FOR REFERENCE

Do Not Take From This Room

ENCYCLOPEDIA OF
ASSOCIATIONS®

AN ASSOCIATIONS UNLIMITED REFERENCE

ISSN 0071-0202

ENCYCLOPEDIA OF ASSOCIATIONS®

AN ASSOCIATIONS UNLIMITED REFERENCE

A Guide to More Than 23,000 National and International Organizations, Including: Trade, Business, and Commercial; Environmental and Agricultural; Legal, Governmental, Public Administration, and Military; Engineering, Technological, and Natural and Social Sciences; Educational; Cultural; Social Welfare; Health and Medical; Public Affairs; Fraternal, Nationality, and Ethnic; Religious; Veterans', Hereditary, and Patriotic; Hobby and Avocational; Athletic and Sports; Labor Unions, Associations, and Federations; Chambers of Commerce and Trade and Tourism; Greek Letter and Related Organizations; and Fan Clubs.

51st EDITION

VOLUME 1
NATIONAL ORGANIZATIONS OF THE U.S.

PART 3
NAME AND KEYWORD INDEX
Includes Association Addresses and Phone Numbers

Tara E. Atterberry, Project Editor

GALE
CENGAGE Learning®

Detroit • New York • San Francisco • New Haven, Conn • Waterville, Maine • London

GALE
CENGAGE Learning·

Encyclopedia of Associations, 51st Edition

Product Management: Michele LaMeau

Project Editor: Tara Atterberry

Composition and Electronic Capture: Gary Oudersluys

Manufacturing: Rita Wimberley

© 2012 Gale, Cengage Learning

For product information and technology assistance, contact us at
Gale Customer Support, 1-800-877-4253.
For permission to use material from this text or product,
submit all requests online at **www.cengage.com/permissions.**
Further permissions questions can be emailed to
permissionrequest@cengage.com

Gale
27500 Drake Rd.
Farmington Hills, MI 48331-3535

ISBN-13: 978-1-4144-5890-8 (vol. 1, 3-part set)
ISBN-10: 1-4144-5890-8 (vol. 1, 3-part set)
ISBN-13: 978-1-4144-5891-5 (vol. 1, part 1)
ISBN-10: 1-4144-5891-6 (vol. 1, part 1)
ISBN-13: 978-1-4144-5892-2 (vol. 1, part 2)
ISBN-10: 1-4144-5892-4 (vol. 1, part 2)
ISBN-13: 978-1-4144-5893-9 (vol. 1, part 3)
ISBN-10: 1-4144-5893-2 (vol. 1, part 3)
ISBN-13: 978-1-4144-5894-6 (vol. 2)
ISBN-10: 1-4144-5894-0 (vol. 2)

ISSN 0071-0202

Printed in the United States of America
1 2 3 4 5 6 7 16 15 14 13 12

Contents

The *Encyclopedia of Associations (EA)*, Volume 1, is the only comprehensive source of detailed information concerning more than 23,000 nonprofit American membership organizations of national scope. For more than fifty years and through 50 earlier editions, *EA's* listing of associations and professional societies is unsurpassed as a "switchboard" connecting persons needing information to highly qualified sources.

Frequently, a phone call, fax, or e-mail to one of the thousands of organizations formed around a specific interest or objective produces more information faster than research in books, periodicals, and other printed materials.

Organizations often operate with small, volunteer staffs. *Many such groups have requested that all written inquiries be accompanied by stamped, self-addressed envelopes.* Replies can then be expedited and costs to the organization kept to a minimum.

Preparation of This Edition

The editorial objective for each edition of *EA* is complete verification or updating of existing entries and the identification and description of new or previously unlisted organizations. Information was compiled or confirmed through written correspondence, through the association's recently updated web site, by telephone or through e-mail.

Scope of the Encyclopedia

The organizations described in *EA* fall into the following seven general categories:

National, nonprofit membership associations, which represent the largest number of organizations listed;

International associations, which are generally North American in scope and membership or binational, representing a direct link between the United States and another country or region; also includes American or North American sections, chapters, or divisions of associations headquartered outside of the United States;

Local and regional associations, only if their subjects or objectives are national in interest;

Nonmembership organizations, if they disseminate information to the public as well as to the researcher;

For-profit associations, if their names suggest that they are nonprofit organizations;

Defunct associations, which appear only in the index with the appropriate "defunct" annotation;

Untraceable associations (After requests for updated information have remained unanswered for two editions, these associations are listed in the index only, with the annotation "address unknown.")

Available in Electronic Formats

Licensing. National Organizations of the U.S. is available for licensing. The complete database is provided in a fielded format and is deliverable on such media as disk or CD-ROM. For more information, contact Gale's Business Development Group at 1-800-877-GALE, or visit us on our web site at http://gale.cengage.com/bizdev.

Online. The complete *Encyclopedia of Associations (EA)* series (including associations listed in the international and regional, state and local editions) is also accessible as File 114 through Dialog and as File ENASSC through LexisNexis. For more information, contact Dialog, 11000 Regency Parkway, Ste. 10, Cary, NC 27518, phone: (919) 462-8600; toll-free: 800-3-DIALOG; or LexisNexis, PO Box 933, Dayton, OH 45401-0933, phone: (937) 865-6800; toll-free: 800-227-9597.

This Directory is also available online as part of the Gale Directory Library. For more information, call 1-800-877-GALE.

Associations Unlimited. Associations Unlimited is a modular approach to the *Encyclopedia of Associations* database, allowing customers to select the pieces of the series that they want to purchase. The four modules include each of the *EA* series (national, international, and regional) as well as one module featuring U.S. government data on more than 400,000 nonprofit organizations.

Associations Unlimited is available on a subscription basis through InfoTrac, Gale's online information resource that features an easy-to-use end-user interface, powerful search capabilities, and ease of access through the World-Wide Web. For more information, call 800-877-GALE.

Acknowledgments

The editors are grateful to the large number of organization officials in the United States and abroad who generously responded to our requests for updated information, provided additional data by telephone, fax, email or website and helped in the shaping of this edition with their comments and suggestions throughout the year. Special thanks go to Jeannine M. James for her research contributions. Appreciation is also extended to the American Society of Association Executives for its ongoing support.

Comments and Suggestions Welcome

Matters pertaining to specific listings in *EA,* as well as suggestions for new listings, should be directed to Tara Atterberry, Editor, *Encyclopedia of Associations.*

Please write or call:

Encyclopedia of Associations
Gale
27500 Drake Rd.
Farmington Hills, MI 48331-3535

Phone: (248) 699-4253
Toll-free: 800-347-GALE
Fax: (248) 699-8075
Email: Tara.Atterberry@Cengage.com

Descriptive Listings

Entries in *EA* are arranged into 18 subject sections, as outlined on the Contents page. Within each section, organizations are arranged in alphabetical order, with numeric listings appearing first, according to the assigned principal subject keyword that appears as a subhead above the organization names. An alphabetical list of keywords used throughout *EA* follows the 'Abbreviations and Symbols' list. Within each keyword, entries are listed alphabetically by organization name.

Access to entries is facilitated by the alphabetical *Name and Keyword Index* found in Part 3 of this edition. An explanation of this index follows the discussion of the sample entry.

Sample Entry

The number preceding each portion of the sample entry designates an item of information that might be included. Each numbered item in the sample entry is explained in the paragraph of the same number following the diagram.

❚1❚ Storytelling

❚2❚ 3348 ■ ❚3❚ Association of Eclectic Storytellers ❚4❚ (AES)
❚5❚ 123 Amanda Ave.
PO Box 1992
Eldridge, NY 13201
❚6❚ Ph: (315)555-9500
❚7❚ Free: (800)555-2000
Fax: (315)555-9505
❚8❚ E-mail: harmersway@aes.org
❚9❚ Website: http://www.aes.org
❚10❚ Contact: Grant Smith, Pres.
❚11❚ **Founded:** 1950. ❚12❚ **Members:** 150,000. ❚13❚ **Membership Dues:** individual, $50 (annual). ❚14❚ **Staff:** 15. ❚15❚ **Budget:** $1,000,000. ❚16❚ **Regional Groups:** 10. **Local Groups:** 20. ❚17❚ **Languages:** English, Dutch. ❚18❚ **Multinational.** ❚19❚ **Description:** Professional society of storytellers, focusing on storytellers that enjoy eclectic themes and others with an interest in this field. Promotes the study and tradition of storytelling. Conducts special programs for various types of audiences. Sponsors special seminars and courses on traditional forms of storytelling. ❚20❚ **Libraries: Type:** lending. **Holdings:** 15,000; archival material, artwork, books, periodicals. **Subjects:** folktales, traditional stories, fairytales. ❚21❚ **Awards:** Yaeko Abe Excellence Endowment. **Frequency:** annual. **Type:** monetary. • Michelle Eads's Founder Prize. **Frequency:** quarterly. **Type:** recognition. ❚23❚ **Committees:** Career Counseling; Cultural Studies; History of Stories. **Divisions:** Education; Literature.

❚24❚ **Affiliated With:** Storytelling Institute. ❚25❚ **Also Known As:** Story Time Society. ❚26❚ **Formerly:** (1975) Storytelling Society of America. ❚27❚ **Publications:** *AES News,* monthly. Newsletter. Contains happenings in the storytelling world, book reviews, and listing of seminars and courses offered. ❚28❚ **Price:** $25. ❚29❚ **ISSN:** 1234-5678. ❚30❚ **Circulation:** 5000. ❚31❚ **Advertising:** accepted. ❚32❚ **Alternate Formats:** online. ❚33❚ **Also Cited As:** *American Society of Eclectic Storytellers.* ❚34❚ **Conventions/Meetings:** annual (with exhibits) - 2011 Nov. 1-9, Boulder, CO.

Description of Numbered Elements

❚1❚ **Keyword.** In each of the sections, keywords are given as subheadings and listed alphabetically. Organizations are listed in alphabetical order under their principal keyword subheading. Because the listings are arranged by keyword, the user will find organizations having similar interests grouped together within each keyword subheading.

❚2❚ **Entry Number.** Entries are numbered sequentially and the entry number (rather than the page number) is used in the Name and Keyword Index to refer to the organization. To facilitate location of the entries in the text, the first entry number on each left-hand page and the last entry number on each right-hand page are provided at the top outer corners of the pages.

❚3❚ **Organization Name.** The formal name is given; 'The' and 'Inc.' are omitted in most listings, unless they are an integral part of the acronym used by the association.

❚4❚ **Acronym.** Indicates the short form or abbreviation of the organization's name, usually composed of the initial letter or syllable of each word in it.

❚5❚ **Address.** The address is generally that of the permanent national headquarters, or of the chief official for groups that have no permanent office.

❚6❚ **Telephone Numbers.** These are listed when furnished by the organization.

❚7❚ **Toll-free, Fax, and Telex.** These are listed when furnished by the organization.

❚8❚ **E-mail.** This is listed when furnished by the organization.

❚9❚ **Website.** The primary web address for the organization or contact person listed.

∎10∎ Chief Official and Title. The name of a full-time executive, an elected officer, or other contact person designated by the association is provided.

∎11∎ Founding Date. Indicates the year in which the organization was formed. If the group has changed its name, the founding date is for the earliest name by which it was known. If, however, the group was formed by a merger or supersedes another group, the founding date refers to the year in which this action took place.

∎12∎ Members. The figure represents individuals, firms, institutions, other associations, or a combination of these categories. Since membership constantly fluctuates, the figure listed should be considered an approximation. If an organization describes itself as nonmembership, such notation is made in the entry preceding the descriptive text.

∎13∎ Membership Dues. Fees required of members as reported by the organization. Dues often vary according to membership category.

∎14∎ Staff. Many associations operate with a small paid or volunteer staff. The fact that an organization has no paid staff does not mean it has a limited program. Many groups carry on extensive activities through volunteer workers and committees.

∎15∎ Budget. The approximate annual budget for all activities is listed as reported by the organization.

∎16∎ Regional, State, and Local Groups. Indicates the number of regional, state, and local associations, chapters, clubs, councils, and posts affiliated with the national organization.

∎17∎ Languages. The official and/or working languages of the organization are listed, if other than English.

∎18∎ Geographic Scope. The boldface word **Multinational** indicates a multinational scope of the organization; otherwise, the geographic scope is assumed to be National.

∎19∎ Description. The description briefly outlines the membership, purpose, and activities of the association. Where no description is given, the title of the group usually is self-explanatory; in some cases, no summary of activities could be obtained.

∎20∎ Libraries. Provides information for organizations that maintain a library. Includes type of collection, holdings, and subject matter of collection, if available.

∎21∎ Awards. Provides information for organizations that offer awards. Includes name, frequency, type, and recipient of award.

∎23∎ Subgroups. Lists those subgroups, including committees, sections, divisions, councils, departments, etc., that give an indication of the activities of the group, as distinguished from such administrative committees such as membership, finance, and convention. This information often supplements the description (see paragraph 19) by providing details about the organization's programs and fields of interest. Geographic divisions are omitted.

∎24∎ Affiliated With. Lists organizations sponsored by or directly related to the listed group. Organizations listed under this rubric can be found in *EA* or in *International Organizations*.

∎25∎ Also Known As. If the group is also known by another name, legally doing business under another name, or otherwise operates under a name different than its official title, that name is provided here.

∎26∎ Supersessions, Mergers, and Former Names. If the group superseded another organization or was formed by a merger, the original organizations are listed. Former names and the date of change to a new name, if available, are also listed.

∎27∎ Publications. The official publications are listed in alphabetical order with frequencies. When available, a brief description of the publication is provided. Additional publications, such as newspaper columns, are listed following the words 'Also publishes.' When provided, languages in which the publications are available are noted. If the group has indicated that no publications are issued, this is noted in the entry's main body.

∎28∎ Price. The figures are as provided by the organization.

∎29∎ ISSN. The International Standard Serial Number is a unique code for the purpose of identifying a specific serial publication. It is listed when provided by the organization; not all publications have been assigned an ISSN.

∎30∎ Circulation. This figure is as reported by the organization.

∎31∎ Advertising. Indicates whether or not the association accepts advertising in the publication.

∎32∎ Alternate Formats. Notes online, CD-ROM, diskette, and microform (includes microfiche and microfilm) availability.

∎33∎ Also Cited As. Lists any alternate or former names of the publication.

∎34∎ Conventions/Meetings. The frequency of national or international sessions and the dates and locations (city, state, and country) of the association's conventions, meetings, or conferences are given, if available at the time of publication. Also noted is the inclusion of commercial exhibits. If the group has indicated that no conventions or meetings are held, this is noted in the entry's main body.

Name and Keyword Index

A comprehensive alphabetical Name and Keyword index is provided in Part 3 of this edition of the Encyclopedia. Note that *each reference refers to the entry number, rather than the page on which the entry is listed*. Alphabetization rules ignore articles, prepositions, and conjunctions. A collection of references in this index would appear this way:

∎1∎ Amer. Soc. of Earth Sciences **[6359]**, 123 Salina St., Syracuse, NY 13201 (315)222-950
∎2∎ Earth Sciences, Amer. Soc. of **[6359]**
∎3∎ Earth Sciences Soc., USA **[★6359]**

I4I Geology
Amer. Soc. of Earth Sciences **[6359]**
I5I *Highways* Asphalt Recycling and Reclaiming Assn **[3728]**
I6I Natl. Soc. of Constitutional Training —Address unknown since 1988
I7I Soc. for the Advancement of Space Travel—Defunct
I8I Turkish Air Assn. **[IO]**

Description of Numbered Index References

I1I Each association's primary reference includes the mailing address and telephone number of the group.

I2I Associations are alphabetized by important words in the name. These references aid in locating organizations whose correct name is unknown to the user.

I3I Any reference with a ★ preceding the entry number indicates that the organization is not listed separately, but is mentioned within the description of another entry. These references would include the organization's former or alternate name as well as names of important committees, projects, or programs.

I4I Associations appear alphabetically by primary and added keywords (see keyword list in this volume). These references allow the user to access all organizations within a particular field of interest.

I5I Keywords that are italicized are added keywords and do not appear as subject headings within a section.

I6I Organizations that are untraceable are noted as 'address unknown.'

I7I Defunct associations are listed as such.

I8I This index includes references to associations listed in the *Encyclopedia of Associations: International Organizations*.

Geographic Index

Entries in *EA*'s Geographic Index are listed according to the state in which the organization's headquarters are located. They are then sub-arranged by city and listed alphabetically according to the names of the organizations within each city.

A sample entry is shown below.

I1I Amer. Soc. of Earth Sciences **I2I** [3348]
I3I 123 Salina St.
PO Box 1992
Allen Park, NY 13201
I4I Ph: (315)555-9500
I5I Patsy, Mrs. Rachel, Pres.

Description of Numbered Elements

I1I **Organization Name.** The formal name is given; 'The' and 'Inc.' are omitted in most listings, unless they are an integral part of the acronym used by the association.

I2I **Entry Number.** Refers to the sequential entry number (rather than the page number) assigned to the organization's main entry in Volume 1, where other details concerning membership, objectives and activities, and publications can be found.

I3I **Address.** The address is generally that of the permanent national headquarters, or of the chief official for groups that have no permanent offices. The city appears in **boldface.**

I4I **Telephone Number.** A telephone number is listed when furnished by the organization.

I5I **Chief Official and Title.** Lists the name of a full-time executive, an elected officer, or other contact person designated by the association.

Executive Index

Entries in *EA*'s Executive Index are listed alphabetically according to the surname of the chief executive of the organization. When an individual is listed as the chief executive of more than one organization, entries are arranged by organization name.

A sample entry is shown below.

I1I Patsy, Mrs. Rachel, Pres.
I2I Amer. Soc. of Earth Sciences **I3I** [3348]
I4I 123 Salina St.
PO Box 1992
Allen Park, NY 13201
I5I Ph: (315)555-9500

Description of Numbered Elements

I1I **Chief Official and Title.** Lists the name of a full-time executive, an elected officer, or other contact person designated by the association.

I2I **Organization Name.** The formal name is given; 'The' and 'Inc.' are omitted in most listings, unless they are an integral part of the acronym used by the association.

I3I **Entry Number.** Refers to the sequential entry number (rather than the page number) assigned to the organization's main entry in Volume 1, where other details concerning membership, objectives and activities, and publications can be found.

I4I **Address.** The address is generally that of the permanent national headquarters, or of the chief official for groups that have no permanent offices.

I5I **Telephone Number.** A telephone number is listed when furnished by the organization.

Geographic Abbreviations

United States and U.S. Territories

AK Alaska
AL Alabama
AR Arkansas
AZ Arizona
CA California
CO Colorado
CT Connecticut
DC District of Columbia
DE Delaware
FL Florida
GA Georgia
GU Guam
HI Hawaii
IA Iowa
ID Idaho
IL Illinois
IN Indiana
KS Kansas
KY Kentucky
LA Louisiana
MA Massachusetts
MD Maryland
ME Maine
MI Michigan
MN Minnesota
MO Missouri
MS Mississippi
MT Montana
NC North Carolina
ND North Dakota
NE Nebraska
NH New Hampshire
NJ New Jersey
NM New Mexico
NV Nevada
NY New York
OH Ohio
OK Oklahoma
OR Oregon

PA Pennsylvania
PR Puerto Rico
RI Rhode Island
SC South Carolina
SD South Dakota
TN Tennessee
TX Texas
UT Utah
VA Virginia
VI Virgin Islands
VT Vermont
WA Washington
WI Wisconsin
WV West Virginia
WY Wyoming

Table of Abbreviations Used in Addresses and the Index

Acad Academy
AFB Air Force Base
Amer American
APO Army Post Office
Apt Apartment
Assn Association
Ave Avenue
Bd Board
Bldg Building
Blvd Boulevard
Br Branch
Bur Bureau
c/o Care of
Co Company
Coll College
Comm Committee
Commn Commission
Conf Conference
Confed Confederation
Cong Congress
Corp Corporation
Coun Council
Ct Court

Dept Department
Div Division
Dr Drive
E East
Expy Expressway
Fed Federation
Fl Floor
Found Foundation
FPO Fleet Post Office
Ft Fort
Fwy Freeway
Govt Government
GPO General Post Office
Hwy Highway
Inc Incorporated
Inst Institute
Intl International
Ln Lane
Ltd Limited
Mfrs Manufacturers
Mgt Management
Mt Mount
N North
Natl National
NE Northeast
No Number
NW Northwest
Pkwy Parkway
Pl Place
PO Post Office
Prof Professor
Rd Road
RD Rural Delivery
RFD Rural Free Delivery
Rm Room
RR Rural Route
Rte Route
S South
SE Southeast
Sect Section
Soc Society

Sq	Square	Subcommn	Subcommission	UN	United Nations
St	Saint, Street	SW	Southwest	Univ	University
Sta	Station	Terr	Terrace, Territory	U.S.	United States
Ste	Sainte, Suite	Tpke	Turnpike	U.S.A.	United States of America
Subcomm	Subcommittee	T.V.	Television	W	West

Currency Abbreviations and Definitions

Arranged by Currency Abbreviation

Abbr.	Currency Unit	Country
$	U.S. dollar	American Samoa, British Virgin Islands, Guam, Marshall Islands, Federated States of Micronesia, U.S.
$A	Australian dollar	Australia, Kiribati, Nauru, Norfolk Island, Tuvalu
$B	Belizean dollar	Belize
$b	boliviano	Bolivia
$F	Fijian dollar	Fiji
œ	pound sterling	England, Northern Ireland, Scotland, Wales
œC	Cyprus pound	Cyprus
œE	Egyptian pound	Egypt
œG	Gibraltar pound	Gibraltar
œS	Sudanese pound	Sudan
Syr	Syrian pound	Syria
A	Argentinian austral	Argentina
Af	afghani	Afghanistan
AF	Aruban florin	Aruba
AS	Austrian Schilling	Austria
B	balboa	Panama
B$	Bahamian dollar	Bahamas
BD	Bahraini dinar	Bahrain
BD$	Barbados dollar	Barbados
BFr	Belgian franc	Belgium
Bht	baht	Thailand
Bm$	Bermuda dollar	Bermuda
Br$	Brunei dollar	Brunei Darussalam
Bs	bolivar	Venezuela
C	colon	Costa Rica, El Salvador
Cd	cedi	Ghana
C$	Canadian dollar	Canada
C$	new cordoba	Nicaragua
CFP	Colonial Francs Pacifique	New Caledonia
ChP	Chilean peso	Chile
CI$	Cayman Island dollar	Cayman Islands
CoP	Colombian peso	Colombia
Cr$	cruzado	Brazil
CRs	Ceylon rupee	Sri Lanka
CuP	Cuban peso	Cuba
D	dalasi	Gambia
DA	dinar	Algeria
Db	dobra	Sao Tome and Principe
DFr	Djibouti franc	Djibouti
Dg	dong	Vietnam
Dh	dirham	Morocco
Din	dinar	Bosnia-Hercegovina, Croatia, Macedonia, Slovenia, Yugoslavia
DKr	Danish krone	Denmark, Faroe Islands, Greenland
DM	Deutsche Mark	Germany
DP	Dominican peso	Dominican Republic
Dr	drachma	Greece
Ec	escudo	Cape Verde
EC$	East Caribbean dollar	Antigua-Barbuda, Dominica, Grenada, Montserrat, St.Christopher-Nevis, St. Lucia, St. Vincent and the Grenadines
ECU	European currency unit	European Economic Community
E$	Ethiopian birr	Ethiopia
Eg	emalangeni	Swaziland
Esc	escudo	Portugal
EUR	Euro	Austria, Belgium, Finland, France, Germany, Greece, Ireland, Italy, Luxembourg, Netherlands, Portugal, Spain
f	florin	Netherlands
FM	Finnish mark	Finland
Fr	franc	Andorra, France, French Guiana, Guadeloupe, Martinique, Monaco, Reunion Island, St. Pierre and Miquelon
FrB	Burundi franc	Burundi
Fr CFA	Communaute Financiere Africaine franc	Benin, Burkina Faso, Cameroon, Central African Republic, Chad, Comoros, Congo, Cote d'Ivoire, Equatorial Guinea, Gabon, Mali, Niger, Senegal, Togo
Ft	forint	Hungary
G	gourde	Haiti
GBP	Guinea-Bissau peso	Guinea-Bissau
G$	Guyana dollar	Guyana
GFr	Guinea franc	Guinea
Gs	guarani	Paraguay
HK$	Hong Kong dollar	Hong Kong
ID	Iraqi dinar	Iraq
IKr	Icelandic krona	Iceland
IRœ	Irish pound	Republic of Ireland
IS	Israel shekel	Israel
It	inti	Peru
J$	Jamaican dollar	Jamaica
JD	Jordanian dinar	Jordan
K	kina	Papua New Guinea
K	new kip	Laos
Kcs	koruna	Czech Republic, Slovakia
KD	Kuwaiti dinar	Kuwait
KSh	Kenyan shilling	Kenya
Ky	kyat	Myanmar (Burma)
Kz	kwanza	Angola
L	leu	Romania
L$	Liberian dollar	Liberia
LD	Libyan dinar	Libya
Le	leone	Sierra Leone
LFr	Luxembourg franc	Luxembourg
Lk	lek	Albania
Lp	lempira	Honduras
L£	Lebanese pound	Lebanon
Lr	lira	Italy, San Marino
Lv	leva	Bulgaria
M$	Malaysian dollar	Malaysia
MFr	Malagasy franc	Madagascar
MKw	Malawi kwacha	Malawi
Ml	maloti	Lesotho
ML	Maltese lira	Malta

MP	Mexican peso	Mexico
MRs	Mauritius rupee	Mauritius
MRu	Maldivian rufiya	Maldives
Mt	metical	Mozambique
N	naira	Nigeria
NAf	Antillean florin	Netherlands Antilles
Ng	ngultrum	Bhutan
NKr	Norwegian krone	Norway
NP	nuevo peso	Uruguay
NRs	Nepalese rupee	Nepal
NTs	New Taiwanese dollar	Taiwan
NZ$	New Zealand dollar	Cook Islands, New Zealand, Niue
Og	ouguiya	Mauritania
P	pula	Botswana
PP	Philippine peso	Philippines
PRs	Pakistan rupee	Pakistan
Ptas	peseta	Spain
Ptcs	pataca	Macao
Q	quetzal	Guatemala
QRl	riyal	Qatar
R	rand	South Africa, Namibia
Rb	ruble	Armenia, Azerbaijan, Belarus, Estonia, Georgia, Kazakhstan, Kirgizstan, Latvia, Lithuania, Moldova, Russia, Tajikstan, Turkmenistan, Ukraine, Uzbekistan
RFr	Rwandan franc	Rwanda
riel	riel	Cambodia
Rl	Iranian rial	Iran
Rlo	rial Omani	Oman

Rp	rupiah	Indonesia
Rs	rupee	India
S	sucre	Ecuador
S$	Singapore dollar	Singapore
Sf	Suriname florin	Suriname
SFr	Swiss franc	Switzerland, Liechtenstein
Sl$	Solomon Island dollar	Soloman Islands
SKr	Swedish krona	Sweden
SRl	Saudi riyal	Saudi Arabia
SRs	Seychelles rupee	Seychelles
SSh	Somali shilling	Somalia
T$	pa'anga	Tonga
TD	Tunisian dinar	Tunisia
Tg	tugrik	Mongolia
Tk	taka	Bangladesh
TL	Turkish lira	Turkey
TSh	Tanzanian shilling	Tanzania
TT$	Trinidad and Tobagoan dollar	Trinidad and Tobago
USh	Ugandan shilling	Uganda
V	vatu	Vanuatu
W	won	Democratic People's Republic of Korea, Republic of Korea
Y	yen	Japan
YRl	Yemen rial	Yemen
Yu	yuan	People's Republic of China
Z	Zaire	Zaire
Z$	Zimbabwe dollar	Zimbabwe
ZKw	Zambian kwacha	Zambia
Zl	zloty	Poland

Keyword List

Following is a list of keywords used in EA. The section(s) in which each keyword appears are listed after each keyword. Within each keyword, entries are arranged alphabetically by organization name.

Abortion	.7, 8
Academic Freedom	.5
Accounting	.1, 3, 8, 9, 17
Accreditation	.5, 7, 8
Acid Maltase Deficiency	.8
Acoustics	.4
Actors	.18
Acupuncture	.8
Adhesives	.1
Adirondacks	.6
Administration	.1, 5
Administrative Services	.1, 3, 15
Admissions	.5
Adoption	.7
Adult Education	.5
Adventist	.7, 11
Advertising	.1, 5
Advertising Auditors	.1
Aerobics	.14
Aerospace	.1, 4, 5, 6, 12, 13, 14
Aerospace Medicine	.8
Afghan	.7, 10, 16
Afghanistan	.2, 7
Africa	.1, 7, 8, 9
African	.5, 6, 7, 10
African-American	.4, 5, 6, 7, 9, 10, 11
Agents	.1
Aging	.7, 8
Agribusiness	.1, 2
Agricultural Development	.2
Agricultural Education	.5, 17
Agricultural Equipment	.1, 2
Agricultural Law	.3
Agricultural Science	.2
Agriculture	.2, 3, 4, 9, 15, 17
AIDS	.7, 8
Aikido	.14
Air Force	.3, 12
Aircraft	.6, 12
Albanian	.9, 10
Alcohol	.9
Alcoholic Beverages	.1, 3, 9, 13
Allergy	.8
Alternative Education	.4, 5
Alternative Lifestyles	.8

Alternative Medicine	.5, 8, 11
Alternative Technology	.2, 4
Alumni	.5, 10
Alzheimer's Disease	.8
Amateur Radio	.13
Ambulatory Care	.8
Amegroid	.6
American	.6, 7, 9
American Indian	.3, 6, 7
American Legion	.12
American Revolution	.6, 12
American South	.6
American West	.6
Americans Overseas	.10
Americas	.9
Amish	.11
Amusement Parks	.13
Anarchism	.9
Anatomy	.8
Andean	.6
Anesthesiology	.8
Anglican	.5, 11
Anglican Catholic	.11
Animal Breeding	.2
Animal Research	.4, 8
Animal Science	.2, 17
Animal Welfare	.2, 7
Animals	.4, 8, 13, 18
Anthropology	.4, 5, 17
Anthroposophical	.11
Anti-Communism	.9
Anti-Poverty	.5, 7, 9
Antiques	.1, 6, 13
Anxiety Disorders	.8
Aphasia	.8
Apiculture	.2
Appalachian	.6, 10
Apparel	.1, 6, 7
Appliances	.1, 13, 15
Appraisers	.1
Appropriate Technology	.9
Aquaculture	.1, 2
Arabic	.6, 7, 10, 16
Arbitration and Mediation	.3
Archaeology	.4

Archery	.14
Architectural Education	.5
Architecture	.1, 3, 4, 5, 6, 17
Archives	.1, 6
Armed Forces	.3, 7, 10, 12
Armenian	.5, 6, 10, 11
Arms	.13
Armwrestling	.14
Army	.12
Art	.1, 6, 8, 13
Art History	.5, 6
Art Therapy	.8
Artifacts	.6, 13
Artificial Intelligence	.4
Artists	.6, 13, 18
Arts	.2, 5, 6, 7, 17
Arts and Sciences	.6, 17
Asatru	.11
Asian	.5, 6, 7, 9, 10
Asian Studies	.5
Asian-American	.6, 9
Asian-Indian	.16
Associations	.1, 7
Assyrian	.6, 7
Astrology	.4
Astronomy	.4, 13
Atheist	.9, 11
Athletes	.14
Athletics	.14
Attorneys	.1, 3
Auctions	.1
Audiology	.8
Audiovisual	.1
Australian	.10
Austrian	.6, 10, 16
Authors	.6
Autism	.7, 8
Auto Racing	.14, 18
Autoimmune Disorders	.8
Automatic Identification	.1
Automation	.4
Automobile	.3, 4, 13, 14, 15
Automotive Education	.5
Automotive Industries	.1
Automotive Manufacturers	.1

Association names are listed alphabetically by name and by keyword subheading (in bold). Index numbers refer to entry numbers, not to page numbers. A star ★ before an entry number signifies that the name is not listed separately, but is mentioned or described within the entry indicated by the entry number.

NUMERIC

1/77th Artillery Vietnam Veterans Assn. [★20829]

1/87 Vehicle Club [21898], PO Box 2701, Carlsbad, CA 92018-2701, (760)721-3393

1-800 Amer. Free Trade Assn. [3588], PO Box 1049, Burlington, VT 05402-1049, (802)383-0816

1planet1ocean [3975], PO Box 53090, Washington, DC 20009, (202)683-9949

1st Fighter Assn. [20872], 504 Southgate Dr., Blacksburg, VA 24060-5437, (757)850-5581

1st Fighter Gp. Assn. [★20872]

1st Marine Div. Assn. [20676], 410 Pier View Way, Oceanside, CA 92054, (760)967-8561

1st Special Response Gp. [11843], PO Box 230, Moffett Field, CA 94035-0230, (650)618-1449

2D Reconnaissance Battalion Assn. [5215], PO Box 56640, Virginia Beach, VA 23456, (615)452-5040

2nd Chance 4 Pets [10897], 1484 Pollard Rd., No. 444, Los Gatos, CA 95032, (408)871-1133

2nd Infantry Div., Korean War Veterans Alliance [20673], Ralph Hockley, Sec., 10027 Pine Forest Rd., Houston, TX 77042-1531, (713)334-0271

2nd Infantry Div., Korean War Veterans Alliance [20673], Ralph Hockley, Sec., 10027 Pine Forest Rd., Houston, TX 77042-1531, (713)334-0271

3-A Sanitary Standards Committees, Inc. [★1012]

3-A Sanitary Standards, Inc. [1012], 6888 Elm St., Ste. 2D, McLean, VA 22101, (703)790-0295

3AI, Affiliated Advertising Agencies Intl. - Defunct.

3HO Found. [20296], 6 Narayan Ct., Espanola, NM 87532, (888)346-2420

4-H Ontario [IO], Guelph, ON, Canada

4-H Prog. and Youth Development [★13521]

4 R Kids Sake [11443], PO Box 77693, Corona, CA 92877, (951)737-2539

4 Real Women Intl. [13447], 277 Broadway, Ste. 1710, New York, NY 10007, (866)494-4794

4Children [IO], London, United Kingdom

4H [IO], Arhus, Denmark

4K for Cancer [13874], PO Box 4730, Baltimore, MD 21211, (443)839-0414

5P- Soc. [★16768]

6th Bomb Gp. Assn. [20318], Warren Higgins, 29277 Garrard Ave., Frontenac, MN 55026

9 to 5, Natl. Assn. of Working Women [17626], 207 E Buffalo St., No. 211, Milwaukee, WI 53202, (414)274-0925

9 to 5 Working Women Educ. Fund [17627], 207 E Buffalo St., No. 211, Milwaukee, WI 53202, (414)274-0925

9/11 Families for a Secure Am. Found. [18710], PO Box 23, Pawling, NY 12564, (914)920-6968

10th Foot Royal Lincolnshire Regimental Assn. Amer. Contingent Br. [★9116]

11th Airborne Div. Assn. [20351], PO Box 367, Town Creek, AL 35672

11th Armored Cavalry's Veterans of Vietnam and Cambodia [20828], PO Box 1948, Plainview, TX 79073-1948

20/20 Vision Natl. Proj. - Address unknown since 2011.

20-30 Intl. [★13049]

21st Century Democrats [17530], 1133 19th St. NW, 9th Fl., Washington, DC 20036, (202)626-5620

25th Infantry Div. Assn. [20352], PO Box 7, Flourtown, PA 19031-0007

29th Infantry Div. Assn. [20353], PO Box 1546, Frederick, MD 21702-0546, (301)695-9558

30 Years After [17999], 9500 W Olympic Blvd., Ste. No. 203, Beverly Hills, CA 90212

30 Years After [17999], 9500 W Olympic Blvd., Ste. No. 203, Beverly Hills, CA 90212

30th Infantry Div. Veterans of WWII [20343], 2915 W SR, No. 235, Brooker, FL 32622-5167, (352)485-1173

32nd Infantry Div. Veterans Assn. [★20344]

32nd Red Arrow Veteran Assn. [20344], 7425 Richter Ln., Larsen, WI 54947-9530, (920)836-3101

33rd Infantry Div. Assn. [20345], 617 143rd St. NW, Marysville, WA 98271-8132

35th Div. Assn. [20346], PO Box 5004, Topeka, KS 66605, (785)267-3295

37th Div. Veterans Assn. - Defunct.

41pounds.org [4232], 41 W Saratoga St., Ferndale, MI 48220

43rd Bomb Gp. [20319], Edward L. Gammill, Sec., 5337 E Earll Dr., Phoenix, AZ 85018-8045, (602)301-7224

43rd Infantry Div. Veterans Assn. - Address unknown since 2010.

50 Years is Enough: U.S. Network for Global Economic Justice - Address unknown since 2010.

51st Medical Battalion Assn. - Defunct.

52 Assn. for the Handicapped - Defunct.

52 Plus Joker [21291], Clarence Peterson, Sec., 12290 W 18th Dr., Lakewood, CO 80215

56 Studebaker Golden Hawk Owners Register [★20979]

60 Plus Assn. [10830], 515 King St., Ste. 315, Alexandria, VA 22314, (703)807-2070

63rd Infantry Div. Assn. [20354], Donna LaCosse, Sec.-Treas., PO Box 86, Morocco, IN 47963, (219)285-2861

70th Infantry Div. Assn. [20845], Ms. Diane Kessler, Sec., 73 Providence Hill Rd., Atkinson, NH 03811, (603)362-9737

71 429 Mustang Registry [20977], 6250 Germantown Pike, Dayton, OH 45418-1634

73rd Bomb Wing Assn. - Defunct.

77th Artillery Assn. [20829], PO Box 141, Boonville, MO 65233-0141, (660)888-1129

78th Div. Veterans Assn. [20762], Barb Cashdollar, Membership Sec., 438 Watters Sta. Rd., Evans City, PA 16033, (724)538-3502

80-20 Initiative [17204], 13337 S St., No. 189, Cerritos, CA 90703

80th Fighter Squadron Headhunters' Assn. [5195], 905 Arapaho Ct., Columbus, GA 31904-1242

82nd Airborne Div. Assn. [20763], PO Box 87482, Fayetteville, NC 28304-7482, (910)223-1182

86th Chem. Mortar Battalion Assn. [20846], 818 W 62nd St., Anniston, AL 36206, (256)820-4415

90th Div. Assn. [20764], James Reid, Exec. Sec.-Treas., 17 Lake Shore Dr., Willowbrook, IL 60527-2221, (630)789-0204

92nd St. Y [12400], 1395 Lexington Ave., New York, NY 10128, (212)415-5500

94th Infantry Div. Assn. [20355], 609 Dogwood Dr., Downingtown, PA 19335-3907, (610)363-7826

95th Infantry Div. Assn. [20356], 620 Grant Rd., Folcroft, PA 19032

96th Infantry Div. Assn. [20357], 128 N Musket Ridge Dr., Sun Prairie, WI 53590, (608)837-7479

99th Infantry Div. Assn. [20358], PO Box 99, Marion, KS 66861, (620)382-2922

100 Black Men of Am. [18842], 141 Auburn Ave., Atlanta, GA 30303, (404)688-5100

100% Recycled Paperboard Alliance[2616], 1156 15th St., NW, Ste. 1020, Washington, DC 20005-1754, (202)347-8000

100 Women in Hedge Funds Assn. [1275], 331 W 57th St., No. 239, New York, NY 10019

100th Infantry Div. Assn. [20359], PO Box 629, Bedford, PA 15522, (814)632-8308

104th Infantry Div. Natl. Timberwolf Assn. [20360], 4002 Jasmine Dr., Wichita, KS 67226, (316)636-5334

106th Infantry Division Association - Address unknown since 2010.

107th Engineer Assn. [5216], 900 Palms Ave., Ishpeming, MI 49849-1064, (906)486-8741

129th Alumni and Heritage Assn. [19270], 6718 Zerillo Dr., Riverbank, CA 95367-2122, (209)869-2879

146th Alumni Assn. [7727], 1534 N Moorpark Rd., No. 365, Thousand Oaks, CA 91360

200 Orphanages Worldwide [11172], 2921 35th St. N, Sartell, MN 56377-2432, (320)217-4944

200 Orphanages Worldwide [11172], 2921 35th St. N, Sartell, MN 56377-2432, (320)217-4944

210 Class [★22345]

303rd Bomb Gp. (H) Assn. [20847], 303rd Bomb Gp., 4483 Palmer Dr., West Valley City, UT 84120-5052

325th Glider Infantry Association - Address unknown since 2010.

369th Fighter Squadron Assn., 359th Fighter Gp. - Address unknown since 2010.

369th Veterans' Assn. [20765], PO Box 1206, New York, NY 10037-1206

381st Bomb Gp. Memorial Assn. [20320], 145 Kimel Park Dr., Ste. 370, Winston-Salem, NC 27103-6972

401st Bombardment Gp. Heavy Assn. [20321], PO Box 15356, Savannah, GA 31416

401st Bombardment Gp. Heavy Assn. [20321], PO Box 15356, Savannah, GA 31416

452nd Bomb Wing/Group Assn. - Address unknown since 2010.

461st Bombardment Gp. Assn. [20322], PO Box 926, Gunnison, CO 81230

483rd Bombardment Gp. H Assn. [20323], Sandee West Maeda, Sec., 1050 E 5th Ave., Escondido, CA 92025, (760)747-6615

494th Bombardment Gp. (H) Assn. 7th Air Force [20324], 3160 E Main St., No. 103, Mesa, AZ 85213-9519, (480)924-6801

501 Soc. [★9641]

504th Parachute Infantry Regiment Assn. [20848], 22 Club Hill Dr., Garner, NC 27529, (919)803-4554

507th Parachute Infantry Assn. - Defunct.

508th Parachute Infantry Regiment Assn. [20849], 3630 Townsend Dr., Dallas, TX 75229

509th Parachute Infantry Assn. [20850], PO Box 860, Huntsville, AL 35804-0860

511 Engineer Light Ponton Company Veterans - Defunct.

517th Parachute Regimental Combat Team Assn. **[20851]**, Leo P. Dean, Sec.-Treas., 14 Stonehenge Ln., Albany, NY 12203
526th Armored Infantry Battalion Assn. **[20852]**, PO Box 456, Yolo, CA 95697, (530)662-8160
550th Airborne Infantry Assn. - Defunct.
605th Ordnance Battalion Assn. - Defunct.
606 Soc. **[★9641]**
800-COCAINE - Defunct.
826 Natl. **[9071]**, 826 Valencia St., San Francisco, CA 94110, (415)642-5905
911 Indus. Alliance **[804]**, Reid French, Vice Chm., 1611 N Kent St., Ste. 802, Arlington, VA 22209, (202)737-6001
1000 Jobs **[12713]**, 316 W Main Rd., Little Compton, RI 02837
1000 Jobs **[12713]**, 316 W Main Rd., Little Compton, RI 02837
1394 High Performance Serial Bus Trade Assn. **[3385]**, 315 Lincoln, Ste. E, Mukilteo, WA 98275, (425)870-6574
1904 World's Fair Soc. **[22205]**, 2605 Causeway Dr., St. Louis, MO 63125
1929 Silver Anniversary Buick Club **[IO]**, Toronto, ON, Canada
1937-1938 Buick Club - Address unknown since 2011.
1950s Amer. Bandstand Fan Club **[★23916]**
1953-54 Buick Skylark Club **[20978]**, 51 Statesville Quarry Rd., Lafayette, NJ 07848, (973)383-6035
1956 Studebaker Golden Hawk Owners Register **[20979]**, 31654 Wekiva River Rd., Sorrento, FL 32776-9233
1965-66 Full Size Chevrolet Club **[20980]**, 831 Londonderry Blvd., Palmyra, PA 17078, (717)838-6122
1970 Dart Swinger 340s Registry **[20981]**, PO Box 9, Wethersfield, CT 06129-0009, (860)257-8434
1971 GTO and Judge Convertible Registry **[20982]**, 9746 Rocky Hollow, La Porte, TX 77571, (281)452-0855
1995 Corvette Pace Car Registry - Address unknown since 2011.

A

A. J. Muste Memorial Inst. **[18228]**, 339 Lafayette St., New York, NY 10012, (212)533-4335
A. J. Muste Memorial Inst. **[18228]**, 339 Lafayette St., New York, NY 10012, (212)533-4335
A. Philip Randolph Inst. **[18610]**, 815 16th St. NW, 4th Fl., Washington, DC 20006-4101, (202)508-3710
A-T Medical Res. Found. - Address unknown since 2010.
AAA Found. for Traffic Safety **[12971]**, 607 14th St. NW, Ste. 201, Washington, DC 20005, (202)638-5944
AAAS Sci. and Human Rights Coalition **[17806]**, Amer. Assn. for the Advancement of Sci., 1200 New York Ave. NW, Washington, DC 20005, (202)326-6400
AACC Intl. **[6385]**, 3340 Pilot Knob Rd., St. Paul, MN 55121, (651)454-7250
AACC Intl. **[6385]**, 3340 Pilot Knob Rd., St. Paul, MN 55121, (651)454-7250
AACE Intl. **[6580]**, 1265 Suncrest Towne Ctr Dr., Morgantown, WV 26505-1876, (304)296-8444
AACE Intl. **[6580]**, 1265 Suncrest Towne Ctr Dr., Morgantown, WV 26505-1876, (304)296-8444
AACSB Intl. **[7780]**, 777 S Harbour Island Blvd., Ste. 750, Tampa, FL 33602-5730, (813)769-6500
AACSB Intl. **[7780]**, 777 S Harbour Island Blvd., Ste. 750, Tampa, FL 33602-5730, (813)769-6500
AACSB-The Intl. Assn. for Mgt. Educ. **[★7780]**
AACSB-The Intl. Assn. for Mgt. Educ. **[★7780]**
AACTION Autism **[13776]**, 1861 Manor Ln., Park Ridge, IL 60068, (847)825-3423
AAFRC Trust for Philanthropy **[★12669]**
Aahung **[IO]**, Karachi, Pakistan
AAKSIS **[★14694]**
AAMED - The Amer. Assn. of Multiple Enchondroma Diseases - Address unknown since 2010.
AAP Political Action Comm. - Defunct.
Aaron Burr Assn. **[10650]**, 1004 Butterworth Ln., Upper Marlboro, MD 20774-2205, (301)641-0494

AARP **[12914]**, 601 E St. NW, Washington, DC 20049, (202)434-2560
AARP | Grief and Loss Prog. **[13446]**, 601 E St. NW, Washington, DC 20049, (888)687-2277
AASP - The Palynological Soc. **[7216]**, PO Box 2197, Houston, TX 77252-2197
AAU/U.S.A Junior Olympics **[★22960]**
AAU Youth Sports Prog. **[★22960]**
AAUW Legal Advocacy Fund **[5639]**, 1111 16th St. NW, Washington, DC 20036, (202)785-7700
ABA Marketing Network **[2385]**, 1120 Connecticut Ave. NW, Washington, DC 20036, (202)663-5269
Abandoned Animals Protect Assn. of Macau **[IO]**, Macau, Macao
Abbott and Costello Fan Club **[★23795]**
Abbott and Costello Intl. Fan Club **[23795]**, PO Box 5566, Fort Wayne, IN 46895-5566
ABCD: The Microcomputer Indus. Assn. **[★6532]**
Abdominal Surgeons; Amer. Soc. of **[16800]**
Abdus Salam Intl. Centre for Theoretical Physics **[IO]**, Trieste, Italy
Aberdeen-Angus Cattle Soc. **[IO]**, Perth, United Kingdom
Aberdeen Formation Evaluation Soc. **[IO]**, Aberdeen, United Kingdom
Aberdeen Geological Soc. **[IO]**, Aberdeen, United Kingdom
Aberdeen and Grampian Chamber of Commerce **[IO]**, Aberdeen, United Kingdom
Aberfeldie Bowls Club **[IO]**, Essendon, Australia
ABET **[6764]**, 111 Market Pl., Ste. 1050, Baltimore, MD 21202, (410)347-7700
ABET Inc. **[★6764]**
ABF Auxiliary - Defunct.
ABG Division United Steel Workers - Defunct.
Abhivyakti Media for Development **[IO]**, Nashik, India
Abilities! **[11751]**, 201 I.U. Willets Rd., Albertson, NY 11507-1599, (516)465-1400
Ability Soc. **[IO]**, Calgary, AB, Canada
Abingdon Pottery Club - Address unknown since 2010.
ABJS **[★16030]**
ABLE: Assn. for Better Living and Educ. Intl. **[11537]**, 7065 Hollywood Blvd., Los Angeles, CA 90028, (323)960-3530
ABLE: Assn. for Better Living and Educ. Intl. **[11537]**, 7065 Hollywood Blvd., Los Angeles, CA 90028, (323)960-3530
Able Australia Services **[IO]**, Camberwell, Australia
Abolitionist Party of Canada **[IO]**, Brantford, ON, Canada
Aboriginal Evangelical Fellowship of Australia **[IO]**, Tanilba Bay, Australia
Aboriginal Nurses Assn. of Canada **[IO]**, Ottawa, ON, Canada
Aboriginal Peoples Training and Employment Comm. **[IO]**, Truro, NS, Canada
Aboriginal Rights Coalition **[IO]**, Ottawa, ON, Canada
Abortion
   Abortion Access Proj. **[10763]**
   Abortion Care Network **[10764]**
   Coalition on Abortion/Breast Cancer **[13569]**
   Elliot Inst. **[10765]**
   Exhale **[10766]**
   Life and Liberty for Women **[10767]**
   Natl. Abortion Fed. **[10768]**
   Natl. Network of Abortion Funds **[10769]**
   Natl. Pro-Life Alliance **[18558]**
   One More Soul **[18561]**
   Pro-Choice Public Educ. Proj. **[10770]**
   Republican Majority for Choice **[18539]**
Abortion Access Proj. **[10763]**, PO Box 410164, Cambridge, MA 02141-0002, (617)661-1161
Abortion Care Network **[10764]**, 1425 K St. NW, No. 350, Washington, DC 20005, (202)419-1444
Abortion Rights **[IO]**, London, United Kingdom
Abortion Rights Assn. **[★18525]**
About Books, Inc. **[2910]**, 1618 W Colorado Ave., Colorado Springs, CO 80904, (719)632-8226
About-Face **[13448]**, PO Box 77665, San Francisco, CA 94107, (415)839-0212
AboutFace Intl. **[IO]**, Toronto, ON, Canada
ABRADEMI - Brazilian Manga and Illustration Artists Assn. **[IO]**, Sao Paulo, Brazil

Abraham Lincoln Assn. **[10651]**, One Old State Capitol Plz., Springfield, IL 62701-1507, (866)865-8500
Abrahamic Alliance Intl. **[19824]**, 1900 Camden Ave., Ste. 201-E, San Jose, CA 95124, (408)728-8943
Abrasive Engg. Soc. **[1795]**, 144 Moore Rd., Butler, PA 16001, (724)282-6210
Abrasive Engg. Soc. **[1795]**, 144 Moore Rd., Butler, PA 16001, (724)282-6210
Abrasive Grain Assn. **[★2347]**
Abrasive Grain Assn. **[★1875]**
Abri Intl. **[★IO]**
Abriendo Mentes **[12950]**, Opening Minds Latin America, 3310 Crosspark Ln., Houston, TX 77007, (713)893-8334
Absorbents; Inst. for Polyacrylate **[756]**
Abstinence CH **[16643]**, 801 E 41st St., Sioux Falls, SD 57105, (605)335-3643
Abundant Life Seeds **[3976]**, PO Box 279, Cottage Grove, OR 97424, (541)767-9606
Abundant Wildlife Soc. of North Am. **[5019]**, PO Box 2, Beresford, SD 57004, (605)751-0979
Abuse; Natl. Comm. for the Prevention of Elder **[10860]**
Abused Deaf Women's Advocacy Services **[12136]**, 8623 Roosevelt Way NE, Seattle, WA 98115, (206)726-0093
ABW Ministries **[19305]**, PO Box 851, Valley Forge, PA 19482-0851, (800)ABC-3USA
Abwenzi African Stud. - Address unknown since 2010.
Abyssinian Cat Club of Am. **[21242]**, 23700 Stagecoach Rd., Volcano, CA 95689, (209)296-7390
A.C. Gilbert Heritage Soc. **[22168]**, 4 Ronald Dr., Poestenkill, NY 12140
ACA Intl. **[1030]**, PO Box 390106, Minneapolis, MN 55439-0106, (952)926-6547
ACA Intl. **[1030]**, PO Box 390106, Minneapolis, MN 55439-0106, (952)926-6547
Acacia Fraternity **[23648]**, 8777 Purdue Rd., Ste. 225, Indianapolis, IN 46268, (317)872-8210
Acadamh Rioga na hEireann **[★IO]**
Academi - Yr Academi Gymreig **[IO]**, Cardiff, United Kingdom
Academia Argentina de Letras **[★IO]**
Academia Brasileira de Ciencias **[★IO]**
Academia Brasileira de Letras **[★IO]**
Academia Chilena de Bellas Artes **[IO]**, Santiago, Chile
Academia Chilena de la Historia **[★IO]**
Academia de Ciencias de Am. Latina **[★IO]**
Academia de Ciencias Fisicas, Matematicas y Naturales **[★IO]**
Academia das Ciencias de Lisboa **[★IO]**
Academia das Ciencias de Lisboa **[★IO]**
Academia de Ciencias Politicas y Sociales **[IO]**, Caracas, Venezuela
Academia Colombiana de Ciencias Exactas, Fisicas y Naturales **[IO]**, Bogota, Colombia
Academia Colombiana de Ciencias Exactas, Fisicas y Naturales **[★IO]**
Academia Europaea **[IO]**, London, United Kingdom
Academia Mexicana de Ciencias **[★IO]**
Academia Mexicana de Dermatologia **[★IO]**
Academia Musicale Chigiana **[IO]**, Siena, Italy
Academia Nacional de Agronomia y Veterinaria **[IO]**, Buenos Aires, Argentina
Academia Nacional de Ciencias de Bolivia **[★IO]**
Academia Nacional de Ciencias Exactas, Fisicas y Naturales **[★IO]**
Academia Nacional de Geografia **[★IO]**
Academia Nacional de la Historia de la Republica Argentina **[IO]**, Buenos Aires, Argentina
Academia Nacional de la Historia de la Republica Argentina **[★IO]**
Academia Portuguesa da Historia **[★IO]**
Academia Romana **[★IO]**
Academia Scientiarum et Artium Croatian **[★IO]**
Academia Sinica **[IO]**, Taipei, Taiwan
Academia de Stiinte a Moldovei **[★IO]**
Academic Admin. Internship Prog. **[★7655]**
Academic Automotive Assn. **[IO]**, Minsk, Belarus
Academic Collective Bargaining Information Service - Defunct.

A star before a book entry number signifies that the name is not listed separately, but is mentioned within the entry.

Academic Cooperation Assn. **[IO]**, Brussels, Belgium

Academic Coun. on the United Nations Sys. **[IO]**, Waterloo, ON, Canada

Academic Freedom
  Amer. Coun. of Trustees and Alumni **[7640]**
  Coalition for Student and Academic Rights **[7641]**
  Student Veterans of Am. **[9032]**

Academic Hea. Centers: Responses to the Malpractice Insurance Crisis **[★14701]**

Academic Language Therapy Assn. **[12420]**, 14070 Proton Rd., Ste. 100, LB 9, Dallas, TX 75244, (972)233-9107

Academic Medicine Club **[★8596]**

Academic Orthopaedic Soc. - Address unknown since 2010.

Academic Pediatric Assn. **[16137]**, 6728 Old McLean Village Dr., McLean, VA 22101, (703)556-9222

Academic Resource Network - Defunct.

Academics for the Second Amendment - Address unknown since 2011.

Academie internationale de droit et de sante mentale **[★IO]**

Academie chretienne de dialogue europeen **[★IO]**

Academie internationale de droit compare **[★IO]**

Academie suisse des sciences naturelles **[★IO]**

Academie des Beaux-Arts **[IO]**, Paris, France

Academie Canadienne de Chirurgie Plastique et Reconstructive Faciale **[★IO]**

Academie Canadienne du Cinema et de la TV **[★IO]**

Academie Canadienne d'Endodontie **[★IO]**

L'Academie Canadienne du Genie **[★IO]**

L' Academie Canadienne de Medecine du Sport **[★IO]**

Academie Canadienne de Parodontologie **[★IO]**

Academie des Chefs de Direction en Soins Infirmiers **[★IO]**

Academie nationale de Chirurgie **[★IO]**

Academie d'Agriculture de France **[IO]**, Paris, France

Academie Europeenne d'Allergologie et d'Immunologie Clinique **[★IO]**

Academie Francaise **[IO]**, Paris, France

Academie des Inscriptions et Belles-Lettres **[IO]**, Paris, France

Academie Internationale de la Ceramique **[★IO]**

Academie Internationale d'Astronautique **[★IO]**

L'Academie Internationale De Cytologie **[★IO]**

Academie Internationale de Droit Linguistique **[★IO]**

Academie Internationale de Medecine Aeronautique et Spatiale **[★IO]**

Academie Internationale de Medecine Legale **[★IO]**

Academie Mondiale de l'Art et de la Sci. **[★9331]**

Academie Mondiale de l'Art et de la Sci. **[★9331]**

Academie Royale de Medecine de Belgique **[★IO]**

Academie Royale des Sciences d'Outre-Mer **[★IO]**

Academie Royale des Sciences, des Lettres, et des Beaux-Arts de Belgique **[★IO]**

Academie des Sciences **[IO]**, Paris, France

Academie des Sciences - Institut de France **[★IO]**

Academie des Sciences Morales et Politiques **[IO]**, Paris, France

Acad. of Accounting Historians **[9738]**, Case Western Reserve Univ., Weatherhead School of Mgt., 10900 Euclid Ave., Cleveland, OH 44106-7177, (216)368-2058

Acad. of Ambulatory Foot and Ankle Surgery **[16282]**, 1601 Walnut St., Ste. 1005, Philadelphia, PA 19102, (215)569-3303

Acad. of Ambulatory Foot and Ankle Surgery **[16282]**, 1601 Walnut St., Ste. 1005, Philadelphia, PA 19102, (215)569-3303

Acad. of Amer. Franciscan History **[19377]**, 1712 Euclid Ave., Berkeley, CA 94709, (510)548-1755

Acad. of Amer. Poets **[10446]**, 75 Maiden Ln., Ste. 901, New York, NY 10038, (212)274-0343

Acad. of Aphasia **[13767]**, PO Box 26532, Minneapolis, MN 55426, (952)920-0484

Acad. of Applied Osteopathy **[★16056]**

Acad. of Applied Sci. **[7351]**, 24 Warren St., Concord, NH 03301, (603)228-4530

Acad. of Behavioral Medicine Res. **[13812]**, Univ. of Miami, Dept. of Psychology, PO Box 248185, Coral Gables, FL 33124-0751, (305)284-5507

Acad. of Canadian Cinema and TV **[IO]**, Toronto, ON, Canada

Acad. of Canadian Executive Nurses **[IO]**, Ottawa, ON, Canada

Acad. of Certified Archivists **[244]**, 1450 Western Ave., Ste. 101, Albany, NY 12203, (518)694-8471

Acad. of Certified Hazardous Materials Managers **[★4518]**

Acad. of Clinical Lab. Physicians and Scientists **[16244]**, 500 Chipeta Way, Salt Lake City, UT 84108, (801)583-2787

Acad. of Clinical Lab. Physicians and Scientists **[16244]**, 500 Chipeta Way, Salt Lake City, UT 84108, (801)583-2787

Acad. of Clinical Mental Hea. Counselors **[★11678]**

Acad. Conf. **[★7378]**

Acad. of Country Music **[10132]**, 5500 Balboa Blvd., Ste. 200, Encino, CA 91316, (818)788-8000

Acad. of Country and Western Music **[★10132]**

Acad. of Criminal Justice Sciences **[11698]**, PO Box 960, Greenbelt, MD 20768-0960, (301)446-6300

Acad. of Dental Materials **[14222]**, Thomas Hilton, Treas., Oregon Hea. and Sci. Univ., School of Dentistry, Dept. of Restorative Dentistry, 611 SW Campus Dr., Portland, OR 97239, (503)494-8672

Acad. of Dentistry Intl. **[14223]**, 3813 Gordon Creek Dr., Hicksville, OH 43526, (419)542-0101

Acad. of Dentistry Intl. **[14223]**, 3813 Gordon Creek Dr., Hicksville, OH 43526, (419)542-0101

Acad. of Dentistry for Persons with Disabilities **[★14310]**

Acad. of Dispensing Audiologists **[★14909]**

Acad. of Doctors of Audiology **[14909]**, 3493 Lansdowne Dr., Ste. 2, Lexington, KY 40517-1147, (866)493-5544

Acad. for Eating Disorders **[14429]**, 111 Deer Lake Rd., Ste. 100, Deerfield, IL 60015, (847)498-4274

Acad. for Educational Development **[7989]**, 1825 Connecticut Ave. NW, Washington, DC 20009-5721, (202)884-8000

Acad. for Educational Development **[7989]**, 1825 Connecticut Ave. NW, Washington, DC 20009-5721, (202)884-8000

Academy of Elecl. Contracting **[★936]**

Acad. for Ethics in Medicine **[IO]**, Gottingen, Germany

Acad. of Experts **[IO]**, London, United Kingdom

Acad. of Family Psychology **[★16370]**

Acad. of Forensic and Indus. Chiropractic Consultants **[14115]**, 1629 West Ave. J, Ste. 101, Lancaster, CA 93534, (661)942-2273

Acad. of Gen. Dentistry **[14224]**, 211 E Chicago Ave., Ste. 900, Chicago, IL 60611-1999, (888)243-3368

Acad. of Gen. Practice of Pharmacy **[★16176]**

Acad. of Homiletics **[19814]**, 100 E 27th St., Austin, TX 78705

Acad. of Horror Films and Sci. Fiction Films **[★9591]**

Academy of Humanism **[★19819]**

Academy of Humanism **[★19819]**

Acad. for Implants and Transplants - Address unknown since 2010.

Acad. of Indus. Hygiene **[★15902]**

Acad. of Intl. Bus. **[7781]**, Michigan State Univ., The Eli Broad Coll. of Bus., 7 Eppley Center, East Lansing, MI 48824-1121, (517)432-1452

Acad. of Intl. Bus. **[7781]**, Michigan State Univ., The Eli Broad Coll. of Bus., 7 Eppley Center, East Lansing, MI 48824-1121, (517)432-1452

Acad. for Intl. Hea. Stud.

Acad. for Intl. Hea. Stud. - Address unknown since 2011.

Acad. for Interscience Methodology - Defunct.

Acad. of Laser Dentistry **[14225]**, 9900 W Sample Rd., Ste. 400, Coral Springs, FL 33065, (954)346-3776

Acad. of Learned Societies for the Social Sciences **[IO]**, London, United Kingdom

Acad. of Legal Stud. in Bus. **[8496]**, Miami Univ., Dept. of Finance, 3111 Farmer School of Bus., Oxford, OH 45056, (800)831-2903

Acad. of Legal Stud. in Bus. **[8496]**, Miami Univ., Dept. of Finance, 3111 Farmer School of Bus., Oxford, OH 45056, (800)831-2903

Acad. of Leisure Sciences **[IO]**, Waterloo, ON, Canada

Acad. of Managed Care Pharmacy **[16163]**, 100 N Pitt St., Ste. 400, Alexandria, VA 22314, (703)683-8416

Acad. of Managed Care Providers **[14848]**, 1945 Palo Verde Ave., Ste. 202, Long Beach, CA 90815-3445, (562)682-3559

Acad. of Mgt. **[8546]**, PO Box 3020, Briarcliff Manor, NY 10510-8020, (914)923-2607

Acad. of Marketing Sci. **[8553]**, PO Box 3072, Ruston, LA 71272, (318)257-2612

Acad. of Medical Surgical Nurses **[15698]**, PO Box 56, Pitman, NJ 08071, (866)877-2676

Acad. of Medicine, Singapore **[IO]**, Singapore, Singapore

Acad. of Model Aeronautics **[20877]**, 5161 E Memorial Dr., Muncie, IN 47302, (765)287-1256

Acad. of Molecular Imaging **[15388]**, 5839 Green Valley Cir., Ste. 209, Culver City, CA 90230-6963, (310)215-9730

Acad. of Motion Picture Arts and Sciences **[1247]**, 8949 Wilshire Blvd., Beverly Hills, CA 90211, (310)247-3000

Acad. of Natural Sciences **[7135]**, 1900 Benjamin Franklin Pkwy., Philadelphia, PA 19103-1195, (215)299-1000

Acad. of Natural Sciences **[7135]**, 1900 Benjamin Franklin Pkwy., Philadelphia, PA 19103-1195, (215)299-1000

Acad. of Operative Dentistry **[14226]**, Dr. Richard G. Stevenson, III, Sec., PO Box 34425, Los Angeles, CA 90034, (310)794-4387

Acad. of Oral Dynamics - Address unknown since 2010.

Acad. of Organizational and Occupational Psychiatry **[15897]**, Sandra Gabel-Onkels, Admin., 402 E Yakima Ave., No. 330, Yakima, WA 98901, (509)457-4611

Acad. of Organizational and Occupational Psychiatry **[15897]**, Sandra Gabel-Onkels, Admin., 402 E Yakima Ave., No. 330, Yakima, WA 98901, (509)457-4611

Acad. of Osseointegration **[14227]**, 85 W Algonquin Rd., Ste. 550, Arlington Heights, IL 60005, (847)439-1919

Acad. of Osteopathic Directors of Medical Education - Defunct.

Acad. of Parish Clergy **[19981]**, 2249 Florinda St., Sarasota, FL 34231-4414, (941)922-8633

Acad. for Peace Res. **[18229]**, 600 Park Ave., Apt. 4D, Capitola, CA 95010, (831)475-4250

Acad. of Pharmaceutical Physicians and Investigators **[8583]**, 500 Montgomery St., Ste. 800, Alexandria, VA 22314, (703)254-8100

Acad. of Pharmaceutical Res. and Sci. **[16164]**, Amer. Pharmacists Assn., 2215 Constitution Ave. NW, Washington, DC 20037, (202)628-4410

Acad. of Pharmaceutical Sciences **[★16164]**

Acad. of Pharmacy Practice **[★16176]**

Acad. of Pharmacy Practice and Mgt. **[★16176]**

Acad. of Physical, Mathematical and Natural Sciences **[IO]**, Caracas, Venezuela

Acad. of Political Sci. **[7283]**, 475 Riverside Dr., Ste. 1274, New York, NY 10115-1274, (212)870-2500

Acad. of Psychic Arts and Sciences **[7220]**, PO Box 191129, Dallas, TX 75219-8129, (214)219-2020

Acad. of Psychoanalysis **[★16351]**

Acad. of Psychosomatic Medicine **[16442]**, 5272 River Rd., Ste. 630, Bethesda, MD 20816-1453, (301)718-6520

Acad. of Rehabilitative Audiology **[14910]**, PO Box 2323, Albany, NY 12220-0323

Acad. of Religion and Psychical Res. **[★7221]**

Acad. of Religion and Psychical Res. **[★7221]**

Acad. of Sci. Fiction, Fantasy, and Horror Films **[9591]**, 334 W 54th St., Los Angeles, CA 90037, (323)752-5811

Acad. of Sciences of Cuba **[IO]**, Havana, Cuba

Acad. of Sciences of the Czech Republic **[IO]**, Prague, Czech Republic

Acad. of Sciences for the Developing World **[IO]**, Trieste, Italy

Acad. of Sciences of Lisbon **[IO]**, Lisbon, Portugal

Acad. of Sciences of Moldova **[IO]**, Chisinau, Moldova

Acad. of Sciences - Uzbekistan **[IO]**, Tashkent, Uzbekistan

Acad. of Sci. Interrogation **[★5475]**

Acad. of Security Educators and Trainers - Address unknown since 2010.

Reference to "IO" in place of a book number signifies that the association may be found in the 50th edition of International Organizations.

Acad. of the Social Sciences in Australia [IO], Canberra, Australia

Acad. for Spatial Res. and Planning [IO], Hannover, Germany

Acad. of Spinal Cord Injury Professionals, Nurses Sect. [15699], 206 S 6th St., Springfield, IL 62701, (217)753-1190

Acad. of Spirituality and Paranormal Stud., Inc. [7221], PO Box 614, Bloomfield, CT 06002-0614, (860)242-4593

Acad. of Spirituality and Paranormal Stud., Inc. [7221], PO Box 614, Bloomfield, CT 06002-0614, (860)242-4593

Acad. for Sports Dentistry [16709], 118 Faye St., Farmersville, IL 62533, (217)227-3431

Acad. for Sports Dentistry [★16709]

Acad. for Sports Dentistry [16709], 118 Faye St., Farmersville, IL 62533, (217)227-3431

Acad. of Students of Pharmacy [★16177]

Acad. of Surgical Res. [15335], 7500 Flying Cloud Dr., Ste. 900, Eden Prairie, MN 55344, (952)253-6240

Acad. of TV Arts and Sciences [477], 5220 Lankershim Blvd., North Hollywood, CA 91601-3109, (818)754-2800

Acad. of Upper Cervical Chiropractic Organizations - Address unknown since 2010.

Acad. of Veterinary Homeopathy [16971], PO Box 232282, Encinitas, CA 92023-2282, (866)652-1590

Academy of Wind and Percussion Arts [★10255]

AcademyHealth [14691], 1150 17th St. NW, Ste. 600, Washington, DC 20036, (202)292-6700

Acadian Cultural Soc. - Address unknown since 2011.

Acadian Entomological Soc. [IO], St. John's, NL, Canada

Acadian Genealogical and Historical Assn. [★20615]

Acadian Genealogical and Historical Assn. [★20615]

Acadian Genealogical and Historical Assn. of New Hampshire [★20615]

Acadian Genealogical and Historical Assn. of New Hampshire [★20615]

Acarological Soc. of Am.

Acarological Soc. of Am. - Address unknown since 2011.

ACB Radio Amateurs [20930], 2200 Wilson Blvd., Ste. 650, Arlington, VA 22201, (202)467-5081

Accademia Agraria [IO], Pesaro, Italy

Accademia Americana in Rome [★IO]

Accademia d'Arte e Design - Leonetto Cappiello [IO], Florence, Italy

Accademia di Medicina di Torino [IO], Turin, Italy

Accademia Nazionale dei Lincei [IO], Rome, Italy

Accademia Pontaniana [IO], Naples, Italy

Accademia delle Scienze di Torino [IO], Turin, Italy

ACCE Communications Coun. - Address unknown since 2011.

Accelerated Cure Proj. for Multiple Sclerosis [15560], 300 Fifth Ave., Waltham, MA 02451, (781)487-0008

Accellera Org. [6644], 1370 Trancas St., No. 163, Napa, CA 94558, (707)251-9977

Accent on Information - Defunct.

ACCESS: An International Affairs Information Service - Defunct.

Access to Benefits Coalition [17760], 1901 L St. NW, 4th Fl., Washington, DC 20036, (202)479-6670

access Cinema [IO], Dublin, Ireland

Access Copyright, The Canadian Copyright Licensing Agency [IO], Toronto, ON, Canada

Access to Empowerment Intl. [11901], 12523 Limonite Ave., No. 440-222, Mira Loma, CA 91752, (951)440-5542

Access Flooring Assn. [IO], Hull, United Kingdom

Access Fund [22959], PO Box 17010, Boulder, CO 80308, (303)545-6772

ACCESS Hea. Intl. [14744], 3053 P St. NW, Washington, DC 20007

Access to Justice [IO], Lagos, Nigeria

Access to Justice Network [IO], Edmonton, AB, Canada

Access Proj. [14745], 89 South St., Ste. 202, Lincoln Plz., Boston, MA 02111, (617)654-9911

Access Res. Network [8833], PO Box 38069, Colorado Springs, CO 80937-8069, (719)633-1772

Access Tech. Assn. - Defunct.

Accessibility Equip. Mfrs. Assn. [11752], PO Box 380, Metamora, IL 61548-0380, (800)514-1100

Accessibility Interoperability Alliance [6966], 401 N Michigan Ave., Chicago, IL 60611-4267

Accessible Housing Soc. [IO], Calgary, AB, Canada

Accessories Coun. [198], 390 Fifth Ave., Ste. 710, New York, NY 10018, (212)947-1135

Accident Reconstruction Specialists; Natl. Assn. of Professional [5965]

Accidental Nuclear War Prevention Proj. [★18270]

Accidental Nuclear War Prevention Proj. [★18270]

Accio dels Cristians per l'Abolicio de la Tortura [IO], Barcelona, Spain

Accio Psoriasi [IO], Barcelona, Spain

Accion Ciudadana [IO], Guatemala City, Guatemala

Accion de los Cristianos para la Abolocion de la Tortura [★IO]

ACCION Intl. [17366], 56 Roland St., Ste. 300, Boston, MA 02129, (617)625-7080

ACCION Intl. [17366], 56 Roland St., Ste. 300, Boston, MA 02129, (617)625-7080

Accion Permanente Por la Paz [★18161]

Accion Permanente Por la Paz [★18161]

Acclimatization Experiences Inst. [★8144]

Acclimatization Experiences Inst. [★8144]

Accokeek Found. [9659], 3400 Bryan Point Rd., Accokeek, MD 20607, (301)283-2113

ACCORD [20169], PO Box 2336 ., Colorado Springs, CO 80901

Accord Alliance [13114], 531 Rte. 22 E No. 244, Whitehouse Station, NJ 08889, (908)349-0534

Accordion Fed. of North Am. - Address unknown since 2010.

Accordion Soc. of Australia [IO], Earlwood, Australia

Accordion Teachers' Guild [★8637]

Accordion Teachers' Guild [★8637]

Accordionists and Teachers Guild, Intl. [8637], PO Box 68012, Minneapolis, MN 55418, (612)781-8192

Accordionists and Teachers Guild, Intl. [8637], PO Box 68012, Minneapolis, MN 55418, (612)781-8192

Accountability in Intl. Development [12308], 324 S Pacific Coast Hwy., Ste. 202, Redondo Beach, CA 90277, (310)279-7026

Accountability in Intl. Development [12308], 324 S Pacific Coast Hwy., Ste. 202, Redondo Beach, CA 90277, (310)279-7026

Accountant's Advanced Marketing Network Assn. [★2]

Accountants and Auditors Assn. [IO], Sharjah, United Arab Emirates

Accountants Global Network [1], 2851 S Parker Rd., Ste. 850, Aurora, CO 80014, (303)743-7880

Accountants Global Network [1], 2851 S Parker Rd., Ste. 850, Aurora, CO 80014, (303)743-7880

Accountants Motivational Marketing Org. [2], 1 Country Club Exec. Park, Glen Carbon, IL 62034, (618)288-8795

Accountants for the Public Interest - Defunct.

Accounting

Accountants Global Network [1]

Accountants Global Network [1]

Accountants Motivational Marketing Org. [2]

Accounting and Finance Benchmarking Consortium [637]

Accreditation Coun. for Accountancy and Taxation [3]

Advt. and Marketing Intl. Network [77]

AGN Intl. North Am. [4]

Amer. Accounting Assn. [5]

Amer. Accounts Payable Assn. [6]

Amer. Assn. of Attorney-Certified Public Accountants [7]

Amer. Inst. of Certified Public Accountants [8]

Amer. Soc. of Women Accountants [9]

Amer. Woman's Soc. of Certified Public Accountants [10]

Ascend [11]

Assn. for Accounting Admin. [12]

Assn. of Chartered Accountants in the U.S. [13]

Assn. of Govt. Accountants [5180]

Assn. of Insolvency and Restructuring Advisors [14]

Assn. of Latino Professionals in Finance and Accounting [15]

Auditing Assn. of Canada [11769]

Beta Alpha Psi [23459]

BKR Intl. [16]

BKR Intl. [16]

Community Banking Advisory Network [17]

Constr. Indus. CPAs/Consultants Assn. [18]

Controllers Coun. [19]

Coun. of Petroleum Accountants Societies [20]

CPA Associates Intl. [21]

CPA Associates Intl. [21]

CPA Auto Dealer Consultants Assn. [22]

CPA Mfg. Services Assn. [23]

CPAmerica Intl. [24]

CPAmerica Intl. [24]

DFK International/USA [25]

Financial Accounting Standards Bd. [26]

Forensic Accountants Soc. of North Am. [27]

Found. for Accounting Educ. [28]

Governmental Accounting Standards Bd. [5181]

IGAF Worldwide [29]

Inst. of Chartered Accountants of Guyana [11916]

Inst. of Internal Auditors [30]

Inst. of Internal Auditors [30]

Inst. of Mgt. Accountants [31]

Interamerican Accounting Assn. [32]

Interamerican Accounting Assn. [32]

Intl. Accounts Payable Professionals [33]

Intl. Assn. for Res. in Income and Wealth [17139]

Intl. Assn. for Res. in Income and Wealth [17139]

Intl. Budget Partnership [34]

Intl. Budget Proj. of the Center on Budget and Policy Priorities [34]

Intl. Fed. of Accountants [35]

Intl. Fed. of Accountants [35]

Intl. Gp. of Accounting Firms [29]

Intl. Soc. of Filipinos in Finance and Accounting [36]

Leading Edge Alliance [37]

Medical Dental Hosp. Bus. Associates [38]

Moore Stephens North Am. [39]

Natl. Accounting and Finance Coun. [40]

Natl. Assoc. CPA Firms [41]

Natl. Assn. of Black Accountants [42]

Natl. Assn. of Certified Public Bookkeepers [43]

Natl. Assn. of Certified Valuation Analysts [44]

Natl. Assn. of Certified Valuators and Analysts [44]

Natl. Assn. of Forensic Accountants [45]

Natl. Assn. of State Boards of Accountancy [5182]

Natl. Conf. of CPA Practitioners [46]

Natl. CPA Hea. Care Advisors Assn. [13570]

Natl. Fed. of Municipal Analysts [47]

Natl. Soc. of Accountants [48]

Natl. Soc. of Accountants for Cooperatives [49]

Not-For-Profit Services Assn. [50]

PKF North Amer. Network [51]

PKF North Amer. Network [51]

Professional Accounting Soc. of Am. [52]

Professional Animal Auditor Certification Org. [53]

Professional Assn. of Small Bus. Accountants [54]

Soc. of Depreciation Professionals [55]

Traffic Audit Bur. for Media Measurement [56]

Accounting and Auditing Org. for Islamic Financial Institutions [IO], Manama, Bahrain

Accounting and Finance Assn. of Australia and New Zealand [IO], Carlton, Australia

Accounting and Finance Benchmarking Consortium [637], 4606 FM 1960 W, Ste. 250, Houston, TX 77069-9949, (800)324-4685

Accounting Technicians Ireland [IO], Dublin, Ireland

ACCRA [★23358]

Accreditation

Accreditation Coun. for Graduate Medical Educ. [7642]

Accrediting Commn. of Career Schools and Colleges of Tech. [7643]

Accrediting Coun. for Independent Colleges and Schools [7644]

Amer. Assn. of Christian Schools [7645]

Amer. Commn. for Accreditation of Reflexology Educ. and Training [7726]

Assn. for the Accreditation of Human Res. Protection Programs [10771]

A star before a book entry number signifies that the name is not listed separately, but is mentioned within the entry.

Certification of Disability Mgt. Specialists Commn. [13571]

Commn. on Accreditation of Ambulance Services [13572]

Healthcare Laundry Accreditation Coun. [2192]

Healthcare Quality Certification Bd. [13573]

Intl. Christian Accrediting Assn. [7646]

Intl. Christian Accrediting Assn. [7646]

Natl. Accrediting Commn. of Cosmetology Arts and Sciences [7647]

Natl. Assn. of Private Catholic and Independent Schools [7648]

Natl. Bd. of Surgical Tech. and Surgical Assisting [13574]

Natl. Coun. for Accreditation of Teacher Educ. [7649]

Natl. Coun. for Private School Accreditation [7650]

Accreditation Assn. for Ambulatory Hea. Care [13725], 5250 Old Orchard Rd., Ste. 200, Skokie, IL 60077, (847)853-6060

Accreditation Bd. for Engg. and Tech. - ABET [★6764]

Accreditation Commn. for Acupuncture and Oriental Medicine [16009], 14502 Greenview Dr., Ste. 300B, Laurel, MD 20708, (301)313-0855

Accreditation Comm. on Educ. for Physicians Assistants [★16234]

Accreditation Coun. for Accountancy [★3]

Accreditation Coun. for Accountancy and Taxation [3], 1010 N Fairfax St., Alexandria, VA 22314-1574, (888)289-7763

Accreditation Coun. for Bus. Schools and Programs [7867], 11520 W 119th St., Overland Park, KS 66213, (913)339-9356

Accreditation Coun. for Continuing Medical Educ. [15389], 515 N State St., Ste. 1801, Chicago, IL 60654, (312)527-9200

Accreditation Coun. for Facilities for the Mentally Retarded [★12501]

Accreditation Coun. for Facilities for the Mentally Retarded [★12501]

Accreditation Coun. for Graduate Medical Educ. [7642], 515 N State St., Ste. 2000, Chicago, IL 60610-4322, (312)755-5000

Accreditation Coun. on Optometric Educ. [15986], Amer. Optometric Assn., 243 N Lindbergh Blvd., 1st Fl., St. Louis, MO 63141-7881, (314)991-4100

Accreditation Coun. for Pharmacy Educ. [16165], 135 S LaSalle St., Ste. 4100, Chicago, IL 60603-4810, (312)664-3575

Accreditation Coun. for Services for Mentally Retarded and Other Developmentally Disabled Persons [★12501]

Accreditation Coun. for Services for Mentally Retarded and Other Developmentally Disabled Persons [★12501]

Accreditation Coun. on Services for People with Developmental Disabilities [★12501]

Accreditation Coun. on Services for People with Developmental Disabilities [★12501]

Accreditation Coun. on Services for People with Disabilities [★12501]

Accreditation Coun. on Services for People with Disabilities [★12501]

Accreditation Rev. Commn. on Educ. for the Physician Asst. [16234], 12000 Findley Rd., Ste. 150, Johns Creek, GA 30097, (770)476-1224

Accreditation Rev. Comm. on Educ. for Physician Assistants [★16234]

Accreditation Rev. Comm. for Educational Programs in Surgical Tech. [★15361]

Accreditation Rev. Coun. on Educ. in Surgical Tech. and Surgical Assisting [15361], 6 W Dry Creek Cir., Ste. 110, Littleton, CO 80120, (303)694-9262

Accredited Certifiers Assn. [4760], PO Box 472, Port Crane, NY 13833, (607)648-3259

Accredited Gemologists Assn. [2152], 3315 Juanita St., San Diego, CA 92105, (619)501-5444

Accredited Home Newspapers of Am. [★2967]

Accredited Pet Cemetery Soc. - Address unknown since 2010.

Accredited Rev. Appraisers Coun. - Address unknown since 2010.

Accredited Standards Comm. NCITS, Natl. Comm. for Info. Tech. Standards [★7510]

Accredited Standards Comm. X3, Info. Tech. [★7510]

Accrediting Agency for Clinical Lab. Sciences; Natl. [15379]

Accrediting Assn. of Bible Colleges [★7850]

Accrediting Bur. of Hea. Educ. Schools [15362], 7777 Leesburg Pike, Ste. 314 N, Falls Church, VA 22043, (703)917-9503

Accrediting Bur. of Medical Lab. Schools [★15362]

Accrediting Commn. of Career Schools and Colleges of Tech. [7643], 2101 Wilson Blvd., Ste. 302, Arlington, VA 22201, (703)247-4212

Accrediting Commn. for Cosmetology Educ. [★7647]

Accrediting Coun. for Continuing Educ. and Training [7919], 1722 N St. NW, Washington, DC 20036, (202)955-1113

Accrediting Coun. on Educ. in Journalism and Mass Communications [8434], Stauffer-Flint Hall, 1435 Jayhawk Blvd., Lawrence, KS 66045-7575, (785)864-3973

Accrediting Coun. for Independent Colleges and Schools [7644], 750 1st St. NE, Ste. 980, Washington, DC 20002-4241, (202)336-6780

Accrediting Coun. for Theological Educ. in Africa [IO], Ndola, Zambia

Accuracy in Academia [8104], 4455 Connecticut Ave. NW, Ste. 330, Washington, DC 20008, (202)364-3085

Accuracy in Media [17332], 4455 Connecticut Ave. NW, Ste. 330, Washington, DC 20008, (202)364-4401

ACDI/VOCA [4174], 50 F St. NW, Ste. 1075, Washington, DC 20001, (202)469-6000

ACDI/VOCA [4174], 50 F St. NW, Ste. 1075, Washington, DC 20001, (202)469-6000

ACFO [IO], Petersfield, United Kingdom

Achieve in Africa [11173], 1104 Woodridge Ave., Thousand Oaks, CA 91362

Achieve in Africa [11173], 1104 Woodridge Ave., Thousand Oaks, CA 91362

Achievers Intl. [IO], London, United Kingdom

Achilles Intl. [22499], 42 W 38th St., Ste. 400, New York, NY 10018, (212)354-0300

Achilles Track Club [★22499]

Achromatopsia Network [17055], 230 Gosset's Turn Dr., Middletown, RI 02842, (401)848-9699

ACI - Financial Markets Assn. [IO], Paris, France

Acid Maltase Deficiency

Acid Maltase Deficiency Assn. [13575]

Acid Maltase Deficiency Assn. [13575], PO Box 700248, San Antonio, TX 78270-0248, (210)494-6144

The Acid Rain Found. - Defunct.

ACIL [★7019]

Acindar Found. [IO], Buenos Aires, Argentina

ACJ-YMCA Guatemala [IO], Guatemala City, Guatemala

Ackerman Inst. for the Family [11992], 149 E 78th St., New York, NY 10075, (212)879-4900

Ackerman Inst. for Family Therapy [★11992]

ACLU | Natl. Prison Proj. [11699], 915 15th St. NW, 7th Fl., Washington, DC 20005, (202)393-4930

ACM Hong Kong Chap. [IO], Hong Kong, People's Republic of China

ACM Japan Chap. [IO], Tokyo, Japan

ACM SIGCHI [★6267]

ACM SIGGRAPH [6441], PO Box 30777, New York, NY 10087-0777, (212)626-0500

ACM SIGGRAPH [6441], PO Box 30777, New York, NY 10087-0777, (212)626-0500

ACMHA: The Coll. for Behavioral Hea. Leadership [15440], 7804 Loma del Norte Rd. NE, Albuquerque, NM 87109, (505)822-5038

ACMP - The Chamber Music Network [10133], 1123 Broadway, Ste. 904, New York, NY 10010-2007, (212)645-7424

ACMP - The Chamber Music Network [10133], 1123 Broadway, Ste. 904, New York, NY 10010-2007, (212)645-7424

ACORD [1921], 2 Blue Hill Plz., 3rd Fl., PO Box 1529, Pearl River, NY 10965-8529, (845)620-1700

ACORD [1921], 2 Blue Hill Plz., 3rd Fl., PO Box 1529, Pearl River, NY 10965-8529, (845)620-1700

Acoustic Neuroma Assn. [16080], 600 Peachtree Pkwy., Ste. 108, Cumming, GA 30041-6899, (770)205-8211

Acoustic Neuroma Assn. of Canada [IO], Peterborough, ON, Canada

Acoustical Soc. of Am. [6078], 2 Huntington Quadrangle, Ste. 1N01, Melville, NY 11747-4505, (516)576-2360

Acoustical Soc. of China [IO], Beijing, People's Republic of China

Acoustical Soc. of the Netherlands [IO], Nieuwegein, Netherlands

Acoustical Soc. of Scandinavia [IO], Lyngby, Denmark

Acoustics

Acoustical Soc. of Am. [6078]

IEEE | Signal Processing Soc. [6079]

IEEE | Ultrasonics, Ferroelectrics, and Frequency Control Soc. [6080]

ACP-EU Joint Parliamentary Assembly [IO], Brussels, Belgium

ACP-UE Assembee Parlementaire Paritaire [★IO]

ACRES, Inc. [★3977]

Acres Land Trust [3977], 1802 Chapman Rd., Huntertown, IN 46748, (260)637-2273

Acronym Inst. for Disarmament Diplomacy [IO], London, United Kingdom

Across [IO], Nairobi, Kenya

Acrylonitrile Gp. [740], 1250 Connecticut Ave. NW, Ste. 700, Washington, DC 20036, (202)419-1500

ACT [8982], PO Box 168, Iowa City, IA 52244-0168, (319)337-1000

Act for Africa Intl. [12951], PO Box 2031, Manassas, VA 20108, (571)212-6167

ACT Assn. for the Teaching of English [IO], Hawker, Australia

ACT Canada [IO], Ajax, ON, Canada

ACT New Zealand [IO], Auckland, New Zealand

ACT Palliative Care Soc. [IO], Canberra, Australia

ACT and Region Chamber of Commerce and Indus. [IO], Deakin West, Australia

ACT Right to Life Assn. [IO], Canberra, Australia

Act Together [IO], London, United Kingdom

Acting

Directors Guild of Am. [23187]

Intl. Guild of Symphony, Opera and Ballet Musicians [23272]

Natl. Assn. Broadcast Employees and Technicians | Communications Workers of Am. [23162]

Richard Burgi Fan Club [23781]

Acting for Life [IO], Paris, France

Action 81 - Defunct.

Action Against Allergy [IO], Twickenham, United Kingdom

Action Against Hunger [11844], 247 W 37th St., 10th Fl., New York, NY 10018, (212)967-7800

Action Against Hunger [11844], 247 W 37th St., 10th Fl., New York, NY 10018, (212)967-7800

Action Against Hunger - France [IO], Paris, France

Action Against Medical Accidents [IO], Croydon, United Kingdom

Action for Animals [10898], PO Box 45843, Seattle, WA 98145, (206)227-5752

Action for Autism [IO], New Delhi, India

Action for Blind People [IO], London, United Kingdom

Action Cancer [IO], Belfast, United Kingdom

Action for Child Protection [11174], 2101 Sardis Rd. N, Ste. 204, Charlotte, NC 28227, (704)845-2121

Action Children Aid [IO], Copenhagen, Denmark

Action for Children in Conflict [IO], Abingdon, United Kingdom

Action for Children - Zambia [11175], 20855 Kensington Blvd., Lakeville, MN 55044

Action des Chretiens pour l'Abolition de la Torture - Belgium [IO], Brussels, Belgium

Action des Chretiens pour l'Abolition de la Torture - France [★IO]

Action des Chretiens pour l'Abolition de la Torture - Switzerland [IO], Bern, Switzerland

Action by Churches Together Intl. [IO], Geneva, Switzerland

Action for Clean Energy [4224], 614 Massachusetts Ave., Cambridge, MA 02139, (510)673-2440

Action Coalition for Media Educ. [18088], 2808 El Tesoro Escondido NW, Albuquerque, NM 87120, (505)893-9702

Action Comm. Ser. for Peace [IO], Bonn, Germany

Action for Community and Human Development [IO], Monrovia, Liberia

Action for Concern of Crisis Victims in Africa [IO], Monrovia, Liberia

Action Consulting Assn. [★11538]

Action Consulting Assn. [★11538]

Action Contre la Faim [★IO]

Action to Cure Kidney Cancer [13875], 150 W 75th St., Ste. 4, New York, NY 10023, (212)714-5341

Action Damien [★IO]

Action for Development [IO], Kampala, Uganda

Action in Disabilities - India [IO], Chennai, India

Action on Disability and Development [IO], Frome, United Kingdom

Action on Elder Abuse [IO], London, United Kingdom

Action for Enterprise [11538], 2009 N 14th St., Ste. 301, Arlington, VA 22201, (703)243-9172

Action for Enterprise [11538], 2009 N 14th St., Ste. 301, Arlington, VA 22201, (703)243-9172

Action for Food Production [IO], New Delhi, India

Action Hea. - Nigeria [IO], Lagos, Nigeria

Action for Healthy Bones [IO], Graz, Austria

Action for Healthy Kids [14054], 600 W Van Buren St., Ste. 720, Chicago, IL 60607, (800)416-5136

Action for Humanity - Uganda [IO], Kampala, Uganda

Action for Independent Maturity [★12914]

Action Intl. Ministries [19728], PO Box 398, Mount-lake Terrace, WA 98043-0398, (425)775-4800

Action Intl. Ministries [19728], PO Box 398, Mount-lake Terrace, WA 98043-0398, (425)775-4800

Action from Ireland [IO], Dublin, Ireland

Action Jeunesses pour la Paix [★IO]

Action for Market Towns [IO], Bury St. Edmunds, United Kingdom

Action for Nature [4233], 2269 Chestnut St., No. 263, San Francisco, CA 94123, (415)513-2421

Action for Post-Soviet Jewry [17564], 24 Crescent St., Ste. 306, Waltham, MA 02453-4089, (781)893-2331

Action for Post-Soviet Jewry [17564], 24 Crescent St., Ste. 306, Waltham, MA 02453-4089, (781)893-2331

Action Reconciliation Ser. for Peace [IO], Berlin, Germany

Action for Sick Children [IO], Stockport, United Kingdom

Action for Singapore Dogs Soc. [IO], Singapore, Singapore

Action on Smoking and Hea. [16671], 701 4th St. NW, Washington, DC 20001, (202)659-4310

Action on Smoking and Hea. - England [IO], London, United Kingdom

Action on Smoking and Hea. - Ireland [IO], Dublin, Ireland

Action on Smoking and Hea. - Scotland [IO], Edinburgh, United Kingdom

Action for Solidarity, Equality, Env. and Development [IO], Tokyo, Japan

Action for Solidarity, Equality, Env. and Diversity - Europe [IO], Amsterdam, Netherlands

Action for Southern Africa [IO], London, United Kingdom

Action for Soviet Jewry [★17564]

Action for Soviet Jewry [★17564]

Action for Victims of Medical Accidents [★8116]

Action Volunteers for Animals [IO], Unionville, ON, Canada

Action Without Borders/Idealist.org [17726], 302 5th Ave., 11th Fl., New York, NY 10001, (212)843-3973

Action Without Borders/Idealist.org [17726], 302 5th Ave., 11th Fl., New York, NY 10001, (212)843-3973

Action for World Solidarity [IO], Berlin, Germany

ActionAid [IO], London, United Kingdom

ActionAid - Brasil [IO], Rio de Janeiro, Brazil

ActionAid - Cambodia [IO], Phnom Penh, Cambodia

ActionAid Intl. USA [11539], 1420 K St. NW, Ste. 900, Washington, DC 20005, (202)835-1240

ActionAid Intl. USA [11539], 1420 K St. NW, Ste. 900, Washington, DC 20005, (202)835-1240

ActionAid - Nepal [IO], Kathmandu, Nepal

ActionAid - Sierra Leone [IO], Nairobi, Kenya

ActionAid - Vietnam [IO], Hanoi, Vietnam

Actions for Intl. Solidarity - France [IO], Paris, France

Actions de Solidarite Internationale - France [★IO]

ACTIS/ATIS [★13597]

Activ Found. [IO], Wembley, Australia

Active 20-30 Assn. of U.S./Canada [13049], 915 L St., Ste. 1000, Sacramento, CA 95814, (916)447-3217

Active 20-30 Intl. [★13049]

Active Intl. [★13049]

Active Learning Network for Accountability and Performance in Humanitarian Action [IO], London, United Kingdom

Active Living Alliance for Canadians with a Disability [IO], Ottawa, ON, Canada

Active Minds [15441], 2001 S St. NW, Ste. 450, Washington, DC 20009, (202)332-9595

Active Retirement Ireland [IO], Dublin, Ireland

Active - Sobriety, Friendship and Peace [IO], Stockholm, Sweden

Active: Water [13410], PO Box 37, Mattawan, MI 49071, (269)492-6470

Acton Inst. for the Stud. of Religion and Liberty [20172], 161 Ottawa Ave. NW, Ste. 301, Grand Rapids, MI 49503, (616)454-3080

Actors

Ann-Margret's Official Fan Club [23760]

Beyond the Rainbow [23761]

Bruce Boxleitner's Official Fan Club [23762]

Conrad Veidt Soc. [23763]

David Birney Intl. Fan Club [23764]

David Birney Intl. Fan Club [23764]

Dinah Shore Memorial Fan Club [23765]

Directors Guild of Am. [23187]

Elvira Fan Club [23766]

Friends of Debbie Reynolds Fan Club [23767]

Friends of Hopalong Cassidy Fan Club [23768]

Gale Storm Appreciation Soc. [23769]

Gary's Web Intl. [23770]

Intl. Crosby Circle [23857]

Intl. Guild of Symphony, Opera and Ballet Musicians [23272]

Jeanette MacDonald Intl. Fan Club [23771]

Jon-Erik Hexum Fan Club [23772]

Leslie Charleson Fan Club [23773]

Linda Gray's Official Fan Club [23774]

Lindsay Wagner's Official Fan Club [23775]

Louise Brooks Soc. [23776]

Louise Brooks Soc. [23776]

Michael Crawford Intl. Fan Assn. [23777]

Michele Lee Fan Club/Michele Lee Online [23778]

Natl. Assn. Broadcast Employees and Technicians I Communications Workers of Am. [23162]

Official Intl. Michael York Fan Club [23779]

Official Robert Newman Fan Club [23780]

Richard Burgi Fan Club [23781]

Rick's Loyal Supporters [23886]

Rita Hayworth Fan Club [23782]

Robert Redford Fan Club [23783]

Shatner and Friends Intl. [23784]

Stars for Stripes [20417]

Stefanie Powers' Official Fan Club [23785]

We Love Lucy/International Lucille Ball Fan Club [23786]

Zuzu News [23787]

Actors and Athletes Against Drunk Driving; Recording Artists, [13003]

Actors' Equity Assn. [23264], 165 W 46th St., New York, NY 10036, (212)869-8530

Actors' Fund [11968], 729 Seventh Ave., 10th Fl., New York, NY 10019, (212)221-7300

Actors and Others for Animals [10899], 11523 Burbank Blvd., North Hollywood, CA 91601, (818)755-6045

Actuarial Assn. [IO], Utrecht, Netherlands

Actuarial Soc. of Am. [★2038]

Actuarial Soc. of Hong Kong [IO], Hong Kong, People's Republic of China

Actuarial Soc. of South Africa [IO], Cape Town, Republic of South Africa

Actuarieel Genootschap [★IO]

ACU Educ. Res. Inst. [★17721]

ACUO [8094], PO Box 6063, McLean, VA 22106-6063, (202)659-2104

Acupressure; Jin Shin Do Found. for Bodymind [16015]

Acupressure; Jin Shin Do Found. for Bodymind [16015]

Acupuncture

Acupuncture for Veterans [13576]

Acupuncturists Without Borders [13577]

Acupuncturists Without Borders [13577]

Amer. Abdominal Acupuncture Medical Assn. [13578]

Amer. Assn. of Traditional Chinese Veterinary Medicine [13653]

Community Acupuncture Network [13579]

Coun. for Acupuncture Res. and Educ. [13580]

Coun. of Chiropractic Acupuncture [14128]

HealingWorks [13681]

Mindful Medicine Worldwide [13693]

Soc. for Acupuncture Res. [13581]

Soc. for Acupuncture Res. [13581]

Traditional Chinese Medicine Assn. and Alumni [13714]

Acupuncture; Amer. Acad. of Medical [16010]

Acupuncture Detoxification Assn; Natl. [16745]

Acupuncture Detoxification Assn; Natl. [16745]

Acupuncture Found. of Canada Inst. [IO], Scarborough, ON, Canada

Acupuncture and Oriental Medicine; Accreditation Commn. for [16009]

Acupuncture and Oriental Medicine; Amer. Acad. of [13649]

Acupuncture and Oriental Medicine; Coun. of Colleges of [16012]

Acupuncture and Oriental Medicine; Natl. Certification Commn. for [16016]

Acupuncture Res. Inst. - Defunct.

Acupuncture for Veterans [13576], 119-40 Metropolitan Ave., Concourse 102, Kew Gardens, NY 11415-2642, (718)847-7278

Acupuncturists Without Borders [13577], 909 Virginia NE, Ste. 211, Albuquerque, NM 87108, (505)266-3878

Acupuncturists Without Borders [13577], 909 Virginia NE, Ste. 211, Albuquerque, NM 87108, (505)266-3878

ACURIL [★9964]

ACURIL [★9964]

ACURP [★16505]

ACUTA: The Assn. of Coll. and Univ. Telecommunications Administrators Inc. [★8301]

ACUTA: The Assn. for Communications Tech. Professionals in Higher Educ. [8301], 152 W Zandale Dr., Ste. 200, Lexington, KY 40503, (859)278-3338

ACUTA: The Assn. for Telecommunication Professionals in Higher Educ. [★8301]

Acute Long Term Hosp. Assn. [15024], 1667 K St. NW, Ste. 1050, Washington, DC 20006, (202)266-9800

ACV - Bouw en Industrie [IO], Brussels, Belgium

Ad Coun. [18410], 815 2nd Ave., 9th Fl., New York, NY 10017, (212)922-1500

Ad Hoc Coalition on Block Grants [★13179]

Ad Hoc Comm. to Bring Nazi War Criminals to Justice [★17787]

Ad Hoc Gp. on Latin Amer. Anthropology [★6154]

Ad Hoc Gp. on Latin Amer. Anthropology [★6154]

Ad Hoc Gp. for Medical Res. [17761], 2450 N St. NW, Washington, DC 20037-1126, (202)828-0525

Ad Hoc Low Income Housing Coalition [★12193]

Ada Cole Rescue Stables [IO], Waltham Abbey, United Kingdom

Adam Hawkes Family Assn. [20418], 65 Center St., Danvers, MA 01923

Adam Smith Inst. [IO], London, United Kingdom

Adaptive Sports Assn. [22500], PO Box 1884, Durango, CO 81302, (970)259-0374

ADARA [★14911]

ADARA: Professionals Networking for Excellence in Ser. Delivery with Individuals who are Deaf or Hard of Hearing [14911], PO Box 480, Myersville, MD 21773

Adbusters Media Found. [IO], Vancouver, BC, Canada

Addgene [7110], Bldg. 600, 3rd Fl., 1 Kendall Sq., Ste. B6302, Cambridge, MA 02139-1666, (617)225-9000

Addiction Coun; Natl. Black Alcoholism and [13276]

A star before a book entry number signifies that the name is not listed separately, but is mentioned within the entry.

Addiction Medicine; Amer. Osteopathic Acad. of [16735]
Addiction Medicine; Amer. Soc. of [16736]
Addiction Rehabilitation Assn; Christian [13241]
Addiction Res. and Treatment Corp. [13229], 22 Chapel St., Brooklyn, NY 11201, (718)260-2900
Addictions Ontario [IO], Windsor, ON, Canada
Addington Assn. [20419], 100 Oak Beech Ct., Holly Springs, NC 27540
Addison's Disease Self Help Gp. [IO], Guildford, United Kingdom
ADED: The Assn. for Driver Rehabilitation Specialists [7978], 2425 N Center St., No. 369, Hickory, NC 28601, (828)855-1623
ADED: The Assn. for Driver Rehabilitation Specialists [7978], 2425 N Center St., No. 369, Hickory, NC 28601, (828)855-1623
Adelaide Hosp. Soc. [IO], Dublin, Ireland
Adelynrood Retreat Center [★19716]
Adenoid Cystic Carcinoma Org. Intl. [13876], PO Box 112186, Tacoma, WA 98411, (888)223-7983
ADHD Norge [IO], Lysaker, Norway
Adhesion Soc. [6386], 2 Davidson Hall - 0201, Blacksburg, VA 24061, (540)231-7257
Adhesive and Sealant Coun. [57], 7101 Wisconsin Ave., Ste. 990, Bethesda, MD 20814, (301)986-9700

Adhesives
Adhesive and Sealant Coun. [57]
Pressure Sensitive Tape Coun. [58]
Sealant Waterproofing and Restoration Inst. [59]
Sealant Waterproofing and Restoration Inst. [59]
Adhesives Mfrs. Assn. - Defunct.
The Adirondack Coun. [3978], 103 Hand Ave., Ste. 3, PO Box D-2, Elizabethtown, NY 12932, (877)873-2240
Adirondack Forty-Sixers [23075], PO Box 180, Cadyville, NY 12918-0180, (518)293-6401
Adirondack Historical Assn. [9085], Adirondack Museum, PO Box 89, Blue Mountain Lake, NY 12812-0099, (518)352-7311
Adirondack Mountain Club [23076], 814 Goggins Rd., Lake George, NY 12845, (518)668-4447
Adirondack Trail Improvement Soc. [23077], PO Box 565, Keene Valley, NY 12943, (518)576-9949

Adirondacks
Adirondack Historical Assn. [9085]
Adizes Network Intl. [★2268]
Adizes Network Intl. [★2268]
Adjutants Gen. Assn. of the U.S. [5791], 1 Massachusetts Ave. NW, Washington, DC 20001-1401, (202)789-0031
Adlerian Psychology; North Amer. Soc. of [16415]

Administration
African Amer. Fed. Executive Assn. [5504]
Amer. Assn. of School Administrators [7651]
Amer. Assn. of School Personnel Administrators [7652]
Amer. Assn. of School Personnel Administrators [7652]
Amer. Assn. of Univ. Administrators [7653]
Amer. Coll. of Healthcare Info. Administrators [14753]
Amer. Conf. of Academic Deans [7654]
Amer. Coun. on Educ., Fellows Prog. [7655]
Amer. Fed. of School Administrators [7656]
Assn. for the Advancement of Intl. Educ. [8388]
Assn. of Coll. Admin. Professionals [7657]
Assn. of Coll. and Univ. Auditors [7658]
Assn. of Coll. and Univ. Auditors [7658]
Assn. of Dermatology Administrators and Managers [14323]
Assn. of Governing Boards of Universities and Colleges [7659]
Assn. of Intl. Educ. Administrators [7660]
Assn. of Intl. Educ. Administrators [7660]
Assn. of Latino Administrators and Superintendents [7661]
Assn. of School Bus. Officials Intl. [7662]
Assn. of School Bus. Officials Intl. [7662]
Assn. of Schools of Journalism and Mass Commun. [7663]
Australian Coun. for Educational Leaders [23890]
Educational Res. Ser. [7664]
Executives Without Borders [60]

Intl. Assn. of Schools and Institutes of Admin. [4336]
Jesuit Assn. of Student Personnel Administrators [7665]
NASPA - Student Affairs Administrators in Higher Educ. [7666]
Natl. Assn. of Coll. and Univ. Bus. Officers [7667]
Natl. Assn. of Educational Off. Professionals [7668]
Natl. Assn. of Educational Procurement [7669]
Natl. Assn. of Fed. Educ. Prog. Administrators [7670]
Natl. Assn. of Peoplecultural Engg. Prog. Advocates [8127]
Natl. Assn. of Pupil Services Administrators [7671]
Natl. Assn. of State Directors of Special Educ. [8888]
Natl. Assn. of Student Affairs Professionals [7672]
Natl. Center for Higher Educ. Mgt. Systems [7673]
Natl. Orientation Directors Assn. [7674]
Natl. School Plant Mgt. Assn. [7675]
Natl. Staff Development Coun. [7676]
Natl. Title I Assn. [7677]
Univ. Coun. for Educational Admin. [7678]
Administrative Personnel Assn. of the Presbyterian Church [19609], 1201 W Wall, Midland, TX 79701-6619, (432)682-5297

Administrative Services
AFL-CIO I SEIU I District 925 [23140]
Amer. Coll. of Healthcare Info. Administrators [14753]
Assn. of Celebrity Personal Assistants [61]
Assn. of Executive and Administrative Professionals [62]
Assn. for Financial Tech. [63]
Assn. of Healthcare Administrative Professionals [64]
Assn. of Local Govt. Auditors [5183]
Black Data Processing Associates [65]
Chartered Secretaries Australia [16540]
Executive Women Intl. [66]
Executive Women Intl. [66]
Info. Systems Audit and Control Assn. and Found. [67]
Info. Systems Audit and Control Assn. and Found. [67]
Intl. Assn. for Human Rsrc. Info. Mgt. [68]
Intl. Assn. for Human Rsrc. Info. Mgt. [68]
Intl. Virtual Assistants Assn. [69]
Legal Secretaries Intl. [70]
Legal Secretaries Intl. [70]
MEMA Tech. Coun. [71]
Natl. Assn. of Legal Secretaries Intl. [72]
Natl. Assn. of Legal Secretaries Intl. [72]
Off. Bus. Center Assn. Intl. [73]
Off. and Professional Employees Intl. Union [23141]
Soc. of Corporate Secretaries and Governance Professionals [74]

Admissions
Amer. Assn. of Collegiate Registrars and Admissions Officers [7679]
Amer. Intl. Recruitment Coun. [7680]
Assn. of Independent School Admission Professionals [7681]
Assn. of Intl. Graduate Admissions Consultants [7682]
Coll. Summit [8234]
Educ. Conservancy [7683]
Natl. Assn. for Coll. Admission Counseling [7684]
Natl. Assn. of Graduate Admissions Professionals [7685]
North Amer. Coalition for Christian Admissions Professionals [7686]
Overseas Assn. for Coll. Admission Counseling [7687]
Adolescent Psychiatry; Amer. Soc. for [16333]
Adolescent Psychiatry; Amer. Soc. for [16333]
Adolescent Scoliosis Soc. of North Am. [16638], PO Box 1178, Rocky Mount, NC 27802-1178
Adolph and Esther Gottlieb Found. [9216], 380 W Broadway, New York, NY 10012, (212)226-0581
Adopt-A-Church Intl. [19610], PO Box 510, Allen-dale, MI 49401, (616)892-4260

Adopt-A-Church Intl. [19610], PO Box 510, Allen-dale, MI 49401, (616)892-4260
Adopt-A-Hawk Prog. [★7200]
Adopt-A-Hawk Prog. [★7200]
Adopt-A-Horse Prog. [★4572]
Adopt A Husky [10900], PO Box 87226, Carol Stream, IL 60188-7226, (262)909-2244
Adopt-A-Minefield [IO], London, United Kingdom
Adopt-a-Village Intl. [11540], PO Box 26599, Colorado Springs, CO 80936, (719)492-8736
Adopt Am. Network [10772], 1500 N Superior St., Ste. 303, Toledo, OH 43604, (419)726-5100
Adopt a Building Prog. [★11683]
Adopt a Dr. [16245], 101 Dyer St., Providence, RI 02903, (401)421-0606
Adopt a Special Kid [10773], 8201 Edgewater Dr., Ste. 103, Oakland, CA 94621, (510)553-1748
AdoptaPlatoon [11081], PO Box 1457, Seabrook, NH 03874
Adoptee-Birthparent Support Network [10774], 6439 Woodridge Rd., Alexandria, VA 22312-1336, (301)442-9106
Adoptees and Natural Parents Org. - Defunct.

Adoption
Adopt Am. Network [10772]
Adopt a Special Kid [10773]
Adoptee-Birthparent Support Network [10774]
Adoption Info. Services [10775]
Adoptions Together [10776]
Adoptions Together [10776]
ALMA Soc. [10777]
Am. World Adoption Assn. [10778]
Am. World Adoption Assn. [10778]
Amer. Adoption Cong. [10779]
Amer. World War II Orphans Network [10780]
Amer. World War II Orphans Network [10780]
Assn. of Administrators of the Interstate Compact on Adoption and Medical Assistance [10781]
Bastard Nation: The Adoptee Rights Org. [10782]
Catholic Guardian Soc. and Home Bur. [11208]
Children with AIDS Proj. of Am. [10783]
Children Awaiting Parents [10784]
Concerned Persons for Adoption [10785]
Concerned United Birthparents [10786]
Echo Dogs White Shepherd Rescue [10954]
Embracing Orphans [11267]
Families with Children from China [10787]
Families for Private Adoption [10788]
Friends in Adoption [10789]
Heaven on Earth Soc. for Animals [10977]
Inst. for Adoption Info. [10790]
Intl. Adoption Assn. - Ireland [14988]
Intl. Soundex Reunion Registry [10791]
Intl. Soundex Reunion Registry [10791]
Interracial Family Circle [12012]
Jewish Children's Adoption Network [10792]
Joint Coun. on Intl. Children's Services [10793]
Joint Coun. on Intl. Children's Services [10793]
Kidsave Intl. [10794]
Kidsave Intl. [10794]
Latin Am. Parents Assn. [10795]
Natl. Adoption Center [10796]
Natl. Coun. for Adoption [10797]
North Amer. Coun. on Adoptable Children [10798]
Oper. Identity [10799]
Orphan's Lifeline of Hope Intl. [11385]
Pact, An Adoption Alliance [10800]
Single Mothers By Choice [12622]
Stars of David Intl. [10801]
Stars of David Intl. [10801]
Adoption Coun. of Canada [IO], Ottawa, ON, Canada
Adoption and Family Reunion Center - Defunct.
Adoption Info. Services [10775], 1840 Old Nocross Rd., Ste. 400, Lawrenceville, GA 30044, (770)339-7236
Adoption Roots and Rights [IO], Dorchester, ON, Canada
Adoptions Together [10776], 10230 New Hampshire Ave., Ste. 200, Silver Spring, MD 20903, (301)439-2900
Adoptions Together [10776], 10230 New Hampshire Ave., Ste. 200, Silver Spring, MD 20903, (301)439-2900
Adoptive Families of America - Defunct.

Reference to "IO" in place of a book number signifies that the association may be found in the 50th edition of International Organizations.

ADOREMUS - Soc. for the Renewal of the Sacred Liturgy **[19378]**, PO Box 300561, St. Louis, MO 63130, (314)863-8385
ADOREMUS - Soc. for the Renewal of the Sacred Liturgy **[19378]**, PO Box 300561, St. Louis, MO 63130, (314)863-8385
ADR Inst. of Canada **[IO]**, Toronto, ON, Canada
ADSC: The Intl. Assn. of Found. Drilling **[894]**, 8445 Freeport Pkwy., Ste. 325, Irving, TX 75063, (469)359-6000
ADSC: The Intl. Assn. of Found. Drilling **[894]**, 8445 Freeport Pkwy., Ste. 325, Irving, TX 75063, (469)359-6000
Adsum for Women and Children **[IO]**, Halifax, NS, Canada
Adult Children of Alcoholics, Central Ser. Bd. **[★13034]**
Adult Children of Alcoholics, Central Ser. Bd. **[★13034]**
Adult Children of Alcoholics World Ser. Org. **[13034]**, PO Box 3216, Torrance, CA 90510, (562)595-7831
Adult Children of Alcoholics World Ser. Org. **[13034]**, PO Box 3216, Torrance, CA 90510, (562)595-7831
Adult Christian Educ. Found. **[19667]**, 315 N Carroll St., Madison, WI 53703-2005, (608)241-9220
Adult Congenital Heart Assn. **[13996]**, 6757 Greene St., Ste. 335, Philadelphia, PA 19119-3508, (215)849-1260

Adult Education
Adult Higher Educ. Alliance **[7688]**
Assn. for Non-Traditional Students in Higher Educ. **[7689]**
Assn. for Non-Traditional Students in Higher Educ. **[7689]**
Center for Consumer Affairs **[17448]**
European Soc. for Res. on the Educ. of Adults **[15484]**
Natl. Adult Educ. Honor Soc. **[7690]**
Natl. Adult Educ. Professional Development Consortium **[7691]**
Natl. Assn. for Educational Guidance for Adults **[19538]**
Natl. Coun. for Continuing Educ. and Training **[7928]**
Women in Adult and Vocational Educ. **[822]**
World Educ. **[7692]**
World Educ. **[7692]**

Adult Educ. Assn. of the U.S.A. **[★7920]**
Adult Higher Educ. Alliance **[7688]**, Montana State Univ., Dept. of Educ., Reid Hall, Bozeman, MT 59717, (406)994-6419
Adult Learning Australia **[IO]**, Canberra, Australia
Adult Residential Colleges Assn. **[IO]**, Felixstowe, United Kingdom
Adult Services Division of ALA **[★10008]**
Adults Surviving Child Abuse **[IO]**, Milsons Point, Australia
Advanced Authoring Format Assn. **[★3386]**
Advanced Biofuels Assn. **[1533]**, 2099 Pennsylvania Ave. NW Ste. 100, Washington, DC 20006, (202)469-5140
Advanced Biofuels USA **[6108]**, 507 N Bentz St., Frederick, MD 21701, (301)644-1395
Advanced Conservation Strategies **[3979]**, PO Box 1201, Midway, UT 84049, (435)200-3031
Advanced Foods and Materials Network **[IO]**, Guelph, ON, Canada
Advanced Mfg. Australia **[IO]**, Wantirna South, Australia
Advanced Media Workflow Assn. **[3386]**, 436 N Westfield Rd., Madison, WI 53717, (608)513-5992
Advanced Medical Tech. Assn. **[14840]**, 701 Pennsylvania Ave. NW, Ste. 800, Washington, DC 20004-2654, (202)783-8700
Advanced TV Systems Comm. **[478]**, 1776 K St. NW, Ste. 200, Washington, DC 20006-2304, (202)872-9160
Advanced Transit Assn. **[7578]**, PO Box 293, Maple Valley, WA 98038
Advancement for Rural Kids **[11176]**, 6 E 65th St., Ste. 4A, New York, NY 10065
Advancing Canadian Entrepreneurship **[IO]**, Toronto, ON, Canada
Advancing Churches in Missions Commitment - Defunct.

Advancing Human Rights **[17807]**, 277 Park Ave., 49th Fl., New York, NY 10172, (212)207-5042
Advancing the Ministries of the Gospel **[★20008]**
Advancing the Ministries of the Gospel **[★20008]**
Advancing Native Missions **[19532]**, PO Box 5303, Charlottesville, VA 22905, (540)456-7111
Advancing Native Missions **[19532]**, PO Box 5303, Charlottesville, VA 22905, (540)456-7111
Advancing Women Professionals and the Jewish Community **[13449]**, 1114 Ave. of the Americas, Ste. 3400, New York, NY 10036, (212)869-9700
Advent Christian Gen. Conf. **[19287]**, PO Box 690848, Charlotte, NC 28227, (704)545-6161
Advent Christian Gen. Conf. **[19287]**, PO Box 690848, Charlotte, NC 28227, (704)545-6161
Advent Mission Society; American **[★19287]**
Adventist
Advent Christian Gen. Conf. **[19287]**
Advent Christian Gen. Conf. **[19287]**
Adventist Hea. Intl. **[15138]**
Adventist World Aviation **[10802]**
Adventist World Aviation **[10802]**
Adventist Community Services **[20237]**, 12501 Old Columbia Pike, Silver Spring, MD 20904, (301)680-6438
Adventist Development and Relief Agency - Canada **[IO]**, Oshawa, ON, Canada
Adventist Development and Relief Agency Intl. **[12795]**, 12501 Old Columbia Pike, Silver Spring, MD 20904, (800)424-2372
Adventist Development and Relief Agency Intl. **[12795]**, 12501 Old Columbia Pike, Silver Spring, MD 20904, (800)424-2372
Adventist Development and Relief Agency - Japan **[IO]**, Tokyo, Japan
Adventist Food Ser. Assn. - Address unknown since 2011.
Adventist Hea. Intl. **[15138]**, 11060 Anderson St., Loma Linda, CA 92350, (909)558-4540
Adventist Hea. Intl. **[15138]**, 11060 Anderson St., Loma Linda, CA 92350, (909)558-4540
Adventist World Aviation **[10802]**, PO Box 251, Berrien Springs, MI 49103-0251, (269)473-0135
Adventist World Aviation **[10802]**, PO Box 251, Berrien Springs, MI 49103-0251, (269)473-0135
Adventrek **[12256]**, PO Box 793, Chicago, IL 60690
Adventrek **[12256]**, PO Box 793, Chicago, IL 60690
Adventure Cycling Assn. **[22474]**, PO Box 8308, Missoula, MT 59807, (406)721-1776
Adventure Found. Pakistan **[IO]**, Abbottabad, Pakistan
Adventure Tour Operators Assn. of India **[IO]**, New Delhi, India
Adventure Travel Trade Assn. **[3545]**, 601 Union St., 42nd Fl., Seattle, WA 98101, (360)805-3131
Adventures in Movement for the Handicapped **[16830]**, 945 Danbury Rd., Dayton, OH 45420, (937)294-4611
Adventures in Preservation **[9660]**, 1557 North St., Boulder, CO 80304, (303)444-0128
Adventures in Preservation **[9660]**, 1557 North St., Boulder, CO 80304, (303)444-0128
Adversity.Net - Address unknown since 2011.
Advertisers' Assn. **[IO]**, Istanbul, Turkey
Advertising
Advt. Club of New York **[75]**
Advt. Coun. **[76]**
Advt. Fed. of Australia **[12133]**
Advt. and Marketing Intl. Network **[77]**
Advt. Res. Found. **[78]**
Advt. Standards Canada **[14174]**
Advt. Women of New York **[79]**
Amer. Acad. of Advt. **[7693]**
Amer. Advt. Fed. **[80]**
Amer. Assn. of Advt. Agencies **[81]**
Antique Advt. Assn. of Am. **[82]**
Asian Amer. Advt. Fed. **[83]**
Assn. of Entertainment Marketing Agencies **[1189]**
Assn. of Hispanic Advt. Agencies **[84]**
Assn. of Independent Commercial Producers **[85]**
Assn. of Independent Creative Editors **[2811]**
Assn. of Natl. Advertisers **[86]**
BPA Worldwide **[87]**
BPA Worldwide **[87]**
Cabletelevision Advt. Bur. **[88]**

Catalog and Multichannel Marketing Coun. **[1605]**
Children's Advt. Rev. Unit **[89]**
Digital Signage Assn. **[90]**
Eight Sheet Outdoor Advt. Assn. **[91]**
European Fed. of Illuminated Signs **[15013]**
Inflatable Advt. Dealers Assn. **[92]**
Interactive Advt. Bur. **[93]**
Interactive Advt. Bur. **[93]**AdvertisingIntl. Advt. Assn.
Intl. Vintage Poster Dealers Assn. **[94]**
Intl. Vintage Poster Dealers Assn. **[94]**
Mailing and Fulfillment Ser. Assn. **[95]**
Marketing and Advt. Global Network **[96]**
Marketing and Advt. Global Network **[96]**
Mobile Marketing Assn. **[97]**
Mobile Marketing Assn. **[97]**AdvertisingNatl. Advt. Assn. - Venezuela
Natl. Advt. Div. Coun. of Better Bus. Bureaus **[98]**
Natl. Advt. Golf Assn. **[22616]**
Natl. Advt. Rev. Bd. **[99]**
Natl. Agri-Marketing Assn. **[100]**
Newspaper Target Marketing Coalition **[2576]**
Old Sleepy Eye Collectors' Club of Am. **[21268]**
Outdoor Advt. Assn. of Am. **[101]**
Peanut Pals **[21396]**
Peruvian Assn. of Advt. Agencies **[19145]**
Point-of-Purchase Advt. Intl. **[102]**
Promotion Marketing Assn. **[2422]**
Promotional Products Assn. Intl. **[103]**
Promotional Products Assn. Intl. **[103]**
Radio Advt. Bur. **[104]**
Retail Advt. and Marketing Assn. **[105]**
Southern Classified Advt. Managers Assn. **[106]**
Syndicated Network TV Assn. **[107]**
TV Bur. of Advt. **[108]**
thinkLA **[109]**
Trade Promotion Mgt. Associates **[110]**
Transworld Advt. Agency Network **[111]**
Transworld Advt. Agency Network **[111]**
Underfashion Club **[112]**
Advt. Agencies Assn. of Bangladesh **[IO]**, Dhaka, Bangladesh
Advt. Agencies Assn. of India **[IO]**, Mumbai, India
Advt. Agency Production Club of New York **[★1599]**
Advt. Assn. of Sweden **[IO]**, Stockholm, Sweden
Advt. Assn. of Thailand **[IO]**, Bangkok, Thailand
Advt. Assn. of the United Kingdom **[IO]**, London, United Kingdom
Advertising Auditors
Audit Bur. of Circulations **[113]**
Certified Audit of Circulations **[114]**
Publishers Info. Bur. **[115]**
Advt. Bd. of the Philippines **[IO]**, Makati City, Philippines
Advt. Club of New York **[75]**, 235 Park Ave. S, 6th Fl., New York, NY 10003-1450, (212)533-8080
Advt. Coun. **[76]**, 815 2nd Ave., 9th Fl., New York, NY 10017, (212)922-1500
Advt. and Design Club of Canada **[IO]**, Toronto, ON, Canada
Advt. Fed. of Am. **[★80]**
Advt. Fed. of Australia **[IO]**, Sydney, Australia
Advt. Funeral Directors of Am. **[★2543]**
Advt. Funeral Directors of Am. **[★2543]**
Advt. and Illustrative Photographers Assn. **[IO]**, Auckland, New Zealand
Advt. Mail Marketing Assn. **[★2232]**
Advt. and Marketing Intl. Network **[77]**, 3587 Northshore Dr., Wayzata, MN 55391, (952)457-1116
Advt. and Marketing Intl. Network **[77]**, 3587 Northshore Dr., Wayzata, MN 55391, (952)457-1116
Advt. Media Credit Executives Assn. **[1276]**, PO Box 40036, Bay Village, OH 44140-0036
Advt. Men's League of New York **[★75]**
Advt. Photographers of Am. **[★2708]**
Advt. Producers Assn. **[IO]**, London, United Kingdom
Advt. Production Club of New York **[1599]**, Euro RSCG Life, 7th Fl., 200 Madison Ave., New York, NY 10016, (212)251-7295
Advt. Res. Found. **[78]**, 432 Park Ave. S, 6th Fl., New York, NY 10016-8013, (212)751-5656
Advt. Standards Authority **[IO]**, London, United Kingdom
Advt. Standards Canada **[IO]**, Toronto, ON, Canada
Advt. Women of New York **[79]**, 25 W 45th St., Ste. 403, New York, NY 10036, (212)221-7969

A star before a book entry number signifies that the name is not listed separately, but is mentioned within the entry.

Advice UK [IO], London, United Kingdom
Advisory Bd. for Medical Specialties [★15355]
Advisory Bd. on Veterinary Specialties [★16992]
Advisory Centre for Educ. [IO], London, United Kingdom
Advisory Comm. on Protection of the Sea [IO], Cambridge, United Kingdom
Advisory Comm. on X-Ray and Radium Protection [★5954]
Advisory Coun. on Camps - Defunct.
Advisory Coun. for Children with Impaired Hearing [IO], Blackburn, Australia
Advisory Coun. on Historic Preservation [9661], Old Post Off. Bldg., 1100 Pennsylvania Ave. NW, Ste. 803, Washington, DC 20004, (202)606-8503
Advisory Coun. for Orthopedic Resident Educ. [★16019]
Advisory Coun. for Orthopedic Resident Educ. [★16019]
Advocacy Initiative for Development [IO], Freetown, Sierra Leone
Advocacy Inst. - Address unknown since 2010.
Advocacy Tasmania [IO], Sandy Bay, Australia
Advocaten Zonder Grenzen [★IO]
Advocates for the Amer. Osteopathic Assn. [16055], 142 E Ontario St., Chicago, IL 60611-2864, (312)202-8190
Advocates for Animals [IO], Edinburgh, United Kingdom
Advocates for Better Children's Diets [15813], 1050 17th St. NW, Ste. 600, Washington, DC 20036, (202)659-1858
Advocates for Child Psychiatric Nursing [★15759]
Advocates for Child Psychiatric Nursing [★15759]
Advocates for Commun. Tech. for Deaf/Blind People - Defunct.
Advocates for Highway and Auto Safety [12972], 750 1st St. NE, Ste. 901, Washington, DC 20002, (202)408-1711
Advocates Intl. [5640], 9691 Main St., Ste. D, Fairfax, VA 22031-3754, (703)894-1084
Advocates Intl. [5640], 9691 Main St., Ste. D, Fairfax, VA 22031-3754, (703)894-1084
Advocates for Self-Government [18076], 1010 N Tennessee St., Ste. 215, Cartersville, GA 30120, (770)386-8372
Advocates' Soc. [IO], Toronto, ON, Canada
Advocates for Women in Sci., Engg., and Mathematics - Address unknown since 2011.
Advocates for Youth [12025], 2000 M St. NW, Ste. 750, Washington, DC 20036, (202)419-3420
Advocates for Youth [12025], 2000 M St. NW, Ste. 750, Washington, DC 20036, (202)419-3420
Advocating Change Together [11753], 1821 Univ. Ave. W, Ste. 306-S, St. Paul, MN 55104, (651)641-0297
ADVOCIS [IO], Toronto, ON, Canada
AE/AEO Sailors Assn. [5865], 89 W Union St., Canton, PA 17724, (570)673-4167
AeA - Advancing the Bus. of Tech.
AeA - Advancing the Bus. of Tech. - Address unknown since 2011.
AEC - TEA Volunteer Centre [IO], Capim Grosso, Brazil
AED Natl. Inst. for Work and Learning [18038], 1825 Connecticut Ave. NW, Washington, DC 20009, (202)464-3798
AEM Marketing Communications Coun. [★2390]
Aeras Global TB Vaccine Found. [14510], 1405 Res. Blvd., Rockville, MD 20850, (301)547-2900
Aeras Global TB Vaccine Found. [14510], 1405 Res. Blvd., Rockville, MD 20850, (301)547-2900
Aerial Agricultural Assn. of Australia [IO], Mitchell, Australia
Aerial Firefighting Indus. Assn. - Defunct.
Aero Club of Am. [★144]
Aero Club of Canada [IO], St. John, NB, Canada
Aero Club d'Italia [IO], Rome, Italy
Aero Club de France [IO], Paris, France
Aero Club of India [IO], New Delhi, India
Aero Club of Israel [IO], Tel Aviv, Israel
Aero Club of Lithuania [IO], Vilnius, Lithuania
Aero Club of Poland [IO], Warsaw, Poland
Aero-club Royal de Belgique [★IO]
Aero Club of South Africa [IO], Germiston, Republic of South Africa

Aero Medical Assn. [★13582]
Aero Medical Assn. [★13582]
Aero Philatelic Soc. of Am. [★22006]
Aero Philatelists [★22006]
Aerobatics Canada [IO], Toronto, ON, Canada
Aerobics
    Intl. Fitness Assn. [16227]
    Natl. Exercise Trainers Assn. [22208]
    U.S. Competitive Aerobics Fed. [22209]
Aerobics and Fitness Assn. of Am. [16219], 15250 Ventura Blvd., Ste. 200, Sherman Oaks, CA 91403, (877)968-7263
Aerobics and Fitness Assn. of Am. [16219], 15250 Ventura Blvd., Ste. 200, Sherman Oaks, CA 91403, (877)968-7263
Aerobics Intl. Res. Soc. - Defunct.
Aeroclub de Monaco [IO], Monaco, Monaco
Aeroclube do Brasil [IO], Rio de Janeiro, Brazil
Aeroklub Polski [★IO]
Aeromedical Evacuation
    Vietnam Dustoff Assn. [20836]
Aeronautical Chamber of Commerce of Am. [★117]
Aeronautical Repair Sta. Assn. [116], 121 N Henry St., Alexandria, VA 22314-2903, (703)739-9543
Aeronautical Soc. of India [IO], Hyderabad, India
Aeronca Club [★20908]
Aerophilatelic Fed. of the Americas [★22006]
Aerosol Assn. of Australia [IO], Parramatta, Australia
Aerosol Soc. [IO], Bristol, United Kingdom
Aerospace
    Acad. of Model Aeronautics [20877]
    Aeronautical Repair Sta. Assn. [116]
    Aerospace Dept. Chair's Assn. [7694]
    Aerospace Indus. Assn. of Am. [117]
    Aerostar Owners Assn. [20878]
    Air Carrier Assn. of Am. [118]
    Air Mail Pioneers [20879]
    Air Sailing Club [21272]
    Air Traffic Control Assn. [119]
    Air Traffic Control Assn. [119]
    Air Transport Assn. of Am. [120]
    Aircraft Electronics Assn. [121]
    Aircraft Electronics Assn. [121]
    Aircraft Owners and Pilots Assn. [122]
    Airlift/Tanker Assn. [20311]
    Airlift/Tanker Assn. [20311]
    Airline Indus. Relations Conf. [123]
    Airports Coun. Intl. North Am. [124]
    Airports Coun. Intl. North Am. [124]
    Amer. Assn. of Airport Executives [125]
    Amer. Astronautical Soc. [6081]
    Amer. Astronautical Soc. [6081]
    Amer. Aviation Historical Soc. [20880]
    Amer. Bonanza Soc. [20881]
    Amer. Bonanza Soc. [20881]
    Amer. Fighter Aces Assn. [20312]
    Amer. Helicopter Soc. [126]
    Amer. Helicopter Soc. [126]
    Amer. Inst. of Aeronautics and Astronautics [6082]
    Amer. Pilots' Assn. [127]
    Amer. Yankee Assn. [20882]
    Antique Airplane Assn. [20883]
    Apollo Soc. [9086]
    Assn. for Aviation Psychology [6083]
    Assn. of Intl. Airlines [1677]
    Assn. of Space Explorers U.S.A. [6084]
    Assn. of Space Explorers U.S.A. [6084]
    Astronaut Scholars Honor Soc. [23629]
    Aviation Development Coun. [128]
    Aviation Distributors and Mfrs. Assn. [129]
    Aviation Indus. CBT Comm. [130]
    Aviation Technician Educ. Coun. [7695]
    Avionics Maintenance Conf. [131]
    B-52 Stratofortress Assn. [20331]
    Baltic Air Charter Assn. [12065]
    Bellanca-Champion Club [20884]
    Canadian Aerial Applicators Assn. [21346]
    Canadian Aviation Maintenance Coun. [16062]
    Cargo Airline Assn. [132]
    Cessna Owner Org. [20885]
    Cessna Pilots Assn. [20886]
    Cherokee Pilots' Assn. [20887]
    Civil Air Operations Officers Assn. of Australia [6495]
    Collegiate Soaring Assn. [22210]

    Combat Helicopter Pilots Assn. [20313]
    Commemorative Air Force [20888]
    Continental Luscombe Assn. [20889]
    Corben Club [20890]
    Coun. of Defense and Space Indus. Associations [133]
    Daedalian Found. [20314]
    Distinguished Flying Cross Soc. [20374]
    EAA Vintage Aircraft Assn. [20891]
    EAA Warbirds of Am. [20892]
    Ercoupe Owners Club [20893]
    Experimental Aircraft Assn. [6085]
    F-4 Phantom II Soc. [20894]
    F-4 Phantom II Soc. [20894]
    Fairchild Club [20895]
    First Flight Soc. [20896]
    Flight Safety Found. [134]
    Flight Safety Found. [134]
    Funk Aircraft Owners Assn. [20897]
    Gen. Aviation Mfrs. Assn. [135]
    Helicopter Assn. Intl. [136]
    Helicopter Assn. Intl. [136]
    Helicopter Found. Intl. [137]
    Helicopter Found. Intl. [137]
    Helicopter Safety Advisory Conf. [138]
    High Frontier [6086]
    IEEE | Aerospace and Electronics Systems Soc. [6654]
    Intl. Aerobatic Club [22211]AerospaceIntl. Assn. of Air Travel Couriers
    Intl. Assn. of Space Entrepreneurs [139]
    Intl. Assn. of Space Entrepreneurs [139]
    Intl. Bird Dog Assn. [20898]
    Intl. Cessna 120/140 Assn. [20899]
    Intl. Cessna 120/140 Assn. [20899]
    The Intl. Cessna 170 Assn. [20900]
    Intl. Coordinating Coun. of Aerospace Indus. Associations [140]
    Intl. Coordinating Coun. of Aerospace Indus. Associations [140]
    Intl. Coun. of Air Shows [20901]
    Intl. Coun. of Air Shows [20901]
    Intl. Coun. of Aircraft Owner and Pilot Associations [141]
    Intl. Coun. of Aircraft Owner and Pilot Associations [141]
    Intl. Experimental Aerospace Soc. [6087]
    Intl. Experimental Aerospace Soc. [6087]
    Intl. Lunar Observatory Assn. [6231]
    Intl. Pietenpol Assn. [20902]
    Intl. Scale Soaring Assn. [21904]
    Intl. Soc. for Aviation Photography [2724]
    Intl. Soc. of Transport Aircraft Trading [142]
    Intl. Soc. of Transport Aircraft Trading [142]
    Intl. Soc. of Women Airline Pilots [143]
    Intl. Soc. of Women Airline Pilots [143]
    Intl. Space Exploration and Colonization Company [6088]
    Intl. Space Exploration and Colonization Company [6088]
    Intl. Wheelchair Aviators [20903]
    Intl. Wheelchair Aviators [20903]
    Interstate Club [20904]
    Italian Indus. Assn. for Aerospace Systems and Defence [4613]
    Jack Knight Air Mail Soc. [22047]
    League of World War I Aviation Historians [20905]
    League of World War I Aviation Historians [20905]
    Luscombe Endowment [20906]
    Military Aviation Preservation Soc. [9087]
    Monocoupe Club [20907]
    Natl. Aeronautic Assn. [144]
    Natl. Aeronca Assn. [20908]
    Natl. Air Carrier Assn. [145]
    Natl. Air-Racing Gp. [22212]
    Natl. Air Trans. Assn. [146]
    Natl. Aircraft Appraisers Assn. [147]
    Natl. Aircraft Resale Assn. [148]
    Natl. Assn. of Flight Instructors [149]
    Natl. Biplane Assn. [20909]
    Natl. Bus. Aviation Assn. [150]
    Natl. InterCollegiate Flying Assn. [20910]
    Natl. Space Club [6089]
    Natl. Space Soc. [6090]
    Natl. Stinson Club [20911]

Reference to "IO" in place of a book number signifies that the association may be found in the 50th edition of International Organizations.

Natl. World War II Glider Pilots Assn. [20315]
Naval Airship Assn. [6091]
Negro Airmen Intl. [6092]
Ninety-Nines, Intl. Org. of Women Pilots [151]
Ninety-Nines, Intl. Org. of Women Pilots [151]
Org. of Black Airline Pilots [152]
Pacific Rocket Soc. [6093]
Pedro Rescue Helicopter Assn. [20316]
Pilatus Owners and Pilots Assn. [153]
Piper Owner Soc. [20912]
Planetary Soc. [6094]
Planetary Soc. [6094]
Popular Rotorcraft Assn. [20913]
Precision Aerobatics Model Pilots Assn. [20914]
Professional Aviation Maintenance Assn. [154]
Regional Airline Assn. [155]
SAFE Assn. [6095]
Seaplane Pilots Assn. [156]
Short Wing Piper Club [20915]
Silver Wings Fraternity [20916]
Soaring Soc. of Am. [22213]
Soc. of Antique Modelers [20917]
Soc. of Experimental Test Pilots [6096]
Soc. of Flight Test Engineers [6097]
Space Energy Assn. [6098]
Space Enterprise Coun. [157]
Space Found. [7696]
Space Stud. Inst. [6099]
Space Topic Stud. Unit [22080]
Space Trans. Assn. [6100]
Stearman Restorers Assn. [20918]
Students for the Exploration and Development of
   Space [7697]
Swift Museum Found. [20919]
Trans Lunar Res. [6101]
Tuskegee Airmen, Inc. [20317]
Twirly Birds [20920]
United Flying Octogenarians [20921]
U.S. Hang Gliding and Paragliding Assn. [22214]
U.S. Pilots Assn. [158]
U.S. Ultralight Assn. [20922]
Universities Space Res. Assn. [6102]
Univ. Aviation Assn. [7698]
Vintage Sailplane Assn. [22215]
Whirly-Girls - Intl. Women Helicopter Pilots
   [20923]
Women in Aerospace [6103]
World Airline Historical Soc. [20924]
World Airline Historical Soc. [20924]
World War I Aeroplanes [20925]
Aerospace Dept. Chair's Assn. [7694], Prof. Gary
   Balas, Chm., Univ. of Minnesota, 107 Akerman
   Hall, 110 Union St. SE, Minneapolis, MN 55455,
   (612)625-8000
Aerospace Educ. Found. [★5792]
Aerospace and Electronics Systems Soc; IEEE I
   [6654]
Aerospace Indus. Assn. of Am. [117], 1000 Wilson
   Blvd., Ste. 1700, Arlington, VA 22209-3928,
   (703)358-1000
Aerospace Indus. Assn. of Canada [IO], Ottawa,
   ON, Canada
Aerospace Medical Assn. [13582], 320 S Henry St.,
   Alexandria, VA 22314-3579, (703)739-2240
Aerospace Medical Assn. [13582], 320 S Henry St.,
   Alexandria, VA 22314-3579, (703)739-2240
Aerospace Medicine
   Aerospace Medical Assn. [13582]
   Aerospace Medical Assn. [13582]
   Airlines Medical Directors Assn. [13583]
   Civil Aviation Medical Assn. [13584]
   Civil Aviation Medical Assn. [13584]AerospaceIntl.
      Assn. of Military Flight Surgeon-Pilots
   Natl. Assn. of Air Medical Commun. Specialists
      [13585]
   Soc. of U.S. Air Force Flight Surgeons [13586]
   Soc. of U.S. Naval Flight Surgeons [13587]
Aerospace Sys. Safety Soc. [★3144]
Aerostar Owners Assn. [20878], 2608 W Kenosha
   St., No. 704, Broken Arrow, OK 74012, (918)258-
   2346
Aesthetic Realism Found. [10367], 141 Greene St.,
   New York, NY 10012, (212)777-4490
Aestheticians Intl. Assn. [★966]
Aestheticians Intl. Assn. [★966]

Aesthetics Intl. Assn. [966], 310 E Interstate 30, Ste.
   B107, Garland, TX 75043, (469)429-9300
Aesthetics Intl. Assn. [966], 310 E Interstate 30, Ste.
   B107, Garland, TX 75043, (469)429-9300
Aetherius Soc. [20243], 6202 Afton Pl., Los Angeles,
   CA 90028, (323)465-9652
Aetherius Soc. [20243], 6202 Afton Pl., Los Angeles,
   CA 90028, (323)465-9652
Aetherius Soc. - United Kingdom [IO], London,
   United Kingdom
AFAPAC Found. [IO], Amsterdam, Netherlands
AFASIC - Unlocking Speech and Language [IO],
   London, United Kingdom
AFBA [18924], 909 N Washington St., Alexandria,
   VA 22314, (800)776-2322
AFCOM [6502], 742 E Chapman Ave., Orange, CA
   92866, (714)997-7966
Affiliated/Associated Drug Stores [★2691]
Affiliated Boards of Officials [★23027]
Affiliated Dress Mfrs. - Defunct.
Affiliated Drug Stores [★2691]
Affiliated Leadership League of and for the Blind of
   America - Defunct.
Affiliated Tribes of Northwest Indians [19151], 1827
   NE 44th Ave., Ste. 130, Portland, OR 97213-1443,
   (503)249-5770
Affiliated Warehouse Companies [3617], PO Box
   295, Hazlet, NJ 07730-0295, (732)739-2323
Affiliated Woodcarvers [9261], PO Box 104, Betten-
   dorf, IA 52722, (563)676-8264
Affiliated Woodcarvers [9261], PO Box 104, Betten-
   dorf, IA 52722, (563)676-8264
Affinity Gp. of Evolutionary Anarchists [★17180]
Affirm United [IO], Ottawa, ON, Canada
Affirmation/Gay and Lesbian Mormons [19783], PO
   Box 1435, Palm Springs, CA 92263-1435,
   (661)367-2421
Affirmation: United Methodists for Lesbian, Gay,
   Bisexual and Transgender Concerns [19784], PO
   Box 1021, Evanston, IL 60204
Affirmation: United Methodists for Lesbian/Gay
   Concerns [★19784]
Affirmative Action; Chinese for [17277]
Affirmative Action; Filipinos for [18314]
Affirmative/Gay Mormons United [★19783]
Affirming Anglican Catholicism [19292], 84
   Broadway, New Haven, CT 06511, (203)787-3195
Affordable Housing Investors Coun. [514], Toni
   Sylvester, Exec. Admin., PO Box 986, Irmo, SC
   29063, (803)781-1638
Affordable Housing Tax Credit Coalition [515], 401
   9th St. NW, Ste. 900, Washington, DC 20004,
   (202)585-8162
Afghan
   Afghan-American Chamber of Commerce [23323]
   Afghan Amer. Muslim Outreach [18837]
   Afghan Friends Network [18838]
   Afghan Hands [10803]
   Afghan Hindu Assn. of Am. [19810]
   Afghans4Tomorrow [11541]
   Assn. for the Protection of Afghan Archaeology
      [6163]
   Educational Help for Afghanistan Assn. [8916]
   Global Partnership for Afghanistan [3716]
   Nutrition and Educ. Intl. [12586]
   Solace Intl. [13479]
   Women of Hope Proj. [13487]
Afghan-American Chamber of Commerce [23323],
   8201 Greensboro Dr., Ste. 103, McLean, VA
   22102, (703)442-5005
Afghan Amer. Muslim Outreach [18837], 1339 E Ka-
   tella Ave., No. 333, Orange, CA 92867, (877)663-
   2266
Afghan Amputee Bicyclist for Rehabilitation and
   Recreation [IO], Kabul, Afghanistan
Afghan Assn. for Physical Therapy [IO], Kabul,
   Afghanistan
Afghan Chamber of Commerce and Indus. [IO],
   Kabul, Afghanistan
Afghan Cmpt. Sci. Assn. [IO], Kabul, Afghanistan
Afghan Development Assn. [IO], Kabul, Afghanistan
Afghan Friends Network [18838], PO Box 170368,
   San Francisco, CA 94117, (650)931-4527
Afghan Hands [10803], 395 S End Ave., Ste. 11E,
   New York, NY 10280, (212)786-3309

Afghan Hea. and Development Services [IO], Kabul,
   Afghanistan
Afghan Hindu Assn. of Am. [19810], 45-32 Bowne
   St., Flushing, NY 11355, (718)961-8838
Afghan Hound Club of Am. [21475], 2515 Winsted
   Dr., Dallas, TX 75214-3843, (214)327-0719
Afghan Land Consulting Org. [IO], Kabul,
   Afghanistan
Afghan Natl. Assn. for Adult Educ. [IO], Kabul,
   Afghanistan
Afghan Paiwand Assn. [IO], Willesden, United
   Kingdom
Afghan Refugee Fund - Defunct.
Afghan Soc. Against Cancer [IO], Kabul, Afghanistan
Afghan Women Counselling and Integration Com-
   munity Support Org. [IO], Toronto, ON, Canada
Afghan Women Services and Educ. Org. [IO], Kabul,
   Afghanistan
Afghan Women's Assn. Intl.
Afghan Women's Assn. Intl. - Address unknown
   since 2011.
Afghan Women's Bus. Fed. [IO], Kabul, Afghanistan
Afghan Women's Network [IO], Kabul, Afghanistan
Afghanaid [IO], London, United Kingdom
Afghanistan
   Afghan Hindu Assn. of Am. [19810]
   Afghans4Tomorrow [11541]
   Amer. Support for Afghanistan [10804]
   Assn. for the Protection of Afghan Archaeology
      [6163]
   Educational Help for Afghanistan Assn. [8916]
   Global Partnership for Afghanistan [3716]
   Global Partnership for Afghanistan [3716]
   Noshaq [12958]
   Nutrition and Educ. Intl. [12586]
   Solace Intl. [13479]
   U.S.-Afghanistan Reconstruction Coun. [10805]
   Women's Alliance for Peace and Human Rights in
      Afghanistan [12253]
Afghanistan Assn. of Professional Accountants [IO],
   Kabul, Afghanistan
Afghanistan Athletic Fed. [IO], Kabul, Afghanistan
Afghanistan Badminton Fed. [IO], Kabul,
   Afghanistan
Afghanistan Banks Assn. [IO], Kabul, Afghanistan
Afghanistan Builders Assn. [IO], Kabul, Afghanistan
Afghanistan Civil Soc. Forum - organization [IO],
   Kabul, Afghanistan
Afghanistan Cricket Fed. [IO], Kabul, Afghanistan
Afghanistan Football Fed. [IO], Kabul, Afghanistan
Afghanistan Handball Fed. [IO], Kabul, Afghanistan
Afghanistan Human Rights Org. [IO], Kabul,
   Afghanistan
Afghanistan Independent Human Rights Commn.
   [IO], Kabul, Afghanistan
Afghanistan Microfinance Assn. [IO], Kabul,
   Afghanistan
Afghanistan Natl. Seed Assn. [IO], Kabul,
   Afghanistan
Afghanistan Paralympic Comm. [IO], Kabul,
   Afghanistan
Afghanistan Peace Assn. [18230], 4136 Coll. Point
   Blvd., Ste. 2A, Flushing, NY 11355-4229,
   (718)461-6799
Afghanistan Peace Assn. [18230], 4136 Coll. Point
   Blvd., Ste. 2A, Flushing, NY 11355-4229,
   (718)461-6799
Afghanistan Red Crescent [IO], Kabul, Afghanistan
Afghanistan Relief Comm. - Defunct.
Afghanistan Relief Org. [12796], PO Box 866,
   Cypress, CA 90630, (877)276-2440
Afghanistan Res. and Evaluation Unit [IO], Kabul,
   Afghanistan
Afghanistan/Southwest Asia Resource Center -
   Defunct.
Afghanistan Studies Assn. - Defunct.
Afghanistan Tennis Fed. [IO], Kabul, Afghanistan
Afghanistan Veterinary Assn. [IO], Kabul,
   Afghanistan
Afghanistan Watch [IO], Kabul, Afghanistan
Afghanistan Weightlifting Fed. [IO], Kabul,
   Afghanistan
Afghans for Civil Soc. [17255], 806 N Charles St.,
   Baltimore, MD 21201, (410)385-1445
Afghans for Civil Soc. [17255], 806 N Charles St.,
   Baltimore, MD 21201, (410)385-1445

A star before a book entry number signifies that the name is not listed separately, but is mentioned within the entry.

Afghans4Tomorrow **[11541]**, PO Box 22, Larkspur, CA 94977-0022
Afghans4Tomorrow **[11541]**, PO Box 22, Larkspur, CA 94977-0022
AFL-CIO **[23217]**, 815 16th St. NW, Washington, DC 20006, (202)637-5000
AFL-CIO/ALA Joint Comm. on Lib. Ser. to Labor Groups - Address unknown since 2010.
AFL-CIO I Building and Constr. Trades Dept. **[23163]**, 815 16th St., Ste. 600, Washington, DC 20006, (202)347-1461
AFL-CIO I Community Action Field Mobilization Dept. **[11658]**, 815 16th St. NW, Washington, DC 20006
AFL-CIO Community Services Activities **[★11658]**
AFL-CIO Dept. of Community Services **[★11658]**
AFL-CIO I Dept. Professional Employees **[23223]**, 815 16th St. NW, 7th Fl., Washington, DC 20006, (202)638-0320
AFL-CIO I Intl. Labor Communications Assn. **[2911]**, 815 16th St. NW, 4 N, Washington, DC 20006, (202)637-5068
AFL-CIO I Intl. Org. of Masters, Mates and Pilots **[23245]**, 700 Maritime Blvd., Ste. B, Linthicum Heights, MD 21090-1953, (410)850-8700
AFL-CIO I Maritime Trades Dept. **[23246]**, 815 16th St. NW, Washington, DC 20006-4101, (202)628-6300
AFL-CIO I Metal Trades Dept. **[23253]**, 815 16th St. NW, Washington, DC 20006, (202)508-3705
AFL-CIO I SEIU I District 925 **[23140]**, 1914 N 34th St., Ste. 100, Seattle, WA 98103, (206)322-3010
AFL-CIO I Union Label and Ser. Trades Dept. **[23304]**, 815 16th St. NW, Washington, DC 20006, (202)508-3700
AFL-CIO I Utility Workers Union of Am. **[23315]**, 815 16th St. NW, Washington, DC 20006, (202)974-8200
AFL-CIO I Working for Am. Inst. **[11926]**, 815 16th St. NW, Washington, DC 20006, (202)508-3717
AFL Community Relations Comm. **[★11658]**
Afoakom-USA **[9863]**, 5031 Charlestown Crossing Way, New Albany, IN 47150, (217)220-2302
Afoakom-USA **[9863]**, 5031 Charlestown Crossing Way, New Albany, IN 47150, (217)220-2302
Africa
　Achieve in Africa **[11173]**
　Act for Africa Intl. **[12951]**
　Afoakom-USA **[9863]**
　Africa Action **[17140]**
　Africa Action **[17140]**
　Africa Am. Crisis Assistance Network **[12797]**
　Africa-America Inst. **[17141]**
　Africa-America Inst. New York **[17142]**
　Africa Environmental Watch **[3980]**
　Africa Faith and Justice Network **[17143]**
　Africa News Ser. **[17144]**
　Africa Peace and Conflict Network **[12625]**
　African Bus. Alliance **[159]**AfricaAfrican Development Inst.
　Africare **[17145]**
　Africare **[17145]**
　AfriHope Intl., Inc. **[10806]**
　Aid Africa **[12714]**
　All for Africa **[10807]**
　All for Africa **[10807]**
　All-African People's Revolutionary Party **[17146]**
　All Kids Can Learn Intl. **[11446]**
　All One People **[10808]**
　Alternative Medicine Intl. **[13648]**
　Amara Conservation **[5022]**
　Amman Imman: Water is Life **[13413]**
　Answer Africa **[14374]**
　Anti-Poverty Initiative **[17188]**
　Assn. for Africanist Anthropology **[6133]**
　Assn. of Concerned African Scholars **[17147]**
　Assn. of Concerned African Scholars **[17147]**
　BERWA **[12315]**
　Blessings on Africa **[12719]**
　Blood: Water Mission **[10809]**
　BLOOM Africa **[11199]**
　Building Tomorrow **[12659]**
　Change Exchange **[12205]**
　CHAP Intl. **[12817]**
　Child Aid Africa **[11212]**

The Child is Innocent **[11219]**
Communities Without Borders **[11258]**
Computers for Africa **[7910]**
Congo Helping Hands **[10810]**
Constituency for Africa **[17148]**
Corporate Coun. on Africa **[160]**
Corporate Coun. on Africa **[160]**
Debt AIDS Trade Africa **[17149]**
Debt AIDS Trade Africa **[17149]**
Educate These Children **[11462]**
Eliminate Poverty Now **[11066]**
Emofra Africa **[15157]**
Empower Tanzania, Inc. **[12954]**
Empowerment Works **[11579]**
Friends of Africa Intl. **[17830]**
Friends of Mali **[18246]**
FUNDaFIELD **[11288]**
Global Alliance for Africa **[17150]**
Global Alliance for Community Empowerment **[10811]**
Global Associates for Hea. Development **[15161]**
Guinea Development Found. **[17151]**
Guinea Development Found. **[17151]**
Hands Across the Water **[11297]**
Heart for Africa **[11299]**
Help Aid Africa **[11594]**
HIS Nets **[13588]**
HomeAID for Africa **[10812]**
Human Touch Intl. **[13589]**
Idoma Assn. USA **[19176]**
Indego Africa Proj. **[10813]**
Innovation: Africa **[6114]**
Intl. Agro Alliance **[4940]**
Intl. Partnership for Reproductive Hea. **[16587]**
Intl. Refugee Rights Initiative **[17843]**
Invisible Children **[17237]**
Jamii Moja **[11603]**
Jewish Heart for Africa **[10822]**
Kasese Wildlife Conservation Awareness Org. **[5074]**
Life in Abundance Intl. **[10814]**
Malawi Proj. **[10815]**
Malawi Proj. **[10815]**
Mali Assistance Proj. **[10816]**
Medical Relief Alliance **[12864]**
Medicine for Mali **[12468]**
NextAid **[11369]**
One Hundred Days **[14732]**
Oper. Crossroads Africa **[17152]**
Oper. Crossroads Africa **[17152]**
Orphans Africa **[11621]**
Pilgrim Africa **[12878]**
Rain for the Sahel and Sahara **[12359]**
Rebuild A Nation **[11077]**
Relief for Africa **[12882]**
Rwanda Knits **[11626]**
Rwanda Partners **[12364]**
Seeds For Hope **[11861]**
Solar Light for Africa **[11640]**
SpanAfrica **[11642]**
Strategies for Intl. Development **[12372]**
SunPower Afrique **[13227]**
ThinkImpact **[12373]**
Touch the Life of a Child Org. **[11418]**
Touching Hearts **[10817]**
TransAfrica Forum **[17153]**
TransAfrica Forum **[17153]**
Ubuntu Africa **[11421]**
Ugandan Amer. Partnership Org. **[12307]**
US Doctors for Africa **[15221]**
Voices of African Mothers **[12638]**
Water Alliance for Africa **[13434]**
Water for People I PlayPumps Intl. **[10827]**
Water to Thrive **[13439]**
WICUDA-USA **[9095]**
Women Watch Afrika **[18797]**
Africa 2000Plus Network - Zimbabwe **[IO]**, Harare, Zimbabwe
Africa Action **[17140]**, 1634 Eye St. NW, Ste. 1000, Washington, DC 20006, (202)546-7961
Africa Action **[17140]**, 1634 Eye St. NW, Ste. 1000, Washington, DC 20006, (202)546-7961
Africa Alliance of YMCAs **[IO]**, Nairobi, Kenya
Africa Am. Crisis Assistance Network **[12797]**, PO Box 440151, Kennesaw, GA 30160, (678)467-7202

Africa-America Inst. **[17141]**, 420 Lexington Ave., Ste. 1706, New York, NY 10170-0002, (212)949-5666
Africa-America Inst. New York **[17142]**, 420 Lexington Ave., Ste. 1706, New York, NY 10170-0002, (212)949-5666
Africa-America Inst. New York **[17142]**, 420 Lexington Ave., Ste. 1706, New York, NY 10170-0002, (212)949-5666
Africa-American Friendship Soc.
Africa-American Friendship Soc. - Address unknown since 2011.
Africa Bridge **[11177]**, PO Box 115, Marylhurst, OR 97036, (503)699-6162
Africa-Canada Development and Info. Services Assn. **[IO]**, Vancouver, BC, Canada
Africa Centre **[IO]**, London, United Kingdom
Africa Comm. **[IO]**, Basel, Switzerland
Africa Environmental Watch **[3980]**, 4207 Plummers Promise Dr., Ste. 100, Bowie, MD 20720, (240)417-2545
Africa - Europe Faith and Justice Network **[IO]**, Brussels, Belgium
Africa-Europe Gp. for Interdisciplinary Stud. **[IO]**, London, United Kingdom
Africa Evangelical Fellowship - Defunct.
Africa Faith and Justice Network **[17143]**, 125 Michigan Ave. NE, Ste. 480, Washington, DC 20017, (202)884-9780
The Africa Fund **[★17140]**
The Africa Fund **[★17140]**
Africa Groups of Sweden **[IO]**, Stockholm, Sweden
Africa Hope **[11178]**, PO Box 127, Dacula, GA 30019, (770)573-0676
Africa Inland Mission **[★20004]**
Africa Inland Mission **[★20004]**
Africa Inland Mission Intl. **[20004]**, PO Box 178, Pearl River, NY 10965, (845)735-4014
Africa Inland Mission Intl. **[20004]**, PO Box 178, Pearl River, NY 10965, (845)735-4014
Africa Inland Mission Intl. - Brazil **[IO]**, Londrina, Brazil
Africa Inland Mission Intl. - Canada **[IO]**, Scarborough, ON, Canada
Africa Inland Mission Intl. - France **[IO]**, Le Breuil-Bernard, France
Africa Inland Mission Intl. Hong Kong Comm. **[IO]**, Hong Kong, People's Republic of China
Africa Inland Mission Intl. - Netherlands **[IO]**, Zeist, Netherlands
Africa Inland Mission Intl. - South Africa **[IO]**, Plumstead, Republic of South Africa
Africa Inland Mission Intl. - United Kingdom **[IO]**, Nottingham, United Kingdom
Africa Inland Mission New Zealand **[IO]**, Auckland, New Zealand
Africa Leadership Forum **[IO]**, Ota, Nigeria
Africa Network **[17808]**, 110 Hofstra Univ., 205 Davison Hall, Hempstead, NY 11549
Africa News Ser. **[17144]**, 920 M St. SE, Washington, DC 20003, (202)546-0777
Africa Peace and Conflict Network **[12625]**, Nova Southern Univ., SHSS/Maltz Bldg., 3301 Coll. Ave., Fort Lauderdale, FL 33314, (954)262-3064
Africa Peace and Conflict Network **[12625]**, Nova Southern Univ., SHSS/Maltz Bldg., 3301 Coll. Ave., Fort Lauderdale, FL 33314, (954)262-3064
Africa Rainforest and River Conservation - Address unknown since 2010.
Africa Reconciliation Comm. **[IO]**, Tokyo, Japan
Africa Rice Center **[IO]**, Bouake, Cote d'Ivoire
Africa - The African Travel Assn. **[★3546]**
Africa - The African Travel Assn. **[★3546]**
Africa Travel Assn. **[3546]**, 166 Madison Ave., 5th Fl., New York, NY 10016, (212)447-1357
Africa Travel Assn. **[3546]**, 166 Madison Ave., 5th Fl., New York, NY 10016, (212)447-1357
Africa Youth Ministries **[IO]**, Kampala, Uganda
Africaine De Developpement **[★IO]**
AFRICALINK - Address unknown since 2010.
African
　Achieve in Africa **[11173]**
　Afoakom-USA **[9863]**AfricanAfrica-American Friendship Soc.
　Africa-Canada Development and Info. Services Assn. **[11152]**

Reference to "IO" in place of a book number signifies that the association may be found in the 50th edition of International Organizations.

Africa News Ser. [17144]
African Children's Choir [9088]
African Children's Choir [9088]
African Cultural Alliance of North Am. [10818]
African Family Film Found. [9089]
African Family Film Found. [9089]
African Fed., Inc. [17900]
African Hea. Now [15139]
African Kids In Need [11179]
African Stud. Assn. [9090]
African Stud. Assn. [9090]
African Univ. Found. [7699]
African Univ. Found. [7699]
All for Africa [10807]
All One People [10808]
Amazigh Cultural Assn. in Am. [9091]
Amer. Inst. for Maghrib Stud. [7700]
Amer. Inst. for Maghrib Stud. [7700]
Anti-Poverty Initiative [17188]
Art Aids Art [10819]
Asaba Natl. Assn. [18839]
Assn. of African Stud. Programs [7701]
Assn. for Africanist Anthropology [6133]
Assn. for the Stud. of Classical African Civiliza-
    tions [9092]
Assn. for the Stud. of the Middle East and Africa
    [8619]
Assn. for the Stud. of the Worldwide African Di-
    aspora [7702]
BERWA [12315]
Black World Found. [9093]
Bridge Kids Intl. [13515]
Center for African Studies [18789]
Change Exchange [12205]
A Child For All [11216]
Darfur Human Rights Org. [17825]
Develop Africa [10820]
Educate These Children [11462]
Exodus Guild [10821]
Friends of Mali [18246]
From Us With Love [12235]
Global Alliance for Community Empowerment
    [10811]
Global Youth Partnership for Africa [9875]
HomeAID for Africa [10812]
Homowo African Arts and Cultures [9094]
Human Touch Intl. [13589]
Idoma Assn. USA [19176]
Invisible Children [17237]
Jewish Heart for Africa [10822]
Kenyan Americans Community Org. [10823]
KEZA [210]
Krochet Kids Intl. [12735]
Life in Abundance Intl. [10814]
Maasai Assn. [10824]
Medicine for Mali [12468]
Natl. Org. for Manyu Advancement [18840]
Nubian United Benevolent Intl. Assn. [12787]
Ota Benga Alliance [10825]
Play Soccer [10826]
Rwanda Gift for Life [13099]
Rwanda Partners [12364]
Solar Light for Africa [11640]
Sudan Stud. Assn. [7703]
Sudan Stud. Assn. [7703]
ThinkImpact [12373]
Touch the Life of a Child Org. [11418]
Touching Hearts [10817]AfricanUganda Soc.
Ugandan Amer. Partnership Org. [12307]
Ugandan North Amer. Assn. [18841]
UHAI for Hea. [15217]
Voices of African Mothers [12638]
Water for People I PlayPumps Intl. [10827]
WICUDA-USA [9095]
Women Watch Afrika [18797]
World Against AIDS [12386]
African Acad. of Sciences [IO], Nairobi, Kenya
African Aid Org. [10872], 1325 G St. NE, Ste. 500,
    Washington, DC 20005, (202)449-7708
African Airlines Assn. [IO], Nairobi, Kenya
African-American
100 Black Men of Am. [18842]
African Amer. Art Song Alliance [10134]
African Amer. Cultural Alliance [9096]
African Amer. Environmentalist Assn. [4234]

African Amer. Fed. Executive Assn. [5504]
African Amer. Lutheran Assn. [19920]
African Amer. Museum [10103]
African Amer. Women in Cinema Org. [9592]
African-American Women in Tech. [6104]
African Cultural Alliance of North Am. [10818]
Afro-American Historical and Genealogical Soc.
    [9097]
Afro-American Historical Soc. Museum [9098]
Assn. of African Amer. Financial Advisors [1334]
Assn. for the Stud. of African-American Life and
    History [9099]
Before Columbus Found. [10036]
Black Community Crusade for Children [11198]
Black Entomologists [6840]
Black Fashion Designers Assn. [1037]
Black Flight Attendants of Am. [18843]
Black Flight Attendants of Am. [18843]
Black Holocaust Soc. [17154]
Black Leadership Forum [18844]
Black Radical Cong. [18845]
Black Theatre Network [10571]
Black Women of Essence [10828]
Bridge Kids Intl. [13515]
Change Exchange [12205]
Charles H. Wright Museum of African Amer. His-
    tory [9100]
Charles H. Wright Museum of African Amer. His-
    tory [9100]
Coalition on Urban Renewal and Educ. [18755]
Cong. of Racial Equality [17155]
Friends of Mali [18246]
Inst. for the Advanced Stud. of Black Family Life
    and Culture [9101]
Inst. for Social Res. I Prog. for Res. on Black
    Americans [6105]
Intl. Black Writers and Authors [10721]
Land Loss Fund [12417]
Lincoln Inst. for Res. and Educ. [17156]
Minority Peace Corps Assn. [18307]
Museum of African Amer. History [9102]
Natl. Assn. of African Amer. Stud. [7704]
Natl. Assn. of African Americans for Positive
    Imagery [17157]
Natl. Assn. of Black Women in Constr. [848]
Natl. Black Catholic Cong. [19462]
Natl. Black Environmental Justice Network [4284]
Natl. Black Graduate Student Assn. [18846]
Natl. Black United Fed. of Charities [17158]
Natl. Center of Afro-American Artists [9103]
Natl. Coalition of Blacks for Reparations in Am.
    [17159]
Natl. Juneteenth Observance Found. [17160]
Natl. Org. for African-American Women [10829]
Natl. Trust for the Development of African Amer.
    Men [17161]
Nubian United Benevolent Intl. Assn. [12787]
Prostate Hea. Educ. Network [13971]
San Francisco African Amer. Historical and
    Cultural Soc. [9104]
Schomburg Center for Res. in Black Culture
    [9105]
Schomburg Center for Res. in Black Culture
    [9105]
Soc. for the Anal. of African-American Public Hea.
    Issues [16497]
Student African Amer. Brotherhood [19288]
Thurgood Marshall Coll. Fund [7705]
African Amer. Alliance for Homeownership [1781],
    PO Box 11531, Portland, OR 97211, (503)595-
    3517
African-Amer. Art Song Alliance [10134], 15 Newton
    Ct., Irvine, CA 92604, (949)468-8031
African-Amer. Assn. of Fitness Professionals - Ad-
    dress unknown since 2010.
African Amer. Breast Cancer Alliance [13877], PO
    Box 8981, Minneapolis, MN 55408, (612)825-3675
African Amer. Cinema Soc. - Address unknown since
    2010.
African Amer. Cultural Alliance [9096], PO Box
    22173, Nashville, TN 37202, (615)251-0007
African Amer. Environmentalist Assn. [4234], 1629 K
    St. NW, Ste. 300, Washington, DC 20006-1631,
    (443)569-5102
African Amer. Fed. Executive Assn. [5504], 1205
    Heritage Hills Dr., Upper Marlboro, MD 20774,
    (866)600-4894

African-American Female Entrepreneurs Alliance
    [3673], 45 Scottdale Ave., Lansdowne, PA 19050,
    (215)747-9282
African-Amer. History Assn. - Defunct.
African Amer. Holiday Assn. - Address unknown
    since 2011.
African-American Inst. [★17141]
African-Amer. Labor Center - Defunct.
African-American Lib. and Info. Sci. Assn. - Defunct.
African-Amer. Life Alliance - Address unknown since
    2011.
African Amer. Literature and Culture Soc. [10030],
    Aldon L. Nielsen, PhD, Pres., The Pennsylvania
    State Univ., 116 Burrowes, University Park, PA
    16802-6200, (814)865-0091
African Amer. Lutheran Assn. [19920], 335 E Alber-
    toni St., No. 200-641, Carson, CA 90746
African Amer. Museum [10103], 1765 Crawford Rd.,
    Cleveland, OH 44106
African Amer. Museum [10103], 1765 Crawford Rd.,
    Cleveland, OH 44106
African-Amer. Museums Assn. [10104], PO Box 427,
    Wilberforce, OH 45384, (937)352-5084
African-Amer. Natural Foods Assn. - Defunct.
African Amer. Post Traumatic Stress Disorder Assn.
    [20766], 9129 Veterans Dr. SW, Lakewood, WA
    98498, (253)589-0766
African Amer. Visual Arts Assn. - Address unknown
    since 2011.
African Amer. Wine Tasting Soc. [173], PO Box 681,
    Powder Springs, GA 30127, (770)437-1753
African-American Women in Cinema Org. [9592], 545
    8th Ave., Ste. 401, New York, NY 10018, (212)769-
    7949
African-American Women in Tech. [6104], 619 E
    Coll. Ave., Ste. C3, Decatur, GA 30030
African-Americans for Humanism [★19819]
African-Americans for Humanism [★19819]
African Assn. for Lexicography [IO], Pretoria,
    Republic of South Africa
African Assn. of Physiological Sciences [IO], Dur-
    ban, Republic of South Africa
African Assn. for Public Admin. and Mgt. [IO],
    Nairobi, Kenya
African Assn. of Remote Sensing of the Env. [IO],
    Enschede, Netherlands
African Assn. for the Stud. of Liver Diseases [IO],
    Cairo, Egypt
African Assn. of Zoos and Aquaria [IO], Pretoria,
    Republic of South Africa
African Baseball Network [22260], PO Box 1579,
    New York, NY 10027, (646)785-1471
African Bird Club [IO], Cambridge, United Kingdom
African Blackwood Conservation Proj. [3981], PO
    Box 26, Red Rock, TX 78662
African Blackwood Conservation Proj. [3981], PO
    Box 26, Red Rock, TX 78662
African Books Collective [IO], Oxford, United
    Kingdom
African Bus. Alliance [159], 5805 State Bridge Rd.,
    Ste. G255, Duluth, GA 30097, (770)409-8780
African Capacity Building Found. [IO], Harare,
    Zimbabwe
African, Caribbean and Pacific Gp. of States [IO],
    Brussels, Belgium
African Centre for Democracy and Human Rights
    Stud. [IO], Serrekunda, Gambia
African Centre of Meteorological Applications for
    Development [IO], Niamey, Niger
African Centre for Tech. Stud. [IO], Nairobi, Kenya
African Chap. of Intl. Assn. of Agricultural Medicine
    and Rural Hea. - Egypt [IO], Cairo, Egypt
African Child Assn. [IO], London, United Kingdom
African Child Care Assn., Inc. [★10872]
African Children's Choir [9088], PO Box 29690, Bell-
    ingham, WA 98228-1690, (604)575-4500
African Children's Choir [9088], PO Box 29690, Bell-
    ingham, WA 98228-1690, (604)575-4500
African Children's Intl. Peace Forum and Ambas-
    sadors for Global Peace Intl. [IO], Lagos, Nigeria
African Civil Aviation Commn. [IO], Dakar, Senegal
African Civil Ser. Observatory [IO], Cotonou, Benin
African Commn. on Human and Peoples' Rights
    [IO], Banjul, Gambia
African Community Involvement Assn. [IO], Surrey,
    United Kingdom

A star before a book entry number signifies that the name is not listed separately, but is mentioned within the entry.

African Conservation Trust [IO], Pietermaritzburg, Republic of South Africa

African Coun. of AIDS Ser. Organizations [IO], Dakar, Senegal

African Coun. for Commun. Educ. [IO], Nairobi, Kenya

African Cradle [11444], 2672 Bayshore Pkwy., Ste. 1000, Mountain View, CA 94043, (650)461-9192

African Cultural Alliance of North Am. [10818], 5530 Chester Ave., Philadelphia, PA 19143-5328, (215)729-8225

African Development Bank [IO], Abidjan, Cote d'Ivoire

African Development Fund [IO], Abidjan, Cote d'Ivoire

African Development Inst.

African Development Inst. - Address unknown since 2011.

African Dream Found. [IO], Abeokuta, Nigeria

African Economic Community [IO], Addis Ababa, Ethiopia

African Economic Res. Consortium [IO], Nairobi, Kenya

African Educational Res. Network [7990], Albany State Univ., Coll. of Educ., 504 Coll. Dr., Albany, GA 31705

African Educational Res. Network [7990], Albany State Univ., Coll. of Educ., 504 Coll. Dr., Albany, GA 31705

African Energy Policy Res. Network/Foundation for Woodstove Dissemination [IO], Nairobi, Kenya

African Energy Policy Res. Network - Kenya [IO], Nairobi, Kenya

African Enterprise [IO], Kampala, Uganda

African Enterprise Canada [IO], Vancouver, BC, Canada

African Environmental Res. and Consulting Gp. [4235], 14912 Walmer St., Overland Park, KS 66223, (913)897-6132

African Environmental Res. and Consulting Gp. [4235], 14912 Walmer St., Overland Park, KS 66223, (913)897-6132

African Export-Import Bank [IO], Cairo, Egypt

African Family Film Found. [9089], PO Box 630, Santa Cruz, CA 95061-0630

African Family Film Found. [9089], PO Box 630, Santa Cruz, CA 95061-0630

African Family Relief Income Creation Assistance - Address unknown since 2011.

African Fed. of Gastroenterology [IO], Congella, Republic of South Africa

African Fed., Inc. [17900], 228 Park Ave. S, Ste. 25965, New York, NY 10003-1502, (646)863-5880

African Fed., Inc. [17900], 228 Park Ave. S, Ste. 25965, New York, NY 10003-1502, (646)863-5880

African Football Confed. [IO], 6th October City, Egypt

African Forum and Network on Debt and Development [IO], Harare, Zimbabwe

African Found. for Development [IO], London, United Kingdom

African Gender Inst. [IO], Rondebosch, Republic of South Africa

African Great Lakes Initiative [13165], 1001 Park Ave., St. Louis, MO 63104, (314)647-1287

African Hea. For Empowerment and Development [IO], London, United Kingdom

African Hea. Now [15139], PO Box 3243, New York, NY 10163, (646)673-0405

African Hea. Now [15139], PO Box 3243, New York, NY 10163, (646)673-0405

African Hockey Fed. [IO], Alexandria, Egypt

African Info. and Documentation Center [IO], Madrid, Spain

African Info. Soc. Initiative [IO], Addis Ababa, Ethiopia

African Inst. for Economic Development and Planning [IO], Dakar, Senegal

African Insurance Org. [IO], Douala, Cameroon

African Intellectual Property Org. [IO], Yaounde, Cameroon

African Kids In Need [11179], 137 N Larchmont Blvd., Los Angeles, CA 90004

African Kids In Need [11179], 137 N Larchmont Blvd., Los Angeles, CA 90004

African Language Assn. of Southern Africa [IO], Pretoria, Republic of South Africa

African Language Teachers Assn. [8939], Univ. of Wisconsin - Madison, 4231 Humanities Bldg., 455 N Park St., Madison, WI 53706, (608)265-7902

African Love Bird Soc. [21207], PO Box 142, San Marcos, CA 92079-0142

African Medical and Res. Found. [15140], 4 W 43rd St., 2nd Fl., New York, NY 10036, (212)768-2440

African Medical and Res. Found. [15140], 4 W 43rd St., 2nd Fl., New York, NY 10036, (212)768-2440

African Medical and Res. Found. - Canada [IO], Toronto, ON, Canada

African Medical and Res. Found. - France [IO], Paris, France

African Medical and Res. Found. - Italy [IO], Rome, Italy

African Medical and Res. Found. - Kenya [IO], Nairobi, Kenya

African Medical and Res. Found. - Sweden [IO], Stockholm, Sweden

African Medical and Res. Found. - Tanzania [IO], Dar es Salaam, United Republic of Tanzania

African Medical and Res. Found. - Uganda [IO], Kampala, Uganda

African Natl. Network [★17808]

African Network for Agriculture, Agroforestry and Natural Resources Educ. [IO], Nairobi, Kenya

African Network for Prevention and Protection Against Child Abuse and Neglect [IO], Nairobi, Kenya

African Network of Sci. and Technological Institutions [IO], Nairobi, Kenya

African Org. of Supreme Audit Institutions [IO], Tripoli, Libyan Arab Jamahiriya

African Peace Support Trainers' Assn. [IO], Pretoria, Republic of South Africa

African Publishers Network [IO], Harare, Zimbabwe

African Refugees Found. [IO], Lagos, Nigeria

African Regional Intellectual Property Org. [IO], Harare, Zimbabwe

African Regional Labour Admin. Centre - Zimbabwe [IO], Harare, Zimbabwe

African Regional Org. for Standardization - Kenya [IO], Nairobi, Kenya

African Regional Youth Initiative [IO], Dar es Salaam, United Republic of Tanzania

African Reinsurance Corp. [IO], Lagos, Nigeria

African Relief and Development Found. [★12895]

African Relief and Development Found. [★12895]

African Res. Found. [★15140]

African Res. Found. [★15140]

African Rural and Agricultural Credit Assn. [IO], Nairobi, Kenya

African Sci. Inst. [7352], PO Box 12161, Oakland, CA 94604, (510)653-7027

African Seed Trade Assn. [IO], Nairobi, Kenya

African Sky [11542], PO Box 203, Munroe Falls, OH 44262

African Sky [11542], PO Box 203, Munroe Falls, OH 44262

African Soc. for Bioinformatics and Computational Biology [IO], Bellville, Republic of South Africa

African Soc. of Chemotherapy [IO], Casablanca, Morocco

African Soc. for Toxicological Sciences [7567], 35 Gatehouse Dr., Waltham, MA 02451, (781)472-5984

African Sports Confed. of Disabled [IO], Giza, Egypt

African Stud. Assn. [9090], Rutgers Univ., Livingston Campus, 54 Joyce Kilmer Ave., Piscataway, NJ 08854-8045, (848)445-8173

African Stud. Assn. [9090], Rutgers Univ., Livingston Campus, 54 Joyce Kilmer Ave., Piscataway, NJ 08854-8045, (848)445-8173

African Stud. Assn. of Australasia and the Pacific [IO], Melbourne, Australia

African Stud. Assn. of the United Kingdom [IO], London, United Kingdom

African Stud. Centre [IO], Leiden, Netherlands

African Training and Res. Centre in Admin. for Development [IO], Tangier, Morocco

African Union of the Blind - Kenya [IO], Nairobi, Kenya

African Univ. Found. [7699], 3737 N Meridian St., Ste. 204, Indianapolis, IN 46208, (317)926-2175

African Univ. Found. [7699], 3737 N Meridian St., Ste. 204, Indianapolis, IN 46208, (317)926-2175

African Venture Capital Assn. [IO], Nairobi, Kenya

African Violet Soc. of Am. [21763], 2375 North St., Beaumont, TX 77702, (409)839-4725

African Violet Soc. of Canada [IO], St. Albert, AB, Canada

African Wild Dog Conservancy [5020], 208 N California Ave., Silver City, NM 88061

African Wild Dog Conservancy [5020], 208 N California Ave., Silver City, NM 88061

African Wildlife Found. [5021], 1400 16th St. NW, Ste. 120, Washington, DC 20036, (202)939-3333

African Wildlife Found. [5021], 1400 16th St. NW, Ste. 120, Washington, DC 20036, (202)939-3333

African Wildlife Leadership Found. [★5021]

African Wildlife Leadership Found. [★5021]

African Wind Energy Assn. [IO], Darling, Republic of South Africa

African Women Global Network [18789], Ohio State Univ., 314 Oxley Hall, 1712 Neil Ave., Columbus, OH 43210-1219, (614)292-8169

African Women's Development and Commun. Network [IO], Nairobi, Kenya

Africans in Partnership Against AIDS [IO], Toronto, ON, Canada

Africare [17145], 440 R St. NW, Washington, DC 20001, (202)462-3614

Africare [17145], 440 R St. NW, Washington, DC 20001, (202)462-3614

Africare - Angola [IO], Luanda, Angola

Africare - Benin [IO], Cotonou, Benin

Africare - Nigeria [IO], Abuja, Nigeria

Africare - Sierra Leone [IO], Freetown, Sierra Leone

Africare - Tanzania [IO], Dar es Salaam, United Republic of Tanzania

AfriHope Intl., Inc. [10806], PO Box 190796, Boston, MA 02119, (617)957-1613

Afrika Komitee [★IO]

Afrika-Studiecentrum [★IO]

Afrikagrupperna [★IO]

Afrikanerbond [IO], Auckland Park, Republic of South Africa

Afro-American Cultural and Historical Soc. [★10103]

Afro-American Cultural and Historical Soc. [★10103]

Afro-American Historical and Genealogical Soc. [9097], PO Box 73067, Washington, DC 20056-3067

Afro-American Historical Soc. Museum [9098], Neal E. Brunson, Esq., Dir., 1841 Kennedy Blvd., Jersey City, NJ 07305, (201)547-5262

Afro-American Museum of Detroit [★9100]

Afro-American Museum of Detroit [★9100]

Afro-Asian Book Coun. [IO], New Delhi, India

Afro-Asian Philosophy Assn. [IO], Cairo, Egypt

Afro-Asian Rural Development Org. [IO], New Delhi, India

Afro-Asian Soc. of Nematologists [IO], Luton, United Kingdom

AFS Austauschprogramme fur interkulturelles Lernen [★IO]

AFS Del Peru Programas Interculturales [★IO]

AFS Intercultura [★IO]

AFS Intercultura Brasil [★IO]

AFS Intercultura Portugal [★IO]

AFS Intercultural Programmes - New Zealand [IO], Wellington, New Zealand

AFS Intercultural Programs [8336], 71 W 23rd St., 6th Fl., New York, NY 10010-4102, (212)807-8686

AFS Intercultural Programs [8336], 71 W 23rd St., 6th Fl., New York, NY 10010-4102, (212)807-8686

AFS Intercultural Programs - Argentina [IO], Buenos Aires, Argentina

AFS Intercultural Programs - Australia [IO], Sydney, Australia

AFS Intercultural Programs - Austria [IO], Vienna, Austria

AFS Intercultural Programs - Brazil [IO], Rio de Janeiro, Brazil

AFS Intercultural Programs - Chile [IO], Santiago, Chile

AFS Intercultural Programs - China [IO], Beijing, People's Republic of China

AFS Intercultural Programs - Costa Rica [IO], San Jose, Costa Rica

Reference to "IO" in place of a book number signifies that the association may be found in the 50th edition of International Organizations.

AFS Intercultural Programs - Czech Republic **[IO]**, Prague, Czech Republic

AFS Intercultural Programs - Denmark **[IO]**, Frederiksberg, Denmark

AFS Intercultural Programs - Dominican Republic **[IO]**, Santo Domingo, Dominican Republic

AFS Intercultural Programs - Ecuador **[IO]**, Quito, Ecuador

AFS Intercultural Programs - Finland **[IO]**, Helsinki, Finland

AFS Intercultural Programs - Germany **[IO]**, Hamburg, Germany

AFS Intercultural Programs - Ghana **[IO]**, Accra, Ghana

AFS Intercultural Programs - Guatemala **[IO]**, Guatemala City, Guatemala

AFS Intercultural Programs - Honduras **[IO]**, Tegucigalpa, Honduras

AFS Intercultural Programs - Hong Kong **[IO]**, Hong Kong, People's Republic of China

AFS Intercultural Programs - Hungary **[IO]**, Budapest, Hungary

AFS Intercultural Programs - Iceland **[IO]**, Reykjavik, Iceland

AFS Intercultural Programs - India **[IO]**, New Delhi, India

AFS Intercultural Programs - Italy **[IO]**, Siena, Italy

AFS Intercultural Programs - Latvia **[IO]**, Riga, Latvia

AFS Intercultural Programs - Malaysia **[IO]**, Petaling Jaya, Malaysia

AFS Intercultural Programs - Panama **[IO]**, Panama City, Panama

AFS Intercultural Programs - Peru **[IO]**, Lima, Peru

AFS Intercultural Programs - Portugal **[IO]**, Lisbon, Portugal

AFS Intercultural Programs - Slovakia **[IO]**, Bratislava, Slovakia

AFS Intercultural Programs - Spain **[IO]**, Madrid, Spain

AFS Intercultural Programs - Sweden **[IO]**, Stockholm, Sweden

AFS Intercultural Programs - Thailand **[IO]**, Nonthaburi, Thailand

AFS Intercultural Programs - Venezuela **[IO]**, Caracas, Venezuela

AFS Interculture Canada **[IO]**, Montreal, QC, Canada

AFS Interculture South Africa **[IO]**, Rosebank, Republic of South Africa

AFS Interkultur **[★IO]**

AFS Interkulturell Utbildning **[★IO]**

AFS Interkulturelle Begegnungen e.V. **[★IO]**

AFS Intl. **[7947]**, 71 W 23rd St., 6th Fl., New York, NY 10010, (212)807-8686

AFS Intl. **[7947]**, 71 W 23rd St., 6th Fl., New York, NY 10010, (212)807-8686

AFS a Islandi **[★IO]**

AFS Mezikulturni Programy - Ceska Republika **[★IO]**

AFS Norge **[IO]**, Oslo, Norway

AFS Norge Internasjonal Utvekslings **[★IO]**

AFS Programas Interculturales - Argentina **[★IO]**

AFS Programas Interculturales - Costa Rica **[★IO]**

AFS Programas Interculturales - Ecuador **[★IO]**

AFS Programas Interculturales - Panama **[★IO]**

AFS Programas Interculturales - Venezuela **[★IO]**

AFT Healthcare **[23213]**, 555 New Jersey Ave. NW, Washington, DC 20001, (202)879-4400

Aftab Soc. **[IO]**, Tehran, Iran

After Death Commun. Res. Found. **[15072]**, PO Box 20238, Houma, LA 70360

Aftermarket Body Parts Assn. **[★348]**

Aftermarket Body Parts Assn. **[★348]**

Aftermarket Body Parts Distributors Assn. **[★348]**

Aftermarket Body Parts Distributors Assn. **[★348]**

Aftermarket Coun. on Electronic Commerce - Address unknown since 2011.

Afterschool Alliance **[11146]**, 1616 H St. NW, Ste. 820, Washington, DC 20006, (202)347-2030

AG Communications in Educ. **[★3737]**

Ag Container Recycling Coun. **[4865]**, 223 S Main St., Lexington, VA 24450, (877)952-2272

Aga Khan Found. - Canada **[IO]**, Ottawa, ON, Canada

Aga Khan Found. - India **[IO]**, New Delhi, India

Aga Khan Trust for Culture **[IO]**, Geneva, Switzerland

Agac Mamuelleri ve Oman Ueruenleri Ikhracatcilari Biligi **[★IO]**

Against Child Abuse **[IO]**, Hong Kong, People's Republic of China

Agami **[7824]**, PO Box 3178, Fremont, CA 94539

Agape Center **[IO]**, Zama, Japan

Agatha Christie Appreciation Soc.: Partners in Crime - Defunct.

Agatha Christie Appreciation Soc.: Postern of Murder - Defunct.

Age Action Ireland **[IO]**, Dublin, Ireland

Age Concern England **[IO]**, London, United Kingdom

Age Concern Scotland **[IO]**, Edinburgh, United Kingdom

Age Platform Europe **[IO]**, Brussels, Belgium

Aged Care Assn. Australia **[IO]**, Curtin, Australia

Aged Care Assn. Australia - South Australia **[IO]**, Frewville, Australia

Aged Care Assn. Australia - Tasmania **[IO]**, Claremont, Australia

Aged Care Assn. Australia - Western Australia **[IO]**, South Perth, Australia

Aged Care Assn. of Victoria **[IO]**, Malvern, Australia

Aged Care Queensland **[IO]**, Brisbane, Australia

Aged and Community Services Australia **[IO]**, South Melbourne, Australia

Aged Rights Advocacy Ser. **[IO]**, Adelaide, Australia

Agence Canadienne des Droits de Reproduction Musicaux **[★IO]**

Agence de Consultation, de Commandement et de Conduite des Operations de l'OTAN **[★IO]**

Agence d'Aide a la Cooperation Technique Et au Developpement **[★IO]**

Agence de Developpement et de Secours Adventiste Canada **[★IO]**

Agence islamique Intl. de Presse **[★IO]**

Agence Internationale ISBN **[★IO]**

Agence Internationale de l'Energie **[★IO]**

Agence Internationale de l'Energie Atomique **[★IO]**

Agence de l'OCDE pour l'energie nucleaire **[★IO]**

Agence de Presse de l'OPEC **[★IO]**

Agence Spatiale Europeenne **[★IO]**

Agence Universitaire De La Francophonie **[★IO]**

Agence Universitaire de la Francophone, Bur. Afrique de l'Quest **[IO]**, Dakar, Senegal

Agence Universitaire de la Francophonie **[★IO]**

Agence Universitaire de la Francophonie **[★IO]**

Agence Universitaire de la Francophonie **[★IO]**

Agence Universitaire de la Francophonie Antenne de Bruxelles **[★IO]**

Agencia de Informacao de Mocambique **[★IO]**

Agencia Latinoamericana de Informacion **[★IO]**

Agency for Instructional Tech. **[8302]**, Box A, 1800 N Stonelake Dr., Bloomington, IN 47402-0120, (812)339-2203

Agency for Instructional TV **[★8302]**

Agency for the Prohibition of Nuclear Weapons in Latin Am. and the Caribbean **[IO]**, Mexico City, Mexico

Agency for Tech. Cooperation and Development **[IO]**, Paris, France

AGENDA Feminist Media **[IO]**, Durban, Republic of South Africa

Agent Orange
   VietNow Natl. **[13358]**

Agent Orange Victims Intl. **[★13353]**

Agents
   Assn. of Authors' Representatives **[161]**
   Assn. of Talent Agents **[162]**
   Natl. Assn. of Independent Real Estate Brokers **[3021]**
   Natl. Conf. of Personal Managers **[163]**
   North Amer. Performing Arts Managers and Agents **[164]**

Agents Assn. of Great Britain **[IO]**, London, United Kingdom

Agenturforetagen **[★IO]**

Aggregate and Concrete Executives - Defunct.

Aggregate and Sand Producers Assn. of South Africa **[IO]**, Gauteng, Republic of South Africa

Aggregation of Congregation of Our Lady of Cenacle **[★19391]**

Agility Dog Assn. of Australia **[IO]**, Gailes, Australia

Agility Dog Club of Queensland **[IO]**, Brisbane, Australia

Aging
   60 Plus Assn. **[10830]**
   Aging in Am. **[10831]**
   Alliance for Aging Res. **[10832]**
   Amer. Assn. of Homes and Services for the Aging **[10851]**
   Amer. Soc. on Aging **[10833]**
   Assn. of Jewish Aging Services **[10834]**
   Beverly Found. **[10835]**
   Center for Advocacy for the Rights and Interests of the Elderly **[10836]**
   The Center for Social Gerontology **[10837]**
   Center for the Stud. of Aging of Albany **[10838]**
   Children of Aging Parents **[10839]**
   Consumer Consortium on Assisted Living **[10840]**
   Coun. of Professional Geropsychology Training Programs **[14663]**
   Elder Craftsmen **[10841]**
   Environmental Alliance for Senior Involvement **[4048]**
   Families U.S.A. Found. **[10842]**
   Gay and Lesbian Assn. of Retiring Persons **[10843]**
   Grace and Compassion Benedictines **[9763]**
   Gray is Green: The Natl. Senior Conservation Corps **[4072]**
   Gray Panthers **[10844]**
   Grey Muzzle Org. **[10971]**
   Hea. Promotion Inst. **[10845]**
   Intl. Assn. of Homes and Services for the Ageing **[10846]**
   Intl. Assn. of Homes and Services for the Ageing **[10846]**
   Intl. Soc. for Aging and Physical Activity **[13590]**
   Intl. Soc. for Aging and Physical Activity **[13590]**
   Jewish Assn. for Services for the Aged **[10847]**
   John A. Hartford Found. **[10848]**
   Latino Center on Aging **[10849]**
   Latino Center on Aging **[10849]**
   Leadership Coun. of Aging Organizations **[10850]**
   LeadingAge **[10851]**
   Lifespan Resources **[10852]**
   Little Bros. - Friends of the Elderly **[10853]**
   Natl. Acad. for Teaching and Learning About Aging **[10854]**
   Natl. Adult Day Services Assn. **[10855]**
   Natl. Asian Pacific Center on Aging **[10856]**
   Natl. Assn. of Area Agencies on Aging **[10857]**
   Natl. Assn. of State United for Aging and Disabilities **[10858]**
   Natl. Assn. of Triads **[12992]**
   Natl. Caucus and Center on Black Aged **[10859]**
   Natl. Comm. for the Prevention of Elder Abuse **[10860]**
   Natl. Coun. on Aging **[10861]**
   Natl. Coun. on the Aging | Natl. Inst. of Senior Centers **[10862]**
   Natl. Hispanic Coun. on Aging **[10863]**
   Natl. Indian Coun. on Aging **[10864]**
   Natl. Inst. on Community-Based Long-Term Care **[10865]**
   Natl. Senior Citizens Law Center **[10866]**
   Natl. Soc. for Amer. Indian Elderly **[19162]**
   Old Lesbians Organizing for Change **[10867]**
   Private Duty Homecare Assn. **[15015]**
   Rebuilding Together **[12200]**
   Retirement Res. Found. **[10868]**
   Senior Gleaners **[12291]**
   Senior Roller Skaters of Am. **[22899]**
   The Seniors Coalition **[10869]**
   Significant Living **[10870]**
   Silver Age Yoga **[17138]**
   Support Our Aging Religious **[10871]**

Aging in Am. **[10831]**, 1500 Pelham Pkwy. S, Bronx, NY 10461, (877)AGING-NY

Aging with Autism **[13777]**, 704 Marten Rd., Princeton, NJ 08540

Aging Services Programs; Natl. Assn. of Nutrition and **[15840]**

AGIR Ici **[IO]**, Paris, France

Aglow Intl. **[20284]**, PO Box 1749, Edmonds, WA 98020-1749, (425)775-7282

A star before a book entry number signifies that the name is not listed separately, but is mentioned within the entry.

Aglow Intl. [20284], PO Box 1749, Edmonds, WA 98020-1749, (425)775-7282
Aglow New Zealand [IO], Porirua, New Zealand
AGN Intl. North Am. [4], 2851 S Parker Rd., Ste. 850, Aurora, CO 80014, (303)743-7880
Agni Yoga Soc. [20297], 319 W 107th St., New York, NY 10025, (212)864-7752
Agoraphobics in Motion [12691], PO Box 725363, Berkley, MI 48072, (248)547-0400
Agostiniani dell'Assunzione [★IO]
Agrarian Cooperators Union [IO], Tirana, Albania
Agri-Club Natl. Togo [IO], Lome, Togo
Agri-Energy Roundtable [17901], PO Box 5565, Washington, DC 20016, (202)887-0528
Agri-Energy Roundtable [17901], PO Box 5565, Washington, DC 20016, (202)887-0528
Agri-Horticultural Soc. of India [IO], Calcutta, India
Agri-Service Ethiopia [IO], Addis Ababa, Ethiopia
Agribition Canadienne de l'Ouest [★IO]

Agribusiness
Agribusiness Coun. [3717]
Agricultural Development Initiatives [3727]
Amer. Farmers for the Advancement and Conservation of Tech. [4347]
Amer. Soc. of Agricultural Consultants [3718]
Amer. Soc. of Agricultural Consultants [3718]
Australian Inst. of Agricultural Sci. and Tech. [14819]
Communicating for Am. [3719]
CUMELA Nederland [6813]
Demeter Biodynamic Trade Assn. [4350]
Ecova Mali [3754]
Food Trade Sustainability Leadership Assn. [1387]
Geode Rsrc., Conservation, and Development [3720]
German Foods North Am. [4715]
Hazelnut Coun. [4750]
Intl. Sugar Trade Coalition [3367]
Natl. Alliance of Independent Crop Consultants [3721]
Natl. Assn. of Farm Bus. Anal. Specialists [165]
Natl. Coun. of Agricultural Employers [3722]
Org. for Competitive Markets [3723]
Samuel Roberts Noble Found. [3724]
Southern U.S. Trade Assn. [3725]
United Agribusiness League [3726]
Agribusiness Assn. of Australia [IO], Farrell Flat, Australia
Agribusiness Coun. [3717], 3312 Porter St. NW, Washington, DC 20008, (202)296-4563
Agribusiness Employers Fed. [IO], Adelaide, Australia
Agricultural and Applied Economics Assn. [6606], 555 E Wells St., Ste. 1100, Milwaukee, WI 53202, (414)918-3190
Agricultural and Applied Economics Assn. [6606], 555 E Wells St., Ste. 1100, Milwaukee, WI 53202, (414)918-3190
Agricultural Coll. Magazines Assoc. [★8445]
Agricultural Commodities Certification Assn. [3749], PO Box 23175, Washington, DC 20026-3175, (571)377-0722
Agricultural Communicators in Educ. [★3737]
Agricultural Cooperative Development Intl. [★4174]
Agricultural Cooperative Development Intl. [★4174]
Agricultural Cooperative Development Intl. and Volunteers in Cooperative Assistance [★4174]
Agricultural Cooperative Development Intl. and Volunteers in Cooperative Assistance [★4174]

Agricultural Development
Agricultural Commodities Certification Assn. [3749]
Agricultural Development Initiatives [3727]
Alliance for Sustainability [4345]
Amer. Farmers for the Advancement and Conservation of Tech. [4347]
Armenian Tech. Gp. [3728]
Armenian Tech. Gp. [3728]
Australian Women in Agriculture [2150]
Canadian Agricultural Economics Soc. [21688]
Community Agroecology Network [4938]
Compatible Tech. Intl. [3729]
Compatible Tech. Intl. [3729]
Demeter Biodynamic Trade Assn. [4350]

Double Harvest [3730]
Double Harvest [3730]
Farm and Ranch Freedom Alliance [4352]
Farmers Market Coalition [3731]
Intl. Agro Alliance [4940]
Intl. Sprout Growers Assn. [3732]
Intl. Sprout Growers Assn. [3732]
Multinational Exchange for Sustainable Agriculture [4941]
Natl. Women in Agriculture Assn. [3762]
Pan-American Fed. for Info. Tech. in Agriculture [6106]
Reach Across [20084]
Sustainable Agriculture Educ. [4944]
Sustainable Agriculture Educ. Assn. [7717]
Women Organizing for Change in Agriculture and NRM [3769]
Agricultural Development Coun. [★17171]
Agricultural Development Coun. [★17171]
Agricultural Development Initiatives [3727], PO Box 50006, Nashville, TN 37205, (615)599-2015
Agricultural Development and Training Soc. [IO], Bagepalli, India
Agricultural Drainage Mgt. Coalition [5003], PO Box 592, Owatonna, MN 55060, (507)451-0073
Agricultural Economics Assn. of South Africa [IO], Pretoria, Republic of South Africa
Agricultural Economics Soc. [IO], Banbury, United Kingdom

Agricultural Education
Alpha Tau Alpha [23460]
Amer. Assn. for Agricultural Educ. [7706]
Assn. for Intl. Agricultural and Extension Educ. [7707]
Assn. for Intl. Agricultural and Extension Educ. [7707]
Assn. for Intl. Agriculture and Rural Development [7708]
Assn. for Intl. Agriculture and Rural Development [7708]
Coun. for Agricultural Sci. and Tech. [7709]
Farm-Based Educ. Assn. [7710]
Multinational Exchange for Sustainable Agriculture [4941]
Natl. Assn. of Agricultural Educators [7711]
Natl. Assn. of Supervisor of Agricultural Educ. [7712]
Natl. Coalition for Food and Agricultural Res. [3744]
Natl. Coun. for Agricultural Educ. [7713]
Natl. FFA Org. [7714]
Natl. FFA Org. [7714]
Natl. Postsecondary Agricultural Student Org. [7715]
North Amer. Colleges and Teachers of Agriculture [7716]
North Amer. South Devon Assn. [3934]
Sustainable Agriculture Educ. Assn. [7717]
Tech. for the Poor [4945]
Agricultural Educ. Natl. HQ [★7713]

Agricultural Engineering
Alpha Epsilon [23516]AgriculturalArgentine Center of Agricultural Engineers
Coachmakers' and Coach Harness Makers' Company [14628]
Intl. Network on Participatory Irrigation Mgt. [7016]
Agricultural Engineers' Assn. [IO], Peterborough, United Kingdom

Agricultural Equipment
Assn. Equip. Mfrs. [166]
Assn. Equip. Mfrs. [166]
Canada West Equip. Dealers Assn. [14409]
Equip. Mfrs. Coun. [167]
Farm Equip. Mfrs. Assn. [168]
Intl. Silo Assn. [169]
Intl. Silo Assn. [169]
Irrigation Assn. [170]
Irrigation Assn. [170]
Midwest Equip. Dealers Assn. [3733]
Natl. Greenhouse Mfrs. Assn. [171]
Natl. Russell Collectors Assn. [21382]
North Amer. Equip. Dealers Assn. [172]
Tech. for the Poor [4945]
Agricultural and Food Transporters Conf. [3498], 950 N Glebe Rd., Ste. 210, Arlington, VA 22203-4181, (703)838-7964

Agricultural and Forestry Machinery Assn. [IO], Brno, Czech Republic
Agricultural Groups Concerned About Resources and the Env. [IO], Guelph, ON, Canada
Agricultural History Soc. [9739], Alan I. Marcus, Treas., PO Box H, Mississippi State, MS 39762, (662)268-2247
Agricultural and Indus. Manufacturer's Representatives Assn. [★2317]
Agricultural Insecticide and Fungicide Assn. [★753]
Agricultural Insecticides and Fungicide Mfrs. Assn. [★753]
Agricultural Inst. of Canada [IO], Ottawa, ON, Canada

Agricultural Law
Amer. Agricultural Law Assn. [5184]
Agricultural Law Assn. [IO], Colchester, United Kingdom
Agricultural Libraries Network [IO], Rome, Italy
Agricultural Lime Assn. [IO], London, United Kingdom
Agricultural Mfrs. of Canada [IO], Regina, SK, Canada
Agricultural Missions Found. [★20005]
Agricultural Missions, Inc. [20005], 475 Riverside Dr., Rm. 725, New York, NY 10115, (212)870-2553
Agricultural Nitrogen Inst. [★1245]
Agricultural Personnel Mgt. Assn. [4344], 512 Pajaro St., Ste. 7, Salinas, CA 93901, (831)422-8023
Agricultural Producers Union [IO], Longueuil, QC, Canada
Agricultural Relations Coun. [2906], PO Box 156, New Prague, MN 56071, (952)758-5811
Agricultural Res. Coun. [IO], Pretoria, Republic of South Africa
Agricultural Res. Coun. - Biometry Unit [IO], Pretoria, Republic of South Africa
Agricultural Res. Inst. - Defunct.
Agricultural Res. Trust [IO], Harare, Zimbabwe
Agricultural Retailers Assn. [3092], 1156 15th St. NW, Ste. 500, Washington, DC 20005, (202)457-0825
Agricultural and Rural Development Assn. in Ghana [IO], Agona Swedru, Ghana

Agricultural Science
Agriculture, Food and Human Values Soc. [3734]
Amer. Farm Bur. Found. for Agriculture [3735]
Amer. Soc. of Agronomy [3736]
Assn. for Commun. Excellence in Agriculture, Natural Resources, and Life and Human Sciences [3737]
Bangladesh Assn. of Agricultural Scientists in Am. [3738]
Crop Sci. Soc. of Am. [3739]
Crop Sci. Soc. of Am. [3739]
Demeter Biodynamic Trade Assn. [4350]
Ecological Farming Assn. [3740]
Farm Found. [3741]
Intl. Weed Sci. Soc. [3742]
Intl. Weed Sci. Soc. [3742]
Josephine Porter Inst. for Applied Bio-Dynamics [3743]
Natl. Coalition for Food and Agricultural Res. [3744]
Natl. Inst. for Sci., Law and Public Policy [3745]
Network of European Agricultural Tropically and Sub-tropically Oriented Universities and Sci. Complexes Related with Agricultural Development [18905]
North Amer. Weed Mgt. Assn. [3746]
North Amer. Weed Mgt. Assn. [3746]
Rural Advancement Found. Intl. USA [3747]
Rural Advancement Found. Intl. USA [3747]
Sustainable Agriculture Educ. Assn. [7717]
Weed Sci. Soc. of Am. [3748]
Weed Soc. of Victoria [15007]
Agricultural Societies Coun. of New South Wales [IO], Hunters Hill, Australia
Agricultural Transporters Conf. [★3498]

Agriculture
Agricultural Commodities Certification Assn. [3749]
Agricultural Development Initiatives [3727]
Agricultural Societies Coun. of New South Wales [16781]

Reference to "IO" in place of a book number signifies that the association may be found in the 50th edition of International Organizations.

Alliance for Sustainability [4345]
Alpha Epsilon [23516]
Alpha Gamma Rho [23461]
Alpha Zeta [23462]
Amer. Agri-Women [17162]
Amer. Agri-Women Rsrc. Center [17163]
Amer. Agriculture Movement [17164]
Amer. Farmers for the Advancement and
   Conservation of Tech. [4347]
Amer. Farmland Trust [17165]
Assn. for the Advancement of Indus. Crops [3750]
Assn. of Amer. Feed Control Officials [5185]
Assn. of Amer. Plant Food Control Officials [5186]
Assn. of Amer. Seed Control Officials [5187]
Assn. of Amer. Seed Control Officials [5187]
Assn. of Official Seed Analysts [5188]
Assn. of Official Seed Analysts [5188]
Assn. of Official Seed Certifying Agencies [5189]
Assn. of Public and Land Grant Universities |
   Commn. on Intl. Programs [17903]
Black Farmers and Agriculturists Assn. [3751]
Center for Rural Affairs [17166]
Community Agroecology Network [4938]
Compost Tea Indus. Assn. [3752]
Consortium for Intl. Crop Protection [3758]
Controlled Release Soc. [6404]
Coun. on Food, Agricultural and Rsrc. Economics
   [3753]
Demeter Biodynamic Trade Assn. [4350]
Ecova Mali [3754]
Ecova Mali [3754]
Experience Intl. [4054]
Farm Aid [17167]
Farm Financial Standards Coun. [3755]
Farm Labor Organizing Comm. [23142]
Farm Rescue [12041]
Farmer-Veteran Coalition [20610]
Food Trade Sustainability Leadership Assn.
   [1387]
Gamma Sigma Delta [23463]
Gamma Sigma Delta [23463]
German Foods North Am. [4715]
Hawaii Agriculture Res. Center [4936]
Hazelnut Coun. [4750]
IFDC [3756]
IFDC [3756]
Independent Professional Seedsmen Assn. [3757]
Inst. for Agriculture and Trade Policy [17168]
Integrated Plant Protection Center [3758]
Intl. Agro Alliance [4940]
Intl. Assn. for the Plant Protection Sciences
   [3759]
Intl. Assn. for the Plant Protection Sciences
   [3759]
Intl. Network on Participatory Irrigation Mgt.
   [7016]
Intl. Ser. for the Acquisition of Agri-biotech Ap-
   plications [3760]
Intl. Ser. for the Acquisition of Agri-biotech Ap-
   plications [3760]
Intl. Sugar Trade Coalition [3367]
Minorities in Agriculture, Natural Resources and
   Related Sciences [3761]
Multinational Exchange for Sustainable Agriculture
   [4941]
Namibia Agricultural Union [3219]
Natl. Assn. of African Palm Growers [22878]
Natl. Assn. of Agricultural Produce Trading
   Companies [18772]
Natl. Assn. of Agriculture Employees [5190]
Natl. Assn. of County Agricultural Agents [5191]
Natl. Assn. of Farm Bus. Anal. Specialists [165]
Natl. Assn. of State Departments of Agriculture
   [5192]AgricultureNatl. Chamber of Agriculture
   and Agro-Industry
Natl. Family Farm Coalition [17169]
Natl. Org. for Raw Materials [17170]
Natl. Plant Bd. [5193]
Natl. Sustainable Agriculture Coalition [4942]
Natl. Women in Agriculture Assn. [3762]
North Amer. Farm Show Coun. [3763]
Organic Seed Growers and Trade Assn. [4883]
Pan-American Fed. for Info. Tech. in Agriculture
   [6106]
Pan-American Fed. for Info. Tech. in Agriculture
   [6106]

Planting Empowerment [4410]
Proj. Food, Land and People [3764]
Sustainable Agriculture Educ. [4944]
Sustainable Agriculture Educ. Assn. [7717]
Sustainable Harvest Intl. [3765]
Tech. for the Poor [4945]
Truth About Trade and Tech. [6337]
United Farm Workers of Am. [23143]
U.S. Dept. of Agriculture | Org. of Professional
   Employees [5194]
Urban Farming [4366]
U.S.A. Dry Pea and Lentil Coun. [3766]
Wallace Genetic Found. [3767]
We're Welcome on Organic Farms - Austria
   [20889]
Western U.S. Agricultural Trade Assn. [3768]
Willing Workers on Organic Farms - New Zealand
   [2131]
Willing Workers on Organic Farms - Norway
   [18344]
Winrock Intl. [17171]
Winrock Intl. [17171]
Women Involved in Farm Economics [17172]
Women Organizing for Change in Agriculture and
   NRM [3769]
Women's Horticultural Assn. [4680]
World Wide Opportunities on Organic Farms - UK
   [16088]
World Wide Opportunities on Organic Farms -
   USA [17173]
Zambia Natl. Farmers' Union [20756]
Agriculture Coun. of America - Defunct.
Agriculture, Food and Human Values Soc. [3734],
   6802 SW 13th, Gainesville, FL 32608, (352)392-
   0958
Agriculture Tech. Services Assn. [IO], Phnom Penh,
   Cambodia
Agromisa Found. [IO], Wageningen, Netherlands
Agronomy Soc. of New Zealand [IO], Palmerston
   North, New Zealand
Agrupacion Espanola del Genero de Punto [★IO]
Agua Muisne [13411], 6014 The Terraces, Baltimore,
   MD 21209, (443)858-5869
Agua Muisne [13411], 6014 The Terraces, Baltimore,
   MD 21209, (443)858-5869
Aguayuda [13412], 7418 Tour Dr., Easton, MD
   21601, (410)463-1455
Aguayuda [13412], 7418 Tour Dr., Easton, MD
   21601, (410)463-1455
Aguda Leumit le Kimum Mefagrim Be'Israel [★IO]
Agudat Achsaniot Noar Beisrael [★IO]
Agudat Hachershim Beisrael [★IO]
Agudat Hametargmim Beyisrael [★IO]
Agustinians of the Assumption [IO], Rome, Italy
ah Adurzia [★19829]
AHA Intl. [8337], 70 NW Couch St., Ste. 242,
   Portland, OR 97209, (503)295-7730
AHA Intl. [8337], 70 NW Couch St., Ste. 242,
   Portland, OR 97209, (503)295-7730
AHEAD [★7970]
AHEAD [★7970]
AHEAD-INC., African Hea. Educ. and Development
   [14692], PO Box 600379, Dallas, TX 75206,
   (214)823-0007
Ahern Clan Assn. [20420], 298 Central St., Acton,
   MA 01720-2444
Ahl-ul-Bait World Assembly [IO], Tehran, Iran
Ahmadiyya Anjuman Isha'at-e-Islam Lahore [★IO]
Ahmadiyya Anjuman Isha'at-e-Islam Lahore, Canada
   [★IO]
Ahmadiyya Movement in Islam, Canada [★20446]
Ahmadiyya Muslim Community [IO], London, United
   Kingdom
AHOPE for Children [11180], 104 Hume Ave.,
   Alexandria, VA 22301, (703)683-7500
Ahoto Partnership for Ghana [15141], 366 Winthrop
   Mail Ctr., 32 Mill St., Cambridge, MA 02138
AHRA: The Assn. for Medical Imaging Mgt. [16516],
   490B Boston Post Rd., Ste. 200, Sudbury, MA
   01776, (978)443-7591
Ahsas Disabled People Org. [IO], Mansehra,
   Pakistan
AI Foundation [★13050]
AI Foundation [★13050]
AIB Intl. [384], 1213 Bakers Way, PO Box 3999,
   Manhattan, KS 66505-3999, (785)537-4750

AIC Foundation [★6392]
Aicardi Syndrome Newsl. [14581], PO Box 3202, St.
   Charles, IL 60174, (800)374-8518
Aicardi Syndrome Newsl. [14581], PO Box 3202, St.
   Charles, IL 60174, (800)374-8518
Aid Afghanistan for Educ. [IO], Kabul, Afghanistan
Aid Africa [12714], 3916 Pennsylvania Ave., La
   Crescenta, CA 91214, (818)249-2398
Aid Africa [12714], 3916 Pennsylvania Ave., La
   Crescenta, CA 91214, (818)249-2398
Aid for AIDS [13591], 515 Greenwich St., Ste. 506,
   New York, NY 10013, (212)337-8043
Aid for AIDS [13591], 515 Greenwich St., Ste. 506,
   New York, NY 10013, (212)337-8043
Aid to Artisans [12309], 1030 New Britain Ave., Ste.
   102, West Hartford, CT 06110, (860)756-5550
Aid to the Church in Need [19379], 725 Leonard St.,
   PO Box 220384, Brooklyn, NY 11222, (718)609-
   0939
Aid to the Church in Need [IO], Konigstein, Germany
Aid to Incarcerated Mothers [11700], 434 Mas-
   sachusetts Ave., Ste. 503, Boston, MA 02118,
   (617)536-0058
Aid for Refugees and Orphans [IO], Peshawar,
   Pakistan
Aid Still Required [11845], PO Box 7353, Santa
   Monica, CA 90406, (310)454-4646
Aid for the World [12715], 20 Murray St., Fl. 2, New
   York, NY 10007, (877)424-3911
Aide et Action - France [IO], Paris, France
Aide aux Aines [★IO]
Aide a l'Eglise en Detresse [★IO]
Aiding Leukemia Stricken Amer. Children [★14096]
Aiding Mothers and Fathers Experiencing Neonatal
   Death [11744], 1559 Ville Rosa, Hazelwood, MO
   63042, (314)291-0892
Aiding Romania's Children [11181], 212 W Lan-
   caster Ave., Paoli, PA 19301
AIDIS-USA [7348], PO Box 7737, McLean, VA
   22106-7737, (703)734-0367
AIDIS-USA Sect. [7348], PO Box 7737, McLean, VA
   22106-7737, (703)734-0367

AIDS
   African Aid Org. [10872]
   Africans in Partnership Against AIDS [21858]
   AHOPE for Children [11180]
   Aid for AIDS [13591]
   Aid for AIDS [13591]
   Aiding Romania's Children [11181]
   AIDS Alliance for Children, Youth and Families
      [13592]
   AIDS Clinical Trials Gp. [13593]
   AIDS Clinical Trials Gp. [13593]
   AIDS-Free World [13594]
   AIDS-Free World [13594]
   AIDS Relief Intl. [10873]
   AIDS Relief Intl. [10873]
   AIDS Res. Alliance [13595]
   AIDS Rsrc. Found. for Children [13596]
   AIDS Treatment Activists Coalition [10874]
   AIDS Trust of Australia [38]
   AIDSinfo [13597]
   Amer. Acad. of HIV Medicine [13598]
   Amer. Found. for AIDS Res. [13603]
   Ardent Lion Soc. [11659]
   Assn. of Nurses in AIDS Care [13599]
   Balm in Gilead [13600]
   Balm in Gilead [13600]
   Blood: Water Mission [10809]
   Broadway Cares/Equity Fights AIDS [10875]
   CDC Natl. Prevention Info. Network [13601]
   Children with AIDS Proj. of Am. [10783]
   Children of Grace [11236]
   Children of Nowhere [11239]
   Children's AIDS Fund [10876]
   Children's AIDS Fund [10876]
   Children's Cancer and Blood Found. [14964]
   Damien Ministries [19633]
   Debt AIDS Trade Africa [17149]
   Design Indus. Found. Fighting AIDS [10877]
   Do It Now Found. [13248]
   Educ. Fights AIDS Intl. [10878]
   Elton John AIDS Found. [10879]
   Emofra Africa [15157]
   FACE AIDS [13602]

A star before a book entry number signifies that the name is not listed separately, but is mentioned within the entry.

The Found. for AIDS Res. [13603]
Friends Women's Assn. [13461]
Gardens for Hea. Intl. [13604]
Gardens for Hea. Intl. [13604]
Gay Men's Hea. Crisis [13605]
Global AIDS Alliance [13606]
Global AIDS Interfaith Alliance [13607]
Global AIDS Interfaith Alliance [13607]
Global Bus. Coalition on HIV/AIDS [10880]
Global Bus. Coalition on HIV/AIDS, Tuberculosis and Malaria [10880]
Global Medic Force [15173]
Global Partnership for Family Hea. [13608]
Global Strategies for HIV Prevention [13609]
Global Strategies for HIV Prevention [13609]
Global Youth Coalition on HIV/AIDS [10881]
Grassroot Soccer [10882]
Hea. Global Access Proj. [10883]
HIV/AIDS Prevention Grants Prog. [10884]
HIV Medicine Assn. [13610]
HomeAID for Africa [10812]
Horizon Intl. [11316]
Housing Works [13611]AIDSInfoshare Intl.
Intl. AIDS Soc. USA [13612]
Intl. AIDS Soc. USA [13612]
Intl. AIDS Vaccine Initiative [13613]
Intl. AIDS Vaccine Initiative [13613]
Intl. Alliance for the Prevention of AIDS [13614]
Intl. Partnership for Microbicides [13615]
Intl. Partnership for Microbicides [13615]
Intl. Union Against Sexually Transmitted Infections, Regional Off. for North Am. [16656]
Kidlinks World [11332]
LIFEbeat [10885]
Lily of the Valley Endeavor [10886]
Mobilization Against AIDS [10887]
Mothers' Voices [13616]
Names Proj. Found. I AIDS Memorial Quilt [13617]
Natl. AIDS Treatment Advocacy Proj. [13618]
Natl. AIDS Treatment Advocacy Proj. [13618]
Natl. Alliance of State and Territorial AIDS Directors [10888]
Natl. Assn. of People with AIDS [13619]
Natl. Black Gay Men's Advocacy Coalition [12099]
Natl. Catholic AIDS Network [13620]
Natl. Coalition of Anti-Violence Programs [18770]
Natl. Coalition of Pastors' Spouses [13195]
Natl. Episcopal AIDS Coalition [10889]
Natl. Minority AIDS Coun. [13621]
Natl. Native Amer. AIDS Prevention Center [10890]
NextAid [11369]
Orphan Support Africa [11380]
Orphans Against AIDS [11383]
Peace House Africa [11389]
Pediatric AIDS Found. [13622]
Proj. Inform [13623]
River Fund [10891]
Rwanda Gift for Life [13099]
San Francisco AIDS Found. [13624]
Seventh Day Adventist Kinship Intl. [19800]
Sociologists' AIDS Network [13625]
Solidarity and Action Against the HIV Infection in India [10892]
Solidarity and Action Against the HIV Infection in India [10892]
SOTENI Intl. [10893]
Support for Intl. Change [15214]
Treatment Action Gp. [13626]
Ubuntu Africa [11421]
Well Proj. [13627]
Who's Positive [10894]
Women Alive Coalition [13628]
Women Organized to Respond to Life-Threatening Diseases [13629]
Women Organized to Respond to Life-Threatening Diseases [13629]
World Against AIDS [12386]
World Hea. Clinicians [13630]
World Partners for Development [13210]
World Wide AIDS Coalition [13631]
AIDS Action Coun. and Natl. AIDS Fund [★18318]
AIDS Action Europe [IO], Amsterdam, Netherlands
AIDS Alliance for Children, Youth and Families [13592], 2000 L St. NW, Ste. 717, Washington, DC 20036-4964, (202)785-3564

AIDS Calgary [IO], Calgary, AB, Canada
AIDS Clinical Trials Gp. [13593], 8757 Georgia Ave., Ste. 1200, Silver Spring, MD 20910, (301)628-3338
AIDS Clinical Trials Gp. [13593], 8757 Georgia Ave., Ste. 1200, Silver Spring, MD 20910, (301)628-3338
AIDS-Free World [13594], 857 Broadway, 3rd Fl., New York, NY 10003, (212)729-5084
AIDS-Free World [13594], 857 Broadway, 3rd Fl., New York, NY 10003, (212)729-5084
AIDS Intl. [★2258]
AIDS/Kaposi's Sarcoma Res. and Educ. Found. [★13624]
AIDS Medical Found. [★13603]
AIDS, Medicine and Miracles - Address unknown since 2010.
AIDS Natl. Interfaith Network - Defunct.
AIDS Relief Intl. [10873], PO Box 2081, Providence, RI 02912
AIDS Relief Intl. [10873], PO Box 2081, Providence, RI 02912
AIDS Res. Alliance [13595], 1400 S Grand Ave., Ste. 701, Los Angeles, CA 90015, (310)358-2423
AIDS Rsrc. Found. for Children [13596], 77 Acad. St., Newark, NJ 07102, (973)643-0400
AIDS Soc. for Asia and the Pacific [IO], Bangkok, Thailand
AIDS Task Force for the Amer. Coll. Health Assn. - Defunct.
AIDS Treatment Activists Coalition [10874], 611 Broadway, No. 308, New York, NY 10012, (646)284-3801
AIDS Trust of Australia [IO], Darlinghurst, Australia
AIDS United [18318], 1424 K St. NW, Ste. 200, Washington, DC 20005, (202)408-4848
AIDSinfo [13597], PO Box 6303, Rockville, MD 20849-6303, (301)315-2816
AIESEC Alumni Intl. [IO], Brussels, Belgium
AIESEC Bahrain [IO], Manama, Bahrain
AIESEC Canada [IO], Toronto, ON, Canada
AIESEC China [IO], Beijing, People's Republic of China
AIESEC Kenya [IO], Nairobi, Kenya
AIESEC Pakistan [IO], Karachi, Pakistan
AIESEC Qatar [IO], Doha, Qatar
AIESEC U.S. [7782], 127 W 26th St., 10th Fl., New York, NY 10001, (212)757-3774
AIESEC U.S. [7782], 127 W 26th St., 10th Fl., New York, NY 10001, (212)757-3774
AIIM - The Enterprise Content Mgt. Assn. [1894], 1100 Wayne Ave., Ste. 1100, Silver Spring, MD 20910, (301)587-8202
Aik Hunar Aik Nagar [IO], Lahore, Pakistan
Aiki-Kai Australia Natl. Aikido Assn. [IO], Melbourne, Australia

Aikido
Aikido Assn. of Am. [22216]
Aikido Yoshokai Assn. of North Am. [22217]
Aikido Yoshokai Assn. of North Am. [22217]
Intl. Aikido Assn. [22218]
U.S. Aikido Fed. [22219]
World Martial Arts Assn. [22771]
Aikido Aikikai Fed. of Russia [IO], Moscow, Russia
Aikido Assn. of Am. [22216], 1016 W Belmont Ave., Chicago, IL 60657, (773)525-3141
Aikido Assn. of North Am. - Address unknown since 2010.
Aikido Assn. of Thailand [IO], Bangkok, Thailand
Aikido Assn. U.S.A; Japan [★22752]
Aikido Federacija Srbije i Crne Gore - Aikikai SCG [★IO]
Aikido Fed. of Serbia and Montenegro - Aikikai SCG [IO], Belgrade, Serbia
Aikido Fed. of South Africa [IO], Heidelberg, Republic of South Africa
Aikido Yoshokai Assn. of North Am. [22217], Genyo-kan Dojo, 3796 Plaza Dr., Ste. 3, Ann Arbor, MI 48108, (734)662-4686
Aikido Yoshokai Assn. of North Am. [22217], Genyo-kan Dojo, 3796 Plaza Dr., Ste. 3, Ann Arbor, MI 48108, (734)662-4686
Aikikai Deutschland - Fachverband fur Aikido in Deutschland [IO], Viechtach, Germany
Aikikai Found. [★22219]

Aikikai Malaysia [IO], Kuching, Malaysia
Aikikai Singapore [IO], Singapore, Singapore
AIM - European Brands Assn. [IO], Brussels, Belgium
Aim For Success [8860], PO Box 550336, Dallas, TX 75355, (972)422-2322
AIM Global [279], One Landmark N, 20399 Rte. 19, Ste. 203, Cranberry Township, PA 16066, (724)742-4470
AIM Intl. [★20004]
AIM Intl. [★20004]
AIM Intl. - Australia [IO], Wyee, Australia
AIM U.S.A. [★279]
AINA [IO], Paris, France
AIPPI Natl. Gp. of Lithuania [IO], Vilnius, Lithuania
Air Balance Consultants - Defunct.
Air Barrier Assn. of Am. [516], 1600 Boston-Providence Hwy., Walpole, MA 02081, (866)956-5888
Air Brake Assn. [2982], 2098 E 10140 S, Sandy, UT 84092, (801)944-5270
Air-Britain Historians [IO], Woodbridge, United Kingdom
Air Cadet League of Canada [IO], Ottawa, ON, Canada
Air Care Alliance - Defunct.
Air Carrier Assn. of Am. [118], 1776 K St. NW, Washington, DC 20006, (202)719-7420
Air Charity Network [14447], 4620 Haygood Rd., Ste. 1, Virginia Beach, VA 23455, (800)549-9980
Air Commando Assn. [20767], PO Box 7, Mary Esther, FL 32569, (850)581-0099
AIR Commercial Real Estate Assn. [2998], 800 W 6th St., Ste. 800, Los Angeles, CA 90017-2741, (213)687-8777
Air Compassion for Veterans [20768], 4620 Haygood Rd., Ste. 1, Virginia Beach, VA 23455, (757)271-2289
Air Conditioning Contractors of Am. [1694], 2800 Shirlington Rd., Ste. 300, Arlington, VA 22206, (703)575-4477
Air Conditioning Equip. Mfrs'. Assn. [IO], Madrid, Spain
Air-Conditioning Heating and Refrigeration Inst. [1695], 2111 Wilson Blvd., Ste. 500, Arlington, VA 22201, (703)524-8800
Air Conditioning and Mech. Contractors Assn. - Australian Capital Territory [IO], Epping, Australia
Air Conditioning and Mech. Contractors Assn. - New South Wales [IO], Epping, Australia
Air Conditioning and Mech. Contractors Assn. - Queensland [IO], Ashgrove, Australia
Air Conditioning and Mech. Contractors Assn. - South Australia [IO], Mile End, Australia
Air Conditioning and Mech. Contractors Assn. - Western Australia [IO], Victoria Park, Australia
Air Conditioning and Refrigeration Contractors of Am. [★1694]
Air Conditioning and Refrigeration European Assn. [IO], Brussels, Belgium
Air-Conditioning and Refrigeration Inst. [★1695]
Air-Conditioning and Refrigeration Machinery Assn. [★1695]
Air Conditioning and Refrigeration Mfrs'. Assn. [IO], Istanbul, Turkey
Air-Conditioning and Refrigeration Wholesalers Intl. [★1702]
Air-Conditioning and Refrigeration Wholesalers Intl. [★1702]
AIR Conf. [★123]
Air Courier Conf. of Am. [★3247]
Air Diffusion Coun. [1696], 1901 N Roselle Rd., Ste. 800, Schaumburg, IL 60195, (847)706-6750
Air Distribution Inst. [2546], 4415 W Harrison St., Ste. 426, Hillside, IL 60162, (708)449-2933
Air Filter Inst. [★1695]
Air Force
6th Bomb Gp. Assn. [20318]
43rd Bomb Gp. [20319]
80th Fighter Squadron Headhunters' Assn. [5195]
129th Alumni and Heritage Assn. [19270]
146th Alumni Assn. [7727]
381st Bomb Gp. Memorial Assn. [20320]
401st Bombardment Gp. Heavy Assn. [20321]
401st Bombardment Gp. Heavy Assn. [20321]

Reference to "IO" in place of a book number signifies that the association may be found in the 50th edition of International Organizations.

461st Bombardment Gp. Assn. [20322]
483rd Bombardment Gp. H Assn. [20323]
494th Bombardment Gp. (H) Assn. 7th Air Force [20324]
Air Force Navigators Observer Assn. [20325]
Air Forces Escape and Evasion Soc. [20326]
Assn. of Air Force Missileers [20327]
Cell Phones for Soldiers [11086]
Combat Helicopter Pilots Assn. [20313]
Distinguished Flying Cross Soc. [20374]
Hof Reunion Assn. [20349]
Mosquito Assn. [20328]
Never Forget Our Fallen [11095]
Oper. Paperback [11100]
Second Bombardment Assn. [20329]
Soc. of Air Force Physician Assistants [20330]
Support Our Troops [11110]
T-34 Assn. [21202]
Air Force Aid Soc. [18925], 241 18th St. S, Ste. 202, Arlington, VA 22202, (800)769-8951
Air Force Assn. [5792], 1501 Lee Hwy., Arlington, VA 22209-1198, (703)247-5800
Air Force Assn. of Canada [IO], Ottawa, ON, Canada
Air Force Clinical Surgeons; Soc. of [16821]
Air Force; Commemorative [20888]
Air Force Historical Found. [10087], 1535 Command Dr., Ste. C102, Andrews AFB, MD 20762-7002, (301)736-1959
Air Force Navigators Observer Assn. [20325], Clem Smith, Treas., 1095 Harriet, Canyon Lake, TX 78133-5244
Air Force Public Affairs Alumni Assn. [5914], PO Box 447, Locust Grove, VA 22508-0447
Air Force Sergeants Assn. [5793], 5211 Auth Rd., Suitland, MD 20746, (301)899-3500
Air Forces Escape and Evasion Soc. [20326], PO Box 2501, Wichita Falls, TX 76307-2501, (940)692-6700
Air Freight Assn. of Am. [★132]
Air Freight Forwarders Assn. of Am. [★132]
Air Horn and Steam Whistle Enthusiasts [★21348]
Air, Inc. - Aviation Info. Resources - Defunct.
Air League [IO], London, United Kingdom
Air Line Pilots Assn. [★23146]
Air Line Pilots Assn. [★23146]
Air Line Pilots Assn. Intl. [23146], 1625 Massachusetts Ave. NW, Washington, DC 20036, (703)689-2270
Air Line Pilots Assn. Intl. [23146], 1625 Massachusetts Ave. NW, Washington, DC 20036, (703)689-2270
Air Line Pilots Assn. Intl. - Canada [IO], Ottawa, ON, Canada
Air Mail Pioneers [20879], PMB 504 C5, 26910 92nd Ave. NW, Stanwood, WA 98292-5437, (360)387-2009
Air Medical Physician Assn. [16246], Patricia Petersen, Exec. Dir., 951 E Montana Vista Ln., Salt Lake City, UT 84124, (801)263-2672
Air Movement and Control Assn. [★1697]
Air Movement and Control Assn. [★1697]
Air Movement and Control Assn. Intl. [1697], 30 W Univ. Dr., Arlington Heights, IL 60004, (847)394-0150
Air Movement and Control Assn. Intl. [1697], 30 W Univ. Dr., Arlington Heights, IL 60004, (847)394-0150
Air Moving and Conditioning Assn. [★1697]
Air Moving and Conditioning Assn. [★1697]
Air Pollution and Climate Secretariat [IO], Goteborg, Sweden
Air Pollution Control Assn. [★4779]
Air Pollution Control Assn. [★4779]
Air Reserve Assn. [★5792]
Air Sailing Club [IO], Guelph, ON, Canada
Air Serv Intl. [12798], 410 Rosedale Ct., Ste. 190, Warrenton, VA 20186, (540)428-2323
Air Serv Intl. [12798], 410 Rosedale Ct., Ste. 190, Warrenton, VA 20186, (540)428-2323
Air Supply Fan Club [23809], PO Box 4084, Santa Monica, CA 90411-4084, (310)888-4201
Air and Surface Transport Nurses Assn. [15700], 7995 E Prentice Ave., Ste. 100, Greenwood Village, CO 80111, (720)488-0492

Air Traffic Control Assn. [119], 1101 King St., Ste. 300, Alexandria, VA 22314, (703)299-2430
Air Traffic Control Assn. [119], 1101 King St., Ste. 300, Alexandria, VA 22314, (703)299-2430
Air Transport Action Gp. [IO], Geneva, Switzerland
Air Transport Assn. of Am. [120], 1301 Pennsylvania Ave. NW, Ste. 1100, Washington, DC 20004-7017, (202)626-4000
Air Transport Assn. of Canada [IO], Ottawa, ON, Canada
Air and Waste Mgt. Assn. [4779], 1 Gateway Ctr., 3rd Fl., 420 Ft. Duquesne Blvd., Pittsburgh, PA 15222-1435, (412)232-3444
Air and Waste Mgt. Assn. [4779], 1 Gateway Ctr., 3rd Fl., 420 Ft. Duquesne Blvd., Pittsburgh, PA 15222-1435, (412)232-3444
Air Weather Assn. [20769], 1697 Capri Way, Charlottesville, VA 22911-3534, (434)296-2832
Air Weather Reconnaissance Assn. [20770], Bernard Barris, Membership Chm., 11019 Oak Park, San Antonio, TX 78249-4440, (907)694-4992
Airborne Law Enforcement Assn. [5683], 50 Carroll Creek Way, Ste. 260, Frederick, MD 21701, (301)631-2406
Aircraft
Air Mail Pioneers [20879]
Aircraft Carrier Indus. Base Coalition [1034]
Aircraft Engine Historical Soc. [9106]
Angel Wing Flights [12445]
Aviation for Humanity [12807]
B-52 Stratofortress Assn. [20331]
Cherokee Pilots' Assn. [20887]
Combat Helicopter Pilots Assn. [20313]
F-14 Tomcat Assn. [21201]
Fairchild Club [20895]
First Flight Soc. [20896]
Intl. Assn. of Missionary Aviation [20052]
Intl. Bird Dog Assn. [20898]
Intl. Coun. of Air Shows [20901]
Intl. Scale Soaring Assn. [21904]
Intl. Soc. for Aviation Photography [2724]
Jack Knight Air Mail Soc. [22047]
Motion Picture Pilots Assn. [380]
Natl. Assn. of Priest Pilots [19459]
Natl. Conf. of Catholic Airport Chaplains [19528]
Natl. World War II Glider Pilots Assn. [20315]
OV-10 Bronco Assn. [9107]
Piper Owner Soc. [20912]
Popular Rotorcraft Assn. [20913]
Professional Airways Systems Specialists [23155]
Scale Warbird Racing Assn. [21910]
T-34 Assn. [21202]
U.S. Powered Paragliding Assn. [22796]
Whirly-Girls - Intl. Women Helicopter Pilots [20923]
World Airline Historical Soc. [20924]
Aircraft Carrier Indus. Base Coalition [1034], 700 13th St. NW, Ste. 1000, Washington, DC 20005, (202)585-2141
Aircraft Electronics Assn. [121], 3570 NE Ralph Powell Rd., Lee's Summit, MO 64064, (816)347-8400
Aircraft Electronics Assn. [121], 3570 NE Ralph Powell Rd., Lee's Summit, MO 64064, (816)347-8400
Aircraft Engine Historical Soc. [9106], 4608 Charles Dr. NW, Huntsville, AL 35816, (256)683-1458
Aircraft Fleet Recycling Assn. [12768], 2233 Wisconsin Ave. NW, Ste. 503, Washington, DC 20007, (202)347-6899
Aircraft Fleet Recycling Assn. [12768], 2233 Wisconsin Ave. NW, Ste. 503, Washington, DC 20007, (202)347-6899
Aircraft Indus. Assn. of Am. [★117]
Aircraft Locknut Mfrs. Assn. [1644], 994 Old Eagle School Rd., Ste. 1019, Wayne, PA 19087-1802, (610)971-4850
Aircraft Maintenance Engineers Assn. [★21114]
Aircraft Mechanics Fraternal Assn. [23147], 14001 E Iliff Ave., Ste. 217, Aurora, CO 80014, (303)752-2632
Aircraft Owners and Pilots Assn. [122], 421 Aviation Way, Frederick, MD 21701, (301)695-2000
Aircraft Owners and Pilots Assn. - Australia [IO], Georges Hall, Australia

Aircraft Owners and Pilots Assn. - Austria [IO], Vienna, Austria
Aircraft Owners and Pilots Assn. - Belgium [IO], Antwerp, Belgium
Aircraft Owners and Pilots Assn. - Brazil [IO], Sao Paulo, Brazil
Aircraft Owners and Pilots Assn. - Colombia [IO], Bogota, Colombia
Aircraft Owners and Pilots Assn. - Cyprus [IO], Nicosia, Cyprus
Aircraft Owners and Pilots Assn. - Denmark [IO], Roskilde, Denmark
Aircraft Owners and Pilots Assn. - Finland [IO], Helsinki, Finland
Aircraft Owners and Pilots Assn. - Hungary [IO], Budapest, Hungary
Aircraft Owners and Pilots Assn. - Iceland [IO], Reykjavik, Iceland
Aircraft Owners and Pilots Assn. - India [IO], Bangalore, India
Aircraft Owners and Pilots Assn. - Ireland [IO], Athlone, Ireland
Aircraft Owners and Pilots Assn. - Italy [IO], Milan, Italy
Aircraft Owners and Pilots Assn. - Jamaica [IO], Kingston, Jamaica
Aircraft Owners and Pilots Assn. - Japan [IO], Tokyo, Japan
Aircraft Owners and Pilots Assn. - Liberia [IO], Monrovia, Liberia
Aircraft Owners and Pilots Assn. - Lithuania [IO], Vilnius, Lithuania
Aircraft Owners and Pilots Assn. - Luxembourg [IO], Luxembourg, Luxembourg
Aircraft Owners and Pilots Assn. - Malta [IO], Luqa, Malta
Aircraft Owners and Pilots Assn. - Monaco [IO], Monte Carlo, Monaco
Aircraft Owners and Pilots Assn. - Netherlands [IO], Lelystad, Netherlands
Aircraft Owners and Pilots Assn. - New Zealand [IO], Dunedin, New Zealand
Aircraft Owners and Pilots Assn. - Norway [IO], Sola, Norway
Aircraft Owners and Pilots Assn. - Pakistan [IO], Lahore, Pakistan
Aircraft Owners and Pilots Assn. - Philippines [IO], Pasay City, Philippines
Aircraft Owners and Pilots Assn. - Poland [IO], Warsaw, Poland
Aircraft Owners and Pilots Assn. - Romania [IO], Bucharest, Romania
Aircraft Owners and Pilots Assn. - Russia [IO], Moscow, Russia
Aircraft Owners and Pilots Assn. - Singapore [IO], Singapore, Singapore
Aircraft Owners and Pilots Assn. - Slovenia [IO], Ljubljana, Slovenia
Aircraft Owners and Pilots Assn. - Spain [IO], Barcelona, Spain
Aircraft Owners and Pilots Assn. - Sweden [IO], Bromma, Sweden
Aircraft Owners and Pilots Assn. - Switzerland [IO], Zurich, Switzerland
Aircraft Owners and Pilots Assn. - Turkey [IO], Ankara, Turkey
Aircraft Owners and Pilots Assn. - United Kingdom [IO], London, United Kingdom
Aircraft Owners and Pilots Assn. - Venezuela [IO], Caracas, Venezuela
Aircraft Res. Assn. [IO], Bedford, United Kingdom
Airedale Terrier Club of Am. [21476], Shirley Vanover, Sec., 1897 S Tulane Rd., Hernando, MS 38632, (901)484-3815
Airfields Env. Trust [IO], London, United Kingdom
Airflow Club of Am. [20983], 1651 209th Pl. NE, Sammamish, WA 98074-4212, (425)868-7448
Airforwarders Assn. [2227], 750 Natl. Press Bldg., 529 14th St. NW, Washington, DC 20045, (202)393-2818
AirLifeLine [★14447]
Airlift Assn. [★20311]
Airlift Assn. [★20311]
Airlift/Tanker Assn. [20311], 9312 Convento Terr., Fairfax, VA 22031-3809, (703)385-2802

A star before a book entry number signifies that the name is not listed separately, but is mentioned within the entry.

Airlift/Tanker Assn. [**20311**], 9312 Convento Terr., Fairfax, VA 22031-3809, (703)385-2802

Airline Ambassadors Intl. [**13166**], 1020 16th St. NW, Ste. 603, Washington, DC 20036, (202)466-3428

Airline Ambassadors Intl. [**13166**], 1020 16th St. NW, Ste. 603, Washington, DC 20036, (202)466-3428

Airline Credit Union Assn. - Defunct.

Airline Ground Trans. Assn. [★**3499**]

Airline Indus. Relations Conf. [**123**], 1300 19th St. NW, Ste. 750, Washington, DC 20036, (202)861-7550

Airline Medical Examiners Assn. [★**13584**]

Airline Medical Examiners Assn. [★**13584**]

Airline Passenger Experience Assn. [**373**], 355 Lexington Ave., 15th Fl., New York, NY 10017, (212)297-2177

Airline Passengers Assn. [★**22190**]

Airline Passengers Assn. [★**22190**]

Airline Pilots Security Alliance [**374**], 1 Park Ln., Ste. 412, Boston, MA 02210, (615)479-4140

Airline Services Assn. [★**116**]

Airline Sports and Cultural Assn. [**IO**], Vienna, Austria

Airline Stewards and Stewardesses Assn. [★**23151**]

Airline Suppliers Assn. [★**2331**]

Airlines Electronic Engg. Comm. [**6765**], ARINC Inc., 2551 Riva Rd., Annapolis, MD 21401-7435, (410)266-4113

Airlines Medical Directors Assn. [**13583**], Ralph G. Fennell, MD, Sec., 46155 Black Spruce Ln., Parker, CO 80138-4919

Airport Consultants Coun. [**854**], 908 King St., Ste. 100, Alexandria, VA 22314, (703)683-5900

Airport Ground Trans. Assn. [**3499**], USML Center for Trans. Stud., 154 Univ. Ctr., One Univ. Blvd., St. Louis, MO 63121-4499, (314)516-7271

Airport Minority Advisory Coun. [**2518**], 2345 Crystal Dr., Ste. 902, Arlington, VA 22202, (703)414-2622

Airport Operators Assn. [**IO**], London, United Kingdom

Airports Coun. Intl. - Asia-Pacific Region [**IO**], Hong Kong, People's Republic of China

Airports Coun. Intl. - Europe [**IO**], Brussels, Belgium

Airports Coun. Intl. - Latin America-Caribbean Off. [**IO**], Merida, Mexico

Airports Coun. Intl. North Am. [**124**], 1775 K St. NW, Ste. 500, Washington, DC 20006, (202)293-8500

Airports Coun. Intl. North Am. [**124**], 1775 K St. NW, Ste. 500, Washington, DC 20006, (202)293-8500

Airports Coun. Intl. - Switzerland [**IO**], Geneva, Switzerland

Airship Assn. [**IO**], Folkestone, United Kingdom

Airspace Action on Smoking and Hea. [**IO**], Delta, BC, Canada

Airts Cooncil o Norlin Airlann [★**IO**]

Airways Club [★**22190**]

Airways Club [★**22190**]

AIVS Newsl. [★**10148**]

Akademie fuer Ethik in der Medizin [★**IO**]

Akademie fur Raumforschung und Landesplanung [★**IO**]

Akademie Ved Ceske Republiky [★**IO**]

Akademiet for de Tekniske Videnskaber [★**IO**]

Akademikerforbundet SSR [**IO**], Stockholm, Sweden

Akademio Internacia de la Sciencoj [★**IO**]

Akademischer Arbeitskreis Japan [★**IO**]

Akerne Orchids [**IO**], Antwerp, Belgium

Akhal-Teke Assn. of Am. [**4522**], PO Box 1635, Rolla, MO 65402, (573)426-5207

Akita Club of Am. [**21477**], PO Box 103, Islip Terrace, NY 11752-0103

Akita Kennel Club of Am. [★**21477**]

Aktion Boernehjaelp [★**IO**]

Aktion Gesunde Knochen [★**IO**]

Aktion Suehnezeichen Friedensdienste [★**IO**]

Aktionsgemeinschaft Dienst fuer den Frieden [★**IO**]

Aktionsgemeinschaft Solidarische Welt [★**IO**]

Al-Anon Familjegrupper i Sverige [★**IO**]

Al-Anon Family Gp. HQ World Ser. Off. [**13230**], 1600 Corporate Landing Pkwy., Virginia Beach, VA 23454-5617, (757)563-1600

Al-Anon Family Gp. HQ World Ser. Off. [**13230**], 1600 Corporate Landing Pkwy., Virginia Beach, VA 23454-5617, (757)563-1600

Al-Anon Family Groups - United Kingdom and Eire [**IO**], London, United Kingdom

Al-Bakorah Adurzia [★**19829**]

Al-Bustan Seeds of Culture [**9135**], 526 S 46th St., Philadelphia, PA 19143, (267)303-0070

Al-Haq [**IO**], Ramallah, Israel

Al-Itihad al-Arabi Linakl al-Jawi [★**IO**]

A.L. Mailman Family Found. [**11445**], 707 Westchester Ave., White Plains, NY 10604, (914)683-8089

Al-Mu'asasat al -Arabiyye l-Hoquq al-Insan [★**IO**]

Alabama Fan Club [**23810**], PO Box 680529, Fort Payne, AL 35968-1606, (256)845-1646

Aladdin Knights of the Mystic Light [**21877**], 550 Pioneer Ln., Calvert City, KY 42029, (270)559-7900

Alagille Syndrome Alliance [**14582**], 10500 SW Starr Dr., Tualatin, OR 97062, (503)885-0455

Alan Jackson Fan Club [**23811**], PO Box 440328, Nashville, TN 37244, (615)321-5221

Alaska Coalition [**3982**], 122 C St. NW, Ste. 240, Washington, DC 20001, (505)438-4245

Alaska Collectors' Club [**22005**], 5300 N Paseo del Arenal, Tucson, AZ 85750

Alaskan Malamute Assistance League [**10901**], PO Box 4, Verona, VA 24482, (419)512-2423

Alaskan Malamute Club of Am. [**21478**], 640 E 50 N, Hyrum, UT 84319, (435)245-3634

Alaskan Malamute Protection League [★**10901**]

Alateen [**13231**], 1600 Corporate Landing Pkwy., Virginia Beach, VA 23454-5617, (757)563-1600

Alateen [★**13230**]

Alateen [**IO**], Ottawa, ON, Canada

Alateen [★**13230**]

Albacore Assn. [★**22401**]

Alban Inst. [**19611**], 2121 Cooperative Way, Ste. 100, Herndon, VA 20171, (703)964-2700

Albanian

   Albanian Amer. Civic League [**17174**]

   Albanian Amer. Civic League [**17174**]

   Albanian Amer. Medical Soc. [**15390**]

   Center for the Stud. of Aging of Albany [**10838**]

   Natl. Albanian Amer. Coun. [**18847**]

Albanian Amateur Radio Assn. [**IO**], Tirana, Albania

Albanian Amer. Civic League [**17174**], PO Box 70, Ossining, NY 10562, (914)762-5530

Albanian Amer. Civic League [**17174**], PO Box 70, Ossining, NY 10562, (914)762-5530

Albanian Amer. Medical Soc. [**15390**], 58 E Springfield St., Ste. 2, Boston, MA 02118, (617)236-0113

Albanian-American Trade and Development Assn. [**23409**], 159 E 4th St., Dunkirk, NY 14048, (954)802-3166

Albanian-American Trade and Development Assn. [**23409**], 159 E 4th St., Dunkirk, NY 14048, (954)802-3166

Albanian Assn. of Consulting Engineers [**IO**], Tirana, Albania

Albanian Catholic Info. Center [★**18514**]

Albanian Catholic Info. Center [★**18514**]

Albanian Catholic Inst. [**18514**], Univ. of San Francisco, 650 Parker Ave., San Francisco, CA 94118, (415)422-6966

Albanian Catholic Inst. [**18514**], Univ. of San Francisco, 650 Parker Ave., San Francisco, CA 94118, (415)422-6966

Albanian Dance Sport Fed. [**IO**], Tirana, Albania

Albanian League Against Epilepsy [**IO**], Tirana, Albania

Albanian Orthodontic Soc. [**IO**], Tirana, Albania

Albanian Pain Assn. [**IO**], Tirana, Albania

Albanian Political Sci. Assn. [**IO**], Tirana, Albania

Albanian Red Cross [**IO**], Tirana, Albania

Albanian Soc. of Cardiology [**IO**], Tirana, Albania

Albanian Soc. of Rheumatology [**IO**], Tirana, Albania

Albanian Taekwondo Fed. [**IO**], Tirana, Albania

Albanian Tennis Fed. [**IO**], Tirana, Albania

Albany Natural Trail Riders [**IO**], Albany, Australia

Alberg 37 Intl. Owners Assn. [**22314**], PO Box 32, Kinsale, VA 22488

Albert A. List Found. - Defunct.

Albert Einstein Institution [**18163**], PO Box 455, East Boston, MA 02128, (617)247-4882

Albert Ellis Inst. [**16444**], 45 E 65th St., New York, NY 10021, (212)535-0822

Albert Schweitzer Coun. on Animals and the Environment - Defunct.

Albert Schweitzer Ecological Centre [**IO**], Neuchatel, Switzerland

Albert Schweitzer Fellowship [**10652**], 330 Brookline Ave., Boston, MA 02215, (617)667-5111

Alberta Amateur Boxing Assn. [**IO**], Edmonton, AB, Canada

Alberta Amateur Softball Assn. [**IO**], Edmonton, AB, Canada

Alberta Amputee Sports and Recreation Assn. [**IO**], Calgary, AB, Canada

Alberta Angus Assn. [**IO**], Olds, AB, Canada

Alberta Arbitration and Mediation Soc. [**IO**], Edmonton, AB, Canada

Alberta Assn. for Community Living [**IO**], Edmonton, AB, Canada

Alberta Assn. on Gerontology [**IO**], Edmonton, AB, Canada

Alberta Assn. of Landscape Architects [**IO**], Edmonton, AB, Canada

Alberta Assn. of Naturopathic Practitioners [**IO**], Calgary, AB, Canada

Alberta Ballet [**IO**], Calgary, AB, Canada

Alberta Bottle Depot Assn. [**IO**], Edmonton, AB, Canada

Alberta Community Crime Prevention Assn. [**IO**], Calgary, AB, Canada

Alberta Constr. Assn. [**IO**], Edmonton, AB, Canada

Alberta Constr. Safety Assn. [**IO**], Edmonton, AB, Canada

Alberta Equestrian Fed. [**IO**], Calgary, AB, Canada

Alberta Family Histories Soc. [**IO**], Calgary, AB, Canada

Alberta Ferret Soc. [**IO**], Edmonton, AB, Canada

Alberta Forest Products Assn. [**IO**], Edmonton, AB, Canada

Alberta Foster Parent Assn. [**IO**], Edmonton, AB, Canada

Alberta Funeral Ser. Assn. [**IO**], Red Deer, AB, Canada

Alberta Golf Assn. [**IO**], Calgary, AB, Canada

Alberta Irrigation Projects Assn. [**IO**], Lethbridge, AB, Canada

Alberta Lung Assn. [**IO**], Edmonton, AB, Canada

Alberta Magazine Publishers Assn. [**IO**], Calgary, AB, Canada

Alberta Motion Picture Indus. Assn. [**IO**], Edmonton, AB, Canada

Alberta Motor Assn. [**IO**], Calgary, AB, Canada

Alberta Motor Transport Assn. [**IO**], Rocky View, AB, Canada

Alberta Occupational Hea. Nurses Assn. [**IO**], Edmonton, AB, Canada

Alberta Orienteering Assn. [**IO**], Cochrane, AB, Canada

Alberta Real Estate Assn. [**IO**], Calgary, AB, Canada

Alberta Rockies Gay Rodeo Assn. [**IO**], Calgary, AB, Canada

Alberta Senior Citizens' Housing Assn. [**IO**], Edmonton, AB, Canada

Alberta Snowboarding Assn. [**IO**], Calgary, AB, Canada

Alberta Standardbred Horse Assn. [**IO**], Calgary, AB, Canada

Alberta Table Tennis Assn. [**IO**], Edmonton, AB, Canada

Alberta Teachers' Assn. [**IO**], Edmonton, AB, Canada

Alberta Wilderness Assn. [**IO**], Calgary, AB, Canada

Albinism and Hypopigmentation; Natl. Org. for [**15503**]

Albinism World Alliance

Albinism World Alliance - Defunct.

Alcohol

   Assn. of Recovering Motorcyclists [**13236**]

   Center for Sci. in the Public Interest I Alcohol Policies Proj. [**17175**]

   Christian Addiction Rehabilitation Assn. [**13241**]

   Do It Now Found. [**13248**]

   Eastern Coast Breweriana Assn. [**20928**]

   Narcotic Educational Found. of Am. [**13267**]

   Sonoma County Vintners [**5173**]

   Sonoma County Winegrape Commission [**5174**]

Alcohol Abuse

   Amer. Osteopathic Acad. of Addiction Medicine [**16735**]

   Assn. of Recovering Motorcyclists [**13236**]

Reference to "IO" in place of a book number signifies that the association may be found in the 50th edition of International Organizations.

Center for Sci. in the Public Interest | Alcohol Policies Proj. [17175]
Christian Addiction Rehabilitation Assn. [13241]
Do It Now Found. [13248]
Intl. Assn. of Addictions and Offender Counselors [11674]
Luz Social Services [13263]
Narcotic Educational Found. of Am. [13267]
Alcohol Beverage Legislative Coun. [5196], 5101 River Rd., Ste. 108, Bethesda, MD 20816-1560, (301)656-1494
Alcohol Concern [IO], London, United Kingdom
Alcohol and Drug Abuse Directors; Natl. Assn. of State [13275]
Alcohol, Drugs and Disability; Natl. Assn. on [16748]
Alcohol Focus Scotland [IO], Glasgow, United Kingdom
Alcohol and Other Drugs Coun. of Australia [IO], Woden, Australia
Alcohol Policy Coun. - Defunct.
Alcohol Res. Info. Ser. [13232], 430 Lanthrop St., Lansing, MI 48912, (517)485-9900
Alcohol Testing Indus. Assn; Drug and [13249]
Alcoholic Beverages
African Amer. Wine Tasting Soc. [173]
Alcohol Beverage Legislative Coun. [5196]
Amer. Assn. of Wine Economists [3670]
Amer. Beverage Licensees [174]
Amer. Breweriana Assn. [20926]
Amer. Homebrewers Assn. [175]
Amer. Sommelier Assn. [176]
Assn. of African Amer. Vintners [177]
Assn. of Beer and Malt Mfrs. [18866]
Assn. of Bordeaux Wine and Alcohol Wholesalers [2159]
Assn. of the Producers and Merchants of Wines and Spirits in Bulgaria [20552]
Beer Inst. [178]
Brewers Assn. [179]
Brewmeisters Anonymous [20927]
Caffeine Awareness Assn. [13828]
Distilled Spirits Coun. of the U.S. [180]
Eastern Coast Breweriana Assn. [20928]
El Dorado Winery Assn. [181]
Fermenters Intl. Trade Assn. [182]
Fermenters Intl. Trade Assn. [182]
Flair Bartenders' Assn. [183]
Free the Grapes! [17176]
German Wine Inst. [9716]
Intl. Bird Beer Label Assn. [20929]
Intl. Bird Beer Label Assn. [20929]
Intl. Brotherhood of Teamsers | Brewery and Soft Drink Workers Conf. [23158]
Intl. Center for Alcohol Policies [184]
Intl. Center for Alcohol Policies [184]
Joint Comm. of the States [5197]
Latin Amer. Brewers Assn. [17109]
Liquor Merchants Assn. of Australia [3771]
Minnesota Beer Wholesalers Assn. [185]
Natl. Alcohol Beverage Control Assn. [5198]
Natl. Assn. of Beverage Importers [186]
Natl. Beer Wholesalers Assn. [187]
Natl. Conf. of State Liquor Administrators [5199]
North Amer. Brewers' Assn. [188]
North Amer. Brewers' Assn. [188]
Norwegian Brewers and Soft Drink Producers [22114]
Sommelier Soc. of Am. [189]
Sonoma County Vintners [5173]
Sonoma County Winegrape Commission [5174]AlcoholicSpanish Assn. of Beer and Malt Technicians
Tasters Guild Intl. [190]
U.S. Sommelier Assn. [191]
Wine and Spirits Shippers Assn. [192]
Wine and Spirits Wholesalers of Am. [193]
World Assn. of the Alcohol Beverage Indus. [194]
World Assn. of the Alcohol Beverage Indus. [194]
Alcoholic Clergy Assn; Recovered [13286]
Alcoholics Anonymous - Australia [IO], Arncliffe, Australia
Alcoholics Anonymous - Brazil [IO], Sao Paulo, Brazil
Alcoholics Anonymous - England [IO], York, United Kingdom

Alcoholics Anonymous - French Gen. Services Off. [IO], Paris, France
Alcoholics Anonymous - Gen. Ser. Bd. for French-speaking Belgium [IO], Brussels, Belgium
Alcoholics Anonymous World Services [13233], PO Box 459, New York, NY 10163, (212)870-3400
Alcoholics Anonymous World Services [13233], PO Box 459, New York, NY 10163, (212)870-3400
Alcoholics Anonymous World Services | New Zealand Gen. Ser. Bd. of Acloholics Anonymous Inc [IO], Wellington, New Zealand
Alcoholics Anonymous World Services - Swedish Gen. Services Off. [IO], Jarfalla, Sweden
Alcoholics; Natl. Assn. for Children of [13273]
Alcoholism and Addiction Coun; Natl. Black [13276]
Alcoholism and Drug Dependence; Natl. Coun. on [13278]
Alcoholism; Res. Soc. on [16753]
Alcoolicos Anonimos no Brasil [★IO]
Alcooliques Anonymes France [★IO]
Alcooliques anonymes : bureau des Services generaux de Belgique francophone [★IO]
Alcor Found. [★14210]
Alcor Found. [★14210]
Alcor Life Extension Found. [14210], 7895 E Acoma Dr., Ste. 110, Scottsdale, AZ 85260-6916, (480)905-1906
Alcor Life Extension Found. [14210], 7895 E Acoma Dr., Ste. 110, Scottsdale, AZ 85260-6916, (480)905-1906
Alcort Sailfish-Sunfish Class [★22362]
Alcort Sailfish-Sunfish Class [★22362]
Alcuin Club [IO], Royston, United Kingdom
Alcuin Soc. [IO], Vancouver, BC, Canada
Alden Kindred of Am.ı[20421], PO Box 2754, Duxbury, MA 02331-2754, (781)934-9092
Alderson Cousins - Defunct.
Aldrig Mere Krig [★IO]
Aleksandr Solzhenitsyn Soc. for Freedom and Justice - Defunct.
ALEPH: Alliance for Jewish Renewal [18190], 7000 Lincoln Dr., No. B2, Philadelphia, PA 19119-3046, (215)247-9700
ALEPH: Alliance for Jewish Rènewal [18190], 7000 Lincoln Dr., No. B2, Philadelphia, PA 19119-3046, (215)247-9700
A.L.E.R.T. Intl. [14480], PO Box 1236, Bloomington, IN 47402, (812)369-9995
Alexander Graham Bell Assn. for the Deaf [★14912]
Alexander Graham Bell Assn. for the Deaf [★14912]
Alexander Graham Bell Assn. for the Deaf and Hard of Hearing [14912], 3417 Volta Pl. NW, Washington, DC 20007, (202)337-5220
Alexander Graham Bell Assn. for the Deaf and Hard of Hearing [14912], 3417 Volta Pl. NW, Washington, DC 20007, (202)337-5220
Alexander Technique; Amer. Center for the [13654]
Alexander Technique; Amer. Soc. for the [13660]
Alexander Technique Intl. [13646], 1692 Massachusetts Ave., 3rd Fl., Cambridge, MA 02138, (617)497-5151
Alexander Technique Intl. [13646], 1692 Massachusetts Ave., 3rd Fl., Cambridge, MA 02138, (617)497-5151
Alexander Thomson Soc. [IO], Glasgow, United Kingdom
Alexandra Writers' Centre Soc. [IO], Calgary, AB, Canada
Alfa Romeo Assn. [20984], PO Box 1458, Alameda, CA 94501
Alfa Romeo Club of Canada [IO], Toronto, ON, Canada
Alfa Romeo Owners Club [20985], PO Box 12340, Kansas City, MO 64116-0340, (816)459-7462
Alfalfa Coun. [★4372]
Alford Amer. Family Assn. [20422], PO Box 1297, Florissant, MO 63031, (314)831-8648
Alfred Adler Inst. [16364], 594 Broadway, Ste. 1213, New York, NY 10012, (212)254-1048
Alfred Adler Inst. for Individual Psychology [★16364]
Alfred P. Sloan Found. [18411], 630 5th Ave., Ste. 2550, New York, NY 10111, (212)649-1649
Algal Biomass Org. [6680], PO Box 369, Preston, MN 55965-0369, (763)458-0068
Algemeen Christelijk Vakverbond van Belgie [IO], Brussels, Belgium

Algemene Centrale der Openbare Diensten Sector Onderwijs [IO], Brussels, Belgium
Algemene Nederlandse Bond van Geitenhouders [★IO]
Algemene Nederlandse Branche Organisatie Schoonheidsverzorging [★IO]
Algerian Amer. Scientists Assn. [7353], 1825 Madison Ave., Ste. 6H, New York, NY 10035, (646)641-7615
Algerian Badminton Assn. [IO], Algiers, Algeria
Algerian League Against Epilepsy [IO], Algiers, Algeria
Algerian Ostomy Assn. [IO], Tizi Ouzou, Algeria
Algerian Red Crescent [IO], Algiers, Algeria
Algerian Soc. of Cardiology [IO], Algiers, Algeria
Algerian Soc. of Dermatology [IO], Algiers, Algeria
Algerian Soc. of Hypertension [IO], Algiers, Algeria
Algerian Taekwondo Fed. [IO], Algiers, Algeria
Algerian Tennis Fed. [IO], Algiers, Algeria
Algonquin Arts Coun. [IO], Bancroft, ON, Canada
ALI-ABA Continuing Professional Educ. - Address unknown since 2010.
Alice in Wonderland Collectors Network - Address unknown since 2011.
Aliran Kesedaran Negara [★IO]
Alisa Ann Ruch Burn Found. [13870], Southern CA Off., 2501 W Burbank Blvd., Ste. 201, Burbank, CA 91505, (818)848-0223
Alive Alone [11125], PO Box 182, Van Wert, OH 45891
Alkan Soc. [IO], Hemel Hempstead, United Kingdom
AlKoura League [12428], PO Box 95, Norwood, MA 02062, (617)435-8687
Alkylphenols and Ethoxylates Res. Coun. [741], 1250 Connecticut Ave. NW, Ste. 700, Washington, DC 20036, (202)419-1506
All for Africa [10807], 245 Park Ave., 38 Fl., New York, NY 10167, (212)351-0055
All for Africa [10807], 245 Park Ave., 38 Fl., New York, NY 10167, (212)351-0055
All Africa Leprosy, Tuberculosis and Rehabilitation Training Centre [IO], Addis Ababa, Ethiopia
All-African People's Revolutionary Party [17146], PO Box 42126, Atlanta, GA 30311-0126, (770)808-6062
All Am. Karate Fed. [★22721]
All-America Rose Selections [4664], PO Box 2612, Mill Valley, CA 94942, (415)381-5055
All-American Indian Motorcycle Club [21915], 140 N Centennial Rd., Holland, OH 43528
All-American Judges Assn. of Michigan - Defunct.
All Amer. Premier Breeds Admin. [21479], 141 3rd Ave. SW, Castle Rock, WA 98611, (360)274-4209
All-Amer. Soap Box Derby [22929], PO Box 7225, Akron, OH 44306, (330)733-8723
All As One, UAE [IO], Dubai, United Arab Emirates
All Breeds Cat Club [IO], Cape Town, Republic of South Africa
All-Breeds Rescue Conservancy - Defunct.
All the Children are Children [11182], PO Box 153012, Cape Coral, FL 33915, (239)214-4922
All China Fed. of Indus. and Commerce [IO], Beijing, People's Republic of China
All China Fed. of Trade Unions [IO], Beijing, People's Republic of China
All China Women's Fed. [IO], Beijing, People's Republic of China
All Dressage Assn. - Defunct.
All England Lawn Tennis and Croquet Club [IO], London, United Kingdom
All England Netball Assn. [IO], Hitchin, United Kingdom
All European Academies [IO], Amsterdam, Netherlands
All Hands Volunteers [11846], PO Box 546, Carlisle, MA 01741
All Healers Mental Hea. Alliance [15442], 2 W 64th St., Rm. 505, New York, NY 10023, (917)677-8550
All India Assn. of Indus. [IO], Mumbai, India
All India Biotech Assn. [IO], New Delhi, India
All India Chess Fed. for the Blind [IO], Mumbai, India
All India Dance Sport Fed. [IO], Bhubaneswar, India
All India Darts Assn. [IO], Calcutta, India
All India Disaster Mitigation Inst. [IO], Ahmedabad, India

A star before a book entry number signifies that the name is not listed separately, but is mentioned within the entry.

All India Exporters' Chamber [IO], Mumbai, India
All-India Fine Arts and Crafts Soc. [IO], New Delhi, India
All India Indus. Gases Mfrs. Assn. [IO], New Delhi, India
All India Mgt. Assn. [IO], New Delhi, India
All India Manufacturer's Org. [IO], Chennai, India
All India Occupational Therapists Assn. [IO], Udupi, India
All India Ophthalmological Soc. [IO], New Delhi, India
All India Plastics Mfrs. Assn. [IO], Mumbai, India
All India Railwaymen's Fed. [IO], New Delhi, India
All India Rubber Indus. Assn. [IO], Mumbai, India
All India Skin and Hide Tanners' and Merchants' Assn. [IO], Chennai, India
All India Stainless Steel Indus. Assn. [IO], Mumbai, India
All India Tennis Assn. [IO], New Delhi, India
All India Women's Conf. [IO], New Delhi, India
All Indian Pueblo Coun. [18147], 2401 12th St. NW, Albuquerque, NM 87104-2302, (505)881-1992
All-Industry Res. Advisory Coun. [★1978]
All-Japan Aikido Fed. [IO], Tokyo, Japan
All Japan Ju-Jitsu Intl. Fed. [22720], 5460 White Oak Ave., Unit F207, Encino, CA 91316, (818)578-6671
All-Japan Prefectural and Municipal Workers' Union [IO], Tokyo, Japan
All Japan Seamen's Union [IO], Tokyo, Japan
All Japan Taekwondo Fed. [IO], Tokyo, Japan
All Kids Can Learn Intl. [11446], 224 N Washington St., Havre de Grace, MD 21078, (800)785-1015
All Navy Women's Natl. Alliance [5866], PO Box 147, Goldenrod, FL 32733-0147
All Nepal Tennis Assn. [IO], Lalitpur, Nepal
All Nippon Nonwovens Assn. [IO], Osaka, Japan
All One Heart - Address unknown since 2011.
All One People [10808], 460 E 100 N, Manti, UT 84642, (435)835-6062
All Our Children Intl. Outreach [11183], PO Box 1807, Claremont, CA 91711, (909)450-1177
All Out Arts [9262], CSV Cultural Center, 107 Suffolk St., New York, NY 10002, (212)477-9945
All Pakistan Cement Mfrs. Assn. [IO], Lahore, Pakistan
All Pakistan CNG Assn. [IO], Rawalpindi, Pakistan
All Pakistan Contractors Assn. [IO], Lahore, Pakistan
All Pakistan Customs Agents Assn. [IO], Karachi, Pakistan
All Pakistan LPG Distributors Assn. [IO], Karachi, Pakistan
All Pakistan Security Agencies Assn. [IO], Karachi, Pakistan
All Pakistan Textile Mills Assn. [IO], Karachi, Pakistan
All Pakistan Women's Assn. [IO], Karachi, Pakistan
All-Poland Alliance of Trade Unions [IO], Warsaw, Poland
All Russia Assn. of the Blind [IO], Moscow, Russia
All-Russia Athletic Fed. [IO], Moscow, Russia
All-Russian Soc. for Disabled [IO], Moscow, Russia
All Services Postal Chess Club [21273], 1805 S Van Buren St., Amarillo, TX 79102-3058, (806)374-5991
All Star Assn. [1013], PO Box 911050, Lexington, KY 40591-1050, (859)255-3644
All Together Now Intl. - Address unknown since 2011.
All Trinidad Sugar and Gen. Workers' Trade Union [IO], Couva, Trinidad and Tobago
All of Us or None [17256], Legal Services for Prisoners with Children, 1540 Market St., Ste. 490, San Francisco, CA 94102, (415)255-7036
All4Israel [12389], 53 Dewhurst St., Staten Island, NY 10314, (877)812-7162
All4Israel [12389], 53 Dewhurst St., Staten Island, NY 10314, (877)812-7162
Allan Savory Center for Holistic Mgt. [★4078]
Allegro Vivo Music Assn. [IO], San Marino, San Marino
Allen Family Circle - Defunct.
Allergy
　Allergy Soc. of South Africa [18713]

Amer. Acad. of Allergy, Asthma and Immunology [13632]
Amer. Acad. of Otolaryngic Allergy and Found. [13633]
Amer. Bd. of Allergy and Immunology [13634]
Amer. Celiac Society | Dietary Support Coalition [15817]
Amer. Coll. of Allergy, Asthma and Immunology [13635]
Amer. Latex Allergy Assn. [13636]
Asthma and Allergy Found. of Am. [13637]
Environmental Res. Found. [13638]
Food Allergy and Anaphylaxis Network [13639]
Food Allergy Initiative [13640]
Joint Coun. of Allergy, Asthma and Immunology [13641]
Kids with Food Allergies Found. [13642]
Pan-American Allergy Soc. [13643]
World Allergy Org. [13644]
World Allergy Org. [13644]
Allergy/Asthma Info. Assn. [IO], Toronto, ON, Canada
Allergy and Asthma Network Mothers of Asthmatics [16602], 8201 Greensboro Dr., Ste. 300, McLean, VA 22102, (800)878-4403
Allergy Found. of Am. [★13637]
Allergy Soc. of South Africa [IO], Cape Town, Republic of South Africa
Alley Cat Allies [10902], 7920 Norfolk Ave., Ste. 600, Bethesda, MD 20814-2525, (240)482-1980
Alley Farming Network for Tropical Africa [IO], Ibadan, Nigeria
Allgemeiner Deutscher Automobil-Club [IO], Munich, Germany
Allgemeiner Deutscher Tanzlehrerverband [★IO]
Allgood Ancestry - Defunct.
The Alliance [★8338]
Alliance des manufacturiers de vitrage isolant [★IO]
L'alliance canadienne des associations etudiantes [★IO]
The Alliance [★8338]
L'Alliance 7 [★IO]
Alliance for Academic Internal Medicine [8334], 330 John Carlyle St., Ste. 610, Alexandria, VA 22314-5946, (703)341-4540
Alliance for Addiction Solutions [15561], 1450 S Havana St., No. 712, Aurora, CO 80012, (303)888-9617
Alliance for Advancing Nonprofit Hea. Care [14746], PO Box 41015, Washington, DC 20018, (877)299-6497
The Alliance Against Alveolar Soft Part Sarcoma - Address unknown since 2010.
Alliance Against Fraud in Telemarketing and Electronic Commerce [17441], Natl. Consumers League, 1701 K St. NW, Ste. 1200, Washington, DC 20006, (202)835-3323
Alliance Against IP Theft [IO], London, United Kingdom
Alliance for Aging Res. [10832], 750 17th St. NW, Ste. 1100, Washington, DC 20006, (202)293-2856
Alliance of the Amer. Dental Assn. [14228], 211 E Chicago Ave., Ste. 730, Chicago, IL 60611, (312)440-2865
Alliance of Amer. Insurers [★2031]
Alliance of Amer. Insurers - Defunct.
Alliance for Amer. Mfg. [2325], 727 15th St. NW, Ste. 700, Washington, DC 20005, (202)393-3430
Alliance for Amer. Quilts [21423], 125 S Lexington Ave., Ste. 101, Asheville, NC 28801, (828)251-7073
Alliance for Animals [10903], 232 Silver St., South Boston, MA 02127-2206, (617)268-7800
Alliance of Area Bus. Publications [2912], 1970 E Grand Ave., Ste. 330, El Segundo, CA 90245, (310)364-0193
Alliance of Artists and Recording Companies [3047], 700 N Fairfax St., Ste. 601, Alexandria, VA 22314, (703)535-8101
Alliance of Artists and Recording Companies [3047], 700 N Fairfax St., Ste. 601, Alexandria, VA 22314, (703)535-8101
Alliance for the Arts [9263], 330 W 42nd St., Ste. 1701, New York, NY 10036, (212)947-6340
Alliance for Arts and Culture [★10836]

Alliance for Arts Educ. [★7749]
Alliance for Asian Amer. Arts and Culture [★9277]
Alliance of Atomic Veterans - Defunct.
Alliance of Auto. Mfrs. [310], 1401 Eye St. NW, Ste. 900, Washington, DC 20005, (202)326-5500
Alliance of Auto. Mfrs. [310], 1401 Eye St. NW, Ste. 900, Washington, DC 20005, (202)326-5500
Alliance for Beverage Cartons and the Env. - Belgium [IO], Brussels, Belgium
Alliance for Beverage Cartons and the Env. - United Kingdom [IO], Wrexham, United Kingdom
Alliance Biblique du Benin [★IO]
Alliance Biblique au Gabon [★IO]
Alliance Biblique de la Republique Democratique du Congo [★IO]
Alliance Biblique du Togo [★IO]
Alliance Bielarusienne du Canada [★IO]
Alliance for Biking and Walking [18731], PO Box 65150, Washington, DC 20035, (202)449-9692
Alliance for Biking and Walking [18731], PO Box 65150, Washington, DC 20035, (202)449-9692
Alliance for Biotherapies [16831], 1120 G St. NW, Ste. 1000, Washington, DC 20005, (202)331-2196
Alliance for Building Regulatory Reform in the Digital Age [6372], 10702 Midsummer Dr., Reston, VA 20191, (703)568-2323
Alliance of Canadian Cinema, TV and Radio Artists [IO], Toronto, ON, Canada
Alliance for Canadian New Music Proj. [IO], Toronto, ON, Canada
Alliance Canadienne du Camionnage [★IO]
Alliance Canadienne des Organismes de Reglementation de la Physiotherapie [★IO]
Alliance Canadienne pour la Paix [★IO]
Alliance Canadienne des Victimes d'Accidents et de Maladies du Travail [★IO]
L'Alliance de vie active des Canadiens/Canadiennes ayant un handicap [★IO]
Alliance of Cardiovascular Professionals [13997], PO Box 2007, Midlothian, VA 23113, (804)632-0078
Alliance Catholique Canadienne de la Sante [★IO]
Alliance for Child Survival - Defunct.
Alliance for Childhood [11160], PO Box 20973, New York, NY 10025, (917)363-1982
Alliance for Childhood Cancer [13878], 2318 Mill Rd., Ste. 800, Alexandria, VA 22314, (571)483-1670
Alliance for Children and Families [11993], 11700 W Lake Park Dr., Milwaukee, WI 53224-3099, (414)359-1040
Alliance for Children and Families [11993], 11700 W Lake Park Dr., Milwaukee, WI 53224-3099, (414)359-1040
Alliance for Children and TV [IO], Montreal, QC, Canada
Alliance for Choices in Child Care [11147], 858 Woodlands Rd., Charlottesville, VA 22911, (434)973-2587
Alliance of Claims Assistance Professionals [1922], Rebecca Stephenson, ACAP, Co-Pres., 9600 Escarpment, Ste. 745-65, Austin, TX 78749, (512)394-0008
Alliance for a Clean Rural Environment - Defunct.
Alliance for Climate Educ. [4315], 360 22nd St., Ste. 730, Oakland, CA 94612, (510)251-5990
Alliance for Climate Educ. [4315], 360 22nd St., Ste. 730, Oakland, CA 94612, (510)251-5990
Alliance of Community Hea. Plans [14849], 1825 Eye St. NW, Ste. 401, Washington, DC 20006, (202)785-2247
Alliance for Community Media [17333], 1760 Old Meadow Rd., No. 500, McLean, VA 22102, (703)556-7175
Alliance for Community Trees [4386], 4603 Calvert Rd., College Park, MD 20740-3421, (301)277-0040
Alliance for Conflict Transformation [17399], PO Box 9117, Alexandria, VA 22304, (703)879-7039
Alliance for Continuing Medical Educ. [8584], Southcrest Bldg., 1025 Montgomery Hwy., Ste. 105, Birmingham, AL 35216, (205)824-1355
Alliance for Contraception in Cats and Dogs [12647], 14245 NW Belle Ct., Portland, OR 97229, (503)358-1438
Alliance Cooperative Internationale [★IO]

Reference to "IO" in place of a book number signifies that the association may be found in the 50th edition of International Organizations.

Alliance Credit Counseling - Address unknown since 2010.

Alliance for Cultural Democracy **[9264]**, PO Box 192244, San Francisco, CA 94119-2244, (415)821-9652

Alliance for Customers' Telecommunications Rights; TeleTruth; The **[17474]**

Alliance Defense Fund **[17498]**, 15100 N 90th St., Scottsdale, AZ 85260, (480)444-0020

Alliance for Democracy **[18412]**, PO Box 540115, Waltham, MA 02454-0115, (781)894-1179

Alliance Des Arts Mediatiques Independants **[★IO]**

Alliance for Digital Equality **[7492]**, 1447 Peachtree St., Ste. 550, Atlanta, GA 30309-3032, (404)815-9484

Alliance for Eating Disorders Awareness **[14430]**, PO Box 2562, West Palm Beach, FL 33402-2562, (561)841-0900

Alliance to End Childhood Lead Poisoning **[★13320]**

Alliance to End Hunger **[12264]**, 425 3rd St. SW, Ste. 1200, Washington, DC 20024, (202)639-9400

Alliance to End Repression **[★17304]**

Alliance for Energy and Economic Growth **[6681]**, 1615 H St. NW, Washington, DC 20062, (202)463-5642

Alliance of Energy Suppliers - Address unknown since 2011.

Alliance for Environmental Tech. **[1492]**, 1250 24th St. NW, Ste. 300, Washington, DC 20037, (800)999-PULP

Alliance of European Voluntary Ser. Organizations **[IO]**, Copenhagen, Denmark

Alliance Europeenne pour l'Ethique en Publicite **[★IO]**

Alliance for Excellent Educ. **[8854]**, 1201 Connecticut Ave. NW, Ste. 901, Washington, DC 20036, (202)828-0828

Alliance of Faith and Feminism **[17628]**, PO Box 4323, Tallahassee, FL 32315

Alliance for Fire and Emergency Mgt. **[★5445]**

Alliance for Fire and Emergency Mgt. **[★5445]**

Alliance for Fire and Smoke Containment and Control **[1349]**, 4 Brookhollow Rd. SW, Rome, GA 30165-6509, (706)291-9355

Alliance of Foam Packaging Recyclers **[4978]**, 1298 Cronson Blvd., Ste. 201, Crofton, MD 21114, (410)451-8340

Alliance de la Fonction Publique du Canada **[★IO]**

Alliance For Animal Rights **[IO]**, Dublin, Ireland

Alliance For Relief Mission in Haiti **[12799]**, PO Box 250028, Brooklyn, NY 11225, (516)499-7452

Alliance Francaise **[★IO]**

Alliance Francaise de New York **[★9629]**

Alliance Francaise of St. Kitts and Nevis **[IO]**, Basseterre, St. Kitts and Nevis

Alliance of France **[IO]**, Paris, France

Alliance for Full Acceptance **[12066]**, PO Box 22088, Charleston, SC 29413, (843)883-0343

Alliance for Full Participation **[11754]**, 202 Lexington Dr., Silver Spring, MD 20901, (301)706-6252

Alliance of Genetic Support Groups **[★16770]**

Alliance of Genetic Support Groups **[★15494]**

Alliance of Girls' Schools Australasia **[IO]**, Hobart, Australia

Alliance for Global Conservation **[3983]**, PO Box 1200, Washington, DC 20013-1200, (202)739-8155

Alliance for Global Conservation **[3983]**, PO Box 1200, Washington, DC 20013-1200, (202)739-8155

Alliance for Global Sustainability **[IO]**, Goteborg, Sweden

Alliance Graphique Internationale **[IO]**, St. Gallen, Switzerland

Alliance for Green Heat **[6682]**, 6930 Carroll Ave., Ste. 407, Takoma Park, MD 20912, (301)841-7755

Alliance of Guardian Angels **[11681]**, 982 E 89th St., Brooklyn, NY 11236, (212)860-5575

Alliance of Guardian Angels **[11681]**, 982 E 89th St., Brooklyn, NY 11236, (212)860-5575

Alliance of Hazardous Materials Professionals **[4518]**, 9650 Rockville Pike, Bethesda, MD 20814, (301)634-7430

Alliance for Hea. Reform **[17762]**, 1444 Eye St. NW, Ste. 910, Washington, DC 20005-6573, (202)789-2300

Alliance for a Healthier Generation **[14055]**, 606 SE 9th Ave., Portland, OR 97214, (888)KID-HLTH

Alliance for Healthy Homes **[13320]**, 50 F St. NW, Ste. 300, Washington, DC 20001, (202)347-7610

Alliance for Higher Educ. **[8226]**, PO Box 836696, Richardson, TX 75083-6696, (972)883-4920

Alliance for Human Res. Protection **[17809]**, 142 W End Ave., Ste. 28P, New York, NY 10023-6123

Alliance for Inclusion in the Arts **[10559]**, 1560 Broadway, Ste. 709, New York, NY 10036, (212)730-4750

Alliance of Independent Academic Medical Centers **[15319]**, 401 N Michigan Ave., Ste. 1200, Chicago, IL 60611, (312)836-3712

Alliance of Info. and Referral Systems **[6967]**, 11240 Waples Mill Rd., Ste. 200, Fairfax, VA 22030, (703)218-2477

Alliance of Info. and Referral Systems **[6967]**, 11240 Waples Mill Rd., Ste. 200, Fairfax, VA 22030, (703)218-2477

Alliance of Intl. Aromatherapists **[13647]**, 9956 W Remington Pl., Unit A10, Ste. 323, Littleton, CO 80128, (303)531-6377

Alliance for Intl. Conflict Prevention and Resolution **[★17404]**

Alliance for Intl. Conflict Prevention and Resolution **[★17404]**

Alliance for Intl. Educational and Cultural Exchange **[8338]**, 1828 L St. NW, Ste. 1150, Washington, DC 20036-1912, (202)293-6141

Alliance for Intl. Educational and Cultural Exchange **[8338]**, 1828 L St. NW, Ste. 1150, Washington, DC 20036-1912, (202)293-6141

Alliance for Intl. Market Res. Institutes **[IO]**, London, United Kingdom

Alliance for Intl. Monasticism **[IO]**, Vanves, France

Alliance for Intl. Reforestation **[3984]**, 1721 N Woodland Blvd., DeLand, FL 32720, (386)748-2454

Alliance for Intl. Reforestation **[3984]**, 1721 N Woodland Blvd., DeLand, FL 32720, (386)748-2454

Alliance for Intl. Women's Rights **[18804]**, PO Box 165, East Chatham, NY 12060, (518)632-4797

Alliance Internationale des Femmes **[★IO]**

Alliance Internationale de Tourisme **[★IO]**

Alliance of Jamaican and Amer. Humanitarians **[11543]**, 264 S La Cienega Blvd., Ste. 1004, Beverly Hills, CA 90211, (424)249-8135

Alliance for Jewish Renewal; ALEPH: **[18190]**

Alliance for Jewish Renewal; ALEPH: **[18190]**

Alliance for Justice **[5932]**, 11 Dupont Cir. NW, 2nd Fl., Washington, DC 20036, (202)822-6070

Alliance of Legal Document Asst. Professionals **[5751]**, 7290 Navajo Rd., Ste. 113, San Diego, CA 92119, (888)201-8622

Alliance pour l'enfant et la television **[★IO]**

Alliance for Life Ministries **[19533]**, PO Box 5468, Madison, WI 53705

Alliance de L'Industrie Canadienne de L'Aquiculture **[★IO]**

Alliance of Literary Societies **[IO]**, Kidderminster, United Kingdom

Alliance for Lupus Res. **[15251]**, 28 W 44th St., Ste. 501, New York, NY 10036, (212)218-2840

Alliance for Lupus Res. **[15251]**, 28 W 44th St., Ste. 501, New York, NY 10036, (212)218-2840

Alliance of Marine Mammal Parks and Aquariums **[4699]**, 2850 Ranch Reserve Ln., Westminster, CO 80234, (720)887-5921

Alliance of Marine Mammal Parks and Aquariums **[4699]**, 2850 Ranch Reserve Ln., Westminster, CO 80234, (720)887-5921

Alliance of Maritime Regional Interests in Europe **[IO]**, Brussels, Belgium

Alliance for Marriage **[12435]**, PO Box 2490, Merrifield, VA 22116-2490, (703)934-1212

Alliance for Massage Therapy Educ. **[8560]**, 1760 Old Meadow Rd., Ste. 500, McLean, VA 22102, (703)506-2888

Alliance for a Media Literate Am. **[★8574]**

Alliance of Meeting Mgt. Companies **[2442]**, PO Box 1857, West Jefferson, NC 28694, (336)846-7270

Alliance of Meeting Mgt. Consultants **[★2442]**

Alliance of Merger and Acquisition Advisors **[638]**, 200 E Randolph St., 24th Fl., Chicago, IL 60601, (877)844-2535

Alliance of Metalworking Industries - Defunct.

Alliance for Microbicide Development - Defunct.

Alliance of Minority Medical Associations - Address unknown since 2011.

Alliance Mondiale des Unions Chretiennes Feminines **[★IO]**

Alliance des Moniteurs de Ski du Canada **[★IO]**

Alliance of Motion Picture and TV Producers **[1248]**, 15301 Ventura Blvd., Bldg. E, Sherman Oaks, CA 91403, (818)995-3600

Alliance for Natl. Defense **[6071]**, PO Box 22241, Alexandria, VA 22304

Alliance of Natl. Heritage Areas **[9522]**, 444 N Capitol St. NW, Ste. 342, Washington, DC 20001-1538, (202)625-4393

Alliance for Natl. Renewal - Defunct.

Alliance Nationale des Unions Chretiennes de Jeunes Gens de France **[★IO]**

Alliance for Natural Hea. USA **[16302]**, 1350 Connecticut Ave. NW, 5th Fl., Washington, DC 20036, (800)230-2762

Alliance for Neighborhood Govt. **[★11532]**

Alliance for a New Trans. Charter **[6026]**, Surface Trans. Policy Proj., 1707 L St. NW, Ste. 1050, Washington, DC 20036, (202)466-2636

Alliance New Zealand **[IO]**, Dunedin, New Zealand

Alliance of Nonprofit Mailers **[2228]**, 1211 Connecticut Ave. NW, Ste. 610, Washington, DC 20036-2705, (202)462-5132

Alliance for Nonprofit Mgt. **[260]**, 731 Market St., Ste. 200, San Francisco, CA 94103, (415)704-5058

Alliance for Nuclear Accountability **[18180]**, 903 W Alameda St., No. 505, Santa Fe, NM 87501, (505)473-1670

Alliance of the Orders of St. John of Jerusalem **[IO]**, Basel, Switzerland

Alliance of Organisations of Disabled People Slovakia **[IO]**, Bratislava, Slovakia

Alliance for Paired Donation **[15540]**, 3661 Briarfield Blvd., Ste. 105, Maumee, OH 43537, (419)866-5505

Alliance Party of Northern Ireland **[IO]**, Belfast, United Kingdom

Alliance for a Paving Moratorium **[17391]**, Culture Change, PO Box 4347, Arcata, CA 95518, (215)243-3144

Alliance for Peacebuilding **[17404]**, 1320 19th St. NW, Ste. 410, Washington, DC 20036, (202)822-2047

Alliance for Peacebuilding **[17404]**, 1320 19th St. NW, Ste. 410, Washington, DC 20036, (202)822-2047

Alliance for Plasma Therapies **[★16831]**

Alliance for the Polyurethanes Indus. A Bus. Unit of the Amer. Plastics Coun. **[★2765]**

Alliance for Preventive Hea. **[14864]**, 817 Broadway, 5th Fl., New York, NY 10003, (212)257-6105

Alliance des Producteurs de Cacao **[★IO]**

Alliance of Professional Consultants **[855]**, 8200 Brownleigh Dr., Raleigh, NC 27617-7411, (919)510-9696

Alliance of Professional Tattooists **[3379]**, 215 W 18th St., Ste. 210, Kansas City, MO 64108, (816)979-1300

Alliance pour des Projets de Musique Canadienne Nouvelle **[★IO]**

Alliance for the Prudent Use of Antibiotics **[16166]**, 75 Kneeland St., Boston, MA 02111-1901, (617)636-0966

Alliance for Rabies Control **[14370]**, 529 Humboldt St., Ste. 1, Manhattan, KS 66502, (570)899-4885

Alliance for Rail Competition **[2983]**, 412 First St. SE, Ste. 1, Washington, DC 20003-1804, (202)484-7133

Alliance Reformee Mondiale **[★IO]**

Alliance for Regional Stewardship **[18060]**, 4875 Eisenhower Ave., Ste. 250, Alexandria, VA 22304, (703)998-0072

Alliance of Registered Homeopaths **[IO]**, Nutley, United Kingdom

Alliance of Religions and Conservation **[IO]**, Bath, , United Kingdom

Alliance for Renewable Energy **[6683]**, PO Box 63, Amherst, MA 01004, (413)549-8118

A star before a book entry number signifies that the name is not listed separately, but is mentioned within the entry.

Alliance of Resident Theatres/New York [10560], 520 8th Ave., Ste. 319, New York, NY 10018, (212)244-6667

Alliance for Responsible Atmospheric Policy [742], 2111 Wilson Blvd., Ste. 850, Arlington, VA 22201, (703)243-0344

Alliance for Responsible CFC Policy [★742]

Alliance for Responsible Trade [3480], PO Box 5206, Hyattsville, MD 20782, (301)699-0042

Alliance for Responsible Trade [3480], PO Box 5206, Hyattsville, MD 20782, (301)699-0042

Alliance for Retired Americans [18548], 815 16th St. NW, 4th Fl., Washington, DC 20006, (202)637-5399

The Alliance for Safe Children [14056], 213 Adahi Rd., Vienna, VA 22180-5937, (703)652-3873

Alliance to Save Energy [6684], 1850 M St. NW, Ste. 600, Washington, DC 20036-5817, (202)857-0666

Alliance for School Choice [8822], 1660 L St. NW, Ste. 1000, Washington, DC 20036, (202)280-1990

Alliance for Sci. and Tech. Res. in Am. [7354], Oth-mer Bldg., Rm. 320, 1155 16th St. NW, Washington, DC 20036, (202)872-6160

Alliance for the Separation of School and State [7991], 3100 Willow Ave., Ste. 110, Clovis, CA 93612, (888)325-1776

Alliance of Small Island States [17902], 800 Second Ave., Ste. 400k, New York, NY 10017, (212)599-0301

Alliance of Small Island States [17902], 800 Second Ave., Ste. 400k, New York, NY 10017, (212)599-0301

Alliance for Smiles [14189], 2565 3rd St., Ste. 237, San Francisco, CA 94107, (415)647-4481

Alliance de Societes Feminines Suisses [★IO]

Alliance for South Asian AIDS Prevention [IO], Tor-onto, ON, Canada

Alliance for Southern African Progress [12310], 1424 31st Ave., Ste. 3R, Astoria, NY 11106, (877)375-5778

Alliance for Southern African Progress [12310], 1424 31st Ave., Ste. 3R, Astoria, NY 11106, (877)375-5778

Alliance of Special Effects and Pyrotechnic Opera-tors [2975], 12522 Moorpark St., Ste. 111, Studio City, CA 91604, (818)506-8173

Alliance of State Pain Initiatives - Address unknown since 2011.

Alliance for a Stronger FDA [17696], PO Box 7508, Silver Spring, MD 20907-7508, (202)887-4211

Alliance for Student Activities [8911], 1129 Ortega Rd. NW, Albuquerque, NM 87114, (800)658-6082

Alliance of Supplier Diversity Professionals [2969], Lisa Barr, Treas., PO Box 560211, Rockledge, FL 32955, (877)405-6565

Alliance in Support of Independent Res. [3085], 1990 M St. NW, Ste. 660, Washington, DC 20036, (202)223-4418

Alliance for Sustainability [4345], Univ. of Minnesota, 1521 Univ. Ave. SE, Minneapolis, MN 55414, (612)331-1099

Alliance for Sustainable Built Environments [517], 5150 N Port Washington Rd., Ste. 260, Milwaukee, WI 53217, (866)913-9473

Alliance for a Sustainable U.S.A. [10895], 56 Do-lores Way, Orinda, CA 94563, (925)377-0376

Alliance for Tech. Access [11755], 1119 Old Hum-boldt Rd., Jackson, TN 38305, (731)554-5282

Alliance for Telecommunications Indus. Solutions [3397], 1200 G St. NW, Ste. 500, Washington, DC 20005, (202)628-6380

Alliance of Third-Class Nonprofit Mailers [★2228]

Alliance for Tompotika Conservation [3985], 21416 86th Ave. SW, Vashon, WA 98070, (206)463-7720

Alliance for Traffic Safety - Defunct.

Alliance for Transforming the Lives of Children [11184], 901 Preston Ave., Ste. 400, Charlottes-ville, VA 22903, (888)574-7580

Alliance of Unitarian Women [★20273]

Alliance of Universities for Democracy [IO], Pecs, Hungary

Alliance of Veterinarians for the Env. [4325], 836 W Hillwood Dr., Nashville, TN 37205, (615)353-0272

Alliance for Water Educ. [8149], 120 Village Sq., Ste. 137, Orinda, CA 94563, (925)386-0515

Alliance for Water Efficiency [4986], 300 W Adams St., Ste. 601, Chicago, IL 60606, (773)360-5100

Alliance for Wellness ROI [16303], 390 Main St., Ste. 400, Worcester, MA 01608

Alliance for Women in Media [479], 1760 Old Meadow Rd., Ste. 500, McLean, VA 22102, (703)506-3290

Alliance for Work-Life Progress [2890], 14040 N Northsight Blvd., Scottsdale, AZ 85260-3601, (480)922-2007

Alliance for Worker Freedom [23316], 722 12th St. NW, 4th Fl., Washington, DC 20005, (202)785-0266

Alliance for Youth Achievement [11185], PO Box 6634, Maryville, TN 37802, (865)983-5863

Allied Airborne Assn. - Defunct.

Allied Artists of Am. [9217], 15 Gramercy Park S, New York, NY 10003

Allied Beauty Assn. [IO], Mississauga, ON, Canada

Allied Farm Equip. Mfrs. Assn. [★168]

Allied Hea. Assn. [967], 5420 S Quebec St., Ste. 102, Englewood, CO 80111, (800)444-7546

Allied Pilots Assn. [23148], O'Connell Bldg., 14600 Trinity Blvd., Ste. 500, Fort Worth, TX 76155-2512, (817)302-2272

Allied Purchasing Company [1014], PO Box 1249, Mason City, IA 50402, (800)247-5956

Allied Social Sci. Associations [7408], 2014 Broadway, Ste. 305, Nashville, TN 37203, (615)322-3509

Allied States Assn. of Motion Picture Exhibitors [★1209]

Allied Stone Indus. [3357], Butch Coleman, Dir., PO Box 273, Susquehanna, PA 18847, (570)465-7200

Allied Trades of the Baking Indus. [385], Cereal Food Processors, Inc., 2001 Shawnee Mission Pkwy., Mission Woods, KS 66205

Allies Building Community [9332], PO Box 57250, Washington, DC 20037-0250, (202)496-1555

Allison Family Assn. - Address unknown since 2010.

AlloSource [16895], 6278 S Troy Cir., Centennial, CO 80111, (720)873-0213

Alloway Family Assn. - Defunct.

Alloy Casting Inst. [★1870]

Alloy Casting Inst. [★1870]

ALMA Soc. [10777], PO Box 85, Denville, NJ 07834

ALMA - The Intl. Loudspeaker Assn. [1090], 55 Littleton Rd., 13B, Ayer, MA 01432, (617)314-6977

Alma Wesley Millet Family Org. - Defunct.

Almond Bd. of California [4744], 1150 9th St., Ste. 1500, Modesto, CA 95354, (209)549-8262

Almond Control Bd. [★4744]

Almshouse Assn. [IO], Wokingham, United Kingdom

Aloe Tech. Assn. - Defunct.

Alopecia Areata Found; Natl. [16633]

Alpaca Assn. New Zealand [IO], Christchurch, New Zealand

Alpaca Breeders of the Rockies [3771], PO Box 1965, Estes Park, CO 80517, (970)586-5589

Alpaca Llama Show Assn. [20947], 607 California Ave., Pittsburgh, PA 15202, (412)761-0211

Alpaca Owners and Breeders Assn. [3772], 5000 Linbar Dr., Ste. 297, Nashville, TN 37211, (615)834-4195

Alpacas Without Borders [3773], Prairie Lake Alpacas, 13711 John Kline Rd., Smithsburg, MD 21783, (301)416-0833

Alpenlite Travel Club - Address unknown since 2011.

Alpha-1 Advocacy Alliance [14583], PO Box 202, Wolftown, VA 22748, (540)948-6777

Alpha 1 Antitrypsin Support Gp. [★16603]

Alpha-1 Assn. [16603], 2937 SW 27th Ave., Ste. 106, Miami, FL 33133, (305)648-0088

Alpha 1 Found. [14584], 2937 SW 27th Ave., Ste. 302, Miami, FL 33133, (305)567-9888

Alpha-1 Kids [14585], PO Box 132, Coltons Point, MD 20626, (410)227-9524

Alpha-66

Alpha-66 - Address unknown since 2011.

Alpha Beta Gamma [★23486]

Alpha Beta Gamma [★23486]

Alpha Beta Gamma Intl. [23486], 75 Grasslands Rd., Valhalla, NY 10595, (914)606-6877

Alpha Beta Gamma Intl. [23486], 75 Grasslands Rd., Valhalla, NY 10595, (914)606-6877

Alpha Chi [23551], Harding Univ., Box 12249, 915 E Market Ave., Searcy, AR 72149-2249, (501)279-4443

Alpha Chi Omega [23710], 5939 Castle Creek Pkwy., North Dr., Indianapolis, IN 46250-4343, (317)579-5050

Alpha Chi Omega Foundation [★23710]

Alpha Chi Rho [23649], 109 Oxford Way, Neptune, NJ 07753, (732)869-1895

Alpha Chi Sigma [23489], 2141 N Franklin Rd., Indianapolis, IN 46219-2497, (317)357-5944

Alpha Delta Gamma [23650], 946 Sanders Dr., St. Louis, MO 63126

Alpha Delta Kappa [23509], 1615 W 92nd St., Kansas City, MO 64114, (816)363-5525

Alpha Delta Kappa [23509], 1615 W 92nd St., Kansas City, MO 64114, (816)363-5525

Alpha Delta Phi [23651], 6126 Lincoln Ave., Morton Grove, IL 60053, (847)965-1832

Alpha Delta Pi [23652], 1386 Ponce de Leon Ave. NE, Atlanta, GA 30306, (404)378-3164

Alpha Delta Tau Fraternity [★23556]

Alpha Epsilon [23516], Univ. of Illinois in Urbana-Champaign, Dept. of Agricultural and Biological Engg., 1304 W Pennsylvania Ave., Urbana, IL 61801, (217)333-3570

Alpha Epsilon Delta [23591], Texas Christian Univ., Box 298810, Fort Worth, TX 76129, (817)257-4550

Alpha Epsilon Phi [23711], 11 Lake Ave. Ext., Ste. 1A, Danbury, CT 06811, (203)748-0029

Alpha Epsilon Pi [23653], 8815 Wesleyan Rd., Indianapolis, IN 46268-1171, (317)876-1913

Alpha Epsilon Pi Found. [★23653]

Alpha Epsilon Rho [★23472]

Alpha Gamma Delta [23712], 8701 Founders Rd., Indianapolis, IN 46268-1338, (317)872-2655

Alpha Gamma Rho [23461], 10101 NW Ambassador Dr., Kansas City, MO 64153-1395, (816)891-9200

Alpha Gamma Upsilon [★23657]

Alpha Iota Delta [23473], Univ. of Detroit Mercy, Coll. of Bus. Admin., 4001 W McNichols Rd., Detroit, MI 48221, (313)993-1219

Alpha Iota Sorority [23474], 3219 SE 18th Ct., Des Moines, IA 50320-1901, (515)282-4896

Alpha Iota Sorority [23474], 3219 SE 18th Ct., Des Moines, IA 50320-1901, (515)282-4896

Alpha Kappa Alpha [23639], 5656 S Stony Island Ave., Chicago, IL 60637, (773)684-1282

Alpha Kappa Delta [23737], Le Moyne Coll., 1419 Salt Springs Rd., Syracuse, NY 13214, (315)445-5452

Alpha Kappa Delta [23737], Le Moyne Coll., 1419 Salt Springs Rd., Syracuse, NY 13214, (315)445-5452

Alpha Kappa Lambda [23654], 354 Gradle Dr., Car-mel, IN 46032, (317)564-8003

Alpha Kappa Lambda Educational Foundation [★23654]

Alpha Kappa Mu [23552], 101 Longwood Ln., Greenwood, SC 29646, (864)229-1546

Alpha Kappa Pi [★23657]

Alpha Kappa Psi [23475], 7801 E 88th St., Indianapolis, IN 46256-1233, (317)872-1553

Alpha Micro Users Soc. - Defunct.

Alpha Mu Gamma [★23576]

Alpha Mu Gamma Natl. [23576], 855 N Vermont Ave., Los Angeles, CA 90029, (323)644-9752

Alpha Omega Alpha [★23592]

Alpha Omega Alpha Honor Medical Soc. [23592], 525 Middlefield Rd., Ste. 130, Menlo Park, CA 94025, (650)329-0291

Alpha Omega Intl. Dental Fraternity [23497], 50 W Edmonston Dr., No. 303, Rockville, MD 20852, (301)738-6400

Alpha Omega Intl. Dental Fraternity [23497], 50 W Edmonston Dr., No. 303, Rockville, MD 20852, (301)738-6400

Alpha Omicron Pi [23713], 5390 Virginia Way, Brent-wood, TN 37027, (615)370-0920

Alpha Phi Alpha Fraternity [23634], 2313 St. Paul St., Baltimore, MD 21218-5211, (410)554-0040

Alpha Phi Delta [23655], 257 E Camden Wyoming Ave., Ste. A, Camden, DE 19934, (302)531-7854

Alpha Phi Intl. Fraternity [23714], 1930 Sherman Ave., Evanston, IL 60201, (847)475-0663

Reference to "IO" in place of a book number signifies that the association may be found in the 50th edition of International Organizations.

Alpha Phi Intl. Fraternity [23714], 1930 Sherman Ave., Evanston, IL 60201, (847)475-0663
Alpha Phi Omega Natl. Ser. Fraternity [23635], 14901 E 42nd St., Independence, MO 64055-7347, (816)373-8667
Alpha Pi Mu [23517], PO Box 773, Portland, OR 97207-0773, (503)297-3604
Alpha Pi Sigma [23530], PO Box 15983, San Diego, CA 92175
Alpha Psi Lambda Natl. [23656], PO Box 804835, Chicago, IL 60680
Alpha Psi Omega [23503], Dr. Bret Jones, Bus. Mgr., Wichita State Univ., 1845 Fairmount St., Box 153, Wichita, KS 67260, (908)737-4427
Alpha Rho Lambda Sorority - Address unknown since 2011.
Alpha Sigma Alpha [23715], 9002 Vincennes Cir., Indianapolis, IN 46268, (317)871-2920
Alpha Sigma Nu [23553], PO Box 1881, Milwaukee, WI 53201-1881, (414)288-7542
Alpha Sigma Nu [23553], PO Box 1881, Milwaukee, WI 53201-1881, (414)288-7542
Alpha Sigma Phi [23657], 710 Adams St., Carmel, IN 46032-7541, (317)843-1911
Alpha Sigma Tau [23716], 3334 Founders Rd., Indianapolis, IN 46268, (205)978-2179
Alpha Sigma Tau [★23553]
Alpha Sigma Tau [★23553]
Alpha Tau Alpha [23460], 455 Ag Hall, Stillwater, OK 74074
Alpha Tau Delta [23608], 1904 Poinsettia Ave., Manhattan Beach, CA 90266
Alpha Tau Omega [23658], 1 N Pennsylvania St., 12th Fl., Indianapolis, IN 46204-3136, (317)684-1865
Alpha Xi Delta Women's Fraternity [23717], 8702 Founders Rd., Indianapolis, IN 46268, (317)872-3500
Alpha Zeta [23462], 16020 Swingley Ridge Rd., Ste. 300, Chesterfield, MO 63017, (636)449-5090
Alpha Zeta Omega [23615], 140 Hepburn Rd., Apt. 15B, Clifton, NJ 07012
Alpha Zeta Pi [★23577]
Alphabetisation mondiale Canada [★IO]
Alpine Club of Canada [IO], Canmore, AB, Canada
Alpine Club of England [IO], London, United Kingdom
Alpine Coach Assn. [22132], 5808 A Summitview Ave., No. 337, Yakima, WA 98908, (509)457-4133
Alpine Garden Soc. [IO], Pershore, United Kingdom
Alpines Intl. Club [3774], Tina Antes, Sec.-Treas., 7195 City Rd. 315, Silt, CO 81652
Alpines Intl. Club [3774], Tina Antes, Sec.-Treas., 7195 City Rd. 315, Silt, CO 81652
ALS Assn. [★15569]
ALS Diagnostic Support Gp. [IO], Baarn, Netherlands
ALS Forbes Norris Res. Center [★15590]
ALS Liga Belgie [★IO]
ALS and Neuromuscular Res. Found. [★15590]
ALS Res. Center [★15590]
ALS Res. Fund [IO], Baarn, Netherlands
ALS Support Gp. - Belgium [IO], Leuven, Belgium
Alston Wilkes Soc. [★11701]
Alston Wilkes Veterans Home [11701], Palmetto State Base Camp, Inc., 3519 Medical Dr., Columbia, SC 29203
Alstrom Syndrome Intl. [14586], 14 Whitney Farm Rd., Mount Desert, ME 04660, (800)371-3628
Alstrom Syndrome Intl. [14586], 14 Whitney Farm Rd., Mount Desert, ME 04660, (800)371-3628
Alstrom Syndrome Intl. - United Kingdom [IO], Paignton, United Kingdom
Alternating Hemiplegia of Childhood Vereniging Nederland [IO], Rhoon, Netherlands
Alternative Aquaculture Assn. [3819], 630 Independent Rd., Breinigsville, PA 18031, (610)398-1062
Alternative Communities Trade in Vanuatu Assn. [IO], Port Vila, Vanuatu

Alternative Education
Commun. Inst. for Online Scholarship [6107]
Consciousness-Based Educ. Assn. [8762]
Eta Sigma Alpha Natl. Home School Honor Soc. [7718]
Intl. Assn. for K-12 Online Learning [7719]
Intl. Assn. for K-12 Online Learning [7719]
Intl. Assn. for Learning Alternatives [7720]
Intl. Assn. for Learning Alternatives [7720]
Intl. E-Learning Assn. [7721]
Natl. Alternative Educ. Assn. [7722]
Natl. Assn. for Legal Support of Alternative Schools [7723]
Natl. Coalition of Alternative Community Schools [7724]
Natl. Coalition for Telecommunications Educ. and Learning [8981]
Parents' Rights Org. [7725]
Alternative Educ. Rsrc. Org. [7992], 417 Roslyn Rd., Roslyn Heights, NY 11577, (516)621-2195
Alternative Energy Resources Org. [6685], 432 N Last Chance Gulch, Helena, MT 59601-5014, (406)443-7272
Alternative Investment Mgt. Assn. [IO], London, United Kingdom
Alternative Investment Mgt. Assn. - Australia [IO], Sydney, Australia
Alternative Investment Mgt. Assn. - Cayman Chap. [IO], Grand Cayman, Cayman Islands
Alternative Investment Mgt. Assn. - Japan [IO], Tokyo, Japan
Alternative Investments Compliance Assn. [2127], 3 Park Ave., 14th Fl., New York, NY 10016, (212)515-2800

Alternative Lifestyles
Everyday Ayurveda [13645]
Hanuman Found. [12208]

Alternative Medicine
Acupuncture for Veterans [13576]
Alexander Technique Intl. [13646]
Alexander Technique Intl. [13646]
Alliance for Addiction Solutions [15561]
Alliance for Biotherapies [16831]
Alliance of Intl. Aromatherapists [13647]
Alliance for Massage Therapy Educ. [8560]
Alternative Medicine Intl. [13648]
Amer. Abdominal Acupuncture Medical Assn. [13578]
Amer. Acad. of Acupuncture and Oriental Medicine [13649]
Amer. Alternative Medical Assn. [13650]
Amer. Apitherapy Soc. [13651]
Amer. Assn. of Drugless Practitioners [13652]
Amer. Assn. of Naturopathic Midwives [15530]
Amer. Assn. of Traditional Chinese Veterinary Medicine [13653]
Amer. Bd. of Integrative Holistic Medicine [14991]
Amer. Bd. of Oriental Reproductive Medicine [16595]
Amer. Center for the Alexander Technique [13654]
Amer. Commn. for Accreditation of Reflexology Educ. and Training [7726]
Amer. Herbal Pharmacopoeia [13655]
Amer. Herbalists Guild [14989]
Amer. Manual Medicine Assn. [13656]
Amer. Osteopathic Assn. of Medical Informatics [16065]
Amer. Polarity Therapy Assn. [13657]
Amer. Reflexology Certification Bd. [13658]
Amer. Reiki Master Assn. [13659]
Amer. Soc. for the Alexander Technique [13660]
Amer. Soc. of Alternative Therapists [13661]
Anahata Intl. [13662]
Angel Harps [16454]
Aromatherapy Registration Coun. [13663]
Art Therapy Connection [13772]
Assn. of Ayurvedic Professionals of North Am. [13664]
Assn. for Catholic Chiropractors [14121]
Assn. for Holotropic Breathwork Intl. [13665]
Assn. for Network Care [13666]
Attunement Guild [13667]
Be Healthy [13668]
Breathecure [13669]
Chiropractic Diplomatic Corps [14125]
Chiropractic Orthopedists of North Am. [14126]
Citizens for Hea. [13670]
Citizens for Hea. [13670]
Commn. on Religious Counseling and Healing [19289]
Commn. on Religious Counseling and Healing [19289]
Community Acupuncture Network [13579]
Complementary and Alternative Medicine Initiative [13671]
Coun. for Acupuncture Res. and Educ. [13580]
Coun. of Chiropractic Acupuncture [14128]
Coun. on Chiropractic Guidelines and Practice Parameters [14130]
Coun. on Chiropractic Practice [14132]
Coun. for Healing [13672]
Councils on Chiropractic Educ. Intl. [7849]
Craniosacral Therapy Assn. of the UK [10385]
Creative Children Therapy [16846]
Dinshah Hea. Soc. [13673]
Dinshah Hea. Soc. [13673]
Emergency Response Massage Intl. [15266]
Energy Kinesiology Assn. [13674]
Energy Kinesiology Awareness Coun. [13675]
Father Josef's Method of Reflexology [13676]
Feldenkrais Guild of North Am. [9834]
Friends of Hea. [13677]
Gerson Inst. [13678]
Global Initiative for the Advancement of Nutritional Therapy [16851]
Global Natural Hea. Alliance [13679]
Guild for Structural Integration [13680]
HALTER, Inc. [16852]
HealingWorks [13681]
Holistic Mentorship Network [14998]
Holistic Pediatric Assn. [13682]
Hospital-Based Massage Network [15267]
Imagery Intl. [15073]
Inst. for Traditional Medicine and Preventive Hea. Care [13683]
Inst. for Traditional Medicine and Preventive Hea. Care [13683]
Intl. Alliance of Professional Hypnotists [15089]
Intl. Aromatherapy and Herb Assn. [13684]
Intl. Aromatherapy and Herb Assn. [13684]
Intl. Assn. of Attunement Practitioners [13685]
Intl. Assn. of Medical and Therapeutic Specialists [13686]
Intl. Assn. of Reiki Professionals [13687]
Intl. Assn. of Reiki Professionals [13687]
Intl. Assn. of Structural Integrators [13688]
Intl. Assn. of Structural Integrators [13688]AlternativeIntl. Found. of Bio-Magnetics
Intl. Holistic Practitioner Assn. [13689]
Intl. Meta-Medicine Assn. [13690]
Intl. Soc. for Ayurveda and Hea. [13691]
Intl. Soc. for Complementary Medicine Res. [13692]
Intl. Soc. for Complementary Medicine Res. [13692]
Journey to Solidarity [14139]
Kate's Voice [8764]
Mindful Medicine Worldwide [13693]
Mindful Medicine Worldwide [13693]
Music Therapy for Healing [16467]
Natl. Assn. of Certified Professionals of Equine Therapy [13694]
Natl. Ayurvedic Medical Assn. [13695]
Natl. Center for Complementary and Alternative Medicine [13696]
Natl. Qigong Chi Kung Assn. [13697]
Natl. Spiritualist Assn. of Churches I Healers League [20145]
Naturopathic Medical Student Assn. [15535]
Naturopathic Medicine for Global Hea. [15536]
Naturopathic Physicians Bd. of Aesthetic Medicine [15537]
Non-Profit Chiropractic Org. [14142]
North Amer. Studio Alliance [13698]
North Amer. Tang Shou Tao Assn. [13699]
Oncology Assn. of Naturopathic Physicians [15539]
Pediatric Assn. of Naturopathic Physicians [8681]
Physicians' Assn. for Anthroposophic Medicine [13700]
Professional Football Chiropractic [14143]
A Promise of Hea. [14827]
Qigong Alliance Intl. [13701]
QiGong Res. Soc. [13702]
The Radiance Technique Intl. Assn. [13703]

A star before a book entry number signifies that the name is not listed separately, but is mentioned within the entry.

The Radiance Technique Intl. Assn. [13703]
Radix Inst. [13704]
Reflexology Assn. of Am. [13705]
Reflexology Assn. of Am. [13705]
Reiki Alliance [13706]
Reiki Alliance [13706]
Reiki Educ. [16580]
Reiki Rays of Hope for Caregivers [13707]
Rolf Inst. of Structural Integration [13708]
Shelter Animal Reiki Assn. [16581]
Shibumi Intl. Reiki Assn. [16582]
Shine Therapy [15274]
Silver Age Yoga [17138]
Soc. for Animal Homeopathy [15023]
Soc. of Ortho-Bionomy Intl. [13709]
Soc. of Ortho-Bionomy Intl. [13709]
Soc. for Orthomolecular Hea. Medicine [13710]
Sound Healers Assn. [13711]
Surfing Medicine Intl. [13712]
Touch for Hea. Kinesiology Assn. [13713]
Touch of Relief [15004]
Traditional Chinese Medicine Assn. and Alumni [13714]
Unite for HER [13989]
United Plant Savers [13715]
United Plant Savers [13715]
U.S. Trager Assn. [13716]
Upledger Inst. [13717]
Veterinary Botanical Medicine Assn. [17046]
Visionary Alternatives [13718]
World Fed. of Therapeutic Communities [13719]
World Sound Healing Org. [12640]
Worldwide Aquatic Bodywork Assn. [13720]
Yoga Bear [13721]
ZY Qigong [13722]
Alternative Medicine Intl. [13648], 7639 Houghton Rd., Bakersfield, CA 93313, (661)330-2828
Alternative Press Center [10472], PO Box 47739, Chicago, IL 60647, (312)451-8133
Alternative Religions Educational Network [20148], PO Box 1893, Trenton, FL 32693, (321)243-2337
Alternative Sources of Energy - Defunct.

Alternative Technology
Advanced Biofuels Assn. [1533]
Advanced Biofuels USA [6108]
Algal Biomass Org. [6680]
Alliance for Green Heat [6682]
Alliance for Renewable Energy [6683]
Amer. Biogas Coun. [6109]
Amer. Solar Action Plan [7437]
Assn. of Certified Green Tech. Auditors [6692]
Biomass Power Assn. [7292]
Biomass Thermal Energy Coun. [6697]
Citizens for Affordable Energy [6701]
Clean Economy Network [6605]
Clean Tech. Trade Alliance [6110]
ClimateTalk Alliance [6111]
Distributed Wind Energy Assn. [3666]
EarthSpark Intl. [6711]
Electrification Coalition [3510]
Elephant Energy [6715]
Energy Extraction Technologies [6718]
Energy Farm [6719]
Energy Vision [6724]
Focus the Nation [17616]
FutureGen Alliance [6112]
Global Biofuels Alliance [1535]
GreenMotion [4227]
Growth Energy [6728]
HeatGreen Coun. [6113]
Hydrogen 2000 [6729]
Innovation: Africa [6114]
Intl. Biochar Initiative [6115]
Intl. Biochar Initiative [6115]
Intl. DME Assn. [3770]
Intl. DME Assn. [3770]
Intl. Green Energy Coun. [6116]
Light Elec. Vehicle Assn. [3518]
Natl. Algae Assn. [6117]
New Fuels Alliance [6885]
New Generation Energy [6743]
Plug In Am. [6118]
Power to the People [7440]
Quantal Energy [8121]
Renewable Energy for Medicine and Educ. [6749]

Renewable Energy Resources [6750]
Rural Renewable Energy Alliance [6754]
Seventh Generation Advisors [4304]
Show Me Solar [7443]
Solar Household Energy [4931]
Strategic Energy, Environmental and Trans. Alternatives [8122]
Sustainable Biomaterials Collaborative [6119]
Sweet Sorghum Ethanol Assn. [6120]
U.S. Water and Power [6121]
Vote Solar Initiative [7451]
Waste-to-Energy Res. and Tech. Coun. [7593]
The Wind Alliance [7624]
Alternative Tech. Assn. [IO], Melbourne, Australia
Alternative World Org. [★18167]
Alternative World Org. [★18167]
Alternatives to Abortion [★12931]
Alternatives to Abortion [★12931]
Alternatives to Abortion/Women's Hea. and Educ. Found. [★12931]
Alternatives to Abortion/Women's Hea. and Educ. Found. [★12931]
Alternatives, Action and Commun. Network for Intl. Development [IO], Montreal, QC, Canada
Alternatives to Marriage Proj. [18087], 358 7th Ave., PMB 131, Brooklyn, NY 11215, (347)987-1068
Alternatives to Marriage Proj. [18087], 358 7th Ave., PMB 131, Brooklyn, NY 11215, (347)987-1068
Alternatives in Publication Task Force [★9956]
Alternatives, Reseau d'Action et de Commun. pour le Developpement Intl. [★IO]
Alternatives for Simple Living - Address unknown since 2011.
Altrusa Intl. [13050], 332 S Michigan Ave., Ste. 1123, Chicago, IL 60604, (312)427-4410
Altrusa Intl. [13050], 332 S Michigan Ave., Ste. 1123, Chicago, IL 60604, (312)427-4410
Aluminium Assn. of India [IO], Bangalore, India
Aluminium Extruders Assn. [IO], West Bromwich, United Kingdom
Aluminium Fed. [IO], West Bromwich, United Kingdom
Aluminium Packaging Recycling Org. [IO], Redditch, United Kingdom
Aluminium Powder and Paste Assn. [IO], Birmingham, United Kingdom
Aluminium Primary Producers Assn. [IO], West Bromwich, United Kingdom
Aluminium Rolled Products Mfrs. Assn. [IO], West Bromwich, United Kingdom
Aluminium Stockholders Assn. [IO], Birmingham, United Kingdom
Aluminium Verband Schweiz [★IO]
Aluminum Anodizers Coun. [786], 1000 N Rand Rd., No. 214, Wauconda, IL 60084, (847)526-2010
Aluminum Assn. [2460], 1525 Wilson Blvd., Ste. 600, Arlington, VA 22209, (703)358-2967
Aluminum Extruders Coun. [2461], 1000 N Rand Rd., Ste. 214, Wauconda, IL 60084, (847)526-2010
Aluminum Foil Container Mfrs. Assn. [870], 10 Vecilla Ln., Hot Springs Village, AR 71909, (501)922-7425
Aluminum Recycling Assn. - Defunct.
Aluminum Siding Assn. [★518]
Aluminum Wares Assn. [★1776]
Aluminum Window Mfrs. Assn. [★518]
Aluminum Workers of Am. [★23256]

Alumni
129th Alumni and Heritage Assn. [19270]
146th Alumni Assn. [7727]
Alumni Assn., Framingham State Coll. [18848]
Alumni Assn. of the Universidad del Valle [18849]
Alumni Assn. of the Univ. of Michigan [18850]
Angelo State Univ. Alumni Assn. [18851]
Assn. of Graduates of the U.S. Air Force Acad. [18852]
Astronaut Scholars Honor Soc. [23629]
Auburn Univ. Montgomery Alumni Assn. [18853]
Benedict Coll. Natl. Alumni Soc. [18854]
Bethune-Cookman Coll. Natl. Alumni Assn. [18855]
Brandeis Univ. Alumni Assn. [18856]
Brooklyn Coll. of the City Univ. of New York Alumni Assn. [18857]
Cal State San Marcos Alumni Assn. [18858]

California Coll. of the Arts and Crafts Alumni Assn. [18859]
California State Univ. I Northridge Alumni Assn. [18860]
Catholic Alumni Clubs Intl. [18861]
Catholic Alumni Clubs Intl. [18861]
Centenary Coll. of Louisiana Alumni Assn. [18862]
Coastal Carolina Univ. Alumni Assn. [18863]
Coll. for Creative Stud. Alumni Assn. [18864]
Coll. of St. Scholastica Alumni Assn. [18865]
Colorado Christian Univ. Alumni Assn. [18866]
Columbia Coll. of Nursing Alumni Assn. [18867]
Coun. of Alumni Marketing and Membership Professionals [2397]
Defense Intel Alumni Assn. [18868]
D'Youville Coll. Alumni Assn. [18869]
Emerson Coll. Alumni Assn. [18870]
Erskine Alumni Assn. [18871]
Excelsior Coll. Alumni Assn. [18872]
Gallaudet Univ. Alumni Assn. [18873]
Hope Intl. Univ. Alumni Assn. [18874]
Indiana State Univ. Alumni Assn. [18875]
Intl. Alumni Assn. of Shri Mahavir Jain Vidyalaya [19219]
Iowa Wesleyan Coll. Alumni Assn. [18876]
Jackson State Univ. Natl. Alumni Assn. [18877]
Kent State Univ. Alumni Assn. [18878]
Keuka Coll. Alumni Assn. [18879]
Lawrence Technological Univ. Alumni Assn. [18880]
LDS Bus. Coll. Alumni Assn. [18881]
Lincoln Univ. Alumni Assn. [18882]
Long Island Univ. - Southampton Coll. Alumni Assn. [18883]
Marquette Univ. Alumni Assn. [18884]
Montreat Coll. Alumni Assn. [18885]
Mt. Marty Coll. Alumni Assn. [18886]
Nebraska Christian Coll. Alumni Assn. [18887]
Network of Gay and Lesbian Alumni/ae Associations [18888]
North Dakota State Univ. Alumni Assn. [18889]
Northern Michigan Univ. Alumni Assn. [18890]
Northwest Nazarene Univ. Alumni Assn. [18891]
Oklahoma Baptist Univ. Alumni Assn. [18892]
Oklahoma City Univ. Alumni Off. [18893]
Oklahoma Univ. Alumni Assn. [18894]
Ouachita Baptist Univ. Alumni Assn. [18895]
Prescott Coll. Alumni Assn. [18896]
St. Mary's Coll. of California Alumni Assn. [18897]
Southern Connecticut State Univ. Alumni Assn. [18898]
Spalding Univ. Alumni Assn. [18899]
Stanford Chicano/Latino Alumni Assn. [18900]
Texas A&M Univ. - Commerce Alumni Assn. [18901]
Tufts Univ. Alumni Assn. [18902]
UERMMMC Nursing Alumni Assn. U.S.A. [18903]
United Negro Coll. Fund I Natl. Alumni Coun. [18904]
Univ. of Alaska Fairbanks Alumni Assn. [18905]
Univ. of Iowa Alumni Assn. [18906]
Univ. of Louisville Alumni Assn. [18907]
Univ. of Mary Alumni Assn. [18908]
Univ. of Minnesota - Crookston Alumni Assn. [18909]
Univ. of South Dakota Alumni Assn. [18910]
Univ. of Texas at Brownsville and Texas Southmost Coll. Alumni Assn. [18911]
Univ. of Texas I Pan-American Alumni Assn. [18912]
Univ. of Wisconsin I Eau Claire Alumni Assn. [18913]
Washburn Alumni Assn. [18914]
Wellesley Coll. Alumnae Assn. [18915]
Western New Mexico Univ. Alumni Assn. [18916]
William Penn Univ. Alumni Assn. [18917]
Wofford Coll. Natl. Alumni Assn. [18918]
Worcester Polytechnic Inst. Alumni Assn. [18919]
Alumni Assn., Framingham State Coll. [18848], PO Box 9101, Framingham, MA 01701-9101, (508)626-4035
Alumni Assn. of Regents Coll. [★18872]
Alumni Assn. of the Universidad del Valle [18849], 4712 Richland Ave., Metairie, LA 70002, (504)842-3930

Reference to "IO" in place of a book number signifies that the association may be found in the 50th edition of International Organizations.

Alumni Assn. of the Univ. of Michigan [18850], 200 Fletcher St., Ann Arbor, MI 48109-1007, (734)764-0384

Alveolar Capillary Dysplasia Assn. [13837], Steve Hanson, Co-Exec. Dir., 5902 Marcie Ct., Garland, TX 75044-4958

Alvis Owner Club [IO], Wokingham, United Kingdom

Always Patsy Cline World Wide Fan Org. [23812], PO Box 462, Joelton, TN 37080

Alzheimer Angehorige Austria [IO], Vienna, Austria

Alzheimer Europe [IO], Luxembourg, Luxembourg

Alzheimer Keskusliitto [IO], Helsinki, Finland

Alzheimer Nederland [IO], Bunnik, Netherlands

Alzheimer Scotland-Action on Dementia [IO], Edinburgh, United Kingdom

Alzheimer Soc. of Alberta and Northwest Territories [IO], Edmonton, AB, Canada

Alzheimer Soc. of Canada [IO], Toronto, ON, Canada

Alzheimer Soc. of Ireland [IO], Dublin, Ireland

Alzheimerforeningen [IO], Hellerup, Denmark

Alzheimerforeningen i Sverige [IO], Lund, Sweden

Alzheimer's Assn. [13723], 225 N Michigan Ave., 17th Fl., Chicago, IL 60601-7633, (312)335-8700

Alzheimer's Assn. Japan [IO], Kyoto, Japan

Alzheimer's Australia [IO], Hawker, Australia

Alzheimer's Australia Australian Capital Territory [IO], Kaleen, Australia

Alzheimer's Australia Central Queensland [IO], Rockhampton, Australia

Alzheimer's Australia Darling Downs and South West [IO], Toowoomba, Australia

Alzheimer's Australia Gold Coast [IO], Arundel, Australia

Alzheimer's Australia North Queensland [IO], Thuringowa Central, Australia

Alzheimer's Australia Northern Territory [IO], Darwin, Australia

Alzheimer's Australia NSW [IO], North Ryde, Australia

Alzheimer's Australia South Australia [IO], Glenside, Australia

Alzheimer's Australia Sunshine Coast [IO], Kuluin, Australia

Alzheimer's Australia Victoria [IO], Hawthorn, Australia

Alzheimer's Australia WA - Albany Regional Off. [IO], Albany, Australia

Alzheimer's Australia WA - Bunbury Br. [IO], Bunbury, Australia

Alzheimer's Australia WA - Kalgoorlie Regional Off. [IO], Kalgoorlie, Australia

Alzheimer's Australia WA - Mandurah Regional Off. [IO], Mandurah, Australia

Alzheimer's Australia WA - Rockingham Br. [IO], Rockingham, Australia

Alzheimer's Australia WA - York Regional Off. [IO], York, Australia

Alzheimer's Australia Western Australia [IO], Subiaco, Australia

Alzheimer's Disease
Alzheimer Nederland [16022]
Alzheimer Scotland-Action on Dementia [22]
Alzheimer Soc. of Ireland [598]
Alzheimerforeningen i Sverige [5306]
Alzheimer's Assn. [13723]
Alzheimer's Australia NSW [18686]
Alzheimer's Found. of Am. [13724]
Alzheimer's and Related Disorders Soc. of India [16122]
Alzheimer's Soc. [23]
Fundacion Alzheimer Espana [6651]
Hong Kong Alzheimer's Disease Assn. [13042]Alzheimer'sSpanish Confed. of Family Alzheimer Associations

Alzheimer's Disease Assn. of Nigeria [IO], Nnewi, Nigeria

Alzheimer's Disease Assn. of the Philippines [IO], Quezon City, Philippines

Alzheimer's Disease Assn. Singapore [IO], Singapore, Singapore

Alzheimer's Disease Found. Malaysia [IO], Petaling Jaya, Malaysia

Alzheimer's Disease Intl. [IO], London, United Kingdom

Alzheimer's Disease and Related Disorders Assn. [★13723]

Alzheimer's Disease Soc. [★23]

Alzheimer's Found. of Am. [13724], 322 Eighth Ave., 7th Fl., New York, NY 10001, (866)232-8484

Alzheimer's NZ [IO], Wellington, New Zealand

Alzheimer's Pakistan [IO], Lahore, Pakistan

Alzheimer's and Related Disorders Soc. of India [IO], Kunnamkulam, India

Alzheimer's Soc. [IO], London, United Kingdom

Am Cham Cuba [★23346]

AM/FM Intl. [★6535]

Amalgamated Assn. of St., Elec. Railway and Motor Coach Employees of Am. [★23300]

Amalgamated Meat Cutters and Bucher Workmen of North Am. [★23191]

Amalgamated Printers' Assn. [1635], Phillip Driscoll, Sec., 135 East Church St., Clinton, MI 49236

Amalgamated Printers' Assn. [1635], Phillip Driscoll, Sec., 135 East Church St., Clinton, MI 49236

Amalgamated Transit Union [23300], 5025 Wisconsin Ave. NW, Washington, DC 20016, (202)537-1645

Amara Conservation [5022], 1531 Packard St., No. 12, Ann Arbor, MI 48104, (734)761-5357

Amarun Org. [3986], 9505 Seany Dr., Leland, NC 28451, (910)508-3630

Amaryllis Res. Inst. [★6356]

Amaryllis Res. Inst. [★6356]

Amateur Astronomers Assn. [6220], PO Box 150253, Brooklyn, NY 11215, (212)535-2922

Amateur Astronomers Assn. of New York City [★6220]

Amateur Astronomers, Inc. [20975], PO Box 111, Garwood, NJ 07027-0111, (908)241-2843

Amateur Athletes Intl. - Defunct.

Amateur Athletic Assn. of Barbados [IO], Bridgetown, Barbados

Amateur Athletic Assn. of Cyprus [IO], Nicosia, Cyprus

Amateur Athletic Fed. of Iran [IO], Tehran, Iran

Amateur Athletic Fed. of Turkmenistan [IO], Ashgabat, Turkmenistan

Amateur Athletic Union [22960], PO Box 22409, Lake Buena Vista, FL 32830-2409, (407)934-7200

Amateur Baseball Assn. of Thailand [IO], Ayutthaya, Thailand

Amateur Baseball Umpires' Assn. [22261], 200 S Wilcox St., No. 508, Castle Rock, CO 80104, (303)290-7411

Amateur Basketball Assn. of the U.S.A. [★22302]

Amateur Bicycle League of Am. [★22489]

Amateur Boxing Assn. of England [IO], Sheffield, United Kingdom

Amateur Chamber Music Players [★10133]

Amateur Chamber Music Players [★10133]

Amateur Entomologists' Soc. [IO], London, United Kingdom

Amateur Fencers League of Amer. [★22565]

Amateur Field Trial Clubs of Am. [21480], Mrs. Linda Hunt, Sec.-Treas., 1300 Tripp Rd., Somerville, TN 38068, (901)465-1556

Amateur Fisherman's Assn. of the Northern Territory [IO], Casuarina, Australia

Amateur Hockey Assn. of the U.S. [★22647]

Amateur Motorcycle Assn. [IO], Cannock, United Kingdom

Amateur Organists and Keyboard Assn. Intl. - Defunct.

Amateur Radio
ACB Radio Amateurs [20930]
Amer. Radio Relay League [20931]
Amer. Shortwave Listeners Club [20932]
ARRL Found. [20933]
Assn. of Clandestine Radio Enthusiasts [20934]
Collins Collectors Assn. [20935]AmateurFriends of Radio for Peace Intl.
Intl. Amateur Radio Union [20936]
Intl. Radio Club of Am. [20937]
Longwave Club of Am. [20938]
New Zealand Assn. of Radio Transmitters [19252]
No-Code Intl. [20939]
North Amer. Radio Archives [22120]
North Amer. Shortwave Assn. [20940]
Old Old Timers Club [20941]

Quarter Century Wireless Assn. [20942]
Worldwide Television-FM DX Assn. [20943]
Worldwide Television-FM DX Assn. [20943]

Amateur Radio Lighthouse Soc. [9662], 114 Woodbine Ave., Merchantville, NJ 08109

Amateur Radio Soc. of India [IO], Mumbai, India

Amateur Radio Soc. of Kenya [IO], Nairobi, Kenya

Amateur Rose Breeders Assn. [IO], Northampton, United Kingdom

Amateur Ski Instructors Assn. [22906], 28 Park Dr., Woodstock, NY 12498-1726, (845)679-4609

Amateur Softball Assn. of Am. [22950], 2801 NE 50th St., Oklahoma City, OK 73111, (405)424-5266

Amateur SpeedSkating Union of the U.S. [★22903]

Amateur SpeedSkating Union of the U.S. - Defunct.

Amateur Swimming Assn. [IO], Loughborough, United Kingdom

Amateur Trapshooting Assn. [22871], 601 W Natl. Rd., Vandalia, OH 45377, (937)898-4638

Amateur Yacht Res. Soc. [IO], London, United Kingdom

AmateurJudo Assn. [★22706]

Amateurs Radio Republic of San Marino [IO], San Marino, San Marino

Amatorteaterns Riksforbund [★IO]

Amaury Sport Org. [IO], Issy-les-Moulineaux, France

Amazigh Cultural Assn. in Am. [9091], PO Box 3371, Lisle, IL 60532-8371

Amazon Conservation Assn. [3987], 1822 R St. NW, 4th Fl., Washington, DC 20009, (202)234-2356

Amazon Conservation Team Suriname [IO], Paramaribo, Suriname

Amazon Promise [16162], PO Box 1304, Newburyport, MA 01950, (800)775-5704

Amazon Watch [3988], 221 Pine St., 4th Fl., San Francisco, CA 94104, (415)487-9600

Amazona Guildingii
Population Rsrc. Center [12708]

Amazonas Hope for Hea. [14747], Dr. Ruth A. Hayes, Treas., 15 Peterson Pl., Wilmington, OH 45177, (937)383-3382

Amazone [IO], Brussels, Belgium

Ambassador Programs [★17982]

Ambassador Programs [★17982]

Ambassadors for Children [11447], 7399 N Shadeland Ave., No. 116, Indianapolis, IN 46250, (317)660-1135

Ambassadors for Friendship [★17967]

Ambassadors for Friendship [★17967]

Ambassadors for Sustained Hea. [14748], 3 Petrel St., West Roxbury, MA 02132, (646)481-0844

Ambrose Monell Found. [13124], 1 Rockefeller Plz., Ste. 301, New York, NY 10020-2002, (212)586-0700

Ambrose Monell Found. [13124], 1 Rockefeller Plz., Ste. 301, New York, NY 10020-2002, (212)586-0700

AMBUCS [13051], PO Box 5127, High Point, NC 27262, (800)838-1845

Ambulance Services; Commn. on Accreditation of [13572]

Ambulatory Behavioral Healthcare; Assn. for [16335]

Ambulatory Care
Accreditation Assn. for Ambulatory Hea. Care [13725]
Amer. Acad. of Urgent Care Medicine [13726]
Natl. Assn. for Ambulatory Urgent Care [13727]
North Amer. Primary Care Res. Gp. [13728]
Urgent Care Assn. of Am. [13729]

Ambulatory Care Nursing; Amer. Acad. of [15701]

Ambulatory Pediatric Assn. [★16137]

Ambulatory Surgery Center Assn. [16789], 1012 Cameron St., Alexandria, VA 22314, (703)836-8808

AMC Inst. [261], 100 N 20th St., 4th Fl., Philadelphia, PA 19103-1443, (215)564-3484

AMC Inst. [261], 100 N 20th St., 4th Fl., Philadelphia, PA 19103-1443, (215)564-3484

AMC Rambler Club [20986], 6 Murolo Rd., North Grosvenordale, CT 06255-1814, (860)923-0485

AMC Rambler Club [20986], 6 Murolo Rd., North Grosvenordale, CT 06255-1814, (860)923-0485

AMCHA, the Natl. Israeli Centre for Psychosocial Support of Holocaust Survivors and the Second Generation [IO], Jerusalem, Israel

---

A star before a book entry number signifies that the name is not listed separately, but is mentioned within the entry.

Amcot, Inc. **[3946]**, PO Box 2827, Lubbock, TX 79408, (806)763-8011

AME Assn. Atlantic **[IO]**, Fredericton, NB, Canada

Amegroid
   Amegroid Soc. of Am. **[9108]**

Amegroid Soc. of Am. **[9108]**, 5432 Price Ave., Baltimore, MD 21215, (410)367-5308

Ameinu **[19086]**, 114 W 26th St., Ste. 1005, New York, NY 10001, (212)366-1194

AMEND - Address unknown since 2011.

AMER Medical Div., Amer. Near East Refugee Aid - Defunct.

Amerasians for Intl. Aid and Adoption **[★11372]**

Am. Abroad Media **[18089]**, 1020 19th St. NW, Ste. 650, Washington, DC 20036, (202)457-8050

Am. the Beautiful Fund **[4236]**, 725 15th St. NW, Ste. 605, Washington, DC 20005-6093, (202)638-1649

Am. Bikes **[11131]**, 1612 K St. NW, Ste. 802, Washington, DC 20006, (202)223-3726

Am. in Bloom **[3971]**, 2130 Stella Ct., Columbus, OH 43215-1033, (614)487-1117

Am. Bus. Conf. **[1062]**, 1828 L St. NW, Ste. 908, Washington, DC 20036, (202)822-9300

Am. Celiac Soc. **[★15817]**

Am. Continental 2000 **[11847]**, PO Box 771753, Coral Springs, FL 33077, (800)435-7352

Am. Coun. on Educ., Off. of Minorities in Higher Educ. **[★8629]**

America-Georgia Bus. Coun. **[2092]**, 2300 M St. NW, Ste. 800, Washington, DC 20037, (202)416-1606

America-Georgia Bus. Coun. **[2092]**, 2300 M St. NW, Ste. 800, Washington, DC 20037, (202)416-1606

Am. Individual and Gp. Home Hea. Care Assn. **[★12157]**

America-Israel Coun. for Israeli-Palestinian Peace **[18111]**, 224 Lake Dr., Kensington, CA 94708-1132, (510)526-8449

America-Israel Cultural Found. **[9895]**, 1140 Broadway, Ste. No. 304, New York, NY 10001, (212)557-1600

America-Israel Cultural Found. **[9895]**, 1140 Broadway, Ste. No. 304, New York, NY 10001, (212)557-1600

America-Israel Friendship League **[9896]**, 134 E 39th St., New York, NY 10016, (212)213-8630

America-Israel Soc. **[★9895]**

America-Israel Soc. **[★9895]**

America-MidEast Educational and Training Services **[18112]**, 1730 M St. NW, Ste. 1100, Washington, DC 20036, (202)776-9600

America-MidEast Educational and Training Services **[18112]**, 1730 M St. NW, Ste. 1100, Washington, DC 20036, (202)776-9600

Am. on the Move Found. **[14693]**, 13001 E 17th Pl., Campus Box C263, Aurora, CO 80045

Am. Outdoors Assn. **[22835]**, PO Box 10847, Knoxville, TN 37939, (865)558-3595

Am. Scores **[22931]**, 520 8th Ave., 11th Fl., New York, NY 10018, (212)868-9510

Am. Sings! **[10135]**, 904 Polaris Way, Missoula, MT 59803, (800)372-1222

Am. Walks **[18775]**, PO Box 2834, Alexandria, VA 22301, (703)738-4889

Am. World Adoption Assn. **[10778]**, 6723 Whittier Ave., Ste. 202, McLean, VA 22101, (703)356-8447

Am. World Adoption Assn. **[10778]**, 6723 Whittier Ave., Ste. 202, McLean, VA 22101, (703)356-8447

Americal Div. Veterans Assn. **[20853]**, Mr. Roger Gilmore, Natl. Adjutant, PO Box 830662, Richardson, TX 75080

American
   Alliance for Amer. Mfg. **[2325]**
   Alliance for a Sustainable U.S.A. **[10895]**
   Amer. Civil Liberties Union **[17260]**
   Amer. Coun. on Consumer Interests **[17442]**
   Amer. Patriots Assn. **[20742]**
   Amer. Stud. Assn. **[9109]**
   Americans for Peace Now **[18010]**
   Armenian Amer. Chamber of Commerce **[23352]**
   Assn. of Concerned African Scholars **[17147]**
   Australian New Zealand - Amer. Chambers of Commerce **[23339]**

Bridges of Understanding **[17938]**
Center for Constitutional Rights **[17273]**
Common Dreams **[17177]**
Confederate Memorial Assn. **[9110]**
Confederate Memorial Literary Soc. **[9761]**
Congressional Automotive Caucus **[17410]**
The Conservative Caucus **[17420]**
Coun. for Amer. Students in Intl. Negotiations **[8386]**
English in Action **[17964]**
Freedom Alliance **[9111]**
Friends of the Amer. Museum in Britain/Halcyon Found. **[9112]**
Friends of the Amer. Museum in Britain/Halcyon Found. **[9112]**
Hall of Fame for Great Americans **[10665]**
The Hospitality and Info. Ser. **[17973]**
Irish Amer. Unity Conf. **[18009]**
Laotian Amer. Soc. **[19102]**
Lebanese Amer. Coun. for Democracy **[18069]**
Natl. Center for Constitutional Stud. **[17440]**
Natl. Comm. for an Effective Cong. **[17413]**
Natl. Day of the Cowboy **[9124]**
Nepali Amer. Friendship Assn. **[19172]**
Pakistan Chamber of Commerce USA **[23435]**
Partners for Rural Am. **[18574]**
Peace Alliance **[18272]**
People for the Amer. Way **[17317]**
People's Medical Soc. **[17768]**
Polish Amer. Golf Assn. **[22620]**
Polish-American-Jewish Alliance for Youth Action **[13551]**
Sedgwick Soc. **[10738]**
Soc. of Early Americanists **[9113]**
Turkish-American Chamber of Commerce and Indus. **[23455]**
Twelve Lights League **[18073]**
Ugandan North Amer. Assn. **[18841]**
U.S. Assn. of Former Members of Cong. **[17414]**
Young America's Found. **[17432]**

Amer. Abdominal Acupuncture Medical Assn. **[13578]**, 41790 Winchester Rd., Ste. B, Temecula, CA 92590, (951)296-1688

Amer. Aberdeen-Angus Breeder's Assn. **[★3865]**

Amer. Abstract Artists **[9218]**, PO Box 1076, New York, NY 10013

Amer. Acad. of Actuaries **[1923]**, 1850 M St. NW, Ste. 300, Washington, DC 20036, (202)223-8196

Amer. Acad. of Acupuncture and Oriental Medicine **[13649]**, 1925 W County Rd. B2, Roseville, MN 55113, (651)631-0204

Amer. Acad. of Addiction Psychiatry **[16316]**, 400 Massasoit Ave., Ste. 307, East Providence, RI 02914, (401)524-3076

Amer. Acad. of Adoption Attorneys **[5222]**, PO Box 33053, Washington, DC 20033, (202)832-2222

Amer. Acad. of Advt. **[7693]**, 24710 Shaker Blvd., Beachwood, OH 44122, (786)393-3333

Amer. Acad. of Algology **[★16093]**

Amer. Acad. of Allergy, Asthma and Immunology **[13632]**, 555 E Wells St., Ste. 1100, Milwaukee, WI 53202-3823, (414)272-6071

Amer. Acad. of Ambulatory Care **[★13726]**

Amer. Acad. of Ambulatory Care Nursing **[15701]**, PO Box 56, Pitman, NJ 08071-0056, (856)256-2350

Amer. Acad. of Ambulatory Nursing Admin. **[★15701]**

Amer. Acad. of Anesthesiologist Assistants **[13733]**, 2209 Dickens Rd., Richmond, VA 23230-2005, (804)565-6353

Amer. Acad. of Anti-Aging Medicine **[15363]**, 1510 W Montana St., Chicago, IL 60614, (773)528-1000

Amer. Acad. of Appellate Lawyers **[5223]**, 9707 Key West Ave., Ste. 100, Rockville, MD 20850, (240)404-6498

Amer. Acad. of Arts and Letters **[9841]**, 633 W 155 St., New York, NY 10032, (212)368-5900

Amer. Acad. of Arts and Sciences **[9328]**, 136 Irving St., Cambridge, MA 02138, (617)576-5000

Amer. Acad. of Audiology **[16679]**, 11730 Plaza Am. Dr., Ste. 300, Reston, VA 20190, (703)790-8466

Amer. Acad. for Cerebral Palsy **[★15562]**

Amer. Acad. for Cerebral Palsy and Developmental Medicine **[15562]**, 555 E Wells St., Ste. 1100, Milwaukee, WI 53202, (414)918-3014

Amer. Acad. of Child and Adolescent Psychiatry **[16317]**, 3615 Wisconsin Ave. NW, Washington, DC 20016-3007, (202)966-7300

Amer. Acad. of Child Psychiatry **[★16317]**

Amer. Acad. of Cleft Palate Prosthesis **[★14190]**

Amer. Acad. of Clinical Neurophysiology **[★15643]**

Amer. Acad. of Clinical Neuropsychology **[15643]**, Univ. of Michigan Hea. Sys., Dept. of Psychiatry, 1500 E Medical Center Dr., SPC 5295, Ann Arbor, MI 48109-5295, (734)936-8269

Amer. Acad. of Clinical Psychiatrists **[16318]**, PO Box 458, Glastonbury, CT 06033, (860)635-5533

Amer. Acad. of Clinical Toxicology **[16890]**, 110 W Lancaster Ave., Ste. 230, Wayne, PA 19087, (703)556-9222

Amer. Acad. on Commun. in Healthcare **[16247]**, 16020 Swingley Ridge Rd., Ste. 300, Chesterfield, MO 63017, (636)449-5080

Amer. Acad. of Cosmetic Dentistry **[14229]**, 402 W Wilson St., Madison, WI 53703, (608)222-8583

Amer. Acad. of Cosmetic Surgery **[14169]**, 737 N Michigan Ave., Ste. 2100, Chicago, IL 60611-5641, (312)981-6760

Amer. Acad. of Counseling Psychology - Address unknown since 2011.

Amer. Acad. of Craniofacial Pain **[16018]**, 12100 Sunset Hills Rd., Ste. 130, Reston, VA 20190-3221, (703)234-4142

Amer. Acad. of Craniomandibular Disorders **[★14241]**

Amer. Acad. of Craniomandibular Orthopedics **[★14241]**

Amer. Acad. of Crown and Bridge Prosthodontics **[★14233]**

Amer. Acad. of Dental Gp. Practice **[14230]**, 2525 E Arizona Biltmore Cir., Ste. 127, Phoenix, AZ 85016, (602)381-1185

American Acad. of Dental Gp. Practice **[★14230]**

Amer. Acad. of Dental Practice Admin. **[14231]**, 1063 Whippoorwill Ln., Palatine, IL 60067-7064, (847)934-4404

Amer. Acad. of Dental Radiology **[★14239]**

Amer. Acad. of Dental Sleep Medicine **[16659]**, 2510 N Frontage Rd., Darien, IL 60561, (630)737-9761

Amer. Acad. of Dermatology **[14313]**, PO Box 4014, Schaumburg, IL 60168, (847)240-1280

Amer. Acad. of Dermatology **[14313]**, PO Box 4014, Schaumburg, IL 60168, (847)240-1280

Amer. Acad. of Dermatology and Syphilology **[★14313]**

Amer. Acad. of Dermatology and Syphilology **[★14313]**

Amer. Acad. of Diplomacy **[5466]**, 1200 18th St. NW, Ste. 902, Washington, DC 20036, (202)331-3721

Amer. Acad. of Disability Evaluating Physicians **[14164]**, 223 W Jackson Blvd., Ste. 1104, Chicago, IL 60606, (312)663-1171

Amer. Acad. of Emergency Medicine **[14457]**, 555 E Wells St., Ste. 1100, Milwaukee, WI 53202-3823, (800)884-AAEM

Amer. Acad. of Environmental Engineers **[6766]**, 130 Holiday Ct., Ste. 100, Annapolis, MD 21401, (410)266-3311

Amer. Acad. of Environmental Medicine **[14496]**, 6505 E Central Ave., No. 296, Wichita, KS 67206, (316)684-5500

Amer. Acad. of Environmental Medicine **[14496]**, 6505 E Central Ave., No. 296, Wichita, KS 67206, (316)684-5500

Amer. Acad. of Equine Art **[9151]**, PO Box 1364, Georgetown, KY 40324, (859)281-6031

Amer. Acad. of Estate Planning Attorneys **[5224]**, 9444 Balboa Ave., Ste. 300, San Diego, CA 92123, (858)453-2128

Amer. Acad. of Esthetic Dentistry **[14232]**, 303 W Madison St., Ste. 2650, Chicago, IL 60606, (312)981-6770

Amer. Acad. of Experts in Traumatic Stress **[16921]**, 203 Deer Rd., Ronkonkoma, NY 11779-4801, (631)543-2217

Amer. Acad. of Facial Plastic and Reconstructive Surgery **[14170]**, 310 S Henry St., Alexandria, VA 22314, (703)299-9291

Amer. Acad. of Family Physicians **[14523]**, PO Box 11210, Shawnee Mission, KS 66207-1210, (913)906-6000

Reference to "IO" in place of a book number signifies that the association may be found in the 50th edition of International Organizations.

Amer. Acad. of Fed. Civil Ser. Physicians [★16263]

Amer. Acad. of Fertility Care Professionals [12026], 11700 Studt Ave., Ste. C, St. Louis, MO 63131, (402)489-3733

Amer. Acad. of Fixed Prosthodontics [14233], Dr. Richard D. Jordan, Treas., 36 N Mission Hills Ct., Arden, NC 28704-5500, (866)254-0280

Amer. Acad. of Forensic Psychology [5468], Roger Williams Univ., Dept. of Psychology, One Old Ferry Rd., Bristol, RI 02809, (401)254-5333

Amer. Acad. of Forensic Sciences [5469], 410 N 21st St., Colorado Springs, CO 80904, (719)636-1100

Amer. Acad. of Gen. Practice [★14523]

Amer. Acad. of Gnathologic Orthopedics [14234], 2651 Oak Grove Rd., Walnut Creek, CA 94598, (800)510-AAGO

Amer. Acad. of Gold Foil Operators [14235], Dr. Robert C. Keene, Sec., 1 Woods End Rd., Etna, NH 03750-4318, (603)643-2899

Amer. Acad. of Head, Neck and Facial Pain [★16018]

Amer. Acad. of Hea. Care Providers [★15563]

Amer. Acad. of Hea. Care Providers in the Addictive Disorders [15563], 314 W Superior St., Ste. 508, Duluth, MN 55802, (218)727-3940

Amer. Acad. of Hea. Physics [16832], 1313 Dolley Madison Blvd., Ste. 402, McLean, VA 22101, (703)790-1745

Amer. Acad. of Healthcare Attorneys [★5510]

Amer. Acad. of the History of Dentistry [14236], 684 W Napa St., Sonoma, CA 95476

Amer. Acad. of HIV Medicine [13598], 1705 DeSales St. NW, Ste. 700, Washington, DC 20036, (202)659-0699

Amer. Acad. of Home Care Physicians [15007], PO Box 1037, Edgewood, MD 21040-0337, (410)676-7966

Amer. Acad. of Homiletics [★19814]

Amer. Acad. of Hospice and Palliative Medicine [16248], 4700 W Lake Ave., Glenview, IL 60025-1468, (847)375-4712

Amer. Acad. of Hosp. Attorneys [★5510]

Amer. Acad. of Husband-Coached Childbirth [15860], PO Box 5224, Sherman Oaks, CA 91413-5224, (818)788-6662

Amer. Acad. of Implant Dentistry [14237], 211 E Chicago Ave., Ste. 750, Chicago, IL 60611, (312)335-1550

Amer. Acad. of Implant Dentures [★14237]

Amer. Acad. of Insurance Medicine [IO], Ottawa, ON, Canada

Amer. Acad. for Jewish Res. - Defunct.

Amer. Acad. of Kinesiology and Physical Educ. [★8717]

Amer. Acad. of Laser Dentistry [★14225]

Amer. Acad. for Liberal Educ. [8513], 526 King St., Ste. 203, Alexandria, VA 22314, (703)299-9030

Amer. Acad. of Matrimonial Lawyers [5422], 150 N Michigan Ave., Ste. 1420, Chicago, IL 60601, (312)263-6477

Amer. Acad. of Maxillofacial Prosthetics [14238], UT MD Anderson Cancer Center, 1515 Holcomber Blvd., Unit 1445, Houston, TX 77030-4009

Amer. Acad. of Mechanics - Address unknown since 2011.

Amer. Acad. of Medical Acupuncture [16010], 1970 E Grand Ave., Ste. 330, El Segundo, CA 90245, (310)364-0193

Amer. Acad. of Medical Administrators [15276], 701 Lee St., Ste. 600, Des Plaines, IL 60016-4516, (847)759-8601

Amer. Acad. of Medical Administrators Res. and Educational Found. [15277], 701 Lee St., Ste. 600, Des Plaines, IL 60016, (847)759-8601

Amer. Acad. of Medical Directors [★15285]

Amer. Acad. of Medical Esthetic Professionals [15702], 2000 S Andrews Ave., Fort Lauderdale, FL 33316, (954)463-5594

Amer. Acad. of Medical Hypnoanalysts [15080], 1022 Depot Hill Rd., Broomfield, CO 80020, (888)454-9766

Amer. Acad. of Medical Mgt. [15320], Crossville Commons, 560 W Crossville Rd., Ste. 103, Roswell, GA 30075, (770)649-7150

Amer. Acad. of Medical Preventics [★16305]

Amer. Acad. of Medical Preventics [★16305]

Amer. Acad. of Microbiology [6282], 1752 N St. NW, Washington, DC 20036-2804, (202)737-3600

Amer. Acad. of Microbiology [6282], 1752 N St. NW, Washington, DC 20036-2804, (202)737-3600

Amer. Acad. of Micropigmentation [14171], 2709 Medical Off. Pl., Goldsboro, NC 27534, (919)736-3937

Amer. Acad. of Natural Family Planning [★12026]

Amer. Acad. of Neurological and Orthopaedic Surgeons [15681], 10 Cascade Creek Ln., Las Vegas, NV 89113, (702)388-7390

Amer. Acad. of Neurology [15644], 1080 Montreal Ave., St. Paul, MN 55116, (651)695-2717

Amer. Acad. of Nurse Practitioners [15703], PO Box 12846, Austin, TX 78711, (512)442-4262

Amer. Acad. of Nursing [15704], 1000 Vermont Ave. NW, Ste. 910, Washington, DC 20005, (202)777-1170

Amer. Acad. of Obstetrics and Gynecology [★15865]

Amer. Acad. of Occupational Medicine [★15900]

Amer. Acad. of Ophthalmology [15936], PO Box 7424, San Francisco, CA 94120-7424, (415)561-8500

Amer. Acad. of Optometry [15987], 6110 Executive Blvd., Ste. 506, Rockville, MD 20852, (301)984-1441

Amer. Acad. of Optometry [15987], 6110 Executive Blvd., Ste. 506, Rockville, MD 20852, (301)984-1441

Amer. Acad. of Optometry - British Chap. [IO], Woodbridge, United Kingdom

Amer. Acad. of Oral and Maxillofacial Pathology [16109], 214 N Hale St., Wheaton, IL 60187, (630)510-4552

Amer. Acad. of Oral and Maxillofacial Radiology [14239], PO Box 231422, New York, NY 10023, (304)293-3773

Amer. Acad. of Oral Medicine [14240], PO Box 2016, Edmonds, WA 98020-9516, (425)778-6162

Amer. Acad. Oral Pathology [★16109]

Amer. Acad. of Oral Roentgenology [★14239]

Amer. Acad. of Orofacial Pain [14241], 19 Mantua Rd., Mount Royal, NJ 08061, (856)423-3629

Amer. Acad. of Orthodontics for the Gen. Practitioner - Address unknown since 2011.

Amer. Acad. of Orthopaedic Manual Physical Therapists [16833], 12100 Sunset Hills Rd., Ste. 130, Reston, VA 20190, (703)234-4079

Amer. Acad. of Orthopaedic Surgeons [16019], 6300 N River Rd., Rosemont, IL 60018-4262, (847)823-7186

Amer. Acad. of Orthopaedic Surgeons [16019], 6300 N River Rd., Rosemont, IL 60018-4262, (847)823-7186

Amer. Acad. of Orthotists and Prosthetists [16048], 1331 H St. NW, Ste. 501, Washington, DC 20005, (202)380-3663

Amer. Acad. of Osteopathic Surgeons [★16058]

Amer. Acad. of Osteopathy [16056], 3500 DePauw Blvd., Ste. 1080, Indianapolis, IN 46268, (317)879-1881

Amer. Acad. of Otolaryngic Allergy and Found. [13633], 1990 M St. NW, Ste. 680, Washington, DC 20036, (202)955-5010

Amer. Acad. of Otolaryngology - Head and Neck Surgery [16081], 1650 Diagonal Rd., Alexandria, VA 22314, (703)836-4444

Amer. Acad. of Pain Mgt. [16092], 13947 Mono Way, Ste. A, Sonora, CA 95370, (209)533-9744

Amer. Acad. of Pain Medicine [16093], 4700 W Lake Ave., Glenview, IL 60025, (847)375-4731

Amer. Acad. of Pediatric Dentistry [14242], 211 E Chicago Ave., Ste. 1700, Chicago, IL 60611-2637, (312)337-2169

Amer. Acad. of Pediatrics [16138], 141 NW Point Blvd., Elk Grove Village, IL 60007-1098, (847)434-4000

Amer. Acad. of Pedodontics [★14242]

Amer. Acad. of Periodontology [14243], 737 N Michigan Ave., Ste. 800, Chicago, IL 60611-6660, (312)787-5518

Amer. Acad. of Pharmaceutical Physicians Educ. Found. [★8583]

Amer. Acad. of Philately [★22009]

Amer. Acad. of Physical Educ. [★8717]

Amer. Acad. of Physical Medicine and Rehabilitation [16552], 9700 W Bryn Mawr Ave., Ste. 200, Rosemont, IL 60018-5706, (847)737-6000

Amer. Acad. of Physician Assistants [16235], 2318 Mill Rd., Ste. 1300, Alexandria, VA 22314-6868, (703)836-2272

Amer. Acad. of Physician Assistants in Occupational Medicine [15898], 174 Monticello Pl., Elizabethtown, KY 42701

Amer. Acad. on Physician and Patients [★16247]

Amer. Acad. for Plastics Res. in Dentistry [★14222]

Amer. Acad. Podiatric Admin. [★16283]

Amer. Acad. of Podiatric Mgt. [★16283]

Amer. Acad. of Podiatric Practice Mgt. [16283], 1000 W. St. Joseph St., Ste. 200, Lansing, MI 48915, (517)484-1930

Amer. Acad. of Podiatric Sports Medicine [16710], Rita J. Yates, Exec. Dir., 109 Greenwich Dr., Walkersville, MD 21793, (301)845-9887

Amer. Acad. of Political and Social Sci. [7284], Annenberg Policy Center, 202 S 36th St., Philadelphia, PA 19104-3806, (215)746-6500

Amer. Acad. of Polygraph Examiners [★5475]

Amer. Acad. of Practice Mgt. in Podiatry [★16283]

Amer. Acad. of Procedural Coders [★14865]

Amer. Acad. of Professional Coders [14865], 2480 S 3850 W, Ste. B, Salt Lake City, UT 84120, (801)236-2200

Amer. Acad. of Psychiatry and the Law [5507], One Regency Dr., PO Box 30, Bloomfield, CT 06002-0030, (860)242-5450

Amer. Acad. of Psychoanalysis [★16351]

Amer. Acad. of Psychoanalysis and Dynamic Psychiatry [16351], PO Box 30, Bloomfield, CT 06002, (888)691-8281

Amer. Acad. of Psychotherapists [16445], 111 W Main St., No. 100, Garner, NC 27529, (919)779-5051

Amer. Acad. of Religion [7993], 825 Houston Mill Rd. NE, Ste. 300, Atlanta, GA 30329, (404)727-3049

Amer. Acad. of Res. Historians of Medieval Spain [9740], Prof. Mark Johnston, Treas., DePaul Univ., Dept. of Modern Languages, McGaw Hall, Ste. 315-2, 802 W Belden, Chicago, IL 60614

Amer. Acad. of Restorative Dentistry [14244], Southwestern Medical Found., 2305 Cedar Springs Rd., Ste. 150, Dallas, TX 75201

Amer. Acad. in Rome [IO], Rome, Italy

Amer. Acad. of Sanitarians [16632], 1568 LeGrand Cir., Lawrenceville, GA 30043-8191, (678)407-1051

Amer. Acad. of Sanitary Engineers [★6766]

Amer. Acad. of Sleep Medicine [16660], 2510 N Frontage Rd., Darien, IL 60561, (630)737-9700

Amer. Acad. of Somnology - Address unknown since 2010.

Amer. Acad. of Teachers of Singing [8638], 777 W End Ave., New York, NY 10025-5551, (212)666-1166

Amer. Acad. of Urgent Care Medicine [13726], 2813 S Hiawassee Rd., Ste. 206, Orlando, FL 32835, (407)521-5789

Amer. Acad. of Veterinary and Comparative Toxicology - Address unknown since 2010.

Amer. Acad. of Veterinary Nutrition [16972], 721 Inverness Dr., West Chester, PA 19380

Amer. Acad. of Veterinary Pharmacology and Therapeutics [16973], PO Box 18188, Portland, ME 04112-8188, (207)766-6944

Amer. Acad. of Wound Mgt. [16922], 1155 15th St. NW, Ste. 500, Washington, DC 20005, (202)457-8408

Amer. Accordion Musicological Soc. [10136], 322 Haddon Ave., Westmont, NJ 08108, (856)854-6628

Amer. Accordionists' Assn. [10137], 152 Home Fair Dr., Fairfield, CT 06825, (203)335-2045

Amer. Accounting Assn. [5], 5717 Bessie Dr., Sarasota, FL 34233-2330, (941)921-7747

Amer. Accounts Payable Assn. [6], 660 N Main Ave., Ste. 200, San Antonio, TX 78205-1217, (210)630-4373

Amer. Accreditation Healthcare Commn. [14850], 1220 L St. NW, Ste. 400, Washington, DC 20005, (202)216-9010

A star before a book entry number signifies that the name is not listed separately, but is mentioned within the entry.

Amer. Action Fund for Blind Children and Adults [17056], 1800 Johnson St., Baltimore, MD 21230, (410)659-9315

Amer. Adoption Cong. [10779], PO Box 42730, Washington, DC 20015, (202)483-3399

American Advent Mission Society [★19287]

American Advent Mission Society [★19287]

Amer. Advt. Fed. [80], 1101 Vermont Ave. NW, Ste. 500, Washington, DC 20005-6306, (202)898-0089

Amer. Affiliation of Tall Clubs [★13307]

Amer. Affiliation of Tall Clubs [★13307]

Amer. Affiliation of Visiting Nurses Associations and Services [★15806]

Amer. and African Bus. Women's Alliance - Address unknown since 2010.

Amer. Aging Assn. [14657], Mark A. Smith, Exec. Dir., Dept. of Pathology, 2103 Cornell Rd., Rm. 5125, Cleveland, OH 44106, (216)368-3671

Amer. Aging Assn. [14657], Mark A. Smith, Exec. Dir., Dept. of Pathology, 2103 Cornell Rd., Rm. 5125, Cleveland, OH 44106, (216)368-3671

Amer. Agri-Women [17162], 2103 Zeandale Rd., Manhattan, KS 66502, (785)537-6171

Amer. Agri-Women Rsrc. Center [17163], Amer. Agri-Women, 2103 Zeandale Rd., Manhattan, KS 66502, (785)537-6171

Amer. Agricultural Economics Assn. [★6606]

Amer. Agricultural Economics Assn. [★6606]

Amer. Agricultural Editors' Assn. [2793], PO Box 156, New Prague, MN 56071, (952)758-6502

Amer. Agricultural Law Assn. [5184], Robert P. Achenbach, Jr., Exec. Dir., 127 Young Rd., Kelso, WA 98626, (360)200-5699

Amer. Agricultural Movement [★17164]

Amer. Agriculture Movement [17164], Natl. Treas., 24800 Sage Creek Rd., Scenic, SD 57780, (620)463-3513

Amer. Aid Soc. of German Descendants [18999], 6540 N Milwaukee Ave., Chicago, IL 60631-1750

Amer. Aid Soc. of German Descendants [18999], 6540 N Milwaukee Ave., Chicago, IL 60631-1750

Amer. Air Mail Soc. [22006], Stephen Reinhard, Treas., PO Box 110, Mineola, NY 11501

Amer. Airborne Assn. [20361], 10301 McKinstry Mill Rd., New Windsor, MD 21776-7903, (888)567-2927

Amer. Airgun Field Target Assn. - Address unknown since 2011.

Amer. Albacore Fishing Assn. [1357], 4364 Bonita Rd., Box 311, Bonita, CA 91902, (619)941-2307

American-Albanian Catholic Charity [★18514]

American-Albanian Catholic Charity [★18514]

Amer. Alfalfa Processors Assn. [★4370]

Amer. Allergy Assn. - Defunct.

Amer. Alliance Against Violence [★17684]

Amer. Alliance of Ethical Movers [13341], 1200 De-Kalb Pike, Center Square, PA 19422

Amer. Alliance for Hea., Physical Educ. and Recreation [★8715]

Amer. Alliance for Hea., Physical Educ., Recreation and Dance [8715], 1900 Assn. Dr., Reston, VA 20191-1598, (703)476-3400

Amer. Alliance of Hypnotists [15081], 107 Picket Row, Savannah, GA 31410, (912)897-9799

Amer. Alliance for Medical Cannabis [15259], 44500 Tide Ave., Arch Cape, OR 97102, (503)436-1882

Amer. Alliance of Paralegals, Inc. [5870], 4001 Kennett Pike, Ste. 134-146, Wilmington, DE 19807

Amer. Alliance of Ser. Providers - Address unknown since 2010.

Amer. Alliance for Theatre and Educ. [10561], 4908 Auburn Ave., Bethesda, MD 20814, (301)280-1682

Amer. Alliance of TMD Organizations [14245], 536 School of Dentistry Bldg., 1530 3rd Ave. S, Birmingham, AL 35294-0007, (205)934-0126

Amer. Alpine Club [6856], 710 10th St., Ste. 100, Golden, CO 80401, (303)384-0110

Amer. Alternative Medical Assn. [13650], 2200 Market St., Ste. 803, Galveston, TX 77550-1530, (409)621-2600

Amer. Alumni Coun. [★8013]

Amer. Amaryllis Soc. Gp. [★6356]

Amer. Amaryllis Soc. Gp. [★6356]

Amer. Amateur Baseball Cong. [22262], 100 W Broadway, Farmington, NM 87401, (505)327-3120

Amer. Amateur Karate Fed. [22721], 445 S Figueroa St., Ste. 2600, Los Angeles, CA 90071, (888)939-8882

Amer. Amateur Press Assn. [22105], 1327 NE 73rd Ave., Portland, OR 97213-6112

Amer. Amateur Racquetball Assn. [★22832]

Amer. Ambulance Assn. [14448], 8400 Westpark Dr., 2nd Fl., McLean, VA 22102, (703)610-9018

Amer. Amputee Found. [11756], PO Box 94227, North Little Rock, AR 72190, (501)835-9290

Amer. Amputee Hockey Assn. [22961], 41 Buena Vista Way, Hanover, MA 02339

Amer. Amputee Soccer Assn. [22932], PO Box 6002, Wilmington, DE 19804, (302)683-0997

Amer. Amusement Machine Assn. [1186], 450 E Higgins Rd., Ste. 201, Elk Grove Village, IL 60007, (847)290-9088

Amer. Amusement Machine Assn. [1186], 450 E Higgins Rd., Ste. 201, Elk Grove Village, IL 60007, (847)290-9088

Amer. Andalusian Assn. [★4594]

Amer. Andalusian Assn. [★4594]

Amer. Angora Goat Breeder's Assn. [3775], PO Box 195, Rocksprings, TX 78880, (830)683-4483

Amer. Angus Assn. [3865], 3201 Frederick Ave., St. Joseph, MO 64506, (816)383-5100

Amer. Animal Hosp. Assn. [16974], 12575 W Bayaud Ave., Lakewood, CO 80228, (303)986-2800

Amer. Anorexia Bulimia Assn. [★14439]

Amer. Anthropological Assn. [6125], 2200 Wilson Blvd., Ste. 600, Arlington, VA 22201-3357, (703)528-1902

Amer. Anthropological Assn. I Assn. of Latina and Latino Anthropologists [6126], Indiana Univ. Bloomington, 701 E Kirkwood Ave., SB 242, Bloomington, IN 47405, (812)855-3901

Amer. Anthropological Assn. I Assn. for Political and Legal Anthropology [6127], George Mason Univ., Inst. for Conflict Anal. and Resolution, 3401 Fairfax Dr., MS 4D3, Arlington, VA 22201, (703)993-9407

Amer. Anthropological Assn. I Coun. for Museum Anthropology [10105], Univ. of Connecticut, Dept. of Anthropology, Academic Bldg. 114A, 1084 Shennecossett Rd., Groton, CT 06340, (860)405-9059

Amer. Anthropological Assn. I Soc. for the Anthropology of Europe [6128], 2200 Wilson Blvd., Ste. 600, Arlington, VA 22201, (703)528-1902

Amer. Anti-Vivisection Soc. [10904], 801 Old York Rd., Ste. 204, Jenkintown, PA 19046, (215)887-0816

Amer. Antiquarian Soc. [9663], 185 Salisbury St., Worcester, MA 01609-1634, (508)755-5221

Amer. Antique Playing Card Collector's Club [★21291]

Amer. Apitherapy Soc. [13651], 14942 S Eagle Crest Dr., Draper, UT 84020, (631)470-9446

Amer. Appaloosa Assn. Worldwide [4523], PO Box 429, Republic, MO 65738-0429, (417)466-2046

Amer. Appaloosa Assn. Worldwide [4523], PO Box 429, Republic, MO 65738-0429, (417)466-2046

Amer. Apparel Contractors Assn. [★200]

Amer. Apparel Contractors Assn. [★200]

Amer. Apparel and Footwear Assn. [199], 1601 N Kent St., Ste. 1200, Arlington, VA 22209, (703)797-9037

Amer. Apparel and Footwear Mfrs. Assn. [★199]

Amer. Apparel Producers Assn. [★200]

Amer. Apparel Producers Assn. [★200]

Amer. Apparel Producers' Network [200], PO Box 720693, Atlanta, GA 30358, (404)843-3171

Amer. Apparel Producers' Network [200], PO Box 720693, Atlanta, GA 30358, (404)843-3171.

Amer. APS Assn. [13808], 6942 FM 1960 Rd. E, No. 363, Humble, TX 77346, (281)812-3384

Amer. Arab Affairs Coun. [★18130]

Amer. Arab Affairs Coun. [★18130]

American-Arab Anti-Discrimination Comm. [17257], 1732 Wisconsin Ave. NW, Washington, DC 20007-2313, (202)244-2990

Amer. Arab Chamber of Commerce [23324], 12740 W Warren Ave., Ste. 101, Dearborn, MI 48126, (313)945-1700

Amer. Arbitration Assn. [5201], 1633 Broadway, 10th Fl., New York, NY 10019, (212)716-5800

Amer. Archery Coun. - Defunct.

Amer. Architectural Found. [6181], 1799 New York Ave. NW, Washington, DC 20006, (202)626-7318

Amer. Architectural Mfrs. Assn. [518], 1827 Walden Off. Sq., Ste. 550, Schaumburg, IL 60173-4268, (847)303-5664

Amer. Armsport Assn. [22229], 176 Dean Rd., Mooresburg, TN 37811, (423)272-6162

Amer. Art Pottery Assn. [9152], Marie Latta, Admin., 907 Maurer, Wilton, IA 52778

Amer. Art Therapy Assn. [16446], 225 N Fairfax St., Alexandria, VA 22314, (703)548-5860

Amer. Artists of Chinese Brush Painting - Address unknown since 2010.

Amer. Artists Professional League [9219], 47 5th Ave., New York, NY 10003, (212)645-1345

Amer. Arts Alliance [★9313]

Amer. Asperger's Assn. [15564], 1301 Seminole Blvd., Ste. B-112, Largo, FL 33770, (727)518-7294

Amer. Assembly [18438], 475 Riverside Dr., Ste. 456, New York, NY 10115-0456, (212)870-3500

Amer. Assembly of Collegiate Schools of Bus. [★7780]

Amer. Assembly of Collegiate Schools of Bus. [★7780]

Amer. Assembly for Men in Nursing [15705], Byron McCain, Exec. Dir., PO Box 130220, Birmingham, AL 35213, (205)956-0146

Amer. Assisted Living Nurses Assn. [15706], PO Box 10469, Napa, CA 94581, (707)253-7299

Amer. Assoc. Rental Operators [★3076]

Amer. Associates Ben-Gurion Univ. of the Negev [8417], 1430 Broadway, 8th Fl., New York, NY 10018, (212)687-7721

Amer. Assn. for Accreditation of Ambulatory Plastic Surgery Facilities [★16790]

Amer. Assn. for Accreditation of Ambulatory Surgery Facilities [16790], 5101 Washington St., Ste. 2F, Gurnee, IL 60031, (888)545-5222

Amer. Assn. for Accreditation of Lab. Animal Care [★13760]

Amer. Assn. for Accreditation of Lab. Animal Care [★13760]

Amer. Assn. for Acupuncture and Oriental Medicine [★16011]

Amer. Assn. of Acupuncture and Oriental Medicine [16011], PO Box 96503, Washington, DC 20090-6503, (866)455-7999

Amer. Assn. of Acupuncture and Oriental Medicine [16011], PO Box 96503, Washington, DC 20090-6503, (866)455-7999

Amer. Assn. for Acupuncture and Oriental Medicine [★16011]

Amer. Assn. of adaptedSPORTS Programs [22501], PO Box 451047, Atlanta, GA 31145, (404)294-0070

Amer. Assn. for Adult and Continuing Educ. [7920], 10111 Martin Luther King, Jr. Hwy., Ste. 200C, Bowie, MD 20720, (301)459-6261

Amer. Assn. for Advancement of Physical Educ. [★8715]

Amer. Assn. for the Advancement of Sci. [7355], 1200 New York Ave. NW, Washington, DC 20005, (202)326-6400

Amer. Assn. for the Advancement of Slavic Stud. [★10534]

Amer. Assn. of Advt. Agencies [81], 405 Lexington Ave., 18th Fl., New York, NY 10174-1801, (212)682-2500

Amer. Assn. for Aerosol Res. [6387], 15000 Commerce Pkwy., Ste. C, Mount Laurel, NJ 08054, (856)439-9080

Amer. Assn. for Affirmative Action [11927], 888 16th St. NW, Ste. 800, Washington, DC 20006, (202)349-9855

Amer. Assn. of Agricultural Coll. Editors [★3737]

Amer. Assn. of Agricultural Communicators of Tomorrow [★8445]

Amer. Assn. for Agricultural Educ. [7706], Ohio State Univ., Human and Community Rsrc. Development, 203A Ag. Admin. Bldg., 2120 Fyffe Rd., Columbus, OH 43210, (614)292-6321

Amer. Assn. for Agricultural Engg. and Vocational Agriculture [★9037]

Amer. Assn. of Airport Executives [125], 601 Madison St., Ste. 400, Alexandria, VA 22314, (703)824-0500

Reference to "IO" in place of a book number signifies that the association may be found in the 50th edition of International Organizations.

Amer. Assn. of Ambulatory Surgery Centers and Federated Ambulatory Surgery Assn. [★16789]

Amer. Assn. of Anatomists [13730], 9650 Rockville Pike, Bethesda, MD 20814-3998, (301)634-7910

Amer. Assn. of Anger Mgt. Providers [15443], 12301 Wilshire Blvd., Ste. 418, Los Angeles, CA 90025, (310)207-3591

Amer. Assn. of Anthropological Genetics [6895], Univ. of Oklahoma, Dept. of Anthropology, 455 W Lindsey Ave., DAHT 521, Norman, OK 73019, (405)325-7609

Amer. Assn. for Applied Linguistics [10021], 2900 Delk Rd., Ste. 700, Marietta, GA 30067-5350, (678)229-2892

Amer. Assn. for Artificial Intelligence [★6209]

Amer. Assn. of Attorney-Certified Public Accountants [7], 3921 Old Lee Hwy., Ste. 71A, Fairfax, VA 22030, (703)352-8064

Amer. Assn. of Automatic Door Mfrs. [1046], 1300 Sumner Ave., Cleveland, OH 44115-2851, (216)241-7333

Amer. Assn. for Automotive Medicine [★12978]

Amer. Assn. of Avian Pathologists [16975], 12627 San Jose Blvd., Ste. 202, Jacksonville, FL 32223-8638, (904)425-5735

Amer. Assn. of Ayurvedic Medicine - Defunct.

Amer. Assn. of Bank Directors [395], 1250 24th St. NW, Ste. 700, Washington, DC 20037, (202)463-4888

Amer. Assn. of Behavioral and Social Sciences [6246], Univ. of Tampa, Dept. of SSME, 401 W Kennedy Blvd., Tampa, FL 33606-1490

Amer. Assn. of Behavioral Therapists - Address unknown since 2010.

Amer. Assn. of Bible Colleges [★7850]

Amer. Assn. of Bioanalysts [15229], 906 Olive St., Ste. 1200, St. Louis, MO 63101-1448, (314)241-1445

Amer. Assn. of Birth Centers [15861], 3123 Gottschall Rd., Perkiomenville, PA 18074, (215)234-8068

Amer. Assn. of Blacks in Energy [6686], 1625 K St. NW, Ste. 405, Washington, DC 20006, (202)371-9530

Amer. Assn. of Blood Banks [13848], 8101 Glenbrook Rd., Bethesda, MD 20814-2749, (301)907-6977

Amer. Assn. of Botanical Gardens and Arboreta [★4666]

Amer. Assn. of Botanical Gardens and Arboretums [★4666]

Amer. Assn. of Bovine Practitioners [16976], PO Box 3610, Auburn, AL 36831-3610, (334)821-0442

Amer. Assn. of Breast Care Professionals [13858], 3375 Westpark Dr., No. 573, Houston, TX 77005, (800)892-1683

Amer. Assn. of Breeders of Holsteiner Horses [★4536]

Amer. Assn. of Brief and Strategic Therapists - Address unknown since 2011.

Amer. Assn. for Budget and Prog. Anal. [5915], PO Box 1157, Falls Church, VA 22041, (703)941-4300

Amer. Assn. for Cancer Educ. [13879], San Diego Hospice and Palliative Care, 4311 3rd Ave., San Diego, CA 92103-1407, (619)278-6164

Amer. Assn. for Cancer Res. [15912], 615 Chestnut St., 17th Fl., Philadelphia, PA 19106-4404, (215)440-9300

Amer. Assn. for Cancer Res. [15912], 615 Chestnut St., 17th Fl., Philadelphia, PA 19106-4404, (215)440-9300

Amer. Assn. for Cancer Res. | Women in Cancer Res. [17120], 615 Chestnut St., 17th Fl., Philadelphia, PA 19106-4404, (215)440-9300

Amer. Assn. of Candy Technologists [6868], PO Box 266, Princeton, WI 54968, (920)295-6969

Amer. Assn. of Cardiovascular Nurses [★15707]

Amer. Assn. of Cardiovascular and Pulmonary Rehabilitation [13998], 401 N Michigan Ave., Ste. 2200, Chicago, IL 60611-4267, (312)321-5146

Amer. Assn. of Caregiving Youth [13505], 1515 N Fed. Hwy., No. 214, Boca Raton, FL 33432, (561)391-7401

Amer. Assn. of Cat Enthusiasts [21243], 780 E Peenpack Trail, Sparrow Bush, NY 12780, (973)335-3335

Amer. Assn. of Ceramic Indus. [★731]

Amer. Assn. of Cereal Chemists [★6385]

Amer. Assn. of Cereal Chemists [★6385]

Amer. Assn. of Certified Allied Hea. Personnel in Ophthalmology [★15950]

Amer. Assn. of Certified Orthoptists [15937], 3914 Nakoma Rd., Madison, WI 53711, (608)233-5383

Amer. Assn. of Chairmen of Medical School Departments of Pathology [★16120]

Amer. Assn. of Chairs of Departments of Psychiatry [16319], Lucille F. Meinsler, Exec. Sec., 1594 Cumberland St., Lebanon, PA 17042, (717)270-1673

Amer. Assn. of Cheerleading Coaches and Administrators [22449], 6745 Lenox Center Ct., Ste. 318, Memphis, TN 38115, (800)533-6583

Amer. Assn. for Child Psychoanalysis [★16355]

Amer. Assn. of Children's Residential Centers [13506], 11700 W Lake Park Dr., Milwaukee, WI 53224, (877)332-2272

Amer. Assn. for Chinese Companies - Defunct.

Amer. Assn. for Chinese Stud. [7839], Prof. Peter C.Y. Chow, Exec. Dir., The City Coll. - CUNY, NAC R4/116, Convent Ave. and 138th St., New York, NY 10031, (212)650-6206

Amer. Assn. of Christian Counselors [19629], PO Box 739, Forest, VA 24551, (434)525-9470

Amer. Assn. of Christian Counselors [19629], PO Box 739, Forest, VA 24551, (434)525-9470

Amer. Assn. of Christian Schools [7645], 602 Belvoir Ave., East Ridge, TN 37412, (423)629-4280

Amer. Assn. for Chronic Fatigue Syndrome [★14391]

Amer. Assn. of Classified School Employees [23177], 555 New Jersey Ave. NW, Washington, DC 20001

Amer. Assn. for Cleft Palate Rehabilitation [★14190]

Amer. Assn. of Clinical Anatomists [13731], H. Wayne Lambert, PhD, West Virginia Univ., Robert C. Byrd Hea. Sciences Ctr., MN225 Chandler Medical Ctr., 4052 HSN, Morgantown, WV 26506-0610, (304)293-0610

Amer. Assn. for Clinical Chemistry [6388], 1850 K St. NW, Ste. 625, Washington, DC 20006, (202)857-0717

Amer. Assn. for Clinical Chemistry [6388], 1850 K St. NW, Ste. 625, Washington, DC 20006, (202)857-0717

Amer. Assn. of Clinical Chemists [★6388]

Amer. Assn. of Clinical Chemists [★6388]

Amer. Assn. of Clinical Coders and Auditors [14866], 1142 S Diamond Bar Blvd., No. 796, Diamond Bar, CA 91765, (909)579-0507

Amer. Assn. of Clinical Directors [16249], 520 N Northwest Hwy., Park Ridge, IL 60068-2573, (847)825-5586

Amer. Assn. of Clinical Endocrinologists [14485], 245 Riverside Ave., Ste. 200, Jacksonville, FL 32202, (904)353-7878

Amer. Assn. for Clinical Histocompatibility Testing [★15099]

Amer. Assn. of Clinical Lab. Supervisors and Administrators [★15233]

Amer. Assn. of Clinical Urologists [16936], 1100 E Woodfield Rd., Ste. 520, Schaumburg, IL 60173, (847)517-1050

Amer. Assn. of Code Enforcement [5684], 5310 E Main St., Ste. 104, Columbus, OH 43213, (614)552-2633

Amer. Assn. of Coll. Baseball Coaches [★22263]

Amer. Assn. of Coll. Baseball Coaches [★22263]

Amer. Assn. of Coll. Bus. Officers [★7667]

Amer. Assn. of Coll. and Univ. Bus. Officers [★7667]

American Assn. of Colleges [★12669]

Amer. Assn. of Colleges of Chiropody [★16284]

Amer. Assn. of Colleges of Nursing [8585], 1 Dupont Cir. NW, Ste. 530, Washington, DC 20036, (202)463-6930

Amer. Assn. of Colleges of Osteopathic Medicine [16057], 5550 Friendship Blvd., Ste. 310, Chevy Chase, MD 20815-7231, (301)968-4100

Amer. Assn. of Colleges of Pharmacy [16167], 1727 King St., Alexandria, VA 22314, (703)739-2330

Amer. Assn. of Colleges of Podiatric Medicine [16284], 15850 Crabbs Br. Way, Ste. 320, Rockville, MD 20855, (301)948-9760

Amer. Assn. of Colleges of Podiatry [★16284]

Amer. Assn. of Colleges for Teacher Educ. [8940], 1307 New York Ave. NW, Ste. 300, Washington, DC 20005-4701, (202)293-2450

Amer. Assn. for Collegiate Independent Stud. - Address unknown since 2010.

Amer. Assn. of Collegiate Registrars [★7679]

Amer. Assn. of Collegiate Registrars and Admissions Officers [7679], 1 Dupont Cir. NW, Ste. 520, Washington, DC 20036, (202)293-9161

Amer. Assn. of Collegiate Schools of Bus. [★7780]

Amer. Assn. of Collegiate Schools of Bus. [★7780]

Amer. Assn. of Community Colleges [7889], 1 Dupont Cir. NW, Ste. 410, Washington, DC 20036-1176, (202)728-0200

Amer. Assn. for Community Dental Programs [14246], 635 W 7th St., Ste. 309, Cincinnati, OH 45203, (513)621-0248

Amer. Assn. of Community and Junior Colleges [★7889]

Amer. Assn. of Community Psychiatrists [16320], Francis Roton Bell, Admin. Dir., PO Box 570218, Dallas, TX 75357-0218, (972)613-0985

Amer. Assn. of Community Theatre [10562], 1300 Gendy St., Fort Worth, TX 76107, (817)732-3177

Amer. Assn. for the Comparative Stud. of Law [★5586]

Amer. Assn. for Comprehensive Hea. Planning [★14697]

Amer. Assn. of Cmpt. Rental Professionals [6525], Adams Hill Rd., Box 34, South Newfane, VT 05351, (877)846-6404

Amer. Assn. of Concerned Engineers - Defunct.

Amer. Assn. for Conservation Info. [★4002]

Amer. Assn. for Contamination Control [★7331]

Amer. Assn. of Correctional Psychologists [★11715]

Amer. Assn. Correctional Training Personnel [★11716]

Amer. Assn. Correctional Training Personnel [★11716]

Amer. Assn. of Cosmetic Surgeons [★14169]

Amer. Assn. of Cosmetology Schools [7935], 9927 E Bell Rd., Ste. 110, Scottsdale, AZ 85260, (480)281-0431

Amer. Assn. of Cost Engineers [★6580]

Amer. Assn. of Cost Engineers [★6580]

Amer. Assn. for Counseling and Development [★11667]

Amer. Assn. of Critical-Care Nurses [15707], 101 Columbia, Aliso Viejo, CA 92656-4109, (949)362-2000

Amer. Assn. of Crop Insurers [1924], 1 Massachusetts Ave. NW, Ste. 800, Washington, DC 20001, (202)789-4100

Amer. Assn. for Crystal Growth [6587], 6986 S. Wadsworth Ct., Littleton, CO 80128, (888)506-1271

Amer. Assn. of Daily Money Managers [1333], 174 Crestview Dr., Bellefonte, PA 16823, (877)326-5991

Amer. Assn. of the Deaf-Blind [14913], 8630 Fenton St., Ste. 121, Silver Spring, MD 20910-4500, (301)495-4403

Amer. Assn. of Dental Boards [14247], 211 E Chicago Ave., Ste. 760, Chicago, IL 60611, (312)440-7464

Amer. Assn. of Dental Consultants [1925], 10032 Wind Hill Dr., Greenville, IN 47124, (812)923-2600

Amer. Assn. of Dental Editors [2794], 750 N Lincoln Memorial Dr., Ste. 422, Milwaukee, WI 53202, (414)272-2759

Amer. Assn. for Dental Res. [14248], 1619 Duke St., Alexandria, VA 22314-3406, (703)548-0066

Amer. Assn. Dental Schools [★7964]

Amer. Assn. Dental Schools [★7964]

Amer. Assn. of Diabetes Educators [14343], 200 W Madison St., Ste. 800, Chicago, IL 60606, (800)338-3633

Amer. Assn. of Directors of Psychiatric Residency Training [16321], Lucille F. Meinsler, Admin. Mgr., Executive Off., 1594 Cumberland St., Lebanon, PA 17042, (717)270-1673

Amer. Assn. of Drilling Engineers [7234], PO Box 107, Houston, TX 77001-0107, (281)293-9800

Amer. Assn. of Drugless Practitioners [13652], 2200 Market St., Ste. 329, Galveston, TX 77550-1530, (409)621-2600

A star before a book entry number signifies that the name is not listed separately, but is mentioned within the entry.

Amer. Assn. of Early Childhood Educators - Defunct.

Amer. Assn. of Economic Entomologists and Entomological Soc. of Am. [★6844]

Amer. Assn. of Electromyography and Electrodiagnosis [★15565]

Amer. Assn. of Electronic Reporters and Transcribers [2891], PO Box 9826, Wilmington, DE 19809-9826, (800)233-5306

Amer. Assn. - Electronic Voice Phenomena [★7246]

Amer. Assn. of Electronic Voice Phenomena [★7246]

Amer. Assn. of Electronic Voice Phenomena [★7246]

Amer. Assn. - Electronic Voice Phenomena [★7246]

Amer. Assn. for Employment in Educ. [8726], 3040 Riverside Dr., Ste. 117, Columbus, OH 43221, (614)485-1111

Amer. Assn. of Endodontists [14249], 211 E Chicago Ave., Ste. 1100, Chicago, IL 60611-2691, (312)266-7310

Amer. Assn. of Endodontists I Amer. Bd. of Endodontics [14250], 211 E Chicago Ave., Ste. 1100, Chicago, IL 60611-2691, (312)266-7310

Amer. Assn. of Engg. Societies [6767], 1801 Alexander Bell Dr., Reston, VA 20191, (202)296-2237

Amer. Assn. of Engineers [★6816]

Amer. Assn. of English Jewish Newspapers [★2797]

Amer. Assn. of Environmental Technicians [4332], PO Box 20434, West Palm Beach, FL 33416, (561)644-1208

Amer. Assn. of Equine Practitioners [16977], 4075 Iron Works Pkwy., Lexington, KY 40511, (859)233-0147

Amer. Assn. of Equine Veterinary Technicians [16978], 539 Wild Horse Ln., San Marcos, CA 92078

Amer. Assn. of Equine Veterinary Technicians [16978], 539 Wild Horse Ln., San Marcos, CA 92078

Amer. Assn. of Equip. Lessors [★3078]

Amer. Assn. of Equip. Lessors [★3078]

Amer. Assn. of Examiners and Administrators of Educational Personnel [★7652]

Amer. Assn. of Examiners and Administrators of Educational Personnel [★7652]

Amer. Assn. of Exporters and Importers [2093], 1050 17th St. NW, Ste. 810, Washington, DC 20036, (202)857-8009

Amer. Assn. of Eye and Ear Hospitals

Amer. Assn. of Eye and Ear Hospitals - Address unknown since 2011.

Amer. Assn. of Family and Consumer Sciences [12152], 400 N Columbus St., Ste. 202, Alexandria, VA 22314, (703)706-4600

Amer. Assn. of Feed Microscopists Div. [★4371]

Amer. Assn. of Feline Practitioners [16979], 390 Amwell Rd., Ste. 402, Hillsborough, NJ 08844, (908)359-9351

Amer. Assn. of Food Hygiene Veterinarians - Address unknown since 2010.

Amer. Assn. of Food Stamp Directors [★5975]

Amer. Assn. of Former Soviet Political Prisoners [★17840]

Amer. Assn. of Former Soviet Political Prisoners [★17840]

Amer. Assn. of Franchisees and Dealers [1525], PO Box 81887, San Diego, CA 92138-1887, (619)209-3755

Amer. Assn. of Fundraising Counsel [★1539]

Amer. Assn. of Genito-Urinary Surgeons [16937], Univ. of Michigan, Dept. of Urology, 3875 Taubman Center SPC 5330, 1500 E Medical Center Dr., Ann Arbor, MI 48109-5330, (734)232-4943

Amer. Assn. for Geodetic Surveying [7485], 6100 Ingleston Dr., No. 724, Sparks, NV 89436, (775)626-6295

Amer. Assn. for Geriatric Psychiatry [16322], 7910 Woodmont Ave., Ste. 1050, Bethesda, MD 20814-3004, (301)654-7850

Amer. Assn. for Gifted Children [8214], Duke Univ., PO Box 90539, Durham, NC 27708-0539, (919)783-6152

Amer. Assn. of Grain Inspection and Weighing Agencies [1590], PO Box 26426, Kansas City, MO 64196, (816)569-4020

Amer. Assn. of Grant Professionals [★12671]

Amer. Assn. of Gp. Workers [★13222]

Amer. Assn. of Gynecologic Laparoscopists [15862], 6757 Katella Ave., Cypress, CA 90630-5105, (714)503-6200

Amer. Assn. of Gynecological Laparoscopists [★15862]

Amer. Assn. for Hand Surgery [14678], 900 Cummings Ctr., Ste. 221-U, Beverly, MA 01915, (978)927-8330

Amer. Assn. of Handwriting Analysts [10751], 4143 Lorna Ct. SE, Lacey, WA 98503, (360)455-4551

Amer. Assn. for the Hard of Hearing [★16682]

Amer. Assn. on Hea. and Disability [14359], 110 N Washington St., Ste. 328-J, Rockville, MD 20850, (301)545-6140

Amer. Assn. for Hea. Educ. [16476], 1900 Assn. Dr., Reston, VA 20191-1599, (703)476-3400

Amer. Assn. for Hea. Freedom [★16302]

Amer. Assn. for Hea., Physical Educ. and Recreation [★8715]

Amer. Assn. of Healthcare Administrative Mgt. [15278], 11240 Waples Mill Rd., Ste. 200, Fairfax, VA 22030, (703)281-4043

Amer. Assn. of Healthcare Consultants [15031], 1205 Johnson Ferry Rd., Ste. 136-420, Marietta, GA 30068, (770)635-8758

Amer. Assn. of Heart Failure Nurses [15708], 15000 Commerce Pkwy., Ste. C, Mount Laurel, NJ 08054, (856)642-4422

Amer. Assn. of Hide, Skin and Leather Merchants [★2207]

Amer. Assn. of Hip and Knee Surgeons [16791], 6300 N River Rd., Ste. 615, Rosemont, IL 60018-4237, (847)698-1200

Amer. Assn. of Hispanic CPAs [★15]

Amer. Assn. for History and Computing [6944], 1900 W 7th St., CMB 480, Plainview, TX 79072

Amer. Assn. for the History of Medicine [9741], 4609 Gustafson Dr. NW, Gig Harbor, WA 98335

Amer. Assn. for the History of Nursing [9742], 10200 W 44th Ave., Ste. 304, Wheat Ridge, CO 80033, (303)422-2685

Amer. Assn. for Home-Based Early Interventionists [17234], Utah State Univ., 6500 Old Main Hill, Logan, UT 84322-6500, (800)396-6144

Amer. Assn. for Homecare [14841], 2011 Crystal Dr., Ste. 725, Arlington, VA 22202, (703)836-6263

Amer. Assn. of Homes for the Aging [★10851]

Amer. Assn. of Homes for the Aging [★10851]

Amer. Assn. of Homes and Services for the Aging [10851], 2519 Connecticut Ave. NW, Washington, DC 20008-1520, (202)783-2242

Amer. Assn. of Homes and Services for the Aging [★10851]

Amer. Assn. for Horsemanship Safety [12973], 4125 Fish Creek Rd., Estes Park, CO 80517, (512)488-2220

Amer. Assn. of Hosp. Accountants [★15258]

Amer. Assn. of Hosp. Consultants [★15031]

Amer. Assn. of Hosp. Dentists [★14310]

Amer. Assn. of Hosp. and Healthcare Podiatrists [16285], 8508 18th Ave., Brooklyn, NY 11214, (718)259-1822

Amer. Assn. of Hosp. Podiatrists [★16285]

Amer. Assn. of Housecall and Mobile Veterinarians [16980], Shannon Stanek, DVM, 609 N Pottstown Pike, Exton, PA 19341-1678, (610)363-7479

Amer. Assn. of Housing Educators - Address unknown since 2010.

Amer. Assn. of Human-Animal Bond Veterinarians [10905], 618 Church St., Ste. 220, Nashville, TN 37219, (615)254-3687

Amer. Assn. of Human Design Practitioners [1036], PO Box 195, Ranchos de Taos, NM 87557-0195

Amer. Assn. for Humanistic Psychology [★16388]

Amer. Assn. of Immunologists [15096], 9650 Rockville Pike, Bethesda, MD 20814-3998, (301)634-7178

Amer. Assn. of Importers and Breeders of Belgian Draft Horses [★4570]

Amer. Assn. for the Improvement of Boxing [22433], 86 Fletcher Ave., Mount Vernon, NY 10552-3319, (914)664-4571

Amer. Assn. of Independent Coll. and Univ. Presidents [★8285]

Amer. Assn. of Independent Music [3048], 853 Broadway, Ste. 1406, New York, NY 10003, (212)999-6113

Amer. Assn. of Independent News Distributors [2795], 93 2nd St., Harrison, NY 10528, (877)GOA-AIND

Amer. Assn. on Indian Affairs [★18150]

Amer. Assn. of Individual Investors [8184], 625 N Michigan Ave., Chicago, IL 60611, (312)280-0170

Amer. Assn. of Indus. Editors [★809]

Amer. Assn. of Indus. Editors [★809]

Amer. Assn. of Indus. Nurses [★15713]

Amer. Assn. of Inhalation Therapists [★16834]

Amer. Assn. for Inhalation Therapy [★16834]

Amer. Assn. of Inside Sales Professionals [3156], 14530 Florissant Path, Apple Valley, MN 55124, (800)604-7085

Amer. Assn. of Insurance Mgt. Consultants [856], Texas Insurance Consulting, 8980 Lakes at 610 Dr., Ste. 100, Houston, TX 77054, (713)664-6424

Amer. Assn. of Insurance Services [1926], 1745 S Naperville Rd., Wheaton, IL 60189-8132, (630)681-8347

Amer. Assn. of Integrated Healthcare Delivery Systems [15279], 4435 Waterfront Dr., Ste. 101, PO Box 4913, Glen Allen, VA 23060, (804)747-5823

Amer. Assn. of Integrative Medicine [15391], 2750 E Sunshine St., Springfield, MO 65804, (417)881-9995

Amer. Assn. on Intellectual and Developmental Disabilities [15487], 501 3rd St. NW, Ste. 200, Washington, DC 20001-1512, (202)387-1968

Amer. Assn. for the Intl. Commn. of Jurists [17810], 280 Madison Ave., Ste. 1102, New York, NY 10016, (212)972-0883

Amer. Assn. for the Intl. Commn. of Jurists [17810], 280 Madison Ave., Ste. 1102, New York, NY 10016, (212)972-0883

Amer. Assn. for Jewish Educ. [★8426]

Amer. Assn. for Junior Colleges [★7889]

Amer. Assn. for Justice [6041], 777 6th St. NW, Ste. 200, Washington, DC 20001, (202)965-3500

Amer. Assn. of Kidney Patients [15541], 3505 E Frontage Rd., Ste. 315, Tampa, FL 33607-1796, (800)749-2257

Amer. Assn. for Klinefelter Syndrome Info. and Support [14694], 2945 W Farwell Ave., Chicago, IL 60645-2925, (888)466-5747

Amer. Assn. for Lab. Accreditation [7017], 5301 Buckeystown Pike, Ste. 350, Frederick, MD 21704, (301)644-3248

Amer. Assn. for Lab. Animal Sci. [13757], 9190 Crestwyn Hills Dr., Memphis, TN 38125-8538, (901)754-8620

The Amer. Assn. of Language Specialists [3495], PO Box 27306, Washington, DC 20038-7306

The Amer. Assn. of Language Specialists [3495], PO Box 27306, Washington, DC 20038-7306

Amer. Assn. of Law Libraries [9951], 105 W Adams St., Ste. 3300, Chicago, IL 60603, (312)939-4764

Amer. Assn. of Legal Nurse Consultants [15240], 401 N Michigan Ave., Chicago, IL 60611, (877)402-2562

Amer. Assn. for Leisure and Recreation and Amer. Assn. for Active Lifestyles and Fitness [★12762]

Amer. Assn. of Lib. Trustees [★9970]

Amer. Assn. for Long-Term Care Insurance [1927], 3835 E Thousand Oaks Blvd., Ste. 336, Westlake Village, CA 91362, (818)597-3227

Amer. Assn. of Lost Children [12542], 539 Fred Rogers Dr., Latrobe, PA 15650, (724)537-6970

Amer. Assn. of Managed Care Nurses [15709], 4435 Waterfront Dr., Ste. 101, Glen Allen, VA 23060, (804)747-9698

Amer. Assn. of Managing Gen. Agents [1928], 150 S Warner Rd., Ste. 156, King of Prussia, PA 19406, (610)225-1999

Amer. Assn. of Marriage Counselors [★16447]

Amer. Assn. of Marriage and Family Counselors [★16447]

Amer. Assn. for Marriage and Family Therapy [16447], 112 S Alfred St., Alexandria, VA 22314-3061, (703)838-9808

Amer. Assn. of Meat Processors [2430], PO Box 269, Elizabethtown, PA 17022, (717)367-1168

Reference to "IO" in place of a book number signifies that the association may be found in the 50th edition of International Organizations.

Amer. Assn. of Medical Assistants [15315], 20 N Wacker Dr., Ste. 1575, Chicago, IL 60606, (312)899-1500

Amer. Assn. of Medical Audit Specialists [15280], 10200 W 44th Ave., Ste. 304, Wheat Ridge, CO 80033, (720)881-6045

Amer. Assn. for Medical Chronobiology and Chronotherapeutics [13834], Univ. of Minnesota, Dept. of Pathology, 640 Jackson St., St. Paul, MN 55101, (651)254-9630

Amer. Assn. of Medical Clinics [★14891]

Amer. Assn. of Medical Dosimetrists [15354], 2325 Dulles Corner Blvd., Ste. 500, Herndon, VA 20171, (703)677-8071

Amer. Assn. of Medical Record Librarians [★15331]

Amer. Assn. of Medical Rev. Officers [14867], PO Box 12873, Research Triangle Park, NC 27709, (800)489-1839

Amer. Assn. of Medical Social Workers [★13222]

Amer. Assn. of Medical Soc. Executives [15392], 555 E Wells St., Ste. 1100, Milwaukee, WI 53202-3823, (414)221-9275

Amer. Assn. for Medical Systems and Informatics [★14219]

Amer. Assn. for Medical Transcription [★15318]

Amer. Assn. of Medico-Legal Consultants - Defunct.

Amer. Assn. on Mental Deficiency [★15487]

Amer. Assn. on Mental Retardation [★15487]

Amer. Assn. of Minority Enterprise Small Bus. Investment Companies [★2522]

Amer. Assn. of Motor Vehicle Administrators [5290], 4301 Wilson Blvd., Ste. 400, Arlington, VA 22203, (703)522-4200

Amer. Assn. for Museum Volunteers [10106], PO Box 9494, Washington, DC 20016

Amer. Assn. of Museums [10107], 1575 Eye St. NW, Ste. 400, Washington, DC 20005, (202)289-1818

Amer. Assn. for Music Therapy [★16451]

Amer. Assn. of Naturopathic Midwives [15530], PO Box 672, Meredith, NH 03253

Amer. Assn. of Naturopathic Physicians [15531], 4435 Wisconsin Ave. NW, Ste. 403, Washington, DC 20016, (202)237-8150

Amer. Assn. of Nephrology Nurses and Technicians [★15543]

Amer. Assn. of Neurological Surgeons [15682], 5550 Meadowbrook Dr., Rolling Meadows, IL 60008, (847)378-0500

Amer. Assn. of Neurological Surgeons [15682], 5550 Meadowbrook Dr., Rolling Meadows, IL 60008, (847)378-0500

Amer. Assn. of Neuromuscular and Electrodiagnostic Medicine [15565], 2621 Superior Dr. NW, Rochester, MN 55901, (507)288-0100

Amer. Assn. of Neuropathologists [16110], Peggy Harris, Admin., Case Western Reserve Univ., 2103 Cornell Rd., WRB 5101, Cleveland, OH 44106, (216)368-3671

Amer. Assn. of Neuroscience Nurses [15710], 4700 W Lake Ave., Glenview, IL 60025, (847)375-4733

Amer. Assn. of Neuroscience Nurses [15710], 4700 W Lake Ave., Glenview, IL 60025, (847)375-4733

Amer. Assn. for Nude Recreation [10340], 1703 N Main St., Ste. E, Kissimmee, FL 34744, (407)933-2064

Amer. Assn. of Nurse Anesthetists [15711], 222 S Prospect Ave., Park Ridge, IL 60068, (847)692-7050

Amer. Assn. of Nurse Assessment Coordinators [14749], 400 S Colorado Blvd., Ste. 600, Denver, CO 80246, (800)768-1880

Amer. Assn. of Nurse Attorneys [15241], PO Box 14218, Lenexa, KS 66285-4218, (877)538-2262

Amer. Assn. of Nurse Life Care Planners [15712], 3267 E 3300 S, No. 309, Salt Lake City, UT 84109, (801)274-1184

Amer. Assn. of Nurse-Midwives [★15719]

Amer. Assn. of Nurserymen [★4740]

Amer. Assn. of Nurserymen, Florists and Seedsmen [★4740]

Amer. Assn. of Nursing Homes [★14696]

Amer. Assn. of Nutritional Consultants [15814], 400 Oakhill Dr., Winona Lake, IN 46590, (888)828-2262

Amer. Assn. of Obstetricians and Gynecologists [★15868]

Amer. Assn. of Occupational Hea. Nurses [15713], 7794 Grow Dr., Pensacola, FL 32514, (850)474-6963

Amer. Assn. of Oilwell Drilling Contractors [★2654]

Amer. Assn. of Oilwell Drilling Contractors [★2654]

Amer. Assn. for Ophthalmic Standardized Echography [15938], 1345 Cedar St., Iowa City, IA 52245, (319)337-4066

Amer. Assn. of Ophthalmology [★15936]

Amer. Assn. of Oral and Maxillofacial Surgeons [16002], 9700 W Bryn Mawr Ave., Rosemont, IL 60018-5701, (847)678-6200

Amer. Assn. of Oral and Plastic Surgeons [★14172]

Amer. Assn. of Oriental Healing Arts [★15263]

Amer. Assn. of Oriental Medicine and Acupuncture and Oriental Medicine Alliance [★16011]

Amer. Assn. of Oriental Medicine and Acupuncture and Oriental Medicine Alliance [★16011]

Amer. Assn. of Orthodontists [14251], 401 N Lindbergh Blvd., St. Louis, MO 63141-7816, (314)993-1700

Amer. Assn. of Orthopaedic Executives [16020], 6300 N River Rd., Ste. 727, Rosemont, IL 60018, (800)247-9699

Amer. Assn. of Orthopedic Medicine [16021], 600 Pembrook Dr., Woodland Park, CO 80863, (800)992-2063

Amer. Assn. of Orthopic Technicians [★15937]

Amer. Assn. of Osteopathic Colleges [★16057]

Amer. Assn. of Osteopathic Specialists [★16058]

Amer. Assn. of Paging Carriers [★808]

Amer. Assn. for Paralegal Educ. [8497], 19 Mantua Rd., Mount Royal, NJ 08061, (856)423-2829

Amer. Assn. of Paranormal Investigators [2624], 13973 E Utah Cir., Aurora, CO 80012, (303)260-9634

Amer. Assn. of Parenthood Physicians [★12027]

Amer. Assn. for Partial Hospitalization [★16335]

Amer. Assn. of Pastoral Counselors [19630], 9504A Lee Hwy., Fairfax, VA 22031-2303, (703)385-6967

Amer. Assn. of Pathologists [★16116]

Amer. Assn. of Pathologists' Assistants [16111], 2345 Rice St., Ste. 220, St. Paul, MN 55113, (651)697-9264

Amer. Assn. of Pathologists and Bacteriologists [★16116]

Amer. Assn. of Pediatric Ophthalmology [★15939]

Amer. Assn. for Pediatric Ophthalmology and Strabismus [15939], PO Box 193832, San Francisco, CA 94119-3832, (415)561-8505

Amer. Assn. of People with Disabilities [11757], 1629 K St. NW, Ste. 950, Washington, DC 20006, (202)457-0046

Amer. Assn. of Pesticide Safety Educators [4326], PO Box 4535, Ithaca, NY 14852-4535, (607)255-7525

Amer. Assn. of Petroleum Geologists [6907], PO Box 979, Tulsa, OK 74101-0979, (918)584-2555

Amer. Assn. of Petroleum Landmen [★2637]

Amer. Assn. of Pharmaceutical Scientists [7243], 2107 Wilson Blvd., Ste. 700, Arlington, VA 22201-3042, (703)243-2800

Amer. Assn. of Pharmaceutical Scientists [7243], 2107 Wilson Blvd., Ste. 700, Arlington, VA 22201-3042, (703)243-2800

Amer. Assn. of Pharmacy Technicians [16168], PO Box 1447, Greensboro, NC 27402, (336)333-9356

Amer. Assn. of Philosophy Teachers [8701], 1245 7th Ave. N, St. Cloud, MN 56303

Amer. Assn. of Phonetic Sciences [10433], PO Box 23005, St. Louis, MO 63156, (314)293-1940

Amer. Assn. for Physical Activity and Recreation [12762], 1900 Assn. Dr., Reston, VA 20191-1598, (703)476-3430

Amer. Assn. of Physical Anthropologists,[6129], Univ. of South Florida, Dept. of Anthropology, Tampa, FL 33620-8100, (800)627-0326

Amer. Assn. of Physician-Hospital Organizations [★15279]

Amer. Assn. of Physician Offices and Labs. [15230], 10401 Kingston Pike, Knoxville, TN 37922, (865)470-9605

Amer. Assn. of Physician Specialists [16058], 5550 W Executive Dr., Ste. 400, Tampa, FL 33609, (813)433-2277

Amer. Assn. of Physicians for Human Rights [★14577]

Amer. Assn. of Physicians of Indian Origin [16250], 600 Enterprise Dr., Ste. 108, Oak Brook, IL 60523, (630)530-2277

Amer. Assn. of Physicists in Medicine [16275], 1 Physics Ellipse, College Park, MD 20740, (301)209-3350

Amer. Assn. of Physicists in Medicine [16275], 1 Physics Ellipse, College Park, MD 20740, (301)209-3350

Amer. Assn. of Physics Teachers [8725], 1 Physics Ellipse, College Park, MD 20740-3845, (301)209-3300

Amer. Assn. of Plastic Surgeons [14172], 500 Cummings Ctr., Ste. 4550, Beverly, MA 01915, (978)927-8330

Amer. Assn. of Poison Control Centers [16891], 515 King St., Ste. 510, Alexandria, VA 22314, (703)894-1858

Amer. Assn. of Police Polygraphists [5470], PO Box 657, Waynesville, OH 45068-0657, (937)728-7827

Amer. Assn. of Political Consultants [18372], 8400 Westpark Dr., 2nd Fl., Washington, DC 20003, (703)245-8020

Amer. Assn. of Port Authorities [5505], 1010 Duke St., Alexandria, VA 22314-3589, (703)684-5700

Amer. Assn. of Port Authorities [5505], 1010 Duke St., Alexandria, VA 22314-3589, (703)684-5700

Amer. Assn. of Preferred Provider Organizations [14851], 222 S First St., Ste. 303, Louisville, KY 40202, (502)403-1122

Amer. Assn. of Presidents of Independent Colleges and Universities [8285], Box 7070, Provo, UT 84602-7070, (801)422-5624

Amer. Assn. of Private Railroad Car Owners [2984], 622 N Reed St., Joliet, IL 60435, (815)722-8877

Amer. Assn. of Pro Life Obstetricians and Gynecologists [18549], 339 River Ave., Holland, MI 49423, (616)546-2639

Amer. Assn. of Professional Apiculturists [3814], USDA ARS Honey Bee Lab, 1157 Ben Hur Rd., Baton Rouge, LA 70808, (225)767-9284

Amer. Assn. of Professional Bridal Consultants [★469]

Amer. Assn. of Professional Bridal Consultants [★469]

Amer. Assn. of Professional Consultants [★861]

Amer. Assn. of Professional Hypnotherapists [15082], 16055 SW Walker Rd., No. 406, Beaverton, OR 97006, (503)533-7106

Amer. Assn. of Professional Landmen [2637], 4100 Fossil Creek Blvd., Fort Worth, TX 76137-2723, (817)847-7700

Amer. Assn. of Professional Standards Rev. Organizations [★16506]

Amer. Assn. of Professional Tech. Analysts [3387], 209 W Jackson Blvd., 6th Fl., Chicago, IL 60606, (972)213-5816

Amer. Assn. to Promote the Teaching of Speech to the Deaf [★14912]

Amer. Assn. to Promote the Teaching of Speech to the Deaf [★14912]

Amer. Assn. for Protecting Children [★11187]

Amer. Assn. of Psychiatric Administrators [15032], PO Box 570218, Dallas, TX 75357-0218, (800)650-5888

Amer. Assn. of Psychiatric Social Workers [★13222]

Amer. Assn. of Psychiatric Technicians [16323], 1220 S St., Ste. 100, Sacramento, CA 95811-7138, (800)391-7589

Amer. Assn. for Psychoanalysis in Clinical Social Work [13212], Deborah Dale, Admin., 4834 Highgate Dr., Durham, NC 27713, (919)933-4055

Amer. Assn. of Psychoanalytic Physicians [★16354]

Amer. Assn. of Public Hea. Dentistry [14252], 3085 Stevenson Dr., Ste. 200, Springfield, IL 62703, (217)529-6941

Amer. Assn. of Public Hea. Dentists [★14252]

Amer. Assn. of Public Hea. Physicians [16477], 1605 Pebble Beach Blvd., Green Cove Springs, FL 32043-8077, (904)860-9208

Amer. Assn. of Public Hea. Veterinarians [16981], 3221 Briarcliff Dr., Anchorage, AK 99508

Amer. Assn. of Public Human Services - Defunct.

A star before a book entry number signifies that the name is not listed separately, but is mentioned within the entry.

Amer. Assn. for Public Opinion Res. [18395], 111 Deer Lake Rd., Ste. 100, Deerfield, IL 60015, (847)205-2651

Amer. Assn. of Public Welfare Info. Systems Mgt. [★13170]

Amer. Assn. of Radon Scientists and Technologists [6892], PO Box 2109, Fletcher, NC 28732, (866)772-2778

Amer. Assn. of Railroad Superintendents [2985], PO Box 200, LaFox, IL 60147, (630)762-0754

Amer. Assn. of the Red Cross [★12803]

Amer. Assn. of Registration Executives [★5930]

Amer. Assn. for Respiratory Care [16834], 9425 N MacArthur Blvd., Ste. 100, Irving, TX 75063-4706, (972)243-2272

Amer. Assn. for Respiratory Therapy [★16834]

Amer. Assn. of Retirement Communities [12915], PO Box 2931, Statesboro, GA 30459, (706)496-7047

Amer. Assn. of Riding Schools [22673], 8375 Coldwater Rd., Davison, MI 48423-8966, (810)496-0360

Amer. Assn. for Russian Language, Culture and Educ. [10516], 451 Hungerford Dr., Ste. 300, Rockville, MD 20850, (240)813-0610

Amer. Assn. of Safety Councils [12974], Brandy Howard, 1145 Court St., Clearwater, FL 33756, (727)373-7233

Amer. Assn. of Safety Councils [12974], Brandy Howard, 1145 Court St., Clearwater, FL 33756, (727)373-7233

Amer. Assn. of School Administrators [7651], 801 N Quincy St., Ste. 700, Arlington, VA 22203, (703)528-0700

Amer. Assn. of School Librarians [9952], 50 E Huron St., Chicago, IL 60611-2729, (312)280-4382

Amer. Assn. of School Personnel Administrators [7652], 11863 W 112th St., Ste. 100, Overland Park, KS 66210, (913)327-1222

Amer. Assn. of School Personnel Administrators [7652], 11863 W 112th St., Ste. 100, Overland Park, KS 66210, (913)327-1222

Amer. Assn. of School Photographers [★2733]

Amer. Assn. of School Photographers [★2733]

Amer. Assn. of School Physicians [★14892]

Amer. Assn. of Schools and Dept. of Journalism [★7663]

Amer. Assn. of Schools of Theological Schools [★9007]

Amer. Assn. of Schools of Theological Schools [★9007]

Amer. Assn. of Senior Physicians [★15395]

Amer. Assn. of Ser. Coordinators [1792], PO Box 1178, Powell, OH 43065-1178, (614)848-5958

Amer. Assn. of Sex Educators and Counselors [★16644]

Amer. Assn. of Sexuality Educators, Counselors and Therapists [16644], 1444 I St. NW, Ste. 700, Washington, DC 20005, (202)449-1099

Amer. Assn. of Sheep and Goat Practitioners [★16982]

Amer. Assn. of Sheriff Posses and Riding Clubs - Defunct.

Amer. Assn. of Sleep Disorders [★16660]

Amer. Assn. of Sleep Disorders Centers [★16660]

Amer. Assn. of Sleep Technologists [16661], 2510 N Frontage Rd., Darien, IL 60561, (630)737-9704

Amer. Assn. for Small Dredging and Marine Constr. Companies [★2355]

Amer. Assn. of Small Ruminant Practitioners [16982], PO Box 3614, Montgomery, AL 36109, (334)517-1233

Amer. Assn. of SNAP Directors [5975], Division of Family Support Services, Dept. of Human Services, PO Box 25352, Oklahoma City, OK 73125-5352, (405)521-2937

Amer. Assn. of Snowboard Instructors [22923], 133 S Van Gordon St., Ste. 200, Lakewood, CO 80228, (303)987-9390

Amer. Assn. of Social Workers [★13222]

Amer. Assn. of Spanish Timbrado Breeders [21208], 122 Quail Dr., Chula Vista, CA 91911, (619)426-8276

Amer. Assn. of Spinal Cord Injury Professionals, Nurses Sect. [★15699]

Amer. Assn. of Spinal Cord Injury Professionals, Psychologists and Social Workers Sect. [16695], 801 18th St. NW, Washington, DC 20006, (202)416-7704

Amer. Assn. State Boards, Veterinary [★16988]

Amer. Assn. of State Climatologists [7103], State Climatologist, California Dept. of Water Resources, Division of Flood Mgt., 3310 El Camino Ave., Rm. 200, Sacramento, CA 95821, (916)574-2830

Amer. Assn. of State Colleges and Universities [7868], 1307 New York Ave. NW, Washington, DC 20005-4701, (202)293-7070

Amer. Assn. of State Compensation Insurance Funds [1929], 855 Front St., Helena, MT 59601, (406)495-5015

Amer. Assn. of State Compensation Insurance Funds [1929], 855 Front St., Helena, MT 59601, (406)495-5015

Amer. Assn. of State Counseling Boards [14187], 305 N Beech Cir., Broken Arrow, OK 74012-2293, (918)994-4413

Amer. Assn. of State Highway Officials [★6027]

Amer. Assn. of State Highway and Trans. Officials [6027], 444 N Capitol St. NW, Ste. 249, Washington, DC 20001-1539, (202)624-5800

Amer. Assn. for State and Local History [9743], 1717 Church St., Nashville, TN 37203-2921, (615)320-3203

Amer. Assn. of State Psychology Boards [★16392]

Amer. Assn. of State Psychology Boards [★16392]

Amer. Assn. of State Ser. Commissions [5903], 1875 K St. NW, 5th Fl., Washington, DC 20006, (202)729-8179

Amer. Assn. of State Social Work Boards [★13215]

Amer. Assn. of State Troopers [5685], 1949 Raymond Diehl Rd., Tallahassee, FL 32308, (850)385-7904

Amer. Assn. of Stomatologists - Defunct.

Amer. Assn. of Stratigraphic Palynologists [★7216]

Amer. Assn. of Stratigraphic Palynologists [7216], PO Box 2197, Houston, TX 77252-2197

Amer. Assn. for the Stud. of the Feebleminded [★15487]

Amer. Assn. for the Stud. of Goiter [★16883]

Amer. Assn. for the Stud. of Headache [★14686]

Amer. Assn. for the Stud. of Liver Diseases [14978], 1001 N Fairfax, Ste. 400, Alexandria, VA 22314-1587, (703)299-9766

Amer. Assn. for the Study of Neoplastic Diseases - Defunct.

Amer. Assn. of Suicidology [13293], 5221 Wisconsin Ave. NW, Washington, DC 20015, (202)237-2280

Amer. Assn. of Sunday and Feature Editors [★2872]

Amer. Assn. of Surgeon Assistants [★16792]

Amer. Assn. for the Surgery of Trauma [16923], 633 N St. Clair St., Ste. 2600, Chicago, IL 60611, (312)202-5252

Amer. Assn. of Surgical Physician Assistants [16792], PO Box 781688, Sebastian, FL 32978, (772)388-0498

Amer. Assn. of Swine Practitioners [★16983]

Amer. Assn. of Swine Practitioners [★16983]

Amer. Assn. of Swine Veterinarians [16983], 830 26th St., Perry, IA 50220-1703, (515)465-5255

Amer. Assn. of Swine Veterinarians [16983], 830 26th St., Perry, IA 50220-1703, (515)465-5255

Amer. Assn. of Teacher Educators in Agriculture [★7706]

Amer. Assn. of Teachers of Arabic [8457], 3416 Primm Ln., Birmingham, AL 35216, (205)822-6800

Amer. Assn. of Teachers of Chinese Language and Culture [★7839]

Amer. Assn. of Teachers Colleges [★8940]

Amer. Assn. of Teachers of Esperanto [8458], Sally Lawton, 12 Stage Rd., Westhampton, MA 01027-9603

Amer. Assn. of Teachers of French [8459], Southern Illinois Univ., Mail Code 4510, Carbondale, IL 62901, (618)453-5731

Amer. Assn. of Teachers of French [8459], Southern Illinois Univ., Mail Code 4510, Carbondale, IL 62901, (618)453-5731

Amer. Assn. of Teachers of German [8460], 112 Haddontowne Ct., No. 104, Cherry Hill, NJ 08034-3668, (856)795-5553

Amer. Assn. of Teachers of Italian [8461], Indiana Univ., Dept. of French and Italian, Ballentine Hall 642, 1020 E Kirkwood Ave., Bloomington, IN 47405-6601

Amer. Assn. of Teachers of Italian [8461], Indiana Univ., Dept. of French and Italian, Ballentine Hall 642, 1020 E Kirkwood Ave., Bloomington, IN 47405-6601

Amer. Assn. of Teachers of Journalism [★8437]

Amer. Assn. of Teachers of Korean - Defunct.

Amer. Assn. of Teachers of Slavic and East European Languages [8462], PO Box 569, Beloit, WI 53512-0569, (608)361-9697

Amer. Assn. of Teachers of Spanish and Portuguese [8463], 900 Ladd Rd., Walled Lake, MI 48390, (248)960-2180

Amer. Assn. of Teachers of Spanish and Portuguese [8463], 900 Ladd Rd., Walled Lake, MI 48390, (248)960-2180

Amer. Assn. of Teachers of Turkic Languages [9021], Princeton Univ., Near Eastern Stud., 110 Jones Hall, Princeton, NJ 08544-1008, (609)258-1435

Amer. Assn. of Teachers of Turkish [★9021]

Amer. Assn. for Teaching and Curriculum [8941], Lynne Bailey, Exec. Sec., 4240 Yorketowne Rd., Orlando, FL 32812-7958

Amer. Assn. of Tech. High Schools and Inst. [★8964]

Amer. Assn. of Tech. High Schools and Inst. [★8964]

Amer. Assn. for Tech. in Psychiatry [16324], PO Box 11, Bronx, NY 10464-0011, (718)502-9469

Amer. Assn. of Textile Chemists and Colorists [7563], PO Box 12215, Research Triangle Park, NC 27709-2215, (919)549-8141

Amer. Assn. of Textile Chemists and Colorists [7563], PO Box 12215, Research Triangle Park, NC 27709-2215, (919)549-8141

Amer. Assn. for Textile Technology - Defunct.

Amer. Assn. of Theatre Organ Enthusiasts [★10157]

Amer. Assn. of Theological Schools [★9007]

Amer. Assn. of Theological Schools [★9007]

Amer. Assn. for Therapeutic Humor [★16841]

Amer. Assn. for Thoracic Surgery [16877], 500 Cummings Ctr., Ste. 4550, Beverly, MA 01915-6183, (978)927-8330

Amer. Assn. of Tissue Banks [16896], 1320 Old Chain Bridge Rd., Ste. 450, McLean, VA 22101, (703)827-9582

Amer. Assn. of Traditional Chinese Veterinary Medicine [13653], Cheryl Chrisman, DVM, 10145 SW 52nd Rd., Gainesville, FL 32608, (352)672-6400

Amer. Assn. for the Treatment of Opioid Dependence [16734], 225 Varick St., 4th Fl., New York, NY 10014, (212)566-5555

Amer. Assn. for Ukrainian Stud. [8397], 34 Kirkland St., Cambridge, MA 02138, (617)495-4053

Amer. Assn. for Ukrainian Stud. [8397], 34 Kirkland St., Cambridge, MA 02138, (617)495-4053

Amer. Assn. for the United Nations [★18748]

Amer. Assn. of Univ. Administrators [7653], PO Box 29, Stoughton, MA 02072, (781)752-7878

Amer. Assn. of Univ. Affiliated Programs for the Developmentally Disabled [★12497]

Amer. Assn. of Univ. Affiliated Programs for Persons With Developmental Disabilities [★12497]

Amer. Assn. of Univ. Instructors in Accounting [★5]

Amer. Assn. of Univ. Professors [8756], 1133 19th St. NW, Ste. 200, Washington, DC 20036, (202)737-5900

Amer. Assn. of Univ. Teachers of Insurance [★8322]

Amer. Assn. of Univ. Women [9051], 1111 16th St. NW, Washington, DC 20036, (202)785-7700

Amer. Assn. of Univ. I Women Educational Found. [9052], 1111 16th St. NW, Washington, DC 20036, (800)326-AAUW

Amer. Assn. of Univ. Women I Legal Advocacy Fund [6072], 1111 16th St. NW, Washington, DC 20036, (202)785-7700

Amer. Assn. of Utilization Mgt. Nurses - Defunct.

Amer. Assn. of Variable Star Observers [6221], 49 Bay State Rd., Cambridge, MA 02138, (617)354-0484

Amer. Assn. of Veterinary Anatomists - Defunct.

Amer. Assn. of Veterinary Clinicians [16984], 422 Peppers Ferry Rd., No. 309, Christiansburg, VA 24073, (614)358-0417

Reference to "IO" in place of a book number signifies that the association may be found in the 50th edition of International Organizations.

Amer. Assn. of Veterinary Immunologists [16985], Univ. of Tennessee, Animal Sci. Dept., 114 McCord Hall, 2460 Morgan Cir., Knoxville, TN 37996-4588, (865)974-7225

Amer. Assn. of Veterinary Lab. Diagnosticians [16986], PO Box 1770, Davis, CA 95617, (530)754-9719

Amer. Assn. of Veterinary Nutritionists [★16972]

Amer. Assn. of Veterinary Parasitologists [16987], Bayer HealthCare LLC, Animal Hea., 12809 Shawnee Mission Pkwy., Shawnee, KS 66216, (913)268-2503

Amer. Assn. of Veterinary State Boards [16988], 380 W 22nd St., Ste. 101, Kansas City, MO 64108, (816)931-1504

Amer. Assn. of Visually Impaired Attorneys - Address unknown since 2010.

Amer. Assn. for Vital Records and Public Hea. Statistics [★5930]

Amer. Assn. for Vocational Instructional Materials [9037], 220 Smithonia Rd., Winterville, GA 30683, (706)742-5355

Amer. Assn. of Wardens and Superintendents [★11727]

Amer. Assn. of Wardens and Superintendents [★11727]

Amer. Assn. of Webmasters [6526], PO Box 1284, Burlingame, CA 94011, (888)519-9119

Amer. Assn. of Wedding Planners [2427], Weddings Beautiful Worldwide, 2225 Grove Ave., Richmond, VA 23220-4444, (804)342-6061

Amer. Assn. of Wildlife Veterinarians [16989], Dr. Mark Drew, Treas., Idaho Dept. of Fish and Game, 16569 S 10th Ave., Caldwell, ID 83607

Amer. Assn. of Wine Economists [3670], New York Univ., Economics Dept., 19 W 4th St., 6th Fl., New York, NY 10012, (212)992-8083

Amer. Assn. of Women [18439], 337 Washington Blvd., Ste. 1, Marina del Rey, CA 90292, (310)822-4449

Amer. Assn. for Women in Community Colleges [9053], Salt Lake Community Coll., PO Box 30808, Salt Lake City, UT 84130-0808, (801)975-4225

Amer. Assn. for Women in Community and Junior Colleges [★9053]

Amer. Assn. of Women Dentists [14253], 216 W Jackson Blvd., Ste. 625, Chicago, IL 60606, (800)920-2293

Amer. Assn. for Women Podiatrists [16286], Sheryl Strich, DPM, Pres., 6042 Sierra Siena, Irvine, CA 92603, (949)854-3636

Amer. Assn. for Women Radiologists [16517], 4550 Post Oak Pl., Ste. 342, Houston, TX 77027, (713)965-0566

Amer. Assn. of Women Radiologists [★16517]

Amer. Assn. of Women Voters [★18439]

Amer. Assn. of Woodturners [21424], 222 Landmark Ctr., 75 W 5th St., St. Paul, MN 55102, (651)484-9094

Amer. Assn. of Woodturners [21424], 222 Landmark Ctr., 75 W 5th St., St. Paul, MN 55102, (651)484-9094

Amer. Assn. of Working People [11928], 4435 Waterfront Dr., Ste. 101, Glen Allen, VA 23060, (804)527-1905

Amer. Assn. for World Hea. - Defunct.

Amer. Assn. of Yellow Pages Publishers [★2968]

Amer. Assn. of Youth Museums [★10113]

Amer. Assn. of Zoo Keepers [7628], 3601 SW 29th St., Ste. 133, Topeka, KS 66614-2054, (785)273-9149

Amer. Assn. of Zoo Veterinarians [16990], 581705 White Oak Rd., Yulee, FL 32097, (904)225-3275

Amer. Assn. of Zoological Parks and Aquariums [★7633]

Amer. Associations of Spanish Speaking CPA's [★15]

Amer. Astronautical Soc. [6081], 6352 Rolling Mill Pl., Ste. 102, Springfield, VA 22152-2370, (703)866-0020

Amer. Astronautical Soc. [6081], 6352 Rolling Mill Pl., Ste. 102, Springfield, VA 22152-2370, (703)866-0020

Amer. Astronomical Soc. [6222], 2000 Florida Ave. NW, Ste. 400, Washington, DC 20009-1231, (202)328-2010

Amer. Atheist Women - Defunct.

Amer. Atheists [19302], PO Box 158, Cranford, NJ 07016, (908)276-7300

Amer. Athletic Assn. for the Deaf [★22531]

Amer. Auction Bridge League [★21239]

Amer. Auction Bridge League [★21239]

Amer. Audiology Soc. [★14914]

Amer. Auditory Soc. [14914], 19 Mantua Rd., Mount Royal, NJ 08061, (856)423-3118

Amer. Austin/Bantam Club [20987], Marilyn Sanson, Treas., 7704 Bridgeport Kirkville Rd., Kirkville, NY 13082, (315)656-7568

Amer. Australian Assn. [18939], 50 Broadway, Ste. 2003, New York, NY 10004, (212)338-6860

American-Austrian Cultural Soc. [18940], Mr. Michael Korenchuk, Treas., 116 E Melrose St., Chevy Chase, MD 20815

American-Austrian Soc. [★18940]

Amer. Autism Alliance [13778], 501 N Wymore Park Rd., Winter Park, FL 32789, (407)342-1259

Amer. Auto Racing Writers and Broadcasters Assn. [22240], 922 N Pass Ave., Burbank, CA 91505-2703, (818)842-7005

Amer. Autoduel Assn. [21739], PO Box 18957, Austin, TX 78760, (512)447-7866

Amer. Autoimmune Related Diseases Assn. [15097], 22100 Gratiot Ave., Eastpointe, MI 48021, (586)776-3900

Amer. Auto. Assn. [346], AAA Mid-Atlantic, One River Pl., Wilmington, DE 19801, (800)763-9900

Amer. Automobile Mfrs. Assn. - Defunct.

Amer. Auto. Touring Alliance [3547], Natl. Auto. Club, 1151 E Hillsdale Blvd., Foster City, CA 94404, (650)294-7000

Amer. Automotive Leasing Assn. [3074], 675 N Washington St., Ste. 410, Alexandria, VA 22314, (703)548-0777

Amer. Automotive Policy Coun. [284], 1401 H St., Nw, Ste. 780, Washington, DC 20005, (202)789-0030

Amer. Autonomic Soc. [15675], Ms. Anita Zeller, Exec. Sec., 18915 Inca Ave., Lakeville, MN 55044, (952)469-5837

Amer. Avalanche Assn. [12975], PO Box 2831, Pagosa Springs, CO 81147, (970)946-0822

Amer. Aviation Historical Soc. [20880], PO Box 3023, Huntington Beach, CA 92605-3023

Amer. Award Mfrs. Assn. [★382]

Amer. Azteca Horse Intl. Assn. [4524], PO Box 1577, Rapid City, SD 57709, (605)342-2322

Amer. Azteca Horse Intl. Assn. [4524], PO Box 1577, Rapid City, SD 57709, (605)342-2322

Amer. Back Soc. [16022], 2648 Intl. Blvd., Ste. 502, Oakland, CA 94601, (510)536-9929

Amer. Backflow Prevention Assn. [7587], PO Box 3051, Bryan, TX 77805-3051, (979)846-7606

Amer. Backflow Prevention Assn. [7587], PO Box 3051, Bryan, TX 77805-3051, (979)846-7606

Amer. Bahraini Friendship Soc. [17932], PO Box 5934, Friendship Sta. 234, Washington, DC 20016, (301)897-2162

Amer. Bail Coalition [383], 3857 Lewiston Pl., Fairfax, VA 22030, (877)385-9009

Amer. Bakers Assn. [386], 1300 I St. NW, Ste. 700 W, Washington, DC 20005, (202)789-0300

Amer. Balint Soc. [16365], 12 Goldfinch Dr., Wyomissing, PA 19610, (610)777-9456

Amer. Ballet Competition [9530], 4701 Bath St., No. 46, Philadelphia, PA 19137-2229, (215)636-9000

Amer. Ballet Theatre [★9537]

American Ballet Theatre [★9537]

Amer. Bamboo Soc. [6339], 315 S Coast Hwy. 101, Ste. U, PMB 212, Encinitas, CA 92024-3555

Amer. Bamboo Soc. [6339], 315 S Coast Hwy. 101, Ste. U, PMB 212, Encinitas, CA 92024-3555

Amer. Bandmasters Assn. [10138], 4250 Shorebrook Dr., Columbia, SC 29206, (803)787-6540

Amer. Bandstand Fan Club [23916], PO Box 131, Adamstown, PA 19501

Amer. Bandstand Memory Club [★23916]

Amer. Banjo Fraternity - Address unknown since 2010.

Amer. Bankers Assn. [396], 1120 Connecticut Ave. NW, Washington, DC 20036, (202)663-5564

Amer. Bankers Assn. and America's Community Bankers [★396]

Amer. Bankruptcy Inst. [5315], 44 Canal Center Plz., Ste. 400, Alexandria, VA 22314, (703)739-0800

Amer. Bantam Assn. [4802], PO Box 127, Augusta, NJ 07822, (973)383-8633

Amer. Baptist Foreign Mission Soc. [★19317]

Amer. Baptist Foreign Mission Soc. [★19317]

Amer. Baptist Historical Soc. [19306], 3001 Mercer Univ. Dr., Atlanta, GA 30341, (678)547-6680

Amer. Baptist Homes and Caring Ministries [19307], Judson Park, 23600 Marine View Dr. S, Des Moines, WA 98198, (800)ABC-3USA

Amer. Baptist Missionary Union [★19317]

Amer. Baptist Missionary Union [★19317]

Amer. Baptist Women [★19305]

Amer. Bar Assn. [5225], 321 N Clark St., Chicago, IL 60610, (312)988-5000

Amer. Bar Assn. Center on Children and the Law [11186], 740 15th St. NW, Washington, DC 20005-1019, (202)662-1720

Amer. Bar Assn. Center for Professional Responsibility [5226], 321 N Clark St., Chicago, IL 60654, (312)988-5325

Amer. Bar Assn. Commn. on Homelessness and Poverty [12153], 740 15th St. NW, Washington, DC 20005-1022, (202)662-1693

Amer. Bar Assn. I Commn. on Law and Aging [5641], 740 15th St. NW, Washington, DC 20005-1022, (202)662-8690

Amer. Bar Assn. I Commn. on Mental and Physical Disability Law [5508], 740 15th St. NW, 9th Fl., Washington, DC 20005, (202)662-1570

Amer. Bar Assn. Comm. on the Resolution of Minor Disputes [★5202]

Amer. Bar Assn. Criminal Justice Sect. [5642], 740 15th St. NW, 10th Fl., Washington, DC 20005-1019, (202)662-1500

Amer. Bar Assn. - Hea. Law Sect. [5509], 321 N Clark St., Chicago, IL 60610, (312)988-5000

Amer. Bar Assn. - Law Student Div. [8498], 321 N Clark St., Chicago, IL 60654, (312)988-5624

Amer. Bar Assn. I Natl. Conf. of Bar Foundations [5643], Div. for Bar Services, 321 N Clark St., Ste. 2000, Chicago, IL 60654, (312)988-5344

Amer. Bar Assn. Representation of the Homeless Proj. [★12153]

Amer. Bar Assn. Sect. of Dispute Resolution [5202], 740 15th St. NW, 9th Fl., Washington, DC 20005-1009, (202)662-1680

Amer. Bar Assn. - Sect. of Individual Rights and Responsibilities [17258], 740 15th St. NW, Washington, DC 20005-1009, (202)662-1030

Amer. Bar Assn. Sect. of Intl. Law [5584], 740 15th St. NW, Washington, DC 20005, (202)662-1661

Amer. Bar Assn. Sect. of Intl. Law [5584], 740 15th St. NW, Washington, DC 20005, (202)662-1661

Amer. Bar Assn. Special Comm. on Dispute Resolution [★5202]

Amer. Bar Assn. Standing Comm. on Dispute Resolution [★5202]

Amer. Bar Assn. Young Lawyers Div. [5227], 321 N Clark St., Chicago, IL 60610, (312)988-5611

Amer. Bar Found. [5644], 750 N Lake Shore Dr., 4th Fl., Chicago, IL 60611-4403, (312)988-6500

Amer. Barefoot Waterski Club [23114], PO Box 1084, Erie, CO 80516-1084, (303)833-5450

Amer. Barred Plymouth Rock Club [★4812]

Amer. Barrel Racing Assn. - Address unknown since 2011.

Amer. Baseball Coaches Assn. [22263], 108 S Univ. Ave., Ste. 3, Mount Pleasant, MI 48858-2327, (989)775-3300

Amer. Baseball Coaches Assn. [22263], 108 S Univ. Ave., Ste. 3, Mount Pleasant, MI 48858-2327, (989)775-3300

Amer. Baseball Cong. [★22262]

Amer. Baseball Found. [22264], 2660 10th Ave. S, Ste. 620, Birmingham, AL 35205, (205)558-4235

Amer. Bashkir Curly Registry [4525], 71 Cavalier Blvd., No. 124, Florence, KY 41042, (859)485-9700

Amer. Bearing Mfrs. Assn. [1796], 2025 M St. NW, Ste. 800, Washington, DC 20036-2422, (202)367-1155

Amer. Beauty Assn. [★975]

Amer. Bee Breeders Assn. - Defunct.

A star before a book entry number signifies that the name is not listed separately, but is mentioned within the entry.

Amer. Beefalo Assn. [3776], PO Box 295, Benton City, WA 99320, (573)732-5763

Amer. Beefalo Assn. [3776], PO Box 295, Benton City, WA 99320, (573)732-5763

Amer. Beekeeping Fed. [3815], 3525 Piedmont Rd., Bldg. 5, Ste. 300, Atlanta, GA 30305, (404)760-2875

Amer. Beethoven Soc. [9493], San Jose State Univ., Ira F. Brilliant Center for Beethoven Studies, 1 Washington Sq., San Jose, CA 95192-0171, (408)808-2058

Amer. Begonia Soc. [21764], PO Box 471651, San Francisco, CA 94147-1651

Amer. Behcet's Assn. [★13827]

Amer. Behcet's Disease Assn. [13827], PO Box 869, Smithtown, NY 11787-0869, (800)7-BEHCET

Amer. Behcet's Found. [★13827]

Amer. Belarussian Relief Org. [12800], PO Box 365, Zebulon, NC 27597, (919)269-6033

Amer. Belgian Blue Assn. [★3866]

Amer. Belgian Blue Breeders [3866], 245 W Main St., Stanley, IA 50671, (319)230-0671

Amer. Belgian Blue Breeders Assn. [★3866]

Amer. Belgian Hare Club [4828], 15330 Sharp Rd., Rockton, IL 61072, (815)629-2465

Amer. Belgian Malinois Club [21481], 994 Lowell Dr., Idaho Falls, ID 83402, (208)542-6552

Amer. Belgian Malinois Club [21481], 994 Lowell Dr., Idaho Falls, ID 83402, (208)542-6552

Amer. Bell Assn. Intl. [21292], 7210 Bellbrook Dr., San Antonio, TX 78227-1002

Amer. Belted Galloway Cattle Breeders' Assn. [★3906]

Amer. Benedictine Acad. [19380], St. Benedict's House, 415 S Crow St., Pierre, SD 57501, (605)224-0969

Amer. Benefits Coun. [5887], 1501 M St. NW, Ste. 600, Washington, DC 20005, (202)289-6700

Amer. Berkshire Assn. [4946], 2637 Yeager Rd., West Lafayette, IN 47906, (765)497-3618

Amer. Beverage Assn. [442], 1101 16th St. NW, Washington, DC 20036, (202)463-6732

Amer. Beverage Inst. [443], 1090 Vermont Ave. NW, Ste. 800, Washington, DC 20005, (202)463-7110

Amer. Beverage Licensees [174], 5101 River Rd., Ste. 108, Bethesda, MD 20816-1560, (301)656-1494

Amer. Beveren Rabbit Club - Address unknown since 2010.

Amer. Bible Soc. [19338], 1865 Broadway, New York, NY 10023-7505, (212)408-1200

Amer. Bible Soc. [19338], 1865 Broadway, New York, NY 10023-7505, (212)408-1200

Amer. Biblical Encyclopedia Soc. - Defunct.

Amer. Bicycle Assn. [22475], PO Box 718, Chandler, AZ 85244, (480)961-1903

Amer. Bicycle Polo Assn. [22811], Bicycle Polo Assn. of Am., 305 Magnolia Lake Ct., Aiken, SC 29803, (803)648-4993

Amer. Bicycle Racing [22820], PO Box 487, Tinley Park, IL 60477-0487, (708)532-7204

Amer. Biofuels Coun. [1534], 9655 S Dixie Hwy., Ste. 116, Miami, FL 33156, (305)409-4285

Amer. Biogas Coun. [6109], 1211 Connecticut Ave. NW, Ste. 600, Washington, DC 20036, (202)640-6595

Amer. Biographical Inst. Res. Assn. [20614], Amer. Biographical Inst., 5126 Bur Oak Cir., Raleigh, NC 27612, (919)781-8710

Amer. Biological Safety Assn. [3134], 1200 Allanson Rd., Mundelein, IL 60060-3808, (847)949-1517

Amer. Bird Beer Label Assn. [★20929]

Amer. Bird Beer Label Assn. [★20929]

Amer. Bird Conservancy [5023], PO Box 249, The Plains, VA 20198-0249, (540)253-5780

Amer. Birders' Exchange - Defunct.

Amer. Birding Assn. [7191], 4945 N 30th St., Ste. 200, Colorado Springs, CO 80919, (719)578-9703

Amer. Birding Assn. [7191], 4945 N 30th St., Ste. 200, Colorado Springs, CO 80919, (719)578-9703

Amer. Birkebeiner Ski Found. [22907], PO Box 911, Hayward, WI 54843, (715)634-5025

Amer. Birth Control League [★12040]

Amer. Bison Assn. [★3793]

Amer. Black Hereford Assn. [3867], 719 Walnut St., Kansas City, MO 64106, (816)472-1111

Amer. Bladesmith Soc. [21425], PO Box 905, Salida, CO 81201, (419)832-0400

Amer. Blake Found. - Defunct.

Amer. Blasting Assn. [★6803]

Amer. Blasting Assn. [★6803]

Amer. Blind Bowling Assn. [22502], 111 S Dwyer, Arlington Heights, IL 60005, (248)853-0209

Amer. Blind Skiing Found. [22503], Jim Hynan, Treas., 8100 Foster Ln., No. 310, Niles, IL 60714-1159, (312)409-1605

Amer. Blonde d'Aquitaine Assn. [3868], 7407 VZ County Rd. 1507, Grand Saline, TX 75140, (903)570-0568

Amer. Blood Resources Assn. [★13852]

Amer. Bloodhound Club [21482], Cindy Andrews, Membership Chair, 129 Little Bear Trail, Elkton, VA 22827, (540)298-9899

Amer. Bd. of Abdominal Surgery [16793], 824 Main St., 2nd Fl., Ste. 1, Melrose, MA 02176, (781)665-6102

Amer. Bd. of Allergy and Immunology [13634], 111 S Independence Mall E, Ste. 701, Philadelphia, PA 19106-2512, (215)592-9466

Amer. Bd. of Anesthesiology [13734], Mark A. Rockoff, MD, Pres., 4208 Six Forks Rd., Ste. 900, Raleigh, NC 27609-5735, (919)881-2570

Amer. Bd. of Bariatric Medicine [15850], 2821 S Parker Rd., Ste. 625, Aurora, CO 80014, (303)752-4000

Amer. Bd. of Bioanalysis [7018], 906 Olive St., Ste. 1200, St. Louis, MO 63101-1448, (314)241-1445

Amer. Bd. of Bioanalysts [★7018]

Amer. Bd. of Cardiovascular Perfusion [13999], 207 N 25th Ave., Hattiesburg, MS 39401, (601)582-2227

Amer. Bd. of Certification [5228], 101 2nd St. SE, Ste. 904, Cedar Rapids, IA 52401, (319)365-2222

Amer. Bd. for Certification in Orthotics, Prosthetics and Pedorthics [16049], 330 John Carlyle St., Ste. 210, Alexandria, VA 22314, (703)836-7114

Amer. Bd. of Chelation Therapy [★16892]

Amer. Bd. of Clinical Hea. Psychology [★16367]

Amer. Bd. of Clinical Metal Toxicology [16892], 4889 Smith Rd., West Chester, OH 45069, (513)863-6277

Amer. Bd. of Clinical Neuropsychology [★16367]

Amer. Bd. of Cognitive and Behavioral Psychology [★16367]

Amer. Bd. of Colon and Rectal Surgery [16313], 20600 Eureka Rd., Ste. 600, Taylor, MI 48180, (734)282-9400

Amer. Bd. of Counseling Psychology [★16367]

Amer. Bd. on Counseling Services [★7943]

Amer. Bd. on Counseling Services [★7943]

Amer. Bd. of Criminalistics [5471], PO Box 1358, Palmetto, FL 34220

Amer. Bd. of Dental Public Hea. - Address unknown since 2010.

Amer. Bd. of Dermatology [14314], Henry Ford Hea. Sys., 1 Ford Pl., Detroit, MI 48202-3450, (313)874-1088

Amer. Bd. of Disability Analysts [16553], Belle Mead Off. Park, 4525 Harding Rd., 3rd Fl., Nashville, TN 37205, (615)327-2984

Amer. Bd. of Emergency Medicine [14458], 3000 Coolidge Rd., East Lansing, MI 48823-6319, (517)332-4800

Amer. Bd. of Examiners in Professional Psychology [★16367]

Amer. Bd. of Examiners of Psychodrama, Sociometry, and Gp. Psychotherapy [16448], PO Box 15572, Washington, DC 20003-0572, (202)483-0514

Amer. Bd. of Examiners in Psychological Hypnosis [★15084]

Amer. Bd. of Facial Plastic and Reconstructive Surgery [16794], 115C S St. Asaph St., Alexandria, VA 22314, (703)549-3223

Amer. Bd. of Family Medicine [14524], 1648 McGrathiana Pkwy., Ste. 550, Lexington, KY 40511-1342, (859)269-5626

Amer. Bd. of Family Practice [★14524]

Amer. Bd. of Family Psychology [★16367]

Amer. Bd. of Forensic Anthropology [14543], Susan M.T. Myster, PhD, Sec., Hamline Univ., Dept. of Anthropology, PO Box 196, St. Paul, MN 55104, (651)523-2554

Amer. Bd. of Forensic Document Examiners [5472], 7887 San Felipe, Ste. 122, Houston, TX 77063, (713)784-9537

Amer. Bd. of Forensic Examiners [★5473]

Amer. Bd. of Forensic Examiners [★5473]

Amer. Bd. of Forensic Odontology [14544], Forensic Sciences Found., Inc., 410 N 21st St., Colorado Springs, CO 80904, (719)636-1100

Amer. Bd. of Forensic Psychiatry - Defunct.

Amer. Bd. of Forensic Psychology [★16367]

Amer. Bd. of Funeral Ser. Educ. [2526], 3414 Ashland Ave., Ste. G, St. Joseph, MO 64506, (816)233-3747

Amer. Bd. of Genetic Counseling [14640], PO Box 14216, Lenexa, KS 66285, (913)895-4617

Amer. Bd. of Hair Restoration Surgery [14672], 419 Ridge Rd., Ste. C, Munster, IN 46321-1535, (219)836-5858

Amer. Bd. of Hea. Physics [16276], Nancy J. Johnson, Program Dir., 1313 Dolley Madison Blvd., Ste. 402, McLean, VA 22101, (703)790-1745

Amer. Bd. of Hypnotherapy [15083], PO Box 531605, Henderson, NV 89053, (702)456-3267

Amer. Bd. of Independent Medical Examiners [15327], 6470-A Merritts Creek Rd., Huntington, WV 25702, (304)733-0095

Amer. Bd. of Independent Medical Examiners [15327], 6470-A Merritts Creek Rd., Huntington, WV 25702, (304)733-0095

Amer. Bd. of Indus. Hygiene [15899], 6015 W St. Joseph, Ste. 102, Lansing, MI 48917-3980, (517)321-2638

Amer. Bd. of Integrative Holistic Medicine [14991], Nancy Sudak, MD, Exec. Dir., 5313 Colorado St., Duluth, MN 55804, (218)525-5651

Amer. Bd. of Internal Medicine [15132], 510 Walnut St., Ste. 1700, Philadelphia, PA 19106-3699, (215)446-3500

Amer. Bd. of Lab. Animal Medicine [★16995]

Amer. Bd. of Lower Extremity Surgery [16287], 6421 Inkster Rd., Ste. 102, Bloomfield Hills, MI 48301, (248)855-7740

Amer. Bd. of Managed Care Nursing [15714], 4435 Waterfront Dr., Ste. 101, Glen Allen, VA 23060, (804)527-1905

Amer. Bd. of Medical Genetics [14641], 9650 Rockville Pike, Bethesda, MD 20814-3998, (301)634-7315

American Bd. of Medical Lab. Immunology [★6282]

American Bd. of Medical Lab. Immunology [★6282]

American Bd. of Medical Microbiology [★6282]

American Bd. of Medical Microbiology [★6282]

Amer. Bd. of Medical Specialties [15355], 222 N LaSalle St., Ste. 1500, Chicago, IL 60601, (312)436-2600

Amer. Bd. of Medical Specialties in Podiatry [★16288]

Amer. Bd. of Medical Toxicology [★16893]

Amer. Bd. of Missions to the Jews [★19738]

Amer. Bd. of Multiple Specialties in Podiatry [16288], 1350 Broadway, Ste. 1705, New York, NY 10018, (212)356-0690

Amer. Bd. of Neurological Surgery [15683], 6550 Fannin St., Ste. 2139, Houston, TX 77030, (713)441-6015

Amer. Bd. of Neuroscience Nursing [15715], 4700 W Lake Ave., Glenview, IL 60025, (847)375-4733

Amer. Bd. of Nuclear Medicine [15691], 4555 Forest Park Blvd., Ste. 119, St. Louis, MO 63108, (314)367-2225

Amer. Bd. of Nursing Specialties [15716], 610 Thornhill Ln., Aurora, OH 44202, (330)995-9172

Amer. Bd. of Nutrition [15815], 8630 Fenton St., Ste. 412, Silver Spring, MD 20910, (301)587-6312

Amer. Bd. of Obstetrics and Gynecology [15863], 2915 Vine St., Dallas, TX 75204, (214)871-1619

Amer. Bd. for Occupational Hea. Nurses [15717], 201 E Ogden Ave., Ste. 114, Hinsdale, IL 60521-3658, (630)789-5799

Amer. Bd. of Operative Dentistry [14254], Univ. of Iowa, Coll. of Dentistry, Dept. of Operative Dentistry, Loma Linda, CA 92350, (319)335-7583

Amer. Bd. for Ophthalmic Examinations [★15940]

Amer. Bd. of Ophthalmology [15940], 111 Presidential Blvd., Ste. 241, Bala Cynwyd, PA 19004-1075, (610)664-1175

Reference to "IO" in place of a book number signifies that the association may be found in the 50th edition of International Organizations.

Amer. Bd. of Opticianry [15980], 6506 Loisdale Rd., Ste. 209, Springfield, VA 22150, (703)719-5800

Amer. Bd. of Opticianry [★15983]

Amer. Bd. of Opticianry [15980], 6506 Loisdale Rd., Ste. 209, Springfield, VA 22150, (703)719-5800

Amer. Bd. of Oral and Maxillofacial Pathology [16112], PO Box 25915, Tampa, FL 33622-5915, (813)286-2444

Amer. Bd. of Oral and Maxillofacial Surgery [16003], 625 N Michigan Ave., Ste. 1820, Chicago, IL 60611-3177, (312)642-0070

Amer. Bd. of Oral Pathology [★16112]

Amer. Bd. of Oral Surgery [★16003]

Amer. Bd. of Organizational and Bus. Consulting [★16367]

Amer. Bd. of Oriental Reproductive Medicine [16595], Raymond E. Rubio, Pres., 910 Hampshire Rd., Ste. A, Westlake Village, CA 91361, (805)497-1335

Amer. Bd. of Orthodontia [★14255]

Amer. Bd. of Orthodontics [14255], 401 N Lindbergh Blvd., Ste. 300, St. Louis, MO 63141-7839, (314)432-6130

Amer. Bd. of Orthodontics I Coll. of Diplomates [14256], 3260 Upper Bottom Rd., St. Charles, MO 63303, (636)922-5551

Amer. Bd. of Orthopaedic Surgery [16023], 400 Silver Cedar Ct., Chapel Hill, NC 27514, (919)929-7103

Amer. Bd. of Otolaryngology [16082], 5615 Kirby Dr., Ste. 600, Houston, TX 77005, (713)850-0399

Amer. Bd. of Pain Medicine [16094], 4700 W Lake Ave., Glenview, IL 60025-1468, (847)375-4726

Amer. Bd. of Pathology [16113], PO Box 25915, Tampa, FL 33622-5915, (813)286-2444

Amer. Bd. of Pediatric Dentistry - Defunct.

Amer. Bd. of Pediatrics [16139], 111 Silver Cedar Ct., Chapel Hill, NC 27514, (919)929-0461

Amer. Bd. of Perianesthesia Nursing Certification [15718], 475 Riverside Dr., 6th Fl., New York, NY 10115-0089, (800)6-ABPANC

Amer. Bd. of Periodontology [14257], 877 Baltimore Annapolis Blvd., Ste. 111, Severna Park, MD 21146, (410)647-1324

Amer. Bd. of Physical Medicine and Rehabilitation [16554], 3015 Allegro Park Ln. SW, Rochester, MN 55902-4139, (507)282-1776

Amer. Bd. of Physician Nutrition Specialists [15816], Amer. Soc. for Parenteral and Enteral Nutrition, 8630 Fenton St., Ste. 412, Silver Spring, MD 20910, (301)587-6315

Amer. Bd. of Plastic Surgery [14173], 7 Penn Center, Ste. 400, 1635 Market St., Philadelphia, PA 19103-2204, (215)587-9322

Amer. Bd. of Podiatric Orthopedics [★16289]

Amer. Bd. of Podiatric Orthopedics and Primary Medicine [★16289]

Amer. Bd. of Podiatric Orthopedics and Primary Podiatric Medicine [16289], 3812 Sepulveda Blvd., Ste. 530, Torrance, CA 90505, (310)375-0700

Amer. Bd. of Podiatric Surgery [16290], 445 Fillmore St., San Francisco, CA 94117-3404, (415)553-7800

Amer. Bd. of Preventive Medicine [16304], 111 W Jackson Blvd., Ste. 1110, Chicago, IL 60604, (312)939-2276

Amer. Bd. of Preventive Medicine and Public Hea. [★16304]

Amer. Bd. of Proctology [★16313]

Amer. Bd. of Professional Liability Attorneys [5771], 4355 Cobb Pkwy., Ste. J-208, Atlanta, GA 30339, (404)989-7663

Amer. Bd. of Professional Neuropsychology [16366], John Heinz Inst. of Rehabilitation Medicine, 150 Mundy St., Wilkes-Barre, PA 18702, (570)826-3771

Amer. Bd. of Professional Psychology [16367], 600 Market St., Ste. 300, Chapel Hill, NC 27516, (919)537-8031

Amer. Bd. of Professional Psychology in Hypnosis [★15084]

Amer. Bd. on Professional Standards in Vocational Counseling [★7943]

Amer. Bd. on Professional Standards in Vocational Counseling [★7943]

Amer. Bd. of Prosthodontics [14258], PO Box 271894, West Hartford, CT 06127-1894, (860)679-2649

Amer. Bd. of Psychiatry and Neurology [16325], 2150 E Lake Cook Rd., Ste. 900, Buffalo Grove, IL 60089, (847)229-6500

Amer. Bd. of Psychoanalysis in Psychology [★16367]

Amer. Bd. of Psychological Hypnosis [15084], Charles E. Burbridge, Sec., 1421 Rte. 44, Pleasant Valley, NY 12569, (845)635-3214

Amer. Bd. of Quality Assurance and Utilization Rev. Physicians [16504], 6640 Cong. St., New Port Richey, FL 34653, (727)569-0190

Amer. Bd. of Rabbis - Vaad Harabonim of Am. [19837], 292 5th Ave., 4th Fl., New York, NY 10001, (212)714-3598

Amer. Bd. of Radiology [16518], 5441 E Williams Blvd., Ste. 200, Tucson, AZ 85711, (520)790-2900

Amer. Bd. of Registration of EEG and EP Technologists [14442], 2509 W Iles Ave., Ste. 102, Springfield, IL 62704, (217)726-7980

Amer. Bd. of Registration of EEG Technologists [★14442]

Amer. Bd. of Rehabilitation Psychology [★16367]

Amer. Bd. of School Psychology [★16367]

Amer. Bd. of Sci. in Nuclear Medicine [15692], John J. Bower, PhD, 3000 Spout Run Pkwy., Apt. D401, Arlington, VA 22201-4220, (571)814-0227

Amer. Bd. of Sexology [16645], PO Box 1166, Winter Park, FL 32790-1166, (407)645-1641

Amer. Bd. of Sleep Medicine [16662], 2510 N. Frontage Rd., Carien, IL 60561, (630)737-9700

Amer. Bd. of Surgery [16795], 1617 John F. Kennedy Blvd., Ste. 860, Philadelphia, PA 19103-1841, (215)568-4000

Amer. Bd. of Thoracic Surgery [16878], 633 N St. Clair St., Ste. 2320, Chicago, IL 60611, (312)202-5900

Amer. Bd. of Toxicology [7568], PO Box 30054, Raleigh, NC 27622-0054, (919)841-5022

Amer. Bd. of Toxicology [7568], PO Box 30054, Raleigh, NC 27622-0054, (919)841-5022

Amer. Bd. of Trial Advocates [6042], 2001 Bryan St., Ste. 3000, Dallas, TX 75201-3078, (214)871-7523

Amer. Bd. of Trial Advocates Found. [5229], 2001 Bryan St., Ste. 3000, Dallas, TX 75201, (214)871-7523

Amer. Bd. of Tropical Medicine - Defunct.

Amer. Bd. of Urologic Allied Hea. Professionals [★16944]

Amer. Bd. of Urology [16938], Stuart S. Howards, MD, Exec. Sec., 600 Peter Jefferson Pkwy., Ste. 150, Charlottesville, VA 22911, (434)979-0059

Amer. Bd. of Veterinary Practitioners [16991], 618 Church St., Ste. 220, Nashville, TN 37219, (615)250-7794

Amer. Bd. of Veterinary Radiology [★17003]

Amer. Bd. of Veterinary Specialties [16992], Amer. Veterinary Medical Assn., 1931 N Meacham Rd., Ste. 100, Schaumburg, IL 60173-4340, (847)925-8070

Amer. Bd. of Veterinary Toxicology [16993], Covance Labs., Inc., 2701 E Ryan Rd., Chandler, AZ 85286, (480)384-3638

Amer. Bd. of Vocational Experts [9038], 3540 Soquel Ave., Ste. A, Santa Cruz, CA 95062-1776, (831)464-4890

Amer. Boarding Kennels Assn. [★2683]

Amer. Boat Builders and Repairers Assn. [2348], 50 Water St., Warren, RI 02885, (401)247-0318

Amer. Boat and Yacht Coun. [2349], 613 3rd St., Ste. 10, Annapolis, MD 21403, (410)990-4460

Amer. Boating Assn. [22315], PO Box 456, Centerville, MA 02632, (508)534-9893

Amer. Boccaccio Assn. [9345], Univ. of Massachusetts Amherst, Dept. of Languages, Literatures and Cultures, 312 Herter Hall, UMass Amherst, Amherst, MA 01003, (413)545-2314

Amer. Boiler Mfrs. Assn. [1797], 8221 Old Courthouse Rd., Ste. 207, Vienna, VA 22182, (703)356-7172

Amer. Bonanza Soc. [20881], PO Box 12888, Wichita, KS 67277, (316)945-1700

Amer. Bonanza Soc. [20881], PO Box 12888, Wichita, KS 67277, (316)945-1700

Amer. Bone Marrow Donor Registry [13854], PO Box 8841, Mandeville, LA 70470-8841, (985)626-1749

Amer. Bonsai Soc. [21765], PO Box 351604, Toledo, OH 43635-1604, (734)848-9207

Amer. Book Center for War Devastated Libraries [★10016]

Amer. Book Producers Assn. [2913], 151 W 19th St., 3rd Fl., New York, NY 10011, (212)645-2368

Amer. Book Publishers Coun. [★2918]

Amer. Booksellers Assn. [3093], 200 White Plains Rd., Ste. 600, Tarrytown, NY 10591, (800)637-0037

Amer. Booksellers Found. for Free Expression [17727], 19 Fulton St., Ste. 407, New York, NY 10038, (212)587-4025

Amer. Bop Assn. [9531], 1438 Cedarcrest Dr., Barnhart, MO 63012, (636)464-1253

Amer. Border Leicester Assn. [4885], PO Box 500, Cuba, IL 61427, (309)785-5058

Amer. Botanical Coun. [6340], 6200 Manor Rd., Austin, TX 78723, (512)926-4900

Amer. Bottled Water Assn. [★447]

Amer. Bottled Water Assn. [★447]

Amer. Bottlers of Carbonated Beverages [★442]

Amer. Bouvier des Flandres Club [21483], 79 W Indian Springs Dr., Glenmoore, PA 19343-3989

Amer. Bowling Cong. [★22429]

Amer. Bowling Cong. [★22429]

Amer. Boxer Club [21484], Mrs. Sandy Orr, Sec., 7106 N 57th St., Omaha, NE 68152-2301, (402)571-0389

Amer. Boxer Rescue Assn. [10906], PO Box 184, Carmel, IN 46082, (334)272-2590

Amer. Boxwood Soc. [21766], PO Box 85, Boyce, VA 22620-0085

Amer. Brachytherapy Soc. [13880], 12100 Sunset Hills Rd., Ste. 130, Reston, VA 20190, (703)234-4078

Amer. Brahman Breeders Assn. [3869], 3003 S Loop W, Ste. 520, Houston, TX 77054, (713)349-0854

Amer. Brahmousin Coun. [3870], PO Box 88, Whitesboro, TX 76273, (903)564-3995

Amer. Brahms Soc. [9494], Univ. of Washington, School of Music, PO Box 353450, Seattle, WA 98195-3450, (206)543-0400

Amer. Braille Press for War and Civilian Blind [★17085]

Amer. Braille Press for War and Civilian Blind [★17085]

Amer. Brain Coalition [15566], 6257 Quantico Ln. N, Maple Grove, MN 55311, (763)557-2913

Amer. Brain Tumor Assn. [13881], 2720 River Rd., Des Plaines, IL 60018, (847)827-9910

Amer. Brangus Breeders Assn. [★3916]

Amer. Brazilian Cultural Exchange [9513], 1075 E 33rd St., Oakland, CA 94610, (510)280-4862

Amer. Breeders Assn. [★6896]

Amer. Breeds Coalition [3871], 3003 S Loop W, Ste. 520, Houston, TX 77054

Amer. Breweriana Assn. [20926], PO Box 595767, Fort Gratiot, MI 48059-5767, (810)385-7101

Amer. Bridge Assn. [21237], 2828 Lakewood Ave. SW, Atlanta, GA 30315, (404)768-5517

Amer. Bridge League [★21239]

Amer. Bridge League [★21239]

Amer. Bridge Teachers' Assn. [21238], 490 N Winnebago Dr., Lake Winnebago, MO 64034-9321, (816)537-5165

Amer. Bridge, Tunnel, and Turnpike Assn. [★6032]

Amer. Bridge, Tunnel, and Turnpike Assn. [★6032]

Amer. British White Park Assn. [3872], PO Box 409, Myerstown, PA 17067, (270)563-9733

Amer. Brittany Club [21485], Mary Jo Trimble, Sec., 10370 Fleming Rd., Carterville, IL 62918, (618)985-2336

American Broadcasting Network [★17715]

Amer. Broncho-Esophagological Assn. [13868], Boston Medical Center, FGH Bldg., Dept. of Otolaryngology-Head and Neck Surgery, 820 Harrison Ave., 4th Fl., Boston, MA 02118, (617)638-7934

Amer. Bronchoscopic Soc. [★13868]

Amer. Brotherhood for the Blind [★17056]

Amer. Brugmansia and Datura Soc. [★21738]

Amer. Brush Mfrs. Assn. [1775], 2111 Plum St., Ste. 274, Aurora, IL 60506, (720)392-2262

A star before a book entry number signifies that the name is not listed separately, but is mentioned within the entry.

Amer. Brussels Griffon Assn. [21486], PO Box 11, Shirley, IL 61772-0011, (309)828-4311

Amer. Bryological and Lichenological Soc. [6341], James Bennett, Sec.-Treas., Univ. of Wisconsin, Dept. of Botany, 430 Lincoln Dr., Madison, WI 53706, (608)262-5489

Amer. Bryological and Lichenological Soc. [6341], James Bennett, Sec.-Treas., Univ. of Wisconsin, Dept. of Botany, 430 Lincoln Dr., Madison, WI 53706, (608)262-5489

Amer. Bryological Soc. [★6341]

Amer. Bryological Soc. [★6341]

Amer. Buckskin Registry Assn. [4526], PO Box 493850, Redding, CA 96049, (530)223-1420

Amer. Buddhist Acad. [★19358]

Amer. Buddhist Assn. - Address unknown since 2010.

Amer. Buddhist Stud. Center [19358], 331 Riverside Dr., New York, NY 10025, (212)864-7424

Amer. Budgerigar Soc. [21209], Larry Moore, Sec., 521 Westview St. SW, Lenoir, NC 28645, (828)754-2480

Amer. Buffalo Assn. [★3793]

Amer. Bugatti Club [20988], 600 Lakeview Terr., Glen Ellyn, IL 60137, (630)469-4920

Amer. Bullmastiff Assn. [21487], 1020 S Schwamberger Rd., Swanton, OH 43558, (419)825-2427

Amer. Bunka Embroidery Assn. [21960], Beverly Enos, Treas., 296 Andover St., Georgetown, MA 01833

Amer. Bur. for Medical Advancement in China - Defunct.

Amer. Bur. of Metal Statistics [7088], PO Box 805, Chatham, NJ 07928, (973)701-2299

Amer. Bur. of Shipping [2376], 16855 Northchase Dr., Houston, TX 77060, (281)877-5800

Amer. Burn Assn. [13871], 311 S Wacker Dr., Ste. 4150, Chicago, IL 60606, (312)642-9260

Amer. Bus. Assn. [3500], 111 K St. NE, 9th Fl., Washington, DC 20002, (202)842-1645

Amer. Bus. Assn. of Russian-speaking Professionals [2892], 2600 El Camino Real, Ste. 505, Palo Alto, CA 94306

Amer. Bus. Clubs Spastic Paralysis Fund [★11808]

Amer. Bus. Commun. Assn. [★7783]

Amer. Bus. Conf. [17712], 1828 L St. NW, Ste. 908, Washington, DC 20036, (202)822-9300

Amer. Bus. Coun. of Dubai and the Northern Emirates [IO], Dubai, United Arab Emirates

Amer. Bus. Coun. of Pakistan [IO], Karachi, Pakistan

Amer. Bus. Gp. of Jeddah [IO], Jeddah, Saudi Arabia

Amer. Bus. Law Assn. [★8496]

Amer. Bus. Law Assn. [★8496]

Amer. Bus. Media [2914], 675 3rd Ave., 7th Fl., New York, NY 10017-5704, (212)661-6360

Amer. Bus. Men's Res. Found. [★13232]

American Bus. Network [★23384]

Amer. Bus. Press [★2914]

Amer. Bus. Women's Assn. [639], PO Box 8728, Kansas City, MO 64114-0728, (800)228-0007

Amer. Bus. Writing Assn. [★7783]

Amer. Businesspersons Assn. - Address unknown since 2010.

Amer. Butter Inst. [1015], 2101 Wilson Blvd., Ste. 400, Arlington, VA 22201, (703)243-5630

Amer. Buyers of Meeting and Incentive Travel - Defunct.

Amer. Byron Soc. [★9356]

Amer. Cable Assn. [723], 1 Parkway Ctr., Ste. 212, Pittsburgh, PA 15220, (412)922-8300

Amer. Camaro Assn. [20989], 5786 Buckeye Rd., Macungie, PA 18062, (610)966-2492

Amer. Camellia Soc. [21767], Massee Ln. Gardens, 100 Massee Ln., Fort Valley, GA 31030, (478)967-2358

Amer. Camp Assn. [22440], 5000 State Rd., 67 N, Martinsville, IN 46151-7902, (765)342-8456

Amer. Campaign for Prevention of Child Abuse and Family Violence [★11893]

Amer. Camping Assn. [★22440]

American-Canadian Genealogical Soc. [20615], PO Box 6478, Manchester, NH 03108-6478, (603)622-1554

American-Canadian Genealogical Soc. [20615], PO Box 6478, Manchester, NH 03108-6478, (603)622-1554

Amer. Canal Soc. [9466], Charles W. Derr, Sec.-Treas., 117 Main St., Freemansburg, PA 18017, (610)691-0956

Amer. Canal Soc. [9466], Charles W. Derr, Sec.-Treas., 117 Main St., Freemansburg, PA 18017, (610)691-0956

Amer. Canary Fanciers Assn. [21210], 1198 Hilda St., Anaheim, CA 92806, (714)287-4590

Amer. Cancer Soc. [13882], PO Box 22718, Oklahoma City, OK 73123-1718, (800)227-2345

Amer. Canine Educ. Found. [21488], 7200 Tanager St., Springfield, VA 22150, (703)451-5656

Amer. Canine Educ. Fund [★21488]

Amer. Canine Sports Medicine Assn. [16994], PO Box 07412, Fort Myers, FL 33919

Amer. Canoe Assn. [23120], 108 Hanover St., Fredericksburg, VA 22401, (540)907-4460

Amer. Canyoneering Assn. [21281], 148 N 100 W, Cedar City, UT 84720, (435)590-8889

Amer. Car Rental Assn. [3075], PO Box 225, Clifton Park, NY 12065, (888)200-2795

Amer. Car Rental Assn. - Defunct.

Amer. Carbon Comm. [★6389]

Amer. Carbon Soc. [6389], Air Force Res. Lab., AFRL/PRSM, 10 E Saturn Blvd., Edwards, CA 93524, (661)275-5768

Amer. Cardiology Technologists Assn. [★13997]

Amer. Cargo War Risk Reinsurance Exchange - Defunct.

Amer. Carnival Glass Assn. [21828], 5951 Fredericksburg Rd., Wooster, OH 44691-9491, (330)264-3703

Amer. Carp Soc. [21730], 106 N Denton Tap Rd., Ste. 210-178, Coppell, TX 75019, (818)240-4842

Amer. Carpal Tunnel Syndrome Assn. [★15906]

Amer. Cartographic Assn. [★6379]

Amer. Case Mgt. Assn. [15281], 11701 W 36th St., Little Rock, AR 72211, (501)907-2262

Amer. Cast Metals Assn. [★8963]

Amer. Casting Assn. [22569], 1773 Lance End Ln., Fenton, MO 63026-2674, (636)225-9443

Amer. Cat Fanciers Assn. [21244], PO Box 1949, Nixa, MO 65714-1949, (417)725-1530

Amer. Cat Fanciers Assn. [21244], PO Box 1949, Nixa, MO 65714-1949, (417)725-1530

Amer. Catholic Church Assn. - Defunct.

Amer. Catholic Correctional Chaplains Assn. [19516], 738 Guernsey Ct., Slinger, WI 53086, (262)627-0636

Amer. Catholic Historical Assn. [9744], Catholic Univ. of Am., Mullen Lib., Rm. 320, Washington, DC 20064, (202)319-5079

Amer. Catholic Historical Soc. [9745], 263 S 4th St., Philadelphia, PA 19106, (610)517-0835

Amer. Catholic Historical Soc. [9745], 263 S 4th St., Philadelphia, PA 19106, (610)517-0835

Amer. Catholic Lawyers Assn. [5645], U.S. Highway Rt. 46, Ste. 7, PO Box 10092, Fairfield, NJ 07004, (973)244-9895

Amer. Catholic Philosophical Assn. [8702], Univ. of St. Thomas, Center for Thomistic Stud., 3800 Montrose Blvd., Houston, TX 77006, (713)942-3483

Amer. Catholic Prison Chaplains Assn. [★19516]

Amer. Catholic Psychological Assn. [★16382]

Amer. Catholic Sociological Soc. [★7425]

Amer. Catholic Union - Address unknown since 2011.

The Amer. Cause [17728], 501 Church St., Ste. 315, Vienna, VA 22180, (703)255-2632

Amer. Cavalier King Charles Spaniel Club [21489], 2 Bud Davis Rd., Newnan, GA 30263

Amer. Cave Conservation Assn. [3989], PO Box 409, 119 E Main St., Horse Cave, KY 42749, (270)786-1466

Amer. Cave and Karst Center [★3989]

Amer. Cave Museum [★3989]

Amer. Cavy Breeders Assn. [3777], 1157 E San Angelo Ave., Gilbert, AZ 85234, (480)545-1785

Amer. Celiac Disease Alliance [14549], 2504 Duxbury Pl., Alexandria, VA 22308, (703)622-3331

Amer. Celiac Society | Dietary Support Coalition [15817], PO Box 23455, New Orleans, LA 70183-0455, (504)737-3293

Amer. Cemetery Assn. [★2535]

Amer. Cemetery Assn. [★2535]

Amer. Cemetery-Mortuary Comm. - Defunct.

Amer. Center for the Alexander Technique [13654], 39 W 14th St., Rm. 507, New York, NY 10011, (212)633-2229

Amer. Center for Design - Defunct.

Amer. Center for Law and Justice [12920], PO Box 90555, Washington, DC 20090-0555, (757)226-2489

Amer. Center for Physics [7262], 1 Physics Ellipse, College Park, MD 20740, (301)209-3000

Amer. Center for Polish Culture [★10461]

Amer. Center for Polish Culture [★10461]

Amer. Ceramic Soc. [6382], 600 N Cleveland Ave., Ste. 210, Westerville, OH 43082, (614)794-5855

Amer. Ceramic Soc. [6382], 600 N Cleveland Ave., Ste. 210, Westerville, OH 43082, (614)794-5855

Amer. Cetacean Soc. [7038], PO Box 1391, San Pedro, CA 90733-1391, (310)548-6279

Amer. Chain Assn. [1798], 5672 Strand Ct., Ste. 2, Naples, FL 34110, (239)514-3441

Amer. Chain of Warehouses [3618], 156 Flamingo Dr., Beecher, IL 60401-9725, (708)946-9792

Amer. Chamber of Commerce [★23388]

Amer. Chamber of Commerce [★23388]

Amer. Chamber of Commerce in Algeria [IO], Algiers, Algeria

Amer. Chamber of Commerce in Argentina [IO], Buenos Aires, Argentina

Amer. Chamber of Commerce in Australia [IO], Sydney, Australia

Amer. Chamber of Commerce in Australia - Melbourne Br. [IO], Melbourne, Australia

Amer. Chamber of Commerce in Australia - National/New South Wales Off. [IO], Sydney, Australia

Amer. Chamber of Commerce in Australia - Perth Br. [IO], Perth, Australia

Amer. Chamber of Commerce in Austria [IO], Vienna, Austria

Amer. Chamber of Commerce in Azerbaijan [IO], Baku, Azerbaijan

Amer. Chamber of Commerce in Belgium [IO], Brussels, Belgium

Amer. Chamber of Commerce of Belize [IO], Belize City, Belize

Amer. Chamber of Commerce of Bolivia [IO], La Paz, Bolivia

Amer. Chamber of Commerce of Brazil - Rio de Janeiro [IO], Rio de Janeiro, Brazil

Amer. Chamber of Commerce of Brazil - Sao Paulo [IO], Sao Paulo, Brazil

Amer. Chamber of Commerce of Bulgaria [IO], Sofia, Bulgaria

Amer. Chamber of Commerce of Cuba in the U.S. [23346], 910 17th St. NW, Ste. 422, Washington, DC 20006-2605, (202)833-3548

Amer. Chamber of Commerce in the Czech Republic [IO], Prague, Czech Republic

Amer. Chamber of Commerce of the Dominican Republic [IO], Santo Domingo, Dominican Republic

Amer. Chamber of Commerce in Egypt [IO], Cairo, Egypt

Amer. Chamber of Commerce of El Salvador [IO], San Salvador, El Salvador

Amer. Chamber of Commerce Estonia [IO], Tallinn, Estonia

Amer. Chamber of Commerce to the European Union [IO], Brussels, Belgium

Amer. Chamber of Commerce Executives [23451], 4875 Eisenhower Ave., Ste. 250, Alexandria, VA 22304, (703)998-0072

Amer. Chamber of Commerce in France [IO], Paris, France

Amer. Chamber of Commerce in Germany [IO], Frankfurt, Germany

Amer. Chamber of Commerce in Germany - Frankfurt [IO], Frankfurt, Germany

Amer. Chamber of Commerce of Guatemala [IO], Guatemala City, Guatemala

Amer. Chamber of Commerce in Hong Kong [IO], Hong Kong, People's Republic of China

Amer. Chamber of Commerce in Hungary [IO], Budapest, Hungary

Reference to "IO" in place of a book number signifies that the association may be found in the 50th edition of International Organizations.

Encyclopedia of Associations, 51st Edition

2527

Amer. Chamber of Commerce in Indonesia [IO], Jakarta, Indonesia

Amer. Chamber of Commerce and Indus. of Panama [IO], Panama City, Panama

Amer. Chamber of Commerce Ireland [IO], Dublin, Ireland

Amer. Chamber of Commerce in Italy [IO], Milan, Italy

Amer. Chamber of Commerce of Jamaica [IO], Kingston, Jamaica

Amer. Chamber of Commerce in Japan [IO], Tokyo, Japan

Amer. Chamber of Commerce in Korea [IO], Seoul, Republic of Korea

Amer. Chamber of Commerce in the Kyrgyz Republic [IO], Bishkek, Kirgizstan

Amer. Chamber of Commerce in Latvia [IO], Riga, Latvia

Amer. Chamber of Commerce in Lithuania [IO], Vilnius, Lithuania

Amer. Chamber of Commerce in Luxembourg [IO], Luxembourg, Luxembourg

Amer. Chamber of Commerce in Macau [IO], Macau, Macao

Amer. Chamber of Commerce of Mexico - Guadalajara [IO], Guadalajara, Mexico

Amer. Chamber of Commerce of Mexico - Mexico City [IO], Mexico City, Mexico

Amer. Chamber of Commerce in Moldova [IO], Chisinau, Moldova

Amer. Chamber of Commerce in Morocco [IO], Casablanca, Morocco

Amer. Chamber of Commerce in the Netherlands [IO], Amsterdam, Netherlands

Amer. Chamber of Commerce in New Zealand [IO], Auckland, New Zealand

Amer. Chamber of Commerce in Norway [IO], Oslo, Norway

Amer. Chamber of Commerce in Okinawa [IO], Okinawa, Japan

Amer. Chamber of Commerce - People's Republic of China [IO], Beijing, People's Republic of China

Amer. Chamber of Commerce of Peru [IO], Lima, Peru

Amer. Chamber of Commerce of the Philippines [IO], Makati City, Philippines

Amer. Chamber of Commerce in Poland [IO], Warsaw, Poland

Amer. Chamber of Commerce in Portugal [IO], Lisbon, Portugal

Amer. Chamber of Commerce Researchers Assn. [★23358]

Amer. Chamber of Commerce in Romania [IO], Bucharest, Romania

Amer. Chamber of Commerce in Russia [IO], Moscow, Russia

Amer. Chamber of Commerce in Shanghai [IO], Shanghai, People's Republic of China

Amer. Chamber of Commerce in Singapore [IO], Singapore, Singapore

Amer. Chamber of Commerce in the Slovak Republic [IO], Bratislava, Slovakia

Amer. Chamber of Commerce in South Africa [IO], Johannesburg, Republic of South Africa

Amer. Chamber of Commerce in South China [IO], Guangzhou, People's Republic of China

Amer. Chamber of Commerce in Spain - Barcelona [IO], Barcelona, Spain

Amer. Chamber of Commerce in Spain - Madrid [IO], Madrid, Spain

Amer. Chamber of Commerce in Sri Lanka [IO], Colombo, Sri Lanka

Amer. Chamber of Commerce in Sweden [IO], Stockholm, Sweden

Amer. Chamber of Commerce in Switzerland [★23444]

Amer. Chamber of Commerce in Taipei [IO], Taipei, Taiwan

Amer. Chamber of Commerce in Thailand [IO], Bangkok, Thailand

Amer. Chamber of Commerce of Trinidad and Tobago [IO], Port of Spain, Trinidad and Tobago

Amer. Chamber of Commerce in the Ukraine [IO], Kiev, Ukraine

Amer. Chamber of Commerce in Uzbekistan [IO], Tashkent, Uzbekistan

Amer. Chamber of Commerce in Vietnam - Hanoi [IO], Hanoi, Vietnam

Amer. Chamber of Commerce in Vietnam - Ho Chi Minh City [IO], Ho Chi Minh City, Vietnam

Amer. Chap., Intl. Real Estate Fed. [★3012]

Amer. Charbray Breeders Assn. [★3881]

Amer. Charbray Breeders Assn. [★3881]

Amer. Charities for Reasonable Fundraising Regulation [12047], 9112 Tetterton Ave., Vienna, VA 22182, (703)938-1809

Amer. Charolais Breeders Assn. [★3881]

Amer. Charolais Breeders Assn. [★3881]

Amer. Checker Assn. [★21740]

Amer. Checker Assn. [★21740]

Amer. Checker Fed. [21740], Kim Willis, Sec., 31 Sandston Rd., Eldon, MO 65026

Amer. Checker Fed. [21740], Kim Willis, Sec., 31 Sandston Rd., Eldon, MO 65026

Amer. Checkered Giant Club [★4829]

Amer. Checkered Giant Rabbit Club [4829], David Freeman, Sec., 1119 Klondyke Rd., Milford, OH 45150

Amer. Cheese Soc. [1016], 2696 S Colorado Blvd., Ste. 570, Denver, CO 80222-5954, (720)328-2788

Amer. Chem. Coun. [★743]

Amer. Chem. Soc. [771], 1155 16th St. NW, Washington, DC 20036, (202)872-4600

Amer. Chem. Soc., Rubber Div. [3131], PO Box 499, Akron, OH 44309-0499, (330)972-6527

Amer. Chemistry Coun. [743], 700 2nd St. NE, Washington, DC 20002, (202)249-7000

Amer. Chemistry Coun., Chlorine Chemistry Div. [6390], 700 2nd St. NE, Washington, DC 20002, (202)249-7000

Amer. Chemistry Coun. I Plastics Foodservice Packaging Gp. [2604], 1300 Wilson Blvd., Arlington, VA 22209, (703)741-5000

Amer. Chesapeake Club [21490], PO Box 58082, Salt Lake City, UT 84158

Amer. Chess Assn. - Address unknown since 2010.

Amer. Chess Found. [★21275]

Amer. Chesterton Soc. [9346], 4117 Pebblebrook Cir., Minneapolis, MN 55437, (952)831-3096

Amer. Chesterton Soc. [9346], 4117 Pebblebrook Cir., Minneapolis, MN 55437, (952)831-3096

The Amer. Chestnut Found. [6342], 160 Zillicoa St., Ste. D, Asheville, NC 28801, (828)281-0047

Amer. Chevelle Enthusiasts Soc. [20990], 900 Conf. Dr., Ste. 1B, No. 222, Goodlettsville, TN 37072, (615)643-2237

Amer. Cheviot Sheep Soc. [4886], 10015 Flush Rd., St. George, KS 66535, (785)494-2436

Amer. Chianina Assn. [3873], 1708 N Prairie View Rd., PO Box 890, Platte City, MO 64079, (816)431-2808

Amer. Childhood Cancer Org. [13883], PO Box 498, Kensington, MD 20895-0498, (202)262-9949

Amer. Children of SCORE [10139], PO Box 3423, 8031 Great Run Ln., Warrenton, VA 20188, (540)428-2313

American-Chinese CEO Soc. [773], 225 S Lake Ave., No. 610, Pasadena, CA 91101, (714)817-1988

Amer. Chinese Medical Exchange Soc. [14750], 15 New England Executive Park, Burlington, MA 01803, (781)791-5066

Amer. Chinese Medical Soc. [★15407]

Amer. Chinese Pharmaceutical Assn. [16169], PO Box 10193, Rockville, MD 20849-0193

Amer. Chiropractic Assn. [14116], 1701 Clarendon Blvd., Arlington, VA 22209, (703)276-8800

Amer. Chiropractic Assn. Coun. on Sports Injuries and Physical Fitness [14117], Kelly Lange, DC, Sec., 120 N 2nd St., Ashland, OR 97520, (541)482-3492

Amer. Chiropractic Coll. of Radiology [14118], PO Box 986, Plainfield, IL 60544

Amer. Chiropractic Coun. on Roentgenology [★16532]

Amer. Chiropractic Registry of Radiologic Technologists [16519], 52 W Colfax St., Palatine, IL 60067, (847)705-1178

Amer. Choral Directors Assn. [10140], 545 Couch Dr., Oklahoma City, OK 73102-2207, (405)232-8161

Amer. Choral Found. Lib. [★10189]

Amer. Christian Fiction Writers [10698], PO Box 101066, Palm Bay, FL 32910-1066

Amer. Chronic Pain Assn. [16095], PO Box 850, Rocklin, CA 95677, (800)533-3231

Amer. Church Building Fund Commn. [★19698]

Amer. Cichlid Assn. [21721], Claudia Dickinson, PO Box 5078, Montauk, NY 11954, (631)668-5125

Amer. Cinema Editors [1249], 2282 Verna Fields Bldg., Rm. 190, 100 Universal City Plz., Universal City, CA 91608, (818)777-2900

Amer. Citizens Abroad [18920], 1051 N George Mason Dr., Arlington, VA 22205, (703)276-0949

Amer. Citizens Abroad [IO], Geneva, Switzerland

American Citizens Abroad
Amer. Citizens Abroad [18920]

Amer. Citizens for Justice [17259], PO Box 851163, Westland, MI 48185, (248)347-1663

Amer. Civic Assn. [12300], 131 Front St., Binghamton, NY 13905-3101, (607)723-9419

The Amer. Civil Defense Assn. [5305], 11576 S State St., Ste. No. 502, Draper, UT 84020, (801)501-0077

Amer. Civil Liberties Union [17260], 125 Broad St., 18th Fl., New York, NY 10004, (212)549-2500

Amer. Civil Liberties Union Found. [17261], 125 Broad St., 18th Fl., New York, NY 10004-2400, (212)549-2500

Amer. Civil Rights Inst. [17262], PO Box 188350, Sacramento, CA 95818-8350, (916)444-2278

Amer. Civil Rights Union [17263], 3213 Duke St., No. 625, Alexandria, VA 22314, (703)807-0242

Amer. Civil War Assn. [9746], PO Box 1652, Tracy, CA 95378

Amer. Civil War Round Table - United Kingdom [IO], London, United Kingdom

Amer. Clan Gregor Soc. [20423], 238 W 1220 N, American Fork, UT 84003, (801)763-0663

Amer. Classical League [8464], Miami Univ., 422 Wells Mills Dr., Oxford, OH 45056-1694, (513)529-7741

Amer. Cleaning Inst. [744], 1331 L St. NW, Ste. 650, Washington, DC 20005, (202)347-2900

Amer. Cleft Palate Assn. [★14190]

Amer. Cleft Palate-Craniofacial Assn. [14190], 1504 E Franklin St., Ste. 102, Chapel Hill, NC 27514-2820, (919)933-9044

Amer. Cleft Palate Educational Found. [★14194]

Amer. Clematis Soc. [4665], PO Box 17085, Irvine, CA 92623-7085

Amer. Clergy Leadership Conf. [20173], 3224 16th St. NW, Washington, DC 20010, (202)319-3200

Amer. CLG of Foot Orthopedists [★16291]

Amer. Clinical and Climatological Assn. [14149], 2320 Kleinert Ave., Baton Rouge, LA 70806, (225)215-1311

Amer. Clinical Lab. Assn. [15231], 1100 New York Ave. NW, Ste. 725 W, Washington, DC 20005, (202)637-9466

Amer. Clinical Neurophysiology Soc. [14443], PO Box 30, Bloomfield, CT 06002, (860)243-3977

Amer. Clipper Owners Club - Address unknown since 2010.

Amer. Club of Lyon [IO], Lyon, France

Amer. Club of Paris [IO], Paris, France

Amer. Clydesdale Assn. [★4576]

Amer. Coal Ash Assn. [3629], 15200 E Girard Ave., Ste. 3050, Aurora, CO 80014, (720)870-7897

Amer. Coal Coun. [778], 1101 Pennsylvania Ave. NW, Ste. 600, Washington, DC 20004, (202)756-4540

Amer. Coal Found. [779], 101 Constitution Ave. NW, Ste. 525 E, Washington, DC 20001-2133, (202)463-9875

Amer. Coal Sales Assn. [★785]

Amer. Coalition for Clean Coal Electricity [6638], 333 John Carlyle St., Ste. 530, Alexandria, VA 22314, (703)684-6292

Amer. Coalition for Fathers and Children [12602], 1718 M St. NW, No. 187, Washington, DC 20036-4504, (202)330-3248

Amer. Coaster Enthusiasts [20944], 1100-H Brandywine Blvd., Zanesville, OH 43701-7303, (740)450-1560

Amer. Coatings Assn. [2613], 1500 Rhode Island Ave. NW, Washington, DC 20005, (202)462-6272

A star before a book entry number signifies that the name is not listed separately, but is mentioned within the entry.

Amer. Cockatiel Soc. [**21211**], PO Box 980055, Houston, TX 77098-0055, (888)221-1161

Amer. Cocoa Res. Comm. [★**4369**]

Amer. Cocoa Res. Inst. [★**4369**]

Amer. Coke and Coal Chemicals Inst. [**780**], 1140 Connecticut Ave. NW, Ste. 705, Washington, DC 20036, (202)452-7198

Amer. Collectors Assn. [★**1030**]

Amer. Collectors Assn. [★**1030**]

Amer. Collectors of Infant Feeders [**21293**], Sara Jean Binder, Treas., 13851 Belle Chasse Blvd., Ste. 412, Laurel, MD 20707

Amer. Collectors of Infant Feeders [**21293**], Sara Jean Binder, Treas., 13851 Belle Chasse Blvd., Ste. 412, Laurel, MD 20707

Amer. Coll. of Addiction Treatment Administrators - Address unknown since 2011.

Amer. Coll. for Advancement in Medicine [**16305**], 8001 Irvine Center Dr., Ste. 825, Irvine, CA 92618, (949)309-3520

Amer. Coll. for Advancement in Medicine [**16305**], 8001 Irvine Center Dr., Ste. 825, Irvine, CA 92618, (949)309-3520

Amer. Coll. of Allergy, Asthma and Immunology [**13635**], 85 W Algonquin Rd., Ste. 550, Arlington Heights, IL 60005-4425, (847)427-1200

Amer. Coll. of Apothecaries [**16170**], 2830 Summer Oaks Dr., Bartlett, TN 38134, (901)383-8119

Amer. Coll. of Bankruptcy [**5316**], 11350 Random Hills Rd., Ste. 800, Fairfax, VA 22030-6044, (703)934-6154

Amer. Coll. of Cardiology [**14000**], 2400 N St. NW, Washington, DC 20037-1153, (202)375-6000

Amer. Coll. of Cardiovascular Administrators [**15282**], Amer. Acad. of Medical Administrators, 701 Lee St., Ste. 600, Des Plaines, IL 60016-4516, (847)759-8601

Amer. Coll. of Cardiovascular Invasive Specialists [★**13997**]

Amer. Coll. of Chemosurgery [★**15913**]

Amer. Coll. of Chest Physicians [**14001**], 3300 Dundee Rd., Northbrook, IL 60062, (847)498-1400

Amer. Coll. of Chest Physicians [**14001**], 3300 Dundee Rd., Northbrook, IL 60062, (847)498-1400

Amer. Coll. of Chiropractic Consultants [**14119**], 2741 Ridge Rd., Lansing, IL 60438, (708)895-3141

Amer. Coll. of Chiropractic Orthopedists [**14120**], 35 S Lake St., North East, PA 16428, (781)665-1497

Amer. Coll. of Chiropractic Orthopedists [**14120**], 35 S Lake St., North East, PA 16428, (781)665-1497

Amer. Coll. of Chiropractic Specialists [★**14120**]

Amer. Coll. of Chiropractic Specialists [★**14120**]

Amer. Coll. of Clinic Managers [★**15283**]

Amer. Coll. of Clinical Pharmacology [**16171**], PO Box 1637, Rockville, MD 20849, (240)399-9070

Amer. Coll. of Clinical Pharmacy [**16172**], 13000 W 87th St. Pkwy., Lenexa, KS 66215-4530, (913)492-3311

Amer. Coll. of Community Midwives [**15864**], 3889 Middlefield Rd., Palo Alto, CA 94303-4718, (650)328-8491

Amer. Coll. of Constr. Lawyers [**5230**], PO Box 4646, Austin, TX 78765, (512)343-1808

Amer. Coll. of Contingency Planners [**14751**], Amer. Acad. of Medical Administrators, 701 Lee St., Ste. 600, Des Plaines, IL 60016, (847)759-8601

Amer. Coll. Counseling Assn. [**7936**], 5999 Stevenson Ave., Alexandria, VA 22304-3300, (703)823-9800

Amer. Coll. Counseling Assn. [**7936**], 5999 Stevenson Ave., Alexandria, VA 22304-3300, (703)823-9800

Amer. Coll. of Counselors [**11994**], 273 Glossip Ave., Highlandville, MO 65669-8133, (417)885-4030

Amer. Coll. Dance Festival Assn. [**9532**], 2275 Res. Blvd., Ste. 500, Rockville, MD 20850, (301)670-2820

Amer. Coll. of Dentists [**14259**], 839J Quince Orchard Blvd., Gaithersburg, MD 20878-1614, (301)977-3223

Amer. Coll. of Emergency Physicians [**14459**], PO Box 619911, Irving, TX 75038-2522, (972)550-0911

Amer. Coll. of Emergency Physicians I Amer. Assn. of Women Emergency Physicians [**14460**], PO Box 619911, Dallas, TX 75261-9911, (972)550-0911

Amer. Coll. of Environmental Lawyers [**5410**], 1300 SW 5th Ave., Ste. 2300, Portland, OR 97201-5630, (207)774-1200

Amer. Coll. of Epidemiology [**14511**], 1500 Sunday Dr., Ste. 102, Raleigh, NC 27607, (919)861-5573

Amer. Coll. of Eye Surgeons [**16796**], 334 E Lake Rd., No. 135, Palm Harbor, FL 34685-2427, (727)366-1487

Amer. Coll. of Foot and Ankle Orthopedics and Medicine [**16291**], 5272 River Rd., Ste. 630, Bethesda, MD 20816, (301)718-6505

Amer. Coll. of Foot and Ankle Surgeons [**16292**], 8725 W Higgins Rd., Ste. 555, Chicago, IL 60631-2724, (773)693-9300

Amer. Coll. of Foot Surgeons [★**16292**]

Amer. Coll. of Forensic Examiners [★**5473**]

Amer. Coll. of Forensic Examiners [★**5473**]

Amer. Coll. of Forensic Examiners Intl. [**5473**], 2750 E Sunshine St., Springfield, MO 65804, (417)881-3818

Amer. Coll. of Forensic Examiners Intl. [**5473**], 2750 E Sunshine St., Springfield, MO 65804, (417)881-3818

Amer. Coll. of Forensic Psychiatry [**5474**], PO Box 130458, Carlsbad, CA 92012-0458, (760)929-9777

Amer. Coll. of Forensic Psychology [**14546**], PO Box 130458, Carlsbad, CA 92012-0458, (760)929-9777

Amer. Coll. of Gastroenterology [**14550**], PO Box 342260, Bethesda, MD 20827-2260, (301)263-9000

Amer. Coll. of Gen. Practitioners in Osteopathic Medicine and Surgery [★**16059**]

Amer. Coll. Hea. Assn. [**14888**], 891 Elkridge Landing Rd., Ste. 100, Linthicum, MD 21090, (410)859-1500

Amer. Coll. of Hea. Care Administrators [**15809**], 1321 Duke St., Ste. 400, Alexandria, VA 22314, (202)536-5120

Amer. Coll. of Hea. Plan Mgt. - Address unknown since 2011.

Amer. Coll. of Healthcare Architects [**14752**], PO Box 14548, Lenexa, KS 66285-4548, (913)895-4604

Amer. Coll. of Healthcare Architects [**14752**], PO Box 14548, Lenexa, KS 66285-4548, (913)895-4604

Amer. Coll. of Healthcare Executives [**15033**], 1 N Franklin St., Ste. 1700, Chicago, IL 60606, (312)424-2800

Amer. Coll. of Healthcare Info. Administrators [**14753**], Amer. Acad. of Medical Administrators, 701 Lee St., Ste. 600, Des Plaines, IL 60016-4516, (847)759-8601

Amer. Coll. of Heraldry [**20616**], 1643-B Savannah Hwy., Ste. 396, Charleston, SC 29407

Amer. Coll. of Hosp. Administrators [★**15033**]

Amer. Coll. of Intl. Physicians [**15142**], 9323 Old Mt. Vernon Rd., Alexandria, VA 22309-2714, (703)221-1500

Amer. Coll. of Intl. Physicians [**15142**], 9323 Old Mt. Vernon Rd., Alexandria, VA 22309-2714, (703)221-1500

Amer. Coll. of Lab. Animal Medicine [**16995**], 96 Chester St., Chester, NH 03036, (603)887-2467

Amer. Coll. of Legal Medicine [**15242**], 2 Woodfield Lake, 1100 E Woodfield Rd., Ste. 520, Schaumburg, IL 60173-5125, (847)969-0283

Amer. Coll. of Medical Genetics [**14642**], 7220 Wisconsin Ave., Ste. 300, Bethesda, MD 20814, (301)718-9603

Amer. Coll. of Medical Gp. Administrators [★**15283**]

Amer. Coll. of Medical Informatics [★**14219**]

Amer. Coll. of Medical Physics - Defunct.

Amer. Coll. of Medical Practice Executives [**15283**], 104 Inverness Terr. E, Englewood, CO 80112-5306, (303)799-1111

Amer. Coll. of Medical Practice Mgt. [★**15320**]

Amer. Coll. of Medical Quality [**16505**], 5272 River Rd., Ste. 630, Bethesda, MD 20816, (301)718-6516

Amer. Coll. of Medical Staff Development [★**15320**]

Amer. Coll. of Medical Toxicology [**16893**], 10645 N Tatum Blvd., Ste. 200-111, Phoenix, AZ 85028, (623)533-6340

Amer. Coll. of Mental Hea. Admin. [★**15440**]

Amer. Coll. of Mohs Micrographic Surgery and Cutaneous Oncology [★**15913**]

Amer. Coll. of Mohs Surgery [**15913**], 555 E Wells St., Ste. 1100, Milwaukee, WI 53202-3823, (414)347-1103

Amer. Coll. of Musicians [**8639**], PO Box 1807, Austin, TX 78767, (512)478-5775

Amer. Coll. of Neuropsychopharmacology [**16173**], 5034-A Thoroughbred Ln., Brentwood, TN 37027, (615)324-2360

Amer. Coll. of Nuclear Medicine [**15693**], 1850 Samuel Morse Dr., Reston, VA 20190, (703)326-1190

Amer. Coll. of Nurse-Midwifery [★**15719**]

Amer. Coll. of Nurse-Midwives [**15719**], 8403 Colesville Rd., Ste. 1550, Silver Spring, MD 20910, (240)485-1800

Amer. Coll. of Nurse Practitioners [**15720**], 1501 Wilson Blvd., Ste. 509, Arlington, VA 22209, (703)740-2529

Amer. Coll. of Nursing Home Administrators [★**15809**]

Amer. Coll. of Nutrition [**15818**], 300 S Duncan Ave., Ste. 225, Clearwater, FL 33755, (727)446-6086

Amer. Coll. of Nutrition [**15818**], 300 S Duncan Ave., Ste. 225, Clearwater, FL 33755, (727)446-6086

Amer. Coll. of Obstetricians and Gynecologists [**15865**], PO Box 96920, Washington, DC 20090-6920, (202)638-5577

Amer. Coll. of Obstetricians and Gynecologists I Coun. on Resident Educ. in Obstetrics and Gynecology [**15866**], PO Box 96920, Washington, DC 20090-6920, (202)638-5577

Amer. Coll. of Occupational and Environmental Medicine [**15900**], 25 NW Point Blvd., Ste. 700, Elk Grove Village, IL 60007-1030, (847)818-1800

Amer. Coll. of Occupational Medicine [★**15900**]

Amer. Coll. of Oncology Administrators [**15284**], Amer. Acad. of Medical Administrators, 701 Lee St., Ste. 600, Des Plaines, IL 60016-4516, (847)759-8601

Amer. Coll. of Oral and Maxillofacial Surgeons [**16004**], 2025 M St. NW, Ste. 800, Washington, DC 20036, (202)367-1182

Amer. Coll. of Oral and Maxillofacial Surgeons [**16004**], 2025 M St. NW, Ste. 800, Washington, DC 20036, (202)367-1182

Amer. Coll. of Orgonomy [**16008**], PO Box 490, Princeton, NJ 08542, (732)821-1144

Amer. Coll. of Osteopathic Emergency Physicians [**14461**], 142 E Ontario St., Ste. 1500, Chicago, IL 60611, (312)587-3709

Amer. Coll. of Osteopathic Family Physicians [**16059**], 330 E Algonquin Rd., Ste. 1, Arlington Heights, IL 60005, (847)952-5108

Amer. Coll. of Osteopathic Internists [**16060**], 3 Bethesda Metro Ctr., Ste. 508, Bethesda, MD 20814, (301)656-8877

Amer. Coll. of Osteopathic Neurologists and Psychiatrists - Address unknown since 2010.

Amer. Coll. of Osteopathic Obstetricians and Gynecologists [**15867**], 8851 Camp Bowie W, Ste. 120, Fort Worth, TX 76116, (817)377-0421

Amer. Coll. of Osteopathic Pain Mgt. and Sclerotherapy [★**16062**]

Amer. Coll. of Osteopathic Pediatricians [**16061**], 2209 Dickens Rd., Richmond, VA 23230-2005, (804)565-6333

Amer. Coll. of Osteopathic Sclerotherapeutic Pain Mgt. [**16062**], 303 S Ingram Ct., Middletown, DE 19709, (302)530-2489

Amer. Coll. of Osteopathic Surgeons [**16063**], 123 N Henry St., Alexandria, VA 22314-2903, (703)684-0416

Amer. Coll. of Pain Medicine [★**16094**]

Amer. Coll. Personnel Assn. [**8699**], 1 Dupont Cir. NW, Ste. 300, Washington, DC 20036-1188, (202)835-2272

Amer. Coll. of Phlebology [**16956**], 101 Callan Ave., Ste. 210, San Leandro, CA 94577, (510)346-6800

Amer. Coll. of Physician Executives [**15285**], 400 N Ashley Dr., Ste. 400, Tampa, FL 33602, (813)287-2000

Amer. Coll. of Physicians [**15133**], 190 N Independence Mall W, Philadelphia, PA 19106-1572, (215)351-2600

Reference to "IO" in place of a book number signifies that the association may be found in the 50th edition of International Organizations.

Amer. Coll. of Preventive Medicine **[16306]**, 455 Massachusetts Ave. NW, Ste. 200, Washington, DC 20001, (202)466-2044

Amer. Coll. of Probate Counsel **[★5896]**

Amer. Coll. of Prosthodontists **[14260]**, 211 E Chicago Ave., Ste. 1000, Chicago, IL 60611, (312)573-1260

Amer. Coll. of Psychiatrists **[16326]**, 122 S Michigan Ave., Ste. 1360, Chicago, IL 60603, (312)662-1020

Amer. Coll. Public Relations Assn. **[★8013]**

Amer. Coll. of Radiation Oncology **[16511]**, 5272 River Rd., Ste. 630, Bethesda, MD 20816, (301)718-6515

Amer. Coll. of Radiology **[16520]**, 1891 Preston White Dr., Reston, VA 20191, (703)648-8900

Amer. Coll. of Real Estate Lawyers **[5231]**, 11300 Rockville Pike, Ste. 903, Rockville, MD 20852, (301)816-9811

Amer. Coll. of Rheumatology **[16616]**, 2200 Lake Blvd. NE, Atlanta, GA 30319, (404)633-3777

Amer. Coll. of Rheumatology **[16616]**, 2200 Lake Blvd. NE, Atlanta, GA 30319, (404)633-3777

Amer. Coll. of Spine Surgeons **[★15672]**

Amer. Coll. of Spine Surgeons **[★15672]**

Amer. Coll. of Sports Medicine **[16711]**, 401 W Michigan St., Indianapolis, IN 46202-3233, (317)637-9200

Amer. Coll. of Surgeons **[16797]**, 633 N St. Clair St., Chicago, IL 60611-3211, (312)202-5000

Amer. Coll. of Surgeons **[16797]**, 633 N St. Clair St., Chicago, IL 60611-3211, (312)202-5000

Amer. Coll. of Tax Counsel **[5646]**, 750 Natl. Press Bldg., 529 14th St. NW, Washington, DC 20045, (202)637-3243

Amer. Coll. Testing **[★8982]**

Amer. Coll. of Theriogenologists **[16996]**, PO Box 3065, Montgomery, AL 36109-0065, (334)395-4666

Amer. Coll. of Toxicology **[7569]**, 9650 Rockville Pike, Bethesda, MD 20814, (301)634-7840

Amer. Coll. of Toxicology **[7569]**, 9650 Rockville Pike, Bethesda, MD 20814, (301)634-7840

Amer. Coll. of Trial Lawyers **[6043]**, 19900 MacArthur Blvd., Ste. 530, Irvine, CA 92612, (949)752-1801

Amer. Coll. of Trust and Estate Counsel **[5896]**, 901 15th St., Ste. 525 NW, Washington, DC 20005, (202)684-8460

Amer. Coll. of Veterinary Anesthesiologists **[16997]**, PO Box 1100, Middleburg, VA 20118

Amer. Coll. of Veterinary Dermatology **[16998]**, 1411 El Camino Real, Redwood City, CA 94063, (650)365-6826

Amer. Coll. of Veterinary Emergency and Critical Care **[16999]**, Tufts Cummings School of Veterinary Medicine, 200 Westboro Rd., North Grafton, MA 01536, (508)839-5395

Amer. Coll. of Veterinary Internal Medicine **[17000]**, 1997 Wadsworth Blvd., Ste. A, Lakewood, CO 80214-5293, (303)231-9933

Amer. Coll. of Veterinary Ophthalmologists **[17001]**, PO Box 1311, Meridian, ID 83680, (208)466-7624

Amer. Coll. of Veterinary Pathologists **[17002]**, 2424 Amer. Ln., Madison, WI 53704, (608)443-2466

Amer. Coll. of Veterinary Radiology **[17003]**, PO Box 8820, Harrisburg, PA 17105-8820, (717)558-7865

Amer. Coll. of Veterinary Surgeons **[17004]**, 19785 Crystal Rock Dr., Ste. 305, Germantown, MD 20874, (301)916-0200

Amer. Collegians for Life **[★12945]**

Amer. Collegiate Hockey Assn. **[22639]**, PO Box 827, Union Lake, MI 48387-0827, (248)366-7914

Amer. Collegiate Horsemen's Assn. **[4527]**, 135 Poole Agricultural Bldg., Clemson, SC 29631, (864)656-4028

Amer. Collegiate Retailing Assn. **[8554]**, Am. Collegiate Retailing Assn., 312 Sandels Bldg., Tallahassee, FL 32306

Amer. Colon Therapy Assn. **[★16315]**

Amer. Colon Therapy Assn. **[★16315]**

Amer. Color Print Soc. **[9153]**, 205 Woodside Ave., Narberth, PA 19072

Amer. Combat Veterans of War **[20771]**, 3350 La Jolla Village Dr., Rm. 1580, San Diego, CA 92161-0002, (858)552-7501

Amer. Commercial Collectors Assn. **[★1033]**

Amer. Commercial Collectors Assn. **[★1033]**

Amer. Comm. for Accreditation of Reflexology Educ. and Training **[7726]**, 1309 Hillcrest Dr., Anchorage, AK 99503, (907)278-4646

Amer. Comm. for the Advancement of Torah Educ. **[★8421]**

Amer. Comm. on Africa **[★17140]**

Amer. Comm. on Africa **[★17140]**

Amer. Comm. for Aid to Poland - Defunct.

Amer. Comm. for the Brotherhood of Saint Andrew in Japan **[★12311]**

Amer. Comm. for Crystal Growth **[★6587]**

Amer. Comm. for the Evangelization of the Greeks **[★20008]**

Amer. Comm. for the Evangelization of the Greeks **[★20008]**

Amer. Comm. on the History of the Second World War **[★9818]**

Amer. Comm. on the History of the Second World War **[★9818]**

Amer. Comm. for Human Rights **[★17860]**

Amer. Comm. for Human Rights **[★17860]**

Amer. Comm. for Intl. Conservation - Defunct.

Amer. Comm. for Irish Stud. **[★9883]**

Amer. Comm. for Irish Stud. **[★9883]**

Amer. Comm. on Italian Migration **[19074]**, 25 Carmine St., New York, NY 10014, (212)247-7373

Amer. Comm. for KEEP **[12311]**, 825 Green Bay Rd., Ste. 122, Wilmette, IL 60091-2500, (847)853-2500

Amer. Comm. for Peace in Chechnya

Amer. Comm. for Peace in Chechnya - Address unknown since 2011.

Amer. Comm. for Rescue and Resettlement of Iraqi Jews - Address unknown since 2010.

Amer. Comm. for Shaare Zedek Hosp. in Jerusalem **[12390]**, 55 W 39th St., 4th Fl., New York, NY 10018, (212)764-8116

Amer. Comm. for Shaare Zedek Hosp. in Jerusalem **[12390]**, 55 W 39th St., 4th Fl., New York, NY 10018, (212)764-8116

Amer. Comm. for Shenkar Coll. - Address unknown since 2010.

Amer. Comm. of Slavists - Address unknown since 2010.

Amer. Comm. for South Asian Art **[★9154]**

Amer. Comm. for Ulster Justice - Defunct.

Amer. Comm. for the Weizmann Inst. of Sci. **[7356]**, 633 3rd Ave., New York, NY 10017, (212)895-7900

Amer. Commodity Distribution Assn. **[3947]**, 11358 Barley Field Way, Marriottsville, MD 21104, (410)442-4612

Amer. Communities Helping Israel **[12396]**, PO Box 550, Monsey, NY 10952-0550, (646)463-2531

Amer. Community Gardening Assn. **[21768]**, 1777 E Broad St., Columbus, OH 43203-2040, (877)275-2242

Amer. Community Theatre Assn. **[★10562]**

Amer. Comparative Literature Assn. **[10031]**, Univ. of South Carolina, Dept. of Languages, Literatures & Cultures, 1620 Coll. St., Rm. 813A, Columbia, SC 29208, (803)777-3021

Amer. Compensation Assn. **[★1162]**

Amer. Compensation Assn. **[★1162]**

Amer. Composers Alliance **[10141]**, 802 W 190th St., 1st Fl., New York, NY 10040, (212)925-0458

Amer. Composers Forum **[9495]**, 332 Minnesota St., Ste. E-145, St. Paul, MN 55101-1300, (651)228-1407

Amer. Composites Mfrs. Assn. **[519]**, 1010 N Glebe Rd., Ste. 450, Arlington, VA 22201, (703)525-0511

Amer. Cmpt. Barrel Racing Assn. **[22649]**, 14211 Rd. 35, Madera, CA 93636, (559)907-7976

Amer. Cmpt. Sci. League **[7902]**, 10 Brisas Dr., West Warwick, RI 02893

Amer. Cmpt. Scientists Assn. - Address unknown since 2011.

Amer. Concord Grape Assn. **[★4445]**

Amer. Concrete Inst. **[6570]**, 38800 Country Club Dr., Farmington Hills, MI 48331, (248)848-3700

Amer. Concrete Pavement Assn. **[820]**, 500 New Jersey Ave. NW, 7th Fl., Washington, DC 20001, (202)638-2272

Amer. Concrete Pipe Assn. **[2744]**, 1303 W Walnut Hill Ln., Ste. 305, Irving, TX 75038-3008, (972)506-7216

Amer. Concrete Pressure Pipe Assn. **[2745]**, 3900 Univ. Dr., Ste. 110, Fairfax, VA 22030-2513, (703)273-7227

Amer. Concrete Pumping Assn. **[821]**, 606 Enterprise Dr., Lewis Center, OH 43035-9432, (614)431-5618

Amer. Confed. of Reciprocating, Examining and Licensing Medical Boards **[★15411]**

Amer. Confed. of Reciprocating, Examining and Licensing Medical Boards **[★15411]**

Amer. Confed. of State Medical Examining Boards **[★15411]**

Amer. Confed. of State Medical Examining Boards **[★15411]**

Amer. Conf. of Academic Deans **[7654]**, Laura A. Rzepka, Exec. Dir., 1818 R St. NW, Washington, DC 20009, (202)884-7419

Amer. Conf. of Cantors **[19838]**, 1305 Remington Rd., Ste. D, Schaumburg, IL 60173, (847)781-7800

Amer. Conf. of Certified Cantors **[★19838]**

Amer. Conf. of Governmental Indus. Hygienists **[15901]**, 1330 Kemper Meadow Dr., Cincinnati, OH 45240, (513)742-2020

Amer. Conf. for Irish Stud. **[9883]**, Nicholas Wolf, Treas., PO Box 842001, Richmond, VA 23284-2001

Amer. Conf. for Irish Stud. **[9883]**, Nicholas Wolf, Treas., PO Box 842001, Richmond, VA 23284-2001

Amer. Conf. of Pharmaceutical Faculties **[★16167]**

Amer. Congregational Assn. **[19627]**, 14 Beacon St., 2nd Fl., Boston, MA 02108, (617)523-0470

Amer. Cong. of Community Supports and Employment Services **[17367]**, 1501 M St., 7th Fl., Washington, DC 20005, (202)466-3355

Amer. Cong. of Physical Medicine **[★16555]**

Amer. Cong. of Physical Medicine and Rehabilitation **[★16555]**

Amer. Cong. of Rehabilitation Medicine **[16555]**, PO Box 759272, Baltimore, MD 21275, (317)471-8760

Amer. Cong. on Surveying and Mapping **[7486]**, 6 Montgomery Village Ave., Ste. 403, Gaithersburg, MD 20879, (240)632-9716

Amer. Conifer Soc. **[4966]**, 175 Charisma Ln., Lewisville, NC 27023-9611, (336)945-0483

Amer. Connemara Pony Soc. **[4528]**, PO Box 100, Middlebrook, VA 24459

Amer. Conservative Defense Alliance **[17499]**, 1920 L St. NW, Ste. 200, Washington, DC 20036

Amer. Conservative Union **[17418]**, 1007 Cameron St., Alexandria, VA 22314, (703)836-8602

Amer. Conservatives for Freedom - Defunct.

Amer. Conservatory Theater Found. **[10563]**, 30 Grant Ave., 6th Fl., San Francisco, CA 94109-5800, (415)834-3200

Amer. Constitution Soc. for Law and Policy **[5336]**, 1333 H St. NW, 11th Fl., Washington, DC 20005, (202)393-6181

Amer. Constr. Inspectors Assn. **[839]**, 530 S Lake Ave., No. 431, Pasadena, CA 91101, (626)797-2242

Amer. Consular Assn. **[★23197]**

Amer. Consultants League` - Defunct.

Amer. Consumer Credit Counseling **[988]**, 130 Rumford Ave., Ste. 202, Auburndale, MA 02466-1370, (617)559-5700

Amer. Contact Dermatitis Soc. **[14315]**, 2323 N State St., Unit 30, Bunnell, FL 32110-4395, (386)437-4405

Amer. Contract Bridge League **[21239]**, 6575 Windchase Blvd., Horn Lake, MS 38637-1523, (662)253-3100

Amer. Contract Bridge League **[21239]**, 6575 Windchase Blvd., Horn Lake, MS 38637-1523, (662)253-3100

Amer. Contract Compliance Assn. **[11929]**, 17 E Monroe St., No. 150, Chicago, IL 60603, (866)222-2298

Amer. Coon Hunters Assn. **[22696]**, PO Box 453, Grayson, KY 41143, (606)474-9740

Amer. Coordinating Comm. for Equality in Sport and Soc. - Defunct.

Amer. Copper Coun. **[2462]**, 2 S End Ave., No. 4C, New York, NY 10280, (212)945-4990

Amer. Copy Editors Soc. **[2796]**, 7 Avenida Vista Grande, Ste. B7, No. 467, Santa Fe, NM 87508

A star before a book entry number signifies that the name is not listed separately, but is mentioned within the entry.

Amer. Cordage and Netting Mfrs. [★960]

Amer. Cormo Sheep Assn. [4887], 100 E River Rd., Broadus, MT 59317, (406)427-5449

Amer. Corn Millers' Fed. [★2502]

Amer. Corn Millers' Fed. - Defunct.

Amer. Corporate Counsel Assn. [★5345]

Amer. Correctional Assn. [11702], 206 N Washington St., Ste. 200, Alexandria, VA 22314, (703)224-0000

Amer. Correctional Chaplains Assn. [19517], PO Box 85840, Seattle, WA 98145-1840, (206)985-0577

Amer. Correctional Food Ser. Assn. [★1442]

Amer. Correctional Food Ser. Assn. [★1442]

Amer. Correctional Hea. Services Assn. [14889], 3990 Bullard Rd., Monticello, GA 31064, (855)825-5559

Amer. Corrective Therapy Assn. [★16556]

Amer. Corriedale Assn. [4888], Marcia E. Craig, Exec. Sec., PO Box 391, Clay City, IL 62824, (618)676-1046

Amer. Cotswold Record Assn. [4889], PO Box 59, Plympton, MA 02367, (781)585-2026

Amer. Cotswold Sheep Assn. [★4889]

Amer. Cotton Cooperative [★3946]

Amer. Cotton Shippers Assn. [977], 88 Union Ave., Ste. 1204, Memphis, TN 38103, (901)525-2272

Amer. Coun. of Academic Plastic Surgeons [14174], 900 Cummings Ctr., Ste. 221-U, Beverly, MA 01915, (978)927-8330

Amer. Coun. for Accredited Certification [4780], PO Box 11599, Glendale, AZ 85318-1599, (623)516-8381

Amer. Coun. on Alcoholism and Treatment - Address unknown since 2010.

Amer. Coun. for the Arts [★9271]

Amer. Coun. for Better Broadcasts [★9462]

Amer. Coun. of the Blind [17057], 2200 Wilson Blvd., Ste. 650, Arlington, VA 22201, (202)467-5081

Amer. Coun. of the Blind | Amer. Coun. of Blind Students [17058], 1155 15th St. NW, Ste. 1004, Washington, DC 20005, (202)467-5081

Amer. Coun. of the Blind Lions [17059], 148 Vernon Ave., Louisville, KY 40206, (502)897-1472

Amer. Coun. of the Blind Parents [★17073]

Amer. Coun. for Capital Formation [17475], 1750 K St. NW, Ste. 400, Washington, DC 20006, (202)293-5811

Amer. Coun. on Capital Gains and Estate Taxation [★17475]

Amer. Coun. of Certified Podiatric Physicians and Surgeons [★16287]

Amer. Coun. on Chiropractic Physiotherapy [★14131]

Amer. Coun. on Chiropractic Roentgenology [★16532]

Amer. Coun. of Christian Churches [19534], PO Box 5455, Bethlehem, PA 18015-0455, (610)865-3009

Amer. Coun. of Commercial Labs. [★7019]

Amer. Coun. for Competitive Telecommunications [★3592]

Amer. Coun. for Constr. Educ. [7915], 1717 N Loop 1604 E, Ste. 320, San Antonio, TX 78232-1570, (210)495-6161

Amer. Coun. on Consumer Interests [17442], 5100 E Vogel Rd., Ste. 202, Evansville, IN 47715, (812)470-1985

Amer. Coun. on Criminal Justice Training [5368], PO Box 1702, Missoula, MT 59806, (406)241-6150

Amer. Coun. for Drug Educ. [13234], 50 Jay St., Brooklyn, NY 11201, (646)505-2061

Amer. Coun. on Educ. [7994], 1 Dupont Cir. NW, Washington, DC 20036-1193, (202)939-9300

Amer. Coun. on Educ. | Center for Intl. Initiatives [8482], 1 Dupont Cir. NW, Washington, DC 20036, (202)939-9313

Amer. Coun. on Educ. | Center for Lifelong Learning [8171], 1 Dupont Cir. NW, Washington, DC 20036-1193, (202)939-9475

Amer. Coun. on Educ., Fellows Prog. [7655], 1 Dupont Cir. NW, Washington, DC 20036-1193, (202)939-9300

Amer. Coun. on Educ. for Journalism [★8434]

Amer. Coun. on Educ. | Off. of Women in Higher Educ. [9054], 1 Dupont Cir. NW, Washington, DC 20036, (202)939-9300

Amer. Coun. for an Energy-Efficient Economy [6687], 529 14th St. NW, Ste. 600, Washington, DC 20045, (202)507-4000

Amer. Coun. of Engg. Companies [6768], 1015 15th St., 8th Fl. NW, Washington, DC 20005-2605, (202)347-7474

Amer. Coun. of Engg. Companies | Coun. of Professional Surveyors [3370], 1015 15th St. NW, 8th Fl., Washington, DC 20005-2605, (202)347-7474

Amer. Coun. of Engineering Companies | Res. and Mgt. Found. [6769], 1015 15th St. NW, 8th Fl., Washington, DC 20005-2605, (202)347-7474

Amer. Coun. on Exercise [16220], 4851 Paramount Dr., San Diego, CA 92123, (858)576-6500

Amer. Coun. for Fitness and Nutrition - Address unknown since 2011.

Amer. Coun. on Germany [19000], 14 E 60th St., Ste. 1000, New York, NY 10022, (212)826-3636

Amer. Coun. on Germany [19000], 14 E 60th St., Ste. 1000, New York, NY 10022, (212)826-3636

Amer. Coun. on Global Nuclear Competitiveness [7174], PO Box 4520, Washington, DC 20015, (301)656-1859

Amer. Coun. for Headache Educ. [★14687]

Amer. Coun. of Hypnotist Examiners [15085], 700 S Central Ave., Glendale, CA 91204, (818)242-1159

Amer. Coun. on Immersion Educ. [8942], Univ. of Minnesota, Center for Advanced Res. on Language Acquisition, 140 Univ. Intl. Ctr., 331 17th Ave. SE, Minneapolis, MN 55414

Amer. Coun. of Independent Labs. [7019], 1875 I St. NW, Ste. 500, Washington, DC 20006, (202)887-5872

Amer. Coun. of Indus. Arts Supervisors [★8968]

Amer. Coun. of Indus. Arts Supervisors [★8968]

Amer. Coun. on Indus. Arts Teacher Educ. [★8297]

Amer. Coun. on Indus. Arts Teacher Educ. [★8297]

Amer. Coun. on Intl. InterCultural Educ. - Defunct.

Amer. Coun. on Intl. Personnel [1139], 1101 15th St. NW, Ste. 750, Washington, DC 20005, (202)371-6789

Amer. Coun. on Intl. Personnel [1139], 1101 15th St. NW, Ste. 750, Washington, DC 20005, (202)371-6789

Amer. Coun. for Intl. Stud. [8339], 343 Cong. St., Ste. 3100, Boston, MA 02210, (617)236-2051

Amer. Coun. for Intl. Stud. [8339], 343 Cong. St., Ste. 3100, Boston, MA 02210, (617)236-2051

Amer. Coun. for Judaism [19839], PO Box 2836, Ponte Vedra Beach, FL 32004-2836, (904)280-3131

Amer. Coun. for Kosovo [18036], PO Box 14522, Washington, DC 20044

Amer. Coun. of Learned Societies [9842], 633 Third Ave., 8th Fl., New York, NY 10017-6795, (212)697-1505

Amer. Coun. of Life Insurers [1930], 101 Constitution Ave. NW, Ste. 700, Washington, DC 20001-2133, (202)624-2000

Amer. Coun. on Marijuana and Other Psychoactive Drugs [★13234]

Amer. Coun. of Nanny Schools - Defunct.

Amer. Coun. of Parent Cooperatives [★7834]

Amer. Coun. of Parent Cooperatives [★7834]

Amer. Coun. on Pharmaceutical Educ. [★16165]

Amer. Coun. of Polish Cultural Clubs [★19186]

Amer. Coun. for Polish Culture [19186], Mrs. Florence Langrige, Membership Chair, 78 Meadow Ln., West Hartford, CT 06107, (860)521-4034

Amer. Coun. on Public Relations [★2908]

Amer. Coun. for Quebec Stud. [★7810]

Amer. Coun. for Quebec Stud. [★7810]

Amer. Coun. on Reclamation Res. [★5838]

Amer. Coun. on Renewable Energy [6688], 1600 K St. NW, Ste. 700, Washington, DC 20006, (202)393-0001

Amer. Coun. on Rural Special Educ. [8875], Cathy Galyon Keramidas, Chair, West Virginia Univ., PO Box 6122, Morgantown, WV 26506, (304)293-4384

Amer. Coun. on Sci. and Hea. [14695], 1995 Broadway, Ste. 202, New York, NY 10023-5860, (212)362-7044

Amer. Coun. of Snowmobile Associations [22924], Christine Jourdain, Exec. Dir., 271 Woodland Pass, Ste. 216, East Lansing, MI 48823, (517)351-4362

Amer. Coun. for Southern Asian Art [9154], Univ. of Illinois at Chicago, Dept. of Art History, 211A Henry Hall, 935 W Harrison St., Chicago, IL 60607-3553, (312)996-3303

Amer. Coun. of Spotted Asses [3778], Coreen Eaton, Sec.-Treas., 914 Riske Ln., Wentzville, MO 63385, (636)828-5955

Amer. Coun. of State Savings Supervisors [397], 1129 20th St. NW, 9th Fl., Washington, DC 20036-3403, (202)728-5757

Amer. Coun. of Teachers of Russian/American Coun. for Collaboration and Language Stud. [★7995]

Amer. Coun. of Teachers of Russian/American Coun. for Collaboration and Language Stud. [★7995]

Amer. Coun. on the Teaching of Foreign Languages [8465], 1001 N Fairfax St., Ste. 200, Alexandria, VA 22314, (703)894-2900

Amer. Coun. for Tech. [5535], 3040 Williams Dr., Ste. 610, Fairfax, VA 22031, (703)208-4800

Amer. Coun. of Trustees and Alumni [7640], 1726 M St. NW, Ste. 802, Washington, DC 20036, (202)467-6787

Amer. Coun. of Vedic Astrology [★6217]

Amer. Coun. for Voluntary Intl. Action [★12340]

Amer. Coun. for Voluntary Intl. Action [★12340]

Amer. Coun. of Young Political Leaders [18061], 2131 K St. NW, Ste. 400, Washington, DC 20037, (202)857-0999

Amer. Coun. of Young Political Leaders [18061], 2131 K St. NW, Ste. 400, Washington, DC 20037, (202)857-0999

Amer. Councils for Intl. Educ. [7995], 1828 L St. NW, Ste. 1200, Washington, DC 20036, (202)833-7522

Amer. Councils for Intl. Educ. [7995], 1828 L St. NW, Ste. 1200, Washington, DC 20036, (202)833-7522

Amer. Councils for Intl. Educ. | ACTR/ACCELS in the Kyrgyz Republic [IO], Bishkek, Kirgizstan

Amer. Counseling Assn. [11667], 5999 Stevenson Ave., Alexandria, VA 22304, (800)347-6647

Amer. Countertrade Assn. [★2098]

Amer. Court and Commercial Newspapers [2915], Public Notice Rsrc. Center, PO Box 5337, Arlington, VA 22205, (703)237-9806

Amer. Craft Assn. - Defunct.

Amer. Craft Coun. [21426], 72 Spring St., 6th Fl., New York, NY 10012-4019, (212)274-0630

Amer. Crafts Coun. [★21426]

Amer. Craftsmen's Coun. [★21426]

Amer. CranioSacral Therapy Assn. [14992], Upledger Inst., 11211 Prosperity Farms Rd., Ste. D-325, Palm Beach Gardens, FL 33410, (561)622-4334

Amer. Crappie Assn. [21731], 125 Ruth Ave., Benton, KY 42025, (270)395-4204

Amer. Cream Draft Horse Assn. [4529], 193 Crossover Rd., Bennington, VT 05201

Amer. Cream Draft Horse Assn. of Am. [★4529]

Amer. Creativity Assn. [9819], Drexel Univ., Goodwin Coll., 3001 Market St., Philadelphia, PA 19104, (215)895-5930

Amer. Credit Card Collectors Soc. [17485], PO Box 2465, Midland, MI 48641

Amer. Credit Union Mortgage Assn. [994], PO Box 400955, Las Vegas, NV 89140, (877)442-2862

Amer. Credit Union Mortgage Assn. and Amer. CU Housing Alliance [★994]

Amer. Criminal Justice Assn. | Lambda Alpha Epsilon [11703], PO Box 601047, Sacramento, CA 95860-1047, (916)484-6553

Amer. Crop Protection Assn. [★753]

Amer. Cross Country Skiers [22908], PO Box 604, Bend, OR 97709, (541)317-0217

Amer. Crossbow Fed. - Address unknown since 2011.

Amer. Cryonics Soc. [14211], PO Box 1509, Cupertino, CA 95015, (408)446-9001

Amer. Cryptogram Assn. [21473], 56 Sanders Ranch Rd., Moraga, CA 94556-2806

Amer. Crystallographic Assn. [6588], PO Box 96 Ellicot Station, Buffalo, NY 14205-0096, (716)898-8692

Amer. Cuemakers Assn. [455], Steven Klein, Sec.-Treas., 125A Marshall Creek Rd., Roanoke, TX 76262, (817)683-5652

Reference to "IO" in place of a book number signifies that the association may be found in the 50th edition of International Organizations.

Amer. CueSports Alliance [22307], 101 S Military Ave., Ste. P, No. 131, Green Bay, WI 54303, (920)662-1705

Amer. Culinary Fed. [734], 180 Center Place Way, St. Augustine, FL 32095, (904)824-4468

Amer. Cultural Exchange [★7948]

Amer. Cultural Resources Assn. [9265], 5024-R Campbell Blvd., Baltimore, MD 21236, (410)933-3483

Amer. Culture Assn. [10466], Michigan State Univ., 276 Bessey Hall, East Lansing, MI 48824, (517)355-6660

Amer. Custom Gunmakers Guild [1352], 22 Vista View Ln., Cody, WY 82414-9606, (307)587-4297

Amer. Cut Glass Assn. [21829], PO Box 482, Ramona, CA 92065-0482

Amer. Cutlery Mfrs. Assn. [★3375]

Amer. Cutting Horse Assn. [22674], PO Box 2443, Brenham, TX 77834, (979)836-3370

Amer. Daffodil Soc. [21769], PO Box 522, Hawkinsville, GA 31036

Amer. Daffodil Soc. [21769], PO Box 522, Hawkinsville, GA 31036

Amer. Dairy Assn. - Defunct.

Amer. Dairy Goat Assn. [3779], PO Box 865, Spindale, NC 28160, (828)286-3801

Amer. Dairy Goat Products Assn. - Defunct.

Amer. Dairy Products Inst. [1017], 116 N York St., Elmhurst, IL 60126, (630)530-8700

Amer. Dairy Sci. Assn. [4180], 2441 Village Green Pl., Champaign, IL 61822, (217)356-5146

Amer. Dance Festival [9533], Box 90772, Durham, NC 27708-0772, (919)684-6402

Amer. Dance Guild [9534], 240 W 14th St., New York, NY 10011, (212)627-9407

Amer. Dance Therapy Assn. [16449], 10632 Little Patuxent Pkwy., Ste. 108, Columbia, MD 21044, (410)997-4040

Amer. Darters Assn. [22496], PO Box 627, Wentzville, MO 63385-0627, (636)614-4380

Amer. Darts Org. [22497], Katie Harris, 230 N Crescent Way, Ste. K, Anaheim, CA 92801-6707, (714)254-0212

Amer. Deafness and Rehabilitation Assn. [★14911]

Amer. Debate Assn. - Address unknown since 2011.

Amer. Decency Assn. [17433], PO Box 202, Fremont, MI 49412, (231)924-4050

Amer. Decentralized Wastewater Assn. [3645], 918 Cong. Ave., Ste. 200, Austin, TX 78701, (800)993-5002

Amer. Deer and Wildlife Alliance [5024], PO Box 10, Liberty, TX 78642, (512)331-8607

Amer. Defenders of Bataan and Corregidor [20854], 945 Main St., Wellsburg, WV 26070, (304)737-1551

Amer. Defense Inst. [17500], 1055 N Fairfax St., Ste. 200, Alexandria, VA 22314, (703)519-7000

Amer. Delaine and Merino Record Assn. [4890], 7744 State Rte. 613, McComb, OH 45858, (419)293-2871

Amer. Dental Assistants Assn. [14261], 35 E Wacker Dr., Ste. 1730, Chicago, IL 60601-2211, (312)541-1550

Amer. Dental Assn. [14262], 211 E Chicago Ave., Chicago, IL 60611-2678, (312)440-2500

Amer. Dental Educ. Assn. [7964], 1400 K St. NW, Ste. 1100, Washington, DC 20005, (202)289-7201

Amer. Dental Educ. Assn. [7964], 1400 K St. NW, Ste. 1100, Washington, DC 20005, (202)289-7201

Amer. Dental Hygienists' Assn. [14263], 444 N Michigan Ave., Ste. 3400, Chicago, IL 60611, (312)440-8900

Amer. Dental Inst. - Defunct.

Amer. Dental Soc. of Anesthesiology [14264], 211 E Chicago Ave., Ste. 780, Chicago, IL 60611-6983, (312)664-8270

Amer. Dermatologic Soc. of Allergy and Immunology - Defunct.

Amer. Dermatological Assn. [14316], PO Box 551301, Davie, FL 33355, (954)452-1113

Amer. Desalting Assn. [★7595]

Amer. Desalting Assn. [★7595]

Amer. Design Drafting Assn. [6931], 105 E Main St., Newbern, TN 38059, (731)627-0802

Amer. Devon Cattle Assn. [3874], PO Box 261, Lampasas, TX 76550, (512)556-6593

Amer. Devon Cattle Club [★3874]

Amer. Dexter Cattle Assn. [3875], 4150 Merino Ave., Watertown, MN 55388, (952)215-2206

Amer. Diabetes Assn. [14344], 1701 N Beauregard St., Alexandria, VA 22311, (800)342-2383

Amer. Dialect Soc. [10022], MacMurray Coll., Dept. of English, 447 E Coll. Ave., Jacksonville, IL 62650, (217)479-7014

Amer. Die Casting Inst. [★1855]

Amer. Dietetic Assn. [15819], 120 S Riverside Plz., Ste. 2000, Chicago, IL 60606-6995, (312)899-0040

Amer. Digestive Hea. Found. [★14562]

American Dinner Theatre Inst. - Address unknown since 2010.

Amer. Disabled for Accessible Public Transit [★11758]

Amer. Disabled for Attendant Programs Today [11758], 201 S Cherokee St., Denver, CO 80223, (303)733-9324

Amer. Disc Jockey Assn. [2547], 20118 N 67th Ave., Ste. 300-605, Glendale, AZ 85308, (888)723-5776

Amer. Distance Educ. Consortium [7996], Univ. of Nebraska, C218 Animal Sci. Bldg., Lincoln, NE 68583-0952, (402)472-7000

Amer. Ditchley Found. [17933], 445 Park Ave., 9th Fl., New York, NY 10022, (212)541-3791

Amer. Dobermann Assn. [21491], PO Box 2231, Snohomish, WA 98291-2231, (425)397-7630

Amer. Documentation Inst. [★6968]

Amer. Dog Breeders Assn. [21492], PO Box 1771, Salt Lake City, UT 84110, (801)936-7513

Amer. Dog Owner's Assn. [10907], PO Box 41194, Fredericksburg, VA 22404, (540)786-8337

Amer. Dog Show Judges [21493], 9144 W Mt. Morris Rd., Flushing, MI 48433, (810)639-7075

Amer. Donkey and Mule Soc. [3780], PO Box 1210, Lewisville, TX 75067, (972)219-0781

Amer. Donkey and Mule Soc. | Miniature Donkey Registry [3781], PO Box 1210, Lewisville, TX 75067, (972)219-0781

Amer. Dorper Sheep Breeders' Soc. [4891], PO Box 259, Hallsville, MO 65255-0259, (573)696-2550

Amer. Dorper Sheep Breeders' Soc. [4891], PO Box 259, Hallsville, MO 65255-0259, (573)696-2550

Amer. Double Dutch League [22852], PO Box 567, Cherry Hill, NJ 08003-0567, (800)982-ADDL

Amer. Dove Assn. [21212], 15706 Bowsprit Ln., Houston, TX 77062-4518

Amer. Down Assn. [★2057]

Amer. Down Assn. - Defunct.

Amer. Drag Racing Assn. [★22241]

Amer. Dream Coalition [17264], 3711 NW 59th Pl., Gainesville, FL 32653, (352)281-5817

Amer. Driver Educ. Assn. [★7979]

Amer. Driver and Safety Educ. Assn. [★7979]

Amer. Driver and Traffic Safety Educ. Assn. [7979], Highway Safety Services, LLC, 1434 Trim Tree Rd., Indiana, PA 15701, (724)801-8246

Amer. Driving Soc. [22693], PO Box 278, Cross Plains, WI 53528, (608)237-7382

Amer. Drum Horse Assn. [4530], 3822 Bluff Cir., Coarsegold, CA 93614, (559)676-7990

Amer. Druze Soc. [19829], PO Box 17718, Sugar Land, TX 77479, (877)ADS-7330

Amer. Dry Milk [★1017]

Amer. Dutch Bantam Soc. - Address unknown since 2011.

Amer. Dutch Rabbit Club [4830], Rick Billups, Sec.-Treas., 488 Pratt Rd., Blanchester, OH 45107, (937)655-8657

Amer. Ecological Engg. Soc. [4191], Dr. Stewart Diemont, Treas., SUNY-ESF, 402 Baker Lab, 1 Forestry Dr., Syracuse, NY 13210-2778

Amer. Economic Assn. [6607], 2014 Broadway, Ste. 305, Nashville, TN 37203, (615)322-2595

Amer. Economic Development Coun. [★5534]

Amer. Economic Development Coun. [★5534]

Amer. Edged Products Mfrs. Assn. [3375], 21165 Whitfield Pl., No. 105, Potomac Falls, VA 20165, (703)433-9281

Amer. Educ. Finance Assn. [★8096]

Amer. Educational Gender Info. Ser. [★13104]

Amer. Educational Publishers Inst. [★2918]

Amer. Educational Res. Assn. [8790], 1430 K St. NW, Ste. 1200, Washington, DC 20005-2504, (202)238-3200

Amer. Educational Res. Assn. Women's Caucus [★9067]

Amer. Educational Stud. Assn. [7997], Philip Kovacs, Communications Dir., Univ. of Alabama in Huntsville, Dept. of Educ., 235 Morton Hall, Huntsville, AL 35899

Amer. Educational Stud. Assn. [7997], Philip Kovacs, Communications Dir., Univ. of Alabama in Huntsville, Dept. of Educ., 235 Morton Hall, Huntsville, AL 35899

Amer. Educational Trust [18113], PO Box 53062, Washington, DC 20009, (202)939-6050

Amer. Egg Bd. [4803], 1460 Renaissance Dr., Ste. 301, Park Ridge, IL 60068, (847)296-7043

Amer. Egyptian Cooperation Found. [17931], 200 E 61st St., Ste. 12B, New York, NY 10065, (212)867-2323

Amer. Egyptian Cooperation Found. [17931], 200 E 61st St., Ste. 12B, New York, NY 10065, (212)867-2323

Amer. Elasmobranch Soc. [7059], Daniel S. Ha, Treas., 1058 Cobblestone Ln., Lancaster, PA 17601, (717)569-1061

Amer. Electrochemical Soc. [★6406]

Amer. Electroencephalographic Soc. [★14443]

Amer. Electrology Assn. [14445], 6 Market Pl., Ste. 1, Essex Junction, VT 05452, (802)879-1898

Amer. Electrolysis Assn. [★14445]

Amer. Electrophoresis Soc. [6639], 1202 Ann St., Madison, WI 53713, (608)258-1565

Amer. Embryo Transfer Assn. [3801], 2441 Village Green Pl., Champaign, IL 61822, (217)398-2217

Amer. Employment Law Coun. [5232], 4800 Hampden Ln., 7th Fl., Bethesda, MD 20814, (301)951-9326

Amer. Emu Assn. [4685], 1201 W Main St., Ste. 2, Ottawa, IL 61350, (541)332-0675

Amer. Endodontic Soc. [14265], 265 N Main St., Glen Ellyn, IL 60137, (773)519-4879

Amer. Endurance Ride Conf. [23078], PO Box 6027, Auburn, CA 95604, (530)823-2260

Amer. Energy Alliance [17614], 1100 H St. NW, Ste. 400, Washington, DC 20005, (202)621-2940

Amer. Engg. Alliance [6770], Bowling Green Sta., PO Box 1446, New York, NY 10274-1446, (212)606-4053

Amer. Engg. Assn. [6771], Harold Ruchelman, 533 Waterside Blvd., Monroe Township, NJ 08831, (201)664-6954

Amer. Engg. Standards Comm. [★5982]

Amer. English Spot Rabbit Club - Address unknown since 2010.

Amer. Enterprise Assn. [★18440]

Amer. Enterprise Inst. for Public Policy Res. [18440], 1150 17th St. NW, Washington, DC 20036, (202)862-5800

Amer. Enterprise Inst. for Public Policy Res. and Natl. Legal Center for the Public Interest [★18440]

Amer. Entrepreneurs Assn. - Defunct.

Amer. Envelope Mfrs. Assn. [★3348]

Amer. Environmental Hea. Found. [14497], 8345 Walnut Hill Ln., Ste. 225, Dallas, TX 75231, (214)361-9515

Amer. Epilepsy Soc. [14517], 342 N Main St., Ste. 301, West Hartford, CT 06117-2507, (860)586-7505

Amer. Equestrian Alliance [1733], PO Box 6230, Scottsdale, AZ 85261, (602)992-1570

Amer. Equestrian Trade Assn. [4531], 107 W St. Rd., Kennett Square, PA 19348-1613, (610)444-2025

Amer. Equilibration Soc. [14266], 207 E Ohio St., Ste. 399, Chicago, IL 60611, (847)965-2888

Amer. Escrow Assn. [1277], 211 N Union St., Ste. 100, Alexandria, VA 22314, (703)519-1240

Amer. Eskimo Dog Club of Am. [21494], Bonnie Hardenstine, VP, RR 3, Box 3389, Stroudsburg, PA 18360, (724)926-1111

Amer. Ethical Union [19817], 2 W 64th St., New York, NY 10023-7104, (212)873-6500

Amer. Ethnological Soc. [6130], Univ. of Wisconsin, Dept. of Rural Sociology, Madison, WI 53701, (608)262-1217

Amer. Eugenics Soc. [★6598]

American-European Greyhound Alliance [4514], Louise Coleman, Pres., 167 Saddle Hill Rd., Hopkinton, MA 01748, (508)435-5969

A star before a book entry number signifies that the name is not listed separately, but is mentioned within the entry.

American-European Greyhound Alliance **[4514]**, Louise Coleman, Pres., 167 Saddle Hill Rd., Hopkinton, MA 01748, (508)435-5969

Amer. Evaluation Assn. **[6853]**, 16 Sconticut Neck Rd., No. 290, Fairhaven, MA 02719-1914, (508)748-3326

Amer. Ex-Prisoners of War **[20755]**, 3201 E Pioneer Pkwy., No. 40, Arlington, TX 76010-5396, (817)649-2979

Amer. Executives for Mgt. Excellence - Defunct.

Amer. Exploration and Production Coun. **[2638]**, 1350 Eye St. NW, Ste. 510, Washington, DC 20005, (202)652-2359

Amer. Face Brick Assn. **[★536]**

Amer. Facsimile Assn. **[3398]**, 2200 Benjamin Franklin Pkwy., Ste. E105A, Philadelphia, PA 19130, (215)981-0292

Amer. Family Assn. **[17334]**, PO Drawer 2440, Tupelo, MS 38803-2440, (662)844-5036

Amer. Family Communiversity - Address unknown since 2010.

Amer. Family Found. **[★19640]**

Amer. Family Rights Assn. **[17622]**, PO Box 1560, Cotuit, MA 02635

Amer. Family Soc. - Defunct.

Amer. Family Therapy Acad. **[11668]**, 1608 20th St. NW, 4th Fl., Washington, DC 20009, (202)483-8001

Amer. Family Therapy Assn. **[★11668]**

Amer. Fan Collectors Assn. **[★21303]**

Amer. Fancy Rat and Mouse Assn. **[21949]**, 9230 64th St., Riverside, CA 92509-5924, (909)238-5231

Amer. Farm Bur. Fed. **[4346]**, 600 Maryland Ave. SW, Ste. 1000W, Washington, DC 20024, (202)406-3600

Amer. Farm Bur. Found. for Agriculture **[3735]**, 600 Maryland Ave. SW, Ste. 1000W, Washington, DC 20024, (800)443-8456

Amer. Farm Bur. Res. Found. **[★3735]**

Amer. Farm Economic Assn. **[★6606]**

Amer. Farm Economic Assn. **[★6606]**

Amer. Farm Mgt. Assn. **[★6606]**

Amer. Farm Mgt. Assn. **[★6606]**

Amer. Farm Res. Assn. **[★3735]**

Amer. Farmers for the Advancement and Conservation of Tech. **[4347]**, 4255 S Buckley Rd., No. 178, Aurora, CO 80013, (800)340-0737

Amer. Farmland Trust **[17165]**, 1200 18th St. NW, Ste. 800, Washington, DC 20036, (202)331-7300

Amer. Farrier's Assn. **[459]**, 4059 Iron Works Pkwy., Ste. 1, Lexington, KY 40511, (859)233-7411

Amer. Fashion Assn. - Defunct.

Amer. Fed. for Aging Res. **[14658]**, 55 W 39th St., 16th Fl., New York, NY 10018, (212)703-9977

Amer. Fed. of Arts **[9266]**, 305 E 47th St., 10th Fl., New York, NY 10017, (212)988-7700

Amer. Fed. of Astrologers **[6213]**, 6535 S Rural Rd., Tempe, AZ 85283-3746, (480)838-1751

Amer. Fed. of Aviculture **[21213]**, PO Box 91717, Austin, TX 78709-1717, (512)585-9800

Amer. Fed. for Clinical Res. **[★14150]**

Amer. Fed. of German Folk Dance Groups **[9535]**, 308 Magnolia Dr., Plainfield, IN 46168

Amer. Fed. of Govt. Employees **[23195]**, 80 F St. NW, Washington, DC 20001, (202)737-8700

Amer. Fed. of Grain Millers - Defunct.

Amer. Fed. of Jazz Societies **[9914]**, 1400 16th St., Ste. 420, Washington, DC 20036, (202)939-1780

Amer. Fed. of Labor **[★23217]**

Amer. Fed. of Labor and Cong. of Indus. Organizations **[★23217]**

Amer. Fed. for Medical Res. **[14150]**, 500 Cummings Ctr., Ste. 221-U, Beverly, MA 01915, (978)927-8330

Amer. Fed. of Mineralogical Societies **[7119]**, PO Box 302, Glyndon, MD 21071-0302, (410)833-7926

Amer. Fed. of Motorcyclists **[21916]**, 6167 Jarvis Ave., No. 333, Newark, CA 94560, (510)796-7005

Amer. Fed. of Musicians of the U.S. and Canada **[23265]**, 1501 Broadway, Ste. 600, New York, NY 10036, (212)869-1330

Amer. Fed. of Musicians of the U.S. and Canada **[23265]**, 1501 Broadway, Ste. 600, New York, NY 10036, (212)869-1330

Amer. Fed. of New Zealand Rabbit Breeders **[4831]**, 626 Alabama St., Sulphur, LA 70663, (337)533-9005

Amer. Fed. of Organizations for the Hard of Hearing **[★16682]**

Amer. Fed. of Police **[★5686]**

Amer. Fed. of Police and Concerned Citizens **[5686]**, 6350 Horizon Dr., Titusville, FL 32780, (321)264-0911

Amer. Fed. of Radio Artists **[★23160]**

Amer. Fed. of Railroad Police - Defunct.

Amer. Fed. of Ramallah, Palestine **[9136]**, 27484 Ann Arbor Trail, Westland, MI 48185, (734)425-1600

Amer. Fed. of Reformed Young Men Societies **[★19606]**

Amer. Fed. of Reformed Young Women Societies **[★19606]**

Amer. Fed. of Representatives of Intl. Companies in Africa **[★3546]**

Amer. Fed. of Representatives of Intl. Companies in Africa **[★3546]**

Amer. Fed. of School Administrators **[7656]**, 1101 17th St. NW, Ste. 408, Washington, DC 20036, (202)986-4209

Amer. Fed. of Security Officers - Address unknown since 2011.

Amer. Fed. of Soroptimist Clubs **[★13077]**

Amer. Fed. of Soroptimist Clubs **[★13077]**

Amer. Fed. of State, County and Municipal Employees **[23196]**, 1625 L St. NW, Washington, DC 20036-5687, (202)429-1000

Amer. Fed. of Teachers **[23178]**, 555 New Jersey Ave. NW, Washington, DC 20001, (202)879-4400

Amer. Fed. of Tech. Engineers **[★6802]**

Amer. Fed. of TV and Radio Artists **[23160]**, 260 Madison Ave., 9th Fl., New York, NY 10016-2401, (212)532-0800

Amer. Feed Indus. Assn. **[4370]**, 2101 Wilson Blvd., Ste. 916, Arlington, VA 22201, (703)524-0810

Amer. Feed Mfrs. Assn. **[★4370]**

Amer. Feline Soc. - Defunct.

Amer. Fence Assn. **[840]**, 800 Roosevelt Rd., Bldg. C-312, Glen Ellyn, IL 60137, (630)942-6598

Amer. Fence Assn. **[840]**, 800 Roosevelt Rd., Bldg. C-312, Glen Ellyn, IL 60137, (630)942-6598

Amer. Fern Soc. **[6343]**, PO Box 299, St. Louis, MO 63166-0299

Amer. Ferret Assn. **[20948]**, PO Box 554, Frederick, MD 21705-0554, (888)FERRET-1

Amer. Fertility Assn. **[14529]**, 315 Madison Ave., Ste. 901, New York, NY 10017, (888)917-3777

Amer. Fertility Soc. **[★14530]**

Amer. Fertility Soc. **[★14530]**

Amer. Festival of Microtonal Music **[10142]**, 318 E 70th St., Ste. 5FW, New York, NY 10021, (212)517-3550

Amer. Fiber Mfrs. Assn. **[3432]**, 1530 Wilson Blvd., Ste. 690, Arlington, VA 22209-2418, (703)875-0432

Amer. Fiber, Textile, Apparel Coalition - Defunct.

Amer. Fiberboard Assn. **[520]**, 1935 S Plum Grove Rd., No. 283, Palatine, IL 60067, (847)934-8394

Amer. Fiberboard Assn. **[520]**, 1935 S Plum Grove Rd., No. 283, Palatine, IL 60067, (847)934-8394

Amer. Fibromyalgia Syndrome Assn. **[14536]**, PO Box 32698, Tucson, AZ 85751, (520)733-1570

Amer. Field Ser. **[★7947]**

Amer. Field Ser. **[★8336]**

Amer. Field Ser. **[★7947]**

Amer. Field Ser. **[★8336]**

Amer. Fighter Aces Assn. **[20312]**, 9404 E Marginal Way S, Seattle, WA 98108-4907, (206)764-5700

Amer. Film Inst. **[9593]**, 2021 N Western Ave., Los Angeles, CA 90027-1657, (323)856-7600

Amer. Film Inst. Alumni Assn. Writers Workshop **[★10749]**

Amer. Film Marketing Assn. **[1257]**, 10850 Wilshire Blvd., 9th Fl., Los Angeles, CA 90024-4321, (310)446-1000

Amer. Filtration and Separations Soc. **[7493]**, 7608 Emerson Ave. S, Richfield, MN 55423, (612)861-1277

Amer. Finance Assn. **[1278]**, Univ. of California, Haas School of Bus., Berkeley, CA 94720-1900, (800)835-6770

Amer. Financial Services Assn. **[2208]**, 919 18th St. NW, Ste. 300, Washington, DC 20006-5526, (202)296-5544

Amer. Fine Arts Soc. **[★9226]**

Amer. Fire Safety Coun. - Address unknown since 2011.

Amer. Fire Sprinkler Assn. **[3135]**, 12750 Merit Dr., Ste. 350, Dallas, TX 75251, (214)349-5965

Amer. Fired Arts Alliance **[9267]**, PO Box 14, Waupun, WI 53963, (920)296-5456

Amer. First Day Cover Soc. **[22007]**, PO Box 16277, Tucson, AZ 85732-6277, (520)321-0880

Amer. Fisheries Soc. **[6951]**, 5410 Grosvenor Ln., Ste. 110, Bethesda, MD 20814-2199, (301)897-8616

Amer. Fisheries Soc. **[6951]**, 5410 Grosvenor Ln., Ste. 110, Bethesda, MD 20814-2199, (301)897-8616

Amer. Flock Assn. **[3433]**, 6 Beacon St., Ste. 1125, Boston, MA 02108, (617)303-6288

Amer. Floorcovering Alliance **[2050]**, 210 W Cuyler St., Dalton, GA 30720, (706)278-4101

Amer. Floorcovering Assn. **[★3129]**

Amer. Floorcovering Assn. **[★3129]**

Amer. Floral Indus. Assn. **[★1368]**

Amer. Floral Marketing Coun. - Defunct.

Amer. Flower Importers Assn. **[★1368]**

Amer. Flute Guild **[10143]**, PO Box 1515, South Pasadena, CA 91031, (626)441-6314

Amer. Fly-Fishing Trade Assn. **[3304]**, 901 Front St., Ste. B-125, Louisville, CO 80027, (303)604-6132

Amer. Folklore Soc. **[9618]**, Ohio State Univ., Mershon Center, 1501 Neil Ave., Columbus, OH 43201-2602, (614)292-3375

Amer. Football Coaches Assn. **[22585]**, 100 Legends Ln., Waco, TX 76706, (254)754-9900

American Football Conf. **[★22591]**

American Football League **[★22591]**

Amer. Forage and Grassland Coun. **[4862]**, PO Box 867, Berea, KY 40403, (800)944-AFGC

Amer. Forces Guild for Infant Survival **[★16758]**

Amer. and Foreign Christian Union **[19535]**, 244 5th Ave., No. 1890, New York, NY 10001

Amer. Foreign Law Assn. **[5585]**, Emma Lindsay, Sec., Simpson Thatcher and Bartlett LLP, 425 Lexington Ave., New York, NY 10017-3954

Amer. Foreign Ser. Assn. **[23197]**, 2101 E St. NW, Washington, DC 20037, (202)338-4045

Amer. Foreign Ser. Protective Assn. **[19041]**, 1716 N St. NW, Washington, DC 20036-2902, (202)833-4910

Amer. Forensic Assn. **[8890]**, PO Box 256, River Falls, WI 54022, (800)228-5424

Amer. Forensic Nurses **[15721]**, 255 N El Cielo Rd., Ste. 140-195, Palm Springs, CA 92262, (760)322-9925

Amer. Forest History Found. **[★9765]**

Amer. Forest and Paper Assn. **[4387]**, 1111 19th St. NW, Ste. 800, Washington, DC 20036, (202)463-2700

Amer. Forestry Assn. **[★3990]**

Amer. Forests **[3990]**, PO Box 2000, Washington, DC 20013, (202)737-1944

Amer. Formalwear Assn. **[★208]**

Amer. Formalwear Assn. **[★208]**

Amer. Forum: Educ. in a Global Age **[★8340]**

Amer. Forum for Global Educ. **[8340]**, 120 Wall St., Ste. 2600, New York, NY 10005, (212)624-1300

Amer. Found. for Aging Res. **[14659]**, Univ. of Albany, Dept. of Biological Sciences, 1400 Washington Ave., Albany, NY 12222, (518)437-4448

Amer. Found. for AIDS Res. **[13603]**, 120 Wall St., 13th Fl., New York, NY 10005-3908, (212)806-1600

Amer. Found. for Allergic Diseases **[★13637]**

Amer. Found. for Alternative Health Care, Res. and Development - Defunct.

Amer. Found. for the Blind **[17060]**, 2 Penn Plz., Ste. 1102, New York, NY 10121, (212)502-7600

Amer. Found. for Mgt. Res. **[★2263]**

Amer. Found. for Mgt. Res. **[★2263]**

Amer. Found. for Overseas Blind **[★17085]**

Amer. Found. for Overseas Blind **[★17085]**

Amer. Found. for Pharmaceutical Educ. **[16174]**, 1 Church St., Ste. 400, Rockville, MD 20850-4184, (301)738-2160

Reference to "IO" in place of a book number signifies that the association may be found in the 50th edition of International Organizations.

Amer. Found. for Psychoanalysis and Psychoanalysis in Groups [★16351]

Amer. Found. for Resistance Intl. - Defunct.

Amer. Found. for Suicide Prevention [13294], 120 Wall St., 22nd Fl., New York, NY 10005, (212)363-3500

Amer. Found. for Surgery of the Hand [14679], 6300 N River Rd., Ste. 600, Rosemont, IL 60018-4256, (847)384-8300

Amer. Found. for Urologic Diseases [★16943]

Amer. Found. for Vision Awareness - Defunct.

Amer. Foundry Soc. [8963], 1695 N Penny Ln., Schaumburg, IL 60173-4555, (847)824-0181

Amer. Foundrymen's Assn. [★8963]

Amer. Foundrymen's Soc. [★8963]

Amer. Fox Terrier Club [21495], Mrs. Anne E. Smith, Membership Chair, 6838 Lake Shore Rd., Derby, NY 14047

Amer. Fracture Assn. - Address unknown since 2010.

Amer. Franchisee Assn. [1526], 53 W Jackson Blvd., Ste. 1256, Chicago, IL 60604, (312)431-0545

Amer. Fraternal Alliance [19042], 1301 W 22nd St., Ste. 700, Oak Brook, IL 60523, (630)522-6322

Amer. Fraternal Insurance Company [★19065]

Amer. Fraternal Union [19043], PO Box 59, Ely, MN 55731-0059, (218)365-3143

Amer. Freedom Alliance [18515], 11500 W Olympic Blvd., Ste. 400, Los Angeles, CA 90064, (310)444-3085

Amer. Freedom Coalition - Defunct.

Amer. Freedom from Hunger Found. [★12279]

American-French Genealogical Soc. [20617], PO Box 830, Woonsocket, RI 02895-0870, (401)765-6141

Amer. Friends of ALYN Hosp. [12794], 51 E 42nd St., Ste. 308, New York, NY 10017, (212)869-8085

Amer. Friends of ALYN Hosp. [12794], 51 E 42nd St., Ste. 308, New York, NY 10017, (212)869-8085

Amer. Friends of the Anglican Centre in Rome [19293], PO Box 300, St. Francisville, LA 70775, (225)252-3231

Amer. Friends of the Anglican Centre in Rome [19293], PO Box 300, St. Francisville, LA 70775, (225)252-3231

Amer. Friends of the Anne Frank Center [★17782]

Amer. Friends of the Anne Frank Center [★17782]

Amer. Friends of the Australian Natl. Gallery Found. [★10109]

Amer. Friends of Boys Town Jerusalem [★13513]

Amer. Friends of Cambridge Univ. [★9023]

Amer. Friends of Chung-Ang Univ. - Defunct.

Amer. Friends of the Czech Republic [18970], 4410 Massachusetts Ave. NW, No. 391, Washington, DC 20016-5572, (202)413-5528

Amer. Friends of the Fed. of Jewish Organizations and Communities of Russia - Defunct.

Amer. Friends of For Survival [13306], 5333 42nd St. NW, Washington, DC 20015

Amer. Friends of Guinea [15143], 12012 Wickchester Ln., Ste. 475, Houston, TX 77079, (713)353-9400

Amer. Friends of the Hakluyt Soc. [10032], Maureen O'Donnell, Sec., The John Carter Brown Lib., Box 1894, Providence, RI 02912

Amer. Friends of the Israel Museum [10108], 500 5th Ave., Ste. 2540, New York, NY 10110, (212)997-5611

Amer. Friends of Julio Iglesias Fan Club - Address unknown since 2010.

Amer. Friends of Lafayette [10653], Lafayette Coll., Farinon Ctr., Box 9463, Easton, PA 18042-1798

Amer. Friends of Magen David Adom [12801], 352 7th Ave., Ste. 400, New York, NY 10001, (212)757-1627

Amer. Friends of Magen David Adom [12801], 352 7th Ave., Ste. 400, New York, NY 10001, (212)757-1627

Amer. Friends of the Middle East [★18112]

Amer. Friends of the Middle East [★18112]

Amer. Friends of the Natl. Gallery of Australia [10109], 50 Broadway, Ste. 2003, New York, NY 10004, (212)338-6863

Amer. Friends of Neot Kedumim - Address unknown since 2010.

Amer. Friends of the Paris Opera and Ballet [9268], 972 5th Ave., New York, NY 10021, (212)439-1426

Amer. Friends of St. David's Cathedral [9664], St. David's Episcopal Church, 5150 Macomb St. NW, Washington, DC 20016

Amer. Friends of Scottish Opera [★10170]

Amer. Friends of Scottish Opera [★10170]

Amer. Friends Ser. Comm. [13167], 1501 Cherry St., Philadelphia, PA 19102, (215)241-7000

Amer. Friends Ser. Comm. [13167], 1501 Cherry St., Philadelphia, PA 19102, (215)241-7000

Amer. Friends of the Shakespeare Birthplace Trust [10699], 625 Slaters Ln., Ste. 103, Alexandria, VA 22314-1176, (703)684-7703

Amer. Friends of the Shakespeare Birthplace Trust [10699], 625 Slaters Ln., Ste. 103, Alexandria, VA 22314-1176, (703)684-7703

Amer. Friends of Switzerland [★19250]

Amer. Friends of Switzerland [★19250]

Amer. Friends of Tel Aviv Univ. [8418], 39 Broadway, Ste. 1510, New York, NY 10006, (212)742-9070

Amer. Friends of the Tel Aviv Univ. [★8418]

Amer. Friends of The Hebrew Univ. [8419], 1 Battery Park Plz., 25th Fl., New York, NY 10004, (212)607-8500

Amer. Friends of Turkey [18736], 1111 14th St. NW, Ste. 1050, Washington, DC 20005, (202)783-0483

Amer. Friends of Turkey [18736], 1111 14th St. NW, Ste. 1050, Washington, DC 20005, (202)783-0483

Amer. Friends of the Univ. of the Negev [★8417]

Amer. Friends of the Vatican Lib. [9953], 3535 Indian Trail, Orchard Lake, MI 48324, (248)683-0311

Amer. Friends of the Wildfowl and Wetlands Trust - Defunct.

Amer. Frozen Food Inst. [1371], 2000 Corporate Ridge, Ste. 1000, McLean, VA 22102, (703)821-0770

Amer. Fruit and Vegetable Shippers Assn. [★4476]

Amer. Fuchsia Soc. [21770], 6979 Clark Rd., Paradise, CA 95969, (530)876-8517

Amer. Fund for Alternatives to Animal Res. - Defunct.

Amer. Fund for Czech and Slovak Relief [12771], Bohemian Natl. Hall, 321 E 73rd St., New York, NY 10021

Amer. Fund for Czech and Slovak Relief [12771], Bohemian Natl. Hall, 321 E 73rd St., New York, NY 10021

Amer. Fund for Czechoslovak Relief [★12771]

Amer. Fund for Czechoslovak Relief [★12771]

Amer. Fund for Czechosloval Refugees [★12771]

Amer. Fund for Czechosloval Refugees [★12771]

Amer. Fund for Dental Educ. [★7966]

Amer. Fund for Dental Hea. [★7966]

Amer. Fund for Israel Institutions [★9895]

Amer. Fund for Israel Institutions [★9895]

Amer. Fund for Palestine Institutions [★9895]

Amer. Fund for Palestine Institutions [★9895]

Amer. Fur Indus. [★206]

Amer. Furniture Mfrs. Assn. [★1543]

Amer. Fuzzy Lop Rabbit Club [22113], Deb Levisay, Sec., 1007 Country Club Ln., Spencer, IA 51301-2639

Amer. Galloway Breeders' Assn. [3876], 395 Double J Ln., New Castle, PA 16101

Amer. Galvanizers Assn. [787], 6881 S Holy Cir., Ste. 108, Centennial, CO 80112, (720)554-0900

Amer. Galvanizers Assn. [787], 6881 S Holy Cir., Ste. 108, Centennial, CO 80112, (720)554-0900

Amer. Game Collectors Assn. [★21742]

Amer. Game Fowl Soc. [3840], PO Box 800, Belton, SC 29627, (864)237-5280

Amer. Game Protective Assn. [★5044]

Amer. Gaming Assn. [21759], 1299 Pennsylvania Ave. NW, Ste. 1175, Washington, DC 20004, (202)552-2675

Amer. Gas Assn. [4486], 400 N Capitol St. NW, Ste. 450, Washington, DC 20001, (202)824-7000

Amer. Gastroenterological Assn. [14551], 4930 Del Ray Ave., Bethesda, MD 20814, (301)654-2055

Amer. Gastroscopic Club [★14554]

Amer. Gastroscopic Soc. [★14554]

Amer. Gathering of Jewish Holocaust Survivors and Their Descendants - Address unknown since 2010.

Amer. Gear Mfrs. Assn. [1799], 1001 N Fairfax St., 5th Fl., Alexandria, VA 22314-1587, (703)684-0211

Amer. Gear Mfrs. Assn. [1799], 1001 N Fairfax St., 5th Fl., Alexandria, VA 22314-1587, (703)684-0211

Amer. Gelbvieh Assn. [3877], 10900 Dover St., Westminster, CO 80021, (303)465-2333

Amer. Gem Soc. [2153], 8881 W Sahara Ave., Las Vegas, NV 89117, (702)255-6500

Amer. Gem Trade Assn. [2154], 3030 LBJ Fwy., Ste. 840, Dallas, TX 75234, (214)742-4367

Amer. Genetic Assn. [6896], 2030 SE Marine Sci. Dr.; Newport, OR 97365, (541)867-0334

Amer. Geographical Soc. [6902], 32 Court St., Ste. 201, Brooklyn, NY 11201-4404, (718)624-2212

Amer. Geological Inst. [6908], 4220 King St., Alexandria, VA 22302-1502, (703)379-2480

Amer. Geophysical Union [6916], 2000 Florida Ave. NW, Washington, DC 20009-1277, (202)462-6900

Amer. Gerbil Soc. [20949], 18893 Lawrence 2100, Mount Vernon, MO 65712

Amer. Geriatrics Soc. [14660], 350 5th Ave., Ste. 801, New York, NY 10118, (212)308-1414

Amer. German Shepherd Rescue Assn. [10908], PO Box 7113, Clearlake, CA 95422, (707)994-5241

Amer. Ghost Soc. [7219], Chicago, IL, (312)666-5255

Amer. GI Forum of U.S. [20772], Dottie Bruton, Mgr., 2870 Speed Blvd., No. 103, Denver, CO 80211, (866)244-3628

Amer. Glovebox Soc. [7163], PO Box 9099, Santa Rosa, CA 95405, (800)530-1022

Amer. Gloxina Soc. [★21797]

Amer. Gloxina Soc. [★21797]

Amer. Gloxinia and Gesneriad Soc. [★21797]

Amer. Gloxinia and Gesneriad Soc. [★21797]

Amer. Go Assn. [21741], PO Box 397, New York, NY 10113-0397, (917)817-7080

Amer. Goat Soc. [3782], PO Box 63748, 735 Oakridge Ln., Pipe Creek, TX 78063, (830)535-4247

Amer. Goiter Assn. [★16883]

Amer. Gold Star Mothers [20698], 2128 Leroy Pl. NW, Washington, DC 20008, (202)265-0991

Amer. Gourd Soc. [21771], PO Box 2186, Kokomo, IN 46904-2186

Amer. Grandprix Assn. - Defunct.

Amer. Graniteware Assn. [★21380]

Amer. Grant Writers' Assn. [12654], PO Box 8481, Seminole, FL 33775, (727)366-9334

Amer. Grassfed Assn. [4686], PO Box 461090, Denver, CO 80246, (877)774-7277

Amer. Grassland Coun. [★4862]

Amer. Green Movement [★18358]

Amer. Greenhouse Vegetable Growers Assn. - Defunct.

Amer. Greyhound Track Operators Assn. [22554], Palm Beach Kennel Club, 1111 N Cong. Ave., West Palm Beach, FL 33409, (561)688-5799

Amer. Grooming Shop Assn. - Defunct.

Amer. Ground Water Trust [3646], 50 Pleasant St., Concord, NH 03301, (603)228-5444

Amer. Gp. Gymnastics Assn. - Address unknown since 2010.

Amer. Gp. Practice Assn. [★14891]

Amer. Gp. Psychotherapy Assn. [16450], 25 E 21st St., 6th Fl., New York, NY 10010, (212)477-2677

Amer. Guernsey Assn. [3878], 1224 Alton Darby Creek Rd., Ste. G, Columbus, OH 43228, (614)864-2409

Amer. Guernsey Cattle Club [★3878]

Amer. Guild of Authors and Composers [★5582]

Amer. Guild of Banjoists, Mandolinists and Guitarists [★10145]

Amer. Guild of Court Videographers [5752], 2241 Mariposa Blvd., Casper, WY 82604, (866)688-8441

Amer. Guild of English Handbell Ringers [10144], 1055 E Centerville Sta. Rd., Dayton, OH 45459, (937)438-0085

Amer. Guild of Hypnotherapists [15086], 2200 Veterans Blvd., Ste. 108, Kenner, LA 70062-4005

Amer. Guild for Infant Survival [16758], 301 Eastwood Cir., Virginia Beach, VA 23454-4014, (757)463-3845

Amer. Guild of Judaic Art [9155], 135 Shaker Hallow, Alpharetta, GA 30022, (404)981-2308

A star before a book entry number signifies that the name is not listed separately, but is mentioned within the entry.

Amer. Guild of Music **[10145]**, PO Box 599, Warren, MI 48090-0599, (248)686-1975

Amer. Guild of Musical Artists **[23266]**, 1430 Broadway, 14th Fl., New York, NY 10018, (212)265-3687

Amer. Guild of Organists **[10146]**, 475 Riverside Dr., Ste. 1260, New York, NY 10115, (212)870-2310

Amer. Guild of Patient Account Mgt. **[★15278]**

Amer. Guild of Patient Account Managers **[★15278]**

Amer. Guild of Town Criers **[10475]**, 121 S Div. Ave., Holland, MI 49424, (616)396-1943

Amer. Guinea Hog Assn. **[4947]**, 1820 P Ave., Jefferson, IA 50129, (515)370-1021

Amer. Gulf War Veterans Assn. **[20773]**, PO Box 85, Versailles, MO 65084, (573)378-6049

Amer. Gymnastic Union **[★22964]**

Amer. Gynecological and Obstetrical Soc. **[15868]**, 230 W Monroe St., Ste. 710, Chicago, IL 60606-4702, (312)235-4060

Amer. Gynecological Soc. **[★15868]**

Amer. Hackney Horse Soc. **[4532]**, 4059 Iron Works Pkwy., A-3, Lexington, KY 40511-8462, (859)255-8694

Amer. Haflinger Registry **[4533]**, 1686 E Waterloo Rd., Akron, OH 44306, (330)784-0000

Amer. Hair Loss Assn. **[14673]**, 23679 Calabasas Rd., No. 682, Calabasas, CA 91302-1502

Amer. Hair Loss Coun. **[14317]**, 30 S Main St., Shenandoah, PA 17976-2331, (570)462-1101

Amer. Half Quarter Horse Registry **[4534]**, PO Box 211, Carlsbad, NM 88221-0211, (480)982-1551

Amer. Hampshire Sheep Assn. **[4892]**, 15603 173rd Ave., Milo, IA 50166-8940, (641)942-6402

Amer. Handel Soc. **[9496]**, Univ. of Maryland, School of Music, College Park, MD 20742, (909)607-3568

Amer. Handwriting Anal. Found. **[10752]**, PO Box 460385, Escondido, CA 92046-0385, (760)489-0692

Amer. Hanoverian Soc. **[4535]**, 4067 Iron Works Pkwy., Ste. 1, Lexington, KY 40511-8483, (859)255-4141

Amer. Hardboard Assn. **[★1503]**

Amer. Hardboard Assn. **[★1503]**

Amer. Hardboard Assn. - Defunct.

Amer. Hardware Mfrs. Assn. **[1645]**, 801 N Plaza Dr., Schaumburg, IL 60173, (847)605-1025

Amer. Hardwood Export Coun. **[1464]**, 1825 Michael Faraday Dr., Reston, VA 20190, (703)435-2900

Amer. Harlequin Rabbit Club **[4832]**, 14991 Opera Rd., Leopold, IN 47551, (812)843-5460

Amer. Harp Soc. **[10147]**, PO Box 38334, Los Angeles, CA 90038-0334, (323)469-3050

Amer. Hatpin Soc. **[21294]**, Cathy Miller, VP, 2505 Indian Creek Rd., Diamond Bar, CA 91765-3307

Amer. Head and Neck Soc. **[16083]**, 11300 W Olympic Blvd., Ste. 600, Los Angeles, CA 90064, (310)437-0559

Amer. Headache Soc. **[14686]**, 19 Mantua Rd., Mount Royal, NJ 08061, (856)423-0043

Amer. Headache Soc. I Comm. for Headache Educ. **[14687]**, 19 Mantua Rd., Mount Royal, NJ 08061, (856)423-0043

Amer. Healing Arts Alliance **[14993]**, 3157 Rolling Rd., Edgewater, MD 21037, (410)956-0055

Amer. Hea. Assistance Found. **[15336]**, 22512 Gateway Center Dr., Clarksburg, MD 20871-2005, (800)437-2423

Amer. Hea. and Beauty Aids Inst. **[1666]**, PO Box 19510, Chicago, IL 60619-0510, (708)633-6328

Amer. Hea. Care Assn. **[14696]**, 1201 L St. NW, Washington, DC 20005, (202)842-4444

Amer. Hea. Care Assn. **[★14813]**

Amer. Hea. Decisions - Address unknown since 2011.

Amer. Hea. Info. Mgt. Assn. **[15331]**, 233 N Michigan Ave., 21st Fl., Chicago, IL 60601, (312)233-1100

Amer. Hea. Lawyers Assn. **[5510]**, 1620 Eye St. NW, 6th Fl., Washington, DC 20006-4010, (202)833-1100

Amer. Hea. Planning Assn. **[14697]**, 7245 Arlington Blvd., Ste. 300, Falls Church, VA 22042, (703)573-3103

Amer. Hea. Quality Assn. **[16506]**, 1776 I St. NW, 9th Fl., Washington, DC 20036, (202)331-5790

Amer. Healthcare Radiology Administrators **[★16516]**

Amer. Hearing Aid Associates **[14915]**, 225 Wilmington W, Chester Pike, Chadds Ford, PA 19317, (800)984-3272

Amer. Hearing Impaired Hockey Assn. **[22504]**, 4214 W 77th Pl., Chicago, IL 60652, (312)226-5880

Amer. Hearing Res. Found. **[14916]**, 8 S Michigan Ave., Ste. 814, Chicago, IL 60603-4539, (312)726-9670

Amer. Hearing Soc. **[★16682]**

Amer. Heart Assn. **[14002]**, 7272 Greenville Ave., Dallas, TX 75231, (301)223-2307

Amer. Heart Assn. I Coun. on Arteriosclerosis, Thrombosis and Vascular Biology - Address unknown since 2011.

Amer. Heartworm Soc. **[17005]**, PO Box 8266, Wilmington, DE 19803-8266, (302)691-5371

Amer. Helicopter Soc. **[126]**, 217 N Washington St., Alexandria, VA 22314-2538, (703)684-6777

Amer. Helicopter Soc. **[126]**, 217 N Washington St., Alexandria, VA 22314-2538, (703)684-6777

American-Hellenic Chamber of Commerce **[IO]**, Athens, Greece

Amer. Hellenic Educational Progressive Assn. **[19010]**, 1909 Q St. NW, Ste. 500, Washington, DC 20009, (202)232-6300

Amer. Hellenic Inst. **[23403]**, 1220 16th St. NW, Washington, DC 20036, (202)785-8430

Amer. Helvetia Philatelic Soc. **[22008]**, Richard T. Hall, Sec., PO Box 15053, Asheville, NC 28813-0053

Amer. Helvetia Philatelic Soc. **[22008]**, Richard T. Hall, Sec., PO Box 15053, Asheville, NC 28813-0053

Amer. Hemerocallis Soc. **[21772]**, 32 Mylod St., Walpole, MA 02081-4026, (508)668-7399

Amer. Hemisphere Assn. of the Intl. Cooperative Insurance Fed. **[★1985]**

Amer. Hemochromatosis Soc. **[14698]**, Sandra Thomas, Pres./Founder, 4044 W Lake Mary Blvd., Unit No. 104, PMB 416, Lake Mary, FL 32746-2012, (407)829-4488

Amer. Hepato-Pancreato-Biliary Assn. **[14979]**, 341 N Maitland Ave., Ste. 130, Maitland, FL 32751, (407)647-8839

Amer. Hepato-Pancreato-Biliary Assn. **[14979]**, 341 N Maitland Ave., Ste. 130, Maitland, FL 32751, (407)647-8839

Amer. Heraldry Soc. **[20618]**, PO Box 96503, Washington, DC 20090-6503

Amer. Herb Assn. **[6344]**, PO Box 1673, Nevada City, CA 95959, (530)265-9552

Amer. Herbal Pharmacopoeia **[13655]**, PO Box 66809, Scotts Valley, CA 95067, (831)461-6318

Amer. Herbal Products Assn. **[1723]**, 8630 Fenton St., Ste. 918, Silver Spring, MD 20910-5606, (301)588-1171

Amer. Herbalists Guild **[14989]**, PO Box 230741, Boston, MA 02123-0741, (857)350-3128

Amer. Hereford Assn. **[3879]**, PO Box 014059, Kansas City, MO 64101, (816)842-3757

Amer. Heritage Assn. Intl. **[★8337]**

Amer. Heritage Assn. Intl. **[★8337]**

Amer. Hernia Soc. **[16798]**, PO Box 4834, Englewood, CO 80155, (303)567-7899

Amer. Hernia Soc. **[16798]**, PO Box 4834, Englewood, CO 80155, (303)567-7899

Amer. Hibiscus Soc. **[21773]**, PO Box 1580, Venice, FL 34284-1580

Amer. Hibiscus Soc. **[21773]**, PO Box 1580, Venice, FL 34284-1580

Amer. Highland Cattle Assn. **[3880]**, Livestock Exchange Bldg., 4701 Marion St., Ste. 200, Denver, CO 80216-2139, (303)292-9102

Amer. Highway Freight Assn. **[★3504]**

Amer. Highway Proj. - Address unknown since 2010.

Amer. Highway Users Alliance **[12976]**, 1101 14th St. NW, Ste. 750, Washington, DC 20005, (202)857-1200

Amer. Hiking Soc. **[23079]**, 1422 Fenwick Ln., Silver Spring, MD 20910, (301)565-6704

Amer. Himalayan Rabbit Assn. **[4833]**, 7715 Callan Ct., New Port Richey, FL 34654, (727)847-1001

Amer. Himalayan Rabbit Assn. **[4833]**, 7715 Callan Ct., New Port Richey, FL 34654, (727)847-1001

Amer. Hindu Assn. **[19811]**, PO Box 55405, Madison, WI 53705, (608)234-8634

Amer. Hippotherapy Assn. **[16835]**, PO Box 2014, Fort Collins, CO 80522, (877)851-4592

Amer. Hippotherapy Assn. **[16835]**, PO Box 2014, Fort Collins, CO 80522, (877)851-4592

Amer. Histadrut Development Found. **[★12393]**

Amer. Histadrut Development Found. **[★12393]**

Amer. Historic Inns **[9665]**, PO Box 669, Dana Point, CA 92629, (949)481-6256

Amer. Historic Monument Soc. **[★2539]**

Amer. Historic Racing Motorcycle Assn. **[21917]**, 2375 Midway Rd. SE, Bolivia, NC 28422, (910)253-8012

Amer. Historical Assn. **[9747]**, 400 A St. SE, Washington, DC 20003-3889, (202)544-2422

Amer. Historical Assn. I Conf. on Asian History **[9333]**, H&SS 4062, Univ. of California San Diego, 9500 Gilmann Dr., La Jolla, CA 92093, (858)534-3401

Amer. Historical Assn. I Conf. on Asian History **[9333]**, H&SS 4062, Univ. of California San Diego, 9500 Gilmann Dr., La Jolla, CA 92093, (858)534-3401

Amer. Historical Print Collectors Soc. **[20955]**, 94 Marine St., Farmingdale, NY 11735-5605

Amer. Historical Soc. of Germans From Russia **[19001]**, 631 D St., Lincoln, NE 68502-1199, (402)474-3363

Amer. Historical Soc. of Germans From Russia **[19001]**, 631 D St., Lincoln, NE 68502-1199, (402)474-3363

Amer. History Forum I Civil War Educ. Assn. **[8251]**, PO Box 78, Winchester, VA 22604, (540)678-8598

Amer. Hockey Coaches Assn. **[22640]**, 7 Concord St., Gloucester, MA 01930, (781)245-4177

Amer. Hockey League **[22641]**, 1 Monarch Pl., Ste. 2400, Springfield, MA 01144-4004

Amer. Hockey League **[22641]**, 1 Monarch Pl., Ste. 2400, Springfield, MA 01144-4004

Amer. Holistic Hea. Assn. **[14994]**, PO Box 17400, Anaheim, CA 92817, (714)779-6152

Amer. Holistic Medical Assn. **[14995]**, 23366 Commerce Park, Ste. 101B, Beachwood, OH 44122, (216)292-6644

Amer. Holistic Medical Found. - Defunct.

Amer. Holistic Nurses' Assn. **[14996]**, 323 N San Francisco St., Ste. 201, Flagstaff, AZ 86001, (928)526-2196

Amer. Holistic Veterinary Medical Assn. **[17006]**, PO Box 630, Abingdon, MD 21009, (410)569-0795

Amer. Holstein Horse Assn. **[★4536]**

Amer. Holsteiner Horse Assn. **[4536]**, 222 E Main St., Ste. 1, Georgetown, KY 40324-1712, (502)863-4239

Amer. Home Bus. Assn. **[1730]**, 965 E 4800, Ste. 3c, Salt Lake City, UT 84117, (866)396-7773

Amer. Home Economics Assn. **[★12152]**

Amer. Home Furnishings Alliance **[1543]**, 317 W High Ave., 10th Fl., High Point, NC 27260, (336)884-5000

Amer. Home Laundry Mfrs. Assn. **[★218]**

Amer. Home Laundry Mfrs. Assn. and the Consumer Products Division of the Natl. Elecl. Mfrs. Assn. **[★5838]**

Amer. Home Life Intl. **[8341]**, 2137 Embassy Dr., Ste. 202, Lancaster, PA 17603, (717)560-2840

Amer. Home Life Intl. **[8341]**, 2137 Embassy Dr., Ste. 202, Lancaster, PA 17603, (717)560-2840

Amer. Home Lighting Assn. **[★2216]**

Amer. Homebrewers Assn. **[175]**, 736 Pearl St., Boulder, CO 80302-5006, (303)447-0816

Amer. Homeowners Assn. **[2239]**, PO Box 16817, Stamford, CT 06905, (203)323-7715

Amer. Homeowners Grassroots Alliance **[17798]**, 6776 Little Falls Rd., Arlington, VA 22213-1213, (800)489-7776

Amer. Homeowners' Rsrc. Center - Address unknown since 2011.

Amer. Honey Producers Assn. **[3816]**, PO Box 162, Power, MT 59468, (406)463-2227

Amer. Horse Coun. **[4537]**, 1616 H St. NW, 7th Fl., Washington, DC 20006, (202)296-4031

Amer. Horse Defense Fund **[4538]**, 1718 M St. NW, Unit 191, Washington, DC 20036-4505, (866)956-2433

Reference to "IO" in place of a book number signifies that the association may be found in the 50th edition of International Organizations.

Amer. Horse League [12166], 1612 Junction Ave., Ste. 4, Sturgis, SD 57785, (605)347-1730

Amer. Horse Protection Assn. [★5053]

Amer. Horse Publications [2916], 49 Spinnaker Cir., South Daytona, FL 32119, (386)760-7743

Amer. Horse Shows Assn. [★22689]

Amer. Horse Trials Found. [22675], 221 Grove Cove Rd., Centreville, MD 21617-2686, (443)262-9555

Amer. Horticultural Marketing Coun. - Defunct.

Amer. Horticultural Soc. [21774], 7931 E Boulevard Dr., Alexandria, VA 22308-1300, (703)768-5700

Amer. Horticultural Therapy Assn. [16836], 150 S Warner Rd., Ste. 156, King of Prussia, PA 19406, (484)654-0357

Amer. Hosp. Assn. [15034], 155 N Wacker Dr., Chicago, IL 60606, (312)422-3000

Amer. Hosp. Assn. I Amer. for the Healthcare Environmental [15035], 155 N Wacker Dr., Ste. 400, Chicago, IL 60606, (312)422-3860

Amer. Hosp. Assn. I Amer. Soc. for Healthcare Engg. [15036], 155 N Wacker Dr., Ste. 400, Chicago, IL 60606, (312)422-3800

Amer. Hosp. Assn. I Amer. Soc. for Healthcare Environmental Services [15035], 155 N Wacker Dr., Ste. 400, Chicago, IL 60606, (312)422-3860

Amer. Hosp. Assn. I Amer. Soc. for Healthcare Human Resources Admin. [15037], 155 N Wacker Dr., Ste. 400, Chicago, IL 60606, (312)422-3720

Amer. Hosp. Assn. I Assn. for Healthcare Rsrc. and Materials Mgt. [15038], 155 N Wacker Dr., Chicago, IL 60606, (312)422-3840

Amer. Hosp. Assn., Sect. for Long Term Care and Rehabilitation [15039], 155 N Wacker, Ste. 400, Chicago, IL 60606, (312)422-3302

Amer. Hosp. Assn., Sect. for Metropolitan Hospitals [15040], 155 N Wacker Dr., Chicago, IL 60606, (312)422-3000

Amer. Hosp. Assn., Sect. for Psychiatric and Substance Abuse Services [16327], 155 N Wacker Dr., Chicago, IL 60606-3421, (312)422-3303

Amer. Hosp. Assn. I Soc. for Healthcare Consumer Advocacy [15243], 155 N Wacker Dr., Ste. 155, Chicago, IL 60606, (312)422-3700

Amer. Hosp. Assn. I Soc. for Healthcare Strategy and Market Development [15041], 155 N Wacker Dr., Ste. 400, Chicago, IL 60606, (312)422-3888

Amer. Hosp. Radiology Administrators [★16516]

Amer. Hosta Soc. [21775], Sandie Markland, Membership Sec., PO Box 7539, Kill Devil Hills, NC 27948

Amer. Hot Dip Galvanizers Assn. [★787]

Amer. Hot Dip Galvanizers Assn. [★787]

Amer. Hot Rod Assn. [22241], N 102 Hayford Rd., Spokane, WA 99224, (509)244-3663

Amer. Hotel Assn. [★1735]

Amer. Hotel Found. [★1736]

Amer. Hotel and Lodging Assn. [1735], 1201 New York Ave. NW, No. 600, Washington, DC 20005-3931, (202)289-3100

Amer. Hotel and Lodging Educational Found. [1736], 1201 New York Ave. NW, No. 600, Washington, DC 20005-3931, (202)289-3100

Amer. Hotel and Motel Assn. [★1735]

Amer. Hotel and Motel Brokers [★3013]

Amer. Hotel and Motel Brokers [★3013]

Amer. Hovercraft Assn. [★21860]

Amer. Humane Assn. [13168], 63 Inverness Dr. E, Englewood, CO 80112-5117, (303)792-9900

Amer. Humane Assn. Children's Div. [★11187]

Amer. Humane Assn. Children's Services [11187], 63 Inverness Dr. E, Englewood, CO 80112-5117, (303)792-9900

Amer. Humane Educ. Soc. [★11004]

Amer. Humanics [★8493]

Amer. Humanics Found. [★8493]

Amer. Humanist Assn. [19818], 1777 T St. NW, Washington, DC 20009-7125, (202)238-9088

Amer. Humor Stud. Assn. [9851], St. Louis Univ., Dept. of English, 3800 Lindell Blvd., St. Louis, MO 63108-3414

Amer. Hungarian Catholic Soc. [★19063]

Amer. Hungarian Educators' Assn. [8284], 4515 Willard Ave., No. 2210, Chevy Chase, MD 20815-3685

Amer. Hungarian Educators' Assn. [8284], 4515 Willard Ave., No. 2210, Chevy Chase, MD 20815-3685

Amer. Hungarian Fed. [19028], Tamas Teglassy, Treas., 1805 Snow Meadow Ln., No. 103, Baltimore, MD 21209, (202)737-0127

Amer. Hungarian Found. [19029], PO Box 1084, New Brunswick, NJ 08903, (732)846-5777

Amer. Hungarian Lib. and Historical Soc. [19030], Hungarian House, 213 E 82nd St., New York, NY 10028-2701, (212)744-5298

Amer. Hungarian Stud. Found. [★19029]

Amer. Hydrangea Soc. [21776], PO Box 53234, Atlanta, GA 30355

Amer. Hydrogen Assn. [6689], 2350 W Shangri La Rd., Phoenix, AZ 85029-4724, (602)328-4238

Amer. Hyperlexia Assn. - Address unknown since 2010.

Amer. Hypnosis Assn. [15087], Hypnosis Motivation Inst., 18607 Ventura Blvd., Ste. 310, Tarzana, CA 91356, (818)758-2747

Amer. Iatrogenic Assn. - Address unknown since 2011.

Amer. Immigration and Citizenship Conf. [★17883]

Amer. Immigration and Citizenship Conf. [★17883]

Amer. Immigration Control Found. [17878], PO Box 525, Monterey, VA 24465, (540)468-2022

Amer. Immigration Coun. [5527], 1331 G St. NW, Ste. 200, Washington, DC 20005, (202)507-7500

Amer. Immigration Law Found. [★5527]

Amer. Immigration Lawyers Assn. [5528], 1331 G St. NW, Ste. 300, Washington, DC 20005-3142, (202)216-2400

Amer. Immunization Registry Assn. [15098], 1025 Thomas Jefferson St. NW, Ste. 500 E, Washington, DC 20007, (202)527-7000

Amer. Import Shippers Assn. [3241], 662 Main St., New Rochelle, NY 10801, (914)633-3770

Amer. Imported Auto. Dealers Assn. [★347]

Amer. Imported Auto. Dealers Assn. [★347]

Amer. Importers Assn. [2094], 214 7th St. N, Safety Harbor, FL 34695, (727)204-8500

Amer. Importers Assn. [★2093]

Amer. Impressionist Soc. [9220], 856 5th Pl., Vero Beach, FL 32962, (772)569-0597

Amer. Incense Mfrs. Assn. - Defunct.

Amer. Independent Bus. Alliance [3280], 222 S Black Ave., Bozeman, MT 59715, (406)582-1255

Amer. Independent Cockpit Alliance [23149], PO Box 220670, St. Louis, MO 63122-0670, (603)528-2552

Amer. Independent Refiners Assn. - Defunct.

American Indian

Amer. Indian Law Alliance [5200]

Assn. of Kannada Kootas of Am. [19035]

Assn. for the Stud. of Amer. Indian Literatures [10322]AmericanBear Butte Intl. Alliance

Black Indians and Intertribal Native Amer. Assn. [19152]

First Americans in the Arts [9114]

Indian Defense League of Am. [19156]

Lakota Student Alliance [19158]

Natl. Indian Child Care Assn. [12564]

Natl. Soc. for Amer. Indian Elderly [19162]

Natl. Tribal Development Assn. [19163]

Native Amer. Bus. Alliance [19164]

Native Amer. Coalition for Healthy Alternatives [12567]

Native Amer. Leadership Alliance [20147]

Native Workplace [10896]

Old Sleepy Eye Collectors' Club of Am. [21268]

Phi Sigma Nu Native Amer. Fraternity [23685]

Red Feather Development Gp. [12201]

United Indian Missions Intl. [20102]

Unreserved Amer. Indian Fashion and Art Alliance [9134]

Amer. Indian Archaeological Inst. [★6169]

Amer. Indian Arts Coun. - Address unknown since 2010.

Amer. Indian Bus. Leaders [640], Gallagher Bus. Bldg., Ste. 366, Missoula, MT 59812, (877)245-2425

Amer. Indian Coun. of Architects and Engineers [6182], 1707 E Highland Ave., Ste. 200, Phoenix, AZ 85016, (602)222-5300

Amer. Indian Culture Res. Center [10319], PO Box 98, Marvin, SD 57251-0098, (605)398-9200

Amer. Indian Defense Assn. [★18150]

Amer. Indian Ethnohistoric Conf. [★9585]

Amer. Indian Graduate Center [8189], 3701 San Mateo Blvd. NE, 2nd Fl., Albuquerque, NM 87109, (505)881-4584

Amer. Indian Heritage Found. [10320], PO Box 750, Pigeon Forge, TN 37868

Amer. Indian Higher Educ. Consortium [8673], 121 Oronoco St., Alexandria, VA 22314, (703)838-0400

Amer. Indian Horse Registry [4539], Rancho San Francisco, 9028 State Park Rd., Lockhart, TX 78644, (512)398-6642

Amer. Indian Inst. [10321], Univ. of Oklahoma, Coll. of Continuing Educ., 1639 Cross Center Dr., Norman, OK 73019-2219, (405)325-4127

Amer. Indian Law Alliance [5200], 11 Broadway, 2nd Fl., New York, NY 10004

Amer. Indian Law Students Assn. [★8510]

Amer. Indian Lib. Assn. [9954], 12 Highfield Rd., No. 2, Roslindale, MA 02131

Amer. Indian Movement [18148], PO Box 13521, Minneapolis, MN 55414

Amer. Indian Ritual Object Repatriation Found. [18149], 463 E 57th St., New York, NY 10022-3003, (212)980-9441

Amer. Indian Scholarships [★8189]

Amer. Indian Sci. and Engg. Soc. [6772], PO Box 9828, Albuquerque, NM 87119-9828, (505)765-1052

Amer. Indian Summer Seminar - Defunct.

Amer. Indian Youth Running Strong [12558], 2550 Huntington Ave., Ste. 200, Alexandria, VA 22303-1499, (703)317-9881

Amer. Indonesian Chamber of Commerce [23408], 317 Madison Ave., Ste. 1619, New York, NY 10017, (212)687-4505

Amer. Indoor Air Quality Coun. [★4780]

Amer. Indus. Arts Assn. [★8967]

Amer. Indus. Arts Assn. [★8967]

Amer. Indus. Arts Student Assn. [★8299]

Amer. Indus. Bankers Assn. [★2208]

Amer. Indus. Development Coun. [★5534]

Amer. Indus. Development Coun. [★5534]

Amer. Indus. Extension Alliance [2326], Center for Indus. Res. and Ser., 2272 Howe Hall, Ste. 2620, Ames, IA 50011-2272, (515)294-9592

Amer. Indus. Hygiene Assn. [15902], 2700 Prosperity Ave., Ste. 250, Fairfax, VA 22031, (703)849-8888

Amer. Indus. Radium and X-Ray Soc. [★7555]

Amer. Infertility Assn. [★14529]

Amer. Inst. of Actuaries [★2038]

Amer. Inst. of Aeronautics and Astronautics [6082], 1801 Alexander Bell Dr., Ste. 500, Reston, VA 20191-4344, (703)264-7500

Amer. Inst. of Architects [6183], 1735 New York Ave. NW, Washington, DC 20006-5292, (202)626-7300

Amer. Inst. of Architects Found. [★6181]

Amer. Inst. of Architecture Students [238], 1735 New York Ave. NW, Washington, DC 20006, (202)626-7472

Amer. Inst. of Bangladesh Stud. [7766], Univ. of Wisconsin-Madison, 203 Ingraham, 1155 Observatory Dr., Madison, WI 53706, (608)265-4304

Amer. Inst. of Biological Sciences [6283], 1313 Dolley Madison Blvd., McLean, VA 22101, (703)790-1745

Amer. Inst. of Biomedical Climatology - Defunct.

Amer. Inst. of Bolt, Nut and Rivet Mfrs. [★1651]

Amer. Inst. of Building Design [6184], 7059 Blair Rd. NW, Ste. 201, Washington, DC 20012, (800)366-2423

Amer. Inst. for Cancer Res. [13884], 1759 R St. NW, Washington, DC 20009, (202)328-7744

Amer. Inst. of Certified Public Accountants [8], 1211 Ave. of the Americas, New York, NY 10036-8775, (212)596-6200

Amer. Inst. for Chartered Property Casualty Underwriters [★1931]

Amer. Inst. of Chem. Engineers [6391], 3 Park Ave., New York, NY 10016-5991, (646)495-1380

Amer. Inst. of Chem. Engineers I Soc. for Biological Engg. [6284], 3 Park Ave., 19th Fl., New York, NY 10016, (212)591-8888

Amer. Inst. of Chemists [6392], 315 Chestnut St., Philadelphia, PA 19106-2702, (215)873-8224

A star before a book entry number signifies that the name is not listed separately, but is mentioned within the entry.

Amer. Inst. of Commemorative Art [2527], 8015 Van Ness Way, Indianapolis, IN 46240, (317)731-6556

Amer. Inst. for Conservation of Historic and Artistic Works [9666], 1156 15th St., Ste. 320, Washington, DC 20005-1714, (202)452-9545

Amer. Inst. for Conservation of Historic and Artistic Works [9666], 1156 15th St., Ste. 320, Washington, DC 20005-1714, (202)452-9545

Amer. Inst. of Constructors [6571], 700 N Fairfax St., Ste. 510, Alexandria, VA 22314, (703)683-4999

Amer. Inst. of Consulting Engineers [★6768]

Amer. Inst. for Contemporary German Stud. [9634], 1755 Massachusetts Ave. NW, Ste. 700, Washington, DC 20036-2121, (202)332-9312

Amer. Inst. for Contemporary German Stud. [9634], 1755 Massachusetts Ave. NW, Ste. 700, Washington, DC 20036-2121, (202)332-9312

Amer. Inst. for CPCU [1931], 720 Providence Rd., Ste. 100, Malvern, PA 19355-3433, (800)644-2101

Amer. Inst. for Decision Sciences [★7789]

Amer. Inst. for Design and Drafting [★6931]

Amer. Inst. for Economic Res. [6608], PO Box 1000, Great Barrington, MA 01230, (888)528-1216

Amer. Inst. of Employment Counseling [★1156]

Amer. Inst. of Engineers [6773], 4630 Appian Way, Ste. 206, El Sobrante, CA 94803-1875, (510)758-6240

Amer. Inst. of Fellows in Free Enterprise - Defunct.

Amer. Inst. of Fishery Res. Biologists [6952], Allen Shimada, Treas., 7909 Sleaford Pl., Bethesda, MD 20814

Amer. Inst. of Floral Designers [1365], 720 Light St., Baltimore, MD 21230, (410)752-3318

Amer. Inst. of Food Distribution [1372], 10 Mountainview Rd., Ste. S125, Upper Saddle River, NJ 07458, (201)791-5570

Amer. Inst. of Food Distribution [1372], 10 Mountainview Rd., Ste. S125, Upper Saddle River, NJ 07458, (201)791-5570

Amer. Inst. for Foreign Stud. [8398], River Plz., 9 W Broad St., Stamford, CT 06902-3734, (203)399-5000

Amer. Inst. for Foreign Stud. Found. [8399], 9 W Broad St., River Plz., Stamford, CT 06902, (203)399-5414

Amer. Inst. for Foreign Stud. Scholarship Found. [★8399]

Amer. Inst. for Full Employment [11930], 2636 Biehn St., Klamath Falls, OR 97601, (541)273-6731

Amer. Inst. for Full Employment [11930], 2636 Biehn St., Klamath Falls, OR 97601, (541)273-6731

Amer. Inst. of Graphic Arts [1600], 164 5th Ave., New York, NY 10010-5901, (212)807-1990

Amer. Inst. of Grapho Anal. [★10755]

Amer. Inst. of Grapho Anal. [★10755]

Amer. Inst. of the History of Pharmacy [16175], 777 Highland Ave., Madison, WI 53705-2222, (608)262-6234

Amer. Inst. of Homeopathy [15017], 101 S Whiting St., Ste. 16, Alexandria, VA 22304, (703)273-5250

Amer. Inst. of Hydrology [7594], Southern Illinois Univ. Carbondale, 1230 Lincoln Dr., Carbondale, IL 62901, (618)453-7809

Amer. Inst. of Indian Stud. [8293], 1130 E 59th St., Chicago, IL 60637, (773)702-8638

Amer. Inst. of Indus. Engineers [★6799]

Amer. Inst. of Inspectors [1913], PO Box 248, Lower Lake, CA 95457, (800)877-4770

Amer. Inst. for Intl. Steel [2463], 8400 Westpark Dr., McLean, VA 22102, (703)245-8075

Amer. Inst. for Intl. Steel [2463], 8400 Westpark Dr., McLean, VA 22102, (703)245-8075

Amer. Inst. of Iranian Stud. [9880], 118 Riverside Dr., No. 13A, New York, NY 10024

Amer. Inst. of Iranian Stud. [9880], 118 Riverside Dr., No. 13A, New York, NY 10024

Amer. Inst. for Islamic Affairs [★18129]

Amer. Inst. for Islamic Affairs [★18129]

Amer. Inst. of Kitchen Dealers [★2070]

Amer. Inst. of Landscape Architects [★6187]

Amer. Inst. of Laundering [★2191]

Amer. Inst. of Laundering [★2191]

Amer. Inst. for Maghrib Stud. [7700], Center for Middle Eastern Stud., Marshall Bldg., Rm. 477, 845 N Park Ave., PO Box 210158-B, Tucson, AZ 85721-0158, (520)626-6498

Amer. Inst. for Maghrib Stud. [7700], Center for Middle Eastern Stud., Marshall Bldg., Rm. 477, 845 N Park Ave., PO Box 210158-B, Tucson, AZ 85721-0158, (520)626-6498

Amer. Inst. of Maintenance [★2245]

Amer. Inst. for Managing Diversity [17495], 1200 W Peachtree St. NW, Ste. 3, Atlanta, GA 30309, (404)575-2131

Amer. Inst. of Marine Underwriters [1932], 14 Wall St., New York, NY 10005, (212)233-0550

Amer. Inst. for Medical and Biological Engg. [6897], 1701 K St. NW, Ste. 510, Washington, DC 20006, (202)496-9660

Amer. Inst. of Merchant Shipping [★5789]

Amer. Inst. of Mining and Metallurgical Engineers [★7125]

Amer. Inst. of Mining, Metallurgical, and Petroleum Engineers [7125], PO Box 270728, Littleton, CO 80127-0013, (303)948-4255

Amer. Inst. of Mortgage Brokers [★427]

Amer. Inst. of Musical Stud. [8640], 28 E 69th St., Kansas City, MO 64113, (816)268-3657

Amer. Inst. of Musical Stud. [8640], 28 E 69th St., Kansas City, MO 64113, (816)268-3657

Amer. Inst. of Nautical Archeology [★6170]

Amer. Inst. of Nautical Archeology [★6170]

Amer. Inst. of Nutrition [★15821]

Amer. Inst. of Nutrition [★15822]

Amer. Inst. of Oral Biology [14267], PO Box 1338, Loma Linda, CA 92354, (909)558-4671

Amer. Inst. of Organbuilders [2548], PO Box 35306, Canton, OH 44735, (330)806-9011

Amer. Inst. of Parliamentarians [10350], 550M Richie Hwy., No. 271, Severna Park, MD 21146, (888)664-0428

Amer. Inst. of Philanthropy [12655], PO Box 578460, Chicago, IL 60657, (773)529-2300

Amer. Inst. of Physics [7263], 1 Physics Ellipse, College Park, MD 20740, (301)209-3100

Amer. Inst. of Planners [★5327]

Amer. Inst. of Planners [★5326]

Amer. Inst. of Plant Engineers [★6785]

Amer. Inst. of Polish Culture [10459], 1440 79th St. Causeway, Ste. 117, Miami, FL 33141, (305)864-2349

Amer. Inst. of Polish Culture [10459], 1440 79th St. Causeway, Ste. 117, Miami, FL 33141, (305)864-2349

Amer. Inst. for Preventive Medicine [16307], 30445 Northwestern Hwy., Ste. 350, Farmington Hills, MI 48334, (248)539-1800

Amer. Inst. for Preventive Medicine [16307], 30445 Northwestern Hwy., Ste. 350, Farmington Hills, MI 48334, (248)539-1800

Amer. Inst. of Professional Geologists [6909], 12000 Washington St., Ste. 285, Thornton, CO 80241, (303)412-6205

Amer. Inst. for Property and Liability Underwriters [★1931]

Amer. Inst. of Real Estate Appraisers [★225]

Amer. Inst. for Shippers' Associations [3242], PO Box 33457, Washington, DC 20033-0457, (202)628-0933

Amer. Inst. of Steel Constr. [6572], 1 E Wacker Dr., Ste. 700, Chicago, IL 60601-1802, (312)670-2400

Amer. Inst. of Stress [16723], 124 Park Ave., Yonkers, NY 10703, (914)963-1200

Amer. Inst. for Stuttering Treatment and Professional Training [16680], 27 W 20th St., Ste. 1203, New York, NY 10011, (212)633-6400

Amer. Inst. of Supply Associations [★2779]

Amer. Inst. of Swedish Arts, Literature, and Sci. [★10552]

Amer. Inst. of Swedish Arts, Literature, and Sci. [★10552]

Amer. Inst. of Timber Constr. [1493], 7012 S Revere Pkwy., Ste. 140, Centennial, CO 80112, (303)792-9559

Amer. Inst. of Ultrasound in Medicine [16675], 14750 Sweitzer Ln., Ste. 100, Laurel, MD 20707-5906, (301)498-4100

Amer. Inst. of Verdi Stud. [10148], New York Univ., Dept. of Music, 24 Waverly Pl., Rm. 268, New York, NY 10003, (212)998-2587

Amer. Inst. of Wine and Food [21844], 26384 Carmel Rancho Ln., Ste. 200E, Carmel, CA 93923, (831)250-7595

Amer. Inst. of Wood Engg. [★4415]

Amer. Institutes for Res. [7324], 1000 Thomas Jefferson St. NW, Washington, DC 20007, (202)403-5000

Amer. Institutes for Res. in the Behavioral Sciences - Address unknown since 2011.

Amer. Institutions Food Service Assn. - Defunct.

Amer. Instructors of the Deaf [★14927]

Amer. Insurance Assn. [1933], 2101 L St. NW, Ste. 400, Washington, DC 20037, (202)828-7100

American Insurance Highway Safety Association [★12985]

Amer. Insurance Marketing and Sales Soc. [1934], PO Box 35718, Richmond, VA 23235, (804)674-6466

Amer. Integrative Medical Assn. [15393], 9201 Edgeworth Dr., No. 5631, Capitol Heights, MD 20791-5631, (757)292-7710

Amer. Intellectual Property Law Assn. [5559], 241 18th St. S, Ste. 700, Arlington, VA 22202, (703)415-0780

Amer. Intercultural Student Exchange [8342], 707 Lakehall Rd., Lake Village, AR 71653, (870)265-5050

Amer. Intl. Auto. Dealers Assn. [347], 211 N Union St., Ste. 300, Alexandria, VA 22314, (703)519-7800

Amer. Intl. Auto. Dealers Assn. [347], 211 N Union St., Ste. 300, Alexandria, VA 22314, (703)519-7800

Amer. Intl. Chamber of Commerce [23338], 333 S Grand Ave., 25th Fl., Los Angeles, CA 90071, (213)255-2066

Amer. Intl. Chamber of Commerce [23338], 333 S Grand Ave., 25th Fl., Los Angeles, CA 90071, (213)255-2066

American-International Charolais Assn. [3881], 11700 NW Plaza Cir., Kansas City, MO 64153, (816)464-5977

American-International Charolais Assn. [3881], 11700 NW Plaza Cir., Kansas City, MO 64153, (816)464-5977

Amer. Intl. Freight Assn. - Defunct.

Amer. Intl. Hea. Alliance [14890], 1250 Eye St. NW, Ste. 350, Washington, DC 20005, (202)789-1136

Amer. Intl. Hea. Alliance [14890], 1250 Eye St. NW, Ste. 350, Washington, DC 20005, (202)789-1136

Amer. Intl. Marchigiana Soc. [★3922]

Amer. Intl. Marchigiana Soc. [3882], PO Box 198, Walton, KS 67151-0198, (620)837-3303

Amer. Intl. Recruitment Coun. [7680], 4710 Rosedale Ave., Ste. 200, Bethesda, MD 20814, (240)547-6400

American/International Reiki Assn. [★13703]

American/International Reiki Assn. [★13703]

Amer. Intl. Women's Assn. of Rabat [IO], Rabat, Morocco

American/International Women's Club of Casablanca [IO], Casablanca, Morocco

Amer. Intl. Women's Club of Genoa [IO], Genoa, Italy

Amer. Intl. Women's Club of Torino [IO], Turin, Italy

Amer. Intersociety Acad. for Certification of Sanitarians [★16632]

Amer. Intra-Ocular Implant Soc. [★15943]

Amer. Iranian Coun. [18000], 29A Wiggins St., Princeton, NJ 08540, (609)252-9099

Amer. Ireland Fund [18005], 211 Cong. St., 10th Fl., Boston, MA 02110, (617)574-0720

Amer. Ireland Fund [18005], 211 Cong. St., 10th Fl., Boston, MA 02110, (617)574-0720

Amer. Iris Soc. [21777], PO Box 177, De Leon Springs, FL 32130, (386)277-2057

Amer. Iris Soc. [21777], PO Box 177, De Leon Springs, FL 32130, (386)277-2057

Amer. Irish Historical Soc. [9884], 991 5th Ave., New York, NY 10028, (212)288-2263

Amer. Iron and Steel Assn. [★2464]

Amer. Iron and Steel Inst. [2464], 1140 Connecticut Ave. NW, Ste. 705, Washington, DC 20036, (202)452-7100

Amer. Islamic Chamber of Commerce [23347], PO Box 93033, Albuquerque, NM 87199-3033

Amer. Islamic Chamber of Commerce [23347], PO Box 93033, Albuquerque, NM 87199-3033

Amer. Israel Chamber of Commerce - Southeast Region [23348], 400 Northridge Rd., Ste. 250, Atlanta, GA 30350, (404)843-9426

Reference to "IO" in place of a book number signifies that the association may be found in the 50th edition of International Organizations.

Amer. Israel Chamber of Commerce - Southeast Region [23348], 400 Northridge Rd., Ste. 250, Atlanta, GA 30350, (404)843-9426

American-Israel Numismatic Assn. [21962], PO Box 20255, Fountain Hills, AZ 85268, (818)225-1348

Amer. Israel Public Affairs Comm. [18114], 251 H St. NW, Washington, DC 20001, (202)639-5198

Amer. Italian Cong. - Defunct.

Amer. Italian Historical Assn. [9898], Queens College/City Univ. of New York, John D. Calandra Italiam Amer. Inst., 25 W 43rd St., 17th Fl., New York, NY 10036, (708)756-7168

Amer. Italian Historical Assn. [9898], Queens College/City Univ. of New York, John D. Calandra Italiam Amer. Inst., 25 W 43rd St., 17th Fl., New York, NY 10036, (708)756-7168

Amer. Italian Historical Soc. [★9902]

Amer. Italian Historical Soc. [★9902]

Amer. Ivy Soc. [21778], PO Box 163, Deerfield Street, NJ 08313

Amer. Ivy Soc. [21778], PO Box 163, Deerfield Street, NJ 08313

Amer. Jail Assn. [11704], 1135 Professional Ct., Hagerstown, MD 21740-5853, (301)790-3930

Amer. Jeepster Club [20991], PO Box 653, Lincoln, CA 95648, (916)645-8761

Amer. Jersey Cattle Assn. [3883], 6486 E Main St., Reynoldsburg, OH 43068-2362, (614)861-3636

Amer. Jersey Cattle Club [★3883]

Amer. Jesuit Missionary Assn. [★19437]

Amer. Jewelers Protective Assn. [★2167]

Amer. Jewish Archives [★9926]

Amer. Jewish Comm. [19840], PO Box 705, New York, NY 10150, (212)751-4000

Amer. Jewish Conf. on Soviet Jewry [★17568]

Amer. Jewish Conf. on Soviet Jewry [★17568]

Amer. Jewish Cong. [19841], 115 E 57 St., Ste. 11, New York, NY 10022, (212)879-4500

Amer. Jewish Historical Soc. [9917], 15 W 16th St., New York, NY 10011-6301, (212)294-6160

Amer. Jewish Joint Distribution Comm. [12401], 711 3rd Ave., New York, NY 10017-4014, (212)687-6200

Amer. Jewish Joint Distribution Comm. [12401], 711 3rd Ave., New York, NY 10017-4014, (212)687-6200

Amer. Jewish League for Israel [19842], PO Box 543, New York, NY 10116, (212)371-1583

Amer. Jewish Physicians' Comm. [★8419]

Amer. Jewish Press Assn. [2797], 107 S Southgate Dr., Chandler, AZ 85226, (480)403-4602

Amer. Jewish Publication Soc. [★9924]

Amer. Jewish Relief Comm. [★12401]

Amer. Jewish Relief Comm. [★12401]

Amer. Jewish Soc. for Ser. [12402], 10319 Westlake Blvd., Ste. 193, Bethesda, MD 20817, (240)205-5940

Amer. Jewish World Ser. [12802], 45 W 36th St., 10th Fl., New York, NY 10018-7641, (212)792-2900

Amer. Jewish World Ser. [12802], 45 W 36th St., 10th Fl., New York, NY 10018-7641, (212)792-2900

Amer. Joint Comm. on Cancer [15914], 633 N St. Clair St., Chicago, IL 60611-3211, (312)202-5313

Amer. Joint Comm. for Cancer Staging and End Results Reporting [★15914]

Amer. Journalism Historians Assn. [8252], OBU Box 61201, 500 W Univ., Shawnee, OK 74804-2590, (405)878-2221

Amer. Judges Assn. [5612], 300 Newport Ave., Williamsburg, VA 23185-4147, (757)259-1841

Amer. Judicature Soc. [5613], Drake Univ., The Opperman Ctr., 2700 Univ. Ave., Des Moines, IA 50311, (515)271-2281

Amer. Judo and Jujitsu Fed. [22703], PO Box 596, Penryn, CA 95663, (541)772-8190

American Junior Acad. of Sci. [★7378]

Amer. Junior Brahman Assn. [3884], Amer. Brahman Breeders Assn., 3003 S Loop W, Ste. 520, Houston, TX 77054, (713)349-0854

Amer. Junior Chianina Assn. [3885], Amer. Chianina Assn., 1708 N Prairie View Rd., PO Box 890, Platte City, MO 64079, (816)431-2808

Amer. Junior Golf Assn. [22603], 1980 Sports Club Dr., Braselton, GA 30517, (770)868-4200

Amer. Junior Hereford Assn. [★3926]

Amer. Junior Paint Horse Assn. [4540], PO Box 961023, Fort Worth, TX 76161-0023, (817)834-2742

Amer. Junior Quarter Horse Assn. [★4549]

Amer. Junior Rodeo Assn. [22839], 2301 Boyd Rd., Granbury, TX 76049, (817)559-0287

Amer. Junior Shorthorn Assn. [3886], Amer. Shorthorn Assn., 8288 Hascall St., Omaha, NE 68124, (402)393-7200

Amer. Junior Simmental Assn. [★3899]

Amer. Karakul Fur Sheep Registry [★4893]

Amer. Karakul Sheep Registry [4893], 11500 Hwy. 5, Boonville, MO 65233, (660)838-6340

Amer. Kempo-Karate Assn. [22722], Acad. of Kempo-Karate, 5760 Oak Dr., Charlotte, NC 28216, (704)393-1077

Amer. Kennel Club [21496], 260 Madison Ave., New York, NY 10016, (212)696-8200

Amer. Kennel Club Companion Animal Recovery [10909], 8051 Arco Corporate Dr., Ste. 200, Raleigh, NC 27617, (800)252-7894

Amer. Kenpo Karate Intl. [22709], PO Box 768, Evanston, WY 82931, (307)789-4124

Amer. Kerry Bog Pony Soc. [4541], 13010 W Darrow Rd., Vermilion, OH 44089, (440)967-2680

Amer. Kerry Bog Pony Soc. [4541], 13010 W Darrow Rd., Vermilion, OH 44089, (440)967-2680

Amer. Kerry and Dexter Club [★3875]

Amer. Keuda Cat Assn. - Address unknown since 2010.

Amer. Kidney Fund [15542], 6110 Executive Blvd., Ste. 1010, Rockville, MD 20852-3914, (800)638-8299

Amer. Kiko Goat Assn. [4497], 14551 County Rd. 7130, Moody, MO 65777, (254)423-5914

Amer. Killifish Assn. [21722], Barry Cooper, 27505 Riggs Hill Rd., Sweet Home, OR 97386

Amer. Kinesiotherapy Assn. [16556], 118 Coll. Dr., No. 5142, Hattiesburg, MS 39406, (800)296-2582

Amer. Kitefliers Assn. [22712], PO Box 22365, Portland, OR 97269, (609)755-5483

Amer. Knowledge Rescue [★12154]

Amer. Kurdish Info. Network [18037], 2722 Connecticut Ave. NW, No. 42, Washington, DC 20008-5316, (202)483-6444

Amer. Kurdish Info. Network [18037], 2722 Connecticut Ave. NW, No. 42, Washington, DC 20008-5316, (202)483-6444

Amer. Kuvasz Assn. [11870], 3831 Broad St. Rd., Gum Spring, VA 23065-2135

American-Kuwaiti Alliance - Address unknown since 2010.

Amer. Ladder Inst. [1646], 401 N Michigan Ave., Chicago, IL 60611, (312)644-6610

Amer. Laminators Assn. - Defunct.

Amer. Lancia Club - Address unknown since 2011.

Amer. Land Conservancy [3991], 369 Pine St., Ste. 700, San Francisco, CA 94104, (415)912-3660

Amer. Land Development Assn. [★3000]

Amer. Land Rights Assn. [5901], PO Box 400, Battle Ground, WA 98604, (360)687-3087

Amer. Land Title Assn. [2999], 1828 L St. NW, Ste. 705, Washington, DC 20036, (202)296-3671

Amer. Landrace Assn. - Address unknown since 2010.

Amer. Lands Access Assn. [22129], Ruth Bailey, Treas., 2857 Addison Pl., Santa Clara, CA 95051-1705

Amer. Lands Alliance - Defunct.

Amer. Langshan Club - Address unknown since 2010.

Amer. Language Acad. [★8523]

Amer. Laryngeal Papilloma Found. - Defunct.

Amer. Laryngological Assn. [16084], PO Box 128186, Nashville, TN 37212-8186, (615)509-5525

Amer. Laryngological, Rhinological and Otological Soc. [16085], 13930 Gold Cir., Ste. 103, Omaha, NE 68144, (402)346-5500

Amer. Latex Allergy Assn. [13636], PO Box 198, Slinger, WI 53086, (262)677-9707

Amer. Latvian Assn. [19107], 400 Hurley Ave., Rockville, MD 20850-3121, (301)340-1914

Amer. Law and Economics Assn. [5647], PO Box 208245, New Haven, CT 06520-8245, (203)432-7801

Amer. Law Enforcement Officers Assn. [★5686]

Amer. Law Firms for African Relief - Defunct.

Amer. Law Inst. [5648], 4025 Chestnut St., Philadelphia, PA 19104-3099, (215)243-1600

Amer. Law Student Assn. [★8498]

Amer. Lawn Bowls Assn. [★22430]

Amer. Leadership Forum [18062], 3101 Richmond Ave., Ste. 140, Houston, TX 77098, (713)807-1253

Amer. League Against Epilepsy [★14517]

Amer. League for Deaf-Blind [★14913]

Amer. League of Lobbyists [18373], Patti Jo Baber, Exec. Dir., PO Box 30005, Alexandria, VA 22310, (703)960-3011

Amer. League of Professional Baseball Clubs [★22275]

Amer. Leather Belting Assn. [★1853]

Amer. Leather Chemists Assn. [6393], 1314 50th St., Ste. 103, Lubbock, TX 79412-2940, (806)744-1798

Amer. Lebanese Coalition [18068], 4900 Leesburg Pike, Ste. 203, Alexandria, VA 22302, (703)578-4214

Amer. Lebanese Engg. Soc. - Address unknown since 2010.

Amer. Lebanese Medical Assn. [15394], 501 Swanson Ave., Placentia, CA 92870, (909)562-9474

Amer. Legacy Found. [18728], 1724 Massachusetts Ave. NW, Washington, DC 20036, (202)454-5555

Amer. Legal Finance Assn. [1279], 228 Park Ave. S, No. 23315, New York, NY 10003, (914)242-2023

Amer. Legal Found. [★5940]

Amer. Legal Studies Assn. - Defunct.

Amer. Legend [3783], Motorcycle Trailers Inc., 903 S Prairieview Rd., Mahomet, IL 61853, (217)586-2201

Amer. Legion [20332], Public Relations Div., PO Box 1055, Indianapolis, IN 46206, (317)630-1200

American Legion
Amer. Legion [20332]
Forty and Eight [20333]
Natl. Amer. Legion Press Assn. [20334]

Amer. Legion Auxiliary [20699], 8945 N Meridian St., 2nd Fl., Indianapolis, IN 46260, (317)569-4500

Amer. Legion Auxiliary Girls Nation [17245], 8945 N Meridian St., 2nd Fl., Indianapolis, IN 46260, (317)569-4500

Amer. Legion Baseball [22265], 700 N Pennsylvania St., Indianapolis, IN 46204, (317)630-1200

Amer. Legion Press Assn. [★20334]

Amer. Legislative Exchange Coun. [18441], 1101 Vermont Ave. NW, 11th Fl., Washington, DC 20005, (202)466-3800

Amer. Legislators Assn. [★5988]

Amer. Leprosy Found. [★15248]

Amer. Leprosy Found. [★15248]

Amer. Leprosy Missions [15247], 1 ALM Way, Greenville, SC 29601, (864)271-7040

Amer. Leprosy Missions [15247], 1 ALM Way, Greenville, SC 29601, (864)271-7040

Amer. Leprosy Missions I Leonard Wood Memorial [15248], 1 ALM Way, Greenville, SC 29601, (877)241-1736

Amer. Lhasa Apso Club [21497], Joyce Johanson, Membership Chair, 126 Kurlene Dr., Macomb, IL 61455, (309)837-1665

Amer. Lib. Assn. [9955], 50 E Huron St., Chicago, IL 60611, (312)944-6780

Amer. Lib. Assn. I Alternatives Media Task Force [9956], Social Responsibilities Round Table, 50 E Huron St., Chicago, IL 60611, (312)344-7072

Amer. Lib. Assn. I Ethnic and Peoplecultural Info. Exchange Roundtable - Address unknown since 2011.

Amer. Lib. Assn. I Gay, Lesbian, Bisexual and Transgendered Roundtable [9633], 50 E Huron St., Chicago, IL 60611, (800)545-2433

Amer. Lib. Assn. I Off. for Res. and Statistics [10509], 50 E Huron St., Chicago, IL 60611, (312)280-4274

Amer. Lib. Assn. - Public Info. Off. [10476], 50 E Huron St., Chicago, IL 60611, (312)280-4020

Amer. Lib. Assn. I Social Responsibilities Round Table Feminist Task Force [17629], 50 E Huron St., Chicago, IL 60611, (800)545-2433

Amer. Lib. Trustee Assn. [★9970]

A star before a book entry number signifies that the name is not listed separately, but is mentioned within the entry.

Amer. Libyan Freedom Alliance [17513], PO Box 22262, Lehigh Valley, PA 18002, (610)703-1382

Amer. Life Educ. and Res. Trust [★12921]

Amer. Life League [12921], PO Box 1350, Stafford, VA 22555, (540)659-4171

Amer. Lifesaving Emergency Response Team [★12912]

Amer. Lighting Assn. [2216], PO Box 420288, Dallas, TX 75342-0288, (214)698-9898

Amer. Liszt Soc. [9497], 1136 Hog Mountain Rd., Fleischmanns, NY 12430, (845)586-4457

Amer. Literacy Coun. [8523], 1441 Mariposa Ave., Boulder, CO 80302, (303)440-7385

Amer. Literary Translators Assn. [10614], Univ. of Texas at Dallas, 800 W Campbell Rd., Mail Sta. J051, Richardson, TX 75080-3021, (972)883-2092

Amer. Literature Assn. [10033], Texas A&M Univ., Dept. of English, College Station, TX 77843-4227

Amer. Littoral Soc. Northeast Region [7050], 28 W 9th Rd., Broad Channel, NY 11693, (718)318-9344

Amer. Livebearer Assn.

Amer. Livebearer Assn. - Address unknown since 2010.

Amer. Liver Found. [14980], 39 Broadway, Ste. 2700, New York, NY 10006, (212)668-1000

Amer. Livestock Breeds Conservancy [4687], PO Box 477, Pittsboro, NC 27312, (919)542-5704

Amer. Lock Collectors Assn. [21295], 8576 Barbara Dr., Mentor, OH 44060, (440)257-2346

Amer. Loggers Coun. [1465], PO Box 966, Hemphill, TX 75948, (409)625-0206

Amer. Logistics Assn. [5794], 1133 15th St. NW, Ste. 640, Washington, DC 20005, (202)466-2520

Amer. Longevity Assn. - Defunct.

Amer. Loudspeaker Mfrs. Assn. [★1090]

Amer. Loudspeaker Mfrs. Assn. [★1090]

Amer. Luggage Dealers Assn. - Address unknown since 2010.

Amer. Luggage Dealers Assn. - Defunct.

Amer. Lumber Standard Comm. [1494], PO Box 210, Germantown, MD 20875-0210, (301)972-1700

Amer. Lumber Standard Comm. [1494], PO Box 210, Germantown, MD 20875-0210, (301)972-1700

Amer. Lumberjack Assn. [22962], 51A Kirkpatrick Rd., Elk, WA 99009-9533, (509)292-2386

Amer. Lunar Soc. [6223], 722 Mapleton Rd., Rockville, MD 20850

Amer. Lunar Soc. [6223], 722 Mapleton Rd., Rockville, MD 20850

Amer. Lung Assn. [16604], 1301 Pennsylvania Ave. NW, Ste. 800, Washington, DC 20004, (212)315-8700

Amer. Lutheran Church [★19932]

Amer. Lutheran Church Men [★19932]

Amer. Lutheran Educ. Assn. [★8543]

Amer. Lutheran Publicity Bur. [19921], Donna Roche, Off. Mgr., PO Box 327, Delhi, NY 13753-0327, (607)746-7511

Amer. Lyme Disease Found. [14371], PO Box 466, Lyme, CT 06371

Amer. Machine Tool Distributors' Assn. [1800], 7361 Calhoun Pl., Ste. 320, Rockville, MD 20855, (301)738-1200

Amer. Made Alliance [21427], 3000 Chestnut Ave., Ste. 300, Baltimore, MD 21211, (410)889-2933

Amer. Magnolia Soc. [★6362]

Amer. Maine-Anjou Assn. [3887], PO Box 1100, 204 Marshall Rd., Platte City, MO 64079-1100, (816)431-9950

Amer. Malacological Soc. [7035], Tunison Lab. of Aquatic Sci., 3075 Gracie Rd., Cortland, NY 13045

Amer. Malacological Union [★7035]

American-Malaysian Chamber of Commerce [IO], Kuala Lumpur, Malaysia

Amer. Maltese Assn. [21498], 3002 Oakwood Dr., Charleston, IL 61920

Amer. Malting Barley Assn. [3948], 740 N Plankinton Ave., Ste. 830, Milwaukee, WI 53203-2403, (414)272-4640

Amer. Mammoth Jack Stock Registry [★3784]

Amer. Mammoth Jackstock Registry [3784], PO Box 1723, Johnson City, TX 78636, (830)330-0499

Amer. Managed Behavioral Healthcare Assn. [★14756]

Amer. Managed Care Pharmacy Assn. [★16211]

Amer. Mgt. Assn. [2263], 1601 Broadway, New York, NY 10019-7420, (212)586-8100

Amer. Mgt. Assn. [2263], 1601 Broadway, New York, NY 10019-7420, (212)586-8100

Amer. Mgt. Assn. I Oper. Enterprise [8547], 1601 Broadway, New York, NY 10019-7420, (800)634-4262

Amer. Manchester Terrier Club [21499], Susan Thrasher, Sec., 511 Hosier Dr., New Castle, IN 47362, (765)529-5196

Amer. Manual Medicine Assn. [13656], 2040 Raybrook SE, Ste. 103, Grand Rapids, MI 49546, (888)375-7245

Amer. Mfrs. Assn. and Affiliated Indus. [★1797]

Amer. Mfrs. Assn. of Products From Corn [★1381]

Amer. Mfrs. of Toilet Articles [★1670]

Amer. Mfg. Trade Action Coalition [2327], 910 16th St. NW, Ste. 760, Washington, DC 20006, (202)452-0866

Amer. Marine Insurance CH - Defunct.

Amer. Marinelife Dealers Assn. [4700], Liz Harris, Sec., Creatures Featured, PO Box 1052, Madison, FL 32341, (850)973-3488

Amer. Maritain Assn. [10368], Walsh Univ., 2020 E Maple St. NW, North Canton, OH 44720-3336, (330)490-7042

Amer. Maritime Cong. [5788], 444 N Capitol St. NW, Ste. 800, Washington, DC 20001, (202)347-8020

Amer. Maritime Safety [2350], 445 Hamilton Ave., Ste. 1204, White Plains, NY 10601-1833, (914)997-2916

Amer. Marketing Assn. [2386], 311 S Wacker Dr., Ste. 5800, Chicago, IL 60606, (312)542-9000

Amer. Marketing Soc. [★2386]

Amer. Massage Therapy Assn. [15261], 500 Davis St., Ste. 900, Evanston, IL 60201-4695, (847)864-0123

Amer. Massage and Therapy Assn. [★15261]

Amer. Masters of Foxhounds Assn. [★22699]

Amer. Match Coun. - Defunct.

Amer. Matchcover Collecting Club [21296], PO Box 18481, Asheville, NC 28814-0481

Amer. Material Handling Soc. [★7064]

Amer. Material Handling Soc. [★7064]

Amer. Mathematical Assn. of Two-Year Colleges [8561], Southwest Tennessee Community Coll., 5983 Macon Cove, Memphis, TN 38134, (901)333-6243

Amer. Mathematical Soc. [7068], 201 Charles St., Providence, RI 02904-2213, (401)455-4000

Amer. Mathematics Project - Defunct.

Amer. Matthay Assn. [8641], 319 Parker Dr., Jackson, TN 38305-9495

Amer. Measuring Tool Mfrs. Assn. [7463], 8652 East Ave., Mentor, OH 44060, (440)974-6829

Amer. Meat Goat Assn. - Address unknown since 2011.

Amer. Meat Inst. [2431], 1150 Connecticut Ave. NW, 12th Fl., Washington, DC 20036, (202)587-4200

Amer. Meat Packers Assn. [★2431]

Amer. Meat Sci. Assn. [6869], 2441 Village Green Pl., Champaign, IL 61822, (800)517-AMSA

Amer. Medallic Sculpture Assn. - Defunct.

Amer. Medical Assn. [15395], 515 N State St., Chicago, IL 60654, (312)464-5262

Amer. Medical Assn. Alliance [15396], 515 N State St., 9th Fl., Chicago, IL 60654, (312)464-4470

Amer. Medical Assn. Auxiliary [★15396]

Amer. Medical Assn. for the Conservation of Vision [★17112]

Amer. Medical Assn. I Coun. on Medical Educ. [8575], 515 N State St., Chicago, IL 60654-4854, (800)621-8335

Amer. Medical Assn. Educ. and Res. Found. [★8586]

Amer. Medical Assn. I Fed. of State Physician Hea. Programs [16251], 515 N State St., Rm. 8584, Chicago, IL 60610, (312)464-4574

Amer. Medical Assn. Found. [8586], 515 N State St., Chicago, IL 60654, (312)464-2593

Amer. Medical Assn. I Liaison Comm. on Medical Educ. [8576], 515 N State St., Chicago, IL 60654, (312)464-4933

Amer. Medical Athletic Assn. [22802], 4405 E West Hwy., Ste. 405, Bethesda, MD 20814, (301)913-9517

Amer. Medical Billing Assn. [15286], 2465 E Main St., Davis, OK 73030, (580)369-2700

Amer. Medical Directors Assn. [15810], 11000 Broken Land Pkwy., Ste. 400, Columbia, MD 21044, (410)740-9743

Amer. Medical Educ. Found. [★8586]

American Medical Equestrian Association/Safe Riders Foundation - Address unknown since 2010.

Amer. Medical Fly Fishing Assn. [3992], PO Box 768, Lock Haven, PA 17745, (570)769-7375

Amer. Medical Golf Assn. - Defunct.

Amer. Medical Gp. Assn. [14891], One Prince St., Alexandria, VA 22314-3318, (703)838-0033

Amer. Medical Informatics Assn. [14219], 4915 St. Elmo Ave., Ste. 401, Bethesda, MD 20814, (301)657-1291

Amer. Medical Joggers Assn. [★22802]

Amer. Medical Massage Assn. [15262], 2040 Raybrook St. SE, Ste. 103, Grand Rapids, MI 49546, (888)375-7245

Amer. Medical Network - Defunct.

Amer. Medical Peer Rev. Assn. [★16506]

Amer. Medical Political Action Comm. [18319], 25 Massachusetts Ave. NW, Ste. 600, Washington, DC 20001, (202)789-7400

American Medical Publishers' Assn. - Address unknown since 2010.

Amer. Medical Records Assn. [★15331]

Amer. Medical Rehabilitation Providers Assn. [16557], 1710 N St. NW, Washington, DC 20036, (202)223-1920

Amer. Medical Res. Found. [★8586]

Amer. Medical Resources Found. [15144], PO Box 3609, Brockton, MA 02304-3609, (508)580-3301

Amer. Medical Resources Found. [15144], PO Box 3609, Brockton, MA 02304-3609, (508)580-3301

Amer. Medical Soc. on Alcoholism and Other Drug Dependencies [★16736]

Amer. Medical Soc. for Sports Medicine [16712], 4000 W 114th St., Ste. 100, Leawood, KS 66211, (913)327-1415

Amer. Medical Student Assn. [8587], 1902 Assn. Dr., Reston, VA 20191, (703)620-6600

Amer. Medical Technologists [15364], 10700 W Higgins Rd., Ste. 150, Rosemont, IL 60018, (847)823-5169

Amer. Medical Tennis Assn. [23051], 1803 Cobblestone Dr., Provo, UT 84604, (800)326-2682

Amer. Medical Women's Assn. [14868], 100 N 20th St., 4th Fl., Philadelphia, PA 19103, (215)320-3716

Amer. Medical Writers Assn. [2798], 30 W Gude Dr., Ste. 525, Rockville, MD 20850-1161, (301)294-5303

Amer. Medico Psychological Assn. [★16330]

Amer. Membrane Tech. Assn. [7595], 2409 SE Dixie Hwy., Stuart, FL 34996, (772)463-0820

Amer. Membrane Tech. Assn. [7595], 2409 SE Dixie Hwy., Stuart, FL 34996, (772)463-0820

Amer. Menopause Found. [17121], 866 United Nations Plz., Ste. 508, New York, NY 10117, (212)714-2398

Amer. Men's Stud. Assn. [12204], 1507 Pebble Dr., Greensboro, NC 27410, (336)323-2672

Amer. Mensa [9638], 1229 Corporate Dr. W, Arlington, TX 76006-6103, (817)607-0060

Amer. Mental Hea. Alliance [15444], PO Box 4075, Portland, OR 97208-4075, (503)227-2027

Amer. Mental Hea. Counselors Assn. [15445], 801 N Fairfax St., Ste. 304, Alexandria, VA 22314, (703)548-6002

Amer. Merchant Marine Inst. [★5789]

Amer. Merchant Marine Lib. Assn. - Address unknown since 2010.

Amer. Merchant Marine Veterans [20855], PO Box 186, Ferndale, CA 95536, (707)786-4554

Amer. Messianic Fellowship [★19758]

Amer. Messianic Fellowship [★19758]

Amer. Metal Detector Mfrs. Assn. - Address unknown since 2010.

Amer. Metal Etching Mfrs. Trade Assn. [★2484]

Amer. Metal Stamping Assn. [★2491]

Amer. Meteor Soc. [6224], Vladimir Getman, Treas., Pennsylvania State Univ., Dept. of Astronomy and Astrophysics, 121 EEE, University Park, PA 16802

Amer. Meteorological Soc. [7104], 45 Beacon St., Boston, MA 02108-3693, (617)227-2425

Reference to "IO" in place of a book number signifies that the association may be found in the 50th edition of International Organizations.

Amer. Methanol Inst. [★6894]

Amer. MGB Assn. [20992], PO Box 11401, Chicago, IL 60611, (773)878-5055

Amer. MGC Register [20993], 560 Acorn Ln., Damascus, VA 24236, (276)338-3724

Amer. Microchemical Soc. [6394], 2 June Way, Middlesex, NJ 08846

Amer. Microscopical Soc. [7113], The Citadel, 171 Moultrie St., Charleston, SC 29407, (843)953-7511

Amer. Middle-Eastern Christian Assn. - Address unknown since 2011.

Amer. MidEast Leadership Network [17934], PO Box 2156, Long Island City, NY 11102, (347)924-9674

Amer. Military Family [20700], PO Box 1101, Brighton, CO 80601, (303)746-8195

Amer. Military History Found. [★10098]

Amer. Military Inst. [★10098]

Amer. Military Retirees Assn. [20774], 5436 Peru St., Ste. 1, Plattsburgh, NY 12901, (518)563-9479

Amer. Military Soc. [5795], PO Box 90740, Washington, DC 20090-0740, (800)379-6128

Amer. Milking Devon Cattle Assn. [3888], Sue Randall, Registrar, 135 Old Bay Rd., New Durham, NH 03855, (603)859-6611

Amer. Milking Shorthorn Junior Soc. [3889], 800 Pleasant St., Beloit, WI 53511-5456, (608)365-3332

Amer. Milking Shorthorn Soc. [3890], 800 Pleasant St., Beloit, WI 53511-5456, (608)365-3332

Amer. Miniature Cheviot Sheep Breeders Assn. [4894], 403 Cheryl Way, Silver Springs, NV 89429, (775)629-1211

Amer. Miniature Horse Assn. [4542], 5601 S Interstate 35 W, Alvarado, TX 76009, (817)783-5600

Amer. Miniature Llama Assn. [3785], PO Box 8, Kalispell, MT 59903, (406)755-3438

Amer. Miniature Schnauzer Club [21500], Mary Ann Shandor, 2302 Cumberland Ct. SW, Decatur, AL 35603-2617

Amer. Mining Cong. - Defunct.

Amer. Minor Breeds Conservancy [★4687]

Amer. Miscellaneous Soc. - Defunct.

Amer. Mission to Greeks [★20008]

Amer. Mission to Greeks [★20008]

Amer. Missionary Fellowship [20006], PO Box 370, Villanova, PA 19085-0370, (610)527-4439

Amer. Mizrachi Women [★19845]

Amer. Mobile Groomers Assn. [2675], Barkleigh Mgt. Gp., Inc., 970 W Trindle Rd., Mechanicsburg, PA 17055, (717)691-3388

Amer. Mobile Telecommunications Assn. [★3407]

Amer. Mobile Telecommunications Assn. - Defunct.

Amer. Mobilehome Assn. - Defunct.

Amer. Mock Trial Assn. [9020], 2700 Westown Pkwy., Ste. 410, West Des Moines, IA 50266-1411, (515)283-0803

Amer. Model Yachting Assn. [21899], PO Box 360374, Melbourne, FL 32936-0374, (888)237-9524

Amer. Mold Builders Assn. [1801], 3601 Algonquin Rd., Ste. 304, Rolling Meadows, IL 60008, (847)222-9402

American Money Management Group - Address unknown since 2011.

Amer. Montessori Soc. [8632], 281 Park Ave. S, New York, NY 10010-6102, (212)358-1250

Amer. Mookee Assn. [3841], 1109 Lancaster Ave., Fort Lupton, CO 80621, (864)876-2543

Amer. Morgan Horse Assn. [4543], 4066 Shelburne Rd., Ste. 5, Shelburne, VT 05482-6908, (802)985-4944

Amer. Morphological Soc. [★7638]

Amer. Mosquito Control Assn. [4769], 15000 Commerce Pkwy., Ste. C, Mount Laurel, NJ 08054, (856)439-9222

Amer. Mosquito Control Assn. [4769], 15000 Commerce Pkwy., Ste. C, Mount Laurel, NJ 08054, (856)439-9222

Amer. Mothers Comm. [★11995]

Amer. Mothers, Inc. [11995], 1666 K St. NW, Ste. 260, Washington, DC 20006, (877)242-4264

Amer. Motility Soc. [★14552]

Amer. Motivational Assn. - Defunct.

Amer. Motorcycle Assn. [★22777]

Amer. Motorcycle Heritage Found. [22776], 13515 Yarmouth Dr., Pickerington, OH 43147, (614)856-2222

Amer. Motorcyclist Assn. [22777], 13515 Yarmouth Dr., Pickerington, OH 43147-8214, (614)856-1900

Amer. Motors Owners Assn. [20994], 1615 Purvis Ave., Janesville, WI 53548, (608)752-8247

Amer. Mountain Guides Assn. [21282], PO Box 1739, Boulder, CO 80306, (303)271-0984

Amer. Movers Conf. [★3243]

Amer. Movers Conf. [★3243]

Amer. Movers Inst. [★3243]

Amer. Movers Inst. [★3243]

Amer. Moving and Storage Assn. [3243], 1611 Duke St., Alexandria, VA 22314-3406, (703)683-7410

Amer. Moving and Storage Assn. [3243], 1611 Duke St., Alexandria, VA 22314-3406, (703)683-7410

Amer. Moving and Storage Tech. Found. [★3243]

Amer. Moving and Storage Tech. Found. [★3243]

Amer. Mule Assn. [3786], 260 Neilson Rd., Reno, NV 89521, (775)849-9437

Amer. Mule Racing Assn. [22821], 1600 Exposition Blvd., Sacramento, CA 95815-5104, (916)263-1529

Amer. Municipal Assn. [★5854]

Amer. Murray Grey Assn. [3891], PO Box 43515, Louisville, KY 40253-0515, (502)384-2335

Amer. Museum of Natural History [7136], Central Park W at 79th St., New York, NY 10024-5192, (212)769-5100

Amer. Museum of Negro History [★9102]

Amer. Mushroom Inst. [4423], 1 Massachusetts Ave. NW, Ste. 800, Washington, DC 20001-1401, (202)842-4344

Amer. Music Center [10149], 322 8th Ave., Ste. 1401, New York, NY 10001, (212)366-5260

Amer. Music Conf. - Address unknown since 2010.

Amer. Music Educator's Repair Assn. [2549], PO Box 32, Normal, IL 61761, (309)830-4257

Amer. Music Scholarship Assn. [★10314]

Amer. Music Therapy Assn. [16451], 8455 Colesville Rd., Ste. 1000, Silver Spring, MD 20910, (301)589-3300

Amer. Musical Instrument Soc. [10150], Joanne Kopp, Treas., 1106 Garden St., Hoboken, NJ 07030, (201)656-0107

Amer. Musicological Soc. [10151], 6010 Coll. Sta., Brunswick, ME 04011, (207)798-4243

Amer. Muslim Alliance [18142], 39675 Cedar Blvd., Ste. 220 E, Newark, CA 94560, (510)252-9858

Amer. Muslim Coun. - Address unknown since 2011.

Amer. Muslim Law Enforcement Officers Assn. - Address unknown since 2011.

Amer. Muslim Women Physicians Assn. [16252], 6300 Stonewood Dr., Ste. 412, Plano, TX 75024, (817)938-0792

Amer. Muslim Women Physicians Assn. [16252], 6300 Stonewood Dr., Ste. 412, Plano, TX 75024, (817)938-0792

Amer. Muslims for Global Peace and Justice - Defunct.

Amer. Muslims Intent on Learning and Activism [10316], PO Box 420 614, San Francisco, CA 94142

Amer. Mustang and Burro Assn. [4544], PO Box 608, Greenwood, DE 19950

Amer. Mutual Life Assn. [19235], 19424 S Waterloo Rd., Cleveland, OH 44119, (216)531-1900

Amer. Mycological Soc. [★6351]

Amer. Name Soc. [10344], Binghamton Univ., State Univ. of New York, Off. of the Provost, Binghamton, NY 13902-6000, (607)777-2143

Amer. Name Soc. [10344], Binghamton Univ., State Univ. of New York, Off. of the Provost, Binghamton, NY 13902-6000, (607)777-2143

Amer. Naprapathic Assn. [15526], 800 E South St., Woodstock, IL 60098, (312)912-7984

Amer. Natl. CattleWomen [3892], 9110 E Nichols Ave., Ste. 302, Centennial, CO 80112, (303)694-0313

Amer. Natl. CowBelles [★3892]

Amer. Natl. Metric Coun. [18672], 900 Mix Ave., Ste. 1, Hamden, CT 06514-5106, (203)287-9849

Amer. Natl. Red Cross [★12803]

Amer. Natl. Standards Comm. - Z39 [★6987]

Amer. Natl. Standards Inst. [5982], 1899 L St. NW, 11th Fl., Washington, DC 20036, (202)293-8020

Amer. Nationalist Union [18352], 10161 Park Run Dr., Ste. 150, Las Vegas, NV 89145

Amer. Natural Hygiene Soc. [★15529]

Amer. Natural Soda Ash Corp. [1573], 15 Riverside Ave., 2nd Fl., Westport, CT 06880, (203)226-9056

Amer. Naturopathic Medical Assn. [15532], PO Box 96273, Las Vegas, NV 89193, (702)897-7053

Amer. Nazi Party [★18786]

Amer. Nazi Party [★18786]

Amer. Near East Refugee Aid [12772], 1111 14th St. NW, No. 400, Washington, DC 20005, (202)266-9700

Amer. Near East Refugee Aid [12772], 1111 14th St. NW, No. 400, Washington, DC 20005, (202)266-9700

Amer. Needlepoint Guild [21428], 2424 Amer. Ln., Madison, WI 53704-3102, (608)443-2476

Amer. Nephrology Nurses' Assn. [15543], E Holly Ave., Box 56, Pitman, NJ 08071, (856)256-2320

Amer. Netherland Dwarf Rabbit Club [4834], 864 Barkers Creek Rd., Whittier, NC 28789

Amer. Netherlands Club of Rotterdam [IO], Rotterdam, Netherlands

Amer. Network of Community Options and Resources [12494], 1101 King St., Ste. 380, Alexandria, VA 22314, (703)535-7850

Amer. Neurogastroenterology and Motility Soc. [14552], 45685 Harmony Ln., Belleville, MI 48111, (734)699-1130

Amer. Neurological Assn. [15645], 5841 Cedar Lake Rd. S, Ste. 204, Minneapolis, MN 55416, (952)545-6284

Amer. Neuromodulation Soc. [★16106]

Amer. Neuropsychiatric Assn. [16328], 700 Ackerman Rd., Ste. 625, Columbus, OH 43202, (614)447-2077

Amer. Neurotology Soc. [16681], 1980 Warson Rd., Springfield, IL 62704, (217)638-0801

Amer. News Women's Club [2799], 1607 22nd St. NW, Washington, DC 20008, (202)332-6770

Amer. Newspaper Guild [★23258]

Amer. Newspaper Publishers Assn. [★2953]

Amer. Newspaper Women's Club [★2799]

Amer. Nigerian Dwarf Dairy Assn. [4498], 21181 E Hwy. 28A, Chelsea, OK 74016, (918)342-1425

Amer. Nobel Center - Defunct.

Amer. Non-Governmental Organizations Coalition for the Intl. Criminal Court [17488], 801 2nd Ave., 2nd Fl., New York, NY 10017, (212)907-1317

American Nonsmokers' Rights Foundation [★16672]

Amer. Nordic Walking Assn. [16221], PO Box 491205, Los Angeles, CA 90049, (323)244-2519

Amer. Normande Assn. [★3931]

Amer. North Country Cheviot Sheep Assn. [4895], 1201 N 500 E, Rolling Prairie, IN 46371, (574)323-3506

Amer. Nuclear Energy Coun. [★6746]

Amer. Nuclear Insurers [1935], 95 Glastonbury Blvd., Ste. 300, Glastonbury, CT 06033-4453, (860)682-1301

Amer. Nuclear Soc. [7164], 555 N Kensington Ave., La Grange Park, IL 60526, (708)352-6611

Amer. Numismatic and Archaeological Soc. [★21964]

Amer. Numismatic Assn. [21963], 818 N Cascade Ave., Colorado Springs, CO 80903-3279, (719)632-2646

Amer. Numismatic Soc. [21964], 75 Varick St., 11th Fl., New York, NY 10038, (212)571-4470

Amer. Nursery and Landscape Assn. [4740], 1200 G St., NW, Ste. 800, Washington, DC 20005, (202)789-2900

Amer. Nurses Assn. [15722], 8515 Georgia Ave., Ste. 400, Silver Spring, MD 20910, (301)628-5000

Amer. Nurses Credentialing Center [15723], 8515 Georgia Ave., Ste. 400, Silver Spring, MD 20910-3492, (800)284-2378

Amer. Nurses Found. [15724], 8515 Georgia Ave., Ste. 400, Silver Spring, MD 20910, (301)628-5227

Amer. Nursing Home Assn. [★14696]

Amer. Nursing Informatics Assn. [15725], 1908 S El Camino Real, Ste. H, San Clemente, CA 92672, (866)552-6404

Amer. Nutraceutical Assn. [14754], 5120 Selkirk Dr., Ste. 100, Birmingham, AL 35242, (205)980-5710

A star before a book entry number signifies that the name is not listed separately, but is mentioned within the entry.

Amer. Nutrition Assn. [15820], PO Box 262, Western Springs, IL 60558, (708)246-3663

Amer. Nyckelharpa Assn. [10152], 1280 Taylorsville Rd., Washington Crossing, PA 18977

Amer. Nyckelharpa Assn. [10152], 1280 Taylorsville Rd., Washington Crossing, PA 18977

Amer. Nystagmus Network [17061], 303-D Beltline Pl., No. 321, Decatur, AL 35603

Amer. Oat Assn. [★2502]

Amer. Oat Assn. - Defunct.

Amer. Obesity Assn. - Address unknown since 2010.

Amer. Occupational Medical Assn. [★15900]

Amer. Occupational Therapy Assn. [16837], 4720 Montgomery Ln., PO Box 31220, Bethesda, MD 20824-1220, (301)652-2682

Amer. Occupational Therapy Certification Bd. [★16863]

Amer. Occupational Therapy Found. [15903], PO Box 31220, Bethesda, MD 20824-1220, (301)652-6611

Amer. Oceans Campaign - Defunct.

Amer. Officers of the Great War [★20874]

Amer. Officers of the Great War [★20874]

Amer. Oil Chemists' Soc. [6395], PO Box 17190, Urbana, IL 61803-7190, (217)359-2344

Amer. Oil Chemists' Soc. [6395], PO Box 17190, Urbana, IL 61803-7190, (217)359-2344

Amer. Oil and Gas Historical Soc. [2639], 3204 18th St. NW, Washington, DC 20010, (202)857-4785

Amer. Olive Oil Assn. [★2591]

Amer. Olive Oil Assn. [★2591]

Amer. Olympic Assn. [★22791]

Amer. Ophthalmological Soc. [15941], PO Box 193940, San Francisco, CA 94119, (415)561-8578

Amer. Optical Assn. [★15988]

Amer. Optometric Assn. [15988], 243 N Lindbergh Blvd., St. Louis, MO 63141, (314)991-4100

Amer. Optometric Found. [15989], 6110 Executive Blvd., Ste. 506, Rockville, MD 20852, (301)984-4734

Amer. Optometric Student Assn. [15990], 243 N Lindbergh Blvd., St. Louis, MO 63141, (314)983-4321

Amer. Orchid Soc. [6345], 16700 AOS Ln., Delray Beach, FL 33446-4351, (561)404-2000

Amer. Orchid Soc. [6345], 16700 AOS Ln., Delray Beach, FL 33446-4351, (561)404-2000

Amer. Order of the French Croix de Guerre - Defunct.

Amer. Ordnance Assn. [★5814]

Amer. Orff-Schulwerk Assn. [10153], PO Box 391089, Cleveland, OH 44139-8089, (440)543-5366

Amer. Organ Transplant Assn. [16897], 21175 Tomball Pkwy., No. 194, Houston, TX 77070, (713)344-2402

Amer. Org. for Bodywork Therapies of Asia [15263], 1010 Haddonfield-Berlin Rd., Ste. 408, Voorhees, NJ 08043-3514, (856)782-1616

Amer. Org. for the Development of Bihar [12302], 210 Alden Ln., Livermore, CA 94550, (925)961-1988

Amer. Org. of Nurse Executives [15726], 325 Seventh St. NW, Liberty Pl., Washington, DC 20004, (202)626-2240

Amer. Oriental Bodywork Therapy Assn. [★15263]

Amer. Oriental Soc. [9334], Univ. of Michigan, Hatcher Graduate Lib., Ann Arbor, MI 48109-1205, (734)647-4760

Amer. Oriental Soc. [9334], Univ. of Michigan, Hatcher Graduate Lib., Ann Arbor, MI 48109-1205, (734)647-4760

Amer. Ornithologists' Union [7192], 5405 Villa View Dr., Farmington, NM 87402, (505)326-1579

Amer. Ort Fed. [★12413]

Amer. Ort Fed. [★12413]

Amer. ORT and Women's Amer. ORT [★12413]

Amer. ORT and Women's Amer. ORT [★12413]

Amer. Orthodontic Soc. [14268], 11884 Greenville Ave., Ste. 112, Dallas, TX 75243-3537, (800)448-1601

Amer. Orthopaedic Assn. [16024], 6300 N River Rd., Ste. 505, Rosemont, IL 60018, (847)318-7330

Amer. Orthopaedic Foot and Ankle Soc. [16025], 6300 N River Rd., Ste. 510, Rosemont, IL 60018, (847)698-4654

Amer. Orthopaedic Foot Soc. [★16025]

Amer. Orthopaedic Soc. for Sports Medicine [16713], 6300 N River Rd., Ste. 500, Rosemont, IL 60018, (847)292-4900

Amer. Orthopsychiatric Assn. [16329], Clemson Univ., IFNL, 225 S Pleasantburg Dr., Ste. B-11, Greenville, SC 29607, (864)250-4622

Amer. Orthoptic Coun. [15942], Ms. Leslie France, CO, Admin., 3914 Nakoma Rd., Madison, WI 53711, (608)233-5383

Amer. Orthotic and Prosthetic Assn. [1679], PO Box 34711, Alexandria, VA 22334-0711, (571)431-0876

Amer. Osler Soc. [15397], 3575 N Pantano Rd., Tucson, AZ 85750, (520)296-6662

Amer. Osteopathic Acad. of Addiction Medicine [16735], PO Box 280, La Grange, IL 60525-0280, (708)572-8006

Amer. Osteopathic Acad. Addictionology [★16735]

Amer. Osteopathic Acad. of Orthopedics [16026], 2209 Dickens Rd., Richmond, VA 23230-2005, (804)565-6370

Amer. Osteopathic Acad. of Physical Medicine and Rehabilitation [★16071]

Amer. Osteopathic Acad. of Public Hea. and Preventive Medicine [★16069]

Amer. Osteopathic Acad. of Sports Medicine [16714], 2424 Amer. Ln., Madison, WI 53704, (608)443-2477

Amer. Osteopathic Assn. [16064], 142 E Ontario St., Chicago, IL 60611, (312)202-8000

Amer. Osteopathic Assn. of Medical Informatics [16065], 142 E Ontario St., Chicago, IL 60611, (312)202-8142

Amer. Osteopathic Bd. of Emergency Medicine [14462], 8765 W. Higgins Rd., Ste. 200, Chicago, IL 60631, (773)724-3161

Amer. Osteopathic Bd. of Family Physicians [16066], 330 E Algonquin Rd., Ste. 6, Arlington Heights, IL 60005, (847)640-8477

Amer. Osteopathic Bd. of Gen. Practice [★16066]

Amer. Osteopathic Bd. of Pediatrics [16067], 142 E Ontario St., 4th Fl., Chicago, IL 60611, (800)621-1773

Amer. Osteopathic Bd. of Preventive Medicine [16068], 142 E Ontario St., 4th Fl., Chicago, IL 60611, (800)621-1773

American Osteopathic Bd. of Rehabilitation Medicine [★16071]

Amer. Osteopathic Coll. of Anesthesiologists [13735], 2260 E Saginaw St., Ste. B, East Lansing, MI 48823, (517)339-0919

Amer. Osteopathic Coll. of Dermatology [14318], PO Box 7525, Kirksville, MO 63501, (660)665-2184

Amer. Osteopathic Coll. of Occupational and Preventive Medicine [16069], Mr. Jeffrey J. LeBoeuf, CAE, Exec. Dir., PO Box 3043, Tulsa, OK 74101, (800)558-8686

Amer. Osteopathic Coll. of Pathologists [16070], 142 E Ontario St., Chicago, IL 60611-8224, (312)202-8197

Amer. Osteopathic Coll. of Physical Medicine and Rehabilitation [16071], Stephanie Wilson, Exec. Dir., PO Box 4, Phillipsburg, NJ 08865-0004, (908)329-0270

Amer. Osteopathic Coll. of Preventive Medicine [★16069]

Amer. Osteopathic Coll. of Radiology [16521], 119 E 2nd St., Milan, MO 63556-1331, (660)265-4011

Amer. Osteopathic Coll. of Rehabilitation Medicine [★16071]

Amer. Osteopathic Colleges of Opthalmology and Otolaryngology - Head and Neck Surgery [16072], 4764 Fishburg Rd., Ste. F, Huber Heights, OH 45424, (937)233-5653

Amer. Osteopathic Found. [16073], 142 E Ontario St., Ste. 1450, Chicago, IL 60611, (312)202-8234

Amer. Osteopathic Occupational Medical Assn. [★16069]

Amer. Osteopathic Soc. of Anesthesiologists [★13735]

Amer. Ostrich Assn. [3787], PO Box 166, Ranger, TX 76470, (254)647-1645

Amer. Otological Soc. [16086], Ms. Shirley Gossard, Admin., 3096 Riverdale Rd., The Villages, FL 32162, (352)751-0932

Amer. Otorhinologic Soc. for Plastic Surgery [★14170]

Amer. Outreach to Ethiopia [12265], 1121 S Diamond St., Jacksonville, IL 62650, (217)245-8792

Amer. Overseas Assn. [★12804]

Amer. Overseas Schools Historical Soc. [9667], 704 W Douglas Ave., Wichita, KS 67203-6401, (316)265-6837

Amer. Oxford Down Record Assn. [★4896]

Amer. Oxford Sheep Assn. [4896], 1960 E 2100 North Rd., Stonington, IL 62567, (217)325-3515

Amer. Pain Found. [16096], 201 N Charles St., Ste. 710, Baltimore, MD 21201-4111, (888)615-7246

Amer. Pain Soc. [16097], 4700 W Lake Ave., Glenview, IL 60025, (847)375-4715

Amer. Paint Horse Assn. [4545], PO Box 961023, Fort Worth, TX 76161-0023, (817)834-2742

Amer. Paint Horse Assn. [★4540]

Amer. Paint Mfrs. Assn. [★2613]

Amer. Paintball Players Assn. [22798], 1133 Indus. Blvd., No. 6, Chippewa Falls, WI 54729, (715)720-9131

Amer. Palestine Fund [★9895]

Amer. Palestine Fund [★9895]

Amer. Paper Machinery Assn. [★1809]

American-Paraguayan Cultural Center [IO], Asuncion, Paraguay

Amer. Paralysis Assn. [★16700]

Amer. Paraplegia Soc. [16696], 75-20 Astoria Blvd., East Elmhurst, NY 11370, (718)803-3782

Amer. Parkinson Disease Assn. [15567], Natl. Off., 135 Parkinson Ave., Staten Island, NY 10305, (718)981-8001

Amer. Parliamentary Debate Assn. [8891], Princeton Univ., One Wbig Hall, Princeton, NJ 08544

Amer. Parole Assn. [★11690]

Amer. Part-Blooded Horse Registry [4546], PO Box 986, Oregon City, OR 97045, (503)895-1680

Amer. Partnership for Eosinophilic Disorders [14553], PO Box 29545, Atlanta, GA 30359, (713)493-7749

Amer. Paso Fino Horse Assn. [4547], PO Box 2363, Pittsburgh, PA 15230, (724)437-5170

Amer. Pastured Poultry Producers Assn. [4804], PO Box 87, Boyd, WI 54726

Amer. Patent Law Assn. [★5559]

Amer. Pathology Found. [16114], 1540 S Coast Hwy., No. 203, Laguna Beach, CA 92651, (877)993-9935

Amer. Patriots Assn. [20742], Terry Lynch, Pres./ Founder, PO Box 241035, Montgomery, AL 36124-1035

Amer. Pax Assn. [★18175]

Amer. Payroll Assn. [1140], 660 N Main Ave., Ste. 100, San Antonio, TX 78205-1217, (210)226-4600

Amer. Peanut Coun. [4745], 1500 King St., Ste. 301, Alexandria, VA 22314, (703)838-9500

Amer. Peanut Coun. - European Off. [IO], London, United Kingdom

Amer. Peanut Res. and Educ. Assn. [★4746]

Amer. Peanut Res. and Educ. Soc. [4746], Dr. James L. Starr, Exec. Off., 2132 Texas A and M Univ., Dept. of Plant Pathology and Microbiology, 118B Peterson Bldg., College Station, TX 77843, (979)845-8278

Amer. Peanut Shellers Assn. [4747], 2336 Lake Park Dr., Albany, GA 31707, (229)888-2508

Amer. Pediatric Soc. [16140], 3400 Res. Forest Dr., Ste. B-7, The Woodlands, TX 77381, (281)419-0052

Amer. Pediatric Surgical Assn. [16141], 111 Deer Lake Rd., Ste. 100, Deerfield, IL 60015, (847)480-9576

Amer. Pediatric Surgical Nurses Assn. [15727], 111 Deer Lake Rd., Ste. 100, Deerfield, IL 60015, (608)262-2146

Amer. Pencil Collectors Soc. [21297], Marilyn James, Sec., 720 N 13th St., Chariton, IA 50049

Amer. Penstemon Soc. [21779], 1050 Camino Rancheros, Santa Fe, NM 87505

Amer. Peony Soc. [21780], 713 White Oak Ln., Kansas City, MO 64116-4607, (816)459-9386

Amer. Personal Chef Assn. [★735]

Amer. Personal and Private Chef Assn. [735], 4572 Delaware St., San Diego, CA 92116, (619)294-2436

Reference to "IO" in place of a book number signifies that the association may be found in the 50th edition of International Organizations.

Amer. Personnel and Guidance Assn. [★11667]
Amer. Peruvian Paso Horse Registry [★4630]
Amer. Peruvian Paso Horse Registry [★4630]
Amer. Pet Products Assn. [2676], 255 Glenville Rd., Greenwich, CT 06831, (203)532-0000
Amer. Pet Products Mfrs. Assn. [★2676]
Amer. Pet Soc. - Address unknown since 2011.
Amer. Pet Stock Assn. [★4835]
Amer. Petanque Assn. U.S.A. [★22801]
Amer. Petroleum Credit Assn. [★1307]
Amer. Petroleum Credit Assn. [★1307]
Amer. Petroleum Equip. Suppliers [★2666]
Amer. Petroleum Inst. [2640], 1220 L St. NW, Washington, DC 20005-4070, (202)682-8000
Amer. Pewter Guild - Defunct.
Amer. Pharmaceutical Assn. - Acad. of Pharmacy Practice and Mgt. [★16176]
Amer. Pharmaceutical Assn. Acad. of Students of Pharmacy [★16177]
Amer. Pharmaceutical Assn. Student Sect. [★16177]
Amer. Pharmacists Assn. I Acad. of Pharmacy Practice and Mgt. [16176], APhA-APPM Nominating Community, 2215 Constitution Ave., NW, Washington, DC 20037, (202)628-4410
Amer. Pharmacists Assn. I Acad. of Student Pharmacists [16177], 2215 Constitution Ave. NW, Washington, DC 20037, (202)628-4410
Amer. Pheasant Soc. [★5025]
Amer. Pheasant and Waterfowl Soc. [5025], 6220 Bullbeggar Rd., Withams, VA 23488-2700, (757)824-5828
Amer. Philatelic Cong. [22009], Mr. Ross A. Towle, Sec.-Treas., 400 Clayton St., San Francisco, CA 94117-1912
Amer. Philatelic Res. Lib. [22010], 100 Match Factory Pl., Bellefonte, PA 16823, (814)933-3803
Amer. Philatelic Soc. [22011], 100 Match Factory Pl., Bellefonte, PA 16823, (814)933-3803
Amer. Philatelic Soc. Writers Unit [22012], 2501 Drexel St., Vienna, VA 22180-6906
Amer. Philological Assn. [9935], Univ. of Pennsylvania, 220 S 40th St., Ste. 201E, Philadelphia, PA 19104-3543, (215)898-4975
Amer. Philosophical Assn. [10369], Univ. of Delaware, 31 Amstel Ave., Newark, DE 19716-4797, (302)831-1112
Amer. Philosophical Practitioners Assn. [8703], The City Coll. of New York, 160 Convent Ave., New York, NY 10031, (212)650-7647
Amer. Philosophical Soc. [7357], 104 S 5th St., Philadelphia, PA 19106-3387, (215)440-3400
Amer. Photographic Artists [2708], PO Box 725146, Atlanta, GA 31139, (888)889-7190
Amer. Photographic Artists Guild [2709], 2269 N 400 Rd., Eudora, KS 66025, (785)883-4166
Amer. Photoplatemakers Assn. [★6934]
Amer. Photoplatemakers Assn. [★6934]
Amer. Physical Educ. Assn. [★8715]
Amer. Physical Soc. [7264], One Physics Ellipse, College Park, MD 20740-3844, (301)209-3200
Amer. Physical Soc. [7264], One Physics Ellipse, College Park, MD 20740-3844, (301)209-3200
Amer. Physical Therapy Assn. [16838], 1111 N Fairfax St., Alexandria, VA 22314-1488, (703)684-2782
Amer. Physical Therapy Assn., Orthopaedic Sect. [16839], 2920 E Ave. S, Ste. 200, La Crosse, WI 54601, (608)788-3982
American Physical Therapy Assn., Private Practice Sect. [16840], 1055 N Fairfax St., Ste. 100, Alexandria, VA 22314, (703)299-2410
Amer. Physician Art Assn. [9156], 521 WS R434, Ste. 106, Longwood, FL 32750, (407)834-5255
Amer. Physician Scientists Assn. [8588], 111 Deer Lake Rd., Ste. 100, Deerfield, IL 60015, (847)480-9080
Amer. Physicians Assn. of Computer Medicine - Defunct.
Amer. Physicians Fellowship for the Israel Medical Assn. [★12391]
Amer. Physicians Fellowship for the Israel Medical Assn. [★12391]
Amer. Physicians Fellowship for Medicine in Israel [12391], 2001 Beacon St., Ste. 210, Boston, MA 02135, (617)232-5382
Amer. Physicians Fellowship for Medicine in Israel [★12391]

Amer. Physicians and Friends for Medicine in Israel [12391], 2001 Beacon St., Ste. 210, Boston, MA 02135, (617)232-5382
Amer. Physiological and Natural Hygiene Soc. [★15529]
Amer. Physiological Soc. [7274], 9650 Rockville Pike, Bethesda, MD 20814-3991, (301)634-7164
Amer. Physiotherapy Assn. [★16838]
Amer. Phytopathological Soc. [6346], 3340 Pilot Knob Rd., St. Paul, MN 55121, (651)454-7250
Amer. Pianists Assn. [21953], 4603 Clarendon Rd., Ste. 030, Indianapolis, IN 46208, (317)940-9945
Amer. Pie Coun. [387], PO Box 368, Lake Forest, IL 60045, (847)371-0170
Amer. Piedmontese Assn. [★3936]
Amer. Pilots' Assn. [127], 499 S Capitol St. SW, Ste. 409, Washington, DC 20003, (202)484-0700
Amer. Pinzgauer Assn. [3893], PO Box 1097, Lake Ozark, MO 65049, (573)964-2389
Amer. Pioneers [★20597]
Amer. Planning Assn. [5326], 122 S Michigan Ave., Ste. 1600, Chicago, IL 60603-6107, (312)431-9100
Amer. Planning Assn. I Amer. Inst. of Certified Planners [5327], 1030 15th St. NW, Ste. 750 W, Washington, DC 20005-1503, (202)872-0611
Amer. Plant Life Soc. [★6356]
Amer. Plant Life Soc. [★6356]
Amer. Plate Number Single Soc. [22013], PO Box 1023, Palatine, IL 60078-1023
Amer. Platform Tennis Assn. [23052], 109 Wesport Dr., Pittsburgh, PA 15238, (888)744-9490
Amer. Plywood Assn. [★1497]
Amer. Podiatric Medical Assn. [16293], 9312 Old Georgetown Rd., Bethesda, MD 20814-1621, (301)581-9200
Amer. Podiatric Medical Assn. Auxilliary - Defunct.
Amer. Podiatric Medical Students' Assn. [16294], 9312 Old Georgetown Rd., Bethesda, MD 20814, (301)493-9667
Amer. Podiatric Multiple Specialties Bd. [★16288]
Amer. Podiatric Students Assn. [★16294]
Amer. Podiatry Assn. [★16293]
Amer. Pointer Club [21501], Susan Bleckley, Recording Sec., 327 Lugonia St., Newport Beach, CA 92663, (949)515-4454
Amer. Polar Soc. [7279], PO Box 300, Searsport, ME 04974
Amer. Polar Soc. [7279], PO Box 300, Searsport, ME 04974
Amer. Polarity Therapy Assn. [13657], 122 N Elm St., Ste. 512, Greensboro, NC 27401, (336)574-1121
Amer. Police Acad. - Defunct.
Amer. Police Hall of Fame and Museum [★5686]
Amer. Political Items Collectors [22102], PO Box 55, Avon, NY 14414, (585)226-8620
Amer. Political Sci. Assn. [7285], 1527 New Hampshire Ave. NW, Washington, DC 20036-1206, (202)483-2512
Amer. Polled Hereford Assn. [★3879]
Amer. Polled Shorthorn Soc. - Defunct.
Amer. Polo Horse Assn. [22812], 4095 State Rd. 7, Ste. L, PMB No. 183, Lake Worth, FL 33449, (561)312-5201
Amer. Polocrosse Assn. [22505], PO Box 158, Bonneau, SC 29431, (843)825-2686
Amer. Polygraph Assn. [5475], PO Box 8037, Chattanooga, TN 37414-0037, (423)892-3992
Amer. Polypay Sheep Assn. [4897], 15603 173rd Ave., Milo, IA 50166, (641)942-6402
Amer. Pomeranian Club [21502], Linda Pelz, Membership Chair, 161 Houston Dr., Hewitt, TX 76643, (254)420-1724
Amer. Pomological Soc. [4424], Dr. Robert Crassweller, Treas., 103 Tyson Bldg., University Park, PA 16802-4200, (814)863-6163
Amer. Porphyria Found. [15491], 4900 Woodway, Ste. 780, Houston, TX 77056-1837, (713)266-9617
Amer. Portuguese Engg. and Architecture Soc. - Address unknown since 2010.
Amer. Portuguese Stud. Assn. [8737], Univ. of New Mexico, Dept. of Spanish and Portuguese, MSC01-2100, Albuquerque, NM 87131-1000
Amer. Postal Workers Union [23278], 1300 L St. NW, Washington, DC 20005, (202)842-4200

Amer. Poultry Assn. [4805], PO Box 306, Burgettstown, PA 15021, (724)729-3459
Amer. Poultry Intl. [4806], 5420 Interstate 55 N, Ste. A, Jackson, MS 39211, (601)956-1715
Amer. Poultry Intl. [4806], 5420 Interstate 55 N, Ste. A, Jackson, MS 39211, (601)956-1715
Amer. Powder Metallurgy Inst. [★7089]
Amer. Powder Metallurgy Inst. [★7089]
Amer. Power Boat Assn. [22316], PO Box 377, Eastpointe, MI 48021, (586)773-9700
Amer. Pre-Veterinary Medical Assn. [17007], Dillon Harvey, 2635 N 5th St., Lincoln, NE 68521
Amer. Precision Optics Mfrs. Assn. [3172], PO Box 20001, Rochester, NY 14602, (585)346-9513
Amer. Pregnancy Assn. [15869], 1425 Greenway Dr., Ste. 440, Irving, TX 75038, (972)550-0140
Amer. Prepaid Legal Services Inst. [5753], 321 N Clark St., 19th Fl., Chicago, IL 60654, (312)988-5751
Amer. Press Inst. [8435], 11690 Sunrise Valley Dr., Reston, VA 20191-1498, (703)620-3611
Amer. Preventive Medical Assn. [★16302]
Amer. Primrose Soc. [21781], Mr. Jon Kawaguchi, Treas., 3524 Bowman Ct., Alameda, CA 94502
Amer. Print Alliance [9269], 302 Larkspur Turn, Peachtree City, GA 30269-2210
Amer. Print Alliance [9269], 302 Larkspur Turn, Peachtree City, GA 30269-2210
Amer. Printing History Assn. [9643], PO Box 4519, Grand Central Sta., New York, NY 10163-4519
Amer. Printing House for the Blind [17062], 1839 Frankfort Ave., PO Box 6085, Louisville, KY 40206-0085, (502)895-2405
Amer. Prison Assn. [★11702]
Amer. Probation and Parole Assn. [5883], 2760 Res. Park Dr., Lexington, KY 40511-8482, (859)244-8203
Amer. Producers of Italian Type Cheese Assn. - Defunct.
Amer. Production and Inventory Control Soc. [★6960]
Amer. Production and Inventory Control Soc. [★6960]
Amer. Productivity Center [★2265]
Amer. Productivity & Quality Center [★2265]
Amer. Professional Partnership for Lithuanian Educ. [8541], PO Box 179017, San Diego, CA 92177
Amer. Professional Pet Distributors - Defunct.
Amer. Professional Practice Assn. - Address unknown since 2010.
Amer. Professional Soc. on the Abuse of Children [11188], 350 Poplar Ave., Elmhurst, IL 60126, (630)941-1235
Amer. Professional Soc. of the Deaf - Defunct.
Amer. Professional Wedding Photographers Assn. [2710], 1155 Sherman St., No. 203, Denver, CO 80203, (800)725-1650
Amer. Professional Wound Care Assn. [16924], 853 Second St. Pike, Ste. A1, Richboro, PA 18954, (215)364-4100
Amer. Prosecutors Res. Inst. - Address unknown since 2011.
Amer. Prospect Res. Assn. [★12050]
Amer. Prostate Soc. [16939], PO Box 870, Hanover, MD 21076, (410)859-3735
Amer. Prosthodontic Soc. [14269], 303 W Madison St., Ste. 2650, Chicago, IL 60611, (312)981-6780
Amer. Protestants for Truth About Ireland - Defunct.
Amer. Pseudo-Obstruction and Hirschsprung's Disease Soc. [★14567]
Amer. Pseudo-Obstruction and Hirschsprung's Disease Soc. [★14567]
Amer. Pseudo-Obstruction and Hirschsprung's Disease Soc. - Defunct.
Amer. Psychiatric Assn. [16330], 1000 Wilson Blvd., Ste. 1825, Arlington, VA 22209-3901, (703)907-7300
Amer. Psychiatric Assn. Alliance [16331], PO Box 285, North Boston, NY 14110, (703)907-7304
Amer. Psychiatric Assn. I Inst. on Psychiatric Services [16332], 1000 Wilson Blvd., Ste. 1825, Arlington, VA 22209-3901, (703)907-7300
Amer. Psychiatric Nurses Assn. [15728], 1555 Wilson Blvd., Ste. 530, Arlington, VA 22209, (703)243-2443

A star before a book entry number signifies that the name is not listed separately, but is mentioned within the entry.

Amer. Psychoanalytic Assn. [16352], 309 E 49th St., New York, NY 10017-1601, (212)752-0450

Amer. Psychoanalytic Found. [16353], Amer. Psychoanalytic Assn., 309 E 49th St., New York, NY 10017, (212)752-0450

American Psychological Association [★16393]

Amer. Psychological Assn. [16368], 750 First St. NE, Washington, DC 20002-4242, (202)336-5500

Amer. Psychological Assn. l Amer. Soc. for the Advancement of Pharmacotherapy [16369], Keith Cooke, Div. Services Off., 750 1st St. NE, Washington, DC 20002-4242, (202)216-7602

Amer. Psychological Assn. l Division of Family Psychology [16370], 750 1st St. NE, Washington, DC 20002-4242, (202)216-7602

Amer. Psychological Assn. l Division of Independent Practice [16371], 919 W Marshall Ave., Phoenix, AZ 85013, (602)284-6219

Amer. Psychological Assn. l Division of Intl. Psychology [16372], Univ. of Missouri-Columbia, School of Medicine, 5400 Arsenal St., St. Louis, MO 63139, (314)877-6464

Amer. Psychological Assn. - Division of Intl. Psychology [16372], Univ. of Missouri-Columbia, School of Medicine, 5400 Arsenal St., St. Louis, MO 63139, (314)877-6464

Amer. Psychological Assn. l Division of of Psychotherapy [16373], Div. 29 Central Off., 6557 E Riverdale St., Mesa, AZ 85215-0722, (602)363-9211

Amer. Psychological Assn. l Div. of State, Provincial, and Territorial Psychological Assn. Affairs [16374], Univ. of Washington, William H. Gates Hall, Box 353020, Seattle, WA 98195-3020

Amer. Psychological Assn. l Division of Trauma Psychology [16375], 750 1st St. NE, Washington, DC 20002-4242

Amer. Psychological Assn. of Graduate Students [16376], 750 1st St. NE, Washington, DC 20002-4242, (202)336-6014

Amer. Psychological Assn. - Hea. Psychology Div. [16377], PO Box 1838, Ashland, VA 23005-2544, (804)752-4987

Amer. Psychological Assn. - Media Psychology Div. [16378], Div. Services Office, 750 1st St NE, Washington, DC 20002-4242, (202)336-6013

Amer. Psychological Assn. l Soc. of Addictions Psychology [16379], Div. Services Office, 750 1st St. NE, Washington, DC 20002-4242, (202)336-6013

Amer. Psychological Assn. l Soc. of Psychological Hypnosis [16380], Division Services Office, 750 First St NE, Washington, DC 20002-4242

Amer. Psychological Assn. l Soc. for the Study of Peace, Conflict and Violence [16381], Div. Services Off., 750 1st St NE, Washington, DC 20002, (202)336-6013

Amer. Psychological Assn. l Soc. for the Study of Religion and Spirituality [16382], Div. Services Off., 750 1st St. NE, Washington, DC 20002-4242, (202)336-6013

Amer. Psychological Soc. [★16390]

Amer. Psychology-Law Soc. [16383], PO Box 11488, Southport, NC 28461-3936, (910)933-4018

Amer. Psychopathological Assh. [16438], Linda B. Cottler, PhD, Treas., Washington Univ. School of Medicine, Dept. of Psychiatry, 40 N Kings Hwy., Ste. 4, St. Louis, MO 63108

Amer. Psychosocial Oncology Soc. [15915], 154 Hansen Rd., Ste. 201, Charlottesville, VA 22911, (434)293-5350

Amer. Psychosomatic Soc. [16443], 6728 Old McLean Village Dr., McLean, VA 22101, (703)556-9222

Amer. Psychotherapy Assn. [16452], 2750 E Sunshine St., Springfield, MO 65804, (417)823-0173

Amer. Public Communications Coun. [3399], 625 Slaters Ln., Ste. 104, Alexandria, VA 22314, (703)739-1322

Amer. Public Gardens Assn. [4666], 351 Longwood Rd., Kennett Square, PA 19348-1807, (610)708-3010

Amer. Public Gas Assn. [3589], 201 Massachusetts Ave. NE, Ste. C-4, Washington, DC 20002, (202)464-2742

Amer. Public Hea. Assn. [16478], 800 I St. NW, Washington, DC 20001, (202)777-2742

Amer. Public Human Services Assn. [13169], 1133 19th St. NW, Ste. 400, Washington, DC 20036, (202)682-0100

Amer. Public Human Services Assn. l IT Solutions Mgt. for Human Services [13170], Connecticut Dept. of Social Services, 25 Sigourney St., Hartford, CT 06106, (860)424-5508

Amer. Public Human Services Assn. l Natl. Coun. of State Human Ser. Administrators [13171], 1133 19th St. NW, Ste. 400, Washington, DC 20036, (202)682-0100

Amer. Public Info. on the Env. - Address unknown since 2011.

Amer. Public Policy Assn. [★5915]

Amer. Public Power Assn. [6050], 1875 Connecticut Ave. NW, Ste. 1200, Washington, DC 20009-5715, (202)467-2900

Amer. Public Relations Assn. [★2908]

Amer. Public Transit Assn. [★3501]

Amer. Public Transit Assn. [★3501]

Amer. Public Trans. Assn. [3501], 1666 K St. NW, Ste. 1100, Washington, DC 20006, (202)496-4800

Amer. Public Trans. Assn. [3501], 1666 K St. NW, Ste. 1100, Washington, DC 20006, (202)496-4800

Amer. Public Welfare Assn. [★13169]

Amer. Public Works Assn. [5944], 2345 Grand Blvd., Ste. 700, Kansas City, MO 64108-2625, (816)472-6100

Amer. Pulp and Paper Mill Superintendents Assn. [★2621]

Amer. Pulpwood Assn. [★1468]

Amer. Purchasing Soc. [2970], PO Box 256, Aurora, IL 60506, (630)859-0250

Amer. Pyrotechnics Assn. [2976], PO Box 30438, Bethesda, MD 20824, (301)907-8181

Amer. Qigong Assn. - Address unknown since 2010.

Amer. Quarter Horse Assn. [4548], 1600 Quarter Horse Dr., Amarillo, TX 79168, (806)376-4811

Amer. Quarter Horse Youth Assn. [4549], PO Box 200, Amarillo, TX 79120, (806)376-4811

Amer. Quarter Pony Assn. [4550], PO Box 30, New Sharon, IA 50207, (641)675-3669

Amer. Quaternary Assn. [7137], Brian Carter, Treas., 2209 W 104th St., Perkins, OK 74059-4149, (405)744-9585

Amer. Quilt Study Group [21429], 1610 L St., Lincoln, NE 68508-2509, (402)477-1181

Amer. Quilter's Soc. [21430], PO Box 3290, Paducah, KY 42002-3290, (270)898-7903

Amer. Rabbit Breeders Assn. [4835], PO Box 5667, Bloomington, IL 61702-5667, (309)664-7500

Amer. Rabbit and Cavy Breeders Assn. [★4835]

Amer. Racing Pigeon Union [22096], PO Box 18465, Oklahoma City, OK 73154-0465, (405)848-5801

Amer. Radio Assn. [23161], 1755 E Plumb Ln., Ste. 111, Reno, NV 89502, (775)562-0883

Amer. Radio Relay League [20931], 225 Main St., Newington, CT 06111-1494, (860)594-0200

Amer. Radiological Nurses Assn. [★15739]

Amer. Radium Soc. [15916], 11300 W Olympic Blvd., Ste. 600, Los Angeles, CA 90064, (310)437-0581

Amer. Railway and Airline Supervisors Assn. [★23290]

Amer. Railway Bridge and Building Assn. [★2986]

Amer. Railway Bridge and Building Assn. [★2986]

American Railway Car Inst. - Address unknown since 2010.

Amer. Railway Engg. and Maintenance Assn. [★2986]

Amer. Railway Engg. and Maintenance Assn. [★2986]

Amer. Railway Engg. and Maintenance of Way Assn. [2986], 10003 Derekwood Ln., Ste. 210, Lanham, MD 20706-4875, (301)459-3200

Amer. Railway Engg. and Maintenance of Way Assn. [2986], 10003 Derekwood Ln., Ste. 210, Lanham, MD 20706-4875, (301)459-3200

Amer. Rainwater Catchment Systems Assn. [7596], 823 Cong. Ave., Ste. 230, Austin, TX 78701, (512)617-6528

Amer. Rambouillet Sheep Breeders' Assn. [4898], 15603 173rd Ave., Milo, IA 50166, (641)942-6402

Amer. Ranch Horse Assn. [4551], PO Box 186, Nancy, KY 42544, (606)636-4112

Amer. Rare Breed Assn. [21503], 9921 Frank Tippett Rd., Cheltenham, MD 20623, (301)868-5718

Amer. Real Estate Soc. [8787], Diane Quarles, Membership Services Mgr., Clemson Univ., Dept. of Finance, 424 Sirrine Hall, Clemson, SC 29634-1343, (864)656-1373

Amer. Real Estate and Urban Economics Assn. [8788], PO Box 9958, Richmond, VA 23228-9958, (866)273-8321

Amer. Recorder Soc. [10154], Kathy Sherrick, Admin. Dir., 1129 Ruth Dr., St. Louis, MO 63122-1019, (314)966-4082

Amer. Recorder Teachers Assn. - Address unknown since 2010.

Amer. Records Mgt. Assn. [★1895]

Amer. Records Mgt. Assn. [★1895]

Amer. Recovery Assn. [1031], 5525 N MacArthur Blvd., Ste. 135, Irving, TX 75038, (972)755-4755

Amer. Recreation Coalition [12763], 1225 New York Ave. NW, Ste. 450, Washington, DC 20005-6405, (202)682-9530

Amer. Recreational Equip. Assn. [★1187]

Amer. Recreational Equip. Assn. [★1187]

Amer. Red Brangus Assn. [3894], 3995 E Hwy. 290, Dripping Springs, TX 78620, (512)858-7285

Amer. Red Cross Natl. HQ [12803], 2025 E St. NW, Washington, DC 20006, (202)303-4498

Amer. Red Cross Overseas Assn. [12804], 200 S Lebanon Rd., Loveland, OH 45140, (513)683-1377

Amer. Red Poll Assn. [3895], PO Box 847, Frankton, IN 46044, (765)425-4515

Amer. Reef Coalition [3993], PO Box 844, Kihei, HI 96753, (808)870-5817

Amer. Reflexology Certification Bd. [13658], PO Box 141553, Grand Rapids, MI 49514, (303)933-6921

Amer. Refugee Comm. [12773], 430 Oak Grove St., Ste. 204, Minneapolis, MN 55403, (612)872-7060

Amer. Refugee Comm. [12773], 430 Oak Grove St., Ste. 204, Minneapolis, MN 55403, (612)872-7060

Amer. Registry of Diagnostic Medical Sonography [16676], Plaza East One, 51 Monroe St., Rockville, MD 20850-2400, (301)738-8401

Amer. Registry of Inhalation Therapists [★16864]

Amer. Registry of Medical Assistants [15316], 61 Union St., Ste. 5, Westfield, MA 01085-2476, (413)562-7336

Amer. Registry of Pathology - Address unknown since 2011.

Amer. Registry of Professional Animal Scientists [3802], 2441 Village Green Pl., Champaign, IL 61822, (217)356-5390

Amer. Registry of Professional Entomologists [★6844]

Amer. Registry of Radiologic Technologists [15365], 1255 Northland Dr., St. Paul, MN 55120-1155, (651)687-0048

Amer. Registry of Radiological Technicians [★15365]

Amer. Registry of X-Ray Technicians [★15365]

Amer. RehabACTion Network [18511], PO Box 249, Boston, MA 02117, (617)720-2233

Amer. Rehabilitation Assn. [★16557]

Amer. Rehabilitation Counseling Assn. [16558], School of Educ. and Human Performance, Dept. of Human Performance and Sports Sciences, 601 S Martin Luther King Dr., 02 A Old Nursing Bldg., Rm. 116, Winston-Salem, NC 27110, (336)750-2586

Amer. Rehabilitation Found. [★16576]

Amer. Reiki Assn. [★13703]

Amer. Reiki Assn. [★13703]

Amer. Reiki Master Assn. [13659], PO Box 130, Lake City, FL 32056-0130, (904)755-9638

Amer. Relief for Italy [★13514]

Amer. Renewal Found. [18320], PO Box 930, Corbin, VA 22446

Amer. Rental Assn. [3076], 1900 19th St., Moline, IL 61265-4179, (309)764-2475

Amer. Repossessors Assn. [★1031]

Amer. Rescue Dog Assn. [12905], PO Box 613, Bristow, VA 20136, (703)213-4747

Amer. Rescue Dog Assn. [12905], PO Box 613, Bristow, VA 20136, (703)213-4747

Amer. Rescue Team Intl. [12154], PO Box 237, San Francisco, CA 94127, (415)533-2231

Reference to "IO" in place of a book number signifies that the association may be found in the 50th edition of International Organizations.

Amer. Rescue Workers [13172], 25 Ross St., Williamsport, PA 17701, (570)323-8693

Amer. Res. Inst. in Turkey [10616], Univ. of Pennsylvania Museum, 3260 South St., Philadelphia, PA 19104-6324, (215)898-3474

Amer. Res. Inst. in Turkey [10616], Univ. of Pennsylvania Museum, 3260 South St., Philadelphia, PA 19104-6324, (215)898-3474

Amer. Resort Development Assn. [3000], 1201 15th St. NW, Ste. 400, Washington, DC 20005-2842, (202)371-6700

Amer. Resort and Residential Development Assn. [★3000]

Amer. Resources Gp. [3994], 374 Maple Ave. E, Ste. 310, Vienna, VA 22180-4751, (800)476-8733

Amer. Restaurant Inst. [★1765]

Amer. Restitution Assn. - Defunct.

Amer. Restroom Assn. [13013], PO Box 65111, Baltimore, MD 21209, (202)470-3011

Amer. Retail Fed. [★3118]

Amer. Retirees Assn. [20693], PO Box 2333, Redlands, CA 92373-0781, (909)557-0107

Amer. Reusable Textile Assn. [3434], PO Box 1142, Mission, KS 66222, (863)660-5350

Amer. Revenue Assn. [22014], PO Box 74, Grosse Ile, MI 48138, (734)676-2649

Amer. Revenue Assn. [22014], PO Box 74, Grosse Ile, MI 48138, (734)676-2649

American Revolution

Amer. Revolution Round Table [9115]

Centennial Legion of Historic Military Commands [20743]

Daughters of the Cincinnati [20335]

Descendants of the Signers of the Declaration of Independence [20336]

Gen. Soc. of Mayflower Descendants [20746]

Gen. Soc., Sons of the Revolution [20337]

His Majesty's 10th Regiment of Foot [9116]

Junior Amer. Citizens [9117]

Natl. Soc. of the Children of the Amer. Revolution [20338]

Natl. Soc., Daughters of the Amer. Revolution [20339]

Natl. Soc., Sons of the Amer. Revolution [20340]

Natl. Soc. of Women Descendants of the Ancient and Honorable Artillery Company [20403]

Northwest Territory Alliance [9118]

Soc. of the Ark and the Dove [20407]

Soc. of the Cincinnati [20341]

Soc. of the Cincinnati [20341]

Soc. of the Descendants of Washington's Army at Valley Forge [20342]

Amer. Revolution Round Table [9115], 6 Grovedale Rd., Niantic, CT 06357

Amer. Reye's Syndrome Soc. [★16615]

Amer. Rheumatism Assn. [★16616]

Amer. Rheumatism Assn. [★16616]

Amer. Rhinologic Soc. [16087], PO Box 495, Warwick, NY 10990, (845)988-1631

Amer. Rhododendron Soc. [21782], PO Box 525, Niagara Falls, NY 14304, (416)424-1942

Amer. Riding Instructors Assn. [22676], 28801 Trenton Ct., Bonita Springs, FL 34134-3337, (239)948-3232

Amer. Right of Way Assn. [★5958]

Amer. Right of Way Assn. [★5958]

Amer. Rights at Work [18039], 1616 P St. NW, Ste. 150, Washington, DC 20036, (202)822-2127

Amer. Risk and Insurance Assn. [8322], 716 Providence Rd., Malvern, PA 19355-3402, (610)640-1997

Amer. Risk Retention Coalition - Address unknown since 2011.

Amer. River Touring Assn. [3995], 24000 Casa Loma Rd., Groveland, CA 95321, (209)962-7873

Amer. Rivers [3996], 1101 14th St. NW, Ste. 1400, Washington, DC 20005, (202)347-7550

Amer. Rivers Conservation Coun. [★3996]

Amer. Road Builders Assn. [★6028]

Amer. Road Makers [★6028]

Amer. Road and Trans. Builders Assn. [6028], 1219 28th St. NW, Washington, DC 20007-3389, (202)289-4434

Amer. Rock Art Res. Assn. [6159], 3711 W Deer Valley Rd., Glendale, AZ 85308-2038

Amer. Rock Garden Soc. [★21816]

Amer. Rock Garden Soc. [★21816]

Amer. Rock Mechanics Assn. [3358], Peter H. Smeallie, Exec. Dir., 600 Woodland Terr., Alexandria, VA 22302, (703)683-1808

Amer. Rocket Soc. [★6082]

Amer. Roentgen Ray Soc. [16522], 44211 Slatestone Ct., Leesburg, VA 20176, (703)729-3353

Amer. Roentgen Ray Soc. [16522], 44211 Slatestone Ct., Leesburg, VA 20176, (703)729-3353

Amer. Romagnola Assn. - Address unknown since 2011.

Amer. Romanian Acad. of Arts and Sciences - Address unknown since 2010.

Amer. Romanian Orthodox Youth [20226], 2041 Tyler Dr., Commerce Township, MI 48390-2701, (734)395-9707

Amer. Romanian Orthodox Youth [20226], 2041 Tyler Dr., Commerce Township, MI 48390-2701, (734)395-9707

Amer. Romney Breeders' Assn. [4899], 12775 NW Oak Ridge Rd., Yamhill, OR 97148, (503)662-4249

Amer. Rose Found. [★21783]

Amer. Rose Soc. [21783], PO Box 30000, Shreveport, LA 71130-0030, (318)938-5402

Amer. Rosie the Riveter Assn. [20856], 209 Univ. Park Dr., Birmingham, AL 35209, (205)822-4106

Amer. Rosie the Riveter Assn. [20856], 209 Univ. Park Dr., Birmingham, AL 35209, (205)822-4106

Amer. Rottweiler Club [21504], 16005 Pine Creek Way, Magnolia, TX 77355-3351, (281)252-0585

Amer. Royal Assn. [4688], 1701 Amer. Royal Ct., Kansas City, MO 64102, (816)221-9800

Amer. RSDHope - Address unknown since 2010.

Amer. Running Assn. [22803], 4405 East-West Hwy., Ste. 405, Bethesda, MD 20814, (800)776-2732

Amer. Rural Hea. Assn. [★16492]

American-Russian Chamber of Commerce and Indus. [23349], Aon Center, 200 E Randolph St., Ste. 2200, Chicago, IL 60601, (312)494-6562

American-Russian Chamber of Commerce and Indus. [23349], Aon Center, 200 E Randolph St., Ste. 2200, Chicago, IL 60601, (312)494-6562

Amer. Russian Theatrical Alliance [10564], 1409 Midvale Ave., Ste. 105, Los Angeles, CA 90024, (310)312-4989

Amer. Sabbath Tract and Commun. Coun. [★19328]

Amer. Sabbath Tract Soc. [★19328]

Amer. Sable Rabbit Soc. - Defunct.

Amer. Saddle Horse Breeders Assn. [★4552]

Amer. Saddle Makers Assn. [2198], 12155 Donovan Ln., Colorado Springs, CO 80908, (719)494-2848

Amer. Saddlebred Horse Assn. [4552], 4083 Iron Works Pkwy., Lexington, KY 40511, (859)259-2742

Amer. Saddlebred Pleasure Horse Assn. [★4552]

Amer. Saddlebred Sporthorse Assn. [4553], 520 Byers Rd., Chester Springs, PA 19425

Amer. Safe Climbing Assn. [21283], PO Box 1814, Bishop, CA 93515, (650)843-1473

Amer. Sail Training Assn. [22317], PO Box 1459, Newport, RI 02840, (401)846-1775

Amer. Sailing Assn. [22318], 5301 Beethoven St., Ste. 265, Los Angeles, CA 90066, (310)822-7171

Amer. Sailing Assn. Found. - Address unknown since 2011.

Amer. Sailing Educ. Assn. [★8551]

Amer. Salers Assn. [3896], 19590 E Main St., Ste. 202, Parker, CO 80138, (303)770-9292

Amer. Salers Junior Assn. [3897], Amer. Salers Assn., 19590 E Main St., No. 202, Parker, CO 80138, (303)770-9292

Amer. Salvage Pool Assn. [285], PMB 709, 2900 Delk Rd., Ste. 700, Marietta, GA 30067, (678)560-6678

Amer. Salvation Army [★13172]

Amer. Sambo Assn. [22723], PO Box 5773, Long Island City, NY 11105, (718)728-8054

Amer. Samoa Archery Assn. [IO], Pago Pago, American Samoa

Amer. Samoa Bar Assn. [IO], Pago Pago, American Samoa

Amer. Samoa Community Cancer Coalition [IO], Pago Pago, American Samoa

Amer. Samoa Coral Reef Advisory Gp. [IO], Pago Pago, American Samoa

Amer. Samoa Humane Soc. [IO], Pago Pago, American Samoa

Amer. Samoa Judo Assn. [IO], Pago Pago, American Samoa

Amer. Samoa Natl. Olympic Comm. [IO], Pago Pago, American Samoa

Amer. Samoa Rugby Union [IO], Pago Pago, American Samoa

Amer. Samoa Track and Field Assn. [IO], Pago Pago, American Samoa

Amer. Samoa Volleyball Assn. [IO], Pago Pago, American Samoa

Amer. Sanatorium Assn. [★16879]

Amer. Sanatorium Assn. [★16879]

Amer. Sanctuary Assn. [10910], 2308 Chatfield Dr., Las Vegas, NV 89128, (702)804-8562

Amer. Santal Mission [★19944]

Amer. Santal Mission [★19944]

Amer. Satellite TV Alliance - Defunct.

Amer. Satin Rabbit Breeders' Assn. [4836], 3500 S Wagner Rd., Ann Arbor, MI 48103, (734)668-6709

Amer./Saudi Business Roundtable - Defunct.

Amer. Savings Educ. Coun. [8199], 1100 13th St. NW, Ste. 878, Washington, DC 20005-4204, (202)659-0670

American-Scandinavian Found. [10518], 58 Park Ave., 38th St., New York, NY 10016, (212)779-3587

American-Scandinavian Found. [10518], 58 Park Ave., 38th St., New York, NY 10016, (212)779-3587

Amer. Scandinavian Student Exchange [★8346]

Amer. Scandinavian Student Exchange [★8346]

Amer. Schizophrenia Assn. - Defunct.

American/Schleswig-Holstein Heritage Soc. [18994], PO Box 506, Walcott, IA 52773-0506, (563)284-4184

Amer. Scholastic Associates Intl. [★7999]

Amer. Scholastic Associates Intl. [★7999]

Amer. School Band Directors' Assn. [8642], PO Box 696, Guttenberg, IA 52052, (563)252-2500

Amer. School Counselor Assn. [7937], 1101 King St., Ste. 625, Alexandria, VA 22314, (703)683-2722

Amer. School Counselor Assn. [7937], 1101 King St., Ste. 625, Alexandria, VA 22314, (703)683-2722

Amer. School Food Ser. Assn. [★8909]

Amer. School Hea. Assn. [14892], 4340 East West Hwy., Ste. 403, Bethesda, MD 20814, (301)652-8072

Amer. Schools Assn. [7938], PO Box 577820, Chicago, IL 60657-7820, (800)230-2263

Amer. Schools of Oriental Res. [9335], 656 Beacon St., 5th Fl., Boston, MA 02215, (617)353-6570

Amer. Schools of Oriental Res. [9335], 656 Beacon St., 5th Fl., Boston, MA 02215, (617)353-6570

Amer. Sci. Affiliation [20231], PO Box 668, Ipswich, MA 01938, (978)356-5656

Amer. Sci. Glassblowers Soc. [3173], PO Box 453, Machias, NY 14101, (716)353-8062

Amer. Scotch Highland Breeders Assn. [★3880]

Amer. Scottish Found. [19220], 575 Madison Ave., Ste. 1006, New York, NY 10022-2511, (212)605-0338

Amer. Scouting Traders Assn. [★21361]

Amer. Screenwriters Assn. - Address unknown since 2010.

Amer. Seafood Distributors Assn. - Defunct.

Amer. Sealyham Terrier Club [21505], 14111 Rehoboth Church Rd., Lovettsville, VA 20180-3217, (540)882-3492

Amer. Seat Belt Coun. [★321]

Amer. Sect., Intl. Assn. for Testing Materials [★7557]

Amer. Sect. of the Intl. Solar Energy Soc. [★7438]

Amer. Security Coun. [18587], 1250 24th St. NW, Ste. 300, Washington, DC 20037, (202)263-3661

Amer. Security Coun. Educ. Found. [★18588]

Amer. Security Coun. Found. [18588], 1250 24th St. NW, Ste. 300, Washington, DC 20037, (202)263-3661

Amer. Seed Res. Found. [4879], 1701 Duke St., Ste. 275, Alexandria, VA 22314, (703)837-8140

Amer. Seed Trade Assn. [4880], 1701 Duke St., Ste. 675, Alexandria, VA 22314, (703)837-8140

Amer. Self-Help CH [★13035]

Amer. Self-Help Gp. CH [13035], 375 E McFarlan St., Dover, NJ 07801, (973)989-1122

A star before a book entry number signifies that the name is not listed separately, but is mentioned within the entry.

Amer. Self-Protection Assn. [22870], 825 Greengate Oval, Sagamore Hills, OH 44067-2311

Amer. Seminar Leaders Assn. [7921], 2405 E Washington Blvd., Pasadena, CA 91104, (626)791-1211

Amer. Senior Benefits Assn. [3281], PO Box 300777, Chicago, IL 60630-0777, (773)714-7990

Amer. Senior Citizens Assn. - Defunct.

Amer. Senior Fitness Assn. [16222], PO Box 2575, New Smyrna Beach, FL 32170, (386)423-6634

Amer. Seniors Housing Assn. [12169], 5225 Wisconsin Ave. NW, Ste. 502, Washington, DC 20015, (202)237-0900

Amer. Sephardi Fed. [19843], 15 W 16th St., New York, NY 10011-6301, (212)294-8350

Amer. Sepsis Alliance [15114], 610 W Azeele St., Ste. 230, Tampa, FL 33606, (813)874-2552

Amer. Sewing Guild [21431], 9660 Hillcroft, Ste. 510, Houston, TX 77096, (713)729-3000

Amer. Shagya Arabian Verband [4554], 15918 Porter Rd., Verona, KY 41092

Amer. Shark Assn. [22319], 2605 Bainbridge Blvd., Chesapeake, VA 23324-1862

Amer. Sheep Indus. Assn. [4900], 9785 Maroon Cir., Ste. 360, Centennial, CO 80112, (303)771-3500

Amer. Sheep Producers' Coun. [★4900]

Amer. Shetland Pony Club | Amer. Miniature Horse Registry [4555], 81-B Queenwood Rd., Morton, IL 61550, (309)263-4044

Amer. Shetland Sheepdog Assn. [21506], 41044 N Savage Rd., Antioch, IL 60002-7222, (847)838-3049

Amer. Shiatsu Assn. [★15263]

Amer. Shih Tzu Club [21507], 279 Sun Valley Ct., Ripon, CA 95366

Amer. Shipbuilding Assn. - Address unknown since 2011.

Amer. Shire Horse Assn. [4556], Pamela Correll, Sec., 1211 Hill Harrell Rd., Effingham, SC 29541, (843)629-0072

Amer. Shooting Sports Coun. - Defunct.

Amer. Shore and Beach Preservation Assn. [3997], Kate Gooderham, Exec. Dir., 5460 Beaujolais Ln., Fort Myers, FL 33919-2704, (239)489-2616

Amer. Short Line Railroad Assn. [★2987]

Amer. Short Line and Regional Railroad Assn. [2987], 50 F St. NW, Ste. 7020, Washington, DC 20001-1507, (202)628-4500

Amer. Shorthorn Assn. [3898], 8288 Hascall St., Omaha, NE 68124-3234, (402)393-7200

Amer. Shorthorn Breeders Assn. [★3898]

Amer. Shortwave Listeners Club [20932], 16182 Ballad Ln., Huntington Beach, CA 92649-2272, (714)846-1685

Amer. Shotcrete Assn. [822], 38800 Country Club Dr., Farmington Hills, MI 48331, (248)848-3780

Amer. Shoulder and Elbow Surgeons [16799], 6300 N River Rd., Ste. 727, Rosemont, IL 60018-4226, (847)698-1629

Amer. Shropshire Registry Assn. [4901], Becky Peterson, Sec., 41 Bell Rd., Leyden, MA 01337, (413)624-9652

Amer. Sickle Cell Anemia Assn. [16658], 10300 Carnegie Ave., Cleveland, OH 44106, (216)229-8600

Amer. Sickle Cell Anemia Soc. [★16658]

Amer. Sickle Cell Soc. [★16658]

Amer. SIDS Inst. [★16759]

Amer. Sighthound Field Assn. [21508], 3052 Mann Rd., Blacklick, OH 43004, (614)855-5067

Amer. Sign Language Teachers Assn. [14917], PO Box 92426, Rochester, NY 14692

Amer. Silkie Bantam Club [4807], Carina Moncrief, Sec.-Treas., 23754 Spenser Butte Dr., Perris, CA 92570, (951)240-2939

Amer. Simmental Assn. [3899], 1 Simmental Way, Bozeman, MT 59715, (406)587-4531

Amer. Singers Club [21214], 8908 S Yates Blvd., Chicago, IL 60617-3863, (773)750-8691

Amer. Single Shot Rifle Assn. [22872], 15770 Rd. 1037, Oakwood, OH 45873, (419)393-2976

Amer. Single Shot Rifle Assn. [22872], 15770 Rd. 1037, Oakwood, OH 45873, (419)393-2976

Amer. Singles Golf Assn. [22604], PO Box 848, Pineville, NC 28134, (704)889-4600

Amer. Ski-Bike Assn. [22963], 3401 Arthur St., Wichita Falls, TX 76308, (888)203-3530

Amer. Skin Assn. [14319], 6 E 43rd St., 28th Fl., New York, NY 10017, (212)889-4858

Amer. Sleep Apnea Assn. [16663], 6856 Eastern Ave. NW, Ste. 203, Washington, DC 20012, (202)293-3650

American-Slovenian Polka Found. - Address unknown since 2011.

Amer. Slow Sand Assn. - Defunct.

Amer. Small Bus. Assn. [★3281]

Amer. Small Bus. Coalition [3282], PO Box 2786, Columbia, MD 21045-1786, (410)381-7378

Amer. Small Bus. League [3283], 3910 Cypress Dr., Ste. B, Petaluma, CA 94954, (707)789-9575

Amer. Small Bus. Travelers Alliance [3548], PO Box 270543, Flower Mound, TX 75027-0543, (972)836-8064

Amer. Small Businesses Assn. [★3281]

Amer. Small Mfrs. Coalition [2328], PO Box 15289, Washington, DC 20003, (202)341-7066

Amer. Small and Rural Hosp. Assn. [★16492]

Amer. Social Hea. Assn. [16654], PO Box 13827, Research Triangle Park, NC 27709, (919)361-8400

Amer. Social Hea. Assn. | Herpes Rsrc. Center [16655], PO Box 13827, Research Triangle Park, NC 27709, (919)361-8400

Amer. Social Hygiene Assn. [★16654]

Amer. Soc. of Abdominal Surgeons [16800], 824 Main St., 2nd Fl., Ste. 1, Melrose, MA 02176, (781)665-6102

Amer. Soc. for Abrasive Methods [★1795]

Amer. Soc. for Abrasive Methods [★1795]

Amer. Soc. for Abrasives [★1795]

Amer. Soc. for Abrasives [★1795]

Amer. Soc. of Access Professionals [5536], 1444 I St. NW, Ste. 700, Washington, DC 20005-6542, (202)712-9054

Amer. Soc. of Addiction Medicine [16736], 4601 N Park Ave., Upper Arcade No. 101, Chevy Chase, MD 20815, (301)656-3920

Amer. Soc. for Adolescent Psychiatry [16333], PO Box 570218, Dallas, TX 75357-0218, (972)613-0985

Amer. Soc. for Adolescent Psychiatry [16333], PO Box 570218, Dallas, TX 75357-0218, (972)613-0985

Amer. Soc. of Adults with Pseudo-Obstruction [★14555]

Amer. Soc. of Adults with Pseudo-Obstruction [★14555]

Amer. Soc. for Advancement of Anesthesia in Dentistry [★13736]

Amer. Soc. for Advancement of Anesthesia in Dentistry [★13736]

Amer. Soc. for Advancement of Anesthesia and Sedation in Dentistry [13736], 6 E Union Ave., Bound Brook, NJ 08805, (732)469-9050

Amer. Soc. for Advancement of Anesthesia and Sedation in Dentistry [13736], 6 E Union Ave., Bound Brook, NJ 08805, (732)469-9050

Amer. Soc. for Advancement of Gen. Anesthesia in Dentistry [★13736]

Amer. Soc. for Advancement of Gen. Anesthesia in Dentistry [★13736]

Amer. Soc. for Advancement of Haifa Inst. of Tech. [★8420]

Amer. Soc. for the Advancement of Proj. Mgt. [2264], 6547 N Acad., No. 404, Colorado Springs, CO 80918, (719)488-3850

Amer. Soc. for the Advancement of Proj. Mgt. [2264], 6547 N Acad., No. 404, Colorado Springs, CO 80918, (719)488-3850

Amer. Soc. for the Advancement of Violin Making [★10310]

Amer. Soc. of Aeronautical Engineers [★6243]

Amer. Soc. for Aesthetic Plastic Surgery [14175], 11262 Monarch St., Garden Grove, CA 92841, (562)799-2356

Amer. Soc. for Aesthetics [9270], PO Box 915, Pooler, GA 31322, (912)961-3189

Amer. Soc. for Aesthetics [9270], PO Box 915, Pooler, GA 31322, (912)961-3189

Amer. Soc. on Aging [10833], 71 Stevenson St., Ste. 1450, San Francisco, CA 94105-2938, (415)974-9600

Amer. Soc. of Agricultural Appraisers [222], PO Box 186, Twin Falls, ID 83303-0186, (208)733-1122

Amer. Soc. of Agricultural and Biological Engineers [6774], 2950 Niles Rd., St. Joseph, MI 49085-8607, (269)429-0300

Amer. Soc. of Agricultural and Biological Engineers [6774], 2950 Niles Rd., St. Joseph, MI 49085-8607, (269)429-0300

Amer. Soc. of Agricultural Consultants [3718], N78W14573 Appleton Ave., No. 287, Menomonee Falls, WI 53051, (262)253-6902

Amer. Soc. of Agricultural Consultants [3718], N78W14573 Appleton Ave., No. 287, Menomonee Falls, WI 53051, (262)253-6902

Amer. Soc. of Agricultural Engineers [★6774]

Amer. Soc. of Agricultural Engineers [★6774]

Amer. Soc. of Agronomy [3736], 5585 Guilford Rd., Madison, WI 53711, (608)273-8080

Amer. Soc. of Alderian Psychology [★16415]

Amer. Soc. for the Alexander Technique [13660], PO Box 2307, Dayton, OH 45401-2307, (937)586-3732

Amer. Soc. of Allied Hea. Professions [★8598]

Amer. Soc. of Alternative Therapists [13661], PO Box 303, Topsfield, MA 01983, (978)561-1639

Amer. Soc. for Amusement Park Safety and Security - Address unknown since 2011.

Amer. Soc. of Andrology [16940], 1100 E Woodfield Rd., Ste. 520, Schaumburg, IL 60173, (847)619-4909

Amer. Soc. of Anesthesia Technologists and Technicians [15317], 7044 S 13th St., Oak Creek, WI 53154-1429, (414)908-4942

Amer. Soc. of Anesthesiologists [13737], 520 N Northwest Hwy., Park Ridge, IL 60068-2573, (847)825-5586

Amer. Soc. of Anesthetists [★13737]

Amer. Soc. of Animal Sci. [3803], 2441 Village Green Pl., Champaign, IL 61822, (217)356-9050

Amer. Soc. of Appraisers [2550], 555 Herndon Pkwy., Ste. 125, Herndon, VA 20170, (703)478-2228

Amer. Soc. of Architectural Hardware Consultants [★1649]

Amer. Soc. of Architectural Hardware Consultants [★1649]

Amer. Soc. of Architectural Illustrators [239], 1022 Tait St., Oceanside, CA 92054, (760)453-2544

Amer. Soc. of Artists [9221], PO Box 1326, Palatine, IL 60078, (312)751-2500

Amer. Soc. of Assn. Executives [262], 1575 I St. NW, Washington, DC 20005, (202)371-0940

Amer. Soc. of Assn. Executives [262], 1575 I St. NW, Washington, DC 20005, (202)371-0940

Amer. Soc. for Automation in Pharmacy [2689], 492 Norristown Rd., Ste. 160, Blue Bell, PA 19422, (610)825-7783

Amer. Soc. of Bakery Engineers [★388]

Amer. Soc. of Baking [388], PO Box 336, Swedesboro, NJ 08085, (800)713-0462

Amer. Soc. of Bariatric Physicians [15851], 2821 S Parker Rd., Ste. 625, Aurora, CO 80014, (303)770-2526

Amer. Soc. for Bariatric Surgery [★16804]

Amer. Soc. for Biochemistry and Molecular Biology [6268], 11200 Rockville Pike, Ste. 302, Rockville, MD 20852-3110, (240)283-6600

Amer. Soc. for Bioethics and Humanities [8589], 4700 W Lake Ave., Glenview, IL 60025-1468, (847)375-4745

Amer. Soc. of Biological Chemists [★6268]

Amer. Soc. of Biomechanics [6285], Univ. of Iowa, Iowa City, IA 52242, (319)335-8135

Amer. Soc. for Blood and Marrow Transplantation [16898], 85 W Algonquin Rd., Ste. 550, Arlington Heights, IL 60005, (847)427-0224

Amer. Soc. for Bone and Mineral Res. [16053], 2025 M St. NW, Ste. 800, Washington, DC 20036-3309, (202)367-1161

Amer. Soc. for Bookplate Collectors and Designers [21298], PO Box 14964, Tucson, AZ 85732-4964

Amer. Soc. of Botanical Artists [9222], The New York Botanical Garden, 200th St. and Kazimiroff Blvd., Bronx, NY 10458-5126, (212)691-9080

Amer. Soc. of Breast Disease [13859], PO Box 140186, Dallas, TX 75214, (214)368-6836

Amer. Soc. of Breast Surgeons [16801], 5950 Symphony Woods Rd., Ste. 212, Columbia, MD 21044, (410)992-5470

Reference to "IO" in place of a book number signifies that the association may be found in the 50th edition of International Organizations.

Amer. Soc. of Brewing Chemists [6396], 3340 Pilot Knob Rd., St. Paul, MN 55121-2097, (651)454-7250

Amer. Soc. of Brewing Chemists [6396], 3340 Pilot Knob Rd., St. Paul, MN 55121-2097, (651)454-7250

Amer. Soc. of Bus. Press Editors [★2800]

Amer. Soc. of Bus. Publication Editors [2800], 214 N Hale St., Wheaton, IL 60187, (630)510-4588

Amer. Soc. of Cardiovascular Professionals/Society for Cardiovascular Mgt. [★13997]

Amer. Soc. of Cataract and Refractive Surgery [15943], 4000 Legato Rd., Ste. 700, Fairfax, VA 22033, (703)591-2220

Amer. Soc. for Cell Biology [6286], 8120 Woodmont Ave., Ste. 750, Bethesda, MD 20814-2762, (301)347-9300

Amer. Soc. of Certified Engg. Technicians [6775], PO Box 1536, Brandon, MS 39043, (601)824-8991

Amer. Soc. of Check Collectors [21965], 473 E Elm St., Sycamore, IL 60178

Amer. Soc. of Christian Ethics [★11985]

Amer. Soc. of Christian Social Ethics in the U.S. and Canada [★11985]

Amer. Soc. for Church Growth [★19619]

Amer. Soc. of Church History [19812], PO Box 2216, Hewitt, TX 76643-2216, (254)666-2457

Amer. Soc. of Church History [19812], PO Box 2216, Hewitt, TX 76643-2216, (254)666-2457

Amer. Soc. of Cinematographers [1250], PO Box 2230, Hollywood, CA 90078, (323)969-4333

Amer. Soc. of Civil Engineers [6776], 1801 Alexander Bell Dr., Reston, VA 20191-4400, (703)295-6300

Amer. Soc. of Civil Engineers | Architectural Engg. Inst. [6185], 1801 Alexander Bell Dr., Reston, VA 20191-4400, (703)295-6370

Amer. Soc. for Clinical Evoked Potentials - Defunct.

Amer. Soc. of Clinical Hypnosis [15088], 140 N Bloomingdale Rd., Bloomingdale, IL 60108-1017, (630)980-4740

Amer. Soc. for Clinical Investigation [14151], 15 Res. Dr., Ann Arbor, MI 48103, (734)222-6050

Amer. Soc. for Clinical Lab. Sci. [15232], 2025 M St. NW, Ste. 800, Washington, DC 20036, (202)367-1174

Amer. Soc. of Clinical Lab. Technicians [★15232]

Amer. Soc. for Clinical Nutrition [15821], 9650 Rockville Pike, Bethesda, MD 20814-3998, (301)634-7050

Amer. Soc. of Clinical Oncology [15917], 2318 Mill Rd., Ste. 800, Alexandria, VA 22314, (571)483-1300

Amer. Soc. of Clinical Pathologists [★16115]

Amer. Soc. for Clinical Pathology [16115], 33 W Monroe, Ste. 1600, Chicago, IL 60603, (312)541-4999

Amer. Soc. of Clinical Pharmacology and Chemotherapy [★16178]

Amer. Soc. for Clinical Pharmacology and Therapeutics [16178], 528 N Washington St., Alexandria, VA 22314-2314, (703)836-6981

Amer. Soc. of Clinical Psychopharmacology [16179], 5034 A. Thoroughbred Ln., Brentwood, TN 37027, (615)649-3085

Amer. Soc. of Clinical Radiation Oncology [15918], 9909 Le Grand Dr., Wexford, PA 15090, (412)721-4311

Amer. Soc. of CLU and ChFC [★2039]

Amer. Soc. of CLU and ChFC [★2039]

Amer. Soc. of Colon and Rectal Surgeons [16314], 85 W Algonquin Rd., Ste. 550, Arlington Heights, IL 60005, (847)290-9184

Amer. Soc. for Colposcopy and Cervical Pathology [15870], 152 W Washington St., Hagerstown, MD 21740, (301)733-3640

Amer. Soc. for Colposcopy and Colpomicroscopy [★15870]

Amer. Soc. of Comparative Law [5586], Univ. of Iowa Coll. of Law, 290 Boyd Law Bldg., Iowa City, IA 52242-1113, (319)335-9086

Amer. Soc. for Competitiveness [7777], PO Box 1658, Indiana, PA 15705, (724)357-5928

Amer. Soc. of Composers, Authors and Publishers [5560], 1 Lincoln Plz., New York, NY 10023, (212)621-6000

Amer. Soc. for Composites [6373], Prof. Steven L. Donaldson, Treas., Univ. of Dayton, Dept. of Civil and Environmental Engg., 422 Kettering Lab., 300 Coll. Park Ave., Dayton, OH 45469-0243, (937)229-3847

Amer. Soc. for Cmpt. Dealers [★6530]

Amer. Soc. for Concrete Constr. [★895]

Amer. Soc. of Concrete Contractors [895], 2025 S Brentwood Blvd., Ste. 105, St. Louis, MO 63144, (314)962-0210

Amer. Soc. of Consultant Pharmacists [16180], 1321 Duke St., Alexandria, VA 22314-3563, (703)739-1300

Amer. Soc. of Consulting Arborists [4967], 9707 Key W Ave., Ste. 100, Rockville, MD 20850, (301)947-0483

Amer. Soc. of Consulting Planners - Address unknown since 2010.

Amer. Soc. of Contemporary Artists [9223], 453 FDR Dr., No. 1805, New York, NY 10002, (212)673-1620

Amer. Soc. for the Control Cancer [★13882]

Amer. Soc. of Corporate Secretaries [★74]

Amer. Soc. of Cosmetic Surgeon [★14169]

Amer. Soc. of Cost Segregation Professionals [3381], 1001 Pennsylvania Ave. NW, 6th Fl., Washington, DC 20004, (202)756-1959

Amer. Soc. of Crime Lab. Directors [5476], 139K Tech. Dr., Garner, NC 27529, (919)773-2044

Amer. Soc. of Criminology [11740], 1314 Kinnear Rd., Ste. 212, Columbus, OH 43212-1156, (614)292-9207

Amer. Soc. of Critical Care Anesthesiologists [13738], 520 N Northwest Hwy., Park Ridge, IL 60068-2573, (847)825-5586

Amer. Soc. of Cybernetics [6442], 2033 K St. NW, Ste. 230, Washington, DC 20052, (202)994-1642

Amer. Soc. of Cytology [★14214]

Amer. Soc. of Cytopathology [14214], 100 W 10th St., Ste. 605, Wilmington, DE 19801, (302)543-6583

Amer. Soc. for Cytotechnology [14215], 1500 Sunday Dr., Ste. 102, Raleigh, NC 27607, (919)861-5571

Amer. Soc. for Deaf Children [14918], 800 Florida Ave. NE, No. 2047, Washington, DC 20002-3600, (800)942-2732

Amer. Soc. for the Defense of Tradition, Family and Property [★19536]

Amer. Soc. for the Defense of Tradition, Family and Property - Defunct.

Amer. Soc. for Dental Aesthetics [14270], 635 Madison Ave., New York, NY 10022-1009, (212)751-3263

Amer. Soc. for Dental Aesthetics [14270], 635 Madison Ave., New York, NY 10022-1009, (212)751-3263

Amer. Soc. of Dental Ceramics [★14244]

Amer. Soc. of Dentist Anesthesiologists [14271], Ms. Amy Brown, Exec. Dir., 304 Patrick St. SW, Vienna, VA 22180-6742, (703)462-9196

Amer. Soc. of Dentistry for Children - Defunct.

Amer. Soc. for Dermatologic Surgery [14320], 5550 Meadowbrook Dr., Ste. 120, Rolling Meadows, IL 60008, (847)956-0900

Amer. Soc. of Dermatology [14321], First Financial Plz., No. 1006, 411 Hamilton Blvd., Peoria, IL 61602, (309)676-4074

Amer. Soc. of Dermatopathology [14322], 111 Deer Lake Rd., Ste. 100, Deerfield, IL 60015, (847)400-5820

Amer. Soc. of Design Engineers - Defunct.

Amer. Soc. of Diagnostic and Interventional Nephrology [15544], 134 Fairmont St., Ste. B, Clinton, MS 39056, (601)924-2220

Amer. Soc. of Digital Forensics and eDiscovery [6883], 2451 Cumberland Pkwy., Ste. 3382, Atlanta, GA 30339-6157, (866)534-9734

Amer. Soc. of Directors of Volunteer Services [★13384]

Amer. Soc. of Dowsers [7245], PO Box 24, Danville, VT 05828, (802)684-3417

Amer. Soc. of Echocardiography [14003], 2100 Gateway Centre Blvd., Ste. 310, Morrisville, NC 27560, (919)861-5574

Amer. Soc. for Eighteenth-Century Stud. [9748], Wake Forest Univ., PO Box 7867, Winston-Salem, NC 27109, (336)727-4694

Amer. Soc. of Electroencephalographic Technologists [★14444]

Amer. Soc. of Electroneurodiagnostic Technologists [14444], 402 E Bannister Rd., Ste. A, Kansas City, MO 64131-3019, (816)931-1120

Amer. Soc. of Embalmers [2528], PO Box 0685, Forest Park, IL 60130-0685, (708)488-9185

Amer. Soc. of Emergency Radiology [16523], 4550 Post Oak Pl., Ste. 342, Houston, TX 77027, (713)965-0566

Amer. Soc. of Employers [1141], 19575 Victor Pkwy., Ste. 100, Livonia, MI 48152, (248)353-4500

Amer. Soc. for Engg. Educ. [8123], 1818 N St. NW, Ste. 600, Washington, DC 20036-2479, (202)331-3500

Amer. Soc. for Engg. Educ. [8123], 1818 N St. NW, Ste. 600, Washington, DC 20036-2479, (202)331-3500

Amer. Soc. for Engg. Mgt. [6777], PO Box 820, Rolla, MO 65402-0820, (573)341-6228

Amer. Soc. of Enologists [★5161]

Amer. Soc. for Enology and Viticulture [5161], PO Box 1855, Davis, CA 95617-1855, (530)753-3142

Amer. Soc. for Environmental History [8139], Univ. of Washington, Interdisciplinary Arts and Sciences Prog., 1900 Commerce St., Tacoma, WA 98402

Amer. Soc. for Environmental History [8139], Univ. of Washington, Interdisciplinary Arts and Sciences Prog., 1900 Commerce St., Tacoma, WA 98402

Amer. Soc. for Ethnohistory [9585], Duke Univ. Press, PO Box 906660, Durham, NC 27708-0660, (919)687-3602

Amer. Soc. of Exercise Physiologists [16278], Coll. of St. Scholastica, 1200 Kenwood Ave., Duluth, MN 55811, (218)723-6297

Amer. Soc. of Exodontists [★16002]

Amer. Soc. for Experimental Neuro Therapeutics [15646], 342 N Main St., West Hartford, CT 06117, (860)586-7523

Amer. Soc. for Experimental Pathology [★16116]

Amer. Soc. of Extra-Corporeal Tech. [15366], 2209 Dickens Rd., Richmond, VA 23230-2005, (804)565-6363

Amer. Soc. of Extracorporeal Circulation Technicians [★15366]

Amer. Soc. of Facial Plastic Surgery [★14170]

Amer. Soc. of Farm Equip. Appraisers [223], PO Box 186, Twin Falls, ID 83303-0186, (208)733-2323

Amer. Soc. of Farm Managers [★224]

Amer. Soc. of Farm Managers and Rural Appraisers [224], 950 S Cherry St., Ste. 508, Denver, CO 80246-2664, (303)758-3513

Amer. Soc. of Forensic Odontology [14272], PMB 121, 4414 82nd St., Ste. 212, Lubbock, TX 79424

Amer. Soc. of Forensic Podiatry [14545], PO Box 549, Bandon, OR 97411

Amer. Soc. forReconstructive Microsurgery [16802], 20 N Michigan Ave., Ste. 700, Chicago, IL 60602, (312)456-9579

Amer. Soc. for Friendship with Switzerland [★19250]

Amer. Soc. for Friendship with Switzerland [★19250]

Amer. Soc. of Furniture Designers [1544], 144 Woodland Dr., New London, NC 28127, (910)576-1273

Amer. Soc. of Gas Engineers [6690], PO Box 66, Artesia, CA 90702

Amer. Soc. for Gastrointestinal Endoscopy [14554], 1520 Kensington Rd., Ste. 202, Oak Brook, IL 60523, (630)573-0600

Amer. Soc. of Gene and Cell Therapy [14643], 555 E Wells St., Ste. 1100, Milwaukee, WI 53202, (414)278-1341

Amer. Soc. of Gene Therapy [★14643]

Amer. Soc. of Gene Therapy [14643], 555 E Wells St., Ste. 1100, Milwaukee, WI 53202, (414)278-1341

Amer. Soc. of Genealogists [20619], PO Box 26836, San Diego, CA 92196

Amer. Soc. of Genealogists [20619], PO Box 26836, San Diego, CA 92196

Amer. Soc. of Gen. Surgeons [16803], PO Box 4834, Englewood, CO 80155, (303)771-5948

A star before a book entry number signifies that the name is not listed separately, but is mentioned within the entry.

Amer. Soc. for Genomic Medicine [14644], PO Box 2946, La Jolla, CA 92038

Amer. Soc. for Genomic Medicine [14644], PO Box 2946, La Jolla, CA 92038

Amer. Soc. of Geolinguistics

Amer. Soc. of Geolinguistics - Address unknown since 2011.

Amer. Soc. for Geriatric Dentistry [★14310]

Amer. Soc. of Golf Course Architects [6186], 125 N Executive Dr., Ste. 302, Brookfield, WI 53005, (262)786-5960

Amer. Soc. of Greek and Latin Epigraphy [10753], CWRU Dept. of Classics, 111 Mather House, 11201 Euclid Ave., Cleveland, OH 44106-7111

Amer. Soc. of Gp. Psychotherapy and Psychodrama [16453], 301 N Harrison St., Ste. 508, Princeton, NJ 08540, (609)737-8500

Amer. Soc. of Hair Restoration Surgery [14674], Amer. Acad. of Cosmetic Surgery, 737 N Michigan Ave., Ste. 2100, Chicago, IL 60611, (312)981-6760

Amer. Soc. of Hair Restoration Surgery [14674], Amer. Acad. of Cosmetic Surgery, 737 N Michigan Ave., Ste. 2100, Chicago, IL 60611, (312)981-6760

Amer. Soc. of Hand Therapists [14680], 15000 Commerce Pkwy., Ste. C, Mount Laurel, NJ 08054, (856)380-6856

Amer. Soc. for the Hard of Hearing [★16682]

Amer. Soc. of Head and Neck Radiology [16524], 2210 Midwest Rd., Ste. 207, Oak Brook, IL 60523-8205, (630)574-0220

Amer. Soc. of Head and Neck Surgeons [★16083]

Amer. Soc. for Head and Neck Surgery [★16083]

Amer. Soc. of Hea. Sys. Pharmacists [16181], 7272 Wisconsin Ave., Bethesda, MD 20814, (301)657-3000

Amer. Soc. for Healthcare Central Ser. Mgt. [★15058]

Amer. Soc. for Healthcare Education and Training of the Amer. Hospital Assn. - Defunct.

American Soc. for Healthcare Food Ser. Administrators [★15044]

Amer. Soc. for Healthcare Marketing and Public Relations [★15041]

Amer. Soc. for Healthcare Materials Mgt. [★15038]

Amer. Soc. of Healthcare Publication Editors [14755], 8870 Darrow Rd., Ste. F106-155, Twinsburg, OH 44087, (330)487-0344

Amer. Soc. for Healthcare Risk Mgt. [15042], 155 N Wacker Dr., Ste. 400, Chicago, IL 60606, (312)422-3980

Amer. Soc. Heating and Air-Conditioning Engineers [★6778]

Amer. Soc. Heating and Air-Conditioning Engineers [★6778]

Amer. Soc. of Heating, Refrigerating and Air-Conditioning Engineers [6778], 1791 Tullie Cir. NE, Atlanta, GA 30329, (404)636-8400

Amer. Soc. of Heating, Refrigerating and Air-Conditioning Engineers [6778], 1791 Tullie Cir. NE, Atlanta, GA 30329, (404)636-8400

Amer. Soc. of Hematology [14960], 2021 L St. NW, Ste. 900, Washington, DC 20036, (202)776-0544

Amer. Soc. for Histocompatibility and Immunogenetics [15099], 15000 Commerce Pkwy., Ste. C, Mount Laurel, NJ 08054-2212, (856)638-0428

Amer. Soc. of Home Inspectors [521], 932 Lee St., Ste. 101, Des Plaines, IL 60016, (847)759-2820

Amer. Soc. for Horticultural Sci. [6347], 1018 Duke St., Alexandria, VA 22314, (703)836-4606

Amer. Soc. of Hosp. Attorneys [★5510]

Amer. Soc. of Hospital-Based Emergency Air Medical Services [★14449]

Amer. Soc. of Hospital-Based Emergency Air Medical Services [★14449]

Amer. Soc. for Hosp. Central Ser. Personnel [★15058]

Amer. Soc. for Hosp. Engg. [★15036]

Amer. Soc. for Hosp. Food Ser. Administrators [★15044]

Amer. Soc. for Hosp. Marketing and Public Relations [★15041]

Amer. Soc. for Hosp. Materials Mgt. [★15038]

Amer. Soc. for Hosp. Nursing Ser. Administrators [★15726]

Amer. Soc. of Hosp. Pharmacists Res. and Educ. Found. [★16184]

Amer. Soc. for Hosp. Public Relations [★15041]

Amer. Soc. for Hosp. Purchasing Agents [★15038]

Amer. Soc. for Hosp. Purchasing and Materials Mgt. [★15038]

Amer. Soc. of Human Genetics [6898], 9650 Rockville Pike, Bethesda, MD 20814-3998, (301)634-7300

Amer. Soc. of Hypertension [15075], 148 Madison Ave., 5th Fl., New York, NY 10016, (212)696-9099

Amer. Soc. of Hypertension [15075], 148 Madison Ave., 5th Fl., New York, NY 10016, (212)696-9099

Amer. Soc. of Ichthyologists and Herpetologists [6939], Florida Intl. Univ., Coll. of Arts and Sci., Dept. of Biological Sciences, 11200 SW 8th St., Miami, FL 33199, (305)348-1235

Amer. Soc. of Indexers [★9957]

Amer. Soc. for Indexing [9957], 10200 W 44th Ave., Ste. 304, Wheat Ridge, CO 80033, (303)463-2887

Amer. Soc. for Indus. Security [★1883]

Amer. Soc. for Indus. Security [★1883]

Amer. Soc. for Info. Sci. and Tech. [6968], 1320 Fenwick Ln., Ste. 510, Silver Spring, MD 20910, (301)495-0900

Amer. Soc. of Inspectors of Plumbing and Sanitary Engg. [★7349]

Amer. Soc. of Instrument Engineers [★6999]

Amer. Soc. of Instrument Engineers [★6999]

Amer. Soc. of Insurance Mgt. [★2034]

Amer. Soc. of Interior Designers [2051], 608 Massachusetts Ave. NE, Washington, DC 20002-6006, (202)546-3480

Amer. Soc. of Internal Medicine - Defunct.

Amer. Soc. of Intl. Law [5587], 2223 Massachusetts Ave. NW, Washington, DC 20008, (202)939-6000

Amer. Soc. of Intl. Law [5587], 2223 Massachusetts Ave. NW, Washington, DC 20008, (202)939-6000

Amer. Soc. of Interpreters - Defunct.

Amer. Soc. of Interventional Pain Physicians [16098], 81 Lakeview Dr., Paducah, KY 42001, (270)554-9412

Amer. Soc. of Interventional and Therapeutic Neuroradiology [★16545]

Amer. Soc. of Inventors [7011], PO Box 58426, Philadelphia, PA 19102, (215)546-6601

Amer. Soc. for Investigative Pathology [16116], 9650 Rockville Pike, Ste. E133, Bethesda, MD 20814, (301)634-7130

Amer. Soc. of Irrigation Consultants [7597], PO Box 426, Rochester, MA 02770-0426, (508)763-8140

Amer. Soc. of Jewelry Historians [9916], 1333A North Ave., No. 103, New Rochelle, NY 10804, (914)235-0983

Amer. Soc. of Jewelry Historians [9916], 1333A North Ave., No. 103, New Rochelle, NY 10804, (914)235-0983

Amer. Soc. for Jewish Heritage in Poland [9918], 1202 Lexington Ave., No. 121, New York, NY 10028-1425, (212)330-6588

Amer. Soc. for Jewish Heritage in Poland [9918], 1202 Lexington Ave., No. 121, New York, NY 10028-1425, (212)330-6588

Amer. Soc. for Jewish Music [10155], Center for Jewish History, 15 W 16th St., New York, NY 10011, (212)294-8328

Amer. Soc. of Journalism School Administrators [★7663]

Amer. Soc. of Journalists and Authors [10700], 1501 Broadway, Ste. 302, New York, NY 10036, (212)997-0947

Amer. Soc. for Kurds [13173], 227 N Bronough St., Ste. 1001, Tallahassee, FL 32301

Amer. Soc. for Kurds [13173], 227 N Bronough St., Ste. 1001, Tallahassee, FL 32301

Amer. Soc. of Landscape Architects [6187], 636 Eye St. NW, Washington, DC 20001-3736, (202)898-2444

Amer. Soc. of Landscape Architects Found. [★6199]

Amer. Soc. for Laser Medicine and Surgery [15236], 2100 Stewart Ave., Ste. 240, Wausau, WI 54401-1709, (715)845-9283

Amer. Soc. of Law and Medicine [★15244]

Amer. Soc. of Law, Medicine and Ethics [15244], 765 Commonwealth Ave., Ste. 1634, Boston, MA 02215-1401, (617)262-4990

Amer. Soc. for Legal History [9749], Western Kentucky Univ., 1906 Coll. Heights Blvd., No. 21086, Bowling Green, KY 42101-1086

Amer. Soc. of Limnology and Oceanography [★7177]

Amer. Soc. of Limnology and Oceanography [7177], 5400 Bosque Blvd., Ste. 680, Waco, TX 76710-4446, (254)399-9635

Amer. Soc. of Lipo-Suction Surgery - Address unknown since 2010.

Amer. Soc. of Lubrication Engineers [★6831]

Amer. Soc. of Lubrication Engineers [★6831]

Amer. Soc. of Magazine Editors [2801], 810 7th Ave., 24th Fl., New York, NY 10019, (212)872-3700

Amer. Soc. of Magazine Photographers [★2711]

Amer. Soc. of Mammalogists [7039], PO Box 1897, Lawrence, KS 66044, (785)843-1235

Amer. Soc. of Marine Artists [9224], PO Box 247, Smithfield, VA 23430, (757)357-3785

Amer. Soc. for Mass Spectrometry [7457], 2019 Galisteo St., Bldg. I-1, Santa Fe, NM 87505, (505)989-4517

Amer. Soc. of Master Dental Technologists [14273], 146-21 13th Ave., Whitestone, NY 11357-2420, (718)746-8355

Amer. Soc. for Matrix Biology [6287], 9650 Rockville Pike, Bethesda, MD 20814, (301)634-7814

Amer. Soc. of Maxillofacial Surgeons [16005], 900 Cummings Ctr., Ste. 221-U, Beverly, MA 01915, (978)927-8330

Amer. Soc. for Measurement Control [★6999]

Amer. Soc. for Measurement Control [★6999]

Amer. Soc. of Mech. Engineers [7079], 3 Park Ave., New York, NY 10016-5990, (973)882-1170

Amer. Soc. of Mech. Engineers Auxiliary - Address unknown since 2011.

Amer. Soc. of Media Photographers [2711], 150 N 2nd St., Philadelphia, PA 19106, (215)451-2767

Amer. Soc. of Medical Technologists [★15232]

Amer. Soc. for Medical Tech. [★15232]

Amer. Soc. of Medication Safety Officers [14869], 200 Lakeside Dr., Ste. 200, Horsham, PA 19044, (508)499-3043

Amer. Soc. for Metabolic and Bariatric Surgery [16804], 100 SW 75th St., Ste. 201, Gainesville, FL 32607, (352)331-4900

Amer. Soc. for Metals [★7090]

Amer. Soc. for Metals [★7090]

Amer. Soc. for Microbiology [6288], 1752 N St. NW, Washington, DC 20036, (202)737-3600

Amer. Soc. of Military Comptrollers [5796], 415 N Alfred St., Alexandria, VA 22314, (703)549-0360

Amer. Soc. of Military Insignia Collectors [21883], 526 Lafayette Ave., Palmerton, PA 18071-1621

Amer. Soc. of Milling and Baking Tech. [★6385]

Amer. Soc. of Milling and Baking Tech. [★6385]

Amer. Soc. of Mining and Reclamation [5838], 3134 Montavesta Rd., Lexington, KY 40502-3548, (859)351-9032

Amer. Soc. of Minority Hea. and Transplant Professionals [★16899]

Amer. Soc. of Missiology [20007], 2100 S Summit Ave., Sioux Falls, SD 57105, (605)336-6588

Amer. Soc. for Mohs Histotechnology [15367], 555 E Wells St., Ste. 1100, Milwaukee, WI 53202, (414)347-1103

Amer. Soc. for Mohs Surgery [15919], 5901 Warner Ave., Private Mail Box 391, Huntington Beach, CA 92649-4659, (714)379-6262

Amer. Soc. for Mohs Surgery [15919], 5901 Warner Ave., Private Mail Box 391, Huntington Beach, CA 92649-4659, (714)379-6262

Amer. Soc. of Multicultural Hea. and Transplant Professionals [16899], 700 N 4th St., Richmond, VA 23219, (877)742-2630

Amer. Soc. of Municipal Engineers [★5944]

Amer. Soc. of Music Arrangers [★10156]

Amer. Soc. of Music Arrangers and Composers [10156], PO Box 17840, Encino, CA 91416, (818)994-4661

Amer. Soc. for Muslim Advancement [9889], 475 Riverside Dr., Ste. 248, New York, NY 10115, (212)870-2552

Amer. Soc. for Nanomedicine [15398], Georgetown Univ. Medical Center, 3970 Reservoir Rd. NW, Washington, DC 20007-2126, (202)687-8418

Amer. Soc. of Naturalists [7138], Univ. of Chicago Press, 1427 E 60th St., Chicago, IL 60637, (773)702-0446

Reference to "IO" in place of a book number signifies that the association may be found in the 50th edition of International Organizations.

Amer. Soc. of Naval Engineers **[7051]**, 1452 Duke St., Alexandria, VA 22314-3458, (703)836-6727

Amer. Soc. of Nephrology **[15545]**, 1510 H St. NW, Ste. 800, Washington, DC 20005-1003, (202)640-4660

Amer. Soc. for Neural Therapy and Repair **[15647]**, Donna C. Morrison, Univ. of South Florida, Center for Aging and Brain Repair, Dept. of Neurosurgery, MDC-78, 12901 Bruce B. Downs Blvd., Tampa, FL 33612-4799, (813)974-3154

Amer. Soc. for Neural Transplantation **[★15647]**

Amer. Soc. for Neural Transplantation and Repair **[★15647]**

Amer. Soc. for Neurochemistry **[7154]**, 9037 Ron Den Ln., Windermere, FL 34786, (407)909-9064

Amer. Soc. of Neuroimaging **[16525]**, 5841 Cedar Lake Rd., Ste. 204, Minneapolis, MN 55416, (952)545-6291

Amer. Soc. of Neurophysiological Monitoring **[15648]**, 20 N Michigan Ave., Ste. 700, Chicago, IL 60602, (800)479-7979

Amer. Soc. of Neuroradiology **[16526]**, 2210 Midwest Rd., Ste. 207, Oak Brook, IL 60523, (630)574-0220

Amer. Soc. of Neurorehabilitation **[15649]**, 5841 Cedar Lake Rd., Ste. 204, Minneapolis, MN 55416, (952)545-6324

Amer. Soc. of News Editors **[2802]**, 11690B Sunrise Valley Dr., Reston, VA 20191-1436, (703)453-1122

Amer. Soc. of Newspaper Editors **[★2802]**

Amer. Soc. for Nondestructive Testing **[7555]**, PO Box 28518, Columbus, OH 43228-0518, (614)274-6003

Amer. Soc. of Notaries **[5867]**, PO Box 5707, Tallahassee, FL 32314-5707, (850)671-5164

Amer. Soc. of Nuclear Cardiology **[14004]**, 4340 East-West Hwy., Ste. 1120, Bethesda, MD 20814-4578, (301)215-7575

Amer. Soc. for Nursing Ser. Administrators **[★15726]**

Amer. Soc. for Nutrition **[15822]**, 9650 Rockville Pike, Bethesda, MD 20814-3998, (301)634-7050

Amer. Soc. for Nutritional Sciences **[★15822]**

Amer. Soc. for Oceanography **[★7054]**

Amer. Soc. of Ocularists **[15356]**, PO Box 608, Earlysville, VA 22936-0608, (434)973-4066

Amer. Soc. of Ophthalmic Administrators **[15287]**, 4000 Legato Rd., Ste. 700, Fairfax, VA 22033, (703)788-5777

Amer. Soc. of Ophthalmic Plastic and Reconstructive Surgery **[14176]**, 5841 Cedar Lake Rd., Ste. 204, Minneapolis, MN 55416, (952)646-2038

Amer. Soc. of Ophthalmic Registered Nurses **[15729]**, PO Box 193030, San Francisco, CA 94119-3030, (415)561-8513

Amer. Soc. of Ophthalmologic and Otolaryngologic Allergy **[★13633]**

Amer. Soc. of Oral Surgeons **[★16002]**

Amer. Soc. of Orthodontists **[★14251]**

Amer. Soc. of Orthopaedic Physician's Assistants **[16027]**, 8365 Keystone Crossing, Ste. 107, Indianapolis, IN 46240, (800)280-2390

Amer. Soc. of Orthopedic Professionals **[16028]**, PO Box 7440, Seminole, FL 33775, (727)394-1700

Amer. Soc. of Outpatient Surgeons **[★16789]**

Amer. Soc. of Pain Educators **[16099]**, 6 Erie St., Montclair, NJ 07042, (973)233-5570

Amer. Soc. for Pain Mgt. Nursing **[15730]**, PO Box 15473, Lenexa, KS 66285-5473, (913)895-4606

Amer. Soc. of Papyrologists **[10349]**, Duke Univ., Dept. of Classical Stud., 233 Allen Bldg., PO Box 90103, Durham, NC 27708-0103

Amer. Soc. for Parenteral and Enteral Nutrition **[15823]**, 8630 Fenton St., Ste. 412, Silver Spring, MD 20910-3805, (301)587-6315

Amer. Soc. of Pediatric Hematology/Oncology **[14961]**, 4700 W Lake Ave., Glenview, IL 60025-1485, (847)375-4716

Amer. Soc. of Pediatric Nephrology **[15546]**, 3400 Res. Forest Dr., Ste. B7, The Woodlands, TX 77381, (281)419-0052

Amer. Soc. of Pediatric Neuroradiology **[16527]**, 2210 Midwest Rd., Ste. 207, Oak Brook, IL 60523-8205, (630)574-0220

Amer. Soc. of Pension Actuaries **[★1121]**

Amer. Soc. of Pension Professionals and Actuaries **[1121]**, 4245 N Fairfax Dr., Ste. 750, Arlington, VA 22203, (703)516-9300

Amer. Soc. of Perfumers **[1519]**, PO Box 1551, West Caldwell, NJ 07007, (201)991-0040

Amer. Soc. of PeriAnesthesia Nurses **[15731]**, 90 Frontage Rd., Cherry Hill, NJ 08034-1424, (856)616-9600

Amer. Soc. of PeriAnesthesia Nurses **[15731]**, 90 Frontage Rd., Cherry Hill, NJ 08034-1424, (856)616-9600

Amer. Soc. of Periodontists **[★14243]**

Amer. Soc. for Personnel Admin. **[★2632]**

Amer. Soc. for Personnel Admin. Intl. **[★2631]**

Amer. Soc. for Personnel Admin. Intl. **[★2631]**

Amer. Soc. of Pharmacognosy **[16182]**, David J. Slatkin, Treas., 3149 Dundee Rd., No. 260, Northbrook, IL 60062, (773)995-3748

Amer. Soc. of Pharmacognosy **[16182]**, David J. Slatkin, Treas., 3149 Dundee Rd., No. 260, Northbrook, IL 60062, (773)995-3748

Amer. Soc. of Pharmacology and Experimental Therapeutics **[16183]**, 9650 Rockville Pike, Bethesda, MD 20814-3995, (301)634-7060

Amer. Soc. of Pharmacy Law **[15245]**, 3085 Stevenson Dr., Ste. 200, Springfield, IL 62703-4270, (217)529-6948

Amer. Soc. for Philosophy Counseling and Psychotherapy - Address unknown since 2011.

Amer. Soc. for Photobiology **[6289]**, PO Box 1897, Lawrence, KS 66044, (800)627-0629

Amer. Soc. for Photobiology **[6289]**, PO Box 1897, Lawrence, KS 66044, (800)627-0629

Amer. Soc. for Photogrammetry **[★7259]**

Amer. Soc. for Photogrammetry and Remote Sensing **[★7259]**

Amer. Soc. of Photographers **[10434]**, 3120 N Argonne Dr., Milwaukee, WI 53222, (414)871-6600

Amer. Soc. of Physical Medicine and Rehabilitation **[★16552]**

Amer. Soc. of Physician Analysts **[★16354]**

Amer. Soc. of Piano Technicians **[★2571]**

Amer. Soc. of Picture Professionals **[2712]**, 217 Palos Verdes Blvd., No. 700, Redondo Beach, CA 90277, (424)247-9944

Amer. Soc. of Planning Officials **[★5326]**

Amer. Soc. of Plant Biologists **[6348]**, 15501 Monona Dr., Rockville, MD 20855-2768, (301)251-0560

Amer. Soc. of Plant Physiologists **[★6348]**

Amer. Soc. of Plant Taxonomists **[6349]**, Univ. of Wyoming, Dept. of Botany 3165, 1000 E Univ. Ave., Laramie, WY 82071-2000, (307)766-2556

Amer. Soc. of Plastic and Reconstructive Surgeons **[★14178]**

Amer. Soc. of Plastic and Reconstructive Surgical Nurses **[★15732]**

Amer. Soc. of Plastic Surgeons **[14177]**, 444 E Algonquin Rd., Arlington Heights, IL 60005, (847)228-9900

Amer. Soc. of Plastic Surgeons | Plastic Surgery Educ. Found. **[14178]**, 444 E Algonquin Rd., Arlington Heights, IL 60005, (847)228-9900

Amer. Soc. of Plastic Surgical Nurses **[15732]**, 500 Cummings Ctr., Ste. 4550, Beverly, MA 01915, (877)337-9315

Amer. Soc. for Plasticulture - Address unknown since 2011.

Amer. Soc. of Plumbing Engineers **[6779]**, 2980 S River Rd., Des Plaines, IL 60018, (847)296-0002

American Soc. of Plumbing Engineers Res. Foundation **[★6779]**

Amer. Soc. of Podiatric Medical Assistants **[16295]**, 1616 N 78th Ct., Elmwood Park, IL 60707, (888)882-7762

Amer. Soc. of Polar Philatelists **[22015]**, PO Box 39, Exton, PA 19341-0039

Amer. Soc. of Portrait Artists **[9225]**, PO Box 230216, Montgomery, AL 36106, (800)62-ASOPA

Amer. Soc. of Post Anesthesia Nurses **[★15731]**

Amer. Soc. of Post Anesthesia Nurses **[★15731]**

Amer. Soc. for Precision Engg. **[6780]**, PO Box 10826, Raleigh, NC 27605-0826, (919)839-8444

Amer. Soc. for the Prevention of Cruelty to Animals **[10911]**, 424 E 92nd St., New York, NY 10128-6804, (212)876-7700

Amer. Soc. of Preventive Oncology **[15920]**, Heidi Sahel, 330 WARF Bldg., 610 Walnut St., Madison, WI 53726, (608)263-9515

Amer. Soc. of Primatologists **[6131]**, Trinity Univ., Dept. of Psychology, One Trinity Pl., San Antonio, TX 78212, (210)999-7102

Amer. Soc. of Professional Appraisers - Defunct.

Amer. Soc. of Professional Biologists **[★6283]**

Amer. Soc. of Professional Communicators **[805]**, 4885 McKnight Rd., Ste. 325, Pittsburgh, PA 15237, (412)695-4009

Amer. Soc. of Professional Estimators **[7916]**, 2525 Perimeter Place Dr., Ste. 103, Nashville, TN 37214, (615)316-9200

Amer. Soc. of Professional Graphologists **[1641]**, 23 South Dr., Great Neck, NY 11021, (516)487-5287

Amer. Soc. for the Protection of Nature in Israel **[3998]**, 28 Arrandale Ave., Great Neck, NY 11024, (800)411-0966

Amer. Soc. for the Protection of Nature in Israel **[3998]**, 28 Arrandale Ave., Great Neck, NY 11024, (800)411-0966

Amer. Soc. for Psychical Res. **[7222]**, 5 W 73rd St., New York, NY 10023, (212)799-5050

Amer. Soc. of Psychoanalytic Physicians **[16354]**, 13528 Wisteria Dr., Germantown, MD 20874, (301)540-3197

Amer. Soc. for Psychoprophylaxis in Obstetrics **[★15885]**

Amer. Soc. for Psychoprophylaxis in Obstetrics **[★15885]**

Amer. Soc. for Public Admin. **[5904]**, 1301 Pennsylvania Ave. NW, Ste. 840, Washington, DC 20004-1735, (202)393-7878

Amer. Soc. for Public Admin. **[5904]**, 1301 Pennsylvania Ave. NW, Ste. 840, Washington, DC 20004-1735, (202)393-7878

Amer. Soc. for Quality **[7316]**, PO Box 3005, Milwaukee, WI 53201-3005, (414)272-8575

Amer. Soc. for Quality Control **[★7316]**

Amer. Soc. of Questioned Document Examiners **[5477]**, PO Box 18298, Long Beach, CA 90807, (562)901-3376

Amer. Soc. of Radiographers **[★15368]**

Amer. Soc. of Radiologic Technologists **[15368]**, 15000 Central Ave. SE, Albuquerque, NM 87123-3909, (505)298-4500

Amer. Soc. of Range Mgt. **[★4863]**

Amer. Soc. of Real Estate Counselors **[★3009]**

Amer. Soc. of Real Estate Counselors **[★3009]**

Amer. Soc. for Reconstructive Microsurgery **[16802]**, 20 N Michigan Ave., Ste. 700, Chicago, IL 60602, (312)456-9579

Amer. Soc. for Reformation Res. **[★10506]**

Amer. Soc. of Refrigerating Engineers **[★6778]**

Amer. Soc. of Refrigerating Engineers **[★6778]**

Amer. Soc. of Regional Anesthesia and Pain Medicine **[13739]**, 520 N Northwest Hwy., Park Ridge, IL 60068-2573, (847)825-7246

Amer. Soc. of Regional Anesthesia and Pain Medicine **[13739]**, 520 N Northwest Hwy., Park Ridge, IL 60068-2573, (847)825-7246

Amer. Soc. of Regional Anesthesia and Pain Practice **[★13739]**

Amer. Soc. of Regional Anesthesia and Pain Practice **[★13739]**

Amer. Soc. for Reproductive Medicine **[14530]**, 1209 Montgomery Hwy., Birmingham, AL 35216-2809, (205)978-5000

Amer. Soc. for Reproductive Medicine **[14530]**, 1209 Montgomery Hwy., Birmingham, AL 35216-2809, (205)978-5000

Amer. Soc. for Res. in Psychosomatic Problems **[★16443]**

Amer. Soc. of Safety Engineers **[7345]**, 1800 E Oakton St., Des Plaines, IL 60018, (847)699-2929

Amer. Soc. of Sanitary Engg. **[7349]**, 901 Canterbury Rd., Ste. A, Westlake, OH 44145, (440)835-3040

Amer. Soc. of Spine Radiology **[16528]**, 2210 Midwest Rd., Ste. 207, Oak Brook, IL 60523-8205, (630)574-0220

Amer. Soc. for Steel Treating **[★7090]**

Amer. Soc. for Steel Treating **[★7090]**

Amer. Soc. for Stereotactic and Functional Neurosurgery **[15684]**, Ohio State Univ., Dept. of Neurological Surgery, N1021 Doan Hall, 410 W 10th Ave., Columbus, OH 43210, (614)366-2420

A star before a book entry number signifies that the name is not listed separately, but is mentioned within the entry.

Amer. Soc. for Stereotactic and Functional Neurosurgery **[15684]**, Ohio State Univ., Dept. of Neurological Surgery, N1021 Doan Hall, 410 W 10th Ave., Columbus, OH 43210, (614)366-2420

Amer. Soc. for the Study of Ideological Belief Systems - Defunct.

Amer. Soc. for the Stud. of Orthodontics - Address unknown since 2011.

Amer. Soc. for the Stud. of Sterility **[★14530]**

Amer. Soc. for the Stud. of Sterility **[★14530]**

Amer. Soc. of Sugar Beet Technologists **[6870]**, 800 Grant St., Ste. 300, Denver, CO 80203-2944, (303)832-4460

Amer. Soc. of Sugar Cane Technologists **[4932]**, Ag-Center, Sturgis Hall No. 128, Baton Rouge, LA 70803, (225)578-6930

Amer. Soc. for the Support of Injured Survivors of Terrorism **[13359]**, 4371 Dinner Lake Blvd., Lake Wales, FL 33859-2135, (863)223-1818

Amer. Soc. for Surface Mining and Reclamation **[★5838]**

Amer. Soc. for Surgery of the Hand **[14681]**, 6300 N River Rd., Ste. 600, Rosemont, IL 60018, (847)384-8300

Amer. Soc. of Swedish Engineers - Address unknown since 2011.

Amer. Soc. of Sydney **[IO]**, Sydney, Australia

Amer. Soc. of Tax Problem Solvers **[6006]**, 2250 Wehrle Dr., Ste. 3, Williamsville, NY 14221, (716)630-1650

Amer. Soc. of Tech. Appraisers **[★2550]**

Amer. Soc. of Test Engineers **[7556]**, PO Box 389, Nutting Lake, MA 01865-0389

Amer. Soc. of Theatre Consultants **[857]**, Edgar L. Lustig, Sec./CFO, 12226 Mentz Hill Rd., St. Louis, MO 63128, (314)843-9218

Amer. Soc. of Theatre Consultants **[857]**, Edgar L. Lustig, Sec./CFO, 12226 Mentz Hill Rd., St. Louis, MO 63128, (314)843-9218

Amer. Soc. for Theatre Res. **[10565]**, PO Box 1798, Boulder, CO 80306-1798, (303)530-1838

Amer. Soc. of Therapeutic Radiologists **[★16529]**

Amer. Soc. for Therapeutic Radiology and Oncology **[16529]**, 8280 Willow Oaks Corporate Dr., Ste. 500, Fairfax, VA 22031, (703)502-1550

Amer. Soc. of Tool Engineers **[★7048]**

Amer. Soc. of Tool and Mfg. Engineers **[★7048]**

Amer. Soc. of Traffic and Trans. **[★3502]**

Amer. Soc. for Training and Development **[2893]**, 1640 King St., Box 1443, Alexandria, VA 22314-2746, (703)683-8100

Amer. Soc. for Training and Development **[★7786]**

Amer. Soc. for Training and Development **[2893]**, 1640 King St., Box 1443, Alexandria, VA 22314-2746, (703)683-8100

Amer. Soc. of Training Directors **[★7786]**

Amer. Soc. of Transplant Surgeons **[16900]**, 2461 S Clark St., Ste. 640, Arlington, VA 22202, (703)414-7870

Amer. Soc. of Transplantation **[16901]**, 15000 Commerce Pkwy., Ste. C, Mount Laurel, NJ 08054, (856)439-9986

Amer. Soc. of Trans. and Logistics **[3502]**, PO Box 3363, Warrenton, VA 20188, (202)580-7270

Amer. Soc. of Travel Agents **[3549]**, 1101 King St., Ste. 200, Alexandria, VA 22314

Amer. Soc. of Trial Consultants **[6247]**, 1941 Greenspring Dr., Timonium, MD 21093, (410)560-7949

Amer. Soc. of Tropical Medicine **[★16932]**

Amer. Soc. of Tropical Medicine and Hygiene **[16932]**, 111 Deer Lake Rd., Ste. 100, Deerfield, IL 60015, (847)480-9592

Amer. Soc. of Ultrasound Tech. Specialists **[★16678]**

Amer. Soc. of Univ. Composers **[★9506]**

Amer. Soc. of Utility Investors - Defunct.

Amer. Soc. for Value Inquiry - Address unknown since 2010.

Amer. Soc. of Veterinary Ethology **[★17011]**

Amer. Soc. of Veterinary Ophthalmology - Address unknown since 2011.

Amer. Soc. of Victimology **[13360]**, Washburn Univ., 1700 SW Coll. Ave., Topeka, KS 66621, (785)231-1010

Amer. Soc. for Virology **[6269]**, Univ. of Toledo Coll. of Medicine, Dept. of Medical Microbiology and Immunology, 3000 Arlington Ave., Mail Stop 1021, Toledo, OH 43614, (419)383-5173

Amer. Soc. of Wedding Professionals - Address unknown since 2011.

Amer. Soc. of Wireless Pioneers of the Seven Seas **[★3421]**

Amer. Soc. of Women Accountants **[9]**, 1760 Old Meadow Rd., Ste. 500, McLean, VA 22102, (703)506-3265

Amer. Soc. of Writers on Legal Subjects **[★5325]**

Amer. Soc. for X-Ray and Electron Diffraction **[★6588]**

Amer. Soc. of X-Ray Technicians **[★15368]**

Amer. Soc. of Zoologists **[★7638]**

Amer. Sociological Assn. **[7421]**, 1430 K St. NW, Ste. 600, Washington, DC 20005, (202)383-9005

Amer. Sociological Assn. I Comm. on the Status of Women in Sociology **[9589]**, 1430 K St. NW, Ste. 600, Washington, DC 20005, (202)383-9005

Amer. Sociological Assn. I Honors Prog. **[23738]**, 1430 K St. NW, Ste. 600, Washington, DC 20005, (202)383-9005

Amer. Sociological Soc. **[★7421]**

Amer. Sod Producers Assn. **[★4513]**

Amer. Sod Producers Assn. **[★4513]**

Amer. Software Users Group - Defunct.

Amer. Sokol Org. **[18971]**, 9126 Ogden Ave., Brookfield, IL 60513, (708)255-5397

Amer. Solar Action Plan **[7437]**, 52 Columbia St., Farmingdale, NY 11735

Amer. Solar Energy Assn. **[★7438]**

Amer. Solar Energy Soc. **[7438]**, 4760 Walnut St., Ste. 106, Boulder, CO 80301, (303)443-3130

Amer. Sommelier Assn. **[176]**, 580 Broadway, Ste. 716, New York, NY 10012, (212)226-6805

Amer. Sons of Liberty **[17265]**, 1142 S Diamond Bar Blvd., Ste. 305, Diamond Bar, CA 91765

American South
   Center for Southern Folklore **[9119]**
   Inst. for Southern Stud. **[9120]**
   Southern Historical Assn. **[9121]**

Amer. Southdown Breeders' Assn. **[4902]**, 100 Cornerstone Rd., Fredonia, TX 76842, (325)429-6226

Amer. Sovereignty Task Force **[17935]**, PO Box 6102, Woodland Hills, CA 91365

Amer. Soybean Assn. **[3949]**, 12125 Woodcrest Executive Dr., Ste. 100, St. Louis, MO 63141-5009, (314)576-1770

Amer. Spaniel Club **[21509]**, PO Box 4194, Frankfort, KY 40604-4194, (502)875-4489

Amer. Spaniel Club **[21509]**, PO Box 4194, Frankfort, KY 40604-4194, (502)875-4489

Amer. Spasmodic Torticollis Assn. **[★15623]**

Amer. Specialty Toy Retailing Assn. **[2174]**, 432 N Clark Ave., Ste. 401, Chicago, IL 60654, (312)222-0984

Amer. Speech Language Hearing Assn. **[16682]**, 2200 Res. Blvd., Rockville, MD 20850, (301)296-5700

Amer. Spelean Historical Assn. **[9750]**, 6304 Kaybro St., Laurel, MD 20707, (301)725-5877

Amer. Spice Trade Assn. **[1373]**, 2025 M St. NW, Ste. 800, Washington, DC 20036, (202)367-1127

Amer. Spinal Injury Assn. **[16697]**, 2020 Peachtree Rd. NW, Atlanta, GA 30309-1402, (404)355-9772

Amer. Spoon Collectors **[21299]**, PO Box 243, Rhinecliff, NY 12574, (845)876-0303

Amer. Spoon Collectors **[21299]**, PO Box 243, Rhinecliff, NY 12574, (845)876-0303

Amer. Sport Fishing Assn. **[★22570]**

Amer. Sportfishing Assn. **[22570]**, 225 Reinekers Ln., Ste. 420, Alexandria, VA 22314, (703)519-9691

Amer. Sportpony Registry **[★4560]**

Amer. Sports Assn. **[3322]**, 2 Sarah Ln., Monroe, NJ 08831, (732)446-8794

Amer. Sports Builders Assn. **[896]**, 8480 Baltimore Natl. Pike, No. 307, Ellicott City, MD 21043, (410)730-9595

Amer. Sports Education Inst./Boosters Clubs of America - Defunct.

Amer. Sports Inst. **[7998]**, PO Box 1837, Mill Valley, CA 94942, (415)383-5750

Amer. Sports Medicine Inst. **[16715]**, 2660 10th Ave. S, Ste. 505, Birmingham, AL 35205, (205)918-0000

Amer. Sportscasters Assn. **[480]**, 225 Broadway, Ste. 2030, New York, NY 10007, (212)227-8080

Amer. Spotted Poland China Record **[★4952]**

Amer. Sprocket Chain Mfrs. Assn. **[★1798]**

Amer. Staffing Assn. **[1142]**, 277 S Washington St., Ste. 200, Alexandria, VA 22314-3675, (703)253-2020

Amer. Stamp Dealers Assn. **[1727]**, 217-14 Northern Blvd., Ste. 205, Bayside, NY 11361, (718)224-2500

Amer. Standard Chinchilla Assn. **[★4837]**

Amer. Standard Chinchilla Rabbit Assn. **[★4837]**

Amer. Standard Chinchilla Rabbit Breeders Assn. **[4837]**, Patricia Gest, Sec., 1607 9th St. W, Palmetto, FL 34221, (941)729-1184

Amer. Standardbred Breeders Assn. - Defunct.

Amer. Standards Assn. **[★5982]**

Amer. attorneys in good standing. seeks to improve the administration of civil and criminal justice, and the availability of legal services to the public. Assn. I Amer. Lawyers Auxiliary **[5233]**, 1809 Vine St., Midland, MI 48642

Amer. Sta. Wagon Owners Assn. **[20995]**, PO Box 914, Matthews, NC 28106, (704)847-7510

Amer. Statistical Assn. **[7471]**, 732 N Washington St., Alexandria, VA 22314-1943, (703)684-1221

Amer. Steamship Historical Soc. **[★22158]**

Amer. Steamship and Tourist Agents Assn. **[★3549]**

Amer. Steel Treaters' Soc. **[★7090]**

Amer. Steel Treaters' Soc. **[★7090]**

Amer. String Teachers Assn. **[8643]**, 4155 Chain Bridge Rd., Fairfax, VA 22030, (703)279-2113

Amer. Stroke Assn. **[16728]**, Natl. Center, 7272 Greenville Ave., Dallas, TX 75231, (888)478-7653

Amer. Student Assn. of Community Colleges **[8912]**, 2250 N Univ. Pkwy., Ste. 4865, Provo, UT 84604-1510, (888)140-4993

American Student Coun. Association **[★8749]**

Amer. Student Dental Assn. **[7965]**, 211 E Chicago Ave., Ste. 700, Chicago, IL 60611-2687, (312)440-2795

Amer. Student Govt. Assn. **[8913]**, 412 NW 16th Ave., Gainesville, FL 32602, (352)373-6907

Amer. Student Hea. Assn. **[★14888]**

Amer. Stud. Assn. **[9109]**, 1120 19th St. NW, Ste. 301, Washington, DC 20036, (202)467-4783

Amer. Subcontractors Assn. **[897]**, 1004 Duke St., Alexandria, VA 22314-3588, (703)684-3450

Amer. Sudden Infant Death Syndrome Inst. **[16759]**, 528 Raven Way, Naples, FL 34110-1166, (239)431-5425

Amer. Suffolk Horse Assn. **[4557]**, Mary Margaret M. Read, Sec., 4240 Goehring Rd., Ledbetter, TX 78946-5004, (979)249-5795

Amer. Sugar Alliance **[1374]**, 2111 Wilson Blvd., Ste. 600, Arlington, VA 22201, (703)351-5055

Amer. Sugar Cane League of the U.S.A. **[4933]**, 206 E Bayou Rd., Thibodaux, LA 70301-2941, (985)448-3707

Amer. Sugarbeet Growers Assn. **[4934]**, 1156 15th St. NW, Ste. 1101, Washington, DC 20005-1704, (202)833-2398

Amer. Sulphur Horse Assn. **[21855]**, 1245 S 6300 W, Cedar City, UT 84720-9206

Amer. Sulphur Horse Assn. **[21855]**, 1245 S 6300 W, Cedar City, UT 84720-9206

Amer. Sunbathing Assn. **[★10340]**

Amer. Sunday School Union **[★20006]**

Amer. Sunrise **[12170]**, 454 Soledad, Ste. 300, San Antonio, TX 78205, (210)228-9693

Amer. Supplier Inst. **[7494]**, 30200 Telegraph Rd., Ste. 100, Bingham Farms, MI 48025, (734)464-1395

Amer. Supply Assn. **[2779]**, 222 Merchandise Mart Plz., Ste. 1400, Chicago, IL 60654, (312)464-0090

Amer. Supply and Machinery Mfrs. Assn. **[★1830]**

Amer. Support for Afghanistan **[10804]**, 3905 State St., Ste. 7-177, Santa Barbara, CA 93105, (805)455-4066

Amer. Surgical Assn. **[16805]**, 500 Cummings Ctr., Ste. 4550, Beverly, MA 01915, (978)927-8330

Amer. Surgical Trade Assn. **[★1683]**

Amer. Swan Boat Assn. **[22822]**, 312 Duff Ave., Wenonah, NJ 08090, (856)468-4646

Amer. Swedish Historical Museum **[10551]**, 1900 Pattison Ave., Philadelphia, PA 19145-5901, (215)389-1776

Reference to "IO" in place of a book number signifies that the association may be found in the 50th edition of International Organizations.

Amer. Swedish Inst. [10552], 2600 Park Ave., Minneapolis, MN 55407-1090, (612)871-4907

Amer. Swedish Inst. [10552], 2600 Park Ave., Minneapolis, MN 55407-1090, (612)871-4907

Amer. Swimming Coaches Assn. [23037], 5101 NW 21st Ave., Ste. 200, Fort Lauderdale, FL 33309, (954)563-4930

American-Swiss Assn. [★19250]

American-Swiss Assn. [★19250]

American-Swiss Found. [19250], 500 5th Ave., Ste. 1800, New York, NY 10110, (212)754-0130

American-Swiss Found. [19250], 500 5th Ave., Ste. 1800, New York, NY 10110, (212)754-0130

Amer. Symphony Orchestra League [★10234]

Amer. Synesthesia Assn. [15550], 515 Greenwich St., Ste. 304, New York, NY 10013

Amer. Syringomyelia and Chiari Alliance Proj. [15568], PO Box 1586, Longview, TX 75606-1586, (903)236-7079

Amer. Tai Chi Assn. [★16827]

Amer. Tai Chi and Qigong Assn. [16827], 2465 Centreville Rd., No. J17, Ste. 150, Herndon, VA 20171

Amer. Tapestry Alliance [9157], PO Box 28600, San Jose, CA 95159-8600

Amer. Tapestry Alliance [9157], PO Box 28600, San Jose, CA 95159-8600

Amer. Tarentaise Assn. [3900], 9150 N 216th St., Elkhorn, NE 68022, (402)639-9808

Amer. Tarot Assn. [22160], 2901 Richmond Rd., Ste. 130, No. 123, Lexington, KY 40509-1763, (800)372-1524

Amer. Tarot Assn. [22160], 2901 Richmond Rd., Ste. 130, No. 123, Lexington, KY 40509-1763, (800)372-1524

Amer. Task Force for Lebanon [19113], 1100 Connecticut Ave. NW, Ste. 1250, Washington, DC 20036, (202)223-9333

Amer. Task Force on Palestine [17936], 1634 Eye St. NW, Ste. 725, Washington, DC 20006, (202)887-0177

Amer. Tax Policy Inst. [18690], The Kellen Company, 529 14th St., Ste. 750, Washington, DC 20045, (202)637-3243

Amer. Tax Token Soc. [21966], Robert Frye, Ed., PO Box 14514, Lenexa, KS 66285-4514

Amer. Taxation Assn. [6007], 9201 Univ. City Blvd., Charlotte, NC 28223, (704)687-7696

Amer. Taxicab Assn. [★3537]

Amer. Taxicab Assn. [★3537]

Amer. Teachers Assn. [★23181]

Amer. Teachers Assn. of the Martial Arts [22724], 11990 Sunset Hill Rd., Penn Valley, CA 95946, (530)432-5588

Amer. Tech. Educ. Assn. [8964], North Dakota State Coll. of Sci., 800 N 6th St., Wahpeton, ND 58076-0002, (701)671-2240

Amer. Tech. Educ. Assn. [8964], North Dakota State Coll. of Sci., 800 N 6th St., Wahpeton, ND 58076-0002, (701)671-2240

Amer. Technion Soc. [8420], 55 E 59th St., New York, NY 10022-1112, (212)407-6300

Amer. Technion Soc. [★8420]

Amer. Technion Soc. [8420], 55 E 59th St., New York, NY 10022-1112, (212)407-6300

Amer. Teilhard Assn. [9347], 29 Spoke Dr., Woodbridge, CT 06525

Amer. Teilhard Assn. for the Future of Man [★9347]

Amer. Teilhard de Chardin Assn. [★9347]

Amer. TeleEdCommunications Alliance - Address unknown since 2010.

Amer. Telemarketing Assn. [★2387]

Amer. Telemedicine Assn. [16828], 1100 Connecticut Ave. NW, Ste. 540, Washington, DC 20036, (202)223-3333

Amer. Teleservices Assn. [2387], 3815 River Crossing Pkwy., Ste. 20, Indianapolis, IN 46240, (317)816-9336

Amer. TV Soc. [★494]

Amer. Telugu Assn. [9514], PO Box 4496, Naperville, IL 60567, (630)783-2250

Amer. Tennis Assn. [23053], 9701 Apollo Dr., Ste. 301, Largo, MD 20774, (240)487-5953

Amer. Tennis Indus. Fed. [★3319]

Amer. Textbook Coun. [8994], 1150 Park Ave., 12th Fl., New York, NY 10128, (212)289-5177

Amer. Textile Machinery Assn. [1802], 201 Park Washington Ct., Falls Church, VA 22046, (703)538-1789

Amer. Textile Mfrs. Inst. - Defunct.

Amer. TFP [19536], PO Box 341, Hanover, PA 17331, (717)225-7147

Amer. Theatre Arts for Youth [10566], 1429 Walnut St., Philadelphia, PA 19102, (215)563-3501

Amer. Theatre Assn. [★8999]

Amer. Theatre Critics Assn. [10567], Barry Gaines, Admin., 12809 Northern Sky NE, Albuquerque, NM 87111-8089, (505)856-2101

Amer. Theatre and Drama Soc. [10568], 61 Carey Rd., Needham, MA 02494

Amer. Theatre and Drama Soc. [10568], 61 Carey Rd., Needham, MA 02494

Amer. Theatre Organ Enthusiasts [★10157]

Amer. Theatre Organ Soc. [10157], PO Box 5327, Fullerton, CA 92838-0327, (714)773-4354

Amer. Theological Lib. Assn. [9958], 300 S Wacker Dr., Ste. 2100, Chicago, IL 60606-6701, (312)454-5100

Amer. Therapeutic Recreation Assn. [16559], 629 N Main St., Hattiesburg, MS 39401, (601)450-2872

Amer. Therapeutic Soc. [★16178]

Amer. Thoracic Soc. [16879], 25 Broadway, 18th Fl., New York, NY 10004, (212)315-8600

Amer. Thoracic Soc. [16879], 25 Broadway, 18th Fl., New York, NY 10004, (212)315-8600

Amer. Thoroughbred Breeders Assn. [★22667]

Amer. Thoroughbred Owners Assn. [★22667]

Amer. Thrombosis and Hemostasis Network [14962], 72 Treasure Ln., Riverwoods, IL 60015, (847)607-9479

Amer. Thyroid Assn. [16883], 6066 Leesburg Pike, Ste. 550, Falls Church, VA 22041, (703)998-8890

Amer. Tilapia Assn. [4378], PO Box 1647, Pine Bluff, AR 71613, (870)850-7900

Amer. Tinnitus Assn. [16683], PO Box 5, Portland, OR 97207-0005, (503)248-9985

Amer. Title Assn. [★2999]

Amer. Toll Bridge Assn. [★6032]

Amer. Toll Bridge Assn. [★6032]

Amer. Topical Assn. [22016], PO Box 8, Carterville, IL 62918-0008, (618)985-5100

Amer. Topical Assn., Americana Unit [22017], 17 Peckham Rd., Poughkeepsie, NY 12603

Amer. Topical Assn., Biology Unit [22018], 1401 Linmar Dr. NE, Cedar Rapids, IA 52402

Amer. Topical Assn. I Casey Jones Railroad Unit [22019], PO Box 18615, Rochester, NY 14618-8615

Amer. Torah Shelemah Comm. - Defunct.

Amer. Tort Reform Assn. [5649], 1101 Connecticut Ave. NW, Ste. 400, Washington, DC 20036, (202)682-1163

Amer. Tortoise Rescue [5026], 22631 Pacific Coast Hwy., Ste. 928, Malibu, CA 90265

Amer. Toy Fox Terrier Club [21510], Roger Pritchard, Corresponding Sec., 310 S Sooner Rd., Midwest City, OK 73110, (405)732-1873

Amer. Toy Manchester Terrier Club [★21499]

Amer. Track Racing Assn. [22476], PO Box 93245, Atlanta, GA 30377

Amer. Tract Soc. [19729], PO Box 462008, Garland, TX 75046-2008, (972)276-9408

Amer. Tractor Pullers Assn. [★23074]

Amer. Trade Assn. Executives [★262]

Amer. Trade Assn. Executives [★262]

Amer. Traffic Safety Control Devices Assn. [★3136]

Amer. Traffic Safety Services Assn. [3136], 15 Riverside Pkwy., Ste. 100, Fredericksburg, VA 22406-1077, (540)368-1701

Amer. Traffic Services Assn. [★3136]

Amer. Trails [23080], PO Box 491797, Redding, CA 96049-1797, (530)547-2060

Amer. Trails Network [★23080]

Amer. Train Dispatchers Assn. [23286], 4239 W 150th St., Cleveland, OH 44135, (216)251-7984

Amer. Trakehner Assn. [4558], 1536 W Church St., Newark, OH 43055, (740)344-1111

Amer. Trakehner Assn. [4558], 1536 W Church St., Newark, OH 43055, (740)344-1111

Amer. Transit Assn. [★3501]

Amer. Transit Assn. [★3501]

Amer. Translation and Interpreting Stud. Assn. [9015], Dr. Erik Angelone, Sec.-Treas., Kent State Univ., MCLS, Satterfield Hall 109, Kent, OH 44242, (330)672-3241

Amer. Translators Assn. [3496], 225 Reinekers Ln., Ste. 590, Alexandria, VA 22314-2875, (703)683-6100

Amer. Transplant Assn. [16902], 47 W Polk St., Ste. 100-133, Chicago, IL 60605, (800)494-4527

Amer. Trauma Soc. [16925], 7611 S Osborne Rd., Ste. 202, Upper Marlboro, MD 20772, (301)574-4300

Amer. Trial Lawyers Assn. [★6041]

Amer. Trote and Trocha Assn. [4559], 17050 SW 20th Avenue Rd., Ocala, FL 34473-8808, (352)454-5880

Amer. Trotting Assn. [★22672]

Amer. Truck Dealers [3503], 8400 Westpark Dr., McLean, VA 22102, (703)821-7230

Amer. Truck Historical Soc. [22195], PO Box 901611, Kansas City, MO 64190-1611, (816)891-9900

Amer. Trucking Associations [3504], 950 N Glebe Rd., Ste. 210, Arlington, VA 22203-4181, (703)838-1700

Amer. Trucking Associations I Tech. and Maintenance Coun. [3505], 950 N Glebe Rd., Ste. 210, Arlington, VA 22203-4181, (703)838-1763

Amer. Trudeau Soc. [★16879]

Amer. Trudeau Soc. [★16879]

Amer. Tube Assn. and Tube and Pipe Fabricators Assn., Intl. [★2759]

Amer. Tube Assn. and Tube and Pipe Fabricators Assn., Intl. [★2759]

Amer. Tunaboat Assn. - Defunct.

Amer. Tunis Sheep Breeders' Assn. [★4914]

American-Turkish Coun. [18737], 1111 14th St. NW, Ste. 1050, Washington, DC 20005, (202)783-0483

American-Turkish Coun. [18737], 1111 14th St. NW, Ste. 1050, Washington, DC 20005, (202)783-0483

American-Turkish Friendship Coun. [★18737]

Amer. Turkish Friendship Coun. [17937], 1266 W Paces Ferry Rd., No. 257, Atlanta, GA 30327-2306, (404)848-9600

American-Turkish Friendship Coun. [★18737]

Amer. Turkish Soc. [19257], 3 Dag Hammarskjold Plz., New York, NY 10017, (212)583-7614

Amer. Turkish Soc. [19257], 3 Dag Hammarskjold Plz., New York, NY 10017, (212)583-7614

Amer. Turnerbund [★22964]

Amer. Turners [22964], PO Box 4216, Louisville, KY 40204, (502)636-2395

Amer. Type Culture Coll. [6290], PO Box 1549, Manassas, VA 20108, (703)365-2700

Amer. Ukrainian Medical Soc. [★15437]

Amer. Ultrarunning Assn. [22862], 5825 W Dry Creek Rd., Healdsburg, CA 95448, (707)431-9898

Amer. Underground Assn. [★7484]

Amer. Underground Constr. Assn. [7484], 3001 Hennepin Ave. S, Ste. D202, Minneapolis, MN 55408, (212)465-5541

American-Underground-Space Assn. [★7484]

Amer. Union of Men [18105], PO Box 80131, Santa Barbara, CA 93117

Amer. Union of Swedish Singers - Defunct.

Amer. Universities Field Staff -Inst. of World Affairs [★8407]

Amer. Universities Field Staff -Inst. of World Affairs [★8407]

Amer. Univ. in Moscow [8343], 1800 Connecticut Ave. NW, Washington, DC 20009, (202)364-0200

Amer. Univ. in Moscow [8343], 1800 Connecticut Ave. NW, Washington, DC 20009, (202)364-0200

Amer. Urogynecologic Soc. [16941], 2025 M St. NW, Ste. 800, Washington, DC 20036-2422, (202)367-1167

Amer. Urological Assn. [16942], 1000 Corporate Blvd., Linthicum, MD 21090, (410)689-3700

Amer. Urological Assn. Found. [16943], 1000 Corporate Blvd., Linthicum, MD 21090, (410)689-3700

Amer. Uveitis Soc. [15944], Univ. of Miami, Bascom Palmer Eye Inst., Miller School of Medicine, Miami, FL 33101-6880, (305)326-6377

American-Uzbekistan Chamber of Commerce [23350], 1300 Connecticut Ave. NW, Ste. 501, Washington, DC 20036, (202)223-1770

A star before a book entry number signifies that the name is not listed separately, but is mentioned within the entry.

American-Uzbekistan Chamber of Commerce **[23350]**, 1300 Connecticut Ave. NW, Ste. 501, Washington, DC 20036, (202)223-1770

Amer. Vacuum Soc. **[★7592]**

Amer. Vaulting Assn. **[23108]**, 8205 Santa Monica Blvd., No. 1-288, West Hollywood, CA 90046, (323)654-0800

Amer. Vecturist Assn. **[22182]**, Richard Mallicote, Sec., 1039 Arbor Dr., Lakemont, GA 30552-1704

Amer. Vegan Soc. **[10623]**, 56 Dinshah Ln., PO Box 369, Malaga, NJ 08328, (856)694-2887

Amer. Venous Forum **[16957]**, 100 Cummings Ctr., Ste. 124A, Beverly, MA 01915, (978)927-7800

Amer. Veterans **[★20776]**

Amer. Veterans Alliance **[20775]**, 2260 SW 8th St., Ste. 304, Miami, FL 33135, (305)642-1113

Amer. Veterans Comm. - Defunct.

Amer. Veterans for Equal Rights **[12067]**, PO Box 2115, Decatur, GA 30031, (404)429-1316

Amer. Veterans of Foreign Ser. **[★20813]**

Amer. Veterans of Israel **[20671]**, 136 E 39th St., New York, NY 10016-0914, (212)685-8548

Amer. Veterans of World War II, Korea and Vietnam **[★20776]**

Amer. Veterinary Chiropractic Assn. **[17008]**, 442154 E 140 Rd., Bluejacket, OK 74333, (918)784-2231

Amer. Veterinary Dental Soc. **[17009]**, PO Box 803, Fayetteville, TN 37334, (931)438-0238

Amer. Veterinary Distributors Assn. **[2677]**, 2105 Laurel Bush Rd., Ste. 200, Bel Air, MD 21015, (443)640-1040

Amer. Veterinary Holistic Medical Assn. **[★17006]**

Amer. Veterinary Medical Assn. **[17010]**, 1931 N Meacham Rd., Ste. 100, Schaumburg, IL 60173-4340, (847)925-8070

American Veterinary Medical Assn. Found. **[★17010]**

Amer. Veterinary Medical Law Assn. **[5650]**, 1666 K St. NW, Ste. 260, Washington, DC 20006, (202)449-3818

Amer. Veterinary Soc. of Animal Behavior **[17011]**, 2715 N Monticello Ave., Chicago, IL 60647

Amer. Veterinary Soc. for the Stud. of Breeding Soundness **[★17039]**

Amer. Victims of Abortion - Address unknown since 2010.

Amer. Viewpoint **[★17250]**

Amer. Viewpoint Soc. **[★17250]**

Amer. Vineyard Found. **[5162]**, PO Box 5779, Napa, CA 94581-0779, (707)252-6911

Amer. Vinland Assn. **[19300]**, 537 Jones St., PMB 2154, San Francisco, CA 94102-2007

Amer. Viola Soc. **[10158]**, 14070 Proton Rd., Ste. 100, LB 9, Dallas, TX 75244-3601, (972)233-9107

Amer. Vision **[19537]**, PO Box 220, Powder Springs, GA 30127, (770)222-7266

Amer. Viticultural Area Assn. - Defunct.

Amer. Vocational Assn. **[★9039]**

Amer. Vocational Education Personnel Development Assn. - Defunct.

Amer. Vocational Educ. Res. Assn. **[★9040]**

Amer. Volkssport Assn. **[22965]**, 1001 Pat Booker Rd., Ste. 101, Universal City, TX 78148, (210)659-2112

Amer. Volleyball Coaches Assn. **[23110]**, 2365 Harrodsburg Rd., Ste. A325, Lexington, KY 40504, (859)226-4315

Amer. Voyager Assn. **[21918]**, 2015 Powers Dr., Lewiston, ID 83501, (208)746-3530

Amer. Voyager Assn. **[21918]**, 2015 Powers Dr., Lewiston, ID 83501, (208)746-3530

Amer. Wagyu Assn. **[3901]**, PO Box 547, Pullman, WA 99163, (509)335-0519

Amer. Wagyu Assn. **[3901]**, PO Box 547, Pullman, WA 99163, (509)335-0519

Amer. Waldensian Aid Soc. **[★20281]**

Amer. Waldensian Soc. **[20281]**, PO Box 398, Valdese, NC 28690, (828)874-3500

Amer. Walnut Mfrs. Assn. **[1495]**, 1007 N 725 W, West Lafayette, IN 47906-9431

Amer. War Mothers **[20701]**, 5415 Connecticut Ave. NW, Ste. L30, Washington, DC 20015, (202)362-0090

Amer. Warehouse Assn. **[★3621]**

Amer. Warehouse Assn. **[★3621]**

Amer. Warehousemen's Assn. **[★3621]**

Amer. Warehousemen's Assn. **[★3621]**

Amer. Warmblood Registry **[4560]**, PO Box 197, Carter, MT 59420, (406)734-5499

Amer. Warmblood Soc. **[4561]**, 24516 Taylor Rd., Lincoln, MO 65338, (660)668-3673

Amer. Watchmaker Inst. **[★2155]**

Amer. Watchmakers-Clockmakers Inst. **[2155]**, 701 Enterprise Dr., Harrison, OH 45030, (513)367-9800

Amer. Watchmakers Inst. **[★2155]**

Amer. Water Buffalo Assn. **[4689]**, PO Box 13533, Gainesville, FL 32604, (352)392-2643

Amer. Water Buffalo Assn. **[4689]**, PO Box 13533, Gainesville, FL 32604, (352)392-2643

Amer. Water Resources Assn. **[7598]**, PO Box 1626, Middleburg, VA 20118-1626, (540)687-8390

Amer. Water Resources Assn. **[7598]**, PO Box 1626, Middleburg, VA 20118-1626, (540)687-8390

Amer. Water Ski Assn. **[★23119]**

Amer. Water Ski Educational Found. **[23115]**, 1251 Holy Cow Rd., Polk City, FL 33868-8200, (863)324-2472

Amer. Water Spaniel Club **[21511]**, 6 Golfview Ln., Lake Barrington, IL 60010-1941, (847)277-7948

Amer. Water Spaniel Club **[21511]**, 6 Golfview Ln., Lake Barrington, IL 60010-1941, (847)277-7948

Amer. Water Works Assn. **[3647]**, 6666 W Quincy Ave., Denver, CO 80235-3098, (303)794-7711

Amer. Water Works Assn. **[3647]**, 6666 W Quincy Ave., Denver, CO 80235-3098, (303)794-7711

Amer. Watercolor Soc. **[9158]**, 47 5th Ave., New York, NY 10003, (212)206-8986

Amer. Watercraft Assn. **[23121]**, PO Box 1993, Ashburn, VA 20146-1993, (800)913-2921

Amer. Waterpark Assn. **[★1220]**

Amer. Waterpark Assn. **[★1220]**

Amer. Waterslager Soc. **[21215]**, 556 S Cactus Wren St., Gilbert, AZ 85296, (480)892-5464

Amer. Waterslager Soc. **[21215]**, 556 S Cactus Wren St., Gilbert, AZ 85296, (480)892-5464

Amer. Waterways Operators **[2351]**, 801 N Quincy St., Ste. 200, Arlington, VA 22203, (703)841-9300

Amer. Welara Pony Soc. **[4562]**, PO Box 3309, Landers, CA 92285-0309

Amer. Welara Pony Soc. **[4562]**, PO Box 3309, Landers, CA 92285-0309

Amer. Welding Soc. **[7617]**, 550 NW LeJeune Rd., Miami, FL 33126, (305)443-9353

Amer. Welding Soc. **[7617]**, 550 NW LeJeune Rd., Miami, FL 33126, (305)443-9353

American West

  Natl. Cowboy Symposium and Celebration | Amer. Cowboy Culture Assn. **[9122]**

  Natl. Cowboy and Western Heritage Museum **[9123]**

  Natl. Day of the Cowboy **[9124]**

  PEN Center USA **[10731]**

  Rodeo Historical Soc. **[9125]**

  Superstition Mountain Historical Soc. **[9126]**

  Traditional Cowboy Arts Assn. **[9127]**

  Western History Assn. **[9128]**

  Western Literature Assn. **[10052]**

  Westerners Intl. **[9129]**

Amer. West Overseas Assn. - Defunct.

Amer. Wheelchair Bowling Assn. **[22506]**, PO Box 69, Clover, VA 24534-0069, (434)454-2269

Amer. Whippet Club **[21512]**, Jackie Hubble, Membership Chair, 5472 Spoked Wheel Dr., Colorado Springs, CO 80918, (719)270-7037

Amer. White Shepherd Assn. **[21513]**, Cindy McCann, Membership Chair, PO Box 22, Stoutsville, OH 43154

Amer. Whitewater **[22836]**, PO Box 1540, Cullowhee, NC 28723-1540, (828)586-1930

Amer. Whitewater Affiliation **[★22836]**

Amer. Wholesale Marketers Assn. **[1375]**, 2750 Prosperity Ave., Ste. 530, Fairfax, VA 22031, (703)208-3358

Amer. Widows of World War II **[★20705]**

Amer. Wilderness Coalition **[5010]**, PO Box 2622, Durango, CO 81302-2622

Amer. Wildlands - Address unknown since 2011.

Amer. Wildlife Found. **[★5044]**

Amer. Wildlife Inst. **[★4164]**

Amer. Wildlife Inst. **[★5044]**

Amer. Willow Growers Network **[4968]**, 412 County Rd. 31, Norwich, NY 13815-3149, (607)336-9031

Amer. Wind Energy Assn. **[7621]**, 1501 M St. NW, Ste. 1000, Washington, DC 20005, (202)383-2500

Amer. Window Covering Mfrs. Assn. **[★2076]**

Amer. Wine Alliance for Res. and Educ. **[5163]**, PO Box 765, Washington, DC 20004-0765, (800)700-4050

Amer. Wine Soc. **[5164]**, PO Box 279, Englewood, OH 45322, (937)529-7800

Amer. Wire Cloth Inst. **[1803]**, 25 N Broadway, Tarrytown, NY 10591, (914)332-0040

Amer. Wire Producers Assn. **[1804]**, 801 N Fairfax St., Ste. 211, Alexandria, VA 22314-1757, (703)299-4434

Amer. Woman's Soc. of Certified Public Accountants **[10]**, 136 S Keowee St., Dayton, OH 45402, (937)222-1872

Amer. Women of Berkshire and Surrey **[IO]**, Virginia Water, United Kingdom

Amer. Women in Radio and TV **[★479]**

Amer. Women of Surrey **[IO]**, Cobham, United Kingdom

Amer. Women of Ticino **[IO]**, Carona, Switzerland

Amer. Women's Assn. of Hong Kong **[IO]**, Hong Kong, People's Republic of China

Amer. Women's Assn. of Kenya **[IO]**, Nairobi, Kenya

Amer. Women's Assn. of Rome **[IO]**, Rome, Italy

Amer. Women's Assn. of Vienna **[IO]**, Vienna, Austria

Amer. Woman's Auxiliary to the Royal Children's Hosp. Melbourne **[IO]**, Toorak, Australia

Amer. Women's Club of Amsterdam **[IO]**, Amsterdam, Netherlands

Amer. Women's Club of Basel **[IO]**, Basel, Switzerland

Amer. Women's Club of Brussels **[IO]**, Brussels, Belgium

Amer. Women's Club of Cairo **[IO]**, Cairo, Egypt

Amer. Women's Club of Central Scotland **[IO]**, Edinburgh, United Kingdom

Amer. Women's Club of Cologne **[IO]**, Cologne, Germany

Amer. Women's Club of Curacao **[IO]**, Curacao, Netherlands Antilles

Amer. Women's Club of Dublin **[IO]**, Dublin, Ireland

Amer. Women's Club of Dusseldorf **[IO]**, Dusseldorf, Germany

Amer. Women's Club in Finland **[IO]**, Helsinki, Finland

Amer. Women's Club of Gothenburg **[IO]**, Goteborg, Sweden

Amer. Women's Club of Hamburg **[IO]**, Hamburg, Germany

Amer. Women's Club of Lausanne **[IO]**, Lausanne, Switzerland

Amer. Women's Club of Liechtenstein **[IO]**, Schaan, Liechtenstein

Amer. Women's Club of London **[IO]**, London, United Kingdom

Amer. Women's Club of Luxembourg **[IO]**, Luxembourg, Luxembourg

Amer. Women's Club of Madrid **[IO]**, Madrid, Spain

Amer. Women's Club of Malmo **[IO]**, Malmo, Sweden

Amer. Women's Club of Oslo **[IO]**, Oslo, Norway

Amer. Women's Club of Perth **[IO]**, Perth, Australia

Amer. Women's Club of the Philippines **[IO]**, Makati City, Philippines

Amer. Women's Club in Stockholm **[IO]**, Stockholm, Sweden

Amer. Women's Club of the Taunus **[IO]**, Oberursel, Germany

Amer. Women's Club of Thailand **[IO]**, Bangkok, Thailand

Amer. Women's Club of The Hague **[IO]**, The Hague, Netherlands

Amer. Women's Club of Zurich **[IO]**, Zurich, Switzerland

Amer. Women's Gp. of Languedoc-Roussillon **[IO]**, Montpellier, France

Amer. Women's Gp. in Paris **[IO]**, Paris, France

Amer. Women's Hospitals **[★15043]**

Amer. Women's Hospitals Ser. **[★15043]**

Amer. Women's Hospitals Ser. Comm. of AMWA **[15043]**, 100 N 20th St., 4th Fl., Philadelphia, PA 19103, (215)320-3716

Reference to "IO" in place of a book number signifies that the association may be found in the 50th edition of International Organizations.

Amer. Women's Lawn Bowls Assn. [★22430]

Amer. Women's Org. of Greece [IO], Athens, Greece

Amer. Women's Physical Therapeutic Assn. [★16838]

Amer. Women's Self-Defense Assn. [★13031]

Amer. Women's Self-Defense Assn. [★13031]

Amer. Wood Chip Export Assn. - Defunct.

Amer. Wood Coun. [3699], 803 Sycolin Rd., Ste. 201, Leesburg, VA 20175, (202)463-2766

Amer. Wood-Preservers' Assn. [★1496]

Amer. Wood Preservers Inst. - Defunct.

Amer. Wood Protection Assn. [1496], PO Box 361784, Birmingham, AL 35236-1784, (205)733-4077

Amer. Wool Coun. [3435], Amer. Sheep Indus. Assn., 9785 Maroon Cir., Ste. 360, Englewood, CO 80112, (303)771-3500

Amer. Workers Party [★18784]

Amer. Workers Party [★18784]

Amer. Working Collie Assn. [21514], 26695 Snell Ln., Los Altos Hills, CA 94022, (650)941-1022

Amer. Working Dog Fed. [21515], 4282 Illinois Hwy. 17, Alpha, IL 61413, (309)334-3403

Amer. Working Malinois Assn. [20950], Dana Williams, Membership Chair, 20322 Riverside Dr., Newport Beach, CA 92660

Amer. World War II Orphans Network [10780], 5745 Lee Rd., Indianapolis, IN 46216, (540)310-0750

Amer. World War II Orphans Network [10780], 5745 Lee Rd., Indianapolis, IN 46216, (540)310-0750

Amer. Wrestling Coaches and Officials Assn. [★23132]

Amer. Wu Shu Soc. [22725], PO Box 5898, Long Island City, NY 11105-5898

Amer. Wu Shu Soc. [22725], PO Box 5898, Long Island City, NY 11105-5898

Amer. Y-Flyer Yacht Racing Assn. [22320], 7349 Scarborough Blvd., East Dr., Indianapolis, IN 46256-2052, (317)849-7588

Amer. Yachtmen's Assn. [★22324]

Amer. Yangjia Michuan Taijiquan Assn. [22726], PO Box 173, Grand Haven, MI 49417

Amer. Yankee Assn. [20882], PO Box 1531, Cameron Park, CA 95682-1531, (530)676-4292

Amer. Yarn Spinners Assn. [3436], 2500 Lowell Rd., Gastonia, NC 28053, (704)824-3522

Amer. Yo-Yo Assn. - Address unknown since 2011.

Amer. Yoga Assn. [10760], PO Box 19986, Sarasota, FL 34276

Amer. Yorkshire Club - Address unknown since 2010.

Amer. Youth Circus Org. [9482], PO Box 96, Temple, NH 03084, (603)654-5523

Amer. Youth Football [★22586]

Amer. Youth Football and Cheer [22586], 1000 S Point Dr., TH-9, Miami, FL 33139

Amer. Youth Found. [20303], 6357 Clayton Rd., St. Louis, MO 63117, (314)963-1321

Amer. Youth Horse Coun. [4563], 577 N Boyero Ave., Pueblo West, CO 81007, (719)594-9778

Amer. Youth Hostels [★12766]

Amer. Youth Hostels [★12766]

Amer. Youth Policy Forum [13507], 1836 Jefferson Pl. NW, Washington, DC 20036-2505, (202)775-9731

Amer. Youth Soccer Org. [22933], 19750 S Vermont Ave., Ste. 200, Torrance, CA 90502, (800)872-2976

Amer. Youth Understanding Diabetes Abroad [14345], 1700 N Moore St., Arlington, VA 22209, (703)527-3860

Amer. Youth Understanding Diabetes Abroad [14345], 1700 N Moore St., Arlington, VA 22209, (703)527-3860

Amer. Youth Work Center [13508], 1331 H St. NW, Ste. 701, Washington, DC 20005, (202)785-0764

Amer. Zinc Assn. [★2476]

Amer. Zionist Comm. for Public Affairs [★18114]

Amer. Zionist Coun. [★19844]

Amer. Zionist Emergency Coun. [★19844]

Amer. Zionist Fed. [★19844]

Amer. Zionist Movement [19844], 633 3rd Ave., New York, NY 10017, (212)318-6100

Amer. Zoo and Aquarium Assn. [★7633]

Americana Music Assn. [10159], PO Box 128077, Nashville, TN 37212, (615)386-6936

Americanism Educational League [17713], PO Box 1287, Monrovia, CA 91017, (626)357-7733

Americans Against Union Control of Govt. - Address unknown since 2011.

Americans Against World Empire [18776], 3220 N St. NW, Ste. 281, Washington, DC 20007

Americans for the Arts [9271], 1000 Vermont Ave. NW, 6th Fl., Washington, DC 20005, (202)371-2830

Americans to Ban Cloning [17266], 1100 H St. NW, Ste. 700, Washington, DC 20005, (202)347-6840

Americans for Better Care [★17458]

Americans for Better Care of the Dying [13315], 1700 Diagonal Rd., Ste. 635, Alexandria, VA 22314, (703)647-8505

Americans for Better Immigration - Address unknown since 2011.

Americans Care and Share [12805], PO Box 600370, San Diego, CA 92160, (619)481-3085

Americans Caring for Children Worldwide [★13186]

Americans Caring for Children Worldwide [★13186]

Americans for Civic Participation [★18390]

Americans for Constitutional Justice - Defunct.

Americans for Customary Weight and Measure [18673], PO Box 24A, Wiscasset, ME 04578

Americans for Decency [17434], 5830 W Thunderbird Rd., Ste. B8, No. 110, Glendale, AZ 85306

Americans for Democratic Action [18074], 1625 K St. NW, Ste. 210, Washington, DC 20006, (202)785-5980

Americans for Effective Law Enforcement [5381], PO Box 75401, Chicago, IL 60675-5401, (847)685-0700

Amers. for Energy Independence - Defunct.

Americans for Fair Electronic Commerce Transactions [17562], 111 G St. NW, Washington, DC 20001, (202)662-9200

Americans for Fairness in Lending - Defunct.

Americans for Free Choice in Medicine [15399], 1525 Superior Ave., Ste. 101, Newport Beach, CA 92663

Amers. for Generational Equity - Defunct.

Americans for Immigration Control [17879], PO Box 738, Monterey, VA 24465, (540)468-2023

Americans for Indian Opportunity [12559], 1001 Marquette Ave. NW, Albuquerque, NM 87102, (505)842-8677

Americans for Informed Democracy [17514], 218 D St. SE, 1st Fl., Washington, DC 20003, (202)544-9662

Americans for Intl. Aid [★11372]

Americans for Medical Progress [13758], 526 King St., Ste. 201, Alexandria, VA 22314, (703)836-9595

Americans for Medical Progress [★13758]

Americans for Middle East Understanding [18115], 475 Riverside Dr., Rm. 245, New York, NY 10115-0245, (212)870-2053

Americans for Middle East Understanding [18115], 475 Riverside Dr., Rm. 245, New York, NY 10115-0245, (212)870-2053

Amers. for the Natl. Voter Initiative Amendment - Defunct.

Americans for a Non-Violent Soc. - Defunct.

Americans for Nonsmokers' Rights [16672], 2530 San Pablo Ave., Ste. J, Berkeley, CA 94702, (510)841-3032

Americans Overseas

Amer. Citizens Abroad [18920]

Americans for Peace Now [18010], 1101 14th St. NW, 6th Fl., Washington, DC 20005, (202)408-9898

Americans for Peace Now [18010], 1101 14th St. NW, 6th Fl., Washington, DC 20005, (202)408-9898

Americans for Religious Liberty [17267], PO Box 6656, Silver Spring, MD 20916-6656, (301)260-2988

Americans for Safe Access [15260], 1322 Webster St., Ste. 402, Oakland, CA 94612, (510)251-1856

Americans for a Safe Israel [18116], 1751 2nd Ave., New York, NY 10128-5363, (800)235-3658

Americans for a Safe Israel [18116], 1751 2nd Ave., New York, NY 10128-5363, (800)235-3658

Americans for a Sound AIDS/HIV Policy [★10876]

Americans for a Sound AIDS/HIV Policy [★10876]

Americans for a Sound AIDS Policy [★10876]

Americans for a Sound AIDS Policy [★10876]

Americans for Tax Reform [18691], 722 12th St. NW, Ste. 400, Washington, DC 20005-3957, (202)785-0266

Americans for Trans. Mobility [6029], U.S. Chamber of Commerce, Congressional and Public Affairs, Trans. and Infrastructure, 1615 H St. NW, Washington, DC 20062, (202)463-5600

Americans for UNESCO - Address unknown since 2011.

Americans United for Life [12922], 655 15th St. NW, Ste. 410, Washington, DC 20005, (202)289-1478

Amers. United to Outlaw Fluoridation - Defunct.

Americans United for Separation of Church and State [19607], 1301 K St. NW, Ste. 850, E Tower, Washington, DC 20005, (202)466-3234

Americans With Disabilities Act - Address unknown since 2011.

AmeriCares Found. [12806], 88 Hamilton Ave., Stamford, CT 06902, (203)658-9500

Americas

Americas Soc. [17178]

Americas Soc. [17178]

Coun. on Hemispheric Affairs [17179]

Coun. on Hemispheric Affairs [17179]

North Amer. Cong. on Latin Am. [17180]

Org. of Amer. States [17181]

Org. of Amer. States [17181]

Pan Amer. Development Found. [17182]

Pan Amer. Development Found. [17182]

Pan-American Fed. for Info. Tech. in Agriculture [6106]

Partners of the Americas [17183]

Partners of the Americas [17183]

Salvadoran Amer. Natl. Network [18979]

Westerners Intl. [9129]

America's Angel [11996], PO Box 3124, San Diego, CA 92103

Americas Assn. of Cooperative/Mutual Insurance Societies [★1985]

America's Blood Centers [13849], 725 15th St. NW, Ste. 700, Washington, DC 20005, (202)393-5725

America's Charities [12048], 14150 Newbrook Dr., Ste. 110, Chantilly, VA 20151, (800)458-9505

America's Children Hunger Network [11189], 25263 N 67th Dr., Peoria, AZ 85383, (623)376-0727

America's Children Hunger Network [11189], 25263 N 67th Dr., Peoria, AZ 85383, (623)376-0727

America's Corvette Club [20996], PO Box 250754, West Bloomfield, MI 48325, (248)208-0323

America's Development Found. [17515], 101 N Union St., Ste. 200, Alexandria, VA 22314, (703)836-2717

America's Edge [17599], 1212 New York Ave. NW, Ste. 300, Washington, DC 20005, (202)408-9284

America's Found. [20372], PO Box 434, Downingtown, PA 19335-0434, (610)825-7033

America's Fund for Afghan Children - Address unknown since 2010.

America's Future [17714], 7800 Bonhomme Ave., St. Louis, MO 63105, (314)725-6003

America's Hea. Insurance Plans [14852], 601 Pennsylvania Ave. NW, Ste. 500, Washington, DC 20004, (202)778-3200

America's Heroes of Freedom [20347], PO Box 18984, Washington, DC 20036-8984

America's Natural Gas Alliance [2641], 701 Eighth St. NW, Ste. 800, Washington, DC 20001, (202)789-2642

America's Nazi Party [★18784]

America's Nazi Party [★18784]

America's Promise - The Alliance for Youth [13509], 1110 Vermont Ave. NW, Ste. 900, Washington, DC 20005, (202)657-0600

America's Second Harvest [★12272]

America's Ser. Commissions [★5903]

Americas Soc. [17178], 680 Park Ave., New York, NY 10021, (212)249-8950

Americas Soc. [17178], 680 Park Ave., New York, NY 10021, (212)249-8950

America's Survival, Inc. [17268], PO Box 146, Owings, MD 20736, (301)855-2679

AmeriCorps VISTA [13381], 1201 New York Ave. NW, Washington, DC 20005, (202)606-5000

A star before a book entry number signifies that the name is not listed separately, but is mentioned within the entry.

AmeriFace [14191], PO Box 751112, Las Vegas, NV 89136, (702)769-9264

AmeriGhana [12312], 11000 W McNichols Rd., No. 100, Detroit, MI 48221, (866)417-2494

AmeriGhana [12312], 11000 W McNichols Rd., No. 100, Detroit, MI 48221, (866)417-2494

Amerika Katolika Esperanto-Societo - Defunct.

Amerikaanse Kamer van Koophandel [★IO]

Amerikos Lietuviu Taryba [★19115]

Amerind Found. [6132], PO Box 400, Dragoon, AZ 85609, (520)586-3666

Amerind Found. [6132], PO Box 400, Dragoon, AZ 85609, (520)586-3666

Amerindian Peoples Assn. [IO], Georgetown, Guyana

AMF Alcort Sailfish-Sunfish Class [★22362]

AMF Alcort Sailfish-Sunfish Class [★22362]

AMF Intl. [★19758]

AMF Intl. [★19758]

AMF Sunfish Racing Class Assn. [★22362]

AMF Sunfish Racing Class Assn. [★22362]

AMG Intl. [20008], 6815 Shallowford Rd., Chattanooga, TN 37421, (423)894-6060

AMG Intl. [20008], 6815 Shallowford Rd., Chattanooga, TN 37421, (423)894-6060

Amici della Terra - Italia [★IO]

Amici Thomae Mori [★IO]

Amigos de las Americas [13382], 5618 Star Ln., Houston, TX 77057, (713)782-5290

Amigos de las Americas [13382], 5618 Star Ln., Houston, TX 77057, (713)782-5290

AMIGOS Bibliographic Coun. [★9959]

Amigos for Christ [12574], 1845 S Lee Ct., Ste. A, Buford, GA 30518, (770)614-9250

AMIGOS Lib. Services [9959], 14400 Midway Rd., Dallas, TX 75244-3509, (972)851-8000

Amigos da Terra - Brasil [★IO]

Amigos de la Tierra - Argentina [★IO]

Amigos de la Tierra El Salvador [★IO]

Amigos de la Tierra - Espana [★IO]

Amigos de la Tierra - Uruguay [★IO]

Amis de la Reliure d'Art [★IO]

Amis de la Terre [★IO]

Amis de la Terre - Togo [★IO]

Amish

Natl. Comm. for Amish Religious Freedom [19290]

AMISTAD Am. [8253], 746 Chapel St., Ste. 300, New Haven, CT 06510, (203)495-1839

AMIT [19845], 817 Broadway, New York, NY 10003, (212)477-4720

Amizade Global Service-Learning and Volunteer Programs [13383], 4 Smithfield St., 7th Fl., Pittsburgh, PA 15222, (412)586-4986

Amizade Global Service-Learning and Volunteer Programs [13383], 4 Smithfield St., 7th Fl., Pittsburgh, PA 15222, (412)586-4986

Amman Imman: Water is Life [13413], 7700 Old Georgetown Rd., Ste. 550, Bethesda, MD 20814

Amman World Trade Center [IO], Amman, Jordan

Amnesty Intl. - Algeria [IO], Algiers, Algeria

Amnesty Intl. - Argentina [IO], Buenos Aires, Argentina

Amnesty Intl. - Australia, NSW Br. [IO], Broadway, Australia

Amnesty Intl. - Austria [IO], Vienna, Austria

Amnesty Intl. - Bahamas [IO], Nassau, Bahamas

Amnesty Intl. - Barbados [IO], Bridgetown, Barbados

Amnesty Intl. - Benin [IO], Cotonou, Benin

Amnesty Intl. - Bermuda [IO], Hamilton, Bermuda

Amnesty Intl. - Burkina Faso [IO], Ouagadougou, Burkina Faso

Amnesty Intl. - Canadian Sect. [IO], Ottawa, ON, Canada

Amnesty Intl. - Chile [IO], Santiago, Chile

Amnesty Intl. - Cote d'Ivoire [IO], Abidjan, Cote d'Ivoire

Amnesty Intl. - Croatia [IO], Zagreb, Croatia

Amnesty Intl. - Czech Republic [IO], Prague, Czech Republic

Amnesty Intl. - Danish Sect. [IO], Copenhagen, Denmark

Amnesty Intl. - European Union Assn. [IO], Brussels, Belgium

Amnesty Intl. - Faroe Islands [IO], Torshavn, Faroe Islands

Amnesty Intl. - Finnish Sect. [IO], Helsinki, Finland

Amnesty Intl. - France [IO], Paris, France

Amnesty Intl. - Hong Kong [IO], Hong Kong, People's Republic of China

Amnesty Intl. - Hungary [IO], Budapest, Hungary

Amnesty Intl. - Icelandic Sect. [IO], Reykjavik, Iceland

Amnesty Intl. - Intl. Secretariat [IO], London, United Kingdom

Amnesty Intl. - Ireland [IO], Dublin, Ireland

Amnesty Intl. - Israel Sect. [IO], Tel Aviv, Israel

Amnesty Intl. - Italy [IO], Rome, Italy

Amnesty Intl. - Jamaica [IO], Kingston, Jamaica

Amnesty Intl. - Japan [IO], Tokyo, Japan

Amnesty Intl. - Luxembourg [IO], Luxembourg, Luxembourg

Amnesty Intl. - Malaysia [IO], Petaling Jaya, Malaysia

Amnesty Intl. - Mali [IO], Bamako, Mali

Amnesty Intl. - Mexican Sect. [IO], Mexico City, Mexico

Amnesty Intl. - Mongolia [IO], Ulan Bator, Mongolia

Amnesty Intl. - New Zealand Sect. [IO], Auckland, New Zealand

Amnesty Intl. Norge [★IO]

Amnesty Intl. - Norway [IO], Oslo, Norway

Amnesty Intl. Osterreich [★IO]

Amnesty Intl. - Paraguay [IO], Asuncion, Paraguay

Amnesty Intl. - Peru [IO], Lima, Peru

Amnesty Intl. - Philippines [IO], Quezon City, Philippines

Amnesty Intl. - Poland [IO], Warsaw, Poland

Amnesty Intl. - Puerto Rico [17811], 54 Calle Robles, Ste. 6, Rio Piedras, PR 00925, (787)763-8318

Amnesty Intl. - Puerto Rico [17811], 54 Calle Robles, Ste. 6, Rio Piedras, PR 00925, (787)763-8318

Amnesty Intl. - Russia [IO], Moscow, Russia

Amnesty Intl. Sect. Francaise [★IO]

Amnesty Intl. - Senegal [IO], Dakar, Senegal

Amnesty Intl. - Sierra Leone [IO], Freetown, Sierra Leone

Amnesty Intl. - South Africa [IO], Johannesburg, Republic of South Africa

Amnesty Intl. - Spain [IO], Madrid, Spain

Amnesty Intl., Suomen Osasto [★IO]

Amnesty Intl. - Swiss Sect. [IO], Bern, Switzerland

Amnesty Intl. - Taiwan [IO], Taipei, Taiwan

Amnesty Intl. - Thailand [IO], Bangkok, Thailand

Amnesty Intl. - Tunisia [IO], Tunis, Tunisia

Amnesty Intl. - Turkey [IO], Istanbul, Turkey

Amnesty Intl. - Ukraine [IO], Kiev, Ukraine

Amnesty Intl. - United Kingdom [IO], London, United Kingdom

Amnesty Intl. - United Kingdom Scottish Off. [IO], Edinburgh, United Kingdom

Amnesty Intl. of the U.S.A. [17812], 5 Penn Plz., New York, NY 10001, (212)807-8400

Amnesty Intl. of the U.S.A. [17812], 5 Penn Plz., New York, NY 10001, (212)807-8400

Amnesty Intl. - Zimbabwe [IO], Harare, Zimbabwe

Amnesty for Women [IO], Hamburg, Germany

Amnet - Defunct.

Amnistia Internacional [★IO]

Amnistia Internacional Argentina [★IO]

Amnistia Internacional - Chile [★IO]

Amnistia Internacional - Paraguay [★IO]

Amnistia Internacional, Seccion Mexicana [★IO]

AMOA Natl. Dart Assn. [22498], 9100 Purdue Rd., Ste. 200, Indianapolis, IN 46268, (317)387-1299

AMOA Natl. Dart Assn. [22498], 9100 Purdue Rd., Ste. 200, Indianapolis, IN 46268, (317)387-1299

Amphibian Veterinarians; Assn. of Reptilian and [17014]

Amphibians and Reptiles; Soc. for the Stud. of [6941]

Amputation Found; Natl. [11809]

Amputee Coalition of Am. [14360], 900 E Hill Ave., Ste. 205, Knoxville, TN 37915-2566, (865)524-8772

Amputee Found; Amer. [11756]

Amputee Hockey Assn; Amer. [22961]

Amputee Network; Intl. Child [11796]

Amputee Network; Intl. Child [11796]

Amputee Shoe and Glove Exchange - Defunct.

Amputees in Motion [★11759]

Amputees in Motion [★11759]

Amputees in Motion Intl. [11759], PO Box 19236, San Diego, CA 92159, (858)454-9300

Amputees in Motion Intl. [11759], PO Box 19236, San Diego, CA 92159, (858)454-9300

AMURT [IO], Brussels, Belgium

Amusement Indus. Mfrs. and Suppliers Intl. [1187], 3026 S Orange, Santa Ana, CA 92707, (714)425-5747

Amusement Indus. Mfrs. and Suppliers Intl. [1187], 3026 S Orange, Santa Ana, CA 92707, (714)425-5747

Amusement and Music Operators Assn. [1188], 600 Spring Hill Ring Rd., Ste. 111, West Dundee, IL 60118, (847)428-7699

Amusement Parks

Amer. Coaster Enthusiasts [20944]

Darkride and Funhouse Enthusiasts [20945]

Natl. Amusement Park Historical Assn. [20946]

AMVETS [20776], 4647 Forbes Blvd., Lanham, MD 20706-4380, (301)459-9600

Amy Beth Fan Club [23813], Peridot Records, PO Box 8846, Cranston, RI 02920, (401)785-2677

Amyloidosis Found. [14372], 7151 N Main St., Ste. 2, Clarkston, MI 48346, (248)922-9610

Amyloidosis Support Groups [14373], Muriel Finkel, Pres., 232 Orchard Dr., Wood Dale, IL 60191, (847)350-7540

Amyloidosis Support Groups [14373], Muriel Finkel, Pres., 232 Orchard Dr., Wood Dale, IL 60191, (847)350-7540

Amyotrophic Lateral Sclerosis Assn. [15569], 1275 K St. NW, Ste. 1050, Washington, DC 20005, (818)880-9007

Amyotrophic Lateral Sclerosis Soc. of Am. [★15569]

Amyotrophic Lateral Sclerosis Soc. of Canada [IO], Markham, ON, Canada

Amy's Doll Lover's Club [21687], 399 Winfield Rd., Rochester, NY 14622, (585)266-4956

Anabaptist Assn. of Australia and New Zealand [IO], Mona Vale, Australia

Anabaptist Sociology and Anthropology Assn. - Address unknown since 2011.

Anaerobe Soc. of the Americas [6291], PO Box 452058, Los Angeles, CA 90045, (310)216-9265

Anaerobe Soc. of the Americas [6291], PO Box 452058, Los Angeles, CA 90045, (310)216-9265

Anaesthetic Res. Soc. [IO], Nottingham, United Kingdom

Anahata Intl. [13662], 1450 P St. NW, Washington, DC 20005

Analystes des mineraux canadiens [★IO]

Analytical Lab. Managers Assn. [★7021]

Analytical and Life Sci. Systems Assn. [7358], 500 Montgomery St., Ste. 400, Alexandria, VA 22314, (703)647-6214

ANAND Soc. Intl. - Address unknown since 2011.

Ananda Marga [20298], 97-38 42nd Ave., 1F, Corona, NY 11368, (718)898-1603

Ananda Marga [IO], New Delhi, India

Ananda Marga Pracarka Samgha - Berlin Sector [IO], Mainz, Germany

Ananda Marga Universal Relief Team - Brazil [IO], Sao Paulo, Brazil

Ananda Marga Yoga Soc. [★20298]

Ananda Yoga Teachers Assn. [10761], The Expanding Light, 14618 Tyler Foote Rd., Nevada City, CA 95959, (530)478-7518

Anaphylaxis Australia Inc. [IO], Asquith, Australia

Anaphylaxis Canada [IO], Toronto, ON, Canada

Anaphylaxis Network; Food Allergy and [13639]

AnarchismAnarchismVoluntary Cooperation Movement

Workers Solidarity Alliance [17184]

Anatomical Soc. [IO], Erlangen, Germany

Anatomical Soc. of Great Britain and Ireland [IO], London, United Kingdom

Anatomical Soc. of Paris [IO], Paris, France

Anatomische Gesellschaft [★IO]

Anatomy

Amer. Assn. of Anatomists [13730]

Amer. Assn. of Clinical Anatomists [13731]AnatomyEuropean Fed. for Experimental Morphology Human Anatomy and Physiology Soc. [13732]

Ancestry Res. Club - Defunct.

Reference to "IO" in place of a book number signifies that the association may be found in the 50th edition of International Organizations.

Ancient Accepted Scottish Rite of Free-Masonry, Northern Masonic Jurisdiction | Supreme Coun. **[19124]**, PO Box 519, Lexington, MA 02420-0519, (781)862-4410

Ancient and Accepted Scottish Rite of Free Masonry, Southern Jurisdiction | Supreme Coun. 33rd Degree **[19125]**, 1733 16th St. NW, Washington, DC 20009-3103, (202)232-3579

Ancient Astronaut Soc. - Defunct.

Ancient Coin Collectors Guild **[21967]**, PO Box 911, Gainesville, MO 65655, (417)679-2142

Ancient Coins for Educ. **[8685]**, PO Box 90193, Springfield, MA 01139

Ancient Egypt and Middle East Soc. **[IO]**, Skegness, United Kingdom

Ancient Egyptian Arabic Order Nobles of the Mystic Shrine **[19126]**, 2239 Democrat Rd., Memphis, TN 38132-1802, (901)395-0150

Ancient Egyptian Order of Sciots - Address unknown since 2010.

Ancient Forest Intl. **[3999]**, PO Box 1850, Redway, CA 95560, (707)923-4475

Ancient Forest Intl. **[3999]**, PO Box 1850, Redway, CA 95560, (707)923-4475

Ancient and Honorable Artillery Company of Massachusetts **[20702]**, Armory Faneuil Hall, 4th Fl., Boston, MA 02109, (617)227-1638

Ancient Monuments Soc. **[IO]**, London, United Kingdom

Ancient Mystic Order of Bagmen of Bagdad Imperial Guild - Defunct.

Ancient Mystical Order Rosae Crucis **[★19213]**

Ancient Order of Foresters of the Pacific Coast Jurisdiction - Defunct.

Ancient Order of Gleaners **[★19047]**

Ancient Order of Hibernians in Am. **[19071]**, 31 Logan St., Auburn, NY 13021-3925, (315)252-3895

Ancient Order United Workmen - Defunct.

Ancients **[★20702]**

And Justice for All **[18639]**, PO Box 53079, Washington, DC 20009, (202)547-0508

Andean
  Inst. of Andean Stud. **[9130]**
  Inst. of Andean Stud. **[9130]**

Andean Commn. of Jurists **[IO]**, Lima, Peru

Andean Community - Gen. Secretariat **[IO]**, Lima, Peru

Andean Hea. and Development **[15145]**, 2039 Winnebago St., No. 8, Madison, WI 53704, (619)788-6833

Andean Info. Network **[IO]**, Cochabamba, Bolivia

Anderson Assn. **[IO]**, Merrow, United Kingdom

Andolan - Organizing South Asian Workers **[12516]**, PO Box 720364, Jackson Heights, NY 11372, (718)426-2774

Andorra Chamber of Commerce, Indus. and Services **[IO]**, Andorra la Vella, Andorra

Andorra Natl. Comm. for UNICEF **[IO]**, Andorra la Vella, Andorra

Andorra Radioamateur Union **[IO]**, Andorra la Vella, Andorra

Andorra Squash Rackets Assn. **[IO]**, Andorra la Vella, Andorra

Andorran Coll. of Dentists **[IO]**, Andorra la Vella, Andorra

Andre Agassi Fan Club **[IO]**, Reading, United Kingdom

Andrew Furuseth Found. for Maritime Res. **[★3273]**

Andrew Jackson Papers Proj. **[★10676]**

Andrew W. Mellon Found. **[10363]**, 140 E 62nd St., New York, NY 10065-8124, (212)838-8400

Androgen Insensitivity Syndrome Support Gp. - U.S.A. **[14587]**, PO Box 2148, Duncan, OK 73534-2148

Andrology; Amer. Soc. of **[16940]**

The Andy Griffith Show Rerun Watchers Club **[23917]**, 9 Music Sq. S, PMB 146, Nashville, TN 37203-3286, (336)786-1604

Anemia Action Coun; Natl. **[14971]**

Anemia Found; Cooley's **[14966]**

Anemia and MDS Intl. Found; Aplastic **[14963]**

Anemia and MDS Intl. Found; Aplastic **[14963]**

Anemia Res. Fund; Fanconi **[14596]**

Anesthesia Awareness Campaign **[13740]**, 1658 Parkcrest Cir., No. 200, Reston, VA 20190-4946, (703)437-7327

Anesthesia Educational Programs; Coun. on Accreditation of Nurse **[8580]**

Anesthesia History Assn. **[13741]**, 201 Delafield Rd., Pittsburgh, PA 15215, (412)559-7010

Anesthesia Nurses; Amer. Soc. of Peri **[15731]**

Anesthesia Overseas **[★16044]**

Anesthesia Overseas **[★16044]**

Anesthesia Patient Safety Found. **[13742]**, 8007 S Meridian St., Bldg. 1, Ste. 2, Indianapolis, IN 46217-2922

Anesthesiologists; Amer. Coll. of Veterinary **[16997]**

Anesthesiology
  Amer. Acad. of Anesthesiologist Assistants **[13733]**
  Amer. Bd. of Anesthesiology **[13734]**
  Amer. Osteopathic Coll. of Anesthesiologists **[13735]**
  Amer. Soc. for Advancement of Anesthesia and Sedation in Dentistry **[13736]**
  Amer. Soc. for Advancement of Anesthesia and Sedation in Dentistry **[13736]**
  Amer. Soc. of Anesthesiologists **[13737]**
  Amer. Soc. of Critical Care Anesthesiologists **[13738]**
  Amer. Soc. of Regional Anesthesia and Pain Medicine **[13739]**
  Amer. Soc. of Regional Anesthesia and Pain Medicine **[13739]**
  Anesthesia Awareness Campaign **[13740]**
  Anesthesia History Assn. **[13741]**
  Anesthesia Patient Safety Found. **[13742]**
  Assn. of Univ. Anesthesiologists **[13743]**
  Assn. of Veterans Affairs Anesthesiologists **[13744]**
  Chinese Amer. Soc. Of Anesthesiology **[13745]**
  Congenital Cardiac Anesthesia Soc. **[13746]**
  Congenital Cardiac Anesthesia Soc. **[13746]**
  Dannemiller, Inc. **[13747]**
  European Soc. for Computing and Tech. in Anaesthesia and Intensive Care **[10425]**
  Global Partners in Anesthesia and Surgery **[16814]**
  Intl. Anesthesia Res. Soc. **[13748]**
  Intl. Anesthesia Res. Soc. **[13748]**
  Intl. Soc. for Anaesthetic Pharmacology **[13749]**
  Intl. Soc. for Anaesthetic Pharmacology **[13749]**
  Intl. Trauma Anesthesia and Critical Care Soc. **[13750]**
  Intl. Trauma Anesthesia and Critical Care Soc. **[13750]**
  Navy Anesthesia Soc. **[13751]**
  Soc. for Ambulatory Anesthesia **[13752]**
  Soc. of Cardiovascular Anesthesiologists **[13753]**
  Soc. of Cardiovascular Anesthesiologists **[13753]**
  Soc. for Educ. in Anesthesia **[13754]**
  Soc. for Pediatric Anesthesia **[13755]**
  Soc. for Tech. in Anesthesia **[13756]**
  Soc. for Tech. in Anesthesia **[13756]**

Anesthesiology; Amer. Dental Soc. of **[14264]**

Anesthetists; Amer. Assn. of Nurse **[15711]**

Aneurysm Outreach Inc. **[14699]**, 17222 Hwy. 929, Prairieville, LA 70769, (225)622-1577

Angel Capital Assn. **[2128]**, 10977 Granada Ln., Ste. 103, Overland Park, KS 66211, (913)894-4700

Angel Covers **[11190]**, PO Box 6891, Broomfield, CO 80021, (303)947-5215

Angel Flight Am. **[★14447]**

Angel Flight West **[12444]**, 3161 Donald Douglas Loop S, Santa Monica, CA 90405, (310)390-2958

Angel Harps **[16454]**, PO Box 704, Wildomar, CA 92595, (951)246-0320

The Angel Planes **[★14454]**

Angel Wing Flights **[12445]**, PO Box 2926, Canyon Country, CA 91386-2926, (310)598-6294

Angela Thirkell Soc. **[9348]**, PO Box 7109, San Diego, CA 92167

Angelcare **[11448]**, PO Box 600370, San Diego, CA 92160-0370, (888)264-5227

Angelcare **[11448]**, PO Box 600370, San Diego, CA 92160-0370, (888)264-5227

Angeles que Aguardan **[★IO]**

Angelman Syndrome Assn. **[IO]**, Sutherland, Australia

Angelman Syndrome Found. **[16763]**, 4255 Westbrook Dr., Ste. 219, Aurora, IL 60504, (630)978-4245

Angelo State Univ. Alumni Assn. **[18851]**, ASU Sta. No. 11049, San Angelo, TX 76909, (325)942-2122

Angelo State Univ. Ex-Students Assn. **[★18851]**

The Angels **[★20351]**

Angels In Waiting **[11171]**, PO Box 1221, Blue Jay, CA 92317, (800)974-4274

Angels 'n Camouflage - Address unknown since 2011.

Angels With Special Needs **[11760]**, PO Box 25555, Columbia, SC 29224-5555, (803)419-5136

Angioma Alliance **[15570]**, 520 W 21st St., Ste. G2-411, Norfolk, VA 23517-1950, (571)306-2873

Angioma Alliance **[15570]**, 520 W 21st St., Ste. G2-411, Norfolk, VA 23517-1950, (571)306-2873

Anglers for Conservation **[4000]**, PO Box 373257, Satellite Beach, FL 32937, (321)446-8240

Anglican
  Anglican Assn. of Biblical Scholars **[19291]**
  Anglican Assn. of Biblical Scholars **[19291]**
  Colleges and Universities of the Anglican Communion **[7728]**
  Colleges and Universities of the Anglican Communion **[7728]**
  Commn. of the Churches on Intl. Affairs **[19828]**
  Natl. Episcopal Scouters Assn. **[13024]**
  Soc. of Anglican Missionaries and Senders **[20094]**

Anglican Assn. of Biblical Scholars **[19291]**, 2 Museum Sq., Ste. 313, Lawrence, MA 01840

Anglican Assn. of Biblical Scholars **[19291]**, 2 Museum Sq., Ste. 313, Lawrence, MA 01840

Anglican Catholic
  Affirming Anglican Catholicism **[19292]**
  Amer. Friends of the Anglican Centre in Rome **[19293]**
  Amer. Friends of the Anglican Centre in Rome **[19293]**
  Anglican Fellowship of Prayer **[19294]**
  Fellowship of Concerned Churchmen **[19295]**
  Fellowship of Concerned Churchmen **[19295]**
  Soc. of Anglican Missionaries and Senders **[20094]**
  Soc. of King Charles the Martyr **[19296]**

Anglican Church in Japan **[IO]**, Tokyo, Japan

Anglican Fellowship of Prayer **[19294]**, 1106 Mansfield Ave., Indiana, PA 15701, (724)463-6436

Anglican Found. of Canada **[IO]**, Toronto, ON, Canada

Anglican Pacifist Fellowship **[IO]**, Milton Keynes, United Kingdom

Anglican Soc. - Address unknown since 2010.

Anglicans for Life **[12923]**, 405 Frederick Ave., Sewickley, PA 15143-1522, (412)749-0455

Anglicans United **[19689]**, PO Box 763217, Dallas, TX 75376-3217, (972)293-7443

Angling Trades Assn. **[IO]**, Coventry, United Kingdom

Angling Trust **[IO]**, Leominster, United Kingdom

Anglo-Austrian Music Soc. **[IO]**, London, United Kingdom

Anglo Chilean Soc. **[IO]**, London, United Kingdom

Anglo Danish Soc. **[IO]**, London, United Kingdom

Anglo-European Coll. of Chiropractic **[IO]**, Bournemouth, United Kingdom

Anglo-German Found. for the Stud. of Indus. Soc. **[IO]**, London, United Kingdom

Anglo-Jewish Assn. **[IO]**, London, United Kingdom

Angola Red Cross **[IO]**, Luanda, Angola

Angolan Taekwondo Fed. **[IO]**, Luanda, Angola

Angora Goat Record and Registry - Defunct.

Anguilla Amateur Athletic Fed. **[IO]**, The Valley, Anguilla

Anguilla Archeological and Historical Soc. **[IO]**, The Valley, Anguilla

Anguilla Chamber of Commerce and Indus. **[IO]**, The Valley, Anguilla

Anguilla Financial Services Assn. **[IO]**, The Valley, Anguilla

Anguilla Hotel and Tourism Assn. **[IO]**, The Valley, Anguilla

Anguilla Natl. Trust **[IO]**, The Valley, Anguilla

Anguilla Sailing Assn. **[IO]**, The Valley, Anguilla

Anguilla Tourist Bd. **[23446]**, 246 Central Ave., White Plains, NY 10606, (914)287-2400

Anguilla Tourist Info. Off. **[★23446]**

A star before a book entry number signifies that the name is not listed separately, but is mentioned within the entry.

Anguilla Tourist Info. and Reservation Off. [★23446]
Angus Soc. of Australia [IO], Armidale, Australia
Angus Youth Australia [IO], Armidale, Australia
Anheuser-Busch Collectors Club [21300], 14 N 679 Rte. 25, Ste. A, East Dundee, IL 60118, (847)428-3150
Animal Agents - Defunct.
Animal Agriculture Alliance [1376], PO Box 9522, Arlington, VA 22219, (703)562-5160
Animal Air Trans. [★10921]
Animal Alliance of Canada [IO], Toronto, ON, Canada
Animal Behavior Mgt. Alliance [7629], 3650 S Pointe Cir., No. 205, Laughlin, NV 89029
Animal Behavior Soc. [7630], Indiana Univ., 402 N Park Ave., Bloomington, IN 47408, (812)856-5541
Animal Breeders Assn. of Estonia [IO], Rapla, Estonia

Animal Breeding
  Alaskan Malamute Club of Am. [21478]
  Alpaca Breeders of the Rockies [3771]
  Alpaca Owners and Breeders Assn. [3772]
  Alpacas Without Borders [3773]
  Alpines Intl. Club [3774]
  Alpines Intl. Club [3774]
  Amer. Angora Goat Breeder's Assn. [3775]
  Amer. Assn. of Cat Enthusiasts [21243]
  Amer. Azteca Horse Intl. Assn. [4524]
  Amer. Beefalo Assn. [3776]
  Amer. Beefalo Assn. [3776]
  Amer. Buckskin Registry Assn. [4526]
  Amer. Canine Educ. Found. [21488]
  Amer. Cavy Breeders Assn. [3777]
  Amer. Cockatiel Soc. [21211]
  Amer. Cotswold Record Assn. [4889]
  Amer. Coun. of Spotted Asses [3778]
  Amer. Cream Draft Horse Assn. [4529]
  Amer. Dairy Goat Assn. [3779]
  Amer. Donkey and Mule Soc. [3780]
  Amer. Donkey and Mule Soc. | Miniature Donkey Registry [3781]
  Amer. Fox Terrier Club [21495]
  Amer. Galloway Breeders' Assn. [3876]
  Amer. Game Fowl Soc. [3840]
  Amer. Gelbvieh Assn. [3877]
  Amer. Goat Soc. [3782]
  Amer. Himalayan Rabbit Assn. [4833]
  Amer. Holsteiner Horse Assn. [4536]
  Amer. Kuvasz Assn. [11870]
  Amer. Legend [3783]
  Amer. Mammoth Jackstock Registry [3784]
  Amer. Milking Shorthorn Soc. [3890]
  Amer. Miniature Llama Assn. [3785]
  Amer. Mule Assn. [3786]
  Amer. Ostrich Assn. [3787]
  Amer. Rottweiler Club [21504]
  Amer. Shetland Sheepdog Assn. [21506]
  ARCA: Amer. Romeldale/CVM Assn. [4903]
  Australian Shepherd Club of Am. [21517]
  Berger Picard Club of Am. [21523]
  Bluetick Breeders of Am. [21527]
  Boykin Spaniel Club and Breeders Assn. of Am. [21531]
  Canary and Finch Soc. [3843]
  Canine Defense Fund [10936]
  Caucasian Ovcharka Club of Am. [21536]
  Chinese Shar-Pei Club of Am. [21539]
  Club de l'Epagneul Breton of the U.S. [21541]
  Coast to Coast Dachshund Rescue [10944]
  Cockapoo Club of Am. [21543]
  Companion Animal Protection Soc. [12649]
  Continental Mi-Ki Assn. [21546]
  Cotswold Breeders Assn. [3788]
  Dales Pony Assn. of North Am. [4579]
  The Designer Cat Assn. [21248]
  Dogs for the Deaf [14933]
  Dogue de Bordeaux Soc. of Am. [21555]
  Echo Dogs White Shepherd Rescue [10954]
  Empress Chinchilla Breeders Cooperative [3789]
  Exmoor Pony Assn. Intl. [4581]
  Field Spaniel Soc. of Am. [21562]
  Fullblood Simmental Fleckvieh Fed. [3912]
  Hartz Club of Am. [7198]
  Havana Silk Dog Assn. of Am. [21578]
  Icelandic Sheepdog Assn. of Am. [21582]

Intl. Assn. of Butterfly Exhibitions [1232]
Intl. Fed. of Amer. Homing Pigeon Fanciers [22097]
Intl. German Coolie Soc. and Registry [21585]
Intl. Nubian Breeders Assn. [3790]
Intl. Nubian Breeders Assn. [3790]
Intl. Pedigree Assignment and Bloodline Res. Assn. [4602]
Intl. Trotting and Pacing Assn. [22656]
Intl. Yak Assn. [4694]
Japanese Soc. of Breeding [17520]
Jews for Animal Rights [10996]
Llama Assn. of North Am. [3791]
Miniature and Novelty Sheep Breeders Assn. and Registry [4910]
Mohair Coun. of Am. [3792]
Natl. Birman Fanciers [21254]
Natl. Bison Assn. [3793]
Natl. Pedigreed Livestock Coun. [3794]
Natl. Pygmy Goat Assn. [3795]
Natl. Saanen Breeders Assn. [3796]
North Amer. Corriente Assn. [3928]
North Amer. Deutsch Kurzhaar Club [21617]
North Amer. Gamebird Assn. [3797]
North Amer. Llewellin Breeders Assn. [21620]
North Amer. Normande Assn. [3931]
North Amer. Potbellied Pig Assn. [3798]
North Amer. South Devon Assn. [3934]
North Amer. Teckel Club [21622]
Norwegian Forest Cat Breed Coun. [21255]
Norwegian Lundehund Assn. of Am. [21625]
Oberhasli Breeders of Am. [3799]
Painted Desert Sheep Soc. [4921]
Peruvian Inca Orchid Dog Club of Am. [21633]
Professional Rabbit Meat Assn. [4853]
Rescue Alliance of Hairless and Other Breeds [11031]
Rocky Mountain Llama and Alpaca Assn. [3800]
Samoyed Club of Am. [21646]
Savannah Cat Club [3864]
Soays of Am. [4922]
Soc. of Border Leicester Sheep Breeders [17773]
Spanish Water Dog Assn. of Am. [21654]
Support Dogs, Inc. [11832]
Thoroughbred Club of Am. [22666]
Tiger Horse Assn. [4653]
United Beagle Gundog Fed. [21661]
United Poodle Breeds Assn. [21664]
U.S.A. Coton de Tulear Club [21666]
U.S. Mondioring Assn. [22552]
United White Shepherd Club [21673]
Unwanted Horse Coalition [11053]
West Highland White Terrier Club of Am. [21677]
Western Intl. Walking Horse Assn. [4662]
Animal Care Coll. [IO], Ascot, United Kingdom
Animal Care Panel [★13757]
Animal Defence League of Canada [IO], Ottawa, ON, Canada
Animal Defenders Intl. U.S.A. [10912], 6100 Wilshire Blvd., Ste. 1150, Los Angeles, CA 90048, (323)935-2234
Animal Feed Mfrs. Assn. [IO], Centurion, Republic of South Africa
Animal Hea. Distributors Assn. [IO], Stamford, United Kingdom
Animal Hea. Found. [17012], 3615 Bassett Rd., Pacific, MO 63069
Animal Hea. Info. Specialists [IO], Hatfield, United Kingdom
Animal Hea. Inst. [2690], 1325 G St. NW, Ste. 700, Washington, DC 20005-3127, (202)637-2440
Animal Hea. Trust [IO], Newmarket, United Kingdom
Animal House Rescue [10913], PO Box 313, Neapolis, OH 43547, (419)276-5699
Animal Indus. Found. [★1376]
Animal Kind Intl. [10914], PO Box 300, Jemez Springs, NM 87025
Animal Law Coalition [10915], 907 Hanshaw Rd., No. 213, Ithaca, NY 14850, (607)220-8938
Animal Legal Defense Fund [10916], 170 E Cotati Ave., Cotati, CA 94931, (707)795-2533
Animal Liberation [IO], Courtenay, BC, Canada
Animal Medical Center [10917], 510 E 62nd St., New York, NY 10065, (212)838-8100
Animal Mission [IO], Surrey, United Kingdom

Animal Nutrition Assn. of Canada [IO], Ottawa, ON, Canada
Animal Nutrition Res. Coun. - Defunct.
Animal Place [10918], PO Box 1118, Grass Valley, CA 95945, (530)477-1757
Animal and Plant Hea. Assn. [IO], Blackrock, Ireland
Animal Protection Inst. of Am. [★10934]
Animal Protection Soc. of Samoa [IO], Apia, Western Samoa
Animal Protective Assn. [★10975]

Animal Research
  Amer. Assn. for Lab. Animal Sci. [13757]
  Americans for Medical Progress [13758]
  Animal Venom Res. Intl. [13759]
  Assn. for Assessment and Accreditation of Lab. Animal Care Intl. [13760]
  Boykin Spaniel Club and Breeders Assn. of Am. [21531]
  Comparative Cognition Soc. [6122]
  Evidenced-Based Veterinary Medicine Assn. [17024]
  Found. for BioMedical Res. [13761]
  German Shepherd Dog Club of Am. | Working Dog Assn. [21569]
  Global Res. and Rescue [5012]
  Global Wildlife Resources [5013]
  Hawk Mountain Sanctuary [5063]
  Inst. for Lab. Animal Res. [13762]
  Intl. Pedigree Assignment and Bloodline Res. Assn. [4602]
  Jews for Animal Rights [10996]
  Lab. Animal Mgt. Assn. [13763]
  Natl. Assn. for Biomedical Res. [13764]
  Walking Horse Trainers Assn. [4660]
Animal Res. and Conservation Center [★4162]

Animal Rights
  Amer. Assn. for Lab. Animal Sci. [13757]
  Amer. Horse League [12166]
  Animal House Rescue [10913]
  Animal Welfare Advocacy [10922]
  Animal Welfare Coun. [3807]
  Animals Deserve Absolute Protection Today and Tomorrow [10924]
  Animals Voice [10926]
  Born Free USA [10934]
  Canine Defense Fund [10936]
  Coast to Coast Dachshund Rescue [10944]
  Companion Animal Protection Soc. [12649]
  DreamCatcher Wild Horse and Burro Sanctuary [10953]
  Echo Dogs White Shepherd Rescue [10954]
  Fur Free Alliance [10968]
  Global Animal Partnership [3811]
  Global Fed. of Animal Sanctuaries [10970]
  Humane Soc. Veterinary Medical Assn. [10985]
  Intl. Aid for Korean Animals [10988]
  Intl. Defenders of Animals [10989]
  Jews for Animal Rights [10996]
  Kinship Circle [10998]
  Millennium Wildlife Sciences [5015]
  Natl. Dog Registry [11009]
  Natl. Endowment for the Animals [11010]
  Rescue Alliance of Hairless and Other Breeds [11031]
  Ridgeback Rescue of the U.S. [11034]
  SPCA Intl. [11041]
  Stolen Horse Intl. [11042]
  Unexpected Wildlife Refuge [11049]
  U.S.A. Defenders of Greyhounds [11054]
  VeterinaryVentures [11055]
  WildCat Conservation Legal Aid Soc. [5016]
Animal Rights Aruba [IO], San Nicolas, Aruba
Animal Rights Coalition [10919], 317 W 48th St., Minneapolis, MN 55419, (612)822-6161
Animal Rights Info. Ser. [★11047]
Animal Rights Intl.
Animal Rights Intl. - Defunct.
Animal Rights Kollective [IO], Toronto, ON, Canada
Animal Rights Mobilization [10920], PO Box 671, Placitas, NM 87043, (505)681-1682
Animal Rights Network/Animals' Agenda [★10925]
Animal Rights Sweden [IO], Alvsjo, Sweden
Animal Samaritans [IO], Bexleyheath, United Kingdom

Animal Science
  Amer. Assn. for Lab. Animal Sci. [13757]

Reference to "IO" in place of a book number signifies that the association may be found in the 50th edition of International Organizations.

A star before a book entry number signifies that the name is not listed separately, but is mentioned within the entry.

Stolen Horse Intl. [11042]
Stolen Horse Intl. [11042]
Support Our Shelters [11043]
Tattoo-a-Pet [11044]
Thoroughbred Club of Am. [22666]
Thoroughbred Retirement Found. [11045]
Tiger Horse Assn. [4653]
Tree House Humane Soc. [11046]
The True Nature Network [11047]
Tufts Center for Animals and Public Policy [11048]
Turtle Island Restoration Network [4156]
Unexpected Wildlife Refuge [11049]
United Action for Animals [11050]
United Poodle Breeds Assn. [21664]
United Poultry Concerns [11051]
United White Shepherd Club [21673]
United Yorkie Rescue [11052]
Unwanted Horse Coalition [11053]
U.S.A. Defenders of Greyhounds [11054]
VeterinaryVentures [11055]
Viva! USA [11056]
Viva! USA [11056]
Voice for Animals [11057]
Wild Animal Orphanage [11058]
Wild Animals Worldwide [5144]
Wild Burro Rescue and Preservation Proj. [11059]
Wild Horse Sanctuary [11060]
Wild Horse Spirit [11061]
WildCat Conservation Legal Aid Soc. [5016]
Wildlife in Need [5017]
Women's Humane Soc. Animal Shelter [11062]
World Nature Coalition [5159]
World Soc. for the Protection of Animals [11063]
World Soc. for the Protection of Animals [11063]
World Vets [11064]
Animal Welfare Advocacy [10922], PO Box 737, Mamaroneck, NY 10543, (914)381-6177
Animal Welfare Coun. [3807], PO Box 85, Eastwood, KY 40018-0085
Animal Welfare Inst. [10923], PO Box 3650, Washington, DC 20027, (202)337-2332
Animal World USA [3808], 5255 Brantford Dr., Memphis, TN 38120, (901)791-2455
Animalia - Fed. for the Protection of Animals [IO], Helsinki, Finland
Animals
Alaskan Malamute Club of Am. [21478]
Alliance for Contraception in Cats and Dogs [12647]
Alliance for Rabies Control [14370]
Alpaca Llama Show Assn. [20947]
Alpacas Without Borders [3773]
Amer. Assn. of Cat Enthusiasts [21243]
Amer. Assn. for Lab. Animal Sci. [13757]
Amer. Azteca Horse Intl. Assn. [4524]
Amer. Beefalo Assn. [3776]
Amer. Buckskin Registry Assn. [4526]
Amer. Canine Educ. Found. [21488]
Amer. Cockatiel Soc. [21211]
Amer. Coll. of Veterinary Dermatology [16998]
Amer. Cream Draft Horse Assn. [4529]
Amer. Ferret Assn. [20948]
Amer. Fox Terrier Club [21495]
Amer. Galloway Breeders' Assn. [3876]
Amer. Game Fowl Soc. [3840]
Amer. Gelbvieh Assn. [3877]
Amer. Gerbil Soc. [20949]
Amer. Holsteiner Horse Assn. [4536]
Amer. Horse League [12166]
Amer. Kiko Goat Assn. [4497]
Amer. Kuvasz Assn. [11870]
Amer. Milking Shorthorn Soc. [3890]
Amer. Rottweiler Club [21504]
Amer. Shetland Sheepdog Assn. [21506]
Amer. Working Malinois Assn. [20950]
Animal Hea. Inst. [2690]
Animal House Rescue [10913]
Animal Law Coalition [10915]
Animal Venom Res. Intl. [13759]
Animal Welfare Advocacy [10922]
Animal Welfare Coun. [3807]
Animal World USA [3808]
Animals Deserve Absolute Protection Today and Tomorrow [10924]

Another Chance 4 Horses [10927]
Ape Action Africa [5027]
Ape Conservation Effort [5028]
ARCA: Amer. Romeldale/CVM Assn. [4903]
Assn. of Professional Wildlife Educators [9050]
Assn. for Veterinary Family Practice [17016]
Australian Shepherd Club of Am. [21517]
Berger Picard Club of Am. [21523]
Big Wildlife [5034]
Bluetick Breeders of Am. [21527]
Bonobo Conservation Initiative [5038]
Born Free USA [10934]
Boykin Spaniel Club and Breeders Assn. of Am. [21531]
Brighter Green [4014]
British Camelids Assn. [15372]
Canary and Finch Soc. [3843]
Canine Defense Fund [10936]
Canine Freestyle Fed. [22545]
CATalyst Coun. [10938]
Cats in Crisis [10939]
Caucasian Ovcharka Club of Am. [21536]
Chinese Shar-Pei Club of Am. [21539]
Club de l'Epagneul Breton of the U.S. [21541]
Coast to Coast Dachshund Rescue [10944]
Cockapoo Club of Am. [21543]
Companion Animal Protection Soc. [12649]
Continental Mi-Ki Assn. [21546]
Controlled Release Soc. [6404]
Dales Pony Assn. of North Am. [4579]
Darwin Animal Doctors [3809]
The Designer Cat Assn. [21248]
Divine Canines [16848]
Doberman Assistance Network [11871]
Dogs for the Deaf [14933]
Dogue de Bordeaux Soc. of Am. [21555]
Echo Dogs White Shepherd Rescue [10954]
Elephants Without Borders [5011]
Equine Protection Network [5053]
Evidenced-Based Veterinary Medicine Assn. [17024]
Exmoor Pony Assn. Intl. [4581]
Fed. for the Amer. Staffordshire Terrier [20951]
Feral Cat Caretakers' Coalition [3810]
Field Spaniel Soc. of Am. [21562]
Friends of Roman Cats [3859]
Fullblood Simmental Fleckvieh Fed. [3912]
Galgo Rescue Intl. Network [10969]
German Shepherd Dog Club of Am. I Working Dog Assn. [21569]
Global Animal Partnership [3811]
Global Animal Relief [3812]
Global Fed. of Animal Sanctuaries [10970]
Global Res. and Rescue [5012]
Global Wildlife Resources [5013]
Gorilla Found. [6123]
Grey Muzzle Org. [10971]
Hartz Club of Am. [7198]
Havana Silk Dog Assn. of Am. [21578]
Heaven on Earth Soc. for Animals [10977]
HOPE Animal-Assisted Crisis Response [12906]
Humane Soc. Veterinary Medical Assn. [10985]
Icelandic Sheepdog Assn. of Am. [21582]
Intl. Aid for Korean Animals [10988]
Intl. Alliance for Animal Therapy and Healing [13765]
Intl. Alliance for Animal Therapy and Healing [13765]
Intl. Defenders of Animals [10989]
Intl. Fed. of Amer. Homing Pigeon Fanciers [22097]
Intl. German Coolie Soc. and Registry [21585]
Intl. Lama Registry [20952]
Intl. Lama Registry [20952]
Intl. Pedigree Assignment and Bloodline Res. Assn. [4602]
Intl. Trotting and Pacing Assn. [22656]
Intl. Veterinarians Dedicated to Animal Hea. [17029]
Intl. Yak Assn. [4694]
Jews for Animal Rights [10996]
Kids Making a Difference [3813]
Kinship Circle [10998]AnimalsLittle Mouse Club
Marine Animal Rescue Soc. [4093]
Marine Mammal Conservancy [5079]

Miniature and Novelty Sheep Breeders Assn. and Registry [4910]
Natl. Birman Fanciers [21254]
Natl. Block and Bridle Club [23464]
Natl. Coun. on Pet Population Stud. and Policy [6124]
Natl. Dog Registry [11009]
Natl. Endowment for the Animals [11010]
Natl. Pygmy Goat Assn. [3795]
Natl. Versatility Ranch Horse Assn. [22686]
Natl. Wolfdog Alliance [21615]
North Amer. Deutsch Kurzhaar Club [21617]
North Amer. Dog Agility Coun. [22548]
North Amer. Hunting Club [22700]
North Amer. Llewellin Breeders Assn. [21620]
North Amer. Pet Hea. Insurance Assn. [14863]
North Amer. Saddle Mule Assn. [20953]
North Amer. Teckel Club [21622]
North Amer. Wildlife Park Found. [5098]
North Amer. Wolf Assn. [5099]
Norwegian Forest Cat Breed Coun. [21255]
Norwegian Lundehund Assn. of Am. [21625]
Out of Love Sugar Glider Rescue [11017]
Pacific Marine Mammal Center [5103]
Painted Desert Sheep Soc. [4921]
Pan African Sanctuary Alliance [5106]
Panthera [5108]
Personal Ponies Ltd. [11822]
Peruvian Inca Orchid Dog Club of Am. [21633]
The Pig Preserve Assn. [11025]
Princess Kitty Fan Club [23788]
Professional Rabbit Meat Assn. [4853]
Reptile and Amphibian Ecology Intl. [5118]
Rescue Alliance of Hairless and Other Breeds [11031]
Responsible Policies for Animals [11032]
Ridgeback Rescue of the U.S. [11034]
Samoyed Club of Am. [21646]
Savannah Cat Club [3864]
Save-A-Vet [11036]
Save the Frogs! [4137]
Save the Turtles [5123]
Saving Horses, Inc. [12167]
Saving Wildlife Intl. [5125]
Self-Guided Hunting Assn. [21867]
Shark Alliance [5128]
Shark Savers [5129]
Shelter Animal Reiki Assn. [16581]
Snow Leopard Network [5130]
Soays of Am. [4922]
Soc. for Animal Homeopathy [15023]
Soul Friends [16873]
Southwestern Donkey and Mule Soc. [20954]
Spanish Water Dog Assn. of Am. [21654]
SPCA Intl. [11041]
State of the World's Sea Turtles [5134]
Stolen Horse Intl. [11042]
Support Dogs, Inc. [11832]
Thoroughbred Club of Am. [22666]
Tiger Horse Assn. [4653]
Turtle Survival Alliance [5140]
Unexpected Wildlife Refuge [11049]
United Beagle Gundog Fed. [21661]
United Natl. Weight Pull Assn. [22550]
United Poodle Breeds Assn. [21664]
U.S.A. Coton de Tulear Club [21666]
U.S. Complete Shooting Dog Assn. [21668]
U.S. Hunter Jumper Assn. [22691]
U.S. Mondioring Assn. [22552]
United White Shepherd Club [21673]
United Yorkie Rescue [11052]
Unwanted Horse Coalition [11053]
U.S.A. Defenders of Greyhounds [11054]
Veterinary Botanical Medicine Assn. [17046]
VeterinaryVentures [11055]
Walking Horse Trainers Assn. [4660]
West Highland White Terrier Club of Am. [21677]
Western Intl. Walking Horse Assn. [4662]
Wild Animals Worldwide [5144]
Wild Felid Res. and Mgt. Assn. [5145]
WildCat Conservation Legal Aid Soc. [5016]
Wildlife in Need [5017]
Wonderful World of Wildlife [5157]
World Nature Coalition [5159]
World Vets [11064]

Reference to "IO" in place of a book number signifies that the association may be found in the 50th edition of International Organizations.

Animals Australia **[IO]**, North Melbourne, Australia

Animals Deserve Absolute Protection Today and Tomorrow **[10924]**, PO Box 725, Royal Oak, MI 48068

Animals in Distress Sanctuary **[IO]**, Manchester, United Kingdom

Animals as Intermediaries **[★11016]**

Animals in Mind **[IO]**, Worle, United Kingdom

Animals Safety Org., Pakistan **[IO]**, Multan, Pakistan

Animals and Soc. Inst. **[10925]**, 2512 Carpenter Rd., Ste. 202-A, Ann Arbor, MI 48108, (734)677-9240

Animals Voice **[10926]**, 1354 E Ave., No. R-252, Chico, CA 95926, (800)82-VOICE

Animals Voice **[10926]**, 1354 E Ave., No. R-252, Chico, CA 95926, (800)82-VOICE

Animation; Soc. for the Promotion of Japanese **[9205]**

Animation; Women in **[1272]**

Anisa Found. **[IO]**, Mexicali, Mexico

Anita Borg Inst. for Women and Tech. **[12697]**, 1501 Page Mill Rd., MS 1105, Palo Alto, CA 94304, (650)236-4756

Anita Borg Inst. for Women and Tech. **[12697]**, 1501 Page Mill Rd., MS 1105, Palo Alto, CA 94304, (650)236-4756

Aniz **[12257]**, Zina Age, CEO/Founder, 233 Mitchell St., Ste. 200, Atlanta, GA 30303, (404)521-2410

Anjoman Mostanadsazane Cinemaye Iran **[★IO]**

Ankina Breeders - Defunct.

Ankole Watusi Intl. Registry **[3902]**, 22484 W 239 St., Spring Hill, KS 66083-9306, (913)592-4050

Ankole Watusi Intl. Registry **[3902]**, 22484 W 239 St., Spring Hill, KS 66083-9306, (913)592-4050

Ankylosing Spondylitis Assn. **[★16627]**

Ankylosing Spondylitis Assn. of Ireland **[IO]**, Dublin, Ireland

Ankylosing Spondylitis Soc. in Hungary **[IO]**, Budapest, Hungary

Ankylosing Spondylitis Soc. in Italy **[IO]**, Bologna, Italy

Ann-Margret's Official Fan Club **[23760]**, All Media Public Relations, PO Box 2045, Toluca Lake, CA 91610

Annalee Club **[21688]**, 71 NH Rte. 104, Unit 15, Meredith, NH 03253, (800)433-6557

Annalee Doll Soc. **[★21688]**

Annapolis Coalition on the Behavioral Hea. Workforce **[15446]**, 1001 Barton St., Columbia, SC 29203, (803)708-4030

Annapolis Naval Sailing Assn. **[22321]**, Richard S. Gavlak, Treas., 6807 Crofton Colony Ct., Crofton, MD 21114

Anne Frank Center U.S.A. **[17782]**, 38 Crosby St., 5th Fl., New York, NY 10013, (212)431-7993

Anne Frank Center U.S.A. **[17782]**, 38 Crosby St., 5th Fl., New York, NY 10013, (212)431-7993

Anne Frank - Fonds **[IO]**, Basel, Switzerland

Anne Frank House **[IO]**, Amsterdam, Netherlands

Anne Frank Inst. of Philadelphia **[★17789]**

Anne Frank Inst. of Philadelphia **[★17789]**

Anne Frank Stichting **[★IO]**

Anneke Jans and Everardus Bogardus Descendants Assn. **[20424]**, 1121 Linhof Rd., Wilmington, OH 45177-2917

Annie Sims Intl. Fan Club - Address unknown since 2011.

Annonsorforeningen **[★IO]**

Annual Steel Guitar Convention **[★10227]**

Annual Steel Guitar Convention **[★10227]**

Annular Bearing Engineers Comm. **[★1796]**

Anodizing Assn; Intl. Hard **[2473]**

Anonymous for Animal Rights **[IO]**, Tel Aviv, Israel

Anonymous Families History Project - Defunct.

Anorexia Nervosa Aid Soc. **[★14439]**

Anorexia Nervosa and Assoc. Disorders **[★14437]**

Anorexia Nervosa and Assoc. Disorders; Natl. Assn. of **[14437]**

Another Chance 4 Horses **[10927]**, 166 Sta. Rd., Bernville, PA 19506-8820, (610)621-5290

Ansar Burney Welfare Trust Intl. **[IO]**, Karachi, Pakistan

Ansari Rehabilitation Assn. for Afghanistan **[IO]**, Herat, Afghanistan

Ansley Family Assn. - Address unknown since 2011.

Answer Africa **[14374]**, 203 E Avenida San Juan, San Clemente, CA 92672, (949)498-5274

Antahkarana Soc. Intl. **[13319]**, PO Box 1543, Bozeman, MT 59771-1543, (406)581-5963

Antarabudaya Malaysia **[★IO]**

Antarctic Inst. of Canada **[IO]**, Edmonton, AB, Canada

Antarctic Prog. of the Intl. Geophysical Year **[★7282]**

Antarctic and Southern Ocean Coalition **[7280]**, 1630 Connecticut Ave. NW, 3rd Fl., Washington, DC 20009, (202)234-2480

Antarctic and Southern Ocean Coalition **[7280]**, 1630 Connecticut Ave. NW, 3rd Fl., Washington, DC 20009, (202)234-2480

The Antarctica Proj. - Defunct.

Antenna Measurement Techniques Assn. **[6645]**, MI Technologies, 1125 Satellite Blvd., Ste. 100, Suwanee, GA 30024

Anthology Film Archives **[9594]**, 32 2nd Ave., New York, NY 10003, (212)505-5181

Anthracite Railroads Historical Soc. **[10484]**, PO Box 519, Lansdale, PA 19446-0519

Anthropological Assn. of Greece **[IO]**, Athens, Greece

Anthropological Assn. of Ireland **[IO]**, Rostrevor, United Kingdom

Anthropology

   Amer. Anthropological Assn. **[6125]**

   Amer. Anthropological Assn. | Assn. of Latina and Latino Anthropologists **[6126]**

   Amer. Anthropological Assn. | Assn. for Political and Legal Anthropology **[6127]**

   Amer. Anthropological Assn. | Soc. for the Anthropology of Europe **[6128]**

   Amer. Assn. of Anthropological Genetics **[6895]**

   Amer. Assn. of Physical Anthropologists **[6129]**

   Amer. Ethnological Soc. **[6130]**

   Amer. Soc. of Primatologists **[6131]**

   Amerind Found. **[6132]**

   Amerind Found. **[6132]**AnthropologyAnthropological Assn. of Ireland

   Assn. for Africanist Anthropology **[6133]**

   Assn. of Black Anthropologists **[6134]**

   Assn. for Queer Anthropology **[6135]**

   Assn. of Senior Anthropologists **[6136]**

   Assn. for Social Anthropology in Oceania **[6137]**

   Assn. for Social Anthropology in Oceania **[6137]**

   Biological Anthropology Sect. **[6138]**

   Coun. on Anthropology and Educ. **[6139]**

   Dental Anthropology Assn. **[14279]**

   Evolutionary Anthropology Soc. **[6140]**

   Gen. Anthropology Division of the Amer. Anthropological Assn. **[6141]**

   Inst. for the Stud. of Man **[6142]**

   Intl. Primatological Soc. **[6143]**

   Intl. Primatological Soc. **[6143]**

   Intl. Union of Anthropological and Ethnological Sciences **[21650]**

   Intl. Women's Anthropology Conf. **[6144]**

   Intl. Women's Anthropology Conf. **[6144]**

   Kroeber Anthropological Soc. **[6145]**

   Lambda Alpha **[23465]**

   Natl. Assn. for the Practice of Anthropology **[6146]**

   Paleoanthropology Soc. **[7211]**

   Soc. for Anthropology in Community Colleges **[7729]**

   Soc. for the Anthropology of Consciousness **[7730]**

   Soc. for the Anthropology of Europe **[6128]**

   Soc. for the Anthropology of Food and Nutrition **[6147]**

   Soc. for the Anthropology of North Am. **[6148]**

   Soc. for the Anthropology of Religion **[6149]**

   Soc. for Applied Anthropology **[6150]**

   Soc. for Applied Anthropology **[6150]**

   Soc. for Cultural Anthropology **[6151]**

   Soc. for East Asian Anthropology **[6152]**

   Soc. for Economic Anthropology **[6153]**

   Soc. for Ethnomusicology **[10293]**

   Soc. for Latin Amer. Anthropology **[6154]**

   Soc. for Latin Amer. Anthropology **[6154]**

   Soc. for Linguistic Anthropology **[6155]**

   Soc. for Medical Anthropology **[6156]**

   Soc. for Urban, Natl. and Transnational/Global Anthropology **[6157]**

   Soc. for Visual Anthropology **[6158]**

Anthropology; Amer. Bd. of Forensic **[14543]**

Anthroposophic Medicine; Physicians' Assn. for **[13700]**

Anthroposophical

   Anthroposophical Soc. in Am. **[19297]**

Anthroposophical Nurses Assn. of Am. - Address unknown since 2011.

Anthroposophical Soc. in Am. **[19297]**, 1923 Geddes Ave., Ann Arbor, MI 48104, (734)662-9355

Anthroposophical Soc. in Canada **[IO]**, Thornhill, ON, Canada

Anthroposophical Soc. in Great Britain **[IO]**, London, United Kingdom

Anthroposophical Translators and Editors Assn. - Defunct.

Anti-Child Pornography Org. **[12710]**, PO Box 22338, Eagan, MN 55122-0388

Anti-Child Pornography Org. **[12710]**, PO Box 22338, Eagan, MN 55122-0388

Anti Copying In Design **[IO]**, Gloucester, United Kingdom

Anti-Corruption Commn. of Bhutan **[IO]**, Thimphu, Bhutan

Anti-Counterfeiting Gp. **[IO]**, High Wycombe, United Kingdom

Anti-Cruelty Soc. **[10928]**, 157 W Grand Ave., Chicago, IL 60610, (312)644-8338

Anti-Defamation League **[17269]**, 605 3rd Ave., New York, NY 10158, (212)885-7700

Anti Defamation League of B'nai B'rith **[★17269]**

Anti-Defamation League | Braun Holocaust Inst. **[17783]**, One E Camelback, Ste. 670, Phoenix, AZ 85012

Anti-Fascist Network - Defunct.

Anti-Friction Bearing Distributors Assn. **[★1813]**

Anti-Friction Bearing Mfrs. Assn. **[★1796]**

Anti-Malware Testing Standards Org. **[6478]**, One Ferry Bldg., Ste. 200, San Francisco, CA 94111, (415)963-3553

Anti Narcotic Welfare Org. **[IO]**, Karachi, Pakistan

Anti-Poverty Initiative **[17188]**, 10444 Kensington Way, Indianapolis, IN 46234, (317)272-0753

Anti-Poverty Initiative **[17188]**, 10444 Kensington Way, Indianapolis, IN 46234, (317)272-0753

Anti-Racist Action-Los Angeles/People Against Racist Terror **[17270]**, PO Box 1055, Culver City, CA 90232-1055, (310)495-0299

Anti-Racist Action-Los Angeles/People Against Racist Terror **[17270]**, PO Box 1055, Culver City, CA 90232-1055, (310)495-0299

Anti-Racist Action/People Against Racist Terror **[★17270]**

Anti-Racist Action/People Against Racist Terror **[★17270]**

Anti-Slavery Intl. **[IO]**, London, United Kingdom

Anti-Slavery Intl. **[★12234]**

Anti-Communism

   Captive Nations Comm. **[17185]**

   Cardinal Mindszenty Found. **[17186]**

   Christian Anti-Communism Crusade **[17187]**

Antigua and Barbuda Assn. of Persons with Disabilities **[IO]**, St. Johns, Antigua-Barbuda

Antigua Barbuda Horticultural Soc. **[IO]**, St. Johns, Antigua-Barbuda

Antigua and Barbuda Humane Soc. **[IO]**, St. Johns, Antigua-Barbuda

Antigua and Barbuda Inst. of Architects **[IO]**, St. Johns, Antigua-Barbuda

Antigua and Barbuda Netball Assn. **[IO]**, St. Johns, Antigua-Barbuda

Antigua and Barbuda Red Cross Soc. **[IO]**, St. Johns, Antigua-Barbuda

Antigua and Barbuda Search and Rescue **[IO]**, Falmouth, Antigua-Barbuda

Antigua and Barbuda Squash Rackets Assn. **[IO]**, St. Johns, Antigua-Barbuda

Antigua and Barbuda Tennis Assn. **[IO]**, St. Johns, Antigua-Barbuda

Antigua Hotels and Tourist Assn. **[IO]**, St. Johns, Antigua-Barbuda

Antigua Planned Parenthood Assn. **[IO]**, St. Johns, Antigua-Barbuda

Antillean Fed. for Youth Care **[IO]**, Curacao, Netherlands Antilles

Antilles Episcopal Conf. **[IO]**, Port of Spain, Trinidad and Tobago

---

A star before a book entry number signifies that the name is not listed separately, but is mentioned within the entry.

Antilliaanse Gewichthef Bond **[IO]**, Curacao, Netherlands Antilles

Anti-Poverty
Americans Care and Share **[12805]**
Anti-Poverty Initiative **[17188]**
Anti-Poverty Initiative **[17188]**
Children of Tanzania **[11065]**
Community Empowerment Network **[12953]**
Edurelief **[12834]**
Eliminate Poverty Now **[11066]**
Equator Initiative **[11581]**
Exit Poverty Empowerment **[11067]**
Fashion Fights Poverty **[12725]**
Generation for Change and Growth **[12328]**
Global Fac. for Disaster Reduction and Recovery **[11851]**
Green for All **[17189]**
Haiti Outreach **[11068]**
HavServe Volunteer Ser. Network **[11069]**
Hearts for Kenya **[11070]**
Human Development and Capability Assn. **[12210]**
Initiative for Global Development **[12731]**
Innovations for Poverty Action **[17190]**
Jamaica Unite **[11602]**
Liberian Anti Poverty Assn. **[11071]**
Liberian Anti Poverty Assn. **[11071]**
LIFT **[11072]**
Long Way Home **[11073]**
Millennium Campus Network **[17191]**
Millennium Promise **[11074]**
Millennium Promise **[11074]**
Moms Against Poverty **[12742]**
Nourish Intl. **[11075]**
Nuru Intl. **[11076]**
Out of Poverty thru Educ. **[7731]**
Partners in Sustainable Development Intl. **[12745]**
Poverty Awareness Coalition for Equality **[12747]**
Rain for the Sahel and Sahara **[12359]**
Rebuild A Nation **[11077]**
Rebuild A Nation **[11077]**
RISE-UP From Poverty **[12751]**
Rising Intl. **[11078]**
Sabu Help **[12962]**
Serving Our World **[11405]**
Shining Hope for Communities **[11635]**
Tusubira - We Have Hope **[12755]**
Union MicroFinanza **[12964]**
Village Focus Intl. **[11650]**

Antipsychiatry Coalition **[16334]**, Carrie L. Drake, 2040 Polk St., Box 234, San Francisco, CA 94109
Antiquarian Booksellers Assn. of Am. **[9437]**, 20 W 44th St., Ste. 507, New York, NY 10036-6604, (212)944-8291
Antiquarian Booksellers' Assn. of Canada **[IO]**, Ottawa, ON, Canada
Antiquarian Booksellers Assn. of the United Kingdom **[IO]**, London, United Kingdom
Antiquarian Horological Soc. **[IO]**, Sussex, United Kingdom
Antique Advt. Assn. of Am. **[82]**, 13915 David Rd., Woodstock, IL 60098
Antique Airplane Assn. **[20883]**, 22001 Bluegrass Rd., Ottumwa, IA 52501-8569, (641)938-2773
Antique and Amusement Photographers Intl. **[2713]**, PO Box 15117, Arlington, VA 22215, (479)253-8554
Antique Appraisal Assn. of America - Defunct.
Antique and Art Glass Salt Shaker Collectors Soc. **[★21304]**
Antique Auto Racing Assn. **[20997]**, 5295 S Linden Rd., Swartz Creek, MI 48473, (810)655-2219
Antique Auto. Club of Am. **[20998]**, PO Box 417, Hershey, PA 17033, (717)534-1910
Antique Barbed Wire Soc. **[21301]**, 2720 Camino Chueco, Santa Fe, NM 87505-5250
Antique Boat Club **[★22329]**
Antique Caterpillar Machinery Owners Club **[21878]**, 7501 N Univ., Ste. 119, Peoria, IL 61614, (309)691-5002
Antique and Classic Boat Soc. **[22322]**, 422 James St., Clayton, NY 13624, (315)686-2628
Antique Collectors' Club **[IO]**, Woodbridge, United Kingdom
Antique Dealers Assn. of Czech Republic **[IO]**, Prague, Czech Republic

Antique Dealers Assn. of Poland **[IO]**, Krakow, Poland
Antique and Decorative Arts League **[★246]**
Antique Doorknob Collectors of Am. **[21302]**, PO Box 31, Chatham, NJ 07928-0031, (973)635-6338
Antique Fan Collectors Assn. **[21303]**, 2245 Harrison Ave., Lincoln, NE 68502
Antique Glass Salt and Sugar Shaker Club **[21304]**, 64 Burt Rd., Springfield, MA 01118-1848
Antique Motorcycle Club of Am. **[21919]**, Trudi Johnson-Richards, Natl. Sec., 3295 Victoria St., Shoreview, MN 55126, (651)482-0096
Antique Motorcycle Club of Am. **[21919]**, Trudi Johnson-Richards, Natl. Sec., 3295 Victoria St., Shoreview, MN 55126, (651)482-0096
Antique Outboard Motor Club **[22323]**, PO Box 2526, Walla Walla, WA 99362
Antique Poison Bottle Collectors Assn. **[21305]**, 312 Summer Ln., Huddleston, VA 24104, (540)297-4498
Antique Radio Club of Am. **[★22118]**
Antique Radio Club of Am. **[★22118]**
Antique Reloading Tool Collector's Assn. - Address unknown since 2011.
Antique Small Engine Collectors Club **[21702]**, 5655 US Hwy., 50 E, Bedford, IN 47421-8688
Antique Snowmobile Club of Am. **[22133]**, 8660 Fawn Lake Dr. NE, Stacy, MN 55079, (651)462-4497
The Antique Stove Assn. **[20956]**, 2321 E Pioneer Rd., Duluth, MN 55804
Antique Studebaker Club **[20999]**, PO Box 1743, Maple Grove, MN 55311, (763)420-7829
Antique Telephone Collectors Assn. **[22162]**, PO Box 1252, McPherson, KS 67460, (620)245-9555
Antique Telescope Soc. **[20957]**, 1878 Robinson Rd., Dahlonega, GA 30533
Antique Tribal Art Dealers Assn. **[245]**, 215 Sierra Dr. SE, Albuquerque, NM 87108, (415)927-3717
Antique Truck Club of Am. **[22196]**, 85 S Walnut St., Boyertown, PA 19512, (610)367-2567
Antique Wireless Assn. **[22118]**, PO Box 421, Bloomfield, NY 14469
Antique Wireless Assn. **[22118]**, PO Box 421, Bloomfield, NY 14469

Antiques
1965-66 Full Size Chevrolet Club **[20980]**
Aladdin Knights of the Mystic Light **[21877]**
Amer. Historical Print Collectors Soc. **[20955]**
Amer. Lock Collectors Assn. **[21295]**
Amer. Numismatic Soc. **[21964]**
Amer. Pencil Collectors Soc. **[21297]**
Amer. Philatelic Res. Lib. **[22010]**
Amer. Philatelic Soc. Writers Unit **[22012]**
Amer. Soc. of Military Insignia Collectors **[21883]**
Amer. Topical Assn. **[22016]**
America's Corvette Club **[20996]**
Ancient Coin Collectors Guild **[21967]**
Ancient Coins for Educ. **[8685]**
Antique Advt. Assn. of Am. **[82]**
Antique Caterpillar Machinery Owners Club **[21878]**
Antique Glass Salt and Sugar Shaker Club **[21304]**
Antique Motorcycle Club of Am. **[21919]**
Antique Small Engine Collectors Club **[21702]**
The Antique Stove Assn. **[20956]**
Antique Telescope Soc. **[20957]**
Antiques and Collectibles Natl. Assn. **[195]**
Antiques Coun. **[196]**
Antiques Coun. **[196]**
Assoc. Collectors of El Salvador **[22020]**
Assn. of Coffee Mill Enthusiasts **[21306]**
Assn. of Restorers **[197]**
Blue/White Pottery Club **[20958]**
Brazil Philatelic Assn. **[22022]**
Brewery Collectibles Club of Am. **[21311]**
British Antique Furniture Restorers Assn. **[12109]**
Browning Collectors Assn. **[21712]**
Canadian Antique Phonograph Soc. **[21406]**
Chess Collectors Intl. **[21274]**
Chevrolet Nomad Assn. **[21022]**
Chicago Map Soc. **[20959]**
Chrysler Town and Country Owners Registry **[21026]**

Citizens' Stamp Advisory Comm. **[22029]**
Citroen Quarterly Car Club **[21027]**
Civil War Dealers and Collectors Assn. **[21280]**
Civil War Token Soc. **[21970]**
Cobra Owners Club of Am. **[21032]**
Collectors of Religion on Stamps **[22032]**
Colonial Coin Collectors Club **[21971]**
Combined Organizations of Numismatic Error Collectors of Am. **[21972]**
Confederate Stamp Alliance **[22033]**
Corvair Soc. of Am. **[21035]**
Cover Collectors Circuit Club **[22034]**
Doll Costumer's Guild **[21690]**
Egg Cup Collectors' Corner **[21336]**
Errors, Freaks and Oddities Collectors' Club **[22037]**
Erskine Registry **[21052]**
F-14 Tomcat Assn. **[21201]**
Fairchild Club **[20895]**
Ferguson Enthusiasts of North Am. **[22174]**
Firehawk Assn. of Am. **[21057]**
First Flight Soc. **[20896]**
First Issues Collectors Club **[22038]**
Ford/Fordson Collectors Assn. **[22175]**
Fostoria Glass Collectors **[21831]**
Found. for the Stud. of the Arts and Crafts Movement at Roycroft **[20960]**
France and Colonies Philatelic Soc. **[22039]**
Future Corvette Owners Assn. **[21060]**
Guild of Antique Dealers and Restorers **[15391]**
Gull Wing Gp. Intl. **[21065]**
Harley Hummer Club **[21929]**
Hudson-Essex-Terraplane Club **[21070]**
Intl. Bank Note Soc. **[21976]**
Intl. Coun. of Air Shows **[20901]**
Intl. Doll Makers Assn. **[21692]**
Intl. Fire Buff Associates **[21708]**
Intl. Radio Club of Am. **[20937]**
Jack Knight Air Mail Soc. **[22047]**
Karmann Ghia Club of North Am. **[21087]**
Kissel Kar Klub **[21088]**
Knife Collectors Club **[21875]**
Korea Stamp Soc. **[22048]**
Kustom Kemps of Am. **[21089]**
Les Amis de Panhard and Deutsch-Bonnet USA **[21091]**
Liberty Seated Collectors Club **[21979]**
Magic Lantern Soc. of the U.S. and Canada **[20961]**
Mailer's Postmark Permit Club **[22050]**
Marmon Club **[21098]**
Maserati Info. Exchange **[21100]**
Massey Collectors Assn. **[22178]**
Meter Stamp Soc. **[22053]**
Metropolitan Owners Club of North Am. **[21105]**
Mexico Elmhurst Philatelic Soc. Intl. **[22055]**
Midstates Jeepster Assn. **[21107]**
Model A Ford Cabriolet Club **[21108]**
Modern Car Soc. **[21114]**
Morgan Car Club **[21116]**
Napoleonic Age Philatelists **[22058]**
Natl. Button Soc. **[21378]**
Natl. Corvette Owners Assn. **[21124]**
Natl. Duncan Glass Soc. **[21839]**
Natl. Mossberg Collectors Assn. **[21716]**
Natl. Pop Can Collectors **[21381]**
Natl. Russell Collectors Assn. **[21382]**
Natl. World War II Glider Pilots Assn. **[20315]**
North Amer. Collectors **[21984]**
North Amer. Mini Moke Registry **[21137]**
North Amer. Radio Archives **[22120]**
Numismatic Literary Guild **[21986]**
Numismatics Intl. **[21987]**
Old Sleepy Eye Collectors' Club of Am. **[21268]**
Org. of Bricklin Owners **[21143]**
Peanut Pals **[21396]**
Plasticville Collectors Assn. **[22100]**
Plymouth Owners Club **[21151]**
Popular Rotorcraft Assn. **[20913]**
Professional Car Soc. **[21155]**
The Questers **[20962]**
Riva Club USA **[21232]**
Saving Antiquities for Everyone **[9131]**
Tea Leaf Club Intl. **[21269]**
United Four-Wheel Drive Associations **[21184]**

Reference to "IO" in place of a book number signifies that the association may be found in the 50th edition of International Organizations.

U.S. Mexican Numismatic Assn. [21996]
Vintage Garden Tractor Club of Am. [22181]
Vintage Thunderbird Club Intl. [21190]
Volkswagen Club of Am. [21193]
Wagner And Griswold Soc. [21859]
Whirly-Girls - Intl. Women Helicopter Pilots [20923]
World Airline Historical Soc. [20924]
Worldwide Camaro Club [21197]
Wreck and Crash Mail Soc. [22093]
Antiques and Collectibles Natl. Assn. [195], PO Box 4389, Davidson, NC 28036, (704)895-9088
Antiques Coun. [196], PO Box 1508, Warren, MA 01083, (413)436-7064
Antiques Coun. [196], PO Box 1508, Warren, MA 01083, (413)436-7064
Antiques Dealers Assn. of Am. [795], PO Box 529, Newtown, CT 06470-0529, (203)364-9913

Antiquities
Ancient Coin Collectors Guild [21967]
Antique Caterpillar Machinery Owners Club [21878]
Antique Small Engine Collectors Club [21702]
Colonial Coin Collectors Club [21971]
Wagner And Griswold Soc. [21859]

Anti-Racism
Turkish Amer. Alliance for Fairness [19260]
A World of Difference Inst. [11525]

Anti-Semitism
Anti-Defamation League [17269]
A World of Difference Inst. [11525]
Antwerp Diamond High Coun. [IO], Antwerp, Belgium
Anuvrat Global Org. [IO], Rajsamand, India

Anxiety Disorders
Anxiety UK [190]
Intl. Soc. for Bipolar Disorders [13766]
Anxiety Disorders Assn. of Am. [12692], 8730 Georgia Ave., Ste. 600, Silver Spring, MD 20910, (240)485-1001
Anxiety Disorders Assn. of Victoria [IO], Kew, Australia
Anxiety Disorders Special Interest Gp. - Address unknown since 2010.
Anxiety and Phobia Clinic [★12693]
Anxiety and Phobia Treatment Center [12693], White Plains Hosp., Davis Ave. at E Post Rd., White Plains, NY 10601, (914)681-1038
Anxiety Self Help Assn. [IO], Nedlands, Australia
Anxiety UK [IO], Manchester, United Kingdom
Any Soldier [11082], PO Box 29, Hoagland, IN 46745-0029
AOAC Intl. [6397], 481 N Frederick Ave., Ste. 500, Gaithersburg, MD 20877-2417, (301)924-7077
AOAC Intl. [6397], 481 N Frederick Ave., Ste. 500, Gaithersburg, MD 20877-2417, (301)924-7077
Aontas Fiontair Agus Spoirt [★IO]
Aontas Innealtoireacht Bithleighis na hEireann [★IO]
Aontas Muinteoiri Eireann [★IO]
Aontas Teilgin Agus Amais na h'Eireann [★IO]
Aos-Oideachas Naisiunta Tri Aontu Soarlach [★IO]
Aosdana [IO], Dublin, Ireland
AOTCB [★16863]
APA: The Engineered Wood Assn. [1497], 7011 S 19th St., Tacoma, WA 98466, (253)565-6600
Apartment Owners and Managers Assn. of America - Defunct.
APB Registry [★4546]
APCA [★4779]
APCA [★4779]
Ape Action Africa [5027], 205 S Dixie Dr., No. 1014, Haines City, FL 33844
Ape Conservation Effort [5028], 800 Cherokee Ave. SE, Atlanta, GA 30315, (404)624-5963

Aphasia
Acad. of Aphasia [13767]
Natl. Aphasia Assn. [13768]
Aphra Behn Soc. [10701], Seton Hall Univ., Dept. of English, 400 S Orange Ave., South Orange, NJ 07079
Apiary Inspectors of Am. [3817], Minnesota Dept. of Agriculture, 32736 180th St., Starbuck, MN 56381, (320)239-4725
APICS Canadian District [IO], Toronto, ON, Canada
APICS — The Educational Soc. for Rsrc. Mgt. [6960]

APICS — The Educational Soc. for Rsrc. Mgt. [6960]

Apiculture
Amer. Assn. of Professional Apiculturists [3814]
Amer. Beekeeping Fed. [3815]
Amer. Honey Producers Assn. [3816]
Apiary Inspectors of Am. [3817]
Eastern Apicultural Soc. of North Am. [3818]
Apistogramma Study Group [21723], PO Box 504, Elkhorn, WI 53121
Apistogramma Study Group [21723], PO Box 504, Elkhorn, WI 53121
Apitherapy Soc; Amer. [13651]
Aplastic Anemia Found. of Am. [★14963]
Aplastic Anemia Found. of Am. [★14963]
Aplastic Anemia and MDS Intl. Found. [14963], 100 Park Ave., Ste. 108, Rockville, MD 20850, (301)279-7202
Aplastic Anemia and MDS Intl. Found. [14963], 100 Park Ave., Ste. 108, Rockville, MD 20850, (301)279-7202
Aplastic Anemia and Myelodysplasia Assn. of Canada [IO], Richmond Hill, ON, Canada
APLIC [9960], Princeton Univ., Stokes Lib., Wallace Hall, Princeton, NJ 08544
APLIC [9960], Princeton Univ., Stokes Lib., Wallace Hall, Princeton, NJ 08544
APMI Intl. [7089], 105 Coll. Rd. E, Princeton, NJ 08540-6692, (609)452-7700
APMI Intl. [7089], 105 Coll. Rd. E, Princeton, NJ 08540-6692, (609)452-7700
Apnea Assn; Amer. Sleep [16663]
APOG [★18344]
Apollo Alliance [6691], 330 Townsend St., Ste. 205, San Francisco, CA 94107, (415)371-1700
Apollo Soc. [9086], PO Box 61206, Honolulu, HI 96839-1206
Apostleship of Prayer [19381], 3211 S Lake Dr., Ste. 216, Milwaukee, WI 53235, (414)486-1152
Apostleship of Prayer [IO], Toronto, ON, Canada
Apostleship of the Sea in the U.S.A. [19382], US-CCB/Cultural Diversity, 3211 4th St. NE, Washington, DC 20017-1194, (202)541-3035
Apostolate for Family Consecration [19383], 3375 County Rd. 36, Bloomingdale, OH 43910, (740)765-5500
Apothecaries; Amer. Coll. of [16170]
Apoyo Para el Campesino-Indigena del Oriente Boliviano [★IO]
APPA: The Assn. of Higher Educ. Facilities Officers [8087], 1643 Prince St., Alexandria, VA 22314-2818, (703)684-1446
APPA: The Assn. of Higher Educ. Facilities Officers [8087], 1643 Prince St., Alexandria, VA 22314-2818, (703)684-1446

Appalachian
Appalachian Consortium [9132]
Appalachian Stud. Assn. [9133]
Melungeon Heritage Assn. [18921]
Appalachian Consortium [9132], Center for Appalachian Stud., Appalachian State Univ., ASU Box 32018, Boone, NC 28608-2018, (828)262-4089
Appalachian Families - Defunct.
Appalachian Finance Assn. [★1294]
Appalachian Hardwood Club [★1498]
Appalachian Hardwood Mfrs., Inc. [1498], PO Box 427, High Point, NC 27261, (336)885-8315
Appalachian Mountain Club [23081], 5 Joy St., Boston, MA 02108, (617)523-0655
Appalachian Stud. Assn. [9133], Mary K. Thomas, Exec. Dir., Marshall Univ., 1 John Marshall Dr., Huntington, WV 25755, (304)696-2904
Appalachian Trail Conf. [★23082]
Appalachian Trail Conservancy [23082], PO Box 807, Harpers Ferry, WV 25425-0807, (304)535-6331
Appaloosa Horse Assn. of New Zealand [IO], Whakatane, New Zealand
Appaloosa Horse Club [4564], 2720 W Pullman Rd., Moscow, ID 83843, (208)882-5578
Appaloosa Horse Club [4564], 2720 W Pullman Rd., Moscow, ID 83843, (208)882-5578
Appaloosa Horse Club of Canada [IO], Claresholm, AB, Canada
Apparatus Makers Assn. of Am. [★3180]

Apparel
Accessories Coun. [198]
Amer. Apparel and Footwear Assn. [199]
Amer. Apparel Producers' Network [200]
Amer. Apparel Producers' Network [200]
Argentine Chamber of the Clothing Indus. [13606]
Assn. of Knitwear Designers [201]
Assn. of Knitwear Designers [201]
Assn. of Sewing and Design Professionals [202]
Bangladesh Garment Mfrs. and Exporters Assn. [4554]
Black Fashion Designers Assn. [1037]
Coun. of Fashion Designers of Am. [203]
Custom Tailors and Designers Assn. of Am. [204]
Estonian Clothing and Textile Assn. [20504]
Fashion Gp. Intl. [205]
Fashion Gp. Intl. [205]
Fur Info. Coun. of Am. [206]
The Hosiery Assn. [207]
Intl. Apparel Fed. [14584]ApparelIntl. Assn. of Clothing Designers and Executives.
Intl. Bridal Mfrs. Assn. [472]
Intl. Formalwear Assn. [208]
Intl. Formalwear Assn. [208]
Intl. Wooden Bow Tie Club [209]
KEZA [210]
Natl. Assn. of Uniform Mfrs. and Distributors [211]
Natl. Button Soc. [21378]
Natl. Costumers Assn. [212]
Natl. Fashion Accessories Assn. [213]
Sew Much Comfort [11079]
Unreserved Amer. Indian Fashion and Art Alliance [9134]
World Shoe Assn. [214]
World Shoe Assn. [214]
Worldwide Responsible Accredited Production [215]
Worldwide Responsible Accredited Production [215]
YMA Fashion Scholarship Fund [216]
Apparel Guild - Defunct.
Apparel Retailers of Am. [★3118]
APPEAL: Asian Pacific Partners for Empowerment and Leadership [11544], 300 Frank H. Ogawa Plz., Ste. 620, Oakland, CA 94612, (510)272-9536
APPEAL: Asian Pacific Partners for Empowerment and Leadership [11544], 300 Frank H. Ogawa Plz., Ste. 620, Oakland, CA 94612, (510)272-9536
Appeal of Conscience Found. [18516], 119 W 57th St., New York, NY 10019-2401, (212)535-5800
Appita [IO], Rotorua, New Zealand
Appita - Tech. Assn. for the Australian and New Zealand Pulp and Paper Indus. [IO], Carlton, Australia
Apple Processors Assn. [4425], 1666 K St. NW, Ste. 260, Washington, DC 20006, (202)785-6715
Apple Products Res. and Educ. Coun. [4426], 1100 Johnson Ferry Rd., Ste. 300, Atlanta, GA 30342, (404)252-3663
Apple's Kin - Defunct.
AppleWorks Users Gp. [6479], PO Box 701010, Plymouth, MI 48170, (734)454-1969
Appliance Parts Distributors Assn. [217], 3621 N Oakley Ave., Chicago, IL 60618, (773)230-9851
Appliance Parts Jobbers Assn. [★217]

Appliances
The Antique Stove Assn. [20956]
Appliance Parts Distributors Assn. [217]
Assn. of Home Appliance Mfrs. [218]
Hoover Historical Center [20963]
Intl. Brotherhood of Boilermakers I Stove, Furnace, Energy and Allied Appliance Workers Div. [23144]
Natl. Appliance Parts Suppliers Assn. [219]
Natl. Appliance Ser. Assn. [220]
The Old Appliance Club [20964]
TopTen USA [1178]
Vacuum Dealers Trade Assn. [221]
Application Ser. Provider Indus. Consortium [3388], Computing Tech. Indus. Assn., 3500 Lacey Rd., Ste. 100, Downers Grove, IL 60515, (630)678-8300
Applied Computational Electromagnetics Soc. [6646], Florida Intl. Univ., ECE Dept., 10555 W Flagler St., EAS-3983, Miami, FL 33174, (305)348-3040

A star before a book entry number signifies that the name is not listed separately, but is mentioned within the entry.

Applied Linguistics Assn. of New Zealand **[IO]**, Palmerston North, New Zealand

Applied Res. Center **[18637]**, 900 Alice St., Ste. 400, Oakland, CA 94607, (510)653-3415

Applied Res. Ethics Natl. Assn. **[15337]**, 126 Brookline Ave., Ste. 202, Boston, MA 02115-3920, (617)423-4112

Applied Tech. Coun. **[6781]**, 201 Redwood Shores Pkwy., Ste. 240, Redwood City, CA 94065, (650)595-1542

Applied Vision Assn. **[IO]**, Bristol, United Kingdom

Applied Voice Input/Output Soc. **[6443]**, PO Box 20817, San Jose, CA 95160, (408)323-1783

The Applique Soc. **[21432]**, PO Box 89, Sequim, WA 98382-0089, (800)597-9827

The Applique Soc. **[21432]**, PO Box 89, Sequim, WA 98382-0089, (800)597-9827

Appraisal Inst. **[225]**, 550 W Van Buren St., Ste. 1000, Chicago, IL 60607, (312)335-4100

Appraisal Inst. of Canada **[IO]**, Ottawa, ON, Canada

Appraisers

Amer. Soc. of Agricultural Appraisers **[222]**

Amer. Soc. of Farm Equip. Appraisers **[223]**

Amer. Soc. of Farm Managers and Rural Appraisers **[224]**

Appraisal Inst. **[225]**

Appraisers Assn. of Am. **[226]**

Assn. of Appraiser Regulatory Officials **[227]**

Assn. of Online Appraiser **[228]**

Equip. Appraisers Assn. of North Am. **[229]**

Equip. Appraisers Assn. of North Am. **[229]**

Found. of Real Estate Appraisers **[230]**

Haitian Art Educ. and Appraisal Soc. **[9651]**

Independent Automotive Damage Appraisers Assn. **[231]**

Inst. of Bus. Appraisers **[232]**

Intl. Soc. of Appraisers **[233]**

Intl. Soc. of Appraisers **[233]**

Natl. Assn. of Independent Fee Appraisers **[234]**

Natl. Assn. of Real Estate Appraisers **[235]**

Appraisers Assn. of Am. **[226]**, 386 Park Ave. S, 20th Fl., Ste. 2000, New York, NY 10016, (212)889-5404

Appropriate Infrastructure Development Gp. **[11545]**, PO Box 104, Weston, MA 02493, (800)401-3860

Appropriate Rural Tech. Inst. **[IO]**, Pune, India

Appropriate Technology

Aguayuda **[13412]**

Aprovecho Res. Center **[17192]**

Aprovecho Res. Center **[17192]**

EnterpriseWorks/VITA **[17193]**

EnterpriseWorks/VITA **[17193]**

Natl. Center for Appropriate Tech. **[17194]**

New Economics Inst. **[17195]**

Planet Drum Found. **[17196]**

Planet Drum Found. **[17196]**

Prog. for Appropriate Tech. in Hea. **[17197]**

Prog. for Appropriate Tech. in Hea. **[17197]**

Servants in Faith and Tech. **[17198]**

Servants in Faith and Tech. **[17198]**

Appropriate Tech. ASIA **[IO]**, Chatteris, United Kingdom

Appropriate Tech. Intl. **[★17193]**

Appropriate Tech. Intl. **[★17193]**

Approval of Schools Comm. **[★8580]**

Approved Driving Instructors Natl. Joint Coun. **[IO]**, Lichfield, United Kingdom

APQC **[2265]**, 123 N Post Oak Ln., 3rd Fl., Houston, TX 77024, (713)681-4020

Apraxia of Speech Assn; Childhood **[16684]**

Apricot Producers of California **[4427]**, PO Box 974, Turlock, CA 95381, (209)632-9777

Aprovecho Inst. **[★17192]**

Aprovecho Inst. **[★17192]**

Aprovecho Res. Center **[17192]**, 80574 Hazelton Rd., Cottage Grove, OR 97424, (541)942-8198

Aprovecho Res. Center **[17192]**, 80574 Hazelton Rd., Cottage Grove, OR 97424, (541)942-8198

APSE: The Network on Employment **[11761]**, 451 Hungerford Dr., Ste. 700, Rockville, MD 20850, (301)279-0060

APT Enterprise Development **[IO]**, Moreton-in-Marsh, United Kingdom

APVA Preservation Virginia **[9668]**, 204 W Franklin St., Richmond, VA 23220, (804)648-1889

Aquaculture

Alternative Aquaculture Assn. **[3819]**

Aquaculture Intl. **[3820]**

Aquaculture Intl. **[3820]**AquacultureCanadian Aquaculture Indus. Alliance

The Catfish Inst. **[3821]**

Florida Tropical Fish Farms Assn. **[3822]**

Global Aquaculture Alliance **[3823]**

Global Aquaculture Alliance **[3823]**

Intl. Assn. of Meiobenthologists **[8153]**

Intl. Professional Pond Contractors Assn. **[236]**

Intl. Seafood Sustainability Assn. **[1361]**

Marine Aquarium Coun. **[3824]**

Marine Aquarium Coun. **[3824]**

Marine Aquarium Societies of North Am. **[3825]**

Muskies Inc. **[3826]**

Natl. Aquaculture Assn. **[3827]**

Natl. Assn. of Pond Professionals **[237]**

Natl. Assn. of State Aquaculture Coordinators **[3828]**

Pacific Shellfish Inst. **[3829]**

Sustainable Fisheries Partnership **[3830]**

U.S. Aquaculture Soc. **[3831]**

U.S. Trout Farmers Assn. **[3832]**

World Aquaculture Soc. **[3833]**

World Aquaculture Soc. **[3833]**

Aquaculture Assn. of Canada **[IO]**, St. Andrews, NB, Canada

Aquaculture Assn. of Southern Africa **[IO]**, Pretoria, Republic of South Africa

Aquaculture Intl. **[3820]**, 405 Union St., Murfreesboro, NC 27855

Aquaculture Intl. **[3820]**, 405 Union St., Murfreesboro, NC 27855

Aquarium Soc; Natl. **[10061]**

Aquarium and Zoo Facilities Assn. **[7631]**, 3900 Wildlife Way, Cleveland, OH 44109

Aquatic Animal Life Support Operators **[7060]**, PO Box 690067, Orlando, FL 32869-0067

Aquatic Exercise Assn. **[22804]**, PO Box 1609, Nokomis, FL 34274-1609, (941)486-8600

Aquatic and Fitness Professional Assn. Intl. **[22805]**, 547 WCR 18, Longmont, CO 80504, (888)966-5939

Aquatic Gardeners Assn. **[4495]**, Cheryl Rogers, Membership Coor., PO Box 51536, Denton, TX 76206-1536

Aquatic Gardeners Assn. **[4495]**, Cheryl Rogers, Membership Coor., PO Box 51536, Denton, TX 76206-1536

Aquatic Injury Safety Found. **[★12984]**

Aquatic Plant Mgt. Soc. **[6350]**, PO Box 821265, Vicksburg, MS 39182-1265, (601)634-2656

Aquatic Plants

ReefGuardian Intl. **[4709]**

Aquatic Resources Educ. Assn. **[9048]**, Steve Marshall, Coor., Florida Fish and Wildlife Conservation Commn., Division of Freshwater Fisheries Mgt., 9557 Majestic Way, Boynton Beach, FL 33437, (561)292-6050

Aquatics

Fed. of Amer. Aquarium Societies **[6953]**

ReefGuardian Intl. **[4709]**

U.S. Aquaculture Soc. **[3831]**

ARA Intl. **[IO]**, Niederanven, Luxembourg

Arab

Amer. MidEast Leadership Network **[17934]**

Arab Amer. Bus. Women's Coun. **[3674]**

Bridges of Understanding **[17938]**

Egyptian Student Assn. in North America **[8917]**

Iraqi Human Rights Network **[17846]**

Natl. United States-Arab Chamber of Commerce **[23374]**

Syrian-American Relations Coun. **[17951]**

Arab African Soc. of GE and Endoscopy **[IO]**, Cairo, Egypt

Arab Air Carriers Org. **[IO]**, Beirut, Lebanon

Arab Amer. Assn. of Engineers and Architects **[6188]**, PO Box 1536, Chicago, IL 60690-1536, (312)409-8560

Arab Amer. Bus. Women's Coun. **[3674]**, 22952 Outer Dr., Dearborn, MI 48124, (313)277-1986

Arab Amer. Democratic Fed. **[★18063]**

Arab Amer. Inst. **[18374]**, 1600 K St. NW, Ste. 601, Washington, DC 20006, (202)429-9210

Arab Amer. Inst. **[18374]**, 1600 K St. NW, Ste. 601, Washington, DC 20006, (202)429-9210

Arab Amer. Leadership Coun. **[18063]**, 1600 K St. NW, Ste. 601, Washington, DC 20006, (202)429-9210

Arab Amer. Medical Assn. **[★14882]**

Arab Amer. Republican Fed. **[★18063]**

Arab Amer. Women's Coun. **[18922]**, Amer. Arab Chamber of Commerce, 12740 W Warren Ave., Ste. 101, Dearborn, MI 48126, (313)945-1700

Arab Assn. for Human Rights **[IO]**, Nazareth, Israel

Arab Atomic Energy Agency **[IO]**, Tunis, Tunisia

Arab Bankers Assn. of North Am. **[398]**, 150 W 28th St., Ste. 801, New York, NY 10001, (212)599-3030

Arab Bankers Assn. of North Am. **[398]**, 150 W 28th St., Ste. 801, New York, NY 10001, (212)599-3030

Arab Cable Mfrs. Assn. **[IO]**, Manama, Bahrain

Arab Center for the Stud. of Arid Zones and Dry Lands **[IO]**, Damascus, Syrian Arab Republic

Arab Community Center for Economic and Social Services **[18923]**, 2651 Saulino Ct., Dearborn, MI 48120, (313)842-7010

Arab Fertilizer Assn. **[IO]**, Cairo, Egypt

Arab Gulf Programme for United Nations Development Organizations **[IO]**, Riyadh, Saudi Arabia

Arab Horse Soc. **[IO]**, Marlborough, United Kingdom

Arab Hotel Assn. **[IO]**, Jerusalem, Israel

Arab Inst. of Navigation **[IO]**, Alexandria, Egypt

Arab Intl. Women's Forum **[IO]**, London, United Kingdom

Arab-Israeli Relations

Assn. for Peace and Understanding in the Middle East **[18117]**

Coalition for Peace with Justice **[18236]**

Ishmael and Isaac **[18126]**

Middle East Peace Dialogue Network **[12515]**

Arab Knowledge and Mgt. Soc. **[IO]**, Amman, Jordan

Arab Mahgreb Union **[IO]**, Rabat, Morocco

Arab Org. for Agricultural Development **[IO]**, Khartoum, Sudan

Arab Org. for Human Rights **[IO]**, Cairo, Egypt

Arab Palestine Assn. **[IO]**, Mississauga, ON, Canada

Arab Planning Inst. **[IO]**, Safat, Kuwait

Arab Satellite Communications Org. **[IO]**, Riyadh, Saudi Arabia

Arab Soc. of Chemotherapy, Microbiology and Infectious Diseases **[IO]**, Riyadh, Saudi Arabia

Arab Soc. for Intellectual Property **[IO]**, Amman, Jordan

Arab Soc. for Plant Protection **[IO]**, Beirut, Lebanon

Arab Towns Org. **[IO]**, Kaifan, Kuwait

Arab Union for Cement and Building Materials **[IO]**, Damascus, Syrian Arab Republic

Arab Union of Producers, Transporters and Distributors of Electricity **[IO]**, Amman, Jordan

Arab Urban Development Inst. **[IO]**, Riyadh, Saudi Arabia

Arab Women's Solidarity Assn. **[13450]**, New York Univ., Center for the Stud. of Gender and Sexuality, 285 Mercer St., 3rd Fl., Rm. 307, New York, NY 10003-6653, (212)992-9543

Arab Women's Solidarity Assn. UNITED **[13450]**, New York Univ., Center for the Stud. of Gender and Sexuality, 285 Mercer St., 3rd Fl., Rm. 307, New York, NY 10003-6653, (212)992-9543

Arab World Inst. **[IO]**, Paris, France

Arab World and Islamic Resources and School Services **[9137]**, PO Box 174, Abiquiu, NM 87510, (505)685-4533

Arab World and Islamic Resources and School Services **[9137]**, PO Box 174, Abiquiu, NM 87510, (505)685-4533

Arabian F.O.A.L. Assn. **[10929]**, PO Box 198, Parksville, NY 12768-0198, (845)292-7797

Arabian Horse Assn. **[4565]**, 10805 E Bethany Dr., Aurora, CO 80014, (303)696-4500

Arabian Horse Breeders Alliance **[4566]**, 28150 N Alma School Pkwy., Ste. 103-474, Scottsdale, AZ 85262, (480)415-8921

Arabian Horse Breeders Alliance **[4566]**, 28150 N Alma School Pkwy., Ste. 103-474, Scottsdale, AZ 85262, (480)415-8921

Arabian Horse Club Registry of Am. **[★4565]**

Arabian Horse Owners Found. **[4567]**, 4101 N Bear Canyon Rd., Tucson, AZ 85749, (520)760-0682

Reference to "IO" in place of a book number signifies that the association may be found in the 50th edition of International Organizations.

Arabian Horse Registry of Am. and Intl. Arabian
Horse Assn. [★4565]
Arabian Jockey Club [22650], 10805 E Bethany Dr.,
Aurora, CO 80014, (303)696-4523
Arabian Professional and Amateur Horseman's Assn.
[4568], Carole Stohlmann, Membership Chair,
12367 187th St., Mokena, IL 60448-8277,
(405)749-7819
Arabic
Al-Bustan Seeds of Culture [9135]
Amer. Arab Chamber of Commerce [23324]
Amer. Assn. of Teachers of Arabic [8457]
Amer. Fed. of Ramallah, Palestine [9136]
Arab Amer. Women's Coun. [18922]
Arab Community Center for Economic and Social
Services [18923]
Arab World and Islamic Resources and School
Services [9137]
Arab World and Islamic Resources and School
Services [9137]
Bilateral US-Arab Chamber of Commerce [23325]
Bilateral US-Arab Chamber of Commerce [23325]
Birzeit Soc. [9138]
Bridges of Understanding [17938]
Chaldean Fed. of Am. [9139]
Inst. for Palestine Stud. [9140]
Inst. for Palestine Stud. [9140]
Musical Missions of Peace [10352]
Women of Yemen Assn. [11080]
Zawaya [9141]
Aragti Relief and Development Org. [IO], Mogad-
ishu, Somalia
Aranzadi Zientzi Elkartea [★IO]
Arba Sicula [19228], St. John's Univ., Languages
and Literature Dept., Jamaica, NY 11439,
(718)990-5203
Arba Sicula [19228], St. John's Univ., Languages
and Literature Dept., Jamaica, NY 11439,
(718)990-5203
Arbeitsgemeinschaft 13 August [★IO]
Arbeitsgemeinschaft Alpenlander [★IO]
Arbeitsgemeinschaft Spina Bifida und Hydrocephalus
[IO], Dortmund, Germany
Arbeitsgemeinschaft fur Sportpsychologie [★IO]
Arbeitsgemeinschaft fur Wissenschaft und Politik
[★IO]
Arbeitsgemeinschaft der Wissenschaftlichen Mediz-
inischen Fachgesellschaften [★IO]
Arbeitskreis kulinarischer Fachjournalisten [★IO]
Arbetarnas Bildningsforbund [★IO]
Arbitration Found. [★5201]
**Arbitration and MediationArbitrationADR Inst. of
Canada**
Amer. Arbitration Assn. [5201]
Amer. Bar Assn. Sect. of Dispute Resolution
[5202]
Assn. for Conflict Resolution [5203]
Center for Dispute Settlement [5204]
CPR Intl. Inst. for Conflict Prevention and Resolu-
tion [5205]
Inst. for Mediation and Conflict Resolution [5206]
Intl. Centre for Settlement of Investment Disputes
[5207]
Intl. Centre for Settlement of Investment Disputes
[5207]
Mediators Without Borders [5208]
Natl. Acad. of Arbitrators [5209]
Natl. Assn. for Community Mediation [5210]
Professional Mediation Assn. [5211]
Soc. of Maritime Arbitrators [5212]
Veterinary Assn. for Arbitration and Jurisprudence
[14321]
Arbitration and Mediation Inst. of Canada [★12379]
Arbitration Soc. of Am. [★5201]
Arbor Day Found. [18668], 100 Arbor Ave.,
Nebraska City, NE 68410, (402)873-8733
Arboricultural Assn. [IO], Cheltenham, United
Kingdom
ARC-Institute for Tropical and Subtropical Crops
[IO], Nelspruit, Republic of South Africa
Arc of the US. [12495], 1660 L St. NW, Ste. 301,
Washington, DC 20036, (202)534-3700
ARC Videodance [★9536]
ARCA: Amer. Romeldale/CVM Assn. [4903], 1039
State Rte. 168, Darlington, PA 16115, (724)843-
2084

Archaeological Conservancy [6160], 5301 Central
Ave. NE, Ste. 902, Albuquerque, NM 87108,
(505)266-1540
Archaeological Inst. of Am. [6161], 656 Beacon St.,
6th Fl., Boston, MA 02215-2006, (617)353-9361
Archaeological Inst. of Am. [6161], 656 Beacon St.,
6th Fl., Boston, MA 02215-2006, (617)353-9361
Archaeology
Amer. Rock Art Res. Assn. [6159]
Archaeological Conservancy [6160]
Archaeological Inst. of Am. [6161]
Archaeological Inst. of Am. [6161]
Archaeology Scotland [2407]
Archeology Division of the Amer. Anthropological
Assn. [6162]
Assn. for the Protection of Afghan Archaeology
[6163]
Center for Amer. Archeology [6164]
Center for the Stud. of Beadwork [6165]
Center for the Stud. of Beadwork [6165]
Epigraphic Soc. [6166]
Etruscan Found. [6167]
Exploring Solutions Past: The Maya Forest Alli-
ance [6168]
Exploring Solutions Past: The Maya Forest Alli-
ance [6168]
Fed. of Metal Detector and Archaeological Clubs
[21851]
Inst. for Amer. Indian Stud. [6169]
Inst. of Nautical Archaeology [6170]
Inst. of Nautical Archaeology [6170]
Intl. Assn. for Obsidian Stud. [6171]
Intl. Assn. for Obsidian Stud. [6171]
Natl. Assn. of State Archaeologists [6172]
Near East Archaeological Soc. [6173]
Near East Archaeological Soc. [6173]
New England Antiquities Res. Assn. [6174]
Register of Professional Archaeologists [6175]
Soc. for Amer. Archaeology [6176]
Soc. of Bead Researchers [6177]
Soc. of Bead Researchers [6177]
Soc. for Historical Archaeology [6178]
Soc. for Historical Archaeology [6178]
Soc. for Indus. Archeology [6179]
Soc. for Post-Medieval Archaeology [10901]
Ulster Archaeological Soc. [14923]
World Archaeological Soc. [6180]
World Archaeological Soc. [6180]
Archaeology Abroad [IO], London, United Kingdom
Archaeology Scotland [IO], Musselburgh, United
Kingdom
Archbishop Oscar Arnulfo Romero Relief Fund
[★18507]
Archbishop Oscar Arnulfo Romero Relief Fund
[★18507]
Archconfraternity of the Holy Ghost [19384], 6230
Brush Run Rd., Bethel Park, PA 15102, (412)831-
0302
L'Arche Australia [IO], Hobart, Australia
Arche Noah [IO], Schiltern, Austria
Archeology Division of the Amer. Anthropological
Assn. [6162], School of Human Evolution and Soc.
Change, Arizona State Univ., Box 872402, Tempe,
AZ 85287-2402, (480)965-6215
Archeology Sect. [★6162]
Archer Assn. [20425], PO Box 6233, McLean, VA
22106
Archery
Archery Shooters Assn. [22220]
Christian Bowhunters of Am. [22221]
Natl. Alliance for the Development of Archery
[22222]
Natl. Archery Assn. of the U.S. [22223]
Natl. Bowhunter Educ. Found. [22224]
The Natl. Crossbowmen of the U.S.A. [22225]
Natl. Field Archery Assn. [22226]
North Am. Bowhunting Coalition [21866]
Pope and Young Club [22227]
Professional Bowhunter's Soc. [22228]
Archery Australia [IO], Panania, Australia
Archery Lane Operators Assn. [★3323]
Archery Mfrs. Assn. [★3305]
Archery Mfrs. Assn. [★3305]
Archery Mfrs. and Dealers Assn. [★3305]
Archery Mfrs. and Dealers Assn. [★3305]

Archery Mfrs. and Merchants Org. [★3305]
Archery Mfrs. and Merchants Org. [★3305]
Archery Mfrs. Org. [★3305]
Archery Mfrs. Org. [★3305]
Archery New Zealand [IO], Porirua, New Zealand
Archery Range and Retailers Org. [3323], 156 N
Main, Ste. D, Oregon, WI 53575, (608)835-9060
Archery Shooters Assn. [22220], PO Box 399, Ken-
nesaw, GA 30156, (770)795-0232
Archery Trade Assn. [3305], 101 N German St., Ste.
3, New Ulm, MN 56073, (507)233-8130
Archery Trade Assn. [3305], 101 N German St., Ste.
3, New Ulm, MN 56073, (507)233-8130
Architects Coun. of Europe [IO], Brussels, Belgium
Architects/Designers/Planners for Social Responsibil-
ity [18191], PO Box 9126, Berkeley, CA 94709,
(510)845-1000
Architects Regional Coun. Asia [IO], Seoul, Republic
of Korea
Architects Registration Bd. [IO], London, United
Kingdom
Architects for Social Responsibility [★18191]
Architects Without Borders - Address unknown since
2011.
Architectural Aluminum Mfrs. Assn. [★518]
Architectural Anodizers Coun. [★786]
Architectural Assn. [IO], London, United Kingdom
Architectural Assn. of Ireland [IO], Dublin, Ireland
Architectural Cladding Assn. [IO], Leicester, United
Kingdom
Architectural Education
ArchVoices [6190]
Building Tech. Educators' Soc. [7732]
Carpenters' Company [9674]
Ulster Architectural Heritage Soc. [15129]
Architectural Engg. Inst. [6185], 1801 Alexander Bell
Dr., Reston, VA 20191-4400, (703)295-6370
Architectural Glass and Metal Contractors Assn.
[IO], Pickering, ON, Canada
Architectural Heritage Found. [9669], Old City Hall,
45 School St., Boston, MA 02108-3204, (617)523-
7210
Architectural Heritage Soc. of Scotland [IO], Edin-
burgh, United Kingdom
Architectural Inst. of the Republic of China [IO],
Taipei, Taiwan
Architectural League of New York [17392], 594
Broadway, Ste. 607, New York, NY 10012,
(212)753-1722
Architectural Precast Assn. [823], 6710 Winkler Rd.,
Ste. 8, Fort Myers, FL 33919, (239)454-6989
Architectural Res. Centers Consortium [6189], Prof.
Stephen Weeks, Treas., Herberger Inst. for Design
& the Arts, Arizona State Univ., Tempte, AZ 85281,
(480)965-5561
Architectural Res. Centers Consortium [6189], Prof.
Stephen Weeks, Treas., Herberger Inst. for Design
& the Arts, Arizona State Univ., Tempte, AZ 85281,
(480)965-5561
Architectural Soc. of China [IO], Beijing, People's
Republic of China
Architectural and Specialist Door Mfrs. Assn. [IO],
High Wycombe, United Kingdom
Architectural Woodwork Inst. [522], 46179 Westlake
Dr., Ste. 120, Potomac Falls, VA 20165, (571)323-
3636
Architectural Woodwork Mfrs. Assn. of Canada [IO],
High River, AB, Canada
**ArchitectureArchitectureAlexander Thomson
Soc.**
Amer. Architectural Found. [6181]
Amer. Indian Coun. of Architects and Engineers
[6182]
Amer. Inst. of Architects [6183]
Amer. Inst. of Architecture Students [238]
Amer. Inst. of Building Design [6184]
Amer. Soc. of Architectural Illustrators [239]
Amer. Soc. of Civil Engineers | Architectural Engg.
Inst. [6185]
Amer. Soc. of Golf Course Architects [6186]
Amer. Soc. of Landscape Architects [6187]
Amer. Underground Constr. Assn. [7484]
Arab Amer. Assn. of Engineers and Architects
[6188]
Architectural Engg. Inst. [6185]

A star before a book entry number signifies that the name is not listed separately, but is mentioned within the entry.

Architectural League of New York [17392]
Architectural Res. Centers Consortium [6189]
Architectural Res. Centers Consortium [6189]
ArchVoices [6190]
Asian Amer. Architects and Engineers [6191]
Assn. of Architecture Organizations [6192]
Assn. for Bridge Constr. and Design [6193]
Assn. of Collegiate Schools of Architecture [7733]
Assn. of Licensed Architects [240]
Assn. of Licensed Architects [240]
Assn. of Univ. Architects [6194]
Assn. for Women in Architecture [241]
Atomic Age Alliance [9672]
Building Commissioning Assn. [538]
Building Enclosure Coun. Natl. [6374]
Building Res. Coun. [7734]
Building Tech. Educators' Soc. [7732]
Carpenters' Company [9674]
Coalition of Organic Landscapers [2179]
Commonwealth Assn. of Architects [9694]
Community Associations Inst. [17373]
Coun. of Landscape Architectural Registration
    Boards [6195]
Coun. on Tall Buildings and Urban Habitat [6196]
Coun. on Tall Buildings and Urban Habitat [6196]
DOCOMOMO US [9683]
Environmental Design Res. Assn. [5213]
Frank Lloyd Wright Assn. [7735]
Fusion Architecture [6197]
Graham Found. [242]
House Plan Marketing Assn. [1038]
Inst. for Urban Design [6198]
Intl. Assn. for Bridge Maintenance and Safety
    [6369]
Intl. Soc. of the Arts, Mathematics, and
    Architecture [7003]
Landscape Architecture Found. [6199]
Latino Engineers, Architects and Developers Soc.
    [7029]
Ministry Architecture [6200]
Natl. Architectural Accrediting Bd. [7736]
Natl. Building Museum [6201]
Natl. Coun. of Architectural Registration Boards
    [5214]
Natl. Coun. of Architectural Registration Boards
    [5214]
Natl. Org. of Minority Architects [6202]
Phi Kappa Upsilon Fraternity [23521]
Public Architecture [243]
Public Art Fund [17395]
Rice Design Alliance [6203]
Sculpture in the Env. [17396]
Short Span Steel Bridge Alliance [6371]
Soc. of Amer. Registered Architects [6204]
Soc. for Design Admin. [6205]
Soc. of Iranian Architects and Planners [6206]
Soc. of Iranian Architects and Planners [6206]
Tau Sigma Delta [23466]
Twentieth Century Soc. [11791]
Urbanists Intl. [6207]
Van Alen Inst.: Projects in Public Architecture
    [7737]
Vernacular Architecture Forum [6208]
Walter Burley Griffin Soc. of Am. [9142]
Water Design-Build Coun. [634]
Architecture 2030 [4333], 607 Cerrillos Rd., Santa
    Fe, NM 87505, (505)988-5309
Architecture and Culture Soc. of China [IO], Hang-
    zhou, People's Republic of China
Architecture for Humanity [11546], 848 Folsom St.,
    Ste. 201, San Francisco, CA 94107, (415)963-3511
Architecture for Humanity [11546], 848 Folsom St.,
    Ste. 201, San Francisco, CA 94107, (415)963-3511
Archives
    Acad. of Certified Archivists [244]
    Black Archives of Mid-America [9143]
    Irish Soc. for Archives [658]
    Midwest Archives Conf. [9144]
    Soc. of Amer. Archivists [9145]
Archives of Amer. Art [9159], PO Box 37012,
    Washington, DC 20013-7012, (202)633-7940
Archives and Museum of the Polish Catholic Union
    of Am. [★10464]
Archives for UFO Res. [IO], Norrkoping, Sweden
Archivio Disarmo [IO], Rome, Italy

Archivists and Librarians in the History of the Hea.
    Sciences [9961], Arlene Shaner, Treas., The New
    York Acad. of Medicine, 1216 5th Ave., New York,
    NY 10029, (212)822-7313
Archonist Club - Defunct.
ArchVoices [6190], 1014 Curtis St., Albany, CA
    94706, (510)757-6213
A.R.C.I Nuova Associazione [IO], Rome, Italy
ARCNET Trade Assn. - Defunct.
Arcosanti [★4192]
Arcosanti, A Proj. of the Cosanti Found. [4192], HC
    74, Box 4136, Mayer, AZ 86333, (928)632-7135
Arctic Cat Club of Am. [22134], Paul Wustrack, Mgr./
    Webmaster, PO Box 528, Rosendale, WI 54974-
    0528
Arctic Club [★6858]
Arctic Club [★6858]
Arctic Inst. of North Am. [IO], Calgary, AB, Canada
Arctic Monitoring and Assessment Programme [IO],
    Oslo, Norway
Arctic Region Found. of Vocational Training [IO],
    Overtornea, Sweden
Arctic Res. Program [★7381]
Arctic Winter Games Intl. Comm. [IO], Whitehorse,
    YT, Canada
Arcus Found. [18311], 402 E Michigan Ave.,
    Kalamazoo, MI 49007, (269)373-4373
Ardent Lion Soc. [11659], PO Box 356, White
    Plains, NY 10605, (914)874-4480
ARF Tzeghagrons [★18146]
Argentina
    Argentine-American Chamber of Commerce
        [23351]
Argentina Chamber of Commerce [IO], Buenos
    Aires, Argentina
Argentina Israel Chamber of Commerce [IO], Bue-
    nos Aires, Argentina
Argentina Oils and Fats Assn. [IO], Buenos Aires,
    Argentina
Argentine Acad. of Geophysicists and Geodesists
    [IO], Buenos Aires, Argentina
Argentine Acad. of Letters [IO], Buenos Aires,
    Argentina
Argentine Advt. Agencies' Assn. [IO], Buenos Aires,
    Argentina
Argentine-American Chamber of Commerce [23351],
    630 5th Ave., 25th Fl., Rockefeller Ctr., New York,
    NY 10111, (212)698-2238
Argentine Assn. of Biology and Nuclear Medicine
    [IO], Buenos Aires, Argentina
Argentine Assn. of Doctors for the Env. [IO], Buenos
    Aires, Argentina
Argentine Assn. of Ecology [IO], Buenos Aires,
    Argentina
Argentine Assn. of Insurance Companies [IO], Bue-
    nos Aires, Argentina
Argentine Assn. of Medical Informatics [IO], Buenos
    Aires, Argentina
Argentine Assn. of Non-Destructive and Structural
    Evaluation [IO], Buenos Aires, Argentina
Argentine Assn. for Photogrammetry and Related
    Sciences [IO], Buenos Aires, Argentina
Argentine Assn. of Travel and Tourism Agencies
    [IO], Buenos Aires, Argentina
Argentine Bank Marketing Assn. [IO], Buenos Aires,
    Argentina
Argentine Bible Soc. [IO], Buenos Aires, Argentina
Argentine Biochemical Assn. [IO], Buenos Aires,
    Argentina
Argentine Cable TV Assn. [IO], Buenos Aires,
    Argentina
Argentine Canadian Chamber of Commerce [IO],
    Buenos Aires, Argentina
Argentine Center of Agricultural Engineers [IO], Bue-
    nos Aires, Argentina
Argentine Centre of Engg. [IO], Buenos Aires,
    Argentina
Argentine Chamber of Aerosols [IO], Buenos Aires,
    Argentina
Argentine Chamber of the Aluminum, Metals and
    Related Indus. [IO], Buenos Aires, Argentina
Argentine Chamber of Book Publishers [IO], Buenos
    Aires, Argentina
Argentine Chamber of the Clothing Indus. [IO], Bue-
    nos Aires, Argentina

Argentine Chamber of Constr. [IO], Buenos Aires,
    Argentina
Argentine Chamber of Elecl. Material Distributors
    [IO], Buenos Aires, Argentina
Argentine Chamber of Electronics Indus. [IO], Bue-
    nos Aires, Argentina
Argentine Chamber of Exporters [IO], Buenos Aires,
    Argentina
Argentine Chamber of Informatics and Communica-
    tions [IO], Buenos Aires, Argentina
Argentine Chamber of Limited Companies [IO], Bue-
    nos Aires, Argentina
Argentine Chamber of the Plastics Indus. [IO], Bue-
    nos Aires, Argentina
Argentine Chamber of Producers of Pharmaceutical
    Chemicals [IO], Buenos Aires, Argentina
Argentine Chamber of Stationers, Bookshops and
    Related Businesses [IO], Buenos Aires, Argentina
Argentine Chamber of Supermarkets [IO], Buenos
    Aires, Argentina
Argentine Chinese Chamber of Production, Indus.
    and Commerce [IO], Buenos Aires, Argentina
Argentine Coun. of Shopping Centers [IO], Buenos
    Aires, Argentina
Argentine Cricket Assn. [IO], Buenos Aires,
    Argentina
Argentine Fiscal Associations [IO], La Plata,
    Argentina
Argentine Franchising Assn. [IO], Buenos Aires,
    Argentina
Argentine Game Developers Assn. [IO], Buenos
    Aires, Argentina
Argentine Indus. Assn. [IO], Buenos Aires, Argentina
Argentine Magazine Publishers' Assn. [IO], Buenos
    Aires, Argentina
Argentine Marketing Assn. [IO], Buenos Aires,
    Argentina
Argentine Metallurgical Indus'. Assn. [IO], Buenos
    Aires, Argentina
Argentine-North Amer. Assn. for the Advancement of
    Science, Technology and Culture - Defunct.
Argentine Oil Indus. Chamber [IO], Buenos Aires,
    Argentina
Argentine Orthopedic and Traumatology Assn. [IO],
    Buenos Aires, Argentina
Argentine Packaging Inst. [IO], Buenos Aires,
    Argentina
Argentine Paleontological Assn. [IO], Buenos Aires,
    Argentina
Argentine Soc. of Bioengineering [IO], Corrientes,
    Argentina
Argentine Soc. of Biology [IO], Buenos Aires,
    Argentina
Argentine Soc. of Botany [IO], Buenos Aires,
    Argentina
Argentine Soc. of Cancerology [IO], Buenos Aires,
    Argentina
Argentine Soc. of Cardiology [IO], Buenos Aires,
    Argentina
Argentine Soc. of Dermatology [IO], Buenos Aires,
    Argentina
Argentine Soc. of Endocrinology and Metabolism
    [IO], Buenos Aires, Argentina
Argentine Soc. of Gastroenterology [IO], Buenos
    Aires, Argentina
Argentine Soc. of Geographical Stud. [IO], Buenos
    Aires, Argentina
Argentine Soc. of Hematology [IO], Buenos Aires,
    Argentina
Argentine Soc. of Hypertension [IO], Buenos Aires,
    Argentina
Argentine Soc. of Infectious Diseases [IO], Buenos
    Aires, Argentina
Argentine Soc. of Medical Genetics [IO], Buenos
    Aires, Argentina
Argentine Soc. of Ophthalmology [IO], Buenos Aires,
    Argentina
Argentine Soc. of Osteoporosis [IO], Buenos Aires,
    Argentina
Argentine Soc. of Pediatrics [IO], Buenos Aires,
    Argentina
Argentine Soc. of Psychosomatic Obstetrics and Gy-
    naecology [IO], Buenos Aires, Argentina
Argentine Soc. for Psychotrauma [IO], Buenos Aires,
    Argentina

Reference to "IO" in place of a book number signifies that the association may be found in the 50th edition of International Organizations.

Argentine Sugar Center [IO], Buenos Aires, Argentina

Argentine TV and Radio Assn. [IO], Buenos Aires, Argentina

Argentinian Assn. of Dermatology [IO], Buenos Aires, Argentina

Argentinian Soc. of EEG and Clinical Neurophysiology [IO], Buenos Aires, Argentina

ARIAS: Canadian Opera Student Development Fund [IO], Toronto, ON, Canada

Arias Found. for Peace and Human Progress [IO], San Jose, Costa Rica

Arica Inst. [9820], PO Box 645, Kent, CT 06757-0645, (860)927-1006

Arica Inst. [9820], PO Box 645, Kent, CT 06757-0645, (860)927-1006

Arica Inst. in Am. [★9820]

Arica Inst. in Am. [★9820]

Ariel Motorcycle Club North Am. [21920], PO Box 77737, Stockton, CA 95267

Ariel Owners' Motorcycle Club [★21920]

The Aril Soc. [★21784]

Aril Soc. Intl. [21784], Reita Jordan, Membership Sec.-Treas., 3500 Avenida Charada NW, Albuquerque, NM 87107

Arise Intl. [★20009]

Arise Intl. [★20009]

ARISE Intl. Mission [20009], PO Box 1014, College Park, MD 20741, (301)395-2385

ARISE Intl. Mission [20009], PO Box 1014, College Park, MD 20741, (301)395-2385

Arise Medical Missions [15146], 1350 Grantham Dr., Sarasota, FL 34234, (253)355-0179

Aristolochite Soc. [★23619]

Aristos Guild - Defunct.

Aristotelian Soc. [IO], London, United Kingdom

Arizona Cactus [★6426]

Arizona Cactus and Native Flora Soc. [★6352]

Arizona Cactus and Succulent Res.

Arizona Cactus and Succulent Res. - Address unknown since 2011.

Arizona Cotton Planting Seed Distributors [★3962]

Arizona Macintosh Users Gp. [6503], 5235 E Southern Ave., Ste. D106, PMB 445, Mesa, AZ 85206

ARJD [★5615]

Ark-La-Tex Genealogical Assn. [20620], PO Box 4463, Shreveport, LA 71134-0463

Ark Mission [11191], 830 S Buffalo Grove Rd., Ste. 103, Buffalo Grove, IL 60089, (847)215-2755

Arkivet for UFO-Forskning [★IO]

Arkleton Trust [IO], Streatley, United Kingdom

Arktisen Laaketieteen Keskus [★IO]

Arktisk Institut [★IO]

ARLIS/UK and Ireland: Art Libraries Soc. of the United Kingdom and Ireland [IO], London, United Kingdom

ARMA Intl. - Canadian Region [IO], Fredericton, NB, Canada

ARMA Intl. - The Assn. of Info. Mgt. Professionals [1895], 11880 Coll. Blvd., Ste. 450, Overland Park, KS 66210, (913)341-3808

ARMA Intl. - The Assn. of Info. Mgt. Professionals [1895], 11880 Coll. Blvd., Ste. 450, Overland Park, KS 66210, (913)341-3808

Armateurs du Saint-Laurent [★IO]

Arme Schulschwestern von Unserer Lieben Frau [★IO]

Armed Females of Am. [17682], 2702 E Univ. Dr., Ste. 103, PMB 213, Mesa, AZ 85213, (480)924-8202

Armed Forces

2D Reconnaissance Battalion Assn. [5215]

30th Infantry Div. Veterans of WWII [20343]

32nd Red Arrow Veteran Assn. [20344]

33rd Infantry Div. Assn. [20345]

35th Div. Assn. [20346]

107th Engineer Assn. [5216]

129th Alumni and Heritage Assn. [19270]

AdoptaPlatoon [11081]

AFBA [18924]

Air Force Aid Soc. [18925]

America's Heroes of Freedom [20347]

Any Soldier [11082]

Army and Air Force Mutual Aid Assn. [18926]

Army Emergency Relief [18927]

Army Engineer Assn. [5217]

Assn. for Counselors and Educators in Govt. [11669]

Books For Soldiers [11083]

Building Homes for Heroes [11084]

Cause - Comfort for America's Uniformed Services [11085]

Cell Phones for Soldiers [11086]

Coalition for Tactical Medicine [15907]

Combat Helicopter Pilots Assn. [20313]

Distinguished Flying Cross Soc. [20374]

For the Fallen [12531]

Forgotten Soldiers Outreach [11087]

Give an Hour [11088]

Grateful Amer. Coin [11089]

Hero's Welcome [20348]

Hof Reunion Assn. [20349]

Homefront Am. [11090]

Hope for the Warriors [11091]

Hugs for Our Soldiers [11092]

Hugs Proj. [11093]

Laptops for the Wounded [11526]

Marine Corps Veterans Assn. [20683]

Marines Helping Marines [12433]

Military Benefit Assn. [18928]

Military Intelligence Corps Assn. [5218]

Military Order of the Purple Heart of the U.S.A. [20378]

Military Space [11094]

Mothers of Military Support [12529]

Natl. Assn. of Medics and Corpsmen [5219]

Navy-Marine Corps Relief Soc. [18929]

Never Forget Our Fallen [11095]

Oper. First Response [11096]

Oper. Gratitude [11097]

Oper. Gratitude [11097]

Oper. Homelink [11098]

Oper. Hug-A-Hero [12533]

Oper. Interdependence [12530]

Oper. Never Forgotten [11099]

Oper. Paperback [11100]

Oper. Quiet Comfort [11101]

Oper. ShoeBox [11102]

Oper. Stars and Stripes [11103]

Oper. Support Our Troops [11104]

Oper.: Take a Soldier to the Movies [11105]

Oper. Troop Aid [11106]

Our Military Kids [12534]

Salute Military Golf Assn. [22624]

Salute Our Services [11107]

SATS/EAF Assn. [20686]

Soldiers' Angels [18930]

A Soldier's Wish List [11108]

Stand for the Troops [20350]

Stars for Stripes [20417]

Step Up 4 Vets [13354]

Support Our Soldiers Am. [11109]

Support Our Troops [11110]

Tragedy Assistance Prog. for Survivors [11111]

Troops Out Now Coalition [18292]

U.S. Entertainment Force [11112]

U.S. Marine Corps Scout/Sniper Assn. [20688]

United We Serve [20712]

USMC Vietnam Tankers Assn. [20824]

USO World HQ [18931]

USO World HQ [18931]

USS Nitro AE-2/AE-23 Assn. [5220]

Veterans Assn. of Am. [20809]

Vietnam Dustoff Assn. [20836]

Vietnam Era Seabees [20826]

West-Indian Amer. Military Members Assn. [5221]

Armed Forces Benefit and Aid Assn. - Defunct.

Armed Forces Benefit Assn. [★18924]

Armed Forces Chem. Assn. [★5814]

Armed Forces Communications and Electronics Assn. [5797], 4400 Fair Lakes Ct., Fairfax, VA 22033, (703)631-6100

Armed Forces Communications and Electronics Assn. [5797], 4400 Fair Lakes Ct., Fairfax, VA 22033, (703)631-6100

Armed Forces Communications and Electronics Assn. of Canada [IO], Nepean, ON, Canada

Armed Forces Enlisted Personnel Benefit Assn. [★18928]

Armed Forces Hostess Assn. [5798], The Pentagon, Rm. 1E541, 6604 Army Pentagon, Washington, DC 20310, (703)614-0350

Armed Forces Inst. of Pathology - Address unknown since 2011.

Armed Forces Inst. of Pathology | Dept. of Environmental and Toxicologic Pathology [16117], Armed Forces Inst. of Pathology, 6825 16th St. NW, Washington, DC 20306-6000

Armed Forces Inst. of Pathology | Dept. of Environmental and Toxicologic Pathology [16117], Armed Forces Inst. of Pathology, 6825 16th St. NW, Washington, DC 20306-6000

Armed Forces Judo Assn. [★22705]

Armed Forces Mgt. Assn. [★5814]

Armed Forces Marketing Coun. - Defunct.

Armed Forces Relief and Benefit Assn. [★18924]

Armed Forces Sports [5799], The Summit Center, 4700 King St., 4th Fl., Alexandria, VA 22302-4418, (888)875-PLAY

Armed Forces Sports Comm. [★5799]

Armed Forces Stamp Exchange Club - Address unknown since 2010.

Armed Forces Writers League [★5324]

Armenia

Armenian Amer. Chamber of Commerce [23352]

Armenia Skating Fed. [IO], Yerevan, Armenia

Armenian

Armenian Amer. Chamber of Commerce [23352]

Armenian Amer. Cultural Assn. [9146]

Armenian Assembly of Am. [9147]

Armenian Assembly of Am. [9147]

Armenian Church Youth Org. of Am. [19298]

Armenian Film Found. [9148]

Armenian Film Found. [9148]

Armenian Gen. Benevolent Union [18932]

Armenian Gen. Benevolent Union [18932]

Armenian Intl. Women's Assn. [13451]

Armenian Missionary Assn. of Am. [19299]

Armenian Natl. Comm. of Am. [18933]

Armenian Natl. Comm. of Am. [18933]

Armenian Natl. Educ. Comm. [7738]

Armenian Natl. Educ. Comm. [7738]

Armenian Relief Soc. of Eastern U.S.A. [18934]

Armenian Relief Soc. of Eastern U.S.A. [18934]

Armenian Students' Assn. of Am. [18935]

Hairenik Assn. [18936]

Natl. Assn. for Armenian Stud. and Res. [9149]

Soc. for Armenian Stud. [9150]

Soc. for Armenian Stud. [9150]

Soc. for Orphaned Armenian Relief [12892]

Armenian Amer. Chamber of Commerce [23352], 225 E Broadway, Ste. 313C, Glendale, CA 91205, (818)247-0196

Armenian Amer. Cultural Assn. [9146], 1300 Crystal Dr., Ste. 1504, Arlington, VA 22202, (703)416-2555

Armenian Amer. Democratic Leadership Coun. - Address unknown since 2011.

Armenian Amer. Soc. for Stud. on Stress and Genocide [15447], 185 E 85th St., Mezzanine No. 4, New York, NY 10028, (201)723-9578

Armenian Assembly of Am. [9147], 1334 G St. NW, Washington, DC 20005, (202)393-3434

Armenian Assembly of Am. [9147], 1334 G St. NW, Washington, DC 20005, (202)393-3434

Armenian Assn. of Orthodontists [IO], Yerevan, Armenia

Armenian Assn. of Women with Univ. Educ. [IO], Yerevan, Armenia

Armenian Bar Assn. [5234], PO Box 29111, Los Angeles, CA 90029, (323)666-6288

Armenian Bar Assn. [5234], PO Box 29111, Los Angeles, CA 90029, (323)666-6288

Armenian Behavioral Sci. Assn. - Address unknown since 2010.

Armenian Cardiologists Assn. [IO], Yerevan, Armenia

Armenian Church Youth Org. of Am. [19298], Eastern Diocese of the Armenian Church of Am., 630 2nd Ave., New York, NY 10016, (212)686-0710

Armenian Coin Club [★21968]

Armenian Dance Sport Fed. [IO], Yerevan, Armenia

Armenian Draughts Fed. [IO], Yerevan, Armenia

Armenian Educational Found. [8095], 600 W Broadway, Ste. 130, Glendale, CA 91204, (818)242-4154

A star before a book entry number signifies that the name is not listed separately, but is mentioned within the entry.

Armenian Electron Microscopy Soc. [IO], Yerevan, Armenia

Armenian Engineers and Scientists of Am. [7359], 417 W Arden Ave., Ste. 112C, Glendale, CA 91203-4046, (818)547-3372

Armenian Engineers and Scientists of Am. [7359], 417 W Arden Ave., Ste. 112C, Glendale, CA 91203-4046, (818)547-3372

Armenian Film Found. [9148], 2219 Thousand Oaks Blvd., Ste. 292, Thousand Oaks, CA 91362, (805)495-0717

Armenian Film Found. [9148], 2219 Thousand Oaks Blvd., Ste. 292, Thousand Oaks, CA 91362, (805)495-0717

Armenian Gen. Benevolent Union [18932], 55 E 59th St., New York, NY 10022-1112, (212)319-6383

Armenian Gen. Benevolent Union [18932], 55 E 59th St., New York, NY 10022-1112, (212)319-6383

Armenian Gen. Benevolent Union of Am. [★18932]

Armenian Gen. Benevolent Union of Am. [★18932]

Armenian Handball Fed. [IO], Yerevan, Armenia

Armenian Intl. Women's Assn. [13451], 65 Main St., No. 3A, Watertown, MA 02472, (617)926-0171

Armenian Junior Chamber [IO], Yerevan, Armenia

Armenian Lib. Assn. [IO], Yerevan, Armenia

Armenian Literary Soc. - Defunct.

Armenian Medical Assn. [IO], Yerevan, Armenia

Armenian Missionary Assn. of Am. [19299], 31 W Century Rd., Paramus, NJ 07652, (201)265-2607

Armenian Natl. Comm. of Am. [18933], 1711 N St. NW, Washington, DC 20036, (202)775-1918

Armenian Natl. Comm. of Am. [18933], 1711 N St. NW, Washington, DC 20036, (202)775-1918

Armenian Natl. Educ. Comm. [7738], The Armenian Prelacy, 138 E 39th St., New York, NY 10016, (212)689-7810

Armenian Natl. Educ. Comm. [7738], The Armenian Prelacy, 138 E 39th St., New York, NY 10016, (212)689-7810

Armenian Natl. League Against Epilepsy [IO], Yerevan, Armenia

Armenian Natl. Paralympic Comm. [IO], Yerevan, Armenia

Armenian Numismatic Soc. [21968], 8511 Beverly Park Pl., Pico Rivera, CA 90660-1920, (562)695-0380

Armenian Numismatics and Artifact Soc. [★21968]

Armenian Red Cross [★18934]

Armenian Red Cross [★18934]

Armenian Relief Soc. [IO], Yerevan, Armenia

Armenian Relief Soc. [★18934]

Armenian Relief Soc. [★18934]

Armenian Relief Soc. of Eastern U.S.A. [18934], 80 Bigelow Ave., Ste. 200, Watertown, MA 02472, (617)926-3801

Armenian Relief Soc. of Eastern U.S.A. [18934], 80 Bigelow Ave., Ste. 200, Watertown, MA 02472, (617)926-3801

Armenian Revolutionary Fed. [18145], 80 Bigelow Ave., Watertown, MA 02472, (617)923-1933

Armenian Revolutionary Fed. [18145], 80 Bigelow Ave., Watertown, MA 02472, (617)923-1933

Armenian Revolutionary Fed. of Am. [★18145]

Armenian Revolutionary Fed. of Am. [★18145]

Armenian Rheumatological Assn. [IO], Yerevan, Armenia

Armenian Rugs Soc. [9160], PO Box 696, Palo Alto, CA 94302-0696, (650)343-8585

Armenian Squash Fed. [IO], Yerevan, Armenia

Armenian Students' Assn. of Am. [18935], 333 Atlantic Ave., Warwick, RI 02888, (401)461-6114

Armenian Tech. Gp. [3728], PO Box 5969, Fresno, CA 93755-5969, (559)224-1000

Armenian Tech. Gp. [3728], PO Box 5969, Fresno, CA 93755-5969, (559)224-1000

Armenian Tennis Fed. [IO], Yerevan, Armenia

Armenian Women's Welfare Assn. - Address unknown since 2011.

Armenian Youth Fed. [18146], 80 Bigelow Ave., Watertown, MA 02472, (617)923-1933

Armenian Youth Fed. of Am. [★18146]

Arming Women Against Rape and Endangerment [★13485]

Arms

Amer. Heraldry Soc. [20618]

Global Network Against Weapons and Nuclear Power in Space [18199]

Intl. Panel on Fissile Materials [18203]

Japanese Sword Soc. of the U.S. [20965]

Japanese Sword Soc. of the U.S. [20965]

Miniature Arms Collectors/Makers Soc. [20966]

Miniature Arms Collectors/Makers Soc. [20966]

Natl. Automatic Pistol Collectors Assn. [20967]

Winchester Arms Collectors Assn. [20968]

Arms and Armour Soc. [IO], London, United Kingdom

Arms Control Assn. [17546], 1313 L St. NW, Ste. 130, Washington, DC 20005, (202)463-8270

ARMS/FIRMS Users Assn. - Defunct.

Armstrong Clan Soc. [10525], Peter A. Armstrong, Membership Chm./Treas./Dir., 128 Essex Dr., Summerville, SC 29485

Armstrong Clan Soc. [10525], Peter A. Armstrong, Membership Chm./Treas./Dir., 128 Essex Dr., Summerville, SC 29485

Armstrong Siddeley Owners Club [IO], Sutton Cold-field, United Kingdom

Armwrestling

Amer. Armsport Assn. [22229]

Army

11th Airborne Div. Assn. [20351]

25th Infantry Div. Assn. [20352]

29th Infantry Div. Assn. [20353]

63rd Infantry Div. Assn. [20354]

70th Infantry Div. Assn. [20845]

94th Infantry Div. Assn. [20355]

95th Infantry Div. Assn. [20356]

96th Infantry Div. Assn. [20357]

99th Infantry Div. Assn. [20358]

100th Infantry Div. Assn. [20359]

104th Infantry Div. Natl. Timberwolf Assn. [20360]

Amer. Airborne Assn. [20361]

Army Sniper Assn. [20362]

Cell Phones for Soldiers [11086]

DUSTOFF Assn. [20363]

For the Fallen [12531]

Fourth Armored Div. Assn. [20364]

Give an Hour [11088]

Hof Reunion Assn. [20349]

Mothers of Military Support [12529]

Natl. 4th Infantry Ivy Div. Assn. [20365]

Natl. Assn. of Medics and Corpsmen [5219]

Natl. Assn. of the Sixth Infantry Div. [20366]

Never Forget Our Fallen [11095]

Oper. Interdependence [12530]

Oper. Paperback [11100]

Our Military Kids [12534]

Signal Corps Regimental Assn. [20367]

Soc. of the First Infantry Div. [20368]

Soc. of the Third Infantry Div. [20369]

A Soldier's Wish List [11108]

Stars for Stripes [20417]

Support Our Troops [11110]

Troops Out Now Coalition [18292]

U.S. Army Ranger Assn. [20370]

U.S. Marine Corps Scout/Sniper Assn. [20688]

United We Serve [20712]

Women's Army Corps Veterans' Assn. [20371]

Army and Air Force Mutual Aid Assn. [18926], 102 Sheridan Ave., Bldg. 468, Fort Myer, VA 22211-1110, (703)707-4600

Army Aviation Assn. of Am. [5800], 755 Main St., Ste. 4D, Monroe, CT 06468-2830, (203)268-2450

Army Cadet League of Canada [IO], Ottawa, ON, Canada

Army Emergency Relief [18927], 200 Stovall St., Alexandria, VA 22332, (703)428-0000

Army Engineer Assn. [5217], PO Box 30260, Alexandria, VA 22310-8260, (703)428-7084

Army Families Fed. [IO], Pewsey, United Kingdom

Army Historical Found. [10088], 2425 Wilson Blvd., Arlington, VA 22201, (703)522-7901

Army Hostess Assn. [★5798]

Army Mutual Aid Assn. [★18926]

Army, Navy, and Air Force Veterans in Canada [IO], Ottawa, ON, Canada

Army and Navy Legion of Valor of the U.S. [★20377]

Army and Navy Union U.S.A. [20777], 528 A Canton Rd., Akron, OH 44312, (330)798-0880

Army Nurse Corps Assn. [15509], PO Box 39235, San Antonio, TX 78218-1235, (210)650-3534

Army Ordnance Assn. [★5814]

Army of the Philippines [★20813]

Army Physician Assistants; Soc. of [16240]

Army Records Soc. [IO], Baldock, United Kingdom

Army Relief Soc. [★18927]

Army Sniper Assn. [20362], 3100 Gentian Blvd., Ste. 107-F, Columbus, GA 31904, (706)566-0319

Army Transport Assn. [★5815]

Army Widows' Assn. [IO], Upavon, United Kingdom

Arnold Air Soc. [23596], Executive Mgt. Ctr., 9 E Lockerman St., Ste. 2B, Dover, DE 19901

Arnold Chiari Malformation Assn; World [16788]

Arnold Chiari Malformation Assn; World [16788]

Arnold and Mabel Beckman Center for History of Chemistry [★9759]

Aromatherapy; Natl. Assn. for Holistic [15002]

Aromatherapy Registration Coun. [13663], 530 1st St., Ste. A, Lake Oswego, OR 97034, (503)244-0726

Aromatherapy Trade Coun. [IO], Ipswich, United Kingdom

ARRB Gp. [IO], Vermont South, Australia

Arrhythmia Death Syndromes Found; Sudden [14631]

ARRL Found. [20933], 225 Main St., Newington, CT 06111, (860)594-0397

ARROW - Defunct.

Ars Baltica [IO], Kiel, Germany

Art

Alliance for Cultural Democracy [9264]

Amer. Acad. of Equine Art [9151]

Amer. Art Pottery Assn. [9152]

Amer. Color Print Soc. [9153]

Amer. Coun. for Southern Asian Art [9154]

Amer. Guild of Judaic Art [9155]

Amer. Physician Art Assn. [9156]

Amer. Tapestry Alliance [9157]

Amer. Tapestry Alliance [9157]

Amer. Watercolor Soc. [9158]

Antique Glass Salt and Sugar Shaker Club [21304]

Antique Tribal Art Dealers Assn. [245]

Architectural League of New York [17392]

Archives of Amer. Art [9159]

Armenian Rugs Soc. [9160]

Art Aids Art [10819]

Art Alliance for Contemporary Glass [9161]

Art Alliance for Contemporary Glass [9161]

Art and Antique Dealers League of Am. [246]

Art Dealers Assn. of Am. [247]

Art Directors Club [9162]

Art Directors Club [9162]

Art Dreco Inst. [9163]

Art Services Intl. [9164]

Art Services Intl. [9164]

Art Therapy Connection [13772]

Art21 [9165]

Artfully AWARE [9275]

Artists for Israel Intl. [9166]

Artists for Israel Intl. [9166]

Artists Rights Soc. [248]

Arts and Crafts Soc. [9167]

Assn. of Architecture Organizations [6192]

Assn. of Historians of Nineteenth-Century Art [9168]

Assn. of Historians of Nineteenth-Century Art [9168]

Assn. of Medical Illustrators [13769]

Assn. of Medical Illustrators [13769]

Assn. for Professional Art Advisors [249]

Assn. of Sci. Fiction and Fantasy Artists [250]

Assn. of Stained Glass Lamp Artists [251]

Assn. for Textual Scholarship in Art History [9169]

Assn. for Textual Scholarship in Art History [9169]

Atomic Age Alliance [9672]

Audubon Artists [9170]

Center for the Stud. of Political Graphics [9171]

Chess Collectors Intl. [21274]

Christian Comic Arts Soc. [9172]

Colonial Coverlet Guild of Am. [21326]

Colored Pencil Soc. of Am. [9173]

Reference to "IO" in place of a book number signifies that the association may be found in the 50th edition of International Organizations.

Colored Pencil Soc. of Am. **[9173]**
Comicbook Artists' Guild **[9489]**
Complex Weavers **[252]**
Conservation Center for Art and Historic Artifacts **[9174]**
Dart Music Intl. **[10187]**
Dedham Pottery Collectors Soc. **[21333]**
Digital Watermarking Alliance **[6932]**
Diverse Emerging Music Org. **[10188]**
DOCOMOMO US **[9683]**
Doll Costumer's Guild **[21690]**
The Drawing Center **[9175]**
Fed. of Modern Painters and Sculptors **[9230]**
Fine Art Dealers Assn. **[253]**
Found. for Hosp. Art **[13770]**
Franklin Furnace Archv. **[9176]**
Friends of Fiber Art Intl. **[9177]**
Gen Art **[9178]**
Global Alliance of Artists **[9234]**ArtGlobal Alliance for Intelligent Arts
Global Inheritance **[18826]**
Haitian Art Educ. and Appraisal Soc. **[9651]**
Hero Initiative **[9490]**
Independent Arts and Media **[9179]**
Independent Curators Intl. **[9180]**
Independent Curators Intl. **[9180]**
Insight Arts **[9293]**
Integrity: Arts and Culture Assn. **[9181]**
Intl. Alliance of Composers **[10213]**
Intl. Assn. of Pastel Societies **[9182]**
Intl. Assn. of Pastel Societies **[9182]**
Intl. Assn. for Professional Art Advisors **[249]**
Intl. Coun. of the Museum of Modern Art **[9183]**
Intl. Coun. of the Museum of Modern Art **[9183]**
Intl. Doll Makers Assn. **[21692]**
Intl. Fine Print Dealers Assn. **[254]**
Intl. Fine Print Dealers Assn. **[254]**
Intl. Found. for Art Res. **[9184]**
Intl. Found. for Art Res. **[9184]**
Intl. Guild of Glass Artists **[255]**
Intl. Guild of Glass Artists **[255]**
Intl. Hajji Baba Soc. **[9185]**
Intl. Hajji Baba Soc. **[9185]**
Intl. Performing Arts for Youth **[10359]**
Intl. Soc. for the Stud. of Pilgrimage Art **[9186]**
Intl. Soc. for the Stud. of Pilgrimage Art **[9186]**
James Renwick Alliance **[9187]**
Kids with Cameras **[12694]**
Leslie-Lohman Gay Art Found. **[9188]**
Master Drawings Assn. **[9189]**
Mid Atlantic Fiber Assn. **[256]**
Napoleonic Age Philatelists **[22058]**
Natl. Alliance of Craftsmen Associations **[11611]**
Natl. Antique and Art Dealers Assn. of Am. **[257]**
Natl. Art Museum of Sport **[9190]**
Natl. Coun. for Taekwondo Masters Certification **[22746]**
Natl. Duncan Glass Soc. **[21839]**
Natl. Guild of Decoupeurs **[21457]**
Natl. Ice Carving Assn. **[9191]**
Natl. Oil and Acrylic Painters' Soc. **[9192]**
Natl. Watercolor Soc. **[9193]**
Natural Fibers Gp. **[21705]**
New Art Dealers Alliance **[9194]**
North Amer. Quilling Guild **[20969]**
Pacific Arts Assn. **[9195]**
Pacific Arts Assn. **[9195]**
Pastel Soc. of Am. **[9196]**
Pastel Soc. of Am. **[9196]**
Peace of Art **[10354]**
PeaceArt Intl. **[9312]**
Philip Boileau Collectors' Soc. **[20970]**
Polish Arts and Culture Found. **[19191]**
Portrait Soc. of Am. **[9197]**
Print Coun. of Am. **[9198]**
Private Art Dealers Assn. **[258]**
Professional Picture Framers Assn. **[9199]**
Public Art Fund **[17395]**
Quimper Club Intl. **[20971]**
Radical Art Caucus **[9200]**
The Rock Poster Soc. **[9201]**
Saving and Preserving Arts and Cultural Environments **[9202]**
Sculpture in the Env. **[17396]**
Silvermine Guild Arts Center **[9203]**

Soc. for the Arts in Healthcare **[13771]**
Soc. for the Arts in Healthcare **[13771]**
Soc. for Asian Art **[9204]**
Soc. for Eighteenth-Century Music **[10291]**
Soc. for Folk Arts Preservation **[9626]**
Soc. for the Promotion of Japanese Animation **[9205]**
Spinning and Weaving Assn. **[3456]**
Stencilers and Decorative Artists Guild **[20972]**
Stock Artists Alliance **[2737]**
Sumi-e Soc. of Am. **[9206]**
Taos Natl. Soc. of Watercolorists **[9207]**
Thomas Nast Soc. **[9208]**
Union Internationale de la Marionnette I Amer. CTR **[22112]**
Unreserved Amer. Indian Fashion and Art Alliance **[9134]**
Western Assn. for Art Conservation **[259]**
Where Peace Lives **[10355]**
WordTheatre **[10550]**
YLEM: Artists Using Sci. and Tech. **[9260]**
Art Aids Art **[10819]**, PO Box 6038, Altadena, CA 91003
Art Alliance for Contemporary Glass **[9161]**, 11700 Preston Rd., No. 660-327, Dallas, TX 75230-2718, (214)890-0029
Art Alliance for Contemporary Glass **[9161]**, 11700 Preston Rd., No. 660-327, Dallas, TX 75230-2718, (214)890-0029
Art and Antique Dealers League of Am. **[246]**, PO Box 2066, Lennox Hill Sta., New York, NY 10021, (212)879-7558
Art in a Box **[11113]**, Valentina DuBasky, Founder/ Dir., 463 West St., Ste. G-122, New York, NY 10014, (212)691-2543
Art Child **[IO]**, Paris, France
Art and Craft Materials Inst. **[★1601]**
Art and Creative Materials Inst. **[1601]**, PO Box 479, Hanson, MA 02341-0479, (781)293-4100
Art Dealers Assn. of Am. **[247]**, 205 Lexington Ave., Ste. 901, New York, NY 10016, (212)488-5550
Art Dealers Assn. of Canada **[IO]**, Toronto, ON, Canada
Art Directors Club **[9162]**, 106 W 29th St., New York, NY 10001, (212)643-1440
Art Directors Club **[9162]**, 106 W 29th St., New York, NY 10001, (212)643-1440
Art Directors Guild **[9595]**, 11969 Ventura Blvd., 2nd Fl., Studio City, CA 91604, (818)762-9995
Art Dreco Inst. **[9163]**, PMB 131, 2570 Ocean Ave., San Francisco, CA 94132

Art Galleries
Art Services Intl. **[9164]**
Art Glass Assn. **[1574]**, PO Box 2537, Zanesville, OH 43702-2537, (740)450-6547
Art Glass Assn. **[1574]**, PO Box 2537, Zanesville, OH 43702-2537, (740)450-6547
Art Glass Suppliers Assn. **[★1574]**
Art Glass Suppliers Assn. **[★1574]**
Art Glass Suppliers Assn. Intl. **[★1574]**
Art Glass Suppliers Assn. Intl. **[★1574]**
Art Greenhaw Official Intl. Fan Club **[23814]**, 105 Broad St., Mesquite, TX 75149, (972)285-5441
Art Hazards Information Center - Defunct.
Art with Heart **[11741]**, PO Box 94402, Seattle, WA 98124, (206)362-4047

Art History
Art Dreco Inst. **[9163]**
Atomic Age Alliance **[9672]**
Catalogue Raisonne Scholars Assn. **[7739]**
DOCOMOMO US **[9683]**
Haitian Art Educ. and Appraisal Soc. **[9651]**
Historians of British Art **[9209]**
Japan Art History Forum **[9210]**
Native Amer. Art Stud. Assn. **[7740]**
Pre-Raphaelite Soc. **[23174]**
Soc. for Eighteenth-Century Music **[10291]**
Art Libraries Soc. of North Am. **[IO]**, Calgary, AB, Canada
Art of Living, Oman Chap. **[IO]**, Muscat, Oman
Art Museum Assn. of Am. **[★9266]**
Art in the Public Interest **[9272]**, PO Box 68, Saxapahaw, NC 27340, (336)376-8404
Art for Refugees in Transition **[12774]**, 401 E 76th St., New York, NY 10021, (917)757-6191

Art Resources in Collaboration **[9536]**, 123 W 18th St., 7th Fl., New York, NY 10011-4127, (212)206-6492
Art Schools Network **[7741]**, 33 Off. Park Dr., Ste. A156, Hilton Head, SC 29928, (843)686-5060
Art Schools Network **[7741]**, 33 Off. Park Dr., Ste. A156, Hilton Head, SC 29928, (843)686-5060
Art and Sci. Collaborations, Inc. **[9329]**, 130 E End Ave. 1A, New York, NY 10028, (505)990-0781
Art and Sci. Collaborations, Inc. **[9329]**, 130 E End Ave. 1A, New York, NY 10028, (505)990-0781
Art Services Intl. **[9164]**, 1319 Powhatan St., Alexandria, VA 22314, (703)548-4554
Art Services Intl. **[9164]**, 1319 Powhatan St., Alexandria, VA 22314, (703)548-4554
Art Students League of New York **[9226]**, 215 W 57th St., New York, NY 10019, (212)247-4510
Art Teachers' Assn. **[IO]**, Halifax, NS, Canada
Art Therapy
Art Therapy Connection **[13772]**
Artfully AWARE **[9275]**ArtArts in Therapy Network
Intl. Expressive Arts Therapy Assn. **[13773]**
Intl. Expressive Arts Therapy Assn. **[13773]**
Art Therapy Connection **[13772]**, 1800 Ridge Ave., Unit 211, Evanston, IL 60201
Art Through Touch **[IO]**, London, United Kingdom
Art Watch Intl. **[9273]**, Columbia Univ., 931 Schermerhorn, New York, NY 10027, (212)854-4569
Art Watch Intl. **[9273]**, Columbia Univ., 931 Schermerhorn, New York, NY 10027, (212)854-4569
Art for the World **[IO]**, Milan, Italy
Art21 **[9165]**, 286 Spring St., Ste. 405, New York, NY 10013, (212)741-7133
ARTDO Intl. **[IO]**, San Juan, Philippines
Arte Sana **[11114]**, PO Box 1334, Dripping Springs, TX 78620
ArteEast **[9274]**, 1178 Broadway, 3rd Fl., New York, NY 10001, (646)375-5222
Arterial Hypertension Soc. of Mexico **[IO]**, Mexico City, Mexico
Artfoundation **[IO]**, London, United Kingdom
Artfully AWARE **[9275]**, 201 E 17th St., 27D, New York, NY 10003
Arthritis Care **[IO]**, London, United Kingdom
Arthritis Care - Central England **[IO]**, Nottingham, United Kingdom
Arthritis Care - North England **[IO]**, Wakefield, United Kingdom
Arthritis Care - Scotland **[IO]**, Glasgow, United Kingdom
Arthritis Care - South England **[IO]**, London, United Kingdom
Arthritis Care - Southeast England **[IO]**, London, United Kingdom
Arthritis Care - Wales **[IO]**, Cardiff, United Kingdom
Arthritis Found. **[16617]**, PO Box 7669, Atlanta, GA 30357-0669, (800)283-7800
Arthritis Found. of Ireland **[★2780]**
Arthritis Hea. Professions Assn. **[IO]**, Newmarket, ON, Canada
Arthritis Ireland **[IO]**, Dublin, Ireland
Arthritis New Zealand **[IO]**, Wellington, New Zealand
Arthritis New Zealand - Auckland **[IO]**, North Shore City, New Zealand
Arthritis New Zealand - Bay of Plenty **[IO]**, Tauranga, New Zealand
Arthritis New Zealand - Gisborne **[IO]**, Gisborne, New Zealand
Arthritis New Zealand - Hawkes Bay **[IO]**, Hastings, New Zealand
Arthritis New Zealand - Manawatu **[IO]**, Palmerston North, New Zealand
Arthritis New Zealand - Manukau **[IO]**, Manukau City, New Zealand
Arthritis New Zealand - Northland **[IO]**, Whangarei, New Zealand
Arthritis New Zealand - Taranaki **[IO]**, New Plymouth, New Zealand
Arthritis New Zealand - Tauranga/Western Bay of Plenty **[IO]**, Tauranga, New Zealand
Arthritis New Zealand - Waikato **[IO]**, Hamilton, New Zealand
Arthritis New Zealand - Wairarapa **[IO]**, Masterton, New Zealand
Arthritis New Zealand - Waitakere **[IO]**, Auckland, New Zealand

A star before a book entry number signifies that the name is not listed separately, but is mentioned within the entry.

Arthritis New Zealand - Wanganui [IO], Wanganui, New Zealand

Arthritis New Zealand - Wellington [IO], Wellington, New Zealand

Arthritis Res. Campaign [IO], Chesterfield, United Kingdom

Arthritis and Rheumatism Found. [★16617]

The Arthritis Soc. [IO], Toronto, ON, Canada

The Arthritis Trust of Am. [★16624]

Arthroscopy Assn. of North Am. [16029], 6300 N River Rd., Ste. 104, Rosemont, IL 60018, (847)292-2262

Arthur Miller Soc. [10702], 100-14 160th Ave., Howard Beach, NY 11414

Arthur Morgan Inst. for Community Solutions [17368], PO Box 243, Yellow Springs, OH 45387, (937)767-2161

Arthur Rackham Soc. - Address unknown since 2011.

The Arthur Ransome Soc. [IO], Cumbria, United Kingdom

Arthur Rubinstein Intl. Music Soc. [IO], Tel Aviv, Israel

Arthur Szyk Soc. [9227], 1200 Edgehill Dr., Burlin-game, CA 94010, (650)343-9588

Arthur Vining Davis Foundations [11902], 225 Water St., Ste. 1510, Jacksonville, FL 32202-5185, (904)359-0670

Article 19 - Global Campaign for Free Expression [IO], London, United Kingdom

Article Numbering Assn. of Bosnia and Herzegovina [IO], Sarajevo, Bosnia-Hercegovina

Article Numbering Assn. of Tunisia [★107]

Article Numbering Assn. of Ukraine [★16763]

Artifacts
Authentic Artifact Collectors Assn. [20973]
Early Amer. Indus. Assn. [9211]
Historical Soc. of Early Amer. Decoration [9212]
Holy Shroud Guild [19431]
Midwest Old Settlers and Threshers Assn. [9213]
Natl. Threshers Assn. [9214]
Soc. for Commercial Archeology [9215]
World Wide Assn. of Treasure Seekers [22109]

Artificial Intelligence
Assn. for the Advancement of Artificial Intelligence [6209]
Cognitive Sci. Soc. [6210]
Intl. Soc. of Applied Intelligence [6211]
Intl. Soc. of Applied Intelligence [6211]
Special Interest Gp. on Artificial Intelligence [6212]

Artificial and Synthetic Fibers Mfrs'. Assn. [IO], Sao Paulo, Brazil

Artisans' Assn. of Cambodia [IO], Phnom Penh, Cambodia

Artisans Order of Mutual Protection [19044], 8100 Roosevelt Blvd., Philadelphia, PA 19152, (215)708-1000

Artist-Blacksmith's Assn. of North Am. [460], 259 Muddy Fork Rd., Jonesborough, TN 37659, (423)913-1022

Artist-Blacksmith's Assn. of North Am. [460], 259 Muddy Fork Rd., Jonesborough, TN 37659, (423)913-1022

Artist Boat [3834], 2415 Ave. K, Galveston, TX 77550, (409)770-0722

Artistes Sin Fronteras [★IO]

Artists
Adolph and Esther Gottlieb Found. [9216]
Alliance for Cultural Democracy [9264]
Allied Artists of Am. [9217]
Amer. Abstract Artists [9218]
Amer. Artists Professional League [9219]
Amer. Impressionist Soc. [9220]
Amer. Soc. of Artists [9221]
Amer. Soc. of Botanical Artists [9222]
Amer. Soc. of Contemporary Artists [9223]
Amer. Soc. of Marine Artists [9224]
Amer. Soc. of Portrait Artists [9225]
Art Aids Art [10819]
Art Dreco Inst. [9163]
Art Greenhaw Official Intl. Fan Club [23814]
Art Students League of New York [9226]
Arthur Szyk Soc. [9227]
Artists Helping Artists [9228]

Artists Helping Artists [9228]
Artists Striving to End Poverty [12716]
Artists United for Social Justice [18640]
A.R.T.S. Anonymous [13036]
ArtTable [9229]
Assn. of Independent Creative Editors [2811]
Assn. for Korean Music Res. [10165]
Chris Young Fan Club [23825]
Comicbook Artists' Guild [9489]
Creativity Coaching Assn. [22458]
Dance/Drill Team Directors of Am. [9544]
Dart Music Intl. [10187]
Diverse Emerging Music Org. [10188]
European Coun. of Artists [9220]
Fed. of Modern Painters and Sculptors [9230]
Fractured Atlas [9231]
Frere Independent [9232]
Friends of Dennis Lee Fan Club [23789]
Friends-in-Art of Amer. Coun. of the Blind [9233]
Global Alliance of Artists [9234]
Global Inheritance [18826]
Graphic Artists Guild [9235]
Graphic Artists Guild [9235]
The Grascals Fan Club [23851]
Grassroots Artists MovEment [9236]
Haitian Art Educ. and Appraisal Soc. [9651]
Hero Initiative [9490]
Independent Arts and Media [9179]
Insight Arts [9293]
Intercultural Alliance of Artists and Scholars [9237]
Intl. Doll Makers Assn. [21692]
Intl. Guild of Musicians in Dance [23271]
Intl. Guild of Symphony, Opera and Ballet Musi-cians [23272]
Intl. Performing Arts for Youth [10359]
Intl. Soc. for Improvised Music [10226]
Iraqi Artists Assn. [9238]
Jeannie Seely's Circle of Friends [23860]
Jew's Harp Guild [10231]
Johnnie Ray Intl. Fan Club [23865]
Jussi Bjorling Soc. U.S.A. [9239]
Landscape Artists Intl. [9240]
Landscape Artists Intl. [9240]
Michael Jackson Fan Club [23878]
Natl. Assn. of Independent Artists [9241]
Natl. Assn. of Women Artists [9242]
Natl. Cartoonists Soc. [9243]
Natl. Puro Conjunto Music Assn. [10263]
Natl. Soc. of Artists [9244]
Natl. Soc. of Mural Painters [9245]
Natl. Soc. of Painters in Casein and Acrylic [9246]
North Amer. Irish Dance Fed. [9563]
NURTUREart Non-Profit [9247]
NURTUREart Non-Profit [9247]
Oil Painters of Am. [9248]
PeaceArt Intl. [9312]
Pen and Brush [9249]
Philip Boileau Collectors' Soc. [20970]
Pollock-Krasner Found. [9250]
Pollock-Krasner Found. [9250]
The Print Center [9251]
The Print Center [9251]
Professional Org. of Women in the Arts [9315]
Public Art Fund [17395]
Richard Burgi Fan Club [23781]
Salisbury Univ. | Ward Museum of Wildfowl Art [9252]
Sandicast Collectors Guild [20974]
Sculpture in the Env. [17396]
Silk Painters Intl. [9253]
Soc. for All Artists [1289]
Soc. of Amer. Mosaic Artists [9254]
Soc. of Animal Artists [9255]
Soc. of Illustrators [9256]
Soc. of Illustrators [9256]
Soc. of Tempera Painters [9257]
Stars for Stripes [20417]
Stencilers and Decorative Artists Guild [20972]
Stock Artists Alliance [2737]
Tamizdat [9518]
Union Internationale de la Marionnette | Amer. CTR [22112]
U.S. Artists [9258]
Visual Artists and Galleries Assn. [5583]

Visual Effects Soc. [1270]
Women's Caucus for Art [9259]
World Artists Experiences [9325]
YLEM: Artists Using Sci. and Tech. [9260]

Artists Against Racism [IO], Toronto, ON, Canada

Artists Aid Soc. [★19148]

Artists' Assn. of Finland [IO], Helsinki, Finland

Artists for a Better World Intl. [9276], PO Box 1872, Ventura, CA 93002, (877)809-1659

Artists for a Better World Intl. [9276], PO Box 1872, Ventura, CA 93002, (877)809-1659

Artists in Christian Testimony [19730], PO Box 1649, Brentwood, TN 37024-1649, (615)376-7861

Artists in Christian Testimony [19730], PO Box 1649, Brentwood, TN 37024-1649, (615)376-7861

Artists' Fellowship [19148], 47 5th Ave., New York, NY 10003, (212)255-7740

Artists Helping Artists [9228], 300 Redwood Dr., Santa Cruz, CA 95060, (831)227-6588

Artists Helping Artists [9228], 300 Redwood Dr., Santa Cruz, CA 95060, (831)227-6588

Artists for Human Rights [17813], 23679 Calabasas Rd., Ste. 636, Calabasas, CA 91302, (800)334-2802

Artists for Israel Intl. [9166], PO Box 2056, New York, NY 10163-2056, (718)253-0974

Artists for Israel Intl. [9166], PO Box 2056, New York, NY 10163-2056, (718)253-0974

Artists Managers Guild [★162]

Artists for a New South Africa [17516], 2999 Overland Ave., Ste. 102, Los Angeles, CA 90064, (310)204-1748

Artists for a New South Africa [17516], 2999 Overland Ave., Ste. 102, Los Angeles, CA 90064, (310)204-1748

Artists for Peace and Justice [13152], 1507 7th St., Ste. 403, Santa Monica, CA 90401, (424)238-5225

Artists Recovering Through the Twelve Steps [★13036]

Artists Rights Soc. [248], 536 Broadway, 5th Fl., New York, NY 10012, (212)420-9160

Artists in Stained Glass Canada [IO], Parry Sound, ON, Canada

Artists Striving to End Poverty [12716], 165 W 46th St., Ste. 1303, New York, NY 10036, (212)921-1227

Artists United for Social Justice [18640], 5042 Wilshire Blvd. No.131, Los Angeles, CA 90036

Artists Without Borders [IO], Tokyo, Japan

Arts
Affiliated Woodcarvers [9261]
Affiliated Woodcarvers [9261]
Algonquin Arts Coun. [5261]
All Out Arts [9262]
Alliance for the Arts [9263]
Alliance for Cultural Democracy [9264]
Amer. Cultural Resources Assn. [9265]
Amer. Fed. of Arts [9266]
Amer. Fired Arts Alliance [9267]
Amer. Friends of the Paris Opera and Ballet [9268]
Amer. Print Alliance [9269]
Amer. Print Alliance [9269]
Amer. Soc. for Aesthetics [9270]
Amer. Soc. for Aesthetics [9270]
Americans for the Arts [9271]
Architectural League of New York [17392]
ARLIS/UK and Ireland: Art Libraries Soc. of the United Kingdom and Ireland [1396]
Art in a Box [11113]
Art Greenhaw Official Intl. Fan Club [23814]
Art in the Public Interest [9272]
Art Schools Network [7741]
Art Schools Network [7741]
Art Watch Intl. [9273]
Art Watch Intl. [9273]
Arte Sana [11114]
ArteEast [9274]
Artfully AWARE [9275]
Artist Boat [3834]
Artists for a Better World Intl. [9276]
Artists for a Better World Intl. [9276]
Artists in Stained Glass Canada [21251]
Artists Striving to End Poverty [12716]
Arts, Crafts and Theatre Safety [12977]

Reference to "IO" in place of a book number signifies that the association may be found in the 50th edition of International Organizations.

Arts Educ. Partnership [7742]
Asian Amer. Arts Alliance [9277]
Asian Amer. Arts Centre [9278]
Asian Amer. Arts Centre [9278]
The Assn. of Amer. Cultures [9279]
Assn. of Architecture Organizations [6192]
Assn. of Arts Admin. Educators [7743]
Assn. for the Calligraphic Arts [9280]
Assn. of Israel's Decorative Arts [9281]
Assn. of Israel's Decorative Arts [9281]
Assn. for Korean Music Res. [10165]
Assn. for Modern and Contemporary Art of the
   Arab World, Iran, and Turkey [9282]
Assn. for Native Development in the Performing
   and Visual Arts [19031]
Assn. of Performing Arts Presenters [7744]
Atomic Age Alliance [9672]
Beaux Arts Alliance [9283]
Beyond Baroque Literary/Arts Center [9284]
Cartoonists Northwest [9285]
Chinese-American Arts Coun. [9286]
Christians in the Visual Arts [9287]
Coll. Art Assn. [7745]
Coun. for Art Educ. [7746]
Coun. of Colleges of Arts and Sciences [7747]
Creative Time [9288]
Creativity Coaching Assn. [22458]
Dance Theater Workshop [9289]
Dart Music Intl. [10187]
Decorative Arts Trust [9290]
Diverse Emerging Music Org. [10188]
DOCOMOMO US [9683]
Doll Costumer's Guild [21690]
Enrichment Educ. [8276]
Friends of the Kennedy Center [9291]
Global Alliance of Artists [9234]
Global Inheritance [18826]
Greater Vancouver Alliance for Arts and Culture
   [10836]
Independent Arts and Media [9179]
Indo-American Arts Coun. [9292]
Indo-American Arts Coun. [9292]
Insight Arts [9293]
Intercultural Alliance of Artists and Scholars
   [9237]
Interlochen Center for the Arts [9294]
Interlochen Center for the Arts [9294]
Intl. Alliance of Composers [10213]
Intl. Arts and Artists [9295]
Intl. Arts and Artists [9295]
Intl. Assn. of Art Critics - U.S. Sect. [9296]
Intl. Assn. of Arts and Cultural Mgt. [723]
Intl. Coun. of Fine Arts Deans [7748]
Intl. Coun. of Fine Arts Deans [7748]
Intl. Guild of Musicians in Dance [23271]
Intl. Guild of Realism [9297]
Intl. Guild of Symphony, Opera and Ballet Musi-
   cians [23272]
Intl. Performing Arts for Youth [10359]
Intl. Soc. of the Arts, Mathematics, and
   Architecture [7003]
Intl. Soc. of Glass Beadmakers [9298]
Intl. Soc. of Glass Beadmakers [9298]
Intl. Soc. for Improvised Music [10226]
Intl. Soc. for the Performing Arts [9299]
Intl. Soc. for the Performing Arts [9299]
Intl. Soc. for the Performing Arts Found. [9300]
Intl. Soc. for the Performing Arts Found. [9300]
Intl. Soc. of Phenomenology, Aesthetics, and the
   Fine Arts [9301]
Intl. Soc. of Phenomenology, Aesthetics, and the
   Fine Arts [9301]
Jew's Harp Guild [10231]
Kappa Pi Intl. Honorary Art Fraternity [23467]
Kappa Pi Intl. Honorary Art Fraternity [23467]
Kennedy Center Alliance for Arts Educ. Network
   [7749]
Kids with Cameras [12694]
Kollaboration [13534]
Labor Heritage Found. [9302]
Midori and Friends [7750]
Movable Book Soc. [21233]
Musicians for Harmony [10353]
Natl. Alliance of Craftsmen Associations [11611]
Natl. Alliance for Media Arts and Culture [9303]

Natl. Art Educ. Assn. [7751]
Natl. Art Exhibitions by the Mentally Ill [9304]
Natl. Assembly of State Arts Agencies [9305]
Natl. Assn. of Latino Arts and Culture [9306]
Natl. Assn. of Schools of Art and Design [7752]
Natl. Assn. for the Visual Arts [7153]
Natl. Basketry Org. [21455]
Natl. Endowment for the Arts [9307]
Natl. Found. for Advancement in the Arts [9308]
Natl. Guild for Community Arts Educ. [7753]
Natl. League of Amer. Pen Women [9309]
Natl. Puro Conjunto Music Assn. [10263]
Natural Fibers Gp. [21705]
Omega Theatre and the Omega Arts Network
   [9310]
PaintAmerica [9311]
Peace of Art [10354]
PeaceArt Intl. [9312]
Performing Arts Alliance [9313]
Performing Arts Found. [9314]
Phi Beta [23468]
Philip Boileau Collectors' Soc. [20970]
Professional Org. of Women in the Arts [9315]
P.S.1 Contemporary Art Center [9316]
Public Radio Capital [10483]
Retailers of Art Glass and Supplies [1581]
River of Words [3835]
Salmagundi Club [9317]
Scandinavian Soc. for Prehistoric Art [20223]
Schomburg Center for Res. in Black Culture
   [9105]
Soc. for the Arts, Religion and Contemporary
   Culture [9318]
Soc. for Eighteenth-Century Music [10291]
Stencilers and Decorative Artists Guild [20972]
Studio Art Quilt Associates [9319]
Subud Intl. Cultural Assn. U.S.A. [9320]
Symphony for United Nations [9321]
Symphony for United Nations [9321]
Textile Soc. for the Stud. of Art, Design and His-
   tory [2601]
Topaz Arts [9322]
Traditional Fine Arts Org. [9323]
Union Internationale de la Marionnette I Amer.
   CTR [22112]
U.S./Japan Cultural Trade Network [9519]
U.S. Soc. for Educ. Through Art [7754]
Unreserved Amer. Indian Fashion and Art Alliance
   [9134]
Visual Arts Ontario [3216]
Weave a Real Peace [11115]
Where Peace Lives [10355]
Wolf Trap Found. for the Performing Arts [9324]
WordTheatre [10550]
World Artists Experiences [9325]
Young Audiences Arts for Learning [9326]
Youth Educ. in the Arts [9327]
Youth Educ. in the Arts [9327]
Arts for Am., Natl. Assembly of Local Arts Agencies
   [★9271]
A.R.T.S. Anonymous [13036], PO Box 230175, New
   York, NY 10023, (212)873-7075
Arts and Bus. [IO], London, United Kingdom
Arts Centre Gp. [IO], London, United Kingdom
Arts Coun. of England [IO], London, United Kingdom
Arts Coun. of Ireland [IO], Dublin, Ireland
Arts Coun. of Mongolia-US [10101], 2025 23rd Ave.
   E, Seattle, WA 98112
Arts Coun. of Northern Ireland [IO], Belfast, United
   Kingdom
Arts Coun. of Wales [IO], Cardiff, United Kingdom
Arts and Crafts
   Automotive Aftermarket Indus. Assn. I Natl.
      Catalog Managers Assn. [317]
   Colonial Coverlet Guild of Am. [21326]
   Craft Retailers Assn. for Tomorrow [987]
   Doll Costumer's Guild [21690]
   Intl. Doll Makers Assn. [21692]
   Intl. Guild of Candle Artisans [21443]
   Intl. Internet Leather Crafters' Guild [2200]
   Krochet Kids Intl. [12735]
   Natl. Basketry Org. [21455]
   Natl. Guild of Decoupeurs [21457]
   Natural Fibers Gp. [21705]
   Philip Boileau Collectors' Soc. [20970]

Professional Org. of Women in the Arts [9315]
Retailers of Art Glass and Supplies [1581]
Soc. for Folk Arts Preservation [9626]
Union Internationale de la Marionnette I Amer.
   CTR [22112]
Arts and Crafts Soc. [9167], 5015 SE Hawthorne
   Blvd., Ste. C, Portland, OR 97215, (503)459-4422
Arts, Crafts and Theatre Safety [12977], 181
   Thompson St., Ste. 23, New York, NY 10012-2586,
   (212)777-0062
Arts Educ. Partnership [7742], 1 Massachusetts Ave.
   NW, Ste. 700, Washington, DC 20001-1431,
   (202)326-8693
Arts Marketing Assn. [IO], Cambridge, United
   Kingdom
Arts Sans Frontieres [★IO]
Arts and Sciences
   Amer. Acad. of Arts and Sciences [9328]
   Art and Sci. Collaborations, Inc. [9329]
   Art and Sci. Collaborations, Inc. [9329]
   Canadian Commn. for UNESCO [45]
   Leonardo, The Intl. Soc. for the Arts, Sciences
      and Tech. [9330]
   Leonardo, The Intl. Soc. for the Arts, Sciences
      and Tech. [9330]
   Phi Beta Kappa [23469]
   Visual Effects Soc. [1270]
   World Acad. of Art and Sci. [9331]
   World Acad. of Art and Sci. [9331]
Arts in Therapy Network
Arts in Therapy Network - Address unknown since
   2011.
The Arts We Need - Address unknown since 2011.
ArtTable [9229], 137 Varick St., Ste. 402, New York,
   NY 10013, (212)343-1735
Aruba Amateur Radio Club [IO], San Nicolas, Aruba
Aruba Athletic Fed. [IO], Oranjestad, Aruba
Aruba Badminton Club [IO], Noord, Aruba
Aruba Bodybuilding and Powerlifting Fed. [IO],
   Oranjestad, Aruba
Aruba Chamber of Commerce and Indus. [IO],
   Oranjestad, Aruba
Aruba Judo Assn. [IO], Noord, Aruba
Aruba Lawn Tennis Bond [IO], Oranjestad, Aruba
Aruba Squash Assn. [IO], Oranjestad, Aruba
Aruba Surf Assn. [IO], Pepeganga, Aruba
Aruba Taekwondo Assn. [IO], Oranjestad, Aruba
Aruba Timeshare Assn. [IO], Oranjestad, Aruba
Arubaanse Atletiek Bond [★IO]
ARZA - Canada [IO], Toronto, ON, Canada
Arztinnen und Arzte fur eine Gesunde Umwelt [★IO]
As You Sow Found. [17478], 311 California St., Ste.
   510, San Francisco, CA 94104, (415)391-3212
ASA Intl. [7999], 119 Cooper St., Babylon, NY
   11702, (631)893-4540
ASA Intl. [7999], 119 Cooper St., Babylon, NY
   11702, (631)893-4540
Asaba Natl. Assn. [18839], PO Box 1627, Sugar
   Land, TX 77487-1627, (678)860-9602
ASARian - Address unknown since 2011.
Asatru
   Amer. Vinland Assn. [19300]
   Asatru Alliance [19301]
Asatru Alliance [19301], PO Box 961, Payson, AZ
   85547
Asatru Free Assembly [★19301]
Asbestos
   White Lung Assn. [13329]
Asbestos Disease Awareness Org. [16888], 1525
   Aviation Blvd., Ste. 318, Redondo Beach, CA
   90278
Asbestos Disease Awareness Org. [16888], 1525
   Aviation Blvd., Ste. 318, Redondo Beach, CA
   90278
Asbestos Removal Contractors Assn. [IO], Burton-
   on-Trent, United Kingdom
Ascend [11], Arthur Chin, Exec. Dir., 120 Wall St.,
   3rd Fl., New York, NY 10005, (212)248-4888
Ascension Poetry Reading Series - Defunct.
Ascociacion Peruana de Terapistas Fisicos [IO],
   Lima, Peru
ASCP [★13997]
ASD-STAN [IO], Brussels, Belgium
ASEAN Bankers Assn. [IO], Taipei, Taiwan
ASEAN Confed. of Employers [IO], Makati City,
   Philippines

A star before a book entry number signifies that the name is not listed separately, but is mentioned within the entry.

ASEAN Coun. on Petroleum - Indonesia **[IO]**, Jakarta, Indonesia

ASEAN Fed. of Elecl. Engg. Contractors **[IO]**, Quezon City, Philippines

Asean Football Fed. **[IO]**, Petaling Jaya, Malaysia

ASEAN Free Trade Area **[IO]**, Jakarta, Indonesia

ASEAN Inst. for Hea. Development **[IO]**, Bangkok, Thailand

ASEAN Inter-Parliamentary Assembly **[IO]**, Jakarta, Indonesia

ASEAN Network for Women in Skills Training **[IO]**, Jakarta, Indonesia

ASEAN Neurological Assn. **[IO]**, Kuala Lumpur, Malaysia

ASEAN Ports Assn. **[IO]**, Manila, Philippines

ASEAN Promotion Centre on Trade, Investment and Tourism **[IO]**, Tokyo, Japan

ASEAN Regional Forum **[IO]**, Jakarta, Indonesia

ASEAN Univ. Network **[IO]**, Bangkok, Thailand

ASEAN Vegetable Oils Club **[IO]**, Petaling Jaya, Malaysia

Aseptic Packaging Coun. - Address unknown since 2011.

ASFE **[6917]**, 8811 Colesville Rd., Ste. G106, Silver Spring, MD 20910, (301)565-2733

ASFE: Professional Firms Practicing in the Geosciences **[★6917]**

ASFE/The Assn. of Engg. Firms Practicing in the Geosciences **[★6917]**

ASGCA **[★6186]**

ASGM **[19339]**, PO Box 240, Kissimmee, FL 34747, (321)251-8494

ASH Australia **[IO]**, Kings Cross, Australia

Ash Development Assn. of Australia **[IO]**, Wollongong, Australia

ASHA Intl. **[15448]**, 2969 NW 127th Ave., Portland, OR 97229, (971)340-7190

Ashburn Inst. **[18343]**, 198 Okatie Village Dr., Bluffton, SC 29909, (843)705-7643

Ashburn Inst. **[18343]**, 198 Okatie Village Dr., Bluffton, SC 29909, (843)705-7643

Ashburton Jaycee **[IO]**, Ashburton, New Zealand

Ashland, The Henry Clay Estate **[★10667]**

Ashoka: Innovators for the Public **[12313]**, 1700 N More St., Ste. 2000, Arlington, VA 22209, (703)527-8300

Ashoka: Innovators for the Public **[12313]**, 1700 N More St., Ste. 2000, Arlington, VA 22209, (703)527-8300

ASHP Found. **[16184]**, 7272 Wisconsin Ave., Bethesda, MD 20814, (301)664-8612

ASHP Res. and Educ. Found. **[★16184]**

Asia

Amer. Buddhist Stud. Center **[19358]**

The Asia Found. **[18413]**

Asian-American Network Against Abuse of Human Rights **[17814]**

Buddhist Churches of Am. Fed. of Buddhist Women's Associations **[19359]**

Dharma Drum Mountain Buddhist Assn. **[19364]**

DROKPA **[11575]**

Lebanese Amer. Coun. for Democracy **[18069]**

Omnilogy, Inc. **[12353]**

Outreach Asia **[11116]**

Asia Acad. of Mgt. **[IO]**, Hong Kong, People's Republic of China

Asia Am. Initiative **[11547]**, 1523 16th St. NW, Washington, DC 20036, (202)232-7020

Asia Am. Initiative **[11547]**, 1523 16th St. NW, Washington, DC 20036, (202)232-7020

Asia Catalyst **[12580]**, PO Box 20839, New York, NY 10009, (718)514-2855

Asia Crime Prevention Found. **[IO]**, Tokyo, Japan

The Asia Found. **[18413]**, PO Box 193223, San Francisco, CA 94119-3223, (415)982-4640

The Asia Found. **[18413]**, PO Box 193223, San Francisco, CA 94119-3223, (415)982-4640

Asia-Japan Women's Rsrc. Center **[IO]**, Tokyo, Japan

Asia-Josei-Siryo-Center **[★IO]**

Asia Keisei Zaidan **[★IO]**

Asia Middle East Bottled Water Assn. **[IO]**, Jakarta, Indonesia

Asia Monitor Rsrc. Centre **[IO]**, Hong Kong, People's Republic of China

Asia-Oceania Assn. for the Stud. of Obesity **[IO]**, Kuala Lumpur, Malaysia

Asia and Oceania Thyroid Assn. **[IO]**, Nagoya, Japan

Asia and Pacific Alliance of YMCAs **[IO]**, Hong Kong, People's Republic of China

Asia/Pacific Amer. Librarians Assn. **[9962]**, Loyola Law School, William M. Rains Lib., 919 Albany St., Los Angeles, CA 90015, (213)736-1431

Asia-Pacific Assn. of Agricultural Res. Institutions **[IO]**, Bangkok, Thailand

Asia Pacific Assn. of Agricultural Res. Institutions - India **[IO]**, Bangkok, Thailand

Asia-Pacific Assn. of Catalysis Societies **[IO]**, Dalian, People's Republic of China

Asia-Pacific Assn. of Forestry Res. Institutions **[IO]**, Selangor, Malaysia

Asia-Pacific Assn. for Machine Translation **[IO]**, Toyohashi, Japan

Asia Pacific Assn. of Paediatric Urologists **[IO]**, Hong Kong, People's Republic of China

Asia-Pacific Broadcasting Union **[IO]**, Kuala Lumpur, Malaysia

Asia-Pacific Coun. of Amer. Chambers of Commerce **[IO]**, Singapore, Singapore

Asia/Pacific Cultural Centre for UNESCO **[IO]**, Tokyo, Japan

Asia-Pacific Economic Cooperation **[IO]**, Singapore, Singapore

Asia-Pacific Forestry Commn. **[IO]**, Bangkok, Thailand

Asia Pacific Forum on Women, Law and Development **[IO]**, Chiang Mai, Thailand

Asia Pacific Found. of Canada **[IO]**, Vancouver, BC, Canada

Asia Pacific Hospice Palliative Care Network **[IO]**, Singapore, Singapore

Asia-Pacific Implant Centre **[IO]**, Hong Kong, People's Republic of China

Asia-Pacific Inst. for Broadcasting Development **[IO]**, Kuala Lumpur, Malaysia

Asia and Pacific Internet Assn. **[IO]**, Petaling Jaya, Malaysia

Asia Pacific Lab. Accreditation Cooperation **[IO]**, North Melbourne, Australia

Asia Pacific League of Associations for Rheumatology **[IO]**, Singapore, Singapore

Asia-Pacific Legal Metrology Forum **[IO]**, Beijing, People's Republic of China

Asia Pacific Loan Market Assn. **[IO]**, Hong Kong, People's Republic of China

Asia Pacific Lottery Assn. **[IO]**, Osborne Park, Australia

Asia Pacific Marketing Fed. **[IO]**, Singapore, Singapore

Asia Pacific Menopause Fed. **[IO]**, Hong Kong, People's Republic of China

Asia-Pacific Migration Res. Network **[IO]**, Suva, Fiji

Asia Pacific Mountain Network **[IO]**, Lalitpur, Nepal

Asia Pacific Natural Gas Vehicles Assn. **[IO]**, Selangor, Malaysia

Asia Pacific Network for Food Anal. **[IO]**, Archerfield, Australia

Asia Pacific Network for Global Change Res. **[IO]**, Kobe, Japan

Asia-Pacific Network for Intl. Educ. and Values Educ. **[IO]**, Mitcham, Australia

Asia-Pacific Network of People Living with HIV/AIDS **[IO]**, Bangkok, Thailand

Asia Pacific Occupational Safety and Hea. Org. **[IO]**, Hong Kong, People's Republic of China

Asia Pacific Orthopaedic Assn. **[IO]**, Singapore, Singapore

Asia Pacific Paedeatric Endocrine Soc. **[IO]**, Westmead, Australia

Asia Pacific Peace Res. Assn. **[IO]**, Carseldine, Australia

Asia and Pacific Plant Protection Commn. **[IO]**, Bangkok, Thailand

Asia-Pacific Population Info. Network **[IO]**, Bangkok, Thailand

Asia-Pacific Professional Services Marketing Assn. **[IO]**, Chatswood, Australia

Asia-Pacific Programme of Educational Innovation for Development **[IO]**, Bangkok, Thailand

Asia and Pacific Regional Bur. for Educ. **[IO]**, Bangkok, Thailand

Asia-Pacific Risk and Insurance Assn. **[IO]**, Singapore, Singapore

Asia-Pacific Satellite Communications Coun. **[IO]**, Seongnam, Republic of Korea

Asia and Pacific Seed Assn. **[IO]**, Bangkok, Thailand

Asia Pacific Smart Card Assn. **[IO]**, Shanghai, People's Republic of China

Asia Pacific Sociological Assn. **[IO]**, Wollongong, Australia

Asia Pacific Telecommunity **[IO]**, Bangkok, Thailand

Asia Pacific Top Level Domains Assn. **[IO]**, Hong Kong, People's Republic of China

Asia Pacific Tourism Assn. **[IO]**, Busan, Republic of Korea

Asia Pacific - USA Chamber of Commerce

Asia Pacific - USA Chamber of Commerce - Address unknown since 2011.

Asia Partnership for Human Development **[IO]**, Bangkok, Thailand

Asia Soc. **[9336]**, 725 Park Ave., 70th St., New York, NY 10021, (212)327-9217

Asia Soc. **[9336]**, 725 Park Ave., 70th St., New York, NY 10021, (212)327-9217

Asia Soil Conservation Network for the Humid Tropics **[IO]**, Jakarta, Indonesia

Asia Watch Comm. **[★17835]**

Asia Watch Comm. **[★17835]**

ASIAN **[18937]**, 1167 Mission St., 4th Fl., San Francisco, CA 94103, (415)928-5910

Asian

Allies Building Community **[9332]**

Amer. Buddhist Stud. Center **[19358]**

Amer. Historical Assn. I Conf. on Asian History **[9333]**

Amer. Historical Assn. I Conf. on Asian History **[9333]**

Amer. Oriental Soc. **[9334]**

Amer. Oriental Soc. **[9334]**

Amer. Schools of Oriental Res. **[9335]**

Amer. Schools of Oriental Res. **[9335]**

Asia Soc. **[9336]**

Asia Soc. **[9336]**

ASIAN **[18937]**

Asian-American Network Against Abuse of Human Rights **[17814]**

Asian Chefs Assn. **[736]**

Asian Cinema Stud. Soc. **[7755]**

Asian Cinema Stud. Soc. **[7755]**

Asian Hea. Care Leaders Assn. **[15288]**

Asian/Pacific Amer. Heritage Assn. **[18938]**

Asian Pacific Americans for Progress **[17205]**

Asian and Pacific Islander Inst. on Domestic Violence **[11880]**

Assn. for the Development of Pakistan **[12601]**

Buddhist Churches of Am. Fed. of Buddhist Women's Associations **[19359]**

Champa Cultural Preservation Assn. of USA **[10636]**

Comm. Against Anti-Asian Violence **[17199]**

Coun. of Teachers of Southeast Asian Languages **[7756]**

Cultural Integration Fellowship **[9337]**

Dharma Drum Mountain Buddhist Assn. **[19364]**

DROKPA **[11575]**

East-West Cultural Center **[9338]**

European Assn. for South East Asian Stud. **[5360]**

Inst. for the Intl. Educ. of Students **[7757]**

Inst. for the Intl. Educ. of Students **[7757]**

Intercollegiate Taiwanese Amer. Students Assn. **[19252]**

Intl. Soc. for Comparative Stud. of Chinese and Western Philosophy **[8707]**

Intl. Soc. of Filipinos in Finance and Accounting **[36]**

Intl. Tamil Tech. Professionals' Org. **[12346]**

Kappa Phi Gamma Sorority **[23746]**

Kollaboration **[13534]**

Leadership Educ. for Asian Pacifics **[9339]**

Lebanese Amer. Coun. for Democracy **[18069]**

Mai Wah Soc. **[9340]**

Mai Wah Soc. **[9340]**

Natl. Alliance for Filipino Concerns **[17200]**

Natl. Assn. for Asian and Pacific Amer. Educ. **[7758]**

Reference to "IO" in place of a book number signifies that the association may be found in the 50th edition of International Organizations.

A star before a book entry number signifies that the name is not listed separately, but is mentioned within the entry.

Asian Professional Security Assn. - Singapore Chap. [IO], Singapore, Singapore

Asian Racing Fed. [IO], Sydney, Australia

Asian Regional Exchange for New Alternatives [IO], Seoul, Republic of Korea

Asian Reinsurance Corp. [IO], Bangkok, Thailand

Asian Resources [11931], 5709 Stockton Blvd., Sacramento, CA 95824, (916)454-1892

Asian Rural Inst. [IO], Tochigi, Japan

Asian Securities and Investments Fed. [IO], Tokyo, Japan

Asian Sleep Res. Soc. [IO], Sapporo, Japan

Asian Soc. for Cardiovascular and Thoracic Surgery [IO], Tokyo, Japan

Asian Soc. for Environmental Geotechnology [IO], Nanjing, People's Republic of China

Asian Soc. for Environmental Protection [IO], Pathumthani, Thailand

Asian Soc. for Pigment Cell Res. [IO], Chandigarh, India

Asian Studies
  Assn. for Asian Amer. Stud. [7759]
  Assn. for Asian Stud. [7760]
  Assn. for Asian Stud. [7760]
  Intl. Assn. of Asian Stud. [7761]
  Intl. Assn. of Asian Stud. [7761]
  Intl. Soc. for Comparative Stud. of Chinese and Western Philosophy [8707]

Asian Stud. Assn. of Australia [IO], Canberra, Australia

Asian Surgical Assn. [IO], Hong Kong, People's Republic of China

Asian Tennis Fed. [IO], Hong Kong, People's Republic of China

Asian Women in Bus. [642], 42 Broadway, Ste. 1748, New York, NY 10004, (212)868-1368

Asian Women in Bus. [642], 42 Broadway, Ste. 1748, New York, NY 10004, (212)868-1368

Asian Women's Human Rights Coun. [IO], Bangalore, India

Asian Women's Rsrc. Centre for Culture and Theology [IO], Kuala Lumpur, Malaysia

Asian Youth Centre [IO], Chennai, India

Asian Youth Orchestra [IO], Hong Kong, People's Republic of China

Asiana Educ. Development - Address unknown since 2010.

Asians for Miracle Marrow Matches [16903], 244 S San Pedro St., No. 503, Los Angeles, CA 90012, (888)236-4673

Asiatic Breeders Assn. - Defunct.

Asiatic Philharmonia Soc. [10161], PO Box 2799, Sunnyvale, CA 94087, (408)331-4909

Asiatic Philharmonia Soc. [10161], PO Box 2799, Sunnyvale, CA 94087, (408)331-4909

ASIS Intl. [1883], 1625 Prince St., Alexandria, VA 22314-2818, (703)519-6200

ASIS Intl. [1883], 1625 Prince St., Alexandria, VA 22314-2818, (703)519-6200

Asleep at the Wheel Fan Club [23815], PO Box 463, Austin, TX 78767, (512)444-9885

ASM Found. for Educ. and Research [★7090]

ASM Found. for Educ. and Research [★7090]

ASM Intl. [7090], 9639 Kinsman Rd., Novelty, OH 44072, (440)338-5151

ASM Intl. [7090], 9639 Kinsman Rd., Novelty, OH 44072, (440)338-5151

ASME Intl. Gas Turbine Inst. [6782], 6525 The Corners Pkwy., Ste. 115, Norcross, GA 30092, (404)847-0072

ASME Intl. Gas Turbine Inst. [6782], 6525 The Corners Pkwy., Ste. 115, Norcross, GA 30092, (404)847-0072

Asmita Women's Publishing House, Media and Rsrc. Org. [IO], Kathmandu, Nepal

ASMP - The Soc. of Photographers in Communications [★2711]

Asociacao Fiscal Portuguesa [★IO]

Asociacao Interamericana de Engenharia Sanitaria [★7348]

Asociacao Interamericana de Engenharia Sanitaria [★7348]

Asociace fotografu [★IO]

Asociace ceskych pojistovacich makleru [★IO]

Asociace sklarskeho a keramickeho prumyslu Ceske republiky [★IO]

Asociace Ceskeho Papirenskeho Prumyslu [★IO]

Asociace Ceskych Cestovnich Kancelari a Agentur [★IO]

Asociace Ceskych Reklamnich Agentur a Marketingove Komunikace [★IO]

Asociace Cestovnich Kancelari Ceske Republiky [★IO]

Asociace Skolnich Sportovnich Klubu CR [★IO]

Asociace Zemedelske A Lesnicke Techniky [★IO]

Asociacia Marfanovho Syndromu [★IO]

Asociacia Organizacii Zdravotne Postihnutych Obeanov Sr [★IO]

Asociacia Public Relations Slovenskej Republiky [★IO]

Asociacia Slovenskych Geomorfologov [★IO]

Asociacija Lietuvos Keliai [★IO]

Asociacion internacional de relaciones del trabajo [★IO]

Asociacion Accion Intl. para la Salud [★IO]

Asociacion de Administradores de Riesgos de la Republica Argentina [IO], Buenos Aires, Argentina

Asociacion de Afectados Sindrome de Marfan [IO], Alicante, Spain

Asociacion de Amigos de los Amigos [★19782]

Asociacion de Amistad Omani Espanola [★IO]

Asociacion Andar Costa Rica [IO], San Jose, Costa Rica

Asociacion Argentina de Agencias de Publicidad [★IO]

Asociacion Argentina de Agencias de Viajes y Turismo [★IO]

Asociacion Argentina de Aikido [IO], Buenos Aires, Argentina

Asociacion Argentina de Baile Deportivo [IO], San Isidro, Argentina

Asociacion Argentina de Biologia y Medicina Nuclear [★IO]

Asociacion Argentina de Codificacion de Productos Comerciales [★IO]

Asociacion Argentina de Companias de Seguros [★IO]

Asociacion Argentina de Dermatologia [★IO]

Asociacion Argentina de Ecologia [★IO]

Asociacion Argentina de Economia Politica [IO], Buenos Aires, Argentina

Asociacion Argentina de Editores de Revistas [★IO]

Asociacion Argentina para el Estudio del Dolor [IO], Buenos Aires, Argentina

Asociacion Argentina de Franchising [★IO]

Asociacion Argentina de Geofisicos y Geodestas [★IO]

Asociacion Argentina de Ginecologia y Obstetricia Psicosomatica [★IO]

Asociacion Argentina de Grasas y Aceites [★IO]

Asociacion Argentina de Informatica Medica [★IO]

Asociacion Argentina de Marketing [★IO]

Asociacion Argentina de Medicos por el Medio Ambiente [★IO]

Asociacion Argentina de Ortopedia y Traumatologia [★IO]

Asociacion Argentina de Osteologia y Metabolismo Mineral [IO], Buenos Aires, Argentina

Asociacion Argentina de Proteccion Familiar [IO], Buenos Aires, Argentina

Asociacion Argentina de Rosicultura [★IO]

Asociacion Argentina de Sedimentologia [IO], La Plata, Argentina

Asociacion Argentina de Squash Rackets [IO], Buenos Aires, Argentina

Asociacion Argentina de TV por Cable [★IO]

Asociacion Argentina de Tenis [IO], Buenos Aires, Argentina

Asociacion Argentina de Terapistas Ocupacionales [IO], Buenos Aires, Argentina

Asociacion Bancaria Costarricense [★IO]

Asociacion Bancaria de Guatemala [★IO]

Asociacion Bancaria de Panama [★IO]

Asociacion Bancaria de Venezuela [★IO]

Asociacion de Bancos de la Argentina [★IO]

Asociacion de Bancos Privados de Bolivia [★IO]

Asociacion de Bancos Privados del Ecuador [★IO]

Asociacion de Bancos Publicos y Privados de la Republica Argentina [★IO]

Asociacion de Bibliotecarios Graduados de la Republica Argentina [★IO]

Asociacion Bioquimica Argentina [★IO]

Asociacion Boliviana de Aseguradores [★IO]

Asociacion Boliviana para Estudio and Tratamiento del Dolor [IO], La Paz, Bolivia

Asociacion Boliviana de Ingenieria Geotecnica [IO], La Paz, Bolivia

Asociacion Chilena de Albergues Turisticos Juveniles [★IO]

Asociacion Chilena de Control Automatico [IO], Santiago, Chile

Asociacion Chilena de Distribuidores de Software [★IO]

Asociacion Chilena de Empresas de Tecnologias de Informacion [★IO]

Asociacion Chilena de Empresas de Turismo [★IO]

Asociacion Chilena para el Estudio del Dolor [IO], Santiago, Chile

Asociacion Chilena de la Rosa [IO], Santiago, Chile

Asociacion Chilena de Sismologia e Ingenieria Antisismica [★IO]

Asociacion Civil de Planificacion Familiar [IO], Caracas, Venezuela

Asociacion Colombiana para el Avance de la Ciencia [★IO]

Asociacion Colombiana de Baille Deportivo [IO], Manizales, Colombia

Asociacion Colombiana de Dermatologia [★IO]

Asociacion Colombiana para el Estudio del Dolor [IO], Bogota, Colombia

Asociacion Colombiana de Fertilidad Y Esterilidad [★IO]

Asociacion Colombiana de Industrias Plasticas [★IO]

Asociacion Colombiana de Neurofisiologia Clinica [★IO]

Asociacion Colombiana de Osteologia y Metabolismo Mineral [IO], Bogota, Colombia

Asociacion Colombiana de Psiquiatria [★IO]

Asociacion Colombiana de Terapia Ocupacional [IO], Bogota, Colombia

Asociacion de Comerciantes y Distribuidores de Viveres y Similares de Panama [★IO]

Asociacion de Companias Consultoras del Ecuador [★IO]

Asociacion Cosarricense de Climaterio y Menopausia y Osteoporosis [★IO]

Asociacion Costarricense de Badminton [IO], Cartago, Costa Rica

Asociacion Costarricense de Geotecnia [IO], San Jose, Costa Rica

Asociacion Costarricense de la Industria del Plastico [★IO]

Asociacion Costarricense para Organizaciones de Desarrollo [IO], San Jose, Costa Rica

Asociacion de Cricket Argentino [★IO]

Asociacion Cristiana Femenin de la Republica Argentina [★IO]

Asociacion Cristiana Femenina [★13567]

Asociacion Cristiana Femenina [★13567]

Asociacion Cristiana Femenina de Chile [★IO]

Asociacion Cristiana Femenina de Colombia [★IO]

Asociacion Cristiana Femenina Nacional de la Republica Mexicana [★IO]

Asociacion Cristiana Femenina de Peru [★IO]

Asociacion Cristiana Femenina de Uruguay [★IO]

Asociacion Cristiana Feminina Nacional del Salvador [★IO]

Asociacion Cristiana de Jovenes del Peru [★IO]

Asociacion Cubana de Reconocimiento de Patrones [★IO]

Asociacion de Cultivadores de Cana de Azucar de Colombia [★IO]

Asociacion Demografica Costarricense [★IO]

Asociacion Demografica Salvadorena [★IO]

Asociacion Dental Mexicana [IO], Mexico City, Mexico

Asociacion por los Derechos Civiles [★IO]

Asociacion de Desarrolladores de Videojuegos Argentina [★IO]

Asociacion Di Ingeniero y Arquitectonan Arubano [IO], Santa Cruz, Aruba

Asociacion de Diarios y Revistas del Peru [IO], Lima, Peru

Asociacion de Distribuidores de Golosinas y Afines [★IO]

Reference to "IO" in place of a book number signifies that the association may be found in the 50th edition of International Organizations.

Asociacion Distrofia Muscular **[IO]**, Buenos Aires, Argentina

Asociacion Dominicana de Empresas de Inversion Extranjera **[★IO]**

Asociacion Dominicana Pro-Bienestar de la Familia **[IO]**, Santo Domingo, Dominican Republic

Asociacion de Economia de Am. Latina y el Caribe **[★IO]**

Asociacion de Economistas del Caribe **[★IO]**

Asociacion Ecuatoriana de Editores de Periodicos **[★IO]**

Asociacion Ecuatoriana de Radiodifusion **[★IO]**

Asociacion Editores de Diarios de la Ciudad de Buenos Aires **[IO]**, Buenos Aires, Argentina

Asociacion de Editores de Diarios Espanoles **[IO]**, Madrid, Spain

Asociacion de Editores de los Estados **[IO]**, Mexico City, Mexico

Asociacion para la Educacion Teologica Hispana **[9006]**, 2620 S Parker Rd., Ste. 274, Aurora, CO 80014, (720)535-5435

Asociacion Empresarial de Fabricantes y Comerciantes Mayoristas de Articulos de Regalo **[★IO]**

Asociacion de Empresarios Detallistas de Frutas y Hortalizas **[★IO]**

Asociacion de Entidades Periodisticas Argentinas **[IO]**, Buenos Aires, Argentina

Asociacion de Entidades Periodisticas del Paraguay **[IO]**, Asuncion, Paraguay

Asociacion espanola de Entomologia **[★IO]**

Asociacion de fotografos profesionales de Espana **[IO]**, Barcelona, Spain

Asociacion Espanola de Aerosoles **[★IO]**

Asociacion Espanola de Anunciantes **[IO]**, Madrid, Spain

Asociacion Espanola de Baile Deportivo y de Competicion **[★IO]**

Asociacion Espanola de Bioempresas **[★IO]**

Asociacion Espanola de Codificacion Comercial **[★IO]**

Asociacion Espanola de Consultores en Ingenieria **[IO]**, Madrid, Spain

Asociacion Espanola Contra La Osteoporosis **[★IO]**

Asociacion Espanola para el Deficit de Alfa-1 **[★IO]**

Asociacion Espanola de Economia **[★IO]**

Asociacion Espanola para la Economia Energetica **[★IO]**

Asociacion Espanola de Empresas de la Carne **[★IO]**

Asociacion Espanola de Esclerosis Lateral Amiotrofica **[IO]**, Madrid, Spain

Asociacion Espanola de Esclerosis Multiple **[★IO]**

Asociacion Espanola de Fabricantes de Automoviles y Camiones **[★IO]**

Asociacion Espanola de Fabricantes de Caramelos y Chicles **[★IO]**

Asociacion Espanola de Fabricantes Exportadores de Bisuteria **[★IO]**

Asociacion Espanola de Fabricantes de Juguetes **[★IO]**

Asociacion Espanola de Fabricantes de Pasta, Papel y Carton **[★IO]**

Asociacion Espanola de Fabricantes de Pequenos Electrodomesticos **[★IO]**

Asociacion Espanola de Fabricantes de Pinturas y Tintas de Imprimir **[★IO]**

Asociacion Espanola de Fisioterapeutas **[IO]**, Madrid, Spain

Asociacion Espanola de Gerencia de Riesgos y Seguros **[IO]**, Madrid, Spain

Asociacion Espanola de la Industria y el Comercio Exportador del Aceite de Oliva **[★IO]**

Asociacion Espanola de Ingenieria de Proyectos **[IO]**, Valencia, Spain

Asociacion Espanola de Joyeros, Plateros y Relojeros **[★IO]**

Asociacion Espanola de Operadores de Productos Petroliferos **[★IO]**

Asociacion Espanola de Productores de Huevos **[★IO]**

Asociacion Espanola de Reconocimiento de Formas y Analisis de Imagenes **[★IO]**

Asociacion Espanola de la Rosa **[IO]**, Valencia, Spain

Asociacion Espanola de Sistemas de Informacion Geografica **[IO]**, Madrid, Spain

Asociacion Espanola de Tecnicos de Cerveza y Malta **[★IO]**

Asociacion Espanola de Unihockey y Floorball **[★IO]**

Asociacion de Estados del Caribe **[★IO]**

Asociacion Europea de Coleopterologia **[★IO]**

Asociacion Europea de Suministradores de Servicios para Personas con Minusvalias Disabilities **[★IO]**

Asociacion de Exportadores e Industriales de Aceitunas de Mesa **[★IO]**

Asociacion de Exportadores de Manufacturas de Chile **[★IO]**

Asociacion de Fabricantes Artesanales de Helados y Afines **[★IO]**

Asociacion de Fabricantes de Cemento Portland **[★IO]**

Asociacion de Fabricantes de Complementos Alimentarios **[★IO]**

Asociacion de Fabricantes de Equipos de Climatizacion **[★IO]**

Asociacion de Fabricantes de Harinas y Semolas de Espana **[★IO]**

Asociacion de Fabricantes de Riego Espanoles **[★IO]**

Asociacion de Fabricas de Automotores **[★IO]**

Asociacion Farmaceutica Mexicana **[★IO]**

Asociacion Feldenkrais Argentina **[IO]**, Buenos Aires, Argentina

Asociacion Filosofica de Mexico **[IO]**, Mexico City, Mexico

Asociacion Fisica Argentina **[★IO]**

Asociacion de Fisioterapeutas del Uruguay **[IO]**, Montevideo, Uruguay

Asociacion para la Formacion y Actividades Interculturales para la Juventud **[★IO]**

Asociacion de Gerentes de Guatemala **[★IO]**

Asociacion Gremial de Industriales Quimicos de Chiles **[★IO]**

Asociacion Gremial de Supermercados de Chile **[★IO]**

Asociacion Guatemalteca de Deportes Aereos **[IO]**, Guatemala City, Guatemala

Asociacion Guatemalteca de Dermatologia **[IO]**, Antigua, Guatemala

Asociacion Guatemalteca de Fertilidad Y Reproduccion Humana **[IO]**, Guatemala City, Guatemala

Asociacion Guatemalteca de Medicina Deportiva **[IO]**, Guatemala City, Guatemala

Asociacion Hondurena de Instituciones Bancarias **[★IO]**

Asociacion Hondurena de Maquiladores **[★IO]**

Asociacion de Hoteles de Turismo de la Republica Argentina **[★IO]**

Asociacion de la Industria de la Piel para el Comercio Exterior **[★IO]**

Asociacion de la Industria del Salmon **[★IO]**

Asociacion Indus. Textil de Proceso Algodonero **[★IO]**

Asociacion de Industriales Metalurgicos y de Mineria de Venezuela **[★IO]**

Asociacion de Industriales Metalurgicos de la Republica Argentina **[★IO]**

Asociacion de Industrias de la Carne de Espana **[★IO]**

Asociacion de Industrias Metalurgicas y Metalmecanicas **[★IO]**

Asociacion de Ingenieros Cubanos **[★6784]**

Asociacion de Ingenieros y Tecnicos del Automotor **[★IO]**

Asociacion de Inquilinos del Ecuador **[IO]**, Quito, Ecuador

Asociacion Interamericana de Contabilidad **[★32]**

Asociacion Interamericana de Intenieria Sanitaria **[★7348]**

Asociacion Interamericana de Intenieria Sanitaria **[★7348]**

Asociacion Interamericana de la Propiedad Intelectual **[★IO]**

Asociacion Internacional de Asmologia **[★IO]**

Asociacion Internacional de Estudios en Comunicacion Social **[★IO]**

Asociacion Internacional de Ferias de Am. **[★IO]**

Asociacion Internacional de Hidrogeologos Grupo Espanol **[★IO]**

Asociacion Internacional de Hispanistas **[★IO]**

Asociacion Internacional de Lectura **[★8780]**

Asociacion Internacional de Lectura **[★8780]**

Asociacion Latinoamericana de Botanica **[★IO]**

Asociacion Latinoamericana de Diabetes **[★IO]**

Asociacion Latinoamericana de Fitopatologia **[★IO]**

Asociacion Latinoamericana de Instituciones Financieras Para el Desarrollo **[★IO]**

Asociacion Latinoamericana de Investigadores de la Comunicacion **[★IO]**

Asociacion Latinoamericana de Organizaciones de Promocion **[★IO]**

Asociacion de Lineas Aereas Internacionales **[★IO]**

Asociacion Madres de Plaza de Mayo **[★IO]**

Asociacion de Marketing Bancario Argentino **[★IO]**

Asociacion Medica Argentina **[IO]**, Buenos Aires, Argentina

Asociacion Medica Nacional de la Republica de Panama **[IO]**, Panama City, Panama

Asociacion Mexicana de Agencias de Investigacion de Mercado y Opinion Publica **[★IO]**

Asociacion Mexicana de Agencias de Investigacion de Mercado y Opinion Publica **[★IO]**

Asociacion Mexicana de Agencias de Publicidad **[★IO]**

Asociacion Mexicana Automovilistica **[★IO]**

Asociacion Mexicana de Distribuidores de Automotores **[★IO]**

Asociacion Mexicana de Distribuidores de Maquinaria **[★IO]**

Asociacion Mexicana de la Enfermidad De Huntington I.A.P. **[IO]**, Mexico City, Mexico

Asociacion Mexicana de Estandares papa el Comercio Electronico **[★IO]**

Asociacion Mexicana de Fabricantes de Articulos para Regalo, Decoracion y Artesanias **[★IO]**

Asociacion Mexicana de Facultades y Escuelas de Medicina **[IO]**, Mexico City, Mexico

Asociacion Mexicana de Hoteles y Moteles **[IO]**, Mexico City, Mexico

Asociacion Mexicana de la Industria Automotriz **[IO]**, Mexico City, Mexico

Asociacion Mexicana de Mecatronica **[★IO]**

Asociacion Mexicana de Parques Industriales **[★IO]**

Asociacion Mexicana de Productores de Fonogramas AC **[IO]**, Mexico City, Mexico

Asociacion Mexicana de Profesionales de Ferias, Exposiciones y Convenciones **[★IO]**

Asociacion Mexicana de Restaurantes **[★IO]**

Asociacion Mondial de Radios Communautarias **[★IO]**

Asociacion de Mujeres Universitarias de El Salvador **[IO]**, San Salvador, El Salvador

Asociacion de Mujeres Universitarias de Vizcaya **[IO]**, Leioa, Spain

Asociacion Mundial de las Guias Scouts **[★IO]**

Asociacion Mundial Veterinaria de Avicola **[★IO]**

Asociacion de Musica Electroacustica de Espana **[IO]**, Barcelona, Spain

Asociacion Mutual Israelita Argentina **[★IO]**

Asociacion Nacional de Actores **[IO]**, San Rafael, Mexico

Asociacion Nacional de Anunciantes Colombia **[IO]**, Bogota, Colombia

Asociacion Nacional de Anunciantes del Peru **[IO]**, Lima, Peru

Asociacion Nacional de Anunciantes-Venezuela **[★IO]**

Asociacion Nacional de Anunciantes Venezuela **[IO]**, Caracas, Venezuela

Asociacion Nacional de Avisadores **[IO]**, Santiago, Chile

Asociacion Nacional de Comerciantes en Automoviles **[★IO]**

Asociacion Nacional Contra el Cancer **[IO]**, Panama City, Panama

Asociacion Nacional de Cultivadores de Palma Africana **[★IO]**

Asociacion Nacional de Distribuidores de Llantas y Plantas Renovadoras **[★IO]**

Asociacion Nacional de Economistas y Contadores de Cuba **[★IO]**

Asociacion Nacional de la Empresa Privada **[★IO]**

Asociacion Nacional Empresarial de la Industria Farmaceutica **[★IO]**

Asociacion Nacional de Empresas de Aguas de Bebida Envasada **[★IO]**

A star before a book entry number signifies that the name is not listed separately, but is mentioned within the entry.

Asociacion Nacional de Empresas Comercializa-doras de Productores del Campo [★IO]
Asociacion Nacional de Especialidades Farmaceuti-cas Publicitarias [★IO]
Asociacion Nacional de Estabecimientos Financieros de Credito [★IO]
Asociacion Nacional de Exportadores de Cacao [★IO]
Asociacion Nacional de Fabricantes de Bebidas Re-frescantes Analcoholicas [★IO]
Asociacion Nacional de Fabricantes de Chocolate, Dulces y Similares [★IO]
Asociacion Nacional de Fabricantes e Importadores de Electrodomesticos de Linea Blanca [★IO]
Asociacion Nacional de Fabricantes de Pinturas y Tintas [★IO]
Asociacion Nacional de Fisioterapistas de Guatemala [IO], Guatemala City, Guatemala
Asociacion Nacional de Hoteles y Restaurantes [★IO]
Asociacion Nacional de Importadores y Exportado-res [★IO]
Asociacion Nacional de la Industria del Cafe [★IO]
Asociacion Nacional de la Industria Quimica [★IO]
Asociacion Nacional de Industriales de Honduras [★IO]
Asociacion Nacional de Industrias de Aceites y Man-tecas Comestibles [★IO]
Asociacion Nacional de Industrias del Plastico [★IO]
Asociacion Nacional de Instituciones Financieras [★IO]
Asociacion Nacional de Personas Impedidas [IO], Panama City, Panama
Asociacion Nacional de la Prensa - Chile [IO], San-tiago, Chile
Asociacion Nacional de Productores de Semillas de Chile [★IO]
Asociacion Nacional de Proveedores para la Indus-tria del Calzado [★IO]
Asociacion Nacional de la Publicidad [★IO]
Asociacion Nacional de la Publicidad [IO], Mexico City, Mexico
Asociacion Nacional de Scouts de Panama [★IO]
Asociacion Nacional de Squash de Guatemala [IO], Guatemala City, Guatemala
Asociacion Nacional de Supermercados y Autoservi-cios [★IO]
Asociacion Nacional de Tiendas de Autoservicio y Departamentales [★IO]
Asociacion Nacional de Vendedores Vehiculos a Mo-tor Reparacion y Recambios [★IO]
Asociacion Odontologica Argentina [★IO]
Asociacion de Orquideologia de Quito [IO], Quito, Ecuador
Asociacion de Padres de Personas con Autismo [★IO]
Asociacion Paleontologica Argentina [★IO]
Asociacion Panamena de Fisioterapia Kinesiologia [IO], Panama City, Panama
Asociacion Panamena de Juego de Damas [IO], Panama City, Panama
Asociacion Panamena para el Planeamiento de la Familia [★IO]
Asociacion Panamena de Polo [IO], Panama City, Panama
Asociacion Panamena de Taekwondo [IO], Panama City, Panama
Asociacion Panamericana de Instituciones de Credito Educativo [★IO]
Asociacion Paraguaya de Aikido [IO], Asuncion, Paraguay
Asociacion Paraguaya de Tenis [IO], Asuncion, Paraguay
Asociacion de Periodistas y Escritores Agrarios Es-panoles [IO], Saragossa, Spain
Asociacion Peruana de Agencias de Publicidad [★IO]
Asociacion Peruana de Arquitectura del Paisaje [IO], Lima, Peru
Asociacion Peruana para la Conservacion de la Naturaleza [★IO]
Asociacion Peruana para el Estudio del Dolor [IO], Lima, Peru
Asociacion Petroquimica y Quimica Latinoamericana [★IO]

Asociacion de Prensa Profesional [★IO]
Asociacion Pro-Bienestar de la Familia Colombiana [IO], Bogota, Colombia
Asociacion Pro-Bienestar de la Familia Ecuatoriana [IO], Guayaquil, Ecuador
Asociacion Pro-Bienestar de la Familia de Guatemala [IO], Guatemala City, Guatemala
Asociacion de Productores Fonograficos de Venezuela [IO], Caracas, Venezuela
Asociacion de Productores de Salmon y Trucha de Chile [★IO]
Asociacion Regional de Empresas de Petroleo, Gas Natural en Latino Am., el Caribe [★IO]
Asociacion de Revistas de Informacion [IO], Madrid, Spain
Asociacion Salvadorena de Industriales [★IO]
Asociacion Tecnica para la gestion de Residues y Medio Ambiente [★IO]
Asociacion de Teleradiodifusoras Argentinas [★IO]
Asociacion de TV Educativa Iberoamericana [★IO]
Asociacion Universitaria Iberoamericana de Post-grado [★IO]
Asociacion Uruguaya de Badminton [IO], Montev-ideo, Uruguay
Asociacion Uruguaya para el Estudio del Dolor [★IO]
Asociacion Uruguaya de Planificacion Familiar [★IO]
Asociacion Uruguaya de Psicoterapia Psicoanalitica [★IO]
Asociacion Uruguaya de la Rosa [★IO]
Asociacion Uruguaya de Tenis [IO], Barra de Carrasco, Uruguay
Asociacion Uruguaya para la Tutela Organizada de los derechos Reprograficos [IO], Montevideo, Uruguay
Asociacion de Usuarios de la Zona Libre de Colon [★IO]
Asociacion Venezolana para el Estudio del Dolor [IO], Caracas, Venezuela
Asociacion Venezolana de Exportadores [★IO]
Asociacion Venezolana de Huntington [IO], Caracas, Venezuela
Asociacion Venezolana de la Industria Quimica y Petroquimica [★IO]
Asociacion Venezolana de Industrias Plasticas [★IO]
Asociacion Venezolana de Pilotos Privados y Propi-etarios de Aeronaves [★IO]
Asociacion Venezolana de Productores de Pulpa, Papel y Carton [★IO]
Asociatia pentru Compatibiltate Electromagnetica din Romania [★IO]
Asociatia Femeilor din Romania [★IO]
Asociatia Generala a Inginerilor din Romania [★IO]
Asociatia Handicapatilor Neuromotor din Romania [★IO]
Asociatia Medicilor Stomatologi cu Practica Privata din Romania [★IO]
Asociatia Nationala A Femeilor Cu Diploma Universi-tara Din Romania [IO], Bucharest, Romania
Asociatia Nationala a Internet Ser. Providerilor din Romania [★IO]
Asociatia Nationala Romana de Ortodontie [IO], Iasi, Romania
Asociatia Pentru Protectia Consumatorilor Din Romania [★IO]
Asociatia Pilotilor si Proprietarilor de Aeronave din Romania [★IO]
Asociatia Presei Independente [★IO]
Asociatia Producatorilor si Importatorilor De Auto. [★IO]
Asociatia Romana a Bancilor [★IO]
Asociatia Romana de Psihologie Transpersonala [★IO]
Asociatia Romana pentru Telelucru si Teleactivitati [★IO]
Asociatia Youth Hostel Romania [★IO]
Association Argentina Amigos de la Astronomia [IO], Buenos Aires, Argentina
Association Argentina de Ensayos No Destructivos y Estructurales [★IO]
Association Colombiana de Endoscopia Digestiva [IO], Bogota, Colombia
Asociacion Espanola del Gas [★IO]
Asociacion de Exportadores del Peru [★IO]

Asociation Ivoirienne de Medicine Sportive [IO], Abid-jan, Cote d'Ivoire
Asociation Quimica Argentina [IO], Buenos Aires, Argentina
Asosiasi Penyelenggara Jasa Internet Indonesia [★IO]
ASPA Accreditation Inst. [★2628]
Asparagus Growers Assn. [IO], Louth, United Kingdom
ASPECT Found. [8345], 211 Sutter St., 10th Fl., San Francisco, CA 94108, (800)879-6884
Aspen Inst. [9839], 1 Dupont Cir. NW, Ste. 700, Washington, DC 20036-1133, (202)736-5800
Aspen Inst. Berlin [IO], Berlin, Germany
Aspen Inst. for Humanistic Stud. [★9839]
Asperger Syndrome Assn. of Ireland [IO], Dublin, Ireland
Asperger Syndrome Coalition of the U.S. [★15607]
Asperger Syndrome; MAAP Services for Autism and [15607]
Asperger's Syndrome; Families of Adults Afflicted with [16765]
Asphalt Assn. [★524]
Asphalt Assn. [★524]
Asphalt Emulsion Mfrs. Assn. [523], 3 Church Cir., PMB 250, Annapolis, MD 21401, (410)267-0023
Asphalt Inst. [524], 2696 Res. Park Dr., Lexington, KY 40511-8480, (859)288-4960
Asphalt Inst. [524], 2696 Res. Park Dr., Lexington, KY 40511-8480, (859)288-4960
Asphalt Interlayer Assn. [525], 1811 Hampshire Pl., El Dorado Hills, CA 95762, (916)933-9140
Asphalt Pavement Alliance [526], Asphalt Inst., 2696 Res. Park Dr., Lexington, KY 40511, (859)288-4960
Asphalt Recycling and Reclaiming Assn. [3630], PMB 250, 3 Church Cir., Annapolis, MD 21401, (410)267-0023
Asphalt Roofing Indus. Bur. [★527]
Asphalt Roofing Mfrs. Assn. [527], Public Info. Dept., 750 Natl. Press Bldg., 529 14th St. NW, Washington, DC 20045, (202)207-0917
Asphalt Rubber Producers Gp. [★613]
Asphalt Rubber Producers Gp. [★613]
Asphalt Tile Inst. [★611]
Asphalt and Vinyl Asbestos Tile Inst. [★611]
Aspira of Am. [★8000]
ASPIRA Assn. [8000], 1444 I St. NW, Ste. 800, Washington, DC 20005, (202)835-3600
ASPIRE - Assn. of Special People Inspired to Riding Excellence - Defunct.
Aspley Orchid Soc. [IO], Browns Plains, Australia
ASPRS - Amer. Soc. of Plastic and Reconstructive Surgery [★14177]
ASPRS - The Imaging and Geospatial Info. Soc. [7259], 5410 Grosvenor Ln., Ste. 210, Bethesda, MD 20814-2160, (301)493-0290
Assassination Archives and Res. Center [18768], 1003 K St. NW, Ste. 640, Washington, DC 20001, (202)393-1921
Assassination Info. Bur. [★18768]
Assault
    Intl. Center for Assault Prevention [11889]
Assaulted Women's Helpline [IO], Toronto, ON, Canada
ASSE Intl. Student Exchange Programs [8346], 228 N Coast Hwy., Laguna Beach, CA 92651, (949)494-4100
ASSE Intl. Student Exchange Programs [8346], 228 N Coast Hwy., Laguna Beach, CA 92651, (949)494-4100
Assemble Europenne des Academiques Turcs [★IO]
L'Assemblee Canadienne de la Danse [★IO]
Assemblee des Chambres Francaises de Commerce et d'industrie [★IO]
Assemblee Des Regions D'Europe [★IO]
Assemblee des Ordinaires Catholiques de Terre Sainte [★IO]
Assemblee Parlementaire de l'Otan [★IO]
Assemblee des Premieres Nations [★IO]
Assemblee des Regions Europeennes Viticoles [★IO]
Assembly of Episcopal Healthcare Chaplains [19690], Somerset Medical Center, 110 Rehill Ave., Somerville, NJ 08876-2519, (908)685-2200

Reference to "IO" in place of a book number signifies that the association may be found in the 50th edition of International Organizations.

Assembly of European Regions [IO], Strasbourg, France

Assembly of First Nations [IO], Ottawa, ON, Canada

Assembly of French Chambers of Commerce and Indus. [IO], Paris, France

Assembly of Governmental Employees - Defunct.

Assembly for the Teaching of English Grammar [8466], PO Box 92, Fishkill, NY 12524

Assembly of Turkish Amer. Associations [19258], 1526 18th St. NW, Washington, DC 20036, (202)483-9090

Assembly of Wine Producing European Regions [IO], Chalons-en-Champagne, France

Asset Based Finance Assn. [IO], Richmond, United Kingdom

Asset Managers Forum [1281], 120 Broadway, New York, NY 10017, (212)213-1000

Asset Managers Forum [1281], 120 Broadway, New York, NY 10017, (212)213-1000

Assist Card Intl. [3550], 175 SW 7th St., Miami, FL 33130, (877)369-2774

Assist Card Intl. [3550], 175 SW 7th St., Miami, FL 33130, (877)369-2774

Assist Intl. [12446], PO Box 66396, Scotts Valley, CA 95067-6396, (831)438-4582

Assist Intl. [12446], PO Box 66396, Scotts Valley, CA 95067-6396, (831)438-4582

ASSIST-Rwanda [IO], Kigali, Rwanda

Assistance Dogs of Am., Inc. [11762], 8806 State Rte. 64, Swanton, OH 43558, (419)825-3622

Assistance Dogs Australia [IO], Engadine, Australia

Assistance Dogs Intl. [11763], PO Box 5174, Santa Rosa, CA 95402

Assistance Dogs Intl. [11763], PO Box 5174, Santa Rosa, CA 95402

Assistance for Indigenous People of Eastern Bolivia [IO], Santa Cruz, Bolivia

Assistance League [13052], PO Box 6637, Burbank, CA 91510-6637, (818)846-3777

Assistance in Ministries - Defunct.

Asst. Directors Local 161 [★23187]

Assisted Living; Consumer Consortium on [10840]

Assisted Living Facilities Assn. of Am. [★12171]

Assisted Living Fed. of Am. [12171], 1650 King St., Ste. 602, Alexandria, VA 22314-2747, (703)894-1805

Assisted Living; Natl. Center for [14813]

Assisting Children in Need [11148], 600 Cameron St., Alexandria, VA 22314, (703)340-1677

ASSITEJ/USA [★10608]

ASSOCARTA - Italian Assn. of Paper, Cardboard and Pulp Mfrs. [IO], Milan, Italy

Assocazione Italiana di Geologia Applicata e Ambientale [IO], Rome, Italy

Associacao de Apoio Aos Deficientes [IO], Praia, Cape Verde

Associacao de Atletismo de Macau [IO], Macau, Macao

Associacao de Badminton de Macau [IO], Macau, Macao

Associacao Brasil Huntington [IO], Atibaia, Brazil

Associacao Brasileiara Interdisciplinar de AIDS [★IO]

Associacao Brasileira de Aerossois e Saneantes Domissanitarios [★IO]

Associacao Brasileira de Agencias de Viagens [★IO]

Associacao Brasileira de Anunciantes [★IO]

Associacao Brasileira de Arquitetos Paisagistas [IO], Sao Paulo, Brazil

Associacao Brasileira de Aviacao Geral [IO], Sao Paulo, Brazil

Associacao Brasileira de Bancos [★IO]

Associacao Brasileira de Bancos [★IO]

Associacao Brasileira de Bebidas [★IO]

Associacao Brasileira de Bioinformatica e Bioligia Computacional [★IO]

Associacao Brasileira de Cafes Especiais [★IO]

Associacao Brasileira de Ceramica [★IO]

Associacao Brasileira de Cimento Portland [★IO]

Associacao Brasileira de Consultores de Engenharia [★IO]

Associacao Brasileira de Cosmetologia [★IO]

Associacao Brasileira Da Infra-Estrutura E Industrias De Base [★IO]

Associacao Brasileira De Shopping Centers [★IO]

Associacao Brasileira de Direitos Reprograficos [IO], Sao Paulo, Brazil

Associacao Brasileira de Distrofia Muscular [★IO]

Associacao Brasileira de Embalagem [★IO]

Associacao Brasileira das Empresas de Cartoes de Credito e Servicos [★IO]

Associacao Brasileira das Empresas de Coleta de Dados [★IO]

Associacao Brasileira das Empresas de Software [★IO]

Associacao Brasileira de Empresas de Vendas Diretas [★IO]

Associacao Brasileira de Engenharia Automotiva [★IO]

Associacao Brasileira de Esclerose Lateral Amiotrofica [★IO]

Associacao Brasileira de Esclerose Multipla [IO], Sao Paulo, Brazil

Associacao Brasileira dos Fabricantes de Brinquedos [★IO]

Associacao Brasileira de Franchising [★IO]

Associacao Brasileira de Geossinteticos [★IO]

Associacao Brasileira de Gerencia de Riscos [IO], Sao Paulo, Brazil

Associacao Brasileira de Imprensa [★IO]

Associacao Brasileira da Industria de Aguas Minerais [IO], Sao Paulo, Brazil

Associacao Brasileira da Industria de Cafe [★IO]

Associacao Brasileira da Industria Eletrica e Eletronica [★IO]

Associacao Brasileira da Industria do Fumo [★IO]

Associacao Brasileira da Industria de Hoteis [★IO]

Associacao Brasileira da Industria de Maquinas e Equipamentos [★IO]

Associacao Brasileira da Industria Quimica [★IO]

Associacao Brasileira da Industria Textil e de Confeccao [★IO]

Associacao Brasileira das Industrias da Alimentacao [★IO]

Associacao Brasileira das Industrias do Mobiliario [★IO]

Associacao Brasileira das Industrias de Naotecidos e Tecidos Tecnicos [★IO]

Associacao Brasileira das Industrias de Oleos Vegetais [★IO]

Associacao Brasileira de Jet Ski [★IO]

Associacao Brasileira de Mecanica dos Solos e Engenharia Geotecnica [★IO]

Associacao Brasileira de Metalurgia e Materiais [★IO]

Associacao Brasileira de Mulheres Universitarias [IO], Porto Alegre, Brazil

Associacao Brasileira de Ortondontia e Ortopedia Facial [★IO]

Associacao Brasileira do Papelao Ondulado [★IO]

Associacao Brasileira Para o Desenvolvimento de Liderancas [IO], Sao Paulo, Brazil

Associacao Brasileira de Private Equity and Venture Capital [IO], Rio de Janeiro, Brazil

Associacao Brasileira dos Produtores de Discos [IO], Rio de Janeiro, Brazil

Associacao Brasileira dos Produtores e Exportadores de Frangos [★IO]

Associacao Brasileira dos Produtores de Fibras Artificiais e Sinteticas [★IO]

Associacao Brasileira de Quimica [★IO]

Associacao Brasileira de Representantes de Veiculos de Comunicacao [★IO]

Associacao Brasileira de Supermercados [★IO]

Associacao Brasileria de Floorball [★IO]

Associacao Comercial Do Porto [★IO]

Associacao Comercial de Macau [★IO]

Associacao do Comercio Automovel de Portugal [IO], Lisbon, Portugal

Associacao Crista Feminina do Brasil [★IO]

Associacao De Universidades Amazonicas [★IO]

Associacao para o Desenvolvimento Infantil de Macau [★IO]

Associacao dos Dirigentes de Vendas e Marketing do Brasil [★IO]

Associacao das Empresas de Vinho do Porto [★IO]

Associacao de Engenheiros Brazil - Alemanha [★IO]

Associacao Evangelica de Acampamento [★IO]

Associacao dos Exportadores e Importadores de Macau [★IO]

Associacao de Fabricantes para a Industria Automovel [★IO]

Associacao Fonografica Portuguesa [IO], Lisbon, Portugal

Associacao dos Fumicultores do Brasil [★IO]

Associacao de Gastao de Recursos Humanos de Macau [★IO]

Associacao de Grossistas de Produtos Quimicos e Farmaceuticos [★IO]

Associacao de Guia Turistico de Macau [★IO]

Associacao da Hotelaria de Portugal [★IO]

Associacao dos Industriais Metalurgicos, Metalomecanicos e Afins de Portugal [IO], Porto, Portugal

Associacao Indus. de Macau [★IO]

Associacao dos Inquilinos Lisbonenses [IO], Lisbon, Portugal

Associacao dos Inquilinos do Norte de Portugal [IO], Porto, Portugal

Associacao Internacional de Estudantes de Agricultura [★IO]

Associacao Latinoamericana de Estradas de Ferro [★IO]

Associacao Medica Braseleira [IO], Sao Paulo, Brazil

Associacao Medica Homeopatica Brasileira [★IO]

Associacao Medico Espirita do Brasil [★IO]

Associacao Nacional dos Comerciantes Exportadores de Vinhos e Bebidas Espirituosas [★IO]

Associacao Nacional de Comerciantes e Industriais de Produtos Alimentares [★IO]

Associacao Nacional De Deficientes Angolanos [★IO]

Associacao Nacional para a Difusao de Adubos [★IO]

Associacao Nacional dos Doentes com Artrites e outros Reumatismos da Infancia [★IO]

Associacao Nacional de Editores de Revistas [★IO]

Associacao Nacional des Empresas do Comercio e da Reparacao Automovel [IO], Lisbon, Portugal

Associacao Nacional dos Fabricantes de Ceramica para Revestimento [★IO]

Associacao Nacional dos Fabricantes de Veiculos Automotores [★IO]

Associacao Nacional das Farmacias [★IO]

Associacao Nacional dos Industriais de Arroz [★IO]

Associacao Nacional dos Industriais de Lanificios [★IO]

Associacao Nacional dos Industriais de Refrigerantes e Sumos de Frutos [★IO]

Associacao Nacional das Industrias de Vestuario e Confeccao [IO], Porto, Portugal

Associacao Nacional de Jornais [IO], Brasilia, Brazil

Associacao Nacional do Ramo Automovel [★IO]

Associacao Nacional das industrias de Vestuario e Confeccao [★IO]

Associacao Orquestra Sinfonica Jovem de Macau [★IO]

Associacao de Pilotos e Proprietarios de Aeronaves [★IO]

Associacao Portuguesa Antiquarios [★IO]

Associacao Portuguesa das Agencias de Viagens e Turismo [★IO]

Associacao Portuguesa de Anunciantes [IO], Lisbon, Portugal

Associacao Portuguesa de Centros Comerciais [★IO]

Associacao Portuguesa da Classe FINN [★IO]

Associacao Portuguesa de Controlo Automatico [IO], Lisbon, Portugal

Associacao Portuguesa de Deficientes [IO], Lisbon, Portugal

Associacao Portuguesa de Doentes de Huntington [IO], Portimao, Portugal

Associacao Portuguesa dos Editores e Livreiros [★IO]

Associacao Portuguesa de Educacao Ambiental [★IO]

Associacao Portuguesa de Educacao Musical [★IO]

Associacao Portuguesa de Empresas de Distribucao [★IO]

Associacao Portuguesa de Empresas Petroliferas [★IO]

Associacao Portuguesa de Geomorfologos [IO], Porto, Portugal

Associacao Portuguesa da Industria Farmaceutica [★IO]

A star before a book entry number signifies that the name is not listed separately, but is mentioned within the entry.

Associacao Portuguesa da Industria Papeleira [★IO]

Associacao Portuguesa da Industria de Plasticos [★IO]

Associacao Portuguesa dos Industriais de Aguas Minerais e de Nascente [★IO]

Associacao Portuguesa dos Industriais de Calcado, Componentes, Artigos de Pele e seus Sucedaneos [★IO]

Associacao Portuguesa dos Industriais de Curtumes [★IO]

Associacao Portuguesa de Investigacao Operacional [★IO]

Associacao Portuguesa Para o Desenvolvimento do Teletrabalho [★IO]

Associacao Portuguesa de Radiodifusao [★IO]

Associacao Portuguesa de Reconhecimento de Padroes [IO], Porto, Portugal

Associacao Portuguesa dos Tecnicos das Industrias de Celulose e Papel [★IO]

Associacao dos Profissionais e Empresas de Mediacao Imobiliaria de Portugal [★IO]

Associacao de Reabilitacao de Toxicodependentes de Macau [★IO]

Associacao de Regentes de Banda de Macau [★IO]

Associacao Spina Bifida e Hidrocefalia de Portugal [IO], Lisbon, Portugal

Associacao desportiva Taekwondo de Mocambique [IO], Maputo, Mozambique

Associacao Tecnica Brasileira das Industrias Automaticas de Vidro [★IO]

Associacao das Universidades de Lingua Portuguesa [★IO]

Associacio Catalana d'Intel-ligencia Artificial [★IO]

Associacion Colombiana de Endocrinologia [IO], Bogota, Colombia

Associacion Colombiana de Facultades de Medicina [★IO]

Associacion Colombiana de Fisioterapia [IO], Bogota, Colombia

Associacion Comunitaria de Autosuficiencia [IO], Jocotepec, Mexico

Associacion Costarricense de Terapeutas Fisicos de Costa Rica [IO], San Jose, Costa Rica

Associacion para el Desarrollo de las Microempresas [★IO]

Associacion de Diarios Colombianos [IO], Bogota, Colombia

Associacion de Importadores y Exportadores de la Republica Argentina [★IO]

Associacion Mexicana de Endoscopia Gastrointestinal [IO], Mexico City, Mexico

Associacion Mexicana de Fisioterapia [IO], Mexico City, Mexico

Associacion Nicaraguense de Medicina del Deporte [IO], Managua, Nicaragua

Associate Missionaries of the Assumption [20010], 16 Vineyard St., Worcester, MA 01603, (508)767-1356

Associate Missionaries of the Assumption [20010], 16 Vineyard St., Worcester, MA 01603, (508)767-1356

Associate Reformed Presbyterian Church, World Witness [★20114]

Associate Reformed Presbyterian Church, World Witness [★20114]

Assoc. Actors and Artistes of Am. [23267], 165 W 46th St., New York, NY 10036, (212)869-0358

Assoc. Actors and Artistes of Am. [23267], 165 W 46th St., New York, NY 10036, (212)869-0358

Assoc. Advt. Clubs of the World [★80]

Assoc. Air Balance Coun. [528], 1518 K St. NW, Washington, DC 20005, (202)737-0202

Assoc. Bakers of Am. [★394]

Assoc. Bakers of Am. - Retail and Wholesale [★394]

Assoc. Boards for Christian Colleges in China [★8396]

Assoc. Boards for Christian Colleges in China [★8396]

Assoc. Bodywork and Massage Professionals [15264], 25188 Genesee Trail Rd., Ste. 200, Golden, CO 80401, (303)674-8478

Assoc. Builders and Contractors [898], 4250 N Fairfax Dr., 9th Fl., Arlington, VA 22203-1607, (703)812-2000

Assoc. Builders and Contractors I Natl. Elecl. Contractors Coun. [899], 4250 N Fairfax Dr., 9th Fl., Arlington, VA 22203-1607, (703)812-2000

Assoc. Builders and Contractors I Natl. Mech. Contractors Coun. [900], 4250 N Fairfax Dr., 9th Fl., Arlington, VA 22203-1607, (703)812-2000

Assoc. Bus. Publications [★2914]

Assoc. Bus. Writers of Am. [★2858]

Assoc. Camera Clubs of Am. [★22095]

Assoc. Chain Drug Stores [★2691]

Assoc. Chambers of Commerce and Indus. of India [IO], New Delhi, India

Assoc. Chinese Chambers of Commerce and Indus. of Malaysia [IO], Kuala Lumpur, Malaysia

Assoc. Church Press [2917], PO Box 621001, Oviedo, FL 32762-1001, (407)341-6615

Assoc. Coffee Indus. of Am. [★451]

Assoc. Collectors of El Salvador [22020], PO Box 02-5364, Miami, FL 33102

Assoc. Colleges of the Midwest [7869], 205 W Wacker Dr., Ste. 220, Chicago, IL 60606, (312)263-5000

Assoc. Collegiate Press [8436], Univ. of Minnesota, 2221 Univ. Ave. SE, Ste. 121, Minneapolis, MN 55414, (612)625-8335

Assoc. Constr. Distributors Intl. [529], 1605 SE Delaware Ave., Ste. B, Ankeny, IA 50021, (515)964-1335

Assoc. Constr. Distributors Intl. [529], 1605 SE Delaware Ave., Ste. B, Ankeny, IA 50021, (515)964-1335

Assoc. Cooperage Indus. of Am. [871], 8923 Stone Green Way, 2nd Fl., Louisville, KY 40220-4073, (502)499-9808

Assoc. Corn Products Mfrs. [★1381]

Assoc. Court and Commercial Newspapers [★2915]

Assoc. Credit Bureaus [★1290]

Assoc. Daughters of Early Amer. Witches [20843], 269 Bluff Ct., Lake Barrington, IL 60010-7312

Assoc. Designers of Canada [IO], Toronto, ON, Canada

Associated Dress Carriers of Brooklyn and Queens - Defunct.

Assoc. Equip. Distributors [1805], 600 Hunter Dr., Ste. 220, Oak Brook, IL 60523, (630)574-0650

Assoc. Fraternities of Am. [★19042]

Assoc. Gen. Contractors of Am. [901], 2300 Wilson Blvd., Ste. 400, Arlington, VA 22201, (703)548-3118

Assoc. Humane Societies [10930], 124 Evergreen Ave., Newark, NJ 07114-2133, (973)824-7080

Assoc. Humane Societies of New Jersey [★10930]

Assoc. Humans [IO], Paris, France

Assoc. Independent Elecl. Contractors of Am. [★913]

Assoc. Japan-America Societies of the U.S. [★19083]

Assoc. Koi Clubs of Am. [21724], 40211 Redbud Dr., Oakhurst, CA 93644, (559)658-5295

Assoc. Koi Clubs of Am. [21724], 40211 Redbud Dr., Oakhurst, CA 93644, (559)658-5295

Assoc. Landscape Contractors of Am. and Professional Lawn Care Assn. of Am. [★2183]

Assoc. Locksmiths of Am. [1647], 3500 Easy St., Dallas, TX 75247, (214)819-9733

Assoc. Mail and Parcel Centers [2229], 5411 E State St., Ste. 202, Rockford, IL 61108, (815)316-8255

Assoc. Male Choruses of Am. [IO], Dunsford, ON, Canada

Assoc. Mfrs. of Elecl. and Supplies [★1080]

Assoc. Mfrs. of Elecl. and Supplies [★1080]

Assoc. Mfrs. of Toilet Articles [★1670]

Assoc. Medical Services [IO], Toronto, ON, Canada

Assoc. Minority Contractors of Am. [★927]

Assoc. Owners and Developers [841], PO Box 4163, McLean, VA 22103-4163, (703)734-2397

Assoc. Parishes for Liturgy and Mission [19691], PO Box 543, Hughsonville, NY 12537

Assoc. Pipe Organ Builders of Am. [2551], PO Box 155, Chicago Ridge, IL 60415, (660)747-3066

Assoc. Police Communications Officers [★5960]

Assoc. Police Communications Officers [★5960]

Assoc. Press [2804], 450 W 33rd St., New York, NY 10001, (212)621-1500

Assoc. Press Broadcast [481], AP Broadcast News Center, 1100 13th St., Ste. 700, Washington, DC 20005, (202)641-9921

Assoc. Press Broadcasters Assn. [★481]

Assoc. Press Managing Editors [2805], Sally Jacobsen, 450 W 33rd St., New York, NY 10001, (212)621-1838

Assoc. Press Photo Managers [2714], 450 W 33rd St., New York, NY 10001

Assoc. Press Radio-Television Assn. [★481]

Assoc. Professional Massage Therapists and Allied Hea. Practitioners Intl. [★15264]

Assoc. Professional Massage Therapists and Bodyworkers [★15264]

Assoc. Professional Sleep Societies [16664], 2510 N Frontage Rd., Darien, IL 60561, (630)737-9700

Assoc. Public-Safety Communications Officers [★5960]

Assoc. Public-Safety Communications Officers [★5960]

Assoc. Regional Accounting Firms [★51]

Assoc. Regional Accounting Firms [★51]

Assoc. Retail Bakers of Am. [★394]

Assoc. Retail Confectioners of North Am. [★1429]

Assoc. Retail Confectioners of North Am. [★1429]

Assoc. Retail Confectioners of the U.S. [★1429]

Assoc. Retail Confectioners of the U.S. [★1429]

Assoc. Schools of Constr. [7917], PO Box 1312, Fort Collins, CO 80522, (970)222-4459

Assoc. Schools of Constr. [7917], PO Box 1312, Fort Collins, CO 80522, (970)222-4459

Assoc. Services for the Blind [17063], 919 Walnut St., Philadelphia, PA 19107, (215)627-0600

Assoc. Ship Chandlers [★2362]

Assoc. Soc. of Locomotive Engineers and Firemen [IO], London, United Kingdom

Assoc. Soil and Found. Engineers [★6917]

Assoc. Specialty Contractors [902], 3 Bethesda Metro Ctr., Ste. 1100, Bethesda, MD 20814

Assoc. Stenotypists of Am. [★5359]

Assoc. Surplus Dealers [3368], 11835 W Olympic Blvd., Ste. 550E, Los Angeles, CA 90064-5810, (310)481-7300

Assoc. Telephone Answering Exchanges [★3401]

Assoc. Telephone Answering Exchanges [★3401]

Assoc. Telephone Exchanges [★3401]

Assoc. Telephone Exchanges [★3401]

Assoc. Third Class Mail Users [★2232]

Assoc. Traffic Clubs [★3538]

Assoc. Traffic Clubs [★3538]

Assoc. Wire Rope Fabricators [1806], PO Box 748, Walled Lake, MI 48390-0748, (248)994-7753

Assoc. Writing Programs [★10703]

Associates of the Amer. Foreign Ser. Worldwide [23198], 4001 N 9th St., Ste. 214, Arlington, VA 22203, (703)820-5420

Associates of the Amer. Foreign Ser. Worldwide [23198], 4001 N 9th St., Ste. 214, Arlington, VA 22203, (703)820-5420

Associates for Biblical Res. [19340], PO Box 144, Akron, PA 17501, (717)859-3443

Associates for Biblical Res. [19340], PO Box 144, Akron, PA 17501, (717)859-3443

Associates of Clinical Pharmacology [★16185]

Associates of Clinical Pharmacology [★16185]

Associates in Cultural Exchange [7948], 200 W Mercer St., Ste. 108, Seattle, WA 98119-3958, (206)217-9644

Associates of Vietnam Veterans of Am. [20830], 8719 Colesville Rd., Ste. 100, Silver Spring, MD 20910, (301)585-4000

Associates for Youth Development - Defunct.

Assn. nationale des etudiantes handicapes au niveau postsecondaire [★IO]

Assn. canadienne des etudiantes catholiques [★IO]

L'Association canadienne des musiciens educateurs [★IO]

Assn. canadienne des entraineurs [★IO]

Assn. canadienne de crosse [★IO]

L'Association canadienne des specialistes en emploi et des employeurs [★IO]

Assn. canadienne des professionnels de la securite routicre [★IO]

Assn. canadienne des revues savantes [★IO]

Assn. canadienne des conseillers en management [★IO]

Assn. canadienne des assistantes dentaires [★IO]

Assn. canadienne pour les etudes superieures [★IO]

Reference to "IO" in place of a book number signifies that the association may be found in the 50th edition of International Organizations.

Assn. nationale des distributeurs aux petites surfaces alimentaires [★IO]

Assn. canadienne des importateurs et exportateurs [★IO]

Assn. canadienne des etudes environnementales [★IO]

Assn. canadienne des redacteurs scientifiques [★IO]

Assn. canadienne des epices [★IO]

Assn. des regions frontalieres europeenes [★IO]

Assn. canadienne des administrateurs de regimes de retraite [★IO]

Assn. des manufacturiers de vetements pour hommes [★IO]

Assn. des industries canadiennes de defense et de securite [★IO]

Assn. nationale des grands usagers postaux [★IO]

L'Association canadienne des estudes sur les femmes [★IO]

Assn. canadienne de justice penale [★IO]

Assn. canadienne des infirmieres et infirmiers en sante communautaire [★IO]

Assn. canadienne des telecommunications sans fil [★IO]

Assn. canadienne des infirmieres en oncologie [★IO]

Assn. canadienne des restaurateurs et des services alimentaires [★IO]

Assn. canadienne de counseling et de psychotherapie [★IO]

Assn. canadienne des infirmieres et infirmiers et des technologues de nephrologie [★IO]

Assn. canadienne des organismes de controle des regimes retraite [★IO]

Assn. canadienne des professeurs de langues secondes [★IO]

Assn. canadienne en protheses et orthese [★IO]

Assn. canadienne du personnel administratif universitaire [★IO]

L'Association canadienne de sports pour paralytiques cerebraux [★IO]

Assn. canadienne des physiciens et physiciennes [★IO]

Assn. cycliste canadienne [★IO]

Assn. canadienne des reviseurs [★IO]

Assn. des etudes juives canadiennes [★IO]

Assn. canadienne de taxe fonciere [★IO]

Assn. canadienne de la paie [★IO]

Assn. canadienne de science politique [★IO]

Assn. canadienne de la poesie [★IO]

Assn. canadienne de gerontologie [★IO]

Assn. canadienne des soins de sante [★IO]

Assn. europeenne de demolition [★IO]

Assn. europeenne de societies de neurochirugie [★IO]

Assn. canadienne des bibliotheques [★IO]

Assn. nationale des revetements de sol [★IO]

Assn. canadienne des chefs de pompiers [★IO]

Assn. canadienne des automobilistes [★IO]

Assn. canadienne des preteurs sur salaire [★IO]

L'Association canadienne pour la sante mentale [★IO]

Assn. quebecoise des sport en fauteil roulant [★IO]

Assn. canadienne de soins palliatifs [★IO]

Assn. of 40th Infantry Div. Korean War Veterans - Defunct.

Assn. of Academic Chairmen of Plastic Surgery [★14174]

Assn. of Academic Hea. Centers [14701], 1400 16th St. NW, Ste. 720, Washington, DC 20036, (202)265-9600

Assn. of Academic Museums and Galleries [10110], Jordan Schnitzer Museum of Art, 1223 Univ. of Oregon, Eugene, OR 97403-1223, (541)346-0972

Assn. of Academic Physiatrists [16560], 7250 Parkway Dr., Ste. 130, Hanover, MD 21076, (410)712-7120

Assn. for Academic Surgery [16806], 11300 W Olympic Blvd., Ste. 600, Los Angeles, CA 90064, (310)437-1606

Assn. of Academies of Sci. [★7378]

Assn. for Accounting Admin. [12], 136 S Keowee St., Dayton, OH 45402, (937)222-0030

Assn. of Accounting Administrators [★12]

Assn. of Accounting Companies in Bulgaria [IO], Sofia, Bulgaria

Assn. for Accounting Marketing [2388], 15000 Commerce Pkwy., Ste. C, Mount Laurel, NJ 08054, (856)380-6850

Assn. of Accounting Technicians [IO], London, United Kingdom

Assn. for the Accreditation of Human Res. Protection Programs [10771], 2301 M St. NW, Ste. 500, Washington, DC 20037, (202)783-1112

Assn. of Accredited Advt. Agents of Hong Kong [IO], Hong Kong, People's Republic of China

Assn. of Accredited Advt. Agents Singapore [IO], Singapore, Singapore

Assn. of Accredited Naturopathic Medical Colleges [8680], 4435 Wisconsin Ave. NW, Ste. 403, Washington, DC 20016, (202)237-8150

Assn. of Accredited Naturopathic Medical Colleges [8680],.4435 Wisconsin Ave. NW, Ste. 403, Washington, DC 20016, (202)237-8150

Assn. of Accredited School and Departments of Journalism [★7663]

Assn. for Achievement and Improvement through Assessment [IO], Hinckley, United Kingdom

Assn. Actuarielle Internationale [★IO]

Assn. for Addiction Professionals; NAADAC: The [16744]

Assn. des Adjoints Administratifs [★IO]

Assn. des Administrations Portuaires Canadiennes [★IO]

Assn. of Administrative Assistants [IO], Oakville, ON, Canada

Assn. of Administrative Law Judges [5614], 601 Pinetree Dr., Decatur, GA 30030-2327

Assn. of Administrative Law Judges, Dept. of Hea. and Human Services [★5614]

Assn. of Administrative Professionals New Zealand [IO], Wellington, New Zealand

Assn. of Administrative Professionals New Zealand - Auckland Gp. [IO], Auckland, New Zealand

Assn. of Administrative Professionals New Zealand - Dunedin Gp. [IO], Dunedin, New Zealand

Assn. of Administrative Professionals New Zealand - Manawatu Gp. [IO], Palmerston North, New Zealand

Assn. of Administrative Professionals New Zealand - Marlborough Gp. [IO], Blenheim, New Zealand

Assn. of Administrative Professionals New Zealand - Taranaki Gp. [IO], New Plymouth, New Zealand

Assn. of Administrators of the Interstate Compact on Adoption and Medical Assistance [10781], 1133 19th St. NW, Washington, DC 20036, (202)682-0100

Assn. of Administrators of the Interstate Compact on the Placement of Children [11192], Amer. Public Human Services Assn., 1133 19th St. NW, Ste. 400, Washington, DC 20036, (202)682-0100

Assn. of Adult Musicians with Hearing Loss [14919], PO Box 522, Rockville, MD 20848

Assn. to Advance Collegiate Schools of Bus. [★7780]

Assn. to Advance Collegiate Schools of Bus. [★7780]

Assn. for Advanced Life Underwriting [1936], 11921 Freedom Dr., Ste. 1100, Reston, VA 20190, (703)641-9400

Assn. for Advanced Training in the Behavioral Sciences [8761], 5126 Ralston St., Ventura, CA 93003, (805)676-3030

Assn. for the Advancement of Applied Sport Psychology [★16716]

Assn. for the Advancement of Applied Sport Psychology [★16716]

Assn. for the Advancement of Artificial Intelligence [6209], 445 Burgess Dr., Ste. 100, Menlo Park, CA 94025, (650)328-3123

Assn. for the Advancement of Automotive Medicine [12978], PO Box 4176, Barrington, IL 60011-4176, (847)844-3880

Assn. for the Advancement of Baltic Stud. [9431], Univ. of Washington, Box 353420, Seattle, WA 98195-3420

Assn. for the Advancement of Baltic Stud. [9431], Univ. of Washington, Box 353420, Seattle, WA 98195-3420

Assn. for Advancement of Behavior Therapy [★13813]

Assn. for the Advancement of the Behavioral Therapies [★13813]

Assn. for Advancement of Blind Children [★17064]

Assn. for the Advancement of Blind and Retarded [17064], 1508 Coll. Point Blvd., 2nd Fl., College Point, NY 11356, (718)321-3800

Assn. for the Advancement of Computing in Educ. [8971], PO Box 1545, Chesapeake, VA 23327-1545, (757)366-5606

The Assn. for the Advancement of Cost Engg. [★6580]

The Assn. for the Advancement of Cost Engg. [★6580]

Assn. for the Advancement of Creative Musicians [10162], 410 S Michigan Ave., Ste. 943, Chicago, IL 60680, (312)922-1900

Assn. for the Advancement of Documentation Sciences and Techniques [IO], Montreal, QC, Canada

Assn. for the Advancement of Dutch-American Stud. [9576], The Joint Archives of Holland, Hope Coll., PO Box 9000, Holland, MI 49422-9000, (616)395-7798

Assn. for the Advancement of Dutch-American Stud. [9576], The Joint Archives of Holland, Hope Coll., PO Box 9000, Holland, MI 49422-9000, (616)395-7798

Assn. for the Advancement of Feminism [IO], Hong Kong, People's Republic of China

Assn. for the Advancement of Gestalt Therapy [16384], Cathy Gray, Pres., 426 Haverford Ave., Narberth, PA 19072, (610)667-4770

Assn. for the Advancement of Hea. Educ. [★16476]

Assn. for the Advancement of Indus. Crops [3750], Valerie Teetor, PO Box 210036, Tucson, AZ 85721-0036, (520)621-2817

Assn. for the Advancement of Intl. Educ. [8388], Nova Southeastern Univ., Fischler School of Educ. and Human Services, 3970 RCA Blvd., Ste. 7000, Palm Beach Gardens, FL 33410, (954)262-5691

Assn. for the Advancement of Intl. Educ. [8388], Nova Southeastern Univ., Fischler School of Educ. and Human Services, 3970 RCA Blvd., Ste. 7000, Palm Beach Gardens, FL 33410, (954)262-5691

Assn. for the Advancement of Medical Instrumentation [6325], 4301 N Fairfax Dr., Ste. 301, Arlington, VA 22203-1633, (703)525-4890

Assn. for the Advancement of Medical Instrumentation [6325], 4301 N Fairfax Dr., Ste. 301, Arlington, VA 22203-1633, (703)525-4890

Assn. for the Advancement of Mexican Americans [11548], 6001 Gulf Fwy., B1, Houston, TX 77023, (713)967-6700

Assn. for the Advancement of Modelling and Simulation Techniques in Enterprises - France [IO], Tassin-la-Demi-Lune, France

Assn. for the Advancement of Modelling and Simulation Techniques in Enterprises - Spain [IO], Barcelona, Spain

Assn. for the Advancement of Philosophy and Psychiatry [8704], Univ. of Louisville, Dept. of Philosophy, Louisville, KY 40292

Assn. for the Advancement of Philosophy and Psychiatry [8704], Univ. of Louisville, Dept. of Philosophy, Louisville, KY 40292

Assn. for Advancement of Psychoanalysis (of the Karen Horney Psychoanalytic Inst. and Center) - Address unknown since 2010.

Assn. for the Advancement of Psychology [16385], PO Box 38129, Colorado Springs, CO 80937-8129, (800)869-6595

Assn. for the Advancement of Psychotherapy [16455], T. Byram Karasu, MD, Ed.-in-Chief, Belfer Educ. Ctr., Rm. 405, 1300 Morris Park Ave., Bronx, NY 10461, (718)430-3503

Assn. for Advancement of Res. on Multiple Sclerosis [★15619]

Assn. for the Advancement of Sports Potential [★16717]

Assn. for the Advancement of Sustainability in Higher Educ. [8227], 213 1/2 N Limestone, Lexington, KY 40507, (859)258-2551

Assn. for the Advancement of Sustainability in Higher Educ. [8227], 213 1/2 N Limestone, Lexington, KY 40507, (859)258-2551

Assn. for the Advancement of Wound Care [14702], 83 Gen. Warren Blvd., Ste. 100, Malvern, PA 19355, (610)560-0484

A star before a book entry number signifies that the name is not listed separately, but is mentioned within the entry.

Assn. of Adventist Forums [20238], PO Box 619047, Roseville, CA 95661-9047, (916)774-1080

Assn. of Adventist Forums [20238], PO Box 619047, Roseville, CA 95661-9047, (916)774-1080

Assn. for Adventure Sports [IO], Ramelton, Ireland

Assn. of Advertisers in Ireland [IO], Dublin, Ireland

Assn. of Advt., Commercial and Magazine Photographers of Australia [IO], North Sydney, Australia

Assn. of Advt. and Commun. Agencies [IO], Paris, France

Assn. of AE Bus. Leaders [2266], 948 Capp St., San Francisco, CA 94110-3911, (415)713-5379

Assn. Aeronautique et Astronautique de France [IO], Paris, France

Assn. for Aerosol Res. [IO], Karlsruhe, Germany

Assn. for Affiliated Coll. and Univ. Offices [★8094]

Assn. Africaine du Commerce des Semences [★IO]

Assn. Africaine de Credit Rural et Agricole [★IO]

Assn. Africaine des Formateurs au Soutien de la Paix [★IO]

Assn. of African Amer. Financial Advisors [1334], PO Box 4853, Capitol Heights, MD 20791-4853, (240)396-2530

Assn. of African Amer. Vintners [177], 101 W Amer. Canyon Rd., American Canyon, CA 94503, (707)478-7222

Assn. of African Biomedical Scientists [7360], Vincent K. Tsiagbe, PhD, Pres., Univ. of Medicine and Dentistry of New Jersey, 185 S Orange Ave., MSB C-636, Newark, NJ 07103, (973)972-2612

Assn. of African Stud. Programs [7701], Judith A. Byfield, Cornell Univ., Stud. and Res. Center, 310 Triphammer Rd., Ithaca, NY 14850

Assn. of African Universities [IO], Accra, Ghana

Assn. of African Women Scholars [8807], Indiana Univ., French and Women's Stud., Cavanaugh Hall, Rm. 001C, 425 Univ. Blvd., Indianapolis, IN 46202, (317)278-2038

Assn. of African Women Scholars [8807], Indiana Univ., French and Women's Stud., Cavanaugh Hall, Rm. 001C, 425 Univ. Blvd., Indianapolis, IN 46202, (317)278-2038

Assn. for Africanist Anthropology [6133], Amer. Anthropological Assn., 2200 Wilson Blvd., Ste. 600, Arlington, VA 22201-3357, (703)528-1902

Assn. des Agences Conseils en Commun. [★IO]

Assn. des Agences-Conseils en Commun. [IO], Paris, France

Assn. of Agents, Brokers and Valuers of Wine and Foreign Spirits [IO], Amsterdam, Netherlands

Assn. for Agricultural Colleges in DENM smgacisark [IO], Arhus, Denmark

Assn. of Agricultural Res. Institutions in the Near East and North Africa [IO], Amman, Jordan

Assn. for the Aid of Crippled Children [★11163]

Assn. for Aid and Relief, Japan [IO], Tokyo, Japan

Assn. des Aides Familiales du Quebec [IO], Montreal, QC, Canada

Assn. of Air Force Missileers [20327], PO Box 5693, Breckenridge, CO 80424, (970)453-0500

Assn. of Air Medical Services [14449], 909 N Washington St., Ste. 410, Alexandria, VA 22314-3143, (703)836-8732

Assn. of Air Medical Services [14449], 909 N Washington St., Ste. 410, Alexandria, VA 22314-3143, (703)836-8732

Assn. Albanaise des Femmes Diplomees des Universites [IO], Tirana, Albania

Assn. of Albanian Girls and Women [18408], 9510 Tirana Pl., Dulles, VA 20189-9510, (310)291-9205

Assn. of Albanian Girls and Women [18408], 9510 Tirana Pl., Dulles, VA 20189-9510, (310)291-9205

Assn. Algerienne pour la Planification Familiale [IO], Oran, Algeria

Assn. of Alternate Postal Systems [2230], 1725 Oaks Way, Oklahoma City, OK 73131, (405)478-0006

Assn. of Alternative Newsweeklies [2806], 1156 15th St. NW, Ste. 905, Washington, DC 20005, (202)289-8484

Assn. Alzheimer Suisse [IO], Yverdon-les-Bains, Switzerland

Assn. of Amazonian Universities [IO], Sao Bras, Brazil

Assn. for Ambulatory Behavioral Healthcare [16335], 247 Douglas Ave., Portsmouth, VA 23707, (757)673-3741

Assn. for Ambulatory Pediatric Services [★16137]

Assn. of Amer. Battery Mfrs. [★323]

Assn. of Amer. Battery Mfrs. [★323]

Assn. of Amer. Bd. of Examiners in Veterinary Medicine [★16988]

Assn. of Amer. Cancer Institutes [13885], Medical Arts Bldg., 3708 5th Ave., Ste. 503, Pittsburgh, PA 15213, (412)647-6111

Assn. of Amer. Ceramic Component Mfrs. [730], 600 N Cleveland Ave., Ste. 210, Westerville, OH 43082, (614)794-5821

Assn. of Amer. Chambers of Commerce in Latin Am. [23423], 1615 H St. NW, Washington, DC 20062-2000, (202)463-5485

Assn. of American-Chinese Professionals [★18961]

Assn. of Amer. Choruses [★10189]

Assn. of Amer. Colleges [★7870]

Assn. of Amer. Colleges and Universities [7870], 1818 R St. NW, Washington, DC 20009, (202)387-3760

Assn. of Amer. Consumers [★13337]

The Assn. of Amer. Cultures [9279], 1635 S 15th St., Lincoln, NE 68502, (402)472-0208

Assn. for the Amer. Dance Festival [★9533]

Assn. of Amer. Editorial Cartoonists [2807], 3899 N Front St., Harrisburg, PA 17110, (717)703-3003

Assn. of Amer. Feed Control Officials [5185], Purdue Univ., Off. of Indiana State Chemist, 175 S Univ. St., West Lafayette, IN 47907-2063, (765)494-1561

Assn. of Amer. Fertilizer Control Officials [★5186]

Assn. of Amer. Foreign Ser. Women [★23198]

Assn. of Amer. Foreign Ser. Women [★23198]

Assn. of Amer. Geographers [6903], 1710 16th St. NW, Washington, DC 20009-3198, (202)234-1450

Assn. on Amer. Historic Inns [★9665]

Assn. on Amer. Indian Affairs [18150], 966 Hungerford Dr., Ste. 12-B, Rockville, MD 20850, (240)314-7155

Assn. of Amer. Indian Physicians [16253], 1225 Sovereign Row, Ste. 103, Oklahoma City, OK 73108-1854, (405)946-7072

Assn. of Amer. Intl. Colleges and Universities [8389], Dr. Arthur H. Charles, 136 Boylston St., Boston, MA 02116

Assn. of Amer. Intl. Colleges and Universities [8389], Dr. Arthur H. Charles, 136 Boylston St., Boston, MA 02116

Assn. of Amer. Law Schools [8499], 1201 Connecticut Ave. NW, Ste. 800, Washington, DC 20036-2717, (202)296-8851

Assn. of Amer. Law Schools I Sect. on Sexual Orientation and Gender Identity Issues [8500], Prof. Mark E. Wojcik, Chm., The John Marshall Law School, 315 S Plymouth Ct., Chicago, IL 60604, (312)987-2391

Assn. of Amer. Medical Colleges [8590], 2450 N St. NW, Washington, DC 20037-1126, (202)828-0400

Assn. of Amer. Medical Colleges-Women in Medicine Prog. [8591], 2450 N St. NW, Washington, DC 20037-1126, (202)478-9867

Assn. of Amer. Military Uniform Collectors [21884], PO Box 1876, Elyria, OH 44036, (440)365-5321

Assn. of Amer. Pesticide Control Officials [5888], PO Box 466, Milford, DE 19963, (302)422-8152

Assn. of Amer. Physicians - Defunct.

Assn. of Amer. Physicians and Surgeons [16254], 1601 N Tucson Blvd., No. 9, Tucson, AZ 85716, (800)635-1196

Assn. of Amer. Plant Food Control Officials [5186], Univ. of Missouri-Columbia, Fertilizer/Ag Lime Control Ser., Columbia, MO 65211-8080, (573)882-0007

Assn. of Amer. Publishers [2918], 71 5th Ave., 2nd Fl., New York, NY 10003-3004, (212)255-0200

Assn. of Amer. Railroads [2988], 425 Third St. SW, Ste. 1000, Washington, DC 20024, (202)639-2100

Assn. of Amer. Rhodes Scholars [19218], Joyce Knight, 8229 Boone Blvd., Ste. 240, Vienna, VA 22182-2623, (703)821-7377

Assn. of Amer. Schools in Central Am., Colombia, Caribbean and Mexico [IO], Quito, Ecuador

Assn. of Amer. Schools in South Am. [8390], 1911 NW 150 Ave., Ste. 101, Pembroke Pines, FL 33028, (954)436-4034

Assn. of Amer. Secretaries of State [★5992]

Assn. of Amer. Seed Control Officials [5187], 101 E State St., No. 214, Ithaca, NY 14850, (607)256-3313

Assn. of Amer. Seed Control Officials [5187], 101 E State St., No. 214, Ithaca, NY 14850, (607)256-3313

Assn. of Amer. State Geologists [6910], Kentucky Geological Survey, 228 Mining and Mineral Resources Bldg., Lexington, KY 40506-0107, (859)257-5500

Assn. of Amer. Trial Lawyers [★6041]

Assn. of Amer. Universities [7871], 1200 New York Ave. NW, Ste. 550, Washington, DC 20005, (202)408-7500

Assn. of Amer. Univ. Presses [8303], 28 W 36th St., Ste. 602, New York, NY 10018, (212)989-1010

Assn. of Amer. Veterinary Medical Colleges [9033], 1101 Vermont Ave. NW, Ste. 301, Washington, DC 20005, (202)371-9195

Assn. of Amer. Wives of Europeans [IO], Paris, France

Assn. of Amer. Women Dentists [★14253]

Assn. of Amer. Wood Pulp Importers - Defunct.

Assn. of Americans and Canadians in Israel [IO], Jerusalem, Israel

Assn. of Americans for Civic Responsibility [17252], 13316 Foxhall Dr., Silver Spring, MD 20906, (301)933-1494

Assn. of Americans Resident Overseas [IO], Paris, France

Assn. of America's Young Democratic Azerbaijanian Friends [IO], Baku, Azerbaijan

Assn. des Amidonneries de Cereales de l'UE [★IO]

Assn. des Amis de la Republique Arabe Sahraouie Democratique [IO], Paris, France

Assn. of Anaesthetists of Great Britain and Ireland [IO], London, United Kingdom

Assn. des Anciens Fonctionnaires Internationaux [★IO]

Assn. des Anciens de l'OMS [★IO]

Assn. of Ancient Historians [9751], 215 S Central Campus Dr., Rm. 312, Salt Lake City, UT 84112

Assn. of Anglican Musicians [20119], PO Box 7530, Little Rock, AR 72217, (501)661-9925

Assn. for the Anthropological Stud. of Play [★10445]

Assn. of Apex Clubs of Australia [IO], Sydney, Australia

Assn. of Applied Biologists [IO], Warwick, United Kingdom

Assn. for Applied and Clinical Sociology [7422], Martin Fonda, Admin., Eastern Michigan Univ., Dept. of Sociology, Anthropology, and Criminology Off., 712 Pray Harrold, Ypsilanti, MI 48197, (734)487-0012

Assn. of Applied Geochemists [IO], Nepean, ON, Canada

Assn. of Applied Insect Ecologists [★4770]

Assn. of Applied IPM Ecologists [4770], PO Box 1119, Coarsegold, CA 93614, (559)761-1064

Assn. for Applied Poetry [16456], 81 Shadymere Ln., Columbus, OH 43213, (614)986-1881

Assn. for Applied Psychoanalysis - Defunct.

Assn. for Applied Psychophysiology and Biofeedback [13832], 10200 W 44th Ave., Ste. 304, Wheat Ridge, CO 80033, (303)422-8436

Assn. for Applied Sport Psychology [16716], 2424 Amer. Ln., Madison, WI 53704, (608)443-2475

Assn. for Applied Sport Psychology [16716], 2424 Amer. Ln., Madison, WI 53704, (608)443-2475

Assn. for Applied and Therapeutic Humor [16841], 65 Enterprise, Aliso Viejo, CA 92656, (949)715-4681

Assn. of Appraiser Regulatory Officials [227], 13200 Strickland Rd., Ste. 114-264, Raleigh, NC 27613, (919)235-4544

Assn. of Approved Tourist Guides of Ireland [IO], Dublin, Ireland

Assn. Aquacole du Canada [★IO]

Assn. of Arab Universities [IO], Amman, Jordan

Assn. for Arab Youth - Baladna [IO], Haifa, Israel

Assn. of Architectural Librarians - Defunct.

Assn. of Architecture Organizations [6192], 224 S Michigan Ave., Ste. 116, Chicago, IL 60604, (312)922-3432

Reference to "IO" in place of a book number signifies that the association may be found in the 50th edition of International Organizations.

Assn. of Architecture School Librarians [9963], Iowa State Univ., 152 Parks Lib., Ames, IA 50011-2140, (515)294-6863

Assn. of Area Bus. Publications [★2912]

Assn. of Argentine Banks [IO], Buenos Aires, Argentina

Assn. for Arid Lands Stud. - Address unknown since 2010.

Assn. of Armenian Church Choirs of Am. - Defunct.

Assn. des Arpenteurs des Terres du Canada [★IO]

Assn. of Art and Antique Dealers [IO], London, United Kingdom

Assn. of Art Editors [2919], Phil Freshman, Pres., 3912 Natchez Ave. S, St. Louis Park, MN 55416, (952)922-1374

Assn. of Art Galleries in Switzerland [IO], Basel, Switzerland

Assn. of Art Historians [IO], London, United Kingdom

Assn. of Art Museum Curators [10111], 174 E 80th St., New York, NY 10075, (646)405-8065

Assn. of Art Museum Curators [10111], 174 E 80th St., New York, NY 10075, (646)405-8065

Assn. of Art Museum Directors [10112], 120 E 56th St., Ste. 520, New York, NY 10022, (212)754-8084

Assn. of Arts Admin. Educators [7743], 4222 Oakland Dr., Kalamazoo, MI 49008, (608)561-2040

Assn. of Asia Pacific Airlines [IO], Kuala Lumpur, Malaysia

Assn. of Asia Pacific Physical Societies [IO], Beijing, People's Republic of China

Assn. of Asian Amer. Investment Managers [2129], 50 California St., Ste. 2320, San Francisco, CA 94111

Assn. for Asian Amer. Stud. [7759], 104 Scott Hall, 72 Pleasant St. SE, Minneapolis, MN 55455-0134, (612)626-2022

Assn. of Asian Indians in Am. [★19034]

Assn. of Asian Pacific Community Hea. Organizations [14893], 300 Frank H. Ogawa Plz., Ste. 620, Oakland, CA 94612, (510)272-9536

Assn. of Asian-Pacific Operational Res. Societies [IO], Mandaluyong City, Philippines

Assn. of Asian Performing Arts Festivals [IO], Singapore, Singapore

Assn. of Asian Social Sci. Res. Councils [IO], Canberra, Australia

Assn. for Asian Stud. [7760], 1021 E Huron St., Ann Arbor, MI 48104, (734)665-2490

Assn. for Asian Stud. [7760], 1021 E Huron St., Ann Arbor, MI 48104, (734)665-2490

Assn. Asiatique des Bureaux de Congres et de Tourisme [★IO]

Assn. of Asphalt Paving Technologists [6573], 6776 Lake Dr., Ste. 215, Lino Lakes, MN 55014-1191, (651)293-9188

Assn. for Assessment and Accreditation of Lab. Animal Care Intl. [13760], 5283 Corporate Dr., Ste. 203, Frederick, MD 21703, (301)696-9626

Assn. for Assessment and Accreditation of Lab. Animal Care Intl. [13760], 5283 Corporate Dr., Ste. 203, Frederick, MD 21703, (301)696-9626

Assn. for Assessment in Counseling [★8983]

Assn. for Assessment in Counseling and Educ. [8983], Amer. Counseling Assn., 5999 Stevenson Ave., Alexandria, VA 22304-3300, (800)347-6647

Assn. of Asset Mgt. Companies [IO], Bratislava, Slovakia

Assn. of Assistive Tech. Act Programs [14361], PO Box 32, Delmar, NY 12054, (518)439-1263

Assn. des Assureurs Cooperatifs et Mutualistes Europeens [★IO]

Assn. of Asthma Educators [16605], 1215 Anthony Ave., Columbia, SC 29201-1701, (888)988-7747

Assn. for Astrological Networking [6214], 8306 Wilshire Blvd., PMB 537, Beverly Hills, CA 90211, (404)477-4121

Assn. for Astrological Psychology [★6215]

Assn. for Astronomy Educ. [IO], London, United Kingdom

Assn. of Astronomy Educators - Defunct.

Assn. of Atlantic Women Bus. Owners [IO], Halifax, NS, Canada

Assn. of Attenders and Alumni of The Hague Acad. of Intl. Law [IO], The Hague, Netherlands

Assn. of Attorney-Mediators [5235], PO Box 741955, Dallas, TX 75374-1955, (972)669-8101

Assn. of Audiovisual and Film Indus. of Austria [IO], Vienna, Austria

L'Association des Auditeurs at Anciens Auditeurs de L'Academie de Droit Intl. de la Haye [★IO]

Assn. of Australasian Diesel Specialists [IO], Crows Nest, Australia

Assn. of Australasian Palaeontologists [IO], Sydney, Australia

Assn. of Australian Boutique Winemakers [IO], Ashfield, Australia

Assn. of the Austrian Chem. Indus. [IO], Vienna, Austria

Assn. of Austrian Clothing Indus. [IO], Vienna, Austria

Assn. of the Austrian Elecl. and Electronics Indus. [IO], Vienna, Austria

Assn. of Austrian Librarians [IO], Bregenz, Austria

Assn. of the Austrian Machinery and Metalware Indus. [IO], Vienna, Austria

Assn. of the Austrian Paper Indus. [IO], Vienna, Austria

Assn. of Austrian Textile Indus. [IO], Vienna, Austria

Assn. of Authorised Public Accountants [IO], London, United Kingdom

Assn. of Authors' Agents [IO], London, United Kingdom

Assn. of Authors' Representatives [161], 676A 9th Ave., Ste. 312, New York, NY 10036, (212)840-5777

Assn. of Auto and Truck Recyclers [★3632]

Assn. for Automatic Identification and Mobility North Am. [280], 1 Landmark N, 20399 Rte., Ste. 203, Cranberry Township, PA 16066, (724)742-4473

Assn. for Automatic Language Processing [IO], Paris, France

Assn. of Automotive Aftermarket Distributors [★311]

Assn. of Automotive Aftermarket Distributors/Parts Plus [311], 3085 Fountainside Dr., No. 210, Germantown, TN 38138, (800)727-8112

Assn. of the Automotive Indus. [IO], Berlin, Germany

Assn. of Automotive Tech. Societies in Finland [IO], Helsinki, Finland

Assn. of Average Adjusters [IO], London, United Kingdom

Assn. of Average Adjusters of the U.S. [1937], Eileen M. Fellin, Sec., 126 Midwood Ave., Farmingdale, NY 11735

Assn. of Avian Veterinarians USA [17013], Summit Meetings, Inc., 90 Madison St., Ste. 403, Denver, CO 80206, (303)756-8380

Assn. of Avian Veterinarians USA [17013], Summit Meetings, Inc., 90 Madison St., Ste. 403, Denver, CO 80206, (303)756-8380

Assn. for Aviation Psychology [6083], Lori McDonnell, Membership Ser. Coor., NASA Ames Res. Center, Mail Stop 262-4, Moffett Field, CA 94035

Assn. of Ayurvedic Professionals of North Am. [13664], 567 Thomas St., Coopersburg, PA 18036

Assn. for Baha'i Stud. [IO], Ottawa, ON, Canada

Assn. of Bakery Ingredients Mfrs. [IO], London, United Kingdom

Assn. Bancaire pour l'Evro [★IO]

Assn. of Bangkok Alumni of Dermatology - Pakistan [IO], Peshawar, Pakistan

Assn. of Bank Holding Companies [★413]

Assn. of Banks in Cambodia [IO], Phnom Penh, Cambodia

Assn. of Banks in Jordan [IO], Amman, Jordan

Assn. of Banks in Lebanon [IO], Beirut, Lebanon

Assn. of Banks in Malaysia [IO], Kuala Lumpur, Malaysia

Assn. of Banks in Singapore [IO], Singapore, Singapore

Assn. of Banks in Slovakia [IO], Bratislava, Slovakia

Assn. des Banques et Banquiers Luxembourg [★IO]

Assn. des Banquiers Canadiens [★IO]

Assn. of Baptist Chaplains - Defunct.

Assn. of Baptist Homes and Hospitals [★19307]

Assn. of Baptist Professors of Religion [★9013]

Assn. of Baptists for Evangelism in the Orient [★19308]

Assn. of Baptists for Evangelism in the Orient [★19308]

Assn. of Baptists for Scouting [13016], PO Box 152079, Irving, TX 75015-2079

Assn. of Baptists for World Evangelism [19308], PO Box 8585, Harrisburg, PA 17105-8585, (717)774-7000

Assn. of Baptists for World Evangelism [19308], PO Box 8585, Harrisburg, PA 17105-8585, (717)774-7000

Assn. of Baptists for World Evangelism - Canada [IO], London, ON, Canada

L'Association du Barreau Canadien [★IO]

Assn. of Bearing Specialists [★1813]

Assn. of Beer and Malt Mfrs. [IO], Rome, Italy

Assn. for Behavior Anal. [6248], 550 W Centre Ave., Ste. 1, Portage, MI 49024, (269)492-9310

Assn. for Behavioral and Cognitive Therapies [13813], 305 7th Ave., 16th Fl., New York, NY 10001-6008, (212)647-1890

Assn. for Behavioral Hea. and Wellness [14756], 1325 G St. NW, Ste. 500, Washington, DC 20005, (202)756-7726

Assn. for the Behavioral Sciences and Medical Educ. [6249], 1460 N Center Rd., Burton, MI 48509, (810)715-4365

Assn. for the Behavioral Treatment of Sexual Abusers [★6253]

Assn. for the Behavioral Treatment of Sexual Aggression [★6253]

Assn. Belge des Architectes de Jardins et des Architectes Paysagistes [IO], Brussels, Belgium

Assn. Belge de Documentation [★IO]

Assn. Belge des Journalistes Agricoles [★IO]

Assn. Belge du Marketing Direct [★IO]

Assn. Belge des patients Osteoporotiques [★IO]

Assn. Belge des Syndicats Medicaux [IO], Brussels, Belgium

Assn. of the Belgian Pulp, Paper and Bd. Indus. [IO], Brussels, Belgium

Assn. of Belgian Relocation Agents [IO], Waterloo, Belgium

Assn. for Benchmarking Hea. Care [1672], 4606 FM 1960 W, Ste. 250, Houston, TX 77069-9949, (281)440-5044

Assn. of Benedictin Children [★13838]

Assn. of Bermuda Compliance Officers [IO], Hamilton, Bermuda

Assn. of Better Bus. Bureaus [★17445]

Assn. of Better Bus. Bureaus [★17445]

Assn. of Better Cmpt. Dealers [★6532]

Assn. for Better Insulation [530], 3906 Auburn Hills Dr., Greensboro, NC 27407, (603)768-3984

Assn. for Better Living and Educ. Intl; ABLE: [11537]

Assn. for Better Living and Educ. Intl; ABLE: [11537]

Assn. of Bible Institutes and Bible Colleges [★7850]

Assn. of Biblical Counselors [19631], 209 N Indus. Blvd., Ste. 237, Bedford, TX 76021, (877)222-4551

Assn. for Biblical Higher Educ. [7850], 5850 T.G. Lee Blvd., Ste. 130, Orlando, FL 32822, (407)207-0808

Assn. for the Bibliography of History [9752], Thomas Helde, Georgetown Univ., Dept. of History, Washington, DC 20057

Assn. des Bibliotheques de Recherche du Canada [★IO]

Assn. des Bibliotheques de la Sante du Canada [★IO]

Assn. of Biomedical Communications Directors [14161], SUNY Downstate Medical Center, Box 18, Brooklyn, NY 11203, (423)439-2402

Assn. for Biomedical Res. [★13764]

Assn. of Biomolecular Rsrc. Facilities [7020], 9650 Rockville Pike, Bethesda, MD 20814, (301)634-7306

Assn. of Biotechnology Companies [★457]

Assn. of Biotechnology Led Enterprises [IO], Bangalore, India

Assn. of Birth Defect Children [★13838]

Assn. for Birth Psychology [16386], 9115 Ridge Blvd., Brooklyn, NY 11209, (347)517-4607

Assn. of Black Anthropologists [6134], AAA Member Services, 2200 Wilson Blvd., Ste. 600, Arlington, VA 22201-3357, (703)528-1902

Assn. of Black Cardiologists [14005], 2400 N St. NW, Ste. 604, Washington, DC 20037, (202)375-6618

Assn. of Black Catholics Against Abortion - Defunct.

Assn. of Black Nursing Faculty [8592], PO Box 580, Lisle, IL 60532, (630)969-0221

A star before a book entry number signifies that the name is not listed separately, but is mentioned within the entry.

Assn. of Black Psychologists **[16387]**, PO Box 55999, Washington, DC 20040-5999, (202)722-0808

Assn. of Black Sociologists **[7423]**, 4200 Wisconsin Ave. NW, PMB 106-257, Washington, DC 20016-2143, (202)365-1759

Assn. of Black Storytellers **[★10545]**

Assn. of Black Women Attorneys **[5236]**, 255 W 36th St., Ste. 800, New York, NY 10018, (212)300-2193

Assn. of Black Women in Higher Educ. **[9055]**, PO Box 210, Princeton, NJ 08540, (609)258-7801

Assn. for the Bladder Exstrophy Community **[14375]**, 2901 W Kinnickinnic River Pkwy., Ste. 311, Milwaukee, WI 53215, (414)385-7100

Assn. for the Bladder Exstrophy Community **[14375]**, 2901 W Kinnickinnic River Pkwy., Ste. 311, Milwaukee, WI 53215, (414)385-7100

Assn. of Blauvelt Descendants **[20426]**, 3367 W 113th Ave., Westminster, CO 80031-7179, (303)438-7267

Assn. of Blauvelt Descendants **[20426]**, 3367 W 113th Ave., Westminster, CO 80031-7179, (303)438-7267

Assn. of the Blind in Cambodia **[IO]**, Phnom Penh, Cambodia

Assn. of Blind and Partially Sighted Teachers and Students **[IO]**, London, United Kingdom

Assn. of Blind Piano Tuners **[IO]**, Darwen, United Kingdom

Assn. for the Blind of Western Australia **[IO]**, Victoria Park, Australia

The Assn. of Boarding Schools **[8752]**, 1 N Pack Square., Ste. 301, Asheville, NC 28801, (828)258-5354

Assn. of Boards of Certification **[6051]**, 2805 SW Snyder Blvd., Ste. 535, Ankeny, IA 50023, (515)232-3623

Assn. of Boards of Certification for Operating Personnel **[★6051]**

Assn. of Boards of Certification for Operating Personnel in Water and Wastewater Utilities **[★6051]**

Assn. of Bone and Joint Surgeons **[16030]**, 6300 N River Rd., Ste. 605, Rosemont, IL 60018-4237, (847)720-4186

Assn. of Booksellers for Children **[466]**, 6538 Collin Ave., No. 168, Miami Beach, FL 33141, (617)390-7759

Assn. of Bordeaux Wine and Alcohol Wholesalers **[IO]**, Bordeaux, France

Assn. for Borderlands Stud. **[8400]**, Univ. of Texas at El Paso, Dept. of Political Sci., 500 W Univ. Ave., El Paso, TX 79902, (915)747-7985

Assn. for Borderlands Stud. **[8400]**, Univ. of Texas at El Paso, Dept. of Political Sci., 500 W Univ. Ave., El Paso, TX 79902, (915)747-7985

L'Association Botanique du Canada **[★IO]**

Assn. for Brain Tumor Res. **[★13881]**

Assn. des Brasseurs du Canada **[★IO]**

Assn. for Breastfeeding Fashions - Defunct.

Assn. of Breastfeeding Mothers **[IO]**, Bridgwater, United Kingdom

Assn. of Breeders of Thoroughbred Holstein Cattle **[★3914]**

Assn. of Brethren Caregivers - Address unknown since 2010.

Assn. of Brewers and Brewers' Assn. of Am. **[★179]**

Assn. of Bridal Consultants **[469]**, 56 Danbury Rd., Ste. 11, New Milford, CT 06776, (860)355-7000

Assn. of Bridal Consultants **[469]**, 56 Danbury Rd., Ste. 11, New Milford, CT 06776, (860)355-7000

Assn. for Bridge Constr. and Design **[6193]**, 400 Penn Ctr. Blvd., Ste. 600, Pittsburgh, PA 15235, (412)824-2910

Assn. of British Certification Bodies **[IO]**, Chislehurst, United Kingdom

Assn. of British Choral Directors **[IO]**, Sherborne, United Kingdom

Assn. of British Climatologists **[IO]**, Reading, United Kingdom

Assn. of British Climbing Walls **[IO]**, London, United Kingdom

Assn. of British Columbia Drama Educators **[IO]**, Vanderhoof, BC, Canada

Assn. of British Credit Unions Limited **[IO]**, Manchester, United Kingdom

Assn. of British Dispensing Opticians **[IO]**, London, United Kingdom

Assn. of British Drivers **[IO]**, Kenley, United Kingdom

Assn. of British Healthcare Indus. **[IO]**, London, United Kingdom

Assn. of British Insurers **[IO]**, London, United Kingdom

Assn. of British Introduction Agencies **[IO]**, London, United Kingdom

Assn. of British Investigators **[IO]**, Blackpool, United Kingdom

Assn. of British Mining Equip. Companies **[IO]**, Wakefield, United Kingdom

Assn. of British Neurologists **[IO]**, London, United Kingdom

Assn. of British Offshore Indus. **[IO]**, London, United Kingdom

Assn. of British Orchestras **[IO]**, London, United Kingdom

Assn. of the British Pharmaceutical Indus. **[IO]**, London, United Kingdom

Assn. of British Philatelic Societies **[IO]**, Warwickshire, United Kingdom

Assn. of British Professional Conf. Organisers **[IO]**, Belfast, United Kingdom

Assn. of British Riding Schools **[IO]**, Penzance, United Kingdom

Assn. of British Sci. Writers **[IO]**, London, United Kingdom

Assn. of British Theatre Technicians **[IO]**, London, United Kingdom

Assn. of British Theological and Philosophical Libraries **[IO]**, London, United Kingdom

Assn. of British Travel Agents **[IO]**, London, United Kingdom

Assn. of British Wild Animal Keepers **[IO]**, Edinburgh, United Kingdom

Assn. of Broadcasting Doctors **[IO]**, Ely, United Kingdom

Assn. of Brokers and Yacht Agents **[IO]**, Petersfield, United Kingdom

Assn. of Building Engineers **[IO]**, Northampton, United Kingdom

Assn. of Bulgarians with Bronchial Asthma **[IO]**, Sofia, Bulgaria

Assn. Burkinabe des Femmes Diplomees des Universites **[IO]**, Ouagadougou, Burkina Faso

Assn. Burundaise des Femmes Diplomees des Universites **[IO]**, Bujumbura, Burundi

Assn. for Bus. Commun. **[7783]**, PO Box 6143, Nacogdoches, TX 75962-0001, (936)468-6280

Assn. of Bus. Executives **[IO]**, London, United Kingdom

Assn. of Bus. Incubators and Technoparks of the Republic of Uzbekistan **[IO]**, Tashkent, Uzbekistan

Assn. of Bus. Process Mgt. Professionals **[2267]**, 47 W Polk St., Ste. 100-279, Chicago, IL 60605-2085

Assn. of Bus. Psychologists **[IO]**, London, United Kingdom

Assn. of Bus. Publishers **[★2914]**

Assn. of Bus. Recovery Professionals **[IO]**, London, United Kingdom

Assn. of Bus. Schools **[IO]**, London, United Kingdom

Assn. for Bus. Simulation and Experiential Learning **[7784]**, Arcadia Univ., Bus/EC/HA Dept., 450 S Easton Rd., Glenside, PA 19038, (215)572-2849

Assn. for Bus. Simulation and Experiential Learning **[7784]**, Arcadia Univ., Bus/EC/HA Dept., 450 S Easton Rd., Glenside, PA 19038, (215)572-2849

Assn. of Business Support Services Intl. - Defunct.

Assn. of Bus. Travellers **[IO]**, North Sydney, Australia

Assn. of Bus. Women of Serbia **[IO]**, Belgrade, Serbia

Assn. of C and C Users **[IO]**, Abingdon, United Kingdom

Assn. of Cable Communicators **[5321]**, PO Box 75007, Washington, DC 20013-0007, (202)222-2370

Assn. des Cadres d'Institutions Culturelles **[★IO]**

Assn. of Cajun Music Enthusiasts **[10163]**, 5274 Paramont Dr., Birmingham, AL 35210, (205)951-3463

Assn. for the Calligraphic Arts **[9280]**, 26 Main St., East Greenwich, RI 02818

Assn. Camerounaise de Femmes Diplomees des Universites **[★IO]**

Assn. of Camp Nurses **[15734]**, 8630 Thorsonveien NE, Bemidji, MN 56601, (218)586-2633

Assn. of Camp Nurses **[15734]**, 8630 Thorsonveien NE, Bemidji, MN 56601, (218)586-2633

Assn. of Camphill Communities **[IO]**, Aberdeen, United Kingdom

Assn. Canadienne de Femmes Diplomees des **[★IO]**

Assn. du the du Canada **[★IO]**

Assn. mineralogique du Canada **[★IO]**

L'Association des architectes paysagistes du Canada **[★IO]**

Assn. des universites et colleges du Canada **[★IO]**

Assn. des urologues du Canada **[★IO]**

Assn. geologique du Canada **[★IO]**

L'Association internationale de la gestion du personnel - Canada **[★IO]**

Assn. des critiques de theatre du Canada **[★IO]**

Assn. des industries aerospatiales du Canada **[★IO]**

Assn. of Canada Lands Surveyors **[IO]**, Ottawa, ON, Canada

Assn. of Canadian Academic Healthcare Organizations **[IO]**, Ottawa, ON, Canada

Assn. of Canadian Advertisers **[IO]**, Toronto, ON, Canada

Assn. of Canadian Archivists **[IO]**, Ottawa, ON, Canada

Assn. of Canadian Biscuit Mfrs. **[IO]**, Don Mills, ON, Canada

Assn. of Canadian Choral Communities **[IO]**, Halifax, NS, Canada

Assn. of Canadian Coll. and Univ. Teachers of English **[IO]**, Montreal, QC, Canada

Assn. of Canadian Community Colleges **[IO]**, Ottawa, ON, Canada

Assn. of Canadian Distillers **[IO]**, Ottawa, ON, Canada

Assn. of Canadian Ergonomists **[IO]**, Calgary, AB, Canada

Assn. of Canadian Faculties of Dentistry **[IO]**, Ottawa, ON, Canada

Assn. of Canadian Film Craftspeople **[IO]**, Burnaby, BC, Canada

Assn. for Canadian Jewish Stud. **[IO]**, Montreal, QC, Canada

Assn. of Canadian Map Libraries and Archives **[IO]**, Gatineau, QC, Canada

Assn. of Canadian Mountain Guides **[IO]**, Canmore, AB, Canada

Assn. of Canadian Pension Mgt. **[IO]**, Toronto, ON, Canada

Assn. of Canadian Port Authorities **[IO]**, Ottawa, ON, Canada

Assn. of Canadian Publishers **[IO]**, Toronto, ON, Canada

Assn. of Canadian Search, Employment and Staffing Services **[IO]**, Mississauga, ON, Canada

Assn. for Canadian Stud. **[IO]**, Montreal, QC, Canada

Assn. for Canadian Stud. in the U.S. **[7809]**, 2030 M St. NW, Ste. 350, Washington, DC 20036, (202)775-9007

Assn. for Canadian Stud. in the U.S. **[7809]**, 2030 M St. NW, Ste. 350, Washington, DC 20036, (202)775-9007

Assn. of Canadian Travel Agencies **[IO]**, Mississauga, ON, Canada

Assn. of Canadian Universities for Northern Stud. **[IO]**, Ottawa, ON, Canada

Assn. of Canadian Univ. and Coll. Teachers of French **[IO]**, Mississauga, ON, Canada

Assn. of Canadian Univ. Presses **[IO]**, Toronto, ON, Canada

Assn. of Canadian Women Composers **[IO]**, Toronto, ON, Canada

Assn. of Canadians in Bermuda **[IO]**, Hamilton, Bermuda

Assn. Canadiene Des Indus. De La Musique **[★IO]**

Assn. Canadiene d'experts-conseils en Patrimoine **[★IO]**

Assn. Canadienne pour la recherche sur les services et les politiques de la sante **[★IO]**

Assn. Canadienne des moniteurs de surf des neiges **[★IO]**

Reference to "IO" in place of a book number signifies that the association may be found in the 50th edition of International Organizations.

Assn. Canadienne et de recherche institutionelles [★IO]
Assn. Canadienne des employes professionels [★IO]
Assn. Canadienne des paiements [★IO]
L'Association Canadienne des organismes artistiques [★IO]
L'Association Canadienne du medicament generique [★IO]
Assn. Canadienne du beton prepare [★IO]
Assn. Canadienne des 5 Quilles [★IO]
Assn. Canadienne des Administrateurs Solaires [★IO]
Assn. Canadienne pour la sante des Adolescents [★IO]
Assn. Canadienne des Agences de Voyages [★IO]
Assn. Canadienne des Agents de Commun. en Educ. [★IO]
Assn. Canadienne des Aliements de Sante [★IO]
Assn. Canadienne des Artistes de la Scene [★IO]
Assn. Canadienne des Ataxies Familiales [★IO]
Assn. Canadienne des Bibliotheques, Archives et Centres de Documentation Musicaux [★IO]
Assn. Canadienne des Bibliotheques de Droit [★IO]
Assn. Canadienne du Bison [★IO]
Assn. Canadienne de la Boulangerie [★IO]
Assn. Canadienne de Boxe Amateur [★IO]
Assn. Canadienne de Cadeaux et d'accessoires de Table [★IO]
Assn. Canadienne du Camionnage d'Entreprise [★IO]
Assn. Canadienne du Capital de Risque et d'Investissement [★IO]
Assn. Canadienne de Cartographie [★IO]
Assn. Canadienne des Centres Contre les Agressions a Caractere Sexuel [★IO]
Assn. Canadienne des Chaines de Pharmacies [★IO]
Assn. Canadienne des Chefs de Police [★IO]
Assn. Canadienne Chirurgie Pediatrique [★IO]
Assn. Canadienne des Chirurgiens Generaux [★IO]
Assn. Canadienne du Ciment [★IO]
L'Association Canadienne du Commerce des Semences [★IO]
Assn. Canadienne des Commisions de Police [★IO]
L'Association Canadienne des Commissions/Conseils Scolaires [★IO]
Assn. Canadienne des Compagnies d'Assurance Mutuelles [★IO]
Assn. Canadiennes des Compagnies d'Assurances de Personnes [★IO]
Assn. Canadienne du Comptables d'Assurance [★IO]
Assn. Canadienne des Conseillers en Genetique [★IO]
Assn. Canadienne des Conseillers Hypothecaires Accredites [★IO]
Assn. Canadienne des Conseillers et Juridiques d'Entreprises [★IO]
Assn. Canadienne des Conseillers Professionnels en Immigration [★IO]
Assn. Canadienne pour la Conservation et la Restauration des Biens Culturels [★IO]
Assn. Canadienne de Constructeurs de Vehicules [★IO]
Assn. Canadienne de la Constr. [★IO]
Assn. Canadienne du Contreplaque [★IO]
Assn. Canadienne du Contreplaque et des Placages de Bois Dur [★IO]
Assn. Canadienne du Controle du Trafic Aerien [★IO]
Assn. Canadienne des Cosmetiques, Produits de Toilette et Parfums [★IO]
Assn. Canadienne de Counselling Universitaire et Collegial [★IO]
Assn. Canadienne de la Courtepointe [★IO]
Assn. Canadienne de Cricket [★IO]
Assn. Canadienne des Croix Bleue [★IO]
Assn. Canadienne de Curling [★IO]
Assn. Canadienne D' Hydrographie [★IO]
Assn. Canadienne d'Acoustique [★IO]
Assn. Canadienne d'Acoustique [★IO]
Assn. Canadienne D'Alarme Incendie [★IO]
Assn. Canadienne d'Anatomie, de Neurobiologie et de Biologie Cellulaire [★IO]

L'Association Canadienne d'Art Photographique [★IO]
Assn. Canadienne d'Articles de Sport [★IO]
Assn. Canadienne d'Auto Distribution [★IO]
L' Assn. Canadienne De Cultures Speciales [★IO]
L'Association Canadienne De Droit Maritime [★IO]
Assn. Canadienne De L'Industrie Du Caoutchouc [★IO]
L'Association Canadienne De Pharmacie En Oncologie [★IO]
Assn. Canadienne De Sante Publique [★IO]
Assn. Canadienne d'Economique [★IO]
Assn. Canadienne d'Economique de Energie [★IO]
Assn. Canadienne d'Education [★IO]
Assn. Canadienne d'Equitation Therapeutique [★IO]
Assn. Canadienne d'Ergonomie [★IO]
Assn. Canadienne de Dermatologie [★IO]
Assn. Canadienne Des Annonceurs [★IO]
Assn. Canadienne Des Barrages [★IO]
L'Association Canadienne Des Commissaires D'Ecoles Catholiques [★IO]
Assn. Canadienne Des Experts Independants [★IO]
Assn. Canadienne Des Geographes [★IO]
Assn. Canadienne Des Infirmieres Et Infirmiers En Pratique Avancee [★IO]
Assn. Canadienne D'etudes Cinematographiques [★IO]
Assn. Canadienne d'Etudes du Developpement Intl. [★IO]
Assn. Canadienne d'Etudes Fiscales [★IO]
Assn. Canadienne d'Habitation et de Renovation Urbaine [★IO]
Assn. Canadienne D'Histoire Ferroviaire [★IO]
Assn. Canadienne du Diabete [★IO]
Assn. Canadienne des Directeurs Medicaux en Assurance-Vie [★IO]
Assn. Canadienne de Distributeurs d'Equipement [★IO]
Assn. Canadienne des Distributeurs de Films [★IO]
L'Association Canadienne des Distributeurs de Produits Chimiques [★IO]
Assn. Canadienne de la Distribution des Fruits et Legumes [★IO]
Assn. Canadienne de Distribution de Radiodiffusion [★IO]
Assn. Canadienne de Documentation Professionnelle [★IO]
Assn. Canadienne d'Oncologie Psychosociale [★IO]
Assn. Canadienne d'Orthopedie [★IO]
Assn. Canadienne Droit et Societe [★IO]
Assn. Canadienne Du Diabete [★IO]
Assn. Canadienne Du Diabete [★IO]
Assn. Canadienne Du Diabete [★IO]
L'Association Canadienne Du Quarter Horse [★IO]
Assn. Canadienne de la Dyslexie [★IO]
Assn. Canadienne des Eaux Embouteilles [★IO]
Assn. Canadienne des Eaux Potables et Usees [★IO]
Assn. Canadienne des Eaux Souterraines [★IO]
Assn. Canadienne des Echecs par Correspondance [★IO]
Assn. Canadienne des Ecoles de sciences infirmieres [★IO]
Assn. Canadienne des Editeurs de Musique [★IO]
Assn. Canadienne des Educateurs en Radiodiffusion [★IO]
Assn. Canadienne des Enterprises de Messagerie [★IO]
Assn. Canadienne des Entrepreneur Electriciens [★IO]
Assn. Canadienne des Entrepreneurs en Couverture [★IO]
Assn. Canadienne des Entreprises Familiales [★IO]
Assn. Canadienne des Entreprises de Geomatique [★IO]
Assn. Canadienne des Ergotherapeutes [★IO]
Assn. Canadienne des Etudes Aseatiques [★IO]
Assn. Canadienne des Etudes Neoplatonicicennes [★IO]
Assn. Canadienne des Etudiants et des Internes en Pharmacie [★IO]
Assn. Canadienne des Ex-Parlementaires [★IO]
Assn. Canadienne des Exportateurs d'Equipements et Services Miniers [★IO]
L'Association Canadienne des Fabricants Confiseries [★IO]

Assn. Canadienne de Fabricants d'Armoires de Cuisine [★IO]
Assn. Canadienne des Fabricants de Grignotines [★IO]
Assn. Canadienne des Fabricants des Portes et des Cadres d'Acier [★IO]
L'Association Canadienne des Fabricants de Produits Chimiques [★IO]
Assn. Canadienne des Fabricants de Produits de Quincaillerie et d'Articles Menagers [★IO]
Assn. Canadienne des Fabricants de Tuyaux de Beton [★IO]
Assn. Canadienne des Femmes Cadres et Entrepreneurs [★IO]
L'Association Canadienne des Femmes en Communications [★IO]
Assn. Canadienne de Financement et de Location [★IO]
Assn. Canadienne des Foires et Expositions [★IO]
L'Association Canadienne des Fonds de Revenu [★IO]
Assn. Canadienne de Forage au Diamant [★IO]
Assn. Canadienne de la Formation Professionnelle [★IO]
Assn. Canadienne des Fournisseurs de laboratoire [★IO]
Assn. Canadienne de la Franchise [★IO]
Assn. Canadienne de Gastroenterologie [★IO]
Assn. Canadienne du Gaz [★IO]
Assn. Canadienne de Gerance de Tirage [★IO]
Assn. Canadienne de Gestion D'Expositions [★IO]
Assn. Canadienne de Gestion Environnementale [★IO]
Assn. Canadienne de la Gestion Parasitaire [★IO]
Assn. Canadienne de Golf des Sourds [★IO]
Assn. Canadienne des Golfeurs Professionnels [★IO]
Assn. Canadienne pour les Handicapes Neurologiques [★IO]
Assn. Canadienne des Harmonies [★IO]
Assn. Canadienne de Hockey-Balle [★IO]
Assn. Canadienne des Hygienistes Dentaires [★IO]
Assn. Canadienne des Importateurs Reglementes [★IO]
Assn. Canadienne des Indus. du Recyclage [★IO]
Assn. Canadienne des Inedecins Recidents [★IO]
Assn. Canadienne des Infirmieres et Infirmiers en Orthopedie [★IO]
Assn. Canadienne des Infirmieres et Infirmiers en Sante du Travail [★IO]
Assn. Canadienne des Infirmieres et Infirmiers en Sciences Neurologiques [★IO]
Assn. Canadienne des Infirmieres et Infirmiers en Sidologie [★IO]
Assn. Canadienne des Infirmieres et Infirmiers en Soins aux Brules [★IO]
Assn. Canadienne des Infirmiers et Infirmieres en Gerontologie [★IO]
Assn. Canadienne des Informieres en Approches Holistiques de Soins [★IO]
Assn. Canadienne des Inspecteurs de Biens Immobiliers [★IO]
Assn. Canadienne des Institutions de Sante Universtaires [★IO]
Assn. Canadienne des Intervenants en Formation Policiere [★IO]
Assn. Canadienne pour les Jeunes Enfants [★IO]
L'Association Canadienne de Jouet [★IO]
L'Association Canadienne des Journalistes [★IO]
Assn. Canadienne des Journaux [★IO]
Assn. Canadienne des Juges de Cours Provinciales [★IO]
Assn. Canadienne de l' Energie Eolienne [★IO]
Assn. Canadienne pour l'Avancement des Femmes du Sport et de l'Activite Physique [★IO]
Assn. Canadienne de L'emballage [★IO]
Assn. Canadienne de l'enseigne [★IO]
Assn. Canadienne de l'Enseignement Cooperatif [★IO]
Assn. Canadienne pour l'Etude du Curriculum [★IO]
L'Association Canadienne pour l'Etude de l'Education des Adultes [★IO]
Assn. Canadienne pour l'Etude du Quarternaire [★IO]
Assn. Canadienne pour l'Histoire du Nursing [★IO]
Assn. Canadienne des Libertes Civiles [★IO]

A star before a book entry number signifies that the name is not listed separately, but is mentioned within the entry.

Assn. Canadienne de l'Imprimerie [★IO]

Assn. Canadienne de l'Industrie du Bois [★IO]

L'Association Canadienne de l'Industrie de la Peinture et du Revetement [★IO]

Assn. Canadienne de l'industrie des Plastiques [★IO]

Assn. Canadienne de l'informatique [★IO]

Assn. Canadienne de Linguistique [★IO]

Assn. Canadienne pour l'Integration Communautaire [★IO]

Assn. Canadienne de Literature Comparee [★IO]

Assn. Canadienne pour L'Obtention de Services aux Personnes Autistiques [★IO]

Assn. Canadienne de Lutte Amateur [★IO]

L'Association Canadienne des Maitres de Poste et Adjoints [★IO]

L'Association Canadienne de la Maladie Coeliaque [★IO]

Assn. Canadienne des Manufacturiers de Biscuits [★IO]

Assn. Canadienne des Manufacturiers de Palettes et Contenants [★IO]

L'Association Canadienne Marchands Numismatiques [★IO]

Assn. Canadienne des Marches des Capitaux [★IO]

Assn. Canadienne du Marketing [★IO]

Assn. Canadienne des Massotherapeutes du Sport [★IO]

Assn. Canadienne des Medecins d'Urgence [★IO]

Assn. Canadienne des Medecins Veterinaires [★IO]

Assn. Canadienne des Membres des Tribunaux d'Utilite Publique [★IO]

Assn. Canadienne de Microbiologie Clinique et des Maladies [★IO]

Assn. Canadienne des Mouleurs sous Pression [★IO]

L'Association Canadienne des entrepreneurs en Mousse de Polyurethane [★IO]

Assn. Canadienne pour les Nations-Unies [★IO]

Assn. Canadienne pour les Nations Unies - Div. de la Region du Saguenay-Lac-Saint-Jean [★IO]

Assn. Canadienne pour les Nations Unies - Montreal [★IO]

Assn. Canadienne pour les Nations Unies - Region de Quebec [★IO]

Assn. Canadienne des docteurs en Naturopathie [★IO]

Assn. Canadienne de Neurologie Pediatrique [★IO]

Assn. Canadienne des Neuropathologistes [★IO]

Assn. Canadienne des Optometristes [★IO]

Assn. Canadienne des Orthodontistes [★IO]

Assn. Canadienne des Orthophonistes et Audiologistes [★IO]

Assn. Canadienne des Palynologues [★IO]

L'Association Canadienne de Parachutisme Sportiff [★IO]

Assn. Canadienne des Parajuristes [★IO]

Assn. Canadienne des Paraplegiques [★IO]

Assn. Canadienne des Parcs et Loisirs [★IO]

Assn. Canadienne des Pathologistes [★IO]

Assn. Canadienne de Philosophie [★IO]

Assn. Canadienne de Photographes et Illustrateurs de Publicite [★IO]

Assn. Canadienne de Physiotherapie [★IO]

Assn. Canadienne des Pilotes de Ligne Internationale [★IO]

Assn. Canadienne de Pipelines d'Energie [★IO]

Assn. Canadienne du Plegage Humanitaire [★IO]

Assn. Canadienne des Policiers [★IO]

Assn. Canadienne Pou La Sante Mentale - Div. du Quebec [★IO]

L'Association Canadienne Pour les Etudes de Renseignement et de Securite [★IO]

Assn. Canadienne Pour La Sante Mentale [★IO]

Assn. Canadienne Pour La Sante Mentale, Filiale de Chatham-Kent [★IO]

Assn. Canadienne Pour La Sante Metale [★IO]

Assn. Canadienne pour la Pratique et l'Education Pastorales [★IO]

Assn. Canadienne pour la Prevention du Suicide [★IO]

Assn. Canadienne des Producteurs de Semences [★IO]

Assn. Canadienne de Production de Film et de TV [★IO]

Assn. Canadienne des Profesionnels en dons Planifies [★IO]

Assn. Canadienne des Professeurs de Comptabilite [★IO]

L' Assn. Canadienne des Professeurs de Danse [★IO]

Assn. Canadienne des Professeurs d'Immersion [★IO]

Assn. Canadienne des Professionnels de l'Insolvabilite et de la reorganisation [★IO]

L'association Canadienne des Professionnels de la Vente [★IO]

Assn. Canadienne de Programmes en Admin. Publique [★IO]

Assn. Canadienne des Programmes de Ressources pour la Famille [★IO]

Assn. Canadienne de Protection Medicale [★IO]

Assn. Canadienne des Radiodiffuseurs [★IO]

Assn. Canadienne des Radiologistes [★IO]

Assn. Canadienne de Radioprotection [★IO]

Assn. Canadienne pour la Recherche en Economie Familials [★IO]

Assn. Canadienne de Recherches Dentaires [★IO]

Assn. Canadienne de Reflexologie [★IO]

Assn. Canadienne de Rehabilitation des Sites Degrades [★IO]

Assn. Canadienne des Relations Industrielles [★IO]

Assn. Canadienne des Representants de Ventes en Gros [★IO]

Assn. Canadienne des Resources Hydriques [★IO]

Assn. Canadienne des Responsables de l'Aide Financiere au Etudiants [★IO]

Assn. Canadienne des Restaurateurs Professionnels [★IO]

Assn. Canadienne des Sage-Femmes [★IO]

Assn. Canadienne de Sante Dentaire Publique [★IO]

Assn. Canadienne pour la Sante Mentale [★IO]

Assn. Canadienne pour la Sci. des Animaux de Laboratoire [★IO]

Assn. Canadienne de Sci. Economique des Affaires [★IO]

Assn. Canadienne des Sciences Geomatiques [★IO]

L'Association Canadienne des Sciences de l'Information [★IO]

L'Association Canadienne de la Securite [★IO]

Assn. Canadienne de Securite Incendie [★IO]

Assn. Canadienne de Semiotique [★IO]

Assn. Canadienne de Sensibilisation a l'Infertilite [★IO]

Assn. Canadienne des Slavistes [★IO]

Assn. Canadienne des Snowbirds [★IO]

Assn. Canadienne de Soccer [★IO]

Assn. Canadienne des Societes Elizabeth Fry [★IO]

Assn. Canadienne du Soin des Plaies [★IO]

Assn. Canadienne de Soins et Services a Domicile [★IO]

Assn. Canadienne du Sport Collegial [★IO]

Assn. Canadienne des Sports pour Amputes [★IO]

Assn. Canadienne des Sports en Fauteuil Roulant [★IO]

Assn. Canadienne des Sports pour Skieurs Handicapes [★IO]

Assn. Canadienne du Stationnement [★IO]

Assn. Canadienne des Stomotherapeutes [★IO]

Assn. Canadienne pour les Structures et Materiaux Composites [★IO]

Assn. Canadienne des Surintendants de Golf [★IO]

Assn. Canadienne de la Technologie de l'information [★IO]

Assn. Canadienne des Technologues en Electroneurophysiologie [★IO]

Assn. Canadienne des Technologues en Radiation Medicale [★IO]

Assn. Canadienne du Telephone Independant [★IO]

Assn. Canadienne de Tennis du Table [★IO]

Assn. Canadienne des Therapeutes du Sport [★IO]

Assn. Canadienne de Traductologie [★IO]

Assn. Canadienne de Traitement d'Images et de Reconnaissance des Formes [★IO]

Assn. Canadienne de Transport Industriel [★IO]

Assn. Canadienne du Transport Urbain [★IO]

Assn. Canadienne des Travailleuses et Travailleurs Sociaux [★IO]

Assn. Canadienne du Vehicule Recreatif [★IO]

Assn. Canadienne de Verification [★IO]

Assn. Canadienne des Veterans de la Coree [★IO]

L'Association Canadienne de Vexillologie [★IO]

L'Association Canadienne de Vol a Voile [★IO]

Assn. Canadienne de Yachting [★IO]

Assn. of Cancer Executives [13886], 2300 N St. NW, Ste. 710, Washington, DC 20037, (202)521-1886

Assn. of Cancer Inst. Directors [★13885]

Assn. of Cancer Online Resources [13887], 173 Duane St., Ste. 3A, New York, NY 10013-3334, (212)226-5525

Assn. Candienne des Pepinieristes et des Paysagistes [★IO]

Assn. Cannadienne des Radio-Oncologues [★IO]

Assn. of Capitol Reporters and Editors [5894], Alan Johnson, Treas., 34 S Third St., Columbus, OH 43215

Assn. of Car Rental Indus. Systems Standards [IO], Uckfield, United Kingdom

Assn. for Car and Truck Rental Independents and Franchisees [★3075]

Assn. Caraibe pour l'Environnement [★IO]

Assn. of Cardiologists of Bosnia and Herzegovina [IO], Sarajevo, Bosnia-Hercegovina

Assn. of Cardiothoracic Anaesthetists [IO], London, United Kingdom

Assn. for the Care of Children's Health - Defunct.

Assn. of Career Firms Intl. [1143], 8509 Crown Crescent C., Ste. ACF, Charlotte, NC 28227, (704)849-2500

Assn. of Career Firms North America [1143], 8509 Crown Crescent C., Ste. ACF, Charlotte, NC 28227, (704)849-2500

Assn. of Career Mgt. Consulting Firms Intl. [★1143]

Assn. of Career Mgt. Consulting Firms Intl. [★1143]

Assn. for Career and Tech. Educ. [9039], 1410 King St., Alexandria, VA 22314, (703)683-3111

Assn. for Career and Tech. Educ. Res. [9040], North Carolina State Univ., 300C Poe Hall, Raleigh, NC 27695, (919)208-1697

Assn. for Careers Educ. and Guidance [IO], Banbury, United Kingdom

Assn. of Caribbean Economists [IO], Kingston, Jamaica

Assn. of Caribbean Electoral Organizations - Address unknown since 2011.

Assn. of Caribbean States [IO], Port of Spain, Trinidad and Tobago

Assn. of Caribbean Univ., Res. and Institutional Libraries [9964], PO Box 21609, San Juan, PR 00931-1906, (787)763-6199

Assn. of Caribbean Univ., Res. and Institutional Libraries [9964], PO Box 21609, San Juan, PR 00931-1906, (787)763-6199

Assn. Cartographique Internationale [★IO]

Assn. des Cartotheques et Archieves Cartographiques du Canada [★IO]

Assn. of Casualty Accountants and Statisticians [★1328]

Assn. of Casualty and Surety Companies [★1933]

Assn. for Catering Excellence [IO], Woking, United Kingdom

Assn. for Catholic Chiropractors [14121], 2049 Kolb Ridge Ct. SW, Marietta, GA 30008

Assn. of Catholic Colleges and Universities [7813], 1 Dupont Cir., Ste. 650, Washington, DC 20036, (202)457-0650

Assn. of Catholic Institutes of Educ. [IO], Angers, France

Assn. of Catholic Publishers [2920], 4725 Dorsey Hall Dr., Ste. A, PMB No. 709, Ellicott City, MD 21042, (410)988-2926

Assn. of Celebrity Personal Assistants [61], 914 Westwood Blvd., No. 507, Los Angeles, CA 90024-2905

Assn. of Centers of Medieval and Renaissance Stud. [★10078]

Assn. Centrafricaine pour le Bien-Etre Familial [IO], Bangui, Central African Republic

Assn. for Central Asian Studies - Defunct.

Assn. of Ceramic Educators [★7819]

Assn. of Ceramic Educators [★7819]

Assn. of Ceramic Tile Mfrs. of Spain [IO], Castellon, Spain

Reference to "IO" in place of a book number signifies that the association may be found in the 50th edition of International Organizations.

Assn. of Cereal Starch Producers in the EU [IO], Brussels, Belgium

Assn. of Certified Adizes Practitioners Intl. [2268], 6404 Via Real, Carpinteria, CA 93013, (805)565-2901

Assn. of Certified Adizes Practitioners Intl. [2268], 6404 Via Real, Carpinteria, CA 93013, (805)565-2901

Assn. of Certified Anti-Money Laundering Specialists [399], Brickell Bayview Center, 80 SW 8th St., Ste. 2350, Miami, FL 33130, (305)373-0020

Assn. of Certified Anti-Money Laundering Specialists [399], Brickell Bayview Center, 80 SW 8th St., Ste. 2350, Miami, FL 33130, (305)373-0020

Assn. of Certified Background Investigators [5594], PO Box 80413, Staten Island, NY 10308

Assn. of Certified Fraud Examiners [1884], The Gregor Bldg., 716 West Ave., Austin, TX 78701-2727, (512)478-9000

Assn. of Certified Fraud Examiners [1884], The Gregor Bldg., 716 West Ave., Austin, TX 78701-2727, (512)478-9000

Assn. of Certified Fraud Examiners, Belgium Chap. 127 [IO], Vilvoorde, Belgium

Assn. of Certified Fraud Examiners, Hong Kong Chap. [IO], Hong Kong, People's Republic of China

Assn. of Certified Fraud Examiners, South African Chap. [IO], Menlo Park, Republic of South Africa

Assn. of Certified Fraud Examiners, United Kingdom Chap. [IO], London, United Kingdom

Assn. of Certified Fraud Specialists [1885], PO Box 340850, Sacramento, CA 95834-8777, (916)419-6319

Assn. of Certified Green Tech. Auditors [6692], 1802 N Univ. Dr., Ste. 112, Plantation, FL 33322, (855)932-2482

Assn. of Certified Green Tech. Auditors [6692], 1802 N Univ. Dr., Ste. 112, Plantation, FL 33322, (855)932-2482

Assn. of Certified Marine Surveyors [2352], 209/241 Nooseneck Hill Rd., West Greenwich, RI 02817, (401)397-1888

Assn. of Certified Professional Wedding Consultants [2428], 122 Destry Ct., San Jose, CA 95136, (408)227-2792

Assn. of Certified Public Accountant Examiners [★5182]

Assn. of Certified Treasury Managers [IO], Hyderabad, India

Assn. Chaine d'approvisionement et logistique Canada [★IO]

Assn. of Chairmen of Departments of Mechanics [8571], Virginia Polytechnic Inst. and State Univ., Dept. of Engg. Sci. and Mechanics, 223 Norris Hall - MC 0219, Blacksburg, VA 24061, (540)231-6651

Assn. for Challenge Course Tech. [2599], PO Box 47, Deerfield, IL 60015, (800)991-0286

Assn. des Chambres de Commerce et d'Industrie de la Mediterranee [★IO]

Assn. of Champagne Producers [IO], Reims, France

Assn. fiscale internationale - Chapitre Canadien [★IO]

Assn. of Charitable Foundations [IO], London, United Kingdom

Assn. of Charity Officers [IO], Potters Bar, United Kingdom

Assn. of Chartered Accountants in the U.S. [13], 1050 Winter St., Ste. 1000, Waltham, MA 02451, (508)395-0224

Assn. of Chartered Certified Accountants - Australia and New Zealand [IO], Sydney, Australia

Assn. of Chartered Certified Accountants - Botswana [IO], Gaborone, Botswana

Assn. of Chartered Certified Accountants - Cambodia [IO], Phnom Penh, Cambodia

Assn. of Chartered Certified Accountants - Canada [IO], Toronto, ON, Canada

Assn. of Chartered Certified Accountants - Caribbean [IO], Port of Spain, Trinidad and Tobago

Assn. of Chartered Certified Accountants - Central and Eastern Europe Off. [IO], Prague, Czech Republic

Assn. of Chartered Certified Accountants - Cyprus [IO], Nicosia, Cyprus

Assn. of Chartered Certified Accountants - Ethiopia [IO], Addis Ababa, Ethiopia

Assn. of Chartered Certified Accountants - Ghana [IO], Accra, Ghana

Assn. of Chartered Certified Accountants - Gulf States [IO], Dubai, United Arab Emirates

Assn. of Chartered Certified Accountants - Hong Kong [IO], Hong Kong, People's Republic of China

Assn. of Chartered Certified Accountants - Ireland [IO], Dublin, Ireland

Assn. of Chartered Certified Accountants - Kenya [IO], Nairobi, Kenya

Assn. of Chartered Certified Accountants - Malaysia [IO], Kuala Lumpur, Malaysia

Assn. of Chartered Certified Accountants - Mauritius [IO], Ebene City, Mauritius

Assn. of Chartered Certified Accountants - Pakistan [IO], Lahore, Pakistan

Assn. of Chartered Certified Accountants - Poland [IO], Warsaw, Poland

Assn. of Chartered Certified Accountants - Singapore [IO], Singapore, Singapore

Assn. of Chartered Certified Accountants - South Africa [IO], Saxonwold, Republic of South Africa

Assn. of Chartered Certified Accountants - Sri Lanka [IO], Colombo, Sri Lanka

Assn. of Chartered Certified Accountants - Uganda [IO], Kampala, Uganda

Assn. of Chartered Certified Accountants - United Kingdom [IO], London, United Kingdom

Assn. of Chartered Certified Accountants - Vietnam [IO], Ho Chi Minh City, Vietnam

Assn. of Chartered Certified Accountants - Zambia [IO], Lusaka, Zambia

Assn. of Chartered Certified Accountants - Zimbabwe [IO], Harare, Zimbabwe

Assn. of Chartered Indus. Designers of Ontario [IO], Toronto, ON, Canada

Assn. of Chem. Indus. [IO], Ljubljana, Slovenia

Assn. of Chem. Indus. of Slovenia [IO], Ljubljana, Slovenia

Assn. of Chem. Indus. of the Czech Republic [IO], Prague, Czech Republic

Assn. of Chem. Indus. of Germany [IO], Frankfurt, Germany

Assn. of Chem. Pulp and Paper Chemists and Engineers [IO], Darmstadt, Germany

Assn. des Chemins de fer du Canada [★IO]

Assn. of Chemists of the Textile Indus. [IO], Clichy, France

Assn. for Chemoreception Sciences [6398], 5841 Cedar Lake Rd., Minneapolis, MN 55416, (952)646-2035

Assn. for Chemoreception Sciences [6398], 5841 Cedar Lake Rd., Minneapolis, MN 55416, (952)646-2035

Assn. des Chercheurs Iraniens [IO], London, United Kingdom

Assn. of Chess Professionals [IO], Paris, France

Assn. des Chevaux Morgan Canadien [★IO]

Assn. of Chief Estate Surveyors and Property Managers in Local Govt. [IO], Cheshire, United Kingdom

Assn. of Chief Executives of Voluntary Organisations [IO], London, United Kingdom

Assn. of Chief Police Officers of England, Wales and Northern Ireland [IO], London, United Kingdom

Assn. of Chief Police Officers in Scotland [IO], Glasgow, United Kingdom

Assn. of Chiefs and Officials of Bureaus of Labor [★5635]

Assn. of Child Abuse Lawyers [IO], Surbiton, United Kingdom

Assn. for Child and Adolescent Mental Hea. [IO], London, United Kingdom

Assn. of Child and Adolescent Psychiatric Nurses [★15759]

Assn. of Child and Adolescent Psychiatric Nurses [★15759]

Assn. of Child Advocates [★11426]

Assn. for Child Hea. [IO], Lagos, Nigeria

Assn. of Child Neurology Nurses [15735], Blue Chip Mgt. Services Inc., 303 Concord Ave., Exton, PA 19341-1761

Assn. of Child Neurology Nurses [15735], Blue Chip Mgt. Services Inc., 303 Concord Ave., Exton, PA 19341-1761

Assn. for Child Psychoanalysis [16355], 7820 Enchanted Hills Blvd., No. A-233, Rio Rancho, NM 87144, (505)771-0372

Assn. for Child Psychotherapists [IO], London, United Kingdom

Assn. for Childhood Educ. Intl. [7825], 17904 Georgia Ave., Ste. 215, Olney, MD 20832, (301)570-2111

Assn. for Childhood Educ. Intl. [7825], 17904 Georgia Ave., Ste. 215, Olney, MD 20832, (301)570-2111

Assn. for Children and Adults with Learning Disabilities [★12425]

Assn. for Children with a Disability [IO], Hawthorn, Australia

Assn. for Children with Down Syndrome [12496], 4 Fern Pl., Plainview, NY 11803, (516)933-4700

Assn. for Children for Enforcement of Support - Address unknown since 2011.

Assn. for Children with Learning Disabilities [★12425]

Assn. for Children with Retarded Mental Development [★12505]

Assn. of Children's Museums [10113], 2711 Jefferson Davis Hwy., No. 600, Arlington, VA 22202, (703)224-3100

Assn. of Children's Prosthetic-Orthotic Clinics [16050], 6300 N River Rd., Ste. 727, Rosemont, IL 60018-4226, (847)698-1637

Assn. of Children's Welfare Agencies [IO], Haymarket, Australia

Assn. of Chilean Tourism Agencies [IO], Santiago, Chile

Assn. des Chimistes de l'Industrie Textile [★IO]

Assn. of China and Mongolia Intl. Schools [IO], Hong Kong, People's Republic of China

Assn. of Chinese Amer. Physicians [16255], Alex Chan, 33-70 Prince St., Ste. 703, Flushing, NY 11354, (718)321-8893

Assn. of Chinese-American Professionals [18961], 10303 Westoffice Dr., Houston, TX 77042-5306

Assn. for the Chinese Blind [★17085]

Assn. for the Chinese Blind [★17085]

Assn. of Chinese Finance Professionals [1282], 240 Hazelwood Ave., San Francisco, CA 94127

Assn. of Chinese Food Scientists and Technologists in Am. [★6874]

Assn. of Chinese Graduate Schools [IO], Beijing, People's Republic of China

Assn. of Chinese from Indochina [★18509]

Assn. of Chinese from Indochina [★18509]

Assn. of Chinese Professors of Social Sciences in the U.S. [7409], Dr. Shaorong Huang, Treas., Univ. of Cincinnati, Raymond Walters Coll., Dept. of English and Commun., 9555 Plainfield Rd., Cincinnati, OH 45236

Assn. of Chinese Scientists and Engineers U.S.A. [6783], PO Box 59715, Schaumburg, IL 60159

Assn. of Chinese Scientists and Engineers U.S.A. [6783], PO Box 59715, Schaumburg, IL 60159

Assn. Chinoise de Handball [IO], Beijing, People's Republic of China

Assn. of Chiropractic Coll. Presidents [★14122]

Assn. of Chiropractic Coll. Presidents [★14122]

Assn. of Chiropractic Colleges [14122], 4424 Montgomery Ave., Ste. 202, Bethesda, MD 20814, (800)284-1062

Assn. of Chiropractic Colleges [14122], 4424 Montgomery Ave., Ste. 202, Bethesda, MD 20814, (800)284-1062

Assn. Chiropratique Canadienne [★IO]

Assn. of the Chocolate, Biscuit and Confectionery Indus. of the European Union [IO], Brussels, Belgium

Assn. of Christian Church Educators - Defunct.

Assn. for Christian Ethics [19385], PO Box 1007, New York, NY 10150, (718)357-4830

Assn. of Christian Inst. of Social Concern of Asia [IO], Pune, India

Assn. of Christian Investigators [5595], 2553 Jackson Keller, Ste. 200, San Antonio, TX 78230, (210)342-0509

Assn. of Christian Journalists [IO], St. Petersburg, Russia

Assn. of Christian Lay Centres in Africa [IO], Nairobi, Kenya

---

A star before a book entry number signifies that the name is not listed separately, but is mentioned within the entry.

Assn. of Christian Librarians [9965], PO Box 4, Cedarville, OH 45314-0004, (937)766-2255

Assn. of Christian Librarians [9965], PO Box 4, Cedarville, OH 45314-0004, (937)766-2255

Assn. of Christian Schools Intl. [7851], PO Box 65130, Colorado Springs, CO 80962-5130, (800)367-0798

Assn. of Christian Schools Intl. [7851], PO Box 65130, Colorado Springs, CO 80962-5130, (800)367-0798

Assn. of Christian Teachers [IO], St. Albans, United Kingdom

Assn. of Christian Therapists [19538], 6728 Old McLean Village Dr., McLean, VA 22101, (703)556-9222

Assn. for Christian Training and Service - Defunct.

Assn. of Christian Truckers [19982], PO Box 187, Brownstown, IL 62418, (618)427-3737

Assn. of Christian Universities and Colleges in Asia [IO], Daegu, Republic of Korea

Assn. of Christians in the Mathematical Sciences [19539], Dr. Robert Brabanec, Exec. Sec., Wheaton Coll., Dept. of Mathematics, 501 Coll. Ave., Wheaton, IL 60187, (630)752-5869

Assn. of the Cider and Fruit Wine Indus. of the European Union [IO], Brussels, Belgium

Assn. of Cinema Labs. [★1251]

Assn. of Cinema and Video Labs. [1251], Peter Bulcke, Treas., 1833 Centinela Ave., Santa Monica, CA 90404, (310)828-1098

Assn. of Cities of the Kyrgyz Republic [IO], Bishkek, Kirgizstan

Assn. of Cities and Regions for Recycling and Sustainable Rsrc. Mgt. [IO], Skipton, United Kingdom

Assn. for Civil Rights [IO], Buenos Aires, Argentina

Assn. for Civil Rights in Israel [IO], Jerusalem, Israel

Assn. of Civilian Technicians [23199], 12620 Lake Ridge Dr., Woodbridge, VA 22192-2335, (703)494-4845

Assn. of Clandestine Radio Enthusiasts [20934], PO Box 1, Belfast, NY 14711-0001

Assn. of Classical and Christian Schools [8823], PO Box 9741, Moscow, ID 83843, (208)882-6101

Assn. of Classical and Christian Schools [8823], PO Box 9741, Moscow, ID 83843, (208)882-6101

Assn. of Climate Change Officers [4237], 1900 K St. NW, Washington, DC 20006, (202)496-7390

Assn. of Clinic Managers [★15294]

Assn. for Clinical Biochemistry [IO], London, United Kingdom

Assn. for Clinical Data Mgt. [IO], St. Albans, United Kingdom

Assn. of Clinical Embryologists [IO], Manchester, United Kingdom

Assn. for Clinical Pastoral Educ. [19668], 1549 Clairmont Rd., Ste. 103, Decatur, GA 30033-4635, (404)320-1472

Assn. of Clinical Pastoral Educators [★19668]

Assn. of Clinical Pathologists [IO], Hove, United Kingdom

Assn. of Clinical Res. Organizations [14152], 915 15th St. NW, 2nd Fl., Washington, DC 20005, (202)464-9340

Assn. of Clinical Res. Professionals [16185], 500 Montgomery St., Ste. 800, Alexandria, VA 22314, (703)254-8100

Assn. of Clinical Res. Professionals [16185], 500 Montgomery St., Ste. 800, Alexandria, VA 22314, (703)254-8100

Assn. of Clinical Scientists [14153], PO Box 1287, Middlebury, VT 05753, (802)458-3351

Assn. of Clinicians for the Underserved [14757], 1420 Spring Hill Rd., Ste. 600, Tysons Corner, VA 22102, (703)442-5318

Assn. of Club Executives [1738], 601 Pennsylvania Ave. NW, Ste. 900 S, Washington, DC 20004, (202)220-3019

Assn. of Coffee Mill Enthusiasts [21306], PO Box 86, Olivet, MI 49076-0086

Assn. of Collecting Clubs [21307], 18222 Flower Hill Way, No. 299, Gaithersburg, MD 20879, (301)926-8663

Assn. of Coll. Admin. Professionals [7657], PO Box 1389, Staunton, VA 24402, (540)885-1873

Assn. of Coll. Admissions Counselors [★7684]

Assn. of Coll. Auxiliary Services [★3170]

Assn. of Coll. Geology Teachers [★8212]

Assn. of Coll. Honor Societies [23554], 4990 Northwind Dr., Ste. 140, East Lansing, MI 48823-5031, (517)351-8335

Assn. of Coll. Honor Societies [★23527]

Assn. of Coll. Honor Societies [★23527]

Assn. of Coll. Police Training Officials [★11740]

Assn. of Coll. Professors of Textiles and Clothing [★3445]

Assn. of Coll. Professors of Textiles and Clothing [★3445]

Assn. of Coll. and Reference Libraries [★9966]

Assn. of Coll. and Res. Libraries [9966], 50 E Huron St., Chicago, IL 60611-2795, (312)280-2523

Assn. of Coll. Unions [★8903]

Assn. of Coll. Unions [★8903]

Assn. of Coll. Unions Intl. [8903], One City Centre, Ste. 200, 120 W 7th St., Bloomington, IN 47404-3925, (812)245-2284

Assn. of Coll. Unions Intl. [8903], One City Centre, Ste. 200, 120 W 7th St., Bloomington, IN 47404-3925, (812)245-2284

Assn. of Coll. and Univ. Auditors [7658], PO Box 14306, Lenexa, KS 66285-4306, (913)895-4620

Assn. of Coll. and Univ. Auditors [7658], PO Box 14306, Lenexa, KS 66285-4306, (913)895-4620

Assn. of Coll. and Univ. Clubs [7872], 1733 King St., Alexandria, VA 22314-2720, (703)299-2630

Assn. of Coll. and Univ. Clubs [7872], 1733 King St., Alexandria, VA 22314-2720, (703)299-2630

Assn. of Coll., Univ. and Community Arts Administrators [★7744]

Assn. of Coll. and Univ. Concert Managers [★7744]

Assn. of Coll. and Univ. Housing Officers Intl. [8904], 941 Chatham Ln., Ste. 318, Columbus, OH 43221-2416, (614)292-0099

Assn. of Coll. and Univ. Housing Officers Intl. [8904], 941 Chatham Ln., Ste. 318, Columbus, OH 43221-2416, (614)292-0099

Assn. of Coll. and Univ. Museums and Galleries [★10110]

Assn. of Coll. and Univ. Offices [★8094]

Assn. of Coll. and Univ. Religious Affairs [8905], Rev. Susan Henry-Crowe, Treas., Emory Univ., Atlanta, GA 30322, (404)727-6226

Assn. of Colleges [IO], London, United Kingdom

Assn. des Colleges Communautaires du Canada [★IO]

Assn. of Collegiate Alumnae [★9051]

Assn. of Collegiate Bus. Schools and Programs [★7867]

Assn. of Collegiate Conf. and Events Directors Intl. [2443], 419 Canyon Ave., Ste. 311, Fort Collins, CO 80521, (970)449-4960

Assn. of Collegiate Conf. and Events Directors Intl. [2443], 419 Canyon Ave., Ste. 311, Fort Collins, CO 80521, (970)449-4960

Assn. of Collegiate Licensing Administrators [★2407]

Assn. of Collegiate Schools of Architecture [7733], 1735 New York Ave. NW, 3rd Fl., Washington, DC 20006, (202)785-2324

Assn. of Collegiate Schools of Nursing [★15781]

Assn. of Collegiate Schools of Planning [9024], 6311 Mallard Trace Dr., Tallahassee, FL 32312, (850)385-2054

Assn. of Coloproctology of Great Britain and Ireland [IO], London, United Kingdom

The Assn. of Comedy Artists - Defunct.

Assn. des Comites Nationaux Olympiques [★IO]

Assn. des Comites Nationaux Olympiques d'Afrique [★IO]

Assn. des Commercants d'Art de la Suisse [IO], Zurich, Switzerland

Assn. des Commercants de Vehicules Recreatifs du Canada [★IO]

Assn. Commercial Banks of Latvia [IO], Riga, Latvia

Assn. of Commercial Diving Educators [23102], Santa Barbara City Coll., 721 Cliff Dr., Santa Barbara, CA 93109-2394, (805)965-0581

Assn. of Commercial Finance Attorneys [5237], Hahn & Hessen LLP, 488 Madison Ave., New York, NY 10022, (212)478-7348

Assn. of Commercial Finance Companies of New York [★2209]

Assn. of Commercial Finance Companies of New York [★2209]

Assn. of Commercial Records Centers [★1907]

Assn. of Commercial Records Centers [★1907]

Assn. of Commercial Stock Image Licensors [1252], 630 9th Ave., Ste. 1012, New York, NY 10036, (917)338-6417

Assn. of Commercial TV in Europe [IO], Brussels, Belgium

Assn. for Common European Nursing Diagnoses, Interventions and Outcomes [IO], Dublin, Ireland

Assn. of Commonwealth Archivists and Records Managers [IO], London, United Kingdom

Assn. of Commonwealth Literature and Language Stud. [IO], Aachen, Germany

Assn. of Commonwealth Universities [IO], London, United Kingdom

Assn. for Communal Harmony in Asia [12626], 4410 Verda Ln. NE, Keizer, OR 97303, (503)393-6944

Assn. des Communautes Chorales Canadiennes [★IO]

Assn. for Commun. Excellence in Agriculture, Natural Resources, and Life and Human Sciences [3737], 59 Coll. Rd., Durham, NH 03824, (855)657-9544

Assn. of Communications Enterprises [★3592]

Assn. for Communications Tech. Professionals in Higher Educ; ACUTA: The [8301]

Assn. for Community Affiliated Plans [14758], 1015 15th St. NW, Ste. 950, Washington, DC 20005, (202)204-7508

Assn. of Community Cancer Centers [13888], 11600 Nebel St., Ste. 201, Rockville, MD 20852-2557, (301)984-9496

Assn. of Community Coll. Trustees [7890], 1233 20th St. NW, Ste. 301, Washington, DC 20036-2363, (202)775-4667

Assn. of Community Colleges [IO], Odder, Denmark

Assn. of Community and Comprehensive Schools [IO], Dublin, Ireland

Assn. for Community Design - Defunct.

Assn. for Community Hea. Improvement [16479], 155 N Wacker Dr., Ste. 400, Chicago, IL 60606-1725, (312)422-2193

Assn. for Community Hea. Improvement [16479], 155 N Wacker Dr., Ste. 400, Chicago, IL 60606-1725, (312)422-2193

Assn. of Community Hea. Nursing Educators [15736], 10200 W 44th Ave., No. 304, Wheat Ridge, CO 80033, (303)422-0769

Assn. for Community Networking [7896], 1375 E 54th St., No. 2, Chicago, IL 60615

Assn. for Community Networking [7896], 1375 E 54th St., No. 2, Chicago, IL 60615

Assn. for Community Org. and Social Admin. [13213], 20560 Bensley Ave., Lynwood, IL 60411, (708)757-4187

Assn. of Community Organizations for Reform Now [11527], 739 8th St. SE, Washington, DC 20003

Assn. of Community Organizations for Reform Now [IO], Toronto, ON, Canada

Assn. of Community Rail Partnerships [IO], Huddersfield, United Kingdom

Assn. of Community Tribal Schools [8674], 5370 Paragon St., Rocklin, CA 95677, (916)315-0906

Assn. for Community-Wide Protection from Nuclear Attack [★5305]

Assn. for Commuter Trans. [13331], 1341 G St. NW, 10th Fl., Washington, DC 20005, (202)719-5331

Assn. for Commuter Trans. [13331], 1341 G St. NW, 10th Fl., Washington, DC 20005, (202)719-5331

Assn. of Companion Animal Behavior Counselors [7632], PO Box 104, Seville, FL 32190-0104, (866)224-2728

Assn. for Comparative Economic Stud. [6609], Prof. Josef Brada, Exec. Sec., Arizona State Univ., Dept. of Economics, PO Box 879801, Tempe, AZ 85287-3806

Assn. for Comparative Economics [★6609]

Assn. for Competitive Tech. [3389], 1401 K St. NW, Ste. 502, Washington, DC 20005, (202)331-2130

Assn. of Compliance Officers Netherlands Antilles [IO], Curacao, Netherlands Antilles

Assn. for Comprehensive Energy Psychology [16439], 233 E Lancaster Ave., Ste. 104, Ardmore, PA 19003, (619)861-2237

Reference to "IO" in place of a book number signifies that the association may be found in the 50th edition of International Organizations.

Assn. for Comprehensive Energy Psychology **[16439]**, 233 E Lancaster Ave., Ste. 104, Ardmore, PA 19003, (619)861-2237

Assn. for Comprehensive NeuroTherapy **[15651]**, PO Box 2198, Broken Arrow, OK 74013, (561)798-0472

Assn. of Comptrollers and Accounting Officers **[★5918]**

Assn. of Comptrollers and Accounting Officers **[★5918]**

Assn. of Computational Linguistics **[10023]**, 209 N Eighth St., Stroudsburg, PA 18360-1721, (570)476-8006

Assn. of Computational Linguistics **[10023]**, 209 N Eighth St., Stroudsburg, PA 18360-1721, (570)476-8006

Assn. for Cmpt. Aided Design in Architecture **[6444]**, Prof. Anijo Punnen Mathew, IIT Inst. of Design, 350 N Lasalle St., 4th Fl., Chicago, IL 60654

Assn. for Cmpt. Educators **[★7907]**

Assn. for Cmpt. Educators **[★7907]**

Assn. of the Cmpt. and Multimedia Indus. Malaysia **[IO]**, Petaling Jaya, Malaysia

Assn. of Cmpt. Operations Mgt. **[★6502]**

Assn. of Cmpt. Professionals **[IO]**, Arlington, United Kingdom

Assn. of Cmpt. Professionals - Defunct.

Assn. of Computer Users - Defunct.

Assn. for Computers and Taxation **[3382]**, PO Box 1093, Warwick, NY 10990, (845)987-9690

Assn. for Computing Machinery **[6504]**, 2 Penn Plz., Ste. 701, New York, NY 10121-0701, (212)869-7440

Assn. for Computing Machinery | Special Interest Gp. on Algorithms and Computation Theory **[7296]**, Univ. of Washington, Dept. of Cmpt. Sci. and Engg., Box 352350, Seattle, WA 98195, (206)543-9347

Assn. for Computing Machinery | Special Interest Gp. on the APL and J Languages **[7297]**, 1515 Broadway, New York, NY 10036, (212)626-0500

Assn. for Computing Machinery | Special Interest Gp. on Cmpt. Sci. Educ. **[7903]**, 2 Penn Plz., Ste. 701, New York, NY 10121-0701, (212)869-7440

Assn. for Computing Machinery | Special Interest Gp. on Mgt. Info. Systems **[6527]**, Villanova Univ., Coll. of Commerce and Finance, 800 Lancaster Ave., Villanova, PA 19085, (610)519-4347

Assn. for Computing Machinery | Special Interest Gp. on Measurement and Evaluation **[6445]**, 1501 Page Mill Rd., Palo Alto, CA 94304, (212)626-0500

Assn. for Computing Machinery | Special Interest Group on MultiMedia **[6528]**, 2 Penn Plz., Ste. 701, New York, NY 10121-0701, (212)869-7440

Assn. for Computing Machinery | Special Interest Gp. on Security, Audit and Control **[6446]**, Purdue Univ., CS Dept., 305 N Univ. St., West Lafayette, IN 47907, (765)496-2399

Assn. for Computing Machinery | Special Interest Gp. on Software Engg. **[6480]**, Univ. of Nebraska, Dept. of Cmpt. Sci. and Engg., 256 Avery Hall, Lincoln, NE 68588-0115, (402)472-2186

Assn. for Computing Machinery | Special Interest Gp. for Symbolic and Algebraic Manipulation **[7069]**, PO Box 352, Crawfordsville, IN 47933-0352, (765)361-6354

Assn. of Concerned African Scholars **[17147]**, Northern Arizona Univ., Flagstaff, AZ 86011

Assn. of Concerned African Scholars **[17147]**, Northern Arizona Univ., Flagstaff, AZ 86011

Assn. of Concerned Citizens **[★18961]**

Assn. of Concert Bands **[10164]**, Nada Vencl Montgomery, Sec., 6613 Cheryl Ann Dr., Independence, OH 44131-3718, (800)726-8720

Assn. of Concert Bands of Am. **[★10164]**

Assn. of Conductors in the Netherlands **[IO]**, Arnhem, Netherlands

Assn. of Confectionery Indus. **[IO]**, Buenos Aires, Argentina

Assn. for Conferences and Events **[IO]**, Huntingdon, United Kingdom

Assn. for Configuration and Data Mgt. **[6969]**, PO Box 58888, Salt Lake City, UT 84158-0888, (256)536-1096

Assn. for Conflict Resolution **[5203]**, 12100 Sunset Hills Rd., Ste. 130, Reston, VA 20190, (703)234-4141

Assn. for the Conservation of Energy **[IO]**, London, United Kingdom

Assn. of Conservation Engineers **[4001]**, Kathy Dillmon, Sec., Wyoming Game & Fish U.S. Department of, 5400 Bishop Blvd., Cheyenne, WY 82006

Assn. for Conservation Info. **[4002]**, Robert L. Wines, Treas., 149 State Park Trail, Roanoke, WV 26447, (304)269-0440

Assn. des Consommateurs du Canada **[★IO]**

Assn. for Consortium Leadership **[8228]**, Virginia Tidewater Consortium for Higher Educ., 4900 Powhatan Ave., Norfolk, VA 23508-1836, (757)683-3183

Assn. des Constructeurs Europeens de Motocycles **[★IO]**

Assn. of Constr. Inspectors **[1914]**, PO Box 879, Palm Springs, CA 92263, (760)327-5284

Assn. of Constr. Material Producers of Estonia **[IO]**, Tallinn, Estonia

Assn. of Constr. Proj. Managers **[IO]**, Benmore, Republic of South Africa

Assn. for Constructivist Teaching **[8943]**, Dr. Brenda Fyfe, Webster Univ., School of Educ., 470 E Lockwood Ave., St. Louis, MO 63119-3141

Assn. des Constructuers Europeens d'Automobiles **[★IO]**

Assn. for Consultancy and Engg. **[IO]**, London, United Kingdom

Assn. of Consultant Architects **[IO]**, Bromley, United Kingdom

Assn. of Consultants in Access - Australia **[IO]**, Herne Hill, Australia

Assn. des Consultants et des Laboratoires Experts **[★IO]**

Assn. of Consulting Actuaries **[IO]**, London, United Kingdom

Assn. of Consulting Architects - Australia **[IO]**, Melbourne, Australia

Assn. of Consulting Chemists and Chem. Engineers **[6399]**, PO Box 297, Sparta, NJ 07871-0297, (973)729-6671

Assn. of Consulting Engineers of Australia - New South Wales **[IO]**, St. Leonards, Australia

Assn. of Consulting Engineers of Australia - Northern Territory **[IO]**, Marden, Australia

Assn. of Consulting Engineers of Australia - South Australia **[IO]**, Marden, Australia

Assn. of Consulting Engineers of Australia - Tasmania **[IO]**, Southbank, Australia

Assn. of Consulting Engineers of Australia - Victoria **[IO]**, Southbank, Australia

Assn. of Consulting Engineers of Botswana **[IO]**, Gaborone, Botswana

Assn. of Consulting Engineers of Canada **[IO]**, Ottawa, ON, Canada

Assn. of Consulting Engineers of Ireland **[IO]**, Dublin, Ireland

Assn. of Consulting Engineers of Kenya **[IO]**, Nairobi, Kenya

Assn. of Consulting Engineers of Malaysia **[IO]**, Kuala Lumpur, Malaysia

Assn. of Consulting Engineers of Namibia **[IO]**, Windhoek, Namibia

Assn. of Consulting Engineers of New Zealand **[IO]**, Wellington, New Zealand

Assn. of Consulting Engineers of Nigeria **[IO]**, Lagos, Nigeria

Assn. of Consulting Engineers, Norway **[IO]**, Oslo, Norway

Assn. of Consulting Engineers of Pakistan **[IO]**, Karachi, Pakistan

Assn. of Consulting Engineers of Zambia **[IO]**, Lusaka, Zambia

Assn. of Consulting Foresters **[★4388]**

Assn. of Consulting Foresters of Am. **[4388]**, 312 Montgomery St., Ste. 208, Alexandria, VA 22314, (703)548-0990

Assn. of Consulting Mgt. Engineers **[★2270]**

Assn. of Consulting Scientists **[IO]**, West Midlands, United Kingdom

Assn. for Consumer Res. **[17443]**, Univ. of Minnesota Duluth, Labovitz School of Bus. and Economics, 11 E Superior St., Ste. 210, Duluth, MN 55802, (218)726-7853

Assn. for Consumer Res. **[17443]**, Univ. of Minnesota Duluth, Labovitz School of Bus. and Economics, 11 E Superior St., Ste. 210, Duluth, MN 55802, (218)726-7853

Assn. for Consumer Trends **[17444]**, 7076 Drinkard Way, Mechanicsville, VA 23111, (804)559-6519

Assn. of Contact Lens Mfrs. **[IO]**, Devizes, United Kingdom

Assn. of Container Reconditioners **[★888]**

Assn. for Contextual Behavioral Sci. **[6250]**, 42398 Haltom Rd., Hammond, LA 70403, (269)267-4249

Assn. for Continence Advice **[IO]**, Bathgate, United Kingdom

Assn. for Continuing Dental Educ.

Assn. for Continuing Dental Educ. - Address unknown since 2011.

Assn. for Continuing Education - Defunct.

Assn. for Continuing Educ. | Senior Scholars **[7922]**, Off. of Continuing Educ., 341 Sears Bldg., CASE, 10900 Euclid Ave., Cleveland, OH 44106-7116, (216)368-2090

Assn. for Continuing Higher Educ. **[7923]**, OCCE Admin Bldg., Rm. 233, 1700 Asp Ave., Norman, OK 73072, (405)329-0249

Assn. for Continuing Legal Educ. **[8501]**, PO Box 4646, Austin, TX 78765, (512)453-4340

Assn. of Continuing Legal Educ. Administrators **[★8501]**

Assn. for Contract Textiles **[3437]**, PO Box 101981, Fort Worth, TX 76185, (817)924-8048

Assn. of Contract Tribal Schools **[★8674]**

Assn. of Convenience Stores **[IO]**, Farnborough, United Kingdom

Assn. for Convention Marketing Executives **[1739]**, 204 E St., NE, Washington, DC 20002, (202)547-8030

Assn. for Convention Operations Mgt. **[2444]**, 191 Clarksville Rd., Princeton Junction, NJ 08550, (609)799-3712

Assn. for Convention Operations Mgt. **[2444]**, 191 Clarksville Rd., Princeton Junction, NJ 08550, (609)799-3712

Assn. of Conveyor and Material Preparation Equip. Mfrs. **[★1818]**

Assn. of Convulsive Therapy

Assn. for Convulsive Therapy - Address unknown since 2011.

Assn. of Cooking Schools **[★1444]**

Assn. of Cooking Schools **[★1444]**

Assn. of Cooperation in Tunisia **[IO]**, Tunis, Tunisia

Assn. de Cooperation en Tunisie **[★IO]**

Assn. of Cooperative Educators **[7931]**, Sarah Pike, 29630-109th Ave. N, Hanover, MN 55341, (763)432-2032

Assn. of Cooperative Educators **[7931]**, Sarah Pike, 29630-109th Ave. N, Hanover, MN 55341, (763)432-2032

Assn. of Cooperative Lib. Organizations **[★9974]**

Assn. for the Coordination of Univ. Religious Affairs **[★8905]**

Assn. for Core Texts and Courses **[8514]**, Saint Mary's Coll. of California, 1928 St. Mary's Rd., Moraga, CA 94556, (925)631-8597

Assn. for Core Texts and Courses **[8514]**, Saint Mary's Coll. of California, 1928 St. Mary's Rd., Moraga, CA 94556, (925)631-8597

Assn. for Corporate Computing Tech. Professionals **[★6515]**

Assn. for Corporate Computing Tech. Professionals **[★6515]**

Assn. of Corporate Contributions Professionals **[961]**, 1150 Hungryneck Blvd., Mount Pleasant, SC 29464, (843)216-3442

Assn. of Corporate Counsel **[5345]**, 1025 Connecticut Ave. NW, Ste. 200, Washington, DC 20036-5425, (202)293-4103

Assn. for Corporate Growth **[643]**, 71 S Wacker Dr., Ste. 2760, Chicago, IL 60606, (312)957-4260

Assn. for Corporate Growth and Diversification **[★643]**

Assn. for Corporate Growth - Toronto Chap. **[IO]**, Toronto, ON, Canada

Assn. of Corporate Travel Executives **[3551]**, 515 King St., Ste. 440, Alexandria, VA 22314, (703)683-5322

Assn. of Corporate Treasurers **[IO]**, London, United Kingdom

Assn. of Corporate Treasurers Singapore **[IO]**, Singapore, Singapore

---

A star before a book entry number signifies that the name is not listed separately, but is mentioned within the entry.

Assn. of Corporate Treasurers of Southern Africa [IO], Cresta, Republic of South Africa

Assn. of Correctional Food Ser. Affiliates [1442], 210 N Glenoaks Blvd., Ste. C, Burbank, CA 91502, (818)843-6608

Assn. of Correctional Food Ser. Affiliates [1442], 210 N Glenoaks Blvd., Ste. C, Burbank, CA 91502, (818)843-6608

Assn. of Cosmetics and Perfume Mfrs., Importers and Distributors [IO], Geneva, Switzerland

Assn. of Cost Engineers [IO], Sandbach, United Kingdom

Assn. Costarricense de Taekwondo [IO], San Jose, Costa Rica

Assn. of Coun. Secretaries [★19661]

Assn. of Coun. Secretaries and Solicitors [IO], Horsham, United Kingdom

Assn. for Counselling at Work [IO], Lutterworth, United Kingdom

Assn. for Counselor Educ. and Supervision [7939], 5999 Stevenson Ave., Alexandria, VA 22304, (703)212-2237

Assn. for Counselors and Educators in Govt. [11669], 5999 Stevenson Ave., Alexandria, VA 22304-3300, (800)347-6647

Assn. for Couples in Marriage Enrichment [12436], PO Box 21374, Winston-Salem, NC 27120, (336)724-1526

Assn. of Coupon Professionals [3095], 1051 Pontiac Rd., PO Box 512, Drexel Hill, PA 19026, (610)789-1478

Assn. for Craft Producers [IO], Kathmandu, Nepal

Assn. for Crafts and Creative Industries - Defunct.

Assn. for Creative Change - Defunct.

Assn. of Credit Card Investigators [★5600]

Assn. of Credit Card Investigators [★5600]

Assn. of Credit Union Internal Auditors [995], 815 King St., Ste. 308, Alexandria, VA 22314, (703)535-5757

Assn. of Cricket Statisticians and Historians [IO], Cardiff, United Kingdom

Assn. for Crime Scene Reconstruction [11682], Matthew Noedel, Treas., 4227 S Meridian, No. 583, Puyallup, WA 98373, (253)227-5880

Assn. of Cuban Engineers [6784], PO Box 557575, Miami, FL 33255-7575

Assn. for Cultural Economics Intl. [6610], Neil Alper, Acting Exec. Sec.-Treas., Northeastern Univ., Dept. of Economics, Boston, MA 02115, (617)373-2839

Assn. for Cultural Economics Intl. [6610], Neil Alper, Acting Exec. Sec.-Treas., Northeastern Univ., Dept. of Economics, Boston, MA 02115, (617)373-2839

Assn. for Cultural Evolution [9523], PO Box 2382, Mill Valley, CA 94942, (415)409-3220

Assn. for Cultural Exchange, ACE Cultural Tours [IO], Cambridge, United Kingdom

Assn. of Cultural Executives [IO], Waterloo, ON, Canada

Association of Cultural Mythologists - Defunct.

Assn. Culturelle Suisse d'Aikido, Aïkikai Suisse [IO], Illnau-Effretikon, Switzerland

Assn. Cuore-Vita of the Republic of San Marino [IO], San Marino, San Marino

Assn. of the Customs Bar [★5388]

Assn. of the Customs Bar [★5388]

Assn. of Customs Brokers of Kazakhstan [IO], Almaty, Kazakhstan

Assn. of Cycle Traders [IO], Hove, United Kingdom

Assn. of Cytogenetic Technologists [★6292]

Assn. of Czech Advt. Agencies and Marketing Commun. [IO], Prague, Czech Republic

Assn. of Czech Insurance Brokers [IO], Prague, Czech Republic

Assn. canadienne des producteurs d'acier [★IO]

Assn. suisse d'action pour les juifs de l'ancienne Union societique [★IO]

Assn. canadienne d'agri-marketing - Alberta [★IO]

Assn. canadienne d'agri-marketing - Manitoba [★IO]

Assn. canadienne d'agri-marketing - Saskatchewan [★IO]

Assn. for Dance Movement Psychotherapy - United Kingdom [IO], Torquay, United Kingdom

Assn. of Danish Advertisers [IO], Frederiksberg, Denmark

Assn. of Danish Bus. Economists [IO], Copenhagen, Denmark

Assn. of Danish Cosmetics, Toiletries, Soap and Detergent Indus. [IO], Copenhagen, Denmark

Assn. of Danish Energy Companies [IO], Frederiksberg, Denmark

Assn. of Danish Fish Processing Indus. and Exporters [IO], Copenhagen, Denmark

Assn. of Danish Fruit and Vegetables Indus. [IO], Copenhagen, Denmark

Assn. of Danish Landscape Architects [IO], Copenhagen, Denmark

Assn. of Danish Lawyers and Economists [IO], Copenhagen, Denmark

Assn. of Danish Oil and Oilseed Processors [IO], Arhus, Denmark

Assn. of Danish Pharmacists [IO], Copenhagen, Denmark

Assn. of Danish Physiotherapists [IO], Copenhagen, Denmark

Assn. of Danish Res. Libraries [IO], Arhus, Denmark

Assn. of Danish Shoe Retailers [IO], Hellerup, Denmark

Assn. of Danish Travel Agents [IO], Copenhagen, Denmark

Assn. canadienne d'archeologie [★IO]

Assn. of Dark Leaf Tobacco Dealers and Exporters - Address unknown since 2010.

Assn. internationale des critiques d'art - Irlande [★IO]

Assn. d'assurances du Barreau canadien [★IO]

Assn. des courtiers d'assurances du Canada [★IO]

Assn. for Data Center, Networking and Enterprise Systems [★6502]

Assn. of the Deaf in Israel [IO], Tel Aviv, Israel

Assn. of Deans of Amer. Colleges of Veterinary Medicine [★9033]

Assn. of Deans of Pharmacy of Canada [IO], Saskatoon, SK, Canada

Assn. for Death Educ. and Counseling [11745], 111 Deer Lake Rd., Ste. 100, Deerfield, IL 60015, (847)509-0403

Assn. canadienne des directeurs d'ecole [★IO]

Assn. D'Editeurs de la Press Libre et Independante [IO], Libreville, Gabon

Assn. in Defence of the Wrongly Convicted [IO], Toronto, ON, Canada

Assn. of Defense Communities [5533], 734 15th St. NW, Ste. 900, Washington, DC 20005, (202)822-5256

Assn. of Defense Trial Attorneys [5548], 4135 Topsail Trail, New Port Richey, FL 34652, (727)859-0350

Assn. of Defensive Spray Mfrs. [3229], 906 Olive St., Ste. 1200, St. Louis, MO 63101-1448, (314)241-1445

Assn. of Democratic Pharmacists [IO], Hamburg, Germany

Assn. for Democratic Prosperity ZID [IO], Podgorica, Montenegro

Assn. Dentair Canadienne [★IO]

Assn. Dentaire Francaise [IO], Paris, France

Assn. of Dental Dealers in Europe [IO], Bern, Switzerland

Assn. for Dental Educ. in Europe [IO], Dublin, Ireland

Assn. of Departments of English [8130], 26 Broadway, 3rd Fl., New York, NY 10004-1789, (646)576-5130

Assn. of Departments of English in Amer. Colleges and Universities [★8130]

Assn. of Departments of Foreign Languages [8467], 26 Broadway, 3rd Fl., New York, NY 10004, (646)576-5140

Assn. d'equipement du transport canadienne [★IO]

Assn. of Dermato-Venerologists of Latvia [IO], Riga, Latvia

Assn. of Dermatology Administrators and Managers [14323], 1120 G St. NW, Ste. 1000, Washington, DC 20005, (866)480-3573

Assn. Des Banquiers Prives Suisses [★IO]

Assn. Des Cooperatives Du Canada [★IO]

Assn. Des Marchands D'Art du Canada [★IO]

Assn. of Descendants of Defenders of Baltimore [★20840]

Assn. des Designers Canadiens [★IO]

Assn. of Desk and Derrick Clubs [2642], 5153 E 51st St., Ste. 107, Tulsa, OK 74135, (918)622-1749

Assn. of Desk and Derrick Clubs of North Am. [★2642]

Assn. of Destination Mgt. Executives [3552], PO Box 2307, Dayton, OH 45401-2307, (937)586-3727

Assn. of Destination Mgt. Executives [3552], PO Box 2307, Dayton, OH 45401-2307, (937)586-3727

Assn. d'etudes canadiennes [★IO]

Assn. d'Etudes Baha'ies [★IO]

Assn. d'Etudes Politiques Transeuropeennes [★IO]

Assn. d'Europe des Etudes feministes internationales [★IO]

Assn. for the Development of Aerospace Medicine [IO], Montreal, QC, Canada

Assn. for the Development of Children's Residential Facilities [IO], Dartmouth, NS, Canada

Assn. for the Development of Educ. in Africa [IO], Tunis, Tunisia

Assn. of Development Financing Institutions in Asia and the Pacific [IO], Makati City, Philippines

Assn. for the Development of Human Potential [9833], 406 S Coeur d'Alene St., No. T, Spokane, WA 99204, (509)838-3575

Assn. for Development and Innovation of the Furniture Indus. [IO], Paris, France

Assn. for the Development of Intl. Exchange of Food and Agricultural Productions and Techniques [IO], Paris, France

Assn. for the Development of Microenterprise [IO], Santo Domingo, Dominican Republic

Assn. for the Development of Pakistan [12601], PO Box 2492, San Francisco, CA 94126

Assn. pour le Developpement des Echanges Electroniques Professionnels [★IO]

Assn. pour le Developpement des Echanges Internationaux de Produits et Techniques Agro-Alimentaires [★IO]

Assn. d'Experts Europeens du Batiment et de la Constr. [★IO]

Assn. des grands parcs d'expositions europeens [★IO]

Assn. des Diabetiques en Centrafrique [★IO]

Assn. of Diesel Specialists [1180], 400 Admiral Blvd., Kansas City, MO 64106, (816)285-0810

Assn. of Diesel Specialists [1180], 400 Admiral Blvd., Kansas City, MO 64106, (816)285-0810

Assn. d'information sur l'allergie et l'asthme [★IO]

Assn. d'Instituts Europeens de Conjoncture Economique [★IO]

Assn. of Diplomates of the Amer. Bd. of Oral Surgery [★16004]

Assn. of Diplomates of the Amer. Bd. of Oral Surgery [★16004]

Assn. des Diplomes de l'Ecole des Hautes Etudes Commerciales [★IO]

Assn. des Diplomes de Polytechnique [★IO]

Assn. for Direct Instruction [8001], PO Box 10252, Eugene, OR 97440, (541)485-1293

Assn. of Direct Marketing Agencies [★2400]

Assn. of Directors of Children's Services [IO], Manchester, United Kingdom

Assn. of Directors of Geriatric Academic Programs [14661], Erin Corley, Sr., Coor., 40 Fulton St., 18th Fl., New York, NY 10038, (212)308-1414

Assn. for Directors of Radiation Oncology Programs [16512], 8280 Willow Oaks Corporate Dr., Ste. 500, Fairfax, VA 22031, (703)502-1550

Assn. of Directors of Social Work [IO], Edinburgh, United Kingdom

Assn. of Dir. Marketing [2389], 1187 Thorn Run Rd., Ste. 630, Moon Township, PA 15108-3198

Assn. of Dir. Publishers [2921], PO Box 1929, Traverse City, MI 49685-1929, (800)267-9002

Assn. for disAbility and Development [IO], Male, Maldives

Assn. of Disabled Professionals [IO], London, United Kingdom

Assn. of Dissatisfied Candidates of Afghanistan [IO], Kabul, Afghanistan

Assn. des Distillateurs Canadiens [★IO]

Assn. of Dive Prog. Administrators [22538], 225 Baker St., Atlanta, GA 30313, (404)581-4310

Assn. of Diving Contractors [★903]

Assn. of Diving Contractors [★903]

Assn. of Diving Contractors Intl. [903], 5206 FM 1960 W, Ste. 202, Houston, TX 77069-4406, (281)893-8388

Reference to "IO" in place of a book number signifies that the association may be found in the 50th edition of International Organizations.

Encyclopedia of Associations, 51st Edition   2585

Assn. of Diving Contractors Intl. **[903]**, 5206 FM 1960 W, Ste. 202, Houston, TX 77069-4406, (281)893-8388

Assn. of Divorce Financial Planners **[1335]**, 514 Fourth St., East Northport, NY 11731, (631)754-6125

Assn. Djiboutienne pour l'Equilibre et la Promotion de la Famille **[IO]**, Djibouti, Djibouti

Assn. of Doctors for the Env. I ISDE Italy **[IO]**, Arezzo, Italy

Assn. of Donor Relations Professionals **[12657]**, Syracuse Univ., 200 Eggers Hall, Syracuse, NY 13244, (315)443-5056

Assn. for Downloadable Media **[2436]**, 611 Pennsylvania Ave. SE, No. 164, Washington, DC 20003-4303

Assn. des Doyens de Pharmacie du Canada **[★IO]**

Assn. of Drainage Authorities **[IO]**, Manby, United Kingdom

Assn. for Dressings and Sauces **[1377]**, 1100 Johnson Ferry Rd., Ste. 300, Atlanta, GA 30342, (404)252-3663

Assn. of Drilled Shaft Contractors **[★894]**

Assn. of Drilled Shaft Contractors **[★894]**

Assn. of Driver Educators for the Disabled **[★7978]**

Assn. of Driver Educators for the Disabled **[★7978]**

Assn. for Driver Rehabilitation Specialists; ADED: The **[7978]**

Assn. for Driver Rehabilitation Specialists; ADED: The **[7978]**

Assn. de Droit Intl. **[★IO]**

Assn. pour le Droit de Mourir dans la Dignite **[★IO]**

Assn. of Ductwork Contractors and Allied Services **[IO]**, Reading, United Kingdom

Assn. canadienne des professeures et professeurs d'universite **[★IO]**

Assn. of the Dutch Adhesive Indus. **[IO]**, Leidschendam, Netherlands

Assn. of Dutch Businessmen in Singapore **[IO]**, Singapore, Singapore

Assn. of the Dutch Chem. Indus. **[IO]**, Leidschendam, Netherlands

Assn. of Dutch Designers **[IO]**, Amsterdam, Netherlands

Assn. of Dutch Fruit and Vegetable Exporters **[IO]**, The Hague, Netherlands

Assn. of Dutch Poultry Processing Indus. **[IO]**, Houten, Netherlands

Assn. of the Dutch Univ. Libraries and the Royal Lib. **[IO]**, The Hague, Netherlands

Assn. of Dutch Wholesalers in Paint **[IO]**, Leidschendam, Netherlands

Assn. of Early Intervention for Children with Special Needs **[IO]**, Mina Al Fahal, Oman

Assn. of Earth Sci. Editors **[2808]**, Mary Ann Schmidt, 554 Chess St., Pittsburgh, PA 15205-3212

Assn. of Earth Sci. Editors **[2808]**, Mary Ann Schmidt, 554 Chess St., Pittsburgh, PA 15205-3212

Assn. of East Asian Res. Universities **[IO]**, Hong Kong, People's Republic of China

Assn. of Eastern Foresters **[★4405]**

Assn. Echecs et Maths **[★IO]**

Assn. des Ecoles de Sante Publique de la Regional Europeenne **[★IO]**

Assn. of Ecological not-for-profit Organizations of Turkmenistan **[IO]**, Ashgabat, Turkmenistan

Assn. of Economic Poisons Control Officials **[★5888]**

Assn. of Economic Sci. Institutions **[IO]**, Moscow, Russia

Assn. des Economistes de l'Energie **[★IO]**

Assn. Ecosystem **[IO]**, Moscow, Russia

Assn. of Ecosystem Res. Centers **[4193]**, Robin Graham, Sec., Environmental Sciences Div., Oak Ridge Natl. Lab., PO Box 2008, Oak Ridge, TN 37831, (865)576-7756

L'Association des Ecrivains Italo Canadiens **[★IO]**

Assn. of Edison Illuminating Companies **[3590]**, Earl B. Parsons, Jr., Exec. Dir./Sec.-Treas., PO Box 2641, Birmingham, AL 35291, (205)257-2530

Assn. des Editeurs Belges **[★IO]**

Assn. des Editeurs de la Presse Privee du Mali **[IO]**, Bamako, Mali

Assn. of Editorial Businesses - Defunct.

Assn. for the Educ. of Children with Medical Needs **[7836]**, 7065 Hillgreen Dr., Dallas, TX 75214, (214)456-5930

Assn. for Educ. Finance and Policy **[8096]**, Susanna Loeb, Pres., 524 Ceras, 520 Galvez Mall, Stanford, CA 94305, (650)736-1258

Assn. for Educ. in Healthcare Info. Tech. **[15369]**, 401 N Michigan Ave., Ste. 2400, Chicago, IL 60611, (312)321-6839

Assn. for Educ. in Intl. Bus. **[★7781]**

Assn. for Educ. in Intl. Bus. **[★7781]**

Assn. for Educ. in Journalism **[★8437]**

Assn. for Educ. in Journalism and Mass Commun. **[8437]**, 234 Outlet Pointe Blvd., Columbia, SC 29210-5667, (803)798-0271

Assn. of Educ. Practitioners and Provider **[★8947]**

Assn. for Educ. and Rehabilitation of the Blind and Visually Impaired **[17065]**, 1703 N Beauregard St., Ste. 440, Alexandria, VA 22311, (703)671-4500

Assn. for the Educ. of Teachers in Sci. **[★8944]**

Assn. for Educ. in World Govt. **[★17711]**

Assn. for Educ. in World Govt. **[★17711]**

Assn. for Educational Activity **[IO]**, Helsinki, Finland

Assn. for Educational Communications and Tech. **[8304]**, 1800 N Stonelake Dr., Ste. 2, Bloomington, IN 47404, (812)335-7675

Assn. for Educational Development - Defunct.

Assn. of Educational Negotiators **[★23182]**

Assn. of Educational Psychologists **[IO]**, Durham, United Kingdom

Assn. of Educational Publishers **[8744]**, 300 Martin Luther King Blvd., Ste. 200, Wilmington, DE 19801, (302)295-8350

Assn. Educative des Amateurs d'Astronomie du Centre **[IO]**, Orleans, France

Assn. of Educators of Gifted Children **[★8215]**

Assn. of Educators for Homebound and Hospitalized Children **[★11788]**

Assn. of Educators for Homebound and Hospitalized Children **[★8879]**

Assn. of Educators for Homebound and Hospitalized Children **[★11788]**

Assn. of Educators in Imaging and Radiologic Sciences **[8834]**, PO Box 90204, Albuquerque, NM 87199-0204, (505)823-4740

Assn. of Educators in Private Practice **[★8947]**

Assn. of Educators in Radiological Sciences **[★8834]**

Assn. of Electoral Administrators **[IO]**, Liverpool, United Kingdom

Assn. of Elecl. Contractors - Ireland **[IO]**, Celbridge, Ireland

Assn. for Elecl., Electronic and Info. Technologies **[IO]**, Frankfurt, Germany

Assn. of Elecl. Engineers in Finland **[IO]**, Helsinki, Finland

Assn. of Elecl. and Mech. Trades **[IO]**, York, United Kingdom

Assn. of Electricity Producers **[IO]**, London, United Kingdom

Assn. for Electronic Hea. Care Transactions - Address unknown since 2011.

Assn. for Electronics Mfg. of the Soc. of Mfg. Engineers **[★6673]**

Assn. for Electronics Mfg. of the Soc. of Mfg. Engineers **[★6673]**

Assn. of the Electrotechnical Indus. of the Slovak Republic **[IO]**, Bratislava, Slovakia

Assn. des Eleveurs Ayrshire du Canada **[★IO]**

Assn. of Emergency Physicians **[14463]**, 911 Whitewater Dr., Mars, PA 16046, (866)772-1818

Assn. for Emissions Control by Catalyst **[IO]**, Brussels, Belgium

Assn. of Energy Engineers **[6693]**, 4025 Pleasantdale Rd., Ste. 420, Atlanta, GA 30340, (770)447-5083

Assn. of Energy Engineers **[6693]**, 4025 Pleasantdale Rd., Ste. 420, Atlanta, GA 30340, (770)447-5083

Assn. of Energy Engineers, Bulgaria/Sofia **[IO]**, Sofia, Bulgaria

Assn. of Energy Engineers, Poland/Czestochowa **[IO]**, Czestochowa, Poland

Assn. of Energy Engineers, Poland/Warsaw **[IO]**, Warsaw, Poland

Assn. of Energy Engineers, West Georgia Chap. **[IO]**, Batumi, Georgia

Assn. of Energy and Environmental Real Estate Professionals **[8150]**, 3082 Evergreen Pkwy., Ste. H, Evergreen, CO 80439, (303)674-7770

Assn. of Energy Ser. Companies **[2643]**, 14531 FM 529, Ste. 250, Houston, TX 77095, (713)781-0758

Assn. of Energy Services Professionals **[6694]**, 15215 S 48th St., Ste. 170, Phoenix, AZ 85044, (480)704-5900

Assn. of Energy Services Professionals **[6694]**, 15215 S 48th St., Ste. 170, Phoenix, AZ 85044, (480)704-5900

Assn. for Engg. Graphics and Imaging Systems - Address unknown since 2010.

Assn. of Enrolled Agents **[★6015]**

Assn. for Enterprise Info. **[644]**, 2111 Wilson Blvd., Ste. 400, Arlington, VA 22201, (703)247-9474

Assn. for Enterprise Integration **[★644]**

Assn. for Enterprise Opportunity **[3284]**, 1111 16th St. NW, Ste. 410, Washington, DC 20036, (202)650-5580

Assn. for Entertainment Marketing Agencies **[1189]**, 110 S Fairfax Ave. A11, No. 183, Los Angeles, CA 90036

Assn. for Env. Conscious Building **[IO]**, Llandysul, United Kingdom

Assn. for Environmental Archaeology **[IO]**, Plymouth, United Kingdom

Assn. of Environmental and Engg. Geologists **[6911]**, PO Box 460518, Denver, CO 80246, (303)757-2926

Assn. of Environmental Engg. Professors **[★8757]**

Assn. of Environmental Engg. and Sci. Professors **[8757]**, 2303 Naples Ct., Champaign, IL 61822, (217)398-6969

Assn. of Environmental Hea. Academic Programs **[4327]**, 8620 Roosevelt Way NE, Ste. A, Seattle, WA 98115, (206)522-5272

Assn. for Environmental Hea. and Sciences **[4924]**, 150 Fearing St., Amherst, MA 01002, (413)549-5170

Assn. of Environmental and Rsrc. Economists **[4003]**, Iowa State Univ., Dept. of Economics, 568 Heady Hall, Ames, IA 50011-1070, (515)294-5767

Assn. of Episcopal Colleges **[8162]**, Colleges and Universities of the Anglican Communion, 815 2nd Ave., New York, NY 10017-4594, (212)716-6148

Assn. of Episcopal Colleges **[8162]**, Colleges and Universities of the Anglican Communion, 815 2nd Ave., New York, NY 10017-4594, (212)716-6148

Assn. for Episcopal Deacons **[19692]**, Executive Off. , PO Box 160, Bettendorf, IA 52722-0003, (563)359-0541

Assn. of Equip. Lessors **[★3078]**

Assn. of Equip. Lessors **[★3078]**

Assn. of Equip. Mgt. Professionals **[1807]**, PO Box 1368, Glenwood Springs, CO 81602-1368, (970)384-0510

Assn. of Equip. Mgt. Professionals **[1807]**, PO Box 1368, Glenwood Springs, CO 81602-1368, (970)384-0510

Assn. Equip. Mfrs. **[166]**, 6737 W Washington St., Ste. 2400, Milwaukee, WI 53214, (414)272-0943

Assn. of Equip. Mfrs. **[166]**, 6737 W Washington St., Ste. 2400, Milwaukee, WI 53214, (414)272-0943

Assn. of Equip. Mfrs. I AEM Marketing Coun. **[2390]**, 6737 W Washington St., Ste. 2400, Milwaukee, WI 53214-5647, (414)298-4146

Assn. of Equip. Mfrs. - Canada **[IO]**, Ottawa, ON, Canada

Assn. Espanola de Constructores de Maquinaria Textil **[★IO]**

Assn. Espanola de Esclerosis Lateral Amiotrofica **[★IO]**

Assn. of Estonian Broadcasters **[IO]**, Tallinn, Estonia

Assn. of the Estonian Food Indus. **[IO]**, Tallinn, Estonia

Assn. des Etats Genereaux des Etudiants de l'Europe **[IO]**, Brussels, Belgium

Assn. des Etudiantes Infirmiereres du Canada **[★IO]**

Assn. des Etudiants en Pharmacie au Rwanda **[★IO]**

Assn. of European Adhesives Mfrs. **[IO]**, Brussels, Belgium

A star before a book entry number signifies that the name is not listed separately, but is mentioned within the entry.

Assn. of European Airlines [IO], Brussels, Belgium

Assn. of European Border Regions [IO], Gronau, Germany

Assn. of European Building Surveyors and Constr. Experts [IO], London, United Kingdom

Assn. of European Businesses [IO], Moscow, Russia

Assn. of European Cancer Leagues [IO], Brussels, Belgium

Assn. of European Candle Mfrs. [IO], Neuilly-sur-Seine, France

Assn. of European Chambers of Commerce and Indus. [IO], Brussels, Belgium

Assn. of European Cities Interested in Elec. Vehicles [IO], Brussels, Belgium

Assn. of European Civil Engg. Faculties [IO], Prague, Czech Republic

Assn. of European Conjuncture Institutes [IO], Louvain-la-Neuve, Belgium

Assn. of European Election Officials [IO], Budapest, Hungary

Assn. of European Gas Meter Mfrs. [IO], Nivelles, Belgium

Assn. of European Geological Societies [IO], Essen, Germany

Assn. of European Gypsum Indus. [IO], Brussels, Belgium

Assn. of European Journalists [IO], Kraainem, Belgium

Assn. of European Mfrs. of Sporting Ammunition [IO], Rome, Italy

Assn. of European Market Res. Institutes [★18123]

Assn. of European Migration Institutions [IO], Alborg, Denmark

Assn. of European Operational Res. Societies within IFORS [IO], Brussels, Belgium

Assn. of European Operational Res. Societies within IFORS France [IO], Paris, France

Assn. of European Police Colleges [IO], Vienna, Austria

Assn. of European Producers of Steel for Packaging [IO], Brussels, Belgium

Assn. of European Psychiatrists [IO], Strasbourg, France

Assn. of European Public Postal Operators [IO], Brussels, Belgium

Assn. of European Radios [IO], Brussels, Belgium

Assn. of European Refrigeration Component Mfrs. [IO], Berlin, Germany

Assn. of European Schools of Planning [IO], Reims, France

Assn. of European Sci. and Tech. Transfer Professionals [IO], The Hague, Netherlands

Assn. of the European Self-Medication Indus. [IO], Brussels, Belgium

Assn. of the European Space Indus. [IO], Paris, France

Assn. of European Storage Battery Mfrs. [IO], Brussels, Belgium

Assn. of European Trade Mark Owners [IO], Leicester, United Kingdom

Assn. for European Transport [IO], London, United Kingdom

Assn. of European Wheel Mfrs. [IO], Ceriano Laghetto, Italy

Assn. Europeene des Centres D'Ethique Medicale [★IO]

Assn. Europeene des Galvanisateurs [★IO]

Assn. Europeene des Petites et Moyennes Entreprises du PPE [★IO]

Assn. Europeene des Pharmaciens des Hopitaux [★IO]

Assn. Europeene de Sci. Regionale [★IO]

Assn. Europeene des Sous-Officiers de Reserve [★IO]

Assn. Europeene des Universites Ecoles et Colleges d'Optometrie [★IO]

Assn. Europeenne des Academiciens Turcs Belgie [★IO]

Assn. Europeenne des Acarologistes [★IO]

Assn. Europeenne des Agents Artistiques [★IO]

Assn. Europeenne des Anthropologues Sociaux [★IO]

Assn. Europeenne de Cautionnement Mutuel [★IO]

Assn. Europeenne des Centres Anti-Poisons et de Toxicologie Clinique [★IO]

Assn. Europeenne des Centres Nationaux de Productivite [★IO]

Assn. Europeenne du Ciment [★IO]

Assn. Europeenne des Conservatoires, Academies de Musique et Musikhochschulen [★IO]

Assn. Europeenne des Constructeurs de Pompes [★IO]

Assn. Europeenne d'Anatomie Clinique [★IO]

Assn. Europeenne d'Apitherapie [★IO]

Assn. Europeenne d'Athletisme [★IO]

Assn. Europeenne d'Emballages Alimentaires a Usage Unique [★IO]

Assn. Europeenne pour la Direction du Personnel [★IO]

Assn. Europeenne pour le Droit de l'Alimentation [★IO]

Assn. Europeenne des Ecoles d' Hotelleerie et de Tourisme [★IO]

Assn. Europeenne des Editeurs d'Annuaires et Bases de Donrees [★IO]

Assn. Europeenne des Editeurs de Journaux [★IO]

Assn. Europeenne des Enseignants [★IO]

Assn. Europeenne des Enseignants [★IO]

Assn. Europeenne des Etablissements d'Enseignment Veterinaire [★IO]

Assn. Europeenne des Etudes Juives [★IO]

Assn. Europeenne des Fabricants de Composants Electroniques [★IO]

Assn. Europeenne des Femmes Pour la Recherche Theologique [★IO]

Assn. Europeenne des Festivals [★IO]

Assn. Europeenne des Gaz de Petrole Liquefies [★IO]

Assn. Europeenne des Graveurs et des Flexographes [★IO]

Assn. Europeenne des Instituts Recherche et de Formation en Matiere de Developpement [★IO]

Assn. Europeenne de Laboratoires de Teledetection [★IO]

Assn. Europeenne pour l'Administration de la Recherche Industrielle [★IO]

Assn. Europeenne de l'Asphalte [★IO]

Assn. Europeenne pour l'Etude de l'Alimentation et du Developpement de l'Enfant [★IO]

Assn. Europeenne pour l'Etude de la Population [★IO]

Assn. Europeenne de Libre-Echange [★IO]

Assn. Europeenne de l'Industrie Solaire Thermique [★IO]

L'Association Europeenne de Mgt. et Marketing Financiers [★IO]

Assn. Europeenne des Medicins des Hopitaux [★IO]

Assn. Europeenne des Musees d'Histoire des Sciences Medicales [★IO]

Assn. Europeenne des Organizations Nationales des Detaillants en Textile [★IO]

Assn. Europeenne Pour L'Information Sur Le Developpement Local [★IO]

Assn. Europeenne pour la Protection Passive contre l'Incendie [★IO]

Assn. Europeenne des Syndicats de Fabricants de Bougies et de Cierges [★IO]

Assn. Europeenne de Terminologie [★IO]

Assn. Europeenne Thyroide [★IO]

Assn. Europeenne de Tisseurs de Verre [★IO]

Assn. Europeenne des Vehicules Electriques Routiers [★IO]

Assn. Europeenne des Voies Vertes [★IO]

Assn. Europenne De L'Universite [★IO]

Assn. of Evangelical Friends [★19777]

Assn. of Evangelical Friends [★19777]

Assn. of Evangelical Lutheran Church [★19932]

Assn. of Evangelical Relief and Development Organizations [★20169]

Assn. of Evangelicals in Africa [IO], Nairobi, Kenya

Assn. des Evangeliques d'Afrique [★IO]

Assn. of Event Organisers [IO], Berkhamsted, United Kingdom

Assn. for Evolutionary Economics [6611], Eric Hake, Sec., Catawba Coll., 2300 W Innes St., Salisbury, NC 28144-2488, (704)637-4293

Assn. of Executive and Administrative Professionals [62], 900 S Washington St., Ste. G-13, Falls Church, VA 22046, (703)237-8616

Assn. of Executive Directors of Halls of Fame [★22984]

Assn. of Executive Recruiting Consultants [★1144]

Assn. of Executive Recruiting Consultants [★1144]

Assn. of Executive Search Consultants [1144], 12 E 41st St., 17th Fl., New York, NY 10017, (212)398-9556

Assn. of Executive Search Consultants [1144], 12 E 41st St., 17th Fl., New York, NY 10017, (212)398-9556

Assn. of Executive Secretaries [★19661]

Assn. for Experiential Educ. [8173], 3775 Iris Ave., Ste. 4, Boulder, CO 80301-2043, (303)440-8844

Assn. des Experts-Comptables Internationaux [★IO]

Assn. for Explosive Detection K-9s, Intl. [5687], PO Box 176, Aquilla, TX 76622, (386)788-4083

Assn. for Explosive Detection K-9s, Intl. [5687], PO Box 176, Aquilla, TX 76622, (386)788-4083

Assn. de Fabricants Europeens d'Accumulateurs [★IO]

Assn. des Fabricants Europeens d'Emulsifiants Alimentaires [★IO]

Assn. des Fabricants Europeens de Rubans Auto-Adhesifs [★IO]

Assn. des Fabricants, Importateurs et Fournisseurs de Produits de Cosmetique et de Parfumerie [★IO]

Assn. des Fabricants Internationaux d'Automobiles du Canada [★IO]

Assn. des Fabricants de Pates, Papiers et Cartons de Belgique [★IO]

Assn. for Facilities Engg. [6785], 12801 Worldgate Dr., Ste. 500, Herndon, VA 20170, (571)203-7171

Assn. des Facultes Dentaires du Canada [★IO]

Assn. des Facultes de Medecine du Canada [★IO]

Assn. des Facultes de Pharmacie du Canada [★IO]

Assn. of Faculties of Medicine of Canada [IO], Ottawa, ON, Canada

Assn. of Faculties of Pharmacy of Canada [IO], Vancouver, BC, Canada

Assn. des Familles Gosselin [★IO]

Assn. of Family and Conciliation Courts [5423], 6525 Grand Teton Plz., Madison, WI 53719, (608)664-3750

Assn. of Family Medicine Residency Directors [15289], 11400 Tomahawk Creek Pkwy., Ste. 670, Leawood, KS 66211-2672, (913)906-6000

Assn. of Family Practice Administrators - Address unknown since 2011.

Assn. of Family Practice Physician Assistants [14870], 1905 Woodstock Rd., Ste. 2150, Roswell, GA 30075, (770)640-7605

Assn. of Family Practice Residency Directors [★15289]

Assn. of Farmworker Opportunity Programs [12517], 1726 M St. NW, Ste. 602, Washington, DC 20036, (202)826-6006

Assn. of Fashion and Image Consultants [★858]

Assn. of Fashion and Image Consultants [★858]

Assn. of Fashion Retailers in Finland [IO], Helsinki, Finland

Assn. of Fed. Communications Consulting Engineers [7537], PO Box 19333, Washington, DC 20036

Assn. for Fed. Info. Resources Mgt. [5537], 400 N Washington St., Ste. 300, Alexandria, VA 22314, (703)778-4646

Assn. of Fed. Investigators [★5383]

Assn. des Federations Internationales Olympiques d'Ete [★IO]

Assn. des Federations Internationales des Sports d'Hiver [★IO]

Assn. Feline Canadienne [★IO]

Assn. Feminine d'Education et d'Action Sociale [★IO]

Assn. for Feminist Ethics and Social Theory [10370], Dr. Chris Frakes, Treas., 619 N Prospect St., Colorado Springs, CO 80903

Assn. des Femmes Autochtones du Canada [★IO]

Assn. des Femmes Chefs d'Entreprises du Cote d'Ivoire [IO], Abidjan, Cote d'Ivoire

Assn. des Femmes Chefs d'Entreprises du Maroc [IO], Casablanca, Morocco

Assn. des Femmes Compositeurs Canadiennes [★IO]

Assn. des Femmes d'Affaires et Chefs d'Entreprises du Benin [IO], Cotonou, Benin

Assn. des Femmes d'Affaires et Chefs d'Entreprises du Gabon [IO], Libreville, Gabon

Reference to "IO" in place of a book number signifies that the association may be found in the 50th edition of International Organizations.

Assn. des Femmes Entrepreneurs Chefs d'Entreprises [IO], Kinshasa, Republic of the Congo

Assn. des Femmes contre l'Osteoporose [IO], Neuilly-sur-Seine, France

Assn. of Feng Shui Consultants [IO], Eastwood, Australia

Assn. of Fertilizer and Phosphate Chemists [6400], PO Box 1645, Bartow, FL 33831

Assn. of Festival Organisers [IO], Matlock, United Kingdom

Assn. of Field Ornithologists [7193], Kathryn Purcell, VP, Sierra Nevada Res. Center, 2081 E Sierra Ave., Fresno, CA 93710, (559)868-6233

Assn. of Film Commissioners [★1253]

Assn. of Film Commissioners [★1253]

Assn. of Film Commissioners Intl. [1253], 2110 Artesia Blvd., Ste. 234, Redondo Beach, CA 90278, (323)461-2324

Assn. of Film Commissioners Intl. [1253], 2110 Artesia Blvd., Ste. 234, Redondo Beach, CA 90278, (323)461-2324

Assn. of Finance and Insurance Professionals [1938], PO Box 1933, Colleyville, TX 76034, (817)428-2434

Assn. of Financial Advisers [IO], Sydney, Australia

Assn. for Financial Counseling and Planning Educ. [1336], 1940 Duke St., Ste. 200, Alexandria, VA 22314, (703)684-4484

Assn. of Financial Guaranty Insurers [1939], 139 Lancaster St., Albany, NY 12210-1903, (518)449-4698

Assn. for Financial Markets in Europe [IO], London, United Kingdom

Assn. for Financial Professionals [1283], 4520 E West Hwy., Ste. 750, Bethesda, MD 20814, (301)907-2862

Assn. for Financial Tech. [63], 34 N High St., New Albany, OH 43054, (614)895-1208

Assn. of Fine Art Dealers in the Netherlands [IO], Amsterdam, Netherlands

Assn. of Finnish Advertisers [IO], Helsinki, Finland

Assn. of Finnish Furniture and Joinery Indus. [IO], Helsinki, Finland

Assn. of Finnish Music Schools [IO], Helsinki, Finland

Assn. of Finnish Pharmacies [IO], Helsinki, Finland

Assn. of Finnish Symphony Orchestras [IO], Helsinki, Finland

Assn. for Fire Ecology [4194], PO Box 1054, Redlands, CA 92373, (541)852-7903

Assn. for Fire Ecology of the Tropics [4195], Prof. Mark A. Cochrane, South Dakota State Univ., Geographic Info. Sci. Center of Excellence, Wecota Hall, 1021 Medary Ave., Brookings, SD 57007, (605)688-5353

Assn. of Firearm and Tool Mark Examiners [6864], Andy G. Smith, Membership Sec., San Francisco Police Dept., PO Box 34426, San Francisco, CA 94134, (415)671-3264

Assn. Fiscale Internationale [★IO]

Assn. of Fish and Wildlife Agencies [4004], 444 N Capitol St. NW, Ste. 725, Washington, DC 20001, (202)624-7890

Assn. of Fish and Wildlife Agencies [4004], 444 N Capitol St. NW, Ste. 725, Washington, DC 20001, (202)624-7890

Assn. of Flight Attendants [★23150]

Assn. of Flight Attendants [★23150]

Assn. of Flight Attendants - CWA [23150], 501 3rd St. NW, Washington, DC 20001, (202)434-1300

Assn. of Flight Attendants - CWA [23150], 501 3rd St. NW, Washington, DC 20001, (202)434-1300

Assn. des Fonderies Canadiennes [★IO]

Assn. of Food Distributors [★1378]

Assn. of Food and Drug Officials [5460], 2550 Kingston Rd., Ste. 311, York, PA 17402, (717)757-2888

Assn. of Food and Drug Officials of the U.S. [★5460]

Assn. of Food Indus. [1378], 3301 Rte. 66, Ste. 205, Bldg. C, Neptune, NJ 07753, (732)922-3008

Assn. of Food Indus. [IO], Paris, France

Assn. of Food Indus. Sanitarians [★2246]

Assn. of Food Journalists [2809], 7 Avenida Vista Grande, Ste. B7, No. 467, Santa Fe, NM 87508-9199, (505)466-4742

Assn. of Food Journalists [2809], 7 Avenida Vista Grande, Ste. B7, No. 467, Santa Fe, NM 87508-9199, (505)466-4742

Assn. of Football Badge Collectors [IO], Liverpool, United Kingdom

Assn. of Football Statisticians [IO], London, United Kingdom

L'Association des Forces aeriennes du Canada [★IO]

Assn. of Foreign Banks [IO], London, United Kingdom

Assn. of Foreign Investors in Real Estate [2130], Ronald Reagan Bldg., 1300 Pennsylvania Ave. NW, Washington, DC 20004, (202)312-1400

Assn. of Foreign Investors in Real Estate [2130], Ronald Reagan Bldg., 1300 Pennsylvania Ave. NW, Washington, DC 20004, (202)312-1400

Assn. of Foreign Investors in U.S. Real Estate [★2130]

Assn. of Foreign Investors in U.S. Real Estate [★2130]

Assn. of Forensic DNA Analysts and Administrators [5478], Laura Schile, Vice Chair, 3701-A S Harvard Ave., No. 212, Tulsa, OK 74135-2282

Assn. of Forensic DNA Analysts and Administrators [5478], Laura Schile, Vice Chair, 3701-A S Harvard Ave., No. 212, Tulsa, OK 74135-2282

Assn. of Forensic Document Examiners [5479], 5432 E Karen Dr., Scottsdale, AZ 85254-8205

Assn. of Forensic Document Examiners [5479], 5432 E Karen Dr., Scottsdale, AZ 85254-8205

Assn. of Forensic Quality Assurance Managers [5480], Suzanne Smith, Sec./Membership Chair, 1 Tinder Ct., Stafford, VA 22554

Assn. of Forensic Quality Assurance Managers [5480], Suzanne Smith, Sec./Membership Chair, 1 Tinder Ct., Stafford, VA 22554

Assn. of Foresters and Wood Technologists [IO], Warsaw, Poland

Assn. Forestiere Canadienne [★IO]

Assn. for Forests, Development and Conservation [IO], Beirut, Lebanon

Assn. for Formation and Activities Intercultural for Youth [IO], Madrid, Spain

Assn. pour la Formation des Enseignants en Europe [★IO]

Assn. of Former Agents of the U.S. Secret Ser. [5596], 525 SW 5th St., Ste. A, Des Moines, IA 50309, (515)282-8192

Assn. of Former Intelligence Officers [5597], 6723 Whittier Ave., Ste. 200, McLean, VA 22101-4533, (703)790-0320

Assn. of Former Intelligence Officers [5597], 6723 Whittier Ave., Ste. 200, McLean, VA 22101-4533, (703)790-0320

Assn. of Former Intl. Civil Servants [IO], Geneva, Switzerland

Assn. of Former Intl. Civil Servants - New York [5309], 1 United Nations Plz., Rm. DC1-580, New York, NY 10017, (212)963-2943

Assn. of Former Trainees of the European Union [IO], Brussels, Belgium

Assn. of Former UNESCO Staff Members [IO], Paris, France

Assn. of Former WHO Staff Members [IO], Geneva, Switzerland

Assn. for the Foundations of Sci., Language and Cognition [IO], Brussels, Belgium

Assn. Francaise des Banques [★IO]

Assn. Francaise d'Assurance Qualite en Anatomie et Cytologie Pathologiques [★IO]

Assn. Francaise d'Astronomie [IO], Paris, France

Assn. Francaise d'Etude de la Concurrence [★IO]

Assn. Francaise des Diabetiques [★IO]

Assn. Francaise des Femmes Diplomees des Universites [IO], Paris, France

Assn. Francaise de Floorball [★IO]

Assn. Francaise du Froid [★IO]

Assn. Francaise du Froid [IO], Paris, France

Assn. Francaise pour l'Etude des Sols [IO], Rennes, France

Assn. Francaise de Lutte Anti-Rhumatismale [IO], Paris, France

Assn. Francaise de Micromineralogie [★IO]

Assn. Francaise de Normalisation [★IO]

Assn. Francaise des Observateurs d'Etoiles Variables [★IO]

Assn. Francaise de Protection des Plantes [★IO]

Assn. Francaise pour la Reconnaisance et l'Interpretation des Formes [★IO]

Assn. Francaise du Syndrome de Marfan [IO], Torcy, France

Assn. Francaise des Ynglings [IO], La Rochelle, France

Assn. des malaisiens en France [★IO]

Assn. France Alzheimer [IO], Paris, France

Assn. France-Etats-Unis [★IO]

Assn. Francois-Xavier Bagnoud [IO], Geneva, Switzerland

Assn. Francophone Internationale des Directeurs d'Etablissements Scolaires [★IO]

Assn. Francophone de Mgt. de Projet [★IO]

Assn. Francophone pour le Savoir [★IO]

Assn. Francophone pour le Savoir [IO], Montreal, QC, Canada

Assn. of Fraternal Leadership and Values [23531], PO Box 1576, Fort Collins, CO 80522-1576, (970)372-1174

Assn. of Fraternity Advisors [23532], 9640 N Augusta Dr., Ste. 433, Carmel, IN 46032, (317)876-1632

Assn. of Free Community Papers [2922], 7445 Morgan Rd., Ste. 103, Liverpool, NY 13090, (877)203-2327

Assn. of Free Community Papers [2922], 7445 Morgan Rd., Ste. 103, Liverpool, NY 13090, (877)203-2327

Assn. of Free French in the U.S. - Defunct.

Assn. of Freestanding Radiation Oncology Centers [16513], 12100 Sunset Hills Rd., Ste. 130, Reston, VA 20190, (703)234-4050

Assn. for French Language Stud. [IO], Belfield, Ireland

Assn. of French-Speaking Physicians of Canada [IO], Montreal, QC, Canada

Assn. of French-Speaking Planetariums [IO], Strasbourg, France

Assn. of Friends of Classical Art [IO], Basel, Switzerland

Assn. for Frontotemporal Degeneration [15571], Radnor Sta. Bldg. No. 2, Ste. 320, 290 King of Prussia Rd., Radnor, PA 19087, (267)514-7221

Assn. for Frontotemporal Dementias [★15571]

Assn. of Fruit and Vegetable Enterprises [IO], Bishkek, Kirgizstan

Assn. of Fruit and Vegetable Inspection and Standardization Agencies [4428], Phillip Sutton, Pres., PO Box 4149, Albany, GA 31706, (229)432-9155

Assn. of Fruit and Vegetable Retailers [IO], Madrid, Spain

Assn. of Fruit and Vegetable Wholesalers [IO], Milan, Italy

Assn. of Full Gospel Women Clergy - Address unknown since 2011.

Assn. of Fund Raisers and Direct Sellers [★1537]

Assn. of Fund-Raising Distributors and Suppliers [1537], 1100 Johnson Ferry Rd., Ste. 300, Atlanta, GA 30342, (404)252-3663

Assn. of Fundraising Professionals [12049], 4300 Wilson Blvd., Ste. 300, Arlington, VA 22203, (703)684-0410

Assn. of Fundraising Professionals Edmonton and Area Chap. [IO], Spruce Grove, AB, Canada

Assn. of Fundraising Professionals Nova Scotia [IO], Halifax, NS, Canada

Assn. of Fundraising Professionals - Ottawa Chap. [IO], Ottawa, ON, Canada

Assn. Gabonaise de Medecine du Sport [IO], Libreville, Gabon

Assn. Gabonaise des Olympiens [IO], Libreville, Gabon

Assn. of Game and Puzzle Collectors [21742], PMB 321, 197M Boston Post Rd. W, Marlborough, MA 01752

Assn. of Gaming Equip. Mfrs. [1567], Marcus Prater, Exec. Dir., PO Box 50049, Henderson, NV 89016, (702)812-6932

Assn. of Gardens Trusts [IO], London, United Kingdom

A star before a book entry number signifies that the name is not listed separately, but is mentioned within the entry.

Assn. of Gastroenterologists of Bosnia and Herzegovina [IO], Sarajevo, Bosnia-Hercegovina

Assn. of Gastrointestinal Motility Disorders [14555], 12 Roberts Dr., Bedford, MA 01730, (781)275-1300

Assn. of Gastrointestinal Motility Disorders [14555], 12 Roberts Dr., Bedford, MA 01730, (781)275-1300

Assn. for Gay, Lesbian, and Bisexual Issues in Counseling [★12069]

Assn. for Gay and Lesbian Issues in Counseling [★12069]

Assn. of Gay and Lesbian Psychiatrists [12068], 4514 Chester Ave., Philadelphia, PA 19143-3707, (215)222-2800

Assn. for Gender Equity Leadership in Educ. [8164], 317 S Div. St., PMB 54, Ann Arbor, MI 48104, (734)769-2456

Assn. of Genealogists and Researchers in Archives [IO], Kent, United Kingdom

Assn. for Gen. and Liberal Stud. [8515], Ball State Univ., English Dept., RB 2109, Muncie, IN 47306, (765)285-8406

Assn. of Gen. Merchandise Chains [★3125]

Assn. Generale des Handicapes du Rwanda [IO], Kigali, Rwanda

Assn. Generale de l'Industrie du Medicame [★IO]

Assn. of Genetic Technologists [6292], PO Box 19193, Lenexa, KS 66285, (913)895-4605

Assn. of Geographic Info. [IO], London, United Kingdom

Assn. for the Geological Collaboration in Japan [IO], Tokyo, Japan

Assn. of Geology Teachers [★8212]

Assn. of Geomorphologists of Ukraine [IO], Kiev, Ukraine

Assn. of Geotechnical and Geoenvironmental Specialists [IO], Beckenham, United Kingdom

Assn. of German Archivists [IO], Fulda, Germany

Assn. of German Coal Importers [IO], Hamburg, Germany

Assn. of German Concert Choirs [IO], Weimar, Germany

Assn. of German Dental Mfrs. [IO], Cologne, Germany

Assn. of German Elecl. Engineers [★IO]

Assn. of German Elecl. Engineers [IO], Frankfurt, Germany

Assn. of German Engineers [IO], Dusseldorf, Germany

Assn. of German Engineers - Natl. Brazil [IO], Sao Paulo, Brazil

Assn. of the German Fruit Juice Indus. [IO], Bonn, Germany

Assn. of German Home Textiles Indus. [IO], Wuppertal, Germany

Assn. of the German Hotdip Galvanizing Indus. [IO], Dusseldorf, Germany

Assn. of the German Leather Indus. [IO], Frankfurt, Germany

Assn. of German Librarians [IO], Augsburg, Germany

Assn. of the German Margarine Indus. [IO], Bonn, Germany

Assn. of German Mortgage Banks [★7047]

Assn. of German Music Dealers [IO], Bonn, Germany

Assn. of German Music Publishers [IO], Bonn, Germany

Assn. of the German Petroleum Indus. [IO], Berlin, Germany

Assn. of German Pfandbrief Banks [IO], Berlin, Germany

Assn. of the German Rubber Mfg. Indus. [IO], Frankfurt, Germany

Assn. for German Stud. in Great Britain and Ireland [IO], Leeds, United Kingdom

Assn. of the German Trade Fair Indus. [IO], Berlin, Germany

Assn. of German Transport Undertakings [IO], Cologne, Germany

Assn. of German Urologists [IO], Dusseldorf, Germany

Assn. of German Wine Experts [IO], Geisenheim, Germany

Assn. for Gerontology Educ. in Social Work - Address unknown since 2011.

Assn. for Gerontology in Higher Educ. [8213], 1220 L St. NW, Ste. 901, Washington, DC 20005-4018, (202)289-9806

Assn. of Gerontology India [IO], Varanasi, India

Assn. de Gestion Internationale Collective des Oeuvres Audiovisuelles [★IO]

Assn. of Ghana Indus. [IO], Accra, Ghana

The Assn. for the Gifted [8215], Ball State Univ., BU 109, Muncie, IN 47306, (765)285-5390

Assn. of Girl Scout Executive Staff [13017], 1601 N Bond St., Ste. 303, Naperville, IL 60563, (630)369-7781

Assn. of Girl Scout Professional Workers [★13017]

Assn. of the Glass and Ceramics Indus. of the Czech Republic [IO], Prague, Czech Republic

Assn. Global View [7785], PO Box 3324, Chico, CA 95927, (530)892-9696

Assn. Global View [7785], PO Box 3324, Chico, CA 95927, (530)892-9696

Assn. for Glycogen Storage Disease [15492], PO Box 896, Durant, IA 52747, (563)514-4022

Assn. for Gnotobiotics [4238], North Carolina State Univ., Coll. of Veterinary Medicine, 4700 Hillsborough St., Raleigh, NC 27606, (919)513-6278

Assn. of Golf Merchandisers [3306], PO Box 7247, Phoenix, AZ 85011-7247, (602)604-8250

Assn. of Golf Writers [IO], Chilham, United Kingdom

Assn. for Gospel Rescue Missions [13174], 7222 Commerce Center Dr., Ste. 120, Colorado Springs, CO 80919, (719)266-8300

Assn. of Gospel Rescue Missions [13174], 7222 Commerce Center Dr., Ste. 120, Colorado Springs, CO 80919, (719)266-8300

Assn. of Governing Boards of State Universities and Allied Institutions [★7659]

Assn. of Governing Boards of Universities and Colleges [7659], 1133 20th St. NW, Ste. 300, Washington, DC 20036, (202)296-8400

Assn. of Governing Bodies of Independent Schools [IO], Welwyn, United Kingdom

Assn. of Govt. Accountants [5180], 2208 Mt. Vernon Ave., Alexandria, VA 22301-1314, (703)684-6931

Assn. of Govt. Accounts Organizations of Asia [IO], New Delhi, India

Assn. of Govt. Marketing Assistance Specialists [★1585]

Assn. of Govt. Officials in Indus. of the U.S. and Canada [★5635]

Assn. of Governmental Appraisers [★2550]

Assn. of Governmental Labor Officials [★5635]

Assn. for Governmental Leasing and Finance [5916], 19 Mantua Rd., Mount Royal, NJ 08061, (856)423-3259

Assn. of Governmental Risk Pools [5549], PO Box J, Prague, OK 74864-1045, (405)567-2611

Assn. of Grace Brethren Ministers [19355], PO Box 694, Winona Lake, IN 46590

Assn. of Graduate Careers Advisory Services [IO], Sheffield, United Kingdom

Assn. for Graduate Educ. and Res. [★8226]

Assn. of Graduate Liberal Stud. Programs [8516], Duke Univ., Box 90095, Durham, NC 27708, (919)684-1987

Assn. of Graduate Librarians of Argentina [IO], Buenos Aires, Argentina

Assn. of Graduate Recruiters [IO], Warwick, United Kingdom

Assn. of Graduate Schools - Address unknown since 2011.

Assn. of Graduates [8622], 3116 Acad. Dr., USAF Academy, CO 80840-4475, (719)472-0300

Assn. of Graduates of the School of Advanced Bus. Stud. [IO], Montreal, QC, Canada

Assn. of Graduates of the U.S. Air Force Acad. [18852], 3116 Acad. Dr., USAF Academy, CO 80840-4475, (719)472-0300

Assn. of Graphic Arts Consultants [★1628]

Assn. for Graphic Arts Training - Address unknown since 2011.

Assn. of Graphic Communications - Defunct.

Assn. of Graphic Solutions Providers; IPA - [6934]

Assn. of Graphic Solutions Providers; IPA - [6934]

Assn. for Gravestone Stud. [9670], 101 Munson St., Ste. 108, Greenfield, MA 01301, (413)772-0836

Assn. of Greek Producers of Phonograms [IO], Chalandri, Greece

Assn. of Greek Tourist Enterprises [IO], Athens, Greece

Assn. of Green Property Owners and Managers [2900], 3400 Capitol Blvd. SE, Ste. 101, Tumwater, WA 98501, (425)646-6425

Assn. des Grossistes en Medicaments du Canada [★IO]

Assn. for Gp. and Individual Psychotherapy [IO], London, United Kingdom

Assn. for Group Psychoanalysis and Process - Defunct.

Assn. of Group Travel Executives - Defunct.

Assn. of Guilds of Weavers, Spinners and Dyers [IO], Henley-on-Thames, United Kingdom

Assn. Guineenne d'Education et d'Aide aux Diabetiques [★IO]

Assn. des Haitens Vivant A L'estranger Pour Le Development [★IO]

Assn. for Haitian Amer. Development [12126], PO Box 158, Atlanta, GA 30301-0158

Assn. of Haitian Physicians Abroad [15400], 1166 Eastern Pkwy., Brooklyn, NY 11213, (718)245-1015

Assn. of Haitian Professionals [19021], PO Box 34071, Washington, DC 20043-0071

Assn. of Haitians Living Abroad for Development [IO], St. Marc, Haiti

Assn. Haitienne de Taekwondo [IO], Petionville, Haiti

Assn. of Halfway House Alcoholism Programs of North Am. [13235], 401 E Sangamon Ave., Springfield, IL 62702, (217)523-0527

Assn. of Heads of Outdoor Educ. Centres [IO], Cumbria, United Kingdom

Assn. of Hea. Care Journalists [2810], 10 Neff Hall, Columbia, MO 65211, (573)884-5606

Assn. of Hea. Care Journalists [2810], 10 Neff Hall, Columbia, MO 65211, (573)884-5606

Assn. of Hea. Fac. Licensure and Certification Directors [★5924]

Assn. of Hea. Fac. Survey Agencies [5924], 5105 Solemn Grove Rd., Garner, NC 27529

Assn. of Hea. Food Mfrs. [IO], Calw, Germany

Assn. of Hea. Insurance Advisors - Address unknown since 2011.

Assn. of Health Occupations Teacher Educators - Defunct.

Assn. of Healthcare Administrative Professionals [64], 455 S 4th St., Ste. 650, Louisville, KY 40202, (502)574-9040

Assn. for Healthcare Documentation Integrity [15318], 4230 Kiernan Ave., Ste. 130, Modesto, CA 95356, (209)527-9620

Assn. for Healthcare Foodservice [15044], 455 S Fourth St., Ste. 650, Louisville, KY 40202, (502)574-9930

Assn. for Healthcare Internal Auditors [15290], 10200 W 44th Ave., Ste. 304, Wheat Ridge, CO 80033, (303)327-7546

Assn. for Healthcare Philanthropy [15045], 313 Park Ave., Ste. 400, Falls Church, VA 22046-3303, (703)532-6243

Assn. for Healthcare Philanthropy [15045], 313 Park Ave., Ste. 400, Falls Church, VA 22046-3303, (703)532-6243

Assn. of Healthcare Philanthropy Canada [IO], Stratford, ON, Canada

Assn. of Healthcare Professionals [IO], York, United Kingdom

Assn. of Healthcare Value Anal. Professionals [14759], 1000 Westgate Dr., Ste. 252, St. Paul, MN 55114, (651)290-6288

Assn. for Healthcare Volunteer Rsrc. Professionals [13384], 155 N Wacker Dr., Ste. 400, Chicago, IL 60606-1725, (312)422-3939

Assn. of Hebrew Catholics [19386], 4120 W Pine Blvd., St. Louis, MO 63108-2802

Assn. to Help Chernobyl [IO], Nagoya, Japan

Assn. for the Help of Retarded Children [15488], 83 Maiden Ln., New York, NY 10038, (212)780-2500

Assn. for Heritage Interpretation [IO], Kent, United Kingdom

Assn. for High Tech Distribution [★1092]

Assn. of High Tech Distributors [★1092]

Assn. for High Tech. Distribution [1092], N19 W24400 Riverwood Dr., Waukesha, WI 53188, (262)696-3645

Reference to "IO" in place of a book number signifies that the association may be found in the 50th edition of International Organizations.

Assn. for Higher Educ. Access and Disability [IO], Dublin, Ireland

Assn. for Higher Educ. and Development [IO], Ottawa, ON, Canada

Assn. on Higher Educ. and Disability [7970], 107 Commerce Center Dr., Ste. 204, Huntersville, NC 28078, (704)947-7779

Assn. on Higher Educ. and Disability [7970], 107 Commerce Center Dr., Ste. 204, Huntersville, NC 28078, (704)947-7779

Assn. for Higher Educ. of North Texas [★8226]

Assn. of Himalayan Yoga Meditation Societies

Assn. of Himalayan Yoga Meditation Societies - Address unknown since 2011.

Assn. of Hispanic Advt. Agencies [84], 8400 Westpark Dr., 2nd Fl., McLean, VA 22102, (703)610-9014

Assn. of Hispanic Arts - Address unknown since 2010.

Assn. of Hispanic Fed. Executives [★5434]

Assn. of Hispanic Healthcare Executives [14871], PO Box 230832, Ansonia Sta., New York, NY 10023, (212)877-1615

Assn. of Hispanists of Great Britain and Ireland [IO], Newcastle upon Tyne, United Kingdom

Assn. of Historians of Nineteenth-Century Art [9168], Karen Pope, Membership Coor., PO Box 5730, Austin, TX 78763

Assn. of Historians of Nineteenth-Century Art [9168], Karen Pope, Membership Coor., PO Box 5730, Austin, TX 78763

Assn. of Historic Sites Officials [★9743]

Assn. for Historical Fencing [22562], PO Box 2013, Secaucus, NJ 07096-2013

Assn. for Historical Fencing [22562], PO Box 2013, Secaucus, NJ 07096-2013

Assn. for the History of Chiropractic [14123], 4430 8th St., Rock Island, IL 61201, (309)788-0799

Assn. for History and Computing UK Br. [IO], Liverpool, United Kingdom

Assn. of Holistic Animal Practitioners - Defunct.

Assn. of Holistic Biodynamic Massage Therapists [IO], Macclesfield, United Kingdom

Assn. of Holocaust Organizations [17784], PO Box 230317, Hollis, NY 11423, (516)582-4571

Assn. of Holocaust Organizations [17784], PO Box 230317, Hollis, NY 11423, (516)582-4571

Assn. for Holotropic Breathwork Intl. [13665], PO Box 400267, Cambridge, MA 02140, (617)674-2474

Assn. of Home Appliance Mfrs. [218], 1111 19th St. NW, Ste. 402, Washington, DC 20036, (202)872-5955

Assn. of Home Info. Pack Providers [IO], Market Harborough, United Kingdom

Assn. of Home Off. Underwriters [1940], 2300 Windy Ridge Pkwy., Ste. 600, Atlanta, GA 30339, (770)984-3715

Assn. of Home Off. Underwriters [1940], 2300 Windy Ridge Pkwy., Ste. 600, Atlanta, GA 30339, (770)984-3715

Assn. for Honest Attorneys [5238], 7145 Blueberry Ln., Derby, KS 67037, (316)788-0901

Assn. of Hong Kong Nursing Staff [IO], Hong Kong, People's Republic of China

Assn. of Hosp. Directors of Medical Educ. [★15046]

Assn. of Hosp. Hea. and Fitness [★16229]

Assn. for Hosp. Medical Educ. [15046], PO Box 725, Indiana, PA 15701, (724)864-7321

Assn. of Hosp. Superintendents of U.S. and Canada [★15034]

Assn. of the Hotel, Restaurant, and Tourism Indus. in Denmark [IO], Frederiksberg, Denmark

Assn. des Hotels du Canada [★IO]

Assn. of Hotels, Restaurants, Catering and Related Businesses of Angola [IO], Luanda, Angola

Assn. of Human Rsrc. Systems Professionals [★68]

Assn. of Human Rsrc. Systems Professionals [★68]

Assn. of Human Resources Mgt. and Organizational Behavior [★6251]

Assn. of Human Resources Mgt. and Organizational Behavior [★6251]

Assn. of Human Rights and Torture Defenders - Cameroon [IO], Buea, Cameroon

Assn. for the Humane Treatment of Animals in Mauritania [IO], Nouakchott, Mauritania

Assn. for Humanist Sociology [7424], 11 Gates Ave., East Brunswick, NJ 08816

Assn. for Humanistic Counseling [8278], PO Box 791006, Baltimore, MD 21279-1006, (703)823-9800

Assn. for Humanistic Education - Defunct.

Assn. for Humanistic Educ. and Development [★8278]

Assn. for Humanistic Psychology [16388], PO Box 1190, Tiburon, CA 94920, (415)435-1604

Assn. of Humanistic Psychology Practitioners [IO], London, United Kingdom

Assn. of Humanistic Rabbis [19846], 28611 W 12 Mile Rd., Farmington Hills, MI 48334, (248)478-7610

Assn. for Humanitarian Development [IO], Hyderabad, Pakistan

Assn. of the Hungarian Automotive Indus. [IO], Budapest, Hungary

Assn. of Hungarian Consulting Engineers and Architects [IO], Budapest, Hungary

Assn. of the Hungarian Exhibition and Fair Organisers [IO], Budapest, Hungary

Assn. of Hungarian Foundries [IO], Budapest, Hungary

Assn. of Hungarian Geophysicists [IO], Budapest, Hungary

Assn. of Hungarian Inventors [IO], Budapest, Hungary

Assn. of Hungarian Librarians [IO], Budapest, Hungary

Assn. of Hungarian Medical Societies [IO], Budapest, Hungary

Assn. of Hungarian Physiotherapists [IO], Budapest, Hungary

Assn. of Hungarian Record Companies [IO], Budapest, Hungary

Assn. of Hungarian Steel Indus. [IO], Budapest, Hungary

Assn. of Hunt Saboteurs - Ireland [IO], Dublin, Ireland

Assn. Huntington France [★IO]

Assn. Huntington France [IO], Paris, France

Assn. of Iberian and Latin Amer. Stud. of Australasia [IO], Sydney, Australia

Assn. of Ice Cream and Related Products Mfrs. [IO], Buenos Aires, Argentina

Assn. of Icelandic Importers, Exporters, and Wholesale Merchants [IO], Reykjavik, Iceland

Assn. of Icelandic Physiotherapists [IO], Reykjavik, Iceland

L'association de l'industrie canadienne de L'enregistrement [★IO]

Assn. of Illustrators [IO], London, United Kingdom

Assn. for Image Anal. and Recognition [IO], Minsk, Belarus

Assn. of Image Consultants [★858]

Assn. of Image Consultants [★858]

Assn. of Image Consultants Intl. [858], 100 E Grand Ave., Ste. 330, Des Moines, IA 50309, (515)282-5500

Assn. of Image Consultants Intl. [858], 100 E Grand Ave., Ste. 330, Des Moines, IA 50309, (515)282-5500

Assn. for Image Processing [IO], Warsaw, Poland

Assn. of Immigration Attorneys - Defunct.

Assn. of Immigration and Nationality Lawyers [★5528]

Assn. des biens Immobiliers du Canada [★IO]

Assn. of Immunization Managers [15100], 620 Hungerford Dr., Ste. 29, Rockville, MD 20850, (301)424-5439

Assn. of Importers and Exporters of the Republic of Argentina [IO], Buenos Aires, Argentina

Assn. of Importers-Mfrs. for Muzzleloading - Defunct.

Assn. for Improvements in the Maternity Services [IO], Surbiton, United Kingdom

Assn. for Incentive Marketing - Defunct.

Assn. of Independent Asset Managers in Liechtenstein [IO], Balzers, Liechtenstein

Assn. of Independent Colls. of Art and Design - Defunct.

Assn. of Independent Commercial Producers [85], 3 W 18th St., 5th Fl., New York, NY 10011, (212)929-3000

Assn. of Independent Cmpt. Specialists [IO], Stroud, United Kingdom

Assn. of Independent Consultants [IO], Markham, ON, Canada

Assn. of Independent Consumer Credit Counseling Agencies [989], 11350 Random Hills Rd., Ste. 800, PMB 626, Fairfax, VA 22030, (703)934-6118

Assn. of Independent Corrugated Converters [872], PO Box 25708, Alexandria, VA 22313, (703)836-2422

Assn. of Independent Corrugated Converters [872], PO Box 25708, Alexandria, VA 22313, (703)836-2422

Assn. of Independent Creative Editors [2811], 308 W 107th St., No. 5F, New York, NY 10025, (212)665-2679

Assn. of Independent Crop Consultants [IO], Petersfield, United Kingdom

Assn. of Independent European Lawyers [IO], London, United Kingdom

Assn. of Independent Financial Advisers [IO], London, United Kingdom

Assn. of Independent Info. Professionals [1896], 8550 United Plaza Blvd., Ste. 1001, Baton Rouge, LA 70809, (225)408-4400

Assn. of Independent Info. Professionals [1896], 8550 United Plaza Blvd., Ste. 1001, Baton Rouge, LA 70809, (225)408-4400

Assn. of Independent Libraries [IO], Leeds, United Kingdom

Assn. of Independent Mailing Equip. Dealers [★2231]

Assn. of Independent Manufacturers'/Representatives [2316], 16 A Journey, Ste. 200, Aliso Viejo, CA 92656, (949)859-2884

Assn. of Independent Microdealers [★2554]

Assn. of Independent Museums [IO], Gosport, United Kingdom

Assn. for Independent Music - Defunct.

Assn. of Independent Music Publishers [2552], PO Box 69473, Los Angeles, CA 90069, (818)771-7301

Assn. of Independent Optical Wholesalers [★1687]

Assn. of Independent Optical Wholesalers [★1687]

Assn. of Independent Physical Therapists [IO], Bochum, Germany

Assn. of Independent Record Labels [IO], West Melbourne, Australia

Assn. of Independent Res. Institutes [7325], PO Box 844, Westminster, MD 21158, (410)751-8900

Assn. of Independent Res. and Tech. Organisations [IO], Chipping Campden, United Kingdom

Assn. of Independent Retirees [IO], Deakin West, Australia

Assn. of Independent School Admission Professionals [7681], PO Box 709, Madison, CT 06443, (203)421-7051

Assn. of Independent Sci. Engg. and Testing Firms [★7019]

Assn. of Independent Tour Operators [IO], Twickenham, United Kingdom

Assn. of Independent Trust Companies [1337], 8 S Michigan Ave., Ste. 1000, Chicago, IL 60603-3452, (312)223-1611

Assn. of Independents in Radio [482], PO Box 220400, Boston, MA 02122, (617)825-4400

Assn. of Independents in Radio [482], PO Box 220400, Boston, MA 02122, (617)825-4400

Assn. of Indian Muslims [★19033]

Assn. of Indian Muslims of Am. [19033], PO Box 10654, Silver Spring, MD 20914

Assn. of Indian Pathologists in North America [16118], Rajal B. Shah, MD, Co-Treas., 1812 Kings Isle Dr., Plano, TX 75093-2422

Assn. of Indian Universities [IO], New Delhi, India

Assn. of Indians in Am. [19034], 1 Hanson Pl., Ste. 1215, Brooklyn, NY 11243

Assn. for India's Development [12314], PO Box F, College Park, MD 20741-3005, (301)717-1059

Assn. for India's Development [12314], PO Box F, College Park, MD 20741-3005, (301)717-1059

Assn. of Indus. Advertisers [★2392]

Assn. of Indus. Advertisers [★2392]

Assn. for Indus. Archaeology [IO], Telford, United Kingdom

A star before a book entry number signifies that the name is not listed separately, but is mentioned within the entry.

Assn. of Indus. Laser Users [IO], Abingdon, United Kingdom

Assn. of Indus. Metallizers, Coaters and Laminators [788], 201 Springs St., Fort Mill, SC 29715, (803)802-7820

Assn. of Indus. Road Safety Officers [IO], Worthing, United Kingdom

Assn. des Indus. Europeennes du Platre [★IO]

Assn. des Indus. de Marque [★IO]

Assn. of the Indus. of Juices and Nectars from Fruits and Vegetables of the European Union [IO], Brussels, Belgium

Assn. of Indus. Mfrs. Representatives [★2316]

Assn. for Infant Mental Hea., United Kingdom [IO], Bristol, United Kingdom

Assn. des Infirmieres et Infirmiers du Canada [★IO]

Assn. for Informal Logic and Critical Thinking [10371], Ctr. for Critical Thinking, Baker Univ., Baldwin City, KS 66006

Assn. of Info. and Dissemination Centers

Assn. of Info. and Dissemination Centers - Defunct.

Assn. for Info. and Image Mgt. [★1894]

Assn. for Info. Mgt. [IO], Bradford, United Kingdom

Assn. for Info. Media and Equip. [273], PO Box 9844, Cedar Rapids, IA 52409-9844, (319)654-0608

Assn. of Info. Specialists [IO], Tbilisi, Georgia

Assn. for Info. Systems [6447], PO Box 2712, Atlanta, GA 30301-2712, (404)413-7444

Assn. of Info. Technologies Companies and Organizations of Uzbekistan [IO], Tashkent, Uzbekistan

Assn. of Info. Tech. Professionals [7904], 401 N Michigan Ave., Ste. 2400, Chicago, IL 60611-4267, (312)245-1070

Assn. des Ingenieurs-Conseils du Canada [★IO]

Assn. des Ingenieurs Polonais du Canada [★IO]

Assn. of Ingersoll-Rand Distributors [1808], 1300 Sumner Ave., Cleveland, OH 44115-2851, (216)241-7333

Assn. of Insolvency Accountants [★14]

Assn. of Insolvency and Restructuring Advisors [14], 221 Stewart Ave., Ste. 207, Medford, OR 97501, (541)858-1665

Assn. of Inspectors Gen. [5503], John Jay Coll. of Criminal Justice, 445 W 59th St., Rm. 3533N, New York, NY 10019, (212)237-8001

Assn. of the Inst. for Certification of Cmpt. Professionals [★7906]

Assn. for Institutional Res. [8729], 1435 E Piedmont Dr., Ste. 211, Tallahassee, FL 32308, (850)385-4155

Assn. for Institutional Thought [6612], Mary V. Wrenn, Sec.-Treas., Weber State Univ., 3807 Univ. Cir., Ogden, UT 84408

Assn. of Institutions for Feminist Educ. and Res. in Europe [IO], Utrecht, Netherlands

Assn. des Instituts Catholiques de l'Education [★IO]

Assn. of Insurance Attorneys [★5548]

Assn. of Insurance Companies - Greece [IO], Athens, Greece

Assn. of Insurance and Reinsurance Companies of Turkey [IO], Istanbul, Turkey

Assn. of Insurance and Risk Managers [IO], London, United Kingdom

Assn. for Integrative Hea. Care Practitioners [15401], PO Box 5631, Capitol Heights, MD 20791-5631, (757)292-7710

Assn. for Integrative Psychology [16389], 48 Kaiulani St., Hilo, HI 96720-2531, (808)935-7412

Assn. for Integrative Stud. [9868], Miami Univ., Western Prog., 501 E High St., Oxford, OH 45056, (513)529-2659

Assn. for Intelligence Officers [★5597]

Assn. for Intelligence Officers [★5597]

Assn. for Intelligent Systems Technology - Defunct.

Assn. for Intelligent Transport Systems India [IO], Bhopal, India

Assn. for Interactive Marketing [3400], 1430 Broadway, 8th Fl., New York, NY 10018, (888)337-0008

Assn. for Interactive Media [★3400]

Assn. for Interdisciplinary Res. in Values and Social Change [12924], 512 10th St. NW, Washington, DC 20004, (202)626-8800

Assn. of Interior Specialists [IO], Solihull, United Kingdom

Assn. of Internal Mgt. Consultants [2269], 824 Caribbean Ct., Marco Island, FL 34145, (239)642-0580

Assn. of Internal Mgt. Consultants [2269], 824 Caribbean Ct., Marco Island, FL 34145, (239)642-0580

Assn. of Intl. Accountants [IO], Newcastle upon Tyne, United Kingdom

Assn. for Intl. Agricultural Educ. [★7707]

Assn. for Intl. Agricultural Educ. [★7707]

Assn. for Intl. Agricultural and Extension Educ. [7707], Texas A&M Univ., 2116 TAMU, College Station, TX 77843, (979)862-3003

Assn. for Intl. Agricultural and Extension Educ. [7707], Texas A&M Univ., 2116 TAMU, College Station, TX 77843, (979)862-3003

Assn. for Intl. Agriculture and Rural Development [7708], Univ. of California, Davis, Horticulture CRSP, 190 EH Bldg., 1 Shields Ave., Davis, CA 95616-5270, (530)752-7975

Assn. for Intl. Agriculture and Rural Development [7708], Univ. of California, Davis, Horticulture CRSP, 190 EH Bldg., 1 Shields Ave., Davis, CA 95616-5270, (530)752-7975

Assn. of Intl. Airlines [IO], San Jose, Costa Rica

Assn. of Intl. Auto. Mfrs. [297], 1050 K St. NW, Ste. 650, Washington, DC 20001, (202)650-5555

Assn. of Intl. Auto. Mfrs. [★297]

Assn. of Intl. Auto. Mfrs. of Canada [IO], Toronto, ON, Canada

Assn. of Intl. Banks [IO], Bangkok, Thailand

Assn. of Intl. Banks and Trust Companies in the Bahamas [IO], Nassau, Bahamas

Assn. for Intl. Cancer Res. [IO], St. Andrews, United Kingdom

Assn. of Intl. Collective Mgt. of Audiovisual Works [IO], Geneva, Switzerland

Assn. of Intl. Colleges and Universities [★8389]

Assn. of Intl. Colleges and Universities [★8389]

Assn. of Intl. Couriers and Express Services [IO], Colnbrook, United Kingdom

Assn. of Intl. Educ. Administrators [7660], Duke Univ., Franklin Center 107, 2204 Erwin Rd., Durham, NC 27705-3942, (919)668-1928

Assn. of Intl. Educ. Administrators [7660], Duke Univ., Franklin Center 107, 2204 Erwin Rd., Durham, NC 27705-3942, (919)668-1928

Assn. of Intl. Graduate Admissions Consultants [7682], 915 L St., Ste. 1000, Sacramento, CA 95814, (916)446-3670

Assn. of Intl. Healthcare Recruiters and Employers - Defunct.

Assn. of Intl. Insurance Agents [★1987]

Assn. for Intl. Investment [★18484]

Assn. for Intl. Investment [★18484]

Assn. Intl. pour l'Etude de l'Economie de l'Assurance [★IO]

Assn. of Intl. Marathons and Distance Races [IO], London, United Kingdom

Assn. of Intl. Motion Engineers

Assn. of Intl. Motion Engineers - Address unknown since 2011.

Assn. of Intl. Motor Vehicle Mfrs. [IO], Bad Homburg, Germany

Assn. of the Intl. Olympic Winter Sports Federations [IO], Zurich, Switzerland

Assn. of Intl. Pharmaceutical Mfrs. [IO], Moscow, Russia

Assn. of Intl. Photography Art Dealers [10435], 2025 M St. NW, Ste. 800, Washington, DC 20036, (202)367-1158

Assn. of Intl. Photography Art Dealers [10435], 2025 M St. NW, Ste. 800, Washington, DC 20036, (202)367-1158

Assn. for Intl. Practical Training [8347], 10400 Little Patuxent Pkwy., Ste. 250, Columbia, MD 21044-3519, (410)997-2200

Assn. for Intl. Practical Training [8347], 10400 Little Patuxent Pkwy., Ste. 250, Columbia, MD 21044-3519, (410)997-2200

Assn. of Intl. Professional and Bus. Women [IO], Oslo, Norway

Assn. of Intl. Res. Initiatives for Environmental Stud. [IO], Tokyo, Japan

Assn. of Intl. Schools in Africa [IO], Nairobi, Kenya

Assn. of Intl. Trade Fairs of Am. [IO], Bogota, Colombia

Assn. for Intl. Youth-work - Christian Women's Working Group [IO], Frankfurt, Germany

Assn. Internationale des Anatomistes du Bois [★IO]

Assn. Internationale des Anthropobiologistes [★IO]

Assn. Internationale des Approvisionneurs de Navires [★IO]

Assn. Internationale des Arbitres de Water Polo [★IO]

Assn. Internationale des Archives Francophones [★IO]

Assn. Internationale des Assureurs de la Production Agricole [★IO]

Assn. Internationale des Avocats du Monde et des Indus. du Spectacle [★IO]

Assn. Internationale du Barreau [★IO]

Assn. Internationale des Charites [★IO]

Assn. Internationale de Chirurgie Buccale et Maxillo-Faciale [★16006]

Assn. Internationale de Chirurgie Buccale et Maxillo-Faciale [★16006]

Assn. Internationale des Circuits Permanents [★IO]

Assn. Internationale de Climatologie [★IO]

Assn. Internationale Contre les Experiences Douloureuses sur les Animaux [★IO]

Assn. Internationale de la Couleur [★IO]

Assn. Internationale des Critiques d'Art [★IO]

Assn. Internationale des Critiques d'Art - Sect. Canadienne [★IO]

Assn. Internationale des Critiques Litteraires [★IO]

Assn. Internationale des Critiques de Theatre [★IO]

Assn. Internationale des Demographes de Langue Francaise [★IO]

Assn. Internationale Des Etudiants en Sciences Economiques et Commerciales [★7782]

Assn. Internationale Des Etudiants en Sciences Economiques et Commerciales [★7782]

Assn. Internationale Des Magistrats De La Jeunesse Et De La Famille [★IO]

Assn. Internationale du Design Interactif [★IO]

Assn. Internationale d'Essais de Semences [★IO]

Assn. Internationale d'Esthetique Experimentale [★IO]

Assn. Internationale d'Etudes de la Genese des Minerais [★IO]

Assn. Internationale d'Etudes de la Mission [★IO]

Assn. Internationale d'Etudes Patristiques [★IO]

Assn. Internationale du Developpement Urbain [★IO]

Assn. Internationale D'Experts Scientifiques Du Tourisme [★IO]

Assn. Internationale d'Histoire Economique [★IO]

Assn. Internationale d'Institutions d'Histoire Ouvriere [★IO]

Assn. Internationale Droit, Ethique and Sci. [★IO]

Assn. Internationale de Droit de La Consommation [★IO]

Assn. Internationale du Droit Nucleaire [★IO]

Assn. Internationale de Droit Penal [★IO]

Assn. Internationale de Droit Penal [★IO]

Assn. Internationale des Ecoles et Instituts d'Administration [★IO]

Assn. Internationale des Ecoles de Travail Social [★IO]

Assn. Internationale des Ecoles de Voile [★IO]

Assn. Internationale pour les Edulcorants [★IO]

Assn. Internationale des Egyptologues [★IO]

Assn. Internationale des Entrepreneurs en Pipelines [★IO]

Assn. Internationale des Etudes Hongroises [★IO]

Assn. Internationale des Etudes et Recherches sur L'Information et la Commun. [★IO]

Assn. Internationale des Etudiants en Siences Economiques et Commerciales [IO], Rotterdam, Netherlands

Assn. Internationale des Etudiants Veterinaires [★IO]

Assn. Internationale des Experts en Philatelie [★IO]

Assn. Internationale des Fabricants de Caisses en Carton Ondule [★882]

Assn. Internationale des Fabricants de Caisses en Carton Ondule [★882]

Assn. Internationale des Federations di Athletisme [★IO]

Reference to "IO" in place of a book number signifies that the association may be found in the 50th edition of International Organizations.

Assn. Internationale du Film d'Animation [★IO]
Assn. Internationale du Film d'Animation [★IO]
Assn. Internationale Forets Mediterraneenes [★IO]
Assn. Internationale de Geochimie et de Cosmo-
chimie [★IO]
Assn. Internationale de Geodesie [★IO]
Assn. Internationale de Geologie de l'Ingenieur
[★IO]
Assn. Internationale de Geomagnetisme et
d'Aeronomie [★IO]
Assn. Internationale des Geomorphologues [★IO]
Assn. Internationale de Grands Magasins [★IO]
Assn. Internationale des Hautes Juridictions Admin-
istratives [★IO]
Assn. Internationale des Instituts de Navigation
[★IO]
Assn. Internationale des Interpretes de Conf. [★IO]
Assn. Internationale des Jeunes Avocats [★IO]
Assn. Internationale des Laboratoires Textiles
Lainiers [★IO]
Assn. Internationale pour l'Etude des Argiles [★IO]
Assn. Internationale pour l'Etude du Foie [★IO]
Assn. Internationale pour l'Etude de la Musique
Populaire [★IO]
Assn. Internationale pour l'Evaluation du Rendement
Scolaire [★IO]
Assn. Internationale pour l'Histoire des Religions
[★IO]
Assn. Internationale de l'Industrie des Engrais [★IO]
Assn. Internationale pour l'Informatique Statistique
[★IO]
Assn. Internationale de Linguistique Appliquee [★IO]
Assn. Internationale de l'Inspection du Travail [★IO]
Assn. Internationale pour l'Oceanographie Bi-
ologique [★IO]
Assn. Internationale de l'Ozone - EA3G [★IO]
Assn. Internationale des Ludotheques [★IO]
Assn. Internationale des Maires Francophones
[★IO]
Assn. Internationale de Mgt. des Arts et de la
Culture [★IO]
Assn. Internationale de Mecanisation des Essais en
Plein Champ [★IO]
Assn. Internationale de Medecine Agricole et de
Sante Rurale [★IO]
Assn. Internationale de Medecine et de Biologie de
l'Environnement [★IO]
Assn. Internationale des Musees d'Agriculture [★IO]
Assn. Internationale de la Mutualite [IO], Brussels,
Belgium
Assn. Internationale de Mycologie [★7129]
Assn. Internationale de Mycologie [★7129]
Assn. Internationale de Navigation [★IO]
Assn. Internationale des Numismates Professionnels
[★IO]
Assn. Internationale de Papyrologues [★IO]
Assn. Internationale de la Presse Sportive [★IO]
Assn. Internationale des Professeurs d'Anglais des
Universites [★IO]
Assn. Internationale pour la Protection de la Propri-
ete Intellectuelle [★IO]
Assn. Internationale de Psychiatrie de l'Enfant et de
l'Adolescent et des Professionas Associees [★IO]
Assn. Internationale de Psychologie Appliquee [★IO]
Assn. Internationale de Recherche Apicole [★IO]
Assn. Internationale du Registre des Bateaux du
Rhin [★IO]
Assn. Internationale Sans But Lucratif [★IO]
Assn. Internationale Sans But Lucratif [★IO]
Assn. Internationale de la Savonnerie, de la Deter-
gence et des Produits d'Entretien [★IO]
Assn. Internationale de Sci. Politique [★IO]
Assn. Internationale de Sci. et de Technologie pour
le Developpement [★IO]
Assn. Internationale des Sciences Economiques
[★IO]
Assn. Internationale des Sciences Hydrologiques
[★IO]
Assn. Internationale des Sciences Phonetiques
[★IO]
Assn. Internationale de la Securite Sociale [★IO]
Assn. Internationale de Sedimentologistes [★IO]
Assn. Internationale de Semiotique [★IO]
Assn. Internationale des Services d'Installations
Electriques sur lesBateaux [★IO]

Assn. Internationale de Signalisation Maritime [★IO]
Assn. Internationale de Societes s'Occupant des
Agents Mutagenes Presents dans l'Environnement
[★6301]
Assn. Internationale de Societes s'Occupant des
Agents Mutagenes Presents dans l'Environnement
[★6301]
Assn. Internationale de Sociologie [★IO]
Assn. Internationale des Sociologues de Langue
Francaise [★IO]
Assn. Internationale pour le Sport des Aveugles
[★IO]
Assn. Internationale des Statisticiens d'Enquetes
[★IO]
Assn. Internationale pour la Taxonomie Vegetale
[★IO]
Assn. Internationale des Techniciens Biologistes
[★IO]
Assn. Internationale des Technologistes de Labora-
toire Medical [★IO]
Assn. Internationale du Theatre Amateur [★IO]
Assn. Internationale du Theatre pour l'Enfance et la
Jeunesse [★IO]
Assn. Internationale des Traducteurs de Conf. [★IO]
Assn. Internationale Tunnels et de l'Espace Souter-
rain [★IO]
Assn. Internationale des Universites [★IO]
Assn. Internationale Villes et Ports [★IO]
Assn. Internationale pour les Voiles Minces en Beton
[★IO]
Assn. Internationale de Volcanologie et de Chimie
de l'Interieur de la Terre [★IO]
Assn. canadienne des fournisseurs Internet [★IO]
Assn. of Interpretive Naturalists [★7142]
Assn. of Interstate Commerce Commn. Practitioners
[★6030]
Assn. Investissement Responsable [★IO]
Assn. of Investment Companies [IO], London, United
Kingdom
Assn. for Investment Mgt. and Res. [★2133]
Assn. for Investment Mgt. and Res. [★2133]
Assn. of Investment Mgt. Sales Executives [2131],
12100 Sunset Hills Rd., Ste. 130, Reston, VA
20190, (703)234-4098
Assn. of Iranian Endoscopic Surgeons [IO], Tehran,
Iran
Assn. of Iranian Women Entrepreneurs [IO], Tehran,
Iran
Assn. of Irish Composers [IO], Dublin, Ireland
Assn. of Irish Musical Societies [IO], Thurles, Ireland
Assn. of Iron and Steel Engineers [★7091]
Assn. for Iron and Steel Tech. [7091], 186 Thorn Hill
Rd., Warrendale, PA 15086-7528, (724)814-3000
Assn. of Iroquois and Allied Indians [IO], London,
ON, Canada
Assn. of Islamic Charitable Projects [19830], 4431
Walnut St., Philadelphia, PA 19104-2924,
(215)387-8888
Assn. of Israel's Decorative Arts [9281], 110 E 59th
St., 26th Fl., New York, NY 10022, (212)931-0110
Assn. of Israel's Decorative Arts [9281], 110 E 59th
St., 26th Fl., New York, NY 10022, (212)931-0110
Assn. of Italian Canadian Writers [IO], Stouffville,
ON, Canada
Assn. of Italian Clinical Dermatologists [IO], Bari,
Italy
Assn. of Italian Confectionery Mfrs. [IO], Rome, Italy
Assn. of Italian Hosp. Dermatologists [IO], Sorrento,
Italy
Assn. Ivoirienne pour le Bien-Etre Familial [IO],
Abidjan, Cote d'Ivoire
Assn. of Japan Plastics Machinery [IO], Tokyo,
Japan
Assn. of Japanese Consulting Engineers [IO], Tokyo,
Japan
Assn. of Japanese Geographers [IO], Tokyo, Japan
Assn. of Jesuit Colleges and Universities [7814],
One Dupont Cir., Ste. 405, Washington, DC 20036,
(202)862-9893
Assn. Jeunesse Fransaskoise [★IO]
Assn. de la Jeunesse pour la Promotion des Droits
de l'Homme et le Developpement [★IO]
Assn. of Jewish Aging Services [10834], 316
Pennsylvania Ave. SE, Ste. 402, Washington, DC
20003, (202)543-7500

Assn. of Jewish Book Publishers - Defunct.
Assn. of Jewish Ex-Servicemen and Women [IO],
London, United Kingdom
Assn. of Jewish Family and Children's Agencies
[12403], 5750 Park Heights Ave., Baltimore, MD
21215, (410)843-7573
Assn. of Jewish Genealogical Societies [★20634]
Assn. of Jewish Genealogical Societies [★20634]
Assn. of Jewish Libraries [9967], PO Box 1118, Tea-
neck, NJ 07666-1118, (212)725-5359
Assn. of Jewish Libraries [9967], PO Box 1118, Tea-
neck, NJ 07666-1118, (212)725-5359
Assn. of Jewish Religious Professionals from the
Commonwealth of Independent States and Eastern
Europe [IO], Jerusalem, Israel
Assn. for Jewish Retarded [★12503]
Assn. for Jewish Stud. [8423], 15 W 16th St., New
York, NY 10011-6301, (917)606-8249
Assn. for Jewish Stud. [8423], 15 W 16th St., New
York, NY 10011-6301, (917)606-8249
Assn. des Joueurs d'Echecs Professionnels [★IO]
Assn. des Journalistes Auto. du Canada [★IO]
Assn. of Junior Leagues Intl. [13385], 80 Maiden
Ln., Ste. 305, New York, NY 10038, (212)951-8300
Assn. of Junior Leagues Intl. [13385], 80 Maiden
Ln., Ste. 305, New York, NY 10038, (212)951-8300
Assn. des Juristes Franco-Britanniques [★IO]
Assn. of Kannada Kootas of Am. [19035], Mr. Na-
gashankar Chandrashekar, Sec., 12509 Blue Sky
Dr., Clarksburg, MD 20871
Assn. of Knitted Fabrics Mfrs. - Defunct.
Assn. of Knitwear Designers [201], 4532 17th St.,
San Francisco, CA 94114, (415)552-8414
Assn. of Knitwear Designers [201], 4532 17th St.,
San Francisco, CA 94114, (415)552-8414
Assn. of Korean Agricultural Medicine and Rural
Hea. [IO], Daegu, Republic of Korea
Assn. of Korean-Canadian Scientists and Engineers
[IO], North York, ON, Canada
Assn. of Korean Geomorphologists [IO], Jinju,
Republic of Korea
Assn. for Korean Music Res. [10165], Prof. Okon
Hwang, Sec.-Treas., Eastern Connecticut State
Univ., Performing Arts Dept., Willimantic, CT
06226, (860)465-5109
Assn. for Korean Music Res. [10165], Prof. Okon
Hwang, Sec.-Treas., Eastern Connecticut State
Univ., Performing Arts Dept., Willimantic, CT
06226, (860)465-5109
Assn. for Korean Stud. in Europe [IO], Leiden,
Netherlands
Assn. of Labor Assistants and Childbirth Educators -
Address unknown since 2011.
Assn. of Labor-Management Administrators and
Consultants on Alcoholism [★13219]
Assn. of Labor Relations Agencies [23233], Natl.
Labor Relations Bd., 1099 14th St. NW, Ste.
11600, Washington, DC 20570, (202)273-1067
Assn. of Labor Relations Agencies [23233], Natl.
Labor Relations Bd., 1099 14th St. NW, Ste.
11600, Washington, DC 20570, (202)273-1067
Assn. of Lab. Managers [7021], 8630 Guilford Rd.,
Ste. M, Columbia, MD 21046-2654, (800)985-7879
Assn. of Labour Providers [IO], Frimley, United
Kingdom
Assn. of Ladies of Charity of the U.S. [★13191]
Assn. Laitiere Europeene [★IO]
Assn. Laitiere Francaise [★IO]
Assn. genevoise pour l'alimentation infantile [★IO]
Assn. of Land-Grant Colleges and State Universities
[★7873]
Assn. of Landscape Contractors of Ireland [IO],
Bangor, United Kingdom
Assn. of Language Companies [2186], 9707 Key W
Ave., Ste. 100, Rockville, MD 20850, (240)404-
6511
Assn. for Language Learning [IO], Leicester, United
Kingdom
Assn. of Language Testers in Europe [IO],
Cambridge, United Kingdom
Assn. of Language Travel Organisations [IO], Am-
sterdam, Netherlands
Assn. de Langue Francaise pour l'Etude du Diabete
et des Maladies Metaboliques [★IO]
Assn. de Langue Francaise pour l'Etude du Stress
et du Traumatisme [IO], Paris, France

A star before a book entry number signifies that the name is not listed separately, but is mentioned within the entry.

Assn. of Laparoscopic Surgeons of Great Britain and Ireland [IO], London, United Kingdom

Assn. francaise pour la recherche sur l'Asie du Sud-Est [★IO]

Assn. of Late-Deafened Adults [14920], 8038 MacIntosh Ln., Ste. 2, Rockford, IL 61107, (815)332-1515

Assn. for Latin Liturgy [IO], Bristol, United Kingdom

Assn. of Latino Administrators and Superintendents [7661], 65 W Boston Post Rd., Ste. 200, Marlborough, MA 01752, (508)486-4536

Assn. of Latino Professionals in Finance and Accounting [15], 801 S Grand Ave., Ste. 650, Los Angeles, CA 90017, (213)243-0004

Assn. pour l'avancement des sciences et des techniques de la documentation [★IO]

Assn. canadienne pour l'avancement des etudes Neerlandaises [★IO]

Assn. pour l'Avancement des Sciences et des Techniques de la Documentation [IO], Montreal, QC, Canada

Assn. pour l'Avancement des Techniques de Modelisation et de Simulation dans l'Enterprise [★IO]

Assn. of Law Costs Draftsmen [IO], Diss, United Kingdom

Assn. of Law Teachers [IO], Plymouth, United Kingdom

Assn. of Lawyers for Children [IO], East Molesey, United Kingdom

Assn. of Leadership Educators [8483], Univ. of Tennessee, 2621 Morgan Cir., Knoxville, TN 37996, (865)974-4830

Assn. of Learned and Professional Soc. Publishers [IO], Peterborough, United Kingdom

Assn. for Learning Languages en Famille [IO], Bedford, United Kingdom

Assn. for Learning Tech. [IO], Oxford, United Kingdom

Assn. of Leather Exporters [IO], Barcelona, Spain

Assn. canadienne sur la qualite de l'eau [★IO]

Assn. of Lebanese Industrialists [IO], Beirut, Lebanon

Assn. pour le developpment de l'education en Afrique [★IO]

Assn. pour l'Education Permanente dans les Universites du Canada [★IO]

Assn. of Legal Administrators [5653], 75 Tri-State Intl., Ste. 222, Lincolnshire, IL 60069-4435, (847)267-1252

Assn. of Legal Administrators [5653], 75 Tri-State Intl., Ste. 222, Lincolnshire, IL 60069-4435, (847)267-1252

Assn. of Legal Court Interpreters and Translators [IO], Montreal, QC, Canada

Assn. of Legal Writing Directors [6076], Susan Thrower, Sec., DePaul Univ. Coll. of Law, 25 E Jackson Blvd., Chicago, IL 60604

Assn. canadienne de l'electricite [★IO]

Assn. pour l'Enseignement de la Pediatrie en Europe [★IO]

Assn. canadienne de la medecine du travail et de l'environnement [★IO]

Assn. for Lesbian, Gay, Bisexual and Transgender Issues in Counseling [12069], Oakland Univ., 440B Pawley Hall, Rochester, MI 48309, (508)531-2721

L'Association canadienne pour l'etude pratique de la loi dans le systeme educatif [★IO]

Assn. internationale pour l'Etude de la mosaique antique [★IO]

Assn. pour l'etude du droit de la Concurrence [IO], Evere, Belgium

Assn. pour l'Etude des Langues et Litteratures du Commonwealth [★IO]

Assn. canadienne de l'hydroelectricite [★IO]

Assn. Libanaise des Stomises [★IO]

Assn. of Liberian Engineers USA [6786], 10500 Meadowlake Terr., Mitchellville, MD 20721, (918)760-7661

Assn. of Liberian Engineers USA [6786], 10500 Meadowlake Terr., Mitchellville, MD 20721, (918)760-7661

Assn. of Liberian Lawyers in the Americas [5654], 4111 Odessa St., Denver, CO 80249, (303)862-6514

Assn. of Libertarian Feminists [18077], 484 Lake Park Ave., No. 24, Oakland, CA 94610-2730, (925)228-0565

Assn. de la Librairie Ancienne du Canada [★IO]

Assn. of Librarians in the History of the Hea. Sciences [★9961]

Assn. for Lib. Collections and Tech. Services [9968], 50 E Huron St., Chicago, IL 60611, (312)280-5037

Assn. of Lib. and Info. Professionals of the Czech Republic [IO], Prague, Czech Republic

Assn. of Lib. and Info. Professionals - Germany [IO], Reutlingen, Germany

Assn. for Lib. and Info. Sci. Educ. [8520], 65 E Wacker Pl., Ste. 1900, Chicago, IL 60601-7246, (312)795-0996

Assn. for Lib. Ser. to Children [9969], 50 E Huron St., Chicago, IL 60611-2795, (312)280-2162

Assn. of Lib. Trustees, Advocates, Friends and Foundations [9970], 109 S 13th St., Ste. 3-N, Philadelphia, PA 19107, (312)280-2161

Assn. of Lib. Trustees and Advocates and Friends of Libraries U.S.A. [★9970]

Assn. of Licensed Aircraft Engineers [IO], Bagshot, United Kingdom

Assn. of Licensed Architects [240], 22159 N Pepper Rd., Ste. 2N, Barrington, IL 60010, (847)382-0630

Assn. of Licensed Architects [240], 22159 N Pepper Rd., Ste. 2N, Barrington, IL 60010, (847)382-0630

Assn. of Licensed Multiple Retailers [IO], London, United Kingdom

Assn. of Life Agency Officers [★1991]

Assn. of Life Agency Officers [★1991]

Assn. of Life Insurance Counsel [5550], 3815 River Crossing Pkwy., Ste. 100, Indianapolis, IN 46240, (317)566-2154

Assn. of Lifecasters Intl. [10527], 18 Bank St., Summit, NJ 07901, (908)273-5600

Assn. of Lifecasters Intl. [10527], 18 Bank St., Summit, NJ 07901, (908)273-5600

Assn. of Light Aviation of Kazakhstan [IO], Almaty, Kazakhstan

Assn. of Lighting Designers [IO], Oxford, United Kingdom

Assn. of Lighting and Mercury Recyclers [4866], 4139 Rhine Ct., Napa, CA 94558, (707)927-3844

Assn. of Limb Mfrs. of Am. [★1679]

L'Association canadienne de l'immeuble [★IO]

Assn. de L'Industrie Touristique du Canada [★IO]

Assn. for Linen Mgt. [2189], 2161 Lexington Rd., Ste. 2, Richmond, KY 40475, (859)624-0177

Assn. pour la microbiologie medicale et l'infectiology Canada [★IO]

Assn. canadienne du droit des technologies de l'information [★IO]

Assn. de Linguistique du Canada et des Etats Unis [★10028]

Assn. de Linguistique du Canada et des Etats Unis [★10028]

Assn. for Literary and Linguistic Computing [IO], London, United Kingdom

Assn. of Literary Scholars, Critics, and Writers [10034], 650 Beacon St., Ste. 510, Boston, MA 02215, (617)358-1990

Assn. of Lithuania Shipbuilders and Shiprepairers [IO], Klaipeda, Lithuania

Assn. of Lithuanian Banks [IO], Vilnius, Lithuania

Assn. of Lithuanian Chambers of Commerce, Indus. and Crafts [IO], Vilnius, Lithuania

Assn. Litteraire Artistique Canadienne [★IO]

Assn. de Litterature et de Linguistique Computationnelles [★IO]

Assn. for Living Historical Farms and Agricultural Museums [★10114]

Assn. for Living History, Farm and Agricultural Museums [10114], 8774 Rte. 45 NW, North Bloomfield, OH 44450, (440)685-4410

Assn. of Lloyd's Members [IO], London, United Kingdom

Assn. of Loading and Elevating Equip. Mfrs. [IO], Croydon, United Kingdom

Assn. of Local Govt. Auditors [5183], 449 Lewis Hargett Cir., Ste. 290, Lexington, KY 40503-3669, (859)276-0686

Assn. of Local Housing Finance Agencies [★5521]

Assn. of Local Newspapers [IO], Warsaw, Poland

Assn. of Local Public Hea. Agencies [IO], Toronto, ON, Canada

Assn. of Long Distance Telephone Companies [★3592]

Assn. for Long Term Care Financial Managers [15291], 95 West St., Rocky Hill, CT 06067, (860)721-7400

L'Association des counsellers en orientation de l'Ontario [★IO]

Assn. of Loudspeaker Mfrs. and Acoustics Intl. [1090], 55 Littleton Rd., 13B, Ayer, MA 01432, (617)314-6977

Assn. for Low Countries Stud. in Great Britain and Ireland [IO], Sheffield, United Kingdom

Assn. for Low Flow Anaesthesia [IO], Leeds, United Kingdom

Assn. of Lunar and Planetary Observers [20976], Matthew L. Will, Sec.-Treas., PO Box 13456, Springfield, IL 62791-3456

Assn. of Lunar and Planetary Observers [20976], Matthew L. Will, Sec.-Treas., PO Box 13456, Springfield, IL 62791-3456

Assn. of Lutheran Men [★19932]

Assn. of Lutheran Secondary Schools [8542], Concordia Univ. Wisconsin, 12800 N Lake Shore Dr., Mequon, WI 53097-2404, (262)243-4519

Assn. Luxembourg Alzheimer [IO], Luxembourg, Luxembourg

Assn. of Luxembourg Engineers, Architects and Industrialists [IO], Luxembourg, Luxembourg

Assn. Luxembourgeoise Des Kinesitherapeutes [IO], Luxembourg, Luxembourg

Assn. Luxembourgeoise des Ingenieurs, Architectes et Industriels [★IO]

Assn. Luxembourgeoise de Producteurs Professionnels d'Assurances [IO], Luxembourg, Luxembourg

Assn. Luxemburgeoise de Gerontologie et Geriatrie [IO], Ettelbruck, Luxembourg

Assn. of Luxury Suite Directors [3324], 10017 McKelvey Rd., Cincinnati, OH 45231, (513)674-0555

Assn. for Machine Translation in the Americas [7577], 209 N 8th St., Stroudsburg, PA 18360, (570)476-8006

Assn. for Machine Translation in the Americas [7577], 209 N 8th St., Stroudsburg, PA 18360, (570)476-8006

Assn. for Machine Translation and Computational Linguistics [★10023]

Assn. for Machine Translation and Computational Linguistics [★10023]

Assn. for Macintosh Trainers [6529], 117 Portland Ave. S, Ste. 302, Minneapolis, MN 55401, (612)282-5509

Assn. for Macintosh Trainers [6529], 117 Portland Ave. S, Ste. 302, Minneapolis, MN 55401, (612)282-5509

Assn. for Macular Diseases [15945], 210 E 64th St., 8th Fl., New York, NY 10065, (212)605-3719

Assn. of Mailing, Shipping and Off. Automation Specialists [2231], 11310 Wornall Rd., Kansas City, MO 64114, (888)750-6245

Assn. of Major City Building Officials [★5300]

Assn. of Major City/County Building Officials [5300], 505 Huntmar Park Dr., Ste. 210, Herndon, VA 20170, (703)481-2038

Assn. of Malaysian Loss Adjusters [IO], Kuala Lumpur, Malaysia

L'Association des Malentendants Canadiens [★IO]

L'Association des Malentendants Canadiens - Branche d'Edmonton [★IO]

Assn. Malgache des Olympiens [IO], Antananarivo, Madagascar

Assn. Malienne de Lutte contre le Diabete [IO], Bamako, Mali

Assn. of Maltese Arms Collectors and Shooters [IO], Naxxar, Malta

Assn. of Managed Care Dentists [14274], 2355 Westwood Blvd., No. 260, Los Angeles, CA 90064, (310)709-2677

Assn. of Managed Care Providers [★14274]

Assn. of Managed Healthcare Organizations [★14851]

Assn. of Mgt. [★6251]

Assn. of Mgt. [★6251]

Assn. of Mgt. Consultants [★2288]

Assn. of Mgt. Consulting Firms [2270], 370 Lexington Ave., Ste. 2209, New York, NY 10017, (212)262-3055

Assn. of Mgt., Consulting and Tech. for Constr. [IO], Bucharest, Romania

---

Reference to "IO" in place of a book number signifies that the association may be found in the 50th edition of International Organizations.

Assn. for Mgt. Info. in Financial Services [400], 14247 Saffron Cir., Carmel, IN 46032, (317)815-5857

Assn. of Management/International Assn. of Mgt. [6251], 920 S Battlefield Blvd., Ste. 100, Chesapeake, VA 23322, (757)482-2273

Assn. of Management/International Assn. of Mgt. [6251], 920 S Battlefield Blvd., Ste. 100, Chesapeake, VA 23322, (757)482-2273

Assn. for the Mgt. of Org. Design [★2300]

Assn. for the Mgt. of Org. Design [★2300]

Assn. of Mgt. and Professional Staffs [IO], Wakefield, United Kingdom

Assn. of Manpower Franchise Owners [1145], 6737 W Washington St., Ste. 1300, Milwaukee, WI 53214, (414)276-2651

Assn. of Manufactured Goods Exporters [IO], Santiago, Chile

Assn. of Mfrs. of Confectionary and Chocolate [★1426]

Assn. of Mfrs. of Confectionary and Chocolate [★1426]

Assn. of Mfrs. of Domestic Appliances [IO], London, United Kingdom

Assn. of Mfrs. and Formulators of Enzyme Products [IO], Brussels, Belgium

Assn. of Mfrs. of Household Appliances [IO], Paris, France

Assn. of Mfrs. and Importers of Elecl. Household Appliances [IO], Copenhagen, Denmark

Assn. of Mfrs. of Power Generating Systems [IO], Peterborough, United Kingdom

Assn. of Mfrs. and Wholesale Retailers of Gift Items [IO], Madrid, Spain

Assn. of Mfrs. of Woodworking Machinery [★1880]

Assn. des Manufacturiers de la Menuiserie Architecturale du Canada [★IO]

Assn. for Mfg. Excellence [2329], 3701 Algonquin Rd., Ste. 225, Rolling Meadows, IL 60008-3127, (224)232-5980

Assn. for Mfg. Excellence [2329], 3701 Algonquin Rd., Ste. 225, Rolling Meadows, IL 60008-3127, (224)232-5980

Assn. for Mfg. Tech. [7043], 7901 Westpark Dr., McLean, VA 22102-4206, (703)893-2900

Assn. of Marian Helpers [19387], Eden Hill, Stockbridge, MA 01263, (413)298-3931

Assn. of Marina Indus. [2377], 50 Water St., Warren, RI 02885, (866)367-6622

Assn. of Marina Indus. [2377], 50 Water St., Warren, RI 02885, (866)367-6622

Assn. for Marine Exploration [4701], 4820 Olney St., San Diego, CA 92109, (858)337-9418

Assn. of Marine Technicians [2353], 513 River Estates Pkwy., Canton, GA 30114-9419, (770)720-4324

Assn. Marocaine De Squash [IO], Casablanca, Morocco

Assn. Marocaine des Exportateurs [★IO]

Assn. Marocaine de Medecine du Sport [IO], Casablanca, Morocco

Assn. of Marshall Scholars [8808], 3100 Massachusetts Ave. NW, Washington, DC 20008-3600, (866)276-0741

Assn. of Marshall Scholars [8808], 3100 Massachusetts Ave. NW, Washington, DC 20008-3600, (866)276-0741

Assn. of Marshall Scholars and Alumnae/i [★8808]

Assn. of Marshall Scholars and Alumnae/i [★8808]

Assn. for Mascular Degeneration [★15945]

Assn. of Master Upholsterers and Soft Furnishers [IO], Cardiff, United Kingdom

Assn. of Maternal and Child Hea. Programs [14057], 2030 M St. NW, Ste. 350, Washington, DC 20036, (202)775-0436

Assn. for Mathematics Applied to Economic and Social Sciences [IO], Milan, Italy

Assn. of Mature Canadians [IO], Toronto, ON, Canada

Assn. Mauricienne des Femmes Chefs d'Entreprise [IO], Pereybere, Mauritius

Assn. Mauritaninne de Medecine du Sport [IO], Nouakchott, Mauritania

Assn. of Mauritian Mfrs. [IO], Port Louis, Mauritius

Assn. canadienne des specialistes en chirurgie buccale et maxillo-faciale [★IO]

Assn. of MBA's [IO], London, United Kingdom

Assn. for Measurement and Evaluation of Commun. [IO], London, United Kingdom

Assn. for Measurement and Evaluation in Counseling and Development [★8983]

Assn. for Measurement and Evaluation in Guidance [★8983]

Assn. des Medecins Biochimistes du Canada [★IO]

Assn. des Medecins et Medecins Dentistes du Grand-Duche de Luxembourg [IO], Luxembourg, Luxembourg

Assn. for Media Literacy [IO], Toronto, ON, Canada

Assn. of Media Producers [★277]

Assn. of Media Producers [★277]

Assn. Media and Publishing [263], 1760 Old Meadow Rd., Ste. 500, McLean, VA 22102, (703)506-3285

Assn. for Medical and Bio-Informatics, Singapore [IO], Singapore, Singapore

Assn. of Medical Device Reprocessors [15402], 600 New Hampshire Ave. NW, Ste. 500, Washington, DC 20037, (202)518-6796

Assn. of Medical Diagnostics Mfrs. [3174], Rebecca Shames, Admin. Asst., 555 13th St. NW, Ste. 7W-401, Washington, DC 20004, (202)637-6837

Assn. of Medical Directors of Info. Systems [15126], 682 Peninsula Dr., Lake Almanor, CA 96137, (530)596-4477

Assn. of Medical Doctors of Asia [IO], Okayama, Japan

Assn. of Medical Doctors of Kazakhstan [IO], Almaty, Kazakhstan

Assn. for Medical Educ. in Europe [IO], Dundee, United Kingdom

Assn. for Medical Educ. and Res. in Substance Abuse [8593], PO Box 20160, Cranston, RI 02920, (401)243-8460

Assn. of Medical Esthetic Nurses [★15702]

Assn. for Medical Ethics [14872], UC Irvine Spine Center, 101 The City Dr. S, Pavilion 3, 2nd Fl., Orange, CA 92868, (215)322-6654

Assn. for Medical Ethics [16698], 1601 N Sepulveda Blvd., Manhattan Beach, CA 90266, (215)322-6654

Assn. for Medical Humanities [IO], Worthing, United Kingdom

Assn. of Medical Illustrators [13769], 201 E Main St., Ste. 1405, Lexington, KY 40507, (866)393-4264

Assn. of Medical Illustrators [13769], 201 E Main St., Ste. 1405, Lexington, KY 40507, (866)393-4264

Assn. of Medical Lab. Immunologists [15101], Maggie Fogel, Admin., 34 W 83rd St., Ste. R, New York, NY 10024

Assn. of Medical Microbiology and Infectious Disease Canada [IO], Ottawa, ON, Canada

Assn. of Medical Officers of Amer. Institutions of Idiotic and Feebleminded Children [★15487]

Assn. of Medical Physicists of India [IO], Mumbai, India

Assn. of Medical Professionals with Hearing Losses [14921], 10708 Nestling Dr., Miamisburg, OH 45342

Assn. of Medical Professionals with Hearing Losses [14921], 10708 Nestling Dr., Miamisburg, OH 45342

Assn. of Medical Rehabilitation Administrators - Defunct.

Assn. of Medical Res. Charities [IO], London, United Kingdom

Assn. of Medical School Pediatric Dept. Chairs [16142], 6728 Old McLean Village Dr., McLean, VA 22101, (703)556-9222

Assn. of Medical Schools in Europe [IO], Copenhagen, Denmark

Assn. of Medical Secretaries, Practice Managers, Administrators and Receptionists [IO], London, United Kingdom

Assn. of Medical Superintendents of Amer. Institutions for Insane [★16330]

Assn. of Medical Superintendents of Mental Hospitals [★15032]

Assn. Medicale Francaise [IO], Paris, France

Assn. Medicale Haitienne [IO], Port-au-Prince, Haiti

Assn. Medicale Mondiale [★IO]

Assn. Medicale Podiatrique Canadienne [★IO]

Assn. of Medicine and Psychiatry [16336], 4747 N First St., Ste. 140, Fresno, CA 93726, (559)228-6140

Assn. des Medicins de Langue Francaise du Canada [★IO]

Assn. of Mediterranean Chambers of Commerce and Indus. [IO], Barcelona, Spain

Assn. of Meeting Professionals [1740], 2025 M St. NW, Ste. 800, Washington, DC 20036, (202)973-8686

Assn. of Member Episcopal Conferences in Eastern Africa [IO], Nairobi, Kenya

Assn. des Membres des Conferences Episcopales de l'Afrique Orientale [★IO]

Assn. of Memoirists and Family Historians - Defunct.

Assn. of Mental Health Librarians - Defunct.

Assn. canadienne pour la sante mentale, filiale du Bas-du-Fleuve [★IO]

Assn. of Methodist Historical Societies [★10084]

Assn. of Metropolitan Planning Organizations [17369], 1029 Vermont Ave. NW, Ste. 710, Washington, DC 20005, (202)296-7051

Assn. of Metropolitan Sewerage Agencies [★5949]

Assn. of Metropolitan Water Agencies [5859], 1620 I St. NW, Ste. 500, Washington, DC 20006, (202)331-2820

Assn. for Mexican Cave Stud. [7460], PO Box 7672, Austin, TX 78713

Assn. for Mexican Cave Stud. [7460], PO Box 7672, Austin, TX 78713

Assn. of Mezzanine Mfrs. [★1871]

Assn. of Mezzanine Mfrs. - Defunct.

Assn. of Microbiological Diagnostic Mfrs. [★3174]

Assn. for Microbiological Media Mfrs. [★3174]

Assn. of Microfinance Organizations of Tajikistan [IO], Dushanbe, Tajikistan

Assn. for Micrography, Image and Info. Mgt. [IO], Frankfurt am Main, Germany

Assn. of Midwifery Educators [7822], 24 S High St., Bridgton, ME 04009, (207)647-5968

Assn. of Military Banks of Am. [401], PO Box 3335, Warrenton, VA 20188, (540)347-3305

Assn. of Military Colleges and Schools of the U.S. [8623], 3604 Glenbrook Rd., Fairfax, VA 22031, (703)272-8406

Assn. of Military Colleges and Schools of the U.S. [★8623]

Assn. of Military Osteopathic Physicians and Surgeons [16074], 1796 Seven Hills Ln., Severn, MD 21144-1061, (410)519-8217

Assn. of Military Surgeons of the U.S. [15510], 9320 Old Georgetown Rd., Bethesda, MD 20814-1653, (301)897-8800

Assn. of Millwork Distributors [531], 10047 Robert Trent Jones Pkwy., New Port Richey, FL 34655-4649, (727)372-3665

Assn. Miniere du Canada [★IO]

Assn. of Mining Analysts [IO], London, United Kingdom

Assn. of Minor League Umpires [22266], 80 8th Ave., Ste. 205, New York, NY 10011

Assn. of Minority Hea. Professions Schools [8594], PO Box 13778, Atlanta, GA 30324, (678)904-4217

Assn. of the Miraculous Medal [19388], 1811 W St. Joseph St., Perryville, MO 63775-1598, (573)547-2508

Assn. of Missing and Exploited Children's Organizations [12537], PO Box 320338, Alexandria, VA 22320, (703)838-8379

Assn. of Missing and Exploited Children's Organizations [12537], PO Box 320338, Alexandria, VA 22320, (703)838-8379

Assn. for Modern and Contemporary Art of the Arab World, Iran, and Turkey [9282], PO Box 305100, Denton, TX 76203

Assn. of Modified Asphalt Producers [532], PO Box 270006, St. Louis, MO 63127, (314)843-2627

Assn. for Molecular Pathology [16119], 9650 Rockville Pike, Ste. E133, Bethesda, MD 20814-3993, (301)634-7939

Assn. Mondiale des Agences de Voyages [★IO]

Assn. Mondiale des Indus. de Traitement des Algues Marines [★IO]

Assn. Mondiale des Journaux [★IO]

Assn. Mondiale pour l'Advancement de Parasitologie Veterinaire [★17053]

Assn. Mondiale pour l'Advancement de Parasitologie Veterinaire [★17053]

A star before a book entry number signifies that the name is not listed separately, but is mentioned within the entry.

Assn. Mondiale pour l'Ecole Instrument de Paix [★IO]

Assn. Mondiale des Organisations de Recherche Industrielle et Technologique [★IO]

Assn. Mondiale des Radio-Amateurs et des Radio-clubs Chretiens [★IO]

Assn. Mondiale de la Route [★IO]

Assn. Montessori International USA [8633], 410 Alexander St., Rochester, NY 14607-1028, (585)461-5920

Assn. Montessori Internationale [★IO]

Assn. for Moral Educ. [8002], Gordon Coll., Dept. of Psychology, 255 Grapevine Rd., Wenham, MA 01984

Assn. for a More Just Soc. [17272], PO Box 888631, Grand Rapids, MI 49588, (800)897-1135

Assn. of Mormon Counselors and Psychotherapists [16457], PO Box 540385, North Salt Lake, UT 84054, (801)425-3490

Assn. of Moroccan Professionals in Am. [645], 5301 Pooks Hill Rd., Bethesda, MD 20814

Assn. of Motion Picture Sound [IO], London, United Kingdom

Assn. of Motion Picture and TV Producers [★1248]

L'Association Motocycliste Canadienne [★IO]

Assn. of Motor Vehicle Importers - Representatives [IO], Athens, Greece

Assn. of Mountaineering Instructors [IO], Conwy, United Kingdom

Assn. of Mouth and Foot Painting Artists of the World [IO], Schaan, Liechtenstein

Assn. of Moving Image Archivists [9597], 1313 N Vine St., Hollywood, CA 90028, (323)463-1500

Assn. of Moving Image Archivists [9597], 1313 N Vine St., Hollywood, CA 90028, (323)463-1500

Assn. for Multiple Endocrine Neoplasia Disorders [IO], Tunbridge Wells, United Kingdom

Assn. of Municipal Electricity Undertakings Southern Africa [IO], Ferndale, Republic of South Africa

Assn. of Municipal Engineers [IO], London, United Kingdom

Assn. des Musees Canadiens [★IO]

Assn. of Museums in Greenland [IO], Maniitsoq, Greenland

Assn. of Music Producers [2553], 3 W 18th St., 5th Fl., New York, NY 10011, (212)924-4100

Assn. of Music Writers and Photographers - Defunct.

Assn. de Musicotherapie du Canada [★IO]

Assn. of Muslim Amer. Lawyers [5239], Woolworth Bldg., Ste. 801, 233 Broadway, New York, NY 10279-0815

Assn. of Muslim Hea. Professionals [15147], 1284 S Vermont St., Palatine, IL 60067

Assn. of Muslim Lawyers [IO], High Wycombe, United Kingdom

Assn. of Muslim Professionals [IO], Singapore, Singapore

Assn. of Muslim Scientists and Engineers - Address unknown since 2011.

Assn. of Muslim Social Scientists of North Am. [7410], PO Box 5502, Herndon, VA 20172

Assn. of Mutual Fire Insurance Engineers [★1973]

Assn. of Mutual Fund Plan Sponsors [★3200]

Assn. of Mutual Funds in India [IO], Mumbai, India

Assn. of Mutual Insurance Engineers [★1973]

Assn. of Mutual Insurers and Insurance Cooperatives in Europe [IO], Brussels, Belgium

Assn. Mwana Ukundwa [IO], Kigali, Rwanda

Assn. of Myanmar Architects [IO], Yangon, Myanmar

Assn. of Natl. Advertisers [86], 708 3rd Ave., 33rd Fl., New York, NY 10017-4270, (212)697-5950

Assn. Natl. Des Personnes Handicapees Du Gabon [IO], Libreville, Gabon

Assn. of Natl., European and Mediterranean Societies of Gastroenterology [IO], Bologna, Italy

Assn. of Natl. Numbering Agencies [IO], Frankfurt am Main, Germany

Assn. of Natl. Olympic Committees [IO], Lausanne, Switzerland

Assn. of Natl. Olympic Committees of Africa [IO], Abuja, Nigeria

Assn. of Natl. Park Authorities [IO], Cardiff, United Kingdom

Assn. of Natl. Park Rangers [5874], 25958 Genesse Trail Rd., PMB 222, Golden, CO 80401

Assn. for a Natl. Recycling Policy [★3640]

Assn. of Natl. Tourist Off. Representatives UK [IO], Winchester, United Kingdom

Assn. Nationale des Dieteticiens du Luxembourg [★IO]

Assn. Nationale des Editeurs de Livres [★IO]

Assn. Nationale des Enterprises en Recrutement et Placement de Personnel [★IO]

Assn. Nationale Femme et du Droit [★IO]

Assn. Nationale des Indus. Alimentaires [★IO]

Assn. Nationale des Indus. de la Neige [★IO]

Assn. Nationale pour l'Education des Adultes en Haiti [★IO]

Assn. Nationale pour l'Etude de la Neige et des Avalanches [★IO]

Assn. Nationale des Olympiens de Guinee [IO], Conakry, Guinea

Assn. Nationale des Olympiens Tchadiens [IO], N'Djamena, Chad

Assn. Nationale des Retraites Federaux [★IO]

Assn. Nationale des Sourds du Rwanda [★IO]

Assn. of Native Amer. Medical Students [15321], 1225 Sovereign Row, Ste. 103, Oklahoma City, OK 73108, (405)946-7072

Assn. for Native Development in the Performing and Visual Arts [IO], Toronto, ON, Canada

Assn. of Natural Biocontrol Producers [4771], Lynn LeBeck, Exec. Dir., PO Box 1609, Clovis, CA 93613-1609, (559)360-7111

Assn. of Natural Burial Grounds [IO], Winchester, United Kingdom

Assn. of Natural Gasoline Mfrs. [★2650]

Assn. of Natural Medicine Pharmacists [15533], 4815 Minneapolis Ave., Minnetrista, MN 55364, (952)472-5689

Assn. of Natural Resource Enforcement Trainers - Defunct.

Assn. of Natural Rubber Producing Countries [IO], Kuala Lumpur, Malaysia

Assn. of Naval ROTC Colleges and Universities [★8624]

Assn. of Needle-Free Injection Mfrs. [2330], 13755 1st Ave. N, Ste. 100, Minneapolis, MN 55441, (763)475-7769

Assn. of Nepal and Himalayan Stud. [8682], Macalester Coll., Dept. of Anthropology, St. Paul, MN 55105-1801, (651)696-6362

Assn. of Nepal and Himalayan Stud. [8682], Macalester Coll., Dept. of Anthropology, St. Paul, MN 55105-1801, (651)696-6362

Assn. of Nepalis in the Americas [19171], Anil R. Pathak, Treas., 3609 Ox Ridge Ct., Fairfax, VA 22033

Assn. of Nepalis in the Americas [19171], Anil R. Pathak, Treas., 3609 Ox Ridge Ct., Fairfax, VA 22033

Assn. for Network Care [13666], 444 Main St., Longmont, CO 80501, (303)678-8101

Assn. pour les Neurinomes Acoustiques du Canada [★IO]

Assn. for Neuro-Linguistic Programming [IO], Hemel Hempstead, United Kingdom

Assn. for the Neurologically Disabled of Canada [IO], Richmond Hill, ON, Canada

Assn. des Neurologues Liberaux de Langue Francaise [IO], Versailles, France

Assn. of Neuromuscular Disorders [IO], Istanbul, Turkey

Assn. for NeuroPsychoEconomics [6613], Jessica Karp, 750 First St. NE, Washington, DC 20002

Assn. of Neurosurgical Physician Assistants [16236], PO Box 17781, Tampa, FL 33682, (813)988-7795

Assn. for New Canadians [IO], St. John's, NL, Canada

Assn. of New Zealand Advertisers [IO], Auckland, New Zealand

Assn. of Newspaper Classified Advt. Managers [★2953]

Assn. of Newspaper and Magazine Wholesalers [IO], Swindon, United Kingdom

Assn. of Nigerian Petroleum Professionals Abroad [7235], PO Box 218865, Houston, TX 77218

Assn. of Nigerian Petroleum Professionals Abroad [7235], PO Box 218865, Houston, TX 77218

Assn. of Nigerian Physicians in the Americas [16256], 5019 W 147th St., Leawood, KS 66224, (913)402-7102

Assn. of Nigerian Physicians in the Americas [16256], 5019 W 147th St., Leawood, KS 66224, (913)402-7102

Assn. of Nigerians Abroad - Address unknown since 2011.

Assn. Nigerienne de lutte contre la Corruption [IO], Niamey, Niger

Assn. Nigerienne des Olympiens [IO], Niamey, Niger

Assn. of Noise Consultants [IO], St. Albans, United Kingdom

Assn. for Non-Traditional Students in Higher Educ. [7689], Gabe DeGabriele, Consultant, 1202 8th Ave., Olympia, WA 98501, (360)545-3593

Assn. for Non-Traditional Students in Higher Educ. [7689], Gabe DeGabriele, Consultant, 1202 8th Ave., Olympia, WA 98501, (360)545-3593

Assn. of Nordic Paper Historians [IO], Stockholm, Sweden

Assn. Nordique d'Etudes Canadiennes [★IO]

Assn. of North Amer. Dir. Publishers [★2921]

Assn. of North Amer. Missions [20011], PO Box 610, Salem, MO 65560, (573)261-0057

Assn. of Northwest Steelheaders [22571], PO Box 22065, Milwaukie, OR 97269, (503)653-4176

Assn. of Norwegian Economists [IO], Oslo, Norway

Assn. of Norwegian Visual Artists [IO], Oslo, Norway

Assn. of NROTC Colleges and Universities [8624], Univ. of Rochester, 575 Mt. Hope Ave., PO Box 270041, Rochester, NY 14620, (585)273-1765

Assn. Nucleaire Canadienne [★IO]

Assn. of Nurse Advocates for Childbirth Solutions - Address unknown since 2011.

Assn. of Nurses in AIDS Care [13599], 3538 Ridgewood Rd., Akron, OH 44333, (330)670-0101

Assn. of Nurses Endorsing Transplantation [15946], PO Box 320669, Cocoa Beach, FL 32932-0669, (321)698-9117

Assn. de Nutrition Animale du Canada [★IO]

Assn. of Nutrition Departments and Programs [8686], Dr. Deborah Kipp, Univ. of North Carolina at Greensboro, Stone Bldg., Rm. 318, 1000 Spring Garden St., Greensboro, NC 27412

Assn. of Nutrition Services Agencies [14894], 1875 K St. NW, 5th Fl., Washington, DC 20006, (202)729-8031

Assn. of Occupational and Environmental Clinics [15904], 1010 Vermont Ave. NW, Ste. 513, Washington, DC 20005, (202)347-4976

Assn. of Occupational Hea. Professionals in Healthcare [15905], 109 VIP Dr., Ste. 220, Wexford, PA 15090, (800)362-4347

Assn. of Occupational Therapists of Ireland [IO], Kilmainham, Ireland

Assn. of Ocular Pharmacology and Therapeutics [15947], Alcon Res., Ltd., 6201 South Fwy., Fort Worth, TX 76134, (817)551-4921

Assn. of Ocular Pharmacology and Therapeutics [15947], Alcon Res., Ltd., 6201 South Fwy., Fort Worth, TX 76134, (817)551-4921

Assn. of Official Agricultural Chemists [★6397]

Assn. of Official Agricultural Chemists [★6397]

Assn. of Official Analytical Chemists [★6397]

Assn. of Official Analytical Chemists [★6397]

Assn. of Official Seed Analysts [5188], 101 E State St., No. 214, Ithaca, NY 14850, (607)256-3313

Assn. of Official Seed Analysts [5188], 101 E State St., No. 214, Ithaca, NY 14850, (607)256-3313

Assn. of Official Seed Certifying Agencies [5189], 1601 52nd Ave., Ste. 1, Moline, IL 61265, (309)736-0120

Assn. des Officiers des Postes du Canada [★IO]

Assn. of Ohio Longrifle Collectors [21711], 23003 State Rte. 339, Beverly, OH 45715-5028, (740)984-4896

Assn. of Oil and Gas Producing Companies [IO], Hannover, Germany

Assn. of Oil Pipe Lines [2644], 1808 Eye St. NW, Ste. 300, Washington, DC 20006, (202)408-7970

Assn. of Oilwell Servicing Contractors [★2643]

Assn. of Old Crows [6647], 1000 N Payne St., Ste. 300, Alexandria, VA 22314-1652, (703)549-1600

Assn. des Olympiens Mauritaniens [IO], Nouakchott, Mauritania

Assn. of Oncology Social Work [13214], 100 N 20th St., 4th Fl., Philadelphia, PA 19103, (215)599-6093

Reference to "IO" in place of a book number signifies that the association may be found in the 50th edition of International Organizations.

Assn. of Online Appraiser **[228]**, PO Box 1292, Frederick, MD 21702, (301)228-2279

Assn. of Online Insurance Agents **[1941]**, 501 S Idaho St., Ste. 210, La Habra, CA 90631, (888)223-4773

Assn. of Ontario Snowboarders **[IO]**, Collingwood, ON, Canada

Assn. des Operateurs Postaux Publics Europeens **[★IO]**

Assn. of Operating Room Nurses **[★15738]**

Assn. of Operating Room Nurses **[★15738]**

Assn. of Operating Room Technicians **[★15370]**

Assn. for Operations Mgt. **[6960]**, 8430 W Bryn Mawr Ave., Ste. 1000, Chicago, IL 60631, (773)867-1777

Assn. for Operations Mgt. **[6960]**, 8430 W Bryn Mawr Ave., Ste. 1000, Chicago, IL 60631, (773)867-1777

Assn. of Operative Millers **[★2501]**

Assn. of Operative Millers **[★2501]**

Assn. for Ophthalmic Cooperation in Asia **[IO]**, Hyogo, Japan

Assn. des Opticiens du Canada **[★IO]**

Assn. of Optometric Educators - Address unknown since 2010.

Assn. of Optometrists **[IO]**, London, United Kingdom

Assn. of Oral and Maxillofacial Surgeons of India **[IO]**, Madurai, India

Assn. of Organ Procurement Organizations **[14420]**, 8500 Leesburg Pike, Ste. 300, Vienna, VA 22182, (703)556-4242

Assn. Orthodontique Francaise des Specialistres en Orthopedie Dento-Faciale **[IO]**, Saintes, France

Assn. of Orthodox Jewish Scientists **[7361]**, Yossi Bennett, Exec. Dir., 1011 Moss Pl., Lawrence, NY 11559, (718)969-3669

Assn. of Osteopathic Directors and Medical Educators **[16075]**, 142 E Ontario St., Chicago, IL 60611, (312)202-8211

Assn. of Osteopathic State Executive Directors - Address unknown since 2010.

Assn. of Otolaryngology Administrators **[15292]**, 2400 Ardmore Blvd., Ste. 302, Pittsburgh, PA 15221, (412)243-5156

Assn. des Ouellet-te d'Amerique **[★IO]**

Assn. of Outdoor Lighting Professionals **[2217]**, 4305 N 6th St., Ste. A, Harrisburg, PA 17110, (717)238-2504

Assn. of Outdoor Recreation and Educ. **[8688]**, 1100 N Main St., Ste. 111, Ann Arbor, MI 48104, (810)299-2782

Assn. of Outplacement Consulting Firms **[★1143]**

Assn. of Outplacement Consulting Firms **[★1143]**

Assn. of Outplacement Consulting Firms Intl. **[★1143]**

Assn. of Outplacement Consulting Firms Intl. **[★1143]**

Assn. of Overseas Chinese Agricultural, Biological and Food Engineers **[6787]**, Dr. Donghai Wang, Kansas State Univ., Biological and Agricultural Engg., Manhattan, KS 66506, (785)532-2919

Assn. of Pacific Fisheries **[★3188]**

Assn. of Pacific Island Legislatures **[5497]**, 181 E Marine Corps Dr., Carl Rose Bldg., Ste. 207, Hagatna, GU 96910, (671)472-2719

Assn. of Pacific Island Legislatures **[5497]**, 181 E Marine Corps Dr., Carl Rose Bldg., Ste. 207, Hagatna, GU 96910, (671)472-2719

Assn. des musees des iles du Pacifique **[★IO]**

Assn. of Paediatric Anaesthetists of Great Britain and Ireland **[IO]**, London, United Kingdom

Assn. of Painting Craft Teachers **[IO]**, Shrewsbury, United Kingdom

Assn. of Pakistani Physicians **[★16257]**

Assn. of Pakistani Physicians of North Am. **[★16257]**

Assn. of Pakistani Physicians and Surgeons of the United Kingdom **[IO]**, Manchester, United Kingdom

Assn. for Palliative Medicine of Great Britain and Ireland **[IO]**, Southampton, United Kingdom

Assn. Parlementaire du Commonwealth **[★IO]**

Assn. of Paroling Authorities Intl. **[5884]**, Natalie Payne, George J. Beto Criminal Justice Center, Sam Houston State Univ., Huntsville, TX 77341-2296, (877)318-2724

Assn. of Paroling Authorities Intl. **[5884]**, Natalie Payne, George J. Beto Criminal Justice Center, Sam Houston State Univ., Huntsville, TX 77341-2296, (877)318-2724

Assn. of Part-Time Professionals - Defunct.

Assn. for Past Life Res. and Therapies **[★16855]**

Assn. for Past-Life Res. and Therapies **[★16855]**

Assn. for Past-Life Res. and Therapy **[★16855]**

Assn. of Patent Law Firms **[5885]**, 2125 Center Ave., Ste. 406, Fort Lee, NJ 07024, (201)403-0927

Assn. of Pathology Chairmen **[★16120]**

Assn. of Pathology Chairs **[16120]**, 9650 Rockville Pike, Bethesda, MD 20814-3993, (301)634-7880

Assn. for Pathology Informatics **[16121]**, Nova Smith, Univ. of Pittsburgh Cancer Pavilion, Dept. of Biomedical Informatics, 5150 Centre Ave., Ste. 301, Pittsburgh, PA 15232, (412)623-8382

Assn. for Payment Clearing Services **[IO]**, London, United Kingdom

Assn. for Peace **[IO]**, Rome, Italy

Assn. for Peace and Understanding in the Middle East **[18117]**, 2029 Verdugo Blvd., No. 215, Montrose, CA 91020, (818)773-3201

Assn. for Peace and Understanding in the Middle East **[18117]**, 2029 Verdugo Blvd., No. 215, Montrose, CA 91020, (818)773-3201

Assn. of Pedestrian and Bicycle Professionals **[18732]**, PO Box 93, Cedarburg, WI 53012-0093, (262)375-6180

Assn. for Pediatric Educ. in Europe **[IO]**, Bordeaux, France

Assn. of Pediatric Hematology/Oncology Nurses **[15737]**, 4700 W Lake Ave., Glenview, IL 60025-1485, (847)375-4724

Assn. of Pediatric Oncology Nurses **[★15737]**

Assn. of Pediatric Oncology Social Workers **[16143]**, Pat Cornwell, Pres., 5455 Meridian Mark Rd., Ste. 400, Atlanta, GA 30342, (404)785-3608

Assn. of Pediatric Prog. Directors **[8595]**, 6728 Old McLean Village Dr., McLean, VA 22101-3906, (703)556-9222

Assn. of Pediatric Therapists **[16842]**, PO Box 194191, San Francisco, CA 94119

Assn. for Pelvic Organ Prolapse Support **[14760]**, 8225 State Rd. 83, Mukwonago, WI 53149, (262)642-4338

Assn. of Pension Lawyers **[IO]**, London, United Kingdom

Assn. for People with Dogs Named Marty - Address unknown since 2010.

Assn. of People Ethnic Americans - Address unknown since 2011.

Assn. for People With Arthritis - Defunct.

Assn. of Performing Arts Presenters **[7744]**, 1211 Connecticut Ave. NW, Ste. 200, Washington, DC 20036, (202)833-2787

Assn. for Perioperative Practice **[IO]**, Harrogate, United Kingdom

Assn. of PeriOperative Registered Nurses **[15738]**, 2170 S Parker Rd., Ste. 400, Denver, CO 80231-5711, (303)755-6304

Assn. of PeriOperative Registered Nurses **[15738]**, 2170 S Parker Rd., Ste. 400, Denver, CO 80231-5711, (303)755-6304

Assn. of Personal Cmpt. User Groups **[6505]**, PO Box 671294, Dallas, TX 75367-1291, (800)558-6867

Assn. of Personal Counsellors **[IO]**, Homebush, Australia

Assn. of Personal Historians **[9753]**, Marty Walton, Operations Mgr., 43 Beach Ave., Kennebunk, ME 04043, (207)967-0720

Assn. of Personal Injury Lawyers **[IO]**, Nottingham, United Kingdom

Assn. for Persons with Developmental Disabilities and Mental Hea. Needs; NADD - An **[12488]**

Assn. for Persons with Severe Handicaps **[★11833]**

Assn. for Persons in Supported Employment **[★11761]**

Assn. for Persons With Special Needs **[IO]**, Singapore, Singapore

Assn. of Peruvian Exporters **[IO]**, Lima, Peru

Assn. of Pet Behavior Counsellors **[IO]**, Worcester, United Kingdom

Assn. of Pet Dog Trainers **[4188]**, 101 N Main St., Ste. 610, Greenville, SC 29601, (800)PET-DOGS

Assn. of Pet Dog Trainers Australia **[IO]**, Bankstown, Australia

Assn. of Pet Dog Trainers - United Kingdom **[IO]**, Fairford, United Kingdom

Assn. for Pet Loss and Bereavement **[12648]**, PO Box 55, Nutley, NJ 07110, (718)382-0690

Assn. for Petroleum and Explosives Admin. **[IO]**, Saffron Walden, United Kingdom

Assn. of the Pharmaceutical Indus. in Norway **[IO]**, Oslo, Norway

Assn. of Pharmaceutical Mfrs. **[IO]**, Stockholm, Sweden

Assn. des Pharmaciens du Canada **[★IO]**

Assn. of Pharmacy Technicians of United Kingdom **[IO]**, London, United Kingdom

Assn. of Philanthropic Counsel **[859]**, 136 Everett Rd., Albany, NY 12205, (800)957-5666

Assn. of Philippine Orthodontists **[IO]**, Makati City, Philippines

Assn. Phonetique Internationale **[★IO]**

Assn. of Photographers **[IO]**, Prague, Czech Republic

Assn. of Photographers **[IO]**, London, United Kingdom

Assn. for Physical and Mental Rehabilitation **[★16556]**

Assn. of Physical Plant Administrators **[★8087]**

Assn. of Physical Plant Administrators **[★8087]**

Assn. of Physical Plant Administrators of Universities and Colleges **[★8087]**

Assn. of Physical Plant Administrators of Universities and Colleges **[★8087]**

Assn. of Physician Asst. Programs **[★16239]**

Assn. of Physician Assistants in Cardiology **[14006]**, 401 W 15th St., Austin, TX 78701, (866)970-2272

Assn. of Physician Assistants in Cardiovascular Surgery **[14007]**, PO Box 674867, Marietta, GA 30006, (877)221-5651

Assn. of Physician Assistants in Obstetrics and Gynecology **[15871]**, 563 Carter Ct., Ste. B, Kimberly, WI 54136, (800)545-0636

Assn. of Physicians and Medical Workers for Social Responsibility **[IO]**, Nairobi, Kenya

Assn. of Physicians of Pakistani Descent of North Am. **[16257]**, 6414 S Cass Ave., Westmont, IL 60559, (630)968-8585

Assn. of Physiotherapists of Swaziland **[IO]**, Manzini, Swaziland

Assn. of Physiotherapists in Tanzania **[IO]**, Dar es Salaam, United Republic of Tanzania

Assn. des Pilotes Maritimes du Canada **[★IO]**

Assn. des Planetariums de Langue Francaise **[★IO]**

Assn. des Planificateurs de Retraite du Canada **[★IO]**

Assn. of Planned Parenthood Physicians **[★12027]**

Assn. of Planned Parenthood Professionals **[★12027]**

Assn. for the Planning and Development of Services for the Aged in Israel **[IO]**, Jerusalem, Israel

Assn. of Plastic Surgery Physician Assistants **[14179]**, 1050 Pittsford-Victor Rd., Bldg. B, Pittsford, NY 14534, (585)314-8921

Assn. for Play Therapy **[16843]**, 3198 Willow Ave., Ste. 110, Clovis, CA 93612, (559)294-2128

Assn. of Plumbing and Heating Contractors **[IO]**, Solihull, United Kingdom

Assn. for Poetry Therapy **[★16469]**

Assn. of Polar Early Career Scientists **[7281]**, PO Box 757340, Fairbanks, AK 99775-7340, (907)474-1963

Assn. of Police Authorities **[IO]**, London, United Kingdom

Assn. of Policy Market Makers **[IO]**, Sturminster Newton, United Kingdom

Assn. of Polish Agricultural Journalists **[IO]**, Poznan, Poland

Assn. of Polish Engineers in Canada **[IO]**, Toronto, ON, Canada

Assn. of Polish Geomorphologists **[IO]**, Poznan, Poland

Assn. of Polish Operational Res. Societies **[IO]**, Warsaw, Poland

Assn. of Polish Papermakers **[IO]**, Lodz, Poland

Assn. of Polish Women in Am. **[★19195]**

Assn. for Political Theory **[7286]**, Colorado Coll., Dept. of Philosophy, 14 E Cache La Poudre St., Colorado Springs, CO 80903

A star before a book entry number signifies that the name is not listed separately, but is mentioned within the entry.

Assn. for Politics and the Life Sciences - Address unknown since 2010.

Assn. Polysomnographic Technologists [★16661]

Assn. of Polytechnic Graduates [IO], Montreal, QC, Canada

Assn. of Pool and Spa Professionals [3054], 2111 Eisenhower Ave., Ste. 500, Alexandria, VA 22314, (703)838-0083

Assn. of Pool and Spa Professionals [3054], 2111 Eisenhower Ave., Ste. 500, Alexandria, VA 22314, (703)838-0083

Assn. of Population Centers [6594], 1875 Connecticut Ave. NW, Ste. 520, Washington, DC 20009, (202)939-5456

Assn. for Population/Family Planning Libraries and Info. Centers-International [★9960]

Assn. for Population/Family Planning Libraries and Information Centers-Intl. [★9960]

Assn. of Port Hea. Authorities [IO], London, United Kingdom

Assn. of Port Wine Companies [IO], Vila Nova de Gaia, Portugal

Assn. of Portuguese-Language Universities [IO], Lisbon, Portugal

Assn. for Positive Behavior Support [6252], PO Box 328, Bloomsburg, PA 17815, (570)389-4081

Assn. for Post Natal Illness [IO], London, United Kingdom

Assn. for Postal Commerce [2232], 1421 Prince St., Ste. 410, Alexandria, VA 22314-2806, (703)524-0096

Assn. of Postal Officials of Canada [IO], Ottawa, ON, Canada

Assn. of Postconsumer Plastic Recyclers [2763], 1001 G St. NW, Ste. 500 W, Washington, DC 20001, (202)316-3046

Assn. Pour La Lutte Contre Le Psoriasis [IO], Paris, France

Assn. Pour La Prevention Des Infections A l'hopital et dans La Communaute [★IO]

Assn. Pour Le Commerce Et Les Services En Ligne [IO], Paris, France

Assn. of Power Producers of Ontario [IO], Toronto, ON, Canada

Assn. for Practical and Professional Ethics [8705], Indiana Univ., 618 E 3rd St., Bloomington, IN 47405-3602, (812)855-6450

Assn. of Practitioners Before the Interstate Commerce Commn. [★6030]

Assn. for Practitioners in Infection Control [★15115]

Assn. de Pre-Histoire de la Regional Indo-Pacifique [★IO]

Assn. for Pre- and Perinatal Psychology and Hea. [14101], PO Box 1398, Forestville, CA 95436, (707)887-2838

Assn. of Premier Nanny Agencies [772], Ginger Swift, 400 S Colorado Blvd., Ste. 300, Denver, CO 80246

Assn. of Presbyterian Church Educators [19612], PO Box 50761, Arlington, VA 22205-5761, (703)812-9488

Assn. of Presbyterian Colleges [★8738]

Assn. of Presbyterian Colleges and Universities [8738], 100 Witherspoon St., Louisville, KY 40202-1396, (502)569-5364

Assn. of Presbyterian Univ. Pastors and Campus Ministry Assn. [★19682]

Assn. for the Preservation of Civil War Sites [★9675]

Assn. for the Preservation of the Coelacanth [IO], Moroni, Comoros

Assn. pour la Preservation du Gombessa [★IO]

Assn. for Preservation Tech. [★9671]

Assn. for Preservation Tech. [★9671]

Assn. for Preservation Tech. Intl. [9671], 3085 Stevenson Dr., Ste. 200, Springfield, IL 62703, (217)529-9039

Assn. for Preservation Tech. Intl. [9671], 3085 Stevenson Dr., Ste. 200, Springfield, IL 62703, (217)529-9039

Assn. for the Preservation of Virginia Antiquities [★9668]

Assn. to Preserve Cape Cod [4005], PO Box 398, 3010 Main St., Barnstable, MA 02630-0398, (508)362-4226

Assn. des Presses Universitaires Canadiennes [★IO]

Assn. for the Prevention of Atmospheric Pollution [IO], Le Kremlin-Bicetre, France

Assn. pour la Prevention de la Pollution Atmospherique [★IO]

Assn. for Prevention Teaching and Res. [16308], 1001 Connecticut Ave. NW, Ste. 610, Washington, DC 20036, (202)463-0550

Assn. pour la Prevention de la Torture [★IO]

Assn. for the Prevention of Torture [IO], Geneva, Switzerland

Assn. of Principal Fire Officers [IO], Tamworth, United Kingdom

Assn. of Printed Media of Macedonia [IO], Skopje, Macedonia

Assn. of Private Banks of Ecuador [IO], Quito, Ecuador

Assn. of Private Client Investment Managers and Stockbrokers [IO], London, United Kingdom

Assn. of Private Enterprise Educ. [8753], Univ. of Tennessee at Chattanooga, 313 Fletcher Hall, Dept. 6106, 615 McCallie Ave., Chattanooga, TN 37403-2598, (423)425-4118

Assn. of Private Enterprise Educ. [8753], Univ. of Tennessee at Chattanooga, 313 Fletcher Hall, Dept. 6106, 615 McCallie Ave., Chattanooga, TN 37403-2598, (423)425-4118

Assn. of Private Hospitals of Malaysia [IO], Selangor, Malaysia

Assn. of Private Pension and Welfare Plans [★5887]

Assn. of Private Postal Systems [★2230]

Assn. of Private Sector Colleges and Universities [9041], 1101 Connecticut Ave. NW, Ste. 900, Washington, DC 20036, (202)336-6700

Assn. du Prix Albert Londres [IO], Paris, France

Assn. of ProAgria Centres [IO], Vantaa, Finland

Assn. of Problem Gambling Ser. Administrators [12060], Arizona Off. of Problem Gambling, 202 E Earll Dr., Ste. 200, Phoenix, AZ 85012, (602)266-8299

Assn. for Process Philosophy of Educ. - Address unknown since 2011.

Assn. of the Processed Cheese Indus. of the EU [IO], Berlin, Germany

Assn. of Procurement Technical Asistance Centers [1585], 360 Senset Island Trail, Gallatin, TN 37066, (815)268-6644

Assn. of the Producers and Merchants of Wines and Spirits in Bulgaria [IO], Sofia, Bulgaria

Assn. of Productivity Specialists [2271], 521 5th Ave., Ste. 1700, New York, NY 10175, (212)286-0943

Assn. of Productivity Specialists [2271], 521 5th Ave., Ste. 1700, New York, NY 10175, (212)286-0943

Assn. des Produits Forestiers du Canada [★IO]

Assn. des Professeurs d'Allemand des Universites Canadiennes [★IO]

Assn. des Professeurs de Francais des Universites et des Colleges Canadiens [★IO]

Assn. des Professeurs de l'Enseignement Secondaire et Superieur [★IO]

Assn. of Professional Animal Waste Specialists [3631], PO Box 2325, Santa Clarita, CA 91386, (800)787-7667

Assn. of Professional Architects of Belize [IO], Belize City, Belize

Assn. for Professional Art Advisors [249], 433 Third St., Ste. 3, Brooklyn, NY 11215, (718)788-1425

Assn. of Professional Ball Players of Am. [22267], 101 S Kraemer Ave., Ste. 112, Placentia, CA 92870, (714)528-2012

Assn. for Professional Baseball Physicians - Defunct.

Assn. for Professional Basketball Res. [22293], 2006 5th Ave., Sacramento, CA 95818

Assn. for Professional Broadcasting Educ. [★7772]

Assn. for Professional Broadcasting Educ. [★7772]

Assn. of Professional Chaplains [19518], 1701 E Woodfield Rd., Ste. 400, Schaumburg, IL 60173, (847)240-1014

Assn. of Professional Collectors - Defunct.

Assn. of Professional Color Imagers - Defunct.

Assn. of Professional Commun. Consultants [860], 104 Trace Ridge, Clinton, MS 39056, (601)924-2173

Assn. of Professional Commun. Consultants [860], 104 Trace Ridge, Clinton, MS 39056, (601)924-2173

Assn. of Professional Cmpt. Consultants [IO], Toronto, ON, Canada

Assn. of Professional Consultants [861], PO Box 51193, Irvine, CA 92619-1193, (800)745-5050

Assn. of Professional Design Firms [1636], 1448 E 52nd St., No. 201, Chicago, IL 60615, (773)643-7052

Assn. of Professional Directors of YMCAs in the U.S. [★13500]

Assn. of Professional Directors, Young Men's Christian Associations in the U.S. [★13500]

Assn. of Professional Draftsman [★6931]

Assn. of Professional Engineers of Belize [IO], Belize City, Belize

Assn. of Professional Engineers, Geologists and Geophysicists of Alberta [IO], Edmonton, AB, Canada

Assn. of Professional Engineers, Scientists and Managers Australia [IO], Melbourne, Australia

Assn. of Professional Flight Attendants [23151], 1004 W Euless Blvd., Euless, TX 76040, (817)540-0108

Assn. of Professional Futurists [6886], 681 Main St., Ste. 324, Waltham, MA 02451

Assn. of Professional Futurists [6886], 681 Main St., Ste. 324, Waltham, MA 02451

Assn. of Professional Genealogists in Ireland [IO], Dublin, Ireland

Assn. of Professional Geological Scientists [★6909]

Assn. of Professional Humane Educators [11916], The Latham Found., Latham Plaza Bldg., 1826 Clement Ave., Alameda, CA 94501

Assn. of Professional Insurance Women [1942], Susan Barros, Exec. Admin., 990 Cedarbridge Ave., Ste. B, PMB 210, Brick, NJ 08723-4157, (973)941-6024

Assn. of Professional Landscape Designers [2178], 4305 N Sixth St., Ste. A, Harrisburg, PA 17110, (717)238-9780

Assn. of Professional Landscape Designers [2178], 4305 N Sixth St., Ste. A, Harrisburg, PA 17110, (717)238-9780

Assn. of Professional Landscapers [IO], Reading, United Kingdom

Assn. of Professional Material Handling Consultants [862], 8720 Red Oak Blvd., Ste. 201, Charlotte, NC 28217-3992, (704)676-1184

Assn. of Professional Model Makers [6788], PO Box 165, Collinsville, CT 06019, (877)663-2766

Assn. of Professional Music Therapists [IO], London, United Kingdom

Assn. for Professional Observers [4379], PO Box 933, Eugene, OR 97440, (541)344-5503

Assn. of Professional Organizers [★6949]

Assn. of Professional Piercers [3380], PO Box 1287, Lawrence, KS 66044, (785)841-6060

Assn. of Professional Recording Services [IO], Totnes, United Kingdom

Assn. of Professional Recruiters of Canada [IO], Ottawa, ON, Canada

Assn. of Professional Researchers for Advancement [12050], 401 N Michigan Ave., Ste. 2200, Chicago, IL 60611, (312)321-5196

Assn. of Professional Reserve Analysts [2894], W175 N1117 Stonewood Dr., Ste. 204, Germantown, WI 53022, (877)858-5047

Assn. of Professional Responsibility Lawyers [5240], 134 N LaSalle St., Ste. 1600, Chicago, IL 60602, (312)782-4396

Assn. of Professional Schools of Intl. Affairs [8401], 3141 Van Munching Hall, College Park, MD 20742, (301)405-5238

Assn. of Professional Schools of Intl. Affairs [8401], 3141 Van Munching Hall, College Park, MD 20742, (301)405-5238

Assn. of Professional Sleep Societies [★16664]

Assn. of Professional Towsurfers [23030], 758 S Coast Hwy., Laguna Beach, CA 96150, (949)338-1357

Assn. of Professional Vocal Ensembles [★10176]

Assn. of Professional Wildlife Educators [9050], PO Box 365, Escondido, CA 92033

Reference to "IO" in place of a book number signifies that the association may be found in the 50th edition of International Organizations.

Assn. of Professional Writing Consultants [★860]

Assn. of Professional Writing Consultants [★860]

Assn. for Professionals in Infection Control and Epidemiology [15115], 1275 K St. NW, Ste. 1000, Washington, DC 20005-4006, (202)789-1890

Assn. for Professionals in Services for Adolescents [IO], Banbury, United Kingdom

Assn. Professionnelle des Opticiens et Optometristes de Belgique [IO], Brussels, Belgium

Assn. des Professionnels de l'information et de la Documentation [IO], Paris, France

Assn. of Professors of Cardiology [14008], 2400 N St. NW, Washington, DC 20037, (202)375-6191

Assn. of Professors of Gynecology and Obstetrics [15872], 2130 Priest Bridge Dr., Ste. 7, Crofton, MD 21114, (410)451-9560

Assn. of Professors of Higher Educ. [★8230]

Assn. of Professors of Human and Medical Genetics [14645], Miriam G. Blitzer, PhD, Pres., Univ. of Maryland School of Medicine, Dept. of Pediatrics, Division of Human Genetics, 655 W Baltimore St., Rm. 11-037, Baltimore, MD 21201, (410)706-4065

Assn. of Professors of Medicine [8596], 330 John Carlylr St., Ste. 610, Alexandria, VA 22314, (703)341-4540

Assn. of Professors of Mission [20012], Northwestern Coll., 3003 Snelling Ave., St. Paul, MN 55113, (651)631-5229

Assn. of Professors, Practitioners, and Researchers in Religious Educ; Religious Educ. Assn.: An [19686]

Assn. of Professors and Researchers in Religious Educ. [★19686]

Assn. of Professors and Scholars of Iranian Heritage [8411], PO Box 4175, Diamond Bar, CA 91765, (909)869-2569

Assn. of Professors of Secondary and Higher Educ. [IO], Strassen, Luxembourg

Assn. of Prog. Coordinators in Radiology [16530], 820 Jorie Blvd., Oak Brook, IL 60523, (630)368-3737

Assn. of Prog. Directors in Endocrinology, Diabetes and Metabolism [14486], 8401 Connecticut Ave., Ste. 900, Chevy Chase, MD 20815, (301)941-0243

Assn. of Prog. Directors in Endocrinology and Metabolism [★14486]

Assn. of Prog. Directors in Internal Medicine [15134], Alliance for Academic Internal Medicine, 330 John Carlyle St., Ste. 610, Alexandria, VA 22314-5946, (703)341-4540

Assn. of Prog. Directors in Radiology [15322], 820 Jorie Blvd., Oak Brook, IL 60523, (630)368-3737

Assn. of Prog. Directors in Surgery [16807], 6400 Goldsboro Rd., Ste. 450, Bethesda, MD 20817-5846, (301)320-1200

Assn. of Prog. Directors in Vascular Surgery [16808], 633 N St. Clair St., 24th Fl., Chicago, IL 60611, (312)334-2300

Assn. on Programs for Female Offenders [11705], Judy Anderson, Treas., PO Box 5293, Columbia, SC 29250-5293

Assn. of Progressive Rental Organizations [3077], 1504 Robin Hood Trail, Austin, TX 78703, (512)794-0095

Assn. for Proj. Mgt. [IO], Princes Risborough, United Kingdom

Assn. for Proj. Mgt. Hong Kong [IO], Hong Kong, People's Republic of China

Assn. for Proj. Safety [IO], Edinburgh, United Kingdom

Assn. Promoting Educ. and Conservation in Amazonia [5029], 21338 Dumetz Rd., Woodland Hills, CA 91364, (818)340-4212

Assn. Promoting Educ. and Conservation in Amazonia [5029], 21338 Dumetz Rd., Woodland Hills, CA 91364, (818)340-4212

Assn. for the Promotion of African Community Initiatives [IO], Douala, Cameroon

Assn. for the Promotion of Christian Union [★19652]

Assn. pour la Promotion de la Diffusion Internationale de la Presse [★IO]

Assn. pour la Promotion des Initiatives Communautaires Africaines [★IO]

Assn. of Promotion Marketing Agencies Worldwide [★3163]

Assn. of Promotion Marketing Agencies Worldwide [★3163]

Assn. for the Promotion of the Mathematics Educ. of Girls and Women [★8570]

Assn. for Promotion of Skiing [IO], Oslo, Norway

Assn. for the Promotion of Tourism to Africa [3472], PO Box 872, Babylon, NY 11702, (631)661-6871

Assn. for the Promotion of Tourism to Africa [3472], PO Box 872, Babylon, NY 11702, (631)661-6871

Assn. of Property Unit Trusts [★18082]

Assn. of Proposal Mgt. Professionals [2272], PO Box 668, Dana Point, CA 92629-0668

Assn. for Protected Areas Mgt. Organizations [IO], Belize City, Belize

Assn. for the Protection of Afghan Archaeology [6163], PO Box 6798, San Rafael, CA 94903-0798

Assn. pour la Protection des Automobilistes [★IO]

Assn. for Protection of Child Laborers [IO], Tehran, Iran

Assn. for the Protection of Consumers [IO], Bucharest, Romania

Assn. for the Protection of Fur-Bearing Animals [IO], Vancouver, BC, Canada

Assn. for the Protection of Nature and the Env. Kairouan, Tunisia [IO], Kairouan, Tunisia

Assn. for the Protection of Rural Scotland [IO], Edinburgh, United Kingdom

Assn. of Protestant Churches and Missions in Germany [IO], Hamburg, Germany

Assn. Psychanalytique Internationale [★IO]

Assn. des Psychiatres du Canada [★IO]

Assn. for Psychoanalytic Medicine [16356], 333 Central Park W, New York, NY 10025, (718)548-6088

Assn. for Psychoanalytic and Psychosomatic Medicine [★16356]

Assn. for Psychohistory [★9777]

Assn. for Psychological Astrology [6215], 133 Injun Hollow Rd., Haddam Neck, CT 06424, (415)479-5812

Assn. for Psychological Sci. [16390], 1133 15th St. NW, Ste. 1000, Washington, DC 20005, (202)293-9300

Assn. for Psychological Type Intl. [16391], 9650 Rockville Pike, Bethesda, MD 20814-3998, (301)634-7450

Assn. of Psychologists of Nova Scotia [IO], Halifax, NS, Canada

Assn. of Psychology Internship Centers [★8597]

Assn. of Psychology Postdoctoral and Internship Centers [8597], 10 G St. NE, Ste. 440, Washington, DC 20002, (202)589-0600

Assn. for the Psychophysiological Stud. of Sleep [★16669]

Assn. of Public Analysts [IO], London, United Kingdom

Assn. for Public Broadcasting [★483]

Assn. for Public Data Users [6970], PO Box 100155, Arlington, VA 22210, (703)522-4980

Assn. of Public Hea. Labs. [16480], 8515 Georgia Ave., Ste. 700, Silver Spring, MD 20910, (240)485-2745

Assn. of Public Hea. Labs. [16480], 8515 Georgia Ave., Ste. 700, Silver Spring, MD 20910, (240)485-2745

Assn. for Public Justice Educ. Fund [★18448]

Assn. of Public and Land-Grant Universities [7873], 1307 New York Ave. NW, Ste. 400, Washington, DC 20005-4722, (202)478-6040

Assn. of Public and Land Grant Universities I Commn. on Intl. Programs [17903], 1307 New York Ave. NW, Ste. 400, Washington, DC 20005-4722, (202)478-6040

Assn. of Public and Land Grant Universities I Commn. on Intl. Programs [17903], 1307 New York Ave. NW, Ste. 400, Washington, DC 20005-4722, (202)478-6040

Assn. of Public Pension Fund Auditors [23263], PO Box 16064, Columbus, OH 43216

Assn. for Public Policy Anal. and Mgt. [18442], 1029 Vermont Ave. NW, Ste. 1150, Washington, DC 20005, (202)496-0130

Assn. for Public Policy Anal. and Mgt. [18442], 1029 Vermont Ave. NW, Ste. 1150, Washington, DC 20005, (202)496-0130

Assn. of Public and Private Banks of the Argentine Republic [IO], Buenos Aires, Argentina

Assn. of Public Radio Stations [★9461]

Assn. of Public-Safety Communications Officials Intl. [5960], 351 N Williamson Blvd., Daytona Beach, FL 32114-1112, (386)322-2500

Assn. of Public-Safety Communications Officials Intl. [5960], 351 N Williamson Blvd., Daytona Beach, FL 32114-1112, (386)322-2500

Assn. for Public Ser. Excellence [IO], Manchester, United Kingdom

Assn. of Public TV Stations [483], 2100 Crystal Dr., Ste. 700, Arlington, VA 22202, (202)654-4200

Assn. of Public Treasurers of the U.S. and Canada [5917], 962 Wayne Ave., Ste. 910, Silver Spring, MD 20910, (301)495-5560

Assn. of Publicly Traded Investment Funds [★3200]

Assn. of Publishers' Representatives [★2951]

Assn. of Publishing Agencies [IO], London, United Kingdom

Assn. Pulmonaire du Canada [★IO]

Assn. of Pulmonary and Critical Care Medicine Prog. Directors [14207], 3300 Dundee Rd., Northbrook, IL 60062, (847)498-8317

Assn. of the Pulp and Paper Indus. [IO], Prague, Czech Republic

Assn. for Purchasing and Supply [IO], Dublin, Ireland

Assn. of Qualified Volunteers in Youth Services [IO], Montreal, QC, Canada

Assn. of Qualitative Res. [IO], St. Neots, United Kingdom

Assn. for Quality and Participation [★7319]

Assn. Quebecoise des Critiques de Cinema [IO], Montreal, QC, Canada

Assn. Quebecoise des troubles d'apprentissage [★IO]

Assn. Quebecoise de L'Industrie du Disque, du Spectacle et de la Video [IO], Montreal, QC, Canada

Assn. Quebecoise pour la Therapie Conjugale et Familiale [★IO]

Assn. for Queer Anthropology [6135], 4350 N Fairfax Dr., Ste. 640, Arlington, VA 22203-1620, (703)528-1902

Assn. of Racing Commissioners Intl. [5952], 1510 Newtown Pike, Ste. 210, Lexington, KY 40511, (859)224-7070

Assn. of Racing Commissioners Intl. [5952], 1510 Newtown Pike, Ste. 210, Lexington, KY 40511, (859)224-7070

Assn. for Radiation Res. [IO], Manchester, United Kingdom

Assn. of Radical Midwives [IO], Ormskirk, United Kingdom

Assn. of Radio Amateurs of Slovenia [IO], Ljubljana, Slovenia

Assn. of Radio Indus. and Businesses [IO], Tokyo, Japan

Assn. for Radiological and Imaging Nursing [15739], 7794 Grow Dr., Pensacola, FL 32514, (850)474-7292

Assn. of Railroad Advertising and Marketing - Defunct.

Assn. of Railway Communicators - Defunct.

Assn. of Railway Museums [10485], 1016 Rosser St., Conyers, GA 30012, (770)278-0088

Assn. of Railway Training Providers [IO], London, United Kingdom

Assn. of Rain Apparel Contractors - Defunct.

Assn. for Real Change [IO], Chesterfield, United Kingdom

Assn. of Real Estate Brokers of Belize [IO], Belize City, Belize

Assn. of Real Estate Companies of Estonia [IO], Tallinn, Estonia

Assn. of Real Estate Funds [IO], London, United Kingdom

Assn. of Real Estate License Law Officials [5956], 8361 Sangre de Cristo, Ste. 250, Littleton, CO 80127, (303)979-6190

Assn. of Real Estate License Law Officials [5956], 8361 Sangre de Cristo, Ste. 250, Littleton, CO 80127, (303)979-6190

Assn. of Real Estate Women [3002], 1201 Wakarusa Dr., Ste. C3, Lawrence, KS 66049, (212)599-6181

A star before a book entry number signifies that the name is not listed separately, but is mentioned within the entry.

Assn. pour la Recherche sur la Sclerose Laterale Amyotrophique [IO], Paris, France

Assn. de la Recherche Theatrale au Canada [★IO]

Assn. of Record Librarians of North Am. [★15331]

Assn. for Recorded Sound Collections [9971], PO Box 543, Annapolis, MD 21404-0543

Assn. for Recorded Sound Collections [9971], PO Box 543, Annapolis, MD 21404-0543

Assn. of Records Executives and Administrators [★1895]

Assn. of Records Executives and Administrators [★1895]

Assn. of Recovering Motorcyclists [13236], 1503 Market St., La Crosse, WI 54601

Assn. canadienne de Redactologie [★IO]

Assn. of Reef Keepers [IO], Tortola, British Virgin Islands

Assn. of Reflexologists [IO], Taunton, United Kingdom

Assn. of Reform Zionists of Am. [★19847]

Assn. of Reform Zionists of Am. [★19847]

Assn. of Reformed Baptist Churches of Am. [19309], PO Box 289, Carlisle, PA 17013, (717)249-7473

Assn. of Refrigerant and Desuperheating Mfg. - Address unknown since 2011.

Assn. for Refugee Ser. Professionals [12301], 4113 Junius St., Dallas, TX 75246

Assn. of Regional Weed Control Conferences [★3748]

Assn. of Registered Bank Holding Companies [★413]

Assn. des Registraires des Universites et Colleges du Canada [★IO]

Assn. of Registrars of the Universities and Colleges of Canada [IO], Sherbrooke, QC, Canada

Assn. of Regulatory Boards of Optometry [15991], 200 S Coll. St., Ste. 1630, Charlotte, NC 28202, (704)970-2710

Assn. of Regulatory Boards of Optometry [15991], 200 S Coll. St., Ste. 1630, Charlotte, NC 28202, (704)970-2710

Assn. of Regulatory and Clinical Scientists Australia [IO], Crows Nest, Australia

Assn. for the Rehabilitation of the Brain Injured [IO], Calgary, AB, Canada

Assn. of Rehabilitation Centers [★16557]

Assn. for Rehabilitation of Commun. and Oral Skills [IO], Malvern, United Kingdom

Assn. for Rehabilitation of Drug Abusers of Macau [IO], Coloane, Macao

Assn. of Rehabilitation Facilities [★16557]

Assn. of Rehabilitation Marketing [★2391]

Assn. for Rehabilitation Marketing and Sales [2391], 118 Julian Pl., PMB 105, Syracuse, NY 13210

Assn. of Rehabilitation Nurses [15740], 4700 W Lake Ave., Glenview, IL 60025-1485, (847)375-4710

Assn. of Rehabilitation Programs in Cmpt. Tech. [11764], Western Michigan Univ., Educational Leadership, Res. and Tech. Dept., Kalamazoo, MI 49008, (269)387-2053

Assn. for Rehabilitation Programs in Data Processing [★11764]

Assn. for Religion and Intellectual Life [19669], DBA CrossCurrents, 475 Riverside Dr., New York, NY 10115-0021, (212)870-2544

Assn. for Religious and Value Issues in Counseling [★7940]

Assn. of Relocation Professionals [IO], Diss, United Kingdom

Assn. for Renaissance Martial Arts [8559], 105 Gainesborough Walk, Dallas, GA 30157

Assn. for Renaissance Martial Arts [8559], 105 Gainesborough Walk, Dallas, GA 30157

Assn. for Repetitive Motion Syndromes [15906], PO Box 471973, Aurora, CO 80047-1973, (303)369-0803

Assn. of Reporters of Judicial Decisions [5615], 5711 Nevada St., College Park, MD 20740, (202)479-3194

Assn. of Reproductive Hea. Professionals [12027], 1901 L St. NW, Ste. 300, Washington, DC 20036, (202)466-3825

Assn. of Reptilian and Amphibian Veterinarians [17014], PO Box 1897, Lawrence, KS 66044, (785)843-1234

Assn. of Reptilian and Amphibian Veterinarians [17014], PO Box 1897, Lawrence, KS 66044, (785)843-1234

Assn. for Res. of Childhood Cancer [13889], PO Box 251, Buffalo, NY 14225-0251, (716)681-4433

Assn. of Res. Directors [7326], West Virginia State Univ., Institute, WV 25112-1000, (304)766-4291

Assn. for Res. and Enlightenment [7223], 215 67th St., Virginia Beach, VA 23451-2061, (757)428-3588

Assn. for Res. and Enlightenment [7223], 215 67th St., Virginia Beach, VA 23451-2061, (757)428-3588

Assn. of Res. Libraries [9972], 21 Dupont Cir. NW, Ste. 800, Washington, DC 20036-1543, (202)296-2296

Assn. for Res. in Modern History [IO], Bonn, Germany

Assn. for Res. in Nervous and Mental Disease [16337], PO Box 137, Tannersville, PA 18372, (570)460-5670

Assn. for Res. on Nonprofit Organizations and Voluntary Action [13386], 550 W North St., Ste. 301, Indianapolis, IN 46202, (317)684-2120

Assn. for Res. on Nonprofit Organizations and Voluntary Action [13386], 550 W North St., Ste. 301, Indianapolis, IN 46202, (317)684-2120

Assn. for Res. in Ophthalmology [★15948]

Assn. for Res. in Ophthalmology [★15948]

Assn. for Res. in Otolaryngology [16088], 19 Mantua Rd., Mount Royal, NJ 08061, (856)423-0041

Assn. for Res. in Personality [7303], M. Lynne Cooper, Exec. Off., Univ. of Missouri, Dept. of Psychological Sciences, 105 McAlester Hall, Columbia, MO 65211

Assn. for Res. in Vision and Ophthalmology [15948], 1801 Rockville Pike, Ste. 400, Rockville, MD 20852-5622, (240)221-2900

Assn. for Res. in Vision and Ophthalmology [15948], 1801 Rockville Pike, Ste. 400, Rockville, MD 20852-5622, (240)221-2900

Assn. for Res. in the Voluntary and Community Sector [IO], London, United Kingdom

Assn. of Researchers in Medicine and Sci. [IO], London, United Kingdom

Assn. of Reserve City Bankers [★413]

Assn. of Residential Cleaning Services Intl. [2240], 7870 Olentangy River Rd., Ste. 302, Columbus, OH 43235, (614)547-0887

Assn. of Residential Letting Agents [IO], Warwick, United Kingdom

Assn. of Residential Managing Agents [IO], London, United Kingdom

Assn. of Residents in Radiation Oncology [15921], 8280 Willow Oaks Corporate Dr., Ste. 500, Fairfax, VA 22031

Assn. for the Restoration of Church and Home [19613], PO Box 918, Ovid, NY 14521, (315)415-3475

Assn. of Restorers [197], 8 Medford Pl., New Hartford, NY 13413, (315)733-1952

Assn. for Retail Environments [533], 4651 Sheridan St., Ste. 470, Hollywood, FL 33021, (954)893-7300

Assn. for Retail Tech. Standards [3096], 325 7th St. NW, Ste. 1100, Washington, DC 20004-2818, (202)626-8140

Assn. of Retail Travel Agents [3553], 4320 N Miller Rd., Scottsdale, AZ 85251, (866)369-8969

Assn. for Retarded Citizens [★12495]

Assn. for Retarded Citizens of the U.S. [★12495]

Assn. for Retinopathy of Prematurity and Related Diseases [15949], PO Box 250425, Franklin, MI 48025, (800)788-2020

Assn. of Retired Americans [12916], 6505 E 82nd St., No. 130, Indianapolis, IN 46250, (800)806-6160

Assn. of Retired Hispanic Police [5688], PO Box 722, Tallman, NY 10982

Assn. of Retired Intelligence Officers [★5597]

Assn. of Retired Intelligence Officers [★5597]

Assn. of Retirement Housing Managers [IO], London, United Kingdom

Assn. for the Rhetoric of Sci. and Tech. [10510], William J. White, Treas., 3000 Ivyside Park, Altoona, PA 16601

Assn. of Rheumatologists of Russia [IO], Moscow, Russia

Assn. of Rheumatology Hea. Professionals - Address unknown since 2011.

Assn. of Ridesharing Professionals [★13331]

Assn. of Ridesharing Professionals [★13331]

Assn. for the Right to Die with Dignity [IO], Paris, France

Assn. for the Rights of Catholics in the Church [19389], 3150 Newgate Dr., Florissant, MO 63033, (413)527-9929

Assn. of Ringside Physicians [16258], 401 W. Michigan St., Indianapolis, IN

Assn. for Road Traffic Safety and Mgt. [IO], Hampshire, United Kingdom

Assn. of Road Users of Pakistan [IO], Islamabad, Pakistan

Assn. for Roller and Silent Chain Mfrs. [★1798]

Assn. for Roman Archaeology [IO], Swindon, United Kingdom

Assn. of Rotational Molders [★2764]

Assn. of Rotational Molders [★2764]

Assn. of Rotational Molders Intl. [2764], 800 Roosevelt Rd., Ste. C-312, Glen Ellyn, IL 60137, (630)942-6589

Assn. of Rotational Molders Intl. [2764], 800 Roosevelt Rd., Ste. C-312, Glen Ellyn, IL 60137, (630)942-6589

Assn. Royale Belge des Indus. du Biscuit, du Chocolat, de la Confiserie et de la Praline [★IO]

Assn. Royale de Golf du Canada [★IO]

Assn. of Rural Cooperation in Africa and Latin Am. - Nicaragua [IO], Managua, Nicaragua

Assn. for Rural Development and Action Res. [IO], Visakhapatnam, India

Assn. of Russian Auto. Dealers [IO], Moscow, Russia

Assn. of Russian Banks [IO], Moscow, Russia

Assn. Rwandaise pour le Developpement Rural [★IO]

Assn. Rwandaise des Gouvernements Locaux [★IO]

Assn. for Safe Intl. Road Travel [13332], 11769 Gainsborough Rd., Potomac, MD 20854, (301)983-5252

Assn. for Safe Intl. Road Travel [13332], 11769 Gainsborough Rd., Potomac, MD 20854, (301)983-5252

Assn. of Salaried Medical Specialists [IO], Wellington, New Zealand

Assn. for Sales Force Management - Defunct.

Assn. of Sales and Marketing Companies [★1392]

Assn. of Sales and Marketing Companies - Defunct.

The Assn. of Sanctuaries - Defunct.

Assn. for Sandwich Educ. and Training [IO], Sheffield, United Kingdom

Assn. Sans But Lucrative [★IO]

Assn. of School Bus. Officials [★7662]

Assn. of School Bus. Officials [★7662]

Assn. of School Bus. Officials Intl. [7662], 11401 N Shore Dr., Reston, VA 20190-4200, (703)478-0405

Assn. of School Bus. Officials Intl. [7662], 11401 N Shore Dr., Reston, VA 20190-4200, (703)478-0405

Assn. of School Bus. Officials of the U.S. and Canada [★7662]

Assn. of School Bus. Officials of the U.S. and Canada [★7662]

Assn. of School and Coll. Leaders [IO], Leicester, United Kingdom

Assn. for School, Coll. and Univ. Staffing [★8726]

Assn. of Schools of Allied Hea. Professions [8598], 4400 Jenifer St. NW, Ste. 333, Washington, DC 20015, (202)237-6481

Assn. of Schools and Colleges of Optometry [15992], 6110 Executive Blvd., Ste. 420, Rockville, MD 20852, (301)231-5944

Assn. of Schools of Journalism and Mass Commun. [7663], 234 Outlet Pointe Blvd., Columbia, SC 29210-5667, (803)798-0271

Assn. of Schools of Public Hea. [16481], 1900 M St. NW, Ste. 710, Washington, DC 20036, (202)296-1099

Assn. of Schools of Public Hea. in the European Region [IO], Suresnes, France

Assn. for Schools of Social Work in Africa [IO], Addis Ababa, Ethiopia

Assn. of Schoolsports Clubs Czech Republic [IO], Prague, Czech Republic

Reference to "IO" in place of a book number signifies that the association may be found in the 50th edition of International Organizations.

Assn. for Sci. Educ. **[IO]**, Hatfield, United Kingdom

Assn. of Sci. Fiction and Fantasy Artists **[250]**, PO Box 65011, Phoenix, AZ 85082-5011

Assn. for the Sci. and Info. on Coffee **[IO]**, Bussigny-pres-Laussane, Switzerland

Assn. of Sci. Museum Directors **[10115]**, Bonnie W. Styles, Sec.-Treas., Illinois State Museum, 502 S Spring St., Springfield, IL 62706-5000, (217)782-7011

Assn. for Sci. Teacher Educ. **[8944]**, Dr. Bob Hollon, Exec. Dir., 9324 27th Ave., Eau Claire, WI 54703, (715)838-0893

Assn. of Science-Technology Centers **[10116]**, 1025 Vermont Ave. NW, Ste. 500, Washington, DC 20005-6310, (202)783-7200

Assn. for the Sciences of Limnology and Oceanography **[7177]**, 5400 Bosque Blvd., Ste. 680, Waco, TX 76710-4446, (254)399-9635

Assn. for Sciences and Politics **[IO]**, Innsbruck, Austria

Assn. of the Sci. Medical Societies of Germany **[IO]**, Dusseldorf, Germany

Assn. for the Sci. Stud. of Anomalous Phenomena **[IO]**, London, United Kingdom

Assn. for the Sci. Stud. of Consciousness **[7914]**, PO Box 20393, Greenville, NC 27858

Assn. for the Sci. Stud. of Near Death Phenomena **[★7251]**

Assn. for the Sci. Stud. of Near Death Phenomena **[★7251]**

Assn. of Sci. and Tech. Intelligentsia of Tajikistan **[IO]**, Khujand, Tajikistan

Assn. of Sci. and Tech. Translators of Slovenia **[IO]**, Ljubljana, Slovenia

Assn. Scientifique Internationale pour le Cafe **[★IO]**

Assn. Scientifique de l'Industrie Europeenne du Talc **[★IO]**

Assn. Scientifique Mondiale de Cuniculture **[★IO]**

Assn. of Scientists and Physicians of African Descent Intl. - Address unknown since 2010.

Assn. in Scotland to Res. into Astronautics **[IO]**, Glasgow, United Kingdom

Assn. of Scottish Games and Festivals **[19221]**, 3000 Walnut Ave., Altoona, PA 16601-1612, (814)942-0077

Assn. for Scottish Literary Stud. **[IO]**, Glasgow, United Kingdom

Assn. of Scottish Visitor Attractions **[IO]**, Glasgow, United Kingdom

Assn. des Scouts du Canada **[★IO]**

Assn. of Sea Grant Prog. Institutions **[★7057]**

Assn. of Seafood Importers - Defunct.

Assn. of Sealant Applicators **[IO]**, Canvey Island, United Kingdom

Assn. of Secondary Teachers Ireland **[IO]**, Dublin, Ireland

Assn. des Secretaires Generaux des Parlements **[★IO]**

Assn. of Secretaries Gen. of Parliaments **[IO]**, London, United Kingdom

Assn. of Secretaries, Young Men's Christian Associations of North Am. **[★13500]**

Assn. paritaire pour la sante et la securite du travial Secteur fabrication de produits en metal et de produits electriques **[★IO]**

Assn. Sectorielle Fabrication d'Equipement de Transport et de Machines **[★IO]**

Assn. of Securities and Exchange Commn. Alumni **[3192]**, PO Box 5767, Washington, DC 20016, (202)462-1211

Assn. of Security Consultants **[IO]**, Addlestone, United Kingdom

Assn. Senegalaise des Femmes Chefs d'Entreprise **[IO]**, Dakar, Senegal

Assn. of Senior Anthropologists **[6136]**, 2200 Wilson Blvd., Ste. 600, Arlington, VA 22201, (703)528-1902

L'Association professionnelle des agents du Ser. exterieur **[★IO]**

Assn. of Ser. and Cmpt. Dealers Intl. **[6530]**, 131 NW 1st Ave., Delray Beach, FL 33444, (561)266-9016

Assn. des Services aux Etudiants des Universites et Colleges du Canada **[★IO]**

Assn. for Services Mgt. Intl. - Address unknown since 2010.

The Assn. of Settlement Companies **[1284]**, 100 W Cypress Creek Rd., Ste. 700, Fort Lauderdale, FL 33309, (888)657-8272

Assn. of Seventh-Day Adventist Engineers and Architects - Defunct.

Assn. of Seventh-Day Adventist Librarians **[9973]**, Loma Linda Univ., 11072 Anderson St., Loma Linda, CA 92350-1704

Assn. of Seventh Day Pentecostal Assemblies - Defunct.

The Assn. for the Severely Handicapped **[★11833]**

Assn. of Sewing and Design Professionals **[202]**, PO Box 897, Higley, AZ 85236, (877)755-0303

Assn. for Shared Parenting **[IO]**, Dudley, United Kingdom

Assn. of Shareware Professionals **[★6481]**

Assn. of Shelter Veterinarians **[17015]**, 1666 K St. NW, Ste. 260, Washington, DC 20061

Assn. of Shelter Veterinarians **[17015]**, 1666 K St. NW, Ste. 260, Washington, DC 20061

Assn. of Ship Brokers and Agents U.S.A. **[2378]**, 510 Sylvan Ave., Ste. 201, Englewood Cliffs, NJ 07632, (201)569-2882

The Assn. of Shopping Centres **[IO]**, Singapore, Singapore

Assn. for Short Term Psychotherapy - Defunct.

Assn. for Show and Agricultural Organisations **[IO]**, Redhill, United Kingdom

Assn. of SIDS and Infant Mortality Programs **[16760]**, 112 E Allegan, Ste. 500, Lansing, MI 48933, (800)930-7437

Assn. for SIDS Prog. Professionals **[★16760]**

Assn. for Sign Language Interpreters **[IO]**, Milton Keynes, United Kingdom

Assn. of Significant Cemeteries in Europe **[IO]**, Barcelona, Spain

Assn. Sirius d'Astronomie **[★IO]**

Assn. of Sites Advocating Child Protection **[11193]**, 5042 Wilshire Blvd., No. 540, Los Angeles, CA 90036-4305, (323)908-7864

Assn. for Skeptical Enquiry **[IO]**, Sheffield, United Kingdom

Assn. for Skilled and Tech. Sciences **[8294]**, 1931 Mortimer Ct., Boise, ID 83712

Assn. for Slavic, East European and Eurasian Stud. **[10534]**, 203C Bellefield Hall, 315 S Bellefield Ave., Pittsburgh, PA 15260-6424, (412)648-9911

Assn. of Sleep Disorders Centers **[★16660]**

Assn. of Slovak Geomorphologists **[IO]**, Bratislava, Slovakia

Assn. of Slovenia Entrepreneurs **[IO]**, Ljubljana, Slovenia

Assn. of Small Bus. Development Centers **[3285]**, 8990 Burke Lake Rd., 2nd Fl., Burke, VA 22015, (703)764-9850

Assn. of Small Foundations **[18312]**, 1720 N St. NW, Washington, DC 20036, (202)580-6560

Assn. of Small Loan Administrators **[★5342]**

Assn. of Small and Medium Enterprises **[IO]**, Singapore, Singapore

Assn. for Social Advancement **[IO]**, Dhaka, Bangladesh

Assn. of Social Anthropologists of Aoteaora/New Zealand **[IO]**, Dunedin, New Zealand

Assn. of Social Anthropologists of the UK and the Commonwealth **[IO]**, Brighton, United Kingdom

Assn. for Social Anthropology in Eastern Oceania **[★6137]**

Assn. for Social Anthropology in Eastern Oceania **[★6137]**

Assn. for Social Anthropology in Oceania **[6137]**, Eric Silverman, Membership Coor., Wheelock Coll., Amer. Studies/Human Development, 200 The Riverway, Boston, MA 02215, (617)879-2423

Assn. for Social Anthropology in Oceania **[6137]**, Eric Silverman, Membership Coor., Wheelock Coll., Amer. Studies/Human Development, 200 The Riverway, Boston, MA 02215, (617)879-2423

Assn. for Social Economics **[6614]**, Educ. Mgt. Info. Systems, 7116 Wandering Oak Rd., Austin, TX 78749, (512)288-5988

Assn. of Social Sci. Researchers **[IO]**, Wellington, New Zealand

Assn. for the Social Sci. Stud. of Jewry **[8424]**, Gail G. Glicksman, PhD, Pres., 429 Montgomery Ave., B-303, Haverford, PA 19041

Assn. for the Social Sci. Stud. of Jewry **[8424]**, Gail G. Glicksman, PhD, Pres., 429 Montgomery Ave., B-303, Haverford, PA 19041

Assn. for Social Stud. Educators and Teachers **[IO]**, Karachi, Pakistan

Assn. of Social Work Boards **[13215]**, 400 S Ridge Pkwy., Ste. B, Culpeper, VA 22701, (540)829-6880

Assn. des Societes Nationales, Europeennes et Mediterraneennes de Gastroenterologie **[★IO]**

Assn. Sociocyberneering, Inc. **[★18634]**

Assn. of the Sociological Stud. of Jewry **[★8424]**

Assn. of the Sociological Stud. of Jewry **[★8424]**

Assn. for the Sociology of Religion **[7425]**, 618 SW 2nd Ave., Galva, IL 61434-1912, (309)932-2727

Assn. of Software Professionals **[6481]**, Mr. Richard Holler, Exec. Dir., PO Box 1522, Martinsville, IN 46151, (765)349-4740

Assn. for Software Testing **[6482]**, Dee Pizzica, 990 Basswood St., Hoffman Estates, IL 60169, (408)741-4830

Assn. of Soil and Found. Engineers **[★6917]**

Assn. for the Soldiers of Israel **[IO]**, Toronto, ON, Canada

Assn. of Solicitors and Investment Managers **[IO]**, Tonbridge, United Kingdom

Assn. Solidarite Defense Droits de Locataires **[IO]**, Cotonou, Benin

Assn. pour la Solidarite et l'Assistance Socio-Sanitaire - Burundi **[IO]**, Bujumbura, Burundi

Assn. Solidarite Luxembourg-Nicaragua **[★IO]**

Assn. of Solution Oriented Counsellors and Hypnotherapists of Australia **[IO]**, Wendouree, Australia

Assn. of the Sons of Poland **[19187]**, 333 Hackensack St., Carlstadt, NJ 07072, (201)935-2807

Assn. des Sourds du Canada **[★IO]**

Assn. of South African Quantity Surveyors **[IO]**, Halfway House, Republic of South Africa

Assn. of South African Women in Sci. and Engg. **[IO]**, Rhodes Gift, Republic of South Africa

Assn. of South East Asian Stud. in the UK **[IO]**, London, United Kingdom

Assn. of Southern Baptist Campus Ministers - Address unknown since 2010.

Assn. of Southern Baptist Colleges and Schools **[★9012]**

Assn. of Space Explorers U.S.A. **[6084]**, 600 Gemini Ave., Houston, TX 77058, (281)280-8172

Assn. of Space Explorers U.S.A. **[6084]**, 600 Gemini Ave., Houston, TX 77058, (281)280-8172

Assn. of Spanish Costume Jewelry Mfrs. and Exporters **[IO]**, Mahon, Spain

Assn. of Spanish Pulp and Paper Manufactures **[IO]**, Madrid, Spain

Assn. of Spanish Tobacconists **[IO]**, Madrid, Spain

Assn. of Speakers Clubs **[IO]**, Whitley Bay, United Kingdom

Assn. for Special Children **[★12496]**

Assn. for Specialist Fire Protection **[IO]**, Bordon, United Kingdom

Assn. of Specialists in Cleaning and Restoration **[★2258]**

Assn. for Specialists in Gp. Work **[11670]**, Amy Nitza, Sec., Indiana University-Purdue Univ. Fort Wayne, 2101 E Coliseum Blvd., Fort Wayne, IN 46805-1499, (800)347-6647

Assn. of Specialized and Cooperative Lib. Agencies **[9974]**, 50 E Huron St., Chicago, IL 60611-2729, (312)280-4395

Assn. of Specialized and Professional Accreditors **[1063]**, 3304 N Broadway St., No. 214, Chicago, IL 60657, (773)857-7900

Assn. of Specialty Cut Flower Growers **[1366]**, PO Box 268, Oberlin, OH 44074, (440)774-2887

Assn. of Specialty Professors **[8335]**, Alliance for Academic Internal Medicine, 330 John Carlyle St., Ste. 610, Alexandria, VA 22314, (703)341-4540

Assn. of Specialty Professors **[8335]**, Alliance for Academic Internal Medicine, 330 John Carlyle St., Ste. 610, Alexandria, VA 22314, (703)341-4540

Assn. for Spina Bifida and Hydrocephalus **[IO]**, Peterborough, United Kingdom

Assn. for Spirit at Work **[★20248]**

A star before a book entry number signifies that the name is not listed separately, but is mentioned within the entry.

Assn. for Spirit at Work [★20248]

Assn. for Spiritual, Ethical and Religious Values in Counseling [7940], Louisiana State Univ., 122B Peabody Hall, Baton Rouge, LA 70803, (800)347-6647

Assn. Sportive de Monaco - Aikido [IO], Monaco, Monaco

Assn. of Sports Medicine of the Balkans [IO], Bucharest, Romania

Assn. of Sports Medicine of Ghana [IO], Accra, Ghana

Assn. of Sports Museums and Halls of Fame [★22984]

Assn. des Sports des Sourds du Canada [★IO]

Assn. of Staff Employees of the Windward Islands [IO], Philipsburg, Netherlands Antilles

Assn. of Staff Physician Recruiters [16259], 1000 Westgate Dr., Ste. 252, St. Paul, MN 55114, (651)290-7475

Assn. of Staff Physician Recruiters [16259], 1000 Westgate Dr., Ste. 252, St. Paul, MN 55114, (651)290-7475

Assn. of Stained Glass Lamp Artists [251], 5070 Cromwell Dr. NW, Gig Harbor, WA 98335

Assn. of Standardized Patient Educators [15323], Roblynn G. Sliwinski, 1430 Tulane Ave., TB-51, New Orleans, LA 70112-2699, (504)988-6440

Assn. of Starwood Franchisees and Owners North Am. [1741], 420A Lovett Blvd., Houston, TX 77006, (713)523-1352

Assn. of State Baptist Papers - Address unknown since 2011.

Assn. of State Colleges and Universities [★7868]

Assn. of State Correctional Administrators [11706], 213 Court St., Ste. 606, Middletown, CT 06457, (860)704-6410

Assn. of State Dam Safety Officials [5961], 450 Old Vine St., Lexington, KY 40507-1544, (859)257-5140

Assn. of State Drinking Water Administrators [5925], 1401 Wilson Blvd., Ste. 1225, Arlington, VA 22209, (703)812-9505

Assn. of State Energy Res. and Tech. Transfer Institutions [6695], Sherry Benzmiller, Admin., 455 Sci. Dr., Ste. 200, Madison, WI 53711, (608)238-4601

Assn. of State Floodplain Managers [4006], 2809 Fish Hatchery Rd., Ste. 204, Madison, WI 53713, (608)274-0123

Assn. of State and Interstate Water Pollution Control Administrators [5411], 1221 Connecticut Ave. NW, 2nd Fl., Washington, DC 20036, (202)756-0600

Assn. of State Lib. Agencies [★9974]

Assn. of State and Provincial Psychology Boards [16392], PO Box 3079, Peachtree City, GA 30269, (678)216-1175

Assn. of State and Provincial Psychology Boards [16392], PO Box 3079, Peachtree City, GA 30269, (678)216-1175

Assn. of State Public Hea. Veterinarians [★16981]

Assn. of State Sanitary Boards [★17045]

Assn. of State Supervisor of Mathematics [8562], Wisconsin Dept. of Public Instruction, PO Box 7841, Madison, WI 53707-7841

Assn. of State and Territorial Dental Directors [14275], 1838 Fieldcrest Dr., Sparks, NV 89434, (775)626-5008

Assn. of State and Territorial Directors of Hea. Promotion and Public Hea. Educ. [★5928]

Assn. of State and Territorial Directors of Public Hea. Educ. [★5928]

Assn. of State and Territorial Hea. Officers [★5926]

Assn. of State and Territorial Hea. Officials [5926], 2231 Crystal Dr., Ste. 450, Arlington, VA 22202, (202)371-9090

Assn. of State and Territorial Local Hea. Liaison Officials [5927], PO Box 260451, Denver, CO 80226, (303)692-3479

Assn. of State and Territorial Maternal and Child Hea. and Crippled Children's Directors [★14057]

Assn. of State and Territorial Public Hea. Veterinarians [★16981]

Assn. of State and Territorial Solid Waste Mgt. Officials [6065], 444 N Capitol St. NW, Ste. 315, Washington, DC 20001, (202)624-5828

Assn. of State Wetland Managers [4007], 32 Tandberg Trail, Ste. 2A, Windham, ME 04062, (207)892-3399

Assn. of Steam Boiler, Pressure Vessel and Piping Mfrs. [IO], Dusseldorf, Germany

Assn. of Steel Distributors [2465], 401 N Michigan Ave., Ste. 2200, Chicago, IL 60611, (312)673-5793

Assn. of Steel and Metal Forming Indus. [IO], Hagen, Germany

Assn. for sTEm Teacher Educ. [8295], Emily McKinley, Assoc. Mgr., PO Box 2089, West Lafayette, IN 47996

Assn. for Stimulating Know How [IO], Gurgaon, India

Assn. of Stock Exchange Firms [★3206]

Assn. Strabismologique Europeene [★IO]

Assn. for Strategic Alliance Professionals [2273], 960 Turnpike St., Canton, MA 02021, (781)562-1630

Assn. for Strategic Alliance Professionals [2273], 960 Turnpike St., Canton, MA 02021, (781)562-1630

Assn. for Strategic Planning [2761], 12021 Wilshire Blvd., Ste. 286, Los Angeles, CA 90025-1200, (877)816-2080

Assn. for Strengthening Agricultural Res. in Eastern and Central Africa [IO], Entebbe, Uganda

Assn. of Structural Pest Control Regulatory Officials [4772], 2919 Diamond Springs Dr., Las Cruces, NM 88011, (505)522-8040

Assn. of Student Intl. Law Societies [★5589]

Assn. of Student Intl. Law Societies [★5589]

Assn. for Student Teaching [★8945]

Assn. for Stud. in the Conservation of Historic Buildings [IO], London, United Kingdom

Assn. for the Stud. of Abortion [★10768]

Assn. for the Stud. of African-American Life and History [9099], Howard Center, 2225 Georgia Ave. NW, Ste. 331, Washington, DC 20059, (202)238-5910

Assn. for the Stud. of Afro-American Life and History [★9099]

Assn. for the Stud. of Amer. Indian Literatures [10322], 2421 Birchwood Rd., Henrico, VA 23294

Assn. for the Stud. of Animal Behaviour [IO], St. Andrews, United Kingdom

Assn. for the Stud. of Australian Literature [IO], Sydney, Australia

Assn. for the Stud. of Classical African Civilizations [9092], 3645 Marketplace Blvd., Ste. 130-5, East Point, GA 30344-5748, (678)489-2423

Assn. for the Stud. of Community Org. [★13222]

Assn. for the Stud. of the Cuban Economy [7984], PO Box 28267, Washington, DC 20038-8267

Assn. for the Stud. of Dreams [★16666]

Assn. for the Stud. of Food and Soc. [6871], Kingsborough Community Coll., CUNY, Dept. of Tourism and Hospitality, 2001 Oriental Blvd., Brooklyn, NY 11235, (718)368-5809

Assn. for the Stud. of Free Institutions [8229], Univ. of Nebraska at Omaha, Dept. of Political Sci., 275 Arts and Sciences Hall, Omaha, NE 68182, (402)554-4862

Assn. for the Stud. of Higher Educ. [8230], 4505 S Maryland Pkwy., UNLV Box 453068, Las Vegas, NV 89154, (702)895-2737

Assn. for Stud. of Internal Secretions [★14490]

Assn. for the Stud. of Law, Culture and the Humanities [8330], Quinnipiac Univ. School of Law, 275 Mt. Carmel Ave., Hamden, CT 06518, (203)582-3281

Assn. for the Stud. of Literature and Env. [10035], PO Box 502, Keene, NH 03431, (603)357-7411

Assn. for the Study of Man-Environment Relations - Defunct.

Assn. for the Stud. of Medical Educ. [IO], Edinburgh, United Kingdom

Assn. for the Stud. of the Middle East and Africa [8619], PO Box 33699, Washington, DC 20033, (202)429-8860

Assn. for the Stud. of the Middle East and Africa [8619], PO Box 33699, Washington, DC 20033, (202)429-8860

Assn. for the Stud. of Modern and Contemporary France [IO], Bradford, United Kingdom

Assn. for the Stud. of Negro Life and History [★9099]

Assn. for the Stud. of Obesity [IO], Manchester, United Kingdom

Assn. for the Stud. of Peak Oil and Gas U.S.A. [7236], 300 New Jersey Ave. NW, Ste. 900, Washington, DC 20001, (303)744-0954

Assn. for the Stud. of Persianate Societies [8412], 118-18 Union Tpke., Apt. 18E, Kew Gardens, NY 11415

The Assn. for the Stud. of Play [10445], St. Olaf Coll., 1520 St. Olaf Ave., Northfield, MN 55057-1098, (507)786-3624

Assn. for the Stud. and Preservation of Roman Mosaics [IO], Cambridge, United Kingdom

Assn. for the Stud. of Soviet-Type Economies [★6609]

Assn. for the Stud. of Travel in Egypt and the Near East [IO], Cambridge, United Kingdom

Assn. for the Stud. of the World Refugee Problem [IO], Hochberg, Germany

Assn. for the Stud. of the Worldwide African Diaspora [7702], NYU Dept. of History, 53 Washington Sq. S, 7th Fl., New York, NY 10012-1018

Assn. of Subscription Agents and Intermediaries [IO], Suffolk, United Kingdom

Assn. of Sugar Cane Growers of Colombia [IO], Bogota, Colombia

Assn. Suisse des Annonceurs [★IO]

Assn. Suisse pour la Cooperation Internationale [★IO]

Assn. Suisse Des Locataires [★IO]

Assn. Suisse d'Etude de la Concurrence [IO], Zurich, Switzerland

Assn. Suisse des Femmes Diplomees Des Universites [IO], Bivio, Switzerland

Assn. Suisse des Femmes Diplomees des Universites [★IO]

Assn. Suisse de Golf [★IO]

Assn. Suisse des Insurance et Risk Managers [★IO]

Assn. Suisse pour l'equipement technique de l'agriculture [★IO]

Assn. Suisse des Musiciens [★IO]

Assn. Suisse des Proprietaires Yngling [IO], Oberkulm, Switzerland

Assn. Suisse de Recherche Operationnelle [★IO]

Assn. de la Suisse Romande et Italienne Contre les Myopathies [IO], Lavigny, Switzerland

Assn. of Summer Olympic Intl. Federations [IO], Lausanne, Switzerland

Assn. of Superannuation Funds of Australia [IO], Sydney, Australia

Assn. of Superannuation Funds of Papua New Guinea [IO], Boroko, Papua New Guinea

Assn. of Superintendents of Buildings and Grounds of Universities and Colleges [★8087]

Assn. of Superintendents of Buildings and Grounds of Universities and Colleges [★8087]

Assn. of Superintendents and Principals of Amer. Schools for the Deaf [★14926]

Assn. for Supervision and Curriculum Development [7950], 1703 N Beauregard St., Alexandria, VA 22311-1714, (703)578-9600

Assn. for Supervision and Curriculum Development [7950], 1703 N Beauregard St., Alexandria, VA 22311-1714, (703)578-9600

Assn. of Suppliers to the British Clothing Indus. [IO], Halifax, United Kingdom

Assn. of Suppliers of Electronic Instruments and Components [IO], Helsinki, Finland

Assn. of Suppliers of Household Appliances in the Netherlands [IO], Zoetermeer, Netherlands

Assn. of Suppliers to the Paper Indus. [1809], 15 Tech. Pkwy. S, Norcross, GA 30092, (770)209-7521

Assn. for Suppliers of Printing and Publishing and Converting Technologies [★1624]

Assn. of Suppliers for Professional Audio, Video and Lighting Equip. in Sweden [IO], Stockholm, Sweden

Assn. for Support of Graduate Students [8231], PO Box 4698, Incline Village, NV 89450-4698, (775)831-1399

Assn. of Support Professionals [3230], 122 Barnard Ave., Watertown, MA 02472-3414, (617)924-3944

Assn. of Support Professionals [3230], 122 Barnard Ave., Watertown, MA 02472-3414, (617)924-3944

Reference to "IO" in place of a book number signifies that the association may be found in the 50th edition of International Organizations.

Assn. for Support of Social and Community Integration [IO], Porto, Portugal

Assn. of Surfing Lawyers [23031], 12100 Wilshire Blvd., Ste. 905, Los Angeles, CA 90025, (310)826-7900

Assn. of Surfing Professionals [23032], PO Box 309, Huntington Beach, CA 92648, (714)536-3500

Assn. of Surgeons of Great Britain and Ireland [IO], London, United Kingdom

Assn. for Surgical Educ. [8599], SIU School of Medicine, Dept. of Surgery, PO Box 19655, Springfield, IL 62794-9655, (217)545-3835

Assn. for Surgical Educ. [8599], SIU School of Medicine, Dept. of Surgery, PO Box 19655, Springfield, IL 62794-9655, (217)545-3835

Assn. of Surgical Technologists [15370], 6 W Dry Creek Cir., Ste. 200, Littleton, CO 80120-8031, (303)694-9130

Assn. of Swedish Bakeries [IO], Stockholm, Sweden

Assn. of Swedish Engg. Indus. [IO], Stockholm, Sweden

Assn. of Swedish Lighting Designers [IO], Stockholm, Sweden

Assn. of Swiss Advt. and Communications Agencies BSW [IO], Zurich, Switzerland

Assn. for Symbolic Logic [7070], Vassar Coll., 124 Raymond Ave., PO Box 742, Poughkeepsie, NY 12604, (845)437-7080

Assn. for Symbolic Logic [7070], Vassar Coll., 124 Raymond Ave., PO Box 742, Poughkeepsie, NY 12604, (845)437-7080

Assn. of Synthetic Grass Installers [534], 17487 Penn Valley Dr., Ste. B103, Penn Valley, CA 95946, (530)432-5851

Assn. of Synthetic Yarn Mfrs. [★3436]

Assn. of Systematic Kinesiology [IO], East Sussex, United Kingdom

Assn. of Systematics Collections [★6311]

Assn. canadienne de Taekwondo WTF [★IO]

Assn. of Talent Agents [162], 9255 Sunset Blvd., Ste. 930, Los Angeles, CA 90069, (310)274-0628

Assn. of Tank and Cistern Mfrs. [IO], Chepstow, United Kingdom

Assn. of Tankcleaning Companies in the Netherlands [IO], Zoetermeer, Netherlands

Assn. Tchadienne de lutte Contre le Diabete [★IO]

Assn. Tchadienne de Medecine du Sport [IO], N'Djamena, Chad

Assn. for Teacher Educ. in Europe [IO], Brussels, Belgium

Assn. of Teacher Educators [8945], PO Box 793, Manassas, VA 20113, (703)331-0911

Assn. of Teachers of Educ. Institutions [★7868]

Assn. of Teachers of English in Negro Colleges [★8469]

Assn. of Teachers of Japanese [8468], 240 Humanities Bldg., 279 UCB, Boulder, CO 80309-0279, (303)492-5487

Assn. of Teachers and Lecturers [IO], London, United Kingdom

Assn. of Teachers of Lipreading to Adults [IO], East Sussex, United Kingdom

Assn. of Teachers of Mathematics [IO], Derby, United Kingdom

Assn. of Teachers of Preventive Medicine [★16308]

Assn. of Teachers of Singing [IO], Middlesex, United Kingdom

Assn. of Teachers of Tech. Writing [9072], Texas Tech Univ., PO Box 43091, Lubbock, TX 79409

Assn. for Teaching Psychology [IO], Newcastle upon Tyne, United Kingdom

Assn. for the Teaching of the Social Sciences [IO], Manchester, United Kingdom

Assn. of Tech. Employees [★23162]

Assn. of Tech. Lightning and Access Specialists [IO], London, United Kingdom

Assn. of Tech. Personnel in Ophthalmology [15950], 2025 Woodlane Dr., St. Paul, MN 55125-2998, (800)482-4858

Assn. of Tech. and Supervisory Professionals - Address unknown since 2010.

Assn. Technique Canadienne du Bitume [★IO]

Assn. Technique Internationale des Bois Tropicaux [★IO]

Assn. of Tech., Mgt. and Applied Engg. [8296], 1390 Eisenhower Pl., Ann Arbor, MI 48108, (734)677-0720

Assn. for Tech. in Music Instruction [8644], 312 E Pine St., Missoula, MT 59802

Assn. of Telehealth Ser. Providers - Address unknown since 2011.

Assn. of Telemessaging Services Intl. [★3401]

Assn. of Telemessaging Services Intl. [★3401]

Assn. of Telephone Answering Services - Defunct.

Assn. of Teleservices Intl. [3401], 12 Acad. Ave., Atkinson, NH 03811, (603)362-9489

Assn. of Teleservices Intl. [3401], 12 Acad. Ave., Atkinson, NH 03811, (603)362-9489

Assn. for Temperate Agroforestry [4389], Univ. of Missouri, 203 ABNR Bldg., Columbia, MO 65211, (573)884-3216

Assn. of Tenants - BIHUSS-Saravejo [IO], Sarajevo, Bosnia-Hercegovina

Assn. of Tenants of Slovenia [IO], Ljubljana, Slovenia

Assn. of Tequila Producers - Defunct.

Assn. for Terminology and Knowledge Transfer [IO], Cologne, Germany

Assn. for Tertiary Educ. Mgt. [IO], O'Connor, Australia

Assn. of Tertiary Educational Institutions [IO], Bridgetown, Barbados

Assn. of Test Publishers [2923], South Bldg., Ste. 900, 601 Pennsylvania Ave. NW, Washington, DC 20004, (866)240-7909

Assn. of Textile and Footwear Importers and Wholesalers [IO], Helsinki, Finland

Assn. of Textile Retailers - Netherlands [IO], Doorn, Netherlands

Assn. for Textual Scholarship in Art History [9169], 112 Charles St., Beacon Hill, Boston, MA 02114, (617)367-1670

Assn. for Textual Scholarship in Art History [9169], 112 Charles St., Beacon Hill, Boston, MA 02114, (617)367-1670

Assn. of Thai Cmpt. Indus. [IO], Bangkok, Thailand

Assn. of Thai Professionals in Am. and Canada [19255], 1848 Ctr. Ave., Martinez, CA 94553

Assn. of Thai Textile Bleaching, Dyeing, Printing and Finishing Indus. [IO], Bangkok, Thailand

Assn. for The Advancement of Social Potential [★16717]

Assn. for Theatre in Higher Educ. [8999], PO Box 1290, Boulder, CO 80306-1290, (303)530-2167

Assn. of Theatre Movement Educators [9000], Beth Johnson, Sec., Finger Lakes Community Coll., Dept. of Visual and Performing Arts, 3325 Marvin Sands Dr., Canandaigua, NY 14424, (585)785-1242

Assn. of Theatre Movement Educators [9000], Beth Johnson, Sec., Finger Lakes Community Coll., Dept. of Visual and Performing Arts, 3325 Marvin Sands Dr., Canandaigua, NY 14424, (585)785-1242

Assn. of Theatrical Press Agents and Managers [23268], 62 W 45th St., Ste. 901, New York, NY 10036, (212)719-3666

Assn. for Theological Educ. in South East Asia [IO], Manila, Philippines

Assn. of Theological Schools in the U.S. and Canada [9007], 10 Summit Park Dr., Pittsburgh, PA 15275-1110, (412)788-6505

Assn. of Theological Schools in the U.S. and Canada [9007], 10 Summit Park Dr., Pittsburgh, PA 15275-1110, (412)788-6505

Assn. of Therapeutic Communities [IO], Cheltenham, United Kingdom

Assn. on Third World Affairs [17904], 1717 K St. NW, Ste. 600, Washington, DC 20036, (202)973-0157

Assn. on Third World Affairs [17904], 1717 K St. NW, Ste. 600, Washington, DC 20036, (202)973-0157

Assn. of Third World Stud. [17905], Louisiana State Univ., Intl. Lincoln Center for Amer. Stud., Shreveport, LA 71115-2301, (318)797-5349

Assn. of Third World Stud. [17905], Louisiana State Univ., Intl. Lincoln Center for Amer. Stud., Shreveport, LA 71115-2301, (318)797-5349

Assn. of Threat Assessment Professionals [3209], 1215 K St., No. 2290, Sacramento, CA 95814, (916)231-2146

Assn. of Tile, Terrazzo, Marble Contractors and Affiliates [★940]

Assn. of Tongan Univ. Women [IO], Nuku'alofa, Tonga

Assn. of Tongue Depressors - Defunct.

Assn. of Tour Operators and Travel Agents of the Czech Republic [IO], Prague, Czech Republic

Assn. of Tourist Hotels of the Republic of Argentina [IO], Buenos Aires, Argentina

Assn. of Town Centre Mgt. [IO], London, United Kingdom

Assn. of Track and Field Statisticians [IO], Warrandyte, Australia

Assn. of Track and Structures Suppliers [★2992]

Assn. of Track and Structures Suppliers [★2992]

Assn. of Trade Fair and Exhibition Organisers of the Czech Republic [IO], Prague, Czech Republic

Assn. of Trade and Forfaiting in the Americas [1285], 1180 Ave. of the Americas, Ste. 2020, New York, NY 10022, (212)377-2012

Assn. of Trade and Forfaiting in the Americas [1285], 1180 Ave. of the Americas, Ste. 2020, New York, NY 10022, (212)377-2012

Assn. of Traders and Bottlers of Wines and Spirits from Northern Portugal [IO], Porto, Portugal

Assn. des Traducteurs et Interpretes Judiciaires [★IO]

Assn. des Traducteurs et Interpretes de l'Alberta [★IO]

Assn. des Traducteurs et Traductrices Literariness du Canada [★IO]

Assn. of Training and Employment Professionals - Defunct.

Assn. du Traite Atlantique [★IO]

Assn. pour le Traitement Automatique des Langues [★IO]

Assn. TransCommunication [7246], PO Box 13111, Reno, NV 89507-3111

Assn. TransCommunication [7246], PO Box 13111, Reno, NV 89507-3111

Assn. des Transitaires Internationaux Canadiens [★IO]

Assn. of Translation Companies [IO], Brighton, United Kingdom

Assn. of Translators and Interpreters of Alberta [IO], Edmonton, AB, Canada

Assn. for Transpersonal Psychology [9821], PO Box 50187, Palo Alto, CA 94303, (650)424-8764

Assn. du Transport Aerien Intl. [★IO]

Assn. for Trans. Law, Logistics and Policy [★6030]

Assn. of Trans. Law Professionals [6030], PO Box 5407, Annapolis, MD 21403-0702, (410)268-1311

Assn. of Trans. Practitioners [★6030]

Assn. des Transports du Canada [★IO]

Assn. of Traumatic Stress Specialists [11671], 88 Pompton Ave., Verona, NJ 07044, (973)559-9200

Assn. of Traumatic Stress Specialists [11671], 88 Pompton Ave., Verona, NJ 07044, (973)559-9200

Assn. of Travel Agencies of Czech Republic [IO], Prague, Czech Republic

Assn. of Travel Marketing Executives [3554], PO Box 3176, West Tisbury, MA 02575, (508)693-0550

Assn. for the Treatment of Sexual Abusers [6253], 4900 SW Griffith Dr., Ste. 274, Beaverton, OR 97005, (503)643-1023

Assn. for the Treatment of Tobacco Use and Dependence [16737], Univ. of Vermont, Dept. of Psychiatry, 1 S Prospect St., Burlington, VT 05401

Assn. of Trial Behavior Consultants [★6247]

Assn. of Trial Lawyers of Am. [★6041]

Assn. of Trinidad and Tobago Insurance Companies [IO], Port of Spain, Trinidad and Tobago

Assn. for Tropical Biology [★6293]

Assn. for Tropical Biology and Conservation [6293], PO Box 37012, Washington, DC 20013-7012, (202)633-0920

Assn. for Tropical Lepidoptera [6839], PO Box 141210, Gainesville, FL 32614-1210

Assn. Tunisienne de Mecanique des Sols [IO], Tunis, Tunisia

Assn. of Turkish Consulting Engineers and Architects [IO], Ankara, Turkey

Assn. of Uganda Women Medical Doctors [IO], Kampala, Uganda

Assn. of Ukrainian Doctors [IO], Odessa, Ukraine

A star before a book entry number signifies that the name is not listed separately, but is mentioned within the entry.

Assn. of Unclaimed Property Administrators [★5899]

Assn. des anciens fonctionnaires UNESCO [★IO]

The Assn. of Union Constructors [904], 1501 Lee Hwy., Ste. 202, Arlington, VA 22209-1109, (703)524-3336

Assn. for Union Democracy [23234], 104 Montgomery St., Brooklyn, NY 11225, (718)564-1114

Assn. to Unite the Democracies [★18343]

Assn. to Unite the Democracies [★18343]

Assn. of United Kingdom Media Librarians [IO], London, United Kingdom

Assn. of the U.S. Army [5801], 2425 Wilson Blvd., Arlington, VA 22201, (703)841-4300

Assn. of U.S. Chess Journalists [★2818]

Assn. of U.S. Univ. Directors of Intl. Agricultural Programs [★7708]

Assn. of U.S. Univ. Directors of Intl. Agricultural Programs [★7708]

Assn. of United Window Cleaners [2241], PO Box 101, Stephenville, TX 76401, (608)931-8999

Assn. of Unity Churches Canada [IO], Kitchener, ON, Canada

Assn. of Unity Churches Intl. [19614], PO Box 610, Lee's Summit, MO 64063, (816)524-7414

Assn. of Universalist Women [★20273]

Assn. Universelle d'Aviculture Scientifique [★IO]

Assn. Universitaire Canadienne d'Etudes Nordiques [★IO]

Assn. des Universites Africaines [★IO]

Assn. of Universities of Asia and the Pacific [IO], Nakhon Ratchasima, Thailand

Assn. of Universities and Colleges of Canada [IO], Ottawa, ON, Canada

Assn. of Universities for Res. in Astronomy [6225], 1212 New York Ave. NW, Ste. 450, Washington, DC 20005, (202)483-2101

Assn. of Univ. Administrators [IO], Manchester, United Kingdom

Assn. of Univ. Affiliated Facilities [★12497]

Assn. of Univ. Anesthesiologists [13743], 520 N Northwest Hwy., Park Ridge, IL 60068-2573, (847)825-5586

Assn. of Univ. Anesthetists [★13743]

Assn. of Univ. Architects [6194], 1277 Univ. of Oregon, Eugene, OR 97403-1277, (541)346-3537

Assn. for Univ. Business and Economic Res. - Defunct.

Assn. of Univ. Centers on Disabilities [12497], 1010 Wayne Ave., Ste. 920, Silver Spring, MD 20910, (301)588-8252

Assn. for Univ. and Coll. Counseling Center Directors [7941], Claremont Univ. Consortium, 757 Coll. Way, Claremont, CA 91711, (909)621-8355

Assn. for Univ. and Coll. Counseling Center Directors [7941], Claremont Univ. Consortium, 757 Coll. Way, Claremont, CA 91711, (909)621-8355

Assn. of Univ. Environmental Health/Sciences Centers - Defunct.

Assn. of Univ. Evening Colleges [★7923]

Assn. of Univ. Fisheries and Wildlife Prog. Administrators [★8146]

Assn. of Univ. Interior Designers [2052], Carlos Lugo, Ohio State Univ., Off. of Student Life, Fac. Mgt. and Logistics, 1800 Cannon Dr., Ste. 710, Columbus, OH 43210

Assn. of Univ. Leaders for a Sustainable Future [8232], 2100 L St. NW, Washington, DC 20037, (202)778-6133

Assn. of Univ. Leaders for a Sustainable Future [8232], 2100 L St. NW, Washington, DC 20037, (202)778-6133

Assn. of Univ. Professors of French and Heads of Departments of French in Universities in the UK and Ireland [IO], Durham, United Kingdom

Assn. of Univ. Professors of Ophthalmology [15951], PO Box 193030, San Francisco, CA 94119, (415)561-8548

Assn. of Univ. Programs in Hea. Admin. [8600], 2000 4th St. N, Ste. 780, Arlington, VA 22201, (703)894-0940

Assn. of Univ. Programs in Hosp. Admin. [★8600]

Assn. of Univ. Radiologic Technologists [★8834]

Assn. of Univ. Radiologists [16531], 820 Jorie Blvd., Oak Brook, IL 60523, (630)368-3730

Assn. of Univ. Related Res. Parks [★8791]

Assn. of Univ. Res. and Indus. Links [IO], Belfast, United Kingdom

Assn. of Univ. Res. Parks [8791], 6262 N Swan Rd., Ste. 100, Tucson, AZ 85718, (520)529-2521

Assn. of Univ. Teachers - Scotland [IO], Edinburgh, United Kingdom

Assn. of Univ. Tech. Managers [5561], 111 Deer Lake Rd., Ste. 100, Deerfield, IL 60015, (847)559-0846

Assn. for Unmanned Vehicle Systems [★7341]

Assn. for Unmanned Vehicle Systems [★7341]

Assn. for Unmanned Vehicle Systems Intl. [7341], 2700 S Quincy St., Ste. 400, Arlington, VA 22206, (703)845-9671

Assn. for Unmanned Vehicle Systems Intl. [7341], 2700 S Quincy St., Ste. 400, Arlington, VA 22206, (703)845-9671

Assn. of Upper Gastrointestinal Surgeons [IO], London, United Kingdom

Assn. of Upper Level Colleges and Universities [★7868]

Assn. of Vacation Home Rental Managers [★3045]

Assn. of Vacuum Equip. Mfrs. [1810], 201 Park Washington Ct., Falls Church, VA 22046-4527, (703)538-3543

Assn. of Vacuum Equip. Mfrs. [1810], 201 Park Washington Ct., Falls Church, VA 22046-4527, (703)538-3543

Assn. of Vacuum Equip. Mfrs. Intl. [★1810]

Assn. of Vacuum Equip. Mfrs. Intl. [★1810]

Assn. of Valuers of Licensed Property [IO], Sudbury, United Kingdom

Assn. for Vascular Access [16958], 5526 W 13400 S, Ste. 229, Herriman, UT 84096, (801)792-9079

Assn. of Vascular and Interventional Radiographers [16959], 12100 Sunset Hills Rd., Ste. 130, Reston, VA 20190, (703)234-4055

Assn. of Vegetarian Dietitians and Nutrition Educators - Defunct.

Assn. of Veterans Affairs Anesthesiologists [13744], Prof. Nader D. Nader, MD, Pres., 3495 Bailey Ave., No. 203C, Buffalo, NY 14215

Assn. of Veterans Affairs Ophthalmologists [15952], PO Box 193030, San Francisco, CA 94119-3030, (415)561-8523

Assn. of Veterans Affairs Ophthalmologists [15952], PO Box 193030, San Francisco, CA 94119-3030, (415)561-8523

Assn. of Veterinarians for Animal Rights - Address unknown since 2011.

Assn. of Veterinary Anaesthetists [IO], Hatfield, United Kingdom

Assn. of Veterinary and Crop Protection Associations of Southern Africa [IO], Halfway House, Republic of South Africa

Assn. for Veterinary Family Practice [17016], Richard Timmins, Exec. Dir., 1601 N Benton Ave., Helena, MT 59625, (530)902-4201

Assn. of Veterinary Hematology and Transfusion Medicine [17017], 2509 N Campbell Ave., No. 304, Tucson, AZ 85719-3304

Assn. for Veterinary Teaching and Res. Work [IO], Bridgwater, United Kingdom

Assn. of Veterinary Technician Educators [9034], Teresa Sonsthagen, Sec.-Treas., 11428 38 St. S, Horace, ND 58047-9510

Assn. for Victim-Offender Mediation [★18761]

Assn. for Victim-Offender Mediation [★18761]

Assn. europeenne contre les Violences faites aux Femmes au Travail [★IO]

Assn. of Virtual Worlds - Address unknown since 2010.

Assn. of Vision Educators [15953], PO Box 1277, Sayville, NY 11782, (631)563-5007

Assn. of Vision Educators [15953], PO Box 1277, Sayville, NY 11782, (631)563-5007

Assn. of Vision Sci. Librarians [9975], Univ. of Michigan, 1000 Wall St., Ann Arbor, MI 48105, (734)763-9468

Assn. for Visual Arts [IO], Cape Town, Republic of South Africa

Assn. of Visual Communicators [★1259]

Assn. of Visual Communicators [★1259]

Assn. of Visual Language Interpreters of Canada [IO], Squamish, BC, Canada

Assn. of Visual Language Interpreters of New Brunswick [IO], St. John, NB, Canada

Assn. of Visual Sci. Librarians [★9975]

Assn. for Vital Records and Hea. Statistics [★5930]

Assn. of Vitamin Chemists - Defunct.

L'Association Volcanologique Europeenne [★IO]

Assn. of Volleyball Professionals [23297], 960 Knox St., Ste. A, Torrance, CA 90502, (310)426-8000

Assn. of Voluntary Action Scholars [★13386]

Assn. of Voluntary Action Scholars [★13386]

Assn. of Voluntary Ser. Organisations [IO], Brussels, Belgium

Assn. for Voluntary Sterilization [★12031]

Assn. for Voluntary Sterilization [★12031]

Assn. for Voluntary Surgical Contraception [★12031]

Assn. for Voluntary Surgical Contraception [★12031]

Assn. for Volunteer Administration - Defunct.

Assn. for Volunteer Services [IO], Beirut, Lebanon

Assn. of Waldorf Schools of North Am. [8279], Frances Kane, 2344 Nicollet Ave. S, Minneapolis, MN 55404, (612)870-8310

Assn. of Waldorf Schools of North Am. [8279], Frances Kane, 2344 Nicollet Ave. S, Minneapolis, MN 55404, (612)870-8310

Assn. of the Wall and Ceiling Indus. Intl. [535], 513 W Broad St., Ste. 210, Falls Church, VA 22046, (703)538-1600

Assn. of the Wall and Ceiling Indus. Intl. [535], 513 W Broad St., Ste. 210, Falls Church, VA 22046, (703)538-1600

Assn. of Water Technologies [3648], 9707 Key West Ave., Ste. 100, Rockville, MD 20850, (301)740-1421

Assn. of Water Transportation Accounting Officers - Defunct.

Assn. of Wedding Planners Worldwide [★476]

Assn. of Wedding Planners Worldwide [★476]

Assn. for Wedding Professionals Intl. [1742], 6700 Freeport Blvd., Ste. 202, Sacramento, CA 95822, (916)392-5000

Assn. for Wedding Professionals Intl. [1742], 6700 Freeport Blvd., Ste. 202, Sacramento, CA 95822, (916)392-5000

Assn. of Welcoming and Affirming Baptists [19310], PO Box 545, Kensington, MD 20895, (240)515-8664

Assn. of Welding Distributors [IO], Redditch, United Kingdom

Assn. of Western Pulp and Paper Workers [23192], PO Box 4566, Portland, OR 97208-4566, (503)228-7486

Assn. of Wheelchair Children [IO], London, United Kingdom

Assn. of Wholesale Elecl. Bulk Buyers [IO], Ilkeston, United Kingdom

Assn. of Wholesalers of Chem. and Pharmaceutical Goods [IO], Lisbon, Portugal

Assn. of Wireless Tech. [IO], Maidenhead, United Kingdom

Assn. for Women in Architecture [241], 22815 Frampton Ave., Torrance, CA 90501-5034, (310)534-8466

Assn. for Women in Aviation Maintenance [3675], PO Box 1030, Edgewater, FL 32132-1030, (386)416-0248

Assn. of Women Bus. Owners [★685]

Assn. Women and Bus. in Russia [IO], St. Petersburg, Russia

Assn. for Women in Communications [806], 3337 Duke St., Alexandria, VA 22314, (703)370-7436

Assn. for Women in Computing [6506], PO Box 2768, Oakland, CA 94602

Assn. of Women Educators [IO], Sandgate, Australia

Assn. of Women in Environmental Professions [4316], PO Box 748, Seattle, WA 98111-0748

Assn. for Women Geoscientists [6918], 12000 N Washington St., Ste. 285, Thornton, CO 80241, (303)412-6219

Assn. of Women Geoscientists [★6918]

Assn. of Women Indus. Designers [6958], PO Box 468, Old Chelsea Sta., New York, NY 10011

Assn. of Women Indus. Designers [6958], PO Box 468, Old Chelsea Sta., New York, NY 10011

Assn. for Women Journalists [2812], PO Box 2199, Fort Worth, TX 76113, (817)685-3876

Reference to "IO" in place of a book number signifies that the association may be found in the 50th edition of International Organizations.

Assn. of Women Martial Arts Instructors [22727], PO Box 6284, Norfolk, VA 23508, (917)623-9640

Assn. of Women Mathematicians [★7071]

Assn. for Women in Mathematics [7071], 11240 Waples Mill Rd., Ste. 200, Fairfax, VA 22030-6078, (703)934-0163

Assn. of Women in the Metal Indus. [3676], 19 Mantua Rd., Mount Royal, NJ 08061, (856)423-3201

Assn. of Women Painters and Sculptors [★9242]

Assn. for Women Psychologists [★16393]

Assn. for Women in Psychology [16393], Sonoma State Univ., 1801 E Cotati Ave., Rohnert Park, CA 94928, (707)664-3395

Assn. for Women in Sci. [7362], 1321 Duke St., Ste. 21Q, Alexandria, VA 22314, (703)894-4490

Assn. for Women in the Sciences [IO], Hamilton, New Zealand

Assn. of Women Shooters of Canada [IO], Mississauga, ON, Canada

Assn. of Women Soil Scientists [7433], Kelly Counts, PO Box 8264, Kirkland, WA 98034

Assn. of Women Solicitors [IO], London, United Kingdom

Assn. for Women in Sports Media [2813], 3899 N Front St., Harrisburg, PA 17110

Assn. of Women Surgeons [16809], 5204 Fairmont Ave., Ste. 208, Downers Grove, IL 60515, (630)655-0392

Assn. of Women Surgeons [16809], 5204 Fairmont Ave., Ste. 208, Downers Grove, IL 60515, (630)655-0392

Assn. for Women Veterinarians Found. [17018], Lisa C. Freeman, DVM, Chair, Northern Illinois Univ., Lowden Hall 301, DeKalb, IL 60115, (815)753-1883

Assn. of Women's Bus. Centers [3677], PO Box 1255, Camden, ME 04843, (207)236-9753

Assn. of Women's Committees of Art Museums [★10130]

Assn. of Women's Hea., Obstetric and Neonatal Nurses [15741], 2000 L St. NW, Ste. 740, Washington, DC 20036, (202)261-2400

Assn. of Women's Hea., Obstetric and Neonatal Nurses [15741], 2000 L St. NW, Ste. 740, Washington, DC 20036, (202)261-2400

Assn. of Women's Music and Culture - Defunct.

Assn. for Women's Rights in Development [IO], Toronto, ON, Canada

Assn. for Women's Self Defense Advancement [13031], 556 Rte. 17 N, Ste. 7-209, Paramus, NJ 07652, (201)794-2153

Assn. for Women's Self Defense Advancement [13031], 556 Rte. 17 N, Ste. 7-209, Paramus, NJ 07652, (201)794-2153

Assn. of Woodturners of Great Britain [IO], Datchet, United Kingdom

Assn. of Woodworking and Furnishings Suppliers [3700], 500 Citadel Dr., Ste. 200, Commerce, CA 90040, (323)838-9440

The Assn. for Work Process Improvement [★6512]

Assn. for Worksite Hea. Promotion [★16711]

Assn. for Worksite Health Promotion - Defunct.

Assn. of World Citizens [18810], 55 New Montgomery St., Ste. 224, San Francisco, CA 94105, (415)541-9610

Assn. of World Citizens [18810], 55 New Montgomery St., Ste. 224, San Francisco, CA 94105, (415)541-9610

Assn. of World Coun. of Churches Related Development Organisations in Europe [IO], Brussels, Belgium

Assn. for World Travel Exchange [8366], 38 W 88th St., New York, NY 10024, (212)787-7706

Assn. for World Travel Exchange [★8366]

Assn. of Writers and Writing Programs [10703], George Mason Univ., Mail Stop 1E3, Fairfax, VA 22030-4444, (703)993-4301

Assn. of Yemeni Scientists and Professionals - Address unknown since 2010.

Assn. of Yiddish Writers and Journalists in Israel [IO], Tel Aviv, Israel

Assn. of YMCA Professionals [13500], Springfield Coll., 263 Alden St., Springfield, MA 01109, (413)748-3884

Assn. for Young Astrologers [6216], 2019 NW 31st Terr., Gainesville, FL 32605

Assn. of Young Economists of Georgia [IO], Tbilisi, Georgia

Assn. of Youth Museums [★10113]

Assn. Zen Internationale [★IO]

Assn. of Zimbabwe Advertisers [IO], Harare, Zimbabwe

Assn. of Zimbabwe Journalists in the United Kingdom [IO], Burpham, United Kingdom

Assn. of Zoo Veterinary Technicians [17019], Marcie Oliva, Exec. Dir., 581705 White Oak Rd., Yulee, FL 32097, (312)742-7211

Assn. of Zoological Horticulture [4667], PO Box 135776, Clermont, FL 34711, (407)939-1609

Assn. of Zoos and Aquariums [7633], 8403 Colesville Rd., Ste. 710, Silver Spring, MD 20910-3314, (301)562-0777

Assn. des Zoos et Aquariums du Canada [★IO]

Associations

AAAS Sci. and Human Rights Coalition [17806]

Alliance for Nonprofit Mgt. [260]

AMC Inst. [261]

AMC Inst. [261]

Amer. Soc. of Assn. Executives [262]

Amer. Soc. of Assn. Executives [262]

Assn. Media and Publishing [263]

DMA Nonprofit Fed. [264]AssociationsFound. for Educational Futures

Melos Inst. [265]

Natl. Coun. of Nonprofits [266]

Soc. for Nonprofit Organizations [267]

World Assn. of Non-Governmental Organizations [11117]

Associations Coun. of the Natl. Assn. of Mfrs. [★2341]

Associazione Amici de Bambini [IO], Milan, Italy

Associazione Antiquari d'Italia [IO], Florence, Italy

Associazione Bertoni per la Cooperazione e lo Sviluppo nel Terzo Mondo [IO], Verona, Italy

Associazione Centro Aiuti Volontari Cooperazione Sviluppo Terzo Mondo [IO], Trento, Italy

Associazione di Cooperazione Cristiana Internazionale [IO], Trieste, Italy

Associazione di Cultura Tradizionale Giapponese - Aikikai d'Italia [IO], Rome, Italy

Associazione Culturale Antonio Pedrotti [IO], Trento, Italy

L'Associazione Cuore-Vita della Repubblica di San Marino [★IO]

Associazione Dermatologi Ospedalieri Italiani [★IO]

Associazione per il Disegno Industriale [IO], Milan, Italy

Associazione dei Fonografici Italiani [★IO]

Associazione Geotecnica Italiana [IO], Rome, Italy

Associazione Grossisti Ortofrutticoli [★IO]

Associazione degli Industriali della Birra e del Malto [★IO]

Associazione degli Industriali delle Carni [★IO]

Associazione Industrie Dolciarie Italiane [★IO]

Associazione Industrie per l'Aerospazio I Sistemi e la Difesa [★IO]

Associazione Industrie Risiere Italiane [★IO]

Associazione Ingegneri per l'Ambiente ed il Territorio [★IO]

Associazione Internazionale di Archeologia Classica [★IO]

Associazione Internazionale di Volontariato [★IO]

Associazione Italian Sclerosi Laterale Amiotrofica [IO], Novara, Italy

Associazione Italiana Amici di Raoul Follereau [★IO]

Associazione Italiana di Architettura del Paesaggio [IO], Rome, Italy

Associazione Italiana Biblioteche [★IO]

Associazione Italiana Classe Yngling [IO], Rapallo, Italy

Associazione Italiana dei Construttori ed Operatori del Settore Oleoidraulico e Pneumatico [★IO]

Associazione Italiana Costruttori Autoattrezzature [★IO]

Associazione Italiana Costruttori Autoattrezzature [★IO]

Associazione Italiana dell' Industria Olearia [IO], Rome, Italy

Associazione Italiana d'Ingegneria Economica [★IO]

Associazione Italiana per i Diritti di Riproduzione delle Opere dell'ingegno [IO], Milan, Italy

Associazione Italiana Distribuzione Automatica [★IO]

Associazione Italiana per la Documentazione Avanzata [★IO]

Associazione Italiana Economisti dell'Energia [★IO]

Associazione Italiana Editori [★IO]

Associazione Italiana di Ematologia ed Oncologia Pediatrica [★IO]

Associazione Italiana di Fisica Medica [★IO]

Associazione Italiana Fisioterapisti [IO], Rome, Italy

Associazione Italiana del Franchising [★IO]

Associazione Italiana Guide e Scouts d'Europa Cattolici [IO], Rome, Italy

Associazione Italiana per l'Idrogeno e Celle a Combustibile [★IO]

Associazione Italiana di Informatica Medica [★IO]

Associazione Italiana di Ingegneria Agraria [IO], Catania, Italy

Associazione Italiana Lattiero-Casearia [★IO]

Associazione Italiana Manifatturieri Pelli e Succedanei [★IO]

Associazione Italiana di Metallurgia [★IO]

Associazione Italiana di Metallurgia [IO], Milan, Italy

Associazione Italiana Pellicceria [IO], Milan, Italy

Associazione Italiana Periti liquidatori Assicurativi Incendio e Rischi Diversi [★IO]

Associazione Italiana del Private Equity e Venture Capital [★IO]

Associazione Italiana della Rosa [IO], Monza, Italy

Associazione Italiana Sclerosi Multipla [IO], Genoa, Italy

Associazione Italiana Sindrome di Moebius [★IO]

Associazione Italiana Spondiloartriti [★IO]

Associazione Italiana per gli Studi Giapponesi [★IO]

Associazione Italiana Tecnico Economica Cemento [★IO]

Associazione Italiana di Telerilevamento [★IO]

Associazione Italiana di Terapia Occupazionale [IO], Latina, Italy

Associazione Italiana per la Tutela della Concorrenza [IO], Milan, Italy

Associazione Italiana del Vuoto [★IO]

Associazione Librai Italiani [★IO]

Associazione per le Malattie Infiammatorie Croniche dell'Intestino [★IO]

Associazione per la Matematica Applicata alle Scienze Economiche e Sociali [★IO]

Associazione Medici per l'Ambiente I ISDE Italia [★IO]

Associazione Nazionale Calzaturifici Italiani [★IO]

Associazione Nazionale Commercianti in Ferro e Acciai, Metalli Non-Ferrosi, Rottami Ferrosi, Ferramenta e Affini [★IO]

Associazione Nazionale del Commercio dei Prodotti Lattiero-Caseari [★IO]

Associazione Nazionale Cooperativa tra Dettaglianti [★IO]

Associazione Nazionale dell'Industria Farmaceutica [★IO]

Associazione Nazionale Editoria Periodica Specializzata [★IO]

Associazione Nazionale Editoria Specializzata [★IO]

Associazione Nazionale Fabbricanti Articoli Ottici [★IO]

Associazione Nazionale Fotografi Professionisti [IO], Milan, Italy

Associazione Nazionale Fra i Produttori di Articoli Sportivi [★IO]

Associazione Nazionale Imprese Armamento Ferroviario [IO], Rome, Italy

Associazione Nazionale Imprese Trasporti Automobilistici [★IO]

Associazione Nazionale Industriali Conserve Alimentari Vegetali [★IO]

Associazione Nazionale degli Industriali del Vetro [★IO]

Associazione Nazionale fra Industrie Automobilistiche [★IO]

Associazione Nazionale Malati Reumatici [IO], Rome, Italy

Associazione Nazionale Produttori Articoli per Scrittura e Affini [★IO]

Associazione Nazionale dei Produttori di Piastrelle di Ceramica e di Materiali Refrattari [IO], Sassuolo, Italy

Associazione Nazionale Psoriasi e Vitiligine [IO], Milan, Italy

---

A star before a book entry number signifies that the name is not listed separately, but is mentioned within the entry.

Associazione Nazionale di Risk Managers e Responsabili Assicurazioni Aziendali [IO], Milan, Italy

Associazione Nazionale Rivenditori Specialisti di Pneumatici [★IO]

Associazione Nazionale Vendita a Distanza [IO], Milan, Italy

Associazione la Nostra Famiglia [IO], Ponte Lambro, Italy

Associazione per la Pace [★IO]

Associazione Polo San Marino [IO], San Marino, San Marino

Associazione Sammarinese Cuore-Vita [★IO]

Associazione Studi Am. Latina [IO], Rome, Italy

Associazione per lo Studio del Problema Mondiale dei Rifugiati [★IO]

Associazione Tecnica dell'Automobile [★IO]

Associes Benevoles Qualifies au Ser. des Jeunes [★IO]

Associes Canadiens de l'Universite Ben-Gurion du Neguev [★IO]

AssoComunicazione Associazione delle Imprese di Comunicazione [IO], Milan, Italy

ASSUCOPIE [IO], Ottignies-Louvain-la-Neuve, Belgium

Assumption Guild [19390], 330 Market St., Brighton, MA 02135, (617)783-0495

Assyrian
   Assyrian Aid Soc. of Am. [11118]
   Assyrian Aid Soc. of Am. [11118]
   Bet-Nahrain [9342]

Assyrian Academic Soc. [9936], 8324 N Lincoln Ave., Skokie, IL 60077, (847)982-5800

Assyrian Academic Soc. [9936], 8324 N Lincoln Ave., Skokie, IL 60077, (847)982-5800

Assyrian Aid Soc. of Am. [11118], 350 Berkeley Park Blvd., Berkeley, CA 94707, (510)527-9997

Assyrian Aid Soc. of Am. [11118], 350 Berkeley Park Blvd., Berkeley, CA 94707, (510)527-9997

Assyrian Chaldean Athletics of North Am. - Address unknown since 2011.

Assyrian Medical Soc. [15403], 16055 Ventura Blvd., Ste. 1225, Encino, CA 91436, (818)501-8866

Assyrian Medical Soc. [15403], 16055 Ventura Blvd., Ste. 1225, Encino, CA 91436, (818)501-8866

ASTA Chap. of Greece [IO], Athens, Greece

Astara [20138], 10700 Jersey Blvd., Ste. 450, Rancho Cucamonga, CA 91730, (909)948-7412

Astara Found. [★20138]

ASTD [7786], Box 1443, Alexandria, VA 22313-1443, (703)683-8100

Asthma and Allergy Found. of Am. [13637], 8201 Corporate Dr., Ste. 1000, Landover, MD 20785, (202)466-7643

Asthma Found. of New South Wales [IO], St. Leonards, Australia

Asthma and Immunology; Amer. Acad. of Allergy, [13632]

Asthma and Immunology; Amer. Coll. of Allergy, [13635]

Asthma and Immunology; Joint Coun. of Allergy, [13641]

Asthma Network Mothers of Asthmatics; Allergy and [16602]

Asthma Soc. of Canada [IO], Toronto, ON, Canada

Asthma Soc. of Ireland [IO], Dublin, Ireland

ASTM Intl. [7557], PO Box C700, West Conshohocken, PA 19428-2959, (610)832-9500

Aston Martin Owners Club [21000], PO Box 1460, Stockbridge, MA 01262, (413)298-0222

Aston Martin Owners Club [IO], Wallingford, United Kingdom

Astro-Psychology Inst. - Defunct.

Astrological Assn. of Great Britain [IO], London, United Kingdom

Astrology
   Amer. Fed. of Astrologers [6213]
   Assn. for Astrological Networking [6214]
   Assn. for Psychological Astrology [6215]
   Assn. for Young Astrologers [6216]
   Astrological Assn. of Great Britain [1393]
   Coun. of Vedic Astrology [6217]
   Friends of Astrology [6218]
   Intl. Soc. for Astrological Res. [6219]
   Intl. Soc. for Astrological Res. [6219]
Astromusic - Address unknown since 2011.

Astronaut Scholars Honor Soc. [23629], Astronaut Scholarship Found., 6225 Vectorspace Blvd., Titusville, FL 32780, (321)455-7011

Astronomical and Astrophysical Soc. of Am. [★6222]

Astronomical League [6226], 9201 Ward Pkwy., Ste. 100, Kansas City, MO 64114, (816)333-7759

Astronomical Soc. of Australia [IO], Crawley, Australia

Astronomical Soc. of France [IO], Paris, France

Astronomical Soc. of Iran [IO], Tehran, Iran

Astronomical Soc. of Japan [IO], Tokyo, Japan

Astronomical Soc. of New South Wales [IO], Ettalong Beach, Australia

Astronomical Soc. of the Pacific [6227], 390 Ashton Ave., San Francisco, CA 94112, (415)337-1100

Astronomical Soc. of South Australia [IO], Adelaide, Australia

Astronomical Soc. of Southern Africa [IO], Observatory, Republic of South Africa

Astronomical Soc. of Switzerland [IO], Bulach, Switzerland

Astronomical Soc. of Western Australia [IO], Subiaco, Australia

Astronomisk Selskab Danmark [★IO]

Astronomy
   Amateur Astronomers Assn. [6220]
   Amateur Astronomers, Inc. [20975]
   Amer. Assn. of Variable Star Observers [6221]
   Amer. Astronomical Soc. [6222]
   Amer. Lunar Soc. [6223]
   Amer. Lunar Soc. [6223]
   Amer. Meteor Soc. [6224]
   Assn. of Lunar and Planetary Observers [20976]
   Assn. of Lunar and Planetary Observers [20976]
   Assn. of Universities for Res. in Astronomy [6225]
   Astronomical League [6226]
   Astronomical Soc. of the Pacific [6227]
   Central Bur. for Astronomical Telegrams [6228]
   Intl. Amateur-Professional Photoelectric Photometry [6229]
   Intl. Amateur-Professional Photoelectric Photometry [6229]
   Intl. Dark-Sky Assn. [6230]
   Intl. Dark-Sky Assn. [6230]
   Intl. Lunar Observatory Assn. [6231]
   Intl. Occultation Timing Assn. [6232]
   Intl. Occultation Timing Assn. [6232]
   Intl. Planetarium Soc. [6233]
   Intl. Planetarium Soc. [6233]
   Maria Mitchell Assn. [6234]
   North Amer. Meteor Network [7107]
   PlanetQuest [6235]
   SETI League [6236]
   Von Braun Astronomical Soc. [6237]
   Webb Deep-Sky Soc. [6238]
   Webb Deep-Sky Soc. [6238]
Astronomy Ireland [IO], Dublin, Ireland

At-sea Processors Assn. [1358], PO Box 32817, Juneau, AK 99803, (907)523-0970

ATA - A Graphic Communications Assn. - Defunct.

Ataturk Soc. of Am. [18376], 4731 Massachusetts Ave. NW, Washington, DC 20016, (202)362-7173

Ataxia Found.; Natl. [15614]

Ataxia Telangiectasia Children's Proj. [14376], 5300 W Hillsboro Blvd., No. 105, Coconut Creek, FL 33073, (954)481-6611

Ataxia-Telangiectasia Soc. [IO], Harpenden, United Kingdom

Ataxia - UK [IO], London, United Kingdom

ATAYAL [9864], 900 E Pecan St., Ste. 300, Pflugerville, TX 78660, (407)459-7766

Ateliers du Soleil [★IO]

Athanor Fellowship [★20139]

Atheist
   Amer. Atheists [19302]
   Atheist Alliance Intl. [19303]
   Atheists For Human Rights [17207]
   Atheists United [19304]
   Secular Student Alliance [17869]
Atheist Alliance Intl. [19303], 1777 T St. NW, Washington, DC 20009-1725, (866)HERETIC

Atheists For Human Rights [17207], 5146 Newton Ave. N, Minneapolis, MN 55430-3459, (612)529-1200

Atheists United [19304], 4773 Hollywood Blvd., Hollywood, CA 90027-5333, (323)666-4258

Athena Alliance [17590], 911 E Capitol St. SE, Washington, DC 20003-3903, (202)547-7064

Athenaeum of Philadelphia [9976], 219 S 6th St., Philadelphia, PA 19106-3794, (215)925-2688

Athens Chamber of Commerce and Indus. [IO], Athens, Greece

Athens Daily Newspaper Publishers Assn. [IO], Athens, Greece

Athgo Intl. [13510], 13636 Ventura Blvd., Ste. 222, Sherman Oaks, CA 91423, (818)345-6734

Athgo Intl. [13510], 13636 Ventura Blvd., Ste. 222, Sherman Oaks, CA 91423, (818)345-6734

Athletes
   African Baseball Network [22260]
   Aikido Assn. of Am. [22216]
   All Japan Ju-Jitsu Intl. Fed. [22720]
   Am. Outdoors Assn. [22835]
   Amer. Amputee Soccer Assn. [22932]
   Amer. Assn. of Snowboard Instructors [22923]
   Amer. Barefoot Waterski Club [23114]
   Amer. Blind Bowling Assn. [22502]
   Amer. Collegiate Hockey Assn. [22639]
   Amer. Junior Rodeo Assn. [22839]
   Amer. Legion Baseball [22265]
   Amer. Polo Horse Assn. [22812]
   Amer. Ultrarunning Assn. [22862]
   Assn. for Professional Basketball Res. [22293]
   Assn. of Professional Towsurfers [23030]
   Athletes in Action [19731]
   Babe Ruth Baseball/Softball [22268]
   BlazeSports Am. [22508]
   Catholic Athletes for Christ [22230]
   Christian Cheerleaders of Am. [22450]
   Cinderella Softball Leagues [22951]
   Citizenship Through Sports Alliance [22972]
   Coalition for Anabolic Steroid Precursor and Ephedra Regulation [16718]
   Continental Basketball League [22294]
   Coun. of Ivy Gp. Presidents [22975]
   Eastern Coll. Athletic Conf. [22643]
   Fed. of Intl. Lacrosse [22713]
   Football Writers Assn. of Am. [22588]
   Gin Soon Tai Chi Chuan Fed. [22733]
   Global Sports Alliance USA [22977]
   Golf Coaches Assn. of Am. [22608]
   Golf Writers Assn. of Am. [22610]
   Hampton One-Design Class Racing Assn. [22340]
   Harness Horse Youth Found. [22652]
   InterCollegiate Horse Show Assn. [22682]
   Intercollegiate Women's Lacrosse Coaches Assn. [22714]
   Intl. Assn. of Gay and Lesbian Martial Artists [22734]
   Intl. Dodge Ball Fed. [22981]
   Intl. Female Boxers Assn. [22437]
   Intl. Laser Class Assn. - North Amer. Region [22356]
   Intl. League of Professional Baseball Clubs [22272]
   Intl. Natural Bodybuilding and Fitness Fed. [22418]
   Intl. Rafting Fed. [22837]
   Intl. Seven-Star Mantis Style Lee Kam Wing Martial Art Assn. USA [22736]
   Intl. Sungja-Do Assn. [22738]
   Intl. Women's Flag Football Assn. [22589]
   Intl. Yang Style Tai Chi Chuan Assn. [22740]
   Intl. Youth Conditioning Assn. [23139]
   Kids Enjoy Exercise Now [21474]
   Maccabi USA/Sports for Israel [22985]
   Martial Arts Intl. Fed. [22742]
   Martial Arts Teachers' Assn. [22743]
   Men's Collegiate Lacrosse Assn. [22715]
   Natl. Advt. Golf Assn. [22616]
   Natl. Amer. Semi-Professional Baseball Assn. [22279]
   Natl. Assn. of Collegiate Gymnastics Coaches/ Women [22633]
   Natl. Assn. of Left-Handed Golfers [22617]
   Natl. Assn. of Professional Baseball Leagues [22280]
   Natl. Assn. of Underwater Instructors [23104]
   Natl. Club Baseball Assn. [22283]
   Natl. Coalition Against Violent Athletes [22231]
   Natl. Finals Rodeo Comm. [22844]

Natl. Football League [22591]
Natl. Junior Baseball League [22285]
Natl. Scholastic Surfing Assn. [23035]
Natl. Softball Assn. [22954]
Natl. Starwind/Spindrift Class Assn. [22377]
Natl. Surf Schools and Instructors Assn. [23036]
Natl. Team Cheng Martial Arts Assn. [22747]
Natural Fitness Trainers Assn. [22809]
New England Trails Conf. [23090]
NFHS Coaches Assn. [22465]
North Amer. Football League [22593]
North Amer. One-Armed Golfer Assn. [22521]
OrganicAthlete [22232]
Polish Amer. Golf Assn. [22620]
Professional Baseball Athletic Trainers Soc. [22289]
Professional Figure Skaters Cooperative [22897]
Professional Football Chiropractic [14143]
Professional Football Players Mothers' Assn. [22595]
Professional Putters Assn. [22623]
Qajaq U.S.A. [23124]
Race for Peace [18285]
Sikh Sports Assn. of the U.S.A. [22894]
Southeastern Conf. [23006]
Spirit Indus. Trade Assn. [733]
Sport and Recreation Law Assn. [23022]
Sportscar Vintage Racing Assn. [22249]
Table Shuffleboard Assn. [22893]
United Barrel Racing Assn. [22670]
U.S.A. Deaf Basketball [22300]
U.S. Bobsled and Skeleton Fed. [22926]
U.S. Club Soccer [22944]
U.S. Competitive Aerobics Fed. [22209]
U.S. Dental Tennis Assn. [23062]
U.S. Disc Sports [22536]
U.S. Flag Football League [22599]
U.S. Kuo Shu Fed. [22759]
U.S. Modern Pentathlon Assn. [23071]
U.S. Muay Thai Assn. [22761]
U.S. Olympic Comm. [22791]
U.S. ProMiniGolf Assn. [22627]
U.S. Ski Mountaineering Assn. [22917]
U.S. Ski Team Found. [22919]
U.S. Taekwondo Union [22763]
U.S. Women's Curling Assn. [22473]
USA Athletes Intl. [22233]
USA Diving [22544]
USA Gymnastics [22636]
USA Hockey [22647]
U.S.A. Karate Fed. [22766]
USA Natl. Karate-do Fed. [22710]
USA Professional Platform Tennis Assn. [23066]
USA Pulling [23074]
USA Volleyball [23111]
USGA Green Sect. [22628]
Vintage Base Ball Assn. [22292]
Watering Seeds Org. [22532]
Women Outdoors [22797]
Women's All-Star Assn. [22432]
World Fast-Draw Assn. [22891]
The World Kuoshu Fed. [22770]
World Martial Arts Assn. [22771]
World Masters Cross-Country Ski Assn. [22921]
World Mudo Fed. [22773]
World T.E.A.M. Sports [22534]
Athletes in Action [19731], 651 Taylor Dr., Xenia, OH 45385-7246, (937)352-1000
Athletes in Action [19731], 651 Taylor Dr., Xenia, OH 45385-7246, (937)352-1000
Athletes with Disabilities Network [22507], 2845 Crooks Rd., Rochester Hills, MI 48309, (248)829-8353
Athletes United for Peace [18231], 712 Peralta Ave., Berkeley, CA 94707, (510)273-9235
AthletesCAN [IO], Ottawa, ON, Canada
Athletic Assn. of Antigua and Barbuda [IO], St. Johns, Antigua-Barbuda
Athletic Assn. of Ireland [IO], Dublin, Ireland
Athletic Assn. of Sri Lanka [IO], Colombo, Sri Lanka
Athletic Assn. of Thailand [IO], Pathumthani, Thailand
Athletic Equip. Managers Assn. [22966], 460 Hunt Hill Rd., Freeville, NY 13068, (607)539-6300
Athletic Fed. of Bosnia and Herzegovina [IO], Sarajevo, Bosnia-Hercegovina

Athletic Fed. of Georgia [IO], Tbilisi, Georgia
Athletic Fed. of Kyrgyz Republic [IO], Bishkek, Kirgizstan
Athletic Fed. of Nigeria [IO], Abuja, Nigeria
Athletic Fed. of Republic of Armenia [IO], Yerevan, Armenia
Athletic Fed. of Republic of Kazakhstan [IO], Almaty, Kazakhstan
Athletic Fed. of the Republic of Tajikistan [IO], Dushanbe, Tajikistan
Athletic Fed. of Uzbekistan [IO], Tashkent, Uzbekistan
Athletic Footwear Assn. - Defunct.
Athletic Goods Mfrs. Assn. [★3318]
Athletic Goods Mfrs. Assn. [★3318]
Athletic Inst. [3325], Sporting Goods Mfrs. Assn., 8505 Fenton St., Ste. 211, Silver Spring, MD 20910, (301)495-6321
Athletic Solomons [IO], Honiara, Solomon Islands
Athletic Success Inst. [22818], 1933 Winward Point, Discovery Bay, CA 94514, (925)516-8686

Athletics
African Baseball Network [22260]
Aikido Assn. of Am. [22216]
All Japan Ju-Jitsu Intl. Fed. [22720]
Am. Outdoors Assn. [22835]
Amer. Amputee Soccer Assn. [22932]
Amer. Assn. of Snowboard Instructors [22923]
Amer. Barefoot Waterski Club [23114]
Amer. Blind Bowling Assn. [22502]
Amer. Collegiate Hockey Assn. [22639]
Amer. Junior Rodeo Assn. [22839]
Amer. Legion Baseball [22265]
Amer. Polo Horse Assn. [22812]
Amer. Ultrarunning Assn. [22862]
Assn. for Professional Basketball Res. [22293]
Assn. of Professional Towsurfers [23030]
Athletes in Action [19731]
Babe Ruth Baseball/Softball [22268]
Baseball Writers Assn. of Am. [2814]
BlazeSports Am. [22508]
Catholic Athletes for Christ [22230]
Christian Cheerleaders of Am. [22450]
Cinderella Softball Leagues [22951]
Citizenship Through Sports Alliance [22972]
Coalition for Anabolic Steroid Precursor and Ephedra Regulation [16718]
Continental Basketball League [22294]
Coun. of Ivy Gp. Presidents [22975]
Dwarf Athletic Assn. of Am. [22234]
Eastern Coll. Athletic Conf. [22643]
Fed. of Intl. Lacrosse [22713]
Football Writers Assn. of Am. [22588]
Found. for Safer Athletic Field Environments [22235]
Gin Soon Tai Chi Chuan Fed. [22733]
Global Sports Alliance USA [22977]
Golf Coaches Assn. of Am. [22608]
Golf Writers Assn. of Am. [22610]
Hampton One-Design Class Racing Assn. [22340]
Harness Horse Youth Found. [22652]
Impact Sports Intl. [22979]
InterCollegiate Horse Show Assn. [22682]
Intercollegiate Women's Lacrosse Coaches Assn. [22714]
Intl. Assn. of Gay and Lesbian Martial Artists [22734]
Intl. Dodge Ball Fed. [22981]
Intl. Female Boxers Assn. [22437]
Intl. Laser Class Assn. - North Amer. Region [22356]
Intl. League of Professional Baseball Clubs [22272]
Intl. Natural Bodybuilding and Fitness Fed. [22418]
Intl. Rafting Fed. [22837]
Intl. Seven-Star Mantis Style Lee Kam Wing Martial Art Assn. USA [22736]
Intl. Women's Flag Football Assn. [22589]
Intl. Yang Style Tai Chi Chuan Assn. [22740]
Intl. Youth Conditioning Assn. [23139]
Kids Enjoy Exercise Now [21474]
Maccabi USA/Sports for Israel [22985]
Martial Arts Intl. Fed. [22742]
Martial Arts Teachers' Assn. [22743]

Men's Collegiate Lacrosse Assn. [22715]
Natl. Advt. Golf Assn. [22616]
Natl. Amer. Semi-Professional Baseball Assn. [22279]
Natl. Assn. of Collegiate Gymnastics Coaches/Women [22633]
Natl. Assn. of Left-Handed Golfers [22617]
Natl. Assn. of Professional Baseball Leagues [22280]
Natl. Assn. of Underwater Instructors [23104]
Natl. Club Baseball Assn. [22283]
Natl. Coalition Against Violent Athletes [22231]
Natl. Coun. for Taekwondo Masters Certification [22746]
Natl. Finals Rodeo Comm. [22844]
Natl. Football League [22591]
Natl. Junior Baseball League [22285]
Natl. Scholastic Surfing Assn. [23035]
Natl. Softball Assn. [22954]
Natl. Starwind/Spindrift Class Assn. [22377]
Natl. Surf Schools and Instructors Assn. [23036]
Natural Fitness Trainers Assn. [22809]
New England Trails Conf. [23090]
NFHS Coaches Assn. [22465]
North Amer. Football League [22593]
North Amer. One-Armed Golfer Assn. [22521]
North Amer. Sports Fed. [22236]
North Amer. Sports Fed. [22236]
OrganicAthlete [22232]
Org. of Spirit Indus. Providers [22452]
Polish Amer. Golf Assn. [22620]
Professional Baseball Athletic Trainers Soc. [22289]
Professional Figure Skaters Cooperative [22897]
Professional Football Players Mothers' Assn. [22595]
Professional Putters Assn. [22623]
Qajaq U.S.A. [23124]
Race for Peace [18285]
Senior Roller Skaters of Am. [22899]
Sikh Sports Assn. of the U.S.A. [22894]
Southeastern Conf. [23006]
Spirit Indus. Trade Assn. [733]
Sport and Recreation Law Assn. [23022]
Sportscar Vintage Racing Assn. [22249]
Table Shuffleboard Assn. [22893]
United Barrel Racing Assn. [22670]
U.S.A. Deaf Basketball [22300]
U.S. Bobsled and Skeleton Fed. [22926]
U.S. Club Soccer [22944]
U.S. Competitive Aerobics Fed. [22209]
U.S. Dental Tennis Assn. [23062]
U.S. Disc Sports [22536]
U.S. Flag Football League [22599]
U.S. Kuo Shu Fed. [22759]
U.S. Modern Pentathlon Assn. [23071]
U.S. Muay Thai Assn. [22761]
U.S. Olympic Comm. [22791]
U.S. ProMiniGolf Assn. [22627]
U.S. Ski Mountaineering Assn. [22917]
U.S. Ski Team Found. [22919]
U.S. Taekwondo Union [22763]
U.S. Women's Curling Assn. [22473]
Up2Us [13563]
USA Athletes Intl. [22233]
USA Diving [22544]
U.S.A. Fed. of Pankration Ethlima [22237]
USA Gymnastics [22636]
USA Hockey [22647]
U.S.A. Karate Fed. [22766]
USA Natl. Karate-do Fed. [22710]
USA Professional Platform Tennis Assn. [23066]
USA Pulling [23074]
USA Volleyball [23111]
USGA Green Sect. [22628]
Vintage Base Ball Assn. [22292]
Women Outdoors [22797]
Women's All-Star Assn. [22432]
World Fast-Draw Assn. [22891]
The World Kuoshu Fed. [22770]
World Martial Arts Assn. [22771]
World Masters Cross-Country Ski Assn. [22921]
World Mudo Fed. [22773]
World T.E.A.M. Sports [22534]
Athletics Administrators; Natl. Assn. of Collegiate Women [8718]

A star before a book entry number signifies that the name is not listed separately, but is mentioned within the entry.

Athletics Assn. of Malawi [IO], Blantyre, Malawi
Athletics Assn. of Maldives [IO], Male, Maldives
Athletics Associations of Guyana [IO], Georgetown, Guyana
Athletics Australia [IO], Melbourne, Australia
Athletics Canada [IO], Ottawa, ON, Canada
The Athletics Cong. of the U.S.A. [★23072]
Athletics Cook Islands [IO], Rarotonga, Cook Islands
Athletics and Entertainers for Kids - Address unknown since 2011.
Athletics Fed. of India [IO], New Delhi, India
Athletics Fed. of Pakistan [IO], Islamabad, Pakistan
Athletics Fiji [IO], Suva, Fiji
Athletics Kenya [IO], Nairobi, Kenya
Athletics Namibia [IO], Swakopmund, Namibia
Athletics New Zealand [IO], Wellington, New Zealand
Athletics Samoa [IO], Apia, Western Samoa
Athletisme Canada [★IO]
Atira Women's Rsrc. Soc. [IO], Vancouver, BC, Canada
Atlanta Flames Fan Club - Address unknown since 2011.
Atlantic Assn. of Applied Economists [IO], Halifax, NS, Canada
Atlantic Center for the Env. [★4299]
Atlantic Center for the Env. [★4299]
Atlantic Coast Boat Builders and Repairers Assn. [★2348]
Atlantic Coast Conf. [22967], 4512 Weybridge Ln., Greensboro, NC 27407, (336)854-8787
Atlantic Coun. of Canada [IO], Toronto, ON, Canada
Atlantic Coun. of the U.S. [18589], 1101 15th St. NW, 11th Fl., Washington, DC 20005, (202)463-7226
Atlantic Economic Soc. [★6623]
Atlantic Economic Soc. [★6623]
Atlantic Estuarine Res. Soc. [★7052]
Atlantic Film Festival Assn. [IO], Halifax, NS, Canada
Atlantic Flyway Coun. [5030], Virginia Dept. of Game & Inland Fisheries, PO Box 11104, Richmond, VA 23230, (804)367-1000
Atlantic and Gulf Coasts Dry Dock Assn. [★2370]
Atlantic Independent Union - Address unknown since 2010.
Atlantic Legal Found. [5655], 2039 Palmer Ave., Ste. 104, Larchmont, NY 10538, (914)834-3322
Atlantic Offshore Fish and Lobster Assn. [★1356]
Atlantic Offshore Fishermen's Assn. [★1356]
Atlantic Offshore Lobstermen's Assn. [1356], 54 Chatham Dr., Bedford, NH 03110, (603)206-5468
Atlantic Salmon Fed. [IO], St. Andrews, NB, Canada
Atlantic Seaboard Wine Assn. [5165], PO Box 11332, Burke, VA 22009, (703)323-6873
Atlantic States Marine Fisheries Commn. [5453], 1050 N Highlnd St., Ste. 200 A-N, Arlington, VA 22201, (703)842-0740
Atlantic Treaty Assn. [IO], Brussels, Belgium
Atlantic Waterfowl Coun. [★5030]
Atlantis Project - Defunct.
Atlantische Commissie [★IO]
Atlantsammenslutningen [★IO]
Atlas Economic Res. Found. [6615], 1201 L St. NW, Ste. 200, Washington, DC 20005, (202)449-8449
Atletska Zveza Slovenije [IO], Ljubljana, Slovenia
Atletski savez Bosne i Hercegovine [★IO]
ATM Indus. Assn. [402], PO Box 88433, Sioux Falls, SD 57109-8433, (605)271-7371
Atmospheric Res; Univ. Corp. for [7108]
Atmospheric Sci. Librarians Intl. [8518], Univ. of Iowa Libraries, Science Education and Outreach, 453 Van Allen Hall, Iowa, IA 52242-1325, (319)335-3024
ATOL [IO], Leuven, Belgium
Atomic Age Alliance [9672], 2620 S Maryland Pkwy., No. 345, Las Vegas, NV 89109, (888)MID-MOD1
Atomic Energy Coun. [IO], Yonghe, Taiwan
Atomic Energy Soc. of Japan [IO], Tokyo, Japan
Atomic Indus. Forum [★6746]
Attachment Parenting Intl. [12603], PO Box 4615, Alpharetta, GA 30023, (800)520-8320
Attachment Parenting Intl. [12603], PO Box 4615, Alpharetta, GA 30023, (800)520-8320
Attend [IO], London, United Kingdom

Attention Deficit Disorder Assn. [15572], PO Box 7557, Wilmington, DE 19803-9997, (800)939-1019
Attention-Deficit Disorder Assn. [★15572]
Attention Deficit/Hyperactivity Disorder; Children and Adults With [15578]
Atticus Circle [17735], 515 Cong. Ave., Ste. 1320, Austin, TX 78701, (512)450-5188
Attorneys
  Amer. Acad. of Adoption Attorneys [5222]
  Amer. Acad. of Appellate Lawyers [5223]
  Amer. Acad. of Estate Planning Attorneys [5224]
  Amer. Bar Assn. [5225]
  Amer. Bar Assn. Center for Professional Responsibility [5226]
  Amer. Bar Assn. Young Lawyers Div. [5227]
  Amer. Bd. of Certification [5228]
  Amer. Bd. of Trial Advocates Found. [5229]
  Amer. Coll. of Constr. Lawyers [5230]
  Amer. Coll. of Real Estate Lawyers [5231]
  Amer. Employment Law Coun. [5232]
  Amer. attorneys in good standing. seeks to improve the administration of civil and criminal justice, and the availability of legal services to the public. Assn. I Amer. Lawyers Auxiliary [5233]
  Armenian Bar Assn. [5234]
  Armenian Bar Assn. [5234]
  Assn. of Attorney-Mediators [5235]
  Assn. of Black Women Attorneys [5236]
  Assn. of Commercial Finance Attorneys [5237]
  Assn. for Honest Attorneys [5238]
  Assn. of Muslim Amer. Lawyers [5239]
  Assn. of Professional Responsibility Lawyers [5240]
  Assn. of Women Solicitors [20461]
  The Attorney's Gp. [5241]
  Center for Amer. and Intl. Law [5656]
  Croatian Amer. Bar Assn. [5242]
  Croatian Amer. Bar Assn. [5242]
  Decalogue Soc. of Lawyers [5243]
  Employment Law Alliance [5244]
  European Lawyers' Union [18791]
  Fair Elections Legal Network [5245]
  Fed. Bar Assn. [5246]
  Fed. Circuit Bar Assn. [5247]
  Fellows of the Amer. Bar Found. [5248]
  Fellows of the Amer. Bar Found. [5248]
  Hispanic Natl. Bar Assn. [5249]
  Intl. Acad. of Trial Lawyers [5250]
  Intl. Acad. of Trial Lawyers [5250]
  Intl. Amusement and Leisure Defense Assn. [3057]
  Intl. Assn. of Defense Counsel [5251]
  Intl. Assn. of Defense Counsel [5251]
  Intl. Municipal Lawyers Assn. [5252]
  Intl. Municipal Lawyers Assn. [5252]
  Intl. Network of Boutique Law Firms [5253]
  Intl. Network of Boutique Law Firms [5253]
  Intl. Senior Lawyers Proj. [5254]
  Intl. Senior Lawyers Proj. [5254]
  Intl. Soc. of Primerus Law Firms [5255]
  Intl. Soc. of Primerus Law Firms [5255]
  Iranian Amer. Bar Assn. [5256]
  Lawyers Assoc. Worldwide [5257]
  Lawyers Assoc. Worldwide [5257]
  Lex Mundi [5258]
  Lex Mundi [5258]
  Lithuanian-American Bar Assn. [5259]
  Lithuanian-American Bar Assn. [5259]
  Natl. Assn. of Appellate Court Attorneys [5260]
  Natl. Assn. of Asst. U.S. Attorneys [5261]
  Natl. Assn. of Bench and Bar Spouses [5262]
  Natl. Assn. of Consumer Bankruptcy Attorneys [5263]
  Natl. Assn. of Consumer Bankruptcy Attorneys [5263]
  Natl. Assn. of Minority and Women Owned Law Firms [5264]
  Natl. Assn. of Retail Coll. Attorneys [5265]
  Natl. Assn. of Women Lawyers [5266]
  Natl. Bar Assn. [5267]
  Natl. Conf. of Bar Presidents [5268]
  Natl. Conf. of Black Lawyers [5269]
  Natl. Conf. of Black Lawyers [5269]
  Natl. Conf. of Women's Bar Associations [5270]

  Natl. Coun. of Lawyer Disciplinary Boards [5271]
  Natl. District Attorneys Assn. [5272]
  Natl. Employment Lawyers Assn. [5273]
  Natl. Lawyers Assn. [5274]
  Natl. Lawyers Guild [5275]
  Natl. LGBT Bar Assn. [5276]
  Natl. Network of Estate Planning Attorneys [5277]
  Network of Trial Law Firms [5278]
  Network of Trial Law Firms [5278]
  Nigerian Lawyers Assn. [5279]
  North Amer. South Asian Bar Assn. [5678]
  North Amer. South Asian Law Student Assn. [8511]
  People Before Lawyers [5280]
  Personal Injury Lawyers Marketing and Mgt. Assn. [268]
  Renaissance Lawyer Soc. [5281]
  Serbian Bar Assn. of Am. [5282]
  Soc. of Ethical Attorneys at Law [5283]
  State Capital Global Law Firm Gp. [5284]
  State Capital Global Law Firm Gp. [5284]
  Swedish-American Bar Assn. [5285]
  Taiwanese Amer. Lawyers Assn. [5286]
  Taiwanese Amer. Lawyers Assn. [5286]
  Total Practice Mgt. Assn. [5287]
  U.S. Law Firm Gp. [5288]
  U.S. Law Firm Gp. [5288]
  USFN-America's Mortgage Banking Attorneys [5289]
Attorneys for Animal Rights [★10916]
The Attorney's Gp. [5241], Hillsboro Executive Center N, 350 Fairway Dr., Ste. 200, Deerfield Beach, FL 33441-1834, (954)571-1877
Attunement Guild [13667], 5569 N County Rd. 29, Loveland, CO 80538, (970)679-4299
AU [★22096]
Au Bas de l'Echelle [★IO]
Au Pair in Am. [8348], 9 W Broad St., River Plz., Stamford, CT 06902, (203)399-5000
Auburn-Cord-Duesenberg Club [21001], 24218 E Arapahoe Pl., Aurora, CO 80016, (303)748-3579
Auburn Univ. Montgomery Alumni Assn. [18853], PO Box 244023, Montgomery, AL 36124-4023, (334)244-3000
Auckland Bowls [IO], Auckland, New Zealand
Auckland Chamber of Commerce and Indus. [IO], Auckland, New Zealand
Auckland Miniature Horse Club [IO], Albany, New Zealand
Auckland Refugee Coun. Inc. [IO], Auckland, New Zealand
Auction Marketing Inst. [★271]
Auctioneers and Valuers Assn. of Australia [IO], Concord, Australia
Auctions
  Indus. Auctioneers Assn. [269]
  Natl. Assn. of Public Auto Auctions [270]
  Natl. Auctioneers Assn. [271]
  Natl. Auto Auction Assn. [272]
Audience Development Comm. [10569], PO Box 30, New York, NY 10027, (212)368-6906
Audio Engg. Soc. [6648], 60 E 42nd St., Rm. 2520, New York, NY 10165-2520, (212)661-8528
Audio Engg. Soc. - British Sect. [IO], Slough, United Kingdom
Audio Publishers Assn. [3049], 191 Clarksville Rd., Princeton Junction, NJ 08550, (609)799-6327
Audiological Soc. of Australia [IO], Forest Hill, Australia
Audiology
  Acad. of Rehabilitative Audiology [14910]
  Audiology Awareness Campaign [13774]
  Deaf and Hard of Hearing Alliance [14929]
  Dogs for the Deaf [14933]
  Military Audiology Assn. [13775]
  Model Secondary School for the Deaf [14946]
  Natl. Coalition on Auditory Processing Disorders [14949]
Audiology; Amer. Acad. of [16679]
Audiology Awareness Campaign [13774], 1 Windsor Cove, Ste. 305, Columbia, SC 29223, (858)552-7467
Audiovisual
  Assn. for Info. Media and Equip. [273]
  Communications Media Mgt. Assn. [274]

Reference to "IO" in place of a book number signifies that the association may be found in the 50th edition of International Organizations.

Entertainment Merchants Assn. **[275]**
Independent Professional Representatives Org. **[276]**
InfoComm Intl. **[277]**
InfoComm Intl. **[277]**
Intl. Visual Sociology Assn. **[7428]**
Visual Resources Assn. **[278]**
Visual Resources Assn. **[278]**
Audiovisual Communications
Media Action Grassroots Network **[18092]**
Audiovisual Mgt. Assn. **[★274]**
Audit Bur. of Circulations **[113]**, 48 W Seegers Rd., Arlington Heights, IL 60005-3913, (224)366-6939
Audit Bur. of Circulations - India **[IO]**, Mumbai, India
Audit Bur. of Circulations - United Kingdom **[IO]**, Berkhamsted, United Kingdom
Auditing Assn. of Canada **[IO]**, LaSalle, QC, Canada
Auditorium Managers Assn. **[★2441]**
Auditorium Managers Assn. **[★2441]**
Auditors; Assn. of Healthcare Internal **[15290]**
Auditory Soc; Amer. **[14914]**
Audubon Artists **[9170]**, 3 Lamb Rd., Brick, NJ 08724, (732)903-7468
Audubon Intl. **[4008]**, 46 Rarick Rd., Selkirk, NY 12158, (518)767-9051
Audubon Lifestyles **[4196]**, 35246 US Hwy. 19 N, No. 299, Palm Harbor, FL 34684, (727)733-0762
Audubon Naturalist Soc. of the Central Atlantic States **[4009]**, 8940 Jones Mill Rd., Chevy Chase, MD 20815, (301)652-9188
Audubon Soc. of the District of Columbia **[★4009]**
AUFBAU Trust
AUFBAU Trust - Address unknown since 2011.
August 13 Working Comm. **[IO]**, Berlin, Germany
August Derleth Soc. **[9349]**, PO Box 481, Sauk City, WI 53583, (608)643-3242
August Derleth Soc. **[9349]**, PO Box 481, Sauk City, WI 53583, (608)643-3242
Augustan Soc. **[20621]**, PO Box 771267, Orlando, FL 32877-1267, (407)745-0848
Augustan Soc. **[20621]**, PO Box 771267, Orlando, FL 32877-1267, (407)745-0848
The Augustine Fellowship **[★13084]**
Augusto Cesar Sandino Found. **[IO]**, Managua, Nicaragua
AURA - Defunct.
Aurora Ministries **[19983]**, Aurora Mission, PO Box 621, Bradenton, FL 34206, (941)748-4100
AUS-MEAT **[IO]**, Tingalpa, Australia
Aussenhandelsvereinigung des Deutschen Einzelhandels Ev **[★IO]**
Aussies Rescue and Placement Helpline **[★21517]**
Ausstellungs-und Messe-Ausschuss der Deutschen Wirtschaft **[★IO]**
Austin Bantam Soc. **[21002]**, 1036 Creek Crossing, Coppell, TX 75019
Austin Cody's Official Intl. Fan Club **[23816]**, Austin Cody, LLC, PO Box 21, Pomfret, MD 20675, (301)645-3809
Austin Families Genealogical Soc. - Address unknown since 2011.
Austin-Healey Club of Am. **[21003]**, Mr. Mike Schneider, Membership Dir., 110 N Rastetter Ave., Louisville, KY 40206, (877)5-HEALEY
Austin-Healey Club USA **[21004]**, Mark Schneider, Pres., 8002 NE Hwy. 99, Ste. B, PMB 424, Vancouver, WA 98665
Austin-Healey Sports and Touring Club **[21005]**, 309 E Broad St., Quakertown, PA 18951-1703, (215)536-6912
Austin Ten Drivers Club **[IO]**, Banbury, United Kingdom
Australasian Assn. of Bioethics and Hea. Law **[IO]**, Sydney, Australia
Australasian Assn. of Clinical Biochemists **[IO]**, Mount Lawley, Australia
Australasian Assn. of Convenience Stores **[IO]**, Melbourne, Australia
Australasian Assn. of Distance Educ. Schools **[IO]**, Thornbury, Australia
Australasian Assn. for Lexicography **[IO]**, North Ryde, Australia
Australasian Assn. of Philosophy **[IO]**, Hobart, Australia
Australasian Bottled Water Inst. **[IO]**, Rosebery, Australia

Australasian Cartridge Remanufacturers Assn. **[IO]**, Parramatta, Australia
Australasian Cave and Karst Mgt. Assn. **[IO]**, Mount Compass, Australia
Australasian Cemeteries and Crematoria Assn. **[IO]**, Preston, Australia
Australasian Chap. of Intl. Geosynthetics Soc. **[IO]**, Clayton, Australia
Australasian Coll. of Dermatologists **[IO]**, Boronia Park, Australia
Australasian Coll. for Emergency Medicine **[IO]**, West Melbourne, Australia
Australasian Coll. of Physical Scientists and Engineers in Medicine **[IO]**, Mascot, Australia
Australasian Coll. of Tropical Medicine **[IO]**, Red Hill, Australia
Australasian Corrections Educ. Assn. **[IO]**, Darlinghurst, Australia
Australasian Corrosion Assn. **[IO]**, Kerrimuir, Australia
Australasian Critical Incident Stress Assn. **[IO]**, Park Holme, Australia
Australasian Fed. of Family History Organisations **[IO]**, Weston Creek, Australia
Australasian Fleet Managers Assn. **[IO]**, Melbourne, Australia
Australasian Hellenic Educational Progressive Assn. **[IO]**, Balwyn North, Australia
Australasian Inst. of Mining and Metallurgy **[IO]**, Carlton, Australia
Australasian Jet Sports Boating Assn. **[IO]**, Morphett Vale, Australia
Australasian Lighting Indus. Assn. **[IO]**, Sydney, Australia
Australasian Lymphology Assn. **[IO]**, Mount Colah, Australia
Australasian Meat Indus. Employees' Union **[IO]**, Brisbane, Australia
Australasian Mech. Copyright Owners Soc. **[IO]**, Strawberry Hills, Australia
Australasian Medical Writers Assn. **[IO]**, Chatswood, Australia
Australasian Menopause Soc. **[IO]**, Buderim, Australia
Australasian Palliative Link Intl. **[IO]**, East Melbourne, Australia
Australasian Performing Rights Assn. **[IO]**, Ultimo, Australia
Australasian Pharmaceutical Sci. Assn. **[IO]**, Adelaide, Australia
Australasian Pig Sci. Assn. **[IO]**, Bentley, Australia
Australasian Plant Pathology Soc. **[IO]**, Toowoomba, Australia
Australasian Plant Soc. **[IO]**, Canterbury, United Kingdom
Australasian Political Stud. Assn. **[IO]**, Canberra, Australia
Australasian Promotional Products Assn. **[IO]**, Alphington, Australia
Australasian Quaternary Assn. **[IO]**, Brisbane, Australia
Australasian Radiation Protection Soc. **[IO]**, Upper Ferntree Gully, Australia
Australasian Raptor Assn. **[IO]**, Carlton, Australia
Australasian Sci. Educ. Res. Assn. **[IO]**, Perth, Australia
Australasian Sleep Assn. **[IO]**, Blacktown, Australia
Australasian Soc. of Aerospace Medicine **[IO]**, Balwyn, Australia
Australasian Soc. for Behavioural Hea. and Medicine **[IO]**, Herston, Australia
Australasian Soc. of Cataract and Refractive Surgeons **[IO]**, Mount Martha, Australia
Australasian Soc. for Classical Stud. **[IO]**, Bundanoon, Australia
Australasian Soc. of Clinical and Experimental Pharmacologists and Toxicologists **[IO]**, Fitzroy, Australia
Australasian Soc. of Clinical Immunology and Allergy **[IO]**, Balgowlah, Australia
Australasian Soc. for Computers in Learning in Tertiary Educ. **[IO]**, Figtree, Australia
Australasian Soc. for Gen. Relativity and Gravitation **[IO]**, Sydney, Australia
Australasian Soc. for HIV Medicine **[IO]**, Darlinghurst, Australia

Australasian Soc. for Human Biology **[IO]**, Crawley, Australia
Australasian Soc. of Oral Medicine and Toxicology **[IO]**, Sydney, Australia
Australasian Soc. for Phycology and Aquatic Botany **[IO]**, Lyons, Australia
Australasian Soc. for the Stud. of Animal Behaviour **[IO]**, North Ryde, Australia
Australasian Soc. for Traumatic Stress Stud. **[IO]**, Adelaide, Australia
Australasian Soc. for Trenchless Tech. **[IO]**, Greenwood, Australia
Australasian Soc. for Ultrasound in Medicine **[IO]**, Sydney, Australia
Australasian Soc. of Zoo Keeping **[IO]**, Healesville, Australia
Australasian Sound Recordings Assn. **[IO]**, Hepburn Springs, Australia
Australasian Tuberous Sclerosis Soc. **[IO]**, Springwood, Australia
Australasian Union of Jewish Students **[IO]**, Sydney, Australia
Australasian Universities Language and Literature Assn. **[IO]**, Sydney, Australia
Australasian Victorian Stud. Assn. **[IO]**, Crawley, Australia
Australia
Australian New Zealand - Amer. Chambers of Commerce **[23339]**
Soc. of Australasian Specialists/Oceania **[22075]**
Australia Arab Chamber of Commerce and Indus. **[IO]**, Kingston, Australia
Australia Bhutan Friendship Assn. **[IO]**, Thimphu, Bhutan
Australia-Brazil Chamber of Commerce **[IO]**, Artarmon, Australia
Australia-Britain Soc. **[IO]**, Perth, Australia
Australia China Alumni Assn. **[IO]**, Shanghai, People's Republic of China
Australia Coun. for the Arts **[IO]**, Surry Hills, Australia
Australia Defence Assn. **[IO]**, Wanniassa, Australia
Australia Ice Racing Coun. **[IO]**, West Melbourne, Australia
Australia-Israel Chamber of Commerce **[IO]**, Double Bay, Australia
Australia New Guinea Fishes Assn. **[IO]**, Ringwood, Australia
Australia-New Zealand Assn. **[IO]**, Vancouver, BC, Canada
Australia and New Zealand Coll. of Anaesthetists **[IO]**, Melbourne, Australia
Australia and New Zealand Organ Donation Registry **[IO]**, Adelaide, Australia
Australia New Zealand Soc. for Ecological Economics **[IO]**, Canberra, Australia
Australia Pacific Islands Bus. Coun. **[IO]**, Wynnum, Australia
Australia Philippines Bus. Coun. **[IO]**, Mordialloc, Australia
Australia-Singapore Chamber of Commerce and Indus. **[IO]**, Sydney, Australia
Australia-Taiwan Bus. Coun. **[IO]**, Sydney, Australia
Australia Tibet Coun. **[IO]**, Darlinghurst, Australia
Australian
Amer. Australian Assn. **[18939]**
Australian New Zealand - Amer. Chambers of Commerce **[23339]**
Soc. of Australasian Specialists/Oceania **[22075]**
Australian Acad. of the Humanities **[IO]**, Canberra, Australia
Australian Acad. of Sci. **[IO]**, Canberra, Australia
Australian Acad. of Technological Sciences and Engg. **[IO]**, Melbourne, Australia
Australian Acoustical Soc. **[IO]**, Toowong, Australia
Australian Acupuncture and Chinese Medicine Assn. **[IO]**, Coorparoo, Australia
Australian Addison's Disease Assn. **[IO]**, Dorrigo, Australia
Australian Advisory Bd. on Autism Spectrum Disorders **[IO]**, Forestville, Australia
Australian Agency for Intl. Development **[IO]**, Canberra, Australia
Australian Agricultural and Rsrc. Economics Soc. **[IO]**, Canberra, Australia

A star before a book entry number signifies that the name is not listed separately, but is mentioned within the entry.

Australian Amer. Assn. [IO], Yarraville, Australia

Australian-American Fulbright Commn. [IO], Deakin, Australia

Australian Amusement, Leisure and Recreation Assn. [IO], Gold Coast, Australia

Australian Animal Protection Soc. [IO], Keysborough, Australia

Australian Antique and Art Dealers Assn. [IO], Malvern, Australia

Australian Archaeological Assn. [IO], Townsville, Australia

Australian Architecture Assn. [IO], Sydney, Australia

Australian Assn. for Cognitive and Behaviour Therapy [IO], Brisbane, Australia

Australian Assn. of Consultant Pharmacy [IO], Canberra, Australia

Australian Assn. of Consulting Archaeologists [IO], Sydney, Australia

Australian Assn. of the Deaf [★175]

Australian Assn. of Gerontology [IO], Loganholme, Australia

Australian Assn. of Hong Kong [IO], Hong Kong, People's Republic of China

Australian Assn. of Massage Therapists [IO], Melbourne, Australia

Australian Assn. of Mathematics Teachers [IO], Adelaide, Australia

Australian Assn. of Men Barbershop Singers [IO], West Gosford, Australia

Australian Assn. of Natl. Advertisers [IO], Sydney, Australia

Australian Assn. of Practice Managers [IO], Fortitude Valley, Australia

Australian Assn. for Professional and Applied Ethics [IO], Sydney, Australia

Australian Assn. for Psychological Type [IO], Ashfield, Australia

Australian Assn. of Social Workers [IO], Kingston, Australia

Australian Assn. of Social Workers - Hunter Valley Br. [IO], Newcastle, Australia

Australian Assn. of Social Workers - New South Wales Br. [IO], Rozelle, Australia

Australian Assn. of Social Workers - North Queensland Br. [IO], Mackay, Australia

Australian Assn. of Social Workers - Northern Territory Br. [IO], Nightcliff, Australia

Australian Assn. of Social Workers - South Australian Br. [IO], Hindmarsh, Australia

Australian Assn. of Social Workers - Tasmanian Br. [IO], Hobart, Australia

Australian Assn. of Social Workers - Victorian Br. [IO], Carlton, Australia

Australian Assn. of Somatic Psychotherapists [IO], Belgrave, Australia

Australian Assn. for the Stud. of Religions [IO], Lismore, Australia

Australian Assn. for the Teaching of English [IO], Kensington Gardens, Australia

Australian Assn. of Vaginal and Incontinence Surgeons [IO], Wahroonga, Australia

Australian Athletes with a Disability [IO], Homebush, Australia

Australian Auto. Assn. [IO], Canberra, Australia

Australian Automotive Aftermarket Assn. [IO], Clayton, Australia

Australian Banana Growers' Coun. [IO], Brisbane, Australia

Australian Bankers' Assn. [IO], Sydney, Australia

Australian Barramundi Farmers Assn. [IO], Bulimba, Australia

Australian Bartenders Guild [IO], Sydney, Australia

Australian Baseball Fed. [IO], Mudgeeraba, Australia

Australian Beef Assn. [IO], Oakey, Australia

Australian Beverage Coun. Ltd. [IO], Rosebery, Australia

Australian Bird Stud. Assn. [IO], Sydney, Australia

Australian Blind Sports Federations [IO], Milton, Australia

Australian Booksellers Assn. [IO], Kew East, Australia

Australian Bowhunters Assn. [IO], Morayfield, Australia

Australian Braford Soc. [IO], Rockhampton, Australia

Australian Brahman Breeders' Assn. [IO], Rockhampton, Australia

Australian Braunvieh Assn. [IO], Carlsruhe, Australia

Australian Breastfeeding Assn. [IO], Glen Iris, Australia

Australian Bus. in Europe [IO], Melbourne, Australia

Australian Businesswomen's Network [IO], Rosebery, Australia

Australian Camp Connect Assn. [IO], Mount Evelyn, Australia

Australian Cane Farmers Assn. [IO], Brisbane, Australia

Australian Canoeing [IO], Silverwater, Australia

Australian Capital Territory Aeromodellers Assn. [IO], Fyshwick, Australia

Australian Capital Territory History Teachers Assn. [IO], Phillip, Australia

Australian Casino Assn. [IO], Sydney, Australia

Australian Catholic Bishops' Conf. [IO], Canberra, Australia

Australian Catholic Social Justice Coun. [IO], Alexandria, Australia

Australian Cattle Dog Club of Am. [21516], Carla Price, Membership Sec., 91 Harrison Rd., Ellisville, MS 39437

Australian Centre for Intl. Commercial Arbitration [IO], Sydney, Australia

Australian Ceramic Soc. [IO], Hawthorn, Australia

The Australian Ceramics Assn. [IO], Waverley, Australia

Australian Chamber of Commerce and Indus. [IO], Kingston, Australia

Australian Chamber of Fruit and Vegetable Indus. [IO], Sydney, Australia

Australian Chap. of Sexual Hea. Medicine [IO], Sydney, Australia

Australian Chess Fed. [IO], Evatt, Australia

Australian Chicken Meat Fed. [IO], North Sydney, Australia

Australian Cinematographers Soc. [IO], Artarmon, Australia

Australian Circus and Physical Theatre Assn. [IO], North Melbourne, Australia

Australian Civil Liberties Union [IO], Carlton, Australia

Australian Clay Minerals Soc. [IO], Glen Osmond, Australia

Australian Climbing Instructors Assn. [IO], Natimuk, Australia

Australian Coal Assn. [IO], Deakin, Australia

Australian Coffee Traders Assn. [IO], Coogee, Australia

Australian Collaborative Land Evaluation Prog. [IO], Canberra, Australia

Australian Coll. of Educators [IO], Mawson, Australia

Australian Coll. of Hea. Ser. Executives [IO], North Ryde, Australia

Australian Coll. of Pharmacy Practice and Mgt. [IO], Canberra, Australia

Australian Coll. of Rural and Remote Medicine [IO], Brisbane, Australia

Australian Commn. on Safety and Quality in Hea. Care [IO], Sydney, Australia

Australian Comm. for UNICEF [IO], Sydney, Australia

Australian Cmpt. Soc. [IO], Sydney, Australia

Australian Conservation Found. [IO], Carlton, Australia

Australian Consumers' Assn. [IO], Marrickville, Australia

Australian Copyright Coun. [IO], Strawberry Hills, Australia

Australian Coral Reef Soc. [IO], St. Lucia, Australia

Australian Corporate Lawyers Assn. [IO], Melbourne, Australia

Australian Corriedale Assn. [IO], Melbourne, Australia

Australian Coun. of Agricultural Journalists [IO], Geelong, Australia

Australian Coun. on Children and the Media [IO], Glenelg, Australia

Australian Coun. of Deans of Sci. [IO], Melbourne, Australia

Australian Coun. for Educational Leaders [IO], Penrith, Australia

Australian Coun. for Educational Leaders - Newcastle [IO], Newcastle, Australia

Australian Coun. for Educational Leaders - South Australia [IO], Adelaide, Australia

Australian Coun. for Educational Res. [IO], Camberwell, Australia

Australian Coun. for Hea., Physical Educ. and Recreation [IO], Hindmarsh, Australia

Australian Coun. on Healthcare Standards [IO], Sydney, Australia

Australian Coun. for Intl. Development [IO], Deakin, Australia

Australian Coun. for Private Educ. and Training [IO], Melbourne, Australia

Australian Coun. of Superannuation Investors [IO], Melbourne, Australia

Australian Coun. of Trade Unions [IO], Melbourne, Australia

Australian Coun. of Women and Policing [IO], Woden, Australia

Australian Cricketers' Assn. [IO], South Melbourne, Australia

Australian Croquet Assn. [IO], Dickson, Australia

Australian Curriculum Stud. Assn. [IO], Deakin West, Australia

Australian Democrats [IO], Black Forest, Australia

Australian Dental Assn. [IO], St. Leonards, Australia

Australian Dental and Oral Hea. Therapists' Assn. [IO], Modbury North, Australia

Australian Dermatology Nurses Assn. [IO], East Blaxland, Australia

Australian Die Casting Assn. [IO], Bayswater, Australia

Australian Direct Marketing Assn. [IO], Sydney, Australia

Australian Directors Guild [IO], Rozelle, Australia

Australian Draughts Fed. [IO], Kildare, Australia

Australian Dried Fruits Assn. [IO], Mildura, Australia

Australian Drug Found. [IO], North Melbourne, Australia

Australian Earthquake Engg. Soc. [IO], McKinnon, Australia

Australian Educ. Union [IO], Southbank, Australia

Australian Entertainment Indus. Assn. [★23844]

Australian Entomological Soc. [IO], Canberra, Australia

Australian Environmental Pest Managers Assn. [IO], Sydney, Australia

Australian False Memory Assn. [IO], Epping, Australia

Australian Family Assn. [IO], Balwyn, Australia

Australian Fed. Police Assn. [IO], Canberra, Australia

Australian Fed. of AIDS Organisations [IO], Newtown, Australia

Australian Fed. of Civil Celebrants [IO], New Norfolk, Australia

Australian Fed. of Disability Organisations [IO], Melbourne, Australia

Australian Fed. of Friends of Museums [IO], Canberra, Australia

Australian Fed. of Graduate Women [IO], Enmore, Australia

Australian Fed. of Intl. Forwarders [IO], Eastgardens, Australia

Australian Fed. of Modern Language Teachers Associations [IO], Belconnen, Australia

Australian Fed. of SPELD Associations [IO], South Perth, Australia

Australian Fed. of Travel Agents [IO], Sydney, Australia

Australian Fed. of Univ. Women - Tasmania [IO], Hobart, Australia

Australian Film Inst. [IO], South Melbourne, Australia

Australian Finnsheep Breeders Assn. [IO], Inglewood, Australia

Australian Floorball Assn. [IO], Woodvale, Australia

Australian Flower Export Coun. [IO], North Melbourne, Australia

Australian Flying Disc Assn. [IO], Ermington, Australia

Australian Fodder Indus. Assn. [IO], Melbourne, Australia

Australian Food and Grocery Coun. [IO], Kingston, Australia

Australian Football Assn. of North Am. [22587], PO Box 27623, Columbus, OH 43227-0623, (614)571-8986

Reference to "IO" in place of a book number signifies that the association may be found in the 50th edition of International Organizations.

Australian Funeral Directors Assn. **[IO]**, Kew East, Australia

Australian Furniture Removers Assn. **[IO]**, Baulkham Hills, Australia

Australian Galloway Assn. **[IO]**, Westbury, Australia

Australian Garden History Soc. **[IO]**, Melbourne, Australia

Australian Gas Assn. **[IO]**, Braeside, Australia

Australian Gelbvieh Assn. **[IO]**, Armidale, Australia

Australian Geography Teachers Assn. **[IO]**, Clifton Hill, Australia

Australian Geomechanics Soc. **[IO]**, St. Ives, Australia

Australian Geoscience Coun. **[IO]**, Carlton South, Australia

Australian Geoscience Info. Assn. **[IO]**, Perth, Australia

Australian Ginseng Growers Assn. **[IO]**, Huonville, Australia

Australian Glass and Glazing Assn. **[IO]**, Melbourne, Australia

Australian Graphic Design Assn. **[IO]**, Unley, Australia

Australian Gynaecological Endoscopy Soc. **[IO]**, Castlecrag, Australia

Australian Hand Therapy Assn. **[IO]**, Mundaring, Australia

Australian Hea. Promotion Assn. **[IO]**, Maroochydore, Australia

Australian Higher Educ. Indus. Assn. **[IO]**, Melbourne, Australia

Australian Highland Cattle Soc. **[IO]**, Armidale, Australia

Australian Homoeopathic Assn. **[IO]**, Toowoomba, Australia

Australian Horse Alliance **[IO]**, Elanora, Australia

Australian Horticultural Exporters Assn. **[IO]**, Knoxfield, Australia

Australian Hotels Assn. NSW **[IO]**, Sydney, Australia

Australian Hotels Assn. South Australian Br. **[IO]**, Adelaide, Australia

Australian Hotels Assn. Tasmania **[IO]**, Battery Point, Australia

Australian Hotels Assn. Victoria Br. **[IO]**, Melbourne, Australia

Australian Human Rsrc. Inst. **[IO]**, Melbourne, Australia

Australian Huntington Disease Assn. **[IO]**, Nedlands, Australia

Australian Huntington Disease Assn. - New South Wales **[IO]**, West Ryde, Australia

Australian Huntington Disease Assn. - Victoria **[IO]**, Melbourne, Australia

Australian Huntington Disease Assn. - Western Australia **[IO]**, Nedlands, Australia

Australian Indigenous Art Trade Assn. **[IO]**, Port Douglas, Australia

Australian Indigenous Doctors' Assn. **[IO]**, Manuka, Australia

Australian Indus. Gp. **[IO]**, North Sydney, Australia

Australian Infant, Child, Adolescent and Family Mental Hea. Assn. **[IO]**, Stepney, Australia

Australian Infection Control Assn. **[IO]**, Brisbane, Australia

Australian Info. Indus. Assn. **[IO]**, Deakin, Australia

Australian Info. Security Assn. **[IO]**, Sydney, Australia

Australian Inst. of Aboriginal and Torres Strait Islander Stud. **[IO]**, Canberra, Australia

Australian Inst. of Administrative Law **[IO]**, Canberra, Australia

Australian Inst. of Agricultural Sci. and Tech. **[IO]**, Curtin, Australia

Australian Inst. of Architects **[IO]**, Manuka, Australia

Australian Inst. of Biology **[IO]**, Syndal, Australia

Australian Inst. of Building **[IO]**, Canberra, Australia

Australian Inst. of Company Directors **[IO]**, Sydney, Australia

Australian Inst. of Credit Mgt. **[IO]**, St. Leonards, Australia

Australian Inst. of Criminology **[IO]**, Canberra, Australia

Australian Inst. of Energy **[IO]**, Surrey Hills, Australia

Australian Inst. of Food Sci. and Tech. **[IO]**, Alexandria, Australia

Australian Inst. of Genealogical Stud. **[IO]**, Blackburn, Australia

Australian Inst. of Geoscientists **[IO]**, Perth, Australia

Australian Inst. of Intl. Affairs **[IO]**, Deakin, Australia

Australian Inst. of Landscape Architects **[IO]**, Canberra, Australia

Australian Inst. of Mgt. **[IO]**, St. Kilda, Australia

Australian Inst. of Marine Sci. **[IO]**, Townsville, Australia

Australian Inst. of Nuclear Sci. and Engg. **[IO]**, Kirrawee, Australia

Australian Inst. of Packaging **[IO]**, Brisbane, Australia

Australian Inst. of Petroleum **[IO]**, Canberra, Australia

Australian Inst. of Physics **[IO]**, Port Melbourne, Australia

Australian Inst. of Professional Intelligence Officers **[IO]**, Civic Square, Australia

Australian Inst. of Professional Photography **[IO]**, North Melbourne, Australia

Australian Inst. of Proj. Mgt. **[IO]**, Sydney, Australia

Australian Inst. of Quantity Surveyors **[IO]**, Deakin West, Australia

Australian Inst. of Radiography **[IO]**, Collingwood, Australia

Australian Inst. of Urban Stud. **[IO]**, Melbourne, Australia

Australian Insurance Law Assn. **[IO]**, Box Hill, Australia

Australian Interactive Media Indus. Assn. **[IO]**, Sydney, Australia

Australian Intl. Yngling Assn. **[IO]**, Sydney, Australia

Australian Kite Assn. **[IO]**, Torquay, Australia

Australian Kitesurfing Assn. **[IO]**, Coogee, Australia

Australian Koala Found. **[IO]**, Brisbane, Australia

Australian Labor Party **[IO]**, Kingston, Australia

Australian Lancia Register **[IO]**, East Melbourne, Australia

Australian Lavender Indus. **[IO]**, Leichhardt, Australia

Australian Lawyers for Human Rights **[IO]**, Sydney, Australia

Australian Lib. and Info. Assn. **[IO]**, Kingston, Australia

Australian Life Cycle Assessment Soc. **[IO]**, Melbourne, Australia

Australian Linguistic Soc. **[IO]**, Cardiff, Australia

Australian Literacy Educators' Assn. **[IO]**, Norwood, Australia

Australian Logistics Coun. **[IO]**, Deakin, Australia

Australian Lutheran World Ser. **[IO]**, Albury, Australia

Australian Macadamia Soc. **[IO]**, Lismore, Australia

Australian Malaysian Singaporean Assn. **[IO]**, Sydney, Australia

Australian Mammal Soc. **[IO]**, Wanneroo, Australia

Australian Mfg. Workers' Union **[IO]**, Granville, Australia

Australian Marine Conservation Soc. **[IO]**, Brisbane, Australia

Australian Marine Sciences Assn. **[IO]**, Kilkivan, Australia

Australian Market and Social Res. Soc. **[IO]**, Glebe, Australia

Australian Mathematical Soc. **[IO]**, Canberra, Australia

Australian Meat Indus. Coun. **[IO]**, Crows Nest, Australia

Australian Medical Assn. **[IO]**, Kingston, Australia

Australian Medical Coun. **[IO]**, Kingston, Australia

Australian Medical Students' Assn. **[IO]**, Kingston, Australia

Australian Mensa **[IO]**, Midland, Australia

Australian Microscopy and Microanalysis Soc. **[IO]**, Melbourne, Australia

Australian Military Medicine Assn. **[IO]**, Hobart, Australia

Australian Mineral Found. **[IO]**, Glenside, Australia

Australian Mines and Metals Assn. **[IO]**, Melbourne, Australia

Australian Miniature Enthusiasts Assn. **[IO]**, Cherrybrook, Australia

Australian Mining and Petroleum and Law Assn. **[IO]**, Melbourne, Australia

Australian Mobile Telecommunications Assn. **[IO]**, Manuka, Australia

Australian Multiple Birth Assn. **[IO]**, Coogee, Australia

Australian Municipal, Administrative, Clerical and Services Union **[IO]**, Carlton South, Australia

Australian Mushroom Growers Assn. **[IO]**, Windsor, Australia

Australian Music Centre **[IO]**, Grosvenor Place, Australia

Australian Music Retailers Assn. **[IO]**, Malvern, Australia

Australian Music Therapy Assn. **[IO]**, Malvern, Australia

Australian Natl. Flag Assn. **[IO]**, Sydney, Australia

Australian Natl. Kennel Coun. **[IO]**, Fortitude Valley, Australia

Australian Natl. Sportfishing Assn. **[IO]**, Maroubra, Australia

Australian Natl. Sportfishing Assn. - NT Br. **[IO]**, Darwin, Australia

Australian Natl. Sportfishing Assn. - Victoria **[IO]**, Keysborough, Australia

Australian Native Dog Conservation Soc. **[IO]**, Bargo, Australia

Australian Network for Plant Conservation **[IO]**, Canberra, Australia

Australian Neuroscience Soc. **[IO]**, Kent Town, Australia

Australian New Zealand - Amer. Chambers of Commerce **[23339]**, Embassy of Australia, 1601 Massachusetts Ave. NW, Washington, DC 20036

Australian New Zealand - Amer. Chambers of Commerce **[23339]**, Embassy of Australia, 1601 Massachusetts Ave. NW, Washington, DC 20036

Australian and New Zealand Assn. for the Advancement of Sci. **[IO]**, Northcote, Australia

Australian and New Zealand Assn. of Antiquarian Booksellers **[IO]**, Prahran, Australia

Australian and New Zealand Assn. for Leisure Stud. **[IO]**, Canterbury, New Zealand

Australian and New Zealand Assn. for Medieval and Early Modern Stud. **[IO]**, Crawley, Australia

Australian and New Zealand Assn. for Medieval and Renaissance Stud. **[IO]**, Melbourne, Australia

Australian and New Zealand Assn. of Oral and Maxillofacial Surgeons **[IO]**, Crows Nest, Australia

Australian and New Zealand Assn. of Physicians in Nuclear Medicine **[IO]**, Balmain, Australia

Australian and New Zealand Assn. of Psychotherapy **[IO]**, St. Leonards, Australia

Australian and New Zealand Assn. for the Treatment of Sexual Abuse **[IO]**, Haymarket, Australia

Australian and New Zealand Bone and Mineral Soc. **[IO]**, Sydney, Australia

Australian and New Zealand Coun. for the Care of Animals in Res. and Teaching **[IO]**, Adelaide, Australia

Australian and New Zealand Obesity Soc. **[IO]**, Sydney, Australia

Australian and New Zealand Ombudsman Assn. **[IO]**, Melbourne, Australia

Australian and New Zealand Psychodrama Assn. **[IO]**, Adelaide, Australia

Australian and New Zealand Soc. of Blood Transfusion **[IO]**, Sydney, Australia

Australian and New Zealand Soc. of Intl. Law **[IO]**, Canberra, Australia

Australian and New Zealand Soc. of Nuclear Medicine **[IO]**, Upper Ferntree Gully, Australia

Australian and New Zealand Soc. of Palliative Medicine **[IO]**, Watson, Australia

Australian and New Zealand Soc. of Respiratory Sci. **[IO]**, Orange, Australia

Australian and New Zealand Solar Energy Soc. **[IO]**, Frenchs Forest, Australia

Australian and New Zealand Sports Law Assn. **[IO]**, Avoca Beach, Australia

Australian Newsagents' Fed. **[IO]**, St. Leonards, Australia

Australian Nuclear Assn. **[IO]**, Peakhurst, Australia

Australian Nuclear Sci. and Tech. Org. **[IO]**, Menai, Australia

Australian Nudist Fed. **[IO]**, Lake Haven, Australia

Australian Nudist Fed. Supporter Club **[IO]**, North Parramatta, Australia

Australian Numismatic Soc. **[IO]**, Brookvale, Australia

A star before a book entry number signifies that the name is not listed separately, but is mentioned within the entry.

Australian Nurses' Cardiovascular and Hypertension Assn. [IO], Greenslopes, Australia

Australian Nursing Fed. [IO], Kingston, Australia

Australian Oilseeds Fed. [IO], Sydney, Australia

Australian Olive Assn. [IO], Pendle Hill, Australia

Australian Olive Oil Assn. [IO], Carlton, Australia

Australian Optical Soc. [IO], Callaghan, Australia

Australian Orthopaedic Assn. [IO], Sydney, Australia

Australian Orthopaedic Foot and Ankle Soc. [IO], Wantirna, Australia

Australian Packaging and Processing Machinery Assn. [IO], Rose Bay North, Australia

Australian Pain Soc. [IO], North Sydney, Australia

Australian Paint Mfrs. Fed. [IO], North Sydney, Australia

Australian Paralympic Comm. [IO], Sydney, Australia

Australian Parkour Assn. [IO], Melbourne, Australia

Australian Pattern Recognition Soc. [IO], Adelaide, Australia

Australian Payments Clearing Assn. [IO], Sydney, Australia

Australian People for Hea., Educ. and Development Abroad [IO], Sydney, Australia

Australian Petroleum Production and Exploration Assn. [IO], Canberra, Australia

Australian Pharmaceutical Mfrs. Assn. [★13892]

Australian Physiological Soc. [IO], Brisbane, Australia

Australian Physiotherapy Assn. [IO], Camberwell, Australia

Australian Pipeline Indus. Assn. [IO], Kingston, Australia

Australian Plaiters and Whipmakers Assn. [IO], Kuranda, Australia

Australian Plants Soc. - New South Wales Region [IO], Old Toongabbie, Australia

Australian Plants Soc. - South Australia [IO], Unley, Australia

Australian Plants Soc. - Tasmania [IO], Hobart, Australia

Australian Poll Dorset Assn. [IO], Melbourne, Australia

Australian Population Assn. [IO], Acton, Australia

Australian Pork Ltd. [IO], Deakin West, Australia

Australian Prawn Farmers Assn. [IO], Brisbane, Australia

Australian Press Coun. [IO], Sydney, Australia

Australian Private Hospitals Assn. [IO], Canberra, Australia

Australian Property Inst. [IO], Deakin, Australia

Australian Psychological Soc. [IO], Melbourne, Australia

Australian Public Access Network Assn. [IO], Doncaster, Australia

Australian Publishers' Assn. [IO], Ultimo, Australia

Australian Pump Mfrs'. Assn. [★50]

Australian Red Cross ACT [IO], Mawson, Australia

Australian Red Cross Soc. [IO], Carlton, Australia

Australian Red Poll Cattle Breeders [IO], Armidale, Australia

Australian Rehabilitation and Assistive Tech. Assn. [IO], Melbourne, Australia

Australian Reproductive Hea. Alliance [IO], Campbell, Australia

Australian Res. Coun. [IO], Canberra, Australia

Australian Resuscitation Coun. [IO], Melbourne, Australia

Australian Rheumatology Assn. [IO], Sydney, Australia

Australian Rheumatology Assn. - Australian Capital Territory [IO], Canberra, Australia

Australian Rheumatology Assn. - New South Wales [IO], Liverpool, Australia

Australian Rheumatology Assn. - Queensland [IO], Greenslopes, Australia

Australian Rheumatology Assn. - South Australia [IO], Adelaide, Australia

Australian Rheumatology Assn. - Tasmania [IO], Hobart, Australia

Australian Rheumatology Assn. - Western Australia [IO], Subiaco, Australia

Australian Rhododendron Soc. [IO], Park Orchards, Australia

Australian Robotics and Automation Assn. [IO], Sydney, Australia

Australian Rock Art Res. Assn. [IO], Caulfield South, Australia

Australian Sailing and Cruising Club [IO], Potts Point, Australia

Australian Salaried Medical Officers' Fed. [IO], Glebe, Australia

Australian Sci. Teachers Assn. [IO], Deakin, Australia

Australian Screen Editors Guild [IO], Paddington, Australia

Australian Seafood Indus. Coun. [IO], Ascot, Australia

Australian Seed Fed. [IO], Manuka, Australia

Australian Self-Medication Indus. [IO], North Sydney, Australia

Australian Services Union [IO], Carlton South, Australia

Australian Severe Weather Assn. [IO], Kew, Australia

Australian Shareholders' Assn. [IO], Chatswood, Australia

Australian Sheep Breeders Assn. [IO], Bendigo, Australia

Australian Shepherd Club of Am. [21517], 6091 E State Hwy. 21, Bryan, TX 77808-8641, (979)778-1082

Australian Ship Repairers Gp. [IO], Ashmore, Australia

Australian Shipbuilders Assn. [IO], Ashmore, Australia

Australian Shipowners Assn. [IO], Port Melbourne, Australia

Australian Sign Language Interpreters Assn. [IO], Sydney, Australia

Australian Simmental Breeders Assn. [IO], Armidale, Australia

Australian Skeptics - NSW Br. [IO], Roseville, Australia

Australian Small Animal Veterinary Assn. [IO], St. Leonards, Australia

Australian Soc. of Anaesthetists [IO], Edgecliff, Australia

Australian Soc. of Animal Production Sydney Br. [IO], Park Ridge, Australia

Australian Soc. for Antimicrobials [IO], South Perth, Australia

Australian Soc. of Archivists [IO], Virginia, Australia

Australian Soc. of Assn. Executives [IO], Surrey Hills, Australia

Australian Soc. of Authors [IO], Strawberry Hills, Australia

Australian Soc. of Baking [IO], Happy Valley, Australia

Australian Soc. for Biochemistry and Molecular Biology [IO], Melbourne, Australia

Australian Soc. for Biomaterials and Tissue Engg. [IO], Christchurch, New Zealand

Australian Soc. for Biophysics [IO], Canberra, Australia

Australian Soc. of Calligraphers [IO], Willoughby, Australia

Australian Soc. of Clinical Hypnotherapists [IO], Crows Nest, Australia

Australian Soc. of Clinical Neurophysiologists [IO], Sydney, Australia

Australian Soc. of Cosmetic Chemists [IO], Moorebank, Australia

Australian Soc. of Exploration Geophysicists [IO], Perth, Australia

Australian Soc. for Fish Biology [IO], Kingston, Australia

Australian Soc. of Hypnosis [IO], North Willoughby, Australia

Australian Soc. of Legal Philosophy [IO], Clayton, Australia

Australian Soc. for Limnology [IO], Melbourne, Australia

Australian Soc. of Magicians [IO], Toorak, Australia

Australian Soc. for Medical Res. [IO], Sydney, Australia

Australian Soc. for Microbiology [IO], Melbourne, Australia

Australian Soc. for Music Educ. [IO], Mawson, Australia

Australian Soc. for Operations Res. [IO], Canberra, Australia

Australian Soc. for Operations Res. - ACT Chap. [IO], Acton, Australia

Australian Soc. for Operations Res. - Melbourne Chap. [IO], Melbourne, Australia

Australian Soc. for Operations Res. - Queensland Br. [IO], Brisbane, Australia

Australian Soc. for Operations Res. - South Australia Chap. [IO], Adelaide, Australia

Australian Soc. for Operations Res. - Western Australia Chap. [IO], Perth, Australia

Australian Soc. of Orthodontists [IO], Crows Nest, Australia

Australian Soc. of Otolaryngology Head and Neck Surgery [IO], Milsons Point, Australia

Australian Soc. for Parasitology [IO], Darwin, Australia

Australian Soc. of Plant Scientists [IO], Canberra, Australia

Australian Soc. of Soil Sci. [IO], Warragul, Australia

Australian Soc. of Sugar Cane Technologists [IO], Mackay, Australia

Australian Soc. of Teachers of the Alexander Technique [IO], Beechworth, Australia

Australian Soc. of Viticulture and Oenology [IO], Adelaide, Australia

The Australian Sociological Assn. [IO], Hawthorn, Australia

Australian Sonographers Assn. [IO], Moorabbin, Australia

Australian Spatial Info. Bus. Assn. [IO], Deakin West, Australia

Australian Speech Sci. and Tech. Assn. [IO], Canberra, Australia

Australian Spina Bifida and Hydrocephalus Assn. [IO], Nedlands, Australia

Australian Sport Aviation Confed. [IO], Canberra, Australia

Australian Sports Commn. [IO], Belconnen, Australia

Australian Stainless Steel Development Assn. [IO], Brisbane, Australia

Australian Steel Inst. [IO], North Sydney, Australia

Australian Stock Horse Soc. [IO], Scone, Australia

Australian Subscription TV and Radio Assn. [IO], Pyrmont, Australia

Australian Suburban Newspapers Assn. [★16163]

Australian Superfine Wool Growers' Assn. [IO], Brooklyn, Australia

Australian Systematic Botany Soc. [IO], Melbourne, Australia

Australian Teachers of Media [IO], St. Kilda, Australia

Australian Terrier Club of Am. [21518], Sherrill Yates, Corresponding Sec., 2506 Glynnwood Dr., Bartlesville, OK 74006

Australian Texel Stud Breeders Assn. [IO], Melbourne, Australia

Australian Tile Coun. [IO], Hope Valley, Australia

Australian Tinnitus Assn. NSW [IO], Woollahra, Australia

Australian Tourism Export Coun. [IO], Sydney, Australia

Australian Toy Assn. [IO], North Melbourne, Australia

Australian Trade Commn. [23452], 150 E 42nd St., 34th Fl., New York, NY 10017-5612, (646)344-8111

Australian Traditional-Medicine Soc. [IO], Meadowbank, Australia

Australian Trail Horse Riders Assn. [IO], Karuah, Australia

Australian Trail Horse Riders Assn. - New South Wales Br. [IO], Karuah, Australia

Australian Trail Horse Riders Assn. - Queensland [IO], Park Ridge, Australia

Australian Trail Horse Riders Assn. - South Australian Br. [IO], Kersbrook, Australia

Australian Trail Horse Riders Assn. - Victoria Br. [IO], Yarram, Australia

Australian Trucking Assn. [IO], Forrest, Australia

Australian UNIX and Open Systems Users Gp. [IO], Baulkham Hills, Australia

Australian Vaccination Network [IO], Bangalow, Australia

Australian Vascular Biology Soc. [IO], Melbourne, Australia

Australian Vegetables and Potato Growers' Fed. [IO], Camberwell, Australia

Reference to "IO" in place of a book number signifies that the association may be found in the 50th edition of International Organizations.

Australian Vegetarian Soc. [IO], Surry Hills, Australia
Australian Venture Capital Assn. Limited [IO], Sydney, Australia
Australian Veterinary Assn. [IO], St. Leonards, Australia
Australian Volunteer Coast Guard Assn. [IO], Brisbane, Australia
Australian Wagyu Assn. [IO], Armidale, Australia
Australian Water Assn. [IO], St. Leonards, Australia
Australian White Suffolk Assn. [IO], Goodwood, Australia
Australian Wildlife Protection Coun. [IO], Fitzroy, Australia
Australian Wine and Brandy Corp. [IO], Kent Town, Australia
Australian Wine Consumers' Co-operative Soc. [IO], Broadway, Australia
Australian Women in Agriculture [IO], Wangaratta, Australia
Australian Women Lawyers [IO], Hobart, Australia
Australian Women Pilots' Assn. [IO], Cairns, Australia
Australian Women's Hea. Network [IO], Melbourne, Australia
Australian Wool Growers Assn. [IO], Lismore, Australia
Australian Workers' Union [IO], Sydney, Australia
Australian Wound Mgt. Assn. [IO], South Melbourne, Australia
Australian Writers' Guild [IO], Chippendale, Australia
Australians Against Racism [IO], Enfield, Australia
Australians for Animals [IO], Byron Bay, Australia
Australians for Constitutional Monarchy [IO], Sydney, Australia
Austria Natl. Comm. for UNICEF [IO], Vienna, Austria

Austrian
  American-Austrian Cultural Soc. [18940]
  Austrian Cultural Forum [9343]
  Austrian Cultural Forum [9343]
  Austrian Press and Info. Ser. [23327]
  Austrian Tourist Off. [23328]
  Austrian Trade Commn. [23329]
  Center for Austrian Stud. [9344]
  Center for Austrian Stud. [9344]
  U.S. Austrian Chamber of Commerce [23330]
Austrian Acad. of Sciences [IO], Vienna, Austria
Austrian Advt. Res. Assn. [IO], Vienna, Austria
Austrian Assn. for Amer. Stud. [IO], Salzburg, Austria
Austrian Assn. of Music [IO], Vienna, Austria
Austrian Assn. for Pattern Recognition [IO], Graz, Austria
Austrian Assn. for Theatre Technics [IO], Vienna, Austria
Austrian Astronomical Soc. [IO], Vienna, Austria
Austrian Auto. Touring and Motorcycle Club [IO], Vienna, Austria
Austrian Badminton Assn. [IO], Vienna, Austria
Austrian Bankers' Assn. [IO], Vienna, Austria
Austrian Baseball-Softball Fed. [IO], Vienna, Austria
Austrian Bible Soc. [IO], Vienna, Austria
Austrian Booksellers' and Publishers' Assn. [IO], Vienna, Austria
Austrian Brewers' Assn. [IO], Vienna, Austria
Austrian Bus. Coun. Dubai and The Northern Emirates [IO], Dubai, United Arab Emirates
Austrian Cockpit Assn. [IO], Vienna, Austria
Austrian Coffee and Tea Bd. [IO], Vienna, Austria
Austrian Commn. on Geomorphology [IO], Vienna, Austria
Austrian Composers Assn. [IO], Vienna, Austria
Austrian Cmpt. Soc. [IO], Vienna, Austria
Austrian Consultants Assn. [IO], Vienna, Austria
Austrian Coun. for Agricultural Engg. and Rural Development [IO], Vienna, Austria
Austrian Cultural Forum [9343], 11 E 52nd St., New York, NY 10022, (212)319-5300
Austrian Cultural Forum [9343], 11 E 52nd St., New York, NY 10022, (212)319-5300
Austrian Cultural Inst. [★9343]
Austrian Cultural Inst. [★9343]
Austrian DanceSport Fed. [IO], Vienna, Austria
Austrian Doctors for a Healthy Env. [IO], Vienna, Austria

Austrian Fed. Economic Chamber [IO], Vienna, Austria
Austrian Fed. of Independent Loss Adjusters [IO], Vienna, Austria
Austrian Fed. of Roller Skating and Inline Skating [IO], Vienna, Austria
Austrian Fed. of Univ. Women [IO], Vienna, Austria
Austrian Floorball Fed. [IO], Leoben, Austria
Austrian Found. for Development Res. [IO], Vienna, Austria
Austrian Frisbee-Sport Fed. [IO], Vienna, Austria
Austrian Golf Assn. [IO], Vienna, Austria
Austrian Hotels' Assn. [IO], Vienna, Austria
Austrian Huntington Assn. [IO], Vienna, Austria
Austrian Ice Hockey Fed. [IO], Vienna, Austria
Austrian Inst. [★9343]
Austrian Inst. [★9343]
Austrian Inst. of Economic Res. [IO], Vienna, Austria
Austrian-Japan Soc. for Sci. and Art [IO], Vienna, Austria
Austrian Jet Sport Assn. [IO], Vienna, Austria
Austrian League Against Epilepsy [IO], Vienna, Austria
Austrian Ludwig Wittgenstein Soc. [IO], Kirchberg am Wechsel, Austria
Austrian Magazines Assn. [IO], Vienna, Austria
Austrian Medical Chamber [IO], Vienna, Austria
Austrian Medical Students Assn. [IO], Vienna, Austria
Austrian Member Comm. of the World Energy Coun. [IO], Vienna, Austria
Austrian Milling Assn. [IO], Vienna, Austria
Austrian Natl. Tourist Off. [★23328]
Austrian Natl. Union of Students [IO], Vienna, Austria
Austrian Neuroscience Assn. [IO], Innsbruck, Austria
Austrian Newspaper Assn. [IO], Vienna, Austria
Austrian North-South Inst. for Development Cooperation [IO], Vienna, Austria
Austrian Oil Crushers and Processors [IO], Bruck an der Leitha, Austria
Austrian Olympic Comm. [IO], Oberwaltersdorf, Austria
Austrian Paralympic Comm. [IO], Vienna, Austria
Austrian Pharmacological Soc. [IO], Vienna, Austria
Austrian Physical Soc. [IO], Graz, Austria
Austrian Physiological Soc. [IO], Salzburg, Austria
Austrian Physiotherapy Assn. [IO], Vienna, Austria
Austrian Press and Info. Ser. [23327], 3524 Intl. Ct. NW, Washington, DC 20008
Austrian Sci. Fund [IO], Vienna, Austria
Austrian Soc. for Acupuncture [IO], Vienna, Austria
Austrian Soc. of Antimicrobial Chemotherapy [IO], Vienna, Austria
Austrian Soc. for Applied Res. in Tourism [IO], Vienna, Austria
Austrian Soc. of Automotive Engineers [IO], Vienna, Austria
Austrian Soc. for Bone and Mineral Res. [IO], Vienna, Austria
Austrian Soc. of Cardiology [IO], Vienna, Austria
Austrian Soc. for Clinical Neurophysiology [IO], Innsbruck, Austria
Austrian Soc. of Dermatology and Venereology [IO], Vienna, Austria
Austrian Soc. for Electron Microscopy [IO], Vienna, Austria
Austrian Soc. for Geriatrics and Gerontology [IO], Vienna, Austria
Austrian Soc. of Operations Res. [IO], Vienna, Austria
Austrian Soc. of Sports Medicine [IO], Vienna, Austria
Austrian Soc. of Sterility, Fertility and Endocrinology [IO], Graz, Austria
Austrian Sports Fed. [IO], Vienna, Austria
Austrian Statistical Soc. [IO], Vienna, Austria
Austrian Taekwondo Fed. [IO], Innsbruck, Austria
Austrian Tourist Off. [23328], PO Box 1142, New York, NY 10108-1142, (212)994-6880
Austrian Trade Commn. [23329], 120 W 45th St., 9th Fl., New York, NY 10036, (212)421-5250
Austrian Trade Commissions in the U.S. [23353], 11601 Wilshire Blvd., Ste. 2420, Los Angeles, CA 90025, (310)477-9988

Austrian Trade Commissions in the U.S. [23353], 11601 Wilshire Blvd., Ste. 2420, Los Angeles, CA 90025, (310)477-9988
Austrian Trade Commissions in the U.S. and Canada [★23353]
Austrian Trade Commissions in the U.S. and Canada [★23353]
Austrian Trade Union Fed. - Christian Fraction [IO], Vienna, Austria
Austrian Travel Agents and Tour Operators Assn. [IO], Vienna, Austria
Austrian Umbrella Org. for Geographic Info. [IO], Innsbruck, Austria
Austrian Vehicle Indus. Assn. [IO], Vienna, Austria
Austrian Waterski Fed. [IO], Enns, Austria
Austrian Youth Hostel Assn. [IO], Vienna, Austria
Austropapier - Vereinigung der Osterreichischen Papierindustrie [★IO]
AustStab: Pavement Recycling and Stabilisation Assn. [IO], Sydney, Australia
Authentic Artifact Collectors Assn. [20973], 323 Hamme Mill Rd., Warrenton, NC 27589
Authors
  Amer. Boccaccio Assn. [9345]
  Amer. Chesterton Soc. [9346]
  Amer. Chesterton Soc. [9346]
  Amer. Teilhard Assn. [9347]
  Angela Thirkell Soc. [9348]
  August Derleth Soc. [9349]
  August Derleth Soc. [9349]
  Barbara Pym Soc. [9350]
  Bernard Shaw Soc. [9351]
  Bertrand Russell Soc. [9352]
  Betsy-Tacy Soc. [9353]
  Bram Stoker Memorial Assn. [9354]
  Bram Stoker Memorial Assn. [9354]
  Burroughs Bibliophiles [9355]
  Byron Soc. of Am. [9356]
  Charles S. Peirce Soc. [9357]
  Charles S. Peirce Soc. [9357]
  Christopher Morley Knothole Assn. [9358]
  Dante Soc. of Am. [9359]
  D.H. Lawrence Soc. of North Am. [9360]
  D.H. Lawrence Soc. of North Am. [9360]
  Edgar Allan Poe Soc. of Baltimore [9361]
  Eugene O'Neill Soc. [9362]
  Eugene O'Neill Soc. [9362]
  F. Scott Fitzgerald Soc. [9363]
  F. Scott Fitzgerald Soc. [9363]
  Francis Bacon Found. [9364]
  Gene Stratton Porter Memorial Soc. [9365]
  George Sand Assn. [9366]
  Goethe Soc. of North Am. [9367]
  Harry Stephen Keeler Soc. [9368]
  Harry Stephen Keeler Soc. [9368]
  Hegel Soc. of Am. [9369]
  Heinlein Soc. [9370]
  Hemingway Found. and Soc. [9371]
  Horatio Alger Soc. [9372]
  Ibsen Soc. of Am. [9373]
  Ibsen Soc. of Am. [9373]
  Intl. Adam Smith Soc. [10381]
  Intl. Brecht Soc. [9374]
  Intl. Brecht Soc. [9374]
  Intl. Lawrence Durrell Soc. [9375]
  Intl. Lawrence Durrell Soc. [9375]
  Intl. Spenser Soc. [9376]
  Intl. Theodore Dreiser Soc. [9377]
  Intl. Theodore Dreiser Soc. [9377]
  Intl. Thomas Merton Soc. [9378]
  Intl. Thomas Merton Soc. [9378]
  Intl. Virginia Woolf Soc. [9379]
  Intl. Virginia Woolf Soc. [9379]
  Intl. Vladimir Nabokov Soc. [9380]
  Intl. Vladimir Nabokov Soc. [9380]
  Intl. Wizard of Oz Club [9381]
  Intl. Wizard of Oz Club [9381]
  Jack London Res. Center [9382]
  James A. Michener Soc. [9383]
  James Jones Literary Soc. [10725]
  James Joyce Soc. [9384]
  Jane Austen Soc. of North Am. [9385]
  Jane Austen Soc. of North Am. [9385]
  Jesse Stuart Found. [9386]
  Joseph Conrad Soc. of Am. [9387]

A star before a book entry number signifies that the name is not listed separately, but is mentioned within the entry.

Kafka Soc. of Am. and Jour. **[9388]**
Kafka Soc. of Am. and Jour. **[9388]**
Keats-Shelley Assn. of Am. **[9389]**
Langston Hughes Soc. **[9390]**
Laura Ingalls Wilder Memorial Soc. **[9391]**
Lewis Carroll Soc. of North Am. **[9392]**
Louisa May Alcott Memorial Assn. **[9393]**
Lowell Celebrates Kerouac! **[9394]**
Mark Twain Boyhood Home Associates **[9395]**
Mark Twain Circle of New York **[9396]**
Mark Twain Home Found. **[9397]**
Mark Twain House and Museum **[9398]**
Marlowe Soc. of Am. **[9399]**
Melville Soc. **[9400]**
Mencken Soc. **[9401]**
Military Writers Soc. of Am. **[22207]**
Milton Soc. of Am. **[9402]**
Nathaniel Hawthorne Soc. **[9403]**
Natl. Steinbeck Center **[9404]**
New York C.S. Lewis Soc. **[9405]**
Pearl S. Buck Birthplace Found. **[9406]**
PEN Center USA **[10731]**
Pirandello Soc. of Am. **[9407]**
P.N. Elrod Fan Club **[9408]**
P.N. Elrod Fan Club **[9408]**
Poe Found. **[9409]**
Poe Stud. Assn. **[9410]**
Rousseau Assn. **[9411]**
Rousseau Assn. **[9411]**
Sedgwick Soc. **[10738]**
Shakespeare Oxford Soc. **[9412]**
Shakespeare Oxford Soc. **[9412]**
Shakespeare Soc. **[9413]**
Swedenborg Found. **[9414]**
The Thomas Hardy Assn. **[9415]**
Thomas Wolfe Soc. **[9416]**
Thoreau Soc. **[9417]**
Trollope Soc. **[9418]**
Uncle Remus Museum **[9419]**
Vachel Lindsay Assn. **[9420]**
Vergilian Soc. **[9421]**
Walt Whitman Birthplace Assn. **[9422]**
Willa Cather Pioneer Memorial and Educational Found. **[9423]**
William Allen White Found. **[9424]**
William Dean Howells Soc. **[9425]**
William Morris Soc. in the U.S. **[9426]**
The Wodehouse Soc. **[9427]**
Wolfe Pack **[9428]**
W.T. Bandy Center for Baudelaire and Modern French Stud. **[9429]**
Zane Grey's West Soc. **[9430]**
Authors Guild **[10704]**, 31 E 32nd St., 7th Fl., New York, NY 10016, (212)563-5904
Authors League of Am. **[10705]**, The Authors Guild, 31 E 32nd St., 7th Fl., New York, NY 10016, (212)563-5904
Authors' Licensing and Collecting Soc. **[IO]**, London, United Kingdom
Authors and Publishers Assn. - Address unknown since 2011.

Autism
AACTION Autism **[13776]**
Aging with Autism **[13777]**
Amer. Asperger's Assn. **[15564]**
Amer. Autism Alliance **[13778]**
Autism Allies **[13779]**
Autism Assn. - Singapore **[10324]**
Autism Care and Treatment Today! **[13780]**
Autism Community of Africa **[11119]**
Autism-Europe **[8605]**
Autism Network Intl. **[13781]**
Autism Network Intl. **[13781]**
The Autism Res. Found. **[13782]**
Autism Res. Inst. **[13783]**
Autism Res. Inst. **[13783]**
Autism Ser. Dogs of Am. **[13784]**
Autism Services Center **[13785]**
Autism Soc. **[13786]**
Autism Speaks **[13787]**
Bailey's Team for Autism **[13788]**
Face Autism **[13789]**
Families with Autism Spectrum Disorders **[13790]**
Fashion for Autism **[13791]**
Generation Rescue **[13792]**

Girl Power 2 Cure **[15592]**
Global Autism Collaboration **[13793]**
Global Autism Proj. **[13794]**
Global Autism Proj. **[13794]**
Global Communities of Support **[11120]**
Hands for Autistic Children of Ethiopia **[11121]**
Helping Autism through Learning and Outreach **[13795]**
Intl. Coalition for Autism and All Abilities **[13796]**
Intl. Soc. for Autism Res. **[13797]**
Milestones Autism Org. **[13798]**
Natl. Autism Assn. **[13799]**
Org. for Autism Res. **[13800]**
Parents Of Autistic Children **[13801]**
Parents and Professionals and Autism Northern Ireland **[3768]**
Stop Calling It Autism! **[13802]**
Stories of Autism **[13803]**
S.U.C.C.E.S.S. for Autism **[13804]**
Talk About Curing Autism **[13805]**
U.S. Autism and Asperger Assn. **[13806]**
Unlocking Autism **[13807]**
Autism Allies **[13779]**, 2400 Prairie View Ln., Buffalo, MN 55313-2450, (612)384-4265
Autism Asperger ACT **[IO]**, Mawson, Australia
Autism and Asperger Syndrome; MAAP Services for **[15607]**
Autism Assn. - Singapore **[IO]**, Singapore, Singapore
Autism Assn. of Western Australia **[IO]**, Subiaco, Australia
Autism Care and Treatment Today! **[13780]**, 19019 Ventura Blvd., Ste. 200, Tarzana, CA 91356, (818)705-1625
Autism Community of Africa **[11119]**, 8775 Cloud Leap Ct., Ste. 18, Columbia, MD 21045, (443)718-1824
Autism-Europe **[IO]**, Brussels, Belgium
Autism Independent UK **[IO]**, Kettering, United Kingdom
Autism Initiatives UK **[IO]**, Liverpool, United Kingdom
Autism Network Intl. **[13781]**, PO Box 35448, Syracuse, NY 13235-0448, (315)476-2462
Autism Network Intl. **[13781]**, PO Box 35448, Syracuse, NY 13235-0448, (315)476-2462
Autism Northern Territory **[IO]**, Nightcliff, Australia
Autism Queensland **[IO]**, Sunnybank, Australia
The Autism Res. Found. **[13782]**, 715 Albany St., W701, Boston, MA 02118, (617)414-5286
Autism Res. Inst. **[13783]**, 4182 Adams Ave., San Diego, CA 92116, (619)281-7165
Autism Res. Inst. **[13783]**, 4182 Adams Ave., San Diego, CA 92116, (619)281-7165
Autism Ser. Dogs of Am. **[13784]**, 4248 Galewood St., Lake Oswego, OR 97035, (503)314-6913
Autism Services Center **[13785]**, The Keith Albee Bldg., 929 4th Ave., Huntington, WV 25710-0507, (304)525-8014
Autism Soc. **[13786]**, 4340 E West Hwy., Ste. 350, Bethesda, MD 20814, (301)657-0881
Autism Soc. of British Columbia **[IO]**, Burnaby, BC, Canada
Autism Soc. Canada **[IO]**, Ottawa, ON, Canada
Autism Soc. in Norway **[IO]**, Oslo, Norway
Autism Soc. Philippines **[IO]**, Quezon City, Philippines
Autism Soc. of Serbia **[IO]**, Belgrade, Serbia
Autism South Australia **[IO]**, Marleston, Australia
Autism Speaks **[13787]**, 1 E 33rd St., New York, NY 10016, (212)252-8584
Autism Spectrum Australia **[IO]**, Sydney, Australia
Autism Treatment Services of Canada **[IO]**, Calgary, AB, Canada
Autism Victoria **[IO]**, Melbourne, Australia
Autismeforeningen i Norge **[★IO]**
Auto Body Representatives Coun. - Defunct.
Auto-Cycle Union - Motorcycling Great Britain **[IO]**, Rugby, United Kingdom
Auto Intl. Assn. **[312]**, 7101 Wisconsin Ave., Ste. 1300, Bethesda, MD 20814, (301)654-6664
Auto Intl. Assn. **[312]**, 7101 Wisconsin Ave., Ste. 1300, Bethesda, MD 20814, (301)654-6664
Auto- ja Kuljetusalan Tyontekijaliitto **[★IO]**
Auto Mag or Automatic Magazine **[★20967]**
Auto Parts Recyclers Assn. of Australia **[IO]**, Melbourne, Australia

Auto Racing
Derrike Cope Fan Club **[23790]**
Diesel Hot Rod Assn. **[22823]**
Grand Amer. Road Racing Assn. **[22238]**
Johnny Benson Fan Club **[23791]**
Miniature Motorsports Racing Assn. **[22239]**
Safer Racer Tour **[13006]**
Sportscar Vintage Racing Assn. **[22249]**
U.S. Auto Club **[22250]**
Auto Ser. Excellence **[★365]**
Auto Suppliers Benchmarking Assn. **[646]**, 4606 FM 1960 W, Ste. 250, Houston, TX 77069-9949, (281)440-5044
Auto Suppliers Benchmarking Consortium **[★646]**
Autoalan Keskusliitto ry **[★IO]**
Autobody Craftsman Assn. **[313]**, PO Box 745, Cashmere, WA 98815, (509)782-1364
Autoclaved Aerated Concrete Products Assn. - Address unknown since 2011.
Autoimmune Diseases Assn. **[★15097]**
Autoimmune Disorders
Amer. APS Assn. **[13808]**
Churg Strauss Syndrome Assn. **[13809]**
Multiple Sclerosis Coalition **[15609]**
Platelet Disorder Support Assn. **[13810]**
Autoliito **[★IO]**
Automated Builders Consortium - Address unknown since 2011.
Automated Electrified Monorail Product Section - Material Handling Inst. - Defunct.
Automated Imaging Assn. **[7342]**, 900 Victors Way, Ste. 140, Ann Arbor, MI 48108, (734)994-6088
Automated Material Handling Systems Assn. **[IO]**, Leicester, United Kingdom
Automated Storage/Retrieval Systems **[1811]**, 8720 Red Oak Blvd., Ste. 201, Charlotte, NC 28217, (704)676-1190
Automated Vision Assn. **[★7342]**
Automatic Control Soc. of Slovenia **[IO]**, Maribor, Slovenia
Automatic Door Suppliers Assn. **[IO]**, Warlingham, United Kingdom
Automatic Fire Alarm Assn. **[3137]**, PO Box 1569, Jasper, GA 30143, (678)454-3473
Automatic Guided Vehicle Systems **[★1812]**
Automatic Guided Vehicle Systems Sect. of the Material Handling Inst. **[1812]**, 8720 Red Oak Blvd., Ste. 201, Charlotte, NC 28217, (704)676-1190
Automatic Identification
AIM Global **[279]**
Assn. for Automatic Identification and Mobility North Am. **[280]**
GS1 US **[281]**
Integrated Bus. Communications Alliance **[282]**
Intl. RFID Bus. Assn. **[283]**
Automatic Identification Assn. **[IO]**, Moscow, Russia
Automatic Identification Mfrs. **[★279]**
Automatic Identification Mfrs. - Argentina **[IO]**, Buenos Aires, Argentina
Automatic Identification Mfrs. Assn. **[★279]**
Automatic Identification Mfrs. - Belgium **[IO]**, Brussels, Belgium
Automatic Identification Mfrs. - Brazil **[IO]**, Sao Paulo, Brazil
Automatic Identification Mfrs. - Denmark **[IO]**, Lyngby, Denmark
Automatic Identification Mfrs. - Germany **[IO]**, Lampertheim, Germany
Automatic Identification Mfrs. - India **[IO]**, New Delhi, India
Automatic Identification Mfrs. - Italia **[IO]**, Milan, Italy
Automatic Identification Mfrs. - United Kingdom **[IO]**, Halifax, United Kingdom
Automatic Meter Reading Assn. **[★3605]**
Automatic Transmission Rebuilders Assn. **[314]**, 2400 Latigo Ave., Oxnard, CA 93030, (805)604-2000
Automatic Vending Assn. **[IO]**, Sutton, United Kingdom
Automation
Automation Fed. **[6239]**
Automation Fed. **[6239]**, 67 Alexander Dr., Research Triangle Park, NC 27709, (919)314-3920
Automobilclub von Deutschland **[IO]**, Frankfurt, Germany

Reference to "IO" in place of a book number signifies that the association may be found in the 50th edition of International Organizations.

Automobile

71 429 Mustang Registry [20977]
1953-54 Buick Skylark Club [20978]
1956 Studebaker Golden Hawk Owners Register [20979]
1965-66 Full Size Chevrolet Club [20980]
1970 Dart Swinger 340s Registry [20981]
1971 GTO and Judge Convertible Registry [20982]
Airflow Club of Am. [20983]
Alfa Romeo Assn. [20984]
Alfa Romeo Owners Club [20985]
AMC Rambler Club [20986]
AMC Rambler Club [20986]
Amer. Assn. of Motor Vehicle Administrators [5290]
Amer. Austin/Bantam Club [20987]
Amer. Auto Racing Writers and Broadcasters Assn. [22240]
Amer. Bugatti Club [20988]
Amer. Camaro Assn. [20989]
Amer. Chevelle Enthusiasts Soc. [20990]
Amer. Hot Rod Assn. [22241]
Amer. Jeepster Club [20991]
Amer. MGB Assn. [20992]
Amer. MGC Register [20993]
Amer. Motors Owners Assn. [20994]
Amer. Sta. Wagon Owners Assn. [20995]
America's Corvette Club [20996]
Antique Auto Racing Assn. [20997]
Antique Auto. Club of Am. [20998]
Antique Studebaker Club [20999]
Assn. of Automotive Aftermarket Distributors/Parts Plus [311]
Aston Martin Owners Club [21000]
Auburn-Cord-Duesenberg Club [21001]
Austin Bantam Soc. [21002]
Austin-Healey Club of Am. [21003]
Austin-Healey Club USA [21004]
Austin-Healey Sports and Touring Club [21005]
Auto. Competition Comm. for the U.S. FIA [22242]
Auto. License Plate Collectors Assn. [21006]
Auto. Racing Club of Am. [22243]
Automotive Undercar Trade Org. [293]
Avanti Owners Assn. Intl. [21007]
Avanti Owners Assn. Intl. [21007]
Bigfoot Owners Clubs Intl. [21008]
BMW Car Club of Am. [21009]
BMW Vintage and Classic Car Club of Am. [21010]
Boss 302 Registry [21011]
Boss 429 Mustang World Registry [21012]
Brabham Register [21013]
Brabham Register [21013]
Bricklin Intl. Owners Club [21014]
Buick Club of Am. [21015]
Buick GS Club of Am. [21016]
Cadillac-LaSalle Club [21017]
California Assn. of Tiger-Owners [21018]
California Assn. of Tiger-Owners [21018]
Capri Club North Am. [21019]
CarFree City, USA [4961]
Challenger T/A Registry [21020]
Challenger T/A Registry [21020]
Checker Car Club of Am. [21021]
Chevrolet Nomad Assn. [21022]
Chevy and Geo Club [21023]
Christian Motorsports Ministries [21024]
Chrysler 300 Club Intl. [21025]
Chrysler 300 Club Intl. [21025]
Chrysler Town and Country Owners Registry [21026]
Chrysler Town and Country Owners Registry [21026]
Citroen Quarterly Car Club [21027]
Classic Car Club of Am. [21028]
Classic Chevy Intl. [21029]
Classic Chevy Intl. [21029]
Classic Jaguar Assn. [21030]
Classic Thunderbird Club Intl. [21031]
Cobra Owners Club of Am. [21032]
Collision Indus. Electronic Commerce Assn. [1048]
Contemporary Historical Vehicle Assn. [21033]

Corrado Club of Am. [21034]
Corvair Soc. of Am. [21035]
Corvette Club of Am. [21036]
Crosley Auto. Club [21037]
Crown Victoria Assn. [21038]
Cyclone Montego Torino Registry [21039]
DARTS Club [21040]
Davis Registry [21041]
DeLorean Owners Assn. [21042]
DeSoto Club of Am. [21043]
Diesel Hot Rod Assn. [22823]
Dodge Bros. Club [21044]
Early Ford V-8 Club of Am. [21045]
Eastern Museum of Motor Racing [21046]
Eastern Packard Club [21047]
Edsel Club [21048]
Edsel Owner's Club [21049]
Elec. Auto Assn. [6240]
Elec. Drive Trans. Assn. [6241]
Elgin Motorcar Owners Registry [21050]
Emergency Vehicle Owners and Operators Assn. [21051]
Erskine Registry [21052]
Fairlane Club of Am. [21053]
Falcon Club of Am. [21054]
Fed. of British Historic Vehicle Clubs [14626]
Ferrari Club of Am. [21055]
Ferrari Owners Club [21056]
Firehawk Assn. of Am. [21057]
Ford/Fordson Collectors Assn. [22175]
Ford Galaxie Club of Am. [21058]
Ford Owners' Assn. [21059]
Future Corvette Owners Assn. [21060]
GM Futurliner [21061]
GM Futurliner [21061]
Goodguys Rod and Custom Assn. [21062]
Graham Owners Club Intl. [21063]
GTO Assn. of Am. [21064]
Gull Wing Gp. Intl. [21065]
Gull Wing Gp. Intl. [21065]
Henry Nyberg Soc. [21066]
Henry Nyberg Soc. [21066]
H.H. Franklin Club [21067]
Historic Motor Sports Assn. [21068]
Horseless Carriage Club of Am. [21069]
Hudson-Essex-Terraplane Club [21070]
Hudson Essex Terraplane Historical Soc. [21071]
Hurst/Olds Club of Am. [21072]
Inliners Intl. [21073]
Inliners Intl. [21073]
Intl. 190SL Gp. [21074]
Intl. Amphicar Owners Club [21075]
Intl. Assn. of Lemon Law Administrators [5291]
Intl. Edsel Club [21076]
Intl. Hot Rod Assn. [22244]
Intl. King Midget Car Club [21077]
Intl. Mercury Owners Assn. [21078]
Intl. Motor Contest Assn. [22245]
Intl. Motor Sports Assn. [22246]
Intl. Mustang Bullitt Owners Club [21079]
Intl. Thunderbird Club [21080]
Intl. Thunderbird Club [21080]
Intl. Union, United Auto., Aerospace and Agricultural Implement Workers of Am. [23145]
Iso and Bizzarrini Owners Club [21081]
Jaguar Clubs of North Am. [21082]
Jaguar Clubs of North Am. [21082]
Jensen Healey Preservation Soc. [21083]
Johnny Benson Fan Club [23791]
The Judge GTO Intl. [21084]
Kaiser-Darrin Owners Roster [21085]
Kaiser-Frazer Owners Club Intl. [21086]
Kaiser-Frazer Owners Club Intl. [21086]
Karmann Ghia Club of North Am. [21087]
Karmann Ghia Club of North Am. [21087]
Kissel Kar Klub [21088]
Kustom Kemps of Am. [21089]
Lamborghini Club Am. [21090]
Les Amis de Panhard and Deutsch-Bonnet USA [21091]
Lincoln and Continental Owners Club [21092]
Lincoln Zephyr Owner's Club [21093]
London Vintage Taxi Assn. - Amer. Sect. [21094]
Lotus, Ltd. [21095]
LOVEfords [21096]

Marlin Auto Club [21097]
Marmon Club [21098]
The Maserati Club [21099]
The Maserati Club [21099]
Maserati Info. Exchange [21100]
Maverick/Comet Club Intl. [21101]
Mazda Club [21102]
Mercedes-Benz Club of Am. [21103]
Mercedes-Benz M-100 Owner's Gp. [21104]
Metropolitan Owners Club of North Am. [21105]
MG Drivers Club of North Am. [21106]
Midstates Jeepster Assn. [21107]
Model A Ford Cabriolet Club [21108]
Model A Ford Club of Am. [21109]
Model A Ford Found. [21110]
Model A Restorers Club [21111]
Model T Ford Club of Am. [21112]
Model T Ford Club Intl. [21113]
Model T Ford Club Intl. [21113]
Modern Car Soc. [21114]
Morgan 3/4 Gp. [21115]
Morgan Car Club [21116]
Morgan Plus Four Club [21117]
Motor Bus Soc. [21118]
Mustang Club of Am. [21119]
Mustang II Network [21120]
Nash Car Club of Am. [21121]
Natl. Antique Oldsmobile Club [21122]
Natl. Assn. for Stock Car Auto Racing [22247]
Natl. Chevy Assn. [21123]
Natl. Corvette Owners Assn. [21124]
Natl. Corvette Restorers Soc. [21125]
Natl. Coun. of Corvette Clubs [21126]
Natl. DeSoto Club [21127]
Natl. Firebird and Trans Am Club [21128]
Natl. Hot Rod Assn. [22248]
Natl. Impala Assn. [21129]
Natl. Indy 500 Collectors Club [21130]
Natl. Monte Carlo Owners Assn. [21131]
Natl. Nostalgic Nova [21132]
Natl. St. Rod Assn. [21133]
Natural Gas Vehicle for Am. [6242]
New England M.G. "T" Register Limited [21134]
Nissan Infiniti Car Owners Club [21135]
North Amer. English and European Ford Registry [21136]
North Amer. Mini Moke Registry [21137]
NSX Club of Am. [21138]
Oldsmobile Club of Am. [21139]
Online Imperial Club [21140]
Opel Assn. of North Am. [21141]
Opel Motorsports Club [21142]
Org. of Bricklin Owners [21143]
Pacific Northwest Region of the Lincoln and Continental Owners Club [21144]
Packard Auto. Classics [21145]
Packard Club [21146]
Packard Club [21146]
Packards Intl. Motor Car Club [21147]
Packards Intl. Motor Car Club [21147]
Pantera Intl. [21148]
Pantera Intl. [21148]
Partnership for Safe Driving [13002]
PGI [337]
Pierce-Arrow Soc. [21149]
Plymouth Barracuda/Cuda Owners Club [21150]
Plymouth Owners Club [21151]
Police Car Owners of Am. [21152]
Pontiac-Oakland Club Intl. [21153]
Porsche Club of Am. [21154]
Professional Car Soc. [21155]
Renault Owners Club of North Am. [21156]
REO Club of Am. [21157]
REO Club of Am. [21157]
Riviera Owners Assn. [21158]
Road Race Lincoln Register [21159]
Road Race Lincoln Register [21159]
Rolls-Royce Owners' Club [21160]
Saab Club of North Am. [21161]
SAE Intl. [6243]
SAE Intl. [6243]
Safer Racer Tour [13006]
Saleen Club of Am. [21162]
SFI Found. [6244]
Shelby Amer. Auto. Club [21163]

A star before a book entry number signifies that the name is not listed separately, but is mentioned within the entry.

Silver Ghost Assn. [21164]
Soc. of Automotive Historians [21165]
Solid Axle Corvette Club [21166]
Solid Axle Corvette Club [21166]
Sports Car Club of Am. [21167]
Sportscar Vintage Racing Assn. [22249]
Squire SS-100 Registry [21168]
Steam Auto. Club of Am. [21169]
Studebaker Driver's Club [21170]
Stutz Club [21171]
Subaru 360 Drivers' Club [21172]
Sunbeam Rapier Registry [21173]
Super Coupe Club of Am. [21174]
Thunderbird and Cougar Club of Am. [21175]
Tigers East/Alpines East [21176]
Tigers East/Alpines East [21176]
Toyota Owner's and Restorer's Club [21177]
Transmission Rebuilders Network Intl. [341]
Triumph Register of Am. [21178]
Triumph Wedge Owners Assn. [21179]
Tucker Auto. Club of Am. [21180]
TVR Car Club North Am. [21181]
United Coun. of Corvette Clubs [21182]
United Ford Owners [21183]
United Four-Wheel Drive Associations [21184]
U.S. Auto Club [22250]
U.S. Coun. for Automotive Res. [6245]
U.S. Late Model Assn. [22251]
United St. Machine Assn. [21185]
Veteran Motor Car Club of Am. [21186]
Vintage Chevrolet Club of Am. [21187]
Vintage Drivers Club of Am. [21188]
Vintage Sports Car Club of Am. [21189]
Vintage Thunderbird Club Intl. [21190]
Vintage Thunderbird Club Intl. [21190]
Vintage Triumph Register [21191]
Vintage Volkswagen Club of Am. [21192]
Volkswagen Club of Am. [21193]
Volvo Club of Am. [21194]
Willys-Overland-Knight Registry [21195]
Willys-Overland-Knight Registry [21195]
Winged Warriors/National B-Body Owners Assn. [21196]
Worldwide Camaro Club [21197]
WPC Club [21198]
Z Car Club Assn. [21199]
Z Series Car Club of Am. [21200]
Auto. Assn. of Malaysia [IO], Kuala Lumpur, Malaysia
Auto. Club of Ecuador [IO], Quito, Ecuador
Auto. Club de l'Ouest [IO], Le Mans, France
Auto. Competition Comm. for the U.S. FIA [22242], 7800 S Elati St., Ste. 303, Littleton, CO 80120, (303)730-8100
Auto. Film Club of Am. [286], 10 Cross St., Staten Island, NY 10304, (718)447-2255
Auto. Film Club of Am. [286], 10 Cross St., Staten Island, NY 10304, (718)447-2255
Auto. Importers of Am. [★297]
Auto. Importers of Am. [★297]
Auto. Journalists Assn. of Canada [IO], Cobourg, ON, Canada
Auto. License Plate Collectors Assn. [21006], 118 Quaker Rd., Hampton, VA 23669-2024
Auto. Old Timers [★288]
Auto. Protection Assn. [IO], Montreal, QC, Canada
Auto. Racing Club of Am. [22243], PO Box 5217, Toledo, OH 43611-0217, (734)847-6726
Auto. Safety Belt Inst. [★321]
Auto. and Touring Club of Finland [IO], Helsinki, Finland
Automotive
  1965-66 Full Size Chevrolet Club [20980]
  1971 GTO and Judge Convertible Registry [20982]
  America's Corvette Club [20996]
  Assn. of Automotive Aftermarket Distributors/Parts Plus [311]
  Automotive Undercar Trade Org. [293]
  Chevrolet Nomad Assn. [21022]
  Chevy and Geo Club [21023]
  Chrysler Town and Country Owners Registry [21026]
  Citroen Quarterly Car Club [21027]
  Cobra Owners Club of Am. [21032]

Congressional Automotive Caucus [17410]
Corvair Soc. of Am. [21035]
Corvette Club of Am. [21036]
Diesel Hot Rod Assn. [22823]
Electrification Coalition [3510]
Erskine Registry [21052]
Firehawk Assn. of Am. [21057]
Ford/Fordson Collectors Assn. [22175]
Future Corvette Owners Assn. [21060]
Gull Wing Gp. Intl. [21065]
Hudson-Essex-Terraplane Club [21070]
Johnny Benson Fan Club [23791]
Kaiser-Darrin Owners Roster [21085]
Karmann Ghia Club of North Am. [21087]
Kissel Kar Klub [21088]
Kustom Kemps of Am. [21089]
Les Amis de Panhard and Deutsch-Bonnet USA [21091]
Light Elec. Vehicle Assn. [3518]
Marmon Club [21098]
Maserati Info. Exchange [21100]
Mercedes-Benz M-100 Owner's Gp. [21104]
Metropolitan Owners Club of North Am. [21105]
Midstates Jeepster Assn. [21107]
Model A Ford Cabriolet Club [21108]
Modern Car Soc. [21114]
Morgan Car Club [21116]
Natl. Corvette Owners Assn. [21124]
North Amer. Mini Moke Registry [21137]
Opel Assn. of North Am. [21141]
Org. of Bricklin Owners [21143]
Partnership for Safe Driving [13002]
PGI [337]
Plymouth Owners Club [21151]
Professional Car Soc. [21155]
United Four-Wheel Drive Associations [21184]
United St. Machine Assn. [21185]
Vintage Thunderbird Club Intl. [21190]
Volkswagen Club of Am. [21193]
Worldwide Camaro Club [21197]
Automotive Advertisers Coun. [★287]
Automotive Aftermarket Indus. Assn. [★322]
Automotive Aftermarket Indus. Assn. [315], 7101 Wisconsin Ave., Ste. 1300, Bethesda, MD 20814-3415, (301)654-6664
Automotive Aftermarket Indus. Assn. [315], 7101 Wisconsin Ave., Ste. 1300, Bethesda, MD 20814-3415, (301)654-6664
Automotive Aftermarket Indus. Assn. | Heavy Duty Distribution Assn. [316], 7101 Wisconsin Ave., Ste. 1300, Bethesda, MD 20814, (301)654-6664
Automotive Aftermarket Indus. Assn. | Natl. Catalog Managers Assn. [317], 7101 Wisconsin Ave., Ste. 1300, Bethesda, MD 20814-3415, (301)654-6664
Automotive Aftermarket Suppliers Assn. | Brake Mfrs. Coun. [318], PO Box 13966, Research Triangle Park, NC 27709-3966, (919)549-4800
Automotive Body Parts Assn. [348], 1510 Eldridge Pkwy. S, Ste. 110-168, Houston, TX 77077, (281)531-0809
Automotive Body Parts Assn. [348], 1510 Eldridge Pkwy. S, Ste. 110-168, Houston, TX 77077, (281)531-0809
Automotive Chemical Mfrs. Coun. - Defunct.
Automotive Communications Coun. [287], 7101 Wisconsin Ave., Ste. 1300, Bethesda, MD 20814, (240)333-1089
Automotive Component Mfrs. Assn. of India [IO], New Delhi, India
Automotive Consumer Action Prog. - Address unknown since 2011.
Automotive Cooling Systems Inst. - Defunct.
Automotive Dismantlers and Recyclers of Am. [★3632]
Automotive Dismantlers and Recyclers Assn. [★3632]
Automotive Distribution Fed. [IO], Birmingham, United Kingdom
Automotive Education
  Natl. Automotive Technicians Educ. Found. [7762]
  North Amer. Coun. of Automotive Teachers [7763]
Automotive Engine Rebuilders Assn. [319], 500 Coventry Ln., Ste. 180, Crystal Lake, IL 60014-7592, (815)526-7600
Automotive Engine Rebuilders Assn. [319], 500 Coventry Ln., Ste. 180, Crystal Lake, IL 60014-7592, (815)526-7600

Automotive Engineers and Technicians Assn. [IO], Buenos Aires, Argentina
Automotive Exhaust Systems Mfrs. Coun. - Defunct.
Automotive Filter Mfrs. Coun. [★327]
Automotive Filter Mfrs. Coun. [★327]
Automotive Fleet and Leasing Assn. [349], 1000 Westgate Dr., Ste. 252, St. Paul, MN 55114, (651)203-7247
Automotive Hall of Fame [288], 21400 Oakwood Blvd., Dearborn, MI 48124, (313)240-4000
Automotive Industries
  1965-66 Full Size Chevrolet Club [20980]
  1971 GTO and Judge Convertible Registry [20982]
  Amer. Automotive Policy Coun. [284]
  Amer. Salvage Pool Assn. [285]
  America's Corvette Club [20996]
  Assn. of the Hungarian Automotive Indus. [13961]
  Assn. of Intl. Auto. Mfrs. [297]
  Assn. of Motor Vehicle Importers - Representatives [14852]
  Australasian Fleet Managers Assn. [23811]
  Australian Automotive Aftermarket Assn. [23152]
  Austrian Vehicle Indus. Assn. [1625]
  Auto Suppliers Benchmarking Assn. [646]
  Auto. Film Club of Am. [286]
  Auto. Film Club of Am. [286]
  Automotive Aftermarket Indus. Assn. | Heavy Duty Distribution Assn. [316]
  Automotive Communications Coun. [287]
  Automotive Hall of Fame [288]
  Automotive Indus. Action Gp. [289]
  Automotive Indus. Assn. of the Slovak Republic [16769]AutomotiveAutomotive Mfrs'. Assn. - Argentina
  Automotive Market Res. Coun. [290]AutomotiveAutomotive Parts Mfrs. of Mexico
  Automotive Trade Assn. Executives [291]
  Automotive Training Managers Coun. [292]
  Automotive Undercar Trade Org. [293]
  Automotive Women's Alliance [294]
  Automotive Women's Alliance Found. [294]
  Bigfoot Owners Clubs Intl. [21008]
  Brazilian Assn. of Autoparts Mfrs. [22220]
  Car Care Coun. [295]
  Chevrolet Nomad Assn. [21022]
  Chevy and Geo Club [21023]
  Chrysler Town and Country Owners Registry [21026]
  Citroen Quarterly Car Club [21027]
  Cobra Owners Club of Am. [21032]
  Collision Indus. Electronic Commerce Assn. [1048]
  Commercial Vehicle Safety Alliance [296]
  Commercial Vehicle Safety Alliance [296]
  Congressional Automotive Caucus [17410]
  Corvair Soc. of Am. [21035]
  Corvette Club of Am. [21036]
  Electrification Coalition [3510]
  Erskine Registry [21052]
  Future Corvette Owners Assn. [21060]
  Global Automakers [297]
  Global Automotive Mgt. Coun. [298]
  Gull Wing Gp. Intl. [21065]
  Heavy Duty Mfrs. Assn. | Heavy-Duty Bus. Forum [299]
  Hudson-Essex-Terraplane Club [21070]
  Intl. Automotive Remarketers Alliance [300]
  Intl. Automotive Remarketers Alliance [300]
  Intl. Automotive Technicians' Network [301]
  Kaiser-Darrin Owners Roster [21085]
  Karmann Ghia Club of North Am. [21087]
  Kissel Kar Klub [21088]
  Kustom Kemps of Am. [21089]
  Les Amis de Panhard and Deutsch-Bonnet USA [21091]
  Light Elec. Vehicle Assn. [3518]
  Marmon Club [21098]
  Maserati Info. Exchange [21100]
  Mercedes-Benz M-100 Owner's Gp. [21104]
  Metropolitan Owners Club of North Am. [21105]
  Mexican Assn. of Car Dealers [21952]
  Mexican Automotive Assn. [14204]
  Midstates Jeepster Assn. [21107]
  Model A Ford Cabriolet Club [21108]

Reference to "IO" in place of a book number signifies that the association may be found in the 50th edition of International Organizations.

A star before a book entry number signifies that the name is not listed separately, but is mentioned within the entry.

Auxiliary to the Amer. Dental Assn. [★14228]
Auxiliary to the Amer. Osteopathic Assn. [★16055]
Auxiliary to the Natl. Medical Assn. [15404], 8403 Colesville Rd., Ste. 920, Silver Spring, MD 20910, (301)495-3779
Auxiliary to Sons of Union Veterans of the Civil War [20381], 2966 Hayts Corners East Rd., Ovid, NY 14521, (607)869-3720
Avaliku Sona Noukogu [★IO]
Avant Ministries [20013], 10000 N Oak Trafficway, Kansas City, MO 64155, (816)734-8500
Avanti Club of Am. [★21007]
Avanti Club of Am. [★21007]
Avanti Owners Assn. Intl. [21007], PO Box 1743, Maple Grove, MN 55311-6743, (763)420-7829
Avanti Owners Assn. Intl. [21007], PO Box 1743, Maple Grove, MN 55311-6743, (763)420-7829
AVEM Intl. [★1810]
AVEM Intl. [★1810]
Avenues, Natl. Support Gp. for Arthrogryposis Multiplex Congenita [15573], Lynn Staheli, MD, Children's Orthopedic Hosp. and Medical Center, 4800 Sand Point Way NE, Seattle, WA 98105
AVERT [IO], London, United Kingdom
Avian Welfare Coalition [10931], PO Box 40212, St. Paul, MN 55104

Aviation
Air Line Pilots Assn. Intl. [23146]
Air Line Pilots Assn. Intl. [23146]
Air Mail Pioneers [20879]
Aircraft Mechanics Fraternal Assn. [23147]
Airline Passenger Experience Assn. [373]
Airline Pilots Security Alliance [374]
Allied Pilots Assn. [23148]
Amer. Independent Cockpit Alliance [23149]
Assn. of Flight Attendants - CWA [23150]
Assn. of Flight Attendants - CWA [23150]
Assn. of Professional Flight Attendants [23151]
Aviation Crime Prevention Inst. [375]
B-52 Stratofortress Assn. [20331]
Black Pilots of Am. [376]
Cherokee Pilots' Assn. [20887]
Citizens Aviation Watch Assn. [11122]
Citizens Aviation Watch Assn. [11122]
Civil Air Patrol [5292]
Combat Helicopter Pilots Assn. [20313]
F-14 Tomcat Assn. [21201]
Fairchild Club [20895]
First Flight Soc. [20896]
Flying Physicians Assn. [13811]
Independent Pilots Assn. [23152]
Intl. Assn. of Machinists and Aerospace Workers [23153]
Intl. Assn. of Missionary Aviation [20052]
Intl. Assn. of Natural Rsrc. Pilots [3836]
Intl. Assn. of Natural Rsrc. Pilots [3836]
Intl. Aviation Ground Support Assn. [377]
Intl. Aviation Ground Support Assn. [377]
Intl. Aviation Womens Assn. [378]
Intl. Aviation Womens Assn. [378]
Intl. Bird Dog Assn. [20898]
Intl. Coun. of Air Shows [20901]
Intl. Scale Soaring Assn. [21904]
Intl. Soc. for Aviation Photography [2724]
Jack Knight Air Mail Soc. [22047]
Latin Amer. Aeronautical Assn. [379]
Latin Amer. Aeronautical Assn. [379]
Lawyer-Pilots Bar Assn. [5293]
Motion Picture Pilots Assn. [380]
Natl. Agricultural Aviation Assn. [3837]
Natl. Agricultural Aviation Assn. [3837]
Natl. Air Disaster Alliance [11123]
Natl. Air Traffic Controllers Assn. [23154]
Natl. Assn. of Priest Pilots [19459]
Natl. Assn. of State Aviation Officials [5294]
Natl. Aviation and Space Educ. Alliance [7764]
Natl. Black Coalition of Fed. Aviation Employees [5295]
Natl. Coalition for Aviation Educ. [7765]
Natl. Conf. of Catholic Airport Chaplains [19528]
Natl. Gay Pilot's Assn. [381]
Natl. World War II Glider Pilots Assn. [20315]
Pedro Rescue Helicopter Assn. [20316]
Popular Rotorcraft Assn. [20913]
Professional Airways Systems Specialists [23155]

Royal Air Force Historical Soc. [12418]
T-34 Assn. [21202]
U.S. Powered Paragliding Assn. [22796]
Whirly-Girls - Intl. Women Helicopter Pilots [20923]
Women of the Natl. Agricultural Aviation Assn. [3838]
World Airline Entertainment Assn. [373]
World Airline Historical Soc. [20924]
Aviation Crime Prevention Inst. [375], 226 N Nova Rd., Ormond Beach, FL 32174, (386)341-7270
Aviation Development Coun. [128], 141-07 20th Ave., Ste. 404, Whitestone, NY 11357, (718)746-0212
Aviation Distributors and Mfrs. Assn. [129], 100 N 20th St., 4th Fl., Philadelphia, PA 19103-1443, (215)564-3484
Aviation Env. Fed. [IO], London, United Kingdom
Aviation Fellowship; Mission [20061]
Aviation Historical Soc; Amer. [20880]
Aviation for Humanity [12807], 269 S Beverly Dr., No. 674, Beverly Hills, CA 90212, (310)968-3503
Aviation Indus. Assn. of New Zealand [IO], Wellington, New Zealand
Aviation Indus. CBT Comm. [130], PO Box 4067, Federal Way, WA 98063, (253)218-1408
Aviation Indus. Computer-Based Training Comm. [★130]
Aviation Insurance Assn. [1943], 400 Admiral Blvd., Kansas City, MO 64106, (816)221-8488
Aviation Medical Soc. - New Zealand [IO], Auckland, New Zealand
Aviation Sans Frontieres [IO], Orly Aerogares, France
Aviation Suppliers Assn. [2331], 2233 Wisconsin Ave. NW, Ste. 503, Washington, DC 20007, (202)347-6899
Aviation Technician Educ. Coun. [7695], 2090 Wexford Ct., Harrisburg, PA 17112, (717)540-7121
Avicultural Advancement Coun. of Canada [IO], Chemainus, BC, Canada
Avicultural Soc. [IO], Southminster, United Kingdom
Avicultural Soc. of Am. [7194], PO Box 5516, Riverside, CA 92517-5516, (951)780-4102
Avicultural Soc. of Am. [7194], PO Box 5516, Riverside, CA 92517-5516, (951)780-4102
Avionics Maintenance Conf. [131], Aeronautical Radio, Inc., 2551 Riva Rd., Annapolis, MD 21401, (410)266-2008
AVKO Educational Res. Found. [8876], 3084 W Willard Rd., Birch Run, MI 48415-9404, (810)686-9283
AVM Support Group - Defunct.
Avocats Sans Frontieres [IO], Brussels, Belgium
Avoided Deforestation Partners [4390], 134 The Uplands, Berkeley, CA 94705
Avoided Deforestation Partners [4390], 134 The Uplands, Berkeley, CA 94705
Avon and Border Counties Welsh Pony and Cob Assn. [IO], Bristol, United Kingdom
AVRDC - The World Vegetable Center [IO], Tainan, Taiwan
AVS Sci. and Tech. Soc. [7592], Angela Klink, 125 Maiden Ln., 15th Fl., New York, NY 10038, (212)248-0200
AVSC Intl. [★12031]
AVSC Intl. [★12031]
Awaiting Angels [IO], Cusco, Peru
Awake in Am. [18607], PO Box 51601, Philadelphia, PA 19115-1601, (215)764-6568
Awana Clubs Intl. [20304], 1 E Bode Rd., Streamwood, IL 60107-6658, (630)213-2000
Awana Clubs Intl. [20304], 1 E Bode Rd., Streamwood, IL 60107-6658, (630)213-2000
Awana Youth Assn. [★20304]
Awana Youth Assn. [★20304]

Awards
Amer. Sociological Assn. | Honors Prog. [23738]
America's Found. [20372]
Astronaut Scholars Honor Soc. [23629]
Awards and Recognition Assn. [382]
Beta Beta Beta [23470]
Beta Gamma Sigma [23476]
Beta Phi Mu [23583]
Beta Sigma Kappa [23611]

Congressional Medal of Honor Soc. [20373]
Delta Phi Epsilon Professional Foreign Ser. Sorority [23529]
Delta Sigma Delta [23498]
Distinguished Flying Cross Soc. [20374]
Gamma Sigma Delta [23463]
Horatio Alger Assn. of Distinguished Americans [20375]
Intl. Foodservice Mfrs. Assn. | Intl. Gold and Silver Plate Soc. [18941]
Ladies Auxiliary of the Military Order of the Purple Heart U.S.A. [20376]
Legion of Valor of the U.S.A. [20377]
Military Order of the Purple Heart of the U.S.A. [20378]
Mu Beta Psi [23601]
Natl. Block and Bridle Club [23464]
Natl. Women's Hall of Fame [20379]
Phi Chi Medical Fraternity [23594]
Sigma Alpha Iota Intl. Music Fraternity [23605]
Awards and Recognition Assn. [382], 4700 W Lake Ave., Glenview, IL 60025, (847)375-4800
AWARE [★13485]
AWEA [★7621]
Axios USA - Address unknown since 2011.
Ayn Rand Inst. [10372], 2121 Alton Pkwy., Ste. 250, Irvine, CA 92606-4926, (949)222-6550
Ayn Rand Soc. [10373], Prof. Allan Gotthelf, Chm., Univ. of Pittsburgh, Dept. of History and Philosophy of Sci., 1017 Cathedral of Learning, Pittsburgh, PA 15260
Ayrshire Breeders' Assn. [3903], 1224 Alton Darby Creek Rd., Ste. B, Columbus, OH 43228, (614)335-0020
Ayrshire Breeders' Assn. of Canada [IO], St.-Hyacinthe, QC, Canada
Ayurvedic Medical Assn; Natl. [13695]
Azalea Soc. of Am. [21785], Carol Flowers, Sec., 700 New Hampshire Ave. NW, Apt. 1011, Washington, DC 20037, (202)965-5308
Azerbaijan Athletics Fed. [IO], Baku, Azerbaijan
Azerbaijan Cartoonists Union [IO], Baku, Azerbaijan
Azerbaijan Dance Sport Fed. [IO], Baku, Azerbaijan
Azerbaijan Draughts Fed. [IO], Baku, Azerbaijan
Azerbaijan Gadin Ve Inkishaf Merkezi [★IO]
Azerbaijan League Against Epilepsy [IO], Baku, Azerbaijan
Azerbaijan Medical Assn. [IO], Baku, Azerbaijan
Azerbaijan Natl. Sci. Found. [IO], Baku, Azerbaijan
Azerbaijan Red Crescent Soc. [IO], Baku, Azerbaijan
Azerbaijan Republic Badminton Fed. [IO], Baku, Azerbaijan
Azerbaijan Taekwondo Fed. [IO], Baku, Azerbaijan
Azerbaijan Tennis Fed. [IO], Baku, Azerbaijan
Azerbaijan Women and Development Center [IO], Baku, Azerbaijan
Azerbaijan Young Lawyers' Union [IO], Baku, Azerbaijan
Azerbaycan Qizil Aypara Cemiyyeti [★IO]
Azerbaycan Taekvondo Federasiyasina [★IO]
AZRA/World Union for Progressive Judaism North Am. [19847], 633 3rd Ave., 6th Fl., New York, NY 10017-6778, (212)452-6530
AZRA/World Union for Progressive Judaism North Am. [19847], 633 3rd Ave., 6th Fl., New York, NY 10017-6778, (212)452-6530
Azteca Horse Registry of Am. - Address unknown since 2011.
AZUR Development [IO], Brazzaville, Republic of the Congo
AZUR Developpement [★IO]

B
B-26 Marauder Historical Soc. [20857], 3900 E Timrod St., Tucson, AZ 85711, (520)322-6226
B-26 Marauder Historical Soc. [20857], 3900 E Timrod St., Tucson, AZ 85711, (520)322-6226
B-52 Stratofortress Assn. [20331], PO Box 340501, Beavercreek, OH 45434-0501
Babe Ruth Baseball/Softball [22268], Babe Ruth League, Inc., PO Box 5000, Trenton, NJ 08638, (609)695-1434
Babe Ruth Birthplace [22269], 216 Emory St., Baltimore, MD 21230, (410)727-1539

Reference to "IO" in place of a book number signifies that the association may be found in the 50th edition of International Organizations.

Babe Ruth Birthplace Found. [★22269]
Babe Ruth Museum/Sports Legends at Camden Yards [★22269]
Babiker Badri Sci. Assn. for Women Stud. [IO], Omdurman, Sudan
Babraham Inst. [IO], Cambridge, United Kingdom
Baby Milk Action [IO], Cambridge, United Kingdom
Baby Products Assn. [IO], Aylesbury, United Kingdom
BACCHUS and Gamma Peer Educ. Network [★13237]
BACCHUS and Gamma Peer Educ. Network [★13237]
BACCHUS Network [13237], PO Box 100430, Denver, CO 80250-0430, (303)871-0901
BACCHUS Network [13237], PO Box 100430, Denver, CO 80250-0430, (303)871-0901
BACCHUS of the U.S. [★13237]
BACCHUS of the U.S. [★13237]
Bach Elgar Choir [IO], Hamilton, ON, Canada
Bachad Org. [★19851]
Back Bay Lisa - Defunct.
Back Country Horsemen of Am. [22677], PO Box 1367, Graham, WA 98338-1367, (888)893-5161
Back in the Saddle Horse Adoption [4569], 1313 Youngs Rd., Linden, PA 17744, (570)974-1087
BackCare, The Charity for Healthier Backs [IO], Teddington, United Kingdom
Backpackers Club [IO], Chipping Norton, United Kingdom
Bacon Families Assn. - Defunct.
Badan Peguam Malaysia [★IO]
Badger Face Welsh Mountain Sheep Soc. [IO], Hereford, United Kingdom
Badili Club [IO], Port Moresby, Papua New Guinea
Badminton
   U.S.A. Badminton [22252]
Badminton Asian Confed. [IO], Kuala Lumpur, Malaysia
Badminton Assn. of the Cook Islands [IO], Rarotonga, Cook Islands
Badminton Assn. of the Democratic People's Republic of Korea [IO], Pyongyang, Democratic People's Republic of Korea
Badminton Assn. of Ghana [IO], Accra, Ghana
Badminton Assn. of Iceland [IO], Reykjavik, Iceland
Badminton Assn. of Malawi [IO], Zomba, Malawi
Badminton Assn. of Maldives [IO], Male, Maldives
Badminton Assn. of the People's Republic of China [IO], Beijing, People's Republic of China
Badminton Assn. of Thailand [IO], Bangkok, Thailand
Badminton Bond Curacao [IO], Curacao, Netherlands Antilles
Badminton Canada [IO], Ottawa, ON, Canada
Badminton England [IO], Milton Keynes, United Kingdom
Badminton Europe [IO], Brondby, Denmark
Badminton Fed. of Armenia [IO], Yerevan, Armenia
Badminton Fed. of Cambodia [IO], Phnom Penh, Cambodia
Badminton Fed. of Cameroon [IO], Yaounde, Cameroon
Badminton Fed. of the Former Yugoslav Republic of Macedonia [IO], Skopje, Macedonia
Badminton Fed. of Islamic Republic of Iran [IO], Tehran, Iran
Badminton Fed. of Nigeria [IO], Lagos, Nigeria
Badminton Fed. of the Republic of Moldova [IO], Chisinau, Moldova
Badminton Korea Assn. [IO], Seoul, Republic of Korea
Badminton Malta [IO], Valletta, Malta
Badminton Scotland [IO], Glasgow, United Kingdom
Badminton Union of Ireland [IO], Dublin, Ireland
Badminton Union of Namibia [IO], Oranjemund, Namibia
Badminton World Fed. [IO], Kuala Lumpur, Malaysia
Badmintonsamband Foroya [IO], Torshavn, Faroe Islands
Badmintonsamband Islands [★IO]
Badmintonska Zveza Slovenije [IO], Medvode, Slovenia
Baendasamtoek Islands [★IO]
Bagpipe Soc. [IO], Otley, United Kingdom

Baha'i Community of Canada [IO], Thornhill, ON, Canada
Bahamas Agricultural and Indus. Corp. [IO], Nassau, Bahamas
Bahamas Assn. of Athletic Associations [IO], Nassau, Bahamas
Bahamas Baseball Fed. [IO], Nassau, Bahamas
Bahamas Chamber of Commerce - Nassau [IO], Nassau, Bahamas
Bahamas Crisis Centre [IO], Nassau, Bahamas
Bahamas Employers' Confed. [IO], Nassau, Bahamas
Bahamas Historical Soc. [IO], Nassau, Bahamas
Bahamas Inst. of Chartered Accountants [IO], Nassau, Bahamas
Bahamas Lawn Tennis Assn. [IO], Nassau, Bahamas
Bahamas Olympic Assn. [IO], Nassau, Bahamas
Bahamas Real Estate Assn. [IO], Nassau, Bahamas
Bahamas Sailing Assn. [IO], Nassau, Bahamas
Bahamas Squash Raquets Assn. [IO], Nassau, Bahamas
Bahia St. [12717], 1005 NE Boat St., Seattle, WA 98105, (206)633-1724
Bahia St. [12717], 1005 NE Boat St., Seattle, WA 98105, (206)633-1724
Bahrain Arts Soc. [IO], Manama, Bahrain
Bahrain Assn. of Pathologists [IO], Manama, Bahrain
Bahrain Athletics Assn. [IO], Manama, Bahrain
Bahrain Badminton and Squash Assn. [IO], Manama, Bahrain
Bahrain Bowling Assn. [IO], Manama, Bahrain
Bahrain British Bus. Forum [IO], Manama, Bahrain
Bahrain Businesswomen's Soc. [IO], Manama, Bahrain
Bahrain Competitiveness Coun. [IO], Manama, Bahrain
Bahrain Dental Soc. [IO], Manama, Bahrain
Bahrain Disabled Sports Fed. [IO], Manama, Bahrain
Bahrain Emergentologist Assn. [IO], Manama, Bahrain
Bahrain Handball Assn. [IO], Manama, Bahrain
Bahrain Human Rights Watch Soc. [IO], Manama, Bahrain
Bahrain India Soc. [IO], Manama, Bahrain
Bahrain Insurance Assn. [IO], Manama, Bahrain
Bahrain Mgt. Soc. [IO], Manama, Bahrain
Bahrain Maritime Sports Assn. [IO], Manama, Bahrain
Bahrain Mind Sports Assn. [IO], Manama, Bahrain
Bahrain Physical Therapy Assn. [IO], Manama, Bahrain
Bahrain Public Relations Assn. [IO], Manama, Bahrain
Bahrain Red Crescent Soc. [IO], Manama, Bahrain
Bahrain Researchers and Inventors Soc. [IO], Manama, Bahrain
Bahrain Royal Equestrian and Endurance Fed. [IO], Awali, Bahrain
Bahrain Secretarial Assn. [IO], Manama, Bahrain
Bahrain Soc. for Children with Behavioral and Commun. Difficulties [IO], Manama, Bahrain
Bahrain Surgeons Assn. [IO], Manama, Bahrain
Bahrain Tennis Fed. [IO], Manama, Bahrain
Bahrain Weightlifting and Bodybuilding Assn. [IO], Manama, Bahrain
Bahrain Youth Hostels Soc. [IO], Manama, Bahrain
BAIF Development Res. Found. [IO], Pune, India
Baikal Environmental Wave [IO], Irkutsk, Russia
Bail
   Amer. Bail Coalition [383]
   Natl. Assn. of Bail Enforcement Agents [5296]
   Professional Bail Agents of the U.S. [5297]
Bailey's Team for Autism [13788], 164 Westside Ave., North Attleboro, MA 02760, (508)699-4483
Baitulmaal [12808], PO Box 166911, Irving, TX 75016, (972)257-2564
Baja Coalition - Address unknown since 2011.
BAK - Deutsche Rheuma Liga Bundesverband e.V. [IO], Bonn, Germany
Bakers, Food and Allied Workers' Union - Ireland [IO], Dublin, Ireland
Bakers, Food and Allied Workers' Union - United Kingdom [IO], Welwyn Garden City, United Kingdom

Bakery
   Allied Trades of the Baking Indus. [385]
Bakery and Confectionery Indus'. Assn. [IO], Rijswijk, Netherlands
Bakery, Confectionery, Tobacco Workers and Grain Millers Intl. Union [23225], 10401 Connecticut Ave., Kensington, MD 20895
Bakery, Confectionery and Tobacco Workers Intl. Union [★23225]
Bakery and Confectionery Workers' Intl. Union of Am. [★23225]
Baking
   AIB Intl. [384]
   Allied Trades of the Baking Indus. [385]
   Amer. Bakers Assn. [386]
   Amer. Pie Coun. [387]
   Amer. Soc. of Baking [388]
   Assn. of Swedish Bakeries [21934]
   Australian Soc. of Baking [3798]
   Baking Indus. Sanitation Standards Comm. [389]
   Biscuit and Cracker Mfrs. Assn. [390]
   Bread Bakers Guild of Am. [391]
   Bread Bakers Guild of Am. [391]
   Independent Bakers Assn. [392]BakingNatl. Assn. of Bakery Products
   Quality Bakers of Am. Cooperative [393]
   Retail Bakers of Am. [394]
Baking Assn. of Canada [IO], Mississauga, ON, Canada
Baking Indus. Sanitation Standards Comm. [389], PO Box 3999, Manhattan, KS 66505-3999, (785)537-4750
Balalaika and Domra Assn. of Am. [10166], 87 Western Hwy., West Nyack, NY 10994, (608)259-9440
Balearic Assn. of Stutterers [IO], Palma de Mallorca, Spain
Balgarska Akademija na Naukite [★IO]
Balint Soc. [IO], London, United Kingdom
Balkan Acad. of Cosmetic Surgery [IO], Sofia, Bulgaria
Balkan Geophysical Soc. [IO], Chania, Greece
Balkan Physical Union [IO], Thessaloniki, Greece
Ball Games
   African Baseball Network [22260]
   Assn. for Professional Basketball Res. [22293]
   Intl. Dodge Ball Fed. [22981]
   Intl. Women's Flag Football Assn. [22589]
   Men's Collegiate Lacrosse Assn. [22715]
   Natl. Amateur Dodgeball Assn. [22253]
   Natl. Club Baseball Assn. [22283]
   Natl. Paddleball Assn. [22254]
   Professional Football Players Mothers' Assn. [22595]
   Soccer Without Borders [22942]
   U.S.A. Deaf Basketball [22300]
   U.S. Club Soccer [22944]
   U.S. Floorball Assn. [22255]
   U.S. Tchoukball Assn. [22256]
   U.S.A. Broomball [22257]
   U.S.A Team Handball [22258]
   Vintage Base Ball Assn. [22292]
Ball and Roller Bearing Mfrs. Assn. [IO], Birmingham, United Kingdom
Ballet Competition; Amer. [9530]
Ballet Theatre Found. [9537], 890 Broadway, New York, NY 10003-1278, (212)477-3030
Ballew Family Assn. of Am. [20427], 4223 Jordan Rd., Greer, SC 29651, (864)895-1529
Balloon
   Intl. Aeronauts League [21203]
Balloon Fed. of Am. [22259], PO Box 400, Indianola, IA 50125, (515)961-8809
Ballooning
   Balloon Fed. of Am. [22259]
   Intl. Aeronauts League [21203]
Ballroom Dancers' Fed. Intl. [IO], Camberley, United Kingdom
Balm in Gilead [13600], 701 E Franklin St., Ste. 1000, Richmond, VA 23219, (804)644-2256
Balm in Gilead [13600], 701 E Franklin St., Ste. 1000, Richmond, VA 23219, (804)644-2256
Baltic
   Assn. for the Advancement of Baltic Stud. [9431]
   Assn. for the Advancement of Baltic Stud. [9431]

A star before a book entry number signifies that the name is not listed separately, but is mentioned within the entry.

Baltic Amer. Freedom League [17208]
Baltic Amer. Freedom League [17208]
Joint Baltic Amer. Natl. Comm. [17209]
Joint Baltic Amer. Natl. Comm. [17209]
United Baltic Appeal [18942]
United Baltic Appeal [18942]
Baltic Air Charter Assn. [IO], London, United
  Kingdom
Baltic Amer. Freedom League [17208], PO Box
  65056, Los Angeles, CA 90065-0056, (661)549-
  5201
Baltic Amer. Freedom League [17208], PO Box
  65056, Los Angeles, CA 90065-0056, (661)549-
  5201
Baltic Assn. to the United Nations [★18942]
Baltic Assn. to the United Nations [★18942]
Baltic Exchange [IO], London, United Kingdom
Baltic and Intl. Maritime Coun. [IO], Bagsvaerd,
  Denmark
Baltic Marine Biologists [IO], Uppsala, Sweden
Baltic Orthodontic Assn. [IO], Kaunas, Lithuania
Baltic Ports Org. [IO], Gdynia, Poland
Baltimore and Ohio Railroad Historical Soc. [10486],
  PO Box 24225, Baltimore, MD 21227-0725
Baltimore Vegetarians [★10627]
Bamboo of the Americas [4010], Sue Turtle, Treas.,
  30 Myers Rd., Summertown, TN 38483-7323,
  (931)964-4151
Bamboo Soc. of India [IO], Bangalore, India
Banana Link [IO], Norwich, United Kingdom
Banco Centroamericano de Integracion Economica
  [★IO]
Banco Interamericano de Desarrollo [★17579]
Banco Interamericano de Desarrollo [★17579]
Banco Interamericano de Desenvolvimento
  [★17579]
Banco Interamericano de Desenvolvimento
  [★17579]
Bandalag Starfsmanna Rikis og Baeja [★IO]
Bandaleg Islenskra Leikfelaga [★IO]
Bands
  The Grascals Fan Club [23851]
  Phi Beta Mu [23603]
Bands of Am. [10167], 39 W Jackson Pl., Ste. 150,
  Indianapolis, IN 46225, (317)636-2263
Bangalore ACM Chap. [IO], Bangalore, India
Bangkok ACM SIGGRAPH [IO], Pathumthani,
  Thailand
Bangkok Shipowners and Agents Assn. [IO],
  Bangkok, Thailand
Bangladesh Acad. of Sciences [IO], Dhaka, Bang-
  ladesh
Bangladesh Amateur Athletic Assn. [IO], Dhaka,
  Bangladesh
Bangladesh Amateur Radio League [IO], Dhaka,
  Bangladesh
Bangladesh Assn. of Agricultural Scientists in Am.
  [3738], PO Box 721426, Jackson Heights, NY
  11372, (866)504-1642
Bangladesh Assn. of Consulting Engineers [IO],
  Dhaka, Bangladesh
Bangladesh Assn. of Software and Info. Services
  [IO], Dhaka, Bangladesh
Bangladesh Assn. of Sports Medicine [IO], Dhaka,
  Bangladesh
Bangladesh Badminton Fed. [IO], Dhaka, Bang-
  ladesh
Bangladesh Bible Soc. [IO], Dhaka, Bangladesh
Bangladesh Centre for Advanced Stud. [IO], Dhaka,
  Bangladesh
Bangladesh Chem. Soc. [IO], Dhaka, Bangladesh
Bangladesh Dental Soc. [IO], Dhaka, Bangladesh
Bangladesh Economic Assn. [IO], Dhaka, Bang-
  ladesh
Bangladesh Environmental Lawyers Assn. [IO],
  Dhaka, Bangladesh
Bangladesh Fed. of Univ. Women [IO], Dhaka,
  Bangladesh
Bangladesh Fertility Soc. [IO], Dhaka, Bangladesh
Bangladesh Garment Mfrs. and Exporters Assn.
  [IO], Dhaka, Bangladesh
Bangladesh Handball Fed. [IO], Dhaka, Bangladesh
Bangladesh Inst. of Development Stud. [IO], Dhaka,
  Bangladesh
Bangladesh Jute Spinners Assn. [IO], Dhaka, Bang-
  ladesh

Bangladesh Medical Assn. of North Am. [15405],
  87-46 168 St., Jamaica, NY 11432
Bangladesh Medical Stud. and Res. Inst. [IO],
  Dhaka, Bangladesh
Bangladesh Occupational Therapy Assn. [IO],
  Dhaka, Bangladesh
Bangladesh Protibandhi Kallyan Somity [IO], Dhaka,
  Bangladesh
Bangladesh Red Crescent Soc. [IO], Dhaka, Bang-
  ladesh
Bangladesh Shishu Adhikar Forum [IO], Dhaka,
  Bangladesh
Bangladesh Soc. for Stud. of Pain [IO], Dhaka,
  Bangladesh
Bangladesh Squash Rackets Fed. [IO], Dhaka,
  Bangladesh
Bangladesh Taekwondo Fed. [IO], Dhaka, Bang-
  ladesh
Bangladesh Tea Bd. [IO], Chittagong, Bangladesh
Bangladesh Tennis Fed. [IO], Dhaka, Bangladesh
Bangladesh Unnayan Gobeshona Protishthan [★IO]
Bangladesh Unnayan Parishad [IO], Dhaka, Bang-
  ladesh
Bangladesh Weightlifting Fed. [IO], Dhaka, Bang-
  ladesh
Bangladeshi
  Amer. Inst. of Bangladesh Stud. [7766]
  Change Bangladesh [17275]
  Drishtipat Worldwide [11124]
  MAAWS for Global Welfare [12347]
  The Optimists [11377]
Bangladeshi-American Pharmacists' Assn. [16186],
  1596 Dale Ave., East Meadow, NY 11554,
  (646)325-5441
Bank Admin. Inst. [403], 115 S LaSalle St., Ste.
  3300, Chicago, IL 60603, (312)683-2464
Bank Info. Center [404], 1100 H St. NW, Ste. 650,
  Washington, DC 20005, (202)737-7752
Bank Info. Center [404], 1100 H St. NW, Ste. 650,
  Washington, DC 20005, (202)737-7752
Bank Insurance and Securities Assn. [1944], 2025 M
  St. NW, Ste. 800, Washington, DC 20036,
  (202)367-1111
Bank Marketing Assn. [★2385]
Bank Public Relations and Marketing Assn. [★2385]
Bank Securities Assn. [★1944]
Bank Stationers Assn. [★3347]
Bankcard Services Assn. [★409]
Bankcard Services Assn. [★409]
Bankers' Assn. for Finance and Trade [405], 1120
  Connecticut Ave. NW, Washington, DC 20036,
  (202)663-7575
Bankers' Assn. for Finance and Trade [405], 1120
  Connecticut Ave. NW, Washington, DC 20036,
  (202)663-7575
Bankers' Assn. for Foreign Trade [★405]
Bankers' Assn. for Foreign Trade [★405]
Bankers Assn. of the Republic of China [IO], Taipei,
  Taiwan
Bankers Political Action Comm. [★18321]
Banker's Round Table [★413]
Banking
  Amer. Assn. of Bank Directors [395]
  Amer. Bankers Assn. [396]
  Amer. Coun. of State Savings Supervisors [397]
  Amer. Numismatic Soc. [21964]
  Ancient Coin Collectors Guild [21967]
  Arab Bankers Assn. of North Am. [398]
  Arab Bankers Assn. of North Am.
    [398]BankingAssn. of Argentine Banks
  Assn. of Certified Anti-Money Laundering Special-
    ists [399]
  Assn. of Certified Anti-Money Laundering Special-
    ists [399]
  Assn. of German Pfandbrief Banks
    [7047]BankingAssn. of Intl. Banks and Trust
    Companies in the Bahamas
  Assn. for Mgt. Info. in Financial Services [400]
  Assn. of Military Banks of Am. [401]
  Assn. of Private Banks of Ecuador [3528]
  Assn. of Public and Private Banks of the
    Argentine Republic [4012]
  ATM Indus. Assn. [402]
  Bank Admin. Inst. [403]
  Bank Info. Center [404]

  Bank Info. Center [404]
  Bankers' Assn. for Finance and Trade [405]
  Bankers' Assn. for Finance and Trade [405]
  Banking Assn. of Panama [14101]
  Bolivian Private Bankers' Assn. [3829]
  Brazilian Assn. of Commercial Banks [8735]
  Colonial Coin Collectors Club [21971]
  Community Development Bankers Assn. [406]
  Conf. of State Bank Supervisors [5298]
  Consumer Bankers Assn. [407]
  Costa Rican Banking Assn. [14887]BankingDan-
    ish Bankers Assn.
  Development Bank of Southern Africa [515]
  Electronic Funds Transfer Assn. [408]
  Electronic Transactions Assn. [409]
  Electronic Transactions Assn. [409]
  Environmental Bankers Assn. [410]
  Estonian Banking Assn. [13610]
  Farm Credit Coun. [411]
  Financial and Security Products Assn. [412]
  Financial Services Round Table [413]
  Financial Women Intl. [414]
  Financial Women Intl. [414]
  Guatemalan Banks' Assn. [3370]
  Hellenic Amer. Bankers Assn. [415]
  Independent Community Bankers of Am. [416]
  Inst. of Bankers in South Africa [14672]
  Inst. of Intl. Bankers [417]
  Inst. of Intl. Bankers [417]
  Inst. of Intl. Finance [418]
  Inst. of Intl. Finance [418]
  Intl. Assn. of Currency Affairs [419]
  Intl. Bank Note Soc. [21976]
  Intl. Financial Services Assn. [420]
  Liberty Seated Collectors Club [21979]
  Loan Syndications and Trading Assn. [421]
  Loan Syndications and Trading Assn. [421]Bank-
    ingLuxembourg Bankers' Assn.
  Mortgage Bankers Assn. [422]
  NACHA: The Electronic Payments Assn. [423]
  Natl. Assn. of Affordable Housing Lenders [424]
  Natl. Assn. of ATM ISOs and Operators [425]
  Natl. Assn. of Equity Source Banks [426]
  Natl. Assn. of Mortgage Brokers [427]
  Natl. Assn. of Mortgage Processors [428]
  Natl. Assn. of Professional Mortgage Women
    [429]
  Natl. Bankers Assn. [430]
  Natl. Finance Adjusters [431]
  Natl. Investment Banking Assn. [432]
  Natl. Marine Bankers Assn. [433]
  North Amer. Collectors [21984]
  Numismatic Literary Guild [21986]
  Numismatics Intl. [21987]
  Retired Western Union Employees Assn. [434]
  Retirement Indus. Trust Assn. [435]
  Risk Mgt. Assn. [436]
  Single Global Currency Assn. [437]
  Single Global Currency Assn. [437]
  U.S. Mexican Numismatic Assn. [21996]
  Urban Financial Services Coalition [438]
  Western Independent Bankers [439]
Banking Assn. of Panama [IO], Panama City,
  Panama
Banking Assn. South Africa [IO], Marshalltown,
  Republic of South Africa
Banking Assn. of Venezuela [IO], Caracas,
  Venezuela
Banking Law Inst. - Address unknown since 2010.
Banking Profession Political Action Comm. [★18321]
BANKPAC [18321], Amer. Bankers Assn., 1120 Con-
  necticut Ave. NW, Washington, DC 20036,
  (202)663-5121
Bankruptcy Assn. of England and Wales [IO], Lan-
  caster, United Kingdom
Banks
  Amer. Numismatic Soc. [21964]
  Ancient Coin Collectors Guild [21967]
  Colonial Coin Collectors Club [21971]
  Community Development Bankers Assn. [406]
  Intl. Bank Note Soc. [21976]
  Liberty Seated Collectors Club [21979]
  Mech. Bank Collectors of Am. [21204]
  North Amer. Collectors [21984]
  Numismatic Literary Guild [21986]

Reference to "IO" in place of a book number signifies that the association may be found in the 50th edition of International Organizations.

Numismatics Intl. [21987]
   Still Bank Collectors Club of Am. [21205]
   U.S. Mexican Numismatic Assn. [21996]
Banks Assn. of Turkey [IO], Istanbul, Turkey
Banque Canadienne de Tissue du Cerveau [★IO]
Banque Europeenne de Sange Congele de Groupes
   Rares [★IO]
Banque Interamericaine de Developpement
   [★17579]
Banque Interamericaine de Developpement
   [★17579]
Banquet Managers Guild [★1761]
Banquet Managers Guild [★1761]
Banzai Anime Klub of Alberta [IO], Edmonton, AB,
   Canada
Baphalali Swaziland Red Cross Soc. [IO], Mbabane,
   Swaziland
BAPS Care Intl. [★18313]
BAPS Care Intl. [★18313]
BAPS Charities [18313], 81 Suttons Ln., Ste. 201,
   Piscataway, NJ 08854, (732)777-1818
BAPS Charities [18313], 81 Suttons Ln., Ste. 201,
   Piscataway, NJ 08854, (732)777-1818
Baptist
   ABW Ministries [19305]
   Amer. Baptist Historical Soc. [19306]
   Amer. Baptist Homes and Caring Ministries
      [19307]
   Assn. of Baptists for World Evangelism [19308]
   Assn. of Baptists for World Evangelism [19308]
   Assn. of Reformed Baptist Churches of Am.
      [19309]
   Assn. of Welcoming and Affirming Baptists
      [19310]
   Baptist Bible Fellowship Intl. [19311]
   Baptist Bible Fellowship Intl. [19311]
   Baptist Communicators Assn. [19312]
   Baptist Global Response [12809]
   Baptist Joint Comm. for Religious Liberty [19313]
   Baptist Mid-Missions [19314]
   Baptist Women in Ministry/Folio [19315]
   Baptist World Alliance [19316]
   Baptist World Alliance [19316]
   Bd. of Intl. Ministries [19317]
   Bd. of Intl. Ministries [19317]
   Conservative Baptist Assn. of Am. [19318]
   Continental Baptist Missions [19319]
   Ethics and Religious Liberty Commn. of the
      Southern Baptist Convention [19320]
   Gen. Assn. of Gen. Baptists [19321]
   Gen. Assn. of Regular Baptist Churches [19322]
   Master's Men of the Natl. Assn. of Free Will
      Baptists [19323]
   Missions Door [19324]
   Missions Door [19324]
   Natl. Assn. of Free Will Baptists [19325]
   Natl. Baptist Convention U.S.A. [19326]
   Seventh Day Baptist Gen. Conf. [19327]
   Seventh Day Baptist Gen. Conf. of the U.S. and
      Canada [19328]
   Seventh Day Baptist Historical Soc. [19329]
   Seventh Day Baptist Missionary Soc. [19330]
   Seventh Day Baptist World Fed. [19331]
   Seventh Day Baptist World Fed. [19331]
   Southern Baptist Found. [19332]
   Southern Baptist Historical Lib. and Archives
      [19333]
   William H. Whitsitt Baptist Heritage Soc. [19334]
   Woman's Missionary Union [19335]
   Women Nationally Active for Christ [19336]
   WorldVenture [19337]
   WorldVenture [19337]
Baptist Bible Fellowship Intl. [19311], PO Box 191,
   Springfield, MO 65801-0191, (417)862-5001
Baptist Bible Fellowship Intl. [19311], PO Box 191,
   Springfield, MO 65801-0191, (417)862-5001
Baptist Churches of New Zealand [IO], Auckland,
   New Zealand
Baptist Communicators Assn. [19312], Margaret M.
   Dempsey, 1519 Menlo Dr., Kennesaw, GA 30152,
   (770)425-3728
Baptist Foreign Mission Convention [★19326]
Baptist Global Response [12809], 402 BNA Dr., Ste.
   411, Nashville, TN 37217, (615)367-3678
Baptist Historical Soc. [IO], Didcot, United Kingdom

Baptist Joint Comm. on Public Affairs [★19313]
Baptist Joint Comm. for Religious Liberty [19313],
   200 Maryland Ave. NE, Washington, DC 20002,
   (202)544-4226
Baptist Mid-Missions [19314], PO Box 308011,
   Cleveland, OH 44130-8011, (440)826-3930
Baptist Peace Fellowship of North Am. [18232],
   4800 Wedgewood Dr., Charlotte, NC 28210,
   (704)521-6051
Baptist Peace Fellowship of North Am. [18232],
   4800 Wedgewood Dr., Charlotte, NC 28210,
   (704)521-6051
Baptist Public Relations Assn. [★19312]
Baptist Union of Australia [IO], Broadview, Australia
Baptist Union of Denmark [IO], Copenhagen,
   Denmark
Baptist Women in Ministry [★19315]
Baptist Women in Ministry/Folio [19315], PO Box
   941294, Atlanta, GA 31141-1294, (678)547-6475
Baptist World Aid Australia [IO], Frenchs Forest,
   Australia
Baptist World Alliance [19316], 405 N Washington
   St., Falls Church, VA 22046, (703)790-8980
Baptist World Alliance [19316], 405 N Washington
   St., Falls Church, VA 22046, (703)790-8980
Baptistkirken i Danmark [★IO]
Baptists for Life [12925], PO Box 3158, Grand
   Rapids, MI 49501, (616)257-6800
Baqura [★19829]
Bar Assn. Commn. on Homelessness and Poverty;
   Amer. [12153]
Bar Assn. for Local Govt. and the Public Ser. [IO],
   Birmingham, United Kingdom
Baraka Africa [11194], 425 First St., Ste. 1103, San
   Francisco, CA 94105, (415)690-0601
Barbados
   Barbados Tourism Authority [23331]
Barbados Amateur Weightlifting Assn. [IO], Christ
   Church, Barbados
Barbados Assn. of Medical Practitioners [IO], St.
   Michael, Barbados
Barbados Assn. of Off. Professionals [IO], Bridge-
   town, Barbados
Barbados Badminton Assn. [IO], Bridgetown,
   Barbados
Barbados Blackbelly Sheep Assn. Intl. [4904], 1156
   NE 50th Rd., Lamar, MO 64759, (417)398-2875
Barbados Blackbelly Sheep Assn. Intl. [4904], 1156
   NE 50th Rd., Lamar, MO 64759, (417)398-2875
Barbados Bd. of Tourism [★23331]
Barbados Cancer Soc. [IO], St. Michael, Barbados
Barbados Chamber of Commerce and Indus. [IO],
   St. Michael, Barbados
Barbados Employers' Confed. [IO], St. Michael,
   Barbados
Barbados Family Planning Assn. [IO], St. Michael,
   Barbados
Barbados Hotel and Tourism Assn. [IO], St. Michael,
   Barbados
Barbados Labour Party [IO], Bridgetown, Barbados
Barbados Mfrs'. Assn. [IO], St. Michael, Barbados
Barbados Museum and Historical Soc. [IO], St.
   Michael, Barbados
Barbados Natl. Org. for the Disabled [IO], Bridge-
   town, Barbados
Barbados Natl. Trust [IO], St. Michael, Barbados
Barbados Olympic Assn. [IO], St. Michael, Barbados
Barbados Physical Therapy Assn. [IO], St. Michael,
   Barbados
Barbados Red Cross Soc. [IO], Bridgetown,
   Barbados
Barbados Sailing Assn. [IO], Bridgetown, Barbados
Barbados Secondary Teachers' Union [IO], St.
   Michael, Barbados
Barbados Sport Medicine Assn. [IO], St. Michael,
   Barbados
Barbados Squash Rackets Assn. [IO], Bridgetown,
   Barbados
Barbados Taekwondo Assn. [IO], Bridgetown,
   Barbados
Barbados Tennis Assn. [IO], Bridgetown, Barbados
Barbados Tourism Authority [23331], 800 2nd Ave.,
   New York, NY 10017, (212)986-6516
Barbados Union of Teachers [IO], St. Michael,
   Barbados

Barbados Workers' Union [IO], St. Michael,
   Barbados
Barbara Bush Found. for Family Literacy [8524],
   1201 15th St. NW, Ste. 420, Washington, DC
   20005, (202)955-6183
Barbara Eden's Official Fan Club - Address unknown
   since 2011.
Barbara Pym Soc. [9350], 4 Summit Dr., No. 005,
   Reading, MA 01867, (781)942-7471
Barbecue Indus. Assn. [★1699]
Barbers, Beauticians and Allied Indus. Intl. Assn.
   [★23191]
Barbers Company [IO], London, United Kingdom
Barbershop Harmony Soc. [★10297]
Barbie Lovers Club [★21687]
BAREMA [IO], Radley, United Kingdom
Barh Koh Env. and Sustainable Development Aid
   [IO], Toronto, ON, Canada
Bariatric Medicine; Amer. Bd. of [15850]
Bariatric Physicians; Amer. Soc. of [15851]
Bariloche Found. [IO], Bariloche, Argentina
Barisal Young Men's Christian Association [IO], Bar-
   isal City, Bangladesh
Barne- og ungdomsrevmatikergruppen [★IO]
Barney Family Historical Assn. [20428], PO Box
   179, Haymarket, VA 20168
Barnsley and Rotherham Chamber of Commerce
   [IO], Barnsley, United Kingdom
Baromedical Nurses Assn. [15742], PO Box 80423,
   Seattle, WA 98108, (303)918-9686
Baronial Order of Magna Charta [9754], Mr. Robert
   Pond Vivian, 1285 Br. Rd., Wells, ME 04090-6057
Baronial Order of Magna Charta [9754], Mr. Robert
   Pond Vivian, 1285 Br. Rd., Wells, ME 04090-6057
Baronial Order of Runnemede [★9754]
Baronial Order of Runnemede [★9754]
Barre Granite Assn. [3359], PO Box 481, Barre, VT
   05641-0481, (802)476-4131
Barrel Futurities of Am. [22651], Rte. 2, Box 120 K,
   Vian, OK 74962, (918)773-5246
Barrie Constr. Assn. [IO], Barrie, ON, Canada
Bartering
   Intl. Barter Alliance USA [440]
Barzona Breeders Assn. of Am. [3904], 11477 E
   Warren Pl., Aurora, CO 80014, (303)696-5799
Baseball
   African Baseball Network [22260]
   Amateur Baseball Umpires' Assn. [22261]
   Amer. Amateur Baseball Cong. [22262]
   Amer. Baseball Coaches Assn. [22263]
   Amer. Baseball Coaches Assn. [22263]
   Amer. Baseball Found. [22264]
   Amer. Legion Baseball [22265]
   Assn. of Minor League Umpires [22266]
   Assn. of Professional Ball Players of Am. [22267]
   Babe Ruth Baseball/Softball [22268]
   Babe Ruth Birthplace [22269]
   Baseball Writers Assn. of Am. [2814]
   Cosmic Baseball Assn. [22270]
   Coun. of Ivy Gp. Presidents [22975]
   George Khoury Assn. of Baseball Leagues
      [22271]
   Intl. League of Professional Baseball Clubs
      [22272]
   Little League Baseball and Softball [22273]
   Little League Found. [22274]
   Major League Baseball [22275]
   Major League Baseball Players Alumni Assn.
      [22276]
   Major League Baseball Players Assn. [23156]
   Natl. Adult Baseball Assn. [22277]
   Natl. Amateur Baseball Fed. [22278]
   Natl. Amer. Semi-Professional Baseball Assn.
      [22279]
   Natl. Assn. of Professional Baseball Leagues
      [22280]
   Natl. Baseball Cong. [22281]
   Natl. Baseball Hall of Fame and Museum [22282]
   Natl. Club Baseball Assn. [22283]
   Natl. High School Baseball Coaches Assn.
      [22284]
   Natl. Junior Baseball League [22285]
   Natl. Pitching Assn. [22286]
   Negro Leagues Baseball Museum [22287]
   Pony Baseball and Softball [22288]

A star before a book entry number signifies that the name is not listed separately, but is mentioned within the entry.

Professional Baseball Athletic Trainers Soc. [22289]
Soc. for Amer. Baseball Res. [22290]
Southeastern Conf. [23006]
U.S.A. Baseball [22291]
Vintage Base Ball Assn. [22292]
World Umpires Assn. [23157]
World Umpires Assn. [23157]
Baseball Assn; Natl. Beep [22516]
Baseball Canada [IO], Ottawa, ON, Canada
Baseball Fed. of Armenia [IO], Vanadzor, Armenia
Baseball Ireland [IO], Blessington, Ireland
Baseball Nova Scotia [IO], Halifax, NS, Canada
Baseball Softball Assn. of Slovenia [IO], Ljubljana, Slovenia
Baseball and Softball Fed. of the Republic of Kazakhstan [IO], Almaty, Kazakhstan
Baseball Writers Assn. of Am. [2814], PO Box 610611, Bayside, NY 11361, (718)767-2582
Basel Action Network [18780], 206 First Ave. S., Ste. 410, Seattle, WA 98104, (206)652-5555
Basel Action Network [18780], 206 First Ave. S., Ste. 410, Seattle, WA 98104, (206)652-5555
Basenji Club of Am. [21519], 34025 W River Rd., Wilmington, IL 60481-9599
Basic Acrylic Monomer Mfrs. [745], 17260 Vannes Ct., Hamilton, VA 20158, (540)751-2093
Basic Acrylic Monomer Mfrs. Assn. [★745]
Basic Educ. Coalition [8525], 1825 Connecticut Ave. NW, Ste. 600, Washington, DC 20009, (202)884-8751
Basic Hea. Intl. [17122], PO Box 1170, New York, NY 10029-6574, (212)241-0733
Basic Human Needs Assn. [IO], Tokyo, Japan
Basingstoke Conservation Volunteers [IO], Basingstoke, United Kingdom
Basketball
Assn. for Professional Basketball Res. [22293]
Continental Basketball League [22294]
Coun. of Ivy Gp. Presidents [22975]
Intl. Assn. of Approved Basketball Officials [22295]
Naismith Memorial Basketball Hall of Fame [22296]
Natl. Assn. of Basketball Coaches [22297]
Natl. Basketball Assn. [22298]
Natl. Basketball Athletic Trainers Assn. [22299]
Southeastern Conf. [23006]
U.S.A. Deaf Basketball [22300]
U.S. Basketball Writers Assn. [22301]
U.S.A. Basketball [22302]
Women's Basketball Coaches Assn. [22303]
Women's Natl. Basketball Players Assn. [22304]
Basketball Assn; Natl. Wheelchair [22518]
Basketball Nova Scotia [IO], Halifax, NS, Canada
Basketball Players Assn; Natl. [23298]
Basketball Scotland [IO], Edinburgh, United Kingdom
BASO - Assn. for Cancer Surgery [IO], London, United Kingdom
Basque
Basque Educational Org. [9432]
Soc. of Basque Stud. in Am. [9433]
Soc. of Basque Stud. in Am. [9433]
Basque Educational Org. [9432], PO Box 31861, San Francisco, CA 94131-0861, (415)285-0748
B.A.S.S. [★22572]
Bass Anglers Sportsman Soc. [22572], 1170 Celebration Blvd., Ste. 200, Celebration, FL 34747, (877)BAS-SUSA
Basset Hound Club of Am. [21520], Bobbi Brandt, First VP, 11401 Gamache Dr., Anchorage, AK 99516-1676, (907)346-1849
Bass'n Gal - Defunct.
Bastard Nation: The Adoptee Rights Org. [10782], PO Box 1469, Edmond, OK 73083-1469, (415)704-3166
Bat Conservation Intl. [5031], PO Box 162603, Austin, TX 78716, (512)327-9721
Bat Conservation Intl. [5031], PO Box 162603, Austin, TX 78716, (512)327-9721
Bat Conservation Trust - UK [IO], London, United Kingdom
Bataan Relief Org. [★20755]
Bates Assn. for Vision Educ. [IO], Eastbourne, United Kingdom

Batey Relief Alliance [12810], PO Box 300565, Brooklyn, NY 11230-5656, (917)627-5026
Batey Relief Alliance [12810], PO Box 300565, Brooklyn, NY 11230-5656, (917)627-5026
Bath Enclosure Mfrs. Assn. [2780], PO Box 4730, Topeka, KS 66604, (785)273-0393
Bath Inst. for Rheumatic Diseases [IO], Bath, United Kingdom
Bathroom Mfrs. Assn. [IO], Stoke-on-Trent, United Kingdom
Baton Twirling
Natl. Baton Twirling Assn. Intl. [22305]
U.S. Twirling Assn. [22306]
Battelle for Kids [7826], 1160 Dublin Rd., Ste. 500, Columbus, OH 43215, (614)481-3141
Batten Disease Support and Res. Assn. [15574], 166 Humphries Dr., Reynoldsburg, OH 43068, (740)927-4298
Batten Disease Support and Res. Assn. - Australia [IO], Killarney Vale, Australia
Batteries
Battery Recycling Assn. of North Am. [3071]
Natl. Alliance for Advanced Tech. Batteries [441]
Battery Assn. of Japan [IO], Tokyo, Japan
Battery Coun. Intl. [323], 401 N Michigan Ave., 24th Fl., Chicago, IL 60611-4267, (312)644-6610
Battery Coun. Intl. [323], 401 N Michigan Ave., 24th Fl., Chicago, IL 60611-4267, (312)644-6610
Battery Recycling Assn. of North Am. [3071], 12505 N Main St., Ste. 212, Rancho Cucamonga, CA 91739
Battery Vehicle Soc. [IO], Basingstoke, United Kingdom
Battle of Ormoc Bay Assn. - Address unknown since 2011.
Battling to Smile Again [IO], Damascus, Syrian Arab Republic
Bauddha-Grantha-Prakasana Samitiya [★IO]
Bautz Descendants - Defunct.
Bavarian Acad. of Fine Arts [IO], Munich, Germany
Bavarian Acad. of Sciences and Humanities [IO], Munich, Germany
Bay Area Cryonics Soc. [★14211]
Bay Area Independent Publishers Assn. [2924], PO Box E, Corte Madera, CA 94976, (415)456-0247
Bay Area Photographica Assn. [★10439]
Bay Area Photographica Assn. [★10439]
Bay Area Physicians for Human Rights [12070], PO Box 14188, San Francisco, CA 94114-0188
Bay Area Printmakers [★1604]
Bay of Pigs Veterans Assn. - Address unknown since 2011.
Bayerische Akademie der Schonen Kunste [★IO]
Bayerische Akademie der Wissenschaften [★IO]
BBB Wise Giving Alliance [17445], 4200 Wilson Blvd., Ste. 800, Arlington, VA 22203-1838, (703)276-0100
BBB Wise Giving Alliance [17445], 4200 Wilson Blvd., Ste. 800, Arlington, VA 22203-1838, (703)276-0100
BBM Canada [IO], Toronto, ON, Canada
B.C. Assn. of Clinical Counsellors [IO], Victoria, BC, Canada
BC Assn. of Social Workers [IO], Vancouver, BC, Canada
BC Innovation Coun. [IO], Vancouver, BC, Canada
B.C. Road Builders and Heavy Constr. Assn. [IO], Burnaby, BC, Canada
BC Salmon Farmers Assn. [IO], Campbell River, BC, Canada
BC Wheelchair Sports Assn. [IO], Richmond, BC, Canada
The BCA [★1009]
BCA-Credit Info. [★485]
BCM Intl. [19341], 201 Granite Run Dr., Ste. 260, Lancaster, PA 17601, (717)560-9601
BCM Intl. [19341], 201 Granite Run Dr., Ste. 260, Lancaster, PA 17601, (717)560-9601
BCPC [IO], Alton, United Kingdom
BDPA Info. Tech. Thought Leaders [★65]
Be Active, Be Emancipated [IO], Zagreb, Croatia
Be Healthy [13668], 333 W 41st St., Ste. 414, Miami Beach, FL 33140, (305)538-8998
Be and See Inspirations [IO], Lagos, Nigeria
Be The Change Intl. [13344], 1131 N Laura St., Jacksonville, FL 32206, (904)355-0000

Beach Boys Fan Club [23817], 631 N Stephanie St., No. 546, Henderson, NV 89014
Beach Boys Freaks United [★23817]
Beach Educ. Advocates for Culture, Hea., Env. and Safety [10341], PO Box 530702, Miami Shores, FL 33153, (305)620-7090
B.E.A.C.H.E.S. Found. Inst. [★10341]
BeachFront USA [10342], PO Box 328, Moreno Valley, CA 92556-0328
Beacon for Freedom of Expression [IO], Oslo, Norway
The Bead Soc. [★21308]
Bead Soc. of Los Angeles [21308], PO Box 241874, Los Angeles, CA 90024-9674
Beall Family Assn. [20429], 30 SE Gilham Ave., Portland, OR 97215-1366
BEAMA Capacitor Manufacturer's Assn. [IO], London, United Kingdom
BEAMA Installation [IO], London, United Kingdom
BEAMA Metering and Communications Assn. [IO], London, United Kingdom
BEAMA Transmission and Distribution Assn. [IO], London, United Kingdom
Beamtenbund und Tarifunion [★IO]
Bean Assn. [★1378]
Beanies for Baghdad [11195], 6401 Lincoln Ave., Evansville, IN 47715
Bear Biology Assn. [★5065]
Bear Biology Assn. [★5065]
Bear Butte Intl. Alliance
Bear Butte Intl. Alliance - Address unknown since 2010.
Bear Trust Intl. [5032], PO Box 4006, Missoula, MT 59806-4006, (406)523-7779
Bear Trust Intl. [5032], PO Box 4006, Missoula, MT 59806-4006, (406)523-7779
Bearded Collie Club of Am. [21521], 20 Woodmoor Dr., Lucas, TX 75002-7407, (972)442-6824
Bearing Specialists Assn. [1813], 800 Roosevelt Rd., Bldg. C, Ste. 312, Glen Ellyn, IL 60137, (630)858-3838
Beating Disorders Assn. [IO], Norwich, United Kingdom
Beatitudes Soc. [19540], 950 Dena Way, Santa Barbara, CA 93111
Beatles Fans Unite - Address unknown since 2011.
Beatles Info. Center [IO], Stockholm, Sweden
Beatles Unlimited [IO], Nieuwegein, Netherlands
Beaton Inst. of Cape Breton Stud. [IO], Sydney, NS, Canada
Beaumont Soc. [IO], London, United Kingdom
Beautiful Gate Lesotho [IO], Maseru, Lesotho
Beauty 4 Ashes Intl. [13452], 3713 Lexham Ct., High Point, NC 27265, (336)209-7405
Beauty Without Cruelty U.S.A. - Defunct.
Beaux Arts Alliance [9283], 119 E 74th St., New York, NY 10021-3201, (212)639-9120
Beaux-Arts Inst. of Design [★7737]
Beaver Ambassador Club [22135], PO Box 3706, Incline Village, NV 89450, (530)823-3767
Beaver Water World [IO], Kent, United Kingdom
Because I Love You: The Parent Support Gp. [13300], PO Box 2062, Winnetka, CA 91396-2062, (818)884-8242
Because Intl. [12718], 3720 S Palm Springs St., Nampa, ID 83686, (208)989-8867
Becket Fund for Religious Liberty [18517], 3000 K St. NW, Ste. 220, Washington, DC 20007, (202)955-0095
Bed & Breakfast Reservation Services World-Wide - Defunct.
Bedding Plants Intl. - Defunct.
Bedford Systems Users Group - Defunct.
Bedfordshire and Luton Chamber of Commerce, Training and Enterprise [IO], Luton, United Kingdom
Bee Improvement and Bee Breeders' Assn. [IO], Doncaster, United Kingdom
Bee Native [3839], Mantis Farm, 68 Fingar Rd., Hudson, NY 12534, (917)679-0567
Beef Friesian Soc. [★3921]
Beef Improvement Fed. [6872], Box 7621, Raleigh, NC 27695, (919)513-0262
Beef Info. Centre [IO], Mississauga, ON, Canada
Beef Promotion and Res. Bd. [★3911]

Reference to "IO" in place of a book number signifies that the association may be found in the 50th edition of International Organizations.

Beefmaster Breeders United **[3905]**, 6800 Park 10 Blvd., Ste. 290 W, San Antonio, TX 78213, (210)732-3132
Beefmaster Breeders Universal **[★3905]**
Beekeeping
Amer. Honey Producers Assn. **[3816]**
Apiary Inspectors of Am. **[3817]**
Bee Native **[3839]**
Beekeeping Extension Soc. **[IO]**, Zaria, Nigeria
Beer
Brewery Collectibles Club of Am. **[21311]**
Beer Can Collectors of Am. **[★21311]**
Beer Distributors Secretaries of Am. **[★185]**
Beer Inst. **[178]**, 122 C St. NW, Ste. 350, Washington, DC 20001, (202)737-2337
Beet Sugar Development Found. **[4935]**, 800 Grant St., Ste. 300, Denver, CO 80203-2944, (303)832-4460
Beethoven Found. **[★21953]**
Before Columbus Found. **[10036]**, The Raymond House, Ste. 302, 655-13th St., Oakland, CA 94612, (510)268-9775
Befrienders Worldwide **[IO]**, Ewell, United Kingdom
Behavior Genetics Assn. **[14646]**, Rhee Soo Hyun, PhD, Treas., 345 UCB, Dept. of Psychology, Boulder, CO 80309
Behavior Genetics Assn. **[14646]**, Rhee Soo Hyun, PhD, Treas., 345 UCB, Dept. of Psychology, Boulder, CO 80309
Behavioral Medicine
Acad. of Behavioral Medicine Res. **[13812]**
Annapolis Coalition on the Behavioral Hea. Workforce **[15446]**
Assn. for Behavioral and Cognitive Therapies **[13813]**
Assn. for Integrative Psychology **[16389]**
Devereux Natl. **[13814]**
Inst. for the Advancement of Human Behavior **[13815]**
Intercontinental Fed. of Behavioral Optometry **[15994]**
Intl. Soc. for Autism Res. **[13797]**
Intl. Soc. for Comparative Psychology **[16402]**
Mental Hea. Corporations of Am. **[13816]**
Mental Res. Inst. **[13817]**
Natl. Assn. of Therapeutic Schools and Programs **[13818]**
Natl. Inst. for the Clinical Application of Behavioral Medicine **[13819]**
Psychoneuroimmunology Res. Soc. **[13820]**
Sigmund Freud Archives **[16362]**
Soc. of Behavioral Medicine **[13821]**
Soc. for Behavioral Neuroendocrinology **[13822]**
Soc. for the Stud. of Ingestive Behavior **[13823]**
Soc. for the Stud. of Occupation: U.S.A. **[7767]**
U.S.A. Transactional Anal. Assn. **[13824]**
Behavioral Neuropsychology Special Interest Group - Defunct.
Behavioral Pediatrics; Soc. for Developmental and **[16155]**
Behavioral Sciences
Amer. Assn. of Behavioral and Social Sciences **[6246]**
Amer. Psychological Assn. l Soc. of Psychological Hypnosis **[16380]**
Amer. Soc. of Trial Consultants **[6247]**
Annapolis Coalition on the Behavioral Hea. Workforce **[15446]**
Assn. for Advanced Training in the Behavioral Sciences **[8761]**
Assn. for Africanist Anthropology **[6133]**
Assn. for Behavior Anal. **[6248]**
Assn. for the Behavioral Sciences and Medical Educ. **[6249]**
Assn. for Contextual Behavioral Sci. **[6250]**
Assn. of Management/International Assn. of Mgt. **[6251]**
Assn. of Management/International Assn. of Mgt. **[6251]**
Assn. for Positive Behavior Support **[6252]**
Assn. for the Treatment of Sexual Abusers **[6253]**
Cognitive Development Soc. **[13825]**
Consciousness-Based Educ. Assn. **[8762]**
Fed. of Associations in Behavioral and Brain Sciences **[6254]**

Human Behavior and Evolution Soc. **[6255]**
Human Resources Res. Org. **[6256]**
Intercontinental Fed. of Behavioral Optometry **[15994]**
Intl. Assn. of Applied Control Theory **[6257]**
Intl. Positive Psychology Assn. **[16401]**
Intl. Soc. for Adaptive Behavior **[6258]**
Intl. Soc. for Adaptive Behavior **[6258]**
Intl. Soc. for Behavioral Nutrition and Physical Activity **[13826]**
Intl. Soc. for Behavioral Nutrition and Physical Activity **[13826]**
Intl. Soc. for Comparative Psychology **[16402]**
Intl. Soc. for Human Ethology **[6259]**
Intl. Soc. for Human Ethology **[6259]**
Intl. Soc. for Neuroimmunomodulation **[15664]**
Intl. Soc. for Quality of Life Res. **[6260]**
Intl. Soc. for Quality-of-Life Stud. **[7768]**
Intl. Soc. for Quality-of-Life Stud. **[7768]**
Intl. Soc. for Res. on Aggression **[6261]**
Intl. Soc. for Res. on Aggression **[6261]**
Natl. Alliance of Professional Psychology Providers **[16411]**
Natl. Anger Mgt. Assn. **[15465]**
Organizational Behavior Teaching Soc. **[6262]**
Sigmund Freud Archives **[16362]**
Soc. for the Advancement of Behavior Anal. **[6263]**
Soc. for Evolutionary Anal. in Law **[6264]**
Soc. for Evolutionary Anal. in Law **[6264]**
Soc. for the History of Psychology **[7312]**
Soc. for Human Performance in Extreme Environments **[6265]**
Soc. for Quantitative Analyses of Behavior **[6266]**
Soc. of Sensory Professionals **[7391]**
Soc. for the Stud. of Human Development **[6946]**
Soc. for Terrorism Res. **[7554]**
Special Interest Gp. on Cmpt. and Human Interaction **[6267]**
Behavioral Sciences; NTL Inst. for Applied **[8178]**
Behavioral Teratology Soc; Neuro **[15626]**
Behavioral Toxicology Soc. - Defunct.
Behaviorists for Social Action **[★18611]**
Behaviorists for Social Responsibility **[18611]**, 1040 W Harrison St., Chicago, IL 60607
Behcet's Syndrome
Amer. Behcet's Disease Assn. **[13827]**
Behind the Bench - Address unknown since 2011.
Beijing ACM SIGGRAPH **[IO]**, Beijing, People's Republic of China
Beirut Veterans of Am. **[20778]**, 123 Prentice Ave., South River, NJ 08882
Belarus Athletic Fed. **[IO]**, Minsk, Belarus
Belarus Baseball and Softball Fed. **[IO]**, Minsk, Belarus
Belarus Draughts Fed. **[IO]**, Minsk, Belarus
Belarus Sailing Union **[IO]**, Minsk, Belarus
Belarus Tennis Assn. **[IO]**, Minsk, Belarus
Belarusian Assn. of Consulting Engineers **[IO]**, Minsk, Belarus
Belarusian Canadian Alliance **[IO]**, Toronto, ON, Canada
Belarusian Dance Sport Fed. **[IO]**, Minsk, Belarus
Belarusian Lib. Assn. **[IO]**, Minsk, Belarus
Belarusian Physical Soc. **[IO]**, Minsk, Belarus
Belarusian Republican Taekwondo Fed. **[IO]**, Minsk, Belarus
Belarusian Sci. Rheumatological Soc. **[IO]**, Minsk, Belarus
Belarussian
North Amer. Assn. for Belarusian Stud. **[9434]**
North Amer. Assn. for Belarusian Stud. **[9434]**
Belarussian Badminton Fed. **[IO]**, Minsk, Belarus
Belarussian Physiological Soc. **[IO]**, Minsk, Belarus
Beldon Fund - Defunct.
Belgian
Belgian Tourist Off. **[23333]**
Belgian Aerospace Indus. Assn. **[IO]**, Brussels, Belgium
Belgian Aikikai **[IO]**, Brussels, Belgium
Belgian Amer. Chamber of Commerce **[23332]**, 1177 Ave. of the Americas, 8th Fl., New York, NY 10018, (212)541-0779
Belgian Amer. Educational Found. **[9435]**, 195 Church St., New Haven, CT 06510, (203)777-5765

Belgian Assn. for Documentation **[IO]**, Brussels, Belgium
Belgian Assn. for Osteoporosis Patients **[IO]**, Antwerp, Belgium
Belgian Assn. of Regional Anesthesia **[IO]**, Leuven, Belgium
Belgian Assn. for the Stud. of the Liver **[IO]**, Brussels, Belgium
Belgian Assn. for the Stud. of Obesity **[IO]**, Leuven, Belgium
Belgian Aviation History Assn. **[IO]**, Temse, Belgium
Belgian Brewers **[IO]**, Brussels, Belgium
Belgian Centre for Corrosion Stud. **[IO]**, Waterloo, Belgium
Belgian Centre for Music Documentation **[IO]**, Brussels, Belgium
Belgian Chamber of Inventors **[IO]**, Brussels, Belgium
Belgian Clayshooting Fed. **[IO]**, Schilde, Belgium
Belgian Cockpit Assn. **[IO]**, Brussels, Belgium
Belgian Cricket Fed. **[IO]**, Antwerp, Belgium
Belgian Dance Sport Fed. **[IO]**, Brussels, Belgium
Belgian Direct Marketing Assn. **[IO]**, Brussels, Belgium
Belgian Draft Horse Corp. of Am. **[4570]**, PO Box 335, Wabash, IN 46992, (260)563-3205
Belgian Electrotechnical Comm. **[IO]**, Brussels, Belgium
Belgian EMG and Clinical Neurophysiology Soc. **[IO]**, Brussels, Belgium
Belgian Fed. of Baseball and Softball **[★IO]**
Belgian Fed. of Bus and Coach Operators **[IO]**, Brussels, Belgium
Belgian Fed. of Distributors **[IO]**, Brussels, Belgium
Belgian Fed. of Magazines **[IO]**, Brussels, Belgium
Belgian Fed. of Psychologists **[IO]**, Brussels, Belgium
Belgian Fed. of Univ. Graduate Women **[IO]**, Brussels, Belgium
Belgian Floorball Fed. **[IO]**, Iddergem, Belgium
Belgian Flying Disc Fed. **[IO]**, Brussels, Belgium
Belgian Franchise Fed. **[IO]**, Uccle, Belgium
Belgian Fur Trade Fed. **[IO]**, Brussels, Belgium
Belgian Geological Soc. **[IO]**, Liege, Belgium
Belgian Heart League **[IO]**, Brussels, Belgium
Belgian Hypertension Comm. **[IO]**, Brussels, Belgium
Belgian League Against Epilepsy **[IO]**, Gent, Belgium
Belgian-Luxembourg Amer. Stud. Assn. **[IO]**, Brussels, Belgium
Belgian Luxembourg Chamber of Commerce in Great Britain **[IO]**, South Cave, United Kingdom
Belgian Mathematical Soc. **[IO]**, Brussels, Belgium
Belgian Medical Informatics Assn. **[IO]**, Baisy-Thy, Belgium
Belgian Michael Jackson Fan Club **[IO]**, Overpelt, Belgium
Belgian Natl. Comm. for UNICEF **[IO]**, Brussels, Belgium
Belgian Natl. Taekwondo Union **[IO]**, Hasselt, Belgium
Belgian Natl. Tourist Off. **[★23333]**
Belgian Neurological Soc. **[IO]**, Liege, Belgium
Belgian Operations Res. Soc. **[IO]**, Brussels, Belgium
Belgian Pain Soc. **[IO]**, Louvain, Belgium
Belgian Paralympic Comm. **[IO]**, Brussels, Belgium
Belgian Periodical Press Fed. **[IO]**, Brussels, Belgium
Belgian Pharmaceutical Indus. Assn. **[IO]**, Brussels, Belgium
Belgian Pool Billiard Fed. **[IO]**, Westende, Belgium
Belgian Publishers' Assn. **[IO]**, Brussels, Belgium
Belgian Risk Mgt. Assn. **[IO]**, Brussels, Belgium
Belgian Royal Soc. of Rheumatology **[IO]**, Brussels, Belgium
Belgian Sheepdog Club of Am. **[21522]**, Pat Porter, Ed., 11300A SE 362nd Ave., Boring, OR 97009
Belgian Soc. of Cardiology **[IO]**, Brussels, Belgium
Belgian Soc. of Clinical Neurophysiology **[IO]**, Liege, Belgium
Belgian Soc. of Digestive Endoscopy **[IO]**, Brussels, Belgium
Belgian Soc. of Fundamental and Clinical Physiology and Pharmacology **[IO]**, Liege, Belgium

A star before a book entry number signifies that the name is not listed separately, but is mentioned within the entry.

Belgian Soc. of Gerontology and Geriatrics [IO], Wetteren, Belgium

Belgian Soc. of Human Genetics [IO], Brussels, Belgium

Belgian Soc. for Microscopy [IO], Mechelen, Belgium

Belgian Soc. for Reproductive Medicine [IO], Ternat, Belgium

Belgian Teleworking Assn. [IO], Brussels, Belgium

Belgian Tourist Off. [23333], 220 E 42nd St., Ste. 3402, New York, NY 10017, (212)758-8130

Belgian Transplantation Soc. [IO], Brussels, Belgium

Belgian Veterinary Cmpt. Assn. [IO], Liege, Belgium

Belgian Wallonia-Brussels Discgolf Assn. [IO], Namur, Belgium

Belgische Bontfederatie [★IO]

Belgische Confederatie van de Zuivelindustrie [IO], Leuven, Belgium

Belgische DansSport Federatie [★IO]

Belgische Vereniging voor Gerontologie en Geriatrie [★IO]

Belgische Vereniging voor Neurologie [★IO]

Belgische Vereniging Sport-Geneeskunde and Sportwetenschappen [★IO]

Belgische Vereniging Voor Tuinarchitecten En Landschapsarchitecten [★IO]

Belgium
Belgian Amer. Chamber of Commerce [23332]
Belgian Amer. Educational Found. [9435]
Belgian Tourist Off. [23333]

Belgium Assn. of Agricultural Journalists [IO], Brussels, Belgium

Belgium Fed. of Fuel Suppliers [IO], Brussels, Belgium

Belgium-Japan Assn. and Chamber of Commerce [IO], Brussels, Belgium

Belgium-Luxembourg Chamber of Commerce in Hong Kong [IO], Hong Kong, People's Republic of China

Belgium Squash Fed. [IO], Herentals, Belgium

Belgo-Canadian Assn. [IO], Scarborough, ON, Canada

Believe In Tomorrow Natl. Children's Found. [11449], 6601 Frederick Rd., Baltimore, MD 21228, (410)744-1032

Belize Amateur Athletic Assn. [IO], Belize City, Belize

Belize Audubon Soc. [IO], Belize City, Belize

Belize Cancer Soc. [IO], Belize City, Belize

Belize Catholic Principals Assn. [IO], Orange Walk, Belize

Belize Chamber of Commerce and Indus. [IO], Belize City, Belize

Belize Citrus Growers Assn. [IO], Dangriga, Belize

Belize Emergency Response Team [IO], Belize City, Belize

Belize Family Life Assn. [IO], Belize City, Belize

Belize Fishermen Cooperative Assn. [IO], Belize City, Belize

Belize Hotel Assn. [IO], Belize City, Belize

Belize Natl. Assn. of Realtors [IO], Belize City, Belize

Belize Natl. Teachers' Union [IO], Belize City, Belize

Belize Natl. Tour Operators Assn. [IO], Belize City, Belize

Belize Natl. Tourist Guide Assn. [IO], Belize City, Belize

Belize Offshore Practitioners Assn. [IO], Belize City, Belize

Belize Taekwondo Fed. [IO], Belize City, Belize

Belize Tennis Assn. [IO], Belize City, Belize

Belize Tourism Bd. [IO], Belize City, Belize

Belize Tourism Indus. Assn. [IO], Belize City, Belize

Belizean Poets Soc. [IO], Belize City, Belize

Bell Assn. for the Deaf and Hard of Hearing; Parents' Sect. of the Alexander Graham [14955]

Bell Family Assn. of the U.S. [★20443]

Bellanca-Champion Club [20884], PO Box 100, Coxsackie, NY 12051, (518)731-6800

Bellanet Alliance [IO], Chelsea, QC, Canada

Bellona Europa [★IO]

Bellona Europe [IO], Brussels, Belgium

Bellwoods Centres for Community Living [IO], Toronto, ON, Canada

Belorussian Sci. Soc. of Cardiologists [IO], Minsk, Belarus

Below/Hook Lifters Sect. of the Material Handling Inst. [★1847]

Belt Assn. - Defunct.

Belted Galloway Soc. [3906], Hav-A-Belt Galloways, New Glarus, WI 53574, (608)527-4811

Benchmarking Network [2574], 4606 FM 1960 W, Ste. 250, Houston, TX 77069, (281)440-5044

Benedict Coll. Natl. Alumni Soc. [18854], 1600 Harden St., Columbia, SC 29204, (803)253-5000

Benedictine Liturgical Conf. [★19659]

Benedictine Liturgical Conf. [★19659]

Benedictines for Peace [19392], 465 Keuterville Rd., Cottonwood, ID 83522-5183, (208)962-5032

Benefit4Kids [11196], 21660 23 Mile Rd., Macomb, MI 48044, (877)245-5430

BeNeLux Assn. of Bariatric Surgeons [IO], Gent, Belgium

Benelux Assn. for Energy Economics [IO], Petten, Netherlands

Benelux Economic Union [IO], Brussels, Belgium

Benelux Economische Unie [★IO]

Benevolent Fund of the Coll. of Optometrists and the Assn. of Optometrists [IO], Swanley, United Kingdom

Benevolent Org. for Development, Hea., and Insight [IO], Campbell Town, Australia

Benevolent and Protective Order of Elks [18980], 2750 N Lakeview Ave., Chicago, IL 60614-1889, (773)755-4700

Benevolent and Protective Order of Elks of Canada [IO], Regina, SK, Canada

Benevolent Soc. of California [★19053]

Benevoles Canada [★IO]

Bengal
Cultural Assn. of Bengal [9436]

Benign Essential Blepharospasm Res. Found. [15575], PO Box 12468, Beaumont, TX 77726-2468, (409)832-0788

Benishyaka Assn. [IO], Kigali, Rwanda

Benjamin Franklin Educ. Found. [8003], 6275 Hazeltine Natl. Dr., Orlando, FL 32822, (407)240-8009

Bentley Drivers Club [IO], Wroxton, United Kingdom

Benton Found. [11549], 1250 Connecticut Ave. NW, Ste. 200, Washington, DC 20036, (202)638-5770

Benvenuto Club of Milan [IO], Milan, Italy

Berean Bible Soc. [19342], PO Box 756, Germantown, WI 53022, (262)255-4750

Berean Bible Soc. [19342], PO Box 756, Germantown, WI 53022, (262)255-4750

Berean Mission, Inc. [★20034]

Berean Mission, Inc. [★20034]

Bereaved Parents of the USA [11126], John Goodrich, PO Box 95, Park Forest, IL 60466-0095, (708)748-7866

Bereavement
Alive Alone [11125]
Bereaved Parents of the USA [11126]
Bereavement Services [11127]
Children's Grief Educ. Assn. [11128]
Cruse Bereavement Care Scotland [21776]
Hold the Door for Others [11129]
MISS Found. I Alliance of Grandparents, A Support in Tragedy Intl. [12123]
Violent Death Bereavement Soc. [11130]

Bereavement Services [11127], 1900 South Ave., La Crosse, WI 54601, (608)775-4747

Berger Picard Club of Am. [21523], Patricia Coury, Treas., 219 Meadow Ridge, Boones Mill, VA 24065

Beritashvili Physiological Soc. of Georgia [IO], Tbilisi, Georgia

Berkeley Enthusiasts Club [IO], Oswaldkirk, United Kingdom

Berkeley Macintosh Users Gp. - Defunct.

Berkshire Conservation Volunteers [IO], Reading, United Kingdom

Bermuda
Bermuda Dept. of Tourism [23447]

Bermuda Anglers Club [IO], Hamilton, Bermuda

Bermuda Assn. of Landscape Architects [IO], Hamilton, Bermuda

Bermuda Autism Support and Educ. [IO], Flatts Village, Bermuda

Bermuda Badminton Assn. [IO], Devonshire, Bermuda

Bermuda Bar Assn. [IO], Hamilton, Bermuda

Bermuda Basketball Assn. [IO], Hamilton, Bermuda

Bermuda Chamber of Commerce [IO], Hamilton, Bermuda

Bermuda Coun. on Ageing [IO], Hamilton, Bermuda

Bermuda Counsellors Assn. [IO], Devonshire Parish, Bermuda

Bermuda Dental Assn. [IO], Hamilton, Bermuda

Bermuda Dept. of Tourism [23447], 675 3rd Ave., 20th Fl., New York, NY 10017, (212)818-9800

Bermuda Employers' Coun. [IO], Hamilton, Bermuda

Bermuda Feline Assistance Bur. [IO], Warwick Parish, Bermuda

Bermuda Gymnastics Assn. [IO], Flatts, Bermuda

Bermuda Hea. Alliance [IO], Hamilton, Bermuda

Bermuda Hotel Assn. [IO], Hamilton, Bermuda

Bermuda Intl. Bus. Assn. [IO], Hamilton, Bermuda

Bermuda Lawn Tennis Assn. [IO], Hamilton, Bermuda

Bermuda Masters Swimming Assn. [IO], Devonshire, Bermuda

Bermuda Musical and Dramatic Soc. [IO], Devonshire, Bermuda

Bermuda Occupational Therapy Assn. [IO], Devonshire, Bermuda

Bermuda Olympic Assn. [IO], Hamilton, Bermuda

Bermuda Optimist Dinghy Assn. [IO], Hamilton, Bermuda

Bermuda Physiotherapy Assn. [IO], Southampton, Bermuda

Bermuda Public Services Union [IO], Hamilton, Bermuda

Bermuda Rowing Assn. [IO], Hamilton, Bermuda

Bermuda Sailing Assn. [IO], Hamilton, Bermuda

Bermuda Squash Racquets Assn. [IO], Hamilton, Bermuda

Bermuda Taekwondo Assn. [IO], Hamilton, Bermuda

Bermuda Trade Development Bd. [★23447]

Bermuda Union of Teachers [IO], Hamilton, Bermuda

Bernard van Leer Found. [IO], The Hague, Netherlands

Bernard Shaw Soc. [9351], PO Box 1159, Madison Square Sta., New York, NY 10159-1159, (212)982-9885

Berne Declaration [IO], Zurich, Switzerland

Bernese Mountain Dog Club of Am. [21524], 4263 E Hope St., Mesa, AZ 85205, (480)641-3405

Bernoulli Soc. for Mathematical Statistics and Probability [IO], The Hague, Netherlands

Beroepsorganisatie Nederlandse Ontwerpers [★IO]

Bertrand Russell Soc. [9352], Lehman College-CUNY, Philosophy Dept., 250 Bedford Park Blvd. W, Bronx, NY 10468-1527

Berufsverband der Deutschen Urologen [★IO]

Berufsverband Deutscher Markt- und Sozialforscher [★IO]

Berufsverband Info. Bibliothek [★IO]

Berufsverband der Pharmaberater [IO], Worms, Germany

Berufsverband der Yogalehrenden in Deutschland e.V. [★IO]

BERWA [12315], PO Box 6006, South Bend, IN 46660

BEST - Afghanistan [IO], Kabul, Afghanistan

Best Buddies Intl. [12498], 100 SE 2nd St., Ste. 2200, Miami, FL 33131, (305)374-2233

Best Buddies Intl. [12498], 100 SE 2nd St., Ste. 2200, Miami, FL 33131, (305)374-2233

BEST Employers Assn. [3286], 2505 McCabe Way, Irvine, CA 92614, (866)706-2225

Best Friends Animal Sanctuary [★10932]

Best Friends Animal Soc. [10932], 5001 Angel Canyon Rd., Kanab, UT 84741-5000, (435)644-2001

Best Holiday Trav-L-Park Assn. [3055], 4809 E Marshall Dr., Vestal, NY 13850, (607)241-7531

Bet-Nahrain [9342], PO Box 4116, Modesto, CA 95352, (209)538-4130

Beta Alpha Psi [23459], Palladian I, 220 Leigh Farm Rd., Durham, NC 27707, (919)402-4044

Beta Beta Beta [23470], Univ. of North Alabama, PO Box 5079, Florence, AL 35632, (256)765-6220

Beta Chi Theta Natl. Fraternity [23659], 9663 Santa Monica Blvd., Ste. 498, Beverly Hills, CA 90210

Beta Gamma Sigma [23476], 125 Weldon Pkwy., Maryland Heights, MO 63043, (314)432-5650

Reference to "IO" in place of a book number signifies that the association may be found in the 50th edition of International Organizations.

Beta Gamma Sigma [23476], 125 Weldon Pkwy., Maryland Heights, MO 63043, (314)432-5650

Beta Gamma Sigma Alumni [23477], PO Box 297-006, Brooklyn, NY 11229

Beta Gamma Sigma Alumni in New York City [★23477]

Beta Kappa Chi [23630], PO Box 10046, Baton Rouge, LA 70813, (225)771-4845

Beta Phi Alpha [★23723]

Beta Phi Mu [23583], Univ. of Missouri, 303 Townsend Hall, Columbia, MO 65211, (573)882-3258

Beta Phi Mu [23583], Univ. of Missouri, 303 Townsend Hall, Columbia, MO 65211, (573)882-3258

Beta Pi Sigma Sorority [23478], 256 Waterville St., San Francisco, CA 94124

Beta Sigma Kappa [23611], PO Box 5886, Topeka, KS 66605

Beta Sigma Phi [23640], 1800 W 91st Pl., Kansas City, MO 64114, (816)444-6800

Beta Sigma Psi [★23660]

Beta Sigma Psi Natl. Lutheran Fraternity [23660], 2408 Lebanon Ave., Belleville, IL 62221, (618)235-0014

Beta Sigma Rho [★23690]

Beta Theta Pi [23661], 5134 Bonham Rd., PO Box 6277, Oxford, OH 45056, (513)523-7591

Beth Din of Am. [19848], 305 7th Ave., 12th Fl., New York, NY 10001-6008, (212)807-9042

Bethany Care Soc. [IO], Calgary, AB, Canada

Bethany Christian Services Intl. [11197], PO Box 294, Grand Rapids, MI 49501-0294, (616)224-7610

Bethany Christian Services Intl. [11197], PO Box 294, Grand Rapids, MI 49501-0294, (616)224-7610

Bethany Fellowship Missions [★20014]

Bethany Fellowship Missions [★20014]

Bethany International [★20014]

Bethany International [★20014]

Bethany Intl. Missions [20014], 6820 Auto Club Rd., Ste. M, Bloomington, MN 55438-2849, (952)944-2121

Bethany Intl. Missions [20014], 6820 Auto Club Rd., Ste. M, Bloomington, MN 55438-2849, (952)944-2121

Bethel Ministries [★19639]

Bethesda Lutheran Home and Services [★12499]

Bethesda Lutheran Homes and Services [12499], 600 Hoffman Dr., Watertown, WI 53094, (920)261-3050

Bethesda Natl. Found. of Massachusetts [★15930]

Bethesda Natl. Found. of Massachusetts [★15930]

Bethlehem Assn. [18118], PO Box 1111, Media, PA 19063, (610)353-2010

Bethlehem Mission Immensee [IO], Immensee, Switzerland

Bethune-Cookman Coll. Natl. Alumni Assn. [18855], 640 Dr. Mary McLeod Bethune Blvd., Daytona Beach, FL 32114-3099, (386)481-2985

Betonelement-Foreningen [★IO]

Betsy-Tacy Soc. [9353], PO Box 94, Mankato, MN 56002-0094, (507)345-9777

Better BedRest [15873], PO Box 212, Savage, MD 20763, (410)740-7662

Better Boys Found. [11450], 1512 S Pulaski Rd., Chicago, IL 60623, (773)542-7300

A Better Chance [8077], 240 W 35th St., 9th Fl., New York, NY 10001-2506, (646)346-1310

Better Govt. Assn. [18322], 223 W Jackson Blvd., Ste. 620, Chicago, IL 60606, (312)427-8330

Better Hearing Australia [IO], Prahran, Australia

Better Hearing Inst. [14922], 1444 I St. NW, Ste. 700, Washington, DC 20005, (202)449-1100

Better Highway Info. Found. [★6028]

Better Lawn and Turf Institute/American Sod Producers Assn. [★4510]

Better Lawn and Turf Institute/American Sod Producers Assn. [★4510]

Better School Food [8824], 487 E Main St., Mount Kisco, NY 10549, (914)864-1293

Better Sleep Coun. [16665], 501 Wythe St., Alexandria, VA 22314-1917, (703)683-8371

Better Vision Inst. [15954], Vision Coun. of Am., 225 Reinekers Ln., Ste. 700, Alexandria, VA 22314, (703)548-4560

Better World Chorus [12552], PO Box 20934, Park W Finance Sta., New York, NY 10025

Better World Chorus [12552], PO Box 20934, Park W Finance Sta., New York, NY 10025

Better World Soc. - Defunct.

Betty White Fan Club - Address unknown since 2011.

Beverage Network [444], 44 Pleasant St., Ste. 110, Watertown, MA 02472, (617)715-9670

Beverage Ser. Assn. [IO], Northwood, United Kingdom

Beverages
　Amer. Assn. of Wine Economists [3670]
　Amer. Beverage Assn. [442]
　Amer. Beverage Inst. [443]
　Beverage Network [444]
　Caffeine Awareness Assn. [13828]
　Chamber of Soft Drink and Related Mfrs. [3819]
　Chinese-American Tea Assn. [445]
　Intl. Beverage Dispensing Equip. Assn. [446]
　Intl. Beverage Dispensing Equip. Assn. [446]
　Intl. Bottled Water Assn. [447]
　Intl. Bottled Water Assn. [447]
　Intl. Brotherhood of Teamsers I Brewery and Soft Drink Workers Conf. [23158]
　Intl. Soc. of Beverage Technologists [448]
　Intl. Soc. of Beverage Technologists [448]
　Juice Products Assn. [449]
　Master Brewers Assn. of the Americas [450]
　Master Brewers Assn. of the Americas [450]
　Natl. Coffee Assn. of U.S.A. [451]
　Natl. Pop Can Collectors [21381]
　Responsible Hospitality Inst. [11827]
　Royal Fed. of Water and Soft Drinks Indus. [23760]
　Specialty Coffee Assn. of Am. [452]
　Tea Assn. of Canada [7062]
　Tea Assn. of the U.S.A. [453]
　Tea Coun. of the U.S.A. [454]
　Tea Coun. of the U.S.A. [454]

Beverly Found. [10835], 1120 Pennsylvania St. NE, Albuquerque, NM 87110, (505)222-0620

Beyaz Esya Yan Sanayicileri Dernegi [★IO]

Beyond Baroque Found. [★9284]

Beyond Baroque Literary/Arts Center [9284], 681 Venice Blvd., Venice, CA 90291, (310)822-3006

Beyond Borders [12316], PO Box 2132, Norristown, PA 19404, (610)277-5045

Beyond Hunger [14431], PO Box 151148, San Rafael, CA 94915, (415)459-2270

Beyond Nuclear [18192], 6930 Carroll Ave., Ste. 400, Takoma Park, MD 20912, (301)270-2209

Beyond Pesticides [13321], 701 E St. SE, Ste. 200, Washington, DC 20003, (202)543-5450

Beyond the Pond.International Frog Collectors Club [21309], 120 W Front St., Washington, MO 63090

Beyond the Rainbow [23761], PO Box 31672, St. Louis, MO 63131-0672, (314)799-1724

Beyond Tears Worldwide - Address unknown since 2011.

Beyond War Found. [★18244]

Beyondblue [IO], Hawthorn, Australia

Beyondmedia Educ. [8572], 4001 N Ravenswood Ave., No. 204 B, Chicago, IL 60613, (773)857-7300

Beyster Inst. [647], 1241 Cave St., La Jolla, CA 92037, (858)822-6000

BGSA Chap. [★23477]

Bharatiya Janata Party [IO], New Delhi, India

Bhojpuri Assn. of North Am. [9937], 801 Hebron Pkwy., No. 6308, Lewisville, TX 75057, (972)948-0996

Bhojpuri Assn. of North Am. [9937], 801 Hebron Pkwy., No. 6308, Lewisville, TX 75057, (972)948-0996

BHR Gp. [IO], Bedford, United Kingdom

Bhutan Amateur Athletic Assn. [IO], Thimphu, Bhutan

Bhutan Assn. of Women Entrepreneurs [IO], Thimphu, Bhutan

Bhutan Badminton Fed. [IO], Thimphu, Bhutan

Bhutan Chamber of Commerce and Indus. [IO], Thimphu, Bhutan

Bhutan Soc. of the United Kingdom [IO], Guilford, United Kingdom

Bhutan Taekwondo Fed. [IO], Thimphu, Bhutan

Bhutan Tennis Fed. [IO], Thimphu, Bhutan

Biathlon Assn; U.S. [22915]

Bible
　Amer. Bible Soc. [19338]
　Amer. Bible Soc. [19338]
　Amer. Family Assn. [17334]
　ASGM [19339]
　Associates for Biblical Res. [19340]
　Associates for Biblical Res. [19340]
　Assn. of Biblical Counselors [19631]
　BCM Intl. [19341]
　BCM Intl. [19341]
　Berean Bible Soc. [19342]
　Berean Bible Soc. [19342]
　Bethany Intl. Missions [20014]
　Bible League [19343]
　Bible League Intl. [19343]
　Bibles for the Blind and Visually Handicapped Intl. [19344]
　Biblica [19345]
　Catholic Radio Assn. [19406]
　Chalcedon Found. [20219]
　Christ Truth Ministries [19346]
　Christian Media Assn. [19947]
　Dawn Bible Students Assn. [19347]
　Fellowship Intl. Mission [20044]
　Full Gospel Bus. Men's Fellowship Intl. [19574]
　The Gospel Coalition [19576]
　High School Evangelism Fellowship [19751]
　Inst. for Biblical Res. [19348]
　Interdisciplinary Biblical Res. Inst. [19677]
　Intl. Bible Soc. [19345]
　Intl. Org. for Septuagint and Cognate Stud. [19349]
　Intl. Org. for Septuagint and Cognate Stud. [19349]
　Intl. Soc. of Bible Collectors [19350]
　Intl. Soc. of Bible Collectors [19350]
　Life Action Revival Ministries [19757]
　Lutheran Bible Translators [19351]
　New Hope Intl. [20073]
　Pocket Testament League [19352]
　Pocket Testament League [19352]
　Seventh Day Baptist Missionary Soc. [19330]
　Seventh Day Baptist World Fed. [19331]
　Soc. of Biblical Literature [19353]
　Westar Inst. [20198]
　WordAlone Ministries [19943]
　Wycliffe Bible Translators [19354]

Bible Believers [IO], Currabubula, Australia

Bible Believers Fellowship [20166], PO Box 0065, Baldwin, NY 11510-0065, (516)739-7746

Bible Centered Ministries [★19341]

Bible Centered Ministries [★19341]

Bible Christian Union [★20039]

Bible Club Movement [★19341]

Bible Club Movement [★19341]

Bible Holiness Movement [IO], Vancouver, BC, Canada

Bible Inst; Moody [20070]

Bible League [19343], PO Box 28000, Chicago, IL 60628, (866)825-4636

Bible League of Canada [IO], Burlington, ON, Canada

Bible League Intl. [19343], PO Box 28000, Chicago, IL 60628, (866)825-4636

Bible Memory Assn., Intl. - Defunct.

Bible Sabbath Assn. [20229], 802 NW 21st Ave., Battle Ground, WA 98604, (360)687-1541

Bible-Science Assn. - Defunct.

Bible Soc. in Angola [IO], Luanda, Angola

Bible Soc. of Armenia [IO], Yerevan, Armenia

Bible Soc. in Australia [IO], Canberra, Australia

Bible Soc. of Benin [IO], Cotonou, Benin

Bible Soc. in Botswana [IO], Gaborone, Botswana

Bible Soc. of Brazil [IO], Barueri, Brazil

Bible Soc. of Burkina Faso [IO], Ouagadougou, Burkina Faso

Bible Soc. in Burundi [IO], Bujumbura, Burundi

Bible Soc. in Cambodia [IO], Phnom Penh, Cambodia

Bible Soc. of Cameroon [IO], Yaounde, Cameroon

Bible Soc. in Central African Republic [IO], Bangui, Central African Republic

---

A star before a book entry number signifies that the name is not listed separately, but is mentioned within the entry.

Bible Soc. of Chad [IO], N'Djamena, Chad

Bible Soc. in Congo [IO], Brazzaville, Republic of the Congo

Bible Soc. of Costa Rica [IO], San Jose, Costa Rica

Bible Soc. of Cote d'Ivoire [IO], Abidjan, Cote d'Ivoire

Bible Soc. of Cyprus [IO], Nicosia, Cyprus

Bible Soc. of Democratic Republic of Congo [IO], Brazzaville, Republic of the Congo

Bible Soc. of Egypt [IO], Cairo, Egypt

Bible Soc. of El Salvador [IO], San Salvador, El Salvador

Bible Soc. of Eritrea [IO], Asmara, Eritrea

Bible Soc. of Ethiopia [IO], Addis Ababa, Ethiopia

Bible Soc. in Gabon [IO], Libreville, Gabon

Bible Soc. of Ghana [IO], Kumasi, Ghana

Bible Soc. of Guinea [IO], Conakry, Guinea

Bible Soc. of Honduras [IO], Tegucigalpa, Honduras

Bible Soc. of India [IO], Bangalore, India

Bible Soc. in Jordan [IO], Amman, Jordan

Bible Soc. work in Kazakhstan [IO], Almaty, Kazakhstan

Bible Soc. in Kenya [IO], Nairobi, Kenya

Bible Soc. in Lebanon [IO], Beirut, Lebanon

Bible Soc. in Lesotho [IO], Maseru, Lesotho

Bible Soc. in Liberia [IO], Monrovia, Liberia

Bible Soc. of Lithuania [IO], Vilnius, Lithuania

Bible Soc. of Mali [IO], Bamako, Mali

Bible Soc. of Mexico [IO], Mexico City, Mexico

Bible Soc. in Mozambique [IO], Maputo, Mozambique

Bible Soc. of Myanmar [IO], Yangon, Myanmar

Bible Soc. in Namibia [IO], Windhoek, Namibia

Bible Soc. in Netherlands Antilles [IO], Curacao, Netherlands Antilles

Bible Soc. in New Zealand [IO], Wellington, New Zealand

Bible Soc. in Nicaragua [IO], Managua, Nicaragua

Bible Soc. in Nigeria [IO], Lagos, Nigeria

Bible Soc. of Panama [IO], Panama City, Panama

Bible Soc. of Papua New Guinea [IO], Port Moresby, Papua New Guinea

Bible Soc. in Poland [IO], Warsaw, Poland

Bible Soc. of Portugal [IO], Lisbon, Portugal

Bible Soc. of Republic of Belarus [IO], Minsk, Belarus

Bible Soc. in Rwanda [IO], Kigali, Rwanda

Bible Soc. of Senegal [IO], Dakar, Senegal

Bible Soc. in Sierra Leone [IO], Freetown, Sierra Leone

Bible Soc. in Singapore [IO], Singapore, Singapore

Bible Soc. of Spain [IO], Madrid, Spain

Bible Soc. in Sudan [IO], Khartoum, Sudan

Bible Soc. in Swaziland [IO], Manzini, Swaziland

Bible Soc. in Taiwan [IO], Taipei, Taiwan

Bible Soc. of Tanzania [IO], Dodoma, United Republic of Tanzania

Bible Soc. of Togo [IO], Lome, Togo

Bible Soc. of Uzbekistan [IO], Tashkent, Uzbekistan

Bible Soc. of Zimbabwe [IO], Harare, Zimbabwe

The Bible Standard [★19755]

The Bible Standard [★19755]

Bibles for the Blind and Visually Handicapped Intl. [19344], 3228 E Rosehill Ave., Terre Haute, IN 47805-1297, (812)466-4899

Bibles For The World [20015], PO Box 49759, Colorado Springs, CO 80949-9759, (719)630-7733

Bibles For The World [20015], PO Box 49759, Colorado Springs, CO 80949-9759, (719)630-7733

Biblica [19345], 1820 Jet Stream Dr., Colorado Springs, CO 80921, (719)488-9200

Biblical Am. Resistance Front - Defunct.

Biblical Inst. for Social Change [20174], Howard Univ. School of Divinity, 1400 Shepherd St. NE, Suites 264 and 266, Washington, DC 20017, (202)269-4311

Biblical Ministries Worldwide [19732], 1595 Herrington Rd., Lawrenceville, GA 30043, (770)339-3500

Biblical Ministries Worldwide [19732], 1595 Herrington Rd., Lawrenceville, GA 30043, (770)339-3500

Biblical Witness Fellowship [20274], 4150 Belden Village St. NW, Ste. 601, Canton, OH 44718, (800)494-9172

Bibliographical Soc. of Am. [9438], PO Box 1537, Lenox Hill Sta., New York, NY 10121, (212)452-2710

Bibliographical Soc. of Australia and New Zealand [IO], Wagga Wagga, Australia

Bibliographical Soc. of Canada [IO], Toronto, ON, Canada

Bibliographical Soc. - United Kingdom [IO], London, United Kingdom

Bibliotheques Europeennes de Theologie [★IO]

Bichon Frise Club of Am. [21525], 140 Pine Ave., Clarksburg, MA 01247-4602, (413)663-7109

BICSI [3402], 8610 Hidden River Pkwy., Tampa, FL 33637-1000, (813)979-1991

BICSI [3402], 8610 Hidden River Pkwy., Tampa, FL 33637-1000, (813)979-1991

Bicycle
    Am. Bikes [11131]
    Bike and Build [11132]
    Bikes Belong Coalition [21206]
    Bikes to Rwanda [11133]
    Light Elec. Vehicle Assn. [3518]
    World Bicycle Relief [12898]

Bicycle Assn. of Great Britain [IO], Coventry, United Kingdom

Bicycle Fed. of Am. [★22484]

Bicycle Forum [★22474]

Bicycle Helmet Safety Inst. [12979], 4611 7th St. S, Arlington, VA 22204-1419, (703)486-0100

Bicycle New South Wales [IO], Sydney Olympic Park, Australia

Bicycle Nova Scotia [IO], Halifax, NS, Canada

Bicycle Polo Assn; U.S. [22813]

Bicycle Prdt. Suppliers Assn. [3307], PO Box 187, Montgomeryville, PA 18936, (215)393-3144

Bicycle Queensland [IO], West End, Australia

Bicycle Ride Directors' Assn. of Am. [22477], 755 N Leafwood Ct., Brea, CA 92821, (562)690-9693

Bicycle Stamps Club [22021], 21304 2nd Ave. SE, Bothell, WA 98021-7550

Bicycle Tasmania [IO], Hobart, Australia

Bicycle Transportation Action - Defunct.

Bicycle Trans. Alliance [IO], West Perth, Australia

Bicycle Wholesale Distributors Assn. [★3307]

Bide-A-Wee Home Assn. [★10933]

Bide Awhile Animal Shelter Soc. [IO], Dartmouth, NS, Canada

Bideawee [10933], 410 E 38th St., New York, NY 10016, (212)532-6395

Biennial Coun. of Community Churches [★19621]

Biennial Coun. of Community Churches [★19621]

Big Apple Triathlon Club [★23099]

Big Bend Natural History Assn. [7139], PO Box 196, Big Bend National Park, TX 79834-0196, (432)477-2236

Big Bros. of Am. [★11451]

Big Bros. Big Sisters of Am. [11451], 230 N 13th St., Philadelphia, PA 19107, (215)567-7000

Big Bros. Big Sisters of Canada [IO], Burlington, ON, Canada

Big East Conf. [22968], 222 Richmond St., Ste. 110, Providence, RI 02903, (401)453-0660

Big Eight Conf. - Defunct.

Big Little Book Collector's Club [21310], PO Box 1242, Danville, CA 94526, (925)837-2086

Big Little Book Collector's Club of Am. [★21310]

Big Picture Alliance [16717], 4732 Stenton Ave., Philadelphia, PA 19144, (215)381-2588

Big Picture Learning [8105], 325 Public St., Providence, RI 02905, (401)752-3442

Big Sisters, Intl. [★11451]

Big Ten Communications Department [★22969]

Big Ten Conf. [22969], 1500 W Higgins Rd., Park Ridge, IL 60068-6300, (847)696-1010

Big Thicket Assn. [4011], PO Box 198, Saratoga, TX 77585, (936)274-1181

Big Thicket Natural Heritage Trust [4012], Box 1049, Kountze, TX 77625, (936)274-1181

Big West Conf. [22970], 2 Corporate Park, Irvine, CA 92606, (949)261-2525

Big Wild Advocates [5033], 222 Tom Miner Creek Rd., Emigrant, MT 59027, (406)848-7000

Big Wildlife [5034], PO Box 344, Williams, OR 97544, (541)846-1352

Bigelow Soc. [20430], Dee Bigelow, Treas., 1360 E Bigelow Creek Rd., Newaygo, MI 49337

Bigelow Soc. [20430], Dee Bigelow, Treas., 1360 E Bigelow Creek Rd., Newaygo, MI 49337

Bigfoot Owners Clubs Intl. [21008], PO Box 550, Carson City, NV 89702-0550

Bighelp for Educ. [IO], Hyderabad, India

Bihar Assn. of North Am. [9856], 9511 Lily Glen Ln., Katy, TX 77494, (713)504-2228

Bihar Assn. of North Am. [9856], 9511 Lily Glen Ln., Katy, TX 77494, (713)504-2228

Bike and Build [11132], 6109 Ridge Ave., Bldg. 2, Philadelphia, PA 19128, (267)331-8488

Bikecentennial [★22474]

Bikecentennial: The Bicycle Travel Assn. [★22474]

Bikes for Australia [IO], Canberra, Australia

Bikes Belong Coalition [21206], PO Box 2359, Boulder, CO 80306, (303)449-4893

Bikes Not Bombs [18158], 284 Amory St., Jamaica Plain, MA 02130, (617)522-0222

Bikes Not Bombs [18158], 284 Amory St., Jamaica Plain, MA 02130, (617)522-0222

Bikes to Rwanda [11133], 4110 SE Hawthorne Blvd., No. 406, Portland, OR 97214

Bilateral Safety Corridor Coalition [12230], 2050 Wilson Ave., Ste. C, National City, CA 91950, (619)336-0770

Bilateral US-Arab Chamber of Commerce [23325], PO Box 571870, Houston, TX 77257-1870, (713)880-8168

Bilateral US-Arab Chamber of Commerce [23325], PO Box 571870, Houston, TX 77257-1870, (713)880-8168

Bildkonst Upphovsratt i Sverige [IO], Stockholm, Sweden

Bilingual Found. of the Arts [10570], 421 North Ave. 19, Los Angeles, CA 90031, (323)225-4044

Bilingualism
    Intercultural Development Res. Assn. [7769]
    Intercultural Development Res. Assn. [7769]
    Natl. Assn. for Bilingual Educ. [7770]

Bilkent Turkey ACM SIGART [IO], Ankara, Turkey

Bill Glass Evangelistic Assn. [★19735]

Bill Glass Evangelistic Assn. [★19735]

Bill Glass Ministries [★19735]

Bill Glass Ministries [★19735]

Bill and Melinda Gates Found. [12134], PO Box 23350, Seattle, WA 98102, (206)709-3140

Bill Raskob Found. [17597], PO Box 507, Crownsville, MD 21032-0507, (410)923-9123

The Billfish Found. [5035], 5100 N Fed. Hwy., Ste. 200, Fort Lauderdale, FL 33308, (954)938-0150

Billiard and Bowling Inst. of Am. [3308], PO Box 6573, Arlington, TX 76005, (817)385-8120

Billiard Cong. of Am. [22308], 12303 Airport Way, Ste. 140, Broomfield, CO 80021, (303)243-5070

Billiards
    Amer. Cuemakers Assn. [455]
    Amer. CueSports Alliance [22307]
    Billiard Cong. of Am. [22308]
    Canadian Poolplayers Assn. [21004]
    Intl. Cuemakers Assn. [456]
    Intl. Cuemakers Assn. [456]
    U.S. Billiard Assn. [22309]
    U.S. Professional Poolplayers Assn. [22310]
    U.S. Snooker Assn. [22311]
    Women's Professional Billiard Assn. [22312]
    World Confed. of Billiard Sports [22313]

Billing Assn; Amer. Medical [15286]

Billings Ovulation Method Assn. - USA [12028], PO Box 2135, St. Cloud, MN 56302, (651)699-8139

Billy Barty Found. [13115], 929 W Olive Ave., Ste. C, Burbank, CA 91506, (818)953-5410

Billy Barty Found. for Little People [★13115]

Billy Crash Craddock Fan Club [23818], 4101 Pickfair Rd., Springfield, IL 62703, (336)339-9928

Billy Graham Evangelistic Assn. [19733], 1 Billy Graham Pkwy., Charlotte, NC 28201, (704)401-2432

Billy Ray Cyrus Spirit - Address unknown since 2010.

Bimetallic Question [IO], Montreal, QC, Canada

Binational Tourism Alliance [3473], 275 Oak St., Ste. 150, Buffalo, NY 14203, (716)856-6525

Binders' Guild [9439], 2925 Powell St., Eugene, OR 97405, (541)485-6527

Binding Indus. of Am. [★1602]

Reference to "IO" in place of a book number signifies that the association may be found in the 50th edition of International Organizations.

Binding Indus. of Am. [★1602]
Binding Indus. Assn. Intl. [1602], 200 Deer Run Rd., Sewickley, PA 15143, (412)259-1802
Binding Indus. Assn. Intl. [1602], 200 Deer Run Rd., Sewickley, PA 15143, (412)259-1802
BiNet U.S.A. [12071], 4201 Wilson Blvd., No. 110-311, Arlington, VA 22203-1859, (800)585-9368
Binge Eating Disorder Assn. [14432], 637 Emerson Pl., Severna Park, MD 21146, (855)855-2332
Bing's Friends and Collectors Soc. - Address unknown since 2011.
Bio-Electro-Magnetics Inst. - Defunct.
Bio-Gro New Zealand [IO], Wellington, New Zealand
Bio-Integral Rsrc. Center [4773], PO Box 7414, Berkeley, CA 94707, (510)524-2567
BIO IT Coalition [6333], 2918 24th Rd. N, Arlington, VA 22207, (703)927-8757
BIO Ventures for Global Hea. [15148], 1605 Connecticut Ave. NW, 2nd Fl., Washington, DC 20009, (415)446-9440
BIO Ventures for Global Hea. [15148], 1605 Connecticut Ave. NW, 2nd Fl., Washington, DC 20009, (415)446-9440
Bioanalysis; Amer. Bd. of [7018]
Bioanalysts; Amer. Assn. of [15229]
Biochemical, Biophysical and Microbiological Soc. of Finland [IO], Helsinki, Finland
Biochemical Soc. - England [IO], London, United Kingdom

Biochemistry
Amer. Soc. for Biochemistry and Molecular Biology [6268]
Amer. Soc. for Virology [6269]
Analytical and Life Sci. Systems Assn. [7358]
Intl. Assn. for Protein Structure Anal. and Proteomics [6270]
Intl. Isotope Soc. [6271]
Intl. Isotope Soc. [6271]
Intl. Proteolysis Soc. [6272]
Intl. Proteolysis Soc. [6272]
Intl. Soc. of Chem. Ecology [6273]
Intl. Soc. of Chem. Ecology [6273]
Intl. Soc. for Hyaluronan Sciences [6274]
Intl. Soc. for IGF Res. [6851]
Natl. Acad. of Clinical Biochemistry [13829]
Natl. Lipid Assn. [13830]
Oligonucleotide Therapeutics Soc. [16866]
Protein Soc. [6275]
Protein Soc. [6275]
RNA Soc. [6276]
Soc. for Physical Regulation in Biology and Medicine [6277]
Soc. for Physical Regulation in Biology and Medicine [6277]
BioCommunications Assn. [14162], 220 Southwind Ln., Hillsborough, NC 27278, (919)245-0906
BioCommunications Assn. [14162], 220 Southwind Ln., Hillsborough, NC 27278, (919)245-0906
Biodynamic Agricultural Assn. [IO], Stroud, United Kingdom
Biodynamic Agriculture Australia [IO], Bellingen, Australia
Biodynamic Craniosacral Therapy Assn. of North Am. [14206], 150 Cross Creek Ct., Chapel Hill, NC 27517, (734)904-0546
Biodynamic Craniosacral Therapy Assn. of North Am. [14206], 150 Cross Creek Ct., Chapel Hill, NC 27517, (734)904-0546
Biodynamic Farming and Gardening Assn. [4348], 25844 Butler Rd., Junction City, OR 97448, (541)998-0105
Bioelectrical Repair and Growth Soc. [★6277]
Bioelectrical Repair and Growth Soc. [★6277]
Bioelectrochemical Soc. [IO], Toulouse, France

Bioelectromagnetics
Bioelectromagnetics Soc. [6278]
Bioelectromagnetics Soc. [6278], 2412 Cobblestone Way, Frederick, MD 21702-2626, (301)663-4252
Bioenergy Assn. of New Zealand [IO], Wellington, New Zealand
BioEnvironmental Polymer Soc. [6401], Linda Hurtley, Admin., 6751 229th Ave. NE, Stacy, MN 55079, (256)824-6188

Bioethics
Bioethics-In-Action [6279]

Bioethics Intl. [13831]
Center for Bioethics [6281]
Center for Bioethics [6280]
Citizens for Responsible Care and Res. [17210]
Bioethics and Humanities; Amer. Soc. for [8589]
Bioethics-In-Action [6279], Karl Haigler, Exec. Dir., 168 Bermuda Run Dr., Advance, NC 27006, (336)940-2600
Bioethics Intl. [13831], The Graybar Bldg., Ste. 300, 420 Lexington Ave., New York, NY 10170, (212)297-6109

Biofeedback
Assn. for Applied Psychophysiology and Biofeedback [13832]
Biofeedback Certification Intl. Alliance ★[13833]
Biofeedback Certification Inst. of IT. [★13833]
Biofeedback Certification Intl. Alliance [13833], 10200 W 44th Ave., Ste. 310, Wheat Ridge, CO 80033-2840, (303)420-2902
Biofeedback Found. of Europe [IO], Amersfoort, Netherlands
Biofeedback Res. Soc. [★13832]
Biofeedback Soc. of Am. [★13832]
Biofuel Recycling [4867], 5758 Geary Blvd., No. 421, San Francisco, CA 94121, (415)747-2771
BioIndustry Assn. [IO], London, United Kingdom
Bioinformatics Italian Soc. [IO], Bari, Italy
Biokemisk Forening [★IO]
Biological Anthropology Sect. [6138], Univ. of Delaware, Dept. of Anthropology, John Munroe Hall, Newark, DE 19716, (302)831-1855
Biological Farmers of Australia [IO], Chermside, Australia
Biological Info. Processing Org. [★6504]
Biological Photographic Assn. [★14162]
Biological Photographic Assn. [★14162]
Biological Safety Assn. of Pakistan [IO], Karachi, Pakistan
Biological Stain Commn. [6294], Univ. of Rochester, Medical Center, Pathology Dept., 575 Elmwood Ave., Rochester, NY 14620-2945, (585)275-2751

Biology
AASP - The Palynological Soc. [7216]
Addgene [7110]
Amer. Acad. of Microbiology [6282]
Amer. Acad. of Microbiology [6282]
Amer. Assn. of Anthropological Genetics [6895]
Amer. Assn. for Medical Chronobiology and Chronotherapeutics [13834]
Amer. Fern Soc. [6343]
Amer. Inst. of Biological Sciences [6283]
Amer. Inst. of Chem. Engineers I Soc. for Biological Engg. [6284]
Amer. Soc. of Biomechanics [6285]
Amer. Soc. for Cell Biology [6286]
Amer. Soc. for Matrix Biology [6287]
Amer. Soc. for Microbiology [6288]
Amer. Soc. for Photobiology [6289]
Amer. Soc. for Photobiology [6289]
Amer. Type Culture Coll. [6290]
Anaerobe Soc. of the Americas [6291]
Anaerobe Soc. of the Americas [6291]
Analytical and Life Sci. Systems Assn. [7358]
Assn. of Applied Biologists [15908]
Assn. of Genetic Technologists [6292]
Assn. for Tropical Biology and Conservation [6293]
Beta Beta Beta [23470]
Biological Stain Commn. [6294]
Biometric Application Programming Interface Consortium [6295]
Bionomics Intl. [7363]
Chinese Biological Investigators Soc. [6296]
Classification Soc. [7231]
Comm. on the Status of Women in Microbiology [6297]
Environmental Mutagen Soc. [6298]
European Life Scientist Org. [2423]
Fed. of Amer. Societies for Experimental Biology [6299]
Human Biology Assn. [6300]
Intl. Assn. of Environmental Mutagen Societies [6301]
Intl. Assn. of Environmental Mutagen Societies [6301]

Intl. Assn. of Human Biologists [8957]
Intl. Biogeography Soc. [6904]
Intl. Canopy Network [6302]
Intl. Canopy Network [6302]
Intl. Fed. of Cell Biology [6303]
Intl. Fed. of Cell Biology [6303]
Intl. Mammalian Genome Soc. [6900]
Intl. Org. for Mycoplasmology [6304]
Intl. Org. for Mycoplasmology [6304]
Intl. Org. of Plant Biosystematists [6358]
Intl. Soc. for Advancement of Cytometry [6305]
Intl. Soc. for Analytical Cytology [6305]
Intl. Soc. of Artificial Life [6306]
Intl. Soc. of Artificial Life [6306]
Intl. Soc. for Biological and Environmental Repositories [6307]
Intl. Soc. for Biological and Environmental Repositories [6307]
Intl. Soc. for Biosafety Res. [6308]
Intl. Soc. for Biosafety Res. [6308]
Intl. Soc. for Chronobiology [6309]
Intl. Soc. for Chronobiology [6309]
Intl. Soc. of Developmental Biologists [9341]
Intl. Soc. of Differentiation [6310]
Intl. Soc. of Differentiation [6310]
Intl. Soc. for Hyaluronan Sciences [6274]
Intl. Soc. for IGF Res. [6851]BiologyIntl. Soc. for Plant Molecular Biology
Intl. Soc. for Plasmid Biology and other Mobile Genetic Elements [7111]
Japanese Soc. of Developmental Biologists [12259]
Moroccan-American Soc. for Life Sciences [7141]
Natl. Assn. of Biology Teachers [7771]
Natl. Assn. of Bionutritionists [15839]
Natural Sci. Collections Alliance [6311]Biology-Netherlands Biotechnological Soc.
Org. of Biological Field Stations [6312]
Pan-American Aerobiology Assn. [6313]
Pan-American Aerobiology Assn. [6313]
Phi Sigma [23471]
Soc. for Developmental Biology [6314]
Soc. for Developmental Biology [6314]
Soc. of Ethnobiology [6315]
Soc. of Ethnobiology [6315]
Soc. for Experimental Biology and Medicine [6316]
Soc. for In Vitro Biology [6317]
Soc. for Indus. Microbiology [6318]
Soc. for Mathematical Biology [6319]
Soc. for Molecular Biology and Evolution [6320]
Soc. of Systematic Biologists [7639]
Teratology Soc. [6321]
Tropical Biology Assn. [1912]
U.S. Fed. for Culture Collections [6322]
U.S. Human Proteome Org. [6323]
U.S. Human Proteome Org. [6323]
Waksman Found. for Microbiology [6324]
Biomagnetic Therapy Assn. [16844], PO Box 394, Lyons, CO 80540, (303)823-0307
Biomass Energy Res. Assn. [6696], 901 D St. SW, Ste. 100, Washington, DC 20024, (410)953-6202
Biomass Power Assn. [7292], PO Box 9729, Portland, ME 04104-5029, (202)429-4929
Biomass Thermal Energy Coun. [6697], 1211 Connecticut Ave. NW, Ste. 600, Washington, DC 20036-2701, (202)596-3974
Biomechanics; Amer. Soc. of [6285]
Biomedical Computing Soc. [★6504]

Biomedical Engineering
Ad Hoc Gp. for Medical Res. [17761]
Amer. Soc. for Nanomedicine [15398]
Assn. for the Advancement of Medical Instrumentation [6325]
Assn. for the Advancement of Medical Instrumentation [6325]
Biomedical Engg. Assn. of Ireland [23536]
Biomedical Engg. Career Alliance [6326]
Biomedical Engg. Soc. [6327]
Biomedical Engg. Soc. [6327]
Engg. World Hea. [15158]
IEEE Engg. in Medicine and Biology Soc. [6328]
IEEE I Engg. in Medicine and Biology Soc. [6328]
Intl. Fed. for Medical and Biological Engg. [16118]
Intl. Mammalian Genome Soc. [6900]

A star before a book entry number signifies that the name is not listed separately, but is mentioned within the entry.

Soc. For Biomaterials [6329]
Tissue Engg. Intl. and Regenerative Medicine Soc. [13835]
World Assn. for Chinese Biomedical Engineers [6330]
World Assn. for Chinese Biomedical Engineers [6330]
Biomedical Engg. Assn. of Ireland [IO], Wilton, Ireland
Biomedical Engg. Career Alliance [6326], 4809 E Thistle Landing Dr., Ste. 100, Phoenix, AZ 85044, (480)726-7272
Biomedical Engg. Soc. [6327], 8201 Corporate Dr., Ste. 1125, Landover, MD 20785-2224, (301)459-1999
Biomedical Engg. Soc. [6327], 8201 Corporate Dr., Ste. 1125, Landover, MD 20785-2224, (301)459-1999
Biomedical Marketing Assn. [★2399]
Biomedical Res. and Experimental Therapeutics Soc. of Singapore [IO], Singapore, Singapore
Biometric Application Programming Interface Consortium [6295], 11491 Sunset Hills Rd., Reston, VA 20190, (703)579-3064
Biometric Identification Assn; Intl. [7509]
The Biometric Soc. [★7476]
The Biometric Soc. [★7476]
Biometric Soc., Eastern North Amer. Region; Intl. [7477]
Biometric Soc., Western North Amer. Region [★7478]
Biometric Soc., Western North Amer. Region [★7478]
Biometrics Inst. [IO], Crows Nest, Australia
Biomimetics New Zealand [IO], Christchurch, New Zealand
Biomolecular Rsrc. Facilities; Assn. of [7020]
Bioneers [4733], 1607 Paseo de Peralta, Ste. 3, Santa Fe, NM 87501, (505)986-0366
Bionomics Intl. [7363], 3023 Kramer St., Wheaton, MD 20902, (301)942-6316
Biopesticide Indus. Alliance [7233], PO Box 465, McFarland, WI 53558, (202)536-4602
Biophysical Soc. [6331], 11400 Rockville Pike Rd., Ste. 800, Rockville, MD 20852, (240)290-5600
Biophysical Soc. of Argentina [IO], Buenos Aires, Argentina
Biophysical Soc. of China [IO], Beijing, People's Republic of China
Biophysics
Biophysical Soc. [6331]
Soc. for Free Radical Biology and Medicine [6332]
Soc. for Free Radical Biology and Medicine [6332]
Biopolitics Intl. Org. [IO], Athens, Greece
BiOptic Driving Network U.S.A. [15981], 5520 Ridgeton Hill Ct., Fairfax, VA 22032
BIOTECanada [IO], Ottawa, ON, Canada
Biotech Medical Mgt. Assn. - Address unknown since 2011.
Biotechnology
BIO IT Coalition [6333]
Biotechnology Indus. Org. [457]
Coun. for Biotechnology Info. [6334]
Coun. for Biotechnology Info. [6334]
European Assn. for Bioindustries [18860]
HealthGrid.US Alliance [13836]
Intl. Soc. of Lyophilization - Freeze Drying [6335]
Org. of Regulatory and Clinical Associates [458]
Surfaces in Biomaterials Found. [6336]
Truth About Trade and Tech. [6337]
Women in Bio [6338]
Biotechnology Indus. Org. [457], 1201 Maryland Ave. SW, Ste. 900, Washington, DC 20024, (202)962-9200
Biotecnologie per l'Ecologia e l'Agricoltura [IO], Serravalle, San Marino
Bioversity Intl. [IO], Rome, Italy
BioWeapons Prevention Proj. [IO], Geneva, Switzerland
Bipolar Support Alliance; Depression and [15452]
Birambye Intl. [11550], 6948 Howell St., Arvada, CO 80004, (303)596-1401
Bird
African Love Bird Soc. [21207]

Amer. Assn. of Spanish Timbrado Breeders [21208]
Amer. Budgerigar Soc. [21209]
Amer. Canary Fanciers Assn. [21210]
Amer. Cockatiel Soc. [21211]
Amer. Dove Assn. [21212]
Amer. Fed. of Aviculture [21213]
Amer. Game Fowl Soc. [3840]
Amer. Mookee Assn. [3841]
Amer. Singers Club [21214]
Amer. Waterslager Soc. [21215]
Amer. Waterslager Soc. [21215]
Audubon Intl. [4008]
Audubon Naturalist Soc. of the Central Atlantic States [4009]
Avian Welfare Coalition [10931]
Bird Conservation Alliance [3842]
Bird Observation and Conservation Australia [3487]
Birds Australia [7779]BirdBrotogeris Soc. Intl.
Canary and Finch Soc. [3843]
Dove Sportsman's Soc. [3844]
Dove Sportsman's Soc. [3844]
Env. for the Americas [3845]
Exotic Bird Soc. of Am. [21216]
Forest Bird Soc. [4056]
Guinea Fowl Breeders Assn. [3846]
Guinea Fowl Intl. Assn. [3847]
Guinea Fowl Intl. Assn. [3847]
Hartz Club of Am. [7198]
Hawk Mountain Sanctuary [5063]
Hummingbird Monitoring Network [3848]
Hummingbird Soc. [3849]
Intl. Assn. of Avian Trainers and Educators [21217]
Intl. Assn. of Avian Trainers and Educators [21217]
Intl. Aviculturists Soc. [3850]
Intl. Aviculturists Soc. [3850]
Intl. Conure Assn. [21218]
Intl. Conure Assn. [21218]
Intl. Fed. of Amer. Homing Pigeon Fanciers [22097]
Intl. Gloster Breeders Assn. [21219]
Intl. Parrotlet Soc. [21220]
Intl. Parrotlet Soc. [21220]
Natl. Cage Bird Show [21221]
Natl. Cockatiel Soc. [21222]
Natl. Color-Bred Assn. [21223]
Natl. Finch and Softbill Soc. [21224]
Natl. Pigeon Assn. [21225]
North Amer. Cockatiel Soc. [21226]
North Amer. Cockatiel Soc. [21226]
North Amer. Parrot Soc. [21227]
Parrot Intl. [3851]
Parrotlet Alliance [3852]
Parrots and People [3853]
Pionus Breeders Assn. [21228]
Pionus Breeders Assn. [21228]
Quaker Parakeet Soc. [3854]
Quaker Parakeet Soc. [3854]
Soc. of Parrot Breeders and Exhibitors [21229]
Stafford Canary Club of Am. [21230]
Stafford Canary Club of Am. [21230]
The Tanygnathus Soc. [3855]
United Beagle Gundog Fed. [21661]
United Gloster Breeders [21231]
Bird Conservation Alliance [3842], Amer. Bird Conservancy, PO Box 249, The Plains, VA 20198, (202)234-7181
Bird Conservation Soc. of Thailand [IO], Nonthaburi, Thailand
Bird Life Intl. - United Kingdom [IO], Cambridge, United Kingdom
Bird Observation and Conservation Australia [IO], Nunawading, Australia
Bird Observers Club of Australia [★3487]
Bird Strike Comm. U.S.A. [5036], 4300 Glumack Dr., St. Paul, MN 55111, (612)726-5780
Bird Stud. Canada [IO], Port Rowan, ON, Canada
BirdLife Botswana [IO], Gaborone, Botswana
BirdLife Cyprus [IO], Nicosia, Cyprus
BirdLife Intl. [IO], Cambridge, United Kingdom
BirdLife Malta [IO], Ta'Xbiex, Malta
Birdlife South Africa [IO], Randburg, Republic of South Africa

Birds Australia [IO], Carlton, Australia
Birds of Prey
Hawk Mountain Sanctuary [5063]
The Intl. Osprey Found. [5068]
Last Chance Forever [5077]
Birds of Prey Found. [5037], 2290 S 104th St., Broomfield, CO 80020, (303)460-0674
Birds of Prey Working Group [IO], Johannesburg, Republic of South Africa
BirdWatch Ireland [IO], Kilcoole, Ireland
Birmingham Chamber of Commerce and Indus. [IO], Birmingham, United Kingdom
Birmingham Natural History Soc. [IO], Birmingham, United Kingdom
Birth Defect Res. for Children [13838], 976 Lake Baldwin Ln., Ste. 104, Orlando, FL 34747, (407)895-0802
Birth Defects
Alliance for Smiles [14189]
Alveolar Capillary Dysplasia Assn. [13837]
Birth Defect Res. for Children [13838]
Breath of Hope [13839]
CHERUBS - Assn. of Congenital Diaphragmatic Hernia Res., Advocacy and Support [13840]
CHERUBS - Assn. of Congenital Diaphragmatic Hernia Res., Awareness and Support [13840]
Cornelia de Lange Syndrome Found. [13841]
Erb's Palsy Assn. of Ireland [3391]
Hypospadias and Epispadias Assn. [13842]
Klippel-Trenaunay Support Gp. [13843]
March of Dimes Found. [13844]
Natl. Birth Defects Prevention Network [13845]
Org. of Teratology Info. Services [13846]
Rubinstein-Taybi Parent Gp. U.S.A. [13847]
Smile Network Intl. [14203]
Wide Smiles [16786]
Birth Without Boundaries [14102], 8 Riddle Rd., Camp Hill, PA 17011, (717)654-9810
Birthright Intl. [IO], Toronto, ON, Canada
Birthright U.S.A. [12926], PO Box 98363, Atlanta, GA 30359-2063, (800)550-4900
Birzeit Soc. [9138], PO Box 1822, Norwalk, CA 90651, (714)996-3389
Biscuit Bakers Inst. [★390]
Biscuit and Cracker Distributors Assn. - Defunct.
Biscuit and Cracker Mfrs. Assn. [390], 6325 Woodside Ct., Ste. 125, Columbia, MD 21046, (443)545-1645
Bisexual
Atticus Circle [17735]
Campus Pride [12072]
CenterLink [11661]
Equality Fed. [17736]
Gay and Lesbian Assn. of Retiring Persons [10843]
LEAGUE [12096]
Natl. Coalition of Anti-Violence Programs [18770]
POWER UP: Professional Org. of Women in Entertainment Reaching UP! [17737]
Soc. for the Psychological Stud. of Lesbian, Gay, Bisexual and Transgender Issues [16429]
Youth Pride Alliance [12117]
Bishop Baraga Assn. [19393], 347 Rock St., Marquette, MI 49855, (906)227-9117
Bishop Hill Heritage Assn. [20622], PO Box 92, Bishop Hill, IL 61419-0092, (309)927-3899
Bishop Pike Found. [★12226]
Bishops' Commn. for Ecumenical Affairs [★19511]
Bishops' Comm. on the Liturgical Apostolate [★19510]
Bishops' Comm. on the Liturgy [★19510]
Bishops' Comm. for Migrant Workers [★12149]
Bishops' Comm. on Scouting [★13022]
Bishops' Comm. for the Spanish Speaking [★12149]
Bishops' Comm. on Vocations - Address unknown since 2010.
Bishops' Conf. of Scotland [IO], Airdrie, United Kingdom
Bison Hybrid Intl. Assn. [★3776]
Bison Hybrid Intl. Assn. [★3776]
Bitterroot Outfitters [★23087]
Bitumen Waterproofing Assn. [IO], Nottingham, United Kingdom
Bituminous Coal Inst. [★785]
BKR Intl. [16], 19 Fulton St., Ste. 306, New York, NY 10038, (212)964-2115

Reference to "IO" in place of a book number signifies that the association may be found in the 50th edition of International Organizations.

BKR Intl. **[16]**, 19 Fulton St., Ste. 306, New York, NY 10038, (212)964-2115

B.K.S. Iyengar Yoga Natl. Assn. of the U.S. **[23137]**, 1952 1st Ave. S, Ste. 1B, Seattle, WA 98134, (206)623-3562

BKSTS - The Moving Image Soc. **[IO]**, Iver Heath, United Kingdom

Black Alliance for Educational Options **[8078]**, 888 16th St. NW, Ste. 800, Washington, DC 20006, (202)429-2236

Black Amer. Law Students Assn. **[★8509]**

Black Amers. for Bush - Defunct.

Black Americans for Life **[12927]**, 9504 E 63rd St., Raytown, MO 64133, (816)353-4113

Black Archives of Mid-America **[9143]**, 2033 Vine St., Kansas City, MO 64108, (816)241-2272

Black and Asian Stud. Assn. **[IO]**, Mitcham, United Kingdom

Black Awareness in TV - Address unknown since 2011.

Black Bass Found. - Defunct.

Black on Black Love Campaign **[11683]**, 1000 E 87th St., Chicago, IL 60619, (773)978-0868

Black Box Voting **[17605]**, 330 SW 43rd St., Ste. K, PMB 547, Renton, WA 98057-4944, (206)335-7747

Black Bus. and Professional Assn. **[IO]**, Toronto, ON, Canada

Black Bus. Professionals and Entrepreneurs **[648]**, 5710 Ogeechee Rd., Ste. 200-256, Savannah, GA 31405, (912)443-1995

Black Career Women **[19205]**, PO Box 19332, Cincinnati, OH 45219-0332, (513)531-1932

Black Caucus of the Amer. Lib. Assn. **[9977]**, 627 S St., Lafayette, IN 47901, (765)429-0118

Black Coaches and Administrators **[22457]**, Pan Amer. Plaza, 201 S Capitol Ave., Ste. 495, Indianapolis, IN 46225, (317)829-5600

Black Coaches Assn. **[★22457]**

Black Coalition for AIDS Prevention **[IO]**, Toronto, ON, Canada

Black Coll. Radio Org. **[484]**, PO Box 3191, Atlanta, GA 30302, (404)523-6136

Black Community Crusade for Children **[11198]**, 25 E St. NW, Washington, DC 20001, (202)628-8787

Black Cops Against Police Brutality **[5689]**, PO Box 4256, East Orange, NJ 07019, (973)926-5717

Black Country Chamber of Commerce **[IO]**, Walsall, United Kingdom

Black Culinarian Alliance **[1009]**, 244 Madison Ave., New York, NY 10016-2817, (212)643-6570

Black Data Processing Associates **[65]**, 9500 Arena Dr., Ste. 350, Largo, MD 20774, (301)584-3135

Black Entertainment Lawyers Assn. **[★5409]**

Black Entertainment and Sports Lawyers Assn. **[5409]**, Rev. Phyllicia M. Hatton, Conf. Mgr./ Consultant, PO Box 441485, Fort Washington, MD 20749-1485, (301)248-1818

Black Entomologists **[6840]**, USDA, ARS, 59 Lee Rd., Stoneville, MS 38776, (662)686-3646

Black Family Genealogy and History Soc. - Address unknown since 2011.

Black Farmers and Agriculturists Assn. **[3751]**, PO Box 61, Tillery, NC 27887-0061, (252)826-2800

Black Fashion Designers Assn. **[1037]**, PO Box 3567, New York, NY 10163, (718)415-9843

Black Filmmaker Found. - Address unknown since 2011.

Black Flight Attendants of Am. **[18843]**, 1060 Crenshaw Blvd., Ste. 202, Los Angeles, CA 90019, (888)682-2322

Black Flight Attendants of Am. **[18843]**, 1060 Crenshaw Blvd., Ste. 202, Los Angeles, CA 90019, (888)682-2322

Black Gold Gp. - Address unknown since 2011.

Black History Month Assn. **[IO]**, Halifax, NS, Canada

Black Holocaust Soc. **[17154]**, 6622 N Bourbon St., Rm. 16, Milwaukee, WI 53224, (414)446-4377

Black Indians and Intertribal Native Amer. Assn. **[19152]**, PO Box 143, Upperstrasburg, PA 17265, (717)491-1065

Black Info. Tech. Forum **[IO]**, Johannesburg, Republic of South Africa

Black Informed Professionals - Defunct.

Black Law Students Assn; Natl. **[8509]**

Black Leadership Forum **[18844]**, 633 Pennsylvania Ave. NW, 5th Fl., Washington, DC 20004, (202)689-1965

Black Mental Hea. Alliance **[15449]**, 733 W 40th St., Ste. 10, Baltimore, MD 21211, (410)338-2642

Black Methodists for Church Renewal **[19969]**, 201 8th Ave. S, Nashville, TN 37203-3919, (615)749-6351

Black Mothers' Breastfeeding Assn. **[13862]**, 19436 Packard St., Detroit, MI 48234, (313)366-5996

Black Pilots of Am. **[376]**, PO Box 7463, Pine Bluff, AR 71601, (504)214-7346

Black Professional Coaches Alliance - Address unknown since 2011.

Black Radical Cong. **[18845]**, PO Box 24795, St. Louis, MO 63115

Black Retail Action Gp. **[3097]**, Rockefeller Center Sta., PO Box 1192, New York, NY 10185, (212)319-7751

Black Rock Coalition **[9580]**, PO Box 1054, Cooper Sta., New York, NY 10276, (212)713-5097

Black Russian Terrier Club of Am. **[21526]**, 5621 N Kenmore Ave., Chicago, IL 60660, (773)271-5407

Black Sash Trust **[IO]**, Cape Town, Republic of South Africa

Black Theatre Network **[10571]**, 2609 Douglas Rd. SE, Ste. 102, Washington, DC 20020-6540, (202)274-5667

Black-Top Delaine Merino Sheep Breeders' Assn. - Defunct.

Black Veterans **[★20779]**

Black Veterans for Social Justice **[20779]**, 665 Willoughby Ave., Brooklyn, NY 11206, (718)852-6004

Black Wings in Aviation **[★6092]**

Black Women in Church and Soc. **[20285]**, 700 Martin Luther King Jr. Dr. SW, Atlanta, GA 30314, (404)527-5713

Black Women of Essence **[10828]**, PO Box 28061, Baltimore, MD 21239

Black Women Organized for Educational Development - Address unknown since 2011.

Black Women in Sisterhood for Action **[13453]**, PO Box 1592, Washington, DC 20013, (202)543-6013

Black Women United for Action **[13454]**, 6551 Loisdale Ct., Ste. 400, Springfield, VA 22150, (703)922-5757

Black Women United for Action **[13454]**, 6551 Loisdale Ct., Ste. 400, Springfield, VA 22150, (703)922-5757

Black Women's Hea. Imperative **[17123]**, 1726 M St. NW, Ste. 300, Washington, DC 20036, (202)548-4000

Black Women's Hea. Proj. **[★17123]**

Black Women's House of Culture **[IO]**, Santos, Brazil

Black Women's Roundtable on Voter Participation **[18377]**, Natl. Coalition on Black Civic Participation, 1050 Connecticut Ave. NW, 10th Fl., Ste. No. 1000, Washington, DC 20036, (202)659-4929

Black World **[IO]**, Madrid, Spain

Black World Found. **[9093]**, PO Box 22869, Oakland, CA 94609, (734)213-2400

Black Writers Alliance - Defunct.

Blackburn Family Assn. **[20431]**, 13138 Lincoln Dr., Huntington Woods, MI 48070, (248)677-7411

Blackhawk Standbys, Inc. - Address unknown since 2010.

Blacks in Law Enforcement - Address unknown since 2011.

Blacksmiths
 Amer. Farrier's Assn. **[459]**
 Artist-Blacksmith's Assn. of North Am. **[460]**
 Artist-Blacksmith's Assn. of North Am. **[460]**
 Intl. Brotherhood of Boilermakers, Iron Ship Builders, Blacksmiths, Forgers and Helpers **[23159]**
 Natl. Blacksmiths and Weldors Assn. **[461]**

Blackwater Wildlife Rescue **[IO]**, Surrey, United Kingdom

Bladder Cancer Advocacy Network **[13890]**, 4813 St. Elmo Ave., Bethesda, MD 20814, (301)215-9099

Blair Chiropractic Soc. **[14124]**, 550 E Carson Plaza Dr., Ste. 122, Carson, CA 90746, (563)676-6209

Blair Soc. for Genealogical Res. **[20432]**, Bryce D. Blair, Treas., 726 Falling Oaks Dr., Medina, OH 44256-2778

Blair Soc. for Genealogical Res. **[20432]**, Bryce D. Blair, Treas., 726 Falling Oaks Dr., Medina, OH 44256-2778

Blankets for Canada Soc. **[IO]**, Lethbridge, AB, Canada

Blazer Horse Assn. **[4571]**, 820 N Can-Ada Rd., Star, ID 83669, (208)286-7267

BlazeSports Am. **[22508]**, 535 N McDonough St., Decatur, GA 30030, (404)270-2000

BLC Leather Tech. Centre **[IO]**, Northampton, United Kingdom

Blencowe Families Assn. - Address unknown since 2011.

Blessings on Africa **[12719]**, PO Box 645, East Stroudsburg, PA 18301, (800)452-5176

Blessings on Africa **[12719]**, PO Box 645, East Stroudsburg, PA 18301, (800)452-5176

Blessings Intl. **[12447]**, 1650 N Indianwood Ave., Broken Arrow, OK 74012, (918)250-8101

Blessings Intl. **[12447]**, 1650 N Indianwood Ave., Broken Arrow, OK 74012, (918)250-8101

Blind
 Amer. Blind Bowling Assn. **[22502]**
 Amer. Coun. of the Blind **[17057]**
 Blind Ser. Assn. **[17067]**
 Norrie Disease Assn. **[14415]**
 Skating Assn. for the Blind and Handicapped **[22901]**
 Theosophical Book Assn. for the Blind **[20264]**
 World Access for the Blind **[17118]**

Blind; Amer. Found. for the **[17060]**

Blind; Amer. Printing House for the **[17062]**

Blind; Assoc. Services for the **[17063]**

Blind; Carroll Center for the **[17070]**

Blind Children and Adults; Amer. Action Fund for the **[17056]**

Blind Children's Fund **[17066]**, PO Box 363, Three Oaks, MI 49128, (989)779-9966

Blind Citizens Australia **[IO]**, Melbourne, Australia

Blind Friends of Lesbian, Gay, Transgender and Bisexual People - Address unknown since 2011.

Blind Golf Assn; U.S. **[22527]**

Blind; Gospel Assn. for the **[17078]**

Blind; Guide Dog Found. for the **[17079]**

Blind; Guiding Eyes for the **[17083]**

Blind; Guiding Eyes for the **[17083]**

Blind; Jewish Guild for the **[17092]**

Blind; Leader Dogs for the **[17094]**

Blind; Leader Dogs for the **[17094]**

Blind Lions; Amer. Coun. of the **[17059]**

Blind; Natl. Church Conf. of the **[13379]**

Blind; Natl. Fed. of the **[17107]**

Blind; Natl. Indus. for the **[17108]**

Blind Outdoor Leisure Development **[★22509]**

Blind and Retarded; Assn. for the Advancement of **[17064]**

Blind Sailing Intl. **[23109]**, Carroll Center for the Blind, 770 Centre St., Newton, MA 02458, (617)969-6204

Blind Ser. Assn. **[17067]**, 17 N State St., Ste. 1050, Chicago, IL 60602-3510, (312)236-0808

Blind Sport New Zealand **[IO]**, Auckland, New Zealand

Blind and Visually Handicapped Intl; Bibles for the **[19344]**

Blind and Visually Impaired; Assn. for Educ. and Rehabilitation of the **[17065]**

Blind and Visually Impaired; Natl. Accreditation Coun. for Agencies Serving the **[17101]**

Blind; Xavier Soc. for the **[17119]**

Blinded Amer. Veterans Found. **[20411]**, PO Box 65900, Washington, DC 20035-5900, (202)462-4430

Blinded Veterans Assn. **[17068]**, 477 H St. NW, Washington, DC 20001-2617, (202)371-8880

Blindness Am; Prevent **[17112]**

Blindness; Found. Fighting **[17075]**

Bliss Classification Assn. **[IO]**, London, United Kingdom

Blissymbolics Commun. Intl. **[IO]**, Toronto, ON, Canada

Block Booking Conf. **[★8906]**

Block Parent Prog. of Canada **[IO]**, Barrie, ON, Canada

Blood
 Alliance for Biotherapies **[16831]**
 Amer. Assn. of Blood Banks **[13848]**
 America's Blood Centers **[13849]**
 Children's Cancer and Blood Found. **[14964]**
 Intl. Soc. of Radiolabeled Blood Elements **[13850]**

A star before a book entry number signifies that the name is not listed separately, but is mentioned within the entry.

Intl. Soc. of Radiolabeled Blood Elements **[13850]**
Natl. Blood Found. **[13851]**
Plasma Protein Therapeutics Assn. **[13852]**
USBloodDonors.org **[13853]**
Blood and Marrow Transplant Info. Network **[16904]**, 2310 Skokie Valley Rd., Ste. 104, Highland Park, IL 60035, (847)433-3313
Blood and Marrow Transplantation; Amer. Soc. for **[16898]**
Blood: Water Mission **[10809]**, PO Box 60381, Nashville, TN 37206, (615)550-4296
BLOOM Africa **[11199]**, 4605 E Natl. Rd., Springfield, OH 45505
Blossom **[IO]**, Virudhunagar, India
Blue Anchor, Inc. - Defunct.
Blue Army of Our Lady of Fatima U.S.A. **[19394]**, PO Box 976, Washington, NJ 07882, (908)689-1700
Blue Blue Violet **[★23513]**
The Blue Card **[12404]**, 171 Madison Ave., Ste. 1405, New York, NY 10016, (212)239-2251
Blue Cross **[IO]**, Burford, United Kingdom
Blue Cross Assn. **[★15127]**
Blue Cross and Blue Shield Assn. **[15127]**, 225 N Michigan Ave., Chicago, IL 60601, (312)297-6000
Blue Dolphin Alliance **[4702]**, PO Box 312, Watsonville, CA 95077, (831)761-1477
Blue Earth Alliance **[10436]**, Bart J. Cannon, Exec. Dir., PO Box 4490, Seattle, WA 98194, (206)569-8754
Blue Heron Support Services Assn. **[IO]**, Barrhead, AB, Canada
Blue Key Honor Soc. **[23555]**, 7501 Whitehill Ln., Whitehill Farm, Millersburg, OH 44654-9270, (330)674-2570
Blue Knights **[★21921]**
Blue Knights **[★21921]**
Blue Knights Intl. Law Enforcement Motorcycle Club **[21921]**, 38 Alden St., Bangor, ME 04401, (207)947-4600
Blue Knights Intl. Law Enforcement Motorcycle Club **[21921]**, 38 Alden St., Bangor, ME 04401, (207)947-4600
Blue Mountain Proj. **[12397]**, 920 Adams St., Hammond, WI 54015, (715)690-5433
Blue Nile Children's Org. **[11200]**, PO Box 28658, Seattle, WA 98118, (206)760-2873
Blue Ribbon Coalition **[★22834]**
Blue Shield Assn. **[★15127]**
Blue Star Mothers of Am. **[20703]**, 718 Daniel Dr., Grand Junction, CO 81506, (970)242-3845
Blue Ventures Conservation - Madagascar **[IO]**, London, United Kingdom
Blue/White Pottery Club **[20958]**, PO Box 460517, Aurora, CO 80015, (303)690-8649
Bluebell Railway Preservation Soc. **[IO]**, Lewes, United Kingdom
blueEnergy **[11966]**, 972 Mission St., Ste. 500, San Francisco, CA 94103, (415)552-2615
Bluefaced Leicester Sheep Breeders Assn. **[IO]**, Carlisle, United Kingdom
Bluefaced Leicester Union of North Am. **[4905]**, 760 W VW Ave., Schoolcraft, MI 49087, (269)679-5497
Bluefaced Leicester Union of North Am. **[4905]**, 760 W VW Ave., Schoolcraft, MI 49087, (269)679-5497
Bluegrass
The Grascals Fan Club **[23851]**
Natl. Traditional Country Music Assn. **[10265]**
Bluegrass Assn; Southwest **[10300]**
Bluegrass Music Assn; Intl. **[10216]**
Bluegrass Music Assn; Intl. **[10216]**
Blueliners **[23899]**, PO Box 805, St. Louis, MO 63188
BlueRibbon Coalition **[22834]**, 4555 Burley Dr., Ste. A, Pocatello, ID 83202-1945, (208)237-1008
The Blues Found. **[10168]**, 49 Union Ave., Memphis, TN 38103-2492, (901)527-2583
Blues Heaven Found. **[10169]**, 2120 S Michigan Ave., Chicago, IL 60616, (312)808-1286
Bluetick Breeders of Am. **[21527]**, PO Box 171, Sedalia, MO 65302, (660)541-0716
BlueVoice.org **[4013]**, 10 Sunfish Dr., St. Augustine, FL 32080
Bluewater Bus. Card Club **[IO]**, Sarnia, ON, Canada
Bluewater Cruising Assn. **[IO]**, Vancouver, BC, Canada

Bluewater Sportfishing Club **[IO]**, Hyde Park, Australia
BME Career Alliance **[★6326]**
BMMF International/USA **[★20054]**
BMMF International/USA **[★20054]**
BMW 507 Register **[★21010]**
BMW Car Club of Am. **[21009]**, 640 S Main St., Ste. 201, Greenville, SC 29601, (864)250-0022
BMW Club of Canada **[IO]**, New Westminster, BC, Canada
BMW Motorcycle Owners of Am. **[21922]**, PO Box 3982, Ballwin, MO 63022, (636)394-7277
BMW Riders Assn. Intl. **[21923]**, PO Box 599, Troy, OH 45373-0599, (937)339-7100
BMW Vintage and Classic Car Club of Am. **[21010]**, 4862 Silver Sage Ct., Boulder, CO 80301, (303)300-9946
B'nai B'rith **[★19849]**
B'nai B'rith **[★19849]**
B'nai Brith Canada **[IO]**, Toronto, ON, Canada
B'nai B'rith Intl. **[19849]**, 2020 K St. NW, 7th Fl., Washington, DC 20006, (202)857-6600
B'nai B'rith Intl. **[19849]**, 2020 K St. NW, 7th Fl., Washington, DC 20006, (202)857-6600
B'nai B'rith Intl. Commn. on Adult Jewish Educ. **[★8425]**
B'nai B'rith Intl. Commn. on Adult Jewish Educ. **[★8425]**
B'nai B'rith International's Center for Jewish Identity **[8425]**, 801 2nd Ave., 14th Fl., New York, NY 10017, (212)490-3290
B'nai B'rith International's Center for Jewish Identity **[8425]**, 801 2nd Ave., 14th Fl., New York, NY 10017, (212)490-3290
B'nai B'rith Women **[★19876]**
B'nai B'rith Women **[★19876]**
B'nai B'rith Youth Org. **[19850]**, 2020 K St. NW, 7th Fl., Washington, DC 20006, (202)857-6633
Bnai Zion Found. **[19087]**, 136 E 39th St., New York, NY 10016, (212)725-1211
Bnei Akiva of North Am. **[★19851]**
Bnei Akiva of the U.S. and Canada **[19851]**, 520 W 8th Ave., 15 Fl., New York, NY 10018, (212)465-9536
Bd. of Acquisitions of Lib. Materials - of ALA **[★9968]**
Bd. of Airline Representatives in the United Kingdom **[IO]**, London, United Kingdom
Bd. of Canadian Registered Safety Professionals **[IO]**, Mississauga, ON, Canada
Bd. for Certification of Genealogists **[20623]**, PO Box 14291, Washington, DC 20044
Bd. for Certification in Pedorthics and Amer. Bd. for Certification in Orthotics, Prosthetics and Pedorthics **[★16049]**
Bd. of Certified Hazard Control Mgt. **[3138]**, PO Box 515, Helena, AL 35080, (205)664-8412
Bd. of Certified Prdt. Safety Mgt. **[3139]**, PO Box 515, Helena, AL 35080, (205)664-8412
Bd. of Certified Safety Professionals **[7346]**, 208 Burwash Ave., Savoy, IL 61874, (217)359-9263
Board of Examiners in Psychotherapy **[★16452]**
Bd. of Governors of the European Schools **[IO]**, Brussels, Belgium
Bd. of Home Missions of the Natl. Assn. of Free Will Baptists **[★19325]**
Bd. of Hospitals and Homes of The Methodist Church **[★14742]**
Bd. of Intl. Ministries **[19317]**, Amer. Baptist Churches in the U.S.A., PO Box 851, Valley Forge, PA 19482-0851, (800)222-3872
Bd. of Intl. Ministries **[19317]**, Amer. Baptist Churches in the U.S.A., PO Box 851, Valley Forge, PA 19482-0851, (800)222-3872
Bd. of Investment of Sri Lanka **[IO]**, Colombo, Sri Lanka
Bd. of Marine Underwriters of San Francisco **[★3257]**
Bd. on Medicine of the Natl. Acad. of Sciences **[★15416]**
Bd. of Natl. Ministries - Address unknown since 2010.
Bd. of Nephrology Examiners Nursing and Tech. **[15547]**, 1901 Pennsylvania Ave. NW, Ste. 607, Washington, DC 20006, (202)462-1252

Bd. of Nephrology Examiners - Nursing and Tech. **[★15547]**
Bd. for Orthotist/Prosthetist Certification **[16051]**, 10451 Mill Run Cir., Ste. 200, Owings Mills, MD 21117-5575, (410)581-6222
Bd. of Registered Polysomnographic Technologists **[15371]**, 8400 Westpark Dr., 2nd Fl., McLean, VA 22102, (703)610-9020
Bd. Retailers Assn. **[3098]**, PO Box 1170, Wrightsville Beach, NC 28480, (910)509-0109
Bd. of Schools of the ASCP **[★15379]**
Bd. of Schools of Inhalation Therapy **[★16845]**
Bd. of Schools of Medical Tech. **[★15379]**
Bd. on Science and Technology for Intl. Development - Defunct.
Bd. of Specialty Societies **[15521]**, 6300 N River Rd., Rosemont, IL 60018-4206, (847)823-7186
Bd. of Thoracic Surgery **[★16878]**
Bd. of Trade of Kansas City, Missouri **[★3967]**
Bd. of Trustees and Directors of Missions **[★19330]**
Boardgame Players Assn. **[21743]**, 1541 Redfield Rd., Bel Air, MD 21015
Boarding for Breast Cancer Found. **[13891]**, 6230 Wilshire Blvd., No. 179, Los Angeles, CA 90048, (323)467-2663
Boarding Schools Assn. **[IO]**, London, United Kingdom
BoardSource **[12592]**, 750 9th St. NW, Ste. 650, Washington, DC 20001-4793, (202)349-2500
Boat Mfrs. Assn. **[★2365]**
Boat Owners Assn. of the U.S. **[22324]**, 880 S Pickett St., Alexandria, VA 22304, (703)823-9550
Boaters Against Drunk Driving - Address unknown since 2011.
Boating
Alberg 37 Intl. Owners Assn. **[22314]**
Amer. Boating Assn. **[22315]**
Amer. Power Boat Assn. **[22316]**
Amer. Sail Training Assn. **[22317]**
Amer. Sailing Assn. **[22318]**
Amer. Shark Assn. **[22319]**
Amer. Y-Flyer Yacht Racing Assn. **[22320]**
Annapolis Naval Sailing Assn. **[22321]**
Antique and Classic Boat Soc. **[22322]**
Antique Outboard Motor Club **[22323]**
Blind Sailing Intl. **[23109]**
Boat Owners Assn. of the U.S. **[22324]**
Bullseye Assn. **[22325]**
Catalina 22 Natl. Sailing Assn. **[22326]**
Catboat Assn. **[22327]**
Center for Wooden Boats **[22328]**
Chris Craft Antique Boat Club **[22329]**
Classic Yacht Assn. **[22330]**
Coronado 15 Natl. Assn. **[22331]**
Cruising Club of Am. **[22332]**
Day Sailer Assn. **[22333]**
El Toro Intl. Yacht Racing Assn. **[22334]**
Flying Scot Sailing Assn. **[22335]**
Force 5 Class Assn. **[22336]**
Gar Wood Soc. **[22337]**
Geary 18 Intl. Yacht Racing Assn. **[22338]**
Gulf Yachting Assn. **[22339]**
Hampton One-Design Class Racing Assn. **[22340]**
Highlander Class Intl. Assn. **[22341]**
Inland Lake Yachting Assn. **[22342]**
Inter-Lake Yachting Assn. **[22343]**
Interlake Sailing Class Assn. **[22344]**
Intl. 210 Assn. **[22345]**
Intl. 505 Yacht Racing Assn., Amer. Sect. **[22346]**
Intl. Blue Jay Class Assn. **[22347]**
Intl. Blue Jay Class Assn. **[22347]**
Intl. Catalina 27/270 Assn. **[22348]**
Intl. Catalina 400 Assn. **[22349]**
Intl. D.N. Ice Yacht Racing Assn. **[22350]**
Intl. D.N. Ice Yacht Racing Assn. **[22350]**
Intl. Etchells Class Assn. **[22351]**
Intl. Etchells Class Assn. **[22351]**
Intl. Flying Dutchman Class Assn. of the U.S. **[22352]**
Intl. Flying Dutchman Class Assn. of the U.S. **[22352]**
Intl. Hobie Class Assn. **[22353]**
Intl. Hobie Class Assn. **[22353]**
Intl. Hydrofoil Soc. **[22354]**
Intl. Hydrofoil Soc. **[22354]**

Reference to "IO" in place of a book number signifies that the association may be found in the 50th edition of International Organizations.

Intl. J/22 Class Assn. [22355]
Intl. J/22 Class Assn. [22355]
Intl. Laser Class Assn. - North Amer. Region [22356]
Intl. Lightning Class Assn. [22357]
Intl. Lightning Class Assn. [22357]
Intl. Mobjack Assn. [22358]
Intl. Mobjack Assn. [22358]
Intl. Naples Sabot Assn. [22359]
Intl. Penguin Class Dinghy Assn. [22360]
Intl. Penguin Class Dinghy Assn. [22360]
Intl. Shipmasters Assn. [2358]
Intl. Star Class Yacht Racing Assn. [22361]
Intl. Star Class Yacht Racing Assn. [22361]
Intl. Sunfish Class Assn. [22362]
Intl. Sunfish Class Assn. [22362]
Intl. Thunderbird Class Assn. [22363]
J/80 Class Assn. [22364]
Jet 14 Class Assn. [22365]
Joshua Slocum Soc. Intl. [22366]
Lido 14 Class Assn. [22367]
Lyman Boat Owners Assn. [22368]
MC Sailing Assn. [22369]
Metal Boat Soc. [462]
Natl. Assn. of State Boating Law Administrators [5299]
Natl. Boating Fed. [22370]
Natl. Butterfly Assn. [22371]
Natl. C Scow Sailing Assn. [22372]
Natl. C Scow Sailing Assn. [22372]
Natl. Class E Scow Assn. [22373]
Natl. Fisheries Inst. [3184]
Natl. Hospice Regatta Alliance [22374]
Natl. Offshore Dept. [22375]
Natl. One Design Racing Assn. [22376]
Natl. Piers Soc. [14824]
Natl. Starwind/Spindrift Class Assn. [22377]
Natl. Women's Sailing Assn. [22378]
Nautical Res. Guild [22379]
Nautical Res. Guild [22379]
North Amer. Formula 18 Assn. [22380]
North Amer. Steam Boat Assn. [22381]
North Amer. Steam Boat Assn. [22381]
Northwest Schooner Soc. [22382]
Olson 30 Natl. Class Assn. [22383]
Pacific Dragon Boat Assn. [22384]
Professional Windsurfers Assn. [22385]
Rhodes 19 Class Assn. [22386]
Richardson Boat Owners Assn. [22387]
Riva Club USA [21232]
Sail Am. [463]
SailMail Assn. [6679]
San Juan 21 Class Assn. [22388]
Santana 20 Class Assn. [22389]
Seven Seas Cruising Assn. [22390]
Shields Natl. Class Assn. [22391]
Ships on Stamps Unit [22074]
Snipe Class Intl. Racing Assn. [22392]
Snipe Class Intl. Racing Assn. [22392]
Sonar Class Assn. [22393]
States Org. for Boating Access [464]
Swan Owners Assn. of Am. [22394]
T-Ten Class Assn. [22395]
Tanzer 16 Class Assn. [22396]
Thistle Class Assn. [22397]
Traditional Small Craft Assn. [22398]
Tugboat Enthusiasts Soc. of the Americas [22399]
U.S. A-Class Catamaran Assn. [22400]
U.S. Albacore Assn. [22401]
U.S. J/24 Class Assn. [22402]
U.S. J/24 Class Assn. [22402]
U.S. Mariner Class Assn. [22403]
U.S. Naval Sailing Assn. [20727]
U.S. Optimist Dinghy Assn. [22404]
U.S. Power Squadrons [22405]
U.S. Sailing Assn. [22406]
U.S. Sailing Assn. I Coun. of Sailing Associations [22407]
U.S. Sailing Assn. I U.S. Sailing Found. [22408]
U.S. Soling Assn. [22409]
U.S. Superyacht Assn. [465]
U.S. Wayfarer Assn. [22410]
U.S. Windsurfing Assn. [22411]
U.S. Yngling Assn. [22412]
Windmill Class Assn. [22413]

Wooden Canoe Heritage Assn. [22414]
Yachting Club of Am. [22415]
Boating Coun; Natl. Safe [12996]
Boating Indus. Associations [★2365]
Boating Writers Intl. [2815], 108 9th St., Wilmette, IL 60091, (847)736-4142
Boating Writers Intl. [2815], 108 9th St., Wilmette, IL 60091, (847)736-4142
Bob Homan Fan Club - Address unknown since 2011.
Bob und Schlittenverband fur Deutschland e.V. [IO], Berchtesgaden, Germany
Bobby Labonte Fan Club [23900], PO Box 358, Trinity, NC 27370
Bobsled and Skeleton Fed; U.S. [22926]
Bobsleigh
 Fed. Internationale de Bobsleigh et de Tobogganing [13966]
 U.S. Bobsled and Skeleton Fed. [22926]
Bobsleigh Canada Skeleton [IO], Calgary, AB, Canada
Bocce
 U.S. Bocce Fed. [22416]
 World Bocce League [22417]
 World Bocce League [22417]
Bocce Fed. of Australia [IO], Kew East, Australia
Bockus Intl. Soc. of Gastroenterology [14556], North Shore Univ. Hosp., 300 Community Dr., Manhasset, NY 11030, (516)562-2061
Bockus Intl. Soc. of Gastroenterology [14556], North Shore Univ. Hosp., 300 Community Dr., Manhasset, NY 11030, (516)562-2061
BOCS Found. [IO], Szekesfehervar, Hungary
Bodomase Development Assn. USA [11551], 6844 Signature Cir., Alexandria, VA 22310, (703)472-4064
Body Positive - Defunct.
Body Positive Tayside [IO], Dundee, United Kingdom
Body Stress Release Assn. - UK [IO], Lightwater, United Kingdom
Bodybuilding
 Intl. Natural Bodybuilding and Fitness Fed. [22418]
 Intl. Natural Bodybuilding and Fitness Fed. [22418]
 Natl. Amateur Body Builders Assn. U.S.A. [22419]
 Natural Fitness Trainers Assn. [22809]
 North Amer. Natural Bodybuilding Fed. [22420]
 North Amer. Strongman [22421]
Bodymind Acupressure; Jin Shin Do Found. for [16015]
BODYWHYS: The Eating Disorders Assn. of Ireland [IO], Dublin, Ireland
Boer Goat Breeders Assn. of Australia [IO], Armidale, Australia
Boerenbond [IO], Leuven, Belgium
Boersenverein des Deutschen Buchhandels e.V. [★IO]
Boghandlerforeningen [★IO]
Bogra Young Men's Christian Association [IO], Bogra, Bangladesh
Boise Peace Quilt Proj. - Address unknown since 2011.
Boissons rafraichissantes [★IO]
Bol Chumann na hEireann [IO], Carrigtwohill, Ireland
Bold Brave Courageous - Address unknown since 2011.
BOLD/Challenge Aspen [★22509]
Bolivian Assn. of Insurance Companies [IO], La Paz, Bolivia
Bolivian Assn. of Osteology and Mineral Metabolism [IO], Santa Cruz, Bolivia
Bolivian Bible Soc. [IO], Cochabamba, Bolivia
Bolivian Forestry Assn. [IO], Santa Cruz, Bolivia
Bolivian Inst. of Foreign Trade [IO], Santa Cruz, Bolivia
Bolivian Private Bankers' Assn. [IO], La Paz, Bolivia
Bolivian Soc. of Clinical Neurophysiology [IO], La Paz, Bolivia
Bolivian Soc. of Gastroenterology and Digestive Endoscopy [IO], Cochabamba, Bolivia
Bolling Family Assn. [20433], PO Box 591, Vienna, VA 22183-0591, (703)281-7489
Bombardiers Inc. - Defunct.
Bombay Natural History Soc. [IO], Mumbai, India

BOMI Intl. - The Independent Inst. for Property and Fac. Mgt. Educ. [3003], 1 Park Pl., Ste. 475, Annapolis, MD 21401, (410)974-1410
Bonaire Govt. Tourist Off. [23432], Adams Unlimited Public Relations and Marketing, 80 Broad St., 32nd Fl., Ste. 3202, New York, NY 10004, (212)956-5912
Bonaire Tourist Info. Off. [★23432]
Bond Club of New York - Defunct.
Bond van Nederlandse Architecten [★IO]
Bond van Orkestdirigenten en Instructeurs [★IO]
Bond and Share Soc. [★21354]
Bondurant Family Assn. [20434], 750 Glenwood Dr., Athens, GA 30606-4628
Bone
 Amer. Assn. of Orthopaedic Executives [16020]
 Amer. Bone Marrow Donor Registry [13854]
 Bone Marrow Found. [13855]
 Caitlin Raymond Intl. Registry [13856]
 Center for Intl. Blood and Marrow Transplant Res. [13857]
 Center for Intl. Blood and Marrow Transplant Res. [13857]
Bone Marrow Donor Registry-American [★13854]
Bone Marrow Donors Worldwide [IO], Leiden, Netherlands
Bone Marrow Found. [13855], 30 E End Ave., Apt. 1F, New York, NY 10028, (212)838-3029
Bone Marrow Transplant Link; Natl. [16912]
Bone and Mineral Res; Amer. Soc. for [16053]
Bone Res. Soc. [IO], Colchester, United Kingdom
Bonefish and Tarpon Trust [4380], 24 Dockside Ln., PMB 83, Key Largo, FL 33037, (239)283-4733
Bonefish and Tarpon Unlimited [★4380]
Bones Soc. [★16020]
Bonnechere Soaring [IO], Petawawa, ON, Canada
Bonobo Conservation Initiative [5038], 2701 Connecticut Ave. NW, No. 702, Washington, DC 20008, (202)332-1014
Bonobo Conservation Initiative [5038], 2701 Connecticut Ave. NW, No. 702, Washington, DC 20008, (202)332-1014
Bonsai Clubs Assn. [★21786]
Bonsai Clubs Assn. [★21786]
Bonsai Clubs Intl. [21786], PO Box 8445, Metairie, LA 70011-8445, (504)832-8071
Bonsai Clubs Intl. [21786], PO Box 8445, Metairie, LA 70011-8445, (504)832-8071
Bonus Families [11997], PO Box 1238, Discovery Bay, CA 94505, (925)516-2681
Bonus Presskopia [IO], Stockholm, Sweden
Book Aid Intl. [IO], London, United Kingdom
Book Components Manufacturers Assn. - Defunct.
Book Indus. Study Group [2925], 370 Lexington Ave., Ste. 900, New York, NY 10017, (646)336-7141
Book Indus. Study Group [2925], 370 Lexington Ave., Ste. 900, New York, NY 10017, (646)336-7141
Book Mfrs'. Inst. [1603], Two Armand Beach Dr., Ste. 1B, Palm Coast, FL 32137-2612, (386)986-4552
Book and Periodical Coun. [IO], Toronto, ON, Canada
Book Publishers Assn. of Alberta [IO], Edmonton, AB, Canada
Book Publishers Assn. of Israel [IO], Tel Aviv, Israel
Book Publishers' Fed. of Luxembourg [IO], Luxembourg, Luxembourg
Book Publishers' Professional Assn. [IO], Toronto, ON, Canada
Bookplate Soc. [IO], London, United Kingdom
Books
 Antiquarian Booksellers Assn. of Am. [9437]
 Assn. of Booksellers for Children [466]
 Australian and New Zealand Assn. of Antiquarian Booksellers [12941]
 Bibliographical Soc. of Am. [9438]
 Big Little Book Collector's Club [21310]
 Binders' Guild [9439]
 Books For Africa [9440]
 Books For Africa [9440]
 Booksellers' Assn. of Finland [18864]
 Center for Book Arts [9441]
 Children's Book Coun. [9442]

A star before a book entry number signifies that the name is not listed separately, but is mentioned within the entry.

The Christian Sci. Publishing Soc. [2927]Books-Colombian Book Chamber
Dictionary Proj. [11134]
Dictionary Soc. of North Am. [9443]
Gen. Egyptian Book Org. [4260]
Great Books Found. [9444]
Grolier Club [9445]
Guild of Book Workers [9446]
Guild of Book Workers [9446]
Independent Online Booksellers Assn. [467]
Intl. Assn. of Cross-Reference Dir. Publishers [2940]
Jewish Book Coun. [9447]
Latvian Publishers' Assn. [18289]
Libraries Without Borders [8519]
Miniature Book Soc. [9448]
Miniature Book Soc. [9448]
Movable Book Soc. [21233]
Natl. Book Critics Circle [9449]
Natl. Chamber of the Mexican Publishing Indus. [20306]
Oper. Paperback [11100]
Soc. for the History of Authorship, Reading and Publishing [9450]
Soc. for the History of Authorship, Reading and Publishing [9450]
Soc. of Phantom Friends [9451]
Soc. of Phantom Friends [9451]
U.S. Bd. on Books for Young People [9452]
Univ. of Virginia I Bibliographical Soc. [9453]
Books for the Barrios [11903], 2350 Whitman Rd., Ste. D, Concord, CA 94518-2541, (925)687-7701
Books for the Barrios [11903], 2350 Whitman Rd., Ste. D, Concord, CA 94518-2541, (925)687-7701
Books for a Better World [8004], 5025 N Central Ave., Ste. 649, Phoenix, AZ 85012
Books for a Better World [8004], 5025 N Central Ave., Ste. 649, Phoenix, AZ 85012
Books For Africa [9440], 253 E 4th St., Ste. 200, St. Paul, MN 55101, (651)602-9844
Books For Africa [9440], 253 E 4th St., Ste. 200, St. Paul, MN 55101, (651)602-9844
Books For Soldiers [11083], 116 Lowes Food Dr., No. 123, Lewisville, NC 27023
Books for Keeps [IO], London, United Kingdom
Booksellers' Assn. of Finland [IO], Helsinki, Finland
Booksellers Assn. of the United Kingdom and Ireland [IO], London, United Kingdom
Booksellers New Zealand [IO], Wellington, New Zealand
Boomerangs
U.S. Boomerang Assn. [22422]
Boone and Crockett Club [5039], 250 Sta. Dr., Missoula, MT 59801, (406)542-1888
Boone Soc. [20435], 1303 Hunter Ace Way, Cedar Park, TX 78613
Boone Soc. [20435], 1303 Hunter Ace Way, Cedar Park, TX 78613
Boot and Shoe Travelers Assn. of New York [1457], 50 W 34th St., Ste. 8A6, New York, NY 10001-3057, (212)564-1069
Bord na gCon [★IO]
Border Collie Rescue [IO], Richmond, United Kingdom
Border Terrier Club of Am. [21528], Brenda Weintraub, Membership Coor., 532 Mill Creek Crossing, Millboro, VA 24460, (540)997-5570
Borderland Sciences Res. Found. [7247], PO Box 6250, Eureka, CA 95502, (707)497-6911
Boreal Songbird Initiative [5040], 1904 Third Ave., Ste. 305, Seattle, WA 98101, (206)956-9040
Boreal Songbird Initiative [5040], 1904 Third Ave., Ste. 305, Seattle, WA 98101, (206)956-9040
Borgward Owners' Club - Address unknown since 2010.
Born Free Found. [IO], Horsham, United Kingdom
Born Free USA [10934], PO Box 22505, Sacramento, CA 95822, (916)447-3085
Born Young [★20493]
Borzoi Club of Am. [21529], Edna Ogata, Membership Chair, 579 Cotton St., Menlo Park, CA 94025, (630)325-8940
Bosnia and Herzegovina Sports Medicine Assn. [IO], Sarajevo, Bosnia-Hercegovina
Bosniak Amer. Advisory Coun. for Bosnia and Herzegovina [17895], 1634 I St. NW, Ste. 725, Washington, DC 20006, (202)347-6742

BOSPO [IO], Tuzla, Bosnia-Hercegovina
Boss 302 Registry [21011], 1817 Janet Ave., Lebanon, PA 17046-1845, (717)274-5280
Boss 429 Mustang World Registry [21012], PO Box 8035, Spokane, WA 99203, (509)448-0252
Boston Computer Soc. - Defunct.
Boston Intl. Found. for Medical Education/Exchange
Boston Intl. Found. for Medical Education/Exchange - Address unknown since 2011.
Boston Intl. Found. for Medical Exchange [★15295]
Boston Terrier Club of Am. [21530], 3878 Banks Rd., Cincinnati, OH 45245-2602, (513)943-9432
Boston Theological Inst. [9008], 197 Herrick Rd., Newton Centre, MA 02459, (617)527-4880
Boston Univ. Washington Journalism Prog. [★8449]
Boston Women's Hea. Book Collective [★17135]
Bostonian Soc. [9755], Old State House, 206 Washington St., Boston, MA 02109, (617)720-1713
Botanical Gardens
Amer. Penstemon Soc. [21779]
Center for Plant Conservation [4018]
Botanical Gardens Conservation Intl. [IO], Richmond, United Kingdom
Botanical Soc. [★6351]
Botanical Soc. of Am. [6351], PO Box 299, St. Louis, MO 63166, (314)577-9566
Botanical Soc. of the British Isles [IO], London, United Kingdom
Botanical Soc. of Japan [IO], Tokyo, Japan
Botanical Soc. of Lund [IO], Lund, Sweden
Botanical Soc. of Scotland [IO], Edinburgh, United Kingdom
Botanical Soc. of South Africa [IO], Claremont, Republic of South Africa
Botaniese Vereniging van Suid-Afrika [★IO]
Botany
Amer. Bamboo Soc. [6339]
Amer. Bamboo Soc. [6339]
Amer. Botanical Coun. [6340]
Amer. Bryological and Lichenological Soc. [6341]
Amer. Bryological and Lichenological Soc. [6341]
The Amer. Chestnut Found. [6342]
Amer. Fern Soc. [6343]
Amer. Herb Assn. [6344]
Amer. Orchid Soc. [6345]
Amer. Orchid Soc. [6345]
Amer. Penstemon Soc. [21779]
Amer. Phytopathological Soc. [6346]
Amer. Soc. for Horticultural Sci. [6347]
Amer. Soc. of Plant Biologists [6348]
Amer. Soc. of Plant Taxonomists [6349]
Aquatic Plant Mgt. Soc. [6350]BotanyArizona Cactus and Succulent Res.
Australasian Plant Pathology Soc. [6433]
Australian Garden History Soc. [15020]
Botanical Soc. of Am. [6351]
Desert Botanical Garden [6352]
Ethnobotanical Conservation Org. for South East Asia [4053]
Friends of the Natl. Arboretum [6353]
The Gardeners of Am. [21794]BotanyHebe Soc.
Herb Res. Found. [6354]
Herb Soc. of Am. [6355]
Indoor Gardening Soc. of Am. [21801]
Intl. Brugmansia and Datura Soc. [21738]
Intl. Bulb Soc. [6356]
Intl. Bulb Soc. [6356]
Intl. Org. of Citrus Virologists [6357]
Intl. Org. of Citrus Virologists [6357]
Intl. Org. of Plant Biosystematists [6358]
Intl. Org. of Plant Biosystematists [6358]
Intl. Palm Soc. [6359]
Intl. Palm Soc. [6359]
Intl. Phalaenopsis Alliance [4671]
Intl. Soc. for Molecular Plant Microbe Interactions [6360]
Intl. Soc. for Molecular Plant Microbe Interactions [6360]
Intl. Soc. of Photosynthesis Res. [859]
Lady Bird Johnson Wildflower Center [6361]
Magnolia Soc. Intl. [6362]
North Amer. Lily Soc. [21815]
Org. for Flora Neotropica [6363]
Org. for Flora Neotropica [6363]
Phycological Soc. of Am. [6364]

Phycological Soc. of Am. [6364]
Plant Growth Regulation Soc. of Am. [6365]
Plumeria Soc. of Am. [21817]
Rhododendron Species Found. [6366]
Soc. for Economic Botany [6367]
Soc. of Herbarium Curators [6368]
Women's Horticultural Assn. [4680]
World Bamboo Org. [4738]
Both ENDS [IO], Amsterdam, Netherlands
Botswana Athletics Assn. [IO], Gaborone, Botswana
Botswana Badminton Assn. [IO], Gaborone, Botswana
Botswana Natl. Olympic Comm. [IO], Gaborone, Botswana
Botswana Physiotherapy Assn. [IO], Gaborone, Botswana
Botswana Red Cross Soc. [IO], Gaborone, Botswana
Botswana Soc. [IO], Gaborone, Botswana
Botswana Squash Rackets Assn. [IO], Gaborone, Botswana
Botswana-Sweden Friendship Assn. [IO], Stockholm, Sweden
Botswana Tennis Assn. [IO], Gaborone, Botswana
Bottle Caps
Crowncap Collectors Soc. Intl. [21330]
Natl. Pop Can Collectors [21381]
Bottles
Fed. of Historical Bottle Collectors [21234]
Intl. Assn. of Jim Beam Bottle and Specialties Clubs [21235]
Intl. Assn. of Jim Beam Bottle and Specialties Clubs [21235]
Intl. Chinese Snuff Bottle Soc. [21236]
Natl. Pop Can Collectors [21381]
Bounders United [22185], 1211 S Western Skies Dr., Gilbert, AZ 85296-4346, (480)688-6440
Bourbon Inst. [★180]
Bourse de Commerce Europeenne [★IO]
Bowfishing Assn. of Am. [22573], 5 Eldon Starr Ln., Conway, AR 72032, (501)730-3169
Bowhunters of America - Defunct.
Bowhunting Preservation Alliance - Address unknown since 2011.
Bowlers to Veterans Link [22423], 11350 Random Hills Rd., Ste. 800, Fairfax, VA 22030, (703)934-6039
Bowlers' Victory League [★22423]
Bowling
Amer. Blind Bowling Assn. [22502]BowlingBahrain Bowling Assn.
Bowlers to Veterans Link [22423]
Intl. Assn. of Bowling Equipment Specialists [569]
Intl. Bowling Pro Shop and Instructors Assn. [468]
Intl. Gay Bowling Org. [22424]
The Natl. Bowling Assn. [22425]
Natl. Duckpin Bowling Cong. [22426]
Parents-Coaches Assn. [22427]
Professional Bowlers Assn. of Am. [22428]
Scottish Women's Indoor Bowling Assn. [1063]
U.S. Bowling Cong. [22429]
U.S. Bowling Cong. [22429]
U.S. Lawn Bowls Assn. [22430]
Western Women Premier Bowlers [22431]
Women's All-Star Assn. [22432]
Bowling Assn; Amer. Wheelchair [22506]
Bowling Assn; Natl. Deaf Women's [22517]
Bowling Inc. - Address unknown since 2011.
Bowling Proprietors' Assn. of Am. [3326], 621 Six Flags Dr., Arlington, TX 76011, (800)343-1329
Bowling Proprietors' Assn. of Canada [IO], Markham, ON, Canada
Bowling Writers Assn. of Am. [2816], 621 Six Flags Dr., Arlington, TX 76011, (800)343-1329
Bowling Writers Assn. of Am. and Natl. Women Bowling Writers Assn. [★2816]
Bowls Australia [IO], Northcote, Australia
Bowls British Columbia [IO], Vancouver, BC, Canada
Bowls Canada Boulingrin [IO], Ottawa, ON, Canada
Bowls England [IO], Worthing, United Kingdom
Bowls Manitoba [IO], Winnipeg, MB, Canada
Bowls SA [IO], Brooklyn Park, Australia
Bowls Saskatchewan [IO], Regina, SK, Canada
Bowls South Africa [IO], Parklands, Republic of South Africa

Reference to "IO" in place of a book number signifies that the association may be found in the 50th edition of International Organizations.

Box Culvert Assn. **[IO]**, Leicester, United Kingdom
Box Off. Mgt. Intl. **[★1204]**
Box Off. Mgt. Intl. **[★1204]**
Box Proj. **[12811]**, 315 Losher St., Ste. 100, Hernando, MS 38632, (662)449-5002
Box Proj. **[12811]**, 315 Losher St., Ste. 100, Hernando, MS 38632, (662)449-5002
Boxboard Res. and Development Assn. **[★887]**
Boxer Club - Denmark **[IO]**, Otterup, Denmark
Boxer Klubben **[★IO]**
Boxing
   Amer. Assn. for the Improvement of Boxing **[22433]**
   Intl. Boxing Fed. **[22434]**
   Intl. Boxing Fed. **[22434]**
   Intl. Boxing Hall of Fame Museum **[22435]**
   Intl. Chinese Boxing Assn. **[22436]**
   Intl. Chinese Boxing Assn. **[22436]**
   Intl. Female Boxers Assn. **[22437]**
   North Amer. Boxing Fed. **[22438]**
   U.S.A. Boxing **[22439]**
Boxing BC **[IO]**, Richmond, BC, Canada
Boxing Newfoundland **[IO]**, Torbay, NL, Canada
Boxing Nova Scotia **[IO]**, Bedford, NS, Canada
Boxing Ontario **[IO]**, Toronto, ON, Canada
Boxing Saskatchewan **[IO]**, Regina, SK, Canada
Boy Scouts of Am. **[13018]**, PO Box 152079, Irving, TX 75015-2079, (972)580-2000
Boy Scouts Assn. of Zimbabwe **[IO]**, Harare, Zimbabwe
Boykin Spaniel Club and Breeders Assn. of Am. **[21531]**, PO Box 42, Gilbert, SC 29054, (803)532-0990
Boys Baseball **[★22288]**
Boys' Brigade **[IO]**, Hemel Hempstead, United Kingdom
Boys' Club Fed. of Am. **[★13511]**
Boys Clubs of Am. **[★13511]**
Boys and Girls Clubs of Am. **[13511]**, 1275 Peachtree St. NE, Atlanta, GA 30309-3506, (404)487-5700
Boys and Girls Clubs of Canada **[IO]**, Markham, ON, Canada
Boys' and Girls' Clubs of Northern Ireland **[IO]**, Belfast, United Kingdom
Boys Hope **[★13512]**
Boys Hope Girls Hope **[13512]**, 12120 Bridgeton Square Dr., Bridgeton, MO 63044-2607, (314)298-1250
Boys Town Jerusalem Found. of Am. **[13513]**, 1 Penn Plz., Ste. 6250, New York, NY 10119, (800)4MY-BOYS
Boys' Town of Rome **[★13514]**
Boys' Towns of Italy **[13514]**, 250 E 63rd St., Ste. 204, New York, NY 10021, (212)980-8770
Boys of Woodcraft Auxiliary of the Woodmen of the World **[★19285]**
Boys of Woodcraft Sportsmen's Clubs/Girl of Woodcraft Sportsmen's Clubs **[★19285]**
BP Amoco Marketers Assn. **[2645]**, 15 Lake St., Ste. 280, Savannah, GA 31411, (912)598-7939
BP and Amoco Oil Marketers Assn. **[★2645]**
BPA Intl. **[★87]**
BPA Intl. **[★87]**
BPA Worldwide **[87]**, Two Corporate Dr., 9th Fl., Shelton, CT 06484, (203)447-2800
BPA Worldwide **[87]**, Two Corporate Dr., 9th Fl., Shelton, CT 06484, (203)447-2800
BPIF Cartons **[IO]**, London, United Kingdom
BPM-Focus **[649]**, 3640-B3 N Fed. Hwy., No. 421, Lighthouse Point, FL 33064, (954)688-4922
BPM-Focus **[649]**, 3640-B3 N Fed. Hwy., No. 421, Lighthouse Point, FL 33064, (954)688-4922
Brabham Owners Register **[★21013]**
Brabham Owners Register **[★21013]**
Brabham Register **[21013]**, 1611 Alvina Ave., Sacramento, CA 95822, (916)454-1115
Brabham Register **[21013]**, 1611 Alvina Ave., Sacramento, CA 95822, (916)454-1115
BRAC **[IO]**, Dhaka, Bangladesh
Brachytherapy Soc; Amer. **[13880]**
Bradford Chamber of Commerce **[IO]**, Bradford, United Kingdom
Bradley Commn. on History in Schools **[★8260]**
Brady Campaign to Prevent Gun Violence **[17683]**, 1225 Eye St. NW, Ste. 1100, Washington, DC 20005, (202)898-0792

Brady Center to Prevent Gun Violence **[17684]**, 1225 Eye St. NW, Ste. 1100, Washington, DC 20005, (202)289-7319
Brahman Samaj of North Am. **[9652]**, PO Box 716, Belle Mead, NJ 08502, (908)359-3348
Brahman Samaj of North Am. **[9652]**, PO Box 716, Belle Mead, NJ 08502, (908)359-3348
Brahms Soc; Amer. **[9494]**
Braille Assn; Natl. **[17104]**
Braille Authority of North Am. **[17069]**, 1805 N Oakland St., Arlington, VA 22207, (202)707-0722
Braille Authority of North Am. **[17069]**, 1805 N Oakland St., Arlington, VA 22207, (202)707-0722
Braille Books for Children; Seedlings **[9036]**
Braille Chess Assn. **[IO]**, Sheffield, United Kingdom
Braille Evangelism Assn; Lutheran **[17097]**
Braille Evangelism Assn; Lutheran **[17097]**
Braille Found. of Uruguay **[IO]**, Montevideo, Uruguay
Braille Press; Natl. **[17105]**
Braille Revival League - Address unknown since 2010.
Brain Attack Coalition **[16729]**, NINDS, 31 Center Dr., Bldg. 31, Rm. 8A-16, MSC 2540, Bethesda, MD 20892, (301)496-5751
Brain Injury Assn. **[★14683]**
Brain Injury Assn. of Alberta **[IO]**, Red Deer, AB, Canada
Brain Injury Assn. of Am. **[14683]**, 1608 Spring Hill Rd., Ste. 110, Vienna, VA 22182, (703)761-0750
Brain Injury Assn. of Chatham-Kent **[IO]**, Chatham, ON, Canada
Brain Injury Assn. of London and Region **[IO]**, London, ON, Canada
Brain Injury Assn. of New South Wales **[IO]**, Epping, Australia
Brain Injury Assn. of New Zealand **[IO]**, North Shore City, New Zealand
Brain Injury Assn. of New Zealand - Auckland **[IO]**, Auckland, New Zealand
Brain Injury Assn. of New Zealand - Bay of Plenty **[IO]**, Mount Maunganui, New Zealand
Brain Injury Assn. of New Zealand - Canterbury **[IO]**, Christchurch, New Zealand
Brain Injury Assn. of New Zealand - Central Districts **[IO]**, Palmerston North, New Zealand
Brain Injury Assn. of New Zealand - Eastern Bay of Plenty **[IO]**, Whakatane, New Zealand
Brain Injury Assn. of New Zealand - Gisborne **[IO]**, Gisborne, New Zealand
Brain Injury Assn. of New Zealand - Hawkes Bay **[IO]**, Hastings, New Zealand
Brain Injury Assn. of New Zealand - Nelson **[IO]**, Nelson, New Zealand
Brain Injury Assn. of New Zealand - Northland **[IO]**, Whangarei, New Zealand
Brain Injury Assn. of New Zealand - Rotorua **[IO]**, Rotorua, New Zealand
Brain Injury Assn. of New Zealand - Taranaki **[IO]**, New Plymouth, New Zealand
Brain Injury Assn. of New Zealand - Waikato **[IO]**, Hamilton, New Zealand
Brain Injury Assn. of New Zealand - Wanganui **[IO]**, Wanganui, New Zealand
Brain Injury Assn. of New Zealand - Wellington **[IO]**, Wellington, New Zealand
Brain Injury Assn. of Niagara **[IO]**, St. Catharines, ON, Canada
Brain Injury Assn. of North Bay **[IO]**, North Bay, ON, Canada
Brain Injury Assn. of Nova Scotia **[IO]**, Halifax, NS, Canada
Brain Injury Assn. of Ottawa Valley **[IO]**, Ottawa, ON, Canada
Brain Injury Assn. of Peel and Halton **[IO]**, Mississauga, ON, Canada
Brain Injury Assn. of Queensland **[IO]**, South Brisbane, Australia
Brain Injury Assn. of Sarnia and Lambton **[IO]**, Sarnia, ON, Canada
Brain Injury Assn. of Sault Ste. Marie and District **[IO]**, Sault Ste. Marie, ON, Canada
Brain Injury Assn. of Southeastern Ontario **[IO]**, Kingston, ON, Canada
Brain Injury Assn. of Sudbury and District **[IO]**, Sudbury, ON, Canada

Brain Injury Assn. of Tasmania **[IO]**, Moonah, Australia
Brain Injury Assn. of Waterloo-Wellington **[IO]**, Kitchener, ON, Canada
Brain Injury Assn. of Windsor-Essex County **[IO]**, Windsor, ON, Canada
Brain Injury Australia **[IO]**, Marrickville, Australia
Brain Injury Network of South Australia **[IO]**, Adelaide, Australia
Brain Injury Rsrc. Center **[16561]**, PO Box 84151, Seattle, WA 98124-5451, (206)621-8558
Brain Injury Soc. of Toronto **[IO]**, Toronto, ON, Canada
Brain Res. Soc. of Finland **[IO]**, Helsinki, Finland
Brain Tumor Assn; Amer. **[13881]**
Brain Tumor Coalition; North Amer. **[13961]**
Brain Tumor Found. of Canada **[IO]**, London, ON, Canada
Brain Tumor Found; Childhood **[14379]**
Brain Tumor Found. for Children **[14058]**, 6065 Roswell Rd. NE, Ste. 505, Atlanta, GA 30328-4015, (404)252-4107
Brain Tumor Found. of the U.S; Pediatric **[13966]**
Brain Tumour Australia **[IO]**, Kotara, Australia
Brainard-Brainerd-Braynard Family Assn. - Address unknown since 2011.
BrainTrust Canada Assn. **[IO]**, Kelowna, BC, Canada
Brainwave The Irish Epilepsy Assn. **[IO]**, Dublin, Ireland
Brake Lining Mfrs. Assn. **[★328]**
Brake Sys. Parts Mfrs. Coun. **[★318]**
Bram Stoker Club **[IO]**, Dublin, Ireland
Bram Stoker Memorial Assn. **[9354]**, 29 Washington Sq. W, Penthouse N, Ste. 145, New York, NY 10011
Bram Stoker Memorial Assn. **[9354]**, 29 Washington Sq. W, Penthouse N, Ste. 145, New York, NY 10011
Bram Stoker Soc. - Ireland **[IO]**, Dublin, Ireland
Brancheforening for Frugd og Grongindustrien **[★IO]**
Brancheforeningen for Saebe-, Parfumeri-, Toilet- og Kemisk-teknisk Artikler **[★IO]**
Brand-Beskermingsvereniging van Suider-Afraid **[★IO]**
Brandeis - Bardin Inst. - Address unknown since 2011.
Brandeis Univ. Alumni Assn. **[18856]**, PO Box 549110, Waltham, MA 02454-9110, (781)736-4100
Branding Assn. of Malaysia **[IO]**, Selangor, Malaysia
Brangus Beestelersgenootskap van Suid-Afrika **[★IO]**
Brangus Cattle Breeder's Soc. of South Africa **[IO]**, Bloemfontein, Republic of South Africa
Branschforeningen Ljud, Ljus och Bild for professionellt bruk **[★IO]**
Branscombe Richmond Fan Club - Address unknown since 2011.
Brantley Assn. of Am. **[20436]**, 4750 Oakleigh Manor Dr., Powder Springs, GA 30127, (770)428-4402
Brasilian League Against Epilepsy **[IO]**, Sao Paulo, Brazil
Brass Gas Stop Inst. **[★2784]**
Brass Gas Stop Inst. **[★2784]**
Brass Ring Soc. - Address unknown since 2010.
Braun Center for Holocaust Stud. **[★17783]**
Braunvieh Assn. of Am. **[3907]**, 5750 Epsilon, Ste. 200, San Antonio, TX 78249, (210)561-2892
Brave Intl. **[19808]**, 5338 SW 183rd Ave., Miramar, FL 33029, (954)964-2362
Brave Kids **[14059]**, United Cerebral Palsy, 1825 K St. NW, Ste. 600, Washington, DC 20006, (800)872-5827
Brazil
   Amazonas Hope for Hea. **[14747]**
   Amer. Brazilian Cultural Exchange **[9513]**
   Bahia St. **[12717]**
   Brazil Philatelic Assn. **[22022]**
   Brazil-U.S. Bus. Coun. **[23354]**
   Brazilian-American Chamber of Commerce **[23334]**
   Brazilian Govt. Trade Bur. of the Consulate Gen. of Brazil in New York **[23335]**
Brazil-Canada Chamber of Commerce **[IO]**, Toronto, ON, Canada

A star before a book entry number signifies that the name is not listed separately, but is mentioned within the entry.

Brazil Philatelic Assn. [22022], Mr. William V. Kriebel, 1923 Manning St., Philadelphia, PA 19103-5728

Brazil Specialty Coffee Assn. [IO], Machado, Brazil

Brazil-U.S. Bus. Coun. [23354], 1615 H St. NW, Washington, DC 20062, (202)463-5729

Brazilian
Brazil Philatelic Assn. [22022]
Brazil-U.S. Bus. Coun. [23354]
Brazilian Govt. Trade Bur. of the Consulate Gen. of Brazil in New York [23335]

Brazilian Acad. of Letters [IO], Rio de Janeiro, Brazil

Brazilian Acad. of Sciences [IO], Rio de Janeiro, Brazil

Brazilian Agricultural Assn. [IO], Sao Paulo, Brazil

Brazilian Agricultural Res. Corp. [IO], Brasilia, Brazil

Brazilian Agroforestry Network [IO], Rio de Janeiro, Brazil

Brazilian-American Chamber of Commerce [23334], 509 Madison Ave., Ste. 304, New York, NY 10022, (212)751-4691

Brazilian-American Cultural Inst. - Address unknown since 2010.

Brazilian Assn. of Advertisers [IO], Sao Paulo, Brazil

Brazilian Assn. of the Aerosol Indus. [IO], Sao Paulo, Brazil

Brazilian Assn. of Amyotrophic Lateral Sclerosis [IO], Sao Paulo, Brazil

Brazilian Assn. of the Automated Glass Indus. [IO], Sao Paulo, Brazil

Brazilian Assn. of Automotive Engg. [IO], Sao Paulo, Brazil

Brazilian Assn. of Autoparts Mfrs. [IO], Sao Paulo, Brazil

Brazilian Assn. for Bioinformatics and Computational Biology [IO], Ribeirao Preto, Brazil

Brazilian Assn. of Ceramic Tile Mfrs. [IO], Sao Paulo, Brazil

Brazilian Assn. of the Coffee Roasting and Grinding Indus. [IO], Rio de Janeiro, Brazil

Brazilian Assn. of Commercial Banks [IO], Sao Paulo, Brazil

Brazilian Assn. of Credit Card Companies and Services [IO], Sao Paulo, Brazil

Brazilian Assn. of Drinks Producers [IO], Sao Paulo, Brazil

Brazilian Assn. of Engg. Consultants [IO], Rio de Janeiro, Brazil

Brazilian Assn. of Furniture Indus. [IO], Sao Paulo, Brazil

Brazilian Assn. of Homeopathic Medicine [IO], Vitoria, Brazil

Brazilian Assn. of Infrastructure and Basic Indus. [IO], Sao Paulo, Brazil

Brazilian Assn. of Media Companies Representatives [IO], Sao Paulo, Brazil

Brazilian Assn. of Motor Vehicle Mfrs. [IO], Sao Paulo, Brazil

Brazilian Assn. of the Nonwoven and Tech. Textiles Indus. [IO], Sao Paulo, Brazil

Brazilian Assn. of Orthodontics and Facial Orthopedics [IO], Goiania, Brazil

Brazilian Assn. of Sales and Marketing Directors [IO], Sao Paulo, Brazil

Brazilian Assn. of Shopping Centers [IO], Sao Paulo, Brazil

Brazilian Assn. of Software Companies [IO], Sao Paulo, Brazil

Brazilian Assn. of the Textile Indus. [★18938]

Brazilian Assn. of Vegetable Oil Indus. [IO], Sao Paulo, Brazil

Brazilian Automatics Soc. [IO], Porto Alegre, Brazil

Brazilian Banks Assn. [IO], Sao Paulo, Brazil

Brazilian Book Chamber [IO], Sao Paulo, Brazil

Brazilian Cement Mfrs'. Assn. [IO], Sao Paulo, Brazil

Brazilian Center for Planning and Anal. [IO], Sao Paulo, Brazil

Brazilian Ceramics Assn. [IO], Sao Paulo, Brazil

Brazilian Chamber of Commerce in Great Britain [IO], London, United Kingdom

Brazilian Chem. Assn. [IO], Rio de Janeiro, Brazil

Brazilian Chem. Indus. Assn. [IO], Sao Paulo, Brazil

Brazilian Chicken Producers and Exporters Assn. [IO], Sao Paulo, Brazil

Brazilian Corrugated Bd. Assn. [IO], Sao Paulo, Brazil

Brazilian Cosmetics Assn. [★3018]

Brazilian Cosmetology Assn. [IO], Sao Paulo, Brazil

Brazilian Dimensional Embroidery Intl. Guild [22164], 13013 89th Ave. N, Seminole, FL 33776, (727)391-9207

Brazilian Dimensional Embroidery Intl. Guild [22164], 13013 89th Ave. N, Seminole, FL 33776, (727)391-9207

Brazilian Direct Selling Assn. [IO], Sao Paulo, Brazil

Brazilian Elecl. and Electronics Indus. Assn. [IO], Sao Paulo, Brazil

Brazilian Floorball Assn. [IO], Sao Paulo, Brazil

Brazilian Food Indus. Assn. [IO], Sao Paulo, Brazil

Brazilian Franchising Assn. [IO], Sao Paulo, Brazil

Brazilian Genetics Soc. [IO], Ribeirao Preto, Brazil

Brazilian Geomorphological Union [IO], Uberlandia, Brazil

Brazilian Geophysical Soc. [IO], Rio de Janeiro, Brazil

Brazilian Govt. Trade Bur. of the Consulate Gen. of Brazil in New York [23335], 1185 Ave. of the Americas, 21st Fl., New York, NY 10036, (917)777-7777

Brazilian Hotels' Assn. [IO], Brasilia, Brazil

Brazilian Ice Sports Fed. [IO], Rio de Janeiro, Brazil

Brazilian Inst. of Economics [IO], Rio de Janeiro, Brazil

Brazilian Inst. of History and Geography [IO], Rio de Janeiro, Brazil

Brazilian Inst. for Info. in Sci. and Tech. [IO], Brasilia, Brazil

Brazilian Interdisciplinary AIDS Assn. [IO], Rio de Janeiro, Brazil

Brazilian Jet Sports Assn. [IO], Sao Paulo, Brazil

Brazilian Machinery Builders' Assn. [IO], Sao Paulo, Brazil

Brazilian Medical Spiritist Assn. [IO], Sao Paulo, Brazil

Brazilian Metallurgy and Materials Assn. [IO], Sao Paulo, Brazil

Brazilian Muscular Dystrophy Assn. [IO], Sao Paulo, Brazil

Brazilian Olympic Comm. [IO], Rio de Janeiro, Brazil

Brazilian Packaging Assn. [IO], Sao Paulo, Brazil

Brazilian Press Assn. [IO], Rio de Janeiro, Brazil

Brazilian Soc. of Aesthetic Dentistry [IO], Rio de Janeiro, Brazil

Brazilian Soc. of Aesthetic Medicine [IO], Rio de Janeiro, Brazil

Brazilian Soc. of Biochemistry and Molecular Biology [IO], Sao Paulo, Brazil

Brazilian Soc. of Biomedical Engg. [IO], Rio de Janeiro, Brazil

Brazilian Soc. of Clinical Neurophysiology [IO], Conjunto, Brazil

Brazilian Soc. of Dermatology [IO], Rio de Janeiro, Brazil

Brazilian Soc. of Entomology [IO], Curitiba, Brazil

Brazilian Soc. of Hea. Informatics [IO], Sao Paulo, Brazil

Brazilian Soc. of Hypertension [IO], Sao Paulo, Brazil

Brazilian Soc. for Metrology [IO], Rio de Janeiro, Brazil

Brazilian Soc. for Microscopy and Microanalysis [IO], Rio de Janeiro, Brazil

Brazilian Soc. of Operational Res. [IO], Rio de Janeiro, Brazil

Brazilian Soc. of Osteoporosis [IO], Campinas, Brazil

Brazilian Soc. of Pharmacology and Experimental Therapeutics [IO], Sao Paulo, Brazil

Brazilian Soc. of Physiology [IO], Sao Paulo, Brazil

Brazilian Soc. for Soil Mechanics and Geotechnical Engg. [IO], Sao Paulo, Brazil

Brazilian Stud. Assn. [8349], Univ. of Illinois at Urbana-Champaign, 223 Intl. Stud. Bldg., 910 S 5th St., Champaign, IL 61820, (217)333-8248

Brazilian Stud. Assn. [8349], Univ. of Illinois at Urbana-Champaign, 223 Intl. Stud. Bldg., 910 S 5th St., Champaign, IL 61820, (217)333-8248

Brazilian Supermarkets' Assn. [IO], Sao Paulo, Brazil

Brazilian Textile and Apparel Indus. Assn. [IO], Sao Paulo, Brazil

Brazilian Tobacco Indus. Assn. [IO], Brasilia, Brazil

Brazilian Travel Agencies' Assn. [IO], Sao Paulo, Brazil

Brazilian Water Ski Confed. [IO], Campinas, Brazil

The BRC [★9580]

Bread Bakers Guild of Am. [391], 670 W Napa St., Ste. B, Sonoma, CA 95476, (707)935-1468

Bread Bakers Guild of Am. [391], 670 W Napa St., Ste. B, Sonoma, CA 95476, (707)935-1468

Bread for the Journey Intl. [12658], 9 Santa Gabriella Ct., Novato, CA 94945, (415)895-5357

Bread for the Journey Intl. [12658], 9 Santa Gabriella Ct., Novato, CA 94945, (415)895-5357

Bread Loaf Writers Conf. [10706], Middlebury Coll., Middlebury, VT 05753, (802)443-5286

Bread Machine Industry Assn. - Defunct.

Bread and Roses [11969], 233 Tamalpais Dr., Ste. 100, Corte Madera, CA 94925-1415, (415)945-7120

Bread for the World [17870], 425 3rd St. SW, Ste. 1200, Washington, DC 20024, (202)639-9400

Bread for the World [17870], 425 3rd St. SW, Ste. 1200, Washington, DC 20024, (202)639-9400

Break Away [★12764]

Break Away: The Alternative Break Connection [12764], 2451 Cumberland Pkwy., Ste. 3124, Atlanta, GA 30339, (800)903-0646

Break the Chains - Address unknown since 2011.

Break the Cycle [11881], 5777 W Century Blvd., Ste. 1150, Los Angeles, CA 90045, (310)286-3383

Breaking Ground [11552], 104 Neal St., Portland, ME 04102, (206)351-7778

Breakthrough [17815], 4 W 37th St., 4th Fl., New York, NY 10018, (212)868-6500

Breakthrough Collaborative [8005], 545 Sansome St., Ste. 700, San Francisco, CA 94111, (415)442-0600

Breakthroughs Abroad - Address unknown since 2010.

Breast Cancer Action [13892], 55 New Montgomery St., Ste. 323, San Francisco, CA 94105, (415)243-9301

Breast Cancer Advisory Center [★13976]

Breast Cancer Advisory Center; Rose Kushner [13976]

Breast Cancer Alliance; African Amer. [13877]

Breast Cancer Care [IO], London, United Kingdom

Breast Cancer Coalition; Natl. [13947]

Breast Cancer; Men Against [13942]

Breast Cancer; Mothers Supporting Daughters with [13943]

Breast Cancer Network Australia [IO], Camberwell, Australia

Breast Cancer Network of Strength - Address unknown since 2011.

Breast Cancer Soc. of Canada [IO], Sarnia, ON, Canada

Breast Cancer Support Ser. - Northern Ireland [IO], Belfast, United Kingdom

Breast Diseases
Amer. Assn. of Breast Care Professionals [13858]
Amer. Soc. of Breast Disease [13859]
Natl. Consortium of Breast Centers [13860]
Pink Isn't Always Pretty [13969]
Radiology Mammography Intl. [13861]
Radiology Mammography Intl. [13861]

Breast Imaging; Soc. of [16539]

Breast Implants
Command Trust Network [17125]

Breastfeeding
Black Mothers' Breastfeeding Assn. [13862]
Intl. Bd. of Lactation Consultant Examiners [13863]
Intl. Bd. of Lactation Consultant Examiners [13863]
Intl. Soc. for Res. in Human Milk and Lactation [13864]
Intl. Soc. for Res. in Human Milk and Lactation [13864]
Natl. Alliance for Breastfeeding Advocacy [13865]
U.S. Breastfeeding Comm. [13866]
U.S. Lactation Consultant Assn. [13867]

Breastfeeding Promotion Network of India [IO], New Delhi, India

Breath of Hope [13839], PO Box 6627, Charlottesville, VA 22906, (888)264-2340

Reference to "IO" in place of a book number signifies that the association may be found in the 50th edition of International Organizations.

Breathecure [13669], 3641-C Westheimer Rd., Houston, TX 77027, (713)839-9642

Brecht Forum [13125], 451 West St., New York, NY 10014, (212)242-4201

Brecht Forum [13125], 451 West St., New York, NY 10014, (212)242-4201

Brecknock Fed. of Young Farmers Clubs [IO], Brecon, United Kingdom

Brecon and Borders Welsh Pony and Cob Breeders Assn. [IO], Brecon, United Kingdom

Breeder's Registry [21725], 5541 Columbia Dr. N, Fresno, CA 93727

Brennan Center for Justice I NYU School of Law [5889], 161 Ave. of the Americas, 12th Fl., New York, NY 10013, (646)292-8310

Brethren
Assn. of Grace Brethren Ministers [19355]
Center for the Evangelical United Brethren Heritage [19719]

Brethren in Christ Missions [★20016]

Brethren in Christ Missions [★20016]

Brethren in Christ World Missions [20016], PO Box 390, Grantham, PA 17027, (717)697-2634

Brethren in Christ World Missions [20016], PO Box 390, Grantham, PA 17027, (717)697-2634

Brethren/Mennonite Coun. for Gay Concerns [★19785]

Brethren/Mennonite Coun. for Lesbian, Gay, Bisexual and Transgender Interest [19785], PO Box 6300, Minneapolis, MN 55406, (612)343-2060

Brethren/Mennonite Coun. for Lesbian and Gay Concerns [★19785]

Brethren Volunteer Ser. [13387], 1451 Dundee Ave., Elgin, IL 60120, (847)742-5100

Brethren Volunteer Ser. [13387], 1451 Dundee Ave., Elgin, IL 60120, (847)742-5100

Breton
Intl. Comm. for the Defense of the Breton Language, U.S. Br. [9454]
Intl. Comm. for the Defense of the Breton Language, U.S. Branch [9454]

Breton Democratic Union [IO], Nantes, France

Bretton Woods Comm. [17571], 1726 M St. NW, Ste. 200, Washington, DC 20036, (202)331-1616

Bretton Woods Proj. [IO], London, United Kingdom

Breweries Central Off. [IO], The Hague, Netherlands

Brewers Assn. [179], PO Box 1679, Boulder, CO 80306, (303)447-0816

Brewers Assn. of Canada [IO], Ottawa, ON, Canada

Brewers Assn. of Japan [IO], Tokyo, Japan

Brewers of Europe [IO], Brussels, Belgium

Brewers of Spain [IO], Madrid, Spain

Brewery Collectibles Club of Am. [21311], 747 Merus Ct., Fenton, MO 63026-2092, (636)343-6486

Brewing, Food and Beverage Indus. Suppliers Assn. [IO], Wolverhampton, United Kingdom

Brewing and Malting Barley Res. Inst. [IO], Winnipeg, MB, Canada

Brewmeisters Anonymous [20927], 20634 W Narramore Rd., Buckeye, AZ 85326, (602)751-3600

Brewster Kaleidoscope Soc. [21312], PO Box 95, Damascus, MD 20872, (740)352-2310

Brick by Brick for Tanzania! [8739], 539 Braatz Dr., Kewaskum, WI 53040, (262)573-9032

Brick Development Assn. [IO], London, United Kingdom

Brick Indus. Assn. [536], 1850 Centennial Park Dr., Ste. 301, Reston, VA 20191, (703)620-0010

Brick Inst. of Am. [★536]

Brick Mfrs. Assn. [★536]

Brickish Assn. [IO], Basingstoke, United Kingdom

Bricklayers, Masons and Plasterers Intl. of Amer. [★23164]

Bricklin Intl. [★21014]

Bricklin Intl. Owners Club [21014], 38083 Princeton Dr., North Ridgeville, OH 44039

Bridal Assn. of Am. [470], 531 H St., Bakersfield, CA 93304, (661)633-9200

Bridal Services
Amer. Professional Wedding Photographers Assn. [2710]
Assn. of Bridal Consultants [469]
Assn. of Bridal Consultants [469]
Bridal Assn. of Am. [470]

Bridal Show Producers Intl. [471]

Intl. Bridal Mfrs. Assn. [472]

Natl. Black Bridal Assn. [473]

Natl. Bridal Ser. [474]

Wedding Indus. Professionals Assn. [475]

Weddings Beautiful Worldwide [476]

Weddings Beautiful Worldwide [476]

Bridal Show Producers Intl. [471], 17730 W Center Rd., Ste. 110-311, Omaha, NE 68130, (402)330-8900

Bridge
Amer. Bridge Assn. [21237]
Amer. Bridge Teachers' Assn. [21238]
Amer. Contract Bridge League [21239]
Amer. Contract Bridge League [21239]
Bridge Engg. Assn. [6789]
Canadian Bridge Fed. [14379]
Intl. Assn. for Bridge Maintenance and Safety [6369]
Intl. Assn. for Bridge Maintenance and Safety [6369]
Natl. Steel Bridge Alliance [6370]
Short Span Steel Bridge Alliance [6371]
U.S. Bridge Fed. [21240]

A Bridge for Children [11201], PO Box 1054, New York, NY 10268

Bridge Engg. Assn. [6789], 11 Broadway, 21st Fl., New York, NY 10004, (212)286-8014

Bridge Grid Flooring Mfrs. Assn. [537], 300 E Cherry St., North Baltimore, OH 45872, (419)257-3561

Bridge Joint Assn. [IO], Camberley, United Kingdom

Bridge Kids Intl. [13515], 333 Mamaroneck Ave., No. 336, White Plains, NY 10605, (502)457-1910

Bridge Line Historical Soc. [22124], PO Box 13324, Albany, NY 12212

Bridge of Love [11202], PO Box 1869, West Jordan, UT 84084, (801)867-9401

Bridge Pastoral Found. [IO], Birkenhead, United Kingdom

Bridges Across Borders Cambodia [IO], Phnom Penh, Cambodia

Bridges Cambodia Intl. [11203], 2970 Almond Dr., San Jose, CA 95148, (408)223-2359

Bridges to Community [13388], 95 Croton Ave., Ossining, NY 10562, (914)923-2200

Bridges to Community [13388], 95 Croton Ave., Ossining, NY 10562, (914)923-2200

Bridges of Hope [★11448]

Bridges of Hope [★11448]

Bridges to Prosperity [12952], 5007 Victory Blvd., C-126, Yorktown, VA 23693

Bridges of Understanding [17938], 1630 Crescent Pl. NW, Washington, DC 20009, (202)478-4458

Bridging Nations [17939], 1800 K St. NW, Ste. 622, Washington, DC 20006, (202)741-3870

Bridging Nations [17939], 1800 K St. NW, Ste. 622, Washington, DC 20006, (202)741-3870

Bridging Refugee Youth and Children's Services [11452], U.S. Conf. of Catholic Bishops, 3211 4th St. NE, Washington, DC 20017-1104, (888)572-6500

Bridport Arts Centre [IO], Bridport, United Kingdom

Bright Belt Warehouse Assn. - Defunct.

Bright Futures Farm - Address unknown since 2011.

Bright Hope Intl. [12720], 2060 Stonington Ave., Hoffman Estates, IL 60169, (224)520-6100

Bright Hope Intl. [12720], 2060 Stonington Ave., Hoffman Estates, IL 60169, (224)520-6100

Bright Pink [17124], 400 N State St., Ste. 230, Chicago, IL 60654

Brighter Green [4014], 165 Court St., No. 171, Brooklyn, NY 11201

Brinton Assn. of Am. [20624], 21 Oakland Rd., West Chester, PA 19382, (610)399-0913

Brisbane Orchid Soc. [IO], Runcorn, Australia

Brisbane Water Ski Club [IO], Mount Ommaney, Australia

Bristol Chamber of Commerce and Initiative [IO], Bristol, United Kingdom

Bristol Indus. Archaeological Soc. [IO], Bath, United Kingdom

Bristol Owners' Club [IO], Petersfield, United Kingdom

Britain-Nepal Chamber of Commerce [IO], London, United Kingdom

Britain - Nepal Medical Trust [IO], Tonbridge, United Kingdom

Brith Abraham [★19087]

B'Rith Christian Union [★19573]

British
British Trade Off. at Consulate-General [23336]
Cornish Amer. Heritage Soc. [9455]
North Amer. Conf. on British Stud. [9456]
North Amer. Mini Moke Registry [21137]British-Surtees Soc.

British Abrasives Fed. [IO], Hurst, United Kingdom

British Acad. [IO], London, United Kingdom

British Acad. of Film and TV Arts [IO], London, United Kingdom

British Acad. of Film and TV Arts - Scotland [IO], Glasgow, United Kingdom

British Acad. of Forensic Sciences [IO], London, United Kingdom

British Acad. of Songwriters, Composers and Authors [IO], London, United Kingdom

British ACM Chap. [IO], London, United Kingdom

British Activity Holiday Assn. [IO], Chester, United Kingdom

British Actors' Equity Assn. [IO], London, United Kingdom

British Acupuncture Coun. [IO], London, United Kingdom

British Adhesives and Sealants Assn. [IO], Worksop, United Kingdom

British Aerobiology Fed. [IO], Worcester, United Kingdom

British Aerosol Mfrs'. Assn. [IO], London, United Kingdom

British Agricultural and Garden Machinery Assn. [IO], Banbury, United Kingdom

British Agricultural History Soc. [IO], Exeter, United Kingdom

British Aikido Assn. [IO], Ilkley, United Kingdom

British Air Line Pilots Assn. [IO], West Drayton, United Kingdom

British Airports Gp. [IO], London, United Kingdom

British Amateur Rugby League Assn. [IO], Huddersfield, United Kingdom

British-American Bus. Coun. [650], 52 Vanderbilt Ave., 20th Fl., New York, NY 10017, (212)661-5660

British-American Bus. Coun. [650], 52 Vanderbilt Ave., 20th Fl., New York, NY 10017, (212)661-5660

British-American Chamber of Commerce [★23355]

British Amer. Educational Found. [8350], 520 Summit Ave., Oradell, NJ 07649, (201)261-4438

British Amer. Security Info. Coun. [17501], 110 Maryland Ave. NE, Ste. 205, Washington, DC 20002, (202)546-8055

British Amer. Security Info. Coun. [17501], 110 Maryland Ave. NE, Ste. 205, Washington, DC 20002, (202)546-8055

British Amer. Security Info. Coun. - United Kingdom [IO], London, United Kingdom

British Amusement Catering Trade Assn. [IO], London, United Kingdom

British Andrology Soc. [IO], Sheffield, United Kingdom

British Angora Goat Soc. [IO], Warwick, United Kingdom

British Antique Dealers' Assn. [IO], London, United Kingdom

British Antique Furniture Restorers Assn. [IO], Dorchester, United Kingdom

British Appaloosa Soc. [IO], Wolverhampton, United Kingdom

British Approvals Bd. for Telecommunications [IO], Walton-on-Thames, United Kingdom

British Approvals for Fire Equip. [IO], Moreton-in-Marsh, United Kingdom

British Arachnological Soc. [IO], Redditch, United Kingdom

British Art Medal Soc. [IO], London, United Kingdom

British Artist Blacksmiths Assn. [IO], Glasgow, United Kingdom

British Arts Festivals Assn. [IO], London, United Kingdom

British Assn. of Academic Phoneticians [IO], Cambridge, United Kingdom

A star before a book entry number signifies that the name is not listed separately, but is mentioned within the entry.

British Assn. for Adoption and Fostering [IO], London, United Kingdom

British Assn. of Aesthetic Plastic Surgeons [IO], London, United Kingdom

British Assn. for Amer. Stud. [IO], Leicester, United Kingdom

British Assn. for Applied Linguistics [IO], London, United Kingdom

British Assn. of Art Therapists [IO], London, United Kingdom

British Assn. of Aviation Consultants [IO], London, United Kingdom

British Assn. of Barbershop Singers [IO], Bristol, United Kingdom

British Assn. of Beauty Therapy and Cosmetology [IO], Gloucester, United Kingdom

British Assn. of Behavioral Optometrists [IO], Gloucestershire, United Kingdom

British Assn. for Behavioural and Cognitive Psychotherapies [IO], Bury, United Kingdom

British Assn. for Biological Anthropology and Osteoarchaeology [IO], Durham, United Kingdom

British Assn. of Brain Injury Case Managers [IO], Bury, United Kingdom

British Assn. for Canadian Stud. [IO], London, United Kingdom

British Assn. for Cancer Res. [IO], Leeds, United Kingdom

British Assn. for Cemeteries in South Asia [IO], London, United Kingdom

British Assn. for Chem. Specialities [IO], Harrogate, United Kingdom

British Assn. for Chinese Stud. [IO], Leeds, United Kingdom

British Assn. of Clinical Anatomists [IO], Norwich, United Kingdom

British Assn. and Coll. of Occupational Therapists [IO], London, United Kingdom

British Assn. of Colliery Mgt. - Tech., Energy and Administrative Mgt. [IO], Doncaster, United Kingdom

British Assn. of Conf. Destinations [IO], Birmingham, United Kingdom

British Assn. of Cosmetic Doctors [IO], Shorne, United Kingdom

British Assn. for Counselling and Psychotherapy [IO], Lutterworth, United Kingdom

British Assn. of Crystal Growth [IO], Manchester, United Kingdom

British Assn. of Day Surgery [IO], London, United Kingdom

British Assn. of Dental Nurses [IO], Thornton-Cleveleys, United Kingdom

British Assn. of Dermatologists [IO], London, United Kingdom

British Assn. of Dramatherapists [IO], Cheltenham, United Kingdom

British Assn. for Early Childhood Educ. [IO], London, United Kingdom

British Assn. for Fair Trade Shops [IO], Chelmsford, United Kingdom

British Assn. in Forensic Medicine [IO], Glasgow, United Kingdom

British Assn. of Former United Nations Civil Servants [IO], London, United Kingdom

British Assn. of Friends of Museums [IO], Bishop's Waltham, United Kingdom

British Assn. of Golf Course Constructors [IO], Hampshire, United Kingdom

British Assn. of Green Crop Driers [IO], Hythe, United Kingdom

British Assn. of Head and Neck Oncologists [IO], Midhurst, United Kingdom

British Assn. of Homoeopathic Veterinary Surgeons [IO], Nuneaton, United Kingdom

British Assn. of Hospitality Accountants [IO], Wimborne, United Kingdom

British Assn. for Immediate Care [IO], Ipswich, United Kingdom

British Assn. of Indian Anaesthetists [IO], Wakefield, United Kingdom

British Assn. for Japanese Stud. [IO], Colchester, United Kingdom

British Assn. of Journalists [IO], London, United Kingdom

British Assn. of Landscape Indus. [IO], Coventry, United Kingdom

British Assn. of Leisure Parks, Piers and Attractions [IO], London, United Kingdom

British Assn. for Local History [IO], Ashbourne, United Kingdom

British Assn. for Lung Res. [IO], London, United Kingdom

British Assn. of Medical Managers [IO], Stockport, United Kingdom

British Assn. for Modern Mosaic [IO], East Sussex, United Kingdom

British Assn. of Mountain Guides [IO], Conwy, United Kingdom

British Assn. of Neuroscience Nurses [IO], Londonderry, United Kingdom

British Assn. of Numismatic Societies [IO], Manchester, United Kingdom

British Assn. for Nutritional Therapy [IO], London, United Kingdom

British Assn. of Occupational Therapists [IO], London, United Kingdom

British Assn. of Oral and Maxillofacial Surgeons [IO], London, United Kingdom

British Assn. of Otorhinolaryngologists - Head and Neck Surgeons [IO], London, United Kingdom

British Assn. for Paediatric Nephrology [IO], Bristol, United Kingdom

British Assn. of Paediatric Surgeons of England [IO], London, United Kingdom

British Assn. of Paintings Conservator-Restorers [IO], Norwich, United Kingdom

British Assn. of Paper Historians [IO], Dorset, United Kingdom

British Assn. for Performing Arts Medicine [★8015]

British Assn. for Performing Arts Medicine [IO], London, United Kingdom

British Assn. of Perinatal Medicine [IO], London, United Kingdom

British Assn. of Pharmaceutical Physicians [IO], Reading, United Kingdom

British Assn. of Pharmaceutical Wholesalers [IO], London, United Kingdom

British Assn. of Picture Libraries and Agencies [IO], London, United Kingdom

British Assn. of Plastic, Reconstructive and Aesthetic Surgeons [IO], London, United Kingdom

British Assn. of Play Therapists [IO], Surrey, United Kingdom

British Assn. of Prosthetists and Orthotists [IO], Paisley, United Kingdom

British Assn. for Psychopharmacology [IO], Cambridge, United Kingdom

British Assn. of Psychotherapists [IO], London, United Kingdom

British Assn. of Record Dealers [IO], Bournemouth, United Kingdom

British Assn. of Removers [IO], Watford, United Kingdom

British Assn. of Res. Quality Assurance [IO], Ipswich, United Kingdom

British Assn. of Retinal Screeners [IO], Dundee, United Kingdom

British Assn. of Settlements and Social Action Centres [IO], London, United Kingdom

British Assn. for Sexual Hea. and HIV [IO], London, United Kingdom

British Assn. for Sexual and Relationship Therapy [IO], London, United Kingdom

British Assn. for Shooting and Conservation [IO], Wrexham, United Kingdom

British Assn. of Ski Patrollers [IO], Argyllshire, United Kingdom

British Assn. of Skin Camouflage [IO], Chester, United Kingdom

British Assn. for Slavonic and East European Stud. [IO], Aberystwyth, United Kingdom

British Assn. of Snowsport Instructors [IO], Grantown-on-Spey, United Kingdom

British Assn. of Social Workers [IO], Birmingham, United Kingdom

British Assn. for South Asian Stud. [IO], London, United Kingdom

British Assn. of Sport and Exercise Sciences [IO], Leeds, United Kingdom

British Assn. of Sport Rehabilitators and Trainers [IO], Salford, United Kingdom

British Assn. of Stroke Physicians [IO], Wallasey, United Kingdom

British Assn. for the Stud. of Headache [IO], London, United Kingdom

British Assn. for the Stud. of Religions [IO], Bangor, United Kingdom

British Assn. of Symphonic Bands and Wind Ensembles [IO], Anglesey, United Kingdom

British Assn. of Teachers of Dancing [IO], Glasgow, United Kingdom

British Assn. of Teachers of the Deaf [IO], Rochester, United Kingdom

British Assn. of Urological Surgeons [IO], London, United Kingdom

British Assn. for Vedic Astrology [IO], London, United Kingdom

British Assn. of Veterinary Ophthalmologists [IO], Suffolk, United Kingdom

British Assn. of Women Entrepreneurs [IO], Stirling, United Kingdom

British Astronomical Assn. [IO], London, United Kingdom

British Atherosclerosis Soc. [IO], Bristol, United Kingdom

British Audio-Visual Dealers Assn. [IO], London, United Kingdom

British Automatic Fire Sprinkler Assn. [IO], Ely, United Kingdom

British Automation and Robot Assn. [IO], Wallington, United Kingdom

British Ballet Org. [IO], London, United Kingdom

British Balloon and Airship Club [IO], Llanishen, United Kingdom

British Bankers' Assn. [IO], London, United Kingdom

British Baseball Fed. [IO], London, United Kingdom

British Beatles Fan Club [IO], Croydon, United Kingdom

British Bedding and Pot Plant Assn. [IO], Huntingdon, United Kingdom

British Bee-Keepers' Assn. [IO], Kenilworth, United Kingdom

British Beer and Pub Assn. [IO], London, United Kingdom

British Beermat Collectors Soc. [IO], Worcester, United Kingdom

British Belgian Blue Cattle Soc. [IO], Penrith, United Kingdom

British Biker Cooperative [21924], PO Box 371021, Milwaukee, WI 53237-2121, (262)514-2073

British Biophysical Soc. [IO], Sheffield, United Kingdom

British Blind and Shutter Assn. [IO], Stowmarket, United Kingdom

British Blind Sport [IO], Leamington Spa, United Kingdom

British Blood Transfusion Soc. [IO], Manchester, United Kingdom

British Bluegrass Music Assn. [IO], Portsmouth, United Kingdom

British Bd. of Film Classification [IO], London, United Kingdom

British Bobsleigh Assn. [IO], Dorchester, United Kingdom

British Brands Gp. [IO], London, United Kingdom

British Bryological Soc. [IO], Stafford, United Kingdom

British Bus. Assn. of Macao [IO], Macau, Macao

British Bus. and Gen. Aviation Assn. [IO], Aylesbury, United Kingdom

British Cactus and Succulent Soc. [IO], Hornchurch, United Kingdom

British Camelids Assn. [IO], Warwickshire, United Kingdom

British Camelids Owners and Breeders Assn. [★15372]

British Canadian Chamber of Trade and Commerce [IO], Beaconsfield, QC, Canada

British Canoe Union [IO], Nottingham, United Kingdom

British Cardiovascular Soc. [IO], London, United Kingdom

British Cartographic Soc. [IO], London, United Kingdom

Reference to "IO" in place of a book number signifies that the association may be found in the 50th edition of International Organizations.

British Casino Assn. [IO], London, United Kingdom

British Cattle Veterinary Assn. [IO], Frampton-on-Severn, United Kingdom

British Cave Res. Assn. [IO], Buxton, United Kingdom

British Caving Assn. [IO], Buxton, United Kingdom

British Cement Assn. [IO], Camberley, United Kingdom

British Centre of the Intl. Theatre Inst. [IO], London, United Kingdom

British Ceramic Confed. [IO], Stoke-on-Trent, United Kingdom

British Chamber of Commerce in Belgium [IO], Brussels, Belgium

British Chamber of Commerce in China [IO], Beijing, People's Republic of China

British Chamber of Commerce in Germany [IO], Berlin, Germany

British Chamber of Commerce in Hong Kong [IO], Hong Kong, People's Republic of China

British Chamber of Commerce in Hungary [IO], Budapest, Hungary

British Chamber of Commerce for Italy [IO], Milan, Italy

British Chamber of Commerce in Latvia [IO], Riga, Latvia

British Chamber of Commerce for Luxembourg [IO], Luxembourg, Luxembourg

British Chamber of Commerce in Spain [IO], Barcelona, Spain

British Chambers of Commerce [IO], London, United Kingdom

British Cheerleading Assn. [IO], Northwood, United Kingdom

British Chelonia Gp. [IO], Chippenham, United Kingdom

British Chem. Engg. Contractors Assn. [IO], London, United Kingdom

British Cheque Cashers Assn. [IO], Chester, United Kingdom

British Chiropractic Assn. [IO], Reading, United Kingdom

British Christmas Tree Growers Assn. [IO], Edinburgh, United Kingdom

British Cleaning Coun. [IO], London, United Kingdom

British Clematis Soc. [IO], Stratford-upon-Avon, United Kingdom

British Coatings Fed. [IO], Leatherhead, United Kingdom

British Colour Makers Assn. [IO], Buxton, United Kingdom

British Columbia Art Teachers' Assn. [IO], Vancouver, BC, Canada

British Columbia Art Therapy Assn. [IO], Vancouver, BC, Canada

British Columbia Assn. for Marriage and Family Therapy [IO], Victoria, BC, Canada

British Columbia Assn. of Teachers of Modern Languages [IO], Surrey, BC, Canada

British Columbia Bottle Depot Assn. [IO], Surrey, BC, Canada

British Columbia Chefs' Assn. [IO], Vancouver, BC, Canada

British Columbia Constr. Assn. [IO], Victoria, BC, Canada

British Columbia Folklore Soc. [IO], Saanich, BC, Canada

British Columbia Herb Growers Assn. [IO], Kelowna, BC, Canada

British Columbia Historical Fed. [IO], Victoria, BC, Canada

British Columbia Hospice Palliative Care Assn. [IO], Vancouver, BC, Canada

British Columbia Intl. Commercial Arbitration Centre [IO], Vancouver, BC, Canada

British Columbia Play Therapy Assn. [IO], Vancouver, BC, Canada

British Columbia Psychological Assn. [IO], Vancouver, BC, Canada

British Columbia Schizophrenia Soc. [IO], Richmond, BC, Canada

British Columbia School Counsellors' Assn. [IO], Richmond, BC, Canada

British Columbia Snowboard Assn. [IO], Kelowna, BC, Canada

British Columbia Soc. for the Prevention of Cruelty to Animals [IO], Vancouver, BC, Canada

British Columbia Teachers' Fed. [IO], Vancouver, BC, Canada

British Columbia Tech. Indus. Assn. [IO], Vancouver, BC, Canada

British Columbia Water and Waste Assn. [IO], Burnaby, BC, Canada

British Columbia Wheelchair Basketball Soc. [IO], Richmond, BC, Canada

British Comparative Literature Assn. [IO], Manchester, United Kingdom

British Compressed Air Soc. [IO], London, United Kingdom

British Compressed Gases Assn. [IO], Derby, United Kingdom

British Cmpt. Assn. of the Blind [IO], Birmingham, United Kingdom

British Cmpt. Soc. [IO], Swindon, United Kingdom

British Cmpt. Soc. - Sri Lanka Sect. [IO], Colombo, Sri Lanka

British Confectioners' Assn. [IO], Brighton, United Kingdom

British Constructional Steelwork Assn. [IO], London, United Kingdom

British Contact Lens Assn. [IO], London, United Kingdom

British Contract Furnishing Assn. [IO], High Wycombe, United Kingdom

British Contract Mfrs. and Packers Assn. [IO], Amersham, United Kingdom

British Copyright Coun. [IO], London, United Kingdom

British Coun. [IO], London, United Kingdom

British Coun. Canada [IO], Ottawa, ON, Canada

British Coun. for Offices [IO], London, United Kingdom

British Coun. of Shopping Centres [IO], London, United Kingdom

British Coun. - Uzbekistan [IO], Tashkent, Uzbekistan

British Cryogenics Coun. [IO], Leatherhead, United Kingdom

British Crystallographic Assn. [IO], East Kilbride, United Kingdom

British Culinary Fed. [IO], Alcester, United Kingdom

British Cycling [IO], Manchester, United Kingdom

British Dam Soc. [IO], London, United Kingdom

British Dance Coun. [IO], London, United Kingdom

British Deaf Assn. [IO], Coventry, United Kingdom

British Deaf Sports Coun. [IO], Ipswich, United Kingdom

British Deer Soc. [IO], Fordingbridge, United Kingdom

British Dental Assn. [IO], London, United Kingdom

British Dental Practice Managers' Assn. [IO], Gloucester, United Kingdom

British Dental Trade Assn. [IO], Chesham, United Kingdom

British Design and Art Direction [IO], London, United Kingdom

British Dietetic Assn. [IO], Birmingham, United Kingdom

British Disabled Angling Assn. [IO], Walsall, United Kingdom

British Disabled Water Ski Assn. [IO], Wraysbury, United Kingdom

British Disc Golf Assn. [IO], London, United Kingdom

British Display Soc. [IO], Essex, United Kingdom

British Doll Artists Assn. [IO], Rudgwick, United Kingdom

British Dragonfly Soc. [IO], Peterborough, United Kingdom

British Driving Soc. [IO], Stowmarket, United Kingdom

British Dyslexia Assn. [IO], Bracknell, United Kingdom

British Ecological Soc. [IO], London, United Kingdom

British Educational Communications and Tech. Agency [IO], Coventry, United Kingdom

British Educational Leadership, Mgt. and Admin. Soc. [IO], Sheffield, United Kingdom

British Educational Res. Assn. [IO], Macclesfield, United Kingdom

British Educational Suppliers Assn. [IO], London, United Kingdom

British Egg Indus. Coun. [IO], London, United Kingdom

British Electrostatic Control Assn. [IO], Birmingham, United Kingdom

British Electrotechnical and Allied Mfrs'. Assn. [IO], London, United Kingdom

British Endodontic Soc. [IO], Gerrards Cross, United Kingdom

British Engraved Stationery Assn. [IO], London, United Kingdom

British Entomological and Natural History Soc. [IO], Reading, United Kingdom

British Epilepsy Assn. [IO], Leeds, United Kingdom

British Equestrian Fed. [IO], Kenilworth, United Kingdom

British Equestrian Trade Assn. [IO], Wetherby, United Kingdom

British Equine Veterinary Assn. [IO], Fordham, United Kingdom

British Expertise [IO], London, United Kingdom

British Exporters Assn. [IO], London, United Kingdom

British False Memory Soc. [IO], Bradford-on-Avon, United Kingdom

British Fantasy Soc. [IO], Stoke-on-Trent, United Kingdom

British Fed. of Audio [IO], Farnham, United Kingdom

British Fed. of Brass Bands [IO], Barnsley, United Kingdom

British Fed. of Film Societies [IO], Sheffield, United Kingdom

British Fed. of Women Graduates [IO], London, United Kingdom

British Fencing Assn. [IO], London, United Kingdom

British Fertility Soc. [IO], Bristol, United Kingdom

British Film Inst. [IO], London, United Kingdom

British Finn Assn. [IO], Chichester, United Kingdom

British Flue and Chimney Mfrs'. Assn. [IO], Reading, United Kingdom

British Fluid Power Assn. [IO], Chipping Norton, United Kingdom

British Fluid Power Distributors Assn. [IO], Chipping Norton, United Kingdom

British Fluoridation Soc. [IO], Wigan, United Kingdom

British Flute Soc. [IO], Surrey, United Kingdom

British Footwear Assn. [IO], Wellingborough, United Kingdom

British Fragrance Assn. [IO], Cranleigh, United Kingdom

British Franchise Assn. [IO], Abingdon, United Kingdom

British Frozen Food Fed. [IO], Newark, United Kingdom

British Fur Trade Assn. [IO], London, United Kingdom

British Furniture Mfrs. [IO], High Wycombe, United Kingdom

British Gear Assn. [IO], Burton-on-Trent, United Kingdom

British Geological Survey [IO], Nottingham, United Kingdom

British Geophysical Assn. [IO], Bristol, United Kingdom

British Geotechnical Assn. [IO], London, United Kingdom

British Geriatrics Soc. [IO], London, United Kingdom

British - German Jurists Assn. [IO], London, United Kingdom

British Glass [IO], Sheffield, United Kingdom

British Gliding Assn. [IO], Leicester, United Kingdom

British Glove Assn. [IO], Birmingham, United Kingdom

British Goat Soc. [IO], Newton Abbot, United Kingdom

British Grassland Soc. [IO], Kenilworth, United Kingdom

British Guild of Travel Writers [IO], London, United Kingdom

British Gymnastics [IO], Newport, United Kingdom

British Hallmarking Coun. [IO], Birmingham, United Kingdom

British Hang Gliding and Paragliding Assn. [IO], Leicester, United Kingdom

British Hardmetal and Engineers' Cutting Tool Assn. [IO], London, United Kingdom

A star before a book entry number signifies that the name is not listed separately, but is mentioned within the entry.

British Hardware Fed. [IO], Birmingham, United Kingdom

British Hardware and Housewares Mfrs'. Assn. [IO], Northampton, United Kingdom

British Hat Guild [IO], London, United Kingdom

British Hea. Care Assn. [IO], Elgin, United Kingdom

British Healthcare Bus. Intelligence Assn. [IO], St. Albans, United Kingdom

British Heart Found. [IO], London, United Kingdom

British Hedgehog Preservation Soc. [IO], Ludlow, United Kingdom

British Helicopter Advisory Bd. [IO], Woking, United Kingdom

British Hellenic Chamber of Commerce [IO], Athens, Greece

British Herb Trade Assn. [IO], Louth, United Kingdom

British Herbal Medicine Assn. [IO], Exeter, United Kingdom

British Herpetological Soc. [IO], Montrose, United Kingdom

British HIV Assn. [IO], London, United Kingdom

British Holiday and Home Parks Assn. [IO], Gloucester, United Kingdom

British Holistic Medical Assn. [IO], Bridgwater, United Kingdom

British Homeopathic Assn. [IO], London, United Kingdom

British Horn Soc. [IO], West Malling, United Kingdom

British Horological Fed. [IO], Warwickshire, United Kingdom

British Horological Inst. [IO], Newark, United Kingdom

British Horse Soc. [IO], Kenilworth, United Kingdom

British Horse Soc. - Pony Club [★22692]

British Hospitality Assn. [IO], London, United Kingdom

British Hosta and Hemerocallis Soc. [IO], Westbury-on-Severn, United Kingdom

British Housewives' League [IO], London, United Kingdom

British Humanist Assn. [IO], London, United Kingdom

British Hydrological Soc. [IO], London, United Kingdom

British Hydropower Assn. [IO], Wimborne, United Kingdom

British Hypertension Soc. [IO], Leicester, United Kingdom

British In-Vitro Diagnostics Assn. [IO], London, United Kingdom

British Indian Psychiatric Assn. [IO], Berkshire, United Kingdom

British Indoor Cricket Assn. [IO], Sutton Coldfield, United Kingdom

British Indus. Furnace Constructors Assn. [IO], West Bromwich, United Kingdom

British Indus. Truck Assn. [IO], Ascot, United Kingdom

British Infection Soc. [IO], Princes Risborough, United Kingdom

British Infertility Counselling Assn. [IO], Sheffield, United Kingdom

British Inline Puck Hockey Assn. [IO], Rotherham, United Kingdom

British Inline Skater Hockey Assn. [IO], Essex, United Kingdom

British Inst. of Agricultural Consultants [IO], Sittingbourne, United Kingdom

British Inst. of Cleaning Sci. [IO], Northampton, United Kingdom

British Inst. of Dental and Surgical Technologists [IO], Shipley, United Kingdom

British Inst. of Energy Economics [IO], Aylesbury, United Kingdom

British Inst. of Facilities Mgt. [IO], Bishop's Stortford, United Kingdom

British Inst. of Graphologists [IO], Gerrards Cross, United Kingdom

British Inst. of Human Rights [IO], London, United Kingdom

British Inst. of Innkeeping [IO], Camberley, United Kingdom

British Inst. of Intl. and Comparative Law [IO], London, United Kingdom

British Inst. of Learning Disabilities [IO], Kidderminster, United Kingdom

British Inst. of Musculoskeletal Medicine [IO], Bushey, United Kingdom

British Inst. of Non-Destructive Testing [IO], Northampton, United Kingdom

British Inst. of Organ Stud. [IO], London, United Kingdom

British Inst. of Persian Stud. [IO], Tehran, Iran

British Inst. of Persian Stud. - United Kingdom [IO], London, United Kingdom

British Inst. of Professional Photography [IO], Aylesbury, United Kingdom

British Inst. of Radiology [IO], London, United Kingdom

British Insurance Broker's Assn. [IO], London, United Kingdom

British Insurance Law Assn. [IO], Stowmarket, United Kingdom

British Interactive Media Assn. [IO], London, United Kingdom

British Interior Design Assn. [IO], London, United Kingdom

British Interior Textiles Assn. [IO], London, United Kingdom

British and Intl. Fed. of Festivals [IO], Macclesfield, United Kingdom

British Intl. Freight Assn. [IO], Feltham, United Kingdom

British and Intl. Golf Greenkeepers Assn. [IO], York, United Kingdom

British Intl. Spa Assn. [IO], Goudhurst, United Kingdom

British Intl. Stud. Assn. [IO], Aberystwyth, United Kingdom

British Interplanetary Soc. [IO], London, United Kingdom

British Iris Soc. [IO], Rawtenstall, United Kingdom

British and Irish Assn. of Law Librarians [IO], Edinburgh, United Kingdom

British and Irish Law, Educ. and Tech. Assn. [IO], Coventry, United Kingdom

British and Irish Ombudsman Assn. [IO], Twickenham, United Kingdom

British and Irish Orthoptic Soc. [IO], London, United Kingdom

British-Israel-World Fed. Canada [IO], Toronto, ON, Canada

British Jewellers' Assn. [IO], Birmingham, United Kingdom

British Jewellery, Giftware and Finishing Fed. [IO], Birmingham, United Kingdom

British Judo Assn. [IO], Loughborough, United Kingdom

British Kendo Assn. [IO], London, United Kingdom

British Killifish Assn. [IO], Kew, United Kingdom

British Kite Surfing Assn. [IO], Weymouth, United Kingdom

British Korfball Assn. [IO], Chatham, United Kingdom

British Ladder Mfrs. Assn. [★14751]

British Laminate Fabricators Assn. [IO], Nottingham, United Kingdom

British Leafy Salads Assn. [IO], Louth, United Kingdom

British Leprosy Relief Assn. [IO], Colchester, United Kingdom

British Lichen Soc. [IO], London, United Kingdom

British Lime Assn. [IO], London, United Kingdom

British Llama and Alpaca Assn. [IO], Tredington, United Kingdom

British Long Distance Swimming Assn. [IO], Durham, United Kingdom

British Longbow Soc. [IO], Manchester, United Kingdom

British Lung Found. [IO], London, United Kingdom

British Machine Vision Assn. and Soc. for Pattern Recognition [IO], Sheffield, United Kingdom

British Magical Soc. [IO], Birmingham, United Kingdom

British Marine Fed. [IO], Egham, United Kingdom

British Marine Fed. - Scotland [IO], Glasgow, United Kingdom

British Marine Life Stud. Soc. [IO], Shoreham-by-Sea, United Kingdom

British Maritime Law Assn. [IO], London, United Kingdom

British Materials Handling Fed. [IO], West Bromwich, United Kingdom

British Measurement and Testing Assn. [IO], Kent, United Kingdom

British Medical Acupuncture Soc. [IO], Northwich, United Kingdom

British Medical Assn. [IO], London, United Kingdom

British Medical Laser Assn. [IO], Cleveland, United Kingdom

British Medical Ultrasound Soc. [IO], London, United Kingdom

British Menopause Soc. [IO], Marlow, United Kingdom

British Menswear Guild [IO], London, United Kingdom

British Metals Recycling Assn. [IO], Huntingdon, United Kingdom

British Mexican Soc. [IO], Morpeth, United Kingdom

British Microcirculation Soc. [IO], Keele, United Kingdom

British Microlight Aircraft Assn. [IO], Banbury, United Kingdom

British Model Flying Assn. [IO], Leicester, United Kingdom

British Model Soldier Soc. [IO], Denham, United Kingdom

British Motorcyclists Fed. [IO], Leicester, United Kingdom

British Mountaineering Coun. [IO], Manchester, United Kingdom

British Mule Soc. [IO], Swindon, United Kingdom

British Music Hall Soc. [IO], Whitstable, United Kingdom

British Music Rights [IO], London, United Kingdom

British Music Soc. [IO], Upminster, United Kingdom

British Mycological Soc. [IO], Manchester, United Kingdom

British Natural Hygiene Soc. [IO], Frinton-on-Sea, United Kingdom

British Naturalists' Assn. [IO], Corby, United Kingdom

British Naturism [IO], Northampton, United Kingdom

British Naval Equip. Assn. [IO], London, United Kingdom

British Neuropathological Soc. [IO], Plymouth, United Kingdom

British Neuropsychiatry Assn. [IO], London, United Kingdom

British Neuroscience Assn. [IO], Cambridge, United Kingdom

British North Am. Philatelic Soc. [IO], Surrey, BC, Canada

British Nuclear Medicine Soc. [IO], London, United Kingdom

British Numismatic Soc. [IO], London, United Kingdom

British Numismatic Trade Assn. [IO], Rye, United Kingdom

British Nutrition Found. [IO], London, United Kingdom

British Obesity Surgery Patient Assn. [IO], Taunton, United Kingdom

British Occupational Hygiene Soc. [IO], Derby, United Kingdom

British Octopush Assn. [IO], Sanquhar, United Kingdom

British Off. Supplies and Services Fed. [IO], London, United Kingdom

British Oil Spill Control Assn. [IO], London, United Kingdom

British Olympic Assn. [IO], London, United Kingdom

British Orchid Growers Assn. [IO], Leeds, United Kingdom

British Organ Grinders Assn. [IO], Oxon, United Kingdom

British Orienteering Fed. [IO], Matlock, United Kingdom

British Origami Soc. [IO], Leicester, United Kingdom

British Ornithologists' Union [IO], Peterborough, United Kingdom

British Orthodontic Soc. [IO], London, United Kingdom

British Orthopaedic Foot and Ankle Soc. [IO], London, United Kingdom

Reference to "IO" in place of a book number signifies that the association may be found in the 50th edition of International Organizations.

British Osteopathic Assn. [IO], Luton, United Kingdom

British Overseas NGOs for Development [IO], London, United Kingdom

British Packaging Assn. [IO], Kilmarnock, United Kingdom

British Pain Soc. [IO], London, United Kingdom

British Palomino Soc. [IO], Llandysul, United Kingdom

British Parachute Assn. [IO], Leicester, United Kingdom

British Paralympic Assn. [IO], London, United Kingdom

British Parking Assn. [IO], Haywards Heath, United Kingdom

British Peanut Coun. [IO], London, United Kingdom

British Performing Arts Medicine Trust [★8015]

British Pest Control Assn. [IO], Derby, United Kingdom

British Pharmacological Soc. [IO], London, United Kingdom

British Philosophical Assn. [IO], London, United Kingdom

British Phonographic Indus. [IO], London, United Kingdom

British Photodermatology Gp. [IO], Gloucester, United Kingdom

British Phycological Soc. [IO], London, United Kingdom

British Pig Assn. [IO], Cambridge, United Kingdom

British Plastics Fed. [IO], London, United Kingdom

British Polish Chamber of Commerce [IO], Warsaw, Poland

British Porphyria Assn. [IO], Durham, United Kingdom

British Ports Assn. [IO], London, United Kingdom

British Poultry Coun. [IO], London, United Kingdom

British Precast Concrete Fed. [IO], Leicester, United Kingdom

British Press Photographers Assn. [IO], Bournemouth, United Kingdom

British Printing Indus. Fed. [IO], London, United Kingdom

British Professional Toastmasters' Authority [IO], London, United Kingdom

British Promotional Merchandise Assn. [IO], London, United Kingdom

British Property Fed. [IO], London, United Kingdom

British Psychoanalytical Soc. [IO], London, United Kingdom

British Psychodrama Assn. [IO], Helensburgh, United Kingdom

British Psychological Soc. [IO], Leicester, United Kingdom

British Psychosocial Oncology Soc. [IO], Northwood, United Kingdom

British Pteridological Soc. [IO], Isle of Skye, United Kingdom

British Pump Mfrs'. Assn. [IO], West Bromwich, United Kingdom

British Puppet and Model Theatre Guild [IO], London, United Kingdom

British Pyrotechnists Assn. [IO], Cambridge, United Kingdom

British Rabbit Coun. [IO], Newark, United Kingdom

British Record Soc. [IO], London, United Kingdom

British Records Assn. [IO], London, United Kingdom

British Red Cross [IO], London, United Kingdom

British Reflexology Assn. [IO], Worcester, United Kingdom

British Refrigeration Assn. [IO], Reading, United Kingdom

British Retail Consortium [IO], London, United Kingdom

British Retinitis Pigmentosa Soc. [IO], Buckingham, United Kingdom

British Rig Owners' Assn. [IO], London, United Kingdom

British Rowing [IO], London, United Kingdom

British Safety Coun. [IO], London, United Kingdom

British Sandwich Assn. [IO], Chepstow, United Kingdom

British Schools and Universities Club of New York [7874], The Williams Club, 24 E 39th St., New York, NY 10016, (212)713-5713

British Schools and Universities Found. [7875], 575 Madison Ave., Ste. 1006, New York, NY 10022-2511, (212)662-5576

British Schools and Universities Found. [7875], 575 Madison Ave., Ste. 1006, New York, NY 10022-2511, (212)662-5576

British Sci. Assn. [IO], London, United Kingdom

British Sci. Fiction Assn. [IO], New Barnet, United Kingdom

British Security Indus. Assn. [IO], Worcester, United Kingdom

British Sheep Dairying Assn. [IO], Horsted Keynes, United Kingdom

British Shooting [IO], Brookwood, United Kingdom

British Shooting Sports Coun. [IO], London, United Kingdom

British Shops and Stores Assn. [IO], Banbury, United Kingdom

British Show Jumping Assn. [IO], Kenilworth, United Kingdom

British Show Pony Soc. [IO], Huntingdon, United Kingdom

British Sign and Graphics Assn. [IO], Peterborough, United Kingdom

British Sleep Soc. [IO], Huntingdon, United Kingdom

British Slot Car Racing Assn. [IO], Christchurch, United Kingdom

British Small Animal Veterinary Assn. [IO], Gloucester, United Kingdom

British Soc. for Allergy and Clinical Immunology [IO], London, United Kingdom

British Soc. for Allergy, Environmental and Nutritional Medicine [IO], Knighton, United Kingdom

British Soc. of Animal Sci. [IO], Penicuik, United Kingdom

British Soc. for Antimicrobial Chemotherapy [IO], Birmingham, United Kingdom

British Soc. of Audiology [IO], Reading, United Kingdom

British Soc. of Baking [IO], Bicester, United Kingdom

British Soc. for Cell Biology [IO], London, United Kingdom

British Soc. of Cinematographers [IO], Gerrards Cross, United Kingdom

British Soc. of Clinical and Academic Hypnosis [IO], Sheffield, United Kingdom

British Soc. for Clinical Cytology [IO], London, United Kingdom

British Soc. for Clinical Neurophysiology [IO], Bristol, United Kingdom

British Soc. for Clinical Psychophysiology [IO], Birkenhead, United Kingdom

British Soc. of Criminology [IO], London, United Kingdom

British Soc. of Dental Hygiene and Therapy [IO], Gloucester, United Kingdom

British Soc. for Dental and Maxillofacial Radiology [IO], Dundee, United Kingdom

British Soc. for Disability and Oral Hea. [IO], Gosforth, United Kingdom

British Soc. of Dowsers [IO], Hanley Swan, United Kingdom

British Soc. of Echocardiography [IO], London, United Kingdom

British Soc. for Eighteenth Century Stud. [IO], Hatfield, United Kingdom

British Soc. of Enamellers [IO], London, United Kingdom

British Soc. of Flavourists [IO], Brentwood, United Kingdom

British Soc. of Gastroenterology [IO], London, United Kingdom

British Soc. for Geomorphology [IO], London, United Kingdom

British Soc. of Gerontology [IO], York, United Kingdom

British Soc. for Haematology [IO], London, United Kingdom

British Soc. of Hearing Aid Audiologists [IO], London, United Kingdom

British Soc. for Histocompatibility and Immunogenetics [IO], London, United Kingdom

British Soc. for the History of Mathematics [IO], Croydon, United Kingdom

British Soc. for the History of Medicine [IO], London, United Kingdom

British Soc. for the History of Pharmacy [IO], Leicester, United Kingdom

British Soc. for the History of Sci. [IO], Norwich, United Kingdom

British Soc. for Human Genetics [IO], Birmingham, United Kingdom

British Soc. of Hypnotherapists [IO], London, United Kingdom

British Soc. for Immunology [IO], London, United Kingdom

British Soc. of Magazine Editors [IO], Middlesex, United Kingdom

British Soc. of Master Glass Painters [IO], Minehead, United Kingdom

British Soc. for Medical Mycology [IO], London, United Kingdom

British Soc. for Middle Eastern Stud. [IO], Durham, United Kingdom

British Soc. for Music Therapy [IO], London, United Kingdom

British Soc. for Neuroendocrinology [IO], Nottingham, United Kingdom

British Soc. for Oral Medicine [IO], Leeds, United Kingdom

British Soc. for Parasitology [IO], Bedford, United Kingdom

British Soc. of Periodontology [IO], Leeds, United Kingdom

British Soc. of Plant Breeders [IO], Ely, United Kingdom

British Soc. for Plant Pathology [IO], Reading, United Kingdom

British Soc. for Protist Biology [IO], Coventry, United Kingdom

British Soc. of Psychosomatic Obstetrics, Gynaecology and Andrology [IO], Dudley, United Kingdom

British Soc. of Rehabilitation Medicine [IO], London, United Kingdom

British Soc. for Res. on Ageing [IO], Kingston upon Hull, United Kingdom

British Soc. for Restorative Dentistry [IO], Bristol, United Kingdom

British Soc. of Rheology [IO], Aberystwyth, United Kingdom

British Soc. for Rheumatology [IO], London, United Kingdom

British Soc. of Sci. Glassblowers [IO], Thurso, United Kingdom

British Soc. of Soil Sci. [IO], Cranfield, United Kingdom

British Soc. for Strain Measurement [IO], Bedford, United Kingdom

British Soc. for the Stud. of Prosthetic Dentistry [IO], Newcastle upon Tyne, United Kingdom

British Soc. for Surgery of the Hand [IO], London, United Kingdom

British Soc. of Toxicological Pathologists [IO], Isle of Skye, United Kingdom

British Sociological Assn. [IO], Durham, United Kingdom

British Soft Drinks Assn. [IO], London, United Kingdom

British Sound Recording Assn. [IO], Roydon, United Kingdom

British Stainless Steel Assn. [IO], Sheffield, United Kingdom

British Stammering Assn. [IO], London, United Kingdom

British Stammering Assn. - Scotland [IO], Edinburgh, United Kingdom

British Standards Institution [IO], London, United Kingdom

British Stationary Engine Res. Gp. [★22331]

British Stickmakers Guild [IO], Chesterfield, United Kingdom

British Studies Intelligencer - Defunct.

British Sub-Aqua Club [IO], Ellesmere Port, United Kingdom

British Sugarcraft Guild [IO], London, United Kingdom

British Sundial Soc. [IO], Crowthorne, United Kingdom

British Surfing Assn. [IO], Cornwall, United Kingdom

British Suzuki Inst. [IO], London, United Kingdom

British-Swedish Chamber of Commerce in Sweden [IO], Stockholm, Sweden

A star before a book entry number signifies that the name is not listed separately, but is mentioned within the entry.

British-Swiss Chamber of Commerce [IO], Zurich, Switzerland

British Syrian Soc. [IO], Damascus, Syrian Arab Republic

British Taekwondo Control Bd. [IO], Manchester, United Kingdom

British Tarantula Soc. [IO], Polegate, United Kingdom

British Tenpin Bowling Assn. [IO], Ilford, United Kingdom

British Textile Machinery Assn. [IO], Warrington, United Kingdom

British Thematic Assn. [IO], Bishop's Stortford, United Kingdom

British Tinnitus Assn. [IO], Sheffield, United Kingdom

British Toilet Assn. [IO], West Sussex, United Kingdom

British Toxicology Soc. [IO], Colchester, United Kingdom

British Toy and Hobby Assn. [IO], London, United Kingdom

British Toymakers Guild [IO], Uckfield, United Kingdom

British Trade Development Off. [★23336]

British Trade and Investment Off. [★23336]

British Trade Off. at Consulate-General [23336], 845 3rd Ave., New York, NY 10022, (212)745-0200

British Transplantation Soc. [IO], Macclesfield, United Kingdom

British Travelgoods and Accessories Assn. [IO], Birmingham, United Kingdom

British Triathlon Fed. [IO], Loughborough, United Kingdom

British Trombone Soc. [IO], Driffield, United Kingdom

British Trout Assn. [IO], Midlothian, United Kingdom

British Trust for Conservation Volunteers [IO], Doncaster, United Kingdom

British Trust for Ornithology [IO], Thetford, United Kingdom

British Tunnelling Soc. [IO], London, United Kingdom

British Turf and Landscape Irrigation Assn. [IO], Preston, United Kingdom

British Turned-Parts Mfrs. Assn. [IO], Warwick, United Kingdom

British UFO Res. Assn. [IO], London, United Kingdom

British Union for the Abolition of Vivisection [IO], London, United Kingdom

British Universities Film and Video Coun. [IO], London, United Kingdom

British Universities North Am. Club [8351], PO Box 430, Southbury, CT 06488, (203)264-0901

British Urban Regeneration Assn. [IO], London, United Kingdom

British Vacuum Coun. [IO], London, United Kingdom

British Valve and Actuator Assn. [IO], Banbury, United Kingdom

British Vehicle Rental and Leasing Assn. [IO], Amersham, United Kingdom

British Venture Capital Assn. [IO], London, United Kingdom

British Veterinary Assn. [IO], London, United Kingdom

British Veterinary Dental Assn. [IO], Sidcup, United Kingdom

British Veterinary Nursing Assn. [IO], Harlow, United Kingdom

British Video Assn. [IO], London, United Kingdom

British Vintage Wireless Soc. [IO], Swindon, United Kingdom

British Violin Making Assn. [IO], Redhill, United Kingdom

British Virgin Islands Amateur Athletic Fed. [IO], Tortola, British Virgin Islands

British Virgin Islands Assn. of Professional Accountants [IO], Tortola, British Virgin Islands

British Virgin Islands Bar Assn. [IO], Tortola, British Virgin Islands

British Virgin Islands Lawn Tennis Assn. [IO], Tortola, British Virgin Islands

British Water [IO], London, United Kingdom

British Water Ski [IO], Chertsey, United Kingdom

British Weight Lifters' Assn. [IO], Leeds, United Kingdom

British Women Pilots' Assn. [IO], Weybridge, United Kingdom

British Wood Pulp Assn. [IO], Nyon, Switzerland

British Woodworking Fed. [IO], London, United Kingdom

British Wool Marketing Bd. [IO], Bradford, United Kingdom

British Wrestling Assn. [IO], Chesterfield, United Kingdom

British-Yemeni Soc. [IO], London, United Kingdom

BritishAmerican Bus. Inc. [IO], London, United Kingdom

BritishAmerican Bus. Inc. of New York and London [23355], 52 Vanderbilt Ave., 20th Fl., New York, NY 10017, (212)661-4060

Brittany Spaniel Club of Am. [★21485]

BrittiCares Intl. [13893], PO Box 43504, Los Angeles, CA 90043, (323)292-8527

Brittle Bone Soc. [IO], Dundee, United Kingdom

Broad Universe [22206], 51 Watkins Ln., Walnut Creek, CA 94596

Broadband Forum [1897], 48377 Fremont Blvd., Ste. 117, Fremont, CA 94538, (510)492-4020

Broadband Services Forum - Address unknown since 2011.

Broadcast Advt. Bur. [★104]

Broadcast Cable Credit Assn. [485], 550 W Frontage Rd., Ste. 3600, Northfield, IL 60093, (847)881-8757

Broadcast Credit Assn. [★485]

Broadcast Educ. Assn. [7772], 1771 N St. NW, Washington, DC 20036-2800, (202)429-3935

Broadcast Educ. Assn. [7772], 1771 N St. NW, Washington, DC 20036-2800, (202)429-3935

Broadcast Educators Assn. of Canada [IO], London, ON, Canada

Broadcast Pioneers [★486]

Broadcast Promotion and Marketing Executives [★508]

Broadcast Promotion and Marketing Executives [★508]

Broadcast Rating Coun. [★497]

Broadcasters
Amer. Radio Relay League [20931]
Amer. Shortwave Listeners Club [20932]
ARRL Found. [20933]
Catholic Radio Assn. [19406]
Intl. Radio Club of Am. [20937]
Natl. Assn. Broadcast Employees and Technicians | Communications Workers of Am. [23162]
Natl. Lum and Abner Soc. [22119]
North Amer. Radio Archives [22120]
Old Old Timers Club [20941]

Broadcasters' Found. [★486]

Broadcasters' Found. of Am. [486], 125 W 55th St., 21st Fl., New York, NY 10019-5366, (212)373-8250

Broadcasters' Promotion Assn. [★508]

Broadcasters' Promotion Assn. [★508]

Broadcasting
Acad. of TV Arts and Sciences [477]
Advanced TV Systems Comm. [478]
Alliance for Women in Media [479]
Amer. Fed. of TV and Radio Artists [23160]
Amer. Radio Assn. [23161]
Amer. Radio Relay League [20931]
Amer. Shortwave Listeners Club [20932]
Amer. Sportscasters Assn. [480]
ARRL Found. [20933]
Assoc. Press Broadcast [481]
Assn. of Independents in Radio [482]
Assn. of Independents in Radio [482]
Assn. of Public TV Stations [483]
Black Coll. Radio Org. [484]
Broadcast Cable Credit Assn. [485]
Broadcast Educ. Assn. [7772]
Broadcast Educ. Assn. [7772]
Broadcasters' Found. of Am. [486]
Canadian Broadcast Standards Coun. [13856]
Catholic Acad. for Commun. Arts Professionals [9457]
Catholic Radio Assn. [19406]
Center for Commun. [7773]
Christian Media Assn. [19947]
Citizens for Independent Public Broadcasting [17211]
Coll. Broadcasters, Inc. [487]BroadcastingCommercial Radio Australia

Corp. for Public Broadcasting [9458]
Country Radio Broadcasters [488]
CTAM - Cable and Telecommunications Assn. for Marketing [489]
Educational Broadcasting Corp. [9459]
Hollywood Radio and TV Soc. [490]
Integrated Media Assn. [491]
Intercollegiate Broadcasting Sys. [7774]
Intl. Acad. of TV Arts and Sciences [492]
Intl. Acad. of TV Arts and Sciences [492]
Intl. Assn. of Broadcast Monitors [493]
Intl. Assn. of Broadcast Monitors [493]BroadcastingIntl. Nanocasting Assn.
Intl. Radio Club of Am. [20937]
Intl. Radio and TV Soc. Found. [494]
Jones/NCTI [495]
Junior Hollywood Radio and TV Soc. [496]
Media Rating Coun. [497]
Mediawatch - UK [15730]
MRFAC [498]
Natl. Acad. of TV Arts and Sciences [499]
Natl. Assn. of Black Owned Broadcasters [500]
Natl. Assn. Broadcast Employees and Technicians | Communications Workers of Am. [23162]
Natl. Assn. of Broadcasters [501]
Natl. Assn. of Farm Broadcasting [502]
Natl. Assn. of Public Affairs Networks [17212]
Natl. Assn. of Shortwave Broadcasters [503]
Natl. Assn. of TV Prog. Executives [504]
Natl. Assn. of TV Prog. Executives [504]
Natl. Black Programming Consortium [9460]
Natl. Broadcasting Soc. - Alpha Epsilon Rho [23472]
Natl. Cable and Telecommunications Assn. [505]
Natl. Cable TV Assn. [7454]
Natl. Coun. of Churches U.S.A. | Commun. Commn. [19356]
Natl. Fed. of Community Broadcasters [506]
Natl. Lum and Abner Soc. [22119]
Natl. Public Radio [9461]
Natl. Religious Broadcasters [19357]
Natl. Religious Broadcasters [19357]
Natl. TeleMedia Coun. [9462]
Natl. Translator Assn. [507]
Native Amer. Public Telecommunications [9463]
New Am. Media [18099]
North Amer. Radio Archives [22120]
Old Old Timers Club [20941]
OURMedia Network [18100]
PROMAXBDA [508]
PROMAXBDA [508]
Prometheus Radio Proj. [18101]
Public Broadcasting Mgt. Assn. [509]
Public Broadcasting Ser. [9464]
Public Radio Capital [10483]
Public Radio News Directors Incorporated [510]
Radio-Television Digital News Assn. [511]
Traffic Directors Guild of Am. [512]
Women in Cable Telecommunications [513]
World Commun. Assn. [7775]
World Commun. Assn. [7775]

Broadcasting Entertainment Cinematograph and Theatre Union [IO], London, United Kingdom

Broadcasting and Film Commn. [★19356]

Broadway Cares/Equity Fights AIDS [10875], 165 W 46th St., Ste. 1300, New York, NY 10036, (212)840-0770

Broadway Dozen [★10589]

Broadway League [10572], 226 W 47th St., New York, NY 10036, (212)764-1122

Broeders van de Onbevlekte Ontvangenis der Heilige Maagd Maria [★IO]

Broker Mgt. Coun. [1743], PO Box 150229, Arlington, TX 76015, (682)518-6008

Bromeliad Identification Center [★21787]

Bromeliad Identification Center [★21787]

Bromeliad Soc. [★21787]

Bromeliad Soc. [★21787]

Bromeliad Soc. Intl. [21787], 713 Breckenridge Dr., Port Orange, FL 32127-7528

Bromeliad Soc. Intl. [21787], 713 Breckenridge Dr., Port Orange, FL 32127-7528

Bronchoesophagology
Amer. Broncho-Esophagological Assn. [13868]
Intl. Bronchoesophagological Soc. [13869]

Reference to "IO" in place of a book number signifies that the association may be found in the 50th edition of International Organizations.

Intl. Bronchoesophagological Soc. **[13869]**
Bronfman Center for Jewish Life **[★12400]**
Bronte Soc. **[IO]**, Keighley, United Kingdom
Brookdale Found. **[14662]**, 950 3rd Ave., 19th Fl., New York, NY 10022, (212)308-7355
Brookings Institution **[18443]**, 1775 Massachusetts Ave. NW, Washington, DC 20036-2188, (202)797-6000
Brookings Tax Policy Center; Urban- **[18707]**
Brooklyn Coll. of the City Univ. of New York Alumni Assn. **[18857]**, 2900 Bedford Ave., Brooklyn, NY 11210, (718)951-5065
Brooklyn Soc. of Artists **[★9223]**
Brooks Bird Club **[5041]**, PO Box 4077, Wheeling, WV 26003
Brooks and Dunn Fan Club **[23819]**, PO Box 120669, Nashville, TN 37212-0669
Brotherhood of the Amer. Lutheran Church **[★19932]**
Brotherhood Commn. - Defunct.
Brotherhood of the Footboard **[★23287]**
Brotherhood of the Footboard **[★23287]**
Brotherhood of the Knights of the Vine **[5166]**, 3343 Indus. Dr., Ste. 2, Santa Rosa, CA 95403, (707)579-3781
Brotherhood of Locomotive Engineers, Intl. **[★23287]**
Brotherhood of Locomotive Engineers, Intl. **[★23287]**
Brotherhood of Locomotive Engineers and Trainmen **[23287]**, 1370 Ontario St., Mezzanine, Cleveland, OH 44113-1701, (216)241-2630
Brotherhood of Locomotive Engineers and Trainmen **[23287]**, 1370 Ontario St., Mezzanine, Cleveland, OH 44113-1701, (216)241-2630
Brotherhood of Locomotive Firemen and Enginemen **[★23292]**
Brotherhood of Maintenance of Way Employees **[23288]**, 20300 Civic Center Dr., Ste. 320, Southfield, MI 48076-4169, (248)948-1010
Brotherhood of Merchant Seamen and Privateers **[★20869]**
Brotherhood of Motorcycle Campers **[★22779]**
Brotherhood of Motorcycle Campers **[★22779]**
Brotherhood Org. of a New Destiny **[18612]**, PO Box 35090, Los Angeles, CA 90035-0090, (323)782-1980
Brotherhood Org. of a New Destiny **[18612]**, PO Box 35090, Los Angeles, CA 90035-0090, (323)782-1980
Brotherhood of Painters, Decorators and Paperhangers of Am. **[★11941]**
Brotherhood of Painters, Decorators and Paperhangers of Am. **[★11941]**
Brotherhood of Railroad Signalmen **[23289]**, 917 Shenandoah Shores Rd., Front Royal, VA 22630-6418, (540)622-6522
Brotherhood of Railroad Trainmen **[★23292]**
Brotherhood of Railway, Airline and Steamship Clerks, Freight Handlers, Express and Sta. Employees **[★23290]**
Brotherhood Railway Carmen **[★23290]**
Brotherhood Railway Carmen of Am. **[★23291]**
Brotherhood Railway Carmen of the U.S. and Canada **[★23291]**
Brotherhood of Railway and Steamship Clerks, Freight Handlers, Express and Sta. Employees **[★23290]**
Brotherhood of Saint Andrew **[19693]**, PO Box 632, Ambridge, PA 15003, (724)266-5810
Brotherhood of Sleeping Car Porters **[★23290]**
Brotherhood of Working Farriers Assn. **[1241]**, Ralph Casey, Pres./Exec. Dir., 14013 E Hwy. 136, Lafayette, GA 30728, (706)397-8047
Brother's Brother Found. **[12812]**, 1200 Galveston Ave., Pittsburgh, PA 15233-1604, (412)321-3160
Brother's Brother Found. **[12812]**, 1200 Galveston Ave., Pittsburgh, PA 15233-1604, (412)321-3160
Bros. of Charity **[IO]**, Rome, Italy
Bros. of Christian Instruction of Saint Gabriel **[IO]**, Rome, Italy
Bros. of the Christian Schools **[IO]**, Rome, Italy
Bros. of the Immaculate Conception of the Blessed Virgin Mary **[IO]**, Maastricht, Netherlands
Bros. of Our Lady, Mother of Mercy **[IO]**, Tilburg, Netherlands

Bros. and Sisters in Christ **[19541]**, PO Box 633, Grapevine, TX 76099, (228)255-9251
Bros. and Sisters in Christ **[19541]**, PO Box 633, Grapevine, TX 76099, (228)255-9251
Bros. and Sisters of Penance **[★19395]**
Bros. and Sisters of Penance **[★19415]**
Bros. and Sisters of Penance of St. Francis **[19395]**, 65774 County Rd. 31, Northome, MN 56661, (218)897-5974
Brotogeris Soc. Intl.
Brotogeris Soc. Intl. - Defunct.
Brougham Owners Assn. **[★21017]**
Brown Swiss Cattle Breeders Assn. of the U.S.A. **[3908]**, 800 Pleasant St., Beloit, WI 53511-5456, (608)365-4474
Brown Trout Club - Defunct.
Browning Collectors Assn. **[21712]**, 711 Scott St., Covington, KY 41011
Browning Collectors Assn. **[21712]**, 711 Scott St., Covington, KY 41011
Browning Inst. - Defunct.
Bruce Boxleitner's Official Fan Club **[23762]**, PO Box 5513, Sherman Oaks, CA 91403
Bruce Intl., U.S.A. Br. - Defunct.
Bruce Trail Conservancy **[IO]**, Hamilton, ON, Canada
Bruckner Soc. of America - Defunct.
Brunei Amateur Softball and Baseball Assn. **[IO]**, Bandar Seri Begawan, Brunei Darussalam
Brunei Assn. of Hotels **[IO]**, Bandar Seri Begawan, Brunei Darussalam
Brunei-China Friendship Assn. **[IO]**, Bandar Seri Begawan, Brunei Darussalam
Brunei Darussalam Assn. of Food Sci. and Tech. **[IO]**, Bandar Seri Begawan, Brunei Darussalam
Brunei Darussalam Cmpt. Soc. **[IO]**, Bandar Seri Begawan, Brunei Darussalam
Brunei Darussalam Natl. Assn. of the Blind **[IO]**, Bandar Seri Begawan, Brunei Darussalam
Brunei Darussalam Red Crescent Soc. **[IO]**, Kuala Belait, Brunei Darussalam
Brunei Darussalam Tennis Assn. **[IO]**, Bandar Seri Begawan, Brunei Darussalam
Brunei Darussalam Yachting Assn. **[IO]**, Bandar Seri Begawan, Brunei Darussalam
Brunei Energy Assn. **[IO]**, Seria, Brunei Darussalam
Brunei Freight Forwarders Assn. **[IO]**, Bandar Seri Begawan, Brunei Darussalam
Brunei Natl. Badminton Assn. **[IO]**, Bandar Seri Begawan, Brunei Darussalam
Brunei Nature Soc. **[IO]**, Bandar Seri Begawan, Brunei Darussalam
Brunei Squash Rackets Assn. **[IO]**, Berakas, Brunei Darussalam
Bryan Adams BadNews **[IO]**, Vancouver, BC, Canada
Bryggeriforeningen **[★IO]**
BTCV **[IO]**, Doncaster, United Kingdom
BTCV Scotland **[IO]**, Stirling, United Kingdom
Buchereiverband Osterreichs **[★IO]**
Buckeye DeSoto Club **[★21127]**
Buckminster Fuller Inst. **[10654]**, 181 N 11th St., Ste. 402, Brooklyn, NY 11211, (718)290-9280
Buckskin Registry Assn. **[★4526]**
Buddhism and Soc. Development Assn. **[IO]**, Kampong Cham, Cambodia
Buddhist
    Amer. Buddhist Stud. Center **[19358]**
    Buddhist Churches of Am. Fed. of Buddhist Women's Associations **[19359]**
    Buddhist Text Translation Soc. **[19360]**
    Buddhist Vihara **[19361]**
    Cambodian Buddhist Soc. **[19362]**
    Cambodian Buddhist Soc. **[19362]**
    Cambridge Buddhist Assn. **[19363]**
    Dharma Drum Mountain Buddhist Assn. **[19364]**
    Dharma Realm Buddhist Assn. **[19365]**
    First Zen Inst. of Am. **[19366]**
    Found. for the Preservation of the Mahayana Tradition **[19367]**
    Jewel Heart **[19368]**
    Kunzang Palyul Choling **[19369]**
    Mid-America Buddhist Assn. **[19370]**
    Nichiren Buddhist Assn. of Am. **[19371]**
    Soka Gakkai International-United States of Am. **[19372]**

Soka Gakkai International-United States of Am. **[19372]**
Supreme Master Ching Hai Meditation Assn. **[19373]**
Supreme Master Ching Hai Meditation Assn. **[19373]**
Triratna Buddhist Community **[19374]**
Zen Stud. Soc. **[19375]**
Buddhist Churches of Am. Fed. of Buddhist Women's Associations **[19359]**, Buddhist Churches of Am., 1710 Octavia St., San Francisco, CA 94109, (415)776-5600
Buddhist Mission, Hungarian Buddhist Church Arya Maitreya Mandala **[IO]**, Budapest, Hungary
Buddhist Peace Fellowship **[18233]**, PO Box 3470, Berkeley, CA 94703, (510)655-6169
Buddhist Peace Fellowship **[18233]**, PO Box 3470, Berkeley, CA 94703, (510)655-6169
Buddhist Publication Soc. **[IO]**, Kandy, Sri Lanka
Buddhist Soc. of Am. **[★19366]**
Buddhist Soc. for Compassionate Wisdom **[IO]**, Toronto, ON, Canada
Buddhist Soc. UK **[IO]**, London, United Kingdom
Buddhist Text Translation Soc. **[19360]**, Intl. Translation Inst., 1777 Murchison Dr., Burlingame, CA 94010-4504, (415)332-6221
Buddhist Vihara **[19361]**, 5017 16th St. NW, Washington, DC 20011, (202)723-0773
Buddhista Misszio, Magyarorszagi Arya Maitreya Mandala Egyhazkozosseg **[★IO]**
Budgerigar and Foreign Bird Soc. **[IO]**, Toronto, ON, Canada
Budgerigar Soc. of Pakistan **[IO]**, Lahore, Pakistan
Budi aktivna. Budi emancipirana **[★IO]**
Buelingo Beef Cattle Soc. **[3909]**, 15904 W Warren Rd., Warren, IL 61087-9601, (815)745-2147
Buffalo Assn; Amer. Water **[4689]**
Buffalo Bill Historical Center **[10655]**, 720 Sheridan Ave., Cody, WY 82414-3428, (307)587-4771
Buffalo Sabres Booster Club - Address unknown since 2011.
Buick Car Club of Australia in NSW **[IO]**, Merrylands, Australia
Buick Club of Am. **[21015]**, PO Box 360775, Columbus, OH 43236-0775, (614)472-3939
Buick GS Club of Am. **[21016]**, 625 Pine Point Cir., Valdosta, GA 31602, (229)244-0577
Buick St. Rod Assn. **[22114]**, 824 Kay Cir., Chattanooga, TN 37421-4218
Build Change **[12172]**, 1416 Larimer St., Ste. 301, Denver, CO 80202, (303)953-2563
The Builders Exchange Network **[★917]**
The Builders Exchange Network **[★917]**
Builders Hardware Mfrs. Assn. **[1648]**, 355 Lexington Ave., 15th Fl., New York, NY 10017, (212)297-2122
Builders Merchants Fed. **[IO]**, London, United Kingdom
Builders Without Borders **[12173]**, 119 Main St., Hillsboro, NM 88042, (575)895-5400
Builders Without Borders **[12173]**, 119 Main St., Hillsboro, NM 88042, (575)895-5400
Building with Books - Address unknown since 2011.
Building Bridges: Middle East-US **[8385]**, PO Box 1208, Norwich, VT 05055, (802)649-1601
Building Bridges Worldwide **[11553]**, 5-09 48th Ave., Apt. 7B, Long Island City, NY 11101
Building Codes
    Alliance for Building Regulatory Reform in the Digital Age **[6372]**
    Assn. of Major City/County Building Officials **[5300]**
    Building Security Coun. **[3210]**
    Intl. Assn. of Plumbing and Mech. Officials **[5301]**
    Intl. Assn. of Plumbing and Mech. Officials **[5301]**
    Intl. Code Coun. **[5302]**
    Intl. Code Coun. **[5302]**
    Natl. Conf. of States on Building Codes and Standards **[5303]**
    New Buildings Inst. **[5304]**
Building Commissioning Assn. **[538]**, 100 SW Main St., Ste. 1600, Portland, OR 97204, (877)666-2292
Building Community Bridges **[11554]**, 244 5th Ave., Ste. E283, New York, NY 10001, (888)486-4218
Building and Constr. Trades Dept. - Canadian Off. **[IO]**, Ottawa, ON, Canada

A star before a book entry number signifies that the name is not listed separately, but is mentioned within the entry.

Building Cost Info. Ser. of the Royal Institution of Chartered Surveyors [IO], London, United Kingdom

Building Designers Assn. of Australia [IO], Dangar, Australia

Building Educated Leaders for Life [8526], 60 Clayton St., Dorchester, MA 02122, (617)282-1567

Building Enclosure Coun. Natl. [6374], Natl. Inst. of Building Sciences, 1090 Vermont Ave. NW, Ste. 700, Washington, DC 20005-4950, (202)289-7800

Building Enclosure Tech. and Env. Coun. [539], Wiss, Janney, Elstner Associates, Inc., 245 First St., Ste. 1200, Cambridge, MA 02142, (617)225-4900

Building Futures Coun. - Address unknown since 2010.

Building Homes for Heroes [11084], 65 Roosevelt Ave., Ste. 105, Valley Stream, NY 11581, (516)684-9220

Building Industries

Affordable Housing Investors Coun. [514]

Affordable Housing Tax Credit Coalition [515]

Air Barrier Assn. of Am. [516]

Alliance for Building Regulatory Reform in the Digital Age [6372]

Alliance for Sustainable Built Environments [517]

Amer. Architectural Mfrs. Assn. [518]

Amer. Composites Mfrs. Assn. [519]

Amer. Fiberboard Assn. [520]

Amer. Fiberboard Assn. [520]

Amer. Soc. for Composites [6373]

Amer. Soc. of Home Inspectors [521]

Architectural Woodwork Inst. [522]

Asphalt Emulsion Mfrs. Assn. [523]

Asphalt Inst. [524]

Asphalt Inst. [524]

Asphalt Interlayer Assn. [525]

Asphalt Pavement Alliance [526]

Asphalt Roofing Mfrs. Assn. [527]

Assoc. Air Balance Coun. [528]

Assoc. Constr. Distributors Intl. [529]

Assoc. Constr. Distributors Intl. [529]

Assn. of Architecture Organizations [6192]

Assn. for Better Insulation [530]

Assn. of Millwork Distributors [531]

Assn. of Modified Asphalt Producers [532]

Assn. for Retail Environments [533]

Assn. of Synthetic Grass Installers [534]

Assn. of the Wall and Ceiling Indus. Intl. [535]

Assn. of the Wall and Ceiling Indus. Intl. [535]

Brick Indus. Assn. [536]

Bridge Grid Flooring Mfrs. Assn. [537]

Building Commissioning Assn. [538]

Building Designers Assn. of Australia [19929]

Building Enclosure Coun. Natl. [6374]

Building Enclosure Tech. and Env. Coun. [539]

Building Material Dealers Assn. [540]

Building Materials Reuse Assn. [541]

Building Security Coun. [3210]

Building Tech. Educators' Soc. [7732]

Building Trades Employers' Assn. [542]

Cellulose Insulation Mfrs. Assn. [543]

Ceramic Tile Distributors Assn. [544]

Chain Link Fence Mfrs. Inst. [545]

Clay Roof Tile Coun. [14488]

Clean Tech. and Sustainable Indus. Org. [3856]

Concrete Reinforcing Steel Inst. [546]BuildingConfed. of Intl. Contractors' Associations

Constr. Employers Assn. [547]

Constr. Materials Recycling Assn. [548]

Constr. Owners Assn. of Am. [549]

Cool Metal Roofing Coalition [550]

Cool Roof Rating Coun. [551]

Cooling Tech. Inst. [552]

Design-Build Inst. of Am. [553]

Ecological Building Network [3857]

EIFS Indus. Members Assn. [554]

Elevator U [555]

EMerge Alliance [556]

Energy and Environmental Building Assn. [557]

Environmental Info. Assn. [558]

Expanded Shale Clay and Slate Inst. [559]

Finishing Contractors Assn. [560]

Floor Installation Assn. of North Am. [561]

Floor Installation Assn. of North Am. [561]

Found. of the Wall and Ceiling Indus. [562]

Gen. Building Contractors Assn. [563]

Glazing Indus. Code Comm. [564]

Green Builder Coalition [565]

Green Building Initiative [566]

Green Home Coun. [567]

Healthy Building Network [4330]

Heavy Movable Structures [6375]

High Performance Building Coun. [6376]

Home Builders Inst. [568]

House Plan Marketing Assn. [1038]

Intl. Assn. of Bowling Equipment Specialists [569]

Intl. Assn. for Bridge Maintenance and Safety [6369]

Intl. Building Performance Simulation Assn. [6377]

Intl. Building Performance Simulation Assn. [6377]

Intl. Cast Polymer Assn. [570]

Intl. Cast Polymer Assn. [570]

Intl. Door Assn. [571]

Intl. Door Assn. [571]

Intl. Plant Nutrition Inst. | Potash and Phosphate Inst. [572]

Intl. Slurry Surfacing Assn. [573]

Intl. Slurry Surfacing Assn. [573]

Intl. Soc. for Concrete Pavements [574]

Intl. Soc. for Structural Hea. Monitoring of Intelligent Infrastructure [6428]

Intl. Window Film Assn. [575]

Intl. Window Film Assn. [575]

Italian Trade Commn. [576]

Leading Builders of Am. [577]

Maple Flooring Mfrs. Assn. [578]

Maple Flooring Mfrs. Assn. [578]

Materials and Methods Standards Assn. [579]

Metal Building Mfrs. Assn. [580]

Metal Buildings Inst. [7776]

Metal Constr. Assn. [581]

Metal Framing Mfrs. Assn. [582]

Moulding and Millwork Producers Assn. [583]

Natl. Acad. of Building Inspection Engineers [584]

Natl. Asphalt Pavement Assn. [585]

Natl. Assn. of Black Women in Constr. [848]

Natl. Assn. of Building Cooperatives Soc. [3682]

Natl. Assn. of Church Design Builders [586]

Natl. Assn. of Constr. Contractors Cooperation [587]

Natl. Assn. of Home Builders | Leading Suppliers Coun. [588]

Natl. Assn. of the Remodeling Indus. [589]

Natl. Assn. of Tower Erectors [6378]

Natl. Assn. of Waterproofing and Structural Repair Contractors [590]

Natl. Coun. of Acoustical Consultants [591]

Natl. Fenestration Rating Coun. [592]

Natl. Housing Endowment [593]

Natl. One Coat Stucco Assn. [594]

Natl. Pavement Contractors Assn. [595]

Natl. Roof Certification and Inspection Assn. [596]

Natl. Slag Assn. [597]

Natl. Sunroom Assn. [598]

Natl. Town Builders' Assn. [599]

Natl. Wood Flooring Assn. [600]

Natural Building Network [601]

North Amer. Assn. of Floor Covering Distributors [602]

North Amer. Building Material Distribution Assn. [603]

North Amer. Insulation Mfrs. Assn. [604]

North Amer. Laminate Flooring Assn. [605]

North Amer. Laminate Flooring Assn. [605]

Polyisocyanurate Insulation Mfrs. Assn. [606]

Porcelain Enamel Inst. [607]

Post-Tensioning Inst. [608]

Preservation Trades Network [609]

Residential Energy Services Network [610]

Resilient Floor Covering Inst. [611]

Roofing Indus. Comm. on Weather Issues [612]

Rubber Pavements Assn. [613]

Rubber Pavements Assn. [613]

Safety Glazing Certification Coun. [614]

Scaffold Indus. Assn. [615]

Scaffolding, Shoring and Forming Inst. [616]

The Shelter Alliance [11634]

Short Span Steel Bridge Alliance [6371]

Slate Roofing Contractors Assn. of North Am. [617]

Steel Deck Inst. [618]

Steel Door Inst. [619]

Steel Joist Inst. [620]

Steel Window Inst. [621]

Structural Building Components Assn. [622]

Structural Insulated Panel Assn. [623]

Stucco Mfrs. Assn. [624]

Submersible Wastewater Pump Assn. [625]

Sump and Sewage Pump Mfrs. Assn. [626]

Sump and Sewage Pump Mfrs. Assn. [626]

Tesla Engine Builders Assn. [627]

Tile Coun. of North Am. [628]

Tile Roofing Inst. [629]

Timber Frame Bus. Coun. [630]

Truss Plate Inst. [631]

U.S. Green Building Coun. [632]

Vinyl Siding Inst. [633]

Water Design-Build Coun. [634]

Welders Without Borders [7619]

Window and Door Mfrs. Assn. [635]

Wire Reinforcement Inst. [636]

Wood Moulding and Millwork Producers Assn. [583]

Building Material Dealers Assn. [540], 12540 SW Main St., Ste. 200, Tigard, OR 97223-6198, (503)624-0561

Building Materials Fed. [IO], Dublin, Ireland

Building Materials Reuse Assn. [541], PO Box 47776, Chicago, IL 60647, (773)340-2672

Building Owners and Managers Assn. Intl. [3004], 1101 15th St. NW, Ste. 800, Washington, DC 20005, (202)408-2662

Building Owners and Managers Assn. Intl. [3004], 1101 15th St. NW, Ste. 800, Washington, DC 20005, (202)408-2662

Building Owners and Managers Inst. Intl. [★3003]

Building Professionals' Consortium [IO], Winnipeg, MB, Canada

Building Res. Coun. [7734], Univ. of Illinois at Urbana-Champaign, Coll. of Fine and Applied Arts, 117 Temple Hoyne Buell Hall, Champaign, IL 61820, (217)333-1330

Building Res. Est. [IO], Watford, United Kingdom

Building Security Coun. [3210], 1801 Alexander Bell Dr., Reston, VA 20191, (703)295-6314

Building Ser. Contractors Assn. Intl. [2242], 401 N Michigan Ave., Ste. 2200, Chicago, IL 60611-4267, (312)321-5167

Building Ser. Contractors Assn. Intl. [2242], 401 N Michigan Ave., Ste. 2200, Chicago, IL 60611-4267, (312)321-5167

Building Ser. Employees' Intl. Union [★23296]

Building Ser. Employees' Intl. Union [★23296]

Building Services Res. and Info. Assn. [IO], Bracknell, United Kingdom

Building Societies Assn. - England [IO], London, United Kingdom

Building Soc. [IO], Copenhagen, Denmark

Building Stone Inst. [3360], PO Box 419, 5 Riverside Dr., Bldg. 2, Chestertown, NY 12817, (518)803-4336

Building Systems Industry Forum - Defunct.

Building Tech. Educators' Soc. [7732], Univ. of Idaho, Dept. of Architecture and Interior Design, 207 AAS, Moscow, ID 83844-2451

Building Tomorrow [12659], 407 Fulton St., Indianapolis, IN 46202, (317)632-3545

Building Tomorrow [12659], 407 Fulton St., Indianapolis, IN 46202, (317)632-3545

Building Trades

AFL-CIO | Building and Constr. Trades Dept. [23163]

Asphalt Interlayer Assn. [525]

Assn. of Synthetic Grass Installers [534]

Constr. Indus. Trade Alliance [10773]

Cool Metal Roofing Coalition [550]

Intl. Assn. for Bridge Maintenance and Safety [6369]

Intl. Soc. for Concrete Pavements [574]

Intl. Union of Bricklayers and Allied Craftworkers [23164]

Intl. Union of Operating Engineers [23165]

Laborers' Intl. Union of North Am. [23166]

Reference to "IO" in place of a book number signifies that the association may be found in the 50th edition of International Organizations.

Laborers' Intl. Union of North Am. [23166]
Leading Builders of Am. [577]
Ministry Architecture [6200]
Natl. Alliance for Fair Contracting [23167]
Natl. Roof Certification and Inspection Assn. [596]
Operative Plasterers and Cement Masons Intl.
  Assn. of U.S. and Canada [23168]
Operative Plasterers and Cement Masons Intl.
  Assn. of U.S. and Canada [23168]
United Brotherhood of Carpenters and Joiners of
  Am. [23169]
United Union of Roofers, Waterproofers and Allied
  Workers [23170]
Building Trades Employers' Assn. [542], 1430
  Broadway, Ste. 1106, New York, NY 10018,
  (212)704-9745
BuildingBlocks Intl. [11666], 323 Geary St., Ste. 418,
  San Francisco, CA 94102, (415)362-2224
BuildingSMART Alliance [6574], Natl. Inst. of Build-
  ing Sciences, 1090 Vermont Ave. NW, Ste. 700,
  Washington, DC 20005-4905, (202)289-7800
Bukovina Soc. of the Americas [3910], PO Box 81,
  Ellis, KS 67637
Bulgaria Squash Fed. [IO], Sofia, Bulgaria
Bulgarian
  Bulgarian-American Chamber of Commerce
    [23337]
  Bulgarian Stud. Assn. [9465]
  One Heart Bulgaria [11373]
Bulgarian Acad. of Sciences [IO], Sofia, Bulgaria
Bulgarian ACM Chap. [IO], Varna, Bulgaria
Bulgarian Aikido Fed. [IO], Sofia, Bulgaria
Bulgarian-American Chamber of Commerce [23337],
  1427 N Wilcox Ave., Hollywood, CA 90028-8123,
  (323)962-2414
Bulgarian Animal Defence League [IO], Sofia,
  Bulgaria
Bulgarian Assn. Against Epilepsy [IO], Sofia,
  Bulgaria
Bulgarian Assn. on Aging [IO], Sofia, Bulgaria
Bulgarian Assn. for Alternative Tourism [IO], Sofia,
  Bulgaria
Bulgarian Assn. of Consulting Engineers and
  Architects [IO], Sofia, Bulgaria
Bulgarian Assn. of Info. Technologies [IO], Sofia,
  Bulgaria
Bulgarian Assn. of Kinesitherapists and Rehabilita-
  tors [IO], Sofia, Bulgaria
Bulgarian Assn. of Music Producers [IO], Sofia,
  Bulgaria
Bulgarian Assn. of Pattern Recognition [IO], Sofia,
  Bulgaria
Bulgarian Assn. of Sterility and Reproductive Hea.
  [IO], Sofia, Bulgaria
Bulgarian Assn. of Surgeons and Gastroenterolo-
  gists [IO], Sofia, Bulgaria
Bulgarian Assn. of Travel Agents [IO], Sofia,
  Bulgaria
Bulgarian Assn. of Univ. Women [IO], Sofia, Bulgaria
Bulgarian Athletics Fed. [IO], Sofia, Bulgaria
Bulgarian Badminton Fed. [IO], Sofia, Bulgaria
Bulgarian Bible Soc. [IO], Sofia, Bulgaria
Bulgarian Book Assn. [IO], Sofia, Bulgaria
Bulgarian Bus. Coun. [IO], Dubai, United Arab Emir-
  ates
Bulgarian Chamber of Commerce and Indus. [IO],
  Sofia, Bulgaria
Bulgarian Constr. Chamber [IO], Sofia, Bulgaria
Bulgarian Dance Sport Fed. [IO], Sofia, Bulgaria
Bulgarian Fed. of Speleology [IO], Sofia, Bulgaria
Bulgarian Geological Soc. [IO], Sofia, Bulgaria
Bulgarian Geophysical Soc. [IO], Sofia, Bulgaria
Bulgarian Handball Fed. [IO], Sofia, Bulgaria
Bulgarian Hypertension League [IO], Sofia, Bulgaria
Bulgarian Ice Hockey Fed. [IO], Sofia, Bulgaria
Bulgarian Indus. Assn. [IO], Sofia, Bulgaria
Bulgarian League for the Prevention of Osteoporosis
  [IO], Sofia, Bulgaria
Bulgarian Lib. and Info. Assn. [IO], Sofia, Bulgaria
Bulgarian Medical Assn. [IO], Sofia, Bulgaria
Bulgarian Mineralogical Soc. [IO], Sofia, Bulgaria
Bulgarian Natl. Fed. of Karate-Do [IO], Sofia,
  Bulgaria
Bulgarian Olympian Comm. [IO], Sofia, Bulgaria
Bulgarian Operational Res. Soc. [IO], Sofia, Bulgaria

Bulgarian Orienteering Fed. [IO], Sofia, Bulgaria
Bulgarian Orthodontic Soc. [IO], Sofia, Bulgaria
Bulgarian Paralympic Comm. [IO], Sofia, Bulgaria
Bulgarian Red Cross [IO], Sofia, Bulgaria
Bulgarian Sailing Fed. [IO], Sofia, Bulgaria
Bulgarian Skating Fed. [IO], Sofia, Bulgaria
Bulgarian Soc. of Chemotherapy [IO], Varna,
  Bulgaria
Bulgarian Soc. for Clinical Densitometry [IO], Sofia,
  Bulgaria
Bulgarian Soc. of Endocrinology [IO], Sofia, Bulgaria
Bulgarian Soc. of Ophthalmology [IO], Sofia,
  Bulgaria
Bulgarian Soc. for the Protection of Birds [IO], Sofia,
  Bulgaria
Bulgarian Soc. for Rheumatology [IO], Sofia,
  Bulgaria
Bulgarian Sociological Assn. [IO], Sofia, Bulgaria
Bulgarian Stud. Assn. [9465], Martha Forsyth, Sec.-
  Treas., 51 Davis Ave., West Newton, MA 02465-
  1925
Bulgarian Taekwondo Fed. [IO], Sofia, Bulgaria
Bulgarian Telework Assn. [IO], Sofia, Bulgaria
Bulgarian Tennis Fed. [IO], Sofia, Bulgaria
Bulgarian-U.S. Bus. Coun.
Bulgarian-U.S. Bus. Coun. - Address unknown since
  2011.
Bulgarian Volleyball Fed. [IO], Sofia, Bulgaria
Bulgarian Water Polo Fed. [IO], Sofia, Bulgaria
Bulgarian Web Assn. [IO], Sofia, Bulgaria
Bulgarska Federacia Volleyball [★IO]
Bulk Drug Mfrs'. Assn. [IO], Hyderabad, India
Bulk Packaging and Containerization Inst. [★876]
Bull Terrier Club of Am. [21532], Naomi Waynee,
  Exec. Sec., 19135 W Taylor St., Buckeye, AZ
  85326-8506, (623)853-1940
Bull Users Soc. - Defunct.
Bulldog Club of Am. Rescue Network [10935], PO
  Box 1049, Kaysville, UT 84037, (801)546-0265
Bulletin of the Atomic Scientists [7364], 1155 E 60th
  St., Chicago, IL 60637, (773)702-6312
Bullnose Morris Club [IO], Chelmsford, United
  Kingdom
Bullseye Assn. [22325], 203 Washington St., Marble-
  head, MA 01945
Bullseye Cancel Collectors' Club [22023], 2749 Pine
  Knoll Dr., No. 4, Walnut Creek, CA 94595-2044
Bullseye Class Assn. [★22325]
Bullwhip Squadron Assn. [20780], 3590 Round Bot-
  tom Rd., PMB F254301, Cincinnati, OH 45244-
  3026, (334)692-5140
Bunbury Chamber of Commerce and Indus. [IO],
  Bunbury, Australia
Bund der Deutschen Katholischen Jugend [★IO]
Bund der Deutschen Landjugend [★IO]
Bund Deutscher Innenarchitekten [★IO]
Bund Deutscher Landschaftsarchitekten [★IO]
Bund Deutscher Oenologen [★IO]
Bund Freischaffender Foto-Designer [IO], Stuttgart,
  Germany
BUND - Friends of the Earth Germany [IO], Berlin,
  Germany
Bund freiberuflicher Hebammen Deutschlands e.V.
  [★IO]
Bund fur Lebensmittelrecht und Lebensmittelkunde
  e.V. [★IO]
Bund Osterreichischer Innenarchitekten [IO], Vienna,
  Austria
Bund der Steuerzahler Europa [★IO]
Bund fur Umwelt und Naturschutz Deutschland
  [★IO]
Bundersarztekammer [★IO]
Bundesarchitektenkammer [★IO]
Bundesfachverband Fleisch eV [★IO]
Bundesforschungsanstalt fur Ernahrung und Lebens-
  mittel [IO], Detmold, Germany
Bundesfraktion Christlicher Gewerkschafter [★IO]
Bundesgremium des Einrichtungsfachhandels [★IO]
Bundesgremium des Lebensmittelhandels [★IO]
Bundesgremium des Radio- und Elektrohandels
  [★IO]
Bundesinnung der Baecker Osterreichs [★IO]
Bundesinnung der Chemischen Gewerbe [★IO]
Bundesinnung der Fleischer [★IO]
Bundesinnung der Konditoren (Zuckerbaecker)
  [★IO]

Bundesrechtsanwaltskammer [★IO]
Bundesverband Bildender Kuenstlerinnen und Kuen-
  stler [★IO]
Bundesverband des Deutschen Exporthandels [★IO]
Bundesverband der Deutschen Fleischwarenindus-
  trie [★IO]
Bundesverband der Deutschen Industrie [★IO]
Bundesverband der Deutschen Kies- und Sandin-
  dustrie [★IO]
Bundesverband der Deutschen Luft-und Raumfahr-
  tindustrie [★IO]
Bundesverband der Deutschen Spirituosen-Industrie
  und -Importeure e. V. [★IO]
Bundesverband der Deutschen Zementindustrie
  [★IO]
Bundesverband der Deutschen Ziegelindustrie [★IO]
Bundesverband Deutscher Fertigbau [★IO]
Bundesverband Deutscher Galerien E.V. [IO], Berlin,
  Germany
Bundesverband Deutscher Kapitalbeteiligungsgesell-
  schaften e.V. [★IO]
Bundesverband Deutscher Tabakwaren-
  Grosshandler und Automatenaufsteller e.V. [★IO]
Bundesverband Deutscher Unternehmensberater
  [★IO]
Bundesverband Deutscher Versicherungskaufleute
  e.V. [IO], Bonn, Germany
Bundesverband Deutscher Zeitungsverleger [★IO]
Bundesverband Druck und Medien [★IO]
Bundesverband der Edelstein- und Diamantindustrie
  [★IO]
Bundesverband Finanzdienstleistungen [★IO]
Bundesverband Glasindustrie [★IO]
Bundesverband der Hersteller- und Errichterfirmen
  von Sicherheitssystemen [★IO]
Bundesverband Kamera [★IO]
Bundesverband Medizintechnologie e.V. [★IO]
Bundesverband Molkereiprodukte eV [IO], Berlin,
  Germany
Bundesverband der Phonographischen Wirtschaft
  [★IO]
Bundesverband Praktizierender Tierarzte [★IO]
Bundesverband Regie [★IO]
Bundesverband Selbstandiger Physiotherapeuten
  [★IO]
Bundesverband der Steuerberater e.V. [★IO]
Bundesverband Wind Energie e.V. [★IO]
Bundesverband der Zigarrenindustrie [★IO]
Bundesverbandes des Deutschen Briefmarkenhan-
  dels [★IO]
Bundesvereinigung der Deutschen Arbeitgeberver-
  bande [★IO]
Bundesvereinigung der Deutschen Ernahrungsindus-
  trie [★IO]
Bundesvereinigung Deutscher Apothekerverbande
  [★IO]
Bundesvereinigung Lebenshilfe fur Menschen mit
  geistiger Behinderung [★IO]
BundeszahnArztekammer-BZAK [★IO]
BUNDjugend [IO], Berlin, Germany
Bunker Family Assn. of Am. [20437], LiAnn Penning-
  ton, Treas., PO Box 337961, Greeley, CO 80633
Bunker Family Assn. of Am. [20437], LiAnn Penning-
  ton, Treas., PO Box 337961, Greeley, CO 80633
Bunyad Literacy Community Coun. [IO], Lahore,
  Pakistan
Burak Havacilik [★IO]
Bur. des radiocommunications [★IO]
Bur. des Activities Socio-Caritatives - Caritas Camer-
  oun [IO], Yaounde, Cameroon
Bur. of Animal Indus. Veterinarians [★17033]
Bur. of the Budget in Exile Unrequited Marching and
  Chowder Soc. - Defunct.
Bur. Canadien de l'Education Internationale [★IO]
Bur. D'Assurance du Canada [★IO]
Bur. of Envelope Mfrs. of Am. [★3348]
Bur. of European Designers Associations [IO], Brus-
  sels, Belgium
Bur. Europeen pour les Langues Moins Repandues
  [★IO]
Bur. Europeen de l'Environnement [★IO]
Bur. Europeen de l'Objection de Conscience [★IO]
Bur. Europeene des Unions de Consommateurs
  [★IO]
Bur. of Freelance Photographers [IO], London,
  United Kingdom

A star before a book entry number signifies that the name is not listed separately, but is mentioned within the entry.

Reference to "IO" in place of a book number signifies that the association may be found in the 50th edition of International Organizations.

Business and Commerce

A star before a book entry number signifies that the name is not listed separately, but is mentioned within the entry.

Buying Influence [17446]BusinessCameroon-USA Chamber of Commerce
CEO Netweavers [962]
ChristianTrade Assn. Intl. [19561]
Clean Economy Network [6605]
Coalition of Asian Amer. Bus. Organizations [712]
Collision Indus. Electronic Commerce Assn. [1048]
Consultants Assn. for the Natural Products Indus. [713]
Consuming Indus. Trade Action Coalition [714]
Corporate Responsibility Officers Assn. [963]
Coun. of Supplier Diversity Professionals [715]
Craft Retailers Assn. for Tomorrow [987]
Crude Oil Quality Assn. [2647]
Customer Relationship Mgt. Assn. [869]
Cyprus-US Chamber of Commerce [23360]
Decorative Plumbing and Hardware Assn. [2781]
Deep Draft Lubricant Assn. [2225]
Electronic Indus. Citizenship Coalition [1098]
Executives Without Borders [60]
Global Envelope Alliance [3349]
Global India Venture Capital Assn. [1302]
Global Sourcing Coun. [2602]
Green Partners [4177]
Guam Chamber of Commerce [23340]
Guam Chamber of Commerce [23340]
Hardwood Fed. [1508]
Hotel Tech. Next Generation [1753]
Indus. Auctioneers Assn. [269]
Info. Tech. Services Marketing Assn. [2405]
Innovation Norway - U.S. [23368]
Intl. Amusement and Leisure Defense Assn. [3057]
Intl. Assn. for Contract and Commercial Mgt. [716]
Intl. Assn. for Contract and Commercial Mgt. [716]
Intl. Assn. of Space Entrepreneurs [139]
Intl. Assn. of Women in Family Enterprises [3289]
Intl. Bridal Mfrs. Assn. [472]
Intl. Economic Alliance [1065]
Intl. Photovoltaic Equip. Assn. [1170]
Intl. Sugar Trade Coalition [3367]
Internet Merchants Assn. [2117]
Iraqi Amer. Chamber of Commerce and Indus. [23370]
ITAP Intl. Alliance [717]
Jordan Info. Bur. [23421]
Korean Amer. Soc. of Entrepreneurs [718]
Latin Am. Trade Coalition [2187]
LCD TV Assn. [3431]
Leadership for Energy Automated Processing [1171]
Middle East Investment Initiative [1313]
MSPAlliance [6547]
Natl. Assn. for Moisture Mgt. [1223]
Natl. Assn. of Pharmaceutical Representatives [2697]
Natl. Assn. of Small Bus. Contractors [931]
Natl. Black Chamber of Commerce [23341]
Natl. Coalition for Capital [1058]
Natl. Coun. of Asian Amer. Bus. Associations [719]
Natl. Coun. of Minorities in Energy [1173]
Natl. Hair Soc. [1643]
Natl. Latina Bus. Women Assn. [2188]
Natl. United States-Arab Chamber of Commerce [23374]
Natl. Utilities Diversity Coun. [3600]
North Amer. Security Products Org. [3225]
North Amer. Trailer Dealers Assn. [3531]
Pakistan Chamber of Commerce USA [23435]
Parachute Indus. Assn. [2623]
Professional Lighting and Sign Mgt. Companies of Am. [2223]
Retail Energy Supply Assn. [1177]
Rising Tide Capital [1060]
Romanian-U.S. Bus. Coun. [23438]
South African USA Chamber of Commerce [23379]
Support Services Alliance [3300]
Swedish Trade Coun. [3489]
Transmission Rebuilders Network Intl. [341]
Turkish-American Chamber of Commerce and Indus. [23455]
Underground Utility and Leak Locators Assn. [3603]

U.S. Chamber of Commerce [23384]
U.S. Christian Chamber of Commerce [23393]
U.S. Coun. of Better Bus. Bureaus [706]
U.S. Indian Amer. Chamber of Commerce [23407]
United States-Indonesia Soc. [720]
United States-Indonesia Soc. [720]
U.S.-Ukraine Bus. Coun. [721]
US-Ireland Alliance [722]
US-Ireland Alliance [722]
Utility Indus. Gp. [3607]
Utility Supply Mgt. Alliance [3609]
Women's High Tech Coalition [7535]
Bus. Comm. for the Arts - Address unknown since 2010.
Bus. and Community Found. [IO], New Delhi, India
Bus. Continuity Planning Workgroup for Healthcare Organizations [14481], Byron Callies, Treas., 6102 Woodridge Ln. NE, Rochester, MN 55906
Bus. Coun. [18428], PO Box 20147, Washington, DC 20041, (202)298-7650
Bus. Coun. for Africa [IO], London, United Kingdom
Bus. Coun. of Australia [IO], Melbourne, Australia
Bus. Coun. for Intl. Understanding [17940], 1212 Ave. of the Americas, 10th Fl., New York, NY 10036, (212)490-0460
Bus. Coun. for Intl. Understanding [17940], 1212 Ave. of the Americas, 10th Fl., New York, NY 10036, (212)490-0460
Bus. Coun. of Papua New Guinea [IO], Konedobu, Papua New Guinea
Bus. Coun. for Peace [13455], 5 E 22nd St., Ste. 9J, New York, NY 10010, (212)696-9696
Bus. Coun. for Sustainable Energy [1164], 1620 Eye St. NW, Ste. 501, Washington, DC 20006, (202)785-0507
Bus. for Economic Security, Tourism and Trade
Bus. for Economic Security, Tourism and Trade - Address unknown since 2011.

Business Education
AACSB Intl. [7780]
AACSB Intl. [7780]
Acad. of Intl. Bus. [7781]
Acad. of Intl. Bus. [7781]
AIESEC U.S. [7782]
AIESEC U.S. [7782]
Alpha Beta Gamma Intl. [23486]
Alpha Beta Gamma Intl. [23486]
Assn. for Bus. Commun. [7783]
Assn. for Bus. Simulation and Experiential Learning [7784]
Assn. for Bus. Simulation and Experiential Learning [7784]
Assn. Global View [7785]
Assn. Global View [7785]
ASTD [7786]
CDS Intl. [7787]
CDS Intl. [7787]
Community Coll. Bus. Officers [7788]
Decision Sciences Inst. [7789]
Delta Pi Epsilon [23487]
European Consortium for the Learning Org. [6838]
Found. for Student Commun. [7790]
Green Computing Impact Org. [1221]
Intl. Assembly for Collegiate Bus. Educ. [7791]
Intl. Assembly for Collegiate Bus. Educ. [7791]
Intl. Assn. for Bus. and Soc. [7792]
Intl. Assn. for Bus. and Soc. [7792]
Intl. Assn. of Jesuit Bus. Schools [7793]
Intl. Assn. of Jesuit Bus. Schools [7793]
Intl. Soc. for Bus. Educ. [7794]
Intl. Soc. for Bus. Educ. [7794]
Junior Achievement [7795]
Junior Achievement [7795]
Mgt. Educ. Alliance [7796]
My Own Bus., Inc. [7797]
NASBITE Intl. [7798]
NASBITE Intl. [7798]
Natl. Assn. of Blessed Billionaires [7799]
Natl. Assn. for Bus. Teacher Educ. [7800]
Natl. Assn. for Community Coll. Entrepreneurship [7801]
Natl. Assn. of Small Bus. Contractors [931]
Natl. Assn. of Supervisor of Bus. Educ. [7802]
Natl. Black MBA Assn. [7803]

Natl. Bus. Educ. Assn. [7804]
Natl. Found. for Teaching Entrepreneurship [7805]
Org. for Entrepreneurial Development [7806]
Pi Omega Pi [23488]
Soc. for Judgment and Decision Making [7807]
Soc. for Judgment and Decision Making [7807]
Southwest Case Res. Assn. [7808]
Team Success [13560]
Business Educ. Res. Foundation [★7800]
Bus. Educators Australasia [IO], Abbotsford, Australia
Bus. Equip. Mfrs. Assn. [★6539]
Bus. Espionage Controls and Countermeasures Assn. [1886], PO Box 55582, Shoreline, WA 98155-0582
Bus. Espionage Controls and Countermeasures Assn. [1886], PO Box 55582, Shoreline, WA 98155-0582
Bus. Ethics Forum [651], 905 Main St., Houston, TX 77002
Bus. Executives for Natl. Security [18590], 1030 15th St., NW, Ste. 200 E, Washington, DC 20005, (202)296-2125
Bus. Forms Mgt. Assn. [3345], 3800 Old Cheney Rd., Ste. 101-285, Lincoln, NE 68516-5901, (402)216-0479
Business-Higher Educ. Forum [7778], 2025 M St. NW, Ste. 800, Washington, DC 20036-2422, (202)367-1189
Bus. History Conf. [9756], Hagley Museum and Lib., PO Box 3630, Wilmington, DE 19807-0630, (302)658-2400
Bus. and Indus. Advisory Comm. to the OECD [IO], Paris, France
Business-Industry Political Action Comm. [18324], 888 16th St. NW, Ste. 305, Washington, DC 20006, (202)833-1880
Bus. Indus. Promotion Assn. of Pakistan [IO], Lahore, Pakistan
Bus. and Institutional Furniture Manufacturer's Assn. [1545], 678 Front Ave. NW, Ste. 150, Grand Rapids, MI 49504-5368, (616)285-3963
Business Law
National Fraud Information Center/Internet Fraud Watch [17467]
Bus. Leaders for Sensible Priorities [18414], 1333 H St. NW, 10th Fl., Washington, DC 20005
Business Leadership Forum - Defunct.
Bus. Leadership South Africa [IO], Johannesburg, Republic of South Africa
Bus. Mail Found. [★2400]
Bus. Marketing Assn. [2392], 1833 Centre Point Cir., Ste. 123, Naperville, IL 60563, (630)544-5054
Bus. Marketing Assn. [2392], 1833 Centre Point Cir., Ste. 123, Naperville, IL 60563, (630)544-5054
Business, Minority
Native Amer. Bus. Alliance [19164]
Bus. Modeling and Integration Domain Task Force [652], 140 Kendrick St., Bldg. A, Ste. 300, Needham, MA 02494, (781)444-0404
Bus. Network Intl. - Suriname [IO], Paramaribo, Suriname
Bus. NZ [IO], Wellington, New Zealand
Bus. Process Indus. Assn. of India [IO], Gurgaon, India
Bus. Process Mgt. Initiative and Object Mgt. Gp. [★652]
Business Products
Global Envelope Alliance [3349]
North Amer. Security Products Org. [3225]
TopTen USA [1178]
Bus. Products Credit Assn. [1286], 607 Westridge Dr., O'Fallon, MO 63366, (636)294-5775
Bus. Products Indus. Assn. [★1552]
Business/Professional Advt. Assn. [★2392]
Business/Professional Advt. Assn. [★2392]
Bus. and Professional Women Australia [IO], Surrey Hills, Australia
Bus. and Professional Women Intl. [IO], Horsham, United Kingdom
Bus. and Professional Women the Netherlands [IO], Amsterdam, Netherlands
Bus. and Professional Women - UK [IO], Billericay, United Kingdom
Bus. and Professional Women/U.S.A. - Defunct.

Reference to "IO" in place of a book number signifies that the association may be found in the 50th edition of International Organizations.

Bus. and Professional Women's Found. **[10638]**, 1718 M St. NW, No. 148, Washington, DC 20036, (202)293-1100

Bus. Professionals of Am. **[9042]**, 5454 Cleveland Ave., Columbus, OH 43231-4021, (614)895-7277

Bus. Publications Audit of Circulation **[★87]**

Bus. Publications Audit of Circulation **[★87]**

Bus. Retention and Expansion Intl. **[1055]**, PO Box 3212, Bismarck, ND 58502-3212, (800)677-9930

Bus. Roundtable **[18429]**, 1717 Rhode Island Ave. NW, Ste. 800, Washington, DC 20036, (202)872-1260

Bus. for Social Responsibility **[653]**, 111 Sutter St., 12th Fl., San Francisco, CA 94104, (415)984-3200

Bus. Software Alliance **[5562]**, 1150 18th St. NW, Ste. 700, Washington, DC 20036, (202)872-5500

Bus. Software Alliance Australia **[IO]**, North Ryde, Australia

Bus. Software Assn. **[★5562]**

Bus. Solutions Assn. **[3346]**, 5024 Campbell Blvd., Ste. R, Baltimore, MD 21236-5943, (410)931-8100

Business Studies
   Bus. Leaders for Sensible Priorities **[18414]**

Business Systems Assn. - Defunct.

Bus. Tech. Assn. **[2577]**, 12411 Wornall Rd., Ste. 200, Kansas City, MO 64145, (816)941-3100

Bus. Travel Coalition **[23453]**, 214 Grouse Ln., Radnor, PA 19087-2730, (610)999-9247

Bus. Volunteers Unlimited **[13389]**, 1300 E 9th St., Ste. 1805, Cleveland, OH 44114-1509, (216)736-7711

Bus. Women's Assn. of Uzbekistan **[IO]**, Tashkent, Uzbekistan

BusinessEurope **[IO]**, Brussels, Belgium

Businesswomen's Assn. **[IO]**, Killarney, Republic of South Africa

Butchers' Company **[IO]**, London, United Kingdom

Butsuri Tansa Gakkai **[★IO]**

Butter Pat Patter Assn. **[21313]**, 265 Eagle Bend Dr., Bigfork, MT 59911-6235

Butterfly
   Intl. Assn. of Butterfly Exhibitions **[1232]**
   Intl. Butterfly Breeders Assn. **[3858]**
   Intl. Butterfly Breeders Assn. **[3858]**
   Natl. Butterfly Assn. **[22371]**

Butterfly Conservation **[IO]**, Wareham, United Kingdom

Butterfly Soc. of Japan **[IO]**, Tokyo, Japan

Buttonhook Soc. **[IO]**, Maidstone, United Kingdom

Buying Influence **[17446]**, 801 W 47th St., Ste. 110, Country Club Plz., Kansas City, MO 64112, (816)931-7896

BVI Assn. of Compliance Officers **[IO]**, Tortola, British Virgin Islands

BVI Motor Sports Assn. **[IO]**, Tortola, British Virgin Islands

BVI Olympians Assn. **[IO]**, Tortola, British Virgin Islands

BVI's Big Bros. Big Sisters **[IO]**, Tortola, British Virgin Islands

BWHBC **[★17135]**

By Word of Mouth Storytelling Guild - Address unknown since 2010.

Byelorussian-Amer. Veteran Assn. - Defunct.

Byelorussian Anatomical Soc. **[IO]**, Minsk, Belarus

Byelorussian Assn. of the Physicians **[IO]**, Minsk, Belarus

Byelorussian Operational Res. Soc. **[IO]**, Minsk, Belarus

Byggesocietetet **[★IO]**

Byron Soc. of Am. **[9356]**, PO Box 1833, Cathedral Sta., New York, NY 10025

Bytown Railway Soc. **[IO]**, Ottawa, ON, Canada

Byzantine
   Mission Soc. of the Mother of God of Boronyavo **[20191]**
   Soc. for the Promotion of Byzantine Stud. **[3229]**

C

C-Change **[13894]**, 1776 Eye St. NW, 9th Fl., Washington, DC 20006, (202)756-1600

C3: Colorectal Cancer Coalition **[13895]**, 1414 Prince St., Ste. 204, Alexandria, VA 22314, (703)548-1225

CAA/AAA Found. for Traffic Safety **[★12971]**

CAAAV: Organizing Asian Communities **[★17199]**

Cab Res. Bur. **[★3537]**

Cab Res. Bur. **[★3537]**

Cabbage Patch Kids Collectors Club **[21314]**, PO Box 714, Cleveland, GA 30528, (706)865-2171

CABC: Coalition Against Breast Cancer - Defunct.

CABI **[IO]**, Wallingford, United Kingdom

CABI Bioscience Pakistan Centre **[IO]**, Rawalpindi, Pakistan

CABI Bioscience Switzerland Centre **[IO]**, Wallingford, United Kingdom

Cabinet Makers Assn. **[1546]**, PO Box 14276, Milwaukee, WI 53214-0276, (414)377-1340

Cable Europe **[IO]**, Brussels, Belgium

Cable and Satellite Broadcasting Assn. of Asia - Hong Kong Off. **[IO]**, Hong Kong, People's Republic of China

Cable and Telecommunications: A Marketing Soc. **[★489]**

Cable Telecommunications Assn. - Defunct.

Cable and Telecommunications Human Resources Assn. **[1787]**, 1755 Park St., Ste. 260, Naperville, IL 60563, (630)416-1166

Cable Television
   Amer. Cable Assn. **[723]**
   Cable TV Labs. **[724]**
   Natl. Cable TV Cooperative **[725]**

Cable TV Admin. and Marketing Soc. **[★489]**

Cable TV Labs. **[724]**, 858 Coal Creek Cir., Louisville, CO 80027-9750, (303)661-9100

Cable TV Public Affairs Assn. **[★5321]**

Cabletelevision Advt. Bur. **[88]**, 830 Third Ave., 2nd Fl., New York, NY 10022, (212)508-1200

Cabo Verde Children U.S.A. **[11204]**, 1151 Main St., Brockton, MA 02301, (508)588-0400

Cabrini Mission Corps **[20017]**, 610 King of Prussia Rd., Radnor, PA 19087-3623, (610)971-0821

Cactus and Succulent Soc. of Am. **[21788]**, PO Box 1000, Claremont, CA 91711, (626)852-8085

Cactus and Succulent Soc. of Pakistan **[IO]**, Karachi, Pakistan

CAD Soc. **[6483]**, Strategic Reach PR, 7100 N Broadway, Bldg. 2, Ste. 2LPH, Denver, CO 80221, (303)487-7406

Cadillac-LaSalle Club **[21017]**, PO Box 360835, Columbus, OH 43236-0835, (614)478-4622

CAE **[IO]**, Melbourne, Australia

CAEF - The European Foundry Assn. **[IO]**, Dusseldorf, Germany

Caesarean Cycling Club **[IO]**, Jersey, United Kingdom

Caffeine Awareness Assn. **[13828]**, 93 S Jackson St., No. 46673, Seattle, WA 98104, (815)572-8007

Cahill Cooperative Ancestors - Address unknown since 2011.

Cairn Terrier Club of Am. **[21533]**, 12616-215th Ave., Ct. E, Bonney Lake, WA 98391, (253)862-6147

Cairns Chamber of Commerce **[IO]**, Cairns, Australia

Cairo Regional Centre for Intl. Commercial Arbitration **[IO]**, Cairo, Egypt

Caithness Paperweight Collectors Soc. **[IO]**, Devon, United Kingdom

Caitlin Raymond Intl. Registry **[13856]**, UMass Memorial Medical Center, 55 Lake Ave. N, Worcester, MA 01655, (508)334-8969

Cajal Club **[15652]**, Dr. Charles E. Ribak, Sec.-Treas., Univ. of California at Irvine, School of Medicine, Dept. of Anatomy and Neurobiology, Irvine, CA 92697-1275

Cal State San Marcos Alumni Assn. **[18858]**, 333 S Twin Oaks Valley Rd., San Marcos, CA 92096-0001, (760)750-4405

Caledonian Found. USA **[10170]**, PO Box 1242, Edgartown, MA 02539-1242

Caledonian Found. USA **[10170]**, PO Box 1242, Edgartown, MA 02539-1242

Calendar
   Comm. for Crescent Observation Intl. **[9890]**

Calendar Marketing Assn. **[2393]**, 214 N Hale St., Wheaton, IL 60187, (630)510-4564

Calgary Acad. of Chefs and Cooks **[IO]**, Calgary, AB, Canada

Calgary Amateur Radio Assn. **[IO]**, Calgary, AB, Canada

Calgary Apartment Assn. **[IO]**, Calgary, AB, Canada

Calgary BMX Assn. **[IO]**, Calgary, AB, Canada

Calgary Cerebral Palsy Assn. **[IO]**, Calgary, AB, Canada

Calgary Chinese Elderly Citizens' Assn. **[IO]**, Calgary, AB, Canada

Calgary Constr. Assn. **[IO]**, Calgary, AB, Canada

Calgary Coun. for Advanced Tech. **[IO]**, Calgary, AB, Canada

Calgary Down Syndrome Assn. **[IO]**, Calgary, AB, Canada

Calgary Immigrant Women's Assn. **[IO]**, Calgary, AB, Canada

Calgary Minor Basketball Assn. **[IO]**, Calgary, AB, Canada

Calgary Mountain Bike Alliance **[IO]**, Calgary, AB, Canada

Calgary Musicians' Assn. **[IO]**, Calgary, AB, Canada

Calgary Recreational Intl. Folkdance Club **[IO]**, Calgary, AB, Canada

Calgary Seniors Rsrc. Soc. **[IO]**, Calgary, AB, Canada

Calgary United Soccer Assn. **[IO]**, Calgary, AB, Canada

Calgary Women's Soccer Assn. **[IO]**, Calgary, AB, Canada

Calibre Audio Lib. **[IO]**, Aylesbury, United Kingdom

California Artichoke Advisory Bd. - Defunct.

California Assn. of Pet Professionals **[★2688]**

California Assn. of Pet Professionals **[★2688]**

California Assn. of Sanitarians **[★14504]**

California Assn. of Tiger-Owners **[21018]**, 2950 Calle Grande Vista, San Clemente, CA 92672

California Assn. of Tiger-Owners **[21018]**, 2950 Calle Grande Vista, San Clemente, CA 92672

California Assn. of Winegrape Growers **[5167]**, 1325 J St., Ste. 1560, Sacramento, CA 95814, (916)379-8995

California Avocado Advisory Bd. **[★4429]**

California Avocado Assn. **[★4430]**

California Avocado Commn. **[4429]**, 12 Mauchly, Ste. L, Irvine, CA 92618-6305, (949)341-1955

California Avocado Soc. **[4430]**, PO Box 1660, Temecula, CA 92593-1660, (951)225-9102

California Begonia Soc. **[★21764]**

California Cactus Growers Assn. - Defunct.

California Canning Peach Assn. **[4431]**, 2300 River Plaza Dr., Ste. 110, Sacramento, CA 95833, (916)925-9131

California Cling Peach Advisory Bd. **[★4432]**

California Cling Peach Bd. **[4432]**, J.D. Allen, 531-D N Alta Ave., Dinuba, CA 93618-3203, (559)595-1425

California Coll. of the Arts and Crafts Alumni Assn. **[18859]**, 5212 Broadway, Oakland, CA 94618, (510)594-3788

California Conservation Proj. **[★4152]**

California Coun. Against Hea. Fraud **[★17765]**

California Date Administrative Comm. **[4433]**, PO Box 1736, Indio, CA 92202-1736, (760)347-4510

California Date Commn. **[★4433]**

California Dried Fig Advisory Bd. **[★4436]**

California Dried Fruit Export Assn. **[★4472]**

California Dried Plum Bd. **[4434]**, 3840 Rosin Ct., Ste. 170, Sacramento, CA 95834, (916)565-6232

California Dry Bean Advisory Bd. **[4435]**, 531-D N Alta Ave., Dinuba, CA 93618-3203, (559)591-4866

California Fed. of Legal Secretaries **[★72]**

California Fed. of Legal Secretaries **[★72]**

California Fig Advisory Bd. **[4436]**, 600 W Shaw Ave., Ste. 300, Fresno, CA 93704, (559)243-8600

California Forest Protective Assn. **[★1466]**

California Forestry Assn. **[1466]**, 1215 K St., Ste. 1830, Sacramento, CA 95814, (916)444-6592

California Freezers Assn. **[★1371]**

California Grape and Tree Fruit Assn. **[★4437]**

California Grape and Tree Fruit League **[4437]**, 978 W Alluvial, Ste. 107, Fresno, CA 93711, (559)226-6330

California Gp. Against Smoking Pollution **[★16672]**

California Growers and Shippers Protective League **[★4437]**

California Helicopter Assn. **[★136]**

California Helicopter Assn. **[★136]**

California Hungarian Amer. Cultural Found. - Defunct.

A star before a book entry number signifies that the name is not listed separately, but is mentioned within the entry.

California Independent Almond Growers - Defunct.
California Kiwifruit Commn. [4438], 1521 I St., Sacramento, CA 95814, (916)441-0678
California Melon Res. Bd. [4439], 531-D N Alta Ave., Dinuba, CA 93618, (559)591-0435
California Motorama Corp. [★22778]
California Natl. Watercolor Soc. [★9193]
California Pistachio Commn. - Defunct.
California Prune Advisory Bd. [★4434]
California Prune Bd. [★4434]
California Public Employee Relations Prog. [18040], 2521 Channing Way, No. 5555, Berkeley, CA 94720-5555, (510)643-7096
California Raisin Advisory Bd. - Defunct.
California Rare Fruit Growers [4440], PO Box 6850, Fullerton, CA 92834-6850
California Redwood Assn. [1499], 818 Grayson Rd., Ste. 201, Pleasant Hill, CA 94523, (925)935-1499
California Soc. of Etchers [★1604]
California Soc. of Printmakers [1604], PO Box 194202, San Francisco, CA 94119
California State Univ. | Northridge Alumni Assn. [18860], 18111 Nordhoff St., Northridge, CA 91330-8385, (818)677-2137
California State Univ. of San Marcos Alumni Assn. [★18858]
California Strawberry Advisory Bd. [★4441]
California Strawberry Commn. [4441], PO Box 269, Watsonville, CA 95077, (831)724-1301
California Table Grape Commn. [4442], 392 W Fallbrook, Ste. 101, Fresno, CA 93711-6150, (559)447-8350
California Vehicle Leasing Assn. [★3082]
California Vintage Race Gp. [★21917]
California Walnut Bd. [4748], 101 Parkshore Dr., Ste. 250, Folsom, CA 95630, (916)932-7070
California Water Color Soc. [★9193]
California Wheelchair Aviators [★20903]
California Wheelchair Aviators [★20903]
Californian
   Los Californianos [20380]
   Native Daughters of the Golden West [18943]
   Native Sons of the Golden West [18944]
Californian Rabbit Specialty Club [4838], Susan Yeary, Sec.-Treas., 3201 N Alamo Rd., Edinburg, TX 78542-1480, (956)383-2228
Californians for Nonsmokers' Rights [★16672]
Californians for Responsible Res. [★10987]
Calix Soc. [13238], 3881 Highland Ave., Ste. 201, White Bear Lake, MN 55110, (651)773-3117
Calix Soc. [13238], 3881 Highland Ave., Ste. 201, White Bear Lake, MN 55110, (651)773-3117
Call Center Benchmarking Network [★672]
Call Center Benchmarking Network [★672]
Call Centre Mgt. Assn. [IO], Sandbach, United Kingdom
Call Centre Mgt. Assn., Ireland [IO], Naas, Ireland
Call For Action [11660], 11820 Parklawn Dr., Ste. 340, Rockville, MD 20852, (240)747-0229
Call For Action [11660], 11820 Parklawn Dr., Ste. 340, Rockville, MD 20852, (240)747-0229
Call and Response - Address unknown since 2011.
A Call to Serve Intl. [11557], PO Box 7026, Columbia, MO 65205-7026
A Call to Serve Intl. [11557], PO Box 7026, Columbia, MO 65205-7026
Call and Whistle Collectors Assn. - Address unknown since 2011.
Callerlab - Intl. Assn. of Square Dance Callers [9538], 200 SW 30th St., Ste. 104, Topeka, KS 66611, (785)783-3665
Callerlab - Intl. Assn. of Square Dance Callers [9538], 200 SW 30th St., Ste. 104, Topeka, KS 66611, (785)783-3665
Calligraphy and Lettering Arts Soc. [IO], London, United Kingdom
Calligraphy; Soc. for [10757]
Callmakers and Collectors Assn. of Am. [21315], 2925 Ethel Ave., Alton, IL 62002, (618)465-5235
Calmeadow Charitable Found. [IO], Toronto, ON, Canada
Calorie Control Coun. [1379], 1100 Johnson Ferry Rd., Ste. 300, Atlanta, GA 30342, (404)252-3663
Calorie Restriction Soc. [15824], 187 Ocean Dr., Newport, NC 28570, (252)241-3079

Calvin Coolidge Memorial Found. [10656], PO Box 97, Plymouth, VT 05056, (802)672-3389
CAM Intl. [20018], 8625 La Prada Dr., Dallas, TX 75228, (214)327-8206
CAM Intl. [20018], 8625 La Prada Dr., Dallas, TX 75228, (214)327-8206
Camanachd Assn. [IO], Inverness, United Kingdom
Camara Americana de Comercio de Bolivia [★IO]
Camara Americana de Comercio de El Salvador [★IO]
Camara Americana de Comercio de la Republica Dominicana [★IO]
Camara Americana de Comercio de Sao Paulo [★IO]
Camara de Anunciantes del Paraguay [IO], Asuncion, Paraguay
Camara Anunciantes del Uruguay [IO], Montevideo, Uruguay
Camara Argentina del Aerosol [★IO]
Camara Argentina de Anunciantes [IO], Buenos Aires, Argentina
Camara Argentina de Comercio [★IO]
Camara Argentina de la Construccion [★IO]
Camara Argentina de Distribuidores de Materiales Electricos [★IO]
Camara Argentina de la Industria del Aluminio y Metales Afines [★IO]
Camara Argentina de la Industria Plastica [★IO]
Camara Argentina de Industrias Electronicas [★IO]
Camara Argentina del Libro [★IO]
Camara Argentina de Papelerias, Librerias y Afines [★IO]
Camara Argentina de Productores Avicolas [★IO]
Camara Argentina de Productores de Drogas Farmaceuticas [★IO]
Camara Argentina de Shopping Centers [★IO]
Camara Argentina de Supermercados [★IO]
Camara de Aseguradores de Venezuela [★IO]
Camara Automotoriz de Venezuela [★IO]
Camara de Azucareros [★IO]
Camara Brasileira do Livro [★IO]
Camara Chilena de la Construccion [★IO]
Camara Chilena del Libro A.G. [★IO]
Camara Chileno Norteamericana de Comercio [★IO]
Camara Colombiana de Informatica y Telecomunicaciones [★IO]
Camara Colombiana del Libro [★IO]
Camara de Comercio Americana del Peru [★IO]
Camara de Comercio Americana em Portugal [★IO]
Camara de Comercio Argentino-Brasilena [IO], Buenos Aires, Argentina
Camara de Comercio Argentino-Britanica en la Republica Argentina [IO], Buenos Aires, Argentina
Camara de Comercio Argentino-Canadiense [★IO]
Camara de Comercio Argentino-Israeli [★IO]
Camara de Comercio Colombo Americana [★IO]
Camara de Comercio de Costa Rica [★IO]
Camara de Comercio Ecuatoriano- Americana [★IO]
Camara de Comercio de los Estados Unidos en la Republica Argentina [★IO]
Camara de Comercio Exterior de Rosario [IO], Rosario, Argentina
Camara de Comercio Exterior de Salta [IO], Salta, Argentina
Camara de Comercio Guatemalteco-Americana [★IO]
Camara de Comercio Hondureno-Americana [★IO]
Camara de Comercio e Industria de El Salvador [★IO]
Camara de Comercio e Industria Peruano-Alemana [★IO]
Camara de Comercio e Industria Peruano-Francesa [★IO]
Camara do Comercio e Industria de Ponta Delgada [★IO]
Camara de Comercio e Industria de Trenque Lauquen [IO], Buenos Aires, Argentina
Camara de Comercio, Industria Y Servicios de Carlos Casares [IO], Carlos Casares, Argentina
Camara de Comercio Italiana de Rosario [IO], Rosario, Argentina
Camara de Comercio Latina de los EEUU [★23425]
Camara de Comercio de Lima [★IO]
Camara de Comercio de Mocambique [★IO]
Camara de Comercio Paraguaya Americana [★IO]

Camara de Comercio y Produccion de Santiago [★IO]
Camara de Comercio y Produccion de Santo Domingo [★IO]
Camara de Comercio de la Republica de Cuba [IO], Havana, Cuba
Camara de Comercio de Santiago [★IO]
Camara de Comercio Sueco Argentina [IO], Buenos Aires, Argentina
Camara de Comercio Suizo Argentina [★IO]
Camara de Comercio Uruguay - Estados Unidos [★IO]
Camara de la Construccion de Quito [★IO]
Camara Costarricense de la Construccion [★IO]
Camara De Comercio Colombo Americana - Bogota [★IO]
Camara Empresaria Parque Indus. de Pilar [IO], Buenos Aires, Argentina
Camara de Empresarios Madereros y Afines [★IO]
Camara de Empresas de Servicios de Telecomunicaciones [★IO]
Camara de Empresas de Software y Servicios Informaticos [★IO]
Camara Espanola de Comercio de la Republica Argentina [IO], Buenos Aires, Argentina
Camara de Exportadores de la Republica Argentina [★IO]
Camara de Fabricantes de Refrescos y Afines [★IO]
Camara de Fabricantes Venezolanos de Productos Automotores [★IO]
Camara Forestal de Bolivia [★IO]
Camara de Importadores de la Republica Argentina [★IO]
Camara de la Industria Aceitera de la Republica Argentina [★IO]
Camara de la Industria del Calzado del Estado de Guanajuato [★IO]
Camara de Industria y Comercio Argentino-Alemana [IO], Buenos Aires, Argentina
Camara de Industria y Comercio de Matanza [IO], Buenos Aires, Argentina
Camara Indus. Argentina de Indumentaria [★IO]
Camara de Informatica y Comunicaciones de la Republica Argentina [★IO]
Camara Junior Internacional Colombia [★IO]
Camara Junior Internacional de Ecuador [★IO]
Camara Junior Internacional de Republica Dominicana [★IO]
Camara Junior Internacional de Venezuela [★IO]
Camara Junior del Paraguay [IO], San Lorenzo, Paraguay
Camara Junor de Guatemala [IO], Guatemala City, Guatemala
Camara Madrid [★IO]
Camara Mexicana de la Industria de la Construccion [★IO]
Camara Nacional de Agricultura y Agroindustria [★IO]
Camara Nacional de Comercio - Bolivia [★IO]
Camara Nacional de Comercio y Servicios del Uruguay [★IO]
Camara Nacional de Empresas Comercializadoras de Seguros [★IO]
Camara Nacional de Empresas de Consultoria [★IO]
Camara Nacional de la Industria Editorial Mexicana [★IO]
Camara Nacional de la Industria de Farmaceutica [★IO]
Camara Nacional de la Industria Panificadora y Similares de Mexico [★IO]
Camara Nacional de la Industria de Perfumeria, Cosmetica y Articulos de Tocador e Higiene [★IO]
Camara Nacional de la Industria Pesquera [★IO]
Camara Nacional de la Industria de Radio y TV [★IO]
Camara Nacional de la Industria de Restaurantes y Alimentos Condimentados [★IO]
Camara Nacional de la Industria de Telecomunicaciones por Cable [★IO]
Camara Nacional de la Industria de la Transformacion [★IO]
Camara Nacional de la Industria del Vestido [★IO]
Camara Nacional de Manufacturas Electricas [★IO]
Camara Nacional de Productores de Leche [★IO]

Reference to "IO" in place of a book number signifies that the association may be found in the 50th edition of International Organizations.

Camara Oficial de Comercio de Espana en Gran
Bretana [★IO]
Camara Paraguaya de Exportadores de Cereales y
Oleaginosas [★IO]
Camara Peruana de la Construccion [★IO]
Camara de la Produccion, la Industria y el Comercio
Argentino-China [★IO]
Camara de Produccion Y Servicios de La Provincia
de Buenos Aires [IO], La Plata, Argentina
Camara Salvadorena de la Industria de la Construc-
cion [★IO]
Camara Salvadorena de Turismo [★IO]
Camara de Sociedades Anonimas [★IO]
Camara Textil Costarricense [★IO]
Camara Uruguaya del Libro [IO], Montevideo,
Uruguay
Camara Venezolana de Empresas de Tecnologias
de la Informacion [★IO]
Camara Venezolano Americana de Comercio e In-
dustria [★IO]
Camara Venezolano Americana de Comercio e In-
dustria [★23388]
Cambodia Assn. of Travel Agents [IO], Phnom Penh,
Cambodia
Cambodia Bus. Coalition on AIDS [IO], Phnom
Penh, Cambodia
Cambodia Community-Based Ecotourism Network
[IO], Phnom Penh, Cambodia
Cambodia Kids [IO], Sihanoukville, Cambodia
Cambodia Medical Assn. [IO], Phnom Penh,
Cambodia
Cambodia Microfinance Assn. [IO], Phnom Penh,
Cambodia
Cambodia Rural Development Team [IO], Phnom
Penh, Cambodia
Cambodia Tennis Fed. [IO], Phnom Penh, Cambodia
Cambodian
Light of Cambodian Children [11342]
Cambodian Amer. Mobile Clinic [14110], 5249 River-
brook Dr., Stockton, CA 95219, (209)505-6996
Cambodian Assn. of Prosthetists and Orthotist [IO],
Phnom Penh, Cambodia
Cambodian Buddhist Soc. [19362], 13800 New
Hampshire Ave., Silver Spring, MD 20904,
(301)622-6544
Cambodian Buddhist Soc. [19362], 13800 New
Hampshire Ave., Silver Spring, MD 20904,
(301)622-6544
Cambodian Children Against Starvation and Violence
Assn. [IO], Phnom Penh, Cambodia
Cambodian Child's Dream Org. [IO], Siem Reap,
Cambodia
Cambodian Craft Cooperation [IO], Phnom Penh,
Cambodia
Cambodian Disabled People's Org. [IO], Phnom
Penh, Cambodia
Cambodian Economic Assn. [IO], Phnom Penh,
Cambodia
Cambodian Educ. and Waste Mgt. Org. [IO], Phnom
Penh, Cambodia
Cambodian Farmers Assn. Fed. of Agricultural
Producers [IO], Svay Rieng, Cambodia
Cambodian Fed. of Employers and Bus. Associa-
tions [IO], Phnom Penh, Cambodia
Cambodian Hea. Professionals Assn. of Am.
[14761], 1025 Atlantic Ave., Long Beach, CA
90813, (562)491-9292
Cambodian Mutual Assistance Assn. [19271], 787 E
Broad St., Columbus, OH 43205, (614)224-8888
Cambodian Ophthalmological Soc. [IO], Phnom
Penh, Cambodia
Cambodian People's Party [IO], Phnom Penh,
Cambodia
Cambodian Professional Network [IO], Phnom Penh,
Cambodia
Cambodian Red Cross Soc. [IO], Phnom Penh,
Cambodia
Cambodian Sedge Mats Bus. Assn. [IO], Kandal,
Cambodia
Cambodian Volunteers for Community Development
[IO], Phnom Penh, Cambodia
Cambodian War Amputees Rehabilitation Soc. [IO],
Phnom Penh, Cambodia
Cambodia's Hope
Cambodia's Hope - Address unknown since 2011.

Cambra De Comerc Industria Serveis D' Andorra
[★IO]
Cambridge in Am. [9023], 292 Madison Ave., 8th Fl.,
New York, NY 10017, (212)984-0960
Cambridge Buddhist Assn. [19363], 75 Sparks St.,
Cambridge, MA 02138-2215, (617)491-8857
Cambridge Philosophical Soc. [IO], Cambridge,
United Kingdom
Cambridge Refrigeration Tech. [IO], Cambridge,
United Kingdom
Cambridgeshire Chamber of Commerce and Indus.
[IO], Cambridge, United Kingdom
Camelopard Soc. - Defunct.
CAMERA [★18120]
CAMERA [★18120]
Camera de Comercio Espana - Estados Unidos
[★23380]
Camera de Comercio Espana - Estados Unidos
[★23380]
Camera de Comert si Industrie a Romaniei [★IO]
Camera di Commercio Italiana in Cina [★IO]
Camera di Commercio Milano [★IO]
Cameroon Assn. for the Protection and Educ. of the
Child [IO], Kumba, Cameroon
Cameroon Assn. of Univ. Women [IO], Bamenda,
Cameroon
Cameroon Baseball and Softball Fed. [IO], Yaounde,
Cameroon
Cameroon Diabetes Assn. [IO], Yaounde, Cameroon
Cameroon Red Cross Soc. [IO], Yaounde, Cam-
eroon
Cameroon Soc. of Physiological Sciences [IO],
Yaounde, Cameroon
Cameroon Soc. of Physiotherapy [IO], Yaounde,
Cameroon
Cameroon-USA Chamber of Commerce
Cameroon-USA Chamber of Commerce - Address
unknown since 2011.
Cameroon Young Men's Christian Association Alli-
ance [IO], Yaounde, Cameroon
Camex Users Group - Defunct.
Camille and Henry Dreyfus Found. [8006], 555
Madison Ave., 20th Fl., New York, NY 10022-3301,
(212)753-1760
Camogie Assn. [IO], Dublin, Ireland
Camp Directors Assn. of Am. [★22440]
Camp Fire Boys and Girls [★13516]
Camp Fire Club of Am. [4015], 230 Campfire Rd.,
Chappaqua, NY 10514, (914)941-0199
Camp Fire Girls [★13516]
Camp Fire USA [13516], 1100 Walnut St., Ste.
1900, Kansas City, MO 64106-2197, (816)285-
2010
Camp Horsemanship Assn. [★22679]
Camp To Belong [11205], PO Box 1146, Marana, AZ
85653, (520)413-1395
Campaign for the Accountability of Amer. Bases [IO],
Harrogate, United Kingdom
Campaign Against Arms Trade [IO], London, United
Kingdom
Campaign Against U.S. Military Bases in the Philip-
pines - Defunct.
Campaign for America's Future [18415], 1825 K St.
NW, Ste. 400, Washington, DC 20006, (202)955-
5665
Campaign for a Commercial-Free Childhood
[11206], 89 South St., No. 404, Boston, MA 02111,
(617)896-9368
Campaign to End the Death Penalty [17215], PO
Box 25730, Chicago, IL 60625, (773)955-4841
Campaign For Our Children [13517], 1 N Charles
St., 11th Fl., Baltimore, MD 21201-3740, (410)576-
9015
Campaign for Fresh Air and Clean Politics [18646],
2842 N Calvert St., Baltimore, MD 21218,
(443)708-8360
Campaign for Good Governance [IO], Freetown,
Sierra Leone
Campaign for High School Equity [13014], 1050
Connecticut Ave. NW, Ste. 1025, Washington, DC
20036, (202)772-1137
Campaign for Human Development [★12661]
Campaign to Label Genetically Engineered Foods -
Address unknown since 2011.
Campaign Life Coalition Canada [IO], Toronto, ON,
Canada

Campaign for Natl. Parks [IO], London, United
Kingdom
Campaign for Nuclear Disarmament [IO], London,
United Kingdom
Campaign for Nuclear Phaseout [IO], Ottawa, ON,
Canada
Campaign for Peace and Democracy - Defunct.
Campaign for Press and Broadcasting Freedom [IO],
London, United Kingdom
Campaign to Protect Rural England [IO], London,
United Kingdom
Campaign for the Protection of Rural Wales [IO],
Welshpool, United Kingdom
Campaign for Tobacco-Free Kids [★16673]
Campaign for U.N. Reform [★18744]
Campaign for Working Families [18325], PO Box
97163, Washington, DC 20090, (703)671-8800
Campaign for World Govt. - Defunct.
Campana de Solidaridad con Nicaragua [★IO]
Campbell River Head Injury Support Soc. [IO],
Campbell River, BC, Canada
Campden BRI [IO], Chipping Campden, United
Kingdom
Camping
Amer. Camp Assn. [22440]
Camping Women [22441]
Christian Camp and Conf. Assn. [22442]
Escapees [22137]
Family Campers and RVers [22443]
Natl. Assn. of Therapeutic Wilderness Camping
[22444]
Natl. Camp Assn. [22445]
Natl. Episcopal Scouters Assn. [13024]
North Amer. Family Campers Assn. [22446]
RV Mfrs'. Clubs Assn. [22146]
Wilderness Inquiry [22447]
Camping Women [22441], PO Box 1402, Twain
Harte, CA 95383
Camps
Boy Scouts of Am. [13018]
Camping Women [22441]
Christian Camp and Conf. Assn. [22442]
Family Campers and RVers [22443]
Hungarian Scouts Assn. [13020]
North Amer. Family Campers Assn. [22446]
Campus Coalition for Democracy [★8239]
Campus Comm. to Bridge the Gap [★18193]
Campus Compact [8007], 45 Temple Pl., Boston,
MA 02111, (617)357-1881
Campus Crusade for Christ Intl. [19734], 100 Lake
Hart Dr., Orlando, FL 32832, (888)278-7233
Campus Crusade for Christ Intl. [19734], 100 Lake
Hart Dr., Orlando, FL 32832, (888)278-7233
Campus Freethought Alliance [★17729]
Campus Greens [18353], PO Box 57065,
Washington, DC 20037
Campus Outreach Opportunity League [★17726]
Campus Outreach Opportunity League [★17726]
Campus Pride [12072], PO Box 240473, Charlotte,
NC 28224, (704)277-6710
Campus Safety, Hea. and Environmental Mgt. Assn.
[4328], Jack Voorhees, One City Centre, Ste. 204,
120 W Seventh St., Bloomington, IN 47404-3839,
(812)245-8084
Campus Teens [★13531]
CAMUS Intl. [2332], Terry Simpkins, Sec.-Treas.,
45738 Northport Loop W, Fremont, CA 94538,
(757)766-4559
CAMUS Intl. [2332], Terry Simpkins, Sec.-Treas.,
45738 Northport Loop W, Fremont, CA 94538,
(757)766-4559
Camus Stud. Assn. [10374], Boise State Univ.,
Modern Languages and Literatures, Boise, ID
83703, (208)426-3692
Can Makers [IO], London, United Kingdom
Can Mfrs. Inst. [873], 1730 Rhode Island Island Ave.
NW, Ste. 1000, Washington, DC 20036, (202)232-
4677
Canaan Dog Club of Am. [21534], 5704 Timber Ln.,
Raleigh, NC 27606
Canada
Assn. of Amer. Seed Control Officials [5187]
Assn. of Thai Professionals in Am. and Canada
[19255]
Mine Safety Inst. of Am. [5841]

A star before a book entry number signifies that the name is not listed separately, but is mentioned within the entry.

Canada-Arab Bus. Coun. [IO], Toronto, ON, Canada
Canada Atlantic Region of Narcotics Anonymous [IO], St. John, NB, Canada
Canada Basketball [IO], Toronto, ON, Canada
Canada Beef Export Fed. [IO], Calgary, AB, Canada
Canada-China Bus. Coun. [IO], Toronto, ON, Canada
Canada Coun. for the Arts [IO], Ottawa, ON, Canada
Canada-Czech Republic Chamber of Commerce [IO], Oakville, ON, Canada
Canada Employment and Immigration Union [IO], Ottawa, ON, Canada
Canada-Finland Chamber of Commerce [IO], Toronto, ON, Canada
Canada Fox Breeders Assn. [IO], Moncton, NB, Canada
Canada Games Coun. [IO], Ottawa, ON, Canada
Canada Grains Coun. [IO], Winnipeg, MB, Canada
Canada Hippique [★IO]
Canada-India Bus. Coun. [IO], Toronto, ON, Canada
Canada India Village Aid Assn. [IO], Vancouver, BC, Canada
Canada-Israel Comm. [IO], Ottawa, ON, Canada
Canada - Japan Soc. of British Columbia [IO], Vancouver, BC, Canada
Canada-Pakistan Bus. Coun. [IO], Thornhill, ON, Canada
Canada Porc Intl. [★IO]
Canada Pork Intl. [IO], Ottawa, ON, Canada
Canada Safety Coun. [IO], Ottawa, ON, Canada
Canada-Singapore Bus. Assn. [IO], Vancouver, BC, Canada
Canada Tibet Comm. [IO], Montreal, QC, Canada
Canada-UK Chamber of Commerce [IO], London, United Kingdom
Canada-United States Bus. Assn. [2096], 600 Renaissance Ctr., Ste. 1100, Detroit, MI 48243, (313)446-7013
Canada West Equip. Dealers Assn. [IO], Calgary, AB, Canada
Canada West Found. [IO], Calgary, AB, Canada
Canada World Youth [IO], Montreal, QC, Canada
Canada's Assn. for the Fifty-Plus [IO], Toronto, ON, Canada
Canada's Aviation Hall of Fame [IO], Wetaskiwin, AB, Canada
Canada's Natl. History Soc. [IO], Winnipeg, MB, Canada
Canada's Research-Based Pharmaceutical Companies [IO], Ottawa, ON, Canada
Canada's Venture Capital and Private Equity Assn. [IO], Toronto, ON, Canada
Canadian
  Assn. for Canadian Stud. in the U.S. [7809]
  Assn. for Canadian Stud. in the U.S. [7809]
  Center for the Stud. of Canada [7810]
  Center for the Stud. of Canada [7810]
  Nordic Assn. for Canadian Stud. [14463]
Canadian 4-H Coun. [IO], Ottawa, ON, Canada
Canadian 5 Pin Bowlers' Assn. [IO], Ottawa, ON, Canada
Canadian Academic Accounting Assn. [IO], Toronto, ON, Canada
Canadian Acad. of Endodontics [IO], Winnipeg, MB, Canada
Canadian Acad. of Engg. [IO], Ottawa, ON, Canada
Canadian Acad. of Facial, Plastic and Reconstructive Surgery [IO], Mississauga, ON, Canada
Canadian Acad. of Periodontology [IO], Ottawa, ON, Canada
Canadian Acad. of Recording Arts and Sciences [IO], Toronto, ON, Canada
Canadian Acad. of Sport Medicine [IO], Ottawa, ON, Canada
Canadian Acoustical Assn. [IO], Ottawa, ON, Canada
Canadian Acoustical Assn. - Toronto [IO], Ottawa, ON, Canada
Canadian Actors' Equity Assn. [IO], Toronto, ON, Canada
Canadian Addison Soc. [IO], Goderich, ON, Canada
Canadian Adult Congenital Heart Network [IO], Mississauga, ON, Canada
Canadian Adult Recreational Hockey Assn. [IO], Ottawa, ON, Canada

Canadian Advanced Tech. Alliance [IO], Ottawa, ON, Canada
Canadian Advt. Res. Found. [IO], Toronto, ON, Canada
Canadian Aerial Applicators Assn. [IO], Edmonton, AB, Canada
Canadian Aeronautics and Space Inst. [IO], Kanata, ON, Canada
Canadian Aerophilatelic Soc. [IO], Nepean, ON, Canada
Canadian Agri-Marketing Assn. - Alberta [IO], Calmar, AB, Canada
Canadian Agri-Marketing Assn. - Manitoba [IO], Winnipeg, MB, Canada
Canadian Agri-Marketing Assn. - Ontario [IO], Port Elgin, ON, Canada
Canadian Agri-Marketing Assn. - Saskatchewan [IO], Regina, SK, Canada
Canadian Agricultural Economics Soc. [IO], Victoria, BC, Canada
Canadian AIDS Soc. [IO], Ottawa, ON, Canada
Canadian AIDS Treatment Info. Exchange [IO], Toronto, ON, Canada
Canadian Air Line Pilots Assn. [★23146]
Canadian Air Line Pilots Assn. [★23146]
Canadian Air Mail Collectors Club [IO], Nepean, ON, Canada
Canadian Air Traffic Control Assn. | CAW Local 5454 [IO], Ottawa, ON, Canada
Canadian Airports Coun. [IO], Ottawa, ON, Canada
Canadian Alliance of British Pensioners [IO], Toronto, ON, Canada
Canadian Alliance of Physiotherapy Regulators [IO], Toronto, ON, Canada
Canadian Alliance of Student Associations [IO], Ottawa, ON, Canada
Canadian Amateur Boxing Assn. [IO], Ottawa, ON, Canada
Canadian Amateur Dancesport Assn. [IO], Pickering, ON, Canada
Canadian Amateur Diving Assn. [IO], Ottawa, ON, Canada
Canadian Amateur Musicians [IO], Harrington, QC, Canada
Canadian Amateur Wrestling Assn. [IO], Gloucester, ON, Canada
Canadian/American Border Trade Alliance [3481], PO Box 929, Lewiston, NY 14092, (716)754-8824
Canadian/American Border Trade Alliance [3481], PO Box 929, Lewiston, NY 14092, (716)754-8824
Canadian-American Bus. Coun. [654], 1900 K St. NW, Ste. 100, Washington, DC 20006, (202)496-7906
Canadian-American Bus. Coun. [654], 1900 K St. NW, Ste. 100, Washington, DC 20006, (202)496-7906
Canadian Amputee Sports Assn. [IO], Toronto, ON, Canada
Canadian Anesthesiologists' Soc. [IO], Toronto, ON, Canada
Canadian Angus Assn. [IO], Calgary, AB, Canada
Canadian Animal Hea. Inst. [IO], Guelph, ON, Canada
Canadian Antique Phonograph Soc. [IO], Toronto, ON, Canada
Canadian Apparel Fed. [IO], Ottawa, ON, Canada
Canadian Aquaculture Indus. Alliance [IO], Ottawa, ON, Canada
Canadian Aquafitness Leaders Alliance [IO], Toronto, ON, Canada
Canadian Arab Fed. [IO], Toronto, ON, Canada
Canadian Arab Friendship Assn. [IO], Edmonton, AB, Canada
Canadian Arabian Horse Registry [IO], Sherwood Park, AB, Canada
Canadian Archaeological Assn. [IO], Burnaby, BC, Canada
Canadian Arctic Resources Comm. [IO], Ottawa, ON, Canada
Canadian Art Museum Directors' Org. [IO], Ottawa, ON, Canada
Canadian Artists Representation [IO], Ottawa, ON, Canada
Canadian Arts Presenting Assn. [IO], Ottawa, ON, Canada

Canadian Asian Stud. Assn. [IO], Montreal, QC, Canada
Canadian Associates of the Ben-Gurion Univ. of the Negev [IO], Toronto, ON, Canada
Canadian Assn. of Accredited Mortgage Professionals [IO], Toronto, ON, Canada
Canadian Assn. for Adolescent Hea. [IO], Montreal, QC, Canada
Canadian Assn. of Advanced Practice Nurses [IO], St. John's, NL, Canada
Canadian Assn. for the Advancement of Netherlandic Stud. [IO], Wellington, ON, Canada
Canadian Assn. for the Advancement of Women and Sport and Physical Activity [IO], Ottawa, ON, Canada
Canadian Assn. for Amer. Stud. [IO], Kingston, ON, Canada
Canadian Assn. for Anatomy, Neurobiology and Cell Biology [IO], Winnipeg, MB, Canada
Canadian Assn. of Aquarium Clubs [IO], Toronto, ON, Canada
Canadian Assn. of Arts Admin. Educators [IO], Toronto, ON, Canada
Canadian Assn. of Blue Cross Plans [IO], Etobicoke, ON, Canada
Canadian Assn. of Broadcasters [IO], Ottawa, ON, Canada
Canadian Assn. of Burn Nurses [IO], Calgary, AB, Canada
Canadian Assn. for Bus. Economics [IO], Ottawa, ON, Canada
Canadian Assn. of Cardiac Rehabilitation [IO], Winnipeg, MB, Canada
Canadian Assn. of Cardio-Pulmonary Technologists [IO], Toronto, ON, Canada
Canadian Assn. of Career Educators and Employers [IO], Toronto, ON, Canada
Canadian Assn. of Chain Drug Stores [IO], Toronto, ON, Canada
Canadian Assn. of Chem. Distributors [IO], Oakville, ON, Canada
Canadian Assn. of Chiefs of Police [IO], Ottawa, ON, Canada
Canadian Assn. for Child Neurology [IO], Calgary, AB, Canada
Canadian Assn. for Child and Play Therapy [IO], Guelph, ON, Canada
Canadian Assn. of Children's Librarians [IO], Brantford, ON, Canada
Canadian Assn. for Clinical Microbiology and Infectious Diseases [IO], Winnipeg, MB, Canada
Canadian Assn. for Co-operative Educ. [IO], Toronto, ON, Canada
Canadian Assn. of Coll. and Univ. Libraries [IO], Edmonton, AB, Canada
Canadian Assn. of Coll. and Univ. Student Services [IO], Kingston, ON, Canada
Canadian Assn. for Commonwealth Literature and Language Stud. [IO], Saskatoon, SK, Canada
Canadian Assn. of Communicators in Educ. [IO], Ottawa, ON, Canada
Canadian Assn. for Community Living [IO], Toronto, ON, Canada
Canadian Assn. for Composite Structures and Materials [IO], Montreal, QC, Canada
Canadian Assn. for Conservation of Cultural Property [IO], Ottawa, ON, Canada
Canadian Assn. of Critical Care Nurses [IO], London, ON, Canada
Canadian Assn. for Curriculum Stud. [IO], Edmonton, AB, Canada
Canadian Assn. of the Deaf [IO], Ottawa, ON, Canada
Canadian Assn. of Defence and Security Indus. [IO], Ottawa, ON, Canada
Canadian Assn. for Dental Res. [IO], London, ON, Canada
Canadian Assn. for Disabled Skiing [IO], Barrie, ON, Canada
Canadian Assn. of Drilling Engineers [IO], Calgary, AB, Canada
Canadian Assn. of Electroneurophysiology Technologists [IO], Moncton, NB, Canada
Canadian Assn. of Elizabeth Fry Societies [IO], Ottawa, ON, Canada

Reference to "IO" in place of a book number signifies that the association may be found in the 50th edition of International Organizations.

Canadian Assn. of Emergency Physicians **[IO]**, Ottawa, ON, Canada
Canadian Assn. of Energy Ser. Companies **[IO]**, Toronto, ON, Canada
Canadian Assn. for Enterostomal Therapy **[IO]**, Mount Royal, QC, Canada
Canadian Assn. Environmental Mgt. **[IO]**, New Glasgow, NS, Canada
Canadian Assn. of Equip. Distributors **[IO]**, Senneville, QC, Canada
Canadian Assn. of Exposition Mgt. **[IO]**, Toronto, ON, Canada
Canadian Assn. of Fairs and Exhibitions **[IO]**, Ottawa, ON, Canada
Canadian Assn. for Familial Ataxia **[IO]**, Montreal, QC, Canada
Canadian Assn. of Family Enterprise **[IO]**, Oakville, ON, Canada
Canadian Assn. of Family Rsrc. Programs **[IO]**, Ottawa, ON, Canada
Canadian Assn. of Farm Advisors **[IO]**, Blaine Lake, SK, Canada
Canadian Assn. of Fire Chiefs **[IO]**, Ottawa, ON, Canada
Canadian Assn. of Footwear Importers **[IO]**, Toronto, ON, Canada
Canadian Assn. of Former Parliamentarians **[IO]**, Ottawa, ON, Canada
Canadian Assn. for Free Expression **[IO]**, Etobicoke, ON, Canada
Canadian Assn. of Gastroenterology **[IO]**, Oakville, ON, Canada
Canadian Assn. of Gen. Surgeons **[IO]**, Ottawa, ON, Canada
Canadian Assn. of Genetic Counsellors **[IO]**, Oakville, ON, Canada
Canadian Assn. of Geographers **[IO]**, Montreal, QC, Canada
Canadian Assn. of Geophysical Contractors **[IO]**, Calgary, AB, Canada
Canadian Assn. of Gerontology **[IO]**, Toronto, ON, Canada
Canadian Assn. of Gift Planners **[IO]**, Ottawa, ON, Canada
Canadian Assn. for Graduate Stud. **[IO]**, Ottawa, ON, Canada
Canadian Assn. for Hea. Services and Policy Res. **[IO]**, Ottawa, ON, Canada
Canadian Assn. of Heritage Professional **[IO]**, Toronto, ON, Canada
Canadian Assn. for the History of Nursing **[IO]**, Ottawa, ON, Canada
Canadian Assn. of Home and Property Inspectors **[IO]**, Ottawa, ON, Canada
Canadian Assn. for Humane Trapping **[IO]**, Burlington, ON, Canada
Canadian Assn. of Immersion Teachers **[IO]**, Ottawa, ON, Canada
Canadian Assn. of Income Funds **[IO]**, Toronto, ON, Canada
Canadian Assn. of Independent Schools **[IO]**, St. Catharines, ON, Canada
Canadian Assn. for Info. Sci. **[IO]**, London, ON, Canada
Canadian Assn. of Insolvency and Restructuring Professionals **[IO]**, Toronto, ON, Canada
Canadian Assn. of Intl. Development Consultants **[IO]**, Ottawa, ON, Canada
Canadian Assn. of Internet Providers **[IO]**, Ottawa, ON, Canada
Canadian Assn. of Interns and Residents **[IO]**, Ottawa, ON, Canada
Canadian Assn. for Irish Stud. **[IO]**, St. John's, NL, Canada
Canadian Assn. of Journalists **[IO]**, Ottawa, ON, Canada
Canadian Assn. for Lab. Accreditation **[IO]**, Ottawa, ON, Canada
Canadian Assn. for Lab. Animal Sci. **[IO]**, Toronto, ON, Canada
Canadian Assn. of Labour Media **[IO]**, Toronto, ON, Canada
Canadian Assn. of Law Libraries **[IO]**, Kingston, ON, Canada
Canadian Assn. of Learned Journals **[IO]**, Vancouver, BC, Canada

Canadian Assn. of Mgt. Consultants **[IO]**, Toronto, ON, Canada
Canadian Assn. of Media Educ. Organizations **[IO]**, Toronto, ON, Canada
Canadian Assn. of Medical Biochemists **[IO]**, Ottawa, ON, Canada
Canadian Assn. of Medical Radiation Technologists **[IO]**, Ottawa, ON, Canada
Canadian Assn. of Members of Public Utility Tribunals **[IO]**, Oakville, ON, Canada
Canadian Assn. of Midwives **[IO]**, Montreal, QC, Canada
Canadian Assn. for Mine and Explosive Ordinance Security **[IO]**, Cornwall, ON, Canada
Canadian Assn. of Mining Equip. and Services for Export **[IO]**, Markham, ON, Canada
Canadian Assn. of Moldmakers **[IO]**, Windsor, ON, Canada
Canadian Assn. of Music Libraries, Archives, and Documentation Centres **[IO]**, Ottawa, ON, Canada
Canadian Assn. for Music Therapy **[IO]**, Toronto, ON, Canada
Canadian Assn. of Mutual Insurance Companies **[IO]**, Ottawa, ON, Canada
Canadian Assn. of Naturopathic Doctors **[IO]**, Toronto, ON, Canada
Canadian Assn. of Nephrology Nurses and Technologists **[IO]**, Barrie, ON, Canada
Canadian Assn. of Neuropathologists **[IO]**, Halifax, NS, Canada
Canadian Assn. of Neuroscience Nurses **[IO]**, Stittsville, ON, Canada
Canadian Assn. of Numismatic Dealers **[IO]**, Stoney Creek, ON, Canada
Canadian Assn. of Nurses in AIDS Care **[IO]**, Toronto, ON, Canada
Canadian Assn. of Nurses in Oncology **[IO]**, Vancouver, BC, Canada
Canadian Assn. of Occupational Therapists **[IO]**, Ottawa, ON, Canada
Canadian Assn. of Oilwell Drilling Contractors **[IO]**, Calgary, AB, Canada
Canadian Assn. of Optometrists **[IO]**, Ottawa, ON, Canada
Canadian Assn. of Oral and Maxillofacial Surgeons **[IO]**, Ottawa, ON, Canada
Canadian Assn. of Orthodontists **[IO]**, Toronto, ON, Canada
Canadian Assn. of Paediatric Surgeons **[IO]**, Ottawa, ON, Canada
Canadian Assn. of Palynologists **[IO]**, Ottawa, ON, Canada
Canadian Assn. of Paralegals **[IO]**, Montreal, QC, Canada
Canadian Assn. for Pastoral Practice and Educ. **[IO]**, Halifax, NS, Canada
Canadian Assn. of Pathologists **[IO]**, Ottawa, ON, Canada
Canadian Assn. of Pension Supervisory Authorities **[IO]**, North York, ON, Canada
Canadian Assn. for People Who Stutter **[★16915]**
Canadian Assn. of Petroleum Landmen **[IO]**, Calgary, AB, Canada
Canadian Assn. of Petroleum Producers **[IO]**, Calgary, AB, Canada
Canadian Assn. of Petroleum Production Accounting **[IO]**, Calgary, AB, Canada
Canadian Assn. for Pharmacy Distribution Mgt. **[IO]**, Woodbridge, ON, Canada
Canadian Assn. of Pharmacy in Oncology **[IO]**, North Vancouver, BC, Canada
Canadian Assn. of Pharmacy Students and Interns **[IO]**, Toronto, ON, Canada
Canadian Assn. of Pharmacy Technicians **[IO]**, Mississauga, ON, Canada
Canadian Assn. of Photographers and Illustrators in Communications **[IO]**, Toronto, ON, Canada
Canadian Assn. for Photographic Art **[IO]**, Logan Lake, BC, Canada
Canadian Assn. of Physical Medicine and Rehabilitation **[IO]**, Ottawa, ON, Canada
Canadian Assn. of Physicians for the Env. **[IO]**, Toronto, ON, Canada
Canadian Assn. of Physicists **[IO]**, Ottawa, ON, Canada

Canadian Assn. of Police Boards **[IO]**, Ottawa, ON, Canada
Canadian Assn. of Police Educators **[IO]**, Ottawa, ON, Canada
Canadian Assn. for Porphyria **[IO]**, Neepawa, MB, Canada
Canadian Assn. for the Practical Stud. of Law in Educ. **[IO]**, Georgetown, ON, Canada
Canadian Assn. of Principals **[IO]**, Kanata, ON, Canada
Canadian Assn. of Professional Conservators **[IO]**, Ottawa, ON, Canada
Canadian Assn. of Professional Employees **[IO]**, Ottawa, ON, Canada
Canadian Assn. of Professional Immigration Consultants **[IO]**, Toronto, ON, Canada
Canadian Assn. of Professional Pet Dog Trainers **[IO]**, Shelburne, ON, Canada
Canadian Assn. of Professional Speakers **[IO]**, Toronto, ON, Canada
Canadian Assn. of Programs in Public Admin. **[IO]**, Regina, SK, Canada
Canadian Assn. for Prosthetics and Orthotics **[IO]**, Winnipeg, MB, Canada
Canadian Assn. of Provincial Court Judges **[IO]**, Kentville, NS, Canada
Canadian Assn. of Psychoanalytic Child Therapists **[IO]**, Brampton, ON, Canada
Canadian Assn. of Psychosocial Oncology **[IO]**, Toronto, ON, Canada
Canadian Assn. of Public Hea. Dentistry **[IO]**, Manitouwadge, ON, Canada
Canadian Assn. of Public Libraries **[IO]**, Regina, SK, Canada
Canadian Assn. of Radiation Oncologists **[IO]**, Ottawa, ON, Canada
Canadian Assn. of Radiologists **[IO]**, Ottawa, ON, Canada
Canadian Assn. of Recycling Indus. **[IO]**, Ajax, ON, Canada
Canadian Assn. of Regulated Importers **[IO]**, Ottawa, ON, Canada
Canadian Assn. for Renewable Energies **[IO]**, Ottawa, ON, Canada
Canadian Assn. for Res. in Home Economics **[IO]**, Halifax, NS, Canada
Canadian Assn. of Res. Libraries **[IO]**, Ottawa, ON, Canada
Canadian Assn. of Road Safety Professionals **[IO]**, Saskatoon, SK, Canada
Canadian Assn. of Rocketry **[IO]**, Lethbridge, AB, Canada
Canadian Assn. of School Administrators **[IO]**, Oakville, ON, Canada
Canadian Assn. for School Hea. **[IO]**, Surrey, BC, Canada
Canadian Assn. for School Libraries **[IO]**, Calgary, AB, Canada
Canadian Assn. of Schools of Nursing **[IO]**, Ottawa, ON, Canada
Canadian Assn. of Second Language Teachers **[IO]**, Ottawa, ON, Canada
Canadian Assn. for Security and Intelligence Stud. **[IO]**, Ottawa, ON, Canada
Canadian Assn. of Sexual Assault Centres **[IO]**, Vancouver, BC, Canada
Canadian Assn. for Shar-Pei Rescue **[IO]**, Mansfield, ON, Canada
Canadian Assn. of Slavists **[IO]**, Victoria, BC, Canada
Canadian Assn. of Snowboard Instructors **[IO]**, Cambridge, ON, Canada
Canadian Assn. of Social Workers **[IO]**, Ottawa, ON, Canada
Canadian Assn. of Special Libraries and Info. Services **[IO]**, Ottawa, ON, Canada
Canadian Assn. of Specialized Kinesiology **[IO]**, Vancouver, BC, Canada
Canadian Assn. of Speech-Language Pathologists and Audiologists **[IO]**, Ottawa, ON, Canada
Canadian Assn. of Student Activity Advisors **[IO]**, Wainright, AB, Canada
Canadian Assn. of Student Financial Aid Administrators **[IO]**, Fredericton, NB, Canada
Canadian Assn. for the Stud. of Adult Educ. **[IO]**, Ottawa, ON, Canada

A star before a book entry number signifies that the name is not listed separately, but is mentioned within the entry.

Canadian Assn. for the Stud. of Discourse and Writing [IO], Toronto, ON, Canada
Canadian Assn. for the Stud. of Intl. Development [IO], Ottawa, ON, Canada
Canadian Assn. for Suicide Prevention [IO], Winnipeg, MB, Canada
Canadian Assn. for Theatre Res. [IO], Toronto, ON, Canada
Canadian Assn. of Token Collectors [IO], Mississauga, ON, Canada
Canadian Assn. for Translation Stud. [IO], Ottawa, ON, Canada
Canadian Assn. of Univ. Bus. Officers [IO], Ottawa, ON, Canada
Canadian Assn. for Univ. Continuing Educ. [IO], Saskatoon, SK, Canada
Canadian Assn. of Univ. Teachers [IO], Ottawa, ON, Canada
Canadian Assn. of Univ. Teachers of German [IO], Winnipeg, MB, Canada
Canadian Assn. on Water Quality [IO], Burlington, ON, Canada
Canadian Assn. of Wholesale Sales Representatives [IO], Toronto, ON, Canada
Canadian Assn. of Women Executives and Entrepreneurs [IO], Toronto, ON, Canada
Canadian Assn. of Wooden Money Collectors [IO], Newmarket, ON, Canada
Canadian Assn. of Wound Care [IO], Toronto, ON, Canada
Canadian Assn. for Young Children [IO], Calgary, AB, Canada
Canadian Assn. of Zoos and Aquariums [IO], Ottawa, ON, Canada
Canadian Astronomical Soc. [IO], Kingston, ON, Canada
Canadian Athletic Therapists Assn. [IO], Calgary, AB, Canada
Canadian Authors Assn. [IO], Orillia, ON, Canada
Canadian Auto Workers [IO], Toronto, ON, Canada
Canadian Automatic Merchandising Assn. [IO], Mississauga, ON, Canada
Canadian Automatic Sprinkler Assn. [IO], Markham, ON, Canada
Canadian Auto. Assn. [IO], Ottawa, ON, Canada
Canadian Auto. Dealers Assn. [IO], Markham, ON, Canada
Canadian Automotive Repair and Ser. Coun. [IO], Ottawa, ON, Canada
Canadian Avalanche Assn. [IO], Revelstoke, BC, Canada
Canadian Aviation Historical Soc. [IO], Ottawa, ON, Canada
Canadian Aviation Maintenance Coun. [IO], Ottawa, ON, Canada
Canadian Ball Hockey Assn. [IO], Concord, ON, Canada
Canadian Balloon Assn. [IO], Vankleek Hill, ON, Canada
Canadian Band Assn. [IO], Winnipeg, MB, Canada
Canadian Bankers Assn. [IO], Toronto, ON, Canada
Canadian Baptist Ministries [IO], Mississauga, ON, Canada
Canadian Bar Assn. [IO], Ottawa, ON, Canada
Canadian Bar Insurance Assn. [IO], Toronto, ON, Canada
Canadian Battlefields Found. [IO], Ottawa, ON, Canada
Canadian Beef Breeds Coun. [IO], Calgary, AB, Canada
Canadian Belgian Horse Assn. [IO], Schomberg, ON, Canada
Canadian Bible Soc. [IO], Toronto, ON, Canada
Canadian Bison Assn. [IO], Regina, SK, Canada
Canadian Blonde d'Aquitaine Assn. [IO], Ottawa, ON, Canada
Canadian Bd. of Marine Underwriters [IO], Mississauga, ON, Canada
Canadian Boating Fed. [IO], Valleyfield, QC, Canada
Canadian Boiler Soc. [IO], Toronto, ON, Canada
Canadian Bookbinders and Book Artists Guild [IO], Toronto, ON, Canada
Canadian Booksellers Assn. [IO], Toronto, ON, Canada
Canadian Botanical Assn. [IO], Ottawa, ON, Canada

Canadian Bottled Water Assn. [IO], Richmond Hill, ON, Canada
Canadian Brain Tissue Bank [IO], Toronto, ON, Canada
Canadian Breast Cancer Found. [IO], Toronto, ON, Canada
Canadian Brewery and Distillery Workers [★23191]
Canadian Bridge Fed. [IO], Regina, SK, Canada
Canadian Broadcast Distribution Assn. [IO], Mississauga, ON, Canada
Canadian Broadcast Standards Coun. [IO], Ottawa, ON, Canada
Canadian Broomball Fed. [IO], Winnipeg, MB, Canada
Canadian Brown Swiss and Braunvieh Assn. [IO], Guelph, ON, Canada
Canadian Bur. for Intl. Educ. [IO], Ottawa, ON, Canada
Canadian Bus. Aviation Assn. [IO], Ottawa, ON, Canada
Canadian Bus. Coun. - Iran [IO], Tehran, Iran
Canadian Bus. Press [IO], Toronto, ON, Canada
Canadian Call Mgt. Assn. [IO], Grimsby, ON, Canada
Canadian Camping Assn. [IO], Montreal, QC, Canada
Canadian Cancer Soc. [IO], Toronto, ON, Canada
Canadian Cancer Soc. Res. Inst. [IO], Toronto, ON, Canada
Canadian Canoe Assn., Atlantic Div. [IO], Dartmouth, NS, Canada
Canadian Canon Law Soc. [IO], Ottawa, ON, Canada
Canadian Capital Markets Assn. [IO], Toronto, ON, Canada
Canadian Cardiovascular Soc. [IO], Ottawa, ON, Canada
Canadian Career Development Found. [IO], Ottawa, ON, Canada
Canadian Career Info. Assn. [IO], Toronto, ON, Canada
Canadian Carpet Inst. [IO], Ottawa, ON, Canada
Canadian Cartographic Assn. [IO], Ottawa, ON, Canada
Canadian Carwash Assn. [IO], Toronto, ON, Canada
Canadian Casting Fed. [IO], Toronto, ON, Canada
Canadian Cat Assn. [IO], Mississauga, ON, Canada
Canadian Catholic Historical Assn. [IO], Toronto, ON, Canada
Canadian Catholic Org. for Development and Peace [IO], Toronto, ON, Canada
Canadian Catholic Org. for Development and Peace - Alberta [IO], Edmonton, AB, Canada
Canadian Catholic Org. for Development and Peace - Atlantic region [IO], Antigonish, NS, Canada
Canadian Catholic Org. for Development and Peace - British Columbia [IO], Abbotsford, BC, Canada
Canadian Catholic Org. for Development and Peace - Manitoba [IO], Winnipeg, MB, Canada
Canadian Catholic Org. for Development and Peace - Montreal [IO], Montreal, QC, Canada
Canadian Catholic Org. for Development and Peace - Nova Scotia [IO], Antigonish, NS, Canada
Canadian Catholic Org. for Development and Peace - Ontario [IO], Toronto, ON, Canada
Canadian Catholic Org. for Development and Peace - Quebec [IO], Quebec, QC, Canada
Canadian Catholic Org. for Development and Peace - Saskatchewan [IO], Battleford, SK, Canada
Canadian Catholic School Trustees' Assn. [IO], Nepean, ON, Canada
Canadian Catholic Students' Assn. [IO], Toronto, ON, Canada
Canadian Cattlemen's Assn. [IO], Calgary, AB, Canada
Canadian Celiac Assn. [IO], Mississauga, ON, Canada
Canadian Celtic Arts Assn. [IO], Toronto, ON, Canada
Canadian Centre for Architecture [IO], Montreal, QC, Canada
Canadian Centre for Diversity [IO], Toronto, ON, Canada
Canadian Centre for Ecumenism [IO], Montreal, QC, Canada

Canadian Centre for Ethics in Sport [IO], Ottawa, ON, Canada
Canadian Centre for Intl. Stud. and Cooperation - Asia [IO], Kathmandu, Nepal
Canadian Centre for Intl. Stud. and Cooperation - Bolivia [IO], La Paz, Bolivia
Canadian Centre for Intl. Stud. and Cooperation - Burkina Faso [IO], Ouagadougou, Burkina Faso
Canadian Centre for Intl. Stud. and Cooperation - Nepal [IO], Kathmandu, Nepal
Canadian Centre for Intl. Stud. and Cooperation - Republic of Guinea [IO], Conakry, Guinea
Canadian Centre for Intl. Stud. and Cooperation - Senegal [IO], Dakar, Senegal
Canadian Centre for Marine Communications [IO], St. John's, NL, Canada
Canadian Centre for Occupational Hea. and Safety [IO], Hamilton, ON, Canada
Canadian Centre for Policy Alternatives [IO], Ottawa, ON, Canada
Canadian Centre for Pollution Prevention [IO], Mississauga, ON, Canada
Canadian Centre on Substance Abuse [IO], Ottawa, ON, Canada
Canadian Centre for Victims of Torture [IO], Toronto, ON, Canada
Canadian Cerebral Palsy Sports Assn. [IO], Ottawa, ON, Canada
Canadian Chamber of Commerce [IO], Ottawa, ON, Canada
Canadian Chamber of Commerce in Macao [IO], Macau, Macao
Canadian Charolais Assn. [IO], Calgary, AB, Canada
Canadian Chem. Producers' Assn. [IO], Ottawa, ON, Canada
Canadian Child Care Fed. [IO], Ottawa, ON, Canada
Canadian Children's Book Centre [IO], Toronto, ON, Canada
Canadian Children's Opera Company [IO], Toronto, ON, Canada
Canadian Chinese Kuo Shu Fed. [IO], Agincourt, ON, Canada
Canadian Chiropractic Assn. [IO], Toronto, ON, Canada
Canadian Chiropractic Examining Bd. [IO], Calgary, AB, Canada
Canadian Churches' Forum for Global Ministries [IO], Toronto, ON, Canada
Canadian Circulation Mgt. Assn. [IO], Moncton, NB, Canada
Canadian Citizenship Fed. [IO], St. John, NB, Canada
Canadian Civil Liberties Assn. [IO], Toronto, ON, Canada
Canadian Co-operative Assn. [IO], Ottawa, ON, Canada
Canadian Co-Operative Wool Growers [IO], Carleton Place, ON, Canada
Canadian Coalition Against the Death Penalty [IO], Toronto, ON, Canada
Canadian Coalition for Nuclear Responsibility [IO], Montreal, QC, Canada
Canadian Coll. of Hea. Ser. Executives [IO], Ottawa, ON, Canada
Canadian Coll. of Medical Geneticists [IO], Ottawa, ON, Canada
Canadian Coll. of Naturopathic Medicine [IO], Toronto, ON, Canada
Canadian Coll. of Physicists in Medicine [IO], Kanata, ON, Canada
Canadian Colleges Athletic Assn. [IO], Cornwall, ON, Canada
Canadian Commn. for UNESCO [IO], Ottawa, ON, Canada
Canadian Comm. on Cataloguing [IO], Ottawa, ON, Canada
Canadian Comm. on Labour History [IO], Edmonton, AB, Canada
Canadian Comm. on MARC [IO], Ottawa, ON, Canada
Canadian Community Newspapers Assn. [IO], Toronto, ON, Canada
Canadian Comparative Literature Assn. [IO], Prince George, BC, Canada
Canadian Concrete Pipe Assn. [IO], Halton Hills, ON, Canada

Reference to "IO" in place of a book number signifies that the association may be found in the 50th edition of International Organizations.

Canadian Condominium Inst. [IO], Toronto, ON, Canada

Canadian Conf. of the Arts [IO], Ottawa, ON, Canada

Canadian Conf. of Catholic Bishops [IO], Ottawa, ON, Canada

Canadian Conf. of Mennonite Brethren Churches [IO], Winnipeg, MB, Canada

Canadian Conservation Inst. [IO], Ottawa, ON, Canada

Canadian Constr. Assn. [IO], Ottawa, ON, Canada

Canadian Consulting Agrologists Assn. [IO], Calgary, AB, Canada

Canadian Consumer Specialty Products Assn. [IO], Ottawa, ON, Canada

Canadian Continence Found. [IO], Peterborough, ON, Canada

Canadian Copper and Brass Development Assn. [IO], Don Mills, ON, Canada

Canadian Copyright Inst. [IO], Toronto, ON, Canada

Canadian Corkscrew Collectors Club [21316], 1 Madison St., 5B, East Rutherford, NJ 07073, (973)773-9224

Canadian Corkscrew Collectors Club [21316], 1 Madison St., 5B, East Rutherford, NJ 07073, (973)773-9224

Canadian Corporate Counsel Assn. [IO], Toronto, ON, Canada

Canadian Corps of Commissionaires [IO], Ottawa, ON, Canada

Canadian Correspondence Chess Assn. [IO], Ottawa, ON, Canada

Canadian Cosmetic, Toiletry and Fragrance Assn. [IO], Mississauga, ON, Canada

Canadian Coun. for Aboriginal Bus. [IO], Toronto, ON, Canada

Canadian Coun. for Accreditation of Pharmacy Programs [IO], Saskatoon, SK, Canada

Canadian Coun. for the Advancement of Educ. [IO], Ottawa, ON, Canada

Canadian Coun. on Animal Care [IO], Ottawa, ON, Canada

Canadian Coun. of Archives [IO], Ottawa, ON, Canada

Canadian Coun. of Better Bus. Bureaus [IO], Toronto, ON, Canada

Canadian Coun. of the Blind [IO], Ottawa, ON, Canada

Canadian Coun. of Cardiovascular Nurses [IO], Ottawa, ON, Canada

Canadian Coun. of Chief Executives [IO], Ottawa, ON, Canada

Canadian Coun. of Christian Charities [IO], Elmira, ON, Canada

Canadian Coun. of Churches [IO], Toronto, ON, Canada

Canadian Coun. on Continuing Educ. in Pharmacy [IO], Regina, SK, Canada

Canadian Coun. on Ecological Areas [IO], Yellowknife, NT, Canada

Canadian Coun. of Grocery Distributors [IO], Montreal, QC, Canada

Canadian Coun. of Independent Labs. [IO], Ottawa, ON, Canada

Canadian Coun. for Intl. Co-operation [IO], Ottawa, ON, Canada

Canadian Coun. on Intl. Law [IO], Ottawa, ON, Canada

Canadian Coun. of Land Surveyors [IO], St. Albert, AB, Canada

Canadian Coun. of Ministers of the Env. [IO], Winnipeg, MB, Canada

Canadian Coun. of Montessori Administrators [IO], Toronto, ON, Canada

Canadian Coun. of Motor Transport Administrators [IO], Ottawa, ON, Canada

Canadian Coun. of Muslim Women [IO], Gananoque, ON, Canada

Canadian Coun. of Professional Certification [IO], Toronto, ON, Canada

Canadian Coun. of Professional Fish Harvesters [IO], Ottawa, ON, Canada

Canadian Coun. for Public-Private Partnerships [IO], Toronto, ON, Canada

Canadian Coun. for Reform Judaism [IO], Toronto, ON, Canada

Canadian Coun. for Refugees [IO], Montreal, QC, Canada

Canadian Coun. on Rehabilitation and Work [IO], Toronto, ON, Canada

Canadian Coun. of Snowmobile Organizations [IO], Thunder Bay, ON, Canada

Canadian Coun. on Social Development [IO], Ottawa, ON, Canada

Canadian Coun. of Teachers of English Language Arts [IO], Winnipeg, MB, Canada

Canadian Coun. of Technicians and Technologists [IO], Ottawa, ON, Canada

Canadian Coun. for Tobacco Control [IO], Ottawa, ON, Canada

Canadian Counselling and Psychotherapy Assn. [IO], Ottawa, ON, Canada

Canadian Country Music Assn. [IO], Toronto, ON, Canada

Canadian Courier and Logistics Assn. [IO], Toronto, ON, Canada

Canadian Craft and Hobby Assn. [IO], Orangeville, ON, Canada

Canadian Crafts Fed. [IO], Fredericton, NB, Canada

Canadian Credit Inst. Educational Found. [IO], Toronto, ON, Canada

Canadian Criminal Justice Assn. [IO], Ottawa, ON, Canada

Canadian Critical Care Soc. [IO], Toronto, ON, Canada

Canadian Crossroads Intl. [IO], Toronto, ON, Canada

Canadian Culinary Fed. - Edmonton Br. [IO], Edmonton, AB, Canada

Canadian Culinary Fed. - Lethbridge Assn. [IO], Lethbridge, AB, Canada

Canadian Culinary Fed. - North Vancouver Island [IO], Courtenay, BC, Canada

Canadian Culinary Fed. - Saskatoon Br. [IO], Saskatoon, SK, Canada

Canadian Culinary Fed. - Winnipeg Br. [IO], Winnipeg, MB, Canada

Canadian Cultural Soc. of the Deaf [IO], Toronto, ON, Canada

Canadian Curling Assn. [IO], Cumberland, ON, Canada

Canadian Cutting Horse Assn. [IO], Innisfail, AB, Canada

Canadian Cycling Assn. [IO], Ottawa, ON, Canada

Canadian Cystic Fibrosis Found. [IO], Toronto, ON, Canada

Canadian Dairy Commn. [IO], Ottawa, ON, Canada

Canadian Dam Assn. [IO], Moose Jaw, SK, Canada

Canadian Dance Assembly [IO], Toronto, ON, Canada

Canadian Dance Teachers' Assn. [IO], Mississauga, ON, Canada

Canadian Deaf Golf Assn. [IO], London, ON, Canada

Canadian Deaf Sports Assn. [IO], Montreal, QC, Canada

Canadian Decorating Products Assn. [★2073]

Canadian Decorating Products Assn. [★2073]

Canadian Dental Assistants' Assn. [IO], Ottawa, ON, Canada

Canadian Dental Assn. [IO], Ottawa, ON, Canada

Canadian Dental Hygienists' Assn. [IO], Ottawa, ON, Canada

Canadian Dental Protective Assn. [IO], Burlington, ON, Canada

Canadian Dermatology Assn. [IO], Ottawa, ON, Canada

Canadian Dexter Cattle Assn. [IO], Ottawa, ON, Canada

Canadian Diabetes Assn. [IO], Toronto, ON, Canada

Canadian Diabetes Assn. - Barrie Br. Simcoe County/Muskokas/Parry Sound [IO], Barrie, ON, Canada

Canadian Diabetes Assn. - Bellville Br. Hastings and Prince Edward [IO], Belleville, ON, Canada

Canadian Diabetes Assn. - Brantford Br. [IO], Brantford, ON, Canada

Canadian Diabetes Assn. - Brockville Br. Tri-County [IO], Brockville, ON, Canada

Canadian Diabetes Assn. - Calgary and District Br. [IO], Calgary, AB, Canada

Canadian Diabetes Assn. - Cambridge and District Br. [IO], Kitchener, ON, Canada

Canadian Diabetes Assn. - Cape Breton Br. [IO], Sydney, NS, Canada

Canadian Diabetes Assn. - Chatham and District Br. [IO], Chatham-Kent, ON, Canada

Canadian Diabetes Assn. - Cornwall and District Br. [IO], Cornwall, ON, Canada

Canadian Diabetes Assn. - Diabetes Educator Sect. [IO], Toronto, ON, Canada

Canadian Diabetes Assn. - Durham Region Br. [IO], Toronto, ON, Canada

Canadian Diabetes Assn. - Edmonton and District Br. [IO], Edmonton, AB, Canada

Canadian Diabetes Assn. - Elliot Lake/Blind River [IO], Sudbury, ON, Canada

Canadian Diabetes Assn. - Elmira and District Br. [IO], Kitchener, ON, Canada

Canadian Diabetes Assn. - Fredericton and District Br. [IO], Fredericton, NB, Canada

Canadian Diabetes Assn. - Greater Vancouver and District Br. [IO], Vancouver, BC, Canada

Canadian Diabetes Assn. - Guelph and South Wellington Br. [IO], Kitchener, ON, Canada

Canadian Diabetes Assn. - Haldimand/Norfolk Community Gp. [IO], Dunnville, ON, Canada

Canadian Diabetes Assn. - Hamilton and District Br. [IO], Hamilton, ON, Canada

Canadian Diabetes Assn. - Kelowna Br. [IO], Kelowna, BC, Canada

Canadian Diabetes Assn. - Kingston and District Br. [IO], Kingston, ON, Canada

Canadian Diabetes Assn. - Kitchener-Waterloo Br. [IO], Kitchener, ON, Canada

Canadian Diabetes Assn. - Lakeshore Br. [IO], Peterborough, ON, Canada

Canadian Diabetes Assn. - Lethbridge and District Br. [IO], Lethbridge, AB, Canada

Canadian Diabetes Assn. - Lindsay Br. [IO], Lindsay, ON, Canada

Canadian Diabetes Assn. - London Br. [IO], London, ON, Canada

Canadian Diabetes Assn. - Medicine Hat and District Br. [IO], Medicine Hat, AB, Canada

Canadian Diabetes Assn. - Midland/Penetanguishene Br. [IO], Penetanguishene, ON, Canada

Canadian Diabetes Assn. - Nanaimo and District Br. [IO], Nanaimo, BC, Canada

Canadian Diabetes Assn. - New Brunswick [IO], Fredericton, NB, Canada

Canadian Diabetes Assn. - Newfoundland and Labrador Region [IO], St. John's, NL, Canada

Canadian Diabetes Assn. - Niagara Br. [IO], St. Catharines, ON, Canada

Canadian Diabetes Assn. - North Bay and District Br. [IO], Sudbury, ON, Canada

Canadian Diabetes Assn. - North Perth/North Wellington Br. [IO], Harriston, ON, Canada

Canadian Diabetes Assn. - Nova Scotia [IO], Halifax, NS, Canada

Canadian Diabetes Assn. - Oakville Br. [IO], Oakville, ON, Canada

Canadian Diabetes Assn. - Orangeville and District Br. [IO], Kitchener, ON, Canada

Canadian Diabetes Assn. - Ottawa and District Br. [IO], Ottawa, ON, Canada

Canadian Diabetes Assn. - Peel Region Br. [IO], Toronto, ON, Canada

Canadian Diabetes Assn. - Pembroke and District Br. [IO], Pembroke, ON, Canada

Canadian Diabetes Assn. - Peterborough Br. Kawarthas/Lakeshore [IO], Peterborough, ON, Canada

Canadian Diabetes Assn. - Prince Edward Island [IO], Charlottetown, PE, Canada

Canadian Diabetes Assn. - Prince George and District Br. [IO], Prince George, BC, Canada

Canadian Diabetes Assn. - Red Deer and District Br. [IO], Red Deer, AB, Canada

Canadian Diabetes Assn. - Regina Br. [IO], Regina, SK, Canada

Canadian Diabetes Assn. - Sarnia and District Br. [IO], Sarnia, ON, Canada

Canadian Diabetes Assn. - Saskatoon Br. [IO], Saskatoon, SK, Canada

Canadian Diabetes Assn. - Sault Ste. Marie and District Br. [IO], Sault Ste. Marie, ON, Canada

A star before a book entry number signifies that the name is not listed separately, but is mentioned within the entry.

Canadian Diabetes Assn. - Sect. de Bathurst [IO], Fredericton, NB, Canada

Canadian Diabetes Assn. - South Parklands Br. [IO], Dauphin, MB, Canada

Canadian Diabetes Assn. - Sudbury and District Br. [IO], Sudbury, ON, Canada

Canadian Diabetes Assn. - Thunder Bay and District Br. [IO], Thunder Bay, ON, Canada

Canadian Diabetes Assn. - Timmins and District Br. [IO], Timmins, ON, Canada

Canadian Diabetes Assn. - Toronto Br. [IO], Toronto, ON, Canada

Canadian Diabetes Assn. - Victoria and District Br. [IO], Victoria, BC, Canada

Canadian Diabetes Assn. - Westman Br. [IO], Brandon, MB, Canada

Canadian Diabetes Assn. - Williams Lake and District Br. [IO], Kelowna, BC, Canada

Canadian Diabetes Assn. - Windsor and District Br. [IO], Windsor, ON, Canada

Canadian Diabetes Assn. - York Region Br. [IO], Toronto, ON, Canada

Canadian Diamond Drilling Assn. [IO], North Bay, ON, Canada

Canadian Die Casters Assn. [IO], Renfrew, ON, Canada

Canadian Disarmament Info. Ser. [IO], Toronto, ON, Canada

Canadian Disc Jockey Assn. [IO], Arva, ON, Canada

Canadian Doll Artists Assn. [IO], Milton, ON, Canada

Canadian Dove Assn. [IO], Plattsville, ON, Canada

Canadian Down Syndrome Soc. [IO], Calgary, AB, Canada

Canadian Dressage Owners and Riders Assn. [IO], Hamilton, ON, Canada

Canadian Driving Soc. [★315]

Canadian Dyslexia Assn. [IO], Gatineau, QC, Canada

Canadian Economics Assn. [IO], Montreal, QC, Canada

Canadian Educ. Assn. [IO], Toronto, ON, Canada

Canadian Educ. Centre Network [IO], Vancouver, BC, Canada

Canadian Educational Standards Inst. [IO], St. Catharines, ON, Canada

Canadian Elecl. Contractors Assn. [IO], Toronto, ON, Canada

Canadian Electricity Assn. [IO], Ottawa, ON, Canada

Canadian Electronic and Appliance Ser. Assn. [IO], Mississauga, ON, Canada

Canadian Energy Pipeline Assn. [IO], Calgary, AB, Canada

Canadian Energy Res. Inst. [IO], Calgary, AB, Canada

Canadian Energy Workers Assn. [IO], Edmonton, AB, Canada

Canadian Environmental Auditing Assn. [★11769]

Canadian Environmental Law Assn. [IO], Toronto, ON, Canada

Canadian Environmental Network [IO], Ottawa, ON, Canada

Canadian Esperanto Assn. [IO], Montreal, QC, Canada

Canadian Ethnic Stud. Assn. [IO], Winnipeg, MB, Canada

Canadian Ethnocultural Coun. [IO], Ottawa, ON, Canada

Canadian Evaluation Soc. [IO], Ottawa, ON, Canada

Canadian Executive Ser. Org. [IO], Toronto, ON, Canada

Canadian Family Camping Fed. [IO], Rexdale, ON, Canada

Canadian Farm Animal Care Trust [IO], Barrie, ON, Canada

Canadian Farm Builders Assn. [IO], Stratford, ON, Canada

Canadian Farm and Indus. Equip. Inst. [★10197]

Canadian Farm Writers' Fed. [IO], Ormstown, QC, Canada

Canadian Fed. of Aromatherapists [IO], Waterloo, ON, Canada

Canadian Fed. of Biological Societies [IO], Ottawa, ON, Canada

Canadian Fed. of Bus. and Professional Women's Clubs [IO], London, ON, Canada

Canadian Fed. of Bus. School Deans [IO], Montreal, QC, Canada

Canadian Fed. of Earth Sciences [IO], Calgary, AB, Canada

Canadian Fed. of Engg. Students [IO], Ottawa, ON, Canada

Canadian Fed. of Friends of Museums [IO], Ottawa, ON, Canada

Canadian Fed. of Humane Societies [IO], Ottawa, ON, Canada

Canadian Fed. for the Humanities and Social Sciences [IO], Ottawa, ON, Canada

Canadian Fed. of Independent Bus. [IO], Toronto, ON, Canada

Canadian Fed. of Independent Grocers [IO], Willowdale, ON, Canada

Canadian Fed. of Junior Leagues [IO], Calgary, AB, Canada

Canadian Fed. of Medical Students [IO], Ottawa, ON, Canada

Canadian Fed. of Mental Hea. Nurses [IO], Toronto, ON, Canada

Canadian Fed. of Music Teachers' Associations [IO], London, ON, Canada

Canadian Fed. of Nurses Unions [IO], Ottawa, ON, Canada

Canadian Fed. of Poets [IO], Burlington, ON, Canada

Canadian Fed. for Sexual Hea. [IO], Ottawa, ON, Canada

Canadian Fed. of Students [IO], Ottawa, ON, Canada

Canadian Fed. of Univ. Women [IO], Ottawa, ON, Canada

Canadian Feed The Children [IO], Toronto, ON, Canada

Canadian Fencing Fed. [IO], St. Catharines, ON, Canada

Canadian Fertility and Andrology Soc. [IO], Montreal, QC, Canada

Canadian Fertilizer Inst. [IO], Ottawa, ON, Canada

Canadian Film Centre [IO], Toronto, ON, Canada

Canadian Film Inst. [IO], Ottawa, ON, Canada

Canadian Film and TV Production Assn. [IO], Ottawa, ON, Canada

Canadian Filmmakers Distribution Centre [IO], Toronto, ON, Canada

Canadian Finance and Leasing Assn. [IO], Toronto, ON, Canada

Canadian Fire Alarm Assn. [IO], Markham, ON, Canada

Canadian Fire Safety Assn. [IO], North York, ON, Canada

Canadian Firefighters Curling Assn. [IO], Victoria, BC, Canada

Canadian Fitness and Lifestyle Res. Inst. [IO], Ottawa, ON, Canada

Canadian Fjord Horse Assn. [IO], Beausejour, MB, Canada

Canadian Flag Assn. [IO], Toronto, ON, Canada

Canadian Food Exporters Assn. [IO], Toronto, ON, Canada

Canadian Football Hall of Fame and Museum [IO], Hamilton, ON, Canada

Canadian Football League [IO], Toronto, ON, Canada

Canadian Football League Players Assn. [IO], Oakville, ON, Canada

Canadian Forestry Assn. [IO], Pembroke, ON, Canada

Canadian Found. for AIDS Res. [IO], Toronto, ON, Canada

Canadian Found. for the Americas [IO], Ottawa, ON, Canada

Canadian Found. for the Awareness of Miracles [IO], Lefaivre, ON, Canada

Canadian Found. for Dietetic Res. [IO], Toronto, ON, Canada

Canadian Found. for Drug Policy [IO], Ottawa, ON, Canada

Canadian Found. for Economic Educ. [IO], Toronto, ON, Canada

Canadian Found. for Masorti Judaism [IO], Toronto, ON, Canada

Canadian Found. for Physically Disabled Persons [IO], Toronto, ON, Canada

Canadian Found. for the Stud. of Infant Deaths [IO], Toronto, ON, Canada

Canadian Found. for Ukrainian Stud. [IO], Toronto, ON, Canada

Canadian Foundry Assn. [IO], Ottawa, ON, Canada

Canadian Franchise Assn. [IO], Toronto, ON, Canada

Canadian Friends of Bar-Ilan Univ. [IO], Concord, ON, Canada

Canadian Friends of Burma [IO], Ottawa, ON, Canada

Canadian Friends of Givat Haviva [IO], Toronto, ON, Canada

Canadian Friends of the Hebrew Univ. of Jerusalem [IO], Toronto, ON, Canada

Canadian Friends Historical Assn. [IO], Newmarket, ON, Canada

Canadian Friends of Peace Now [IO], Thornhill, ON, Canada

Canadian Friends Ser. Comm. [IO], Toronto, ON, Canada

Canadian Friends of Soviet People [IO], Toronto, ON, Canada

Canadian Galloway Assn. [IO], Ottawa, ON, Canada

Canadian Gas Assn. [IO], Ottawa, ON, Canada

Canadian Gelbvieh Assn. [IO], Calgary, AB, Canada

Canadian Gemmological Assn. [IO], Toronto, ON, Canada

Canadian Gen. Standards Bd. [IO], Gatineau, QC, Canada

Canadian Generic Pharmaceutical Assn. [IO], Toronto, ON, Canada

Canadian Genetic Diseases Network [IO], Vancouver, BC, Canada

Canadian Geomorphological Res. Gp. [IO], Ottawa, ON, Canada

Canadian Geophysical Union [IO], Calgary, AB, Canada

Canadian Geotechnical Soc. [IO], Richmond, BC, Canada

Canadian Geriatrics Soc. [IO], Markham, ON, Canada

Canadian German Chamber of Indus. and Commerce [IO], Toronto, ON, Canada

Canadian Gerontological Nursing Assn. [IO], Vancouver, BC, Canada

Canadian Gift and Tableware Assn. [IO], Toronto, ON, Canada

Canadian Ging Wu Kung Fu Martial Art Assn. [IO], Edmonton, AB, Canada

Canadian Girls Rodeo Assn. [IO], Calgary, AB, Canada

Canadian Goat Soc. [IO], Ottawa, ON, Canada

Canadian Golf Superintendents Assn. [IO], Mississauga, ON, Canada

Canadian Grand Masters Fiddling Assn. [IO], Ottawa, ON, Canada

Canadian Ground Water Assn. [IO], Bedford, NS, Canada

Canadian Guernsey Assn. [IO], Guelph, ON, Canada

Canadian Guide Dogs for the Blind [IO], Manotick, ON, Canada

Canadian Guild of Pakistani Women [IO], Willowdale, ON, Canada

Canadian Hackney Soc. [IO], North Gower, ON, Canada

Canadian Haflinger Assn. [IO], Windsor, NS, Canada

Canadian Hard of Hearing Assn. [IO], Ottawa, ON, Canada

Canadian Hard of Hearing Assn. - Alberni Valley Br. [IO], Port Alberni, BC, Canada

Canadian Hard of Hearing Assn. - BC Parents' Br. [IO], Chilliwack, BC, Canada

Canadian Hard of Hearing Assn. - British Columbia Chap. [IO], Chilliwack, BC, Canada

Canadian Hard of Hearing Assn. - Calgary [IO], Calgary, AB, Canada

Canadian Hard of Hearing Assn. - Edmonton Br. [IO], Edmonton, AB, Canada

Canadian Hard of Hearing Assn. - Kelowna Br. [IO], Kelowna, BC, Canada

Canadian Hard of Hearing Assn. - Lethbridge Br. [IO], Lethbridge, AB, Canada

Canadian Hard of Hearing Assn. - Manitoba Chap. [IO], Winnipeg, MB, Canada

Reference to "IO" in place of a book number signifies that the association may be found in the 50th edition of International Organizations.

Canadian Hard of Hearing Assn. - Moncton Br. **[IO]**, Dieppe, NB, Canada

Canadian Hard of Hearing Assn. - Nanaimo Br. **[IO]**, Nanaimo, BC, Canada

Canadian Hard of Hearing Assn. - New Brunswick Chap. **[IO]**, St. John, NB, Canada

Canadian Hard of Hearing Assn. - Newfoundland and Labrador Chap. **[IO]**, Mount Pearl, NL, Canada

Canadian Hard of Hearing Assn. - North Shore Br. **[IO]**, North Vancouver, BC, Canada

Canadian Hard of Hearing Assn. - Ontario Chap. **[IO]**, Ottawa, ON, Canada

Canadian Hard of Hearing Assn. - Orillia and District Br. **[IO]**, Orillia, ON, Canada

Canadian Hard of Hearing Assn. - Outaouais Br. **[IO]**, Gatineau, QC, Canada

Canadian Hard of Hearing Assn. - Prince George Br. **[IO]**, Prince George, BC, Canada

Canadian Hard of Hearing Assn. - Quebec Chap. **[IO]**, Gatineau, QC, Canada

Canadian Hard of Hearing Assn. - Regina and District Br. **[IO]**, Regina, SK, Canada

Canadian Hard of Hearing Assn. - Saskatoon Br. **[IO]**, Saskatoon, SK, Canada

Canadian Hard of Hearing Assn. - Sudbury Br. **[IO]**, Sudbury, ON, Canada

Canadian Hard of Hearing Assn. - Vancouver Br. **[IO]**, Vancouver, BC, Canada

Canadian Hard of Hearing Assn. - Victoria Br. **[IO]**, Victoria, BC, Canada

Canadian Hard of Hearing Assn. - Yellowknife Br. **[IO]**, Yellowknife, NT, Canada

Canadian Hardware and Housewares Mfrs. Assn. **[IO]**, Scarborough, ON, Canada

Canadian Hardwood Plywood and Veneer Assn. **[IO]**, St. Sauveur, QC, Canada

Canadian Harvard Aircraft Assn. **[IO]**, Tillsonburg, ON, Canada

Canadian Hatching Egg Producers **[IO]**, Ottawa, ON, Canada

Canadian Hays Converter Assn. **[IO]**, Calgary, AB, Canada

Canadian Hea. Coalition **[IO]**, Ottawa, ON, Canada

Canadian Hea. Food Assn. **[IO]**, Toronto, ON, Canada

Canadian Hea. Info. Mgt. Assn. **[IO]**, London, ON, Canada

Canadian Hea. Libraries Assn. **[IO]**, Toronto, ON, Canada

Canadian Healthcare Assn. **[IO]**, Ottawa, ON, Canada

Canadian Healthcare Engg. Soc. **[IO]**, Kingston, ON, Canada

Canadian Hearing Soc. **[IO]**, Toronto, ON, Canada

Canadian Hematology Soc. **[IO]**, Ottawa, ON, Canada

Canadian Hemochromatosis Soc. **[IO]**, Richmond, BC, Canada

Canadian Hemophilia Soc. **[IO]**, Montreal, QC, Canada

Canadian Hereford Assn. **[IO]**, Calgary, AB, Canada

Canadian Heritage Info. Network **[IO]**, Gatineau, QC, Canada

Canadian Highland Cattle Soc. **[IO]**, Exeter, ON, Canada

Canadian Historical Assn. **[IO]**, Ottawa, ON, Canada

Canadian HIV/AIDS Legal Network **[IO]**, Toronto, ON, Canada

Canadian Hockey League **[IO]**, Scarborough, ON, Canada

Canadian Holistic Nurses Assn. **[IO]**, Red Deer, AB, Canada

Canadian Home Builders' Assn. **[IO]**, Ottawa, ON, Canada

Canadian Home Care Assn. **[IO]**, Mississauga, ON, Canada

Canadian Honey Coun. **[IO]**, Calgary, AB, Canada

Canadian Horticultural Coun. **[IO]**, Ottawa, ON, Canada

Canadian Hospice Palliative Care Assn. **[IO]**, Ottawa, ON, Canada

Canadian Host Family Assn. **[IO]**, Chestermere, AB, Canada

Canadian Housing and Renewal Assn. **[IO]**, Ottawa, ON, Canada

Canadian Human-Computer Communications Soc. **[IO]**, Mississauga, ON, Canada

Canadian Hydrogen and Fuel Cell Assn. **[IO]**, Vancouver, BC, Canada

Canadian Hydrographic Assn. **[IO]**, Burlington, ON, Canada

Canadian Hydrographic Assn. - Ottawa Br. **[IO]**, Ottawa, ON, Canada

Canadian Hydropower Assn. **[IO]**, Ottawa, ON, Canada

Canadian Hypertension Soc. **[IO]**, Markham, ON, Canada

Canadian Icelandic Horse Fed. **[IO]**, Woodlawn, ON, Canada

Canadian Image Processing and Pattern Recognition Soc. **[IO]**, London, ON, Canada

Canadian Imaging Trade Assn. **[IO]**, Newmarket, ON, Canada

Canadian Immigration Historical Soc. **[IO]**, Ottawa, ON, Canada

Canadian Independent Adjusters' Assn. **[IO]**, Etobicoke, ON, Canada

Canadian Independent Music Assn. **[IO]**, Toronto, ON, Canada

Canadian Independent Telephone Assn. **[IO]**, Alton, ON, Canada

Canadian Indus. Relations Assn. **[IO]**, Quebec, QC, Canada

Canadian Indus. Trans. Assn. **[IO]**, Ottawa, ON, Canada

Canadian Info. Processing Soc. **[IO]**, Mississauga, ON, Canada

Canadian Injured Workers Alliance **[IO]**, Thunder Bay, ON, Canada

Canadian Innovation Centre **[IO]**, Waterloo, ON, Canada

Canadian Inst. **[IO]**, Toronto, ON, Canada

Canadian Inst. of Actuaries **[IO]**, Ottawa, ON, Canada

Canadian Inst. for the Admin. of Justice **[IO]**, Montreal, QC, Canada

Canadian Inst. for Advanced Res. **[IO]**, Toronto, ON, Canada

Canadian Inst. of Certified Administrative Managers **[IO]**, Toronto, ON, Canada

Canadian Inst. of Chartered Accountants **[IO]**, Toronto, ON, Canada

Canadian Inst. of Chartered Bus. Valuators **[IO]**, Toronto, ON, Canada

Canadian Inst. of Child Hea. **[IO]**, Ottawa, ON, Canada

Canadian Inst. for Climate Stud. **[IO]**, Victoria, BC, Canada

Canadian Inst. for Conflict Resolution **[IO]**, Ottawa, ON, Canada

Canadian Inst. of Cultural Affairs **[IO]**, Toronto, ON, Canada

Canadian Inst. of Energy **[IO]**, Vancouver, BC, Canada

Canadian Inst. for Energy Training **[IO]**, Orangeville, ON, Canada

Canadian Inst. for Environmental Law and Policy **[IO]**, Toronto, ON, Canada

Canadian Inst. of Financial Planning **[IO]**, Mississauga, ON, Canada

Canadian Inst. of Food Sci. and Tech. **[IO]**, Toronto, ON, Canada

Canadian Inst. of Forestry **[IO]**, Mattawa, ON, Canada

Canadian Inst. of Gemmology **[IO]**, Vancouver, BC, Canada

Canadian Inst. of Geomatics **[IO]**, Ottawa, ON, Canada

Canadian Inst. of Hea. Care and Bus. **[IO]**, Toronto, ON, Canada

Canadian Inst. for Hea. Info. **[IO]**, Ottawa, ON, Canada

Canadian Inst. for Jewish Res. **[IO]**, Montreal, QC, Canada

Canadian Inst. of Mgt. **[IO]**, Barrie, ON, Canada

Canadian Inst. of Marketing **[IO]**, Halton Hills, ON, Canada

Canadian Inst. of Mining, Metallurgy, and Petroleum **[IO]**, Montreal, QC, Canada

Canadian Inst. for NDE **[IO]**, Hamilton, ON, Canada

Canadian Inst. of Planners **[IO]**, Ottawa, ON, Canada

Canadian Inst. of Plumbing and Heating **[IO]**, Toronto, ON, Canada

Canadian Inst. of Professional Home Inspectors **[IO]**, Vancouver, BC, Canada

Canadian Inst. of Public Hea. Inspectors **[IO]**, Vancouver, BC, Canada

Canadian Inst. of Quantity Surveyors **[IO]**, Markham, ON, Canada

Canadian Inst. of Resources Law **[IO]**, Calgary, AB, Canada

Canadian Inst. of Steel Constr. **[IO]**, Markham, ON, Canada

Canadian Inst. of Strategic Stud. **[IO]**, Toronto, ON, Canada

Canadian Inst. for Theatre Tech. **[IO]**, Ottawa, ON, Canada

Canadian Inst. of Traffic and Trans. **[IO]**, Toronto, ON, Canada

Canadian Inst. of Travel Counsellors **[IO]**, Toronto, ON, Canada

Canadian Inst. of Ukrainian Stud. **[IO]**, Edmonton, AB, Canada

Canadian Institutional Res. and Planning Assn. **[IO]**, Ottawa, ON, Canada

Canadian Insurance Accountants Assn. **[IO]**, Toronto, ON, Canada

Canadian Insurance Claims Managers' Assn. **[IO]**, Burlington, ON, Canada

Canadian Intl. Coun. **[IO]**, Toronto, ON, Canada

Canadian Intl. Dragon Boat Festival Soc. **[IO]**, Vancouver, BC, Canada

Canadian Intl. DX Club **[IO]**, St. Lambert, QC, Canada

Canadian Intl. Freight Forwarders Assn. **[IO]**, Toronto, ON, Canada

Canadian Intl. Grains Inst. **[IO]**, Winnipeg, MB, Canada

Canadian Intl. Inst. of Applied Negotiation **[IO]**, Ottawa, ON, Canada

Canadian Interuniversity Sport **[IO]**, Ottawa, ON, Canada

Canadian Investor Relations Inst. **[IO]**, Toronto, ON, Canada

Canadian Iris Soc. **[IO]**, Brantford, ON, Canada

Canadian IT Law Assn. **[IO]**, Thornhill, ON, Canada

Canadian Jackie Chan Fan Club **[IO]**, Scarborough, ON, Canada

Canadian Jesuits Intl. **[IO]**, Toronto, ON, Canada

Canadian Jewellers Assn. **[IO]**, Toronto, ON, Canada

Canadian Jewish Cong. **[IO]**, Ottawa, ON, Canada

Canadian Journalists for Free Expression **[IO]**, Toronto, ON, Canada

Canadian Junior Football League **[IO]**, St. Leonard, QC, Canada

Canadian Kendo Fed. **[IO]**, Burnaby, BC, Canada

Canadian Kennel Club **[IO]**, Etobicoke, ON, Canada

Canadian Kitchen Cabinet Assn. **[IO]**, Ottawa, ON, Canada

Canadian Lab. Suppliers Assn. **[IO]**, Kitchener, ON, Canada

Canadian Labour Cong. **[IO]**, Ottawa, ON, Canada

Canadian Lacrosse Assn. **[IO]**, Ottawa, ON, Canada

Canadian Land Reclamation Assn. **[IO]**, Calgary, AB, Canada

Canadian Landmine Found. **[IO]**, Waterloo, ON, Canada

Canadian Law and Economics Assn. **[IO]**, Toronto, ON, Canada

Canadian Law and Soc. Assn. **[IO]**, Toronto, ON, Canada

Canadian Lawyers for Intl. Human Rights **[IO]**, Toronto, ON, Canada

Canadian League Against Epilepsy **[IO]**, London, ON, Canada

Canadian League of Composers **[IO]**, Toronto, ON, Canada

Canadian Lebanon Soc. of Halifax **[IO]**, Halifax, NS, Canada

Canadian Lib. Assn. **[IO]**, Ottawa, ON, Canada

Canadian Lib. Trustees Assn. **[IO]**, Ottawa, ON, Canada

Canadian Life and Hea. Insurance Assn. **[IO]**, Toronto, ON, Canada

A star before a book entry number signifies that the name is not listed separately, but is mentioned within the entry.

Canadian Life Insurance Medical Officers Assn. [IO], Ottawa, ON, Canada

Canadian Lifeboat Institution [IO], Vancouver, BC, Canada

Canadian Limousin Assn. [IO], Calgary, AB, Canada

Canadian Linguistic Assn. [IO], St. John's, NL, Canada

Canadian Liver Found. [IO], Toronto, ON, Canada

Canadian Livestock Records Corp. [IO], Ottawa, ON, Canada

Canadian Llama and Alpaca Assn. [IO], Calgary, AB, Canada

Canadian Long Distance Riding Assn. [IO], Stouffville, ON, Canada

Canadian Lumbermen's Assn. [IO], Ottawa, ON, Canada

Canadian Lung Assn. [IO], Ottawa, ON, Canada

Canadian Maine-Anjou Assn. [IO], Calgary, AB, Canada

Canadian Mgt. Centre [IO], Toronto, ON, Canada

Canadian Manufactured Housing Inst. [IO], Ottawa, ON, Canada

Canadian Mfrs. and Exporters [IO], Ottawa, ON, Canada

Canadian Marfan Assn. [IO], Mississauga, ON, Canada

Canadian Marine Pilots' Assn. [IO], Ottawa, ON, Canada

Canadian Maritime Law Assn. [IO], Montreal, QC, Canada

Canadian Marketing Assn. [IO], Don Mills, ON, Canada

Canadian Masters' Cross Country Ski Assn. [IO], Stephenville, NL, Canada

Canadian Mathematical Soc. [IO], Ottawa, ON, Canada

Canadian Meat Coun. [IO], Ottawa, ON, Canada

Canadian Media Guild [IO], Toronto, ON, Canada

Canadian Medical Assn. [IO], Ottawa, ON, Canada

Canadian Medical and Biological Engg. Soc. [IO], Ottawa, ON, Canada

Canadian Medical Protective Assn. [IO], Ottawa, ON, Canada

Canadian MedicAlert Found. [IO], Toronto, ON, Canada

Canadian Mental Hea. Assn. [IO], Ottawa, ON, Canada

Canadian Mental Hea. Assn. - Alberta Div. [IO], Ottawa, ON, Canada

Canadian Mental Hea. Assn., Barrie - Simcoe Br. [IO], Barrie, ON, Canada

Canadian Mental Hea. Assn., Bas-du-Fleuve Br. [IO], Rimouski, QC, Canada

Canadian Mental Hea. Assn. - BC Div. [IO], Vancouver, BC, Canada

Canadian Mental Hea. Assn. - Brant County Br. [IO], Brantford, ON, Canada

Canadian Mental Hea. Assn. - Calgary Region [IO], Calgary, AB, Canada

Canadian Mental Hea. Assn. - Central Alberta Region [IO], Red Deer, AB, Canada

Canadian Mental Hea. Assn., Chatham - Kent Br. [IO], Chatham-Kent, ON, Canada

Canadian Mental Hea. Assn., Chaudiere - Appalaches Br. [IO], Levis, QC, Canada

Canadian Mental Hea. Assn. - Cochrane Timiskaming Br. [IO], Timmins, ON, Canada

Canadian Mental Hea. Assn. - Courtenay Br. [IO], Courtenay, BC, Canada

Canadian Mental Hea. Assn. - Cowichan Valley Br. [IO], Duncan, BC, Canada

Canadian Mental Hea. Assn. - Dartmouth Br. [IO], Halifax, NS, Canada

Canadian Mental Hea. Assn. - Durham Br. [IO], Oshawa, ON, Canada

Canadian Mental Hea. Assn. - East Central Region [IO], Camrose, AB, Canada

Canadian Mental Hea. Assn. - Edmonton Region [IO], Edmonton, AB, Canada

Canadian Mental Hea. Assn. - Elgin County Br. [IO], St. Thomas, ON, Canada

Canadian Mental Hea. Assn. - Estevan Br. [IO], Estevan, SK, Canada

Canadian Mental Hea. Assn. - Fredericton/Oromocto Region [IO], Fredericton, NB, Canada

Canadian Mental Hea. Assn. - Grand River Br. [IO], Guelph, ON, Canada

Canadian Mental Hea. Assn., Grey - Bruce Br. [IO], Owen Sound, ON, Canada

Canadian Mental Hea. Assn. - Hamilton Br. [IO], Hamilton, ON, Canada

Canadian Mental Hea. Assn. - Hastings and Prince Edward Br. [IO], Belleville, ON, Canada

Canadian Mental Hea. Assn., Haut-Richelieu Br. [IO], St.-Jean-sur-Richelieu, QC, Canada

Canadian Mental Hea. Assn., Huron - Perth Br. [IO], Stratford, ON, Canada

Canadian Mental Hea. Assn. - Interlake Region [IO], Selkirk, MB, Canada

Canadian Mental Hea. Assn. - Kamloops Br. [IO], Kamloops, BC, Canada

Canadian Mental Hea. Assn. - Kelowna Br. [IO], Kelowna, BC, Canada

Canadian Mental Hea. Assn. - Kingston Br. [IO], Kingston, ON, Canada

Canadian Mental Hea. Assn. - Kootenays [IO], Cranbrook, BC, Canada

Canadian Mental Hea. Assn. - Lac St. Jean Br. [IO], Roberval, QC, Canada

Canadian Mental Hea. Assn. - Lambton County Br. [IO], Sarnia, ON, Canada

Canadian Mental Hea. Assn., Leeds - Grenville Br. [IO], Brockville, ON, Canada

Canadian Mental Hea. Assn., London - Middlesex Br. [IO], London, ON, Canada

Canadian Mental Hea. Assn. - Manitoba Div. [IO], Winnipeg, MB, Canada

Canadian Mental Hea. Assn., Mid-Island Br. [IO], Nanaimo, BC, Canada

Canadian Mental Hea. Assn. - Moncton Region [IO], Moncton, NB, Canada

Canadian Mental Hea. Assn. - Montreal Br. [IO], Montreal, QC, Canada

Canadian Mental Hea. Assn. - Moose Jaw Br. [IO], Moose Jaw, SK, Canada

Canadian Mental Hea. Assn. - New Brunswick Div. [IO], Fredericton, NB, Canada

Canadian Mental Hea. Assn. - Newfoundland and Labrador Div. [IO], St. John's, NL, Canada

Canadian Mental Hea. Assn. - Niagara Br. [IO], St. Catharines, ON, Canada

Canadian Mental Hea. Assn. - Nipissing Regional Br. [IO], North Bay, ON, Canada

Canadian Mental Hea. Assn. - North Battlefords Br. [IO], North Battleford, SK, Canada

Canadian Mental Hea. Assn. - North and South Okanagan Br. [IO], Kelowna, BC, Canada

Canadian Mental Hea. Assn. - North West Region [IO], Grande Prairie, AB, Canada

Canadian Mental Hea. Assn. - North and West Vancouver Br. [IO], North Vancouver, BC, Canada

Canadian Mental Hea. Assn. - Northwest Territories Div. [IO], Yellowknife, NT, Canada

Canadian Mental Hea. Assn. - Nova Scotia Div. [IO], Dartmouth, NS, Canada

Canadian Mental Hea. Assn. - Ontario Div. [IO], Toronto, ON, Canada

Canadian Mental Hea. Assn. - Ottawa Br. [IO], Ottawa, ON, Canada

Canadian Mental Hea. Assn. - Oxford County Br. [IO], Woodstock, ON, Canada

Canadian Mental Hea. Assn. - Peel Br. [IO], Brampton, ON, Canada

Canadian Mental Hea. Assn. - Peterborough Br. [IO], Peterborough, ON, Canada

Canadian Mental Hea. Assn. - Pincher Creek Br. [IO], Pincher Creek, AB, Canada

Canadian Mental Hea. Assn. - Port Alberni Br. [IO], Port Alberni, BC, Canada

Canadian Mental Hea. Assn. - Prince Albert Br. [IO], Prince Albert, SK, Canada

Canadian Mental Hea. Assn. - Prince County Br. [IO], Summerside, PE, Canada

Canadian Mental Hea. Assn. - Prince Edward Island Div. [IO], Charlottetown, PE, Canada

Canadian Mental Hea. Assn. - Prince George Br. [IO], Prince George, BC, Canada

Canadian Mental Hea. Assn. - Quebec Div. [IO], Montreal, QC, Canada

Canadian Mental Hea. Assn. - Regina Br. [IO], Regina, SK, Canada

Canadian Mental Hea. Assn. - Region III Br. [IO], Fredericton, NB, Canada

Canadian Mental Hea. Assn. - Region IV Edmundston [IO], Edmundston, NB, Canada

Canadian Mental Hea. Assn. - Region V Campbellton [IO], Campbellton, NB, Canada

Canadian Mental Hea. Assn. - Region VII Miramichi [IO], Miramichi, NB, Canada

Canadian Mental Hea. Assn. - Richmond Br. [IO], Richmond, BC, Canada

Canadian Mental Hea. Assn., Rive-Sud de Montreal Br. [IO], Longueuil, QC, Canada

Canadian Mental Hea. Assn., S. D. and G. Prescott - Russel Br. [IO], Cornwall, ON, Canada

Canadian Mental Hea. Assn. - Saint John Br. [IO], St. John, NB, Canada

Canadian Mental Hea. Assn. - Saskatchewan Div. [IO], Regina, SK, Canada

Canadian Mental Hea. Assn. - Saskatoon Br. [IO], Saskatoon, SK, Canada

Canadian Mental Hea. Assn. - Sault Ste. Marie Br. [IO], Sault Ste. Marie, ON, Canada

Canadian Mental Hea. Assn. - Simon Fraser Br. [IO], New Westminster, BC, Canada

Canadian Mental Hea. Assn. - South East Region [IO], Medicine Hat, AB, Canada

Canadian Mental Hea. Assn. - South Okanagan Similkameen Br. [IO], Penticton, BC, Canada

Canadian Mental Hea. Assn. - South Region [IO], Lethbridge, AB, Canada

Canadian Mental Hea. Assn. - Swift Current Br. [IO], Swift Current, SK, Canada

Canadian Mental Hea. Assn. - Thompson Region [IO], Thompson, MB, Canada

Canadian Mental Hea. Assn. - Thunder Bay Br. [IO], Thunder Bay, ON, Canada

Canadian Mental Hea. Assn. - Toronto Br. [IO], Toronto, ON, Canada

Canadian Mental Hea. Assn. - Vancouver/Burnaby Br. [IO], Vancouver, BC, Canada

Canadian Mental Hea. Assn. - Vernon District Br. [IO], Vernon, BC, Canada

Canadian Mental Hea. Assn. - Westman Region [IO], Brandon, MB, Canada

Canadian Mental Hea. Assn. - Weyburn Br. [IO], Weyburn, SK, Canada

Canadian Mental Hea. Assn., Windsor - Essex County Br. [IO], Windsor, ON, Canada

Canadian Mental Hea. Assn. - Winnipeg Region [IO], Winnipeg, MB, Canada

Canadian Mental Hea. Assn. - Yorkton Br. [IO], Yorkton, SK, Canada

Canadian Mental Hea. Assn. - Yukon Div. [IO], Whitehorse, YT, Canada

Canadian Merchant Ser. Guild [IO], Ottawa, ON, Canada

Canadian Meteorological and Oceanographic Soc. [IO], Ottawa, ON, Canada

Canadian Micro Mineral Assn. [IO], Toronto, ON, Canada

Canadian Milking Shorthorn Soc. [IO], Guelph, ON, Canada

Canadian Mineral Analysts [IO], Winnipeg, MB, Canada

Canadian Morgan Horse Assn. [IO], Port Perry, ON, Canada

Canadian Motion Picture Distribution Assn. [IO], Toronto, ON, Canada

Canadian Motorcycle Assn. [IO], Hamilton, ON, Canada

Canadian Murray Grey Assn. [IO], Stettler, AB, Canada

Canadian Museum of Nature [IO], Ottawa, ON, Canada

Canadian Museums Assn. [IO], Ottawa, ON, Canada

Canadian Mushroom Growers' Assn. [IO], Guelph, ON, Canada

Canadian Music Centre [IO], Toronto, ON, Canada

Canadian Music Educators Assn. [IO], Waterloo, ON, Canada

Canadian Music Publishers Assn. [IO], Toronto, ON, Canada

Canadian Musical Reproduction Rights Agency [IO], Toronto, ON, Canada

Reference to "IO" in place of a book number signifies that the association may be found in the 50th edition of International Organizations.

Canadian Natl. Exhibition [IO], Toronto, ON, Canada

Canadian Natl. Fed. of Independent Unions [IO], Campbellville, ON, Canada

Canadian Natl. Inst. for the Blind [IO], Toronto, ON, Canada

Canadian Natl. Soc. of the Deaf-Blind [IO], North York, ON, Canada

Canadian Native Friendship Centre [IO], Edmonton, AB, Canada

Canadian Nautical Res. Soc. [IO], Ottawa, ON, Canada

Canadian Navigation Soc. [IO], Kanata, ON, Canada

Canadian Netherlands Bus. and Professional Assn. [IO], Toronto, ON, Canada

Canadian Network for Asthma Care [IO], Bolton, ON, Canada

Canadian Network for Innovation in Educ. [IO], Ottawa, ON, Canada

Canadian Network of Toxicology Centres [IO], Guelph, ON, Canada

Canadian Neurological Sciences Fed. [IO], Calgary, AB, Canada

Canadian Neuropathy Assn. [IO], Pefferlaw, ON, Canada

Canadian Neurosurgical Soc. [IO], Calgary, AB, Canada

Canadian Newspaper Assn. [IO], Toronto, ON, Canada

Canadian Northern Soc. [IO], Camrose, AB, Canada

Canadian Norwegian Bus. Assn. [IO], Sandvika, Norway

Canadian Nuclear Assn. [IO], Ottawa, ON, Canada

Canadian Nuclear Soc. [IO], Toronto, ON, Canada

Canadian Numismatic Res. Soc. [IO], Victoria, BC, Canada

Canadian Nursery Landscape Assn. [IO], Milton, ON, Canada

Canadian Nurses Assn. [IO], Ottawa, ON, Canada

Canadian Nurses Found. [IO], Ottawa, ON, Canada

Canadian Nurses Protective Soc. [IO], Ottawa, ON, Canada

Canadian Nursing Students' Assn. [IO], Ottawa, ON, Canada

Canadian Occupational Hea. Nurses Assn. [IO], Edmonton, AB, Canada

Canadian Occupational Therapy Found. [IO], Ottawa, ON, Canada

Canadian Off-Highway Vehicle Distributors Coun. [IO], Markham, ON, Canada

Canadian Off. Products Assn. [IO], Mississauga, ON, Canada

Canadian Oil Heat Assn. [IO], Markham, ON, Canada

Canadian Oilseed Processors Assn. [IO], Winnipeg, MB, Canada

Canadian Olympic Comm. [IO], Toronto, ON, Canada

Canadian Operational Res. Soc. [IO], Ottawa, ON, Canada

Canadian Ophthalmological Soc. [IO], Ottawa, ON, Canada

Canadian Oral History Assn. [IO], Winnipeg, MB, Canada

Canadian Organic Growers [IO], Ottawa, ON, Canada

Canadian Org. for Development Through Educ. [IO], Ottawa, ON, Canada

Canadian Org. for Rare Disorders [IO], Toronto, ON, Canada

Canadian Orienteering Fed. [IO], Calgary, AB, Canada

Canadian Ornamental Plant Found. [IO], North Bay, ON, Canada

Canadian Orthopaedic Assn. [IO], Westmount, QC, Canada

Canadian Orthopaedic Found. [IO], Innisfil, ON, Canada

Canadian Orthopaedic Nurses Assn. [IO], Chambly, QC, Canada

Canadian Orthopractic Manual Therapy Assn. [IO], Edmonton, AB, Canada

Canadian Orthoptic Coun. [IO], Ste.-Foy, QC, Canada

Canadian Osteopathic Assn. [IO], London, ON, Canada

Canadian Overseas Telecommunications Union [IO], Montreal, QC, Canada

Canadian Owners and Pilots Assn. [IO], Ottawa, ON, Canada

Canadian Paediatric Soc. [IO], Ottawa, ON, Canada

Canadian Pain Soc. [IO], Oshawa, ON, Canada

Canadian Paint and Coatings Assn. [IO], Ottawa, ON, Canada

Canadian - Palestinian Educational Exchange [IO], Ottawa, ON, Canada

Canadian Palestinian Found. of Quebec [IO], St.-Laurent, QC, Canada

Canadian Pallet Coun. [IO], Cobourg, ON, Canada

Canadian Palomino Horse Assn. [IO], Hannon, ON, Canada

Canadian Paper Money Soc. [IO], Pickering, ON, Canada

Canadian Paralympic Comm. [IO], Ottawa, ON, Canada

Canadian Paraplegic Assn. [IO], Ottawa, ON, Canada

Canadian Parents for French [IO], Ottawa, ON, Canada

Canadian Parking Assn. [IO], Ottawa, ON, Canada

Canadian Parks and Recreation Assn. [IO], Ottawa, ON, Canada

Canadian Parks and Wilderness Soc. [IO], Ottawa, ON, Canada

Canadian Payday Loan Assn. [IO], Hamilton, ON, Canada

Canadian Payments Assn. [IO], Ottawa, ON, Canada

Canadian Payroll Assn. [IO], Toronto, ON, Canada

Canadian Peace Alliance [IO], Toronto, ON, Canada

Canadian Peacekeeping Veterans Assn. [IO], Kingston, ON, Canada

Canadian Pension and Benefits Inst. [IO], Montreal, QC, Canada

Canadian Pensioners Concerned [IO], Toronto, ON, Canada

Canadian Peregrine Found. [IO], Toronto, ON, Canada

Canadian Pest Mgt. Assn. [IO], Moncton, NB, Canada

Canadian Pharmacists Assn. [IO], Ottawa, ON, Canada

Canadian Philosophical Assn. [IO], Ottawa, ON, Canada

Canadian Physicians for Aid and Relief [IO], Toronto, ON, Canada

Canadian Physicians for Aid and Relief - Malawi [IO], Lilongwe, Malawi

Canadian Physicians for Aid and Relief - Uganda [IO], Kampala, Uganda

Canadian Physiological Soc. [IO], Toronto, ON, Canada

Canadian Physiotherapy Assn. [IO], Ottawa, ON, Canada

Canadian Phytopathological Soc. [IO], Morden, MB, Canada

Canadian Picture Pioneers [IO], Toronto, ON, Canada

Canadian Pinto Horse Assn. [IO], Acheson, AB, Canada

Canadian Pinzgauer Assn. [IO], Olds, AB, Canada

Canadian Plastics Indus. Assn. [IO], Mississauga, ON, Canada

Canadian Plywood Assn. [IO], North Vancouver, BC, Canada

Canadian Podiatric Medical Assn. [IO], Sherwood Park, AB, Canada

Canadian Poetry Assn. [IO], Moncton, NB, Canada

Canadian Police Assn. [IO], Ottawa, ON, Canada

Canadian Polish Cong. [IO], Toronto, ON, Canada

Canadian Political Sci. Assn. [IO], Ottawa, ON, Canada

Canadian Polo Assn. [IO], Toronto, ON, Canada

Canadian Pony Club [IO], Baldur, MB, Canada

Canadian Poolplayers Assn. [IO], Walkerton, ON, Canada

Canadian Population Soc. [IO], Ottawa, ON, Canada

Canadian Pork Coun. [IO], Ottawa, ON, Canada

Canadian Porphyria Found. [★21000]

Canadian Post-MD Educ. Registry [IO], Ottawa, ON, Canada

Canadian Postmasters and Assistants Assn. [IO], Ottawa, ON, Canada

Canadian Poultry and Egg Processors Coun. [IO], Ottawa, ON, Canada

Canadian Power and Sail Squadrons [IO], Scarborough, ON, Canada

Canadian Powerlifting Union [IO], Mount Pearl, NL, Canada

Canadian Precast/Prestressed Concrete Inst. [IO], Ottawa, ON, Canada

Canadian Printing Indus. Assn. [IO], Ottawa, ON, Canada

Canadian Printing Ink Mfrs'. Assn. [IO], Whitby, ON, Canada

Canadian Process Control Assn. [IO], Oakville, ON, Canada

Canadian Produce Marketing Assn. [IO], Ottawa, ON, Canada

Canadian Professional Golfers' Assn. [IO], Acton, ON, Canada

Canadian Professional Logistics Inst. [IO], Toronto, ON, Canada

Canadian Professional Rodeo Assn. [IO], Airdrie, AB, Canada

Canadian Professional Sales Assn. [IO], Toronto, ON, Canada

Canadian Progress Club [IO], New Glasgow, NS, Canada

Canadian Property Tax Assn. [IO], Toronto, ON, Canada

Canadian Prostate Cancer Network [IO], Lakefield, ON, Canada

Canadian Psychiatric Assn. [IO], Ottawa, ON, Canada

Canadian Psychoanalytic Soc. [IO], Montreal, QC, Canada

Canadian Psychological Assn. [IO], Ottawa, ON, Canada

Canadian Public Hea. Assn. [IO], Ottawa, ON, Canada

Canadian Public Relations Soc. [IO], Toronto, ON, Canada

Canadian Publishers' Coun. [IO], Toronto, ON, Canada

Canadian Quarter Horse Assn. [IO], Carberry, MB, Canada

Canadian Quaternary Assn. [IO], Montreal, QC, Canada

Canadian Quilters' Assn. [IO], Pasadena, NL, Canada

Canadian Racing Pigeon Union [IO], Tillsonburg, ON, Canada

Canadian Radiation Protection Assn. [IO], Carleton Place, ON, Canada

Canadian Railroad Historical Assn. [IO], St. Constant, QC, Canada

Canadian Ready-Mixed Concrete Assn. [IO], Mississauga, ON, Canada

Canadian Real Estate Assn. [IO], Ottawa, ON, Canada

Canadian Recording Indus. Assn. [IO], Toronto, ON, Canada

Canadian Recreational Vehicle Assn. [IO], Toronto, ON, Canada

Canadian Red Angus Promotion Soc. [IO], Taber, AB, Canada

Canadian Red Cross [IO], Ottawa, ON, Canada

Canadian Red Poll Cattle Assn. [IO], Ottawa, ON, Canada

Canadian Register of Hea. Ser. Providers in Psychology [IO], Ottawa, ON, Canada

Canadian Reiki Assn. [IO], Burnaby, BC, Canada

Canadian Religious Conf. [IO], Montreal, QC, Canada

Canadian Remote Sensing Soc. [IO], Kanata, ON, Canada

Canadian Renewable Fuels Assn. [IO], Ottawa, ON, Canada

Canadian Res. Inst. for the Advancement of Women [IO], Ottawa, ON, Canada

Canadian Resort Development Assn. [IO], Toronto, ON, Canada

Canadian Restaurant and Foodservices Assn. [IO], Toronto, ON, Canada

Canadian Retransmission Collective [IO], Toronto, ON, Canada

A star before a book entry number signifies that the name is not listed separately, but is mentioned within the entry.

Canadian Rheumatology Assn. [IO], Newmarket, ON, Canada

Canadian Roofing Contractors Assn. [IO], Ottawa, ON, Canada

Canadian Rose Soc. [IO], Toronto, ON, Canada

Canadian Sanitation Supply Assn. [IO], Whitby, ON, Canada

Canadian-Scandinavian Found. [IO], Montreal, QC, Canada

Canadian School Boards Assn. [IO], Montreal, QC, Canada

Canadian School Sport Fed. [IO], Ottawa, ON, Canada

Canadian Sci. Writers' Assn. [IO], Toronto, ON, Canada

Canadian Securities Inst. [IO], Toronto, ON, Canada

Canadian Security Assn. [IO], Markham, ON, Canada

Canadian Seed Growers' Assn. [IO], Ottawa, ON, Canada

Canadian Seed Trade Assn. [IO], Ottawa, ON, Canada

Canadian Semiotic Assn. [IO], Edmonton, AB, Canada

Canadian ShareOwners Assn. [IO], Toronto, ON, Canada

Canadian Sheep Breeders' Assn. [IO], Deerville, NB, Canada

Canadian Sheep Fed. [IO], Guelph, ON, Canada

Canadian Sheet Steel Building Inst. [IO], Cambridge, ON, Canada

Canadian Shipowners Assn. [IO], Ottawa, ON, Canada

Canadian Shooting Sports Assn. [IO], Vaughan, ON, Canada

Canadian Shorthorn Assn. [IO], Regina, SK, Canada

Canadian Simmental Assn. [IO], Calgary, AB, Canada

Canadian Ski Coun. [IO], Collingwood, ON, Canada

Canadian Ski Instructors' Alliance [IO], Montreal, QC, Canada

Canadian Ski Patrol Sys. [IO], Ottawa, ON, Canada

Canadian Ski and Snowboard Professionals [IO], Montreal, QC, Canada

Canadian Sleep Soc. [IO], Westmount, QC, Canada

Canadian Snack Food Assn. [IO], Mississauga, ON, Canada

Canadian Snowbird Assn. [IO], Toronto, ON, Canada

Canadian Snowboard Fed. [IO], Vancouver, BC, Canada

Canadian Soccer Assn. [IO], Ottawa, ON, Canada

Canadian Soc. for 18th Century Stud. [IO], Burnaby, BC, Canada

Canadian Soc. for Aesthetic (Cosmetic) Plastic Surgery [IO], Pickering, ON, Canada

Canadian Soc. for Aesthetics [IO], Westmount, QC, Canada

Canadian Soc. of Agronomy [IO], Pinawa, MB, Canada

Canadian Soc. of Air Safety Investigators [IO], Vancouver, BC, Canada

Canadian Soc. of Allergy and Clinical Immunology [IO], Ottawa, ON, Canada

Canadian Soc. for Analytical Sciences and Spectroscopy [IO], Ottawa, ON, Canada

Canadian Soc. of Animal Sci. [IO], Truro, NS, Canada

Canadian Soc. of Assn. Executives [IO], Toronto, ON, Canada

Canadian Soc. of Atherosclerosis, Thrombosis and Vascular Biology [IO], Ste.-Foy, QC, Canada

Canadian Soc. of Biblical Stud. [IO], Sudbury, ON, Canada

Canadian Soc. of Biochemistry, Molecular and Cellular Biology [IO], Ottawa, ON, Canada

Canadian Soc. for Bioengineering [IO], Winnipeg, MB, Canada

Canadian Soc. for Biomechanics [IO], Fredericton, NB, Canada

Canadian Soc. for Brain, Behaviour and Cognitive Sci. [IO], Vancouver, BC, Canada

Canadian Soc. of Cardiology Technologists [IO], Winnipeg, MB, Canada

Canadian Soc. for Chem. Engg. [IO], Ottawa, ON, Canada

Canadian Soc. for Chem. Tech. [IO], Ottawa, ON, Canada

Canadian Soc. for Chemistry [IO], Ottawa, ON, Canada

Canadian Soc. of Children's Authors, Illustrators and Performers [IO], Toronto, ON, Canada

Canadian Soc. of Church History [IO], Langley, BC, Canada

Canadian Soc. of Cinematographers [IO], Toronto, ON, Canada

Canadian Soc. for Civil Engg. [IO], Montreal, QC, Canada

Canadian Soc. of Clinical Chemists [IO], Kingston, ON, Canada

Canadian Soc. for Clinical Investigation [IO], Ottawa, ON, Canada

Canadian Soc. of Clinical Neurophysiologists [IO], Calgary, AB, Canada

Canadian Soc. for Clinical Pharmacology [IO], Hamilton, ON, Canada

Canadian Soc. of Club Managers [IO], Etobicoke, ON, Canada

Canadian Soc. of Customs Brokers [IO], Ottawa, ON, Canada

Canadian Soc. of Diagnostic Medical Sonographers [IO], Kemptville, ON, Canada

Canadian Soc. of Dowsers [IO], Kitchener, ON, Canada

Canadian Soc. for Educ. through Art [IO], Victoria, BC, Canada

Canadian Soc. of Endocrinology and Metabolism [IO], Ottawa, ON, Canada

Canadian Soc. of Environmental Biologists [IO], Toronto, ON, Canada

Canadian Soc. of Exploration Geophysicists [IO], Calgary, AB, Canada

Canadian Soc. of Forensic Sci. [IO], Ottawa, ON, Canada

Canadian Soc. of Gastroenterology Nurses and Associates [IO], Oakville, ON, Canada

Canadian Soc. of the History of the Catholic Church - French Sect. [IO], Trois-Rivieres, QC, Canada

Canadian Soc. for the History and Philosophy of Sci. [IO], Sydney, NS, Canada

Canadian Soc. of Hosp. Pharmacists [IO], Ottawa, ON, Canada

Canadian Soc. for Immunology [IO], Saskatoon, SK, Canada

Canadian Soc. for Independent Radio Production [IO], Ottawa, ON, Canada

Canadian Soc. for Indus. Security [IO], Hamilton, ON, Canada

Canadian Soc. of Internal Medicine [IO], Ottawa, ON, Canada

Canadian Soc. for Intl. Hea. [IO], Ottawa, ON, Canada

Canadian Soc. for the Investigation of Child Abuse [IO], Calgary, AB, Canada

Canadian Soc. for Italian Stud. [IO], Montreal, QC, Canada

Canadian Soc. of Landscape Architects [IO], Ottawa, ON, Canada

Canadian Soc. of Mayflower Descendants [IO], Ottawa, ON, Canada

Canadian Soc. for Mech. Engg. [IO], Kingston, ON, Canada

Canadian Soc. for Medical Lab. Sci. [IO], Hamilton, ON, Canada

Canadian Soc. for Mesopotamian Stud. [IO], Toronto, ON, Canada

Canadian Soc. for Microbiologists [IO], Ottawa, ON, Canada

Canadian Soc. for Mucopolysaccharide and Related Diseases [IO], North Vancouver, BC, Canada

Canadian Soc. for Neoplatonic Stud. [IO], Quebec, QC, Canada

Canadian Soc. of Nuclear Medicine [IO], Ottawa, ON, Canada

Canadian Soc. for Nutritional Sciences [IO], Ste.-Anne-de-Bellevue, QC, Canada

Canadian Soc. of Occupational Scientists [IO], London, ON, Canada

Canadian Soc. of Orthopaedic Technologists [IO], North York, ON, Canada

Canadian Soc. of Otolaryngology - Head and Neck Surgery [IO], Elora, ON, Canada

Canadian Soc. of Painters in Water Colour [IO], Toronto, ON, Canada

Canadian Soc. of Petroleum Geologists [IO], Calgary, AB, Canada

Canadian Soc. of Plant Physiologists [IO], Regina, SK, Canada

Canadian Soc. of Plastic Surgeons [IO], Montreal, QC, Canada

Canadian Soc. for the Prevention of Cruelty to Children [IO], Midland, ON, Canada

Canadian Soc. of Professional Engineers [IO], Toronto, ON, Canada

Canadian Soc. of Professional Event Planners [IO], Newmarket, ON, Canada

Canadian Soc. of Questers [IO], Vancouver, BC, Canada

Canadian Soc. of Respiratory Therapists [IO], Ottawa, ON, Canada

Canadian Soc. of Safety Engg. [IO], Toronto, ON, Canada

Canadian Soc. of Soil Sci. [IO], Pinawa, MB, Canada

Canadian Soc. for the Stud. of Educ. [IO], Ottawa, ON, Canada

Canadian Soc. for the Stud. of Higher Educ. [IO], Ottawa, ON, Canada

Canadian Soc. for the Stud. of Religion [IO], Toronto, ON, Canada

Canadian Soc. of Teachers of the Alexander Technique [IO], London, ON, Canada

Canadian Soc. for Traditional Music [IO], Edmonton, AB, Canada

Canadian Soc. for Training and Development [IO], Toronto, ON, Canada

Canadian Soc. for Women in Philosophy [IO], Toronto, ON, Canada

Canadian Soc. of Zoologists [IO], Edmonton, AB, Canada

Canadian Sociology Assn. [IO], Montreal, QC, Canada

Canadian Space Soc. [IO], Toronto, ON, Canada

Canadian Special Crops Assn. [IO], Winnipeg, MB, Canada

Canadian Sphagnum Peat Moss Assn. [IO], St. Albert, AB, Canada

Canadian Spice Assn. [IO], Toronto, ON, Canada

Canadian Sport Horse Assn. [IO], Richmond, ON, Canada

Canadian Sport Massage Therapists Assn. [IO], Victoria, BC, Canada

Canadian Sport Parachuting Assn. [IO], Russell, ON, Canada

Canadian Sporting Goods Assn. [IO], Montreal, QC, Canada

Canadian Steel Door Mfrs. Assn. [IO], Toronto, ON, Canada

Canadian Steel Producers Assn. [IO], Ottawa, ON, Canada

Canadian Stud. of Parliament Gp. [IO], Ottawa, ON, Canada

Canadian Stuttering Assn. [IO], Sherwood Park, AB, Canada

Canadian Sugar Inst. [IO], Toronto, ON, Canada

Canadian Swine Breeder Assn. [IO], Ottawa, ON, Canada

Canadian Table Tennis Assn. [IO], Ottawa, ON, Canada

Canadian Tanzer 16 Assn. [★22396]

Canadian Tarentaise Assn. [IO], Shellbrook, SK, Canada

Canadian Tax Found. [IO], Toronto, ON, Canada

Canadian Taxicab Assn. [IO], Toronto, ON, Canada

Canadian Taxpayers' Fed. [IO], Ottawa, ON, Canada

Canadian Teachers' Fed. [IO], Ottawa, ON, Canada

Canadian Team Handball Fed. [IO], Sherbrooke, QC, Canada

Canadian Tech. Asphalt Assn. [IO], Victoria, BC, Canada

Canadian Telecommunications Consultants Assn. [IO], St. Davids, ON, Canada

Canadian Tenpin Fed. [IO], Lethbridge, AB, Canada

Canadian Testing Assn. [IO], Montreal, QC, Canada

Canadian Texel Assn. [IO], Denfield, ON, Canada

Canadian Textiles Inst. [IO], Ottawa, ON, Canada

Canadian Theatre Critics Assn. [IO], Toronto, ON, Canada

Reference to "IO" in place of a book number signifies that the association may be found in the 50th edition of International Organizations.

Canadian Therapeutic Riding Assn. [IO], Guelph, ON, Canada
Canadian Thoracic Soc. [IO], Ottawa, ON, Canada
Canadian Thoroughbred Horse Soc. [IO], Rexdale, ON, Canada
Canadian Tooling and Machining Assn. [IO], Cambridge, ON, Canada
Canadian Tourism Res. Inst. [IO], Ottawa, ON, Canada
Canadian Toy Assn. [IO], Concord, ON, Canada
Canadian Toy Collectors' Soc. [IO], Scarborough, ON, Canada
Canadian Toy Testing Coun. [IO], Ottawa, ON, Canada
Canadian Trakehner Horse Soc. [IO], New Hamburg, ON, Canada
Canadian Translators, Terminologists and Interpreters Coun. [IO], Ottawa, ON, Canada
Canadian Transplant Assn. [IO], Edmonton, AB, Canada
Canadian Trans. Equip. Assn. [IO], St. Thomas, ON, Canada
Canadian Trucking Alliance [IO], Ottawa, ON, Canada
Canadian Trucking Human Resources Coun. [IO], Ottawa, ON, Canada
Canadian Ukrainian Immigrant Aid Soc. [IO], Toronto, ON, Canada
Canadian Ultimate Players Assn. [IO], Winnipeg, MB, Canada
Canadian Union of Postal Workers [IO], Ottawa, ON, Canada
Canadian Union of Public Employees [IO], Ottawa, ON, Canada
Canadian Unitarian Coun. [IO], Toronto, ON, Canada
Canadian Univ. and Coll. Counselling Assn. [IO], Kingston, ON, Canada
Canadian Univ. Football Coaches Assn. [IO], Waterloo, ON, Canada
Canadian Univ. Music Soc. [IO], Toronto, ON, Canada
Canadian Univ. Press [IO], Toronto, ON, Canada
Canadian Urban Transit Assn. [IO], Toronto, ON, Canada
Canadian Urethane Foam Contractors Assn. [IO], Winnipeg, MB, Canada
Canadian Urethane Mfrs. Assn. [IO], Penetanguishene, ON, Canada
Canadian Urologic Oncology Gp. [IO], Montreal, QC, Canada
Canadian Urological Assn. [IO], Montreal, QC, Canada
Canadian Vascular Access Assn. [IO], Toronto, ON, Canada
Canadian Vehicle Mfrs. Assn. [IO], Toronto, ON, Canada
Canadian Veterinary Medical Assn. [IO], Ottawa, ON, Canada
Canadian Viola Soc. [IO], Brossard, QC, Canada
Canadian Vocational Assn. [IO], Longueuil, QC, Canada
Canadian Voice of Women for Peace [IO], Toronto, ON, Canada
Canadian Water Quality Assn. [IO], Toronto, ON, Canada
Canadian Water Resources Assn. [IO], Lethbridge, AB, Canada
Canadian Water and Wastewater Assn. [IO], Ottawa, ON, Canada
Canadian Welding Bur. [IO], Milton, ON, Canada
Canadian Well Logging Soc. [IO], Calgary, AB, Canada
Canadian Welsh Black Cattle Soc. [IO], Ottawa, ON, Canada
Canadian Western Agribition [IO], Regina, SK, Canada
Canadian Western Horse Assn. [IO], Dugald, MB, Canada
Canadian Wheat Bd. [IO], Winnipeg, MB, Canada
Canadian Wheelchair Sports Assn. [IO], Ottawa, ON, Canada
Canadian Wildlife Fed. [IO], Kanata, ON, Canada
Canadian Wind Energy Assn. [IO], Ottawa, ON, Canada

Canadian Window and Door Mfrs. Assn. [IO], Ottawa, ON, Canada
Canadian Wireless Telecommunications Assn. [IO], Ottawa, ON, Canada
Canadian Women in Communications [IO], Toronto, ON, Canada
Canadian Women's Found. [IO], Toronto, ON, Canada
Canadian Women's Hea. Network [IO], Winnipeg, MB, Canada
Canadian Women's Stud. Assn. [IO], Prince George, BC, Canada
Canadian Wood Coun. [IO], Ottawa, ON, Canada
Canadian Wood Preservers Bur. [IO], Ottawa, ON, Canada
Canadian Wooden Pallet and Container Assn. [IO], Ottawa, ON, Canada
Canadian Writers Found. [IO], Ottawa, ON, Canada
Canadian Yachting Assn. [IO], Kingston, ON, Canada
Canadiana.org [IO], Ottawa, ON, Canada
Canadians Against Violence - BC [IO], Langley, BC, Canada
Canadians Concerned About Violence in Entertainment [IO], Toronto, ON, Canada
Canadians for Ethical Treatment of Food Animals [IO], Vancouver, BC, Canada
Canadians for Hea. Res. [IO], Westmount, QC, Canada
Canadienne Croix-Rouge [★IO]
Canadiens pour la Recherche Medicale [★IO]
Canal Soc. of New York State [9467], 2527 Cherry Valley Tpke., Marcellus, NY 13108, (315)730-4495
Canals
    Amer. Canal Soc. [9466]
    Amer. Canal Soc. [9466]
    Canal Soc. of New York State [9467]
CANARIE [IO], Ottawa, ON, Canada
Canary and Finch Soc. [3843], Helen Jones, Treas., 348 Magnolia Dr., Huffman, TX 77336, (281)259-7951
Canberra Ornithologists Gp. [IO], Civic Square, Australia
Cancer
    4K for Cancer [13874]
    Action to Cure Kidney Cancer [13875]
    Adenoid Cystic Carcinoma Org. Intl. [13876]
    African Amer. Breast Cancer Alliance [13877]
    Alliance for Childhood Cancer [13878]
    Amer. Assn. of Breast Care Professionals [13858]
    Amer. Assn. for Cancer Educ. [13879]
    Amer. Brachytherapy Soc. [13880]
    Amer. Brain Tumor Assn. [13881]
    Amer. Cancer Soc. [13882]
    Amer. Childhood Cancer Org. [13883]
    Amer. Inst. for Cancer Res. [13884]
    Assn. of Amer. Cancer Institutes [13885]
    Assn. of Cancer Executives [13886]
    Assn. of Cancer Online Resources [13887]
    Assn. of Community Cancer Centers [13888]
    Assn. for Res. of Childhood Cancer [13889]
    Bladder Cancer Advocacy Network [13890]
    Boarding for Breast Cancer Found. [13891]
    Breast Cancer Action [13892]
    BrittiCares Intl. [13893]
    C-Change [13894]
    C3: Colorectal Cancer Coalition [13895]
    Canadian Breast Cancer Found. [10783]
    Cancer Care [13896]
    Cancer Control Soc. [13897]
    Cancer Fed. [13898]
    Cancer Hope Network [13899]
    Cancer Info. Ser. [13900]
    Cancer Leadership Coun. [13901]
    Cancer Prevention Coalition [13902]
    Cancer Prevention Coalition [13902]
    Cancer Support Community [13903]
    CancerClimber Assn. [13904]
    Carcinoid Cancer Found. [13905]
    Chemotherapy Found. [15922]
    Children's Cancer and Blood Found. [14964]
    Children's Cause for Cancer Advocacy [13906]
    Children's Leukemia Res. Assn. [13907]
    CLIC Sargent [1492]
    Coalition of Cancer Cooperative Groups [13908]

    Comedy Fights Cancer [13909]
    Community Oncology Alliance [15923]
    Concern Found. [13910]
    Corporate Angel Network [13911]
    Cure Alveolar Soft Part Sarcoma Intl. [13912]
    Cure Kids Cancer Coalition [13913]
    Cure Res. Found. [13914]
    CureSearch for Children's Cancer [13915]
    Damon Runyon Cancer Res. Found. [13916]
    Dana-Farber Cancer Inst. [13917]
    Dana-Farber Cancer Inst. [13917]
    DES Action USA [13918]
    Educ. Network to Advance Cancer Clinical Trials [13919]
    Esophageal Cancer Awareness Assn. [13920]
    Facing Our Risk of Cancer Empowered [13921]
    Flashes of Hope [11135]
    Found. for Advancement in Cancer Therapy [13922]
    Friends-4-Cures [13923]CancerFriends of the Jose Carreras Intl. Leukemia Found.
    Gilda Radner Familial Ovarian Cancer Registry [13924]
    Gilda Radner Familial Ovarian Cancer Registry [13924]
    Gilda's Club [13925]
    Golf Fights Cancer [13926]
    Golf Fights Cancer [13926]
    Grind for Life [11136]
    Grounds for Hea. [13927]
    Haitian Amer. Assn. Against Cancer [13928]
    Hematology/Oncology Pharmacy Assn. [16194]
    Hong Kong Anti-Cancer Soc. [4467]
    Hope for Two. The Pregnant With Cancer Network [13929]
    Intercultural Cancer Coun. [13930]
    Intercultural Cancer Coun. [13930]
    Intl. Assn. for the Stud. of Lung Cancer [13931]
    Intl. Myeloma Found. [13932]
    Intl. Myeloma Found. [13932]
    Intl. Partnership for Reproductive Hea. [16587]
    Intl. Psycho-Oncology Soc. [13933]
    Intl. Psycho-Oncology Soc. [13933]
    Intl. Skeletal Soc. [16533]
    Intl. Soc. for Biological Therapy of Cancer [13982]
    Intl. Soc. for Children with Cancer [13934]
    Intl. Soc. of Gastrointestinal Oncology [14568]
    Kidney Cancer Assn. [13935]
    KIDSCOPE [11137]
    Leukemia and Lymphoma Soc. [13936]
    Life Raft Gp. [13937]
    Lung Cancer Alliance [13938]
    Lymphoma Res. Found. [13939]
    Lynch Syndrome Intl. [14609]
    Marie Curie Cancer Care [2557]
    Melanoma Awareness [13940]
    Melanoma Res. Found. [13941]
    Men Against Breast Cancer [13942]
    Mothers Supporting Daughters with Breast Cancer [13943]
    Multinational Assn. of Supportive Care in Cancer [13944]
    Multiple Myeloma Res. Found. [13945]
    Natl. Black Leadership Initiative on Cancer [13946]
    Natl. Breast Cancer Coalition [13947]
    Natl. Breast and Ovarian Cancer Connection [13948]
    Natl. Cancer Registrars Assn. [15929]
    Natl. Cervical Cancer Coalition [13949]
    Natl. Children's Cancer Soc. [13950]
    Natl. Coalition for Cancer Survivorship [13951]
    Natl. Coalition of Oncology Nurse Navigators [15778]
    Natl. Coalition for Quality Colorectal Cancer Screening and Care [13952]
    Natl. Comprehensive Cancer Network [13953]
    Natl. Coun. on Skin Cancer Prevention [13954]
    Natl. Lung Cancer Partnership [13955]
    Natl. Melanoma Alliance [13956]
    Natl. Ovarian Cancer Coalition [13957]
    Native Amer. Cancer Res. [13958]
    Neuroblastoma Children's Cancer Soc. [13959]
    North Amer. Assn. of Central Cancer Registries [13960]

A star before a book entry number signifies that the name is not listed separately, but is mentioned within the entry.

North Amer. Assn. of Central Cancer Registries [13960]
North Amer. Brain Tumor Coalition [13961]
Oncology Assn. of Naturopathic Physicians [15539]
Ovarian Cancer Natl. Alliance [13962]
Ovations for the Cure [13963]
Pancreatic Cancer Action Network [13964]
Patient Advocates for Advanced Cancer Treatments [13965]
Patients Against Lymphoma [15257]
Pediatric Brain Tumor Found. of the U.S. [13966]
People Against Cancer [13967]
Pink Door Nonprofit Org. [13968]
Pink Isn't Always Pretty [13969]
Prevent Cancer Found. [13970]
Prostate Hea. Educ. Network [13971]
R.A. Bloch Cancer Found. [13972]
Reach to Recovery [13973]
Reel Recovery [11138]
Retinoblastoma Intl. [13974]
Retinoblastoma Intl. [13974]
Rock Against Cancer [13975]
Rose Kushner Breast Cancer Advisory Center [13976]
Sarcoma Alliance [13977]
Sharsheret [13978]
Shine Therapy [15274]
Show Me A Cure [13979]
Sino-American Network for Therapeutic Radiology and Oncology [16871]
Sisters Network [13980]
Skin Cancer Found. [13981]
Soc. for Immunotherapy and Cancer [13982]
Soc. for Melanoma Res. [13983]
Soc. for Melanoma Res. [13983]
Soc. for Translational Oncology [15935]
Sun Safety Alliance [13984]
Support Connection [13985]
Support for People with Oral and Head and Neck Cancer [13986]
Susan G. Komen for the Cure [13987]
Tamika and Friends [13988]
Unite for HER [13989]
Us TOO Intl. [13990]
Us TOO Intl. [13990]
William H. Donner Found. [13991]
Women Against Prostate Cancer [13992]
Women's Cancer Network [13993]
Yoga Bear [13721]
Young Survival Coalition [13994]
Young Survival Coalition [13994]
ZERO - The Proj. to End Prostate Cancer [13995]
Cancer; Amer. Joint Comm. on [15914]
Cancer Assn. of South Africa [IO], Gauteng, Republic of South Africa
Cancer Care [13896], 275 7th Ave., New York, NY 10001-6708, (212)712-8400
Cancer Care Ontario [IO], Toronto, ON, Canada
Cancer Center; Natl. [15928]
Cancer Connection [★13972]
Cancer Control Soc. [13897], 2043 N Berendo St., Los Angeles, CA 90027, (323)663-7801
Cancer Coordinators [★13879]
Cancer Coun. Australia [IO], Sydney, Australia
Cancer Coun. Australian Capital Territory [IO], Fairbairn, Australia
Cancer Coun. Tasmania [IO], Hobart, Australia
Cancer Coun. Western Australia [IO], Perth, Australia
Cancer Cytology Found. of Am. [★15928]
Cancer Fed. [13898], PO Box 1298, Banning, CA 92220-0009, (951)849-4325
Cancer Hope Network [13899], 2 North Rd., Ste. A, Chester, NJ 07930, (908)879-4039
Cancer Info. Ser. [13900], Natl. Cancer Inst., 6116 Executive Blvd., Rm. 3036 A, Bethesda, MD 20892-8322, (800)422-6237
Cancer Leadership Coun. [13901], 2446 39th St. NW, Washington, DC 20007, (202)333-4041
Cancer Prevention Coalition [13902], Univ. of Illinois at Chicago, School of Public Hea., MC 922, 2121 W Taylor St., Chicago, IL 60612, (312)996-2297
Cancer Prevention Coalition [13902], Univ. of Illinois at Chicago, School of Public Hea., MC 922, 2121 W Taylor St., Chicago, IL 60612, (312)996-2297

Cancer Quality Alliance - Address unknown since 2011.
Cancer Registrars Assn; Natl. [15929]
Cancer Registry of Norway [IO], Oslo, Norway
Cancer Res. and Prevention Found. [★13970]
Cancer Res. Soc. [IO], Montreal, QC, Canada
Cancer Soc. of Finland [IO], Helsinki, Finland
Cancer Soc. of New Zealand [IO], Wellington, New Zealand
Cancer Soc; Veterinary [17047]
Cancer Support Community [13903], 1050 17th St. NW, Ste. 500, Washington, DC 20036-5558, (202)659-9709
CancerClimber Assn. [13904], PO Box 3051, Breckenridge, CO 80424
Candle Mfrs. Assn. [★2067]
Candlelighters Childhood Cancer Found. [★13883]
Candlelighters Found. [★13883]
CANDU Owners Gp. [IO], Toronto, ON, Canada
Candy Container Collectors of Am. [21317], 115 MacBeth Dr., Lower Burrell, PA 15068-2628
Canegrowers [IO], Brisbane, Australia
Canfield Family Assn. - Defunct.
Canhelp, Tajikistan [IO], Khujand, Tajikistan
Canine Assistants [11765], 3160 Francis Rd., Milton, GA 30004, (770)664-7178
Canine Assn. of Western Australia [IO], Southern River, Australia
Canine Cancer Awareness [17020], 44 Devoe St., Brooklyn, NY 11211
Canine Companions for Independence [11766], PO Box 446, Santa Rosa, CA 95402-0446, (707)577-1700
Canine Defense Fund [10936], Amer. Dog Owners Assn., PO Box 41194, Fredericksburg, VA 22404, (888)714-7220
Canine Freestyle Fed. [22545], Carl Tennille, Treas., 14430 Overlook Ridge Ln., Beaverdam, VA 23015-1787
Canines for Disabled Kids [11767], 299 Redemption Rock Trail S, Princeton, MA 01541, (978)422-5299
Cannabis Consumers; Friends and Families of [18085]
Canoe Kayak Canada [IO], Ottawa, ON, Canada
Canoe Kayak Nova Scotia [IO], Halifax, NS, Canada
Canoeing
    Amer. Canoe Assn. [23120]
    Camping Women [22441]
    Qajaq U.S.A. [23124]
    Trade Assn. of Paddlesports [3320]
    Wooden Canoe Heritage Assn. [22414]
Canoes of the Marshall Islands [IO], Majuro, Marshall Islands
Canola Assn. of Australia [IO], Sydney, Australia
Canola Coun. of Canada [IO], Winnipeg, MB, Canada
Canolfan Gymreig Materion Rhyngwladol [★IO]
Canon Collins Educational Trust for Southern Africa [IO], Cape Town, Republic of South Africa
Canon Law Soc. of Am. [19396], The Hecker Center, Ste. 111, 3025 Fourth St. NE, Washington, DC 20017-1102, (202)832-2350
Canon Law Soc. of the Orthodox Catholic Church
Canon Law Soc. of the Orthodox Catholic Church - Address unknown since 2011.
Canseil Canadien des distributeurs en Alimentation [★IO]
Canterbury Historical Assn. [IO], Christchurch, New Zealand
Cantonese Language Assn. - Address unknown since 2010.
Cantors Assembly [19852], 464 S Hawkins Ave., Akron, OH 44320, (330)864-8533
Cantors Assembly [19852], 464 S Hawkins Ave., Akron, OH 44320, (330)864-8533
Canvas Products Intl. [★3444]
Canvas Products Intl. [★3444]
Canyonlands Field Inst. [4197], PO Box 68, Moab, UT 84532, (435)259-7750
Capacity Building Initiative [IO], Yangon, Myanmar
Cape Lancia Club [IO], Cape Town, Republic of South Africa
Cape Town Regional Chamber of Commerce and Indus. [IO], Cape Town, Republic of South Africa
Capital PC User Gp. [6507], 19209 Mt. Airey Rd., Brookeville, MD 20833, (301)560-6442

Capital PC User Gp. [6507], 19209 Mt. Airey Rd., Brookeville, MD 20833, (301)560-6442
Capital Press Club - Address unknown since 2010.
Capital Punishment
    Campaign to End the Death Penalty [17215]
    Capital Punishment Proj. [17216]
    Death Penalty Info. Center [17217]
    Lamp of Hope Proj. [17218]
    Murder Victims' Families for Reconciliation [17219]
    Natl. Coalition to Abolish the Death Penalty [17220]
    People of Faith Against the Death Penalty [17221]
    Proj. Hope to Abolish the Death Penalty [17222]
    Southern Center for Human Rights [17223]
Capital Punishment Proj. [17216], 125 Broad St., 18th Fl., New York, NY 10004, (212)549-2500
Capital Quarter Horse Registry [★4619]
Capitol Hill Club [★18533]
Capitol Hill Restoration Soc. [9673], PO Box 15264, Washington, DC 20003-0264, (202)543-0425
Capri Club North Am. [21019], PO Box 701, Johnstown, OH 43031
Captain Cook Soc. [IO], Thornhill, United Kingdom
Caption Center [★12418]
Captive Daughters [18409], PO Box 34682, Los Angeles, CA 90034-0682, (888)373-7888
Captive Insurance Companies Assn. [1945], 4248 Park Glen Rd., Minneapolis, MN 55416, (952)928-4655
Captive Nations Comm. [17185], PO Box 540, Gracie Sta., New York, NY 10028-0005
Captive Nations Comm. New York [★17185]
Capuchin-Franciscans [19397], 3407 S Archer Ave., Chicago, IL 60608, (773)475-6206
CAPUTO [★1407]
Car Care Coun. [295], 7101 Wisconsin Ave., Ste. 1300, Bethesda, MD 20814, (240)333-1088
Car Collectors Assn; Toy [22171]
Car Rental Assn. of Namibia [IO], Windhoek, Namibia
Car Rental Coun. of Ireland [IO], Dublin, Ireland
Caracas ACM SIGGRAPH [IO], Caracas, Venezuela
Caravan Farm Theatre [IO], Armstrong, BC, Canada
Carbon Mgt. Coun. - Address unknown since 2011.
Carbonated Beverage Container Mfrs. Assn. [★873]
CarCanMadCarLan Assn. U.S.A. - Address unknown since 2011.
Carcinoid Cancer Found. [13905], 333 Mamaroneck Ave., No. 492, White Plains, NY 10605, (914)683-1001
Carded Yarn Assn. [★3436]
Cardiac Arrhythmias Res. and Educ. Found. [14009], PO Box 69, Seymour, WI 54165, (920)833-7000
Cardiac Soc. of Australia and New Zealand [IO], Sydney, Australia
Cardiac Soc. of Nepal [IO], Kathmandu, Nepal
Cardigan Welsh Corgi Club of Am. [21535], Rte. 940, Ste. A, Mount Pocono, PA 18344, (570)350-2299
Cardinal Club - Address unknown since 2011.
Cardinal Mindszenty Found. [17186], PO Box 11321, St. Louis, MO 63105, (314)727-6279
Cardiology
    Adult Congenital Heart Assn. [13996]
    Albanian Soc. of Cardiology [16246]
    Alliance of Cardiovascular Professionals [13997]
    Amer. Assn. of Cardiovascular and Pulmonary Rehabilitation [13998]
    Amer. Bd. of Cardiovascular Perfusion [13999]
    Amer. Coll. of Cardiology [14000]
    Amer. Coll. of Chest Physicians [14001]
    Amer. Coll. of Chest Physicians [14001]
    Amer. Heart Assn. [14002]
    Amer. Soc. of Echocardiography [14003]
    Amer. Soc. of Nuclear Cardiology [14004]
    Assn. of Black Cardiologists [14005]
    Assn. of Cardiologists of Bosnia and Herzegovina [18424]
    Assn. of Physician Assistants in Cardiology [14006]
    Assn. of Physician Assistants in Cardiovascular Surgery [14007]
    Assn. of Professors of Cardiology [14008]

Reference to "IO" in place of a book number signifies that the association may be found in the 50th edition of International Organizations.

Encyclopedia of Associations, 51st Edition												2659

Austrian Soc. of Cardiology [12293]
Brain Attack Coalition [16729]
British Lung Found. [9740]
Cardiac Arrhythmias Res. and Educ. Found.
    [14009]
Cardiovascular Credentialing Intl. [14010]
Cardiovascular Credentialing Intl. [14010]
Cardiovascular and Interventional Radiological
    Soc. of Europe [20605]
Children's HeartLink [14011]
Congenital Heart Info. Network [14012]
Congenital Heart Info. Network [14012]
Cyprus Soc. of Cardiology [6266]
Czech Soc. of Cardiology [7313]
Danish Soc. of Cardiology [16427]
Donald W. Reynolds Found. [14013]
Georgian Soc. of Cardiology [12140]
German Cardiac Soc. [12758]
Heart Care Intl. [14014]
Heart Care Intl. [14014]
Heart Failure Soc. of Am. [14015]
Heart Rhythm Soc. [14016]
Heart Rhythm Soc. [14016]
Heart Valve Soc. of Am. [14017]
Hellenic Cardiological Soc. [18639]
Hypertrophic Cardiomyopathy Assn. [14018]
Hypertrophic Cardiomyopathy Assn.
    [14018]CardiologyIndo-American Soc. of Inter-
    ventional Cardiology
InterAmerican Heart Found. [14019]
Intl. Atherosclerosis Soc. [14020]
Intl. Palestinian Cardiac Relief Org. [14021]
Intl. Palestinian Cardiac Relief Org. [14021]
Intl. Partnership for Critical Markers of Disease
    [14022]
Intl. Soc. for Adult Congenital Heart Disease
    [14023]
Intl. Soc. for Adult Congenital Heart Disease
    [14023]
Intl. Soc. for Cardiovascular Translational Res.
    [14024]
Intl. Soc. for Cardiovascular Translational Res.
    [14024]
Intl. Soc. of Cardiovascular Ultrasound [14440]
Intl. Soc. for Computerized Electrocardiology
    [14025]
Intl. Soc. for Computerized Electrocardiology
    [14025]
Intl. Soc. for Minimally Invasive Cardiothoracic
    Surgery [14026]
Intl. Soc. for Minimally Invasive Cardiothoracic
    Surgery [14026]
Intl. Soc. of Rotary Blood Pumps [14027]
Irish Cardiac Soc. [18689]
Israel Heart Soc. [18426]
It's My Heart [14028]
Kids With Heart Natl. Assn. for Children's Heart
    Disorders [14029]
Latvian Soc. of Cardiology [23893]
Lithuanian Soc. of Cardiology [5492]
Mended Hearts, Inc. [14030]
Michael E. DeBakey Intl. Surgical Soc. [14031]
Michael E. DeBakey Intl. Surgical Soc. [14031]
Moldavian Soc. of Cardiology [14835]
Natl. Alliance for Thrombosis and Thrombophilia
    [14032]
Natl. Emphysema Found. [14033]
Natl. Heart Coun. [14034]
Natl. Heart Savers Assn. [14035]
North Amer. Soc. for Cardiovascular Imaging
    [14036]
North Amer. Soc. for Cardiovascular Imaging
    [14036]
Perfusion Prog. Directors' Coun. [14037]
Peripheral Arterial Disease Coalition [14038]
Peruvian Heart Assn. [14039]
Peruvian Heart Assn. [14039]
Polish Cardiac Soc. [8761]CardiologyPortuguese
    Soc. of Cardiology
Preemptive Love Coalition [14040]
Proj. Kids Worldwide [14095]
Saving Little Hearts [14041]
Slovenian Soc. of Cardiology [6281]
Soc. for Cardiovascular Angiography and
    Interventions [14042]

Soc. for Cardiovascular Pathology [14043]
Soc. for Cardiovascular Pathology [14043]
Soc. for Clinical Vascular Surgery [14044]
Soc. for Heart Attack Prevention and Eradication
    [14045]
Soc. for Heart Brain Medicine [14046]
Soc. of Invasive Cardiovascular Professionals
    [14047]
Spanish Soc. of Cardiology [6280]
Sudden Cardiac Arrest Assn. [14048]
Swedish Soc. of Cardiology [19718]
Swiss Soc. of Cardiology [10376]
Ukrainian Soc. of Cardiology [19089]
WomenHeart: Natl. Coalition for Women with
    Heart Disease [14049]
Cardiomyopathy Assn. of Australia [IO], Melbourne,
    Australia
Cardiomyopathy Assn; Hypertrophic [14018]
Cardiomyopathy Assn; Hypertrophic [14018]
Cardiovascular Administrators; Amer. Coll. of [15282]
Cardiovascular Credentialing Intl. [14010], 1500
    Sunday Dr., Ste. 102, Raleigh, NC 27607,
    (919)861-4539
Cardiovascular Credentialing Intl. [14010], 1500
    Sunday Dr., Ste. 102, Raleigh, NC 27607,
    (919)861-4539
Cardiovascular Credentialing International/Board of
    Cardiovascular Tech. [★14010]
Cardiovascular Credentialing International/Board of
    Cardiovascular Tech. [★14010]
Cardiovascular Disease
    Heart Rhythm Soc. [14016]
    Intl. Pediatric Hypertension Assn. [15076]
    Intl. Soc. for Cardiovascular Translational Res.
        [14024]
Cardiovascular and Interventional Radiological Soc.
    of Europe [IO], Vienna, Austria
Cardiovascular Nurses Assn; Preventive [15797]
Care 2 Share [13373], PO Box 911, West Chester,
    OH 45069, (513)860-3076
Care of Afghan Families [IO], Kabul, Afghanistan
CARE Austria [IO], Vienna, Austria
CARE Canada [IO], Ottawa, ON, Canada
CARE Canada - Defunct.
Care for Children Intl. [11207], Neuropsychological
    and Family Therapy Associates, 13310 Compton
    Rd., Clifton, VA 20124, (703)830-6052
Care for Children Intl. [11207], Neuropsychological
    and Family Therapy Associates, 13310 Compton
    Rd., Clifton, VA 20124, (703)830-6052
CARE Danmark [IO], Copenhagen, Denmark
CARE Deutschland (Germany) [★6057]
CARE Deutschland-Luxemburg [IO], Bonn, Germany
CARE Egypt [IO], Cairo, Egypt
Care Forum Wales [IO], Wrexham, United Kingdom
Care Found. [★14009]
CARE France [IO], Paris, France
CARE Guatemala [IO], Guatemala City, Guatemala
Care Highway Intl. [12814], Mickey Meneses, Sec.,
    4569 Edgewood Pl., Riverside, CA 92506
Care Highway Intl. [12814], Mickey Meneses, Sec.,
    4569 Edgewood Pl., Riverside, CA 92506
CARE Honduras [IO], Tegucigalpa, Honduras
CARE India [IO], New Delhi, India
CARE Intl. Belgium [IO], Brussels, Belgium
CARE Intl. Japan [IO], Tokyo, Japan
CARE Intl. UK [IO], London, United Kingdom
CARE Intl. USA [12815], 151 Ellis St. NE, Atlanta,
    GA 30303-2440, (404)681-2552
CARE Intl. USA [12815], 151 Ellis St. NE, Atlanta,
    GA 30303-2440, (404)681-2552
Care for Life [★11823]
Care for Life [★11823]
Care Ministries [20280], PO Box 1830, Starkville,
    MS 39760-1830, (662)323-4999
CARE Nederland [★IO]
CARE Nepal [IO], Kathmandu, Nepal
Care Net [17435], 44180 Riverside Pkwy., Ste. 200,
    Lansdowne, VA 20176, (703)554-8734
CARE Netherlands [IO], The Hague, Netherlands
CARE Norge Norway [IO], Oslo, Norway
CARE Osterreich [★IO]
CARE Peru [IO], Lima, Peru
CARE Philippines [IO], Quezon City, Philippines
Care Through Educ. Intl. [11453], 13810 Sutton Park
    Dr. N, No. 137, Jacksonville, FL 32224, (904)992-
    0977

Care USA [17447], PO Box 7039, Merrifield, VA
    22116, (404)681-2552
Care for the Wild Deutschland [★IO]
Care for the Wild Germany [IO], Stuttgart, Germany
Care for the Wild Intl. [IO], Horsham, United
    Kingdom
Care for the Wild Kenya [IO], Nairobi, Kenya
Care4Dystonia [15576], 440 E 78th St., New York,
    NY 10075
Career Apparel Inst. - Defunct.
Career Coll. Assn. [★9041]
Career Counseling
    Beauty 4 Ashes Intl. [13452]
    Career Mgt. Alliance [726]
    Intl. Mentoring Network Org. [11139]
    Intl. Mentoring Network Org. [11139]
    Natl. Org. for Career Credentialing [727]
    Way to Work [11962]
Career Development Assn. of Alberta [IO], Edmon-
    ton, AB, Canada
Career Development Assn. of Australia [IO], Dul-
    wich, Australia
Career Education
    Canadian Assn. of Career Educators and Employ-
        ers [21355]
    Inst. for Women in Trades, Tech. and Sci. [3684]
    Natl. Org. for Career Credentialing [727]
    Soc. for Financial Educ. and Professional
        Development [7811]
Career Gear [12645], 120 Broadway, 36th Fl., New
    York, NY 10271, (212)577-6190
Career Mgt. Alliance [726], 1 Phoenix Mill Ln., 3rd
    Fl., Peterborough, NH 03458, (603)924-0900
Career Planning and Adult Development Network
    [11932], 543 Vista Mar Ave., Pacifica, CA 94044,
    (650)773-0982
Career Transition For Dancers [11933], The Caroline
    and Theodore Newhouse Centre for Dancers, The
    Actors' Equity Bldg., 165 W 46th St., Ste. 701,
    New York, NY 10036, (212)764-0172
Career Women's Forum [IO], Geneva, Switzerland
Careers Res. and Advisory Centre [IO], Cambridge,
    United Kingdom
Carers Assn. [IO], Tullamore, Ireland
Carers Assn. of South Australia [IO], Goodwood,
    Australia
Carers Australia [IO], Deakin, Australia
Carers Australian Capital Territory [IO], Canberra,
    Australia
Carers New South Wales [IO], Sydney, Australia
Carers Northern Ireland [IO], Belfast, United
    Kingdom
Carers Queensland [IO], Holland Park, Australia
Carers Queensland - Brisbane South [IO], Camp
    Hill, Australia
Carers Queensland - Brisbane West [IO], Holland
    Park, Australia
Carers Queensland - Darling Downs/South West
    Queensland [IO], Toowoomba, Australia
Carers Queensland - Far North Queensland [IO],
    Cairns, Australia
Carers Queensland - Mackay [IO], Mackay, Australia
Carers Queensland - Sunshine Coast [IO], Ma-
    roochydore, Australia
Carers Queensland - Toowoomba/Ipswich [IO], Too-
    woomba, Australia
Carers Queensland - Wide Bay [IO], Hervey Bay,
    Australia
Carers Tasmania [IO], Hobart, Australia
Carers UK [IO], London, United Kingdom
Carers Victoria [IO], Melbourne, Australia
Carers Western Australia [IO], Perth, Australia
Caretakers of the Env. Intl. [IO], Bergen,
    Netherlands
Caretakers of the Env. Intl. - Cameroon [IO],
    Yaounde, Cameroon
Caretakers of the Env. Intl. - Canada Nova Scotia
    [IO], Halifax, NS, Canada
Caretakers of the Env. Intl. - Portugal [IO], Lisbon,
    Portugal
Caretakers of the Env. Intl. - Scotland [IO], Aber-
    deen, United Kingdom
CARF, Commn. on Accreditation of Rehabilitation
    Facilities [★16562]
CarFree City, USA [4961], PO Box 2841, Berkeley,
    CA 94702-0841, (510)849-4412

A star before a book entry number signifies that the name is not listed separately, but is mentioned within the entry.

Cargo Airline Assn. **[132]**, 1620 L St. NW, Ste. 610, Washington, DC 20036, (202)293-1030
Cargo Reinsurance Assn. - Defunct.
Caribbean
  Assn. of Haitian Professionals **[19021]**
  Basic Hea. Intl. **[17122]**
  Caribbean Amer. Medical and Sci. Assn. **[14873]**
  Caribbean Culture Center African Diaspora Inst. **[9468]**
  Caribbean Hea. Outreach **[15149]**
  Caribbean Stud. Assn. **[7812]**
  Caribbean Stud. Assn. **[7812]**
  Caribbean Tourism Org., Amer. Br. **[23342]**
  Grenada Bd. of Tourism **[23343]**
  Intl. Assn. of Caribbean Organizations **[11140]**
  Natl. Assn. of The Bahamas **[11141]**
  Promised Land Intl. **[19376]**
  Saint Kitts Tourism Authority **[23344]**
  Saint Lucia Tourist Bd. **[23345]**
  United Confed. of Taino People **[18945]**
Caribbean and African Chamber of Commerce of Ontario **[IO]**, Toronto, ON, Canada
Caribbean Amer. Chamber of Commerce and Indus. **[23356]**, 63 Flushing Ave., Brooklyn Navy Yard, Bldg. No. 5, Unit 239, Brooklyn, NY 11205, (718)834-4544
Caribbean Amer. Chamber of Commerce and Indus. **[23356]**, 63 Flushing Ave., Brooklyn Navy Yard, Bldg. No. 5, Unit 239, Brooklyn, NY 11205, (718)834-4544
Caribbean Amer. Medical and Sci. Assn. **[14873]**, 6144 Rte. 25A, Ste. 6, Wading River, NY 11792, (631)929-5961
Caribbean Amer. Netball Assn. **[22787]**, PO Box 250-057, Lefferts Sta., Brooklyn, NY 11225, (347)221-0050
Caribbean Assn. for Feminist Res. and Action **[IO]**, Tunapuna, Trinidad and Tobago
Caribbean Assn. of Home Economists **[IO]**, St. Michael, Barbados
Caribbean Assn. of Indus. and Commerce **[IO]**, Maraval, Trinidad and Tobago
Caribbean Assn. of Natl. Telecommunication Organizations **[IO]**, Port of Spain, Trinidad and Tobago
Caribbean Assn. of Sports Medicine **[IO]**, St. Thomas, Barbados
Caribbean Assn. for Tech. and Vocational Educ. and Training **[★1456]**
Caribbean Assn. of Theological Schools **[IO]**, St. John, Barbados
Caribbean Banana Exporters Assn. **[IO]**, London, United Kingdom
Caribbean and Central Am. Tennis Confed. **[IO]**, La Libertad, El Salvador
Caribbean-Central Amer. Action **[12317]**, 1710 Rhode Island Ave., NW, Ste. 300, Washington, DC 20036, (202)331-9467
Caribbean/Central Amer. Action **[★12317]**
Caribbean-Central Amer. Action **[12317]**, 1710 Rhode Island Ave., NW, Ste. 300, Washington, DC 20036, (202)331-9467
Caribbean/Central Amer. Action **[★12317]**
Caribbean Community **[IO]**, Georgetown, Guyana
Caribbean Conf. of Churches **[IO]**, Port of Spain, Trinidad and Tobago
Caribbean Conservation Assn. **[IO]**, St. Michael, Barbados
Caribbean Conservation Corp. **[★5127]**
Caribbean Conservation Corp. **[★5127]**
Caribbean Cultural Comm. **[IO]**, Toronto, ON, Canada
Caribbean Culture Center African Diaspora Inst. **[9468]**, 408 W 58th St., New York, NY 10019, (212)307-7420
Caribbean Desalination Assn. **[IO]**, Curacao, Netherlands Antilles
Caribbean Development Bank **[IO]**, St. Michael, Barbados
Caribbean Diaspora Assn. - Address unknown since 2011.
Caribbean Elec. Utility Ser. Corp. **[IO]**, Gros Islet, St. Lucia
Caribbean Engg. and Tech. Professionals **[IO]**, Carapichaima, Trinidad and Tobago

Caribbean Environmental Hea. Inst. **[IO]**, Castries, St. Lucia
Caribbean Examinations Coun. **[IO]**, St. Michael, Barbados
Caribbean Export Development Agency **[IO]**, St. Michael, Barbados
Caribbean Hea. Outreach **[15149]**, 4300 W 58th Pl., Los Angeles, CA 90043, (626)274-3282
Caribbean Hotel Assn. **[★3555]**
Caribbean Hotel Assn. **[★3555]**
Caribbean Hotel Coun. of the Caribbean Travel Assn. **[★3555]**
Caribbean Hotel Coun. of the Caribbean Travel Assn. **[★3555]**
Caribbean Hotel and Tourism Assn. **[3555]**, 2655 Le Jeune Rd., Ste. 910, Coral Gables, FL 33134, (305)443-3040
Caribbean Hotel and Tourism Assn. **[3555]**, 2655 Le Jeune Rd., Ste. 910, Coral Gables, FL 33134, (305)443-3040
Caribbean Inst. for Meteorology and Hydrology **[IO]**, Bridgetown, Barbados
Caribbean/Latin Amer. Action **[★12317]**
Caribbean/Latin Amer. Action **[★12317]**
Caribbean Meteorological Org. **[IO]**, Port of Spain, Trinidad and Tobago
Caribbean Natural Resources Inst. **[IO]**, Laventille, Trinidad and Tobago
Caribbean Policy Development Centre **[IO]**, Bridgetown, Barbados
Caribbean Public Hea. Coalition **[16482]**, 15515 Symondsbury Way, Upper Marlboro, MD 20774, (240)602-0103
Caribbean Soc. of Hotel Assn. Executives - Address unknown since 2010.
Caribbean Solidarity Assn. **[★18159]**
Caribbean Solidarity Assn. **[★18159]**
Caribbean Stud. Assn. **[7812]**, York Coll. (CUNY), Off. of Academic Affairs, 94-20 Guy R. Brewer Blvd., Jamaica, NY 11451, (718)262-5338
Caribbean Stud. Assn. **[7812]**, York Coll. (CUNY), Off. of Academic Affairs, 94-20 Guy R. Brewer Blvd., Jamaica, NY 11451, (718)262-5338
Caribbean Stud; Inst. of **[12337]**
Caribbean Stud; Inst. of **[12337]**
Caribbean Tourism Assn. **[★23342]**
Caribbean Tourism Organization **[★23342]**
Caribbean Tourism Org. **[IO]**, St. Michael, Barbados
Caribbean Tourism Org., Amer. Br. **[23342]**, 80 Broad St., Ste. 3200, New York, NY 10004, (212)635-9530
Caribbean Tourism Res. and Development Center **[★23342]**
Caribbean Tourist Assn. **[★23342]**
Caribbean Water and Sewerage Assn. **[IO]**, Gros Islet, St. Lucia
Caribou Carnival Assn. **[IO]**, Yellowknife, NT, Canada
Caricature Carvers of Am. **[21433]**, Donald K. Mertz, Sec., 729 Prairie Rd., Wilmington, OH 45177-9683, (316)788-0175
Caring Ambassadors Hepatitis C Prog. **[14981]**, PO Box 1748, Oregon City, OR 97045, (503)632-9032
Caring for Cambodia **[7827]**, 4815 W Braker Ln., Ste. 502, Austin, TX 78759
Caring Hand for Children **[11440]**, 20315 Nordhoff St., Chatsworth, CA 91311, (818)727-9740
Caring Voice Coalition **[12660]**, 8249 Meadowbridge Rd., Mechanicsville, VA 23116, (804)427-6468
Caritas Andorrana **[IO]**, Andorra la Vella, Andorra
Caritas de Angola **[IO]**, Luanda, Angola
Caritas Aotearoa New Zealand **[IO]**, Wellington, New Zealand
Caritas Argentina **[IO]**, Buenos Aires, Argentina
Caritas Australia **[IO]**, Alexandria, Australia
Caritas Bangladesh **[IO]**, Dhaka, Bangladesh
Caritas Belarus **[IO]**, Minsk, Belarus
Caritas Benin **[IO]**, Cotonou, Benin
Caritas Bolivia **[IO]**, Cochabamba, Bolivia
Caritas Bulgaria **[IO]**, Sofia, Bulgaria
Caritas Caboverdeana **[IO]**, Santiago, Cape Verde
Caritas Cambodia **[IO]**, Phnom Penh, Cambodia
Caritas Catholica Belgica **[IO]**, Brussels, Belgium
Caritas Centrafrique **[IO]**, Bangui, Central African Republic

Caritas Colombia **[IO]**, Bogota, Colombia
Caritas Comoros **[IO]**, Moroni, Comoros
Caritas Coreana **[IO]**, Seoul, Republic of Korea
Caritas Cote d'Ivoire **[IO]**, Abidjan, Cote d'Ivoire
Caritas Cuba **[IO]**, Havana, Cuba
Caritas Denmark **[IO]**, Copenhagen, Denmark
Caritas Djibouti **[IO]**, Djibouti, Djibouti
Caritas Dominicana **[IO]**, Santo Domingo, Dominican Republic
Caritas Ecuador **[IO]**, Quito, Ecuador
Caritas Egypte **[IO]**, Cairo, Egypt
Caritas El Salvador **[IO]**, San Salvador, El Salvador
Caritas Eritrea **[IO]**, Asmara, Eritrea
Caritas Ethiopia **[IO]**, Addis Ababa, Ethiopia
Caritas Gabon **[IO]**, Libreville, Gabon
Caritas Gambia **[IO]**, Serrekunda, Gambia
Caritas Georgia **[IO]**, Tbilisi, Georgia
Caritas Guinea Ecuatorial **[IO]**, Malabo, Equatorial Guinea
Caritas Hellas **[IO]**, Athens, Greece
Caritas de Honduras **[IO]**, Tegucigalpa, Honduras
Caritas Hong Kong **[IO]**, Hong Kong, People's Republic of China
Caritas Hungarica **[IO]**, Budapest, Hungary
Caritas Iceland **[IO]**, Reykjavik, Iceland
Caritas Ile Maurice **[IO]**, Port Louis, Mauritius
Caritas India **[IO]**, New Delhi, India
Caritas Indonesia **[IO]**, Jakarta, Indonesia
Caritas Internationalis - Vatican City **[IO]**, Vatican City, Vatican City
Caritas Iran **[IO]**, Tehran, Iran
Caritas Iraq **[IO]**, Baghdad, Iraq
Caritas Italiana **[IO]**, Rome, Italy
Caritas Jordan **[IO]**, Amman, Jordan
Caritas Karuna Myanmar **[IO]**, Yangon, Myanmar
Caritas Kazakhstan **[IO]**, Karaganda, Kazakhstan
Caritas Kenya **[IO]**, Nairobi, Kenya
Caritas Latvia **[IO]**, Riga, Latvia
Caritas Lesotho **[IO]**, Maseru, Lesotho
Caritas Liberia **[IO]**, Monrovia, Liberia
Caritas Libie **[IO]**, Tripoli, Libyan Arab Jamahiriya
Caritas Macedonia **[IO]**, Skopje, Macedonia
Caritas Maroc **[IO]**, Rabat, Morocco
Caritas Mauritanie **[IO]**, Nouakchott, Mauritania
Caritas Mocambicana **[IO]**, Maputo, Mozambique
Caritas Moldova **[IO]**, Chisinau, Moldova
Caritas Monaco **[IO]**, Monaco, Monaco
Caritas Mongolia **[IO]**, Ulan Bator, Mongolia
Caritas Nepal **[IO]**, Kathmandu, Nepal
Caritas Nicaragua **[IO]**, Managua, Nicaragua
Caritas Niger **[IO]**, Niamey, Niger
Caritas Nigeria **[IO]**, Lagos, Nigeria
Caritas Pakistan **[IO]**, Lahore, Pakistan
Caritas Paraguay **[IO]**, Asuncion, Paraguay
Caritas Puerto Rico **[12816]**, PO Box 8812, San Juan, PR 00910-0812, (787)727-7373
Caritas Republique du Congo **[IO]**, Brazzaville, Republic of the Congo
Caritas Rwanda **[IO]**, Kigali, Rwanda
Caritas Sao Tome and Principe **[IO]**, Sao Tome, Sao Tome and Principe
Caritas Senegal **[IO]**, Dakar, Senegal
Caritas Seychelles **[IO]**, Victoria, Seychelles
Caritas South Africa **[IO]**, Pretoria, Republic of South Africa
Caritas Swaziland **[IO]**, Manzini, Swaziland
Caritas Switzerland **[IO]**, Lucerne, Switzerland
Caritas Tanzania **[IO]**, Dar es Salaam, United Republic of Tanzania
Caritas Tunisie **[IO]**, Tunis, Tunisia
Caritas Uganda **[IO]**, Kampala, Uganda
Caritas Ukraine **[IO]**, Kiev, Ukraine
Carl Duisberg Soc. **[★7787]**
Carl Duisberg Soc. **[★7787]**
Carl Orff Canada - Music for Children **[IO]**, Amherst, NS, Canada
Carl Orff Canada Musique pour Enfants **[★IO]**
Carla Riggs-Hall Intl. Fan Club - Address unknown since 2011.
Carlton/Reed/Ashley/Williams/ Bradford/McGoffier/ Mattews/Reade Family Org. - Defunct.
Carmarthenshire Welsh Pony and Cob Assn. **[IO]**, Ammanford, United Kingdom
Carmen Division of the Brotherhood of Railway, Airline and Steamship Clerks, Freight Handlers, Express and Sta. Employees **[★23291]**

Reference to "IO" in place of a book number signifies that the association may be found in the 50th edition of International Organizations.

Carnegie Commn. on Science, Technology, and Govt. - Defunct.

Carnegie Corp. of New York [8008], 437 Madison Ave., New York, NY 10022, (212)371-3200

Carnegie Coun. for Ethics in Intl. Affairs [19827], Merrill House, 170 E 64th St., New York, NY 10065-7478, (212)838-4120

Carnegie Coun. on Ethics and Intl. Affairs [19827], Merrill House, 170 E 64th St., New York, NY 10065-7478, (212)838-4120

Carnegie Endowment for Intl. Peace [17941], 1779 Massachusetts Ave. NW, Washington, DC 20036-2103, (202)483-7600

Carnegie Endowment for Intl. Peace [17941], 1779 Massachusetts Ave. NW, Washington, DC 20036-2103, (202)483-7600

Carnegie Forum on Educ. and the Economy [★8045]

Carnegie Found. for the Advancement of Teaching [8946], 51 Vista Ln., Stanford, CA 94305-8703, (650)566-5100

Carnegie Hero Fund Commn. [13053], 436 7th Ave., Ste. 1101, Pittsburgh, PA 15219-1841, (412)281-1302

Carnegie Institution for Sci. [7327], 1530 P St. NW, Washington, DC 20005, (202)387-6400

Carnegie Institution of Washington [★7327]

Carol Burnett Fund for Responsible Journalism [8438], Univ. of Hawaii, School of Communications, 2550 Campus Rd., Honolulu, HI 96822-2217, (808)956-8715

Carousel Organ Assn. of Am. [21954], 12906 Raytown Rd., Kansas City, MO 64149

Carousel Theatre Soc. [IO], Vancouver, BC, Canada

Carousels
  Natl. Carousel Assn. [21241]

Carp Anglers Gp. [21732], PO Box 1502, Bartlesville, OK 74005-1502, (888)227-7118

Carpatho-Rusyn Soc. [10517], 915 Dickson St., Munhall, PA 15120, (412)567-3077

Carpenters' Company [9674], 320 Chestnut St., Carpenters' Hall, Philadelphia, PA 19106, (215)925-0167

Carpenters' Company [IO], London, United Kingdom

Carpenters' Company of the City and County of Philadelphia [★9674]

Carper Family Assn. - Defunct.

Carpet Cleaners Inst. of the Northwest [746], 2661 N Pearl St., Tacoma, WA 98407, (253)759-5762

Carpet Cushion Coun. [2053], 23 Courtney Cir., Bryn Mawr, PA 19010, (610)527-3880

Carpet Export Promotion Coun. [IO], New Delhi, India

Carpet Inst. of Australia Limited [IO], Melbourne, Australia

Carpet and Rug Inst. [2054], PO Box 2048, Dalton, GA 30722-2048, (706)278-3176

Carpet Yarn Assn. [★3436]

Carr-Loker Descendants Assn. - Defunct.

CARR Support Gp. [IO], Toronto, ON, Canada

Carrefour Canadien Intl. [★IO]

Carriage Assn. of Am. [21318], 3915 Jay Trump Rd., Lexington, KY 40511-8936, (859)231-0971

Carriage Operators of North Am. [728], PO Box 944, North Branch, MN 55056, (651)303-4157

Carriage Operators of North Am. [728], PO Box 944, North Branch, MN 55056, (651)303-4157

Carriage Travel Club [22186], 514 Americans Way, No. 3384, Box Elder, SD 57719-7600, (407)414-8652

Carriages
  Carriage Operators of North Am. [728]
  Carriage Operators of North Am. [728]

Carrie Estelle Doheny Found. [13175], 707 Wilshire Blvd., Ste. 4960, Los Angeles, CA 90017, (213)488-1122

Carrier Liaison Comm. [★3397]

Carriers and Locals Soc. [22103], PO Box 74, Grosse Ile, MI 48138, (734)676-2649

Carroll Center for the Blind [17070], 770 Centre St., Newton, MA 02458, (617)969-6200

Carroll Rehabilitation Center for the Visually Impaired [★17070]

Carroll Soc. of North Am; Lewis [9392]

Carrom Assn. of Maldives [IO], Male, Maldives

Carruthers Clan Soc. - Defunct.

Carrying Capacity [★6595]

Carrying Capacity Network [6595], PO Box 1419, Anaheim, CA 92815, (714)204-3465

CarryOn.com - Address unknown since 2011.

Carson McCullers Soc. [10707], Jackson State Community Coll., Dept. of English and Foreign Languages, 2046 N Pkwy., Jackson, TN 38301, (800)355-5722

Carter Center [18416], One Copenhill, 453 Freedom Pkwy., Atlanta, GA 30307, (404)420-5100

CARTHA [18402], Usha R. Balakrishnan, Pres./Chm./CEO, 33 Buchanan Ct., Iowa City, IA 52246, (319)248-9625

Carto-Philatelists [★22024]

Cartographic Assn. of Tanzania [IO], Dar es Salaam, United Republic of Tanzania

Cartographic Soc. of the Slovak Republic [IO], Bratislava, Slovakia

Cartography
  Cartography and Geographic Info. Soc. [6379]
  Indian Soc. of Geomatics [12926]
  Intl. Map Trade Assn. [6380]
  Intl. Map Trade Assn. [6380]
  North Amer. Cartographic Info. Soc. [6381]

Cartography Division of the Amer. Cong. on Surveying and Mapping [★6379]

Cartography and Geographic Info. Soc. [6379], PO Box 1107, Mount Pleasant, SC 29465, (843)324-0665

Cartooning
  Thomas Nast Soc. [9208]

Cartoonist Guild of New York [★9235]

Cartoonist Guild of New York [★9235]

Cartoonists' Club of Great Britain [IO], Sandy, United Kingdom

Cartoonists Northwest [9285], PO Box 31122, Seattle, WA 98103

Cartoonists Soc; Natl. [9243]

Cartoons
  Cartoonists' Club of Great Britain [1329]
  Disneyana Fan Club [23792]
  Official Gumby Fan Club [23793]
  Pogo Fan Club and Walt Kelly Soc. [23794]

CartoPhilatelic Soc. [22024], 1117 Douglas Ave., Unit 209, North Providence, RI 02904

Carver-Scott Humane Soc. [10937], PO Box 215, Chaska, MN 55318, (952)368-3553

CAS Collectors [21261], 2000 Wisconsin Ave. N, Golden Valley, MN 55427

CAS Forum [★10171]

CAS Forum of the Violin Soc. of Am. [10171], Violin Soc. of Am., 341 N Maitland Ave., Ste. 130, Maitland, FL 32751, (407)647-8839

Casa de Cultura da Mulher Negra [★IO]

Casa Vacanza [★21853]

Case Collectors Club [21873], PO Box 4000, Bradford, PA 16701, (800)523-6350

Case Mgt. Soc. of Am. [15293], 6301 Ranch Dr., Little Rock, AR 72223, (501)221-9068

Case Mgt. Soc. of Am. [15293], 6301 Ranch Dr., Little Rock, AR 72223, (501)221-9068

Case Mgt. Soc. of Australia [IO], Castle Hill, Australia

Case Res. Assn. [★3708]

Casey Jones Railroad Unit [★22019]

Cash Mgt. Practitioners Assn. [★1283]

Cash Registers Collectors Club [21319], PO Box 20534, Dayton, OH 45420-0534

Cashew Export Promotion Coun. of India [IO], Cochin, India

Cashmere and Camel Hair Mfrs. Inst. [3438], 6 Beacon St., Ste. 1125, Boston, MA 02108, (617)542-7481

Casino Assn. of South Africa [IO], Vlaeberg, Republic of South Africa

Casino Chip and Gaming Token Collectors Club [21320], PO Box 691085, Houston, TX 77269-1085

Casino Operators Assn. of the UK [IO], Sheffield, United Kingdom

Casket and Funeral Supply Assn. of Am. [2529], 49 Sherwood Terr., Ste. Y, Lake Bluff, IL 60044-2231, (847)295-6630

Casket Mfrs. Assn. of Am. [★2529]

Caspian Breed Soc. UK [IO], Chippenham, United Kingdom

Caspian Horse Soc. of the Americas [4573], Vicki Hudgins, Registrar, PO Box 1589, Brenham, TX 77834-1589, (979)830-9046

Cast Bronze Bearings Inst. [★1854]

Cast Bullet Assn. [22873], Paul Gans, Membership Dir., 7600 SE Maple Ave., Vancouver, WA 98664-1737, (360)882-0502

Cast Iron Pipe Inst. [★2747]

Cast Iron Pipe Publicity Bur. [★2747]

Cast Iron Pipe Res. Assn. [★2747]

Cast Iron Seat Collectors Assn. [21868], 604 Washington St., Woodstock, IL 60098-2251, (815)338-6464

Cast Iron Soil Pipe Inst. [2746], 1064 Delaware Ave. SE, Atlanta, GA 30316, (404)622-0073

Cast Metals Fed. [IO], West Bromwich, United Kingdom

Cast Metals Inst. [★8963]

Cast Stone Inst. [824], PO Box 68, Lebanon, PA 17042, (717)272-3744

Casting Indus. Suppliers Assn. [1814], 14175 W Indian School Rd., Ste. B4-504, Goodyear, AZ 85395, (623)547-0920

Castings Tech. Intl. [IO], Rotherham, United Kingdom

Castle Coalition [18403], 901 N Glebe Rd., Ste. 900, Arlington, VA 22203, (703)682-9320

Casual Furniture Retailers - Address unknown since 2010.

Casual Games Assn. [21744], PO Box 305, Smithfield, UT 84335

Casualty Actuarial Soc. [1946], 4350 N Fairfax Dr., Ste. 250, Arlington, VA 22203, (703)276-3100

Cat
  Abyssinian Cat Club of Am. [21242]
  Alliance for Contraception in Cats and Dogs [12647]
  Amer. Assn. of Cat Enthusiasts [21243]
  Amer. Cat Fanciers Assn. [21244]
  Amer. Cat Fanciers Assn. [21244]
  Cat Fanciers' Assn. [21245]
  Cat Fanciers' Fed. [21246]
  CATalyst Coun. [10938]
  Cats in Crisis [10939]
  Companion Animal Protection Soc. [12649]
  Cornell Feline Hea. Center [17023]
  Cornish Rex Soc. [21247]
  The Designer Cat Assn. [21248]
  Feline Control Coun. of Victoria [647]
  Feral Cat Caretakers' Coalition [3810]
  Feral Cat Friends [21249]
  Friends of Feral Felines [21250]
  Friends of Roman Cats [3859]
  Happy Household Pet Cat Club [21251]
  The Intl. Bengal Breeders' Assn. [3860]
  The Intl. Bengal Breeders' Assn. [3860]
  The Intl. Bengal Cat Soc. [3861]
  The Intl. Bengal Cat Soc. [3861]
  The Intl. Cat Assn. [21252]
  The Intl. Cat Assn. [21252]
  Intl. Desert Lynx Cat Assn. [3862]
  Intl. Desert Lynx Cat Assn. [3862]
  LaPerm Soc. of Am. [21253]
  Natl. Alliance of Burmese Breeders [3863]
  Natl. Birman Fanciers [21254]
  Norwegian Forest Cat Breed Coun. [21255]
  Rex Breeders United [21256]
  Sacred Cat of Burma Fanciers [21257]
  Savannah Cat Club [3864]
  Savannah Cat Club [3864]
  Somali Intl. Cat Club [21258]
  Traditional Cat Assn. [21259]
  United Silver and Golden Fanciers [21260]
  Wild Felid Res. and Mgt. Assn. [5145]
  WildCat Conservation Legal Aid Soc. [5016]

Cat Collectors - Address unknown since 2011.

Cat Fanciers' Assn. [21245], 1805 Atlantic Ave., Manasquan, NJ 08736, (732)528-9797

Cat Fanciers' Fed. [21246], PO Box 661, Gratis, OH 45330, (937)787-9009

Cat Fund [★11023]

Cat Soc. of Bahrain And Pet Animals [IO], Diraz, Bahrain

A star before a book entry number signifies that the name is not listed separately, but is mentioned within the entry.

Catalan Assn. for Artificial Intelligence **[IO]**, Bellaterra, Spain

Catalina 22 Natl. Sailing Assn. **[22326]**, 3790 Post Gate Dr., Cumming, GA 30040, (770)887-9728

Catalina 27 Natl. Assn. **[★22348]**

Catalog and Multichannel Marketing Coun. **[1605]**, 1120 Ave. of the Americas, New York, NY 10036-6700, (212)768-7277

Catalogue Raisonne Scholars Assn. **[7739]**, Nancy Mowll Mathews, Pres., Williams Coll. Museum of Art, 15 Lawrence Hall Dr., Ste. 2, Williamstown, MA 01267, (413)597-2335

Catalysis Soc. **[★7383]**

Catalysis Soc. (North Am.) - Defunct.

Catalysis Soc; North Amer. **[7383]**

Catalyst **[10639]**, 120 Wall St., 5th Fl., New York, NY 10005-3904, (212)514-7600

CATalyst Coun. **[10938]**, PO Box 5872, Timonium, MD 21094

Cataraqui Archaeological Res. Found. **[IO]**, Kingston, ON, Canada

Catboat Assn. **[22327]**, PO Box 775, Sudbury, MA 01776-0775, (508)733-3062

Catching the Dream **[8190]**, 8200 Mountain Rd. NE, Ste. 203, Albuquerque, NM 87110, (505)262-2351

Catering Equip. Distributors Assn. of Great Britain **[IO]**, Inkberrow, United Kingdom

Catering Equip. Suppliers Assn. **[IO]**, London, United Kingdom

Caterpillar Club - Defunct.

Catfish Farmers of Am. - Address unknown since 2010.

The Catfish Inst. **[3821]**, 6311 Ridgewood Rd., Ste. W404, Jackson, MS 39211, (601)977-9559

Catharsis Found. **[IO]**, Calgary, AB, Canada

Catholic

Acad. of Amer. Franciscan History **[19377]**

ADOREMUS - Soc. for the Renewal of the Sacred Liturgy **[19378]**

ADOREMUS - Soc. for the Renewal of the Sacred Liturgy **[19378]**

Aid to the Church in Need **[19379]**

Amer. Benedictine Acad. **[19380]**

Apostleship of Prayer **[19381]**

Apostleship of the Sea in the U.S.A. **[19382]**

Apostolate for Family Consecration **[19383]**

Archconfraternity of the Holy Ghost **[19384]**

Assn. for Catholic Chiropractors **[14121]**

Assn. of Catholic Colleges and Universities **[7813]**

Assn. for Christian Ethics **[19385]**

Assn. of Hebrew Catholics **[19386]**

Assn. of Jesuit Colleges and Universities **[7814]**

Assn. of Marian Helpers **[19387]**

Assn. of the Miraculous Medal **[19388]**

Assn. for the Rights of Catholics in the Church **[19389]**

Assumption Guild **[19390]**

Auxiliaries of Our Lady of the Cenacle **[19391]**

Benedictines for Peace **[19392]**

Bishop Baraga Assn. **[19393]**

Blue Army of Our Lady of Fatima U.S.A. **[19394]**

Bros. and Sisters of Penance of St. Francis **[19395]**

Cabrini Mission Corps **[20017]**

Canadian Catholic Historical Assn. **[16149]**

Canon Law Soc. of Am. **[19396]**CatholicCanon Law Soc. of the Orthodox Catholic Church

Capuchin-Franciscans **[19397]**

Catholic Acad. of Sciences in the U.S.A. **[19670]**

Catholic Assn. of Foresters **[18946]**

Catholic Assn. of Latino Leaders **[19398]**

Catholic Athletes for Christ **[22230]**

Catholic Campus Ministry Assn. **[19399]**

Catholic Central Union of Am. I Central Bur. **[19400]**

Catholic Church Extension Soc. of the U.S.A. **[19401]**

Catholic Coalition on Climate Change **[4016]**

Catholic Daughters of the Americas **[18947]**

Catholic Financial Life **[18948]**

Catholic Golden Age **[19402]**

Catholic Guardian Soc. and Home Bur. **[11208]**

Catholic Kolping Soc. of Am. **[19403]**

Catholic League for Religious and Civil Rights **[19404]**

Catholic Life Insurance Union **[18949]**

Catholic Network of Volunteer Ser. **[19405]**

Catholic Order of Foresters **[18950]**

Catholic Radio Assn. **[19406]**

Catholic Social Workers Natl. Assn. **[13216]**

Catholic Theological Soc. of Am. **[9469]**

Catholic Traditionalist Movement **[19407]**

Catholic Truth Soc. **[9383]**

Catholic United Financial **[18951]**

Catholic War Veterans Auxiliary of the U.S.A. **[20704]**

Catholic War Veterans of the U.S.A. **[20781]**

Catholic Worker Movement **[18164]**

Catholics in Alliance for the Common Good **[19408]**

Catholics Speak Out **[19488]**

Catholics United for the Faith **[19409]**

Catholics United for the Faith **[19409]**

Center for Applied Res. in the Apostolate **[19410]**

Central Assn. of the Miraculous Medal **[19411]**

The Christophers **[19412]**

Claretian Volunteers and Lay Missionaries **[19413]**

Coll. of St. Scholastica Alumni Assn. **[18865]**

Conf. of Major Superiors of Men **[19414]**

Confraternity of Penitents **[19415]**

Congregation of the Blessed Sacrament **[19416]**

Congregation of Sisters of Saint Agnes **[19417]**

CORPUS **[19418]**

Courage Intl. **[19787]**

CUSA: An Apostolate for People with Chronic Illness or with Disabilities **[19419]**

Daughters of Isabella, Intl. Circle **[18952]**

Daughters of Isabella, Intl. Circle **[18952]**

Dept. of Boards and Councils of Catholic Educ. **[7815]**

Disciples Ecumenical Consultative Coun. **[19618]**

Family Rosary **[19420]**

Fed. of Diocesan Liturgical Commissions **[19421]**

Fellowship of Catholic Scholars **[9470]**

Focolare Movement **[19422]**

Focolare Movement **[19422]**

Foundations and Donors Interested in Catholic Activities **[19423]**

Friends of Old St. Ferdinand **[19424]**

FutureChurch **[19425]**

Glenmary Res. Center **[19426]**

Grailville **[19427]**

Holy Childhood Assn. **[19428]**

Holy Cross Foreign Mission Soc. **[19429]**

Holy Face Assn. **[19430]**

Holy Shroud Guild **[19431]**

Humility of Mary Ser. **[19432]**

Humility of Mary Ser. **[19432]**

Inst. of Apostolic Oblates **[19433]**

Instituto Nacional Hispano de Liturgia **[19434]**

Intl. Catholic Deaf Assn. U.S. Sect. **[19435]**

Intl. Catholic Stewardship Coun. **[19436]**

Intl. Catholic Stewardship Coun. **[19436]**

Intl. Order of Alhambra **[18953]**

Intl. Order of Alhambra **[18953]**

Jesuit Conf. **[19437]**

Jesuit Secondary Educ. Assn. **[7816]**

Jesuit Volunteer Corps: Northwest **[19438]**

Junior Knights of Peter Claver **[18954]**

Knights of Columbus **[18955]**

Knights of Columbus **[18955]**

Knights of Peter Claver **[18956]**

Knights of Saint John Intl. **[18957]**

Knights of Saint John Intl. **[18957]**

Knightsbridge Intl. **[12859]**

Ladies of Charity of the U.S.A. **[13191]**

Laity for Life **[19439]**

Latin Liturgy Assn. **[19440]**

Lay Carmelite Order of the Blessed Virgin Mary **[19441]**

Lay Mission-Helpers Assn. **[19442]**

Lay Mission-Helpers Assn. **[19442]**

Leadership Conf. of Women Religious **[19443]**

League of St. Dymphna **[19444]**

Legatus **[19445]**

Lithuanian Catholic Religious Aid **[19446]**

Mariannhill Mission Soc. **[19447]**

Mariological Soc. of Am. **[19448]**

Maryheart Crusaders **[19449]**

Maryknoll Fathers and Bros. **[19450]**

Maryknoll Fathers and Bros. **[19450]**

Militia of the Immaculata Movement **[19451]**

Mission Soc. of the Mother of God of Boronyavo **[20191]**

Missionary Sisters of the Holy Rosary **[19452]**

Missionary Sisters of Our Lady of the Holy Rosary **[19452]**

Missionary Sisters of the Soc. of Mary **[20068]**

Missionary Soc. of Saint Columban **[19453]**

Missionary Soc. of Saint Paul the Apostle **[19454]**

Natl. Assn. of Asian-Pacific Amer. Deacons **[20202]**

Natl. Assn. of Catholic Family Life Ministers **[19997]**

Natl. Assn. of Catholic School Teachers **[7817]**

Natl. Assn. of Catholic Youth Ministry Leaders **[19455]**

Natl. Assn. of Diaconate Directors **[19456]**

Natl. Assn. of Hispanic Priests of the USA **[19457]**

Natl. Assn. of the Holy Name Soc. **[19458]**

Natl. Assn. of Priest Pilots **[19459]**

Natl. Assn. of State Catholic Conf. Directors **[19460]**

Natl. Black Catholic Clergy Caucus **[19461]**

Natl. Black Catholic Cong. **[19462]**

Natl. Black Sisters' Conf. **[19463]**

Natl. Catholic Coll. Admission Assn. **[19464]**

Natl. Catholic Conf. for Total Stewardship **[19465]**

Natl. Catholic Development Conf. **[19466]**

Natl. Catholic Educational Assn. **[7818]**

Natl. Catholic Off. for the Deaf **[19467]**

Natl. Catholic Partnership on Disability **[19468]**

Natl. Catholic Rural Life Conf. **[19469]**

Natl. Catholic Rural Life Conf. **[19469]**

Natl. Catholic Soc. of Foresters **[18958]**

Natl. Christ Child Soc. **[19470]**

Natl. Christian Life Community of the U.S.A. **[19471]**

Natl. Conf. of Catholic Airport Chaplains **[19528]**

Natl. Coun. of Catholic Women **[19472]**

Natl. Cursillo Movement **[19473]**

Natl. Enthronement Center **[19474]**

Natl. Evangelization Teams **[19475]**

Natl. Fed. for Catholic Youth Ministry **[19476]**

Natl. Fed. of Priests' Councils **[19477]**

Natl. Religious Vocation Conf. **[19478]**

Natl. Ser. Committee/Chariscenter USA **[19479]**

Natl. Shrine of St. Elizabeth Ann Seton **[19480]**

Nocturnal Adoration Soc. **[19481]**

North Amer. Assn. for the Catechumenate **[19482]**

North Amer. Assn. for the Catechumenate **[19482]**

North Amer. Forum on the Catechumenate **[19483]**

Paulist Evangelization Ministries **[19484]**

Pius X Secular Inst. **[19485]**

Pius X Secular Inst. **[19485]**

Pontifical Mission Societies in the U.S. **[19486]**

Pro Sanctity Movement **[19487]**

Quixote Center **[19488]**

Raskob Found. for Catholic Activities **[19489]**

Raskob Found. for Catholic Activities **[19489]**

Religious Bros. Conf. **[19490]**

Religious Formation Conf. **[19491]**

Response-Ability **[20085]**

Sacred Heart League **[19492]**

St. Jude League **[19493]**

Saints' Stories **[19494]**

Secretariat for Family, Laity, Women, and Youth **[12020]**

Secular Inst. of Saint Francis de Sales **[19495]**

Secular Inst. of Saint Francis de Sales **[19495]**

Serra Intl. **[19496]**

Serra Intl. **[19496]**

Soc. of African Missions **[19497]**

Soc. of African Missions **[19497]**

Soc. of the Little Flower **[19498]**

Soc. of Missionaries of Africa **[19499]**

Soc. of Our Lady of the Most Holy Trinity **[19500]**

Soc. for the Propagation of the Faith **[19501]**

Soc. of Saint Mary Magdalene **[19502]**

Soc. of Saint Peter Apostle **[19503]**

Soc. of Traditional Roman Catholics **[19504]**

Supreme Ladies Auxiliary Knights of Saint John **[18959]**

Reference to "IO" in place of a book number signifies that the association may be found in the 50th edition of International Organizations.

Tekakwitha Conf. Natl. Center **[19505]**
UNANIMA Intl. **[18645]**
United Catholic Music and Video Assn. **[19506]**
U.S. Assn. of Consecrated Virgins **[19507]**
U.S. Catholic Mission Assn. **[19508]**
U.S. Conf. of Catholic Bishops **[19509]**
U.S. Conf. of Catholic Bishops l Bishops' Comm. on Priestly Formation **[19688]**
United States Conference of Catholic Bishops l Comm. on Divine Worship **[19510]**
U.S. Conf. of Catholic Bishops l Ecumenical and Interreligious Affairs **[19511]**
Volunteer Missionary Movement - U.S. Off. **[19512]**
Wanderer Forum Found. **[19513]**
Western Catholic Union **[18960]**
Women for Faith and Family **[19514]**
Women's Ordination Conf. **[19515]**
Catholic Acad. for Commun. Arts Professionals **[9457]**, 1645 Brook Lynn Dr., Ste. 2, Dayton, OH 45432-1933, (937)458-0265
Catholic Acad. of Sciences in the U.S.A. **[19670]**, 1205 Carol Raye St., McLean, VA 22101-2620
Catholic Action for St. Children **[IO]**, Accra, Ghana
Catholic Agency for Overseas Development **[IO]**, London, United Kingdom
Catholic Aid Assn. **[★18951]**
Catholic Alliance; Lithuanian **[19116]**
Catholic Alumni Clubs Intl. **[18861]**, 13517 Teakwood Ln., Germantown, MD 20874-1034
Catholic Alumni Clubs Intl. **[18861]**, 13517 Teakwood Ln., Germantown, MD 20874-1034
Catholic Artists of America - Defunct.
Catholic Assn. of Diocesan Ecumenical and Inter-religious Officers **[19649]**, 1009 Stafford Ave., Fredericksburg, VA 22401, (540)373-6491
Catholic Assn. of Foresters **[18946]**, 182 Forbes Rd., Ste. 119, Braintree, MA 02184-2636, (781)848-8221
Catholic Assn. of Latino Leaders **[19398]**, 2718 W Woodlawn Ave., San Antonio, TX 78228, (210)734-1653
Catholic Assn. for Lesbian and Gay Ministry **[19786]**, 1798 Scenic Ave., Berkeley, CA 94709, (510)849-8281
Catholic Assn. of Persons With Visual Impairment - Defunct.
Catholic Athletes for Christ **[22230]**, 3703 Cameron Mills Rd., Alexandria, VA 22305, (703)299-3005
Catholic Biblical Assn. of Am. **[9009]**, Catholic Univ. of Am., 433 Caldwell Hall, Washington, DC 20064, (202)319-5519
Catholic Biblical Fed. **[IO]**, Stuttgart, Germany
Catholic Bishops' Conf. of England and Wales **[IO]**, London, United Kingdom
Catholic Bishops' Conf. of India **[IO]**, New Delhi, India
Catholic Bishops' Conf. of Malaysia, Singapore, and Brunei **[IO]**, Kuala Lumpur, Malaysia
Catholic Bishops' Conf. of Nigeria **[IO]**, Abuja, Nigeria
Catholic Bishops' Conf. of the Philippines **[IO]**, Manila, Philippines
Catholic Book Publishers Assn. **[★2920]**
Catholic Broadcasters Assn. **[★9457]**
Catholic Campaign for Human Development **[12661]**, 3211 4th St. NE, Washington, DC 20017-1194, (202)541-3210
Catholic Campus Ministry Assn. **[19399]**, 1118 Pendleton St., Ste. 300, Cincinnati, OH 45202-8805, (513)842-0167
Catholic Cemetery Conf. **[2530]**, 1400 S Wolf Rd., Bldg. No. 3, Hillside, IL 60162-2197, (708)202-1242
Catholic Central Union **[★18950]**
Catholic Central Union of Am. - Address unknown since 2010.
Catholic Central Union of Am. l Central Bur. **[19400]**, 3835 Westminster Pl., St. Louis, MO 63108-3409, (314)371-1653
Catholic Chaplains; Natl. Assn. of **[19525]**
Catholic Charities USA **[13176]**, 66 Canal Center Plz., Ste. 600, Alexandria, VA 22314, (703)549-1390
Catholic Church Extension Soc. of the U.S.A. **[19401]**, 150 S Wacker Dr., 20th Fl., Chicago, IL 60606, (312)795-5112

Catholic Coalition on Climate Change **[4016]**, PO Box 60205, Washington, DC 20039, (301)920-1442
Catholic Commn. on Intellectual and Cultural Affairs - Defunct.
Catholic Comm. of Appalachia **[20019]**, 885 Orchard Run Rd., Spencer, WV 25276, (304)927-5798
Catholic Comm. on Scouting **[★13022]**
Catholic Counselors in APGA **[★7940]**
Catholic Daughters of Am. **[★18947]**
Catholic Daughters of the Americas **[18947]**, 10 W 71st St., New York, NY 10023, (212)877-3041
Catholic Democrats **[17531]**, PO Box 290331, Boston, MA 02129, (617)308-1584
Catholic Development Commn. - Caritas Zimbabwe **[IO]**, Harare, Zimbabwe
Catholic Development Commn. in Malawi - Caritas Malawi **[IO]**, Lilongwe, Malawi
Catholic Economic Assn. **[★6614]**
Catholic Educ. Assn. **[★7818]**
Catholic Educational Assn. of the Philippines **[IO]**, Quezon City, Philippines
Catholic Extension **[★19401]**
Catholic Family History Soc. **[IO]**, Ilford, United Kingdom
Catholic Family Services of Regina **[IO]**, Regina, SK, Canada
Catholic Family Services Windsor-Essex County **[IO]**, Windsor, ON, Canada
Catholic Fed. Central Coun; Italian **[19077]**
Catholic Financial Life **[18948]**, 1100 W Wells St., Milwaukee, WI 53233, (414)273-6266
Catholic Golden Age **[19402]**, PO Box 249, Olyphant, PA 18447, (800)836-5699
Catholic Guardian Soc. and Home Bur. **[11208]**, 1011 1st Ave., 10th Flr., New York, NY 10022, (212)371-1000
Catholic Guild for All the Blind **[★17070]**
Catholic Hea. Alliance of Canada **[IO]**, Ottawa, ON, Canada
Catholic Hea. Assn. of the U.S. **[15047]**, 4455 Woodson Rd., St. Louis, MO 63134-3797, (314)427-2500
Catholic Healthcare Audit Network **[★8011]**
Catholic Historical Assn; Amer. **[9744]**
Catholic Historical Soc; Amer. **[9745]**
Catholic Historical Soc; Amer. **[9745]**
Catholic Hosp. Assn. **[★15047]**
Catholic Hosp. Assn. of U.S. and Canada **[★15047]**
Catholic Intl. Educ. Off. **[IO]**, Brussels, Belgium
Catholic Interracial Coun. of New York - Defunct.
Catholic Knights and Catholic Family Life Insurance **[★18948]**
Catholic Knights Insurance Soc. **[★18948]**
Catholic Knights of Saint George **[★19063]**
Catholic Kolping Soc. of Am. **[19403]**, 1223 Van Houten Ave., Clifton, NJ 07013, (201)666-1169
Catholic League for Religious and Civil Rights **[19404]**, 450 7th Ave., New York, NY 10123, (212)371-3191
Catholic Legal Immigration Network **[19822]**, 415 Michigan Ave. NE, Ste. 200, Washington, DC 20017, (202)635-2556
Catholic Lib. Assn. **[9978]**, 205 W Monroe St., Ste. 314, Chicago, IL 60606-5061, (312)739-1776
Catholic Life Insurance Union **[18949]**, PO Box 659527, San Antonio, TX 78265-9527, (210)828-9921
Catholic Media Coun. **[IO]**, Aachen, Germany
Catholic Medical Assn. **[16260]**, 29 Bala Ave., Ste. 205, Bala Cynwyd, PA 19004-3206, (484)270-8002
Catholic Medical Mission Bd. **[12448]**, 10 W 17th St., New York, NY 10011-5765, (212)242-7757
Catholic Medical Mission Bd. **[12448]**, 10 W 17th St., New York, NY 10011-5765, (212)242-7757
Catholic Missions In Canada **[IO]**, Toronto, ON, Canada
Catholic Near East Welfare Assn. **[18119]**, 1011 1st Ave., New York, NY 10022-4195, (212)826-1480
Catholic Near East Welfare Assn. **[18119]**, 1011 1st Ave., New York, NY 10022-4195, (212)826-1480
Catholic Near East Welfare Assn. l Pontifical Mission for Palestine **[12775]**, 1011 1st Ave., New York, NY 10022-4195, (212)826-1480
Catholic Network of Volunteer Ser. **[19405]**, 6930 Carroll Ave., Ste. 820, Takoma Park, MD 20912-4481, (301)270-0900

Catholic News Ser. **[2817]**, 3211 4th St. NE, Washington, DC 20017, (202)541-3250
Catholic Order of Foresters **[18950]**, PO Box 3012, Naperville, IL 60566-7012, (630)983-4900
Catholic Parents Network - Address unknown since 2011.
Catholic Peace Fellowship **[18234]**, PO Box 4232, South Bend, IN 46634, (574)232-2811
Catholic Philosophical Assn; Amer. **[8702]**
Catholic Press Assn. **[2926]**, 205 W Monroe St., Ste. 470, Chicago, IL 60606, (312)380-6789
Catholic Press Soc; Lithuanian **[19117]**
Catholic Radio Assn. **[19406]**, 121 Broad St., Charleston, SC 29401, (843)853-2300
Catholic Record Soc. **[IO]**, Durham, United Kingdom
Catholic Relief Services **[12776]**, 228 W Lexington St., Baltimore, MD 21201-3413, (888)277-7575
Catholic Relief Services **[12776]**, 228 W Lexington St., Baltimore, MD 21201-3413, (888)277-7575
Catholic Relief Services - El Salvador **[IO]**, San Salvador, El Salvador
Catholic Relief Services - Natl. Catholic Welfare Conf. **[★12776]**
Catholic Relief Services - Natl. Catholic Welfare Conf. **[★12776]**
Catholic Social Workers Natl. Assn. **[13216]**, PO Box 498531, Cincinnati, OH 45249-8531, (317)416-8285
Catholic Theological Soc. of Am. **[9469]**, Dr. Dolores Christie, Exec. Dir., John Carroll Univ., 20700 N Park Blvd., University Heights, OH 44118, (216)397-1631
Catholic Traditionalist Movement **[19407]**, 210 Maple Ave., Westbury, NY 11590-3117, (516)333-6470
Catholic Truth Soc. **[IO]**, London, United Kingdom
Catholic Union of the Sick in Am. **[★19419]**
Catholic United Financial **[18951]**, 3499 N Lexington Ave., St. Paul, MN 55126, (651)490-0170
Catholic War Veterans Auxiliary of the U.S.A. **[20704]**, 441 N Lee St., Alexandria, VA 22314-2301, (703)549-3622
Catholic War Veterans of the U.S.A. **[20781]**, 441 N Lee St., Alexandria, VA 22314, (703)549-3622
Catholic War Veterans of the U.S.A. Auxiliary **[★20704]**
Catholic Women's League Australia **[IO]**, Braddon, Australia
Catholic Women's League of Canada **[IO]**, Winnipeg, MB, Canada
Catholic Worker Movement **[18164]**, 36 E 1st St., New York, NY 10003, (212)777-9617
Catholics in Alliance for the Common Good **[19408]**, 1612 K St. NW, Ste. 400, Washington, DC 20006, (202)466-1665
Catholics for Choice **[18522]**, 1436 U St. NW, Ste. 301, Washington, DC 20009-3997, (202)986-6093
Catholics for a Free Choice **[★18522]**
Catholics Speak Out **[★19488]**
Catholics Speak Out **[19488]**, PO Box 5206, Hyattsville, MD 20782, (301)699-0042
Catholics United for the Faith **[19409]**, 827 N 4th St., Steubenville, OH 43952, (740)283-2484
Catholics United for the Faith **[19409]**, 827 N 4th St., Steubenville, OH 43952, (740)283-2484
Catholics United for Life **[12928]**, 3050 Gap Knob Rd., New Hope, KY 40052-6927, (502)325-3061
Catholics United for Spiritual Action **[★19419]**
Catlow/Whitney Family Org. - Defunct.
Cato Inst. **[18444]**, 1000 Massachusetts Ave. NW, Washington, DC 20001-5403, (202)842-0200
Cats in Crisis **[10939]**, PO Box 7324, Penndel, PA 19047
Cats Protection **[IO]**, Sussex, United Kingdom
Cattle
  Amer. Angus Assn. **[3865]**
  Amer. Beefalo Assn. **[3776]**
  Amer. Belgian Blue Breeders **[3866]**
  Amer. Black Hereford Assn. **[3867]**
  Amer. Blonde d'Aquitaine Assn. **[3868]**
  Amer. Brahman Breeders Assn. **[3869]**
  Amer. Brahmousin Coun. **[3870]**
  Amer. Breeds Coalition **[3871]**
  Amer. British White Park Assn. **[3872]**
  Amer. Chianina Assn. **[3873]**
  Amer. Devon Cattle Assn. **[3874]**

A star before a book entry number signifies that the name is not listed separately, but is mentioned within the entry.

Amer. Dexter Cattle Assn. [3875]
Amer. Galloway Breeders' Assn. [3876]
Amer. Gelbvieh Assn. [3877]
Amer. Guernsey Assn. [3878]
Amer. Hereford Assn. [3879]
Amer. Highland Cattle Assn. [3880]
American-International Charolais Assn. [3881]
American-International Charolais Assn. [3881]
Amer. Intl. Marchigiana Soc. [3882]
Amer. Jersey Cattle Assn. [3883]
Amer. Junior Brahman Assn. [3884]
Amer. Junior Chianina Assn. [3885]
Amer. Junior Shorthorn Assn. [3886]
Amer. Maine-Anjou Assn. [3887]
Amer. Milking Devon Cattle Assn. [3888]
Amer. Milking Shorthorn Junior Soc. [3889]
Amer. Milking Shorthorn Soc. [3890]
Amer. Murray Grey Assn. [3891]
Amer. Natl. CattleWomen [3892]
Amer. Pinzgauer Assn. [3893]
Amer. Red Brangus Assn. [3894]
Amer. Red Poll Assn. [3895]
Amer. Salers Assn. [3896]
Amer. Salers Junior Assn. [3897]
Amer. Shorthorn Assn. [3898]
Amer. Simmental Assn. [3899]
Amer. Tarentaise Assn. [3900]
Amer. Wagyu Assn. [3901]
Amer. Wagyu Assn. [3901]
Angus Soc. of Australia [1752]
Ankole Watusi Intl. Registry [3902]
Ankole Watusi Intl. Registry [3902]
Australian Beef Assn. [11904]
Ayrshire Breeders' Assn. [3903]
Barzona Breeders Assn. of Am. [3904]
Beefmaster Breeders United [3905]
Belted Galloway Soc. [3906]
Braunvieh Assn. of Am. [3907]
Brown Swiss Cattle Breeders Assn. of the U.S.A. [3908]
Buelingo Beef Cattle Soc. [3909]
Bukovina Soc. of the Americas [3910]
Canadian Maine-Anjou Assn. [17467]
Cattlemen's Beef Promotion and Res. Bd. [3911]
Fullblood Simmental Fleckvieh Fed. [3912]Cattle-Galloway Cattle Soc. of Great Britain and Ireland
Heifer Proj. Intl. [3913]
Highland Cattle Soc. [3696]
Holstein Assn. U.S.A. [3914]
Holstein Junior Prog. [3915]
Intl. Brangus Breeders Assn. [3916]
Intl. Junior Brangus Breeders Assn. [3917]
Intl. Junior Brangus Breeders Assn. [3917]
Intl. Miniature Cattle Breeders Soc. and Registry [3918]
Intl. Miniature Zebu Assn. [3919]
Intl. Texas Longhorn Assn. [3920]
Intl. Texas Longhorn Assn. [3920]
Intl. Yak Assn. [4694]
Irish Blacks Assn. [3921]
Marky Cattle Assn. [3922]
Miniature Hereford Breeders Assn. [3923]
Miniature Hereford Breeders Assn. [3923]
Natl. Dairy Herd Improvement Assn. [3924]
Natl. Junior Angus Assn. [3925]
Natl. Junior Hereford Assn. [3926]
Natl. Junior Santa Gertrudis Assn. [3927]
North Amer. Corriente Assn. [3928]
North Amer. Limousin Found. [3929]
North Amer. Limousin Junior Assn. [3930]
North Amer. Normande Assn. [3931]
North Amer. Piedmontese Assn. [3932]
North Amer. Piedmontese Assn. [3932]
North Amer. Romagnola and RomAngus Assn. [3933]
North Amer. South Devon Assn. [3934]
Parthenais Cattle Breeders Assn. [3935]
Piedmontese Assn. of the U.S. [3936]
Public Lands Coun. [4824]
Purebred Dexter Cattle Assn. of North Am. [3937]
Red Angus Assn. of Am. [3938]
Santa Gertrudis Breeders Intl. [3939]
Santa Gertrudis Breeders Intl. [3939]
Senepol Cattle Breeders Assn. [3940]

South African Holstein Breeders' Assn. [3867]
Texas Longhorn Breeders Assn. of Am. [3941]
United Braford Breeders [3942]
United Stockgrowers of Am. | Ranchers-Cattlemen Action Legal Fund [3943]
Welsh Black Cattle Soc. [14433]
Whitebred Shorthorn Assn. [9058]
Women in Livestock Development [3913]
World Watusi Assn. [3944]
World Watusi Assn. [3944]
Cattle Breeders' Assn. of Turkey [IO], Ankara, Turkey
Cattlemen's Beef Promotion and Res. Bd. [3911], 9000 E Nichols Ave., Ste. 215, Centennial, CO 80112-3450, (303)220-9890
Catweazle Fan Club [IO], Blackburn, United Kingdom
Caucasian Ovcharka Club of Am. [21536], PO Box 227, Chardon, OH 44024, (440)286-2374
Caucasus Environmental NGO Network [IO], Tbilisi, Georgia
Caucus-Association of High Tech Procurement Professionals [7153], Drawer 2970, Winter Park, FL 32790-2970, (407)740-5600
Caucus of Black Anthropologists [★6134]
Caucus of Black Economists [★6629]
Caucus of Black Sociologists [★7423]
Caucus on Children's Rights [★11317]
Caucus on Children's Rights [★11317]
Caucus of Gay Counselors [★12069]
Caucus of Gay, Lesbian, and Bisexual Members of the Amer. Psychiatric Assn. [★12068]
Caucus for a New Political Sci. [7287], Univ. of Massachusetts, 285 Old Westport Rd., North Dartmouth, MA 02747-2300
Caucus for TV Producers, Writers, and Directors [17335], PO Box 11236, Burbank, CA 91510-1236, (818)843-7572
Caucus for Women in Statistics [7472], Anna Nevius, Treas., 7732 Rydal Terr., Rockville, MD 20855-2057, (301)827-0170
Caucus for Women in Statistics [7472], Anna Nevius, Treas., 7732 Rydal Terr., Rockville, MD 20855-2057, (301)827-0170
CAUSA USA - Defunct.
Cause - Comfort for America's Uniformed Services [11085], 6315 Bren Mar Dr., Ste. 175, Alexandria, VA 22312, (703)750-6458
Cavalier King Charles Spaniel Club of Am. [21537], 2301 E Emory Rd., Knoxville, TN 37938, (865)688-2484
Cave Res. Found. [7461], Bob Hoke, Treas., 6304 Kaybro St., Laurel, MD 20707-2621
Cayman Eco [IO], Grand Cayman, Cayman Islands
Cayman Islands Amateur Athletic Assn. [IO], Grand Cayman, Cayman Islands
Cayman Islands Badminton Assn. [IO], Grand Cayman, Cayman Islands
Cayman Islands Cancer Soc. [IO], Grand Cayman, Cayman Islands
Cayman Islands Chamber of Commerce [IO], Grand Cayman, Cayman Islands
Cayman Islands Compliance Assn. [IO], Grand Cayman, Cayman Islands
Cayman Islands Dept. of Tourism [23448], Empire State Bldg., 350 5th Ave., Ste. 1801, New York, NY 10118, (212)889-9009
Cayman Islands Directors Assn. [IO], Grand Cayman, Cayman Islands
Cayman Islands Fund Administrators Assn. [IO], Grand Cayman, Cayman Islands
Cayman Islands Natural Bodybuilding, Powerlifting and Weightlifting Assn. [IO], Grand Cayman, Cayman Islands
Cayman Islands Real Estate Brokers Assn. [IO], Grand Cayman, Cayman Islands
Cayman Islands Sailing Club [IO], Grand Cayman, Cayman Islands
Cayman Islands Small Bus. Assn. [IO], Grand Cayman, Cayman Islands
Cayman Islands Soc. of Human Resources Professionals [IO], Grand Cayman, Cayman Islands
Cayman Islands Tourism Assn. [IO], Grand Cayman, Cayman Islands
Cayman Islands Triathlon Assn. [IO], George Town, Cayman Islands

Cayman Music and Entertainment Assn. [IO], Grand Cayman, Cayman Islands
Cayman Soc. of Architects, Surveyors and Engineers [IO], Grand Cayman, Cayman Islands
Cayman Wildlife Connection [IO], Grand Cayman, Cayman Islands
CB Radio Patrol of Amer. Fed. of Police [★5686]
CBA [3099], PO Box 62000, Colorado Springs, CO 80962-2000, (719)265-9895
CBA [3099], PO Box 62000, Colorado Springs, CO 80962-2000, (719)265-9895
CBAmerica [★19318]
CBHL [★9983]
CBHL [★9983]
CBInternational [★19337]
CBInternational [★19337]
CBM Australia [IO], Box Hill, Australia
CBM Ministries [★19319]
CCCO/An Agency for Military and Draft Counseling [★17561]
CCDR [★9542]
CCDR [★9542]
CCHS Family Network [14377], Al Pope, Treas., 11201 Fairfield St., Livonia, MI 48150
CCIM Inst. [3005], 430 N Michigan Ave., Ste. 800, Chicago, IL 60611-4092, (312)321-4460
CCIM Inst. [3005], 430 N Michigan Ave., Ste. 800, Chicago, IL 60611-4092, (312)321-4460
CCNG Intl. [2394], 2201 Long Prairie Rd., Ste. 107-365, Flower Mound, TX 75022, (303)459-7754
C.D. Howe Inst. [IO], Toronto, ON, Canada
CDA Natl. Credentialing Prog. [★11150]
CDC Development Solutions [17906], 1030 15th St. NW, Ste. 730 E, Washington, DC 20005, (202)872-0933
CDC Natl. Prevention Info. Network [13601], PO Box 6003, Rockville, MD 20849-6003, (404)679-3860
CDG Family Network Found. [16764], PO Box 860847, Plano, TX 75074, (800)250-5273
CDMA Development Gp. [7495], 575 Anton Blvd., Ste. 560, Costa Mesa, CA 92626, (714)545-5211
CDS Intl. [7787], 440 Park Ave. S, New York, NY 10016, (212)497-3500
CDS Intl. [7787], 440 Park Ave. S, New York, NY 10016, (212)497-3500
Ceardchumann Teicniuil, Innealtoireachta and Leic-treachais [★IO]
CEC ArtsLink [17496], 435 Hudson St., 8th Fl., New York, NY 10014, (212)643-1985
CEC ArtsLink [17496], 435 Hudson St., 8th Fl., New York, NY 10014, (212)643-1985
CEC Intl. Partners [★17496]
CEC Intl. Partners [★17496]
Cecchetti Coun. of Am. [7956], 23393 Meadows Ave., Flat Rock, MI 48134, (734)379-6710
CED - Caritas Burundi [IO], Bujumbura, Burundi
CEDAM Intl. [4017], 2 Fox Rd., Croton-on-Hudson, NY 10520, (914)271-5365
CEDAM Intl. [4017], 2 Fox Rd., Croton-on-Hudson, NY 10520, (914)271-5365
Cedar Shake and Shingle Bur. [1500], PO Box 1178, Sumas, WA 98295-1178
Cedar Shake and Shingle Bur. [1500], PO Box 1178, Sumas, WA 98295-1178
Cedar Tree - Address unknown since 2011.
Cedefop - European Centre for the Development of Vocational Training [IO], Thessaloniki, Greece
Ceilings and Interior Systems Constr. Assn. [905], 405 Illinois Ave., Unit 2B, St. Charles, IL 60174, (630)584-1919
Ceilings and Interior Systems Contractors Assn. [★905]
Celebrate Adoption [★10790]
Celebration U.S.A. [8734], 17853 Santiago Blvd., Ste. 107, Villa Park, CA 92861, (714)283-1892
Celiac Disease Found. [14557], 13251 Ventura Blvd., Ste. 1, Studio City, CA 91604, (818)990-2354
Celiac Sprue Assn. U.S.A. [14558], PO Box 31700, Omaha, NE 68131-0700, (402)558-0600
Ce.L.I.M. Milano Volunteers for Intl. Ser. [IO], Milan, Italy
Cell Biology; Intl. Fed. of [6303]
Cell Phones for Soldiers [11086], 243 Winter St., Norwell, MA 02061, (781)588-2608

Reference to "IO" in place of a book number signifies that the association may be found in the 50th edition of International Organizations.

Cell Proliferation Soc. - Address unknown since 2010.

Cell Res; Intl. Soc. for Stem [14652]

Cell Res; Intl. Soc. for Stem [14652]

Cell Res; PanAmerican Soc. for Pigment [15349]

Cell Res; Student Soc. for Stem [15352]

Cell Res; Student Soc. for Stem [15352]

Cell Stress Soc. Intl. [16724], Univ. of Connecticut, MCB Dept., 91 N Eagleville Rd., Storrs Mansfield, CT 06269-3125, (860)486-6304

Cell Stress Soc. Intl. [16724], Univ. of Connecticut, MCB Dept., 91 N Eagleville Rd., Storrs Mansfield, CT 06269-3125, (860)486-6304

Cellular Communications Indus. Assn. [★3406]

Cellular Operators Assn. of India [IO], New Delhi, India

Cellular Radio Communications Assn. [★3406]

Cellular Telecommunications Indus. Assn. [★3406]

Cellulose Indus. Standards Enforcement Prog. [★543]

Cellulose Insulation Mfrs. Assn. [543], 136 S Keowee St., Dayton, OH 45402, (937)222-2462

Celtic
Celtic Coun. of Australia [19344]
North Amer. Celtic Buyers Assn. [729]
North Amer. Celtic Buyers Assn. [729]
Royal Celtic Soc. [16189]
Southwest Celtic Music Assn. [9471]

Celtic Coun. of Australia [IO], Mosman, Australia

Celtic Film and TV Festival [IO], Glasgow, United Kingdom

Celtic Language Teachers; North Amer. Assn. for [8479]

Celtic League [IO], Caerphilly, United Kingdom

Celtic League, Amer. Br. - Address unknown since 2010.

CEMAFON: The European Foundry Equip. Suppliers Assn. [IO], Frankfurt, Germany

Cement Admixtures Assn. [IO], Solihull, United Kingdom

Cement Assn. of Canada [IO], Ottawa, ON, Canada

Cement and Concrete Assn. of Malaysia [IO], Petaling Jaya, Malaysia

Cement and Concrete Assn. of New Zealand [IO], Wellington, New Zealand

Cement and Concrete Inst. [IO], Gauteng, Republic of South Africa

Cement Kiln Recycling Coalition [4868], PO Box 7553, Arlington, VA 22207, (703)869-4718

Cement, Lime, Gypsum, and Allied Workers Div. [23175], Intl. Brotherhood of Boilermakers, 753 State Ave., Kansas City, KS 66101, (913)371-2640

Cement Mfrs'. Assn. [IO], Noida, India

Cemented Carbide Producers Assn. [2466], 30200 Detroit Rd., Cleveland, OH 44145-1967, (440)899-0010

Cementitious Slag Makers Assn. [IO], Oxted, United Kingdom

Cemetery Consumer Ser. Coun. - Address unknown since 2010.

Cemetery Supply Assn. [★2536]

Cemetery Supply Assn. [★2536]

Censeil des Editeurs Européens [★IO]

Censorship
Free Expression Policy Proj. [17290]
Free Speech Coalition [17224]
Freedom to Read Found. [17225]CensorshipIntl. Freedom to Publish Comm.
Natl. Coalition Against Censorship [17226]
Proj. Censored [17227]
Rock the Vote [17228]

Centar Za Prava Deteta [★IO]

Centar Za Zene Rosa [★IO]

Centenary Coll. of Louisiana Alumni Assn. [18862], 2911 Centenary Blvd., Shreveport, LA 71104, (318)869-5115

Centennial Legion of Historic Military Commands [20743], 46 Highland Ave., Jaffrey, NH 03452, (603)532-6415

Center for Academic Ethics - Defunct.

Center for Acid Rain and Clean Air Policy Analyses [★4781]

Center for Adaptive Learning [★6888]

Center for Adaptive Learning [★6888]

Center on Addiction and the Family [13239], 50 Jay St., Brooklyn, NY 11201, (646)505-2061

Center for Adult Learning and Educational Credentials [★8171]

Center for Adult Life and Learning [★12400]

Center to Advance Palliative Care [15048], 1255 5th Ave., Ste. C-2, New York, NY 10029-3852, (212)201-2670

Center for the Advancement of the Covenant - Defunct.

Center for Advancement of Public Policy [18445], 323 Morning Sun Trail, Corrales, NM 87048

Center for Advancement of Racial and Ethnic Equity [8627], 1 Dupont Cir. NW, Washington, DC 20036-1193, (202)939-9395

Center for Advancement of Racial and Ethnic Equity I Amer. Coun. on Educ. [8629], 1 Dupont Cir. NW, Washington, DC 20036-1193, (202)939-9300

Center for Advocacy for the Rights and Interests of the Elderly [10836], 1500 Land Title Bldg., 100 S Broad St., Philadelphia, PA 19110, (215)545-5728

Center for African Studies [18789], Ohio State Univ., 314 Oxley Hall, 1712 Neil Ave., Columbus, OH 43210-1219, (614)292-8169

Center for Amer. Archeology [6164], PO Box 366, Kampsville, IL 62053, (618)653-4316

Center of the Amer. Experiment [17419], 12 S 6th St., Ste. 1024, Minneapolis, MN 55402-1502, (612)338-3605

Center for Amer. and Intl. Law [5656], 5201 Democracy Dr., Plano, TX 75024-3561, (972)244-3400

Center for Amer. and Intl. Law [5656], 5201 Democracy Dr., Plano, TX 75024-3561, (972)244-3400

Center for Amer. Women and Politics [17630], Rutgers Univ., Eagleton Inst. of Politics, 191 Ryders Ln., New Brunswick, NJ 08901-8557, (732)932-9384

Center for Applications of Psychological Type [16394], 2815 NW 13th St., Ste. 401, Gainesville, FL 32609-2865, (352)375-0160

Center for Applied Christian Ethics [19718], Wheaton Coll., 117 Blanchard Hall, 501 Coll. Ave., Wheaton, IL 60187-5593, (630)752-5886

The Center for Applied Judaism [★19902]

Center for Applied Linguistics [10024], 4646 40th St. NW, Washington, DC 20016-1859, (202)362-0700

Center for Applied Res. in the Apostolate [19410], 2300 Wisconsin Ave. NW, Ste. 400, Washington, DC 20007, (202)687-8080

Center for the Applied Stud. of Prejudice and Ethnoviolence [★17320]

Center for Architectural and Design Res. - Defunct.

Center for Asian Amer. Media [17336], 145 9th St., Ste. 350, San Francisco, CA 94103, (415)863-0814

Center for Assessment and Policy Development [18638], 268 Barren Hill Rd., Conshohocken, PA 19428, (610)828-1063

Center for Attitudinal Healing [★15451]

Center for Attitudinal Healing [★15451]

Center for Austrian Stud. [9344], Univ. of Minnesota, 314 Social Sci. Bldg., 267 19th Ave. S, Minneapolis, MN 55455, (612)624-9811

Center for Austrian Stud. [9344], Univ. of Minnesota, 314 Social Sci. Bldg., 267 19th Ave. S, Minneapolis, MN 55455, (612)624-9811

Center for Auto Safety [12980], 1825 Connecticut Ave. NW, Ste. 330, Washington, DC 20009-5708, (202)328-7700

Center for Aviation Res. and Educ. - Address unknown since 2010.

Center for Bead Res. - Defunct.

Center for Bigfoot Stud. [7248], 10926 Milano Ave., Norwalk, CA 90650-1638

Center for Bio-Ethical Reform [18550], PO Box 219, Lake Forest, CA 92609, (949)206-0600

Center for Bioethics [6281], Univ. of Pennsylvania, 3401 Market St., Ste. 320, Philadelphia, PA 19104-3308, (215)898-7136

Center for Bioethics [6280], N504 Boynton Hea. Center, 410 Church St. SE, Minneapolis, MN 55455-0346, (612)624-9440

Center for Biologics Evaluation and Research - Address unknown since 2010.

Center for the Book [10037], Lib. of Cong., 101 Independence Ave. SE, Washington, DC 20540-4920, (202)707-5221

Center for Book Arts [9441], 28 W 27th St., 3rd Fl., New York, NY 10001, (212)481-0295

Center on Budget and Policy Priorities [18430], 820 1st St. NE, Ste. 510, Washington, DC 20002, (202)408-1080

Center for Campus Organizing - Address unknown since 2011.

Center for Canadian Stud. and Intl. Programs [★7810]

Center for Canadian Stud. and Intl. Programs [★7810]

Center for Chem. Plant Safety [★747]

Center for Chem. Process Safety [747], 3 Park Ave., 19th Fl., New York, NY 10016-5991, (646)495-1370

Center for the Child Care Workforce, A Proj. of the Amer. Fed. of Teachers Educational Found. - Address unknown since 2010.

Center for Children with Chronic Illness and Disability - Defunct.

Center for Chinese Res. Materials - Address unknown since 2010.

Center for Chinese Stud. [IO], Taipei, Taiwan

Center for Christian/Jewish Understanding [19650], Sacred Heart Univ., 5151 Park Ave., Fairfield, CT 06825-1000, (203)371-7999

Center for Christian Stud. [19542], Fifth Avenue Presbyterian Church, 7 W 55th St., New York, NY 10019, (212)247-0490

Center for Citizen Initiatives [17960], The Presidio of San Francisco, PO Box 29249, San Francisco, CA 94129, (415)561-7777

Center for Citizen Initiatives [17960], The Presidio of San Francisco, PO Box 29249, San Francisco, CA 94129, (415)561-7777

Center for Civic Network - Defunct.

Center for Civic Networking - Defunct.

Center for Civil and Human Rights [12231], Notre Dame Law School, 2150 Eck Hall of Law, Notre Dame, IN 46556, (574)631-8555

Center for Civil Soc. Intl. [★17565]

Center for Civil Soc. Intl. [★17565]

Center for Clean Air Policy [4781], 750 First St. NE, Ste. 940, Washington, DC 20002, (202)408-9260

Center for Clinical Integration [★14887]

Center for Commercial-Free Public Educ. [8009], 1714 Franklin St., Ste. 100-306, Oakland, CA 94612, (510)268-1100

Center for Commun. [7773], 110 E 23rd St., Ste. 900, New York, NY 10010, (212)686-5005

Center for Commun. Programs [12698], Johns Hopkins Bloomberg School of Public Hea., 111 Market Pl., Ste. 310, Baltimore, MD 21202, (410)659-6300

Center for Commun. Programs [12698], Johns Hopkins Bloomberg School of Public Hea., 111 Market Pl., Ste. 310, Baltimore, MD 21202, (410)659-6300

Center for Community Action of B'Nai B'rith Intl. [11558], 2020 K St. NW, 7th Fl., Washington, DC 20006, (202)857-6600

Center for Community Action of B'Nai B'rith Intl. [11558], 2020 K St. NW, 7th Fl., Washington, DC 20006, (202)857-6600

Center for Community Change [12721], 1536 U St. NW, Washington, DC 20009, (202)339-9300

Center for Community Justice [★5204]

Center for Community and Org. Development [11528], DePaul Univ., 1 E Jackson Blvd., Chicago, IL 60604, (773)325-4250

Center for Community Solutions [17631], 4508 Mission Bay Dr., San Diego, CA 92109, (858)272-5777

Center for Computer-Assisted Legal Instruction [6508], 565 W Adams St., Chicago, IL 60661-3691, (312)906-5307

Center of Concern [17816], 1225 Otis St. NE, Washington, DC 20017-2516, (202)635-2757

Center of Concern [17816], 1225 Otis St. NE, Washington, DC 20017-2516, (202)635-2757

Center for Confucian Sci. [20175], 5821 Queens Chapel Rd., No. 133, Hyattsville, MD 20782

Center on Conscience and War [17560], 1830 Connecticut Ave. NW, Washington, DC 20009-5732, (202)483-2220

Center on Conscience and War [17560], 1830 Connecticut Ave. NW, Washington, DC 20009-5732, (202)483-2220

A star before a book entry number signifies that the name is not listed separately, but is mentioned within the entry.

Center for Constitutional Rights [17273], 666 Broadway, 7th Fl., New York, NY 10012, (212)614-6464

Center for Consumer Affairs [17448], UWM School of Continuing Educ., Univ. of Wisconsin-Milwaukee, 161 W Wisconsin Ave., Ste. 6000, Milwaukee, WI 53203-2602, (414)227-3200

Center for Contemporary Opera [10172], 338 W 23rd St., New York, NY 10011, (347)265-8943

Center for Corporate Public Involvement - Defunct.

Center for Correctional Justice [★5204]

Center for Craniofacial Development and Disorders [14192], 733 N Broadway, Ste. 411, Rm. 419, Baltimore, MD 21205, (410)955-4160

Center for Creative Leadership [2274], PO Box 26300, Greensboro, NC 27438-6300, (336)545-2810

Center for Creative Leadership [2274], PO Box 26300, Greensboro, NC 27438-6300, (336)545-2810

Center for Creative Stud. - Coll. of Art and Design Alumni Assn. [★18864]

Center for Critical Thinking [7951], The Found. for Critical Thinking, PO Box 196, Tomales, CA 94971, (707)878-9100

Center for Critical Thinking and Moral Critique [★7951]

Center for Cuban Stud. [9512], 231 W 29th St., 4th Fl., New York, NY 10011, (212)242-0559

Center for Cultural and Tech. Interchange Between East and West [★17962]

Center for Cultural and Tech. Interchange Between East and West [★17962]

Center for Dao-Confucianism [★20175]

Center for Death Educ. and Bioethics - Address unknown since 2010.

Center for the Defense of Free Enterprise [17715], Liberty Park, 12500 NE 10th Pl., Bellevue, WA 98005, (425)455-5038

Center for Defense Info. [17502], 1779 Massachusetts Ave. NW, Washington, DC 20036-2109, (202)332-0600

Center for Democracy and Free Enterprise [IO], Prague, Czech Republic

Center for Democracy and Tech. [17337], 1634 Eye St. NW, Ste. 1100, Washington, DC 20006, (202)637-9800

Center for Democratic Renewal - Address unknown since 2010.

Center for Dispute Settlement [5204], 1666 Connecticut Ave. NW, Washington, DC 20009-1039, (202)265-9572

Center for Documentation and Res. of Peace and Conflicts [IO], Lyon, France

Center for Ecoliteracy [4198], David Brower Ctr., 2150 Allston Way, Ste. 270, Berkeley, CA 94704-1377, (510)845-4595

Center for Economic Conversion [17547], 222 View St., Mountain View, CA 94041-1344, (650)968-8798

Center for Economic Options [11934], 910 Quarrier St., Ste. 206, Charleston, WV 25301, (304)345-1298

Center for Economic and Policy Res. [17591], 1611 Connecticut Ave. NW, Ste. 400, Washington, DC 20009-1033, (202)293-5380

Center for Economic and Social Justice [11900], PO Box 40711, Washington, DC 20016-0711, (703)243-5155

Center for Educ. and Res. in Free Enterprise [★17722]

Center on Educ. and Training for Employment [9043], Ohio State Univ., 1900 Kenny Rd., Columbus, OH 43210-1016, (614)292-6991

Center for the Educ. of Women [9056], 330 E Liberty St., Ann Arbor, MI 48104, (734)764-6005

Center for Electronic Packaging Res. [7207], Univ. of Arizona, Dept. of Elecl. and Cmpt. Engg., PO Box 210104, Tucson, AZ 85721-0104, (520)621-2434

Center for Energy Efficiency and Renewable Technologies [4225], 1100 11th St., Ste. 311, Sacramento, CA 95814, (916)442-7785

Center for Energy, Env. and Economics [6698], New York Inst. of Tech., Dept. of Energy Mgt., Harry Schure Hall, Rm. 116, Northern Blvd., Old Westbury, NY 11568-8000, (516)686-7990

Center for Energy Policy and Res. [★6698]

Center for Environmental Educ. [★4115]

Center for Environmental Educ. [★4115]

Center for Environmental Info. [4239], 249 Highland Ave., Rochester, NY 14620, (585)262-2870

Center for Environmental Investigation and Planning [IO], Santiago, Chile

Center for Equal Opportunity [9855], 7700 Leesburg Pike, Ste. 231, Falls Church, VA 22043, (703)442-0066

Center for Ergonomic Res. - Address unknown since 2011.

Center for the Evangelical United Brethren Heritage [19719], 4501 Denlinger Rd., Dayton, OH 45426, (937)529-2201

Center for Excellence in Assn. Leadership [★265]

Center for Excellence in Govt. [★5429]

Center for Excellence in Hea. Care Journalism [★2810]

Center for Excellence in Hea. Care Journalism [★2810]

Center for Exhibition Indus. Res. [1228], 12700 Park Central Dr., Ste. 308, Dallas, TX 75251, (972)687-9242

Center for Expressive Anal. [★16461]

Center for Expressive Psychotherapy [★16461]

Center for Family Planning Prog. Development [★12034]

Center for Family Support [12500], 333 7th Ave., 9th Fl., New York, NY 10001-5004, (212)629-7939

Center for Field Res. at Earthwatch Inst. [★7335]

Center for Field Res. at Earthwatch Inst. [★7335]

Center for Food Safety [6873], 660 Pennsylvania Ave. SE, Ste. 302, Washington, DC 20003, (202)547-9359

Center For Hea., Env. and Justice [4979], PO Box 6806, Falls Church, VA 22040-6806, (703)237-2249

Center for Foreign Journalists [★2830]

Center for Foreign Journalists [★2830]

Center for Foreign Policy Development - Defunct.

Center for Global Educ. [8406], Augsburg Coll., 2211 Riverside Ave., Minneapolis, MN 55454, (612)330-1159

Center for Global Educ. [8406], Augsburg Coll., 2211 Riverside Ave., Minneapolis, MN 55454, (612)330-1159

Center for Governmental Res. [18446], 1 S Washington St., Ste. 400, Rochester, NY 14614-1125, (585)325-6360

Center for Hazardous Materials Res. - Defunct.

Center for Hea. Design [14762], 1850 Gateway Blvd., Ste. 1083, Concord, CA 94520, (925)521-9404

Center for Hea. and the Global Env. [14498], Harvard Medical School, 401 Park Dr., 2nd Fl. E, Boston, MA 02115, (617)384-8530

Center for Hea. and the Global Env. [14498], Harvard Medical School, 401 Park Dr., 2nd Fl. E, Boston, MA 02115, (617)384-8530

Center for Hearing and Commun. [14923], 50 Broadway, 6th Fl., New York, NY 10004, (917)305-7700

Center for the History of Amer. Needlework - Defunct.

Center for History of Chemistry [★9759]

Center for Holistic Mgt. [★4078]

Center for Hosp. Mgt. Engg. [★15057]

Center on Human Policy [11768], Syracuse Univ., School of Educ., 805 S Crouse Ave., Syracuse, NY 13244-2280, (315)443-3851

Center for Human Services [13126], 7200 Wisconsin Ave., Ste. 600, Bethesda, MD 20814, (301)654-8338

Center for Human Services [13126], 7200 Wisconsin Ave., Ste. 600, Bethesda, MD 20814, (301)654-8338

Center for Humane Options in Childbirth Experiences [15874], 5721 N High St., Worthington, OH 43085, (614)263-2229

Center for Immigration Stud. [17880], 1522 K St. NW, Ste. 820, Washington, DC 20005-1202, (202)466-8185

Center to Improve Care of the Dying [★11746]

Center for Improved Learning Environments [★8818]

Center for Independent Documentary [9598], 680 S Main St., Sharon, MA 02067, (781)784-3627

Center for Inquiry [17729], 3965 Rensch Rd., Amherst, NY 14228, (716)636-4869

Center for Institutional and Intl. Initiatives [★8482]

Center for Interdisciplinary Res. in Bioethics [IO], Brussels, Belgium

Center for Intl. Affairs [★17959]

Center for Intl. Affairs [★17959]

Center for Intl. Blood and Marrow Transplant Res. [13857], Froedtert and the Medical Coll. of Wisconsin Clinical Cancer Center, 9200 W Wisconsin Ave., Ste. C5500, Milwaukee, WI 53226, (414)805-0700

Center for Intl. Blood and Marrow Transplant Res. [13857], Froedtert and the Medical Coll. of Wisconsin Clinical Cancer Center, 9200 W Wisconsin Ave., Ste. C5500, Milwaukee, WI 53226, (414)805-0700

Center for Intl. Disaster Info. [11848], 529 14th St. NW, Ste. 700, Washington, DC 20045, (202)821-1999

Center for Intl. Disaster Info. [11848], 529 14th St. NW, Ste. 700, Washington, DC 20045, (202)821-1999

Center for Intl. Env. Info. [★4167]

Center for Intl. Env. Info. [★4167]

Center for Intl. Environmental Law [5412], 1350 Connecticut Ave. NW, Ste. 1100, Washington, DC 20036, (202)785-8700

Center for Intl. Environmental Law [5412], 1350 Connecticut Ave. NW, Ste. 1100, Washington, DC 20036, (202)785-8700

Center for Intl. Policy [17817], 1717 Massachusetts Ave. NW, Ste. 801, Washington, DC 20036, (202)232-3317

Center for Intl. Policy [17817], 1717 Massachusetts Ave. NW, Ste. 801, Washington, DC 20036, (202)232-3317

Center for Intl. Private Enterprise [655], 1155 15th St. NW, Ste. 700, Washington, DC 20005, (202)721-9200

Center for Intl. Private Enterprise [655], 1155 15th St. NW, Ste. 700, Washington, DC 20005, (202)721-9200

Center for Intl. Private Enterprise - Egypt Off. [IO], Cairo, Egypt

Center for Intl. Private Enterprise - Romania Off. [IO], Bucharest, Romania

Center for Intl. Private Enterprise - Russia Off. [IO], Moscow, Russia

Center for Investigation and Development of Educ. [IO], Santiago, Chile

Center for Investigative Reporting [17338], 2130 Center St., Ste. 103, Berkeley, CA 94704, (510)809-3160

Center for Jewish Community Stud. [18017], 7 Church Ln., Ste. 9, Baltimore, MD 21208, (410)653-7779

Center for Jewish History [19088], 15 W 16th St., New York, NY 10011, (212)294-8301

Center for Judicial Accountability [18025], 283 Soundview Ave., White Plains, NY 10606, (914)421-1200

Center for Judicial Studies - Defunct.

Center on Juvenile and Criminal Justice [5369], 440 9th St., San Francisco, CA 94103, (415)621-5661

Center for Labor and Community Res. [18041], 3411 W Diversey Ave., Ste. 10, Chicago, IL 60647-6207, (773)278-5418

Center for Labor Res. and Educ. [8452], Inst. of Res. on Labor and Employment, 2521 Channing Way, No. 5555, Berkeley, CA 94720-5555, (510)642-0323

Center for Law and Educ. [5394], 1875 Connecticut Ave. NW, Ste. 510, Washington, DC 20009, (202)986-3000

Center for Law and Justice Intl. [5657], 6375 New Hope Rd., New Hope, KY 40052, (502)549-5454

Center for Law in the Public Interest - Defunct.

Center for Law and Religious Freedom [18518], Christian Legal Soc., 8001 Braddock Rd., Ste. 300, Springfield, VA 22151, (703)642-1070

Center for Leadership Development and Academic Admin. [★8482]

Reference to "IO" in place of a book number signifies that the association may be found in the 50th edition of International Organizations.

Encyclopedia of Associations, 51st Edition

2667

Center for Lesbian and Gay Stud. [12073], City Univ. of New York, Graduate Center, Rm. 7115, 365 Fifth Ave., New York, NY 10016, (212)817-1955

Center for Liberal Strategies [IO], Sofia, Bulgaria

Center for Local Tax Res. [★18692]

Center for Loss in Multiple Birth [12604], PO Box 91377, Anchorage, AK 99509, (907)222-5321

Center for Mgt. Effectiveness [2275], 15332 Antioch St., Ste. 46, Pacific Palisades, CA 90272-3628, (310)459-6052

Center for Marine Conservation [★4115]

Center for Marine Conservation [★4115]

Center for Marketing Commun. [★78]

Center for Media and Public Affairs [17339], 933 N Kenmore St., Ste. 405, Arlington, VA 22201, (571)319-0029

Center for Medical Consumers [14703], 239 Thompson St., New York, NY 10012, (212)674-7105

Center for Medical Consumers and Hea. Care Info. [★14703]

Center for Medical Ethics and Mediation - Address unknown since 2011.

Center for Medicare Advocacy [14853], PO Box 350, Willimantic, CT 06226, (860)456-7790

Center for Medieval and Early Renaissance Stud. [★10074]

Center for Medieval and Renaissance Stud. [10074], PO Box 6000, Binghamton, NY 13902-6000, (607)777-2730

Center for Migration Stud. of New York [10086], 27 Carmine St., New York, NY 10014-4423, (212)337-3080

Center for Migration Stud. of New York [10086], 27 Carmine St., New York, NY 10014-4423, (212)337-3080

Center for the Ministry of Teaching [19671], 3737 Seminary Rd., Alexandria, VA 22304, (703)461-1885

Center for Moral Democracy [★17267]

Center for Multicultural Leadership - Defunct.

Center on Natl. Labor Policy [18048], 5211 Port Royal Rd., Ste. 103, North Springfield, VA 22151

Center for Natl. Policy [18447], 1 Massachusetts Ave. NW, Ste. 333, Washington, DC 20001, (202)682-1800

Center for Natl. Security Stud. [18591], 1120 19th St. NW, 8th Fl., Washington, DC 20036, (202)721-5650

Center for Native Lands [★5416]

Center for Native Lands [★5416]

Center for Neighborhood Enterprise [17370], 1625 K St. NW, Ste. 1200, Washington, DC 20006-1672, (202)518-6500

Center for Neighborhood Tech. [17371], 2125 W North Ave., Chicago, IL 60647, (773)278-4800

Center for a New Amer. Dream [17415], 455 2nd St. SE, Ste. 101, Charlottesville, VA 22902-5697, (301)891-3683

Center for New Community [17372], PO Box 479327, Chicago, IL 60647-9327, (312)266-0319

Center for New Natl. Security - Address unknown since 2010.

Center for Nonviolent Commun. [18165], 5600 San Francisco Rd. NE, Ste. A, Albuquerque, NM 87109, (505)244-4041

Center for Nonviolent Persuasion [★18165]

Center for Occupational Res. and Development [8106], PO Box 21689, Waco, TX 76702-1689, (254)772-8756

Center for Oceans Law and Policy [7178], Univ. of Virginia, School of Law, 580 Massie Rd., Charlottesville, VA 22903-1789, (434)924-7441

Center for Organ Recovery and Educ. [16905], 204 Sigma Dr., RIDC Park, Pittsburgh, PA 15238, (800)366-6777

Center for Organizational and Ministry Development [19543], PO Box 49488, Colorado Springs, CO 80949, (719)590-8808

Center for Pacific Northwest Stud. [7411], Western Washington Univ., Goltz-Murray Archives Bldg., 808 25th St., Bellingham, WA 98225-9123, (360)650-7747

Center Perzent - Karakalpak Center for Reproductive Hea. and Env. [IO], Karakalpakstan, Uzbekistan

Center for Philosophy and Public Policy [★18468]

Center for Plant Conservation [4018], PO Box 299, St. Louis, MO 63166-0299, (314)577-9450

Center for Policy Anal. on Palestine [★8373]

Center for Political Stud. [★7414]

Center for the Polyurethanes Indus. [2765], 1300 Wilson Blvd., Arlington, VA 22209, (703)741-5103

Center for Popular Economics [6616], PO Box 785, Amherst, MA 01004, (413)545-0743

Center for Population Options [★12025]

Center for Population Options [★12025]

Center to Prevent Handgun Violence [★17684]

Center to Prevent Youth Violence [17685], 100 Wall St., 2nd Fl., New York, NY 10005, (212)269-5100

Center for Process Analysis and Control [6402], Univ. of Washington, Henderson Hall, Box 355640, Seattle, WA 98195-5640, (206)685-2326

Center for Process Stud. [10375], 1325 N Coll. Ave., Claremont, CA 91711, (909)621-5330

Center for Professional Well-Being [14874], 21 W Colony Pl., Ste. 150, Durham, NC 27705, (919)489-9167

Center to Protect Workers Rights [★23163]

Center to Protect Workers' Rights [★23176]

Center for the Protection of Children's Rights Found. [IO], Bangkok, Thailand

Center for Psychological and Spiritual Hea. - Defunct.

Center for Public Integrity [17747], 910 17th St. NW, Ste. 700, Washington, DC 20006, (202)466-1300

Center for Public Justice [18448], PO Box 48368, Washington, DC 20002-0368, (410)571-6300

Center for Public Resources [★5205]

Center for Reclaiming Am. - Defunct.

Center for Reduction of Religious-Based Conflict [18512], 649 5th Ave. S, Ste. 201, Naples, FL 34102-6601, (239)821-4850

Center for Reduction of Religious-Based Conflict [18512], 649 5th Ave. S, Ste. 201, Naples, FL 34102-6601, (239)821-4850

Center for Reflective Community Practice - Address unknown since 2010.

Center of Regional Cooperation for Adult Educ. in Latin Am. and the Caribbean [IO], Patzcuaro, Mexico

Center for Regional Development/Transparency Intl. - Armenia [IO], Yerevan, Armenia

Center for Rehabilitation Hospitals and Services [★15039]

Center on Religion and Soc. - Address unknown since 2010.

Center for Religious Freedom [17818], Hudson Inst., Inc., 1015 15th St. NW, 6th Fl., Washington, DC 20005, (202)974-2400

Center for Religious Freedom [17818], Hudson Inst., Inc., 1015 15th St. NW, 6th Fl., Washington, DC 20005, (202)974-2400

Center for Renewable Energy and Sustainable Tech. I Renewable Energy Policy Project [6699], 1612 K St. NW, Ste. 202, Washington, DC 20006, (202)293-2898

Center for Renewable Resources [★7442]

Center for Renewable Resources [★7442]

Center for Reproductive Law and Policy [★18523]

Center for Reproductive Law and Policy [★18523]

Center for Reproductive Rights [18523], 120 Wall St., New York, NY 10005, (917)637-3600

Center for Reproductive Rights [18523], 120 Wall St., New York, NY 10005, (917)637-3600

Center for Res. on Educ., Diversity and Excellence [★10024]

Center for Res. in Faith and Moral Development - Defunct.

Center for Res. Libraries [9979], 6050 S Kenwood Ave., Chicago, IL 60637-2804, (773)955-4545

Center for Rsrc. Mgt. - Address unknown since 2011.

Center for Resourceful Building Tech. - Defunct.

Center for Respect of Life and Env. - Address unknown since 2010.

Center for Responsive Politics [18378], 1101 14th St. NW, Ste. 1030, Washington, DC 20005-5635, (202)857-0044

Center for Responsive Psychology - Defunct.

Center for the Rights of the Terminally Ill - Defunct.

Center for Rural Affairs [17166], PO Box 136, Lyons, NE 68038-0136, (402)687-2100

Center for School Change [8010], Macalester Coll., Markim Hall, 3rd Fl., St. Paul, MN 55105, (651)696-6848

Center for Sci. in the Public Interest [17449], 1220 L St. NW, Ste. 300, Washington, DC 20005, (202)332-9110

Center for Sci. in the Public Interest I Alcohol Policies Proj. [17175], 1220 L St. NW, Ste. 300, Washington, DC 20005-4053, (202)332-9110

Center for Screen-Time Awareness [11998], 1200 29th St. NW, Lower Level No. 1, Washington, DC 20007, (202)333-9220

Center for Seafarers' Rights [5785], Seamen's Church Inst. of New York/New Jersey, 241 Water St., New York, NY 10038, (212)349-9090

Center for Security Policy [18592], 1901 Pennsylvania Ave. NW, Ste. 201, Washington, DC 20006, (202)835-9077

Center for Self-Sufficiency [11559], 4465 N Oakland Ave., Ste. 200, Milwaukee, WI 53211, (414)332-0050

Center for Sex and Culture [8859], 2215-R Market St., PMB 455, San Francisco, CA 94114, (415)255-1155

Center for Short Lived Phenomena - Defunct.

The Center for Social Gerontology [10837], 2307 Shelby Ave., Ann Arbor, MI 48103, (734)665-1126

Center for Social and Legal Res. [5563], 2 Univ. Plz., Ste. 414, Hackensack, NJ 07601, (201)996-1154

Center for Social and Legal Res. [5563], 2 Univ. Plz., Ste. 414, Hackensack, NJ 07601, (201)996-1154

Center for Social Stud. Educ. - Address unknown since 2010.

Center on Social Welfare Policy and Law [★5943]

Center for Socialist History [9757], PO Box 626, Alameda, CA 94501-8626, (510)601-6460

Center for Southern Folklore [9119], Peabody Place Trolley Stop, 119 S Main St., Memphis, TN 38101, (901)525-3655

Center for Spiritual and Ethical Educ. [8286], PO Box 19807, Portland, OR 97280-0807, (503)232-1531

Center for Sports and Osteopathic Medicine [16309], 317 Madison Ave., New York, NY 10017, (212)685-8113

Center for Statistics [★8046]

Center for Strategic and Budgetary Assessments [18136], 1667 K St. NW, Ste. 900, Washington, DC 20006, (202)331-7990

Center for Strategic and Intl. Stud. [18417], 1800 K St. NW, Ste. 400, Washington, DC 20006, (202)887-0200

Center for Strategic and Intl. Stud. [18417], 1800 K St. NW, Ste. 400, Washington, DC 20006, (202)887-0200

Center for Stud. in Criminal Justice [11707], Univ. of Chicago Law School, 1111 E 60th St., Chicago, IL 60637, (773)834-4068

Center of Stud. of Disaster and Prevention [IO], Lima, Peru

Center for Stud. on the Holocaust [★17783]

Center for the Stud. of Aging of Albany [10838], 706 Madison Ave., Albany, NY 12208, (518)465-6927

Center for the Stud. of Beadwork [6165], PO Box 13719, Portland, OR 97213, (503)655-3078

Center for the Stud. of Beadwork [6165], PO Box 13719, Portland, OR 97213, (503)655-3078

Center for the Stud. of Canada [7810], Plattsburgh State Univ. of New York, 133 Court St., Plattsburgh, NY 12901, (518)564-2086

Center for the Stud. of Canada [7810], Plattsburgh State Univ. of New York, 133 Court St., Plattsburgh, NY 12901, (518)564-2086

Center for the Stud. of the Coll. Fraternity [23533], Indiana Univ., 900 E 7th St., Ste. 371, Bloomington, IN 47405, (812)855-1228

Center for the Study of Commercialism - Defunct.

Center for the Stud. of Democracy [IO], Sofia, Bulgaria

Center for the Stud. of Democratic Societies [17517], Box 475, Manhattan Beach, CA 90267-0475

A star before a book entry number signifies that the name is not listed separately, but is mentioned within the entry.

Center for the Stud. of Democratic Societies **[17517]**, Box 475, Manhattan Beach, CA 90267-0475

Center for the Stud. of Economics **[18692]**, 413 S 10th St., Philadelphia, PA 19147, (215)923-7800

Center for the Stud. of Film and History **[9599]**, Univ. of Wisconsin Oshkosh, Polk 305, Oshkosh, WI 54901, (920)424-0976

Center for the Stud. of Gp. Processes **[7412]**, Univ. of Iowa, Dept. of Sociology, Iowa City, IA 52242-1401, (319)335-2503

Center for the Stud. of Law and Politics **[★5417]**

Center for the Stud. of Multiple Birth **[15520]**, 333 E Superior St., Ste. 464, Chicago, IL 60611, (312)695-1677

Center for Stud. of Multiple Gestation **[★15520]**

Center for the Study of Parent Involvement - Defunct.

Center for the Stud. of Political Graphics **[9171]**, 8124 W 3rd St., Ste. 211, Los Angeles, CA 90048-4340, (323)653-4662

Center for the Stud. of the Presidency **[17246]**, 1020 19th St. NW, Ste. 250, Washington, DC 20010, (202)872-9800

Center for the Stud. of Psychiatry **[★16094]**

Center for the Stud. of Psychiatry and Psychology **[★16094]**

Center for Stud. of Responsive Law **[17450]**, PO Box 19367, Washington, DC 20036, (202)387-8030

Center for the Stud. of Social Policy **[18449]**, 1575 Eye St. NW, Ste. 500, Washington, DC 20005, (202)371-1565

Center for the Stud. of States **[★5990]**

Center for the Stud. of Welfare Policy **[★18449]**

Center for Studying Hea. Sys. Change **[14763]**, 600 Maryland Ave. SW, Ste. 550, Washington, DC 20024, (202)484-5261

Center for Substance Abuse Prevention **[16738]**, SAMHSA, PO Box 2345, Rockville, MD 20847-2345, (240)276-2420

Center for Surrogate Parenting **[13304]**, West Coast Off., 15821 Ventura Blvd., Ste. 675, Encino, CA 91436, (818)788-8288

Center for Sustainable Agriculture - Defunct.

Center for Sustainable Transportation - Defunct.

Center for Teaching About China **[8305]**, 1214 W Schwartz St., Carbondale, IL 62901, (618)549-1555

Center for Tech. and Res. - Address unknown since 2010.

Center for Third World Organizing **[17274]**, 1218 E 21st St., Oakland, CA 94606, (510)533-7583

Center for Third World Organizing **[17274]**, 1218 E 21st St., Oakland, CA 94606, (510)533-7583

Center for UFO Stud. **[★7254]**

Center for U.N. Reform Educ. **[18743]**, PO Box 3195, New York, NY 10163, (212)682-6958

Center for Understanding Aging **[★10854]**

Center for United States-China Arts Exchange **[9475]**, 423 W 118th St., No. 1E, New York, NY 10027, (212)280-4648

Center for U.S.-Mexican Stud. **[17774]**, Univ. of California, San Diego, 9500 Gilman Dr., Dept. 0510, La Jolla, CA 92093-0510, (858)534-4503

Center for U.S.-Mexican Stud. **[17774]**, Univ. of California, San Diego, 9500 Gilman Dr., Dept. 0510, La Jolla, CA 92093-0510, (858)534-4503

Center for U.S. -USSR Initiatives **[★17960]**

Center for U.S. -USSR Initiatives **[★17960]**

Center for Urban Hospitals **[★15040]**

Center on Urban Poverty and Community Development **[12722]**, Case Western Reserve Univ., Mandel School of Applied Social Sciences, 10900 Euclid Ave., Cleveland, OH 44106-7164, (216)368-6946

Center on Urban Poverty and Social Change **[★12722]**

Center for Urban and Regional Stud. **[10622]**, Univ. of North Carolina at Chapel Hill, 108 Battle Ln., Campus Box 3410, Chapel Hill, NC 27599-3410, (919)962-3074

Center for Urban and Regional Stud. **[10622]**, Univ. of North Carolina at Chapel Hill, 108 Battle Ln., Campus Box 3410, Chapel Hill, NC 27599-3410, (919)962-3074

Center for Urban Res. **[IO]**, Quito, Ecuador

Center for Venture Res. **[2132]**, Univ. of New Hampshire, Whittemore School of Bus. and Economics, 15 Academic Way, Durham, NH 03824-2602, (603)862-3341

Center for Veterans Issues **[20782]**, 3312 W Wells St., PO Box 080168, Milwaukee, WI 53208, (414)345-3917

Center for Victims of Torture **[13361]**, St. Paul Healing Center, 649 Dayton Ave., St. Paul, MN 55104, (612)436-4800

Center for Visionary Leadership **[18064]**, PO Box 2241, Arlington, VA 22202, (415)472-2540

Center for Vocational Educ. **[★9043]**

Center for Voting and Democracy **[18379]**, 6930 Carroll Ave., Ste. 610, Takoma Park, MD 20912, (301)270-4616

Center for War/Peace Stud. **[17942]**, 330 E 38th St., Ste. 19Q, New York, NY 10016, (212)490-6494

Center for Waste Reduction Technologies - Address unknown since 2011.

Center for the Well-Being of Hea. Professionals **[★14874]**

Center for Whale Res. **[7040]**, PO Box 1577, Friday Harbor, WA 98250-1577, (360)378-5835

Center for Women Policy Stud. **[17632]**, 1776 Massachusetts Ave. NW, Ste. 450, Washington, DC 20036, (202)872-1770

Center for Women Veterans **[20783]**, Dept. of Veteran Affairs-Central Off., 810 Vermont Ave. NW, Washington, DC 20420, (202)273-6193

Center for Women War Victims **[IO]**, Zagreb, Croatia

Center for Women's Bus. Res. **[3678]**, 1760 Old Meadow Rd., Ste. 500, McLean, VA 22102, (703)556-7162

Center for Women's Stud. **[★17631]**

Center for Women's Stud. and Services **[★17631]**

Center for Wooden Boats **[22328]**, 1010 Valley St., Seattle, WA 98109-4468, (206)382-2628

Center for Work and the Family **[11999]**, 910 Tulare Ave., Berkeley, CA 94707, (925)258-5400

Center for Workers with Disabilities **[11769]**, 810 1st St. NE, Ste. 500, Washington, DC 20002-4207, (202)682-0100

Center for World Indigenous Stud. **[17889]**, PMB 214, 1001 Cooper Point Rd. SW, Ste. 140, Olympia, WA 98502-1107, (360)450-5183

Center for World Indigenous Stud. **[17889]**, PMB 214, 1001 Cooper Point Rd. SW, Ste. 140, Olympia, WA 98502-1107, (360)450-5183

Center for World Thanksgiving **[★20257]**

Center for World Thanksgiving **[★20257]**

Center for Youth Development and Policy Res. **[18822]**, Acad. for Educational Development, 1825 Connecticut Ave. NW, Washington, DC 20009-5721, (202)884-8267

Center for Youth as Resources - Defunct.

Centered Riding **[22678]**, PO Box 157, Perkiomenville, PA 18074, (610)754-0633

CenterLink **[11661]**, PO Box 24490, Fort Lauderdale, FL 33307-4490, (954)765-6024

Centra Cam Vocational Training Assn. **[IO]**, Camrose, AB, Canada

Centraal Brouwerij Kantoor **[★IO]**

Centraal Bur. Levensmiddelenhandel **[★IO]**

Central Africa Diabetes Assn. **[IO]**, Bangui, Central African Republic

Central African Badminton Fed. **[IO]**, Bangui, Central African Republic

Central African Red Cross Soc. **[IO]**, Bangui, Central African Republic

Central Agency for Jewish Educ. **[19089]**, 12 Millstone Campus Dr., St. Louis, MO 63146-5576, (314)432-0020

Central Alberta Brain Injury Soc. **[IO]**, Red Deer, AB, Canada

Central Alliance of Furniture Mfrs. **[IO]**, Heemstede, Netherlands

Central America
Hermandad **[17229]**
Hermandad **[17229]**
Inst. for Global Labour and Human Rights **[17230]**CentralInst. for Regional and Intl. Stud.
Katalysis Partnership **[17231]**
Katalysis Partnership **[17231]**

Natl. Labor Comm. **[17230]**
Neighbor to Neighbor **[17232]**
Neighbor to Neighbor **[17232]**
Off. of the Americas **[17233]**
Off. of the Americas **[17233]**
Paso Pacifico **[4125]**

Central Am. Rsrc. Center **[★18053]**

Central Am. Rsrc. Center **[★18053]**

Central Amer. Bank for Economic Integration **[IO]**, Tegucigalpa, Honduras

Central Amer. Hea. Inst. **[IO]**, Managua, Nicaragua

Central Amer. Mission **[★20018]**

Central Amer. Mission **[★20018]**

Central Amer. Refugee Center **[★18505]**

Central Amer. Refugee Center **[★18505]**

Central Amer. Rsrc. Center **[18505]**, 1460 Columbia Rd. NW, Ste. C-1, Washington, DC 20009, (202)328-9799

Central Amer. Rsrc. Center **[18505]**, 1460 Columbia Rd. NW, Ste. C-1, Washington, DC 20009, (202)328-9799

Central Asia and the Caucasus Assn. of Agricultural Res. Institutions **[IO]**, Tashkent, Uzbekistan

Central Asian Found. for Mgt. Development **[IO]**, Almaty, Kazakhstan

Central Assn. of Agricultural Valuers **[IO]**, Coleford, United Kingdom

Central Assn. of Bee-Keepers **[IO]**, Upminster, United Kingdom

Central Assn. of German Pork Producers **[IO]**, Bonn, Germany

Central Assn. of the Miraculous Medal **[19411]**, 475 E Chelten Ave., Philadelphia, PA 19144-5758, (215)848-1010

Central Assn. of Sci. and Mathematics Teachers **[★8851]**

Central Assn. of Sci. and Mathematics Teachers **[★8851]**

Central Assn. of Women Entrepreneurs **[IO]**, Helsinki, Finland

Central Bur. for Astronomical Telegrams **[6228]**, Mail Stop 18, 60 Garden St., Cambridge, MA 02138, (617)495-7281

Central Canadian Fed. of Mineralogical Societies **[IO]**, Toronto, ON, Canada

Central Carpet Indus. Assn. **[IO]**, Kathmandu, Nepal

Central Chamber of Commerce of Finland **[IO]**, Helsinki, Finland

Central Collegiate Hockey Assn. **[22642]**, 23995 Freeway Park Dr., Farmington Hills, MI 48335, (248)888-0600

Central Commn. for the Navigation on the Rhine **[IO]**, Strasbourg, France

Central Comm. for Conscientious Objectors **[17561]**, 405 14th St., No. 205, Oakland, CA 94612-2715

Central Comm. on Lumber Standards **[★1494]**

Central Comm. on Lumber Standards **[★1494]**

Central Confed. of the Textile Indus. in Germany **[IO]**, Berlin, Germany

Central Conf. of Amer. Rabbis **[19853]**, 355 Lexington Ave., New York, NY 10017, (212)972-3636

Central Conf. of Amer. Rabbis **[19853]**, 355 Lexington Ave., New York, NY 10017, (212)972-3636

Central Coun. of Physical Recreation **[IO]**, London, United Kingdom

Central Dredging Assn. **[IO]**, Delft, Netherlands

Central and East European Mgt. Development Assn. **[IO]**, Bled, Slovenia

Central and Eastern European Networking Assn. **[IO]**, Warsaw, Poland

Central and Eastern European Schools Assn. **[IO]**, Zagreb, Croatia

Central Elec. Railfans' Assn. **[22125]**, PO Box 503, Chicago, IL 60690, (312)346-3723

Central Eurasian Stud. Soc. **[9877]**, Miami Univ., Havighurst Center, Harrison Hall, Oxford, OH 45056, (513)529-0241

Central Eurasian Stud. Soc. **[9877]**, Miami Univ., Havighurst Center, Harrison Hall, Oxford, OH 45056, (513)529-0241

Central House for Deaconesses **[★19692]**

Central Inst. of Medical Medicinal and Aromatic Plants **[IO]**, Lucknow, India

Reference to "IO" in place of a book number signifies that the association may be found in the 50th edition of International Organizations.

Central Inter-Scholastic Press Assn. [★8444]
Central Intercollegiate Athletic Assn. [22971], PO Box 7349, Hampton, VA 23666, (757)865-0071
Central Israel ACM SIGGRAPH [IO], Herzliya, Israel
Central Off. for Bus. and Trade in Food [IO], Leidschendam, Netherlands
Central Opera Ser. [★10274]
Central Org. for the Meat Indus. [IO], Zoetermeer, Netherlands
Central Org. of Trade Unions Kenya [IO], Nairobi, Kenya
Central Rabbinical Cong. of the U.S.A. and Canada [19854], 85 Div. Ave., Brooklyn, NY 11211, (718)384-6765
Central Relief Comm. [★12401]
Central Relief Comm. [★12401]
Central Russia ACM SIGCHI [IO], Moscow, Russia
Central Soc. for Clinical Res. [14154], 555 E Wells St., Ste. 1100, Milwaukee, WI 53202-3823, (414)273-2209
Central States Assn. - Address unknown since 2010.
Central Sta. Alarm Assn. [3140], 8150 Leesburg Pike, Ste. 700, Vienna, VA 22182, (703)242-4670
Central Sta. Elecl. Protection Assn. [★3140]
Central Supply Assn. [★2779]
Central Union of Agricultural Producers and Forest Owners [IO], Helsinki, Finland
Central Union for Child Welfare [IO], Helsinki, Finland
Central Union of Swedish-Speaking Agricultural Producers in Finland [IO], Helsinki, Finland
Central Union of Tenants [IO], Helsinki, Finland
Central Wholesalers Assn. [★2782]
Central Yiddish Culture Org. - Address unknown since 2011.
Centrale des Auberges de Jeunesse Luxembour-geoises [★IO]
Centrale Bond van Meubelfabrikanten [★IO]
Centrale Organisatie voor de Vleessector [★IO]
Centrale des Syndicats du Quebec [★IO]
Centre national de la recherche scientifique [★IO]
Centre Africain des Applications de la Meteorologie pour le Developpement [★IO]
Centre Africain de Formation et de Recherche Ad-ministratives pour le Developpement [★IO]
Centre for African Family Stud. [IO], Nairobi, Kenya
Centre for Agricultural Strategy [IO], Reading, United Kingdom
Centre for Alternative Tech. [IO], Machynlleth, United Kingdom
Centre for Animation, Development, and Res. in Educ. [IO], Montreal, QC, Canada
Centre for Applied Stud. in Intl. Negotiations [IO], Geneva, Switzerland
Centre for Arctic Medicine [IO], Oulu, Finland
Centre des Auteurs Dramatiques [★IO]
Centre Belge d'Etude de la Corrosion [★IO]
Centre Canadien d'Architecture [★IO]
Centre Canadien d'Etude et de Cooperation Interna-tionale - Burkina Faso [★IO]
Centre Canadien d'Hygiene et de Securite au Travail [★IO]
Centre Canadien du Film [★IO]
Centre Canadien pour l'Ethique dans le Sport [★IO]
Centre Canadien de Politiques Alternatives [★IO]
Centre Canadien de Prevention de la Pollution [★IO]
Centre for Commun. and Development [IO], Cal-cutta, India
Centre de Cooperation Internationale en Recherche Agronomique pour le Developpement [★IO]
Centre de Cooperation pour les Recherches Scienti-fiques Relatives au Tabac [★IO]
Centre d'Activites Francaises [★IO]
Centre d'Animation, de Developpement et de Recherche en Educ. [★IO]
Centre for Deaf Stud. [IO], Bristol, United Kingdom
Centre de recherche et d'enseignement sur les droits de la personne [★IO]
Centre d'Estudis Historics Internacionals [★IO]
Centre d'Etudes de la Famille Africaine [★IO]
Centre d'Etudes Oecumeniques [★IO]
Centre d'Etudes Pratiques de la Negociation Interna-tionale [★IO]
Centre for Development Alternatives [IO], Ahmeda-bad, India

Centre for Development Info. and Educ. [IO], Rome, Italy
Centre for Development and Population Activities [12318], 1120 20th St. NW, Ste. 720, Washington, DC 20036, (202)667-1142
Centre for Development and Population Activities - Egypt [IO], Cairo, Egypt
Centre for Development and Population Activities - Nigeria [IO], Abuja, Nigeria
Centre d'Information sur le Boeuf [★IO]
Centre de documentation, de recherches et d'experimentations sur les pollutions accidentelles des eaux [★IO]
Centre de Documentation et de Recherche sur la Paix et les Conflits [★IO]
Centre for Documentation, Res. and Experimentation on Accidental Water Pollution [IO], Brest, France
Centre canadien d'oecumenisme [★IO]
Centre for Early Childhood Development [IO], Clar-einch, Republic of South Africa
Centre Ecologique Albert Schweitzer [★IO]
Centre for Ecology and Hydrology [IO], Wallingford, United Kingdom
Centre for Economic Policy Res. [IO], London, United Kingdom
Centre for Educ. and Documentation [IO], Mumbai, India
Centre for Educational Res. and Innovation [IO], Paris, France
Centre for Env. and Development [★IO]
Centre Europeen des Entreprises a Participation Publique et des Enterprises d Interet Economique Gen. [★IO]
Centre Europeen pour les Langues Vivantes [★IO]
Centre Europeen pour l'Enseignement Superieur [★IO]
Centre Europeen de Recherche en Politique Sociale [★IO]
Centre Europeen des Silicones [IO], Brussels, Belgium
Centre of Films for Children and Young People in Germany [IO], Remscheid, Germany
Centre de Formation et de Recherche Cooperatives [★IO]
Centre for Hea. Educ., Training and Nutrition Aware-ness [IO], Ahmedabad, India
Centre for Importers of Paraguay [IO], Asuncion, Paraguay
Centre for Indian Scholars [IO], Vancouver, BC, Canada
Centre of Indian Trade Unions [IO], New Delhi, India
Centre for Indigenous Theatre [IO], Toronto, ON, Canada
Centre for Interfirm Comparison [IO], Winchester, United Kingdom
Centre Internacional Escarre per a les Minories Et-niques i les Nacions [★IO]
Centre Intl. pour le credit Communal [★IO]
Centre Intl. de Criminologie Comparee [★IO]
Centre Intl. d'Etude de Tantale et de Niobium [★IO]
Centre Intl. de recherches et d'Etudes touristiques [★IO]
Centre Intl. d'Etudes Agricoles [★IO]
Centre Intl. d'Etudes pour la Conservation et la Res-tauration des Biens Culturels [★IO]
Centre Intl. d'Etudes Monetaires et Bancaires [★IO]
Centre Intl. du Film pour l'Enfance et la Jeunesse [★IO]
Centre Intl. pour la Formation et les Echanges Geo-sciences [★IO]
Centre Intl. de Hautes Etudes Agronomiques Medi-terraneennes [★IO]
Centre for Intl. Historical Stud. [IO], Barcelona, Spain
Centre Intl. de Liaison des Ecoles de Cinema et de TV [★IO]
Centre Intl. des Marees Terrestres [★IO]
Centre Intl. de Mathematiques Pures et Appliquees [★IO]
Centre Intl. de Recherche sur le Cancer [★IO]
Centre Intl. de Recherches et d'Information sur l'Economie Publique, Sociale et Cooperative [★IO]
Centre Intl. des Sciences Mecaniques [★IO]
Centre for Intl. Stud. and Cooperation - India [IO], Dehradun, India

Centre Islamique pour le Developpement du Com-merce [★IO]
Centre du riz pour l'Afrique de l'Ouest [★IO]
Centre canadien de lutte contre l'alcoolisme et les toxicomanies [★IO]
Centre for Latin Amer. Monetary Stud. [IO], Mexico City, Mexico
Centre for Latin Amer. Res. and Documentation [IO], Amsterdam, Netherlands
Centre for Medical, Legal and Cultural Assistance for Foreigners in Austria [IO], Graz, Austria
Centre de Musique Canadienne [★IO]
Centre Natl. Interprofessionnel de l'Economie Lait-iere [IO], Paris, France
Centre Natl. de Pastorale Liturgique [IO], Paris, France
Centre du Patrimoine Mondial [★IO]
Centre for Photographic Conservation [IO], London, United Kingdom
Centre for Policy on Ageing [IO], London, United Kingdom
Centre for the Promotion of Imports from Developing Countries Netherlands [IO], Rotterdam, Netherlands
Centre pour la Recherche et l'Innovation dans l'Enseignement [★IO]
Centre de Recherches Interdisciplinaires en Bioeth-hique [★IO]
Centre de Recherches pour l'Expansion de l'Economie et le Developpment des Enterprises [★IO]
Centre de Recherches sur l'histoire, l'art et la Culture Islamiques [★IO]
Centre de Recherches sur les Meningites et les Schistosomiases [★IO]
Centre for Res. Ethics and Bioethics [IO], Uppsala, Sweden
Centre de Ressources sur la non-violence [★IO]
Centre for Rural Tech., Nepal [IO], Patan, Nepal
Centre Scientifique de Monaco [★IO]
Centre Seismologique Intl. [★IO]
Centre Sismologique Euro-Mediterraneen [★IO]
Centre for Stud. and Res. in Intl. Law and Intl. Rela-tions [IO], The Hague, Netherlands
Centre for the Stud. of Developing Societies [IO], New Delhi, India
Centre for Tech. Geoscience [IO], Delft, Netherlands
Centre Technique du Papier [★IO]
Centre Technique des Tuiles et Briques [★IO]
Centre for Women in Bus. [IO], Halifax, NS, Canada
Centre for Women's Development Stud. [IO], New Delhi, India
Centre for Women's Hea. [IO], Glasgow, United Kingdom
Centro Administracion de Derechos Reprograficos Asociacion Civil [IO], Buenos Aires, Argentina
Centro Agronomico Tropical de Investigacion y Ensenanza [★IO]
Centro Andino de Accion Popular [IO], Quito, Ecuador
Centro de Apoyo al Nino de la Calle de Oaxaca [IO], Oaxaca, Mexico
Centro Argentino de Arquitectos Paisajistas [IO], Buenos Aires, Argentina
Centro Argentino de Ingenieros [★IO]
Centro Azucarero Argentino [★IO]
Centro Brasileiro de Analise e Planejamento [★IO]
Centro Canadiense de Estudios y Cooperacion Inter-nacional - Bolivia [★IO]
Centro Cientifico Tropical [★IO]
Centro de Cooperacion del Mediterraneo de la UICN [★IO]
Centro de Cooperacion Regional para la Educacion de Adultos en Am. Latina y el Caribe [★IO]
Centro Cultural Paraguayo Americano [★IO]
Centro De Investigacion y Accion Social [IO], Bue-nos Aires, Argentina
Centro de Derecho Ambiental y de los Recursos Naturales [★IO]
Centro de Desarrollo y Asesoria Psicosocial [★IO]
Centro de Documentacao e Pesquisa para a Africa Austral [★IO]
Centro de Documentacion de Honduras [★IO]
Centro Documentacion Sobre la Mujer [★IO]
Centro Ecologico Akumal [IO], Akumal, Mexico

A star before a book entry number signifies that the name is not listed separately, but is mentioned within the entry.

Centro Espanol de Derechos Reprograficos [★IO]
Centro de Estudios para el Desarrollo de la Mujer [IO], Santiago, Chile
Centro de Estudios y Documentacion Latinoamericanos [★IO]
Centro de Estudios Monetarios Latinoamericanos [★IO]
Centro de Estudios y Prevencion de Desastres [★IO]
Centro de Estudios y Promocion del Desarrollo [★IO]
Centro Experimental de la Vivienda Economica [IO], Cordoba, Argentina
Centro Gerontologico Latino [★10849]
Centro Gerontologico Latino [★10849]
Centro de Importadores del Paraguay [★IO]
Centro de la Industria Lechera [★IO]
Centro de Informacion y Documentacion Africana [★IO]
Centro Informazione e Educazione allo Sviluppo [★IO]
Centro Inox [★IO]
Centro Interamericano de Investigacion y Documentacion Sobre Formacion Profesional [★IO]
Centro Internacional de Agricultura Tropical [★IO]
Centro Internacional de Informacion Sobre Cultivos de Cobertura [★IO]
Centro Internacional de Mejoramiento de Maiz y Trigo [★IO]
Centro Internacional de la Papa [★IO]
Centro Internazionale di Ipnosi Medica e Psicologica [★IO]
Centro de Investigacion y Desarrollo de la Educacion [★IO]
Centro de Investigacion y Documentacion para el Desarrollo del Beni [IO], Trinidad, Bolivia
Centro de Investigacion para la Paz [★IO]
Centro de Investigacion y Planificacion del Medio Ambiente [★IO]
Centro de Investigaciones Ciudad [★IO]
Centro Italiano di Solidarieta [★IO]
Centro Laici Italiani per le Missioni [★IO]
Centro Latino Americano de Ecologia Social [★IO]
Centro Latinoamericano de Administracion para el Desarrollo [★IO]
Centro Latinoamericano y Caribeno de Demografia [★IO]
Centro Latinoamericano de Fisica [★IO]
Centro Nacional para la Prevencion y Control del VIH/SIDA [★IO]
Centro Oaxaqueno de Rehabilitacion de Audicion y Lenguaje [IO], Oaxaca, Mexico
Centro Panamericano de Fiebre Aftosa [★IO]
Centro Panamericano de Ingenieria Sanitaria y Ciencias del Ambiente [★IO]
Centro Paraguayo de Estudios de Poblacion [IO], Asuncion, Paraguay
Centro de Pesquisas e Conservacao Iracambi [★IO]
Centro Regional de Sismologia para Am. del Sur [★IO]
Centro Studi Americanistici [★IO]
Centro Uruguayo de Tecnologias Apropiadas [IO], Montevideo, Uruguay
CENTROMARCA - Associacao Portuguesa de Empresas de Produtos de Marca [★IO]
Centrum pro demokracii a svobodne podnikani [★IO]
Centurions of the Deafness Res. Foundation [★14932]
Century Coun. [16739], 2345 Crystal Dr., Ste. 910, Arlington, VA 22202, (202)637-0077
The Century Found. [18450], 41 E 70th St., New York, NY 10021, (212)535-4441
CEO Netweavers [962], PO Box 700393, Dallas, TX 75370
CEOs for Cities [18754], 8 E Randolph St., No. 2603, Chicago, IL 60601, (312)553-4630
CEPS - The European Spirits Org. [IO], Brussels, Belgium
CERAM [IO], Stoke-on-Trent, United Kingdom
Ceramic Arts Fed. Intl. [★1728]
Ceramic Arts Studio Collectors Assn. [★21261]
Ceramic Distributors of Am. [★1728]
Ceramic Educational Coun. [7819], Elliot Slamovich, Purdue Univ., 701 W. Stadium Ave., School of Materials Engineering, West Lafayette, IN 47907, (765)494-6853

Ceramic Educational Coun. [7819], Elliot Slamovich, Purdue Univ., 701 W. Stadium Ave., School of Materials Engineering, West Lafayette, IN 47907, (765)494-6853
Ceramic Mfrs. Assn. [731], Myra Warne, Exec. Dir., PO Box 2489, Zanesville, OH 43702, (740)588-0828
Ceramic Sanitary Wares Mfrs'. Assn. [IO], Istanbul, Turkey
Ceramic Soc. of Japan [IO], Tokyo, Japan
Ceramic Tile Distributors of Am. [★544]
Ceramic Tile Distributors Assn. [544], 800 Roosevelt Rd., Bldg. C, Ste. 312, Glen Ellyn, IL 60137, (630)545-9415
Ceramic Tile Inst. of Am. [906], 12061 Jefferson Blvd., Culver City, CA 90230-6219, (310)574-7800
Ceramic Tiles Mfrs'. Assn. [IO], Istanbul, Turkey
Ceramics
    Amer. Ceramic Soc. [6382]
    Amer. Ceramic Soc. [6382]
    Assn. of Amer. Ceramic Component Mfrs. [730]
    CAS Collectors [21261]
    Ceramic Educational Coun. [7819]
    Ceramic Educational Coun. [7819]
    Ceramic Mfrs. Assn. [731]
    Dedham Pottery Collectors Soc. [21333]
    Egg Cup Collectors' Corner [21336]
    Haviland Collectors Intl. Found. [21262]
    Intl. Assn. of Duncan Certified Ceramic Teachers [21263]
    Intl. Assn. of Duncan Certified Ceramic Teachers [21263]
    Intl. Nippon Collectors Club [21264]
    Intl. Nippon Collectors Club [21264]
    Majolica Intl. Soc. [21265]
    Majolica Intl. Soc. [21265]
    McCoy Pottery Collectors' Soc. [21266]
    M.I. Hummel Club [21267]
    Natl. Inst. of Ceramic Engineers [6383]
    Old Sleepy Eye Collectors' Club of Am. [21268]
    Potters Coun. [9472]
    Potters Coun. [9472]
    The Refractories Inst. [6384]
    Refractory Ceramic Fibers Coalition [732]
    Tea Leaf Club Intl. [21269]
    Transferware Collectors Club [21270]
    Wedgwood Intl. Seminar [21271]
    Wedgwood Intl. Seminar [21271]
    Wedgwood Soc. of Great Britain [21935]
    White Ironstone China Assn. [21272]
Cercle des Benevoles du Musee des Beaux-Arts du Canada [★IO]
Cercle Intl. pour la Promotion de la Creation [★IO]
Cercles des Jeunes Naturalistes [★IO]
Cereals, Pulses, Oily Seeds and Products Exporter Union [IO], Istanbul, Turkey
Cerebral Palsy Intl. Sports and Recreation Assn. [IO], Wildeshausen, Germany
Cerebral Palsy Soc. of New Zealand [IO], Auckland, New Zealand
Ceredigion Welsh Pony and Cob Assn. [IO], Ceredigion, United Kingdom
Certification Bd. of Infection Control and Epidemiology [14875], 555 E Wells St., Ste. 1100, Milwaukee, WI 53202, (414)918-9796
Certification Bd. for Music Therapists [16458], 506 E Lancaster Ave., Ste. 102, Downingtown, PA 19335, (610)269-8900
Certification Bd. Perioperative Nursing [★15051]
Certification Bd. for Sterile Processing and Distribution [15357], 148 Main St., Ste. B-1, Lebanon, NJ 08833, (908)236-0530
Certification Bd. for Urologic Nurses and Associates [16944], 601 Pavonia Ave., Ste. 201, Jersey City, NJ 07306, (856)256-2351
Certification of Disability Mgt. Specialists Commn. [13571], 1699 E Woodfield Rd., Ste. 300, Schaumburg, IL 60173, (847)944-1335
Certified Audit of Circulations [114], 155 Willowbrook Blvd., Ste. 400, Wayne, NJ 07470, (973)785-3000
Certified Builders Assn. of New Zealand [IO], Tauranga, New Zealand
Certified Claims Professional Accreditation Coun. [3506], PO Box 550922, Jacksonville, FL 32255-0922, (904)390-1506

Certified Color Mfrs. Assn. [★800]
Certified Color Mfrs. Assn. [★800]
Certified Contractor's Network [907], 134 Sibley Ave., Ardmore, PA 19003, (610)642-9505
Certified Financial Planner Bd. of Standards [1338], 1425 K St. NW, Ste. 500, Washington, DC 20005, (202)379-2200
Certified Interior Decorators Intl. [2055], 649 SE Central Pkwy., Stuart, FL 34994, (772)287-1855
Certified Interior Decorators Intl. [2055], 649 SE Central Pkwy., Stuart, FL 34994, (772)287-1855
Certified Metrication Specialist Bd. [★7470]
Certified Milk Producers Assn. of America - Defunct.
Certified Practicing Accountants of Maldives [IO], Male, Maldives
Certified Practising Accountants Papua New Guinea [IO], Port Moresby, Papua New Guinea
Certified Professional Insurance Agents Soc. [★1934]
Certifying Bd. of Gastroenterology Nurses and Associates [15743], 401 N Michigan Ave., Chicago, IL 60611, (800)245-7462
Cerveceros de Espana [★IO]
Cerveceros Latinoamericanos [★IO]
Cervical Barrier Advancement Soc. [16646], 17 Dunster St., Ste. 201, Cambridge, MA 02138, (617)349-0049
Cervical Cancer Coalition; Natl. [13949]
Cervical Spine Res. Soc. [16699], 6300 N River Rd., Ste. 727, Rosemont, IL 60018-4226, (847)698-1628
Cervical Spine Res. Soc. [16699], 6300 N River Rd., Ste. 727, Rosemont, IL 60018-4226, (847)698-1628
Cesarean Prevention Movement [★15881]
Cesarean Prevention Movement [★15881]
Ceska asociace konzultacnich inzenyru [★IO]
Ceska asociace pojistovne [★IO]
Ceska gerontologicka a geriatricka spolecnost [★IO]
Ceska meteorologicka spolecnost [★IO]
Ceska spolecnost pro mechaniku [★IO]
Ceska fyziologicka spolecnost [★IO]
Ceska Advokatni Komora [★IO]
Ceska Asociace Aikido [★IO]
Ceska Asociace Franchisingu [★IO]
Ceska Asociace pro Geoinformace [★IO]
Ceska Asociace Geomorfologu [★IO]
Ceska Asociace Squashe [★IO]
Ceska Bankovni Asociace [★IO]
Ceska Biblicka Spolecnost [★IO]
Ceska Bioklimatologicka Spolecnost [★IO]
Ceska Florbalova Unie [★IO]
Ceska Gynekologicka a Porodnicka Spolecnost [★IO]
Ceska Hostelova Asociace [★IO]
Ceska Lekarska Spolecnost J.E. Purkyne [★IO]
Ceska Liga proti Epilepsii [★IO]
Ceska Ortodonticka Spolecnost [★IO]
Ceska Radiologicka Spolecnost [★IO]
Ceska Spolecnost Chemicka [★IO]
Ceska Spolecnost pro Experimentalni a Klinickou Farmakologii a Toxicologii [★IO]
Ceska Spolecnost pro Kybernetiku a Informatiku [★IO]
Ceska Spolecnost Telovychovneho Lekarstvi [★IO]
Ceske sdruzeni pro znackove vyrobky [★IO]
Ceske hnuti specialnich olympiad [★IO]
Ceske A Slovenske Sdruzeni V Kanade [★IO]
Ceskeho Olmpijskeho Vyboru [★IO]
Ceskeho Paralympijskeho Vyboru [★IO]
Cesko Moravska Slechtitelska a Semenarska Asociace [★IO]
Ceskomoravska psychologicka spolecnost [★IO]
Ceskomoravska Elektrotechnicka Asociace [★IO]
Ceskomoravska Slechtitelska A Semenarska Asociace [★IO]
Ceskoslovenska mikroskopicka spolecnost [★IO]
Cesky svaz vynalezcu a zlepsovatelu [★IO]
Cesky radioklub [★IO]
Cesky krasobruslarsky svaz [★IO]
Cesky Badmintonovy Svaz [★IO]
Cesky Cerveny Kriz [★IO]
Cesky Plynarensky Svaz [★IO]
Cesky Svaz Biatlonu [★IO]
Cesky Svaz Tanecniho Sportu [★IO]

Reference to "IO" in place of a book number signifies that the association may be found in the 50th edition of International Organizations.

Cesky svaz Taekwondo WTF [★IO]
Cessna 120/140 Assn. [★20899]
Cessna 120/140 Assn. [★20899]
Cessna 182 Assn. of Australia [IO], Cremorne, Australia
Cessna Centurion Soc. [★20885]
Cessna Owner Org. [20885], N7450 Aanstad Rd., Iola, WI 54945, (715)252-3326
Cessna Pilots Assn. [20886], 3940 Mitchell Rd., Santa Maria, CA 93455, (805)934-0493
Cessna Skyhawk Assn. [★20885]
Cessna Skylane Soc. [★20885]
Ceta-Research [IO], Trinity, NL, Canada
Cetacean Soc; Amer. [7038]
Cetacean Soc. Intl. [5042], PO Box 953, Georgetown, CT 06829, (203)770-8615
Cetacean Soc. Intl. [5042], PO Box 953, Georgetown, CT 06829, (203)770-8615
Cetos Res. Org. [4199], 11 Des Isle Ave., Bar Harbor, ME 04609, (207)266-6252
Ceylon Chamber of Commerce [IO], Colombo, Sri Lanka
Ceylon (Sri Lanka) Tourist Dept. [23443], Embassy of Sri Lanka, 2148 Wyoming Ave. NW, Washington, DC 20008, (202)483-4025
Cezky svaz vodniho lyzovani [★IO]
CFA Assn. of Pakistan [IO], Karachi, Pakistan
CFA Inst. [2133], 560 Ray C. Hunt Dr., Charlottesville, VA 22903-2981, (434)951-5499
CFA Inst. [2133], 560 Ray C. Hunt Dr., Charlottesville, VA 22903-2981, (434)951-5499
CFA Singapore [IO], Singapore, Singapore
CFA Soc. of the Cayman Islands [IO], Grand Cayman, Cayman Islands
CFA Soc. of the Netherlands [IO], Naarden, Netherlands
CFA Soc. of the UK [IO], London, United Kingdom
CFC Intl. [14588], 183 Brown Rd., Vestal, NY 13850, (607)772-9666
CFC Intl. [14588], 183 Brown Rd., Vestal, NY 13850, (607)772-9666
CFFI Ceredigion YFC [IO], Aberaeron, United Kingdom
CFIDS Assn. [★14378]
CFIDS Assn. of Am. [14378], PO Box 220398, Charlotte, NC 28222-0398, (704)365-2343
CFU Junior Cultural Fed. [9510], Croatian Fraternal Union, 100 Delaney Dr., Pittsburgh, PA 15235, (412)843-0380
C.G. Jung Found. for Analytical Psychology [16395], 28 E 39th St., New York, NY 10016-2587, (212)697-6430
CHA-Association for Horsemanship Safety and Educ. [★22679]
CHA - Certified Horsemanship Assn. [22679], 4037 Iron Works Pkwy., Ste. 180, Lexington, KY 40511, (859)259-3399
Chabad Lubavitch [19855], 770 Eastern Pkwy., Brooklyn, NY 11213, (718)774-4000
Chabad Movement [★19855]
Chad Assn. for the Fight Against Diabetes [IO], N'Djamena, Chad
Chain Drug Marketing Associates [★2691]
Chain Drug Marketing Assn. [2691], PO Box 995, 43157 W Nine Mile Rd., Novi, MI 48376-0995, (248)449-9300
Chain Drug Marketing Assn. [2691], PO Box 995, 43157 W Nine Mile Rd., Novi, MI 48376-0995, (248)449-9300
Chain Link Fence Mfrs. Inst. [545], 10015 Old Columbia Rd., Ste. B-215, Columbia, MD 21046, (301)596-2583
Chaine Bleue Mondiale pour la Protection des Animaux et de la Nature [★IO]
Chaine Educ. Fund [★21845]
Chaipattana Found. [IO], Bangkok, Thailand
The Chairmen's Gp. [★1001]
Chalcedon Found. [20219], PO Box 158, Vallecito, CA 95251, (209)736-4365
Chaldean Fed. of Am. [9139], 29850 Northwestern Hwy., Ste. 250, Southfield, MI 48034, (248)996-8384
Challah for Hunger [12266], 2936 Barton Skyway, No. 435, Austin, TX 78746, (512)200-4234
Challah for Hunger [12266], 2936 Barton Skyway, No. 435, Austin, TX 78746, (512)200-4234

Challenge Aspen at Snowmass [22509], PO Box 6639, Snowmass Village, CO 81615, (970)923-0578
Challenge Coin Assn. [21969], 1375 Mistletoe Ridge Pl. NW, Concord, NC 28027, (704)723-1170
Challenged Am. [14362], Disabled Businesspersons Assn., 2240 Shelter Island Dr., Ste. 108, San Diego, CA 92106, (619)523-9318
Challenger Soc. for Marine Sci. [IO], Southampton, United Kingdom
Challenger T/A Car Club [★21020]
Challenger T/A Car Club [★21020]
Challenger T/A Registry [21020], PO Box 9632, Ketchikan, AK 99901-4632, (907)225-2709
Challenger T/A Registry [21020], PO Box 9632, Ketchikan, AK 99901-4632, (907)225-2709
Challenges Worldwide [IO], Edinburgh, United Kingdom
CHALLENGES - Youth Action for Sustainable Development [IO], Lome, Togo
Chama Cha Wakutubi Tanzania [★IO]
Chama Cha Wanariadha [★IO]
Chamber of Commerce, Agriculture, Indus., and Handicrafts of Niger [IO], Niamey, Niger
Chamber of Commerce; Amer. Indonesian [23408]
Chamber of Commerce Amsterdam [IO], Amsterdam, Netherlands
Chamber of Commerce; Brazilian-American [23334]
Chamber of Commerce of Costa Rica [IO], San Jose, Costa Rica
Chamber of Commerce East Lancashire [IO], Accrington, United Kingdom
Chamber of Commerce Executives; Amer. [23451]
Chamber of Commerce; French-American [23400]
Chamber of Commerce of Greater Miami; Colombian-American [23395]
Chamber of Commerce, Herefordshire and Worcestershire [IO], Worcester, United Kingdom
Chamber of Commerce; Honolulu Japanese [23414]
Chamber of Commerce, Indus. and Agriculture of Beirut and Mount Lebanon [IO], Beirut, Lebanon
Chamber of Commerce and Indus. of the Azores [IO], Ponta Delgada, Portugal
Chamber of Commerce and Indus. of El Salvador [IO], San Salvador, El Salvador
Chamber of Commerce and Indus. of Hawaii; Japanese [23419]
Chamber of Commerce and Indus. - Johannesburg [IO], Johannesburg, Republic of South Africa
Chamber of Commerce and Indus. of Mali [IO], Bamako, Mali
Chamber of Commerce and Indus. of New Caledonia [IO], Noumea, New Caledonia
Chamber of Commerce and Indus. of New York; Japanese [23420]
Chamber of Commerce and Indus. of the Republic of Uzbekistan [IO], Tashkent, Uzbekistan
Chamber of Commerce and Indus. of Romania [IO], Bucharest, Romania
Chamber of Commerce and Indus. of Slovenia [IO], Ljubljana, Slovenia
Chamber of Commerce and Indus. of Suriname [IO], Paramaribo, Suriname
Chamber of Commerce, Indus. and Trades of Burkina Faso [IO], Ouagadougou, Burkina Faso
Chamber of Commerce and Indus. of Western Australia [IO], East Perth, Australia
Chamber of Commerce; Italian-American [23411]
Chamber of Commerce; Italy-America [23412]
Chamber of Commerce; Philippine Amer. [23436]
Chamber of Commerce and Production of Santiago [IO], Santiago, Dominican Republic
Chamber of Commerce; Swiss-American [23444]
Chamber of Commerce - The Hague [IO], The Hague, Netherlands
Chamber of Commerce; U.S. Austrian [23330]
Chamber of Commerce; U.S. Hispanic [23405]
Chamber of Commerce in the U.S; Netherlands [23431]
Chamber of Commerce of the U.S. - U.S. Chamber [★23384]
Chamber of Commerce Uruguay - USA [IO], Montevideo, Uruguay
Chamber of Commerce of U.S.A; Latin [23425]
Chamber of Craft, Artists and Artisans [IO], Kigali, Rwanda

Chamber of Crafts of Luxembourg [IO], Luxembourg, Luxembourg
Chamber of the Footwear Indus. in the State of Guanajuato [IO], Leon, Mexico
Chamber of Furniture Indus. of the Philippines [IO], Pasig City, Philippines
Chamber of Furniture Mfrs. [IO], Buenos Aires, Argentina
Chamber of Geological Engineers of Turkey [IO], Ankara, Turkey
Chamber of Geophysical Engineers [IO], Ankara, Turkey
Chamber of Mech. Engineers [IO], Ankara, Turkey
Chamber of Mines of Namibia [IO], Windhoek, Namibia
Chamber of Mines of South Africa [IO], Johannesburg, Republic of South Africa
Chamber Music Am. [10173], 305 7th Ave., New York, NY 10001-6008, (212)242-2022
Chamber of Shipping [IO], London, United Kingdom
Chamber of Shipping of Am. [5789], 1730 M St. NW, Ste. 407, Washington, DC 20036-4517, (202)775-4399
Chamber of Soft Drink and Related Mfrs. [IO], Buenos Aires, Argentina
Chamber of Software Businesses and Info. Services [IO], Buenos Aires, Argentina
Chamber of Sugar Producers [IO], San Jose, Costa Rica
Chamber of Tax Advisers of the Czech Republic [IO], Brno, Czech Republic
Chamber of Telecommunications Businesses [IO], Caracas, Venezuela
Chamber of Venezuelan Auto. Products Mfrs. [IO], Caracas, Venezuela
Chamber of Women Entrepreneurs [IO], Kigali, Rwanda
Chamber of Young Entrepreneurs [IO], Kigali, Rwanda
Chambers of Commerce
   Aberdeen and Grampian Chamber of Commerce [23888]
   Amer. Chamber of Commerce in Australia [5321]
   Amer. Chamber of Commerce of Cuba in the U.S. [23346]
   Amer. Islamic Chamber of Commerce [23347]
   Amer. Islamic Chamber of Commerce [23347]
   Amer. Israel Chamber of Commerce - Southeast Region [23348]
   Amer. Israel Chamber of Commerce - Southeast Region [23348]
   American-Russian Chamber of Commerce and Indus. [23349]
   American-Russian Chamber of Commerce and Indus. [23349]
   American-Uzbekistan Chamber of Commerce [23350]
   American-Uzbekistan Chamber of Commerce [23350]
   Argentine-American Chamber of Commerce [23351]
   Armenian Amer. Chamber of Commerce [23352]ChambersAsia Pacific - USA Chamber of Commerce.
   Australia-Singapore Chamber of Commerce and Indus. [20735]
   Australia-Taiwan Bus. Coun. [69]
   Australian New Zealand - Amer. Chambers of Commerce [23339]
   Austrian Trade Commn. [23329]
   Austrian Trade Commissions in the U.S. [23353]
   Austrian Trade Commissions in the U.S. [23353]ChambersBedfordshire and Luton Chamber of Commerce, Training and Enterprise
   Birmingham Chamber of Commerce and Indus. [18916]
   Black Country Chamber of Commerce [1526]
   Bradford Chamber of Commerce [20457]
   Brazil-U.S. Bus. Coun. [23354]
   Brazilian Chamber of Commerce in Great Britain [22680]
   Brazilian Govt. Trade Bur. of the Consulate Gen. of Brazil in New York [23335]
   Britain-Nepal Chamber of Commerce [2702]

A star before a book entry number signifies that the name is not listed separately, but is mentioned within the entry.

British Chamber of Commerce in Belgium [18906]
British Chamber of Commerce in China [18876]
British Chamber of Commerce in Hong Kong [20514]
British Chamber of Commerce for Luxembourg [18910]ChambersBritish Hellenic Chamber of Commerce
British Polish Chamber of Commerce [20591]
BritishAmerican Bus. Inc. of New York and London [23355]
Cambridgeshire Chamber of Commerce and Indus. [21262]
Cape Town Regional Chamber of Commerce and Indus. [1862]
Caribbean Amer. Chamber of Commerce and Indus. [23356]
Caribbean Amer. Chamber of Commerce and Indus. [23356]ChambersChamber of Commerce East Lancashire
Chamber of Commerce, Herefordshire and Worcestershire [18890]
Chamber of Commerce and Indus. of Western Australia [11320]
Chamber of Commerce and Production of Santiago [14140]
Channel Chamber of Commerce [12983]
Chile-U.S. Chamber of Commerce [23357]
Chile-U.S. Chamber of Commerce [23357]
Clonmel Chamber of Commerce [22492]
Colombian-American Chamber of Commerce - Bogota [23395]
Congleton Chamber of Commerce and Enterprise [20521]
Coun. for Community and Economic Res. [23358]
Cyprus Embassy Trade Center [23359]
Cyprus Embassy Trade Center [23359]
Cyprus-US Chamber of Commerce [23360]
Danish Amer. Chamber of Commerce [23361]
Dublin Chamber of Commerce [2812]
Ecuadorian-American Chamber of Commerce - Quito [23397]
European-American Bus. Coun. [23362]
European-American Bus. Coun. [23362]
Fed. of Philippine Amer. Chambers of Commerce [23363]
Fed. of Philippine Amer. Chambers of Commerce [23363]
Franco-British Chamber of Commerce and Indus. [18885]
Galway Chamber of Commerce and Indus. [4924]
German Amer. Chamber of Commerce [23364]
German-Australian Chamber of Indus. and Commerce [19025]
Ghana-USA Chamber of Commerce [23365]
Ghana-USA Chamber of Commerce [23365]ChambersGrand Bahama Chamber of Commerce
Greek Amer. Chamber of Commerce [23366]
Greek Amer. Chamber of Commerce [23366]
Hemispheric Cong. of Latin Chambers of Commerce [23367]
Hemispheric Cong. of Latin Chambers of Commerce [23367]
Hertfordshire Chamber of Commerce and Indus. [20503]
Innovation Norway - United States [23368]
Innovation Norway - U.S. [23368]
Intl. Chamber of Commerce - USA [23369]
Intl. Chamber of Commerce - USA [23369]
Iraqi Amer. Chamber of Commerce and Indus. [23370]
Iraqi Amer. Chamber of Commerce and Indus. [23370]
Ireland Chamber of Commerce U.S.A. [23371]
Ireland Chamber of Commerce U.S.A. [23371]
Isle of Wight Chamber of Commerce [18848]
Italian Chamber of Commerce and Indus. for the UK [4599]
Jamaica USA Chamber of Commerce [23372]
Jamaica USA Chamber of Commerce [23372]
Jordan Info. Bur. [23421]
Korean Chamber of Commerce in Hong Kong [21706]
Leeds Chamber of Commerce [22683]
Limerick Chamber of Commerce [14176]ChambersLithuanian-U.S. Bus. Coun.

Liverpool Chamber of Commerce and Indus. [18917]
Londonderry Chamber of Commerce [1922]ChambersMacclesfield Chamber of Commerce and Enterprise
Madrid Chamber of Commerce and Indus. [1718]
Malta Chamber of Commerce and Enterprise [4983]
Milton Keynes and North Buckinghamshire Chamber of Commerce [18914]
Natl. Assn. of Chamber Ambassadors [23373]
Natl. United States-Arab Chamber of Commerce [23374]
Netherlands British Chamber of Commerce [18870]
Netherlands Chamber of Commerce Australia [20410]
Norfolk Chamber of Commerce and Indus. [20604]
North American-Bulgarian Chamber of Commerce [23375]
North American-Bulgarian Chamber of Commerce [23375]
North American-Chilean Chamber of Commerce [23376]ChambersNorth Hampshire Chamber of Commerce and Indus.
Northamptonshire Chamber of Commerce [20639]
Norwegian-American Chamber of Commerce [23377]
Norwegian-American Chamber of Commerce [23377]
Osaka Chamber of Commerce and Indus. [3726]
Pakistan Chamber of Commerce USA [23435]
Polish Amer. Chamber of Commerce [23378]
Polish Amer. Chamber of Commerce [23378]
Portsmouth and South East Hampshire Chamber of Commerce and Indus. [18853]
Romanian-U.S. Bus. Coun. [23438]
St. Helens Chamber of Commerce [18887]
Santiago Chamber of Commerce [22469]
Santo Domingo Chamber of Commerce and Production [18796]
Sheffield Chamber of Commerce and Indus. [20560]
Shropshire Chamber of Commerce and Enterprise [20479]
South African USA Chamber of Commerce [23379]
South African USA Chamber of Commerce [23379]
South Wales Chamber of Commerce [18878]
Southampton and Fareham Chamber of Commerce and Indus. [20590]
Spain-United States Chamber of Commerce [23380]
Spain-United States Chamber of Commerce [23380]
Spanish Chamber of Commerce in Great Britain [23151]
Stockholm Chamber of Commerce [5519]
Suffolk Chamber of Commerce [18879]
Surrey Chambers of Commerce [9507]
Swedish-American Chambers of Commerce, U.S.A. [23381]
Swedish-American Chambers of Commerce, U.S.A. [23381]
Swedish Trade Coun. [3489]
Swiss - Amer. Chamber of Commerce [23444]
Thames Valley Chamber of Commerce [18909]
Thanet and East Kent Chamber [18899]
Turkish-American Chamber of Commerce and Indus. [23455]
Turkish British Chamber of Commerce and Indus. [18863]
U.S.-Angola Chamber of Commerce [23382]
U.S.-Angola Chamber of Commerce [23382]
United States-Azerbaijan Chamber of Commerce [23383]
United States-Azerbaijan Chamber of Commerce [23383]
U.S. Chamber of Commerce [23384]
U.S. Christian Chamber of Commerce [23393]
U.S. Indian Amer. Chamber of Commerce [23407]
U.S. Mexico Chamber of Commerce [23385]
United States Mexico Chamber of Commerce [23385]

U.S. Pan Asian Amer. Chamber of Commerce [23386]
U.S. Pan Asian Amer. Chamber of Commerce [23386]
U.S. Qatar Bus. Coun. [23387]
United States Qatar Bus. Coun. [23387]
Venezuelan-American Chamber of Commerce [23388]
Venezuelan-American Chamber of Commerce and Indus. [23388]
Wales North Am. Bus. Chamber [23389]
Wales North Am. Bus. Chamber [23389]
West Kent Chamber of Commerce and Indus. [20501]
Wexford Chamber of Indus. and Commerce [5224]
Chambers of Commerce of Ireland [IO], Dublin, Ireland
Chambre Algerienne de Commerce et d'Industrie [★IO]
Chambre Belge des Inventeurs [★IO]
Chambre de Commerce, d'Agriculture, d'Industrie et d'Artisanat du Niger [★IO]
Chambre de Commerce, d'Industrie et d'Artisanat du Burkina Faso [★IO]
Chambre de Commerce et d'Industrie Franco-Argentine [★IO]
Chambre de Commerce et d'Industrie de l'Ile Maurice [★IO]
Chambre de Commerce et d'Industrie du Mali [★IO]
Chambre de Commerce et d'Industrie de Nouvelle-Caledonie [★IO]
Chambre de Commerce et d'Industrie de Paris [IO]
Chambre de Commerce et d'Industrie du Togo [★IO]
Chambre de Commerce Francaise de Grande Bretagne [★IO]
Chambre de Commerce du Grand-Duche de Luxembourg [★IO]
Chambre de Commerce Internationale [★IO]
Chambre des Ingenieurs-Conseils de France [IO], Paris, France
Chambre Internationale de la Marine Marchande [★IO]
Chambre des Metiers du Grand-Duche de Luxembourg [★IO]
Chambre Nationale des Femmes Chefs d'Entreprise [IO], Tunis, Tunisia
Chambre Royale des Antiquaires de Belgique [★IO]
Chambre Syndicale des Emballages en Matiere Plastique [★IO]
Chambre Syndicale de l'Estampe, du Dessin et du Tableau [IO], Paris, France
Chambre Syndicale Nationale des Fabricants de Confiserie [★IO]
Chambre Syndicale de la Repartition Pharmaceutique [★IO]
Champa Cultural Preservation Assn. of USA [10636], PO Box 62061, Sunnyvale, CA 94088, (408)674-4099
Champa Cultural Preservation Assn. of USA [10636], PO Box 62061, Sunnyvale, CA 94088, (408)674-4099
Champagne d'Argent Rabbit Fed. - Address unknown since 2010.
Champagne Horse Breeders' and Owners' Assn. [4574], 619 Raiford Rd., Erwin, NC 28339, (910)891-5022
Champagne Wines Information Bur. - Defunct.
Champions for Life Intl. [19735], PO Box 761101, Dallas, TX 75376-1101, (972)298-1101
Champions for Life Intl. [19735], PO Box 761101, Dallas, TX 75376-1101, (972)298-1101
Champlain Soc. [IO], Toronto, ON, Canada
CHAN Healthcare Auditors [8011], 231 S Bemiston Ave., Ste. 300, Clayton, MO 63105, (314)802-2000
Chances4Cambodia [IO], Phnom Penh, Cambodia
Change Bangladesh [17275], 505 Nan Cir., Little Rock, AR 72211, (501)255-2814
Change Exchange [12205], PO Box 912, Northville, MI 48167, (734)578-8485
The Change Exchange [12205], PO Box 912, Northville, MI 48167, (734)578-8485
Change in Life Experience, Pakistan [IO], Lahore, Pakistan

Reference to "IO" in place of a book number signifies that the association may be found in the 50th edition of International Organizations.

Change to Win [23305], 1900 L St. NW, Ste. 900, Washington, DC 20036, (202)721-0660
Change to Win [23305], 1900 L St. NW, Ste. 900, Washington, DC 20036, (202)721-0660
ChangeALife Uganda [11209], 58 Fairview Ave., Brick, NJ 08724, (732)899-8483
Changing Children's Lives [15150], 136 Sherman Ave., Ste. 407, New Haven, CT 06511, (203)907-0040
Changing Children's Lives [15150], 136 Sherman Ave., Ste. 407, New Haven, CT 06511, (203)907-0040
Channel Chamber of Commerce [IO], Folkestone, United Kingdom
Channel Swimming Assn. [IO], Loughborough, United Kingdom
CHAP Intl. [12817], PO Box 412, Denver, PA 17517, (717)629-4329
Chapitre Congolais de l'Internet Soc. [★IO]
Chaplains
  Amer. Catholic Correctional Chaplains Assn. [19516]
  Amer. Correctional Chaplains Assn. [19517]
  Assn. of Professional Chaplains [19518]
  Fed. of Fire Chaplains [19519]
  Intl. Assn. of Christian Chaplains [19520]
  Intl. Conf. of Police Chaplains [19521]
  Intl. Conf. of Police Chaplains [19521]
  Intl. Police and Fire Chaplain's Assn. [19522]
  JWB Jewish Chaplains Coun. [19523]
  Military Chaplains Assn. of the U.S.A. [19524]
  Natl. Assn. of Catholic Chaplains [19525]
  Natl. Assn. of Jewish Chaplains [19526]
  Natl. Assn. of Veterans Affairs Chaplains [19527]
  Natl. Conf. of Catholic Airport Chaplains [19528]
  Pediatric Chaplains Network [19529]
  Race Track Chaplaincy of Am. [19530]
Chaplains' Aid Assn./Seminary Education Fund - Defunct.
Chaplains Assn. of the Amer. Protestant Hosp. Assn. [★19518]
Chaplains' Assn. of U.S. [★19524]
Chapman Family Assn. [20439], 770 S Post Oak Ln., Ste. 435, Houston, TX 77056-1913, (713)877-8333
Chap. of Agassiz Assn. [★7206]
Character Education Inst. - Defunct.
Character Educ. Partnership [11904], 1025 Connecticut Ave. NW, Ste. 1011, Washington, DC 20036, (202)296-7743
Charbonneau Connection - Defunct.
Charcot-Marie-Tooth Assn. [15577], 2700 Chestnut St., Chester, PA 19013-4867, (610)499-9264
Charcot-Marie-Tooth Disease
  Charcot-Marie-Tooth Assn. [15577]
Charette/Charest Family Assn. [20440], Ray Thomas, Treas., 22 Ludlow Rd., Plantsville, CT 06095
Chariot Racing
  World Championship Cutter and Chariot Racing Assn. [22448]
Charismatic Renewal Services [★19479]
Charitable Humanitarian Org. in Cambodia by Expats [IO], Phnom Penh, Cambodia
Charities Aid Found. [★13155]
Charities Aid Found. Am. [13155], 1800 Diagonal Rd., Ste. 150, King St. Sta., Alexandria, VA 22314-2840, (703)549-8931
Charity Law Assn. [IO], Harrogate, United Kingdom
Charity Music [12553], 14975 Cong. Dr., Sterling Heights, MI 48313, (586)247-7444
charity: water [13414], 200 Varick St., Ste. 201, New York, NY 10014, (646)688-2323
charity: water [13414], 200 Varick St., Ste. 201, New York, NY 10014, (646)688-2323
CharityHelp Intl. [11210], PO Box 1904, Annapolis, MD 21404, (443)283-0677
Charles A. and Anne Morrow Lindbergh Found. [4240], 2150 3rd Ave. N, Ste. 310, Anoka, MN 55303-2200, (763)576-1596
Charles A. Lindbergh Fund [★4240]
Charles Babbage Inst. for the History of Info. Tech. [9758], Univ. of Minnesota, 211 Andersen Lib., 222 21st Ave. S, Minneapolis, MN 55455, (612)624-5050

Charles Darwin Found. [★4067]
Charles Darwin Found. for the Galapagos Islands [IO], Quito, Ecuador
Charles Darwin Found. for the Galapagos Isles [★4067]
Charles Edison Memorial Youth Fund [★8484]
Charles Edison Memorial Youth Fund [★8484]
Charles Edison Youth Fund [★8484]
Charles Edison Youth Fund [★8484]
Charles H. Wright Museum of African Amer. History [9100], 315 E Warren Ave., Detroit, MI 48201, (313)494-5800
Charles H. Wright Museum of African Amer. History [9100], 315 E Warren Ave., Detroit, MI 48201, (313)494-5800
Charles Homer Haskins Soc. [10075], Frederick Suppe, Treas., Ball State Univ., Dept. of History, Muncie, IN 47306
Charles Homer Haskins Soc. [10075], Frederick Suppe, Treas., Ball State Univ., Dept. of History, Muncie, IN 47306
Charles Ives Soc. [10174], Indiana Univ., School of Music, Bloomington, IN 47405
Charles Johnson Soc. [10708], Penn State Univ., 116 Burrowes Bldg., University Park, PA 16802
Charles Ray III Diabetes Assn. [14346], PO Box 792, Apex, NC 27502, (919)303-6949
Charles Ray III Diabetes Assn. [14346], PO Box 792, Apex, NC 27502, (919)303-6949
Charles Rennie Mackintosh Soc. [IO], Glasgow, United Kingdom
Charles S. Peirce Soc. [9357], Univ. of West Georgia, Philosophy Prog., 1601 Maple St., Carrollton, GA 30118, (678)839-5000
Charles S. Peirce Soc. [9357], Univ. of West Georgia, Philosophy Prog., 1601 Maple St., Carrollton, GA 30118, (678)839-5000
Charles Stewart Mott Found. [13127], Mott Found. Bldg., 503 S Saginaw St., Ste. 1200, Flint, MI 48502-1851, (810)238-5651
Charles W. Chesnutt Assn. [10709], Susan Prothro Wright, PhD, VP, Clark Atlanta Univ., Dept. of English, Atlanta, GA 30314, (404)880-6163
Charles Williams Soc. [IO], Milton Keynes, United Kingdom
Charley Pride Fan Club [23820], 3198 Royal Ln., No. 200, Dallas, TX 75229, (214)350-8477
Charlotte Perkins Gilman Soc. [10710], Univ. of New England, Dept. of English, 11 Hills Beach Rd., Biddeford, ME 04005
Charlotte W. Newcombe Found. [11770], 35 Park Pl., Princeton, NJ 08542-6918, (609)452-7022
Charolais Soc. of Australia [IO], Armidale, Australia
Chart and Nautical Instrument Trade Assn. [IO], London, United Kingdom
Charted Designers Assn. - Address unknown since 2011.
Chartered Alternative Investment Analyst Assn. [2134], 100 Univ. Dr., Amherst, MA 01002, (413)253-7373
Chartered Inst. of Arbitrators [IO], London, United Kingdom
Chartered Inst. of Architectural Technologists [IO], London, United Kingdom
Chartered Inst. of Bankers in Scotland [IO], Edinburgh, United Kingdom
Chartered Inst. of Building [IO], Ascot, United Kingdom
Chartered Inst. of Environmental Hea. [IO], London, United Kingdom
Chartered Inst. of Housing [IO], Coventry, United Kingdom
Chartered Inst. of Journalists [IO], London, United Kingdom
Chartered Inst. of Lib. and Info. Professionals [IO], London, United Kingdom
Chartered Inst. of Lib. and Info. Professionals in Scotland [IO], Hamilton, United Kingdom
Chartered Inst. of Linguists [IO], London, United Kingdom
Chartered Inst. of Logistics and Transport [IO], Corby, United Kingdom
Chartered Inst. of Logistics and Transport in Australia [IO], Robina, Australia
Chartered Inst. of Logistics and Transport in Hong Kong [IO], Hong Kong, People's Republic of China

Chartered Inst. of Logistics and Transport in Ireland [IO], Dublin, Ireland
Chartered Inst. of Logistics and Transport in North America [IO], Ottawa, ON, Canada
Chartered Inst. of Logistics and Transport - Zimbabwe [IO], Harare, Zimbabwe
Chartered Inst. of Loss Adjusters [IO], London, United Kingdom
Chartered Inst. of Mgt. Accountants [IO], London, United Kingdom
Chartered Inst. of Mgt. Accountants - Australia [IO], Sydney, Australia
Chartered Inst. of Mgt. Accountants - Hong Kong Div. [IO], Hong Kong, People's Republic of China
Chartered Inst. of Mgt. Accountants - Ireland [IO], Ballsbridge, Ireland
Chartered Inst. of Mgt. Accountants - Sri Lanka [IO], Colombo, Sri Lanka
Chartered Inst. of Marketing [IO], Maidenhead, United Kingdom
Chartered Inst. of Patent Agents [IO], London, United Kingdom
Chartered Inst. of Personnel and Development [IO], London, United Kingdom
Chartered Inst. of Plumbing and Heating Engg. [IO], Hornchurch, United Kingdom
Chartered Inst. of Public Finance and Accountancy [IO], London, United Kingdom
Chartered Inst. of Public Relations [IO], London, United Kingdom
Chartered Inst. of Purchasing and Supply [IO], Stamford, United Kingdom
Chartered Inst. of Taxation [IO], London, United Kingdom
Chartered Institution of Building Services Engineers - England [IO], London, United Kingdom
Chartered Institution of Civil Engg. Surveyors [IO], Sale, United Kingdom
Chartered Institution of Highways and Trans. [IO], London, United Kingdom
Chartered Institution of Wastes Mgt. [IO], Northampton, United Kingdom
Chartered Institution of Water and Environmental Mgt. [IO], London, United Kingdom
Chartered Insurance Inst. [IO], London, United Kingdom
Chartered Property Casualty Underwriter Soc. [★1954]
Chartered Quality Inst. [IO], London, United Kingdom
Chartered Secretaries Australia [IO], Sydney, Australia
Chartered Secretaries Australia - Queensland Br. [IO], Brisbane, Australia
Chartered Secretaries Australia - South Australia Br. [IO], Kent Town, Australia
Chartered Secretaries Australia - Tasmania Br. [IO], Melbourne, Australia
Chartered Secretaries Australia - Victoria Br. [IO], Melbourne, Australia
Chartered Secretaries Australia - Western Australia Br. [IO], Perth, Australia
Chartered Secretaries New Zealand [IO], Auckland, New Zealand
Chartered Soc. of Designers [IO], London, United Kingdom
Chartered Soc. of Physiotherapy [IO], London, United Kingdom
C.H.A.S.E. for Life [14450], PO Box 443, Little Silver, NJ 07739, (888)547-4460
Chase Purinton Family Assn. - Defunct.
Chatham House [IO], London, United Kingdom
Chatlos Found. [20263], PO Box 915048, Longwood, FL 32791-5048, (407)862-5077
Chatlos Found. [20263], PO Box 915048, Longwood, FL 32791-5048, (407)862-5077
CHEA of CA [★8267]
CHEA of California [★8267]
Check Collectors Roundtable [★21965]
Check Payment Systems Assn. [3347], 2025 M St. NW, Ste. 800, Washington, DC 20036-3309, (202)367-1144
Checker Car Club of Am. [21021], 160 Willard Dr., North East, MD 21901-1631
CHEER for Viet Nam [13374], PO Box 341, Culver City, CA 90232

A star before a book entry number signifies that the name is not listed separately, but is mentioned within the entry.

Cheerleading

Amer. Assn. of Cheerleading Coaches and Administrators [22449]
Christian Cheerleaders of Am. [22450]
Natl. Coun. for Spirit Safety and Educ. [22451]
NFHS Spirit Assn. [22466]
Org. of Spirit Indus. Providers [22452]
Spirit Indus. Trade Assn. [733]
Cheese Importers Assn. of Am. [1018], 204 E St. NE, Washington, DC 20002, (202)547-0899
Chef Assn. of Bermuda [IO], Hamilton, Bermuda

Chefs

Amer. Culinary Fed. [734]
Amer. Personal and Private Chef Assn. [735]
Asian Chefs Assn. [736]
Chefs for Humanity [12267]
Intl. Culinary Tourism Assn. [737]
U.S. Personal Chef Assn. [738]
Women Chefs and Restaurateurs [739]
Chefs for Humanity [12267], Mr. Jaime Wolf, Pelosi, Wolf, Effron & Spates, LLP, The Woolworth Bldg., 233 Broadway, Ste. 2208, New York, NY 10279
Chefs for Humanity [12267], Mr. Jaime Wolf, Pelosi, Wolf, Effron & Spates, LLP, The Woolworth Bldg., 233 Broadway, Ste. 2208, New York, NY 10279
Chem. and Allied Indus. Assn. [IO], Auckland Park, Republic of South Africa
Chem. Bus. Assn. [IO], Crewe, United Kingdom
Chem. Coater Assn. [★748]
Chem. Coaters Assn. Intl. [748], 5040 Old Taylor Mill Rd., PMB 13, Taylor Mill, KY 41015, (859)356-1030
Chem. Fabrics and Film Assn. [2766], 1300 Sumner Ave., Cleveland, OH 44115-2851, (216)241-7333
Chem. Fabrics and Film Assn. [2766], 1300 Sumner Ave., Cleveland, OH 44115-2851, (216)241-7333
Chem. Fiber Indus. Assn. [IO], Frankfurt, Germany
Chem. Hazards Commun. Soc. [IO], Lymington, United Kingdom
Chem. Heritage Found. [9759], 315 Chestnut St., Philadelphia, PA 19106-2702, (215)925-2222
Chem. and Indus. Consultants Assn. [IO], Oswestry, United Kingdom
Chem. Indus. Assn. [IO], London, United Kingdom
Chem. Indus. Coun. of Malaysia [IO], Kuala Lumpur, Malaysia
Chem. Indus. Assn. [IO], Santiago, Chile
Chem. Indus. and Engg. Soc. of China [IO], Beijing, People's Republic of China
Chem. Indus. Fed. of Finland [IO], Helsinki, Finland
Chem. Indus. Inst. of Toxicology [★7571]
Chem. Injury Info. Network [16889], PO Box 301, White Sulphur Springs, MT 59645, (406)547-2255
Chem. Injury Info. Network [16889], PO Box 301, White Sulphur Springs, MT 59645, (406)547-2255
Chem. Inst. of Canada [IO], Ottawa, ON, Canada
Chem. Mfrs. Assn. [★743]
Chem. Org. of Mexico [IO], Mexico City, Mexico
Chem. Pharmaceutical Generic Assn. [IO], Milan, Italy
Chem. Producers and Distributors Assn. [749], 1730 Rhode Island Ave. NW, Ste. 812, Washington, DC 20036, (202)386-7407
Chemical Res. Applied to World Needs Committee [★6424]
Chemical Res. Applied to World Needs Committee [★6424]
Chem. Soc. of Ethiopia [IO], Addis Ababa, Ethiopia
Chem. Soc. of Japan [IO], Tokyo, Japan
Chem. Soc. of Pakistan [IO], Islamabad, Pakistan
Chem. Soc. of Vietnam [IO], Hanoi, Vietnam
Chem. Sources Assn. [1520], Diane Davis, 3301 Rte. 66, Ste. 205, Bldg. C, Neptune, NJ 07753, (732)922-3008
Chem. Specialties Mfrs. Assn. [★752]
Chem. Waste Trans. Inst. [★3260]

Chemicals

Acrylonitrile Gp. [740]
Alkylphenols and Ethoxylates Res. Coun. [741]
Alliance for Responsible Atmospheric Policy [742]
Amer. Chemistry Coun. [743]
Amer. Chemistry Coun., Chlorine Chemistry Div. [6390]
Amer. Cleaning Inst. [744]
Argentine Chamber of Aerosols [17558]

Basic Acrylic Monomer Mfrs. [745]
Brazilian Chem. Indus. Assn. [21534]
Carpet Cleaners Inst. of the Northwest [746]
Center for Chem. Process Safety [747]
Chem. and Allied Indus. Assn. [9138]
Chem. Coaters Assn. Intl. [748]
Chem. Hazards Commun. Soc. [2762]
Chem. Indus. Assn. [5211]
Chem. Producers and Distributors Assn. [749]
Chlorinated Paraffins Indus. Assn. [750]
Chlorine Inst. [751]
Coalition for SafeMinds [15580]
Consumer Specialty Products Assn. [752]
CropLife Am. [753]
Ethylene Oxide Sterilization Assn. [754]
European Isocyanate and Polyol Producers Assn. [21469]
Focus Fusion Soc. [6725]
Halogenated Solvents Indus. Alliance [755]
Inst. for Polyacrylate Absorbents [756]
Inst. for Polyacrylate Absorbents [756]
Intl. Brotherhood of DuPont Workers [23171]
Israeli Assn. for Aerosol Res. [19533]
Latvian Biochemical Soc. [1678]
Materials Tech. Inst. [757]
Methacrylate Producers Assn. [758]
Moms Against Mercury [13322]
Natl. Assn. of Chem. Distributors [759]
Natl. Assn. of Sci. Materials Managers [3179]
Natl. Chem. Indus. Assn. [2140]
Natl. Lime Assn. [760]
Partnership for Advancing the Transition to Hydrogen [6748]
Phosphate Chemicals Export Assn. [761]
Pine Chemicals Assn. [762]
SB Latex Coun. [763]
Silicones Environmental, Hea. and Safety Coun. [764]
Soc. for Chem. Hazard Commun. [765]
Soc. of Chem. Mfrs. and Affiliates [766]
Styrene Info. and Res. Center [767]
The Sulphur Inst. [768]
The Sulphur Inst. [768]
Synthetic Amorphous Silica and Silicates Indus. Assn. [769]
Tributyl Phosphate Task Force [770]
Chemicals and Allied Products Export Promotion Coun. [IO], Calcutta, India

Chemistry

AACC Intl. [6385]
AACC Intl. [6385]
Adhesion Soc. [6386]
Alpha Chi Sigma [23489]
Amer. Assn. for Aerosol Res. [6387]
Amer. Assn. for Clinical Chemistry [6388]
Amer. Assn. for Clinical Chemistry [6388]
Amer. Carbon Soc. [6389]
Amer. Chem. Soc. [771]
Amer. Chemistry Coun., Chlorine Chemistry Div. [6390]
Amer. Inst. of Chem. Engineers [6391]
Amer. Inst. of Chemists [6392]
Amer. Leather Chemists Assn. [6393]
Amer. Microchemical Soc. [6394]
Amer. Oil Chemists' Soc. [6395]
Amer. Oil Chemists' Soc. [6395]
Amer. Soc. of Brewing Chemists [6396]
Amer. Soc. of Brewing Chemists [6396]
Analytical and Life Sci. Systems Assn. [7358]
AOAC Intl. [6397]
AOAC Intl. [6397]
Assn. for Chemoreception Sciences [6398]
Assn. for Chemoreception Sciences [6398]
Assn. of Consulting Chemists and Chem. Engineers [6399]
Assn. of Fertilizer and Phosphate Chemists [6400]
BioEnvironmental Polymer Soc. [6401]
Center for Process Analysis and Control [6402]
Chemists Without Borders [12449]
Commercial Development and Marketing Assn. [6403]
Controlled Release Soc. [6404]
Coun. for Chem. Res. [6405]
Electrochemical Soc. [6406]

Emulsion Polymers Inst. [6407]
Fed. of Analytical Chemistry and Spectroscopy Societies [6408]
Focus Fusion Soc. [6725]
Histochemical Soc. [6409]
Inst. for Chem. Educ. [7820]
Intl. Maillard Reaction Soc. [6410]
Intl. Soc. for Hyaluronan Sciences [6274]
Intl. Soc. for IGF Res. [6851]
Intl. Union of Pure and Applied Chemistry [6411]
Intl. Union of Pure and Applied Chemistry [6411]
Iota Sigma Pi [23490]
Iranian Chemists' Assn. of the Amer. Chem. Soc. [6412]
Natl. Mole Day Found. [6413]
Natl. Org. for the Professional Advancement of Black Chemists and Chem. Engineers [6414]
Natl. Registry of Certified Chemists [6415]
North Amer. Chinese Clinical Chemists Assn. [6416]
North Amer. Chinese Clinical Chemists Assn. [6416]
Organic Reactions Catalysis Soc. [6417]
Partnership for Advancing the Transition to Hydrogen [6748]
Radiochemistry Soc. [6418]
Royal Netherlands Chem. Soc. [17115]
Societe de Chimie Industrielle, Amer. Sect. [6419]
Societe de Chimie Industrielle, Amer. Sect. [6419]
Soc. of Biological Inorganic Chemistry [6420]
Soc. for Biomolecular Sciences [6423]
Soc. of Cosmetic Chemists [6421]
Soc. of Flavor Chemists [6422]
Soc. for Lab. Automation and Screening [6423]
U.S. Natl. Comm. for the Intl. Union of Pure and Applied Chemistry [6424]
U.S. Natl. Comm. for the Intl. Union of Pure and Applied Chemistry [6424]
Women Members Network of the Royal Soc. of Chemistry [20466]
Chemistry Consortium - Defunct.
Chemistry and Physics on Stamps Stud. Unit [22025], Prof. Foil A. Miller, Ed.-Emeritus, 960 Lakemont Dr., Pittsburgh, PA 15243
Chemistry and Physics Stud. Unit [★22025]
Chemistry Stud. Unit [★22025]
Chemists' Club [19239], 30 W 44th St., New York, NY 10036, (212)582-5454
Chemists and Colorists; Amer. Assn. of Textile [7563]
Chemists Without Borders [12449], 745 S Bernardo Ave., No. A121, Sunnyvale, CA 94087, (888)595-5604
CHEMOcare [★13899]
Chemotherapists Assn. of Ukraine [IO], Kiev, Ukraine
Chemotherapy Found. [15922], 183 Madison Ave., Ste. 403, New York, NY 10016, (212)213-9292
Chemtrec Center Non-Emergency Services - Defunct.
Chen Qingzhou Martial Arts Assn., USA [22728], 325M Sharon Park Dr., No. 729, Menlo Park, CA 94025, (650)618-1485
Cherish Life Queensland [IO], Toowong, Australia
Chernobyl Children Proj., U.S.A. [12818], 145 High St., Canton, MA 02021, (781)828-8119
Chernobyl Children's Fund - Japan [IO], Tokyo, Japan
Cherokee Heritage Center [★10323]
Cherokee Natl. Historical Soc. [10323], PO Box 515, Tahlequah, OK 74465-0515, (918)456-6007
Cherokee Pilots' Assn. [20887], PO Box 1996, Lutz, FL 33549, (813)500-2909
Cherry Central Cooperative [4443], PO Box 988, Traverse City, MI 49685-0988, (231)946-1860
Cherry Growers and Indus. Found. [★4459]
Cherry Marketing Inst. [4444], PO Box 30285, Lansing, MI 48909
CHERUBS - Assn. of Congenital Diaphragmatic Hernia Res., Advocacy and Support [★13840]
CHERUBS - Assn. of Congenital Diaphragmatic Hernia Res., Advocacy and Support [13840], 3650 Rogers Rd., No. 290, Wake Forest, NC 27587, (919)610-0129
CHERUBS - Assn. of Congenital Diaphragmatic Hernia Res., Awareness and Support [13840], 3650 Rogers Rd., No. 290, Wake Forest, NC 27587, (919)610-0129

Reference to "IO" in place of a book number signifies that the association may be found in the 50th edition of International Organizations.

Chesapeake Bay Yacht Racing Association [★22340]
Chesapeake and Ohio Historical Soc. [10487], 312 E Ridgeway St., Clifton Forge, VA 24422, (540)862-2210
Cheshire Ireland [IO], Dublin, Ireland
Chess
  All Services Postal Chess Club [21273]
  Chess Collectors Intl. [21274]
  Chess Collectors Intl. [21274]
  Chess in the Schools [21275]
  Correspondence Chess League of Am. [21276]
  U.S. Braille Chess Assn. [21277]
  U.S. Chess Fed. [21278]
Chess Collectors Intl. [21274], PO Box 166, Commack, NY 11725, (631)543-1330
Chess Collectors Intl. [21274], PO Box 166, Commack, NY 11725, (631)543-1330
Chess Journalists of Am. [2818], 284 Sea View Dr., Key Biscayne, FL 33149, (305)767-2143
Chess in the Schools [21275], 520 8th Ave., 2nd Fl., New York, NY 10018, (212)643-0225
Chess Scotland [IO], Edinburgh, United Kingdom
Chess'n Math Assn. [IO], Toronto, ON, Canada
Chester White Swine Record Assn. [4948], PO Box 9758, Peoria, IL 61612-9758, (309)691-0151
Chet Atkins Appreciation Soc. [23821], 3716 Timberlake Rd., Knoxville, TN 37920, (865)577-2828
Chevra Agudath Achim Chesed Shel Emeth [★19865]
Chevrolet
  1965-66 Full Size Chevrolet Club [20980]
  Chevrolet Nomad Assn. [21022]
  Corvette Club of Am. [21036]
Chevrolet Dealers Alliance [★354]
Chevrolet Nomad Assn. [21022], Tom Roberts, 10405 Miller Rd., Johnstown, OH 43031, (740)967-1955
Chevy Assn; Natl. [21123]
Chevy and Geo Club [21023], PO Box 11238, Chicago, IL 60611, (773)769-6262
Chevy GMC Intl. Truck Club - Address unknown since 2011.
Chewings Fescue and Creeping Red Fescue Commn. - Address unknown since 2010.
CHF Intl. [★12175]
CHF - Partners in Rural Development [IO], Ottawa, ON, Canada
Chi Eta Phi Sorority [23609], 3029 13th St. NW, Washington, DC 20009-5303, (202)232-3858
Chi Omega [23718], 3395 Players Club Pkwy., Memphis, TN 38125, (901)748-8600
Chi Phi [23662], 1160 Satellite Blvd., Suwanee, GA 30024, (404)231-1824
Chi Psi [23663], Jeffrey Hall, 45 Rutledge St., Nashville, TN 37210, (615)736-2520
Chi Psi Educational Trust [★23663]
Chi Sigma Iota [14188], PO Box 35448, Greensboro, NC 27425-5448, (336)841-8180
Chian Fed. [19011], 44-01 Broadway, Astoria, NY 11103, (718)204-2550
Chicago Action for Jews in the Former Soviet Union
Chicago Action for Jews in the Former Soviet Union - Defunct.
Chicago Area Agricultural Advt. Assn. [★100]
Chicago Bd. Options Exchange [3193], 400 S LaSalle St., Chicago, IL 60605, (312)786-5600
Chicago Fan Club [23822], PO Box 195, Landing, NJ 07850
Chicago Hebrew Mission [★19758]
Chicago Hebrew Mission [★19758]
Chicago Map Soc. [20959], Newberry Lib., 60 W Walton St., Chicago, IL 60610, (312)255-3689
Chicago Playing Card Collectors [21321], 2307 Cooper Rd., Atco, NJ 08004
Chicago Saab Club [★21161]
Chicago Stock Exchange [3194], One Financial Pl., 440 S LaSalle St., Chicago, IL 60605, (312)663-2222
Chicago True Advocates [23823], PO Box 195, Landing, NJ 07850
Chickasaw Horse Assn. - Defunct.
Chicos Perdidos in Argentina and Latin Am. and Europe [IO], Mendoza, Argentina
Chief Cultural and Leisure Officers Assn. [IO], Norfolk, United Kingdom

Chief Executives Forum [★656]
Chief Executives Org. [656], 7920 Norfolk Ave., Ste. 400, Bethesda, MD 20814-2507, (301)656-9220
Chief Officers of State Lib. Agencies [9980], 201 E Main St., Ste. 1405, Lexington, KY 40507, (859)514-9151
Chief Warrant and Warrant Officers Assn. I U.S. Coast Guard [5802], 200 V St. SW, Washington, DC 20024, (202)554-7753
Chiefs of Police of the U.S. and Canada [★5696]
Chiefs of Police of the U.S. and Canada [★5696]
Chiens Guides Canadiens pour Aveugles [★IO]
Chigaku Dantai Kenkyu-Kai [★IO]
Chihuahua Club of Am. [21538], 2016 Hidden Hills Dr., Dripping Springs, TX 78620-3941, (216)631-0008
Chihuahuan Desert Res. Inst. [4019], PO Box 905, Fort Davis, TX 79734, (432)364-2499
Child Abuse
  Amer. Professional Soc. on the Abuse of Children [11188]
  Anti-Child Pornography Org. [12710]
  Catholic Guardian Soc. and Home Bur. [11208]
  Children of the Americas [11234]
  Dreamcatchers for Abused Children [11142]
  Face Forward [11885]
  First Star [11278]
  Generation Five [13086]
  Hedge Funds Care [11143]
  Innocents at Risk [12241]
  Intl. Initiative on Exploitative Child Labor [11325]
  Leadership Coun. on Child Abuse and Interpersonal Violence [11890]
  Love Our Children USA [11343]
  MaleSurvivor: The Natl. Org. Against Male Sexual Victimization [13089]
  Minga [11351]
  Natl. Org. to Halt the Abuse and Routine Mutilation of Males [11521]
  Polly Klaas Found. [12540]
  RedLight Children [11144]
  Stop the Silence [11145]
  Whole Child Intl. [11429]
Child Abuse Defense and Rsrc. Center; Natl. [13368]
Child Abuse Inst. of Res. - Defunct.
Child Abuse Listening and Mediation [11211], 1236 Chapala St., PO Box 90754, Santa Barbara, CA 93101, (805)965-2376
Child Action Nepal [IO], London, United Kingdom
Child and Adolescent Psychiatry; Amer. Acad. of [16317]
Child and Adolescent Psychiatry; Soc. of Professors of [16346]
Child Aid [14924], 917 SW Oak St., Ste. 208, Portland, OR 97205, (503)223-3008
Child Aid [14924], 917 SW Oak St., Ste. 208, Portland, OR 97205, (503)223-3008
Child Aid Africa [11212], 535 Rosaire Dr., Hummelstown, PA 17036, (717)566-6118
Child Aid Intl. [11213], 10 Chestnut St., Salem, MA 01970, (978)338-4240
Child Care
  200 Orphanages Worldwide [11172]
  Action for Children - Zambia [11175]
  Advancement for Rural Kids [11176]
  Africa Bridge [11177]
  Africa Hope [11178]
  Afterschool Alliance [11146]
  AHOPE for Children [11180]
  Aiding Romania's Children [11181]
  All the Children are Children [11182]
  All Kids Can Learn Intl. [11446]
  Alliance for Choices in Child Care [11147]
  The Alliance for Safe Children [14056]
  Amer. Bar Assn. Center on Children and the Law [11186]
  Amer. Professional Soc. on the Abuse of Children [11188]
  Angel Covers [11190]
  Anti-Child Pornography Org. [12710]
  Ark Mission [11191]
  Assisting Children in Need [11148]
  Assn. of Premier Nanny Agencies [772]
  Baraka Africa [11194]

Beanies for Baghdad [11195]
Benefit4Kids [11196]
BLOOM Africa [11199]
Blue Nile Children's Org. [11200]
Boys' Towns of Italy [13514]
A Bridge for Children [11201]
Cambodian Amer. Mobile Clinic [14110]
Camp To Belong [11205]
Catholic Guardian Soc. and Home Bur. [11208]
ChangeALife Uganda [11209]
Child Aid Africa [11212]
Child Care Law Center [11149]
A Child For All [11216]
Child Hope Intl. [11218]
Child Literacy [11221]
Child Protection Intl. [11222]
Child Vikaas Intl. [11161]
Child Watch of North Am. [11225]
ChildFund Intl. [11231]
Childreach Intl. USA [11233]
Children of the Americas [11234]
Children of the Dump [11235]
Children of Grace [11236]
Children, Inc. [11455]
Children of the Nations Intl. [11237]
Children of Nowhere [11239]
Children of Vietnam [11242]
Children's Hea. Intl. [14066]
Children's Hope Intl. Literacy and Development [11245]
Children's Intl. Hea. Relief [14067]
Children's Medical Mission of Haiti [11247]
Children's Relief Mission [11250]
Children's Vision Intl., Inc. [11458]
Children's Welfare Intl. [11253]
ChildVoice Intl. [11254]
Chosen Children Intl. [11255]
Communities Without Borders [11258]
Coun. for Professional Recognition [11150]
Cover Me With Love [11261]
Creative Children Therapy [16846]
Dads Rights [11865]
Deaf Bilingual Coalition [12137]
Developing Hands [11264]
Distressed Children and Infants Intl. [11265]
Dreamcatchers for Abused Children [11142]
Ecuador Children's Hope Org. [11266]
Embracing Orphans [11267]
Empower Orphans [11269]
Esther's Aid for Needy and Abandoned Children [11270]
Ethiopian Orphan Relief [11271]
Ethiopia's Tomorrow [11272]
Families for Private Adoption [10788]
Feed My Hungry Children [11274]
Firefly [11277]
First Star [11278]
Flashes of Hope [11135]
Flying Kites [11279]
Forever Found [11280]
Friends in Adoption [10789]
Friends of the Children of Angola [11284]
Friends of Jamaica USA [11285]
Friends of Kenyan Orphans [11286]
Friends of Nutre Hogar [14112]
Generation Five [13086]
Ghana Relief Org. [11289]
Global Children's Org. [11467]
Global Neuro Rescue [15593]
Global Pediatric Alliance [16146]
God's Child Proj. [11294]
God's Kids [11295]
Goods for Good [11296]
Hands for Autistic Children of Ethiopia [11121]
Heart for Africa [11299]
Heart4Kids [11301]
Hearts Across Romania [11302]
Hearts for Zambia [11303]
Helping Children Worldwide [11304]
Helping Hands [11305]
Helping Honduras Kids [11306]
Helping and Loving Orphans [11307]
Helping Orphans Worldwide [11308]
Heshima Kenya [11310]
Home of Hope [11311]

A star before a book entry number signifies that the name is not listed separately, but is mentioned within the entry.

Hope and Future for Children in Bolivia [11314]
Horizon Intl. [11316]
Humanity for Children [16147]
Infancy Intl. [14113]
Intl. Children Assistance Network [11323]
Intl. Initiative on Exploitative Child Labor [11325]
Intl. Nanny Assn. [11151]
Intl. Nanny Assn. [11151]
Intl. Soc. for Children with Cancer [13934]
Island Dolphin Care [11797]
Jeena [11798]
JOY for Our Youth [11330]
Kempe Center for the Prevention and Treatment
    of Child Abuse and Neglect [11331]
Kidlinks World [11332]
Kids Home Intl. [11334]
Kids Together [11802]
Kids Without Borders [11337]
KinderUSA [11479]
Kupenda for the Children [11340]
Loving Hands for the Needy [11345]
Malama Intl. [11346]
Malawi Children's Mission [11347]
Medical Missions for Children [14087]
Medicines for Humanity [14088]
Meds and Food for Kids [11348]
Mike's Angels [11349]
Mil Milagros [11350]
Miracles of Hope Network [11352]
Mocha Moms [13466]
Natl. AfterSchool Assn. [11152]
Natl. Assn. of Child Care Professionals [11153]
Natl. Assn. of Child Care Rsrc. and Referral Agen-
    cies [11154]
Natl. Assn. of Non-Custodial Moms [12610]
Natl. Assn. for Sick Child Daycare [11155]
Natl. Child Care Assn. [11156]
Natl. Coalition for Campus Children's Centers
    [11157]
Natl. Foster Care Coalition [11366]
Natl. Indian Child Care Assn. [12564]
Natl. Practitioners Network for Fathers and
    Families [12018]
Natl. Rsrc. Center for Hea. and Safety in Child
    Care and Early Educ. [11158]
Newborns in Need [11438]
NewPlace Intl. [11368]
Ninos del Lago [11370]
Nuestros Pequenos Hermanos Intl. [20077]
One Heart Bulgaria [11373]
Oper. Help The Children [11375]
Oper. Hug-A-Hero [12533]
The Optimists [11377]
Org. for Medical and Psychological Assistance for
    Children Overseas [14094]
Orphan Support Africa [11380]
Orphan World Relief [11381]
OrphanAid Africa [11382]
Orphans Against AIDS [11383]
Orphans to Ambassadors [11384]
Orphan's Lifeline of Hope Intl. [11385]
Outreach Africa [11386]
Para Sa Bata [11387]
Parents Of Autistic Children [13801]
Partners in Foster Care [12046]
Peace House Africa [11389]
Personal Ponies Ltd. [11822]
Playworks [12696]
Pocketful of Joy [11391]
Preemptive Love Coalition [14040]
Pura Vida for Children [11395]
RedLight Children [11144]
Romania Reborn [11397]
Safe Passage [11401]
Safe Sitter [11159]
Samaritan's Feet [11402]
Scottish Out of School Care Network [7746]
Sequoia Helping Hands [11404]
Serving Our World [11405]
Sky of Love [11406]
Soc. for Orphaned Armenian Relief [12892]
Spark Ventures [11407]
Start Thinking About Romanian Children Relief
    [11410]
Stop the Silence [11145]

Surviving Parents Coalition [11511]
Sweet Sleep [11414]
Tiny Hands Intl. [11416]
Together for Kids [15070]
Touch the Life of a Child Org. [11418]
Twins Found. [12551]
Two Hearts for Hope [11420]
Ubuntu Africa [11421]
Ukrainian Children's Aid and Relief Effort [11422]
uNight [11423]
US Coalition for Child Survival [11514]
Whole Child Intl. [11429]
World Camp for Kids [11431]
World Orphans [11433]
World Relief Org. for Children [11434]
World Spark [11435]
Zambia Hope Intl. [11437]
Child Care Action Campaign - Defunct.
Child Care Found. [★11471]
Child Care Found. [★11471]
Child Care Law Center [11149], 445 Church St., San
    Francisco, CA 94114, (415)558-8005
The Child Connection [12538], 2210 Meadow Dr.,
    Ste. 28, Louisville, KY 40218, (502)459-6888
The Child Connection [12538], 2210 Meadow Dr.,
    Ste. 28, Louisville, KY 40218, (502)459-6888

Child Custody
Adoptee-Birthparent Support Network [10774]
ALMA Soc. [10777]
Catholic Guardian Soc. and Home Bur. [11208]
Children of the Americas [11234]
Dads Rights [11865]
Friends in Adoption [10789]
Natl. Assn. of Non-Custodial Moms [12610]
Single Mothers By Choice [12622]

Child Development
AACTION Autism [13776]
Action for Children - Zambia [11175]
Advancement for Rural Kids [11176]
Africa Hope [11178]
Agami [7824]
Aging with Autism [13777]
All Our Children Intl. Outreach [11183]
Alliance for Childhood [11160]
Alliance for Choices in Child Care [11147]
Amer. Professional Soc. on the Abuse of Children
    [11188]
Americans Care and Share [12805]
Assisting Children in Need [11148]
Autism Community of Africa [11119]
Bailey's Team for Autism [13788]
Baraka Africa [11194]
Battelle for Kids [7826]
BLOOM Africa [11199]
Blue Nile Children's Org. [11200]
Brick by Brick for Tanzania! [8739]
Bridging Refugee Youth and Children's Services
    [11452]
Camp To Belong [11205]
Caring for Cambodia [7827]
ChangeALife Uganda [11209]
Child Aid Africa [11212]
Child Empowerment Intl. [11214]
A Child For All [11216]
The Child is Innocent [11219]
Child Literacy [11221]
Child Vikaas Intl. [11161]
Childreach Intl. USA [11233]
Children of Grace [11236]
Children, Inc. [11455]
Children of Vietnam [11242]
Children's Future Intl. [11244]
Children's Hope Intl. Literacy and Development
    [11245]
Children's Medical Mission of Haiti [11247]
Children's Vision Intl., Inc. [11458]
Children's Welfare Intl. [11253]
Coalition for Sci. After School [8836]
Dance It Forward USA [9546]
Developmental Delay Resources [14050]
Distressed Children and Infants Intl. [11265]
e-Learning for Kids [7828]
Empower the Children [11268]
Empower Orphans [11269]
Ethiopia's Tomorrow [11272]

Every Person Influences Children [11162]
Firefly [11277]
First Signs [14051]
Found. for Child Development [11163]
Friends of Jamaica USA [11285]
Friends of Kenyan Orphans [11286]
Ghana Relief Org. [11289]
Global Children's Org. [11467]
God's Kids [11295]
Goods for Good [11296]
Growing Liberia's Children [11441]
Hands for Autistic Children of Ethiopia [11121]
Heart4Kids [11301]
Hearts Across Romania [11302]
Hearts for Zambia [11303]
Helping Hands [11305]
HELPSudan [11442]
Heshima Kenya [11310]
Home of Hope [11311]
Hope and Future for Children in Bolivia [11314]
Hope for Kenya's Kids [11906]
Hypospadias and Epispadias Assn. [13842]
Infancy Intl. [14113]
Intl. Children Assistance Network [11323]
Kids Home Intl. [11334]
Kids Together [11802]
Kids Without Borders [11337]
KinderUSA [11479]
Kindness in a Box [11339]
Kupenda for the Children [11340]
Loving Hands for the Needy [11345]
Mil Milagros [11350]
Milestones Autism Org. [13798]
Miracles of Hope Network [11352]
Natl. Black Child Development Inst. [11164]
Natl. Indian Child Care Assn. [12564]
Natl. Inst. on Out-of-School Time [11165]
Natl. Sci. Coun. on the Developing Child [14052]
NepalAama [7833]
Newborns in Need [11438]
NewPlace Intl. [11368]
One Hen [7821]
Orphan Support Africa [11380]
Orphan World Relief [11381]
Orphans Against AIDS [11383]
Orphans to Ambassadors [11384]
Orphan's Lifeline of Hope Intl. [11385]
Parents Of Autistic Children [13801]
Partners in Foster Care [12046]
Playing for Keeps [11166]
Playworks [12696]
Pocketful of Joy [11391]
Proj. Sunshine [11394]
Prospect Hill Found. [11167]
Sequoia Helping Hands [11404]
Soc. for Res. in Child Development [11168]
Soc. for Res. in Child Development [11168]
Start Thinking About Romanian Children Relief
    [11410]
Talk About Curing Autism [13805]
Twinkle Little Stars [11419]
Two Hearts for Hope [11420]
Ukrainian Children's Aid and Relief Effort [11422]
Unlocking Autism [13807]
US Coalition for Child Survival [11514]
U.S.A. Toy Lib. Assn. [11169]
William T. Grant Found. [11170]
William T. Grant Found. [11170]
World Camp for Kids [11431]
World Orphans [11433]
Youth Action Intl. [11436]
Zero to Three: Natl. Center for Infants, Toddlers
    and Families [14053]
Child Development Associate Consortium [★11150]
Child Development Associate Natl. Credentialing
    Prog. [★11150]
Child Empowerment Intl. [11214], PO Box 66274,
    Scotts Valley, CA 95067, (800)725-8098
Child Evangelism Fellowship [19736], PO Box 348,
    Warrenton, MO 63383-0348, (636)456-4321
Child Evangelism Fellowship [19736], PO Box 348,
    Warrenton, MO 63383-0348, (636)456-4321
Child Evangelism Fellowship of Canada [IO], Win-
    nipeg, MB, Canada
Child Evangelism Fellowship Intl. [★19736]

Reference to "IO" in place of a book number signifies that the association may be found in the 50th edition of International Organizations.

Child Evangelism Fellowship Intl. [★19736]
Child Family Hea. Intl. [14060], 995 Market St., Ste. 1104, San Francisco, CA 94103, (415)957-9000
Child Family Hea. Intl. [14060], 995 Market St., Ste. 1104, San Francisco, CA 94103, (415)957-9000
Child and Family Policy Center [12000], 505 5th Ave., Ste. 404, Des Moines, IA 50309-4013, (515)280-9027
Child Find [★11215]
Child Find of Am. [11215], PO Box 277, New Paltz, NY 12561-0277, (845)883-6060
Child Find Canada [IO], Oakville, MB, Canada
Child Focus [IO], Brussels, Belgium
A Child For All [11216], 21 Arbor Ln., Stafford, VA 22554, (540)659-6497
A Child For All [11216], 21 Arbor Ln., Stafford, VA 22554, (540)659-6497
Child-Friendly Initiative [11217], 210 W Hamilton Ave., Ste. 183, State College, PA 16801, (877)448-0500

Child Health
AACTION Autism [13776]
Action for Children - Zambia [11175]
Action for Healthy Kids [14054]
Aging with Autism [13777]
Aicardi Syndrome Newsl. [14581]
Alliance for a Healthier Generation [14055]
The Alliance for Safe Children [14056]
Alliance for Smiles [14189]
Amer. Professional Soc. on the Abuse of Children [11188]
Angels In Waiting [11171]
Assn. of Maternal and Child Hea. Programs [14057]
Autism Allies [13779]
Autism Community of Africa [11119]
Autism Ser. Dogs of Am. [13784]
Bailey's Team for Autism [13788]
Benefit4Kids [11196]
Blue Nile Children's Org. [11200]
Brain Tumor Found. for Children [14058]
Brave Kids [14059]
Cambodian Amer. Mobile Clinic [14110]
Catholic Guardian Soc. and Home Bur. [11208]
Changing Children's Lives [15150]
Child Family Hea. Intl. [14060]
Child Family Hea. Intl. [14060]
A Child For All [11216]
Child Hea. Found. [14061]
Child Hea. Found. [14061]
Child Life Coun. [14062]
Child Life Coun. [14062]
ChildAlive [15151]
ChildFund Intl. [11231]
Childhood Influenza Immunization Coalition [15102]
Children of the Americas [11234]
Children, Inc. [11455]
Children's Brain Tumor Found. [14063]
Children's Cross Connection Intl. [14064]
Children's Cross Connection Intl. [14064]
Children's Dialysis Intl. [15548]
Children's Hea. Fund [14065]
Children's Hea. Intl. [14066]
Children's Intl. Hea. Relief [14067]
Children's Medical Ministries [14068]
Children's Medical Mission of Haiti [11247]
Children's Organ Transplant Assn. [14069]
Childspring Intl. [14070]
CityMatch [14071]
Coalition for a Healthy and Active Am. [15852]
Creative Children Therapy [16846]
CURE Intl. [14072]
Docs for Tots [14073]
Dravet.org [14519]
Eunice Kennedy Shriver Natl. Inst. of Child Hea. and Human Development [14074]
Evans Syndrome Res. and Support Gp. [15104]
Every Child By Two [14075]
Face Autism [13789]
Families for Private Adoption [10788]
Family Voices [14076]
Fashion for Autism [13791]
Fed. of Pediatric Organizations [16145]
First Star [11278]

Flashes of Hope [11135]
Friends of Jamaica USA [11285]
Friends of Nutre Hogar [14112]
Generation Green [14077]
Generation Rescue [13792]
Gift from the Heart Found. [14078]
Gift from the Heart Found. [14078]
Girl Power 2 Cure [15592]
Giving Vision [17076]
Global Alliance to Prevent Prematurity and Stillbirth [14105]
Global Neuro Rescue [15593]
Global Nutrition Alliance [15833]
Global Pediatric Alliance [16146]
GlobeMed [15175]
God's Child Proj. [11294]
Gp. B Strep Assn. [14079]
Hands Across the Water [11297]
Hea. and Educ. Relief Org. [12334]
Healthy Child Healthy World [14080]
Healthy Kids Challenge [14081]
Heart4Kids [11301]
Hearts Across Romania [11302]
Holistic Pediatric Assn. [13682]
Home of Hope [11311]
Humanity for Children [16147]
Hypospadias and Epispadias Assn. [13842]
Infancy Intl. [14113]
Intl. Pediatric Hypertension Assn. [15076]
Intl. Soc. for Children with Cancer [13934]
It's My Heart [14028]
Kempe Center for the Prevention and Treatment of Child Abuse and Neglect [11331]
Kids in Flight [14082]
Kids With A Cause [11336]
Kids Without Borders [11337]
KinderUSA [11479]
Klingenstein Third Generation Found. [14083]
Little Hearts [14084]
Locks of Love [14085]
MAGIC Found. [14086]
Medical Missions for Children [14087]
Medicines for Humanity [14088]
Meds and Food for Kids [11348]
Mending Kids Intl. [14089]
Mil Milagros [11350]
Milestones Autism Org. [13798]
Mothers Against Munchausen Syndrome by Proxy Allegations [14090]
Natl. AfterSchool Assn. [11152]
Natl. Assn. for Sick Child Daycare [11155]
Natl. Center for Educ. in Maternal and Child Hea. [14091]
Natl. Initiative for Children's Healthcare Quality [14092]
Natl. Org. to Halt the Abuse and Routine Mutilation of Males [11521]
Natl. Vaccine Info. Center [14093]
Network Ethiopia [15199]
Nuestros Pequenos Hermanos Intl. [20077]
One Heart Bulgaria [11373]
Options for Children in Zambia [11378]
Org. for Medical and Psychological Assistance for Children Overseas [14094]
Org. for Medical and Psychological Assistance for Children Overseas [14094]
Outreach Africa [11386]
Parents Of Autistic Children [13801]
Preemptive Love Coalition [14040]
Proj. Kids Worldwide [14095]
Proj. Sunshine [11394]
Rock Against Cancer [13975]
Saint Jude Children's Res. Hosp. [14096]
Shriners Hospitals for Children [14097]
Smile Network Intl. [14203]
Soc. for Adolescent Hea. and Medicine [14098]
Spoons Across Am. [15845]
Syndromes Without a Name USA [14419]
Talk About Curing Autism [13805]
Together for Kids [15070]
Touch the Life of a Child Org. [11418]
Ubuntu Africa [11421]
Unlocking Autism [13807]
US Coalition for Child Survival [11514]
Wings and Dreams for Kids [14099]

World Camp for Kids [11431]
Child Hea. Found. [14061], 10630 Little Patuxent Pkwy., Ste. 126, Columbia, MD 21044, (410)992-5512
Child Hea. Found. [14061], 10630 Little Patuxent Pkwy., Ste. 126, Columbia, MD 21044, (410)992-5512
Child Hope Intl. [11218], PO Box 3677, Redondo Beach, CA 90277, (888)808-9595
Child Hope Intl. [11218], PO Box 3677, Redondo Beach, CA 90277, (888)808-9595
CHILD, Inc. [★15246]
The Child is Innocent [11219], 139 E Berkeley St., Ste. 501, Boston, MA 02118, (617)877-0068
The Child is Innocent [11219], 139 E Berkeley St., Ste. 501, Boston, MA 02118, (617)877-0068
Child Labor Coalition [★17466]
Child Labor Coalition [11220], Natl. Consumers League, 1701 K St. NW, Ste. 1200, Washington, DC 20006-1566
Child Life Activity Stud. Sect. [★14062]
Child Life Activity Stud. Sect. [★14062]
Child Life Coun. [14062], 11821 Parklawn Dr., Ste. 310, Rockville, MD 20852-2539, (301)881-7090
Child Life Coun. [14062], 11821 Parklawn Dr., Ste. 310, Rockville, MD 20852-2539, (301)881-7090
Child Life Specialist Comm. [★14062]
Child Life Specialist Comm. [★14062]
Child Life Task Force [★14062]
Child Life Task Force [★14062]
Child Literacy [11221], 105 Greene St., No. 1202, Jersey City, NJ 07302, (212)531-1111
Child Mirror Liberia [IO], Monrovia, Liberia
Child Neurology Soc. [15653], 1000 W County Rd. E, Ste. 290, St. Paul, MN 55126, (651)486-9447
Child Protection Alliance [IO], Bakau, Gambia
Child Protection Intl. [11222], 267 19th Ave. S, Ste. 214, Minneapolis, MN 55455
Child Quest Intl. [11223], 1060 N 4th St., Ste. 200, San Jose, CA 95112, (408)287-4673
Child Quest Intl. [11223], 1060 N 4th St., Ste. 200, San Jose, CA 95112, (408)287-4673
Child Reach [★11496]
Child Reach [★11496]
Child Relief and You Am. [★11224]
Child Relief and You Am. [★11224]
Child Rights Centre [IO], Belgrade, Serbia
Child Rights Info. Network [IO], London, United Kingdom
Child Rights and You Am. [11224], PO Box 850948, Braintree, MA 02185-0948, (339)235-0792
Child Rights and You Am. [11224], PO Box 850948, Braintree, MA 02185-0948, (339)235-0792
Child Rights and You - Mumbai [IO], Mumbai, India
Child Support Resistance - Address unknown since 2011.
Child Trends [11454], 4301 Connecticut Ave. NW, Ste. 350, Washington, DC 20008, (202)572-6000
Child Vikaas Intl. [11161], 6674 E Bonita Ct., Orange, CA 92867
Child Watch of North Am. [11225], PO Box 691782, Orlando, FL 32869, (407)290-5100
Child Welfare
200 Orphanages Worldwide [11172]
200 Orphanages Worldwide [11172]
Achieve in Africa [11173]
Achieve in Africa [11173]
Action for Child Protection [11174]
Action for Children - Zambia [11175]
Adoptee-Birthparent Support Network [10774]
Advancement for Rural Kids [11176]
Africa Bridge [11177]
Africa Hope [11178]
African Kids In Need [11179]
African Kids In Need [11179]
AHOPE for Children [11180]
Aiding Romania's Children [11181]
All the Children are Children [11182]
All Kids Can Learn Intl. [11446]
All Our Children Intl. Outreach [11183]
Alliance for Choices in Child Care [11147]
The Alliance for Safe Children [14056]
Alliance for Transforming the Lives of Children [11184]
Alliance for Youth Achievement [11185]

A star before a book entry number signifies that the name is not listed separately, but is mentioned within the entry.

ALMA Soc. [10777]
Amer. Assn. for Home-Based Early Intervention-ists [17234]
Amer. Bar Assn. Center on Children and the Law [11186]
Amer. Humane Assn. [13168]
Amer. Humane Assn. Children's Services [11187]
Amer. Professional Soc. on the Abuse of Children [11188]
Amer. Youth Work Center [13508]
Americans Care and Share [12805]
America's Children Hunger Network [11189]
America's Children Hunger Network [11189]
America's Promise - The Alliance for Youth [13509]
Angel Covers [11190]
Angels In Waiting [11171]
Anti-Child Pornography Org. [12710]
Ark Mission [11191]
Artists Striving to End Poverty [12716]
Assisting Children in Need [11148]
Assn. of Administrators of the Interstate Compact on the Placement of Children [11192]
Assn. of Children's Welfare Agencies [1237]
Assn. of Sites Advocating Child Protection [11193]
Bailey's Team for Autism [13788]
Baraka Africa [11194]
Beanies for Baghdad [11195]
Benefit4Kids [11196]
Bethany Christian Services Intl. [11197]
Bethany Christian Services Intl. [11197]
Black Community Crusade for Children [11198]
BLOOM Africa [11199]
Blue Nile Children's Org. [11200]
Boys' Towns of Italy [13514]
Brick by Brick for Tanzania! [8739]
A Bridge for Children [11201]
Bridge of Love [11202]
Bridges Cambodia Intl. [11203]
Bridging Refugee Youth and Children's Services [11452]
Cabo Verde Children U.S.A. [11204]ChildCambo-dia's Hope
Camp To Belong [11205]
Campaign for a Commercial-Free Childhood [11206]
Care for Children Intl. [11207]
Care for Children Intl. [11207]
Caring for Cambodia [7827]
Caring Hand for Children [11440]
Catholic Guardian Soc. and Home Bur. [11208]
Change Exchange [12205]
ChangeALife Uganda [11209]
CharityHelp Intl. [11210]
Child Abuse Listening and Mediation [11211]
Child Aid Africa [11212]
Child Aid Intl. [11213]
Child Empowerment Intl. [11214]
Child and Family Policy Center [12000]
Child Find of Am. [11215]
A Child For All [11216]
A Child For All [11216]
Child-Friendly Initiative [11217]
Child Hope Intl. [11218]
Child Hope Intl. [11218]
The Child is Innocent [11219]
The Child is Innocent [11219]
Child Labor Coalition [11220]
Child Literacy [11221]
Child Protection Intl. [11222]
Child Quest Intl. [11223]
Child Quest Intl. [11223]
Child Rights and You Am. [11224]
Child Rights and You Am. [11224]
Child Vikaas Intl. [11161]
Child Watch of North Am. [11225]
Child Welfare Info. Gateway [11226]
Child Welfare Inst. [11227]
Child Welfare League of Am. [11228]
Child Welfare and Policy and Practice Gp. [11229]
Childcare Worldwide [11230]
Childcare Worldwide [11230]
ChildFund Intl. [11231]
ChildFund Intl. [11231]

Childhelp [11232]
Childreach Intl. USA [11233]
Children of the Americas [11234]
Children of the Americas [11234]
Children Beyond Our Borders [17235]
Children of the Dump [11235]
Children of Grace [11236]
Children, Inc. [11455]
Children of the Nations Intl. [11237]
Children Now [11238]
Children of Nowhere [11239]
Children of Persia [11240]
Children of Russia [11241]
Children of Russia Found. [11241]
Children of Tanzania [11065]
Children of Vietnam [11242]
Children Without a Voice, USA [11243]
Children's Cup [12819]
Children's Future Intl. [11244]
Children's Hea. Intl. [14066]
Children's Hope Intl. Literacy and Development [11245]
Children's Hope Intl. Literacy and Development [11245]
Children's HopeChest [11246]
Children's Medical Mission of Haiti [11247]
Children's Network Intl. [11248]
Children's Network Intl. [11248]
The Children's Partnership [11249]
Children's Relief Mission [11250]
Children's Relief Network [11251]
Children's Relief Network [11251]
Children's Safety Network [11252]
Children's Vision Intl., Inc. [11458]
Children's Welfare Intl. [11253]
A Child's Right [13415]
ChildVoice Intl. [11254]
ChildVoice Intl. [11254]
Chosen Children Intl. [11255]
Commn. on Missing and Exploited Children [11256]
Comm. for Children [11257]
Communities Without Borders [11258]
Community of Caring [11259]
Coptic Orphans Support Assn. [11260]
Coptic Orphans Support Assn. [11260]
Cover Me With Love [11261]
Crutches 4 Kids [11262]
CURE Intl. [14072]
Dance It Forward USA [9546]
Darkness to Light [11263]
Deaf Bilingual Coalition [12137]
Developing Hands [11264]
Distressed Children and Infants Intl. [11265]
Distressed Children and Infants Intl. [11265]
Dreamcatchers for Abused Children [11142]
Ecuador Children's Hope Org. [11266]
Educate the Children [11461]
Educate These Children [11462]
Embracing Orphans [11267]
Empower the Children [11268]
Empower Orphans [11269]
End Childhood Hunger [12271]
Esther's Aid for Needy and Abandoned Children [11270]
Ethiopian Orphan Relief [11271]
Ethiopia's Tomorrow [11272]
European Found. for St. Children Worldwide [6526]
Expanding Opportunities [11273]
Families for Private Adoption [10788]
Feed My Hungry Children [11274]
Fight 4 Kids [11275]
Fight Crime: Invest in Kids [17236]
Find the Children [11276]
Firefly [11277]
First Star [11278]
Flying Kites [11279]
Forever Found [11280]
Foster Care Alumni of Am. [11281]
Foster Family-Based Treatment Assn. [11282]
Friends in Adoption [10789]
Friends of the Children [11283]
Friends of the Children of Angola [11284]
Friends of Jamaica USA [11285]

Friends of Kenyan Orphans [11286]
Friends of Rwanda Assn. [11287]
Friends of Rwanda Assn. [11287]
FUNDaFIELD [11288]
FUNDaFIELD [11288]
Generation Five [13086]
Generation Green [14077]
Ghana Relief Org. [11289]
Giraffe Club [18680]
Girls for a Change [11290]
Giving Children Hope [11291]
Giving Children Hope [11291]
Global Centurion [11292]
Global Children [11293]
Global Children [11293]
Global Children's Org. [11467]
Global Nutrition Alliance [15833]
God's Child Proj. [11294]
God's Kids [11295]
Goods for Good [11296]
Growing Liberia's Children [11441]
Hagar USA [12237]
Hands Across the Water [11297]
Hands Across the Water [11297]
Hands to Hearts Intl. [11298]
Heart for Africa [11299]
Heart of Romania's Children Found. [11300]
Heart4Kids [11301]
Hearts Across Romania [11302]
Hearts for the Hungry [12282]
Hearts for Zambia [11303]
Hedge Funds Care [11143]
Helping Children Worldwide [11304]
Helping Children Worldwide [11304]
Helping Hands [11305]
Helping Honduras Kids [11306]
Helping and Loving Orphans [11307]
Helping and Loving Orphans [11307]
Helping Orphans Worldwide [11308]
Helping Orphans Worldwide [11308]
HELPSudan [11442]
Herbalife Family Found. [11309]
Herbalife Family Found. [11309]
Heshima Kenya [11310]
Heshima Kenya [11310]
Home of Hope [11311]
Homeless Children Intl. [11312]
Hope for the Child [11313]
Hope for the Child [11313]
Hope and Future for Children in Bolivia [11314]
Hope for Haiti's Children [11315]
Hope for Kenya's Kids [11906]
Horizon Intl. [11316]
Human Rights Watch | Children's Rights Div. [11317]
Human Rights Watch | Children's Rights Div. [11317]
Humanitarian Services for Children of Vietnam [11318]
Humanitarian Services for Children of Vietnam [11318]
Infancy Intl. [14113]
Innocence in Danger U.S.A. [11319]
Innocence in Danger - U.S.A. [11319]
Innocents at Risk [12241]
Inst. for Children, Poverty and Homelessness [11320]
Intl. Aid Serving Kids [11321]
Intl. Aid Serving Kids [11321]
Intl. Child Rsrc. Inst. [11322]
Intl. Child Rsrc. Inst. [11322]
Intl. Children Assistance Network [11323]
Intl. Comm. for the Children of Chechnya [11324]
Intl. Comm. for the Children of Chechnya [11324]
Intl. Initiative on Exploitative Child Labor [11325]
Intl. Initiative on Exploitative Child Labor [11325]
Intl. Org. for Adolescents [11326]
Intl. Org. for Adolescents [11326]
Intl. Orphan Care [11327]
Intl. Soc. for Prevention of Child Abuse and Neglect [11328]
Intl. Soc. for Prevention of Child Abuse and Neglect [11328]
Invisible Children [17237]
Inyana - League of Rwandan Children and Youth [11474]

Reference to "IO" in place of a book number signifies that the association may be found in the 50th edition of International Organizations.

Island Dolphin Care [11797]
Jacob Wetterling Rsrc. Center [11329]
Jeena [11798]
JOY for Our Youth [11330]
Kempe Center for the Prevention and Treatment of Child Abuse and Neglect [11331]
Kidlinks World [11332]
Kids Against Hunger [12283]
KIDS COUNT [11333]
Kids Home Intl. [11334]
Kids In Danger [11335]
Kids Need Both Parents [17623]
Kids Together [11802]
Kids With A Cause [11336]
Kids Without Borders [11337]
Kids Without Borders [11337]
KidsPeace [11338]
KinderUSA [11479]
Kindness in a Box [11339]
Kindness in a Box [11339]
Kupenda for the Children [11340]
Larger Than Life [11341]
Legal Services for Children [12429]
Light of Cambodian Children [11342]
Long Way Home [11073]
Love Our Children USA [11343]
Love146 [11344]
Love146 [11344]
Loving Hands for the Needy [11345]
Malama Intl. [11346]
Malawi Children's Mission [11347]
MaleSurvivor: The Natl. Org. Against Male Sexual Victimization [13089]
Medical Missions for Children [14087]
Meds and Food for Kids [11348]
Meds and Food for Kids [11348]
Mike's Angels [11349]
Mil Milagros [11350]
Mil Milagros [11350]
Minga [11351]
Miracles of Hope Network [11352]
Miracles of Hope Network [11352]
Missing Children in Am. [11353]
Mocha Moms [13466]
Moms Against Poverty [12742]
Mothers and Fathers Aligned Saving Kids [17238]
Mothers Without Borders [11354]
Mothers Without Borders [11354]
Natl. AfterSchool Assn. [11152]
Natl. Assn. of Former Foster Care Children of Am. [11355]
Natl. Assn. for Native Amer. Children of Alcoholics [11356]
Natl. Assn. to Protect Children [11357]
Natl. Assn. of Public Child Welfare Administrators [11358]
Natl. Assn. for Sick Child Daycare [11155]
Natl. Center for Missing and Exploited Children [11359]
Natl. Center for Prosecution of Child Abuse [11360]
Natl. Children's Alliance [11361]
Natl. Coalition for Child Protection Reform [11362]
Natl. Collaboration for Youth [11363]
Natl. Court Appointed Special Advocate Assn. [11364]
Natl. Exchange Club Found. [11365]
Natl. Foster Care Coalition [11366]
Natl. Indian Child Care Assn. [12564]
Natl. Org. to Halt the Abuse and Routine Mutilation of Males [11521]
Natl. Rsrc. Center for Youth Services [11367]
NepalAama [7833]
NewPlace Intl. [11368]
NextAid [11369]
NextAid [11369]
Ninos del Lago [11370]
Ninos del Lago [11370]
North Amer. Reggio Emilia Alliance [11371]
Nurses for the Rights of the Child [11523]
One Child at a Time [11372]
One Heart Bulgaria [11373]
One Heart Bulgaria [11373]
Only a Child [11374]
Only a Child [11374]

Oper. Help The Children [11375]
Oper. Help The Children [11375]
Oper. Hug-A-Hero [12533]
Oper. Kid-To-Kid [11376]
The Optimists [11377]
Options for Children in Zambia [11378]
Orphan Resources Intl. [11379]
Orphan Resources Intl. [11379]
Orphan Support Africa [11380]
Orphan World Relief [11381]
OrphanAid Africa [11382]
OrphanAid Africa [11382]
Orphans Africa [11621]
Orphans Against AIDS [11383]
Orphans to Ambassadors [11384]
Orphan's Lifeline of Hope Intl. [11385]
Orphan's Lifeline of Hope Intl. [11385]
Our Military Kids [12534]
Out of Poverty thru Educ. [7731]
Outreach Africa [11386]
Para Sa Bata [11387]
Parents Anonymous [11388]
Parents Of Autistic Children [13801]
Partners in Foster Care [12046]
Peace House Africa [11389]
Pearl S. Buck Intl. [11390]
Pearl S. Buck Intl. [11390]
Personal Ponies Ltd. [11822]
Pocketful of Joy [11391]
Polly Klaas Found. [12540]
Prevent Child Abuse [11392]
Prevent Child Abuse [11392]
Proj. Cuddle [11393]
Proj. Sunshine [11394]
Pura Vida for Children [11395]
Ray Helfer Soc. [14100]
Reach the Children [11396]
Reach the Children [11396]
Reconstruction Efforts Aiding Children without Homes [11624]
RedLight Children [11144]
Robert F. Kennedy Center for Justice and Human Rights [11385]
Romania Reborn [11397]
RUGMARK Found. [11398]
RUGMARK Found. [11398]
Russian Children's Welfare Soc. [11399]
Russian Children's Welfare Soc. [11399]
Safe Kids Worldwide [11400]
Safe Passage [11401]
Safe Passage [11401]
Samaritan's Feet [11402]
Save the Children Australia [2347]
Seeds of HOPE Intl. [11403]
Sequoia Helping Hands [11404]
Serving Our World [11405]
Serving Our World [11405]
Single Mothers By Choice [12622]
Sky of Love [11406]
Smile Network Intl. [14203]
Soc. for Orphaned Armenian Relief [12892]
Soles for Kidz [19531]
Spark Ventures [11407]
Spirit Quilts [11408]
StandUp for Kids [11409]
Start Thinking About Romanian Children Relief [11410]
Stop it Now! [11411]
Stop the Silence [11145]
Supervised Visitation Network [11412]
Supervised Visitation Network [11412]
Surviving Parents Coalition [11511]
Survivors And Victims Empowered [11413]
Sweet Sleep [11414]
Teachers Resisting Unhealthy Children's Entertainment [11415]
Tiny Hands Intl. [11416]
To Love a Child [11417]
Touch the Life of a Child Org. [11418]
Touch the Life of a Child Org. [11418]
Touching Hearts [10817]
Trans Youth Family Allies [12585]
Twinkle Little Stars [11419]
Two Cents of Hope [8292]
Two Hearts for Hope [11420]

Ubuntu Africa [11421]
Ubuntu Africa [11421]
Ukrainian Children's Aid and Relief Effort [11422]
uNight [11423]
US Coalition for Child Survival [11514]
Variety Intl. - The Children's Charity [11424]
Variety Intl. - The Children's Charity [11424]
Vibha [11425]
Voices for America's Children [11426]
Watchlist on Children and Armed Conflict [11427]
Watchlist on Children and Armed Conflict [11427]
Water for People | PlayPumps Intl. [10827]
Web Wise Kids [11428]
Whole Child Intl. [11429]
World Assn. for Children and Parents [11430]
World Assn. for Children and Parents [11430]
World Camp for Kids [11431]
World Family Ethiopian Orphans and Medical Care [11432]
World Orphans [11433]
World Orphans [11433]
World Relief Org. for Children [11434]
World Spark [11435]
Youth Action Intl. [11436]ChildYouth Advocate Prog. Intl.
Youth for Human Rights Intl. [12255]
Zambia Hope Intl. [11437]
Child Welfare Info. Gateway [11226], 1250 Maryland Ave. SW, 8th Fl., Washington, DC 20024, (703)385-7565
Child Welfare Inst. [11227], 111 E Wacker Dr., Ste. 325, Chicago, IL 60601, (312)949-5640
Child Welfare League of Am. [11228], 1726 M St. NW, Ste. 500, Washington, DC 20036-4522, (202)688-4200
Child Welfare League of Canada [IO], Ottawa, ON, Canada
Child Welfare and Policy and Practice Gp. [11229], 428 E Jefferson St., Montgomery, AL 36104, (334)264-8300
Child Workers in Nepal Concerned Centre [IO], Kathmandu, Nepal
ChildAlive [15151], 14505 Gilpin Rd., Silver Spring, MD 20906, (301)598-1163
Childbirth
Assn. of Midwifery Educators [7822]
Assn. for Pre- and Perinatal Psychology and Hea. [14101]
Birth Without Boundaries [14102]
Childbirth and Postpartum Professional Assn. [14103]
Childbirth and Postpartum Professional Assn. [14103]
Citizens for Midwifery [14104]
Coun. of Intl. Neonatal Nurses [15745]
Global Alliance to Prevent Prematurity and Stillbirth [14105]
Intl. Midwife Assistance [15883]
Intl. Stillbirth Alliance [14106]
Intl. Stillbirth Alliance [14106]
Mama Baby Haiti [14107]
Mama Baby Haiti [14107]
Midwifery Educ. Accreditation Coun. [7823]
Natl. Campaign to Prevent Teen Pregnancy [13540]
Newborns in Need [11438]
North Amer. Registry of Midwives [14108]
Waterbirth Intl. [14109]
Waterbirth Intl. [14109]
White Ribbon Alliance for Safe Motherhood [11439]
Childbirth Connection [15875], 260 Madison Ave., 8th Fl., New York, NY 10016, (212)777-5000
Childbirth Experiences; Center for Humane Options in [15874]
Childbirth and Postpartum Professional Assn. [14103], PO Box 491448, Lawrenceville, GA 30049, (888)MY-CAPPA
Childbirth and Postpartum Professional Assn. [14103], PO Box 491448, Lawrenceville, GA 30049, (888)MY-CAPPA
Childcare Intl. [★11230]
Childcare Intl. [★11230]
Childcare Worldwide [11230], 1971 Midway Ln., Ste. N, Bellingham, WA 98226, (360)647-2283

A star before a book entry number signifies that the name is not listed separately, but is mentioned within the entry.

Childcare Worldwide [11230], 1971 Midway Ln., Ste. N, Bellingham, WA 98226, (360)647-2283
ChildFund [11231], 2821 Emerywood Pkwy., Richmond, VA 23294, (804)756-2700
ChildFund Australia [IO], Surry Hills, Australia
ChildFund Intl. [11231], 2821 Emerywood Pkwy., Richmond, VA 23294, (804)756-2700
ChildFund Ireland [IO], Dublin, Ireland
ChildFund New Zealand [IO], Auckland, New Zealand
Childhelp [11232], 15757 N 78th St., Ste. B, Scottsdale, AZ 85260, (480)922-8212
Childhood Apraxia of Speech Assn. [16684], 416 Lincoln Ave., 2nd Fl., Millvale, PA 15209, (412)343-7102
Childhood Arthritis and Rheumatology Res. Alliance [16618], Dept. of Pediatrics, Div. of Rheumatology, Boswell Bldg. A081, 300 Pasteur Dr., Stanford, CA 94305-5208, (650)736-4364
Childhood Arthritis and Rheumatology Res. Alliance [16618], Dept. of Pediatrics, Div. of Rheumatology, Boswell Bldg. A081, 300 Pasteur Dr., Stanford, CA 94305-5208, (650)736-4364
Childhood Brain Tumor Found. [14379], 20312 Watkins Meadow Dr., Germantown, MD 20876, (301)515-2900
Childhood Cancer Found. - Candlelighters Canada [IO], Toronto, ON, Canada
Childhood Education
Advancement for Rural Kids [11176]
African Kids In Need [11179]
Agami [7824]
Assn. for Childhood Educ. Intl. [7825]
Assn. for Childhood Educ. Intl. [7825]
Baraka Africa [11194]
Battelle for Kids [7826]
Blue Nile Children's Org. [11200]
Brick by Brick for Tanzania! [8739]
Care Through Educ. Intl. [11453]
Caring for Cambodia [7827]
Caring Hand for Children [11440]
Child Empowerment Intl. [11214]
A Child For All [11216]
ChildFund Intl. [11231]
Children of the Dump [11235]
Children, Inc. [11455]
Children of Tanzania [11065]
Children's Future Intl. [11244]
Children's Medical Mission of Haiti [11247]
Coalition for Sci. After School [8836]
Dance It Forward USA [9546]
Delta Phi Upsilon [23491]
Developing Hands [11264]
e-Learning for Kids [7828]
Educate the Children [11461]
Educate These Children [11462]
Everybody Wins! USA [7829]
Friends of Jamaica USA [11285]
Friends of Kenyan Orphans [11286]
GalaxyGoo [7830]
God's Child Proj. [11294]
GreatSchools [7831]
Growing Liberia's Children [11441]
HELPSudan [11442]
Hope for Kenya's Kids [11906]
Natl. Alternative Educ. Assn. [7722]
Natl. Assn. for the Educ. of Young Children [7832]
Natl. Title I Assn. [7677]
NepalAama [7833]
One Hen [7821]
Orphans Against AIDS [11383]
Out of Poverty thru Educ. [7731]
Parent Cooperative Preschools Intl. [7834]
Parent Cooperative Preschools Intl. [7834]
Two Cents of Hope [8292]
Van Andel Educ. Inst. [8066]
World Org. for Early Childhood Educ., U.S. Natl. Comm. [7835]
Childhood Eye Cancer Trust [IO], London, United Kingdom
Childhood Influenza Immunization Coalition [15102], 139 5th Ave., 3rd Fl., New York, NY 10010, (212)886-2277
Childhope - Zambia [IO], Lusaka, Zambia
Childless By Choice - Defunct.

Childminding Ireland [IO], Kilcoole, Ireland
Childreach Intl. USA [11233], 4132 RFD, Long Grove, IL 60047, (773)303-8261
Childreach, U.S. Member of Plan Intl. [★11496]
Childreach, U.S. Member of Plan Intl. [★11496]
Children
4 R Kids Sake [11443]
200 Orphanages Worldwide [11172]
AACTION Autism [13776]
ABLE: Assn. for Better Living and Educ. Intl. [11537]
Achieve in Africa [11173]
Action for Children - Zambia [11175]
Adoptee-Birthparent Support Network [10774]
Advancement for Rural Kids [11176]
Africa Hope [11178]
African Cradle [11444]
African Kids In Need [11179]
AHOPE for Children [11180]
Aicardi Syndrome Newsl. [14581]
Aiding Romania's Children [11181]
A.L. Mailman Family Found. [11445]
All the Children are Children [11182]
All Kids Can Learn Intl. [11446]
All Our Children Intl. Outreach [11183]
Alliance for Choices in Child Care [11147]
The Alliance for Safe Children [14056]
Alliance for Smiles [14189]
ALMA Soc. [10777]
Ambassadors for Children [11447]
Amer. Assn. of Caregiving Youth [13505]
Amer. Bar Assn. Center on Children and the Law [11186]
Amer. Civil Liberties Union [17260]
Amer. Junior Brahman Assn. [3884]
Amer. Professional Soc. on the Abuse of Children [11188]
Amer. Youth Work Center [13508]
Angel Covers [11190]
Angelcare [11448]
Angelcare [11448]
Angels In Waiting [11171]
Anti-Child Pornography Org. [12710]
Ark Mission [11191]
Art Therapy Connection [13772]
Artists for Peace and Justice [13152]
Assisting Children in Need [11148]
Assn. for Children with Down Syndrome [12496]
Assn. for the Educ. of Children with Medical Needs [7836]
Baraka Africa [11194]
Beanies for Baghdad [11195]
Believe In Tomorrow Natl. Children's Found. [11449]
Benefit4Kids [11196]
Better Boys Found. [11450]
Big Bros. Big Sisters of Am. [11451]
BLOOM Africa [11199]
Blue Nile Children's Org. [11200]
Boys' Towns of Italy [13514]
A Bridge for Children [11201]
Bridge of Love [11202]
Bridges Cambodia Intl. [11203]
Bridging Refugee Youth and Children's Services [11452]
Cambodian Amer. Mobile Clinic [14110]
Care Through Educ. Intl. [11453]
Caring for Cambodia [7827]
Caring Hand for Children [11440]
Catholic Guardian Soc. and Home Bur. [11208]
ChangeALife Uganda [11209]
Child Aid Africa [11212]
Child Empowerment Intl. [11214]
A Child For All [11216]
Child Hope Intl. [11218]
The Child is Innocent [11219]
Child Literacy [11221]
Child Protection Intl. [11222]
Child Trends [11454]
Child Vikaas Intl. [11161]
Child Watch of North Am. [11225]
Child Welfare and Policy and Practice Gp. [11229]
ChildFund [11231]
Childhood Influenza Immunization Coalition [15102]

Childreach Intl. USA [11233]
Children with AIDS Proj. of Am. [10783]
Children of the Americas [11234]
Children Beyond Our Borders [17235]
Children of the Dump [11235]
Children of the Earth [12627]
Children of Grace [11236]
Children, Inc. [11455]
Children of the Nations Intl. [11237]
Children and Nature Network [4241]
Children of Nowhere [11239]
Children of Vietnam [11242]
Children's Art Found. [9473]
Children's Creative Response to Conflict Prog. [11456]
Children's Cup [12819]
Children's Defense Fund [11457]
Children's Future Intl. [11244]
Children's Hea. Intl. [14066]
Children's Hope Intl. Literacy and Development [11245]
Children's Medical Mission of Haiti [11247]
Children's Relief Mission [11250]
Children's Vision Intl., Inc. [11458]
Children's Welfare Intl. [11253]
Children's Wish Found. Intl. [11459]
Children's Wish Found. Intl. [11459]
A Child's Right [13415]
Childspring Intl. [14070]
ChildVoice Intl. [11254]
Chosen Children Intl. [11255]
Coalition for Sci. After School [8836]
COLAGE [12074]
Communities Without Borders [11258]
Coun. on Accreditation [13182]
Coun. for Children with Behavioral Disorders [8878]
Cover Me With Love [11261]
Crutches 4 Kids [11262]
DAD: Drums and Disabilities [12422]
Dads Rights [11865]
Dance It Forward USA [9546]
Deaf Bilingual Coalition [12137]
Developing Hands [11264]
Diaper Free Baby [14111]
Distressed Children and Infants Intl. [11265]
Dream Factory [11460]
Dreamcatchers for Abused Children [11142]
e-Learning for Kids [7828]
EcoMom Alliance [13459]
Ecuador Children's Hope Org. [11266]
Educate the Children [11461]
Educate These Children [11462]
Embracing Orphans [11267]
Empower the Children [11268]
Empower Orphans [11269]
End Childhood Hunger [12271]
Enrichment Educ. [8276]
Esther's Aid for Needy and Abandoned Children [11270]
Ethiopian North Amer. Hea. Professionals Assn. [14776]
Ethiopian Orphan Relief [11271]
Ethiopia's Tomorrow [11272]
Face Autism [13789]
Fair Play for Children Assn. [14812]
Families for Private Adoption [10788]
Family of the Americas Found. [12032]
Famous Fone Friends [11463]
Fed. of Pediatric Organizations [16145]
Firefly [11277]
First Star [11278]
Flashes of Hope [11135]
Flying Kites [11279]
Focus on the Family [12009]
For Victims of War and Poverty [12455]
Forever Found [11280]
Friends in Adoption [10789]
Friends of the Children of Angola [11284]
Friends of Jamaica USA [11285]
Friends of Karen [11464]
Friends of Kenyan Orphans [11286]
Friends of Nutre Hogar [14112]
Futures for Children [11465]
Generation Five [13086]

Reference to "IO" in place of a book number signifies that the association may be found in the 50th edition of International Organizations.

Generation Green [14077]
Ghana Relief Org. [11289]
Gifted Learning Proj. [12424]
Giraffe Club [18680]
Give Kids the World Village [11466]
Give Kids the World Village [11466]
Giving Vision [17076]
Global Ambassadors for Children [18249]
Global Centurion [11292]
Global Children [11293]
Global Children's Org. [11467]
Global Neuro Rescue [15593]
Global Nutrition Alliance [15833]
God's Child Proj. [11294]
God's Kids [11295]
Goods for Good [11296]
GreatSchools [7831]
Green Parent Assn. [4075]
Growing Liberia's Children [11441]
Hagar USA [12237]
Hands to Hearts Intl. [11298]
Healing the Children [11468]
Hea. and Educ. Relief Org. [12334]
Heart for Africa [11299]
Heart4Kids [11301]
Hearts Across Romania [11302]
Hearts for the Hungry [12282]
Hearts for Zambia [11303]
Hedge Funds Care [11143]
Helping Children Worldwide [11304]
Helping Hands [11305]
Helping Honduras Kids [11306]
Helping and Loving Orphans [11307]
Helping Orphans Worldwide [11308]
Heshima Kenya [11310]
Hollywood Unites For Haiti [12128]
Holt Intl. Children's Services [11469]
Holt Intl. Children's Services [11469]
Home of Hope [11311]
Hope for the Child [11313]
Hope and Future for Children in Bolivia [11314]
Hope for Haiti's Children [11315]
Hope for Kenya's Kids [11906]
Horizon Intl. [11316]
Humanitarian Services for Children of Vietnam
    [11318]ChildrenHumanity United in Giving
    Internationally
Infancy Intl. [14113]
Innocents at Risk [12241]
Institutes for the Achievement of Human Potential
    [11470]
Intl. Child Care U.S.A. [11471]
Intl. Child Care U.S.A. [11471]
Intl. Child Empowerment Network [11472]
Intl. Children Assistance Network [11323]
Intl. Initiative on Exploitative Child Labor [11325]
Intl. Lactation Consultant Assn. [11473]
Intl. Lactation Consultant Assn. [11473]
Intl. Pediatric Hypertension Assn. [15076]
Internet Keep Safe Coalition [17996]
Interracial Family Circle [12012]
Invisible Children [17237]
Inyana - League of Rwandan Children and Youth
    [11474]
Island Dolphin Care [11797]
Jack and Jill of Am. [11475]
Jack and Jill of Am. Found. [11476]
Jeena [11798]
JOY for Our Youth [11330]
Kempe Center for the Prevention and Treatment
    of Child Abuse and Neglect [11331]
Kidlinks World [11332]
Kids Against Hunger [12283]
Kids with Cameras [12694]
Kids Ecology Corps [4322]
Kids Home Intl. [11334]
Kids at Hope [11477]
Kids Konnected [11478]
Kids Making a Difference [3813]
Kids Need Both Parents [17623]
Kids for Peace [18262]
Kids Together [11802]
Kids With A Cause [11336]
Kids Without Borders [11337]
KinderUSA [11479]

Kindness in a Box [11339]
Kupenda for the Children [11340]
La Leche League Intl. [11480]
Light of Cambodian Children [11342]
Loving Hands for the Needy [11345]
Make-A-Wish Found. of Am. [11481]
Make a Child Smile [11482]
Malama Intl. [11346]
Malawi Children's Mission [11347]
Marine Toys for Tots Found. [11483]
Medical Missions for Children [14087]
Meds and Food for Kids [11348]
Mike's Angels [11349]
Miracles of Hope Network [11352]
MISS Found. l Alliance of Grandparents, A Sup-
    port in Tragedy Intl. [12123]
Missing Children in Am. [11353]
Mocha Moms [13466]
Moms Against Poverty [12742]
Mothers of Murdered Youth [11484]
Natl. Abandoned Infants Assistance Rsrc. Center
    [11485]
Natl. AfterSchool Assn. [11152]
Natl. Alliance for Grieving Children [11486]
Natl. Assn. of Counsel for Children [11487]
Natl. Assn. of Non-Custodial Moms [12610]
Natl. Assn. for Sick Child Daycare [11155]
Natl. Center for Children in Poverty [11488]
Natl. Foster Care Coalition [11366]
Natl. Indian Child Care Assn. [12564]
Natl. Practitioners Network for Fathers and
    Families [12018]
Natl. Tribal Child Support Assn. [11489]
NepalAama [7833]
New Parents Network [8692]
Newborns in Need [11438]
NewPlace Intl. [11368]
NIDCAP Fed. Intl. [14114]
Ninos del Lago [11370]
Nuestros Pequenos Hermanos Intl. [20077]
Nursing Mothers Counsel [11490]
One Heart Bulgaria [11373]
One Hen [7821]
Oper. Help The Children [11375]
Oper. Hug-A-Hero [12533]
The Optimists [11377]
Org. for Medical and Psychological Assistance for
    Children Overseas [14094]
Orphan Found. of Am. [11491]
Orphan Support Africa [11380]
OrphanAid Africa [11382]
Orphans Africa [11621]
Orphans Against AIDS [11383]
Orphans to Ambassadors [11384]
Orphans Intl. Worldwide [11492]
Orphan's Lifeline of Hope Intl. [11385]
Our Family Orphan Communities [11493]
Our Military Kids [12534]
Out of Poverty thru Educ. [7731]
Outreach Africa [11386]
Para Sa Bata [11387]
Parents Of Autistic Children [13801]
Partners in Foster Care [12046]
Partnership for Educ. of Children in Afghanistan
    [11494]
Peace House Africa [11389]
Pediatric Chaplains Network [19529]
People for Children [11495]
People for Children [11495]
Personal Ponies Ltd. [11822]
Plan U.S.A. [11496]
Plan U.S.A. [11496]
Playworks [12696]
Pocketful of Joy [11391]
Preemptive Love Coalition [14040]
Proj. Children [11497]
Proj. Children [11497]
Proj. Kids Worldwide [14095]
Proj. Sunshine [11394]
Promise World Wide [12358]
Pura Vida for Children [11395]
RAINBOWS [11498]
RAINBOWS [11498]
RandomKid [13554]
Reconstruction Efforts Aiding Children without
    Homes [11624]

RedLight Children [11144]
Robert F. Kennedy Center for Justice and Human
    Rights [13555]
Rock Against Cancer [13975]
Romania Reborn [11397]
Rosenberg Fund for Children [11499]
Safe Passage [11401]
Samaritan's Feet [11402]
Santa Am. [11500]
Save Africa's Children [11501]
Save the Children [11502]
Seeds of HOPE Intl. [11403]
Sequoia Helping Hands [11404]
Serving Our World [11405]
Sesame Workshop [9474]
Show Mercy Intl. [11503]
Single Mothers By Choice [12622]
Sky of Love [11406]
Smile Alliance Intl. [11504]
Smile Alliance Intl. [11504]
Smile Network Intl. [14203]
Soc. for Orphaned Armenian Relief [12892]
Soles for Kidz [19531]
Southern Early Childhood Assn. [11505]
Spark Ventures [11407]
Sparrow Clubs U.S.A. [11506]
A Special Wish Found. [11507]
Spirit Quilts [11408]
StandUp for Kids [11409]
Starlight Children's Found. [11508]
Start Thinking About Romanian Children Relief
    [11410]
Stepfamily Found. [12021]
Stop the Silence [11145]
Students Helping St. Kids Intl. [11509]
Students Helping St. Kids Intl. [11509]
Sudan-American Found. for Educ. [7837]
Sunshine Found. [11510]
Surviving Parents Coalition [11511]
Sweet Sleep [11414]
Syndromes Without a Name USA [14419]
TAALK: Talk About Abuse to Liberate Kids [11512]
Tiny Hands Intl. [11416]
To Love a Child [11417]
Together for Kids [15070]
Total Family Care Coalition [12023]
Touch the Life of a Child Org. [11418]
Trucker Buddy Intl. [7838]
Twinkle Little Stars [11419]
Twins Found. [12551]
Two Cents of Hope [8292]
Two Hearts for Hope [11420]
Ukrainian Children's Aid and Relief Effort [11422]
Umoja Intl. [12969]
uNight [11423]
Uplift a Child Intl. [11513]
US Coalition for Child Survival [11514]
Warm Blankets Orphan Care Intl. [11515]
Water for People l PlayPumps Intl. [10827]
Whole Child Intl. [11429]
A Wish With Wings [11516]
Women in Fatherhood, Inc. [13151]
Women in Toys [3479]
World Camp for Kids [11431]
World Orphans [11433]
World Relief Org. for Children [11434]
World Spark [11435]
Youth Action Intl. [11436]
Youth for Human Rights Intl. [12255]
Zambia Hope Intl. [11437]
Children and Adults With Attention Deficit Disorder
    [★15578]
Children and Adults With Attention Deficit/Hyperactiv-
    ity Disorder [15578], 8181 Professional Pl., Ste.
    150, Landover, MD 20785, (301)306-7070
Children of Aging Parents [10839], PO Box 167,
    Richboro, PA 18954, (215)355-6611
Children with AIDS Proj. of Am. [10783], PO Box
    23778, Tempe, AZ 85285-3778, (602)405-2196
Children of Alcoholic Parents - Defunct.
Children of Alcoholics Found. [★13239]
Children of the Americas [11234], Jody Greenlee,
    VP, 1781 Eastwood Dr., Lexington, KY 40502,
    (859)269-4721
Children of the Americas [11234], Jody Greenlee,
    VP, 1781 Eastwood Dr., Lexington, KY 40502,
    (859)269-4721

A star before a book entry number signifies that the name is not listed separately, but is mentioned within the entry.

Children of the Andes [IO], London, United Kingdom

Children with Attention-Deficit Disorders [★15578]

Children Awaiting Parents [10784], 595 Blossom Rd., Ste. 306, Rochester, NY 14610, (585)232-5110

Children Beyond Our Borders [17235], 530 W Univ. Ave., Gainesville, FL 32601, (352)301-3513

Children of Chernobyl [IO], Minsk, Belarus

Children of the Confederacy [20382], Mrs. Janet Johnson, UDC Bus. Off., 328 N Blvd., Richmond, VA 23220-4009

Children of the Dawn [IO], Banbury, Republic of South Africa

Children of Deaf Adults [14925], PO Box 30715, Santa Barbara, CA 93130-0715, (805)682-0997

Children of the Dump [11235], 718 Griffin Ave., PMB 207, Enumclaw, WA 98022, (360)825-1099

Children of the Earth [12627], 26 Baycrest Dr., South Burlington, VT 05403, (802)862-1936

Children of the Earth [12627], 26 Baycrest Dr., South Burlington, VT 05403, (802)862-1936

Children of the Earth United [4317], PO Box 258035, Madison, WI 53725, (608)237-6577

Children of the Earth United [4317], PO Box 258035, Madison, WI 53725, (608)237-6577

Children England [IO], London, United Kingdom

Children of Grace [11236], PO Box 2394, Danville, CA 94526, (925)855-4697

Children of the Holocaust Assn. in Poland [IO], Warsaw, Poland

Children, Inc. [11455], 4205 Dover Rd., Richmond, VA 23221-3267, (804)359-4565

Children Intl. [20020], PO Box 219055, Kansas City, MO 64121, (816)942-2000

Children Intl. [20020], PO Box 219055, Kansas City, MO 64121, (816)942-2000

Children of Lesbians and Gays Everywhere [★12074]

Children and Life Assn. [IO], Phnom Penh, Cambodia

Children Living with Inherited Metabolic Diseases [IO], Crewe, United Kingdom

Children of the Nations Intl. [11237], PO Box 3970, Silverdale, WA 98383, (360)698-7227

Children and Nature Network [4241], 7 Avenida Vista Grande B-7, No. 502, Santa Fe, NM 87508

Children of the Night [12946], 14530 Sylvan St., Van Nuys, CA 91411, (818)908-4474

Children in Northern Ireland [IO], Belfast, United Kingdom

Children Now [11238], 1212 Broadway, 5th Fl., Oakland, CA 94612, (510)763-2444

Children of Nowhere [11239], 601 W 26th St., Ste. 1105, New York, NY 10001

Children Out of Detention [IO], Neutral Bay, Australia

Children as the Peacemakers - Address unknown since 2010.

Children of Persia [11240], PO Box 2602, Montgomery Village, MD 20886, (301)315-0750

Children: Priority One; Young [★13062]

Children at Risk in Ireland [IO], Dublin, Ireland

Children of the Rosary [18551], PO Box 1028, Scottsdale, AZ 85252-1028, (602)548-3131

Children of Russia [11241], 434 Hao St., Honolulu, HI 96821, (808)737-5248

Children of Russia Found. [11241], 434 Hao St., Honolulu, HI 96821, (808)737-5248

Children in Scotland [IO], Edinburgh, United Kingdom

Children, Sons and Daughters of the U.S.A. [★9117]

Children of Tanzania [11065], 3 Little Cove Ln., Old Greenwich, CT 06870, (203)637-0191

Children of Vietnam [11242], 817 W End Blvd., Winston-Salem, NC 27101, (336)727-1110

Children in Wales [IO], Cardiff, United Kingdom

The Children of War [18235], PO Box 223602, Chantilly, VA 20153-3602, (703)625-9147

The Children of War [18235], PO Box 223602, Chantilly, VA 20153-3602, (703)625-9147

Children With Hairloss [12125], 12776 Dixie Hwy., South Rockwood, MI 48179, (734)379-4400

Children Without a Voice, USA [11243], PO Box 4351, Alpharetta, GA 30023, (404)474-4020

Children's Advt. Rev. Unit [89], 70 W 36th St., 12th Fl., New York, NY 10018, (866)334-6272

Children's Aid Intl. [★11448]

Children's Aid Intl. [★11448]

Children's AIDS Fund [10876], PO Box 16433, Washington, DC 20041, (703)433-1560

Children's AIDS Fund [10876], PO Box 16433, Washington, DC 20041, (703)433-1560

Children's Angelcare Aid Intl. [★11448]

Children's Angelcare Aid Intl. [★11448]

Children's Art Found. [9473], PO Box 83, Santa Cruz, CA 95063, (831)426-5557

Children's Bible Ministries [19737], PO Box 278, Townsend, TN 37882, (865)448-1200

Children's Bible Mission, Inc. [★19737]

Children's Blood Found. [★14964]

Children's Book Coun. [9442], 54 W 39th St., 14th Fl., New York, NY 10018, (212)966-1990

Children's Book Coun. of Australia [IO], Norwood, Australia

Children's Book Coun. of Iran [IO], Tehran, Iran

Children's Books Ireland [IO], Dublin, Ireland

Children's Brain Tumor Found. [14063], 274 Madison Ave., Ste. 1004, New York, NY 10016, (866)228-4673

Children's Campaign for Nuclear Disarmament - Defunct.

Children's Cancer and Blood Found. [14964], 333 E 38th St., Ste. 830, New York, NY 10016, (212)297-4336

Children's Cause for Cancer Advocacy [13906], 750 1st St. NE, 7th Fl., Washington, DC 20002, (202)336-8374

Children's Comm. 10 - Defunct.

Children's Corrective Surgery Soc. [16810], PO Box 500578, San Diego, CA 92150, (800)803-9190

Children's Craniofacial Assn. [14193], 13140 Coit Rd., Ste. 517, Dallas, TX 75240, (214)570-9099

Children's Creative Response to Conflict Prog. [11456], 521 N Broadway, Box 271, Nyack, NY 10960, (845)353-1796

Children's Cross Connection Intl. [14064], 220 Avon Dr., Fayetteville, GA 30214, (404)992-7182

Children's Cross Connection Intl. [14064], 220 Avon Dr., Fayetteville, GA 30214, (404)992-7182

Children's Cup [12819], PO Box 400, Prairieville, LA 70769, (225)673-4505

Children's Defense Fund [11457], 25 E St. NW, Washington, DC 20001, (202)628-8787

Children's Defense Fund of the Washington Res. Proj. [★11457]

Children's Dialysis Intl. [15548], 25604 NW 2nd Ave., Newberry, FL 32669, (352)472-2651

Children's Environmental Hea. Network [14499], 110 Maryland Ave. NE, Ste. 402, Washington, DC 20002-5619, (202)543-4033

Children's Exocrine Found. [★16607]

Children's Express Found. - Defunct.

Children's Eye Care Found. [★15955]

Children's Eye Found. [15955], 1631 Lancaster Dr., Ste. 200, Grapevine, TX 76051-2116, (817)310-2641

Children's Film Soc., India [IO], Mumbai, India

Children's Found. - Defunct.

Children's Friendship Proj. for Northern Ireland - Address unknown since 2011.

Children's Fund of the Slovak Republic [IO], Bratislava, Slovakia

Children's Future Intl. [11244], 22 Hartley Rd., Great Neck, NY 11023

Children's Grief Educ. Assn. [11128], 6883 Wyman Way, Westminster, CO 80030, (303)246-3826

Children's Hea. Environmental Coalition [★14080]

Children's Hea. Fund [14065], 215 W 125th St., Ste. 301, New York, NY 10027, (212)535-9400

Children's Hea. Intl. [14066], PO Box 3505, Silver Spring, MD 20918, (301)681-8307

Children's Healthcare is a Legal Duty [15246], PO Box 2604, Sioux City, IA 51106-0604, (712)948-3500

Children's Heart Fund [★14011]

Children's HeartLink [14011], 5075 Arcadia Ave., Minneapolis, MN 55436, (952)928-4860

Children's Hemiplegia and Stroke Assn. [16730], 4101 W Green Oaks Blvd., Ste. 305, No. 149, Arlington, TX 76016, (817)492-4325

Children's HIV Assn. of UK and Ireland [IO], London, United Kingdom

Children's Hope Intl. Literacy and Development [11245], 1526 Brookhollow Dr., Ste. 82, Santa Ana, CA 92705, (714)545-3050

Children's Hope Intl. Literacy and Development [11245], 1526 Brookhollow Dr., Ste. 82, Santa Ana, CA 92705, (714)545-3050

Children's HopeChest [11246], PO Box 63842, Colorado Springs, CO 80962-3842, (719)487-7800

Children's Hospice Intl. [15025], 1101 King St., Ste. 360, Alexandria, VA 22314, (703)684-0330

Children's Hospice Intl. [15025], 1101 King St., Ste. 360, Alexandria, VA 22314, (703)684-0330

Children's Hospices UK [IO], Bristol, United Kingdom

Children's Intl. Hea. Relief [14067], 4218 S Steele St., Ste. 220, Tacoma, WA 98409, (253)476-0556

Children's Intl. Summer Villages - Canada [IO], Toronto, ON, Canada

Children's Intl. Summer Villages - England [IO], Newcastle upon Tyne, United Kingdom

Children's Legal Centre [IO], Colchester, United Kingdom

Children's Leukemia Res. Assn. [13907], 585 Stewart Ave., Ste. 18, Garden City, NY 11530, (516)222-1944

Children's Lib. Assn. [★9969]

Children's Literacy Initiative [8527], 2314 Market St., Philadelphia, PA 19103, (215)561-4676

Children's Literature Assn. [10038], PO Box 138, Battle Creek, MI 49016-0138, (269)965-8180

Children's Liver Assn. for Support Services [14982], 25379 Wayne Mills Pl., Ste. 143, Valencia, CA 91355, (661)263-9099

Children's Medical Ministries [14068], PO Box 3382, Crofton, MD 21114, (301)261-3211

Children's Medical Mission of Haiti [11247], 925 Hertzler Rd., Mechanicsburg, PA 17055, (717)796-1852

Children's Network Intl. [11248], 5449 Robin Hill Ct., Norcross, GA 30093, (404)259-8818

Children's Network Intl. [11248], 5449 Robin Hill Ct., Norcross, GA 30093, (404)259-8818

Children's Organ Transplant Assn. [14069], 2501 W COTA Dr., Bloomington, IN 47403, (800)366-2682

The Children's Partnership [11249], 2000 P St. NW, Ste. 330, Washington, DC 20036, (202)429-0033

Children's PKU Network [15493], 3306 Bumann Rd., Encinitas, CA 92024, (858)756-0079

Children's Protective Soc. [★11211]

Children's Relief Mission [11250], PO Box 597, Owensville, MO 65066, (818)502-1989

Children's Relief Network [11251], PO Box 668, Deerfield Beach, FL 33443, (561)620-2970

Children's Relief Network [11251], PO Box 668, Deerfield Beach, FL 33443, (561)620-2970

Children's Rights [17276], 330 7th Ave., 4th Fl., New York, NY 10001, (212)683-2210

Children's Rights Alliance [IO], Dublin, Ireland

Children's Rights Alliance for England [IO], London, United Kingdom

Children's Rights Coun. [11864], 9470 Annapolis Rd., Ste. 310, Lanham, MD 20706-3022, (301)459-1220

Children's Rights, Inc. [★11257]

Children's Rights Proj. - ACLU [★17276]

Children's Safety Network [11252], Educ. Development Center, Inc., 55 Chapel St., Newton, MA 02458-1060, (617)618-2918

Children's Services Div. [★9969]

Children's TV Workshop [★9474]

Children's Tumor Found. [15579], 95 Pine St., 16th Fl., New York, NY 10005, (212)344-6633

Children's Village U.S.A. [★11232]

Children's Vision Intl., Inc. [11458], PO Box 380, Bangor, WI 54614, (608)486-4357

Children's Voice [IO], Goma, Democratic Republic of the Congo

Children's Welfare Intl. [11253], 223 Pacific Ave. S, Pacific, WA 98047, (206)859-3847

Children's Wish Found. [★11459]

Children's Wish Found. [★11459]

Children's Wish Found. of Canada [IO], Ajax, ON, Canada

Children's Wish Found. Intl. [11459], 8615 Roswell Rd., Atlanta, GA 30350-7526, (770)393-9474

Reference to "IO" in place of a book number signifies that the association may be found in the 50th edition of International Organizations.

Children's Wish Found. Intl. [11459], 8615 Roswell Rd., Atlanta, GA 30350-7526, (770)393-9474

A Child's Right [13415], 1127 Broadway, Ste. 102, Tacoma, WA 98402, (253)327-1707

Childspring Intl. [14070], 1328 Peachtree St. NE, Atlanta, GA 30309, (404)228-7744

ChildVoice Intl. [11254], PO Box 579, Durham, NH 03824, (603)842-0132

ChildVoice Intl. [11254], PO Box 579, Durham, NH 03824, (603)842-0132

Childwatch Intl. Res. Network [IO], Oslo, Norway

Chile-U.S. Chamber of Commerce [23357], PO Box 560181, Miami, FL 33256-0181, (305)890-3547

Chile-U.S. Chamber of Commerce [23357], PO Box 560181, Miami, FL 33256-0181, (305)890-3547

Chilean Acad. of History [IO], Santiago, Chile

Chilean Amer. Chamber of Commerce [IO], Santiago, Chile

Chilean Assn. of Info. Tech. Companies [IO], Santiago, Chile

Chilean Assn. of Publishers, Distributors and Booksellers [IO], Santiago, Chile

Chilean Assn. of Seismology and Earthquake Engg. [IO], Santiago, Chile

Chilean Bible Soc. [IO], Santiago, Chile

Chilean Cmpt. Sci. Soc. [IO], Santiago, Chile

Chilean Constr. Chamber [IO], Santiago, Chile

Chilean Salmon Indus. Assn. [IO], Santiago, Chile

Chilean Salmon and Trout Farmers' Assn. [IO], Santiago, Chile

Chilean Seed Producers' Assn. [IO], Santiago, Chile

Chilean Soc. of Cardiology and Cardiovascular Surgery [IO], Santiago, Chile

Chilean Soc. of Clinical Neurophysiology [IO], Santiago, Chile

Chilean Soc. of Dermatology and Venereology [IO], Santiago, Chile

Chilean Soc. of Hypertension [IO], Santiago, Chile

Chilean Soc. of Infectious Diseases [IO], Santiago, Chile

Chilean Soc. of Obstetrics and Gynecology [IO], Santiago, Chile

Chilean Soc. of Osteology and Mineral Metabolism [IO], Santiago, Chile

Chilean Soc. of Physiological Sciences [IO], Santiago, Chile

Chilean Supermarkets' Assn. [IO], Santiago, Chile

Chilean Textile Inst. [IO], Santiago, Chile

Chilean Wood Corp. [IO], Santiago, Chile

Chilled Food Assn. [IO], Kettering, United Kingdom

Chilled Foods Assn. - Defunct.

Chilterns Amer. Women's Club [IO], Gerrards Cross, United Kingdom

Chimera Educational Found. [★13474]

Chimes Hour Youth Caravan [★20106]

Chimes Hour Youth Caravan [★20106]

Chimney Rock Found. [★20158]

Chimney Safety Inst. of Am. [2243], 2155 Commercial Dr., Plainfield, IN 46168, (317)837-5362

Chimney Sweep Guild [★2255]

Chimp Haven [10940], 13600 Chimpanzee Pl., Keithville, LA 71047, (318)925-9575

Chimpanzee

    Bonobo Conservation Initiative [5038]

Chin Human Rights Org. [IO], Nepean, ON, Canada

China

    Chen Qingzhou Martial Arts Assn., USA [22728]

    China Aid Assn. [20209]

    Chinese Amer. Cooperation Coun. [9873]

    Families with Children from China [10787]

    Global China Connection [8387]

    Intl. Assn. for China Planning [18315]

    Overseas Young Chinese Forum [7845]

    Sino-American Bridge for Educ. and Hea. [9876]

    Taipei Economic and Cultural Off. in New York [9480]

    Tea Leaf Club Intl. [21269]

    US-China Green Energy Coun. [6760]

China Acad. of Traditional Chinese Medicine [IO], Beijing, People's Republic of China

China ACM SIGCHI [IO], Beijing, People's Republic of China

China-Africa Bus. Coun. [IO], Beijing, People's Republic of China

China Aid Assn. [20209], PO Box 8513, Midland, TX 79708, (432)689-6985

China AIDS Network [IO], Beijing, People's Republic of China

China Amer. Psychoanalytic Alliance [16396], 455 FDR Dr., No. 1704B, New York, NY 10002-5916, (212)533-0310

China Animal Agriculture Assn. [IO], Beijing, People's Republic of China

China Arms Control and Disarmament Assn. [IO], Beijing, People's Republic of China

China Assn. of Amusement Parks and Attractions [IO], Beijing, People's Republic of China

China Assn. of Bakery and Confectionery Indus. [IO], Beijing, People's Republic of China

China Assn. For Pharmaceutical Equip. [IO], Beijing, People's Republic of China

China Assn. for Intl. Sci. and Tech. Cooperation [IO], Beijing, People's Republic of China

China Assn. of Inventions [IO], Beijing, People's Republic of China

China Assn. of the Lighting Indus. [IO], Beijing, People's Republic of China

China Assn. for Medical Devices Indus. [IO], Beijing, People's Republic of China

China Assn. of Microfinance [IO], Beijing, People's Republic of China

China Assn. of Natl. Advertisers [IO], Beijing, People's Republic of China

China Assn. for NGO Cooperation [IO], Beijing, People's Republic of China

China Assn. of Plant Engg. Consultants [IO], Beijing, People's Republic of China

China Assn. of Rsrc. Comprehensive Utilization [IO], Beijing, People's Republic of China

China Assn. for Sci. and Tech. [IO], Beijing, People's Republic of China

China Assn. of Shipping Agencies and Non-Vessel-Operating Common Carriers [IO], Beijing, People's Republic of China

China Assn. of Trade in Services [IO], Beijing, People's Republic of China

China Assn. of Work Safety [IO], Beijing, People's Republic of China

China Audio Indus. Assn. [IO], Shanghai, People's Republic of China

China Banking Assn. [IO], Beijing, People's Republic of China

China Bearing Indus. Assn. [IO], Beijing, People's Republic of China

China Bicycle Assn. [IO], Beijing, People's Republic of China

China-Britain Bus. Coun. [IO], London, United Kingdom

China-Burma-India Hump Pilot Assn. - Address unknown since 2010.

China-Burma-India Veterans Assn. - Defunct.

China Bus. Coun. for Sustainable Development [IO], Beijing, People's Republic of China

China Centre for Intl. Stud. [IO], Beijing, People's Republic of China

China Chain Store and Franchise Assn. [IO], Beijing, People's Republic of China

China Chamber of Commerce for Import and Export of Machinery and Electronic Products [IO], Beijing, People's Republic of China

China Chem. Fibers Assn. [IO], Beijing, People's Republic of China

China Civil Engg. Soc. [IO], Beijing, People's Republic of China

China Clay Producers Assn. [2510], 113 Arkwright Landing, Macon, GA 31210, (478)757-1211

China Clay Producers Trade Assn. [★2510]

China Communications Standards Assn. [IO], Beijing, People's Republic of China

China Connection [12319], 458 S Pasadena Ave., Pasadena, CA 91105, (626)793-3737

China Connection [12319], 458 S Pasadena Ave., Pasadena, CA 91105, (626)793-3737

China Cotton Assn. [IO], Beijing, People's Republic of China

China Coun. [★9336]

China Coun. [★9336]

China Coun. for the Promotion of Intl. Trade [IO], Beijing, People's Republic of China

China Customs Brokers Assn. [IO], Beijing, People's Republic of China

China Disabled Persons' Fed. [IO], Beijing, People's Republic of China

China Educ. Assn. for Intl. Exchange [IO], Beijing, People's Republic of China

China Elec. Vehicle Assn. [IO], Shanghai, People's Republic of China

China Engg. Cost Assn. [IO], Beijing, People's Republic of China

China Enterprise Confed. [IO], Beijing, People's Republic of China

China-EU Assn. [IO], Beijing, People's Republic of China

China Feather and Down Indus. Assn. [IO], Beijing, People's Republic of China

China Fed. of Indus. Economics [IO], Beijing, People's Republic of China

China Folklore Photographic Assn. [IO], Beijing, People's Republic of China

China Food and Packaging Machinery Indus. Assn. [IO], Beijing, People's Republic of China

China Foundry Assn. [IO], Beijing, People's Republic of China

China, Glass and Giftware Assn. - Defunct.

China Hong Kong Soc. for Trenchless Tech. [IO], Hong Kong, People's Republic of China

China Inland Mission [★20079]

China Inland Mission [★20079]

China Inland Mission Overseas Missionary Fellowship [★20079]

China Inland Mission Overseas Missionary Fellowship [★20079]

China Inst. [★9476]

China Inst. [★9476]

China Inst. in Am. [9476], 125 E 65th St., New York, NY 10065, (212)744-8181

China Inst. in Am. [9476], 125 E 65th St., New York, NY 10065, (212)744-8181

China Intl. Cooperation Assn. of Small and Medium Enterprises [IO], Beijing, People's Republic of China

China Intl. Found. [★12344]

China Intl. Found. [★12344]

China Intl. Mining Gp. [IO], Beijing, People's Republic of China

China Internship Soc. [IO], Dalian, People's Republic of China

China Iron and Steel Assn. [IO], Beijing, People's Republic of China

China-Italy Chamber of Commerce [IO], Beijing, People's Republic of China

China Lab. Primate Breeding and Development Assn. [IO], Beijing, People's Republic of China

China Medical Bd. of New York - Address unknown since 2010.

China Medical Informatics Assn. [IO], Beijing, People's Republic of China

China Mergers and Acquisitions Assn. [IO], Beijing, People's Republic of China

China Mining Assn. [IO], Beijing, People's Republic of China

China Natl. Assn. of Engg. Consultants [IO], Beijing, People's Republic of China

China Nonwovens and Indus. Textiles Assn. [IO], Beijing, People's Republic of China

China Nuclear Energy Assn. [IO], Beijing, People's Republic of China

China Optical Goods' Indus. Assn. [IO], Beijing, People's Republic of China

China Optometric and Optical Assn. [IO], Beijing, People's Republic of China

China Packaging Fed. [IO], Beijing, People's Republic of China

China Peniel Missionary Soc. [★20104]

China Peniel Missionary Soc. [★20104]

China Productivity Center [IO], Taipei, Taiwan

China Rose Soc. [IO], Beijing, People's Republic of China

China School Sport Fed. [IO], Beijing, People's Republic of China

China Security and Protection Indus. Assn. [IO], Beijing, People's Republic of China

China Sewing Machinery Assn. [IO], Beijing, People's Republic of China

China Shipowners' Assn. [IO], Beijing, People's Republic of China

---

A star before a book entry number signifies that the name is not listed separately, but is mentioned within the entry.

China Small Animal Protection Assn. **[IO]**, Beijing, People's Republic of China

China Soc. of Plant Protection **[IO]** Beijing, People's Republic of China

China Soc. for Promotion of the Guangcai Prog. **[IO]**, Beijing, People's Republic of China

China Soc. on Tibet Plateau **[IO]**, Beijing, People's Republic of China

China Software Indus. Assn. **[IO]**, Beijing, People's Republic of China

China Stamp Soc. **[22026]**, PO Box 20711, Columbus, OH 43220, (614)370-1195

China Toothpaste Indus. Assn. **[IO]**, Beijing, People's Republic of China

China Toy Assn. **[IO]**, Beijing, People's Republic of China

China-U.S. Energy Efficiency Alliance **[6700]**, 1 Embarcadero Ctr., Ste. 1550, San Francisco, CA 94111, (415)951-8975

China Users Assn. for Satellite Communications, Broadcasting and TV **[IO]**, Beijing, People's Republic of China

China Venture Capital Assn. **[IO]**, Beijing, People's Republic of China

China Welding Assn. **[IO]**, Harbin, People's Republic of China

China Working Dog Mgt. Assn. **[IO]**, Nanjing, People's Republic of China

China Zoological Soc. **[IO]**, Beijing, People's Republic of China

China's Children Fund **[★11231]**

China's Children Fund **[★11231]**

Chinchilla Breeders' Gp. **[IO]**, Cape Town, Republic of South Africa

Chinese

Amer. Assn. for Chinese Stud. **[7839]**

American-Chinese CEO Soc. **[773]**

Amer. Chinese Medical Exchange Soc. **[14750]**

Assn. of Chinese-American Professionals **[18961]**

Assn. of Chinese Professors of Social Sciences in the U.S. **[7409]**

Center for United States-China Arts Exchange **[9475]**

Chen Qingzhou Martial Arts Assn., USA **[22728]**

China Aid Assn. **[20209]**

China Inst. in Am. **[9476]**

China Inst. in Am. **[9476]**

Chinese Amer. Citizens Alliance **[18962]**

Chinese Amer. Doctors Assn. **[16261]**

Chinese Amer. Educational Res. and Development Assn. **[7840]**

Chinese-American Professors in Environmental Engg. and Sci. **[6425]**

Chinese-American Professors in Environmental Engg. and Sci. **[6425]**

Chinese-American Soc. of Nuclear Medicine **[15694]**

Chinese Amer. Soc. Of Anesthesiology **[13745]**

Chinese Chamber of Commerce of Hawaii **[23390]**

Chinese Consolidated Benevolent Assn. **[18963]**

Chinese Culture Found. of San Francisco **[9477]**

Chinese Entrepreneur Assn. **[774]**

Chinese Finance Assn. **[1287]**

Chinese Historical Soc. of Am. **[9478]**

Chinese Historical Soc. of Am. **[9478]**

Chinese Language Assn. of Secondary-Elementary Schools **[7841]**

Chinese Language Teachers Assn. **[7842]**

Chinese School Assn. in the U.S. **[8825]**

Coun. of Overseas Chinese Services **[18964]**

Educ. Advancement Fund Intl. **[7843]**

European Assn. of Chinese Stud. **[7112]**

European Found. for Chinese Music Res. **[11108]**

Free the Fathers **[17239]**

Friends of Falun Gong **[17240]**

HandReach **[11517]**ChineseIndependent Fed. of Chinese Students and Scholars

Inst. of Chinese Culture **[9479]**

Intl. Assn. for Teachers of Chinese to Speakers of Other Languages **[7844]**

Intl. Chinese Boxing Assn. **[22436]**

Intl. Soc. for Comparative Stud. of Chinese and Western Philosophy **[8707]**

June 4th Found. **[17241]**

Natl. Chinese Honor Soc. **[23492]**

Natl. Comm. on United States-China Relations **[17242]**

Natl. Comm. on United States-China Relations **[17242]**

North Am. Chinese Clean-tech and Semiconductor Assn. **[1112]**

Org. of Chinese Americans **[17243]**

Org. of Chinese Americans **[17243]**

Overseas Chinese-American Entrepreneurs Assn. **[775]**

Overseas Chinese Entomologists Assn. **[6849]**

Overseas Young Chinese Forum **[7845]**

Soc. for the Stud. of Early China **[7846]**

Soc. for the Stud. of Early China **[7846]**

Taipei Economic and Cultural Off. in New York **[9480]**

Traditional Chinese Medicine Assn. and Alumni **[13714]**

Travel China Roads **[7847]**

U.S. of America-China Chamber of Commerce **[23391]**

U.S. of America-China Chamber of Commerce **[23391]**

U.S.-China Educ. Found. **[8377]**

U.S.-China Peoples Friendship Assn. **[17244]**

U.S.-China Peoples Friendship Assn. **[17244]**

US-China Higher Educ. Alliance **[7848]**

Wildflowers Inst. **[9481]**

Wildflowers Inst. **[9481]**

ZY Qigong **[13722]**

Chinese Acad. of Agricultural Sciences **[IO]**, Beijing, People's Republic of China

Chinese Acad. of Forestry **[IO]**, Beijing, People's Republic of China

Chinese Acad. of Meteorological Sciences **[IO]**, Beijing, People's Republic of China

Chinese Acad. of Sciences **[IO]**, Beijing, People's Republic of China

Chinese Acad. of Space Tech. **[IO]**, Beijing, People's Republic of China

Chinese for Affirmative Action **[17277]**, 17 Walter U. Lum Pl., San Francisco, CA 94108, (415)274-6750

Chinese-American Arts Coun. **[9286]**, 456 Broadway, 3rd Fl., New York, NY 10013-5800, (212)431-9740

Chinese Amer. Assn. of Engg. **[6790]**, PO Box 869, New York, NY 10268, (718)591-6012

Chinese Amer. Assn. of Engg. **[6790]**, PO Box 869, New York, NY 10268, (718)591-6012

Chinese Amer. Citizens Alliance **[18962]**, 1044 Stockton St., San Francisco, CA 94108

Chinese-American Cmpt. Assn. - Address unknown since 2011.

Chinese Amer. Cooperation Coun. **[9873]**, PO Box 12028, Pleasanton, CA 94588

Chinese Amer. Doctors Assn. **[16261]**, 8775 Centre Park Dr., No. 501, Columbia, MD 21045, (713)201-7928

Chinese Amer. Doctors Assn. **[16261]**, 8775 Centre Park Dr., No. 501, Columbia, MD 21045, (713)201-7928

Chinese Amer. Educational Res. and Development Assn. **[7840]**, PO Box 853, Ardmore, PA 19003, (704)687-8716

Chinese Amer. Food Soc. **[6874]**, Dr. Vivian Wu, Treas., Univ. of Maine, 5735 Hitchner Hall 101A, Orono, ME 04469-5735

Chinese-American Golf Assn. **[22605]**, 2 Doloree Dr., East Brunswick, NJ 08816, (732)422-9558

Chinese Amer. Medical Soc. **[15407]**, 41 Elizabeth St., Ste. 403, New York, NY 10013, (212)334-4760

Chinese-American Professors in Environmental Engg. and Sci. **[6425]**, Dr. Jianpeng Zhou, PhD, Treas., Engineering Bldg. 2050, Southern Illinois Univ. - Edwardsville, Edwardsville, IL 62026-1800, (302)831-3104

Chinese-American Professors in Environmental Engg. and Sci. **[6425]**, Dr. Jianpeng Zhou, PhD, Treas., Engineering Bldg. 2050, Southern Illinois Univ. - Edwardsville, Edwardsville, IL 62026-1800, (302)831-3104

Chinese Amer. Semiconductor Professional Assn. **[1093]**, 1159 Sonora Ct., Ste. 105, Sunnyvale, CA 94086, (408)940-4600

Chinese Amer. Semiconductor Professional Assn. **[1093]**, 1159 Sonora Ct., Ste. 105, Sunnyvale, CA 94086, (408)940-4600

Chinese-American Soc. of Nuclear Medicine **[15694]**, 19786 Colby Ct., Saratoga, CA 95070-3202

Chinese-American Soc. of Nuclear Medicine **[15694]**, 19786 Colby Ct., Saratoga, CA 95070-3202

Chinese Amer. Soc. Of Anesthesiology **[13745]**, 4 Hickory Ln., Warren, NJ 07059

Chinese-American Tea Assn. **[445]**, 8721 Santa Monica Blvd., No. 1238, Los Angeles, CA 90069-4507, (800)682-0823

Chinese Anti-Cancer Assn. **[IO]**, Tianjin, People's Republic of China

Chinese Assn. for Physiological Sciences **[IO]**, Beijing, People's Republic of China

Chinese Assn. for the Stud. of Pain, People's Republic of China **[IO]**, Beijing, People's Republic of China

Chinese Assn. for the Stud. of Pain, Taiwan **[IO]**, Xizhi, Taiwan

Chinese Athletic Assn. **[IO]**, Beijing, People's Republic of China

Chinese Bamboo Soc. **[IO]**, Fuyang, People's Republic of China

Chinese Baseball Assn. **[IO]**, Beijing, People's Republic of China

Chinese Biological Investigators Soc. **[6296]**, Linheng, Li, 1120 15th St., Augusta, GA 30912, (706)721-8775

Chinese Biopharmaceutical Assn., U.S.A. **[16187]**, PO Box 61362, Potomac, MD 20859-1362

Chinese Burn Assn. of the Integration of Traditional and Western Medicine **[IO]**, Beijing, People's Republic of China

Chinese Canadian Natl. Coun. **[IO]**, Toronto, ON, Canada

Chinese Ceramic Soc. **[IO]**, Beijing, People's Republic of China

Chinese Chamber of Commerce of Hawaii **[23390]**, 8 S King St., Ste. 201, Honolulu, HI 96813, (808)533-3181

Chinese Chem. Soc. **[IO]**, Beijing, People's Republic of China

Chinese Christian Mission **[20021]**, PO Box 750759, Petaluma, CA 94975-0759, (707)762-1314

Chinese Consolidated Benevolent Assn. **[18963]**, 62 Mott St., New York, NY 10013, (212)226-6280

Chinese Coordination Centre of World Evangelism **[IO]**, Hong Kong, People's Republic of China

Chinese Cultural Center **[★9480]**

Chinese Culture Center of San Francisco **[★9477]**

Chinese Culture Found. of San Francisco **[9477]**, 750 Kearny St., 3rd Fl., San Francisco, CA 94108-1809, (415)986-1822

Chinese DanceSport Fed. **[IO]**, Beijing, People's Republic of China

Chinese Economists Soc. **[6617]**, 1007 E Huron St., Ste. 301, Ann Arbor, MI 48104-1690, (734)647-9610

Chinese Economists Soc. **[6617]**, 1007 E Huron St., Ste. 301, Ann Arbor, MI 48104-1690, (734)647-9610

Chinese Entrepreneur Assn. **[774]**, PO Box 2752, Acton, MA 01720, (978)266-1254

Chinese Fed. for Corporate Social Responsibility **[IO]**, Beijing, People's Republic of China

Chinese Figure Skating Assn. **[IO]**, Beijing, People's Republic of China

Chinese Finance Assn. **[1287]**, PO Box 2018, New York, NY 10008

Chinese Gen. Chamber of Commerce **[IO]**, Hong Kong, People's Republic of China

Chinese Geophysical Soc. **[IO]**, Beijing, People's Republic of China

Chinese Hea. Qigong Assn. **[IO]**, Beijing, People's Republic of China

Chinese Historians in the U.S. **[8254]**, Univ. of Houston, Dept. of History, Houston, TX 77204, (713)743-3096

Chinese Historians in the U.S. **[8254]**, Univ. of Houston, Dept. of History, Houston, TX 77204, (713)743-3096

Chinese Historical Soc. of Am. **[9478]**, 965 Clay St., San Francisco, CA 94108, (415)391-1188

Chinese Historical Soc. of Am. **[9478]**, 965 Clay St., San Francisco, CA 94108, (415)391-1188

Reference to "IO" in place of a book number signifies that the association may be found in the 50th edition of International Organizations.

Encyclopedia of Associations, 51st Edition   **2685**

Chinese Hydraulic Engg. Soc. [IO], Beijing, People's Republic of China

Chinese Hypertension League [IO], Beijing, People's Republic of China

Chinese Info. and Networking Assn. [6971], 142 N Milpitas Blvd., No. 267, Milpitas, CA 95035, (408)504-7177

Chinese Info. Ser. [★9480]

Chinese Inst. of Certified Public Accountants [IO], Beijing, People's Republic of China

Chinese Inst. of Electronics [IO], Beijing, People's Republic of China

Chinese Inst. of Engineers [IO], Taipei, Taiwan

Chinese Inst. of Food Sci. and Tech. [IO], Beijing, People's Republic of China

Chinese Language Assn. of Secondary-Elementary Schools [7841], PO Box 2348, Livingston, NJ 07039

Chinese Language Teachers Assn. [7842], PO Box 413, Milwaukee, WI 53201, (414)229-5837

Chinese Mfrs. Assn. of Hong Kong [IO], Hong Kong, People's Republic of China

Chinese Material Res. Soc. [IO], Beijing, People's Republic of China

Chinese Mathematical Soc. [IO], Beijing, People's Republic of China

Chinese Mech. Engg. Soc. [IO], Beijing, People's Republic of China

Chinese Medical Assn. [IO], Beijing, People's Republic of China

Chinese Medical Dr. Assn. [IO], Beijing, People's Republic of China

Chinese Medicine and Acupuncture Assn. of Canada [IO], London, ON, Canada

Chinese Music Soc. of North Am. - Address unknown since 2010.

Chinese Natl. Assn. of Indus. and Commerce [IO], Taipei, Taiwan

Chinese Natl. Export Enterprises Assn. [IO], Taipei, Taiwan

Chinese News Ser. [★9480]

Chinese Nuclear Soc. [IO], Beijing, People's Republic of China

Chinese Orthodontic Soc. [IO], Beijing, People's Republic of China

Chinese Overseas Trans. Assn. [3507], Univ. of Washington, Dept. of Civil and Environmental Engg., Seattle, WA 98195-2700, (206)616-2696

Chinese Pharmacological Soc. [IO], Beijing, People's Republic of China

Chinese Professionals Assn. of Canada [IO], Scarborough, ON, Canada

Chinese Psychological Soc. [IO], Beijing, People's Republic of China

Chinese Radio Sports Assn. [IO], Beijing, People's Republic of China

Chinese Rural Hea. Assn. China [IO], Beijing, People's Republic of China

Chinese School Assn. in the U.S. [8825], 639 Nichole Ln., Geneva, IL 60134, (877)294-3484

Chinese Shar-Pei Club of Am. [21539], Roy Anderson, 33853 SE Doyle Rd., Estacada, OR 97023-7527, (503)630-3422

Chinese Snuff Bottle Soc. of Am. [★21236]

Chinese Soc. of Clinical Oncology [IO], Beijing, People's Republic of China

Chinese Soc. of Digestive Endoscopy [IO], Beijing, People's Republic of China

Chinese Soc. of Elecl. Engg. [IO], Beijing, People's Republic of China

Chinese Soc. of EMG and Clinical Neurophysiology [IO], Beijing, People's Republic of China

Chinese Soc. for EU Stud. [IO], Shanghai, People's Republic of China

Chinese Soc. of Forestry [IO], Beijing, People's Republic of China

Chinese Soc. for Metals [IO], Beijing, People's Republic of China

Chinese Soc. of Mineralogy, Petrology, and Geochemistry [IO], Guiyang, People's Republic of China

Chinese Soc. of Plant Nematologists [IO], Guangzhou, People's Republic of China

Chinese Soc. for Plant Pathology [IO], Beijing, People's Republic of China

Chinese Soc. of Theoretical and Applied Mechanics [IO], Beijing, People's Republic of China

Chinese Soc. of Toxicology [IO], Beijing, People's Republic of China

Chinese Squash Assn. [IO], Beijing, People's Republic of China

Chinese Stud. Assn. of Australia [IO], Sydney, Australia

Chinese Taekwondo Assn. [IO], Beijing, People's Republic of China

Chinese Taipei Badminton Assn. [IO], Taipei, Taiwan

Chinese Taipei DanceSport Fed. [IO], Taipei, Taiwan

Chinese Taipei Flying Disc Assn. [IO], Taipei, Taiwan

Chinese Taipei Olympic Comm. [IO], Taipei, Taiwan

Chinese Taipei Soc. of Photogrammetry and Remote Sensing [IO], Taipei, Taiwan

Chinese Taipei Tennis Assn. [IO], Taipei, Taiwan

Chinese Taipei Track and Field Assn. [IO], Taipei, Taiwan

Chinese Taipei Water Ski Assn. [IO], Taipei, Taiwan

Chinese Taipei Weightlifting Assn. [IO], Taipei, Taiwan

Chinese Taipei Yachting Assn. [IO], Taipei, Taiwan

Chinese Taiwan Landscape Architects Soc. [IO], Taipei, Taiwan

Chinese Taiwan Osteoporosis Assn. [IO], Kaohsiung, Taiwan

Chinese Taiwan Soc. of Digestive Endoscopy [IO], Taipei, Taiwan

Chinese Veterinary Medical Assn. [IO], Beijing, People's Republic of China

Chinese Women's Bus. Assn., ROC [IO], Taipei, Taiwan

Chinese Working Dog Mgt. Assn. [IO], Nanjing, People's Republic of China

Chinese Yachting Assn. [IO], Beijing, People's Republic of China

Chinese Young Economists Soc. [★6617]

Chinese Young Economists Soc. [★6617]

Chinook Area of Narcotics Anonymous [IO], Calgary, AB, Canada

Chiropractic

Acad. of Forensic and Indus. Chiropractic Consultants [14115]

Alliance for Biotherapies [16831]

Amer. Chiropractic Assn. [14116]

Amer. Chiropractic Assn. Coun. on Sports Injuries and Physical Fitness [14117]

Amer. Chiropractic Coll. of Radiology [14118]

Amer. Coll. of Chiropractic Consultants [14119]

Amer. Coll. of Chiropractic Orthopedists [14120]

Amer. Coll. of Chiropractic Orthopedists [14120]

Assn. for Catholic Chiropractors [14121]

Assn. of Chiropractic Colleges [14122]

Assn. of Chiropractic Colleges [14122]

Assn. for the History of Chiropractic [14123]

Assn. for Network Care [13666]

Blair Chiropractic Soc. [14124]

Chiropractic Diplomatic Corps [14125]

Chiropractic Orthopedists of North Am. [14126]

Cong. of Chiropractic State Associations [14127]

Coun. of Chiropractic Acupuncture [14128]

Coun. on Chiropractic Educ. [14129]

Coun. on Chiropractic Guidelines and Practice Parameters [14130]

Coun. of Chiropractic Physiological Therapeutics and Rehabilitation [14131]

Coun. on Chiropractic Practice [14132]

Councils on Chiropractic Educ. Intl. [7849]

Energy Kinesiology Assn. [13674]

Fed. of Chiropractic Licensing Boards [14133]

Fed. of Chiropractic Licensing Boards [14133]

Gonstead Clinical Stud. Soc. [14134]

Intl. Acad. of Olympic Chiropractic Officers [14135]

Intl. Acad. of Olympic Chiropractic Officers [14135]

Intl. Chiropractic Pediatric Assn. [14136]

Intl. Chiropractic Pediatric Assn. [14136]

Intl. Chiropractors Assn. [14137]

Intl. Chiropractors Assn. [14137]

Intl. Fed. of Chiropractors and Organizations [14138]

Japanese Assn. of Chiropractors [9319]

Journey to Solidarity [14139]

Natl. Bd. of Chiropractic Examiners [14140]

Natl. Upper Cervical Chiropractic Assn. [14141]

Non-Profit Chiropractic Org. [14142]

Professional Football Chiropractic [14143]

Sacro Occipital Res. Soc. Intl. [14144]

Sacro Occipital Res. Soc. Intl. [14144]

Sacro Occipital Technique Org. U.S.A. [14145]

Soc. of Chiropractic Orthospinology [14146]

Victims of Chiropractic Abuse [14147]

World Chiropractic Alliance [14148]

World Chiropractic Alliance [14148]

World Fed. of Chiropractic [12231]

Chiropractic Assn; Amer. Veterinary [17008]

Chiropractic Assn. of South Africa [IO], Bethlehem, Republic of South Africa

Chiropractic Diplomatic Corps [14125], 17602 17th St., Ste. 102, Tustin, CA 92780, (800)600-7032

Chiropractic Doctors' Assn. of Hong Kong [IO], Hong Kong, People's Republic of China

Chiropractic Hea. Bur. [★14137]

Chiropractic Hea. Bur. [★14137]

Chiropractic Orthopedics; Coun. on [16033]

Chiropractic Orthopedists of North Am. [14126], Dr. Philip Rake, Treas., 2048 Montrose Ave., Montrose, CA 91020, (818)249-8326

Chiropractic Registry of Radiologic Technologists; Amer. [16519]

Chiropractors' Assn. of Australia [IO], Penrith, Australia

Chiropractors Assn; Christian [19547]

Chiropraktiese Vereniging van Suid-Afrika [★IO]

Chittagong Young Men's Christian Association [IO], Chittagong, Bangladesh

Chlorinated Paraffins Indus. Assn. [750], 1250 Connecticut Ave. NW, Ste. 700, Washington, DC 20036, (202)419-1500

Chlorine Inst. [751], 1300 Wilson Blvd., Arlington, VA 22209, (703)741-5760

Chlorobenzene Producers Assn. - Defunct.

Chlotrudis Soc. for Independent Film [9600], PO Box 301237, Jamaica Plain, MA 02130, (781)526-5384

Chocolate Mfrs. Assn. of the U.S.A. - Address unknown since 2010.

Chocosuisse [★IO]

CHOICE [12029], 1233 Locust St., Ste. 301, Philadelphia, PA 19107, (215)985-3355

Choice in Dying - Defunct.

Choice in Personal Safety [IO], Middlesborough, United Kingdom

Choices [12258], 4701 N Keystone Ave., Ste. 150, Indianapolis, IN 46205, (317)726-2121

Choir Schools' Assn. [IO], Winchester, United Kingdom

Chol Chol Found. for Human Development [IO], Temuco, Chile

Choose Cruelty Free [IO], Melbourne, Australia

Choose Responsibility [13240], PO Box 284, Ardsley-on-Hudson, NY 10503, (202)543-8760

Chopin Found. of the U.S. [10175], 1440 79th St. Causeway, Ste. 117, Miami, FL 33141, (305)868-0624

Chopin Soc. [IO], Marianske Lazne, Czech Republic

Choreographers Found; Stage Directors and [10603]

Choristers Guild [20120], 12404 Park Central Dr., Ste. 100, Dallas, TX 75251-1802, (469)398-3606

Chorus Am. [10176], 1156 15th St. NW, Ste. 310, Washington, DC 20005, (202)331-7577

Chorus Am.: Assn. of Professional Vocal Ensembles [★10176]

CHOSEN [12450], 3638 W 26th St., Erie, PA 16506-2037, (814)833-3023

Chosen Children Intl. [11255], PO Box 3046, Colorado Springs, CO 80934, (866)599-5437

CHOSEN Mission Proj. [★12450]

Chosen People Ministries [19738], 241 E 51st St., New York, NY 10022, (212)223-2252

Chosin Few [20674], 238 Cornwall Cir., Chalfont, PA 18914-2318, (215)822-9093

Chosin Few [20674], 238 Cornwall Cir., Chalfont, PA 18914-2318, (215)822-9093

Chow Chow Club, Inc. [21540], Phil DeGruy, Admin./ Webmaster, 9828 E County Rd. A, Janesville, WI 53546, (608)756-2008

Choy Lee Fut Martial Arts Fed. of Am. [22729], 500 1/2E Live Oak Ave., Arcadia, CA 91006, (626)574-1523

A star before a book entry number signifies that the name is not listed separately, but is mentioned within the entry.

Chris Blair Fan Club - Address unknown since 2011.
Chris Cares Intl. [11560], 119 Britton Ave., Stoughton, MA 02072
Chris Craft Antique Boat Club [22329], 112 14th St. SE, Cedar Rapids, IA 52403, (319)247-7207
Chris LeDoux Intl. Fan Club [23824], PO Box 41052, San Jose, CA 95160
Chris Young Fan Club [23825], PO Box 14338, Huntsville, AL 35815
Christ in Action Ministries [19739], PO Box 4200, Manassas, VA 20108, (703)368-6286
Christ in Action Ministries [19739], PO Box 4200, Manassas, VA 20108, (703)368-6286
Christ for the City Intl. [19984], PO Box 390395, Omaha, NE 68139, (402)592-8332
Christ for the City Intl. [19984], PO Box 390395, Omaha, NE 68139, (402)592-8332
Christ for the Nations [20022], 444 Fawn Ridge Dr., Dallas, TX 75224-4502, (214)302-6438
Christ for the Nations [20022], 444 Fawn Ridge Dr., Dallas, TX 75224-4502, (214)302-6438
Christ for the Poor [8789], PO Box 60118, North Miami Beach, FL 33160, (305)891-2242
Christ Truth Ministries [19346], PO Box 610, Upland, CA 91785, (909)981-2838
Christ Truth Radio Crusade [★19346]
CHRISTAR [20023], PO Box 850357, Richardson, TX 75085, (214)838-3800
CHRISTAR [20023], PO Box 850357, Richardson, TX 75085, (214)838-3800
Christar-North America [★20023]
Christar-North America [★20023]
Christchurch Folk Music Club [IO], Christchurch, New Zealand
Christelijk Onderwijzersverbond van Belgie [★IO]
Christelijke Onderwijscentrale [IO], Brussels, Belgium

Christian
  Abrahamic Alliance Intl. [19824]
  Acad. of Homiletics [19814]
  Adopt-A-Church Intl. [19610]
  Advancing Native Missions [19532]
  Advancing Native Missions [19532]
  Advent Christian Gen. Conf. [19287]
  African Amer. Lutheran Assn. [19920]
  Alliance for Life Ministries [19533]
  Amer. Coun. of Christian Churches [19534]
  Amer. and Foreign Christian Union [19535]
  Amer. TFP [19536]
  Amer. Vision [19537]
  Anglicans United [19689]
  ASGM [19339]
  Assn. of Biblical Counselors [19631]
  Assn. for Biblical Higher Educ. [7850]
  Assn. of Christian Schools Intl. [7851]
  Assn. of Christian Schools Intl. [7851]
  Assn. of Christian Therapists [19538]
  Assn. of Christians in the Mathematical Sciences [19539]
  Assn. of Episcopal Colleges [8162]
  Assn. of Reformed Baptist Churches of Am. [19309]
  Assn. for Religion and Intellectual Life [19669]
  Assn. for the Restoration of Church and Home [19613]
  Athletes in Action [19731]
  Baptist Mid-Missions [19314]
  BCM Intl. [19341]
  Beatitudes Soc. [19540]
  Bethany Intl. Missions [20014]
  Brave Intl. [19808]
  Brotherhood of Saint Andrew [19693]
  Bros. and Sisters in Christ [19541]
  Bros. and Sisters in Christ [19541]
  Catholic Acad. of Sciences in the U.S.A. [19670]
  Catholic Assn. of Latino Leaders [19398]
  Catholic Athletes for Christ [22230]
  Catholic Campus Ministry Assn. [19399]
  Catholic Central Union of Am. | Central Bur. [19400]
  Catholic Radio Assn. [19406]
  Catholic Social Workers Natl. Assn. [13216]
  Catholic War Veterans Auxiliary of the U.S.A. [20704]
  Catholic War Veterans of the U.S.A. [20781]

Center for Christian/Jewish Understanding [19650]
Center for Christian Stud. [19542]
Center for the Evangelical United Brethren Heritage [19719]
Center for the Ministry of Teaching [19671]
Center for Organizational and Ministry Development [19543]
Center for Public Justice [18448]
China Aid Assn. [20209]
Christ Truth Ministries [19346]
Christian Action Network [19544]
Christian Addiction Rehabilitation Assn. [13241]
Christian Adult Higher Educ. Assn. [7852]
Christian Bus. Men's Comm. [19545]
Christian Camp and Conf. Assn. [22442]
Christian Century Found. [19546]
Christian Cheerleaders of Am. [22450]
Christian Chiropractors Assn. [19547]
Christian Coll. Consortium [7853]
Christian Communications, Inc. [19548]
Christian Deer Hunters Assn. [19549]
Christian Defense League [19550]
Christian Family Life [12001]
Christian Friends of Israel USA [19551]
Christian Friends of Israel - U.S.A. [19551]
Christian Golfers' Assn. [22453]
Christian Herald Assn. [19552]
Christian Hunters and Anglers Assn. [21279]
Christian Labor Assn. of the U.S.A. [23172]
Christian Ladies All together Standing against Social Injustice Corp. [13456]
Christian Law Assn. [19553]
Christian Legal Soc. [19554]
Christian Media Assn. [19947]
Christian Military Fellowship [19555]
A Christian Ministry in the Natl. Parks [19556]
Christian Overcomers [11771]
Christian Res. Inst. [19557]
Christian Res. Inst. [19557]
Christian Restoration Assn. [19558]
The Christian Sci. Publishing Soc. [2927]
Christian Seniors Assn. [19559]
Christian Sports Intl. [22454]
Christian Sports Intl. [22454]
Christian Universalist Assn. [19560]
Christian Wrestling Fed. [23131]
ChristianTrade Assn. Intl. [19561]
Claretian Volunteers and Lay Missionaries [19413]
CLOUT - Christian Lesbians Out [19562]
CLOUT - Christian Lesbians Out [19562]
Coalition of Spirit-filled Churches [19616]
Commn. of the Churches on Intl. Affairs [19828]
Communities First Assn. [11564]
Community Aid Relief and Development [12826]
Community of Celebration [19563]
Concerned Women for Am. [19564]
Confessing Synod Ministries [20242]
Coun. for Christian Colleges and Universities [7854]
Cowboys for Christ [19565]
Cowboys for Christ [19565]
A Cup of Water Intl. [20282]
Disciples Ecumenical Consultative Coun. [19618]
Disciples Justice Action Network [19566]
Engg. Ministries Intl. [19567]
Engg. Ministries Intl. [19567]
Episcopalians for Global Reconciliation [19703]
Equestrian Ministries Intl. [19816]
European Conf. on Christian Educ. [22424]
Ex-Masons for Jesus [19568]
Family Fed. for World Peace and Unification [20151]
Fellowship of Christian Cowboys [19569]
Fellowship of Christian Magician Intl. [19570]
Fellowship of Christian Peace Officers U.S.A. [19571]
Fellowship of Companies for Christ Intl. [19572]
Fellowship of Companies for Christ Intl. [19572]
Fellowship of Saint James [19573]
Focus on the Family [12009]
Forum for Scriptural Christianity [19972]
Found. for Amer. Christian Educ. [7855]
Full Gospel Bus. Men's Fellowship Intl. [19574]

Full Gospel Bus. Men's Fellowship Intl. [19574]
Global Univ. [19575]
Global Univ. [19575]
God's Kids [11295]
The Gospel Coalition [19576]
Greek Orthodox Ladies Philoptochos Soc. [19804]
Hagiography Soc. [20212]
High School Evangelism Fellowship [19751]
Holy Childhood Assn. [19428]
Holy Shroud Guild [19431]
Hospitals of Hope [15188]
Intercessors for Am. [19577]
Interdisciplinary Biblical Res. Inst. [19677]
Intl. Assn. of Christian Chaplains [19520]
Intl. Assn. of Missionary Aviation [20052]
Intl. Catholic Deaf Assn. U.S. Sect. [19435]
Intl. Christian Concern [19578]
Intl. Christian Concern [19578]
Intl. Christian Stud. Assn. [19579]
Intl. Christian Stud. Assn. [19579]
Intl. Coalition of Apostles [19991]
Intl. Convention of Faith Ministries [19580]
Intl. Convention of Faith Ministries [19580]
Intl. Cops for Christ [19581]
Intl. Coun. of Iranian Christians [19582]
Intl. Coun. of Iranian Christians [19582]
Intl. Network of Children's Ministry [19583]
Intl. Network of Children's Ministry [19583]
Intl. Order of the King's Daughters and Sons [19584]
Intl. Order of the King's Daughters and Sons [19584]
Intl. Orthodox Christian Charities [19585]
Intl. Orthodox Christian Charities [19585]
Intl. Police and Fire Chaplain's Assn. [19522]
InterServe U.S.A. [20054]
Iraqi Christian Relief Coun. [12857]
Kingdom Chamber of Commerce [23392]
Legatus [19445]
Liberal Religious Educators Assn. [20268]
Life Action Revival Ministries [19757]
Master's Men of the Natl. Assn. of Free Will Baptists [19323]
Mission Am. Coalition [19586]
Mission Builders Intl. [19587]
Missionary Soc. of Saint Paul the Apostle [19454]
Narramore Christian Found. [19588]
Natl. Alliance Against Christian Discrimination [19589]
Natl. Assn. of Catholic Family Life Ministers [19997]
Natl. Assn. of Catholic Youth Ministry Leaders [19455]
Natl. Assn. of Christian Child and Family Agencies [19590]
Natl. Assn. for Episcopal Christian Educ. Directors [7856]
Natl. Assn. of Evangelicals [19766]
Natl. Assn. of Family Ministries [19998]
Natl. Assn. of Hispanic Priests of the USA [19457]
Natl. Assn. of Melkite Youth [19591]
Natl. Assn. of Priest Pilots [19459]
Natl. Assn. of University-Model Schools [7885]
Natl. Christian Barrel Racers Assn. [22660]
Natl. Coalition of Ministries to Men [19592]
Natl. Episcopal Scouters Assn. [13024]
Natl. Org. of Iraqi Christians [12630]
Natl. Spiritualist Assn. of Churches | Healers League [20145]
The Navigators [19593]
Nazarene Compassionate Ministries Intl. [19594]
Nazarene Compassionate Ministries Intl. [19594]
Network of Intl. Christian Schools [7857]
New Life Intl. Alliance [19999]
North Am. Christian Creative Assn. [19595]
North Amer. Professors of Christian Educ. [7858]
Officers' Christian Fellowship of the U.S.A. [19596]
Oper. Blessing Intl. [19597]
Oper. Blessing Intl. [19597]
Oral Roberts Univ. Educational Fellowship [7859]
Partners Worldwide [19598]
Peace Officers for Christ Intl. [19599]
Peace Officers for Christ Intl. [19599]
Pocket Testament League [19352]

Reference to "IO" in place of a book number signifies that the association may be found in the 50th edition of International Organizations.

Polish-American-Jewish Alliance for Youth Action [13551]
Probe Ministries Intl. [7860]
Probe Ministries Intl. [7860]
Promise Keepers [19600]
Quixote Center [19488]
Reach Across [20084]
Response-Ability [20085]
Seventh Day Baptist Missionary Soc. [19330]
Seventh Day Baptist World Fed. [19331]
Soc. of Anglican Missionaries and Senders [20094]
Soc. of the Companions of the Holy Cross [19716]
Soc. for Hindu-Christian Stud. [20215]
Soc. for the Stud. of Christian Spirituality [19601]
Sojourners [19602]
Teen Missions Intl. [20099]
Theosophical Book Assn. for the Blind [20264]
Truckers for Christ [19603]
United People in Christ [19980]
U.S. Assn. of Consecrated Virgins [19507]
U.S. Christian Chamber of Commerce [23393]
U.S. Conf. of Catholic Bishops | Bishops' Comm. on Priestly Formation [19688]
United States Conference of Catholic Bishops | Comm. on Divine Worship [19510]
Unity Fellowship Church Movement [19802]
Urban Awareness USA [19604]
Walking on Water [19605]
WordAlone Ministries [19943]
Young Women's Christian Association - Puerto Rico [13567]
Christian Acad. for European Dialogue [IO], Leuven, Belgium
Christian Action for the Abolition of Torture - France [IO], Paris, France
Christian Action Coun. [★17435]
Christian Action Network [19544], PO Box 606, Forest, VA 24551-0606, (434)851-5584
Christian Action and Relief for Haiti [12820], PO Box 880145, Port St. Lucie, FL 34988-0145, (772)345-1404
Christian Addiction Rehabilitation Assn. [13241], Whosoever Gospel Mission, 101 E Chelten Ave., Philadelphia, PA 19144, (215)438-3094
Christian Adult Higher Educ. Assn. [7852], 2100 Westway Ave., Garland, TX 75042, (972)864-2010
Christian Aid [IO], London, United Kingdom
Christian Aid Ministries [18570], PO Box 360, Berlin, OH 44610, (330)893-2428
Christian Aid Ministries [18570], PO Box 360, Berlin, OH 44610, (330)893-2428
Christian Aid Mission [20024], PO Box 9037, Charlottesville, VA 22906, (434)977-5650
Christian Aid Mission [20024], PO Box 9037, Charlottesville, VA 22906, (434)977-5650
Christian Aid for Romania [★18570]
Christian Aid for Romania [★18570]
Christian Alcoholic Rehabilitation Assn. [★13241]
Christian Alliance For Humanitarian Aid [12821], PO Box 84803, Pearland, TX 77584, (281)412-2285
Christian Amers. for Life - Defunct.
Christian Anti-Communism Crusade [17187], PO Box 129, Manitou Springs, CO 80829, (719)685-9043
Christian Anti-Defamation Commn. [17278], PO Box 1115, Vista, CA 92085, (866)508-2232
Christian Anti-Defamation League [★17278]
Christian Assn. of Primetimers [★10870]
Christian Assn. for Psychological Stud. [16397], PO Box 365, Batavia, IL 60510-0365, (630)639-9478
Christian Assn. of Senior Adult Ministries [★10870]
Christian Blind Mission [IO], Bensheim, Germany
Christian Blind Mission Intl. [17071], 450 E Park Ave., Greenville, SC 29601, (864)239-0065
Christian Blind Mission Intl. [17071], 450 E Park Ave., Greenville, SC 29601, (864)239-0065
Christian Blind Mission Intl. - Canada [IO], Stouffville, ON, Canada
Christian Blind Mission Intl. - New Zealand [IO], North Shore City, New Zealand
Christian Blind Mission Intl. - UK [IO], Cambridge, United Kingdom
Christian Boaters Assn. [19740], 193 Plantation Dr., Tavernier, FL 33070, (305)852-4799

Christian Booksellers Assn. [★3099]
Christian Booksellers Assn. [★3099]
Christian Booksellers Assn. of New Zealand [IO], Wanganui, New Zealand
Christian Bookselling Assn. of Australia [IO], Bargo, Australia
Christian Bowhunters of Am. [22221], 2205 State Rte. 571, Greenville, OH 45331-9425, (937)548-0623
Christian Bros. Volunteer [★20055]
Christian Bus. Men's Comm. [19545], PO Box 8009, Chattanooga, TN 37414-0009, (423)698-4444
Christian Bus. Men's Comm. Intl. [★19545]
Christian Camp and Conf. Assn. [22442], PO Box 62189, Colorado Springs, CO 80962-2189, (719)260-9400
Christian Camping Intl. [★22442]
Christian Camping Intl. - Brazil [IO], Anapolis, Brazil
Christian Camping Intl. - Jamaica [IO], Kingston, Jamaica
Christian Camping Intl. - Russia [IO], St. Petersburg, Russia
Christian Camping Intl. - United Kingdom [IO], Milton Keynes, United Kingdom
Christian Camping - New Zealand [IO], Taupo, New Zealand
Christian Century Found. [19546], 104 S Michigan Ave., Ste. 700, Chicago, IL 60603-5943, (312)263-7510
The Christian Challenge [★19708]
The Christian Challenge [★19708]
Christian Chamber of Commerce [★23392]
Christian Cheerleaders of Am. [22450], PO Box 49, Bethania, NC 27010, (877)243-3722
Christian Children's Fund [★11231]
Christian Children's Fund [★11231]
Christian Children's Fund of Canada [IO], Markham, ON, Canada
Christian Chiropractors Assn. [19547], 2550 Stover St., No. B-102, Fort Collins, CO 80525, (970)482-1404
Christian Coalition [★17436]
Christian Coalition of Am. [17436], PO Box 37030, Washington, DC 20013-7030, (202)479-6900
Christian Coll. Coalition [★7854]
Christian Coll. Consortium [7853], 255 Grapevine Rd., Wenham, MA 01984, (978)867-4802
Christian Comic Arts Soc. [9172], PO Box 254, Temple City, CA 91780
Christian Committees of Correspondence [★8058]
Christian Communications, Inc. [19548], 9600 Bellaire Blvd., No. 111, Houston, TX 77036, (713)778-1155
Christian Community Development Assn. [19985], PO Box 08094, Chicago, IL 60608, (312)733-0200
Christian Conf. of Asia [IO], Chiang Mai, Thailand
Christian Connections for Intl. Hea. [14704], Ray Martin, Exec. Dir., 1817 Rupert St., McLean, VA 22101, (703)556-0123
Christian Connections for Intl. Hea. [14704], Ray Martin, Exec. Dir., 1817 Rupert St., McLean, VA 22101, (703)556-0123
Christian Coun. on Persons with Disabilities [★11804]
Christian Coun. on Persons with Disabilities [★11804]
Christian Coun. of Sweden [IO], Sundbyberg, Sweden
Christian Counsellors Assn. of Australia - New South Wales [IO], Palm Beach, Australia
Christian Counsellors Assn. of Australia - Queensland [IO], Carindale, Australia
Christian Counsellors Assn. of Australia - South Australia [IO], Unley, Australia
Christian Counsellors Assn. of Australia - Victoria [IO], Ormond, Australia
Christian Counsellors Assn. of Australia - Western Australia [IO], Guilford, Australia
Christian Dance Fellowship of Australia [IO], Marsfield, Australia
Christian Deer Hunters Assn. [19549], PO Box 432, Silver Lake, MN 55381, (320)327-2266
Christian Defense League [19550], PO Box 25, Mandeville, LA 70470, (601)749-8565
Christian Democrat Intl. [IO], Brussels, Belgium

Christian Democratic Union [IO], Berlin, Germany
Christian Dental Soc. [14276], PO Box 296, Sumner, IA 50674, (563)578-8887
Christian Educ. [IO], Birmingham, United Kingdom
Christian Educators Assn. [★19672]
Christian Educators Assn. [★19672]
Christian Educators Assn. Intl. [19672], PO Box 45610, Westlake, OH 44145, (440)250-9566
Christian Educators Assn. Intl. [19672], PO Box 45610, Westlake, OH 44145, (440)250-9566
Christian Educators Fellowship of the United Methodist Church [19673], PO Box 24930, Nashville, TN 37202-4930, (615)749-6870
Christian Engineers in Development [IO], Crieff, United Kingdom
Christian European Visual Media Assn. [IO], Wetzlar, Germany
Christian Family Life [12001], Two Becoming One, 1075 Maxwell Mill Rd., Fort Mill, SC 29708, (800)264-3876
Christian Family Movement [12002], PO Box 925, Evansville, IN 47706-0925, (812)962-5508
Christian Fellowship of Art Music Composers [9498], Greatbatch School of Music, Houghton Coll., Houghton, NY 14744, (585)567-9424
Christian Fencers Assn. [22563], Rev. Robert Bruce Sikes, 912 S Rock Hill Rd., St. Louis, MO 63119
Christian Found. for Children [★13177]
Christian Found. for Children [★13177]
Christian Found. for Children and Aging [13177], 1 Elmwood Ave., Kansas City, KS 66103, (913)384-6500
Christian Found. for Children and Aging [13177], 1 Elmwood Ave., Kansas City, KS 66103, (913)384-6500
Christian Freedom Institutes [★8058]
Christian Freedom Intl. [20210], 215 Ashmun St., Sault Ste. Marie, MI 49783, (906)253-2336
Christian Freedom Intl. [20210], 215 Ashmun St., Sault Ste. Marie, MI 49783, (906)253-2336
Christian Friends of Israel - U.S.A. [19551], PO Box 470258, Charlotte, NC 28247-0258, (704)552-1283
Christian Friends of Israel USA [19551], PO Box 470258, Charlotte, NC 28247-0258, (704)552-1283
Christian Golfers' Assn. [22453], 1285 Clara Louise Kellogg Dr., Sumter, SC 29153, (803)773-2171
Christian Hea. Assn. of Kenya [IO], Nairobi, Kenya
Christian Herald Assn. [19552], 132 Madison Ave., New York, NY 10016, (212)674-3456
Christian Heritage Center - Defunct.
Christian Heritage Party of Canada [IO], Ottawa, ON, Canada
Christian Home Educators Assn. [★8267]
Christian Home Educators Assn. of California [8267], PO Box 2009, Norwalk, CA 90651-2009, (562)864-2432
Christian Hospitals Overseas Secure Equip. Needs [12450]
Christian Hunters and Anglers Assn. [21279], PO Box 132379, Tyler, TX 75712-0072, (903)312-7390
Christian Instrumental Directors Assn. [★20121]
Christian Instrumentalists and Directors Assn. [20121], Andrew Kamper, Treas., 1401 Ferndale SW, Grand Rapids, MI 49504
Christian Ireland Ministries - Address unknown since 2010.
Christian Jujitsu Assn. [22730], PO Box 7174, Kalispell, MT 59904-0174, (406)257-3245
Christian Labor Assn. of the U.S.A. [23172], PO Box 65, Zeeland, MI 49464, (616)772-9164
Christian Ladies All together Standing against Social Injustice Corp. [13456], PO Box 3795, Cartersville, GA 30120, (770)769-6392
Christian Law Assn. [19553], PO Box 4010, Seminole, FL 33775, (727)399-8300
Christian Leadership Alliance [20200], 635 Camino de los Mares, Ste. 216, San Clemente, CA 92673, (949)487-0900
Christian League for the Handicapped [★11793]
Christian Legal Soc. [19554], 8001 Braddock Rd., Ste. 300, Springfield, VA 22151-2110, (703)642-1070
Christian Librarians' Fellowship [★9965]
Christian Librarians' Fellowship [★9965]
Christian Life Commn. of the Southern Baptist Convention [★19320]

A star before a book entry number signifies that the name is not listed separately, but is mentioned within the entry.

Christian Life Community [IO], Rome, Italy
Christian Literacy Associates [8528], 541 Perry Hwy., Pittsburgh, PA 15229-1851, (412)364-3777
Christian Literacy Associates [8528], 541 Perry Hwy., Pittsburgh, PA 15229-1851, (412)364-3777
Christian Literature and Bible Center [20025], 2005 Prince William Dr., North Augusta, SC 29841
Christian Literature and Bible Center [20025], 2005 Prince William Dr., North Augusta, SC 29841
Christian Media Assn. [19947], 176 Wayland Rd., Culpeper, VA 22701, (540)829-8101
Christian Medical and Dental Associations [19948], PO Box 7500, Bristol, TN 37621, (423)844-1000
Christian Medical and Dental Associations [19948], PO Box 7500, Bristol, TN 37621, (423)844-1000
Christian Medical and Dental Soc. [IO], Steinbach, MB, Canada
Christian Medical and Dental Soc. [★19948]
Christian Medical and Dental Soc. [★19948]
Christian Medical Found. Intl. - Address unknown since 2010.
Christian Medical Soc. [★19948]
Christian Medical Soc. [★19948]
Christian Methodist Episcopal Church l Women's Missionary Coun. [19970], 2309 Bonnie Ave., Bastrop, LA 71220-4171, (318)281-3044
Christian Military Fellowship [19555], PO Box 1207, Englewood, CO 80150-1207, (303)761-1959
A Christian Ministry in the Natl. Parks [19556], 9185 E Kenyon Ave., Ste. 230, Denver, CO 80237, (303)220-2808
Christian Mission Aid [IO], Nairobi, Kenya
Christian Mission for the Deaf [20026], PO Box 1651, Aledo, TX 76008
Christian Mission for Deaf Africans [★20026]
Christian Missionary Fellowship [20027], PO Box 501020, Indianapolis, IN 46250-6020, (317)578-2700
Christian Missionary Fellowship [20027], PO Box 501020, Indianapolis, IN 46250-6020, (317)578-2700
Christian Missions to the Communist World [★20105]
Christian Missions in Many Lands [20028], PO Box 13, Spring Lake, NJ 07762-0013, (732)449-8880
Christian Motorcyclists Assn. [21925], PO Box 9, Hatfield, AR 71945, (870)389-6196
Christian Motorsports Ministries [21024], 1006 W Taft, Ste. 225, Sapulpa, OK 74066, (607)742-3407
Christian Movement for Evangelization, Counseling and Reconciliation [IO], Kigali, Rwanda
Christian Orthopaedic Partners [★16032]
Christian Orthopaedic Partners [★16032]
Christian Outreach to the Handicapped [IO], Singapore, Singapore
Christian Overcomers [11771], PO Box 2007, Garfield, NJ 07026, (973)253-2343
Christian Patriot Assn. - Defunct.
Christian Peace Conf. [IO], Prague, Czech Republic
Christian Pharmacists Fellowship Intl. [16188], PO Box 24708, West Palm Beach, FL 33416-4708, (561)803-2737
Christian Pharmacists Fellowship Intl. [16188], PO Box 24708, West Palm Beach, FL 33416-4708, (561)803-2737
Christian Pilots Assn. [20029], PO Box 90452, Los Angeles, CA 90009, (562)208-2912
Christian Record Benevolent Assn. [★17072]
Christian Record Braille Found. [★17072]
Christian Record Services [17072], PO Box 6097, Lincoln, NE 68506-0097, (402)488-0981
Christian Record Services [IO], Oshawa, ON, Canada
Christian Reformed
 Assn. of Reformed Baptist Churches of Am. [19309]
 Dynamic Youth Ministries [19606]
 Natl. Assn. of Melkite Youth [19591]
Christian Reformed World Relief Comm. [12320], 2850 Kalamazoo Ave. SE, Grand Rapids, MI 49560, (616)241-1691
Christian Reformed World Relief Comm. [12320], 2850 Kalamazoo Ave. SE, Grand Rapids, MI 49560, (616)241-1691
Christian Relief and Development Assn. [IO], Addis Ababa, Ethiopia

Christian Relief and Development Org. [IO], Bujumbura, Burundi
Christian Relief Services [12822], 2550 Huntington Ave., Ste. 200, Alexandria, VA 22303, (703)317-9086
Christian Relief Services [12822], 2550 Huntington Ave., Ste. 200, Alexandria, VA 22303, (703)317-9086
Christian Renewal Ministry - Defunct.
Christian Res. - Address unknown since 2011.
Christian Res. Assn. [IO], Swindon, United Kingdom
Christian Res. Inst. [19557], PO Box 8500, Charlotte, NC 28271-8500, (704)887-8200
Christian Res. Inst. [19557], PO Box 8500, Charlotte, NC 28271-8500, (704)887-8200
Christian Res. Inst. Intl. [★19557]
Christian Res. Inst. Intl. [★19557]
Christian Response Intl. [★20210]
Christian Response Intl. [★20210]
Christian Restoration Assn. [19558], 7133 Central Parke Blvd., Mason, OH 45040, (513)229-8000
Christian Rural Overseas Prog. [★12823]
Christian Rural Overseas Prog. [★12823]
Christian Schools Australia [IO], North Ryde, Australia
The Christian Sci. Publishing Soc. [2927], 1 Norway St., Boston, MA 02115, (617)450-2000
Christian Seniors Assn. [19559], 139 C St. SE, Washington, DC 20003-1807, (202)547-4400
Christian Ser. Brigade [★20305]
Christian Servicemen Fellowship [★19555]
Christian Small Publishers Assn. [2928], PO Box 481022, Charlotte, NC 28269, (704)277-7194
Christian Small Publishers Assn. [2928], PO Box 481022, Charlotte, NC 28269, (704)277-7194
Christian Social Party [IO], Luxembourg, Luxembourg
Christian Sociological Soc. [7426], Paul J. Serwinek, 2385 Learmont Ln., Milford, MI 48381, (248)685-1299
Christian Solidarity Intl. [20211], 870 Hampshire Rd., Ste. T, Westlake Village, CA 91361, (805)777-7107
Christian Solidarity Intl. [20211], 870 Hampshire Rd., Ste. T, Westlake Village, CA 91361, (805)777-7107
Christian Solidarity Intl. [IO], Binz, Switzerland
Christian Solidarity Intl., U.S.A. [★20210]
Christian Solidarity Intl., U.S.A. [★20210]
Christian Solidarity, U.S.A. [★20210]
Christian Solidarity, U.S.A. [★20210]
Christian Sports Intl. [22454], PO Box 254, Zelienople, PA 16063, (724)453-1400
Christian Sports Intl. [22454], PO Box 254, Zelienople, PA 16063, (724)453-1400
Christian Stewardship Assn. and Christian Mgt. Assn. [★20200]
Christian Stewardship Coun. [★20200]
Christian Tapes for the Disabled - Defunct.
Christian Teachers Fed. of Belgium [IO], Brussels, Belgium
Christian TV Mission - Address unknown since 2010.
Christian Universalist Assn. [19560], PO Box 107, Fairfax, VA 22038, (703)879-1792
Christian Vegetarian Assn. [20279], PO Box 201791, Cleveland, OH 44120, (216)283-6702
Christian Vegetarian Assn. [20279], PO Box 201791, Cleveland, OH 44120, (216)283-6702
Christian Venues Assn. [IO], South Windsor, Australia
Christian Veterinary Missions of Canada [IO], Dundas, ON, Canada
Christian Women Connection [19615], PO Box 2328, Anderson, IN 46018-2328, (765)648-2102
Christian Women's Assn. of Russia [IO], Moscow, Russia
Christian Wrestling Fed. [23131], 331 County Line Rd., Rockwall, TX 75032, (214)460-0477
Christian Writers Guild [★20295]
Christianiki Enosi Neanidon [★IO]
Christianity
 Acad. of Homiletics [19814]
 Adopt-A-Church Intl. [19610]
 Advent Christian Gen. Conf. [19287]
 African Amer. Lutheran Assn. [19920]
 Anglicans United [19689]
 ASGM [19339]

 Assn. of Christian Truckers [19982]
 Assn. of Reformed Baptist Churches of Am. [19309]
 Assn. for Religion and Intellectual Life [19669]
 Assn. for the Restoration of Church and Home [19613]
 Athletes in Action [19731]
 Baptist Mid-Missions [19314]
 BCM Intl. [19341]
 Bethany Intl. Missions [20014]
 Brotherhood of Saint Andrew [19693]
 Bros. and Sisters in Christ [19541]
 Catholic Acad. of Sciences in the U.S.A. [19670]
 Catholic Assn. of Latino Leaders [19398]
 Catholic Athletes for Christ [22230]
 Catholic Campus Ministry Assn. [19399]
 Catholic Central Union of Am. l Central Bur. [19400]
 Catholic Radio Assn. [19406]
 Catholic War Veterans Auxiliary of the U.S.A. [20704]
 Catholic War Veterans of the U.S.A. [20781]
 Center for Christian/Jewish Understanding [19650]
 Center for the Evangelical United Brethren Heritage [19719]
 Center for the Ministry of Teaching [19671]
 China Aid Assn. [20209]
 Christ Truth Ministries [19346]
 Christian Hunters and Anglers Assn. [21279]
 Christian Media Assn. [19947]
 Christian Vegetarian Assn. [20279]
 ChristianTrade Assn. Intl. [19561]
 Claretian Volunteers and Lay Missionaries [19413]
 Coalition of Spirit-filled Churches [19616]
 Commn. of the Churches on Intl. Affairs [19828]
 Confessing Synod Ministries [20242]
 Disciples Ecumenical Consultative Coun. [19618]
 Disciples Justice Action Network [19566]
 Episcopalians for Global Reconciliation [19703]
 Equestrian Ministries Intl. [19816]
 Forum for Scriptural Christianity [19972]
 Found. for Traditional Values [18513]
 Full Gospel Bus. Men's Fellowship Intl. [19574]
 Greek Orthodox Ladies Philoptochos Soc. [19804]
 Hagiography Soc. [20212]
 High School Evangelism Fellowship [19751]
 Holy Childhood Assn. [19428]
 Holy Shroud Guild [19431]
 Interdisciplinary Biblical Res. Inst. [19677]
 Intl. Assn. of Christian Chaplains [19520]
 Intl. Assn. of Missionary Aviation [20052]
 Intl. Catholic Deaf Assn. U.S. Sect. [19435]
 Intl. Police and Fire Chaplain's Assn. [19522]
 InterServe U.S.A. [20054]
 Legatus [19445]
 Liberal Religious Educators Assn. [20268]
 Life Action Revival Ministries [19757]
 Master's Men of the Natl. Assn. of Free Will Baptists [19323]
 Missionary Soc. of Saint Paul the Apostle [19454]
 Natl. Alliance Against Christian Discrimination [19589]
 Natl. Assn. of Catholic Family Life Ministers [19997]
 Natl. Assn. of Evangelicals [19766]
 Natl. Assn. of Hispanic Priests of the USA [19457]
 Natl. Assn. of Priest Pilots [19459]
 Natl. Christian Barrel Racers Assn. [22660]
 Natl. Church Conf. of the Blind [13379]
 Natl. Spiritualist Assn. of Churches l Healers League [20145]
 North Am. Christian Creative Assn. [19595]
 Pocket Testament League [19352]
 Quixote Center [19488]
 Response-Ability [20085]
 Seventh Day Baptist Missionary Soc. [19330]
 Seventh Day Baptist World Fed. [19331]
 Soc. of Anglican Missionaries and Senders [20094]
 Soc. of the Companions of the Holy Cross [19716]
 Soc. for Hindu-Christian Stud. [20215]
 Soc. for the Stud. of Christian Spirituality [19601]

Reference to "IO" in place of a book number signifies that the association may be found in the 50th edition of International Organizations.

Teen Missions Intl. [20099]
Theosophical Book Assn. for the Blind [20264]
United People in Christ [19980]
U.S. Assn. of Consecrated Virgins [19507]
U.S. Conf. of Catholic Bishops | Bishops' Comm. on Priestly Formation [19688]
United States Conference of Catholic Bishops | Comm. on Divine Worship [19510]
Christians Abroad [IO], Essex, United Kingdom
Christians Afloat [★19740]
Christians Assoc. for Relationships with Eastern Europe [IO], Ancaster, ON, Canada
Christians in Crisis [20239], PO Box 293627, Sacramento, CA 95829
Christians' Israel Public Action Campaign [18011], The Ronald Reagan Bldg., 1300 Pennsylvania Ave. NW, Ste. 700, Washington, DC 20004-3024
Christians' Israel Public Action Campaign [18011], The Ronald Reagan Bldg., 1300 Pennsylvania Ave. NW, Ste. 700, Washington, DC 20004-3024
Christians for Peace in El Salvador [20030], 215 E 14 St., Cincinnati, OH 45202, (513)831-4520
Christians in Visual Arts [★9287]
Christians in the Visual Arts [9287], 255 Grapevine Rd., Wenham, MA 01984-1813, (978)867-4124
ChristianTrade Assn. Intl. [19561], PO Box 62187, Colorado Springs, CO 80962-2187, (719)432-8428
Christic Inst. - Defunct.
Christina Noble Children's Found. - Vietnam [IO], Ho Chi Minh City, Vietnam
Christlich Demokratische Union [★IO]
Christlich-Demokratische Volkspartei der Schweiz [★IO]
Christliche Europaische Arbeitsgemeinschaft fur Visuelle Medien [★IO]
Christlicher Friedensdienst e.V. [★IO]
Christmas in April - U.S.A. [★12200]
Christmas Philatelic Club [22027], 312 Northwood Dr., Lexington, KY 40505-2104
Christmas Seal and Charity Stamp Soc. [21322], Mrs. Florence H. Wright, Sec.-Treas., PO Box 18615, Rochester, NY 14618-0615
Christmas Seal and Charity Stamp Soc. [21322], Mrs. Florence H. Wright, Sec.-Treas., PO Box 18615, Rochester, NY 14618-0615
Christoffel-Blindenmission [★IO]
Christoffel Blindenmission [★IO]
Christopher Columbus Philatelic Soc. [22028], Leslie Seff, Sec., 3750 Hudson Manor, Terr. E, Bronx, NY 10463-1126
Christopher and Dana Reeve Found. [16700], 636 Morris Tpke., Ste. 3A, Short Hills, NJ 07078, (800)225-0292
Christopher Morley Knothole Assn. [9358], Bryant Lib., Paper Mill Rd., Roslyn, NY 11576
Christopher Reeve Found. [★16700]
Christopher Reeve Paralysis Found. [★16700]
Christopher St. Liberation Day Comm. [★12086]
The Christophers [19412], 5 Hanover Sq., 11th Fl., New York, NY 10004, (212)759-4050
Christos Stelios Ioannou Found. [IO], Nicosia, Cyprus
Chromatographic Soc. [IO], Glasgow, United Kingdom
Chromosome 9P Network [14589], PO Box 524, Appleton, WI 54912
Chromosome 9P Network [14589], PO Box 524, Appleton, WI 54912
Chromosome 16 Found; Disorders of [14594]
Chromosome 16 Found; Disorders of [14594]
Chromosome 18 Registry and Res. Soc. [14590], 7155 Oakridge Dr., San Antonio, TX 78229, (210)657-4968
Chromosome 18 Registry and Res. Soc. [14590], 7155 Oakridge Dr., San Antonio, TX 78229, (210)657-4968
Chromosome Deletion Outreach [★14591]
Chromosome Deletion Outreach [★14591]
Chromosome Disorder Outreach [14591], PO Box 724, Boca Raton, FL 33429-0724, (561)395-4252
Chromosome Disorder Outreach [14591], PO Box 724, Boca Raton, FL 33429-0724, (561)395-4252
Chronic Fatigue Syndrome and Fibromyalgia Assn; Natl. [14406]
Chronic Fatigue Syndrome; Intl. Assn. for [14391]

Chronic Granulomatous Disease Assn. [14380], 2616 Monterey Rd., San Marino, CA 91108-1646, (626)441-4118
Chronic Granulomatous Disease Assn. [14380], 2616 Monterey Rd., San Marino, CA 91108-1646, (626)441-4118
Chronic Lymphocytic Leukaemia Support Assn. [IO], London, United Kingdom
Chronic Pain Assn. of Canada [IO], Edmonton, AB, Canada
Chronic Syndrome Support Assn. [14381], 801 Riverside Dr., Lumberton, NC 28358-4625

Chrysler
Chrysler Town and Country Owners Registry [21026]
Plymouth Owners Club [21151]
Chrysler 300 Club [★21025]
Chrysler 300 Club [★21025]
Chrysler 300 Club Intl. [21025], PO Box 40, Benson, MD 21018
Chrysler 300 Club Intl. [21025], PO Box 40, Benson, MD 21018
Chrysler Power [★21024]
Chrysler Town and Country Owners Registry [21026], 3006 S 40 St., Milwaukee, WI 53215, (414)384-1843
Chrysler Town and Country Owners Registry [21026], 3006 S 40 St., Milwaukee, WI 53215, (414)384-1843
Chrysotile Inst. [IO], Montreal, QC, Canada
C.H.U.C.K. - Defunct.
Chuck Negron Fan Club - Address unknown since 2011.
Chud Rodo Saigai Boshi Kyokai [★IO]
Chung Nip Hwe Gwan [★IO]
Church Army [19694], 115 W Atlantic St., Ste. 104, Branson, MO 65616, (417)544-9019
Church Army Soc. [★19694]
Church Assn. for Seamen's Work [★19715]
Church Benefits Assn. [20152], 15000 Commerce Pkwy., Ste. C, Mount Laurel, NJ 08054, (856)439-0500
Church of England Record Soc. [IO], London, United Kingdom

Church of God
Mission Soc. of the Mother of God of Boronyavo [20191]
Church of God World Missions [20031], PO Box 8016, Cleveland, TN 37320-8016, (423)478-7190
Church of God World Missions [20031], PO Box 8016, Cleveland, TN 37320-8016, (423)478-7190
Church Growth Inc. [20220], PO Box 541, Monrovia, CA 91017-0541, (800)844-9286
Church Historical Soc. [★19710]
Church Literature Found. [★19712]
Church Mission Soc. [IO], Oxford, United Kingdom
Church Monuments Soc. [IO], Plymouth, United Kingdom
Church Music Assn. of Am. [20122], 12421 New Point Dr., Richmond, VA 23233, (334)703-0884
Church Music Publishers Assn. [20123], PO Box 158992, Nashville, TN 37215, (615)791-0273
Church and Peace [IO], Schoeffengrund, Germany
Church Peace Union [★19827]
Church Peace Union [★19827]
Church Pension Fund [19695], 445 5th Ave., New York, NY 10016, (800)223-6602
Church Pensions Conf. [★20152]
Church Periodical Club [19696], 815 2nd Ave., New York, NY 10017-4594, (800)334-7626
Church Planting Intl.
Church Planting Intl. - Address unknown since 2011.
Church Proj. on U.S. Investments in Southern Africa [★17481]
Church and School of Wicca
Church and School of Wicca - Address unknown since 2011.
Church of Scotland Guild [IO], Edinburgh, United Kingdom

Church and State
Americans United for Separation of Church and State [19607]
Atheists For Human Rights [17207]
Catholic Acad. of Sciences in the U.S.A. [19670]
Freedom From Religion Found. [19608]

Church and Sunday School Music Publishers Assn. [★20123]
Church and Synagogue Lib. Assn. [9981], 2920 SW Dolph Ct., Ste. 3A, Portland, OR 97219-4055, (503)244-6919
Church Universal and Triumphant [20176], 63 Summit Way, Gardiner, MT 59030, (406)848-9500
Church Women United [20286], 475 Riverside Dr., Ste. 1626A, New York, NY 10115, (212)870-2347
Church Women United in the U.S.A. [★20286]
Church World Ser. [12823], PO Box 968, Elkhart, IN 46515, (574)264-3102
Church World Ser. [12823], PO Box 968, Elkhart, IN 46515, (574)264-3102
Church World Service Aids for the Horn of Africa - Defunct.
Church World Ser. Community Appeal [★12823]
Church World Ser. Community Appeal [★12823]
Church World Ser., Immigration and Refugee Prog. [18506], 475 Riverside Dr., Ste. 700, New York, NY 10115, (212)870-2061
Church World Ser., Immigration and Refugee Prog. [18506], 475 Riverside Dr., Ste. 700, New York, NY 10115, (212)870-2061
Church World Ser. - Vietnam [IO], Hanoi, Vietnam

Churches
Acad. of Homiletics [19814]
Administrative Personnel Assn. of the Presbyterian Church [19609]
Adopt-A-Church Intl. [19610]
Adopt-A-Church Intl. [19610]
African Amer. Lutheran Assn. [19920]
Alban Inst. [19611]
Anglicans United [19689]
Assn. of Presbyterian Church Educators [19612]
Assn. of Reformed Baptist Churches of Am. [19309]
Assn. for Religion and Intellectual Life [19669]
Assn. for the Restoration of Church and Home [19613]
Assn. of Unity Churches Intl. [19614]
Baptist Mid-Missions [19314]
BCM Intl. [19341]
Bethany Intl. Missions [20014]
Brotherhood of Saint Andrew [19693]
China Aid Assn. [20209]
Christian Media Assn. [19947]
Christian Women Connection [19615]
Coalition of Spirit-filled Churches [19616]
Commn. of the Churches on Intl. Affairs [19828]
Confessing Synod Ministries [20242]
Disciple Nations Alliance [19617]
Disciples Ecumenical Consultative Coun. [19618]
Disciples Justice Action Network [19566]
Divine Sci. Ministers Assn. [19645]
Episcopalians for Global Reconciliation [19703]
Family Fed. for World Peace and Unification [20151]
Fellowship Intl. Mission [20044]
Forum for Scriptural Christianity [19972]
Full Gospel Bus. Men's Fellowship Intl. [19574]
The Gospel Coalition [19576]
Great Commission Res. Network [19619]
Greek Orthodox Ladies Philoptochos Soc. [19804]
High School Evangelism Fellowship [19751]
Historical Soc. of the United Methodist Church [9768]
IFCA Intl. [19620]
IFCA Intl. [19620]
Interdisciplinary Biblical Res. Inst. [19677]
Intl. Coalition of Apostles [19991]
Intl. Coun. of Community Churches [19621]
Intl. Coun. of Community Churches [19621]
InterServe U.S.A. [20054]
Liberal Religious Educators Assn. [20268]
Life Action Revival Ministries [19757]
Master's Men of the Natl. Assn. of Free Will Baptists [19323]
Mission Soc. of the Mother of God of Boronyavo [20191]
Missionary Soc. of Saint Paul the Apostle [19454]
Morris Pratt Inst. Assn. [20142]
Natl. Assn. of Catholic Family Life Ministers [19997]
Natl. Assn. of Evangelicals [19766]

A star before a book entry number signifies that the name is not listed separately, but is mentioned within the entry.

Natl. Assn. of Family Ministries [19998]
Natl. Assn. of Melkite Youth [19591]
Natl. Conf. of Catholic Airport Chaplains [19528]
Natl. Coun. of Churches [19622]
Natl. Spiritualist Assn. of Churches I Healers League [20145]
New Life Intl. Alliance [19999]
New Wineskins Missionary Network [20075]
Pocket Testament League [19352]
Quixote Center [19488]
Seventh Day Baptist Missionary Soc. [19330]
Seventh Day Baptist World Fed. [19331]
Sikh Coun. on Religion and Educ. [20241]
Soc. of Anglican Missionaries and Senders [20094]
Soc. for Hindu-Christian Stud. [20215]
Theosophical Book Assn. for the Blind [20264]
United Indian Missions Intl. [20102]
U.S. Conf. of Catholic Bishops I Bishops' Comm. on Priestly Formation [19688]
United States Conference of Catholic Bishops I Comm. on Divine Worship [19510]
Willow Creek Assn. [19623]
WordAlone Ministries [19943]
Churches' Center for Theology and Public Policy - Address unknown since 2010.
Churches of ChristChristian Churches
Disciples of Christ Historical Soc. [19624]
Full Gospel Bus. Men's Fellowship Intl. [19574]
Natl. Chaplains Assn. [19625]
World Convention of Churches of Christ [19626]
World Convention of Churches of Christ [19626]
Churches' Commn. for Migrants in Europe [IO], Brussels, Belgium
The Churches Conservation Trust [IO], London, United Kingdom
Churches' Coun. for Child and Youth Care [IO], Bangalore, India
Churches Together in Britain and Ireland [IO], London, United Kingdom
Churches Uniting in Christ [19651], Elder James N. Tse, Treas., 8717 85th St., Woodhaven, NY 11421-1913, (718)849-1608
Churchill Centre [10657], 200 W Madison St., Ste. 1700, Chicago, IL 60606, (312)658-5006
Churchill Soc. London [IO], Ipswich, United Kingdom
Churg Strauss Syndrome Assn. [13809], PO Box 671, Southampton, MA 01073-0671, (413)862-3636
Churro; Navajosa [★4916]
CHWMEG [3633], 470 William Pitt Way, Pittsburgh, PA 15238, (412)826-3055
CID Agents Assn. [20714], 165 Birch Creek Cir., Mc-Donough, GA 30253-5137, (770)363-1188
Cigar Makers' Intl. Union of Am. [★23293]
Cigarette Pack Collectors Assn. [21323], 86 Plymouth Grove Dr., Kennebunk, ME 04043
CIIT Centers for Hea. Res. [★7571]
CILT - The Natl. Centre for Languages [IO], London, United Kingdom
CIMA Marketing Communications Coun. [★2390]
CIMTA [796], 18453 Shaddox Hollow Ln., Rogers, AR 72756, (479)925-7056
CIMTECH [IO], Hatfield, United Kingdom
Cincinnati Music Scholarship Assn. [★10314]
Cinderella Softball Leagues [22951], PO Box 1411, Corning, NY 14830, (607)937-5469
Cinderella Stamp Club [IO], Ludlow, United Kingdom
Cinema Theatre Assn. [IO], London, United Kingdom
Cinema Tropical [9601], 611 Broadway, Ste. 836, New York, NY 10012, (212)254-5474
Cinnamon Rabbit Breeders Assn. [4839], Nancy Searle, Sec.-Treas., 550 Amherst Rd., Belchertown, MA 01007, (413)253-7721
CIO Community Services Comm. [★11658]
CIO Editors and Public Relations Conf. [★2911]
Circle of Earth - Address unknown since 2011.
Circle of Friends for Amer. Veterans [20784], 210 E Broad St., Ste. 202, Falls Church, VA 22046, (703)237-8980
Circle of Hea. Intl. [12130], 90 Coventry Wood Rd., Bolton, MA 01740, (512)517-3220
Circle of Hea. Intl. [12130], 90 Coventry Wood Rd., Bolton, MA 01740, (512)517-3220
Circle K Intl. [13054], 3636 Woodview Trace, Indianapolis, IN 46268-3196, (317)875-8755

Circle K Intl. [13054], 3636 Woodview Trace, Indianapolis, IN 46268-3196, (317)875-8755
Circle Sanctuary [20244], PO Box 9, Barneveld, WI 53507, (608)924-2216
Circle Sanctuary [20244], PO Box 9, Barneveld, WI 53507, (608)924-2216
Circle Sanctuary Network [★20244]
Circle Sanctuary Network [★20244]
Circle of Wine Writers [IO], London, United Kingdom
Circle of Women: Reach and Teach Across Borders [13015], PO Box 381365, Cambridge, MA 02238-1365
Circles of Exchange [★20250]
Circolo Amatori Lancia Sicilia [IO], Palermo, Italy
Circolo Amerindiano [IO], Perugia, Italy
Circuits Intl. [IO], Nurburg, Germany
Circulation Coun. of DMA [2395], 1120 Ave. of the Americas, New York, NY 10036-6700, (212)768-7277
Circulo de Cultura Panamericano [★9949]
Circulo de Cultura Panamericano [★9949]
Circulo Dermatologico del Peru [IO], Lima, Peru
Circulo Uruguayo de la Publicidad [★IO]
Circum-Pacific Coun. for Energy and Mineral Resources [7120], 12201 Sunrise Valley Dr., MS-917, Reston, VA 20192, (703)648-5042
Circum-Pacific Coun. for Energy and Mineral Resources [7120], 12201 Sunrise Valley Dr., MS-917, Reston, VA 20192, (703)648-5042
Circumcision
Doctors Opposing Circumcision [11518]
Intl. Coalition for Genital Integrity [11519]
Intl. Coalition for Genital Integrity [11519]
Natl. Org. of Circumcision Info. Rsrc. Centers [11520]
Natl. Org. of Circumcision Info. Rsrc. Centers [11520]
Natl. Org. to Halt the Abuse and Routine Mutilation of Males [11521]
Natl. Org. of Restoring Men [11522]
Nurses for the Rights of the Child [11523]
Circumnavigators Club [6857], 24 E 39th St., New York, NY 10016-2555, (201)612-9100
Circus
Amer. Youth Circus Org. [9482]
Circus Fans Assn. of Am. [9483]
Circus Historical Soc. [9484]
Natl. Circus Preservation Soc. [9485]
Natl. Circus Proj. [9486]
Circus Educ. Specialists [★9486]
Circus Ethiopia [IO], Addis Ababa, Ethiopia
Circus Fans Assn. of Am. [9483], 2704 Marshall Ave., Lorain, OH 44052-4315, (440)960-2811
Circus Historical Soc. [9484], 2707 Zoar Rd., Cheraw, SC 29520
Circus Model Builders Intl. [21900], 6701 Manlius Center Rd., Ste. 111-128, East Syracuse, NY 13057
Circus Model Builders, Intl. [21900], 6701 Manlius Center Rd., Ste. 111-128, East Syracuse, NY 13057
CIRIA [IO], London, United Kingdom
CISV Intl. [IO], Newcastle upon Tyne, United Kingdom
CISV - Japan [IO], Tokyo, Japan
CISV - Netherlands [IO], Rotterdam, Netherlands
CISV Norge, Internasjonale Barneleire [★IO]
CISV - Norway [IO], Oslo, Norway
Cities in Schools [★8079]
CitiHope Intl. [12824], PO Box 38, 143 Main St., Andes, NY 13731, (845)676-4400
CitiHope Intl. [12824], PO Box 38, 143 Main St., Andes, NY 13731, (845)676-4400
Citizen Advocacy Center [17769], 1400 16th St. NW, Ste. 101, Washington, DC 20036, (202)462-1174
Citizen Exchange Corps [★17496]
Citizen Exchange Corps [★17496]
Citizen Exchange Coun. [★17496]
Citizen Exchange Coun. [★17496]
Citizen Involvement Training Prog. [★11528]
Citizen Soldier [5803], 267 5th Ave., No. 901, New York, NY 10016, (212)679-2250
Citizen Works [17247], PO Box 18478, Washington, DC 20036, (202)265-6164
Citizens for Affordable Energy [6701], 1302 Waugh Dr., No. 940, Houston, TX 77019, (713)523-7333

Citizens Against Chemtrails U.S. - Address unknown since 2011.
Citizens Against Govt. Waste [17748], 1301 Pennsylvania Ave. NW, Ste. 1075, Washington, DC 20004, (202)467-5300
Citizens Against Human Rights Abuse [★17851]
Citizens Against Human Rights Abuse [★17851]
Citizens Against UFO Secrecy - Address unknown since 2010.
Citizens' Alliance for Responsible Energy [6702], PO Box 52103, Albuquerque, NM 87181, (505)239-8998
Citizens for an Alternative Tax Sys. - Address unknown since 2011.
Citizens for Alternatives to Chem. Contamination [4782], 8735 Maple Grove Rd., Lake, MI 48632-9511, (989)544-3318
Citizens Aviation Watch Assn. [11122], 97-37 63rd Rd. 15 E, Rego Park, NY 11374, (718)275-3932
Citizens Aviation Watch Assn. [11122], 97-37 63rd Rd. 15 E, Rego Park, NY 11374, (718)275-3932
Citizens for a Balanced Budget - Defunct.
Citizens for a Better Am. [17279], PO Box 7647, Van Nuys, CA 91409-7647, (818)574-8911
Citizens CH for Hazardous Waste [★4979]
Citizens Coal Coun. [3945], PO Box 964, Washington, PA 15301, (412)257-2223
Citizens Coalition for Nursing Home Reform; Natl. [★17465]
Citizens Coalition for Rational Traffic Laws [★13335]
Citizens' Commn. on Civil Rights - Address unknown since 2010.
Citizens Comm. for the Right to Keep and Bear Arms [17280], Liberty Park, 12500 NE 10th Pl., Bellevue, WA 98005, (425)454-4911
Citizens for a Competitive America - Defunct.
Citizens for Conservation [★19009]
Citizens for Constitutional Concerns [★17317]
Citizens' Coun. on Hea. Care [17770], 1954 Univ. Ave. W, Ste. 8, St. Paul, MN 55104-3460, (651)646-8935
Citizens' Councils of Am. [★18676]
Citizens Crusade Against Poverty [★12721]
Citizens for a Debt Free America - Defunct.
Citizens Development Corps [★17906]
Citizens Development Corps [17906], 1030 15th St. NW, Ste. 730 E, Washington, DC 20005, (202)872-0933
Citizens for Educational Freedom [8091], 498 Woods Mill Rd., Manchester, MO 63011, (636)686-7101
Citizens for Effective Schools [8769], 8209 Hamilton Spring Ct., Bethesda, MD 20817, (301)469-8000
Citizens to End Animal Suffering and Exploitation [10941], PO Box 440456, Somerville, MA 02144, (617)379-0535
Citizens for Energy Freedom [6703], 2020 Pennsylvania Ave. NW, Ste. 263, Washington, DC 20006
Citizens Energy Plan [6704], MinnWest Tech. Campus, 1700 Tech. Dr., Ste. 212, Willmar, MN 56201, (320)222-3060
Citizens Equal Rights Alliance [12232], PO Box 379, Gresham, WI 54128
Citizens Flag Alliance [5338], PO Box 7197, Indianapolis, IN 46207-7197, (317)630-1253
Citizens Forum on Self-Government/National Municipal League [★5852]
Citizens for Global Solutions [18744], 420 7th St. SE, Washington, DC 20003, (202)546-3950
Citizens for Hea. [13670], 2104 Stevens Ave. S, Minneapolis, MN 55404
Citizens for Hea. [13670], 2104 Stevens Ave. S, Minneapolis, MN 55404
Citizens for Independent Public Broadcasting [17211], 901 Old Hickory Rd., Pittsburgh, PA 15243, (412)341-1967
Citizens for Legitimate Govt. [17745], PO Box 1142, Bristol, CT 06011-1142
Citizens for Midwifery [14104], PO Box 82227, Athens, GA 30608-2227, (888)CFM-4880
Citizens Network for Foreign Affairs [17943], 1828 L St. NW, Ste. 710, Washington, DC 20036-5104, (202)296-3920
Citizens Network for Sustainable Development [11561], ISF, PO Box 7458, Silver Spring, MD 20907, (301)588-5550

Reference to "IO" in place of a book number signifies that the association may be found in the 50th edition of International Organizations.

Citizens for Proportional Representation [★18379]
Citizens for Rational Traffic Laws [★13335]
Citizens for Reliable and Safe Highways [18576], Truck Safety Coalition, 2020 14th St. N, Ste. 710, Arlington, VA 22201, (703)294-6404
Citizens for Renewable Energy [IO], Lion's Head, ON, Canada
Citizens for Responsible Care and Res. [17210], 1024 N 5th St., Philadelphia, PA 19123-1404, (215)627-5335
Citizens for Roadside Safety - Address unknown since 2011.
Citizens for Safe Drivers Against Drunk Drivers/ Chronic Offenders - Defunct.
Citizens' Scholarship Found. of Am. [★8814]
Citizens for Sensible Safeguards - Address unknown since 2010.
Citizens' Stamp Advisory Comm. [22029], Stamp Development, U.S. Postal Ser., 475 L'Enfant Plz. SW, Rm. 3300, Washington, DC 20260
Citizens to Stop Nuclear Terrorism [18711], 612 S Laurel St., Richmond, VA 23220, (214)478-8314
Citizens for Tax Justice [18693], 1616 P St. NW, Ste. 200, Washington, DC 20036, (202)299-1066
Citizens United [17746], 1006 Pennsylvania Ave. SE, Washington, DC 20003, (202)547-5420
Citizens United for Alternatives to the Death Penalty [5370], PMB 335, 2603 Dr. Martin Luther King Jr. Hwy., Gainesville, FL 32609, (800)973-6548
Citizens United for Rehabilitation of Errants [11708], PO Box 2310, Washington, DC 20013-2310, (202)789-2126
Citizens United for Res. in Epilepsy [14518], 223 W Erie St., Ste. 2SW, Chicago, IL 60654, (312)255-1801
Citizens United Resisting Euthanasia [11987], 303 Truman St., Berkeley Springs, WV 25411, (304)258-5433
Citizenship
Amer. Legion Auxiliary Girls Nation [17245]
Assn. for Refugee Ser. Professionals [12301]
Center for the Stud. of the Presidency [17246]
Citizen Works [17247]
Citizenship Through Sports Alliance [22972]
Claremont Inst. [17248]
Close Up Found. [17249]
Community Development Soc. [17374]
Ethics Rsrc. Center [17250]
Immigration Voice [5529]
Natl. Alliance Against Racist and Political Repression [17304]
Natl. Comm. for an Effective Cong. [17413]
Natl. Conf. on Citizenship [17251]
People's Medical Soc. [17768]
U.S. Assn. of Former Members of Cong. [17414]
Voices for Global Change [17254]
Citizenship Educational Ser. [★17250]
Citizenship Through Sports Alliance [22972], Ted Breidenthal, 2537 Madison Ave., Kansas City, MO 64108, (913)645-4623
Citroen Car Club [IO], Steyning, United Kingdom
Citroen Quarterly Car Club [21027], PO Box 130030, Boston, MA 02113-0001
Citrus Australia [IO], Mildura, Australia
Citrus Label Soc. [21324], 131 Miramonte Dr., Fullerton, CA 92835, (714)871-2864
Citrus Marketing Bd. of Israel [IO], Beit Dagan, Israel
City Farmer Soc. [IO], Vancouver, BC, Canada
City and Guilds of London Inst. [IO], London, United Kingdom
City of Hope [15338], 1500 E Duarte Rd., Duarte, CA 91010, (626)256-4673
City Parks Alliance [18227], 2121 Ward Ct. NW, 5th Fl., Washington, DC 20037, (202)974-5120
City Planning Inst. of Japan [IO], Tokyo, Japan
City and Regional Magazine Assn. [2929], 1970 E Grand Ave., Ste. 330, El Segundo, CA 90245, (310)364-0193
City Walls [★17395]
City Women's Network [IO], Uxbridge, United Kingdom
CityKids Found. [13518], 57 Leonard St., New York, NY 10013, (212)925-3320
CityMatch [14071], Magda G. Peck, ScD, Founder/ Sr. Advisor, Dept. of Pediatrics, 982170 Nebraska Medical Ctr., Omaha, NE 68198-2170, (402)561-7500

CityTeam Ministries [12825], 2304 Zanker Rd., San Jose, CA 95131, (408)232-5600
Civic Educ. Proj. - Defunct.
Civics
30 Years After [17999]
Assn. of Americans for Civic Responsibility [17252]
Assn. for Refugee Ser. Professionals [12301]
Center for the Stud. of the Presidency [17246]
Hands Across the Mideast Support Alliance [18124]
Innovations in Civic Participation [17253]
Innovations in Civic Participation [17253]
Light Millennium [17299]
Natl. Alliance for Civic Educ. [7861]
Patriotic Educ. Inc. [7862]
Peace Alliance [18272]
Prometheus Radio Proj. [18101]
Pushback Network [18491]
Voices for Global Change [17254]
Washington Workshops Found. [7863]
CIVICUS: World Alliance for Citizen Participation [18370], 1420 K St. NW, Ste. 350, Washington, DC 20005, (202)331-8518
CIVICUS: World Alliance for Citizen Participation [18370], 1420 K St. NW, Ste. 350, Washington, DC 20005, (202)331-8518
Civil Affairs Assn. [5804], 10130 Hyla Brook Rd., Columbia, MD 21044-1705, (410)992-7724
Civil Affairs Assn. [5804], 10130 Hyla Brook Rd., Columbia, MD 21044-1705, (410)992-7724
Civil Air Operations Officers Assn. of Australia [IO], Port Melbourne, Australia
Civil Air Patrol [5292], 105 S Hansell St., Bldg. 714, Maxwell AFB, AL 36112, (877)227-9142
Civil Aviation Medical Assn. [13584], PO Box 2382, Peachtree City, GA 30269-0382, (770)487-0100
Civil Aviation Medical Assn. [13584], PO Box 2382, Peachtree City, GA 30269-0382, (770)487-0100
Civil Censorship Study Group [22030], 15091 Ridgefield Ln., Colorado Springs, CO 80921
Civil Censorship Study Group [22030], 15091 Ridgefield Ln., Colorado Springs, CO 80921
Civil Constr. Indus. Union of the State of Rio de Janeiro [IO], Rio de Janeiro, Brazil
Civil Defense
The Amer. Civil Defense Assn. [5305]
DRI Intl. [5306]
Intl. Assn. Emergency Managers [5307]
Intl. Assn. Emergency Managers [5307]
Intl. Resources Gp. [5308]
Intl. Resources Gp. [5308]
Natl. Security and Law Soc. [5970]
U.S. Homeland Emergency Response Org. [12911]
Civil Engineering
Geosynthetics Materials Assn. [6426]
Intl. Assn. of Civil Engg. Students [13656]
Intl. Geosynthetics Soc. [6427]
Intl. Geosynthetics Soc. [6427]
Intl. Soc. for Structural Hea. Monitoring of Intelligent Infrastructure [6428]
Intl. Soc. for Structural Hea. Monitoring of Intelligent Infrastructure [6428]
North Amer. Geosynthetics Soc. [6429]
North Amer. Geosynthetics Soc. [6429]
Civil Engg. Contractors Assn. [IO], London, United Kingdom
Civil Engg. Forum for Innovation - Defunct.
Civil Rights Legal Defense Fund [★17273]
Civil Rights and Liberties
30 Years After [17999]
Advancing Human Rights [17807]
Afghans for Civil Soc. [17255]
Afghans for Civil Soc. [17255]
All of Us or None [17256]
Alliance of Faith and Feminism [17628]
American-Arab Anti-Discrimination Comm. [17257]
Amer. Bar Assn. - Sect. of Individual Rights and Responsibilities [17258]
Amer. Citizens for Justice [17259]
Amer. Civil Liberties Union [17260]
Amer. Civil Liberties Union Found. [17261]
Amer. Civil Rights Inst. [17262]
Amer. Civil Rights Union [17263]

Amer. Dream Coalition [17264]
Amer. Family Rights Assn. [17622]
Amer. Libyan Freedom Alliance [17513]
Amer. Patriots Assn. [20742]
Amer. Sons of Liberty [17265]
Americans to Ban Cloning [17266]
Americans for Religious Liberty [17267]
America's Survival, Inc. [17268]
Anti-Defamation League [17269]
Anti-Racist Action-Los Angeles/People Against Racist Terror [17270]
Anti-Racist Action-Los Angeles/People Against Racist Terror [17270]
Armed Females of Am. [17682]
Asian Amer. Legal Defense and Educ. Fund [17271]
Asian-American Network Against Abuse of Human Rights [17814]
Assn. for a More Just Soc. [17272]
Atheists For Human Rights [17207]
Atticus Circle [17735]
Bastard Nation: The Adoptee Rights Org. [10782]
Burmese Amer. Democratic Alliance [17213]
Castle Coalition [18403]
Center for Constitutional Rights [17273]
Center for Third World Organizing [17274]
Center for Third World Organizing [17274]
Change Bangladesh [17275]
Children's Rights [17276]
Chinese for Affirmative Action [17277]
Christian Anti-Defamation Commn. [17278]
Citizens for a Better Am. [17279]
Citizens Comm. for the Right to Keep and Bear Arms [17280]
Coalition for Genetic Fairness [17281]
Coalition for Tax Fairness [18694]
COLAGE [12074]
Commn. for Social Justice [17282]
Compassionate Coalition [18084]
Dalit Freedom Network [17823]
Dalit Solidarity [17824]
Darfur Human Rights Org. [17825]
Death with Dignity Natl. Center [17283]
Defending Dissent Found. [17284]
Democracy for Am. [18329]
Discussion Club [17285]
Drug Policy Alliance [17286]
Election Defense Alliance [17607]
Equality Fed. [17736]
European/American Issues Forum [17287]
European-American Unity and Rights Org. [17288]
Faith Alliance Against Slavery and Trafficking [17289]
Free Expression Policy Proj. [17290]
Freedom Forum [17291]
Freedom Forum [17291]
Friends of Africa Intl. [17830]
Gay and Lesbian Advocates and Defenders [17292]
Global Youth Connect [18828]
Hands Across the Mideast Support Alliance [18124]
Heritage Preservation Assn. [17293]
Hispanas Organized for Political Equality [17776]
Human and Civil Rights Organizations of Am. [11524]
Humanity in Action [8277]
Independence Inst. [17294]
Intl. Refugee Rights Initiative [17843]
Iran Democratic Union [17845]
Iraqi Human Rights Network [17846]
Jews for the Preservation of Firearms Ownership [17295]
Judge David L. Bazelon Center for Mental Hea. Law [17296]
Justice Inc. [17490]
Korean Amer. Voters' Coun. [18034]
Leadership Conf. on Civil Rights [17297]
Leadership Conf. Educ. Fund [7864]
League of the South [17298]
League of Young Voters [18384]
Light Millennium [17299]
Media Coalition [17300]
NAACP [17301]

A star before a book entry number signifies that the name is not listed separately, but is mentioned within the entry.

NAACP | Legal Defense and Educational Fund [17302]
Natl. Action Network [17303]
Natl. Advocates for Pregnant Women [17854]
Natl. Alliance Against Christian Discrimination [19589]
Natl. Alliance Against Racist and Political Repression [17304]
Natl. Alliance for Filipino Concerns [17200]
Natl. Assn. for Gun Rights [17305]
Natl. Assn. of Korean Americans [17306]
Natl. Assn. for Rights Protection and Advocacy [17307]
Natl. Catholic Conf. for Interracial Justice [17308]
Natl. Coalition of Anti-Violence Programs [18770]
Natl. Coalition of Pro-Democracy Advocates [17526]
Natl. Comm. to Reopen the Rosenberg Case [17309]
Natl. Drug Strategy Network [17310]
Natl. Hea. Freedom Coalition [14816]
Natl. Juneteenth Observance Found. [17160]
Natl. Latina/Latino Law Student Assn. [18057]
Natl. Minorities with Disabilities Coalition [17545]
Natl. Org. for the Reform of Marijuana Laws [17311]
Natl. Urban League [17312]
New Age Citizen [17313]
Nonprofit VOTE [18162]
November Coalition [18681]
Nurses for the Rights of the Child [11523]
Omega First Amendment Legal Fund [17314]
Online Privacy Alliance [17315]
Partnership for Civil Justice Legal Defense and Educ. Fund [17316]
Peace Alliance [18272]
People for the Amer. Way [17317]
People's Rights Fund [17318]
Peoples Rights Org. [17319]
Picture the Homeless [17792]
Prejudice Institute/Center for the Applied Stud. of Ethnoviolence [17320]
Private Citizen, Inc. [17321]
Progressive Democrats of Am. [17542]
Prometheus Radio Proj. [18101]
Puerto Rican Legal Defense and Educ. Fund [17322]
Racial Justice 911 [17323]
Resisting Defamation [17324]
Rigoberta Menchu Tum Found. [17325]
Rigoberta Menchu Tum Found. [17325]
Second Amendment Found. [17326]
South Asian Amer. Voting Youth [18392]
South Asian Americans Leading Together [18644]
Southern Poverty Law Center [17327]
Southern Poverty Law Center [17327]
Southern Regional Coun. [17328]
SouthernChristian Leadership Conf. [17329]
Special Comm. on the Situation with Regard to the Implementation of the Declaration on the Granting of Independence to Colonial Countries and Peoples [17330]
Special Comm. on the Situation with Regard to the Implementation of the Declaration on the Granting of Independence to Colonial Countries and Peoples [17330]
Students for the Second Amendment [17693]
Total Family Care Coalition [12023]
Turkish Amer. Alliance for Fairness [19260]
Universal Human Rights Network [17865]
US Human Rights Network [17866]
Voices for Global Change [17254]
Women's Intl. Coalition for Economic Justice [17596]
Women's Voices. Women Vote [18802]
A World of Difference Inst. [11525]
A World of Difference Inst. [11525]
Young Americans for Liberty [18836]
Youth for Human Rights Intl. [12255]
Youth Pride Alliance [12117]
Civil Rights Mobilization [★17297]
Civil Rights Trail [★17249]
Civil Service
Assn. of Former Intl. Civil Servants - New York [5309]

Natl. Assn. of State Retirement Administrators [5310]
Natl. Conf. on Public Employee Retirement Systems [5311]
Natl. Org. of Blacks in Govt. [5312]
Partnership for Public Ser. [17331]
Public Employees Roundtable [5313]
Scientists and Engineers for Am. [5314]
Civil Ser. Employees Assn. [23200], 143 Washington Ave., Albany, NY 12210, (518)257-1000
Civil Soc. Forum of Tonga [IO], Nuku'alofa, Tonga
Civil Soc. and Human Rights Network [IO], Kabul, Afghanistan
Civil Soc. Intl. [17565], 38 Miller Ave., No. 155, Mill Valley, CA 94941, (206)523-4755
Civil Soc. Intl. [17565], 38 Miller Ave., No. 155, Mill Valley, CA 94941, (206)523-4755
Civil Soc. of Multimedia Authors [IO], Paris, France
Civil War
Auxiliary to Sons of Union Veterans of the Civil War [20381]
Children of the Confederacy [20382]
Civil War Dealers and Collectors Assn. [21280]
Civil War Token Soc. [21970]
Confederate Memorial Literary Soc. [9761]
Daughters of Union Veterans of the Civil War, 1861-1865 [20383]
Hood's Texas Brigade Assn. [20384]
Ladies of the Grand Army of the Republic [20385]
Military Order of the Loyal Legion of the U.S. [20386]
Military Order of the Stars and Bars [20387]
Natl. Assn. for Civil War Brass Music [10251]
North-South Skirmish Assn. [22885]
Sons of Confederate Veterans [20388]
Sons of Union Veterans of the Civil War [20389]
Ulysses S. Grant Assn. [10695]
uNight [11423]
United Daughters of the Confederacy [20390]
Civil War Assn; Amer. [9746]
Civil War Dealers and Collectors Assn. [21280], PO Drawer 631, Orange, VA 22960
Civil War Historians; Soc. of [9800]
Civil War Preservation Trust [★9675]
Civil War Round Table Associates - Address unknown since 2010.
Civil War Token Soc. [21970], 26548 Mazur Dr., Rancho Palos Verdes, CA 90275
Civil War Trust [9675], 1156 15th St. NW, Ste. 900, Washington, DC 20005, (202)367-1861
Civilian-Based Defense Assn. - Defunct.
Civilian Conservation Corps Legacy [19009], PO Box 341, Edinburg, VA 22824, (540)984-8735
Civilokonomerne [★IO]
Civitan Intl. [13055], PO Box 130744, Birmingham, AL 35213-0744, (205)591-8910
Civitan Intl. [13055], PO Box 130744, Birmingham, AL 35213-0744, (205)591-8910
Civitas - Address unknown since 2011.
CIVITAS: Citizens for Planetary Hea. [★10943]
Civitas Found. for the Civil Soc. [IO], Cluj-Napoca, Romania
CJM Orquideas [IO], Lima, Peru
Cladan Cultural Exchange Inst. of Australia [IO], Double Bay, Australia
An Claidheamh Soluis [★9887]
Claims Support Professional Assn. [1947], 6451 N Fed. Hwy., Ste. 121, Fort Lauderdale, FL 33308, (800)523-3680
CLAL - The Natl. Jewish Center for Learning and Leadership [19856], 440 Park Ave. S, 4th Fl., New York, NY 10016-8012, (212)779-3300
Clan Anderson Soc. [20441], 19411 Center St., Cornelius, NC 28031, (704)892-5608
Clan Archibald Family Assn. - Defunct.
Clan Arthur Assn. USA [20442], Nancy McArthur Cochener, Exec. Sec., 10821 E Glengate Cir., Wichita, KS 67206-8902
Clan Bell Intl. [20443], 12147 Holly Knoll Cir., Great Falls, VA 22066, (703)430-6745
Clan Boyd [★20535]
Clan Boyd [★20535]
Clan Brown Soc. [20444], 38 High Rock St., Lynn, MA 01902-3815
Clan Campbell Soc. [★20445]

Clan Campbell Soc., North Am. [20445], 3704 Kantrel Pl., Valrico, FL 33596-6920
Clan Carmichael U.S.A. [20446], 3298 S Beddow St., Terre Haute, IN 47802
Clan Chisholm in Am. [★20447]
Clan Chisholm Soc. [IO], Sidney, BC, Canada
Clan Chisholm Soc., Australia [IO], Hornsby Heights, Australia
Clan Chisholm Soc., Canada Br. [IO], Calgary, AB, Canada
Clan Chisholm Soc., New Zealand [IO], Palmerston North, New Zealand
Clan Chisholm Soc., United Kingdom [IO], Inverness, United Kingdom
Clan Chisholm Soc., U.S. Br. [20447], 1352 Dewfrost Pl., Castle Rock, CO 80104-7742
Clan Colquhoun Soc. of North Am. - Address unknown since 2011.
Clan Craig Assn. of Am. [20448], 1245 NE 91st St., Seattle, WA 98115
Clan Cunning Assn. - Defunct.
Clan Cunningham Soc. of Am. [20449], 421 Sunnyview St., Carlsbad, NM 88220
Clan Currie Soc. [20450], PO Box 541, Summit, NJ 07902-0541, (908)273-3509
Clan Currie Soc. [20450], PO Box 541, Summit, NJ 07902-0541, (908)273-3509
Clan Davidson Soc. [20451], Elaine Davidson, Treas., 235 Fairmont Dr., North Wilkesboro, NC 28659
Clan Donald Canada [IO], Trenton, NS, Canada
Clan Douglas Soc. of North Am. [20452], Jim Morton, Sec., 4115 Bent Oak Ct., Douglasville, GA 30135, (770)949-4797
Clan Drummond Soc. of North Am. [20453], 6 Bernard Ln., Methuen, MA 01844, (978)682-0130
Clan Ewing in Am. [★19224]
Clan Farquharson Assn. of Canada [IO], Dartmouth, NS, Canada
Clan Fergusson Soc. of North Am. [20454], B. J. Ferguson, Sec., 192 Hawthorne Hill Rd., Jasper, GA 30143
Clan Fergusson Soc. of North Am. [20454], B. J. Ferguson, Sec., 192 Hawthorne Hill Rd., Jasper, GA 30143
Clan Forrester Soc. [20455], Ben Forrester, Membership Chm., 1034 Blue Heron Dr., Commerce, GA 30529, (706)335-7688
Clan Forsyth Soc. of Canada [IO], Toronto, ON, Canada
Clan Forsyth Soc. U.S.A. [20456], 4336 S 3150 W, West Valley City, UT 84119-5856
Clan Fraser Soc. of Canada [IO], Toronto, ON, Canada
Clan Graham Soc. [20457], 2919 Denson Ave., Knoxville, TN 37921, (865)368-2543
Clan Guthrie USA [20458], Carrie Guthrie-Whitlow, Treas., PO Box 121, Port Orchard, WA 98366
Clan Hamilton Soc. - Address unknown since 2010.
Clan Hunter Assn. [IO], West Kilbride, United Kingdom
Clan Irwin Assn. [20459], 226 1750th Ave., Mount Pulaski, IL 62548-6635, (217)792-5226
Clan Johnston in Am. [20460], 215 SE Maynard Rd., Cary, NC 27511, (919)380-7707
Clan Johnston in Am. [20460], 215 SE Maynard Rd., Cary, NC 27511, (919)380-7707
Clan Keith Soc. [20461], Alice M. Hall Hattenbrun, Sec., 119 South Rd., Kensington, NH 03833-6820
Clan Leslie Soc. [★20462]
Clan Leslie Soc. Intl. [20462], Linda Flowers, 302 SW 3rd St., Tuttle, OK 73089-8927, (405)381-3577
Clan MacAlpine Soc. [20463], 32682 Rosemont Dr., Trabuco Canyon, CA 92679-3386
Clan MacCarthy Soc. [20464], PO Box 69, Plains, MT 59859
Clan MacDuff Soc. of Am. [20465], 526 E Charleston Ave., Phoenix, AZ 85022, (602)866-2570
Clan MacGillivray Soc. - Australia [IO], Seaford, Australia
Clan MacInnes Soc. [★20539]
Clan MacIntyre Assn. [20466], Carole M. McIntyre, Membership Coor., 617 E 400 N, Centerville, UT 84014-1956, (801)298-8334

Reference to "IO" in place of a book number signifies that the association may be found in the 50th edition of International Organizations.

Clan MacIntyre Soc. **[20467]**, Alan Wright, Treas., 11936 NE 153rd Pl., Bothell, WA 98011

Clan Mackay Assn. of Canada **[IO]**, Etobicoke, ON, Canada

Clan MacKay Soc. **[20468]**, Doug McCoy, Treas., 1898 Prince Dr., Lawrenceville, GA 30043, (423)543-3775

Clan MacKenzie Soc. in the Americas **[20469]**, PO Box 300603, Waterford, MI 48330, (248)666-3708

Clan Mackenzie Soc. in the Americas - Canada **[IO]**, Oakville, ON, Canada

Clan MacKinnon Soc. **[20470]**, PO Box 832, Wilton, CA 95693, (916)687-7973

Clan Mackintosh of North Am. **[20471]**, 43 Brucewood St., West Roxbury, MA 02132

Clan MacLennan, Central Ontario Br. **[IO]**, Burlington, ON, Canada

Clan Macneil Assn. of Am. **[20472]**, Ms. Rhonwyn Darby McNeill, Membership VP, PO Box 230693, Montgomery, AL 36123-0693, (334)834-0612

Clan MacNeil in Canada **[IO]**, Bedford, NS, Canada

Clan Macpherson Assn. **[20473]**, 46345 River View Dr., Oakhurst, CA 93644, (559)658-6189

Clan Macpherson Assn. **[20473]**, 46345 River View Dr., Oakhurst, CA 93644, (559)658-6189

Clan MacRae Soc. of North Am. **[20474]**, 306 Surrey Rd., Savannah, GA 31410-4407

Clan MacThomas Soc. **[★20555]**

Clan Maitland Soc. of North am. **[20475]**, Rosemary Maitland Thom, Sec., 7016 Carrondale Way, Las Vegas, NV 89128-3339

Clan Matheson Soc. **[20476]**, PO Box 307, The Plains, VA 20198, (540)687-6836

Clan Maxwell Soc. of the USA **[20477]**, Nancy Dirkes, Sec., 803 Armstrong Dr., Georgetown, TX 78628

Clan McAlister of Am. **[20478]**, Robert W. McAlister, Membership Chm., 208 Annapolis Ln., Rotonda West, FL 33947, (941)698-1112

Clan Menzies Soc., North Amer. Br. **[20479]**, 323 Rough Water Point, Canton, NC 28716-8196, (828)648-4255

Clan Moffat Soc. **[20480]**, Roger Moffat, 3020 76th St. SE, Caledonia, MI 49316-8398

Clan Moncreiffe Soc. **[20481]**, Charlotte Moncrief, Treas., 1405 Plaza St. SE, Decatur, AL 35603

Clan Moncreiffe Soc. of North Am. **[★20481]**

Clan Moncreiffe Soc. of North Am. **[20481]**, Charlotte Moncrief, Treas., 1405 Plaza St. SE, Decatur, AL 35603

Clan Montgomery Intl. **[★20482]**

Clan Montgomery Intl. **[★20482]**

Clan Montgomery Soc. Intl. **[20482]**, 2803 Kinnett Rd., Bethel, OH 45106

Clan Montgomery Soc. Intl. **[20482]**, 2803 Kinnett Rd., Bethel, OH 45106

Clan Munro Assn. **[20483]**, Doris Munro Small, Membership Sec., 176 Neptune Rd., Orange Park, FL 32073-3231, (904)272-2931

Clan Munro Assn. of Canada **[IO]**, Scarborough, ON, Canada

Clan Phail Soc. in North America **[20484]**, Bill McPhail, 403 1/2 Garfield St. S, Box 16, Tacoma, WA 98444

Clan Pollock **[20485]**, PO Box 404, Greenville, KY 42345, (615)456-1699

Clan Ramsey Assn. of North Am. **[20486]**, David F. Ramsey, Membership Chm./Treas., 434 Skinner Blvd., Ste. 105, Dunedin, FL 34698, (727)409-4639

Clan Rose Soc. of Am. **[20487]**, Patrice A. May, Sec.-Treas., 1188 Cragmont Ave., Berkeley, CA 94708, (510)848-1188

Clan Ross Assn. of Canada **[IO]**, London, ON, Canada

Clan Ross Assn. of the U.S. **[20488]**, 5044 Via Donaldo, Yorba Linda, CA 92886, (714)779-8425

Clan Scott Soc. **[20489]**, PO Box 13021, Austin, TX 78711-3021

Clan Scott Soc. of the Americas **[★20489]**

Clan Scott, U.S.A. **[★20489]**

Clan Shaw Soc. **[20490]**, Mr. Meredith L. Shaw, Pres., 3031 Appomattox Ave., No. 102, Olney, MD 20832-1498

Clan Sinclair Assn. of Canada **[IO]**, Toronto, ON, Canada

Clan Sinclair Assn. U.S.A. **[20491]**, 224 Bransfield Rd., Greenville, SC 29615, (864)268-3550

Clan Sutherland Soc. of North Am. **[20492]**, 9613 Highstream Ct., Charlotte, NC 28269

Clan Young **[20493]**, 5414 Tim Donald Rd., Justin, TX 76247

Clan Young Soc. **[★20493]**

Clanranald Trust for Scotland **[IO]**, Kincardine, United Kingdom

Clanwilliam Inst. **[IO]**, Dublin, Ireland

Clara Haskil Assn. **[IO]**, Vevey, Switzerland

Clare Animal Welfare **[IO]**, Crusheen, Ireland

Claremont Inst. **[17248]**, 937 W Foothill Blvd., Ste. E, Claremont, CA 91711, (909)621-6825

Claretian Volunteers **[★19413]**

Claretian Volunteers and Lay Missionaries **[19413]**, 205 W Monroe St., Chicago, IL 60606, (312)236-7782

Clarinet Intl. **[★10217]**

Clarinet and Saxophone Soc. of Great Britain **[IO]**, Darlington, United Kingdom

Clarity **[5746]**, Box 13038, Lansing, MI 48901-3038, (517)371-5140

Clarsach Soc. **[IO]**, Edinburgh, United Kingdom

Classic Car Club of Am. **[21028]**, 1645 Des Plaines River Rd., Ste. 7A, Des Plaines, IL 60018-2206, (847)390-0443

Classic Chevy Club Intl. **[★21029]**

Classic Chevy Club Intl. **[★21029]**

Classic Chevy Intl. **[21029]**, 5200 S Washington Ave., Titusville, FL 32780, (800)284-4096

Classic Chevy Intl. **[21029]**, 5200 S Washington Ave., Titusville, FL 32780, (800)284-4096

Classic Jaguar Assn. **[21030]**, Reed Van Rozeboom, 11321 Loch Lomond Rd., Rossmoor, CA 90720

Classic Thunderbird Club Intl. **[21031]**, 1308 E 29th St., Signal Hill, CA 90755-1842, (562)426-2709

Classic Yacht Assn. **[22330]**, 5267 Shilshole Ave. NW, Ste. 107, Seattle, WA 98107, (206)937-6211

Classical Assn. of Ireland **[IO]**, Dublin, Ireland

Classical Assn. of South Africa **[IO]**, Pretoria, Republic of South Africa

Classical Music Broadcasters Assn. - Defunct.

Classical Music Lovers' Exchange **[10177]**, PO Box 275, Santa Barbara, CA 93102-0275

Classical Studies

Ancient Coins for Educ. **[8685]**

Australasian Soc. for Classical Stud. **[17177]**

Classical Assn. of Ireland **[15319]**

Eta Sigma Phi, Natl. Classics Honorary Soc. **[23493]**

Natl. Comm. for Latin and Greek **[9487]**

Natl. Junior Classical League **[7865]**

Natl. Senior Classical League **[7866]**

Women's Classical Caucus **[9488]**

Classification and Compensation Soc. - Defunct.

Classification Soc. **[7231]**, Univ. of Illinois - Chicago, IDS Dept., (MC 294), 601 S Morgan St., Chicago, IL 60607-7100, (312)996-2676

Classroom Publishers Assn. and Assn. of Educational Publishers **[★8744]**

Clay Minerals Soc. **[7121]**, 3635 Concorde Pkwy., Ste. 500, Chantilly, VA 20151-1125, (703)652-9960

Clay Pigeon Shooting Assn. **[IO]**, Woking, United Kingdom

Clay Pipe Development Assn. **[IO]**, Chesham, United Kingdom

Clay Roof Tile Coun. **[IO]**, Stoke-on-Trent, United Kingdom

Clay Target Shooting Assn. South Africa **[IO]**, Great Brak River, Republic of South Africa

Clayton Fund - Address unknown since 2011.

Clean Air Soc. of Australia and New Zealand **[IO]**, Surrey Hills, Australia

Clean Air Task Force **[4783]**, 18 Tremont St., Ste. 530, Boston, MA 02108, (617)624-0234

Clean Air Watch **[4784]**, 1250 Connecticut Ave. NW, Ste. 200, Washington, DC 20036, (202)558-3527

Clean Beaches Coun. **[4242]**, 700 13th St. NW, Ste. 600, Washington, DC 20005, (202)380-9300

Clean Economy Network **[6605]**, 1101 14th St. NW, Ste. 1200, Washington, DC 20005-5637, (202)380-1950

Clean Energy Coun. **[IO]**, Southbank, Australia

Clean Energy Gp. **[6705]**, 50 State St., Ste. 1, Montpelier, VT 05602, (802)223-2554

Clean Energy States Alliance **[6706]**, 50 State St., Ste. 1, Montpelier, VT 05602, (802)223-2554

Clean Fuels Development Coalition **[4785]**, 4641 Montgomery Ave., Ste. 350, Bethesda, MD 20814, (301)718-0077

Clean Islands Intl. **[4243]**, 8219 Elvaton Dr., Pasadena, MD 21122-3903, (410)647-2500

Clean Islands Intl. **[4243]**, 8219 Elvaton Dr., Pasadena, MD 21122-3903, (410)647-2500

Clean Production Action **[4334]**, PO Box 153, Spring Brook, NY 14140, (716)805-1056

Clean Production Action **[4334]**, PO Box 153, Spring Brook, NY 14140, (716)805-1056

Clean and Safe Energy Coalition **[6707]**, 607 14th St. NW, Ste. 300, Washington, DC 20005, (202)338-2273

Clean Sites, Inc. - Defunct.

Clean Tech. and Sustainable Indus. Org. **[3856]**, 3925 W Braker Ln., Austin, TX 78759, (512)692-7267

Clean Tech. Trade Alliance **[6110]**, 2817 Wheaton Way, Ste. 202, Bremerton, WA 98310, (360)692-7286

Clean Up Australia **[IO]**, Royal Exchange, Australia

Clean Up the World **[IO]**, Sydney, Australia

Clean Water Action **[4987]**, 1010 Vermont Ave. NW, Ste. 1100, Washington, DC 20005-4918, (202)895-0420

Clean Water Action Proj. **[★4987]**

Clean Water Am. Alliance **[4988]**, 1816 Jefferson Pl. NW, Washington, DC 20036-2505, (202)223-2299

Clean Water Constr. Coalition **[4989]**, PO Box 728, Allenwood, NJ 08720, (732)292-4300

Clean Water Fund **[4990]**, 1010 Vermont Ave. NW, Ste. 1100, Washington, DC 20005, (202)895-0432

Clean Water for Haiti **[4991]**, 4606 NW Grant Pl., Vancouver, WA 98663

Clean Water for Haiti **[4991]**, 4606 NW Grant Pl., Vancouver, WA 98663

Clean Water for the World **[13416]**, 3504 Madison St., Kalamazoo, MI 49008, (269)342-1354

Clean the World **[4869]**, 400A Pittman St., Orlando, FL 32801, (407)574-8353

Cleaning Equip. Trade Assn. **[2244]**, PO Box 1710, Indian Trail, NC 28079, (704)635-7362

Cleaning Equip. Trade Assn. **[2244]**, PO Box 1710, Indian Trail, NC 28079, (704)635-7362

Cleaning and Hygiene Suppliers' Assn. **[IO]**, Marlow, United Kingdom

Cleaning Industry

Cleaning Mgt. Inst. **[2245]**

Cleaning Mgt. Inst. **[2245]**, 19 British Amer. Blvd. W, Latham, NY 12110, (518)540-9163

Cleaning and Support Services Assn. **[IO]**, London, United Kingdom

Clear Path Intl. **[17548]**, 321 High School Rd. NE, No. 574, Bainbridge Island, WA 98110, (206)780-5964

Clear Path Intl. **[17548]**, 321 High School Rd. NE, No. 574, Bainbridge Island, WA 98110, (206)780-5964

Clearer Vision Ministries **[13378]**, PO Box 297, St. Augustine, FL 32085-0297

Clearer Vision Ministries **[13378]**, PO Box 297, St. Augustine, FL 32085-0297

CH on Child Abuse and Neglect Info. **[★11226]**

CH on Disability Info. **[11772]**, Off. of Special Educ. and Rehabilitative Services, Commun. and Media Support Services, U.S. U.S. Department of of Educ., 550 12th St. SW, Rm. 5133, Washington, DC 20202-2550, (202)245-7307

CH on the Handicapped **[★11772]**

CH on Women's Issues **[17633]**, 10401 Grosvenor Pl., No. 917, Rockville, MD 20852, (301)493-0002

Clearpoint Financial Solutions **[1288]**, 8000 Franklin Farms Dr., Richmond, VA 23229-5004, (877)422-9040

Cleft Lip and Palate Assn. **[IO]**, London, United Kingdom

Cleft Lip and Palate Assn. of Ireland **[IO]**, Dun Laoghaire, Ireland

Cleft Palate-Craniofacial Assn; Amer. **[14190]**

Cleft Palate Found. **[14194]**, 1504 E Franklin St., Ste. 102, Chapel Hill, NC 27514-2820, (919)933-9044

A star before a book entry number signifies that the name is not listed separately, but is mentioned within the entry.

Clemens, Samuel
Mark Twain Circle of New York **[9396]**

Clergy
Coalition of Spirit-filled Churches **[19616]**
Intl. Assn. of Christian Chaplains **[19520]**
Intl. Police and Fire Chaplain's Assn. **[19522]**
Natl. Assn. of Jewish Chaplains **[19526]**
Natl. Assn. of Veterans Affairs Chaplains **[19527]**

Clerkship Directors in Internal Medicine **[15135]**, 330 John Carlyle St., Ste. 610, Alexandria, VA 22314-5946, (703)341-4540
Clerkship Directors in Internal Medicine **[15135]**, 330 John Carlyle St., Ste. 610, Alexandria, VA 22314-5946, (703)341-4540
Cleveland Barons Booster Club **[★23901]**
Cleveland Bay Horse Soc. of Australasia **[IO]**, Minnipa, Australia
Cleveland Bay Horse Soc. of North Am. **[4575]**, PO Box 483, Goshen, NH 03752, (865)300-7133
Cleveland Hockey Booster Club **[23901]**, Marsha Hess, 13118 Tyler Ave., Cleveland, OH 44111, (216)251-0606
Cleveland Vessel Owners Assn. **[★2381]**
CLFMA of India **[IO]**, Mumbai, India
CLIC Sargent **[IO]**, Glasgow, United Kingdom
Cliff Richard Fan Club of Am. **[23826]**, 3 Kelley Rd., Acton, MA 01720-3614
Cliff Richard Movement - USA **[★23826]**
Climate Action Network Australia **[IO]**, Ultimo, Australia
Climate Action Network Europe **[IO]**, Brussels, Belgium
Climate, Community and Biodiversity Alliance **[4020]**, 2011 Crystal Dr., Ste. 500, Arlington, VA 22202, (703)341-2748
Climate Counts **[4021]**, PO Box 4844, Manchester, NH 03108, (603)216-3788
Climate Crisis Coalition **[4022]**, PO Box 125, South Lee, MA 01260, (413)243-5665
Climate Gp. **[4023]**, 444 Park Ave. S, 2nd Fl., New York, NY 10016, (646)233-0550
Climate Inst. **[4244]**, 900 17th St. NW, Ste. 700, Washington, DC 20006, (202)552-4723
Climate Registry **[4786]**, 523 W 6th St., Ste. 445, Los Angeles, CA 90014, (213)891-6922
Climate Trust **[4787]**, 65 SW Yamhill St., Ste. 400, Portland, OR 97204, (503)238-1915
ClimateTalk Alliance **[6111]**, 2400 Camino Ramon, Ste. 375, San Ramon, CA 94583, (925)275-6641
Climatological Assn; Amer. Clinical and **[14149]**
Climatologists; Amer. Assn. of State **[7103]**
Climb Nova Scotia **[IO]**, Halifax, NS, Canada

Climbing
Amer. Canyoneering Assn. **[21281]**
Amer. Mountain Guides Assn. **[21282]**
Amer. Safe Climbing Assn. **[21283]**
New England Trails Conf. **[23090]**
Professional Climbing Instructors Assn. **[22455]**
Tree Climber's Coalition **[21284]**
Tree Climbers Intl. **[21285]**
Tree Climbing USA **[21286]**
U.S. Mountain Guides Assn. **[22456]**
U.S. Ski Mountaineering Assn. **[22917]**
U.S.A. Climbing **[21287]**

Cling Peach Advisory Bd. **[★4432]**
Clinic at a Time **[15152]**, PO Box 14457, Madison, WI 53708, (608)239-3091
Clinical Cytometry Soc. **[16122]**, SPLtrak, 5250 Old Orchard Rd., Skokie, IL 60077, (847)983-3519
Clinical Dental Technicians Assn. **[IO]**, Longfield, United Kingdom
Clinical Directors Network **[14895]**, 5 W 37th St., 10th Fl., New York, NY 10018-6222, (212)382-0699
Clinical Genetics Soc. **[IO]**, Birmingham, United Kingdom
Clinical Immunology Soc. **[15103]**, 555 E Wells St., Ste. 1100, Milwaukee, WI 53202-3823, (414)224-8095
Clinical Lab. and Analytical Sciences - Address unknown since 2010.
Clinical Lab. Mgt. Assn. **[15233]**, 401 N Michigan Ave., Ste. 2200, Chicago, IL 60611, (312)321-5111
Clinical and Lab. Standards Inst. **[15234]**, 940 W Valley Rd., Ste. 1400, Wayne, PA 19087-1898, (610)688-0100

Clinical and Lab. Standards Inst. **[15234]**, 940 W Valley Rd., Ste. 1400, Wayne, PA 19087-1898, (610)688-0100
Clinical Legal Educ. Assn. **[8502]**, New York Univ. School of Law, 245 Sullivan St., 5th Fl., New York, NY 10012, (212)998-6430
Clinical Magnetic Resonance Soc. **[14155]**, 5620 W Sligh Ave., Tampa, FL 33634-4490, (813)806-1080
Clinical Neurophysiology Soc; Amer. **[14443]**
Clinical Orthopaedic Soc. **[16031]**, 2209 Dickens Rd., Richmond, VA 23230-2005, (804)565-6366
Clinical Pathology Accreditation **[IO]**, Sheffield, United Kingdom
Clinical Res. Associates **[★14277]**
Clinical Sci. Club **[★14153]**
Clinical Social Work Assn. **[13217]**, PO Box 3740, Arlington, VA 22203, (703)340-1456
Clinical Social Work Fed. **[★13217]**
Clinical Sociology Assn. **[★7422]**

Clinical Studies
Amer. Clinical and Climatological Assn. **[14149]**
Amer. Fed. for Medical Res. **[14150]**
Amer. Soc. for Clinical Investigation **[14151]**
Assn. of Clinical Res. Organizations **[14152]**
Assn. of Clinical Scientists **[14153]**
Central Soc. for Clinical Res. **[14154]**
Clinical Magnetic Resonance Soc. **[14155]**
CR Found. **[14277]**
Evidenced-Based Veterinary Medicine Assn. **[17024]**
Forbes Norris MDA/ALS Res. Center **[15590]**
Found. for Advances in Medicine and Sci. **[14156]**
Intl. Coun. on Nanotechnology **[6430]**
Intl. Soc. for Cardiovascular Translational Res. **[14024]**
Intl. Soc. for IGF Res. **[6851]**
Natl. Assn. of Bionutritionists **[15839]**
Soc. of Clinical Res. Associates **[14157]**
Soc. of Clinical Res. Associates **[14157]**
Soc. for Clinical and Translational Sci. **[14158]**
Soc. for Clinical Trials **[14159]**
Soc. for Translational Oncology **[15935]**

Clinicians for Choice - Address unknown since 2010.
Clinicians of the World **[15153]**, PO Box 116, Rochester, MN 55903, (612)353-8632
Cliometric Soc. **[17572]**, Univ. of Wisconsin - La Crosse, Dept. of Economics, 1725 State St., La Crosse, WI 54601, (608)785-6863
Clock Mfrs. and Marketing Assn. - Defunct.
Clonmel Chamber of Commerce **[IO]**, Clonmel, Ireland
Close Up Found. **[17249]**, 1220 Braddock Pl., Ste. 400, Alexandria, VA 22314, (703)706-3300
Closed Circuit TV Mfrs. Assn. - Defunct.
Closure Comm. of the Glass Packaging Inst. **[★874]**
Closure Manufacturers Assn. **[874]**, PO Box 1358, Kilmarnock, VA 22482, (804)435-9580
Cloth Diaper Found. **[11749]**, 16346 Flint Run Way, Sugar Land, TX 77498, (888)411-7151

Clothing
Clothworkers' Company **[18594]**
Natl. Button Soc. **[21378]**
YMA Fashion Scholarship Fund **[216]**

Clothing Mfrs. Assn. of India **[IO]**, Mumbai, India
Clothworkers' Company **[IO]**, London, United Kingdom
Cloud Family Assn. **[20494]**, 508 Crestwood Dr., Eastland, TX 76448
CLOUT - Christian Lesbians Out **[19562]**, 3653-F Flakes Mill Rd., No. 306, Decatur, GA 30034-5255
CLOUT - Christian Lesbians Out **[19562]**, 3653-F Flakes Mill Rd., No. 306, Decatur, GA 30034-5255
Clown Club of Am. **[★21288]**
Clown Club of Am. **[★21288]**
Clowner Utan Granser **[★IO]**

Clowns
Clowns of Am. Intl. **[21288]**
Clowns of Am. Intl. **[21288]**
Intl. Shrine Clown Assn. **[21289]**
Intl. Shrine Clown Assn. **[21289]**
World Clown Assn. **[21290]**

Clowns of Am. **[★21288]**
Clowns of Am. **[★21288]**
Clowns of Am. Intl. **[21288]**, PO Box 1171, Englewood, FL 34295-1171, (941)474-4351

Clowns of Am. Intl. **[21288]**, PO Box 1171, Englewood, FL 34295-1171, (941)474-4351
Clowns Sans Frontieres **[★IO]**
Clowns Without Borders **[IO]**, Barcelona, Spain
Clowns Without Borders - Canada **[IO]**, Montreal, QC, Canada
Clowns Without Borders - Sweden **[IO]**, Norsborg, Sweden
Clowns Without Borders - U.S.A. **[11562]**, PO Box 460523, San Francisco, CA 94146, (603)724-4840
Clowns Without Borders - U.S.A. **[11562]**, PO Box 460523, San Francisco, CA 94146, (603)724-4840
Club Alpin Francais **[★IO]**
Club Artritas **[IO]**, Kaunas, Lithuania
Club du Basset Hound **[IO]**, St.-Maur-des-Fosses, France
Club du Braque Francais **[IO]**, Bouisse, France
Club of Budapest **[IO]**, Budapest, Hungary
Club of Cambodian Journalists **[IO]**, Phnom Penh, Cambodia
Club Canin Canadien **[★IO]**
Club of Catholic Intelligentsia **[IO]**, Warsaw, Poland
Club des Chiens Tibetains de France **[IO]**, Fort Bloque, France
Club Delahaye **[IO]**, Paris, France
Club Du Vieux Manoir **[IO]**, Pontpoint, France
Club des Epagneuls Nains Anglais **[IO]**, Landeronde, France
Club Francais du Braqwue Hongrois **[★IO]**
Club Francais du Bullmastiff et du Mastiff **[★IO]**
Club Francais de l'Airedale Terrier et de Divers Terriers **[★IO]**
Club Garcons and Filles du Canada **[★IO]**
Club de Inventores Espanoles **[★IO]**
Club de l'Epagneul Breton of the U.S. **[21541]**, PO Box 251, Brookston, IN 47923, (765)496-3786
Club Managers Assn. of Am. **[776]**, 1733 King St., Alexandria, VA 22314, (703)739-9500
Club Managers Assn. Australia **[IO]**, Sydney, Australia
Club Managers' Assn. of Hong Kong, Macau and China **[IO]**, Hong Kong, People's Republic of China
Club of Neuropathologists **[★16110]**
Club di Roma **[★IO]**
Club of Rome **[IO]**, Winterthur, Switzerland

Clubs
Am. Outdoors Assn. **[22835]**
Amer. Barefoot Waterski Club **[23114]**
Amer. Junior Rodeo Assn. **[22839]**
Aston Martin Owners Club **[21000]**
Austin-Healey Club USA **[21004]**
Boy Scouts of Am. **[13018]**
Canadian Soc. of Club Managers **[13659]**
Cinderella Softball Leagues **[22951]**
Club Managers Assn. of Am. **[776]**
Fed. of Intl. Lacrosse **[22713]**
Fed. of Metal Detector and Archaeological Clubs **[21851]**
Hampton One-Design Class Racing Assn. **[22340]**
Harness Horse Youth Found. **[22652]**
Hungarian Scouts Assn. **[13020]**
Intl. Assn. of Gay and Lesbian Martial Artists **[22734]**
Maccabi USA/Sports for Israel **[22985]**
Natl. Assn. of Underwater Instructors **[23104]**
Natl. Club Assn. **[777]**
Natl. History Club **[8261]**
Natl. Junior Baseball League **[22285]**
Natl. Scholastic Surfing Assn. **[23035]**
Natl. Softball Assn. **[22954]**
Natl. Starwind/Spindrift Class Assn. **[22377]**
New England Trails Conf. **[23090]**
Norwegian Forest Cat Breed Coun. **[21255]**
Professional Baseball Athletic Trainers Soc. **[22289]**
Sportscar Vintage Racing Assn. **[22249]**
U.S. Bobsled and Skeleton Fed. **[22926]**
U.S. Competitive Aerobics Fed. **[22209]**
U.S. Dental Tennis Assn. **[23062]**
U.S. Disc Sports **[22536]**
USA Diving **[22544]**
U.S.A. Karate Fed. **[22766]**
USA Volleyball **[23111]**
USGA Green Sect. **[22628]**

Reference to "IO" in place of a book number signifies that the association may be found in the 50th edition of International Organizations.

Women Outdoors [22797]
Women's All-Star Assn. [22432]
World Fast-Draw Assn. [22891]
World Masters Cross-Country Ski Assn. [22921]
Clubs for Young People [IO], London, United Kingdom
Clubul Roman de Presa [★IO]
Cluid Housing Assn. - North East [IO], Dublin, Ireland
Clumber Spaniel Club of Am. [21542], Vonda R. Poole, Membership Sec., 874 Orchard Terrace Dr., New Wilmington, PA 16142-4222
Clutch Facing and Brake Lining Standards Inst. [★328]
Clutterers Anonymous [13037], PO Box 91413, Los Angeles, CA 90009-1413, (310)281-6064
Clwyd Welsh Pony and Cob Assn. [IO], Ruthin, United Kingdom
Clydesdale Breeders Assn. of the U.S. [★4576]
Clydesdale Breeders of the U.S.A. [4576], 17346 Kelley Rd., Pecatonica, IL 61063, (815)247-8780
CN Lines Special Interest Gp. [IO], Regina, SK, Canada
CNR Books [★18181]
CNR Books [★18181]
Co-Anon Family Groups [13242], PO Box 12722, Tucson, AZ 85732-2722, (520)513-5028
Co-Dependents Anonymous [13038], PO Box 33577, Phoenix, AZ 85067-3577, (602)277-7991
Co-Dependents of Sex Addicts [★13082]
Co-Dependents of Sex Addicts [★13082]
Co-op Am. [★957]
Co-operation for the Development of Emerging Countries [IO], Florence, Italy
Co-operative Union of Tanzania [★5097]
Co-operative Women's Guild [IO], Colchester, United Kingdom
Co-Operettes [★13063]
Co-Operettes [★13063]
COACH: Canada's Hea. Informatics Assn. [IO], Toronto, ON, Canada
Coach Operators Fed. [IO], Bristol, United Kingdom
Coaches Assn; Amer. Swimming [23037]

Coaching
Amer. Assn. of Snowboard Instructors [22923]
Black Coaches and Administrators [22457]
Citizenship Through Sports Alliance [22972]
Creativity Coaching Assn. [22458]
Golf Coaches Assn. of Am. [22608]
Intl. Coach Fed. [22459]
Intl. Coach Fed. [22459]
Intl. Mental Game Coaching Assn. [22460]
Natl. Alliance for Youth Sports [22461]
Natl. Assn. of Collegiate Gymnastics Coaches/ Women [22633]
Natl. High School Athletic Coaches Assn. [22462]
Natl. High School Golf Coaches Assn. [22463]
Natl. Surf Schools and Instructors Assn. [23036]
Natl. Throws Coaches Assn. [22464]
Natural Fitness Trainers Assn. [22809]
NFHS Coaches Assn. [22465]
NFHS Spirit Assn. [22466]
Positive Coaching Alliance [22467]
Professional Climbing Instructors Assn. [22455]
Professional Coaches, Mentors and Advisors [22468]
Professional Golf Teachers Assn. of Am. [22621]
TeamPact [18631]
U.S. Elite Coaches' Assn. for Women's Gymnastics [22469]
U.S. Twirling Assn. [22306]
USA Athletes Intl. [22233]
USA Gymnastics [22636]
Coaching Assn. of Canada [IO], Ottawa, ON, Canada
Coachmakers' and Coach Harness Makers' Company [IO], Chalfont St. Giles, United Kingdom
Coady Intl. Inst. [IO], Antigonish, NS, Canada

Coal
Amer. Coal Coun. [778]
Amer. Coal Found. [779]
Amer. Coke and Coal Chemicals Inst. [780]
Citizens Coal Coun. [3945]
Coal Exporters Assn. of the U.S. [781]
Coal Tech. Assn. [782]

Coal Trading Assn. [783]
FutureGen Alliance [6112]
Natl. Coal Trans. Assn. [784]
Natl. Mining Assn. [785]CoalSouth African Coal Processing Soc.
Coal Assn. of Canada [IO], Calgary, AB, Canada
Coal Exporters Assn. of the U.S. [781], Natl. Mining Assn., 101 Constitution Ave. NW, Ste. 500 E, Washington, DC 20001, (202)463-2600
Coal Exporters of the U.S. [★781]
Coal Merchants' Fed. - England [IO], Alfreton, United Kingdom
Coal Tech. Assn. [782], 12548 Granite Ridge Dr., North Potomac, MD 20878, (301)330-2256
Coal Trading Assn. [783], 2001 Jefferson Davis Hwy., Ste. 1004, Arlington, VA 22202-3617, (703)418-0392
Coalition of 9/11 Families - Address unknown since 2010.
Coalition to Abolish Slavery and Trafficking [12233], 5042 Wilshire Blvd., No. 586, Los Angeles, CA 90036, (213)365-1906
Coalition on Abortion/Breast Cancer [13569], PO Box 957133, Hoffman Estates, IL 60195, (847)421-4000
Coalition to Address Sexual Exploitation of Children in Cambodia [IO], Phnom Penh, Cambodia
Coalition for the Advancement of Jewish Educ. - Address unknown since 2010.
Coalition for the Advancement of Medical Res. [15339], 750 17th St. NW, Ste. 1100, Washington, DC 20006, (202)725-0339
Coalition for Affordable Hea. Coverage [14854], 750 9th St. NW, Ste. 750, Washington, DC 20001, (202)559-0192
Coalition Against Bigger Trucks [13333], 1001 N Fairfax St., Ste. 515, Alexandria, VA 22314, (703)535-3131
Coalition Against Childhood Lead Poisoning and Parents Against Lead [★4245]
Coalition Against Counterfeiting and Piracy [5564], U.S. Chamber of Commerce, Global Intellectual Property Center, 1615 H St. NW, Washington, DC 20062, (202)463-5601
Coalition Against Domain Name Abuse [7006], 1632 Wisconsin Ave. NW, Washington, DC 20007, (202)223-9355
Coalition Against Genocide [17738], 8480 Baltimore Natl. Pike, No. 286, Ellicott City, MD 21043, (443)927-9039
Coalition Against Insurance Fraud [1948], 1012 14th St. NW, Ste. 200, Washington, DC 20005, (202)393-7330
Coalition Against Landmines [11841], 1516 Crittenden St. NW, Washington, DC 20011, (202)465-5213
Coalition Against Pipeline Pollution - Defunct.
Coalition Against Trafficking in Women [17819], Norma Ramos, Esq., Co-Exec. Dir., PO Box 7427, New York, NY 10116
Coalition Against Trafficking in Women [17819], Norma Ramos, Esq., Co-Exec. Dir., PO Box 7427, New York, NY 10116
Coalition Against Unsolicited Commercial Email [6676], PO Box 727, Trumansburg, NY 14886, (303)800-6345
Coalition for Amer. Leadership Abroad
Coalition for Amer. Leadership Abroad - Address unknown since 2011.
Coalition of Amer. Pro-Life Univ. Students [★12945]
Coalition for Amer. Trauma Care [16926], Marcia Mabee, PhD, Exec. Dir., 11479 Waterview Cluster, Ste. 200, Reston, VA 20190, (703)709-3001
Coalition for America's Children - Defunct.
Coalition for Anabolic Steroid Precursor and Ephedra Regulation [16718], 2099 Pennsylvania Ave. NW, Ste. 850, Washington, DC 20006, (202)419-2521
Coalition for Animal Rescue and Educ. [10942], PO Box 2203, Hillsboro, MO 63050, (636)208-6267
Coalition of Asian Amer. Bus. Organizations [712], 255 Rex Blvd., Auburn Hills, MI 48326, (248)760-5125
Coalition of Asian Pacifics in Entertainment [1190], 10 Universal City Plz., 20th Fl., Universal City, CA 91608, (818)508-1421

Coalition for Auto Glass Safety and Public Awareness - Address unknown since 2011.
Coalition for Auto-Insurance Reform - Address unknown since 2011.
Coalition of Black Trade Unionists [23306], PO Box 66268, Washington, DC 20036-6268, (202)429-1203
Coalition on Block Grants and Human Needs [★13179]
Coalition Canadienne de la Sante [★IO]
Coalition of Cancer Cooperative Groups [13908], 1818 Market St., Ste. 1100, Philadelphia, PA 19103, (215)789-3600
Coalition for Christian Colleges and Universities [★7854]
Coalition for Common Sense in Govt. Procurement [★1586]
Coalition for Community Schools [8826], Inst. for Educational Leadership, 4455 Connecticut Ave. NW, Ste. 310, Washington, DC 20008, (202)822-8405
Coalition for Consumer Health and Safety - Defunct.
Coalition for a Democratic Majority - Defunct.
Coalition of Digestive Disease Organizations [★14561]
Coalition for Drug-Free Horse Racing - Defunct.
Coalition for Economic Survival [13178], 514 Shatto Pl., Ste. 270, Los Angeles, CA 90020, (213)252-4411
Coalition for Educ. in the Life Sciences [8835], Univ. of Wisconsin - Madison, Center for Biology Educ., 425 Henry Mall, 1271 Genetics/Biotechnology Bldg., Madison, WI 53706, (608)262-5266
Coalition for Emotional Literacy [13039], 10801 Old Manchaca Rd., Ste. 1908, Austin, TX 78748, (512)351-5538
Coalition to End Childhood Lead Poisoning [4245], 2714 Hudson St., Baltimore, MD 21224, (410)534-6447
Coalition on the Env. and Jewish Life [19857], 116 E 27th St., 10th Fl., New York, NY 10016, (212)532-7436
Coalition for Environmentally Responsible Economies [4246], 99 Chauncy St., 6th Fl., Boston, MA 02111, (617)247-0700
Coalition for Environmentally Safe Communities [11974], 6642 Fisher Ave., Falls Church, VA 22046, (703)534-8334
Coalition for the Equitable Treatment of Publicly Traded Limited Partnerships [★2144]
Coalition of Essential Schools [7952], Great Schools Partnership, 482 Cong. St., Ste. 500, Portland, ME 04101, (510)433-1451
Coalition for Fair Lumber Imports [1501], 1750 K St. NW, Ste. 1200, Washington, DC 20006, (202)582-0021
Coalition for Fire-Safe Cigarettes [12045], Natl. Fire Protection Assn., 1 Batterymarch Park, Quincy, MA 02169, (617)984-7275
Coalition for Genetic Fairness [17281], 4301 Connecticut Ave. NW, No. 404, Washington, DC 20008-2369, (202)966-5557
Coalition on Govt. Information - Defunct.
Coalition for Govt. Procurement [1586], 1990 M St. NW, Ste. 450, Washington, DC 20036, (202)331-0975
Coalition of Handwriting Analysts Intl. [6937], Uliana Sisombath, Sec.-Treas., 4708 Homestead Trail NW, Albuquerque, NM 87120
Coalition for Healthcare Commun. [14764], 405 Lexington Ave., New York, NY 10174-1801, (212)850-0708
Coalition for Healthcare eStandards [14765], 2025 M St. NW, Ste. 800, Washington, DC 20036, (202)367-1162
Coalition for a Healthy and Active Am. [15852], PO Box 387, Tampa, FL 33601, (866)881-7666
Coalition for Healthy India [15154], 1615 H St. NW, Washington, DC 20062, (202)463-5727
Coalition for Hemophilia B [14965], 825 Third Ave., Ste. 226, New York, NY 10022, (212)520-8272
Coalition for Heritable Disorders of Connective Tissue [14592], 4301 Connecticut Ave. NW, Ste. 404, Washington, DC 20008, (202)362-9599
Coalition of Higher Educ. Assistance Organizations [8097], 1101 Vermont Ave. NW, Ste. 400, Washington, DC 20005-3586, (202)289-3910

A star before a book entry number signifies that the name is not listed separately, but is mentioned within the entry.

Coalition of Higher Educ. Associations for Substance Abuse Prevention [13243], Fort Hays State Univ., 600 Park St., Hays, KS 67601-4099, (785)628-4231

Coalition on Human Needs [13179], 1120 Connecticut Ave. NW, Ste. 312, Washington, DC 20036, (202)223-2532

Coalition of Immokalee Workers [13499], PO Box 603, Immokalee, FL 34143, (239)657-8311

Coalition for Improving Maternity Services [15876], PO Box 33590, Raleigh, NC 27607, (866)424-3635

Coalition to Insure Against Terrorism [1949], 1875 Eye St. NW, Ste. 600, Washington, DC 20006, (202)739-9454

Coalition for Intellectual Property Rights [5565], Tom Thomson, Exec. Dir., 1150 18th St. NW, Ste. 325, Washington, DC 20036, (202)466-6210

Coalition Interagence Sida Et Developpement [★IO]

Coalition for Intl. Cooperation and Peace - Defunct.

Coalition for an Intl. Criminal Court [17489], World Federalist Movement, 708 3rd Ave., 24th Fl., New York, NY 10017, (212)687-2863

Coalition for an Intl. Criminal Court [17489], World Federalist Movement, 708 3rd Ave., 24th Fl., New York, NY 10017, (212)687-2863

Coalition for Intl. Justice - Defunct.

Coalition of Jamaican Organizations [9905], Mr. Kenneth Guscott, Consul, 351 Massachusetts Ave., Boston, MA 02115, (617)266-8604

Coalition for Jobs, Peace, and Freedom in the Americas [★18476]

Coalition of Journalists for Open Govt. - Defunct.

Coalition for Justice in the Maquiladoras

Coalition for Justice in the Maquiladoras - Address unknown since 2011.

Coalition for Juvenile Justice [6077], 1710 Rhode Island Ave. NW, 10th Fl., Washington, DC 20036, (202)467-0864

Coalition to Keep Alaska Oil - Defunct.

Coalition of Labor Union Women [23307], 815 16th St. NW, 2nd Fl. S, Washington, DC 20006, (202)508-6969

Coalition of Labor Union Women I Center for Educ. and Res. [23308], 815 16th St. NW, 2nd Fl. S, Washington, DC 20006, (202)508-6969

Coalition of Landlords, Homeowners and Merchants [18404], 656C N Wellwood Ave., Lindenhurst, NY 11757, (631)376-2110

Coalition for Literacy [★8535]

Coalition of Natl. Hea. Educ. Organizations [8601], Mark A. Temple, PhD, Coor., Illinois Sta. Univ., ISU Campus Mail 5220, Normal, IL 61790-5220, (309)438-2324

Coalition of Natl. Park Ser. Retirees [4766], 5625 N Wilmot Rd., Tucson, AZ 85750, (520)615-9417

Coalition of Natl. Voluntary Organizations [★12675]

Coalition for Natural Hea. - Address unknown since 2011.

Coalition for Networked Info. [6972], 21 Dupont Cir., Ste. 800, Washington, DC 20036, (202)296-5098

Coalition for Non-Violent Food - Address unknown since 2011.

Coalition for Nonprofit Health Care - Defunct.

Coalition to Oppose the Arms Trade [IO], Ottawa, ON, Canada

Coalition of Organic Landscapers [2179], 1125 NE 152nd St., Shoreline, WA 98155-7053, (206)362-8947

Coalition for Patients' Rights [14766], 8515 Georgia Ave., Ste. 400, Silver Spring, MD 20910-3492, (301)628-5093

Coalition for Peace with Justice [18236], PO Box 2081, Chapel Hill, NC 27515, (919)490-5546

Coalition to Promote Minority Hea. [15853], 1107-E Spring St., Ste. 2F, Silver Spring, MD 20910, (240)988-0400

Coalition for Prompt Pay - Address unknown since 2011.

Coalition to Protect America's Hea. Care [15049], PO Box 30211, Bethesda, MD 20824-0211, (877)422-2349

Coalition to Protect Animals in Parks and Refuges [10943], PO Box 26, Swain, NY 14884-0026

Coalition on the Public Understanding of Sci. [7365], Amer. Inst. of Biological Sciences, 1900 Campus Commons Dr., Ste. 200, Reston, VA 20191

Coalition of Publicly Traded Limited Partnerships [★2144]

Coalition of Publicly Traded Partnerships [★2144]

Coalition for Pulmonary Fibrosis [16606], 1659 Branham Ln., Ste. F, No. 227, San Jose, CA 95118, (888)222-8541

Coalition for Quality in Care [IO], London, United Kingdom

Coalition for Rainforest Nations [4856], 370 Lexington Ave., 26th Fl., New York, NY 10017, (646)448-6870

Coalition of Ratepayers for Affordable Green Electricity [★18185]

Coalition for a Realistic Foreign Policy [17698], 1220 L St. NW, Ste. 100-221, Washington, DC 20005-4018

Coalition to Reduce Nuclear Dangers - Defunct.

Coalition for Religious Freedom [★18519]

Coalition for Religious Freedom [★18519]

Coalition for Responsible Genetics [★18585]

Coalition for Responsible Waste Incineration [3634], 1615 L St. NW, Ste. 1350, Washington, DC 20036, (202)452-1241

Coalition for Road Safety [IO], Phnom Penh, Cambodia

Coalition for Safe Community Needle Disposal [14842], 1001 Fannin St., Ste. 4000, Houston, TX 77002, (713)980-3120

Coalition for SafeMinds [15580], 16033 Bolsa Chica St., No. 104-142, Huntington Beach, CA 92649, (404)934-0777

Coalition to Salute America's Heroes [20785], 12 Godfrey Pl., Wilton, CT 06897, (914)432-5400

Coalition for Scenic Beauty [★4303]

Coalition for Sci. After School [8836], Univ. of California, Lawrence Hall of Sci., REA No. 5200, Berkeley, CA 94720, (510)642-8106

Coalition for a Secure Driver's License [18593], 1300 Pennsylvania Ave. NW, Ste. 880, Washington, DC 20004, (202)312-1540

Coalition of Ser. Indus. [3231], 1090 Vermont Ave. NW, Ste. 420, Washington, DC 20005, (202)289-7460

Coalition on Smoking or Health - Defunct.

Coalition for Spanish Speaking Mental Hea. Organizations [★13194]

Coalition of Spirit-filled Churches [19616], PO Box 6606, Newport News, VA 23606, (877)272-2427

Coalition for State Prompt Pay - Defunct.

Coalition of State Rheumatology Organizations [16619], 1121 Military Cutoff Rd., No. 337, Wilmington, NC 28405, (910)256-9898

Coalition to Stop Gun Violence [17686], 1424 L St. NW, Ste. 2-1, Washington, DC 20005, (202)408-0061

Coalition to Stop the Use of Child Soldiers [IO], London, United Kingdom

Coalition for the Strategic Defense Initiative - Defunct.

Coalition for Student and Academic Rights [7641], PO Box 491, Solebury, PA 18963, (215)862-9096

Coalition for Tactical Medicine [15907], 341-11 S Coll. Rd., PMB 2053, Wilmington, NC 28403, (910)799-9357

Coalition for Tax Fairness [18694], PO Box 9205, Arlington, VA 22219-1205, (301)515-6584

Coalition for Tobacco Control - Pakistan [IO], Islamabad, Pakistan

Coalition for Unborn Children [★12921]

Coalition of Urban and Metropolitan Universities [7876], Towson Univ., 8000 York Rd., Towson, MD 21252, (410)704-3700

Coalition on Urban Renewal and Educ. [18755], 1300 Pennsylvania Ave. NW, Ste. 700, Washington, DC 20004, (202)204-2575

Coalition of Visionary Resources [2575], 8751 E Hampden Ave., Ste. C1, Denver, CO 80231, (303)368-8055

Coalition of Visionary Retailers [★2575]

Coalition for Women in Intl. Development - Defunct.

Coalition on Women and Religion - Defunct.

Coalition of Women's Art Orgs. - Defunct.

COAR Peace Mission [17601], 28700 Euclid Ave., Wickliffe, OH 44092-2527, (440)943-7615

Coast to Coast Dachshund Rescue [10944], PO Box 147, Jacobus, PA 17407

Coast Defense Study Group [10089], Alan Hardey, Membership Chm., 1577 Braeburn Rd., Altadena, CA 91001-2603, (626)791-5034

Coast Guard
   Australian Volunteer Coast Guard Assn. [976]
   Cell Phones for Soldiers [11086]
   Coast Guard Auxiliary Assn. [20391]
   Coast Guard Combat Veterans Assn. [20786]
   Oper. Paperback [11100]
   U.S. Coast Guard Chief Petty Officers Assn. [20392]

Coast Guard Auxiliary Assn. [20391], 9449 Watson Indus. Park, St. Louis, MO 63126, (314)962-8828

Coast Guard Combat Veterans Assn. [20786], Gary Sherman, Sec.-Treas., 3245 Ridge Pk., Eagleville, PA 19403, (610)539-1000

Coast Seamen's Union [★23250]

Coastal Carolina Alumni Assn. [★18863]

Coastal Carolina Univ. Alumni Assn. [18863], Coastal Carolina Univ., PO Box 261954, Conway, SC 29528-6054, (843)349-2846

Coastal Conservation Assn. [4024], 6919 Portwest Dr., Ste. 100, Houston, TX 77024, (713)626-4234

Coastal and Estuarine Res. Fed. [7052], PO Box 510, Port Republic, MD 20676, (410)326-7467

The Coastal Soc. [7179], PO Box 3590, Williamsburg, VA 23187-3590, (757)565-0999

Coastal States Org. [7180], Hall of States, 444 N Capitol St. NW, Ste. 322, Washington, DC 20001, (202)508-3860

Coated Abrasives Mfrs. Inst. [★2347]

Coatings
   Aluminum Anodizers Coun. [786]
   Amer. Galvanizers Assn. [787]
   Amer. Galvanizers Assn. [787]
   Assn. of Indus. Metallizers, Coaters and Laminators [788]
   Intl. Soc. of Coating Sci. and Tech. [6431]
   Intl. Soc. of Coating Sci. and Tech. [6431]
   Natl. Assn. of Pipe Coating Applicators [789]
   Natl. Assn. of Pipe Coating Applicators [789]
   Natl. Coil Coating Assn. [790]
   Powder Coating Inst. [791]
   Roof Coatings Mfrs. Assn. [792]
   Soc. for Mfg. Engineers I Assn. for Finishing Processes [6432]
   Soc. for Mfg. Engineers I Assn. for Finishing Processes [6432]
   Soc. of Vacuum Coaters [793]
   Surface Engg. Coating Assn. [6433]
   Thermoset Resin Formulators Assn. [794]

Cobalt Development Inst. [IO], Guildford, United Kingdom

Cobbett Assn. for Chamber Music Res. [10178], 601 Timber Trail, Riverwoods, IL 60015-3846, (847)374-1800

Cobequid Salmon Assn. [IO], Truro, NS, Canada

Coblentz Soc. [7458], Univ. of South Carolina, 631 Sumter St., Columbia, SC 29208, (803)777-5264

Cobra Club [★21163]

Cobra Owners Club of Am. [21032], 672 N Ranchroad Dr., Orange, CA 92869, (714)546-5670

Cocaine Anonymous World Services [13244], 21720 S Wilmington Ave., Ste. 304, Long Beach, CA 90810, (310)559-5833

Cocaine Anonymous World Services [13244], 21720 S Wilmington Ave., Ste. 304, Long Beach, CA 90810, (310)559-5833

Cochrane Collaboration [IO], Oxford, United Kingdom

Cockapoo Club of Am. [21543], PO Box 2, Christmas Valley, OR 97641

Cocoa Merchants' Assn. of Am. [1380], World Financial Ctr., One N End Ave., 13th Fl., New York, NY 10282-1101, (212)201-8819

Cocoa Producers' Alliance [IO], Lagos, Nigeria

Cocoa Res. Inst. of Ghana [IO], New Tafo, Ghana

Code Pink Women's Pre-Emptive Strike for Peace [18237], 2010 Linden Ave., Venice, CA 90291-3912, (310)827-4320

Code Pink Women's Pre-Emptive Strike for Peace [18237], 2010 Linden Ave., Venice, CA 90291-3912, (310)827-4320

CodeBlueNow! [16483], 705 2nd, Ste. 901, Seattle, WA 98104, (206)217-9430

Reference to "IO" in place of a book number signifies that the association may be found in the 50th edition of International Organizations.

Coecoceiba Amigos de la Tierra Costa Rica [★IO]
Coeliac Soc. of Ireland [IO], Dublin, Ireland
Coeliac UK [IO], High Wycombe, United Kingdom
The Coexistence Initiative [★12628]
The Coexistence Initiative [★12628]
Coexistence Intl. [12628], Mailstop 086, Waltham,
  MA 02454, (781)736-5017
Coexistence Intl. [12628], Mailstop 086, Waltham,
  MA 02454, (781)736-5017
Coffee
  Assn. of Coffee Mill Enthusiasts [21306]
  Caffeine Awareness Assn. [13828]CoffeeNatl.
  Assn. of the Coffee Indus. - Mexico
  Natl. Fed. of Coffee Growers of Colombia [4497]
Coffee Assn. of Canada [IO], Toronto, ON, Canada
Coffee Kids [11563], 1751 Old Pecos Trail, Ste. K,
  Santa Fe, NM 87505, (505)820-1443
Coffee Kids [11563], 1751 Old Pecos Trail, Ste. K,
  Santa Fe, NM 87505, (505)820-1443
Coffee Trade Fed. [IO], London, United Kingdom
Coffin-Lowry Syndrome Found. [14593], 675 Kalmia
  Pl. NW, Issaquah, WA 98027, (425)427-0939
Coffs Harbour Chamber of Commerce and Indus.
  [IO], Coffs Harbour, Australia
COFORD: Natl. Coun. for Forest Res. and Develop-
  ment [IO], Dublin, Ireland
Cogeneration and Competitive Power Institute
  [★6693]
Cogeneration and Competitive Power Institute
  [★6693]
Cogitation Org. - Address unknown since 2011.
Cognac Information Bur. - Defunct.
Cognitive-Behavioral Therapists; Natl. Assn. of
  [16440]
Cognitive Development Soc. [13825], Krista Ouaja,
  Taylor and Francis, 325 Chestnut St., Philadelphia,
  PA 19106, (800)354-1420
Cognitive Neuroscience Soc. [15676], Center for
  Mind and Brain, 267 Cousteau Pl., Davis, CA
  95618
Cognitive Neuroscience Soc. [15676], Center for
  Mind and Brain, 267 Cousteau Pl., Davis, CA
  95618
Cognitive Sci. Soc. [6210], Deborah Gruber, Bus.
  Mgr., Univ. of Texas, Dept. of Psychology, 1 Univ.
  Sta. A8000, Austin, TX 78712-0187, (512)471-2030
Cogswell Family Assn. [20495], Edward R.
  Cogswell, Sec., 21321 107th Ave. SW, Snohomish,
  WA 98296
The Coin Coalition - Defunct.
Coin Laundry Assn. [2190], 1 S 660 Midwest Rd.,
  Ste. 205, Oakbrook Terrace, IL 60181, (630)953-
  7920
Coin Operated Collectors Assn. [21325], 4075 Red
  Oak Cir. NW, Massillon, OH 44646-1389
Coin Operated Collectors Assn. [21325], 4075 Red
  Oak Cir. NW, Massillon, OH 44646-1389
Coins
  Amer. Numismatic Soc. [21964]
  Ancient Coin Collectors Guild [21967]
  Civil War Token Soc. [21970]
  Colonial Coin Collectors Club [21971]
  Combined Organizations of Numismatic Error Col-
    lectors of Am. [21972]
  Intl. Bank Note Soc. [21976]
  Liberty Seated Collectors Club [21979]
  North Amer. Collectors [21984]
  Numismatic Literary Guild [21986]
  Numismatics Intl. [21987]
  U.S. Mexican Numismatic Assn. [21996]
Coir Bd. of India [IO], Kochi, India
Cojolya Assn. of Maya Women Weavers [IO],
  Solola, Guatemala
COLA [15408], 9881 Broken Land Pkwy., Ste. 200,
  Columbia, MD 21046, (800)981-9883
COLAGE [12074], 1550 Bryant St., Ste. 830, San
  Francisco, CA 94103, (415)861-5437
Cold Finished Steel Bar Inst. [2467], PO Box 5137,
  Chicago, IL 60680-5137, (708)735-8000
Cold Formed Parts and Machine Inst. - Address
  unknown since 2010.
Cold Spring Harbor Whaling Museum [★10068]
Cold War Veterans Assn. [20787], PO Box 13042,
  Overland Park, KS 66282-3042
Colegio De Contadores, Economistas y Administra-
  dores del Uruguay [IO], Montevideo, Uruguay

Colegio De Economistas Del Paraguay [IO], Asun-
  cion, Paraguay
Colegio Ibero-LatinoAmericano de Dermatologia
  [★IO]
Colegio de Ingenieros de Chile A.G [★IO]
Colegio Internacional de Medicos Nucleares [★IO]
Colegio Mexicano de Interpretes de Conferencias
  [★IO]
Coleman Found. [13180], 651 W Washington Blvd.,
  Ste. 306, Chicago, IL 60661, (312)902-7120
Coleopterists Soc. [6841], 3294 Meadowview Rd.,
  Sacramento, CA 95832-1448, (916)262-1168
Colitis Found. of Am; Crohn's and [14559]
Colitis; Reach Out for Youth with Ileitis and [16780]
Collaborative Family Healthcare Assn. [14767], PO
  Box 23980, Rochester, NY 14692-3980, (585)482-
  8210
Collaborative on Hea. and the Env. [14500], PO Box
  316, Bolinas, CA 94924, (415)868-0970
Collaborative Intl. Pesticides Analytical Coun. [IO],
  Parma, Italy
Collectibles
  1965-66 Full Size Chevrolet Club [20980]
  1971 GTO and Judge Convertible Registry
    [20982]
  A.C. Gilbert Heritage Soc. [22168]
  Aladdin Knights of the Mystic Light [21877]
  Amer. Lock Collectors Assn. [21295]
  Amer. Numismatic Soc. [21964]
  Amer. Pencil Collectors Soc. [21297]
  Amer. Philatelic Res. Lib. [22010]
  Amer. Philatelic Soc. Writers Unit [22012]
  Amer. Soc. of Military Insignia Collectors [21883]
  Amer. Topical Assn. [22016]
  America's Corvette Club [20996]
  Amy's Doll Lover's Club [21687]
  Ancient Coin Collectors Guild [21967]
  Anheuser-Busch Collectors Club [21300]
  Antique Advt. Assn. of Am. [82]
  Antique Caterpillar Machinery Owners Club
    [21878]
  Antique Glass Salt and Sugar Shaker Club
    [21304]
  Antique Motorcycle Club of Am. [21919]
  Antique Small Engine Collectors Club [21702]
  The Antique Stove Assn. [20956]
  Antiques and Collectibles Natl. Assn. [195]
  Assoc. Collectors of El Salvador [22020]
  Assn. of Coffee Mill Enthusiasts [21306]
  Assn. of Collecting Clubs [21307]
  Big Little Book Collector's Club [21310]
  Brazil Philatelic Assn. [22022]
  Brewery Collectibles Club of Am. [21311]
  Browning Collectors Assn. [21712]
  Chess Collectors Intl. [21274]
  Chevrolet Nomad Assn. [21022]
  Chevy and Geo Club [21023]
  Chrysler Town and Country Owners Registry
    [21026]
  Citizens' Stamp Advisory Comm. [22029]
  Citroen Quarterly Car Club [21027]
  Civil War Dealers and Collectors Assn. [21280]
  Civil War Token Soc. [21970]
  Cobra Owners Club of Am. [21032]
  Collectors of Religion on Stamps [22032]
  Colonial Coin Collectors Club [21971]
  Colonial Coverlet Guild of Am. [21326]
  Combined Organizations of Numismatic Error Col-
    lectors of Am. [21972]
  Confederate Stamp Alliance [22033]
  Corvair Soc. of Am. [21035]
  Corvette Club of Am. [21036]
  Cover Collectors Circuit Club [22034]
  Dedham Pottery Collectors Soc. [21333]
  Doll Costumer's Guild [21690]
  Egg Cup Collectors' Corner [21336]
  Errors, Freaks and Oddities Collectors' Club
    [22037]
  Erskine Registry [21052]
  Fairy Lamp Club [21337]
  Ferguson Enthusiasts of North Am. [22174]
  Firehawk Assn. of Am. [21057]
  First Issues Collectors Club [22038]
  Ford/Fordson Collectors Assn. [22175]
  Fostoria Glass Collectors [21831]

  France and Colonies Philatelic Soc. [22039]
  Future Corvette Owners Assn. [21060]
  Gull Wing Gp. Intl. [21065]
  Harley Hummer Club [21929]
  Hudson-Essex-Terraplane Club [21070]
  Hudson Essex Terraplane Historical Soc. [21071]
  Intl. Autograph Dealers Alliance and Collectors
    Club [21353]
  Intl. Bank Note Soc. [21976]
  Intl. Doll Makers Assn. [21692]
  Intl. Fed. of Amer. Homing Pigeon Fanciers
    [22097]
  Intl. Fire Buff Associates [21708]
  Intl. Paperweight Soc. [22004]
  Intl. Radio Club of Am. [20937]
  Intl. Soc. of Worldwide Stamp Collectors [22046]
  Jack Knight Air Mail Soc. [22047]
  Kaiser-Darrin Owners Roster [21085]
  Karmann Ghia Club of North Am. [21087]
  Kissel Kar Klub [21088]
  Knife Collectors Club [21875]
  Korea Stamp Soc. [22048]
  Kustom Kemps of Am. [21089]
  Les Amis de Panhard and Deutsch-Bonnet USA
    [21091]
  Liberty Seated Collectors Club [21979]
  Mailer's Postmark Permit Club [22050]
  Marklin Digital Special Interest Gp. [21891]
  Marmon Club [21098]
  Maserati Info. Exchange [21100]
  Massey Collectors Assn. [22178]
  Mercedes-Benz M-100 Owner's Gp. [21104]
  Meter Stamp Soc. [22053]
  Metropolitan Owners Club of North Am. [21105]
  Mexico Elmhurst Philatelic Soc. Intl. [22055]
  Midstates Jeepster Assn. [21107]
  Model A Ford Cabriolet Club [21108]
  Modern Car Soc. [21114]
  Morgan Car Club [21116]
  Napoleonic Age Philatelists [22058]
  Natl. Basketry Org. [21455]
  Natl. Button Soc. [21378]
  Natl. Corvette Owners Assn. [21124]
  Natl. Duncan Glass Soc. [21839]
  Natl. Mossberg Collectors Assn. [21716]
  Natl. Pop Can Collectors [21381]
  Natl. Stamp Dealers Assn. [22060]
  North Amer. Collectors [21984]
  North Amer. Mini Moke Registry [21137]
  North Amer. Radio Archives [22120]
  Numismatic Literary Guild [21986]
  Numismatics Intl. [21987]
  Old Sleepy Eye Collectors' Club of Am. [21268]
  Opel Assn. of North Am. [21141]
  Org. of Bricklin Owners [21143]
  Peanut Pals [21396]
  Philip Boileau Collectors' Soc. [20970]
  Plasticville Collectors Assn. [22100]
  Plymouth Owners Club [21151]
  Professional Car Soc. [21155]
  Riva Club USA [21232]
  Rossica Soc. of Russian Philately [22068]
  Sandicast Collectors Guild [20974]
  Ships on Stamps Unit [22074]
  Soc. of Australasian Specialists/Oceania [22075]
  Soc. for Thai Philately [22079]
  Space Topic Stud. Unit [22080]
  Strawberry Shortcake Chat Gp. [21699]
  Tea Leaf Club Intl. [21269]
  Toy Train Collectors Soc. [21894]
  United Four-Wheel Drive Associations [21184]
  U.S. Mexican Numismatic Assn. [21996]
  United St. Machine Assn. [21185]
  Vintage Garden Tractor Club of Am. [22181]
  Vintage Thunderbird Club Intl. [21190]
  Volkswagen Club of Am. [21193]
  World Airline Historical Soc. [20924]
  World Wide Assn. of Treasure Seekers [22109]
  Worldwide Camaro Club [21197]
  Wreck and Crash Mail Soc. [22093]
  Youth in Model Railroading [21897]
Collectif d'echanges pour la Technologie Approprie
  [★IO]
Collectif des Organisations Oeuvrant pour les per-
  sonnes Handicapees [IO], Antananarivo, Madagas-
  car

A star before a book entry number signifies that the name is not listed separately, but is mentioned within the entry.

Collections and Stories of Amer. Muslims [10317],
   2524 Elvans Rd. SE, Washington, DC 20020,
   (202)678-6906

Collective Bargaining

Assn. of Minor League Umpires [22266]
Intl. Union of Indus. and Independent Workers
   [23312]
Natl. Center for the Stud. of Collective Bargaining
   in Higher Educ. and the Professions [23173]

Collectors

52 Plus Joker [21291]
1965-66 Full Size Chevrolet Club [20980]
1971 GTO and Judge Convertible Registry
   [20982]
A.C. Gilbert Heritage Soc. [22168]
Aladdin Knights of the Mystic Light [21877]
Amer. Bell Assn. Intl. [21292]
Amer. Collectors of Infant Feeders [21293]
Amer. Collectors of Infant Feeders [21293]
Amer. Hatpin Soc. [21294]
Amer. Lock Collectors Assn. [21295]
Amer. Matchcover Collecting Club [21296]
Amer. Numismatic Soc. [21964]
Amer. Pencil Collectors Soc. [21297]
Amer. Philatelic Res. Lib. [22010]
Amer. Philatelic Soc. Writers Unit [22012]
Amer. Soc. of Bookplate Collectors and Designers
   [21298]
Amer. Soc. of Military Insignia Collectors [21883]
Amer. Spoon Collectors [21299]
Amer. Spoon Collectors [21299]
Amer. Topical Assn. [22016]
Amer. Vecturist Assn. [22182]
America's Corvette Club [20996]
Amy's Doll Lover's Club [21687]
Ancient Coin Collectors Guild [21967]
Anheuser-Busch Collectors Club [21300]
Antique Advt. Assn. of Am. [82]
Antique Barbed Wire Soc. [21301]
Antique Caterpillar Machinery Owners Club
   [21878]
Antique Doorknob Collectors of Am. [21302]
Antique Fan Collectors Assn. [21303]
Antique Glass Salt and Sugar Shaker Club
   [21304]
Antique Motorcycle Club of Am. [21919]
Antique Poison Bottle Collectors Assn. [21305]
Antique Small Engine Collectors Club [21702]
The Antique Stove Assn. [20956]
Antiques Dealers Assn. of Am. [795]
Assoc. Collectors of El Salvador [22020]
Assn. of Coffee Mill Enthusiasts [21306]
Assn. of Collecting Clubs [21307]
Bead Soc. of Los Angeles [21308]
Beyond the Pond.International Frog Collectors
   Club [21309]
Big Little Book Collector's Club [21310]
Brazil Philatelic Assn. [22022]
Brewery Collectibles Club of Am. [21311]
Brewster Kaleidoscope Soc. [21312]
Browning Collectors Assn. [21712]
Butter Pat Patter Assn. [21313]
Cabbage Patch Kids Collectors Club [21314]
Callmakers and Collectors Assn. of Am. [21315]
Canadian Corkscrew Collectors Club [21316]
Canadian Corkscrew Collectors Club [21316]
Candy Container Collectors of Am. [21317]
Carriage Assn. of Am. [21318]
Cash Registers Collectors Club [21319]
Casino Chip and Gaming Token Collectors Club
   [21320]
Chess Collectors Intl. [21274]
Chevrolet Nomad Assn. [21022]
Chevy and Geo Club [21023]
Chicago Playing Card Collectors [21321]
Christmas Seal and Charity Stamp Soc. [21322]
Christmas Seal and Charity Stamp Soc. [21322]
Chrysler Town and Country Owners Registry
   [21026]
Cigarette Pack Collectors Assn. [21323]
CIMTA [796]
Citizens' Stamp Advisory Comm. [22029]
Citroen Quarterly Car Club [21027]
Citrus Label Soc. [21324]
Civil War Dealers and Collectors Assn. [21280]

Civil War Token Soc. [21970]
Cobra Owners Club of Am. [21032]
Coin Operated Collectors Assn. [21325]
Coin Operated Collectors Assn. [21325]
Collectors of Religion on Stamps [22032]
Colonial Coin Collectors Club [21971]
Colonial Coverlet Guild of Am. [21326]
Combined Organizations of Numismatic Error Col-
   lectors of Am. [21972]
Conchologists of Am. [21327]
Confederate Stamp Alliance [22033]
Cookie Cutter Collectors Club [21328]
Corvair Soc. of Am. [21035]
Corvette Club of Am. [21036]
Cover Collectors Circuit Club [22034]Collectors-
   Cow Observers Worldwide
Cracker Jack Collectors Assn. [21329]
Crowncap Collectors Soc. Intl. [21330]
Currier and Ives Dinnerware Collectors [21331]
Czech Collector's Assn. [21332]
Czech Collector's Assn. [21332]
Dedham Pottery Collectors Soc. [21333]
Divco Club of Am. [21334]
Doll Costumer's Guild [21690]
Early Amer. Pattern Glass Soc. [21335]
Egg Cup Collectors' Corner [21336]
Errors, Freaks and Oddities Collectors' Club
   [22037]
Erskine Registry [21052]
Fairchild Club [20895]
Fairy Lamp Club [21337]
Fan Assn. of North Am. [21338]
Ferguson Enthusiasts of North Am. [22174]
Figural Cast Iron Collector's Club [21339]
Firehawk Assn. of Am. [21057]
First Issues Collectors Club [22038]
Flow Blue Intl. Collectors Club [21340]
Ford/Fordson Collectors Assn. [22175]
Fostoria Glass Collectors [21831]
France and Colonies Philatelic Soc. [22039]
Frankoma Family Collectors Assn. [21341]
Future Corvette Owners Assn. [21060]
German Gun Collectors Assn. [21342]
German Gun Collectors' Assn. [21342]
Global Lottery Collectors Soc. [21343]
Golf Collectors Soc. [21344]
Golf Collectors Soc. [21344]
Great Britain Collectors Club [21345]
Great Britain Collectors Club [21345]
Gull Wing Gp. Intl. [21065]
Harbour Lights Collectors Soc. [21346]
Harley Hummer Club [21929]
Homer Laughlin China Collectors Assn. [21347]
Homer Laughlin China Collectors Assn. [21347]
Horn and Whistle Enthusiasts Gp. [21348]
Hudson-Essex-Terraplane Club [21070]
Hudson Essex Terraplane Historical Soc. [21071]
Hull Pottery Assn. [21349]
Ice Screamers [21350]
Intl. Assn. of R.S. Prussia Collectors [21351]
Intl. Assn. of Silver Art Collectors [21352]
Intl. Autograph Dealers Alliance and Collectors
   Club [21353]
Intl. Bank Note Soc. [21976]
Intl. Bird Dog Assn. [20898]
Intl. Bond and Share Soc. [21354]
Intl. Bossons Collectors Soc. [21355]
Intl. Brick Collectors' Assn. [21356]
Intl. Coleman Collectors Club [21357]
Intl. Doll Makers Assn. [21692]
Intl. Fed. of Amer. Homing Pigeon Fanciers
   [22097]
Intl. Fight'n Rooster Cutlery Club [21874]
Intl. Fire Buff Associates [21708]
Intl. Match Safe Assn. [21358]
Intl. Paperweight Soc. [22004]
Intl. Perfume Bottle Assn. [21359]
Intl. Perfume Bottle Assn. [21359]
Intl. Radio Club of Am. [20937]
Intl. Sand Collectors Soc. [21360]
Intl. Scouting Collectors Assn. [21361]
Intl. Soc. of Antique Scale Collectors [21362]
Intl. Soc. of Antique Scale Collectors [21362]
Intl. Soc. of Worldwide Stamp Collectors [22046]
Intl. Swizzle Stick Collectors Assn. [21363]

Intl. Swizzle Stick Collectors Assn. [21363]
Intl. Willow Collectors [21364]
Intl. Willow Collectors [21364]
Jack Knight Air Mail Soc. [22047]
Just for Openers [21365]
Kaiser-Darrin Owners Roster [21085]
Karmann Ghia Club of North Am. [21087]
Kissel Kar Klub [21088]
Knife Collectors Club [21875]
Korea Stamp Soc. [22048]
Krystonia Collector's Club [21366]
Kustom Kemps of Am. [21089]
Les Amis de Panhard and Deutsch-Bonnet USA
   [21091]
Liberty Seated Collectors Club [21979]
Mailer's Postmark Permit Club [22050]
M&M's Collectors Club [21367]
Manuscript Soc. [21368]
Marklin Digital Special Interest Gp. [21891]
Marmon Club [21098]
Maserati Info. Exchange [21100]
Massey Collectors Assn. [22178]
Matchbox U.S.A. [21369]
McDonald's Collectors Club [21370]
Mercedes-Benz M-100 Owner's Gp. [21104]
Meter Stamp Soc. [22053]
Metropolitan Owners Club of North Am. [21105]
Mexico Elmhurst Philatelic Soc. Intl. [22055]
Midstates Jeepster Assn. [21107]
Midwest Decoy Collectors Assn. [21371]
Miniature Piano Enthusiast Club [21372]
Model A Ford Cabriolet Club [21108]
Modern Car Soc. [21114]
Morgan Car Club [21116]
Movable Book Soc. [21233]
Napoleonic Age Philatelists [22058]
Natl. Assn. of Avon Collectors [21373]
Natl. Assn. of Breweriana Advt. [21374]
Natl. Assn. of Milk Bottle Collectors [21375]
Natl. Assn. of Miniature Enthusiasts [21376]
Natl. Autumn Leaf Collectors Club [21377]
Natl. Basketry Org. [21455]
Natl. Button Soc. [21378]
Natl. Corvette Owners Assn. [21124]
Natl. Duncan Glass Soc. [21839]
Natl. Firearms Act Trade and Collectors Assn.
   [1354]
Natl. Fishing Lure Collectors Club [21379]
Natl. Graniteware Soc. [21380]
Natl. Mossberg Collectors Assn. [21716]
Natl. Pop Can Collectors [21381]
Natl. Russell Collectors Assn. [21382]
Natl. Shaving Mug Collectors Assn. [21383]
Natl. Shelley China Club [21384]
Natl. Toothpick Holder Collectors' Soc. [21385]
Natl. Valentine Collectors' Assn. [21386]
Nissan Infiniti Car Owners Club [21135]
North Amer. Collectors [21984]
North Amer. Mini Moke Registry [21137]
North Amer. Radio Archives [22120]
North Amer. Soc. of Pipe Collectors [21387]
North Amer. Torquay Soc. [21388]
North Amer. Trap Collector Assn. [21389]
Northeastern Spoon Collectors Guild [21390]
Novelty Salt and Pepper Shakers Club [21391]
Numismatic Literary Guild [21986]
Numismatics Intl. [21987]
Old Reel Collectors Assn. [21392]
Old Reel Collectors Assn. [21392]
Old Sleepy Eye Collectors' Club of Am. [21268]
On the Lighter Side, Intl. Lighter Collectors
   [21393]
On the Lighter Side, Intl. Lighter Collectors
   [21393]
Opel Assn. of North Am. [21141]
Org. of Bricklin Owners [21143]
Oughtred Soc. [21394]
Paperweight Collectors' Assn. [21395]
Peanut Pals [21396]
Pen Collectors of Am. [21397]
Pepsi-Cola Collectors Club [21398]
Pewter Soc. [5450]
Pickard Collectors Club [21399]
Plasticville Collectors Assn. [22100]
Plymouth Owners Club [21151]

Reference to "IO" in place of a book number signifies that the association may be found in the 50th edition of International Organizations.

Potomac Antique Tools and Indus. Assn. [21871]
Professional Autograph Dealers Assn. [797]
Professional Car Soc. [21155]
Promotional Glass Collectors Assn. [21400]
Red Wing Collectors Soc. [21401]
Riva Club USA [21232]
Road Map Collectors Assn. [21402]
Rossica Soc. of Russian Philately [22068]
Sandicast Collectors Guild [20974]
Ships on Stamps Unit [22074]
Soc. of Australasian Specialists/Oceania [22075]
Soc. of Herbarium Curators [6368]
Soc. of Inkwell Collectors [21403]
Soc. of Inkwell Collectors [21403]
Soc. for Thai Philately [22079]
Souvenir Building Collectors Soc. [21404]
Space Topic Stud. Unit [22080]
Statue of Liberty Club [21405]
Steiff Club [21406]
Stein Collectors Intl. [21407]
Stein Collectors Intl. [21407]
Strawberry Shortcake Chat Gp. [21699]
Tea Leaf Club Intl. [21269]
Thimble Collectors Intl. [21408]
Toy Train Collectors Soc. [21894]
Tube Collectors Assn. [21409]
UHL Collectors Soc. [21410]
United Four-Wheel Drive Associations [21184]
U.S. Mexican Numismatic Assn. [21996]
United St. Machine Assn. [21185]
Universal Autograph Collectors Club [21411]
Vaseline Glass Collectors, Inc. [21412]Collectors-
    Vintage Fashion and Costume Jewelry Club
Vintage Garden Tractor Club of Am. [22181]
Vintage Thunderbird Club Intl. [21190]
Volkswagen Club of Am. [21193]
Wagner And Griswold Soc. [21859]
Whisky Pitcher Collectors Assn. of Am. [21413]
Whisky Pitcher Collectors Assn. of Am. [21413]
World Airline Historical Soc. [20924]
World Chap. of Disneyana Enthusiasts [21414]
World Chap. of Disneyana Enthusiasts [21414]
World Wide Assn. of Treasure Seekers [22109]
Worldwide Camaro Club [21197]
Wreck and Crash Mail Soc. [22093]
Youth in Model Railroading [21897]
Zeiss Historical Soc. of Am. [21415]
Zeiss Historical Soc. of Am. [21415]
Collectors Club [22031], 22 E 35th St., New York,
    NY 10016-3806, (212)683-0559
Collectors of Numismatic Errors [★21972]
Collectors of Religion on Stamps [22032], 425 N
    Linwood Ave., No. 110, Appleton, WI 54914-3476
Coll. canadien des directeurs de services de sante
    [★IO]
Coll. of Amer. Pathologists [16123], 325 Waukegan
    Rd., Northfield, IL 60093-2750, (847)832-7000
Coll. Art Assn. [7745], 275 7th Ave., 18th Fl., New
    York, NY 10001, (212)691-1051
Coll. Art Assn. of Am. [★7745]
Coll. and Assn. of Registered Nurses of Alberta [IO],
    Edmonton, AB, Canada
Coll. Athletic Bus. Mgt. Assn. [22973], Pat Manak,
    Asst. Sec., 24651 Detroit Rd., Westlake, OH
    44145, (440)892-4000
Coll. Athletic Bus. Managers Assn. [★22973]
Coll. Band Directors Natl. Assn. [8645], Thomas Ver-
    rier, Sec., Vanderbilt Univ., Blair School of Music,
    2400 Blakemore Ave., Nashville, TN 37212,
    (615)322-7651
The Coll. Bd. [8984], 45 Columbus Ave., New York,
    NY 10023-6992, (212)713-8000
Coll. Bookstore Assn. [★3113]
Coll. Broadcasters, Inc. [487], UPS - Hershey Sq.
    Ctr., 1152 Mae St., Hummelstown, PA 17036,
    (855)ASK-4CBI
Coll. Canadien de Geneticiens Medicaux [★IO]
Coll. of Chaplains [★19518]
Coll. Consortium for Intl. Stud. [7877], 2000 P St.
    NW, Ste. 503, Washington, DC 20036, (202)223-
    0330
Coll. Consortium for Intl. Stud. [7877], 2000 P St.
    NW, Ste. 503, Washington, DC 20036, (202)223-
    0330
Coll. for Creative Stud. Alumni Assn. [18864], 201 E
    Kirby St., Detroit, MI 48202-4034, (313)664-7400

Coll. Democrats [★17532]
Coll. Democrats of Am. [17532], 430 S Capitol St.
    SE, Washington, DC 20003-4024
Coll. English Assn. [8131], Nazareth Coll. of
    Rochester, 4245 East Ave., Rochester, NY 14618-
    3790, (585)389-2645
Coll. Entrance Examination Bd. [★8984]
Coll. of Family Physicians of Canada - Ontario
    Chap. [IO], Mississauga, ON, Canada
Coll. Football Assn. - Defunct.
Coll. Fraternity Editors Assn. [★23507]
Coll. Fraternity Secretaries Assn. [★23534]
Coll. Gymnastics Assn. [22631], 306 Cooke Hall,
    1900 Univ. Ave. SE, Minneapolis, MN 55455,
    (612)625-9567
Coll. of Healthcare Info. Mgt. Executives [1898],
    3300 Washtenaw Ave., Ste. 225, Ann Arbor, MI
    48104-5184, (734)665-0000
Coll. Intl. pour la Recherche en Productique [★IO]
Coll. Language Assn. [8469], Univ. of South Carolina
    Upstate, Division of Academic Affairs, Admin. 222,
    Spartanburg, SC 29303, (864)503-5634
Coll. des Medecins de Famille du Canada [★IO]
Coll. Media Advisers [8439], Univ. of Memphis, Dept.
    of Journalism, 3711 Veterans Ave., Rm. 300,
    Memphis, TN 38152-6661, (901)678-2403
Coll. Music Soc. [8646], 312 E Pine St., Missoula,
    MT 59802, (406)721-9616
Coll. of Operating Dept. Practitioners [IO], London,
    United Kingdom
Coll. of Optometrists [IO], London, United Kingdom
Coll. of Optometrists in Vision Development [15993],
    215 W Garfield Rd., Ste. 200, Aurora, OH 44202,
    (330)995-0718
Coll. of Osteopathic Healthcare Executives - Address
    unknown since 2010.
Coll. Ouest Africain des Chirurgiens [★IO]
Coll. Parents of Am. [8233], 2020 Pennsylvania Ave.
    NW, Ste. 1020, Washington, DC 20006, (888)761-
    6702
Coll. of Performance Mgt. [2276], 101 S Whiting St.,
    Ste. 320, Alexandria, VA 22304, (703)370-7885
Coll. of Performance Mgt. [2276], 101 S Whiting St.,
    Ste. 320, Alexandria, VA 22304, (703)370-7885
Coll. of Piping [IO], Glasgow, United Kingdom
Coll. Placement Coun. [★8727]
College of Preachers [★19662]
Coll. Reading and Learning Assn. [8779], 2 Caracal
    St., Belen, NM 87002, (505)861-2142
Coll. Republican Natl. Comm. [18528], 600
    Pennsylvania Ave. SE, Ste. 215, Washington, DC
    20003, (888)765-3564
Coll. Retirement Equities Fund [★8802]
Coll. Royal des Chirurgiens Dentistes du Canada
    [★IO]
Coll. of St. Scholastica Alumni Assn. [18865], Alumni
    Relations, The Coll. of St. Scholastica, Tower Hall
    1410, 1200 Kenwood Ave., Duluth, MN 55811-
    4199, (218)723-6071
Coll. Savings Plans Network [8191], PO Box 11910,
    Lexington, KY 40578-1910, (859)244-8175
Coll. Ser. Comm. of the Young Republican Natl. Fed.
    [★18528]
Coll. Sports Info. Directors of Am. [22974], Dave
    Wohlhueter, Treas., 202 Tudor Rd., Ithaca, NY
    14850, (607)273-5891
Coll. Summit [8234], 1763 Columbia Rd. NW, 2nd
    Fl., Washington, DC 20009, (202)319-1763
Coll. Swimming Coaches Assn. of Am. [23038],
    1640 Maple Ave., No. 803, Evanston, IL 60201,
    (847)833-3478
Coll. of Teachers [IO], London, United Kingdom
Coll. Theology Soc. [9010], 1726 W Cape Rock Dr.,
    Cape Girardeau, MO 63701, (573)651-4199
Coll. and Univ. Dept. of the Natl. Catholic Educ.
    Assn. [★7813]
Coll. and Univ. Personnel Assn. [★8700]
Coll. and Univ. Professional Assn. for Human
    Resources [8700], 1811 Commons Point Dr.,
    Knoxville, TN 37932, (865)637-7673
Coll. and Univ. Systems Exchange [★8310]
Coll. Young Democrats of Am. [★17532]
Colleges of Medicine of South Africa [IO], Ronde-
    bosch, Republic of South Africa
Colleges and Universities
    Accreditation Coun. for Bus. Schools and
    Programs [7867]

Amer. Assn. of State Colleges and Universities
    [7868]
Amer. Assn. of Univ. Women [9051]
Amer. Collegiate Hockey Assn. [22639]
Amer. Mgt. Assn. I Oper. Enterprise [8547]
Assoc. Colleges of the Midwest [7869]
Assn. of Amer. Colleges and Universities [7870]
Assn. of Amer. Intl. Colleges and Universities
    [8389]
Assn. of Amer. Universities [7871]
Assn. of Coll. and Univ. Clubs [7872]
Assn. of Coll. and Univ. Clubs [7872]
Assn. of Episcopal Colleges [8162]
Assn. of Public and Land-Grant Universities
    [7873]
Assn. for Support of Graduate Students [8231]
Assn. of Univ. Architects [6194]
British Schools and Universities Club of New York
    [7874]
British Schools and Universities Found. [7875]
British Schools and Universities Found. [7875]
Campus Pride [12072]
Center for the Stud. of the Presidency [17246]
Coalition on the Public Understanding of Sci.
    [7365]
Coalition of Urban and Metropolitan Universities
    [7876]
Coll. Consortium for Intl. Stud. [7877]
Coll. Consortium for Intl. Stud. [7877]
Coll. Summit [8234]
Collegiate Assn. of Table Top Gamers [21745]
Comm. on Institutional Cooperation [7878]
Community Coll. Journalism Assn. [8441]
Conf. on Coll. Composition and Commun. [8132]
Consortium for the Advancement of Private Higher
    Educ. [7879]
Coun. for Amer. Students in Intl. Negotiations
    [8386]
Coun. of Ivy Gp. Presidents [22975]
Eastern Coll. Athletic Conf. [22643]
Educ. Conservancy [7683]
Golf Coaches Assn. of Am. [22608]
Great Lakes Colleges Assn. [7880]
Hispanic Assn. of Colleges and Universities
    [7881]
IES Abroad [8170]
InterCollegiate Horse Show Assn. [22682]
Intercollegiate Stud. Inst. [17425]
Intercollegiate Women's Lacrosse Coaches Assn.
    [22714]
Intl. Assn. for Jazz Educ. [8653]
Intl. Fed. of Engg. Educ. Societies [8124]
Jesuit Assn. of Student Personnel Administrators
    [7665]
LASPAU: Academic and Professional Programs
    for the Americas [7882]
LASPAU: Academic and Professional Programs
    for the Americas [7882]
Men's Collegiate Lacrosse Assn. [22715]
Minority Access, Inc. [8631]
Natl. Alliance of Concurrent Enrollment Partner-
    ships [7883]
Natl. Assn. of Diversity Officers in Higher Educ.
    [8238]
Natl. Assn. for Equal Opportunity in Higher Educ.
    [7884]
Natl. Assn. of Hea. Sci. Educ. Partnership [8843]
Natl. Assn. of Peoplecultural Engg. Prog.
    Advocates [8127]
Natl. Assn. of University-Model Schools [7885]
Natl. Club Baseball Assn. [22283]
Natl. Forensic Assn. [8895]
Natl. Journalism Center [17721]
Natl. Multicultural Greek Coun. [23538]
Natl. Senior Classical League [7866]
Nordic Assn. of Univ. Administrators [22187]
North Central Conf. on Summer Schools [8936]
Phi Sigma Nu Native Amer. Fraternity [23685]
Responsible Endowments Coalition [9082]
Scripps Assn. of Families [7886]
Security on Campus [11693]
Soc. for Music Teacher Educ. [8669]
Southeastern Conf. [23006]
Student African Amer. Brotherhood [19288]
Student Press Law Center [17358]

A star before a book entry number signifies that the name is not listed separately, but is mentioned within the entry.

Union of North Amer. Vietnamese Students Assn. [19275]
Universities Allied for Essential Medicines [8384]
University/Resident Theatre Assn. [9005]
Women Educators [9067]
Women and Youth Supporting Each Other [9069]CollegesWorldwide Univ. Consortium
Colleges and Universities of the Anglican Communion [7728], 815 2nd Ave., New York, NY 10017-4594, (212)716-6148
Colleges and Universities of the Anglican Communion [7728], 815 2nd Ave., New York, NY 10017-4594, (212)716-6148
Collegi d-Odontolegs I Estomatolegs [★IO]
Collegians Activated to Liberate Life [12929], PO Box 259806, Madison, WI 53725, (608)256-2255
Collegiate Assn. of Table Top Gamers [21745], North Carolina State Univ., Campus Box 7306, Raleigh, NC 27695, (919)809-9456
Collegiate Broadcasters, Inc. [★487]
Collegiate Gymnastics Assn. [★22631]
Collegiate Network [8440], 3901 Centerville Rd., Wilmington, DE 19807-1938, (302)652-4600
Collegiate Soaring Assn. [22210], PO Box 337081, Greeley, CO 80633
Collegiate Volleyball Coaches Assn. [★23110]
Collegiate Water Polo Assn. [23112], 320 W 5th St., Bridgeport, PA 19405, (610)277-6787
Collie Club of Am. [21544], Ms. Jane H. Clymer, Sec., 3385 Upland Rd., Lost Springs, KS 66859, (785)983-4894
Collingwood Rocks With Elvis Fan Club [IO], Collingwood, ON, Canada
Collins Collectors Assn. [20935], PO Box 316, Huntington Beach, CA 92646
Collision Indus. Electronic Commerce Assn. [1048], 3149 Dundee Rd., No. 181, Northbrook, IL 60062, (847)498-6945
Colm Wilkinson Appreciation Soc. [IO], Whitby, ON, Canada
Colombia
    Colombian Amer. Assn. [23394]
    Colombian-American Chamber of Commerce of Greater Miami [23395]
    Natl. Stamp Dealers Assn. [22060]
    U.S. Off. on Colombia [17956]
Colombian Acad. of Exact, Physical, and Natural Sciences [IO], Bogota, Colombia
Colombian Amer. Assn. [23394], 641 Lexington Ave., Ste. 1430, New York, NY 10022, (212)233-7776
Colombian-American Chamber of Commerce [★23394]
Colombian-American Chamber of Commerce [IO], Bogota, Colombia
Colombian-American Chamber of Commerce - Bogota [IO], Bogota, Colombia
Colombian-American Chamber of Commerce - Cartagena [IO], Cartagena, Colombia
Colombian-American Chamber of Commerce of Greater Miami [23395], 2305 NW 107 Ave., Ste. 2M43, Miami, FL 33172, (305)446-2542
Colombian Assn. for the Advancement of Sci. [IO], Bogota, Colombia
Colombian Assn. of Bioengineering and Medical Electronics [IO], Bucaramanga, Colombia
Colombian Assn. of Clinical Neurophysiology [IO], Cali, Colombia
Colombian Assn. of Dermatology [IO], Bogota, Colombia
Colombian Assn. of Fertility and Reproductive Medicine [IO], Bogota, Colombia
Colombian Assn. of Medical Schools [IO], Bogota, Colombia
Colombian Assn. of Psychiatry [IO], Bogota, Colombia
Colombian Bible Soc. [IO], Bogota, Colombia
Colombian Book Chamber [IO], Bogota, Colombia
Colombian Chamber of Info. Tech. and Telecommunications [IO], Bogota, Colombia
Colombian Federations of YMCAs [IO], Bogota, Colombia
Colombian Inst. of Cement Producers [IO], Bogota, Colombia
Colombian League Against Epilepsy [IO], Cartagena, Colombia

Colombian Olympic Comm. [IO], Bogota, Colombia
Colombian Osteoporosis Found. [IO], Bogota, Colombia
Colombian Plastics Indus. Assn. [IO], Bogota, Colombia
Colombian Soc. of Cardiology [IO], Bogota, Colombia
Colombian Soc. of Engineers [IO], Bogota, Colombia
Colombian Soc. of Physics [IO], Barranquilla, Colombia
Colombo Rubber Traders' Assn. [IO], Colombo, Sri Lanka
Colomborquideas [IO], Medellin, Colombia
Colon Free Zone Users Assn. [IO], Colon, Panama
Colon Hydrotherapy; Intl. Assn. for [14716]
Colon Hydrotherapy; Intl. Assn. for [14716]
Colong Found. for Wilderness [IO], Sydney, Australia
Colonial
    Centennial Legion of Historic Military Commands [20743]
    Colonial Coin Collectors Club [21971]
    Colonial Coverlet Guild of Am. [21326]
    Descendants of Founders of New Jersey [20393]
    Flagon and Trencher Descendants of Colonial Tavern Keepers [20394]
    Gen. Soc. of Colonial Wars [20395]
    Gen. Soc. of Mayflower Descendants [20746]
    Holland Soc. of New York [20396]
    Jacques Timothe Boucher Sieur de Montbrun Heritage Soc. [20397]
    Jamestowne Soc. [20398]
    Natl. Soc. of the Colonial Dames of Am. [20399]
    Natl. Soc. Colonial Dames XVII Century [20400]
    Natl. Soc., Daughters of the Amer. Colonists [20401]
    Natl. Soc., Daughters of the British Empire in the U.S.A. [18965]
    Natl. Soc., Sons of the Amer. Colonists [20402]
    Natl. Soc. of Women Descendants of the Ancient and Honorable Artillery Company [20403]
    Order of Americans of Armorial Ancestry [20404]
    Order of the Founders and Patriots of Am. [20405]
    Pilgrim Edward Doty Soc. [20406]
    Soc. of the Ark and the Dove [20407]
    Soc. of Daughters of Holland Dames [20408]
    Soc. of the Descendants of the Colonial Clergy [20409]
    Sons of Colonial New England Natl. Soc. [20410]
Colonial Coin Collectors Club [21971], Charlie Rohrer, Treas., PO Box 25, Mountville, PA 17554
Colonial Coverlet Guild of Am. [21326], 536 Arizona Ave., Glenwood, IL 60425
Colonial Rottweiler Club [21545], 61 Sea View Ave., Niantic, CT 06357
Colonial Soc. of Massachusetts [9760], 87 Mt. Vernon St., Boston, MA 02108, (617)227-2782
Colonial Soc. of Pennsylvania - Defunct.
Color
    Color Marketing Gp. [798]
    Color Marketing Gp. [798]
    Color Pigments Mfrs. Assn. [799]
    Inter-Society Color Coun. [6434]
    Inter-Society Color Coun. [6434]
    Intl. Assn. of Color Mfrs. [800]
    Intl. Assn. of Color Mfrs. [800]
    Intl. Color Consortium [801]
Color Marketing Gp. [798], 1908 Mt. Vernon Ave., Alexandria, VA 22301, (703)329-8500
Color Marketing Gp. [798], 1908 Mt. Vernon Ave., Alexandria, VA 22301, (703)329-8500
Color Pigments Mfrs. Assn. [799], 300 N Washington St., Ste. 105, Alexandria, VA 22314, (703)684-4044
Colorado Christian Univ. Alumni Assn. [18866], Alumni Relations, 8787 W Alameda Ave., Lakewood, CO 80226, (303)963-3330
Colorado Mining Assn. [2511], 216 16th St., Ste. 1250, Denver, CO 80202, (303)575-9199
Colorado Ranger Horse Assn. [4577], Laurel Kosior, Newsl. Ed./Exec. Sec., 1510 Greenhouse Rd., Wampum, PA 16157, (724)535-4841
Colored Angora Goat Breeders Assn. [4499], 4001 Deer Creek Rd., Selma, OR 97538, (541)582-3705
Colored Intercollegiate Athletic Assn. [★22971]

Colored Pencil Soc. of Am. [9173], Cynthia L. Haase, Membership Dir., 8156-E S Wadsworth Blvd., No. 184, Littleton, CO 80128, (303)972-9210
Colored Pencil Soc. of Am. [9173], Cynthia L. Haase, Membership Dir., 8156-E S Wadsworth Blvd., No. 184, Littleton, CO 80128, (303)972-9210
Colors of Cambodia [IO], Siem Reap, Cambodia
Colposcopy and Cervical Pathology; Amer. Soc. for [15870]
Columban Fathers [★19453]
Columbia Basin Trust [IO], Castlegar, BC, Canada
Columbia Coll. of Nursing Alumni Assn. [18867], 2121 E Newport Ave., Milwaukee, WI 53211-2952, (414)961-3530
Columbia Gay and Lesbian Alliance [★12075]
Columbia Historical Soc. [★9769]
Columbia Queer Alliance [12075], Off. of Multicultural Affairs, 510 Lerner Hall, 2920 Broadway, New York, NY 10027, (212)854-0720
Columbia Scholastic Press Advisers Assn. [8745], Columbia Univ., Mail Code 5711, New York, NY 10027-6902, (212)854-9400
Columbia Scholastic Press Assn. [8746], Columbia Univ., Mail Code 5711, New York, NY 10027-6902, (212)854-9400
Columbia School Press Advisers [★8745]
Columbia School Press Specialists [★8745]
Columbia Sheep Breeders Assn. of Am. [4906], 1371 Dozier Sta. Rd., Columbia, MO 65202, (573)886-9419
Column Res. Coun. [★7483]
COM-U.S.A. - Address unknown since 2010.
Coma
    Coma/Traumatic Brain Injury Recovery Assn. [14160]
Coma/Traumatic Brain Injury Recovery Assn. [14160], 8300 Republic Airport, Ste. 106, Farmingdale, NY 11735, (631)756-1826
CoMamas Assn. [12003], PO Box 231804, Encinitas, CA 92023-1804, (760)942-4572
Comanche Language and Cultural Preservation Comm. [10324], 1375 NE Cline Rd., Elgin, OK 73538-3086, (580)492-4988
Combat Helicopter Pilots Assn. [20313], PO Box 42, Divide, CO 80814-0042, (719)687-4131
Combat Martial Art Practitioners Assn. [22731], 1217 E High St., Lima, OH 45804
Combat Merchant Mariners World War II - Defunct.
Combat Veterans Motorcycle Assn. [21926], 1019 Highland Dr., Liberty, MO 64068
Combed Yarn Spinners Assn. [★3436]
Combined Campaign for Amer. Reform Judaism [★19897]
Combined Edible Nut Trade Assn. [IO], Woodford, United Kingdom
Combined Heat and Power Assn. [IO], London, United Kingdom
Combined Organizations of Numismatic Error Collectors of Am. [21972], PO Box 6351, Rock Island, IL 61204, (407)688-7006
Combustion Inst. [7265], 5001 Baum Blvd., Ste. 635, Pittsburgh, PA 15213-1851, (412)687-1366
COMCARE Alliance [14482], 1701 K St. NW, 4th Fl., Washington, DC 20006-1503, (202)429-0574
COME Intl. Baptist Ministries [19741], PO Box 88085, Grand Rapids, MI 49518, (616)868-9906
Comedy
    Abbott and Costello Intl. Fan Club [23795]
    The Andy Griffith Show Rerun Watchers Club [23917]
    Damfinos: The Intl. Buster Keaton Soc. [23796]
    Intl. Jack Benny Fan Club [23797]
    Three Stooges Fan Club [23798]
    W.C. Fields Fan Club [23799]
Comedy Fights Cancer [13909], Nuforms Media, 116 W 23rd St., Ste. 500, New York, NY 10011, (212)396-2015
Comet Media Found. of Mumbai, India [IO], Mumbai, India
ComexPeru Peruvian Foreign Trading Soc. [IO], Lima, Peru
ComexPeru Sociedad de Comercio Exterior del Peru [★IO]
Comhairle Chaomhnaithe Phortaigh na hEireann [★IO]

Reference to "IO" in place of a book number signifies that the association may be found in the 50th edition of International Organizations.

Comhairle Naisiunta na mBan in Eirinn [★IO]
Comhairle Naisiunta na Nog [★IO]
Comhairle Oilimpeach na hEireann [★IO]
Comhairle Spoirt na hEireann [★IO]
Comhairle Treidlianna na Heireann [★IO]
Comhaltas Ceoltoiri Eireann [★IO]
Comhaontas na Siochana is Neodrachta [★IO]
Comhlamh [IO], Dublin, Ireland
Comic Relief [IO], London, United Kingdom
Comicbook Artists' Guild [9489], 133 Sillimanville
  Rd., Moodus, CT 06469
Comics
  Comicbook Artists' Guild [9489]
  Comics Professional Retailers Org. [802]
  Hero Initiative [9490]
  Natl. Assn. of Comics Art Educators [7887]
  Prism Comics [803]
Comics Creators Guild [IO], London, United
  Kingdom
Comics Professional Retailers Org. [802], PO Box
  75446, Colorado Springs, CO 80970, (877)574-
  8618
Comision Andina de Juristas [★IO]
Comision Catolica Internacional de Migracion [★IO]
Comision para la Conservacion de los Recursos Vi-
  vos Marinos Antarticos [★IO]
Comision Economica para Am. Latina y el Caribe
  [★IO]
Comision de Integracion Energetica Regional [★IO]
Comision Mexicana de Defensa y Promocion de los
  Derechos Humanos [★IO]
Comision Nacional de Badminton del Peru [IO],
  Lima, Peru
Comision Nacional de Seguridad Nuclear y Salva-
  guardias [★IO]
Comision Panamericana de Normas Tecnicas [★IO]
Comision Permanente del Pacifico Sur [★IO]
Comitato Collaborazione Medica [★IO]
Comitato di Coordinamento delle Organizzazioni per
  il Servizio Volontario [IO], Milan, Italy
Comitato Italiano Atlantico [★IO]
Comitato Italiano Paralimpico [★IO]
Comitato Italiano Paralimpico [★IO]
Comitato Olimpico Nazionale Sammarinese [IO],
  Serravalle, San Marino
Comite europeen des constructeurs de machines
  pour plastiques et caoutchouc [★IO]
Comite canadien de catalogage [★IO]
Comite europeen de normalisation electrotechnique
  [★IO]
Comite intergouvernemental de recherches urbaines
  et regionales [★IO]
Comite de Am. Latina y el Caribe para la Defensa
  de los Derechos de la Mujer [★IO]
Comite Argentino del Consejo Mundial de la Energia
  [★IO]
Comite Belge pour l'Investigation Scientifique des
  Phenomenes Reputes Pananormaux [IO], Brus-
  sels, Belgium
Comite Canada-Israel [★IO]
Comite Central des Armateurs de France [★IO]
Comite du Commerce des cereals, aliments du be-
  tail, oleagineux, huile d'olive, huiles et graisses et
  agrofourniture [★IO]
Comite des Constructeurs Francais d'Automobiles
  [★IO]
Comite Consultatif Economique et Industriel aupres
  de l'O.C.D.E. [★IO]
Comite Coordinador de Asociaciones Agricolas,
  Comerciales, Industriales y Financieras [★IO]
Comite d'Andorra per l'UNICEF [★IO]
Comite Electrotechnique Belge [★IO]
Comite Espanol de la Camara de Comercio Interna-
  cional [IO], Barcelona, Spain
Comite Europeen des Associations de Constructeurs
  d'Engrenages et d'Elements de Transmission
  [★IO]
Comite Europeen des Associations d'interet Gen.
  [★IO]
Comite Europeen des Assurances [★IO]
Comite Europeen des Assurances [★IO]
Comite Europeen des Constructeurs de Fours et
  Equipements Thermiques Industriels [★IO]
Comite Europeen de Droit Rural [★IO]
Comite Europeen des Equipements Techniques du
  Batiment [★IO]

Comite Europeen des Fabricants de Sucre [★IO]
Comite Europeen des Instructeurs Professionnels de
  Plongee [★IO]
Comite Europeen pour l'Enseignement Catholique
  [★IO]
Comite Europeen de Liaison des Importateurs de
  Machines-Outils [★IO]
Comite Europeen de l'Industrie de la Robinetterie
  [★IO]
Comite Europeen de Normalisation [★IO]
Comite Europeen des Transmissions Oleohy-
  drauliques et Pneumatiques [★IO]
Comite des Fabricants de Levure de Panification de
  l'Union Europeenne [★IO]
Comite Francais de Lutte contre l'HyperTension Arte-
  rielle [★IO]
Comite Francais pour les Travaux sans Tranchee
  [★IO]
Comite Intl. pour le Controle des Performances en
  Elevage [★IO]
Comite Intl. de Cooperation dans les Recherches
  Nationales en Demographie [★IO]
Comite Intl. de la Croix-Rouge [★IO]
Comite Intl. d'Histoire de la Deuxieme Guerre Mon-
  diale [★IO]
Comite Intl. de l'Inspection Technique Auto. [★IO]
Comite Intl. de Medecine Militaire [★IO]
Comite Intl. pour la Metrologie Historique [★IO]
Comite Intl. Olympique [★IO]
Comite Intl. des Plasticos en Agricultura [★IO]
Comite Intl. pour la Protection des Cables Sous-
  marins [★IO]
Comite Intl. Radio-Maritime [★IO]
Comite Intl. de la Rayonne et des Fibres Synthet-
  iques [★IO]
Comite Intl. des Sciences Historiques [★IO]
Comite Intl. des Transports Ferroviaires [★IO]
Comite des eches pour l'Atlantique Centre-Est [★IO]
Comite pour l'elimination de la discrimination raciale
  [★IO]
Comite pour l'Europe occidentale contre la corrosion
  des conduites souterraines [★IO]
Comite canadien sur l'histoire du travail [★IO]
Comite Maritime Intl. [★IO]
Comite Mundial de Consulta de los Amigos [★IO]
Comite Nacional Pro Defensa de la Flora y Fauna
  [IO], Santiago, Chile
Comite Natl. Olympique du Burundi [IO], Bujumbura,
  Burundi
Comite Natl. Olympique et Sportif Beninois [IO],
  Cotonou, Benin
Comite Natl. Olympique et Sportif du Cameroun
  [IO], Yaounde, Cameroon
Comite Natl. Olympique et Sportif Centrafricain [IO],
  Bangui, Central African Republic
Comite Natl. Olympique et Sportif Congolais [IO],
  Brazzaville, Republic of the Congo
Comite Natl. Paralympique Centrafricain [IO], Ban-
  gui, Central African Republic
Comite Olimpico Angolano [IO], Luanda, Angola
Comite Olimpico Brasileiro [★IO]
Comite Olimpico Caboverdeano [IO], Praia, Cape
  Verde
Comite Olimpico Colombiano [★IO]
Comite Olimpico Ecuatoriano [★IO]
Comite Olimpico Guatemalteco [★IO]
Comite Olimpico Mexicano [★IO]
Comite Olimpico de Portugal [★IO]
Comite Olympique Algerien [IO], Algiers, Algeria
Comite Olympique Bulgare [★IO]
Comite Olympique Canadien [★IO]
Comite Olympique Hongrois [★IO]
Comite Olympique et Sportif Tchadien [IO],
  N'Djamena, Chad
Comite des Organisations Professionnelles Agricoles
  de l'EU [★IO]
Comite Paralimpico Angolano [IO], Luanda, Angola
Comite Paralimpico Espanol [★IO]
Comite Paralympique Canadien [★IO]
Comite Permanent des Indus. du Verre Europ-
  eennes [★IO]
Comite Permanent de Liaison des Orthophonistes-
  Logopedes de l'UE [★IO]
Comite para la Promocion y el Progreso de las Co-
  operativas [★IO]

Comite pour la Recherche Spatiale [★IO]
Comite Royal Belge de la Distribution [IO], Brussels,
  Belgium
Comite Scientifique pour l'Allocation des Frequences
  a la Radio Astronomie et la Recherche Spatiale
  [★IO]
Comite Scientifique sur les Problemes de
  l'Environnement [★IO]
Comite UNICEF Canada [★IO]
Comitetul Natl. Roman al Consiliului Mondial al En-
  ergiei [IO], Bucharest, Romania
Command Trust Network [17125], 11301 W Olympic
  Blvd., Ste. 332, Los Angeles, CA 90064
Commemorative Air Force [20888], PO Box 62000,
  Midland, TX 79711-2000, (432)563-1000
Commemorative Collectors Soc. [IO], Newark,
  United Kingdom
Commerce Queensland [IO], Brisbane, Australia
CommerceNet [7496], 169 Univ. Ave., Palo Alto, CA
  94301, (650)289-4040
Commercial Alert [18418], PO Box 19002,
  Washington, DC 20036, (202)387-8030
Commercial Assn. of Portugal [IO], Porto, Portugal
Commercial Boat Operators Assn. [IO], London,
  United Kingdom
Commercial Development and Marketing Assn.
  [6403], 15000 Commerce Pkwy., Ste. C, Mount
  Laurel, NJ 08054, (856)439-9052
Commercial Farmers' Bur. [★20756]
Commercial Finance Assn. [2209], 370 7th Ave.,
  Ste. 1801, New York, NY 10001-3979, (212)792-
  9390
Commercial Finance Assn. [2209], 370 7th Ave.,
  Ste. 1801, New York, NY 10001-3979, (212)792-
  9390
Commercial Food Equip. Ser. Agencies of Am.
  [★1437]
Commercial Food Equip. Ser. Assn. [1437], 2216 W
  Meadowview Rd., Ste. 100, Greensboro, NC
  27407, (336)346-4700
Commercial Horticultural Assn. [IO], Kenilworth,
  United Kingdom
Commercial Internet Exchange Assn. [★6563]
Commercial Law
  Amer. Bankruptcy Inst. [5315]
  Amer. Coll. of Bankruptcy [5316]
  Commercial Law League of Am. [5317]
  Forfeiture Endangers Amer. Rights [5318]
  Natl. Assn. of Bankruptcy Trustees [5319]
  Natl. Assn. of Shareholder and Consumer At-
    torneys [5320]
Commercial Law Assn. of Australia [IO], Sydney,
  Australia
Commercial Law League of Am. [5317], 205 N
  Michigan, Ste. 2212, Chicago, IL 60601, (312)240-
  1400
Commercial Mortgage Securities Assn. [★3010]
Commercial Photographers Intl. [2715], 229 Peacht-
  ree St. NE, Ste. 2200, Atlanta, GA 30303-1608,
  (800)786-6277
Commercial Photographers Intl. [2715], 229 Peacht-
  ree St. NE, Ste. 2200, Atlanta, GA 30303-1608,
  (800)786-6277
Commercial Radio Australia [IO], Surry Hills,
  Australia
Commercial Refrigerator Mfrs. Div. [★1695]
Commercial Refrigerator Mfrs. Div. - Defunct.
Commercial Trailer Assn. [IO], London, United
  Kingdom
Commercial Vehicle Safety Alliance [296], 6303 Ivy
  Ln., Ste. 310, Greenbelt, MD 20770-6319,
  (301)830-6143
Commercial Vehicle Safety Alliance [296], 6303 Ivy
  Ln., Ste. 310, Greenbelt, MD 20770-6319,
  (301)830-6143
Commercial Vehicle Solutions Network [324], 3943-2
  Baymeadows Rd., Jacksonville, FL 32217,
  (904)737-2900
Commercial Weather Services Assn. - Address
  unknown since 2010.
Commn. on Accreditation of Allied Hea. Educ.
  Programs [8577], 1361 Park St., Clearwater, FL
  33756, (727)210-2350
Commission on Accreditation of Allied Hea. Educ.
  Programs [★15361]

A star before a book entry number signifies that the name is not listed separately, but is mentioned within the entry.

Commn. on Accreditation of Ambulance Services [13572], 1926 Waukegan Rd., Ste. 300, Glenview, IL 60025-1770, (847)657-6828

Commn. on Accreditation for Law Enforcement Agencies [5690], 13575 Heathcote Blvd., Ste. 320, Gainesville, VA 20155, (703)352-4225

Commn. on Accreditation for Marriage and Family Therapy Educ. [8558], Amer. Assn. for Marriage and Family Therapy, 112 S Alfred St., Alexandria, VA 22314, (703)838-9808

Commn. on Accreditation of Rehabilitation Facilities Canada [IO], Edmonton, AB, Canada

Commn. on Accreditation of Ser. Experiences [★8171]

Commn. of Accredited Truck Driving Schools - Defunct.

Commn. Adhoc Congolaise de Badminton [IO], Brazzaville, Republic of the Congo

Commn. Africaine Des Droits De L'Homme et Des Peuples [★IO]

Commn. Africaine de l'Aviation Civile [★IO]

Commn. on Air Pollution Prevention of VDI and DIN - Standards Comm. [IO], Dusseldorf, Germany

Commission on Amer. and Intl. Schools Abroad [★8054]

Commn. on Archives and History of the United Methodist Church [★10084]

Commn. on Benevolent Institutions [★13183]

Commn. of the Bishops' Conferences of the European Community [IO], Brussels, Belgium

Commn. Canadienne du Ble [★IO]

Commn. Canadienne du Lait [★IO]

Commn. for Case Manager Certification [14876], 15000 Commerce Pkwy., Ste. C, Mount Laurel, NJ 08054, (856)380-6836

Commn. for Certification in Geriatric Pharmacy [16189], 1321 Duke St., Ste. 400, Alexandria, VA 22314-3563, (703)535-3036

Commn. on Certification of Work Adjustment and Vocational Evaluation Specialists - Defunct.

Commn. of the Churches on Intl. Affairs [19828], UN HQ Liaison Off., 9D, 777 UN Plz., New York, NY 10017, (212)867-5890

Commn. of the Churches on Intl. Affairs [19828], UN HQ Liaison Off., 9D, 777 UN Plz., New York, NY 10017, (212)867-5890

Commn. du Codex Alimentarius [★IO]

Commn. on Collegiate Nursing Educ. [8602], 1 Dupont Cir. NW, Ste. 530, Washington, DC 20036, (202)463-6930

Commn. for the Conservation of Antarctic Marine Living Resources [IO], North Hobart, Australia

Commn. on Crime Prevention and Criminal Justice [IO], Vienna, Austria

Commn. De la Carte Geologique du Monde [★IO]

Commission on Dental Accreditation [★14250]

Commn. on Dietetic Registration [15825], 120 S Riverside Plz., Ste. 2000, Chicago, IL 60606-6995, (312)899-0040

Commn. on Dietetic Registration [15825], 120 S Riverside Plz., Ste. 2000, Chicago, IL 60606-6995, (312)899-0040

Commn. Electrotechnique Internationale [★IO]

Commn. des Episcopats de la Communaute Europeenne [★IO]

Commn. Europeenne Consultative pour les Peches dans les Eaux Interieures [★IO]

Commn. Europeenne du Tourisme [★IO]

Commn. de la Fonction Publique Internationle [★23259]

Commn. de la Fonction Publique Internationle [★23259]

Commn. Francaise Justice et Paix [★IO]

Commn. on Gay/Lesbian Issues in Social work Educ. [★8869]

Commn. Generale des Peches pour la Mediterranee [★IO]

Commn. for the Geological Map of the World [IO], Paris, France

Commn. on Graduates of Foreign Nursing Schools [15744], 3600 Market St., Ste. 400, Philadelphia, PA 19104-2651, (215)222-8454

Commn. on Hea. and Healing [★19950]

Commission on Independent Schools [★8054]

Commission on Institutions of Higher Education [★8054]

Commn. on Intl. Affairs [★17903]

Commn. on Intl. Affairs [★17903]

Commn. Internationale des Aumoniers Generaux des Prisons [★IO]

Commn. Internationale pour la Conservation des Thonides de l'Atlantique [★IO]

Commn. Internationale de Demographie Historique [★IO]

Commn. Internationale d'Optique [★IO]

Commn. Internationale du Genie Rural [★IO]

Commn. Internationale des Grands Barrages [★IO]

Commn. Internationale des Indus. Agricoles et Alimentaires [★IO]

Commn. Internationale des Irrigations et du Drainage [★IO]

Commn. Internationale de Juristes [★IO]

Commn. Internationale de Juristes - Sect. Canadienne [★IO]

Commn. Internationale de l'Eclairage [★IO]

Commn. Internationale de l'Enseignement Mathematique [★IO]

Commn. Internationale de l'Etat Civil [★IO]

Commn. Internationale pour l'Histoire des Assemblees d'Etats [★IO]

Commn. Internationale pour l'Histoire des Villes [★IO]

Commn. Internationale pour l'Unification des Methodes d'Analyse du Sucre [★IO]

Commn. Internationale de la Microflore du Paleozoique [★IO]

Commn. Internationale de Nomenclature Zoologique [★IO]

Commn. Internationale de Numismatique [★IO]

Commn. Internationale des Oeufs [★IO]

Commn. Internationale Permanente pour l'Epreuve des Armes a Feu Portatives [★IO]

Commn. Internationale pour la Protection des Alpes [★IO]

Commn. Internationale pour la Protection des Alpes [IO], Schaan, Liechtenstein

Commn. Internationale du Riz [★IO]

Commn. Internationale de la Sante au Travail [★IO]

Commn. on Interracial Cooperation [★17328]

Commn. Intersyndicale des Deshydrateurs Europeens [★IO]

Commn. on Jewish Chaplaincy [★19523]

Commn. on Legal Pluralism [IO], Ruschlikon, Switzerland

Commn. on Legal Problems of the Elderly [★5641]

Commn. for Local Admin. in England [IO], London, United Kingdom

Commn. de l'Ocean Indien [★IO]

Commn. canadienne pour l'unesco [★IO]

Commn. Luxembourgeoise - Justice et Paix [IO], Luxembourg, Luxembourg

Commn. on the Mentally Disabled [★5508]

Commn. des migrations, des refugies, et de la Population [★IO]

Commn. on Missing and Exploited Children [11256], 616 Adams Ave., Rm. 200, Memphis, TN 38105, (901)405-8441

Commn. for Music Res. of the Austrian Acad. of Sciences [IO], Vienna, Austria

Commn. on Nuclear Physics [IO], Adelaide, Australia

Commn. Oceanographique Intergouvernementale [★IO]

Commn. on Opticianry Accreditation [15982], PO Box 592, Canton, NY 13617, (703)468-0566

Commn. de Pastorale Sociale - Caritas Mali [IO], Bamako, Mali

Commn. on Peace and Human Rights [★18283]

Commn. on Presidential Debates [18380], 1200 New Hampshire Ave. NW, PO Box 445, Washington, DC 20036, (202)872-1020

Commn. on Professionals in Sci. and Tech. [7366], 1200 New York Ave. NW, Ste. 113, Washington, DC 20005, (202)326-7080

Commission on Public Elementary and Middle Schools [★8054]

Commission on Public Secondary Schools [★8054]

Commn. for Racial Equality [IO], London, United Kingdom

Commn. for Racial Justice [★20276]

Commn. on Rehabilitation Counselor Certification [11672], 1699 E Woodfield Rd., Ste. 300, Schaumburg, IL 60173-4957, (847)944-1325

Commn. on Religious Counseling and Healing [19289], 4202 Newark Ave., Cleveland, OH 44109, (216)543-6377

Commn. on Religious Counseling and Healing [19289], 4202 Newark Ave., Cleveland, OH 44109, (216)543-6377

Commn. on Res. in Pastoral Care and Counseling of the Congress on Ministry in specialized settings - Defunct.

Commn. Seismologique Europeenne [★IO]

Commn. on Sexual Orientation and Gender Expression [★8869]

Commn. on Social Action of Reform Judaism [★19898]

Commn. for Social Justice [17282], 219 E St. NE, Washington, DC 20002-4922, (202)547-2900

Commn. on Standardization of Biological Stains [★6294]

Commn. on the Status of Women [17634], Dept. of Economic and Social Affairs, Div. for the Advancement of Women, 2 UN Plz., DC2-12th Fl., New York, NY 10017

Commn. on the Status of Women [17634], Dept. of Economic and Social Affairs, Div. for the Advancement of Women, 2 UN Plz., DC2-12th Fl., New York, NY 10017

Commn. to Study the Org. of Peace - Defunct.

Commn. on the Stud. of Peace [★18283]

Commn. Syndicale Consultative aupres de l'OCDE [★IO]

Commission on Tech. and Career Institutions [★8054]

Commn. on Undergraduate Educ. in the Biological Sciences [★8835]

Commn. on U.S.-Asian Relations [★17202]

Commn. on U.S.-Asian Relations [★17202]

Commn. on U.S.-Russian Relations - Defunct.

Commn. on Voluntary Ser. and Action [★13390]

Commn. on Women in the Profession [5658], Amer. Bar Assn., 321 N Clark St., 18th Fl., Chicago, IL 60610, (312)988-5715

Commn. for Women's Equality - Address unknown since 2011.

Commn. on Youth Ser. Projects [★13390]

A Commitment to Training and Employment for Women [IO], Toronto, ON, Canada

Committee of 100 [★17302]

Comm. of 100 in Finland [IO], Helsinki, Finland

Comm. of 200 [657], 980 N Michigan Ave., Ste. 1575, Chicago, IL 60611-7540, (312)255-0296

Comm. to Abolish Sport Hunting [10945], PO Box 13815, Las Cruces, NM 88013, (575)640-7372

Committee on Accreditation of Canadian Medical Schools [★8576]

Comm. on Accreditation for Educational Programs for the EMS Professions [8578], 4101 W Green Oaks Blvd., Ste. 305-599, Arlington, TX 76016, (817)330-0080

Comm. on Accreditation of Medical Transport Systems [14483], PO Box 130, Sandy Springs, SC 29677, (864)287-4177

Comm. on Accreditation of Medical Transport Systems [14483], PO Box 130, Sandy Springs, SC 29677, (864)287-4177

Comm. on Accreditation for Ophthalmic Medical Personnel [★8579]

Comm. on Accreditation of Ophthalmic Medical Programs [8579], 2025 Woodlane Dr., St. Paul, MN 55125-2998, (651)731-7244

Comm. on Accreditation for Respiratory Care [16845], 1248 Harwood Rd., Bedford, TX 76021-4244, (817)283-2835

Comm. for Accuracy in Middle East Reporting in Am. [18120], PO Box 35040, Boston, MA 02135-0001, (617)789-3672

Comm. for Accuracy in Middle East Reporting in Am. [18120], PO Box 35040, Boston, MA 02135-0001, (617)789-3672

Comm. for Action for Rural Indians - Defunct.

Comm. for the Advancement of Role-Playing Games [21746], 1127 Cedar St., Bonham, TX 75418-2913

Comm. of Advt. Practice [IO], London, United Kingdom

Comm. Against Anti-Asian Violence [17199], 2473 Valentine Ave., Bronx, NY 10458, (718)220-7391

Reference to "IO" in place of a book number signifies that the association may be found in the 50th edition of International Organizations.

Comm. Against Govt. Waste - Defunct.

Comm. Against the Political Misuse of Psychiatry - Defunct.

Comm. Against Registration and the Draft - Defunct.

Comm. on Allied Hea. Educ. and Accreditation [★8577]

Comm. on Amer. Lib. Resources on South Asia [★9982]

Comm. on Amer. Lib. Resources on South Asia [★9982]

Comm. on Amer. Lib. Resources on Southeast Asia [★9982]

Comm. on Amer. Lib. Resources on Southeast Asia [★9982]

Comm. of Amer. Steamship Lines [★5789]

Comm. of Annuity Insurers [1950], 1455 Pennsylvania Ave. NW, Ste. 1200, Washington, DC 20004, (202)347-2230

Comm. for Asian Women [IO], Bangkok, Thailand

Comm. on Assessing the Progress of Educ. [★8989]

Comm. for Better Transit - Defunct.

Comm. on Boarding Schools [★8752]

Comm. to Bridge the Gap [18193], 13400 Riverside Dr., Ste. 308, Sherman Oaks, CA 91423, (831)336-8003

Comm. on Canada-U.S. Relations - Defunct.

Comm. for the Caribbean [★12317]

Comm. for the Caribbean [★12317]

Comm. for Catholic Unity [★19504]

Comm. for Children [11257], 2815 2nd Ave., Ste. 400, Seattle, WA 98121, (206)343-1223

Comm. on Christian Literature for Women and Children [★12246]

Comm. on Christian Literature for Women and Children [★12246]

Comm. on Clay Minerals of the Natl. Acad. of Sciences—National Res. Coun. [7121]

Comm. of Concerned Journalists [2819], Natl. Press Bldg., 529 14th St. NW, Ste. 425, Washington, DC 20045, (202)662-7155

Comm. of Concerned Parents [★5590]

Comm. of Concerned Parents [★5590]

Comm. of Concerned Scientists [17820], Sophie Cook, Exec. Dir., 400 E 85th St., Apt. 10K, New York, NY 10028

Comm. for a Constructive Tomorrow [17451], PO Box 65722, Washington, DC 20035, (202)429-2737

Comm. on Continuing Education for School Personnel - Defunct.

Comm. for Crescent Observation Intl. [9890], 1069 Ellis Hollow Rd., Ithaca, NY 14850, (607)277-6706

Comm. for Crescent Observation Intl. [9890], 1069 Ellis Hollow Rd., Ithaca, NY 14850, (607)277-6706

Comm. on Data for Sci. and Tech. [IO], Paris, France

Comm. for a Democratic Majority [17533], 501 Capitol Ct. NE, Ste. 100, Washington, DC 20002, (202)544-4889

Comm. for the Development of Art in Negro Colleges [★7745]

Comm. on Earth Observation Satellites [IO], Frascati, Italy

Comm. for Economic Development [17573], 2000 L St. NW, Ste. 700, Washington, DC 20036, (202)296-5860

Comm. for Economic Development of Australia [IO], Melbourne, Australia

Committee for the Economic Growth of Israel - Address unknown since 2010.

Comm. for Educ. Funding [8098], 1640 Rhode Island Ave. NW, Ste. 600, Washington, DC 20036, (202)383-0083

Comm. on the Elimination of Discrimination Against Women [17635], United Nations Div. for the Advancement of Women, 2 United Nations Plz., DC 2-12th Fl., New York, NY 10017

Comm. on the Elimination of Discrimination Against Women [17635], United Nations Div. for the Advancement of Women, 2 United Nations Plz., DC 2-12th Fl., New York, NY 10017

Comm. on the Elimination of Racial Discrimination [IO], Geneva, Switzerland

Comm. Encouraging Corporate Philanthropy [12662], 110 Wall St., Ste. 2-1, New York, NY 10005, (212)825-1000

Comm. for Environmentally Effective Packaging - Defunct.

Comm. of European Coffee Associations [IO], Amsterdam, Netherlands

Comm. for European Constr. Equip. [IO], Brussels, Belgium

Comm. of Experts on Cosmetic Products [IO], Strasbourg, France

Comm. of Experts on Flavouring Substances [IO], Strasbourg, France

Comm. of Experts on the Legal Classification of Medicines as Regards Their Supply [IO], Strasbourg, France

Comm. of Experts on Materials Coming into Contact with Food [IO], Strasbourg, France

Comm. of Experts on Nutrition, Food Safety and Consumer Hea. [IO], Strasbourg, France

Comm. for Food and Shelter [★12160]

Comm. of French Auto. Mfrs. [IO], Paris, France

Comm. of French Speaking Societies [18991], 30 E 40th St., Ste. 906, New York, NY 10016

Comm. for Full Funding of Educ. Programs [★8098]

Comm. for the Furtherance of Torah Observance [★19892]

Comm. for Handicapable Dancers [9539], Tom James, Chm., 1920 Heron Cove Dr., Lutz, FL 33549, (813)948-9555

Comm. on Health and Human Rights - Defunct.

Comm. on Human Rights [17821], The Natl. Academies, 500 5th St. NW, Washington, DC 20001, (202)334-3043

Comm. on Human Rights in Malaysia and Singapore - Defunct.

Comm. on Human Rights of the U.S. Natl. Acad. of Sciences [★17821]

Comm. on Human Rights of the U.S. Natl. Acad. of Sciences, Natl. Acad. of Engg., and Inst. of Medicine [★17821]

Comm. for Humane Legislation - Defunct.

Comm. for Humanitarian Assistance to Iranian Refugees [12777], 17 Battery Pl., Rm. 605N, New York, NY 10004, (212)747-1046

Comm. for Humanitarian Assistance to Iranian Refugees [12777], 17 Battery Pl., Rm. 605N, New York, NY 10004, (212)747-1046

Comm. on Info. Systems [★5544]

Comm. on Institutional Cooperation [7878], 1819 S Neil St., Ste. D, Champaign, IL 61820-7271, (217)333-8475

Comm. for Intl. Cooperation in Natl. Res. in Demography [IO], Paris, France

Comm. on Intl. Exchange of Persons Conf. Bd. of Assoc. Res. Councils [★8354]

Comm. on Intl. Exchange of Persons Conf. Bd. of Assoc. Res. Councils [★8354]

Comm. on Intl. Freedom to Publish [★17222]

Comm. on Intl. Human Rights Inquiry - Defunct.

Comm. on Intl. Non-Theatrical Events [★9602]

Comm. on Intl. Non-Theatrical Events [★9602]

Comm. Internationale pour la Definition des Caracteristiques Microbiologiques des Aliments [★IO]

Comm. of Interns and Residents [23214], 520 8th Ave., Ste. 1200, New York, NY 10018-4183, (212)356-8100

Comm. of Interns and Residents in New York City [★23214]

Comm. to Investigate Assassinations [★18768]

Comm. for Legal Aid to Poor [IO], Cuttack, India

Comm. for the Maintenance of Jewish Standards - Defunct.

Comm. for Mapping the Flora of Europe [IO], Helsinki, Finland

Comm. on Marine Fisheries [IO], Bangkok, Thailand

Comm. on Migration, Refugees, and Population [IO], Strasbourg, France

Comm. of Ministers [IO], Strasbourg, France

Comm. for Missing Children [12539], 242 Stone Mountain St., Lawrenceville, GA 30045, (678)376-6265

Comm. for Missing Children [12539], 242 Stone Mountain St., Lawrenceville, GA 30045, (678)376-6265

Comm. on Missionary Evangelism [★19741]

Comm. for Modern Courts Fund [★5621]

Comm. of Natl. Security Companies [★3222]

Comm. for a New Korea Policy - Defunct.

Comm. on Non-Market Decision Making [★7291]

Comm. for Nonviolent Action [★18177]

Comm. for Nuclear Responsibility [18181], PO Box 421993, San Francisco, CA 94142, (415)776-8299

Comm. for Nuclear Responsibility [18181], PO Box 421993, San Francisco, CA 94142, (415)776-8299

Comm. for Oil Pipe Lines [★2644]

Comm. On State Taxation [★18697]

Comm. Opposed to Militarism and the Draft [5389], PO Box 15195, San Diego, CA 92175, (619)265-1369

Comm. for Pedestrian Tolls - Defunct.

Comm. for Pipe Line Companies [★2644]

Committee on Postgraduate Educational Programs [★6282]

Committee on Postgraduate Educational Programs [★6282]

Comm. on Preservation of Natural Conditions Ecological Soc. of Am. [★4110]

Comm. of Presidents of Statistical Societies [7473], Dept. of Biostatistics, Harvard School of Public Hea. and Dana Farber, CancerInstitute, 44 Binney St., Boston, MA 02115, (617)632-2472

Comm. of Professional Agricultural Organisations in the EU [IO], Brussels, Belgium

Comm. for the Promotion and Advancement of Cooperatives [IO], Geneva, Switzerland

Comm. to Protect Journalists [17340], 330 7th Ave., 11th Fl., New York, NY 10001, (212)465-1004

Comm. to Protect Journalists [17340], 330 7th Ave., 11th Fl., New York, NY 10001, (212)465-1004

Committee for Purchase From People Who Are Blind or Severely Disabled [★17108]

Comm. to Reduce Infection Deaths [15050], 185 E 85th St., Ste. 35B, New York, NY 10028, (212)369-3329

Comm. for the Reexamination of the History of the Second World War - Defunct.

Comm. of the Regions [IO], Brussels, Belgium

Comm. for Rehabilitation Aid to Afghanistan [IO], Peshawar, Pakistan

Comm. to Release Stockpile [★2462]

Comm. for Religious Freedom [★18519]

Comm. for Religious Freedom [★18519]

Comm. on Res. in Dance [★9540]

Comm. on Res. in Dance [★9540]

Comm. on Res. Materials on Southeast Asia [9982], Ohio Univ., Alden Lib., Athens, OH 45701-2978, (740)593-2657

Comm. on Res. Materials on Southeast Asia [9982], Ohio Univ., Alden Lib., Athens, OH 45701-2978, (740)593-2657

Comm. for a Responsible Fed. Budget [18431], 1899 L St. NW, Ste. 400, Washington, DC 20036, (202)986-6599

Comm. for Responsible Genetics [★18585]

Comm. for Responsive Philanthropy [★12679]

Comm. for a SANE Nuclear Policy [★18213]

Comm. on Scholarly Editions [10711], Modern Language Assn. of Am., 26 Broadway, 3rd Fl., New York, NY 10004, (646)576-5000

Committee for the Sci. Examination of Religion [★19819]

Committee for the Sci. Examination of Religion [★19819]

Comm. of Sci. Soc. Presidents [★7367]

Comm. of Scottish Clearing Bankers [IO], Edinburgh, United Kingdom

Comm. for Single Six-Year Presidential Term - Defunct.

Comm. for Skeptical Inquiry [7224], PO Box 703, Amherst, NY 14226, (716)636-1425

Comm. in Solidarity With the People of El Salvador [17602], 1525 Newton St. NW, Washington, DC 20010, (202)521-2510

Comm. in Solidarity With the People of El Salvador [17602], 1525 Newton St. NW, Washington, DC 20010, (202)521-2510

Comm. on South Asian Women [17636], Texas A&M Univ., Dept. of Psychology, College Station, TX 77843-4235, (979)845-2576

Comm. on South Asian Women [17636], Texas A&M Univ., Dept. of Psychology, College Station, TX 77843-4235, (979)845-2576

A star before a book entry number signifies that the name is not listed separately, but is mentioned within the entry.

Comm. on Space Res. [IO], Paris, France

Comm. on the Status of Women in the Economics Profession [5392], PO Box 9300, Portland, ME 04104-9300, (207)228-8245

Comm. on the Status of Women in Microbiology [6297], Nassau County Coll. and Medical Center, Dept. of Allied Hea. Sciences, 1 Educ. Dr., Garden City, NY 11530-6793, (516)572-7915

Comm. on the Status of Women in Philosophy - Defunct.

Comm. on the Status of Women in Sociology; Amer. Sociological Assn. | [9589]

Comm. to Stop Chem. Atrocities [★18476]

Comm. on Sugar Cane Diseases - Defunct.

Comm. to Support the Antitrust Laws - Address unknown since 2011.

Comm. to Support Irish Political Prisoners - Defunct.

Comm. to Support the Revolution in Peru [18371], PO Box 1246, Berkeley, CA 94701, (415)252-5786

Comm. in Support of Solidarity [★17566]

Comm. in Support of Solidarity [★17566]

Comm. for Sustainable Agriculture [★3740]

Comm. on the Teaching of Science of the Intl. Coun. of Scientific Unions - Defunct.

Comm. for Truth in Psychiatry [15450], PO Box 1214, New York, NY 10003, (212)NO-JOLTS

Comm. for a Unified Independent Party [18354], 225 Broadway, Ste. 2010, New York, NY 10007, (212)609-2800

Comm. on Uniform Traffic Accident Statistics [★13010]

Comm. for U.S. Veterans of Hiroshima and Nagasaki [★13351]

Comm. on US/Latin Amer. Relations [19103], 316 Anabel Taylor Hall, Ithaca, NY 14850, (607)255-7293

Comm. on User Instruction for Information Literacy - Defunct.

Comm. on Vacuum Tech. [★7592]

Committees of Correspondence for Democracy and Socialism [5978], 545 8th Ave., Rm. No. 1215, New York, NY 10018, (212)868-3733

Commodities

Amcot, Inc. [3946]

Amer. Commodity Distribution Assn. [3947]

Amer. Malting Barley Assn. [3948]

Amer. Soybean Assn. [3949]

Hop Growers of Am. [3950]

Intl. Cotton Advisory Comm. [3951]

Intl. Cotton Advisory Comm. [3951]

Kamut Assn. of North Am. [3952]

Natl. Assn. of Wheat Growers [3953]

Natl. Barley Growers Assn. [4373]

Natl. Corn Growers Assn. [3954]

Natl. Sorghum Producers [3955]

Natl. Sunflower Assn. [3956]

Natl. Sweet Sorghum Producers and Processors Assn. [3957]

Org. for the Advancement of Knowledge [3958]

Pacific Northwest Grain and Feed Assn. [3959]

Plains Cotton Growers [3960]

Soyfoods Assn. of North Am. [3961]

Supima [3962]

U.S. Durum Growers Assn. [3963]

U.S. Wheat Associates [3964]

U.S. Wheat Associates [3964]

U.S.A. Rice Coun. [3965]

Wheat Quality Coun. [3966]

Commodity Exchanges

Kansas City Bd. of Trade [3967]

Memphis Cotton Exchange [3968]

Minneapolis Grain Exchange [3969]

New Orleans Bd. of Trade [3970]

Commodity Markets Coun. [1591], 1300 L St. NW, Ste. 1020, Washington, DC 20005, (202)842-0400

Common-[★6509]

Common-A Users Gp. [6509], 5515 N Cumberland Ave., Ste. 810, Chicago, IL 60656, (312)279-0192

Common Boundary - Defunct.

Common Cause [18326], 1133 19th St. NW, 9th Fl., Washington, DC 20036, (202)833-1200

Common Destiny Alliance [8012], Univ. of Maryland, 2110 Benjamin Bldg., College Park, MD 20742, (301)405-0639

Common Dreams [17177], PO Box 443, Portland, ME 04112-0443, (207)775-0488

Common Ground [★18695]

Common Ground Alliance [12981], 1421 Prince St., Ste. 410, Alexandria, VA 22314, (703)836-1709

Common Ground Prog. [IO], Kitale, Kenya

Common Ground - U.S.A. [18695], PO Box 57, Evanston, IL 60204, (847)475-0391

Common Hope for Hea. [14768], 212 Highland St., Unit A, Roxbury, MA 02119, (617)418-4163

Common Market for Eastern and Southern Africa [IO], Lusaka, Zambia

Common Sense for Animals [10946], PO Box 589, Broadway, NJ 08808, (908)859-3060

Common Sense for Drug Policy [18451], 1377-C Spencer Ave., Lancaster, PA 17603, (717)299-0600

Common Sense about Kids and Guns [8202], 1225 I St. NW, Ste. 1100, Washington, DC 20005-3914, (202)546-0200

Common Sense Media - Defunct.

Commons, Open Spaces and Footpaths Preservation Soc. [IO], Henley-on-Thames, United Kingdom

Commonwealth Assn. of Architects [IO], London, United Kingdom

Commonwealth Assn. for Corporate Governance [IO], Marlborough, New Zealand

Commonwealth Assn. of Museums [IO], De Winton, AB, Canada

Commonwealth Assn. of Planners [IO], Edinburgh, United Kingdom

Commonwealth Assn. for Public Admin. and Mgt. [IO], Ottawa, ON, Canada

Commonwealth Assn. of Public Sector Lawyers [IO], Mosman, Australia

Commonwealth Assn. of Sci., Tech. and Mathematics Educators [IO], Winchester, United Kingdom

Commonwealth Assn. of Surveying and Land Economy [IO], Bristol, United Kingdom

Commonwealth Assn. of Tax Administrators [IO], London, United Kingdom

Commonwealth Bd. of Architectural Educ. [★9694]

Commonwealth Broadcasting Assn. [IO], London, United Kingdom

Commonwealth Cancer Assn. [IO], Saipan, Northern Mariana Islands

Commonwealth Coun. for Educational Admin. and Mgt. [IO], Johannesburg, Republic of South Africa

Commonwealth Countries League [IO], Sudbury, United Kingdom

Commonwealth Dental Assn. [IO], London, United Kingdom

Commonwealth Forestry Assn. [IO], Craven Arms, United Kingdom

Commonwealth Found. [IO], London, United Kingdom

Commonwealth Fund [16484], 1 E 75th St., New York, NY 10021, (212)606-3800

Commonwealth Fund for Tech. Co-Operation [IO], London, United Kingdom

Commonwealth Games Fed. [IO], London, United Kingdom

Commonwealth Hansard Editors Assn. [IO], London, United Kingdom

Commonwealth Human Ecology Coun. [IO], London, United Kingdom

Commonwealth Human Rights Initiative [IO], New Delhi, India

Commonwealth Inst. [IO], London, United Kingdom

Commonwealth Journalists Assn. [IO], Toronto, ON, Canada

Commonwealth Lawyers' Assn. [IO], London, United Kingdom

Commonwealth of Learning [IO], Vancouver, BC, Canada

Commonwealth Magistrates and Judges' Assn. [IO], London, United Kingdom

Commonwealth Network of Info. Tech. for Development [IO], Gzira, Malta

Commonwealth of the Northern Mariana Islands Bar Assn. [IO], Saipan, Northern Mariana Islands

Commonwealth of the Northern Mariana Islands Coun. on Developmental Disabilities [IO], Saipan, Northern Mariana Islands

Commonwealth Nurses Fed. [IO], London, United Kingdom

Commonwealth Parliamentary Assn. [IO], London, United Kingdom

Commonwealth Partnership for Tech. Mgt. [IO], London, United Kingdom

Commonwealth Pharmaceutical Assn. [IO], London, United Kingdom

Commonwealth Sci. and Indus. Res. Org. [IO], Clayton South, Australia

Commonwealth Secretariat [IO], London, United Kingdom

Commonwealth Soc. for Deaf [IO], London, United Kingdom

Commonwealth Telecommunications Org. [IO], London, United Kingdom

Commonwealth War Graves Commn. [IO], Maidenhead, United Kingdom

Commonwealth Youth Exchange Coun. [IO], London, United Kingdom

Communal Ser. Assn. of North Am; Jewish [12407]

Communal Stud. Assn. [9676], PO Box 122, Amana, IA 52203, (319)622-6446

Communaute Economique des Etats de l'Afrique de l'Ouest [★IO]

Communaute Europeenne du Rail [★IO]

Communaute Europeenne des Cooperatives de Consommateurs [★IO]

Communaute Francaise de Belgique [IO], Brussels, Belgium

Communaute du Pacifique [★IO]

Communaute des Potiers Rwandais [★IO]

Communautee Europeenne des Jeunes de l'Horticulture [★IO]

Communicating for Agriculture [★3719]

Communicating for Agriculture and the Self Employed [★3719]

Communicating for Am. [3719], PO Box 677, Fergus Falls, MN 56538-0677, (218)739-3241

Commun., Advt., and Marketing Educ. Found. [IO], Maidenhead, United Kingdom

Commun. Agencies Assn. of New Zealand [IO], Auckland, New Zealand

Commun. Independence for the Neurologically Impaired [15581], PO Box 263, Manorville, NY 11949, (631)878-0642

Commun. Inst. for Online Scholarship [6107], PO Box 57, Rotterdam Junction, NY 12150, (518)887-2443

Commun. and Media Law Assn. [IO], Glebe, Australia

Commun. Workers' Union [IO], London, United Kingdom

Commun. Workers Union of England [IO], London, United Kingdom

Communications

911 Indus. Alliance [804]

Accuracy in Media [17332]

Alliance for Community Media [17333]

Amer. Family Assn. [17334]

Amer. Lib. Assn. - Public Info. Off. [10476]

Amer. Radio Relay League [20931]

Amer. Soc. of Professional Communicators [805]

ARRL Found. [20933]

Assn. of Biomedical Communications Directors [14161]

Assn. of Cable Communicators [5321]

Assn. for Women in Communications [806]

Benjamin Franklin Educ. Found. [8003]

BioCommunications Assn. [14162]

BioCommunications Assn. [14162]

Caucus for TV Producers, Writers, and Directors [17335]

Cell Phones for Soldiers [11086]

Center for Asian Amer. Media [17336]

Center for Democracy and Tech. [17337]

Center for Investigative Reporting [17338]

Center for Media and Public Affairs [17339]

Comm. to Protect Journalists [17340]

Comm. to Protect Journalists [17340]

Communications Workers of Am. [23174]

Cooperative Assn. for Internet Data Anal. [7007]

Corporate Speech Pathology Network [3303]

Coun. of Commun. Mgt. [807]

Critical Messaging Assn. [808]

Electronic Indus. Citizenship Coalition [1098]

Empowerment Proj. [17341]

Essential Info. [17342]

Fairness and Accuracy in Reporting [17343]

Reference to "IO" in place of a book number signifies that the association may be found in the 50th edition of International Organizations.

Encyclopedia of Associations, 51st Edition   2705

Fed. Communications Bar Assn. [5322]
Fund for Investigative Journalism [17344]
Hea. Sci. Communications Assn. [14163]
Hispanic Public Relations Assn. [17345]
IEEE | Communications Soc. [7539]
Inter Amer. Press Assn. [17346]
Inter Amer. Press Assn. [17346]
Intl. Assn. of Bus. Communicators [809]
Intl. Assn. of Bus. Communicators [809]
Intl. Avaya Users Gp. [3410]
Intl. Communications Agency Network [810]
Intl. Communications Agency Network [810]
Intl. Radio Club of Am. [20937]
Intl. Soc. for Gesture Stud. [6435]
Intl. Soc. for Gesture Stud. [6435]
Intl. Tech. Law Assn. [5323]
Laptops for the Wounded [11526]
Mainstream Media Proj. [18503]
Markle Found. [6436]
Media Access Proj. [17347]
Media Action Grassroots Network [18092]
Media Alliance [17348]
Media and Democracy Coalition [18094]
The Media Inst. [17349]
Media Watch [17350]
Media Watch [17350]
MultiService Forum [811]
Natl. Anxiety Center [18436]
Natl. Assn. of Call Centers [812]
Natl. Assn. of Commun. Systems Engineers [6437]
Natl. Assn. of Govt. Communicators [5324]
Natl. Assn. for Multi-Ethnicity in Communications [813]
Natl. Hispanic Media Coalition [17351]
Near Field Commun. Forum [6438]
New York Women in Communications, Inc. Found. [814]
No-Code Intl. [20939]
North Amer. Radio Archives [22120]
Old Old Timers Club [20941]
OURMedia Network [18100]
Professional Insurance Communicators of Am. [815]
Progress and Freedom Found. [17352]
Prometheus Radio Proj. [18101]
Public Conversations Proj. [17353]
Public Media Center [17354]
Public Radio Capital [10483]
Radio Free Europe/Radio Liberty [17355]
Religious Commun. Assn. [7888]
Reporters Comm. for Freedom of the Press [17356]
Rhetoric Soc. of Am. [10512]
Satellite Indus. Assn. [816]
Scribes - The Amer. Soc. of Legal Writers [5325]
Soc. for the Eradication of TV [17357]
Soc. for New Communications Res. [6439]
Soc. for Tech. Commun. [817]
Soc. for Tech. Commun. [817]
Special Interest Gp. on Design of Commun. [6561]
Student Press Law Center [17358]
Telecommunications Res. and Action Center [17359]
Union for Democratic Communications [17360]
Union for Democratic Communications [17360]
U.S. Connected Communities Assn. [6440]
U.S. Soc. for Augmentative and Alternative Commun. [17361]
Utility Communicators Intl. [818]
Utility Communicators Intl. [818]
Wireless-Life Sciences Alliance [16829]
Women's Inst. for Freedom of the Press [17362]
World Artists Experiences [9325]
World Press Freedom Comm. [17363]
World Press Freedom Comm. [17363]
World Press Inst. [17364]
World Press Inst. [17364]
Zeta Phi Eta [23494]
Communications Alliance [IO], Milsons Point, Australia
Communications Assn. of Hong Kong [IO], Hong Kong, People's Republic of China
Communications Coordination Comm. for the United Nations [18745], 211 E 43rd St., No. 710, New York, NY 10017

Communications Coordination Comm. for the United Nations [18745], 211 E 43rd St., No. 710, New York, NY 10017
Communications, Energy and Paperworkers Union of Canada [IO], Ottawa, ON, Canada
Communications Fraud Control Assn. [1887], 4 Becker Farm Rd., 4th Fl., PO Box 954, Roseland, NJ 07068, (973)871-4032
Communications Fraud Control Assn. [1887], 4 Becker Farm Rd., 4th Fl., PO Box 954, Roseland, NJ 07068, (973)871-4032
Communications and Info. Network Assn. of Japan [IO], Tokyo, Japan
Communications Mgt. Assn. [IO], Swindon, United Kingdom
Communications Managers Assn. - Defunct.
Communications Market Assn. [★3403]
Communications Marketing Assn. [3403], PO Box 36275, Denver, CO 80236, (303)988-3515
Communications Media Mgt. Assn. [274], 20423 State Rd. 7, Ste. F6-491, Boca Raton, FL 33498, (561)477-8100
Communications Platforms Trade Assn. [6531], 3855 SW 153rd Dr., Beaverton, OR 97006, (503)619-0680
Communications Supply Ser. Assn. [3591], 5700 Murray St., Little Rock, AR 72209, (501)562-7666
Communications Users Assn. of South Africa [IO], Randburg, Republic of South Africa
Communications Workers of Am. [23174], 501 3rd St. NW, Washington, DC 20001-2797, (202)434-1100
Communications Workers of America/Canada [IO], Ottawa, ON, Canada
Communications Workers of Am. | Printing, Publishing and Media Workers Sector [23210], 501 3rd St. NW, Washington, DC 20001-2760, (202)434-1235
Communidad de Vida Cristiana [★IO]

Communism

Amer. Fund for Czech and Slovak Relief [12771]
Captive Nations Comm. [17185]

Communism, Anti-

Captive Nations Comm. [17185]
Communism; Historians of Amer. [8257]
Communist Party of Australia [IO], Surry Hills, Australia
Communist Party of Bangladesh [IO], Dhaka, Bangladesh
Communist Party of Canada Marxist-Leninist [IO], Montreal, QC, Canada
Communist Party of India [IO], New Delhi, India
Communist Party of the U.S.A. [18355], 235 W 23rd St., 8th Fl., New York, NY 10011, (212)989-4994
Communitarian Network [18452], Inst. for Communitarian Policy Stud., 1922 F St. NW, Rm. 413, Washington, DC 20052, (202)994-8190
Communities Against Violence Network - Address unknown since 2011.
Communities First Assn. [11564], 234 W 18th St., Holland, MI 49423, (616)403-9309
Communities In Schools [8079], 2345 Crystal Dr., Ste. 801, Arlington, VA 22202, (703)519-8999
Communities Without Borders [11258], 63 Pickwick Rd., West Newton, MA 02465, (617)965-4713

Community

ABLE: Assn. for Better Living and Educ. Intl. [11537]
Amer. Sunrise [12170]
Arthur Morgan Inst. for Community Solutions [17368]
Biofuel Recycling [4867]
Center for Screen-Time Awareness [11998]
Climate, Community and Biodiversity Alliance [4020]
Communities First Assn. [11564]
Community Aid Relief and Development [12826]
Community Associations Inst. [17373]
Community Development Soc. [17374]
Community Members Interested [11569]
GAIA Movement USA [4066]
GesherCity [19091]
Indus. Areas Found. [17379]
Insight Center for Community Economic Development [17578]

Inst. for Community Economics [17380]
Living Waters Org. [11608]
Local Initiatives Support Corp. [17383]
Natl. Assn. for County Community and Economic Development [17384]
Natl. Community Development Assn. [17387]
Natl. Community for Latino Leadership [19112]
Natl. Latina/Latino Law Student Assn. [18057]
Natl. Neighborhood Coalition [17389]
New Ecology, Inc. [11616]
One Earth Designs [4293]
Organize Training Center [11657]
Partners for Rural Am. [18574]
Peace in Focus [18275]
Poetic Unity [11623]
Renew Am. [3973]
Seeking Ecology Educ. and Design Solutions [4216]
Seven Generations Ahead [11632]
Social Integration and Community Development Assn. [11639]
Sustainable Smiles [4876]
SustainUS [13559]

Community Action

4K for Cancer [13874]
9/11 Families for a Secure Am. Found. [18710]
100 Women in Hedge Funds Assn. [1275]
Ardent Lion Soc. [11659]
Assn. of Community Organizations for Reform Now [11527]
Assn. for the Development of Pakistan [12601]
Breaking Ground [11552]
Building Bridges Worldwide [11553]
Burundi Friends Intl. [11555]
Center for Community and Org. Development [11528]
Change Exchange [12205]
Children of Tanzania [11065]
Coalition Against Genocide [17738]
Communities First Assn. [11564]
Community Forestry Intl. [4391]
Dam Safety Coalition [13418]
Disaster Mgt. Alliance [11850]
ecoAmerica [4044]
Equator Initiative [11581]
Freedom Fields USA [11529]
Freedom Fields USA [11529]
Friends of Turkmenistan [11585]
Genocide Intervention Network [17739]
Girls for a Change [11290]
Global Community Initiatives [11589]
Global Helps Network [11530]
Global Urban Development [11591]
Green Team Am. [4076]
Haitian Amer. Professionals Coalition [11592]
Help Brings Hope for Haiti [12845]
ImpactLives [9491]
Intl. Coalition for Haiti [11599]
Intl. Healthy Cities Found. [13345]
Jewish World Watch [17743]
JumpStart Intl. [11605]
Khadarlis for Sierra Leone [11607]
Larger Than Life [11341]
The Love Alliance [17365]
Mama Hope [11609]
Midwest Acad. [11531]
Miracles in Action [12740]
Mobile Medical Disaster Relief [12472]
Natl. Assn. of African Americans for Positive Imagery [17157]
Natl. Assn. of Neighborhoods [11532]
Natl. Assn. of Triads [12992]
Natl. Community Action Found. [11533]
Natl. Community Tax Coalition [18700]
Natl. Latina/Latino Law Student Assn. [18057]
Natl. People's Action [11534]
One Love Worldwide [12874]
One World Medical Relief [15202]
Partners for Rural Improvement and Development in Ethiopia [12959]
People for Haiti [12877]
Plastic Pollution Coalition [4799]
Praxis Proj. [11535]
Rotarian Action Gp. for Population Growth and Sustainable Development [12709]

A star before a book entry number signifies that the name is not listed separately, but is mentioned within the entry.

ShadowBlossom [11633]
Social Integration and Community Development Assn. [11639]
Transition U.S. [4343]
Unity Corps [11536]
University-Community Partnership for Social Action Res. [7895]
Community Action on Latin Am. [18051], PO Box 1565, Madison, WI 53701, (608)251-3241
Community Action on Latin Am. [18051], PO Box 1565, Madison, WI 53701, (608)251-3241
Community Action Partnership [12723], 1140 Connecticut Ave. NW, Ste. 1210, Washington, DC 20036, (202)265-7546
Community Acupuncture Network [13579], PO Box 55951, Portland, OR 97238-5951, (800)404-7376
Community Advice Bur. [IO], Hong Kong, People's Republic of China
Community Agroecology Network [4938], PO Box 7653, Santa Cruz, CA 95061, (831)459-3619
Community Aid [IO], Male, Maldives
Community Aid Relief and Development [12826], PO Box 632162, Littleton, CO 80163, (888)412-6243
Community Anti-Drug Coalitions of Am. [13245], 625 Slaters Ln., Ste. 300, Alexandria, VA 22314-1176, (703)706-0560
Community Associations Inst. [17373], 6402 Arlington Blvd., Ste. 500, Falls Church, VA 22042, (703)970-9220
Community Awareness Raising and Advocacy Ventures Around Needs [IO], Saidu Sharif, Pakistan
Community Banking Advisory Network [17], 624 Grassmere Park Dr., Ste. 15, Nashville, TN 37211, (615)377-3392
Community Blood Bank Coun. [★13849]
Community Broadcasting Assn. of Australia [IO], Alexandria, Australia
Community Broadcasting Found. [IO], Collingwood, Australia
Community Built Assn. [11565], 4217 Montgomery St., Oakland, CA 94611
Community-Campus Partnerships For Hea. [11566], UW Box 354809, Seattle, WA 98195-4809, (206)666-3406
Community of Caring [11259], Univ. of Utah, 1901 E South Campus Dr., No. 1120, Salt Lake City, UT 84112, (801)587-8990
Community Catalyst [14769], 30 Winter St., Boston, MA 02108, (617)338-6035
Community of Celebration [19563], PO Box 309, Aliquippa, PA 15001, (724)375-1510
Community Chests and Councils of Am. [★12056]
Community Coll. Assn. for Instruction and Technology - Defunct.
Community Coll. Baccalaureate Assn. [7891], 25216 Pelican Creek Cir., No. 103, Bonita Springs, FL 34134, (239)947-8085
Community Coll. Bus. Officers [7788], PO Box 5565, Charlottesville, VA 22905-5565, (434)293-2825
Community Coll. Humanities Assn. [8281], Prof. David Berry, Exec. Dir., Essex County Coll., 303 Univ. Ave., Newark, NJ 07102, (973)877-3577
Community Coll. Journalism Assn. [8441], 163 E Loop Dr., Camarillo, CA 93010, (805)389-3744
Community Colleges
  Amer. Assn. of Community Colleges [7889]
  Assn. of Community Coll. Trustees [7890]
  Community Coll. Baccalaureate Assn. [7891]
  League for Innovation in the Community Coll. [7892]
  Natl. Coun. of State Directors of Community Colleges [7893]
Community Colleges for Intl. Development [8352], PO Box 2068, Cedar Rapids, IA 52406-2068, (319)398-1257
Community Colleges for Intl. Development [8352], PO Box 2068, Cedar Rapids, IA 52406-2068, (319)398-1257
Community for Creative Non-Violence [12155], 425 2nd St. NW, Washington, DC 20001, (202)393-1909
Community Development
  100 Women in Hedge Funds Assn. [1275]
  ABLE: Assn. for Better Living and Educ. Intl. [11537]

ABLE: Assn. for Better Living and Educ. Intl. [11537]
Abriendo Mentes [12950]
ACCION Intl. [17366]
ACCION Intl. [17366]
Act for Africa Intl. [12951]
Action for Enterprise [11538]
Action for Enterprise [11538]
ActionAid Intl. USA [11539]
ActionAid Intl. USA [11539]
Active: Water [13410]
Adopt-a-Village Intl. [11540]
Afghans4Tomorrow [11541]
Afghans4Tomorrow [11541]
Africa-America Inst. New York [17142]
Africa-America Inst. New York [17142]
Africa Bridge [11177]
African Sky [11542]
African Sky [11542]
Agami [7824]
Agricultural Development Initiatives [3727]
Aid Africa [12714]
Alliance For Relief Mission in Haiti [12799]
Alliance of Jamaican and Amer. Humanitarians [11543]
Am. in Bloom [3971]
Am. Walks [18775]
Amer. Bar Assn. Commn. on Homelessness and Poverty [12153]
Amer. Cong. of Community Supports and Employment Services [17367]
Amer. Friends of Guinea [15143]
Amer. Planning Assn. [5326]
Amer. Planning Assn. | Amer. Inst. of Certified Planners [5327]
Amer. Sunrise [12170]
Americans Care and Share [12805]
APPEAL: Asian Pacific Partners for Empowerment and Leadership [11544]
APPEAL: Asian Pacific Partners for Empowerment and Leadership [11544]
Appropriate Infrastructure Development Gp. [11545]
Architecture for Humanity [11546]
Architecture for Humanity [11546]
Artfully AWARE [9275]
Arthur Morgan Inst. for Community Solutions [17368]
Asia Am. Initiative [11547]
Asia Am. Initiative [11547]
Assn. for the Advancement of Mexican Americans [11548]
Assn. for the Development of Pakistan [12601]
Assn. for Haitian Amer. Development [12126]
Assn. of Metropolitan Planning Organizations [17369]
Athgo Intl. [13510]
Australian Natl. Flag Assn. [14903]
Benton Found. [11549]
Biofuel Recycling [4867]
Birambye Intl. [11550]
Blessings on Africa [12719]
blueEnergy [11966]
Bodomase Development Assn. USA [11551]
Breaking Ground [11552]
Bridges Cambodia Intl. [11203]
Bridges to Prosperity [12952]
Building Bridges Worldwide [11553]
Building Community Bridges [11554]
Burundi Friends Intl. [11555]
Bus. Alliance for Local Living Economies [11556]
Bus. Alliance for Local Living Economies [11556]
A Call to Serve Intl. [11557]
A Call to Serve Intl. [11557]
Center for Community Action of B'Nai B'rith Intl. [11558]
Center for Community Action of B'Nai B'rith Intl. [11558]
Center for Neighborhood Enterprise [17370]
Center for Neighborhood Tech. [17371]
Center for New Community [17372]
Center for Self-Sufficiency [11559]
Center for Work and the Family [11999]
ChildVoice Intl. [11254]
Choices [12258]

Chris Cares Intl. [11560]
Christ for the Poor [8789]
Christian Action and Relief for Haiti [12820]
Citizens Network for Sustainable Development [11561]
Clean Tech. and Sustainable Indus. Org. [3856]
Clean Water for the World [13416]
Clowns Without Borders - U.S.A. [11562]
Clowns Without Borders - U.S.A. [11562]
Coffee Kids [11563]
Coffee Kids [11563]
Communities First Assn. [11564]
Communities Without Borders [11258]
Community Associations Inst. [17373]
Community Built Assn. [11565]
Community-Campus Partnerships For Hea. [11566]
Community Development Bankers Assn. [406]
Community Development Intl. [11567]
Community Development Soc. [17374]
Community Development Soc. [17374]
Community Development Venture Capital Alliance [11568]
Community Empowerment Network [12953]
Community Hea. Intl. [14896]
Community Managers Intl. Assn. [2277]
Community Members Interested [11569]
Community Solutions for Africa's Development [11570]
Community Trans. Assn. of Am. [11571]
Community Voices [11572]
Computers for Africa [7910]
Connecting Congo [11573]
Conscious Alliance [11574]
Coun. of Religious Volunteer Agencies [13390]
Coun. for Zimbabwe [12322]
Darfur Peace and Development Org. [12324]
Do Something [17375]
Drinking Water for India [13419]
DROKPA [11575]
EarthSpark Intl. [6711]
Educ. for Prosperity [11576]
Edurelief [12834]
Egyptians Relief Assn. [11577]
Empower Tanzania, Inc. [12954]
Empowering the Poor [12326]
Empowerment Soc. Intl. [11578]
Empowerment Works [11579]
Engineers for a Sustainable World [11580]
Engineers for a Sustainable World [11580]
Equator Initiative [11581]
Equator Initiative [11581]
Everyone Needs a Hero [11582]
Everyone Needs a Hero [11582]
FaithWorks Intl. [11583]
FaithWorks Intl. [11583]
Fashion Fights Poverty [12725]
Fed. of Egalitarian Communities [11584]
Fellowship for Intentional Community [17376]
Fields of Growth Intl. [12416]
Found. for Intl. Community Assistance [17377]
Found. for Intl. Community Assistance [17377]
Freedom Fields USA [11529]
Friends of Turkmenistan [11585]
Frontiers Intl. [11586]
Frontiers Intl. [11586]
Funders' Network for Smart Growth and Livable Communities [11587]
A Future Without Poverty [12729]
GesherCity [19091]
Gift of Water [13420]
Global Brigades [11588]
Global Community Initiatives [11589]
Global Helps Network [11530]
Global Partners Running Waters [11590]
Global Urban Development [11591]
Global Urban Development [11591]
Global Water Challenge [4993]CommunityGonja Assn. of North Am.
Green Empowerment [3972]
Green Empowerment [3972]
Gyro Intl. [13058]
Habitat for Humanity Intl. [12179]
Haiti Convention Assn. [12966]
Haiti Outreach [11068]

Reference to "IO" in place of a book number signifies that the association may be found in the 50th edition of International Organizations.

Haitian Amer. Professionals Coalition [11592]
Haitian Amer. Professionals Coalition [11592]
HANDS for Cambodia [11593]
Healing the Divide [12238]
Hearts for Kenya [11070]
Help Aid Africa [11594]
Help Brings Hope for Haiti [12845]
Helping Hand for Nepal [12847]
Helping Hearts Helping Hands [12730]
HELPSudan [11442]
Hispanas Organized for Political Equality [17776]
Hope for Haiti [11595]
HOUR Money Network [17378]
Idoma Assn. USA [19176]
Igbere Progressive Assn. Intl. [12576]
ImpactLives [9491]
ImpactLives [9491]
In Our Own Quiet Way [13424]
Indigo Threads [11596]
Indus. Areas Found. [17379]
Innovation: Africa [6114]
Inst. for Community Economics [17380]
Inst. for Local Self-Reliance [11597]
Inst. for Sustainable Communities [11598]
Inst. for Sustainable Communities [11598]
Intl. Action [13425]CommunityIntl. Alliance in Ser.
   and Educ. CommunityIntl. Assn. of Character
   Cities
Intl. Assn. for China Planning [18315]
Intl. Coalition for Haiti [11599]
Intl. Coalition for Haiti [11599]
Intl. Coalition for Sustainable Production and
   Consumption [17381]
Intl. Coalition for Sustainable Production and
   Consumption [17381]
Intl. Coun. for Caring Communities [5328]
Intl. Development Collaborative [12341]
Intl. Org. for Haitian Development [7894]
Intl. Relief and Development [11600]
Intl. Relief and Development [11600]
Intl. Women's Coffee Alliance [11601]
Intl. Women's Coffee Alliance [11601]
Into Your Hands [12967]
Jamaica Unite [11602]
Jamii Moja [11603]
Join Hands Day [11604]
JumpStart Intl. [11605]
Junior Optimist Octagon Intl. [13060]
Kageno Worldwide [11606]
Key Club Intl. [13061]
Khadarlis for Sierra Leone [11607]
Kids with Cameras [12694]
Kids Home Intl. [11334]
Kiwanis Intl. [13062]
Leadership Development Network [17382]
Liberian Anti Poverty Assn. [11071]
LIFT [11072]
Liquid Water [13426]
Living Waters Org. [11608]
Local Initiatives Support Corp. [17383]
Long Way Home [11073]
MAAWS for Global Welfare [12347]
Malawi Children's Mission [11347]
Mama Hope [11609]
Mercy Beyond Borders [12738]
Miracles in Action [12740]
Moringa Community [11610]
Moringa Community [11610]
Natl. Alliance of Community Economic Develop-
   ment Associations [17582]
Natl. Alliance of Craftsmen Associations [11611]
Natl. Assn. of Community Development Extension
   Professionals [11612]
Natl. Assn. for County Community and Economic
   Development [17384]
Natl. Assn. of County Planners [5329]
Natl. Assn. of Development Organizations [5330]
Natl. Assn. of Development Organizations Res.
   Found. [17385]
Natl. Assn. for Olmsted Parks [5331]
Natl. Assn. of Triads [12992]
Natl. Australia Day Coun. [6494]
Natl. Coalition for Asian Pacific Amer. Community
   Development [11613]
Natl. Coalition Building Inst. [17386]

Natl. Community Development Assn. [17387]
Natl. Community for Latino Leadership [19112]
Natl. Community Reinvestment Coalition [17388]
Natl. Community Tax Coalition [18700]
Natl. Housing and Rehabilitation Assn. [12191]
Natl. Neighborhood Coalition [17389]
Natl. Student Campaign Against Hunger and
   Homelessness [12286]
Native Movement [19166]
Nature Healing Nature [11614]
Nepal SEEDS: Social Educational Environmental
   Development Services in Nepal [11615]
NetHope [12872]
New Ecology, Inc. [11616]
New Hope Constr. [12198]
Newah Org. of Am. [11617]
North Amer. Alliances for Social Relief [12352]
North Amer. Sankethi Assn. [9492]
Noshaq [12958]
One Common Unity [11618]
One Earth Designs [4293]
One Love Worldwide [12874]
One Vision Intl. [11619]
OneWorld U.S. [17858]
Oper. HOPE, Inc. [11620]
Opportunity Finance Network [17390]
Optimist Intl. [13071]
Organize Training Center [11657]
Orphans Africa [11621]
Outreach Africa [11386]
Partners for Livable Communities [5332]
Partners for Rural Am. [18574]
Partners for Rural Improvement and Development
   in Ethiopia [12959]
Partners in Sustainable Development Intl. [12745]
Peace House Africa [11389]
PeaceArt Intl. [9312]
Planting Hope [11622]
Poetic Unity [11623]
Proj. Baobab [13553]
Pueblo a Pueblo [12124]
Reach Intl. Healthcare and Training [15206]
Reach Out to Romania [12750]
Rebuild A Nation [11077]
Rebuilding Haiti Now [12881]
Reconstruction Efforts Aiding Children without
   Homes [11624]
Red Feather Development Gp. [12201]
Regional Sci. Assn. Intl. [5333]
Regional Sci. Assn. Intl. [5333]
Renew Am. [3973]
Restoring Institutions Services and Empowering
   Liberia [11625]
Rights and Resources Initiative [4412]
Rigoberta Menchu Tum Found. [17325]
Rising Intl. [11078]
River Intl. [12887]
Roots of Development [12960]
Roots and Wings Intl. [12363]
Rotarian Action Gp. for Population Growth and
   Sustainable Development [12709]
Rural Initiative Development Assn. [12961]
Rwanda Knits [11626]
Sabu Help [12962]
Samaritan's Feet [11402]
Sarvodaya U.S.A. [11627]
SeaAid [11628]
Senior Gleaners [12291]
Serendib [11629]
ServeHAITI [11630]
ServeHAITI [11630]
Ser. for the Love of God [11631]
Serving Our World [11405]
Seven Generations Ahead [11632]
ShadowBlossom [11633]
The Shelter Alliance [11634]
Shining Hope for Communities [11635]
Sierra Leone Relief and Development Outreach
   [12890]
Simple Hope [12891]
Sister Island Proj. [11636]
Smart Growth Am. [11637]
Soccer in the Streets [11638]
Social Integration and Community Development
   Assn. [11639]

Solar Light for Africa [11640]
Solar Light for Africa [11640]
Solar for Peace [7447]
Southern Mutual Help Assn. [11641]
SpanAfrica [11642]
SpanAfrica [11642]
Sudan Sunrise [12636]
Sunstove Org. [11643]
SurfAid Intl. [11644]
SurfAid Intl. [11644]
Sustainable Agriculture Educ. [4944]
Sustainable Organic Integrated Livelihoods
   [11645]
SustainUS [13559]
Team Success [13560]
Teen Missions Intl. [20099]
To Love a Child [11417]
Together for Tanzania [11646]
Touching Hearts [10817]
Trust in Educ. [11647]
Tusubira - We Have Hope [12755]
Under The Baobab Tree [7901]
Union MicroFinanza [12964]
United Neighborhood Centers of Am. [11648]
UNITED SIKHS [12228]
University-Community Partnership for Social Ac-
   tion Res. [7895]
Urban Ed [9031]
Urban Homesteading Assistance Bd. [12203]
Urban Land Inst. [5334]
Urbanists Intl. [6207]
Urhobo Natl. Assn. of North Am. [19178]
Vietnam Relief Effort [12896]
Village Earth: CSVBD [11649]
Village Earth: CSVBD [11649]
Village Focus Intl. [11650]
Village Missions Intl. [11651]
Water Alliance for Africa [13434]
Water for People I PlayPumps Intl. [10827]
The Waterfront Center [11652]
WAVES for Development [18683]
We, The World [13123]
Well Done Org. [11653]
WICUDA-USA [9095]
Wild Gift [5146]
World Bicycle Relief [12898]
World Family Ethiopian Orphans and Medical
   Care [11432]
World Water Org. [13444]
World Water Relief [13445]
World Wins Intl. [11654]
WorldHope Corps [11655]
Community Development Bankers Assn. [406], 1801
   K St. NW, Ste. M-100, Washington, DC 20006,
   (202)689-8935
Community Development Finance Assn. [IO],
   London, United Kingdom
Community Development Found. [★11502]
Community Development Intl. [11567], PO Box
   3417, New York, NY 10163
Community Development Soc. [17374], 17 S High
   St., Ste. 200, Columbus, OH 43215, (614)221-
   1900
Community Development Soc. [17374], 17 S High
   St., Ste. 200, Columbus, OH 43215, (614)221-
   1900
Community Development Venture Capital Alliance
   [11568], 424 W 33rd St., Ste. 320, New York, NY
   10001, (212)594-6747
Community and District Nursing Assn. [IO], London,
   United Kingdom
Community Economics, Inc. [12174], 538 9th St.,
   Ste. 200, Oakland, CA 94607, (510)832-8300
Community Education
   Abriendo Mentes [12950]
   All One People [10808]
   Alliance of Jamaican and Amer. Humanitarians
      [11543]
   Amer. Cong. of Community Supports and Employ-
      ment Services [17367]
   Assn. for Community Networking [7896]
   Assn. for Community Networking [7896]
   Christ for the Poor [8789]
   Circle of Women: Reach and Teach Across
      Borders [13015]

A star before a book entry number signifies that the name is not listed separately, but is mentioned within the entry.

Educ. for Prosperity [11576]
EducationWorks [7897]
Grassroots Alliance for Community Educ. [7898]
HELPSudan [11442]
Intl. Assn. for Res. on Service-Learning and Community Engagement [7899]
Intl. Org. for Haitian Development [7894]
Into Your Hands [12967]
Libraries Without Borders [8519]
Natl. Community Educ. Assn. [7900]
Roots and Wings Intl. [12363]
Ser. for the Love of God [11631]
Touching Hearts [10817]
Under The Baobab Tree [7901]
Community Educ. Development Assn. [IO], Male, Maldives
Community Educ. Rsrc. Center [★11528]
Community Empowerment Network [12953], 1685 Grandview Pl., Ferndale, WA 98248, (206)329-6244
Community Environmental Coun. [4980], 26 W Anapamu St., 2nd Fl., Santa Barbara, CA 93101, (805)963-0583
Community of European Railways [IO], Brussels, Belgium
Community of European Shipyards' Associations [IO], Brussels, Belgium
Community Financial Services Assn. [1289], 515 King St., Ste. 300, Alexandria, VA 22314, (888)572-9329
Community Food Security Coalition [12268], 3830 SE Div. St., Portland, OR 97202, (503)954-2970
Community Food Security Coalition [12268], 3830 SE Div. St., Portland, OR 97202, (503)954-2970
Community Forestry Intl. [4391], 1356 Mokelumne Dr., Antioch, CA 94531, (925)706-2906
Community Found. Network [IO], London, United Kingdom
Community Hea. Charities [12051], 200 N Glebe Rd., Ste. 801, Arlington, VA 22203, (703)528-1007
Community Hea. Intl. [14896], 59 Windsor Rd., Brookline, MA 02445, (617)739-2638
Community Hea. Nurses Assn. of Canada [IO], Toronto, ON, Canada
Community and Hosp. Infection Control Assn. - Canada [IO], Winnipeg, MB, Canada
Community Hospitals Assn. [IO], Ilminster, United Kingdom
Community Housing Fed. of Australia [IO], Woden, Australia
Community Housing for the Hearing Impaired Prog. [★14930]
Community Improvement
100 Women in Hedge Funds Assn. [1275]
Act for Africa Intl. [12951]
Adopt-a-Village Intl. [11540]
African Sky [11542]
Alliance for a Paving Moratorium [17391]
Am. Walks [18775]
Amer. Bar Assn. Commn. on Homelessness and Poverty [12153]
Architectural League of New York [17392]
Assn. for the Development of Pakistan [12601]
Assn. of Haitian Professionals [19021]
Athgo Intl. [13510]
blueEnergy [11966]
Bodomase Development Assn. USA [11551]
Breaking Ground [11552]
Bridges to Prosperity [12952]
Burundi Friends Intl. [11555]
Center for Work and the Family [11999]
Chris Cares Intl. [11560]
Christian Action and Relief for Haiti [12820]
Clean Water for the World [13416]
Communities First Assn. [11564]
Community Development Bankers Assn. [406]
Community Development Intl. [11567]
Community Forestry Intl. [4391]
Community Managers Intl. Assn. [2277]
Community Solutions for Africa's Development [11570]
Coun. of Religious Volunteer Agencies [13390]
Educ. for Prosperity [11576]
Egyptians Relief Assn. [11577]
Equator Initiative [11581]

Freedom Fields USA [11529]
Friends of Turkmenistan [11585]
Funders' Network for Smart Growth and Livable Communities [11587]
Global Brigades [11588]
Global Community Initiatives [11589]
Global Helps Network [11530]
Global Partners Running Waters [11590]
Global Urban Development [11591]
Global Youth Connect [18828]
Gyro Intl. [13058]
Haiti Convention Assn. [12966]
Haitian Amer. Professionals Coalition [11592]
HANDS for Cambodia [11593]
Help Aid Africa [11594]
Help Brings Hope for Haiti [12845]
Hope for Haiti [11595]
ImpactLives [9491]
Intl. Coalition for Haiti [11599]
Intl. Healthy Cities Found. [13345]
Into Your Hands [12967]
Jamii Moja [11603]
JumpStart Intl. [11605]
Junior Optimist Octagon Intl. [13060]
Kageno Worldwide [11606]
Key Club Intl. [13061]
Khadarlis for Sierra Leone [11607]
Kiwanis Intl. [13062]
Living Waters Org. [11608]
MAAWS for Global Welfare [12347]
Mama Hope [11609]
Mercy Beyond Borders [12738]
Moringa Community [11610]
Natl. Alliance for Family Court Justice [5624]
Natl. Alliance of Highway Beautification Agencies [5948]
Natl. Assn. of African Americans for Positive Imagery [17157]
Natl. Trust Main St. Center [17393]
Nepal SEEDS: Social Educational Environmental Development Services in Nepal [11615]
NetHope [12872]
New Hope Constr. [12198]
One Vision Intl. [11619]
Optimist Intl. [13071]
Organize Training Center [11657]
Partners for Rural Improvement and Development in Ethiopia [12959]
Planetwork [4214]
Proj. for Public Spaces [17394]
Public Art Fund [17395]
Renew Am. [3973]
Rotarian Action Gp. for Population Growth and Sustainable Development [12709]
Rural Initiative Development Assn. [12961]
Sabu Help [12962]
Sculpture in the Env. [17396]
SeaAid [11628]
Ser. for the Love of God [11631]
Seven Generations Ahead [11632]
ShadowBlossom [11633]
Shining Hope for Communities [11635]
Social Integration and Community Development Assn. [11639]
Sunstove Org. [11643]
SustainUS [13559]
Team Success [13560]
Together for Tanzania [11646]
Tusubira - We Have Hope [12755]
Under The Baobab Tree [7901]
University-Community Partnership for Social Action Res. [7895]
Vietnam Relief Effort [12896]
Village Focus Intl. [11650]
Village Missions Intl. [11651]
Water for People | PlayPumps Intl. [10827]
WICUDA-USA [9095]
WorldHope Corps [11655]
Community Info. and Epidemiological Technologies [11978], 511 Ave. of the Americas, No. 132, New York, NY 10011, (212)242-3428
Community Info. and Epidemiological Technologies [11978], 511 Ave. of the Americas, No. 132, New York, NY 10011, (212)242-3428
Community Leadership Assn.

Community Leadership Assn. - Address unknown since 2010.
Community Learning and Info. Network
Community Learning and Info. Network - Address unknown since 2011.
Community Managers Intl. Assn. [2277], PO Box 848, Dana Point, CA 92629, (888)900-2642
Community Matters: The Natl. Fed. of Community Organisations [IO], London, United Kingdom
Community Media Assn. [IO], Sheffield, United Kingdom
Community Members Interested [11569], 205 Yoakum Pkwy., Unit 807, Alexandria, VA 22304, (703)945-7258
Community Mental Health
Amer. Cong. of Community Supports and Employment Services [17367]
Natl. Center for Victims of Crime [13367]
Community Newspapers of Australia [IO], Sydney, Australia
Community Oncology Alliance [15923], 1101 Pennsylvania Ave. NW, Ste. 700, Washington, DC 20004, (202)756-2258
Community Organization
Assn. for Community Org. and Social Admin. [13213]CommunityCommunity Leadership Assn.
Global Rsrc. Alliance [3974]
Interreligious Found. for Community Org. [11656]
Organize Training Center [11657]
ShadowBlossom [11633]
Work for Progress [12583]
Community Ownership Organizing Proj. [★12174]
Community Pharmacy Scotland [IO], Edinburgh, United Kingdom
Community Promotion Development Liberation [12646], 703 W Monroe St., Chicago, IL 60661, (312)234-9592
Community Sanitation and Recycling Org. [IO], Phnom Penh, Cambodia
Community Ser. [★17368]
Community Service
Abrahamic Alliance Intl. [19824]
Accountability in Intl. Development [12308]
Act for Africa Intl. [12951]
Adopt-a-Village Intl. [11540]
AFL-CIO | Community Action Field Mobilization Dept. [11658]
Aguayuda [13412]
Aid Africa [12714]
Amer. Bar Assn. Commn. on Homelessness and Poverty [12153]
Amer. Sunrise [12170]
Amer. Youth Work Center [13508]
Americans Care and Share [12805]
Ardent Lion Soc. [11659]
Artfully AWARE [9275]
Bahia St. [12717]
blueEnergy [11966]
Break Away: The Alternative Break Connection [12764]
Breaking Ground [11552]
Bridges to Prosperity [12952]
Building Bridges Worldwide [11553]
Building Community Bridges [11554]
BuildingBlocks Intl. [11666]
Burundi Friends Intl. [11555]
Call For Action [11660]
Call For Action [11660]
CenterLink [11661]
ChildVoice Intl. [11254]
Choices [12258]
Christian Action and Relief for Haiti [12820]
Communities Without Borders [11258]
Community Managers Intl. Assn. [2277]
Community Members Interested [11569]
Community Solutions for Africa's Development [11570]
The Compassionate Listening Proj. [11662]
Coun. of Religious Volunteer Agencies [13390]
Coun. for Zimbabwe [12322]
Credit Builders Alliance [990]
Dam Safety Coalition [13418]
The Dinner Garden [12269]
DROKPA [11575]

Reference to "IO" in place of a book number signifies that the association may be found in the 50th edition of International Organizations.

Educ. for Prosperity [11576]
Empower Tanzania, Inc. [12954]
Everyone Needs a Hero [11582]
Farm Rescue [12041]
Farmer-Veteran Coalition [20610]
Fifty Lanterns Intl. [7439]
Food Res. and Action Center [12278]
Friends of Mali [18246]
Friends of Turkmenistan [11585]
GAIA Movement USA [4066]
Gift of Water [13420]
Global Family Rescue [13158]
Global Helps Network [11530]
Global Rsrc. Alliance [3974]
Gyro Intl. [13058]
Haiti Healthcare Partners [15176]
Haiti Outreach [11068]
HANDS for Cambodia [11593]
HavServe Volunteer Ser. Network [11069]
Healing the Divide [12238]
Helping Hand for Nepal [12847]
Helping Hearts Helping Hands [12730]
Igbere Progressive Assn. Intl. [12576]
Indigo Threads [11596]
Intl. Development Stewardship [12343]
Junior Optimist Octagon Intl. [13060]
Kageno Worldwide [11606]
Key Club Intl. [13061]
Kiwanis Intl. [13062]
Mama Hope [11609]
Minority Peace Corps Assn. [18307]
Miracles in Action [12740]
Natl. Assn. of Triads [12992]
Natl. Center for Victims of Crime [13367]
Natl. Local Tech. Assistance Prog. Assn. [13196]
Natl. Partnership for Community Leadership
  [11663]
Nature Healing Nature [11614]
Neighbors Without Borders [12350]
Nepal SEEDS: Social Educational Environmental
  Development Services in Nepal [11615]
New Hope Constr. [12198]
Nuru Intl. [11076]
Nyaya Hea. [15201]
One Vision Intl. [11619]
Optimist Intl. [13071]
Organize Training Center [11657]
Outreach Africa [11386]
Planting Hope [11622]
Power to the People [7440]
Prana Intl. [12749]
Pro Mujer [13475]
Pueblo a Pueblo [12124]
Restoring Institutions Services and Empowering
  Liberia [11625]
Rights and Resources Initiative [4412]
Roots of Development [12960]
Roots and Wings Intl. [12363]
Rural Hea. Intl. Non-Profit Org. [15208]
Rwanda Knits [11626]
Save Darfur Coalition [17744]
Scottish Community Care Forum [21959]
ServeHAITI [11630]
Serving Our World [11405]
Social Integration and Community Development
  Assn. [11639]
SpanAfrica [11642]
Spark Ventures [11407]
Spirit Quilts [11408]
Stop Hunger Now [12294]
Sustainable Organic Integrated Livelihoods
  [11645]
Tusubira - We Have Hope [12755]
Unchartered Intl. [12377]
United States Women of Today [13079]
Urhobo Natl. Assn. of North Am. [19178]
U.S.A. Harvest [12298]
Village Volunteers [12379]
Wheel Wishers [7407]
Women's Global Connection [13493]
World Family Ethiopian Orphans and Medical
  Care [11432]
World Water Org. [13444]
World Wins Intl. [11654]
Worldhealer [12384]

Community Services [★20237]
Community Solutions for Africa's Development
  [11570], 4624 Hillsboro Ave. N, Minneapolis, MN
  55428, (763)521-0100
Community Systems Found. [15826], 219 S Main
  St., Ste. 206, Ann Arbor, MI 48104, (734)761-1357
Community: The Union for Life [IO], London, United
  Kingdom
Community Transport Assn. [IO], Hyde, United
  Kingdom
Community Trans. Assn. of Am. [11571], 1341 G St.
  NW, 10th Fl., Washington, DC 20005, (202)247-
  1922
Community United Against Violence [12076], 427 S
  Van Ness Ave., San Francisco, CA 94103,
  (415)777-5500
Community and Veteran Ser. [★11558]
Community and Veteran Ser. [★11558]
Community Voices [11572], Natl. Center for Primary
  Care, Morehouse School of Medicine, 720 West-
  view Dr. SW, Atlanta, GA 30310, (404)752-8649
Community Volunteer Services Commn. of B'Nai
  Birth Intl. [★11558]
Community Volunteer Services Commn. of B'Nai
  Birth Intl. [★11558]
Community Water Solutions [13417], 46 Ledgetree
  Rd., Medfield, MA 02052
Community on Youth Smoking Prevention [IO], Hong
  Kong, People's Republic of China
Commuter Airline Assn. [★155]
Commuter Airline Assn. of Am. [★155]
Comoros Red Crescent [IO], Moroni, Comoros
Comox Valley Head Injury Soc. [IO], Courtenay, BC,
  Canada
CompactFlash Assn. [6448], PO Box 130, Cuper-
  tino, CA 95015-0130, (650)843-1220
Compagnie des Experts Agrees [IO], Paris, France
Companion Animal Parasite Coun. [17021], 1210
  Vance Ct., Bel Air, MD 21014
Companion Animal Protection Soc. [12649], 759
  CJC Hwy., No. 332, Cohasset, MA 02025,
  (339)309-0272
Company Chemists Assn. [IO], London, United
  Kingdom
Company of Fifers and Drummers [10179], PO Box
  277, Ivoryton, CT 06442-0277, (860)767-2237
Company of Military Collectors and Historians
  [★21885]
Company of Military Historians [21885], PO Box
  910, Rutland, MA 01543-0910, (508)845-9229
Comparative Cognition Soc. [6122], Auburn Univ.,
  Dept. of Psychology, 226 Thach Hall, Auburn, AL
  36849-5214
Comparative Educ. Soc. [★8402]
Comparative Educ. Soc. [★8402]
Comparative and Intl. Educ. Soc. [8402], SUNY,
  Univ. at Albany, School of Educ., Dept. Educational
  Admin. and Policy Stud., ED342, 1400 Washington
  Ave., Albany, NY 12222, (518)442-5165
Comparative and Intl. Educ. Soc. [8402], SUNY,
  Univ. at Albany, School of Educ., Dept. Educational
  Admin. and Policy Stud., ED342, 1400 Washington
  Ave., Albany, NY 12222, (518)442-5165
Comparative Nutrition Soc. [15827], Kendall Clem-
  ents, PO Box 120551, San Diego, CA 92112-0551
Compassion into Action Network - Direct Outcome
  Org. [11849], 578 Washington Blvd., Ste. 390,
  Marina Del Rey, CA 90292, (877)226-3697
Compassion Care for Disabled Children [16032], PO
  Box 4712, Crofton, MD 21114, (301)261-3211
Compassion Care for Disabled Children [16032], PO
  Box 4712, Crofton, MD 21114, (301)261-3211
Compassion and Choices [11988], PO Box 101810,
  Denver, CO 80250-1810, (800)247-7421
Compassion First [12827], 16055 SW Walker Rd.,
  PMB 239, Beaverton, OR 97006-4942, (503)207-
  1320
Compassion First [12827], 16055 SW Walker Rd.,
  PMB 239, Beaverton, OR 97006-4942, (503)207-
  1320
Compassion In World Farming - Ireland [IO], Cork,
  Ireland
Compassion Intl. - Defunct.
Compassion Over Killing [10947], PO Box 9773,
  Washington, DC 20016, (301)891-2458

Compassion Without Borders [10948], PO Box
  14995, Santa Rosa, CA 95402, (707)474-3345
Compassion in World Farming [IO], Godalming,
  United Kingdom
Compassionate Coalition [18084], 1500 Oliver Rd.,
  Ste. K, Fairfield, CA 94534-3473, (707)720-7593
Compassionate Cooks [13346], PO Box 18512,
  Oakland, CA 94619, (510)531-2665
The Compassionate Friends [12605], PO Box 3696,
  Oak Brook, IL 60522-3696, (630)990-0010
Compassionate Kids [8140], PO Box 18131, Atlanta,
  GA 30316-8131, (404)317-9087
Compassionate Kids [8140], PO Box 18131, Atlanta,
  GA 30316-8131, (404)317-9087
The Compassionate Listening Proj. [11662], PO Box
  17, Indianola, WA 98342, (360)626-4411
Compatible Tech. [★3729]
Compatible Tech. [★3729]
Compatible Tech. Intl. [3729], 800 Transfer Rd., Ste.
  6, St. Paul, MN 55114, (651)632-3912
Compatible Tech. Intl. [3729], 800 Transfer Rd., Ste.
  6, St. Paul, MN 55114, (651)632-3912
Compensation Medicine
  Amer. Acad. of Disability Evaluating Physicians
    [14164]
  Natl. Assn. of Disability Examiners [14165]
Compete Am. [8119], 1615 H St. NW, Washington,
  DC 20062
Competency and Credentialing Inst. [15051], 2170 S
  Parker Rd., Ste. 295, Denver, CO 80231,
  (303)369-9566
Competition Law Assn. [IO], London, United
  Kingdom
Competitive Livestock Marketing Assn. [★4716]
Competitive Swimming Comm. of the Amateur
  Athletic Union [★23047]
Competitive Telecommunications Assn. [★3592]
Complementary and Alternative Medicine Initiative
  [13671], 75 Winchell Dr., Rock Tavern, NY 12575,
  (718)877-0292
Completion Engg. Assn. [6961], Lewis Ledlow,
  Chm., 16945 Northchase Dr., Houston, TX 77060,
  (281)654-6817
Complex Weavers [252], 1615 4th Ave. N, Seattle,
  WA 98109
Component Mfrs. Coun. of the Truss Plate Inst.
  [★631]
Composers
  African Amer. Art Song Alliance [10134]
  Amer. Beethoven Soc. [9493]
  Amer. Brahms Soc. [9494]
  Amer. Composers Forum [9495]
  Amer. Handel Soc. [9496]
  Amer. Liszt Soc. [9497]
  Assn. of Canadian Women Composers [19395]
  Christian Fellowship of Art Music Composers
    [9498]
  Gilbert and Sullivan Soc. [9499]
  Intl. Alliance of Composers [10213]
  Intl. Percy Grainger Soc. [9500]
  Intl. Percy Grainger Soc. [9500]
  Jack Point Preservation Soc. [9501]
  Johnnie Ray Intl. Fan Club [23865]
  Leopold Stokowski Club [9502]
  Mozart Soc. of Am. [9503]
  Rebecca Clarke Soc. [9504]
  Roger Sessions Soc. [9505]
  Soc. of Composers, Inc. [9506]
  Songwriters of Wisconsin Intl. [9507]
  Southeastern Composers' League [10299]
Composers and Authors Soc. of Hong Kong [IO],
  Hong Kong, People's Republic of China
Composers and Authors Soc. of Singapore [IO], Sin-
  gapore, Singapore
Composite Can and Tube Inst. [875], 50 S Pickett
  St., Ste. 110, Alexandria, VA 22304-7206,
  (703)823-7234
Composite Can and Tube Inst. [875], 50 S Pickett
  St., Ste. 110, Alexandria, VA 22304-7206,
  (703)823-7234
Composite Lumber Mfrs. Assn. [1502], 750 Natl.
  Press Bldg., 529 14th St. NW, Washington, DC
  20005, (202)207-0906
Composite Panel Assn. [1503], 19465 Deerfield
  Ave., Ste. 306, Leesburg, VA 20176, (703)724-
  1128

A star before a book entry number signifies that the name is not listed separately, but is mentioned within the entry.

Composite Panel Assn. [1503], 19465 Deerfield Ave., Ste. 306, Leesburg, VA 20176, (703)724-1128

Composite Wood Coun. - Address unknown since 2010.

Composites Assn. of New Zealand [IO], Manukau City, New Zealand

Composites Fabricators Assn. [★519]

Compost Tea Indus. Assn. [3752], PO Box 71894, Eugene, OR 97401, (541)343-8727

Composting Coun. [★6068]

Composting Coun. of Canada [IO], Toronto, ON, Canada

Comprehensive Hea. Educ. Found. [8603], 159 S Jackson St., Ste. 510, Seattle, WA 98104, (206)824-2907

Compressed Air and Gas Inst. [1815], 1300 Sumner Ave., Cleveland, OH 44115-2851, (216)241-7333

Compressed Gas Assn. [1569], 4221 Walney Rd., 5th Fl., Chantilly, VA 20151-2923, (703)788-2700

Compressed Gas Mfrs. Assn. [★1569]

COMPTEL [3592], 900 17th St. NW, Ste. 400, Washington, DC 20006, (202)296-6650

CompTel/ASCENT Alliance and Assn. for Local Telecommunications Services [★3592]

Compton Found. [13128], 101 Montgomery St., Ste. 850, San Francisco, CA 94104-4126, (415)391-9001

Compton Found. [13128], 101 Montgomery St., Ste. 850, San Francisco, CA 94104-4126, (415)391-9001

Compu-Forum - Defunct.

CompuMentor [★7533]

Computational Intelligence Soc. [6791], Jo-Ellen B. Snyder, Exec. Admin., PO Box 1331, Piscataway, NJ 08855, (732)465-5892

Computational Mechanics; U.S. Assn. for [7080]

Cmpt. Aid Intl. [IO], London, United Kingdom

Computer Aided Design
Intl. Building Performance Simulation Assn. [6377]

Computer-Aided Learning in Veterinary Educ. [IO], Edinburgh, United Kingdom

Cmpt. Assisted Language Instruction Consortium [8306], Texas State Univ., 214 Centennial Hall, 601 Univ. Dr., San Marcos, TX 78666, (512)245-1417

Cmpt. Assisted Language Instruction Consortium [8306], Texas State Univ., 214 Centennial Hall, 601 Univ. Dr., San Marcos, TX 78666, (512)245-1417

Cmpt. Assisted Language, Learning and Instruction Consortium [★8306]

Cmpt. Assisted Language, Learning and Instruction Consortium [★8306]

Cmpt. Assn. of Nepal [IO], Kathmandu, Nepal

Cmpt. and Bus. Equip. Mfrs. Assn. [★6539]

Cmpt. and Communications Indus. Assn. [3404], 900 17th St. NW, Ste. 1100, Washington, DC 20006, (202)783-0070

Cmpt. Conservation Soc. [IO], Aldershot, United Kingdom

Cmpt. Distributors' and Dealers' Assn. [IO], Makati City, Philippines

Cmpt. Educ. Mgt. Assn. - Europe [IO], High Wycombe, United Kingdom

Cmpt. Ethics Inst. [8792], 1775 Massachusetts Ave. NW, Washington, DC 20036, (202)797-6183

Cmpt. Event Marketing Assn. [★2396]

Cmpt. Indus. Assn. [★3404]

Cmpt. Indus. Coun. [★6532]

Cmpt. Integrated Textile Design Assn. - Defunct.

Cmpt. Law Assn. [★5323]

Cmpt. Measurement Gp. [6449], 151 Fries Mill Rd., Ste. 104, PO Box 1124, Turnersville, NJ 08012, (856)401-1700

Cmpt. Musician Coalition [★2554]

Cmpt. Musicians Cooperative [★2554]

Cmpt. Professionals for Social Responsibility [18194], PO Box 20046, Stanford, CA 94309-0046, (650)989-1294

Computer Science
ACM SIGGRAPH [6441]
Amer. Cmpt. Sci. League [7902]
Amer. Soc. for Cybernetics [6442]
Anti-Malware Testing Standards Org. [6478]

Applied Voice Input/Output Soc. [6443]

Assn. for Cmpt. Aided Design in Architecture [6444]

Assn. for Computing Machinery [6504]

Assn. for Computing Machinery | Special Interest Gp. on Cmpt. Sci. Educ. [7903]

Assn. for Computing Machinery | Special Interest Gp. on Measurement and Evaluation [6445]

Assn. for Computing Machinery | Special Interest Group on MultiMedia [6528]

Assn. for Computing Machinery | Special Interest Gp. on Security, Audit and Control [6446]

Assn. for Info. Systems [6447]

Assn. of Info. Tech. Professionals [7904]

CompactFlash Assn. [6448]

Cmpt. Measurement Gp. [6449]

Cmpt. Sci. Teachers Assn. [7905]

Computing Res. Assn. [6450]

Ethernet Alliance [7499]

IEEE | Cmpt. Soc. [6451]

IEEE | Systems, Man, and Cybernetics Soc. [6452]

IMAGE Soc. [6453]

InCommon [6537]

InfiniBand Trade Assn. [6454]

Inst. for Certification of Computing Professionals [7906]

Intl. Assn. for Artificial Intelligence and Law [6455]

Intl. Assn. for Cmpt. and Info. Sci. [6456]

Intl. Assn. for Cmpt. Info. Systems [7907]

Intl. Assn. for Cmpt. Info. Systems [7907]

Intl. Assn. of Cmpt. Investigative Specialists [7908]

Intl. Assn. of Cmpt. Investigative Specialists [7908]

Intl. Assn. for Mathematics and Computers in Simulation [6457]

Intl. Assn. for Mathematics and Computers in Simulation [6457]

Intl. Building Performance Simulation Assn. [6377]

Intl. Disk Drive Equip. and Materials Assn. [6458]

Intl. Disk Drive Equip. and Materials Assn. [6458]

Intl. Game Developers Assn. [6459]

Intl. Game Developers Assn. [6459]

Intl. Soc. for Ethics and Info. Tech. [6979]

Intl. Soc. of Parametric Analysts [6460]

Intl. Soc. of Parametric Analysts [6460]

Intl. Soc. for Tech. in Educ. [7909]

Intl. Soc. for Tech. in Educ. [7909]

Intl. Training and Simulation Alliance [6461]

Intl. Training and Simulation Alliance [6461]

Korea Info. Tech. Network [6462]

Korea Info. Tech. Network [6462]

Multicore Assn. [6463]

Natl. Assn. of Internet Ser. Providers of Romania [21199]

Natl. Training and Simulation Assn. [6464]

Network Professional Assn. [6465]

North Amer. Computational Social and Org. Sciences [6466]

Open DeviceNet Vendor Assn. [6492]Computer-Personal Cmpt. Memory Card Intl. Assn.

RapidIO Trade Assn. [6467]

Schools Interoperability Framework Assn. [6468]

SD Assn. [6469]

Serial ATA Intl. Org. [6559]

Soc. for Design and Process Sci. [6601]

Soc. for Info. Display [6470]

Soc. for Info. Display [6470]

Soc. for Modeling and Simulation Intl. [6471]

Soc. for Modeling and Simulation Intl. [6471]

Special Interest Gp. for Design Automation [6472]

Special Interest Gp. on Design of Commun. [6561]

Special Interest Gp. on Mgt. of Data [6473]

Special Interest Gp. on Programming Languages [7302]

Special Interest Gp. on Simulation [6474]

Storage Networking Indus. Assn. [6475]

Top Level Domain Assn. [2118]

Transaction Processing Performance Coun. [6476]

Upsilon Pi Epsilon Assn. [23495]

Upsilon Pi Epsilon Assn. [23495]

World Sci. and Engg. Acad. and Soc. [6837]

World Wide Web Consortium [6477]

World Wide Web Consortium [6477]

Cmpt. Sci. Bd. [★6450]

Cmpt. Sci. Teachers Assn. [7905], PO Box 30778, New York, NY 10117-3509, (212)626-0530

Computer Security
Internet Keep Safe Coalition [17996]
Transported Asset Protection Assn. [7396]

Cmpt. Security Inst. [1888], 350 Hudson St., Ste. 300, New York, NY 10014, (212)600-3026

Cmpt. Soc. of India [IO], Mumbai, India

Cmpt. Soc. of Malta [IO], Paola, Malta

Cmpt. Soc. of Zimbabwe [IO], Harare, Zimbabwe

Computer Software
Advanced Media Workflow Assn. [3386]
Anti-Malware Testing Standards Org. [6478]
AppleWorks Users Gp. [6479]
Assn. for Computing Machinery | Special Interest Gp. on Software Engg. [6480]
Assn. of Software Professionals [6481]
Assn. for Software Testing [6482]
CAD Soc. [6483]
Educational Software Cooperative [6484]
Educational Software Cooperative [6484]
Entertainment Software Assn. [6485]
Ethernet Alliance [7499]
Free Software Found. [6486]
Free Software Found. [6486]
InCommon [6537]
InfraGard Natl. Members Alliance [5968]
Intl. Assn. of Microsoft Channel Partners [6487]
Intl. Assn. of Software Architects [6488]
Intl. Assn. of Software Architects [6488]
Intl. Building Performance Simulation Assn. [6377]
Intl. DB2 Users Gp. [6592]
Intl. .NET Assn. [6489]
Internet Systems Consortium [6490]
New Parents Network [8692]
ODF Alliance [6990]
Online Trust Alliance [6550]
Open Applications Gp. [6491]
Open DeviceNet Vendor Assn. [6492]
Open DeviceNet Vendor Assn. [6492]
The Open Planning Proj. [6493]
Oracle Applications Users Gp. [6494]
Oracle Development Tools User Gp. [6495]
Physical Security Interoperability Alliance [6819]
Soc. for Software Quality [6496]
Software in the Public Interest [6497]
Software and Tech. Vendors' Assn. [819]
Systems and Software Consortium, Inc. [6498]
TechAmerica [6499]
U.S. PostgreSQL Assn. [6500]
Wireless Innovation Forum [6501]

Computer Users
ACM SIGGRAPH [6441]
AFCOM [6502]
Alliance for Digital Equality [7492]
Arizona Macintosh Users Gp. [6503]
Assn. for Computing Machinery [6504]
Assn. for Computing Machinery | Special Interest Group on MultiMedia [6528]
Assn. of Personal Cmpt. User Groups [6505]
Assn. for Women in Computing [6506]
Capital PC User Gp. [6507]
Capital PC User Gp. [6507]
Center for Computer-Assisted Legal Instruction [6508]
Common-A Users Gp. [6509]
Connect Worldwide [6510]
Epicor Users Gp. [6511]
Ethernet Alliance [7499]
FORTH Interest Gp. [7298]
Global Tech. Distribution Coun. [3392]
InCommon [6537]
The Inst. of Financial Operations [6512]
Intl. Assn. for Cmpt. and Info. Sci. [6456]
Intl. Oracle Users Gp. [6513]
Intl. Oracle Users Gp. [6513]
Internet Keep Safe Coalition [17996]
Internet Merchants Assn. [2117]
NAQP Cmpt. Users Gp. [6514]
NaSPA [6515]
Network and Systems Professionals Assn. [6515]
Online Trust Alliance [6550]

Reference to "IO" in place of a book number signifies that the association may be found in the 50th edition of International Organizations.

SailMail Assn. **[6679]**
SAS Global Forum **[6516]**
SAS Global Forum **[6516]**
Special Interest Gp. on Accessible Computing
[6517]
Special Interest Gp. on Data Communications of
the Assn. for Computing Machinery **[6518]**
Special Interest Gp. on Programming Languages
[7302]
SunGard Public Sector Users' Gp. Assn. **[6519]**
Top Level Domain Assn. **[2118]**
Transported Asset Protection Assn. **[7396]**
UniForum Assn. **[6520]**
UniForum Assn. **[6520]**
U.S. Internet Indus. Assn. **[6521]**
USENIX Assn. **[6522]**
Vivit **[6523]**
XyUser Gp. **[6524]**
Computer Users for Social Responsibility - Defunct.
Cmpt. Vision and Pattern Recognition Gp. of Korea
Info. Sci. Soc. **[IO]**, Seoul, Republic of Korea
Computerized Books for the Blind **[★17095]**
Computerized Electrocardiology; Intl. Soc. for
[14025]
Computers
Alliance for Digital Equality **[7492]**
Amer. Assn. of Cmpt. Rental Professionals **[6525]**
Amer. Assn. of Webmasters **[6526]**
Assn. for Computing Machinery **[6504]**
Assn. of Computing Machinery | Special Interest
Gp. on Mgt. Info. Systems **[6527]**
Assn. for Computing Machinery | Special Interest
Gp. on Measurement and Evaluation **[6445]**
Assn. for Computing Machinery | Special Interest
Group on MultiMedia **[6528]**
Assn. of Macintosh Trainers **[6529]**
Assn. of Macintosh Trainers **[6529]**
Assn. of Ser. and Cmpt. Dealers Intl. **[6530]**
Chilean Assn. of Info. Tech. Companies **[5881]**
Communications Platforms Trade Assn. **[6531]**
Computers for Africa **[7910]**
Computers for Children **[7911]**
Computers for Children **[7911]**
Computers for Youth **[7912]**
Computing Tech. Indus. Assn. **[6532]**
Connect Worldwide **[6510]**
Cooperative Assn. for Internet Data Anal. **[7007]**
Distributed Computing Indus. Assn. **[6533]**
e-Learning for Kids **[7828]**
East West Educ. Development Found. **[12664]**
Edutechnia **[6976]**
Entertainment and Leisure Software Publishers
Assn. **[1368]**
Ethernet Alliance **[7499]**
FORTH Interest Gp. **[7298]**ComputersGeeks
Without Borders
GeoData Alliance **[6534]**
Geospatial Info. and Tech. Assn. **[6535]**
HTML Writers Guild **[6536]**
InCommon **[6537]**
Info. Storage Indus. Consortium **[6538]**
Info. Tech. Indus. Coun. **[6539]**
Info. Tech. Services Marketing Assn. **[2405]**
InfraGard Natl. Members Alliance **[5968]**
InterConnection **[11664]**
Intl. Assn. for Obsidian Stud. **[6171]**
Intl. Info. Systems Security Certification
Consortium **[6540]**
Intl. Info. Systems Security Certification
Consortium **[6540]**
Intl. Soc. for Computers and Their Applications
[6541]
Intl. Soc. for Ethics and Info. Tech. **[6979]**
Intl. Webmasters Assn. **[6542]**
Intl. Webmasters Assn. **[6542]**
Internet Corp. for Assigned Names and Numbers
[6543]
Internet Keep Safe Coalition **[17996]**
Internet Merchants Assn. **[2117]**
Internet Ser. Providers Assn. **[14141]**
Internet Soc. **[6544]**
Internet Soc. **[6544]**
IVI Found. **[6545]**
League of Professional Sys. Administrators **[6546]**
League of Professional Sys. Administrators **[6546]**

MSPAlliance **[6547]**
NAQP Cmpt. Users Gp. **[6514]**
Natl. Assn. of Govt. Webmasters **[6548]**
Natl. Coalition for Telecommunications Educ. and
Learning **[8981]**
Natl. States Geographic Info. Coun. **[6549]**
ODF Alliance **[6990]**
One Laptop Per Child **[11665]**
Online Policy Gp. **[17397]**
Online Trust Alliance **[6550]**
Open DeviceNet Vendor Assn. **[6492]**
Open Geospatial Consortium **[6551]**
Organizers' Collaborative **[17398]**
Pan-American Fed. for Info. Tech. in Agriculture
[6106]
PC Gaming Alliance **[6552]**
PCI Indus. Cmpt. Mfrs. Gp. **[6553]**
Physical Security Interoperability Alliance **[6819]**
Pro vs. GI Joe **[21762]**
Professional Assn. for SQL Server **[6554]**
PXI Systems Alliance **[6555]**
Retail Solutions Providers Assn. **[6556]**
SailMail Assn. **[6679]**
Schedules Direct **[6557]**
Scrum Alliance **[6558]**
Serial ATA Intl. Org. **[6559]**
SIGAPP - Special Interest Gp. on Applied
Computing **[6560]**
Special Interest Gp. on Design of Commun.
[6561]
Special Interest Gp. on Mobility of Systems Users,
Data, and Computing **[6562]**
Special Interest Gp. on Programming Languages
[7302]
TechServe Alliance **[868]**
Top Level Domain Assn. **[2118]**
Transported Asset Protection Assn. **[7396]**
U.S. Internet Ser. Provider Assn. **[6563]**
USB Implementers Forum **[6564]**ComputersVen-
ezuelan Chamber of Info. Tech. Businesses
VITA **[6565]**
Web3D Consortium **[6566]**
Wi-Fi Alliance **[6567]**
WiMedia Alliance **[6568]**
World Cmpt. Exchange **[7913]**ComputersX.Org
Found.
YLEM: Artists Using Sci. and Tech. **[9260]**
Computers for Africa **[7910]**, PO Box 34262,
Omaha, NE 68134-0262, (402)933-6456
Computers for Children **[7911]**, 2558 Delaware Ave.,
Buffalo, NY 14216, (716)823-7248
Computers for Children **[7911]**, 2558 Delaware Ave.,
Buffalo, NY 14216, (716)823-7248
Computers for Youth **[7912]**, 520 Eighth Ave., 25th
Fl., New York, NY 10018, (212)563-7300
Computing Res. Assn. **[6450]**, 1828 L St. NW, Ste.
800, Washington, DC 20036-4632, (202)234-2111
Computing Res. Bd. **[★6450]**
Computing Tech. Indus. Assn. **[6532]**, 3500 Lacey
Rd., Ste. 100, Downers Grove, IL 60515,
(630)678-8300
ComSource Independent Foodservice Companies
[★1433]
Comunicacion Intercambio y Desarrollo Humano en
Am. Latina, A.C. **[IO]**, Cuernavaca, Mexico
Comunidad Andina - Secretaria Gen. **[★IO]**
Comunidad Electroacustica de Chile **[IO]**, Santiago,
Chile
Comunidad Oscar A. Romero Peace Mission
[★17601]
Comunn na Clarsaich **[★IO]**
An Comunn Gaidhealach Ameireaganach **[10526]**,
PO Box 103069, Denver, CO 80250
An Comunn Gaidhealach Ameireaganach **[10526]**,
PO Box 103069, Denver, CO 80250
Conaidhm Eireannach na Muinteoiri Ollscoile **[★IO]**
Concern - Address unknown since 2010.
Concern Am. **[12828]**, PO Box 1790, Santa Ana, CA
92702, (714)953-8575
Concern Am. **[12828]**, PO Box 1790, Santa Ana, CA
92702, (714)953-8575
Concern for Children Trust **[IO]**, Karachi, Pakistan
Concern Found. **[13910]**, 1026 S Robertson Blvd.,
Ste. 300, Los Angeles, CA 90035-1545, (310)360-
6100

Concern for Hea. Options - Info., Care and Educ.
[★12029]
Concern for Helping Animals in Israel **[10949]**, PO
Box 3341, Alexandria, VA 22302, (703)658-9650
Concern for Helping Animals in Israel **[10949]**, PO
Box 3341, Alexandria, VA 22302, (703)658-9650
Concern Worldwide **[12829]**, 355 Lexington Ave.,
New York, NY 10017, (212)557-8000
Concern Worldwide **[12829]**, 355 Lexington Ave.,
New York, NY 10017, (212)557-8000
Concerned Alliance of Responsible Employers -
Defunct.
Concerned Children's Advertisers **[IO]**, Toronto, ON,
Canada
Concerned Citizens for Nuclear Safety **[18195]**, 107
Cienega St., Santa Fe, NM 87501, (505)986-1973
Concerned Citizens for Racially Free Am. - Address
unknown since 2011.
Concerned Educators Against Forced Unionism
[18042], 8001 Braddock Rd., Springfield, VA
22160, (703)321-8519
Concerned Educators Allied for a Safe Env. **[18196]**,
55 Frost St., Cambridge, MA 02140, (617)661-
8347
Concerned Persons for Adoption **[10785]**, Anna
Marie O'Loughlin, Membership Chair, 7 Elizabeth
St., Bloomingdale, NJ 07403
Concerned Pet Owners' Assn. - Defunct.
Concerned Philosophers for Peace **[10376]**, Arnold
Farr, Treas., Univ. of Kentucky, Dept. of
Philosophy, 1415 Patterson Off. Tower, Lexington,
KY 40506-0027
Concerned United Birthparents **[10786]**, PO Box
503475, San Diego, CA 92150-3475, (800)822-
2777
Concerned Women for Am. **[19564]**, 1015 15th St.
NW, Ste. 1100, Washington, DC 20005-2619,
(202)488-7000
Concerns of Police Survivors **[12419]**, PO Box 3199,
Camdenton, MO 65020, (573)346-4911
Conchological Soc. of Great Britain and Ireland **[IO]**,
Reading, United Kingdom
Conchologists of Am. **[21327]**, 7529 Ensemble Ln.,
Melbourne, FL 32904-2603
Conchology Assn. of Maldives **[IO]**, Male, Maldives
Concord Coalition **[17574]**, 1011 Arlington Blvd., Ste.
300, Arlington, VA 22209, (703)894-6222
Concord Grape Assn. **[4445]**, 1100 Johnson Ferry
Rd., Ste. 300, Atlanta, GA 30342, (404)252-3663
Concord Grape Coun. **[★4445]**
Concord Video and Film Coun. **[IO]**, Ipswich, United
Kingdom
Concorde Collectors Club **[★22006]**
Concordia Deaconess Conf. **[19922]**, Deaconess
Kim Schave, Treas., St. Paul Lutheran Church,
5433 Madison Rd., Cincinnati, OH 45227
Concordia Historical Inst. **[19923]**, 804 Seminary Pl.,
St. Louis, MO 63105-3014, (314)505-7900
Concordia Historical Soc. **[★19923]**
Concordia - Youth Ser. Volunteers **[IO]**, Brighton,
United Kingdom
Concrete
Amer. Concrete Pavement Assn. **[820]**
Amer. Concrete Pumping Assn. **[821]**
Amer. Shotcrete Assn. **[822]**
Architectural Precast Assn. **[823]**
Asphalt Interlayer Assn. **[525]**
Brazilian Cement Mfrs'. Assn. **[4771]**
Cast Stone Inst. **[824]**
Cement, Lime, Gypsum, and Allied Workers Div.
[23175]
Concrete Anchor Mfrs. Assn. **[825]**
Concrete Sawing and Drilling Assn. **[826]**
Concrete Sawing and Drilling Assn. **[826]**
Concrete Tile Mfrs. Assn. **[827]**
Insulating Concrete Form Assn. **[828]**
Interlocking Concrete Pavement Inst. **[829]**
Interlocking Concrete Pavement Inst. **[829]**
Intl. Concrete Repair Inst. **[830]**
Intl. Concrete Repair Inst. **[830]**
Intl. Grooving and Grinding Assn. **[831]**
Intl. Grooving and Grinding Assn. **[831]**
Intl. Soc. for Concrete Pavements **[574]**
Natl. Concrete Masonry Assn. **[832]**
Natl. Pavement Contractors Assn. **[595]**

A star before a book entry number signifies that the name is not listed separately, but is mentioned within the entry.

Natl. Precast Concrete Assn. [833]
Natl. Ready Mixed Concrete Assn. [834]
Ornamental Concrete Producers Assn. [835]
Portland Cement Assn. [836]
Precast/Prestressed Concrete Inst. [837]
Slag Cement Assn. [838]
Concrete Anchor Mfrs. Assn. [825], 136 S Main St., No. 2E, St. Charles, MO 63301, (314)889-7116
Concrete Block Assn. [IO], Leicester, United Kingdom
Concrete Corrosion Inhibitors Assn. - Address unknown since 2011.
Concrete Foundations Assn. [908], PO Box 204, Mount Vernon, IA 52314, (319)895-6940
Concrete Inst. of Australia [IO], Rhodes, Australia
Concrete Paver Inst. [★832]
Concrete Pipe Assn. [★5775]
Concrete Pipe Assn. of Australasia [IO], St. Leonards, Australia
Concrete Pipeline Systems Assn. [IO], Leicester, United Kingdom
Concrete Plant Mfrs. Bur. [★834]
Concrete Pumpers Assn. of Southern California [★821]
Concrete Reinforcing Steel Inst. [546], 933 N Plum Grove Rd., Schaumburg, IL 60173-4758, (847)517-1200
Concrete Repair Assn. [IO], Bordon, United Kingdom
Concrete Sawing and Drilling Assn. [826], 13577 Feather Sound Dr., Ste. 560, Clearwater, FL 33762, (727)577-5004
Concrete Sawing and Drilling Assn. [826], 13577 Feather Sound Dr., Ste. 560, Clearwater, FL 33762, (727)577-5004
Concrete Soc. [IO], Camberley, United Kingdom
Concrete Soc. of Southern Africa [IO], Lynnwood Ridge, Republic of South Africa
Concrete Tile Mfrs. Assn. [827], PO Box 6225, Buena Park, CA 90622, (714)535-0791
Conductors Guild [10180], 719 Twinridge Ln., Richmond, VA 23235, (804)553-1378
CONDUIT - Defunct.
Confectionery Mfrs. Assn. of Canada [IO], Don Mills, ON, Canada
Confectionery Mfrs. of Australasia [IO], Camberwell, Australia
Confederacao dos Agricultores de Portugal [★IO]
Confederacao das Associacoes Comerciais do Brasil [★IO]
Confederacao Brasileira de Badminton [IO], Campinas, Brazil
Confederacao Brasileira do Desporto Escolar [IO], Brasilia, Brazil
Confederacao Brasileira de Desportos no Gelo [★IO]
Confederacao Brasileira de Esqui-Aquatico [★IO]
Confederacao Brasileira de Taekwondo [IO], Rio de Janeiro, Brazil
Confederacao Brasileira de Tenis [IO], Sao Paulo, Brazil
Confederacao Brasileira de Vela e Motor [IO], Rio de Janeiro, Brazil
Confederacao Brasileira de Squash [IO], Florianopolis, Brazil
Confederacao de Comercio e Servicos de Portugal [★IO]
Confederacao Nacional do Comercio [★IO]
Confederacao Nacional dos Trabalhadores em Educacao [★IO]
Confederacion Atletica del Uruguay [IO], Montevideo, Uruguay
Confederacion de Camaras Industriales [★IO]
Confederacion de Empresarios Privados de Bolivia [★IO]
Confederacion Espanola de Asociaciones Profesionales de Informadores Tecnicos Sanitarios [★IO]
Confederacion Espanola de Empresarios de Plasticos [★IO]
Confederacion Espanola de Fabricantes de Alimentos Compuestos para Animales [★IO]
Confederacion Espanola de Familiares de Enfermos de Alzheimer y Otras Demencias [★IO]
Confederacion Espanola de Hoteles y Alojamientos Turisticos [★IO]
Confederacion Espanola de Organizaciones Empresariales [★IO]

Confederacion Espanola de Organizaciones en favor de las Personas con Discapacidad Intelectual [IO], Madrid, Spain
Confederacion Espanola de la Pequena y Mediana Empresa [★IO]
Confederacion Interamericana de Educacion Catolica [★IO]
Confederacion de Kinesiologos y Fisioterapeutas de la Republica Argentina [IO], Parana, Argentina
Confederacion Latinoamericana de Sociedades de Anestesiologia [★IO]
Confederacion Medica Republica Argentina [IO], Buenos Aires, Argentina
Confederacion Mundial de Centros Comunitarios Judios [IO]
Confederacion Nacional de Squash de Panama [IO], Panama City, Panama
Confederacion de Organizaciones Turisticas de la Am. Latina [★IO]
Confederacion Paraguaya de Taekwondo [IO], Asuncion, Paraguay
Confederacion Sindical Internacional [★IO]
Confederacion Sudamericana de Atletismo [★IO]
Confederacion Sudamericana de Tenis [IO], Santiago, Chile
Confederacion de Tenis de Centroamerica Y El Caribe [★IO]
Confederacion Venezolana de Industriales [★IO]
Confederate Air Force [★20888]
Confederate Memorial Assn. [9110], PO Box 6010, Washington, DC 20005, (202)483-5700
Confederate Memorial Literary Soc. [9761], The Museum of the Confederacy, 1201 E Clay St., Richmond, VA 23219, (804)649-1861
Confederate Stamp Alliance [22033], 501 Rosebud Ln., Greer, SC 29650
Confederated Unions of Am. [★23314]
Confed. of Aerial Indus. [IO], Watford, United Kingdom
Confed. Africaine de Football [★IO]
Confed. Africaine de Tennis [★IO]
Confed. of African Medical Associations and Societies [IO], Lagos, Nigeria
Confed. of African Tennis [IO], Tunis, Tunisia
Confed. of Asian and Pacific Accountants [IO], Kuala Lumpur, Malaysia
Confed. of Asian-Pacific Chambers of Commerce and Indus. [IO], Taipei, Taiwan
Confed. des Associations d'Entreprises de Commerce Intl. [★IO]
Confed. des Associations Internationales d'Entrepreneurs [★IO]
Confed. des Associations Nationales de l'Hotellerie, de la Restauration et des Cafes de l'Union Europeenne [★IO]
Confed. des Associations et Societes Medicales D'Afrique [★IO]
Confed. Belge du Commerce et de la Reparation Automobiles et des Secteurs Connexes a.s.b.l. [★IO]
Confed. Belge de l'industrie laitiere [★IO]
Confed. of Bolivian Private Entrepreneurs [IO], La Paz, Bolivia
Confed. of British Indus. [IO], London, United Kingdom
Confed. of British Metalforming [IO], West Bromwich, United Kingdom
Confed. of British Wool Textiles [IO], Huddersfield, United Kingdom
Confed. of Commercial Associations of Brazil [IO], Brasilia, Brazil
Confed. of Danish Employers [IO], Copenhagen, Denmark
Confed. of Danish Indus. [IO], Copenhagen, Denmark
Confed. of Dental Employers [IO], Holsworthy, United Kingdom
Confed. of European Baseball [IO], Frankfurt, Germany
Confed. of European Forest Owners [IO], Brussels, Belgium
Confed. of European Paper Indus. [IO], Brussels, Belgium
Confed. of European Pest Control Associations [IO], Brussels, Belgium

Confed. Europeene des Independents [★IO]
Confed. Europeene des Relations Publiques [★IO]
Confed. Europeenne des Administrateurs de Biens aisbl [★IO]
Confed. Europeenne de Baseball [★IO]
Confed. Europeenne des Cadres [★IO]
Confed. Europeenne des Cooperatives de Travail Associe, des Cooperatives Sociales et des Entreprises Sociales et Participatives [★IO]
Confed. Europeenne des Distributeurs d'Energie Publics Communaux [★IO]
Confed. Europeenne des Indus. du Bois [★IO]
Confed. Europeenne de l'Immobilier [★IO]
Confed. Europeenne des ONG d'urgence et de Developpement [★IO]
Confed. Europeenne des Produceurs de Spiritueux [★IO]
Confed. Europeenne des Proprietaires Forestiers [★IO]
Confed. Europeenne des Syndicats Independants [★IO]
Confed. Europeenne des Universities du Rhin Superieur [★IO]
Confed. of Family Organisations in the European Union [IO], Brussels, Belgium
Confed. Fiscale Europeenne [IO], Berlin, Germany
Confed. of the Food and Drink Indus. of the EU [IO], Brussels, Belgium
Confed. of Forest Indus. [IO], Edinburgh, United Kingdom
Confed. Francaise Democratique du Travail [★IO]
Confed. Francaise de L'industrie des Papiers, Cartons and Celluloses [★IO]
Confed. of German Employers' Associations [IO], Berlin, Germany
Confed. of Icelandic Employers [IO], Reykjavik, Iceland
Confed. of Independent Trade Unions in Bulgaria [IO], Sofia, Bulgaria
Confed. of Indian Indus. [IO], New Delhi, India
Confed. of Indian Indus. - United Kingdom [IO], London, United Kingdom
Confed. of Indus. Chambers [IO], Mexico City, Mexico
Confed. of Indus. of the Czech Republic [IO], Prague, Czech Republic
Confed. of Inspection and Certification Organisations [IO], Brussels, Belgium
Confed. of Intl. Contractors' Associations [IO], Paris, France
Confed. of Intl. Soft Drinks Associations [IO], Brussels, Belgium
Confed. Internationale des Accordeonistes [★IO]
Confed. Internationale des Banques Populaires [★IO]
Confed. Internationale des Betteraviers Europeens [★IO]
Confed. Internationale de la Boucherie et de la Charcuterie [★IO]
Confed. Internationale du Commerce et des Indus. des Legumes Secs [★IO]
Confed. Internationale du Credit Agricole [★IO]
Confed. Internationale des Fabricants de Tissus d'Ameublement [★IO]
Confed. Internationale des Musees d'Architecture [★IO]
Confed. Internationale de Musique Electroacoustique [★IO]
Confed. Internationale des Sages-Femmes [★IO]
Confed. Internationale des Societes d'Auteurs et Compositeurs [★IO]
Confed. of Italian Indus. [IO], Rome, Italy
Confed. of Labour "Podkrepa" Sofia, BulgariaIO
Confed. of Latin Amer. Societies of Anesthesiology [IO], Buenos Aires, Argentina
Confed. of Latin Amer. Tourism Organizations [IO], Buenos Aires, Argentina
Confed. des organisations familiales de l'Union europeenne [★IO]
Confed. Mondiale des Activites Subaquatiques [★IO]
Confed. Mondiale pour la Therapie Physique [★IO]
Confed. of Natl. Associations of Hotels, Restaurants, Cafes and Similar Establishments [IO], Brussels, Belgium

Reference to "IO" in place of a book number signifies that the association may be found in the 50th edition of International Organizations.

Confed. of Natl. Associations of Tanners and Dressers of the European Community [IO], Brussels, Belgium

Confed. of Natl. Trade Unions [IO], Montreal, QC, Canada

Confed. Nationale de la Boulangerie-Patisserie Francaise [★IO]

Confed. Nationale des Glaciers de France [★IO]

Confed. Nationale du Logement [IO], Montreuil, France

Confed. of Nordic Bank, Finance and Insurance Employees' Unions [IO], Stockholm, Sweden

Confed. of Norwegian Enterprise [IO], Oslo, Norway

Confed. of Paper Indus. [IO], Swindon, United Kingdom

Confed. of Passenger Transport - UK [IO], London, United Kingdom

Confed. of Portuguese Farmers [IO], Lisbon, Portugal

Confed. of Roofing Contractors [IO], Colchester, United Kingdom

Confed. of Swedish Enterprise [IO], Stockholm, Sweden

Confed. of Swiss Employers [IO], Zurich, Switzerland

Confed. Syndicale Internationale - Org. Regionale Africaine [★IO]

Confed. des Syndicats Chretiens de Belgique [★IO]

Confed. des Syndicats Nationaux [★IO]

Confed. of Tanzania Indus. [IO], Dar es Salaam, United Republic of Tanzania

Confed. of Trade Unions of Monaco [IO], Monaco, Monaco

Confed. of Turkish Trade Unions [IO], Ankara, Turkey

Confed. of Unions for Professional and Managerial Staff in Finland [IO], Helsinki, Finland

Confed. of Zimbabwe Indus. [IO], Harare, Zimbabwe

Confed. of Zonta Clubs [★13081]

Confed. of Zonta Clubs [★13081]

Confederazione Cooperative Italiane [★IO]

Confederazione Generale dell'Industria Italiana [★IO]

Conf. of Actuaries in Public Practice [★1951]

Conf. of Biological Editors [★2822]

The Conf. Bd. [6618], 845 3rd Ave., New York, NY 10022, (212)759-0900

The Conf. Bd. [6618], 845 3rd Ave., New York, NY 10022, (212)759-0900

Conf. Bd. of Assoc. Res. Councils [★8354]

Conf. Bd. of Assoc. Res. Councils [★8354]

Conf. Bd. of Canada [IO], Ottawa, ON, Canada

Conf. Bd. Europe [IO], Brussels, Belgium

Conf. Bd. of the Mathematical Sciences [7072], 1529 18th St. NW, Washington, DC 20036-1358, (202)293-1170

Conf. on British Stud. [★9456]

Conf. des eveques catholiques du Canada [★IO]

Conf. Canadienne des arts [★IO]

Conf. of Chief Justices [5616], 300 Newport Ave., Williamsburg, VA 23185-4147, (757)259-1841

Conf. Chretienne pour la Paix [★IO]

Conf. on Christianity and Literature [10039], Pepperdine Univ., 24255 Pacific Coast Hwy., Malibu, CA 90263-3999, (310)506-4095

Conf. of Church Workers Among the Deaf [★19700]

Conf. on Coll. Composition and Commun. [8132], 1111 W Kenyon Rd., Urbana, IL 61801-1096, (217)328-3870

Conf. of Consulting Actuaries [1951], 3880 Salem Lake Dr., Ste. H, Long Grove, IL 60047-5292, (847)719-6500

Conf. on Consumer Finance Law [5340], Prof. Alvin C. Harrell, Exec. Dir., Oklahoma City Univ. School of Law, 2501 N Blackwelder Ave., Oklahoma City, OK 73106, (405)208-5198

Conf. des Directerus des Gymnases Suisses [★IO]

Conf. of Drama Schools [IO], London, United Kingdom

Conf. of Educational Administrators of Schools and Programs for the Deaf [14926], PO Box 1778, St. Augustine, FL 32085-1778, (904)810-5200

Conf. of Educational Administrators Serving the Deaf [★14926]

Conf. des Eglises Europeennes [★IO]

Conf. on English Leadership [8112], Natl. Coun. of Teachers of English, 1111 W Kenyon Rd., Urbana, IL 61801-1096, (217)328-3870

Conf. of European Churches [IO], Geneva, Switzerland

Conf. of European Natl. Librarians [IO], Frankfurt, Germany

Conf. of European Rabbis [IO], London, United Kingdom

Conf. of European Schools for Advanced Engg. Educ. and Res. [IO], Leuven, Belgium

Conf. Europeenne des Administrations des Postes et des Telecommunications [★IO]

Conf. Europeenne de l'Aviation Civile [★IO]

Conf. des Eveques Catholiques de l'Ontario [★IO]

Conf. of Executives of Amer. Schools for the Deaf [★14926]

Conf. of Executives of State Associations of Counties [★5353]

Conference on Fair Foreign Investment - Defunct.

Conf. on Faith and History [19813], Paul E. Michelson, Sec., Huntington Univ., Dept. of History, 2303 Coll. Ave., Huntington, IN 46750, (260)359-4242

Conf. of Funeral Ser. Examining Boards of the U.S. [★5845]

Conf. Gp. of U.S. Natl. Organizations on the United Nations [★18748]

Conf. de la Haye de Droit Intl. Prive [★IO]

Conf. of Intl. Non-Governmental Organizations [IO], Paris, France

Conf. Internationale pour les Bateaux de Sauvetage [★IO]

Conf. on Jesuit Student Personnel Administrators [★7665]

Conf. on Jewish Communal Ser. [★12407]

Conf. on Jewish Communal Ser. [★12407]

Conf. on Jewish Material Claims Against Germany [12405], 1359 Broadway, Rm. 2000, New York, NY 10018, (646)536-9100

Conf. on Latin Amer. History [9945], Univ. of North Carolina at Charlotte, U.S. Department of of History and Prog. in Latin Amer. Studies, 9201 Univ. City blvd., Charlotte, NC 28223, (704)687-2027

Conf. of Local Environmental Hea. Administrators [★16489]

Conf. of Major Religious Superiors of Men's Institutes of the U.S. [★19414]

Conf. of Major Religious Superiors of Women's Institutes of the United States of Am. [★19443]

Conf. of Major Superiors of Men [19414], 8808 Cameron St., Silver Spring, MD 20910, (301)588-4030

Conf. of Minority Public Administrators [5905], PO Box 17476, Fort Worth, TX 76102

Conf. of Minority Trans. Officials [3508], 2025 M St. NW, Ste. 800, Washington, DC 20036-3309, (202)367-1181

Conf. of Municipal Public Hea. Engineers [★16489]

Conf. of Natl. Park Concessionaires [★1214]

Conf. des Nations Unies sur le Commerce et le Developpement [★IO]

Conf. des Organisations Internationales Non-Gouvernementales [★IO]

Conference of Patriotic and Historic Societies - Defunct.

Conf. of Peripheral Maritime Regions of Europe [IO], Rennes, France

Conf. Permanente Europeenne des Associations de Professeurs d'Histoire [★IO]

Conf. Permanente Europeenne de la Probation [★IO]

Conf. on Personal Finance Law [★5340]

Conf. of Personal Managers, East [★163]

Conf. of Personal Managers, West [★163]

Conf. of Presidents of Major Amer. Jewish Organizations [19858], 633 3rd Ave., 21st Fl., New York, NY 10017, (212)318-6111

Conf. of Professors of Preventive Medicine [★16308]

Conf. of Public Health Laboratorians - Defunct.

Conf. of Radiation Control Prog. Directors [5953], 1030 Burlington Ln., Ste. 4B, Frankfort, KY 40601, (502)227-4543

Conf. des Regions Peripheriques Maritimes d'Europe [★IO]

Conf. Religieuse Canadienne [★IO]

Conf. of Res. Workers in Animal Diseases [17022], Colorado State Univ., Dept. of Microbiology, Immunology and Pathology, Microbiology Bldg., Rm. A 102, Fort Collins, CO 80523-1682, (970)491-5740

Conf. of Res. Workers in Animal Diseases [17022], Colorado State Univ., Dept. of Microbiology, Immunology and Pathology, Microbiology Bldg., Rm. A 102, Fort Collins, CO 80523-1682, (970)491-5740

Conf. on Sci. and Religion [★17987]

Conf. on Sci. and Religion [★17987]

Conf. of Speakers and Presiding Officers of the Commonwealth [IO], Ottawa, ON, Canada

Conf. of State Bank Supervisors [5298], 1129 20th St. NW, 9th Fl., Washington, DC 20036, (202)296-2840

Conf. of State Social Security Administrators [★5973]

Conf. of State and Territorial Directors of Public Hea. Educ. [★5928]

Conf. of State and Territorial Epidemiologists [★14512]

Conf. of State Utility Commn. Engineers [★6056]

Conf. of Theological Seminaries of the U.S. and Canada [★9007]

Conf. of Theological Seminaries of the U.S. and Canada [★9007]

Conf. of U.N. Representatives [★18752]

Conf. of Utility Commn. Engineers [★6056]

Conf. on Utopian Stud. [★10430]

Conf. on Utopian Stud. [★10430]

Conf. on Visual Literacy [★8035]

Conf. on Visual Literacy [★8035]

Conf. on World Affairs [★18811]

Conf. on World Affairs [★18811]

Conferencia de Iglesias del Caribe [★IO]

Conferencia Interamericana de Seguridad Social [★IO]

Confesercenti [★IO]

Confessing Synod Ministries [20242], East Liberty Lutheran Church, 5707 Penn Ave., Pittsburgh, PA 15206-3603, (412)362-1712

Conflict

Africa Peace and Conflict Network [12625]

Alliance for Conflict Transformation [17399]

CRU Inst. [17400]

Genocide Intervention Network [17739]

HALO Trust [17401]

HALO USA [17401]

Intl. Campaign to Ban Landmines [17553]

Intl. Crisis Gp., Washington Off. [17402]

Intl. Crisis Gp., Washington Off. [17402]

Not on Our Watch [17857]

Pugwash Conferences on Sci. and World Affairs [17403]

Pugwash Conferences on Sci. and World Affairs [17403]

Save Darfur Coalition [17744]

Terra Segura Intl. [17559]

Conflict Res. Soc. [IO], Newport Pagnell, United Kingdom

Conflict Resolution

African Great Lakes Initiative [13165]

Alliance for Peacebuilding [17404]

Alliance for Peacebuilding [17404]

Black Holocaust Soc. [17154]

Conflict Solutions Intl. [17405]

Empower Peace [18241]

Global Majority [17406]

Global Majority [17406]

Global Peace Services [18251]

Grace Contrino Abrams Peace Educ. Found. [17407]

Independent Diplomat [17898]

Intl. Commn. of Peace [17408]

Just Vision [17409]

Peace Boat US [8695]

Professional Mediation Assn. [5211]

U.S. Assn. for the Univ. for Peace [18294]

Conflict Resolution Center Intl. - Defunct.

Conflict Solutions Intl. [17405], 1629 K St. NW, Ste. 300, Washington, DC 20006

Confraternity of the Blessed Sacrament [19697], 224 E 34th St., Savannah, GA 31401

A star before a book entry number signifies that the name is not listed separately, but is mentioned within the entry.

Confraternity of Christian Doctrine [★19683]
Confraternity of the Most Holy Name of Jesus [★19458]
Confraternity of Penitents [19415], 520 Oliphant Ln., Middletown, RI 02842-4600, (401)849-5421
Confrerie de la Chaine des Rotisseurs, Bailliage des U.S.A. [21845], 285 Madison Ave., Madison, NJ 07940-1099, (973)360-9200
Confrerie des Chevaliers du Tastevin [IO], Nuits-Saint-Georges, France
Congenital Cardiac Anesthesia Soc. [13746], PO Box 11086, Richmond, VA 23230, (804)282-9780
Congenital Cardiac Anesthesia Soc. [13746], PO Box 11086, Richmond, VA 23230, (804)282-9780
Congenital Diaphragmatic Hernia Res., Advocacy and Support; CHERUBS - Assn. of [13840]
Congenital Heart Defects Awareness - Address unknown since 2011.
Congenital Heart Info. Network [14012], 101 N Washington Ave., Ste. 1A, Margate City, NJ 08402, (609)822-1572
Congenital Heart Info. Network [14012], 101 N Washington Ave., Ste. 1A, Margate City, NJ 08402, (609)822-1572
Congleton Chamber of Commerce and Enterprise [IO], Sandbach, United Kingdom
Congo Helping Hands [10810], 8170 Hague Rd., Indianapolis, IN 46256-1649
Congolese Chap. of the Internet Soc. [IO], Bukavu, Democratic Republic of the Congo
Congolese Osteoporosis Soc. [IO], Kinshasa, Republic of the Congo
Congolese Red Cross [IO], Brazzaville, Republic of the Congo
Congregacion de San Basilio [★IO]
Congregation of the Blessed Sacrament [19416], 5384 Wilson Mills Rd., Cleveland, OH 44143-3023, (440)442-6311
Congregation of the Holy Spirit [IO], Rome, Italy
Congregation of Saint Basil [IO], Toronto, ON, Canada
Congregation Shema Yisrael [19859], PO Box 804, Southfield, MI 48037, (248)593-5150
Congregation of Sisters of Saint Agnes [19417], 320 County Rd. K, Fond du Lac, WI 54937-8158, (920)907-2300
Congregational Christian
   Amer. Congregational Assn. [19627]
   Natl. Assn. of Congregational Christian Churches [19628]
Congres du travail du Canada [★IO]
Congres Canadien Polonais [★IO]
Congres Juif Canadien [★IO]
Congres Mondiaux du Petrole [★IO]
Congres des Peuples Autochtones [★IO]
Congress
   Amer. Conservative Union [17418]
   The Conservative Caucus [17420]
   The Conservative Caucus Res., Anal. and Educ. Found. [17421]
   Natl. Traditionalist Caucus [17429]
Cong. of Aboriginal Peoples [IO], Ottawa, ON, Canada
Cong. of Chiropractic State Associations [14127], 12531 E Meadow Dr., Wichita, KS 67206, (316)613-3386
Cong. of Indus. Organizations [★23217]
Cong. for Jewish Culture [9919], 25 E 21st St., New York, NY 10010, (212)505-8040
Cong. of Lung Assn. Staff - Address unknown since 2010.
Cong. of Neurological Surgeons [15685], 10 N Martingale Rd., Ste. 190, Schaumburg, IL 60173, (847)240-2500
Cong. of Neurological Surgeons [15685], 10 N Martingale Rd., Ste. 190, Schaumburg, IL 60173, (847)240-2500
Cong. for the New Urbanism [6049], The Marquette Bldg., 140 S Dearborn St., Ste. 404, Chicago, IL 60603, (312)551-7300
Cong. of Orgs. of the Physically Handicapped - Defunct.
Cong. of Racial Equality [17155], 817 Broadway, 3rd Fl., New York, NY 10003, (212)598-4000
Cong. on Res. in Dance [9540], 3416 Primm Ln., Birmingham, AL 35216, (205)823-5517

Cong. on Res. in Dance [9540], 3416 Primm Ln., Birmingham, AL 35216, (205)823-5517
Cong. of Romanian Americans [19210], 1000 Gelston Cir., McLean, VA 22102, (703)356-2280
Cong. of Russian Americans [19214], 2460 Sutter St., San Francisco, CA 94115, (415)928-5841
Cong. of Secular Jewish Organizations [9920], 320 Claymore Blvd., Cleveland, OH 44143-1730, (866)874-8608
Cong. of South African Trade Unions [IO], Johannesburg, Republic of South Africa
Cong. of Southeast Asian Librarians [IO], Darussalam, Brunei Darussalam
Cong. Watch [★17471]
Congressional
   Congressional Automotive Caucus [17410]
   Congressional Black Caucus [17411]
   Congressional Mgt. Found. [17412]
   Natl. Comm. for an Effective Cong. [17413]
   U.S. Assn. of Former Members of Cong. [17414]
Congressional Auto Conf. [★17410]
Congressional Automotive Caucus [17410], 2107 Rayburn House Off. Bldg., Washington, DC 20515, (202)225-3611
Congressional Black Caucus [17411], 1433 Longworth House Off. Bldg., Washington, DC 20515, (202)226-9776
Congressional Caucus for Women's Issues [17637], 2332 Rayburn HOB, Washington, DC 20515-3214, (202)225-7944
Congressional Clearinghouse on the Future - Defunct.
Congressional Club [19281], 2001 New Hampshire Ave. NW, Washington, DC 20009, (202)332-1155
Congressional Coalition for Soviet Jews - Defunct.
Congressional Competitiveness Caucus - Defunct.
Congressional Hispanic Caucus [17775], 2466 Rayburn HOB, Washington, DC 20515, (202)225-2410
Congressional Mgt. Found. [17412], 513 Capitol Ct. NE, Ste. 300, Washington, DC 20002, (202)546-0100
Congressional Medal of Honor Soc. [20373], 40 Patriots Point Rd., Mount Pleasant, SC 29464, (843)884-8862
Congressional Rural Caucus - Defunct.
Congressional Space Caucus - Defunct.
Congressional Travel and Tourism Caucus - Defunct.
Congressional Wives for Soviet Jewry - Defunct.
Congresswomen's Caucus [★17637]
Congresswomen's Caucus Corp. [★17678]
The Conifer Soc. [★4966]
CONNECT: The Union for Professionals in Communications [IO], London, United Kingdom
Connect Worldwide [6510], PO Box 204086, Austin, TX 78720-4086, (800)807-7560
Connected Intl. Meeting Professionals Assn. [2445], 9200 Bayard Pl., Fairfax, VA 22032, (512)684-0889
Connected Intl. Meeting Professionals Assn. [2445], 9200 Bayard Pl., Fairfax, VA 22032, (512)684-0889
Connecticut Cetacean Soc. [★5042]
Connecticut Cetacean Soc. [★5042]
Connecticut River Watershed Coun. [4025], 15 Bank Row, Greenfield, MA 01301, (413)772-2020
Connecting Congo [11573], 1416 S 43rd St., Tacoma, WA 98418, (206)351-9293
Connective Tissue Oncology Soc. [15924], PO Box 320574, Alexandria, VA 22320, (301)502-7371
Connective Tissue Oncology Soc. [15924], PO Box 320574, Alexandria, VA 22320, (301)502-7371
Connemara Pony Breeders Soc. [IO], Galway, Ireland
Connexions Info. Sharing Services [IO], Toronto, ON, Canada
Connie Francis Intl. Fan Club [23827], Patrick Niglio, 13499 Biscayne Blvd., Ste. 905, North Miami, FL 33181
Conrad N. Hilton Found. [13181], 10100 Santa Monica Blvd., Ste. 1000, Los Angeles, CA 90067, (310)556-4694
Conrad Veidt Soc. [23763], 407 Kingston Ct., York County, VA 23693
Conscience Canada [IO], Toronto, ON, Canada
Conscientious Objectors
   Center on Conscience and War [17560]
   Central Comm. for Conscientious Objectors [17561]

Conscious Alliance [11574], 2525 Arapahoe Ave., Ste. E4 - 182, Boulder, CO 80302, (720)406-7871
Consciousness-Based Educ. Assn. [8762], 1100 Univ. Manor Dr., B-24, Fairfield, IA 52556
Consciousness Studies
   Assn. for the Sci. Stud. of Consciousness [7914]
   Intl. Soc. for the Stud. of Subtle Energies and Energy Medicine [14166]
   Intl. Soc. for the Stud. of Subtle Energies and Energy Medicine [14166]
Conseil canadien pour le controle du tabac [★IO]
Conseil de la recherch en sante pur le development [★IO]
Conseil canadien de la securite [★IO]
Conseil canadien de protection des animaux [★IO]
Conseil canadien de fromages internationaux [★IO]
Conseil canadien des professionnels en securite agrees [★IO]
Conseil des 4-H du Canada [★IO]
Conseil des Aeroports du Canada [★IO]
Conseil des Arts de Ile-du-Prince-Edouard [★IO]
Conseil des Barreaux Europeens [★IO]
Conseil de recherches en sciences humaines de Canada [★IO]
Conseil international du Canada [★IO]
Conseil national de recherches Canada [★IO]
Conseil oecumenique des chretiennes du Canada [★IO]
Conseil Canadien des Aires Ecologiques [★IO]
Conseil Canadien des Archives [★IO]
Conseil Canadien des Aveugles [★IO]
Conseil Canadien des Bureaux d'ethique Commerciale [★IO]
Conseil Canadien des Chefs d'Enterprise [★IO]
Conseil Canadien pour le Commerce Autochtone [★IO]
Conseil Canadien pour la Cooperation Internationale [★IO]
Conseil Canadien de Developpement Social [★IO]
Conseil Canadien D'Orthoptique [★IO]
Conseil Canadien des Eglises [★IO]
Conseil Canadien des Femmes Musulmanes [★IO]
Conseil Canadien de la Fourrure [★IO]
Conseil Canadien des Infirmieres en Nursing Cardio-vasculaire [★IO]
Conseil Canadien des Laboratoires Independants [★IO]
Conseil Canadien de l'Horticulture [★IO]
Conseil Canadien du Miel [★IO]
Conseil Canadien des Normes [★IO]
Conseil Canadien des Normes de la Radiotelevision [★IO]
Conseil Canadien des Organismes de la Motoneige [★IO]
Conseil Canadien des Pecheurs Professionnels [★IO]
Conseil Canadien du Porc [★IO]
Conseil Canadien pour les Refugies [★IO]
Conseil Canadien des Resources Humaines en Camionnage [★IO]
Conseil Canadien du Ski [★IO]
Conseil Canadien des Societes Publiques-Privees [★IO]
Conseil Canadien des Techniciens et Technologues [★IO]
Conseil Canadien des Transformateurs d'Oeufs et de Volailles [★IO]
Conseil des Canadiens [★IO]
Conseil de Canola du Canada [★IO]
Conseil de Commerce Canada-Inde [★IO]
Conseil de Commerce Canado-Arabe [★IO]
Conseil Commercial Canada-Chine [★IO]
Conseil du Commonwealth pour l'Ecologie Humaine [★IO]
Conseil des Communes et Regions d'Europe [★IO]
Conseil canadien du Compostage [★IO]
Conseil Consultatif Canadiene de la Radio [★IO]
Conseil Consultatif sur la Condition de la Femme Nouveau-Brunswick [★IO]
Conseil d'adoption du Canada [★IO]
Conseil Des Architectes D'Europe [★IO]
Conseil Des Arts De L'Ontatio [★IO]
Conseil national d'Ethique en recherche chez l'Humain [★IO]
Conseil pour le Developpement de la Recherche en Sciences Sociales en Afrique [★IO]

Reference to "IO" in place of a book number signifies that the association may be found in the 50th edition of International Organizations.

Conseil Ethnoculturel du Canada [★IO]
Conseil Europeen des Artistes [★IO]
Conseil Europeen des Associations Nationales d'Ecoles Independantes [★IO]
Conseil Europeen De L'Information Sur L'Alimentation [★IO]
Conseil Europeen pour les Langues [★IO]
Conseil Europeen des Producteurs de Materiaux de Constr. [★IO]
Conseil Europeen des Urbanistes [★IO]
Conseil des Examens Chiropratique Canadien [★IO]
Conseil des Grains du Canada [★IO]
Conseil Intl. des Agences Benevoles [★IO]
Conseil Intl. des Archives [★IO]
Conseil Intl. des Associations Graphiques [★IO]
Conseil Intl. des Associations des Indus. Nautiques [★IO]
Conseil Intl. du Batiment pour la Recherche, l'Etude et la Documentation [★IO]
Conseil Intl. des Cereales [★IO]
Conseil Intl. de la Danse [★IO]
Conseil Intl. d'Education des Adultes [★IO]
Conseil Intl. d'Etudes Canadiennes [★IO]
Conseil Intl. d'Etudes sur l'Europe centrale et Orientale [★IO]
Conseil Intl. du Droit de l'Environnement [★IO]
Conseil Intl. des Femmes [★IO]
Conseil Intl. des Grands Reseaux Electriques [★IO]
Conseil Intl. des Infirmieres [★IO]
Conseil Intl. de l'Action Sociale [★IO]
Conseil Intl. de la Langue Francaise [★IO]
Conseil Intl. pour l'Education Physique et la Sci. du Sport [★IO]
Conseil Intl. de l'Enseignement a Distance [★IO]
Conseil Intl. pour l'Exploration de la Mer [★IO]
Conseil Intl. pour L'Information Scientifique et Technique [★IO]
Conseil Intl. des Monuments et des Sites [★IO]
Conseil Intl. des Musees [★IO]
Conseil Intl. des Musees Africains [★IO]
Conseil Intl. de la Musique [★IO]
Conseil Intl. des Normes Comptables [★IO]
Conseil Intl. de la Philosophie et des Sciences Humaines [★IO]
Conseil Intl. sur les Problemes de l'Alcoolisme et des Toxicomanies [★IO]
Conseil Intl. des Sciences de L'Ingenieur et de la Technologie [★IO]
Conseil Intl. des Sciences Sociales [★IO]
Conseil Intl. du Sport Militaire [★IO]
Conseil Intl. des Tanneurs [★IO]
Conseil Interparlementaire Consultatif de Benelux [★IO]
Conseil des Jeux du Canada [★IO]
Conseil canadien de l'education permanente en pharmacie [★IO]
Conseil des ministres de l'Education, Canada [★IO]
Conseil canadien de l'energie [★IO]
Conseil canadien de l'entretien des aeronefs [★IO]
Conseil de l'Europe [★IO]
Conseil pour l'Homologation des Etablissements Theologiques en Afrique [★IO]
Conseil Mondial des Associations D'education Comparee [★IO]
Conseil Mondial de l'Energie [★IO]
Conseil Natl. du Cuir [★IO]
Conseil Natl. des Ingenieurs et des Scientifiques de France [IO], Paris, France
Conseil Natl. de la Recherche Scientifique [★IO]
Conseil Natl. de Recherches Canada Institut de Recherche en Constr. [★IO]
Conseil Oecumenique des Eglises [★IO]
Conseil Oecumenique de la Jeunesse en Europe [★IO]
Conseil Oleicole Intl. [★IO]
Conseil des Organisations Internationales des Sciences Medicales [★IO]
Conseil des Palettes du Canada [★IO]
Conseil du Peuplier [★IO]
Conseil Superieur des Ecoles Europeennes [★IO]
Conseil des Technologies de l'Information et des Communications [★IO]
Conseil des traducteurs, terminologues et interpretes du Canada [★IO]
Conseil Unitarien du Canada [★IO]

Conseil des Viandes du Canada [★IO]
Consejo Cultural Mundial [★IO]
Consejo Dominicano Contra la Osteoporosis [★IO]
Consejo Gen. de Colegios Oficiales de Odontologos y Estomatologos de Espana [IO], Madrid, Spain
Consejo Hondurenos de la Empresa Privada [★IO]
Consejo Internacional de los Frutos Secos [★IO]
Consejo Internacional de las Organizaciones de Festivales de Folclor y de Artes Tradicionales [★IO]
Consejo Latinoamericano de Iglesias [★IO]
Consejo Mundial de Boxeo [★IO]
Consejo Nacional de Ciencia y Tecnologia [IO], Mexico City, Mexico
Consejo Nacional de la Empresa Privada [★IO]
Consejo Nacional de la Empresa Privada [★IO]
Consejo Profesional de Ingeniera Agronomica [★IO]
Consejo Superior de la Empresa Privada [★IO]
Conselho Nacional de Desenvolvimento Cientifico e Tecnologico [★IO]
Conservacao Internacional - Brasil [★IO]
Conservacion Internacional Bolivia [IO], La Paz, Bolivia
ConservAmerica [4026], 971 S Centerville Rd., No. 139, Sturgis, MI 49091-2502, (269)651-1808
Conservancy Assn. [IO], Hong Kong, People's Republic of China
Conservation
  1planet1ocean [3975]
  Abundant Life Seeds [3976]
  Acres Land Trust [3977]
  Action for Clean Energy [4224]
  The Adirondack Coun. [3978]
  Advanced Conservation Strategies [3979]
  Africa Environmental Watch [3980]
  African Blackwood Conservation Proj. [3981]
  African Blackwood Conservation Proj. [3981]
  Alaska Coalition [3982]
  Alliance for Climate Educ. [4315]
  Alliance for Energy and Economic Growth [6681]
  Alliance for Global Conservation [3983]
  Alliance for Global Conservation [3983]
  Alliance for Intl. Reforestation [3984]
  Alliance for Intl. Reforestation [3984]
  Alliance for Tompotika Conservation [3985]
  Alliance for Water Educ. [8149]
  Alliance for Water Efficiency [4986]
  Amara Conservation [5022]
  Amarun Org. [3986]
  Amazon Conservation Assn. [3987]
  Amazon Watch [3988]
  Amer. Cave Conservation Assn. [3989]
  Amer. Forests [3990]
  Amer. Land Conservancy [3991]
  Amer. Medical Fly Fishing Assn. [3992]
  Amer. Reef Coalition [3993]
  Amer. Resources Gp. [3994]
  Amer. River Touring Assn. [3995]
  Amer. Rivers [3996]
  Amer. Shore and Beach Preservation Assn. [3997]
  Amer. Soc. for the Protection of Nature in Israel [3998]
  Amer. Soc. for the Protection of Nature in Israel [3998]
  Amer. Wilderness Coalition [5010]
  Ancient Forest Intl. [3999]
  Ancient Forest Intl. [3999]
  Anglers for Conservation [4000]
  Animal Venom Res. Intl. [13759]
  Animal World USA [3808]
  Ape Action Africa [5027]
  Ape Conservation Effort [5028]
  Assn. of Climate Change Officers [4237]
  Assn. of Conservation Engineers [4001]
  Assn. for Conservation Info. [4002]
  Assn. of Environmental and Rsrc. Economists [4003]
  Assn. of Fish and Wildlife Agencies [4004]
  Assn. of Fish and Wildlife Agencies [4004]
  Assn. to Preserve Cape Cod [4005]
  Assn. of Professional Wildlife Educators [9050]
  Assn. of State Floodplain Managers [4006]
  Assn. of State Wetland Managers [4007]
  Audubon Intl. [4008]

Audubon Naturalist Soc. of the Central Atlantic States [4009]
Avoided Deforestation Partners [4390]
Bamboo of the Americas [4010]
Bee Native [3839]
Big Thicket Assn. [4011]
Big Thicket Natural Heritage Trust [4012]
Big Wildlife [5034]
BlueVoice.org [4013]
Bonobo Conservation Initiative [5038]
Brighter Green [4014]
Camp Fire Club of Am. [4015]
Catholic Coalition on Climate Change [4016]
CEDAM Intl. [4017]
CEDAM Intl. [4017]
Center for a New Amer. Dream [17415]
Center for Plant Conservation [4018]
Chihuahuan Desert Res. Inst. [4019]
Children and Nature Network [4241]
Climate, Community and Biodiversity Alliance [4020]
Climate Counts [4021]
Climate Crisis Coalition [4022]
Climate Gp. [4023]
Coalition of Natl. Park Ser. Retirees [4766]
Coalition for Rainforest Nations [4856]
Coastal Conservation Assn. [4024]
Community Agroecology Network [4938]
Community Forestry Intl. [4391]
Connecticut River Watershed Coun. [4025]
ConservAmerica [4026]
Conservation Breeding Specialist Gp. [4027]
Conservation Breeding Specialist Gp. [4027]
The Conservation Campaign [17416]
The Conservation Fund [4028]
Conservation Intl. USA [4029]
Conservation Intl. USA [4029]
Conservation Leaders Network [4734]
Conservation through Poverty Alleviation Intl. [4030]
Conservation and Preservation Charities of Am. [4031]
Conservation and Res. Found. [4032]
Conservation and Res. Found. [4032]
Conservation Tech. Info. Center [4033]
Conservation Treaty Support Fund [4034]
Conservatree [4035]
Consumer Energy Alliance [6708]
Cork Forest Conservation Alliance [4036]
Coun. for Endangered Species Act Reliability [5413]
Coun. for Responsible Energy [6709]
The Cycad Soc. [4037]
The Cycad Soc. [4037]
Darwin Animal Doctors [3809]
David and Lucile Packard Found. [4038]
David and Lucile Packard Found. [4038]
Defense of Place [4039]
Desert Fishes Coun. [4040]
Desert Fishes Coun. [4040]
Desert Protective Coun. [4041]
Desert Tortoise Preserve Comm. [4042]
EarthEcho Intl. [4043]
EarthEcho Intl. [4043]
Eco-Life Concepts [4318]
ecoAmerica [4044]
Ecological Res. and Development Gp. [4045]
Ecology Proj. Intl. [8154]
Efficiency First [4046]
Elephant Energy [6715]
Elephants Without Borders [5011]
Endangered Species Intl. [4047]
EndOil [6716]
Energy Conservation Org. [8120]
Env. for the Americas [3845]
Environmental Alliance for Senior Involvement [4048]
Environmental Commons [4049]
Environmental Educ. and Conservation Global [8155]
Environmental Entrepreneurs [4050]
Environmental Monitoring Gp. [15415]
Environmental Paper Network [4051]
Environmental Paper Network [4051]ConservationEnvironmental Rights Action

A star before a book entry number signifies that the name is not listed separately, but is mentioned within the entry.

Equator Initiative [11581]
ERTHNXT [4052]
Ethnobotanical Conservation Org. for South East Asia [4053]
Experience Intl. [4054]
Exploring Solutions Past: The Maya Forest Alliance [6168]
FishAmerica Found. [4055]
FishWise [1359]
Forest Bird Soc. [4056]
Forest Guild [4057]
Forest Partners Intl. [4395]
Forest Planters Intl. [4396]
Forest Trends [4058]
Forestry Conservation Communications Assn. [4059]
Found. for Res. on Economics and the Env. [4060]
Friends of the Earth [4061]
Friends of the Earth - Cameroon [9034]
Friends of the Earth - El Salvador [17797]
Friends of the Earth - Georgia [14770]
Friends of the Earth - Haiti [18985]
Friends of the Earth - Hungary [18983]
Friends of the Earth - Indonesia [17856]
Friends of the Earth - Luxembourg [11862]
Friends of the Earth - Mauritius/Maudesco [22505]
Friends of the Everglades [4062]
Friends of the Osa [4063]
Friends of the River [4064]
Friends of the Trees Soc. [4065]
GAIA Movement USA [4066]
Galapagos Conservancy [4067]
Garden Conservancy [4068]
Global Coral Reef Alliance [4069]
Global Parks [4070]
Global Res. and Rescue [5012]
Global Rsrc. Alliance [3974]
Global Underwater Explorers [4703]
Global Wildlife Conservation [5060]
Global Wildlife Resources [5013]
Go Green Initiative Assn. [8156]
Grassland Heritage Found. [4071]
Gray is Green: The Natl. Senior Conservation Corps [4072]
Great Lakes United [4073]
Greater Yellowstone Coalition [4074]
Green Parent Assn. [4075]
Green Partners [4177]
Green Team Am. [4076]
Green Yoga Assn. [5179]
Greensward Found. [4077]
Growing Planet [4400]
Hawk Mountain Sanctuary [5063]
Healthy Building Network [4330]
Holistic Mgt. Intl. [4078]
Human-Wildlife Conflict Collaboration [5014]
Hummingbird Monitoring Network [3848]
Iemanya Oceanica [5064]
Indo-Pacific Conservation Alliance [4079]
Instream Flow Coun. [4080]
Intergovernmental Renewable Energy Org. [6731]
Intl. Assn. for the Stud. of the Commons [4081]
Intl. Assn. for the Stud. of the Commons [4081]
Intl. BioExploration Soc. [8180]
Intl. Commn. for the Protection of Alpine Regions [20559]
Intl. Erosion Control Assn. [4082]
Intl. Erosion Control Assn. [4082]
Intl. Soc. of Sustainability Professionals [4340]
Intl. Union for the Conservation of Nature and Natural Resources U.S. [4083]
Intl. Union for the Conservation of Nature and Natural Resources U.S. [4083]
Irrigation Water Mgt. Soc. [5005]
Island Conservation [4084]
Izaak Walton League of Am. [4085]
Izaak Walton League of Am. Endowment [4086]
Journey Toward Sustainability [8159]
Kasese Wildlife Conservation Awareness Org. [5074]
Kids Ecology Corps [4322]
Land Improvement Contractors of Am. [4087]
Land Trust Alliance [4088]

LandChoices [4089]
League for Earth and Animal Protection [4090]
League to Save Lake Tahoe [4091]
LightHawk [4092]
Marine Animal Rescue Soc. [4093]
Marine Fish Conservation Network [4094]
Marine Mammal Conservancy [5079]
MarineBio Conservation Soc. [4714]
Millennium Wildlife Sciences [5015]
Natl. Assn. of Conservation Districts [4095]
Natl. Assn. of Rsrc. Conservation and Development Councils [4096]
Natl. Assn. of State Conservation Agencies [4097]
Natl. Audubon Soc. [4098]
Natl. Center for Preservation Tech. and Training [6942]
Natl. Coalition for Marine Conservation [4099]
Natl. Flood Determination Assn. [4732]
Natl. Forest Found. [4100]
Natl. Mitigation Banking Assn. [4101]
Natl. Oceanic Soc. [4102]
Natl. Org. of Professional Hispanic Natural Resources Conservation Ser. Employees [4521]
Natl. Sustainable Agriculture Coalition [4942]
Natl. Wildlife Fed. [4103]
Natl. Wind Watch [18788]
Natl. Wolfdog Alliance [21615]
Native Amer. Environmental Protection Coalition [4104]
Native Cultural Alliance [4290]
Native Forest Coun. [4105]
Native Forest Network [4106]
Native Seeds/SEARCH [4107]
Natural Areas Assn. [4108]
Natural Resources Defense Coun. [4109]
Nature Abounds [4291]
Nature Conservancy [4110]
Nature and Culture Intl. [4111]
Nature's Voice Our Choice [4998]
Neotropical Grassland Conservancy [4112]
Neotropical Grassland Conservancy [4112]
Network of Conservation Educators and Practitioners [4113]
New England Wild Flower Soc. [4114]
NOAH Nature Alliance [5090]
North Amer. Wildlife Park Found. [5098]
Ocean Champions [17417]
Ocean Conservancy [4115]
Ocean Conservancy [4115]
Ocean Conservation Res. [4116]
Ocean Res. and Conservation Assn. [4117]
Oceana [4118]
Oceana [4118]
Oceanic Preservation Soc. [4119]
Oceanic Preservation Soc. [4119]
Oikonos [4213]
One Earth Designs [4293]
Orchid Conservation Alliance [4120]
OurEarth.org [4121]
Ozark Soc. [4122]
Pacific Islands Conservation Res. Assn. [4123]
Pan African Sanctuary Alliance [5106]
Panthera [5108]
Partners in Parks [4124]
Paso Pacifico [4125]
Planetwork [4214]
Poetic Unity [11623]
Rainforest Action Network [4126]
Rainforest Action Network [4126]
Rainforest Alliance [4127]
Rainforest Alliance [4127]
Rainforest Partnership [4859]
ReefGuardian Intl. [4709]
Renew Am. [3973]
Renewable Natural Resources Found. [4128]
Reptile and Amphibian Ecology Intl. [5118]
Republicans for Environmental Protection [4129]
Responsible Purchasing Network [1222]
Reverb [4130]
Rights and Resources Initiative [4412]
Rising Tide North Am. [4131]
River Mgt. Soc. [4132]
River Network [4133]
Rivers Without Borders [4134]

Sailors for the Sea [4135]
Save America's Forests [4136]
Save the Frogs! [4137]
Save Our Seas [4138]
Save Our Seas [4138]
Save the Rain [13430]
Save the Redwoods League [4139]
Save the Turtles [5123]
Save Yemen's Flora and Fauna [4140]ConservationScottish Wild Land Gp.
Seacology [4141]
Shark Alliance [5128]
Shark Savers [5129]
Snow Leopard Network [5130]
Soc. for Conservation GIS [6569]
Soc. of Wetland Scientists [4142]
Soil Carbon Coalition [4928]
Soil and Water Conservation Soc. [4143]
Spirit of the Sage Coun. [4144]
Sri Lanka Wildlife Conservation Soc. [5133]
State of the World's Sea Turtles [5134]
The Steamboaters [4145]
Student Conservation Assn. [4146]
Sustainable Smiles [4876]
Sustainable World Coalition [4147]
Tall Timbers Land Conservancy [4148]
Tall Timbers Res. Sta. [4149]
Theodore Roosevelt Conservation Partnership [4150]
TopTen USA [1178]
Tree Musketeers [4151]
TreePeople [4152]
Tropical Forest Gp. [4153]
Tropical Forestry Initiative [4154]
Tropical Forestry Initiative [4154]
Trust for Public Land [4155]
Turtle Island Restoration Network [4156]
Turtle Survival Alliance [5140]
U.S. Climate Emergency Coun. [4157]
Upper Mississippi River Conservation Comm. [4158]
Vision Earth Soc. [4223]
Water for Life Intl. [13436]
Waterfowl U.S.A. [4159]
Wild Animals Worldwide [5144]ConservationWild Earth
Wild Gift [5146]
Wilderness Intl. [4160]
The Wilderness Soc. [4161]
The Wilderness Soc. [4161]
Wildfowl and Wetlands Trust [5276]
Wildlife Conservation Network [5152]
Wildlife Conservation Soc. [4162]
Wildlife Habitat Coun. [4163]
Wildlife Mgt. Inst. [4164]
Wildlife Media [5155]
Wildlife in Need [5017]
Wind Energy Works! [7625]
Wolf Haven Intl. [4165]
Wolf Haven Intl. [4165]
Women Organizing for Change in Agriculture and NRM [3769]
Wonderful World of Wildlife [5157]
World Assn. of Soil and Water Conservation [4166]
World Assn. of Soil and Water Conservation [4166]
World Bamboo Org. [4738]
World Env. Center [4167]
World Env. Center [4167]
World Environmental Org. [4168]
World Fed. for Coral Reef Conservation [4169]
World Fed. for Coral Reef Conservation [4169]
World Nature Coalition [5159]
World Resources Inst. [4170]
World Resources Inst. [4170]
World Sturgeon Conservation Soc. U.S.A. [4171]
World Whale Police [5018]
World Wildlife Fund [4172]
World Wildlife Fund [4172]
Conservation Alliance for Tigers [5159], 601 Pennsylvania Ave. NW, South Bldg., Ste. 900, Washington, DC 20004, (202)379-2974
Conservation Alliance for Tigers [★5159]
Conservation Breeding Specialist Gp. [4027], 12101 Johnny Cake Ridge Rd., Apple Valley, MN 55124-8151, (952)997-9800

Reference to "IO" in place of a book number signifies that the association may be found in the 50th edition of International Organizations.

Conservation Breeding Specialist Gp. [4027], 12101 Johnny Cake Ridge Rd., Apple Valley, MN 55124-8151, (952)997-9800

The Conservation Campaign [17416], 33 Union St., Boston, MA 02108, (617)367-9092

Conservation Center for Art and Historic Artifacts [9174], 264 S 23rd St., Philadelphia, PA 19103, (215)545-0613

Conservation Coun. of Ontario [IO], Toronto, ON, Canada

Conservation Education Assn. - Defunct.

Conservation, Educ., Diving, Awareness, Marine Res. [★4017]

Conservation, Educ., Diving, Awareness, Marine Res. [★4017]

Conservation Farmers Inc. [IO], Toowoomba, Australia

Conservation Found. [IO], London, United Kingdom

Conservation Found. [★4172]

Conservation Found. [★4172]

The Conservation Fund [4028], 1655 N Ft. Myer Dr., Ste. 1300, Arlington, VA 22209-3199, (703)525-6300

Conservation Intl. - Brazil [IO], Belo Horizonte, Brazil

Conservation Intl. USA [4029], 2011 Crystal Dr., Ste. 500, Arlington, VA 22202, (703)341-2400

Conservation Intl. USA [4029], 2011 Crystal Dr., Ste. 500, Arlington, VA 22202, (703)341-2400

Conservation Leaders Network [4734], PO Box 46, Wedderburn, OR 97491, (541)247-8079

Conservation Northwest [4247], 1208 Bay St., No. 201, Bellingham, WA 98225-4301, (360)671-9950

Conservation through Poverty Alleviation Intl. [4030], 221 Lincoln Rd., Lincoln, MA 01773

Conservation and Preservation Charities of Am. [4031], 1100 Larkspur Landing Cir., Ste. 340, Larkspur, CA 94939, (800)626-6685

Conservation and Res. Found. [4032], PO Box 909, Shelburne, VT 05482-0909

Conservation and Res. Found. [4032], PO Box 909, Shelburne, VT 05482-0909

Conservation Tech. Info. Center [4033], 3495 Kent Ave., Ste. J100, West Lafayette, IN 47906, (765)494-9555

Conservation Tillage Info. Center [★4033]

Conservation Treaty Support Fund [4034], 3705 Cardiff Rd., Chevy Chase, MD 20815, (301)654-3150

Conservation Volunteers Alliance [IO], Ballarat, Australia

Conservation Volunteers Australia [IO], Ballarat, Australia

Conservation Volunteers Australia - Canberra [IO], Civic Square, Australia

Conservation Volunteers Northern Ireland [IO], Belfast, United Kingdom

Conservationists

Assn. of Conservation Engineers [4001]

Audubon Naturalist Soc. of the Central Atlantic States [4009]

Catholic Coalition on Climate Change [4016]

Climate Gp. [4023]

Environmental Entrepreneurs [4050]

Hawk Mountain Sanctuary [5063]

Land Trust Alliance [4088]

League to Save Lake Tahoe [4091]

Natl. Wildlife Fed. [4103]

Natl. Wolfdog Alliance [21615]

North Amer. Wildlife Park Found. [5098]

Conservative

Amer. Conservative Union [17418]

Center of the Amer. Experiment [17419]

The Conservative Caucus [17420]

The Conservative Caucus Res., Anal. and Educ. Found. [17421]

Eagle Forum [17422]

Freedom House [17423]

Freedom House [17423]

Frontiers of Freedom [5335]

Future of Freedom Found. [17424]

Intercollegiate Stud. Inst. [17425]

Intl. Freedom Found. [17426]

John Birch Soc. [17427]

LibertyTree [17428]

Natl. Traditionalist Caucus [17429]

Third Generation [17430]

Young Americans for Freedom [17431]

Young America's Found. [17432]

Conservative Baptist Assn. of Am. [19318], 3686 Stagecoach Rd., Ste. F, Longmont, CO 80504-5660, (303)772-1205

Conservative Baptist Foreign Mission Soc. [★19337]

Conservative Baptist Foreign Mission Soc. [★19337]

Conservative Baptist Home Mission Soc. [★19324]

Conservative Baptist Home Mission Soc. [★19324]

The Conservative Caucus [17420], 450 Maple Ave. E, Vienna, VA 22180-4724, (703)938-9626

Conservative Caucus Found. [★17421]

The Conservative Caucus Res., Anal. and Educ. Found. [17421], 450 Maple Ave. E, Vienna, VA 22180, (703)281-6782

Conservative Democratic Forum - Defunct.

Conservative Future [IO], London, United Kingdom

Conservative Future Scotland [IO], Edinburgh, United Kingdom

Conservative Leadership Youth Found. [★8490]

Conservative Majority for Citizen's Rights - Address unknown since 2010.

Conservative Mennonite Bd. of Missions and Charities [★19962]

Conservative Mennonite Bd. of Missions and Charities [★19962]

Conservative Party [18356], 486 78th St., Brooklyn, NY 11209, (718)921-2158

Conservative Party Central Off. [IO], London, United Kingdom

Conservative Party of Norway [IO], Oslo, Norway

Conservative People's Party [IO], Copenhagen, Denmark

Conservative Traditionalists

Amer. Decency Assn. [17433]

Americans for Decency [17434]

Care Net [17435]

Christian Coalition of Am. [17436]

Conservatives for a Constitutional Convention - Defunct.

Conservatory Theater Found; Amer. [10563]

Conservatree [4035], PO Box 29304, San Francisco, CA 94129-0304, (415)561-6264

Consiglio Mondiale dell' Energia Comitato Nazionale Italiano [★IO]

Consiglio Nazionale delle Ricerche [★IO]

Consilium Conferentiarum Episcoporum Europae [★IO]

Consistent Life [18238], PO Box 9295, Silver Spring, MD 20916-9295, (866)444-7245

Consolidated Assn. of Nurses in Substance Abuse Intl. [★15756]

Consolidated Assn. of Nurses in Substance Abuse Intl. [★15756]

Consolidated Tape Assn. [3195], Thompson Financial, 195 Broadway, New York, NY 10007, (646)822-6070

Consorcio Nacional de Industriales del Caucho [★IO]

Consortia of Administrators for Native Amer. Rehabilitation [19153], 176 Martin Loop, Winnfield, LA 71483, (318)727-9793

Consortium on Advanced Biosensors - Defunct.

Consortium for Advanced Mgt. Intl. [2333], 6836 Bee Cave, Ste. 256, Austin, TX 78746, (512)617-6428

Consortium for Advanced Mfg. Intl. [2333], 6836 Bee Cave, Ste. 256, Austin, TX 78746, (512)617-6428

Consortium for the Advancement of Private Higher Educ. [7879], The Coun. of Independent Colleges, 1 Dupont Cir. NW, Ste. 320, Washington, DC 20036-1142, (202)466-7230

Consortium for the Advancement of Private Higher Educ. [★8287]

Consortium on AIDS and Intl. Development [IO], London, United Kingdom

Consortium for Citizens with Disabilities [11773], 1660 L St. NW, Ste. 700, Washington, DC 20036, (202)783-2229

Consortium of Coll. and Univ. Media Centers [8307], Indiana Univ., Franklin Hall 0009, 601 E Kirkwood Ave., Bloomington, IN 47405-1223, (812)855-6049

Consortium for Conservation Medicine [15409], 460 W 34th St., 17th Fl., New York, NY 10001, (212)380-4460

Consortium for Conservation Medicine [15409], 460 W 34th St., 17th Fl., New York, NY 10001, (212)380-4460

Consortium of Doctors [11935], 2207 Glynnwood Dr., Savannah, GA 31404, (912)354-4634

Consortium for Energy Efficiency [1165], 98 N Washington St., Ste. 101, Boston, MA 02114-1918, (617)589-3949

Consortium of European Building Control [IO], Ipswich, United Kingdom

Consortium of European Res. Libraries [IO], London, United Kingdom

Consortium on Financing Higher Educ. [8793], Ms. Isabel Bourelle, Off. Admin., 238 Main St., Ste. 402, Cambridge, MA 02142, (617)253-5030

Consortium for Graduate Stud. in Bus. for Negros [★8548]

Consortium for Graduate Stud. in Mgt. [8548], 5585 Pershing Ave., Ste. 240, St. Louis, MO 63112-1795, (314)877-5500

Consortium of Humanities Centers and Institutes [12263], Duke Univ., John Hope Franklin Humanities Inst., 2204 Erwin Rd., Durham, NC 27708-0403, (919)668-0107

Consortium of Humanities Centers and Institutes [12263], Duke Univ., John Hope Franklin Humanities Inst., 2204 Erwin Rd., Durham, NC 27708-0403, (919)668-0107

Consortium of Institutes of Higher Educ. in Hea. and Rehabilitation in Europe [IO], Gent, Belgium

Consortium of Institutions for Development and Res. in Educ. in Europe [IO], Sint-Katelijne-Waver, Belgium

Consortium for Intl. Crop Protection [3758], Oregon State Univ., Dept. of Environmental and Molecular Toxicology, 2040 Cordley Hall, Corvallis, OR 97331, (541)737-3541

Consortium for North Amer. Higher Educ. Collaboration

Consortium for North Amer. Higher Educ. Collaboration - Address unknown since 2011.

Consortium on Peace Res., Educ. and Development [★18276]

Consortium Perfectae Caritatis - Defunct.

Consortium pour la Recherche Economique en Afrique [★IO]

Consortium of Registered Nurses for Eye Acquisition [★15946]

Consortium for School Networking [8308], 1025 Vermont Ave. NW, Ste. 1010, Washington, DC 20005, (202)861-2676

Consortium on Sci., Tech. and Innovation for the South [IO], Trieste, Italy

Consortium of Social Sci. Associations [7413], 1701 K St. NW, Ste. 1150, Washington, DC 20006, (202)842-3525

Consortium for the Stud. of Intelligence - Address unknown since 2010.

Consortium for Sustainable Village-Based Development [★11649]

Consortium for Sustainable Village-Based Development [★11649]

Consortium of Univ. Film Centers [★8307]

Constantian Soc. - Defunct.

Constellation Found. [★10059]

Constellation Historical Preservation Corp. [★10059]

Constituency for Africa [17148], 316 F St. NE, Ste. 101-102, Washington, DC 20002, (202)371-0588

Constitution

Amer. Civil Rights Union [17263]

Amer. Constitution Soc. for Law and Policy [5336]

Armed Females of Am. [17682]

Constitution Soc. [5337]

Constitutional Rights Found. [17437]

Found. for Rational Economics and Educ. [17438]

Jefferson Found. [17439]

Natl. Center for Constitutional Stud. [17440]

Peoples Rights Org. [17319]

Students for the Second Amendment [17693]

Twelve Lights League [18073]

Young Americans for Liberty [18836]

Constitution Soc. [5337], 2900 W Anderson Ln., C-200-322, Austin, TX 78757-1102, (512)299-5001

Constitutional Amendment Partnership; Natl. Victims' [18760]

A star before a book entry number signifies that the name is not listed separately, but is mentioned within the entry.

Constitutional Govt; Fund for [17749]
Constitutional Law
  Citizens Flag Alliance [5338]
  First Amendment Lawyers Assn. [5339]
  Peoples Rights Org. [17319]
Constitutional Revival - Defunct.
Constitutional Rights Found. [17437], 601 S Kingsley Dr., Los Angeles, CA 90005, (213)487-5590
Constitutional Rights Proj. [IO], Abuja, Nigeria
Construction
  Amer. Concrete Inst. [6570]
  Amer. Constr. Inspectors Assn. [839]
  Amer. Coun. for Constr. Educ. [7915]
  Amer. Fence Assn. [840]
  Amer. Fence Assn. [840]
  Amer. Inst. of Constructors [6571]
  Amer. Inst. of Steel Constr. [6572]
  Amer. Soc. of Professional Estimators [7916]
  Amer. Underground Constr. Assn. [7484]
  Asphalt Interlayer Assn. [525]
  Assoc. Owners and Developers [841]
  Assoc. Schools of Constr. [7917]
  Assoc. Schools of Constr. [7917]
  Assn. of Architecture Organizations [6192]
  Assn. of Asphalt Paving Technologists [6573]
  Assn. for Better Insulation [530]
  Assn. of Constr. Inspectors [1914]
  Bridge Engg. Assn. [6789]
  Building Commissioning Assn. [538]
  Building Enclosure Coun. Natl. [6374]
  Building Enclosure Tech. and Env. Coun. [539]
  Building Security Coun. [3210]
  Building Tech. Educators' Soc. [7732]
  BuildingSMART Alliance [6574]
  Constr. Chamber of Quito [15121]
  Constr. History Soc. [6336]
  Constr. Indus. Round Table [842]
  Constr. Innovation Forum [843]
  Constr. Innovation Forum [843]
  Constr. Specifications Inst. [6575]
  Costa Rican Chamber of Constr. [7527]
  CPWR - The Center for Constr. Res. and Training [23176]
  Crane Certification Assn. of Am. [844]
  Ecological Building Network [3857]
  Equip. Managers Coun. of Am. [845]
  Firestop Contractors Intl. Assn. [846]
  Firestop Contractors Intl. Assn. [846]
  Found. for Pavement Preservation [847]
  Green Builder Coalition [565]
  Green Building Initiative [566]
  Green Home Coun. [567]
  High Performance Building Coun. [6376]
  Homes for Scotland [14755]
  Intl. Assn. for Bridge Maintenance and Safety [6369]
  Intl. Building Performance Simulation Assn. [6377]
  Intl. Soc. for Concrete Pavements [574]
  Intl. Soc. for Structural Hea. Monitoring of Intelligent Infrastructure [6428]
  The Masonry Soc. [6576]
  The Masonry Soc. [6576]
  Mexican Chamber of the Constr. Indus. [14787]
  Natl. Alliance of Highway Beautification Agencies [5948]
  Natl. Assn. of Black Women in Constr. [848]
  Natl. Assn. of Constr. Contractors Cooperation [587]
  Natl. Commn. for the Certification of Crane Operators [849]
  Natl. Inst. of Building Sciences [6577]
  Natl. Pavement Contractors Assn. [595]
  Natl. Roof Certification and Inspection Assn. [596]
  Natl. Roofing Found. [7918]
  Portland Cement Mfrs'. Assn. [16249]
  Quartzite Rock Assn. [850]
  Residential Constr. Workers' Assn. [851]
  Resin Flooring Assn. [12104]
  Salvadoran Chamber of the Constr. Indus. [8202]
  Short Span Steel Bridge Alliance [6371]
  SPRI [852]
  Steel Erectors Assn. of Am. [6578]
  Terrazzo Tile and Marble Assn. of Canada [5941]
  Voluntary Protection Prog. Assn. for Constr. [15910]

  Water Design-Build Coun. [634]
  Western Coun. of Constr. Consumers [853]
  Wood I-Joist Mfrs. Assn. [1517]
Constr. Assn. of Bermuda [IO], Hamilton, Bermuda
Constr. Assn. of Bhutan [IO], Thimphu, Bhutan
Constr. Assn. of Korea [IO], Seoul, Republic of Korea
Constr. Assn. of New Brunswick [IO], Fredericton, NB, Canada
Constr. Assn. of Prince Edward Island [IO], Charlottetown, PE, Canada
Constr. Chamber of Quito [IO], Quito, Ecuador
Constr. Confed. [IO], London, United Kingdom
Constr. Employers Assn. [547], Michael Walton, Sec., 1646 N California Blvd., Ste. 500, Walnut Creek, CA 94596-4148, (925)930-8184
Constr. Employers' Fed. [IO], Belfast, United Kingdom
Constr. Equip. Advertisers [★2390]
Constr. Equip. Advertisers and Public Relations Coun. [★2390]
Constr. Equip. Assn. [IO], Croydon, United Kingdom
Constr. Financial Mgt. Assn. [909], 100 Village Blvd., Ste. 200, Princeton, NJ 08540, (609)452-8000
Constr. Fixings Assn. [IO], Oakham, United Kingdom
Constr. History Soc. [IO], Ascot, United Kingdom
Constr. Indus. Coun. [IO], London, United Kingdom
Constr. Indus. CPAs/Consultants Assn. [18], 15011 E Twilight View Dr., Fountain Hills, AZ 85268, (480)836-0300
Constr. Indus. Fed. [IO], Dublin, Ireland
Constr. Indus. Mfrs. Assn. [★166]
Constr. Indus. Mfrs. Assn. [★166]
Construction Industry Mfrs. Assn. - Defunct.
Constr. Indus. Round Table [842], 8115 Old Dominion Dr., Ste. 210, McLean, VA 22102-2324, (202)466-6777
Constr. Indus. Trade Alliance [IO], Carmarthen, United Kingdom
Constr. Innovation Forum [843], 6494 Latcha Rd., Walbridge, OH 43465, (419)725-3108
Constr. Innovation Forum [843], 6494 Latcha Rd., Walbridge, OH 43465, (419)725-3108
Constr. Labour Relations Assn. of Manitoba [IO], Winnipeg, MB, Canada
Constr. Mgt. Assn. of Am. [2278], 7926 Jones Br. Dr., Ste. 800, McLean, VA 22102, (703)356-2622
Constr. Materials Recycling Assn. [548], PO Box 122, Eola, IL 60519, (630)585-7530
Constr. Owners Assn. of Am. [549], Overlook III, Ste. 445, 2859 Paces Ferry Rd. SE, Atlanta, GA 30339, (770)433-0820
Constr. Plant-hire Assn. [IO], London, United Kingdom
Constr. Products Assn. [IO], London, United Kingdom
Constr. Specifications Canada [IO], Toronto, ON, Canada
Constr. Specifications Inst. [6575], 110 S Union St., Ste. 100, Alexandria, VA 22314-3351, (800)689-2900
Constr. Writers Assn. [2820], PO Box 14784, Chicago, IL 60614-0784, (773)687-8726
Constr. Writers Assn. [2820], PO Box 14784, Chicago, IL 60614-0784, (773)687-8726
Consult Australia [IO], Sydney, Australia
Consultant Dieticians Special Interest Gp. [★15829]
Consultant Dietitians in Hea. Care Facilities [★15829]
Consultant Quantity Surveyors Assn. [IO], Cookham, United Kingdom
Consultants
  Innovation Network [1912]
Consultants Assn. for the Natural Products Indus. [713], PO Box 4014, Clovis, CA 93613, (559)325-7192
Consultants Consortium [863], PO Box 7052, Alexandria, VA 22307, (703)768-6987
Consultants' Network - Defunct.
Consultation on Church Union [★19651]
Consultative Gp. to Assist the Poor [17907], 900 19th St. NW, Ste. 300, Washington, DC 20006, (202)473-9594
Consultative Gp. to Assist the Poor [17907], 900 19th St. NW, Ste. 300, Washington, DC 20006, (202)473-9594

Consultative Gp. on Intl. Agricultural Res. [12321], World Bank, MSN G6-601, 1818 H St. NW, Washington, DC 20433, (202)473-8951
Consultative Gp. on Intl. Agricultural Res. [12321], World Bank, MSN G6-601, 1818 H St. NW, Washington, DC 20433, (202)473-8951
Consulting
  Airport Consultants Coun. [854]
  Alliance of Professional Consultants [855]
  Amer. Assn. of Insurance Mgt. Consultants [856]
  Amer. Soc. of Theatre Consultants [857]
  Amer. Soc. of Theatre Consultants [857]
  Assn. of Image Consultants Intl. [858]
  Assn. of Image Consultants Intl. [858]
  Assn. of Philanthropic Counsel [859]
  Assn. of Professional Commun. Consultants [860]
  Assn. of Professional Commun. Consultants [860]
  Assn. of Professional Consultants [861]
  Assn. of Professional Material Handling Consultants [862]
  Bus. Retention and Expansion Intl. [1055]
  Canadian Assn. of Intl. Development Consultants [1786]
  Chem. and Indus. Consultants Assn. [844]
  Coalition to Insure Against Terrorism [1949]
  Consultants Consortium [863]
  The Fed. of Image Consultants [15273]
  Foodservice Consultants Soc. Intl. [864]
  Foodservice Consultants Soc. Intl. [864]
  Intl. Assn. of Protocol Consultants [865]
  Intl. Assn. of Protocol Consultants [865]ConsultingIntl. Guild of Professional Consultants and Coaches
  Intl. Soc. of Hospitality Consultants [866]
  Intl. Soc. of Hospitality Consultants [866]
  Natl. Assn. of Foreclosure Prevention Professionals [2899]
  Natl. Assn. of Real Estate Consultants [3027]ConsultingNatl. Chamber of Consultancy Businesses
  NHS Consultants Assn. [15399]
  Professional and Tech. Consultants Assn. [867]
  TechServe Alliance [868]
Consulting Australia - Australian Capital Territory [IO], St. Leonards, Australia
Consulting Engineers Assn. of India [IO], New Delhi, India
Consulting Engineers Assn. of Thailand [IO], Bangkok, Thailand
Consulting Engineers Coun. [★6768]
Consulting Engineers South Africa [IO], Johannesburg, Republic of South Africa
Consumer Action [17452], 221 Main St., Ste. 480, San Francisco, CA 94105, (415)777-9648
Consumer Bankers Assn. [407], 1000 Wilson Blvd., Ste. 2500, Arlington, VA 22209-3912, (703)276-1750
Consumer Coalition for Quality Hea. Care [14770], 1612 K St., Ste. 400, Washington, DC 20006, (202)789-3606
Consumer Consortium on Assisted Living [10840], 2342 Oak St., Falls Church, VA 22046, (732)212-9036
Consumer Coun. of Hong Kong [IO], Hong Kong, People's Republic of China
Consumer Credit Counseling Services [★17486]
Consumer Credit Indus. Assn. [1952], 6300 Powers Ferry Rd., Ste. 600-286, Atlanta, GA 30339, (312)939-2242
Consumer Credit Trade Assn. [IO], Shipley, United Kingdom
Consumer Data Indus. Assn. [1290], 1090 Vermont Ave. NW, Ste. 200, Washington, DC 20005-4964, (202)371-0910
Consumer Electronics Assn. [1094], 1919 S Eads St., Arlington, VA 22202, (703)907-7600
Consumer Electronics Assn., TechHome Div. [1095], 1919 S Eads St., Arlington, VA 22202, (703)907-7600
Consumer Electronics Retailers Coalition [3100], 317 Massachusetts Ave. NE, Ste. 200, Washington, DC 20006, (202)292-4600
Consumer Energy Alliance [6708], 2211 Norfolk St., Ste. 614, Houston, TX 77098-4044, (713)337-8800
Consumer Energy Coun. of Am. Res. Found. [17615], 2737 Devonshire Pl., Ste. 102, Washington, DC 20008, (202)468-8440

Reference to "IO" in place of a book number signifies that the association may be found in the 50th edition of International Organizations.

A star before a book entry number signifies that the name is not listed separately, but is mentioned within the entry.

Continental Dorset Club [4907], Debra Hopkins, Exec. Sec.-Treas., PO Box 506, North Scituate, RI 02857-0506, (401)647-4676

Continental Luscombe Assn. [20889], Ellie Madison, 410 Mission Trl., Wimberley, TX 78676, (818)343-4983

Continental Mi-Ki Assn. [21546], 112 Catlin Hill Rd., Owego, NY 13827, (607)687-8067

Continental Motorsport Club [22778], PO Box 3178, Mission Viejo, CA 92690-3178, (949)367-1141

Continental Quilting Cong. [★21464]

Continua Hea. Alliance [14771], 3855 SW 153rd Dr., Beaverton, OR 97006, (503)619-0867

Continuing Care Accreditation Commn. [16562], 1730 Rhode Island Ave. NW, Ste. 209, Washington, DC 20036, (202)587-5001

Continuing Christian Development [★19683]

Continuing Education
  Accrediting Coun. for Continuing Educ. and Training [7919]
  Amer. Assn. for Adult and Continuing Educ. [7920]
  Amer. Seminar Leaders Assn. [7921]
  Assn. for Continuing Educ. I Senior Scholars [7922]
  Assn. for Continuing Higher Educ. [7923]
  Circle of Women: Reach and Teach Across Borders [13015]
  Elderhostel, Inc. [7924]
  Elderhostel, Inc. [7924]
  Energy Training Coun. [6723]
  Intl. Assn. for Continuing Educ. and Training [7925]
  Intl. Assn. for Continuing Educ. and Training [7925]
  Latin Amer. Women's Assn. [13464]
  Learning Resources Network [7926]
  Natl. Assn. for Continuing Educ. [7927]
  Natl. Coun. for Continuing Educ. and Training [7928]
  Spirituality and Practice [7929]
  Univ. Continuing Educ. Assn. [7930]
  Univ. Professional & Continuing Educ. Assn. [7930]

Continuing Educ. Coun. [★7919]

Continuing Lib. Educ. Network and Exchange [★9991]

Continuing Lib. Educ. Network and Exchange Round Table [★9991]

Contract Flooring Assn. [IO], Nottingham, United Kingdom

Contract Furnishings Forum [★1552]

Contract Mfg. and Packaging Assn. [★2605]

Contract Packagers Assn. [★2605]

Contract Packaging Assn. [2605], 1833 Centre Point Cir., Ste. 123, Naperville, IL 60563, (630)544-5053

Contract Stationers Forum [★3353]

Contractors
  ADSC: The Intl. Assn. of Found. Drilling [894]
  ADSC: The Intl. Assn. of Found. Drilling [894]
  Alliance for Building Regulatory Reform in the Digital Age [6372]
  Amer. Soc. of Concrete Contractors [895]
  Amer. Sports Builders Assn. [896]
  Amer. Subcontractors Assn. [897]
  Assoc. Builders and Contractors [898]
  Assoc. Builders and Contractors I Natl. Elecl. Contractors Coun. [899]
  Assoc. Builders and Contractors I Natl. Mech. Contractors Coun. [900]
  Assoc. Gen. Contractors of Am. [901]
  Assoc. Specialty Contractors [902]
  Assn. for Better Insulation [530]
  Assn. of Diving Contractors Intl. [903]
  Assn. of Diving Contractors Intl. [903]
  The Assn. of Union Constructors [904]
  Building Enclosure Coun. Natl. [6374]
  Building Enclosure Tech. and Env. Coun. [539]
  Ceilings and Interior Systems Constr. Assn. [905]
  Ceramic Tile Inst. of Am. [906]
  Certified Contractor's Network [907]
  Concrete Foundations Assn. [908]
  Constr. Financial Mgt. Assn. [909]
  Deep Foundations Inst. [910]
  Deep Foundations Inst. [910]

  Engg. Contractors Assn. [911]
  Floor Covering Installation Contractors Assn. [912]
  High Performance Building Coun. [6376]
  Independent Elecl. Contractors [913]
  Instrument Contracting and Engg. Assn. [914]
  Insulation Contractors Assn. of Am. [915]
  Intl. Assn. of Geosynthetic Installers [916]
  Intl. Assn. of Geosynthetic Installers [916]
  Intl. Builders Exchange Executives [917]
  Intl. Builders Exchange Executives [917]
  Intl. Certified Floorcovering Installers Assn. [918]
  Intl. Certified Floorcovering Installers Assn. [918]
  Intl. Masonry Inst. [919]
  Intl. Masonry Inst. [919]
  Intl. Playground Contractors Assn. [920]
  Intl. Playground Contractors Assn. [920]
  Intl. Soc. for Concrete Pavements [574]
  Joint Indus. Bd. of the Elecl. Indus. [921]
  Log. Home Builders Assn. of North Am. [922]
  Mason Contractors Assn. of Am. [923]
  Mech. Contractors Assn. of Am. [924]
  Natl. Assn. of Constr. Contractors Cooperation [587]
  Natl. Assn. of Elevator Contractors [925]
  Natl. Assn. of Home Builders [926]
  Natl. Assn. of Minority Contractors [927]
  Natl. Assn. of Minority Govt. Contractors [928]
  Natl. Assn. of OEW Contractors [929]
  Natl. Assn. of Reinforcing Steel Contractors [930]
  Natl. Assn. of Small Bus. Contractors [931]
  Natl. Assn. of State Contractors Licensing Agencies [932]
  Natl. Assn. of Women in Constr. [933]
  Natl. Assn. of Women in Constr. [933]
  Natl. Demolition Assn. [934]
  Natl. Drilling Assn. [935]
  Natl. Drilling Assn. [935]
  Natl. Elecl. Contractors Assn. [936]
  Natl. Frame Builders Assn. [937]
  Natl. Insulation Assn. [938]
  Natl. Pavement Contractors Assn. [595]
  Natl. Roofing Contractors Assn. [939]
  Natl. Tile Contractors Assn. [940]
  Natl. Utility Contractors Assn. [941]
  Natl. Utility Locating Contractors Assn. [942]
  Natl. Utility Locating Contractors Assn. [942]
  Native Amer. Contractors Assn. [943]
  Painting and Decorating Contractors of Am. [944]
  Pile Driving Contractors Assn. [945]
  Plumbing-Heating-Cooling Contractors Assn. [946]
  Power and Commun. Contractors Assn. [947]
  Professional Constr. Estimators Assn. of Am. [948]
  Professional Women in Constr. [949]
  Roof Consultants Inst. [950]
  Tile Contractors Assn. of Am. [951]
  Tilt-Up Concrete Assn. [952]
  Tilt-Up Concrete Assn. [952]
  Women Constr. Owners and Executives U.S.A. [953]

Contractors Pump Bur. [1816], 6737 W Washington St., Ste. 2400, Milwaukee, WI 53214-5647, (414)272-0943

A Contre-Courant [IO], Montreal, QC, Canada

Control and Info. Systems Integrators Assn. [3371], 22 N Carroll St., Ste. 300, Madison, WI 53703, (800)661-4914

Control Surveys Division of the Amer. Cong. on Surveying and Mapping [★7485]

Controlled Circulations Audit [★87]

Controlled Circulations Audit [★87]

Controlled Env. Testing Assn. [7558], 1500 Sunday Dr., Ste. 102, Raleigh, NC 27607, (919)861-5576

Controlled Mech. Storage Systems [★1811]

Controlled Release Soc. [6404], 3340 Pilot Knob Rd., St. Paul, MN 55121, (651)454-7250

Controllers Coun. [19], Inst. of Mgt. of Accountants, 10 Paragon Dr., Montvale, NJ 07645-1718, (201)573-9000

Controllers Inst. of Am. [★1296]

Controllers Inst. of Am. [★1296]

Controllers Inst. Res. Found. [★2281]

Controllership Found. [★2281]

Convenience Caterers and Food Mfrs. Assn. [1744], 1205 Spartan Dr., Madison Heights, MI 48071, (248)982-5379

Convenient Automotive Services Inst. - Defunct.

Convention of Amer. Instructors of the Deaf [★14927]

Convention sur le Commerce Intl. des Especes de le Faune et de Flore Sauvages Menacees d'Extinction [★IO]

Convention Europeenne de la Constr. Metallique [★IO]

Convention Indus. Coun. [3474], 700 N Fairfax St., Ste. 510, Alexandria, VA 22314, (571)527-3116

Convention on Intl. Trade in Endangered Species of Wild Fauna and Flora [IO], Geneva, Switzerland

Convention of Natl. Societies of Elecl. Engineers of Europe [IO], Brussels, Belgium

Convention of Scottish Local Authorities [IO], Edinburgh, United Kingdom

Converting Equip. Mfrs. Assn. [1817], 201 Springs St., Fort Mill, SC 29715, (803)802-7820

Conveyor Assn. [★1818]

Conveyor Equip. Mfrs. Assn. [1818], 6724 Lone Oak Blvd., Naples, FL 34109, (239)514-3441

Convoy For Kids [IO], Park Orchards, Australia

Convoy of Hope [12830], 330 S Patterson Ave., Springfield, MO 65802, (417)823-8998

Convoy of Hope [12830], 330 S Patterson Ave., Springfield, MO 65802, (417)823-8998

Cook Island Sports and Natl. Olympic Comm. [IO], Rarotonga, Cook Islands

Cook Islands Canoeing Assn. [IO], Avarua, Cook Islands

Cook Islands Chamber of Commerce [IO], Rarotonga, Cook Islands

Cook Islands Family Welfare Assn. [IO], Rarotonga, Cook Islands

Cook Islands Natl. Disability Coun. [IO], Rarotonga, Cook Islands

Cook Islands Red Cross Soc. [IO], Rarotonga, Cook Islands

Cook Islands Res. Assn. [IO], Rarotonga, Cook Islands

Cook Islands Squash Racquets Assn. [IO], Rarotonga, Cook Islands

Cook Islands Volleyball Assn. [IO], Rarotonga, Cook Islands

Cookie Cutter Club [★21328]

Cookie Cutter Collectors Club [21328], PO Box 417, Cascade, ID 83611

Cooking
  Confrerie de la Chaine des Rotisseurs, Bailliage des U.S.A. [21845]
  Solar Household Energy [4931]
  Sunstove Org. [11643]
  Vinegar Connoisseurs Intl. [21849]

Cooking Advancement Res. and Educ. Found. [★7946]

Cooking Advancement Res. and Educ. Found. [★7946]

Cookware Mfrs. Assn. [1776], PO Box 531335, Birmingham, AL 35253-1335, (205)592-0389

Cool Metal Roofing Coalition [550], 680 Andersen Dr., Pittsburgh, PA 15220, (412)922-2772

Cool Roof Rating Coun. [551], 1610 Harrison St., Oakland, CA 94612, (510)485-7175

Cooley's Anemia Blood and Res. Found. for Children [★14966]

Cooley's Anemia Found. [14966], 330 7th Ave., No. 200, New York, NY 10001, (800)522-7222

Coolidge Memorial Found; Calvin [10656]

Cooling Tech. Inst. [552], PO Box 73383, Houston, TX 77273-3383, (281)583-4087

Cooling Tower Inst. [★552]

Coolmine Rugby Football Club [IO], Dublin, Ireland

Cooltan Arts [IO], London, United Kingdom

Cooper Inst. [16223], 12330 Preston Rd., Dallas, TX 75230, (972)341-3200

Cooper Inst. [16223], 12330 Preston Rd., Dallas, TX 75230, (972)341-3200

Cooper Inst. for Aerobics Res. [★16223]

Cooper Inst. for Aerobics Res. [★16223]

Cooper Ornithological Club [★7195]

Cooper Ornithological Club [★7195]

Cooper Ornithological Soc. [7195], Abby N. Powell, Sec., Univ. of Alaska, Dept. of Biology and Wildlife, Fairbanks, AK 99775-7020, (907)474-5505

Cooper Ornithological Soc. [7195], Abby N. Powell, Sec., Univ. of Alaska, Dept. of Biology and Wildlife, Fairbanks, AK 99775-7020, (907)474-5505

Reference to "IO" in place of a book number signifies that the association may be found in the 50th edition of International Organizations.

Cooperation Centre for Sci. Res. Relative to Tobacco **[IO]**, Paris, France

Cooperation Comm. for Folk Dance **[IO]**, Stockholm, Sweden

Cooperation Internationale pour le Developpement et la Solidarite **[★IO]**

Cooperation for Peace and Unity **[IO]**, Kabul, Afghanistan

Cooperativa Sociale Grado 16 **[★IO]**

Cooperativas Agrarias Federadas de Uruguay **[IO]**, Montevideo, Uruguay

Cooperative for Amer. Remittances Everywhere **[★12815]**

Cooperative for Amer. Remittances Everywhere **[★12815]**

Cooperative Assistance Fund - Defunct.

Cooperative for Assistance and Relief Everywhere **[★12815]**

Cooperative for Assistance and Relief Everywhere **[★12815]**

Cooperative Assn. for Internet Data Anal. **[7007]**, 9500 Gilman Dr., La Jolla, CA 92093, (858)534-5000

Cooperative Assn. of Tractor Dealers **[954]**, Crescent Center, 6075 Poplar Ave., Ste. 125, Memphis, TN 38119, (901)333-8600

Cooperative Birth Center Network **[★15861]**

Cooperative Bus. Intl. **[955]**, 5898 Cleveland Ave., Columbus, OH 43231, (614)839-2700

Cooperative Bus. Intl. **[955]**, 5898 Cleveland Ave., Columbus, OH 43231, (614)839-2700

Cooperative Club Intl. **[★13076]**

Cooperative Club Intl. **[★13076]**

Cooperative Education
  Assn. of Cooperative Educators **[7931]**
  Assn. of Cooperative Educators **[7931]**
  Cooperative Educ. and Internship Assn. **[7932]**
  Future Problem Solving Prog. **[7933]**
  Future Problem Solving Prog. Intl. **[7933]**
  Natl. Commn. for Cooperative Educ. **[7934]**

Cooperative Educ. Assn. **[★7932]**

Cooperative Educ. and Internship Assn. **[7932]**, PO Box 42506, Cincinnati, OH 45242, (513)793-2342

Cooperative Extension
  Epsilon Sigma Phi **[23496]**

Cooperative Extension System **[★13521]**

Cooperative Food Distributors of Am. **[★3117]**

Cooperative Grocers' Info. Network **[956]**, PO Box 399, Arcata, CA 95518, (866)709-2667

Cooperative Housing Found. **[12175]**, 8601 Georgia Ave., Ste. 800, Silver Spring, MD 20910, (301)587-4700

Cooperative Info. Superhighway **[IO]**, Geneva, Switzerland

Cooperative Training and Res. Centre **[IO]**, Kigali, Rwanda

Cooperatives
  ACDI/VOCA **[4174]**
  ACDI/VOCA **[4174]**
  Cooperative Assn. of Tractor Dealers **[954]**
  Cooperative Bus. Intl. **[955]**
  Cooperative Bus. Intl. **[955]**
  Cooperative Grocers' Info. Network **[956]**
  Green Am. **[957]**
  Natl. Cooperative Bus. Assn. **[958]**
  Natl. Cooperative Grocers Assn. **[959]**
  Natl. Coun. of Farmer Cooperatives **[4175]**
  Natl. Renewables Cooperative Org. **[6741]**
  Tanzania Fed. of Cooperatives **[5097]**
  Universal Cooperatives **[4176]**

Cooperazione Internazionale - Italia **[IO]**, Milan, Italy

Cooperazione per lo Sviluppo dei Paesi Emergenti **[★IO]**

Coopers' Company **[IO]**, London, United Kingdom

Coordinadora de ONGD Para el Desarollo Espana **[★IO]**

Coordinating Comm. of Agriculture, Commercial, Indus. and Financial Associations **[IO]**, Guatemala City, Guatemala

Coordinating Comm. for Ellis Island - Defunct.

Coordinating Comm. of Guide Dog Users **[★17080]**

Coordinating Comm. on Women in the Historical Profession/Conference Gp. on Women's History **[★17638]**

Coordinating Coun. for Handicapped Children **[★7971]**

Coordinating Coun. for Women in History **[17638]**, Northern Illinois Univ., Dept. of History and Women's Stud., 715 Zulauf Hall, DeKalb, IL 60115, (815)895-2624

Coordinating Res. Coun. **[2646]**, 3650 Mansell Rd., Ste. 140, Alpharetta, GA 30022, (678)795-0506

Copeland/Sewell Family Org. - Defunct.

Copier Dealers Assn. **[2578]**, Bob Shields, Dir., PO Box 5489, Jacksonville, FL 32207, (904)731-5100

Copper and Brass Res. Assn. **[★2512]**

Copper and Brass Servicenter Assn. **[2468]**, 6734 W 121st St., Overland Park, KS 66209, (913)396-0697

Copper Development Assn. **[2512]**, 260 Madison Ave., 16th Fl., New York, NY 10016, (212)251-7200

Copper Development Assn. **[IO]**, Hemel Hempstead, United Kingdom

Copper Development Assn. - United Kingdom **[IO]**, Hemel Hempstead, United Kingdom

Copper Inst. **[★7088]**

Copper Products Development Assn. **[★7094]**

Copper Products Development Assn. **[★7094]**

Copred Consortium: Peace Res. and Educational Development **[★18276]**

Coptic Orphans **[★11260]**

Coptic Orphans **[★11260]**

Coptic Orphans Support Assn. **[11260]**, PO Box 2881, Merrifield, VA 22116, (703)641-8910

Coptic Orphans Support Assn. **[11260]**, PO Box 2881, Merrifield, VA 22116, (703)641-8910

Copy-Dan **[IO]**, Copenhagen, Denmark

COPYGHANA **[IO]**, Accra, Ghana

Copyright Agency Limited **[IO]**, Sydney, Australia

Copyright Alliance **[5566]**, 1224 M St. NW, Ste. 301, Washington, DC 20005, (202)540-2243

Copyright Clearance Center **[5567]**, 222 Rosewood Dr., Danvers, MA 01923, (978)750-8400

Copyright Info. and Anti-piracy Centre **[IO]**, Helsinki, Finland

Copyright Licensing and Admin. Soc. of Singapore **[IO]**, Singapore, Singapore

Copyright Licensing Agency **[IO]**, London, United Kingdom

Copyright Licensing Limited **[IO]**, North Shore City, New Zealand

Copyright Soc. of the U.S.A. **[5568]**, 352 7th Ave., Ste. 739, New York, NY 10001, (212)354-6401

Copywriter's Coun. of Am. - Address unknown since 2011.

Corben Club **[20890]**, PO Box 127, Blakesburg, IA 52536

Cordage
  Cordage Inst. **[960]**
  Gold and Silver Wyre Drawers' Company **[10033]**

Cordage Inst. **[960]**, 994 Old Eagle School Rd., Ste. 1019, Wayne, PA 19087, (610)971-4854

Cordaid **[IO]**, The Hague, Netherlands

Cordell Hull Found. for Intl. Educ. **[8403]**, 501 5th Ave., Ste. 300, New York, NY 10017, (212)300-2138

Cordell Hull Found. for Intl. Educ. **[8403]**, 501 5th Ave., Ste. 300, New York, NY 10017, (212)300-2138

Cordwainers' Company **[IO]**, London, United Kingdom

CORE **[IO]**, London, United Kingdom

CORE: Coalition for Residential Educ. **[8827]**, 6900 Wisconsin Ave., Ste. 410, Bethesda, MD 20815, (301)656-6101

COREL WTA Tour **[★23061]**

COREL WTA Tour **[★23061]**

CoreNet Global **[3006]**, 260 Peachtree St. NW, Ste. 1500, Atlanta, GA 30303, (404)589-3200

CoreNet Global **[3006]**, 260 Peachtree St. NW, Ste. 1500, Atlanta, GA 30303, (404)589-3200

CorgiAid **[21547]**, Joyce Trittipo, Treas., 4038 Cherokee Dr., Madison, WI 53711

Cork Forest Conservation Alliance **[4036]**, 565 Oxford St., Salem, OR 97302, (503)931-9690

Cork Indus. Fed. **[IO]**, Sidcup, United Kingdom

Cork Inst. of Am. **[1504]**, 715 Fountain Ave., Lancaster, PA 17601, (717)295-3400

Cork Quality Coun. **[1505]**, PO Box 1491, Forestville, CA 95436, (707)887-0141

Cormac McCarthy Soc. **[10712]**, 13850 SW 100th Ave., Miami, FL 33176

Corn Indus. Res. Found. **[★1381]**

Corn Island Storytelling Festival **[★10543]**

Corn Island Storytelling Festival **[★10543]**

Corn Refiners Assn. **[1381]**, 1701 Pennsylvania Ave., Ste. 950, Washington, DC 20006, (202)331-1634

Cornea and Contact Lens Soc. of New Zealand **[IO]**, Nelson, New Zealand

Cornea Res. Found. of Am. **[15340]**, 9002 N Meridian St., Ste. 212, Indianapolis, IN 46260, (317)844-5610

Cornelia de Lange Parents Gp. **[★13841]**

Cornelia de Lange Syndrome Found. **[13841]**, 302 W Main St., No. 100, Avon, CT 06001, (860)676-8166

Cornell Feline Hea. Center **[17023]**, Cornell Univ., Coll. of Veterinary Medicine, PO Box 13, Ithaca, NY 14853-6401, (607)253-3414

Cornell Lab of Ornithology **[7196]**, 159 Sapsucker Woods Rd., Ithaca, NY 14850, (607)254-2473

Cornell Univ. Lab. of Ornithology **[★7196]**

Cornerstone Africa Org. - Address unknown since 2011.

Cornerstone Found. **[IO]**, San Ignacio, Belize

Cornhusker Country Music Club **[★10265]**

Cornish Amer. Heritage Soc. **[9455]**, Ronald Carbis, Treas., 13 St. Ives Pl., Gaithersburg, MD 20877-3457

Cornish Rex Soc. **[21247]**, 57 Pires Dr., Oakdale, CT 06370

Cornwall Archaeological Soc. **[IO]**, Padstow, United Kingdom

Coro **[18453]**, Manatt Phelps, 700 12th St. NW, Ste. 1100, Washington, DC 20005-4075

Coro Found. **[★18453]**

Coro Perosi **[IO]**, Macau, Macao

Corona Worldwide **[IO]**, London, United Kingdom

Coronado 15 Assn. **[★22331]**

Coronado 15 Class Racing Assn. **[★22331]**

Coronado 15 Natl. Assn. **[22331]**, 547 Garden St., Sacramento, CA 95815, (916)832-8015

Coronary Artery Disease Res. Assn. **[IO]**, London, United Kingdom

Corporacion Chilena de la Madera **[★IO]**

Corporacion Chilena de Prevencion del SIDA **[IO]**, Santiago, Chile

Corporacion de Exportadores de El Salvador **[★IO]**

Corporate Accountability Intl. **[18197]**, 10 Milk St., Ste. 610, Boston, MA 02108, (617)695-2525

Corporate Accountability Intl. **[18197]**, 10 Milk St., Ste. 610, Boston, MA 02108, (617)695-2525

Corporate Alliance to End Partner Violence **[11882]**, 2416 E Washington St., Ste. E, Bloomington, IL 61704, (309)664-0667

Corporate Angel Network **[13911]**, Westchester County Airport, 1 Loop Rd., White Plains, NY 10604-1215, (914)328-1313

Corporate Communicators Canada **[★809]**

Corporate Communicators Canada **[★809]**

Corporate Coun. on Africa **[160]**, 1100 17th St. NW, Ste. 1000, Washington, DC 20036, (202)835-1115

Corporate Coun. on Africa **[160]**, 1100 17th St. NW, Ste. 1000, Washington, DC 20036, (202)835-1115

Corporate Data Exchange - Defunct.

Corporate Economics
  Amer. Coun. for Capital Formation **[17475]**
  Amer. Small Bus. Coalition **[3282]**
  Private Sector Coun. **[17476]**
  Small Bus. Coun. of Am. **[17477]**

Corporate Event Marketing Assn. **[2396]**, 5098 Foothills Blvd., Ste. 3-386, Roseville, CA 95747, (916)740-3623

Corporate Info. Center **[★17481]**

Corporate Law
  Assn. of Corporate Counsel **[5345]**
  Minority Corporate Counsel Assn. **[5346]**
  TRACE Intl. **[5347]**

Corporate Real Estate Advisors - Defunct.

Corporate Responsibility
  As You Sow Found. **[17478]**
  Assn. of Certified Green Tech. Auditors **[6692]**
  Assn. of Corporate Contributions Professionals **[961]**

A star before a book entry number signifies that the name is not listed separately, but is mentioned within the entry.

BuildingBlocks Intl. [11666]
CARTHA [18402]
CEO Netweavers [962]
Climate Gp. [4023]
Corporate Responsibility Officers Assn. [963]
Corporate Social Responsibility Assn. [964]
Corporate Voices for Working Families [17479]
Global Integrity [965]
Global Integrity [965]
Green Am. [957]
Green Partners [4177]
Hispanic Assn. on Corporate Responsibility [17480]
Interfaith Center on Corporate Responsibility [17481]
Public Affairs Coun. [17482]
Uplift Intl. [15220]
Corporate Responsibility Officers Assn. [963], 343 Thornall St., Ste. 515, Edison, NJ 08837-2209, (732)476-6160
Corporate Social Responsibility Assn. [964], 155 E Boardwalk Dr., No. 544, Fort Collins, CO 80525, (303)944-4225
Corporate Speech Pathology Network [3303], 10 Glenlake Pkwy., Ste. 130, Atlanta, GA 30328, (678)592-0052
Corporate Theatre Fund [★10588]
Corp. for the Celebration of Jack Kerouac in Lowell [★9394]
Corp. des associations de detaillants d'automobiles [★IO]
Corp. for Enterprise Development [17575], 1200 G St. NW, Ste. 400, Washington, DC 20005, (202)408-9788
Corp. for Public Broadcasting [9458], 401 9th St. NW, Washington, DC 20004-2129, (202)879-9600
Corps Canadien des Commissionaires [★IO]
Corps of Drums Soc. [IO], Kent, United Kingdom
Corps Network [13519], 1100 G St. NW, Ste. 1000, Washington, DC 20005, (202)737-6272
CORPUS [19418], 114 Sunset Dr., Raynham, MA 02767-1383, (508)822-6710
CORPUS - Natl. Assn. for a Married Priesthood [★19418]
CorpWatch [17822], PO Box 29198, San Francisco, CA 94129, (415)800-4004
CorpWatch [17822], PO Box 29198, San Francisco, CA 94129, (415)800-4004
Corrado Club of Am. [21034], PO Box 29, Bala Cynwyd, PA 19004-0029
Correctional
    ACLU | Natl. Prison Proj. [11699]
    All of Us or None [17256]
    Assn. of State Correctional Administrators [11706]
    Center for Stud. in Criminal Justice [11707]
    Corrections Tech. Assn. [17483]
    Intl. Assn. for Correctional and Forensic Psychology [11715]
    Intl. Assn. of Reentry [17484]
    Intl. Assn. of Reentry [17484]
    Natl. Assn. of Victim Ser. Professionals in Corrections [13366]
    November Coalition [18681]
    Way to Work [11962]
Correctional Administrators Assn. of Am. [★11706]
Correctional Educ. Assn. [11709], 8182 Lake Brown Rd., Ste. 202, Elkridge, MD 21075, (443)459-3080
Corrections Tech. Assn. [17483], Conf. Mgt. Solutions, Inc., 8347 Hinsdale Way, Tallahassee, FL 32312
Correspondence
    Cover Collectors Circuit Club [22034]
    Friends' Hea. Connection [21417]
    Golden Threads [21418]
    Golden Threads [21418]
    Intl. Pen Friends [21419]
    Single Booklovers [21420]
    Singles in Agriculture [21421]
    Student Letter Exchange [21422]
Correspondence Chess League of Am. [21276], PO Box 142, Livingston, NJ 07039-0142

Corresponding Surveyors to the Yacht Safety Bur. [★7056]
Corrosion
    World Corrosion Org. [4178]
Corrosion Prevention Assn. [IO], Bordon, United Kingdom
Corrosion Soc; NACE Intl.: The [6809]
Corrugated Bd. Mfrs. Assn. [IO], Istanbul, Turkey
Corrugated Metal Pipe Assn. [★2753]
Corrugated Packaging Alliance [2606], 25 Northwest Point Blvd., Ste. 510, Elk Grove Village, IL 60007, (847)364-9600
Corrugated Packaging Coun. [★2606]
Corrugated Sector of the Confed. of Paper Indus. [IO], Swindon, United Kingdom
Corset and Brassiere Assn. of Am. [★199]
Corset and Brassiere Women's Club [★112]
CORSO [IO], Dunedin, New Zealand
Corson/Colson Family History Assn. [20496], 2300 Cedarfield Pkwy., No. 476, Richmond, VA 23233
CorStone [15451], 250 Camino Alto, Ste. 100A, Mill Valley, CA 94941, (415)388-6161
CorStone [15451], 250 Camino Alto, Ste. 100A, Mill Valley, CA 94941, (415)388-6161
Corvair Soc. of Am. [21035], PO Box 607, Lemont, IL 60439-0607, (630)403-5010
Corvette Club of Am. [21036], PO Box 9879, Bowling Green, KY 42102-9879, (866)482-1191
Corvette Clubs; Natl. Coun. of [21126]
Corvette Owners Assn; Natl. [21124]
Corvette Restorers Soc; Natl. [21125]
COSA [13082], PO Box 14537, Minneapolis, MN 55414, (763)537-6904
COSA [13082], PO Box 14537, Minneapolis, MN 55414, (763)537-6904
COSA [★13082]
Cosmetic Career Women [★1667]
Cosmetic Executive Women [1667], 286 Madison Ave., 19th Fl., New York, NY 10017, (212)685-5955
Cosmetic Indus. Buyers and Suppliers [1668], Mario Magali, Treas., Elite Packaging, 40-E Cotters Ln., East Brunswick, NJ 08816
Cosmetic Ingredient Rev. [1669], 1101 17th St. NW, Ste. 412, Washington, DC 20036-4702, (202)331-0651
Cosmetic and Perfumery Assn. of Hong Kong [IO], Hong Kong, People's Republic of China
Cosmetic Surgery
    Amer. Acad. of Cosmetic Surgery [14169]
    Amer. Acad. of Facial Plastic and Reconstructive Surgery [14170]
    Amer. Acad. of Micropigmentation [14171]
    Amer. Assn. of Plastic Surgeons [14172]
    Amer. Bd. of Plastic Surgery [14173]
    Amer. Coun. of Academic Plastic Surgeons [14174]
    Amer. Soc. for Aesthetic Plastic Surgery [14175]
    Amer. Soc. of Ophthalmic Plastic and Reconstructive Surgery [14176]
    Amer. Soc. of Plastic Surgeons [14177]
    Amer. Soc. of Plastic Surgeons | Plastic Surgery Educ. Found. [14178]
    Assn. of Plastic Surgery Physician Assistants [14179]
    Intl. Alliance of Hair Restoration Surgeons [14675]CosmeticIntl. Soc. of Cosmetic and Laser Surgeons
    Intl. Soc. of Cosmetogynecology [14180]
    Interplast [14185]
    Physicians Coalition for Injectable Safety [14181]
    Plastic Surgery Administrative Assn. [14182]
    Plastic Surgery Found. [14183]
    Plastic Surgery Res. Coun. [14184]
    Plastic Surgery Res. Coun. [14184]
    ReSurge Intl. [14185]
    Soc. of Plastic Surgical Skin Care Specialists [14186]
Cosmetic, Toiletry and Fragrance Assn. [★1670]
Cosmetic, Toiletry and Fragrance Assn. - New Zealand [IO], Auckland, New Zealand
Cosmetic, Toiletry, and Perfumery Assn. - England [IO], London, United Kingdom
Cosmetology
    Aesthetics Intl. Assn. [966]

    Aesthetics Intl. Assn. [966]
    Allied Hea. Assn. [967]
    Amer. Assn. of Cosmetology Schools [7935]
    Barbers Company [3806]CosmetologyBrazilian Cosmetology Assn.
    Fairs and Salons of France [16738]
    Intercoiffure Am. [968]
    Intl. SalonSpa Bus. Network [969]
    Intl. SalonSpa Bus. Network [969]
    Natl. Assn. of Barber Boards of Am. [970]
    Natl. Beauty Culturists' League [971]
    Natl. Coalition of Estheticians, Manufacturers/Distributors and Associations [972]
    Natl. Hair Soc. [1643]
    Natl. - Interstate Coun. of State Boards of Cosmetology [973]
    Professional Beauty Assn. | Nail Mfrs. Coun. [974]
    Professional Beauty Assn. | Natl. Cosmetology Assn. [975]
    Soc. of Permanent Cosmetic Professionals [976]
Cosmetology Accrediting Commn. [★7647]
Cosmetology Arts and Sciences; Natl. Accrediting Commn. of [7647]
Cosmic Baseball Assn. [22270], Jour. of the Cosmic Baseball Assn., 907 6th St. SW, Ste. 214, Washington, DC 20024
Cosmology
    Natl. Coun. for GeoCosmic Res. [6579]
Cosmopolitan Intl. [13056], PO Box 4588, Overland Park, KS 66204, (913)648-4330
Cosmopolitan Intl. [13056], PO Box 4588, Overland Park, KS 66204, (913)648-4330
Cosmopolitan Soccer League [22934], 115 River Rd., Ste. 1029, Edgewater, NJ 07020, (201)943-3390
Cost Estimation
    AACE Intl. [6580]
    AACE Intl. [6580]
Costa Rica Chap. of the ILAE [IO], San Jose, Costa Rica
Costa Rican-American Chamber of Commerce [IO], San Jose, Costa Rica
Costa Rican Assn. of the Plastic Indus. [IO], San Jose, Costa Rica
Costa Rican Banking Assn. [IO], San Jose, Costa Rica
Costa Rican Chamber of the Clothing Indus. [★14793]
Costa Rican Chamber of Constr. [IO], San Jose, Costa Rica
Costa Rican Demographic Assn. [IO], San Jose, Costa Rica
Costa Rican Hypertension League [IO], San Jose, Costa Rica
Costa Rican Textile Chamber [IO], San Jose, Costa Rica
Costa Rican Union of Chambers of Private Sector Enterprises [IO], San Jose, Costa Rica
Costarican Assn. of Climacteric and Menopause and Osteoporosis [IO], San Jose, Costa Rica
Costume Coll. [9508], 601 W 26th St., 3rd Fl., Ste. 325, New York, NY 10001, (212)989-5855
Costume Jewelry Salesmen's Assn. - Defunct.
Costume Soc. of Am. [9509], 390 Amwell Rd., Ste. 402, Hillsborough, NJ 08844, (908)359-1471
Costumes
    Costume Coll. [9508]
    Costume Soc. of Am. [9509]
COTREL [IO], London, United Kingdom
Cotswold Breeders Assn. [3788], PO Box 441, Manchester, MD 21102, (410)374-4383
Cottage Garden Soc. [IO], Cheshire, United Kingdom
Cottage Indus. Miniaturists Trade Assn. [1044], 18453 Shaddox Hollow Ln., Rogers, AR 72756, (479)925-7056
Cottage Indus. Miniaturists Trade Assn., Inc. [★796]
The Cottage Prog. Intl., Inc. [★13252]
The Cottage Prog. Intl., Inc. [★13252]
Cotton
    Amcot, Inc. [3946]
    Amer. Cotton Shippers Assn. [977]
    Cotton Coun. Intl. [978]
    Cotton Coun. Intl. [978]
    Cotton Found. [979]

Reference to "IO" in place of a book number signifies that the association may be found in the 50th edition of International Organizations.

Cotton Incorporated [980]
Cotton Warehouse Assn. of Am. [981]
Memphis Cotton Exchange [3968]
Natl. Cotton Batting Inst. [982]
Natl. Cotton Coun. of Am. [983]
Natl. Cotton Ginners' Assn. [984]
Plains Cotton Growers [3960]
Southern Cotton Assn. [985]
Southern Cotton Ginners Assn. [986]
Cotton Coun. Intl. [978], 1521 New Hampshire Ave. NW, Washington, DC 20036, (202)745-7805
Cotton Coun. Intl. [978], 1521 New Hampshire Ave. NW, Washington, DC 20036, (202)745-7805
Cotton Found. [979], Bill Norman, Exec. Dir./Sec., PO Box 783, Cordova, TN 38088, (901)274-9030
Cotton Incorporated [980], 6399 Weston Pkwy., Cary, NC 27513, (919)678-2220
Cotton Producers' Inst. [★980]
Cotton Textiles Export Promotion Coun. [IO], Mumbai, India
Cotton Warehouse Assn. of Am. [981], 499 S Capitol St. SW, Ste. 408, Washington, DC 20003, (202)479-4371
Cougar
Cougar Network [4179]
Cougar Network [4179], 75 White Ave., Concord, MA 01742
Coun. on Abandoned Military Posts - USA [★9678]
Coun. of Academic and Professional Publishers [IO], London, United Kingdom
Coun. of Academies of Engg. and Technological Sciences [★8840]
Coun. of Academies of Engg. and Technological Sciences [★8840]
Coun. on Accreditation [13182], 45 Broadway 29th Fl., New York, NY 10006, (212)797-3000
Coun. for Accreditation of Counseling and Related Educational Programs [7942], 1001 N Fairfax St., Ste. 510, Alexandria, VA 22314, (703)535-5990
Coun. on Accreditation of Nurse Anesthesia Educational Programs [8580], Amer. Assn. of Nurse Anesthetists, 222 S Prospect Ave., Park Ridge, IL 60068, (847)655-1160
Coun. on Accreditation of Nurse Anesthesia Educational Programs/Schools [★8580]
Coun. for Accreditation in Occupational Hearing Conservation [15908], 555 E Wells St., Ste. 1100, Milwaukee, WI 53202-3823, (414)266-5338
Coun. on Accreditation of Services for Families and Children [★13182]
Coun. for Acupuncture Res. and Educ. [13580], 3448 Horseshoe Bend Rd., Charlottesville, VA 22901
Coun. of Administrators of Special Educ. [8877], Osigian Off. Centre, 101 Katelyn Cir., Ste. E, Warner Robins, GA 31088, (478)333-6892
Coun. for Adult and Experiential Learning [8174], 55 E Monroe St., Ste. 1930, Chicago, IL 60603, (312)499-2600
Coun. of Advanced Automotive Trainers - Address unknown since 2011.
Coun. for the Advancement of Arab-British Understanding [IO], London, United Kingdom
Coun. for the Advancement of Citizenship - Defunct.
Coun. for the Advancement of Experiential Learning [★8174]
Coun. for the Advancement of Psychological Professions and Sciences [★16385]
Coun. for the Advancement of Sci. Writing [2821], PO Box 910, Hedgesville, WV 25427, (304)754-6786
Coun. for the Advancement of Small Colleges [★8287]
Coun. for the Advancement of Standards in Higher Educ. [8914], 1 Dupont Cir. NW, No. 300, Washington, DC 20036-1188, (202)862-1400
Coun. for the Advancement of Standards for Student Services/Development Programs [★8914]
Coun. for Advancement and Support of Educ. [8013], 1307 New York Ave. NW, Ste. 1000, Washington, DC 20005-4701, (202)328-2273
Coun. of Affiliated Assns. of Jewelers of America - Defunct.
Coun. for Affordable Hea. Insurance [14856], 127 S Peyton St., Ste. 210, Alexandria, VA 22314, (703)836-6200

Coun. for Affordable Quality Healthcare [14772], 601 Pennsylvania Ave. NW, South Bldg., Ste. 500, Washington, DC 20004, (202)861-1492
Coun. for Affordable and Rural Housing [12176], 1112 King St., Alexandria, VA 22314-3022, (703)837-9001
Coun. of AFL-CIO Unions for Professional Employees [★23223]
Coun. for Agricultural Sci. and Tech. [7709], 4420 Lincoln Way, Ames, IA 50014-3447, (515)292-2125
Coun. for Aid to Educ. [8099], 215 Lexington Ave., 21st Fl., New York, NY 10016-6023, (212)661-5800
Coun. of the Alleghenies [9677], PO Box 514, Frostburg, MD 21532, (301)689-8178
Coun. for Aluminium in Building [IO], Stonehouse, United Kingdom
Coun. of Alumni Marketing and Membership Professionals [2397], 1520 R St., Lincoln, NE 68501-0129, (402)472-4239
Coun. on Amer. Affairs [★18454]
Coun. of Amer. Instructors of the Deaf [14927], PO Box 377, Bedford, TX 76095-0377, (817)354-8414
Coun. on American-Islamic Relations [19073], 453 New Jersey Ave. SE, Washington, DC 20003-4034, (202)488-8787
Coun. of Amer. Jewish Museums [10117], PO Box 12025, Jackson, MS 39236-2025, (303)871-3015
Coun. of Amer. Maritime Museums [10118], The Whaling Museum, PO Box 25, Cold Spring Harbor, NY 11724, (860)535-0786
Coun. of Amer. Master Mariners [2354], PO Box 5034, Lynnwood, WA 98046-5034, (425)775-2331
Coun. of Amer. Overseas Res. Centers [7328], PO Box 37012, Washington, DC 20013-7012, (202)633-1599
Coun. for Amer. Private Educ. [8754], 13017 Wisteria Dr., No. 457, Germantown, MD 20874-2607, (301)916-8460
Coun. of Amer. Students in Intl. Negotiations [8386], PO Box 2243, New York, NY 10108
Coun. of Amer. Survey Res. Organizations [18396], 170 N Country Rd., Ste. 4, Port Jefferson, NY 11777, (631)928-6954
Coun. of the Americas [23424], 680 Park Ave., New York, NY 10065, (212)628-3200
Coun. on America's Military Past [9678], PO Box 4209, Charlottesville, VA 22905
Coun. for Amusement and Recreational Equip. Safety [5962], PO Box 8236, Des Moines, IA 50301-8236
Coun. on Anthropology and Educ. [6139], Mills Coll., 5000 MacArthur Blvd., Oakland, CA 94613, (510)430-3384
Coun. on Anxiety Disorders - Defunct.
Coun. for Art Educ. [7746], PO Box 479, Hanson, MA 02341-0479, (781)293-4100
Coun. of Australian Postgraduate Associations [IO], Carlton South, Australia
Coun. of Authors and Journalists [★10715]
Coun. of the Bars and Law Societies of Europe [IO], Brussels, Belgium
Coun. for Basic Education - Defunct.
Coun. of Better Bus. Bureaus Found. [★17445]
Coun. of Better Bus. Bureaus Found. [★17445]
Coun. for Better Hearing and Speech Month - Defunct.
Coun. of Biology Editors [★2822]
Coun. for Biotechnology Info. [6334], 1201 Maryland Ave. SW, Ste. 900, Washington, DC 20024, (202)962-9200
Coun. for Biotechnology Info. [6334], 1201 Maryland Ave. SW, Ste. 900, Washington, DC 20024, (202)962-9200
Coun. of Blind Lions [★17059]
Coun. on Botanical and Horticultural Libraries [9983], Auraria Lib., 1100 Lawrence St., Denver, CO 80204-2095, (303)556-2791
Coun. on Botanical and Horticultural Libraries [9983], Auraria Lib., 1100 Lawrence St., Denver, CO 80204-2095, (303)556-2791
Coun. for British Archaeology [IO], York, United Kingdom
Coun. for Bus. and the Arts in Canada [IO], Toronto, ON, Canada

Coun. of Canadians [IO], Ottawa, ON, Canada
Coun. on Certification of Hea., Environmental and Safety Technologists [14705], 208 Burwash Ave., Savoy, IL 61874, (217)359-2686
Coun. on Certification of Nurse Anesthetists [★15775]
Coun. of Chemical Assn. Executives - Defunct.
Coun. for Chem. Res. [6405], 1550 M St. NE, Ste. 500, Washington, DC 20005, (202)429-3971
Coun. of Chief State School Officers [8014], 1 Massachusetts Ave. NW, Ste. 700, Washington, DC 20001-1431, (202)336-7000
Coun. for Children with Behavioral Disorders [8878], 1110 N Glebe Rd., Ste. 300, Arlington, VA 22201-5704, (703)620-3660
Coun. of Chiropractic Acupuncture [14128], 510 Baxter Rd., Ste. 8, Chesterfield, MO 63017, (636)207-6600
Coun. on Chiropractic Educ. [14129], 8049 N 85th Way, Scottsdale, AZ 85258-4321, (480)443-8877
Coun. on Chiropractic Educ. Australasia [IO], Rosewood, Australia
Coun. on Chiropractic Guidelines and Practice Parameters [14130], PO Box 2542, Lexington, SC 29071, (803)356-6809
Coun. on Chiropractic Orthopedics [16033], 4409 Sterling Ave., Kansas City, MO 64133-1854, (816)358-5100
Coun. of Chiropractic Physiological Therapeutics and Rehabilitation [14131], 616 N Columbus St., Lancaster, OH 43130, (740)653-2973
Coun. on Chiropractic Practice [14132], 2950 N Dobson Rd., Ste. 1, Chandler, AZ 85224
Coun. for Christian Colleges and Universities [7854], 321 8th St. NE, Washington, DC 20002, (202)546-8713
Coun. for Christian Medical Work [★19950]
Coun. of Christian Scholarly Societies - Address unknown since 2011.
Coun. on Christian Union [★19652]
Coun. on Christian Unity [19652], PO Box 1986, Indianapolis, IN 46206-1986, (317)713-2586
Coun. of Churches of Malaysia [IO], Petaling Jaya, Malaysia
Coun. of Citizens With Low Vision [★11774]
Coun. of Citizens With Low Vision Intl. [11774], 2200 Wilson Blvd., Ste. 650, Arlington, VA 22201, (800)733-2258
Coun. on Clinical Optometric Care - Defunct.
Coun. for Clinical Training [★19668]
Coun. of Colleges of Acupuncture and Oriental Medicine [16012], 600 Wyndhurst Ave., Baltimore, MD 21210, (410)464-6040
Coun. of Colleges of Arts and Sciences [7747], Coll. of William and Mary, PO Box 8795, Williamsburg, VA 23187-8795, (757)221-1784
Coun. of Collegiate Women's Athletic Administrators [★8718]
Coun. on Commun. Mgt. [807], 65 Enterprise, Aliso Viejo, CA 92656, (866)463-6226
Coun. on Communications Res. [★8437]
Coun. of Community Blood Centers [★13849]
Coun. of Community Coll. Boards [★7890]
Coun. for a Community of Democracies [17518], 1801 F St. NW, Ste. 308, Washington, DC 20006, (202)789-9771
Coun. for a Community of Democracies [17518], 1801 F St. NW, Ste. 308, Washington, DC 20006, (202)789-9771
Coun. for Community and Economic Res. [23358], PO Box 100127, Arlington, VA 22210, (703)522-4980
Coun. on Competitiveness [3482], 1500 K St. NW, Ste. 850, Washington, DC 20005, (202)682-4292
Coun. on Compulsive Gambling of New Jersey [12061], 3635 Quakerbridge Rd., Ste. 7, Hamilton, NJ 08619, (609)588-5515
Coun. of Conservative Citizens [18676], PO Box 221683, St. Louis, MO 63122-8683, (636)940-8474
Coun. on Consumer Info. [★17442]
Coun. on Contemporary Families [12004], Univ. of Illinois at Chicago, 1007 W Harrison St., MC 312, Chicago, IL 60607, (312)996-3074
Coun. on the Continuing Educ. Unit [★7925]
Coun. on the Continuing Educ. Unit [★7925]

A star before a book entry number signifies that the name is not listed separately, but is mentioned within the entry.

Coun. for Continuous Improvement - Defunct.

Coun. for Court Excellence [5617], 1111 14th St. NW, Ste. 500, Washington, DC 20005, (202)785-5917

Coun. for Culture [IO], The Hague, Netherlands

Coun. for Dance Educ. and Training - UK [IO], London, United Kingdom

Coun. of Defense and Space Indus. Associations [133], 1000 Wilson Blvd., Ste. 1800, Arlington, VA 22209, (703)243-2020

Coun. for Democratic and Secular Humanism [★19819]

Coun. for Democratic and Secular Humanism [★19819]

Coun. of Development Finance Agencies [17576], 85 E Gay St., Ste. 700, Columbus, OH 43215, (614)224-1300

Coun. for the Development of Social Sci. Res. in Africa [IO], Dakar, Senegal

Coun. on Diagnostic Imaging [16532], Steven Gould, Sec.-Treas., PO Box 190, Cheney, KS 67025, (316)542-3400

Coun. for Disability Rights - Defunct.

Coun. of Disabled People of Thailand [IO], Bangkok, Thailand

Coun. for Distributive Teacher Educ. [★8557]

Coun. for Early Childhood Professional Recognition [★11150]

Coun. for Educ. in the Commonwealth [IO], London, United Kingdom

Coun. on Educ. of the Deaf [14928], Eastern Kentucky Univ., Wallace 245, Richmond, KY 40475, (859)622-1043

Coun. for the Educ. of the Partially Seeing [★8883]

Coun. on Educ. for Public Hea. [16485], 800 Eye St. NW, Ste. 202, Washington, DC 20001-3710, (202)789-1050

Coun. for Educational Development and Res. [★8797]

Coun. of Educational Fac. Planners Intl. [8088], 9180 E Desert Cove Dr., Ste. 104, Scottsdale, AZ 85260-6231, (480)391-0840

Coun. of Educational Fac. Planners Intl. [8088], 9180 E Desert Cove Dr., Ste. 104, Scottsdale, AZ 85260-6231, (480)391-0840

Coun. for Educational Travel U.S.A. [9016], 32122 Camino Capitrano, Ste. 100, San Juan Capistrano, CA 92675, (949)487-1620

Coun. of Educators in Landscape Architecture [8456], Dee Solco, Interim Bus. Mgr., Univ. of Texas, Box 19108, Arlington, TX 76019-0108, (817)272-2321

Coun. for Electronic Revenue Commun. Advancement [3405], 600 Cameron St., Ste. 309, Alexandria, VA 22314, (703)340-1655

Coun. for Elementary Sci. Intl. [8837], Eastern Connecticut State Univ., 83 Windham St., 151 Webb Hall, Willimantic, CT 06226, (860)465-4532

Coun. for Elementary Sci. Intl. [8837], Eastern Connecticut State Univ., 83 Windham St., 151 Webb Hall, Willimantic, CT 06226, (860)465-4532

Coun. for Emerging Natl. Security Affairs [18594], 150 W 56th St., Ste. 6202, New York, NY 10019-3840, (212)678-8608

Coun. on Employee Benefit Plans [★1122]

Coun. on Employee Benefits [1122], 1311 King St., Alexandria, VA 22314, (703)549-6025

Coun. for Endangered Species Act Reliability [5413], 1990 3rd St., Ste. 400, Sacramento, CA 95811, (916)341-7407

Coun. of Energy Rsrc. Tribes [18151], Greenberg Traurig, 1200 17th St., No. 2400, Denver, CO 80202, (303)282-7576

Coun. of Engg. and Sci. Soc. Executives [6792], PO Box 130656, St. Paul, MN 55113, (952)838-3268

Coun. of Engineers and Scientists Organizations [23309], Stan Sorsche, Coor., SPEEA, IFPTE Local 2001, 15205 52nd Ave. S, Seattle, WA 98188, (206)433-0995

Coun. of Entomology Dept. Administrators [6842], James Harper, North Carolina State Univ., Dept. of Entomology, Box 7613, Raleigh, NC 27695-7613, (919)515-2746

Coun. of Environmental Deans and Directors [8151], Natl. Coun. for Sci. and the Env., 1101 17th St. NW, Ste. 250, Washington, DC 20036, (202)530-5810

Coun. for Environmental Educ. [IO], Reading, United Kingdom

Coun. for Ethical Leadership [658], 1 Coll. and Main, Columbus, OH 43209-7812, (614)236-7222

Coun. of Ethical Organizations [1227], 214 S Payne St., Alexandria, VA 22314, (703)683-7916

Coun. for Ethics in Economics [★658]

Coun. of EU Chambers of Commerce in India [IO], Mumbai, India

Coun. of Europe [IO], Strasbourg, France

Coun. of European Bishops' Conférences [IO], St. Gallen, Switzerland

Coun. of European Employers of the Metal, Engg. and Technology-Based Indus. [IO], Brussels, Belgium

Coun. of European Energy Regulators [IO], Brussels, Belgium

Coun. of European Municipalities and Regions [IO], Brussels, Belgium

Coun. of European Natl. Top-Level Domain Registries [IO], Brussels, Belgium

Coun. of European Producers of Materials for Constr. [IO], Brussels, Belgium

Coun. of European Professional Informatics Societies [IO], Brussels, Belgium

Coun. for European Stud. [8169], Columbia Univ., 420 W 118th St., MC 3310, New York, NY 10027, (212)854-4172

Coun. for European Stud. [8169], Columbia Univ., 420 W 118th St., MC 3310, New York, NY 10027, (212)854-4172

Coun. Europeen des Jeunes Agriculteurs [★IO]

Coun. for Excellence in Govt. [5429], 1301 K St. NW, Ste. 450 W, Washington, DC 20005, (202)728-0418

Coun. for Exceptional Children [8879], 2900 Crystal Dr., Ste. 1000, Arlington, VA 22202-3557, (703)620-3660

Coun. of Families with Visual Impairment [17073], Cindy Van Winkle, Pres., 6686 Capricorn Ln. NE, Bremerton, WA 98311, (360)698-0827

Coun. on Family Health - Defunct.

Coun. of Fashion Designers of Am. [203], 1412 Broadway, Ste. 2006, New York, NY 10018

Coun. of Fleet Specialists and Natl. Wheel and Rim Assn. [★324]

Coun. on Food, Agricultural and Rsrc. Economics [3753], 900 Second St. NE, Ste. 205, Washington, DC 20002, (202)408-8522

Coun. on Foreign Relations [17699], The Harold Pratt House, 58 E 68th St., New York, NY 10065, (212)434-9400

Coun. on Forest Engg. [4392], 620 SW 4th St., Corvallis, OR 97333, (541)754-7558

Coun. of Forest Indus. - Canada [IO], Vancouver, BC, Canada

Coun. on Foundations [12593], 2121 Crystal Dr., Ste. 700, Arlington, VA 22202, (703)879-0655

Coun. of Gen. Motors Credit Unions - Address unknown since 2010.

Coun. of Georgist Organizations [18696], PO Box 57, Evanston, IL 60204, (888)262-9015

Coun. on Governmental Ethics Laws [5985], PO Box 81237, Athens, GA 30608, (706)548-7758

Coun. on Governmental Relations [8794], 1200 New York Ave. NW, Ste. 750, Washington, DC 20005, (202)289-6655

Coun. of Governors' Policy Advisors - Defunct.

Coun. on Graduate Educ. for Public Admin. [★5908]

Coun. of Graduate Schools [8235], 1 Dupont Cir. NW, Ste. 230, Washington, DC 20036-1176, (202)223-3791

Coun. of Graduate Schools in the U.S. [★8235]

Coun. of Graphological Societies [10754], Louie Seibert, Treas., PO Box 615, Hardy, AR 72542

Coun. of the Great City Schools [9028], 1301 Pennsylvania Ave. NW, Ste. 702, Washington, DC 20004, (202)393-2427

Coun. for Healing [13672], PO Box 76, Medford, NJ 08055, (609)714-1885

Coun. for Hea. and Human Ser. Ministries of the United Church of Christ [13183], 700 Prospect Ave., Cleveland, OH 44115, (216)736-2260

Coun. for Hea. and Human Services [★13183]

Coun. on Hea. Res. for Development [IO], Geneva, Switzerland

Coun. for Hea. Ser. Accreditation of South Africa [IO], Pinelands, Republic of South Africa

Coun. for Hea. and Welfare Services, United Church of Christ [★13183]

Coun. on Hemispheric Affairs [17179], 1250 Connecticut Ave. NW, Ste. 1C, Washington, DC 20036, (202)223-4975

Coun. on Hemispheric Affairs [17179], 1250 Connecticut Ave. NW, Ste. 1C, Washington, DC 20036, (202)223-4975

Coun. for Higher Educ. Accreditation [8015], 1 Dupont Cir. NW, Ste. 510, Washington, DC 20036-1135, (202)955-6126

Coun. of Historical Societies [★9743]

Coun. for Holocaust Survivors With Disabilities - Defunct.

Coun. to Homeless Persons [IO], Collingwood, Australia

Coun. for Hospitality Mgt. Educ. [IO], Dorset, United Kingdom

Coun. of Hotel and Restaurant Trainers [1745], PO Box 2835, Westfield, NJ 07091, (908)389-9277

Coun. for Independent Archaeology [IO], Derby, United Kingdom

Coun. of Independent Colleges [8287], 1 Dupont Cir. NW, Ste. 320, Washington, DC 20036-1142, (202)466-7230

Coun. for Indian Educ. [8675], 1240 Burlington Ave., Billings, MT 59102-4224, (406)248-3465

Coun. of Indian Employers [IO], New Delhi, India

Coun. of Indus. Boiler Owners [1819], 6035 Burke Centre Pkwy., Ste. 360, Burke, VA 22015, (703)250-9042

Coun. of Indus. Development Bond Issuers [★17576]

Coun. of Infrastructure Financing Authorities [5945], 316 Pennsylvania Ave. SE, Ste. 404, Washington, DC 20003, (202)547-7886

Coun. of Infrastructure Financing Authorities [5945], 316 Pennsylvania Ave. SE, Ste. 404, Washington, DC 20003, (202)547-7886

Coun. of Institutional Investors [3196], 888 17th St. NW, Ste. 500, Washington, DC 20006, (202)822-0800

Coun. of Insurance Agents and Brokers [1953], 701 Pennsylvania Ave. NW, Ste. 750, Washington, DC 20004-2608, (202)783-4400

Coun. of Insurance Agents and Brokers [1953], 701 Pennsylvania Ave. NW, Ste. 750, Washington, DC 20004-2608, (202)783-4400

Coun. for Inter-American Cooperation [★2087]

Coun. for Inter-American Cooperation [★2087]

Coun. for Interior Design Accreditation [8332], 206 Grandville Ave., Ste. 350, Grand Rapids, MI 49503, (616)458-0400

Coun. on Intl. Banking [★420]

Coun. for Intl. Congresses of Dipterology [IO], Canberra, Australia

Coun. for Intl. Development [IO], Wellington, New Zealand

Coun. on Intl. Educational Exchange USA [8353], 300 Fore St., Portland, ME 04101, (207)553-4000

Coun. on Intl. Educational Exchange USA [8353], 300 Fore St., Portland, ME 04101, (207)553-4000

Coun. for Intl. Exchange of Scholars [★8354]

Coun. for Intl. Exchange of Scholars [★8354]

Coun. for Intl. Exchange of Scholars Conf. Bd. of Assoc. Res. Councils [★8354]

Coun. for Intl. Exchange of Scholars Conf. Bd. of Assoc. Res. Councils [★8354]

Coun. for Intl. Exchange of Scholars I Inst. of Intl. Educ. [8354], 3007 Tilden St. NW, Ste. 5L, Washington, DC 20008-3009, (202)686-4000

Coun. for Intl. Exchange of Scholars I Institute of Intl. Educ. [8354], 3007 Tilden St. NW, Ste. 5L, Washington, DC 20008-3009, (202)686-4000

Coun. of Intl. Investigators [2121], 2150 N 107th St., Ste. 205, Seattle, WA 98133-9009, (206)361-8869

Coun. of Intl. Investigators [2121], 2150 N 107th St., Ste. 205, Seattle, WA 98133-9009, (206)361-8869

Coun. of Intl. Neonatal Nurses [15745], 94 Lyall Terr., Boston, MA 02132, (405)684-1476

Coun. on Intl. Nontheatrical Events [9602], 1112 16th St. NW, Ste. 510, Washington, DC 20036, (202)785-1136

Reference to "IO" in place of a book number signifies that the association may be found in the 50th edition of International Organizations.

Coun. on Intl. Nontheatrical Events [9602], 1112 16th St. NW, Ste. 510, Washington, DC 20036, (202)785-1136

Coun. for Intl. Organizations of Medical Sciences [IO], Geneva, Switzerland

Coun. of Intl. Programs [★13218]

Coun. of Intl. Programs [★13218]

Coun. of Intl. Programs USA [13218], 3500 Lorain Ave., Ste. 504, Cleveland, OH 44113, (216)566-1088

Coun. of Intl. Programs USA [13218], 3500 Lorain Ave., Ste. 504, Cleveland, OH 44113, (216)566-1088

Coun. on Intl. and Public Affairs [18811], 777 UN Plz., Ste. 3C, New York, NY 10017, (212)972-9877

Coun. on Intl. and Public Affairs [18811], 777 UN Plz., Ste. 3C, New York, NY 10017, (212)972-9877

Coun. of Intl. Restaurant Real Estate Brokers [3086], 8350 N Central Expy., Ste. 1300, Dallas, TX 75206, (866)247-2123

Coun. of Intl. Restaurant Real Estate Brokers [3086], 8350 N Central Expy., Ste. 1300, Dallas, TX 75206, (866)247-2123

Coun. for Intl. Tax Educ. [2080], PO Box 1012, White Plains, NY 10602, (914)328-5656

Coun. for Intl. Tax Educ. [2080], PO Box 1012, White Plains, NY 10602, (914)328-5656

Coun. on Ionizing Radiation Measurements and Standards [7320], PO Box 1238, Duluth, GA 30096, (770)622-0026

Coun. on Islamic Educ. [8413], PO Box 20186, Fountain Valley, CA 92728-0186, (714)839-2929

Coun. of Ivy Gp. Presidents [22975], 228 Alexander St., 2nd Fl., Princeton, NJ 08540, (609)258-6426

Coun. of Japan Constr. Indus. Employee's Unions [IO], Tokyo, Japan

Coun. of Khalistan [20240], 730 24th St. NW, No. 310, Washington, DC 20037, (202)337-1904

Coun. of Khalistan [20240], 730 24th St. NW, No. 310, Washington, DC 20037, (202)337-1904

Coun. of Landscape Architectural Registration Boards [6195], 3949 Pender Dr., Ste. 120, Fairfax, VA 22030, (571)432-0332

Coun. for Languages and Other Intl. Stud. [★9943]

Coun. for Languages and Other Intl. Stud. [★9943]

Coun. of Large Public Housing Authorities [5515], 455 Massachusetts Ave. NW, Ste. 425, Washington, DC 20001, (202)638-1300

Coun. for Latin Am. [★23424]

Coun. of Latin-American Students of Architecture - Address unknown since 2011.

Coun. on Law in Higher Educ. [8069], 9386 Via Classico W, Wellington, FL 33411, (561)792-4440

Coun. for Learning Disabilities [12421], 11184 Antioch Rd., Box 405, Overland Park, KS 66210, (913)491-1011

Coun. of Lebanese Amer. Organizations - Address unknown since 2011.

Coun. on Legal Educ. Opportunity [8503], 740 15th St. NW, 9th Fl., Washington, DC 20005, (202)828-6100

Coun. on Lib. and Info. Resources [9984], 1752 N St. NW, Ste. 800, Washington, DC 20036, (202)939-4750

Coun. on Library-Media Technicians [8521], Margaret Barron, Exec. Dir., 28262 Chardon Rd., PMB 168, Willoughby Hills, OH 44092-2793, (202)231-3836

Coun. on Lib. Resources and Commn. on Preservation and Access [★9984]

Coun. on Lib. Technical-Assistants [★8521]

Coun. on Lib. Tech. [★8521]

Coun. on Licensure, Enforcement and Regulation [5986], 403 Marquis Ave., Ste. 200, Lexington, KY 40502, (859)269-1289

Coun. of Literary Magazines and Presses [10473], 154 Christopher St., Ste. 3C, New York, NY 10014-9110, (212)741-9110

Coun. on Litigation Mgt. [5747], 171 W 71st St., 10th Fl., New York, NY 10023, (212)724-2345

Coun. for a Livable World [17549], 322 4th St. NE, Washington, DC 20002, (202)543-4100

Coun. for a Livable World [17549], 322 4th St. NE, Washington, DC 20002, (202)543-4100

Coun. for a Livable World Educ. Fund [17550], 322 4th St. NE, Washington, DC 20002, (202)543-4100

Coun. for a Livable World Educ. Fund [17550], 322 4th St. NE, Washington, DC 20002, (202)543-4100

Coun. of Logistics Mgt. [★3658]

Coun. for Marketing and Opinion Res. - Address unknown since 2011.

Coun. of Mech. Specialty Contracting Indus. [★902]

Coun. for Medical Affairs - Defunct.

Coun. of Medical Specialty Societies [15358], 230 E Ohio St., Ste. 400, Chicago, IL 60611, (312)224-2585

Coun. on Medical Student Educ. in Pediatrics [8604], 6728 Old McLean Village Dr., McLean, VA 22101, (703)556-9222

Coun. of Medical TV [★14163]

Coun. of Ministers of Educ., Canada [IO], Toronto, ON, Canada

Coun. of Mortgage Lenders [IO], London, United Kingdom

Coun. of Musculoskeletal Specialty Societies [★15521]

Coun. for Music in Hospitals [IO], Walton-on-Thames, United Kingdom

Coun. on Music Teacher Educ. [★8669]

Coun. of Natl. Beekeeping Associations in the United Kingdom [IO], Carnforth, United Kingdom

Coun. for the Natl. Interest - Address unknown since 2010.

Coun. on Natl. Literatures [10040], 68-02 Metropolitan Ave., Middle Village, NY 11379, (718)821-3916

Coun. for the Natl. Register of Hea. Ser. Providers in Psychology [16398], Natl. Register, 1120 G St. NW, Ste. 330, Washington, DC 20005, (202)783-7663

Coun. of Natural Waters [★447]

Coun. of Natural Waters [★447]

Coun. on Naturopathic Medical Educ. - Defunct.

Coun. for Noncollegiate Continuing Educ. [★7919]

Coun. for Nongovernmental Organisations in Malawi [IO], Blantyre, Malawi

Coun. of Nordic Trade Unions [IO], Stockholm, Sweden

Coun. on Nutritional Anthropology [★6147]

Coun. on Occupational Educ. [8016], 7840 Roswell Rd., Ste. 325, Bldg. 300, Atlanta, GA 30350, (770)396-3898

Coun. of Occupational Therapists for the European Countries [IO], London, United Kingdom

Coun. On State Taxation [18697], 122 C St. NW, Ste. 330, Washington, DC 20001-2109, (202)484-5222

Coun. of Ontario Constr. Associations [IO], Toronto, ON, Canada

Coun. for Opportunity in Educ. [8080], 1025 Vermont Ave. NW, Ste. 900, Washington, DC 20005, (202)347-7430

Coun. on Optometric Educ. [★15986]

Coun. of Organizations [★18752]

Coun. of Overseas Chinese Services [18964], PO Box 6940, New York, NY 10150, (347)617-2687

Coun. on Packaging in the Environment - Defunct.

Coun. of Parent Attorneys and Advocates [8880], PO Box 6767, Towson, MD 21285, (410)372-0208

Coun. for a Parliament of the World's Religions [20177], 70 E Lake St., Ste. 205, Chicago, IL 60601, (312)629-2990

Coun. for a Parliament of the World's Religions [20177], 70 E Lake St., Ste. 205, Chicago, IL 60601, (312)629-2990

Coun. on Peace Res. in History [★9793]

Coun. of Pediatric Subspecialties [16144], 6728 Old McLean Village Dr., McLean, VA 22101, (703)556-9222

Coun. for Periodical Distributors Assns. - Defunct.

Coun. of Petroleum Accountants Societies [20], 445 Union Blvd., Ste. 207, Lakewood, CO 80228, (303)300-1131

Coun. for Philosophical Studies - Defunct.

Coun. of Planning Librarians - Defunct.

Coun. on Podiatric Medical Educ. [16296], 9312 Old Georgetown Rd., Bethesda, MD 20814-1621, (301)581-9200

Coun. on Podiatry Educ. [★16296]

Coun. on Postsecondary Accreditation - Defunct.

Coun. of Presidents [★17663]

Coun. of Presidents of Women's Natl. Organizations [★17663]

Coun. of Professional Associations on Fed. Statistics [5538], 2121 Eisenhower Ave., Ste. 200, Alexandria, VA 22314, (703)836-0404

Coun. of Professional Geropsychology Training Programs [14663], Center for Aging Resources, 447 N El Molino Ave., Pasadena, CA 91101

Coun. for Professional Recognition [11150], 2460 16th St. NW, Washington, DC 20009, (202)265-9090

Coun. on Professional Standards in Speech-Language Pathology and Audiology - Defunct.

Coun. of Profit Sharing Indus. [★1160]

Coun. of Protocol Executives [2446], 101 W 12th St., Ste. PH-H, New York, NY 10011, (212)633-6934

Coun. for Public Interest Law [★5932]

Coun. of Public Relations Firms [18497], 317 Madison Ave. Ste. 2320, New York, NY 10017, (212)922-1350

Coun. for Qualification of Residential Interior Designers [2056], 164 S Main St., 8th Fl., High Point, NC 27260, (336)884-4437

Coun. on Quality and Leadership [12501], 100 West Rd., Ste. 300, Towson, MD 21204, (410)583-0060

Coun. on Quality and Leadership [12501], 100 West Rd., Ste. 300, Towson, MD 21204, (410)583-0060

Coun. on Quality and Leadership in Supports for People with Disabilities [★12501]

Coun. on Quality and Leadership in Supports for People with Disabilities [★12501]

Coun. of Real Estate Brokerage Managers [3007], 430 N Michigan Ave., Chicago, IL 60611-4011, (312)321-4414

Coun. of Real Estate Brokerage Managers [3007], 430 N Michigan Ave., Chicago, IL 60611-4011, (312)321-4414

Coun. for Refractive Surgery Quality Assurance [16811], 8543 Everglade Dr., Sacramento, CA 95826-3616, (916)381-0769

Coun. of Regional Info. Tech. Associations [★6994]

Coun. of Regional Info. Tech. Associations [★6994]

Coun. of Regional School Accrediting Commns. - Defunct.

Coun. for Registered Gas Installers [IO], Basingstoke, United Kingdom

Coun. for the Registration of Schools Teaching Dyslexic Pupils [IO], Cheltenham, United Kingdom

Coun. for the Regulation of Engg. in Nigeria [IO], Abuja, Nigeria

Coun. of Rehabilitation Counselor Educators [★16571]

Coun. on Rehabilitation Educ. [16563], 1699 E Woodfield Rd., Ste. 300, Schaumburg, IL 60173, (847)944-1345

The Coun. for Religion [★8286]

Coun. for Religion in Independent Schools [★8286]

Coun. on Religion and Intl. Affairs [★19827]

Coun. on Religion and Intl. Affairs [★19827]

Coun. on Religion and Law - Defunct.

Coun. of Religious Volunteer Agencies [13390], Brethren Volunteer Ser., 1451 Dundee Ave., Elgin, IL 60120, (847)742-5100

Coun. for Res. in Music Educ. [8647], Univ. of Illinois at Urbana-Champaign, School of Music, 1114 W Nevada St., Urbana, IL 61801, (217)333-1027

Coun. for Res. in Music Educ. [8647], Univ. of Illinois at Urbana-Champaign, School of Music, 1114 W Nevada St., Urbana, IL 61801, (217)333-1027

Coun. for Res. in Values and Philosophy [10377], 620 Michigan Ave. NE, Washington, DC 20064, (202)319-6089

Coun. for Res. in Values and Philosophy [10377], 620 Michigan Ave. NE, Washington, DC 20064, (202)319-6089

Coun. of Resident Summer Theatres - Defunct.

Coun. of Residential Specialists [3008], 430 N Michigan Ave., Chicago, IL 60611, (312)321-4444

Coun. for Rsrc. Development [8100], 1 Dupont Cir. NW, Ste. 365, Washington, DC 20036, (202)822-0750

Coun. for Responsible Energy [6709], 3030 LBJ Fwy., Ste. 1300, Dallas, TX 75234, (972)620-4018

Coun. for Responsible Genetics [18585], 5 Upland Rd., Ste. 3, Cambridge, MA 02140-2717, (617)868-0870

A star before a book entry number signifies that the name is not listed separately, but is mentioned within the entry.

Coun. for Responsible Nutrition [8687], 1828 L St. NW, Ste. 510, Washington, DC 20036-5114, (202)204-7700

Coun. on Roentgenology to the Amer. Chiropractic Assn. [★16532]

Coun. for Rural Housing and Development [★12176]

Coun. on Safe Trans. of Hazardous Articles [3244], 7803 Hill House Ct., Fairfax Station, VA 22039-2043, (703)451-4031

Coun. on the Safe Trans. of Hazardous Articles [★3244]

Coun. of Sales Promotion Agencies [★3163]

Coun. of Sales Promotion Agencies [★3163]

Coun. of Sci. Editors [2822], 10200 W 44th Ave., Ste. 304, Wheat Ridge, CO 80033, (720)881-6046

Coun. for Sci. and Indus. Res. [IO], Pretoria, Republic of South Africa

Coun. of Sci. Soc. Presidents [7367], 1155 16th St. NW, Washington, DC 20036, (202)872-6230

Coun. for Scottish Archaeology [★2407]

Coun. of Scottish Clan Associations [★19222]

Coun. of Scottish Clans and Associations [19222], PO Box 427, Pinehurst, NC 28370, (980)333-4686

Coun. for Secular Humanism [19819], PO Box 664, Amherst, NY 14226-0664, (716)636-7571

Coun. for Secular Humanism [19819], PO Box 664, Amherst, NY 14226-0664, (716)636-7571

Coun. on Sexual Orientation and Gender Expression [8869], Coun. on Social Work Educ., 1701 Duke St., Ste. 200, Alexandria, VA 22314-3457, (703)683-8080

Coun. on Size and Weight Discrimination [12587], PO Box 305, Mount Marion, NY 12456-0305, (845)679-1209

Coun. for Social and Economic Stud. [18454], 1133 13th St. NW, Washington, DC 20005, (202)371-2700

Coun. on Social Work Educ. [8870], 1701 Duke St., Ste. 200, Alexandria, VA 22314-3457, (703)683-8080

Coun. of Societies for the Stud. of Religion [9011], Rice Univ., PO Box 1892, MIS-156, Houston, TX 77251-1892, (713)348-5721

Coun. on Soil Testing and Plant Anal. [★7434]

Coun. for Spiritual and Ethical Educ. [★8286]

Coun. on Spiritual Practices [20245], PO Box 10086, Berkeley, CA 94709

Coun. on Sports Injuries and Physical Fitness; Amer. Chiropractic Assn. [14117]

Coun. for Standards in Human Ser. Educ. [8867], PMB 297, 1935 S Plum Grove Rd., Palatine, IL 60067

Coun. on Standards for Intl. Educational Travel [8355], 212 S Henry St., Alexandria, VA 22314, (703)739-9050

Coun. on Standards for Intl. Educational Travel [8355], 212 S Henry St., Alexandria, VA 22314, (703)739-9050

Coun. of State Administrators of Vocational Rehabilitation [16564], 1 Res. Ct., Ste. 450, Rockville, MD 20850, (301)519-8023

Coun. of State Community Affairs Agencies [★5987]

Coun. of State Community Development Agencies [5987], 1825 K St., Ste. 515, Washington, DC 20006-1226, (202)293-5820

Coun. of State Governments [5988], PO Box 11910, Lexington, KY 40578, (859)244-8000

Coun. of State Housing Agencies [★5522]

Coun. of State Restaurant Associations [3087], 5024-R Campbell Blvd., Baltimore, MD 21236-5943, (410)931-8100

Coun. of State Sci. Supervisors [8838], C.J. Evans, Treas., 614 Indian Hills Dr., St. Charles, MO 63301-0561, (314)614-7707

Coun. of State and Territorial Epidemiologists [14512], 2872 Woodcock Blvd., Ste. 303, Atlanta, GA 30341, (770)458-3811

Coun. on Students Travel [★8353]

Coun. on Students Travel [★8353]

Coun. on the Stud. of Religion [★9011]

Coun. of Supplier Diversity Professionals [715], PO Box 70226, Rochester, MI 48307

Coun. of Supply Chain Mgt. Professionals [3658], 333 E Butterfield Rd., Ste. 140, Lombard, IL 60148, (630)574-0995

Coun. for Surface Mining and Reclamation Res. in Appalachia [★5838]

Coun. on Synthetic Fuels [★4487]

Coun. on Synthetic Fuels [★4487]

Coun. on Tall Buildings and Urban Habitat [6196], Illinois Inst. of Tech., S.R. Crown Hall, 3360 S State St., Chicago, IL 60616-3796, (312)567-3307

Coun. on Tall Buildings and Urban Habitat [6196], Illinois Inst. of Tech., S.R. Crown Hall, 3360 S State St., Chicago, IL 60616-3796, (312)567-3307

Coun. of Teachers of Southeast Asian Languages [7756], PO Box 3798, Arlington, VA 22203-0798

Coun. of Teaching Hospitals [15052], 15850 Crabbs Br. Way, Ste. 320, Rockville, MD 20850, (301)948-9764

Coun. of Technology Education Assns. - Defunct.

Coun. on Tech. Teacher Educ. [8297], 1914 Assn. Dr., Reston, VA 20191-1539, (703)860-2100

Coun. of Textile and Fashion Indus. of Australia [IO], Collingwood, Australia

Coun. for Textile Recycling - Address unknown since 2010.

Coun. for Tobacco Res. - U.S.A. - Defunct.

Coun. on Undergraduate Res. [8795], 734 15th St. NW, Ste. 550, Washington, DC 20005-1013, (202)783-4810

Coun. on Union-Free Env. [23310], 825 W Bitters Rd., Ste. 203, San Antonio, TX 78216, (866)409-4283

Coun. of Univ. Institutes for Urban Affairs [★9026]

Coun. for Urban Economic Development [★5534]

Coun. for Urban Economic Development [★5534]

Coun. of Vedic Astrology [6217], PO Box 84312, Seattle, WA 98124-5612

Coun. of Vietnam Veterans [★18767]

Coun. of Volunteer Americans [18344], Citizens' Investigative Commn., PO Box 1222, Sterling, VA 20167, (703)379-9188

Coun. for Women in Independent Schools - Defunct.

Coun. of Women of Negara Brunei Darussalam [IO], Bandar Seri Begawan, Brunei Darussalam

Coun. of Women's and Infants' Specialty Hospitals [15053], Natl. Perinatal Info. Center, 225 Chapman St., Ste. 200, Providence, RI 02905, (401)274-0650

Coun. of Writers Orgs. - Defunct.

Coun. of Writing Prog. Administrators [9073], Grand Valley State Univ., 341 Lake Ontario Hall, Allendale, MI 49401

Coun. of Young Israel Rabbis [★19890]

Coun. of Young Men's Hebrew and Kindred Associations [★12408]

Coun. of Yukon First Nations [IO], Whitehorse, YT, Canada

Coun. for Zimbabwe [12322], PO Box 3744, New York, NY 10163

Coun. for Zimbabwe [12322], PO Box 3744, New York, NY 10163

Councils on Chiropractic Educ. Intl. [7849], PO Box 4943, Pocatello, ID 83205, (208)241-4855

Counseil Canadien de droit Intl. [★IO]

Counseil Natl. des Canadiens Chinois [★IO]

Counseling

4 Real Women Intl. [13447]

Amer. Assn. of Christian Counselors [19629]

Amer. Assn. of Christian Counselors [19629]

Amer. Assn. of Pastoral Counselors [19630]

Amer. Assn. of State Counseling Boards [14187]

Amer. Coll. Counseling Assn. [7936]

Amer. Coll. Counseling Assn. [7936]

Amer. Counseling Assn. [11667]

Amer. Family Therapy Acad. [11668]

Amer. Psychological Assn. | Division of Independent Practice [16371]

Amer. School Counselor Assn. [7937]

Amer. School Counselor Assn. [7937]

Amer. Schools Assn. [7938]

Amputees in Motion Intl. [11759]

Assn. for Advanced Training in the Behavioral Sciences [8761]

Assn. of Biblical Counselors [19631]

Assn. for Counselor Educ. and Supervision [7939]

Assn. for Counselors and Educators in Govt. [11669]

Assn. of Mormon Counselors and Psychotherapists [16457]

Assn. for Specialists in Gp. Work [11670]

Assn. for Spiritual, Ethical and Religious Values in Counseling [7940]

Assn. of Traumatic Stress Specialists [11671]

Assn. of Traumatic Stress Specialists [11671]

Assn. for Univ. and Coll. Counseling Center Directors [7941]

Assn. for Univ. and Coll. Counseling Center Directors [7941]

Chi Sigma Iota [14188]

Children of the Americas [11234]

Christian Family Life [12001]

Commn. on Rehabilitation Counselor Certification [11672]

CONTACT USA [19632]

Coun. for Accreditation of Counseling and Related Educational Programs [7942]

Creativity Coaching Assn. [22458]

Damien Ministries [19633]

Do It Now Found. [13248]

Employee Assistance Soc. of North Am. [11673]

Exhale [10766]

Give an Hour [11088]

Grooming Future World Leaders [13528]

Heartbeat [13295]

Hold the Door for Others [11129]

Intl. Assn. of Addictions and Offender Counselors [11674]

Intl. Assn. of Addictions and Offender Counselors [11674]

Intl. Assn. of Biblical Counselors [19634]

Intl. Assn. of Biblical Counselors [19634]

Intl. Assn. of Counseling Services [7943]

Intl. Assn. of Counseling Services [7943]

Intl. Assn. for Marriage and Family Counselors [11675]

Intl. Assn. for Marriage and Family Counselors [11675]

Intl. Org. for Victim Assistance [13364]

LIFE Ministries [19795]

Love in Action [19635]

Loved Ones and Drivers Support [13342]

ManKind Proj. [13043]

Metanoia Ministries [19636]

A Minor Consideration [11676]

MISS Found. | Alliance of Grandparents, A Support in Tragedy Intl. [12123]

Narcotic Educational Found. of Am. [13267]

Natl. Academic Advising Assn. [7944]

Natl. Academic Advising Assn. [7944]

Natl. Assn. of Academic Advisors for Athletics [7945]

Natl. Assn. of Peer Program Professionals [11677]

Natl. Bd. for Certified Counselors and Affiliates [11678]

Natl. Center for Victims of Crime [13367]

Natl. MultiCultural Inst. [11679]

notMYkid [13548]

Nuestros Pequenos Hermanos Intl. [20077]

Pact Training [11680]

Regeneration [19637]

Sigmund Freud Archives [16362]

SingleStop USA [12752]

Suicide Prevention Intl. [13299]

Counselling Assn. of South Australia [IO], Kent Town, Australia

Counselling and Psychotherapy in Scotland [IO], Stirling, United Kingdom

Counsellors and Psychotherapists Assn. of New South Wales [IO], Sydney, Australia

Counselors of Real Estate [3009], 430 N Michigan Ave., Chicago, IL 60611, (312)329-8427

Counselors of Real Estate [3009], 430 N Michigan Ave., Chicago, IL 60611, (312)329-8427

Count Dracula Fan Club [★9354]

Count Dracula Fan Club [★9354]

Counterfeiting Coalition; Intl. Anti [17462]

Counterfeiting Coalition; Intl. Anti [17462]

CounterIntelligence Assn; Marine Corps [19121]

Counterpart Found. [★12323]

Counterpart Found. [★12323]

Counterpart Intl. [12323], 2345 Crystal Dr., Ste. 301, Arlington, VA 22202, (703)236-1200

Counterpart Intl. [12323], 2345 Crystal Dr., Ste. 301, Arlington, VA 22202, (703)236-1200

Reference to "IO" in place of a book number signifies that the association may be found in the 50th edition of International Organizations.

Counterpart - U.S. Off. [**17908**], 2345 Crystal Dr., Ste. 301, Arlington, VA 22202, (703)236-1200
Counterpart - U.S. Off. [**17908**], 2345 Crystal Dr., Ste. 301, Arlington, VA 22202, (703)236-1200
Country Bound - Defunct.
Country Coach Intl. [**22187**], PO Box 575, Junction City, OR 97448, (541)234-2167
Country Dance Soc. of Am. [★**9541**]
Country Dance and Song Soc. [**9541**], PO Box 338, Haydenville, MA 01039-0338, (413)268-7426
Country Dance and Song Soc. of Am. [★**9541**]
Country Day School Headmasters Assn. of the U.S. - Defunct.
Country Land and Bus. Assn. [**IO**], London, United Kingdom
Country Legends Assn. [**10182**], 942 89th Ave. W, No. 102, Duluth, MN 55808, (218)626-9044
Country Music
   Art Greenhaw Official Intl. Fan Club [**23814**]
   Chris Young Fan Club [**23825**]
   Jeannie Seely's Circle of Friends [**23860**]
   Natl. Traditional Country Music Assn. [**10265**]
   Pam Tillis Fan Club [**23881**]
Country Music Assn. [**10183**], 1 Music Cir. S, Nashville, TN 37203-4312, (615)244-2840
Country Music Assn. of Australia [**IO**], Tamworth, Australia
Country Music Found. [**10184**], 222 Fifth Ave. S, Nashville, TN 37203, (615)416-2001
Country Music Showcase Intl. [**10185**], PO Box 368, Carlisle, IA 50047-0368, (515)989-3748
Country Pride Dance Club [**IO**], Red Deer, AB, Canada
Country Radio Broadcasters [**488**], 819 18th Ave. S, Nashville, TN 37203, (615)327-4487
Country-Rock Music
   Lorrie Morgan Intl. Fan Club [**23873**]
   Suzy Bogguss Fan Club [**23893**]
   Trisha Yearwood Fan Club [**23897**]
Country School Assn. of Am. [**9679**], Winthrop Univ., W.T.S. Bldg., 106 Withers, Rock Hill, SC 29733
Country Spirit Dance Soc. [**IO**], Calgary, AB, Canada
Country-Western Music
   Art Greenhaw Official Intl. Fan Club [**23814**]
   George Strait Fan Club [**23848**]
   Kitty Wells-Johnny Wright-Bobby Wright Intl. Fan Club [**23870**]
   Roy Rogers - Dale Evans Collectors Assn. [**23889**]
Country Women's Assn. of Australia [**IO**], Gladstone, Australia
Country Women's Coun. U.S.A. - Defunct.
Countryside Alliance [**IO**], London, United Kingdom
Countryside Coun. for Wales [**IO**], Bangor, United Kingdom
County Government
   Natl. Assn. of Black County Officials [**5348**]
   Natl. Assn. of Counties [**5349**]
   Natl. Assn. of County Info. Officers [**5350**]
   Natl. Assn. of County Recorders, Election Officials, and Clerks [**5351**]
   Natl. Assn. of County Surveyors [**5352**]
   Natl. Coun. of County Assn. Executives [**5353**]
County Intermediate Unit Superintendents [★**7651**]
Couple to Couple League [**12030**], PO Box 111184, Cincinnati, OH 45211-1184, (513)471-2000
Couples Natl. Network [**12077**], PO Box 500699, Marathon, FL 33050-0699, (800)896-0717
Cour permanente d'arbitrage [★**IO**]
Courage [**19787**], 8 Leonard St., Norwalk, CT 06850, (203)803-1564
Courage Intl. [**19787**], 8 Leonard St., Norwalk, CT 06850, (203)803-1564
Courage Stroke Network [★**14002**]
Court Appointed Special Advocates Assn. [★**11364**]
Court of Arbitration for Sport [**IO**], Lausanne, Switzerland
Court Employees
   Fed. Court Clerks Assn. [**5354**]
   Natl. Assn. of Appellate Court Attorneys [**5260**]
   Natl. Assn. for Court Mgt. [**5355**]
   Natl. Assn. for Court Mgt. [**5355**]
   Natl. Assn. of Judiciary Interpreters and Translators [**5356**]
   Natl. Center for State Courts | Conf. of State Court Administrators [**5357**]

   Natl. Conf. of Appellate Court Clerks [**5358**]
   Natl. Court Reporters Assn. [**5359**]
   Soc. for the Technological Advancement of Reporting [**5360**]
   U.S. Court Reporters Assn. [**5361**]
Court Interpreters and Translators Assn. [★**5356**]
Courtiers Indenpendants en securite financiere [★**IO**]
The Cousteau Soc. [**8141**], 732 Eden Way N, Ste. E, No. 707, Chesapeake, VA 23320, (757)523-9335
Cousteau Soc. [★**8141**]
The Cousteau Soc. [**8141**], 732 Eden Way N, Ste. E, No. 707, Chesapeake, VA 23320, (757)523-9335
Cousteau Soc. [★**8141**]
Covenant Fellowship of Presbyterians [★**20165**]
Covenant House [**13520**], 461 8th Ave., New York, NY 10001, (212)613-0300
Covenant of Unitarian Universalist Pagans [**20149**], Sacred Journey Fellowship, 1215 Main St., Garland, TX 75040, (330)892-8877
Covenant World Relief [**12831**], 8303 W Higgins Rd., Chicago, IL 60631, (773)907-3301
Covenant World Relief [**12831**], 8303 W Higgins Rd., Chicago, IL 60631, (773)907-3301
Coventry and Warwickshire Chamber of Commerce [**IO**], Coventry, United Kingdom
Cover Collectors Circuit Club [**22034**], 241 Beachers Brook Ln., Cary, NC 27511
Cover Crops Intl. CH [**IO**], Tegucigalpa, Honduras
Cover Me With Love [**11261**], 22 North Dr., Sag Harbor, NY 11963, (516)443-7909
Cover the Uninsured - Defunct.
Covering Kids and Families - Defunct.
Cow Observers Worldwide
Cow Observers Worldwide - Address unknown since 2011.
Cowart Family - Defunct.
Cowboy Mounted Shooting Assn. [**22874**], PO Box 1529, Columbia, TN 38402-1529, (931)381-2629
Cowboys for Christ [**19565**], Ted K. Pressley, Founder/Pres., PO Box 7557, Fort Worth, TX 76111, (817)236-0023
Cowboys for Christ [**19565**], Ted K. Pressley, Founder/Pres., PO Box 7557, Fort Worth, TX 76111, (817)236-0023
Cowboys Turtle Assn. [★**22849**]
Cowles Family Assn. - Defunct.
Cowsills Fan Club [**23828**], Robin Records, 135 St. Andrews Dr., Ste. 2, Rochester, NY 14626
CP Australia [**IO**], Box Hill, Australia
CPA Associates [★**21**]
CPA Associates [★**21**]
CPA Associates Intl. [**21**], Meadows Off. Complex, 301 Rte. 17 N, Rutherford, NJ 07070, (201)804-8686
CPA Associates Intl. [**21**], Meadows Off. Complex, 301 Rte. 17 N, Rutherford, NJ 07070, (201)804-8686
CPA Associates Intl. Asia Pacific Region [**IO**], Sydney, Australia
CPA Associates Intl. Latin Am. [**IO**], Tampico, Mexico
CPA Australia [**IO**], Melbourne, Australia
CPA Australia - Hong Kong China Div. [**IO**], Hong Kong, People's Republic of China
CPA Auto Dealer Consultants Assn. [**22**], 624 Grassmere Park Dr., Ste. 15, Nashville, TN 37211, (615)377-3392
CPA Mfg. Services Assn. [**23**], 624 Grassmere Park Dr., Ste. 15, Nashville, TN 37211, (615)377-3392
CPAmerica Intl. [**24**], 11801 Res. Dr., Alachua, FL 32615, (386)418-4001
CPAmerica Intl. [**24**], 11801 Res. Dr., Alachua, FL 32615, (386)418-4001
CPCU Soc. [**1954**], 720 Providence Rd., Malvern, PA 19355-3402, (610)251-2727
CPExchange [**7062**], IDEAlliance, 1421 Prince St., St. 230, Alexandria, VA 22314-2805, (703)837-1066
CPPA [★**21024**]
CPPS Volunteer Program - Defunct.
CPR Inst. for Dispute Resolution [★**5205**]
CPR Intl. Inst. for Conflict Prevention and Resolution [**5205**], 575 Lexington Ave., 21st Fl., New York, NY 10022, (212)949-6490

CPRI-HOST - Defunct.
CPWR - The Center for Constr. Res. and Training [**23176**], 8484 Georgia Ave., Ste. 1000, Silver Spring, MD 20910, (301)578-8500
CR Found. [**14277**], 3707 N Canyon Rd., Bldg. 7, Provo, UT 84604, (801)226-2121
Cracker Jack Collectors Assn. [**21329**], Linda Farris, Membership Chair, 4908 N Holborn Dr., Muncie, IN 47304
Craft Australia [**IO**], Barton, Australia
Craft Guild of Chefs [**IO**], Richmond, United Kingdom
Craft and Hobby Assn. [**1728**], 319 E 54th St., Elmwood Park, NJ 07407, (201)835-1200
Craft Org. Development Assn. [**21435**], PO Box 51, Onia, AR 72663, (870)746-5159
Craft Org. Development Assn. [**21435**], PO Box 51, Onia, AR 72663, (870)746-5159
Craft Potters Assn. of Great Britain [**IO**], London, United Kingdom
Craft Retailers Assn. for Tomorrow [**987**], PO Box 293, Islamorada, FL 33036, (305)664-3650
Craft Yarn Coun. of Am. [**21436**], 469 Hosp. Dr., 2nd Fl. Ste. E, Gastonia, NC 28054, (704)824-7838
Crafts
   Alliance for Amer. Quilts [**21423**]
   Amer. Assn. of Woodturners [**21424**]
   Amer. Assn. of Woodturners [**21424**]
   Amer. Bladesmith Soc. [**21425**]
   Amer. Craft Coun. [**21426**]
   Amer. Made Alliance [**21427**]
   Amer. Needlepoint Guild [**21428**]
   Amer. Quilt Study Group [**21429**]
   Amer. Quilter's Soc. [**21430**]
   Amer. Sewing Guild [**21431**]
   The Applique Soc. [**21432**]
   The Applique Soc. [**21432**]
   Caricature Carvers of Am. [**21433**]
   Colonial Coverlet Guild of Am. [**21326**]
   Contemporary Quilt Art Assn. [**21434**]
   Craft Org. Development Assn. [**21435**]
   Craft Org. Development Assn. [**21435**]
   Craft Retailers Assn. for Tomorrow [**987**]
   Craft Yarn Coun. of Am. [**21436**]
   Doll Costumer's Guild [**21690**]
   Embroiderers' Guild of Am. [**21437**]
   Enamelist Soc. [**21438**]
   Firearms Engravers Guild of Am. [**21439**]
   Firearms Engravers Guild of Am. [**21439**]
   Guild of Amer. Papercutters [**21440**]
   Handcrafted Soap Makers Guild [**21441**]
   Handweavers Guild of Am. [**21442**]
   Intl. Doll Makers Assn. [**21692**]
   Intl. Guild of Candle Artisans [**21443**]
   Intl. Guild of Candle Artisans [**21443**]
   Intl. Guild of Miniature Artisans [**21444**]
   Intl. Guild of Miniature Artisans [**21444**]
   Intl. Machine Quilters Assn. [**21445**]
   Intl. Old Lacers, Inc. [**21446**]
   Intl. Old Lacers, Inc. [**21446**]
   Intl. Quilt Assn. [**21447**]
   Intl. String Figure Assn. [**21448**]
   Intl. String Figure Assn. [**21448**]
   Intl. Wildfowl Carvers Assn. [**21449**]
   Intl. Wildfowl Carvers Assn. [**21449**]
   Intl. Wood Collectors Soc. [**22203**]
   Knifemakers' Guild [**21450**]
   The Knitting Guild Assn. [**21451**]
   Krochet Kids Intl. [**12735**]
   Lock Museum of Am. [**21452**]
   Natl. Acad. of Needlearts [**21453**]
   Natl. Acad. of Needlearts [**21453**]
   Natl. Assn. of Wheat Weavers [**21454**]
   Natl. Assn. of Wheat Weavers [**21454**]
   Natl. Basketry Org. [**21455**]
   Natl. Coun. on Educ. for the Ceramic Arts [**21456**]
   Natl. Guild of Decoupeurs [**21457**]
   Natl. Quilting Assn. [**21458**]
   Natl. Wood Carvers Assn. [**21459**]
   Natl. Wood Carvers Assn. [**21459**]
   Natural Fibers Gp. [**21705**]
   Northwest Regional Spinners' Assn. [**21460**]
   Pomegranate Guild of Judaic Needlework [**21461**]
   Potters for Peace [**21462**]
   Potters for Peace [**21462**]CraftsPrecious Metal Clay Guild

A star before a book entry number signifies that the name is not listed separately, but is mentioned within the entry.

Professional Decorative Painters Assn. [2614]
Professional Knifemakers Assn. [21463]
The Quilters Hall of Fame [21464]
Retailers of Art Glass and Supplies [1581]
Roycrofters-at-Large Assn. [21465]
Smocking Arts Guild of Am. [21466]
Soc. of Decorative Painters [21467]
Soc. for Folk Arts Preservation [9626]
Soc. of North Amer. Goldsmiths [21468]
Solace Intl. [13479]
Spinning and Weaving Assn. [3456]
Spirit Quilts [11408]
Stencilers and Decorative Artists Guild [20972]
Union Internationale de la Marionnette l Amer.
  CTR [22112]
United Chainsaw Carvers Guild [21469]
U.S. Faceters Guild [6590]
Victorian Hairwork Soc. [21470]
Wood Engravers Network [21471]
Wood Engravers Network [21471]
Wooden Canoe Heritage Assn. [22414]
World Org. of China Painters [21472]
World Org. of China Painters [21472]
Crafts Coun. [IO], London, United Kingdom
Cranberry Inst. [4446], PO Box 497, Carver, MA
  02330, (508)866-1118
Crandall Family Assn. [20497], PO Box 1472,
  Westerly, RI 02891
Crane Certification Assn. of Am. [844], PO Box
  87907, Vancouver, WA 98687-7907, (360)834-3805
Crane Mfrs. Assn. of Am. [1820], MHIA, 8720 Red
  Oak Blvd., Ste. 201, Charlotte, NC 28217,
  (704)676-1190
Crane-Rogers Found. [★18815]
Crane-Rogers Found. [★18815]
Cranial Acad. [16076], 8202 Clearvista Pkwy., No.
  9-D, Indianapolis, IN 46256, (317)594-0411
Cranio-Mandibular Orthopedics; Intl. Coll. of [16035]
Cranio-Mandibular Orthopedics; Intl. Coll. of [16035]
Craniofacial Abnormalities
  Alliance for Smiles [14189]
  Amer. Cleft Palate-Craniofacial Assn. [14190]
  AmeriFace [14191]
  Center for Craniofacial Development and
    Disorders [14192]
  Changing Children's Lives [15150]
  Children's Craniofacial Assn. [14193]
  Cleft Palate Found. [14194]
  Craniofacial Found. of Am. [14195]
  Craniosynostosis and Positional Plagiocephaly
    Support [14196]
  FACES: The Natl. Craniofacial Assn. [14197]
  Forward Face [14198]
  Freeman-Sheldon Parent Support Gp. [14199]
  Freeman-Sheldon Parent Support Gp. [14199]
  Let's Face It USA [14200]
  Let's Face It USA [14200]
  Natl. Found. for Facial Reconstruction [14201]
  Rotaplast Intl. [14202]
  Smile Network Intl. [14203]
  Soc. for Craniofacial Morphometry [14204]
  World Craniofacial Found. [14205]
Craniofacial Found. of Am. [14195], 975 E 3rd St.,
  Chattanooga, TN 37403, (423)778-9192
Craniofacial Pain; Amer. Acad. of [16018]
Craniofacial Res; Friends of the Natl. Inst. of Dental
  and [14283]
Craniofacial Res; Natl. Inst. of Dental and [14306]
Craniosacral Therapy
  Biodynamic Craniosacral Therapy Assn. of North
    Am. [14206]
  Biodynamic Craniosacral Therapy Assn. of North
    Am. [14206]
CranioSacral Therapy Assn; Amer. [14992]
Craniosacral Therapy Assn. of Australia [IO], Ade-
  laide, Australia
Craniosacral Therapy Assn. of North Am. [★14206]
Craniosacral Therapy Assn. of North Am. [★14206]
Craniosacral Therapy Assn. of the UK [IO], London,
  United Kingdom
Craniosynostosis and Positional Plagiocephaly Sup-
  port [14196], 6905 Xandu Ct., Fredericksburg, VA
  22407
Crappie USA [★21731]
Crayon, Water Color and Craft Inst. [★1601]

Crazy Horse Memorial Found. [10325], 12151 Ave.
  of the Chiefs, Crazy Horse, SD 57730-8900,
  (605)673-4681
CRB Educational Found., Inc. [★9435]
CRE Finance Coun. [3010], 30 Broad St., 28th Fl.,
  New York, NY 10004, (212)509-1844
Creamery Assn. [★3719]
CREATE [IO], Dublin, Ireland
Create A Smile Dental Found. [13318], 115 S Div.
  St., Carterville, IL 62918, (618)925-2140
Creation Res. Soc. [20232], PO Box 8263, St.
  Joseph, MO 64508-8263, (928)636-1153
Creation Social Science and Humanities Soc. -
  Defunct.
Creative Audio and Music Electronics Org. - Defunct.
Creative Children Therapy [16846], 12608 SW 88th
  St., Miami, FL 33186-1867, (305)412-4177
The Creative Coalition [18328], 105 Madison Ave.,
  11th Fl., New York, NY 10016, (212)512-8570
Creative Educ. Found. [8017], 48 N Pleasant St.,
  Ste. 301, Amherst, MA 01002, (508)960-0000
Creative Floral Arrangers of the Americas [1367],
  2295 W Helen Cir., Bartow, FL 33830
Creative Initiative [★18244]
Creative Music Found. [10186], PO Box 671, Wood-
  stock, NY 12498, (845)679-8847
Creative Musicians Coalition [2554], PO Box 6205,
  Peoria, IL 61601-6205, (309)685-4843
Creative New Zealand [IO], Wellington, New
  Zealand
Creative Resources Guild [18614], PO Box 3397,
  Santa Monica, CA 90408-3397, (310)828-0130
Creative Response to Conflict [★11456]
Creative Time [9288], 59 E 4th St. 6E, New York,
  NY 10003, (212)206-6674
Creativity
  Creativity Coaching Assn. [22458]
  Global Inheritance [18826]
  Innovation Network [1912]
Creativity Coaching Assn. [22458], PO Box 328,
  Lake George, NY 12845, (518)798-6933
The Creativity Movement [18781], PO Box 927,
  Zion, IL 60099-0927, (309)830-9485
The Creativity Movement [18781], PO Box 927,
  Zion, IL 60099-0927, (309)830-9485
CredAbility [17486], 100 Edgewood Ave. NE, Ste.
  1500, Atlanta, GA 30303, (800)251-2227
Credit
  Amer. Consumer Credit Counseling [988]
  Amer. Credit Card Collectors Soc. [17485]
  Assn. of Independent Consumer Credit Counsel-
    ing Agencies [989]
  Brazilian Assn. of Credit Card Companies and
    Services [484]
  CredAbility [17486]
  Credit Builders Alliance [990]
  Intl. Assn. of Credit Portfolio Managers [991]
  Natl. Assn. of Mortgage Processors [428]
  Natl. Credit Reporting Assn. [992]
  Natl. Found. for Credit Counseling [2212]
  Printing Indus. Credit Executives [993]
Credit Builders Alliance [990], 1200 G St. NW, Ste.
  400, Washington, DC 20005, (202)730-9390
Credit Inst. of Canada [IO], Toronto, ON, Canada
Credit Professionals Intl. [1291], 10726 Manchester
  Rd., Ste. 210, St. Louis, MO 63122, (314)821-9393
Credit Professionals Intl. [1291], 10726 Manchester
  Rd., Ste. 210, St. Louis, MO 63122, (314)821-9393
Credit Protection Assn. [IO], London, United
  Kingdom
Credit Res. Found. [1292], 8840 Columbia 100
  Pkwy., Columbia, MD 21045, (410)740-5499
Credit Union Executives Soc. [996], PO Box 14167,
  Madison, WI 53708-0167, (608)271-2664
Credit Union Natl. Assn. [997], 5710 Mineral Point
  Rd., Madison, WI 53705, (202)638-5777
Credit Unions
  Amer. Credit Union Mortgage Assn. [994]
  Assn. of Credit Union Internal Auditors [995]
  Credit Union Executives Soc. [996]
  Credit Union Natl. Assn. [997]
  Defense Credit Union Coun. [998]
  Educ. Credit Union Coun. [999]
  LICU [1000]
  Natl. Assn. of Credit Union Chairmen [1001]

Natl. Assn. of Credit Union Services Organizations
  [1002]
Natl. Assn. of Credit Union Supervisory and Audit-
  ing Committees [1003]
Natl. Assn. of Fed. Credit Unions [1004]
Natl. Assn. of State Credit Union Supervisor
  [5362]
Natl. Coun. of Postal Credit Unions [1005]
Natl. Credit Union Mgt. Assn. [1006]
Natl. Fed. of Community Development Credit
  Unions [1007]
World Coun. of Credit Unions [1008]
World Coun. of Credit Unions [1008]
Credit Women - Intl. [★1291]
Credit Women - Intl. [★1291]
Credit Women's Breakfast Clubs of North Am.
  [★1291]
Credit Women's Breakfast Clubs of North Am.
  [★1291]
Cremation Assn. of Am. [★2531]
Cremation Assn. of North Am. [2531], 401 N
  Michigan Ave., Chicago, IL 60611, (312)245-1077
Cremation Soc. of Great Britain [IO], Maidstone,
  United Kingdom
CREW Network [3011], 1201 Wakarusa Dr., Ste. C3,
  Lawrence, KS 66049, (785)832-1808
Cri du Chat Syndrome Soc. [★16768]
Cribbage Bd. Collectors Soc. - Address unknown
  since 2011.
Cricket Assn. of Nepal [IO], Kathmandu, Nepal
Cricket Australia [IO], Jolimont, Australia
Cricket Canada [IO], Toronto, ON, Canada
Cricket Ireland [IO], Dublin, Ireland
Cricket Scotland [IO], Edinburgh, United Kingdom
Crigler-Najjar Assn. - Address unknown since 2011.
Crime
  ABLE: Assn. for Better Living and Educ. Intl.
    [11537]
  Acad. of Criminal Justice Sciences [11698]
  ACLU l Natl. Prison Proj. [11699]
  All of Us or None [17256]
  Alliance of Guardian Angels [11681]
  Alliance of Guardian Angels [11681]
  Amer. Non-Governmental Organizations Coalition
    for the Intl. Criminal Court [17488]
  Amer. Soc. of Digital Forensics and eDiscovery
    [6883]
  Amer. Youth Work Center [13508]
  Anti-Child Pornography Org. [12710]
  Assn. for Crime Scene Reconstruction [11682]
  Assn. of State Correctional Administrators [11706]
  Black on Black Love Campaign [11683]
  Center for Stud. in Criminal Justice [11707]
  Crime Prevention Coalition of Am. [11684]
  Crime Survivors [17487]
  CrimeWatch USA [11685]
  Document Security Alliance [5539]
  Intl. Assn. of Asian Crime Investigators [5363]
  Intl. Assn. of Asian Crime Investigators [5363]
  Intl. Assn. of Bloodstain Pattern Analysts [5364]
  Intl. Assn. for Bloodstain Pattern Analysts [5364]
  Intl. Assn. for Correctional and Forensic Psychol-
    ogy [11715]
  Intl. Assn. for the Stud. of Organized Crime
    [11686]
  Intl. Assn. for the Stud. of Organized Crime
    [11686]
  Intl. Coalition for the Responsibility to Protect
    [18498]
  Intl. Crime Free Assn. [5365]
  Intl. Org. of Asian Crime Investigators and
    Specialists [5366]
  Intl. Org. for Victim Assistance [13364]
  Intl. Soc. of Crime Prevention Practitioners
    [11687]
  Intl. Soc. of Crime Prevention Practitioners
    [11687]
  Jewish Prisoner Services Intl. [19874]
  Milton S. Eisenhower Found. [11688]
  Natl. Alliance of Gang Investigators Associations
    [5367]
  Natl. Assn. of Town Watch [11689]
  Natl. Assn. of Victim Ser. Professionals in Correc-
    tions [13366]
  Natl. Center for Victims of Crime [13367]

Reference to "IO" in place of a book number signifies that the association may be found in the 50th edition of International Organizations.

Natl. Coun. on Crime and Delinquency [11690]
Natl. Crime Prevention Coun. [11691]
Natl. Crime Prevention Inst. [11692]
Natl. Org. of Hispanics in Criminal Justice [5513]
Professional Soc. of Forensic Mapping [5490]
R2P Coalition [13376]
Robert F. Kennedy Center for Justice and Human
    Rights [13555]
Security on Campus [11693]
Stolen Horse Intl. [11042]
TIPS Prog. [11694]
USCCCN Natl. CH on Satanic Crime in Am.
    [11695]
Victims' Assistance Legal Org. [11696]
WeTip [11697]
Crime Prevention Coalition [★11691]
Crime Prevention Coalition of Am. [11684], Natl.
    Crime Prevention Coun., 2345 Crystal Dr., Ste.
    500, Arlington, VA 22202-4801, (202)466-6272
Crime Stoppers Belize [IO], Belize City, Belize
Crime Survivors [17487], PO Box 54552, Irvine, CA
    92619-4552, (949)872-7895
Crime Writers of Canada [IO], Toronto, ON, Canada
CrimeWatch USA [11685], 6671 W Indiantown Rd.,
    Jupiter, FL 33458, (561)247-5113
Criminal Defense Investigation Training Coun.
    [5382], 800 E Ocean Blvd., Ste. D, Stuart, FL
    34994, (772)288-1485
Criminal Justice
    Acad. of Criminal Justice Sciences [11698]
    ACLU | Natl. Prison Proj. [11699]
    Aid to Incarcerated Mothers [11700]
    All of Us or None [17256]
    Alston Wilkes Veterans Home [11701]
    Amer. Correctional Assn. [11702]
    Amer. Coun. on Criminal Justice Training [5368]
    Amer. Criminal Justice Assn. | Lambda Alpha
        Epsilon [11703]
    Amer. Jail Assn. [11704]
    Amer. Non-Governmental Organizations Coalition
        for the Intl. Criminal Court [17488]
    Amer. Youth Work Center [13508]
    Assn. on Programs for Female Offenders [11705]
    Assn. of State Correctional Administrators [11706]
    Center on Juvenile and Criminal Justice [5369]
    Center for Stud. in Criminal Justice [11707]
    Citizens United for Alternatives to the Death
        Penalty [5370]
    Citizens United for Rehabilitation of Errants
        [11708]
    Coalition for an Intl. Criminal Court [17489]
    Coalition for an Intl. Criminal Court [17489]
    Correctional Educ. Assn. [11709]
    Crime Survivors [17487]
    Criminal Justice Legal Found. [5371]
    Families Against Mandatory Minimums Found.
        [11710]
    Family Justice [11711]
    Fortune Soc. [11712]
    Friends Outside [11713]
    Good News Jail and Prison Ministry [11714]
    Good News Jail and Prison Ministry [11714]
    Innocence Proj. [5372]
    Intl. Assn. for Correctional and Forensic Psychol-
        ogy [11715]
    Intl. Assn. of Correctional Training Personnel
        [11716]
    Intl. Assn. of Correctional Training Personnel
        [11716]
    Intl. Assn. of Law Enforcement Planners [5373]
    Intl. Assn. of Law Enforcement Planners [5373]
    Intl. Community Corrections Assn. [11717]
    Intl. Community Corrections Assn. [11717]
    Intl. Prison Ministry [11718]
    Intl. Prison Ministry [11718]
    Jewish Prisoner Services Intl. [19874]
    John Howard Assn. [11719]
    Just Detention Intl. [11720]
    Justice Inc. [17490]
    Justice Res. and Statistics Assn. [11721]
    Life After Exoneration Prog. [17491]
    Natl. Alliance of Sentencing Advocates and Mitiga-
        tion Specialists [5374]
    Natl. Assn. of Blacks in Criminal Justice [11722]
    Natl. Assn. of Fed. Defenders [5375]

Natl. Assn. of Forensic Counselors [5376]
Natl. Assn. for Justice Info. Systems [5377]
Natl. Assn. of Probation Executives [5378]
Natl. Assn. of State Sentencing Commissions
    [5379]
Natl. Center on Institutions and Alternatives
    [11723]
Natl. Center for Juvenile Justice [11724]
Natl. Center for Victims of Crime [13367]
Natl. Correctional Indus. Assn. [11725]
Natl. Criminal Justice Assn. [11726]
Natl. Major Gang Task Force [5380]
Natl. Org. of Fed. Employees Against Abuse and
    Retaliation [23206]
Natl. Org. of Hispanics in Criminal Justice [5513]
Natl. Religious Affairs Assn. [19638]
North Amer. Assn. of Wardens and
    Superintendents [11727]
North Amer. Assn. of Wardens and
    Superintendents [11727]
November Coalition [18681]
Osborne Assn. [11728]
Prison-Ashram Proj. [11729]
Prison Fellowship Intl. [11730]
Prison Fellowship Intl. [11730]
Prison Fellowship Ministries [11731]
Prisoners' Rights Union [11732]
Professional Soc. of Forensic Mapping [5490]
Robert F. Kennedy Center for Justice and Human
    Rights [13555]
Safer Soc. Found. [11733]
SEARCH - The Natl. Consortium for Justice Info.
    and Statistics [11734]
Sentencing Proj. [11735]
Vera Inst. of Justice [11736]
Volunteers in Prevention, Probation, Prisons
    [11737]
We Care Prog. [11738]
Women's Prison Assn. [11739]
Criminal Justice Legal Found. [5371], PO Box 1199,
    Sacramento, CA 95812, (916)446-0345
Criminal Justice Policy Found. [18026], 8730
    Georgia Ave., Ste. 400, Silver Spring, MD 20910,
    (301)589-6020
Criminal Justice Statistics Assn. [★11721]
Criminal Law
    Acad. of Criminal Justice Sciences [11698]
    ACLU | Natl. Prison Proj. [11699]
    Americans for Effective Law Enforcement [5381]
    Assn. of State Correctional Administrators [11706]
    Center for Stud. in Criminal Justice [11707]
    Criminal Defense Investigation Training Coun.
        [5382]
    Fed. Criminal Investigators Assn. [5383]
    Intl. Assn. for Correctional and Forensic Psychol-
        ogy [11715]
    Intl. Assn. for Identification [5485]
    Intl. Criminal Court Alliance [5384]
    Intl. Criminal Court Alliance [5384]
    Justice Inc. [17490]
    Natl. Assn. of Criminal Defense Lawyers [5385]
    Natl. Criminal Defense Coll. [5386]
Criminal Law Soc. of Japan [IO], Tokyo, Japan
Criminology
    Amer. Soc. of Criminology [11740]
    Intl. Assn. of Crime Analysts [5387]
    Intl. Assn. of Crime Analysts [5387]
Crisis Intervention
    Art with Heart [11741]
    Girls and Boys Town [12947]
    Heartbeat [13295]
    Intl. Org. for Victim Assistance [13364]
    Natl. Domestic Violence Hotline [11894]
    North Korea Freedom Coalition [18035]
    Suicide Prevention Intl. [13299]
    Transition U.S. [4343]
CRISTA Ministries [13184], 19303 Fremont Ave. N,
    Seattle, WA 98133, (206)546-7200
Cristina Found; Natl. [11814]
Critical Care
    Assn. of Pulmonary and Critical Care Medicine
        Prog. Directors [14207]
    Natl. Assn. of Long Term Hospitals [15064]
    Neurocritical Care Soc. [14208]
    Neurocritical Care Soc. [14208]

Soc. of Critical Care Medicine [14209]
Soc. of Critical Care Medicine [14209]
Critical Mass [★18185]
Critical Mass Energy Proj. of Public Citizen
    [★18185]
Critical Messaging Assn. [808], 1720 Lakepointe Dr.,
    Ste. 100, Lewisville, TX 75057, (972)353-1879
Critical Resistance [18401], 1904 Franklin St., Ste.
    504, Oakland, CA 94612, (510)444-0484
Crnogorsko Drustvo za Borbu Protiv Raka [★IO]
Crnogorsko Turisticko Udruzenje [★IO]
Croatian
    CFU Junior Cultural Fed. [9510]
    Croatian Acad. of Am. [18966]CroatianCroatian-
        American Chamber of Commerce
    Croatian Fraternal Union of Am. [18967]
    Natl. Fed. of Croatian Americans [9511]
Croatian Acad. of Am. [18966], PO Box 1767, Grand
    Central Sta., New York, NY 10163-1767
Croatian Acad. of Sciences and Arts [IO], Zagreb,
    Croatia
Croatian Aeronautical Fed. [IO], Zagreb, Croatia
Croatian Agricultural Engg. Soc. [IO], Zagreb,
    Croatia
Croatian Amer. Assn. [17944], 6607 W Archer Ave.,
    Chicago, IL 60638
Croatian Amer. Assn. [17944], 6607 W Archer Ave.,
    Chicago, IL 60638
Croatian Amer. Bar Assn. [5242], 6 Papette Cir.,
    Ladera Ranch, CA 92694, (949)274-5360
Croatian Amer. Bar Assn. [5242], 6 Papette Cir.,
    Ladera Ranch, CA 92694, (949)274-5360
Croatian-American Chamber of Commerce
Croatian-American Chamber of Commerce - Address
    unknown since 2011.
Croatian Archery Assn. [IO], Zagreb, Croatia
Croatian Assn. of the Blind [IO], Zagreb, Croatia
Croatian Assn. of Consulting Engineers [IO], Zagreb,
    Croatia
Croatian Assn. of Physiotherapists [IO], Zagreb,
    Croatia
Croatian Assn. for the Treatment of Pain [IO], Os-
    ijek, Croatia
Croatian Assn. of Univ. Women [IO], Zagreb, Croatia
Croatian Athletic Fed. [IO], Zagreb, Croatia
Croatian Badminton Assn. [IO], Zagreb, Croatia
Croatian Baseball Assn. [IO], Zagreb, Croatia
Croatian Bible Soc. [IO], Zagreb, Croatia
Croatian Canoe Fed. [IO], Zagreb, Croatia
Croatian Cardiac Soc. [IO], Zagreb, Croatia
Croatian Chess Fed. [IO], Zagreb, Croatia
Croatian Composers Soc. [IO], Zagreb, Croatia
Croatian Cycling Fed. [IO], Zagreb, Croatia
Croatian Dance Sport Fed. [IO], Zagreb, Croatia
Croatian Dental Soc. [IO], Zagreb, Croatia
Croatian Dermatovenerological Soc. of the Croatian
    Medical Assn. [IO], Zagreb, Croatia
Croatian Economic Assn. [IO], Zagreb, Croatia
Croatian Entomological Soc. [IO], Zagreb, Croatia
Croatian Fed. for EEG and Neurophysiology [IO],
    Zagreb, Croatia
Croatian Football Fed. [IO], Zagreb, Croatia
Croatian Fraternal Union of Am. [18967], 100
    Delaney Dr., Pittsburgh, PA 15235, (412)843-0380
Croatian Gas Assn. [IO], Zagreb, Croatia
Croatian Genealogical Soc. - Defunct.
Croatian Geotechnical Soc. [IO], Zagreb, Croatia
Croatian Hockey Fed. [IO], Zagreb, Croatia
Croatian League Against Epilepsy [IO], Zagreb,
    Croatia
Croatian League Against Rheumatism [IO], Zagreb,
    Croatia
Croatian League of Illinois [★18967]
Croatian Lib. Assn. [IO], Zagreb, Croatia
Croatian Managers' and Entrepreneurs Assn. [IO],
    Zagreb, Croatia
Croatian Medical Assn. [IO], Zagreb, Croatia
Croatian Microscopy Soc. [IO], Zagreb, Croatia
Croatian Mineralogical Assn. [IO], Zagreb, Croatia
Croatian Natl. Cong. - Defunct.
Croatian Nuclear Soc. [IO], Zagreb, Croatia
Croatian Olympic Comm. [IO], Zagreb, Croatia
Croatian Operational Res. Soc. [IO], Split, Croatia
Croatian Orienteering Fed. [IO], Zagreb, Croatia
Croatian Osteoporosis Soc. [IO], Zagreb, Croatia

A star before a book entry number signifies that the name is not listed separately, but is mentioned within the entry.

Croatian Pharmaceutical Soc. [IO], Zagreb, Croatia
Croatian Pharmacological Soc. [IO], Osijek, Croatia
Croatian Philatelic Soc. - Address unknown since 2011.
Croatian Physical Soc. [IO], Zagreb, Croatia
Croatian Red Cross [IO], Zagreb, Croatia
Croatian Rock-n-Roll Assn. [IO], Zagreb, Croatia
Croatian Sailing Fed. [IO], Split, Croatia
Croatian Skating Fed. [IO], Zagreb, Croatia
Croatian Soc. for Bird and Nature Protection [IO], Zagreb, Croatia
Croatian Soc. of Chem. Engineers [IO], Zagreb, Croatia
Croatian Soc. of Chemotherapy [IO], Zagreb, Croatia
Croatian Soc. for Communications, Computing, Electronics, Measurement and Control [IO], Zagreb, Croatia
Croatian Soc. of Environmental Hea. [IO], Zagreb, Croatia
Croatian Soc. for Hospice and P.C. [IO], Zagreb, Croatia
Croatian Soc. of Hypertension [IO], Zagreb, Croatia
Croatian Soc. for Medical Informatics [IO], Zagreb, Croatia
Croatian Soc. for Rheumatology [IO], Zagreb, Croatia
Croatian Sports Fed. for the Disabled [IO], Zagreb, Croatia
Croatian Sports Medicine Soc. [IO], Zagreb, Croatia
Croatian Squash Fed. [IO], Zagreb, Croatia
Croatian Taekwondo Fed. [IO], Zagreb, Croatia
Croatian Tennis Assn. [IO], Zagreb, Croatia
Croatian Union of Tenants [IO], Zagreb, Croatia
Croatian Youth Coun. [IO], Zagreb, Croatia
Croatian Youth Hostel Assn. [IO], Zagreb, Croatia
Crochet Guild of Am. [21961], 1100-H Brandywine Blvd., Zanesville, OH 43701-7303, (740)452-4541
Crohn's and Colitis Found. of Am. [14559], 386 Park Ave. S, 17th Fl., New York, NY 10016-8804, (800)932-2423
Crohn's and Colitis Found. of Canada [IO], Toronto, ON, Canada
Croissant Rouge Tunisien [★IO]
Cromwell Assn. [IO], London, United Kingdom
CROP [★12823]
CROP [★12823]
Crop-Hail Insurance Actuarial Assn. [★2019]
Crop Insurance Agents of Am. - Defunct.
Crop Insurance Professionals Assn. [1955], PO Box 368, Memphis, TX 79245, (806)259-1842
Crop Insurance and Reinsurance Bur. [1956], 201 Massachusetts Ave. NE, Ste. C5, Washington, DC 20002, (202)544-0067
Crop Insurance Res. Bur. [★1956]
Crop Protection Assn. [IO], Peterborough, United Kingdom
Crop Sci. Division of the Amer. Soc. of Agronomy [★3739]
Crop Sci. Division of the Amer. Soc. of Agronomy [★3739]
Crop Sci. Soc. of Am. [3739], 5585 Guilford Rd., Madison, WI 53711-5801, (608)273-8080
Crop Sci. Soc. of Am. [3739], 5585 Guilford Rd., Madison, WI 53711-5801, (608)273-8080
Crop Sci. Soc. of Japan [IO], Tokyo, Japan
CropLife Am. [753], 1156 15th St. NW, Washington, DC 20005, (202)296-1585
CropLife Australia [IO], Canberra, Australia
Croquet
  Croquet Found. of Am. [22470]CroquetScottish Croquet Assn.
  U.S. Croquet Assn. [22471]
Croquet Assn. [IO], Cheltenham, United Kingdom
Croquet Assn. Queensland [IO], Brisbane, Australia
Croquet Canada [IO], Toronto, ON, Canada
Croquet Fed. of Belgium [IO], Brussels, Belgium
Croquet Found. of Am. [22470], 700 Florida Mango Rd., West Palm Beach, FL 33406-4461, (561)478-0760
Croquet Victoria [IO], Cairnlea, Australia
Crosier Missions [20032], 4332 N 24th St., Phoenix, AZ 85016-6259, (602)443-7100
Crosier Missions [20032], 4332 N 24th St., Phoenix, AZ 85016-6259, (602)443-7100

Crosley Auto. Club [21037], 307 Schaeffer Rd., Blandon, PA 19510
Cross Country Coaches Assn; U.S. [22868]
Cross Country Ski Areas of Am. [★3327]
Cross Country Ski Areas Assn. [3327], 259 Bolton Rd., Winchester, NH 03470, (603)239-4341
Cross Country Ski Nova Scotia [IO], Halifax, NS, Canada
Cross Country Skiers; Amer. [22908]
Cross Cultural Collaborative [7949], 45 Auburn St., Brookline, MA 02446, (617)277-0482
Cross Cultural Collaborative [7949], 45 Auburn St., Brookline, MA 02446, (617)277-0482
Cross-Cultural Dance Resources [9542], 518 S Agassiz St., Flagstaff, AZ 86001-5711, (928)774-8108
Cross-Cultural Dance Resources [9542], 518 S Agassiz St., Flagstaff, AZ 86001-5711, (928)774-8108
Cross Cultural Hea. Care Prog. [14773], 4700 42nd Ave. SW, Ste. 580, Seattle, WA 98116, (206)860-0329
Cross-Cultural Solutions [11742], 2 Clinton Pl., New Rochelle, NY 10801, (914)632-0022
Cross-Examination Debate Assn. - Defunct.
Cross Stitch Guild [IO], Fairford, United Kingdom
Crosscurrents Intl. Inst. [17961], 7122 Hardin-Wapak Rd., Sidney, OH 45365, (937)492-0407
Crosscurrents Intl. Inst. [17961], 7122 Hardin-Wapak Rd., Sidney, OH 45365, (937)492-0407
Crossdressers Intl.
Crossdressers Intl. - Address unknown since 2011.
Crossdressing
  Soc. for the Second Self [13112]
CrossGlobal Link [20033], PO Box 398, Wheaton, IL 60187, (630)682-9270
CrossRef [2930], 40 Salem St., Lynnfield, MA 01940, (781)295-0072
CrossRef [2930], 40 Salem St., Lynnfield, MA 01940, (781)295-0072
Crossroads [★12078]
Crossroads [★12078]
CrossSphere: the Global Assn. for Packaged Travel [★3569]
CrossWorld [20034], 10000 N Oak Trafficway, Kansas City, MO 64155, (816)479-7300
CrossWorld [20034], 10000 N Oak Trafficway, Kansas City, MO 64155, (816)479-7300
Crotty Family Org. - Defunct.
Crowl Name Assn. [20498], 123 East Rd., Toronto, OH 43964-7783, (740)544-6439
Crown Coun. [14278], 975 Woodoak Ln., Ste. 200, Salt Lake City, UT 84117, (801)293-8522
Crown Victoria Assn. [21038], PO Box 6, Bryan, OH 43506-9141, (419)636-2475
Crowncap Collectors Soc. Intl. [21330], Kevin Kirk, Treas., 1990 Holland Brook Rd., Branchburg, NJ 08876
Croydon Chamber of Commerce and Indus. [IO], Surrey, United Kingdom
CRU Inst. [17400], 2330 130th Ave. NE, Bldg. C, Ste. 102, Bellevue, WA 98005, (425)869-4041
Crucea Rosie Romana [IO], Bucharest, Romania
Crude Accountability [4248], PO Box 2345, Alexandria, VA 22301, (703)299-0854
Crude Oil Quality Assn. [2647], 2324 N Dickerson St., Arlington, VA 22207
Cruise Club of Am. [3556], PO Box 318, North Pembroke, MA 02358, (800)982-2276
Cruise Lines Intl. Assn. [3557], 910 SE 17th St., Ste. 400, Fort Lauderdale, FL 33316, (754)224-2200
Cruise Lines Intl. Assn. [3557], 910 SE 17th St., Ste. 400, Fort Lauderdale, FL 33316, (754)224-2200
Cruiser Olympia Assn. [★20759]
Cruisermen's Assn. - Defunct.
Cruising Assn. [IO], London, United Kingdom
Cruising Club of Am. [22332], 77 Churchills Ln., Milton, MA 02186-3522
Crusade Against Corruption - Defunct.
Cruse Bereavement Care Scotland [IO], Perth, United Kingdom
The Crustacean Soc. [7634], PO Box 7065, Lawrence, KS 66044-7065, (785)843-1234
Crutches 4 Kids [11262], 1350 Avenue of the Americas, 4th Fl., New York, NY 10019

Cruz Roja Argentina [IO], Buenos Aires, Argentina
Cruz Roja Boliviana [IO], La Paz, Bolivia
Cruz Roja Chilena [IO], Santiago, Chile
Cruz Roja Colombiana [IO], Bogota, Colombia
Cruz Roja Costarricense [IO], San Jose, Costa Rica
Cruz Roja Ecuatoriana [IO], Quito, Ecuador
Cruz Roja Guatemalteca [IO], Guatemala City, Guatemala
Cruz Roja Hondurena [IO], Comayaguela, Honduras
Cruz Roja Paraguaya [IO], Asuncion, Paraguay
Cruz Roja Salvadorena [IO], San Salvador, El Salvador
Cruz Roja Uruguaya [IO], Montevideo, Uruguay
Cruz Roja Venezolana [IO], Caracas, Venezuela
Crveni Krst Crne Gore [IO], Podgorica, Montenegro
Cryogenic Engg. Conf. [6581], 1 Res. Cir., K1-EP119, Niskayuna, NY 12309
Cryogenic Soc. of Am. [6582], 218 Lake St., Oak Park, IL 60302-2609, (708)383-6220
Cryogenics
  Cryogenic Engg. Conf. [6581]
  Cryogenic Soc. of Am. [6582]
  Immortalist Soc. [6583]
  Intl. Cryogenic Materials Conf. [6584]
  Soc. for Cryobiology [6585]
Cryonics
  Alcor Life Extension Found. [14210]
  Alcor Life Extension Found. [14210]
  Amer. Cryonics Soc. [14211]
  Cryonics Inst. [14212]
  Immortalist Soc. [6583]
Cryonics Assn. [★6583]
Cryonics Inst. [14212], 24355 Sorrentino Ct., Clinton Township, MI 48035, (586)791-5961
Cryonics Soc. of Canada [IO], Toronto, ON, Canada
Cryonics Soc. of Michigan [★6583]
Cryptography
  Amer. Cryptogram Assn. [21473]
Cryptology
  Intl. Assn. for Cryptologic Res. [6586]
  Intl. Assn. for Cryptologic Res. [6586]
Crystal Ball Cruise Assn. [13228], PO Box 390, Brewerton, NY 13029, (315)668-CARS
Crystallographic Soc. of Am. [★6588]
Crystallography
  Amer. Assn. for Crystal Growth [6587]
  Amer. Crystallographic Assn. [6588]
  Intl. Liquid Crystal Soc. [6589]
  Intl. Liquid Crystal Soc. [6589]
  U.S. Faceters Guild [6590]
C.S. Forester Soc. - Defunct.
CSA Fraternal Life [18972], 122 W 22nd St., Oak Brook, IL 60523, (630)472-0500
CSA Intl. [IO], Toronto, ON, Canada
CSB [★6165]
CSB [★6165]
CSB Ministries [20305], PO Box 150, Wheaton, IL 60187, (630)462-4682
CSC Clearing Corp. - Defunct.
CSLR [★5563]
CSLR [★5563]
CTAM - Cable and Telecommunications Assn. for Marketing [489], 201 N Union St., Ste. 440, Alexandria, VA 22314, (703)549-4200
CTAM, The Marketing Soc. for the Cable and Telecommunications Indus. [★489]
CTC, The Natl. Cyclists' Org. [IO], Guildford, United Kingdom
CTIA - The Wireless Assn. [3406], 1400 16th St. NW, Ste. 600, Washington, DC 20036, (202)736-3200
CTIA - The Wireless Assn. and Wireless Data Forum [★3406]
CTR for Dance Medicine [★16309]
CTSNet: Cardiothoracic Surgery Network [16880], 401 E Pratt St., Ste. 351, Baltimore, MD 21202, (410)385-1949
CTSNet: Cardiothoracic Surgery Network [16880], 401 E Pratt St., Ste. 351, Baltimore, MD 21202, (410)385-1949
CUAMM - Medici con l'Africa [★IO]
CubaCubaAlpha-66
  Center for Cuban Stud. [9512]
  Cuba Res. and Anal. Gp. [17492]
  Cuban Amer. Alliance Educ. Fund [18968]

Reference to "IO" in place of a book number signifies that the association may be found in the 50th edition of International Organizations.

Encyclopedia of Associations, 51st Edition

2731

Cuban Amer. Natl. Found. [17493]
Cuban Amer. Natl. Found. [17493]
Directorio Democratico Cubano [17494]
Directorio Democratico Cubano [17494]
U.S. Women and Cuba Collaboration [17957]
Cuba Information Proj. - Defunct.
Cuba Reconciliation Initiative; US- [17754]
Cuba Reconciliation Initiative; US- [17754]
Cuba Res. and Anal. Gp. [17492], PO Box 6510, Albuquerque, NM 87197-6510, (505)344-5049
Cuba Support Gp. - Ireland [IO], Dublin, Ireland
Cuban
    Havana Silk Dog Assn. of Am. [21578]
    U.S. Women and Cuba Collaboration [17957]
Cuban Amer. Alliance Educ. Fund [18968], PO Box 5113, San Luis Obispo, CA 93403, (805)627-1959
Cuban Amer. Found. [★17493]
Cuban Amer. Found. [★17493]
Cuban Amer. Freedom Coalition [★17493]
Cuban Amer. Freedom Coalition [★17493]
Cuban Amer. Natl. Coun. [13185], 1223 SW 4th St., Miami, FL 33135, (305)642-3484
Cuban Amer. Natl. Found. [17493], 1312 SW 27th Ave., Miami, FL 33145, (305)592-7768
Cuban Amer. Natl. Found. [17493], 1312 SW 27th Ave., Miami, FL 33145, (305)592-7768
Cuban Amer. Public Affairs Comm. [★17493]
Cuban Amer. Public Affairs Comm. [★17493]
Cuban Amer. Republican Women - Defunct.
Cuban Amer. Veterans Assn. - Address unknown since 2011.
Cuban Assn. of Marfan Syndrome [IO], Havana, Cuba
Cuban Assn. for Pattern Recognition [IO], Havana, Cuba
Cuban Clinical Neurophysiology Soc. [IO], Havana, Cuba
Cuban Democratic Directorate [★17494]
Cuban Democratic Directorate [★17494]
Cuban League Against Epilepsy [IO], Havana, Cuba
Cuban Natl. Comm. for the Stud. of Hypertension [IO], Havana, Cuba
Cuban Natl. Planning Coun. [★13185]
Cuban Numismatic Assn. [21973], Robert Freeman, Treas., 523 Meridian St., Tallahassee, FL 32301-1281, (727)531-7337
Cuban Soc. of Physiological Sciences [IO], Havana, Cuba
CUES Financial Suppliers Forum [2398], PO Box 14167, Madison, WI 53708-0167, (608)271-2664
CUES Managers Soc. [★996]
Culinarians - Defunct.
Culinary Arts
    Black Culinarian Alliance [1009]
    Confrerie de la Chaine des Rotisseurs, Bailliage des U.S.A. [21845]
    The Culinary Trust [7946]
    The Culinary Trust [7946]
    Les Dames d'Escoffier Intl. [1010]
    Res. Chefs Assn. [1011]
    Spoons Across Am. [15845]
    Vinegar Connoisseurs Intl. [21849]
Culinary Guild of Windsor [IO], Windsor, ON, Canada
Culinary Inst. of Canada [IO], Charlottetown, PE, Canada
The Culinary Trust [7946], PO Box 273, New York, NY 10013, (646)224-6989
The Culinary Trust [7946], PO Box 273, New York, NY 10013, (646)224-6989
Culion Foundation [★15248]
Culion Foundation [★15248]
Culligan Dealers Assn. of North Am. [1527], 14101 Hwy. 290 W, Bldg. 1600B, Austin, TX 78737, (512)894-4106
Cult Awareness Network - Address unknown since 2010.
Cultivons Biologique Canada [★IO]
Cults
    Free Minds, Inc. [19639]
    Intl. Cultic Stud. Assn. [19640]
    Jews for Judaism [20186]
    Personal Freedom Outreach [19641]
    Spiritual Counterfeits Proj. [19642]
    USCCCN Natl. CH on Satanic Crime in Am. [11695]

Watchman Fellowship [19643]
Cultural Assistance Center [★9263]
Cultural Assn. of Bengal [9436], 141 Grymes Hill Rd., Staten Island, NY 10301
Cultural Centers
    92nd St. Y [12400]
    Schomburg Center for Res. in Black Culture [9105]
Cultural Conservancy [10326], PO Box 29044, San Francisco, CA 94129-0044, (415)561-6594
Cultural Exchange
    Afoakom-USA [9863]
    AFS Intercultural Programs [8336]
    AFS Intl. [7947]
    AFS Intl. [7947]
    Amer. Brazilian Cultural Exchange [9513]
    Amer. Inst. for Managing Diversity [17495]
    Amer. MidEast Leadership Network [17934]
    Amer. Telugu Assn. [9514]
    Associates in Cultural Exchange [7948]
    Assn. for Africanist Anthropology [6133]
    CEC ArtsLink [17496]
    CEC ArtsLink [17496]
    Champa Cultural Preservation Assn. of USA [10636]
    Chinese Amer. Cooperation Coun. [9873]
    Chinese School Assn. in the U.S. [8825]
    Cross Cultural Collaborative [7949]
    Cross Cultural Collaborative [7949]
    Friends of Malawi [9515]
    Friends of Malawi [9515]
    Friends of Turkmenistan [11585]
    Global Routes [9516]
    Haiti Cultural Exchange [9517]
    Intl. Christian Technologists Assn. [19990]
    Intl. Soc. for Iranian Culture [9882]
    Laotian Amer. Soc. [19102]
    The Latino Coalition [9948]
    Multinational Exchange for Sustainable Agriculture [4941]
    My Travel Bug [9018]
    Nepali Amer. Friendship Assn. [19172]
    North Amer. Taiwan Stud. Assn. [8938]
    Panamerican/Panafrican Assn. [17497]
    Qigong Alliance Intl. [13701]
    Sino-American Bridge for Educ. and Hea. [9876]
    Syrian-American Relations Coun. [17951]
    Taipei Economic and Cultural Off. in New York [9480]
    Tamizdat [9518]
    United Burundian-American Community Assn. [17953]
    U.S./Japan Cultural Trade Network [9519]
    United States-Japan Found. [18969]
    United States-Japan Found. [18969]
    Where Peace Lives [10355]
    World Artists Experiences [9325]
    World Assn. for Vedic Stud. [9520]
    World Assn. for Vedic Stud. [9520]
    World Coun. of Elders [9521]
    World Coun. of Elders [9521]
Cultural Integration Fellowship [9337], 2650 Fulton St., 3rd Ave., San Francisco, CA 94118, (415)668-1559
Cultural Orientation Rsrc. Center [★10024]
Cultural Resources
    Afoakom-USA [9863]
    Alliance of Natl. Heritage Areas [9522]
    Assn. for Cultural Evolution [9523]
    Cross-Cultural Solutions [11742]
    European Inst. of Cultural Routes [8774]
    Natl. Initiative for a Networked Cultural Heritage [9524]
    Navy and Marine Living History Assn. [10094]
    Ngwa Natl. Assn. USA [19040]
    Robert Sterling Clark Found. [11743]
    Soc. Farsarotul [9525]
    Tamizdat [9518]
    U.S. Comm. of the Blue Shield [9526]
    Wordcraft Circle of Native Writers and Storytellers [9527]
    Wordcraft Circle of Native Writers and Storytellers [9527]
Cultural Restoration Tourism Proj. [9680], PO Box 6803, Albany, CA 94706, (415)563-7221

Cultural Survival [9822], 215 Prospect St., Cambridge, MA 02139, (617)441-5400
Cultural Survival [9822], 215 Prospect St., Cambridge, MA 02139, (617)441-5400
Cultural Union Brazil U.S. [IO], Paraiso, Brazil
Culturatti Kids Resource Network [9074], 9465 Counselor Row, Ste. 200, Indianapolis, IN 46240, (317)682-4973
Culture and Animals Found. [10950], 3509 Eden Croft Dr., Raleigh, NC 27612, (919)782-3739
Culture and Env. Preservation Assn. [IO], Phnom Penh, Cambodia
Cultured Marble Inst. [★570]
Cultured Marble Inst. [★570]
Cum Laude Soc. [23556], 4100 Springdale Rd., Louisville, KY 40214, (502)814-4631
Cumann Bainistiocht Eolaiocht na h-Eireann [★IO]
Cumann Camogaiochta nan Gael [★IO]
Cumann Cheol Tire Eireann [★IO]
Cumann Comhshaoil Dhoctuiri na heireann [★IO]
Cumann Corpoideachais na hEireann [★IO]
Cumann Geinealais na heireann [★IO]
Cumann Innealtoiri Comhairle na h Eirann [★IO]
Cumann Leabharlann na hEireann [★IO]
Cumann Liathroid Leadoige Na heireann [★IO]
Cumann Lucht Capaillini Chonamara [★IO]
Cumann Luthchleas Gael [★IO]
Cumann na Meanmhuinteori Eire [★IO]
Cumann Muinteoiri Eireann [★IO]
Cumann Peile na hEireann [★IO]
Cumann na Scoileanna Pobail agus Cuimsitheacha [★IO]
Cumann Tireolaiochta na hEireann [★IO]
Cumann Uaigheann Na Laochra Gael [★IO]
Cumbria and North Lancs Campaign for Nuclear Disarmament [IO], Lancaster, United Kingdom
CUMELA Nederland [IO], Nijkerk, Netherlands
Cumunn na Camanachd [★IO]
CUNA Intl. [★997]
A Cup of Water Intl. [20282], PO Box 9809, Kansas City, MO 64134, (267)242-1798
Curacao and Bonaire Tourist Boards [★23433]
Curacao Chamber of Commerce and Indus. [IO], Curacao, Netherlands Antilles
Curacao Convention Bureau/Tourist Bd. [23433], Curacao Tourism Corp., One Gateway Center, Ste. 2600, Newark, NJ 07102, (973)353-6200
Curacao Info. Center [★23433]
Curacao Tourist Bd. [★23433]
Curatio Intl. Found. [IO], Tbilisi, Georgia
Cure Alveolar Soft Part Sarcoma Intl. [13912], 260 Tappan St., Brookline, MA 02445, (617)731-1143
Cure For Lymphoma Found. [★13939]
CURE Intl. [14072], 701 Bosler Ave., Lemoyne, PA 17043, (717)730-6706
CURE Intl. [14072], 701 Bosler Ave., Lemoyne, PA 17043, (717)730-6706
Cure Kids Cancer Coalition [13913], 4525 S 2300 E, Salt Lake City, UT 84117, (800)266-8824
Cure Res. Found. [13914], PO Box 3782, Westlake Village, CA 91359, (805)498-0185
CureSearch for Children's Cancer [13915], 4600 E West Hwy., Ste. 600, Bethesda, MD 20814-3457, (240)235-2200
CuresNow [15372], 10100 Santa Monica Blvd., Ste. 1300, Los Angeles, CA 90067
Curling
    U.S. Curling Assn. [22472]
    U.S. Women's Curling Assn. [22473]
Curling Club Hamburg e.V. [IO], Hamburg, Germany
Curly-Coated Retriever Club of Am. [21548], Andy Ayers, Treas., 7050 Spring Meadows West Dr., Holland, OH 43528, (419)861-7800
Curly Sporthorse Intl. [4578], 17829 Hubbard Gulch, Juliaetta, ID 83535, (208)276-7540
Curly Sporthorse Intl. [4578], 17829 Hubbard Gulch, Juliaetta, ID 83535, (208)276-7540
Curriculum
    Amer. Assn. for Teaching and Curriculum [8941]
    Assn. for Core Texts and Courses [8514]
    Assn. for Supervision and Curriculum Development [7950]
    Assn. for Supervision and Curriculum Development [7950]
    Center for Critical Thinking [7951]

A star before a book entry number signifies that the name is not listed separately, but is mentioned within the entry.

Coalition of Essential Schools **[7952]**
EPIE Inst. **[8311]**
High/Scope Educational Res. Found. **[7953]**
World Coun. for Curriculum and Instruction **[7954]**
World Coun. for Curriculum and Instruction **[7954]**
Currier and Ives Dinnerware Collectors **[21331]**, 308 Jodi Dr., Brownstown, IN 47220, (812)358-4569
Curtis/Curtiss Soc. **[20499]**, 3104 Plaza Dr. NE, No. 17, Grand Rapids, MI 49525
CUSA: An Apostolate for People with Chronic Illness or with Disabilities **[19419]**, 4856 W 29th St., Cicero, IL 60804-3611
CUSA: An Apostolate of the Sick and Disabled **[★19419]**
Cushing's Support and Res. Found. **[14487]**, 65 E India Row, Ste. 22B, Boston, MA 02110, (617)723-3674
Cushman Club of Am. **[21927]**, PO Box 102, Indian Hills, CO 80454
Cushman Found. for Foraminiferal Res. **[7210]**, Smithsonian Inst., Washington, DC 20560-0121, (202)633-1333
CUSO - Canada **[IO]**, Ottawa, ON, Canada
Custer Battlefield Historical and Museum Assn. **[9762]**, PO Box 902, Hardin, MT 59034-0902
Custer, George Armstrong
Little Bighorn History Alliance **[10678]**
Custody Action for Lesbian Mothers - Defunct.
Custom Content Coun. **[2931]**, 30 W 26th St., 3rd Fl., New York, NY 10010, (212)989-4631
Custom Electronic Design Installation Assn. **[3232]**, 7150 Winton Dr., Ste. 300, Indianapolis, IN 46268, (317)328-4336
Custom Publishing Coun. **[★2931]**
Custom Roll Forming Inst. - Address unknown since 2010.
Custom Tailors and Designers Assn. of Am. **[204]**, 42732 Ridgeway Dr., Broadlands, VA 20148, (888)248-2832
Customer Contact Assn. **[IO]**, Glasgow, United Kingdom
Customer Contact Mgt. Assn. **[IO]**, Melbourne, Australia
Customer Relationship Mgt. Assn. **[869]**, 12460 Crabapple Rd., Ste. 202-417, Alpharetta, GA 30004, (404)735-2950
Customer Satisfaction Measurement Benchmarking Assn. **[659]**, 4606 FM 1960 W, Ste. 250, Houston, TX 77069-9949, (281)440-5044
Customers of SirsiDynix User Gp. Inc. **[6973]**, Frances Orton, Membership and Web Coor., 3214 N Univ. Ave., No. 333, Provo, UT 84604, (801)226-6054
Customs
Canadian Soc. of Customs Brokers **[13658]**
Customs and Intl. Trade Bar Assn. **[5388]**
Customs and Intl. Trade Bar Assn. **[5388]**
Customs Brokers and Forwarders Assn. of Am. **[★2103]**
Customs Brokers and Freight Forwarders Assn. of Jamaica **[IO]**, Kingston, Jamaica
Customs Clerks Assn. of the Port of New York **[★2103]**
Customs and Intl. Trade Bar Assn. **[5388]**, Patrick C. Reed, Pres., 220 Fifth Ave., New York, NY 10001, (212)684-5656
Customs and Intl. Trade Bar Assn. **[5388]**, Patrick C. Reed, Pres., 220 Fifth Ave., New York, NY 10001, (212)684-5656
Custumer Satisfaction Measurement Assn. **[★659]**
Cutlery and Allied Trades Res. Assn. **[IO]**, Sheffield, United Kingdom
Cutting Tool Mfrs. of Am. **[★1877]**
Cutting Tool Mfrs. Assn. **[★1877]**
CVJM - Gesamtverband **[IO]**, Kassel, Germany
CWI: Credit Professionals **[★1291]**
CWI: Credit Professionals **[★1291]**
Cyber Conflict Stud. Assn. **[7955]**, Nic Fuqua, 2650 Park Tower Dr., Ste. 400, Vienna, VA 22180
Cyber Security Indus. Alliance **[6974]**, 1401 Wilson Blvd., Ste. 1100, Arlington, VA 22209, (703)284-5353
CyberAngels **[12387]**, 982 E 89th St., Brooklyn, NY 11236
CyberKnife Soc. **[16812]**, 1350 Dell Ave., Ste. 105, Campbell, CA 95008, (408)385-9411

Cybernetics
Cyber Conflict Stud. Assn. **[7955]**
Cybernetics; Amer. Soc. for **[6442]**
Cybernetics Soc. **[IO]**, Welwyn Garden City, United Kingdom
The Cycad Soc. **[4037]**, Dr. Bart Schutzman, Ed., Univ. of Florida, Environmental Horticulture Dept., 1531 Fifield Hall, Gainesville, FL 32611-0670
The Cycad Soc. **[4037]**, Dr. Bart Schutzman, Ed., Univ. of Florida, Environmental Horticulture Dept., 1531 Fifield Hall, Gainesville, FL 32611-0670
Cyclamen Soc. **[IO]**, Sevenoaks, United Kingdom
Cycle Jobbers Assn. **[★3307]**
Cycle Parts and Accessories Assn. - Defunct.
Cycle Polo Fed. of India **[IO]**, Jaipur, India
Cycle Racing Assn. **[IO]**, Gwangmyeong, Republic of Korea
Cyclic Vomiting Syndrome Assn. **[14560]**, 2819 W Highland Blvd., Milwaukee, WI 53208, (414)342-7880
Cyclic Vomiting Syndrome Assn. **[14560]**, 2819 W Highland Blvd., Milwaukee, WI 53208, (414)342-7880
Cycling
4K for Cancer **[13874]**
Adventure Cycling Assn. **[22474]**
Amer. Bicycle Assn. **[22475]**
Amer. Track Racing Assn. **[22476]**
Bicycle Ride Directors' Assn. of Am. **[22477]**
Camping Women **[22441]**
Intl. Christian Cycling Club U.S.A. **[22478]**
Intl. Christian Cycling Club U.S.A. **[22478]**
Intl. Mountain Bicycling Assn. **[22479]**
Intl. Mountain Bicycling Assn. **[22479]**
Intl. Unicycling Fed. **[22480]**
League of Amer. Bicyclists **[22481]**
Natl. Bicycle League **[22482]**
Natl. Bicycle Tour Directors Assn. **[22483]**
Natl. Center for Bicycling and Walking **[22484]**
Randonneurs USA **[22485]**
Ride to Work **[21936]**
Ride for World Hea. **[14213]**
Tandem Club of Am. **[22486]**
Ultra Marathon Cycling Assn. **[22487]**
Ultra Marathon Cycling Assn. **[22487]**
Unicycling Soc. of Am. **[22488]**
U.S. Cycling Fed. **[22489]**
U.S. Handcycling Fed. **[22490]**
The Wheelmen **[22491]**
Women's Mountain Bike and Tea Soc. **[22492]**
Cycling Assn; U.S. Deaf **[22528]**
Cycling Australia **[IO]**, Alexandria, Australia
Cycling Ireland **[IO]**, Dublin, Ireland
Cycling Time Trials **[IO]**, Leigh, United Kingdom
Cyclone Montego Torino Registry **[21039]**, 19 Glyn Dr., Newark, DE 19713-4016, (302)737-4252
Cyclone Torino Montego Registry **[★21039]**
Cykel Motor och Sportfackhandlarna **[★IO]**
Cymbidium Soc. of Am. **[21789]**, 6639 Ibex Woods Ct., Citrus Heights, CA 95621, (510)537-8923
Cymbidium Soc. of Am. **[21789]**, 6639 Ibex Woods Ct., Citrus Heights, CA 95621, (510)537-8923
Cymdeithas Cerddoriaeth Cymru **[★IO]**
Cymdeithas Ddrama Cymru **[★IO]**
Cymdeithas Gwartheg Duon Cymreig **[★IO]**
Cymdeithas Judo Cymru **[★IO]**
Cyngor Cefn Gwlad Cymru **[★IO]**
Cyngor Celfyddydau Cymru **[★IO]**
Cyngor Llyfrau Cymru **[★IO]**
Cyprus
Cyprus Tourism Org. **[23396]**
Cyprus-US Chamber of Commerce **[23360]**
Cyprus Airsports Fed. **[IO]**, Nicosia, Cyprus
Cyprus Amateur Baseball Fed. **[IO]**, Larnaca, Cyprus
Cyprus Amateur Judo, Taekwondo Fed. **[IO]**, Nicosia, Cyprus
Cyprus Amateur Radio Soc. **[IO]**, Limassol, Cyprus
Cyprus Assn. of Medical Physics and Biomedical Engg. **[IO]**, Nicosia, Cyprus
Cyprus Assn. of Physiotherapists **[IO]**, Nicosia, Cyprus
Cyprus Assn. of Professional Quantity Surveyors **[IO]**, Nicosia, Cyprus
Cyprus Assn. of Sports Medicine **[IO]**, Nicosia, Cyprus

Cyprus Badminton Fed. **[IO]**, Nicosia, Cyprus
Cyprus Chamber of Commerce and Indus. **[IO]**, Nicosia, Cyprus
Cyprus Chap. of the Penn State Alumni Assn. **[IO]**, Nicosia, Cyprus
Cyprus Clothing Indus. Assn. **[IO]**, Strovolos, Cyprus
Cyprus Cmpt. Soc. **[IO]**, Nicosia, Cyprus
Cyprus Embassy Trade Center **[23359]**, 13 E 40th St., New York, NY 10016, (212)213-9100
Cyprus Embassy Trade Center **[23359]**, 13 E 40th St., New York, NY 10016, (212)213-9100
Cyprus Employers and Industrialists Fed. **[IO]**, Nicosia, Cyprus
Cyprus Family Planning Assn. **[IO]**, Nicosia, Cyprus
Cyprus Football Assn. **[IO]**, Nicosia, Cyprus
Cyprus Hotel Assn. **[IO]**, Nicosia, Cyprus
Cyprus Ice Skating Fed. **[IO]**, Nicosia, Cyprus
Cyprus Info. Tech. Enterprises Assn. **[IO]**, Nicosia, Cyprus
Cyprus League against Rheumatism **[IO]**, Nicosia, Cyprus
Cyprus Multiple Sclerosis Assn. **[IO]**, Nicosia, Cyprus
Cyprus Natl. Paralympic Comm. **[IO]**, Nicosia, Cyprus
Cyprus Newspaper and Magazines Publishers Assn. **[IO]**, Nicosia, Cyprus
Cyprus Olympic Comm. **[IO]**, Nicosia, Cyprus
Cyprus Org. for Promotion of Quality **[IO]**, Nicosia, Cyprus
Cyprus Orthodontic Soc. **[IO]**, Limassol, Cyprus
Cyprus Professional Engineers Assn. **[IO]**, Nicosia, Cyprus
Cyprus Soc. Against Osteoporosis and Myoskeletal Diseases **[IO]**, Nicosia, Cyprus
Cyprus Soc. of Cardiology **[IO]**, Nicosia, Cyprus
Cyprus Soc. of Chemotherapy and Infectious Diseases **[IO]**, Nicosia, Cyprus
Cyprus Soc. of Dermatology and Venerology **[IO]**, Nicosia, Cyprus
Cyprus Soc. for Rheumatology **[IO]**, Nicosia, Cyprus
Cyprus Sport Org. **[IO]**, Nicosia, Cyprus
Cyprus Squash Rackets Assn. **[IO]**, Nicosia, Cyprus
Cyprus Tennis Fed. **[IO]**, Nicosia, Cyprus
Cyprus Tourism Org. **[IO]**, Nicosia, Cyprus
Cyprus Tourism Org. **[23396]**, 13 E 40th St., New York, NY 10016, (212)683-5280
Cyprus-US Chamber of Commerce **[23360]**, 150 E 57th St., Ste. 25A, New York, NY 10022, (201)444-5609
Cyprus Veterans Assn. World War II **[IO]**, Nicosia, Cyprus
Cyprus Water Ski Fed. **[IO]**, Limassol, Cyprus
Cyprus Weightlifting Fed. **[IO]**, Limassol, Cyprus
Cyprus Yachting Assn. **[IO]**, Limassol, Cyprus
Cyriac Elias Voluntary Assn. **[IO]**, Kochi, India
Cystic Fibrosis Assn. of Ireland **[IO]**, Dublin, Ireland
Cystic Fibrosis Australia **[IO]**, North Ryde, Australia
Cystic Fibrosis Australia - Australian Capital Territory **[IO]**, Civic Square, Australia
Cystic Fibrosis Australia - Victoria **[IO]**, Melbourne, Australia
Cystic Fibrosis Australia - Western Australia **[IO]**, Nedlands, Australia
Cystic Fibrosis Found. **[16607]**, 6931 Arlington Rd., Bethesda, MD 20814, (301)951-4422
Cystic Fibrosis Tasmania **[IO]**, Hobart, Australia
Cystic Fibrosis Trust **[IO]**, Bromley, United Kingdom
Cystic Fibrosis Worldwide **[16608]**, Ms. Christine Noke, Exec. Dir., 210 Park Ave., No. 267, Worcester, MA 01609, (508)762-4232
Cystinosis Found. of California **[★15494]**
Cystinosis Found. **[15494]**, 58 Miramonte Dr., Moraga, CA 94556, (925)631-1588
Cystinosis Res. Network **[15495]**, 302 Whytegate Ct., Lake Forest, IL 60045, (847)735-0471
Cytokine Res; Intl. Soc. for Interferon and **[15345]**
Cytology
Amer. Soc. of Cytopathology **[14214]**
Amer. Soc. for Cytotechnology **[14215]**
European Tissue Culture Soc. **[9531]**
European Tissue Repair Soc. **[8854]**
Intl. Cell Death Soc. **[14216]**
Intl. Cell Death Soc. **[14216]**
Mitochondrial Medicine Soc. **[14217]**

Reference to "IO" in place of a book number signifies that the association may be found in the 50th edition of International Organizations.

Mitochondrial Medicine Soc. [14217]
Papanicolaou Soc. of Cytopathology [14218]
Cytometry Soc; Clinical [16122]
Cytopathology; Amer. Soc. of [14214]
Czech
Amer. Friends of the Czech Republic [18970]
Amer. Fund for Czech and Slovak Relief [12771]
Amer. Sokol Org. [18971]
CSA Fraternal Life [18972]
Czech Catholic Union [18973]
Czechoslovak Soc. of Arts and Sciences [9528]
Czechoslovak Soc. of Arts and Sciences [9528]
Intl. Assn. of Teachers of Czech [9529]
Intl. Assn. of Teachers of Czech [9529]
Slovak-American Cultural Center [10537]
Western Fraternal Life Assn. [18974]
Czech ACM SIGCHI [IO], Prague, Czech Republic
Czech Aikido Assn. - Aikikai of Czech Republic [IO], Prague, Czech Republic
Czech Assn. for Branded Products [IO], Prague, Czech Republic
Czech Assn. of Consulting Engineers [IO], Prague, Czech Republic
Czech Assn. for Geoinformation [IO], Prague, Czech Republic
Czech Assn. of Geomorphologists [IO], Ostrava, Czech Republic
Czech Assn. of Occupational Therapists [IO], Prague, Czech Republic
Czech Assn. of Proj. Mgt. [IO], Brno, Czech Republic
Czech Badminton Fed. [IO], Prague, Czech Republic
Czech Banking Assn. [IO], Prague, Czech Republic
Czech Bar Assn. [IO], Prague, Czech Republic
Czech Baseball Fed. [IO], Prague, Czech Republic
Czech Biathlon Union [IO], Prague, Czech Republic
Czech Bible Soc. [IO], Prague, Czech Republic
Czech Bioclimatological Soc. [IO], Prague, Czech Republic
Czech Catholic Union [18973], 5349 Dolloff Rd., Cleveland, OH 44127, (216)341-0444
Czech Chamber of Commerce [IO], Prague, Czech Republic
Czech Chem. Soc. [IO], Prague, Czech Republic
Czech Collector's Assn. [21332], 810 - 11th St., Ste. 201, Miami Beach, FL 33139-4834
Czech Collector's Assn. [21332], 810 - 11th St., Ste. 201, Miami Beach, FL 33139-4834
Czech Confed. of Commerce and Tourism [IO], Prague, Czech Republic
Czech Dance Sport Fed. [IO], Litomerice, Czech Republic
Czech Figure Skating Assn. [IO], Prague, Czech Republic
Czech Fish Farmers' Assn. [IO], Ceske Budejovice, Czech Republic
Czech Floorball Union [IO], Prague, Czech Republic
Czech Franchise Assn. [IO], Prague, Czech Republic
Czech Gas Assn. [IO], Prague, Czech Republic
Czech Gynecological and Obstetrical Soc. [IO], Prague, Czech Republic
Czech Heritage Preservation Soc. [9681], PO Box 128, Tabor, SD 57063, (605)463-2476
Czech Insurance Assn. [IO], Prague, Czech Republic
Czech League Against Epilepsy [IO], Prague, Czech Republic
Czech League Against Rheumatism [IO], Prague, Czech Republic
Czech Medical Assn. of J.E. Purkyne [IO], Prague, Czech Republic
Czech Member Comm. of the World Energy Coun. [IO], Prague, Czech Republic
Czech Meteorological Soc. [IO], Prague, Czech Republic
Czech-Moravian Assn. of Plant Breeders and Seed Traders [IO], Prague, Czech Republic
Czech and Moravian Elecl. and Electronic Assn. [IO], Prague, Czech Republic
Czech-Moravian Psychological Soc. [IO], Prague, Czech Republic
Czech Multiple Sclerosis Soc. [IO], Prague, Czech Republic

Czech Olympic Comm. [IO], Prague, Czech Republic
Czech Operational Res. Soc. [IO], Prague, Czech Republic
Czech Orthodontic Soc. [IO], Prague, Czech Republic
Czech Osteoporosis League [IO], Prague, Czech Republic
Czech Pain Soc. [IO], Prague, Czech Republic
Czech Paralympic Comm. [IO], Prague, Czech Republic
Czech Pattern Recognition Soc. [IO], Prague, Czech Republic
Czech Physiological Soc. [IO], Prague, Czech Republic
Czech Publishers Assn. [IO], Prague, Czech Republic
Czech Radio Club [IO], Prague, Czech Republic
Czech Radiological Soc. [IO], Plzen, Czech Republic
Czech Red Cross [IO], Prague, Czech Republic
Czech Republic Union of Tenants [IO], Prague, Czech Republic
Czech Rheumatological Soc. [IO], Prague, Czech Republic
Czech Rosa Club [IO], Prague, Czech Republic
Czech Sailing Assn. [IO], Prague, Czech Republic
Czech Seed Trade Assn. [IO], Prague, Czech Republic
Czech and Slovak Assn. of Canada [IO], Toronto, ON, Canada
Czech Soc. of Cardiology [IO], Brno, Czech Republic
Czech Soc. of Chemotherapy [IO], Prague, Czech Republic
Czech Soc. for Clinical Neurophysiology [IO], Simkova, Czech Republic
Czech Soc. for Cybernetics and Informatics [IO], Prague, Czech Republic
Czech Soc. for Experimental and Clinical Pharmacology and Toxicology [IO], Hradec Kralove, Czech Republic
Czech Soc. of Geronology and Geriatrics of the Czech Medical Assn. [IO], Prague, Czech Republic
Czech Soc. of Hypertension [IO], Prague, Czech Republic
Czech Soc. for Infectious Disease [IO], Prague, Czech Republic
Czech Soc. for Mechanics [IO], Prague, Czech Republic
Czech Soc. for Metabolic Skeletal Diseases [IO], Hradec Kralove, Czech Republic
Czech Soc. of Sports Medicine [IO], Brno, Czech Republic
Czech Speed Skating Fed. [IO], Prague, Czech Republic
Czech Squash Assn. [IO], Prague, Czech Republic
Czech Taekwondo Fed. WTF [IO], Prague, Czech Republic
Czech Tenisova Asociace [IO], Prague, Czech Republic
Czech Union of Inventors and Rationalizers [IO], Prague, Czech Republic
Czech Water Ski Fed. [IO], Prague, Czech Republic
Czech Youth Hostel Assn. [IO], Prague, Czech Republic
Czechoslovak Genealogical Soc. [★20625]
Czechoslovak Genealogical Soc. [★20625]
Czechoslovak Genealogical Soc. Intl. [20625], PO Box 16225, St. Paul, MN 55116-0225, (651)450-2322
Czechoslovak Genealogical Soc. Intl. [20625], PO Box 16225, St. Paul, MN 55116-0225, (651)450-2322
Czechoslovak Microscopy Soc. [IO], Prague, Czech Republic
Czechoslovak Natl. Coun. of Am. - Defunct.
Czechoslovak Soc. of Am. [★18972]
Czechoslovak Soc. of Arts and Sciences [9528], 254 Easton Ave., New Brunswick, NJ 08901, (732)745-8504
Czechoslovak Soc. of Arts and Sciences [9528], 254 Easton Ave., New Brunswick, NJ 08901, (732)745-8504
Czechoslovak Soc. of Arts and Sciences in Am. [★9528]

Czechoslovak Soc. of Arts and Sciences in Am. [★9528]
Czechoslovakia
Amer. Fund for Czech and Slovak Relief [12771]
Slovak-American Cultural Center [10537]

D
Dachshund
Dachshund Rescue of North Am. [10951]
North Amer. Teckel Club [21622]
Dachshund Club of Am. [21549], Neal Hamilton, VP, 559 Clover Hill Rd., Flemington, NJ 08822, (908)782-4724
Dachshund Rescue of North Am. [10951], 7821 Sabre Ct., Manassas, VA 20109
Dachverband der Osterreichischen Osteoporose-Selbsthilfegruppen [★IO]
Dachverband Schweizer Lehrerinnen und Lehrer [★IO]
DACOR [5467], 1801 F St. NW, Washington, DC 20006, (202)682-0500
DAD: Drums and Disabilities [12422], PO Box 341, Towaco, NJ 07082, (973)725-5150
Dads Against Discrimination - Defunct.
Dads Rights [11865], 3140 De La Cruz Blvd., Ste. 200, Santa Clara, CA 95054, (415)853-6877
Daedalian Found. [20314], PO Box 249, Universal City, TX 78148-0249, (210)945-2113
Dag Hammarskjold Found. [IO], Uppsala, Sweden
Daguerreian Soc. [10437], PO Box 306, Cecil, PA 15321-0306, (412)221-0306
Daimler and Lanchester Owners' Club - England [IO], Southampton, United Kingdom
Dairy Australia [IO], Southbank, Australia
Dairy Coun. - United Kingdom [IO], London, United Kingdom
Dairy Farmers of Canada [IO], Montreal, QC, Canada
Dairy and Food Indus. Supply Assn. [★1020]
Dairy and Food Indus. Supply Assn. [★1020]
Dairy and Ice Cream Machinery and Supplies Assn. [★1020]
Dairy and Ice Cream Machinery and Supplies Assn. [★1020]
Dairy Indus. Supply Assn. [★1020]
Dairy Indus. Supply Assn. [★1020]
Dairy Mgt., Inc. [1019], 10255 W Higgins Rd., Ste. 900, Rosemont, IL 60018-5616, (847)627-3252
Dairy Products
3-A Sanitary Standards, Inc. [1012]
All Star Assn. [1013]
Allied Purchasing Company [1014]
Amer. Butter Inst. [1015]
Amer. Cheese Soc. [1016]
Amer. Dairy Products Inst. [1017]
Amer. Dairy Sci. Assn. [4180]
Cheese Importers Assn. of Am. [1018]
Dairy Mgt., Inc. [1019]
Dairylea Cooperative [4181]
Estonian Dairy Assn. [20531]
Food Processing Suppliers Assn. [1020]
Food Processing Suppliers Assn. [1020]
Intl. Dairy Fed. [22331]
Intl. Dairy Foods Assn. [1021]
Intl. Dairy Foods Assn. [1021]
Milk Indus. Found. [1022]
Milk Indus. Found. [1022]
Natl. Chamber of Milk Producers [15069]
Natl. Cheese Inst. [1023]
Natl. Conf. on Interstate Milk Shipments [4182]
Natl. Dairy Coun. [4183]
Natl. Dairy Shrine [4184]
Natl. Ice Cream Retailers Assn. [1024]
Natl. Milk Producers Fed. [4185]
Natl. Yogurt Assn. [1025]
Quality Chekd Dairies [1026]
U.S. Dairy Export Coun. [4186]
Wisconsin Cheese Makers' Assn. [1027]
Wisconsin Dairy Products Assn. [4187]
Dairy Shrine [★4184]
Dairy Soc. Intl. - Defunct.
Dairy UK [IO], London, United Kingdom
Dairylea Cooperative [4181], PO Box 4844, Syracuse, NY 13221-4844, (315)433-0100

A star before a book entry number signifies that the name is not listed separately, but is mentioned within the entry.

Dairymen's League Cooperative Assn. [★4181]
Daisy Alliance [18239], 990 Hammond Dr., Ste. 830, Atlanta, GA 30328, (770)261-4274
Daiwa Anglo-Japanese Found. [IO], London, United Kingdom
Dakota Women of All Red Nations - Defunct.
Dakshinayan [IO], New Delhi, India
Dalcroze Soc. of America - Defunct.
Dale Jarrett Fan Club [23902], PO Box 279, Conover, NC 28613, (828)464-8818
Dales Pony Assn. of North Am. [4579], PO Box 585, New Portland, ME 04954, (207)628-6061
Dales Pony Assn. of North Am. [4579], PO Box 585, New Portland, ME 04954, (207)628-6061
Dales Pony Soc. of Am. [4580], 4161 Leon Dr., Clayton, CA 94517, (925)788-0655
Dalit Freedom Network [17823], 631 Pennsylvania Ave. SE, Ste. 2, Washington, DC 20003, (202)375-5000
Dalit Liberation Educ. Trust [IO], Chennai, India
Dalit Solidarity [17824], PO Box 112, Hines, IL 60141, (708)612-4248
Dalmatian Club of Am. [21550], 864 Ettin Ave., Simi Valley, CA 93065, (805)583-5914
Dalton Floor Covering Market Assn. [★2050]
Dam Safety Coalition [13418], 101 Constitution Ave. NW, Ste. 375 E, Washington, DC 20001, (202)789-7850
Dameron Family Assn. [20500], 1326 N Audubon Rd., Indianapolis, IN 46219-3120
Damfinos: The Intl. Buster Keaton Soc. [23796], 2222 S Mesa St., No. 27, San Pedro, CA 90731, (310)547-2207
Damien-Dutton Soc. [★15249]
Damien-Dutton Soc. for Leprosy Aid [15249], 616 Bedford Ave., Bellmore, NY 11710, (516)221-5829
Damien Found. - Belgium [IO], Brussels, Belgium
Damien Ministries [19633], PO Box 10202, Washington, DC 20018-0202, (202)526-3020
Damon Runyon Cancer Res. Found. [13916], One Exchange Plz., 55 Broadway, Ste. 302, New York, NY 10006, (212)455-0500
Damon Runyon Found. for Cancer Res. [★13916]
Damon Runyon Memorial Fund for Cancer Res. [★13916]
Damon Runyon - Walter Winchell Cancer Fund [★13916]
Damon Runyon - Walter Winchell Cancer Res. Fund [★13916]
Dana Alliance for Brain Initiatives [15654], 505 5th Ave., 6th Fl., New York, NY 10017, (212)223-4040
Dana-Farber Cancer Inst. [13917], 450 Brookline Ave., Boston, MA 02215, (617)632-3000
Dana-Farber Cancer Inst. [13917], 450 Brookline Ave., Boston, MA 02215, (617)632-3000
Dance
　Amer. Ballet Competition [9530]
　Amer. Bop Assn. [9531]
　Amer. Coll. Dance Festival Assn. [9532]
　Amer. Dance Festival [9533]
　Amer. Dance Guild [9534]
　Amer. Fed. of German Folk Dance Groups [9535]
　Amer. Soc. for Aesthetics [9270]
　Art Resources in Collaboration [9536]
　Ballet Theatre Found. [9537]
　Callerlab - Intl. Assn. of Square Dance Callers [9538]
　Callerlab - Intl. Assn. of Square Dance Callers [9538]
　Cecchetti Coun. of Am. [7956]
　Comm. for Handicapable Dancers [9539]
　Cong. on Res. in Dance [9540]
　Cong. on Res. in Dance [9540]
　Country Dance and Song Soc. [9541]
　Cross-Cultural Dance Resources [9542]
　Cross-Cultural Dance Resources [9542]
　Dance Critics Assn. [9543]
　Dance/Drill Team Directors of Am. [9544]
　Dance Educators of Am. [7957]
　Dance Films Assn. [7958]
　Dance Heritage Coalition [9545]
　Dance It Forward USA [9546]
　Dance Masters of Am. [7959]
　Dance Notation Bur. [9547]
　Dance USA [9548]

　Intl. Assn. for Creative Dance [9549]
　Intl. Assn. for Creative Dance [9549]
　Intl. Assn. of Gay/Lesbian Country Western Dance Clubs [9550]
　Intl. Assn. of Gay/Lesbian Country Western Dance Clubs [9550]
　Intl. Assn. of Gay Square Dance Clubs [9551]
　Intl. Assn. of Gay Square Dance Clubs [9551]
　Intl. Assn. of Round Dance Teachers [9552]
　Intl. Assn. of Round Dance Teachers [9552]
　Intl. Coun. of Kinetography Laban [9553]
　Intl. Coun. of Kinetography Laban [9553]
　Intl. Guild of Musicians in Dance [23271]
　Intl. Hustle Dance Assn. [9554]
　Intl. Tap Assn. [9555]
　Israeli Dance Inst. [9556]
　Junior Shag Assn. [9557]
　Laban/Bartenieff Inst. of Movement Stud. [9558]
　Lloyd Shaw Found. [7960]
　London Swing Dance Soc. [14612]DanceMorris Fed.
　Natl. Assn. of Schools of Dance [7961]
　Natl. Clogging Org. [9559]
　Natl. Dance Assn. [9560]
　Natl. Dance Coun. of Am. [7962]
　Natl. Dance Educ. Assn. [22493]
　Natl. Dance Inst. [7963]
　Natl. Dance Teacher's Assn. [22494]
　Natl. Fastdance Assn. [9561]
　Natl. Square Dance Convention [9562]
　NFHS Spirit Assn. [22466]
　North Amer. Fed. of German Folk Dance Groups [9535]
　North Amer. Irish Dance Fed. [9563]
　Old Time Dance Soc. [8782]
　Professional Dancers Fed. [22495]
　Royal Acad. of Dance [9564]
　Sacred Dance Guild [9565]
　Sacred Dance Guild [9565]
　Spirit Indus. Trade Assn. [733]
　United Dance Merchants of Am. [1028]
　United Square Dancers of Am. [9566]
　U.S. Competitive Aerobics Fed. [22209]
　U.S.A. Dance [9567]
　World Dance Alliance Americas [9568]
　World Dance Alliance Americas [9568]
　World Salsa Fed. [9569]
　World Swing Dance Coun. [9570]
　World Swing Dance Coun. [9570]
Dance Critics Assn. [9543], PO Box 1882, Old Chelsea Sta., New York, NY 10011
Dance/Drill Team Directors of Am. [9544], 110 S Stadium Rd., Apt. V1, Alice, TX 78332, (214)415-2349
Dance Educators of Am. [7957], PO Box 8607, Pelham, NY 10803-0607, (914)636-3200
Dance Films Assn. [7958], 48 W 21st St., No. 907, New York, NY 10010, (212)727-0764
Dance Films, Inc. [★7958]
Dance Heritage Coalition [9545], 1111 16th St. NW, Ste. 300, Washington, DC 20036, (202)223-8392
Dance History Scholars [★9802]
DANCE, Inc. [★16830]
Dance It Forward USA [9546], 1521 N Jantzen, Ste. 350, Portland, OR 97217, (503)927-9471
Dance It Up-Kids USA [★9546]
Dance Masters of Am. [7959], PO Box 610533, Bayside, NY 11361-0533, (718)225-4013
Dance-Movement Therapy Assn. of Australia [IO], Carlton South, Australia
Dance Notation Bur. [9547], 111 John St., Ste. 704, New York, NY 10038, (212)571-7011
Dance Sport Assn. of Bosnia and Herzegovina [IO], Sarajevo, Bosnia-Hercegovina
Dance Sport Australia [IO], Baulkham Hills, Australia
Dance Sport Coun. of the Philippines [IO], Pasig City, Philippines
Dance Sport Fed. of the Kyrgyz Republic [IO], Bishkek, Kirgizstan
Dance Teachers Guild [★9534]
Dance Theater Workshop [9289], 219 W 19th St., New York, NY 10011, (212)691-6500
Dance USA [9548], 1111 16th St. NW, Ste. 300, Washington, DC 20036, (202)833-1717
DanceSafe [13246], 1440 Broadway, Ste. 510, Oakland, CA 94612, (888)636-2411

DanceSafe [13246], 1440 Broadway, Ste. 510, Oakland, CA 94612, (888)636-2411
DanceSport Fed. of Kazakhstan [IO], Astana, Kazakhstan
Dandie Dinmont Terrier Club of Am. [21551], Peter L. Andrus, MD, Membership Chair, 3130 E Lake Crescent Dr., Kingwood, TX 77339
Danforth Found. - Address unknown since 2010.
Dangerous Goods Advisory Coun. [3245], 1100 H St. NW, Ste. 740, Washington, DC 20005-5484, (202)289-4550
Daniel Boone and Frontier Families Res. Assn. [9763], 1770 Little Bay Rd., Hermann, MO 65041
Danischer Handelsvertreterverband [★IO]
Danish
　Danish Amer. Heritage Soc. [9571]
　Danish Amer. Heritage Soc. [9571]
　Supreme Lodge of the Danish Sisterhood of Am. [18975]
Danish Acad. of Tech. Sciences [IO], Lyngby, Denmark
Danish Acoustic Neuroma Assn. [IO], Elsinore, Denmark
Danish Actors' Assn. [IO], Frederiksberg, Denmark
Danish Agricultural Coun. [IO], Copenhagen, Denmark
Danish Agriculture [IO], Copenhagen, Denmark
Danish Airtaxi Assn. [IO], Norresundby, Denmark
Danish Amateur Theatre Coun. [IO], Grasten, Denmark
Danish Amer. Chamber of Commerce [23361], PO Box 2886, New York, NY 10163, (917)575-3761
Danish Amer. Heritage Soc. [9571], 925 NE 15th St., Salem, OR 97301, (503)588-1331
Danish Amer. Heritage Soc. [9571], 925 NE 15th St., Salem, OR 97301, (503)588-1331
Danish Amer. Trade Coun. [★23361]
Danish Antiquarian Bookseller's Assn. [IO], Copenhagen, Denmark
Danish Arctic Inst. [IO], Copenhagen, Denmark
Danish Article Numbering Assn. [★21219]
Danish Assn. of Advt. and Relationship Agencies [IO], Copenhagen, Denmark
Danish Assn. of Commercial Agents and Exclusive Distributors [IO], Copenhagen, Denmark
Danish Assn. of Consulting Engineers [IO], Copenhagen, Denmark
Danish Assn. of Graduates in Forestry [IO], Copenhagen, Denmark
Danish Assn. of Graduates in Horticulture [IO], Copenhagen, Denmark
Danish Assn. for von Hippel-Lindau [IO], Tjaereborg, Denmark
Danish Assn. of Medical Imaging [IO], Tjele, Denmark
Danish Assn. of the Pharmaceutical Indus. [IO], Copenhagen, Denmark
Danish Assn. for Prdt. Modelling [IO], Lyngby, Denmark
Danish Assn. of Social Workers [IO], Copenhagen, Denmark
Danish Assn. of the Specialist Press [IO], Copenhagen, Denmark
Danish Assn. of Sports Medicine [IO], Kastrup, Denmark
Danish Assn. of State-Authorized Translators and Interpreters [IO], Copenhagen, Denmark
Danish Assn. of Univ. Women [IO], Hellerup, Denmark
Danish Astronomical Assn. [IO], Rodovre, Denmark
Danish Athletic Fed. [IO], Brondby, Denmark
Danish Atlantic Treaty Assn. [IO], Copenhagen, Denmark
Danish Auto. Dealers Assn. [IO], Taastrup, Denmark
Danish Auto. Sports Union [IO], Brondby, Denmark
Danish Bankers Assn. [IO], Copenhagen, Denmark
Danish Baseball Softball Fed. [IO], Brondby, Denmark
Danish Basketball Fed. [IO], Brondby, Denmark
Danish Bible Soc. [IO], Copenhagen, Denmark
Danish Bone Soc. [IO], Arhus, Denmark
Danish Booksellers Assn. [IO], Copenhagen, Denmark
Danish Brain Injury Assn. [IO], Brondby, Denmark
Danish Brewers' Assn. [IO], Valby, Denmark

Reference to "IO" in place of a book number signifies that the association may be found in the 50th edition of International Organizations.

Danish Bus. Coun. Dubai [IO], Dubai, United Arab Emirates
Danish Butchers' Assn. [IO], Odense, Denmark
Danish Cancer Soc. [IO], Copenhagen, Denmark
Danish Chamber of Commerce [IO], Copenhagen, Denmark
Danish Chem. Soc. [IO], Copenhagen, Denmark
Danish Confed. of Trade Unions [IO], Copenhagen, Denmark
Danish Constr. Assn. [IO], Copenhagen, Denmark
Danish Consumer Coun. [IO], Copenhagen, Denmark
Danish Consumer Goods Suppliers' Assn. [IO], Copenhagen, Denmark
Danish Coun. of Ethics [IO], Copenhagen, Denmark
Danish Dairy Bd. [IO], Arhus, Denmark
Danish Dance Sport Fed. [IO], Brondby, Denmark
Danish Deaf Assn. [IO], Copenhagen, Denmark
Danish Dental Assn. [IO], Copenhagen, Denmark
Danish Dental Mfrs. [IO], Copenhagen, Denmark
Danish Dermatological Soc. [IO], Roskilde, Denmark
Danish Designers [IO], Copenhagen, Denmark
Danish Economic Soc. [IO], Copenhagen, Denmark
Danish Epilepsy Soc. [IO], Glostrup, Denmark
Danish Fed. of Graduates in Agricultural Sci., Economics, Forestry, Horticulture and Landscape Architecture [IO], Copenhagen, Denmark
Danish Fed. of Teachers of Tech. Educ. [IO], Copenhagen, Denmark
Danish Fencing Fed. [IO], Brondby, Denmark
Danish Fishermen's Assn. [IO], Fredericia, Denmark
Danish Floorball Fed. [IO], Brondby, Denmark
Danish Football Assn. [IO], Brondby, Denmark
Danish Foreign Policy Soc. [IO], Copenhagen, Denmark
Danish Forest Assn. [IO], Frederiksberg, Denmark
Danish Forest and Landscape Res. Inst. [IO], Hoersholm, Denmark
Danish Galloway Soc. [IO], Tollose, Denmark
Danish Gerontological Assn. [IO], Copenhagen, Denmark
Danish Gymnastics Fed. [IO], Brondby, Denmark
Danish Historical Assn. [IO], Copenhagen, Denmark
Danish Huntington Assn. [IO], Bronshoj, Denmark
Danish Hypertension Soc. [IO], Arhus, Denmark
Danish Ice Cream Indus. [IO], Copenhagen, Denmark
Danish Import Promotion Off. for Products from Developing Countries [IO], Copenhagen, Denmark
Danish Inst. for Intl. Stud. [IO], Copenhagen, Denmark
Danish Insurance Assn. [IO], Copenhagen, Denmark
Danish Inventors Assn. [IO], Farum, Denmark
Danish Irish Soc. [IO], Copenhagen, Denmark
Danish Jazz Fed. [IO], Copenhagen, Denmark
Danish Jockey Club [IO], Charlottenlund, Denmark
Danish Kennel Club [IO], Solrod Strand, Denmark
Danish Lancia Register [IO], Roskilde, Denmark
Danish Lib. Assn. [IO], Copenhagen, Denmark
Danish Literature Centre [IO], Copenhagen, Denmark
Danish Livestock and Meat Bd. [IO], Copenhagen, Denmark
Danish Luncheon Club of New York [★23361]
Danish Magazine Publishers Assn. [IO], Copenhagen, Denmark
Danish Marfan Assn. [IO], Hillerod, Denmark
Danish Maritime [IO], Copenhagen, Denmark
Danish Mathematical Soc. [IO], Lyngby, Denmark
Danish Medical Soc. [IO], Copenhagen, Denmark
Danish Missionary Coun. [IO], Frederiksberg, Denmark
Danish Multiple Sclerosis Soc. [IO], Valby, Denmark
Danish Music Lib. Assn. [IO], Frederiksberg, Denmark
Danish Musicological Soc. [IO], Copenhagen, Denmark
Danish Natl. Fed. of Early Childhood Teachers and Youth Educators [IO], Copenhagen, Denmark
Danish Natl. Union of Upper Secondary School Teachers [IO], Copenhagen, Denmark
Danish Nurses' Org. [IO], Copenhagen, Denmark
Danish Open Source Bus. Assn. [IO], Copenhagen, Denmark
Danish Operations Res. Soc. [IO], Lyngby, Denmark

Danish Ophthalmological Soc. [IO], Copenhagen, Denmark
Danish Optical Soc. [IO], Arhus, Denmark
Danish Org. of Youth with Rheumatism [IO], Gentofte, Denmark
Danish Orienteering Fed. [IO], Brondby, Denmark
Danish Orthopedic Soc. [IO], Copenhagen, Denmark
Danish Pattern Recognition Soc. [IO], Lyngby, Denmark
Danish Physical Soc. [IO], Roskilde, Denmark
Danish Plastics Fed. [IO], Copenhagen, Denmark
Danish Precast Concrete Fed. [IO], Copenhagen, Denmark
Danish Psychologists' Assn. [IO], Copenhagen, Denmark
Danish Publishers' Assn. [IO], Copenhagen, Denmark
Danish Ready-Mixed Concrete Assn. [IO], Copenhagen, Denmark
Danish Red Cross [IO], Copenhagen, Denmark
Danish Refugee Coun. [IO], Copenhagen, Denmark
Danish Retriever Club [IO], Odense, Denmark
Danish Rheumatism Assn. [IO], Copenhagen, Denmark
Danish Rottweiler Club [IO], Hjorring, Denmark
Danish Sailing Assn. [IO], Brondby, Denmark
Danish Samoyed Club [IO], Odense, Denmark
Danish Schoolsport [IO], Nyborg, Denmark
Danish Seed Trade Assn. [IO], Copenhagen, Denmark
Danish Shipowners' Assn. [IO], Copenhagen, Denmark
Danish Shooting Union [IO], Brondby, Denmark
Danish Skating Union [IO], Brondby, Denmark
Danish Slaughterhouses [IO], Copenhagen, Denmark
Danish Social-Liberal Party [IO], Copenhagen, Denmark
Danish Soc. for Biochemistry and Molecular Biology [IO], Glostrup, Denmark
Danish Soc. for Biomedical Engg. [IO], Copenhagen, Denmark
Danish Soc. of Cardiology [IO], Copenhagen, Denmark
Danish Soc. of Clinical Neurophysiology [IO], Glostrup, Denmark
Danish Soc. of Engineers [IO], Copenhagen, Denmark
Danish Soc. of Gastroenterology [IO], Odense, Denmark
Danish Soc. of Heating, Ventilating and Airconditioning Engineers [IO], Ballerup, Denmark
Danish Soc. for Jazz, Rock, and Folk Composers [IO], Copenhagen, Denmark
Danish Soc. for Medical Physics [IO], Copenhagen, Denmark
Danish Soc. for Nature Conservation [IO], Copenhagen, Denmark
Danish Soc. for Neuroscience [IO], Copenhagen, Denmark
Danish Soc. of Obstetrics and Gynaecology [IO], Odense, Denmark
Danish Soc. of Palliative Medicine [IO], Copenhagen, Denmark
Danish Soc. for Patient Safety [IO], Hvidovre, Denmark
Danish Soc. of Periodontology [IO], Arhus, Denmark
Danish Soc. of Pharmacology and Toxicology [IO], Arhus, Denmark
Danish Soc. of Rheumatology [IO], Copenhagen, Denmark
Danish Songwriters Guild [IO], Copenhagen, Denmark
Danish Squash Assn. [IO], Odense, Denmark
Danish Standards [IO], Charlottenlund, Denmark
Danish/Swedish Farmdog Club of Am. [21552], PO Box 1184, Ramona, CA 92065
Danish Taekwondo Fed. [IO], Olgod, Denmark
Danish Technological Inst. [IO], Taastrup, Denmark
Danish Terrier Club [IO], Hjorring, Denmark
Danish Textile Union [IO], Hellerup, Denmark
Danish-UK Chamber of Commerce [IO], London, United Kingdom
Danish Union of Journalists [IO], Copenhagen, Denmark

Danish Union of Teachers [IO], Copenhagen, Denmark
Danish United Nations Assn. [IO], Copenhagen, Denmark
Danish Water Ski Fed. [IO], Kerteminde, Denmark
Danish Wind Indus. Assn. [IO], Frederiksberg, Denmark
Danish Wine and Spirits' Assn. [IO], Copenhagen, Denmark
Danish Women's Soc. [IO], Copenhagen, Denmark
Danish Wound Healing Soc. [IO], Allerod, Denmark
Danish Writers Assn. [IO], Copenhagen, Denmark
Danish Yngling Club [IO], Klampenborg, Denmark
Danish Young Farmers [IO], Arhus, Denmark
Danish Youth Coun. [IO], Copenhagen, Denmark
Danishkadah [IO], Karachi, Pakistan
Danmark-Amerika Fondet [★IO]
Danmarks Apotekerforening [★IO]
Danmarks Automobilforhandler Forening [★IO]
Danmarks Basketball-Forbund [★IO]
Danmarks Biblioteksforening [★IO]
Danmarks Farmaceutiske Selskab [★IO]
Danmarks Fiskeindustri-Og Eksportforening [★IO]
Danmarks Fiskeriforening [★IO]
Danmarks Forskningsbiblioteksforening [★IO]
Danmarks Gymnastik Forbund [★IO]
Danmarks Idraets-Forbund [★IO]
Danmarks Jurist- og Okonomforbund [★IO]
Danmarks Laererforening [★IO]
Danmarks Naturfredningsforening [★IO]
Danmarks Rederiforening [★IO]
Danmarks Rejsebureau Forening [★IO]
Danmarks Skohandlerforening [★IO]
Danmarks Socialdemokratiske Ungdom [★IO]
Dannemiller, Inc. [13747], 5711 Northwest Pkwy., San Antonio, TX 78249, (800)328-2308
Dannemiller Memorial Educational Found. [★13747]
Dansiprottasamband Islands [★IO]
Dansk Acusticusneurinom Forening [★IO]
Dansk Akustik Selskab [★IO]
Dansk Amater Teater Samvirke [★IO]
Dansk Annoncorforening [★IO]
Dansk Arbejdsgiverforening [★IO]
Dansk Atletik Forbund [★IO]
Dansk Automobil Sports Union [★IO]
Dansk Baseball Softball Forbund [★IO]
Dansk Boldspil-Union [★IO]
Dansk Byggeri [★IO]
Dansk Cardiologisk selskab [★IO]
Dansk Dagligvareleverandor Forening [★IO]
Dansk Dermatologisk Selskab [★IO]
Dansk Dobermann Klub [IO], Lynge, Denmark
Dansk Energiokonomisk Selskab [★IO]
Dansk Epilepsiforening [★IO]
Dansk Fabriksbetonforening [★IO]
Dansk Faegte-Forbund [★IO]
Dansk Fagpresse [★IO]
Dansk Floorball Union [★IO]
Dansk Flygtningehjaelp [★IO]
Dansk Forening til Fremme af Opfindelser [★IO]
Dansk Forfatterforening [★IO]
Dansk Frisbee Sport Union [IO], Odense, Denmark
Dansk Frohandlerforening [★IO]
Dansk Fysisk Selskab [★IO]
Dansk Galop [★IO]
Dansk Gastroenterologisk Selskab [★IO]
Dansk Geologisk Forening [★IO]
Dansk Gerontologisk Selskab [★IO]
Dansk Hortonomforening [★IO]
Dansk Hypertensionsselskab [★IO]
Dansk Idraetsmedicinsk Selskab [★IO]
Dansk Industri [★IO]
Dansk Institut for Internationale Studier [★IO]
Dansk Irsk Selskab [★IO]
Dansk Isindustri [★IO]
Dansk Jazz Forbund [★IO]
Dansk Journalistforbund [★IO]
Dansk Kennel Klub [★IO]
Dansk Kunst og Antikvitetshandler Union [IO], Frederiksberg, Denmark
Dansk Kvindesamfund [★IO]
Dansk Lancia Register [★IO]
Dansk Landbrug [★IO]
Dansk Litteraturcenter [★IO]
Dansk Maganipresses Udgiverforening [★IO]

A star before a book entry number signifies that the name is not listed separately, but is mentioned within the entry.

Dansk Matematisk Forening [★IO]
Dansk Medicinsk Selskab [★IO]
Dansk MedikoTeknisk Selskab [★IO]
Dansk Missionsrad [★IO]
Dansk Musikbiblioteks Forening [★IO]
Dansk Oftalmologisk Selskab [★IO]
Dansk Optisk Selskab [★IO]
Dansk Orienterings-Forbund [★IO]
Dansk Ortopaedisk Selskab [★IO]
Dansk Psykolog Forening [★IO]
Dansk Retriever Klub [★IO]
Dansk Reumatologisk Selskab [★IO]
Dansk Rode Kors [★IO]
Dansk Sejlunion [★IO]
Dansk Selskab for Farmakologi og Toksikologi [★IO]
Dansk Selskab for Klinisk Neurofysiologis [★IO]
Dansk Selskab for Medicinsk Fysik [★IO]
Dansk Selskab for Musikforskning [★IO]
Dansk Selskab for Neurovidenskab [★IO]
Dansk Selskab for Obstetrik og Gynaekologi [★IO]
Dansk Selskab for Operationsanalyse [★IO]
Dansk Selskab for Patientsikkerhed [★IO]
Dansk Selskab for Sarheling [★IO]
Dansk Skojte Union [★IO]
Dansk Skoleidraet [★IO]
Dansk Skovforening [★IO]
Dansk Skuespillerforbund [★IO]
Dansk Skytte Union [★IO]
Dansk Socialradgiverforening [★IO]
Dansk Sportsdanserforbund [★IO]
Dansk Squash Forbund [★IO]
Dansk Standard [★IO]
Dansk Sygeplejeraad [★IO]
Dansk Taekwondo Forbund [★IO]
Dansk Tandlaegeforening [★IO]
Dansk Teknisk Laererforbund [★IO]
Dansk Tennis Forbund [IO], Brondby, Denmark
Dansk Terrier Klub [★IO]
Dansk Textil and Beklaedning [★IO]
Dansk Textil Union [★IO]
Dansk Translatorforbund [★IO]
Dansk Ungdoms Faellesrad [★IO]
Dansk Vandski Forbund [★IO]
Dansk Yngling Klub [★IO]
Danske Designere [★IO]
Danske Doves Landsforbund [★IO]
Danske Forstkandidaters Forening [★IO]
Danske Fysioterapeuter [★IO]
Danske Jazz, Beat og Folkemusik Autorer [★IO]
Danske Landbrugsskoler [★IO]
Danske Landskabsarkitekter [★IO]
Danske Malermestre [★IO]
Danske Maritime [★IO]
Danske Populaerautorer [★IO]
Danske Radiologers Org. [★IO]
Danske Reklame- og Relationsbureauers Branche-forening [★IO]
Danske Slagterier [★IO]
Danske Slagtermestres [★IO]
Dante Soc. [★9359]
Dante Soc. of Am. [9359], PO Box 1558, Arlington, MA 02474-0023
Danube Tourist Commn. [IO], Vienna, Austria
Danubian Psychiatric Assn. [IO], Linz, Austria
Daphne Institut Aplikovanej Ekologie [★IO]
Daphne Inst. of Applied Ecology [IO], Bratislava, Slovakia
Dar Serca [★14078]
Dar Serca [★14078]
D.A.R.E. Am. [13247], PO Box 512090, Los Angeles, CA 90051-0090, (310)215-0575
Darfur Human Rights Org. [17825], 8171 Castor Ave., Philadelphia, PA 19152, (267)784-7073
Darfur Human Rights Org. [17825], 8171 Castor Ave., Philadelphia, PA 19152, (267)784-7073
Darfur Peace and Development Org. [12324], PO Box 66475, Washington, DC 20035-6475, (202)393-8150
Darfur Peace and Development Org. [12324], PO Box 66475, Washington, DC 20035-6475, (202)393-8150
Dark Shadows Fan Info. Ser. [★23918]
Dark Shadows Official Fan Club [23918], PO Box 92, Maplewood, NJ 07040
Darkness to Light [11263], 7 Radcliffe St., Ste. 200, Charleston, SC 29403, (843)965-5444

Darkride and Funhouse Enthusiasts [20945], PO Box 484, Vienna, OH 44473-0484
Dart Automotive Refurbishing Tech. Services [★21040]
Dart Music Intl. [10187], 711 San Antonio St., Austin, TX 78701, (707)836-3278
Dartmoor Sheep Breeders' Assn. [IO], Saltash, United Kingdom
Darts
  Amer. Darters Assn. [22496]
  Amer. Darts Org. [22497]
  AMOA Natl. Dart Assn. [22498]
  AMOA Natl. Dart Assn. [22498]
DARTS Club [21040], PO Box 9, Wethersfield, CT 06129-0009, (860)257-8434
Darul Vietii [★IO]
Darwin Animal Doctors [3809], 222 E 89th St., No. 8, New York, NY 10128
DAST Intl. [16813], 42611 Saratoga Park St., Fremont, CA 94538
Data Interchange Standards Assn. [18674], 7600 Leesburg Pike, Ste. 430, Falls Church, VA 22043, (703)970-4480
Data Mgt. Assn. Intl. [6975], 19239 N Dale Mabry Hwy., No. 132, Lutz, FL 33548, (813)778-5495
Data Mgt. Assn. Intl. [6975], 19239 N Dale Mabry Hwy., No. 132, Lutz, FL 33548, (813)778-5495
Data Processing
  Amer. Medical Informatics Assn. [14219]
  Chamber of Software Businesses and Info. Services [3750]
  Hea. Indus. Bus. Communications Coun. [14220]
  Infrared Data Assn. [6591]
  Infrared Data Assn. [6591]
  Intl. Soc. for Ethics and Info. Tech. [6979]
  Latinos in Info. Sciences and Tech. Assn. [6983]
  Software Contractors' Guild [1029]
Data Publishers Assn. [IO], London, United Kingdom
Database Management
  Intl. DB2 Users Gp. [6592]
  Quest Intl. Users Gp. [6593]
DataCenter [18435], 1904 Franklin St., Ste. 900, Oakland, CA 94612-2923, (510)835-4692
Dataworks Users Alliance [★6511]
Date-Able/HI [★11775]
Date-Able/HI [★11775]
Date Administrative Comm. [★4433]
DateAble [11775], 15520 Bald Eagle School Rd., Brandywine, MD 20613, (301)888-1177
DateAble [11775], 15520 Bald Eagle School Rd., Brandywine, MD 20613, (301)888-1177
Dateable Intl. [★11775]
Dateable Intl. [★11775]
Daughters of Cambodia [IO], Phnom Penh, Cambodia
Daughters of the Cincinnati [20335], 20 W 44th St., Rm. 508, New York, NY 10036, (212)991-9945
Daughters of the Elderly Bridging the Unknown Together - Defunct.
Daughters of Isabella, Intl. Circle [18952], PO Box 9585, New Haven, CT 06535, (203)865-2570
Daughters of Isabella, Intl. Circle [18952], PO Box 9585, New Haven, CT 06535, (203)865-2570
Daughters of Isabella, Natl. Circle [★18952]
Daughters of Isabella, Natl. Circle [★18952]
Daughters of Isabella, Supreme Circle [★18952]
Daughters of Isabella, Supreme Circle [★18952]
Daughters of the King [★19714]
Daughters of the Nile, Supreme Temple - Address unknown since 2010.
Daughters of Norway [★19180]
Daughters of Norway [★19180]
Daughters of Penelope [19012], 1909 Q St. NW, Ste. 500, Washington, DC 20009, (202)234-9741
Daughters of Penelope Foundation [★19012]
Daughters of the Republic of Texas [20626], 510 E Anderson Ln., Austin, TX 78752, (512)339-1997
Daughters of Saint Paul - European Off. [IO], Rome, Italy
Daughters of Scotia [19223], 7595 Carter Rd., Saga-more Hills, OH 44067, (330)467-6387
Daughters and Sons United - Defunct.
Daughters of Union Veterans of the Civil War, 1861-1865 [20383], 1932 Clifton Ave., Lansing, MI 48910-3531, (517)484-7795

Daughters of Zion [★19863]
Daughters of Zion [★19863]
David Allan Coe Fan Club [23829], 97 Haybar Dr., Rogersville, MO 65742, (417)753-2567
David Birney Intl. Fan Club [23764], Ruth K. Becht, Pres., 168 N Lehigh Ave., Cranford, NJ 07016
David Birney Intl. Fan Club [23764], Ruth K. Becht, Pres., 168 N Lehigh Ave., Cranford, NJ 07016
David and Lucile Packard Found. [4038], 300 Second St., Los Altos, CA 94022, (650)948-7658
David and Lucile Packard Found. [4038], 300 Second St., Los Altos, CA 94022, (650)948-7658
David Suzuki Found. [IO], Vancouver, BC, Canada
Davis Dyslexia Assn. - UK [IO], Kent, United Kingdom
Davis Registry [21041], Tom Wilson, Dir. Emeritus, 6487 Munger Rd., Ypsilanti, MI 48197-9014, (734)434-5581
DaVita Patient Citizens [★15549]
Dawley Family Assn. - Defunct.
Dawn Bible Students Assn. [19347], 199 Railroad Ave., East Rutherford, NJ 07073, (888)440-DAWN
Dawn Welfare Org. [IO], Gujar Khan, Pakistan
Day-Break Geriatric Massage Inst. [15265], Sharon Puszko, PhD, Dir./Owner, 7434 King George Dr., Ste. A, Indianapolis, IN 46240, (317)722-9896
Day One Christian Ministries [IO], Leominster, United Kingdom
Day Sailer Assn. [22333], Brooks Measures, Sec., 5780 San Pedro Ave., Atascadero, CA 93422-3520, (805)466-2646
Daycare Trust [IO], London, United Kingdom
Daytime Broadcasters Assn. [★501]
DB-Link [★17106]
DB-Link: The Natl. Info. CH on Children Who are Deaf-Blind [★17106]
DB - Panhard Registry [★21091]
DBA ESI - Defunct.
DBA Intl. [1032], 8400 Westpark Dr., 2nd Fl., McLean, VA 22102, (703)610-0224
DBA - The Barge Assn. [IO], Maidenhead, United Kingdom
DC Dance Club [IO], Calgary, AB, Canada
De Havilland Moth Club [IO], Berkhamsted, United Kingdom
De Maatschappij der Nederlandse Letterkunde [★IO]
De Nederlandse Rozenvereniging [IO], Liempde, Netherlands
De Re Militari: The Soc. for Medieval Military History [10090], Carroll Gillmor, Sec.-Treas., PO Box 784, Salt Lake City, UT 84111
Deadline Club [2823], Salmagundi Club, 47 5th Ave., New York, NY 10003, (347)637-8370
Deaf
  Acad. of Rehabilitative Audiology [14910]
  Deaf and Hard of Hearing Alliance [14929]
  Dogs for the Deaf [14933]
  Intl. Catholic Deaf Assn. U.S. Sect. [19435]
  Model Secondary School for the Deaf [14946]
  Natl. Coalition on Auditory Processing Disorders [14949]
  Rainbow Alliance of the Deaf [12110]
  U.S.A. Deaf Basketball [22300]
  U.S. Flag Football for the Deaf [22530]
  Univ. of Colorado Hea. Sciences Center Alumni Assn. [23547]
Deaf Artists of America - Defunct.
Deaf Assn. of New Zealand [IO], Auckland, New Zealand
Deaf Australia [IO], Stafford, Australia
Deaf Bilingual Coalition [12137], 3045 140th Ave. NE, Ham Lake, MN 55304
Deaf-Blind Youths and Adults; Helen Keller Natl. Center for [14941]
Deaf Children's Literacy Proj. [★16689]
Deaf Educ. Through Listening and Talking [IO], Sur-rey, United Kingdom
Deaf Friends Intl. [12138], PO Box 13192, Hamilton, OH 45013, (513)658-4879
Deaf Friends Intl. [12138], PO Box 13192, Hamilton, OH 45013, (513)658-4879
Deaf and Hard of Hearing Alliance [14929], 108 S 63rd St., Milwaukee, WI 53214, (414)888-0508
Deaf and Hard of Hearing Entrepreneurs Coun. - Defunct.

Reference to "IO" in place of a book number signifies that the association may be found in the 50th edition of International Organizations.

Deaf and Hard of Hearing; Parents' Sect. of the Alexander Graham Bell Assn. for the [14955]
Deaf Intl. [12139], PO Box 3838, Olathe, KS 66063-3838, (913)390-9010
Deaf Missions - Defunct.
Deaf Olympics [★22512]
Deaf Olympics [★22512]
Deaf-REACH [14930], 3521 12th St. NE, Washington, DC 20017, (202)832-6681
Deaf Seniors of Am. [14931], 7370 Michael Ave., Easton, MD 21601-4918
Deaf Sports Australia [IO], East Melbourne, Australia
Deaf Sports Fed; U.S.A. [22531]
Deaf Women United [12140], PO Box 141774, Austin, TX 78714-1774
Deaf Women's Bowling Assn; Natl. [22517]
Deafblind Intl. [IO], Perth, Australia
Deafblind Scotland [IO], Glasgow, United Kingdom
Deafblind UK [IO], Peterborough, United Kingdom
DeafHear.ie [IO], Dublin, Ireland
DeafHope [12141], 470 27th St., Oakland, CA 94612, (510)267-8800
Deafness Res. Found. [14932], 363 7th Ave., 10th Fl., New York, NY 10001-3904, (212)257-6140
Dealers Alliance [354], Continental Plz., 401 Hackensack Ave., Hackensack, NJ 07601, (201)342-4542
Dean Martin Fan Center [23802], PO Box 660212, Arcadia, CA 91066-0212
Death with Dignity Natl. Center [17283], 520 SW 6th Ave., Ste. 1220, Portland, OR 97204, (503)228-4415

Death and Dying
Aiding Mothers and Fathers Experiencing Neonatal Death [11744]
Assn. for Death Educ. and Counseling [11745]
Hold the Door for Others [11129]
MISS Found. I Alliance of Grandparents, A Support in Tragedy Intl. [12123]
Palliative Care Policy Center [11746]
Sacred Dying Found. [11747]
Death Penalty; Campaign to End the [17215]
Death Penalty Info. Center [17217], 1015 18th St. NW, Ste. 704, Washington, DC 20036, (202)289-2275
Death Penalty; Natl. Coalition to Abolish the [17220]
Death Penalty; Proj. Hope to Abolish the [17222]
Death Valley '49ers [9682], PO Box 101, Amargosa Valley, NV 89020
Death With Dignity Educ. Center [★17283]
Death With Dignity Educ. Fund [★17283]
Debate and Theatre Assn; NFHS Speech, [8898]
Debbie Fox Found. [★14197]
Debbie Fox Found. for Treatment of Cranio-Facial Deformities [★14197]
Debbie Harry Collector's Soc. - Address unknown since 2011.
DEBRA of Am. [★14325]
DEBRA European [IO], Crowthorne, United Kingdom
DEBRA Intl. [IO], Vienna, Austria
DEBRA Ireland [IO], Dublin, Ireland
Debt AIDS Trade Africa [17149], 1400 Eye St. NW, Ste. 600, Washington, DC 20005, (202)495-2700
Debt AIDS Trade Africa [17149], 1400 Eye St. NW, Ste. 600, Washington, DC 20005, (202)495-2700
Debt Buyers' Assn. [★1032]

Debt Collection
ACA Intl. [1030]
ACA Intl. [1030]
Amer. Recovery Assn. [1031]
DBA Intl. [1032]
Debtors Anonymous [13040]
Intl. Assn. of Commercial Collectors [1033]
Intl. Assn. of Commercial Collectors [1033]
Debt Payment Club - Defunct.
Debtors Anonymous [13040], PO Box 920888, Needham, MA 02492-0009, (781)453-2743
DECA [★23069]
DECA, The Decathlon Assn. [23069], 58 2nd Ave., Emmitsburg, MD 21727-9169, (301)447-6122
Decade of the Brain Coalition [★15666]
Decalogue Soc. of Lawyers [5243], 39 S LaSalle St., Ste. 410, Chicago, IL 60603, (312)263-6493

Decathlon
DECA, The Decathlon Assn. [23069]

DECHEMA [IO], Frankfurt, Germany
Decision Sciences Inst. [7789], 75 Piedmont Ave., Ste. 340, Atlanta, GA 30303, (404)413-7710
Declaration Found. - Address unknown since 2011.
Decorative Arts Trust [9290], 106 Bainbridge St., Philadelphia, PA 19147, (215)627-2859
Decorative Laminate Products Assn. - Defunct.
Decorative Plumbing and Hardware Assn. [2781], 401 N Michigan Ave., Ste. 2200, Chicago, IL 60611, (312)321-5110
Dedham Pottery Collectors Soc. [21333], 248 Highland St., Dedham, MA 02026-5833, (800)283-8070
Deep Draft Lubricant Assn. [2225], Shawn Konrad, Dir./Pres., Belle Chasse Marine Trans., 5813 Citrus Blvd., Harahan, LA 70123, (504)837-3125
Deep Foundations Inst. [910], 326 Lafayette Ave., Hawthorne, NJ 07506, (973)423-4030
Deep Foundations Inst. [910], 326 Lafayette Ave., Hawthorne, NJ 07506, (973)423-4030
Deep Griha Soc. of Pune, India [IO], Pune, India
Deep Purple Appreciation Soc. [IO], Sheffield, United Kingdom
Deep Purple Made in Italy Fan Club [IO], Turin, Italy
Deep Springs Intl. [4992], Etta Casalnova, PO Box 654, Grove City, PA 16127
Deer Commn. for Scotland [IO], Inverness, United Kingdom
Defence for Children Intl. - Angola [IO], Luanda, Angola
Defence for Children Intl. - Bolivia [IO], Cochabamba, Bolivia
Defence for Children Intl. - Canada [IO], Toronto, ON, Canada
Defence for Children Intl. - Chile [IO], Santiago, Chile
Defence for Children Intl. - Costa Rica [IO], San Jose, Costa Rica
Defence for Children Intl. - Czech Republic [IO], Prague, Czech Republic
Defence for Children Intl. - Lebanon [IO], Beirut, Lebanon
Defence for Children Intl. - Netherlands [IO], Leiden, Netherlands
Defence for Children Intl. - Niger [IO], Niamey, Niger
Defence for Children Intl. - Palestine [IO], Jerusalem, Israel
Defence for Children Intl. - Republic of the Congo [IO], Kinshasa, Republic of the Congo
Defence for Children Intl. - Sierra Leone [IO], Freetown, Sierra Leone
Defence for Children Intl. - Switzerland [IO], Geneva, Switzerland
Defence for Children Intl. - Togo [IO], Lome, Togo
Defence Export Promotion Org. [IO], Islamabad, Pakistan
Defence Mfrs. Assn. of Great Britain [IO], Surrey, United Kingdom
Defenders of the Christian Faith [★19548]
Defenders of Furbearers [★5043]
Defenders of Wildlife [5043], 1130 17th St. NW, Washington, DC 20036, (202)682-9400
Defending Dissent Found. [17284], 8630 Fenton St., Ste. 524, Silver Spring, MD 20910, (202)529-4225
Defensa de Ninas y Ninos Internacional - Costa Rica [★IO]
Defensa de Ninas y Ninos Internacional - Seccion Bolivia [★IO]
Defensa de los Ninos Internacional - Chile [★IO]

Defense
Aircraft Carrier Indus. Base Coalition [1034]
Alliance Defense Fund [17498]
Amer. Conservative Defense Alliance [17499]
Amer. Defense Inst. [17500]
British Amer. Security Info. Coun. [17501]
Center for Defense Info. [17502]
Defense Forum Found. [17503]
Inter-American Defense Bd. [17504]
Inter-American Defense Bd. [17504]
Intl. Disabled Self-Defense Assn. [13032]
Intl. Strategic Stud. Assn. [17505]
Intl. Strategic Stud. Assn. [17505]
Jewish Inst. for Natl. Security Affairs [17506]
Jewish Inst. for Natl. Security Affairs [17506]
Leonard Peltier Defense Comm. [17507]

Leonard Peltier Defense Comm. [17507]
Missile Defense Advocacy Alliance [17508]
Natl. Security and Law Soc. [5970]
Natl. Strategy Info. Center [17509]
Naval Submarine League [17510]
Proj. on Defense Alternatives [17511]
Submarine Indus. Base Coun. [1035]
Women in Defense, a Natl. Security Org. [17512]
Defense Advisory Comm. on Women in the Services [5805], 4000 Defense Pentagon, Rm. 2C548A, Washington, DC 20301-4000, (703)697-2122
Defense Budget Proj. [★18136]
Defense Credit Union Coun. [998], 601 Pennsylvania Ave. NW, South Bldg., Ste. 600, Washington, DC 20004-2601, (202)638-3950
Defense des Enfants Intl. [★IO]
Defense des Enfants Intl. - Canada [★IO]
Defense des Enfants Intl. - Liban [★IO]
Defense Forum Found. [17503], 3014 Castle Rd., Falls Church, VA 22044, (703)534-4313
Defense Intel Alumni Assn. [18868], 256 Morris Creek Rd., Cullen, VA 23934, (571)426-0098
Defense Org; Jewish [18018]
Defense Orientation Conf. Assn. [18595], 9271 Old Keene Mill Rd., Ste. 200, Burke, VA 22015-4202, (703)451-1200
Defense of Place [4039], Rsrc. Renewal Inst., 187 E Blithedale Ave., Mill Valley, CA 94941, (415)928-3774
Defense Res. Inst. [5772], 55 W Monroe, Ste. 2000, Chicago, IL 60603, (312)795-1101
Defense Supply Assn. [★5794]

Deforestation
Avoided Deforestation Partners [4390]
Environmental Paper Network [4051]
Tropical Forestry Initiative [4154]
Degree of Honor Protective Assn. [19045], 400 Robert St. N, Ste. 1600, St. Paul, MN 55101-2029, (651)228-7600
Degree of Pocahontas, Improved Order of Red Men [19207], 4521 Speight Ave., Waco, TX 76711-1708, (254)756-1221
DeKalb Families in Action [★13279]
Del Shannon Appreciation Soc. [23830], PO Box 44201, Tacoma, WA 98448-0201
Delancey St. Found. [13041], 600 Embarcadero, San Francisco, CA 94107, (415)512-5104
Delbert McClinton Intl. Fan Club [23831], PO Box 218248, Nashville, TN 37221, (800)335-2378
Delegation Catholique pour la Cooperation [IO], Paris, France
Delegation de la Commn. Europeenne en Republique Democratique du Congo [★IO]
Delegation de la Commn. Europeenne aupres de la Republique Togolaise [★IO]
Delegation of the European Commn. to Guyana, Suriname, Trinidad and Tobago, Aruba and the Netherlands Antilles [IO], Georgetown, Guyana
Delegation of the Finnish Academies of Sci. and Letters [IO], Helsinki, Finland
Delegation for Friendship Among Women [17639], 1630 Edgecumbe Rd., St. Paul, MN 55116
Delhi Mgt. Assn. [IO], New Delhi, India
Deli/Prepared Meats Comm. - Defunct.
Delius Soc. [IO], London, United Kingdom
Deliver the Dream [13042], 3223 NW 10th Terr., Ste. 602, Fort Lauderdale, FL 33309, (954)564-3512
DeLorean Owners Assn. [21042], 879 Randolph Rd., Santa Barbara, CA 93111, (818)576-9932
Delphi Found. [23510], 2020 Pennsylvania Ave. NW, No. 355, Washington, DC 20006-1811, (202)558-2801
Delphi Intl. Prog. of World Learning [★17992]
Delphi Intl. Prog. of World Learning [★17992]
Delphinium Soc. [IO], Chippenham, United Kingdom
Delta Delta Delta [23719], 2331 Brookhollow Plaza Dr., PO Box 5987, Arlington, TX 76005-5987, (817)633-8001
Delta Epsilon Sigma [23557], Univ. of St. Thomas, Mail 4073, 2115 Summit Ave., St. Paul, MN 55105
Delta Gamma [23720], 3250 Riverside Dr., Columbus, OH 43221, (614)481-8169
Delta Gamma [23720], 3250 Riverside Dr., Columbus, OH 43221, (614)481-8169
Delta Gamma Pi Multicultural Sorority [23739], PO Box 1414, New York, NY 10101

A star before a book entry number signifies that the name is not listed separately, but is mentioned within the entry.

Delta Hospice Soc. [IO], Delta, BC, Canada
Delta Kappa Epsilon [23664], PO Box 8360, Ann Arbor, MI 48107-8360, (734)302-4210
Delta Lambda·Phi [★23665]
Delta Lambda Phi Natl. Social Fraternity [23665], 2020 Pennsylvania Ave. NW, No. 355, Washington, DC 20006-1811, (202)527-9453
Delta Mu Delta Honor Soc. [23479], 9217 Broadway Ave., Brookfield, IL 60513-1251, (708)485-8494
Delta Nu Alpha Trans. Fraternity [23756], 265 N Chicago Ave., No. 2, South Milwaukee, WI 53172, (414)764-3063
Delta Omega [★23613]
Delta Omega [23628], 1900 M St. NW, Ste. 710, Washington, DC 20036, (202)296-1099
Delta Omicron [23599], PO Box 752, Jefferson City, TN 37760, (865)471-6155
Delta Org. [★4115]
Delta Org. [★4115]
Delta Phi Alpha [23546], Natl. German Honor Soc., Longwood Univ., Grainger Bldg. 306, 201 High St., Farmville, VA 23909-1801
Delta Phi Epsilon [23721], 251 S Camac St., Philadelphia, PA 19107, (215)732-5901
Delta Phi Epsilon, Professional Foreign Ser. Fraternity [23528], 3401 Prospect St. NW, Washington, DC 20007-3219, (202)337-9702
Delta Phi Epsilon Professional Foreign Ser. Sorority [23529], 3401 Prospect St. NW, Washington, DC 20007-3219
Delta Phi Omega Sorority [23740], Delta Phi Omega Natl. Coun., 2900 Oak Tree Ave., Apt. No. 8103, Norman, OK 73072
Delta Phi Upsilon [23491], PO Box 573013, Houston, TX 77257-3013, (713)800-0802
Delta Pi Epsilon [23487], PO Box 4340, Little Rock, AR 72214, (501)219-1866
Delta Psi [23666], PO Box 876, Ithaca, NY 14851-0876, (607)533-9994
Delta Psi Omega [23504], Wabash Coll., Theater Dept., Crawfordsville, IN 47933-2484, (765)361-6394
Delta Res. and Educational Foundation [★23641]
Delta Sigma Chi Sorority [23741], 114-75 226th St., Cambria Heights, NY 11411, (866)439-6489
Delta Sigma Delta [23498], 296 15th Ave., Nekoosa, WI 54457, (715)325-6320
Delta Sigma Delta [23498], 296 15th Ave., Nekoosa, WI 54457, (715)325-6320
Delta Sigma Epsilon [★23723]
Delta Sigma Pi [23667], 330 S Campus Ave., Oxford, OH 45056-2405, (513)523-1907
Delta Sigma Pi Leadership Foundation [★23667]
Delta Sigma Rho [★23754]
Delta Sigma Rho - Tau Kappa Alpha [23754], Univ. of Alabama, 210j Reese Phifer Hall, PO Box 870172, Tuscaloosa, AL 35487, (205)348-6010
Delta Sigma Theta [23641], 1707 New Hampshire Ave. NW, Washington, DC 20009, (202)986-2400
Delta Soc. [16847], 875 124th Ave. NE, Ste. 101, Bellevue, WA 98005, (425)679-5500
Delta Soc. Australia [IO], Sydney, Australia
Delta Tau Lambda Sorority [23742], PO Box 7714, Ann Arbor, MI 48107, (734)673-9879
Delta Theta Phi [23578], PO Box 117, Elyria, OH 44036-0117, (919)866-4667
Delta Upsilon [23668], 8705 Founders Rd., Indianapolis, IN 46268, (317)875-8900
Delta Upsilon [23668], 8705 Founders Rd., Indianapolis, IN 46268, (317)875-8900
Delta Waterfowl Found. [5044], PO Box 3128, Bismarck, ND 58502, (701)222-8857
Delta Xi Nu Multicultural Sorority [23743], PO Box 36748, Albuquerque, NM 87176-6748
Delta Xi Phi Multicultural Sorority [23722], PO Box 5218, Chicago, IL 60680-5218
Delta Zeta [23723], 202 E Church St., Oxford, OH 45056, (513)523-7597
DEMA, The Assn. for Input Tech. and Mgt. [★6512]
Demand Response and Smart Grid Coalition [6649], Paul Pietsch, 1301 Connecticut Ave. NW, Ste. 350, Washington, DC 20036, (202)296-3636
Demand-Side Mgt. Society [★6693]
Demand-Side Mgt. Society [★6693]
Demarche Alliance - Address unknown since 2010.

Dement Family Assn. - Defunct.
Dementia Advocacy and Support Network Intl. [15582], PO Box 1645, Mariposa, CA 95338
Dementia Advocacy and Support Network Intl. [15582], PO Box 1645, Mariposa, CA 95338
Dementia and Alzheimer's Assn. Tasmania - Hobart [IO], Hobart, Australia
Dementia and Alzheimer's Assn. Tasmania - Launceston [IO], Newnham, Australia
Demeter Assn. [4349], PO Box 1390, Philomath, OR 97370, (541)929-7148
Demeter Biodynamic Trade Assn. [4350], PO Box 264, Talmage, CA 95481
Demir Celik Ureticileri Dernegi [★IO]
Democracia U.S.A. [17606], 2915 Biscayne Blvd., Ste. 210, Miami, FL 33137, (305)573-7329
Democracy
  Amer. Libyan Freedom Alliance [17513]
  Americans for Informed Democracy [17514]
  America's Development Found. [17515]
  Artists for a New South Africa [17516]
  Artists for a New South Africa [17516]
  Burmese Amer. Democratic Alliance [17213]
  Center for the Stud. of Democratic Societies [17517]
  Center for the Stud. of Democratic Societies [17517]
  Change Bangladesh [17275]
  Coun. for a Community of Democracies [17518]
  Coun. for a Community of Democracies [17518]
  Democracy for Am. [18329]
  Democracy Proj. [17519]
  Demos [17520]
  Exit Poverty Empowerment [11067]
  Free Expression Policy Proj. [17290]
  Global Exchange [17521]
  Global Exchange [17521]
  Inst. on Religion and Democracy [17522]
  Inter-American Conf..of Ministers of Labor of the OAS [17523]
  Inter-American Conf. of Ministers of Labor of the OAS [17523]
  Intl. People's Democratic Uhuru Movement [17524]
  Intl. People's Democratic Uhuru Movement [17524]
  Intl. Republican Inst. USA [17525]
  Intl. Republican Inst. USA [17525]
  Karen Natl. League [18722]
  Lebanese Amer. Coun. for Democracy [18069]
  Media and Democracy Coalition [18094]
  Natl. Coalition of Pro-Democracy Advocates [17526]
  Natl. Endowment for Democracy [17527]
  OneAmerica [17528]
  Pushback Network [18491]
  ReclaimDemocracy.org [17529]
Democracy for Am. [18329], PO Box 1717, Burlington, VT 05402, (802)651-3200
Democracy Intl. [18330], 4802 Montgomery Ln., Ste. 200, Bethesda, MD 20814, (301)961-1660
Democracy Intl. [18330], 4802 Montgomery Ln., Ste. 200, Bethesda, MD 20814, (301)961-1660
Democracy Proj. [17519], Campus Watch, 1500 Walnut St., Ste. 1050, Philadelphia, PA 19019
Democracy and Workers Rights Center [IO], Palestine, Israel
Democrat Youth Community of Europe [IO], Nicosia, Cyprus
Democratiaid Rhyddfrydol Cymru [★IO]
Democratic Congressional Campaign Comm. [17534], 430 S Capitol St. SE, Washington, DC 20003, (202)863-1500
Democratic Governors Assn. [5989], 1401 K St. NW, Ste. 200, Washington, DC 20005, (202)772-5600
Democratic Governors Conf. [★5989]
Democratic Leadership Coun. [17535], PO Box 15244, Washington, DC 20003-0244, (202)546-0007
Democratic Natl. Comm. [17536], 430 S Capitol St. SE, Washington, DC 20003, (202)863-8000
Democratic Nursing Org. of South Africa [IO], Pretoria, Republic of South Africa
Democratic Party
  21st Century Democrats [17530]

  Catholic Democrats [17531]
  Coll. Democrats of Am. [17532]
  Comm. for a Democratic Majority [17533]
  Congressional Automotive Caucus [17410]
  Constitutional Rights Found. [17437]
  Democratic Congressional Campaign Comm. [17534]
  Democratic Leadership Coun. [17535]
  Democratic Natl. Comm. [17536]
  Democratic Senatorial Campaign Comm. [17537]
  Democrats Abroad [17538]
  Democrats Abroad [17538]
  Natl. Comm. for an Effective Cong. [17413]
  Natl. Democratic Club [17539]
  Natl. Fed. of Democratic Women [17540]
  New Democratic Dimensions [17541]
  Progressive Democrats of Am. [17542]
  U.S. Assn. of Former Members of Cong. [17414]
  Woman's Natl. Democratic Club [17543]
  Young Democrats of Am. [17544]
Democratic Party Comm. Abroad [★17538]
Democratic Party Comm. Abroad [★17538]
Democratic Party of Hong Kong [IO], Hong Kong, People's Republic of China
Democratic Party of Japan [IO], Tokyo, Japan
Democratic Progressive Party [IO], Taipei, Taiwan
Democratic Rally of Cyprus [IO], Nicosia, Cyprus
Democratic Senatorial Campaign Comm. [17537], PO Box 96047, Washington, DC 20077, (202)224-2447
Democratic Socialism
  Youth for Intl. Socialism [18663]
  Democratic Socialist Fed. [★18339]
  Democratic Socialist Organizing Comm. [★18654]
  Democratic Socialist Organizing Comm. Youth Sect. [★18662]
  Democratic Socialists of Am. [18654], 75 Maiden Ln., Ste. 505, New York, NY 10038, (212)727-8610
  Democratic Socialists of Am. - Youth Sect. [★18662]
Democratic Study Group - Defunct.
Democrats Abroad [17538], 430 S Capitol St. SE, Washington, DC 20003, (202)488-5073
Democrats Abroad [17538], 430 S Capitol St. SE, Washington, DC 20003, (202)488-5073
Democrats for Educ. Reform [17600], 928 Broadway, Ste. 505, New York, NY 10010, (212)614-3213
Democrats for Life of Am. [18552], 601 Pennsylvania Ave. NW, South Bldg., Ste. 900, Washington, DC 20004, (202)220-3066
Demography
  Assn. of Population Centers [6594]
  Carrying Capacity Network [6595]
  Population Assn. of Am. [6596]
  Population Reference Bur. [6597]
  Population Reference Bur. [6597]
  Soc. for the Stud. of Social Biology [6598]
DeMolay Intl. [19240], 10200 NW Ambassador Dr., Kansas City, MO 64153, (816)891-8333
DeMolay Intl. [19240], 10200 NW Ambassador Dr., Kansas City, MO 64153, (816)891-8333
Demos [17520], 220 5th Ave., 5th Fl., New York, NY 10001, (212)633-1405
Demos [IO], Moscow, Russia
Den Danske Antikvarboghandlerforening [★IO]
Den Danske Forlaeggerforening [★IO]
Den Danske Historiske Forening [★IO]
Den norske Forfatterforening [★IO]
Den Nasjonale Forskningsetiske Komite for Medisin [★IO]
Den Norske Forleggerforening [★IO]
Den Norske Revisorforening [★IO]
Den Norske Tannlegeforening [★IO]
Den Norske Turistforening [★IO]
Den Norske Veterinaerforening [★IO]
Den Sociale Hojskole Kobenhavn [★IO]
Denison Soc. [20501], PO Box 42, Mystic, CT 06355-0042, (860)536-9248
Denmark-America Found. [IO], Copenhagen, Denmark
Dennis Brutus Defense Comm. [★17808]
Denominational Ministry Strategy [★20242]
Dental Anthropology Assn. [14279], Univ. of Tennessee, Coll. of Dentistry, 870 Union Ave., Memphis, TN 38163

Reference to "IO" in place of a book number signifies that the association may be found in the 50th edition of International Organizations.

Dental Anxiety and Phobia Assn. [IO], Surrey, United Kingdom

Dental Chamber of Macedonia [IO], Skopje, Macedonia

Dental Gold Inst. - Defunct.

Dental Hea. Found. [IO], Dublin, Ireland

Dental Hygiene

    Amer. Acad. of Restorative Dentistry [14244]

    Amer. Assn. of Endodontists | Amer. Bd. of Endodontics [14250]DentalCanadian Dental Assistants' Assn. DentalCanadian Dental Protective Assn.

        Dental Anthropology Assn. [14279]

        Intl. Fed. of Denturists [5641]

        Intl. Smile Power [14221]

Dental Hygienists' Assn. of Australia - Australian Capital Territory Br. [IO], Canberra, Australia

Dental Hygienists' Assn. of Australia - New South Wales Br. [IO], Sydney, Australia

Dental Hygienists' Assn. of Australia - Queensland Br. [IO], Brisbane, Australia

Dental Hygienists Assn. of Australia - South Australia Br. [IO], Adelaide, Australia

Dental Hygienists Assn. of Australia - Tasmania Br. [IO], Sandy Bay, Australia

Dental Hygienists Assn. of Australia - Victoria Br. [IO], Melbourne, Australia

Dental Hygienists' Assn. of Australia - Western Australia Br. [IO], Bentley, Australia

Dental Labs. Assn. [IO], Nottingham, United Kingdom

Dental Lifeline Network [14280], 1800 15th St., Ste. 100, Denver, CO 80202, (303)534-5360

Dental and Oral Hea. Therapists' Assn. of Queensland [IO], Nundah, Australia

Dental Plans; Natl. Assn. of [15129]

Dental Practitioners Assn. [IO], London, United Kingdom

Dental Soc; Amer. Veterinary [17009]

Dental Therapy and Hygiene Assn. Western Australia [IO], Como, Australia

Dental Trade Alliance [1682], 2300 Clarendon Blvd., Ste. 1003, Arlington, VA 22201, (703)379-7755

Dentalbranchforeningen [★IO]

Dentistry

    Acad. of Dental Materials [14222]

    Acad. of Dentistry Intl. [14223]

    Acad. of Dentistry Intl. [14223]

    Acad. of Gen. Dentistry [14224]

    Acad. of Laser Dentistry [14225]

    Acad. of Operative Dentistry [14226]

    Acad. of Osseointegration [14227]

    Alliance of the Amer. Dental Assn. [14228]

    Alpha Omega Intl. Dental Fraternity [23497]

    Alpha Omega Intl. Dental Fraternity [23497]

    Amer. Acad. of Cosmetic Dentistry [14229]

    Amer. Acad. of Dental Gp. Practice [14230]

    Amer. Acad. of Dental Practice Admin. [14231]

    Amer. Acad. of Esthetic Dentistry [14232]

    Amer. Acad. of Fixed Prosthodontics [14233]

    Amer. Acad. of Gnathologic Orthopedics [14234]

    Amer. Acad. of Gold Foil Operators [14235]

    Amer. Acad. of the History of Dentistry [14236]

    Amer. Acad. of Implant Dentistry [14237]

    Amer. Acad. of Maxillofacial Prosthetics [14238]

    Amer. Acad. of Oral and Maxillofacial Radiology [14239]

    Amer. Acad. of Oral Medicine [14240]

    Amer. Acad. of Orofacial Pain [14241]

    Amer. Acad. of Pediatric Dentistry [14242]

    Amer. Acad. of Periodontology [14243]

    Amer. Acad. of Restorative Dentistry [14244]

    Amer. Alliance of TMD Organizations [14245]

    Amer. Assn. for Community Dental Programs [14246]

    Amer. Assn. of Dental Boards [14247]

    Amer. Assn. for Dental Res. [14248]

    Amer. Assn. of Endodontists [14249]

    Amer. Assn. of Endodontists | Amer. Bd. of Endodontics [14250]

    Amer. Assn. of Orthodontists [14251]

    Amer. Assn. of Public Hea. Dentistry [14252]

    Amer. Assn. of Women Dentists [14253]

    Amer. Bd. of Operative Dentistry [14254]

    Amer. Bd. of Orthodontics [14255]

Amer. Bd. of Orthodontics | Coll. of Diplomates [14256]

Amer. Bd. of Periodontology [14257]

Amer. Bd. of Prosthodontics [14258]

Amer. Coll. of Dentists [14259]

Amer. Coll. of Prosthodontists [14260]

Amer. Dental Assistants Assn. [14261]

Amer. Dental Assn. [14262]

Amer. Dental Educ. Assn. [7964]

Amer. Dental Educ. Assn. [7964]

Amer. Dental Hygienists' Assn. [14263]

Amer. Dental Soc. of Anesthesiology [14264]

Amer. Endodontic Soc. [14265]

Amer. Equilibration Soc. [14266]

Amer. Inst. of Oral Biology [14267]

Amer. Orthodontic Soc. [14268]

Amer. Prosthodontic Soc. [14269]

Amer. Soc. for Dental Aesthetics [14270]

Amer. Soc. for Dental Aesthetics [14270]

Amer. Soc. of Dentist Anesthesiologists [14271]

Amer. Soc. of Forensic Odontology [14272]

Amer. Soc. of Master Dental Technologists [14273]

Amer. Student Dental Assn. [7965]DentistryAssn. for Continuing Dental Educ.

Assn. of Managed Care Dentists [14274]

Assn. of State and Territorial Dental Directors [14275]

Christian Dental Soc. [14276]

Consejo Gen. de Colegios Oficiales de Odontologos y Estomatologos de Espana [16791]

Consumers for Dental Choice [11748]

CR Found. [14277]

Croatian Dental Soc. [19104]

Crown Coun. [14278]

Delta Sigma Delta [23498]

Delta Sigma Delta [23498]

Dental Anthropology Assn. [14279]

Dental Lifeline Network [14280]

Dental Practitioners Assn. [147]

Denturist Assn. of Canada [16288]

European Prosthodontic Assn. [13980]

Fluoride Action Network [14281]

Flying Dentists Assn. [14282]

Friends of the Natl. Inst. of Dental and Craniofacial Res. [14283]

Hellenic Amer. Dental Soc. [14284]

Hispanic Dental Assn. [14285]

Holistic Dental Assn. [14286]

Indian Dental Assn. U.S.A. [14287]

Intl. Acad. of Gnathology-American Sect. [14288]

Intl. Acad. of Oral Medicine and Toxicology [14289]

Intl. Acad. of Oral Medicine and Toxicology [14289]

Intl. Anesthesia Res. Soc. [13748]

Intl. Assn. for Dental Res. [14290]

Intl. Assn. for Dental Res. [14290]

Intl. Assn. for Orthodontics [14291]

Intl. Assn. for Orthodontics [14291]

Intl. Coll. of Dentists [14292]

Intl. Coll. of Dentists [14292]

Intl. Coll. of Prosthodontists [14293]

Intl. Coll. of Prosthodontists [14293]

Intl. Cong. of Oral Implantologists [14294]

Intl. Cong. of Oral Implantologists [14294]

Intl. Fed. of Esthetic Dentistry [14295]

Intl. Fed. of Esthetic Dentistry [14295]

Medicaid/SCHIP Dental Assn. [14296]

Natl. Assn. of Dental Labs. [14297]

Natl. Assn. of Residents and Interns [15425]

Natl. Assn. of Seventh-day Adventist Dentists [14298]

Natl. Bd. for Certification in Dental Lab. Tech. [14299]

Natl. Dental Assistants Assn. [14300]

Natl. Dental Assn. [14301]

Natl. Dental EDI Coun. [14302]

Natl. Dental Hygienists' Assn. [14303]

Natl. Denturist Assn. [14304]

Natl. Flossing Coun. [14305]

Natl. Inst. of Dental and Craniofacial Res. [14306]

Natl. Oral Hea. Info. CH [14307]

North Amer. Sikh Medical and Dental Assn. [15429]

Omicron Kappa Upsilon [23499]

Oral Hea. Am. [7966]

Org. for Safety and Asepsis Procedures [14308]

Pierre Fauchard Acad. [14309]

Psi Omega [23500]DentistrySerbian Amer. Medical and Dental Soc.

Sigma Phi Alpha [23501]

Singapore Dental Assn. [5389]

Special Care Dentistry Assn. [14310]

Student Natl. Dental Assn. [7967]

U.S. Dental Tennis Assn. [23062]

Western Soc. of Periodontology [14311]

Western Soc. of Periodontology [14311]

World Fed. of Orthodontists [14312]

World Fed. of Orthodontists [14312]

Xi Psi Phi [23502]

Dentistry Overseas [★16044]

Dentistry Overseas [★16044]

Dentists Assn. of Argentina [IO], Buenos Aires, Argentina

Dentists for Life [18553], PO Box 1350, Stafford, VA 22555, (540)659-4171

Dentists; Natl. Assn. of Veterans Affairs Physicians and [16271]

Denturist Assn. of British Columbia [IO], Surrey, BC, Canada

Denturist Assn. of Canada [IO], Surrey, BC, Canada

Denturist Assn. of Ontario [IO], Mississauga, ON, Canada

Departement des Metiers de la Constr. - Bur. Canadien [★IO]

Dept. of Audiovisual Instruction [★8304]

Dept. of Boards and Councils of Catholic Educ. [7815], Natl. Catholic Educational Assn., 1005 N Glebe Rd., Ste. 525, Arlington, VA 22201, (202)337-6232

Dept. of Bus. Educ. of the Natl. Educ. Assn. [★7804]

Dept. of Elementary School Principals, NEA [★8749]

Dept. of Environmental and Drug-Induced Pathology [★16117]

Dept. of Environmental and Drug-Induced Pathology [★16117]

Dept. of History and Records Mgt. Services of the Presbyterian Church [★10471]

Dept. for Intl. Development [IO], London, United Kingdom

Dept. of Rural and Agricultural Educ. [★8805]

Dept. of Rural Educ. [★8805]

Dept. of School Nurses/NEA [★15772]

Dept. of School Superintendents of the Natl. Educ. Assn. [★7651]

Dept. of Socio-Economic Development - Caritas Ghana [IO], Accra, Ghana

Dept. of Superintendents of the Natl. Educ. Assn. [★7651]

Dept. of Supervision and Curriculum Development (of NEA) [★7950]

Dept. of Supervisors and Directors of Instruction (of NEA) [★7950]

Dept. of Tourism and Hea. Resorts [★23434]

Dept. of United Church Women of the Natl. Coun. of Churches [★20286]

Dept. of Visual Instruction [★8304]

Depression After Delivery - Address unknown since 2011.

Depression Alliance [IO], London, United Kingdom

Depression Awareness; Families for [15453]

Depression and Bipolar Support Alliance [15452], 730 N Franklin St., Ste. 501, Chicago, IL 60610-7225, (312)642-0049

Derbyshire Conservation Volunteers [IO], Derby, United Kingdom

Derechos Iguales para la Mujer Argentina [★IO]

Dermatological Soc. of Iceland [IO], Reykjavik, Iceland

Dermatological Soc. of Malaysia [IO], Petaling Jaya, Malaysia

Dermatological Soc. of Mauritius [IO], Port Louis, Mauritius

Dermatological Soc. of Singapore [IO], Singapore, Singapore

Dermatological Soc. of South Africa [IO], Johannesburg, Republic of South Africa

Dermatological Soc. of Thailand [IO], Bangkok, Thailand

A star before a book entry number signifies that the name is not listed separately, but is mentioned within the entry.

Dermatology
Amer. Acad. of Dermatology [14313]
Amer. Acad. of Dermatology [14313]
Amer. Bd. of Dermatology [14314]
Amer. Coll. of Veterinary Dermatology [16998]
Amer. Contact Dermatitis Soc. [14315]
Amer. Dermatological Assn. [14316]
Amer. Hair Loss Coun. [14317]
Amer. Osteopathic Coll. of Dermatology [14318]
Amer. Skin Assn. [14319]
Amer. Soc. for Dermatologic Surgery [14320]
Amer. Soc. of Dermatology [14321]
Amer. Soc. of Dermatopathology [14322]
Assn. of Dermatology Administrators and Managers [14323]
Dermatology Found. [14324]
Dystrophic Epidermolysis Bullosa Res. Assn. of Am. [14325]DermatologyEuropean Soc. for Dermatological Res.
Found. for Ichthyosis and Related Skin Types [14326]
Intl. Acad. of Cosmetic Dermatology [14327]
Intl. Acad. of Cosmetic Dermatology [14327]
Intl. Fed. of Psoriasis Associations [14328]
Intl. Fed. of Psoriasis Associations [14328]
Intl. Psoriasis Coun. [14329]
Intl. Soc. of Dermatology [14330]
Intl. Soc. of Dermatology [14330]
Irish Raynaud's and Scleroderma Soc. [14119]
Medical Dermatology Soc. [14331]
Natl. Assn. for Pseudoxanthoma Elasticum [14332]
Natl. Eczema Assn. [14333]
Natl. Psoriasis Found. USA [14334]
Natl. Rosacea Soc. [14335]
Natl. Vitiligo Found. [14336]
North Amer. Clinical Dermatologic Soc. [14337]
North Amer. Clinical Dermatologic Soc. [14337]
Pacific Dermatologic Assn. [14338]
Pacific Dermatologic Assn. [14338]
Psoriasis Assn. of New Zealand [20541]
Soc. for Investigative Dermatology [14339]
Soc. for Pediatric Dermatology [14340]
Vitiligo Support Intl. [14341]
Women's Dermatologic Soc. [14342]
Women's Dermatologic Soc. [14342]
Dermatology; Amer. Coll. of Veterinary [16998]
Dermatology Found. [14324], 1560 Sherman Ave., Ste. 870, Evanston, IL 60201-4808, (847)328-2256
Dermatology Nurses' Assn. [15746], 15000 Commerce Pkwy., Ste. C, Mount Laurel, NJ 08054, (856)439-0500
Dermatology Physician Assistants; Soc. of [16241]
Dermatology Soc; History of [9770]
Dermatovenereology Assn. of Turkey [IO], Izmir, Turkey
Derrike Cope Fan Club [23790], 750 Cartref Rd., Etters, PA 17319
Derwent Valley Horseriders Assn. [IO], New Norfolk, Australia
DES Action, Natl. [★13918]
DES Action USA [13918], PO Box 7296, Jupiter, FL 33468, (800)337-9288
DeSales Secular Inst. [★19495]
DeSales Secular Inst. [★19495]
Descendants of Founders of New Jersey [20393], 816 Grove St., Point Pleasant Beach, NJ 08742
Descendants of Mexican War Veterans [20692], PO Box 461941, Garland, TX 75046-1941
Descendants of the New Jersey Settlers - Defunct.
Descendants of the Signers of the Declaration of Independence [20336], 103 Elmsford Ct., Brentwood, TN 37027-4753
Descendents of Richard Risley [★20578]
Descendents of Richard Risley [★20578]
Desert Botanical Garden [6352], 1201 N Galvin Pkwy., Phoenix, AZ 85008, (480)941-1225
Desert Fishes Coun. [4040], PO Box 337, Bishop, CA 93515, (760)872-8751
Desert Fishes Coun. [4040], PO Box 337, Bishop, CA 93515, (760)872-8751
Desert German Shorthaired Pointer Club [21553], Tina Louie, Sec., 878 E Beargrass Pl., Queen Creek, AZ 85143, (480)862-6896
Desert Protective Coun. [4041], PO Box 3635, San Diego, CA 92163-1635, (619)342-5524

Desert Storm Veterans Assn. [20788], 2425 Wilson Blvd., Arlington, VA 22201, (703)697-7351
Desert Tortoise Coun. [5045], PO Box 1568, Ridgecrest, CA 93556
Desert Tortoise Preserve Comm. [4042], 4067 Mission Inn Ave., Riverside, CA 92501, (951)683-3872
Design
Amer. Assn. of Human Design Practitioners [1036]
Atomic Age Alliance [9672]
Black Fashion Designers Assn. [1037]
Building Commissioning Assn. [538]
Building Enclosure Coun. Natl. [6374]
Building Enclosure Tech. and Env. Coun. [539]
Bur. of European Designers Associations [7]
Decorative Plumbing and Hardware Assn. [2781]
Design Bus. Assn. [23176]
The Designer Cat Assn. [21248]
Fashion Fights Poverty [12725]
Feng Shui Inst. of Am. [9572]
Fusion Architecture [6197]
High Performance Building Coun. [6376]
House Plan Marketing Assn. [1038]
Interaction Design Assn. [6599]
Interaction Design Assn. [6599]
Interior Redesign Indus. Specialists [2060]
Intl. Building Performance Simulation Assn. [6377]
Intl. Feng Shui Guild [9573]
Intl. Feng Shui Guild [9573]
Intl. Soc. for Quality Electronic Design [6600]
Intl. Soc. for Structural Hea. Monitoring of Intelligent Infrastructure [6428]
KEZA [210]
Org. of Black Designers [9574]
Personal Submersibles Org. [7148]
Professional Decorative Painters Assn. [2614]
Public Architecture [243]
Soc. of Boat and Yacht Designers [1039]
Soc. for Design and Process Sci. [6601]
Soc. of Iranian Architects and Planners [6206]
U.S. Faceters Guild [6590]
Universal Design Alliance [1040]
Urbanists Intl. [6207]
Water Design-Build Coun. [634]
Design and Artists Copyright Soc. [IO], London, United Kingdom
Design Austria [IO], Vienna, Austria
Design Automation; Special Interest Gp. for [6472]
Design-Build Inst. of Am. [553], 1100 H St. NW, Ste. 500, Washington, DC 20005-5476, (202)682-0110
Design Bus. Assn. [IO], London, United Kingdom
Design Coun. [IO], London, United Kingdom
Design Forum Finland [IO], Helsinki, Finland
Design History Soc. [IO], Oxford, United Kingdom
Design Indus. Found. for AIDS [★10877]
Design Indus. Found. Fighting AIDS [10877], 200 Lexington Ave., Ste. 910, New York, NY 10016, (212)727-3100
Design Mgt. Inst. [1637], 101 Tremont St., Ste. 300, Boston, MA 02108, (617)338-6380
Design and Tech. Assn. [IO], Warwick, United Kingdom
The Designer Cat Assn. [21248], Nina Adkins, 916 CR 702, Cleburne, TX 76031
Designers Assn; Univ. and Coll. [8321]
Designers Inst. of New Zealand [IO], Auckland, New Zealand
Designs for Change [8770], 814 S Western Ave., Chicago, IL 60612, (312)236-7252
DeSoto Club of Am. [21043], 403 S Thorton, Richmond, MO 64085, (816)470-3048
Despatch Assn. [IO], King's Lynn, United Kingdom
Destination ImagiNation [8697], 1111 S Union Ave., Cherry Hill, NJ 08002, (856)881-1603
Destination Marketing Assn. Intl. [2447], 2025 M St. NW, Ste. 500, Washington, DC 20036, (202)296-7888
Destination Marketing Assn. Intl. [2447], 2025 M St. NW, Ste. 500, Washington, DC 20036, (202)296-7888
Destiny Res. Found. - Defunct.
Det Danske Bibelselskab [★IO]
Det Internationale Rehabiliteringsrad for Torturofre [★IO]
Det Kongelige Norske Videnskabers Selskab [★IO]

Det Norske Bibelselskap [★IO]
Det Norske Videnskaps-Akademi [★IO]
Det Udenrigspolitiske Selskab [★IO]
Detroit Tooling Assn. [★1874]
Detsky Fond Slovenskej Republiky [★IO]
Deutsche Akademie fur Sprache und Dichtung [★IO]
Deutsch-Amerikanische Juristen-Vereinigung e.V. [★IO]
Deutsch-Amerikanischer National-Kongress [★19002]
Deutsch-Armenische Gesellschaft [★IO]
Deutsch-Australische Industrie- und Handelskammer [★IO]
Deutsch Brasilianische Juristenvereinigung [★IO]
Deutsch-Britische Industrie-und Handelskammer [★IO]
Deutsch-Britische Juristenvereinigung [★IO]
Deutsch-Britische Stiftung [★IO]
Deutsch-Chinesische Wirtschaftsvereinigung e.V. [★IO]
Deutsch-Indische Handelskammer [★IO]
Deutsch-Japanische Juristenvereinigung [★IO]
Deutsch-Namibische Gesellschaft e.V. [★IO]
Deutsche Akademie fur Psychoanalyse [★IO]
Deutsche Alzheimer Gesellschaft [IO], Berlin, Germany
Deutsche Arbeitsgemeinschaft fur Mustererkennung [IO], Zurich, Switzerland
Deutsche Atlantische Gesellschaft [★IO]
Deutsche Bibelgesellschaft [★IO]
Deutsche Bunsen-Gesellschaft fur Physikalische Chemie [★IO]
Deutsche China-Gesellschaft [★IO]
Deutsche Dermatologische Gesellschaft [★IO]
Deutsche Forschungsgemeinschaft [★IO]
Deutsche Friedensgesellschaft - Vereinigte KriegsdienstgegnerInnen [★IO]
Deutsche Gartenbauwissenschaftliche Gesellschaft e.V. [★IO]
Deutsche Gemmologische Gesellschaft e.V. [★IO]
Deutsche Gesellschaft fur Allgemein-und Viszeralchirurgie e.V. [★IO]
Deutsche Gesellschaft fur Amerikastudien [★IO]
Deutsche Gesellschaft fur Anaesthesiologie und Intensivmedizin [★IO]
Deutsche Gesellschaft fur Asienkunde e.V. [★IO]
Deutsche Gesellschaft fur Auswartige Politik [★IO]
Deutsche Gesellschaft fur Biomedizinische Technik im VDE [★IO]
Deutsche Gesellschaft fur Eisenbahngeschichte e.V. [★IO]
Deutsche Gesellschaft fur Endokrinologie [★IO]
Deutsche Gesellschaft fur Ernahrung [★IO]
Deutsche Gesellschaft fur Ernahrung e. V. [★IO]
Deutsche Gesellschaft fur Ernahrung e.V. [★IO]
Deutsche Gesellschaft fur Erziehungswissenschaft [★IO]
Deutsche Gesellschaft fur Experimentelle und Klinische Pharmakologie und Toxikologie e.v. [★IO]
Deutsche Gesellschaft fur Fettwissenschaft e.V. [★IO]
Deutsche Gesellschaft Fur Kardiologie [★IO]
Deutsche Gesellschaft fur Gerontologie und Geriatrie [★IO]
Deutsche Gesellschaft fur Hamatologie und Onkologie e.V. [★IO]
Deutsche Gesellschaft fur Humangenetik [★IO]
Deutsche Gesellschaft fur Infektiologie [IO], Freiburg im Breisgau, Germany
Deutsche Gesellschaft fur Informationswissenschaft und Informationspraxis [★IO]
Deutsche Gesellschaft fur Kinder- und Jugendmedizin [★IO]
Deutsche Gesellschaft fur Luft- und Raumfahrt - Lilienthal - Oberth e.V. [★IO]
Deutsche Gesellschaft fur Luft- und Raumfahrtmedizin [★IO]
Deutsche Gesellschaft fur Materialkunde [IO], Frankfurt am Main, Germany
Deutsche Gesellschaft fur Meeresforschung [★IO]
Deutsche Gesellschaft fur Moor- und Torfkunde e.V. [★IO]
Deutsche Gesellschaft fur Musiktherapie e.V. [★IO]
Deutsche Gesellschaft fur Muskelkranke [IO], Freiburg, Germany

Reference to "IO" in place of a book number signifies that the association may be found in the 50th edition of International Organizations.

Encyclopedia of Associations, 51st Edition

2741

Deutsche Gesellschaft fur Neurogenetik [★IO]

Deutsche Gesellschaft fur Online Forschung e.V. [★IO]

Deutsche Gesellschaft fur Ortung und Navigation e.V. [★IO]

Deutsche Gesellschaft fur Padiatrische Infektiologie [IO], Bremen, Germany

Deutsche Gesellschaft fur Parasitologie [IO], Stuttgart, Germany

Deutsche Gesellschaft fur Personalfuhrung e.V. [★IO]

Deutsche Gesellschaft fur Pharmazeutische Medizin [★IO]

Deutsche Gesellschaft fur Philosphie e.V. [IO], Cologne, Germany

Deutsche Gesellschaft fur Photogrammetrie, Fernerkundung, und Geoinformation [★IO]

Deutsche Gesellschaft fur Physikalische Medizin und Rehabilitation [★IO]

Deutsche Gesellschaft fur Plastische und Wiederherstellungschirurgie e.V. [★IO]

Deutsche Gesellschaft fur Rheumatologie [IO], Berlin, Germany

Deutsche Gesellschaft fur Schlafforschung und Schlafmedizin e.V. [★IO]

Deutsche Gesellschaft fur Sexualforschung [★IO]

Deutsche Gesellschaft fur Sozialwissenschaftliche Sexualforschung e.V. [★IO]

Deutsche Gesellschaft fur Sprach- und Stimmheilkunde e.V. [★IO]

Deutsche Gesellschaft fur Tropenmedizin und Internationale Gesundheit [★IO]

Deutsche Gessellschaft fur Reproduktionsmedizin e.V. [★IO]

Deutsche Glastechnische Gesellschaft [★IO]

Deutsche Huntington Hilfe e.V. [★IO]

Deutsche Institut fur Internationale Politik und Sicherheit [★IO]

Deutsche Interdisziplinare Vereinigung fur Intensiv- und Notfallmedizin [★IO]

Deutsche Kakteen-Gesellschaft e.V. [★IO]

Deutsche Kautschuk-Gesellschaft e.V [★IO]

Deutsche Keramische Gesellschaft [★IO]

Deutsche Krankenhausgesellschaft [★IO]

Deutsche Landwirtschafts-Gesellschaft [★IO]

Deutsche Mathematiker Vereinigung [★IO]

Deutsche Mathematiker Vereinigung [★IO]

Deutsche Meteorologische Gesellschaft [IO], Berlin, Germany

Deutsche Meteorologische Gesellschaft [★IO]

Deutsche Mineralogische Gesellschaft [★IO]

Deutsche Multiple Sklerose Gesellschaft Bundesverband E.V. [IO], Hannover, Germany

Deutsche Ophthalmologische Gesellschaft Heidelberg e.V. [★IO]

Deutsche Physikalische Gesellschaft [★IO]

Deutsche Physikalische Gesellschaft [IO], Bad Honnef, Germany

Deutsche Physiologische Gesellschaft [IO], Dusseldorf, Germany

Deutsche Physiologische Gesellschaft [★IO]

Deutsche Phytomedizinische Gesellschaft e.V. [★IO]

Deutsche Public Relations Gesellschaft [★IO]

Deutsche Roemisch Katholisch Unterstuetzungs Gesellschaft von Minnesota [★18951]

Deutsche Statistische Gesellschaft [★IO]

Deutsche Taekwondo Union [IO], Furth, Germany

Deutsche Transpersonale Gesellschaft [★IO]

Deutsche Vereinigung zur Bekampfung der Viruskrankheiten [IO], Jena, Germany

Deutsche Vereinigung fur Datenschutz [★IO]

Deutsche Vereinigung fur Politische Wissenschaft [★IO]

Deutsche Welthungerhilfe [★IO]

Deutsche Yngling Klassenvereinigung e.V [IO], Stutensee, Germany

Deutschen Gesellschaft fur Epileptologie [★IO]

Deutschen Gesellschaft fur Geowissenshaften [★IO]

Deutschen Gesellschaft fur KatastrophenMedizin e.V. [★IO]

Deutschen Gesellschaft fur Sprachwissenschaft [★IO]

Deutschen Gesellschaft fur Zerstorungsfreie Prufung [★IO]

Deutschen Weinbauverband e.V. [★IO]

Deutscher Aero Club [★IO]

Deutscher Akademikerinnenbund [IO], Berlin, Germany

Deutscher Akademischer Austausch Dienst [★8361]

Deutscher Akademischer Austausch Dienst [★8361]

Deutscher Alpenverein [★IO]

Deutscher Anwaltverein [★IO]

Deutscher Arbeitskreis fur Geomorphologie E.V. [IO], Bonn, Germany

Deutscher Asphaltverband [★IO]

Deutscher Badminton Verband [IO], Mulheim an der Ruhr, Germany

Deutscher Behindertensportverband [★IO]

Deutscher Beton- und Bautechnik-verein [★IO]

Deutscher Brauer-Bund [★IO]

Deutscher Cricket Bund [★IO]

Deutscher Direktmarketing Verband [★IO]

Deutscher Entwicklungsdienst Vietnam [★IO]

Deutscher Fleischer-Verband [IO], Frankfurt, Germany

Deutscher Forstwirtschaftsrat e.V. [★IO]

Deutscher Franchise-Verband [★IO]

Deutscher Frauenring e.V. [IO], Berlin, Germany

Deutscher Fruchthandelsverband e.V. [★IO]

Deutscher Giessereiverband [★IO]

Deutscher Hausfrauen-Bund [IO], Bonn, Germany

Deutscher Holstein Verband e.V. [★IO]

Deutscher Hotel- und Gaststattenverband [★IO]

Deutscher Ingenieurinnenbund [★IO]

Deutscher Journalisten Verband [★IO]

Deutscher Journalisten-Verband e.V. [IO], Berlin, Germany

Deutscher Juristinnenbund [IO], Berlin, Germany

Deutscher Kaffee-Verband e.V. [★IO]

Deutscher Kalte- und Klimatechnischer Verein e.V. [★IO]

Deutscher Kunsthandelsverband E.V. [IO], Berlin, Germany

Deutscher Lehrerverband [★IO]

Deutscher Mieterbund [★IO]

Deutscher Museumsbund [★IO]

Deutscher Musikverlegerverband [★IO]

Deutscher Olympischer Sportbund [★IO]

Deutscher Pelzverband e.V. [★IO]

Deutscher Rat fuer Landespflege [★IO]

Deutscher ReiseVerband [★IO]

Deutscher Segler-Verband [IO], Hamburg, Germany

Deutscher Sportlehrerverband [IO], Landau, Germany

Deutscher Squash Rackets Verband E.V. [IO], Bocholt, Germany

Deutscher Stahlbau-Verband [★IO]

Deutscher Steuerberaterverband [★IO]

Deutscher Tanzsportverband [★IO]

Deutscher Tennis Bund [IO], Hamburg, Germany

Deutscher Unihockey Bund [★IO]

Deutscher Verband fur Materialforschung und -prufung [★IO]

Deutscher Verband fur Physiotherapie [★IO]

Deutscher Verband fur Schweissen und verwandte Verfahren [★IO]

Deutscher Verein fur Kunstwissenschaft e.V. [★IO]

Deutscher Verein fur Vermessungswesen e.V. [★IO]

Deutscher Volkshochschul-Verband [★IO]

Deutsches Atomforum [★IO]

Deutsches Historisches Institut [★9766]

Deutsches Jugendherbergswerk [★IO]

Deutsches Kunststoff-Institut [★IO]

Deutsches Nationales Kommitee des Weltenergierats [IO], Berlin, Germany

Deutsches Teppich-Forschungsinstitut [★IO]

Deutsches Tiefkuehlinstitut [IO], Berlin, Germany

Deutsches Weininstitut [★IO]

Deutsches Zentrum fur Altersfragen e.V. [★IO]

Deutsches Zentrum fuer Luft-und Raumfahrt e. V. [★IO]

Deutschsprachige Gesellschaft Fur Psychotraumatologie [IO], Munich, Germany

Develop Africa [10820], 307 Green Valley Dr., Johnson City, TN 37601, (423)282-0006

Developartners [★15045]

Developartners [★15045]

Developing Hands [11264], 6137 Lincoln St., Frederick, CO 80530, (720)352-7716

Developing Technologies [IO], London, United Kingdom

Development and Ability Org. [IO], Kabul, Afghanistan

Development Aid from People to People in Zimbabwe [IO], Harare, Zimbabwe

Development Assistance Comm. [IO], Paris, France

Development Bank of Southern Africa [IO], Midrand, Republic of South Africa

Development and Cooperation in Central Asia [IO], Bishkek, Kirgizstan

Development Educ. Assn. [IO], London, United Kingdom

Development GAP [★17909]

Development GAP [★17909]

Development Gp. for Alternative Policies [17909], 3179 18th St. NW, Washington, DC 20010, (202)898-1566

Development Gp. for Alternative Policies [17909], 3179 18th St. NW, Washington, DC 20010, (202)898-1566

Development Humanitarian Services for Afghanistan [IO], Kabul, Afghanistan

Development Innovations and Networks - Switzerland [IO], Geneva, Switzerland

Development Network of Indigenous Voluntary Associations [IO], Kampala, Uganda

Development and Partnership in Action [IO], Phnom Penh, Cambodia

Development Planning Unit [IO], London, United Kingdom

Development Promotion Gp. [IO], Chennai, India

Development Stud. Assn. [IO], Bideford, United Kingdom

Development Stud. and Promotion Center [IO], Lima, Peru

Development Trusts Assn. [IO], London, United Kingdom

Developmental Delay Registry [★14050]

Developmental Delay Resources [14050], 5801 Beacon St., Pittsburgh, PA 15217, (800)497-0944

Developmental Disabilities Nurses Assn. [15747], PO Box 536489, Orlando, FL 32853-6489, (407)835-0642

Developmental Education

Amer. Assn. of Human Design Practitioners [1036]

Amer. Cong. of Community Supports and Employ ment Services [17367]

Circle of Women: Reach and Teach Across Borders [13015]

Destination ImagiNation [8697]

Lions-Quest [7968]

Natl. Assn. for Developmental Educ. [7969]

Devereux Natl. [13814], PO Box 638, Villanova, PA 19085, (800)345-1292

Devil Pups [20677], 3027 Townsgate Rd., Ste. 210, Westlake Village, CA 91361-3097, (805)497-9810

Devils in Baggy Pants [★20848]

Devils Fan Club [23903], Prudential Center, 165 Mulberry St., Newark, NJ 07102, (201)768-9680

Devis de Constr. Canada [★IO]

DevNet [IO], Georgetown, Guyana

Dewan Perniagaan Melayu Malaysia [★IO]

Dewan Perniagaan dan Perindustrian Antarabangsa Malaysia [★IO]

Dewan Perniagaan dan Perindustrian Kebangsaan Malaysia [★IO]

Dexter Cattle Soc. New Zealand [IO], Papakura, New Zealand

DFA of California [4447], 710 Striker Ave., Sacramento, CA 95834, (916)561-5900

DFK International/USA [25], 1025 Thomas Jefferson St. NW, Ste. 500 E, Washington, DC 20007, (202)452-8100

DG Soc. [★6930]

DG Soc. [★6930]

D.H. Lawrence Soc. of North Am. [9360], Loyola Univ. of Chicago, 6525 N Sheridan, Chicago, IL 60626

D.H. Lawrence Soc. of North Am. [9360], Loyola Univ. of Chicago, 6525 N Sheridan, Chicago, IL 60626

Dhaka Young Men's Christian Association [IO], Dhaka, Bangladesh

Dharma Drum Mountain Buddhist Assn. [19364], 90-56 Corona Ave., Elmhurst, NY 11373, (718)592-6593

A star before a book entry number signifies that the name is not listed separately, but is mentioned within the entry.

Dharma Realm Buddhist Assn. [19365], 1825 Murchison Dr., Burlingame, CA 94010-4504, (415)421-6117

Diabetes
Amer. Assn. of Diabetes Educators [14343]
Amer. Diabetes Assn. [14344]
Amer. Youth Understanding Diabetes Abroad [14345]
Amer. Youth Understanding Diabetes Abroad [14345]
Charles Ray III Diabetes Assn. [14346]
Charles Ray III Diabetes Assn. [14346]
Diabetes Action Res. and Educ. Found. [14347]
Diabetes Exercise and Sports Assn. [14348]
Diabetes Res. Assn. of Am. [14349]
Diabetes Res. Inst. Found. [14350]
Immunology of Diabetes Soc. [14351]
Immunology of Diabetes Soc. [14351]
Indigenous Diabetes Educ. Alliance [14352]
Insulindependence [14353]
Joslin Diabetes Center [14354]
Juvenile Diabetes Res. Found. - Hellas [17689]
Juvenile Diabetes Res. Found. Intl. [14355]
Juvenile Diabetes Res. Found. Intl. [14355]
Natl. Certification Bd. for Diabetes Educators [14356]
Natl. Diabetes Info. CH [14357]
Taking Control of Your Diabetes [14358]
Diabetes ACT [IO], Weston, Australia
Diabetes Action Res. and Educ. Found. [14347], 426 C St. NE, Washington, DC 20002, (202)333-4520
Diabetes Ashburton [IO], Ashburton, New Zealand
Diabetes Assn. of Nigeria [IO], Lagos, Nigeria
Diabetes Assn. of Sri Lanka [IO], Rajagiriya, Sri Lanka
Diabetes Assn. of Zambia [IO], Lusaka, Zambia
Diabetes Auckland [IO], Auckland, New Zealand
Diabetes Australia [IO], Canberra, Australia
Diabetes Australia - New South Wales [IO], Sydney, Australia
Diabetes Australia - Northern Territory [IO], Tiwi, Australia
Diabetes Australia - Queensland [IO], Brisbane, Australia
Diabetes Australia - South Australia [IO], Hilton, Australia
Diabetes Australia - Tasmania [IO], Hobart, Australia
Diabetes Australia - Victoria [IO], Melbourne, Australia
Diabetes Buller [IO], Westport, New Zealand
Diabetes Central Otago [IO], Balclutha, New Zealand
Diabetes Christchurch [IO], Christchurch, New Zealand
Diabetes Exercise and Sports Assn. [14348], 310 W Liberty, Ste. 604, Louisville, KY 40202, (502)581-0207
Diabetes Fed. of Ireland [IO], Dublin, Ireland
Diabetes Found. [★14354]
Diabetes Gisborne [IO], Gisborne, New Zealand
Diabetes Hawkes Bay [IO], Napier, New Zealand
Diabetes Horowhenua [IO], Levin, New Zealand
Diabetes Kapiti Coast [IO], Paraparaumu, New Zealand
Diabetes Manawatu [IO], Palmerston North, New Zealand
Diabetes Marlborough [IO], Blenheim, New Zealand
Diabetes Matamata [IO], Matamata, New Zealand
Diabetes and Metabolism; Assn. of Prog. Directors in Endocrinology, [14486]
Diabetes Milton [IO], Milton, New Zealand
Diabetes Nelson [IO], Nelson, New Zealand
Diabetes New Zealand [IO], Wellington, New Zealand
Diabetes North Otago [IO], Oamaru, New Zealand
Diabetes Northland [IO], Whangarei, New Zealand
Diabetes Otago [IO], Dunedin, New Zealand
Diabetes Res. Assn. of Am. [14349], 10560 Wayzata Blvd., Ste. 19, Minnetonka, MN 55305, (612)730-2789
Diabetes Res. Inst. Found. [14350], 200 S Park Rd., Ste. 100, Hollywood, FL 33021, (954)964-4040
Diabetes Rotorua [IO], Rotorua, New Zealand
Diabetes South Africa [IO], Fontainebleau, Republic of South Africa

Diabetes South Canterbury [IO], Timaru, New Zealand
Diabetes South Otago [IO], Balclutha, New Zealand
Diabetes South Taranaki [IO], Wellington, New Zealand
Diabetes South Waikato [IO], Wellington, New Zealand
Diabetes Southland [IO], Invercargill, New Zealand
Diabetes Taranaki [IO], New Plymouth, New Zealand
Diabetes Taupo [IO], Taupo, New Zealand
Diabetes Tauranga [IO], Tauranga, New Zealand
Diabetes UK [IO], London, United Kingdom
Diabetes Waikato [IO], Hamilton, New Zealand
Diabetes Waimate [IO], Waimate, New Zealand
Diabetes Wairarapa [IO], Wellington, New Zealand
Diabetes Wakatipu [IO], Queenstown, New Zealand
Diabetes Wanganui [IO], Wanganui, New Zealand
Diabetes Wellington [IO], Wellington, New Zealand
Diabetes West Coast [IO], Hokitika, New Zealand
Diabetes Western Australia [IO], Subiaco, Australia
Diabetesliitto [★IO]
Diabetic Soc. of Singapore [IO], Singapore, Singapore
Diagnostic Imaging; Coun. on [16532]
Diagnostic and Interventional Nephrology; Amer. Soc. of [15544]
Diagnostic Marketing Assn. [2399], 10293 N Meridian St., Ste. 175, Indianapolis, IN 46290, (317)816-1640
Diakonia of the Americas and Caribbean [IO], Penticton, BC, Canada
Dialogue on Diversity [8628], 1629 K St. NW, Ste. 300, Washington, DC 20006, (703)631-0650
Dialogue Found. [19917], PO Box 58423, Salt Lake City, UT 84158, (801)274-8210
Dialysis Assn; Kidney Transplant/ [16910]
Dialysis Patient Citizens [15549], 900 7th St. NW, Ste. 670, Washington, DC 20001, (866)877-4242
Dialysis and Transplantation; North Amer. Soc. for [15555]
Diamond Connection [IO], Witham, United Kingdom
Diamond Coun. of Am. [2156], 3212 W End Ave., Ste. 202, Nashville, TN 37203, (615)385-5301
Diamond Dealers Club [2157], 580 5th Ave. at 11 W 47th St., New York, NY 10036, (212)869-9777
Diamond Mfrs. Assn. [★2158]
Diamond Mfrs. and Importers Assn. of Am. [2158], 580 5th Ave., Ste. 2000, New York, NY 10036, (212)944-2066
Diamond Rio Fan Club [23832], PO Box 2195, Hendersonville, TN 37077-2195
Diamond T Register - Address unknown since 2011.
Diamond Wheel Mfrs. Inst. [★1876]
Diamond Wheel Mfrs. Inst. [★2347]
Dian Fossey Fund [★5046]
Dian Fossey Fund [★5046]
Dian Fossey Gorilla Fund Intl. [5046], 800 Cherokee Ave. SE, Atlanta, GA 30315-1440, (404)624-5881
Dian Fossey Gorilla Fund Intl. [5046], 800 Cherokee Ave. SE, Atlanta, GA 30315-1440, (404)624-5881
Diaper
Cloth Diaper Found. [11749]
Real Diaper Assn. [11750]
Diaper Free Baby [14111], PO Box 2604, Westwood, MA 02090
Diaper Ser. Accreditation Coun. - Defunct.
Diar for Rehabilitation and Development Assn. [IO], Rumbek, Sudan
Dickens Fellowship [IO], London, United Kingdom
DICOM Standards Comm. [6957], 1300 N 17th St., Ste. 1752, Rosslyn, VA 22209, (703)841-3285
Dictionary Proj. [11134], PO Box 1845, Charleston, SC 29402, (843)388-8375
Dictionary Soc. of North Am. [9443], Buffalo State Coll., English Dept., Ketchum Hall 326, 1300 Elmwood Ave., Buffalo, NY 14222, (716)878-4049
DidiBahini [IO], Kathmandu, Nepal
Die Casting Res. Found. [★1855]
Die Donau [★IO]
Die Geomorphologische Kommission der Oesterreichischen Geographischen Gesellschaft [★IO]
Die Misstofvereniging van Suid-Afrika [★IO]
Die Set Mfrs. Service Bur. - Defunct.
Die Spitaler der Schweiz [★IO]
Die Suid-Afrikaanse Akademie vir Wetenskap en Kuns [★IO]

Die Suid-Afrikaanse Vereniging van Musiekonderwysers [★IO]
Diecast Toy Collectors Assn. [★22171]
Diecast Toy Collectors Assn. [★22171]
Diecasting Development Coun. - Defunct.
Diemakers and Diecutters Assn. [★1831]
Diemakers and Diecutters Assn. [★1831]
Dierkundige Vereniging van Suidelike Afrika [★IO]
Diesel Hot Rod Assn. [22823], 920 W Walnut St., Albany, IN 47320, (765)768-6400
Dietary Managers Assn. [15828], 406 Surrey Woods Dr., St. Charles, IL 60174, (630)587-6336
Dietetic Assn; Amer. [15819]
Dietetic Products
Amer. Assn. of Nutritional Consultants [15814]
Amer. Bd. of Nutrition [15815]
Amer. Celiac Society | Dietary Support Coalition [15817]
Amer. Soc. for Clinical Nutrition [15821]
Calorie Control Coun. [1379]
Dietetics in Hea. Care Communities [15829], Marla Carlson, Exec. Dir., 2219 Cardinal Dr., Waterloo, IA 50701, (319)235-0991
Dietitians Assn. of Australia [IO], Deakin, Australia
Dietitians of Canada [IO], Toronto, ON, Canada
Digestive Disease Natl. Coalition [14561], 507 Capitol Ct. NE, Ste. 200, Washington, DC 20002, (202)544-7497
Digestive Diseases CH [★14569]
Digit Fund [★5046]
Digit Fund [★5046]
Digital Cinema Soc. [1255], PO Box 1973, Studio City, CA 91614, (818)762-2214
Digital Cinema Soc. [1255], PO Box 1973, Studio City, CA 91614, (818)762-2214
Digital Divide Data [7005], 115 W 30th St., Ste. 400, New York, NY 10001, (212)461-3700
Digital Govt. Soc. of North Am. [6930], Yigal Arens, Treas., USC-ISI, 4676 Admiralty Way, Marina del Rey, CA 90292
Digital Govt. Soc. of North Am. [6930], Yigal Arens, Treas., USC-ISI, 4676 Admiralty Way, Marina del Rey, CA 90292
Digital Imaging and Communications in Medicine [★6957]
Digital Living Network Alliance [1096], 400 Kruse Way Pl., Bldg. 2, Ste. 250, Lake Oswego, OR 97035, (503)908-1115
Digital Media Device Assn. - Defunct.
Digital Pathology Assn. [16124], 10293 N Meridian St., Ste. 175, Indianapolis, IN 46290-1130, (317)816-1630
Digital Printing and Imaging Assn. [1606], Specialty Graphic Imaging Assn., 10015 Main St., Fairfax, VA 22031-3489, (703)385-1335
Digital and Screen Printing Assn. [IO], Barnsley, United Kingdom
Digital Screenmedia Assn. [3233], 13100 Eastpoint Park Blvd., Louisville, KY 40223, (502)489-3915
Digital Signage Assn. [90], 13100 Eastpoint Park Blvd., Louisville, KY 40223, (502)241-7545
Digital TV Gp. [IO], London, United Kingdom
Digital Video Broadcasting [IO], Geneva, Switzerland
Digital Watermarking Alliance [6932], 9405 SW Gemini Dr., Beaverton, OR 97008-7192, (503)469-4717
DigitalEve [7083], 1902 NE 98th St., Seattle, WA 98115
Dignity After Death - Defunct.
Dignity in Dying [IO], London, United Kingdom
Dignity, Inc. [★19788]
Dignity Inst. of Tech. [★7352]
Dignity/U.S.A. [19788], PO Box 376, Medford, MA 02155-0004, (202)861-0017
DIK Assn. [IO], Nacka, Sweden
Dimokratikos Synagermos [★IO]
Dinah Shore Fan Club [23833], 3552 Fed. Ave., Los Angeles, CA 90066-2811
Dinah Shore Memorial Fan Club [23765], 3552 Fed. Ave., Los Angeles, CA 90066
Dinah Shore Memorial Fan Club [★23833]
Dinajpur Young Men's Christian Association [IO], Dinajpur, Bangladesh
Dining for Women [13457], PO Box 25633, Greenville, SC 29616, (864)335-8401

Reference to "IO" in place of a book number signifies that the association may be found in the 50th edition of International Organizations.

The Dinner Garden [12269], PO Box 700686, San Antonio, TX 78270-0686, (210)979-1776
Dinosaur Soc. [IO], Guildford, United Kingdom
Dinshah Hea. Soc. [13673], PO Box 707, Malaga, NJ 08328-0707, (856)692-4686
Dinshah Hea. Soc. [13673], PO Box 707, Malaga, NJ 08328-0707, (856)692-4686
Diplomacy
   Delta Phi Epsilon Professional Foreign Ser. Sorority [23529]
   Independent Diplomat [17898]
   Voices of African Mothers [12638]
Diplomacy Intl. [IO], Brussels, Belgium
Diplomas Nok Magyarorszagi Szovetsege [IO], Budapest, Hungary
Diplomates Sans Frontieres [★IO]
Diplomatic and Consular Officers, Retired [★5467]
Diplomats Without Borders [IO], Geneva, Switzerland
Direccion de Innovacion, Ciencia y Tecnologia para el Desarrollo [★IO]
Direct Aid Intl. [12832], PO Box 394, Northfield, VT 05663
Direct Aid Intl. [12832], PO Box 394, Northfield, VT 05663
Direct Broadcast Satellite Assn. [★3418]
Direct Broadcast Satellite Assn. [★3418]
Direct Care Alliance [1692], Leonila Vega, Esq., Exec. Dir., 4 W 43rd St., Unit 611, New York, NY 10036, (212)730-0741
Direct Gardening Assn. [3102], 5836 Rockburn Woods Way, Elkridge, MD 21075, (410)540-9830
Direct Link for the DisAbled - Defunct.
Direct Mail Advt. Assn. [★2400]
Direct Mail Educational Found. [★8555]
Direct Mail Fundraisers Assn. [★1538]
Direct Mail/Marketing Assn. [★2400]
Direct Mail/Marketing Educational Found. [★8555]
Direct Marketing Assn. [2400], 1120 Ave. of the Americas, New York, NY 10036-6700, (212)768-7277
Direct Marketing Assn. [IO], London, United Kingdom
Direct Marketing Assn. Catalog Coun. [★1605]
Direct Marketing Assn. - India [IO], Mumbai, India
Direct Marketing Assn. of Singapore [IO], Singapore, Singapore
Direct Marketing Assn. - United Kingdom [IO], London, United Kingdom
Direct Marketing Cmpt. Assn. [★2400]
Direct Marketing Educational Found. [8555], 1120 Ave. of the Americas, New York, NY 10036-6700, (212)768-7277
Direct Marketing Fundraisers Assn. [1538], PO Box 1038, New York, NY 10028, (646)675-7314
Direct Marketing Insurance Coun. [★1957]
Direct Marketing Insurance and Financial Services Coun. [1957], Direct Marketing Assn., 1120 Aave. of the Americas, New York, NY 10036-6700, (212)768-7277
Direct Relief Found. [★12451]
Direct Relief Found. [★12451]
Direct Relief Intl. [12451], 27 S La Patera Ln., Santa Barbara, CA 93117, (805)964-4767
Direct Relief Intl. [12451], 27 S La Patera Ln., Santa Barbara, CA 93117, (805)964-4767
Direct Selling Assn. [3157], 1667 K St. NW, Ste. 1100, Washington, DC 20006, (202)452-8866
Direct Selling Assn. - Hungary [IO], Budapest, Hungary
Direct Selling Assn. of New Zealand [IO], Auckland, New Zealand
Direct Selling Assn. - South Africa [IO], Auckland Park, Republic of South Africa
Direct Selling Assn. - United Kingdom [IO], London, United Kingdom
Direct Selling Educ. Found. [3158], 1667 K St. NW, Ste. 1100, Washington, DC 20006-1660, (202)452-8866
Direct Selling Educ. Found. [3158], 1667 K St. NW, Ste. 1100, Washington, DC 20006-1660, (202)452-8866
Direct Selling Women's Alliance [3159], 111 Hekili St., Ste. A139, Kailua, HI 96734, (808)239-8292
Directed Energy Professional Soc. [6710], 7770 Jefferson St. NE, Ste. 440, Albuquerque, NM 87109, (505)998-4910

Directorio Democratico Cubano [17494], PO Box 110235, Hialeah, FL 33011, (305)220-2713
Directorio Democratico Cubano [17494], PO Box 110235, Hialeah, FL 33011, (305)220-2713
Directorio Revolucionario Democratico Cubano [★17494]
Directorio Revolucionario Democratico Cubano [★17494]
Directors Guild of Am. [23187], 7920 Sunset Blvd., Los Angeles, CA 90046, (310)289-2000
Directors Guild of Canada [IO], Toronto, ON, Canada
Directors Guild of Great Britain [IO], London, United Kingdom
Directors of Hea. Promotion and Educ. [5928], 1015 18th St. NW, Ste. 300, Washington, DC 20036, (202)659-2230
Directors UK [IO], London, United Kingdom
Disabilities
   AACTION Autism [13776]
   Acad. of Rehabilitative Audiology [14910]
   Achromatopsia Network [17055]
   Amer. Amputee Soccer Assn. [22932]
   Amer. Asperger's Assn. [15564]
   Amer. Assn. of People with Disabilities [11757]
   Amer. Blind Bowling Assn. [22502]
   Amer. Coun. of the Blind [17057]
   Amer. Hosp. Assn., Sect. for Long Term Care and Rehabilitation [15039]
   Amputees in Motion Intl. [11759]
   Arc of the U.S. [12495]
   BlazeSports Am. [22508]
   Blind Sailing Intl. [23109]
   Blind Ser. Assn. [17067]
   Christian Overcomers [11771]
   DAD: Drums and Disabilities [12422]
   Deaf and Hard of Hearing Alliance [14929]
   Disability Resources [11776]
   Disabled Amer. Veterans [20412]
   Disabled Amer. Veterans Auxiliary [20413]
   Dogs for the Deaf [14933]
   Extensions for Independence [11786]
   Families with Autism Spectrum Disorders [13790]
   Global Communities of Support [11120]
   HALTER, Inc. [16852]
   Inter-National Assn. of Bus., Indus. and Rehabilitation [11794]
   Intl. Disabled Self-Defense Assn. [13032]
   Island Dolphin Care [11797]
   Kids Enjoy Exercise Now [21474]
   Kids Together [11802]
   Kupenda for the Children [11340]
   Model Secondary School for the Deaf [14946]
   Natl. Assn. of the Physically Handicapped [11811]
   Natl. Assn. of State Directors of Special Educ. [8888]
   Natl. Coalition on Auditory Processing Disorders [14949]
   Natl. Inst. for Rehabilitation Engg. [11817]
   Natl. Order of Trench Rats [20414]
   North Amer. One-Armed Golfer Assn. [22521]
   Rebuilding Together [12200]
   Special Recreation for disABLED Intl. [11831]
   Support Dogs, Inc. [11832]
   U.S.A. Deaf Basketball [22300]
   Veterans Educ. Proj. [13357]
   VietNow Natl. [13358]
   Watering Seeds Org. [22532]
   World Access for the Blind [17118]
   World T.E.A.M. Sports [22534]
Disabilities and Gifted Education; ERIC CH on [★11788]
Disability Alliance [IO], London, United Kingdom
Disability Awareness Action Gp. [IO], Freetown, Sierra Leone
Disability Evaluating Physicians; Amer. Acad. of [14164]
Disability Fed. of Ireland [IO], Dublin, Ireland
Disability Insurance Training Coun. - Defunct.
Disability Mgt. Employer Coalition [1146], 5173 Waring Rd., Ste. 134, San Diego, CA 92120-2705, (800)789-3632
Disability Ministries [19924], ELCA Churchwide Org., 8765 W Higgins Rd., Chicago, IL 60631, (773)380-2700

Disability Promotion and Advocacy [IO], Port Vila, Vanuatu
Disability Resources [11776], 4 Glatter Ln., South Setauket, NY 11720-1032, (631)585-0290
Disability Rights Center [11777], PO Box 2007, Augusta, ME 04338-2007, (207)626-2774
Disability Rights Educ. and Defense Fund [11778], 3075 Adeline St., Ste. 210, Berkeley, CA 94703-2578, (510)644-2555
Disability Sport Events [IO], Manchester, United Kingdom
Disabled
   AACTION Autism [13776]
   Abilities! [11751]
   Acad. of Rehabilitative Audiology [14910]
   Accessibility Equip. Mfrs. Assn. [11752]
   Achilles Intl. [22499]
   Achromatopsia Network [17055]
   Adaptive Sports Assn. [22500]
   Advocating Change Together [11753]
   Alliance for Full Participation [11754]
   Alliance for Tech. Access [11755]
   Amer. Amputee Found. [11756]
   Amer. Amputee Soccer Assn. [22932]
   Amer. Assn. of adaptedSPORTS Programs [22501]
   Amer. Assn. on Hea. and Disability [14359]
   Amer. Assn. of People with Disabilities [11757]
   Amer. Blind Bowling Assn. [22502]
   Amer. Blind Skiing Found. [22503]
   Amer. Cong. of Community Supports and Employment Services [17367]
   Amer. Coun. of the Blind [17057]
   Amer. Disabled for Attendant Programs Today [11758]
   Amer. Hearing Impaired Hockey Assn. [22504]
   Amer. Hosp. Assn., Sect. for Long Term Care and Rehabilitation [15039]
   Amer. Polocrosse Assn. [22505]
   Amer. Soc. for the Support of Injured Survivors of Terrorism [13359]
   Amer. Wheelchair Bowling Assn. [22506]
   Amputee Coalition of Am. [14360]
   Amputees in Motion Intl. [11759]
   Amputees in Motion Intl. [11759]
   Angel Harps [16454]
   Angels With Special Needs [11760]
   APSE: The Network on Employment [11761]
   Arc of the U.S. [12495]
   Assistance Dogs of Am., Inc. [11762]
   Assistance Dogs Intl. [11763]
   Assistance Dogs Intl. [11763]
   Assn. of Assistive Tech. Act Programs [14361]
   Assn. for Children with a Disability [14536]
   Assn. for Higher Educ. Access and Disability [1580]
   Assn. on Higher Educ. and Disability [7970]
   Assn. on Higher Educ. and Disability [7970]
   Assn. of Rehabilitation Programs in Cmpt. Tech. [11764]
   Athletes with Disabilities Network [22507]
   BlazeSports Am. [22508]
   Blind Ser. Assn. [17067]
   Canadian Found. for Physically Disabled Persons [21703]
   Canine Assistants [11765]
   Canine Companions for Independence [11766]
   Canines for Disabled Kids [11767]
   Catholic Guardian Soc. and Home Bur. [11208]
   Center on Human Policy [11768]
   Center for Workers with Disabilities [11769]
   Challenge Aspen at Snowmass [22509]
   Challenged Am. [14362]
   Charlotte W. Newcombe Found. [11770]
   Christian Overcomers [11771]
   CH on Disability Info. [11772]
   Comm. for Handicapable Dancers [9539]
   Consortium for Citizens with Disabilities [11773]
   Coun. of Citizens With Low Vision Intl. [11774]
   Crutches 4 Kids [11262]
   DAD: Drums and Disabilities [12422]
   DateAble [11775]
   DateAble [11775]
   Deaf Bilingual Coalition [12137]
   Deaf and Hard of Hearing Alliance [14929]

A star before a book entry number signifies that the name is not listed separately, but is mentioned within the entry.

Deaf Intl. [12139]
DeafHope [12141]
Disability Fed. of Ireland [11058]
Disability Resources [11776]
Disability Rights Center [11777]
Disability Rights Educ. and Defense Fund [11778]
Disabled and Alone/Life Services for the
    Handicapped [11779]
Disabled Amer. Veterans [20412]
Disabled Amer. Veterans Auxiliary [20413]
Disabled Drummers Assn. [11780]
Disabled Online Users Assn. [11781]
Disabled Sports USA [22510]
Disabled Womyn's Educational Proj. [11782]
Div. on Visual Impairments [8883]
Dogs for the Deaf [14933]
DOVE: Advocacy Services for Abused Deaf
    Women and Children [12142]
Dream Catchers USA [11783]
Easter Seals [11784]
Empower the Children [11268]
Enable Am. [11785]
Exodus Guild [10821]
Extensions for Independence [11786]
Family Rsrc. Center on Disabilities [7971]
Follow A Dream [11787]
Found. for Exceptional Children [11788]
Found. for Exceptional Children [11788]
Found. for Sci. and Disability [11789]
Free Wheelchair Mission [11790]
Free Wheelchair Mission [11790]
Gifted Learning Proj. [12424]
Glenkirk [11791]
Global Applied Disability Res. and Info. Network
    [14363]
Global Applied Disability Res. and Info. Network
    [14363]
Global Communities of Support [11120]
Goodwill Indus. Intl. [11792]
Goodwill Indus. Intl. [11792]
HALTER, Inc. [16852]
Handicapped Scuba Assn. [22511]
Handicapped Scuba Assn. [22511]
HEATH Rsrc. Center at the Natl. Youth Transitions
    Center [7972]
Hong Kong PHAB Assn. [21329]
Inspiration Ministries [11793]
Inter-National Assn. of Bus., Indus. and
    Rehabilitation [11794]
Intl. Assn. of Assistance Dog Partners [14364]
Intl. Assn. of Laryngectomees [11795]
Intl. Assn. of Laryngectomees [11795]
Intl. Child Amputee Network [11796]
Intl. Child Amputee Network [11796]
Intl. Comm. of Sports for the Deaf [22512]
Intl. Comm. of Sports for the Deaf [22512]
Intl. Disabled Self-Defense Assn. [13032]
Irish Wheelchair Assn. [6242]
Island Dolphin Care [11797]
Jeena [11798]
Job Accommodation Network [11799]
Joni and Friends [11800]
Just One Break [11801]
Kids Enjoy Exercise Now [21474]
Kids Together [11802]
Knowbility [11803]
Kupenda for the Children [11340]
Lift Disability Network [11804]
Lift Disability Network [11804]
Logan Community Resources [11805]
Mobility Intl. USA [11806]
Mobility Intl. USA [11806]
Model Secondary School for the Deaf [14946]
MOVE Intl.: Mobility Opportunities Via Educ.
    U.S.A. [11807]
MOVE Intl.: Mobility Opportunities Via Educ.
    U.S.A. [11807]
Natl. Ability Center [22513]
Natl. Alliance for Accessible Golf [22514]
Natl. AMBUCS [11808]
Natl. Amputation Found. [11809]
Natl. Amputee Golf Assn. [22515]
Natl. Assn. of ADA Coordinators [11810]
Natl. Assn. for Adults with Special Learning Needs
    [7973]

Natl. Assn. for the Dually Diagnosed [14365]
Natl. Assn. of the Physically Handicapped [11811]
Natl. Assn. of Ser. Dogs [11876]
Natl. Beep Baseball Assn. [22516]
Natl. Black Deaf Advocates [11812]
Natl. Center for the Dissemination of Disability
    Res. [14366]
Natl. Coalition on Auditory Processing Disorders
    [14949]
Natl. Coun. on Independent Living [11813]
Natl. Cristina Found. [11814]
Natl. Cristina Found. [11814]
Natl. Deaf Women's Bowling Assn. [22517]
Natl. Disability Rights Network [11815]
Natl. Dissemination Center for Children with Dis-
    abilities [11816]
Natl. Inst. for Rehabilitation Engg. [11817]
Natl. Minorities with Disabilities Coalition [17545]
Natl. Odd Shoe Exchange [11818]
Natl. Odd Shoe Exchange [11818]
Natl. Order of Trench Rats [20414]
Natl. Org. on Disability [11819]
Natl. Org. on Disability [11819]
Natl. Special Needs Network Found. [14367]
Natl. Wheelchair Basketball Assn. [22518]
Natl. Wheelchair Poolplayer Assn. [22519]
Natl. Wheelchair Poolplayer Assn. [22519]
Natl. Wheelchair Softball Assn. [22520]
NISH [11820]
North Amer. One-Armed Golfer Assn. [22521]
North Amer. Riding for the Handicapped Assn.
    [22522]
One-Arm Dove Hunt Assn. [22523]
PACER Center - Parent Advocacy Coalition for
    Educational Rights [14368]
Parents Of Autistic Children [13801]
Paws With a Cause [11821]
Personal Ponies Ltd. [11822]
Post-Polio Hea. Intl. [11823]
Post-Polio Hea. Intl. [11823]
PRIDE Found. - Promote Real Independence for
    the Disabled and Elderly [11824]
Rebuilding Together [12200]
Rehabilitation Engg. and Assistive Tech. Soc. of
    North Am. [11825]
Res. and Training Center on Independent Living
    [11826]
Responsible Hospitality Inst. [11827]
Responsible Hospitality Inst. [11827]
Riding for the Disabled Assn. - Ireland [15773]
The Rural Inst.: Center for Excellence in Disability
    Educ., Res. and Ser. [11828]
Ski for Light [22524]
Ski for Light [22524]
Soc. for Accessible Travel and Hospitality [11829]
Soc. for Disability Stud. [11830]
Special Olympics [22525]
Special Olympics [22525]DisabledSpecial
    Olympics Andorra
Special Olympics Australia [22235]
Special Olympics Austria [10401]DisabledSpecial
    Olympics Bangladesh
Special Olympics Benin [9656]
Special Olympics Bolivia [21489]
Special Olympics Bulgaria [1632]
Special Olympics Burkina Faso [16353]
Special Olympics Cameroon [3703]
Special Olympics Chad [14871]
Special Olympics Croatia [17795]
Special Olympics Cuba [11045]
Special Olympics Cyprus [17796]
Special Olympics Czech Republic [8002]
Special Olympics El Salvador [1089]DisabledSpe-
    cial Olympics Finland DisabledSpecial Olympics
    Gambia
Special Olympics Ghana [10528]
Special Olympics Honduras [10002]
Special Olympics Iceland [13361]
Special Olympics Italy [5805]
Special Olympics Latvia [18212]
Special Olympics Lesotho [4999]
Special Olympics Moldova [23547]
Special Olympics Netherlands [19073]
Special Olympics Paraguay [1908]
Special Olympics Philippines [14807]

Special Olympics Poland [13829]
Special Olympics Slovenia [10960]
Special Olympics Spain [14108]
Special Olympics Thailand [12242]
Special Olympics Uganda [19867]
Special Olympics Uruguay [22675]
Special Recreation for disABLED Intl. [11831]
Special Recreation for disABLED Intl. [11831]
Step Up 4 Vets [13354]
Steps Charity Worldwide [3694]
STRIDE, Inc. [7974]
Support Dogs, Inc. [11832]
Support Dogs, Inc. [11832]
TASH [11833]
U.S.A. Deaf Basketball [22300]
U.S. Assn. for Blind Athletes [22526]
U.S. Blind Golf Assn. [22527]
U.S. Deaf Cycling Assn. [22528]
U.S. Deaf Ski and Snowboard Assn. [22529]
U.S. Flag Football for the Deaf [22530]
U.S. Intl. Coun. on Disabilities [11834]
U.S. Intl. Coun. on Disabilities [11834]
U.S.A. Deaf Sports Fed. [22531]
Veterans Educ. Proj. [13357]
Veterans2Work [20818]
VietNow Natl. [13358]
VSA arts [11835]
VSA - The Intl. Org. on Arts and Disability [11835]
Watering Seeds Org. [22532]
Wheelchair and Ambulatory Sports, USA [22533]
Wheels for the World [11836]
Wheels for the World [11836]
World Ability Fed. [11837]
World Ability Fed. [11837]
World Access for the Blind [17118]
World Assn. of Persons with disAbilities [14369]
World Assn. of Persons with disAbilities [14369]
World Inst. on Disability [11838]
World Inst. on Disability [11838]
World Rehabilitation Fund [11839]
World Rehabilitation Fund [11839]
World T.E.A.M. Sports [22534]
Disabled and Alone/Life Services for the
    Handicapped [11779], 61 Broadway, Ste. 510,
    New York, NY 10006, (212)532-6740
Disabled Amer. Veterans [20412], 3725 Alexandria
    Pike, Cold Spring, KY 41076, (859)441-7300
Disabled Amer. Veterans Auxiliary [20413], 3725
    Alexandria Pike, Cold Spring, KY 41076, (859)441-
    7300
Disabled Birders Assn. [IO], Kent, United Kingdom
Disabled Businesspersons Assn. [11936], 2240
    Shelter Island Dr., Ste. 108, San Diego, CA 92106,
    (619)523-9318
Disabled Children's Fund [★16032]
Disabled Children's Fund [★16032]
Disabled Drivers' Assn. of Ireland [IO], Claremorris,
    Ireland
Disabled Drummers Assn. [11780], 18901 NW 19th
    Ave., Miami Gardens, FL 33056-2808, (305)621-
    9022
Disabled Living Found. [IO], London, United
    Kingdom
Disabled Motorists Fed. [IO], Chester-Le-Street,
    United Kingdom
Disabled Online Users Assn. [11781], 1806 Vaigneur
    Rd., Port Royal, SC 29935, (843)525-1667
Disabled People's Assn. of Singapore [IO], Sin-
    gapore, Singapore
Disabled Peoples' Intl. [IO], Mount Pearl, NL,
    Canada
Disabled Peoples' Intl. - Europe [IO], Lamezia
    Terme, Italy
Disabled Peoples' Intl. - India [IO], New Delhi, India
Disabled Peoples' Intl. - Jamaica [IO], Kingston,
    Jamaica
Disabled People's Intl. - Korea [IO], Seoul, Republic
    of Korea
Disabled Peoples' Intl. - North Am. and the Carib-
    bean [IO], St. Johns, Antigua-Barbuda
Disabled Peoples' Intl. - Sweden [IO], Leksand,
    Sweden
Disabled Persons Assembly New Zealand [IO], Well-
    ington, New Zealand
Disabled Persons Rehabilitation Assn. [IO], Honiara,
    Solomon Islands

Reference to "IO" in place of a book number signifies that the association may be found in the 50th edition of International Organizations.

Disabled Photographers' Soc. **[IO]**, Kent, United Kingdom
Disabled Sports USA **[22510]**, 451 Hungerford Dr., Ste. 100, Rockville, MD 20850, (301)217-0960
Disabled Veterans
Blinded Amer. Veterans Found. **[20411]**
Disabled Amer. Veterans **[20412]**
Disabled Amer. Veterans Auxiliary **[20413]**
Guitars For Vets **[11840]**
Natl. Order of Trench Rats **[20414]**
Oper. Appreciation **[20415]**
Paralyzed Veterans of Am. **[20416]**
Salute Military Golf Assn. **[22624]**
Step Up 4 Vets **[13354]**
Veterans Educ. Proj. **[13357]**
Veterans2Work **[20818]**
VietNow Natl. **[13358]**
Watering Seeds Org. **[22532]**
DisAbled Women's Network Canada **[IO]**, Montreal, QC, Canada
Disabled Womyn's Educational Proj. **[11782]**, PO Box 8773, Madison, WI 53708-8773, (608)256-8883
Disarm Educ. Fund **[17551]**, 113 Univ. Pl., New York, NY 10003, (212)353-9800
Disarmament
Arms Control Assn. **[17546]**
Canadian Assn. for Mine and Explosive Ordinance Security **[15311]**
Center for Economic Conversion **[17547]**
Clear Path Intl. **[17548]**
Clear Path Intl. **[17548]**
Coalition Against Landmines **[11841]**
Coun. for a Livable World **[17549]**
Coun. for a Livable World **[17549]**
Coun. for a Livable World Educ. Fund **[17550]**
Coun. for a Livable World Educ. Fund **[17550]**
Daisy Alliance **[18239]**
Disarm Educ. Fund **[17551]**
Economists for Peace and Security **[17552]**
Economists for Peace and Security **[17552]**
Intl. Campaign to Ban Landmines **[17553]**
Intl. Campaign to Ban Landmines **[17553]**
Intl. Panel on Fissile Materials **[18203]**
Middle Powers Initiative **[17554]**
NGO Comm. on Disarmament, Peace and Security **[17555]**
NGO Comm. on Disarmament, Peace and Security **[17555]**
Parliamentarians For Global Action **[17556]**
Parliamentarians For Global Action **[17556]**
PeaceTrees Vietnam **[11842]**
Proposition One Comm. **[17557]**
Reaching Critical Will **[17558]**
Terra Segura Intl. **[17559]**
Disaster Aid
1st Special Response Gp. **[11843]**
Action Against Hunger **[11844]**
Action Against Hunger **[11844]**
Aid Still Required **[11845]**
All Hands Volunteers **[11846]**
Am. Continental 2000 **[11847]**
Amer. Friends of Magen David Adom **[12801]**
Baitulmaal **[12808]**
Baptist Global Response **[12809]**
Bus. Continuity Planning Workgroup for Healthcare Organizations **[14481]**
Care Highway Intl. **[12814]**
Center for Intl. Disaster Info. **[11848]**
Center for Intl. Disaster Info. **[11848]**
Children's Cup **[12819]**
Christian Alliance For Humanitarian Aid **[12821]**
Community Aid Relief and Development **[12826]**
Compassion into Action Network - Direct Outcome Org. **[11849]**
Compassion First **[12827]**
Disaster Mgt. Alliance **[11850]**
Global Emergency Relief **[11923]**
Global Fac. for Disaster Reduction and Recovery **[11851]**
Global Fac. for Disaster Reduction and Recovery **[11851]**
Great Commn. Alliance **[11852]**
Haiti Works! **[12333]**
Hand in Hand USA **[12842]**

HEART 9/11: Healing Emergency Aid Response Team 9/11 **[11853]**
HOPE Animal-Assisted Crisis Response **[12906]**
Hope Force Intl. **[11854]**
Hope Force Intl. **[11854]**
Humanitarian Resources Intl. **[12850]**
Humanity First USA **[11855]**
Indonesia Relief - USA **[11856]**
Innovative Support to Emergencies Diseases and Disasters **[11857]**
Innovative Support to Emergencies Diseases and Disasters **[11857]**
Intl. Crisis Aid **[12854]**
Irob Relief and Rehabilitation Operations Brotherhood **[11986]**
Island Aid **[11858]**
Kinship Circle **[10998]**
Knightsbridge Intl. **[12859]**
Korean Amer. Sharing Movement **[12860]**
Medical Aid Comm. **[15306]**
Mobile Medical Disaster Relief **[12472]**
Natl. Assn. of State 911 Administrators **[7547]**
NetHope **[12872]**
Peace Winds Am. **[11859]**
Psychology Beyond Borders **[11860]**
Psychology Beyond Borders **[11860]**
Reconstruction Efforts Aiding Children without Homes **[11624]**
Seeds For Hope **[11861]**
Seeds For Hope **[11861]**
September 11th Families' Assn. **[11862]**
SHIP Aid: Shipping Humanitarian Aid to Impoverished People **[12889]**
Tuesday's Children **[11863]**
Water for Life Intl. **[13436]**
World Assn. of Natural Disaster Awareness and Assistance **[12572]**
World Bicycle Relief **[12898]**
Disaster Emergency Response Assn. **[5397]**, PO Box 797, Longmont, CO 80502, (970)532-3362
Disaster Mgt. Alliance **[11850]**, 1889 F St. NW, 2nd Fl., Washington, DC 20006, (202)458-3969
Disaster Recovery Inst. Intl. **[★5306]**
Disaster Volunteers of Ghana **[IO]**, Ho, Ghana
Disasters Emergency Comm. **[IO]**, London, United Kingdom
Disc Sports
Freestyle Players Assn. **[22535]**
Freestyle Players Assn. **[22535]**
U.S. Disc Sports **[22536]**
U.S.A. Ultimate **[22537]**
Discalced Bros. of the Most Blessed Virgin Mary of Mount Carmel **[IO]**, Rome, Italy
Disciple Nations Alliance **[19617]**, 1110 E Missouri Ave., Ste. 393, Phoenix, AZ 85014, (602)386-4560
Disciples of Christ Historical Soc. **[19624]**, 1101 19th Ave. S, Nashville, TN 37212-2109, (615)327-1444
Disciples Ecumenical Consultative Coun. **[19618]**, Coun. on Christian Unity, PO Box 1986, Indianapolis, IN 46206-1986, (317)713-2586
Disciples Justice Action Network **[19566]**, 1040 Harbor Dr., Annapolis, MD 21403, (410)212-7964
Disciples Peace Fellowship **[18240]**, PO Box 1986, Indianapolis, IN 46206-1986, (888)346-2631
Discipline
Natl. Center for the Stud. of Corporal Punishment and Alternatives **[7975]**
Natl. Coalition to Abolish Corporal Punishment in Schools **[7976]**
Natl. Coalition Against Violent Athletes **[22231]**
Parents and Teachers Against Violence in Educ. **[7977]**
Discover Worlds **[13129]**, 908 B2 Pompton Ave., Cedar Grove, NJ 07009
Discovery Owners Assn., Inc. **[22136]**, PO Box 95, St. George, UT 84771-0095, (888)594-6818
Discussion Club **[17285]**, 2206 Rose Garden Dr., St. Louis, MO 63125, (314)416-7722
Disease
4K for Cancer **[13874]**
Aicardi Syndrome Newsl. **[14581]**
AIDS-Free World **[13594]**
Alliance for Rabies Control **[14370]**
Amer. Celiac Disease Alliance **[14549]**
Amer. Lyme Disease Found. **[14371]**

Amyloidosis Found. **[14372]**
Amyloidosis Support Groups **[14373]**
Amyloidosis Support Groups **[14373]**
Answer Africa **[14374]**
Asperger Syndrome Assn. of Ireland **[1939]**
Assn. for the Bladder Exstrophy Community **[14375]**
Assn. for the Bladder Exstrophy Community **[14375]**
Ataxia Telangiectasia Children's Proj. **[14376]**
Avenues, Natl. Support Gp. for Arthrogryposis Multiplex Congenita **[15573]**
Benign Essential Blepharospasm Res. Found. **[15575]**
Blood: Water Mission **[10809]**
C-Change **[13894]**
CancerClimber Assn. **[13904]**
CCHS Family Network **[14377]**
CFIDS Assn. of Am. **[14378]**
Childhood Brain Tumor Found. **[14379]**
Children's Cancer and Blood Found. **[14964]**
Children's Tumor Found. **[15579]**
Chronic Granulomatous Disease Assn. **[14380]**
Chronic Granulomatous Disease Assn. **[14380]**
Chronic Syndrome Support Assn. **[14381]**
Coalition of State Rheumatology Organizations **[16619]**
Community Oncology Alliance **[15923]**
DEBRA Ireland **[18850]**
DMAA: The Care Continuum Alliance **[14382]**
DMAA: The Care Continuum Alliance **[14382]**
Dysphagia Res. Soc. **[14383]**
Encephalitis Global **[14384]**
Encephalitis Global **[14384]**
The Erythromelalgia Assn. **[14385]**
European Org. for Rare Disorders **[14381]**
Evans Syndrome Res. and Support Gp. **[15104]**
Fabry Support and Info. Gp. **[14386]**
Flashes of Hope **[11135]**
Forbes Norris MDA/ALS Res. Center **[15590]**
Found. for PSP/CBD and Related Brain Diseases **[14387]**
Frontline Hepatitis Awareness **[14983]**
Gardens for Hea. Intl. **[13604]**
Genetic Metabolic Dietitians Intl. **[15497]**
Global AIDS Interfaith Alliance **[13607]**
Global Hea. Soc. **[15171]**
Global Network for Neglected Tropical Diseases **[14388]**
Global Solutions for Infectious Diseases **[15116]**
Global Youth Coalition on HIV/AIDS **[10881]**
Golf Fights Cancer **[13926]**
Grind for Life **[11136]**
Heart Rhythm Soc. **[14016]**
HIS Nets **[13588]**
Human Touch Intl. **[13589]**
Incontinentia Pigmenti Intl. Found. **[14601]**
Inflammation Res. Assn. **[14389]**
Inflammatory Skin Disease Inst. **[14390]**
Intl. Alliance for the Prevention of AIDS **[13614]**
Intl. Assn. for Chronic Fatigue Syndrome **[14391]**
Intl. Atherosclerosis Soc. **[14020]**
Intl. Bronchoesophagological Soc. **[13869]**
Intl. Disease Mgt. Alliance **[14392]**
Intl. Fed. of Psoriasis Associations **[14328]**
Intl. Genetic Epidemiology Soc. **[14514]**
Intl. Lyme and Assoc. Diseases Soc. **[14393]**
Intl. Lyme and Assoc. Diseases Soc. **[14393]**
Intl. Pemphigus and Pemphigoid Found. **[14394]**
Intl. Psoriasis Coun. **[14329]**
Intl. Skeletal Soc. **[16533]**
Intl. Soc. for Children with Cancer **[13934]**
Intl. Soc. for Disease Surveillance **[14395]**
Intl. Soc. for Disease Surveillance **[14395]**
Intl. Soc. for Genetic Eye Diseases and Retinoblastoma **[15964]**
Intl. Soc. on Metabolic Eye Disease **[15966]**
Intl. Soc. for Vaccines **[15109]**
Kidney Care Partners **[15551]**
Kidney Community Emergency Response Coalition **[15552]**
LAM Found. **[14396]**
Leukemia and Lymphoma Soc. **[13936]**
Lily of the Valley Endeavor **[10886]**
Lyme Disease Assn. **[14397]**

A star before a book entry number signifies that the name is not listed separately, but is mentioned within the entry.

Lyme Disease Found. [14398]
Malaria No More [14399]
The Mastocytosis Soc. [14400]
Melanoma Awareness [13940]
Meningitis Angels [14401]
Mesothelioma Applied Res. Found. [14402]
Mitochondria Res. Soc. [14403]
Mitochondria Res. Soc. [14403]
Multiple Sclerosis Coalition [15609]
Natl. Brain Tumor Soc. [14404]
Natl. Capital Lyme and Tick-Borne Disease Assn. [14405]
Natl. Chronic Fatigue Syndrome and Fibromyalgia Assn. [14406]
Natl. Coalition of Pastors' Spouses [13195]
Natl. Disease Clusters Alliance [14407]
Natl. Dysautonomia Res. Found. [14408]
Natl. Hydrocephalus Found. [14409]
Natl. Melanoma Alliance [13956]
Natl. Meningitis Assn. [14410]
Natl. Org. for Rare Disorders [14411]
Natl. Tuberculosis Controllers Assn. [14412]
Netting Nations [14413]
Netting Nations [14413]
Nevus Outreach [14414]
Norrie Disease Assn. [14415]
North Amer. Clinical Dermatologic Soc. [14337]
Parkinson's Action Network [14416]
Patients Against Lymphoma [15257]
Pink Isn't Always Pretty [13969]
Preemptive Love Coalition [14040]
Primary Biliary Cirrhosis Org. [14417]
Prize4Life [15632]
Purine Res. Soc. [15506]
Rock Against Cancer [13975]
Sarcoid Networking Assn. [14418]
Soc. for Heart Valve Disease [14959]
SOTENI Intl. [10893]
Syndromes Without a Name USA [14419]
Tourette Syndrome Assn. [15636]
Venous Disease Coalition [16970]
Vitiligo Support Intl. [14341]
Disease Mgt. Assn. of Am. [★14382]
Disease Mgt. Assn. of Am. [★14382]
Disinfected Mail Stud. Circle [IO], London, United Kingdom
Disneyana Fan Club [23792], PO Box 19212, Irvine, CA 92623-9212, (714)731-4705
Disorders of Chromosome 16 Found. [14594], PO Box 230448, Encinitas, CA 92023-0448, (609)219-9449
Disorders of Chromosome 16 Found. [14594], PO Box 230448, Encinitas, CA 92023-0448, (609)219-9449
Disposable Products
Foodservice and Packaging Inst. [1041]
Mfrs. Representatives of Am. [1042]
Disposables Assn. [★3442]
Dissatisfied Parents Together [★14093]
Distance Educ. and Training Coun. [8268], 1601 18th St. NW, Ste. 2, Washington, DC 20009, (202)234-5100
Distance Running
Amer. Ultrarunning Assn. [22862]
Distilled Spirits Assn. of New Zealand [IO], Auckland, New Zealand
Distilled Spirits Coun. of the U.S. [180], 1250 Eye St. NW, Ste. 400, Washington, DC 20005, (202)628-3544
Distilled Spirits Indus. Coun. of Australia [IO], South Melbourne, Australia
Distilled Spirits Inst. [★180]
Distillers Feed Res. Coun. [★1592]
Distillers Grains Tech. Coun. [1592], Univ. of Louisville, Lutz Hall, Rm. 435, Louisville, KY 40292, (502)852-1575
Distillery, Wine and Allied Workers Intl. Union [★23191]
Distinguished Flying Cross Soc. [20374], PO Box 530250, San Diego, CA 92153-0250, (619)220-0003
Distinguished Inns of North Am., Select Registry [1746], PO Box 150, Marshall, MI 49068, (269)789-0393
Distinguished Restaurants of North Am. [3088], 455 S Fourth St., Ste. 650, Louisville, KY 40202, (502)583-7855

Distressed Children and Infants Intl. [11265], 5 Shipton Ct., Cheshire, CT 06410, (203)376-6351
Distressed Children and Infants Intl. [11265], 5 Shipton Ct., Cheshire, CT 06410, (203)376-6351
Distributed Computing Indus. Assn. [6533], 2838 Cox Neck Rd., Ste. 200, Chester, MD 21619, (410)476-7965
Distributed Wind Energy Assn. [3666], PO Box 1861, Flagstaff, AZ 86002, (928)255-0214
Distribution Bus. Mgt. Assn. [3659], 2938 Columbia Ave., Ste. 1102, Lancaster, PA 17603, (717)295-0033
Distribution Contractors Assn. [23276], 101 W Renner Rd., Ste. 460, Richardson, TX 75082-2024, (972)680-0261
Distribution and LTL Carriers Assn. [3246], 950 N Glebe Rd., Ste. 210, Arlington, VA 22203, (703)838-7970
Distribution Res. and Educ. Found. [★3664]
Distributive Educ. Clubs of Am. [8556], 1908 Assn. Dr., Reston, VA 20191-1594, (703)860-5000
District 1 of Marine Engineers Beneficial Association/ National Maritime Union and Professional Airways Systems Specialists [★23155]
District of Columbia Speleological Soc. [★7462]
Distripress - Assn. for the Promotion of the Intl. Press Distribution [IO], Zurich, Switzerland
Ditchley Found. [IO], Chipping Norton, United Kingdom
Divadelni, Literarni, Audiovizualni Agentura [★IO]
Divadelni Ustav [★IO]
Divco Club of Am. [21334], PO Box 215, Lowell, MI 49331-0215
Divers Alert Network [22539], Peter B. Bennett Ctr., 6 W Colony Pl., Durham, NC 27705, (919)684-2948
Divers Assn. of Maldives [IO], Male, Maldives
Diverse Emerging Music Org. [10188], PO Box 50252, Minneapolis, MN 55405
Diversity
Earth Coun. Alliance [12584]
Diversity Info. Resources [2519], 2105 Central Ave. NE, Minneapolis, MN 55418, (612)781-6819
Diversity Pipeline Alliance - Address unknown since 2010.
Divine Canines [16848], 3736 Bee Cave Rd., No. 1-107, West Lake Hills, TX 78746
Divine Science
Divine Sci. Fed. Intl. [19644]
Divine Sci. Fed. Intl. [19644]
Divine Sci. Ministers Assn. [19645]
Divine Sci. Fed. Intl. [19644], 110 Merchants Row, Ste. 4, Rutland, VT 05701, (802)779-9019
Divine Sci. Fed. Intl. [19644], 110 Merchants Row, Ste. 4, Rutland, VT 05701, (802)779-9019
Divine Sci. Ministers Assn. [19645], 55 W 116th St., No. 265, New York, NY 10026, (646)753-2959
Divine Sci. Ministers Org. [★19645]
Diving
Assn. of Dive Prog. Administrators [22538]
Divers Alert Network [22539]
Historical Diving Soc. U.S.A. [22540]
Intl. Assn. of Nitrox and Tech. Divers [22541]
Natl. Assn. of Underwater Instructors [23104]
U.S. Apnea Assn. [22542]
U.S. Apnea Assn. [22542]
U.S. Parachute Assn. [22800]
U.S. Professional Diving Coaches Assn. [22543]
USA Diving [22544]
Diving Dentists Soc. - Defunct.
Diving Equip. Mfrs. Assn. [★3309]
Diving Equip. Mfrs. Assn. [★3309]
Diving Equip. and Marketing Assn. [3309], 3750 Convoy St., Ste. 310, San Diego, CA 92111-3741, (858)616-6408
Diving Equip. and Marketing Assn. [3309], 3750 Convoy St., Ste. 310, San Diego, CA 92111-3741, (858)616-6408
Diving Historical Soc. Norway [IO], Bergen, Norway
Diving Plongeon Canada [IO], Ottawa, ON, Canada
Div. 54, APA [★16425]
Div. on Career Development of The Coun. for Exceptional Children [★8881]
Div. on Career Development and Transition [8881], Coun. for Exceptional Children, PO Box 79026, Baltimore, MD 21279-0026, (888)232-7733

Div. on Career Development and Transition of the Coun. for Exceptional Children [★8881]
Division of Cataloging and Classification - of ALA [★9968]
Div. for Children with Learning Disabilities [★12421]
Div. for Early Childhood of the Coun. for Exceptional Children [8882], 27 Ft. Missoula Rd., Ste. 2, Missoula, MT 59804, (406)543-0872
Division of Girl's and Women's Sports of the Amer. Assn. of Hea., Physical Educ., and Recreation [★8719]
Division of Hea. and Welfare Ministries of The United Methodist Church [★14742]
Division of Intl. Affairs [★17903]
Division of Intl. Affairs [★17903]
Div. for Physically Handicapped [★11788]
Div. for Physically Handicapped [★11788]
Div. for Physically Handicapped [★8879]
Div. on Physically Handicapped, Homebound and Hospitalized [★8879]
Div. on Physically Handicapped, Homebound and Hospitalized [★11788]
Div. on Physically Handicapped, Homebound and Hospitalized [★11788]
Div. de la Region de la Capitale nationale, Assn. canadienne pour les Nations Unies [★IO]
Div. for the Spanish Speaking [★12149]
Div. on Visual Handicaps [★8883]
Div. on Visual Impairments [8883], 1839 Frankfort Ave., Louisville, KY 40206, (502)899-2325
Div. for the Visually Handicapped [★8883]
Divorce
Assn. of Divorce Financial Planners [1335]
Children's Rights Coun. [11864]
Dads Rights [11865]
Ex-Partners of Servicemembers for Equality [11866]
Fathers for Equal Rights [11867]
Kids Need Both Parents [17623]
Natl. Assn. of Non-Custodial Moms [12610]
North Amer. Conf. of Separated and Divorced Catholics [11868]
Single Mothers By Choice [12622]
Stepfamily Found. [12021]
United Fathers of Am. [11869]
Divorce After 60 - Defunct.
Divya Disha [IO], Secunderabad, India
Dixie Coun. of Authors and Journalists [★10715]
Dizziness and Balance Disorders Assn. [★16091]
Dizziness and Balance Disorders Assn. [★16091]
DKT Intl. - Vietnam [IO], Hanoi, Vietnam
DM - Fagforening for hojtuddannede [IO], Frederiksberg, Denmark
DMA Nonprofit Fed. [264], 1615 L St. NW, Ste. 1100, Washington, DC 20036, (202)861-2410
DMAA Educational Found. [★8555]
DMAA: The Care Continuum Alliance [14382], 701 Pennsylvania Ave. NW, Ste. 700, Washington, DC 20004-2694, (202)737-5980
DMAA: The Care Continuum Alliance [14382], 701 Pennsylvania Ave. NW, Ste. 700, Washington, DC 20004-2694, (202)737-5980
Do Do Club [★20317]
Do It Now Found. [13248], PO Box 27568, Tempe, AZ 85285-7568, (480)736-0599
Do It Yourself Aids
Home Improvement Res. Inst. [1043]
Do-It-Yourself Res. Inst. [★1043]
Do Right Found. [20178], 2540 S Maryland Pkwy., No. 178, Las Vegas, NV 89109
Do Something [17375], 24-32 Union Sq. E, 4th Fl., New York, NY 10003, (212)254-2390
Doane Family Assn. of Am. [20502], Ms. Jane MacDuff, Membership Chair, 2618 Occidental Dr., Vienna, VA 22180
Doberman Assistance Network [11871], 3852 La Colina Rd., El Sobrante, CA 94803
Doberman Pinscher Club of Am. [21554], Lesley Reeves-Hunt, Membership Sec., 6400 Tripp Rd., China, MI 48054-2518, (586)899-2719
Doboku-Gakkai [★IO]
Doc to Dock [15302], 300 Douglass St., Brooklyn, NY 11217, (718)852-0655
DOCARE Intl. [12452], 142 E Ontario St., 4th Fl., Chicago, IL 60611, (312)202-8163

Reference to "IO" in place of a book number signifies that the association may be found in the 50th edition of International Organizations.

DOCARE Intl., N.F.P. **[12452]**, 142 E Ontario St., 4th Fl., Chicago, IL 60611, (312)202-8163

DOCHAS, The Irish Assn. of Non-Governmental Development Organisations **[IO]**, Dublin, Ireland

DOCOMOMO US **[9683]**, PO Box 230977, New York, NY 10023

Docs for Tots **[14073]**, 1000 Vermont Ave. NW, Ste. 700, Washington, DC 20005, (202)589-0103

Dr. to Dr. **[12453]**, 1749 MLK Jr. Way, Berkeley, CA 94709, (510)548-5200

Dr. to Dr. **[12453]**, 1749 MLK Jr. Way, Berkeley, CA 94709, (510)548-5200

Dr. James Naismith Basketball Found. **[IO]**, Almonte, ON, Canada

Dr. John W. Tintera Memorial/Hypoglycemia Lay Group - Defunct.

Dr. Thomas A. Dooley Found. **[★15190]**

Dr. Thomas A. Dooley Found. **[★15190]**

Dr. Who Info. Network **[IO]**, Toronto, ON, Canada

Doctors in Christ **[15303]**, 14359 Miramar Pkwy., Ste. 140, Miramar, FL 33027, (954)483-1215

Doctors for Developing Countries **[IO]**, Turin, Italy

Doctors for Disaster Preparedness **[14451]**, 1601 N Tucson Blvd., No. 9, Tucson, AZ 85716, (520)325-2680

Doctors for the Env. - Australia **[IO]**, Adelaide, Australia

Doctors for the Env. - Switzerland **[IO]**, Basel, Switzerland

Doctors for Life Intl. **[IO]**, Zimbali, Republic of South Africa

Doctors Opposing Circumcision **[11518]**, 2442 NW Market St., Ste. 42, Seattle, WA 98107-4137, (360)385-1882

Doctors for United Medical Missions **[15155]**, 313 Tidewater Dr., Havre de Grace, MD 21078, (410)688-0691

Doctors Without Borders - Australia **[IO]**, Broadway, Australia

Doctors Without Borders - Canada **[IO]**, Toronto, ON, Canada

Doctors Without Borders - France **[IO]**, Paris, France

Doctors Without Borders USA **[12833]**, 333 7th Ave., 2nd Fl., New York, NY 10001-5004, (212)679-6800

Doctors Without Borders USA **[12833]**, 333 7th Ave., 2nd Fl., New York, NY 10001-5004, (212)679-6800

Doctors of the World **[★12461]**

Doctors of the World **[★12461]**

Doctors of the World UK **[★IO]**

Doctors Worldwide **[IO]**, Stockport, United Kingdom

Document Mgt. Indus. Assn. **[★3354]**

Document Security Alliance **[5539]**, 204 E St. NE, Washington, DC 20002, (202)543-5552

Documentaristes du Canada **[★IO]**

Documentary Org. of Canada **[IO]**, Toronto, ON, Canada

Documentation Exchange **[★18053]**

Documentation Exchange **[★18053]**

Dodge Bros. Club **[21044]**, Less Hoffman, PO Box 1648, Cambridge, OH 43725, (740)439-5102

Dodge Family Assn. **[20503]**, 10105 W 17th Pl., Lakewood, CO 80215, (303)237-4947

Dodge Pilothouse Era Truck Club of Am. **[22197]**, 3778 Hoen Ave., Santa Rosa, CA 95405

Doe Network **[12543]**, 420 Airport Rd., Livingston, TN 38570, (931)397-3893

Doe Network **[12543]**, 420 Airport Rd., Livingston, TN 38570, (931)397-3893

Dog
Afghan Hound Club of Am. **[21475]**
Airedale Terrier Club of Am. **[21476]**
Akita Club of Am. **[21477]**
Alaskan Malamute Club of Am. **[21478]**
All Amer. Premier Breeds Admin. **[21479]**
Alliance for Contraception in Cats and Dogs **[12647]**
Amateur Field Trial Clubs of Am. **[21480]**
Amer. Belgian Malinois Club **[21481]**
Amer. Belgian Malinois Club **[21481]**
Amer. Bloodhound Club **[21482]**
Amer. Bouvier des Flandres Club **[21483]**
Amer. Boxer Club **[21484]**
Amer. Brittany Club **[21485]**
Amer. Brussels Griffon Assn. **[21486]**
Amer. Bullmastiff Assn. **[21487]**

Amer. Canine Educ. Found. **[21488]**
Amer. Cavalier King Charles Spaniel Club **[21489]**
Amer. Chesapeake Club **[21490]**
Amer. Dobermann Assn. **[21491]**
Amer. Dog Breeders Assn. **[21492]**
Amer. Dog Show Judges **[21493]**
Amer. Eskimo Dog Club of Am. **[21494]**
Amer. Fox Terrier Club **[21495]**
Amer. Kennel Club **[21496]**
Amer. Kuvasz Assn. **[11870]**
Amer. Lhasa Apso Club **[21497]**
Amer. Maltese Assn. **[21498]**
Amer. Manchester Terrier Club **[21499]**
Amer. Miniature Schnauzer Club **[21500]**
Amer. Pointer Club **[21501]**
Amer. Pomeranian Club **[21502]**
Amer. Rare Breed Assn. **[21503]**
Amer. Rottweiler Club **[21504]**
Amer. Sealyham Terrier Club **[21505]**
Amer. Shetland Sheepdog Assn. **[21506]**
Amer. Shih Tzu Club **[21507]**
Amer. Sighthound Field Assn. **[21508]**
Amer. Spaniel Club **[21509]**
Amer. Spaniel Club **[21509]**
Amer. Toy Fox Terrier Club **[21510]**
Amer. Water Spaniel Club **[21511]**
Amer. Water Spaniel Club **[21511]**
Amer. Whippet Club **[21512]**
Amer. White Shepherd Assn. **[21513]**
Amer. Working Collie Assn. **[21514]**
Amer. Working Dog Fed. **[21515]**
Assn. of Pet Dog Trainers **[4188]**
Australian Cattle Dog Club of Am. **[21516]**
Australian Shepherd Club of Am. **[21517]**
Australian Terrier Club of Am. **[21518]**
Autism Ser. Dogs of Am. **[13784]**
Basenji Club of Am. **[21519]**
Basset Hound Club of Am. **[21520]**
Bearded Collie Club of Am. **[21521]**
Belgian Sheepdog Club of Am. **[21522]**
Berger Picard Club of Am. **[21523]**
Bernese Mountain Dog Club of Am. **[21524]**
Bichon Frise Club of Am. **[21525]**
Black Russian Terrier Club of Am. **[21526]**
Bluetick Breeders of Am. **[21527]**
Border Terrier Club of Am. **[21528]**
Borzoi Club of Am. **[21529]**
Boston Terrier Club of Am. **[21530]**
Boykin Spaniel Club and Breeders Assn. of Am. **[21531]**
Bull Terrier Club of Am. **[21532]**
Cairn Terrier Club of Am. **[21533]**
Canaan Dog Club of Am. **[21534]**
Canine Defense Fund **[10936]**
Canine Freestyle Fed. **[22545]**
Cardigan Welsh Corgi Club of Am. **[21535]**
Caucasian Ovcharka Club of Am. **[21536]**
Cavalier King Charles Spaniel Club of Am. **[21537]**
Chihuahua Club of Am. **[21538]**
Chinese Shar-Pei Club of Am. **[21539]**
Chow Chow Club, Inc. **[21540]**
Club de l'Epagneul Breton of the U.S. **[21541]**
Clumber Spaniel Club of Am. **[21542]**
Cockapoo Club of Am. **[21543]**
Collie Club of Am. **[21544]**
Colonial Rottweiler Club **[21545]**
Companion Animal Protection Soc. **[12649]**
Continental Mi-Ki Assn. **[21546]**
CorgiAid **[21547]**
Curly-Coated Retriever Club of Am. **[21548]**
Dachshund Club of Am. **[21549]**
Dalmatian Club of Am. **[21550]**
Dandie Dinmont Terrier Club of Am. **[21551]**
Danish/Swedish Farmdog Club of Am. **[21552]**
Desert German Shorthaired Pointer Club **[21553]**
Divine Canines **[16848]**
Doberman Assistance Network **[11871]**
Doberman Pinscher Club of Am. **[21554]**
Dog Scouts of Am. **[11872]**
Dogs Against Drugs/Dogs Against Crime **[11873]**
Dogs for the Deaf **[14933]**
Dogs Deserve Better **[11874]**
Dogue de Bordeaux Soc. of Am. **[21555]**
Echo Dogs White Shepherd Rescue **[10954]**

English Cocker Spaniel Club of Am. **[21556]**
English Setter Assn. of Am. **[21557]**
English Shepherd Club **[21558]**
English Springer Spaniel Field Trial Assn. **[21559]**
English Toy Spaniel Club of Am. **[21560]**
Estrela Mountain Dog Assn. of Am. **[21561]**
Field Spaniel Soc. of Am. **[21562]**
Finnish Spitz Club of Am. **[21563]**
Flat-Coated Retriever Soc. of Am. **[21564]**
Fox Terrier Network **[21565]**
French Brittany Gun Dog Assn. **[21566]**
French Bull Dog Club of Am. **[21567]**
Galgo Rescue Intl. Network **[10969]**
German Shepherd Dog Club of Am. **[21568]**
German Shepherd Dog Club of Am. I Working Dog Assn. **[21569]**
German Shorthaired Pointer Club of Am. **[21570]**
German Wirehaired Pointer Club of Am. **[21571]**
Giant Schnauzer Club of Am. **[21572]**
Golden Retriever Club of Am. **[21573]**
Gordon Setter Club of Am. **[21574]**
Great Dane Club of Am. **[21575]**
Great Pyrenees Club of Am. **[21576]**
Grey Muzzle Org. **[10971]**
Greyhound Club of Am. **[21577]**
Havana Silk Dog Assn. of Am. **[21578]**
Heart Bandits Amer. Eskimo Dog Rescue **[11875]**
Heart Bandits Amer. Eskimo Dog Rescue **[11875]**
Heaven on Earth Soc. for Animals **[10977]**
HOPE Animal-Assisted Crisis Response **[12906]**
Hovawart Club of North Am. **[21579]**
Hungarian Pumi Club of Am. **[21580]**
Hunting Retriever Club **[21581]**
Icelandic Sheepdog Assn. of Am. **[21582]**
Intl. Assn. of Canine Professionals **[4189]**
Intl. Assn. of Canine Professionals **[4189]**
Intl. Borzoi Coun. **[21583]**
Intl. Borzoi Coun. **[21583]**
Intl. Forensic Entomology Detection Canine Assn. **[5489]**
Intl. French Brittany Club of Am. **[21584]**
Intl. French Brittany Club of Am. **[21584]**
Intl. German Coolie Soc. and Registry **[21585]**
Intl. Kennel Club of Chicago **[21586]**
Intl. Seppala Assn. **[21587]**
Irish Setter Club of Am. **[21588]**
Irish Terrier Club of Am. **[21589]**
Irish Water Spaniel Club of Am. **[21590]**
Irish Wolfhound Club of Am. **[21591]**
Italian Greyhound Club of Am. **[21592]**
Jack Russell Terrier Club of Am. **[21593]**
Japanese Chin Club of Am. **[21594]**
Keeshond Club of Am. **[21595]**
Komondor Club of Am. **[21596]**
Kuvasz Club of Am. **[21597]**
Ladies Kennel Assn. of Am. **[21598]**
Maremma Sheepdog Club of Am. **[21599]**
Mastiff Club of Am. **[21600]**
Miniature Australian Shepherd Club of Am. **[21601]**
Miniature Bull Terrier Club of Am. **[21602]**
Miniature Pinscher Club of Am. **[21603]**
Musical Dog Sport Assn. **[22546]**
Natl. Amateur Retriever Club **[21604]**
Natl. Amer. Eskimo Dog Assn. **[21605]**
Natl. Amer. Pit Bull Terrier Assn. **[21606]**
Natl. Assn. of Dog Obedience Instructors **[21607]**
Natl. Assn. of Ser. Dogs **[11876]**
Natl. Beagle Club of Am. **[21608]**
Natl. Bird Dog Challenge Assn. **[21609]**
Natl. Entlebucher Mountain Dog Assn. **[21610]**
Natl. Entomology Scent Detection Canine Assn. **[2633]**
Natl. Greyhound Assn. **[21611]**
Natl. Labrador Retriever Club **[21612]**
Natl. Retriever Club **[22547]**
Natl. Shiba Club of Am. **[21613]**
Natl. Toy Fox Terrier Assn. **[21614]**
Natl. Wolfdog Alliance **[21615]**
Newfoundland Club of Am. **[21616]**
North Amer. Border Terrier Welfare **[11877]**
North Amer. Deutsch Kurzhaar Club **[21617]**
North Amer. Dog Agility Coun. **[22548]**
North Amer. Gun Dog Assn. **[21618]**
North Amer. Kai Assn. **[21619]**

A star before a book entry number signifies that the name is not listed separately, but is mentioned within the entry.

North Amer. Llewellin Breeders Assn. [21620]
North Amer. Llewellin Breeders Assn. [21620]
North Amer. Ring Assn. [21621]
North Amer. Ring Assn. [21621]
North Amer. Teckel Club [21622]
North Amer. Working Bouvier Assn. [21623]
Norwegian Elkhound Assn. of Am. [21624]
Norwegian Lundehund Assn. of Am. [21625]
Old English Sheepdog Club of Am. [21626]
Otterhound Club of Am. [21627]
Papillon Club of Am. [21628]
Parson Russell Terrier Assn. of Am. [21629]
Patterdale Terrier Club of Am. [21630]
Pekingese Club of Am. [21631]
Pembroke Welsh Corgi Club of Am. [21632]
Peruvian Inca Orchid Dog Club of Am. [21633]
Polish Tatra Sheepdog Club of Am. [21634]
Poodle Club of Am. [21635]
Portuguese Podengo Club of Am. [21636]
Portuguese Water Dog Club of Am. [21637]
Professional Handlers' Assn. [21638]
Pug Dog Club of Am. [21639]
Puli Club of Am. [21640]
Pyrenean Mastiff Club of Am. [21641]
Rat Terrier Club of Am. [21642]
Rhodesian Ridgeback Club of the U.S. [21643]
Ridgeback Rescue of the U.S. [11034]
Rough and Smooth Collie Training Assn. [8688]
Saint Bernard Club of Am. [21644]
Saluki Club of Am. [21645]
Saluki Tree of Life Alliance [11878]
Samoyed Club of Am. [21646]
Save-A-Vet [11036]
Schipperke Club of Am. [21647]
Scottish Deerhound Club of Am. [21648]
Scottish Terrier Club of Am. [21649]
Search and Rescue Dogs of the U.S. [11879]
Senior Conformation Judges Assn. [21650]
Siberian Husky Club of Am. [21651]
Silky Terrier Club of Am. [21652]
Skye Terrier Club of Am. [21653]
South African Boerboel Breeders Assn. - U.S.A.
    and Canada [22549]
Spanish Water Dog Assn. of Am. [21654]
Staffordshire Terrier Club of Am. [21655]
Standard Schnauzer Club of Am. [21656]
Standard Schnauzer Club of Am. [21656]
Support Dogs, Inc. [11832]
Tasmanian Canine Assn. [18095]
Tibetan Spaniel Club of Am. [21657]
Tibetan Terrier Club of Am. [21658]
Toy Australian Shepherd Assn. of Am. [21659]
Treeing Walker Breeders and Fanciers Assn.
    [21660]
United Beagle Gundog Fed. [21661]
United Doberman Club [21662]
United Kennel Club [21663]
United Natl. Weight Pull Assn. [22550]
United Poodle Breeds Assn. [21664]
United Schutzhund Clubs of Am. [21665]
U.S.A. Coton de Tulear Club [21666]
U.S. Border Collie Club [21667]
U.S. Complete Shooting Dog Assn. [21668]
U.S. Dog Agility Assn. [22551]
U.S. Kerry Blue Terrier Club [21669]
U.S. Lakeland Terrier Club [21670]
U.S. Mondioring Assn. [22552]
U.S. Neapolitan Mastiff Club [21671]
U.S. Rottweiler Club [21672]
United White Shepherd Club [21673]
United Yorkie Rescue [11052]
U.S.A. Defenders of Greyhounds [11054]
Versatility in Poodles [4190]
Vizsla Club of Am. [21674]
Weimaraner Club of Am. [21675]
Welsh Springer Spaniel Club of Am. [21676]
West Highland White Terrier Club of Am. [21677]
Westminster Kennel Club [21678]
White German Shepherd Dog Club of Am.
    [21679]
Wirehaired Vizsla Club of Am. [21680]
Working Pit Bull Terrier Club of Am. [21681]
Working Riesenschnauzer Fed. [21682]
Working Riesenschnauzer Fed. [21682]
World Bulldog Alliance [21683]

World Canine Freestyle Org. [22553]
Worldwide Kennel Club [21684]
Worldwide Kennel Club [21684]
WTCARES [21685]
Yorkshire Terrier Club of Am. [21686]
Dog Assistance in Disability [IO], Birmingham,
    United Kingdom
Dog Center; Natl. Ser. [14954]
Dog Found; Fidelco Guide [17074]
Dog Guides Canada [IO], Oakville, ON, Canada
Dog Racing
  Amer. Greyhound Track Operators Assn. [22554]
  Greyhound Racing Assn. of Am. [22555]
  Intl. Fed. of Sleddog Sports [22556]
  Intl. Sled Dog Racing Assn. [22557]
  Intl. Sled Dog Racing Assn. [22557]
  Lakes Region Sled Dog Club [22558]
  U.S.A. Defenders of Greyhounds [11054]
Dog Scouts of Am. [11872], PO Box 158, Harrison,
    OH 45030, (513)505-5071
Dog Writers' Assn. of Am. [2824], Pat Santi, Sec.,
    173 Union Rd., Coatesville, PA 19320-1326,
    (610)384-2436
Doga Dernegi [IO], Ankara, Turkey
Dogs Against Drugs/Dogs Against Crime [11873],
    4012 W 32nd St., Anderson, IN 46011, (765)642-
    9447
Dogs for the Blind; Leader [17094]
Dogs for the Blind; Leader [17094]
Dogs for the Deaf [14933], 10175 Wheeler Rd.,
    Central Point, OR 97502, (541)826-9220
Dogs for Deaf and Disabled Americans [★14950]
Dogs Deserve Better [11874], PO Box 23, Tipton,
    PA 16684, (814)941-7447
Dogs New South Wales [IO], St. Marys, Australia
Dogs Trust [IO], London, United Kingdom
Dogue de Bordeaux Soc. of Am. [21555], 712 Ban-
    croft Rd., No. 164, Walnut Creek, CA 94598,
    (925)954-8644
Dohne Merino Breed Soc. of South Africa [IO], Stut-
    terheim, Republic of South Africa
Doirse Dochais [★18006]
Doirse Dochais [★18006]
Doitsu Kikai Kogyo Renmei - Nihon Daihyo Jimusho
    [★IO]
Doll Artisan Guild [21689], PO Box 1113, Oneonta,
    NY 13820-5113, (607)432-4977
Doll Artisan Guild [21689], PO Box 1113, Oneonta,
    NY 13820-5113, (607)432-4977
The Doll Center [★21689]
The Doll Center [★21689]
Doll Costumer's Guild [21690], PO Box 247, New
    Harmony, IN 47631, (812)319-5300
Dollars & Sense [★6619]
Dolls
  Amy's Doll Lover's Club [21687]
  Annalee Club [21688]
  Cottage Indus. Miniaturists Trade Assn. [1044]
  Doll Artisan Guild [21689]
  Doll Artisan Guild [21689]
  Doll Costumer's Guild [21690]
  Ginny Doll Club [21691]
  Intl. Doll Makers Assn. [21692]
  Intl. Doll Makers Assn. [21692]
  Intl. Rose O'Neill Club Found. [21693]
  Intl. Rose O'Neill Club Found. [21693]
  Lawton Collector's Guild [21694]
  Natl. Antique Doll Dealers Assn. [21695]
  Natl. Antique Doll Dealers Assn. [21695]
  Natl. Inst. of Amer. Doll Artists [21696]
  Oper. Hug-A-Hero [12533]
  Original Doll Artists Coun. of Am. [21697]
  Original Paper Doll Artists Guild [21698]
  Strawberry Shortcake Chat Gp. [21699]
  United Fed. of Doll Clubs [21700]
Dollywood Found. - Address unknown since 2011.
Dolphin Res. Center [7041], 58901 Overseas Hwy.,
    Grassy Key, FL 33050-6019, (305)289-1121
Domestic Abuse Helpline for Men and Women
    [11883], PO Box 252, Harmony, ME 04942,
    (207)683-5758
Domestic Appliance Ser. Assn. [IO], London, United
    Kingdom
Domestic Energy Producers Alliance [1166], PO Box
    18359, Oklahoma City, OK 73154, (405)424-1699

Domestic/Foreign Missionary Soc. of the Protestant
    Episcopal Church [20035], Episcopal Church
    Center, 815 2nd Ave., New York, NY 10017-4594,
    (212)716-6000
Domestic/Foreign Missionary Soc. of the Protestant
    Episcopal Church [20035], Episcopal Church
    Center, 815 2nd Ave., New York, NY 10017-4594,
    (212)716-6000
Domestic Policy Assn. [★18479]
Domestic Services
  Assn. of Residential Cleaning Services Intl. [2240]
  Intl. Janitorial Cleaning Services Assn. [2248]
  Vacation Rental Housekeeping Professionals
    [1045]
Domestic Violence
  Asian and Pacific Islander Inst. on Domestic
    Violence [11880]
  Break the Cycle [11881]
  Corporate Alliance to End Partner Violence
    [11882]
  DeafHope [12141]
  Domestic Abuse Helpline for Men and Women
    [11883]
  DOVE: Advocacy Services for Abused Deaf
    Women and Children [12142]
  Emerge: Counseling and Educ. to Stop Domestic
    Violence [11884]
  Face Forward [11885]
  FaithTrust Inst. [11886]
  Futures Without Violence [11887]
  Girls Educational and Mentoring Services [18603]
  Illusion Theater [11888]
  Intl. Center for Assault Prevention [11889]
  Leadership Coun. on Child Abuse and
    Interpersonal Violence [11890]
  Love Our Children USA [11343]
  Natl. Center on Elder Abuse [11891]
  Natl. Coalition Against Domestic Violence [11892]
  Natl. Coalition of Anti-Violence Programs [18770]
  Natl. Coun. on Child Abuse and Family Violence
    [11893]
  Natl. Domestic Violence Hotline [11894]
  Natl. Latino Alliance for the Elimination of
    Domestic Violence [11895]
  Natl. Network to End Domestic Violence [11896]
  Stop Abuse for Everyone [11897]
  A Window Between Worlds [11898]
Dominica Amateur Athletic Assn. [IO], Roseau, Do-
    minica
Dominica Amateur Volleyball Assn. [IO], Roseau,
    Dominica
Dominica Assn. of Disabled People [IO], Roseau,
    Dominica
Dominica Assn. of Professional Engineers [IO], Ro-
    seau, Dominica
Dominica Assn. of Teachers [IO], Roseau, Dominica
Dominica Employers' Fed. [IO], Roseau, Dominica
Dominica Hotel and Tourism Assn. [IO], Roseau,
    Dominica
Dominica Lawn Tennis Assn. [IO], Roseau, Dominica
Dominica Natl. Development Corp. [IO], Roseau,
    Dominica
Dominica Organic Agriculture Movement [IO], Ro-
    seau, Dominica
Dominica Red Cross Soc. [IO], Roseau, Dominica
Dominica Soc. of Architects [IO], Roseau, Dominica
Dominica Taekwondo Fed. [IO], Roseau, Dominica
Dominica Watersports Assn. [IO], Roseau, Dominica
Dominican Advance [11899], PO Box 924, Williston,
    VT 05495, (520)908-7324
Dominican Amer. Natl. Roundtable [18976], 1050
    17th St. NW, Ste. 600, Washington, DC 20036,
    (202)238-0097
Dominican Assn. of Foreign Investment Enterprises
    [IO], Santo Domingo, Dominican Republic
Dominican Menopause and Osteoporosis Soc. [IO],
    Santiago, Dominican Republic
Dominican Mission Found. [20036], PO Box 15367,
    San Francisco, CA 94115-0367, (415)931-2183
Dominican Osteoporosis Hea. Coun. [IO], Santo Do-
    mingo, Dominican Republic
Dominican Red Cross [IO], Santo Domingo,
    Dominican Republic
Dominican Republic
  Dominican Advance [11899]

Reference to "IO" in place of a book number signifies that the association may be found in the 50th edition of International Organizations.

Dominican Amer. Natl. Roundtable [18976]
Response-Ability [20085]
Umoja Intl. [12969]
Dominican Republic Bible Soc. [IO], Santo Domingo, Dominican Republic
Dominican Republic League Against Epilepsy [IO], Santo Domingo, Dominican Republic
Dominican Soc. of Cardiology [IO], Santo Domingo, Dominican Republic
Dominican Soc. of EEG and Clinical Neurophysiology [IO], Santo Domingo, Dominican Republic
Dominican Volunteers USA [20037], 1914 S Ashland Ave., Chicago, IL 60608, (708)524-5985
Dominicans on Wall St. [1293], PO Box 4081, New York, NY 10261
Dominicans on Wall St. [1293], PO Box 4081, New York, NY 10261
Dominion Sports Services, Inc. [★22645]
Don DeLillo Soc. [10713], Marni Gauthier, Sec., PO Box 2000, Cortland, NY 13045-0900
DONA Intl. [15877], 1582 S Parker Rd., Ste. 201, Denver, CO 80231, (888)788-DONA
Donald W. Reynolds Found. [14013], 1701 Village Center Cir., Las Vegas, NV 89134, (702)804-6000
Donate Life Am. [14421], 700 N 4th St., Richmond, VA 23219, (804)782-4920
Doncaster Chamber [IO], Doncaster, United Kingdom
Donee Gp. [★12679]
Donizetti Soc. [IO], Morden, United Kingdom
Donkey Breed Soc. [IO], Edenbridge, United Kingdom
Donkey Sanctuary [IO], Sidmouth, United Kingdom
Donna Fargo Fan Club [★23834]
Donna Fargo Intl. Fan Club [23834], PO Box 210877, Nashville, TN 37221-0877, (800)446-8426
Donny Osmond Fan Club [★23835]
Donny Osmond Intl. Network [23835], 223 W Bulldog Blvd., No. 520, Provo, UT 84604, (800)732-2111
Donors
Assn. of Organ Procurement Organizations [14420]
Assn. of Small Foundations [18312]
Donate Life Am. [14421]
Eye Bank Assn. of Am. [14422]
Eye-Bank for Sight Restoration [14423]
LifeBanc [14424]
The Living Bank [14425]
The Living Bank Intl. [14425]
Natl. Marrow Donor Prog. [14426]
Natl. Marrow Donor Prog. [14426]
USBloodDonors.org [13853]
Dooley Foundation/INTERMED [★15190]
Dooley Foundation/INTERMED [★15190]
Door
Amer. Assn. of Automatic Door Mfrs. [1046]
Institutional Locksmiths' Assn. [1047]
Door and Access Systems Mfrs. Assn. Intl. [2334], 1300 Sumner Ave., Cleveland, OH 44115-2851, (216)241-7333
Door and Access Systems Mfrs. Assn. Intl. [2334], 1300 Sumner Ave., Cleveland, OH 44115-2851, (216)241-7333
Door and Hardware Fed. [IO], Tamworth, United Kingdom
Door and Hardware Inst. [1649], 14150 Newbrook Dr., Ste. 200, Chantilly, VA 20151-2223, (703)222-2010
Door and Hardware Inst. [1649], 14150 Newbrook Dr., Ste. 200, Chantilly, VA 20151-2223, (703)222-2010
Door and Operator Dealers of Am. [★571]
Door and Operator Dealers of Am. [★571]
Door and Operator Dealers Assn. [★571]
Door and Operator Dealers Assn. [★571]
Door Operator and Remote Controls Mfrs. Assn. - Defunct.
Doors Collectors Club [23836], TDM Inc., PO Box 1441, Orem, UT 84059-1441, (801)224-7390
Doors of Hope [18006], PO Box 485, Ho-Ho-Kus, NJ 07423, (201)444-4786
Doors of Hope [18006], PO Box 485, Ho-Ho-Kus, NJ 07423, (201)444-4786
Dorcas Medical Mission [15156], 907 Utica Ave., Brooklyn, NY 11203, (718)342-2928

Doris Day Animal League [10952], 2100 L St. NW, Washington, DC 20037, (202)452-1100
Doris Duke Charitable Found. [13130], 650 5th Ave., 19th Fl., New York, NY 10019, (212)974-7000
Dorothy L. Sayers Soc. [IO], Hassocks, United Kingdom
Dorper Sheep Breeders' Soc. of South Africa [IO], Middelburg, Republic of South Africa
Dorpers Skaaptelersgenootskap van Suid-Afrika [★IO]
Dorset Bus., The Chamber of Commerce and Indus. [IO], Poole, United Kingdom
Dorset Horn and Poll Dorset Sheep Breeders Assn. [IO], London, United Kingdom
Dorset Natural History and Archaeological Soc. [IO], Dorchester, United Kingdom
Double Harvest [3730], 55 S Main St., Oberlin, OH 44074, (440)714-1694
Double Harvest [3730], 55 S Main St., Oberlin, OH 44074, (440)714-1694
Double Trouble in Recovery [12485], PO Box 245055, Brooklyn, NY 11224, (718)373-2684
Douglas Fir Plywood Assn. [★1497]
Doulas of North Am. [★15877]
DOVE: Advocacy Services for Abused Deaf Women and Children [12142], PO Box 181118, Denver, CO 80218-8822, (303)831-7932
Dove Sportsman's Soc. [3844], PO Box 610, Edgefield, SC 29824, (803)637-5731
Dove Sportsman's Soc. [3844], PO Box 610, Edgefield, SC 29824, (803)637-5731
Dovenschap [★IO]
Doves Unlimited [★3844]
Doves Unlimited [★3844]
Dow Jones Employees Assn. [★23285]
Dow Jones Newspaper Fund [8442], PO Box 300, Princeton, NJ 08543-0300, (609)452-2820
Down Syndrome Assn. [IO], Teddington, United Kingdom
Down Syndrome Assn. - Singapore [IO], Singapore, Singapore
Down Syndrome Cong; Natl. [12510]
Down Syndrome Fed. of India [IO], Chennai, India
Down Syndrome Ireland [IO], Dublin, Ireland
Downed Bikers Assn. [12547], PO Box 21713, Oklahoma City, OK 73156, (405)789-5565
Down's Syndrome
Arc of the U.S. [12495]
Assn. for Children with Down Syndrome [12496]
Down Syndrome Ireland [18862]
Down's Syndrome Cong. [★12510]
Downwinders
Downwinders - Address unknown since 2011.
Dozenal Soc. of Am. [7464], 472 Village Oaks Ln., Babylon, NY 11702-3123
Dracula Soc. [IO], London, United Kingdom
Dracula Soc. - Great Britain [IO], London, United Kingdom
Draft
Center on Conscience and War [17560]
Center on Conscience and War [17560]
Central Comm. for Conscientious Objectors [17561]
Comm. Opposed to Militarism and the Draft [5389]
Drag Racing
Diesel Hot Rod Assn. [22823]
Natl. Elec. Drag Racing Assn. [22559]
Safer Racer Tour [13006]
United Black Drag Racers Assn. [22560]
Dragonfly Soc. of Am. [★6843]
Dragonfly Soc. of the Americas [6843], Univ. of Texas Insect Coll., 3001 Lake Austin Blvd., Ste. 1.314, Austin, TX 78703
Drama Assn. of Wales [IO], Cardiff, United Kingdom
Drama Desk [10573], Lester Schecter, 244 W 54th St., 9th Fl., New York, NY 10019, (212)586-2600
Drama League [10574], 520 8th Ave., Ste. 320, New York, NY 10018, (212)244-9494
Drama Tree - Defunct.
Dramatic, Artistic and Literary Rights Org. [IO], Braamfontein, Republic of South Africa
Dramatic Order Knights of Khorassan [19094], 613 N River Dr., Marion, IN 46952-2648, (765)664-7925

Dramatics
Alpha Psi Omega [23503]
Amer. Theatre Arts for Youth [10566]
Delta Psi Omega [23504]
Drama Desk [10573]
Intl. Guild of Symphony, Opera and Ballet Musicians [23272]
O'Neill Critics Inst. [10596]
Dramatist Guild [★10575]
Dramatists Centre [IO], Montreal, QC, Canada
Dramatists Guild of Am. [10575], 1501 Broadway, Ste. 701, New York, NY 10036, (212)398-9366
Draugas [★19117]
Draught Proofing Advisory Assn. [IO], Haslemere, United Kingdom
Draughts Fed. of India [IO], Dhuri, India
Draughts Fed. of Turkmenistan [IO], Balkanabat, Turkmenistan
Dravet.org [14519], PO Box 797, Deale, MD 20751, (443)607-8267
The Drawing Center [9175], 35 Wooster St., New York, NY 10013, (212)219-2166
Dream Catchers USA [11783], PO Box 701, Killen, AL 35645, (256)272-0286
Dream Factory [11460], 120 W Broadway, Ste. 300, Louisville, KY 40202, (502)561-3001
DreamCatcher Wild Horse and Burro Sanctuary [10953], PO Box 9, Ravendale, CA 96123, (530)260-0148
Dreamcatchers for Abused Children [11142], PO Box 142, Peck, MI 48466, (810)275-0755
Dredging Contractors of Am. [2355], 503 D St. NW, Ste. 150, Washington, DC 20001, (202)737-2674
Dredging Indus. Size Standard Comm. [18331], Patton, Boggs, 2550 M St. NW, Washington, DC 20037-1301, (202)457-6000
Dress for Success Worldwide [13458], 32 E 31st St., 7th Fl., New York, NY 10016, (212)532-1922
Dress for Success Worldwide [13458], 32 E 31st St., 7th Fl., New York, NY 10016, (212)532-1922
Dressage Canada [IO], Ottawa, ON, Canada
DRI Intl. [5306], 115 Broadway, 12th Fl., New York, NY 10010, (866)542-3744
Dried Fruit Assn. of California [★4447]
Dried Fruit Assn. of New York [★1378]
Drilling Engg. Assn. [2648], Mike Killalea, Sec.-Treas., Intl. Assn. of Drilling Contractors, 10370 Richmond Ave., Ste. 760, Houston, TX 77042, (713)292-1945
Drilling, Observation and Sampling of the Earth's Continental Crust [6602], PO Box 58857, Salt Lake City, UT 84158-0857, (801)583-2150
Drilling and Sawing Assn. [IO], Nottingham, United Kingdom
Drinker Lib. of Choral Music [10189], Free Lib. of Philadelphia, 1901 Vine St., Philadelphia, PA 19103, (215)686-5364
Drinking Water for India [13419], PO Box 244, Plainsboro, NJ 08536-0244, (609)843-0176
Drishtipat Worldwide [11124], PO Box 1581, New York, NY 10156
Drive Canada [IO], Vancouver, BC, Canada
driveAWARE [12982], PO Box 2114, Warminster, PA 18974-2114, (215)343-1919
Driver Education
ADED: The Assn. for Driver Rehabilitation Specialists [7978]
ADED: The Assn. for Driver Rehabilitation Specialists [7978]
Amer. Driver and Traffic Safety Educ. Assn. [7979]
driveAWARE [12982]
Driving School Assn. of the Americas [7980]
North Amer. Trans. Mgt. Inst. [7981]
Safer Racer Tour [13006]
Driver Employment Coun. of Am. [3509], 1150 17th St. NW, Ste. 900, Washington, DC 20036, (202)842-3400
Driver Leasing Coun. of Am. [★3509]
Driving Instructor Register of Ireland [IO], Dublin, Ireland
Driving Instructors Assn. [IO], Croydon, United Kingdom
Driving School Assn. of the Americas [7980], 3090 E Gause Blvd., Ste. 425, Slidell, LA 70461, (800)270-DSAA

A star before a book entry number signifies that the name is not listed separately, but is mentioned within the entry.

DROKPA [11575], 1032 Irving St., San Francisco, CA 94122
Drop Forging Assn. [★2470]
Drug Abuse
　Amer. Osteopathic Acad. of Addiction Medicine [16735]
　Ardent Lion Soc. [11659]
　Assn. of Recovering Motorcyclists [13236]
　Christian Addiction Rehabilitation Assn. [13241]
　Do It Now Found. [13248]
　Giraffe Club [18680]
　Intl. Assn. of Addictions and Offender Counselors [11674]
　Luz Social Services [13263]
　Narcotic Educational Found. of Am. [13267]
　November Coalition [18681]
　VietNow Natl. [13358]
　Way to Work [11962]
Drug and Alcohol Coun. of Seychelles [IO], Victoria, Seychelles
Drug and Alcohol Testing Indus. Assn. [13249], 1325 G St. NW, Ste. 500, No. 5001, Washington, DC 20005, (800)355-1257
Drug, Chem. and Allied Trades Assn. [★2693]
Drug, Chem. and Allied Trades Sect. of the New York Bd. of Trade [★2693]
Drug, Chem. and Assoc. Technologies Assn. [2693], 1 Washington Blvd., Ste. 7, Robbinsville, NJ 08691-3162, (609)448-1000
Drug Educ; Amer. Coun. for [13234]
Drug Info. Assn. [16190], 800 Enterprise Rd., Ste. 200, Horsham, PA 19044, (215)442-6100
Drug Info. Assn. [16190], 800 Enterprise Rd., Ste. 200, Horsham, PA 19044, (215)442-6100
Drug Info. Center [★13279]
Drug Policy
　Access to Benefits Coalition [17760]
　Canadian Found. for Drug Policy [21869]
　Drug Policy Alliance [17286]
　Friends and Families of Cannabis Consumers [18085]
　Giraffe Club [18680]
　MOMSTELL [13265]
　Natl. Alliance for Model State Drug Laws [5390]
　Natl. Assn. of State Controlled Substances Authorities [5391]
　November Coalition [18681]
Drug Policy Alliance [17286], 925 15th St. NW, 2nd Fl., Washington, DC 20005, (202)216-0035
Drug Policy Found. [★17286]
Drug Rehabilitation
　Amer. Osteopathic Acad. of Addiction Medicine [16735]
　Assn. of Recovering Motorcyclists [13236]
　Do It Now Found. [13248]
　Giraffe Club [18680]
　Intl. Assn. of Addictions and Offender Counselors [11674]
　Luz Social Services [13263]
　Narcotic Educational Found. of Am. [13267]
Drug and Therapeutic Info. [★16201]
Drug Wholesalers Assn. [★16193]
Drugs Anonymous [★13283]
DrugScope [IO], London, United Kingdom
Drum Corps Intl. [10190], 110 W Washington St., Ste. C, Indianapolis, IN 46204, (317)275-1212
Drum Corps Intl. [10190], 110 W Washington St., Ste. C, Indianapolis, IN 46204, (317)275-1212
Drums
　Disabled Drummers Assn. [11780]
　Earth Drum Coun. [9575]
Drums No Guns [17687], PO Box 1455, New Haven, CT 06510, (203)675-4827
Drunk Driving; Mothers Against [12990]
Drustvo za borbu protiv side Crne Gore [★IO]
Drustvo Crvenog Kriza Bosne I Hercegovine [★IO]
Drustvo Hrvatskih Intelektualki [★IO]
Drustvo Inzenirjev in Tehnikov Papirnistva [★IO]
Drustvo matematikov, fizikov in astronomov Slov-enije [★IO]
Drustvo Prijatelja Biblije [IO], Zagreb, Croatia
Drustvo fiziologa Republike Srbije [★IO]
Drustvo Slovenskih Pisateljev [★IO]
Drustvo Za Psiholosku Pomoc [★IO]
Drustvo Znanstvenih in Tehniskih Prevajalcev Slov-enije [★IO]

Drutsvo Slovenskih Pisateljev [★IO]
Drutvo prostovoljcev Vincencijeve zveze dobrote [★IO]
Dry Color Mfrs. Assn. [★799]
Dry Stone Walling Assn. of Great Britain [IO], Milnthorpe, United Kingdom
Drycleaning Inst. of Australia [IO], Cessnock, Australia
Drycleaning and Laundry Inst. Intl. [2191], 14700 Sweitzer Ln., Laurel, MD 20707, (301)622-1900
Drycleaning and Laundry Inst. Intl. [2191], 14700 Sweitzer Ln., Laurel, MD 20707, (301)622-1900
DSA [★20505]
DSL Forum [★1897]
DTC Assn. [IO], Hong Kong, People's Republic of China
DUAL [★6511]
Dual Laminate Fabrication Assn. [2767], PO Box 1023, Gatesville, TX 76528, (254)865-9444
Dualchas Nadair na h-Alba [★IO]
Duane Eddy Circle [IO], Sheffield, United Kingdom
Dubai Cares [IO], Dubai, United Arab Emirates
Dublin Chamber of Commerce [IO], Dublin, Ireland
Dublin City Bus. Assn. [IO], Dublin, Ireland
DuBois Family Assn. [20504], 46715 McLeod Rd., Myakka City, FL 34251
Ducks Unlimited [5047], 1 Waterfowl Way, Memphis, TN 38120, (901)758-3825
Ductile Iron Pipe Res. Assn. [2747], 245 Riverchase Pkwy. E, Ste. O, Birmingham, AL 35244, (205)402-8700
Ductile Iron Soc. [7092], 15400 Pearl Rd., Ste. 234, Strongsville, OH 44136, (440)665-3686
Dude Ranchers' Assn. [1747], PO Box 2307, Cody, WY 82414, (307)587-2339
Duke Ellington Jazz Soc. [★10191]
The Duke Ellington Soc. [10191], PO Box 31, Church St. Sta., New York, NY 10008-0031
The Duke Ellington Soc. - New York Chap. [★10191]
Duncan Black Macdonald Center for the Stud. of Islam and Christian/Muslim Relations [★19832]
Duncan Black Macdonald Center for the Stud. of Islam and Christian/Muslim Relations [★19832]
Duncan Surname Assn. [20505], 8080 N Illinois St., Indianapolis, IN 46260-2939
Dunlop - Dunlap Family Soc. [20506], Mr. Peter Dunlop, Pres., PO Box 652, East Aurora, NY 14052, (716)655-2521
Dunya Enerji Konseyi Turk Milli Komitesi [★IO]
Duodecimal Soc. of Am. [★7464]
DuPont Fund; Jessie Ball [12677]
Durango/Purgatory Adaptive Sports Assn. [★22500]
Durene Assn. of Amer. - Defunct.
Durrell Wildlife Conservation Trust [IO], Jersey, United Kingdom
Durum Wheat Inst. [★2502]
Duster Class Yacht Racing Assn. - Defunct.
DUSTOFF Assn. [20363], PO Box 8091, San Antonio, TX 78208
Dutch
　Assn. for the Advancement of Dutch-American Stud. [9576]
　Assn. for the Advancement of Dutch-American Stud. [9576]
　Genealogical Soc. of Flemish Americans [20630]
Dutch Addison and Cushing Soc. [IO], Nijkerk, Netherlands
Dutch Assn. of Abortion Doctors [IO], Utrecht, Netherlands
Dutch Assn. of Commun. Agencies [IO], Amsterdam, Netherlands
Dutch Assn. of Consulting Engineers [IO], The Hague, Netherlands
Dutch Assn. of Corporate Treasurers [IO], Bussum, Netherlands
Dutch Assn. of Cost Engineers [IO], Nijkerk, Netherlands
Dutch Assn. for Medical Records Admin. [IO], Den Helder, Netherlands
Dutch Assn. of Paediatric Nurses [IO], Leiden, Netherlands
Dutch Assn. for Producers and Importers of Audio, Video and Multimedia [IO], Hilversum, Netherlands
Dutch Assn. of Psychiatric Nursing [IO], Utrecht, Netherlands

Dutch Assn. of Sign Language Interpreters [IO], Ugchelen, Netherlands
Dutch Assn. of Soap Mfrs. [IO], Zeist, Netherlands
Dutch Assn. for Soft Drinks, Waters and Juices [IO], The Hague, Netherlands
Dutch Assn. of Subcontracting Indus. [IO], Zoeter-meer, Netherlands
Dutch Bakery Center [IO], Wageningen, Netherlands
Dutch Biscuit, Chocolate and Confectionery Indus. Assn. [IO], Rijswijk, Netherlands
Dutch Cancer Soc. [IO], Amsterdam, Netherlands
Dutch Caribbean Nature Alliance [IO], Kralendijk, Netherlands Antilles
Dutch Corporate Finance Assn. [IO], Amersfoort, Netherlands
Dutch Cosmetics Assn. [IO], Zeist, Netherlands
Dutch Coun. of the Chronically Ill and Disabled [IO], Utrecht, Netherlands
Dutch Deafship [IO], Houten, Netherlands
Dutch Dental Assn. [IO], Nieuwegein, Netherlands
Dutch Fed. of Traders in Livestock [IO], Zoetermeer, Netherlands
Dutch Fish Prdt. Bd. [IO], Rijswijk, Netherlands
Dutch Flower Auctions Assn. [IO], Aalsmeer, Netherlands
Dutch Flying Disc Assn. [IO], Utrecht, Netherlands
Dutch-Friesian Assn. of Am. [★3914]
Dutch Fruit Growers' Org. [IO], Zoetermeer, Netherlands
Dutch Gen. Alliance of Beauty Parlours [IO], Utrecht, Netherlands
Dutch Goatbreeders' Assn. [IO], Heerde, Netherlands
Dutch Intl. Fiscal Assn. Br. [IO], Amsterdam, Netherlands
Dutch Jewelry, Watch and Clock Makers' Br. [IO], Voorburg, Netherlands
Dutch Labour Party [IO], Amsterdam, Netherlands
Dutch Language Union [IO], The Hague, Netherlands
Dutch League Against Epilepsy [IO], Breda, Netherlands
Dutch Newspaper Publishers Assn. [IO], Amsterdam, Netherlands
Dutch Pharmacological Soc. [IO], Zeist, Netherlands
Dutch Physiological Soc. [IO], Maastricht, Netherlands
Dutch Publishers' Assn. [IO], Amsterdam, Netherlands
Dutch Soc. for Biomaterials and Tissue Engg. [IO], Amsterdam, Netherlands
Dutch Soc. for Calcium and Bone Metabolism [IO], Amsterdam, Netherlands
Dutch Soc. for Intl. Affairs [IO], The Hague, Netherlands
Dutch Soc. for Microscopy [IO], Rotterdam, Netherlands
Dutch Soc. of Psychosomatic Obstetrics and Gynae-cology [IO], Tilburg, Netherlands
Dutch Soc. for Quality in Healthcare [IO], Utrecht, Netherlands
Dutch Soc. for Rheumatology [IO], Utrecht, Netherlands
Dutch Textile Inst. [IO], Zeist, Netherlands
Dutch Tourette Syndrome Assn. [IO], Rhoon, Netherlands
Dutch Union of Tenants [IO], Amsterdam, Netherlands
Dutch Warmblood Studbook in North America [★4628]
Dutch Youth Assn. for Astronomy [IO], Utrecht, Netherlands
DVD Assn. [7084], 2250 E Tropicana Ave., Ste. 19-435, Las Vegas, NV 89119, (702)948-0443
DVF [★20342]
Dvizhenje na ekologistite na Makedonija [★IO]
Dwa Fanm [17826], PO Box 23505, Brooklyn, NY 11202, (718)222-6320
Dwarf Athletic Assn. of Am. [22234], 708 Graven-stein Hwy. N, No. 118, Sebastopol, CA 95472, (888)598-3222
Dwarf Fruit Tree Assn. [★4970]
Dwarf Fruit Tree Assn. [★4970]
Dwarf Iris Soc. of Am. [21790], 26231 Shaker Blvd., Beachwood, OH 44122, (216)831-8662

Reference to "IO" in place of a book number signifies that the association may be found in the 50th edition of International Organizations.

Dwarfism
    Alaskan Malamute Club of Am. [21478]
    Billy Barty Found. [13115]
Dyes
    Natural Dyes Intl. [7982]
Dyfed Welsh Pony and Cob Assn. [IO], Ceredigion, United Kingdom
Dying With Dignity [IO], Toronto, ON, Canada
Dying With Dignity Victoria [IO], Melbourne, Australia
DYLEAGUE - Defunct.
Dynamic Youth Ministries [19606], Calvinist Cadet Corps, 1333 Alger St. SE, PO Box 7259, Grand Rapids, MI 49507, (616)241-5616
D'Youville Coll. Alumni Assn. [18869], 631 Niagara St., Buffalo, NY 14201-1084, (716)829-7806
Dysautonomia Found. [15583], 315 W 39th St., Ste. 701, New York, NY 10018, (212)279-1066
Dysautonomia Res. Found; Natl. [14408]
Dysautonomia Youth Network of Am. [15584], 1301 Greengate Ct., Waldorf, MD 20601, (301)705-6995
Dyslexia
    Dyslexia Res. Inst. [14427]
    Intl. Dyslexia Assn. [14428]
    Intl. Dyslexia Assn. [14428]
Dyslexia Action [IO], Egham, United Kingdom
Dyslexia Res. Inst. [14427], 5746 Centerville Rd., Tallahassee, FL 32309, (850)893-2216
Dyson Found. [12663], 25 Halcyon Rd., Millbrook, NY 12545-9611, (845)677-0644
Dysphagia Res. Soc. [14383], Intl. Meeting Managers, Inc., 4550 Post Oak Place Dr., Ste. 342, Houston, TX 77027, (713)965-0566
Dysplasia Soc. of Am; Fibromuscular [15589]
Dyspraxia Assn. of Ireland [IO], Dublin, Ireland
Dyspraxia Found. County Durham [IO], Durham, United Kingdom
Dyspraxia USA [15585], 2502 N Clark St., Ste. 223, Chicago, IL 60614, (773)248-3476
Dystonia Medical Res. Found. [15586], 1 E Wacker Dr., Ste. 2810, Chicago, IL 60601-1905, (312)755-0198
Dystonia Soc. [IO], London, United Kingdom
Dystrophic Epidermolysis Bullosa Res. Assn. of Am. [14325], 16 E 41st St., 3rd Fl., New York, NY 10017, (212)868-1573
Dystrophic Epidermolysis Bullosa Res. Assn. - Europe [IO], Crowthorne, United Kingdom
Dystrophie Musculaire Canada [★IO]
Dzieci Holocaustu w Polsce [★IO]

E

E-Commerce
    Americans for Fair Electronic Commerce Transactions [17562]
    Collision Indus. Electronic Commerce Assn. [1048]
    EC-Council [1049]
    Electronic Commerce Code Mgt. Assn. [1050]
    eMarketing Assn. [1051]
    eMarketing Assn. [1051]
    Internet Merchants Assn. [2117]
    Merchant Risk Coun. [1052]
    Payment Card Indus. Security Alliance [1053]
    WECAI Network [1054]
E. F. Schumacher Soc. [★17195]
e-Learning for Kids [7828], PO Box 754, Ardmore, PA 19003, (888)399-3138
E-quip Africa [12644], PO Box 3178, Willmar, MN 56201-8178, (320)894-1680
E-quip Africa [12644], PO Box 3178, Willmar, MN 56201-8178, (320)894-1680
EAA Antique/Classic Div. [★20891]
EAA Aviation Found. - Defunct.
EAA Vintage Aircraft Assn. [20891], EAA Aviation Center, PO Box 3086, Oshkosh, WI 54903-3086, (920)426-4800
EAA Warbirds of Am. [20892], EAA Aviation Center, PO Box 3086, Oshkosh, WI 54903-3086, (920)426-4874
Eagle Forum [17422], PO Box 618, Alton, IL 62002, (618)462-5415
Eagles
    Grand Aerie, Fraternal Order of Eagles [18977]
Eagras Um Chearta Cheolta [★IO]

EAN Azerbaijan [IO], Baku, Azerbaijan
EAN Croatia [IO], Zagreb, Croatia
EAN Lietuva [★IO]
EAN Lithuania [IO], Vilnius, Lithuania
EAN Mauritius [★18889]
EAPA [★13219]
EAPE/Campolo Ministries - Evangelical Assn. for the Promotion of Educ. [20038], 1300 Eagle Rd., St. Davids, PA 19087, (610)341-5962
EAPE/Campolo Ministries - Evangelical Assn. for the Promotion of Educ. [20038], 1300 Eagle Rd., St. Davids, PA 19087, (610)341-5962
Ear, Nose, and Throat Advances in Children; Soc. for [16089]
Ear Res. Inst. [★16686]
Earl Warren Legal Training Prog. [8504], 99 Hudson St., Ste. 1600, New York, NY 10013, (212)965-2200
Early Amer. Coppers [21974], PO Box 3497, Lake Worth, FL 33465
Early Amer. Indus. Assn. [9211], PO Box 524, Hebron, MD 21830-0524, (410)749-1965
Early Amer. Pattern Glass Soc. [21335], PO Box 266, Colesburg, IA 52035-0266
Early Childhood Australia [IO], Watson, Australia
Early Childhood Music and Movement Assn. [12554], 805 Mill Ave., Snohomish, WA 98290, (360)568-5635
Early Day Gas Engine and Tractor Assn. [21703], 2340 S Luster Ave., Springfield, MO 65804, (417)882-7195
Early English Text Soc. [IO], Oxford, United Kingdom
Early Ford V-8 Club of Am. [21045], PO Box 1715, Maple Grove, MN 55311, (763)420-7829
Early Music Am. [8648], 2366 Eastlake Ave. E, No. 429, Seattle, WA 98102, (206)720-6270
Early Music Network [10192], PO Box 854, Atlanta, GA 30301, (770)638-7554
Early Slavic Stud. Assn. [8863], Eve Levin, VP, 3638 Wescoe Hall, Lawrence, KS 66045, (785)864-9463
Early Years - The Org. for Young Children [IO], Belfast, United Kingdom
Ears for the Deaf [★11821]
Earth Care Intl. [8152], 1235 Siler Rd., Ste. D, Santa Fe, NM 87507, (505)983-6896
Earth Communications [★21062]
Earth Coun. Alliance [12584], 1250 24th St., NW Ste. 300, Washington, DC 20037, (619)595-0760
Earth Coun. Alliance [12584], 1250 24th St., NW Ste. 300, Washington, DC 20037, (619)595-0760
Earth Day 2000 [★4249]
Earth Day Canada [IO], Toronto, ON, Canada
Earth Day Network [4249], 1616 P St. NW, Ste. 340, Washington, DC 20036, (202)518-0044
Earth Drum Coun. [9575], PO Box 1284, Concord, MA 01742, (978)371-2502
Earth Ecology Found. [4200], 4175 S Decatur Blvd., Apt. 205, Las Vegas, NV 89103-6811, (702)268-2595
Earth Energy Soc. of Canada [IO], Ottawa, ON, Canada
Earth Force [4250], 2555 W 34th Ave., Denver, CO 80211, (303)433-0016
Earth Island Inst. [4251], 2150 Allston Way, Ste. 460, Berkeley, CA 94704-1375, (510)859-9108
Earth Island Inst. [4251], 2150 Allston Way, Ste. 460, Berkeley, CA 94704-1375, (510)859-9108
Earth Regeneration Soc. [4252], 1442A Walnut St., No. 57, Berkeley, CA 94709, (510)527-9716
Earth Repair Found. [IO], Katoomba, Australia
Earth Sci. Teachers' Assn. [IO], Northwich, United Kingdom
Earth Sciences
    Drilling, Observation and Sampling of the Earth's Continental Crust [6602]
    Fed. of Earth Sci. Info. Partners [6603]
    Intl. Biogeography Soc. [6904]
    Rock Detective Geoscience Educ. [7983]
Earth, Sea and Sky [IO], Lincoln, United Kingdom
Earth Soc. Found. [4253], 238 E 58th St., Ste. 2400, New York, NY 10022, (212)832-3659
Earth Soc. Found. [4253], 238 E 58th St., Ste. 2400, New York, NY 10022, (212)832-3659
Earth-Spirit, Inc. [★14990]

Earth-Spirit, Inc. [★14990]
EarthAction Intl. [4254], PO Box 63, Amherst, MA 01004, (413)549-8118
EarthAction Intl. [4254], PO Box 63, Amherst, MA 01004, (413)549-8118
EarthConnection - Defunct.
EarthEcho Intl. [4043], 888 16th St. NW, Ste. 800, Washington, DC 20006, (202)349-9828
EarthEcho Intl. [4043], 888 16th St. NW, Ste. 800, Washington, DC 20006, (202)349-9828
Earthjustice [5414], 426 17th St., 6th Fl., Oakland, CA 94612-2820, (510)550-6700
Earthjustice [5414], 426 17th St., 6th Fl., Oakland, CA 94612-2820, (510)550-6700
EarthLink [IO], Munich, Germany
The Earthology Found. [★4200]
Earthquake Engg; Natl. Info. Ser. for [7401]
Earthquake Engg. Res. Inst. [7398], 499 14th St., Ste. 320, Oakland, CA 94612-1934, (510)451-0905
EarthRights Intl. [17827], 1612 K St. NW, Ste. 401, Washington, DC 20006, (202)466-5188
EarthRights Intl. [17827], 1612 K St. NW, Ste. 401, Washington, DC 20006, (202)466-5188
EarthRights Intl. - Asia [IO], Chiang Mai, Thailand
Earthrise [6887], 2151 Michelson Dr., Ste. 258, Irvine, CA 92612, (949)623-0980
Earthroots [IO], Toronto, ON, Canada
Earth's Physical Features Stud. Unit [22035], Fred W. Klein, Sec.-Treas., 515 Magdalena Ave., Los Altos, CA 94024
EarthSave Canada [IO], Vancouver, BC, Canada
Earthsave Found. [★4201]
Earthsave Found. [★4201]
EarthSave Intl. [4201], 20555 Devonshire St., Ste. 105, Chatsworth, CA 91311, (818)407-0289
EarthSave Intl. [4201], 20555 Devonshire St., Ste. 105, Chatsworth, CA 91311, (818)407-0289
EarthShare [8153], 7735 Old Georgetown Rd., Ste. 900, Bethesda, MD 20814, (240)333-0300
EarthSharing [IO], Melbourne, Australia
EarthSpark Intl. [6711], 1616 H St. NW, Ste. 900, Washington, DC 20006-4909
Earthspirit Community [20139], PO Box 723, Williamsburg, MA 01096, (413)238-4240
Earthstewards Network [12206], Box 10697, Bainbridge Island, WA 98110, (206)842-7986
Earthstewards Network [12206], Box 10697, Bainbridge Island, WA 98110, (206)842-7986
Earthtrust [5048], Windward Environmental Center, 1118 Maunawili Rd., Kailua, HI 96734, (808)261-5339
Earthtrust [5048], Windward Environmental Center, 1118 Maunawili Rd., Kailua, HI 96734, (808)261-5339
Earthvote Intl. [★4254]
Earthvote Intl. [★4254]
Earthvote Network [★4254]
Earthvote Network [★4254]
Earthwatch Inst. [8175], 3 Clock Tower Pl., Ste. 100, Box 75, Maynard, MA 01754-0075, (978)461-0081
EarthWave Soc. [4255], 16151 Hwy. 377 S, Fort Worth, TX 76126, (817)443-3780
Earthworks [5839], 1612 K St. NW, Ste. 808, Washington, DC 20006, (202)887-1872
East Africa
    Kasese Wildlife Conservation Awareness Org. [5074]
East African Wild Life Soc. [IO], Nairobi, Kenya
East African Youth Alliance [IO], Nairobi, Kenya
East Anglian Traditional Music Trust [IO], Stowmarket, United Kingdom
East Asia Regional Coun. of Overseas Schools [IO], Laguna, Philippines
East Asian Economic Assn. - Hong Kong Off. [IO], Hong Kong, People's Republic of China
East Bay Fan Guild [★21338]
East Coast Marine Sci. Librarians [★9989]
East Coast Marine Sci. Librarians [★9989]
East Coast Migrant Hea. Proj. [★12520]
East Coast Music Assn. [IO], Charlottetown, PE, Canada
East Coast Timing Assn. [22115], 1081 Dexter Corner Rd., Townsend, DE 19734, (302)378-3013
East Jerusalem YMCA [IO], East Jerusalem, Israel
East Meets West Found. [IO], Da Nang, Vietnam

A star before a book entry number signifies that the name is not listed separately, but is mentioned within the entry.

East Meets West Found. [**17910**], 1611 Telegraph Ave., Ste. 1420, Oakland, CA 94612, (510)763-7045

East Meets West Found. [**17910**], 1611 Telegraph Ave., Ste. 1420, Oakland, CA 94612, (510)763-7045

East Midlands Campaign for Nuclear Disarmament [**IO**], Chesterfield, United Kingdom

East Midlands Welsh Pony and Cob Assn. [**IO**], Worksop, United Kingdom

East Texas Big Thicket Assn. [**★4011**]

East Timor

East Timor and Indonesia Action Network/US [**17563**]

East Timor Action Network/US [**★17563**]

East Timor Human Rights Comm. - Defunct.

East Timor and Indonesia Action Network/US [**17563**], PO Box 21873, Brooklyn, NY 11202-1873, (718)596-7668

East West Acad. of Healing Arts [**16013**], 117 Topaz Way, San Francisco, CA 94131, (415)285-9400

East-West Bridges for Peace - Defunct.

East-West Center [**17962**], 1601 East-West Rd., Honolulu, HI 96848, (808)944-7111

East-West Center [**17962**], 1601 East-West Rd., Honolulu, HI 96848, (808)944-7111

East-West Cultural Center [**9338**], 12329 Marshall St., Culver City, CA 90230, (310)390-9083

East West Educ. Development Found. [**12664**], PO Box 701560, Dallas, TX 75370-1560, (214)265-8300

East West Educ. Development Found. [**12664**], PO Box 701560, Dallas, TX 75370-1560, (214)265-8300

East West News Bur. [**★3709**]

Easter Seals [**11784**], 233 S Wacker Dr., Ste. 2400, Chicago, IL 60606, (312)726-6200

Easter Seals New Brunswick [**IO**], Fredericton, NB, Canada

Easterling Family Genealogical Soc. [**20507**], 1124 Pearl Valley Rd., Wesson, MS 39191-9361, (601)894-2642

Eastern Acad. of Sexual Therapy [**★16653**]

Eastern Africa Assn. [**IO**], London, United Kingdom

Eastern Amputee Golf Assn. [**22606**], 2015 Amherst Dr., Bethlehem, PA 18015-5606, (610)867-9295

Eastern Amputee Golf Assn. [**22606**], 2015 Amherst Dr., Bethlehem, PA 18015-5606, (610)867-9295

Eastern Apicultural Soc. [**★3818**]

Eastern Apicultural Soc. of North Am. [**3818**], 142 Cemetery Rd., Mocksville, NC 27028, (336)998-2975

Eastern Asia Soc. for Trans. Stud. [**IO**], Tokyo, Japan

Eastern Assn. of Mosquito Control Workers [**★4769**]

Eastern Assn. of Mosquito Control Workers [**★4769**]

Eastern Assn. of Rowing Colleges [**22854**], Easter Coll. Athletic Conf., 1311 Craigville Beach Rd., Centerville, MA 02632, (508)771-5060

Eastern Bird Banding Assn. [**7197**], 2366 Springtown Hill Rd., Hellertown, PA 18055-3049, (610)346-7754

Eastern Caribbean Central Bank [**IO**], Basseterre, St. Kitts and Nevis

Eastern Claims Conf. [**1958**], PO Box 2730, Stamford, CT 06906-0730, (203)352-3074

Eastern Coast Breweriana Assn. [**20928**], PO Box 826, South Windsor, CT 06074-0826

Eastern Coll. Athletic Conf. [**22643**], PO Box 3, Centerville, MA 02632, (508)771-5060

Eastern Coll. Soccer Assn. [**22935**], PO Box 3, Centerville, MA 02632, (508)771-5060

Eastern Coll. Soccer Officials Bur. [**★22935**]

Eastern Collegiate Hockey Assn. [**22644**], 18206 Bunker Hill Rd., Parkton, MD 21120-9435, (410)357-9878

Eastern Europe

Action for Post-Soviet Jewry [**17564**]

Action for Post-Soviet Jewry [**17564**]EasternChicago Action for Jews in the Former Soviet Union

Civil Soc. Intl. [**17565**]

Civil Soc. Intl. [**17565**]

Inst. for Democracy in Eastern Europe [**17566**]

Inst. for Democracy in Eastern Europe [**17566**]

Jamestown Found. [**17567**]

Jamestown Found. [**17567**]

NCSJ: Advocates on Behalf of Jews in Russia, Ukraine, the Baltic States and Eurasia [**17568**]

NCSJ: Advocates on Behalf of Jews in Russia, Ukraine, the Baltic States and Eurasia [**17568**]

Raoul Wallenberg Comm. of the U.S. [**17569**]

Raoul Wallenberg Comm. of the U.S. [**17569**]EasternSMOLOSKYP, Ukrainian Info. Ser.

Tamizdat [**9518**]

Ukranian Cong. Comm. of Am. [**18741**]

Union of Councils for Jews in the Former Soviet Union [**17570**]

Union of Councils for Jews in the Former Soviet Union [**17570**]

Eastern European Bible Mission [**★20073**]

Eastern European Bible Mission [**★20073**]

Eastern Finance Assn. [**1294**], Auburn Montgomery, School of Bus., PO Box 244023, Montgomery, AL 36124-4023

Eastern Intercollegiate Gymnastic League [**22632**], Eastern Coll. Athletic Conf., 1311 Craigville Beach Rd., Centerville, MA 02632, (508)771-5060

Eastern Mineral Law Found. [**★5860**]

Eastern Museum of Motor Racing [**21046**], PO Box 688, Mechanicsburg, PA 17055, (717)528-8279

Eastern Orthodox

Fellowship of St. John the Divine [**19646**]

Orthodox Theological Soc. in Am. [**19647**]

Standing Conf. of the Canonical Orthodox Bishops in the Americas [**19648**]

Standing Conf. of the Canonical Orthodox Bishops in the Americas [**19648**]

Eastern Packard Club [**21047**], 127 Westerly Terr., Rocky Hill, CT 06067, (732)738-7859

Eastern Police Bloodhound Assn. [**★5732**]

Eastern Professional River Outfitters Assn. [**★22835**]

Eastern Regional Dance Assn. [**★9565**]

Eastern Regional Dance Assn. [**★9565**]

Eastern Regional Org. for Public Admin. [**IO**], Quezon City, Philippines

Eastern Ski Assn. [**★22918**]

Eastern Ski Representatives Assn. [**★3328**]

Eastern Soccer Officials Bur. [**★22935**]

Eastern and Southern Africa Intl. Assn. for Schools of Social Work [**★383**]

Eastern and Southern Africa Mgt. Inst. [**IO**], Arusha, United Republic of Tanzania

Eastern Surfing Assn. [**23033**], PO Box 625, Virginia Beach, VA 23451, (757)233-1790

Eastern Water Polo Assn. [**★23112**]

Eastern Welsh Pony and Cob Assn. [**IO**], Ely, United Kingdom

Eastern Winter Sports Representatives Assn. [**3328**], PO Box 88, White Haven, PA 18661, (570)443-7180

Easti Fusioterapeutide Liit [**★IO**]

Easti Gerontoloogia ja Geriaatria Assotsiatsioon [**★IO**]

EastWest Inst. [**17896**], 700 Broadway, 2nd Fl., New York, NY 10003-9536, (212)824-4100

EastWest Inst. [**17896**], 700 Broadway, 2nd Fl., New York, NY 10003-9536, (212)824-4100

Eating Disorder Rsrc. Centre of British Columbia [**IO**], Vancouver, BC, Canada

Eating Disorders

Acad. for Eating Disorders [**14429**]

Alliance for Eating Disorders Awareness [**14430**]

Beyond Hunger [**14431**]

Binge Eating Disorder Assn. [**14432**]

Coalition to Promote Minority Hea. [**15853**]

Do It Now Found. [**13248**]

Eating Disorders Coalition for Res., Policy and Action [**14433**]

The Elisa Proj. [**14434**]

Intl. Assn. of Eating Disorders Professionals [**14435**]

Intl. Assn. of Eating Disorders Professionals [**14435**]

Joy Proj. [**14436**]

Natl. Assn. of Anorexia Nervosa and Assoc. Disorders [**14437**]

Natl. Assn. for Males with Eating Disorders [**14438**]

Natl. Eating Disorders Assn. [**14439**]

Eating Disorders Assn. Queensland [**IO**], Greenslopes, Australia

Eating Disorders Awareness and Prevention, Inc. [**★14439**]

Eating Disorders Coalition for Res., Policy and Action [**14433**], 720 7th St. NW, Ste. 300, Washington, DC 20001, (202)543-9570

EC-Council [**1049**], 6330 Riverside Plaza Ln. NW, Ste. 210, Albuquerque, NM 87120, (505)341-3228

EC Seed Crushers' and Oil Processors' Fed. [**IO**], Brussels, Belgium

Ecclesiastical History Soc. [**IO**], London, United Kingdom

ECHO [**IO**], Damascus, Syrian Arab Republic

Echo Dogs White Shepherd Rescue [**10954**], PO Box 16199, Hooksett, NH 03106

Echo Res. Inst. [**IO**], Markham, ON, Canada

Echocardiography

Intl. Soc. of Cardiovascular Ultrasound [**14440**]

Echocardiography; Amer. Soc. of [**14003**]

ECKANKAR [**20179**], PO Box 2000, Chanhassen, MN 55317-2000, (952)380-2222

Ecma Intl. [**IO**], Geneva, Switzerland

Eco-Benin [**IO**], Abomey-Calavi, Benin

Eco-Conservation Initiatives [**IO**], Islamabad, Pakistan

Eco Energy Finance [**6712**], 2307 15th St. NW, Ste. 1, Washington, DC 20009, (202)262-0412

Eco-friendly Nepal [**IO**], Kathmandu, Nepal

Eco-Justice Working Group [**18615**], Natl. Coun. of Churches, 110 Maryland Ave. NE, Ste. 108, Washington, DC 20002, (202)544-2350

Eco-Life Concepts [**4318**], 4300 Old Oak Trace, Cumming, GA 30041, (770)406-8647

Eco-Spirit - Address unknown since 2011.

Ecoagriculture Partners [**4939**], 730 11th St. NW, Ste. 301, Washington, DC 20001, (202)393-5315

ecoAmerica [**4044**], 1900 L St. NW, Ste. 607, Washington, DC 20036, (202)457-1900

EcoFlight [**4202**], 307 L Aspen Airport Bus. Ctr., Aspen, CO 81611, (970)429-1110

EcoHealth Alliance [**5049**], 460 W 34th St., 17th Fl., New York, NY 10001, (212)380-4460

Ecojustice Canada [**IO**], Vancouver, BC, Canada

EcoLogic Development Fund [**4203**], 25 Mt. Auburn St., Ste. 203, Harvard Sq., Cambridge, MA 02138, (617)441-6300

EcoLogic Development Fund [**4203**], 25 Mt. Auburn St., Ste. 203, Harvard Sq., Cambridge, MA 02138, (617)441-6300

Ecologic - Institut fur Internationale und Europaische Umweltpolitik [**★IO**]

Ecologic - Inst. for Intl. and European Environmental Policy [**IO**], Berlin, Germany

Ecological Agriculture Projects [**IO**], Ste.-Anne-de-Bellevue, QC, Canada

Ecological Building Network [**3857**], PO Box 6397, San Rafael, CA 94903, (415)987-7271

Ecological Farming Assn. [**3740**], 2901 Park Ave., Ste. D-2, Soquel, CA 95073, (831)763-2111

Ecological Landscaping Assn. [**4681**], 841 Worcester St., Ste. 326, Natick, MA 01760, (617)436-5838

Ecological Landscaping Assn. [**4681**], 841 Worcester St., Ste. 326, Natick, MA 01760, (617)436-5838

EcoLogical Mail Coalition [**4698**], 6886 Fallsbrook Ct., Granite Bay, CA 95746, (800)620-3975

Ecological Movement of Uzbekistan [**IO**], Tashkent, Uzbekistan

Ecological Res. and Development Gp. [**4045**], 190 Main St., Dover, DE 19901, (302)236-5383

Ecological Soc. of Am. [**4204**], 1990 M St. NW, Ste. 700, Washington, DC 20036, (202)833-8773

Ecological Soc. of Australia [**IO**], Windsor, Australia

Ecological Soc. of Germany, Austria, and Switzerland [**IO**], Berlin, Germany

Ecological Soc. of Japan [**IO**], Kyoto, Japan

Ecological Soc. of Physicians [**IO**], Bremen, Germany

Ecological and Toxicological Assn. of Dyes and Organic Pigments Mfrs. [**IO**], Basel, Switzerland

Ecologist Workshop [**IO**], Rosario, Argentina

Ecologists Union [**★4110**]

Ecology

Amer. Ecological Engg. Soc. [**4191**]

Reference to "IO" in place of a book number signifies that the association may be found in the 50th edition of International Organizations.

A star before a book entry number signifies that the name is not listed separately, but is mentioned within the entry.

Assn. of Specialized and Professional Accreditors [1063]
Assn. for the Stud. of the Cuban Economy [7984]
Athena Alliance [17590]
Atlas Economic Res. Found. [6615]
Australian New Zealand - Amer. Chambers of Commerce [23339]
Austrian Trade Commn. [23329]
Bionomics Intl. [7363]
Brazil-U.S. Bus. Coun. [23354]
Brazilian Govt. Trade Bur. of the Consulate Gen. of Brazil in New York [23335]
British Trade Off. at Consulate-General [23336]
Canadian Found. for Economic Educ. [3733]
Center for Economic and Policy Res. [17591]
Center for Economic and Social Justice [11900]
Center for Popular Economics [6616]
Chinese Economists Soc. [6617]
Chinese Economists Soc. [6617]
Comm. on the Status of Women in the Economics Profession [5392]
The Conf. Bd. [6618]
The Conf. Bd. [6618]
Economic Affairs Bureau/Dollars and Sense [6619]
Economic Soc. of Australia [1611]
Environmental Entrepreneurs [4050]
Estonian Amer. Fund for Economic Educ. [7985]
Estonian Amer. Fund for Economic Educ. [7985]
European Travel Commn. [3558]
Executives Without Borders [60]
Fisher Inst. for Medical Res. [17716]
Found. for Teaching Economics [7986]
Gp. of Thirty [1064]
Innovation Norway - U.S. [23368]
Insight Center for Community Economic Development [17578]
Inst. for Community Economics [17380]
Inst. for Economic Anal. [6620]
Inst. on Taxation and Economic Policy [17592]
Intercollegiate Stud. Inst. [17425]
Intl. Adam Smith Soc. [10381]
Intl. Assn. of Agricultural Economists [6621]
Intl. Assn. of Agricultural Economists [6621]
Intl. Assn. for Feminist Economics U.S.A. [6622]
Intl. Assn. for Feminist Economics U.S.A. [6622]
Intl. Atlantic Economic Soc. [6623]
Intl. Atlantic Economic Soc. [6623]
Intl. Banking, Economics and Finance Assn. [6624]
Intl. Confed. of Associations for Pluralism in Economics [6625]
Intl. Economic Alliance [1065]
Intl. Economics and Finance Soc. [6626]
Intl. Soc. for Ecological Economics [1066]
Intl. Soc. for Ecological Economics [1066]
Iraqi Amer. Chamber of Commerce and Indus. [23370]
Jordan Info. Bur. [23421]
Krochet Kids Intl. [12735]
Lambda Alpha Intl. [23505]
Local Initiatives Support Corp. [17383]
Natl. Alliance of Community Economic Development Associations [17582]
Natl. Assn. for Bus. Economics [6627]
Natl. Assn. for County Community and Economic Development [17384]
Natl. Bur. of Economic Res. [6628]
Natl. Community Development Assn. [17387]
Natl. Coun. on Economic Educ. [7987]
Natl. Economic Assn. [6629]
Natl. Economists Club [6630]
Natl. Fed. of Enterprise Agencies [14308]
Natl. Schools Comm. for Economic Educ. [7988]
Natl. United States-Arab Chamber of Commerce [23374]
New Rules for Global Finance Coalition [17584]
Omicron Delta Epsilon [23506]
The Other Economic Summit of the U.S. [6631]
Pakistan Chamber of Commerce USA [23435]
Romanian-U.S. Bus. Coun. [23438]
Soc. for the Advancement of Economic Theory [6632]
Soc. for the Advancement of Socio-Economics [17593]

Soc. for the Development of Austrian Economics [6633]
Soc. for Energy Educ. [6756]
Soc. of Govt. Economists [5393]
Soc. for Neuroeconomics [6634]
South African USA Chamber of Commerce [23379]
Southern Economic Assn. [6635]
Swedish Trade Coun. [3489]
Turkish-American Chamber of Commerce and Indus. [23455]
Union for Radical Political Economics [6636]
United for a Fair Economy [17594]
U.S. Chamber of Commerce [23384]
U.S. Indian Amer. Chamber of Commerce [23407]
USA Engage [17589]
Western Economic Assn. Intl. [6637]
Western Economic Assn. Intl. [6637]
William E. Simon Found. [17595]
Women's Intl. Coalition for Economic Justice [17596]
Women's Intl. Coalition for Economic Justice [17596]
Economics and Bus. Educ. Assn. [IO], Burgess Hill, United Kingdom
Economics News Broadcasters Assn. [★2874]
Economics Soc. of Calgary [IO], Calgary, AB, Canada
Economiesuisse, The Swiss Bus. Fed. [IO], Zurich, Switzerland
Economists Allied for Arms Reduction [★17552]
Economists Allied for Arms Reduction [★17552]
Economists for Peace and Security [17552], The Levy Inst., PO Box 5000, Annandale-on-Hudson, NY 12504, (845)758-0917
Economists for Peace and Security [17552], The Levy Inst., PO Box 5000, Annandale-on-Hudson, NY 12504, (845)758-0917
ECORYS Nederland BV [★IO]
ECOTERRA Intl. [IO], Nairobi, Kenya
Ecotourism Australia [IO], Brisbane, Australia
Ecotourism Soc. [★3476]
Ecotourism Soc. [★3476]
Ecotourism Soc. of Pakistan [IO], Lahore, Pakistan
The Ecotourism Soc. of Seychelles [IO], Victoria, Seychelles
Ecova Mali [3754], 69 Cherry St., Swampscott, MA 01907, (802)254-5417
Ecova Mali [3754], 69 Cherry St., Swampscott, MA 01907, (802)254-5417
EcoVentures Intl. [4319], 2122 P St. NW, Ste. 302, Washington, DC 20037, (202)667-0802
EcoVentures Intl. [4319], 2122 P St. NW, Ste. 302, Washington, DC 20037, (202)667-0802
ECRI [★15373]
ECRI [★15373]
ECRI Inst. [15373], 5200 Butler Pike, Plymouth Meeting, PA 19462-1298, (610)825-6000
ECRI Inst. [15373], 5200 Butler Pike, Plymouth Meeting, PA 19462-1298, (610)825-6000
Ecuador
  Agua Muisne [13411]
  Ecuador Children's Hope Org. [11266]
  Ecuadorean Amer. Assn. [18978]
  Ecuadorian-American Chamber of Commerce of Miami [23397]
  Global Vaccine Awareness League [14709]
Ecuador Children's Hope Org. [11266], PO Box 20294, Atlanta, GA 30325, (207)370-5838
Ecuador Volunteer [IO], Quito, Ecuador
Ecuadorean Amer. Assn. [18978], 30 Vesey St., Ste. 506, New York, NY 10007, (212)233-7776
Ecuadorian-American Chamber of Commerce of Miami [23397], 3403 NW 82 Ave., Ste. 310, Miami, FL 33122, (305)591-0800
Ecuadorian-American Chamber of Commerce - Quito [IO], Quito, Ecuador
Ecuadorian Assn. of Newspaper Publishers [IO], Quito, Ecuador
Ecuadorian Bible Soc. [IO], Quito, Ecuador
Ecuadorian Broadcasting Assn. [IO], Quito, Ecuador
Ecuadorian Consulting Companies' Assn. [IO], Quito, Ecuador
Ecuadorian Electron Microscopy Soc. [IO], Guayaquil, Ecuador

Ecuadorian Experiment in Intl. Living [IO], Quito, Ecuador
Ecuadorian Hotel Fed. [IO], Quito, Ecuador
Ecuadorian League Against Epilepsy [IO], Quito, Ecuador
Ecuadorian Olympic Comm. [IO], Guayaquil, Ecuador
Ecuadorian Soc. of Dermatology [IO], Guayaquil, Ecuador
Ecuadorian Soc. of Reproductive Medicine [IO], Guayaquil, Ecuador
Ecuatorian Assn. of Exporters [IO], Quito, Ecuador
Ecumenical
  Catholic Assn. of Diocesan Ecumenical and Inter-religious Officers [19649]
  Center for Christian/Jewish Understanding [19650]
  Churches Uniting in Christ [19651]
  Commn. of the Churches on Intl. Affairs [19828]
  Coun. on Christian Unity [19652]
  Ecumenical Celebrations [19653]
  Fellowship in Prayer [19654]
  Fellowship in Prayer [19654]
  Graymoor Ecumenical and Interreligious Inst. [19655]
  Graymoor Ecumenical and Interreligious Inst. [19655]
  The InterChurch Center [19656]
  Intl. Assn. of Ministers Wives and Ministers Widows [19657]
  Intl. Assn. of Ministers Wives and Ministers Widows [19657]
  Koinonia Found. [19658]
  Liturgical Conf. [19659]
  Liturgical Conf. [19659]
  Lumunos [19660]
  Missionary Soc. of Saint Paul the Apostle [19454]
  Natl. Assn. of Ecumenical and Interreligious Staff [19661]
  Natl. Cathedral Assn. [19662]
  Natl. Coun. of Churches of Christ in the U.S.A. [19663]
  North Amer. Acad. of Ecumenists [19664]
  Prayers for Life [19665]
  Seventh Day Baptist World Fed. [19331]
  Societas Liturgica [19666]
  Societas Liturgica [19666]
Ecumenical Assn. of Academies and Laity Centres in Europe [IO], Solingen, Germany
Ecumenical Assn. of Professors [★19664]
Ecumenical Celebrations [19653], The Interchurch Center, 475 Riverside Dr., New York, NY 10115, (212)870-2347
Ecumenical Inst. [★12212]
Ecumenical Migration Centre [IO], Collingwood, Australia
Ecumenical Network for Youth Action [IO], Prague, Czech Republic
Ecumenical Prog. on Central Am. and the Caribbean - Address unknown since 2010.
Ecumenical Theological Center [★19674]
Ecumenical Theological Seminary [19674], 2930 Woodward Ave., Detroit, MI 48201, (313)831-5200
Ecumenical Women's Caucus; Evangelical and [19721]
Ecumenical Women's Caucus; Evangelical and [19721]
Ecumenical Youth Coun. in Europe [IO], Brussels, Belgium
Eczema Assn. of Australasia [IO], Cleveland, Australia
Eczema Assn. for Sci. and Educ. [★14333]
Eddy Family Assn. [20508], Elaine Darrah, Treas., 13151 Erie Ave., Merced, CA 95340-1408
Eddy Raven Fan Club [23837], PO Box 2476, Hendersonville, TN 37077, (615)368-7433
Eden Found. [IO], Falkenberg, Sweden
Edexcel Intl. [IO], London, United Kingdom
Edgar Allan Poe Soc. of Baltimore [9361], Mr. Jeffrey A. Savoye, Sec.-Treas., 1610 Dogwood Hill Rd., Towson, MD 21286-1506, (410)821-1285
Edgar Cayce Found. [★7223]
Edgar Cayce Found. [★7223]
Edge-ucate [11915], PO Box 126, Englewood, CO 80151-0126

Reference to "IO" in place of a book number signifies that the association may be found in the 50th edition of International Organizations.

Edge-ucate [11915], PO Box 126, Englewood, CO 80151-0126
Edinburgh Architectural Assn. [IO], Edinburgh, United Kingdom
Edinburgh Bibliographical Soc. [IO], Edinburgh, United Kingdom
Edinburgh Chamber of Commerce [IO], Edinburgh, United Kingdom
Edinburgh Geological Soc. [IO], Edinburgh, United Kingdom
Edinburgh Mathematical Soc. [IO], Edinburgh, United Kingdom
Edinburgh Ski Touring Club [IO], Cupar, United Kingdom
Edison Birthplace Assn. [10658], Edison Birthplace Museum, PO Box 451, Milan, OH 44846, (419)499-2135
Edison Elec. Inst. [3593], 701 Pennsylvania Ave. NW, Washington, DC 20004-2696, (202)508-5000
Edison Elec. Inst. [3593], 701 Pennsylvania Ave. NW, Washington, DC 20004-2696, (202)508-5000
Edison Welding Inst. [7618], 1250 Arthur E Adams Dr., Columbus, OH 43221-3585, (614)688-5000
Editorial Coun. of the Religious Press [★2917]
Editorial Freelancers Assn. [2825], 71 W 23rd St., 4th Fl., New York, NY 10010, (212)929-5400
Editorial Photographers [2716], PO Box 51192, Seattle, WA 98115
Editorial Projects in Educ. [8018], 6935 Arlington, Ste. 100, Bethesda, MD 20814, (301)280-3100
Editors
    Assn. of Independent Creative Editors [2811]
    Fraternity Communications Assn. [23507]
    Natl. Assn. of Independent Writers and Editors [2844]
    Natl. Panhellenic Conf. I Natl. Panhellenic Editors Conf. [23508]
    Special Interest Gp. on Design of Commun. [6561]
Editors' Assn. of Canada [IO], Toronto, ON, Canada
Edmondson Family Assn. - Defunct.
Edmonton Area Narcotics Anonymous [IO], Edmonton, AB, Canada
Edmonton Chamber of Commerce/World Trade Center Edmonton [IO], Edmonton, AB, Canada
Edmonton Epilepsy Assn. [IO], Edmonton, AB, Canada
Edna Hibel Soc. [10119], PO Box 33332, Palm Beach Gardens, FL 33420, (561)493-7114
EDP Auditors Assn. [★67]
EDP Auditors Assn. [★67]
EdPress - The Assn. of Educational Publishers [★8744]
Edsel Club [21048], 19296 Tuckaway Ct., Fort Myers, FL 33903-1244, (239)731-8027
Edsel Owner's Club [21049], 5865 Cincinnati Dayton Rd., Middletown, OH 45044-9520, (513)755-7655
Edu-Culture Intl. [8356], PO Box 2692, Berkeley, CA 94702, (510)845-2230
Educate the Children [11461], PO Box 414, Ithaca, NY 14851-0414, (607)272-1176
Educate These Children [11462], 5 Meadow Ct., Norwood, NJ 07648, (201)767-5806
Educate Tomorrow [9077], 1717 N Bayshore Dr., Ste. 203, Miami, FL 33132, (305)374-3751
Educating for Justice [8864], 1201 3rd Ave., Ste. A, Spring Lake, NJ 07762, (732)988-7322
Educating for Justice [8864], 1201 3rd Ave., Ste. A, Spring Lake, NJ 07762, (732)988-7322
Education
    92nd St. Y [12400]
    ABLE: Assn. for Better Living and Educ. Intl. [11537]
    Acad. of Criminal Justice Sciences [11698]
    Acad. for Educational Development [7989]
    Acad. for Educational Development [7989]
    Access to Empowerment Intl. [11901]
    Accuracy in Academia [8104]
    ACLU I Natl. Prison Proj. [11699]
    Adult Christian Educ. Found. [19667]
    Adult Learning Australia [18873]
    African Educational Res. Network [7990]
    African Educational Res. Network [7990]
    African Kids In Need [11179]
    Agami [7824]

All One People [10808]
Alliance for Climate Educ. [4315]
Alliance for the Separation of School and State [7991]
Alpha Delta Kappa [23509]
Alpha Delta Kappa [23509]
Alpha Epsilon [23516]
Alternative Educ. Rsrc. Org. [7992]
Amer. Acad. of Religion [7993]
Amer. Assn. of Classified School Employees [23177]
Amer. Assn. for Gifted Children [8214]
Amer. Assn. of Human Design Practitioners [1036]
Amer. Assn. of Teachers of French [8459]
Amer. Assn. for Teaching and Curriculum [8941]
Amer. Assn. of Univ. Women [9051]
Amer. Coun. on Educ. [7994]
Amer. Councils for Intl. Educ. [7995]
Amer. Councils for Intl. Educ. [7995]
Amer. Distance Educ. Consortium [7996]
Amer. Educational Stud. Assn. [7997]
Amer. Educational Stud. Assn. [7997]
Amer. Fed. of Teachers [23178]
Amer. Forum for Global Educ. [8340]
Amer. Mgt. Assn. I Oper. Enterprise [8547]
Amer. Sociological Assn. I Honors Prog. [23738]
Amer. Sports Inst. [7998]
Americans Care and Share [12805]
America's Edge [17599]
Ancient Coins for Educ. [8685]
Arthur Morgan Inst. for Community Solutions [17368]
Arthur Vining Davis Foundations [11902]
ASA Intl. [7999]
ASA Intl. [7999]
Asociacion para la Educacion Teologica Hispana [9006]
ASPIRA Assn. [8000]
Assn. for the Advancement of Intl. Educ. [8388]
Assn. of Amer. Intl. Colleges and Universities [8389]
Assn. for Borderlands Stud. [8400]
Assn. of Chairmen of Departments of Mechanics [8571]
Assn. for Clinical Pastoral Educ. [19668]
Assn. of Concerned African Scholars [17147]
Assn. for Core Texts and Courses [8514]
Assn. for Direct Instruction [8001]
Assn. of Energy and Environmental Real Estate Professionals [8150]
Assn. of Episcopal Colleges [8162]
The Assn. for the Gifted [8215]
Assn. of Latino Administrators and Superintendents [7661]
Assn. for Moral Educ. [8002]
Assn. of Presbyterian Church Educators [19612]
Assn. for Professionals in Services for Adolescents [12143]
Assn. of Professors and Scholars of Iranian Heritage [8411]
Assn. of Public and Land-Grant Universities [7873]
Assn. for Religion and Intellectual Life [19669]
Assn. of State Correctional Administrators [11706]
Assn. for Support of Graduate Students [8231]
Assn. of Teachers of Tech. Writing [9072]
Assn. of Tech., Mgt. and Applied Engg. [8296]
Assn. of Thai Professionals in Am. and Canada [19255]
Assn. of Theatre Movement Educators [9000]
Assn. of Univ. Architects [6194]
Astronaut Scholars Honor Soc. [23629]
Battelle for Kids [7826]
Benjamin Franklin Educ. Found. [8003]
Beta Beta Beta [23470]
Beta Gamma Sigma [23476]
Beta Phi Mu [23583]
Beta Sigma Kappa [23611]
Books for the Barrios [11903]
Books for the Barrios [11903]
Books for a Better World [8004]
Books for a Better World [8004]
Breakthrough Collaborative [8005]
Building Bridges: Middle East-US [8385]

Building Tomorrow [12659]
Camille and Henry Dreyfus Found. [8006]
Campus Compact [8007]
Caring for Cambodia [7827]
Caring Hand for Children [11440]
Carnegie Corp. of New York [8008]
Catholic Acad. of Sciences in the U.S.A. [19670]
Catholic Campus Ministry Assn. [19399]
Center for Commercial-Free Public Educ. [8009]
Center for Consumer Affairs [17448]
Center for the Ministry of Teaching [19671]
Center for School Change [8010]
Center for Stud. in Criminal Justice [11707]
CHAN Healthcare Auditors [8011]
Change Exchange [12205]
Character Educ. Partnership [11904]
Child Aid Africa [11212]
Chinese School Assn. in the U.S. [8825]
Christian Educators Assn. Intl. [19672]
Christian Educators Assn. Intl. [19672]
Christian Educators Fellowship of the United Methodist Church [19673]
Close Up Found. [17249]
Coalition for Sci. After School [8836]
Coll. Summit [8234]
Common Destiny Alliance [8012]
Community Coll. Journalism Assn. [8441]
Community Development Soc. [17374]
Conf. on Coll. Composition and Commun. [8132]
Consciousness-Based Educ. Assn. [8762]
Consortium for the Advancement of Private Higher Educ. [7879]
Consortium of Institutions for Development and Res. in Educ. in Europe [16844]
Coun. for the Advancement of Standards in Higher Educ. [8914]
Coun. for Advancement and Support of Educ. [8013]
Coun. of Chief State School Officers [8014]
Coun. for Children with Behavioral Disorders [8878]
Coun. for Higher Educ. Accreditation [8015]
Coun. on Library-Media Technicians [8521]
Coun. on Occupational Educ. [8016]
Coun. of Teachers of Southeast Asian Languages [7756]
Creative Educ. Found. [8017]
Culturatti Kids Resource Network [9074]
DAD: Drums and Disabilities [12422]
Dance Masters of Am. [7959]
Delphi Found. [23510]
Delta Phi Epsilon Professional Foreign Ser. Sorority [23529]
Delta Sigma Delta [23498]
Democrats for Educ. Reform [17600]
Destination ImagiNation [8697]
e-Learning for Kids [7828]
Ecology Proj. Intl. [8154]
Ecumenical Theological Seminary [19674]
Editorial Projects in Educ. [8018]
Educate the Children [11461]
Educate These Children [11462]
Educ. Commn. of the States [8019]
Educ. Conservancy [7683]
Educ. Development Center [8020]
Educ. Development Center [8020]
Educational Help for Afghanistan Assn. [8916]
Educational Res. Associates [8021]
Edurelief [12834]
Edutechnia [6976]
Edutopia - The George Lucas Educational Found. [8022]
Egyptian Student Assn. in North America [8917]
Empowering the Poor [12326]
Enrichment Educ. [8276]
Environmental Educ. and Conservation Global [8155]
European Coun. for Steiner Waldorf Educ. [17491]
European Soc. for Translation Stud. [8792]
European Univ. Continuing Educ. Network [1948]
Evangelical Training Assn. [19675]
Fed. Educ. Assn. [23179]
Fed. Govt. Distance Learning Assn. [8023]
Fellowship of Christian Released Time Ministries [19676]

A star before a book entry number signifies that the name is not listed separately, but is mentioned within the entry.

Food and Drug Admin. Alumni Assn. [17697]
Future Problem Solving Prog. Intl. [7933]
Gamma Sigma Delta [23463]
Generation for Change and Growth [12328]
Gifted Learning Proj. [12424]
Girls Helping Girls [12118]
Global Explorers [9017]
GreatSchools [7831]
Hands Across the Water [11297]
Hea. and Educ. Relief Org. [12334]
Healthcare Educ. Assn. [8024]
Henry Luce Found. [11905]
Hispanic Coun. for Reform and Educational Options [8025]
Hispanic Educational Tech. Services [8973]
Holy Childhood Assn. [19428]
Home and School Inst. [8026]
Hope for Kenya's Kids [11906]
Hope for Kenya's Kids [11906]
Humanity in Action [8277]
iEARN [8027]
IES Abroad [8170]
Independent Educational Consultants Assn. [8028]
Indigo Threads [11596]
Inst. for Chem. Educ. [7820]
Inst. for Earth Educ. [8144]
Inst. for Educational Leadership [8029]
Inst. of Near Eastern and African Stud. [8030]
Inst. of Near Eastern and African Stud. [8030]
Inst. for People's Educ. and Action [8031]
Inst. for the Transfer of Tech. to Educ. [8314]
Intercollegiate Stud. Inst. [17425]
InterConnection [11664]
Interdisciplinary Biblical Res. Inst. [19677]
Intl. Alumni Assn. of Shri Mahavir Jain Vidyalaya [19219]
Intl. Assn. for Correctional and Forensic Psychology [11715]
Intl. Assn. for Jazz Educ. [8653]
Intl. Assn. for Statistical Educ. [2823]
Intl. Assn. for Teachers of Chinese to Speakers of Other Languages [7844]
Intl. BioExploration Soc. [8180]
Intl. Boys' Schools Coalition [8032]
Intl. Boys' Schools Coalition [8032]
Intl. Coordination Coun. of Educational Institutions Alumni [18697]
Intl. Coun. on Materials Educ. [8033]
Intl. Educ. and Rsrc. Network [8027]
Intl. Fed. of Engg. Educ. Societies [8124]
Intl. Graphic Arts Educ. Assn. [8220]
Intl. Listening Assn. [8034]
Intl. Listening Assn. [8034]
Intl. Org. for Haitian Development [7894]
Intl. Progressive Educ. [8074]
Intl. Soc. of the Arts, Mathematics, and Architecture [7003]
Intl. Soc. for Comparative Stud. of Chinese and Western Philosophy [8707]
Intl. Soc. for Islamic Legal Stud. [8414]
Intl. Soc. for the Social Stud. [8865]
Intl. Visual Literacy Assn. [8035]
Intl. Visual Literacy Assn. [8035]
Inyana - League of Rwandan Children and Youth [11474]
Jagannath Org. for Global Awareness [20213]
Japan Intl. Christian Univ. Found. [19678]
Japan Intl. Christian Univ. Found. [19678]
Jesuit Assn. of Student Personnel Administrators [7665]
Jewish Student Press Ser. [8428]
Joseph Drown Found. [11907]
Judge David L. Bazelon Center for Mental Hea. Law [17296]
Kappa Delta Epsilon [23511]
Kappa Delta Pi [23512]
Kate's Voice [8764]
Latin Amer. Women's Assn. [13464]
Learning First Alliance [8036]
LearnWell Resources [13161]
Legacies of War [8259]
Libraries Without Borders [8519]
LOGOI [19679]
LOGOI [19679]

Louis Finkelstein Inst. for Religious and Social Stud. [19680]
LULAC Natl. Educational Ser. Centers [8037]
Mercy Beyond Borders [12738]
Mid-Atlantic Equity Consortium [8038]
Middle Atlantic Planetarium Soc. [8841]
Middle States Assn. of Colleges and Schools [8039]
Minority Access, Inc. [8631]
Montessori Accreditation Coun. for Teacher Educ. [8040]
Montessori Accreditation Coun. for Teacher Educ. [8040]
Montessori Inst. of Am. [8041]
Mu Beta Psi [23601]
Natl. 4-H Coun. [13536]
Natl. Acad. of Educ. [8042]
Natl. Alternative Educ. Assn. [7722]
Natl. Assn. of Charter School Authorizers [8043]
Natl. Assn. for Continuing Educ. [7927]
Natl. Assn. of Diversity Officers in Higher Educ. [8238]
Natl. Assn. for Episcopal Christian Educ. Directors [7856]
Natl. Assn. of Hea. Sci. Educ. Partnership [8843]
Natl. Assn. for Health Science Educ. Partnerships [8318]
Natl. Assn. of Math Circles [8566]
Natl. Assn. of Parish Catechetical Directors [19681]
Natl. Assn. of Peoplecultural Engg. Prog. Advocates [8127]
Natl. Assn. of State Directors of Special Educ. [8888]
Natl. Assn. of University-Model Schools [7885]
Natl. Assn. for Year-Round Educ. [8044]
Natl. Block and Bridle Club [23464]
Natl. Campus Ministry Assn. [19682]
Natl. Center on Educ. and the Economy [8045]
Natl. Center for Educ. Statistics [8046]
Natl. Center for Res. on Evaluation, Standards, and Student Testing [8047]
Natl. CH for English Language Acquisition and Language Instruction Educational Programs [8048]
Natl. Coalition of Girls' Schools [8049]
Natl. Coalition for Public School Options [8775]
Natl. Collegiate Honors Coun. [8050]
Natl. Conf. for Catechetical Leadership [19683]
Natl. Coun. of Churches, Educ. and Leadership Ministries Commn. [19684]
Natl. Coun. for Continuing Educ. and Training [7928]
Natl. Coun. on Teacher Retirement [23180]
Natl. Dissemination Assn. [8051]
Natl. Educ. Assn. [23181]
Natl. Forensic Assn. [8895]
Natl. Inst. of Ceramic Engineers [6383]
Natl. Journalism Center [17721]
Natl. Kappa Kappa Iota [23513]
Natl. Middle Level Sci. Teachers' Assn. [8848]
Natl. Native Amer. Law Students Assn. [8510]
Natl. Org. for Continuing Educ. of Roman Catholic Clergy [19685]
Natl. Schools Comm. for Economic Educ. [7988]
Natl. Senior Classical League [7866]
Natl. Title I Assn. [7677]
NEA Found. [8052]
NepalAama [7833]
NETWORK [8053]
Network of Intl. Christian Schools [7857]
New England Assn. of Schools and Colleges [8054]
New Parents Network [8692]
North Amer. Assn. of Educational Negotiators [23182]
North Amer. Assn. for Environmental Educ. [8148]
North Amer. South Asian Law Student Assn. [8511]
North Amer. Taiwan Stud. Assn. [8938]
North Central Conf. on Summer Schools [8936]
Northwest Accreditation Commn. [8055]
Northwest Assn. of Accredited Schools [8055]
One Hen [7821]
One Voice of Peace [8694]

One World Educ. [8928]
OneWorld Now! [8929]
Organizational Behavior Teaching Soc, [6262]
Out of Poverty thru Educ. [7731]
Overseas Young Chinese Forum [7845]
Parents for Public Schools [11908]
Per Scholas [8056]
Phelps-Stokes Fund [8057]
Phelps-Stokes Fund [8057]
Phi Chi Medical Fraternity [23594]
Phi Theta Kappa, Intl. Honor Soc. [23514]
Phi Theta Kappa, Intl. Honor Soc. [23514]
Physicians Against World Hunger [12287]
Pi Lambda Theta [23515]
Plymouth Rock Found. [8058]
Polish-American-Jewish Alliance for Youth Action [13551]
Public Educ. Center [18425]
Quality Educ. for Minorities Network [8059]
Reasoning Mind [8569]
Rebuild A Nation [11077]
Religious Educ. Assn.: An Assn. of Professors, Practitioners, and Researchers in Religious Educ. [19686]
Resources for Indispensable Schools and Educators [8961]
Response-Ability [20085]
Responsible Endowments Coalition [9082]
Restore Humanity [12362]
Restoring Institutions Services and Empowering Liberia [11625]
Rock Detective Geoscience Educ. [7983]
Room to Read [11909]
Room to Read [11909]
Serendib [11629]
Sigma Alpha Iota Intl. Music Fraternity [23605]
Sloan Consortium [8060]
Soc. for Energy Educ. [6756]
Soc. for Music Teacher Educ. [8669]
Soc. of Professors of Educ. [8061]
Soc. for the Stud. of Early China [7846]
Soc. for Values in Higher Educ. [19687]
Solace Intl. [13479]
Southern Assn. of Colleges and Schools [8062]
Southern Educ. Found. [8063]
Spencer Found. [11910]
Student African Amer. Brotherhood [19288]
Student Press Law Center [17358]
Student Veterans of Am. [9032]
TeamPact [18631]
Tech. Inst. for Music Educators [8671]
Telluride Assn. [8064]
Thomas B. Fordham Found. [11911]
Total Family Care Coalition [12023]
Touching Hearts [10817]
Two Cents of Hope [8292]
Under The Baobab Tree [7901]
U.S.-China Educ. Found. [8377]
U.S. Conf. of Catholic Bishops I Bishops' Comm. on Priestly Formation [19688]
University/Resident Theatre Assn. [9005]
Up With People [8065]
Urban Ed [9031]
Urban Teacher Residency United [8962]
Utility Tech. Assn. [7591]
Van Andel Educ. Inst. [8066]
Wallace Found. [11912]
Washington Journalism Center [8449]
Welders Without Borders [7619]
Western Assn. of Schools and Colleges [8067]
WICUDA-USA [9095]
Women Educators [9067]
Women and Youth Supporting Each Other [9069]
WoodLINKS USA [8300]
World Care [11913]
World Care [11913]
World Org. for Early Childhood Educ., U.S. Natl. Comm. [7835]
World Savvy [9084]
WorldTeach [8068]
Education-A-Must [11914], PO Box 216, East Derry, NH 03041, (603)437-6286
Educ. Advancement Fund Intl. [7843], 6584 Hawaii Kai Dr., Honolulu, HI 96825
Education, Alternative
Consciousness-Based Educ. Assn. [8762]

Reference to "IO" in place of a book number signifies that the association may be found in the 50th edition of International Organizations.

Encyclopedia of Associations, 51st Edition   2757

Reasoning Mind **[8569]**
Educ. physique et sante Canada **[★IO]**
Educ. Centre for Women in Democracy **[IO]**, Nairobi, Kenya
Educ. for Christian Life and Mission **[★19684]**
The Educ. Coalition **[8081]**, 31 Segovia, San Clemente, CA 92672, (949)369-3867
Educ. Commn. of the States **[8019]**, 700 Broadway, No. 810, Denver, CO 80203-3442, (303)299-3600
Educ. Conservancy **[7683]**, 805 SW Broadway, Ste. 1600, Portland, OR 97205, (503)290-0083
Educ. Coun. of the Graphic Arts Indus. **[★1609]**
Educ. Credit Union Coun. **[999]**, Lorraine Zerfas, Exec. Dir., PO Box 7558, Spanish Fort, AL 36577, (251)626-3399
Education and Cultural Development Assn. - Defunct.
Educ. and Culture Union **[IO]**, Berlin, Germany
Educ. Development Center **[8020]**, 55 Chapel St., Newton, MA 02458, (617)969-7100
Educ. Development Center **[8020]**, 55 Chapel St., Newton, MA 02458, (617)969-7100
Educ. and Enrichment Sect. **[★12005]**
Educ. and Enrichment Sect. of the Natl. Coun. on Family Relations **[12005]**, 1201 W River Pkwy., Ste. 200, Minneapolis, MN 55454-1115, (763)781-9331
Education Excellence Partnership - Defunct.
Educ. Fights AIDS Intl. **[10878]**, PO Box 34114, Washington, DC 20043, (202)290-0416
Educ. Found. of Amer. Soc. of Plastic and Reconstructive Surgeons **[★14183]**
Educ. Indus. Assn. **[★3171]**
Educ. Indus. Assn. **[8947]**, Steven Pines, Exec. Dir., 1839 Batten Hollow Rd., Vienna, VA 22182, (703)938-2429
Educ. Intl. **[IO]**, Brussels, Belgium
Educ. Intl., Africa Regional Off. **[IO]**, Accra, Ghana
Educ. Intl., Asia-Pacific Regional Off. **[IO]**, Kuala Lumpur, Malaysia
Educ. Intl., Latin Am. Regional Off. **[IO]**, San Jose, Costa Rica
Educ. Intl., North America-Caribbean Regional Off. **[IO]**, Babonneau, St. Lucia
Education Law
Center for Law and Educ. **[5394]**
Coun. on Law in Higher Educ. **[8069]**
Educ. Law Assn. **[5395]**
Educ. Law Assn. **[5395]**
Natl. Assn. of Coll. and Univ. Attorneys **[5396]**
North Amer. South Asian Law Student Assn. **[8511]**
Educ. Law Assn. **[5395]**, 300 Coll. Park, Dayton, OH 45469-0528, (937)229-3589
Educ. Law Assn. **[5395]**, 300 Coll. Park, Dayton, OH 45469-0528, (937)229-3589
Educ. Network to Advance Cancer Clinical Trials **[13919]**, 7625 Wisconsin Ave., 3rd Fl., Bethesda, MD 20814, (240)482-4730
Educ. for Peace in Iraq Center **[18003]**, 900 2nd St. NE, Ste. 216, Washington, DC 20002, (202)682-0208
Educ. Pioneers **[8915]**, 1970 Broadway, Ste. 1140, Oakland, CA 94612, (510)893-4374
Educ. for Prosperity **[11576]**, PO Box 302, East Lansing, MI 48826, (517)614-0501
Educ. and Res. Inst. **[★17721]**
Educ. and Sci. Employees' Union of Russia **[IO]**, Moscow, Russia
Educ. and Sci. Trade Union of Slovenia **[IO]**, Ljubljana, Slovenia
Education, Special
DAD: Drums and Disabilities **[12422]**
Model Secondary School for the Deaf **[14946]**
Natl. Assn. of State Directors of Special Educ. **[8888]**
Educ. Through Music **[8649]**, 122 E 42nd St., Ste. 1501, New York, NY 10168, (212)972-4788
Education and Training Found. **[★20416]**
Educ., Training and Res. Associates **[8309]**, 4 Carbonero Way, Scotts Valley, CA 95066-4200, (831)438-4060
Educ. Voters of Am. **[8771]**, 11 Dupont Cir. NW, Ste. 201, Washington, DC 20036, (202)232-3371
Educ. Writers Assn. **[2826]**, 2122 P St. NW, Ste. 201, Washington, DC 20037, (202)452-9830

Education Youth
African Kids In Need **[11179]**
All One People **[10808]**
Caring Hand for Children **[11440]**
Child Literacy **[11221]**
Chinese School Assn. in the U.S. **[8825]**
Coun. for Children with Behavioral Disorders **[8878]**
Educators Serving the Community **[8070]**
Facing the Future **[8071]**
For Inspiration and Recognition of Sci. and Tech. **[8072]**
Girls Helping Girls **[12118]**
Global China Connection **[8387]**
Global Kids **[8073]**
Hope for Kenya's Kids **[11906]**
Humanity in Action **[8277]**
Intl. Progressive Educ. **[8074]**
Kids Universe, Inc. **[8075]**
Latin Amer. Women's Assn. **[13464]**
Natl. 4-H Coun. **[13536]**
Natl. Alternative Educ. Assn. **[7722]**
OneWorld Now! **[8929]**
Proj. Tomorrow **[8076]**
Responsible Endowments Coalition **[9082]**
Urban Ed **[9031]**
World Savvy **[9084]**
Educational Advocacy
Amer. Assn. for Teaching and Curriculum **[8941]**
Assn. for Core Texts and Courses **[8514]**
A Better Chance **[8077]**
Black Alliance for Educational Options **[8078]**
Coll. Summit **[8234]**
Communities In Schools **[8079]**
Coun. for Opportunity in Educ. **[8080]**
Democrats for Educ. Reform **[17600]**
Education-A-Must **[11914]**
The Educ. Coalition **[8081]**
Intl. Assn. for Truancy and Dropout Prevention **[8082]**
Intl. Assn. for Truancy and Dropout Prevention **[8082]**
Natl. Coalition for Public School Options **[8775]**
Natl. Coun. of Educ. Providers **[8083]**
Natl. Dropout Prevention Center/Network **[8084]**
Plan of Action for Challenging Times **[8085]**
Proj. Appleseed: The Natl. Campaign for Public School Improvement **[8086]**
Educational Audiology Assn. **[14934]**, 3030 W 81st Ave., Westminster, CO 80031, (800)460-7322
Educational Audiology Assn. **[14934]**, 3030 W 81st Ave., Westminster, CO 80031, (800)460-7322
Educational Audiology Soc. **[★14934]**
Educational Audiology Soc. **[★14934]**
Educational Book and Media Assn. **[2932]**, PO Box 1399, East Hampton, NY 11937, (631)329-3315
Educational Broadcasting Corp. **[9459]**, 825 8th Ave., New York, NY 10019, (212)560-1313
Educational Buyers Assn. **[★7669]**
Educational Center for Applied Ekistics **[9869]**, 1900 DeKalb Ave. NE, Atlanta, GA 30307-2304, (404)378-2219
Educational Commn. for Foreign Medical Graduates **[16262]**, 3624 Market St., Philadelphia, PA 19104-2685, (215)386-5900
Educational Commn. for Foreign Medical Graduates **[16262]**, 3624 Market St., Philadelphia, PA 19104-2685, (215)386-5900
Educational Commn. for Foreign Veterinary Graduates **[★17010]**
Educational Communications **[8142]**, PO Box 351419, Los Angeles, CA 90035-9119, (310)559-9160
Educational Communications **[8142]**, PO Box 351419, Los Angeles, CA 90035-9119, (310)559-9160
Educational Concerns for Hunger Org. **[12270]**, 17391 Durrance Rd., North Fort Myers, FL 33917, (239)543-3246
Educational Concerns for Hunger Org. **[12270]**, 17391 Durrance Rd., North Fort Myers, FL 33917, (239)543-3246
Educational Coun. for Foreign Medical Graduates **[★16262]**
Educational Coun. for Foreign Medical Graduates **[★16262]**

Educational Dealers and Suppliers Assn. Intl. - Defunct.
Educational Development Assn. **[IO]**, Keighley, United Kingdom
Educational Equity Center **[8165]**, 100 5th Ave., 8th Fl., New York, NY 10011, (212)243-1110
Educational Expeditions Intl. **[★8175]**
Educational Facilities
APPA: The Assn. of Higher Educ. Facilities Officers **[8087]**
APPA: The Assn. of Higher Educ. Facilities Officers **[8087]**EducationalCommunity Learning and Info. Network
Coun. of Educational Fac. Planners Intl. **[8088]**
Coun. of Educational Fac. Planners Intl. **[8088]**
Natl. Assn. for the Exchange of Indus. Resources **[8089]**
Natl. Educational Telecommunications Assn. **[8090]**
Educational Found. of Am. **[11975]**, 35 Church Ln., Westport, CT 06880, (203)226-6498
Educational Found. of Am. **[11975]**, 35 Church Ln., Westport, CT 06880, (203)226-6498
Educational Found. of the Natl. Restaurant Assn. **[★1767]**
Educational Found. for Nuclear Sci. **[★7364]**
Educational Found. for Women in Accounting **[9057]**, 136 S Keowee St., Dayton, OH 45402, (937)424-3391
Educational Freedom
Citizens for Educational Freedom **[8091]**
Home School Legal Defense Assn. **[8092]**
Parents in Control **[8093]**
Educational Fund to End Handgun Violence **[★17688]**
Educational Fund to Stop Gun Violence **[17688]**, 1424 L St. NW, Ste. 2-1, Washington, DC 20005-2602, (202)408-0061
Educational Funding
ACUO **[8094]**
Armenian Educational Found. **[8095]**
Assn. for Educ. Finance and Policy **[8096]**
Bill Raskob Found. **[17597]**
Coalition of Higher Educ. Assistance Organizations **[8097]**
Comm. for Educ. Funding **[8098]**
Coun. for Aid to Educ. **[8099]**
Coun. for Rsrc. Development **[8100]**
Edge-ucate **[11915]**
Edge-ucate **[11915]**
Henry M. Jackson Found. **[17598]**
Natl. Assn. of Federally Impacted Schools **[8101]**
Natl. Assn. of Student Financial Aid Administrators **[8102]**
Natl. Coun. of Higher Educ. Loan Programs **[8103]**
Van Andel Educ. Inst. **[8066]**
Educational Help for Afghanistan Assn. **[8916]**, 610 N Keystone St., Burbank, CA 91506-1922, (818)563-1590
Educational Help for Afghanistan Assn. **[8916]**, 610 N Keystone St., Burbank, CA 91506-1922, (818)563-1590
Educational Inst. of Scotland **[IO]**, Edinburgh, United Kingdom
Educational Paperback Assn. **[★2932]**
Educational Planning **[★8730]**
Educational Planning **[★8730]**
Educational Policy Center **[★8077]**
Educational Press Assn. of Am. **[★8744]**
Educational Products Info. Exchange Inst. **[★8311]**
Educational Publishers Coun. **[IO]**, London, United Kingdom
Educational Records Bur. **[8985]**, 220 E 42nd St., New York, NY 10017, (800)989-3721
Educational Records Bur. **[8985]**, 220 E 42nd St., New York, NY 10017, (800)989-3721
Educational Reform
Accuracy in Academia **[8104]**
America's Edge **[17599]**
Big Picture Learning **[8105]**
Center for Occupational Res. and Development **[8106]**
Democrats for Educ. Reform **[17600]**
Inst. for Learning Technologies **[8107]**

A star before a book entry number signifies that the name is not listed separately, but is mentioned within the entry.

Natl. Acad. of Amer. Scholars [8108]
Natl. Career Pathways Network [8109]
Natl. Paideia Center [8110]
Teaching for Change [8111]
Educational Res. Analysts [8995], PO Box 7518, Longview, TX 75607-7518, (903)753-5993
Educational Res. Associates [8021], PO Box 8795, Portland, OR 97207-8795, (503)228-6345
Educational Res. Ser. [7664], 1001 N Fairfax St., Ste. 500, Alexandria, VA 22314-1587, (703)243-2100
Educational Services [★8020]
Educational Software Cooperative [6484], 127 The Ranch Rd., Del Valle, TX 78617
Educational Software Cooperative [6484], 127 The Ranch Rd., Del Valle, TX 78617
Educational Testing Ser. [8986], Rosedale Rd., Princeton, NJ 08541, (609)921-9000
Educational Theatre Assn. [9001], 2343 Auburn Ave., Cincinnati, OH 45219-2815, (513)421-3900
Educational Trust of the Amer. Hosp. Assn. [★15056]
EducationWorks [7897], 684 Whitehead Rd., Lawrenceville, NJ 08648, (609)392-6662
Educators
Amer. Assn. for Teaching and Curriculum [8941]
Asociacion para la Educacion Teologica Hispana [9006]
Assn. for the Advancement of Intl. Educ. [8388]
Assn. of Presbyterian Church Educators [19612]
Assn. of Professional Humane Educators [11916]
Assn. of Standardized Patient Educators [15323]
Building Tech. Educators' Soc. [7732]
Conf. on English Leadership [8112]
Coun. for the Advancement of Standards in Higher Educ. [8914]
Dance Masters of Am. [7959]
Destination ImagiNation [8697]
Educ. Conservancy [7683]
Experience Corps [8113]
Global Explorers [9017]
Green Schools Alliance [8158]
Home and School Inst. [8026]
Inst. for Chem. Educ. [7820]
Inst. for Earth Educ. [8144]
Intl. Assn. of Educators [8114]
Intl. Assn. for Jazz Educ. [8653]
Intl. Assn. for Teachers of Chinese to Speakers of Other Languages [7844]
Intl. Graphic Arts Educ. Assn. [8220]
Intl. Soc. for the Social Stud. [8865]
Legacies of War [8259]
Martial Arts Teachers' Assn. [22743]
Middle Atlantic Planetarium Soc. [8841]
Natl. Assn. for Alternative Certification [8115]
Natl. Assn. for Episcopal Christian Educ. Directors [7856]
Natl. Assn. of Hea. Sci. Educ. Partnership [8843]
Natl. Assn. of Math Circles [8566]
Natl. Assn. of State Directors of Special Educ. [8888]
Natl. Coun. for Continuing Educ. and Training [7928]
Natl. Coun. for Workforce Educ. [8116]
Natl. Middle Level Sci. Teachers' Assn. [8848]
Natl. Schools Comm. for Economic Educ. [7988]
Natl. Senior Classical League [7866]
Natl. Title I Assn. [7677]
Natural Fitness Trainers Assn. [22809]
Network of Intl. Christian Schools [7857]
One World Educ. [8928]
Resources for Indispensable Schools and Educators [8961]
Soc. of Building Sci. Educators [8117]
Soc. for Music Teacher Educ. [8669]
Student Press Law Center [17358]
Urban Teacher Residency United [8962]
Women Educators [9067]
World Savvy [9084]
Educators Assembly of Am. [★8427]
Educators Assembly of Am. [★8427]
Educators Serving the Community [8070], 1040 West St., Laurel, MD 20707, (301)498-2899
Educators for Social Responsibility [17963], 23 Garden St., Cambridge, MA 02138, (617)492-1764

EDUCAUSE [8310], 4772 Walnut St., Ste. 206, Boulder, CO 80301-2538, (303)449-4430
Edurelief [12834], 85334 Lorane Hwy., Eugene, OR 97405, (541)554-2992
Edurelief [12834], 85334 Lorane Hwy., Eugene, OR 97405, (541)554-2992
Edutechnia [6976], 4849 S Darrow Dr., No. L138, Tempe, AZ 85282
Edutopia - The George Lucas Educational Found. [8022], PO Box 3494, San Rafael, CA 94912, (415)662-1600
Eduwatch [8683], 8817 Swallow Ct., Gaithersburg, MD 20879, (301)869-4720
Edward E. Ford Found. [13131], 66 Pearl St., Ste. 322, Portland, ME 04101, (207)774-2346
Edward E. Ford Found. [13131], 66 Pearl St., Ste. 322, Portland, ME 04101, (207)774-2346
Edwards Family Assn. - Defunct.
EEI—Nuclear Div. [6746]
Eelam Tamils Assn. of America - Defunct.
EEMA [IO], Worcester, United Kingdom
Eesti Ajalehtede Liit [★IO]
Eesti Akadeemiliste Naiste Uhing [★IO]
Eesti Arstide Liit [★IO]
Eesti Ehitusmaterjalide Tootjate Liit [★IO]
Eesti Fuusika Selts [★IO]
Eesti Hambaarstiuliopilaste Liit [★IO]
Eesti Haridustootajate Liit [★IO]
Eesti Hasartmangude Korraldajate Liit [★IO]
Eesti Hotellide Ja Restoranide Liit [★IO]
Eesti Infotehnoloogia Selts [★IO]
Eesti Infotehnoloogia ja Telekommunikatsiooni Liit [★IO]
Eesti Inimoiguste Instituut [★IO]
Eesti Instituut [★IO]
Eesti Jalgpalli Liit [★IO]
Eesti Kardioloogide Selts [★IO]
Eesti Kaubandus-Toostuskoda [★IO]
Eesti Kaupmeeste Liit [★IO]
Eesti Keemiatoostuse Liit [★IO]
Eesti Kergejoustikuliit [★IO]
Eesti Kiirabi Liit [★IO]
Eesti Kindlustusseltside Liit [★IO]
Eesti Kinnisvarafirmade Liit [★IO]
Eesti Kunstnike Liit [★IO]
Eesti Lennuspordi Foderatsioon [IO], Tallinn, Estonia
Eesti Maaturism [★IO]
Eesti Masinatoostuse Liit [★IO]
Eesti Noorte Naiste ja Meeste Kristlike Uhingute Liit [★IO]
Eesti Noorte Reumaliit [★IO]
Eesti Olumpiakomitee [★IO]
Eesti Orienteerumisliit [★IO]
Eesti Osteoporoosi Selts [★IO]
Eesti Pangaliit [★IO]
Eesti Paraolumpiakomitee [★IO]
Eesti Personalitoo Arendamise Uhing [★IO]
Eesti Piimaliit [★IO]
Eesti Psuhholoogide Liit [★IO]
Eesti Purjelaualiit [★IO]
Eesti Raadioamatooride Uhing [★IO]
Eesti Raamatukoguhoidjate Uhing [★IO]
Eesti Rakvuslik Geomorfoloogia Komitee [★IO]
Eesti Reformierakonna Peakontor [★IO]
Eesti Ringhaalingute Liit [★IO]
Eesti Roeiva- ja Tekstiililiit [★IO]
Eesti Saalihoki Liit [★IO]
Eesti Seksuaaltervise Liit [★IO]
Eesti Skautide Uhing [★IO]
Eesti Squashifoderatsioon [★IO]
Eesti Sulgpalliliit [★IO]
Eesti Suurettevotjate Assotsiatsioon [★IO]
Eesti Tantsuspordi Liit [★IO]
Eesti Teaduste Akadeemia [★IO]
Eesti Toiduainetoostuse Liit [★IO]
Eesti Tooandjate Keskliit [★IO]
Eesti Touloomakasvatajate Uhistu [★IO]
Eesti Turbaliit [★IO]
Eesti Turismifirmade Liit [★IO]
Eesti Turvaettevotete Liit [★IO]
Eesti Tuuleenergia Assotsiatsioon [★IO]
Eesti Uisuliit [★IO]
Eesti Uliopilaskondade Liit [★IO]
Eestimaa Looduse Fond [★IO]
E.F. Benson Soc. [IO], Rye, United Kingdom

EF Educational Found. for Foreign Stud. [★8357]
EF Educational Found. for Foreign Stud. [★8357]
EF Found. for Foreign Stud. [8357], One Educ. St., Cambridge, MA 02141, (800)44-SHARE
EF Found. for Foreign Stud. [8357], One Educ. St., Cambridge, MA 02141, (800)44-SHARE
Effective Citizens Org. [★17482]
Effective Citizens Org. Found. [★18461]
Efficiency First [4046], 70 Zoe St., Ste. 201, San Francisco, CA 94107, (415)449-0551
Efficient Windows Collaborative [3668], Mr. Nils Petermann, Proj. Mgr., Alliance to Save Energy, 1850 M St. NW, Ste. 600, Washington, DC 20036, (202)530-2254
EFNARC [IO], Warrington, United Kingdom
The EFT Assn. [★408]
Egale Canada [IO], Toronto, ON, Canada
Egbe Omo Yoruba: Natl. Assn. of Yoruba Descendants in North America [19174], PO Box 204, White Marsh, MD 21162-0204, (314)974-3604
Egbe Omo Yoruba: Natl. Assn. of Yoruba Descendants in North America [19174], PO Box 204, White Marsh, MD 21162-0204, (314)974-3604
Egg CH, Inc. [4808], PO Box 817, Dover, NH 03821, (800)872-3324
Egg Cup Collectors' Corner [21336], 67 Stevens Ave., Old Bridge, NJ 08857
Egg Farmers of Canada [IO], Ottawa, ON, Canada
Egg Nutrition Center [15830], PO Box 738, Park Ridge, IL 60068, (847)296-7055
Egg Packaging Assn. [★1041]
Egypt
Egyptian Student Assn. in North America [8917]
Egyptians Relief Assn. [11577]
Historical Soc. of Jews from Egypt [9923]
Egypt Exploration Soc. [IO], London, United Kingdom
Egypt Flying Disc Fed. [IO], Cairo, Egypt
Egyptian Article Numbering Assn. [IO], Cairo, Egypt
Egyptian Assn. of Univ. Women [IO], Alexandria, Egypt
Egyptian Athletic Fed. [IO], Cairo, Egypt
Egyptian Badminton Fed. [IO], Giza, Egypt
Egyptian Cmpt. Soc. [IO], Cairo, Egypt
Egyptian Family Planning Assn. [IO], Cairo, Egypt
Egyptian Fertility and Sterility Soc. [IO], Cairo, Egypt
Egyptian Gas Assn. [IO], Cairo, Egypt
Egyptian Gen. Company for Tourism and Hotels [IO], Cairo, Egypt
Egyptian Geotechnical Soc. [IO], Giza, Egypt
Egyptian Hotel Assn. [IO], Cairo, Egypt
Egyptian Hypertension Soc. [IO], Cairo, Egypt
Egyptian Medical Assn. [IO], Cairo, Egypt
Egyptian Natl. Gp. of IFPI [IO], Cairo, Egypt
Egyptian Nuclear Physics Assn. [IO], Cairo, Egypt
Egyptian Ophthalmological Soc. [IO], Cairo, Egypt
Egyptian Org. for Human Rights [IO], Cairo, Egypt
Egyptian Orthopaedic Assn. [IO], Cairo, Egypt
Egyptian Osteoporosis Prevention Soc. [IO], Cairo, Egypt
Egyptian Red Crescent Soc. [IO], Cairo, Egypt
Egyptian Seed Assn. [IO], Cairo, Egypt
Egyptian Soc. Against Epilepsy [IO], Cairo, Egypt
Egyptian Soc. of Cardiology [IO], Alexandria, Egypt
Egyptian Soc. of Consulting Engineers [IO], Cairo, Egypt
Egyptian Soc. of Crystallography and Applications [IO], Cairo, Egypt
Egyptian Soc. of Gastrointestinal Endoscopy [IO], Cairo, Egypt
Egyptian Soc. for Intercultural Exchange [IO], Giza, Egypt
Egyptian Soc. for the Mgt. of Pain [IO], Cairo, Egypt
The Egyptian Soc. of South Africa [IO], Cape Town, Republic of South Africa
Egyptian Student Assn. in North America [8917], 916 Armfield Cir., Apt. 203, Norfolk, VA 23505
Egyptian Student Assn. in North America [8917], 916 Armfield Cir., Apt. 203, Norfolk, VA 23505
Egyptian Taekwondo Fed. [IO], Cairo, Egypt
Egyptian Yachting and Water Ski Fed. [IO], Cairo, Egypt
Egyptians Relief Assn. [11577], 6121 Winnepeg Dr., Burke, VA 22015, (703)503-8816
Egyptology
The Egyptian Soc. of South Africa [15006]

Reference to "IO" in place of a book number signifies that the association may be found in the 50th edition of International Organizations.

eHealth Assn. of Pakistan [IO], Karachi, Pakistan
eHealth Initiative [14774], 818 Connecticut Ave. NW, Ste. 500, Washington, DC 20006, (202)624-3270
Ehlers Danlos Natl. Found. [16886], 1760 Old Meadow Rd., Ste. 500, McLean, VA 22102, (703)506-2892
Eichelmann Clan Diggers Assn. - Defunct.
EIDD - Design for All Europe [IO], Bromma, Sweden
EIFS Indus. Members Assn. [554], 513 W Broad St., Ste. 210, Falls Church, VA 22046-3257, (800)294-3462
Eight Sheet Outdoor Advt. Assn. [91], PO Box 2680, Bremerton, WA 98310-0344, (360)377-9867
Eighteenth-Century Scottish Stud. Soc. [8256], New Jersey Inst. of Tech., Univ. Heights, Newark, NJ 07102-1982, (973)596-3377
Eighteenth-Century Scottish Stud. Soc. [8256], New Jersey Inst. of Tech., Univ. Heights, Newark, NJ 07102-1982, (973)596-3377
Eighth Air Force Historical Soc. [20858], Samantha Reid, Mgr., PO Box 956, Pooler, GA 31322, (912)748-8884
Eigse Eireann [★IO]
Eikon Gesellschaft der Freunde der Ikonenkunst e.v. [IO], Recklinghausen, Germany
EIL Intercultural Learning [IO], Cork, Ireland
Einstein Institution; Albert [18163]
Eire Philatelic Assn. [22036], John B. Sharkey, Sec., 1559 Grouse Ln., Mountainside, NJ 07092
EISCAT Sci. Assn. [IO], Kiruna, Sweden
Eisenhower Birthplace Found; Mamie Doud [9707]
Eisenhower Found; Milton S. [11688]
Eisenhower Found. for the Prevention of Violence [★11688]
Eisenhower Inst. [★18456]
Eisenhower Inst. [18419], 818 Connecticut Ave. NW, 8th Fl., Washington, DC 20005-2311, (202)628-4444
Eisenhower Inst. [★18456]
Eisenhower World Affairs Inst. [18456], 818 Connecticut Ave. NW, 18th Fl., Washington, DC 20006, (202)628-4444
Eisenhower World Affairs Inst. [18456], 818 Connecticut Ave. NW, 18th Fl., Washington, DC 20006, (202)628-4444
Ekonomiska Samfundet i Finland [★IO]
El Bireh Palestine Soc. of the U.S.A. - Defunct.
El Dorado Winery Assn. [181], PO Box 1614, Placerville, CA 95667, (916)966-5008
El Rescate [12778], PO Box 57036, Los Angeles, CA 90057, (213)387-3284
El Salvador
   Assoc. Collectors of El Salvador [22020]
   COAR Peace Mission [17601]
   Comm. in Solidarity With the People of El Salvador [17602]
   Comm. in Solidarity With the People of El Salvador [17602]
   Salvadoran Amer. Leadership and Educational Fund [17603]
   Salvadoran Amer. Leadership and Educational Fund [17603]
   Salvadoran Amer. Natl. Network [18979]
   SHARE Found.: Building a New El Salvador Today [17604]
   SHARE Found.: Building a New El Salvador Today [17604]
El Taller [IO], Tunis, Tunisia
El Toro Intl. Yacht Racing Assn. [22334], 1014 Hopper Ave., No. 419, Santa Rosa, CA 95403-1613, (707)526-6621
Elainsuojeluliitto Animalia [★IO]
Elasmobranch Soc; Amer. [7059]
Elbe Alliance - Defunct.
Elberton Granite Assn. [3361], PO Box 640, Elberton, GA 30635, (706)283-2551
ELCINA Electronic Indus. Assn. of India [IO], New Delhi, India
Elder Abuse
   Elder Justice Coalition [11917]
   Face Forward [11885]
   Gary Jones Assn. [11918]
   Natl. Assn. to Stop Guardian Abuse [11919]
Elder Brewster Soc. [20509], Gregory E. Thompson, Historian/Membership Chm., PO Box 355, Branford, CT 06405

Elder Craftsmen [10841], 307 7th Ave., Ste. 1401, New York, NY 10001, (212)319-8128
Elder Hea. Care Rsrc. Center; Native [19165]
Elder Justice Coalition [11917], 1612 K St. NW, Ste. 400, Washington, DC 20006-2829, (202)682-4140
Elder Rights Advocacy [IO], Melbourne, Australia
Elder Support Network [★12403]
Elderhostel, Inc. [7924], 11 Ave. de Lafayette, Boston, MA 02111-1736, (617)426-7788
Elderhostel, Inc. [7924], 11 Ave. de Lafayette, Boston, MA 02111-1736, (617)426-7788
Elderly; Legal Services for the [12430]
Elderly; Natl. Assn. for Hispanic [19024]
Eleanor Assn. [★17640]
Eleanor Found. [17640], 311 W Superior St., Ste. 314, Chicago, IL 60654, (312)337-7766
Eleanor Leff Jewish Women's Rsrc. Center [9921], 820 2nd Ave., New York, NY 10017-4504, (212)687-5030
Eleanor Roosevelt Inst. [★10689]
Eleanor Women's Found. [★17640]
Elected Spanish Speaking Officials [★5846]
Election Defense Alliance [17607], PO Box 3152, Culver City, CA 90231-3152, (617)538-6012
Elections
   Asian Pacific Americans for Progress [17205]
   Black Box Voting [17605]
   Change Bangladesh [17275]
   Democracia U.S.A. [17606]
   Democracy for Am. [18329]
   Election Defense Alliance [17607]
   Electoral Reform Soc. [1794]
   Hall of Fame for Great Americans [10665]
   HeadCount [17608]
   Honest Ballot Assn. [17609]
   Intl. Found. for Election Systems [17610]
   Korean Amer. Voters' Coun. [18034]
   League of Young Voters [18384]
   Mobile Voter [18096]
   Natl. Assn. of State Election Directors [1067]
   Natl. Jewish Democratic Coun. [18387]
   Nonprofit VOTE [18162]
   Open Debates [17611]
   Open Voting Consortium [17612]
   Open Voting Consortium [17612]
   South Asian Amer. Voting Youth [18392]
   Women's Voices. Women Vote [18802]
Elections Res. Center - Defunct.
Electoral Reform Soc. [IO], London, United Kingdom
Electrathon Am. [22824], 2495 Cleveland St., Eugene, OR 97405, (541)915-9834
ELECTRI Intl. - The Found. for Elecl. Contraction [1068], 3 Bethesda Metro Ctr., Ste. 1100, Bethesda, MD 20814-6302, (301)215-4538
Elec. Auto Assn. [6240], 323 Los Altos Dr., Aptos, CA 95003-5248, (831)688-8669
Elec. Consumers Info. Comm. [★17453]
Elec. Drive Trans. Assn. [6241], 1101 Vermont Ave. NW, Ste. 401, Washington, DC 20005, (202)408-0774
Elec. Energy Assn. [★3593]
Elec. Energy Assn. [★3593]
Elec. Generation Assn. [★6714]
Elec. Indus. Truck Assn. [★330]
Elec. Overhead Crane Inst. [★1820]
Elec. Power Club [★1080]
Elec. Power Club [★1080]
Elec. Power Res. Inst. [6713], 3420 Hillview Ave., Palo Alto, CA 94304, (650)855-2121
Elec. Power Soc. [IO], Frankfurt, Germany
Elec. Power Supply Assn. [6714], 1401 New York Ave. NW, Ste. 1230, Washington, DC 20005-2110, (202)628-8200
Elec. Railroaders' Assn. [10488], PO Box 3323, Grand Central Sta., New York, NY 10163-3323, (212)986-4482
Elec. Railway Soc. [IO], Sutton Coldfield, United Kingdom
Elec. Tool Inst. [★1657]
Elec. Utility Benchmarking Assn. [6640], 4606 FM 1960 W, Ste. 250, Houston, TX 77069, (281)440-5044
Elec. Utility Indus. Sustainable Supply Chain Alliance [3594], PO Box 419164, Kansas City, MO 64141, (816)561-5323

Elec. Vehicle Assn. of the Americas [★6241]
Electrical
   Amer. Coalition for Clean Coal Electricity [6638]
   Amer. Electrophoresis Soc. [6639]
   Brazilian Elecl. and Electronics Indus. Assn. [16727]
   Canadian Elecl. Contractors Assn. [2023]
   Demand Response and Smart Grid Coalition [6649]
   ELECTRI Intl. - The Found. for Elecl. Contraction [1068]
   Elec. Utility Benchmarking Assn. [6640]
   Elecl. Apparatus Ser. Assn. [1069]
   Elecl. Apparatus Ser. Assn. [1069]
   Elecl. Equip. Representatives Assn. [1070]
   Elecl. Generating Systems Assn. [1071]
   Elecl. Mfg. and Coil Winding Assn. [1072]
   Electricity Consumers Rsrc. Coun. [1073]
   Electronic Indus. Citizenship Coalition [1098]
   Energy Telecommunications and Elecl. Assn. [1074]
   IEEE | Dielectrics and Elecl. Insulation Soc. [6641]
   IEEE | Power and Energy Soc. [6642]
   IEEE | Solid-State Circuits Soc. [6643]
   Intl. Assn. of Elecl. Inspectors [1075]
   Intl. Assn. of Elecl. Inspectors [1075]
   Intl. Cablemakers' Fed. [15840]
   Intl. Elecl. Testing Assn. [1076]
   Intl. Elecl. Testing Assn. [1076]
   Intl. League of Elecl. Associations [1077]
   Intl. League of Elecl. Associations [1077]
   Intl. Sign Assn. [1078]
   Intl. Sign Assn. [1078]
   Intl. Union of Electronic, Elecl., Salaried, Machine, and Furniture Workers [23184]
   Large Public Power Coun. [5406]
   Lightning Strike and Elec. Shock Survivors Intl. [14441]
   Lightning Strike and Elec. Shock Survivors Intl. [14441]
   Natl. Assn. of Elecl. Distributors [1079]
   Natl. Elecl. Mfrs. Assn. [1080]
   Natl. Elecl. Mfrs. Assn. [1080]
   Natl. Elecl. Mfrs. Representatives Assn. [1081]
   Natl. Fed. of Wholesale Distributors of Elec. Materials [4586]
   Natl. Insulator Assn. [21701]
   Natl. Rural Elec. Cooperative Assn. [1082]
   Natl. Rural Elec. Cooperative Assn. [1082]
   North Amer. Elec. Reliability Corp. [1083]
   Professional Elecl. Apparatus Recyclers League [1084]
   Professional Lighting and Sign Mgt. Companies of Am. [2223]
   Relay and Switch Indus. Assn. [1085]
   SMMA - The Motor and Motion Assn. [1086]
   SMMA - The Motor and Motion Assn. [1086]
   Wiring Harness Manufacturer's Assn. [1087]
   Women's Intl. Network of Utility Professionals [1088]
Elecl. Apparatus Ser. Assn. [1069], 1331 Baur Blvd., St. Louis, MO 63132, (314)993-2220
Elecl. Apparatus Ser. Assn. [1069], 1331 Baur Blvd., St. Louis, MO 63132, (314)993-2220
Elecl. and Communications Assn. of Western Australia [IO], Balcatta, Australia
Elecl. and Cmpt. Engg. Dept. Heads Assn. [6793], 233 S Wacker Dr., Ste. 8400, Chicago, IL 60606-6338, (312)559-3724
Elecl. Constr. Assn. of Hamilton [IO], Hamilton, ON, Canada
Elecl. Contracting Found. [★1068]
Elecl. Contractors Assn. [IO], London, United Kingdom
Elecl. Contractors Assn. of Finland [IO], Espoo, Finland
Elecl. Contractors Assn. of London [IO], Dorchester, ON, Canada
Elecl. Contractors Assn. of New Zealand [IO], Wellington, New Zealand
Elecl. Contractors Assn. of Northern Ontario [IO], Sudbury, ON, Canada
Elecl. Contractors Assn. of Ottawa [IO], Ottawa, ON, Canada

A star before a book entry number signifies that the name is not listed separately, but is mentioned within the entry.

Elecl. Contractors Assn. of Quinte-St. Lawrence **[IO]**, Kingston, ON, Canada

Elecl. Contractors Assn. of Sarnia **[IO]**, Sarnia, ON, Canada

Elecl. Contractors Assn. of Saskatchewan **[IO]**, Regina, SK, Canada

The Elecl. and Electronics Assn. of Malaysia **[IO]**, Kuala Lumpur, Malaysia

Electrical Engineering

Elecl. Engg. and Allied Indus. Assn. **[638]**

Elecl. Engg. and Allied Indus. Assn. **[IO]**, Johannesburg, Republic of South Africa

Elecl. Equip. Representatives Assn. **[1070]**, 638 W 39th St., Kansas City, MO 64111, (816)561-5323

Elecl. Generating Systems Assn. **[1071]**, 1650 S Dixie Hwy., Ste. 400, Boca Raton, FL 33432-7462, (561)750-5575

Elecl. Generating Systems Marketing Assn. **[★1071]**

Elecl. Insulation Assn. **[IO]**, Stafford, United Kingdom

Elecl. Mfg. and Coil Winding Assn. **[1072]**, PO Box 278, Imperial Beach, CA 91933, (619)435-3629

Elecl. Overstress/Electrostatic Discharge Assn. **[6650]**, 7900 Turin Rd., Bldg. 3, Rome, NY 13440-2069, (315)339-6937

Elecl. Rebuilder's Assn. **[325]**, PO Box 906, Union, MO 63084, (636)584-7400

Electrical Sensitivity Network - Defunct.

Elecl. Supply Jobbers Assn. **[★1079]**

Elecl. Trade Coun. **[★899]**

Elecl. Women's Roundtable **[★1088]**

Electricity

Amer. Solar Action Plan **[7437]**

Elec. Utility Indus. Sustainable Supply Chain Alliance **[3594]**

Electrification Coalition **[3510]**

Energy Storage Coun. **[6722]**

Governors' Wind Energy Coalition **[6070]**

GridWise Alliance **[6727]**

GridWise Architecture Coun. **[7293]**

Natl. Alliance for Advanced Tech. Batteries **[441]**

Natl. Renewables Cooperative Org. **[6741]**

Power to the People **[7440]**

Pro Energy Alliance **[1175]**

Solar Light for Africa **[11640]**

Solar for Peace **[7447]**

STG Intl. **[7449]**

SunPower Afrique **[13227]**

Utility Supply Mgt. Alliance **[3609]**

Utility Tech. Assn. **[7591]**

Electricity Consumers Rsrc. Coun. **[1073]**, 1111 19th St. NW, Ste. 700, Washington, DC 20036, (202)682-1390

Electricity Networks Assn. **[IO]**, Wellington, New Zealand

Electricity Storage Assn. **[3595]**, 1155 15th St. NW, Ste. 500, Washington, DC 20005

Electricity Storage Assn. **[3595]**, 1155 15th St. NW, Ste. 500, Washington, DC 20005

Electrification Coalition **[3510]**, 1111 19th St. NW, Ste. 406, Washington, DC 20036, (202)461-2360

Electrification Coun. - Defunct.

Electro-Federation Canada **[IO]**, Toronto, ON, Canada

Electro-Technical Coun. of Ireland **[IO]**, Dublin, Ireland

Electro-Technology Assn. **[IO]**, Manukau City, New Zealand

Electrocardiology; Intl. Soc. for Computerized **[14025]**

Electrocardiology; Intl. Soc. for Computerized **[14025]**

Electrochemical Soc. **[6406]**, 65 S Main St., Bldg. D, Pennington, NJ 08534-2839, (609)737-1902

Electrocoat Assn. **[7497]**, PO Box 541083, Cincinnati, OH 45254-1083, (816)496-2308

Electrodiagnostic Medicine; Amer. Assn. of Neuromuscular and **[15565]**

Electroencephalography

Amer. Bd. of Registration of EEG and EP Technologists **[14442]**

Amer. Clinical Neurophysiology Soc. **[14443]**

Amer. Soc. of Electroneurodiagnostic Technologists **[14444]**

Electrogists Intl. **[★936]**

Electroheat Mfrs. Assn. of BEAMA **[IO]**, London, United Kingdom

Electrolysis

Amer. Electrology Assn. **[14445]**

Soc. for Clinical and Medical Hair Removal **[14446]**

Electrolysis Soc. of Am. **[★14446]**

Electromagnetic Compatibility Soc; IEEE I **[6659]**

Electron Microscope Soc. of India **[IO]**, New Delhi, India

Electron Microscopy Sect. of Moldova Republic **[IO]**, Chisinau, Moldova

Electron Microscopy Soc. of Am. **[★7116]**

Electron Probe Anal. Soc. of Am. **[★7115]**

Electroneurodiagnostic Technologists; Amer. Soc. of **[14444]**

Electronic Commerce Code Mgt. Assn. **[1050]**, 2980 Linden St., Ste. E2, Bethlehem, PA 18017, (610)861-5990

Electronic Components Certification Bd. **[1097]**, PO Box 9041, Midland, TX 79708, (432)697-9970

Electronic Connector Study Group **[★6670]**

Electronic Connector Study Group **[★6670]**

Electronic Data Processing Auditors Assn. **[★67]**

Electronic Data Processing Auditors Assn. **[★67]**

Electronic Defense Assn. **[★6647]**

Electronic Design Automation Consortium **[6651]**, 111 W St. John St., Ste. 220, San Jose, CA 95113-1104, (408)287-3322

Electronic Document Systems Found. **[1899]**, 1845 Precinct Line Rd., Ste. 212, Hurst, TX 76054, (817)849-1145

Electronic Frontier Found. **[7498]**, 454 Shotwell St., San Francisco, CA 94110-1914, (415)436-9333

Electronic Frontiers Australia **[IO]**, North Adelaide, Australia

Electronic Funds Transfer Assn. **[408]**, 11350 Random Hills Rd., Ste. 800, Fairfax, VA 22030, (703)934-6052

Electronic Govt. Directorate **[IO]**, Islamabad, Pakistan

Electronic Indus. Alliance - Defunct.

Electronic Indus. Found. **[★13140]**

Electronic Indus. Citizenship Coalition **[1098]**, Carrie Hoffman, Dir. of Communications, 1155 15th St. NW, Ste. 500, Washington, DC 20005, (202)962-0167

Electronic Literature Org. **[1089]**, Univ. of Maryland, Maryland Inst. for Tech. in the Humanities, B0131 McKeldin Lib., College Park, MD 20742, (301)314-6545

Electronic Media Rating Coun. **[★497]**

Electronic Money Coun. **[★408]**

Electronic Music Found. **[10193]**, PO Box 8748, Albany, NY 12208, (518)434-4110

Electronic Privacy Info. Center **[6977]**, 1718 Connecticut Ave. NW, Ste. 200, Washington, DC 20009, (202)483-1140

Electronic Publishing

Electronic Literature Org. **[1089]**

ICRA **[11920]**

ICRA **[11920]**

Electronic Publishing Assn. **[IO]**, Prague, Czech Republic

Electronic Retailing Assn. **[2401]**, 2000 N 14th St., Ste. 300, Arlington, VA 22201, (703)841-1751

Electronic Retailing Assn. **[2401]**, 2000 N 14th St., Ste. 300, Arlington, VA 22201, (703)841-1751

Electronic Security Assn. **[3211]**, 2300 Valley View Ln., Ste. 230, Irving, TX 75062, (214)260-5970

Electronic Security Distributors Assn. **[IO]**, Benmore, Republic of South Africa

Electronic Transactions Assn. **[409]**, 1101 16th St. NW, Washington, DC 20036, (202)828-2635

Electronic Transactions Assn. **[409]**, 1101 16th St. NW, Washington, DC 20036, (202)828-2635

Electronics

Accellera Org. **[6644]**ElectronicsAeA - Advancing the Bus. of Tech.

ALMA - The Intl. Loudspeaker Assn. **[1090]**

Amer. Soc. of Digital Forensics and eDiscovery **[6883]**

Antenna Measurement Techniques Assn. **[6645]**

Applied Computational Electromagnetics Soc. **[6646]**

Argentine Chamber of Elecl. Material Distributors **[4929]**

Asian Am. MultiTechnology Assn. **[1091]**

Assn. for High Tech. Distribution **[1092]**

Assn. of Loudspeaker Mfrs. and Acoustics Intl. **[1090]**

Assn. of Old Crows **[6647]**

Assn. of Suppliers of Electronic Instruments and Components **[14195]**

Audio Engg. Soc. **[6648]**

Battery Recycling Assn. of North Am. **[3071]**

Center for Electronic Packaging Res. **[7207]**

Chinese Am. Semiconductor Professional Assn. **[1093]**

Chinese Am. Semiconductor Professional Assn. **[1093]**

Consumer Electronics Assn. **[1094]**

Consumer Electronics Assn., TechHome Div. **[1095]**

Demand Response and Smart Grid Coalition **[6649]**

Digital Living Network Alliance **[1096]**

Elecl. Overstress/Electrostatic Discharge Assn. **[6650]**

Electronic Components Certification Bd. **[1097]**

Electronic Design Automation Consortium **[6651]**

Electronic Indus. Citizenship Coalition **[1098]**

Electronics Representatives Assn. **[1099]**

Electronics TakeBack Coalition **[6652]**

Electronics Technicians Assn. Intl. **[1100]**

Electronics Technicians Assn. Intl. **[1100]**

European Electronic Chips and Systems Design Initiative **[15584]**

Fab Owners Assn. **[1101]**

FlexTech Alliance **[3390]**

Global Semiconductor Alliance **[1102]**

Global Semiconductor Alliance **[1102]**

Green Electronics Coun. **[6653]**

GridWise Alliance **[6727]**

HomePlug Powerline Alliance **[1103]**

IEEE I Aerospace and Electronics Systems Soc. **[6654]**

IEEE I Antennas and Propagation Soc. **[6655]**

IEEE I Circuits and Systems Soc. **[6656]**

IEEE I Components, Packaging, and Mfg. Tech. Soc. **[6657]**

IEEE I Consumer Electronics Soc. **[6658]**

IEEE I Electromagnetic Compatibility Soc. **[6659]**

IEEE I Electron Devices Soc. **[6660]**

IEEE I Indus. Electronics Soc. **[6661]**

IEEE Indus. Electronics Soc. **[6661]**

IEEE I Magnetics Soc. **[6662]**

IEEE I Photonics Soc. **[6663]**

IEEE Photonics Soc. **[6663]**

IEEE I Power Electronics Soc. **[6664]**

IEEE I Professional Commun. Soc. **[6665]**

IEEE I Reliability Soc. **[6666]**

IEEE I Robotics and Automation Soc. **[7343]**

IEEE I Vehicular Tech. Soc. **[6667]**

Intl. Auto Sound Challenge Assn. **[1104]**

Intl. Brotherhood of Elecl. Workers **[23183]**

Intl. Coordinating Comm. on Solid State Sensors and Actuators Res. **[6668]**

Intl. Coordinating Comm. on Solid State Sensors and Actuators Res. **[6668]**

Intl. DB2 Users Gp. **[6592]**

Intl. Engg. Consortium **[6669]**

Intl. Engg. Consortium **[6669]**

Intl. Inst. of Connector and Interconnection Tech. **[6670]**

Intl. Inst. of Connector and Interconnection Tech. **[6670]**

Intl. Microelectronic and Packaging Soc. **[6671]**

Intl. Microelectronic and Packaging Soc. **[6671]**

Intl. Soc. of Certified Electronics Technicians **[1105]**

Intl. Soc. of Certified Electronics Technicians **[1105]**

Intl. Soc. for Quality Electronic Design **[6600]**

Intl. Union of Electronic, Elecl., Salaried, Machine, and Furniture Workers **[23184]**

IPC - Assn. Connecting Electronics Indus. **[1106]**

ISRI **[1107]**

ISRI **[1107]**

JEDEC **[1108]**

LCD TV Assn. **[3431]**ElectronicsNatl. Chamber of Elec. Manufactures

---

Reference to "IO" in place of a book number signifies that the association may be found in the 50th edition of International Organizations.

Natl. Coalition for Electronics Educ. [8118]
Natl. Electronic Distributors Assn. [1109]
Natl. Electronics Ser. Dealers Assn. [1110]
Natl. Systems Contractors Assn. [1111]
North Am. Chinese Clean-tech and Semiconductor Assn. [1112]
North Am. Chinese Semiconductor Assn. [1112]
North Amer. Retail Dealers Assn. [1113]
PRBA- The Rechargeable Battery Assn. [1114]
Professional Audio Mfrs. Alliance [1115]
SEMI Intl. [1116]
SEMI Intl. [1116]
Semiconductor Environmental, Safety and Hea. Assn. [6672]
Semiconductor Indus. Assn. [1117]
Serial ATA Intl. Org. [6559]
Soc. of Mfg. Engineers | Electronics Mfg. Tech Gp. [6673]
Soc. of Mfg. Engineers | Electronics Mfg. Tech Gp. [6673]
United Elecl., Radio and Machine Workers of Am. [23185]
Variable Electronic Components Inst. [1118]
Video Electronics Standards Assn. [6674]
Wire and Cable Indus. Suppliers Assn. [1119]
Xtal Set Soc. [6675]
Electronics and Elecl. Engg. Assn. of Slovenia [IO], Ljubljana, Slovenia
Electronics Indus. Assn. [IO], Eastwood, Australia
Electronics Representatives Assn. [1099], 111 N Canal St., Ste. 885, Chicago, IL 60606, (312)559-3050
Electronics TakeBack Coalition [6652], 60 29th St., No. 230, San Francisco, CA 94110, (415)206-9595
Electronics Technicians Assn. Intl. [1100], 5 Depot St., Greencastle, IN 46135, (765)653-8262
Electronics Technicians Assn. Intl. [1100], 5 Depot St., Greencastle, IN 46135, (765)653-8262
Elektriska Hushaallsapparat Leverantoerer [★IO]
Elektroniikan Komponentti-ja Mittalaitetoimittajat [★IO]
Elephant Care Intl. [5050], 166 Limo View Ln., Hohenwald, TN 38462, (931)796-7102
Elephant Care Intl. [5050], 166 Limo View Ln., Hohenwald, TN 38462, (931)796-7102
Elephant Energy [6715], 4369 Xavier St., Denver, CO 80212-2421, (515)991-3114
Elephant Energy [6715], 4369 Xavier St., Denver, CO 80212-2421, (515)991-3114
Elephant Managers Assn. [10955], Animal Programs Admin., PO Box 10, Lake Buena Vista, FL 32830, (407)938-1988
Elephant Managers Assn. [10955], Animal Programs Admin., PO Box 10, Lake Buena Vista, FL 32830, (407)938-1988
Elephant Sanctuary in Tennessee [10956], PO Box 393, Hohenwald, TN 38462, (931)796-6500
Elephants Without Borders [5011], 168 S Marlin Rd., Grand Island, NY 14072, (716)773-1012
Elevator Escalator Safety Found. [1120], 362 Pinehill Dr., Mobile, AL 36606, (251)479-2199
Elevator Escalator Safety Found. of Canada [IO], Mississauga, ON, Canada
Elevator U [555], 751 N Olcott Ave., Harwood Heights, IL 60706
Elevators
Elevator Escalator Safety Found. [1120]
Elevator U [555]
Elgin Motorcar Owners Registry [21050], 2226 E Apache Ln., Vincennes, IN 47591, (812)888-4172
Eliminate Poverty Now [11066], PO Box 67, Mendham, NJ 07945
Elintarviketeollisuusliitto [★IO]
The Elisa Proj. [14434], 3102 Oak Lawn Ave., Ste. 520, Dallas, TX 75219, (214)369-5222
Elizabeth Linington Soc. - Defunct.
Elizabeth Madox Roberts Soc. [10714], Tina Iraca, Sec.-Treas., 16 Montgomery St., Tivoli, NY 12583
Elks
Benevolent and Protective Order of Elks [18980]
Supreme Emblem Club of the U.S.A. [18981]
Elks Natl. Foundation [★18980]
Ella Baker Student Program [★17273]
Eller Family Assn. [20510], 1124 Ridgeleigh Cir., Dalton, GA 30721, (706)278-1516

Ellington Navigators Observers Assn. [★20325]
Elliniki Aerathlitiki Omospondia [IO], Glyfada, Greece
Elliniko Diktio Diaxeiriston Ergon [★IO]
Elliot Clan Soc. USA [20511], Patricia Tennyson-Bell, Treas., 2288 Casa Grande St., Pasadena, CA 91104
Elliot Inst. [10765], PO Box 7348, Springfield, IL 62791-7348, (217)525-8202
Elliot Inst. for Social Sciences Res. [★10765]
Ellis Island Medal of Honor Soc. [18983], Natl. Ethnic Coalition of Organizations, 232 Madison Ave., Ste. 900, New York, NY 10016-2901, (212)755-1492
Ellis-van Creveld Syndrome Support [14595], 17 Bridlewood Trail, Honeoye Falls, NY 14472, (585)737-1500
Elm Res. Inst. [4393], 11 Kit St., Keene, NH 03431, (603)358-6198
Elms Unlimited [★4393]
Elmwood Inst. [★4198]
The Elongated Collectors [21975], PO Box 704, Richlandtown, PA 18955
Elsey Family Assn. - Defunct.
Elton John AIDS Found. [10879], 584 Broadway, Ste. 906, New York, NY 10012
Elva Owners Club [IO], Arundel, United Kingdom
Elvira Fan Club [23766], 4570 Van Nuys Blvd., No. 306, Sherman Oaks, CA 91403
Elvis' Angels Fan Club [23800], 10152 La Hwy. 1, Mooringsport, LA 71060-8948, (318)424-5000
Elvis Costello Info. Ser. [IO], Purmerend, Netherlands
Elvis Presley
Elvis' Angels Fan Club [23800]
ElvisNet Elvis Presley Fan Club [23801]
Elvish Linguistic Fellowship [10025], 2509 Ambling Cir., Crofton, MD 21114
Elvish Linguistic Fellowship [10025], 2509 Ambling Cir., Crofton, MD 21114
Elvisly Yours [IO], Watford, United Kingdom
ElvisNet Elvis Presley Fan Club [23801], The Presley Connection, PO Box 680444, Prattville, AL 36068, (800)238-2000
Elwyn [12259], 111 Elwyn Rd., Elwyn, PA 19063, (610)891-2000
Email
Coalition Against Unsolicited Commercial Email [6676]
Email Experience Coun. [6677]
Email Sender and Provider Coalition [6678]
Online Trust Alliance [6550]
SailMail Assn. [6679]
Email Experience Coun. [6677], 1120 Ave. of the Americas, 13th Fl., New York, NY 10036, (212)790-1483
Email Sender and Provider Coalition [6678], 62 Portland Rd., Ste. 44, Kennebunk, ME 04043, (207)467-3500
Emanuel Family Genealogy - Defunct.
eMarketing Assn. [1051], 91 Point Judith Rd., No. 129, Narragansett, RI 02882, (800)496-2950
eMarketing Assn. [1051], 91 Point Judith Rd., No. 129, Narragansett, RI 02882, (800)496-2950
Embracing Orphans [11267], PO Box 2615, Walla Walla, WA 99362-0333, (509)540-9408
Embroiderers' Guild [IO], East Molesey, United Kingdom
Embroiderers' Guild of Am. [21437], 1355 Bardstown Rd., Ste. 157, Louisville, KY 40202, (502)589-6956
Embroiderers' Guild of London, Amer. Br. [★21437]
Embroidery Coun. of Am. - Defunct.
Embroidery Mfrs. Bur. [★3454]
Embroidery Mfrs. Promotion Bd. [★3453]
Embroidery Software Protection Coalition [2049], 1220G Airport Fwy., Ste. 422, Bedford, TX 76022
Embroidery Trade Assn. [3439], 4230 LBJ Fwy., Ste. 414, Dallas, TX 75244, (888)628-2545
EMDR Assn. of Australia [IO], Hall, Australia
EMDR Europe [IO], Ra'anana, Israel
EMDR - Humanitarian Assistance Programs [12711], 2911 Dixwell Ave., Ste. 201, Hamden, CT 06518, (203)288-4450
EMDR - Humanitarian Assistance Programs [12711], 2911 Dixwell Ave., Ste. 201, Hamden, CT 06518, (203)288-4450

EMDR Intl. Assn. [16459], 5806 Mesa Dr., Ste. 360, Austin, TX 78731, (512)451-5200
EMDR Intl. Assn. [16459], 5806 Mesa Dr., Ste. 360, Austin, TX 78731, (512)451-5200
EMDR Mexico [IO], Mexico City, Mexico
EMDRIA Latinoamerica Asociacion Civil [IO], Buenos Aires, Argentina
Emerald Isle Immigration Center [17881], 59-26 Woodside Ave., Woodside, NY 11377, (718)478-5502
Emerald Isle Immigration Center [17881], 59-26 Woodside Ave., Woodside, NY 11377, (718)478-5502
Emerald Soc. of the Fed. Law Enforcement Agencies [19108], PO Box 16413, Rochester, NY 14616-0413, (202)386-6192
Emerald Soc. of the Fed. Law Enforcement Agencies [19108], PO Box 16413, Rochester, NY 14616-0413, (202)386-6192
Emerge: A Men's Counseling Ser. on Domestic Violence [★11884]
EMerge Alliance [556], 2400 Camino Ramon, Ste. 375, San Ramon, CA 94583, (925)275-6617
Emerge Am. [18790], 111 Pine St., Ste. 1500, San Francisco, CA 94111, (415)344-0323
Emerge: Counseling and Educ. to Stop Domestic Violence [11884], 2464 Massachusetts Ave., Ste. 101, Cambridge, MA 02140, (617)547-9879
Emerge: Counseling and Educ. to Stop Male Violence [★11884]
Emergency Aid
1st Special Response Gp. [11843]
Air Charity Network [14447]
All Hands Volunteers [11846]
Amer. Ambulance Assn. [14448]
Amer. Friends of Magen David Adom [12801]
Assn. of Air Medical Services [14449]
Assn. of Air Medical Services [14449]
Baptist Global Response [12809]
Bus. Continuity Planning Workgroup for Healthcare Organizations [14481]
C.H.A.S.E. for Life [14450]
Children's Cup [12819]
Christian Alliance For Humanitarian Aid [12821]
Compassion into Action Network - Direct Outcome Org. [11849]
Disaster Emergency Response Assn. [5397]
Disaster Mgt. Alliance [11850]
Doctors for Disaster Preparedness [14451]
From Hunger to Harvest [12280]
Global Emergency Relief [11923]
Global Fac. for Disaster Reduction and Recovery [11851]
HEART 9/11: Healing Emergency Aid Response Team 9/11 [11853]
HOPE Animal-Assisted Crisis Response [12906]
Hope Force Intl. [11854]
Humanity First USA [11855]
Indonesia Relief - USA [11856]
Innovative Support to Emergencies Diseases and Disasters [11857]
Intl. Fire Buff Associates [21708]
Intl. Police and Fire Chaplain's Assn. [19522]
Intl. Rescue and Emergency Care Assn. [14452]
Intl. Rescue and Emergency Care Assn. [14452]EmergencyIntl. Soc. of First Responders
Iraqi Christian Relief Coun. [12857]
Island Aid [11858]
Kenya Medical Outreach [12462]
Kidney Community Emergency Response Coalition [15552]
Knightsbridge Intl. [12859]
MedicAlert Found. Intl. [14453]
MedicAlert Found. Intl. [14453]
Medics Without Borders [14469]
Miracle Flights for Kids [14454]
Natl. Assn. of Female Paramedics [14472]
Natl. Assn. of State 911 Administrators [7547]
Natl. Emergency Mgt. Assn. [5398]
Natl. Emergency Number Assn. [14455]
Natl. EMS Mgt. Assn. [14476]
Natl. EMS Pilots Assn. [14456]
Peace Winds Am. [11859]
Relief Liberia Intl. [12884]

A star before a book entry number signifies that the name is not listed separately, but is mentioned within the entry.

U.S. Homeland Emergency Response Org.
[12911]
World Assn. of Natural Disaster Awareness and
Assistance [12572]
Emergency Care Res. Inst. [★15373]
Emergency Care Res. Inst. [★15373]
Emergency Comm. for Amer. Trade [2097], 900 17th
St. NW, Ste. 1150, Washington, DC 20006,
(202)659-5147
Emergency Comm. to Defend Constitutional Welfare
Rights USA [18457], Mr. Martin J. Sawma, Exec.
Dir./Intl. Rep., 3501 Westwood Dr., Rm. 4, Niagara
Falls, NY 14305-3416, (716)297-7273
Emergency Comm. for Full Funding of Educ.
Programs [★8098]
Emergency Comm. to Save America's Marine
Resources - Defunct.
Emergency Comm. to Suspend Immigration -
Defunct.
Emergency Dept. Nurses Assn. [★14467]
Emergency Dept. Practice Mgt. Assn. [14464], 8400
W Park Dr., 2nd Fl., McLean, VA 22102, (703)610-
0314
Emergency Land Fund [★12955]
Emergency Lead-Zinc Producers Comm. [★2487]
Emergency Mgt. Professional Org. for Women's
Enrichment [2279], PO Box 10803, McLean, VA
22102
Emergency Medicine
Amer. Acad. of Emergency Medicine [14457]
Amer. Bd. of Emergency Medicine [14458]
Amer. Coll. of Emergency Physicians [14459]
Amer. Coll. of Emergency Physicians | Amer.
Assn. of Women Emergency Physicians
[14460]
Amer. Coll. of Osteopathic Emergency Physicians
[14461]
Amer. Friends of Magen David Adom [12801]
Amer. Osteopathic Bd. of Emergency Medicine
[14462]
Assn. of Emergency Physicians [14463]
Australasian Coll. for Emergency Medicine
[15546]
Emergency Dept. Practice Mgt. Assn. [14464]
Emergency Medicine Found. [14465]
Emergency Medicine Residents' Assn. [14466]
Emergency Nurses Assn. [14467]
Emergency Response Massage Intl. [15266]
Global Emergency Care Collaborative [15162]
Intl. Assn. of EMTs and Paramedics [23186]
Intl. Assn. of EMTs and Paramedics [23186]
Intl. Assn. of Flight and Critical Care Paramedics
[14468]
Intl. Fire Buff Associates [21708]
Medics Without Borders [14469]
Natl. Assn. of Emergency Medical Technicians
[14470]
Natl. Assn. of Emergency Medical Technicians
[14470]
Natl. Assn. of EMS Physicians [14471]
Natl. Assn. of Female Paramedics [14472]
Natl. Assn. of State EMS Officials [14473]
Natl. Collegiate EMS Found. [14474]
Natl. Emergency Medicine Assn. [14475]
Natl. EMS Mgt. Assn. [14476]
Natl. Registry of Emergency Medical Technicians
[14477]
Residency Rev. Comm. for Emergency Medicine
[14478]
Soc. for Academic Emergency Medicine [14479]
Emergency Medicine Found. [14465], PO Box
619911, Dallas, TX 75261-9911, (800)798-1822
Emergency Medicine Mgt. Assn. - Defunct.
Emergency Medicine Physician Assistants; Soc. of
[16242]
Emergency Medicine Residents' Assn. [14466], 1125
Executive Cir., Irving, TX 75038-2522, (972)550-
0920
Emergency Nurses Assn. [14467], 915 Lee St., Des
Plaines, IL 60016-6569, (847)460-4095
Emergency Planning Soc. [IO], Cardiff, United
Kingdom
Emergency Radiology; Amer. Soc. of [16523]
Emergency Relief Response Fund [13186], PO Box
2300, Redlands, CA 92373, (909)793-2009

Emergency Relief Response Fund [13186], PO Box
2300, Redlands, CA 92373, (909)793-2009
Emergency Rescue Comm. [★12783]
Emergency Response Massage Intl. [15266], 227 S
Peak St., Columbus, NC 28722, (704)763-6099
Emergency Services
1st Special Response Gp. [11843]
A.L.E.R.T. Intl. [14480]
All Hands Volunteers [11846]
Amer. Friends of Magen David Adom [12801]
Bus. Continuity Planning Workgroup for Health-
care Organizations [14481]
COMCARE Alliance [14482]
Comm. on Accreditation of Medical Transport
Systems [14483]
Comm. on Accreditation of Medical Transport
Systems [14483]
Disaster Mgt. Alliance [11850]
Fed. Alliance For Safe Homes [11921]
Fire and Emergency Mfrs. and Services Assn.
[11922]
From Hunger to Harvest [12280]
Global Emergency Relief [11923]
HEART 9/11: Healing Emergency Aid Response
Team 9/11 [11853]
HOPE Animal-Assisted Crisis Response [12906]
Hope Force Intl. [11854]
Innovative Support to Emergencies Diseases and
Disasters [11857]
Intl. Fire Buff Associates [21708]
Intl. Police and Fire Chaplain's Assn. [19522]
Kidney Community Emergency Response Coali-
tion [15552]
Knightsbridge Intl. [12859]
Natl. Academies of Emergency Dispatch [14484]
Natl. Assn. of Female Paramedics [14472]
Natl. Assn. of State 911 Administrators [7547]
Natl. EMS Mgt. Assn. [14476]
Natl. Traffic Incident Mgt. Coalition [13330]
Peace Winds Am. [11859]
U.S. Homeland Emergency Response Org.
[12911]
Emergency Social Services Assn. [IO], Burnaby, BC,
Canada
Emergency Vehicle Owners and Operators Assn.
[21051], PO Box 1149, Airway Heights, WA 99001-
1149
Emerging Humanity [12325], 2279 Makanani Dr.,
Honolulu, HI 96817-2038
Emerging Humanity [12325], 2279 Makanani Dr.,
Honolulu, HI 96817-2038
Emerging Markets Private Equity Assn. [1295], 1077
30th St. NW, Ste. 100, Washington, DC 20007,
(202)333-8171
Emerging Markets Private Equity Assn. [1295], 1077
30th St. NW, Ste. 100, Washington, DC 20007,
(202)333-8171
Emerging Markets Traders Assn. [★3197]
Emerging Markets Traders Assn. [★3197]
Emerging Practitioners in Philanthropy [12665], 10 E
34th St., 10th Fl., New York, NY 10016, (212)584-
8249
Emerson Coll. Alumni Assn. [18870], 120 Boylston
St., Boston, MA 02116-4624, (617)824-8500
Emigration
Amer. Fund for Czech and Slovak Relief [12771]
Emil Gilels Soc. - Defunct.
EMILY's List [18332], 1120 Connecticut Ave. NW,
Ste. 1100, Washington, DC 20036-3949, (202)326-
1400
EMILY'S LIST [IO], Leeds, United Kingdom
Emirates Amateur Radio Soc. [IO], Sharjah, United
Arab Emirates
Emirates Assn. of Respiratory Care Practitioners
[IO], Abu Dhabi, United Arab Emirates
Emirates Assn. of UK Alumni [IO], Abu Dhabi, United
Arab Emirates
Emirates Aviation Assn. [IO], Abu Dhabi, United Arab
Emirates
Emirates Body Building and Weightlifting Fed. [IO],
Dubai, United Arab Emirates
Emirates Cardiac Soc. [IO], Abu Dhabi, United Arab
Emirates
Emirates Culinary Guild [IO], Dubai, United Arab
Emirates

Emirates Diving Assn. [IO], Dubai, United Arab Emir-
ates
Emirates Equestrian Fed. [IO], Abu Dhabi, United
Arab Emirates
Emirates Golf Fed. [IO], Dubai, United Arab Emir-
ates
Emirates Green Building Coun. [IO], Dubai, United
Arab Emirates
Emirates Insurance Assn. [IO], Abu Dhabi, United
Arab Emirates
Emirates Marine Environmental Gp. [IO], Dubai,
United Arab Emirates
Emirates Nursing Assn. [IO], Abu Dhabi, United Arab
Emirates
Emirates Philatelic Assn. [IO], Dubai, United Arab
Emirates
Emirates Physiotherapy Soc. [IO], Dubai, United
Arab Emirates
Emirates Quality Assn. [IO], Abu Dhabi, United Arab
Emirates
Emirates Racing Assn. [IO], Dubai, United Arab
Emirates
Emissary Found. - Defunct.
Emofra Africa [15157], 1815-B Chain Bridge Rd.,
Ste. 34, McLean, VA 22102
Emotions Anonymous Intl. Ser. Center [12486], PO
Box 4245, St. Paul, MN 55104-0245, (651)647-
9712
Emotions Anonymous Intl. Ser. Center [12486], PO
Box 4245, St. Paul, MN 55104-0245, (651)647-
9712
Emphysema Found; Natl. [14033]
Empire Karakul Registry [★4893]
Employed Coun. Officers Assn. [★19661]
Employee Assistance Professionals Assn. [13219],
4350 N Fairfax Dr., Ste. 410, Arlington, VA 22203,
(703)387-1000
Employee Assistance Programs
Inter-National Assn. of Bus., Indus. and
Rehabilitation [11794]
Employee Assistance Soc. of North Am. [11673],
2001 Jefferson Davis Hwy., Ste. 1004, Arlington,
VA 22202-3617, (703)416-0060
Employee Benefit Res. Inst. [1123], 1100 13th St.
NW, Ste. 878, Washington, DC 20005-4058,
(202)659-0670
Employee Benefits
Amer. Soc. of Pension Professionals and Actuar-
ies [1121]
Coun. on Employee Benefits [1122]
Employee Benefit Res. Inst. [1123]
The Employers Assn. [1124]
Employers Coun. on Flexible Compensation
[1125]
ERISA Indus. Comm. [1126]
Fed. of Employers and Workers of Am. [1147]
Global Equity Org. [1127]
Global Equity Org. [1127]
Intl. Found. of Employee Benefit Plans [1128]
Intl. Found. of Employee Benefit Plans [1128]
Intl. Soc. of Certified Employee Benefit Specialists
[1129]
Intl. Soc. of Certified Employee Benefit Specialists
[1129]
Natl. Assn. of Benefits and Work Incentive
Specialists [1130]
Natl. Coordinating Comm. for Multi-employer
Plans [1131]
Natl. Inst. of Pension Administrators [1132]
Natl. Org. of Injured Workers [23319]
Professionals in Workers' Compensation [3704]
Profit Sharing/401k Educ. Found. [1161]
Soc. of Professional Benefit Administrators [1133]
WEB - Worldwide Employee Benefits Network
[1134]
WEB - Worldwide Employee Benefits Network
[1134]
Workplace Benefits Assn. [1135]
Employee Involvement Association [★1149]
Employee Involvement Assn. [1149], 162 S Vista,
Auburn Hills, MI 48326-1447, (248)961-2674
Employee Ownership
ESOP Assn. [1136]
ICA Gp. [1137]
Natl. Center for Employee Ownership [1138]

Reference to "IO" in place of a book number signifies that the association may be found in the 50th edition of International Organizations.

Employee Relocation Real Estate Advisory Coun. [★1163]
Employee Rights
  LEAGUE [12096]
  Natl. Org. of Injured Workers [23319]
  US Human Rights Network [17866]
  Verite [11924]
  Verite [11924]
  Workplace Fairness [11925]
Employee Services Mgt. Assn. [★12765]
Employee Services Mgt. Found. [12765], PO Box 10517, Rockville, MD 20849, (630)559-0020
Employer Assn. Gp. - Address unknown since 2010.
Employers of Am. [3287], 310 Meadow Ln., Mason City, IA 50401, (641)424-3187
The Employers Assn. [1124], 3020 W Arrowood Rd., Charlotte, NC 28273, (704)522-8011
Employers' Assn. of the Swedish Plate Works [IO], Stockholm, Sweden
Employers' Consultative Assn. of Malawi [IO], Blantyre, Malawi
Employers' Consultative Assn. of Trinidad and Tobago [IO], Port of Spain, Trinidad and Tobago
Employers Coun. on Flexible Compensation [1125], 927 15th St. NW, Ste. 1000, Washington, DC 20005, (202)659-4300
Employers' Fed. of Ceylon [IO], Colombo, Sri Lanka
Employers' Fed. of Hong Kong [IO], Hong Kong, People's Republic of China
Employers Forum on Age [IO], London, United Kingdom
Employers Gp. [2280], 1150 S Olive St., Ste. 2300, Los Angeles, CA 90015, (800)748-8484
Employers' Managed Hea. Care Assn. [★14852]
Employers' and Mfrs'. Assn. [IO], Wellington, New Zealand
Employers' and Mfrs'. Assn. Northern [IO], Auckland, New Zealand
Employing Bookbinders of Amer. [★1603]
Employment
  1000 Jobs [12713]
  AFL-CIO | Working for Am. Inst. [11926]
  Amer. Assn. for Affirmative Action [11927]
  Amer. Assn. of Working People [11928]
  Amer. Cong. of Community Supports and Employment Services [17367]
  Amer. Contract Compliance Assn. [11929]
  Amer. Coun. on Intl. Personnel [1139]
  Amer. Coun. on Intl. Personnel [1139]
  Amer. Inst. for Full Employment [11930]
  Amer. Inst. for Full Employment [11930]
  Amer. Payroll Assn. [1140]
  Amer. Soc. of Employers [1141]
  Amer. Staffing Assn. [1142]
  America's Edge [17599]
  Asian Resources [11931]
  Assn. of Career Firms Intl. [1143]
  Assn. of Career Firms North America [1143]
  Assn. of Executive Search Consultants [1144]
  Assn. of Executive Search Consultants [1144]
  Assn. of Manpower Franchise Owners [1145]
  Bahamas Employers' Confed. [19586]
  Barbados Employers' Confed. [801]
  Bermuda Employers' Coun. [21377]
  Career Planning and Adult Development Network [11932]
  Career Transition For Dancers [11933]
  Center for Economic Options [11934]
  Compete Am. [8119]
  Consortium of Doctors [11935]
  Disability Mgt. Employer Coalition [1146]
  Disabled Businesspersons Assn. [11936]
  Dominica Employers' Fed. [13301]
  Employee Involvement Assn. [1149]
  Employment Support Center [11937]
  Equal Employment Advisory Coun. [11938]
  Every Mother is a Working Mother Network [18791]
  Experience Works [11939]
  Experience Works [11939]
  Fed. of Employers and Workers of Am. [1147]
  Fed. of European Employers [16673]
  Fed. of Kenya Employers [16591]
  Green Collar Assn. [1148]
  Homeworkers Organized for More Employment [11940]

IdeasAmerica [1149]
Immigration Voice [5529]
Indus. Found. of Am. [1150]
Insight Center for Community Economic Development [17578]
Inter-National Assn. of Bus., Indus. and Rehabilitation [11794]
Intl. Assn. of Corporate and Professional Recruitment [1151]
Intl. Assn. of Corporate and Professional Recruitment [1151]
Intl. Assn. of Employment Web Sites [1152]
Intl. Assn. of Employment Web Sites [1152]
Intl. Assn. of Indus. Accident Boards and Commissions [5399]
Intl. Assn. of Indus. Accident Boards and Commissions [5399]
Intl. Assn. of Workforce Professionals [5400]
Intl. Assn. of Workforce Professionals [5400]
Intl. Personnel Mgt. Assn. [1153]
Intl. Public Mgt. Assn. for Human Resources [1153]
Intl. Union of Painters and Allied Trades | Joint Apprenticeship and Training Fund [11941]
Intl. Union of Painters and Allied Trades | Joint Apprenticeship and Training Fund [11941]
A Job is a Right Campaign [11942]
Jobs for America's Graduates [11943]
Jobs for the Future [11944]
LEAGUE [12096]
Mauritius Employers' Fed. [7159]
Mothers And More [11945]
Natl. Assn. of Executive Recruiters [1154]
Natl. Assn. of Part-Time and Temporary Employees [1155]
Natl. Assn. of Personnel Services [1156]
Natl. Assn. of Professional Employer Organizations [1157]
Natl. Assn. of State Workforce Agencies [5401]
Natl. Assn. of Workforce Boards [11946]
Natl. Assn. of Workforce Development Professionals [11947]
Natl. Bus. and Disability Coun. [11948]
Natl. Career Development Assn. [11949]
Natl. Coalition of Healthcare Recruiters [15298]
Natl. Employment Counseling Assn. [11950]
Natl. Employment Law Proj. [11951]
Natl. Found. for Unemployment Compensation and Workers Compensation [5402]
Natl. Skills Coalition [11952]
Natl. Soc. for Hispanic Professionals [695]
New Ways to Work [11953]
North Amer. Alliance for Fair Employment [1158]
NTID's Center on Employment [11954]
Opportunities Industrialization Centers of Am. [11955]
POWER: People Organized to Win Employment Rights [11956]
Professional Administrative Co-Employers [1159]
Professional Assn. of Resume Writers and Career Coaches [11957]
Professionals in Workers' Compensation [3704]
Profit Sharing/401k Coun. of Am. [1160]
Profit Sharing/401k Educ. Found. [1161]
Recognition Professionals Intl. [17613]
Senior Community Ser. Employment Prog. [11958]
SER - Jobs for Progress Natl. [11959]
Tradeswomen [11960]
U.S. Equal Employment Opportunity Commn. [5403]
Veterans2Work [20818]
W. E. Upjohn Inst. for Employment Res. [11961]
Way to Work [11962]
Wider Opportunities for Women [11963]
Wildcat Ser. Corp. [11964]
Women Employed [11965]
Work for Progress [12583]
WorldatWork [1162]
WorldatWork [1162]
Worldwide ERC [1163]
Employment Agencies Protective Assn. [★1156]
Employment Law Alliance [5244], 727 Sansome St., San Francisco, CA 94111, (415)835-9011
Employment Support Center [11937], 1556 Wisconsin Ave. NW, Washington, DC 20007, (202)628-2919

Empower the Children [11268], PO Box 1412, Jackson, NJ 08527
Empower Orphans [11269], 1415 Hidden Pond Dr., Yardley, PA 19067, (610)909-1778
Empower Peace [18241], 240 Commercial St., 2nd Fl., Boston, MA 02109, (617)912-3800
Empower Peace [18241], 240 Commercial St., 2nd Fl., Boston, MA 02109, (617)912-3800
Empower Tanzania, Inc. [12954], 5414 Cervantes Dr., Ames, IA 50014
Empower Tanzania, Inc. [12954], 5414 Cervantes Dr., Ames, IA 50014
Empowering Leadership Alliance [8236], Richard A. Tapia, Rice Univ., Center for Excellence and Equity in Educ., 6100 Main St., MS 134, Houston, TX 77005, (713)348-6122
Empowering the Poor [12326], PO Box 42031, Fredericksburg, VA 22404, (540)424-2705
Empowering the Poor [12326], PO Box 42031, Fredericksburg, VA 22404, (540)424-2705
Empowerment Proj. [17341], 8218 Farrington Mill Rd., Chapel Hill, NC 27517, (919)928-0382
Empowerment Soc. Intl. [11578], 4460 S Cobblestone St., Gilbert, AZ 85297
Empowerment Soc. of the U.S.A. - Address unknown since 2011.
Empowerment Works [11579], 1793 Northwood Ct., Oakland, CA 94611, (310)392-6909
Emprender Found. [IO], Santiago, Chile
Empresa Brasileira de Pesquisa Agropecuaria [★IO]
Empress Chinchilla Breeders Cooperative [3789], 43188 Cottonwood Creek Rd., Crawford, CO 81415, (970)921-7231
EMS Educators; Natl. Assn. of [8611]
EMS Educators; Natl. Assn. of [8611]
EMS Professions; Comm. on Accreditation for Educational Programs for the [8578]
EMTA [3197], 360 Madison Ave., 17th Fl., New York, NY 10017, (646)289-5410
EMTA [3197], 360 Madison Ave., 17th Fl., New York, NY 10017, (646)289-5410
Emulsion Polymers Inst. [6407], Lehigh Univ., Iacocca Hall, Rm. D-325, 111 Res. Dr., Bethlehem, PA 18015, (610)758-3602
Emulsion Polymers Liaison Program [★6407]
Emunah of Am. [12392], 7 Penn Plz., New York, NY 10001, (212)564-9045
Emunah Women of Am. [19860], 7 Penn Plz., New York, NY 10001, (212)564-9045
Emunah Women of Am. [19860], 7 Penn Plz., New York, NY 10001, (212)564-9045
Emunah Women of Canada [IO], Montreal, QC, Canada
En Foco [10438], 1738 Hone Ave., Bronx, NY 10461-1403, (718)931-9311
Enable Am. [11785], PO Box 3031, Tampa, FL 33601, (813)222-3212
Enable Intl. [13156], 145 Old Dundee Rd., Barrington, IL 60010
Enable - Ireland [IO], Dublin, Ireland
ENABLE Scotland [IO], Glasgow, United Kingdom
Enabled Artists United - Defunct.
Enameling
  British Soc. of Enamellers [16414]
Enamelist Soc. [21438], PO Box 920220, Norcross, GA 30010
Encephalitis Global [14384], 18 N Broadway, No. 404, Tarrytown, NY 10591
Encephalitis Global [14384], 18 N Broadway, No. 404, Tarrytown, NY 10591
ENCOMPASS, HP-Interex EMEA and Intl. Tandem Users' Gp. [★6510]
EnConsult [IO], Bishkek, Kirgizstan
Encuentro con la Biblica Argentina [★IO]
End Child Prostitution, Abuse and Trafficking in Cambodia [IO], Phnom Penh, Cambodia
End Child Prostitution, Child Pornography and the Trafficking of Children for Sexual Purposes - New Zealand [IO], Auckland, New Zealand
End Child Prostitution, Child Pornography and the Trafficking of Children for Sexual Purposes - UK [IO], London, United Kingdom
End Childhood Hunger [12271], 1080 W Tropical Way, Plantation, FL 33317, (954)792-3852
End Hunger Network [17871], 3819 Hunt Manor Dr., Fairfax, VA 22033, (703)860-1273

A star before a book entry number signifies that the name is not listed separately, but is mentioned within the entry.

ENDA Caribe [IO], Santo Domingo, Dominican Republic
Endangered Language Fund [9938], 300 George St., Ste. 900, New Haven, CT 06511, (203)865-6163
Endangered Species Coalition [5051], PO Box 65195, Washington, DC 20035, (202)320-6467
Endangered Species Intl. [4047], 77 Brady St., San Francisco, CA 94103
Endangered Wildlife Trust [IO], Johannesburg, Republic of South Africa
Endangered Wolf Center [5052], PO Box 760, Eureka, MO 63025, (636)938-5900
Enders Family Assn. [20512], 56 Marie Dr., Halifax, PA 17032, (717)362-8959
Enders Family Assn. [20512], 56 Marie Dr., Halifax, PA 17032, (717)362-8959
Ending Relationship Abuse Soc. of British Columbia [IO], Chilliwack, BC, Canada
Endocrine Fellows Found. [14488], 1310 19th St. NW, Washington, DC 20036, (860)586-7574
Endocrine Nurses Soc. [14489], PO Box 211068, Milwaukee, WI 53221, (414)421-3679
Endocrine Soc. [14490], 8401 Connecticut Ave., Ste. 900, Chevy Chase, MD 20815-5817, (301)941-0200
Endocrine Soc. of Australia [IO], Sydney, Australia
Endocrinology
    Amer. Assn. of Clinical Endocrinologists [14485]
    Assn. of Prog. Directors in Endocrinology, Diabetes and Metabolism [14486]
    Cushing's Support and Res. Found. [14487]
    Endocrine Fellows Found. [14488]
    Endocrine Nurses Soc. [14489]
    Endocrine Soc. [14490]
    European Soc. of Endocrinology [20555]
    Hypoparathyroidism Assn. [14491]
    Hypoparathyroidism Assn. [14491]
    Intl. Hyperhidrosis Soc. [14492]
    Intl. Hyperhidrosis Soc. [14492]
    Natl. Adrenal Diseases Found. [14493]
    Netherlands Soc. for Endocrinology [6791]
    North Amer. NeuroEndocrine Tumor Soc. [14494]
    Women in Endocrinology [14495]
Endocrinology and Infertility; Soc. for Reproductive [16599]
Endocrinology; Intl. Soc. of Psychoneuro [15346]
Endocrinology Nursing Soc; Pediatric [16152]
Endodontic Soc; Amer. [14265]
Endodontists; Amer. Assn. of [14249]
EndOil [6716], 4000 Long Beach Blvd., Ste. 249, Long Beach, CA 90807, (562)424-8200
Endometriosis Assn. [15878], 8585 N 76th Pl., Milwaukee, WI 53223, (414)355-2200
Endometriosis Assn. [15878], 8585 N 76th Pl., Milwaukee, WI 53223, (414)355-2200
Endometriosis New Zealand [IO]; Christchurch, New Zealand
Endometriosis UK [IO], London, United Kingdom
Endorsers Conf. for Veterans Affairs Chaplaincy - Defunct.
Endoscopic Sect. of the Gastroenterological Assn. of Thailand [IO], Bangkok, Thailand
Energetic Healing Assn. [IO], Crows Nest, Australia
Energia-alan Keskusliitto [★IO]
Energia Klub [★IO]
Energiagazdalkodasi Tudomanyos Egyesulet [★IO]
Energy
    Action for Clean Energy [4224]
    Advanced Biofuels Assn. [1533]
    Advanced Biofuels USA [6108]
    Algal Biomass Org. [6680]
    Alliance for Energy and Economic Growth [6681]
    Alliance for Green Heat [6682]
    Alliance for Renewable Energy [6683]
    Alliance to Save Energy [6684]
    Alternative Energy Resources Org. [6685]
    Amer. Assn. of Blacks in Energy [6686]
    Amer. Biogas Coun. [6109]
    Amer. Coun. for an Energy-Efficient Economy [6687]
    Amer. Coun. on Global Nuclear Competitiveness [7174]
    Amer. Coun. on Renewable Energy [6688]
    Amer. Energy Alliance [17614]

    Amer. Hydrogen Assn. [6689]
    Amer. Soc. of Gas Engineers [6690]
    Amer. Solar Action Plan [7437]
    America's Natural Gas Alliance [2641]
    Apollo Alliance [6691]
    Assn. of Certified Green Tech. Auditors [6692]
    Assn. of Certified Green Tech. Auditors [6692]
    Assn. of Climate Change Officers [4237]
    Assn. of Energy Engineers [6693]
    Assn. of Energy Engineers [6693]
    Assn. of Energy and Environmental Real Estate Professionals [8150]
    Assn. of Energy Services Professionals [6694]
    Assn. of Energy Services Professionals [6694]
    Assn. of State Energy Res. and Tech. Transfer Institutions [6695]
    Biofuel Recycling [4867]
    Biomass Energy Res. Assn. [6696]
    Biomass Power Assn. [7292]
    Biomass Thermal Energy Coun. [6697]
    blueEnergy [11966]
    Bus. Coun. for Sustainable Energy [1164]
    Center for Energy Efficiency and Renewable Technologies [4225]
    Center for Energy, Env. and Economics [6698]
    Center for Renewable Energy and Sustainable Tech. I Renewable Energy Policy Project [6699]
    China-U.S. Energy Efficiency Alliance [6700]
    Citizens for Affordable Energy [6701]
    Citizens' Alliance for Responsible Energy [6702]
    Citizens for Energy Freedom [6703]
    Citizens Energy Plan [6704]
    Clean Energy Gp. [6705]
    Clean Energy States Alliance [6706]
    Clean and Safe Energy Coalition [6707]
    ClimateTalk Alliance [6111]
    Consortium for Energy Efficiency [1165]
    Consumer Energy Alliance [6708]
    Consumer Energy Coun. of Am. Res. Found. [17615]
    Coun. for Responsible Energy [6709]
    Demand Response and Smart Grid Coalition [6649]
    Directed Energy Professional Soc. [6710]
    Distributed Wind Energy Assn. [3666]
    Domestic Energy Producers Alliance [1166]
    EarthSpark Intl. [6711]
    Eco Energy Finance [6712]
    Efficiency First [4046]
    Elec. Power Res. Inst. [6713]
    Elec. Power Supply Assn. [6714]
    Elec. Utility Indus. Sustainable Supply Chain Alliance [3594]
    Electrification Coalition [3510]
    Elephant Energy [6715]
    Elephant Energy [6715]
    EndOil [6716]
    Energy Action Coalition [6717]
    Energy Bar Assn. [5404]
    Energy Communities Alliance [4226]
    Energy Conservation Org. [8120]
    Energy Efficiency Bus. Coalition [1167]
    Energy Extraction Technologies [6718]
    Energy Farm [6719]
    Energy Future Coalition [6720]
    Energy Info. Standards Alliance [1168]
    Energy Services Coalition [6721]
    Energy Storage Coun. [6722]
    Energy Training Coun. [6723]
    Energy Vision [6724]
    European Fed. of Energy Traders [2426]
    Fifty Lanterns Intl. [7439]
    Focus Fusion Soc. [6725]
    Focus the Nation [17616]
    Fusion Power Associates [6726]
    Fusion Power Associates [6726]
    FutureGen Alliance [6112]
    Global Biofuels Alliance [1535]
    Global Possibilities [4930]
    Governors' Wind Energy Coalition [6070]
    Green for All [17189]
    GreenMotion [4227]
    GridWise Alliance [6727]
    GridWise Architecture Coun. [7293]
    Growth Energy [6728]

    HeatGreen Coun. [6113]
    High Performance Building Coun. [6376]
    Hydrogen 2000 [6729]
    Impact Carbon [4228]
    Impact Carbon [4228]
    Indus. Energy Consumers of Am. [1169]
    Innovation: Africa [6114]
    Inst. for Energy and Environmental Res. [6730]
    Intergovernmental Renewable Energy Org. [6731]
    Intl. Assn. for the Advancement of Steam Power [7480]
    Intl. Assn. of Directional Drilling [7238]
    Intl. Assn. for Energy Economics [6732]
    Intl. Assn. for Energy Economics [6732]
    Intl. Assn. for Hydrogen Energy [6733]
    Intl. Assn. for Hydrogen Energy [6733]
    Intl. Biochar Initiative [6115]
    Intl. DME Assn. [3770]
    Intl. Green Energy Coun. [6116]
    Intl. Inst. for Energy Conservation [6734]
    Intl. Inst. for Energy Conservation [6734]
    Intl. Photovoltaic Equip. Assn. [1170]
    Intl. Ultraviolet Assn. [6735]
    Interstate Oil and Gas Compact Commn. [5405]
    Interstate Renewable Energy Coun. [6736]
    Large Public Power Coun. [5406]
    Leadership for Energy Automated Processing [1171]
    Natl. Alliance for Advanced Tech. Batteries [441]
    Natl. Alliance of Clean Energy Bus. Incubators [1172]
    Natl. Assn. of Energy Ser. Companies [6737]
    Natl. Assn. of State Energy Officials [5407]
    Natl. Center for Appropriate Tech. [17194]
    Natl. Coun. of Minorities in Energy [1173]
    Natl. Energy Educ. Development Proj. [17617]
    Natl. Energy Mgt. Inst. [6738]
    Natl. Energy Marketers Assn. [1174]
    Natl. Energy Marketers Assn. [1174]
    Natl. Energy Services Assn. [6739]
    Natl. Hydropower Assn. [6740]
    Natl. Petroleum Coun. [5408]
    Natl. Petroleum Mgt. Assn. [2663]
    Natl. Renewables Cooperative Org. [6741]
    Natl. Wind Watch [18788]
    New Energy Indus. Assn. for Asia and the Pacific [6742]
    New Fuels Alliance [6885]
    New Generation Energy [6743]
    North Amer. Bd. of Certified Energy Practitioners [6744]
    Northeast Sustainable Energy Assn. [6745]
    Northwest Energy Efficiency Alliance [4229]
    Nuclear Energy Inst. [6746]
    Ocean Renewable Energy Coalition [6747]
    Oil Change Intl. [4230]
    Partnership for Advancing the Transition to Hydrogen [6748]
    Power to the People [7440]
    Power Up Gambia [7441]
    Pro Energy Alliance [1175]
    Quantal Energy [8121]
    Redwood Alliance [17618]
    Renewable Energy Markets Assn. [1176]
    Renewable Energy for Medicine and Educ. [6749]
    Renewable Energy Resources [6750]
    Renewable Fuels Assn. [6751]
    Res. Partnership to Secure Energy for Am. [6752]
    Retail Energy Supply Assn. [1177]
    Rural Electricity Rsrc. Coun. [6753]
    Rural Renewable Energy Alliance [6754]
    Securing America's Future Energy [6755]
    Set Am. Free [17619]
    Show Me Solar [7443]
    SmartPower [4231]
    Soc. for Energy Educ. [6756]
    Solar Household Energy [4931]
    Solar Light for Africa [11640]
    Solar for Peace [7447]
    Southface Energy Inst. [6757]
    STG Intl. [7449]
    Strategic Energy, Environmental and Trans. Alternatives [8122]
    SunPower Afrique [13227]
    Sunstove Org. [11643]

Reference to "IO" in place of a book number signifies that the association may be found in the 50th edition of International Organizations.

Sweet Sorghum Ethanol Assn. [6120]
TopTen USA [1178]
U.S. Assn. for Energy Economics [6758]
U.S. Energy Assn. [6759]
U.S. Energy Assn. [6759]
U.S. Offshore Wind Collaborative [7623]
U.S. Water and Power [6121]
U.S. Women in Nuclear [7173]
US-China Green Energy Coun. [6760]
Utility Tech. Assn. [7591]
Veggie Van Org. [4872]
Vote Solar Initiative [7451]
Waste-to-Energy Res. and Tech. Coun. [7593]
Western Interstate Energy Bd. [18189]
The Wind Alliance [7624]
Wind Energy Mfrs. Assn. [3667]
Wind Energy Works! [7625]
Women of Wind Energy [7627]
Women's Coun. on Energy and the Env. [6761]
World Alliance for Decentralized Energy [6762]
World Energy Cities Partnership [1179]
Young Professionals in Energy [6763]
Energy Action [IO], Dublin, Ireland
Energy Action Coalition [6717], 1718 21st St. NW,
  Washington, DC 20009-1102, (202)328-1733
Energy Assn. [IO], Ljubljana, Slovenia
Energy Bar Assn. [5404], 1990 M St. NW, Ste. 350,
  Washington, DC 20036, (202)223-5625
Energy Club [IO], Budapest, Hungary
Energy Communities Alliance [4226], 1101 Con-
  necticut Ave. NW, Ste. 1000, Washington, DC
  20036-4374, (202)828-2317
Energy Conservation Org. [8120], 965 Lanini Dr.,
  Hollister, CA 95023-6451, (408)804-2906
Energy Coun. of Canada [IO], Ottawa, ON, Canada
Energy Economics Educational Foundation [★6732]
Energy Economics Educational Foundation [★6732]
Energy Efficiency Bus. Coalition [1167], 5500 E Yale
  St., Ste. 360, Denver, CO 80222, (720)445-3728
Energy Efficient Building Assn. [★557]
Energy Efficient Lighting Assn. - Defunct.
Energy and Environmental Building Assn. [557],
  6520 Edenvale Blvd., Ste. 112, Eden Prairie, MN
  55346, (952)881-1098
Energy Extraction Technologies [6718], 7891 Wig-
  gins Rd., Howell, MI 48843, (517)548-3115
Energy Farm [6719], PO Box 1834, Jackson, MS
  39215
Energy Fed. of New Zealand [IO], Wellington, New
  Zealand
Energy For Opportunity [IO], Freetown, Sierra Leone
Energy Forum of Finland [IO], Helsinki, Finland
Energy Frontiers Intl. [4487], 1425 K St. NW, Ste.
  350, Washington, DC 20005, (202)587-5780
Energy Frontiers Intl. [4487], 1425 K St. NW, Ste.
  350, Washington, DC 20005, (202)587-5780
Energy Future Coalition [6720], 1615 M St. NW, 7th
  Fl., Washington, DC 20036-3209, (202)463-1947
Energy Indus. Coun. [IO], London, United Kingdom
Energy Info. Standards Alliance [1168], 65
  Washington St., Ste. 170, Santa Clara, CA 95050,
  (650)938-6945
Energy Inst. [IO], London, United Kingdom
Energy Kinesiology Assn. [13674], Georgianna Lig-
  uori, VP for Membership, 11322 Golf Round Dr.,
  New Port Richley, FL 34654, (866)365-4336
Energy Kinesiology Awareness Coun. [13675],
  19210 Sonoma Hwy., Sonoma, CA 95476
Energy Mgt. Assn. of New Zealand [IO], Wellington,
  New Zealand
Energy Mgt. and Controls Soc. [★6693]
Energy Mgt. and Controls Soc. [★6693]
Energy in Man's Env. [★8147]
Energy and Mineral Law Found. [5860], 340 S
  Broadway, Ste. 101, Lexington, KY 40508,
  (859)231-0271
Energy Networks Assn. [IO], Barton, Australia
Energy Policy Res. Found., Inc. [7237], 1031 31st
  St. NW, Washington, DC 20007-4401, (202)944-
  3339
Energy Probe Res. Found. [IO], Toronto, ON,
  Canada
Energy Recovery Coun. [4981], 1730 Rhode Island
  Ave. NW, Ste. 700, Washington, DC 20036,
  (202)467-6240

Energy Res. Gp. [IO], Dublin, Ireland
Energy Retailers Assn. of Australia [IO], Sydney,
  Australia
Energy Security Coun. [1889], 2611 FM 1960 Rd.
  W, Ste. F-121, Houston, TX 77068, (281)587-2700
Energy Services Coalition [6721], Bill Skosky, VP,
  9000 Wessex Pl., Louisville, KY 40222, (502)420-
  1966
Energy Storage Coun. [6722], 3963 Flora Pl., 2nd
  Fl., St. Louis, MO 63110, (314)495-4545
Energy Supply Assn. of Australia [IO], Melbourne,
  Australia
Energy Systems Trade Assn. [IO], Benfleet, United
  Kingdom
Energy Telecommunications and Elecl. Assn. [1074],
  5005 Royal Ln., Ste. 116, Irving, TX 75063,
  (888)503-8700
Energy Traffic Assn. [2649], 935 Eldridge Rd., No.
  604, Sugar Land, TX 77478-2809, (832)474-3564
Energy Training Coun. [6723], PO Box 850359,
  Yukon, OK 73085, (405)262-2629
Energy Vision [6724], 138 E 13th St., New York, NY
  10003, (212)228-0225
Enerji Ekonomisi Dernegi [★IO]
Enfants and Developpement [IO], Paris, France
Enfants du Monde [IO], Marseille, France
Enfants Solidaires d'Afrique et du Monde [★IO]
Enforcement Services Assn. [IO], Bristol, United
  Kingdom
ENG Study Group [★16681]
Engelbert's Goils [23838], 22249 Berry Dr.,
  Cleveland, OH 44116-2013
Engel's Angels in Humperdinck Heaven Fan Club
  [23839], 3024 4th Ave., Baltimore, MD 21234-
  3208, (410)665-0744
Engel's Angels in Humperdinck Heaven Fan Club
  [23839], 3024 4th Ave., Baltimore, MD 21234-
  3208, (410)665-0744
Engender [IO], Edinburgh, United Kingdom
EngenderHealth [12031], 440 9th Ave., New York,
  NY 10001, (212)561-8000
EngenderHealth [12031], 440 9th Ave., New York,
  NY 10001, (212)561-8000
Engine Generator Set Mfrs. Assn. [★1071]
Engine Mfrs. Assn. [1181], 333 W Wacker Dr., Ste.
  810, Chicago, IL 60606, (312)929-1970
Engineer Assn; Army [5217]
Engineered Wood Res. Found. [★1506]
Engineered Wood Tech. Assn. [1506], APA - The
  Engineered Wood Assn., 7011 S 19th St., Tacoma,
  WA 98466, (253)565-6600

Engineering
  ABET [6764]
  Airlines Electronic Engg. Comm. [6765]
  Alpha Epsilon [23516]
  Alpha Pi Mu [23517]EngineeringAME Assn.
    Atlantic
  Am. Continental 2000 [11847]
  Amer. Acad. of Environmental Engineers [6766]
  Amer. Assn. of Engg. Societies [6767]
  Amer. Coun. of Engg. Companies [6768]
  Amer. Coun. of Engineering Companies I Res.
    and Mgt. Found. [6769]
  Amer. Engg. Alliance [6770]
  Amer. Engg. Assn. [6771]
  Amer. Indian Coun. of Architects and Engineers
    [6182]
  Amer. Indian Sci. and Engg. Soc. [6772]
  Amer. Inst. of Engineers [6773]
  Amer. Soc. of Agricultural and Biological
    Engineers [6774]
  Amer. Soc. of Agricultural and Biological
    Engineers [6774]
  Amer. Soc. of Certified Engg. Technicians [6775]
  Amer. Soc. of Civil Engineers [6776]
  Amer. Soc. for Engg. Educ. [8123]
  Amer. Soc. for Engg. Educ. [8123]
  Amer. Soc. for Engg. Mgt. [6777]
  Amer. Soc. of Heating, Refrigerating and Air-
    Conditioning Engineers [6778]
  Amer. Soc. of Heating, Refrigerating and Air-
    Conditioning Engineers [6778]
  Amer. Soc. of Plumbing Engineers [6779]
  Amer. Soc. for Precision Engg. [6780]
  Amer. Underground Constr. Assn. [7484]

Applied Tech. Coun. [6781]
ASME Intl. Gas Turbine Inst. [6782]
ASME Intl. Gas Turbine Inst. [6782]
Assn. of Australasian Diesel Specialists [3919]
Assn. of Chinese Scientists and Engineers U.S.A.
  [6783]
Assn. of Chinese Scientists and Engineers U.S.A.
  [6783]
Assn. of Conservation Engineers [4001]
Assn. of Cuban Engineers [6784]
Assn. for Facilities Engg. [6785]EngineeringAssn.
  of Intl. Motion Engineers
Assn. of Liberian Engineers USA [6786]
Assn. of Liberian Engineers USA [6786]
Assn. of Nigerian Petroleum Professionals Abroad
  [7235]
Assn. of Overseas Chinese Agricultural, Biological
  and Food Engineers [6787]
Assn. of Professional Engineers, Scientists and
  Managers Australia [1676]
Assn. of Professional Model Makers [6788]
Astronaut Scholars Honor Soc. [23629]
Bd. of Certified Prdt. Safety Mgt. [3139]
Bridge Engg. Assn. [6789]
Building Commissioning Assn. [538]
Building Enclosure Coun. Natl. [6374]
Building Enclosure Tech. and Env. Coun. [539]
Chinese Amer. Assn. of Engg. [6790]
Chinese Amer. Assn. of Engg. [6790]
Chinese-American Professors in Environmental
  Engg. and Sci. [6425]
Completion Engg. Assn. [6961]
Computational Intelligence Soc. [6791]
Coun. of Engg. and Sci. Soc. Executives
  [6792]EngineeringCroatian Soc. of Chem.
  Engineers
Drilling, Observation and Sampling of the Earth's
  Continental Crust [6602]
Elecl. and Cmpt. Engg. Dept. Heads Assn. [6793]
Electronics TakeBack Coalition [6652]
Engg. Soc. of Detroit [6794]
Engg. Soc. of Detroit [6794]
Engg. Workforce Commn. [6795]
Engineers' Company [11376]
Engineers Without Borders U.S.A. [11967]
Engineers Without Borders U.S.A. [11967]
Eta Kappa Nu [23518]
European Structural Integrity Soc. [15889]
Fusion Architecture [6197]
Geosynthetics Materials Assn. [6426]
Green Mech. Coun. [6796]
High Performance Building Coun. [6376]
IEEE I Aerospace and Electronics Systems Soc.
  [6654]
IEEE I Components, Packaging, and Mfg. Tech.
  Soc. [6657]
IEEE I Control Systems Soc. [6797]
IEEE I Vehicular Tech. Soc. [6667]
Inst. of Domestic Heating and Environmental
  Engineers [14362]
Inst. of Elecl. and Electronics Engineers USA
  [6798]
Inst. of Indus. Engineers [6799]
Inst. of Municipal Engg. of Southern Africa [4301]
Institution of Diagnostic Engineers [13891]
Insulated Cable Engineers Assn. [6800]
Intl. Assn. for Bridge Maintenance and Safety
  [6369]
Intl. Assn. for Cmpt. and Info. Sci. [6456]
Intl. Assn. of Directional Drilling [7238]
Intl. Coun. on Systems Engg. [6801]
Intl. Coun. on Systems Engg. [6801]
Intl. Fed. of Engg. Educ. Societies [8124]
Intl. Fed. of Professional and Tech. Engineers
  [6802]
Intl. Network of Engineers and Scientists for
  Global Responsibility [1897]
Intl. Network on Participatory Irrigation Mgt.
  [7016]
Intl. Soc. of Explosives Engineers [6803]
Intl. Soc. of Explosives Engineers [6803]
Intl. Soc. for Nanoscale Sci., Computation and
  Engg. [7376]
Intl. Soc. of Offshore and Polar Engineers [6804]
Intl. Soc. of Offshore and Polar Engineers [6804]

A star before a book entry number signifies that the name is not listed separately, but is mentioned within the entry.

Intl. Soc. for Productivity Enhancement [6805]
Intl. Soc. for Productivity Enhancement [6805]
Intl. Soc. for Quality Electronic Design [6600]
Intl. Soc. for Structural Hea. Monitoring of Intelligent Infrastructure [6428]
Intl. Systems Security Engg. Assn. [6806]
Intl. Systems Security Engg. Assn. [6806]
Junior Engg. Tech. Soc. [8125]
Korean-American Scientists and Engineers Assn. [6807]
Latino Engineers, Architects and Developers Soc. [7029]
Malayalee Engineers Assn. in North America [6808]
NACE Intl.: The Corrosion Soc. [6809]
NACE Intl.: The Corrosion Soc. [6809]
Natl. Acad. of Engg. [6810]
Natl. Action Coun. for Minorities in Engg. [8126]
Natl. Assn. of County Engineers [6811]
Natl. Assn. of Peoplecultural Engg. Prog. Advocates [8127]
Natl. Consortium for Graduate Degrees for Minorities in Engg. and Sci. [8128]
Natl. Coun. of Examiners for Engg. and Surveying [6812]
Natl. Coun. of Structural Engineers Associations [6813]
Natl. Inst. of Ceramic Engineers [6383]
Natl. Inst. for Certification in Engg. Technologies [6814]
Natl. Soc. of Black Engineers [6815]
Natl. Soc. of Professional Engineers [6816]
NEHRP Coalition [7402]
North Am. Taiwanese Engineers' Assn. [6817]
North Am. Taiwanese Engineers' Assn. [6817]
North Amer. Carbon Capture and Storage Assn. [6818]
Omega Chi Epsilon [23519]
Parachute Indus. Assn. [2623]
Personal Submersibles Org. [7148]
Phi Alpha Epsilon [23520]
Phi Kappa Upsilon Fraternity [23521]
Physical Security Interoperability Alliance [6819]
Pi Tau Sigma [23522]
Pi Tau Sigma [23522]
Public Architecture [243]
Quantal Energy [8121]
Refrigerating Engineers and Technicians Assn. [6820]
Scientists and Engineers for Am. [5314]
Scientists, Engineers, and Technicians Leadership Assn. [6821]
Seeking Ecology Educ. and Design Solutions [4216]
Short Span Steel Bridge Alliance [6371]
Sigma Gamma Tau [23523]
Silicon Valley Chinese Engineers Assn. [6822]
Silicon Valley Chinese Engineers Assn. [6822]
Soc. of Amer. Military Engineers [6823]
Soc. of Cable Telecommunications Engineers [6824]
Soc. for Design and Process Sci. [6601]
Soc. of Engg. Sci. [6825]
Soc. of Hispanic Professional Engineers [6826]
Soc. of Mfg. Engineers Educ. Found. [8129]
Soc. of Mexican Amer. Engineers and Scientists [6827]
Soc. of Motion Picture and TV Engineers [6828]
Soc. of Piping Engineers and Designers [6829]
Soc. of Reliability Engineers [6830]
Soc. of Tribologists and Lubrication Engineers [6831]
Soc. of Tribologists and Lubrication Engineers [6831]
Soc. of Turkish Amer. Architects, Engineers and Scientists [6832]
Soc. of Turkish Amer. Architects, Engineers and Scientists [6832]
Soc. of Women Engineers [6833]
South African Reinforced Concrete Engineers' Assn. [3846]
Tau Alpha Pi [23524]
Tau Beta Pi Assn. [23525]
Theta Tau [23526]
Ukrainian Engineers' Soc. of Am. [6834]

United Engg. Found. [6835]
Visual Indicators Coun. [6836]
Water Design-Build Coun. [634]
Welders Without Borders [7619]
World Sci. and Engg. Acad. and Soc. [6837]
World Sci. and Engg. Acad. and Soc. [6837]
Engg. Constr. Indus. Assn. [IO], London, United Kingdom
Engg. Consulting Firms Assn., Japan [IO], Tokyo, Japan
Engg. Contractors Assn. [911], 8310 Florence Ave., Downey, CA 90240, (562)861-0929
Engg. Coun. UK [IO], London, United Kingdom
Engg. Employers' Fed. [IO], London, United Kingdom
Engg. Equip. and Materials Users Assn. [IO], London, United Kingdom
Engg. Export Promotion Coun. [IO], Calcutta, India
Engg. and Grading Contractors Assn. [★911]
Engg. Indus. Assn. - England [IO], London, United Kingdom
Engg. Inst. of Canada [IO], Kingston, ON, Canada
Engg. Integrity Soc. [IO], Warwickshire, United Kingdom
Engg. Manpower Commn. [★6795]
Engg. Ministries Intl. [19567], 130 E Kiowa St., No. 200, Colorado Springs, CO 80903-1722, (719)633-2078
Engg. Ministries Intl. [19567], 130 E Kiowa St., No. 200, Colorado Springs, CO 80903-1722, (719)633-2078
Engg. and Physical Sciences Res. Coun. [IO], Swindon, United Kingdom
Engg. Soc. of Detroit [6794], 20700 Civic Center Dr., Ste. 450, Southfield, MI 48076, (248)353-0735
Engg. Soc. of Detroit [6794], 20700 Civic Center Dr., Ste. 450, Southfield, MI 48076, (248)353-0735
Engg. Technologist Certification Inst. [★6814]
Engg. Workforce Commn. [6795], 1801 Alexander Bell Dr., Reston, VA 20191, (202)296-2237
Engg. World Hea. [15158], The Prizery, Ste. 230, 302 E Pettigrew St., Durham, NC 27701, (919)682-7788
Engineers' Assn. of Chile [IO], Santiago, Chile
Engineers Canada [IO], Ottawa, ON, Canada
Engineers' Company [IO], London, United Kingdom
Engineers' Coun. - Defunct.
Engineers' Coun. for Professional Development [★6764]
Engineers; Inst. of Trans. [7581]
Engineers Ireland [IO], Dublin, Ireland
Engineers Joint Coun. [★6767]
Engineers for Social Responsibility [IO], Auckland, New Zealand
Engineers; Soc. of Plastics [7278]
Engineers for a Sustainable World [11580], Univ. of California, Merced, 5200 N Lake Rd., Merced, CA 95343
Engineers for a Sustainable World [11580], Univ. of California, Merced, 5200 N Lake Rd., Merced, CA 95343
Engineers Without Borders - Canada [IO], Toronto, ON, Canada
Engineers Without Borders - India [IO], Hyderabad, India
Engineers Without Borders U.S.A. [11967], 4665 Nautilus Ct., Ste. 300, Boulder, CO 80301, (303)772-2723
Engineers Without Borders U.S.A. [11967], 4665 Nautilus Ct., Ste. 300, Boulder, CO 80301, (303)772-2723

Engines
Antique Small Engine Collectors Club [21702]
Assn. of Diesel Specialists [1180]
Assn. of Diesel Specialists [1180]
Brazilian Machinery Builders' Assn. [5680]
Early Day Gas Engine and Tractor Assn. [21703]
Engine Mfrs. Assn. [1181]
Outdoor Power Equip. Aftermarket Assn. [1182]
Outdoor Power Equip. Aftermarket Assn. [1182]
Outdoor Power Equip. and Engine Ser. Assn. [1183]
Outdoor Power Equip. Inst. [1184]
Production Engine Remanufacturers Assn. [1185]
Turbine Inlet Cooling Assn. [6838]

England Basketball [IO], Sheffield, United Kingdom
England Hockey [IO], Marlow, United Kingdom
England and Wales Cricket Bd. [IO], London, United Kingdom
English
Assn. of Departments of English [8130]
Coll. English Assn. [8131]
Conf. on Coll. Composition and Commun. [8132]
English in Action [17964]
English First [9577]
Intl. Assn. for World Englishes [9578]
Intl. Soc. of Anglo-Saxonists [8133]
Intl. Soc. of Anglo-Saxonists [8133]
Natl. Coun. of Teachers of English [8134]
Natl. Coun. of Teachers of English I Conf. on English Educ. [8135]
ProEnglish [9579]
Serendib [11629]
Sigma Tau Delta, Intl. English Honor Soc. [23527]
Sigma Tau Delta, the Intl. English Honor Soc. [23527]
Soc. for the Preservation of English Language and Literature [8136]
Swedish Translators in North America [10615]
Teachers of English to Speakers of Other Languages [8137]
English Acad. of Southern Africa [IO], Wits, Republic of South Africa
English in Action [17964], 144 E 39th St., New York, NY 10016, (212)818-1200
English Amateur Dancesport Assn. [IO], Winchfield, United Kingdom
English Assn. [IO], Leicester, United Kingdom
English Bridge Union [IO], Aylesbury, United Kingdom
English Centre of Intl. PEN [IO], London, United Kingdom
English Chess Fed. [IO], Battle, United Kingdom
English Cocker Spaniel Club of Am. [21556], Mrs. Kate D. Romanski, Corresponding Sec., PO Box 252, Hales Corners, WI 53130, (414)529-9714
English Curling Assn. [IO], Bedford, United Kingdom
English Draughts Assn. [IO], Ryde, United Kingdom
English First [9577], 8001 Forbes Pl., Ste. 102, Springfield, VA 22151, (703)321-8818
English Folk Dance and Song Soc. [IO], London, United Kingdom
English Golf Union [IO], Woodhall Spa, United Kingdom
English Indoor Bowling Assn. [IO], Melton Mowbray, United Kingdom
English Lacrosse Assn. [IO], Manchester, United Kingdom
English Language Editors' Assn. [IO], Jerusalem, Israel
English Language Teachers' Assn. of Afghanistan [IO], Kabul, Afghanistan
English Natl. Assn. of Visually Handicapped Bowlers [IO], London, United Kingdom
English Place-Name Society/Institute for Name Stud. [IO], Nottingham, United Kingdom
English Poetry and Song Soc. [IO], Surrey, United Kingdom
English Pool Assn. [IO], Nottingham, United Kingdom
English Schools Football Assn. [IO], Stafford, United Kingdom
English Schools' Table Tennis Assn. [IO], Loughborough, United Kingdom
English Setter Assn. of Am. [21557], Sandy Miller, Sec., 24562 McCutcheonville Rd., Perrysburg, OH 43551, (419)873-5399
English Shepherd Club [21558], 441 Harding Ave., Odenton, MD 21113
English Shepherd Club of Amer. [★21558]
English Speaking Bd. [IO], Ormskirk, United Kingdom
English Speaking Union of the Commonwealth [IO], London, United Kingdom
English-Speaking Union of the U.S. [19100], 144 E 39th St., New York, NY 10016, (212)818-1200
English Springer Rescue Am. [10957], 19518 Nashville St., Northridge, CA 91326-2240
English Springer Spaniel Field Trial Assn. [21559], Nanci LaMarque, Membership Sec., PO Box 256, Yarmouth, ME 04096, (207)846-6848

Reference to "IO" in place of a book number signifies that the association may be found in the 50th edition of International Organizations.

English Table Tennis Assn. **[IO]**, Hastings, United Kingdom
English Teachers Assn. of NSW **[IO]**, Leichhardt, Australia
English Teachers Assn. of Queensland **[IO]**, Stafford, Australia
English Teachers Assn. of Western Australia **[IO]**, Perth, Australia
English Toy Spaniel Club of Am. **[21560]**, Michael Allen, Ed., 14531 Jefferson St., Midway City, CA 92655-1030, (714)893-0053
English UK **[IO]**, London, United Kingdom
English Westerners Soc. **[IO]**, Kingston Upon Thames, United Kingdom
English Women's Golf Assn. **[IO]**, Birmingham, United Kingdom
Engraved Stationery Manufacturers Assn. - Address unknown since 2010.
Enid Bd. of Trade - Defunct.
ENJOIN for Responsible Govt. - Defunct.
Enkosini Wildlife Sanctuary **[IO]**, Lydenburg, Republic of South Africa
Enlisted Assn. of Natl. Guard of the U.S. **[5806]**, 3133 Mt. Vernon Ave., Alexandria, VA 22305-2640, (703)519-3846
Eno Found. for Highway Traffic Control **[★7579]**
Eno Found. for Trans. **[★7579]**
Eno Trans. Found. **[7579]**, 1250 I St. NW, Ste. 750, Washington, DC 20005-3910, (202)879-4700
Enough Is Enough **[17995]**, 746 Walker Rd., Ste. 116, Great Falls, VA 22066, (703)476-7890
Enrichment Educ. **[8276]**, 13425 Ventura Blvd., Ste. 304, Sherman Oaks, CA 91423, (818)989-7509
Ensaaf **[18641]**, 811 1st Ave., Ste. 401, Seattle, WA 98104, (206)866-5642
Ente Nazionale Italiano di Unificazione **[IO]**, Milan, Italy
Entente des Hopitaux Luxembourgeois **[★IO]**
Enteral Nutrition Coun. - Defunct.
Enterprise Am. **[★17731]**
Enterprise Community Partners **[12177]**, 10227 Wincopin Cir., Columbia, MD 21044, (410)772-2404
Enterprise Cmpt. Telephony Forum - Address unknown since 2011.
Enterprise Found. **[★12177]**
Enterprise Networking Assn. - Defunct.
Enterprise for a Sustainable World **[1056]**, 1609 Shadford Rd., Ann Arbor, MI 48104, (734)369-8060
Enterprise Wireless Alliance **[3407]**, 8484 Westpark Dr., Ste. 630, McLean, VA 22102-3590, (703)528-5115
EnterpriseWorks - Senegal **[IO]**, Dakar, Senegal
EnterpriseWorks/VITA **[17193]**, 1100 H St. NW, Ste. 1200, Washington, DC 20009, (202)639-8660
EnterpriseWorks/VITA **[17193]**, 1100 H St. NW, Ste. 1200, Washington, DC 20009, (202)639-8660
EnterpriseWorks Worldwide and Volunteers in Tech. Assistance **[★17193]**
EnterpriseWorks Worldwide and Volunteers in Tech. Assistance **[★17193]**
Entertainers
  Actors' Fund **[11968]**
  Bread and Roses **[11969]**
  Dart Music Intl. **[10187]**
  Dean Martin Fan Center **[23802]**
  Diverse Emerging Music Org. **[10188]**
  Entertainment Indus. Found. **[11970]**
  Hollywood Unites For Haiti **[12128]**
  Intl. Crosby Circle **[23857]**
  Intl. Performing Arts for Youth **[10359]**
  Intl. Soc. for Improvised Music **[10226]**
  Joni James Intl. Fan Club **[23803]**
  Michael Jackson Fan Club **[23878]**
  Motion Picture and TV Fund **[11971]**
  Natl. Lum and Abner Soc. **[22119]**
  Natl. Puro Conjunto Music Assn. **[10263]**
  North Amer. Irish Dance Fed. **[9563]**
  Reverb **[4130]**
  Stars for Stripes **[20417]**
  Veterans Bedside Network **[11972]**
  WordTheatre **[10550]**
Entertainment
  African Amer. Women in Cinema Org. **[9592]**
  Amer. Amusement Machine Assn. **[1186]**
  Amer. Amusement Machine Assn. **[1186]**

Amusement Indus. Mfrs. and Suppliers Intl. **[1187]**
Amusement Indus. Mfrs. and Suppliers Intl. **[1187]**
Amusement and Music Operators Assn. **[1188]**
Assn. of Entertainment Marketing Agencies **[1189]**
Black Rock Coalition **[9580]**
Canine Freestyle Fed. **[22545]**
Coalition of Asian Pacifics in Entertainment **[1190]**
Dart Music Intl. **[10187]**
Diverse Emerging Music Org. **[10188]**
Entertainment Publicists Professional Soc. **[1191]**
Game Mfrs. Assn. **[1192]**
Game Mfrs. Assn. **[1192]**
Global Mobile Entertainers Assn. **[1193]**
Global Mobile Entertainers Assn. **[1193]**
Haunted Attraction Assn. **[1194]**
Interactive Media Entertainment and Gaming Assn. **[7008]**
Intl. Assn. of Amusement Parks and Attractions **[1195]**
Intl. Assn. of Amusement Parks and Attractions **[1195]**
Intl. Assn. of Corporate Entertainment Producers **[1196]**
Intl. Assn. of Haunted Attractions **[1194]**
Intl. Entertainment Buyers Assn. **[1197]**
Intl. Fed. of Festival Organizations **[1198]**
Intl. Fed. of Festival Organizations **[1198]**
Intl. Festivals and Events Assn. **[1199]**
Intl. Festivals and Events Assn. **[1199]**
Intl. Laser Display Assn. **[1200]**
Intl. Laser Display Assn. **[1200]**
Intl. Performing Arts for Youth **[10359]**
Intl. Recreational Go-Kart Assn. **[1201]**
Intl. Recreational Go-Kart Assn. **[1201]**
Intl. Soc. of Caricature Artists **[1202]**
Intl. Soc. for Improvised Music **[10226]**
Intl. Special Events Soc. **[1203]**
Intl. Special Events Soc. **[1203]**
Intl. Ticketing Assn. **[1204]**
Intl. Ticketing Assn. **[1204]**
Kollaboration **[13534]**
Live Performance Australia **[23844]**
Michael Jackson Fan Club **[23878]**
A Minor Consideration **[11676]**
Motion Picture Pilots Assn. **[380]**
Musicians for Harmony **[10353]**
Natl. Assn. of Amusement Ride Safety Officials **[1205]**
Natl. Assn. of Arms Shows **[21715]**
Natl. Assn. of Black Female Executives in Music and Entertainment **[1206]**
Natl. Assn. of Casino Party Operators **[1207]**
Natl. Assn. of Mobile Entertainers **[1208]**
Natl. Assn. of Theatre Owners **[1209]**
Natl. Assn. of Theatre Owners **[1209]**
Natl. Assn. of Ticket Brokers **[1210]**
Natl. Ballroom and Entertainment Assn. **[1211]**
Natl. Caves Assn. **[1212]**
Natl. Club Indus. Assn. of Am. **[1213]**
Natl. Club Indus. Assn. of Am. **[1213]**
Natl. Lum and Abner Soc. **[22119]**
Natl. Park Hospitality Assn. **[1214]**
Natl. Puro Conjunto Music Assn. **[10263]**
North Amer. Irish Dance Fed. **[9563]**
Org. of Black Screenwriters **[1215]**
Org. of Black Screenwriters **[1215]**
OSU Tour **[11973]**
Outdoor Amusement Bus. Assn. **[1216]**
PeaceArt Intl. **[9312]**
POWER UP: Professional Org. of Women in Entertainment Reaching UP! **[17737]**
Showmen's League of Am. **[8138]**
Stars for Stripes **[20417]**
Talent Managers Assn. **[1217]**
Themed Entertainment Assn. **[1218]**
Themed Entertainment Assn. **[1218]**
Tournament of Roses Assn. **[9581]**
Visual Effects Soc. **[1270]**
Western Fairs Assn. **[1219]**
Women in Toys **[3479]**
WordTheatre **[10550]**
World Waterpark Assn. **[1220]**
World Waterpark Assn. **[1220]**
Entertainment Consumers Assn. **[17457]**, 64 Danbury Rd., Ste. 700, Wilton, CT 06897-4406, (203)761-6180

Entertainment Indus. Coun. **[13250]**, 1856 Old Reston Ave., Ste. 215, Reston, VA 20190, (703)481-1414
Entertainment Indus. Found. **[11970]**, 1201 W 5th St., Ste. T-700, Los Angeles, CA 90017, (213)240-3900
Entertainment Law
  Assn. of Entertainment Marketing Agencies **[1189]**
  Black Entertainment and Sports Lawyers Assn. **[5409]**
Entertainment and Leisure Software Publishers Assn. **[IO]**, London, United Kingdom
Entertainment Merchants Assn. **[275]**, 16530 Ventura Blvd., Ste. 400, Encino, CA 91436-4551, (818)385-1500
Entertainment Operators of Am. **[★1211]**
Entertainment Publicists Professional Soc. **[1191]**, PO Box 5841, Beverly Hills, CA 90209-5841, (310)496-4449
Entertainment Software Assn. **[6485]**, 575 7th St. NW, Ste. 300, Washington, DC 20004
Enthronement of the Sacred Heart in the Home **[★19474]**
Entomological Livestock Gp. **[IO]**, Sheffield, United Kingdom
Entomological Soc. of Am. **[6844]**, 10001 Derekwood Ln., Ste. 100, Lanham, MD 20706-4876, (301)731-4535
Entomological Soc. of Canada **[IO]**, Ottawa, ON, Canada
Entomological Soc. of New Zealand **[IO]**, Canterbury, New Zealand
Entomological Soc. of Southern Africa **[IO]**, Hatfield, Republic of South Africa
Entomologiese Vereniging van Suidelike Afrika **[★IO]**
EntomologyEntomologyAcarological Soc. of Am.
  Assn. for Tropical Lepidoptera **[6839]**
  Black Entomologists **[6840]**
  Coleopterists Soc. **[6841]**
  Coun. of Entomology Dept. Administrators **[6842]**
  Dragonfly Soc. of the Americas **[6843]**
  Entomological Soc. of Am. **[6844]**
  The Intl. Lepidoptera Survey **[6845]**
  Intl. Union for the Stud. of Social Insects **[6846]**
  Intl. Union for the Stud. of Social Insects **[6846]**
  Japanese Soc. of Applied Entomology and Zoology **[1120]**
  Natl. Assn. of Agriculture Employees **[5190]**
  Natl. Entomology Scent Detection Canine Assn. **[2633]**
  North Amer. Forensic Entomology Assn. **[6847]**
  North Amer. Forensic Entomology Assn. **[6847]**
  Orthopterists' Soc. **[6848]**
  Orthopterists' Soc. **[6848]**
  Overseas Chinese Entomologists Assn. **[6849]**
  Overseas Chinese Entomologists Assn. **[6849]**
L'Entraide missionaire **[IO]**, Montreal, QC, Canada
Entrepreneurs Assn. of Slovakia **[IO]**, Bratislava, Slovakia
Entrepreneurs de l'audiovisuel europeene **[★IO]**
Entrepreneurs' Org. **[660]**, 500 Montgomery St., Ste. 500, Alexandria, VA 22314, (703)519-6700
Entrepreneurs' Org. - Pakistan Chap. **[IO]**, Lahore, Pakistan
Entrepreneurship Development Inst. of India **[IO]**, Gandhinagar, India
The Entrepreneurship Inst. **[661]**, 3592 Corporate Dr., Ste. 101, Columbus, OH 43231, (614)895-1153
Envelope Mfrs. Assn. **[3348]**, 500 Montgomery St., Ste. 550, Alexandria, VA 22314-1581, (703)739-2200
Envelope Mfrs. Assn. of Am. **[★3348]**
Envirofit Intl. **[4335]**, 109 North Coll. Ave., Ste. 200, Fort Collins, CO 80524, (970)372-2874
Environic Found. Intl. **[8143]**, 12035 Stonewick Pl., Glen Allen, VA 23059-7152, (804)360-9130
Environic Found. Intl. **[8143]**, 12035 Stonewick Pl., Glen Allen, VA 23059-7152, (804)360-9130
Environment
  41pounds.org **[4232]**
  Action for Nature **[4233]**
  Advanced Conservation Strategies **[3979]**
  Africa Environmental Watch **[3980]**
  African Amer. Environmentalist Assn. **[4234]**

A star before a book entry number signifies that the name is not listed separately, but is mentioned within the entry.

African Environmental Res. and Consulting Gp. [4235]
African Environmental Res. and Consulting Gp. [4235]
Alaska Coalition [3982]
Alliance for Climate Educ. [4315]
Alliance for Global Conservation [3983]
Alliance for Sustainable Built Environments [517]
Alliance for Tompotika Conservation [3985]
Amara Conservation [5022]
Am. the Beautiful Fund [4236]
Amer. Coll. of Environmental Lawyers [5410]
Amer. Coun. for Accredited Certification [4780]
Amer. Energy Alliance [17614]
Amer. Soc. for Environmental History [8139]
Amer. Soc. for Environmental History [8139]
Amer. Wilderness Coalition [5010]
Anglers for Conservation [4000]
Assn. of Climate Change Officers [4237]
Assn. of Energy and Environmental Real Estate Professionals [8150]
Assn. for Fire Ecology [4194]
Assn. for Fire Ecology of the Tropics [4195]
Assn. for Gnotobiotics [4238]
Assn. of Green Property Owners and Managers [2900]
Assn. of Univ. Leaders for a Sustainable Future [8232]
Audubon Intl. [4008]
Audubon Lifestyles [4196]
Avoided Deforestation Partners [4390]
Bee Native [3839]
Beyond Nuclear [18192]
Bioethics Intl. [13831]
Biofuel Recycling [4867]
BlueVoice.org [4013]
Bonobo Conservation Initiative [5038]
Brighter Green [4014]
Building Enclosure Tech. and Env. Coun. [539]
CarFree City, USA [4961]
Catholic Coalition on Climate Change [4016]
Center for Environmental Info. [4239]
Cetos Res. Org. [4199]
Charles A. and Anne Morrow Lindbergh Found. [4240]
Children and Nature Network [4241]
Chinese-American Professors in Environmental Engg. and Sci. [6425]
CHWMEG [3633]
Citizens for Affordable Energy [6701]
Citizens Energy Plan [6704]
Clean Air Task Force [4783]
Clean Beaches Coun. [4242]
Clean Economy Network [6605]
Clean Islands Intl. [4243]
Clean Islands Intl. [4243]
Clean and Safe Energy Coalition [6707]
Clean Tech. and Sustainable Indus. Org. [3856]
Clean Tech. Trade Alliance [6110]
Clean the World [4869]
Climate, Community and Biodiversity Alliance [4020]
Climate Gp. [4023]
Climate Inst. [4244]
Coalition to End Childhood Lead Poisoning [4245]
Coalition on the Env. and Jewish Life [19857]
Coalition for Environmentally Responsible Economies [4246]
Coalition for Environmentally Safe Communities [11974]
Coalition of Natl. Park Ser. Retirees [4766]
Collaborative on Hea. and the Env. [14500]
Community Forestry Intl. [4391]
Compassionate Kids [8140]
Compassionate Kids [8140]
The Conservation Campaign [17416]
Conservation Leaders Network [4734]
Conservation Northwest [4247]
Conservation through Poverty Alleviation Intl. [4030]
Cork Forest Conservation Alliance [4036]
Coun. for Endangered Species Act Reliability [5413]
Coun. for Responsible Energy [6709]
The Cousteau Soc. [8141]

The Cousteau Soc. [8141]
Crude Accountability [4248]
Defense of Place [4039]
Earth Day Network [4249]
Earth Force [4250]
Earth Island Inst. [4251]
Earth Island Inst. [4251]
Earth Regeneration Soc. [4252]
Earth Soc. Found. [4253]
Earth Soc. Found. [4253]
EarthAction Intl. [4254]
EarthAction Intl. [4254]
EarthRights Intl. [17827]
EarthWave Soc. [4255]
Eco-Life Concepts [4318]
ecoAmerica [4044]
Ecological Building Network [3857]
EcoLogical Mail Coalition [4698]
Ecological Res. and Development Gp. [4045]
Ecology Proj. Intl. [8154]
EcoVentures Intl. [4319]
Educational Communications [8142]
Educational Communications [8142]
Educational Found. of Am. [11975]
Educational Found. of Am. [11975]
Elec. Utility Indus. Sustainable Supply Chain Alliance [3594]
Electronics TakeBack Coalition [6652]
Elephants Without Borders [5011]
Energy Action Coalition [6717]
Energy Conservation Org. [8120]
Energy Training Coun. [6723]
Environic Found. Intl. [8143]
Environic Found. Intl. [8143]
Env. Am. [4256]
Env. for the Americas [3845]
Environmental Alliance for Senior Involvement [4048]
Environmental Bus. Coun. of New England [4257]
Environmental Commons [4049]
Environmental Defense Fund [4258]
Environmental Educ. and Conservation Global [8155]
Environmental Entrepreneurs [4050]
Environmental Indus. Associations [3635]
Environmental Outreach and Stewardship Alliance [4259]
Environmental Paper Network [4051]
Environmental Policy Center [5417]
Environmental Risk Resources Assn. [4260]
Environmental Working Group [4261]
Environmentalists Against War [18777]
Ethnobotanical Conservation Org. for South East Asia [4053]
European Soc. for Environmental History [14785]
Experience Intl. [4054]
Exploring Solutions Past: The Maya Forest Alliance [6168]
Forest Bird Soc. [4056]
Forest Partners Intl. [4395]
Forest Planters Intl. [4396]
Freecycle Network [4870]
Friends of the Osa [4063]
FutureGen Alliance [6112]
GAIA Movement USA [4066]
Generation Green [14077]
George Wright Soc. [4262]
George Wright Soc. [4262]
Global Env. Fac. [4263]
Global Green U.S.A. [4264]
Global Parks [4070]
Global Partnership for Afghanistan [3716]
Global Possibilities [4930]
Global Response [4265]
Global Response [4265]
Global Sports Alliance USA [22977]
Global Underwater Explorers [4703]
Global Warming Initiatives [4793]
Global Warming Intl. Center [4266]
Global Warming Intl. Center [4266]
Global Wildlife Conservation [5060]
Go Green Initiative Assn. [8156]
Governors' Wind Energy Coalition [6070]
Gray is Green: The Natl. Senior Conservation Corps [4072]

Green for All [17189]
Green Builder Coalition [565]
Green Building Initiative [566]
Green Bus. Alliance [4267]
Green Computing Impact Org. [1221]
Green Parent Assn. [4075]
Green Partners [4177]
Green Schools Alliance [8158]
The Green Standard [4208]
Green Team Am. [4076]
Green Yoga Assn. [5179]
Green Zionist Alliance [4268]
GreenMotion [4227]
Greenpeace U.S.A. [4269]
Greenpeace U.S.A. [4269]
Growing Planet [4400]
Growth Energy [6728]
Healthy Building Network [4330]
HeatGreen Coun. [6113]
Human-Wildlife Conflict Collaboration [5014]
Iemanya Oceanica [5064]
Impact Carbon [4228]
Indo-Pacific Conservation Alliance [4079]
Inst. for Conservation Leadership [4270]
Inst. for Earth Educ. [8144]
Inst. for Earth Educ. [8144]
Inst. of Global Env. and Soc. [4271]
Inst. of Global Env. and Soc. [4271]
Inst. of Professional Environmental Practice [4272]
Inst. of Professional Environmental Practice [4272]
Intergovernmental Renewable Energy Org. [6731]
Intl. Arid Lands Consortium [4273]
Intl. Arid Lands Consortium [4273]
Intl. Assn. for Ecology and Hea. [6604]
Intl. Assn. for Environmental Philosophy [10382]
Intl. BioExploration Soc. [8180]
Intl. Biogeography Soc. [6904]
Intl. Center for the Solution of Environmental Problems [4274]
Intl. Center for the Solution of Environmental Problems [4274]
Intl. Soc. for Environmental Ethics [4275]
Intl. Soc. for Environmental Ethics [4275]
Intl. Soc. for Indus. Ecology [4276]
Intl. Soc. for Indus. Ecology [4276]
Intl. Soc. for Reef Stud. [4277]
Intl. Soc. for Reef Stud. [4277]
Intl. Soc. for the Stud. of Religion, Nature and Culture [8329]
Intl. Soc. of Sustainability Professionals [4340]
Intl. Sonoran Desert Alliance [4278]
Intl. Sonoran Desert Alliance [4278]
Intl. Sustainability Coun. [4212]
Intl. Water Level Coalition [5004]
Journey Toward Sustainability [8159]
Kasese Wildlife Conservation Awareness Org. [5074]
Keep Am. Beautiful [4279]
Kids for a Clean Env. [4280]
Kids Ecology Corps [4322]
Kids for Saving Earth [8145]
LandChoices [4089]
Merck Family Fund [4281]
NAEM [4282]
Natl. Alliance of Forest Owners [4404]
Natl. Assn. of Environmental Professionals [4283]
Natl. Assn. of Univ. Fisheries and Wildlife Programs [8146]
Natl. Black Environmental Justice Network [4284]
Natl. Coun. on Paint Disposition [4765]
Natl. Coun. for Sci. and the Env. [4285]
Natl. Energy Found. [8147]
Natl. Environmental Satellite, Data, and Info. Ser. [4286]
Natl. Flood Determination Assn. [4732]
Natl. Oceanic Soc. [4102]
Natl. Org. of Professional Hispanic Natural Resources Conservation Ser. Employees [4521]
Natl. Registry of Environmental Professionals [4287]
Natl. Registry of Environmental Professionals [4287]

Reference to "IO" in place of a book number signifies that the association may be found in the 50th edition of International Organizations.

Natl. Tree Soc. **[4288]**
Natl. Wildlife Fed. **[4103]**
Native Amer. Fish and Wildlife Soc. **[4289]**
Native Cultural Alliance **[4290]**
Natural History Network **[7143]**
Nature Abounds **[4291]**
Neotropical Grassland Conservancy **[4112]**
Network of Conservation Educators and Practitioners **[4113]**
New Ecology, Inc. **[11616]**
New Env. Assn. **[4292]**
New Generation Energy **[6743]**
New Zealand Assn. for Environmental Educ. **[2897]**
NOAH Nature Alliance **[5090]**
Noise Free Am. **[4739]**
Nordic Soc. for Aerosol Res. **[3149]**
North Amer. Assn. for Environmental Educ. **[8148]**
Ocean Champions **[17417]**
Ocean Conservation Res. **[4116]**
Oceanic Preservation Soc. **[4119]**
Oikonos **[4213]**
Oil Change Intl. **[4230]**
One Earth Designs **[4293]**
Open Space Inst. **[4294]**
Orchid Conservation Alliance **[4120]**
OrganicAthlete **[22232]**
Our Task **[4295]**
OurEarth.org **[4121]**
Pacific Inst. for Stud. in Development, Env., and Security **[11976]**
Pacific Islands Conservation Res. Assn. **[4123]**
Paso Pacifico **[4125]**
People 4 Earth **[4296]**
Planetwork **[4214]**
Planting Empowerment **[4410]**
Plastic Pollution Coalition **[4799]**
Plastics Division of the Amer. Plastics Coun. **[2774]**
Poetic Unity **[11623]**
Practice Greenhealth **[14506]**
Property and Env. Res. Center **[4297]**
Protect Our Winters **[4298]**
Puerto Rico Water and Env. Assn. **[5006]**
Quebec-Labrador Found. I Atlantic Center for the Env. **[4299]**
Quebec-Labrador Foundation I Atlantic Center for the Env. **[4299]**
Rainforest Partnership **[4859]**
Recycling for Charities **[4871]**
ReefGuardian Intl. **[4709]**
Rene Dubos Center for Human Environments **[4300]**
Renew Am. **[3973]**
Renewable Energy Resources **[6750]**
Reptile and Amphibian Ecology Intl. **[5118]**
Reverb **[4130]**
Rights and Resources Initiative **[4412]**
Rising Tide North Am. **[4131]**
Rivers Without Borders **[4134]**
Rock the Earth **[4301]**
Sacred Earth Network **[4302]**
Sacred Earth Network **[4302]**
Save the Turtles **[5123]**
Save Yemen's Flora and Fauna **[4140]**
Saving Wildlife Intl. **[5125]**
Scenic Am. **[4303]**
Seeking Ecology Educ. and Design Solutions **[4216]**
Seven Generations Ahead **[11632]**
Seventh Generation Advisors **[4304]**
Soc. for Energy Educ. **[6756]**
Soil Carbon Coalition **[4928]**
Solar Household Energy **[4931]**
Sri Lanka Wildlife Conservation Soc. **[5133]**
State of the World's Sea Turtles **[5134]**
Student Environmental Action Coalition **[4305]**
Sustainable Biomaterials Collaborative **[6119]**
Sustainable Smiles **[4876]**
Thornton W. Burgess Soc. **[4306]**
Threshold **[4307]**
Tree of Peace Soc. **[9582]**
Trees, Water and People **[4308]**
Trees, Water and People **[4308]**
Tropical Forest and Climate Coalition **[4861]**

Tropical Forest Gp. **[4153]**
Tropical Forestry Initiative **[4154]**
Turner Found. **[4309]**
Turtle Island Restoration Network **[4156]**
United Nations Env. Program/Global Rsrc. Info. Database **[4310]**
U.S. Offshore Wind Collaborative **[7623]**
US-China Green Energy Coun. **[6760]**
Vision Earth Soc. **[4223]**
WAVES for Development **[18683]**
Wild Gift **[5146]**
Wilderness Intl. **[4160]**
Wildlands Network **[4311]**
Wildlife Conservation Network **[5152]**
Wildlife Media **[5155]**
Wind Energy Works! **[7625]**
Windstar Found. **[4312]**
Women and the Env. Org. **[4323]**
Women Organizing for Change in Agriculture and NRM **[3769]**
Women's Voices for the Earth **[4313]**
Wonderful World of Wildlife **[5157]**
World Corrosion Org. **[4178]**
World Fed. for Coral Reef Conservation **[4169]**
World Land Trust U.S.A. **[4314]**
World Land Trust U.S.A. **[4314]**
World Ocean Coun. **[5009]**
World Peace One **[12229]**
Worldwide Pollution Control Assn. **[2789]**
Env. Africa **[IO]**, Harare, Zimbabwe
Env. Am. **[4256]**, 44 Winter St., 4th Fl., Boston, MA 02108, (617)747-4449
Env. for the Americas **[3845]**, 2129 13th St., Ste. 1, Boulder, CO 80302, (303)499-1950
Env; Assn. for the Stud. of Literature and **[10035]**
Env. Bus. Australia **[IO]**, Sydney, Australia
The Env. Coun. **[IO]**, London, United Kingdom
Env. Coun. of Macao **[IO]**, Macau, Macao
Env., Culture, Agriculture, Res. and Development Soc. in Nepal **[IO]**, Kathmandu, Nepal
Env. and Development in Action **[IO]**, Ho Chi Minh City, Vietnam
Env. and Development Action in the Third World **[IO]**, Dakar, Senegal
Env. and Development in the Arab World **[IO]**, Tunis, Tunisia
Env. and Development Gp. **[IO]**, Oxford, United Kingdom
Env. and Development Inst. **[IO]**, Lima, Peru
Env. and Human Hea., Inc. **[14501]**, 1191 Ridge Rd., North Haven, CT 06473, (203)248-6582
Env. Liaison Centre Intl. **[IO]**, Nairobi, Kenya
Env. and Natural Resources Found. **[IO]**, Buenos Aires, Argentina
Environment-People-Law **[IO]**, Lviv, Ukraine
Env. Soc. of Oman **[IO]**, Muscat, Oman
Env. Tobago **[IO]**, Scarborough, Trinidad and Tobago
Environmental Action Coalition - Defunct.
Environmental Alert **[IO]**, Kampala, Uganda
Environmental Alliance for Senior Involvement **[4048]**, 5615 26th St. N, Arlington, VA 22207-1407, (703)241-4927
Environmental Bankers Assn. **[410]**, 510 King St., Ste. 410, Alexandria, VA 22314, (703)549-0977
Environmental Bur. of Investigation **[IO]**, Toronto, ON, Canada
Environmental Bus. Coun. of New England **[4257]**, 375 Harvard St., Ste. 2, Brookline, MA 02446, (617)505-1818
Environmental Camps for Conservation Awareness **[IO]**, Kathmandu, Nepal
Environmental Careers Org. **[IO]**, Calgary, AB, Canada
Environmental Cleanup Coalition **[4788]**, 10507 E Zayante Rd., Felton, CA 95018, (808)563-9963
Environmental Cleanup Coalition **[4788]**, 10507 E Zayante Rd., Felton, CA 95018, (808)563-9963
Environmental Clinics; Assn. of Occupational and **[15904]**
Environmental Commn. of Democratic Socialists of America - Defunct.
Environmental Commons **[4049]**, 35501 S Hwy. 1, Unit No. 12, Gualala, CA 95445
Environmental Conservation Org. - Address unknown since 2011.

Environmental Contractors Mgt. Assn. **[IO]**, Hong Kong, People's Republic of China
Environmental Coun. of the States **[4336]**, 50 F St. NW, Ste. 350, Washington, DC 20001, (202)266-4920
Environmental Data and Info. Ser. **[★4286]**
Environmental Data Ser. **[★4286]**
Environmental Defence **[IO]**, Toronto, ON, Canada
Environmental Defence Soc. - New Zealand **[IO]**, Waitakere, New Zealand
Environmental Defender's Off. Network of Australia **[IO]**, Sydney, Australia
Environmental Defense Fund **[4258]**, 257 Park Ave. S, New York, NY 10010, (212)505-2100
Environmental Design Res. Assn. **[5213]**, PO Box 7146, Edmond, OK 73083-7146, (405)330-4863
Environmental Development Action in the Third World **[IO]**, Dakar, Senegal
Environmental Education
41pounds.org **[4232]**
Action for Clean Energy **[4224]**
Africa Environmental Watch **[3980]**
Alaska Coalition **[3982]**
Alliance for Climate Educ. **[4315]**
Alliance for Climate Educ. **[4315]**
Alliance for Water Educ. **[8149]**
Amara Conservation **[5022]**
Anglers for Conservation **[4000]**
Assn. of Energy and Environmental Real Estate Professionals **[8150]**
Assn. for Fire Ecology **[4194]**
Assn. of Univ. Leaders for a Sustainable Future **[8232]**
Assn. of Women in Environmental Professions **[4316]**
Audubon Lifestyles **[4196]**
Cetos Res. Org. **[4199]**
Children of the Earth United **[4317]**
Children of the Earth United **[4317]**
Coun. of Environmental Deans and Directors **[8151]**
Crude Accountability **[4248]**
Earth Care Intl. **[8152]**
EarthShare **[8153]**
Eco-Life Concepts **[4318]**
ecoAmerica **[4044]**
Ecology Proj. Intl. **[8154]**
Ecology Proj. Intl. **[8154]**
EcoVentures Intl. **[4319]**
EcoVentures Intl. **[4319]**
Elephants Without Borders **[5011]**
Environmental Alliance for Senior Involvement **[4048]**
Environmental Commons **[4049]**
Environmental Educ. and Conservation Global **[8155]**
Environmental Outreach and Stewardship Alliance **[4259]**
Environmental Policy Center **[5417]**
Experience Intl. **[4054]**
Global Underwater Explorers **[4703]**
Go Green Initiative Assn. **[8156]**
Grassroots Environmental Educ. **[8157]**
Gray is Green: The Natl. Senior Conservation Corps **[4072]**
Green Schools Alliance **[8158]**
The Green Standard **[4208]**
Green Team Am. **[4076]**
Green Yoga Assn. **[5179]**
Green Zionist Alliance **[4268]**
Indigenous Environmental Network **[4320]**
Interdisciplinary Environmental Assn. **[4321]**
Interdisciplinary Environmental Assn. **[4321]**
Intl. BioExploration Soc. **[8180]**
Intl. Sustainability Coun. **[4212]**
Journey Toward Sustainability **[8159]**
Kasese Wildlife Conservation Awareness Org. **[5074]**
Kids Ecology Corps **[4322]**
Kids Making a Difference **[3813]**
Natl. Environmental Educ. Found. **[8160]**
Natl. Wildlife Fed. **[4103]**
Native Cultural Alliance **[4290]**
Oikonos **[4213]**
Paso Pacifico **[4125]**

A star before a book entry number signifies that the name is not listed separately, but is mentioned within the entry.

Population Rsrc. Center [12708]
Protect Our Winters [4298]
Quantal Energy [8121]
Responsible Purchasing Network [1222]
Strategic Energy, Environmental and Trans.
   Alternatives [8122]
Trips for Kids [8161]
Veggie Van Org. [4872]
Women and the Env. Org. [4323]
World Corrosion Org. [4178]
Youth for Environmental Sanity [4324]
Environmental Educ. and Conservation Global
[8155], 204 E Locust St., Coudersport, PA 16915,
(814)260-9138
Environmental and Energy Study Conf. - Defunct.
Environmental and Energy Stud. Inst. [4205], 1112
16th St. NW, Ste. 300, Washington, DC 20036,
(202)628-1400
Environmental and Engg. Geophysical Soc. [6919],
1720 S Bellaire St., Ste. 110, Denver, CO 80222-
4308, (303)531-7517
Environmental and Engg. Geophysical Soc. [6919],
1720 S Bellaire St., Ste. 110, Denver, CO 80222-
4308, (303)531-7517
Environmental Engineers Intersociety Bd. [★6766]
Environmental Engineers and Managers Institute
[★6693]
Environmental Engineers and Managers Institute
[★6693]
Environmental Entrepreneurs [4050], Ying Li, Natural
Resources Defense Coun., 40 W 20th St., New
York, NY 10011, (212)727-4422
Environmental Found. [IO], Colombo, Sri Lanka
Environmental Found. Bellona [IO], Oslo, Norway
Environmental Fund [★12706]
Environmental Health
Action for Clean Energy [4224]
African Amer. Environmentalist Assn. [4234]
Aircraft Fleet Recycling Assn. [12768]
Alliance of Veterinarians for the Env. [4325]
Amer. Acad. of Environmental Medicine [14496]
Amer. Acad. of Environmental Medicine [14496]
Amer. Assn. of Pesticide Safety Educators [4326]
Amer. Environmental Hea. Found. [14497]
Assn. of Environmental Hea. Academic Programs
[4327]
Campus Safety, Hea. and Environmental Mgt.
Assn. [4328]
CarFree City, USA [4961]
Center for Hea. and the Global Env. [14498]
Center for Hea. and the Global Env. [14498]
Children and Nature Network [4241]
Children's Environmental Hea. Network [14499]
Clean Air Task Force [4783]
Climate, Community and Biodiversity Alliance
[4020]
Collaborative on Hea. and the Env. [14500]
Conservation Leaders Network [4734]
Crude Accountability [4248]
Eco-Life Concepts [4318]
ecoAmerica [4044]
EcoVentures Intl. [4319]
Electronics TakeBack Coalition [6652]
EndOil [6716]
Env. and Human Hea., Inc. [14501]
Environmental Cleanup Coalition [4788]
Environmental Outreach and Stewardship Alliance
[4259]
Generation Green [14077]
Global Environmental Mgt. Initiative [4329]
Global Environmental Mgt. Initiative [4329]
Global Possibilities [4930]
Global Wildlife Conservation [5060]
Green Collar Assn. [1148]
The Green Standard [4208]
Green Team Am. [4076]
Green Zionist Alliance [4268]
Hea. and Environmental Funders Network [11977]
Healthy Building Network [4330]
Human Ecology Action League [14502]
Impact Carbon [4228]
Interamerican Assn. for Environmental Defense
[4331]
Interamerican Assn. for Environmental Defense
[4331]

Intl. Coun. on Nanotechnology [6430]
Intl. Soc. of Sustainability Professionals [4340]
Kids Making a Difference [3813]
Natl. Center for Environmental Hea. Strategies
[14503]
Natl. Environmental Hea. Assn. [14504]
Natl. Environmental Hea. Sci. and Protection Ac-
creditation Coun. [14505]
Nature Abounds [4291]
One Earth Designs [4293]
People 4 Earth [4296]
The Pesticide Stewardship Alliance [6850]
Planetwork [4214]
Plastic Pollution Coalition [4799]
Practice Greenhealth [14506]
Practice Greenhealth [14506]
Protect All Children's Env. [14507]
Protect Our Winters [4298]
ReefGuardian Intl. [4709]
Renew Am. [3973]
Responsible Purchasing Network [1222]
Rising Tide North Am. [4131]
Seventh Generation Advisors [4304]
Soc. of Environmental Toxicology and Chemistry
[14508]
Soc. for Human Ecology [14509]
Soc. for Human Ecology [14509]
Strategic Energy, Environmental and Trans.
   Alternatives [8122]
Sustainable Biomaterials Collaborative [6119]
Sustainable Packaging Coalition [4764]
Towards Freedom [17620]
Transition U.S. [4343]
Tropical Forest and Climate Coalition [4861]
Women and the Env. Org. [4323]
World Corrosion Org. [4178]
Worldwide Pollution Control Assn. [2789]
Environmental Hea. Accreditation Coun. [★14505]
Environmental Hea. Assn. of New Jersey [★14503]
Environmental Indus. Commn. [IO], London, United
Kingdom
Environmental Indus. Associations [3635], 4301
Connecticut Ave. NW, Ste. 300, Washington, DC
20008-2304, (202)244-4700
Environmental Info. Assn. [558], 6935 Wisconsin
Ave., Ste. 306, Chevy Chase, MD 20815-6112,
(301)961-4999
Environmental Law
Amer. Coll. of Environmental Lawyers [5410]
Assn. of State and Interstate Water Pollution
Control Administrators [5411]
Bioethics Intl. [13831]
Center for Intl. Environmental Law [5412]
Center for Intl. Environmental Law [5412]
Clean Air Task Force [4783]
Coun. for Endangered Species Act Reliability
[5413]
Crude Accountability [4248]
Earthjustice [5414]
Earthjustice [5414]
EarthRights Intl. [17827]
Environmental Law Alliance Worldwide U.S.
[5415]
Environmental Law Alliance Worldwide U.S.
[5415]
Environmental Law Inst. [5416]
Environmental Law Inst. [5416]
Environmental Policy Center [5417]
Harvard Environmental Law Soc. [5418]
Natl. Assn. of Clean Air Agencies [5419]
Natl. Assn. of Environmental Law Societies [5420]
Natl. Black Environmental Justice Network [4284]
Natl. Endangered Species Act Reform Coalition
[5421]
Noise Free Am. [4739]
Ruckus Soc. [18222]
World Corrosion Org. [4178]
Environmental Law Alliance Worldwide U.S. [5415],
1877 Garden Ave., Eugene, OR 97403, (541)687-
8454
Environmental Law Alliance Worldwide U.S. [5415],
1877 Garden Ave., Eugene, OR 97403, (541)687-
8454
Environmental Law Inst. [5416], 2000 L St. NW, Ste.
620, Washington, DC 20036, (202)939-3800

Environmental Law Inst. [5416], 2000 L St. NW, Ste.
620, Washington, DC 20036, (202)939-3800
Environmental Mgt. Assn. [2246], Nancy K. Kapral,
Dir., 38575 Mallast, Harrison Township, MI 48045,
(586)468-8008
Environmental Mgt. and Law Assn. - Hungary [IO],
Budapest, Hungary
Environmental Media Services [★4726]
Environmental Monitoring Gp. [IO], Mowbray,
Republic of South Africa
Environmental Mutagen Societies; Intl. Assn. of
[6301]
Environmental Mutagen Societies; Intl. Assn. of
[6301]
Environmental Mutagen Soc. [6298], 1821 Michael
Faraday Dr., Ste. 300, Reston, VA 20190,
(703)438-8220
Environmental and Natural Resources Law Center
[IO], San Jose, Costa Rica
Environmental Outreach and Stewardship Alliance
[4259], 230 NE Juniper St., Ste. 201, Issaquah,
WA 98027, (425)270-3274
Environmental Paper Network [4051], 16 Eagle St.,
Ste. 200, Asheville, NC 28801, (828)251-8558
Environmental Paper Network [4051], 16 Eagle St.,
Ste. 200, Asheville, NC 28801, (828)251-8558
Environmental Partners [★17460]
Environmental and Planning Engineers' Assn. [IO],
Milan, Italy
Environmental Policy Center [5417], Univ. of Cincin-
nati, Dept. of Environmental Hea., PO Box 670056,
Cincinnati, OH 45267-0056, (513)558-5439
Environmental Policy Inst. [★4061]
Environmental Protection Assn. of Ghana [IO], Ku-
masi, Ghana
Environmental Protection UK [IO], Brighton, United
Kingdom
Environmental Quality
41pounds.org [4232]
African Amer. Environmentalist Assn. [4234]
Amer. Assn. of Environmental Technicians [4332]
Architecture 2030 [4333]
Assn. of Univ. Leaders for a Sustainable Future
[8232]
Audubon Lifestyles [4196]
CarFree City, USA [4961]
Center for a New Amer. Dream [17415]
Clean Air Task Force [4783]
Clean Production Action [4334]
Clean Production Action [4334]
ClimateTalk Alliance [6111]
Coalition on the Env. and Jewish Life [19857]
Eco-Life Concepts [4318]
EcoVentures Intl. [4319]
Energy Action Coalition [6717]
Energy Farm [6719]
Envirofit Intl. [4335]
Env. and Human Hea., Inc. [14501]
Environmental Commons [4049]
Environmental Coun. of the States [4336]
Environmental Educ. and Conservation Global
[8155]
Environmental Outreach and Stewardship Alliance
[4259]
Environmental Res. and Educ. Found. [4337]
Environmental Risk Resources Assn. [4260]
Filipino Amer. Coalition for Environmental Solidar-
ity [4338]
Filipino Amer. Coalition for Environmental Solidar-
ity [4338]
Get Oil Out! [4792]
Global Warming Initiatives [4793]
Green Partners [4177]
Healthy Building Network [4330]
Healthy Schools Network [4339]
Impact Carbon [4228]
Intl. Assn. for Environmental Philosophy [10382]
Intl. Green Energy Coun. [6116]
Intl. Soc. of Sustainability Professionals [4340]
Natl. Alliance of Forest Owners [4404]
Natl. Assn. for Moisture Mgt. [1223]
Natl. Assn. of Mold Professionals [1224]
Natl. Org. of Remediators and Mold Inspectors
[1225]
Natl. Wildlife Fed. [4103]

Reference to "IO" in place of a book number signifies that the association may be found in the 50th edition of International Organizations.

Nature Abounds [4291]
Network of Conservation Educators and Practitioners [4113]
Noise Free Am. [4739]
Oil Change Intl. [4230]
People 4 Earth [4296]
Plastic Pollution Coalition [4799]
Protect Our Winters [4298]
Religious Witness for the Earth [4341]
Renew Am. [3973]
Rising Tide North Am. [4131]
SkyTruth [4342]
Strategic Energy, Environmental and Trans. Alternatives [8122]
Transition U.S. [4343]
Women and the Env. Org. [4323]
Worldwide Pollution Control Assn. [2789]
Environmental Res. and Educ. Found. [4337], 3301 Benson Dr., Ste. 301, Raleigh, NC 27609, (919)861-6876
Environmental Res. Found. [13638], PO Box 160, New Brunswick, NJ 08903, (732)828-9995
Environmental Rights Action [IO], Benin City, Nigeria
Environmental Risk Resources Assn. [4260], 4901 Pine Cone Cir., Middleton, WI 53562, (877)735-0800
Environmental Safety Gp. [IO], Gibraltar, Gibraltar
Environmental Sciences and Tech; Inst. of [7331]
Environmental Sciences and Tech; Inst. of [7331]
Environmental Services Assn. [IO], London, United Kingdom
Environmental Stud. Assn. of Canada [IO], Waterloo, ON, Canada
Environmental Stud. Gp. [IO], Mexico City, Mexico
Environmental Transport Assn. [IO], Weybridge, United Kingdom
Environmental Working Group [4261], 1436 U St. NW, Ste. 100, Washington, DC 20009, (202)667-6982
Environmentalists Against War [18777], PO Box 27, Berkeley, CA 94701, (510)843-3343
Environnement et developpement du tiers monde [★IO]
Environnement et Developpement du Tiers Monde [★IO]
Environnement Jeunesse [IO], Montreal, QC, Canada
Enzymology
Intl. Soc. for IGF Res. [6851]
Intl. Soc. for IGF Res. [6851]
Epagneul Breton USA [★21541]
Ephemera
Ephemera Soc. of Am. [21704]
Ephemera Soc. [IO], Northwood, United Kingdom
Ephemera Soc. of Am. [21704], PO Box 95, Cazenovia, NY 13035-0095, (315)655-9139
Ephphatha Services [★19924]
Ephphatha Services for the Deaf and Blind [★19924]
Ephphatha Services - Div. for Services and Mission in Am. [★19924]
EPIC - Electronically Published Internet Connection [22110], PO Box 90364, Portland, OR 97290
Epic Enterprises [★337]
Epicor Users Gp. [6511], PO Box 10368, Lancaster, PA 17605-0368, (717)209-7177
Epidemiology
Aeras Global TB Vaccine Found. [14510]
Aeras Global TB Vaccine Found. [14510]
Amer. Coll. of Epidemiology [14511]
Community Info. and Epidemiological Technologies [11978]
Community Info. and Epidemiological Technologies [11978]
Coun. of State and Territorial Epidemiologists [14512]
Intl. Clinical Epidemiology Network [14513]
Intl. Genetic Epidemiology Soc. [14514]
Intl. Genetic Epidemiology Soc. [14514]
Intl. Soc. for Disease Surveillance [14395]
Soc. for Epidemiologic Res. [14515]
Soc. for Healthcare Epidemiology of Am. [14516]
Epidermolysis Bullosa Res. Assn. of Am; Dystrophic [14325]
EPIE Inst. [8311], PO Box 590, Hampton Bays, NY 11946-0509, (631)728-9100

Epigraphic Soc. [6166], Mr. Donal B. Buchanan, Sec.-Treas./Ed., 97 Village Post Rd., Danvers, MA 01923, (978)774-1275
Epilepsi Cymru [★IO]
Epilepsie Canada [★IO]
Epilepsy
Amer. Epilepsy Soc. [14517]
Brainwave The Irish Epilepsy Assn. [10999]
Citizens United for Res. in Epilepsy [14518]
Dravet.org [14519]
Epilepsy Found. [14520]
Epilepsy Scotland [21831]
Epilepsy Therapy Proj. [14521]
Parents Against Childhood Epilepsy [14522]
Epilepsy Action Scotland [★21831]
Epilepsy Assn. of the Australian Capital Territory [IO], Canberra, Australia
Epilepsy Assn. of Calgary [IO], Calgary, AB, Canada
Epilepsy Assn. - Central Alberta Off. [IO], Red Deer, AB, Canada
Epilepsy Assn. of Nova Scotia [IO], Halifax, NS, Canada
Epilepsy Assn. of Pakistan [IO], Karachi, Pakistan
Epilepsy Assn. of Scotland [★21831]
Epilepsy Assn. of South Australia and Northern Territory [IO], Woodville, Australia
Epilepsy Assn. of Tasmania - Burnie [IO], Burnie, Australia
Epilepsy Assn. of Tasmania - Hobart [IO], Launceston, Australia
Epilepsy Assn. of Tasmania - Launceston [IO], Launceston, Australia
Epilepsy Assn. of Western Australia [IO], Nedlands, Australia
Epilepsy Australia - New South Wales [IO], Sydney, Australia
Epilepsy Canada [IO], Toronto, ON, Canada
Epilepsy Care Gp. - Singapore [IO], Singapore, Singapore
Epilepsy Concern Service Group - Defunct.
Epilepsy Cornwall and Area [IO], Cornwall, ON, Canada
Epilepsy Durham Region [IO], Oshawa, ON, Canada
Epilepsy Found. [14520], 8301 Professional Pl., Landover, MD 20785-2223, (301)459-3700
Epilepsy Huron-Perth-Bruce [IO], Seaforth, ON, Canada
Epilepsy Kingston [IO], Kingston, ON, Canada
Epilepsy Mississauga [IO], Mississauga, ON, Canada
Epilepsy New Zealand [IO], Hamilton, New Zealand
Epilepsy New Zealand - Canterbury [IO], Christchurch, New Zealand
Epilepsy New Zealand - North Shore and Rodney [IO], North Shore City, New Zealand
Epilepsy New Zealand - Otago [IO], Dunedin, New Zealand
Epilepsy New Zealand - Rotorua [IO], Rotorua, New Zealand
Epilepsy New Zealand - South Canterbury [IO], Timaru, New Zealand
Epilepsy New Zealand - Southland Br. [IO], Invercargill, New Zealand
Epilepsy New Zealand - Taranaki [IO], New Plymouth, New Zealand
Epilepsy New Zealand - Waikato [IO], Hamilton, New Zealand
Epilepsy New Zealand - Wanganui [IO], Wanganui, New Zealand
Epilepsy New Zealand - Wellington [IO], Wellington, New Zealand
Epilepsy Newfoundland and Labrador [IO], St. John's, NL, Canada
Epilepsy Niagara [IO], Niagara Falls, ON, Canada
Epilepsy North Bay [IO], North Bay, ON, Canada
Epilepsy Ontario [IO], Thornhill, ON, Canada
Epilepsy Ottawa-Carleton [IO], Ottawa, ON, Canada
Epilepsy Peterborough and Area [IO], Peterborough, ON, Canada
Epilepsy Queensland, Inc. [IO], Coorparoo, Australia
Epilepsy Regina [IO], Regina, SK, Canada
Epilepsy Saskatoon [IO], Saskatoon, SK, Canada
Epilepsy Sault Ste. Marie [IO], Sault Ste. Marie, ON, Canada
Epilepsy Scotland [IO], Glasgow, United Kingdom

Epilepsy and Seizure Assn. of Manitoba [IO], Winnipeg, MB, Canada
Epilepsy Simcoe County [IO], Barrie, ON, Canada
Epilepsy Soc. of Australia [IO], Sydney, Australia
Epilepsy Soc. of Cyprus [IO], Nicosia, Cyprus
Epilepsy Soc. of Malta [IO], Msida, Malta
Epilepsy Soc. of Thailand [IO], Bangkok, Thailand
Epilepsy South Africa [IO], Cape Town, Republic of South Africa
Epilepsy Sudbury/Manitoulin [IO], Sudbury, ON, Canada
Epilepsy Therapy Development Proj. [★14521]
Epilepsy Therapy Proj. [14521], PO Box 742, Middleburg, VA 20118, (540)687-8077
Epilepsy Toronto [IO], Toronto, ON, Canada
Epilepsy Wales [IO], Cardiff, United Kingdom
Epilepsy Waterloo-Wellington [IO], Kitchener, ON, Canada
Epilepsy Windsor/Essex County [IO], London, ON, Canada
Epilepsy York Region [IO], Richmond Hill, ON, Canada
Epileptology Soc. of Chile [IO], Santiago, Chile
Epiphyllum Soc. of Am. [21791], PO Box 1395, Monrovia, CA 91017-1395
Episcopal
Anglicans United [19689]
Assembly of Episcopal Healthcare Chaplains [19690]
Assoc. Parishes for Liturgy and Mission [19691]
Assn. of Episcopal Colleges [8162]
Assn. of Episcopal Colleges [8162]
Assn. for Episcopal Deacons [19692]
Brotherhood of Saint Andrew [19693]
Church Army [19694]
Church Pension Fund [19695]
Church Periodical Club [19696]
Confraternity of the Blessed Sacrament [19697]
Episcopal Church Building Fund [19698]
Episcopal Communicators [19699]
Episcopal Conf. of the Deaf [19700]
Episcopal Partnership for Global Mission [19701]
Episcopal Women's Caucus [19702]
Episcopalians for Global Reconciliation [19703]
Evangelical Educ. Soc. [19704]
Faith Alive [19705]
Fellowship of Saint Paul [19706]
Forward in Faith North Am. [19707]
Found. for Christian Theology [19708]
Found. for Christian Theology [19708]
Global Teams [19709]
Global Teams [19709]
Historical Soc. of the Episcopal Church [19710]
Intl. Order of St. Vincent [19711]
Intl. Order of St. Vincent [19711]
Living Church Found. [19712]
Natl. Assn. for Episcopal Christian Educ. Directors [7856]
Natl. Assn. of Episcopal Schools [8163]
Natl. Episcopal Scouters Assn. [13024]
Natl. Network of Episcopal Clergy Associations [19713]
New Wineskins Missionary Network [20075]
Order of the Daughters of the King [19714]
Recovered Alcoholic Clergy Assn. [13286]
Seamen's Church Inst. of New York and New Jersey [19715]
Soc. of Anglican Missionaries and Senders [20094]
Soc. of the Companions of the Holy Cross [19716]
Soc. for Promoting and Encouraging Arts and Knowledge of the Church [19717]
Episcopal Actors' Guild of Am. [10576], Little Church Around the Corner, 1 E 29th St., New York, NY 10016-7405, (212)685-2927
Episcopal Church Building Fund [19698], 583A Southlake Blvd., Richmond, VA 23226, (804)592-3512
Episcopal Church Missionary Community [★20075]
Episcopal Church's Presiding Bishop's Fund for World Relief [★12835]
Episcopal Church's Presiding Bishop's Fund for World Relief [★12835]
Episcopal Communicators [19699], Bill Slocumb, Membership Coor., 15820 S Military Trail, Delray Beach, FL 33484

A star before a book entry number signifies that the name is not listed separately, but is mentioned within the entry.

Episcopal Conf. of the Deaf **[19700]**, 6919 Strathmore St., Bethesda, MD 20815, (301)907-7855
Episcopal Evangelical Educ. Soc. **[★19704]**
Episcopal Evangelical Fellowship **[★19704]**
Episcopal Pacifist Fellowship **[★18616]**
Episcopal Partnership for Global Mission **[19701]**, 4846 N Paulina St., No. 2W, Chicago, IL 60640, (773)944-0820
Episcopal Peace Fellowship **[18616]**, 637 S Dearborn St., Ste. 1, Chicago, IL 60605, (312)922-8628
Episcopal Relief and Development **[12835]**, 815 2nd Ave., 7th Fl., New York, NY 10017, (800)334-7626
Episcopal Relief and Development **[12835]**, 815 2nd Ave., 7th Fl., New York, NY 10017, (800)334-7626
Episcopal School Assn. **[★8163]**
Episcopal Soc. for Ministry on Aging - Defunct.
Episcopal Synod of Am. **[★19707]**
Episcopal Women's Caucus **[19702]**, 413 Buffware Ct., Charleston, SC 29492
Episcopal World Mission **[★19709]**
Episcopal World Mission **[★19709]**
Episcopalian
  Anglicans United **[19689]**
  Brotherhood of Saint Andrew **[19693]**
  Episcopal Women's Caucus **[19702]**
  Evangelical Educ. Soc. **[19704]**
  Global Teams **[19709]**
  New Wineskins Missionary Network **[20075]**
  Soc. of Anglican Missionaries and Senders **[20094]**
  Soc. of the Companions of the Holy Cross **[19716]**
Episcopalians for Global Reconciliation **[19703]**, 2202 Willwood Hollow Dr., Valrico, FL 33596, (813)333-1832
Episcopalians for Life **[★12923]**
Episcopalians United **[★19689]**
Episcopalians United for Revelation, Renewal, and Reformation **[★19689]**
Epitestudomanyi Egyesulet **[★IO]**
Epping Forest Conservation Volunteers **[IO]**, London, United Kingdom
EPS Molders Assn. **[2768]**, 1298 Cronson Blvd., Ste. 201, Crofton, MD 21114, (410)451-8341
Epsilon Eta Phi **[★23483]**
Epsilon Pi Tau **[23755]**, Bowling Green State Univ., 105 A Tech. Bldg., Bowling Green, OH 43403-0296, (419)372-2425
Epsilon Pi Tau **[23755]**, Bowling Green State Univ., 105 A Tech. Bldg., Bowling Green, OH 43403-0296, (419)372-2425
Epsilon Sigma Alpha **[23642]**, 363 W Drake Rd., Fort Collins, CO 80526, (970)223-2824
Epsilon Sigma Phi **[23496]**, 450 Falls Ave., Ste. 106, Twin Falls, ID 83301, (208)736-4495
Equal Access **[8166]**, 271 Austin St., San Francisco, CA 94109, (415)561-4884
Equal Education
  Assn. for Gender Equity Leadership in Educ. **[8164]**
  Educational Equity Center **[8165]**
  Equal Access **[8166]**
  Minority Student Achievement Network **[8167]**
Equal Employment Advisory Coun. **[11938]**, 1501 M St. NW, Ste. 400, Washington, DC 20005, (202)629-5650
Equal Justice Soc. **[5972]**, 260 California St., Ste. 700, San Francisco, CA 94111, (415)288-8700
Equal Justice Works **[5618]**, 2120 L St. NW, Ste. 450, Washington, DC 20037-1541, (202)466-3686
Equal Rights Advocates **[5934]**, 180 Howard St., Ste. 300, San Francisco, CA 94105, (415)621-0672
Equal Rights for Argentine Women **[IO]**, Buenos Aires, Argentina
Equality Commn. for Northern Ireland **[IO]**, Belfast, United Kingdom
Equality Fed. **[17736]**, 567 Sutter St., 3rd Fl., San Francisco, CA 94102, (415)252-0510
Equator Initiative **[11581]**, 405 Lexington Ave., 5th Fl., New York, NY 10174, (212)457-1709
Equator Initiative **[11581]**, 405 Lexington Ave., 5th Fl., New York, NY 10174, (212)457-1709
Equatorial Guinea Badminton Fed. **[IO]**, Malabo, Equatorial Guinea

Equatorial Guinea Tennis Fed. **[IO]**, Malabo, Equatorial Guinea
Equestrian Assn; Gladstone **[22680]**
Equestrian Club of Riyadh **[IO]**, Riyadh, Saudi Arabia
Equestrian Fed. of Ireland **[IO]**, Kildare, Ireland
Equestrian Land Conservation Rsrc. **[★4827]**
Equestrian Ministries Intl. **[19816]**, PO Box 164, Wilmore, KY 40390, (859)858-3511
Equine Advocates **[10958]**, PO Box 354, Chatham, NY 12037-0354, (518)245-1599
Equine Assisted Growth and Learning Assn. **[16460]**, PO Box 993, Santaquin, UT 84655, (801)754-0400
Equine Assisted Growth and Learning Assn. **[16460]**, PO Box 993, Santaquin, UT 84655, (801)754-0400
Equine Canada **[IO]**, Ottawa, ON, Canada
Equine Guided Educ. Assn. **[8275]**, PO Box 415, Valley Ford, CA 94972, (707)876-1908
Equine Land Conservation Rsrc. **[4827]**, 4037 Iron Works Pike, Ste. 120, Lexington, KY 40511, (859)455-8383
Equine Protection Network **[5053]**, PO Box 232, Friedensburg, PA 17933
Equine Rescue League **[10959]**, PO Box 4366, Leesburg, VA 20177, (540)822-4577
EQUIP Liberia **[IO]**, Monrovia, Liberia
Equip. Appraisers Assn. of North Am. **[229]**, 1270 State Rte. 30, Clinton, PA 15026, (800)790-1053
Equip. Appraisers Assn. of North Am. **[229]**, 1270 State Rte. 30, Clinton, PA 15026, (800)790-1053
Equip. Leasing Assn. **[★3078]**
Equip. Leasing Assn. **[★3078]**
Equip. Leasing Assn. of Am. **[★3078]**
Equip. Leasing Assn. of Am. **[★3078]**
Equip. Leasing and Finance Assn. **[3078]**, 1825 K St. NW, Ste. 900, Washington, DC 20006, (202)238-3400
Equip. Leasing and Finance Assn. **[3078]**, 1825 K St. NW, Ste. 900, Washington, DC 20006, (202)238-3400
Equip. Maintenance Coun. **[★1807]**
Equip. Maintenance Coun. **[★1807]**
Equip. Managers Coun. of Am. **[845]**, PO Box 794, South Amboy, NJ 08879-0794, (610)360-1736
Equip. Mfrs. Coun. **[167]**, Amer. Feed Indus. Assn., 2101 Wilson Blvd., Ste. 916, Arlington, VA 22201, (703)524-0810
Equip. Mfrs. Inst. **[★166]**
Equip. Mfrs. Inst. **[★166]**
Equip. Marketing and Distribution Assn. **[2317]**, Box 1347, Iowa City, IA 52244, (319)354-5156
Equip. Ser. Assn. **[3234]**, Heather Phillips, Exec. Dir., PO Box 1420, Cherry Hill, NJ 08034, (856)489-0753
Equip. and Tool Inst. **[326]**, 134 W Univ. Dr., Ste. 205, Rochester, MI 48307, (248)656-5080
Equitable Reserve Assn. **[19046]**, 116 S Commercial St., PO Box 448, Neenah, WI 54957-0448, (800)722-1574
Equitas - Centre Intl. d'education aux droits humains **[★IO]**
Equitas - Intl. Centre for Human Rights Educ. **[IO]**, Montreal, QC, Canada
Equitoy **[IO]**, Cranbrook, United Kingdom
Equity **[IO]**, London, United Kingdom
Erasmus Student Network **[IO]**, Brussels, Belgium
Erb's Palsy Assn. of Ireland **[IO]**, Blackrock, Ireland
Ercoupe Owners Club **[20893]**, 52 Hunters Ln., Timberlake, NC 27583-8781, (919)471-9492
Ergonomics Soc. of South Africa **[IO]**, Parkview, Republic of South Africa
Ergonomics Soc. - Sweden **[IO]**, Stockholm, Sweden
Ergonomisallskapet, Sverige **[★IO]**
ERIC Clearinghouse on Adult, Career, and Vocational Educ. - Defunct.
ERIC CH on Disabilities and Gifted Education **[★8879]**
ERIC CH on Disabilities and Gifted Education **[★11788]**
ERIC CH on Disabilities and Gifted Education **[★11788]**
ERIC CH on Languages and Linguistics **[8470]**, 4646 40th St. NW, Washington, DC 20016-1859, (202)362-0700

Erikoishammasteknikkoliitto ry **[★IO]**
ERISA Indus. Comm. **[1126]**, 1400 L St. NW, Ste. 350, Washington, DC 20005, (202)789-1400
Eritrean Natl. Badminton Fed. **[IO]**, Asmara, Eritrea
Eritrean Natl. War Disabled Veterans Assn. **[IO]**, Asmara, Eritrea
Eritrean Tennis Fed. **[IO]**, Asmara, Eritrea
Erklarung von Bern **[★IO]**
Ernst Bacon Soc. **[10194]**, 8 Drovers Ln., DeWitt, NY 13214
Erosion Control Tech. Coun. **[4925]**, PO Box 18012, St. Paul, MN 55118, (651)554-1895
Erosion Control Tech. Coun. **[4925]**, PO Box 18012, St. Paul, MN 55118, (651)554-1895
Errors, Freaks and Oddities Collectors' Club **[22037]**, 3561 Country Ct. N, Mobile, AL 36619-5335
Erskine Alumni Assn. **[18871]**, Erskine Colorado, 2 Washington St., Due West, SC 29639, (864)369-6319
Erskine Registry **[21052]**, 1144 Dockside Dr., Lutz, FL 33559, (813)948-1822
ERTHNXT **[4052]**, 11100 Wildlife Center Dr., Reston, VA 20190, (703)438-6500
The Erythromelalgia Assn. **[14385]**, 200 Old Castle Ln., Wallingford, PA 19086, (610)566-0797
ESA **[18617]**, 6 E Lancaster Ave., Wynnewood, PA 19096, (610)645-9390
ESA Intl. **[★23642]**
Esalen Inst. **[9823]**, 55000 Hwy. 1, Big Sur, CA 93920-9546, (831)667-3000
Escadrilles Canadiennes de Plaisance **[★IO]**
Escapees **[22137]**, 100 Rainbow Dr., Livingston, TX 77351, (936)327-8873
Escarre Intl. Center for the Ethnic Minorities and Nations **[IO]**, Barcelona, Spain
Esclerosis Multiple Argentina **[IO]**, Buenos Aires, Argentina
Escoffier Soc. of Toronto **[IO]**, Toronto, ON, Canada
Escort Carrier Sailors and Airmen Assn. **[20694]**, Ralph Magerkurth, Membership Chm., 13114 Blue Bonnet Dr., Sun City, AZ 85375, (716)474-1670
ESIB - Natl. Unions of Students in Europe **[★18]**
Eskridge Family Assn. **[20513]**, Fran Markowski, Treas., PO Box 102, Dagsboro, DE 19939
ESOMAR: World Assn. of Opinion and Marketing Res. Professionals **[IO]**, Amsterdam, Netherlands
ESOP Assn. **[1136]**, 1726 M St. NW, Ste. 501, Washington, DC 20036, (202)293-2971
ESOP Coun. of Am. **[★1136]**
Esophageal Cancer Awareness Assn. **[13920]**, PO Box 55071, Boston, MA 02205-5071, (800)601-0613
Espaco t **[★IO]**
Esperanca **[14775]**, 1911 W Earll Dr., Phoenix, AZ 85015, (602)252-7772
Esperanca **[14775]**, 1911 W Earll Dr., Phoenix, AZ 85015, (602)252-7772
Esperantic Stud. Found. **[IO]**, Burnaby, BC, Canada
Esperanto
  Esperanto-USA **[9583]**
  Intl. Soc. of Friendship and Good Will **[9584]**
  Intl. Soc. of Friendship and Good Will **[9584]**
Esperanto-Asocio de Skotlando **[★IO]**
Esperanto Cultural Centre **[IO]**, La Chaux-de-Fonds, Switzerland
Esperanto Info. Center **[★9583]**
Esperanto League for North Am. **[★9583]**
Esperanto-USA **[9583]**, PO Box 1129, El Cerrito, CA 94530, (510)380-6629
ESPRIT **[IO]**, Brussels, Belgium
Esquel Gp. Found. - Brazil **[IO]**, Brasilia, Brazil
Essential Info. **[17342]**, PO Box 19405, Washington, DC 20036, (202)387-8030
Essential Oil Assn. of the U.S.A. **[★1522]**
Essex Chamber of Commerce **[IO]**, Colchester, United Kingdom
Estate Management
  Natl. Assn. of Financial and Estate Planning **[1316]**
  Soc. of Trust and Estate Practitioners USA **[1226]**
Esther A. and Joseph Klingenstein Fund **[15341]**, Mr. John Klingenstein, Pres., 787 7th Ave., 6th Fl., New York, NY 10019-6016, (212)492-6195
Esther Stevens Brazer Guild **[★9212]**

Reference to "IO" in place of a book number signifies that the association may be found in the 50th edition of International Organizations.

Esther's Aid for Needy and Abandoned Children
[11270], 271 North Ave., New Rochelle, NY 10801,
(914)235-5595
Esti Punane Rist **[★IO]**
Estonia
  Estonian Amer. Chamber of Commerce and
  Indus. **[23398]**
Estonia Natl. Comm. of Geomorphology **[IO]**, Tallinn,
  Estonia
Estonia Physiological Soc. **[IO]**, Tartu, Estonia
Estonia Red Cross **[IO]**, Tallinn, Estonia
Estonian
  Estonian Amer. Natl. Coun. **[18982]**
Estonian Acad. of Sciences **[IO]**, Tallinn, Estonia
Estonian Amer. Chamber of Commerce and Indus.
  [23398], 157-61 17th Ave., Whitestone, NY 11357,
  (718)747-3805
Estonian Amer. Fund for Economic Educ. **[7985]**, 4
  Noyes Ct., Silver Spring, MD 20910, (301)587-
  9115
Estonian Amer. Fund for Economic Educ. **[7985]**, 4
  Noyes Ct., Silver Spring, MD 20910, (301)587-
  9115
Estonian Amer. Natl. Coun. **[18982]**, 9814 Hill St.,
  Kensington, MD 20895-3135, (301)587-8353
Estonian Artists' Assn. **[IO]**, Tallinn, Estonia
Estonian Assn. of Info. Tech. and Telecommunica-
  tions **[IO]**, Tallinn, Estonia
Estonian Assn. for Personnel Development **[IO]**,
  Tallinn, Estonia
Estonian Assn. for Rheumatology **[IO]**, Tallinn,
  Estonia
Estonian Assn. of Travel Agencies **[IO]**, Tallinn,
  Estonia
Estonian Assn. of Travel Agents **[★22494]**
Estonian Assn. of Univ. Women **[IO]**, Tartu, Estonia
Estonian Athletic Assn. **[IO]**, Tallinn, Estonia
Estonian Badminton Fed. **[IO]**, Tallinn, Estonia
Estonian Banking Assn. **[IO]**, Tallinn, Estonia
Estonian Bible Soc. **[IO]**, Tallinn, Estonia
Estonian Bus. Assn. **[IO]**, Tallinn, Estonia
Estonian Chamber of Commerce and Indus. **[IO]**,
  Tallinn, Estonia
Estonian Choral Assn. **[IO]**, Tallinn, Estonia
Estonian Clothing and Textile Assn. **[IO]**, Tallinn,
  Estonia
Estonian Clothing and Textiles Mfrs'. Assn. **[★20504]**
Estonian Dairy Assn. **[IO]**, Tallinn, Estonia
Estonian Dance Sport Assn. **[IO]**, Tallinn, Estonia
Estonian Dentistry Students' Assn. **[IO]**, Tartu,
  Estonia
Estonian Draughts Fed. **[IO]**, Tallinn, Estonia
Estonian Economic Assn. **[IO]**, Tallinn, Estonia
Estonian Educ. Personnel Union **[IO]**, Tallinn,
  Estonia
Estonian Employers Confed. **[IO]**, Tallinn, Estonia
Estonian Floorball Union **[IO]**, Tallinn, Estonia
Estonian Football Assn. **[IO]**, Tallinn, Estonia
Estonian Fund for Nature **[IO]**, Tartu, Estonia
Estonian Gambling Operator Assn. **[IO]**, Tallinn,
  Estonia
Estonian Geotechnical Soc. **[IO]**, Tallinn, Estonia
Estonian Gerontology and Geriatrics Assn. **[IO]**,
  Tartu, Estonia
Estonian Heart Assn. **[IO]**, Tallinn, Estonia
Estonian Hotel and Restaurant Assn. **[IO]**, Tallinn,
  Estonia
Estonian Info. Tech. Soc. **[IO]**, Tallinn, Estonia
Estonian Inst. **[IO]**, Tallinn, Estonia
Estonian Inst. of Human Rights **[IO]**, Tallinn, Estonia
Estonian Insurance Assn. **[IO]**, Tallinn, Estonia
Estonian League Against Epilepsy **[IO]**, Tartu,
  Estonia
Estonian Learned Soc. of America - Defunct.
Estonian Librarians' Assn. **[IO]**, Tallinn, Estonia
Estonian Medical Assn. **[IO]**, Tartu, Estonia
Estonian Music Center, U.S.A. - Defunct.
Estonian Newspaper Assn. **[IO]**, Tallinn, Estonia
Estonian Olympic Comm. **[IO]**, Tallinn, Estonia
Estonian Orienteering Fed. **[IO]**, Tallinn, Estonia
Estonian Osteoporosis Soc. **[IO]**, Tartu, Estonia
Estonian Pain Soc. **[IO]**, Tallinn, Estonia
Estonian Paralympic Comm. **[IO]**, Tallinn, Estonia
Estonian Peat Assn. **[IO]**, Tallinn, Estonia
Estonian Physical Soc. **[IO]**, Tartu, Estonia

Estonian Physiotherapists Assn. **[IO]**, Tallinn, Estonia
Estonian Press Coun. **[IO]**, Tallinn, Estonia
Estonian Radio Amateurs Union **[IO]**, Tallinn, Estonia
Estonian Reform Party **[IO]**, Tallinn, Estonia
Estonian Relief Comm. **[12836]**, Estonian House,
  243 E 34th St., New York, NY 10016, (212)684-
  0336
Estonian Relief Comm. **[12836]**, Estonian House,
  243 E 34th St., New York, NY 10016, (212)684-
  0336
Estonian Rural Tourism Org. **[IO]**, Tallinn, Estonia
Estonian Schoolsport Union **[IO]**, Tallinn, Estonia
Estonian Scout Assn. **[IO]**, Tallinn, Estonia
Estonian Security Assn. **[IO]**, Tallinn, Estonia
Estonian Sexual Hea. Assn. **[IO]**, Tallinn, Estonia
Estonian Skating Union **[IO]**, Tallinn, Estonia
Estonian Soc. of Cardiology **[IO]**, Tallinn, Estonia
Estonian Soc. of Clinical Neurophysiology **[IO]**,
  Tallinn, Estonia
Estonian Soc. of Gastrointestinal Endoscopy **[IO]**,
  Tallinn, Estonia
Estonian Soc. of Hypertension **[IO]**, Tallinn, Estonia
Estonian Soc. of Merchants **[IO]**, Tallinn, Estonia
Estonian Sports Medicine Fed. **[IO]**, Tallinn, Estonia
Estonian Squash Fed. **[IO]**, Tallinn, Estonia
Estonian Taekwondo Fed. **[IO]**, Tallinn, Estonia
Estonian Tennis Assn. **[IO]**, Tallinn, Estonia
Estonian Traders Assn. **[★7521]**
Estonian Union of Banks **[★13610]**
Estonian Wind Power Assn. **[IO]**, Tallinn, Estonia
Estonian Windsurfing Assn. **[IO]**, Tallinn, Estonia
Estonian Youth Rheumatism Assn. **[IO]**, Tallinn,
  Estonia
Estrela Mountain Dog Assn. of Am. **[21561]**, Gene
  Blackwell, VP, 51888 Long Br. Rd., Heavener, OK
  74937, (918)653-4366
Estuarine and Coastal Sciences Assn. **[IO]**, Dublin,
  Ireland
Eta Kappa Nu **[23518]**, 445 Hoes Ln., Piscataway,
  NJ 08854, (800)406-2590
Eta Phi Beta **[23480]**, 19983 Livernois Ave., Detroit,
  MI 48235, (313)862-0600
Eta Sigma Alpha Natl. Home School Honor Soc.
  [7718], 11665 Fuqua St., Ste. A-100, Houston, TX
  77034, (281)922-0478
Eta Sigma Phi, Natl. Classics Honorary Soc.
  [23493], Monmouth Coll., Dept. of Classics, 700 E
  Broadway, Monmouth, IL 61462-1963, (309)457-
  2371
ETAD: Ecological and Toxicological Assn. of Dyes
  and Organic Pigments Mfrs. **[4789]**, 1850 M St.
  NW, Ste. 700, Washington, DC 20036, (202)721-
  4154
Ethernet Alliance **[7499]**, 3855 SW 153rd Dr., Bea-
  verton, OR 97006, (503)619-0564
The ETHIC - The Essence of True Humanity is
  Compassion **[18166]**, PO Box 6640, Albany, CA
  94706, (866)THE-ETHIC
Ethics
  AAAS Sci. and Human Rights Coalition **[17806]**
  Assn. for Medical Ethics **[14872]**
  Center for Applied Christian Ethics **[19718]**
  Coun. of Ethical Organizations **[1227]**
  Ethics Rsrc. Center **[17250]**
  Funeral Ethics Org. **[11979]**
  Hastings Center **[11980]**
  Inst. for Global Ethics **[6852]**
  Inst. for Global Ethics **[6852]**
  Intl. Feminist Approaches to Bioethics **[11981]**
  Intl. Feminist Approaches to Bioethics **[11981]**
  Intl. Intelligence Ethics Assn. **[7001]**
  Intl. Soc. for Ethics and Info. Tech. **[6979]**
  Joseph and Edna Josephson Inst. of Ethics
    [11982]
  Joseph P. and Rose F. Kennedy Inst. of Ethics
    [11983]
  Neuroethics Soc. **[15679]**
  Oper. Respect **[8168]**
  Semmelweis Soc. Intl. **[16510]**
  Soc. for Bus. Ethics **[11984]**
  Soc. for Bus. Ethics **[11984]**
  Soc. of Christian Ethics **[11985]**
  Unitarian Universalist Assn. of Congregations
    [12903]
Ethics and Compliance Officer Assn. **[662]**, 411 Wa-
  verley Oaks Rd., Ste. 324, Waltham, MA 02452-
  8420, (781)647-9333

Ethics Inst. **[IO]**, Utrecht, Netherlands
Ethics Officer Assn. **[★662]**
Ethics and Public Policy Center **[18458]**, 1730 M St.
  NW, Ste. 910, Washington, DC 20036, (202)682-
  1200
Ethics and Religious Liberty Commn. of the
  Southern Baptist Convention **[19320]**, 901 Com-
  merce St., Ste. 550, Nashville, TN 37203-3600,
  (615)244-2495
Ethics Rsrc. Center **[17250]**, 2345 Crystal Dr., Ste.
  201, Arlington, VA 22202-4807, (703)647-2185
EthicsCentre CA **[IO]**, Toronto, ON, Canada
Ethiek Instituut **[★IO]**
Ethington Family Org. - Defunct.
Ethiopia
  Amer. Outreach to Ethiopia **[12265]**
  Clinic at a Time **[15152]**
  Ethiopian North Amer. Hea. Professionals Assn.
    [14776]
  Ethiopian Orphan Relief **[11271]**
  Hands for Autistic Children of Ethiopia **[11121]**
  Intl. Partnership for Reproductive Hea. **[16587]**
  Irob Relief and Rehabilitation Operations Brother-
    hood **[11986]**
  Network Ethiopia **[15199]**
  Water is Life Intl. **[13435]**
  Water to Thrive **[13439]**
Ethiopian
  Ethiopian Geophysical Union Intl. **[6920]**
  Ethiopian Orphan Relief **[11271]**
Ethiopian Athletic Fed. **[IO]**, Addis Ababa, Ethiopia
Ethiopian Badminton Fed. **[IO]**, Addis Ababa,
  Ethiopia
Ethiopian Community Development Coun. **[12779]**,
  901 S Highland St., Arlington, VA 22204, (703)685-
  0510
Ethiopian Community Development Coun. **[12779]**,
  901 S Highland St., Arlington, VA 22204, (703)685-
  0510
Ethiopian Diabetes Assn. **[IO]**, Addis Ababa, Ethiopia
Ethiopian Economic Assn. **[IO]**, Addis Ababa,
  Ethiopia
Ethiopian Evangelical Church Mekane Yesus **[IO]**,
  Addis Ababa, Ethiopia
Ethiopian Free-Press Journalists Assn. **[IO]**, Addis
  Ababa, Ethiopia
Ethiopian Geophysical Union Intl. **[6920]**, Univ. of
  Connecticut, Dept. of Civil and Environmental
  Engg., 261 Glenbrook Rd., Unit - 2037, Storrs
  Mansfield, CT 06269-2037
Ethiopian Medical Assn. **[IO]**, Addis Ababa, Ethiopia
Ethiopian North Amer. Hea. Professionals Assn.
  [14776], 6632 Telegraph Rd., Box 150, Bloomfield
  Hills, MI 48301, (313)872-2000
Ethiopian Orphan Relief **[11271]**, 3020 SW Christy
  Ave., Beaverton, OR 97005
Ethiopian Pharmacists Assn. in North Am.
Ethiopian Pharmacists Assn. in North Am. - Address
  unknown since 2011.
Ethiopian Tennis Fed. **[IO]**, Addis Ababa, Ethiopia
Ethiopian Weightlifting Fed. **[IO]**, Addis Ababa,
  Ethiopia
Ethiopian World Taekwondo Fed. **[IO]**, Addis Ababa,
  Ethiopia
Ethiopia's Tomorrow **[11272]**, 28 Hoffman St.,
  Maplewood, NJ 07040
Ethnic Minorities Development Assn. **[IO]**, Blackburn,
  United Kingdom
Ethnic Studies
  Amer. Soc. for Ethnohistory **[9585]**
  Before Columbus Found. **[10036]**
  Ellis Island Medal of Honor Soc. **[18983]**
  Inter-University Prog. for Latino Res. **[18984]**
  Interracial-InterCultural Pride **[12013]**
  Natl. Assn. for Ethnic Stud. **[9586]**
  Natl. Assn. of Hispanic and Latino Stud. **[9587]**
  Natl. Ethnic Coalition of Organizations **[18985]**
  Proj. RACE **[18986]**
Ethnobiology; Soc. of **[6315]**
Ethnobiology; Soc. of **[6315]**
Ethnobotanical Conservation Org. for South East
  Asia **[4053]**, PO Box 77, Mendocino, CA 95460
Ethnobotany Specialist Group - Defunct.
Ethnohistory
  Early Slavic Stud. Assn. **[8863]**

A star before a book entry number signifies that the name is not listed separately, but is mentioned within the entry.

Ethylene Oxide Sterilization Assn. **[754]**, PO Box 33361, Washington, DC 20033, (866)235-5030

Etruscan Found. **[6167]**, Richard F. String, Exec. Dir., PO Box 26, Fremont, MI 49412, (231)519-0675

Etudes d'Oiseaux Canada **[★IO]**

Etudes Tsiganes **[★IO]**

EUCARPIA **[IO]**, Martonvasar, Hungary

EUCC - The Coastal and Marine Union **[IO]**, Leiden, Netherlands

Eucomed **[IO]**, Brussels, Belgium

Eugene L. Garey Cancer Found. **[★15928]**

Eugene O'Neill Memorial Theater Center **[10577]**, 305 Great Neck Rd., Waterford, CT 06385, (860)443-5378

Eugene O'Neill Memorial Theater Found. **[★10577]**

Eugene O'Neill Soc. **[9362]**, 700 Hawthorn Ct., San Ramon, CA 94582, (925)828-0659

Eugene O'Neill Soc. **[9362]**, 700 Hawthorn Ct., San Ramon, CA 94582, (925)828-0659

Eugene V. Debs Found. **[9934]**, PO Box 9454, Terre Haute, IN 47808, (812)232-2163

Eugenics Special Interest Gp. - Address unknown since 2011.

Euler Soc. **[10071]**, Erik R. Tou, Treas., Carthage Coll., Dept. of Mathematics, 2001 Alford Park Dr., Kenosha, WI 53140

Eunice Kennedy Shriver Natl. Inst. of Child Hea. and Human Development **[14074]**, PO Box 3006, Rockville, MD 20847, (301)496-5133

EURATEX: European Apparel and Textile Confed. **[IO]**, Brussels, Belgium

EUREKA **[IO]**, Brussels, Belgium

Eureka - Croatia **[IO]**, Zagreb, Croatia

Eureka Soc. **[20299]**, PO Box 3117, Montrose, CO 81402-3117

Eureka - Ukraine **[IO]**, Kiev, Ukraine

EURISOL, The UK Mineral Wool Assn. **[IO]**, London, United Kingdom

Euro-American Women's Coun. **[17641]**, 147-37 Beech Ave., Ste. 4A, Flushing, NY 11355, (718)321-3179

Euro Banking Assn. **[IO]**, Paris, France

Euro-Children **[IO]**, Antwerp, Belgium

Euro Chlor **[IO]**, Brussels, Belgium

Euro Inst. **[IO]**, Kehl, Germany

Euro-Mediterranean Human Rights Network **[IO]**, Copenhagen, Denmark

EUROAVIA - European Assn. of Aerospace Students **[IO]**, Delft, Netherlands

Eurocare: Advocacy for the Prevention of Alcohol Related Harm in Europe **[IO]**, Brussels, Belgium

Eurocentres Bus. Inst. **[IO]**, London, United Kingdom

EUROCITIES Mobility Forum - ACCESS **[IO]**, Brussels, Belgium

EUROCLIO: European Standing Conf. of History Teachers' Associations **[IO]**, The Hague, Netherlands

EuroCommerce **[IO]**, Brussels, Belgium

Eurofuel **[IO]**, Brussels, Belgium

EuroHealthNet **[IO]**, Brussels, Belgium

Euroheat and Power **[IO]**, Brussels, Belgium

EUROMICRO **[IO]**, St. Augustin, Germany

Euromoulders **[IO]**, Brussels, Belgium

Europa Cantat - European Fed. of Young Choirs **[IO]**, Bonn, Germany

Europa Nostra Pan European Fed. for Heritage **[IO]**, The Hague, Netherlands

Europaeische Evangelikale Akkreditieru **[★IO]**

Europai Folklor Intezet **[★IO]**

Europaische Akademie Otzenhausen **[★IO]**

Europaische Akademie fur stadtische Umwelt **[★IO]**

Europaische Akademie der Wissenschaften und Kunste **[★IO]**

Europaische Baptistische Foderation **[★IO]**

Europaische Baptistische Frauenunion **[★IO]**

Europaische Baptistische Mission **[★IO]**

Europaische Bausparkassenvereinigung **[★IO]**

Europaische Beratervereinigung **[★IO]**

Europaische Evangelische Allianz **[★IO]**

Europaische Fluss-See-Transport Union **[★IO]**

Europaische Foderation der Bergbau-, Chemie-, Und Energie Gewerkschaften **[★IO]**

Europaische Foderation fur Betriebessport **[★IO]**

Europaische Foderation fur Chemie-Ingenieur-Wesen **[★IO]**

Europaische Foderation der Museums - und Touristikbahnen **[★IO]**

Europaische Gesellschaft fur Herbologie **[★IO]**

Europaische Go Fed. **[★IO]**

Europaische Kernenergie-Gesellschaft **[★IO]**

Europaische Marchengesellschaft **[★IO]**

Europaische Metall-Union **[★IO]**

Europaische Musikschul-Union **[★IO]**

Europaische Org. der Militarverbande **[★IO]**

Europaische Radsport Union **[★IO]**

Europaische Schulleitervereinigung **[★IO]**

Europaische Union Judischer Studenten **[★IO]**

Europaische Union der Musikwettbewerbe fur die Jugend **[★IO]**

Europaische Vereinigung der Allgemeinartze **[★IO]**

Europaische Vereinigung der Arzteverbande der besonderen Therapierichtungen **[★IO]**

Europaische Vereinigung der Erdgaswirtschaft **[★IO]**

Europaische Vereinigung der Lack-, Druckfarben- und Kunstlerfarbenindustrie **[★IO]**

Europaische Vereinigung der Verbande der Reformwaren-Hersteller **[★IO]**

Europaische Zentrum fur Minderheitenfragen **[★IO]**

Europaischen Ombudsmann-Institut **[★IO]**

Europaischen Senioren Union **[★IO]**

Europaischen Vereinigung fur Erneuerbare Energien **[★IO]**

Europaischer Fachverband der Arzneimittel-Hersteller **[★IO]**

Europaischer Sportschiffahrtsverband **[★IO]**

Europaischer Verband der Binnenhafen **[★IO]**

Europaischer Verband der Lichtwerbung **[★IO]**

Europaischer Verband der Veranstaltungs-Centren **[★IO]**

Europaischer Verein zur verbrauchsabhangigen Energiekostenabrechnung **[★IO]**

Europaischer Wohnwagen-Verband **[★IO]**

Europaisches Institut fur postgraduale Bildung **[★IO]**

Europaisches Patentamt **[★IO]**

Europalia Intl. **[IO]**, Brussels, Belgium

Europe
Amer. Anthropological Assn. I Soc. for the Anthropology of Europe **[6128]**
Early Slavic Stud. Assn. **[8863]**
Human Rights Watch - Helsinki **[17836]**
New Hope Intl. **[20073]**
U.S. Assn. of Former Members of Cong. **[17414]**

European
Before Columbus Found. **[10036]**
Coun. for European Stud. **[8169]**
Coun. for European Stud. **[8169]**
European-American Unity and Rights Org. **[17288]**
European Democrat Students **[14397]**
European Travel Commn. **[3558]**
European Union Delegation to the U.S. **[17621]**
European Union Delegation to the U.S. **[17621]**
Historians of German and Central European Art and Architecture **[9588]**
IES Abroad **[8170]**
IES Abroad **[8170]**
New Hope Intl. **[20073]**

European Acad. of Allergology and Clinical Immunology **[IO]**, Zurich, Switzerland

European Acad. of Andrology **[IO]**, Rome, Italy

European Acad. of Childhood Disability **[IO]**, Turku, Finland

European Acad. of Dermatology and Venereology **[IO]**, Brussels, Belgium

European Acad. of Design **[IO]**, Lancaster, United Kingdom

European Acad. of Facial Plastic Surgery **[IO]**, Lisbon, Portugal

European Acad. For Aviation Safety **[IO]**, Blagnac, France

European Acad. of Nutritional Sciences **[IO]**, Lausanne, Switzerland

European Acad. Otzenhausen **[IO]**, Nonnweiler, Germany

European Acad. of Paediatric Dentistry **[IO]**, Dublin, Ireland

European Acad. of Sciences and Arts **[IO]**, Salzburg, Austria

European Acad. of Teachers in Gen. Practice **[IO]**, Ljubljana, Slovenia

European Acad. of the Urban Env. **[IO]**, Berlin, Germany

European Accounting Assn. **[IO]**, Brussels, Belgium

European Actuarial Consultative Gp. **[IO]**, Oxford, United Kingdom

European Advt. Standards Alliance **[IO]**, Brussels, Belgium

European Aero-Medical Inst. **[IO]**, Reutlingen, Germany

European Aerosol Fed. **[IO]**, Brussels, Belgium

European Aggregates Assn. **[IO]**, Brussels, Belgium

European AIDS Clinical Soc. **[IO]**, Paris, France

European AIDS Treatment Gp. **[IO]**, Brussels, Belgium

European Alliance of Companies for Energy Efficiency in Buildings **[IO]**, Brussels, Belgium

European Alliance of Neuromuscular Disorders Associations **[IO]**, Gzira, Malta

European Alliance of News Agencies **[IO]**, Stockholm, Sweden

European Aluminium Assn. **[IO]**, Brussels, Belgium

European Aluminum Foil Assn. **[IO]**, Dusseldorf, Germany

European-American Bus. Coun. **[23362]**, 919 18th St. NW, No. 220, Washington, DC 20006, (202)828-9104

European-American Bus. Coun. **[23362]**, 919 18th St. NW, No. 220, Washington, DC 20006, (202)828-9104

European Amer. Chamber of Commerce France **[IO]**, Paris, France

European-American Chamber of Commerce in the U.S. - Address unknown since 2010.

European-American Chamber of Commerce in Washington, DC **[★23362]**

European-American Chamber of Commerce in Washington, DC **[★23362]**

European/American Issues Forum **[17287]**, 1212H El Camino Real, PMB 253, San Bruno, CA 94066, (650)952-8489

European Amer. Musical Alliance **[10195]**, 1160 Fifth Ave., Ste. 201, New York, NY 10029, (212)831-7424

European-American Unity and Rights Org. **[17288]**, PO Box 188, Mandeville, LA 70470, (985)626-7714

European Anti-Poverty Network **[IO]**, Brussels, Belgium

European Apparel and Textile Confed. **[IO]**, Brussels, Belgium

European Aquaculture Soc. **[IO]**, Ostend, Belgium

European Arboricultural Coun. **[IO]**, Bad Honnef, Germany

European Architectural Endoscopy Assn. **[IO]**, Dresden, Germany

European Arenas Assn. **[IO]**, Rotterdam, Netherlands

European Asphalt Pavement Assn. **[IO]**, Brussels, Belgium

European Aspirin Found. **[IO]**, Haslemere, United Kingdom

European Assembly of Turkish Academics **[IO]**, Stuttgart, Germany

European Assn. of Acarologists **[IO]**, Vienna, Austria

European Assn. Against Violence Against Women at Work **[IO]**, Paris, France

European Assn. of Agricultural Economists **[IO]**, The Hague, Netherlands

European Assn. of Air Heater Mfrs. **[IO]**, Menen, Belgium

European Assn. for Amer. Stud. **[IO]**, Halle, Germany

European Assn. for Animal Production **[IO]**, Rome, Italy

European Assn. for Apitherapy **[IO]**, Limoges, France

European Assn. for Aquatic Mammals **[IO]**, Harderwijk, Netherlands

European Assn. of Archaeologists **[IO]**, Prague, Czech Republic

European Assn. of Artists' Managers **[IO]**, Levallois Perret, France

European Assn. of Automotive Suppliers **[IO]**, Brussels, Belgium

European Assn. for Aviation Psychology **[IO]**, Hamburg, Germany

Reference to "IO" in place of a book number signifies that the association may be found in the 50th edition of International Organizations.

European Assn. for Banking and Financial History **[IO]**, Frankfurt am Main, Germany

European Assn. for Battery, Hybrid and Fuel Cell Elec. Vehicles **[IO]**, Brussels, Belgium

European Assn. for Behavioural and Cognitive Therapies **[IO]**, Utrecht, Netherlands

European Assn. for Bioindustries **[IO]**, Brussels, Belgium

European Assn. for Body Psychotherapy **[IO]**, Amsterdam, Netherlands

European Assn. for Cancer Res. **[IO]**, Nottingham, United Kingdom

European Assn. for Cardio-Thoracic Surgery **[IO]**, Windsor, United Kingdom

European Assn. of Centres of Medical Ethics **[IO]**, Maastricht, Netherlands

European Assn. of Chem. Distributors **[IO]**, Brussels, Belgium

European Assn. for Chem. and Molecular Sciences **[IO]**, London, United Kingdom

European Assn. of Chinese Stud. **[IO]**, Cambridge, United Kingdom

European Assn. of Clinical Anatomy **[IO]**, Graz, Austria

European Assn. for Coal and Lignite **[IO]**, Brussels, Belgium

European Assn. of Coleopterology **[IO]**, Barcelona, Spain

European Assn. for Commonwealth Literature and Language Stud. **[IO]**, Liege, Belgium

European Assn. of Communications Agencies **[IO]**, Brussels, Belgium

European Assn. for Comparative Economic Stud. **[IO]**, Brighton, United Kingdom

European Assn. for Cmpt. Assisted Language Learning **[IO]**, Coleraine, Ireland

European Assn. for Cmpt. Graphics **[IO]**, Geneva, Switzerland

European Assn. for Cmpt. Sci. Logic **[IO]**, Bergen, Norway

European Assn. for the Conservation of the Geological Heritage **[IO]**, Uppsala, Sweden

European Assn. of Conservatories **[IO]**, Utrecht, Netherlands

European Assn. of Consultants to and about Not-For-Profit Organisations **[IO]**, Amsterdam, Netherlands

European Assn. for the Consumption-Based Billing of Energy Costs **[IO]**, Bonn, Germany

European Assn. of Cooperative Banks **[IO]**, Brussels, Belgium

European Assn. of Craft, Small and Medium-Sized Enterprises **[IO]**, Brussels, Belgium

European Assn. for Cranio-Maxillofacial Surgery **[IO]**, Midhurst, United Kingdom

European Assn. for Dental Public Hea. **[IO]**, Waiblingen, Germany

European Assn. of Dermato-Oncology **[IO]**, Vienna, Austria

European Assn. of Development Res. and Training Institutes **[IO]**, Bonn, Germany

European Assn. of Dir. and Database Publishers **[IO]**, Brussels, Belgium

European Assn. for Distance Learning **[IO]**, Grootebroek, Netherlands

European Assn. of Distance Teaching Universities **[IO]**, Heerlen, Netherlands

European Assn. for Earthquake Engg. **[IO]**, Istanbul, Turkey

European Assn. for the Educ. of Adults **[IO]**, Brussels, Belgium

European Assn. for Educ. Law and Policy **[IO]**, Antwerp, Belgium

European Assn. for Endoscopic Surgery and Other Interventional Techniques **[IO]**, Veldhoven, Netherlands

European Assn. of Engravers and Flexographers **[IO]**, Wiesbaden, Germany

European Assn. of Environmental and Rsrc. Economists **[IO]**, Venice, Italy

European Assn. of Establishments for Veterinary Educ. **[IO]**, Vienna, Austria

European Assn. of Event Centers **[IO]**, Bad Homburg, Germany

European Assn. for Evolutionary Political Economy **[IO]**, Valbonne, France

European Assn. of Experimental Social Psychology **[IO]**, Munster, Germany

European Assn. of Feldspar Producers **[IO]**, Brussels, Belgium

European Assn. of Fibre Drum Mfrs. **[IO]**, Knaresborough, United Kingdom

European Assn. of Fish Pathologists **[IO]**, Frederiksberg, Denmark

European Assn. of Fisheries Economists **[IO]**, The Hague, Netherlands

European Assn. of Flexible Polyurethane Foam Blocks Mfrs. **[IO]**, Brussels, Belgium

European Assn. for Forensic Child and Adolescent Psychiatry, Psychology and Other Involved Professionals **[IO]**, Manchester, United Kingdom

European Assn. for Geochemistry **[IO]**, Paris, France

European Assn. of Geographers **[IO]**, Liverpool, United Kingdom

European Assn. of Geoscientists and Engineers **[IO]**, Houten, Netherlands

European Assn. for Grain Legume Res. **[IO]**, Paris, France

European Assn. for Hea. Info. and Libraries **[IO]**, Amsterdam, Netherlands

European Assn. for the History of Medicine and Hea. **[IO]**, London, United Kingdom

European Assn. of Hosp. Pharmacists **[IO]**, Leipzig, Germany

European Assn. of Hotel and Tourism Schools **[IO]**, Diekirch, Luxembourg

European Assn. of Indus. Silica Producers **[IO]**, Brussels, Belgium

European Assn. for Info. on Local Development **[IO]**, Brussels, Belgium

European Assn. of Info. Services **[IO]**, Amersfoort, Netherlands

European Assn. for Institutional Res. **[IO]**, Amsterdam, Netherlands

European Assn. of Internal Combustion Engine Mfrs. **[IO]**, Frankfurt, Germany

European Assn. for Intl. Educ. **[IO]**, Amsterdam, Netherlands

European Assn. for Investors in Non-listed Real Estate Vehicles **[IO]**, Amsterdam, Netherlands

European Assn. for Japanese Stud. **[IO]**, Frankfurt, Germany

European Assn. for Jewish Stud. **[IO]**, Oxford, United Kingdom

European Assn. of Labour Economists **[IO]**, Maastricht, Netherlands

European Assn. of Lawyers for Democracy and World Human Rights **[IO]**, Dusseldorf, Germany

European Assn. for Lexicography **[IO]**, Copenhagen, Denmark

European Assn. of Machine Tool Merchants **[IO]**, Brussels, Belgium

European Assn. for Machine Translation **[IO]**, Allschwil, Switzerland

European Assn. of Mfrs. of Moulded Polyurethane Parts for the Automotive Indus. **[IO]**, Brussels, Belgium

European Assn. of Metals **[IO]**, Brussels, Belgium

European Assn. for Microprocessing and Microprogramming **[IO]**, Trondheim, Norway

European Assn. for Middle Eastern Stud. **[IO]**, Mainz, Germany

European Assn. of Mining Indus. **[★402]**

European Assn. of Mining Indus., Metals Ores and Indus. Minerals **[IO]**, Brussels, Belgium

European Assn. of Museums of the History of Medical Sciences **[IO]**, Paris, France

European Assn. of Natl. Organisations of Textile Retailers **[IO]**, Brussels, Belgium

European Assn. of Natl. Productivity Centres **[IO]**, Brussels, Belgium

European Assn. for NeuroOncology **[IO]**, Kaatsheuvel, Netherlands

European Assn. of Neurosurgical Societies **[IO]**, Wiltshire, United Kingdom

European Assn. of Nuclear Medicine **[IO]**, Vienna, Austria

European Assn. of Organic Geochemists **[IO]**, Amsterdam, Netherlands

European Assn. for Osseointegration **[IO]**, Brussels, Belgium

European Assn. for Palliative Care **[IO]**, Milan, Italy

European Assn. for Passive Fire Protection **[IO]**, Bordon, United Kingdom

European Assn. of Perinatal Medicine **[IO]**, Milan, Italy

European Assn. of Personality Psychology **[IO]**, Groningen, Netherlands

European Assn. for Personnel Mgt. **[IO]**, Paris, France

European Assn. of Pharmaceutical Full-Line Wholesalers **[IO]**, Brussels, Belgium

European Assn. for Philanthropy and Giving **[IO]**, London, United Kingdom

European Assn. for Planned Giving **[★20453]**

European Assn. of Plastic Surgeons **[IO]**, Utrecht, Netherlands

European Assn. of Poisons Centres and Clinical Toxicologists **[IO]**, Zurich, Switzerland

European Assn. for Population Stud. **[IO]**, The Hague, Netherlands

European Assn. for Potato Res. **[IO]**, Leuven, Belgium

European Assn. of Professional Secretaries **[IO]**, Bagsvaerd, Denmark

European Assn. for Professions in Biomedical Sci. **[IO]**, Salzburg, Austria

European Assn. for the Promotion of Cogeneration **[IO]**, Brussels, Belgium

European Assn. for the Promotion of Poetry **[IO]**, Gent, Belgium

European Assn. of Psychological Assessment **[IO]**, Ljubljana, Slovenia

European Assn. of Psychology and Law **[IO]**, Erlangen, Germany

European Assn. for Psychotherapy **[IO]**, Vienna, Austria

European Assn. of Pump Mfrs. **[IO]**, Brussels, Belgium

European Assn. of Remote Sensing Labs. **[IO]**, Hannover, Germany

European Assn. for Renewable Energy **[IO]**, Bonn, Germany

European Assn. for Res. on Adolescence **[IO]**, Utrecht, Netherlands

European Assn. for. Res. on Learning and Instruction **[IO]**, Leuven, Belgium

European Assn. of Res. and Tech. Organisations **[IO]**, Brussels, Belgium

European Assn. of the Rubber Indus. (BLIC) **[★197]**

European Assn. of Schools of Occupational Medicine **[IO]**, Utrecht, Netherlands

European Assn. of Schools of Social Work **[IO]**, Geel, Belgium

European Assn. for the Sci. of Air Pollution **[IO]**, Apeldoorn, Netherlands

European Assn. of Sci. Editors **[IO]**, Reading, United Kingdom

European Assn. for the Self-Adhesive Tape Indus. **[IO]**, The Hague, Netherlands

European Assn. of Senior Hosp. Physicians **[IO]**, Brussels, Belgium

European Assn. of Ser. Providers for Persons with Disabilities **[IO]**, Brussels, Belgium

European Assn. for Signal and Image Processing **[IO]**, Kaisariani, Greece

European Assn. of Social Anthropologists **[IO]**, Bristol, United Kingdom

European Assn. for South. East Asian Stud. **[IO]**, Naples, Italy

European Assn. for Speech Signal and Image Processing **[IO]**, Kaisariani, Greece

European Assn. for the Streamlining of Energy Exchange **[IO]**, Brussels, Belgium

European Assn. for Stud. on Nutrition and Child Development **[IO]**, Paris, France

European Assn. for the Stud. of Diabetes **[IO]**, Dusseldorf, Germany

European Assn. for the Stud. of Religions **[IO]**, Leeds, United Kingdom

European Assn. of Teachers **[IO]**, Brussels, Belgium

European Assn. of Teachers - UK Sect. **[IO]**, Shoeburyness, United Kingdom

European Assn. for Terminology **[IO]**, Brussels, Belgium

European Assn. for Textile Polyolefins **[IO]**, Brussels, Belgium

---

A star before a book entry number signifies that the name is not listed separately, but is mentioned within the entry.

European Assn. for Theoretical Cmpt. Sci. [IO], Rio, Greece

European Assn. for the Trade in Jute and Related Products [IO], The Hague, Netherlands

European Assn. of Transactional Anal. [IO], Konstanz, Germany

European Assn. for the Transfer of Technologies, Innovation, and Indus. Info. [IO], Luxembourg, Luxembourg

European Assn. for the Treatment of Addiction - U.K. [IO], London, United Kingdom

European Assn. of Turkish Academics - Belgium [IO], Brussels, Belgium

European Assn. of Universities, Schools and Colleges of Optometry [IO], Bures-sur-Yvette, France

European Assn. of Urology [IO], Arnhem, Netherlands

European Assn. of Veterinary Anatomists [IO], Messina, Italy

European Assn. of Veterinary Diagnostic Imaging [IO], Bern, Switzerland

European Assn. for Vision and Eye Res. [IO], Leuven, Belgium

European Assn. of Work and Organizational Psychology [IO], Liege, Belgium

European Assn. of Youth Orchestras [IO], Dedemsvaart, Netherlands

European Assn. for Zoological Nomenclature [IO], Bern, Switzerland

European Assn. of Zoos and Aquaria [IO], Amsterdam, Netherlands

European Astronomical Soc. [IO], Versoix, Switzerland

European Atherosclerosis Soc. [IO], Goteborg, Sweden

European Athletic Assn. [IO], Lausanne, Switzerland

European Athletics Coaches Assn. [IO], Richmond, United Kingdom

European Atomic Forum [IO], Brussels, Belgium

European Audiovisual Entrepreneurs [IO], Bertrange, Luxembourg

European Auto. Mfrs. Assn. [IO], Brussels, Belgium

European Baha'i Bus. Forum [IO], Chambery, France

European Bank of Frozen Blood of Rare Groups [IO], Amsterdam, Netherlands

European Banking Fed. [IO], Brussels, Belgium

European Baptist Fed. [IO], Prague, Czech Republic

European Baptist Mission [IO], Wustermark, Germany

European Baptist Press Ser. of the European Baptist Fed. [IO], Prague, Czech Republic

European Baptist Women's Union [IO], Riga, Latvia

European Barge Union [IO], Rotterdam, Netherlands

European Battery Recycling Assn. [IO], Brussels, Belgium

European Beer Consumers' Union [IO], St. Albans, United Kingdom

European Behavioral Pharmacology Soc. [IO], Bordeaux, France

European Bentonite Producers Assn. [IO], Brussels, Belgium

European Biological Rhythms Soc. [IO], Oxford, United Kingdom

European Biomass Indus. Assn. [IO], Brussels, Belgium

European Biomedical Res. Assn. [IO], London, United Kingdom

European Biophysical Societies' Assn. [IO], Utrecht, Netherlands

European Biosafety Assn. [IO], Frankfurt, Germany

European Bitumen Assn. [IO], Brussels, Belgium

European Blind Union [IO], Paris, France

European Bd. of Cardiovascular Perfusion [IO], Berlin, Germany

European Bd. and Coll. of Obstetrics and Gynaecology [IO], Belfast, United Kingdom

European Bd. of Ophthalmology [IO], Ljubljana, Slovenia

European Bd. of Plastic, Reconstructive and Aesthetic Surgery [IO], East Grinstead, United Kingdom

European Bd. of Urology [IO], Arnhem, Netherlands

European Bd. of Veterinary Specialization [IO], Limal, Belgium

European Boating Assn. [IO], Southampton, United Kingdom

European Booksellers Fed. [IO], Brussels, Belgium

European Borates Assn. [IO], Brussels, Belgium

European Botanical and Horticultural Libraries Gp. [IO], Richmond, United Kingdom

European Bowling Proprietors Assn. [IO], Norrkoping, Sweden

European Brain and Behaviour Soc. [IO], Leiden, Netherlands

European Brain Coun. [IO], Brussels, Belgium

European Brain Injury Consortium [IO], Rotterdam, Netherlands

European Brain Injury Soc. [IO], Brussels, Belgium

European Brands Assn. [IO], Brussels, Belgium

European Brewery Convention [IO], Brussels, Belgium

European Bridge League [IO], Milan, Italy

European Broadcasting Union [IO], Grand-Saconnex, Switzerland

European Brushware Fed. [IO], Tilburg, Netherlands

European Buddhist Union [IO], Nantes, France

European Building and Services Assn. [IO], Berlin, Germany

European Bur. for Conscientious Objection [IO], Brussels, Belgium

European Bur. for Lesser-Used Languages [IO], Dublin, Ireland

European Bur. of Lib., Info. and Documentation Associations [IO], The Hague, Netherlands

European Burns Assn. [IO], Beverwijk, Netherlands

European Bus. Angel Network [IO], Brussels, Belgium

European Bus. Aviation Assn. [IO], Brussels, Belgium

European Bus. Ethics Network [IO], Leuven, Belgium

European Bus. History Assn. [IO], Frankfurt am Main, Germany

European Bus. and Innovation Centre Network [IO], Brussels, Belgium

European Calcified Tissue Soc. [IO], Bristol, United Kingdom

European Calcium Carbonate Assn. - Europe [IO], Brussels, Belgium

European Calcium Soc. [IO], Brussels, Belgium

European Canoe Assn. [IO], Nottingham, United Kingdom

European Caravan Fed. [IO], Frankfurt, Germany

European Carton Makers Assn. [IO], The Hague, Netherlands

European Casino Assn. [IO], Brussels, Belgium

European Catalysts Mfrs. Assn. [IO], Brussels, Belgium

European Cell Death Org. [IO], Gent, Belgium

European Cement Assn. [IO], Brussels, Belgium

European Central Coun. of Homeopaths [IO], Kenninghall, United Kingdom

European Centre for Development Policy Mgt. [IO], Maastricht, Netherlands

European Centre for Ecotoxicology and Toxicology of Chemicals [IO], Brussels, Belgium

European Centre of Enterprises with Public Participation and of Enterprises of Gen. Economic Interest [IO], Brussels, Belgium

European Centre for Higher Educ. [IO], Bucharest, Romania

European Centre for Medium-Range Weather Forecasts [IO], Reading, United Kingdom

European Centre for Minority Issues [IO], Flensburg, Germany

European Centre for Modern Language of the Coun. of Europe [IO], Graz, Austria

European Centre for Nature Conservation [IO], Tilburg, Netherlands

European Centre for Occupational Hea., Safety and the Env. [IO], Glasgow, United Kingdom

European Centre for Social Welfare Policy and Res. [IO], Vienna, Austria

European Centre for Strategic Mgt. of Universities [IO], Brussels, Belgium

European Centre of Stud. on Linear Alkylbenzene [IO], Brussels, Belgium

European Ceramic Soc. [IO], Mons, Belgium

European Cetacean Soc. [IO], Tromso, Norway

European Charcot Found. [IO], Molenhoek, Netherlands

European Chem. Indus. Coun. [IO], Brussels, Belgium

European Chem. Marketing and Strategy Assn. [IO], The Hague, Netherlands

European Chem. Transport Assn. [IO], Brussels, Belgium

European Chemoreception Res. Org. [IO], Versailles, France

European Children's Network [IO], Brussels, Belgium

European Chilled Food Fed. [IO], Kettering, United Kingdom

European Chinese Soc. for Clinical Magnetic Resonance [IO], Freiburg, Germany

European Chlorinated Solvent Assn. [IO], Brussels, Belgium

European Christian Environmental Network [IO], Brussels, Belgium

European Citric Acid Mfrs. Assn. [IO], Brussels, Belgium

European Civil Aviation Conf. [IO], Neuilly-sur-Seine, France

European Civil Ser. Fed. [IO], Brussels, Belgium

European Coal Combustion Products Assn. [IO], Essen, Germany

European Coalition to End Animal Experiments [IO], London, United Kingdom

European Coastal Assn. for Sci. and Tech. [IO], Cardiff, United Kingdom

European Cockpit Assn. [IO], Brussels, Belgium

European Coffee Fed. [IO], Rijswijk, Netherlands

European Coil Coating Assn. [IO], Brussels, Belgium

European Cold Storage and Logistics Assn. [IO], Brussels, Belgium

European Coll. of Hypnotherapy [IO], Surrey, United Kingdom

European Coll. of Lab. Animal Medicine [IO], Mainz, Germany

European Coll. of Neuropsychopharmacology [IO], Utrecht, Netherlands

European Coll. of Sport Sci. [IO], Cologne, Germany

European Coll. of Veterinary Diagnostic Imaging [IO], Gent, Belgium

European Coll. of Veterinary Internal Medicine - Companion Animals [IO], Dublin, Ireland

European Coll. of Veterinary Pathologists [IO], Liverpool, United Kingdom

European Coll. of Veterinary Surgeons [IO], Zurich, Switzerland

European Colloid and Interface Soc. [IO], Fribourg, Switzerland

European Commn. - Congo Delegation [IO], Kinshasa, Republic of the Congo

European Commn. Delegation in Barbados and Eastern Caribbean [IO], Christ Church, Barbados

European Commn. - Kenya Delegation [IO], Nairobi, Kenya

European Commn. - Mozambique Delegation [IO], Maputo, Mozambique

European Commn. Off. of Press and Public Affairs [★17621]

European Commn. Off. of Press and Public Affairs [★17621]

European Commn. - Suriname Off. [IO], Paramaribo, Suriname

European Commn. - Tanzania Delegation [IO], Dar es Salaam, United Republic of Tanzania

European Commn. - Togo Delegation [IO], Lome, Togo

European Comm. for the Advancement of Thermal Sciences and Heat Transfer [IO], Pisa, Italy

European Comm. of Associations of Mfrs. of Gears and Transmission Parts [IO], Frankfurt, Germany

European Comm. for Catholic Educ. [IO], Brussels, Belgium

European Comm. for Electrotechnical Standardization [IO], Brussels, Belgium

European Comm. for External Quality Assessment Programmes in Lab. Medicine [IO], Leiden, Netherlands

European Comm. of Indus. Furnace and Heating Equip. Associations [IO], Frankfurt, Germany

European Comm. of Machinery Mfrs. for the Plastics and Rubber Indus. [IO], Frankfurt, Germany

Reference to "IO" in place of a book number signifies that the association may be found in the 50th edition of International Organizations.

European Comm. of Mfrs. of Compressors, Vacuum Pumps, and Pneumatic Tools [IO], Brussels, Belgium

European Comm. of the Mfrs. of Fire Protection Equip. and Fire Fighting Vehicles [IO], Wurzburg, Germany

European Comm. of Professional Diving Instructors [IO], Antibes, France

European Comm. for Standardization [IO], Brussels, Belgium

European Comm. for the Stud. of Corrosion and Protection of Pipes [IO], Brussels, Belgium

European Comm. for Sugar Mfrs. [IO], Brussels, Belgium

European Comm. for the Valve Indus. [IO], Brussels, Belgium

European Commodities Exchange [IO], Strasbourg, France

European Community of Consumer Cooperatives [IO], Brussels, Belgium

European Community Info. Ser. [★17621]

European Community Info. Ser. [★17621]

European Community Off. of Press and Public Affairs [★17621]

European Community Off. of Press and Public Affairs [★17621]

European Community Shipowners' Assn. [IO], Brussels, Belgium

European Community of Young Horticulturists [IO], Grunberg, Germany

European Competitive Telecommunications Assn. [IO], Brussels, Belgium

European Cmpt. Driving License Found. [IO], Dublin, Ireland

European Confed. of Executives and Managerial Staff [IO], Brussels, Belgium

European Confed. of the Footwear Indus. [IO], Brussels, Belgium

European Confed. of Independent Trade Unions [IO], Brussels, Belgium

European Confed. of Independents [IO], Berlin, Germany

European Confed. of Intl. Trading Houses Associations [IO], The Hague, Netherlands

European Confed. of Iron and Steel Indus. [IO], Brussels, Belgium

European Confed. of Junior Enterprises [IO], Brussels, Belgium

European Confed. of Natl. Associations of Mfrs. of Insulated Wire and Cable [IO], Brussels, Belgium

European Confed. of Police [IO], Luxembourg, Luxembourg

European Confed. of Property Managers [IO], Brussels, Belgium

European Confed. of Real Estate Agents [IO], Brussels, Belgium

European Confed. of Upper Rhine Universities [IO], Strasbourg, France

European Confed. of Woodworking Indus. [IO], Brussels, Belgium

European Confed. of Workers' Cooperatives, Social Cooperatives and Social and Participative Enterprises [IO], Brussels, Belgium

European Conf. on Christian Educ. [IO], Aachen, Germany

European Conf. of Postal and Telecommunications Administrations [IO], Copenhagen, Denmark

European Conf. of Promoters of New Music [IO], Amsterdam, Netherlands

European Conservation Agriculture Fed. [IO], Brussels, Belgium

European Consortium for Agricultural Res. in the Tropics [IO], Paris, France

European Consortium of Innovative Universities [IO], Dortmund, Germany

European Consortium for the Learning Org. [IO], Wavre, Belgium

European Consortium for Mathematics in Indus. [IO], Eindhoven, Netherlands

European Consortium for Political Res. [IO], Colchester, United Kingdom

European Consortium for Sociological Res. [IO], Groningen, Netherlands

European Constr. Indus. Fed. [IO], Brussels, Belgium

European Constr. Inst. [IO], Loughborough, United Kingdom

European Consultants Unit [IO], Munich, Germany

European Consumers' Org. [IO], Brussels, Belgium

European Contact Gp. - Ecumenical Network for Economic and Social Action [IO], Prague, Czech Republic

European Contact Lens Soc. of Ophthalmologists [IO], Valmont, France

European Container Glass Fed. [IO], Brussels, Belgium

European Convention for Constructional Steelwork [IO], Brussels, Belgium

European Cooperation in Legal Metrology [IO], Ljubljana, Slovenia

European Cooperation in Sci. and Tech. [IO], Brussels, Belgium

European Coordinating Comm. for Artificial Intelligence [IO], Leipzig, Germany

European Copper Inst. [IO], Brussels, Belgium

European Cosmetic, Toiletry and Perfumery Assn. [IO], Brussels, Belgium

European Coun. for Agricultural Law [IO], Gent, Belgium

European Coun. of Amer. Chambers of Commerce [IO], Brussels, Belgium

European Coun. of Applied Sciences and Engg. [IO], Paris, France

European Coun. of Artists [IO], Copenhagen, Denmark

European Coun. for Cardiovascular Res. [IO], London, United Kingdom

European Coun. on Chiropractic Educ. [IO], Havant, United Kingdom

European Coun. of Civil Engineers [IO], Bratislava, Slovakia

European Coun. of Conscripts Organisations [IO], Stockholm, Sweden

European Coun. for Constr. Res., Development and Innovation [IO], Brussels, Belgium

European Coun. of Doctors for Plurality in Medicine [IO], Basel, Switzerland

European Coun. on Eating Disorders [IO], London, United Kingdom

European Coun. for High Ability [IO], Oxford, United Kingdom

European Coun. of Interior Architects [IO], Amsterdam, Netherlands

European Coun. of Intl. Schools [IO], Petersfield, United Kingdom

European Coun. of Legal Medicine [IO], Zurich, Switzerland

European Coun. of Natl. Associations of Independent Schools [IO], Copenhagen, Denmark

European Coun. for Non-Profit Organisations [IO], Brussels, Belgium

European Coun. of the Paint, Printing Ink and Artists' Colours Indus. [IO], Brussels, Belgium

European Coun. for Plasticisers and Intermediates [IO], Brussels, Belgium

European Coun. on Refugees and Exiles [IO], London, United Kingdom

European Coun. of Skeptical Organizations [IO], Rossdorf, Germany

European Coun. of Spatial Planners [IO], Brussels, Belgium

European Coun. for Steiner Waldorf Educ. [IO], Forest Row, United Kingdom

European Coun. for the Village and Small Town [IO], Eastleigh, United Kingdom

European Coun. of Vinyl Mfrs. [IO], Brussels, Belgium

European Coun. of Young Farmers [IO], Brussels, Belgium

European Cricket Coun. [IO], London, United Kingdom

European Crop Protection Assn. [IO], Brussels, Belgium

European Cultural Found. [IO], Amsterdam, Netherlands

European Culture Collections' Org. [IO], Braunschweig, Germany

European Cycling Union [IO], Erlenbach, Switzerland

European Cyclists' Fed. [IO], Brussels, Belgium

European Cystic Fibrosis Soc. [IO], Karup, Denmark

European Dairy Assn. [IO], Brussels, Belgium

European Dehydrators Assn. [IO], Brussels, Belgium

European Democrat Students [IO], Brussels, Belgium

European Demolition Assn. [IO], Copenhagen, Denmark

European Desalination Soc. [IO], L'Aquila, Italy

European Diagnostic Mfrs. Assn. [IO], Brussels, Belgium

European Dialysis and Transplant Nurses Association/European Renal Care Assn. [IO], Prague, Czech Republic

European Disability Forum [IO], Brussels, Belgium

European Disposables and Nonwovens Assn. [IO], Brussels, Belgium

European Diving Tech. Comm. [IO], Stavanger, Norway

European Down and Feather Assn. [IO], Mainz, Germany

European Down Syndrome Assn. [IO], Pula, Croatia

European Dragon Boat Fed. [IO], Newport, United Kingdom

European Dystonia Fed. [IO], Helensburgh, United Kingdom

European Economic Assn. [IO], Milan, Italy

European Educational Res. Assn. [IO], Berlin, Germany

European Electronic Chips and Systems Design Initiative [IO], Gieres, France

European Electronic Component Mfrs. Assn. [IO], Brussels, Belgium

European Elevator Assn. [IO], Brussels, Belgium

European Employers' Comm. of Yeast Mfrs. [IO], Paris, France

European Energy Forum [IO], Brussels, Belgium

European Environmental Bur. [IO], Brussels, Belgium

European Environmental Mutagen Soc. [IO], Lyon, France

European Epilepsy Acad. [IO], Bielefeld, Germany

European Evaluation Soc. [IO], Prague, Czech Republic

European Evangelical Accrediting Assn. [IO], Rome, Italy

European Evangelical Alliance [IO], Driebergen, Netherlands

European Expedition Guild [IO], Paris, France

European Express Assn. [IO], Brussels, Belgium

European Eye Bank Assn. [IO], Venice, Italy

European Fac. Mgt. Network [IO], Naarden, Netherlands

European Fair Trade Assn. [IO], Schin op Geul, Netherlands

European Fairytale Assn. [IO], Rheine, Germany

European Fed. of Accountants [IO], Brussels, Belgium

European Fed. of Accountants and Auditors for Small and Medium Sized Enterprises [IO], Brussels, Belgium

European Fed. Against Hunting [IO], Brussels, Belgium

European Fed. of Agents of Indus. in Indus. Property [IO], Basel, Switzerland

European Fed. of Amer. Football [IO], Frankfurt am Main, Germany

European Fed. of Associations and Centres of Irish Stud. [IO], Siegen, Germany

European Fed. of the Associations of Dietitians [IO], Emmerich am Rhein, Germany

European Fed. of Associations of Families of People with Mental Illness [IO], Leuven, Belgium

European Fed. of Associations of Hea. Prdt. Mfrs. [IO], Brussels, Belgium

European Fed. of Associations of Insulation Contractors [IO], Durham, United Kingdom

European Fed. of Associations of Lock and Builders' Hardware Mfrs. [IO], Leissigen, Switzerland

European Fed. of Associations of Market Res. Organisations [IO], Brussels, Belgium

European Fed. of Audiology Societies [IO], Msida, Malta

European Fed. of Biotechnology [IO], Barcelona, Spain

European Fed. of Biotechnology - Germany [IO], Frankfurt, Germany

---

A star before a book entry number signifies that the name is not listed separately, but is mentioned within the entry.

European Fed. of Building Societies **[IO]**, Brussels, Belgium

European Fed. of Campingsite Organisations and Holiday Park Associations **[IO]**, Gloucester, United Kingdom

European Fed. of Chem. Engg. **[IO]**, Frankfurt, Germany

European Fed. of City Farms **[IO]**, Sint-Martens-Lennik, Belgium

European Fed. of Clean Air and Environmental Protection Associations **[IO]**, Delft, Netherlands

European Fed. of Cleaning Indus. **[IO]**, Brussels, Belgium

European Fed. for Company Sports **[IO]**, Paris, France

European Fed. of the Contact Lens Indus. **[IO]**, Chelmsford, United Kingdom

European Fed. of Corrosion **[IO]**, Frankfurt, Germany

European Fed. of Corrugated Bd. Mfrs. **[IO]**, Brussels, Belgium

European Fed. of Crohn's and Ulcerative Colitis Assn. **[IO]**, Alphen aan den Rijn, Netherlands

European Fed. of Cytology Societies **[IO]**, Brussels, Belgium

European Fed. for Diaconia **[IO]**, Brussels, Belgium

European Fed. of Endocrine Societies **[★20555]**

European Fed. of Energy Traders **[IO]**, Amsterdam, Netherlands

European Fed. of Engg. Consultancy Associations **[IO]**, Brussels, Belgium

European Fed. for Experimental Morphology **[IO]**, Bologna, Italy

European Fed. of Farm and Village Tourism **[IO]**, Almeria, Spain

European Fed. of Financial Analysts Societies **[IO]**, Dreieich, Germany

European Fed. of Food, Agriculture and Tourism Trade Unions **[IO]**, Brussels, Belgium

European Fed. of Food Sci. and Tech. **[IO]**, Wageningen, Netherlands

European Fed. of Found. Contractors **[IO]**, Beckenham, United Kingdom

European Fed. of Frozen Food Products **[IO]**, Paris, France

European Fed. of Geologists **[IO]**, Brussels, Belgium

European Fed. of Green Parties **[IO]**, Brussels, Belgium

European Fed. of Hereditary Ataxias **[IO]**, London, United Kingdom

European Fed. of Illuminated Signs **[IO]**, Bussiere-Galant, France

European Fed. of Immunological Societies **[IO]**, Berlin, Germany

European Fed. of Inland Ports **[IO]**, Brussels, Belgium

European Fed. of Insurance Intermediaries **[IO]**, Brussels, Belgium

European Fed. for Intercultural Learning **[IO]**, Brussels, Belgium

European Fed. of Internal Medicine **[IO]**, Brussels, Belgium

European Fed. of Journalists **[IO]**, Brussels, Belgium

European Fed. of Liberian Associations **[IO]**, Diegem, Belgium

European Fed. of Local Public Energy Distribution Companies **[IO]**, Brussels, Belgium

European Fed. of Loss Adjusting Experts **[IO]**, Rotterdam, Netherlands

European Fed. of Magazine Publishers **[IO]**, Brussels, Belgium

European Fed. of Mgt. Consultancies Associations **[IO]**, Brussels, Belgium

European Fed. of Marine Sci. and Tech. Societies **[IO]**, Paris, France

European Fed. of Materials Handling and Storage Equip. **[IO]**, Brussels, Belgium

European Fed. for Medical Informatics **[IO]**, Munich, Germany

European Fed. for Medicinal Chemistry **[IO]**, Vienna, Austria

European Fed. of Multiwall Paper Sack Mfrs. **[IO]**, Paris, France

European Fed. of Museum and Tourist Railways **[IO]**, Haaksbergen, Netherlands

European Fed. of Natl. Associations of Measurement, Testing and Analytical Labs. **[IO]**, Paris, France

European Fed. of Natl. Associations of Orthopaedics and Traumatology **[IO]**, Zurich, Switzerland

European Fed. of Natl. Engg. Associations **[IO]**, Brussels, Belgium

European Fed. of Natl. Organisations Working with the Homeless **[IO]**, Brussels, Belgium

European Fed. of Neurological Societies **[IO]**, Vienna, Austria

European Fed. of Organizations for Medical Physics **[IO]**, Udine, Italy

European Fed. of Orthodontic Specialists Associations **[IO]**, Falun, Sweden

European Fed. of Parasitologists **[IO]**, Valencia, Spain

European Fed. of the Parquet Indus. **[IO]**, Brussels, Belgium

European Fed. of Periodontology **[IO]**, Madrid, Spain

European Fed. of Pharmaceutical Indus. and Associations **[IO]**, Brussels, Belgium

European Fed. for Pharmaceutical Sciences **[IO]**, Stockholm, Sweden

European Fed. of the Plywood Indus. **[IO]**, Brussels, Belgium

European Fed. for Primatology **[IO]**, Zurich, Switzerland

European Fed. for Psychoanalytic Psychotherapy **[IO]**, London, United Kingdom

European Fed. of Psychoanalytic Self-Psychology **[IO]**, Munich, Germany

European Fed. of Psychology Students' Associations **[IO]**, Brussels, Belgium

European Fed. of Public Ser. Employees **[IO]**, Brussels, Belgium

European Fed. of Public Ser. Unions **[IO]**, Brussels, Belgium

European Fed. of Regional Energy and Environmental Agencies **[IO]**, Brussels, Belgium

European Fed. of Road Traffic Victims **[IO]**, London, United Kingdom

European Fed. of Salaried Doctors **[IO]**, Paris, France

European Fed. for the Sci. and Tech. of Lipids **[IO]**, Frankfurt, Germany

European Fed. of Sexology **[IO]**, Sheffield, United Kingdom

European Fed. of Societies for Ultrasound in Medicine and Biology **[IO]**, London, United Kingdom

European Fed. of Statisticians in the Pharmaceutical Indus. **[IO]**, Reading, United Kingdom

European Fed. for Table and Ornamental Ware **[IO]**, Brussels, Belgium

European Fed. of Therapeutic Communities **[IO]**, Gavere, Belgium

European Fed. of the Trade in Dried Fruit, Edible Nuts, Preserved Food, Spices, Honey, and Similar Foodstuffs **[IO]**, Brussels, Belgium

European Fed. for Transport and Env. **[IO]**, Brussels, Belgium

European Fed. of Waste Mgt. and Environmental Services **[IO]**, Brussels, Belgium

European Fed. for Welding, Joining and Cutting **[IO]**, Brussels, Belgium

European Fed. of Wooden Pallet and Packaging Mfrs. **[IO]**, Tilburg, Netherlands

European Feed Additives and Premixtures Assn. **[IO]**, Brussels, Belgium

European Feed Mfrs'. Fed. **[IO]**, Brussels, Belgium

European Ferrous Recovery and Recycling Fed. **[IO]**, Brussels, Belgium

European Fertilizer Mfrs. Assn. **[IO]**, Brussels, Belgium

European Festivals Assn. **[IO]**, Gent, Belgium

European Film Acad. **[IO]**, Berlin, Germany

European Finance Assn. **[IO]**, Brussels, Belgium

European Financial Mgt. and Marketing Assn. **[IO]**, Paris, France

European Financial Planning Assn. **[IO]**, Rotterdam, Netherlands

European Fire and Security Advisory Coun. **[IO]**, Brussels, Belgium

European Fireworks Assn. **[IO]**, Amsterdam, Netherlands

European Fishing Tackle Trade Assn. **[IO]**, London, United Kingdom

European Flavour and Fragrance Assn. **[IO]**, Brussels, Belgium

European Flexible Intermediate Bulk Container Assn. **[IO]**, Bad Homburg, Germany

European Flexographic Tech. Assn. - UK **[IO]**, Long Sutton, United Kingdom

European Flour Milling Assn. **[IO]**, Brussels, Belgium

European Flying Disc Fed. **[IO]**, Karlsruhe, Germany

European Folk Art and Craft Fed. **[IO]**, Oslo, Norway

European Folklore Inst. **[IO]**, Budapest, Hungary

European Food Emulsifiers Mfrs. Assn. **[IO]**, Brussels, Belgium

European Food Info. Coun. **[IO]**, Brussels, Belgium

European Food Law Assn. **[IO]**, Brussels, Belgium

European Food Phosphates Producers' Assn. **[IO]**, Brussels, Belgium

European Food Ser. and Packaging Assn. **[IO]**, Brussels, Belgium

European Foot and Ankle Soc. **[IO]**, Dun Laoghaire, Ireland

European Forest Genetic Resources Programme **[IO]**, Rome, Italy

European Forest Inst. **[IO]**, Joensuu, Finland

European Forum for Good Clinical Practice **[IO]**, Brussels, Belgium

European Forum of Heritage Associations **[IO]**, Padua, Italy

European Forum for Renewable Energy Sources **[IO]**, Brussels, Belgium

European Forum for Student Guidance **[IO]**, Brussels, Belgium

European Forum for Urban Safety **[IO]**, Paris, France

European Forum for Victim Services **[★12156]**

European Found. Centre **[IO]**, Brussels, Belgium

European Found. for Chinese Music Res. **[IO]**, Leiden, Netherlands

European Found. for the Improvement of Living and Working Conditions **[IO]**, Loughlinstown, Ireland

European Found. for Landscape Architecture **[IO]**, Brussels, Belgium

European Found. for Mgt. Development **[IO]**, Brussels, Belgium

European Found. for Plant Pathology **[IO]**, Wageningen, Netherlands

European Found. for Quality Mgt. **[IO]**, Brussels, Belgium

European Found. for St. Children Worldwide **[IO]**, Luxembourg, Luxembourg

European Free Trade Assn. **[IO]**, Geneva, Switzerland

European Fresh Produce Importers Assn. **[★20506]**

European Fuel Oxygenates Assn. **[IO]**, Brussels, Belgium

European Funds and Asset Mgt. Assn. **[IO]**, Brussels, Belgium

European Fur Breeders Assn. **[IO]**, Brussels, Belgium

European Furniture Mfrs. Fed. **[IO]**, Brussels, Belgium

European Gaming and Amusement Fed. **[IO]**, Brussels, Belgium

European Gaming and Betting Assn. **[IO]**, Brussels, Belgium

European Garage Equip. Assn. **[IO]**, Brussels, Belgium

European Gay and Lesbian Sports Fed. **[IO]**, Amsterdam, Netherlands

European Gen. Galvanizers Assn. **[IO]**, Caterham, United Kingdom

European Generic Medicines Assn. **[IO]**, Brussels, Belgium

European Genetic Alliances Network **[IO]**, Soest, Netherlands

European Genetics Found. **[IO]**, Bologna, Italy

European Geosciences Union **[IO]**, Strasbourg, France

European Glass Weavers Assn. **[IO]**, Paris, France

European Glaucoma Soc. **[IO]**, London, United Kingdom

European Glaziers Assn. **[IO]**, Copenhagen, Denmark

European Go Fed. **[IO]**, Hamburg, Germany

Reference to "IO" in place of a book number signifies that the association may be found in the 50th edition of International Organizations.

European Golf Assn. [IO], Epalinges, Switzerland
European Golf Course Owners Assn. [IO], Amsterdam, Netherlands
European Greenways Assn. [IO], Madrid, Spain
European Gp. for Organizational Stud. [IO], Berlin, Germany
European Gp. of Public Admin. [IO], Brussels, Belgium
The European Gp. of Valuers' Associations [IO], Brussels, Belgium
European Grouping of Societies of Authors and Composers [IO], Brussels, Belgium
European Hair Res. Soc. [IO], Stevington, United Kingdom
European Hea. Indus. Bus. Communications Coun. [IO], The Hague, Netherlands
European Hea. Mgt. Assn. [IO], Brussels, Belgium
European Hea. Psychology Soc. [IO], Aberdeen, United Kingdom
European Hearing Instrument Mfrs. Assn. [IO], Bagsvaerd, Denmark
European Heart and Lung Transplant Fed. [IO], Vienna, Austria
European Heart Network [IO], Brussels, Belgium
European Hematology Assn. [IO], The Hague, Netherlands
European Herbal Infusions Assn. [IO], Hamburg, Germany
European Hernia Soc. [IO], Varese, Italy
European Herpetological Soc. [IO], Pisa, Italy
European Histamine Res. Soc. [IO], Stockholm, Sweden
European Historical Economics Soc. [IO], Oxford, United Kingdom
European Hosp. and Healthcare Fed. [IO], Brussels, Belgium
European Hotel Managers Assn. [IO], Rome, Italy
European Human Rsrc. Forum [IO], Bristol, United Kingdom
European Humanist Fed. [IO], Brussels, Belgium
European Hydrogen Assn. [IO], Brussels, Belgium
European Ichthyological Soc. [IO], Anavyssos, Grenada
European Indus. Minerals Assn. [IO], Brussels, Belgium
European Indus. Res. Mgt. Assn. [IO], Paris, France
European Info. Assn. [IO], Mold, United Kingdom
European Info., Communications and Consumer Electronics Tech. Indus. Assn. [IO], Brussels, Belgium
European Inland Fisheries Advisory Commn. [IO], Mondsee, Austria
European Inst. for Advanced Stud. in Mgt. [IO], Brussels, Belgium
European Inst. for Crime Prevention and Control Affiliated with the United Nations [IO], Helsinki, Finland
European Inst. of Cultural Routes [IO], Luxembourg, Luxembourg
European Inst. of Educ. and Social Policy [IO], Paris, France
European Inst. of Golf Course Architects [IO], Surrey, United Kingdom
European Inst. of Postgraduate Stud. [IO], Dresden, Germany
European Inst. of Printed Circuits [IO], Maastricht, Netherlands
European Inst. of Public Admin. [IO], Maastricht, Netherlands
European Inst. of Purchasing Mgt. [IO], Archamps, France
European Inst. for Res. and Strategic Stud. in Telecommunications GmbH [IO], Heidelberg, Germany
European Inst. of Social Security [IO], Leuven, Belgium
European Insurance Coun. [IO], Brussels, Belgium
European Insurance Fed. [IO], Brussels, Belgium
European Intermodal Assn. [IO], Brussels, Belgium
European Intl. Bus. Acad. [IO], Brussels, Belgium
European Internet Services Providers Assn. [IO], Brussels, Belgium
European Intestinal Transport Gp. [IO], Berlin, Germany
European Investment Casters' Fed. [IO], Redditch, United Kingdom

European Isocyanate and Polyol Producers Assn. [IO], Brussels, Belgium
European Isocyanate Producers Assn. [★21469]
European Journalism Centre [IO], Maastricht, Netherlands
European Journalism Training Assn. [IO], Maastricht, Netherlands
European Judo Union [IO], Valletta, Malta
European Juggling Assn. [IO], Stockholm, Sweden
European Landowners Org. [IO], Brussels, Belgium
European Landscape Contractors Assn. [IO], Bad Honnef, Germany
European Language Coun. [IO], Berlin, Germany
European Language Resources Assn. [IO], Paris, France
European Laryngological Soc. [IO], Madrid, Spain
European Law Faculties Assn. [IO], Bonn, Germany
European Law Students' Assn. [IO], Brussels, Belgium
European Lawyers' Union [IO], Rome, Italy
European League Against Rheumatism [IO], Kilchberg, Switzerland
European League for Economic Cooperation [IO], Brussels, Belgium
European League of Institutes of the Arts [IO], Amsterdam, Netherlands
European League of Stuttering Associations [IO], Cologne, Germany
European Liaison Comm. of Machine Tool Importers [IO], London, United Kingdom
European Liberal Democrat and Reform Party [IO], Brussels, Belgium
European Life Scientist Org. [IO], Dresden, Germany
European Lift Components Assn. [IO], Brussels, Belgium
European Lime Assn. [IO], Brussels, Belgium
European Liquefied Petroleum Gas Assn. [IO], Brussels, Belgium
European Livestock and Meat Trading Union [IO], Brussels, Belgium
European Logistics Assn. [IO], Brussels, Belgium
European Lotteries [IO], Lausanne, Switzerland
European Lupus Erythematosus Fed. [IO], Romford, United Kingdom
European Major Exhibition Centres Assn. [IO], Brussels, Belgium
European Mgt. Assistants [IO], Wels, Austria
European Mfrs. of Expanded Polystyrene [IO], Brussels, Belgium
European Marine Equip. Coun. [IO], Brussels, Belgium
European Maritime Pilots' Assn. [IO], Antwerp, Belgium
European Marketing Acad. [IO], Brussels, Belgium
European Marmoset Res. Gp. [IO], Zurich, Switzerland
European Mastic Asphalt Assn. [IO], Bern, Switzerland
European Materials Res. Soc. [IO], Strasbourg, France
European Mathematical Soc. [IO], Helsinki, Finland
European Mechanics Soc. [IO], Udine, Italy
European Medical Assn. [IO], Brussels, Belgium
European Medical Students' Assn. [IO], Brussels, Belgium
European Medical Writers Assn. [IO], Petersfield, United Kingdom
European and Mediterranean Cereal Rusts Found. [IO], Norwich, United Kingdom
European and Mediterranean Network of the Social Sciences [IO], Valletta, Malta
European and Mediterranean Plant Protection Org. [IO], Paris, France
European-Mediterranean Seismological Centre [IO], Bruyeres-le-Chatel, France
European Membrane Soc. [IO], Toulouse, France
European Metal Trade and Recycling Fed. [IO], Brussels, Belgium
European Metall Union [IO], Brussels, Belgium
European Metallizers Assn. [IO], The Hague, Netherlands
European Metalworkers' Fed. [IO], Brussels, Belgium
European Meteorological Soc. [IO], Berlin, Germany

European Microbeam Anal. Soc. [IO], Antwerp, Belgium
European Microscopy Soc. [IO], Cambridge, United Kingdom
European Mine, Chem., and Energy Workers' Fed. [IO], Brussels, Belgium
European Molecular Biology Lab. [IO], Heidelberg, Germany
European Molecular Biology Org. [IO], Heidelberg, Germany
European Money and Finance Forum [IO], Vienna, Austria
European Mortar Indus. Org. [IO], Duisburg, Germany
European Mortgage Fed. [IO], Brussels, Belgium
European Movement [IO], London, United Kingdom
European Movement - Ireland [IO], Dublin, Ireland
European Multimedia Forum [IO], Brussels, Belgium
European Music Festival for Young People [IO], Neerpelt, Belgium
European Music School Union [IO], Utrecht, Netherlands
European Music Therapy Confed. [IO], Schoten, Belgium
European Mutual Guarantee Assn. [IO], Brussels, Belgium
European Nail Soc. [IO], Brussels, Belgium
European Nature Heritage Fund [IO], Radolfzell, Germany
European Network Against Arms Trade [IO], Amsterdam, Netherlands
European Network Against Racism [IO], Brussels, Belgium
European Network of Building Res. Institutes [IO], Brussels, Belgium
European Network of Cancer Registries [IO], Lyon, France
European Network for Commun. Development in Bus. Educ. [IO], St. Gallen, Switzerland
European Network of Cultural Admin. Training Centres [IO], Brussels, Belgium
European Network on Debt and Development [IO], Brussels, Belgium
European Network for Housing Res. [IO], Gavle, Sweden
European Network of Info. Centres for the Performing Arts [IO], Brussels, Belgium
European Network on Law and Soc. [IO], Rieux-Minervois, France
European Network of Policewomen [IO], Amersfoort, Netherlands
European Network for Sci. Res. Coordination in Organic Farming [IO], Barcelona, Spain
European Network for Smoking Prevention [IO], Brussels, Belgium
European Network of Sport Sci., Educ. and Employment [IO], Cologne, Germany
European Network on St. Children Worldwide [★6526]
European Network of Transmission Sys. Operators for Electricity [IO], Brussels, Belgium
European Network of the Unemployed [IO], Limoges, France
European Network for Workplace Hea. Promotion [IO], Essen, Germany
European Neural Network Soc. [IO], Nijmegen, Netherlands
European Neuroendocrine Assn. [IO], Liege, Belgium
European Neurological Soc. [IO], Basel, Switzerland
European Newspaper Publishers' Assn. [IO], Brussels, Belgium
European NGO Confed. for Relief and Development [IO], Brussels, Belgium
European Non-Governmental Sports Org. [IO], Belgrade, Serbia
European Nuclear Soc. [IO], Brussels, Belgium
European Nut Assn. [IO], Tilburg, Netherlands
European Oil Hydraulic and Pneumatic Comm. [IO], Frankfurt, Germany
European Oleochemicals and Allied Products Gp. [IO], Brussels, Belgium
European Ombudsman Inst. [IO], Innsbruck, Austria
European Oncology Nursing Soc. [IO], Brussels, Belgium

A star before a book entry number signifies that the name is not listed separately, but is mentioned within the entry.

European Operations Mgt. Assn. **[IO]**, Brussels, Belgium

European Optical Soc. **[IO]**, Hannover, Germany

European Org. for Civil Aviation Equip. **[IO]**, Malakoff, France

European Org. for the Exploitation of Meteorological Satellites **[IO]**, Darmstadt, Germany

European Org. for Res. and Treatment of Cancer **[IO]**, Brussels, Belgium

European Org. of Supreme Audit Institutions **[IO]**, Madrid, Spain

European Org. for Tech. Approvals **[IO]**, Brussels, Belgium

European Org. for Caries Res. **[IO]**, Amsterdam, Netherlands

European Org. of Military Associations **[IO]**, Brussels, Belgium

European Org. for Nuclear Res. **[IO]**, Geneva, Switzerland

European Org. for Packaging and the Env. **[IO]**, Brussels, Belgium

European Org. for Quality **[IO]**, Brussels, Belgium

European Org. for Rare Diseases **[IO]**, Paris, France

European Org. for Rare Disorders **[IO]**, Paris, France

European Ornithologists' Union **[IO]**, Wroclaw, Poland

European Orthodontic Soc. **[IO]**, London, United Kingdom

European Ostomy Assn. **[IO]**, Kristiansand, Norway

European Paediatric Neurology Soc. **[IO]**, Bolton, United Kingdom

European Palm Soc. **[IO]**, Richmond, United Kingdom

European Pancreatic Club **[IO]**, Munich, Germany

European Panel Fed. **[IO]**, Brussels, Belgium

European Paralympic Comm. **[IO]**, Rome, Italy

European Parking Assn. **[IO]**, Cologne, Germany

European Parkinson's Disease Assn. **[IO]**, Kent, United Kingdom

European Parliamentarians for Africa **[IO]**, Amsterdam, Netherlands

European Patent Off. **[IO]**, Munich, Germany

European Peace Res. Assn. **[IO]**, Adapazari, Turkey

European Pentecostal Theological Assn. **[IO]**, Mattersey, United Kingdom

European Peoples' Party **[IO]**, Brussels, Belgium

European Perforators Assn. **[IO]**, Brussels, Belgium

European Personal Construct Assn. **[IO]**, London, United Kingdom

European Pet Food Indus. Fed. **[IO]**, Brussels, Belgium

European Petrochemical Assn. **[IO]**, Brussels, Belgium

European Petroleum Indus. Assn. **[IO]**, Brussels, Belgium

European Pharmaceutical Students' Assn. **[IO]**, Brussels, Belgium

European Phenolic Foam Assn. **[IO]**, Bordon, United Kingdom

European Photochemistry Assn. **[IO]**, Geneva, Switzerland

European Photovoltaic Indus. Assn. **[IO]**, Brussels, Belgium

European Physical Educ. Assn. **[IO]**, Sint-Amandsberg, Belgium

European Physical Soc. **[IO]**, Mulhouse, France

European Physics Educ. Network **[IO]**, Gent, Belgium

European Piano Teachers Assn. **[IO]**, London, United Kingdom

European Plastics Converters **[IO]**, Brussels, Belgium

European Plastics Distributors Assn. **[IO]**, Munich, Germany

European Platform for Dutch Educ. **[IO]**, Haarlem, Netherlands

European Pocket Billiard Fed. **[IO]**, Brunssum, Netherlands

European Policy Forum **[IO]**, London, United Kingdom

European Portable Battery Assn. **[IO]**, Brussels, Belgium

European Powder Metallurgy Assn. **[IO]**, Shrewsbury, United Kingdom

European Power Electronics and Drives Assn. **[IO]**, Brussels, Belgium

European Power Tool Assn. **[IO]**, Frankfurt am Main, Germany

European Powerlifting Fed. **[IO]**, Halden, Norway

European Prison Educ. Assn. **[IO]**, Drammen, Norway

European Private Equity and Venture Capital Assn. **[IO]**, Brussels, Belgium

European Professional Women's Network **[IO]**, Paris, France

European Prosthodontic Assn. **[IO]**, London, United Kingdom

European Psychoanalytical Fed. **[IO]**, Tubingen, Germany

European Public Hea. Alliance **[IO]**, Brussels, Belgium

European Public Hea. Assn. **[IO]**, Utrecht, Netherlands

European Public Relations Confed. **[IO]**, London, United Kingdom

European Publishers Coun. **[IO]**, Brussels, Belgium

European Pultrusion Tech. Assn. **[IO]**, Frankfurt am Main, Germany

European Pure Phosphoric Acid Producers' Assn. **[IO]**, Brussels, Belgium

European Pure Plant Oil Assn. **[IO]**, Agen, France

European Rare-Earth Actinide Soc. **[IO]**, Lausanne, Switzerland

European Real Estate Soc. **[IO]**, Helsinki, Finland

European Refractories Producers Fed. **[IO]**, Brussels, Belgium

European Regional Sci. Assn. **[IO]**, Louvain-la-Neuve, Belgium

European Regions Airline Assn. **[IO]**, Woking, United Kingdom

European Registration Plate Assn. **[IO]**, Taunton, United Kingdom

European Relocation Assn. **[IO]**, Diss, United Kingdom

European Renewable Energy Coun. **[IO]**, Brussels, Belgium

European Rental Assn. **[IO]**, Brussels, Belgium

European Res. Consortium for Informatics and Mathematics **[IO]**, Sophia Antipolis, France

European Res. Gp. on Military and Soc. **[IO]**, Gothenburg, Sweden

European Res. Org. of Genital Infection and Neoplasia **[IO]**, Paris, France

European Reserve Non-Commissioned Officers Assn. **[IO]**, Bonn, Germany

European Resin Mfrs'. Assn. **[IO]**, London, United Kingdom

European Rsrc. Centre for Alternatives in Higher Educ. **[IO]**, Utrecht, Netherlands

European Respiratory Soc. **[IO]**, Lausanne, Switzerland

European Rheumatoid Arthritis Surgical Soc. **[IO]**, Zurich, Switzerland

European Rhinologic Soc. **[IO]**, Geneva, Switzerland

European River-Sea-Transport Union **[IO]**, Berlin, Germany

European Rotogravure Assn. **[IO]**, Munich, Germany

European Round Table of Industrialists **[IO]**, Brussels, Belgium

European Safety Fed. **[IO]**, Harelbeke, Belgium

European Sales and Marketing Assn. **[IO]**, Prestwood, United Kingdom

European Salt Producers' Assn. **[IO]**, Brussels, Belgium

European Satellite Operators Assn. **[IO]**, Brussels, Belgium

European Savings Banks Gp. **[IO]**, Brussels, Belgium

European School Heads Assn. **[IO]**, Utrecht, Netherlands

European Sci. Found. **[IO]**, Strasbourg, France

European Sci. Cooperative on Phytotherapy **[IO]**, Exeter, United Kingdom

European Sea Ports Org. **[IO]**, Brussels, Belgium

European Sealing Assn. **[IO]**, Tregarth, United Kingdom

European Seed Assn. **[IO]**, Brussels, Belgium

European Seismological Commn. **[IO]**, Ljubljana, Slovenia

European Senior Citizens Union **[IO]**, Berlin, Germany

European Shippers' Coun. **[IO]**, Brussels, Belgium

European Sign Fed. **[★15013]**

European Slag Assn. **[IO]**, Duisburg, Germany

European Sled Dog Racing Assn. **[IO]**, Stockholm, Sweden

European Sleep Res. Soc. **[IO]**, Brussels, Belgium

European Small Hydropower Assn. **[IO]**, Brussels, Belgium

European Snacks Assn. **[IO]**, London, United Kingdom

European Social Action Network **[IO]**, Brussels, Belgium

European Social Network **[IO]**, Brighton, United Kingdom

European Soc. of Agricultural Engineers **[IO]**, Bedford, United Kingdom

European Soc. for Agronomy **[IO]**, Bologna, Italy

European Soc. of Anaesthesiology **[IO]**, Brussels, Belgium

European Soc. for Analytic Philosophy **[IO]**, Geneva, Switzerland

European Soc. for Animal Cell Tech. **[IO]**, Zurich, Switzerland

European Soc. for Artificial Organs - East European Off. **[IO]**, Warsaw, Poland

European Soc. of Assn. Executives **[IO]**, London, United Kingdom

European Soc. for Biomaterials **[IO]**, London, United Kingdom

European Soc. of Biomechanics **[IO]**, Barcelona, Spain

European Soc. for Biomedical Res. on Alcoholism **[IO]**, Vienna, Austria

European Soc. of Breast Imaging **[IO]**, Vienna, Austria

European Soc. of Cardiology **[IO]**, Sophia Antipolis, France

European Soc. for Cardiovascular Surgery **[IO]**, Brescia, Italy

European Soc. for Cataract and Refractive Surgeons **[IO]**, Dublin, Ireland

European Soc. for Central Asian Stud. **[IO]**, Leiden, Netherlands

European Soc. of Child and Adolescent Psychiatry **[IO]**, Tampere, Finland

European Soc. of Clinical Microbiology and Infectious Diseases **[IO]**, Basel, Switzerland

European Soc. of Clinical Pharmacy **[IO]**, Buitenpost, Netherlands

European Soc. for Clinical Virology **[IO]**, Lyon, France

European Soc. for Cognitive Psychology **[IO]**, Copenhagen, Denmark

European Soc. for the Cognitive Sciences of Music **[IO]**, Brussels, Belgium

European Soc. of Coloproctology **[IO]**, Edinburgh, United Kingdom

European Soc. of Comparative Physiology and Biochemistry **[IO]**, Antwerp, Belgium

European Soc. for Computing and Tech. in Anaesthesia and Intensive Care **[IO]**, Berlin, Germany

European Soc. of Contact Dermatitis **[IO]**, Barcelona, Spain

European Soc. of Contraception **[IO]**, Ternat, Belgium

European Soc. of Culture **[IO]**, Venice, Italy

European Soc. for Dermatological Res. **[IO]**, Geneva, Switzerland

European Soc. for Dermatology and Psychiatry **[IO]**, Brussels, Belgium

European Soc. for Developmental Psychology **[IO]**, Vienna, Austria

European Soc. of Domestic Animal Reproduction **[IO]**, Belfield, Ireland

European Soc. for Emergency Medicine **[IO]**, Nancy, France

European Soc. of Endocrinology **[IO]**, Bristol, United Kingdom

European Soc. for Engg. Educ. **[IO]**, Brussels, Belgium

European Soc. for Engg. and Medicine **[IO]**, Groningen, Netherlands

European Soc. for Environmental History **[IO]**, Darmstadt, Germany

---

Reference to "IO" in place of a book number signifies that the association may be found in the 50th edition of International Organizations.

European Soc. for Evolutionary Biology [IO], Lausanne, Switzerland

European Soc. of Feline Medicine [IO], Tisbury, United Kingdom

European Soc. of Gastrointestinal and Abdominal Radiology [IO], Vienna, Austria

European Soc. of Gastrointestinal Endoscopy [IO], Munich, Germany

European Soc. of Gene and Cell Therapy [IO], Leuven, Belgium

European Soc. for Geography [IO], Brussels, Belgium

European Soc. for Gynaecological Endoscopy [IO], Leuven, Belgium

European Soc. of Gynaecological Oncology [IO], Geneva, Switzerland

European Soc. of Gynecology [IO], Paris, France

European Soc. for Haemapheresis and Haemotherapy [IO], Vienna, Austria

European Soc. for Hair Restoration Surgery [IO], Paris, France

European Soc. of Head and Neck Radiology [IO], Vienna, Austria

European Soc. of Human Genetics [IO], Vienna, Austria

European Soc. of Human Reproduction and Embryology [IO], Grimbergen, Belgium

European Soc. for Hyperthermic Oncology [IO], Rotterdam, Netherlands

European Soc. for Immunodeficiencies [IO], Geneva, Switzerland

European Soc. of Intensive Care Medicine [IO], Brussels, Belgium

European Soc. for Intravenous Anaesthesia [IO], Zurich, Switzerland

European Soc. of Knee Surgery Sports Traumatology and Arthroscopy [★18418]

European Soc. for Lab. Animal Veterinarians [IO], Malov, Denmark

European Soc. for Laser Aesthetic Surgery [IO], Athens, Greece

European Soc. for Laser Dermatology [IO], Bassum, Germany

European Soc. for Magnetic Resonance in Medicine and Biology [IO], Vienna, Austria

European Soc. for Mass Spectrometry [IO], Edinburgh, United Kingdom

European Soc. of Mastology [IO], Florence, Italy

European Soc. for Medical Oncology [IO], Lugano, Switzerland

European Soc. for Microcirculation [IO], Berlin, Germany

European Soc. for Movement Anal. for Adults and Children [IO], Headington, United Kingdom

European Soc. for Nematologists [IO], Belfast, United Kingdom

European Soc. for Neurochemistry [IO], Salamanca, Spain

European Soc. for Neurogastroenterology and Motility [IO], Vienna, Austria

European Soc. of Neuroradiology [IO], Leuven, Belgium

European Soc. of Neurosonology and Cerebral Hemodynamics [IO], Bern, Switzerland

European Soc. for New Methods in Agricultural Res. [IO], Brno, Czech Republic

European Soc. for Oceanists [IO], St. Andrews, United Kingdom

European Soc. of Ophthalmic Plastic and Reconstructive Surgery [IO], Munich, Germany

European Soc. for Oral Laser Applications [★2214]

European Soc. for Organ Transplantation [IO], Edinburgh, United Kingdom

European Soc. for Paediatric Endocrinology [IO], Bristol, United Kingdom

European Soc. for Paediatric Infectious Diseases [IO], Geneva, Switzerland

European Soc. of Paediatric and Neonatal Intensive Care [IO], Geneva, Switzerland

European Soc. of Paediatric Radiology [IO], London, United Kingdom

European Soc. for Paediatric Res. [IO], Geneva, Switzerland

European Soc. for Paediatric Urology [IO], Ankara, Turkey

European Soc. of Pathology [IO], Sheffield, United Kingdom

European Soc. for Pediatric Nephrology [IO], Bron, France

European Soc. for Phenylketonuria and Allied Disorders [IO], Aalter, Belgium

European Soc. for Philosophy and Psychology [IO], Edinburgh, United Kingdom

European Soc. for Photobiology [IO], Pisa, Italy

European Soc. for Photodynamic Therapy in Dermatology [IO], Regensburg, Germany

European Soc. for Pigment Cell Res. [IO], Madrid, Spain

European Soc. for Population Economics [IO], Bilbao, Spain

European Soc. for Precision Engg. and Nanotechnology [IO], Bedford, United Kingdom

European Soc. for Primary Care Gastroenterology [IO], Geldermalsen, Netherlands

European Soc. of Radiology [IO], Vienna, Austria

European Soc. of Reproductive and Development Immunology [IO], Poznan, Poland

European Soc. for Res. on the Educ. of Adults [IO], Linkoping, Sweden

European Soc. of Residents in Urology [IO], Arnhem, Netherlands

European Soc. of Rheology [IO], Huelva, Spain

European Soc. for Rural Sociology [IO], Exeter, United Kingdom

European Soc. of Sports Traumatology, Knee Surgery and Arthroscopy [IO], Luxembourg, Luxembourg

European Soc. for Stereotactic and Functional Neurosurgery [IO], Toulouse, France

European Soc. for the Stud. of Cognitive Systems [IO], Groningen, Netherlands

European Soc. for the Stud. of Purine and Pyrimidine Metabolism in Man [IO], Marburg, Germany

European Soc. for the Stud. of Sci. and Theology [IO], Durham, United Kingdom

European Soc. for Sugar Tech. [IO], Berlin, Germany

European Soc. for Surgery of Shoulder and Elbow [IO], St. Genis Laval, France

European Soc. of Surgical Oncology [IO], Brussels, Belgium

European Soc. for Surgical Res. [IO], Malmo, Sweden

European Soc. for Therapeutic Radiology and Oncology [IO], Brussels, Belgium

European Soc. of Thoracic Imaging [IO], Vienna, Austria

European Soc. of Thoracic Surgeons [IO], Exeter, United Kingdom

European Soc. for Toxicology In Vitro [IO], Compiegne, France

European Soc. for Translation Stud. [IO], Sint-Martens-Latem, Belgium

European Soc. for Traumatic Stress Stud. [IO], Amsterdam, Netherlands

European Soc. of Urogenital Radiology [IO], Vienna, Austria

European Soc. for Vascular Surgery [IO], Frederiksberg, Denmark

European Soc. of Veterinary Cardiology [IO], Stavelot, Belgium

European Soc. of Veterinary Clinical Ethology [IO], Geneva, Switzerland

European Soc. of Veterinary Dermatology [IO], Newton Abbot, United Kingdom

European Soc. of Veterinary Neurology [IO], Glasgow, United Kingdom

European Soc. of Veterinary Orthopaedics and Traumatology [IO], Cremona, Italy

European Soc. of Veterinary Pathology [IO], Bologna, Italy

European Soc. of Veterinary Virology [IO], Brussels, Belgium

European Soc. of Women in Theological Res. [IO], Bern, Switzerland

European Sociological Assn. [IO], Paris, France

European Software Assn. [IO], Brussels, Belgium

European Software Inst. [IO], Bizkaia, Spain

European Solar Indus. Fed. [IO], Brussels, Belgium

European Solar Thermal Indus. Fed. [IO], Brussels, Belgium

European Southern Observatory [IO], Munich, Germany

European Space Agency [IO], Paris, France

European Sponsorship Assn. [IO], Surbiton, United Kingdom

European Sports Press Union [IO], Warsaw, Poland

European Squash Fed. [IO], Battle, United Kingdom

European Stabiliser Producers Assn. [IO], Brussels, Belgium

European Strabismological Assn. [IO], Bologna, Italy

European String Teachers Assn. [IO], Weston Turville, United Kingdom

European Structural Integrity Soc. [IO], Turin, Italy

European Students of Indus. Engg. and Mgt. [IO], Eindhoven, Netherlands

European Study Group on Lysosomal Diseases [IO], Rotterdam, Netherlands

European Sulphuric Acid Assn. [IO], Brussels, Belgium

European Sunglass Assn. [IO], Freiburg, Germany

European Surf Indus. Mfrs. Assn. [IO], Capbreton, France

European Surface Treatment on Aluminium [IO], Zurich, Switzerland

European Surfing Fed. [IO], Penzance, United Kingdom

European Surgical Trade Assn. [IO], Venlo, Netherlands

European Suzuki Assn. [IO], Colchester, United Kingdom

European Table Tennis Union [IO], Wasserbillig, Luxembourg

European Taekwondo Union [IO], Oldenzaal, Netherlands

European Tech. Contractors Comm. for the Constr. Indus. [IO], Brussels, Belgium

European Telecommunications Network Operators' Assn. [IO], Brussels, Belgium

European Telecommunications Satellite Org. [IO], Paris, France

European Telecommunications Standards Inst. [IO], Sophia Antipolis, France

European Tennis Fed. - Tennis Europe [IO], Basel, Switzerland

European Textile Network [IO], Hannover, Germany

European Textile Services Assn. [IO], Brussels, Belgium

European Theological Libraries [IO], Paderborn, Germany

European Thrombosis Res. Org. [IO], Krakow, Poland

European Thyroid Assn. [IO], Regenstauf, Germany

European Tile and Brick Producers Fed. [IO], Brussels, Belgium

European Tissue Culture Soc. [IO], Heidelberg, Germany

European Tissue Repair Soc. [IO], Geneva, Switzerland

European Toner and Inkjet Remanufacturers Assn. [IO], Breda, Netherlands

European Tour Operators Assn. [IO], London, United Kingdom

European Trade Union Confed. [IO], Brussels, Belgium

European Trade Union Inst. for Res., Educ. and Hea. and Safety [IO], Brussels, Belgium

European Training Found. [IO], Turin, Italy

European Training and Simulation Assn. [IO], Havant, United Kingdom

European Transplant Coordinators Org. [IO], Barcelona, Spain

European Transport Safety Coun. [IO], Brussels, Belgium

European Transport Workers' Fed. [IO], Brussels, Belgium

European Travel Agents and Tour Operators' Associations [IO], Brussels, Belgium

European Travel Commn. [3558], 50 W 23rd St., 11th Fl., New York, NY 10010

European Travel Commn. [3558], 50 W 23rd St., 11th Fl., New York, NY 10010

European Travel Commn. - Belgium [IO], Brussels, Belgium

European Tropical Forest Res. Network [IO], Wageningen, Netherlands

A star before a book entry number signifies that the name is not listed separately, but is mentioned within the entry.

European Tube Mfrs. Assn. [IO], Dusseldorf, Germany

European Tyre Recycling Assn. [IO], Paris, France

European Tyre and Rim Tech. Org. [IO], Brussels, Belgium

European Tyre and Rubber Mfrs'. Assn. [IO], Brussels, Belgium

European Umbrella Org. for Geographic Info. [IO], Lisbon, Portugal

European Union of Agreement [IO], Watford, United Kingdom

European Union Choir [IO], Brussels, Belgium

European Union of Coachbuilders [IO], Brussels, Belgium

European Union of Dairy Trade [IO], Brussels, Belgium

European Union Delegation to the U.S. [17621], 2175 K St. SW, Washington, DC 20037, (202)862-9500

European Union Delegation to the U.S. [17621], 2175 K St. SW, Washington, DC 20037, (202)862-9500

European Union of Developers and House Builders [IO], Brussels, Belgium

European Union Fed. of Youth Hostel Associations [IO], Brussels, Belgium

European Union of Gen. Practitioners [IO], Lisbon, Portugal

European Union of Independent Hospitals [IO], Brussels, Belgium

European Union of Jewish Students [IO], Brussels, Belgium

European Union of Medical Specialists [IO], Brussels, Belgium

European Union of Music Competition for Youth [IO], Munich, Germany

European Union of Natl. Associations of Water Suppliers and Waste Water Services [IO], Brussels, Belgium

European Union of the Natural Gas Indus. [IO], Brussels, Belgium

European Union Off. of Press and Public Affairs [★17621]

European Union Off. of Press and Public Affairs [★17621]

European Union for Responsible Incineration and Treatment of Special Waste [IO], London, United Kingdom

European Union of Sci. Journalists' Associations [IO], Hamburg, Germany

European Union of Veterinary Practitioners [IO], Brussels, Belgium

European Union Youth Orchestra [IO], London, United Kingdom

European Univ. Assn. [IO], Brussels, Belgium

European Univ. Center for Peace Stud. [IO], Stadtschlaining, Austria

European Univ. Continuing Educ. Network [IO], Barcelona, Spain

European Vegetable Protein Fed. [IO], Brussels, Belgium

European Vegetarian Union [IO], Neukirch, Switzerland

European Vending Assn. [IO], Brussels, Belgium

European Venous Forum [IO], Greenford, United Kingdom

European Veterans Fencing Comm. [IO], Stroud, United Kingdom

European Veterinary Dental Coll. [IO], Rickmansworth, United Kingdom

European Veterinary Dental Soc. [IO], Studley, United Kingdom

European Veterinary Soc. for Small Animal Reproduction [IO], Budapest, Hungary

European Volcanological Assn. [IO], Paris, France

European Water Assn. [IO], Hennef, Germany

European Water Resources Assn. [IO], Athens, Greece

European Wax Fed. [IO], Brussels, Belgium

European Weed Res. Soc. [IO], Doorwerth, Netherlands

European Weightlifting Fed. [IO], San Marino, San Marino

European Whey Products Assn. [IO], Brussels, Belgium

European Wind Energy Assn. [IO], Brussels, Belgium

European Women in Mathematics [IO], Linz, Austria

European Women's Dermatologic Soc. [IO], Brugge, Belgium

European Women's Lobby [IO], Brussels, Belgium

European Women's Mgt. Development Austria [IO], Vienna, Austria

European Women's Mgt. Development Network [IO], Wiesbaden, Germany

European Women's Mgt. Development Switzerland [IO], Zurich, Switzerland

European Wound Mgt. Assn. [IO], Frederiksberg, Denmark

European Writers' Cong. [IO], Brussels, Belgium

European Writing Instrument Mfrs. Assn. [IO], Nuremberg, Germany

European Young Bar Assn. [IO], St. Albans, United Kingdom

European Youth Forest Action [IO], Amsterdam, Netherlands

European Youth Forum [IO], Brussels, Belgium

European Youth Found. [IO], Strasbourg, France

Europeans Students' Union [IO], Brussels, Belgium

Europees Muziek festival voor de Jeugd [★IO]

Europees Platform voor het Nederlandse Onderwijs [★IO]

Europese Federatie van Verenigingen van Familieleden van de Psychisch Zieken [★IO]

Eurostep: European Solidarity Towards Equal Participation of People [IO], Brussels, Belgium

Eurotransplant Intl. Found. [IO], Leiden, Netherlands

Eurovision [★20092]

Eurovision [★20092]

EuTeCer - European Tech. Ceramics Fed. [IO], Brussels, Belgium

Euthanasia

Citizens United Resisting Euthanasia [11987]

Compassion and Choices [11988]

Euthanasia Res. and Guidance Org. [11989]

EXIT [18513]

Human Life Found. [12933]

Intl. Task Force on Euthanasia and Assisted Suicide [11990]

Natl. Pro-Life Alliance [18558]

Euthanasia Prevention Coalition [IO], London, ON, Canada

Euthanasia Prevention Coalition BC [IO], North Vancouver, BC, Canada

Euthanasia Res. and Guidance Org. [11989], 24829 Norris Ln., Junction City, OR 97448-9559, (541)998-1873

Evaluation

Amer. Coun. on Educ. I Center for Lifelong Learning [8171]

Amer. Evaluation Assn. [6853]

Natl. Assn. of Credential Evaluation Services [8172]

Evaluation Network [★6853]

Evaluation Res. Soc. [★6853]

Evangelical

Adopt-A-Church Intl. [19610]

African Amer. Lutheran Assn. [19920]

BCM Intl. [19341]

Bethany Intl. Missions [20014]

Bros. and Sisters in Christ [19541]

Catholic Radio Assn. [19406]

Center for the Evangelical United Brethren Heritage [19719]

A Cup of Water Intl. [20282]

Equestrian Ministries Intl. [19816]

Evangelical Church Alliance [19720]

Evangelical and Ecumenical Women's Caucus [19721]

Evangelical and Ecumenical Women's Caucus [19721]

Evangelical Educ. Soc. [19704]

Evangelical Philosophical Soc. [19722]

Evangelical Philosophical Soc. [19722]

Evangelical Theological Soc. [19723]

Fellowship Intl. Mission [20044]

Forum for Scriptural Christianity [19972]

High School Evangelism Fellowship [19751]

Interdisciplinary Biblical Res. Inst. [19677]

InterServe U.S.A. [20054]

Life Action Revival Ministries [19757]

Media Associates Intl. [19724]

Media Associates Intl. [19724]

Natl. Assn. of Evangelicals [19725]

Natl. Assn. of Evangelicals [19766]

Pocket Testament League [19352]

Teen Missions Intl. [20099]

World Evangelical Alliance [19726]

World Evangelical Alliance [19726]

World Relief [19727]

World Relief [19727]

The Evangelical Alliance Mission [20039], PO Box 969, Wheaton, IL 60189-0969, (630)653-5300

Evangelical Alliance of the United Kingdom [IO], London, United Kingdom

Evangelical Assn. of the Caribbean [IO], Christ Church, Barbados

Evangelical Assn. for the Promotion of Educ. [★20038]

Evangelical Assn. for the Promotion of Educ. [★20038]

Evangelical Christian Publishers Assn. [2933], 9633 S 48th St., Ste. 140, Phoenix, AZ 85044, (480)966-3998

Evangelical Christian Publishers Assn. [2933], 9633 S 48th St., Ste. 140, Phoenix, AZ 85044, (480)966-3998

Evangelical Church Alliance [19720], 205 W Broadway St., PO Box 9, Bradley, IL 60915, (815)937-0720

Evangelical Church Lib. Assn. [9985], PO Box 353, Glen Ellyn, IL 60138, (630)375-7865

Evangelical Coun. for Financial Accountability [19742], 440 W Jubal Early Dr., Ste. 130, Winchester, VA 22601, (540)535-0103

Evangelical and Ecumenical Women's Caucus [19721], PO Box 78171, Indianapolis, IN 46278-0171

Evangelical and Ecumenical Women's Caucus [19721], PO Box 78171, Indianapolis, IN 46278-0171

Evangelical Educ. Soc. [19704], PO Box 3674, Arlington, VA 22203, (703)807-1862

Evangelical Educ. Soc. of the Protestant Episcopal Church [★19704]

Evangelical Environmental Network [19743], PO Box 2791, Washington, DC 20013-2791, (202)903-0209

Evangelical Fellowship of India Commn. on Relief [IO], New Delhi, India

Evangelical Fellowship of Mission Agencies [★20062]

Evangelical Foreign Missions Assn. [★20062]

Evangelical Free Church of Am. [20040], 901 E 78th St., Minneapolis, MN 55420-1334, (952)854-1300

Evangelical Free Church of Am. [20040], 901 E 78th St., Minneapolis, MN 55420-1334, (952)854-1300

Evangelical Free Church of Am. - Intl. Mission [★20040]

Evangelical Free Church of Am. - Intl. Mission [★20040]

Evangelical Free Church Mission [★20040]

Evangelical Free Church Mission [★20040]

Evangelical Friends Alliance [★19777]

Evangelical Friends Alliance [★19777]

Evangelical Friends Intl. [★19777]

Evangelical Friends Intl. [★19777]

Evangelical Friends Intl. - North Amer. Region [19777], 5350 Broadmoor Cir. NW, Canton, OH 44709, (330)493-1660

Evangelical Friends Intl. - North Amer. Region [19777], 5350 Broadmoor Cir. NW, Canton, OH 44709, (330)493-1660

Evangelical Homiletics Soc. [19815], Eastern Mennonite Seminary, 1200 Park Rd., Harrisonburg, VA 22802, (540)432-4260

Evangelical Literature Overseas [★19724]

Evangelical Literature Overseas [★19724]

Evangelical Lutheran Educ. Assn. [8543], 500 N Estrella Pkwy., Ste. B, Box 601, Goodyear, AZ 85338, (800)500-7644

Evangelical Lutheran Good Samaritan Soc. [13187], 4800 W 57th St., Sioux Falls, SD 57108, (866)382-1406

Evangelical Lutheran Sanatorium Assn. [★19942]

Evangelical Medical Aid Soc. [IO], Stouffville, ON, Canada

Reference to "IO" in place of a book number signifies that the association may be found in the 50th edition of International Organizations.

Evangelical Missiological Soc. [20041], PO Box 794, Wheaton, IL 60187, (630)752-5949

Evangelical Philosophical Soc. [19722], PO Box 1298, La Mirada, CA 90637, (562)906-4570

Evangelical Philosophical Soc. [19722], PO Box 1298, La Mirada, CA 90637, (562)906-4570

Evangelical Press Assn. [19744], PO Box 28129, Crystal, MN 55428, (763)535-4793

Evangelical Press Assn. [19744], PO Box 28129, Crystal, MN 55428, (763)535-4793

Evangelical and Reformed Historical Soc. [20275], 555 W James St., Lancaster, PA 17603, (717)290-8734

Evangelical and Reformed Historical Soc. and Archives of the United Church of Christ [★20275]

Evangelical and Reformed Historical Soc., United Church of Christ [★20275]

Evangelical Social Work Conf. [★13225]

Evangelical Teacher Training Assn. [★19675]

Evangelical Theological Soc. [19723], 2825 Lexington Rd., Louisville, KY 40280-0001, (502)897-4387

Evangelical Training Assn. [19675], 380 S Schmale Rd., Ste. 121, Carol Stream, IL 60188, (800)369-8291

Evangelical Women's Caucus, Intl. [★19721]

Evangelical Women's Caucus, Intl. [★19721]

Evangelicals Concerned [19789], .311 E 72nd St., Ste. 1G, New York, NY 10021

Evangelicals for Social Action [★18617]

Evangelische Frauenarbeit in Deutschland [★IO]

Evangelischer Frauenbund der Schweiz [IO], Zurich, Switzerland

Evangelisches Missionswerk in Deutschland [★IO]

Evangelism
Action Intl. Ministries [19728]
Action Intl. Ministries [19728]
Adopt-A-Church Intl. [19610]
Amer. Tract Soc. [19729]
Artists in Christian Testimony [19730]
Artists in Christian Testimony [19730]
Athletes in Action [19731]
Athletes in Action [19731]
BCM Intl. [19341]
Beatitudes Soc. [19540]
Bethany Intl. Missions [20014]
Biblical Ministries Worldwide [19732]
Biblical Ministries Worldwide [19732]
Billy Graham Evangelistic Assn. [19733]
Bros. and Sisters in Christ [19541]
Campus Crusade for Christ Intl. [19734]
Campus Crusade for Christ Intl. [19734]
Catholic Radio Assn. [19406]
Center for the Evangelical United Brethren Heritage [19719]
Champions for Life Intl. [19735]
Champions for Life Intl. [19735]
Child Evangelism Fellowship [19736]
Child Evangelism Fellowship [19736]
Children's Bible Ministries [19737]
Chosen People Ministries [19738]
Christ in Action Ministries [19739]
Christ in Action Ministries [19739]
Christ Truth Ministries [19346]
Christian Boaters Assn. [19740]
Christian Wrestling Fed. [23131]
COME Intl. Baptist Ministries [19741]
Equestrian Ministries Intl. [19816]
Evangelical Coun. for Financial Accountability [19742]
Evangelical Educ. Soc. [19704]
Evangelical Environmental Network [19743]
Evangelical Press Assn. [19744]
Evangelical Press Assn. [19744]
Fellowship of Associates of Medical Evangelism [19949]
Fellowship of Christian Airline Personnel [19745]
Fellowship of Christian Airline Personnel [19745]
Fellowship of Christian Athletes [19746]
Fellowship Intl. Mission [20044]
First Fruit [19747]
Forum for Scriptural Christianity [19972]
Friends of Israel Gospel Ministry [19748]
The Gideons Intl. [19749]
The Gideons Intl. [19749]

Heart's Home USA [19987]
Hebrew Christian Fellowship [19750]
High School Evangelism Fellowship [19751]
Interdisciplinary Biblical Res. Inst. [19677]
Intl. Alliance of Messianic Congregations and Synagogues [19963]
Intl. Bd. of Jewish Missions [19752]
Intl. Bd. of Jewish Missions [19752]
Intl. Coalition of Apostles [19991]
Intl. Messianic Jewish Alliance [19753]
Intl. Messianic Jewish Alliance [19753]
Intl. Students, Inc. [19754]
Intl. Students, Inc. [19754]
InterServe U.S.A. [20054]
Jews for Judaism [20186]
Laymen's Home Missionary Movement [19755]
Laymen's Home Missionary Movement [19755]
Lederer Messianic Ministries [19756]
Life Action Revival Ministries [19757]
Life in Messiah Intl. [19758]
Life in Messiah Intl. [19758]
Life Outreach Intl. [19759]
Luis Palau Assn. [19760]
Luis Palau Assn. [19760]
Maranatha Volunteers Intl. [19761]
Maranatha Volunteers Intl. [19761]
Media Fellowship Intl. [19762]
Media Fellowship Intl. [19762]
Ministry Architecture [6200]
Missions Intl. [19763]
Missions Intl. [19763]
Morris Cerullo World Evangelism [19764]
Morris Cerullo World Evangelism [19764]
Natl. Apostolate for Inclusion Ministry [19765]
Natl. Assn. of Evangelicals [19766]
North Am. Christian Creative Assn. [19595]
Open Air Campaigners U.S.A. [19767]
Pilots for Christ Intl. [19768]
Pilots for Christ Intl. [19768]
Pocket Testament League [19352]
Pro Athletes Outreach [19769]
Remnant Of Israel [19770]
Saints Alive in Jesus [19771]
Seventh Day Baptist Missionary Soc. [19330]
Skinner Leadership Inst. [19772]
Teen Missions Intl. [20099]
WEC Intl. [19773]
WEC Intl. [19773]
Word of Life Fellowship [19774]
Youth Evangelism Assn. [19775]
Evangelism Assn; Lutheran Braille [17097]
Evangelism Assn; Lutheran Braille [17097]
Evangelism and Home Missions Assn. - Address unknown since 2011.
Evangelism and Missions Info. Ser. - Address unknown since 2010.
Evangelistic Faith Missions [20042], PO Box 609, Bedford, IN 47421, (812)275-7531
Evangelistic Faith Missions [20042], PO Box 609, Bedford, IN 47421, (812)275-7531

Evangelization
Athletes in Action [19731]
BCM Intl. [19341]
Beatitudes Soc. [19540]
Bethany Intl. Missions [20014]
Bros. and Sisters in Christ [19541]
Center for the Evangelical United Brethren Heritage [19719]
Christ Truth Ministries [19346]
Evangelical Educ. Soc. [19704]
Fellowship Intl. Mission [20044]
Forum for Scriptural Christianity [19972]
Heart's Home USA [19987]
High School Evangelism Fellowship [19751]
Interdisciplinary Biblical Res. Inst. [19677]
InterServe U.S.A. [20054]
Life Action Revival Ministries [19757]
Natl. Assn. of Evangelicals [19766]
Pocket Testament League [19352]
Seventh Day Baptist Missionary Soc. [19330]
Teen Missions Intl. [20099]
Evangelize China Fellowship [20043], 437 S Garfield Ave., Monterey Park, CA 91754, (626)288-8828
Evangelize China Fellowship [20043], 437 S Garfield Ave., Monterey Park, CA 91754, (626)288-8828

Evans Scholars Foundation [★22629]
Evans Syndrome Res. and Support Gp. [15104], 1376 Presidential Hwy., Jefferson, NH 03583
Evans Syndrome Res. and Support Gp. [15104], 1376 Presidential Hwy., Jefferson, NH 03583
Evaporated Milk Assn. [★1017]
Evaporative Cooling Inst. [1698], MSC 3ECI - NMSU, PO Box 30001, Las Cruces, NM 88003-8001, (505)646-1846
Evelyn Waugh Soc. - Defunct.
The Event Services Assn. [IO], Chepstow, United Kingdom
Events Indus. Alliance [IO], Berkhamsted, United Kingdom
Evergreen Found. [★12078]
Evergreen Found. [★12078]
Evergreen Freedom Found. [★5941]
Evergreen Intl. [12078], 307 W 200 S, Ste. 3004, Salt Lake City, UT 84101, (801)363-3837
Evergreen Intl. [12078], 307 W 200 S, Ste. 3004, Salt Lake City, UT 84101, (801)363-3837
Everly Bros. Intl. [IO], Gouda, Netherlands
Every Child By Two [14075], 1233 20th St. NW, Ste. 403, Washington, DC 20036-2304, (202)783-7034
Every Mother is a Working Mother Network [18791], PO Box 86681, Los Angeles, CA 90086-0681, (323)292-7405
Every Person Influences Children [11162], 1000 Main St., Buffalo, NY 14202, (716)332-4100
Everybody Wins! USA [7829], 20 William St., No. G25, Wellesley, MA 02481, (781)489-5910
Everyday Ayurveda [13645], PO Box 1783, Nevada City, CA 95959, (530)470-9789
Everyday Democracy [19241], 111 Founders Plz., Ste. 1403, East Hartford, CT 06108, (860)928-2616
Everyone Needs a Hero [11582], 27596 Sweetbrier Ln., Mission Viejo, CA 92691, (619)807-0415
Everyone Needs a Hero [11582], 27596 Sweetbrier Ln., Mission Viejo, CA 92691, (619)807-0415
Evidence Photographers Intl. Coun. [5481], 229 Peachtree St. NE, No. 2200, Atlanta, GA 30303, (866)868-3742
Evidence Photographers Intl. Coun. [5481], 229 Peachtree St. NE, No. 2200, Atlanta, GA 30303, (866)868-3742
Evidenced-Based Veterinary Medicine Assn. [17024], PO Box 5444, Mississippi State, MS 39762

Evolution
Human Behavior and Evolution Soc. [6255]
Inst. of Human Origins [6854]
Paleoanthropology Soc. [7211]
Soc. for the Stud. of Evolution [6855]
Evolution Soc; Human Behavior and [6255]
Evolutionary Anthropology Soc. [6140], Amer. Anthropological Assn., 2200 Wilson Blvd., Ste. 600, Arlington, VA 22201-3357
Evrytania Assn. of Am. [19013], 121 Greenwich Rd., Ste. 212, Charlotte, NC 28211, (704)366-6571
Ewing Family Assn. [19224], 17721 Rd. 123, Cecil, OH 45821
Ewing Marion Kaufman Found. [18823], 4801 Rockhill Rd., Kansas City, MO 64110-2046, (816)932-1000
EWM Global Teams [★19709]
EWM Global Teams [★19709]
EWMD ITALY: European Women's Mgt. Development [IO], Brescia, Italy
Ex-Masons for Jesus [19568], PO Box 28702, Las Vegas, NV 89126
Ex-Partners of Servicemembers for Equality [11866], PO Box 11191, Alexandria, VA 22312, (703)941-5844
Exam Comm., Amer. Assn. of Nurse Anesthetists [★15775]
Examination Bd. of Professional Home Inspectors [1915], 53 Regional Dr., Ste. 1, Concord, NH 03301-8500, (847)298-7750
Excelencia in Educ. [8630], 1717 N St. NW, 2nd Fl., Washington, DC 20036, (202)785-7350
Excelsior Coll. Alumni Assn. [18872], Excelsior Coll., 7 Columbia Cir., Albany, NY 12203-5159, (518)464-8500
Exchange Carrier Assn. [★3598]

A star before a book entry number signifies that the name is not listed separately, but is mentioned within the entry.

Exchange Clubs of Am. [★13069]

Exchange Gp. for Appropriate Tech. [IO], Brussels, Belgium

Executive Leadership Coun. [2520], 1001 N Fairfax St., Ste. 300, Alexandria, VA 22314, (703)706-5200

Executive Search Roundtable

Executive Search Roundtable - Address unknown since 2011.

Executive Stewards and Caterers Assn. [★1446]

Executive Stewards and Caterers Assn. [★1446]

Executive Suite Assn. [★73]

Executive Suite Network [★73]

Executive Women in Govt. [5430], 710 Miller Rd., Annapolis, MD 21401, (410)562-2552

Executive Women Intl. [66], 515 S 700 E, Ste. 2A, Salt Lake City, UT 84102, (801)355-2800

Executive Women Intl. [66], 515 S 700 E, Ste. 2A, Salt Lake City, UT 84102, (801)355-2800

Executive Women Intl. - Calgary Chap. [IO], Calgary, AB, Canada

Executive Women's Coun. [3679], 100 W Sta. Square Dr., Ste. 315, Pittsburgh, PA 15219

Executive Women's Golf Assn. [22607], 300 Ave. of the Champions, Ste. 140, Palm Beach Gardens, FL 33418-3615, (561)691-0096

Executives Assn. of Great Britain [IO], Broadstairs, United Kingdom

Executives' Secretaries [★66]

Executives' Secretaries [★66]

Executives Without Borders [60], 410 Park Ave., 15th Fl., Ste. 1530, New York, NY 10022, (212)202-1995

Exer-Safety Assn. [★16224]

Exercise; Amer. Coun. on [16220]

Exercise Physiologists; Amer. Soc. of [16278]

Exercise Safety Assn. [16224], PO Box 547916, Orlando, FL 32854-7916, (407)246-5090

Exercise and Sports Sci. Australia [IO], Red Hill, Australia

Exhale [10766], 484 Lake Park Ave., No. 63, Oakland, CA 94610, (510)446-7900

Exhibit Designers and Producers Assn. [1229], 10 Norden Pl., Norwalk, CT 06855, (203)852-5698

Exhibition and Event Assn. of Australasia [IO], Chatswood, Australia

Exhibition and Event Assn. of Southern Africa [IO], Halfway House, Republic of South Africa

Exhibition Fed. of Ukraine [IO], Kiev, Ukraine

Exhibition Services Assn. Holland [IO], Breukelen, Netherlands

Exhibition Services and Contractors Assn. [★2448]

Exhibitor Appointed Contractor Assn. [1230], 2214 NW 5th St., Bend, OR 97701, (541)317-8768

Exhibitors

Bridal Show Producers Intl. [471]

Center for Exhibition Indus. Res. [1228]

European Major Exhibition Centres Assn. [7644]

Exhibit Designers and Producers Assn. [1229]

Exhibitor Appointed Contractor Assn. [1230]

Healthcare Convention and Exhibitors Assn. [1231]

Intl. Assn. of Butterfly Exhibitions [1232]

Intl. Assn. of Butterfly Exhibitions [1232]

Intl. Defense Equip. Exhibitors Assn. [1233]

Intl. Defense Equip. Exhibitors Assn. [1233]

Intl. Sport Show Producers Assn. [1234]

Natl. Assn. of Consumer Shows [1235]

Natl. Catholic Educational Exhibitors [1236]

Natl. Convention Assn. [2456]

Soc. of Independent Show Organizers [1237]

Trade Show Exhibitors Assn. [1238]

Existentialism

Merleau-Ponty Circle [10399]

EXIT [IO], Edinburgh, United Kingdom

Exit Poverty Empowerment [11067], 325 S Meadowbreak Ln., Olathe, KS 66062, (816)572-6580

Exmoor Horn Sheep Breeders Soc. [IO], Withypool, United Kingdom

Exmoor Pony Assn. Intl. [4581], Lisa Wojan, PO Box 1517, Litchfield, CT 06759, (860)672-2343

Exodus Guild [10821], 9 Sherer Trail, Worcester, MA 01603, (617)777-9338

Exodus Intl. [19790], PO Box 540119, Orlando, FL 32854, (407)599-6872

Exotic Bird Rescue [10960], PO Box 40041, Eugene, OR 97404-0004, (541)461-4333

Exotic Bird Soc. of Am. [21216], 9724 5th Ave., Orlando, FL 32824-8423, (407)855-3367

Exotic Dancers League of Am. - Address unknown since 2010.

Exotic Pathology Soc. [IO], Paris, France

Exotic Wildlife Assn. [5054], 105 Henderson Br. Rd. W, Ingram, TX 78025, (830)367-7761

Expanded Shale Clay and Slate Inst. [559], 230 E Ohio St., Ste. 400, Chicago, IL 60611, (801)272-7070

Expanded Shale Inst. [★559]

Expanding Opportunities [11273], 84 Payson Rd., Brooks, ME 04921, (207)722-3708

Expansion Joint Mfrs. Assn. [2748], 25 N Broadway, Tarrytown, NY 10591, (914)332-0040

Expansionist Party of the U.S. [18357], 295 Smith St., Newark, NJ 07106-2517, (973)416-6151

Expansionist Party of the U.S. [18357], 295 Smith St., Newark, NJ 07106-2517, (973)416-6151

Expediting Mgt. Assn. [IO], Calgary, AB, Canada

Experience Corps [8113], 601 E St. NW, Washington, DC 20049, (202)434-6400

Experience Intl. [4054], PO Box 680, Everson, WA 98247, (360)966-3876

Experience Works [11939], 4401 Wilson Blvd., Ste. 1100, Arlington, VA 22203, (703)522-7272

Experience Works [11939], 4401 Wilson Blvd., Ste. 1100, Arlington, VA 22203, (703)522-7272

Experiential Education

Assn. for Experiential Educ. [8173]

Coun. for Adult and Experiential Learning [8174]

Earthwatch Inst. [8175]

Experiential Learning Intl. [8176]

Intl. BioExploration Soc. [8180]

Natl. Soc. for Experiential Educ. [8177]

NTL Inst. for Applied Behavioral Sciences [8178]

NTL Inst. for Applied Behavioral Sciences [8178]

Reach the World [8179]

Experiential Learning Intl. [8176], 1557 Ogden St., Denver, CO 80218, (303)321-8278

Experiment in Intl. Living [★8379]

Experiment in Intl. Living [★8379]

Experiment in Intl. Living/School for Intl. Training [★8379]

Experiment in Intl. Living/School for Intl. Training [★8379]

Experimental Aircraft Assn. [6085], EAA Aviation Center, 3000 Poberezny Rd., Oshkosh, WI 54902, (920)426-4800

Experimental Cities, Inc. - Address unknown since 2010.

Experimental Psychology Soc. [IO], Bristol, United Kingdom

Experimento de Convivencia Internacional [★IO]

Exploration

Amer. Alpine Club [6856]

Circumnavigators Club [6857]

Explorers Club [6858]

Explorers Club [6858]

Intl. BioExploration Soc. [8180]

Intl. Soc. for a Complete Earth [12217]

South Amer. Explorers [3577]

Exploratory Comm. on Assessing the Progress of Educ. [★8989]

Explorers Club [6858], 46 E 70th St., New York, NY 10021, (212)628-8383

Explorers Club [6858], 46 E 70th St., New York, NY 10021, (212)628-8383

Exploring Solutions Past: The Maya Forest Alliance [6168], PO Box 3962, Santa Barbara, CA 93130, (805)893-8191

Exploring Solutions Past: The Maya Forest Alliance [6168], PO Box 3962, Santa Barbara, CA 93130, (805)893-8191

Explosives

Inst. of Makers of Explosives [1239]

Intl. Assn. of Bomb Technicians and Investigators [6859]

Intl. Assn. of Bomb Technicians and Investigators [6859]

Natl. Coun. on Fireworks Safety [11991]

Natl. Fireworks Assn. [1240]

Terra Segura Intl. [17559]

Export Advt. Assn. [★98]

Export Coun. of Norway [★23368]

Export Coun. of Norway [★23368]

Export Credit Insurance Org. [IO], Athens, Greece

Export Inst. of the U.S. [3483], 6901 W 84th St., Ste. 301, Minneapolis, MN 55438, (952)943-1505

Export Inst. of the U.S. [3483], 6901 W 84th St., Ste. 301, Minneapolis, MN 55438, (952)943-1505

Export Managers Club of Chicago [★2083]

Export Managers Club of Chicago [★2083]

Exporters' Assn. of Northern Greece [IO], Thessaloniki, Greece

Exposition Nationale Canadienne [★IO]

Exposition Ser. Contractors Assn. [2448], 5068 W Plano Pkwy., Ste. 300, Plano, TX 75093, (972)447-8212

Express Carriers Assn. - Defunct.

Express Delivery and Logistics Assn. [3247], 400 Admiral Blvd., Kansas City, MO 64106, (816)221-0254

Extensions for Independence [11786], 555 Saturn Blvd., No. B-368, San Diego, CA 92154, (619)618-2154

Exterior Insulation Mfrs. Assn. [★554]

Extra Miler Club [22188], PO Box 31, Annandale, VA 22003-0031

Extra Milers [★22188]

Extropy Inst. - Defunct.

Eye Bank Assn. of Am. [14422], 1015 18th St. NW, Ste. 1010, Washington, DC 20036, (202)775-4999

Eye Bank Assn. of India [IO], Hyderabad, India

Eye-Bank for Sight Restoration [14423], 120 Wall St., New York, NY 10005-3902, (212)742-9000

Eye on Jamaica Proj. - Address unknown since 2011.

Eye Level Gallery Soc. [IO], Halifax, NS, Canada

Eye Movement Desensitization and Reprocessing Assn. of Canada [IO], Montreal, QC, Canada

Eye Surgery Educ. Coun. [15958], 4000 Legato Rd., Ste. 700, Fairfax, VA 22033, (703)591-2220

Eyecare Trust [IO], Aylesbury, United Kingdom

Eyes for the Blind; Guiding [17083]

EYH Network [8563], Mills Coll., 5000 MacArthur Blvd., Oakland, CA 94613, (510)430-2222

F

F-4 Phantom II Soc. [20894], 3053 Rancho Vista Blvd., Ste. H-102, Palmdale, CA 93551

F-14 Tomcat Assn. [21201], PO Box 1347, Somis, CA 93066

F. Scott Fitzgerald Soc. [9363], Prof. Ruth Prigozy, Exec. Dir., 107 Hofstra Univ., Hempstead, NY 11549

F. Scott Fitzgerald Soc. [9363], Prof. Ruth Prigozy, Exec. Dir., 107 Hofstra Univ., Hempstead, NY 11549

Fab Owners Assn. [1101], 19925 Stevens Creek Blvd., Ste. 100, Cupertino, CA 95014-2358, (408)725-7127

Fabless Semiconductor Assn. [★1102]

Fabless Semiconductor Assn. [★1102]

Fabric Shop Network [3440], PO Box 820128, Vancouver, WA 98682-0003, (360)892-6500

Fabricants de produits allmentaires du Canada [★IO]

Fabricating Machinery Assn. [★1821]

Fabricating Machinery Assn. [★1821]

Fabricating Mfrs. Assn. [★1821]

Fabricating Mfrs. Assn. [★1821]

Fabricators and Mfrs. Assn. Intl. [1821], 833 Featherstone Rd., Rockford, IL 61107-6301, (815)399-8775

Fabricators and Mfrs. Assn. Intl. [1821], 833 Featherstone Rd., Rockford, IL 61107-6301, (815)399-8775

Fabry Disease; Intl. Center for [16771]

Fabry Support and Info. Gp. [14386], PO Box 510, Concordia, MO 64020, (660)463-1355

FACCT Found. for Accountability - Defunct.

FACE AIDS [13602], PO Box 46, Palo Alto, CA 94302

Face Autism [13789], 5333 Rio Vista St., Sarasota, FL 34232

Face Forward [11885], 8670 Wilshire Blvd., Ste. 200, Beverly Hills, CA 90211, (310)657-2253

FACE Intel - Former and Current Employees of Intel - Address unknown since 2011.

Reference to "IO" in place of a book number signifies that the association may be found in the 50th edition of International Organizations.

Face the Music Fan Club **[23840]**, PO Box 6061-572, Sherman Oaks, CA 91413, (888)539-4628

Faceless Intl. **[13362]**, PO Box 41846, Nashville, TN 37204, (615)852-5131

FACES: The Natl. Craniofacial Assn. **[14197]**, PO Box 11082, Chattanooga, TN 37401, (800)332-2373

Faces and Voices of Recovery **[18679]**, 1010 Vermont Ave., No. 618, Washington, DC 20005, (202)737-0690

Fachverband der Audiovisions- und Filmindustrie Osterreichs **[★IO]**

Fachverband der Bekleidungsindustrie Osterreichs **[★IO]**

Fachverband Biomedizinische Technik **[★IO]**

Fachverband der Chemischen Industrie Oesterreichs **[★IO]**

Fachverband Dampfkessel-, Behaelter- und Rohrleitungsbau e.V. **[★IO]**

Fachverband der Elektro- und Elektronikindustrie **[★IO]**

Fachverband der Fahrzeugindustrie Osterreichs **[★IO]**

Fachverband Gastronomie **[★IO]**

Fachverband der Gewurzindustrie e.V. **[★IO]**

Fachverband der Hotellerie **[★IO]**

Fachverband der Lederverarbeitenden Industrie **[★IO]**

Fachverband Maschinen and Metallwaren Industrie **[★IO]**

Fachverband Messe-und Ausstellungsbau **[★IO]**

Fachverband fur Multimediale Informationsverarbeitung **[★IO]**

Fachverband der Papier und Pappe verarbeitenden Industrie **[★IO]**

Fachverband der Reisebueros **[★IO]**

Fachverband der Textilindustrie Oesterreichs **[★IO]**

Facial Pain Assn. **[15587]**, 480 W Univ. Ave., Ste. 602, Gainesville, FL 32601, (352)331-7009

Facial Reconstruction; Natl. Found. for **[14201]**

Facing the Future **[8071]**, 811 1st Ave., Ste. 454, Seattle, WA 98104, (206)264-1503

Facing History and Ourselves **[★9764]**

Facing History and Ourselves **[★9764]**

Facing History and Ourselves Natl. Found. **[9764]**, 16 Hurd Rd., Brookline, MA 02445, (617)232-1595

Facing History and Ourselves Natl. Found. **[9764]**, 16 Hurd Rd., Brookline, MA 02445, (617)232-1595

Facing Our Risk of Cancer Empowered **[13921]**, 16057 Tampa Palms Blvd. W, PMB No. 373, Tampa, FL 33647, (954)255-8732

Facing Tile Inst. - Defunct.

Fact, Inc **[★4690]**

Facts and Logic About the Middle East **[18121]**, PO Box 590359, San Francisco, CA 94159, (415)356-7801

Facultad Latinoamericana de Estudios Teologicos **[★19679]**

Facultad Latinoamericana de Estudios Teologicos **[★19679]**

Faculty of Actuaries **[IO]**, Edinburgh, United Kingdom

Faculty of Advocates **[IO]**, Edinburgh, United Kingdom

Faculty of Astrological Stud. **[IO]**, London, United Kingdom

Faculty of Dental Surgery **[IO]**, London, United Kingdom

Faculty of Homeopathy **[IO]**, Luton, United Kingdom

Faculty for Human Rights in El Salvador and Central America - Defunct.

Faculty of Occupational Medicine **[IO]**, London, United Kingdom

Faculty of Public Hea. **[IO]**, London, United Kingdom

Faculty of Royal Designers for Indus. **[IO]**, London, United Kingdom

Fagazdasagi Orszagos Szakmai Szovetseg **[★IO]**

Fair Elections Legal Network **[5245]**, 1825 K St. NW, Ste. 450, Washington, DC 20006, (202)331-0114

Fair and Exhibition Assn. **[IO]**, Rheda-Wiedenbruck, Germany

Fair Organ Preservation Soc. **[IO]**, Chorleywood, United Kingdom

Fair Play for Children Assn. **[IO]**, Bognor Regis, United Kingdom

Fair Trade USA **[3484]**, 1500 Broadway, Ste. 400, Oakland, CA 94612, (510)663-5260

Fair-Witness Project - Defunct.

Fairchild Club **[20895]**, 92 N Circle Dr., Coldwater, MI 49036

Fairground Soc. **[IO]**, Telford, United Kingdom

Fairlane Club of Am. **[21053]**, 340 Clicktown Rd., Church Hill, TN 37642, (423)245-6678

Fairness and Accuracy in Reporting **[17343]**, 104 W 27th St., Ste. 10B, New York, NY 10001, (212)633-6700

Fairness Fund **[★12090]**

Fairs and Salons of France **[IO]**, Paris, France

FairTest **[★8991]**

Fairy Lamp Club **[21337]**, PO Box 438, Pine, CO 80470-0438

Faith Alive **[19705]**, 431 Richmond Pl. NE, Albuquerque, NM 87106, (505)255-3233

Faith Alliance Against Slavery and Trafficking **[17289]**, 7 E Baltimore St., Baltimore, MD 21202, (855)333-2278

Faith and Freedom Intl. **[★13188]**

Faith and Joy - Venezuela **[IO]**, Caracas, Venezuela

Faith Victory Assn. **[IO]**, Kigali, Rwanda

Faith at Work **[★19660]**

FaithTrust Inst. **[11886]**, 2400 N 45th St., Ste. 101, Seattle, WA 98103, (206)634-1903

FaithWorks Intl. **[11583]**, 3121 Middletown Rd., Ste. 9D, Bronx, NY 10461, (347)293-5460

FaithWorks Intl. **[11583]**, 3121 Middletown Rd., Ste. 9D, Bronx, NY 10461, (347)293-5460

Falcon Club of Am. **[21054]**, PO Box 113, Jacksonville, AR 72076

Falconry

North Amer. Falconers Assn. **[22561]**

Falkland Islands Overseas Games Assn. **[IO]**, Stanley, Falkland Islands

Falkland Islands Philatelic Study Group **[IO]**, Camberley, United Kingdom

Falklands Conservation **[IO]**, Stanley, Falkland Islands

False Memory Syndrome Found. **[16399]**, 1955 Locust St., Philadelphia, PA 19103-5766, (215)940-1040

Falun Data Info. Center **[17828]**, PO Box 577, New City, NY 10956, (888)842-4797

Famagusta Chamber of Commerce and Indus. **[IO]**, Limassol, Cyprus

FAMILIA Ancestral Res. Assn. **[18995]**, PO Box 10425, Westminster, CA 92685-0359, (714)687-0390

FAMILIA Ancestral Res. Assn. **[18995]**, PO Box 10425, Westminster, CA 92685-0359, (714)687-0390

Familiares y Amigos de Enfermos de la Neurona Motora **[IO]**, Mexico City, Mexico

Families

9/11 Families for a Secure Am. Found. **[18710]**

Ackerman Inst. for the Family **[11992]**

Adoptee-Birthparent Support Network **[10774]**

Ahern Clan Assn. **[20420]**

Alliance for Children and Families **[11993]**

Alliance for Children and Families **[11993]**

Amer. Coalition for Fathers and Children **[12602]**

Amer. Coll. of Community Midwives **[15864]**

Amer. Coll. of Counselors **[11994]**

Amer. Family Rights Assn. **[17622]**

Amer. Heraldry Soc. **[20618]**

Amer. Mothers, Inc. **[11995]**

America's Angel **[11996]**

Assn. for the Restoration of Church and Home **[19613]**

Bonus Families **[11997]**

Center for Screen-Time Awareness **[11998]**

Center for Work and the Family **[11999]**

Charette/Charest Family Assn. **[20440]**

Child and Family Policy Center **[12000]**

Christian Family Life **[12001]**

Christian Family Movement **[12002]**

Clan Arthur Assn. USA **[20442]**

Clan MacAlpine Soc. **[20463]**

Clan MacKinnon Soc. **[20470]**

Clan McAlister of Am. **[20478]**

Clan Phail Soc. in North America **[20484]**Families-Clanwilliam Inst.

CoMamas Assn. **[12003]**

Corporate Voices for Working Families **[17479]**

Coun. on Accreditation **[13182]**

Coun. on Contemporary Families **[12004]**

Educ. and Enrichment Sect. of the Natl. Coun. on Family Relations **[12005]**

Families with Children from China **[10787]**

Families for Private Adoption **[10788]**

Families and Work Inst. **[12006]**

Family of the Americas Found. **[12032]**

Family Campers and RVers **[22443]**

Family, Career and Community Leaders of Am. **[8181]**

Family and Consumer Sciences Educ. Assn. **[8182]**

Family Hea. Alliance **[16584]**

Family Literacy Alliance **[18082]**

Family Res. Coun. **[12007]**

Family Support Am. **[12008]**

Fertile Dreams **[14531]**

Focus on the Family **[12009]**

Foster Family-Based Treatment Assn. **[11282]**

FosterClub **[13522]**

Found. for Child Development **[11163]**

Friends in Adoption **[10789]**

Global Family Rescue **[13158]**

Green Parent Assn. **[4075]**

Greenlaw Family Assn. **[20526]**

Inst. for Amer. Values **[12010]**

Intl. Sect. of the Natl. Coun. on Family Relations **[12011]**

Intl. Sect. of the Natl. Coun. on Family Relations **[12011]**

Interracial Family Circle **[12012]**

Interracial-InterCultural Pride **[12013]**

Kids Need Both Parents **[17623]**

Loved Ones and Drivers Support **[13342]**

Luz Social Services **[13263]**

Malama Intl. **[11346]**

MISS Found. l Alliance of Grandparents, A Support in Tragedy Intl. **[12123]**

Mocha Moms **[13466]**

Natl. Alliance for Caregiving **[12014]**

Natl. Assn. of Family Ministries **[19998]**

Natl. Assn. of Non-Custodial Moms **[12610]**

Natl. Coun. on Family Relations **[12015]**

Natl. Coun. on Family Relations l Feminism and Family Stud. Sect. **[12016]**

Natl. Coun. on Family Relations l Religion and Family Life Sect. **[12017]**

Natl. Coun. on Family Relations l Religion and Family Life Sect. **[12017]**

Natl. Fatherhood Initiative **[17624]**

Natl. Practitioners Network for Fathers and Families **[12018]**

North Amer. Family Campers Assn. **[22446]**

notMYkid **[13548]**

One Missing Link **[12545]**

Partners in Foster Care **[12046]**

Professional Football Players Mothers' Assn. **[22595]**

Reach Global **[13146]**

Save a Family Plan **[12019]**

Save a Family Plan **[12019]**

Secretariat for Family, Laity, Women, and Youth **[12020]**

SingleStop USA **[12752]**

Soc. of Blessed Gianna Beretta Molla **[19776]**

Soc. of Blessed Gianna Beretta Molla **[19776]**

Stepfamily Found. **[12021]**

Teaching-Family Assn. **[12022]**

Total Family Care Coalition **[12023]**

Twins Found. **[12551]**

United We Serve **[20712]**

Women in Fatherhood, Inc. **[13151]**

Families, 4-H, and Nutrition **[13521]**, Cooperative State Res. Educ. and Extension Ser., 1400 Independence Ave. SW, Stop 2225, Washington, DC 20250-2225, (202)720-2908

Families in Action **[★13279]**

Families in Action Drug Info. Center **[★13279]**

Families in Action Natl. Drug Info. Center **[★13279]**

Families of Adults Afflicted with Asperger's Syndrome **[16765]**, PO Box 514, Centerville, MA 02632, (508)790-1930

A star before a book entry number signifies that the name is not listed separately, but is mentioned within the entry.

Families Against Internet Censorship - Defunct.

Families Against Mandatory Minimums Found. **[11710]**, 1612 K St. NW, Ste. 700, Washington, DC 20006, (202)822-6700

Families Anonymous **[13251]**, PO Box 3475, Culver City, CA 90231-3475, (310)815-8010

Families Anonymous **[13251]**, PO Box 3475, Culver City, CA 90231-3475, (310)815-8010

Families with Autism Spectrum Disorders **[13790]**, 5989 Meijer Dr., Ste. 9, Milford, OH 45150, (513)444-4979

Families with Children from China **[10787]**, 255 W 90th St., 11C, New York, NY 10024

Families for Depression Awareness **[15453]**, 395 Totten Pond Rd., Ste. 404, Waltham, MA 02451, (781)890-0220

Families with Maple Syrup Urine Disease **[★15499]**

Families Need Fathers **[IO]**, London, United Kingdom

Families for Private Adoption **[10788]**, PO Box 6375, Washington, DC 20015-0375, (202)722-0338

Families of September 11 **[18712]**, 1560 Broadway, Ste. 305, New York, NY 10036-1518, (212)575-1878

Families of S.M.A. **[15588]**, 925 Busse Rd., Elk Grove Village, IL 60007, (847)367-7620

Families U.S.A. Found. **[10842]**, 1201 New York Ave. NW, Ste. 1100, Washington, DC 20005-6100, (202)628-3030

Families and Work Inst. **[12006]**, 267 5th Ave., 2nd Fl., New York, NY 10016, (212)465-2044

Families Worldwide **[13252]**, 5248 Pinemont Dr., Ste. C-190, Salt Lake City, UT 84123, (801)268-6461

Families Worldwide **[13252]**, 5248 Pinemont Dr., Ste. C-190, Salt Lake City, UT 84123, (801)268-6461

Family of the Americas **[★12032]**

Family of the Americas Found. **[12032]**, 5929 Talbot Rd., Lothian, MD 20711, (301)627-3346

Family Assn. of Am. **[★11993]**

Family Assn. of Am. **[★11993]**

Family Campers and RVers **[22443]**, 4804 Transit Rd., Bldg. 2, Depew, NY 14043, (716)668-6242

Family Care Intl. **[16647]**, 588 Broadway, Ste. 503, New York, NY 10012, (212)941-5300

Family Care Intl. **[16647]**, 588 Broadway, Ste. 503, New York, NY 10012, (212)941-5300

Family Care Intl. - Bolivia **[IO]**, La Paz, Bolivia

Family Care Intl. - Burkina Faso **[IO]**, Ouagadougou, Burkina Faso

Family Care Intl. - Ecuador **[IO]**, Quito, Ecuador

Family Care Intl. - Kenya **[IO]**, Nairobi, Kenya

Family Care Intl. - Mali **[IO]**, Bamako, Mali

Family Care Intl. - Niger **[IO]**, Niamey, Niger

Family Care Intl. - Tanzania **[IO]**, Dar es Salaam, United Republic of Tanzania

Family, Career and Community Leaders of Am. **[8181]**, 1910 Assn. Dr., Reston, VA 20191-1584, (703)476-4900

Family Circle of PenDelfin - Address unknown since 2010.

Family and Consumer Sciences Educ. Assn. **[8182]**, Central Washington Univ., Dept. of Family & Consumer Sci., 400 E 8th Univ. Way, Ellensburg, WA 98926-7565, (509)963-2766

Family Coun. on Drug Awareness **[13253]**, Mikki Norris, PO Box 1716, El Cerrito, CA 94530, (510)215-8326

Family Coun. on Drug Awareness **[13253]**, Mikki Norris, PO Box 1716, El Cerrito, CA 94530, (510)215-8326

Family Educ. Trust **[IO]**, Twickenham, United Kingdom

Family Equality Coun. **[12079]**, PO Box 206, Boston, MA 02133, (617)502-8700

Family Farm Defenders **[4351]**, PO Box 1772, Madison, WI 53701, (608)260-0900

Family Fed. of Finland **[IO]**, Helsinki, Finland

Family Fed. for World Peace and Unification **[20151]**, 481 8th Ave., Ste. 620, New York, NY 10001, (212)997-0050

Family Firm Inst. **[3288]**, 200 Lincoln St., Ste. 201, Boston, MA 02111, (617)482-3045

Family Firm Inst. **[3288]**, 200 Lincoln St., Ste. 201, Boston, MA 02111, (617)482-3045

Family Hea. Alliance **[16584]**, 6520 Platt Ave., Ste. 433, West Hills, CA 91307, (818)610-7278

Family Hea. Intl. **[12033]**, PO Box 13950, Research Triangle Park, NC 27709, (919)544-7040

Family Hea. Intl. **[12033]**, PO Box 13950, Research Triangle Park, NC 27709, (919)544-7040

Family Hea. Intl. - Bangladesh **[IO]**, Dhaka, Bangladesh

Family Hea. Intl. - Burundi **[IO]**, Bujumbura, Burundi

Family Hea. Intl. - Cambodia **[IO]**, Phnom Penh, Cambodia

Family Hea. Intl. - Cote d' Ivore **[IO]**, Abidjan, Cote d'Ivoire

Family Hea. Intl. - Egypt **[IO]**, Cairo, Egypt

Family Hea. Intl. - Ethiopia **[IO]**, Addis Ababa, Ethiopia

Family Hea. Intl. - Ghana **[IO]**, Accra, Ghana

Family Hea. Intl. - Guyana **[IO]**, Georgetown, Guyana

Family Hea. Intl. - Haiti **[IO]**, Port-au-Prince, Haiti

Family Hea. Intl. - India **[IO]**, New Delhi, India

Family Hea. Intl. - Indonesia **[IO]**, Jakarta, Indonesia

Family Hea. Intl. - Kenya **[IO]**, Nairobi, Kenya

Family Hea. Intl. - Laos **[IO]**, Vientiane, Lao People's Democratic Republic

Family Hea. Intl. - Malawi **[IO]**, Lilongwe, Malawi

Family Hea. Intl. - Mozambique **[IO]**, Maputo, Mozambique

Family Hea. Intl. - Namibia **[IO]**, Windhoek, Namibia

Family Hea. Intl. - Nepal **[IO]**, Kathmandu, Nepal

Family Hea. Intl. - Nigeria **[IO]**, Abuja, Nigeria

Family Hea. Intl. - People's Republic of China **[IO]**, Beijing, People's Republic of China

Family Hea. Intl. - Senegal **[IO]**, Dakar, Senegal

Family Hea. Intl. - South Africa **[IO]**, Pretoria, Republic of South Africa

Family Hea. Intl. - Thailand **[IO]**, Bangkok, Thailand

Family Hea. Intl. - Vietnam **[IO]**, Hanoi, Vietnam

Family Hea. Options Kenya **[IO]**, Nairobi, Kenya

Family and Hea. Sect. **[★14526]**

Family and Home Network **[12606]**, PO Box 545, Merrifield, VA 22116

Family of Humanists **[9840]**, PO Box 4153, Salem, OR 97302, (503)371-1255

Family Inst. **[★11992]**

Family Justice **[11711]**, 625 Broadway, 8th Fl., New York, NY 10012, (212)475-1500

Family Law

Amer. Acad. of Matrimonial Lawyers **[5422]**

Amer. Family Rights Assn. **[17622]**

Assn. of Family and Conciliation Courts **[5423]**

Natl. Alliance for Family Court Justice **[5624]**

Natl. Assn. for Family Child Care **[12024]**

Natl. Center for Youth Law **[5424]**

Natl. Child Support Enforcement Assn. **[5425]**

Natl. Juvenile Court Services Assn. **[5426]**

Natl. Law Center for Children and Families **[5427]**

Family Learning Assn. - Address unknown since 2011.

Family Life Achievement Center **[★11392]**

Family Life Achievement Center **[★11392]**

Family Life Assn. of Swaziland **[IO]**, Manzini, Swaziland

Family Life Bur. **[★12020]**

Family Life Div., U.S. Catholic Conf. **[★12020]**

Family Life Info. Exchange **[★12700]**

Family Life Ministry, U.S. Catholic Conf. **[★12020]**

Family Life Mission **[IO]**, Kehl, Germany

Family Literacy Alliance **[18082]**, 325 W Main St., Ste. 300, Louisville, KY 40202-4237, (502)584-1133

Family Mediation Canada **[IO]**, Waterloo, ON, Canada

Family Mediation Manitoba **[IO]**, Winnipeg, MB, Canada

Family Medicine

Amer. Acad. of Family Physicians **[14523]**

Amer. Bd. of Family Medicine **[14524]**

Amer. Coll. of Community Midwives **[15864]**

Interstate Postgraduate Medical Assn. of North Am. **[14525]**

Natl. Coun. on Family Relations, Family and Hea. Sect. **[14526]**

Soc. of Teachers of Family Medicine **[14527]**

Family Motor Coach Assn. **[22138]**, 8291 Clough Pike, Cincinnati, OH 45244, (513)474-3622

Family Name Societies

Adam Hawkes Family Assn. **[20418]**

Addington Assn. **[20419]**

Ahern Clan Assn. **[20420]**

Alden Kindred of Am. **[20421]**

Alford Amer. Family Assn. **[20422]**

Amer. Clan Gregor Soc. **[20423]**

Anneke Jans and Everardus Bogardus Descendants Assn. **[20424]**

Archer Assn. **[20425]**

Assn. of Blauvelt Descendants **[20426]**

Assn. of Blauvelt Descendants **[20426]**

Ballew Family Assn. of Am. **[20427]**

Barney Family Historical Assn. **[20428]**

Beall Family Assn. **[20429]**

Bigelow Soc. **[20430]**

Bigelow Soc. **[20430]**

Blackburn Family Assn. **[20431]**

Blair Soc. for Genealogical Res. **[20432]**

Blair Soc. for Genealogical Res. **[20432]**

Bolling Family Assn. **[20433]**

Bondurant Family Assn. **[20434]**

Boone Soc. **[20435]**

Boone Soc. **[20435]**

Brantley Assn. of Am. **[20436]**

Bunker Family Assn. of Am. **[20437]**

Bunker Family Assn. of Am. **[20437]**

Burleson Family Assn. **[20438]**

Chapman Family Assn. **[20439]**

Charette/Charest Family Assn. **[20440]**

Clan Anderson Soc. **[20441]**

Clan Arthur Assn. USA **[20442]**

Clan Bell Intl. **[20443]**

Clan Brown Soc. **[20444]**

Clan Campbell Soc., North Am. **[20445]**

Clan Carmichael U.S.A. **[20446]**

Clan Chisholm Soc., U.S. Br. **[20447]**

Clan Craig Assn. of Am. **[20448]**

Clan Cunningham Soc. of Am. **[20449]**

Clan Currie Soc. **[20450]**

Clan Currie Soc. **[20450]**

Clan Davidson Soc. **[20451]**

Clan Douglas Soc. of North Am. **[20452]**

Clan Drummond Soc. of North Am. **[20453]**

Clan Fergusson Soc. of North Am. **[20454]**

Clan Forrester Soc. **[20455]**

Clan Forsyth Soc. U.S.A. **[20456]**

Clan Graham Soc. **[20457]**

Clan Guthrie USA **[20458]**

Clan Irwin Assn. **[20459]**

Clan Johnston in Am. **[20460]**

Clan Johnston in Am. **[20460]**

Clan Keith Soc. **[20461]**

Clan Leslie Soc. Intl. **[20462]**

Clan MacAlpine Soc. **[20463]**

Clan MacCarthy Soc. **[20464]**

Clan MacDuff Soc. of Am. **[20465]**

Clan MacIntyre Assn. **[20466]**

Clan MacIntyre Assn. **[20467]**

Clan MacKay Soc. **[20468]**

Clan MacKenzie Soc. in the Americas **[20469]**

Clan MacKinnon Soc. **[20470]**

Clan Mackintosh of North Am. **[20471]**

Clan Macneil Assn. of Am. **[20472]**

Clan Macpherson Assn. **[20473]**

Clan Macpherson Assn. **[20473]**

Clan MacRae Soc. of North Am. **[20474]**

Clan Maitland Soc. of North Am. **[20475]**

Clan Matheson Soc. **[20476]**

Clan Maxwell Soc. of the USA **[20477]**

Clan McAlister of Am. **[20478]**

Clan Menzies Soc., North Amer. Br. **[20479]**

Clan Moffat Soc. **[20480]**

Clan Moncreiffe Soc. **[20481]**

Clan Moncreiffe Soc. of North Am. **[20481]**

Clan Montgomery Soc. Intl. **[20482]**

Clan Montgomery Soc. Intl. **[20482]**

Clan Munro Assn. **[20483]**

Clan Phail Soc. in North America **[20484]**

Clan Pollock **[20485]**

Clan Ramsey Assn. of North Am. **[20486]**

Clan Rose Soc. of Am. **[20487]**

Clan Ross Assn. of the U.S. **[20488]**

Clan Scott Soc. **[20489]**

Clan Shaw Soc. **[20490]**

Reference to "IO" in place of a book number signifies that the association may be found in the 50th edition of International Organizations.

Clan Sinclair Assn. U.S.A. [20491]
Clan Sutherland Soc. of North Am. [20492]
Clan Young [20493]
Cloud Family Assn. [20494]
Cogswell Family Assn. [20495]
Corson/Colson Family History Assn. [20496]
Crandall Family Assn. [20497]
Crowl Name Assn. [20498]
Curtis/Curtiss Soc. [20499]
Dameron Family Assn. [20500]
Denison Soc. [20501]
Doane Family Assn. of Am. [20502]
Dodge Family Assn. [20503]
DuBois Family Assn. [20504]
Duncan Surname Assn. [20505]
Dunlop - Dunlap Family Soc. [20506]
Easterling Family Genealogical Soc. [20507]
Eddy Family Assn. [20508]
Elder Brewster Soc. [20509]
Eller Family Assn. [20510]
Elliot Clan Soc. USA [20511]
Enders Family Assn. [20512]
Enders Family Assn. [20512]
Eskridge Family Assn. [20513]
Felton Family Assn. [20514]
Flippin Family Assn. [20515]
Fretz Family Assn. [20516]
Friend Family Assn. of Am. [20517]
Frisbie - Frisbee Family Assn. of Am. [20518]
Fuller Soc. [20519]
Gaylord Family Org. [20520]
Gilstrap Family Assn. [20521]
Goff/Gough Family Assn. [20522]
Goodenow Family Assn. [20523]
Goodwin Family Org. [20524]
Graves Family Assn. [20525]
Graves Family Assn. [20525]
Greenlaw Family Assn. [20526]
Grinnell Family Assn. [20527]
Groberg - Holbrook Genealogical Org. [20528]
Hamilton Natl. Genealogical Soc. [20529]
Harden - Hardin - Harding Family Assn. [20530]
Hasbrouck Family Assn. [20531]
Hathaway Family Assn. [20532]
Hawkins Assn. [20533]
Higdon Family Assn. [20534]
House of Boyd Soc. [20535]
House of Boyd Soc. [20535]
Hubbell Family Historical Soc. [20536]
Hubbell Family Historical Soc. [20536]
Hudson Family Assn. [20537]
Innes Clan Soc. [20538]
Innes Clan Soc. [20538]
Intl. Assn. of Clan MacInnes [20539]
Intl. Molyneux Family Assn. [20540]
Jacob Hochstetler Family Assn. [20541]
John Clough Genealogical Soc. [20542]
John Libby Family Assn. [20543]
John More Assn. [20544]
Judkins Family Assn. [20545]
Junkins Family Assn. [20546]
Kelsey Kindred of Am. [20547]
Kerr Family Assn. of North Am. [20548]
Kerr Family Assn. of North Am. [20548]
Kilts Family Assn. [20549]
Kjaerulf Family Soc. [20550]
Kump Family Assn. [20551]
Lasher Family Assn. [20552]
Littlefield Family Newsl. [20553]
Litzenberger-Litzenberg Assn. [20554]
MacThomas North Am. [20555]
Marley Family Assn. [20556]
Maybee Soc. [20557]
McAdams Historical Soc. [20558]
Meader Family Assn. [20559]
Miles Merwin Assn. [20560]
Murray Clan Soc. North Am. [20561]
Natl. Assn. of the Van Valkenburg Family [20562]
Natl. Grigsby Family Soc. [20563]
Nesbitt/Nisbet Soc.: A Worldwide Clan Soc.
  [20564]
Nesbitt/Nisbet Soc.: A Worldwide Clan Soc.
  [20564]
Nims Family Assn. [20565]
Ouderkerk Family Genealogical Assn. [20566]

Owen Family Assn. [20567]
Owsley Family Historical Soc. [20568]
Paisley Family Soc. [20569]
Parke Soc. [20570]
Pierre Chastain Family Assn. [20571]
Platt Family Assn. [20572]
Pontius Family Assn. [20573]
Purcell Family of Am. [20574]
Rader Assn. [20575]
Reynolds Family Assn. [20576]
Rich Family Assn. [20577]
Risley Family Assn. [20578]
Risley Family Assn. [20578]
Rose Family Assn. [20579]
Runkle Family Assn. [20580]
Saleeby-Saliba Assn. of Families [20581]
Scruggs Family Assn. [20582]
Sears Family Assn. [20583]
Seeley Genealogical Soc. [20584]
Shirley Family Assn. [20585]
Skinner Family Assn. [20586]
Snodgrass Clan Soc. [20587]
Soc. of the Hawley Family [20588]
Soc. of Mareen Duvall Descendants [20589]
Soc. of Stukely Westcott Descendants of Am.
  [20590]
Sparks Family Assn. [20591]
Stovall Family Assn. [20592]
Streeter Family Assn. [20593]
Strong Family Assn. of Am. [20594]
Studebaker Family Natl. Assn. [20595]
Sumner Family Assn. [20596]
Sumner Family Assn. [20596]
Tackett Family Assn. [20597]
Taft Family Assn. [20598]
Templin Family Assn. [20599]
Thomas Minor Soc. [20600]
Turnbull Clan Assn. [20601]
Urbain Baudreau Graveline Genealogical Assn.
  [20602]
Van Voorhees Assn. [20603]
Vawter - Vauter - Vaughter Family Assn. [20604]
Veitch Historical Soc. [20605]
Wells Family Res. Assn. [20606]
Wells Family Res. Assn. [20606]
Wert Family History Assn. [20607]
Wingfield Family Assn. [20608]
Wingfield Family Soc. [20608]
Wolfensberger Family Assn. [20609]

Family Planning
Advocates for Youth [12025]
Advocates for Youth [12025]
Amer. Acad. of Fertility Care Professionals
  [12026]
Assn. of Reproductive Hea. Professionals [12027]
Billings Ovulation Method Assn. - USA [12028]
CHOICE [12029]
Couple to Couple League [12030]
EngenderHealth [12031]
EngenderHealth [12031]
Family of the Americas Found. [12032]
Family Hea. Alliance [16584]
Family Hea. Intl. [12033]
Family Hea. Intl. [12033]
Fertile Dreams [14531]
Guttmacher Inst. [12034]
Healthy Teen Network [12035]
Intl. Consortium for Emergency Contraception
  [12036]
Intl. Consortium for Emergency Contraception
  [12036]
Intl. Planned Parenthood Fed., Western
  Hemisphere Region [12037]
Intl. Planned Parenthood Fed., Western
  Hemisphere Region [12037]
Natl. Assn. of Ovulation Method Instructors UK
  [2774]
Natl. Family Planning and Reproductive Hea.
  Assn. [12038]
Pathfinder Intl. [12039]
Pathfinder Intl. [12039]
Planned Parenthood Fed. of Am. [12040]
Population Rsrc. Center [12708]
Soc. of Family Planning [14528]
Soft Power Hea. [15213]

WINGS [12904]
World Hea. Partners [15225]
Family Planning Assn. of Bangladesh [IO], Dhaka,
  Bangladesh
Family Planning Assn. of Greece [IO], Athens,
  Greece
Family Planning Assn. of Hong Kong [IO], Hong
  Kong, People's Republic of China
Family Planning Assn. of India [IO], Mumbai, India
Family Planning Assn. of Iran [IO], Tehran, Iran
Family Planning Assn. of Moldova [IO], Chisinau,
  Moldova
Family Planning Assn. of Nepal [IO], Kathmandu,
  Nepal
Family Planning Assn. of New Zealand [IO], Welling-
  ton, New Zealand
Family Planning Assn. of Pakistan [IO], Lahore,
  Pakistan
Family Planning Assn. of Sri Lanka [IO], Colombo,
  Sri Lanka
Family Planning Assn. of Trinidad and Tobago [IO],
  Port of Spain, Trinidad and Tobago
Family Planning Assn. of the United Kingdom [IO],
  London, United Kingdom
Family Planning Org. of the Philippines [IO], Quezon
  City, Philippines
Family Planning and Sexual Hea. Assn. [IO], Vilnius,
  Lithuania
Family Pride Coalition [★12079]
Family Promise [12156], 71 Summit Ave., Summit,
  NJ 07901, (908)273-1100
Family Res. Coun. [12007], 801 G St. NW,
  Washington, DC 20001, (202)393-2100
Family Res. Coun. of Am. [★12007]
Family Res. Gp. [★12007]
Family Res. Inst. [17763], PO Box 62640, Colorado
  Springs, CO 80962-2640, (303)681-3113
Family Rsrc. Center on Disabilities [7971], 20 E
  Jackson Blvd., Rm. 300, Chicago, IL 60604,
  (312)939-3513
Family Rsrc. Coalition of Am. [★12008]
Family Rosary [19420], 518 Washington St., North
  Easton, MA 02356-1202, (508)238-4095
Family Rosary Crusade [★19420]
Family Ser. Assn. of Am. [★11993]
Family Ser. Assn. of Am. [★11993]
Family Support Am. [12008], 307 W 200 S, Ste.
  2004, Salt Lake City, UT 84101
Family Therapy Network [★16472]
Family Therapy Sect. of the Natl. Coun. on Family
  Relations [16849], 1201 W River Pkwy., Ste. 200,
  Minneapolis, MN 55454, (763)231-2891
Family Violence Prevention Fund [★11887]
Family Voices [14076], 3701 San Mateo Blvd. NE,
  Ste. 200, Albuquerque, NM 87110, (505)872-4774
Family Welfare Assn. of Am. [★11993]
Family Welfare Assn. of Am. [★11993]
Famous Fone Friends [11463], 9101 Sawyer St.,
  Los Angeles, CA 90035, (310)204-5683
Famplan Jamaica [IO], St. Ann, Jamaica
Fan Assn. of North Am. [21338], 1011 W G St.,
  Jenks, OK 74037-2521
Fan Circle Intl. [IO], Norwich, United Kingdom
Fan Clubs
Art Greenhaw Official Intl. Fan Club [23814]
Chris Young Fan Club [23825]
Conrad Veidt Soc. [23763]
Damfinos: The Intl. Buster Keaton Soc. [23796]
Diamond Rio Fan Club [23832]
Doors Collectors Club [23836]
The Grascals Fan Club [23851]
Jeannie Seely's Circle of Friends [23860]
Johnnie Ray Intl. Fan Club [23865]
Johnny Benson Fan Club [23791]
Martina McBride Fan Club [23876]
Michael Jackson Fan Club [23878]
Natl. Lum and Abner Soc. [22119]
Richard Burgi Fan Club [23781]
Fan Makers' Company [IO], London, United
  Kingdom
Fanconi Anemia Res. Fund [14596], 1801 Wil-
  lamette St., Ste. 200, Eugene, OR 97401,
  (541)687-4658
Fanconi's Anemia Support Gp. [★14596]
Fanderson [IO], Bradford, United Kingdom

A star before a book entry number signifies that the name is not listed separately, but is mentioned within the entry.

Fans and Friends of Ray Price [★23884]
Fans of Leonard Nimoy and DeForest Kelley - Address unknown since 2011.
Fans of Oz - Address unknown since 2010.
Fantasy Sports Trade Assn. [3329], Charlie Wiegert, Treas., 11756 Borman Dr., St. Louis, MO 63146, (763)269-3609
FAO/UNECE Forestry and Timber Sect. [IO], Geneva, Switzerland
Far Eastern Assn. [★7760]
Far Eastern Assn. [★7760]
Farbard Labor Zionist Order [★19086]
Farm Aid [17167], 501 Cambridge St., 3rd Fl., Cambridge, MA 02141, (617)354-2922
Farm Animal Care Trust [★4690]
Farm Animal Reform Movement [★10961]
Farm Animal Rights Movement [10961], 10101 Ashburton Ln., Bethesda, MD 20817, (301)530-1737
Farm Animal Task Force [★10961]
Farm-Based Educ. Assn. [7710], Minute Man Natl. Historical Park, 231 Liberty St., Concord, MA 01742, (978)318-7871
Farm Bur. [★4346]
Farm Credit Coun. [411], 50 F St. NW, Ste. 900, Washington, DC 20001-1530, (202)626-8710
Farm Electrification Coun. [★6753]
Farm Equipment
Aerial Agricultural Assn. of Australia [10889]
Agricultural Mfrs. of Canada [20811]
Assn. of Equip. Mfrs. - Canada [10197]
Intl. Harvester Collectors [22177]
Mexican Assn. of Machinery Distributors [18604]
Natl. Russell Collectors Assn. [21382]
Farm Equip. Mfrs. Assn. [168], 1000 Executive Pkwy., Ste. 100, St. Louis, MO 63141-6369, (314)878-2304
Farm Financial Standards Coun. [3755], Carroll Merry, Exec. Sec., N78W14573 Appleton Ave., No. 287, Menomonee Falls, WI 53051, (262)253-6902
Farm Forward [10962], PO Box 4120, Portland, OR 97208-4120, (877)313-3276
Farm Found. [3741], 1301 W 22nd St., Ste. 615, Oak Brook, IL 60523, (630)571-9393
Farm Labor Organizing Comm. [23142], 1221 Broadway St., Toledo, OH 43609, (419)243-3456
Farm Labor Res. Proj. - Address unknown since 2011.
Farm and Land Inst. [★3043]
Farm Law Inst. - Defunct.
Farm Management
Farm Financial Standards Coun. [3755]
Farm and Ranch Freedom Alliance [4352]
Multinational Exchange for Sustainable Agriculture [4941]
Farm Publications Reports - Defunct.
Farm Radio Intl. [IO], Ottawa, ON, Canada
Farm and Ranch Freedom Alliance [4352], PO Box 809, Cameron, TX 76520, (254)697-2661
Farm Rescue [12041], PO Box 1100, Jamestown, ND 58402-1100, (701)252-2017
Farm Safety 4 Just Kids [12983], 11304 Aurora Ave., Urbandale, IA 50322, (515)331-6506
Farm Sanctuary [10963], PO Box 150, Watkins Glen, NY 14891, (607)583-2225
Farm Store Merchandising Assn. - Defunct.
Farm Tractor and Machinery Trade Assn. [IO], Naas, Ireland
Farmer-Veteran Coalition [20610], 508 2nd St., Ste. 206, Davis, CA 95616, (530)756-1395
Farmers Assistance Relief Mission - Defunct.
Farmers Assn. of Iceland [IO], Reykjavik, Iceland
Farmers Development Agency [IO], Chickballapur, India
Farmers' Educational and Cooperative Union of Am. [★4359]
Farmers' Legal Action Gp. [5754], 360 N Robert St., Ste. 500, St. Paul, MN 55101-1508, (651)223-5400
Farmers Market Coalition [3731], PO Box 331, Cockeysville, MD 21030
Farmers Union Intl. Assn. Corp. [★4174]
Farmers Union Intl. Assn. Corp. [★4174]
FarmFolk/CityFolk Soc. [IO], Vancouver, BC, Canada
Farmhouse [23669], 7306 NW Tiffany Spring Pkwy., Ste. 210, Kansas City, MO 64153, (816)891-9445

Farming
Agricultural Personnel Mgt. Assn. [4344]
Alliance for Sustainability [4345]
Amer. Assn. of Crop Insurers [1924]
Amer. Farm Bur. Fed. [4346]
Amer. Farmers for the Advancement and Conservation of Tech. [4347]
Biodynamic Farming and Gardening Assn. [4348]
Community Agroecology Network [4938]
Conservation through Poverty Alleviation Intl. [4030]
Demeter Assn. [4349]
Demeter Biodynamic Trade Assn. [4350]
Ecova Mali [3754]
Family Farm Defenders [4351]
Farm Financial Standards Coun. [3755]
Farm and Ranch Freedom Alliance [4352]
Farm Rescue [12041]
Farmer-Veteran Coalition [20610]
Farmers Market Coalition [3731]
FishWise [1359]
Food Trade Sustainability Leadership Assn. [1387]
Global Partnership for Afghanistan [3716]
Intl. Flying Farmers [4353]
Intl. Flying Farmers [4353]
Intl. Network on Participatory Irrigation Mgt. [7016]
The Land Inst. [4354]
Land Loss Fund [12417]
Multinational Exchange for Sustainable Agriculture [4941]
Natl. Assn. of Farm Bus. Anal. Specialists [165]
Natl. Assn. of Farmers' Market Nutrition Programs [4355]
Natl. Black Farmers Assn. [12042]
Natl. Coalition for Food and Agricultural Res. [3744]
Natl. Farm-City Coun. [4356]
Natl. Farm and Ranch Bus. Mgt. Educ. Assn. [4357]
Natl. Farmers Org. [4358]
Natl. Farmers Union [4359]
Natl. Grange [4360]
Natl. Sustainable Agriculture Coalition [4942]
Natl. Women in Agriculture Assn. [3762]
Natl. Young Farmer Educational Assn. [4361]
North Amer. Deer Farmers Assn. [4362]
Organic Crop Improvement Assn. [4363]
Organic Crop Improvement Assn. [4363]
Organic Seed Growers and Trade Assn. [4883]
Pan-American Fed. for Info. Tech. in Agriculture [6106]
Permacultura Am. Latina [4684]
Planting Empowerment [4410]
Professional Farmers of Am. [4364]
Royal Highland Educ. Trust [17419]
Senior Gleaners [12291]
Sustainable Agriculture Educ. [4944]
Truth About Trade and Tech. [6337]
Universal Proutist Farmers Fed. [4365]
Urban Farming [4366]
U.S.A. Ploughing Org. [4367]
Victorian Farmers Fed. [8655]
Vote Hemp [18609]
Wild Farm Alliance [4368]
World Cocoa Found. [4369]
World Wide Opportunities on Organic Farms - USA [17173]
Farmland Indus. - Defunct.
FARMS, Inc. [★12327]
FARMS, Inc. [★12327]
FARMS Intl. [12327], PO Box 270, Knife River, MN 55609-0270, (218)834-2676
FARMS Intl. [12327], PO Box 270, Knife River, MN 55609-0270, (218)834-2676
Farmworker Hea. Services, Inc. [★12520]
Farmworker Justice Fund [12518], 1126 16th St. NW, Ste. 270, Washington, DC 20036, (202)293-5420
Faroe Islands Amateur Theatre Coun. [IO], Torshavn, Faroe Islands
Faroese Volleyball Assn. [IO], Torshavn, Faroe Islands
Farriers
Brotherhood of Working Farriers Assn. [1241]

Guild of Professional Farriers [1242]
World Farriers Assn. [1243]
World Farriers Assn. [1243]
Fashion
YMA Fashion Scholarship Fund [216]
Fashion Accessories Shippers Assn. [★213]
Fashion Assn. [★199]
Fashion for Autism [13791], 274 Clinton Ave., Brooklyn, NY 11205, (917)881-6259
Fashion Fights Poverty [12725], 1101 Wilson Blvd., Arlington, VA 22209, (571)969-3121
Fashion Gp. Intl. [205], 8 W 40th St., 7th Fl., New York, NY 10018, (212)302-5511
Fashion Gp. Intl. [205], 8 W 40th St., 7th Fl., New York, NY 10018, (212)302-5511
Fastener Engg. and Res. Assn. [IO], West Bromwich, United Kingdom
Fat Lip Readers Theater - Defunct.
Fatal Light Awareness Prog. [IO], Toronto, ON, Canada
Father Josef's Method of Reflexology [13676], 1441 High Ridge Rd., Stamford, CT 06903, (203)968-6824
Father Judge Apostolic Center - Defunct.
Father Matters [18224], PO Box 13575, Tempe, AZ 85284-3575, (888)648-0718
Fatherhood Proj. - Defunct.
Fathers for Equal Rights [11867], 701 Commerce St., Ste. 302, Dallas, TX 75202, (214)953-2233
Fathers Network - Defunct.
Fathers Rights and Equality Exchange [★11865]
Fats and Proteins Res. Found. [2583], 801 N Fairfax St., Ste. 205, Alexandria, VA 22314-1776, (703)683-2914
Fats and Proteins Res. Found. [2583], 801 N Fairfax St., Ste. 205, Alexandria, VA 22314-1776, (703)683-2914
Fatty Acid Producers' Coun. [★744]
Fatty Oxidation Disorders Family Support Gp. [16766], PO Box 54, Okemos, MI 48805, (517)381-1940
Fauna and Flora Intl. [IO], Cambridge, United Kingdom
Fauna Found. [IO], Chambly, QC, Canada
Fawcett Soc. [IO], London, United Kingdom
FCIB-NACM Corp. [2081], 8840 Columbia 100 Pkwy., Columbia, MD 21045-2158, (410)423-1840
FCIB-NACM Corp. [2081], 8840 Columbia 100 Pkwy., Columbia, MD 21045-2158, (410)423-1840
FDA [IO], London, United Kingdom
FDI World Dental Fed. [IO], Geneva, Switzerland
Fe y Alegria [★IO]
Fe y Alegria - Colombia [IO], Bogota, Colombia
Fe y Alegria - El Salvador [IO], San Salvador, El Salvador
Fe y Alegria del Peru [IO], Lima, Peru
FEAR [★5318]
Fearing Surname Org. - Defunct.
Feather and Down Assn. - Defunct.
Feathered Pipe Found. [12207], PO Box 1682, Helena, MT 59624, (406)442-8196
FED des associations de fonctionnaires internationaux [★IO]
Federacao Angolana de Andebol [IO], Luanda, Angola
Federacao Angolana de Atletismo [IO], Luanda, Angola
Federacao Angolana de Judo [IO], Luanda, Angola
Federacao Angolana de Tenis [IO], Luanda, Angola
Federacao Angolana de Vela [IO], Luanda, Angola
Federacao de Atletismo da Guinea-Bissau [IO], Bissau, Guinea-Bissau
Federacao Brasileira de Albergues da Juventude [★IO]
Federacao Cabo Verdiana de Tenis [IO], Praia, Cape Verde
Federacao Iberoamericana de Acustica [★IO]
Federacao Mocambicana de Atletismo [IO], Maputo, Mozambique
Federacao Mocambicana de Badminton [IO], Beira, Mozambique
Federacao Mocambicana de Tenis [IO], Maputo, Mozambique
Federacao Mundial de Jovens Lideres e Empreendedores [★IO]

Reference to "IO" in place of a book number signifies that the association may be found in the 50th edition of International Organizations.

Federacao Nacional dos Professores [★IO]
Federacao Portuguesa de Aikido [IO], Carcavelos, Portugal
Federacao Portuguesa de Atletismo [IO], Linda-a-Velha, Portugal
Federacao Portuguesa de Badminton [IO], Caldas da Rainha, Portugal
Federacao Portuguesa de Danca Desportiva [IO], Lisbon, Portugal
Federacao Portuguesa de Desporto para Deficientes [★IO]
Federacao Portuguesa de Futebol [★IO]
Federacao Portuguesa de Orientacao [★IO]
Federacao Portuguesa de Taekwondo [IO], Lisbon, Portugal
Federacao Portuguesa de Tenis [IO], Linda-a-Velha, Portugal
Federacio Andorrana de Ball Esportiu [IO], Escaldes-Engordany, Andorra
Federacio Andorrana de Vela [IO], Encamp, Andorra
Federacio d'Associacions de Veins d'Habitatge Social de Catalunya [★IO]
Federacion Aerea de Chile [IO], Santiago, Chile
Federacion Argentina de Industrias Textiles [★IO]
Federacion Argentina de Medicina del Deporte [IO], Buenos Aires, Argentina
Federacion Argentina de Musica Electroacustica [IO], Buenos Aires, Argentina
Federacion Argentina de Yachting [IO], Buenos Aires, Argentina
Federacion de Asociaciones Molturadores y Refinadores de Aceites Vegetales del Reino de Espana [IO], Madrid, Spain
Federacion de Asociaciones de Productores Audiovisuales Espanoles [★IO]
Federacion Atletica de Chile [IO], Santiago, Chile
Federacion de Badminton de Chile [IO], Santiago, Chile
Federacion de Badminton de la Republica Argentina [IO], Buenos Aires, Argentina
Federacion de Beisbol de Chile [★IO]
Federacion Boliviana De Tennis [IO], Santa Cruz, Bolivia
Federacion Boliviana de Medicina Deportiva [IO], La Paz, Bolivia
Federacion Boliviana de Taekwondo [IO], Santa Cruz, Bolivia
Federacion Chilena de Baile Deportivo [IO], Santiago, Chile
Federacion Chilena de Handball [IO], Santiago, Chile
Federacion Chilena de Squash [★IO]
Federacion Chilena de Taekwondo [IO], Santiago, Chile
Federacion Colombiana de ACJs - YMCA [★IO]
Federacion Colombiana de Albergues Juveniles [★IO]
Federacion Colombiana de Deportes Aereos [IO], Bogota, Colombia
Federacion Colombiana de Squash [IO], Bogota, Colombia
Federacion Colombiana de Taekwondo [IO], Bogota, Colombia
Federacion Colombiana de Tenis [IO], Bogota, Colombia
Federacion Colombiana de Vela [IO], Bogota, Colombia
Federacion Costarricense de Tenis [IO], San Jose, Costa Rica
Federacion Cuban de Taekwondo [IO], Havana, Cuba
Federacion Cubana de Badminton [IO], Havana, Cuba
Federacion Cubana de Medicina del Deporte [IO], Havana, Cuba
Federacion Cubana de Tenis De Ocampo [IO], Havana, Cuba
Federacion del Deporte de Orientacion de la Republica Argentina [IO], Buenos Aires, Argentina
Federacion Deportiva Chilena de Aikido - Aikikai Chile [IO], Santiago, Chile
Federacion Deportiva Peruana de Atletismo [IO], Lima, Peru
Federacion Deportiva Peruana de Taekwondo [IO], Lima, Peru

Federacion Deportiva Peruana de Tenis [IO], Lima, Peru
Federacion Dominicana de Juego de Damas [IO], Santiago, Dominican Republic
Federacion Dominicana Republica de Squash [IO], Santo Domingo, Dominican Republic
Federacion Dominicana de Taekwondo [IO], Santo Domingo, Dominican Republic
Federacion Dominicana de Tenis [IO], Santo Domingo, Dominican Republic
Federacion Dominicana de Vela [IO], Santo Domingo, Dominican Republic
Federacion Ecuatoguineana de Tenis [★IO]
Federacion Ecuatoriana de Badminton [IO], Guayaquil, Ecuador
Federacion Ecuatoriana de Beisbol [IO], Guayaquil, Ecuador
Federacion Ecuatoriana De Fisoterepia [IO], Quito, Ecuador
Federacion Ecuatoriana De Squash [IO], Guayaquil, Ecuador
Federacion Ecuatoriana de Exportadores [★IO]
Federacion Ecuatoriana de Medicina Deportiva [IO], Quito, Ecuador
Federacion Ecuatoriana de Taekwondo [IO], Guayaquil, Ecuador
Federacion Ecuatoriana de Tenis [IO], Guayaquil, Ecuador
Federacion Ecuatoriana de Yachting [IO], Guayaquil, Ecuador
Federacion Empresarial de la Industria Quimica Espanola [IO], Madrid, Spain
Federacion de Ensenanza de Comisiones Obreras [IO], Madrid, Spain
Federacion Equatiguineana de Taekwondo [IO], Malabo, Equatorial Guinea
Federacion Espanola de Asociaciones de Espina Bifida e Hidrocefalia [IO], Madrid, Spain
Federacion Espanola de Badminton [IO], Madrid, Spain
Federacion Espanola de Comerciantes de Electrodomesticos [★IO]
Federacion Espanola de Empresas de la Confeccion [★IO]
Federacion Espanola de Industrias de la Alimentacion y Bebidas [★IO]
Federacion Espanola de Medicina del Deporte [IO], Pamplona, Spain
Federacion Espanola de Taekwondo [IO], Alicante, Spain
Federacion Espanola del Vino [★IO]
Federacion Espeleologica de Am. Latina y el Caribe [★IO]
Federacion de Gremios de Editores de Espana [★IO]
Federacion Hondurena de Tenis [IO], Tegucigalpa, Honduras
Federacion Hotelera del Ecuador [★IO]
Federacion Ibero-Latinoamericana de Cirugia Plastica y Reconstructiva [★IO]
Federacion Iberoamericana de Bolsas [★IO]
Federacion de la Industria Licorista Argentina [★IO]
Federacion de Industrias del Calzado Espanol [★IO]
Federacion Interamericana de Touring y Automovil Clubes [★IO]
Federacion Internacional de actores [★IO]
Federacion Internacional de Asociaciones de Estudiantes de Medicina [★IO]
Federacion Internacional de Asociaciones de Profesores de Ciencias [★IO]
Federacion Internacional de Asociaciones Vexilologicas [★10629]
Federacion Internacional de Asociaciones Vexilologicas [★10629]
Federacion Internacional de Hospitales [★IO]
Federacion Internacional de Patologia Cervical y Colposcopia [★IO]
Federacion Internacional de Pelota Vasca [★IO]
Federacion Internacional de Sociedades de la Cruz Roja y de la Media Luna Roja [★IO]
Federacion Internacional de Sociedades Psicoanaliticas [★IO]
Federacion Internacional de Trabajadores Sociales [★IO]
Federacion Intl. de Juventudes Liberales y Radicales [★IO]

Federacion Latinoamericana de Asociaciones de Familiares de Detenidos-Desaparecidos [★IO]
Federacion Latinoamericana de Bancos [★IO]
Federacion Latinoamericana de la Industria Farmaceutica [★IO]
Federacion Latinoamericana de Sociedades de Obesidad [★IO]
Federacion Medica Colombiana [IO], Bogota, Colombia
Federacion Medica Venezolana [IO], Caracas, Venezuela
Federacion Mexicana de Aikido [IO], Mexico City, Mexico
Federacion Mexicana de Atletismo [IO], Mexico City, Mexico
Federacion Mexicana de Tenis [IO], Mexico City, Mexico
Federacion Mexicana de Vela [IO], Mexico City, Mexico
Federacion Mondiale des Organizations des Femmes Ukrainiennes [★IO]
Federacion Mundial de Medicos que Respectan la Vida Humana [★IO]
Federacion Nacional de Arroceros [★IO]
Federacion Nacional de Asociaciones de la Industria de Conservas Vegetales [★IO]
Federacion Nacional de Badminton de Guatemala [IO], Guatemala City, Guatemala
Federacion Nacional de Badminton de Honduras [IO], Tegucigalpa, Honduras
Federacion Nacional de Beisbol de Guatemala [IO], Guatemala City, Guatemala
Federacion Nacional de Cafeteros de Columbia [★IO]
Federacion Nacional de Comerciantes [★IO]
Federacion Nacional de Cultivadores de Cereales y Leguminosas [IO], Cota, Colombia
Federacion Nacional de Cultivadores de Palma de Aceite [★IO]
Federacion Nacional de Empresas de Publicidad [★IO]
Federacion Nacional de Industrias Lacteas [★IO]
Federacion Nacional Taekwondo de Guatemala [IO], Guatemala City, Guatemala
Federacion Nacional de Taekwondo de Honduras [IO], Tegucigalpa, Honduras
Federacion Nautica de Cuba [IO], Havana, Cuba
Federacion Nicaraguense de Atletismo [IO], Managua, Nicaragua
Federacion Nicaraguense de Taekwondo [IO], Managua, Nicaragua
Federacion Nicaraguense de Tenis [IO], Managua, Nicaragua
Federacion Panamena de Atletismo [IO], Panama City, Panama
Federacion Panamena de Tenis [IO], Panama City, Panama
Federacion Panamericana de Consultores [★IO]
Federacion Panamericana de Lecheria [★IO]
Federacion Paraguaya de Atletismo [IO], Asuncion, Paraguay
Federacion Paraguaya de Halterofilia [IO], Lambare, Paraguay
Federacion Peruana de Squash [IO], Lima, Peru
Federacion Peruana de Vela [★IO]
Federacion Salvadorena de Badminton [IO], San Salvador, El Salvador
Federacion Salvadorena de Beisbol [IO], San Salvador, El Salvador
Federacion Salvadorena De Squash [IO], San Salvador, El Salvador
Federacion Salvadorena de Taekwondo [IO], San Salvador, El Salvador
Federacion Salvadorena de Tenis [IO], San Salvador, El Salvador
Federacion de Squash de Mexico, A.C. [IO], Mexico City, Mexico
Federacion de Tenis de Chile [IO], Santiago, Chile
Federacion Uruguaya de Aikido - Aikikai Uruguay [IO], Montevideo, Uruguay
Federacion Uruguaya de Pesas [IO], Montevideo, Uruguay
Federacion Uruguaya de Squash [IO], Montevideo, Uruguay
Federacion Uruguaya de Taekwondo [IO], Montevideo, Uruguay

A star before a book entry number signifies that the name is not listed separately, but is mentioned within the entry.

Federacion Venezolana de Atletismo **[IO]**, Caracas, Venezuela

Federacion Venezolana de Squash **[IO]**, Caracas, Venezuela

Federacion Venezolana de Tenis **[IO]**, Caracas, Venezuela

Federacion Venezolana de Terapeutas Ocupacionales **[IO]**, Caracas, Venezuela

Federacion Venezolana de Vela **[IO]**, Caracas, Venezuela

Fed. Administrative Law Judges Conf. **[5619]**, PO Box 1772, Washington, DC 20013

Fed. Alliance For Safe Homes **[11921]**, 1427 E Piedmont Dr., Ste. 2, Tallahassee, FL 32308, (877)221-7233

Fed. Assn. of Artists of the Fine Arts **[IO]**, Bonn, Germany

Fed. Assn. of the Chem. Trade **[IO]**, Vienna, Austria

Fed. Assn. of Dealers of Furniture and Interior Products **[IO]**, Vienna, Austria

Fed. Assn. of the Gem, Stone and Diamond Indus. **[IO]**, Idar-Oberstein, Germany

Fed. Assn. of the German Spirits Indus. and Importers **[IO]**, Bonn, Germany

Fed. Assn. of Lebenshilfe of People with Intellectual Disabilities **[IO]**, Marburg, Germany

Fed. Assn. of the Radio and Elecl. Trade **[IO]**, Vienna, Austria

Fed. Assn. of Teachers of Dancing **[IO]**, Taren Point, Australia

Fed. Bakers' Assn. **[IO]**, Vienna, Austria

Fed. Bar Assn. **[5246]**, 1220 N Filmore St., Ste. 444, Arlington, VA 22201, (571)481-9100

Fed. Bur. of Investigation Agents Assn. **[5691]**, PO Box 12650, Arlington, VA 22219, (703)247-2173

Fed. Butchers' Assn. **[IO]**, Vienna, Austria

Fed. Chamber of Architects, Germany **[IO]**, Berlin, Germany

Fed. Circuit Bar Assn. **[5247]**, 1620 I St. NW, Ste. 900, Washington, DC 20006, (202)466-3923

Fed. Communications Bar Assn. **[5322]**, 1020 19th St. NW, Ste. 325, Washington, DC 20036-6101, (202)293-4000

Fed. Confectionery Assn. **[IO]**, Vienna, Austria

Fed. Consumer Info. Center Prog. **[5540]**, 1800 F St. NW, Rm. G-142, Washington, DC 20405, (202)501-1794

Fed. Coun. of Australian Apiarists' Assn. **[IO]**, Toongabbie, Australia

Fed. Court Clerks Assn. **[5354]**, U.S. District Ct. - Eastern District of Tennessee, 800 Market St., Ste. 130, Knoxville, TN 37902, (865)545-4244

Fed. Criminal Investigators Assn. **[5383]**, PO Box 23400, Washington, DC 20026, (630)969-8537

Fed. Editors Assn. **[★5324]**

Fed. Educ. Assn. **[23179]**, 1201 16th St. NW, Ste. 117, Washington, DC 20036, (202)822-7850

Fed. Employee Educ. and Assistance Fund **[19149]**, 3333 S Wadsworth Blvd., Ste. 300, Lakewood, CO 80227, (303)933-7580

Federal Employees Coordinating Comm. - Defunct.

Fed. Employees Veterans Assn. **[★23202]**

Fed. Energy Bar Assn. **[★5404]**

Fed. Facilities Coun. **[5431]**, Natl. Acad. of Sciences, 500 5th St. NW, Washington, DC 20001, (202)334-3505

Fed. Flight Deck Officers Assn. **[5692]**, PO Box 20024, Washington, DC 20041

Fed. Food Retailing Assn. **[IO]**, Vienna, Austria

Federal Government
    African Amer. Fed. Executive Assn. **[5504]**
    Air Mail Pioneers **[20879]**
    Asian Amer. Govt. Executives Network **[5428]**
    Asian Amer. Govt. Executives Network **[5428]**
    Coun. for Excellence in Govt. **[5429]**
    Executive Women in Govt. **[5430]**
    Fed. Facilities Coun. **[5431]**
    Fed. Managers Assn. **[5432]**
    Natl. Active and Retired Fed. Employees Assn. **[5433]**
    Natl. Assn. of Hispanic Fed. Executives **[5434]**
    Natl. Org. of Fed. Employees Against Abuse and Retaliation **[23206]**
    Natl. Priorities Proj. **[17625]**
    Partnership for Public Ser. **[17331]**

Professional Managers Assn. **[5435]**
    Senior Executives Assn. **[5436]**
    Senior Executives Assn. Professional Development League **[5437]**

Fed. Govt. Accountants Assn. **[★5180]**

Fed. Govt. Distance Learning Assn. **[8023]**, 166 Bledsoe Dr., Bellbrook, OH 45305-1351, (937)904-5480

Fed. Hispanic Law Enforcement Officers Assn. **[5693]**, Anita Trujillo, Treas., 20622 Water Point Trail, Kingwood, TX 77346, (305)522-0978

Fed. Hispanic Law Enforcement Officers Assn. **[5693]**, Anita Trujillo, Treas., 20622 Water Point Trail, Kingwood, TX 77346, (305)522-0978

Fed. Info. Center Prog. **[★5540]**

Fed. Investigators Assn. **[★5383]**

Fed. Law Enforcement Officers Assn. **[5598]**, PO Box 326, Lewisberry, PA 17339, (717)938-2300

Federal Librarians Round Table - Defunct.

Fed. Lib. Comm. **[★9986]**

Fed. Lib. and Info. Center Comm. **[9986]**, Lib. of Cong., 101 Independence Ave. SE, Washington, DC 20540-4935, (202)707-4800

Fed. Managers Assn. **[5432]**, 1641 Prince St., Alexandria, VA 22314-2818, (703)683-8700

Federal Music Soc. - Defunct.

Fed. Natl. Assn. of the German Brick and Tile Indus. **[IO]**, Bonn, Germany

Fed. Physicians Assn. **[16263]**, 12427 Hedges Run Dr., Ste. 104, Lake Ridge, VA 22192, (800)528-3492

Fed. Plant Quarantine Inspectors Natl. Assn. **[★5190]**

Fed. Power Bar Assn. **[★5404]**

Fed. Superannuates Natl. Assn. **[IO]**, Ottawa, ON, Canada

Fed. Trial Examiners Conf. **[★5619]**

Fed. Union **[★18343]**

Fed. Union **[★18343]**

Fed. Union of European Nationalities **[IO]**, Flensburg, Germany

Fed. Union of German Associations of Pharmacists **[IO]**, Berlin, Germany

Federalist Caucus - Defunct.

Federalist Soc. for Law and Public Policy Stud. **[5620]**, 1015 18th St. NW, Ste. 425, Washington, DC 20036, (202)822-8138

Federally Employed Women **[17642]**, 700 N Fairfax St., No. 510, Alexandria, VA 22314, (202)898-0994

Federasi Aero Sport Indonesia **[IO]**, Jakarta, Indonesia

Federasie van Afrikaanse Kultuurvereniginge **[★IO]**

Federated Employers **[★2280]**

Federated Farmers of New Zealand **[IO]**, Wellington, New Zealand

Federated Funeral Directors of Am. **[2532]**, PO Box 19244, Springfield, IL 62794-9244, (217)525-1712

Federated Hospitality Assn. of South Africa **[IO]**, Bryanston, Republic of South Africa

Federated Mountain Clubs of New Zealand **[IO]**, Wellington, New Zealand

Federated Pecan Growers' Assns. of the U.S. - Defunct.

Federated Russian Orthodox Clubs **[★20228]**

Federated States of Micronesia Athletic Assn. **[IO]**, Palikir, Federated States of Micronesia

Federated States of Micronesia Football Assn. **[IO]**, Chuuk, Federated States of Micronesia

Federated States of Micronesia Lawn Tennis Assn. **[IO]**, Palikir, Federated States of Micronesia

Federated States of Micronesia Natl. Olympic Comm. **[IO]**, Palikir, Federated States of Micronesia

Federated States of Micronesia Volleyball Assn. **[IO]**, Palikir, Federated States of Micronesia

Federated States of Micronesia Weightlifting Assn. **[IO]**, Palikir, Federated States of Micronesia

Federated Women's Institutes of Canada **[IO]**, St. George, ON, Canada

Federatia de Atletism din Republica Moldova **[IO]**, Chisinau, Moldova

Federatia Educatiei Nationale **[★IO]**

Federatia Moldoveneasca de Fotbal **[★IO]**

Federatia Romana de Atletism **[IO]**, Bucharest, Romania

Federatia Romana de Badminton **[★IO]**

Federatia Romana de Baseball si Softbol **[★IO]**

Federatia Romana de Patinaj **[★IO]**

Federatia Romana de Tenis **[IO]**, Bucharest, Romania

Federatie Antilliaanse Jeugdzorg **[★IO]**

Federatie van Beeldende Kunstenaars in Suriname **[★IO]**

Federatie van het Belgisch Vlees **[IO]**, Brussels, Belgium

Federatie van Belgische Fabrikanten van Vetten en Olien **[IO]**, Brussels, Belgium

Federatie van de Belgische Magazines **[★IO]**

Federatie Nederlandse Gehandicaptenraad **[★IO]**

Federatie van Organisaties in het Bibliotheek-, Informatie-, en Documentatiewezen **[★IO]**

Federatie van Ouders van Dove Kinderen **[IO]**, Houten, Netherlands

Fed. des societes africaines de biochimie et de biologie moleculaire **[★IO]**

Fed. canadienne des societes de biologie **[★IO]**

Fed. europeenne de biotechnologie **[★IO]**

Fed. internationale des associations vexillologiques **[★10629]**

Fed. for Accessible Nursing Educ. and Licensure **[15748]**, PO Box 1418, Lewisburg, WV 24901, (304)645-4357

Fed. Aeronautique Internationale **[IO]**, Lausanne, Switzerland

Fed. Aeronautique Luxembourgeoise **[IO]**, Luxembourg, Luxembourg

Fed. of Aerospace Enterprises in Ireland **[IO]**, Dublin, Ireland

Fed. of African Natl. Insurance Companies **[IO]**, Dakar, Senegal

Fed. of African Societies of Biochemistry and Molecular Biology **[IO]**, Cape Town, Republic of South Africa

Fed. of Afrikaans Cultural Societies **[IO]**, Pretoria, Republic of South Africa

Fed. Against Software Theft **[IO]**, Maidenhead, United Kingdom

Fed. Albanaise de Handball **[IO]**, Tirana, Albania

Fed. of Alberta Naturalists **[IO]**, Edmonton, AB, Canada

Fed. Algerienne de Judo **[IO]**, Algiers, Algeria

Fed. Algerienne des Societes d'Aviron et de Canoe/Kayak **[IO]**, Algiers, Algeria

Fed. Algerienne du Sport Scolaire **[IO]**, Algiers, Algeria

Fed. Algerienne de Voile **[IO]**, Algiers, Algeria

Fed. of Amer. Aquarium Societies **[6953]**, Pat Smith, Membership Chm., 109 Bucknell Rd., West Sayville, NY 11796, (847)478-8110

Fed. of Amer. Consumers and Travelers **[13337]**, PO Box 104, Edwardsville, IL 62025, (800)872-3228

Fed. of Amer. Hea. Systems **[★15054]**

Fed. of Amer. Hospitals **[15054]**, 750 9th St. NW, Ste. 600, Washington, DC 20001-4524, (202)624-1500

Fed. for Amer. Immigration Reform **[17882]**, 25 Massachusetts Ave. NW, Ste. 300, Washington, DC 20001, (202)328-7004

Fed. for Amer. Immigration Reform **[17882]**, 25 Massachusetts Ave. NW, Ste. 300, Washington, DC 20001, (202)328-7004

Fed. of Amer. Scientists **[18459]**, 1725 DeSales St. NW, 6th Fl., Washington, DC 20036, (202)546-3300

Fed. of Amer. Societies for Experimental Biology **[6299]**, 9650 Rockville Pike, Bethesda, MD 20814, (301)634-7000

Fed. for the Amer. Staffordshire Terrier **[20951]**, Leri Hanson, 619 W 35th St., Long Beach, CA 90806, (562)427-2259

Fed. of Amer. Women's Clubs Overseas **[IO]**, Oberanven, Luxembourg

Fed. of Amer. Zionists **[★19913]**

Fed. of Analytical Chemistry and Spectroscopy Societies **[6408]**, PO Box 24379, Santa Fe, NM 87502, (505)820-1648

Fed. Andorrana de Taekwondo **[IO]**, Andorra la Vella, Andorra

Fed. of Animal Sci. Societies **[3804]**, 2441 Village Green Pl., Champaign, IL 61822, (217)356-3182

Reference to "IO" in place of a book number signifies that the association may be found in the 50th edition of International Organizations.

Fed. des Architectes Suisses [★IO]

Fed. of Argentine Textile Indus. [IO], Buenos Aires, Argentina

Fed. of Artistic Roller Skating [IO], Thatcham, United Kingdom

Fed. of ASEAN Shipowners' Associations [IO], Singapore, Singapore

Fed. of Asian Chem. Societies [IO], Beijing, People's Republic of China

Fed. of Asian Sci. Academies and Societies - Malaysia [IO], Kuala Lumpur, Malaysia

Fed. of Associations in Behavioral and Brain Sciences [6254], 750 1st St. NE, Ste. 905, Washington, DC 20002, (202)336-5920

Fed. des Associations de proprietaires de cinemas du Canada [★IO]

Fed. des Associations de Chasse et Conservation de la Faune Sauvage de l'U.E. [★IO]

Fed. des Associations Europeennes des Constructeurs de Fenetres et de Facades [★IO]

Fed. des Associations Europeennes et Internationales etablies en Belgique [★IO]

Fed. des Associations Europeennes de Mousse de Polyurethane Rigide [★IO]

Fed. of Associations of Former Intl. Civil Servants [IO], Geneva, Switzerland

Fed. of Associations of Hea. Regulatory Boards [★14706]

Fed. of Associations for Hunting and Conservation of the E.U. [IO], Brussels, Belgium

Fed. of Associations of Regulatory Boards [14706], 1466 Techny Rd., Northbrook, IL 60062, (847)559-3272

Fed. of Astronomical Societies [IO], Surrey, United Kingdom

Fed. of Atomic Scientists [★18459]

Fed. des Auberges de Jeunesse de l'Union Europeenne [★IO]

Fed. of Australian Astrologers [IO], Waterford, Australia

Fed. of Australian Radio Broadcasters [★13867]

Fed. of Australian Sci. and Technological Societies [IO], Canberra, Australia

Fed. of Auto. Distributors [IO], Paris, France

Fed. of Bakers [IO], London, United Kingdom

Fed. Bancaire de l'Union Europeenne [★IO]

Fed. of Bangladesh Chambers of Commerce and Indus. [IO], Dhaka, Bangladesh

Fed. of Baseball of Chile [IO], Santiago, Chile

Fed. Baseball Softball Ukraine [IO], Kiev, Ukraine

Fed. of BC Writers [IO], Vancouver, BC, Canada

Fed. of Behavioral, Psychological and Cognitive Sciences [★6254]

Fed. Belge des entreprises de distribution [★IO]

Fed. Belge des Exploitants d'Autobus et d'Autocars et des Organisateurs de Voyages [★IO]

Fed. Belge des Femmes Diplomees des Universites [★IO]

Fed. Belge de la Franchise [★IO]

Fed. Belge de Musique Electroacoustique [IO], Brussels, Belgium

Fed. Belge des Negociants en Combustibles et Carburants [★IO]

Fed. Belge des Psychologues [★IO]

Fed. Belge de Tir aux Clays [★IO]

Fed. Belge de la Viande [★IO]

Fed. of the Belgian Chem. Indus. [IO], Brussels, Belgium

Fed. Beninoise d'Athletisme Amateur [IO], Cotonou, Benin

Fed. Beninoise de Lawn Tennis [IO], Cotonou, Benin

Fed. Beninoise de Taekwondo [IO], Cotonou, Benin

Fed. des Brasseurs Luxembourgeois [IO], Luxembourg, Luxembourg

Fed. of British Artists [IO], London, United Kingdom

Fed. of British Hand Tool Mfrs. [IO], London, United Kingdom

Fed. of British Historic Vehicle Clubs [IO], Wallingford, United Kingdom

Fed. Burkinabe De Tennis [IO], Ouagadougou, Burkina Faso

Fed. Burkinabe de Handball [IO], Ouagadougou, Burkina Faso

Fed. Burkinabe de Taekwondo [IO], Ouagadougou, Burkina Faso

Fed. Burundaise de Handball [IO], Bujumbura, Burundi

Fed. Burundaise de Judo [IO], Bujumbura, Burundi

Fed. Camerounaise de Baseball et de Softball [★IO]

Fed. Camerounaise Des Danses Sportives et Assimile [IO], Yaounde, Cameroon

Fed. Camerounaise de Handball [IO], Yaounde, Cameroon

Fed. Camerounaise de Jeu de Dames [IO], Yaounde, Cameroon

Fed. Camerounaise de Taekwondo [IO], Yaounde, Cameroon

Fed. Camerounaise de Tennis [IO], Yaounde, Cameroon

Fed. of Canadian Archers [IO], Ottawa, ON, Canada

Fed. of Canadian Music Festivals [IO], Orleans, ON, Canada

Fed. Canadienne pour la sante sexuelle [★IO]

Fed. Canadienne des Amis de' Musees [★IO]

Fed. Canadienne des Archers [★IO]

Fed. Canadienne de Ballon sur Glace [★IO]

Fed. Canadienne du Civisme [★IO]

Fed. Canadienne de Course d'Orientation [★IO]

Fed. Canadienne Des Doyens Des Ecoles D'Administration [★IO]

Fed. Canadienne d'Escrime [★IO]

Fed. Canadienne des Dix-Quilles [★IO]

Fed. Canadienne des Enseignantes et des Enseignants [★IO]

Fed. Canadienne des Epiciers Independants [★IO]

Fed. Canadienne des Etudiantes et Etudiants [★IO]

Fed. Canadienne des Etudiantes et Etudiants en Genie [★IO]

Fed. Canadienne de la Faune [★IO]

Fed. Canadienne des Femmes Diplomees des Universites [★IO]

Fed. Canadienne des Festivals de Musique [★IO]

Fed. Canadienne des Gemmes et des Mineraux [★IO]

Fed. Canadienne de Handball Olympique [★IO]

Fed. Canadienne des Infirmieres et Infirmiers en Sante Mentale [★IO]

Fed. Canadienne des Jeunes Ligues [★IO]

Fed. Canadienne de Kendo [★IO]

Fed. Canadienne de l'Entreprise Independante [★IO]

Fed. Canadienne des Metiers d'Art [★IO]

Fed. Canadienne du Mouton [★IO]

Fed. Canadienne Nationale des Syndicats Independants [★IO]

Fed. Canadienne des Professeurs de Musique [★IO]

Fed. Canadienne des Sci. Humanies et Sociales [★IO]

Fed. Canadienne des Services de Garde a l'Enfance [★IO]

Fed. Canadienne de Snowboard [★IO]

Fed. Canadienne du Sport Scolaire [★IO]

Fed. Canadienne des Syndicats d'Infirmieres et Infirmiers [★IO]

Fed. Canadienne du Vetement [★IO]

Fed. of Catholic Scouts [IO], Brussels, Belgium

Fed. Catholique des Scouts [★IO]

Fed. Centrafricaine de Handball [IO], Bangui, Central African Republic

Fed. Centrafricaine Taekwondo [IO], Bangui, Central African Republic

Fed. Centrafricaine de Tennis [IO], Bangui, Central African Republic

Fed. of Chambers of Commerce and Indus. of Belgium [IO], Brussels, Belgium

Fed. of Chambers of Commerce and Indus. of Sri Lanka [IO], Colombo, Sri Lanka

Fed. des Chambres de Commerce et D'Industrie de Belgique [★IO]

Fed. for Children with Special Needs [12502], 1135 Tremont St., Ste. 420, Boston, MA 02120, (617)236-7210

Fed. of Children's Book Groups [IO], Leeds, United Kingdom

Fed. of Chinese Amer. and Chinese Canadian Medical Societies [15410], 835 Jackson St., Ste. 304, San Francisco, CA 94133, (415)421-4240

Fed. of Chinese Amer. and Chinese Canadian Medical Societies [15410], 835 Jackson St., Ste. 304, San Francisco, CA 94133, (415)421-4240

Fed. of Chiropractic Licensing Boards [14133], 5401 W 10th St., Ste. 101, Greeley, CO 80634-4400, (970)356-3500

Fed. of Chiropractic Licensing Boards [14133], 5401 W 10th St., Ste. 101, Greeley, CO 80634-4400, (970)356-3500

Fed. of City Farms and Community Gardens [IO], Bristol, United Kingdom

Fed. of Clinical Immunology Societies [15105], 11950 W Lake Park Dr., Ste. 320, Milwaukee, WI 53224, (414)359-1670

Fed. of Clothing Designers and Executives [IO], London, United Kingdom

Fed. of Cocoa Commerce [IO], London, United Kingdom

Fed. du Commerce des Cacaos [★IO]

Fed. of Commun. Services [IO], Beckenham, United Kingdom

Fed. Comorienne d'Halterophilie [IO], Moroni, Comoros

Fed. Congolaise d'Athletisme [IO], Brazzaville, Republic of the Congo

Fed. Congolaise Democratique de Lawn Tennis [IO], Kinshasa, Republic of the Congo

Fed. Congolaise de Handball [IO], Brazzaville, Republic of the Congo

Fed. Congolaise de Lawn Tennis [IO], Brazzaville, Republic of the Congo

Fed. Congolaise de Taekwondo [IO], Brazzaville, Republic of the Congo

Fed. Constr. Coun. [★5431]

Fed. for Continuing Educ. in Tertiary Institutions [IO], Hong Kong, People's Republic of China

Fed. of Crafts and Commerce [IO], Hampshire, United Kingdom

Fed. Culinaire Canadienne Saskatoon Br. [★IO]

Fed. Cynologique Internationale [★IO]

Fed. of Danish Investment Associations [IO], Copenhagen, Denmark

Fed. of Danish Painting Contractors [IO], Copenhagen, Denmark

Fed. of Danish Textile and Clothing [IO], Herning, Denmark

Fed. d'Associations de Techniciens des Indus. des Peintures, Vernis, Emaux et Encres d'Imprimerie de l'Europe Continentale [★IO]

Fed. d'Athletisme du Burundi [IO], Bujumbura, Burundi

Fed. D'Athletisme de Polynesie Francaise [IO], Tahiti, French Polynesia

Fed. d'Athletisme R.I. Mauritanie [IO], Nouakchott, Mauritania

Fed. De Volleyball De Tuvalu [IO], Funafuti, Tuvalu

Fed. of Defense and Corporate Counsel [5551], 11812 N 56th St., Tampa, FL 33617, (813)983-0022

Fed. Des Assocations Des Handicapes Moteurs [IO], Algiers, Algeria

Fed. Des Grandes Tours Du Monde [★IO]

Fed. Des Minerais, Mineraux Industriels Et Metaux Non Ferreux [IO], Paris, France

Fed. of Dining Room Professionals [3089], 1417 Sadler Rd., No. 100, Fernandina Beach, FL 32034, (904)491-6690

Fed. of Dining Room Professionals [3089], 1417 Sadler Rd., No. 100, Fernandina Beach, FL 32034, (904)491-6690

Fed. of Diocesan Liturgical Commissions [19421], 415 Michigan Ave. NE, Ste. 70, Washington, DC 20017, (202)635-6990

Fed. of Distribution Companies [IO], Milan, Italy

Fed. of Distribution and Retailing Companies [IO], Paris, France

Fed. Djiboutienne de Tennis [IO], Djibouti, Djibouti

Fed. of Drug and Alcohol Professionals [IO], London, United Kingdom

Fed. of Earth Sci. Info. Partners [6603], 6300 Creedmoor Rd., Ste. 170-315, Raleigh, NC 27612, (919)870-7140

Fed. of East European Family History Societies [18996], PO Box 510898, Salt Lake City, UT 84151-0898

Fed. des Editeurs Europeens [★IO]

Fed. of Egalitarian Communities [11584], 2 Dancing Rabbit Ln., Rutledge, MO 63563, (660)883-5881

A star before a book entry number signifies that the name is not listed separately, but is mentioned within the entry.

Fed. des Eglises Evangeliques Baptistes de France [IO], Paris, France
Fed. of Employee Benefit Assn. [★1122]
Fed. of Employers and Workers of Am. [1147], 2901 Bucks Bayou Rd., Bay City, TX 77414, (979)245-7577
Fed. des Employeurs Europeens [★IO]
Fed. of Engine Re-Manufacturers [IO], Plymouth, United Kingdom
Fed. des Entreprises du Commerce et de la Distribution [★IO]
Fed. des Entreprises Internationales de la Mecanique et de l'Electronique [★IO]
Fed. of Environmental Technologists [4790], W175 N11081 Stonewood Dr., No. 203, Germantown, WI 53022, (262)437-1700
Fed. of Environmental Trade Associations [IO], Reading, United Kingdom
Fed. Equestre Internationale [★IO]
Fed. of the Estonian Chem. Indus. [IO], Tallinn, Estonia
Fed. of Estonian Engg. Indus. [IO], Tallinn, Estonia
Fed. of Estonian Student Unions [IO], Tallinn, Estonia
Fed. of Estonian Universities [IO], Tallinn, Estonia
Fed. des Etablissements d'Enseignment Prives [IO], Montreal, QC, Canada
Fed. des Etudiant(e)s Francophones [IO], Brussels, Belgium
Fed. des Etudiants et des Etudiantes en Medecine du Canada [★IO]
Fed. of Euro-Asian Stock Exchanges [IO], Istanbul, Turkey
Fed. of European Aquaculture Producers [IO], Liege, Belgium
Fed. of European Associations of Paediatric Anaesthesia [IO], Warsaw, Poland
Fed. of European Biochemical Societies [IO], Rehovot, Israel
Fed. of European Cancer Societies [IO], Brussels, Belgium
Fed. of European Companion Animal Veterinary Associations [IO], Borsbeek, Belgium
Fed. of the European Cutlery, Flatware, Holloware, and Cookware Indus. [IO], Solingen, Germany
Fed. of the European Dental Indus. [IO], Cologne, Germany
Fed. of European Direct and Interactive Marketing [IO], Brussels, Belgium
Fed. of European Direct Selling Associations [IO], Brussels, Belgium
Fed. of European Employers [IO], London, United Kingdom
Fed. of European Ergonomics Soc. [IO], Bedford, United Kingdom
Fed. of European Explosive Mfrs. [IO], Brussels, Belgium
Fed. of European Heating and Air Conditioning Associations [IO], Brussels, Belgium
Fed. of European and Intl. Associations Established in Belgium [IO], Brussels, Belgium
Fed. of European Lab. Animal Sci. Associations [IO], Tamworth, United Kingdom
Fed. of European Materials Societies [IO], Voreppe, France
Fed. of European Microbiological Societies [IO], Delft, Netherlands
Fed. of European Neuroscience Societies - Milan [IO], Kuopio, Finland
Fed. of European Nurses in Diabetes [IO], London, United Kingdom
Fed. of European Pharmacological Societies [IO], Mainz, Germany
Fed. of European Philatelic Associations [IO], Stenlose, Denmark
Fed. of European Physiological Societies - Germany [IO], Munich, Germany
Fed. of European Physiological Societies - Netherlands [IO], Maastricht, Netherlands
Fed. of European Private Port Operators [IO], Brussels, Belgium
Fed. of European Producers of Abrasives [IO], Paris, France
Fed. of European Professional Photographers [IO], Brussels, Belgium

Fed. of European Publishers [IO], Brussels, Belgium
Fed. of European Rigid Polyurethane Foam Associations [IO], Brussels, Belgium
Fed. of European Risk Mgt. Associations [IO], Brussels, Belgium
Fed. of European Rope, Twine and Netting Indus. [IO], Paris, France
Fed. of European Securities Exchanges [IO], Brussels, Belgium
Fed. of European Societies of Plant Biology [IO], Heraklion, Greece
Fed. of European Societies for Surgery of the Hand [IO], Budapest, Hungary
Fed. of European Societies for Tropical Medicine and Intl. Hea. [IO], Hamburg, Germany
Fed. of European Specialty Ingredients [IO], Brussels, Belgium
Fed. of the European Sporting Goods Indus. [IO], Brussels, Belgium
Fed. of European Toxicologists and European Societies of Toxicology [IO], Milan, Italy
Fed. of European Window and Curtain Wall Mfrs. Associations [IO], Nieuwegein, Netherlands
Fed. Europeenae de la Diaconie [★IO]
Fed. Europeene des Associations de Fabricants de Serrures et de Ferrures [★IO]
Fed. Europeene des Associations de Specialistes en Orthodontie [★IO]
Fed. Europeene des Indus. de Colles et Adhesifs [★IO]
Fed. Europeene pour l'Architecture du Paysage [★IO]
Fed. Europeene pour l'Art Populaire et l'Artisanat [★IO]
Fed. Europeene de l'Industrie des Aliments pour Animaux Familiers [★IO]
Fed. Europeene de la Recuperation et du Recyclage des Ferrailles [★IO]
Fed. Europeene des Unions Professionnelles d'Experts en Dammages apres Incendie et Risques Divers [★IO]
Fed. Europeenne des Activites du Dechet et de l'Environnement [★IO]
Fed. Europeenne des Aerosols [★IO]
Fed. Europeenne des Associations de Conseils en Org. [★IO]
Fed. Europeenne des Associations de Dieteticiens [★IO]
Fed. Europeenne des Associations de l'Industrie Pharmaceutique [★IO]
Fed. Europeenne des Associations de Vente Directe [★IO]
Fed. Europeenne du Commerce Chimique [★IO]
Fed. Europeenne du Commerce de Produits Surgeles [★IO]
Fed. Europeenne de la Corrosion [★IO]
Fed. Europeenne de la Coutellerie, Orfevrerie, Couverts de Table et Articles Culinaires [★IO]
Fed. Europeenne des Cyclistes [★IO]
Fed. Europeenne d'Associations Nationales d'Ingenieurs [★IO]
Fed. Europeenne d'Associations Nationales Travaillant avec les Sans-Abri [★IO]
Fed. Europeenne d'Editeurs de Periodiques [★IO]
Fed. Europeenne des Fabricants de Carton Ondule [★IO]
Fed. Europeenne des Fabricants d'Adjuvants pour la Nutrition Animale [★IO]
Fed. Europeenne des Fabricants d'Aliments Composes [★IO]
Fed. Europeenne des Fabricants de Palettes et Emballages en Bois [★IO]
Fed. Europeenne des Fabricants de Produits Abrasifs [★IO]
Fed. Europeenne des Fabricants de Produits Refractaires [★IO]
Fed. Europeenne des Fabricants des Tuiles et de Briques [★IO]
Fed. Europeenne des Geologues [★IO]
Fed. Europeenne des Greffes du Coeur et du Poumon [★IO]
Fed. Europeenne des Indus. de Ficellerie Corderie et Filets [★IO]
Fed. Europeenne des Jeunes Chorales [★IO]
Fed. Europeenne de l'Industrie du Contreplaque [★IO]

Fed. Europeenne des Mandataires de l'Industrie en Propriete Industrielle [★IO]
Fed. Europeenne des Medecins Salaries [★IO]
Fed. Europeenne des Metallurgistes [★IO]
Fed. Europeenne de Psychanalyse [★IO]
Fed. Europeenne des Societes de Cytologie [★IO]
Fed. Europeenne des Syndicats d'Entreprises d'Isolation [★IO]
Fed. Europeenne pour le Transport et l'Environment [★IO]
Fed. Europeenne du Verre d'Emballage [★IO]
Fed. Europeenne des Victimes de la Route [★IO]
Fed. Europeenne de Zootechnie [★IO]
Fed. of Exchange Accommodators [3383], 100 N 20th St., 4th Fl., Philadelphia, PA 19103-1443, (215)564-3484
Fed. des Experts Comptables Europeens [★IO]
Fed. of Families for Children's Mental Hea. [12487], 9605 Medical Center Dr., Rockville, MD 20850, (240)403-1901
Fed. of Family History Societies [IO], Lutterworth, United Kingdom
Fed. des Femmes Chinoises [★IO]
Fed. of Finnish Commerce and Trade [IO], Helsinki, Finland
Fed. of Finnish Fisheries Associations [IO], Helsinki, Finland
Fed. of Finnish Textile and Clothing Indus. [IO], Helsinki, Finland
Fed. of Fire Chaplains [19519], PO Box 437, Meridian, TX 76665, (254)435-2256
Fed. of Floorball of Russia [IO], Moscow, Russia
Fed. of Fly Fishermen [★22574]
Fed. of Fly Fishers [22574], 5237 US Hwy. 89 S, Ste. 11, Livingston, MT 59047, (406)222-9369
Fed. Flying Disc France [IO], Versailles, France
Fed. de la Fonction Publique Europeenne [★IO]
Fed. of Food Indus. [IO], Brussels, Belgium
Fed. Francaise Amateur de Mineralogie et Paleontologie [★IO]
Fed. Francaise de Baseball, Softball and Cricket [IO], Paris, France
Fed. Francaise du Batiment [★IO]
Fed. Francaise de Course d'Orientation [★IO]
Fed. Francaise de la Couture, du Pret-a-Porter des Couturiers et des Createurs de Mode [★IO]
Fed. Francaise d'Aikido, d'Aikibudo et Affinitaires [IO], Paris, France
Fed. Francaise de la Franchise [★IO]
Fed. Francaise des Indus. Jouet et Puericulture [★IO]
Fed. Francaise des Indus. du Sport et des Loisirs [★IO]
Fed. Francaise de la Lingerie et du Balneaire [★IO]
Fed. Francaise des Masseurs Kinesitherapeutes Reeducateurs [IO], Paris, France
Fed. Francaise des Mouvements et Services Feminins [IO], Paris, France
Fed. Francaise du Pret-a-Porter Feminin [★IO]
Fed. Francaise des Societes d'Assurances [★IO]
Fed. Francaise du Sport Auto. [IO], Paris, France
Fed. Francaise de Squash [IO], St.-Maur-des-Fosses, France
Fed. Francaise de Taekwondo et Disciplines Associees [IO], Lyon, France
Fed. Francaise de Tennis [IO], Paris, France
Fed. Francaise de Voile [IO], Paris, France
Fed. Francaise de Voile [★IO]
Fed. of Freight Forwarders' Assn. in India [IO], Mumbai, India
Fed. of French Ladies' Fashion [IO], Paris, France
Fed. of French Maltsters [IO], Paris, France
Fed. of French War Veterans [20873], 39-45 51st St., Apt. 6F, Woodside, NY 11377, (718)426-1474
Fed. Gabonaise d'Athletisme [IO], Libreville, Gabon
Fed. Gabonaise de Judo [IO], Libreville, Gabon
Fed. Gabonaise de Taekwondo [IO], Libreville, Gabon
Fed. Gabonaise de Tennis [IO], Libreville, Gabon
Fed. of Galaxy Explorers [8874], 6404 Ivy Ln., Ste. 810, Greenbelt, MD 20770, (877)761-1266
Fed. for the Gardening Trades [IO], Paris, France
Fed. of Gay Games [22976], 584 Castro St., Ste. 343, San Francisco, CA 94114, (866)459-1261
Fed. of Gay Games [22976], 584 Castro St., Ste. 343, San Francisco, CA 94114, (866)459-1261

Reference to "IO" in place of a book number signifies that the association may be found in the 50th edition of International Organizations.

Fed. of Genealogical Societies [20627], PO Box 200940, Austin, TX 78720-0940, (888)FGS-1500

Fed. of German Catholic Youth [IO], Dusseldorf, Germany

Fed. of the German Export Trade [IO], Berlin, Germany

Fed. of German Indus. [IO], Berlin, Germany

Fed. of German Indus. [★702]

Fed. of German Indus. [★702]

Fed. of German Landscape Architects [IO], Berlin, Germany

Fed. of German Newspaper Publishers [IO], Berlin, Germany

Fed. of the Glass Indus. [IO], Brussels, Belgium

Fed. of Govt. Info. Processing Councils [★5535]

Fed. of Greek Indus. [IO], Athens, Greece

Fed. Guineenne Pour La Promotion Des Associations De et pour Personnes Handicapees [IO], Conakry, Guinea

Fed. Guineenne de Taekwondo [IO], Conakry, Guinea

Fed. Haitienne de Tennis [IO], Port-au-Prince, Haiti

Fed. of Handicraft Associations of Nepal [IO], Kathmandu, Nepal

Fed. of Hellenic Food Indus. [IO], Neo Psychiko, Greece

Fed. of Hellenic Info. Tech. and Communications Enterprises [IO], Athens, Greece

Fed. of Historical Bottle Collectors [21234], 401 Johnston Ct., Raymore, MO 64083, (816)318-0160

Fed. of Home Economics Teachers [IO], Helsinki, Finland

Fed. of Hong Kong Indus. [IO], Hong Kong, People's Republic of China

Fed. of Hong Kong Watch Trades and Indus. [IO], Hong Kong, People's Republic of China

Fed. of Hotel and Restaurant Associations of India [IO], New Delhi, India

Fed. of Huguenot Societies [★20669]

Fed. Hypothecaire Europeenne [★IO]

Fed. of Icelandic Indus. [IO], Reykjavik, Iceland

Fed. of Icelandic Landscape Architects [IO], Reykjavik, Iceland

Fed. of Icelandic Trade [IO], Reykjavik, Iceland

The Fed. of Image Consultants [IO], Hemel Hempstead, United Kingdom

Fed. of Immunological Societies of Asia-Oceania [IO], Dhaka, Bangladesh

Fed. of Independent Practitioner Organisations [IO], London, United Kingdom

Fed. of Indian Chambers of Commerce and Indus. [IO], New Delhi, India

Fed. of Indian Export Organisations [IO], New Delhi, India

Fed. of Indian Ser. Employees [8676], 1218 Lomas Blvd. NW, Albuquerque, NM 87102-1856, (505)243-4088

Fed. des Industriels Luxembourgeois [★IO]

Fed. des Indus. Agro-Alimentaires Luxembourgeoises [★IO]

Fed. des Indus. Chimiques de Belgique [★IO]

Fed. des Indus. et Commerces Utilisateurs des Basses Temperatures, Congelation, Surgeles, Glaces [IO], Paris, France

Fed. des Indus. des Equipements pour Vehicules [★IO]

Fed. des Indus. de la Parfumerie [★IO]

Fed. des Indus. des Peintures, Encres, Couleurs, Colles et Adhesifs [★IO]

Fed. of Indus. Products Systems and Services for Constr. [IO], Rome, Italy

Fed. des Indus. Transformatrices de Papier et Carton [★IO]

Fed. of Inline Speed Skating [IO], Birmingham, United Kingdom

Fed. of Institutes Caring for Protestant Children [★20167]

Fed. of Insurance and Corporate Counsel [★5551]

Fed. of Insurance Counsel [★5551]

Fed. of Intl. Bandy [IO], Soderhamn, Sweden

Fed. of Intl. Civil Servants' Associations [IO], Geneva, Switzerland

Fed. Intl. de Genetique [★IO]

Fed. Intl. des Indus. Textiles [★IO]

Fed. of Intl. Lacrosse [22713], 911 Overbrook Rd., Wilmington, DE 19807, (302)652-4530

Fed. of Intl. Mech. Engg. and Electronics Indus. [IO], Paris, France

Fed. of Intl. Physicians in the U.S. - Address unknown since 2011.

Fed. of Intl. Trade Associations [2082], 172 Fifth Ave., No. 118, Brooklyn, NY 11217, (703)634-3482

Fed. of Intl. Trade Associations [2082], 172 Fifth Ave., No. 118, Brooklyn, NY 11217, (703)634-3482

Fed. of Intl. Trampoline Technical Comm. - Defunct.

Fed. Internationale des Architectes d'Interieur [★IO]

Fed. Internationale des Architectes Paysagistes [★IO]

Fed. Internationale des Archives du Film [★IO]

Fed. Internationale des Armateurs [★IO]

Fed. Internationale des Associations Apicoles [★IO]

Fed. Internationale des Associations Contre la Lepre [★IO]

Fed. Internationale des Associations de Controleurs du Trafic Aerien [★IO]

Fed. Internationale des Associations d'Etudes Classiques [★IO]

Fed. Internationale des Associations d'Inventeurs [★IO]

Fed. Internationale des Associations de l'Electronique de Securite du Trafic Aerien [★IO]

Fed. Internationale des Associations de Medecins Catholiques [★IO]

Fed. Internationale des Associations Medicales Catholiques [★IO]

Fed. Internationale des Associations de Patrons de Navires [★IO]

Fed. Internationale des Associations de Pilotes de Ligne [★IO]

Fed. Internationale des Associations de Producteurs de Film [★IO]

Fed. Internationale des Associations de Thanatologues [★IO]

Fed. Internationale des Associations de Transitaires et Assimilies [★IO]

Fed. Internationale des Autorites Hippiques de Courses au Galop [★IO]

Fed. Internationale de Basketball [★IO]

Fed. Internationale de Bobsleigh et de Tobogganing [IO], Milan, Italy

Fed. Internationale des Bureaux de Justification de la Diffusion [★IO]

Fed. Internationale de Camping et de Caravanning [★IO]

Fed. Internationale des Centres d'Entrainement aux Methodes d'Education Active [★IO]

Fed. Internationale des Chasseurs de Sons [★IO]

Fed. Internationale de Chimie Clinique [★IO]

Fed. Internationale de Chiropratique du Sport [★IO]

Fed. Internationale des Corps et Associations Consulaires [★IO]

Fed. Internationale de Cremation [★IO]

Fed. Internationale de la Croix-Bleu [★IO]

Fed. Internationale des Culturistes [★IO]

Fed. Internationale des fabricants et transformateurs d'Adhesifs et Thermocollants sur papiers et autres supports [★IO]

Fed. Internationale d'Astronautique [★IO]

Fed. Internationale d'Education Physique [★IO]

Fed. Internationale des Demenageurs Internationaux [★IO]

Fed. Internationale d'Ingegnerie Municipal [★IO]

Fed. Internationale des Echecs [★IO]

Fed. Internationale des Enseignants de Rythmique [★IO]

Fed. Internationale des Enterprises de Nettoyage [★IO]

Fed. Internationale des Experts en Auto. [★IO]

Fed. Internationale des Fabricants des Papiers Gommes [★IO]

Fed. Internationale des Femmes Diplomees des Universites [★IO]

Fed. Internationale de Football Assn. [★IO]

Fed. Internationale de Football Assn. [★IO]

Fed. Internationale de Football Assn. [IO], Zurich, Switzerland

Fed. Internationale de Genie Medical et Biologique [★IO]

Fed. Internationale des Geometres [★IO]

Fed. Internationale des Grossistes, Importateurs, et Exporateurs en Fourniture Automobiles [★IO]

Fed. Internationale de Gymnastique [★IO]

Fed. Internationale de Gynecologie et d'Obstetrique [★IO]

Fed. Internationale de Gynecologie Infantile et Juvenile [★IO]

Fed. Internationale de Handball [★IO]

Fed. Internationale de Hockey [★IO]

Fed. Internationale des Indus. Consommatrices d'Energie [★IO]

Fed. Internationale des Ingenieurs Conseils [★IO]

Fed. Internationale des Jeunesses Musicales [★IO]

Fed. Internationale des Journalistes [★IO]

Fed. Internationale de Judo [★IO]

Fed. Internationale de Laiterie [★IO]

Fed. Internationale des Langues et Litteratures Modernes [★IO]

Fed. Internationale de l'art Photographique [★IO]

Fed. Internationale de l'Art Photographique [IO], Paris, France

Fed. Internationale de l'Automobile [★IO]

Fed. Internationale de l'Esthetique-Cosmetique [★IO]

Fed. Internationale pour l'Habitation, l'Urbanisme et l'Amenagement des Territoires [★IO]

Fed. Internationale des Ligues des Droits de l'Homme [★IO]

Fed. Internationale de l'Industrie du Medicament [★IO]

Fed. Internationale de Luge de Course [★IO]

Fed. Internationale des Luttes Associees [★IO]

Fed. Internationale de Medecine Manuelle [★IO]

Fed. Internationale de Medecine du Sport [★IO]

Fed. Internationale de Motocyclisme [★IO]

Fed. Internationale des Mouvements Catholiques d'Action Paroissiales [★IO]

Fed. Internationale des Mouvements d'Adultes Ruraux Catholiques [★IO]

Fed. Internationale des Mouvements d'Agriculture Biologique [★IO]

Fed. Internationale des Mouvements d'Ecole Moderne [★IO]

Fed. Internationale des Musiciens [★IO]

Fed. Internationale de Natation Amateur [★IO]

Fed. Internationale de Navigabilite Aerospatiale [★IO]

Fed. Internationale de Neurophysiologie Clinique [★IO]

Fed. Internationale des Organisations de Donneurs de Sang [★IO]

Fed. Internationale des Organisations Syndicales du Personnel des Transports [★IO]

Fed. Internationale des Organisations de Travailleurs de la Metallurgie [★IO]

Fed. Internationale des Organizations de Festivals [★1198]

Fed. Internationale des Organizations de Festivals [★1198]

Fed. Internationale des Ouvriers du Transport [★IO]

Fed. Internationale du Personnel des Services Publics [★IO]

Fed. Internationale de Petanque et Jeu Provencal [★IO]

Fed. Internationale des Petits Freres des Pauvres [★IO]

Fed. Internationale Pharmaceutique [★IO]

Fed. Internationale de Philatelie [★IO]

Fed. Internationale pour la Planification Familiale [★IO]

Fed. Internationale Pour La Recherche En Histoire Des Femmes [★IO]

Fed. Internationale de la Presse Periodique [★IO]

Fed. Internationale des Producteurs Agricoles [★IO]

Fed. Internationale des Producteurs de Jus de Fruits [★IO]

Fed. Internationale des Professeurs de Francais [★IO]

Fed. Internationale des Professions Immobilieres [★IO]

Fed. Internationale des Quilleurs [★IO]

Fed. Internationale pour la Recherche Theatrale [★IO]

Fed. Internationale des Services des Espaces Verts et de la Recreation [★IO]

Fed. Internationale de Ski [★IO]

Fed. Internationale des Societes d'Aviron [★IO]

A star before a book entry number signifies that the name is not listed separately, but is mentioned within the entry.

Fed. Internationale des Societes d'Ingenieurs des
Techniques de l' Auto. [★IO]
Fed. Internationale des Societes Oto-Rhino-
Laryngologiques [★IO]
Fed. Internationale du Sport Universitaire [★IO]
Fed. Internationale de Tennis [★IO]
Fed. Internationale de Tennis de Table [★IO]
Fed. Internationale de Tir a l'Arc [★IO]
Fed. Internationale des Traducteurs [★IO]
Fed. Internationale pour le Traitement de
l'Information [★IO]
Fed. Internationale des Travailleurs du Textile, de
l'Habillement et du Cuir [★IO]
Fed. Internationale des Universites Catholiques
[★IO]
Fed. Internationale du Vieillissement [★IO]
Fed. Internationale des Vins et Spiritueux [★IO]
Fed. Internationale de Volleyball [★IO]
Fed. of Iraqi Associations in Sweden [IO], Stock-
holm, Sweden
Fed. of Irish Beekeepers Associations [IO], Enfield,
Ireland
Fed. of Israeli Chambers of Commerce [IO], Tel Aviv,
Israel
Fed. of the Italian Associations of Mech. and Engg.
Indus. [IO], Milan, Italy
Fed. Ivoirienne d'Athletisme [IO], Abidjan, Cote
d'Ivoire
Fed. Ivoirienne de Taekwondo [IO], Abidjan, Cote
d'Ivoire
Fed. Ivoirienne de Tennis [IO], Abidjan, Cote d'Ivoire
Fed. of Jain Associations in North America [20180],
43-11 Ithaca St., Elmhurst, NY 11373, (716)606-
2885
Fed. des Jeux du Commonwealth [★IO]
Fed. of Jewish Men's Clubs [19861], 475 Riverside
Dr., Ste. 832, New York, NY 10115-0022,
(212)749-8100
Fed. of Jewish Women's Orgs. - Defunct.
Fed. of Kenya Employers [IO], Nairobi, Kenya
Fed. of Korean Trade Unions [IO], Seoul, Republic
of Korea
Fed. Laique de Centres de Planning Familial [IO],
Brussels, Belgium
Fed. of Latin Amer. Societies of Obesity [IO], Bue-
nos Aires, Argentina
Fed. of Leather Guilds [★2199]
Fed. Libanaise de Badminton [IO], Beirut, Lebanon
Fed. Libanaise d'Athletisme [IO], Jounieh, Lebanon
Fed. Libanaise de Tennis [IO], Jounieh, Lebanon
Fed. Libanaise de Yachting [IO], Jounieh, Lebanon
Fed. de l'Industrie Alimentaire [★IO]
Fed. de l'Industrie du Beton [IO], Brussels, Belgium
Fed. de l'Industrie Dentaire en Europe [★IO]
Fed. de l'Industrie Europeenne de la Constr. [★IO]
Fed. de l'Industrie de l'Huilerie de la CE [★IO]
Fed. de l'Industrie du Verre [★IO]
Fed. Lutherienne Mondiale [★IO]
Fed. of Luxembourg Food Indus. [IO], Luxembourg,
Luxembourg
Fed. of Luxembourg Industrialists [IO], Luxembourg,
Luxembourg
Fed. Luxembourgeoise des Arts Martiaux-Aikido
[IO], Strassen, Luxembourg
Fed. Luxembourgeoise de Badminton [★IO]
Fed. Luxembourgeoise de Danse pour Amateurs
[★IO]
Fed. Luxembourgeoise de Danse pour Amateurs
[IO], Hautcharage, Luxembourg
Fed. Luxembourgeoise d'Athletisme [IO], Strassen,
Luxembourg
Fed. Luxembourgeoise des Editeurs de Livres [★IO]
Fed. Luxembourgeoise des Editeurs de Livres [IO],
Luxembourg, Luxembourg
Fed. Luxembourgeoise de Tennis [IO], Esch-sur-
Alzette, Luxembourg
Fed. Luxembourgoise de Cricket [★IO]
Fed. Malagasy de Badminton [IO], Antananarivo,
Madagascar
Fed. Malagasy d'Athletisme [IO], Antananarivo,
Madagascar
Fed. Malagasy Handisport [IO], Antananarivo, Mada-
gascar
Fed. Malagasy de Judo [IO], Antananarivo, Mada-
gascar

Fed. of Malaysian Consumers Associations [IO],
Petaling Jaya, Malaysia
Fed. of Malaysian Mfrs. [IO], Kuala Lumpur,
Malaysia
Fed. Malgache de Tennis [IO], Antananarivo, Mada-
gascar
Fed. Malienne de Base-Ball et de Softball [IO], Ba-
mako, Mali
Fed. Malienne d'Athletisme [IO], Bamako, Mali
Fed. Malienne du Jeu de Dames [IO], Bamako, Mali
Fed. Malienne de Taekwondo [IO], Bamako, Mali
Fed. Malienne de Tennis [IO], Bamako, Mali
Fed. Maritime du Canada [★IO]
Fed. of Master Builders [IO], London, United
Kingdom
Fed. of Materials Societies [7063], 910 17th St. NW,
Ste. 800, Washington, DC 20006, (202)296-9282
Fed. du Materiel pour l'Automobile [IO], Brussels,
Belgium
Fed. Mauritanienne des Associations Nationales des
Personnes Handicapees [IO], Nouakchott, Maurita-
nia
Fed. Mauritanienne de Judo [IO], Nouakchott, Mauri-
tania
Fed. Mauritanienne de Sport pour Handicapes [IO],
Nouakchott, Mauritania
Fed. Mauritanienne de Tennis [IO], Nouakchott,
Mauritania
Fed. of Mech. Engg. of the Slovak Republic [IO],
Bratislava, Slovakia
Fed. of Medical Societies of Hong Kong [IO], Hong
Kong, People's Republic of China
Fed. of Metal Detector and Archaeological Clubs
[21851], 184 Grange Rd., McClellandtown, PA
15458, (724)439-1380
Fed. Mexicana De Baile A.C. [IO], Mexico City,
Mexico
Fed. of Modern Painters and Sculptors [9230], 113
Greene St., New York, NY 10012, (212)966-4864
Fed. Mondiale des Anciens Combattants [★IO]
Fed. Mondiale des Annonceurs [★IO]
Fed. Mondiale des Concours Internationaux de Mu-
sique [★IO]
Fed. Mondiale des Employes [★IO]
Fed. Mondiale des Ergotherapeutes [★IO]
Fed. Mondiale du Jeu de Dames [★IO]
Fed. Mondiale de Karate [★IO]
Fed. Mondiale pour l'Enseignement de la Medicine
[★IO]
Fed. Mondiale de l'Hemophilie [★IO]
Fed. Mondiale des Missions Islamiques [★IO]
Fed. Mondiale des Organisations d'Ingenieurs [★IO]
Fed. Mondiale des Societes d'Anesthesiologistes
[★IO]
Fed. Mondiale des Travailleurs Scientifiques [★IO]
Fed. Monegasque d'Athletisme [IO], Monaco,
Monaco
Fed. Monegasque De Squash Rackets [IO],
Monaco, Monaco
Fed. Monegasque de Lawn Tennis [★IO]
Fed. of Natl. Associations of Shipbrokers and Agents
[IO], London, United Kingdom
Fed. of Natl. Educ. and Res. Unions [IO], Paris,
France
Fed. Nationale des Associations des P. Handicapees
du Burkina Faso [IO], Bujumbura, Burkina Faso
Fed. Nationale de la Coiffure Francaise [★IO]
Fed. Nationale des Cooperatives Laitieres [★IO]
Fed. Nationale des Hoteliers, Restaurateurs et
Grand Duche Cafetiers de Luxembourg [★IO]
Fed. Nationale des Indus. Laitieres [★IO]
Fed. Nationale de l'Industrie Hoteliere [★IO]
Fed. Nationale des Metiers de la Jardinerie [★IO]
Fed. Nationale de la Presse d'Information Speciali-
see [★IO]
Fed. Nationale de la Presse d'Information Speciali-
see [★IO]
Fed. Nationale des Producteurs de Lait [★IO]
Fed. Nationale des Producteurs de Legumes [★IO]
Fed. Nationale des Producteurs de Plants de Pom-
mes de Terre [★IO]
Fed. Naturiste Internationale [★IO]
Fed. Nautique du Canada [★IO]
Fed. of Nepalese Chambers of Commerce and
Indus. [IO], Kathmandu, Nepal

Fed. Nigerienne d'Athletisme [IO], Niamey, Niger
Fed. Nigerienne des Personnes Handicapees [IO],
Niamey, Niger
Fed. Nigerienne de Taekwondo [IO], Niamey, Niger
Fed. Nigerienne de Tennis [IO], Niamey, Niger
Fed. of Norwegian Indus. [IO], Oslo, Norway
Fed. of Norwegian Mfg. Indus. and Fed. of
Norwegian Process Indus. [★21120]
Fed. of Nurses and Hea. Professionals [★23213]
Fed. of Obstetric and Gynecological Societies of
India [IO], Mumbai, India
Fed. Oceanienne d' Halterophile [★IO]
Fed. of Oils, Seeds, and Fats Associations [IO],
London, United Kingdom
Fed. of Ophthalmic and Dispensing Opticians [IO],
London, United Kingdom
Fed. of Organisations of Disabled People in Angola
[IO], Luanda, Angola
Fed. of Organizations in the Field of Libraries, Info.
and Documentation [IO], The Hague, Netherlands
Fed. of Orthodontic Assns. - Defunct.
Fed. of Paints, Inks, Glues and Adhesives Indus.
[IO], Paris, France
Fed. of the Paints, Varnishes, Lacquers and Printing
Inks Indus. Technologists' Associations of
Continental Europe [IO], Paris, France
Fed. of Pakistan Chambers of Commerce and Indus.
[IO], Karachi, Pakistan
Fed. pan-europeenne du patrimoine [★IO]
Fed. of the Paper and Bd. Converting Indus. [IO],
Brussels, Belgium
Fed. of Partial Hospitalization Stud. Groups
[★16335]
Fed. of Patients and Consumer Organisations in the
Netherlands [IO], Utrecht, Netherlands
Fed. of Pediatric Organizations [16145], 3723 Haven
Rd., MS 3705-190, Menlo Park, CA 94025,
(650)839-1933
Fed. of Petanque of U.S.A. [★22801]
Fed. of Petanque U.S.A. [22801], Frank Pipal, Sec.,
PO Box 180, Kenwood, CA 95452, (707)833-2020
Fed. of Petroleum Suppliers [IO], Knutsford, United
Kingdom
Fed. of Pharmaceutical Mfrs'. Associations of Japan
[IO], Tokyo, Japan
Fed. of Philippine Amer. Chambers of Commerce
[23363], Philippine Consulate Bldg., Stes. 700-701,
447 Sutter St., San Francisco, CA 94108-4601,
(415)398-3043
Fed. of Philippine Amer. Chambers of Commerce
[23363], Philippine Consulate Bldg., Stes. 700-701,
447 Sutter St., San Francisco, CA 94108-4601,
(415)398-3043
Fed. of Piling Specialists [IO], Beckenham, United
Kingdom
Fed. of Plastering and Drywall Contractors [IO],
London, United Kingdom
Fed. de la Plasturgie [★IO]
Fed. of Podiatric Medical Boards [16297], 6551
Malta Dr., Boynton Beach, FL 33437, (561)752-
3735
Fed. of Podiatry Boards [★16297]
Fed. of Podiatry Medical Boards [★16297]
Fed. of Police, Security and Correction Officers -
Defunct.
Fed. Polynesienne de Judo [IO], Tahiti, French
Polynesia
Fed. de la Presse Periodique de Belgique [★IO]
Fed. of the Printing Indus. in Finland [IO], Helsinki,
Finland
Fed. of Private Residents' Associations [IO], Epping,
United Kingdom
Fed. des Proprietaires de lots boises du N-B [★IO]
Fed. of Prosthodontic Orgs. - Defunct.
Fed. of Protestant Welfare Agencies [20167], 281
Park Ave. S, New York, NY 10010, (212)777-4800
Fed. of Reconstructionist Congregations and Fellow-
ships [★19875]
Fed. Reconstructionist Congregations and Havurot
[★19875]
Fed. of Recorded Music Societies [IO], Stoke-on-
Trent, United Kingdom
Fed. of Reproductive Hea. Associations, Malaysia
[IO], Petaling Jaya, Malaysia
Fed. of the Retail Licensed Trade [IO], Belfast,
United Kingdom

Reference to "IO" in place of a book number signifies that the association may be found in the 50th edition of International Organizations.

Fed. of Rose Societies of South Africa [IO], Pretoria, Republic of South Africa
Fed. Roumaine de Taekwondo [★IO]
Fed. Royal Marocaine de Badminton [IO], Casablanca, Morocco
Fed. Royale Belge de Tennis [★IO]
Fed. Royale Belge du Yachting [IO], Antwerp, Belgium
Fed. Royale de l'Industrie des Eaux et des Boissons Rafraichissantes [★IO]
Fed. Royale Marocaine d'Athletisme [IO], Rabat, Morocco
Fed. Royale Marocaine de Judo Aikido et AMA [IO], Casablanca, Morocco
Fed. Royale Marocaine du Sport Scolaire [IO], Rabat, Morocco
Fed. Royale Marocaine de Taekwondo [IO], Rabat, Morocco
Fed. Royale Marocaine de Tennis [IO], Casablanca, Morocco
Fed. Royale Marocaine de Yachting a Voile [IO], Rabat, Morocco
Fed. Rwandaise d'Athletisme [IO], Kigali, Rwanda
Fed. Rwandaise Handisport [IO], Kigali, Rwanda
Fed. Rwandaise de Tennis [IO], Kigali, Rwanda
Fed. of Sci. and Tech. Unions in Bulgaria [IO], Sofia, Bulgaria
Fed. Senegalaise d'Athletisme [IO], Dakar, Senegal
Fed. Senegalaise de Taekwondo [IO], Dakar, Senegal
Fed. Senegalaise de Tennis [IO], Dakar, Senegal
Fed. of Sewage and Indus. Wastes Associations [★4801]
Fed. of Sewage and Indus. Wastes Associations [★4801]
Fed. of Sewage Works Associations [★4801]
Fed. of Sewage Works Associations [★4801]
Fed. of Small Businesses [IO], Blackpool, United Kingdom
Fed. des Societes d'Assurances de Droit Natl. Africaines [★IO]
Fed. des Societes d'Histoire du Quebec [★IO]
Fed. des Societes Nationales des Ingenieurs Ecectriciens de L'Europe [★IO]
Fed. of Southern Cooperatives [★12955]
Fed. of Southern Cooperatives Land Assistance Fund [12955], 2769 Church St., East Point, GA 30344, (404)765-0991
Fed. of Spanish Audiovisual Producer Associations [IO], Madrid, Spain
Fed. of Spanish Footwear Indus. [IO], Madrid, Spain
Fed. of Spanish Publishers' Associations [IO], Madrid, Spain
Fed. of Special Care Organizations in Dentistry [★14310]
Fed. of Sports and Play Associations [IO], Kenilworth, United Kingdom
Fed. de Squash Luxembourgeoise [IO], Luxembourg, Luxembourg
Fed. of State Associations of Independent Colleges and Universities [★8290]
Fed. of State Humanities Councils [9843], 1600 Wilson Blvd., Ste. 902, Arlington, VA 22209, (703)908-9700
Fed. of State Medical Boards of the U.S. [15411], 400 Fuller Wiser Rd., Ste. 300, Euless, TX 76039, (817)868-4000
Fed. of State Medical Boards of the U.S. [15411], 400 Fuller Wiser Rd., Ste. 300, Euless, TX 76039, (817)868-4000
Fed. of State and Municipal Employees [IO], Reykjavik, Iceland
Fed. of Straight Chiropractic Organizations [★14138]
Fed. of Straight Chiropractors and Organizations [★14138]
Fed. Suisse de Basketball Amateur [★IO]
Fed. Suisse des Familles Monoparentales [IO], Bern, Switzerland
Fed. Suisse des Femmes Protestantes [★IO]
Fed. Suisse de Musique Electroacoustique [IO], Geneva, Switzerland
Fed. of Swedish Farmers [IO], Stockholm, Sweden
Fed. of Swiss Architects [IO], Basel, Switzerland
Fed. of Swiss Importers and Wholesalers [IO], Basel, Switzerland

Fed. of Swiss Milk Producers [IO], Bern, Switzerland
Fed. of the Swiss Watch Indus. [IO], Bienne, Switzerland
Fed. Syndicale Europeenne des Services Publics [★IO]
Fed. Syndicale Mondiale [★IO]
Fed. des Syndicats de la Distribution Auto. [★IO]
Fed. des Syndicats Generaux de l'Education Nationale et de la Recherche publique [★IO]
Fed. of Syrian Chambers of Commerce [IO], Damascus, Syrian Arab Republic
Fed. of Taekwondo of the Republic of Moldova [IO], Chisinau, Moldova
Fed. of Tax Administrators [6008], 444 N Capitol St. NW, Ste. 348, Washington, DC 20001, (202)624-5890
Fed. Tchadienne de Handball [IO], N'Djamena, Chad
Fed. Tchadienne de Judo [IO], N'Djamena, Chad
Fed. Tchadienne de Taekwondo [IO], N'Djamena, Chad
Fed. of Tech. and Sci. Societies, Hungary [IO], Budapest, Hungary
Fed. de Tennis du Burundi [IO], Bujumbura, Burundi
Fed. de Tennis de la Guinee-Bissau [IO], Bissau, Guinea-Bissau
Fed. canadienne des sciences de la Terre [★IO]
Fed. of Thai Indus. [IO], Bangkok, Thailand
Fed. Togolaise de Badminton [IO], Lome, Togo
Fed. Togolaise de Base-ball et Soft-ball [IO], Lome, Togo
Fed. Togolaise d'Athletisme [IO], Lome, Togo
Fed. Togolaise Des Associations Des Personnes Handicapees [IO], Lome, Togo
Fed. Togolaise de Taekwondo [IO], Lome, Togo
Fed. of Tour Operators [IO], London, United Kingdom
Fed. Truck Associations of Am. [★3504]
Fed. Tunisienne de Baseball et Softball [IO], Tunis, Tunisia
Fed. Tunisienne d'Athletisme [IO], Tunis, Tunisia
Fed. of Turkish Amer. Associations [19259], 821 UN Plz., New York, NY 10017, (212)682-7688
Fed. of Turkish-American Societies [★19259]
Fed. Unie des Auberges de Jeunesse [★IO]
Fed. of United Arab Emirates Chambers of Commerce and Indus. [IO], Abu Dhabi, United Arab Emirates
Fed. of Univ. Women Russia [IO], Moscow, Russia
Fed. of Veterinarians of Europe [IO], Brussels, Belgium
Fed. Vietnamienne du Canada [★IO]
Fed. of Visual Artists in Suriname [IO], Paramaribo, Suriname
Fed. W/O TV [★18708]
Fed. Without TV [★18708]
Fed. of Worker Writers and Community Publishers [IO], Stoke-on-Trent, United Kingdom
Federauto [IO], Brussels, Belgium
Federazione Alzheimer Italia [IO], Milan, Italy
Federazione Associazioni Imprese Distribuzione [★IO]
Federazione delle Associazioni Nazionali della Industria Meccanica Varia ed Affine [★IO]
Federazione CEMAT [IO], Rome, Italy
Federazione Cricket Italiana [★IO]
Federazione Industria Musicale Italiana [IO], Milan, Italy
Federazione Industrie Prodotti Impianti e Servizi per le Costruzioni [★IO]
Federazione Italiana Amici della Bicicletta [★IO]
Federazione Italiana di Atletica Leggera [IO], Rome, Italy
Federazione Italiana Badminton [IO], Rome, Italy
Federazione Italiana Danza Sportiva [★IO]
Federazione Italiana dell'Industria Alimentare [★IO]
Federazione Italiana Editori Giornali [★IO]
Federazione Italiana di Elettrotecnica, Elettronica, Automazione, Informatica e Telecomunicazioni [★IO]
Federazione Italiana Giuoco Squash [★IO]
Federazione Italiana Industriali, Produttori, Esportatori ed Importatori di Vini, Acquaviti, Liquori, Sciroppi, Aceti Affini [★IO]
Federazione Italiana Laureate e Diplomate di Istituti Superiori [★IO]

Federazione Italiana Mercanti d'Arte [IO], Milan, Italy
Federazione Italiana Tabaccai [★IO]
Federazione Italiana Tennis [IO], Rome, Italy
Federazione Italiana Unihockey Floorball [★IO]
Federazione Italiana Vela [★IO]
Federazione Italiana YMCA [★IO]
Federazione Nazionale Commercianti Calzature [★IO]
Federazione Nazionale Commercianti Mobili [★IO]
Federazione Nazionale del Commercio Oleario [★IO]
Federazione Nazionale Del Commercio Vinicolo [★IO]
Federazione Nazionale dell'Industria Chimica [★IO]
Federazione Nazionale Grossisti Distributori Materiale Elettrico [★IO]
Federazione Nazionale Grossisti Orafi Gioellieri Argentieri [★IO]
Federazione Nazionale delle Impresa di Pesca [★IO]
Federazione Nazionale Imprese Elettrotecniche ed Elettroniche [★IO]
Federazione Nazionale Industria dei Viaggi e del Turismo [★IO]
Federazione Nazionale Orafi Argentieri Gioiellieri Fabbricanti [★IO]
Federazione Nazionale Profumieri Italiani [★IO]
Federazione Nazionale Rivenditori Specialisti di Pneumatici [★IO]
Federazione Nazionale della Stampa Italiana [IO], Rome, Italy
Federazione Ordini Farmacisti Italiani [★IO]
Federazione Radio Televisioni [★IO]
Federazione Sammarinese Atletica Leggera [IO], Serravalle, San Marino
Federazione Sammarinese Tennis [★IO]
Federazione Tchoukball Italia [★IO]
Federazioni Italia Associazion Imprese Viaggi E Turismo [★IO]

Feed
Amer. Feed Indus. Assn. [4370]
Feed Microscopy Div. [4371]
Natl. Alfalfa and Forage Alliance [4372]
Natl. Barley Growers Assn. [4373]
Natl. Grain and Feed Assn. [4374]
Natl. Hay Assn. [4375]
Pet Food Assn. of Canada [4995]
U.S. Grains Coun. [4376]
U.S. Grains Coun. [4376]
Wild Bird Feeding Indus. [4377]
Feed the Children [12837], PO Box 36, Oklahoma City, OK 73101-0036, (405)942-0228
Feed the Children [12837], PO Box 36, Oklahoma City, OK 73101-0036, (405)942-0228
Feed Microscopy Div. [4371], Amer. Oil Chemists' Soc., 2710 S Boulder, Urbana, IL 61802-6996, (217)359-2344
Feed My Hungry Children [11274], PO Box 83775, Phoenix, AZ 85071, (602)241-2873
Feeding Am. [12272], 35 E Whacker Dr., No. 2000, Chicago, IL 60601, (312)263-2303
Feeding Hungry Children Intl. [12273], PO Box 2300, Redlands, CA 92373-0761, (909)793-2009
Feeding Hungry Children Intl. [12273], PO Box 2300, Redlands, CA 92373-0761, (909)793-2009
Feingold Assn. of the U.S. [15831], 37 Shell Rd., 2nd Fl., Rocky Point, NY 11778, (631)369-9340
Felag Heyrnarlausra [★IO]
Felag Islenska Leikskolakennara [★IO]
Felag Islenskra Bokautgefenda [★IO]
Felag Islenskra Hjukrunarfraedinga [★IO]
Felag Islenskra Landslagsarkitekta [★IO]
Felag Islenskra Storkaupmanna [★IO]
Felag Islenzkra Bifreidaeigenda [★IO]
Felag Islenzkra Haskolakvenna [IO], Reykjavik, Iceland
Feldenkrais - Fed. Austria [IO], Vienna, Austria
Feldenkrais-Gilde Deutschland e.V. [IO], Munich, Germany
Feldenkrais Guild of North Am. [9834], 5436 N Albina Ave., Portland, OR 97217, (503)221-6612
Feldenkrais Guild of North Am. [9834], 5436 N Albina Ave., Portland, OR 97217, (503)221-6612
Feldenkrais Verband Osterreich [★IO]
Feline Advisory Bur. [IO], Salisbury, United Kingdom

A star before a book entry number signifies that the name is not listed separately, but is mentioned within the entry.

Feline and Canine Friends - Defunct.

Feline Control Coun. of Victoria [IO], Bayswater, Australia

Feline Control Coun. of Western Australia [IO], Cannington, Australia

Fell Pony Soc. [IO], Cumbria, United Kingdom

Fell Pony Soc. and Conservancy of the Americas [4582], Victoria Tollman, Sec.-Treas., 775 Flippin Rd., Lowgap, NC 27024

Fell Pony Soc. and Conservancy of the Americas [4582], Victoria Tollman, Sec.-Treas., 775 Flippin Rd., Lowgap, NC 27024

Fell Pony Soc. of North Am. [4583], Lisa Lindholm, Gen. Sec., 2626 Diane Ln., Hibbing, MN 55746, (218)263-5217

Fell Pony Soc. of North Am. [4583], Lisa Lindholm, Gen. Sec., 2626 Diane Ln., Hibbing, MN 55746, (218)263-5217

Fellows of the Amer. Bar Found. [5248], 750 N Lake Shore Dr., Chicago, IL 60611-4403, (312)988-6511

Fellows of the Amer. Bar Found. [5248], 750 N Lake Shore Dr., Chicago, IL 60611-4403, (312)988-6511

Fellowship of Amer. Baptist Musicians [20124], 3300 Fairlawn Dr., Columbus, IN 47203, (317)635-3552

Fellowship of Associates of Medical Evangelism [19949], 4545 Southeastern Ave., Indianapolis, IN 46203, (317)358-2480

Fellowship of Australian Writers NSW [IO], Rozelle, Australia

Fellowship of Catholic Scholars [9470], Fordham Univ., Dept. of Philosophy, Bronx, NY 10458, (718)817-3291

Fellowship of Christian Airline Personnel [19745], 136 Providence Rd., Fayetteville, GA 30215, (770)461-9320

Fellowship of Christian Airline Personnel [19745], 136 Providence Rd., Fayetteville, GA 30215, (770)461-9320

Fellowship of Christian Athletes [19746], 8701 Leeds Rd., Kansas City, MO 64129, (816)921-0909

Fellowship of Christian Cowboys [19569], PO Box 1210, Canon City, CO 81215, (719)275-7636

Fellowship of Christian Firefighters Intl. [5438], PO Box 901, Fort Collins, CO 80522-0901, (970)416-9076

Fellowship of Christian Firefighters Intl. [5438], PO Box 901, Fort Collins, CO 80522-0901, (970)416-9076

Fellowship of Christian Magician Intl. [19570], 7739 Everest Ct. N, Maple Grove, MN 55311-1815, (763)494-5655

Fellowship of Christian Musicians [★20121]

Fellowship of Christian Peace Officers [★19571]

Fellowship of Christian Peace Officers U.S.A. [19571], PO Box 3686, Chattanooga, TN 37404-0686, (423)622-1234

Fellowship of Christian Policemen [★19571]

Fellowship of Christian Released Time Ministries [19676], 5722 Lime Ave., Long Beach, CA 90805, (562)428-7733

Fellowship of Christians in the Arts, Media and Entertainment [★19762]

Fellowship of Christians in the Arts, Media and Entertainment [★19762]

Fellowship Club [★13255]

Fellowship of Companies for Christ Intl. [19572], 4201 N Peachtree Rd., Ste. 200, Atlanta, GA 30341, (770)685-6000

Fellowship of Companies for Christ Intl. [19572], 4201 N Peachtree Rd., Ste. 200, Atlanta, GA 30341, (770)685-6000

Fellowship of Concerned Churchmen [19295], 192 Wellesley Dr., Spartanburg, SC 29307, (864)582-2657

Fellowship of Concerned Churchmen [19295], 192 Wellesley Dr., Spartanburg, SC 29307, (864)582-2657

Fellowship of Fire Chaplains [★19519]

Fellowship for Intentional Community [17376], RR 1, Box 156, Rutledge, MO 63563-9720, (660)883-5545

Fellowship of Intl. Communities [★17376]

Fellowship Intl. Mission [20044], 555 S 24th St., Allentown, PA 18104-6666, (610)435-9099

Fellowship Intl. Mission [20044], 555 S 24th St., Allentown, PA 18104-6666, (610)435-9099

Fellowship in Israel for Arab-Jewish Youth - Defunct.

Fellowship of Makers and Researchers of Historical Instruments [IO], Guildford, United Kingdom

Fellowship of Missions [20045], 1608 Aberdeen St. NE, Grand Rapids, MI 49505-3910, (616)361-2396

Fellowship of Orthodox Christians in Am. [20228], Sandra Kapelan, Admin. Sec., 10 Downs Dr., Wilkes-Barre, PA 18705, (570)825-3158

Fellowship in Prayer [19654], 291 Witherspoon St., Princeton, NJ 08542-3227, (609)924-6863

Fellowship in Prayer [19654], 291 Witherspoon St., Princeton, NJ 08542-3227, (609)924-6863

Fellowship for Racial and Economic Equality [★18630]

Fellowship of Reconciliation Task Force on Latin Am. and Caribbean [18052], PO Box 271, Nyack, NY 10960, (845)358-4601

Fellowship of Reconciliation Task Force on Latin Am. and Caribbean [18052], PO Box 271, Nyack, NY 10960, (845)358-4601

Fellowship of Reconciliation - USA [18242], PO Box 271, Nyack, NY 10960, (845)358-4601

Fellowship of Reconciliation - USA [18242], PO Box 271, Nyack, NY 10960, (845)358-4601

Fellowship of Saint James [19573], PO Box 410788, Chicago, IL 60641, (773)481-1090

Fellowship of St. John the Divine [19646], Antiochian Orthodox Christian Archdiocese, PO Box 5238, Englewood, NJ 07631-5238, (201)871-1355

Fellowship of St. Nicholas [IO], St. Leonards-on-Sea, United Kingdom

Fellowship of Saint Paul [19706], The Soc. of Saint Paul, St. Paul's Cathedral, 2728 6th Ave., San Diego, CA 92103-6397, (619)542-8660

Fellowship of United Methodist Musicians [★19971]

Fellowship of United Methodists in Music and Worship Arts [19971], PO Box 24787, Nashville, TN 37202-4787, (615)749-6875

Fellowship of United Methodists in Worship, and Other Arts [★19971]

Fellowship of the White Boar [★10686]

Felt Mfrs. Coun. - Defunct.

Felton Family Assn. [20514], PO Box 215, Wolfeboro, NH 03894

Female Europeans of Medium and Small Enterprises [IO], Brussels, Belgium

Female Leadership Interest Coun. [3680], 182 Turnpike Rd., Westborough, MA 01581, (800)671-FLIC

Females in Info. Tech. and Telecommunications [IO], Deakin West, Australia

Femconsult [IO], The Hague, Netherlands

Feminism

  9 to 5, Natl. Assn. of Working Women [17626]

  9 to 5 Working Women Educ. Fund [17627]

  Alliance of Faith and Feminism [17628]

  Alliance for Intl. Women's Rights [18804]

  Amer. Civil Liberties Union [17260]

  Amer. Lib. Assn. | Social Responsibilities Round Table Feminist Task Force [17629]

  Amer. Sociological Assn. | Comm. on the Status of Women in Sociology [9589]

  Beauty 4 Ashes Intl. [13452]

  Center for Amer. Women and Politics [17630]

  Center for Community Solutions [17631]

  Center for Women Policy Stud. [17632]

  Circle of Women: Reach and Teach Across Borders [13015]

  CH on Women's Issues [17633]

  Commn. on the Status of Women [17634]

  Commn. on the Status of Women [17634]

  Comm. on the Elimination of Discrimination Against Women [17635]

  Comm. on the Elimination of Discrimination Against Women [17635]

  Comm. on South Asian Women [17636]

  Comm. on South Asian Women [17636]

  Congressional Caucus for Women's Issues [17637]

  Coordinating Coun. for Women in History [17638]

  Delegation for Friendship Among Women [17639]

  EcoMom Alliance [13459]

  Eleanor Found. [17640]

  Euro-American Women's Coun. [17641]

  Every Mother is a Working Mother Network [18791]

  Federally Employed Women [17642]

  Feminist Majority Found. [17643]

  Feminists for Free Expression [17644]

  Filipina Women's Network [18792]

  Gen. Commn. on the Status and Role of Women [17645]

  Global Fund for Women [17646]

  Global Fund for Women [17646]

  Inst. of Women Today [17647]

  Inst. for Women's Policy Res. [17648]

  Inter-American Commn. of Women [17649]

  Inter-American Commn. of Women [17649]

  Intl. Assn. for Women of Color Day [17650]

  Intl. Assn. for Women of Color Day [17650]

  Intl. Black Women's Cong. [17651]

  Intl. Black Women's Cong. [17651]

  Intl. Center for Res. on Women [17652]

  Intl. Center for Res. on Women [17652]

  Jewish Orthodox Feminist Alliance [19873]

  Legal Momentum: Advancing Women's Rights [17653]

  Lucy Stone League [17654]

  Lucy Stone League [17654]

  MANA, A Natl. Latina Org. [17655]

  Ms. Found. for Women [17656]

  Natl. Assn. of Commissions for Women [17657]

  Natl. Coalition of 100 Black Women [17658]

  Natl. Comm. on Pay Equity [17659]

  Natl. Conf. of Puerto Rican Women [17660]

  Natl. Coun. of Negro Women [17661]

  Natl. Coun. for Res. on Women [17662]

  Natl. Coun. of Women's Organizations [17663]

  Natl. Hook-Up of Black Women [17664]

  Natl. Org. for Women [17665]

  Natl. Partnership for Women and Families [17666]

  Natl. Woman's Party [17667]

  Natl. Women's Law Center [17668]

  Natl. Women's Political Caucus [17669]

  Org. of Chinese Amer. Women [17670]

  Radical Women [17671]

  Sociologists for Women in Soc. [9590]

  Sociologists for Women in Soc. [9590]

  United Nations Development Fund for Women [17672]

  United Nations Development Fund for Women [17672]

  Veteran Feminists of Am. [17673]

  Woman Within Intl. Ltd. [13486]

  Women of Wind Energy [7627]

  Women's Campaign Fund [17674]

  Women's Env. and Development Org. [17675]

  Women's Env. and Development Org. [17675]

  Women's Intl. Coalition for Economic Justice [17596]

  Women's Intl. Network [17676]

  Women's Intl. Network [17676]

  Women's Law Proj. [17677]

  Women's Res. and Educ. Inst. [17678]

  Women's Rights Comm. [17679]

  Women's Voices Now [18807]

Feminist Dalit Org. [IO], Lalitpur, Nepal

Feminist Intl. Radio Endeavour [IO], Ciudad Colon, Costa Rica

Feminist Karate Union [22732], 1426 S Jackson St., 3rd Fl., Seattle, WA 98144, (206)325-3878

Feminist Karate Union/Alternatives to Fear [★22732]

Feminist Majority Found. [17643], 1600 Wilson Blvd., Ste. 801, Arlington, VA 22209, (703)522-2214

Feminist Teacher Editorial Collective - Address unknown since 2011.

Feministas Unidas [9653], Wake Forest Univ., PO Box 7343, Winston-Salem, NC 27109-7343

Feminists for Animal Rights [10964], PO Box 10017, Berkeley, CA 94709

Feminists for Free Expression [17644], 2525 Times Square Sta., New York, NY 10108-2525, (718)651-1232

Feminists for Life of Am. [18554], PO Box 320667, Alexandria, VA 22320, (703)836-3354

Femme Developpement Entreprise en Afrique [IO], Dakar, Senegal

Femmes sous lois musulmanes [★IO]

Femmes en Detresse [IO], Luxembourg, Luxembourg

Reference to "IO" in place of a book number signifies that the association may be found in the 50th edition of International Organizations.

Fencing

Assn. for Historical Fencing [22562]
Assn. for Historical Fencing [22562]
Christian Fencers Assn. [22563]
Intercollegiate Fencing Assn. [22564]
U.S. Fencing Assn. [22565]
U.S. Fencing Coaches Assn. [22566]

Fencing Contractors Assn. [IO], Monmouth, United Kingdom
Feng Shui Inst. of Am. [9572], 7547 Bruns Ct., Canal Winchester, OH 43110, (614)837-8370
Feng Shui Soc. [IO], Romford, United Kingdom
Fenton Art Glass Collectors of Am. [21830], PO Box 384, Williamstown, WV 26187-0384, (304)375-6196
Fenway Community Hea. [★14576]
Fenway Hea. [14576], 1340 Boylston St., Boston, MA 02215, (617)267-0900
Feral Cat Caretakers' Coalition [3810], PO Box 491244, Los Angeles, CA 90049, (310)820-4122
Feral Cat Friends [21249], 8255 White Oak Rd., Garner, NC 27529, (919)802-3948
FeRFA Resin Flooring Assn. [IO], Farnham, United Kingdom
Ferguson Enthusiasts of North Am. [22174], 730 Shuey, Osage City, KS 66523, (785)528-3681
Fermenters Intl. Trade Assn. [182], Dee Roberson, Sec.-Treas., PO Box 1373, Valrico, FL 33595, (813)685-4261
Fermenters Intl. Trade Assn. [182], Dee Roberson, Sec.-Treas., PO Box 1373, Valrico, FL 33595, (813)685-4261
Ferrari Club of Am. [21055], PO Box 720597, Atlanta, GA 30358, (800)328-0444
Ferrari Owners Club [21056], 19051 Goldenwest St., Ste. 106-328, Huntington Beach, CA 92648, (714)213-4775
Ferret Aid Soc. [IO], Mississauga, ON, Canada
The Ferroalloys Assn. [★2497]
Ferrous Scrap Consumers Coalition - Defunct.
Fertile Dreams [14531], 5931 Brick Ct., Winter Park, FL 32792, (321)397-3868
Fertile Hope - Address unknown since 2011.
Fertiliser Assn. of India [IO], New Delhi, India

Fertility

Amer. Fertility Assn. [14529]
Amer. Soc. for Reproductive Medicine [14530]
Amer. Soc. for Reproductive Medicine [14530]
Family of the Americas Found. [12032]
Fertile Dreams [14531]
Fertility Res. Found. [14532]
Intl. Coun. on Infertility Info. Dissemination [14533]
Intl. Coun. on Infertility Info. Dissemination [14533]
Reproductive Toxicology Center [14534]
Reproductive Toxicology Center [14534]
Resolve, The Natl. Infertility Assn. [14535]

Fertility Care Professionals; Amer. Acad. of [12026]
Fertility Res. Found. [14532], 877 Park Ave., New York, NY 10075, (212)744-5500
Fertility Soc. of Australia [IO], Melbourne, Australia

Fertilizer

Canadian Fertilizer Inst. [3855]
Fertilizer Indus. Round Table [1244]
The Fertilizer Inst. [1245]

Fertilizer Assn. of Ireland [IO], Cork, Ireland
Fertilizer Indus. Round Table [1244], Ms. Peggy Long, Sec., 1701 S Highland Ave., Baltimore, MD 21224, (410)276-4466
The Fertilizer Inst. [1245], 425 3rd St. SW, Ste. 950, Washington, DC 20024, (202)962-0490
Fertilizer; Korean Soc. of Soil Sci. and [IO]
Fertilizer Soc. of South Africa [IO], Lynnwood Ridge, Republic of South Africa
Fetal Alcohol Syndrome; Natl. Org. on [16751]
FFA Org; Natl. [7714]
Ffederasiwn Cerddoriaeth Amatur Cymru [★IO]
FG Syndrome Family Alliance [16767], 922 NW Circle Blvd., Ste. 160, PMB 290, Corvallis, OR 97330
FG Syndrome Family Alliance [16767], 922 NW Circle Blvd., Ste. 160, PMB 290, Corvallis, OR 97330
FIABCI - Andorra [IO], Andorra la Vella, Andorra

FIABCI - Argentina [IO], Buenos Aires, Argentina
FIABCI - Australia [IO], Deakin West, Australia
FIABCI - Austria [IO], Vienna, Austria
FIABCI - Brazil [IO], Sao Paulo, Brazil
FIABCI - Bulgaria [IO], Sofia, Bulgaria
FIABCI - Canada [IO], Oakville, ON, Canada
FIABCI - Colombia [IO], Bogota, Colombia
FIABCI - Costa Rica [IO], San Jose, Costa Rica
FIABCI - Cyprus [IO], Nicosia, Cyprus
FIABCI - Czech Republic [IO], Prague, Czech Republic
FIABCI - Dominican Republic [IO], Santo Domingo, Dominican Republic
FIABCI - Finland [IO], Helsinki, Finland
FIABCI - Germany [IO], Hamburg, Germany
FIABCI - Greece [IO], Athens, Greece
FIABCI - Hungary [IO], Budapest, Hungary
FIABCI - Indonesia [IO], Jakarta, Indonesia
FIABCI - Ireland [IO], Dublin, Ireland
FIABCI - Israel [IO], Jerusalem, Israel
FIABCI - Italy [IO], Milan, Italy
FIABCI - Japan [IO], Tokyo, Japan
FIABCI - Korea [IO], Seoul, Republic of Korea
FIABCI - Latvia [IO], Riga, Latvia
FIABCI - Luxembourg [IO], Luxembourg, Luxembourg
FIABCI - Malaysia [IO], Kuala Lumpur, Malaysia
FIABCI - Mexico [IO], Mexico City, Mexico
FIABCI - Monaco [IO], Monte Carlo, Monaco
FIABCI - Netherlands [IO], Enschede, Netherlands
FIABCI - Nigeria [IO], Lagos, Nigeria
FIABCI - Norway [IO], Oslo, Norway
FIABCI - Panama [IO], Panama City, Panama
FIABCI - Philippines [IO], Quezon City, Philippines
FIABCI - Portugal [IO], Lisbon, Portugal
FIABCI - Russia [IO], St. Petersburg, Russia
FIABCI - Singapore [IO], Singapore, Singapore
FIABCI - Slovenia [IO], Ljubljana, Slovenia
FIABCI - Spain [IO], Barcelona, Spain
FIABCI - Switzerland [IO], Fribourg, Switzerland
FIABCI - Taiwan [IO], Taipei, Taiwan
FIABCI - Thailand [IO], Bangkok, Thailand
FIABCI - Turkey [IO], Ankara, Turkey
FIABCI - United Kingdom [IO], Hereford, United Kingdom
FIABCI - Uruguay [IO], Montevideo, Uruguay
FIABCI-U.S.A. [3012], 1961 Wilson Blvd., Ste. 306, Arlington, VA 22201, (703)524-4279
Fianna Fail [IO], Dublin, Ireland
FIBA Oceania [IO], Toormina, Australia
Fiber Economics Bur. [1246], 1530 Wilson Blvd., Ste. 690, Arlington, VA 22209, (703)875-0676
Fiber Economics Bur. [1246], 1530 Wilson Blvd., Ste. 690, Arlington, VA 22209, (703)875-0676
Fiber Fuels Inst. [★4493]
Fiber Optic Assn. [8972], 1119 S Mission Rd., Ste. 355, Fallbrook, CA 92028, (760)451-3655
Fiber Optic Assn. [8972], 1119 S Mission Rd., Ste. 355, Fallbrook, CA 92028, (760)451-3655
Fiber Soc. [6860], PO Box 8301, North Carolina State Univ., Coll. of Textiles, 2401 Res. Dr., Raleigh, NC 27695-8301, (919)513-0143
Fiberglass Fabrication Assn. [★519]
Fiberglass Tank and Pipe Inst. [877], 11150 S Wilcrest Dr., Ste. 101, Houston, TX 77099-4343

Fibers

Fiber Economics Bur. [1246]
Fiber Economics Bur. [1246]
Fiber Soc. [6860]
Natural Fibers Gp. [21705]
North Amer. Indus. Hemp Coun. [6861]
Vote Hemp [18609]

Fibonacci Assn. [IO], Halifax, NS, Canada
Fibre Box Assn. [2617], 25 NW Point Blvd., Ste. 510, Elk Grove Village, IL 60007, (847)364-9600
Fibre Channel Associates [★3408]
Fibre Channel Indus. Assn. [3408], PO Box 29920, San Francisco, CA 94129-0920, (415)561-6270
Fibreoptic Indus. Assn. [IO], Buntingford, United Kingdom
Fibrodysplasia Ossificans Progressiva Assn; Intl. [14603]
FibroHugs: Support for Fibromyalgia [IO], Regina, SK, Canada
Fibromuscular Dysplasia Soc. of Am. [15589], 20325 Center Ridge Rd., Ste. 620, Rocky River, OH 44116, (216)834-2410

Fibromyalgia

Amer. Fibromyalgia Syndrome Assn. [14536]
Fibromyalgia Coalition Intl. [14537]
Fibromyalgia Network [14538]
Fibromyalgia Network [14538]
Natl. Fibromyalgia Assn. [14539]
Natl. Fibromyalgia and Chronic Pain Assn. [14540]
Natl. Fibromyalgia Partnership [14541]

Fibromyalgia Alliance of Am. - Defunct.
Fibromyalgia Assn. of Greater Washington [★14541]
Fibromyalgia Assn; Natl. Chronic Fatigue Syndrome and [14406]
Fibromyalgia Coalition Intl. [14537], 5201 Johnson Dr., Ste. 210, Mission, KS 66205, (913)384-4673
Fibromyalgia Network [14538], PO Box 31750, Tucson, AZ 85751-1750, (520)290-5508
Fibromyalgia Network [14538], PO Box 31750, Tucson, AZ 85751-1750, (520)290-5508
Fibromyalgia Res. Assn; Natl. [15617]
Fichte Soc; North Amer. [10402]

Fiction

Friends of Freddy [23804]
James Jones Literary Soc. [10725]
Mystery Readers Intl. [23805]
Sedgwick Soc. [10738]

Fidelco Breeder's Found. [★17074]
Fidelco Found. [★17074]
Fidelco Guide Dog Found. [17074], 103 Old Iron Ore Rd., Bloomfield, CT 06002, (860)243-5200
Field Guides Assn. of South Africa [IO], Cresta, Republic of South Africa

Field Hockey

Coun. of Ivy Gp. Presidents [22975]
Natl. Field Hockey Coaches Assn. [22567]
Southeastern Conf. [23006]
U.S. Field Hockey Assn. [22568]

Field Hockey Assn. of Am. [★22568]
Field Hockey Canada [IO], Ottawa, ON, Canada
Field Marketing Services Assn. [★3115]
Field Marketing Services Assn. - Defunct.
Field Naturalists Club of Victoria [IO], Blackburn, Australia
Field Spaniel Soc. of Am. [21562], 351 E Kerley Corners Rd., Tivoli, NY 12583, (845)756-2595
Field Stud. Coun. [IO], Shrewsbury, United Kingdom
Field in Trust [IO], London, United Kingdom
Fields of Growth Intl. [12416], PO Box 751, Notre Dame, IN 46556
Fife Chamber of Commerce and Enterprise [IO], Kirkcaldy, United Kingdom
Fifty Caliber Shooters Assn. [22154], PO Box 111, Monroe, UT 84754-0111, (435)527-9245
Fifty Caliber Shooters Assn. [22154], PO Box 111, Monroe, UT 84754-0111, (435)527-9245
Fifty Lanterns Intl. [7439], PO Box 251173, St. Paul, MN 55125, (651)235-7146
Fifty-Plus Fitness Assn. [★23070]
Fifty-Plus Lifelong Fitness [★23070]
Fifty-Plus Runners Assn. [★23070]
Fifty-Six Fifty-Seven Lincoln Registry [★21159]
Fifty-Six Fifty-Seven Lincoln Registry [★21159]
Fight 4 Kids [11275], PO Box 888884, Atlanta, GA 30356, (800)641-5539
Fight Against Animal Cruelty in Europe [IO], Southport, United Kingdom
Fight Against Child Exploitation [IO], Bangkok, Thailand
Fight Against Hunger Org. [12274], PO Box 2250, Monroe, NY 10949
Fight Crime: Invest in Kids [17236], 1212 New York Ave. NW, Ste. 300, Washington, DC 20005, (202)776-0027
Fight Illiteracy Youth Org. [IO], Kigali, Rwanda
Fighting Robot Assn. [IO], Hemel Hempstead, United Kingdom
Figlie de San Paolo [★IO]
Figural Cast Iron Collector's Club [21339], Stephen J. Greenberg, Sec.-Treas., Duane Morris LLP, 30 S 17th St., Philadelphia, PA 19103-4001
Figure Skating Fed. of the Republic of Uzbekistan [IO], Navoiy, Uzbekistan
Figure Skating Fed. of Russia [IO], Moscow, Russia
Figure and Speed Skating Assn. of Thailand [IO], Bangkok, Thailand

A star before a book entry number signifies that the name is not listed separately, but is mentioned within the entry.

Figures Collectors Club - Address unknown since 2010.
Fiji Disabled Peoples Assn. **[IO]**, Suva, Fiji
Fiji Employers' Fed. **[IO]**, Suva, Fiji
Fiji Islands Blind Sport Assn. **[IO]**, Suva, Fiji
Fiji Islands Hotel and Tourism Assn. **[IO]**, Suva, Fiji
Fiji Law Soc. **[IO]**, Suva, Fiji
Fiji Medical Assn. **[IO]**, Suva, Fiji
Fiji Physiotherapy Assn. **[IO]**, Suva, Fiji
Fiji Red Cross Soc. **[IO]**, Suva, Fiji
Fiji Taekwondo Assn. **[IO]**, Suva, Fiji
Fiji Tennis Assn. **[IO]**, Lautoka, Fiji
Fiji Visitors' Bur. **[IO]**, Nadi, Fiji
Fiji Weightlifting Fed. **[IO]**, Suva, Fiji
Fiji Women's Crisis Centre **[IO]** Suva, Fiji
Fiji Yachting Assn. **[IO]**, Nadi, Fiji
Fikambanana Kristiana hoan'ny Zatovovavy eto Madagasikara **[★IO]**
Filipina Women's Network **[18792]**, PO Box 192143, San Francisco, CA 94119, (415)935-4396
Filipino Amer. Coalition for Environmental Solidarity **[4338]**, PO Box 566, Berkeley, CA 94701-0566, (415)496-6561
Filipino Amer. Coalition for Environmental Solidarity **[4338]**, PO Box 566, Berkeley, CA 94701-0566, (415)496-6561
Filipino Amer. Natl. Historical Soc. **[10364]**, 810 18th Ave., Rm. 100, Seattle, WA 98122, (206)322-0203
Filipino Amer. Natl. Historical Soc. **[10364]**, 810 18th Ave., Rm. 100, Seattle, WA 98122, (206)322-0203
Filipino Amer. Real Estate Professionals Assn. - Address unknown since 2010.
Filipino Shipowners Assn. **[IO]**, Manila, Philippines
Filipinos for Affirmative Action **[18314]**, 310 8th St., Ste. 308, Oakland, CA 94607, (510)465-9876

Film
Acad. of Sci. Fiction, Fantasy, and Horror Films **[9591]**
African Amer. Women in Cinema Org. **[9592]**
Amer. Film Inst. **[9593]**
Amer. Soc. for Aesthetics **[9270]**
Amer. Theatre Arts for Youth **[10566]**
Anthology Film Archives **[9594]**
Art Directors Guild **[9595]**
Asian Cinema Stud. Soc. **[7755]**
Asian CineVision **[9596]**
Assn. of Film Commissioners Intl. **[1253]**
Assn. of Moving Image Archivists **[9597]**
Assn. of Moving Image Archivists **[9597]**
Center for Independent Documentary **[9598]**
Center for the Stud. of Film and History **[9599]**
Chlotrudis Soc. for Independent Film **[9600]**
Cinema Tropical **[9601]**
Content Delivery and Storage Assn. **[1254]**
Coun. on Intl. Nontheatrical Events **[9602]**
Coun. on Intl. Nontheatrical Events **[9602]**
Directors Guild of Am. **[23187]**
Film Advisory Bd. **[9603]**
Golden Raspberry Award Found. **[21706]**
Intl. Animated Film Assn. - Canada **[3870]**
Intl. Crosby Circle **[23857]**
Intl. Film Seminars **[9604]**
Intl. Film Seminars **[9604]**
Intl. Guild of Symphony, Opera and Ballet Musicians **[23272]**
Intl. Network of Somewhere in Time Enthusiasts **[23806]**
Intl. Network of Somewhere in Time Enthusiasts **[23806]**
Intl. Visual Sociology Assn. **[7428]**
Media Fellowship Intl. **[19762]**
Natl. Bd. of Rev. of Motion Pictures **[9605]**
Natl. Center for Jewish Film **[9606]**
Outfest **[9607]**
POWER UP: Professional Org. of Women in Entertainment Reaching UP! **[17737]**
Richard Burgi Fan Club **[23781]**
San Francisco Camerawork **[9608]**
Soc. for Cinema and Media Stud. **[9609]**
Soc. for Cinephiles/Cinecon **[9610]**
Sons of the Desert **[23807]**
Sundance Inst. **[9611]**
Univ. Film and Video Assn. **[8183]**
U.S.A. Film Festival **[9612]**
Visual Effects Soc. **[1270]**

Visual Stud. Workshop **[9613]**
Working Films **[12043]**
Film Advisory Bd. **[9603]**, 263 W Olive Ave., No. 377, Burbank, CA 91502, (323)461-6541
Film Artistes Assn. **[IO]**, London, United Kingdom
Film Arts Found. - Defunct.
Film and Bag Fed. **[878]**, Soc. of the Plastics Indus., Inc., 1667 K St. NW, Ste. 1000, Washington, DC 20006-1620, (202)974-5218
Film Distributors' Assn. **[IO]**, London, United Kingdom

Film Industry
Acad. of Canadian Cinema and TV **[14853]**
Acad. of Motion Picture Arts and Sciences **[1247]**
Advanced Media Workflow Assn. **[3386]**
African Amer. Women in Cinema Org. **[9592]**
Alliance of Motion Picture and TV Producers **[1248]**
Amer. Cinema Editors **[1249]**
Amer. Film Marketing Assn. **[1257]**
Amer. Soc. of Cinematographers **[1250]**
Assn. of Audiovisual and Film Indus. of Austria **[4615]**
Assn. of Cinema and Video Labs. **[1251]**
Assn. of Commercial Stock Image Licensors **[1252]**
Assn. of Film Commissioners Intl. **[1253]**
Content Delivery and Storage Assn. **[1254]**
Digital Cinema Soc. **[1255]**
Digital Cinema Soc. **[1255]**
Independent Feature Proj. **[1256]**
Independent Film and TV Alliance **[1257]**
Intl. Animated Film Soc., ASIFA - Hollywood **[1258]**
Intl. Assn. of Audio Visual Communicators **[1259]**
Intl. Assn. of Audio Visual Communicators **[1259]**
Intl. Cinema Tech. Assn. **[1260]**
Intl. Cinema Tech. Assn. **[1260]**
Intl. Documentary Assn. **[1261]**
Intl. Documentary Assn. **[1261]**
Media Communications Assn. Intl. **[1262]**
Media Communications Assn. Intl. **[1262]**
Motion Picture Assn. of Am. **[1263]**
Motion Picture Pilots Assn. **[380]**
Motion Picture Sound Editors **[1264]**
Natl. Assn. of Latino Independent Producers **[1265]**
Producers Guild of Am. **[1266]**
Stuntmen's Assn. of Motion Pictures **[1267]**
Stuntwomen's Assn. of Motion Pictures **[1268]**
United Drive-In Theatre Owners Assn. **[1269]**
Visual Effects Soc. **[1270]**
Wedding and Event Videographers Assn. Intl. **[1271]**
Wedding and Event Videographers Assn. Intl. **[1271]**
Women in Animation **[1272]**
Women in Film **[1273]**
Women in Film and Video **[1274]**
Film-Makers' Cinematheque **[★9594]**
Film Music Soc. **[10196]**, 1516 S Bundy Dr., Ste. 305, Los Angeles, CA 90025, (310)820-1909
Film Stud. Assn. of Canada **[IO]**, Lethbridge, AB, Canada
Film and TV Archives Advisory Comm. **[★9597]**
Film and TV Archives Advisory Comm. **[★9597]**
Film and TV Inst. of Western Australia **[IO]**, Fremantle, Australia
Film/Video Arts - Address unknown since 2010.
FilmAid Intl. **[12780]**, 363 7th Ave., 20th Fl., New York, NY 10001, (212)529-1088
FilmAid Intl. **[12780]**, 363 7th Ave., 20th Fl., New York, NY 10001, (212)529-1088
Fils de la Charite **[★IO]**
Filter Mfrs. Coun. **[327]**, PO Box 13966, Research Triangle Park, NC 27709-3966, (919)549-4800
Filter Mfrs. Coun. **[327]**, PO Box 13966, Research Triangle Park, NC 27709-3966, (919)549-4800
Filtration Soc. **[IO]**, Exeter, United Kingdom

Finance
100 Women in Hedge Funds Assn. **[1275]**
Advt. Media Credit Executives Assn. **[1276]**
Alliance for Wellness ROI **[16303]**
Alternative Investments Compliance Assn. **[2127]**
Amer. Accounts Payable Assn. **[6]**

Amer. Assn. of Individual Investors **[8184]**
Amer. Assn. of Professional Tech. Analysts **[3387]**
Amer. Escrow Assn. **[1277]**
Amer. Finance Assn. **[1278]**
Amer. Legal Finance Assn. **[1279]**
Amer. Soc. of Cost Segregation Professionals **[3381]**
Anguilla Financial Services Assn. **[14992]**
Asian Financial Soc. **[1280]**
Asset Managers Forum **[1281]**
Asset Managers Forum **[1281]**
Assn. of African Amer. Financial Advisors **[1334]**
Assn. of Chinese Finance Professionals **[1282]**
Assn. of Divorce Financial Planners **[1335]**
Assn. for Financial Professionals **[1283]**
Assn. of Governmental Risk Pools **[5549]**
The Assn. of Settlement Companies **[1284]**
Assn. of Trade and Forfaiting in the Americas **[1285]**
Assn. of Trade and Forfaiting in the Americas **[1285]**
Bus. Products Credit Assn. **[1286]**
Chartered Alternative Investment Analyst Assn. **[2134]**
Chicago Stock Exchange **[3194]**
Chinese Finance Assn. **[1287]**
Clearpoint Financial Solutions **[1288]**
Community Development Bankers Assn. **[406]**
Community Financial Services Assn. **[1289]**
Conf. on Consumer Finance Law **[5340]**
The Conservation Campaign **[17416]**
Consumer Data Indus. Assn. **[1290]**
Credit Builders Alliance **[990]**
Credit Professionals Intl. **[1291]**
Credit Professionals Intl. **[1291]**
Credit Res. Found. **[1292]**
Debtors Anonymous **[13040]**
Dominicans on Wall St. **[1293]**
Dominicans on Wall St. **[1293]**
Eastern Finance Assn. **[1294]**
Emerging Markets Private Equity Assn. **[1295]**
Emerging Markets Private Equity Assn. **[1295]**
Farm Financial Standards Coun. **[3755]**
Finance Proj. **[17680]**
Financial Executives Intl. **[1296]**
Financial Executives Intl. **[1296]**
Financial Markets Assn. **[1297]**
Financial Planning Assn. **[1298]**
Financial Planning Assn. **[1298]**
Financial Publishers Assn. **[2934]**
Financial Women's Assn. of New York **[1299]**
Forius Bus. Credit Resources **[1300]**
Found. for the Advancement of Monetary Educ. **[8185]**
Global Assn. of Risk Professionals **[1301]**
Global Assn. of Risk Professionals **[1301]**
Global India Venture Capital Assn. **[1302]**
Global India Venture Capital Assn. **[1302]**
Govt. Investment Officers Assn. **[5611]**
Gp. Underwriters Assn. of Am. **[1962]**
Hospitality Financial and Tech. Professionals **[1303]**
Hospitality Financial and Tech. Professionals **[1303]**
Insight Center for Community Economic Development **[17578]**
Inst. of Consumer Financial Educ. **[8186]**
Inst. for Economic Anal. **[6620]**
Intl. Assn. of Financial Engineers **[1304]**
Intl. Assn. of Financial Engineers **[1304]**
Intl. Assn. of Registered Financial Consultants **[1305]**
Intl. Assn. of Registered Financial Consultants **[1305]**
Intl. Consortium on Governmental Financial Mgt. **[1306]**
Intl. Consortium on Governmental Financial Mgt. **[1306]**
Intl. Energy Credit Assn. **[1307]**
Intl. Energy Credit Assn. **[1307]**
Intl. Factoring Assn. **[1308]**
Intl. Soc. of Financiers **[1309]**
Intl. Soc. of Financiers **[1309]**
Investment Educ. Inst. **[8187]**
I.T. Financial Mgt. Assn. **[1310]**

Reference to "IO" in place of a book number signifies that the association may be found in the 50th edition of International Organizations.

A star before a book entry number signifies that the name is not listed separately, but is mentioned within the entry.

Intl. Order of Runeberg [9616]
Intl. Order of Runeberg [9616]
Finnish 4H Fed. [IO], Helsinki, Finland
Finnish Air Line Pilots' Assn. [IO], Helsinki, Finland
Finnish Amateur Musicians' Assn. [IO], Helsinki, Finland
Finnish Amateur Radio League [IO], Helsinki, Finland
Finnish Amer. Chamber of Commerce [23399], 866 UN Plz., Ste. 250, New York, NY 10017, (212)821-0225
Finnish Amer. Historical Archives [9614], 601 Quincy St., Hancock, MI 49930, (906)487-7347
Finnish Amer. Historical Archives [9614], 601 Quincy St., Hancock, MI 49930, (906)487-7347
Finnish-American Historical Soc. of the West [18988], PO Box 5522, Portland, OR 97228-5522
Finnish and Amer. Women's Network [13460], PO Box 3623, New York, NY 10163-3623
Finnish Assn. of Civil Engineers [IO], Helsinki, Finland
Finnish Assn. of Consulting Firms [IO], Espoo, Finland
Finnish Assn. of Designers Ornamo [IO], Helsinki, Finland
Finnish Assn. of Graduate Engineers [IO], Helsinki, Finland
Finnish Assn. of Landscape Architects [IO], Helsinki, Finland
Finnish Assn. of Marketing Commun. Agencies [IO], Helsinki, Finland
Finnish Assn. for Mental Hea. [IO], Helsinki, Finland
Finnish Assn. of Palliative Care [IO], Helsinki, Finland
Finnish Assn. of Physiotherapists [IO], Helsinki, Finland
Finnish Badminton Assn. [IO], Helsinki, Finland
Finnish Bakery Assn. [IO], Helsinki, Finland
Finnish Bar Assn. [IO], Helsinki, Finland
Finnish Biathlon Assn. [IO], Helsinki, Finland
Finnish Bible Soc. [IO], Helsinki, Finland
Finnish Billiard Fed. [IO], Helsinki, Finland
Finnish Biochemical Soc. [IO], Helsinki, Finland
Finnish Book Publishers Assn. [IO], Helsinki, Finland
Finnish Cardiac Soc. [IO], Oulu, Finland
Finnish Central Org. for Motor Trades and Repairs [IO], Helsinki, Finland
Finnish Centre of AITA/IATA [IO], Helsinki, Finland
Finnish Comm. for UNICEF [IO], Helsinki, Finland
Finnish Confed. of Salaried Employees [IO], Helsinki, Finland
Finnish Constr. Trade Union [IO], Helsinki, Finland
Finnish Cosmetic, Toiletry and Detergent Assn. [IO], Helsinki, Finland
Finnish Cricket Assn. [IO], Kerava, Finland
Finnish Cultural Found. [IO], Helsinki, Finland
Finnish Curling Assn. [IO], Vantaa, Finland
Finnish Diabetes Assn. [IO], Tampere, Finland
Finnish Direct Marketing Assn. [IO], Helsinki, Finland
Finnish Dramatists' Union [IO], Helsinki, Finland
Finnish Driving School Assn. [IO], Helsinki, Finland
Finnish Egyptological Soc. [IO], Helsinki, Finland
Finnish Elecl. Wholesalers Fed. [IO], Helsinki, Finland
Finnish Energy Indus. Fed. [IO], Helsinki, Finland
Finnish Epilepsy Soc. [IO], Oulu, Finland
Finnish Fed. of the Brewing and Soft Drink Indus. [IO], Helsinki, Finland
Finnish Fed. of Petrol Retailers [IO], Helsinki, Finland
Finnish Fed. of Univ. Women [IO], Helsinki, Finland
Finnish Fed. of the Visually Impaired [IO], Helsinki, Finland
Finnish Fish Farmers' Assn. [IO], Helsinki, Finland
Finnish Floorball Fed. [IO], Helsinki, Finland
Finnish Flying Disc Assn. [IO], Helsinki, Finland
Finnish Folk High School Assn. [IO], Helsinki, Finland
Finnish Food and Drink Indus'. Fed. [IO], Helsinki, Finland
Finnish Food Marketing Assn. [IO], Helsinki, Finland
Finnish Food Workers' Union [IO], Helsinki, Finland
Finnish Forest Indus. Fed. [IO], Helsinki, Finland
Finnish Found. for Share Promotion [IO], Helsinki, Finland

Finnish Franchising Assn. [IO], Helsinki, Finland
Finnish Fur Breeders' Assn. [IO], Vantaa, Finland
Finnish Geodetic Inst. [IO], Masala, Finland
Finnish Gynecological Assn. [IO], Oulu, Finland
Finnish Heart Assn. [IO], Helsinki, Finland
Finnish Historical Soc. [IO], Helsinki, Finland
Finnish Huntington Assn. [IO], Turku, Finland
Finnish Hydraulics and Pneumatics Assn. [IO], Tampere, Finland
Finnish Hypertension Soc. [IO], Tampere, Finland
Finnish Info. Processing Assn. [IO], Espoo, Finland
Finnish Kennel Club [IO], Espoo, Finland
Finnish League for Human Rights [IO], Helsinki, Finland
Finnish Lib. Assn. [IO], Helsinki, Finland
Finnish Literature Info. Centre [IO], Helsinki, Finland
Finnish Marfan Assn. [IO], Helsinki, Finland
Finnish Marketing Assn. [IO], Helsinki, Finland
Finnish Medical Assn. [IO], Helsinki, Finland
Finnish Medical Students' Intl. Comm. [IO], Helsinki, Finland
Finnish MS Soc. [IO], Masku, Finland
Finnish Museums Assn. [IO], Helsinki, Finland
Finnish Music Publishers' Assn. [IO], Helsinki, Finland
Finnish Musicians Union [IO], Helsinki, Finland
Finnish Natural Stone Assn. [IO], Helsinki, Finland
Finnish Newspapers Assn. [IO], Helsinki, Finland
Finnish North Amer. Literature Assn. [9615], 47283 Huron St., Atlantic Mine, MI 49905
Finnish Oil and Gas Fed. [IO], Helsinki, Finland
Finnish Oil Millers' Assn. [IO], Helsinki, Finland
Finnish Olympic Comm. [IO], Helsinki, Finland
Finnish Operations Res. Soc. [IO], Helsinki, Finland
Finnish Osteoporosis Assn. [IO], Helsinki, Finland
Finnish Painters' Union [IO], Helsinki, Finland
Finnish Paper Engineers' Assn. [IO], Helsinki, Finland
Finnish Paralympic Comm. [IO], Helsinki, Finland
Finnish Parkinson's Disease Assn., Huntington Disease Br. [IO], Turku, Finland
Finnish Peatland Soc. [IO], Vantaa, Finland
Finnish Pharmacological Soc. [IO], Tampere, Finland
Finnish Physical Soc. [IO], Helsinki, Finland
Finnish Physiological Soc. [IO], Helsinki, Finland
Finnish Plastics Assn. [IO], Helsinki, Finland
Finnish Port Assn. [IO], Helsinki, Finland
Finnish Psoriasis Assn. [IO], Helsinki, Finland
Finnish Red Cross [IO], Helsinki, Finland
Finnish Refugee Coun. [IO], Helsinki, Finland
Finnish Rheumatism Assn. [IO], Helsinki, Finland
Finnish Rose Soc. [IO], Hameenkyro, Finland
Finnish School Sport Fed. [IO], Helsinki, Finland
Finnish Seamen's Union [IO], Helsinki, Finland
Finnish Shipowners' Assn. [IO], Helsinki, Finland
Finnish Shooting Sport Fed. [IO], Helsinki, Finland
Finnish Social Democratic Party [IO], Helsinki, Finland
Finnish Social and Hea. Informatics Assn. [IO], Helsinki, Finland
Finnish Soc. of Anaesthesiologists [IO], Turku, Finland
Finnish Soc. of Automation [IO], Helsinki, Finland
Finnish Soc. of Gastroenterology [IO], Helsinki, Finland
Finnish Soc. of Rheumatology [IO], Espoo, Finland
Finnish Soc. of Sciences and Letters [IO], Helsinki, Finland
Finnish Soc. of Sports Medicine [IO], Jyvaskyla, Finland
Finnish Spitz Club of Am. [21563], 17177 Superior St., Northridge, CA 91325, (818)882-2171
Finnish Sports Fed. [IO], Helsinki, Finland
Finnish Squash Assn. [IO], Helsinki, Finland
Finnish Taekwondo Fed. [IO], Helsinki, Finland
Finnish Tennis Assn. [IO], Helsinki, Finland
Finnish Tourist Bd. [IO], Helsinki, Finland
Finnish Transport Workers' Union [IO], Helsinki, Finland
Finnish United Nations Assn. [IO], Helsinki, Finland
Finnish Veterinary Assn. [IO], Helsinki, Finland
Finnish Watchmakers' Assn. [IO], Espoo, Finland
Finnish Water Ski Sports Fed. [IO], Harjavalta, Finland
Finnish White Ribbon Union [IO], Helsinki, Finland

Finnish Wind Power Assn. [IO], Tampere, Finland
Finnish Wood and Allied Workers' Union [IO], Helsinki, Finland
Finnish Yachting Assn. [IO], Espoo, Finland
Finnish Youth Co-Operation Allianssi [IO], Helsinki, Finland
Finnish Youth Hostel Assn. [IO], Helsinki, Finland
Finno-Ugrian Soc. [IO], Helsinki, Finland
Finnsheep Breeders Assn. [4908], Deb Olschefski, Sec., 3937 Ridgewood Rd., York, PA 17406, (717)840-7316
FINPRO: Finnish Bus. Solutions Worldwide [IO], Helsinki, Finland
FinSec, Finance and Info. Union [IO], Wellington, New Zealand
Finska Kennelklubben [★IO]
Finska Pappesingeniorsforeningen [★IO]
Fiqh Coun. of North Am. [19831], PO Box 1250, Falls Church, VA 22041
Fire Brigades Union [IO], Kingston upon Thames, United Kingdom
Fire Contractors Fed. [★1559]
Fire Dept. Safety Officers Assn. [5963], PO Box 149, Ashland, MA 01721, (508)881-3114
Fire and Emergency Mfrs. and Services Assn. [11922], PO Box 147, Lynnfield, MA 01940-0147, (781)334-2771
Fire Equip. Mfrs'. Assn. [3141], 1300 Sumner Ave., Cleveland, OH 44115, (216)241-7333
Fire Fighting
  Assn. for Fire Ecology [4194]
  Assn. for Fire Ecology of the Tropics [4195]
  Fellowship of Christian Firefighters Intl. [5438]
  Fellowship of Christian Firefighters Intl. [5438]
  Fire Mark Circle of the Americas [21707]
  Firefighters United for Safety, Ethics and Ecology [5439]
  Intl. Assn. of Arson Investigators [5440]
  Intl. Assn. of Arson Investigators [5440]
  Intl. Assn. of Black Professional Fire Fighters [5441]
  Intl. Assn. of Black Professional Fire Fighters [5441]
  Intl. Assn. of Fire Chiefs [5442]
  Intl. Assn. of Fire Chiefs [5442]
  Intl. Assn. of Fire Fighters [23188]
  Intl. Assn. of Women in Fire and Emergency Services [5443]
  Intl. Fire Buff Associates [21708]
  Intl. Fire Marshals Assn. [5444]
  Intl. Fire Marshals Assn. [5444]
  Intl. Police and Fire Chaplain's Assn. [19522]
  Intl. Soc. for Fire Ser. Instructors [5445]
  Intl. Soc. for Fire Ser. Instructors [5445]
  Natl. Assn. of Hispanic Firefighters [5446]
  Natl. Assn. of State Fire Marshals [5447]
  Natl. Conf. of Firemen and Oilers [23189]
  Natl. Historical Fire Found. [21709]
  Natl. Smokejumper Assn. [5448]
  Natl. Volunteer Fire Coun. [5449]
  Soc. for the Preservation and Appreciation of Antique Motor Fire Apparatus in Am. [21710]
Fire Indus. Assn. [IO], Hampton, United Kingdom
Fire Mark Circle of the Americas [21707], 1010 Allgood Rd., Athens, GA 30606-5367
Fire Marshals Assn. of North Am. [★5444]
Fire Marshals Assn. of North Am. [★5444]
Fire Professionals of Am; Intl. Union, Security, Police and [23295]
Fire Protection
  Alliance for Fire and Smoke Containment and Control [1349]
  Assn. for Fire Ecology [4194]
  Assn. for Fire Ecology of the Tropics [4195]
  Coalition for Fire-Safe Cigarettes [12045]
  European Fire and Security Advisory Coun. [473]FireIntl. Assn. for Fire Safety Sci.
  Intl. Fire Buff Associates [21708]
  Intl. FireStop Coun. [6862]
  Intl. FireStop Coun. [6862]
  Intl. Kitchen Exhaust Cleaning Assn. [1350]
  Natl. Fire Indus. Assn. [1559]
  Natl. Fireproofing Contractors Assn. [1351]
  Soc. of Fire Protection Engineers [6863]
  U.S. Homeland Emergency Response Org. [12911]

Reference to "IO" in place of a book number signifies that the association may be found in the 50th edition of International Organizations.

Fire Protection Assn. - Australia [IO], Box Hill, Australia

Fire Protection Assn. - England [IO], Moreton-in-Marsh, United Kingdom

Fire Protection Assn; Natl. [12995]

Fire Protection Assn. of Pakistan [IO], Karachi, Pakistan

Fire Protection Assn. of Southern Africa [IO], Impala Park, Republic of South Africa

Fire Res. Inst. [★4401]

Fire Res. Inst. [★4401]

Fire Suppression Systems Assn. [3142], 5024 R Campbell Blvd., Baltimore, MD 21236-5974, (410)931-8100

Firearm and Security Trainers Mgt. Assn. - Defunct.

Firearms

Amer. Custom Gunmakers Guild [1352]

Armed Females of Am. [17682]

Assn. of Firearm and Tool Mark Examiners [6864]

Assn. of Ohio Longrifle Collectors [21711]

Brady Campaign to Prevent Gun Violence [17683]

Brady Center to Prevent Gun Violence [17684]

Browning Collectors Assn. [21712]

Browning Collectors Assn. [21712]

Center to Prevent Youth Violence [17685]

Coalition to Stop Gun Violence [17686]

Common Sense about Kids and Guns [8202]

Drums No Guns [17687]

Educational Fund to Stop Gun Violence [17688]

Gun Owners of Am. [5450]

Gun Owners Found. [5451]FirearmsHELP Network

High Standard Collectors' Assn. [21713]

L.C. Smith Collectors Assn. [21714]

Natl. Assn. of Arms Shows [21715]

Natl. Assn. of Firearms Retailers [1353]

Natl. Firearms Act Trade and Collectors Assn. [1354]

Natl. Mossberg Collectors Assn. [21716]

Natl. Rifle Assn. of Am. [22881]

North Amer. Hunting Club [22700]

North-South Skirmish Assn. [22885]

Parker Gun Collectors Assn. [21717]

Peoples Rights Org. [17319]

St. Gabriel Possenti Soc. [17689]

Second Amendment Comm. [5452]

Second Amendment Sisters [17690]

Sharps Collector Assn. [21718]

Sporting Arms and Ammunitions Mfrs. Inst. [1355]

Sportsmen's Assn. for Firearms Educ. [17691]

Student Pledge Against Gun Violence [17692]

Students for the Second Amendment [17693]

Thompson Collectors Assn. [21719]

Thompson Collectors Assn. [21719]

Weatherby Collectors Assn. [21720]

Women Against Gun Control [17694]

Women Against Gun Control [17694]

World Fast-Draw Assn. [22891]

Firearms Engravers Guild of Am. [21439], 1452 Ivanhoe Rd., Ludington, MI 49431, (616)929-6146

Firearms Engravers Guild of Am. [21439], 1452 Ivanhoe Rd., Ludington, MI 49431, (616)929-6146

Firearms Lobby of Am. [★17280]

Firearms Policy Proj. [★18771]

Firefighters United for Safety, Ethics and Ecology [5439], 2852 Willamette St., No. 125, Eugene, OR 97405, (541)338-7671

FireFlag/EMS [5496], 208 W 13th St., New York, NY 10011, (917)885-0127

Firefly [11277], 8317 Woodhaven Blvd., Bethesda, MD 20817, (917)359-7207

Firehawk Assn. of Am. [21057], PO Box 96, Union-town, PA 15401

Fireplace Inst. [★1699]

Firestop Contractors Intl. Assn. [846], 4415 W Harrison St., No. 436, Hillside, IL 60162, (708)202-1108

Firestop Contractors Intl. Assn. [846], 4415 W Harrison St., No. 436, Hillside, IL 60162, (708)202-1108

First Amendment Cong. - Defunct.

First Amendment Found. and Natl. Comm. Against Repressive Legislation [★12684]

First Amendment Lawyers Assn. [5339], Mr. Wayne Giampietro, Gen. Counselor, 123 W Madison St., Ste. 1300, Chicago, IL 60602, (312)236-0606

First Amendment Proj. [18420], 1736 Franklin St., 9th Fl., Oakland, CA 94612, (510)208-7744

First Amendment Rights

Student Press Law Center [17358]

First Americans in the Arts [9114], PO Box 17780, Beverly Hills, CA 90209, (310)270-5388

First Artists - Address unknown since 2011.

First Book [8529], 1319 F St. NW, Ste. 1000, Washington, DC 20004-1155, (202)393-1222

First Candle/SIDS Alliance [16761], 1314 Bedford Ave., Ste. 210, Baltimore, MD 21208, (800)221-7437

First Catholic Slovak Ladies Assn. [19229], 24950 Chagrin Blvd., Beachwood, OH 44122-5634, (216)464-8015

First Catholic Slovak Union of the U.S.A. and Canada [19230], 6611 Rockside Rd., Independence, OH 44131, (216)642-9406

First Day Cover Collectors Club [★22006]

First-Day School Gen. Conf. [★19779]

First Flight Soc. [20896], PO Box 1903, Kitty Hawk, NC 27949, (252)441-1903

First Foundations [13188], PO Box 991, Travelers Rest, SC 29690, (864)834-2300

First Fruit [19747], 14 Corporate Plz., Newport Beach, CA 92660, (949)720-3774

First Hungarian Literary Soc. - Address unknown since 2010.

First Issues Collectors Club [22038], PO Box 453, Brentwood, TN 37024-0453

First Marine Aviation Force Veterans Assn. [★5780]

First Nations Development Inst. [12560], 351 Coffman St., Ste. 200, Longmont, CO 80501, (303)774-7836

First Nations Financial Proj. [★12560]

First Nations Natl. Building Officers Assn. [IO], Shannonville, ON, Canada

First Peoples Worldwide [9865], 857 Leeland Rd., Fredericksburg, VA 22405, (540)899-6545

First Peoples Worldwide [9865], 857 Leeland Rd., Fredericksburg, VA 22405, (540)899-6545

First Person Plural [IO], Wolverhampton, United Kingdom

First Signs [14051], PO Box 358, Merrimac, MA 01860, (978)346-4380

First Special Ser. Force Assn. - Defunct.

First Star [11278], 1666 K St. NW, Ste. 300, Washington, DC 20006, (202)293-3703

First Steps to Freedom [IO], Newquay, United Kingdom

First Voice Intl. - Address unknown since 2011.

First Zen Inst. of Am. [19366], 113 E 30th St., New York, NY 10016, (212)686-2520

FISA [1438], 1207 Sunset Dr., Greensboro, NC 27408, (336)274-6311

Fiscal Stud. Prog. [5990], Rockefeller Inst. of Govt., 411 State St., Albany, NY 12203-1003, (518)443-5522

Fischoff Natl. Chamber Music Assn. [10197], Univ. of Notre Dame, 303 Brownson Hall, Notre Dame, IN 46556, (574)631-0984

Fish

Amer. Carp Soc. [21730]

Amer. Cichlid Assn. [21721]

Amer. Killifish Assn. [21722]FishAmer. Livebearer Assn.

Apistogramma Study Group [21723]

Apistogramma Study Group [21723]

Assoc. Koi Clubs of Am. [21724]

Assoc. Koi Clubs of Am. [21724]

Assn. of Conservation Engineers [4001]

Atlantic Flyway Coun. [5030]

Bass Anglers Sportsman Soc. [22572]

Breeder's Registry [21725]

Carp Anglers Gp. [21732]

Fed. of Fly Fishers [22574]

Goldfish Soc. of Am. [21726]

Goldfish Soc. of Am. [21726]

Intl. Betta Cong. [21727]

Intl. Betta Cong. [21727]

Intl. Seafood Sustainability Assn. [1361]

Natl. Bass Anglers Assn. [22581]

Natl. Fisheries Inst. [3184]

Pacific Coast Cichlid Assn. [21728]FishRainbowfish Study Group of North Am.

Rocky Mountain Cichlid Assn. [21729]

Southeastern Fisheries Assn. [3190]

U.S. Aquaculture Soc. [3831]

Fish and Wildlife Reference Service - Defunct.

FishAmerica Found. [4055], 225 Reinekers Ln., Ste. 420, Alexandria, VA 22314, (703)519-9691

Fisher Inst. [★17716]

Fisher Inst. for Medical Res. [17716], 580 Decker Dr., Ste. 100, Irving, TX 75062, (972)660-3219

Fisher-Price Collector's Club [22169], 38 Main St., Oneonta, NY 13820-2519

Fisher-Price Collector's Club [22169], 38 Main St., Oneonta, NY 13820-2519

The Fisherfolk [★19563]

Fisheries Action Coalition Team [IO], Phnom Penh, Cambodia

Fisheries Comm. of the Org. for Economic Co-Operation and Development [IO], Paris, France

Fisheries and Oceans Canada [IO], Ottawa, ON, Canada

Fisherman's Clean Water Action Proj. [★4987]

Fishery Comm. for the Eastern Central Atlantic [IO], Accra, Ghana

Fishing

Amer. Carp Soc. [21730]

Amer. Casting Assn. [22569]

Amer. Crappie Assn. [21731]

Amer. Sportfishing Assn. [22570]

Anglers for Conservation [4000]

Assn. of Northwest Steelheaders [22571]

Atlantic Offshore Lobstermen's Assn. [1356]

Atlantic States Marine Fisheries Commn. [5453]

Bass Anglers Sportsman Soc. [22572]

Bowfishing Assn. of Am. [22573]

Carp Anglers Gp. [21732]

Christian Hunters and Anglers Assn. [21279]

Fed. of Fly Fishers [22574]

Fishing Has No Boundaries [22575]

FishWise [1359]

Future Fisherman Found. [22576]

Great Lakes Sport Fishing Coun. [22577]

Hawaiian Intl. Billfish Tournament [21733]

Hawaiian Intl. Billfish Tournament [21733]

Inter-American Tropical Tuna Commn. [5454]

Inter-American Tropical Tuna Commn. [5454]

Intl. Assn. of Fly Fishing Veterinarians [21734]

Intl. Fellowship of Fishing Rotarians [21735]

Intl. Fellowship of Fishing Rotarians [21735]

Intl. Game Fish Assn. [22578]

Intl. Pacific Halibut Commn. [5455]

Intl. Pacific Halibut Commn. [5455]

Intl. Seafood Sustainability Assn. [1361]

Intl. Underwater Spearfishing Assn. [22579]

Intl. Underwater Spearfishing Assn. [22579]

Intl. Women Fly Fishers [21736]

Intl. Women Fly Fishers [21736]

Intl. Women's Fishing Assn. [22580]

Intl. Women's Fishing Assn. [22580]

Natl. Bass Anglers Assn. [22581]

Natl. Fisheries Inst. [3184]

Natl. Professional Anglers' Assn. [22582]

Natl. Teen Anglers [21737]

North Amer. Fishing Club [22583]

Pacific Fishery Mgt. Coun. [5456]

Pacific States Marine Fisheries Commn. [5457]

Southeastern Assn. of Fish and Wildlife Agencies [5458]

Southeastern Fisheries Assn. [3190]

Sustainable Fisheries Partnership [3830]

United Fly Tyers [22584]

United Fly Tyers [22584]

U.S. Aquaculture Soc. [3831]

Western Assn. of Fish and Wildlife Agencies [5459]

Fishing Has No Boundaries [22575], PO Box 175, Hayward, WI 54843, (715)634-3185

Fishing Industries

Amer. Albacore Fishing Assn. [1357]

Amer. Carp Soc. [21730]

Amer. Tilapia Assn. [4378]

Assn. for Professional Observers [4379]

At-sea Processors Assn. [1358]

Bonefish and Tarpon Trust [4380]

Canadian Coun. of Professional Fish Harvesters [18576]

Carp Anglers Gp. [21732]

Chilean Salmon and Trout Farmers' Assn. [16400]

A star before a book entry number signifies that the name is not listed separately, but is mentioned within the entry.

Dutch Fish Prdt. Bd. [19153]
FishWise [1359]
Gulf and Caribbean Fisheries Inst. [4381]
Intl. Inst. of Fisheries Economics and Trade [1360]
Intl. Inst. of Fisheries Economics and Trade [1360]
Intl. Seafood Sustainability Assn. [1361]Fishing Natl. Chamber of the Fish Indus.
Natl. Fisheries Inst. [3184]
New Zealand Professional Fishing Guides Assn. [20483]
North Amer. Assn. of Fisheries Economists [1362]
Pacific Coast Fed. of Fishermen's Associations [4382]
Recreational Fishing Alliance [4383]
Southeastern Fisheries Assn. [3190]
Striped Bass Growers Assn. [4384]
Sustainable Fisheries Partnership [3830]
U.S. Aquaculture Soc. [3831]
Women's Fisheries Network [4385]
Fishing Indus. Assn. of Tonga [IO], Nuku'alofa, Tonga
FishWise [1359], PO Box 233, Santa Cruz, CA 95061-0233, (831)427-1707
Fiskeri-og Havbruksnaeringens Landsforening [★IO]
Fitness Forward [16225], 401 Park Dr., 3rd Fl. E, Boston, MA 02215
Fitness Indus. Assn. [IO], London, United Kingdom
Fitness Indus. Suppliers Assn. - North Am. [2742], 3525 Del Mar Heights Rd., Box 381, San Diego, CA 92130, (858)509-0034
Fitness Indus. Suppliers Assn. - North Am. [2742], 3525 Del Mar Heights Rd., Box 381, San Diego, CA 92130, (858)509-0034
The Fitness League [IO], Sunningdale, United Kingdom
Fitzgerald Soc; F. Scott [9363]
Fitzgerald Soc; F. Scott [9363]
Five P Minus Soc. [16768], PO Box 268, Lakewood, CA 90714-0268, (562)804-4506
Five Years Meeting of Friends [★19781]
Five Years Meeting of Friends [★19781]
Fixed Income Analysts Soc. [1339], 244 Fifth Ave., Ste. L230, New York, NY 10001, (212)726-8100
FJ U.S. - Address unknown since 2010.
Fjolis [IO], Reykjavik, Iceland
Flag
Citizens Flag Alliance [5338]
Flag Mfrs. Assn. of Am. [1363]
Flag Res. Center [10628]
Flags Across the Nation [20611]
Natl. Flag Day Found. [20612]
Natl. Independent Flag Dealers Assn. [1364]
Star-Spangled Banner Flag House Assn. [20613]
U.S. Flag Football League [22599]
Flag Cancel Soc. [★22049]
Flag Inst. [IO], London, United Kingdom
Flag Mfrs. Assn. of Am. [1363], 994 Old Eagle School Rd., Ste. 1019, Wayne, PA 19087, (610)971-4850
Flag Plaza Found. [★10630]
Flag Res. Center [10628], PO Box 580, Winchester, MA 01890-0880, (781)729-9410
Flagon and Trencher [★20394]
Flagon and Trencher Descendants of Colonial Tavern Keepers [20394], 1716 Bigley Ave., Charleston, WV 25302-3938
Flags Across the Nation [20611], PO Box 78995, Charlotte, NC 28271-7045, (704)962-1868
Flair Bartenders' Assn. [183], 104 E Fairview Ave., No. 283, Meridian, ID 83642-1733, (208)888-3146
Flanders-Brussels Convention Bur. [IO], Brussels, Belgium
Flashes of Hope [11135], 6009 Landerhaven Dr., Ste. I, Cleveland, OH 44124, (440)442-9700
Flat-Coated Retriever Soc. of Am. [21564], MaryAnn Abbott, Membership Sec., 19275 Whispering Trail, Traverse City, MI 49686, (231)223-4473
Flat Glass Jobbers Assn. [★1575]
Flat Glass Marketing Assn. [★1575]
Flavor and Extract Mfrs. Assn. of the U.S. [1382], 1620 I St. NW, Ste. 925, Washington, DC 20006, (202)293-5800
Flavoring Extract Mfrs. Assn. of the U.S. [★1382]

Flavour Mfrs. Assn. of Canada [IO], Toronto, ON, Canada
Fleet Air Arm Officers Assn. [IO], London, United Kingdom
Fleet Reserve Assn. [20718], 125 N West St., Alexandria, VA 22314-2709, (703)684-1400
Flemish Entomological Soc. [IO], Leefdaal, Belgium
Flemish Org. for Assistance in Development - Belgium [IO], Leuven, Belgium
Flemish Watersports Assn. [IO], Antwerp, Belgium
Fletchers' Company [IO], Richmond upon Thames, United Kingdom
FLEUROSELECT [IO], Noordwijk, Netherlands
Fleuroselect [★IO]
Flexible Intermediate Bulk Container Assn. [879], PO Box 24792, Minneapolis, MN 55424, (866)600-8880
Flexible Intermediate Bulk Container Assn. [879], PO Box 24792, Minneapolis, MN 55424, (866)600-8880
Flexible Packaging Assn. [2607], 971 Corporate Blvd., Ste. 403, Linthicum, MD 21090-2253, (410)694-0800
Flexible Packaging Europe [IO], Dusseldorf, Germany
Flexible Polyurethane Foam Mfrs. Assn. [★2775]
Flexicore Mfrs. Assn. - Defunct.
Flexographic Tech. Assn. [1607], 3920 Veterans Memorial Hwy., Ste. 9, Bohemia, NY 11716, (631)737-6020
Flexographic Tech. Assn. [1607], 3920 Veterans Memorial Hwy., Ste. 9, Bohemia, NY 11716, (631)737-6020
FlexTech Alliance [3390], 3081 Zanker Rd., San Jose, CA 95134, (408)577-1300
Flight Attendants of Am; Black [18843]
Flight Attendants of Am; Black [18843]
Flight Attendants; Assn. of Professional [23151]
Flight Attendants - CWA; Assn. of [23150]
Flight Attendants - CWA; Assn. of [23150]
Flight Attendants and Related Services Assn. [IO], Manukau City, New Zealand
Flight Freedoms Found. - Defunct.
Flight Safety Found. [134], 801 N Fairfax St., Ste. 400, Alexandria, VA 22314, (703)739-6700
Flight Safety Found. [134], 801 N Fairfax St., Ste. 400, Alexandria, VA 22314, (703)739-6700
Flippin Family Assn. [20515], 12206 Brisbane Ave., Dallas, TX 75234-6528, (972)241-2739
Floating Harbor Syndrome Support Gp. of North Am. [14597], 1964 Sheffield Rd., Harmony, NC 28634, (336)831-6955
Floating Harbor Syndrome Support Gp. of North Am. [14597], 1964 Sheffield Rd., Harmony, NC 28634, (336)831-6955
The Floating Hosp. [15055], PO Box 8397, Long Island City, NY 11101, (718)784-2240
Floodplain Mgt. Assn. [4731], PO Box 712080, Santee, CA 92072-2080, (619)204-4380
Floor Covering Installation Contractors Assn. [912], 7439 Millwood Dr., West Bloomfield, MI 48322, (248)661-5015
Floor Installation Assn. of North Am. [561], 1521 E Hampton Ln., Spokane, WA 99208-8506, (509)468-9268
Floor Installation Assn. of North Am. [561], 1521 E Hampton Ln., Spokane, WA 99208-8506, (509)468-9268
Floorball Canada [IO], Laval, QC, Canada
Floorball Fed. of India [IO], Lucknow, India
Flora Neotropica Org. [★6363]
Flora Neotropica Org. [★6363]
Floral Marketing Assn. - Defunct.
Florence Ballard Fan Club [23841], PO Box 360502, Los Angeles, CA 90036
Florence Ballard Fan Club [23841], PO Box 360502, Los Angeles, CA 90036
Florence Ceramics Collectors Soc. - Defunct.
Florence Crittenton Assn. of Amer. [★11228]
Floresta U.S.A. [17912], 4903 Morena Blvd., Ste. 1215, San Diego, CA 92117, (858)274-3718
Floresta U.S.A. [17912], 4903 Morena Blvd., Ste. 1215, San Diego, CA 92117, (858)274-3718
Florida Citrus Commn. [★4449]
Florida Citrus Mutual [4448], PO Box 89, Lakeland, FL 33802, (863)682-1111

Florida Citrus Nurserymen's Assn. - Address unknown since 2011.
Florida Dept. of Citrus [4449], PO Box 9010, Bartow, FL 33831-9010, (863)537-3999
Florida Express Fruit Shippers Assn. [★4451]
Florida Fruit and Vegetable Assn. [4450], PO Box 948153, Maitland, FL 32794-8153, (321)214-5200
Florida Gift Fruit Shippers Assn. [4451], 5500 W Concord Ave., Orlando, FL 32808, (407)295-1491
Florida Keys Wild Bird Rehabilitation Center [5055], 93600 Overseas Hwy., Tavernier, FL 33070, (305)852-4486
Florida Space Coast Writers Conf. [★10742]
Florida Tomato Comm. [4452], 800 Trafalgar Ct., No. 300, Maitland, FL 32751-7135, (407)660-1949
Florida Tomato Exchange [★4452]
Florida Trail Assn. [23084], 5415 SW 13th St., Gainesville, FL 32608, (352)378-8823
Florida Tropical Fish Farms Assn. [3822], PO Box 1519, Winter Haven, FL 33882, (863)293-5710
Florists
Amer. Inst. of Floral Designers [1365]
Assn. of Specialty Cut Flower Growers [1366]
Creative Floral Arrangers of the Americas [1367]
Holiday and Decorative Assn. [1368]
North Amer. Ohara Teachers Assn. [9617]
Soc. of Amer. Florists [1369]
Wholesale Florist and Florist Supplier Assn. [1370]
Zambia Export Growers' Assn. [20680]
Flour Advisory Bur. [IO], London, United Kingdom
Flour Millers Assn. of Japan [IO], Tokyo, Japan
Flow Blue Intl. Collectors Club [21340], Jim Swan, Membership Chm., PO Box 5427, Naperville, IL 60567-5427
Flower Coun. of Holland [IO], Leiden, Netherlands
Flower Essence Soc. [14990], PO Box 459, Nevada City, CA 95959, (530)265-9163
Flower Essence Soc. [14990], PO Box 459, Nevada City, CA 95959, (530)265-9163
Flowers
Amer. Clematis Soc. [4665]
Amer. Penstemon Soc. [21779]
Australian Rhododendron Soc. [6536]
British Orchid Growers Assn. [248]
The Gardeners of Am. [21794]
Indoor Gardening Soc. of Am. [21801]
Intl. Brugmansia and Datura Soc. [21738]
Intl. Phalaenopsis Alliance [4671]
North Amer. Lily Soc. [21815]
Orchid Conservation Alliance [4120]
Passiflora Soc. Intl. [4677]
Plumeria Soc. of Am. [21817]
Flowers Canada [IO], Ottawa, ON, Canada
Flowers and Plants Assn. [IO], London, United Kingdom
Flue-Cured Tobacco Cooperative Stabilization Corp. [★4960]
Fluid Controls Inst. [1822], 1300 Sumner Ave., Cleveland, OH 44115, (216)241-7333
Fluid Power
Intl. Fluid Power Soc. [6865]
Natl. Conf. on Fluid Power [6866]
WaterJet Tech. Association-Industrial and Municipal Cleaning Assn. [6867]
Fluid Power Consultants Intl. - Defunct.
Fluid Power Distributors Assn. [★1824]
Fluid Power Soc. [★6865]
Fluid Sealing Assn. [1823], 994 Old Eagle School Rd., No. 1019, Wayne, PA 19087, (610)971-4850
Fluorescent Mineral Soc. [7122], PO Box 572694, Tarzana, CA 91357-2694
Fluorescent Mineral Soc. [7122], PO Box 572694, Tarzana, CA 91357-2694
Fluoride Action Network [14281], 82 Judson St., Canton, NY 13617, (802)338-5577
Fly By Night: The Bat Specialists [5056], PO Box 562, Osteen, FL 32764-0562, (407)414-2142
Flydressers' Guild [IO], Henfield, United Kingdom
FlygTekniska Foreningen [★IO]
Flying Dentists Assn. [14282], 10032 Wind Hill Dr., Greenville, IN 47124-9673, (812)923-2100
Flying Disc Fed. of India [IO], Ahmedabad, India
Flying Doctors of Am. [12454], PO Box 923563, Norcross, GA 30010, (770)386-5221

Reference to "IO" in place of a book number signifies that the association may be found in the 50th edition of International Organizations.

Flying Doctors of Am. **[12454]**, PO Box 923563, Norcross, GA 30010, (770)386-5221
Flying Doctors of Mercy **[★12464]**
Flying Doctors of Mercy **[★12464]**
Flying Fifteen Intl. **[IO]**, Melbourne, Australia
Flying Kites **[11279]**, PO Box 156, Newport, RI 02840, (401)619-5919
Flying Padres **[★19459]**
Flying Physicians Assn. **[13811]**, 11626 Twain Dr., Montgomery, TX 77356, (936)588-6505
Flying Scot Sailing Assn. **[22335]**, 1 Windsor Cove, Ste. 305, Columbia, SC 29223, (803)252-5646
Flying Veterinarians Assn. - Defunct.
FN-forbundet **[★IO]**
FOCAL Intl. **[IO]**, South Harrow, United Kingdom
Focolare Movement **[19422]**, PO Box 7599, Washington, DC 20044
Focolare Movement **[19422]**, PO Box 7599, Washington, DG 20044
Focolare Movement - Italy **[IO]**, Rocca di Papa, Italy
Focus on the Family **[12009]**, 8605 Explorer Dr., Colorado Springs, CO 80920, (800)232-6459
Focus on the Family - Canada **[IO]**, Vancouver, BC, Canada
Focus Fusion Soc. **[6725]**, PO Box 232, South Bound Brook, NJ 08880
Focus on the Global South **[IO]**, Bangkok, Thailand
Focus Intl. - Kenya **[IO]**, Nairobi, Kenya
Focus the Nation **[17616]**, 240 N Broadway, Ste. 212, Portland, OR 97227, (503)224-9440
Focus Qatar **[IO]**, Doha, Qatar
FOD Family Support Gp. **[15496]**, PO Box 54, Okemos, MI 48805-0054, (517)381-1940
FOD Family Support Gp. **[15496]**, PO Box 54, Okemos, MI 48805-0054, (517)381-1940
Foderalistische Union Europaischer Volksgruppen **[★IO]**
Foderation Der Europaischen Parkett Industrie **[★IO]**
Foil Stamping and Embossing Assn. **[2469]**, 2150 SW Westport Dr., Ste. 101, Topeka, KS 66614, (785)271-5816
Foilsiu Eireann **[★IO]**
Foires Salons et Congres Evenements de France **[★IO]**
Foires Salons and Congres de France **[★IO]**
Folding Paper Box Assn. of Am. **[★2609]**
Folk
    Amer. Folklore Soc. **[9618]**
    Folk Alliance **[9619]**
    Folk Alliance Intl. **[9619]**
    Folk Art Soc. of Am. **[9620]**
    Intl. Assn. for Comparative Mythology **[7133]**
    Jargon Soc. **[9621]**
    Maine Folklife Center **[9622]**
    The Mountain Inst. **[9623]**
    Natl. Coun. for the Traditional Arts **[9624]**
    Slavic and East European Folklore Assn. **[9625]**
    Slavic and East European Folklore Assn. **[9625]**
    Soc. for Folk Arts Preservation **[9626]**
    Tennessee Folklore Soc. **[9627]**
Folk Alliance **[9619]**, 510 S Main St., 1st Fl., Memphis, TN 38103, (901)522-1170
Folk Alliance Intl. **[9619]**, 510 S Main St., 1st Fl., Memphis, TN 38103, (901)522-1170
Folk Art Soc. of Am. **[9620]**, PO Box 17041, Richmond, VA 23226-7041, (804)285-4532
Folk Coll. Assn. of Am. **[★8031]**
Folk Educ. Assn. of Am. **[★8031]**
Folk Music
    Natl. Traditional Country Music Assn. **[10265]**
Folk Music Soc. of Ireland **[IO]**, Dublin, Ireland
Folk-School Assn. of Am. **[★8031]**
FolkArts England **[IO]**, Matlock, United Kingdom
Folkbildningsradet **[★IO]**
Folkecenter for Vedvarende Energi **[★IO]**
Folkkampanjen Mot KarnKraft-Karnvapen **[★IO]**
Folklore Canada Intl. **[IO]**, Montreal, QC, Canada
Folklore Soc. **[IO]**, London, United Kingdom
Folkus **[IO]**, Fleetwood, United Kingdom
Follow A Dream **[11787]**, 381 Old Falmouth Rd., Marstons Mills, MA 02648, (508)420-8319
Fondacioni Shoqeria e Hapur per Shqiperine **[★IO]**
Fondation canadienne de recherche sur le cancer de la prostate **[★IO]**
Fondation canadienne des etudes ukrainiennes **[★IO]**

Fondation canadienne de la fibrose kystique **[★IO]**
Fondation Aga Khan Canada **[★IO]**
Fondation Asie Pacifique du Canada **[★IO]**
Fondation du Basket-Ball Dr. James Naismith **[★IO]**
Fondation Bonderjnstichting **[★IO]**
Fondation Canada Ouest **[★IO]**
Fondation Canada-Scandinavie **[★IO]**
Fondation Canadiene du Foie **[★IO]**
Fondation Canadienne des tumeurs cerebrales **[★IO]**
Fondation Canadienne pour les Ameriques **[★IO]**
Fondation Canadienne du Cancer du Sein **[★IO]**
Fondation Canadienne des Champs de Bataille **[★IO]**
Fondation Canadienne d'Ergotherapie **[★IO]**
Fondation Canadienne pour le Developpement de Carriere **[★IO]**
Fondation Canadienne des Femmes **[★IO]**
Fondation Canadienne un Monde de Reves **[★IO]**
Fondation Canadienne Pour La Securite dans les Ascenseurs et escaliers mechaniques **[★IO]**
Fondation Canadienne de la Recherche en Dietetique **[★IO]**
Fondation Canadienne Reves d'Enfants **[★IO]**
Fondation canadienne d'education economique **[★IO]**
Fondation Europeene Charcot **[★IO]**
Fondation Europeenne de la Culture **[★IO]**
Fondation Europeenne pour le Developpement du Mgt. **[★IO]**
Fondation Fauna **[★IO]**
Fondation Frontiere **[★IO]**
Fondation des Infirmieres et Infirmiers du Canada **[★IO]**
Fondation Internationale pour la Gestion de la Faune **[★IO]**
Fondation Internationale Lelio Basso pour le Droit et la Liberation des Peuples **[★IO]**
Fondation ISREC **[★IO]**
Fondation canadienne de l'ouie **[★IO]**
Fondation Louis Jeantet **[IO]**, Geneva, Switzerland
Fondation de la Maison de la Chimie **[IO]**, Paris, France
Fondation Natl. des Realisations autochtones **[★IO]**
Fondation Recherche Medicale **[★IO]**
Fondation de Recherches sur les Blessures de la Route **[★IO]**
Fondation Scolaire de l'Institut Canadien du Credit **[★IO]**
Fondation du Scoutisme Mondial **[★IO]**
Fondation canadienne de recherche sur le SIDA **[★IO]**
Fondation Suisse pour la sante sexuelle at reproductive **[★IO]**
Fondation Universitaire **[★IO]**
Fondazione Africana per la Medicina e la Ricerca **[★IO]**
Fondazione Giovanni Agnelli **[★IO]**
Fondazione Russolo-Pratella **[IO]**, Varese, Italy
Fondo Ecuatoriano Populorum Progressio **[IO]**, Quito, Ecuador
Fondo Nacional de las Artes **[★IO]**
Fondo de Poblacion de las Naciones Unidas **[★IO]**
Fondo de Poblacion de las Naciones Unidas **[★IO]**
Fondo de Poblacion de las Naciones Unidas Costa Rica **[★IO]**
Fondo de Poblacion de las Naciones Unidas - Republica Dominicana **[★IO]**
Fondos Internacionales de Indemnizacion de Danos Debidos a la Contaminacion por Hidrocarburos **[★IO]**
Fonds Canadien pour la paix **[★IO]**
Fonds Europeen pour la Jeunesse **[★IO]**
Fonds zur Forderung der Wissenschaftlichen Forschung **[★IO]**
Fonds Mondial pour la Nature **[★IO]**
Fonds des Nations Unies pour la Population Benin **[★IO]**
Food
    Allied Trades of the Baking Indus. **[385]**
    Amer. Assn. of Candy Technologists **[6868]**
    Amer. Assn. of Nutritional Consultants **[15814]**
    Amer. Bd. of Nutrition **[15815]**
    Amer. Celiac Society | Dietary Support Coalition **[15817]**

    Amer. Frozen Food Inst. **[1371]**
    Amer. Inst. of Food Distribution **[1372]**
    Amer. Inst. of Food Distribution **[1372]**
    Amer. Meat Sci. Assn. **[6869]**
    Amer. Outreach to Ethiopia **[12265]**
    Amer. Soc. for Clinical Nutrition **[15821]**
    Amer. Soc. of Sugar Beet Technologists **[6870]**
    Amer. Spice Trade Assn. **[1373]**
    Amer. Sugar Alliance **[1374]**
    Amer. Wholesale Marketers Assn. **[1375]**
    Animal Agriculture Alliance **[1376]**
    Asian Chefs Assn. **[736]**
    Assn. for Dressings and Sauces **[1377]**
    Assn. of Food Indus. **[1378]**
    Assn. for the Stud. of Food and Soc. **[6871]**FoodAustralian Food and Grocery Coun.
    Beef Improvement Fed. **[6872]**
    California Melon Res. Bd. **[4439]**
    Calorie Control Coun. **[1379]**
    Center for Food Safety **[6873]**
    Chinese Amer. Food Soc. **[6874]**
    Cocoa Merchants' Assn. of Am. **[1380]**
    Concord Grape Assn. **[4445]**
    Confrerie de la Chaine des Rotisseurs, Bailliage des U.S.A. **[21845]**
    Corn Refiners Assn. **[1381]**
    The Dinner Garden **[12269]**
    End Childhood Hunger **[12271]**
    Farmers Market Coalition **[3731]**
    Fight Against Hunger Org. **[12274]**
    Flavor and Extract Mfrs. Assn. of the U.S. **[1382]**
    Food-Aid **[12275]**
    Food Alliance **[6875]**
    Food Distribution Res. Soc. **[6876]**
    Food Ingredient Distributors Assn. **[1383]**
    Food Inst. **[1384]**
    Food Inst. **[1384]**
    Food Res. and Action Center **[12278]**
    Food Safety Consortium **[1385]**
    Food Shippers Assn. of North Am. **[1386]**
    Food Trade Sustainability Leadership Assn. **[1387]**
    Food and Water Watch **[17695]**
    Fresh Produce Assn. of the Americas **[1388]**
    Fresh Produce Exporters' Assn. of Kenya **[17936]**
    Fresh Produce and Floral Coun. **[1389]**
    Friends of Nutre Hogar **[14112]**
    German Sweets Export Assn. **[9390]**
    Global FoodBanking Network **[12281]**
    The Glutamate Assn. **[1390]**
    Greek Food and Wine Inst. **[1391]**
    Greek Food and Wine Inst. **[1391]**
    Grocery Mfrs. Assn. **[1392]**
    Guard Soc. **[1393]**
    Hazelnut Coun. **[4750]**
    Healthcare Caterers Intl. **[1394]**
    Heritage Foods USA **[6877]**
    Home Baking Assn. **[1395]**
    Home Orchard Soc. **[4453]**
    Inst. for Food Safety and Hea. **[1396]**
    Inst. of Food Technologists **[6878]**
    Intl. Coun. of Grocery Mfr. Associations **[1397]**
    Intl. Coun. of Grocery Mfr. Associations **[1397]**
    Intl. Dairy-Deli-Bakery Assn. **[1398]**
    Intl. Dairy-Deli-Bakery Assn. **[1398]**
    Intl. Fed. of Competitive Eating **[22982]**
    Intl. Food and Agribusiness Mgt. Assn. **[1399]**
    Intl. Food and Agribusiness Mgt. Assn. **[1399]**
    Intl. Food Info. Coun. **[1400]**
    Intl. Foodservice Mfrs. Assn. **[1401]**
    Intl. Foodservice Mfrs. Assn. **[1401]**
    Intl. HACCP Alliance **[4809]**
    Intl. Jelly and Preserve Assn. **[1402]**
    Intl. Jelly and Preserve Assn. **[1402]**
    Intl. Maple Syrup Inst. **[1403]**
    Intl. Maple Syrup Inst. **[1403]**
    Intl. Stevia Coun. **[1404]**
    Intl. Wheat Gluten Assn. **[1405]**
    Intl. Wheat Gluten Assn. **[1405]**
    Islamic Food and Nutrition Coun. of Am. **[1406]**
    Islamic Food and Nutrition Coun. of Am. **[1406]**
    Italian Wine and Food Inst. **[1407]**
    Joint Labor Mgt. Comm. of the Retail Food Indus. **[23190]**
    Kitchen Gardeners Intl. **[9628]**

A star before a book entry number signifies that the name is not listed separately, but is mentioned within the entry.

Kitchen Gardeners Intl. [9628]
Les Amis d'Escoffier Soc. of New York [1408]
Les Amis d'Escoffier Soc. of New York [1408]
Meds and Food for Kids [11348]
Move For Hunger [12285]
Natl. Alliance for Food Safety and Security [1409]
Natl. Assn. of Bionutritionists [15839]
Natl. Assn. of Cocoa Exporters [3301]
Natl. Assn. of Flavors and Food-Ingredient
    Systems [1410]
Natl. Assn. of Flour Distributors [1411]
Natl. Assn. of Pizzeria Operators [1762]
Natl. Assn. for the Specialty Food Trade [1412]
Natl. Barbecue Assn. [1413]
Natl. Chamber of the Restaurant and Seasoned
    Food Indus. [18416]
Natl. Coalition for Food and Agricultural Res.
    [3744]
Natl. Confectioners Assn. of the U.S. [1414]
Natl. Country Ham Assn. [1415]
Natl. Fisheries Inst. [3184]
Natl. Frozen Pizza Inst. [1416]
Natl. Frozen and Refrigerated Foods Assn. [1417]
Natl. Honey Bd. [1418]
Natl. Honey Packers and Dealers Assn. [1419]
Natl. Pasta Assn. [1420]
Natl. Poultry and Food Distributors Assn. [1421]
Natl. Yogurt Assn. [1025]
Network of Ingredient Marketing Specialists
    [1422]
North Amer. Natural Casing Assn. [1423]
North Amer. Natural Casing Assn. [1423]
Northern Ireland Food and Drink Assn. [16041]
OrganicAthlete [22232]
Panamanian Food Retailers and Distributors
    Assn. [11184]
Partnership for Food Safety Educ. [14542]
Peanut and Tree Nut Processors Assn. [1424]
Pickle Packers Intl. [1425]
Pickle Packers Intl. [1425]
PMCA: An Intl. Assn. of Confectioners [1426]
PMCA: An Intl. Assn. of Confectioners [1426]
Popcorn Bd. [1427]
Quality Chekd Dairies [1026]
Refrigerated Foods Assn. [1428]
Res. and Development Associates for Military
    Food and Packaging Systems [6879]
Retail Confectioners Intl. [1429]
Retail Confectioners Intl. [1429]
rock CAN roll [12289]
Rotarian Action Gp. for the Alleviation of Hunger
    and Malnutrition [12290]
Senior Gleaners [12291]
Snack Food Assn. [1430]
Southeastern Fisheries Assn. [3190]
Spoons Across Am. [15845]
Sugar Assn. [1431]
Sugar Indus. Technologists [6880]
Sugar Indus. Technologists [6880]
Tortilla Indus. Assn. [1432]
Tortilla Indus. Assn. [1432]
True Food Network [6881]
UniPro Foodservice [1433]
United Food and Commercial Workers Intl. Union
    [23191]
U.S. Beet Sugar Assn. [1434]
U.S. Canola Assn. [1435]
Urban Farming [4366]
U.S.A. Harvest [12298]
Vinegar Inst. [1436]
Food Additives and Ingredients Assn. [IO], Maid-
    stone, United Kingdom
Food Additives Mfrs'. and Traders' Assn. [IO], Barce-
    lona, Spain
Food and Agriculture Org. of the United Nations [IO],
    Rome, Italy
Food and Agriculture Org. of the United Nations -
    Regional Off. for Europe [IO], Budapest, Hungary
Food and Agriculture Org. of the United Nations -
    Regional Off. for Latin Am. and the Caribbean [IO],
    Santiago, Chile
Food and Agriculture Org. of the United Nations -
    Trinidad and Tobago [IO], Port of Spain, Trinidad
    and Tobago
Food-Aid [12275], PO Box 21062, Raleigh, NC
    27619-1062

Food-Aid [12275], PO Box 21062, Raleigh, NC
    27619-1062
Food Aid Comm. [IO], London, United Kingdom
Food Allergy and Anaphylaxis Network [13639],
    11781 Lee Jackson Hwy., Ste. 160, Fairfax, VA
    22033, (703)691-3179
Food Allergy Initiative [13640], 515 Madison Ave.,
    Ste. 1912, New York, NY 10022-5403, (212)207-
    1974
Food Allergy Network [★13639]
Food Alliance [6875], 1829 NE Alberta, Ste. 5,
    Portland, OR 97211, (503)493-1066
Food Animal Concerns Trust [4690], 3525 W Peter-
    son Ave., Ste. 213, Chicago, IL 60659-3314,
    (773)525-4952
Food Banks Canada [IO], Toronto, ON, Canada
Food Beverage Canada [IO], Edmonton, AB,
    Canada
Food and Beverage Importers Assn. [IO], Carlton,
    Australia
Food Brokers Assn. [★1378]
Food Bus. Forum [★3101]
Food Bus. Forum [★3101]
Food Business Forum [★3101]
Food and Consumer Products of Canada [IO], Tor-
    onto, ON, Canada
Food Distribution Res. Soc. [6876], Rodney Hol-
    comb, Membership VP, Oklahoma State Univ.,
    Dept. of Agricultural Economics, Food &
    Agricultural Products Center, 114 Food &
    Agricultural Products Center, Stillwater, OK 74078,
    (405)744-6272
Food Distributors Intl. - Defunct.
Food and Drink Fed. - England [IO], London, United
    Kingdom
Food and Drink Indus. Ireland [IO], Dublin, Ireland
Food and Drug Admin. Alumni Assn. [17697], 1101
    17th St. NW, Ste. 412, Washington, DC 20036,
    (202)331-0651
Food and Drug Law Inst. [5461], 1155 15th St. NW,
    Ste. 800, Washington, DC 20005, (202)371-1420
Food and Drugs
    Alliance for a Stronger FDA [17696]
    Assn. of Food and Drug Officials [5460]
    Coalition for Anabolic Steroid Precursor and
        Ephedra Regulation [16718]
    Food and Drug Admin. Alumni Assn. [17697]
    Food and Drug Law Inst. [5461]
    Intl. Assn. for Food Protection [5462]
    Intl. Assn. for Food Protection [5462]
    Intl. Assn. of Milk Control Agencies [5463]
    Intl. Assn. of Milk Control Agencies [5463]
    Intl. Narcotic Enforcement Officers Assn. [5464]
    Intl. Narcotic Enforcement Officers Assn. [5464]
    Intl. Narcotics Interdiction Assn. [5465]
    Intl. Narcotics Interdiction Assn. [5465]
    Natl. Assn. of Pharmaceutical Representatives
        [2697]
    Pharmaceutical Indus. Labor-Management Assn.
        [2700]
Food Editors Club Deutschland [IO], Munich,
    Germany
Food and Energy Coun. [★6753]
Food Equipment
    Commercial Food Equip. Ser. Assn. [1437]
    FISA [1438]
    Foodservice Equip. Distributors Assn. [1439]
    Mfrs'. Agents for the Foodservice Indus. [1440]
    North Amer. Assn. of Food Equip. Mfrs. [1441]
Food and Fertilizer Tech. Center for the Asian and
    Pacific Region [IO], Taipei, Taiwan
Food First [★17873]
Food First [★17873]
Food for the Hungry [12276], 1224 E Washington
    St., Phoenix, AZ 85034-1102, (480)998-3100
Food for the Hungry Canada [IO], Abbotsford, BC,
    Canada
Food for the Hungry - UK [IO], Beaconsfield, United
    Kingdom
Food Importers' Assn. [IO], Istanbul, Turkey
Food Indus. Suppliers Assn. [★1438]
Food Indus. Assn. Executives [3103], 5657 W 10770
    N, Highland, UT 84003, (801)599-1095
Food Industry Club of Florida - Defunct.
Food Ingredient Distributors Assn. [1383], 4646 W
    Jefferson, Ste. 200, Fort Wayne, IN 46804,
    (260)432-3033

Food Inst. [1384], 10 Mountainview Rd., Ste. S125,
    Upper Saddle River, NJ 07458, (201)791-5570
Food Inst. [1384], 10 Mountainview Rd., Ste. S125,
    Upper Saddle River, NJ 07458, (201)791-5570
Food Law Inst. [★5461]
Food for Life Global [12838], PO Box 59037, Poto-
    mac, MD 20859, (301)987-5883
Food for Life Global [12838], PO Box 59037, Poto-
    mac, MD 20859, (301)987-5883
Food Marketing Inst. [3104], 2345 Crystal Dr., Ste.
    800, Arlington, VA 22202-4801, (202)452-8444
Food and Nutrition Bd. [15832], Inst. of Medicine,
    500 5th St. NW, Washington, DC 20001, (202)334-
    1732
Food for the Poor [12726], 6401 Lyons Rd., Dept.
    9662, Coconut Creek, FL 33073, (954)427-2222
Food for the Poor [12726], 6401 Lyons Rd., Dept.
    9662, Coconut Creek, FL 33073, (954)427-2222
Food Processing Suppliers Assn. [1020], 1451 Dol-
    ley Madison Blvd., Ste. 101, McLean, VA 22101-
    3847, (703)761-2600
Food Processing Suppliers Assn. [1020], 1451 Dol-
    ley Madison Blvd., Ste. 101, McLean, VA 22101-
    3847, (703)761-2600
Food Processors of Canada [IO], Ottawa, ON,
    Canada
Food Processors Inst. - Defunct.
Food Providers of Am. [12277], PO Box 83775,
    Phoenix, AZ 85071, (602)241-2873
Food Res. and Action Center [12278], 1875 Con-
    necticut Ave. NW, Ste. 540, Washington, DC
    20009-5728, (202)986-2200
Food Safety Consortium [1385], Univ. of Arkansas,
    110 Agriculture Bldg., Fayetteville, AR 72701,
    (479)575-5647
Food Sci. and Nutrition Network for Africa [IO], Addis
    Ababa, Ethiopia
Food Security Working Group [IO], Yangon, Myan-
    mar
Food Service
    Allied Trades of the Baking Indus. [385]
    Asian Chefs Assn. [736]
    Assn. of Correctional Food Ser. Affiliates [1442]
    Assn. of Correctional Food Ser. Affiliates [1442]
    Confrerie de la Chaine des Rotisseurs, Bailliage
        des U.S.A. [21845]
    Foodservice Consultants Soc. Intl. [864]
    Foodservice Sales and Marketing Assn. [1443]
    Healthcare Caterers Intl. [1394]
    Intl. Assn. of Culinary Professionals [1444]
    Intl. Assn. of Culinary Professionals [1444]
    Intl. Flight Services Assn. [1445]
    Intl. Flight Services Assn. [1445]
    Intl. Food Ser. Executive's Assn. [1446]
    Intl. Food Ser. Executive's Assn. [1446]
    Intl. Foodservice Distributors Assn. [1447]
    Intl. Foodservice Distributors Assn. [1447]
    Intl. HACCP Alliance [4809]
    Joint Labor Mgt. Comm. of the Retail Food Indus.
        [23190]
    Multicultural Foodservice and Hospitality Alliance
        [1448]
    Natl. Assn. of Church Food Ser. [1449]
    Natl. Assn. of Coll. and Univ. Food Services
        [1450]
    Natl. Assn. of Concessionaires [1451]
    Natl. Assn. of Pizzeria Operators [1762]
    Natl. Food Ser. Mgt. Inst. [1452]
    Natl. Independent Concessionaires Assn. [1453]
    Restaurant Marketing and Delivery Assn. [1454]
    Soc. for Foodservice Mgt. [1455]
    Women's Foodservice Forum [1456]
Food Ser. Equip. Indus. [★1439]
Food Ser. Executives Assn. [★1446]
Food Ser. Executives Assn. [★1446]
Food Service Marketing Inst. - Defunct.
Food Shippers Assn. of North Am. [1386], 12334 SE
    23rd Pl., Bellevue, WA 98005, (425)649-0555
Food Storage and Distribution Fed. [IO], Reading,
    United Kingdom
Food Trade Sustainability Leadership Assn. [1387],
    PO Box 51267, Eugene, OR 97405, (541)852-
    0745
Food Tray and Bd. Assn. [★1041]
Food and Water Watch [17695], 1616 P St. NW,
    Ste. 300, Washington, DC 20036, (202)683-2500

Reference to "IO" in place of a book number signifies that the association may be found in the 50th edition of International Organizations.

FoodFirst Info. and Action Network [IO], Heidelberg, Germany
Foodservice Consultants Soc. Intl. [864], 455 S 4th St., Ste. 650, Louisville, KY 40202, (502)583-3783
Foodservice Consultants Soc. Intl. [864], 455 S 4th St., Ste. 650, Louisville, KY 40202, (502)583-3783
Foodservice Equip. Distributors Assn. [1439], 2250 Point Blvd., Ste. 200, Elgin, IL 60123-7887, (224)293-6500
Foodservice Gp. [3160], PO Box 681864, Marietta, GA 30068, (770)971-8116
Foodservice Gp. [3160], PO Box 681864, Marietta, GA 30068, (770)971-8116
Foodservice and Lodging Inst. [★1765]
Foodservice Org. of Distributors [★1417]
FoodService Packaging Assn. [IO], Oxon, United Kingdom
Foodservice and Packaging Inst. [1041], 201 Park Washington Ct., Falls Church, VA 22046, (703)538-3552
Foodservice Sales and Marketing Assn. [1443], 9192 Red Br. Rd., Ste. 200, Columbia, MD 21045, (410)715-4084
Football
Amer. Football Coaches Assn. [22585]
Amer. Youth Football and Cheer [22586]
Australian Football Assn. of North Am. [22587]
Coun. of Ivy Gp. Presidents [22975]
Football Writers Assn. of Am. [22588]
Intl. Women's Flag Football Assn. [22589]
Natl. Football Found. and Coll. Hall of Fame [22590]
Natl. Football League [22591]
Natl. Football League Alumni [22592]
North Amer. Football League [22593]
North Amer. Football League [22593]
Pop Warner Little Scholars [22594]
Professional Football Chiropractic [14143]
Professional Football Players Mothers' Assn. [22595]
Professional Football Researchers Assn. [22596]
Professional Football Writers of Am. [22597]
Southeastern Conf. [23006]
Union Youth Football Assn. [22598]
U.S. Flag Football for the Deaf [22530]
U.S. Flag Football League [22599]
U.S. Flag and Touch Football League [22600]
U.S. Football Alliance [22601]
U.S.A. Football [22602]
Football Assn. of the Czech Republic [IO], Prague, Czech Republic
Football Assn. of England [IO], London, United Kingdom
Football Assn. of Iceland [IO], Reykjavik, Iceland
Football Assn. of Iranian Clubs [IO], Tehran, Iran
Football Assn. of Ireland [IO], Dublin, Ireland
Football Assn. of Moldova [IO], Chisinau, Moldova
Football Assn. of Wales [IO], Cardiff, United Kingdom
Football Canada [IO], Ottawa, ON, Canada
Football Fed. of Amer. Samoa [IO], Pago Pago, American Samoa
Football Fed. of Armenia [IO], Yerevan, Armenia
Football Fed. Australia [IO], Sydney, Australia
Football Fed. of Belize [IO], Belize City, Belize
Football Fed. of the Kyrgyz Republic [IO], Bishkek, Kirgizstan
Football Fed. of Ukraine [IO], Kiev, Ukraine
Football Writers Assn. of Am. [22588], 18652 Vista Del Sol Dr., Dallas, TX 75287-4021, (972)713-6198
FootPrints for Peace [18243], 1225 N Bend Rd., Cincinnati, OH 45224, (513)843-1205
FootPrints for Peace [18243], 1225 N Bend Rd., Cincinnati, OH 45224, (513)843-1205
FootSteps: Down Syndrome Ireland [★18862]
Footwear
Boot and Shoe Travelers Assn. of New York [1457]
Chamber of the Footwear Indus. in the State of Guanajuato [14784]
Footwear Distributors and Retailers of Am. [1458]
Natl. Shoe Retailers Assn. [1459]
Pedorthic Footwear Assn. [1460]
Shoe Ser. Inst. of Am. [1461]
Soles for Kidz [19531]

Two/Ten Footwear Found. [1462]
United Shoe Retailers Assn. [1463]
Footwear Caucus - Defunct.
Footwear Distributors and Retailers of Am. [1458], 1319 F St. NW, Ste. 700, Washington, DC 20004-1121, (202)737-5660
Footwear Indus. of Am. [★199]
Footwear Retailers of Am. [★1458]
For the Fallen [12531], 1623 N Vine St., Chicago, IL 60614, (312)498-7950
For Family and Hea. Armenian Assn. [IO], Yerevan, Armenia
For Inspiration and Recognition of Sci. and Tech. [8072], 200 Bedford St., Manchester, NH 03101, (603)666-3906
For the Love of Horses [17794], 7371 Sterrettania Rd., Fairview, PA 16415, (814)474-5382
For Mother Earth [17890], 1101 Bryden Rd., Columbus, OH 43205, (614)252-9255
For Victims of War and Poverty [12455], PO Box 3418, Farmington Hills, MI 48333-3418, (877)976-6754
For Victims of War and Poverty [12455], PO Box 3418, Farmington Hills, MI 48333-3418, (877)976-6754
Foragers Cosmetic Indus. Associates - Address unknown since 2010.
Foraminiferal Res; Cushman Found. for [7210]
Foras Oiliuna agus Forbartha Eireann [★IO]
FORATOM: Assn. of European Atomic Forums [IO], Brussels, Belgium
Forbes Norris MDA/ALS Res. Center [15590], 2324 Sacramento St., Ste. 150, San Francisco, CA 94115, (415)600-3604
Forbrugerraadet [★IO]
Forbundet for manskliga rattigheter [★IO]
Forbundet Blodarsjuka i Sverige [★IO]
Forbundet Djurens Ratt [★IO]
Forbundet Sveriges Arbetsterapeuter [★IO]
Force 5 Class Assn. [22336], Nancy Stutzman, Sec., 3438 Scupper Run SE, Southport, NC 28461
Force Recon Assn. [20719], PO Box 425, Rowe, MA 01367
FORCES Intl. [17829], PO Box 4267, Kaneohe, HI 96744, (808)721-8384
Ford
Cobra Owners Club of Am. [21032]
Ford/Fordson Collectors Assn. [22175]
Model A Ford Cabriolet Club [21108]
Vintage Thunderbird Club Intl. [21190]
Ford Dealers Alliance [★354]
Ford/Fordson Collectors Assn. [22175], PO Box 470, Mahomet, IL 61853-0470, (217)369-4778
Ford Found. [18421], 320 E 43rd St., New York, NY 10017, (212)573-5000
Ford Found. [18421], 320 E 43rd St., New York, NY 10017, (212)573-5000
Ford Galaxie Club of Am. [21058], PO Box 429, Valley Springs, AR 72682-0429, (870)743-9757
Ford, Lincoln, Mercury Minority Dealers Assn. [★355]
Ford Madox Ford Soc. [IO], London, United Kingdom
Ford Motor Minority Dealers Assn. [355], 16000 W 9 Mile Rd., Ste. 603, Southfield, MI 48075, (248)557-2500
Ford Owners' Assn. [21059], 3875 Thornhill Dr., Lilburn, GA 30047
Forderkeis fur Internationales Wettbewerbsrecht [IO], Bad Homburg, Germany
Ford's Theatre Soc. [10578], 511 10th St. NW, Washington, DC 20004, (202)638-2941
Forecourt Equip. Fed. [IO], London, United Kingdom
Foreign Correspondents' Club, Hong Kong [IO], Hong Kong, People's Republic of China
Foreign Correspondents' Club of Japan [IO], Tokyo, Japan
Foreign Credit Insurance Assn. [1959], 125 Park Ave., 14th Fl., New York, NY 10017, (212)885-1500
Foreign Credit Interchange Bur. [★2081]
Foreign Credit Interchange Bur. [★2081]
Foreign Executive Women [IO], Tokyo, Japan
Foreign Investors Assn. of Albania [IO], Tirana, Albania

Foreign Investors' Chamber of Commerce and Indus. [IO], Dhaka, Bangladesh
Foreign Mission Bd. [★20053]
Foreign Mission Bd. [★20053]
Foreign Pharmacy Graduate Examination Commn. [★16191]
Foreign Pharmacy Graduate Examination Comm. [16191], Natl. Assn. of Boards of Pharmacy, 1600 Feehanville Dr., Mount Prospect, IL 60056, (847)391-4406
Foreign Policy
Bosniak Amer. Advisory Coun. for Bosnia and Herzegovina [17895]
Captive Nations Comm. [17185]
Coalition for a Realistic Foreign Policy [17698]
Coun. on Foreign Relations [17699]
Foreign Policy Assn. [17700]
Foreign Policy Assn. [17700]
Foreign Policy in Focus [17701]
Foreign Policy Res. Inst. [17702]
Foreign Policy Res. Inst. [17702]
High Frontier Org. [18678]
Independent Diplomat [17898]
Inst. for Foreign Policy Anal. [17703]
Jewish Comm. on the Middle East [18127]
Jewish Peace Lobby [17704]
Jewish Peace Lobby [17704]
Natl. Comm. on Amer. Foreign Policy [17705]
Natl. Comm. on Amer. Foreign Policy [17705]
New Rules for Global Finance Coalition [17584]
Nixon Center [17706]
Pacific Coun. on Intl. Policy [17707]
Speakers on Asian Topics [17708]
State Dept. Watch [17709]
U.S. Off. on Colombia [17956]
William Penn House [17710]
Win Without War [18178]
World Policy Inst. [17711]
World Policy Inst. [17711]
Foreign Policy Assn. [17700], 470 Park Ave. S, New York, NY 10016, (212)481-8100
Foreign Policy Assn. [17700], 470 Park Ave. S, New York, NY 10016, (212)481-8100
Foreign Policy in Focus [17701], 1112 16th St. NW, Ste. 600, Washington, DC 20036, (202)234-9382
Foreign Policy Res. Inst. [17702], 1528 Walnut St., Ste. 610, Philadelphia, PA 19102, (215)732-3774
Foreign Policy Res. Inst. [17702], 1528 Walnut St., Ste. 610, Philadelphia, PA 19102, (215)732-3774
Foreign Press Assn. [2828], 333 E 46th St., Ste. 1K, New York, NY 10017-7425, (212)370-1054
Foreign Press Assn. [2828], 333 E 46th St., Ste. 1K, New York, NY 10017-7425, (212)370-1054
Foreign Press Assn. - Israel [IO], Tel Aviv, Israel
Foreign Press Assn. in London [IO], London, United Kingdom
Foreign Press Center Japan [IO], Tokyo, Japan
Foreign Press in Japan [IO], Tokyo, Japan
Foreign Service
Amer. Acad. of Diplomacy [5466]
DACOR [5467]
Delta Phi Epsilon, Professional Foreign Ser. Fraternity [23528]
Delta Phi Epsilon Professional Foreign Ser. Sorority [23529]
Foreign Ser. Club [★23197]
Foreign Services Res. Inst. - Defunct.
Foreign Students
Intrax Cultural Exchange [8203]
Intrax Cultural Exchange [8203]
NAFSA: Association of Intl. Educators [8204]
NAFSA: Assn. of Intl. Educators [8204]
Foreningen for Dansk Projektledelse [★IO]
Foreningen af Fabrikanter og Importorer af Elektriske Husholdningsapparater [★IO]
Foreningen Kvindelige Akademikere [★IO]
Foreningen Nordiska Pappershistoriker [★IO]
Foreningen for Open Source Leverandorer i Danmark [★IO]
Foreningen for Produktmodellering i Danmark [★IO]
Foreningen af Radgivende Ingeniorer [★IO]
Foreningen Svensk Dentalhandel [★IO]
Foreningen Svenska Kompositorer av Popularmusik [★IO]
Foreningen Svenska Verktygs-och Verktygsmaskintillverkare [★IO]

A star before a book entry number signifies that the name is not listed separately, but is mentioned within the entry.

Foreningen Svenskt Orgelbyggeri [★IO]
Foreningen af Unge med Gigt [★IO]
Foreningen af Von Hippel-Lindau Patienter [★IO]
Forensic Accountants Soc. of North Am. [27], 4248 Park Glen Rd., Minneapolis, MN 55416, (952)928-4668
Forensic Assn; Amer. [8890]
Forensic Assn; Natl. [8895]
Forensic Expert Witness Assn. [5482], 10820 Beverly Blvd., Ste. A5, Whittier, CA 90601, (562)695-4600
Forensic League; Natl. [8896]
Forensic League; Natl. Catholic [8893]
Forensic Medicine
  Amer. Bd. of Forensic Anthropology [14543]
  Amer. Bd. of Forensic Odontology [14544]
  Amer. Soc. of Forensic Podiatry [14545]
Forensic Sci. Soc. [IO], Harrogate, United Kingdom
Forensic Sciences
  Amer. Acad. of Forensic Psychology [5468]
  Amer. Acad. of Forensic Sciences [5469]
  Amer. Assn. of Police Polygraphists [5470]
  Amer. Bd. of Criminalistics [5471]
  Amer. Bd. of Forensic Document Examiners [5472]
  Amer. Coll. of Forensic Examiners Intl. [5473]
  Amer. Coll. of Forensic Examiners Intl. [5473]
  Amer. Coll. of Forensic Psychiatry [5474]
  Amer. Coll. of Forensic Psychology [14546]
  Amer. Polygraph Assn. [5475]
  Amer. Soc. of Crime Lab. Directors [5476]
  Amer. Soc. of Digital Forensics and eDiscovery [6883]
  Amer. Soc. of Forensic Podiatry [14545]
  Amer. Soc. of Questioned Document Examiners [5477]
  Assn. of Forensic DNA Analysts and Administrators [5478]
  Assn. of Forensic DNA Analysts and Administrators [5478]
  Assn. of Forensic Document Examiners [5479]
  Assn. of Forensic Document Examiners [5479]
  Assn. of Forensic Quality Assurance Managers [5480]
  Assn. of Forensic Quality Assurance Managers [5480]
  Coalition of Handwriting Analysts Intl. [6937]
  Evidence Photographers Intl. Coun. [5481]
  Evidence Photographers Intl. Coun. [5481]
  Forensic Expert Witness Assn. [5482]
  Forensic Sciences Found. [5483]
  Independent Assn. of Questioned Document Examiners [5484]
  Intl. Assn. for Identification [5485]
  Intl. Assn. for Identification [5485]
  Intl. Forensic Entomology Detection Canine Assn. [5489]
  Intl. Soc. of Environmental Forensics [6882]
  Intl. Soc. of Environmental Forensics [6882]
  Natl. Assn. of Document Examiners [5486]
  Natl. Forensic Center [5487]
  Professional Soc. of Forensic Mapping [5490]
  Soc. of Forensic Toxicologists [5488]
Forensic Sciences Found. [5483], 410 N 21st St., Colorado Springs, CO 80904, (719)636-1100
Forensics
  Amer. Soc. of Digital Forensics and eDiscovery [6883]
  Amer. Soc. of Forensic Podiatry [14545]
  Coalition of Handwriting Analysts Intl. [6937]
  Delta Sigma Rho - Tau Kappa Alpha [23754]
  Intl. Assn. for Identification [5485]
  Intl. Forensic Entomology Detection Canine Assn. [5489]
  Natl. Cyber-Forensics and Training Alliance [6884]
  Natl. Org. of Forensic Social Work [8205]
  NFHS Speech, Debate and Theatre Assn. [8898]
  Professional Soc. of Forensic Mapping [5490]
Foresight Inst. [★7501]
Foresight Nanotech Inst. [7501], 1455 Adams Dr., Ste. 2160, Menlo Park, CA 94025, (650)289-0860
Forest Action Network [IO], Bella Coola, BC, Canada
Forest Bird Soc. [4056], 10969 SW 47th Terr., Miami, FL 33165, (305)223-2680

Forest, Farm and Community Tree Network - Defunct.
Forest Farmers Assn. [★4394]
Forest Guild [4057], PO Box 519, Santa Fe, NM 87504-0519, (505)983-8992
Forest History Found. [★9765]
Forest History Soc. [9765], 701 William Vickers Ave., Durham, NC 27701-3162, (919)682-9319
Forest Industries
  Amer. Hardwood Export Coun. [1464]
  Amer. Loggers Coun. [1465]
  Assn. of Western Pulp and Paper Workers [23192]
  California Forestry Assn. [1466]
  Environmental Paper Network [4051]
  Forest Indus. Telecommunications [1467]
  Forest Resources Assn. [1468]
  Hardwood Fed. [1508]
  Intl. Wood Products Assn. [1469]
  Intl. Wood Products Assn. [1469]
  Natl. Alliance of Forest Owners [4404]
  Natl. Coun. for Air and Stream Improvement [4406]
  New England Kiln Drying Assn. [1470]
  North Amer. Wholesale Lumber Assn. [1471]
  Northeastern Loggers Assn. [1472]
  Northwest Forestry Assn. [1473]
  Northwestern Lumber Assn. [1474]
  Pacific Logging Cong. [1475]
  Pacific Logging Cong. [1475]
  Pacific Lumber Exporters Assn. [1476]
  Pacific Lumber Exporters Assn. [1476]
  Pacific Lumber Inspection Bur. [1477]
  Pacific Lumber Inspection Bur. [1477]
  Redwood Inspection Ser. [1478]
  Softwood Export Coun. [1479]
  Softwood Export Coun. [1479]
  Southeastern Lumber Mfrs. Assn. [1480]
  Southern Cypress Mfrs. Assn. [1481]
  Southern Forest Products Assn. [1482]
  Southern Pine Inspection Bur. [1483]
  Southern Pressure Treaters' Assn. [1484]
  Timber Framers Guild [1485]
  Timber Framers Guild [1485]
  Timber Products Mfrs. [1486]
  Washington Forest Protection Assn. [1487]
  West Coast Lumber Inspection Bur. [1488]
  Western Building Material Assn. [1489]
  Western Hardwood Assn. [1490]
  Western Wood Products Assn. [1491]
  WoodLINKS USA [8300]
Forest Indus. Radio Communications [★1467]
Forest Indus. Telecommunications [1467], 1565 Oak St., Eugene, OR 97401, (541)485-8441
Forest Landowners Assn. [4394], 900 Cir. 75 Pkwy., Ste. 205, Atlanta, GA 30339, (404)325-2954
Forest Landowners Tax Coun. [6009], PO Box 784, Alexandria, VA 22313-0784, (703)549-0347
Forest Network; Native [4106]
Forest Partners Intl. [4395], 302 Poplar Rd., Flourtown, PA 19031, (215)836-2114
Forest Peoples Programme [IO], Moreton-in-Marsh, United Kingdom
Forest Planters Intl. [4396], 3120 228th St. SW, Brier, WA 98036
Forest Prdt. Res. Soc. [★4397]
Forest Prdt. Res. Soc. [★4397]
Forest Products
  Alliance for Environmental Tech. [1492]
  Amer. Inst. of Timber Constr. [1493]
  Amer. Lumber Standard Comm. [1494]
  Amer. Lumber Standard Comm. [1494]
  Amer. Walnut Mfrs. Assn. [1495]
  Amer. Wood Protection Assn. [1496]
  APA: The Engineered Wood Assn. [1497]
  Appalachian Hardwood Mfrs., Inc. [1498]
  California Redwood Assn. [1499]
  Cedar Shake and Shingle Bur. [1500]
  Cedar Shake and Shingle Bur. [1500]
  Coalition for Fair Lumber Imports [1501]
  Composite Lumber Mfrs. Assn. [1502]
  Composite Panel Assn. [1503]
  Composite Panel Assn. [1503]
  Cork Inst. of Am. [1504]
  Cork Quality Coun. [1505]

  Engineered Wood Tech. Assn. [1506]
  Environmental Paper Network [4051]
  Hardwood Distributor's Assn. [1507]
  Hardwood Fed. [1508]
  Hardwood Mfrs. Assn. [1509]
  Hardwood Plywood and Veneer Assn. [1510]
  Mulch and Soil Coun. [1511]
  Natl. Hardwood Lumber Assn. [1512]
  Natl. Hardwood Lumber Assn. [1512]
  Natl. Lumber and Building Material Dealers Assn. [1513]
  Northeastern Lumber Mfrs. Assn. [1514]
  Northeastern Retail Lumber Assn. [1515]
  Wood Component Mfrs. Assn. [1516]
  Wood I-Joist Mfrs. Assn. [1517]
  Wood Products Mfrs. Assn. [1518]
Forest Products Assn. of Canada [IO], Ottawa, ON, Canada
Forest Products History Found. of Minnesota Historical Soc. [★9765]
Forest Products Soc. [4397], 2801 Marshall Ct., Madison, WI 53705-2295, (608)231-1361
Forest Products Soc. [4397], 2801 Marshall Ct., Madison, WI 53705-2295, (608)231-1361
Forest Rangers and Rangerettes [★18950]
Forest Resources Assn. [1468], 600 Jefferson Plz., Ste. 350, Rockville, MD 20852-1157, (301)838-9385
Forest School Camps [IO], London, United Kingdom
Forest Ser. Employees for Environmental Ethics [4822], PO Box 11615, Eugene, OR 97440-3815, (541)484-2692
Forest Stewardship Coun. - U.S. [4398], 212 3rd Ave. N, Ste. 504, Minneapolis, MN 55401, (612)353-4511
Forest Trends [4058], 1050 Potomac St. NW, Washington, DC 20007, (202)298-3000
Forest Trust [★4057]
ForestEthics [4399], One Haight St., Ste. B, San Francisco, CA 94102, (415)863-4563
ForestEthics [4399], One Haight St., Ste. B, San Francisco, CA 94102, (415)863-4563
Forestry
  Alliance for Community Trees [4386]
  Amer. Forest and Paper Assn. [4387]
  Assn. of Consulting Foresters of Am. [4388]
  Assn. for Temperate Agroforestry [4389]
  Avoided Deforestation Partners [4390]
  Avoided Deforestation Partners [4390]
  Coalition for Rainforest Nations [4856]
  Community Forestry Intl. [4391]
  Cork Forest Conservation Alliance [4036]
  Coun. on Forest Engg. [4392]
  Elm Res. Inst. [4393]
  Environmental Paper Network [4051]
  European Forest Inst. [7303]ForestryEuropean Tropical Forest Res. Network
  Exploring Solutions Past: The Maya Forest Alliance [6168]
  Forest Landowners Assn. [4394]
  Forest Partners Intl. [4395]
  Forest Planters Intl. [4396]
  Forest Products Soc. [4397]
  Forest Products Soc. [4397]
  Forest Stewardship Coun. - U.S. [4398]
  ForestEthics [4399]
  ForestEthics [4399]
  Growing Planet [4400]
  Growing Planet [4400]
  Intl. Assn. of Wildland Fire [4401]
  Intl. Assn. of Wildland Fire [4401]
  Intl. Soc. of Tropical Foresters [4402]
  Intl. Soc. of Tropical Foresters [4402]
  Live Oak Soc. [4403]
  Natl. Alliance of Forest Owners [4404]
  Natl. Assn. of State Foresters [4405]
  Natl. Coun. for Air and Stream Improvement [4406]
  Natl. Network of Forest Practitioners [4407]
  Natl. Wildfire Suppression Assn. [4408]
  Natl. Woodland Owners Assn. [4409]
  Neotropical Grassland Conservancy [4112]
  Planting Empowerment [4410]
  Planting Empowerment [4410]
  Rainforest Partnership [4859]

Reference to "IO" in place of a book number signifies that the association may be found in the 50th edition of International Organizations.

Redwood Region Logging Conf. [4411]
Rights and Resources Initiative [4412]
Rights and Resources Initiative [4412]
Soc. of Amer. Foresters [4413]
Soc. of Municipal Arborists [4414]
Soc. of Wood Sci. and Tech. [4415]
Tree-Ring Soc. [4416]
Trees for Tomorrow [4417]
Tropical Forest and Climate Coalition [4861]
Tropical Forest Found. [4418]
Tropical Forest Gp. [4153]
Tropical Forestry Initiative [4154]
U.S. Dept. of Agriculture | Forest Ser. Volunteers
Prog. [4419]
Western Forestry and Conservation Assn. [4420]
Western Forestry and Conservation Assn. [4420]
World Forest Inst. [4421]
World Forest Inst. [4421]
World Forestry Center [4422]
World Forestry Center [4422]
Forestry Assn. of Botswana [IO], Gaborone,
Botswana
Forestry Conservation Communications Assn.
[4059], 122 Baltimore St., Gettysburg, PA 17325,
(717)388-1505
Forestry Res. Inst. of Sweden [IO], Uppsala,
Sweden
Forever Found [11280], 1464 Madera Rd., No. 158,
Simi Valley, CA 93065, (805)304-6294
Forfeiture Endangers Amer. Rights [5318], 20 Sun-
nyside Ave., Ste. A-419, Mill Valley, CA 94941,
(415)389-8551
FORGE [12781], PO Box 14425, Santa Rosa, CA
95402, (707)529-3048
Forging Indus. Assn. [2470], 1111 Superior Ave.,
Ste. 615, Cleveland, OH 44114, (216)781-6260
Forging Indus. Educational and Res. Found. [7093],
1111 Superior Ave., Ste. 615, Cleveland, OH
44114, (216)781-6260
Forgotten Heroes [13347], PO Box 5067, Woo-
dridge, IL 60517
Forgotten Soldiers Outreach [11087], 3550 23rd
Ave. S, Ste. 7, Lake Worth, FL 33461, (561)369-
2933
Forgotten Victims [13363], 1666 Garnet Ave., No.
108, San Diego, CA 92109-3116, (877)668-4468
Forius Bus. Credit Resources [1300], 8441 Wayzata
Blvd., Ste. 270, Golden Valley, MN 55426,
(800)279-6226
Fork Lift Truck Assn. [IO], Alton, United Kingdom
ForLIFE - Defunct.
Formaldehyde Inst. - Defunct.
Formed Steel Tube Inst. [★891]
Formed Steel Tube Inst. [★891]
Former Members of Cong. [★17414]
Formerly Employed Mothers at the Leading Edge
[★11945]
Formosan Assn. for Public Affairs [18684], 552 7th
St. SE, Washington, DC 20003, (202)547-3686
Formosan Assn. for Public Affairs [18684], 552 7th
St. SE, Washington, DC 20003, (202)547-3686
Forms Mfrs. Credit Interchange [★1324]
Formula One Spectators Assn. - Defunct.
Foroige, Natl. Youth Development Org. [IO], Dublin,
Ireland
Forrester Genealogical Assn. [★20455]
Forsikringsforeningen [★IO]
Forskerparkforeningen [★IO]
Forskningscentret for Skov Landskab [★IO]
Forskningsradet for miljo, areella naringar och sam-
hallsbyggande [★IO]
Forsvars- og Sikkerhetsindustriens forening [★IO]
Forsyth County Defense League [★18785]
Fortean Soc. [★7252]
Fortean Soc. [★7252]
FORTH Interest Gp. [7298], John Rible, Treas., 317
California St., Santa Cruz, CA 95060-4215,
(831)458-0399
Fortress Study Group [IO], Somerset, United
Kingdom
Fortune Soc. [11712], 29-76 Northern Blvd., Long
Island City, NY 11101, (212)691-7554
Forty and Eight [20333], 777 N Meridian St., Rm.
204, Indianapolis, IN 46204, (317)634-1804
Forum des Activistes Contre Torture [★IO]

Forum for Activists Against Torture [IO], Kigali,
Rwanda
Forum for African Women Educationalists [IO],
Nairobi, Kenya
Forum for African Women Educationalists, Rwanda
Chap. [IO], Kigali, Rwanda
Forum-Asia: Asian Forum for Human Rights and
Development [IO], Bangkok, Thailand
Forum for Bioteknologi [★IO]
Forum for the Built Env. [IO], Nottingham, United
Kingdom
Forum for Databehandling i Helsesektoren [★IO]
Forum for Death Educ. and Counseling [★11745]
Forum on Debt and Development [IO], Amsterdam,.
Netherlands
Forum des Eglises Canadiennes pour les Ministeres
Mondiaux [★IO]
Forum Europeen des Associations pour le Patrio-
moine [★IO]
Forum Europeen de la Jeunesse [★IO]
Forum Europeen de l'Energie [★IO]
Forum Europeen de l'Orientation Academique [★IO]
Forum Europeen des Personnes Handicapees [★IO]
Forum Intl.: Intl. Ecosystems Univ. - Address
unknown since 2010.
Forum Maritime Intl. des Compagnies Petrolieres
[★IO]
Forum of Mauritian Journalists [IO], Flic en Flac,
Mauritius
Forum of Regional Associations of Grantmakers
[12666], 2121 Crystal Dr., Arlington, VA 22202,
(703)879-0812
Forum for Scriptural Christianity [19972], PO Box
132076, The Woodlands, TX 77393-2076,
(832)813-8327
Forum for State Hea. Policy Leadership; Natl. Coun.
of State Legislatures | [17766]
Forum Train Europe [IO], Bern, Switzerland
Forward Face [14198], 317 E 34th St., Ste. 901A,
New York, NY 10016, (212)684-5860
Forward in Faith North Am. [19707], PO Box
210248, Bedford, TX 76095-7248, (800)225-3661
Forward in Hea. [14777], 192 Lawrence St., Gard-
ner, MA 01440, (978)632-7846
FOSFA Intl. [IO], London, United Kingdom
Foster Care Alumni of Am. [11281], 901 N
Washington St., Ste. 208, Alexandria, VA 22314,
(703)299-6767
Foster Care Assn. NSW [IO], Stanhope Gardens,
Australia
Foster Family-Based Treatment Assn. [11282], 294
Union St., Hackensack, NJ 07601, (201)343-2246
Foster Parent Assn; Natl. [12611].
Foster Parents
Adoptee-Birthparent Support Network [10774]
Angels In Waiting [11171]
FosterClub [13522]
Friends in Adoption [10789]
Interracial Family Circle [12012]
Partners in Foster Care [12046]
Foster Parents Plan of Germany [IO], Hamburg,
Germany
Foster Parents Plan - U.S.A. [★11496]
Foster Parents Plan - U.S.A. [★11496]
FosterClub [13522], 753 1st Ave., Seaside, OR
97138, (503)717-1552
Fostering Network [IO], London, United Kingdom
Fostoria Glass Collectors [21831], PO Box 826,
Moundsville, WV 26041, (304)845-9188
Fostoria Glass Soc. of Am. [21832], 511 Tomlinson
Ave., Moundsville, WV 26041, (304)845-9188
Found. for Accounting Educ. [28], PO Box 10490,
Uniondale, NY 11555-0490, (212)719-8383
Found. for Advancement in Cancer Therapy [13922],
PO Box 1242, Old Chelsea Sta., New York, NY
10113
Found. for the Advancement of Chiropractic Educ.
[8605], PO Box 1052, Levittown, PA 19058,
(800)397-9722
Found. for the Advancement of Chiropractic Tenets
and Sci. - Address unknown since 2010.
Found. for the Advancement of Monetary Educ.
[8185], PO Box 625, FDR Sta., New York, NY
10150-0625, (212)818-1206
Found. for the Advancement of Sephardic Stud. and
Culture [19090], 34 W 15th St., 3rd Fl., New York,
NY 10011

Found. for Advances in Medicine and Sci. [14156],
111 Oweno Rd., Mahwah, NJ 07430, (201)828-
9150
Found. Against Trafficking in Women [IO], Amers-
foort, Netherlands
Found. Aiding the Elderly [17458], PO Box 254849,
Sacramento, CA 95865-4849, (916)481-8558
The Found. for AIDS Res. [13603], 120 Wall St.,
13th Fl., New York, NY 10005-3908, (212)806-
1600
Found. for Alternative Cancer Therapies [★13922]
Found. for Amer. Christian Educ. [7855], PO Box
9588, Chesapeake, VA 23321-9588, (757)488-
6601
Found. of Amer. Coll. of Health Care Administrators -
Defunct.
Found. for Amer. Communications - Defunct.
Found. for Aquatic Injury Prevention [12984], 13246
Golden Cir., Fenton, MI 48430, (800)342-0330
Found. for the Arts, Religion and Culture [★9318]
Found. for Australian Literary Stud. [IO], Townsville,
Australia
Found. for BioMedical Res. [13761], 818 Con-
necticut Ave. NW, Ste. 900, Washington, DC
20006, (202)457-0654
Found. Center [12594], 79 5th Ave., 16th St., New
York, NY 10003-3076, (212)620-4230
Found. for Child Development [11163], 295 Madison
Ave., 40th Fl., New York, NY 10017, (212)867-
5777
Found. for Children with Learning Disabilities
[★12427]
Found. for the Children's Oncology Gp. [★13915]
Found. for Chiropractic Educ. and Res. - Address
unknown since 2010.
Found. for a Christian Civilization [★19536]
Found. for Christian Theology [19708], The Christian
Challenge, 1215 Independence Ave. SE,
Washington, DC 20003, (202)547-5409
Found. for Christian Theology [19708], The Christian
Challenge, 1215 Independence Ave. SE,
Washington, DC 20003, (202)547-5409
Found. for Community Encouragement - Defunct.
Found. of Compassionate Amer. Samaritans
[20046], PO Box 428760, Cincinnati, OH 45242,
(513)621-5300
Found. of Compassionate Amer. Samaritans
[20046], PO Box 428760, Cincinnati, OH 45242,
(513)621-5300
Found. for Cooperative Housing [★12175]
Found. for Cotton Res. and Educ. [★979]
Found. for a Course in Miracles [20246], 41397
Buecking Dr., Temecula, CA 92590-5668,
(951)296-6261
Found. for Credit Education - Defunct.
Found. for Depression and Manic Depression -
Defunct.
Found. for Design Integrity - Address unknown since
2010.
Found. for Development Cooperation [IO], Brisbane,
Australia
Found. for Development of Needy Communities -
Uganda [IO], Mbale, Uganda
Found. DIAKONIA World Fed. of Diaconal Associa-
tions and Diaconal Communities [IO], Dusseldorf,
Germany
Found. for Digestive Hea. and Nutrition [14562],
4930 Del Ray Ave., Bethesda, MD 20814-3015,
(301)222-4002
Found. for Economic Educ. [18432], 30 S Broadway,
Irvington, NY 10533, (914)591-7230
Found. on Economic Trends [18618], 4520 E West
Hwy., Ste. 600, Bethesda, MD 20814, (301)656-
6272
Found. for Educational Futures
Found. for Educational Futures - Address unknown
since 2011.
Found. for Elective Mutism, Inc. [★15482]
Found. for Emerging Peoples [★12323]
Found. for Emerging Peoples [★12323]
Found. for Enterprise Development [★647]
Found. for Episcopal Colleges [★8162]
Found. for Episcopal Colleges [★8162]
Found. for Ethics and Meaning - Address unknown
since 2011.

A star before a book entry number signifies that the name is not listed separately, but is mentioned within the entry.

Found. for European Language and Educational Centres [IO], Zurich, Switzerland

Found. Europeenne [★IO]

Found. for Exceptional Children [11788], 1110 N Glebe Rd., Ste. 300, Arlington, VA 22201-5704, (703)264-3660

Found. for Exceptional Children [11788], 1110 N Glebe Rd., Ste. 300, Arlington, VA 22201-5704, (703)264-3660

Found. of the Fed. Bar Assn. [5659], 1220 N Fillmore St., Ste. 444, Arlington, VA 22201, (571)481-9100

Found. Fighting Blindness [17075], 7168 Columbia Gateway Dr., Ste. 100, Columbia, MD 21046, (410)423-0600

Found. for Fundamental Res. on Matter [IO], Utrecht, Netherlands

Found. for Glaucoma Res. [★15960]

Found. for Global Community [18244], 251 High St., Ste. B, Palo Alto, CA 94301, (650)328-7756

Found. for Grandparenting [12120], 108 Farnham Rd., Ojai, CA 93023

Found. for Hand Res. and Educ. - Address unknown since 2010.

Found. for Handgun Educ. [★17688]

Found. for Hospice and Homecare - Defunct.

Found. for Hosp. Art [13770], 4238 Highborne Dr., Marietta, GA 30066, (678)324-1705

Found. of Human Understanding [10081], PO Box 1000, Grants Pass, OR 97528, (541)956-6700

Found. for Ichthyosis and Related Skin Types [14326], 2616 N Broad St., Colmar, PA 18915, (215)997-9400

Found. for Ileitis and Colitis [★14559]

Found. for Illinois Archaeology [★6164]

Found. for Independent Higher Educ. [8288], 1920 N St. NW, Ste. 210, Washington, DC 20036, (202)367-0333

Found. Info-Turk [IO], Brussels, Belgium

Found. for Informed Medical Decision Making [15374], 40 Court St., Ste. 300, Boston, MA 02108, (617)367-2000

Found. for Innovation in Medicine [15412], PO Box 1220, Mountainside, NJ 07092, (908)272-2967

Found. for Interior Design Educ. Res. [★8332]

Found. for Intl. Community Assistance [17377], 1101 14th St. NW, 11th Fl., Washington, DC 20005, (202)682-1510

Found. for Intl. Community Assistance [17377], 1101 14th St. NW, 11th Fl., Washington, DC 20005, (202)682-1510

Found. for Intl. Cooperation [8358], 1237 S Western Ave., Park Ridge, IL 60068

Found. for Intl. Cooperation [8358], 1237 S Western Ave., Park Ridge, IL 60068

Found. for Intl. Environmental Law and Development [IO], London, United Kingdom

Found. for Investment and Development of Exports [IO], Tegucigalpa, Honduras

Found. for the Jewish Natl. Fund [★19872]

Found. for Latin Amer. Anthropological Res. - Defunct.

Found. for Latin-American Economic Res. [IO], Buenos Aires, Argentina

Found. Lib. Center [★12594]

Found. of Lower Saxony [IO], Hannover, Germany

Found. for MicroBiology [★6324]

Found. for Middle East Peace [18122], 1761 N St. NW, Washington, DC 20036, (202)835-3650

Found. for Middle East Peace [18122], 1761 N St. NW, Washington, DC 20036, (202)835-3650

Found. of Motion Picture Pioneers - Defunct.

Found. for Nager and Miller Syndromes [14598], 13210 SE 342nd St., Auburn, WA 98092, (253)333-1483

Found. for Natl. Progress [18460], 222 Sutter St., Ste. 600, San Francisco, CA 94108, (415)321-1700

Found. for the New Freeman - Defunct.

Found. for North Amer. Wild Sheep [★5148]

Found. of Occupational Development [IO], Chennai, India

Found. for Pavement Preservation [847], 8613 Cross Park Dr., Austin, TX 78754, (866)862-4587

Found. for P.E.A.C.E. [18245], PO Box 9151, Asheville, NC 28815-0151, (828)296-0194

Found. for P.E.A.C.E. [18245], PO Box 9151, Asheville, NC 28815-0151, (828)296-0194

Found. for Peace - Spain [IO], Barcelona, Spain

Found. for a Peaceful Env. Among Communities Everywhere [★18245]

Found. for a Peaceful Env. Among Communities Everywhere [★18245]

Found. for People and Community Development [IO], Boroko, Papua New Guinea

Found. for the Peoples of the South Pacific [★12323]

Found. for the Peoples of the South Pacific [★12323]

Found. for the Peoples of the South Pacific - Kiribati [IO], Tarawa, Kiribati

Found. for Pet Provided Therapy; Love on a Leash - The [16861]

Found. for Physical Therapy [16850], Amer. Physical Therapy Assn., 1111 N Fairfax St., Alexandria, VA 22314-1488, (703)684-2782

Found. for the Preservation of the Mahayana Tradition [19367], 1632 SE 11th Ave., Portland, OR 97214-4702, (503)808-1588

Found. for the Promotion of Finnish Music [IO], Helsinki, Finland

Foundation for the Promotion and Preservation of Square Dancing [★9538]

Foundation for the Promotion and Preservation of Square Dancing [★9538]

Found. for the Promotion of Responsible Parenthood - Aruba [IO], San Nicolas, Aruba

Found. for PSP/CBD and Related Brain Diseases [14387], 30 E Padonia Rd., Ste. 201, Timonium, MD 21093, (800)457-4777

Found. for Public Affairs [18461], 2033 K St. NW, Ste. 700, Washington, DC 20006, (202)872-1790

Found. for Public Relations Res. and Educ. [★8765]

Found. for Rational Economics and Educ. [17438], PO Box 1776, Lake Jackson, TX 77566, (979)265-3034

Found. of Real Estate Appraisers [230], 4907 Morena Blvd., No. 1415, San Diego, CA 92117, (800)882-4410

Found. for Res. in Economics and Educ. [★17438]

Found. for Res. on Economics and the Env. [4060], 662 Ferguson Ave., Bozeman, MT 59718, (406)585-1776

Found. for Res. on the Nature of Man [★7229]

Found. for Res. and Sustainable Development [IO], Madurai, India

Found. for Revitalization of Local Hea. Traditions [IO], Bangalore, India

Found. for Safer Athletic Field Environments [22235], Sports Turf Managers Assn., 805 New Hampshire St., Ste. E, Lawrence, KS 66044-2774, (800)323-3875

Found. for Sci. and Disability [11789], 503 NW 89 St., Gainesville, FL 32607-1400, (352)374-5774

Found. for Sci. and the Handicapped [★11789]

Found. for Sci. and Indus. Res. at the Norwegian Inst. of Tech. [IO], Trondheim, Norway

Found. for Shamanic Stud. [20140], PO Box 1939, Mill Valley, CA 94942, (415)380-8414

Found. for Student Commun. [7790], 48 Univ. Pl., Princeton, NJ 08544, (609)258-1111

Found. for Stud. and Res. on Women [IO], Buenos Aires, Argentina

Found. for the Stud. of Women's Literature [IO], Bremen, Germany

Found. for the Stud. of the Arts and Crafts Movement at Roycroft [20960], 46 Walnut St., East Aurora, NY 14052, (716)652-3333

Found. for the Stud. of Independent Social Ideas [18075], 310 Riverside Dr., Ste. 2008, New York, NY 10025, (212)316-3120

Found. for the Stud. of Infant Deaths [IO], London, United Kingdom

Found. for the Stud. of Presidential and Congressional Terms [★17439]

Found. for the Support of Intl. Medical Training [15159], Intl. Assn. for Medical Assistance to Travellers, 1623 Military Rd., No. 279, Niagara Falls, NY 14304-1745, (716)754-4883

Found. for the Support of Intl. Medical Training [15159], Intl. Assn. for Medical Assistance to Travellers, 1623 Military Rd., No. 279, Niagara Falls, NY 14304-1745, (716)754-4883

Found. for Teaching Economics [7986], 260 Russell Blvd., Ste. B, Davis, CA 95616-3839, (530)757-4630

Found. for Traditional Values [18513], Student Statesmanship Inst., PO Box 80108, Lansing, MI 48908, (517)321-6233

Found. of the Wall and Ceiling Indus. [562], Assn. of the Wall and Ceiling Indus., 513 W Broad St., Ste. 210, Falls Church, VA 22046, (703)538-1600

Found. for Wild Life Argentina [IO], Buenos Aires, Argentina

Found. for Women Judges [★5627]

Found. for Women's Equality [IO], Buenos Aires, Argentina

Found. for Women's Hea. Res. and Development [IO], London, United Kingdom

Found. for Women's Resources [9058], 25 Highland Park Village, Ste. 100-371, Dallas, TX 75205, (214)421-5566

Found. for Young Australians [IO], Melbourne, Australia

Foundations and Donors Interested in Catholic Activities [19423], 1350 Connecticut Ave. NW, Ste. 825, Washington, DC 20036, (202)223-3550

Foundry Educational Found. - Defunct.

Foundry Equip. Materials Assn. [★1814]

Foundry Equip. and Supplies Assn. [IO], West Bromwich, United Kingdom

Foundry Supply Mfrs. Gp. [★1814]

Fountain Pen and Mech. Pencil Mfrs. Assn. [★3356]

Fountain Soc. [IO], Bucknell, United Kingdom

Four Counties Brain Injury Assn. [IO], Peterborough, ON, Canada

Fourth Armored Div. Assn. [20364], Richard C. Schenker, Sec., 760 Crestview Dr., Sharpsville, PA 16150-8332

Fourth Freedom Forum [18167], 803 N Main St., Goshen, IN 46528, (574)534-3402

Fourth Freedom Forum [18167], 803 N Main St., Goshen, IN 46528, (574)534-3402

Fourth Marine Div. Assn. [20859], 337 Redwood Rd., Venice, FL 34293-1124

Fourth World Documentation Proj. [17891], Center for World Indigenous Stud., Chief George Manuel Memorial Lib., Fourth World Documentation, 1001 Cooper Point Rd. SW, Ste. 140, PMB 214, Olympia, WA 98502-1107, (360)450-5183

Fourth World Documentation Proj. [17891], Center for World Indigenous Stud., Chief George Manuel Memorial Lib., Fourth World Documentation, 1001 Cooper Point Rd. SW, Ste. 140, PMB 214, Olympia, WA 98502-1107, (360)450-5183

Fox Terrier Network [21565], 31415 Hawthorne St., Menifee, CA 92584, (951)672-2008

FPA [IO], London, United Kingdom

FPDA Motion and Control Network [1824], 105 Eastern Ave., Ste. 104, Annapolis, MD 21403-3300, (410)940-6347

FPWA Sexual Hea. Services [IO], Perth, Australia

Fractured Atlas [9231], 248 W 35th St., 10th Fl., New York, NY 10001, (888)692-7878

Fragile X Found.; Natl. [14616]

Fragile X Soc. [IO], Great Dunmow, United Kingdom

Fragrance Found. [1521], 545 5th Ave., Ste. 900, New York, NY 10017, (212)725-2755

Fragrance Found. [1521], 545 5th Ave., Ste. 900, New York, NY 10017, (212)725-2755

Fragrance Materials Assn. of the U.S. [1522], 1620 I St. NW, Ste. 925, Washington, DC 20006, (202)293-5800

Fragrance Res. Fund [★1524]

Fragrance Res. Fund [★1524]

Fragrances
Amer. Soc. of Perfumers [1519]
Aromatherapy Registration Coun. [13663]
Chem. Sources Assn. [1520]
European Cosmetic, Toiletry and Perfumery Assn. [18898]
Fragrance Found. [1521]
Fragrance Found. [1521]
Fragrance Materials Assn. of the U.S. [1522]
Res. Inst. for Fragrance Materials [1523]
Sense of Smell Inst. [1524]
Sense of Smell Inst. [1524]

Frame Screen Mfrs. Assn. [★1659]

Reference to "IO" in place of a book number signifies that the association may be found in the 50th edition of International Organizations.

Frame Screen Mfrs. Assn. [★1659]
France
  Dogue de Bordeaux Soc. of Am. [21555]
  France and Colonies Philatelic Soc. [22039]
  French-American Chamber of Commerce [23400]
France Amerique Latine [★IO]
France and Colonies Gp. [★22039]
France and Colonies Philatelic Soc. [22039], PO
  Box 102, Brooklyn, NY 11209-0102, (908)233-9318
France Latin Am. [IO], Paris, France
France-Louisiane/Franco-Americanie - Vivre
  l'heritage Franceil aus Etats-Unis [IO], Paris,
  France
France Macau Bus. Assn. [IO], Macao, Macao
France-United States Assn. [IO], Paris, France
Franchise Assn. of Greece [IO], Athens, Greece
Franchise Assn. of New Zealand [IO], Auckland,
  New Zealand
Franchise Assn. of Southern Africa [IO], Bedford-
  view, Republic of South Africa
Franchise Coun. of Australia [IO], Malvern East,
  Australia
Franchise Owners; Assn. of Manpower [1145]
Franchising
  Amer. Assn. of Franchisees and Dealers [1525]
  Amer. Franchisee Assn. [1526]
  Brazilian Franchising Assn. [15105]
  Culligan Dealers Assn. of North Am. [1527]
  French Franchise Fed. [14763]
  Hungarian Franchise Assn. [17240]
  Intl. Franchise Assn. [1528]
  Intl. Franchise Assn. [1528]
  Natl. Franchisee Assn. [1529]
  Natl. Franchisee Assn. [1529]
  Netherlands Franchise Assn. [3708]
  North Amer. Assn. of Subway Franchisees [1530]
  Women in Franchising [1531]
Franchising Assn. of India [IO], Mumbai, India
Franchising and Licensing Assn. Singapore [IO],
  Singapore, Singapore
Francis Bacon Found. [9364], 100 Corson St.,
  Pasadena, CA 91103
Franck Goddio Soc. [IO], Paris, France
Franco-Argentina Chamber of Commerce and Indus.
  [IO], Buenos Aires, Argentina
Franco-British Chamber of Commerce and Indus.
  [IO], Paris, France
Franco-British Lawyers Soc. [IO], London, United
  Kingdom
Franco-British Soc. [IO], London, United Kingdom
Franco-Peruvian Chamber of Commerce and Indus.
  [IO], Lima, Peru
Frank Center U.S.A; Anne [17782]
Frank Center U.S.A; Anne [17782]
Frank Lloyd Wright Assn. [7735], PO Box 4430,
  Scottsdale, AZ 85261-4430, (480)860-2700
Frank Lloyd Wright Found. [★7735]
Frank Lloyd Wright Preservation Trust [9684], 931
  Chicago Ave., Oak Park, IL 60302, (708)848-1976
Frankie Laine Soc. of Am. - Defunct.
Franklin D. Roosevelt Four Freedoms Found.
  [★10689]
Franklin and Eleanor Roosevelt Inst. [★10689]
Franklin Furnace Archv. [9176], 80 Arts - The James
  E. Davis Arts Bldg., 80 Hanson Pl., No. 301,
  Brooklyn, NY 11217-1506, (718)398-7255
Frankoma Family Collectors Assn. [21341], 1300
  Luker Ln., Sapulpa, OK 74066-6024, (918)224-
  6610
Fratelli delle Scuole Cristiane [★IO]
Fraternal Field Managers' Assn. [1960], Catholic
  United Financial, 3499 Lexington Ave. N, St. Paul,
  MN 55126, (651)765-4150
Fraternal Insurance Counsellors Assn. [★2003]
Fraternal Order Orioles [19184], PO Box 530447,
  DeBary, FL 32753
Fraternal Order of Police [19109], 701 Marriott Dr.,
  Nashville, TN 37214, (615)399-0900
Fraternitas Rosae Crucis [★19212]
Fraternite Blanche Universelle [★IO]
Fraternite Mondiale des Bouddhistes [★IO]
Fraternite Saint Pie X [★IO]
Fraternities, Service
  Alpha Epsilon [23516]
  Amer. Sociological Assn. | Honors Prog. [23738]

Beta Beta Beta [23470]
Beta Gamma Sigma [23476]
Beta Phi Mu [23583]
Beta Sigma Kappa [23611]
Delta Phi Epsilon Professional Foreign Ser. Soror-
  ity [23529]
Delta Sigma Delta [23498]
Gamma Sigma Delta [23463]
Mu Beta Psi [23601]
Natl. Block and Bridle Club [23464]
Phi Chi Medical Fraternity [23594]
Psi Sigma Phi Multicultural Fraternity [23638]
Sigma Alpha Iota Intl. Music Fraternity [23605]
Fraternities, Social
  Alpha Delta Phi [23651]
  Alpha Epsilon [23516]
  Amer. Sociological Assn. | Honors Prog. [23738]
  Beta Beta Beta [23470]
  Beta Gamma Sigma [23476]
  Beta Phi Mu [23583]
  Beta Sigma Kappa [23611]
  Beta Sigma Psi Natl. Lutheran Fraternity [23660]
  Delta Phi Epsilon Professional Foreign Ser. Soror-
    ity [23529]
  Delta Psi [23666]
  Delta Sigma Delta [23498]
  Delta Upsilon [23668]
  Gamma Sigma Delta [23463]
  Mu Beta Psi [23601]
  Natl. Block and Bridle Club [23464]
  Phi Chi Medical Fraternity [23594]
  Phi Sigma Nu Native Amer. Fraternity [23685]
  Psi Sigma Phi Multicultural Fraternity [23638]
  Sigma Alpha Iota Intl. Music Fraternity [23605]
  Sigma Alpha Mu [23693]
  Sigma Chi Intl. Fraternity [23695]
  Sigma Phi Soc. [23699]
Fraternities and Sororities
  Alpha Pi Sigma [23530]
  Assn. of Fraternal Leadership and Values [23531]
  Assn. of Fraternity Advisors [23532]
  Center for the Stud. of the Coll. Fraternity [23533]
  Delta Gamma Pi Multicultural Sorority [23739]
  Delta Sigma Chi Sorority [23741]
  Delta Tau Lambda Sorority [23742]
  Fraternity Executives Assn. [23534]
  Kappa Phi Gamma Sorority [23746]
  Kappa Psi Kappa Fraternity [23535]
  Lambda Pi Alumni Assn. [23536]
  Lambda Psi Delta Sorority [23747]
  Lambda Theta Phi [23537]
  Moose Intl. [18989]
  Moose Intl. [18989]
  Natl. Assn. of Latino Fraternal Organizations
    [18990]
  Natl. Multicultural Greek Coun. [23538]
  Natl. Pan-Hellenic Coun. [23539]
  Natl. Panhellenic Conf. [23540]
  North Amer. Interfraternal Found. [23541]
  North-American Interfraternity Conf. [23542]
  Phi Sigma Nu Native Amer. Fraternity [23685]
  Professional Fraternity Assn. [23543]
  Psi Sigma Phi Multicultural Fraternity [23638]
  Zeta Chi Phi Multicultural Sorority [23752]
Fraternity Communications Assn. [23507], 5410
  Meadowlark Ln., Cedar Falls, IA 50613, (319)504-
  5999
Fraternity Executives Assn. [23534], Sydney N.
  Dunn, Admin., 1750 Royalton Dr., Carmel, IN
  46032, (317)496-2411
Fraters van O.L. Vrouw, Moeder van Barmhartigheid
  [★IO]
Fratres Presentationis Mariae [★IO]
Frauen fur den Frieden Schweiz [★IO]
Fraunhofer-Gesellschaft zur Forderung der An-
  gewandten Forschung [IO], Munich, Germany
Fraunhofer-Information Centre for Planning and
  Building [IO], Stuttgart, Germany
Fraunhofer-Informationszentrum Raum und Bau
  [★IO]
FRAXA, the Fragile X Res. Found. [★16769]
FRAXA Res. Found. [16769], 45 Pleasant St., New-
  buryport, MA 01950, (978)462-1866
Fred Bear Sports Club - Defunct.
Fred Hollows Found. - Australia [IO], Alexandria,
  Australia

Fred Hollows Found. - Vietnam [IO], Da Nang,
  Vietnam
Frederick A. Cook Soc. [10659], Sullivan County
  Museum, PO Box 247, Hurleyville, NY 12747,
  (845)434-8044
Frederick Chopin Soc. [IO], Warsaw, Poland
Frederick Law Olmsted Assn. - Defunct.
Fredericton Northwest Constr. Assn. [IO], Frederic-
  ton, NB, Canada
Fredrika - Bremer - Assn. [IO], Stockholm, Sweden
Fredrika - Bremer - Forbundet [★IO]
Free Beaches Coalition [★10342]
Free Beaches Documentation Center [★10343]
Free Beaches Info. Center [★10343]
Free Cong. Found. [18333], 1423 Powhatan St., No.
  2, Alexandria, VA 22314, (703)837-0030
Free Democratic Party [IO], Berlin, Germany
Free Democratic Party of Switzerland [IO], Bern,
  Switzerland
Free Enterprise
  Amer. Bus. Conf. [17712]
  Americanism Educational League [17713]
  America's Future [17714]
  Center for the Defense of Free Enterprise [17715]
  Fisher Inst. for Medical Res. [17716]
  Global Envision [17717]
  Global Envision [17717]
  The Heritage Found. [17718]
  Natl. Center for Constr. Educ. and Res. [17719]
  Natl. Coun. for Public-Private Partnerships
    [17720]
  Natl. Journalism Center [17721]
  Private Enterprise Res. Center [17722]
  Professional Services Coun. [17723]
  Students in Free Enterprise [17724]
  U.S. Bus. and Indus. Coun. [17725]
  World Growth [2079]
Free Enterprise Legal Defense Fund - Address
  unknown since 2010.
Free Europe [★17355]
Free Expression
  Amer. Civil Liberties Union [17260]
  Natl. Freedom of Info. Coalition [18437]
  PEN Center USA [10731]
Free Expression Policy Proj. [17290], 170 W 76 St.,
  No. 301, New York, NY 10023
Free the Fathers [17239], PO Box 85, Signal
  Mountain, TN 37377-0085, (423)886-2373
Free Geek [12769], Community Tech. Center, 1731
  SE 10th Ave., Portland, OR 97214, (503)232-9350
Free the Grapes! [17176], 2700 Napa Valley
  Corporate Dr., Ste. H, Napa, CA 94558, (707)254-
  1107
Free Market Found. [IO], Sandton, Republic of
  South Africa
Free Minds, Inc. [19639], PO Box 3818, Manhattan
  Beach, CA 90266, (310)545-7831
Free Muslims Coalition [18143], 1050 17th St. NW,
  Ste. 1000, Washington, DC 20036, (202)776-7190
Free Muslims Coalition [18143], 1050 17th St. NW,
  Ste. 1000, Washington, DC 20036, (202)776-7190
Free Nation Found. [17730], 3713 Brentwood Rd.,
  Raleigh, NC 27604
Free Press Media [18708], PO Box 580878, Min-
  neapolis, MN 55458-0878
Free the Slaves [12234], 1320 19th St. NW, Ste.
  600, Washington, DC 20036, (202)775-7480
Free Software Found. [6486], 51 Franklin St., Ste.
  500, Boston, MA 02110-1301, (617)542-5942
Free Software Found. [6486], 51 Franklin St., Ste.
  500, Boston, MA 02110-1301, (617)542-5942
Free Speech Coalition [17224], PO Box 10480, Can-
  oga Park, CA 91309, (818)348-9373
Free Speech TV [18709], PO Box 44099, Denver,
  CO 80201, (303)442-8445
Free Store [★12727]
Free Store/Food Bank [12727], 1250 Tennessee
  Ave., Cincinnati, OH 45229, (513)482-4500
Free The Children [IO], Toronto, ON, Canada
Free Throwers Boomerang Soc. - Address unknown
  since.2010.
Free Tibet Campaign [IO], London, United Kingdom
Free TV Australia [IO], Mosman, Australia
Free Univ. Network [★7926]
Free Wallenberg Comm. - Defunct.

A star before a book entry number signifies that the name is not listed separately, but is mentioned within the entry.

Free Wheelchair Mission [11790], 9341 Irvine Blvd., Irvine, CA 92618, (949)273-8470
Free Wheelchair Mission [11790], 9341 Irvine Blvd., Irvine, CA 92618, (949)273-8470
Free Will Baptist Press Assn. - Defunct.
Freecycle Network [4870], PO Box 294, Tucson, AZ 85702
Freedom
  Action Without Borders/Idealist.org [17726]
  Action Without Borders/Idealist.org [17726]
  Advancing Human Rights [17807]
  Amer. Booksellers Found. for Free Expression [17727]
  The Amer. Cause [17728]
  Amer. Civil Liberties Union [17260]
  Amer. Civil Rights Union [17263]
  Amer. Dream Coalition [17264]
  Amer. Libyan Freedom Alliance [17513]
  Assn. for the Stud. of the Middle East and Africa [8619]
  Burmese Amer. Democratic Alliance [17213]
  Canadian Journalists for Free Expression [16750]
  Center for Inquiry [17729]
  Dalit Freedom Network [17823]
  Dalit Solidarity [17824]
  Dwa Fanm [17826]
  Ensaaf [18641]
  Exit Poverty Empowerment [11067]
  Free Expression Policy Proj. [17290]
  Free Nation Found. [17730]
  Freedoms Found. at Valley Forge [17731]
  Iran Democratic Union [17845]
  Karen Natl. League [18722]
  Natl. Hea. Freedom Coalition [14816]
  Natl. Juneteenth Observance Found. [17160]
  Toward Freedom [17732]
  Toward Freedom [17732]
  Young Americans for Liberty [18836]
Freedom to Advertise Coalition - Defunct.
Freedom Alliance [9111], 22570 Markey Ct., Ste. 240, Dulles, VA 20166, (703)444-7940
Freedom of Expression Found. - Address unknown since 2010.
Freedom Fields USA [11529], PO Box 221820, Carmel, CA 93922, (831)998-2058
Freedom Fields USA [11529], PO Box 221820, Carmel, CA 93922, (831)998-2058
Freedom Forum [17291], 555 Pennsylvania Ave. NW, Washington, DC 20001, (202)292-6100
Freedom Forum [17291], 555 Pennsylvania Ave. NW, Washington, DC 20001, (202)292-6100
Freedom Found. [5941], PO Box 552, Olympia, WA 98507, (360)956-3482
Freedom Found. [IO], Bangalore, India
Freedom From Fear [15454], 308 Seaview Ave., Staten Island, NY 10305, (718)351-1717
Freedom From Religion Found. [19608], PO Box 750, Madison, WI 53701, (608)256-8900
Freedom House [17423], 1301 Connecticut Ave. NW, 6th Fl., Washington, DC 20036, (202)296-5101
Freedom House [17423], 1301 Connecticut Ave. NW, 6th Fl., Washington, DC 20036, (202)296-5101
Freedom House/National Forum Found. [★17423]
Freedom House/National Forum Found. [★17423]
Freedom House - Ukraine [IO], Kiev, Ukraine
Freedom from Hunger [12279], 1644 DaVinci Ct., Davis, CA 95618, (530)758-6200
Freedom from Hunger Found. [★12279]
Freedom of Info. CH - Address unknown since 2010.
Freedom is Not Free [12527], 11772 Sorrento Valley Rd., Ste. 160, San Diego, CA 92121, (858)847-9999
Freedom is Not Free [12527], 11772 Sorrento Valley Rd., Ste. 160, San Diego, CA 92121, (858)847-9999
Freedom Org. for the Right to Enjoy Smoking Tobacco [IO], London, United Kingdom
Freedom to Read Found. [17225], 50 E Huron St., Chicago, IL 60611, (800)545-2433
Freedom Road Socialist Org. [5979], PO Box 1386, Stuyvesant Sta., New York, NY 10009
Freedom Socialist Party [18655], Natl. Off., 4710 Univ. Way NE, No. 100, Seattle, WA 98105, (206)985-4621

Freedom States Alliance - Address unknown since 2011.
Freedom to Travel Campaign - Defunct.
Freedom Union [IO], Warsaw, Poland
Freedoms Found. [★17731]
Freedoms Found. at Valley Forge [17731], PO Box 67, Valley Forge, PA 19481, (610)933-8825
FreedomWorks [18334], 400 N Capitol St. NW, Ste. 765, Washington, DC 20001-1564, (202)783-3870
Freelance
  Working Today [1532]
Freelance Editorial Assn. [★2825]
Freelancers Union [23317], 20 Jay St., Ste. 700, Brooklyn, NY 11201, (800)856-9981
Freeland League [★19879]
Freeman-Sheldon Parent Support Gp. [14199], 509 Northmont Way, Salt Lake City, UT 84103, (801)364-7060
Freeman-Sheldon Parent Support Gp. [14199], 509 Northmont Way, Salt Lake City, UT 84103, (801)364-7060
Freemen Inst. [★17440]
Freemuse [IO], Copenhagen, Denmark
Freestyle Players Assn. [22535], 864 Grand Ave., Box 475, San Diego, CA 92109, (800)321-8833
Freestyle Players Assn. [22535], 864 Grand Ave., Box 475, San Diego, CA 92109, (800)321-8833
FreeThoughtAction [10378], PO Box 12238, Charlotte, NC 28220, (913)660-9529
Freie Demokratische Partei [★IO]
Freier Verband Deutscher Zahnarzte [★IO]
Freight Carriers Assn. of Canada [IO], Fort Erie, ON, Canada
Freight Forwarders Assn. of the Kyrgyz Republic [IO], Bishkek, Kirgizstan
Freight Transport Assn. [IO], Tunbridge Wells, United Kingdom
Freight Trans. Consultants Assn. - Address unknown since 2011.
Freisinnig-Demokratische Partei der Schweiz [★IO]
French
  Amer. Assn. of Teachers of French [8459]
  Amer. Assn. of Teachers of French [8459]
  Berger Picard Club of Am. [21523]
  Comm. of French Speaking Societies [18991]
  Dogue de Bordeaux Soc. of Am. [21555]
  France and Colonies Philatelic Soc. [22039]
  French-American Aid for Children [18992]
  French Inst. Alliance Francaise [9629]
  Les Amis de Panhard and Deutsch-Bonnet USA [21091]
  Napoleonic Age Philatelists [22058]
  Order of the Noble Companions of the Swan [9630]
  Order of the Noble Companions of the Swan [9630]
  Pi Delta Phi [23544]
  Union Saint-Jean-Baptiste [18993]
French Acad. of Sciences [IO], Paris, France
French Activities Centre [IO], Penetanguishene, ON, Canada
French Agricultural Res. Centre for Intl. Development [IO], Paris, France
French Airedale Terrier and Various Terriers Club [IO], Heric, France
French Alpine Club [IO], Paris, France
French Amateur Fed. of Mineralogy and Paleontology [IO], Paris, France
French Am. History Inst. [IO], Outremont, QC, Canada
French-American Aid for Children [18992], 150 E 58th St., 23rd Fl., New York, NY 10155, (212)486-9593
French-American Chamber of Commerce [23400], 1350 Broadway, Ste. 2101, New York, NY 10018, (212)867-0123
French-American Chamber of Commerce in the U.S. [★23400]
French Amer. Cultural Exchange [8312], 972 5th Ave., New York, NY 10075, (212)439-1449
French-American Found. [17965], 28 W 44th St., Ste. 1420, New York, NY 10036, (212)829-8800
French-American Found. [17965], 28 W 44th St., Ste. 1420, New York, NY 10036, (212)829-8800
French Assn. of Amateurs in Micromineralogy [IO], Carry le Rouet, France

French Assn. of Banks [IO], Paris, France
French Assn. for Elecl. Equip., Automation and Related Services [IO], Paris, France
French Assn. for Info. Commun. Tech. Development [IO], Neuilly-sur-Seine, France
French Assn. of Landscape Contractors [IO], Paris, France
French Assn. for Pattern Recognition and Interpretation [IO], La Rochelle, France
French Assn. for Plant Protection [IO], Alfortville, France
French Assn. for Quality Assurance in Pathology [IO], Strasbourg, France
French Assn. for Res. on South-East Asia [IO], Paris, France
French Assn. for Standardization [IO], St.-Denis, France
French Assn. of Stud. of Competition [IO], Paris, France
French Assn. of Variable Star Observers [IO], Strasbourg, France
French Brittany Gun Dog Assn. [21566], Randy Meester, Sec., 1905 Taylor Ave., Wilton, IA 52778
French Bruneian Bus. Assn. [IO], Bandar Seri Begawan, Brunei Darussalam
French Building Fed. [IO], Paris, France
French Bull Dog Club of Am. [21567], Pat Kosinar, Sec., 2108 Inverness Dr., Lawrence, KS 66047
French Canadian Assn. for the Advancement of the Sciences [IO], Montreal, QC, Canada
French-Canadian Genealogical Soc. [IO], Montreal, QC, Canada
French/Canadian/Metis Genealogical Soc. [20628], Minnesota Genealogical Soc., 1185 Concord St. N, Ste. 218, South St. Paul, MN 55075-1150, (651)455-9057
French/Canadian/Metis Genealogical Soc. [20628], Minnesota Genealogical Soc., 1185 Concord St. N, Ste. 218, South St. Paul, MN 55075-1150, (651)455-9057
French Ceramic Soc. [IO], Les Ulis, France
French Chamber of Commerce in Great Britain [IO], London, United Kingdom
French Chamber of Commerce in the U.S. [★23400]
French Chem. Soc. [IO], Paris, France
French Comm. Against Hypertension [IO], Paris, France
French Confed. of the Paper, Cardboard and Cellulose Indus. [IO], Paris, France
French Dairy Assn. [IO], Paris, France
French Democratic Union of Labour [IO], Paris, France
French Diabetes Assn. [IO], Paris, France
French Family Assn. - Defunct.
French Fed. of Fragrance, Cosmetics, and Toiletries [IO], Paris, France
French Fed. of Haute Couture and Ready-to-Wear and Fashion Designers [IO], Paris, France
French Fed. of Insurance Companies [IO], Paris, France
French Fed. of Lingerie and Swimwear [IO], Paris, France
French Fed. of the Sporting Goods Indus. [IO], Levallois Perret, France
French Fed. of Toy Indus. [IO], Paris, France
French Fed. of Youth Hostels [IO], Paris, France
French Floorball Assn. [IO], Levallois Perret, France
French Found. for Medical Res. [IO], Paris, France
French Franchise Fed. [IO], Paris, France
French Heritage Soc. [9685], 14 E 60th St., Ste. 605, New York, NY 10022, (212)759-6846
French Inst. Alliance Francaise [9629], 22 E 60th St., New York, NY 10022, (212)355-6100
French Inst. of Intl. Relations [IO], Paris, France
French Inst. of Pondicherry [IO], Pondicherry, India
French Inst. of Social History [IO], Paris, France
French Inst. in the U.S. [★9629]
French Justice and Peace Commn. [IO], Paris, France
French-Language Assn. for the Stud. of Diabetes and Metabolic Disorders [IO], Paris, France
French League Against Epilepsy [IO], Bron, France
French Natl. Center for Sci. Res. [IO], Paris, France
French Natl. Shipowners Assn. [IO], Paris, France
French Optics Mfrs. Assn. [IO], Paris, France

Reference to "IO" in place of a book number signifies that the association may be found in the 50th edition of International Organizations.

French Orchid Soc. [IO], Paris, France
French Orienteering Fed. [IO], Paris, France
French Petroleum Inst. [IO], Rueil-Malmaison, France
French Pharmaceutical Distribution Assn. [IO], Paris, France
French Pharmacology Soc. [IO], Rouen, France
French Physical Soc. [IO], Paris, France
French Plastic Packaging Manufacturer's Trade Assn. [IO], Paris, France
French Refrigeration Assn. [IO], Paris, France
French Road Union [IO], Suresnes, France
French Rubber Mfrs. Assn. [IO], Vitry-sur-Seine, France
French Sailing Fed. [IO], Paris, France
French Soc. of Agricultural Economics [IO], Paris, France
French Soc. of Anesthesia and Intensive Care [IO], Paris, France
French Soc. of Automotive Engineers [IO], Suresnes, France
French Soc. of Cardiology [IO], Paris, France
French Soc. for Clinical Densitometry [IO], Narbonne, France
French Soc. of Dermatology [IO], Paris, France
French Soc. of Digestive Endoscopy [IO], Paris, France
French Soc. of Genetics [IO], Paris, France
French Soc. of Geriatrics and Gerontology [IO], Paris, France
French Soc. for Metallurgy and Materials [IO], Paris, France
French Soc. of Musicology [IO], Paris, France
French Soc. of Orthopaedic and Osteopathic Manual Medicine [IO], Nice, France
French Soc. of Overseas History [IO], St.-Denis, France
French Soc. of Psychosomatic Obstetrics and Gynaecology [IO], Paris, France
French Soc. for Trenchless Tech. [IO], Paris, France
French Soc. for Vitamins and Biofactors [IO], Paris, France
French-speaking Cultural Assn. [IO], Penetanguishene, ON, Canada
French-speaking Proj. Mgt. Assn. [IO], Paris, France
French-Speaking Universities Agency - Caribbean Off. [IO], Port-au-Prince, Haiti
French-Speaking Univ. Agency [IO], Montreal, QC, Canada
French Specialised Periodical Publishers Fed. [IO], Paris, France
French Trade Fairs and Exhibitions [IO], Paris, France
French Union of Petroleum Indus. [IO], Paris, France
French Vacuum Soc. [IO], Paris, France
French Vehicle Equip. Indus. Assn. [IO], Suresnes, France
French Young Men's Christian Association [IO], Paris, France
French Youth Assn. [IO], Saskatoon, SK, Canada
Frequency Coordination Sys. Assn. [IO], Ottawa, ON, Canada
Frequent Bus. Travellers Club [IO], North Sydney, Australia
Frere Independent [9232], 149 W 24th St., No. 3A, New York, NY 10011, (646)827-9205
Freres de la Charite [★IO]
Freres Maristes des Ecoles [★IO]
Freres de Saint Gabriel [★IO]
Fresh Fruit-Vegetables Exporters' Union [IO], Istanbul, Turkey
Fresh Lifelines for Youth [13523], 120 W Mission St., San Jose, CA 95110, (408)263-2630
Fresh Produce Assn. of the Americas [1388], PO Box 848, Nogales, AZ 85628-0848, (520)287-2707
Fresh Produce Consortium - UK [IO], Peterborough, United Kingdom
Fresh Produce Exporters' Assn. of Kenya [IO], Nairobi, Kenya
Fresh Produce and Floral Coun. [1389], 16700 Valley View Ave., Ste. 130, La Mirada, CA 90638, (714)739-0177
Freshfel Europe [IO], Brussels, Belgium
Freshwater Biological Assn. [IO], Cumbria, United Kingdom

Freshwater Mollusk Conservation Soc. [5057], Univ. of Oklahoma, Oklahoma Biological Survey, 111 E Chesapeake St., Norman, OK 73019
Freshwater Soc. [4791], 2500 Shadywood Rd., Excelsior, MN 55331, (952)471-9773
Fretted Instrument Guild of Am. [10198], 2501 Saddleback Dr., Edmond, OK 73034
Fretz Family Assn. [20516], PO Box 434, Kulpsville, PA 19443-0443, (610)756-6697
Freunde Nepals [★IO]
Friars Club [10579], 57 E 55th St., New York, NY 10022, (212)751-7272
Friars Natl. Assn. [★10579]
Friction Materials Standards Inst. [328], 23 Woodland Rd., Ste. B-3, Madison, CT 06443, (203)245-8425
Friedreich's Ataxia
Friedreich's Ataxia Res. Alliance [14547]
Friedreich's Ataxia Res. Alliance [14547], PO Box 1537, Springfield, VA 22151, (703)426-1576
Friedreichs Ataxia Soc. of Ireland [IO], Dublin, Ireland
Friedrich Ebert Found. - Jordan [IO], Amman, Jordan
Friedrich Naumann Found. - Africa Regional Off. [IO], Parklands, Republic of South Africa
Friend Family Assn. of Am. [20517], PO Box 96, Friendsville, MD 21531, (301)746-4690
Friendly Hand Found. - Address unknown since 2010.
Friends
Evangelical Friends Intl. - North Amer. Region [19777]
Evangelical Friends Intl. - North Amer. Region [19777]
Friends Assn. for Higher Educ. [8206]
Friends Comm. on Natl. Legislation [19778]
Friends Coun. on Educ. [8207]
Friends Gen. Conf. [19779]
Friends Historical Assn. [19780]
Friends Historical Assn. [19780]
Friends United Meeting [19781]
Friends United Meeting [19781]
Wider Quaker Fellowship [19782]
Friends-4-Cures [13923], PO Box 324, Henderson, KY 42419-0324, (866)469-2873
Friends of the Abraham Lincoln Museum [10660], Abraham Lincoln Museum, Lincoln Memorial Univ., 6965 Cumberland Gap Pkwy., Harrogate, TN 37752, (423)869-6235
Friends in Adoption [10789], PO Box 1228, Middletown Springs, VT 05757, (800)982-3678
Friends of Africa Intl. [17830], 352 7th Ave., Rm. 1226, New York, NY 10001-5012, (917)213-8710
Friends of Africa Intl. [17830], 352 7th Ave., Rm. 1226, New York, NY 10001-5012, (917)213-8710
Friends of Africa Relief and Development Agency - Sierra Leone [IO], Kenema, Sierra Leone
Friends of Alfred E. Packer in the Nation's Capitol - Defunct.
Friends of Algonquin Park [IO], Whitney, ON, Canada
Friends of Amer. Art in Religion - Defunct.
Friends of the Amer. Museum in Britain/Halcyon Found. [9112], 100 Park Ave., 20th Fl., New York, NY 10017, (212)370-0198
Friends of the Amer. Museum in Britain/Halcyon Found. [9112], 100 Park Ave., 20th Fl., New York, NY 10017, (212)370-0198
Friends of Animals [10965], 777 Post Rd., Ste. 205, Darien, CT 06820, (203)656-1522
Friends of Appropriate Technology - Defunct.
Friends of ARCC [★19389]
Friends of the Asian Elephants [IO], Lampang, Thailand
Friends Assn. for Higher Educ. [8206], 1501 Cherry St., Philadelphia, PA 19102, (215)241-7116
Friends of Astrology [6218], 208 Rosewood Ct., Westmont, IL 60559-1577, (630)654-4742
Friends of the Australian Koala Found. [5058], The Nolan Lehr Gp., Inc., 214 W 29th St., Ste. 1002, New York, NY 10001, (212)967-8200
Friends of Beethoven in Am. [★9493]
Friends of Bezalel Acad. of Arts [9897], 370 Lexington Ave., Ste. 1612, New York, NY 10017, (212)687-0542

Friends of Buckminster Fuller Found. [★10654]
Friends of Canadian Broadcasting [IO], Toronto, ON, Canada
Friends of the Cassidys [23842], 1647 Crystal Downs St., Banning, CA 92220
Friends of the Children [11283], One Penn Center, 1617 JFK Blvd., Ste. 900, Philadelphia, PA 19103, (215)575-1105
Friends of the Children of Angola [11284], 6210 Homespun Ln., Falls Church, VA 22044, (703)237-7468
Friends of Christ in India [19823], 1045 Old Acad. Rd., Fairfield, CT 06824, (203)259-5596
Friends Comm. on Natl. Legislation [19778], 245 2nd St. NE, Washington, DC 20002-5761, (202)547-6000
Friends for Conservation and Development [IO], San Ignacio, Belize
Friends Coun. on Educ. [8207], 1507 Cherry St., Philadelphia, PA 19102, (215)241-7245
Friends of Cyprus - Defunct.
Friends of Debbie Reynolds Fan Club [23767], 5713 Rosario Blvd., North Highlands, CA 95660, (916)331-0247
Friends of Dennis Lee Fan Club [23789], 1130 Summit Place Cir., Apt. C, West Palm Beach, FL 33415, (561)640-5986
Friends of the Disabled Assn. [IO], Beirut, Lebanon
Friends of the Earth [4061], 1100 15th St. NW, 11th Fl., Washington, DC 20005, (202)783-7400
Friends of the Earth - Argentina [IO], Buenos Aires, Argentina
Friends of the Earth - Australia [IO], Fitzroy, Australia
Friends of the Earth - Austria [IO], Vienna, Austria
Friends of the Earth - Brazil [IO], Porto Alegre, Brazil
Friends of the Earth - Cameroon [IO], Yaounde, Cameroon
Friends of the Earth - Costa Rica [IO], San Jose, Costa Rica
Friends of the Earth - Cyprus [IO], Limassol, Cyprus
Friends of the Earth - Czech Republic [IO], Brno, Czech Republic
Friends of the Earth - El Salvador [IO], San Salvador, El Salvador
Friends of the Earth - England, Wales, and Northern Ireland [IO], London, United Kingdom
Friends of the Earth - Europe [IO], Brussels, Belgium
Friends of the Earth - Finland [IO], Turku, Finland
Friends of the Earth - Flanders and Brussels [IO], Gent, Belgium
Friends of the Earth - France [IO], Montreuil, France
Friends of the Earth - Georgia [IO], Tbilisi, Georgia
Friends of the Earth - Ghana [IO], Accra, Ghana
Friends of the Earth - Grenada [IO], St. George's, Grenada
Friends of the Earth - Haiti [IO], Port-au-Prince, Haiti
Friends of the Earth - Hong Kong [IO], Hong Kong, People's Republic of China
Friends of the Earth - Hungary [IO], Budapest, Hungary
Friends of the Earth - Indonesia [IO], Jakarta, Indonesia
Friends of the Earth - Intl. [IO], Amsterdam, Netherlands
Friends of the Earth - Ireland [IO], Dublin, Ireland
Friends of the Earth - Italy [IO], Rome, Italy
Friends of the Earth - Japan [IO], Tokyo, Japan
Friends of the Earth - Latvia [IO], Riga, Latvia
Friends of the Earth - Luxembourg [IO], Luxembourg, Luxembourg
Friends of the Earth - Macedonia [IO], Skopje, Macedonia
Friends of the Earth - Malaysia [IO], Penang, Malaysia
Friends of the Earth - Malta [IO], Valletta, Malta
Friends of the Earth - Mauritius/Maudesco [IO], Port Louis, Mauritius
Friends of the Earth Middle East - Amman [IO], Amman, Jordan
Friends of the Earth - Netherlands [IO], Amsterdam, Netherlands
Friends of the Earth - New Zealand [IO], Auckland, New Zealand

A star before a book entry number signifies that the name is not listed separately, but is mentioned within the entry.

Friends of the Earth - Papua New Guinea [IO], Boroko, Papua New Guinea

Friends of the Earth - Peru [IO], Ilo, Peru

Friends of the Earth - Philippines [IO], Quezon City, Philippines

Friends of the Earth - Scotland [IO], Edinburgh, United Kingdom

Friends of the Earth - Sierra Leone [IO], Freetown, Sierra Leone

Friends of the Earth - Slovakia [IO], Banska Bystrica, Slovakia

Friends of the Earth - Spain [IO], Madrid, Spain

Friends of the Earth - Sweden [IO], Goteborg, Sweden

Friends of the Earth - Switzerland [IO], Basel, Switzerland

Friends of the Earth - Togo [IO], Lome, Togo

Friends of the Earth - Uruguay [IO], Montevideo, Uruguay

Friends Economic Development Assn. [IO], Phnom Penh, Cambodia

Friends Educ. Conf. [★19779]

Friends of Env. and Development Assn. [IO], Cairo, Egypt

Friends of the Everglades [4062], 11767 S Dixie Hwy., No. 232, Miami, FL 33156, (305)669-0858

Friends of Falun Gong [17240], 24 W Railroad Ave., PMB No. 124, Tenafly, NJ 07670-1735, (866)343-7436

Friends of Falun Gong Europe [IO], Harrow, United Kingdom

Friends and Families of Cannabis Consumers [18085], PO Box 1716, El Cerrito, CA 94530, (510)215-8326

Friends of Feral Felines [21250], PO Box 473385, Charlotte, NC 28247, (704)348-1578

Friends of Fiber Art Intl. [9177], Box 468, Western Springs, IL 60558, (708)246-9466

Friends of Franklin [10661], PO Box 40048, Philadelphia, PA 19106, (856)833-1771

Friends of Freddy [23804], PO Box 912, Greenbelt, MD 20768-0912, (301)345-2774

Friends of Free China - Defunct.

Friends Gen. Conf. [19779], 1216 Arch St., Ste. 2B, Philadelphia, PA 19107, (215)561-1700

Friends of George Sand [★9366]

Friends of Hea. [13677], Swankin and Turner, 1400 16th St. NW, Washington, DC 20036, (814)865-2610

Friends' Hea. Connection [21417], PO Box 114, New Brunswick, NJ 08903, (732)418-1811

Friends for Hea. in Haiti [14778], PO Box 122, Pewaukee, WI 53072, (262)227-9581

Friends Historical Assn. [19780], Haverford Coll. Lib., 370 Lancaster Ave., Haverford, PA 19041-1336, (610)896-1161

Friends Historical Assn. [19780], Haverford Coll. Lib., 370 Lancaster Ave., Haverford, PA 19041-1336, (610)896-1161

Friends Historical Soc. of Philadelphia [★19780]

Friends Historical Soc. of Philadelphia [★19780]

Friends of the Hop Marketing Order - Defunct.

Friends of Hopalong Cassidy Fan Club [23768], 6310 Friendship Dr., New Concord, OH 43762-9708

Friends of Humanity Org. of Afghanistan [IO], Kabul, Afghanistan

Friends of IBBY [★9452]

Friends-in-Art of Amer. Coun. of the Blind [9233], Nancy Pendegraph, Pres., 2331 Poincianna St., Huntsville, AL 35801, (800)424-8666

Friends of Israel Disabled Veterans [20672], 1133 Broadway, Ste. 232, New York, NY 10010, (212)689-3220

Friends of Israel Disabled War Veterans [★20672]

Friends of Israel Gospel Ministry [19748], PO Box 908, Bellmawr, NJ 08099, (800)257-7843

Friends of Israel Missionary and Relief SOC [★19748]

Friends for Jamaica - Defunct.

Friends of Jamaica USA [11285], 6417 Commonwealth Dr., Loves Park, IL 61111

Friends of the Jose Carreras Intl. Leukemia Found.

Friends of the Jose Carreras Intl. Leukemia Found. - Address unknown since 2011.

Friends of Josh Groban Fan Club [23843], PO Box 8639, Emeryville, CA 94662

Friends of Julio Intl. - Address unknown since 2011.

Friends of Karen [11464], PO Box 190, Purdys, NY 10578-0190, (914)277-4547

Friends of Kate Smith [★23866]

Friends of Kate Smith [★23866]

Friends of the Kennedy Center [9291], John F. Kennedy Center for the Performing Arts, 2700 F St. NW, Washington, DC 20566, (202)416-8301

Friends of Kenyan Orphans [11286], 920 Berkshire Rd., Grosse Pointe Park, MI 48230, (313)815-9900

Friends of LADDERS [12423], LADDERS, 1 Maguire Rd., Lexington, MA 02421-3114, (781)449-6074

Friends of the Land [★4085]

Friends for Lesbian, Gay, Bisexual, Transgender, and Queer Concerns [19791], Su Penn, Treas., 2206 Iroquois Rd., Okemos, MI 48864

Friends for Lesbian, Gay, Bisexual, Transgender, and Queer Concerns [19791], Su Penn, Treas., 2206 Iroquois Rd., Okemos, MI 48864

Friends of Liberia [13121], 4300 16th St. NW, Washington, DC 20011, (202)545-0139

Friends for Life - Defunct.

Friends of Lindenwald [9686], PO Box 64, Kinderhook, NY 12106, (518)758-3061

Friends of the Louvre Museum [IO], Paris, France

Friends of Malawi [9515], Lance Cole, Treas., 7940 SW 11th Ave., Portland, OR 97219

Friends of Malawi [9515], Lance Cole, Treas., 7940 SW 11th Ave., Portland, OR 97219

Friends of Mali [18246], PO Box 27417, Washington, DC 20038-7417

Friends of Mali [18246], PO Box 27417, Washington, DC 20038-7417

Friends of Morocco [19146], PO Box 2579, Washington, DC 20013-2579, (703)660-9292

Friends of Morocco [19146], PO Box 2579, Washington, DC 20013-2579, (703)660-9292

Friends of the Natl. Arboretum [6353], 3501 New York Ave. NE, Washington, DC 20002, (202)544-8733

Friends of the Natl. Inst. of Dental and Craniofacial Res. [14283], 1901 Pennsylvania Ave. NW, Ste. 607, Washington, DC 20006, (202)223-0667

Friends of the Natl. Libraries [IO], London, United Kingdom

Friends of the Natl. Lib. of Medicine [15413], 7900 Wisconsin Ave., Ste. 200, Bethesda, MD 20814, (202)679-9930

Friends of the Natl. Parks at Gettysburg [9687], PO Box 4629, Gettysburg, PA 17325, (717)338-1243

Friends of the Natl. Zoo [7635], PO Box 37012, Washington, DC 20013-7012, (202)633-3038

Friends of the Nemaiah Valley [IO], Victoria, BC, Canada

Friends of Nepal Assn. [IO], Rotenburg, Germany

Friends of Nigeria [19175], Peter J. Hansen, Treas., 1 Oaknoll Ct., Apt. 439, Iowa City, IA 52246, (319)351-3375

Friends of Nigeria [19175], Peter J. Hansen, Treas., 1 Oaknoll Ct., Apt. 439, Iowa City, IA 52246, (319)351-3375

Friends of Nutre Hogar [14112], 7630 N Boyd Way, Fox Point, WI 53217, (414)588-3501

Friends of Old St. Ferdinand [19424], PO Box 222, Florissant, MO 63031, (314)837-2110

Friends of the Osa [4063], 1822 R St. NW, 4th Fl., Washington, DC 20009, (202)234-2356

Friends Outside [11713], 620 N Aurora St., Stockton, CA 95202, (209)955-0701

Friends of Patrick Henry [10662], PO Box 1776, Hanford, CA 93232, (559)582-8534

Friends of Paul Overstreet [23844], PO Box 320, Pegram, TN 37143, (615)952-3999

Friends of Peace Now [★18010]

Friends of Peace Now [★18010]

Friends of Peace Pilgrim [10663], PO Box 2207, Shelton, CT 06484-1207, (203)926-1581

Friends of Peace Pilgrim [10663], PO Box 2207, Shelton, CT 06484-1207, (203)926-1581

Friends of Photography - Defunct.

Friends of the Pyrenees [IO], Ariege, France

Friends of Radio for Peace Intl.

Friends of Radio for Peace Intl. - Defunct.

Friends Religious Conf. [★19779]

Friends of Richard III [★10686]

Friends of the River [4064], 1418 20th St., Ste. 100, Sacramento, CA 95811, (916)442-3155

Friends of Robert Frost [10447], Robert Frost Stone House Museum, 121 Historic Rte. 7A, Shaftsbury, VT 05262, (802)447-6200

Friends of Roman Cats [3859], PO Box 12571, San Francisco, CA 94112

Friends of Rwanda Assn. [11287], PO Box 1311, Elk Grove, CA 95759-1311, (916)683-3356

Friends of Rwanda Assn. [11287], PO Box 1311, Elk Grove, CA 95759-1311, (916)683-3356

Friends of Sabeel - North Am. [18247], PO Box 9186, Portland, OR 97207, (503)653-6625

Friends of Sabeel - North Am. [18247], PO Box 9186, Portland, OR 97207, (503)653-6625

Friends of St. Luke's Hosp. [IO], Dublin, Ireland

Friends of the Sea Lion Marine Mammal Center [★5103]

Friends of the Sea Otter [5059], PO Box 223260, Carmel, CA 93922

Friends of the Shakers [10532], 707 Shaker Rd., New Gloucester, ME 04260, (207)926-4597

Friends of Shaun Cassidy Fan Club [★23842]

Friends of Taiwan Intl. [17945], 12 S 1st St., Ste. 205, San Jose, CA 95113

Friends of the Tango - Defunct.

Friends of Temperance [IO], Helsinki, Finland

Friends of Tent of Nations North Am. [12629], 6819 Selkirk Dr., Bethesda, MD 20817, (301)320-0049

Friends of Tent of Nations North Am. [12629], 6819 Selkirk Dr., Bethesda, MD 20817, (301)320-0049

Friends of Terra Cotta - Address unknown since 2010.

Friends: The Natl. Assn. of Young People Who Stutter [16685], 38 S Oyster Bay Rd., Syosset, NY 11791, (866)866-8335

Friends of the Third World [12728], 611 W Wayne St., Fort Wayne, IN 46802-2167, (260)422-6821

Friends of the Third World [12728], 611 W Wayne St., Fort Wayne, IN 46802-2167, (260)422-6821

Friends of Thomas More [IO], Angers, France

Friends of Togo [17966], PO Box 9436, Washington, DC 20016

Friends of Togo [17966], PO Box 9436, Washington, DC 20016

Friends of the Trees Soc. [4065], PO Box 826, Tonasket, WA 98855, (509)486-4056

Friends of Turkmenistan [11585], PO Box 75526, Washington, DC 20013-0526

Friends Union for Philanthropic Labor [★19779]

Friends United Meeting [19781], 101 Quaker Hill Dr., Richmond, IN 47374-1926, (765)962-7573

Friends United Meeting [19781], 101 Quaker Hill Dr., Richmond, IN 47374-1926, (765)962-7573

Friends of the United Nations [18746], 866 Union Plz., Ste. 544, New York, NY 10017, (212)355-4192

Friends of the United Nations Env. Prog. [★4310]

Friends of the U.S. Natl. Arboretum [★6353]

Friends of the Valley Railroad [10489], PO Box 452, Essex, CT 06426, (860)930-9880

Friends of Vieilles Maisons Francaises [★9685]

Friends of the Vietnam Veterans Memorial - Defunct.

Friends of Virgin Islands Natl. Park [4767], PO Box 811, St. John, VI 00831, (340)779-4940

Friends Welfare Assn., Pakistan [IO], Mansehra, Pakistan

Friends of the Western Buddhist Order [IO], London, United Kingdom

Friends of the Western Buddhist Order [★19374]

Friends Women's Assn. [13461], African Great Lakes Initiative, 1001 Park Ave., St. Louis, MO 63104

Friends World Comm. for Consultation [18248], 1506 Race St., Philadelphia, PA 19102, (215)241-7250

Friends World Comm. for Consultation [18248], 1506 Race St., Philadelphia, PA 19102, (215)241-7250

Friends World Comm. for Consultation - United Kingdom [IO], London, United Kingdom

Friends of the World Food Prog. [★12299]

Friends for Youth [13524], 1741 Broadway St., Redwood City, CA 94063, (650)368-4444

Reference to "IO" in place of a book number signifies that the association may be found in the 50th edition of International Organizations.

Friendship Ambassadors Found. [17967], 299 Greenwich Ave., Greenwich, CT 06830, (203)542-0652

Friendship Ambassadors Found. [17967], 299 Greenwich Ave., Greenwich, CT 06830, (203)542-0652

Friendship Force Intl. [17968], 127 Peachtree St., Ste. 501, Atlanta, GA 30303, (404)522-9490

Friendship Force Intl. [17968], 127 Peachtree St., Ste. 501, Atlanta, GA 30303, (404)522-9490

Friesian Horse Assn. of North Am. [4584], 4037 Iron Works Pkwy., Ste. 160, Lexington, KY 40511-8483, (859)455-7430

Friesian Horse Assn. of North Am. [4584], 4037 Iron Works Pkwy., Ste. 160, Lexington, KY 40511-8483, (859)455-7430

Frisbees
U.S. Disc Sports [22536]

Frisbie - Frisbee Family Assn. of Am. [20518], 1211 Dewey Ave., Evanston, IL 60202

Frog Pond - Frog Collectors Club [★21309]

From Hunger to Harvest [12280], PO Box 5466, Charlotte, NC 28299-5466, (800)481-2048

From Hunger to Harvest [12280], PO Box 5466, Charlotte, NC 28299-5466, (800)481-2048

From Us With Love [12235], 2000 Corporate Square Blvd., Ste. 101, Jacksonville, FL 32216, (800)392-8717

From Us With Love [12235], 2000 Corporate Square Blvd., Ste. 101, Jacksonville, FL 32216, (800)392-8717

Front Line [IO], Dublin, Ireland

Front Range Equine Rescue [4585], PO Box 307, Larkspur, CO 80118

Frontier Nursing Ser. [15749], 132 FNS Dr., Wendover, KY 41775, (606)672-2317

Frontiers of Am. [★11586]

Frontiers of Am. [★11586]

Frontiers Found. [IO], Toronto, ON, Canada

Frontiers of Freedom [5335], PO Box 69, Oakton, VA 22124, (703)246-0110

Frontiers Intl. [11586], 6301 Crittenden St., Philadelphia, PA 19138, (215)549-4550

Frontiers Intl. [11586], 6301 Crittenden St., Philadelphia, PA 19138, (215)549-4550

Frontline Hepatitis Awareness [14983], 701 W Elizabeth St., No. 54, Monroe, WA 98272, (360)805-1700

Frozen Food Locker Inst. [★2430]

Frozen Foods Action Communications Team [★1371]

Frozen Onion Ring Packers Coun. [★1371]

Frozen Vegetable Coun. - Defunct.

Frugi Venta [★IO]

Frugi Venta: Groenten en Fruit Handelsplatform Nederland [★IO]

Fruit Trade Assn. Netherlands [IO], The Hague, Netherlands

Fruit Wine and Cider Makers of New Zealand [IO], New Plymouth, New Zealand

Fruition Project - Defunct.

Fruits and Vegetables
Amer. Mushroom Inst. [4423]
Amer. Pomological Soc. [4424]
Apple Processors Assn. [4425]
Apple Products Res. and Educ. Coun. [4426]
Apricot Producers of California [4427]
Assn. of Fruit and Vegetable Inspection and Standardization Agencies [4428]
Australian Banana Growers' Coun. [8949]
California Avocado Commn. [4429]
California Avocado Soc. [4430]
California Canning Peach Assn. [4431]
California Cling Peach Bd. [4432]
California Date Administrative Comm. [4433]
California Dried Plum Bd. [4434]
California Dry Bean Advisory Bd. [4435]
California Fig Advisory Bd. [4436]
California Grape and Tree Fruit League [4437]
California Kiwifruit Commn. [4438]
California Melon Res. Bd. [4439]
California Rare Fruit Growers [4440]
California Strawberry Commn. [4441]
California Table Grape Commn. [4442]
Cherry Central Cooperative [4443]

Cherry Marketing Inst. [4444]
Concord Grape Assn. [4445]
Cranberry Inst. [4446]
DFA of California [4447]
Florida Citrus Mutual [4448]
Florida Dept. of Citrus [4449]
Florida Fruit and Vegetable Assn. [4450]
Florida Gift Fruit Shippers Assn. [4451]
Florida Tomato Comm. [4452]
Home Orchard Soc. [4453]
Idaho Potato Commn. [4454]
Intl. Jelly and Preserve Assn. [1402]
Intl. Soc. of Citriculture [4455]
Intl. Soc. of Citriculture [4455]
Leafy Greens Coun. [4456]
Michigan Apple Comm. [4457]
Mushroom Coun. [4458]
Natl. Cherry Growers and Indus. Found. [4459]
Natl. Onion Assn. [4460]
Natl. Potato Coun. [4461]
Natl. Watermelon Assn. [4462]
North Amer. Blueberry Coun. [4463]
North Amer. Strawberry Growers Assn. [4464]
North Amer. Strawberry Growers Assn. [4464]
Northwest Cherry Growers [4465]
Northwest Horticultural Coun. [4466]
Paw Paw Found. [4467]
Pear Bur. Northwest [4468]
Potato Assn. of Am. [4469]
Raisin Bargaining Assn. [4470]
Rare Fruit Coun. Intl. [4471]
Rare Fruit Coun. Intl. [4471]
Spanish Exporters and Mfrs. of Table Olives Assn. [20543]
Specialty Crop Trade Coun. [4472]
Sun-Maid Growers of California [4473]
Sunsweet Growers [4474]
Tomato Genetics Cooperative [4475]
Tomato Genetics Cooperative [4475]
United Fresh Produce Assn. [4476]
United Soybean Bd. [4477]
U.S. Apple Assn. [4478]
U.S. Apple Assn. [4478]
U.S. Dry Bean Coun. [4479]
U.S. Potato Bd. [4480]
U.S. Sweet Potato Coun. [4481]
Valley Fig Growers [4482]
Washington State Apple Commn. [4483]
Western Growers Assn. [4484]
Wild Blueberry Assn. of North Am. [4485]
Wild Blueberry Assn. of North Am. [4485]

FSC/DISC Tax Assn. [★2080]
FSC/DISC Tax Assn. [★2080]
FSC/DISC Tax Club [★2080]
FSC/DISC Tax Club [★2080]
FSH Soc. [15591], 64 Grove St., Watertown, MA 02472, (617)658-7878
FSM Alliance of Non-Governmental Organizations [IO], Kolonia, Federated States of Micronesia
FTD Assn. - Defunct.

Fuel
Advanced Biofuels Assn. [1533]
Advanced Biofuels USA [6108]
Algal Biomass Org. [6680]
Alliance for Green Heat [6682]
Amer. Biofuels Coun. [1534]
Amer. Biogas Coun. [6109]
Amer. Energy Alliance [17614]
Amer. Gas Assn. [4486]
America's Natural Gas Alliance [2641]
Biofuel Recycling [4867]
Biomass Thermal Energy Coun. [6697]
Citizens' Alliance for Responsible Energy [6702]
Citizens for Energy Freedom [6703]
Consumer Energy Alliance [6708]
Coun. for Responsible Energy [6709]
Domestic Energy Producers Alliance [1166]
EarthSpark Intl. [6711]
Energy Frontiers Intl. [4487]
Energy Frontiers Intl. [4487]
Energy Storage Coun. [6722]
Energy Vision [6724]FuelEurofuel
Focus Fusion Soc. [6725]
Gas Tech. Inst. [4488]
Global Biofuels Alliance [1535]

Growth Energy [6728]
HeatGreen Coun. [6113]
Hydrogen 2000 [6729]
Intl. Assn. for the Advancement of Steam Power [7480]
Intl. Biochar Initiative [6115]
Intl. DME Assn. [3770]
Interstate Natural Gas Assn. of Am. [4489]
Natl. Biodiesel Bd. [1536]
Natl. Ethanol Vehicle Coalition [4490]
Natl. Petroleum Mgt. Assn. [2663]
Natl. Propane Gas Assn. [4491]
Natural Gas Supply Assn. [4492]
New Fuels Alliance [6885]
Partnership for Advancing the Transition to Hydrogen [6748]
Pellet Fuels Inst. [4493]
Pipeline Assn. for Public Awareness [2755]
Renewable Energy Markets Assn. [1176]
Res. Partnership to Secure Energy for Am. [6752]
Set Am. Free [17619]
STG Intl. [7449]
Sustainable Biodiesel Alliance [4494]
Sweet Sorghum Ethanol Assn. [6120]
Transition U.S. [4343]
Veggie Van Org. [4872]

Fuel Cell and Hydrogen Energy Assn. [7368], 1133 19th St. NW, No. 947, Washington, DC 20036, (202)736-5738

Fuel Cell Inst. - Defunct.

Fuel for Truth [18608], 165 E 56th St., 2nd Fl., New York, NY 10022, (212)594-4435

Fuellers' Company [IO], London, United Kingdom

Fulbright Assn. [8359], 1320 19th St. NW, Ste. 350, Washington, DC 20036-1647, (202)775-0725

Fulbright Assn. [8359], 1320 19th St. NW, Ste. 350, Washington, DC 20036-1647, (202)775-0725

Fulbright Assn. of Alumni of Intl. Educational and Cultural Exchange [★8359]

Fulbright Assn. of Alumni of Intl. Educational and Cultural Exchange [★8359]

Fulbright Assn. of Uzbekistan [IO], Tashkent, Uzbekistan

Fulfillment Mgt. Assn. [2935], 60 E 42nd St., Ste. 1166, New York, NY 10165, (818)487-2090

Full Gospel Bus. Men's Fellowship Intl. [19574], 3 Holland, Irvine, CA 92618, (949)461-0100

Full Gospel Bus. Men's Fellowship Intl. [19574], 3 Holland, Irvine, CA 92618, (949)461-0100

Fullblood Simmental Fleckvieh Fed. [3912], PO Box 965, Weatherford, TX 76086, (817)776-0346

Fuller Found. [13132], PO Box 479, Rye Beach, NH 03871, (603)964-6998

Fuller Soc. [20519], PO Box 531, Boiling Springs, PA 17007-0531

Fully Informed Jury Assn. [18027], PO Box 5570, Helena, MT 59604-5570

Fund for Amer. Stud. [8484], 1706 New Hampshire Ave. NW, Washington, DC 20009, (202)986-0384

Fund for Amer. Stud. [8484], 1706 New Hampshire Ave. NW, Washington, DC 20009, (202)986-0384

Fund for Animals [10966], 200 W 57th St., New York, NY 10019, (212)246-2096

Fund for a Conservative Majority - Defunct.

Fund for Constitutional Govt. [17749], 122 Maryland Ave. NE, Washington, DC 20002, (202)546-3799

Fund for a Democratic Majority [★17533]

Fund for Dental Educ. [★7966]

Fund for Educ. in World Order [★18812]

Fund for Episcopal Colleges [★8162]

Fund for Episcopal Colleges [★8162]

Fund for the Feminist Majority [★17643]

Fund of Funds Assn. [★2135]

Fund of Funds Assn. [★2135]

Fund for Horses - Address unknown since 2010.

Fund for Investigative Journalism [17344], 1023 15th St. NW, Ste. 350, Washington, DC 20005, (202)391-0206

Fund for Modern Courts [5621], 351 W 54th St., New York, NY 10019, (212)541-6741

Fund for an OPEN Soc. [17894], 14 S Orange Ave., No. 2R, South Orange, NJ 07079, (973)821-4198

Fund for Peace [18812], 1720 I St. NW, 7th Fl., Washington, DC 20006, (202)223-7940

Fund for Renewable Energy and the Env. [★7442]

A star before a book entry number signifies that the name is not listed separately, but is mentioned within the entry.

Fund for Renewable Energy and the Env. [★7442]
Fund for Stockowners Rights - Address unknown since 2010.
Fund for UFO Res. [7249], PO Box 7501, Alexandria, VA 22307
Fundacao de Estudos do Mar [★IO]
Fundacao Grupo Esquel Brasil [★IO]
Fundacao Joaquim Nabuco [★IO]
Fundacao Pro-TAMAR [IO], Salvador, Brazil
Fundacio per la Pau [★IO]
Fundacion mujeres en igualdad [★IO]
Fundacion Acindar [★IO]
Fundacion Alfa-1 de Puerto Rico [16609], 2000 Carr. 8177, Ste. 26, PMB 318, Guaynabo, PR 00966-3762, (787)747-6270
Fundacion Alfa-1 de Puerto Rico [16609], 2000 Carr. 8177, Ste. 26, PMB 318, Guaynabo, PR 00966-3762, (787)747-6270
Fundacion Alzheimer Espana [IO], Madrid, Spain
Fundacion Ambiente y Recursos Naturales [★IO]
Fundacion Anisa, A.C. [★IO]
Fundacion Antidrogas de El Salvador [IO], San Salvador, El Salvador
Fundacion Arias para la Paz y el Progreso Humano [★IO]
Fundacion de Asistencia Sicopedagogica para Ninos, Adolescentes y Adultos con Retardo Mental [IO], Guayaquil, Ecuador
Fundacion Augusto Cesar Sandino [★IO]
Fundacion Bariloche [★IO]
Fundacion Braille del Uruguay [★IO]
Fundacion Charles Darwin para las Islas Galapagos [★IO]
Fundacion para el Desarrollo en Justicia y Paz [IO], Buenos Aires, Argentina
Fundacion Emprender [★IO]
Fundacion Eugenio Espejo [IO], Guayaquil, Ecuador
Fundacion Golondrinas [★IO]
Fundacion Hondurena de Investigacion Agricola [★IO]
Fundacion Internacional Josep Carreras [★IO]
Fundacion para la Inversion y Desarrollo de Exportaciones [★IO]
Fundacion de Investigaciones Economicas Latinoamericanas [★IO]
Fundacion Juconi [IO], Puebla, Mexico
Fundacion Mario Santo Domingo [★IO]
Fundacion Mbong [★IO]
Fundacion Mexicana para la Planeacion Familiar [★IO]
Fundacion Miguel Aleman [IO], Mexico City, Mexico
Fundacion Natura Colombia [IO], Bogota, Colombia
Fundacion Nuestros Jovenes [★IO]
Fundacion Operacion Sonrisa Colombia [★IO]
Fundacion Operacion Sonrisa Ecuador [★IO]
Fundacion Operacion Sonrisa Panama [★IO]
Fundacion Pablo Neruda [IO], Santiago, Chile
Fundacion Paniamor [IO], San Jose, Costa Rica
Fundacion Para El Desarrollo Comunitario [★IO]
Fundacion Para Estudio e Investigacion de la Mujer [★IO]
Fundacion Principe de Asturias [★IO]
Fundacion Puntos de Encuentro [IO], Managua, Nicaragua
Fundacion Sabiduria del Corazon [★IO]
Fundacion SARTAWI [IO], La Paz, Bolivia
Fundacion Uruguaya de Cooperacion y Desarrollo Solidarios [★IO]
Fundacion Vida Silvestre Argentina [★IO]
Fundacion de Viviendas Hogar de Cristo [★IO]
Fundacja Pogranicze [★IO]
Fundacja Stefana Batorego [★IO]
FUNDaFIELD [11288], 20 Alamo Springs Ct., Danville, CA 94526-1740, (925)818-0875
FUNDaFIELD [11288], 20 Alamo Springs Ct., Danville, CA 94526-1740, (925)818-0875
Fundamental Ministerial Assn. [★19720]
Fundatia Biblia Pentru Toti din Romania [★IO]
Fundatia Soros Romania [★IO]
Funders' Collaborative on Youth Organizing [12667], 20 Jay St., 210B, Brooklyn, NY 11201, (212)725-3386
Funders' Network for Smart Growth and Livable Communities [11587], 1500 San Remo Ave., Ste. 249, Coral Gables, FL 33146, (305)667-6350

Fundesarrollo [IO], Barranquilla, Colombia
Fundraising
200 Orphanages Worldwide [11172]
Amer. Charities for Reasonable Fundraising Regulation [12047]
America's Charities [12048]
Angel Covers [11190]
Assn. of Fund-Raising Distributors and Suppliers [1537]
Assn. of Fundraising Professionals [12049]
Assn. of Professional Researchers for Advancement [12050]
CancerClimber Assn. [13904]
Citizens United for Res. in Epilepsy [14518]
Community Hea. Charities [12051]
Coun. for Advancement and Support of Educ. [8013]
Direct Marketing Fundraisers Assn. [1538]
Emerging Practitioners in Philanthropy [12665]
European Assn. for Philanthropy and Giving [20453]
Giving Inst. [1539]
Golf Fights Cancer [13926]
The Grantsmanship Center [1540]
Grind for Life [11136]
H2O for Life [13422]
Hedge Funds Care [11143]
Hero Initiative [9490]
HomeAID for Africa [10812]
Independent Charities of Am. [1541]
Intimate Apparel Square Club [12052]
Ludwick Family Found. [12053]
Natl. Assn. of State Charity Officials [5491]
Partnership for Philanthropic Planning [1542]
Pioneers [12054]
Recycling for Charities [4871]
Soc. of Young Philanthropists [12685]
United Black Fund [12055]
United Way of Am. [12056]
United Way Intl. [12057]
United Way Intl. [12057]
Wine to Water [13443]
WISH List [5492]
Women, Children and Family Ser. Charities of Am. [12058]
Fundza [IO], Mbabane, Swaziland
Funeral Consumers Alliance [2533], 33 Patchen Rd., South Burlington, VT 05403, (802)865-8300
Funeral Directors Assn. of New Zealand [IO], Wellington, New Zealand
Funeral Ethics Org. [11979], 85 Upper Access Rd., Hinesburg, VT 05461, (802)482-6021
Funeral Furnishing Mfrs. Assn. [IO], Solihull, United Kingdom
Funeral and Memorial Societies of Am. [★2533]
Funeral Ser. Assn. of Canada [IO], Aurora, ON, Canada
Funeral Ser. Consumer Assistance Prog. [17459], Celine Clark Haga, Exec. Dir., 13625 Bishop Dr., Brookfield, WI 53005-6607, (877)402-5900
Funk Aircraft Owners Assn. [20897], Thad Shelnutt, Treas., 2836 California Ave., Carmichael, CA 95608, (916)971-3452
Funksjonshemmeds Fellesorganisasjon [★IO]
Fur Commn. U.S.A. [10967], PO Box 1532, Medford, OR 97501, (541)595-8568
Fur Coun. of Canada [IO], Montreal, QC, Canada
Fur Finland [IO], Vantaa, Finland
Fur Free Alliance [10968], PO Box 22505, Sacramento, CA 95822, (916)447-3085
Fur Free Alliance [10968], PO Box 22505, Sacramento, CA 95822, (916)447-3085
Fur Industrialists and Businessmen Assn. [IO], Istanbul, Turkey
Fur Info. Coun. of Am. [206], 8424 A Santa Monica Blvd., No. 860, West Hollywood, CA 90069, (323)782-1700
Fur Inst. of Canada [IO], Ottawa, ON, Canada
Fur Takers of Am. [4962], PO Box 3, Buckley, IL 60918, (217)394-2577
Furnishing Indus. Assn. of Australia [IO], Gosford, Australia
Furniture
Amer. Home Furnishings Alliance [1543]
Amer. Soc. of Furniture Designers [1544]

Brazilian Assn. of Furniture Indus. [14901]
Bus. and Institutional Furniture Manufacturer's Assn. [1545]
Cabinet Makers Assn. [1546]
Contemporary Design Gp. [1547]
Furniture Soc. [1548]
Futon Assn. Intl. [1549]
Futon Assn. Intl. [1549]
High Point Market Authority [1550]
Home Furnishings Independents Assn. [1551]
Independent Off. Products and Furniture Dealers Assn. [1552]
Intl. Development Assn. of the Furniture Indus. of Japan [13517]
Intl. Furniture Rental Assn. [1553]
Intl. Furniture Rental Assn. [1553]
Intl. Home Furnishings Representatives Assn. [1554]
Intl. Home Furnishings Representatives Assn. [1554]
Intl. Union of Electronic, Elecl., Salaried, Machine, and Furniture Workers [23184]
Natl. Furniture Bank Assn. [12059]
Natl. Home Furnishings Assn. [1555]
Natl. Home Furnishings Assn. [1555]
Soc. of Amer. Period Furniture Makers [9631]
Specialty Sleep Assn. [1556]
Summer and Casual Furniture Mfrs. Assn. [1557]
Sustainable Furnishings Coun. [1558]
Unfinished Furniture Assn. [1559]
United Furniture Workers Insurance Fund [23193]
Upholstered Furniture Action Coun. [1560]
Western Home Furnishings Assn. [1561]
Furniture Factories Marketing Assn. of the South [★1550]
Furniture Flammability Comm. [★1560]
Furniture History Soc. [IO], Haywards Heath, United Kingdom
Furniture Indus. Res. Assn. [IO], Stevenage, United Kingdom
Furniture Mfrs. Alliance - Defunct.
Furniture Rental Assn. of Am. [★1553]
Furniture Rental Assn. of Am. [★1553]
Furniture Soc. [1548], 111 Grovewood Rd., Asheville, NC 28804, (828)255-1949
Furniture and Wood Products Assn. of Ghana [IO], Accra, Ghana
Furniture Workers Div., IUE [★23193]
Further Poultry Processors Assn. of Canada [IO], Ottawa, ON, Canada
Fusaliers - Defunct.
Fusion Architecture [6197], PO Box 66853, Phoenix, AZ 85082-6853
Fusion Bonded Coaters Assn. [★546]
Fusion Power Associates [6726], 2 Professional Dr., Ste. 249, Gaithersburg, MD 20879, (301)258-0545
Fusion Power Associates [6726], 2 Professional Dr., Ste. 249, Gaithersburg, MD 20879, (301)258-0545
Fussballverband der Tschechischen Republik [★IO]
Futon Assn. Intl. [1549], 10705-7 Rocket Blvd., Orlando, FL 32824, (407)447-1706
Futon Assn. Intl. [1549], 10705-7 Rocket Blvd., Orlando, FL 32824, (407)447-1706
Futon Assn. of North Am. [★1549]
Futon Assn. of North Am. [★1549]
Future
Assn. of Professional Futurists [6886]
Assn. of Professional Futurists [6886]
Earthrise [6887]
Inst. for Alternative Futures [6888]
Inst. for Alternative Futures [6888]
Inst. for the Future [6889]
Inst. for the Future [6889]
Intl. Inst. of Forecasters [6890]
Intl. Inst. of Forecasters [6890]
Millennium Inst. [17733]
World Future Soc. [6891]
World Future Soc. [6891]
Future 500 [1562], 335 Powell St., 14th Fl., San Francisco, CA 94102, (415)294-7775
Future Bus. Leaders of Am. I Phi Beta Lambda [23481], 1912 Assn. Dr., Reston, VA 20191-1591, (800)325-2946
Future without Corruption [IO], Bishkek, Kirgizstan
Future Corvette Owners Assn. [21060], S68 W17323 Rossmar Ct., Muskego, WI 53150-8575, (414)422-0874

Reference to "IO" in place of a book number signifies that the association may be found in the 50th edition of International Organizations.

Future Farmers of Am. [★**7714**]

Future Farmers of Am. [★**7714**]

Future Fisherman Found. [**22576**], 5998 N Pleasant View Rd., Ponca City, OK 74601, (580)716-4251

Future of Freedom Found. [**17424**], 11350 Random Hills Rd., Ste. 800, Fairfax, VA 22030, (703)934-6101

Future Homemakers of Amer. [★**8181**]

Future of Music Coalition [**10199**], 1615 L St. NW, Ste. 520, Washington, DC 20036, (202)822-2051

Future Problem Solving Prog. [**7933**], 2015 Grant Pl., Melbourne, FL 32901, (321)768-0074

Future Problem Solving Prog. [★**7933**]

Future Problem Solving Prog. Intl. [**7933**], 2015 Grant Pl., Melbourne, FL 32901, (321)768-0074

Future Voters of Am. [**18824**], 205 E 69th St., No. 1A, New York, NY 10021, (212)535-8326

A Future Without Poverty [**12729**], PO Box 73, Ripley, OH 45167-0073

FutureChurch [**19425**], 17307 Madison Ave., Lakewood, OH 44107, (216)228-0869

FutureGen Alliance [**6112**], 73 E Central Park Plz., Jacksonville, IL 62650, (217)243-8215

Futures

   Future 500 [**1562**]

   Futures Indus. Assn. [**1563**]

   Kansas City Bd. of Trade [**3967**]

   Natl. Futures Assn. [**1564**]

   Natl. Introducing Brokers Assn. [**1565**]

Futures for Children [**11465**], 9600 Tennyson St. NE, Albuquerque, NM 87122-2282, (505)821-2828

Futures Indus. Assn. [**1563**], 2001 Pennsylvania Ave. NW, Ste. 600, Washington, DC 20006, (202)466-5460

Futures and Options Assn. [**IO**], London, United Kingdom

Futures Without Violence [**11887**], The Presidio, 100 Montgomery St., San Francisco, CA 94129, (415)678-5500

Futuribles Intl. [**IO**], Paris, France

G

G-Jo Inst. [**16014**], PO Box 1460, Columbus, NC 28722-1460, (828)863-4660

G. Unger Vetlesen Found. [**12668**], 1 Rockefeller Plz., Ste. 301, New York, NY 10020-2002, (212)586-0700

G. Unger Vetlesen Found. [**12668**], 1 Rockefeller Plz., Ste. 301, New York, NY 10020-2002, (212)586-0700

Gabler Family Assn. - Defunct.

Gabonese Red Cross Soc. [**IO**], Libreville, Gabon

Gabriel Marcel Soc. [**10379**], Prof. Brendan Sweetman, PhD, Pres., Rockhurst Univ., 1100 Rockhurst Rd., Kansas City, MO 64110-2561, (816)501-4681

Gabriel Richard Inst. - Defunct.

Gabungan Komputer Nasional Malaysia [★**IO**]

Gabungan Persatuan-Persatuan Pengguna Malaysia [★**IO**]

Gabungan Perusahaan Karet Indonesia [★**IO**]

Gaelic Athletic Assn. [**IO**], Dublin, Ireland

Gaelic Cultural Society [★**11497**]

Gaia Inst. [**4206**], 440 City Island Ave., Bronx, NY 10464

Gaia Intl. Women's Center [**IO**], Moscow, Russia

GAIA Movement USA [**4066**], 8918 S Green St., Chicago, IL 60620, (773)651-7870

Gaillimhe in Aghaidh an Chogaidh [★**IO**]

Gait and Clinical Movement Anal. Soc. [**14707**], 2651 Snowbird Ln., Naperville, IL 60564

Gaited Horse Intl. Assn. [**4586**], Whispering Pine Press, Inc., 507 N Sullivan Rd., Ste. A-Z, Veradale, WA 99037-8531, (509)928-8389

GALA Choruses [★**10200**]

GALA: Globalization and Localization Assn. [**1057**], PO Box 413, Andover, MA 01810, (206)329-2596

GALA: Globalization and Localization Assn. [**1057**], PO Box 413, Andover, MA 01810, (206)329-2596

GALA Performing Arts [★**10200**]

Galapagos Conservancy [**4067**], 11150 Fairfax Blvd., Ste. 408, Fairfax, VA 22030, (703)383-0077

GalaxyGoo [**7830**], 4104 24th St., No. 349, San Francisco, CA 94114

Gale Storm Appreciation Soc. [**23769**], PO Box 212, Coalton, OH 45621

Galgo Rescue Intl. Network [**10969**], 17784 N County Rd. 15, Wellington, CO 80549, (970)481-4299

Galilee Soc. [**IO**], Shefa-'Amr, Israel

Gallaudet Coll. Alumni Assn. [★**18873**]

Gallaudet Univ. Alumni Assn. [**18873**], 800 Florida Ave. NE, Washington, DC 20002, (202)651-5060

GalloSuisse - Assn. des producteurs d'oeufs suisses [★**IO**]

Galloway Cattle and Beef Marketing Assn. [**IO**], Hall, Australia

Galloway Cattle Soc. of Great Britain and Ireland [**IO**], Castle Douglas, United Kingdom

Galloway Foreningen Danmark [★**IO**]

Galloway Performance Intl. [★**3876**]

Gallups Island Radio Assn. - Defunct.

Galpin Soc. [**IO**], St. Albans, United Kingdom

Galvanizers Assn. [**IO**], Sutton Coldfield, United Kingdom

Galway Alliance Against War [**IO**], Dublin, Ireland

Galway Chamber of Commerce and Indus. [**IO**], Galway, Ireland

Gam-Anon Intl. Ser. Off. [**12062**], PO Box 157, Whitestone, NY 11357, (718)352-1671

Gam-Anon Intl. Ser. Off. [**12062**], PO Box 157, Whitestone, NY 11357, (718)352-1671

GAMA Intl. [**1961**], 2901 Telestar Ct., Ste. 140, Falls Church, VA 22042-1205, (800)345-2687

GAMA Intl. [**1961**], 2901 Telestar Ct., Ste. 140, Falls Church, VA 22042-1205, (800)345-2687

Gambia Assn. of the Physically Disabled [**IO**], Banjul, Gambia

Gambia Chamber of Commerce and Indus. [**IO**], Serrekunda, Gambia

Gambia Lawn Tennis Assn. [**IO**], Serrekunda, Gambia

Gambia Natl. Olympic Comm. [**IO**], Bakau, Gambia

Gambia Red Cross Soc. [**IO**], Banjul, Gambia

Gambia Women's Finance Assn. [**IO**], Banjul, Gambia

Gambia YMCAs [**IO**], Banjul, Gambia

GAMBICA, Assn. for Instrumentation, Control, Automation and Lab. Tech. [**IO**], London, United Kingdom

Gamblers Anonymous [**12063**], PO Box 17173, Los Angeles, CA 90017, (213)386-8789

Gambling

   Assn. of Problem Gambling Ser. Administrators [**12060**]

   Coun. on Compulsive Gambling of New Jersey [**12061**]

   Gam-Anon Intl. Ser. Off. [**12062**]

   Gam-Anon Intl. Ser. Off. [**12062**]

   Gamblers Anonymous [**12063**]

   Gambling Portal Webmasters Assn. [**1566**]

   Natl. Assn. for Gambling Stud. [**18548**]

   Natl. Coun. on Problem Gambling [**12064**]

   Natl. Indian Gaming Assn. [**5493**]

   North Amer. Gaming Regulators Assn. [**5494**]

   Stop Predatory Gambling Found. [**12065**]

Gambling Portal Webmasters Assn. [**1566**], 95 Wells Ave., Newton Centre, MA 02459, (617)332-2850

Game Audio Network Guild [**21747**], 1611-A S Melrose Dr., No. 290, Vista, CA 92081-5471, (415)626-2931

Game Developers' Assn. of Australia [**IO**], Melbourne, Australia

Game Mfrs. Assn. [**1192**], 280 N High St., Columbus, OH 43215, (614)255-4500

Game Mfrs. Assn. [**1192**], 280 N High St., Columbus, OH 43215, (614)255-4500

Game and Wildlife Conservation Trust [**IO**], Fordingbridge, United Kingdom

Gamers Intl. [**21760**], Maj. Pete Panzeri, Dir., 8230 Golf Green Cir., Houston, TX 77036, (713)774-3373

Games

   Amer. Autoduel Assn. [**21739**]

   Amer. Checker Fed. [**21740**]

   Amer. Checker Fed. [**21740**]

   Amer. Go Assn. [**21741**]

   Assn. of Game and Puzzle Collectors [**21742**]

   Boardgame Players Assn. [**21743**]

   Casual Games Assn. [**21744**]

   Chess Collectors Intl. [**21274**]

   Collegiate Assn. of Table Top Gamers [**21745**]

   Comm. for the Advancement of Role-Playing Games [**21746**]

   Game Audio Network Guild [**21747**]

   Games for Change [**17734**]

   Impact Sports Intl. [**22979**]

   Interactive Media Entertainment and Gaming Assn. [**7008**]

   Intl. Dodge Ball Fed. [**22981**]

   Intl. Fantasy Gaming Soc. [**21748**]

   Intl. Fantasy Gaming Soc. [**21748**]

   Intl. Fed. of Competitive Eating [**22982**]

   Intl. Laser Tag Assn. [**21749**]

   Intl. Masters of Gaming Law [**5495**]

   Intl. Shuffleboard Assn. [**22892**]

   Natl. 42 Players Assn. [**21750**]

   Natl. Amateur Dodgeball Assn. [**22253**]

   Natl. Horseshoe Pitchers Assn. of Am. [**22695**]

   Natl. Mah Jongg League [**21751**]

   Natl. Puzzlers' League [**21752**]

   Natl. Scrabble Assn. [**21753**]

   North Amer. Soc. of Ancient and Medieval Wargamers [**21754**]

   North Amer. Tiddlywinks Assn. [**21755**]

   Playworks [**12696**]

   Pro vs. GI Joe [**21762**]

   Puzzle Buffs Intl. [**21756**]

   Table Shuffleboard Assn. [**22893**]

   U.S. Boomerang Assn. [**22422**]

   U.S. Bridge Fed. [**21240**]

   U.S. Disc Sports [**22536**]

   U.S. ProMiniGolf Assn. [**22627**]

   U.S. Snooker Assn. [**22311**]

   U.S. Table Soccer Fed. [**21757**]

   Valley Intl. Foosball Assn. [**21758**]

   Valley Intl. Foosball Assn. [**21758**]

   World Confed. of Billiard Sports [**22313**]

Games for Change [**17734**], 78 5th Ave., 5th Fl., New York, NY 10011, (212)242-4922

Gamewardens of Vietnam Assn. [**20831**], 80 E Campus Dr., Belfair, WA 98528, (866)220-7477

Gaming

   Amer. Gaming Assn. [**21759**]

   Assn. of Gaming Equip. Mfrs. [**1567**]

   Collegiate Assn. of Table Top Gamers [**21745**]

   Gamers Intl. [**21760**]

   Gaming Standards Assn. [**21761**]

   Gaming Standards Assn. [**21761**]

   Interactive Media Entertainment and Gaming Assn. [**7008**]

   Intl. Masters of Gaming Law [**5495**]

   Intl. Simulation and Gaming Assn. [**8208**]

   Intl. Simulation and Gaming Assn. [**8208**]

   Natl. 42 Players Assn. [**21750**]

   North Amer. Simulation and Gaming Assn. [**8209**]

   Pro vs. GI Joe [**21762**]

   Table Shuffleboard Assn. [**22893**]

   U.S. Bridge Fed. [**21240**]

Gaming Standards Assn. [**21761**], 48377 Fremont Blvd., Ste. 117, Fremont, CA 94538, (510)492-4060

Gaming Standards Assn. [**21761**], 48377 Fremont Blvd., Ste. 117, Fremont, CA 94538, (510)492-4060

Gaming Technologies Assn. [**IO**], Sydney, Australia

Gamma Alpha Omega Sorority [**23643**], PO Box 427, Tempe, AZ 85280

Gamma Alpha Rho [★**23523**]

Gamma Beta Phi Soc. [**23558**], 78A Mitchell Rd., Oak Ridge, TN 37830, (865)483-6212

Gamma Delta [★**19934**]

Gamma Delta Pi [**23744**], 900 Asp Ave., Rm. 181, Norman, OK 73019

Gamma Gamma Chi Sorority [**23745**], PO Box 503, Talbott, TN 37877, (571)606-5053

Gamma Iota Sigma [**23571**], PO Box 227, Norristown, PA 19404, (484)991-4471

Gamma Iota Sigma [**23571**], PO Box 227, Norristown, PA 19404, (484)991-4471

Gamma Phi Beta [**23724**], 12737 E Euclid Dr., Centennial, CO 80111-6437, (303)799-1874

Gamma Phi Beta [**23724**], 12737 E Euclid Dr., Centennial, CO 80111-6437, (303)799-1874

Gamma Pi Epsilon [★**23553**]

Gamma Pi Epsilon [★**23553**]

A star before a book entry number signifies that the name is not listed separately, but is mentioned within the entry.

Gamma Sigma Delta [23463], Animal Sci., C220f Animal Sci. Bldg., Lincoln, NE 68583-0908, (402)472-6446
Gamma Sigma Delta [23463], Animal Sci., C220f Animal Sci. Bldg., Lincoln, NE 68583-0908, (402)472-6446
Gamma Sigma Sigma [23644], PO Box 248, Rindge, NH 03461-0248, (800)585-7508
Gandhi Peace Center - Defunct.
Gar Wood Soc. [22337], The Antique Boat Museum, 750 Mary St., Clayton, NY 13624, (315)686-4104
Garage Door Coun. - Defunct.
Garage Equip. Assn. [IO], Daventry, United Kingdom
Garden Centers of Am. [4741], PO Box 2945, LaGrange, GA 30241, (706)298-0287
Garden Centre Assn. [IO], Witney, United Kingdom
Garden Club of Am. [21792], 14 E 60th St., 3rd Fl., New York, NY 10022-7147, (212)753-8287
Garden Club of Bermuda [IO], Hamilton, Bermuda
Garden Conservancy [4068], PO Box 219, Cold Spring, NY 10516, (845)265-2029
Garden Design Soc. of New Zealand [IO], Auckland, New Zealand
Garden History Soc. [IO], London, United Kingdom
Garden Indus. Mfrs. Assn. [IO], Birmingham, United Kingdom
Garden Plant Conservation Assn. of Australia [IO], South Yarra, Australia
Garden Writers Assn. [21793], 10210 Leatherleaf Ct., Manassas, VA 20111, (703)257-1032
Garden Writers Assn. of Am. [★21793]
The Gardeners of Am. [21794], PO Box 241, Johnston, IA 50131-0241, (515)278-0295
The Gardeners of Am. I Men's Garden Clubs of Am. [21795], PO Box 241, Johnston, IA 50131-6245, (515)278-0295
GARDENEX: Fed. of Garden and Leisure Mfrs. [IO], Brasted, United Kingdom
Gardening
    African Violet Soc. of Am. [21763]
    Amer. Begonia Soc. [21764]
    Amer. Bonsai Soc. [21765]
    Amer. Boxwood Soc. [21766]
    Amer. Camellia Soc. [21767]
    Amer. Community Gardening Assn. [21768]
    Amer. Daffodil Soc. [21769]
    Amer. Daffodil Soc. [21769]
    Amer. Fuchsia Soc. [21770]
    Amer. Gourd Soc. [21771]
    Amer. Hemerocallis Soc. [21772]
    Amer. Hibiscus Soc. [21773]
    Amer. Hibiscus Soc. [21773]
    Amer. Horticultural Soc. [21774]
    Amer. Hosta Soc. [21775]
    Amer. Hydrangea Soc. [21776]
    Amer. Iris Soc. [21777]
    Amer. Iris Soc. [21777]
    Amer. Ivy Soc. [21778]
    Amer. Ivy Soc. [21778]
    Amer. Penstemon Soc. [21779]
    Amer. Peony Soc. [21780]
    Amer. Primrose Soc. [21781]
    Amer. Rhododendron Soc. [21782]
    Amer. Rose Soc. [21783]
    Aquatic Gardeners Assn. [4495]
    Aquatic Gardeners Assn. [4495]
    Aril Soc. Intl. [21784]
    Azalea Soc. of Am. [21785]
    Bonsai Clubs Intl. [21786]
    Bonsai Clubs Intl. [21786]
    Bromeliad Soc. Intl. [21787]
    Bromeliad Soc. Intl. [21787]
    Cactus and Succulent Soc. of Am. [21788]
    Coalition of Organic Landscapers [2179]
    Cymbidium Soc. of Am. [21789]
    Cymbidium Soc. of Am. [21789]
    The Dinner Garden [12269]
    Dwarf Iris Soc. of Am. [21790]
    Epiphyllum Soc. of Am. [21791]
    Garden Club of Am. [21792]
    Garden Writers Assn. [21793]
    The Gardeners of Am. [21794]
    The Gardeners of Am. I Men's Garden Clubs of Am. [21795]
    Gardens for Hea. Intl. [13604]

Gesneriad Hybridizers Assn. [21796]
Gesneriad Soc. [21797]
Gesneriad Soc. [21797]
Heritage Rose Found. [21798]
Heritage Roses Gp. [21799]
Hobby Greenhouse Assn. [21800]
Indoor Gardening Soc. of Am. [21801]
Intl. Aroid Soc. [21802]
Intl. Aroid Soc. [21802]
Intl. Brugmansia and Datura Soc. [21738]
Intl. Carnivorous Plant Soc. [21803]
Intl. Carnivorous Plant Soc. [21803]
Intl. Lilac Soc. [21804]
Intl. Lilac Soc. [21804]
Intl. Oleander Soc. [21805]
Intl. Oleander Soc. [21805]
Intl. Soc. for Plant Pathology [5403]
Intl. Waterlily and Water Gardening Soc. [21806]
Intl. Waterlily and Water Gardening Soc. [21806]
Lawn and Garden Dealers Assn. [1568]
Median Iris Soc. [21807]
Natl. Assn. of Pond Professionals [237]
Natl. Begonia Soc. [18755]
Natl. Chrysanthemum Soc. [21808]
Natl. Garden Bur. [4673]
Natl. Garden Clubs [21809]
Natl. Gardening Assn. [21810]
Natl. Junior Horticultural Assn. [21811]
North Amer. Fruit Explorers [21812]
North Amer. Gladiolus Coun. [21813]
North Amer. Heather Soc. [21814]
North Amer. Heather Soc. [21814]
North Amer. Lily Soc. [21815]
North Amer. Rock Garden Soc. [21816]
North Amer. Rock Garden Soc. [21816]
Plumeria Soc. of Am. [21817]
Professional Gardeners Guild [4261]
Progressive Gardening Trade Assn. [4496]
Reblooming Iris Soc. [21818]
Rose Hybridizers Assn. [21819]
Royal Horticultural Soc. of Ireland [3713]
Scottish Rock Garden Club [14844]
Seed Savers Exchange [21820]
Soc. for Japanese Irises [21821]
Soc. for Louisiana Irises [21822]
Soc. for Pacific Coast Native Iris [21823]
Soc. for Pacific Coast Native Iris [21823]
Soc. for Siberian Irises [21824]
Species Iris Gp. of North Am. [21825]
Spuria Iris Soc. [21826]
Spuria Iris Soc. [21826]
Tall Bearded Iris Soc. [21827]
Urban Farming [4366]
Women's Horticultural Assn. [4680]
Gardening From The Heart [★21794]
Gardens for All [★21810]
Gardens For All, the Natl. Assn. for Gardening [★21810]
Gardens for Hea. Intl. [13604], 9 Avon St., Cambridge, MA 02138
Gardens for Hea. Intl. [13604], 9 Avon St., Cambridge, MA 02138
Garin Yarden - Young Kibbutz Movement [★18013]
Garment Assn. of Nepal [IO], Kathmandu, Nepal
Garment Mfrs. Assn. in Cambodia [IO], Phnom Penh, Cambodia
Gartlan USA's Collectors' League - Address unknown since 2011.
Gary Jones Assn. [11918], 17330 W Center Rd., Ste. 110, PMB 120, Omaha, NE 68130, (402)334-2948
Gary Morris Fan Club [23845], Gary Morris Productions, PO Box 187, Chromo, CO 81128, (970)264-6791
Gary's Web Intl. [23770], Polaris Public Relations, 431 S Fairfax Ave., Los Angeles, CA 90036
Gas Appliance Engineers Soc. [★6690]
Gas Appliance Mfrs. Assn. of Australia [IO], Mulgrave, Australia
Gas Assn. of Bosnia and Herzegovina [IO], Sarajevo, Bosnia-Hercegovina
Gas Assn. of New Zealand [IO], Wellington, New Zealand
Gas Assn. of Serbia [IO], Belgrade, Serbia
Gas Consumers Gp; Process [17468]

Gas Forum [IO], London, United Kingdom
Gas Infrastructure Europe [IO], Brussels, Belgium
Gas Inst. and Natl. Commercial Gas Assn. [★4486]
Gas Processors Assn. [2650], 6526 E 60th St., Tulsa, OK 74145-9202, (918)493-3872
Gas Processors Suppliers Assn. [2651], 6526 E 60th St., Tulsa, OK 74145, (918)493-3872
Gas Res. Inst. [★4488]
Gas Tech. Inst. [4488], 1700 S Mt. Prospect Rd., Des Plaines, IL 60018-1804, (847)768-0500
Gas Turbine Div. [★6782]
Gas Turbine Div. [★6782]
Gases
    Amer. Assn. of Radon Scientists and Technologists [6892]
    Completion Engg. Assn. [6961]
    Compressed Gas Assn. [1569]
    Consumer Energy Alliance [6708]
    Coun. for Responsible Energy [6709]
    Domestic Energy Producers Alliance [1166]
    EndOil [6716]
    Focus Fusion Soc. [6725]
    Gasification Technologies Coun. [1570]
    Gasification Technologies Coun. [1570]
    Intl. Assn. of Directional Drilling [7238]
    Intl. DME Assn. [3770]
    Intl. Oxygen Mfrs. Assn. [1571]
    Intl. Oxygen Mfrs. Assn. [1571]
    Intl. Ozone Assn. [6893]
    Intl. Ozone Assn. [6893]
    Methanol Inst. [6894]
    Natl. Home Oxygen Patients Assn. [14548]
    Partnership for Advancing the Transition to Hydrogen [6748]
Gases and Welding Distributors Assn. [1825], 100 N 20th St., 4th Fl., Philadelphia, PA 19103, (215)564-3484
Gasification Technologies Coun. [1570], 4301 N Fairfax Dr., Ste. 300, Arlington, VA 22203, (703)276-0110
Gasification Technologies Coun. [1570], 4301 N Fairfax Dr., Ste. 300, Arlington, VA 22203, (703)276-0110
Gasket Cutters Assn. [IO], St. Albans, United Kingdom
Gasket Fabricators Assn. [1826], 994 Old Eagle School Rd., Ste. 1019, Wayne, PA 19087, (610)971-4850
Gasoline and Automotive Ser. Dealers Assn. [356], 372 Doughty Blvd., Ste. 2C, Inwood, NY 11096, (516)371-6201
Gasoline Merchants [★356]
GaSp Network - Defunct.
Gastro-Intestinal Res. Found. [14563], 70 E Lake St., Ste. 1015, Chicago, IL 60601, (312)332-1350
Gastroenterological and Digestive Endoscopy Soc. of Sri Lanka [IO], Colombo, Sri Lanka
Gastroenterological Soc. of Australia [IO], Mulgrave, Australia
Gastroenterological Soc. of Singapore [IO], Singapore, Singapore
Gastroenterology
    Amer. Celiac Disease Alliance [14549]
    Amer. Coll. of Gastroenterology [14550]
    Amer. Gastroenterological Assn. [14551]
    Amer. Neurogastroenterology and Motility Soc. [14552]
    Amer. Partnership for Eosinophilic Disorders [14553]
    Amer. Soc. for Gastrointestinal Endoscopy [14554]
    Assn. of Gastrointestinal Motility Disorders [14555]
    Assn. of Gastrointestinal Motility Disorders [14555]
    Bockus Intl. Soc. of Gastroenterology [14556]
    Bockus Intl. Soc. of Gastroenterology [14556]
    Celiac Disease Found. [14557]
    Celiac Sprue Assn. U.S.A. [14558]
    Crohn's and Colitis Found. of Am. [14559]
    Cyclic Vomiting Syndrome Assn. [14560]
    Cyclic Vomiting Syndrome Assn. [14560]
    Digestive Disease Natl. Coalition [14561]
    European Soc. for Primary Care Gastroenterology [5524]

Reference to "IO" in place of a book number signifies that the association may be found in the 50th edition of International Organizations.

Found. for Digestive Hea. and Nutrition [14562]
Gastro-Intestinal Res. Found. [14563]
Gastroenterology Physician Assistants [14564]
Gastroparesis Patient Assn. for Cures and Treat-
ments [14565]
Get Your Guts in Gear [14566]
Hong Kong Soc. of Gastroenterology [18858]
Intl. Found. for Functional Gastrointestinal
Disorders [14567]
Intl. Found. for Functional Gastrointestinal
Disorders [14567]
Intl. Soc. of Gastrointestinal Oncology [14568]
Natl. Digestive Diseases Info. CH [14569]
North Amer. Soc. for Pediatric Gastroenterology,
Hepatology and Nutrition [14570]
Paratuberculosis Awareness and Res. Assn.
[14571]
Paratuberculosis Awareness and Res. Assn.
[14571]
Pediatric/Adolescent Gastroesophageal Reflux
Assn. [14572]
Pediatric/Adolescent Gastroesophageal Reflux
Assn. [14572]
Pull-thru Network [14573]GastroenterologyScandi-
navian Assn. for Gastrointestinal Motility
Soc. of Amer. Gastrointestinal and Endoscopic
Surgeons [14574]
Soc. of Amer. Gastrointestinal and Endoscopic
Surgeons [14574]
Soc. of Gastroenterology Nurses and Associates
[14575]
United European Gastroenterology Fed. [15092]
Gastroenterology Physician Assistants [14564], PO
Box 82511, Tampa, FL 33682, (813)988-7795
Gastrointestinal Radiologists; Soc. of [16542]
Gastronomy
Slow Food USA [9632]
Slow Food USA [9632]
Gastroparesis Patient Assn. for Cures and Treat-
ments [14565], 702 Winebary Cir., Lewisberry, PA
17339, (717)938-2538
Gateway Intl. Center [IO], Kanagawa, Japan
Gathering of Nations [10327], 3301 Coors Blvd. NW,
Ste. R300, Albuquerque, NM 87120-1229,
(505)836-2810
Gaucher Disease Registry [★15500]
Gauchers Assn. [IO], Gloucester, United Kingdom
Gauge and Tool Makers' Assn. [IO], Princes Risbor-
ough, United Kingdom
Gavel Clubs [10477], PO Box 9052, Mission Viejo,
CA 92690-9052, (949)858-8255
GAVI Alliance [14897], 1776 I Eye St. NW, Ste. 600,
Washington, DC 20006, (202)478-1050
Gay Asian Pacific Alliance [12080], PO Box 421884,
San Francisco, CA 94142-1884
Gay Asian Pacific Support Network [12081], PO Box
691093, West Hollywood, CA 90069, (213)368-
6488
Gay, Bisexual and Transgender U.S. Peace Corps
Alumni; Lesbian, [18306]
Gay Caucus of Members of the Amer. Psychiatric
Assn. [★12068]
Gay Fathers Coalition [★12079]
Gay Fathers Coalition Intl. [★12079]
Gay Games [★22976]
Gay Games [★22976]
Gay HIV Strategies [IO], Dublin, Ireland
Gay/Lesbian
Affirmation/Gay and Lesbian Mormons [19783]
Affirmation: United Methodists for Lesbian, Gay,
Bisexual and Transgender Concerns [19784]
Alliance for Full Acceptance [12066]
Amer. Civil Liberties Union [17260]
Amer. Lib. Assn. I Gay, Lesbian, Bisexual and
Transgendered Roundtable [9633]
Amer. Veterans for Equal Rights [12067]
Assn. of Gay and Lesbian Psychiatrists [12068]
Assn. for Lesbian, Gay, Bisexual and Transgender
Issues in Counseling [12069]
Atticus Circle [17735]
Bay Area Physicians for Human Rights [12070]
BiNet U.S.A. [12071]
Brethren/Mennonite Coun. for Lesbian, Gay,
Bisexual and Transgender Interest [19785]
Campus Pride [12072]

Catholic Assn. for Lesbian and Gay Ministry
[19786]
Center for Lesbian and Gay Stud. [12073]
CenterLink [11661]
COLAGE [12074]
Columbia Queer Alliance [12075]
Community United Against Violence [12076]
Couples Natl. Network [12077]
Courage [19787]
Courage Intl. [19787]
Dignity/U.S.A. [19788]
Equality Fed. [17736]
Evangelicals Concerned [19789]
Evergreen Intl. [12078]
Evergreen Intl. [12078]
Exodus Intl. [19790]
Family Equality Coun. [12079]
Fenway Hea. [14576]
FireFlag/EMS [5496]
Friends for Lesbian, Gay, Bisexual, Transgender,
and Queer Concerns [19791]
Friends for Lesbian, Gay, Bisexual, Transgender,
and Queer Concerns [19791]
Gay Asian Pacific Alliance [12080]
Gay Asian Pacific Support Network [12081]
Gay, Lesbian and Affirming Disciples Alliance
[19792]
Gay Lesbian Alliance Against Defamation [12082]
Gay and Lesbian Assn. of Retiring Persons
[10843]
Gay, Lesbian, Bisexual, and Transgender Natl.
Hotline [12083]
Gay and Lesbian Medical Assn. [14577]
Gay and Lesbian Rowing Fed. [22855]
Gay, Lesbian, and Straight Educ. Network [8210]
Gay Officers' Action League [12084]
HeartStrong [12085]
Heritage of Pride [12086]
Hetrick-Martin Inst. [12087]
Homosexual Info. Center [12088]
Homosexuals Anonymous Fellowship Services
[12089]
Human Rights Campaign [12090]
Immigration Equality [12091]
Integrity USA [19793]
Intl. Assn. of Gay and Lesbian Martial Artists
[22734]
Intl. Fed. of Black Prides [12092]
Intl. Gay and Lesbian Aquatics [23040]
Intl. Gay and Lesbian Football Assn. [22936]
Intl. Gay and Lesbian Human Rights Commn.
[12093]
Intl. Gay and Lesbian Human Rights Commn.
[12093]
InterPride [12094]
InterPride [12094]
Interweave Continental: Unitarian Universalists for
Lesbian, Gay, Bisexual and Transgender
Concerns [19794]
Lambda Legal Defense and Educ. Fund [12095]
LEAGUE [12096]
Lesbian Hea. Fund [14578]
Lesbian Hea. Fund [14578]
Lesbian Rsrc. Center [12097]
LIFE Ministries [19795]
Love in Action [19635]
Lutherans Concerned/North Am. [19796]
Mautner Proj. for Lesbian Hea. [14579]
Metanoia Ministries [19636]
Metropolitan Community Churches [19797]
More Light Presbyterians for Lesbian, Gay,
Bisexual and Transgender concerns [19798]
Natl. Assn. for Res. and Therapy of Homosexual-
ity [14580]
Natl. Assn. of Social Workers Natl. Comm. on
Lesbian, Gay and Bisexual Issues [12098]
Natl. Black Gay Men's Advocacy Coalition [12099]
Natl. Center for Lesbian Rights [12100]
Natl. Coalition of Anti-Violence Programs [18770]
Natl. Coalition for LGBT Hea. [12101]
Natl. Coming Out Day [12102]
Natl. Gay and Lesbian Chamber of Commerce
[23401]
Natl. Gay and Lesbian Task Force [12103]
Natl. Org. for Lesbians of Size [12104]

Out and Equal Workplace Advocates [12105]
Parents, Families, and Friends of Lesbians and
Gays [12106]
Parents and Friends of Ex-Gays and Gays
[12107]
Partners Task Force for Gay and Lesbian Couples
[12108]
POWER UP: Professional Org. of Women in
Entertainment Reaching UP! [17737]
Presbyterian Parents of Gays and Lesbians
[12109]
Rainbow Alliance of the Deaf [12110]
Reconciling Ministries Network [19799]
Regeneration [19637]
Senior Action in a Gay Env. [12111]
Seventh Day Adventist Kinship Intl. [19800]
Seventh Day Adventist Kinship Intl. [19800]
Soc. for the Psychological Stud. of Lesbian, Gay,
Bisexual and Transgender Issues [16429]
Soulforce [12112]
Sylvia Rivera Law Proj. [18730]
Tangent Gp. [12113]
Trikone [12114]
Truth Wins Out [12115]
United Church of Christ Coalition for Lesbian,
Gay, Bisexual and Transgender Concerns
[19801]
Unity Fellowship Church Movement [19802]
We Are Family [12116]
World Cong. of Gay, Lesbian, Bisexual, and
Transgender Jews [19803]
World Cong. of Gay, Lesbian, Bisexual, and
Transgender Jews [19803]
Youth Pride Alliance [12117]
Gay and Lesbian Adolescent Social Services - Ad-
dress unknown since 2011.
Gay and Lesbian Advocates and Defenders [17292],
30 Winter St., Ste. 800, Boston, MA 02108,
(617)426-1350
Gay, Lesbian and Affirming Disciples Alliance
[19792], PO Box 44400, Indianapolis, IN 46244-
0400
Gay Lesbian Alliance Against Defamation [12082],
5455 Wilshire Blvd., Ste. 1500, Los Angeles, CA
90036, (323)933-2240
Gay and Lesbian Alliance Against Defamation New
York [★12082]
Gay and Lesbian Alumni/ae Associations; Network of
[18888]
Gay and Lesbian Assn. of Choruses [10200], PO
Box 99998, Pittsburgh, PA 15233, (412)322-4260
Gay and Lesbian Assn. of Retiring Persons [10843],
10940 Wilshire Blvd., Ste. 1600, Los Angeles, CA
90024, (310)722-1807
Gay, Lesbian, and Bisexual Caucus of the Amer.
Psychiatric Assn. [★12068]
Gay, Lesbian, Bisexual, Transgender Historical Soc.
[9688], 657 Mission St., No. 300, San Francisco,
CA 94105, (415)777-5455
Gay, Lesbian, Bisexual, and Transgender Natl. Hot-
line [12083], PMB No. 296, 2261 Market St., San
Francisco, CA 94114, (415)355-0003
Gay, Lesbian, Bisexual, and Transgendered
Disabled Veterans of Am. - Address unknown since
2010.
Gay, Lesbian, and Bisexual Veterans of Am.
[★12067]
Gay and Lesbian Coalition Intl. [★12079]
Gay and Lesbian Dominican Empowerment Org. -
Address unknown since 2011.
Gay and Lesbian Media Coalition [★9607]
Gay and Lesbian Medical Assn. [14577], 1326 18th
St. NW, Ste. 22, Washington, DC 20036, (202)600-
8037
Gay and Lesbian Press Assn. - Defunct.
Gay and Lesbian Rowing Fed. [22855], 10153
Riverside Dr., Ste. 698, Toluca Lake, CA 91602,
(323)774-1903
Gay and Lesbian Scientists and Tech. Professionals;
Natl. Org. of [7379]
Gay, Lesbian, and Straight Educ. Network [8210], 90
Broad St., 2nd Fl., New York, NY 10004, (212)727-
0135
Gay/Lesbian Straight Teachers Network [★8210]
Gay and Lesbian Task Force [★9633]

A star before a book entry number signifies that the name is not listed separately, but is mentioned within the entry.

Gay and Lesbian Tennis Alliance [23054], Mike My-
ers, Treas., 5510 Curdy Rd., Howell, MI 48855
Gay and Lesbian Tennis Alliance [23054], Mike My-
ers, Treas., 5510 Curdy Rd., Howell, MI 48855
Gay and Lesbian Underwater Gp. [IO], London,
United Kingdom
Gay Men's Hea. Crisis [13605], 446 W 33rd St.,
New York, NY 10001-2601, (212)367-1000
Gay Officers' Action League [12084], PO Box 1774,
New York, NY 10113, (212)NY1-GOAL
Gay People at Columbia [★12075]
Gay Police Assn. [IO], London, United Kingdom
Gay Task Force of ALA [★9633]
Gay Theatre Alliance - Defunct.
Gay Women's Alliance [★12097]
Gaylactic Network [10519], PO Box 7587,
Washington, DC 20044-7587
Gaylactic Network [10519], PO Box 7587,
Washington, DC 20044-7587
Gaylord Family Org. [20520], 1910 S Church St.,
Lodi, CA 95240, (209)366-2773
Gays Against Abortion [★12944]
Gays and Lesbians in Foreign Affairs [★23201]
Gays and Lesbians in Foreign Affairs Agencies USA
[23201], PO Box 18774, Washington, DC 20036-
8774
Gazette Intl. Networking Inst. [★11823]
Gazette Intl. Networking Inst. [★11823]
Gazi Entomological Res. Soc. [IO], Ankara, Turkey
GDF [★17079]
GE Stockholders' Alliance for a Sustainable Nuclear-
Free Future - Defunct.
Geary 18 Intl. Yacht Racing Assn. [22338], PO Box
4763, Federal Way, WA 98063-4763
Geburtshilfe und Gynakologie FMH [★IO]
Geekcorps [3391], 1900 M St. NW, Ste. 500,
Washington, DC 20036, (202)589-2600
Geeks Without Borders
Geeks Without Borders - Address unknown since
2011.
Geelong Chamber of Commerce [IO], Geelong,
Australia
Geelong and District Olive Assn. [IO], Torquay,
Australia
Geelong Hospice Care Assn. [IO], Geelong,
Australia
Geelong Waterski Club [IO], Geelong, Australia
Gelatine Mfrs. of Europe [IO], Brussels, Belgium
Gem and Jewelry Export Promotion Coun. [IO],
Mumbai, India
Gem and Lapidary Dealers Assn. [2159], 120 Der-
wood Cir., Rockville, MD 20850, (301)294-1640
Gem and Mineral Fed. of Canada [IO], Winfield, BC,
Canada
Gemmological Assn. of Australia [IO], Melbourne,
Australia
Gemmological Assn. and Gem Testing Lab. of Great
Britain. [IO], London, United Kingdom
Gemological Inst. of Am. [2160], The Robert
Mouawad Campus, 5345 Armada Dr., Carlsbad,
CA 92008, (760)603-4000
Gemological Inst. of Am. Alumni Assn. [19085], The
Robert Mouawad Campus, 5345 Armada Dr.,
Carlsbad, CA 92008, (760)603-4135
Gemological Inst. of Am. Alumni Assn. [19085], The
Robert Mouawad Campus, 5345 Armada Dr.,
Carlsbad, CA 92008, (760)603-4135
Gemology
  U.S. Faceters Guild [6590]
Gems and Aces [★10651]
Gemstone Assn; Intl. Colored [3363]
Gemstone Assn; Intl. Colored [3363]
Gen Art [9178], 627 N La Peer Dr., West Hollywood,
CA 90069, (323)863-2600
Gender Action [18805], 1875 Connecticut Ave. NW,
Ste. 500, Washington, DC 20009, (202)939-5463
Gender Educ. and Advocacy [13104], PO Box 256,
Pine Lake, GA 30072-0256
Gender and Sci. and Tech. Assn. [IO], Brighton,
United Kingdom
Gene Pitney Fan Club [★23846]
Gene Pitney Intl. Fan Club [23846], 6201 - 39th
Ave., Kenosha, WI 53142
Gene Stratton Porter Memorial Soc. [9365], 1205
Pleasant Point, Box 639, Rome City, IN 46784-
9644, (260)854-3790

Gene Summers Intl. Fan Club [23847], 222 Tulane
St., Garland, TX 75043-2239
Gene Summers Intl. Fan Club [23847], 222 Tulane
St., Garland, TX 75043-2239
Genealogical Assn. of Nova Scotia [IO], Halifax, NS,
Canada
Genealogical and Heraldry Soc. ADLER [IO], Vi-
enna, Austria
Genealogical Inst. [20629], PO Box 129, Tremonton,
UT 84337, (435)579-1743
Genealogical Soc. of Am; Italian [9901]
Genealogical Soc. of Flemish Americans [20630],
18740 13 Mile Rd., Roseville, MI 48066, (810)776-
9579
Genealogical Soc. of Flemish Americans [20630],
18740 13 Mile Rd., Roseville, MI 48066, (810)776-
9579
Genealogical Soc. of Ireland [IO], Dun Laoghaire,
Ireland
Genealogical Soc. of South Africa [IO], Houghton,
Republic of South Africa
Genealogical Speakers Guild [10478], PO Box
38314, Olmsted Falls, OH 44138-0314
Genealogy
Ahern Clan Assn. [20420]
Alford Amer. Family Assn. [20422]
ALMA Soc. [10777]
Amer. Biographical Inst. Res. Assn. [20614]
American-Canadian Genealogical Soc. [20615]
American-Canadian Genealogical Soc. [20615]
Amer. Coll. of Heraldry [20616]
American-French Genealogical Soc. [20617]
Amer. Heraldry Soc. [20618]
American/Schleswig-Holstein Heritage Soc.
[18984]
Amer. Soc. of Genealogists [20619]
Amer. Soc. of Genealogists [20619]
Ark-La-Tex Genealogical Assn. [20620]
Augustan Soc. [20621]
Augustan Soc. [20621]
Barney Family Historical Assn. [20428]
Bishop Hill Heritage Assn. [20622]
Blackburn Family Assn. [20431]
Bd. for Certification of Genealogists [20623]
Brantley Assn. of Am. [20436]
Brinton Assn. of Am. [20624]
Burleson Family Assn. [20438]
Catholic War Veterans Auxiliary of the U.S.A.
[20704]
Charette/Charest Family Assn. [20440]
Clan Arthur Assn. USA [20442]
Clan Fergusson Soc. of North Am. [20454]
Clan Keith Soc. [20461]
Clan MacAlpine Soc. [20463]
Clan MacCarthy Soc. [20464]
Clan MacGillivray Soc. - Australia [8021]
Clan MacKenzie Soc. in the Americas [20469]
Clan MacKinnon Soc. [20470]
Clan McAlister of Am. [20478]
Clan Phail Soc. in North America [20484]
Clan Ramsey Assn. of North Am. [20486]
Clan Scott Soc. [20489]
Czechoslovak Genealogical Soc. Intl. [20625]
Czechoslovak Genealogical Soc. Intl. [20625]
Daniel Boone and Frontier Families Res. Assn.
[9763]
Daughters of the Republic of Texas [20626]
Duncan Surname Assn. [20505]
Eller Family Assn. [20510]
Elliot Clan Soc. USA [20511]
FAMILIA Ancestral Res. Assn. [18995]
FAMILIA Ancestral Res. Assn. [18995]
Fed. of East European Family History Societies
[18996]
Fed. of Genealogical Societies [20627]
French/Canadian/Metis Genealogical Soc. [20628]
French/Canadian/Metis Genealogical Soc. [20628]
Genealogical Inst. [20629]
Genealogical Soc. of Flemish Americans [20630]
Genealogical Soc. of Flemish Americans
[20630]GenealogyGenealogical Soc. of Ireland
Genealogical Soc. of South Africa [22221]
Gen. Soc. of Mayflower Descendants [20746]
German Genealogical Soc. of Am. [20631]
German Genealogical Soc. of Am. [20631]

Gosselin Family Assn. [15669]
Greenlaw Family Assn. [20526]
Harden - Hardin - Harding Family Assn. [20530]
Hathaway Family Assn. [20532]
Hispanic Genealogical Soc. [20632]
House of Boyd Soc. [20535]
Hudson Family Assn. [20537]
Immigrant Genealogical Soc. [20633]
Immigrant Genealogical Soc. [20633]
Intl. Assn. of Jewish Genealogical Societies
[20634]
Intl. Assn. of Jewish Genealogical Societies
[20634]
Intl. Molyneux Family Assn. [20540]
Intl. Soc. for British Genealogy and Family History
[20635]
Intl. Soc. for British Genealogy and Family History
[20635]
The Irish Ancestral Res. Assn. [18997]
The Irish Ancestral Res. Assn. [18997]
Irish Family History Forum [20636]
Irish Genealogical Found. [20637]
Irish Genealogical Found. [20637]
Irish Genealogical Soc. Intl. [20638]
Italian Genealogical Gp. [20639]
Jewish Genealogical Soc. [20640]
Johannes Schwalm Historical Assn. [20641]
Knowles/Knoles/Noles Family Assn. [20642]
Lancaster Mennonite Historical Soc. [20643]
Lancaster Mennonite Historical Soc. [20643]
McAdams Historical Soc. [20558]
Military Order of the Loyal Legion of the U.S.
[20386]
Morse Soc. [20644]
Mountain Press Res. Center [20645]
Murray Clan Soc. North Am. [20561]
Natl. Genealogical Soc. [20646]
Natl. Orphan Train Complex [20647]
Natl. Soc. of Madison Family Descendants
[20648]
Natl. Soc. of Women Descendants of the Ancient
and Honorable Artillery Company [20403]
Nesbitt/Nisbet Soc.: A Worldwide Clan Assn.
[20564]
New England Historic Genealogical Soc. [20649]
New York Genealogical and Biographical Soc.
[20650]
Norwegian Amer. Genealogical Center [20651]
Ohio Genealogical Soc. [20652]
Orangeburgh German Swiss Genealogical Soc.
[20653]
Palatines to Am.: Researching German-Speaking
Ancestry [20654]
Palatines to Am.: Researching German-Speaking
Ancestry [20654]
Parke Soc. [20570]
Pierre Chastain Family Assn. [20571]
Polish Genealogical Soc. of Am. [20655]
Polish Genealogical Soc. of Am. [20655]
Presidential Families of Am. [20656]
Puerto Rican Hispanic Genealogical Soc. [20657]
Pursuing Our Italian Names Together [20658]
Pursuing Our Italian Names Together [20658]
Russian Nobility Assn. in Am. [20659]
Saint Nicholas Soc. of the City of New York
[20660]
Scotch-Irish Found. [20661]
Scotch-Irish Found. [20661]
Scotch-Irish Soc. of the U.S.A. [20662]
Soc. of the Ark and the Dove [20407]
Soc. of Mareen Duvall Descendants [20589]
Spencer Historical and Genealogical Soc. [20663]
Studebaker Family Natl. Assn. [20595]
Templin Family Assn. [20599]
Ulster-Scots Soc. of Am. [20664]
Welsh-American Genealogical Soc. [20665]
World Chamberlain Genealogical Soc. [20666]
Genealogy Copy Ser. [★20629]
Gen. Agents and Managers Assn. [★1961]
Gen. Agents and Managers Assn. [★1961]
Gen. Agents and Managers Conf. of NALU [★1961]
Gen. Agents and Managers Conf. of NALU [★1961]
Gen. Anthropology Division of the Amer.
Anthropological Assn. [6141], Luke Eric Lassiter,
PhD, Communications Off., Marshall Univ. Gradu-
ate Coll., 100 Angus E Peyton Dr., South
Charleston, WV 25303-1600, (304)746-1923

Reference to "IO" in place of a book number signifies that the association may be found in the 50th edition of International Organizations.

General Arbitration Coun. of the Textile and Apparel Industries - Address unknown since 2010.

Gen. Assembly Binding Women for Reforms, Integrity, Equality, Leadership, and Action [IO], Manila, Philippines

Gen. Assn. of Engineers in Romania [IO], Bucharest, Romania

Gen. Assn. of Gen. Baptists [19321], 100 Stinson Dr., Poplar Bluff, MO 63901, (573)785-7746

Gen. Assn. of Regular Baptist Churches [19322], 1300 N Meacham Rd., Schaumburg, IL 60173-4806, (847)843-1600

Gen. Aviation Mfrs. Assn. [135], 1400 K St. NW, Ste. 801, Washington, DC 20005, (202)393-1500

Gen. Building Contractors Assn. [563], PO Box 15959, Philadelphia, PA 19103, (215)568-7015

Gen. Chiropractic Coun. [IO], London, United Kingdom

Gen. Commn. on Archives and History of the United Methodist Church [10084], PO Box 127, Madison, NJ 07940, (973)408-3189

Gen. Commn. on the Status and Role of Women [17645], 77 W Washington St., Ste. 1009, Chicago, IL 60602, (312)346-4900

Gen. Contractors Assn. of Ottawa [IO], Ottawa, ON, Canada

Gen. Convention of the Baptist Denomination in the U.S. for Foreign Missions [★19317]

Gen. Convention of the Baptist Denomination in the U.S. for Foreign Missions [★19317]

Gen. Coun. of the Bar [IO], London, United Kingdom

Gen. Coun. of the Bar of Northern Ireland [IO], Belfast, United Kingdom

Gen. Coun. of Cooperating Baptist Missions [★19314]

Gen. Coun. and Register of Naturopaths [IO], Street, United Kingdom

Gen. Counsels' Assn. of Accident and Hea. Counsels [★5251]

Gen. Counsels' Assn. of Accident and Hea. Counsels [★5251]

Gen. Dental Coun. [IO], London, United Kingdom

Gen. Dental Practitioners Assn. [★147]

Gen. Egyptian Book Org. [IO], Cairo, Egypt

Gen. Fed. of Trade Unions [IO], London, United Kingdom

Gen. Fed. of Women's Clubs [19282], 1734 N St. NW, Washington, DC 20036-2990, (202)347-3168

Gen. Fed. of Women's Clubs [19282], 1734 N St. NW, Washington, DC 20036-2990, (202)347-3168

Gen. Fisheries Commn. for the Mediterranean [IO], Rome, Italy

Gen. Grand Chap., Order of the Eastern Star [19127], 1618 New Hampshire Ave. NW, Washington, DC 20009-2549, (202)667-4737

Gen. Grand Chap., Order of the Eastern Star [19127], 1618 New Hampshire Ave. NW, Washington, DC 20009-2549, (202)667-4737

Gen. Grand Chap. of Royal Arch Masons Intl. [19128], PO Box 128, Greenfield, IN 46140-0128, (317)467-3600

Gen. Grand Chap. of Royal Arch Masons Intl. [19128], PO Box 128, Greenfield, IN 46140-0128, (317)467-3600

Gen. Hypnotherapy Register [IO], Lymington, United Kingdom

Gen. Insurance Assn. of Cambodia [IO], Phnom Penh, Cambodia

Gen. Insurance Assn. of Japan [IO], Tokyo, Japan

Gen. Insurance Assn. of Singapore [IO], Singapore, Singapore

Gen. Medical Coun. [IO], London, United Kingdom

Gen. Merchandise Distributors Coun. [★3660]

Gen. Optical Coun. [IO], London, United Kingdom

Gen. Osteopathic Coun. [IO], London, United Kingdom

Gen. Practice Sect. of APhA [★16176]

Gen. Retailers and Traders Union [IO], Valletta, Malta

Gen. Ser. Consumer Arbitration Prog. [★17459]

Gen. Ser. Employees Union Local 73 [23226], 300 S Ashland Ave., Ste. 400, Chicago, IL 60607, (312)787-5868

Gen. Soc. of Colonial Wars [20395], Langsdale Lib., 1420 Maryland Ave., Baltimore, MD 21201

Gen. Soc. of Mayflower Descendants [20746], PO Box 3297, Plymouth, MA 02361-3297, (508)746-3188

Gen. Soc. of Mayflower Descendants [20746], PO Box 3297, Plymouth, MA 02361-3297, (508)746-3188

Gen. Soc. of Mechanics and Tradesmen [★8965]

Gen. Soc. of Mechanics and Tradesmen of the City of New York [8965], 20 W 44th St., New York, NY 10036, (212)840-1840

Gen. Soc., Sons of the Revolution [20337], 108 S Liberty St., Independence, MO 64050, (816)254-1776

Gen. Soc. of the War of 1812 [20840], 678 Fox Rd., Lino Lakes, MN 55014-1968, (763)746-6580

Gen. Teaching Coun. for Scotland [IO], Edinburgh, United Kingdom

Gen. Union of Romanian Mfrs. [IO], Bucharest, Romania

Gen. Union of Workers [IO], Madrid, Spain

Gen. Workers' Union [IO], Valletta, Malta

Generation for Change and Growth [12328], 419 Cedar Ave. No. g248, Minneapolis, MN 55454, (612)520-1109

Generation for Change and Growth [12328], 419 Cedar Ave. No. g248, Minneapolis, MN 55454, (612)520-1109

Generation Five [13086], PO Box 1715, Oakland, CA 94604, (510)251-8552

Generation Green [14077], Center for Environmental Hea., 2201 Broadway, Ste. 302, Oakland, CA 94612, (510)655-3900

Generation Iraq [12388], 1972 W Winona St., No.3, Chicago, IL 60640, (847)814-5905

Generation Rescue [13792], 13636 Ventura Blvd., Ste. 259, Sherman Oaks, CA 91423, (877)98-AUTISM

Generation Rwanda [13525], 16 Highland St., Cambridge, MA 02138, (707)654-4254

Generation Rwanda [IO], Kigali, Rwanda

GenerationEngage - Address unknown since 2011.

Generations [IO], Montreal, QC, Canada

Generations for Life [★18565]

Generations for Life [★18565]

Generations United [13189], 1331 H St. NW, Ste. 900, Washington, DC 20005, (202)289-3979

Generative Linguistics in the Old World [IO], Utrecht, Netherlands

Generic Pharmaceutical Assn. [2694], 777 6th St. NW, Ste. 510, Washington, DC 20001, (202)249-7100

Generic Pharmaceutical Indus. Assn. [★2694]

Genesis Expeditions [IO], Ensenada, Mexico

Genesis Inst. [20233], PO Box 10436, Spokane, WA 99209, (509)467-7913

Genetic Alliance [16770], 4301 Connecticut Ave. NW, Ste. 404, Washington, DC 20008, (202)966-5557

Genetic Alliance Registry and BioBank [14647], 4301 Connecticut Ave. NW, Ste. 404, Washington, DC 20008, (202)966-5557

Genetic Alliance UK [IO], London, United Kingdom

Genetic Defects

Intl. Cellular Medicine Soc. [14649]

Purine Res. Soc. [15506]

Genetic Disorders

Aicardi Syndrome Newsl. [14581]

Aicardi Syndrome Newsl. [14581]

Alagille Syndrome Alliance [14582]

Alpha-1 Advocacy Alliance [14583]

Alpha 1 Found. [14584]

Alpha-1 Kids [14585]

Alstrom Syndrome Intl. [14586]

Alstrom Syndrome Intl. [14586]

Androgen Insensitivity Syndrome Support Gp. - U.S.A. [14587]

Canadian Assn. for Porphyria [21000]

CFC Intl. [14588]

CFC Intl. [14588]

Charcot-Marie-Tooth Assn. [15577]

Chromosome 9P Network [14589]

Chromosome 9P Network [14589]

Chromosome 18 Registry and Res. Soc. [14590]

Chromosome 18 Registry and Res. Soc. [14590]

Chromosome Disorder Outreach [14591]

Chromosome Disorder Outreach [14591]

Coalition for Heritable Disorders of Connective Tissue [14592]

Coffin-Lowry Syndrome Found. [14593]

Disorders of Chromosome 16 Found. [14594]

Disorders of Chromosome 16 Found. [14594]

Ellis-van Creveld Syndrome Support [14595]

Fanconi Anemia Res. Fund [14596]

Floating Harbor Syndrome Support Gp. of North Am. [14597]

Floating Harbor Syndrome Support Gp. of North Am. [14597]

Found. for Nager and Miller Syndromes [14598]

Genetic Metabolic Dietitians Intl. [15497]

Hermansky-Pudlak Syndrome Network [14599]

Hermansky-Pudlak Syndrome Network [14599]

HHT Found. Intl. [14600]

HHT Found. Intl. [14600]

Incontinentia Pigmenti Intl. Found. [14601]

Incontinentia Pigmenti Intl. Found. [14601]

Intl. Cellular Medicine Soc. [14649]

Intl. Fed. of Marfan Syndrome Organizations [14602]

Intl. Fed. of Marfan Syndrome Organizations [14602]

Intl. Fibrodysplasia Ossificans Progressiva Assn. [14603]

Intl. Myotonic Dystrophy Org. [14604]

Intl. Soc. for Genetic Eye Diseases and Retino-blastoma [15964]

Intl. Soc. for Mannosidosis and Related Diseases [14605]

Intl. Soc. for Mannosidosis and Related Diseases [14605]

Joubert Syndrome Found. and Related Cerebellar Disorders [14606]

Laurence-Moon-Bardet-Biedl Syndrome Network [14607]

Lowe Syndrome Assn. [14608]

Lynch Syndrome Intl. [14609]

Make Early Diagnosis to Prevent Early Death [14610]

Make Early Diagnosis to Prevent Early Death [14610]

Malignant Hyperthermia Assn. of the U.S. [14611]

MHE Coalition [14612]

Michael Fund (Intl. Found. for Genetic Res.) [14613]

Michael Fund (Intl. Found. for Genetic Res.) [14613]

Nail Patella Syndrome Worldwide [14614]

Nail Patella Syndrome Worldwide [14614]

Natl. Found. for Ectodermal Dysplasias [14615]

Natl. Fragile X Found. [14616]

Neurofibromatosis [14617]

Noah's Never Ending Rainbow [14618]

Oligonucleotide Therapeutics Soc. [16866]

Organic Acidemia Assn. [14619]

Pierre Robin Network [14620]

PKS Kids [14621]

Prader-Willi Syndrome Assn. USA [14622]

PRISMS: Parents and Researchers Interested In Smith-Magenis Syndrome [14623]

PRISMS: Parents and Researchers Interested In Smith-Magenis Syndrome [14623]

Progressive Osseous Heteroplasia Assn. [14624]

Prune Belly Syndrome Network [14625]

Prune Belly Syndrome Network [14625]

Purine Res. Soc. [15506]

PXE Intl. [14626]

Share and Care Cockayne Syndrome Network [14627]

Shwachman Diamond Am. [14628]

Sotos Syndrome Support Assn. [14629]

Sotos Syndrome Support Assn. [14629]

Stickler Involved People [14630]

Stickler Involved People [14630]

Sudden Arrhythmia Death Syndromes Found. [14631]

Support Org. for Trisomy 18, 13, and Related Disorders [14632]

Turner Syndrome Soc. of the U.S. [14633]

U.S. Hereditary Angioedema Assn. [14634]

Velo-Cardio-Facial Syndrome [14635]

Velo-Cardio-Facial Syndrome [14635]

A star before a book entry number signifies that the name is not listed separately, but is mentioned within the entry.

VHL Family Alliance [14636]
Williams Syndrome Assn. [14637]
Xeroderma Pigmentosum Soc. [14638]
Zellweger Baby Support Network [14639]
Genetic Engg. Action Network - Defunct.
Genetic Found; Wallace [3767]
Genetic Metabolic Dietitians Intl. [15497], PO Box 33985, Fort Worth, TX 76162, (866)611-6346
Genetic Technologists; Assn. of [6292]
Genetic Toxicology Assn. [7570], Leon Stankowski, Treas., Covance Labs., 14920 Broschart Rd., Rockville, MD 20850, (301)610-2887
Genetics
Addgene [7110]
Alpacas Without Borders [3773]
Amer. Assn. of Anthropological Genetics [6895]
Amer. Bd. of Genetic Counseling [14640]
Amer. Bd. of Medical Genetics [14641]
Amer. Coll. of Medical Genetics [14642]
Amer. Genetic Assn. [6896]
Amer. Inst. for Medical and Biological Engg. [6897]
Amer. Soc. of Gene and Cell Therapy [14643]
Amer. Soc. of Gene Therapy [14643]
Amer. Soc. for Genomic Medicine [14644]
Amer. Soc. for Genomic Medicine [14644]
Amer. Soc. of Human Genetics [6898]
Assn. of Professors of Human and Medical Genetics [14645]
Behavior Genetics Assn. [14646]
Behavior Genetics Assn. [14646]GeneticsCanadian Assn. of Genetic Counsellors
Genetic Alliance Registry and BioBank [14647]
Genetic Metabolic Dietitians Intl. [15497]
Genetics Policy Inst. [14648]
Genetics Policy Inst. [14648]
Genetics Soc. [15898]
Genetics Soc. of Am. [6899]
Intl. Cellular Medicine Soc. [14649]
Intl. Genetic Epidemiology Soc. [14514]
Intl. Mammalian Genome Soc. [6900]
Intl. Soc. of Nurses in Genetics [14650]
Intl. Soc. of Nurses in Genetics [14650]
Intl. Soc. of Pharmacogenomics [16200]
Intl. Soc. for Phylogenetic Nomenclature [6901]
Intl. Soc. for Phylogenetic Nomenclature [6901]
Intl. Soc. for Plasmid Biology and other Mobile Genetic Elements [7111]
Intl. Soc. of Psychiatric Genetics [14651]
Intl. Soc. of Psychiatric Genetics [14651]
Intl. Soc. for Stem Cell Res. [14652]
Intl. Soc. for Stem Cell Res. [14652]
Mountain States Genetics Found. [14653]
Natl. Coalition for Hea. Professional Educ. in Genetics [14654]
Natl. Soc. of Genetic Counselors [14655]
Oligonucleotide Therapeutics Soc. [16866]
Preimplantation Genetic Diagnosis Intl. Soc. [14656]GeneticsProteome Soc.
Tissue Engg. Intl. and Regenerative Medicine Soc. [13835]
Genetics Policy Inst. [14648], 11924 Forest Hill Blvd., Ste. 22, Wellington, FL 33414-6208, (888)238-1423
Genetics Policy Inst. [14648], 11924 Forest Hill Blvd., Ste. 22, Wellington, FL 33414-6208, (888)238-1423
Genetics Soc. [IO], Midlothian, United Kingdom
Genetics Soc. of Am. [6899], 9650 Rockville Pike, Bethesda, MD 20814-3998, (301)634-7300
Genetics Soc. of Australasia [IO], Melbourne, Australia
Genetics Soc. of Canada [IO], Aulac, NB, Canada
Genetics Soc. of Japan [IO], Mishima, Japan
Geneva Infant Feeding Assn. [IO], Geneva, Switzerland
Genito-Urinary Nurses Assn. [IO], London, United Kingdom
Genocide
Armenian Amer. Soc. for Stud. on Stress and Genocide [15447]
Coalition Against Genocide [17738]
Facing History and Ourselves Natl. Found. [9764]
Generation Rwanda [13525]
Genocide Intervention Network [17739]

Genocide Watch [17740]
Genocide Watch [17740]
Help Darfur Now [17741]
Help Darfur Now [17741]
Holocaust Survivors and Friends in Pursuit of Justice [17787]
Inst. for the Stud. of Genocide [17837]
Intl. Assn. of Genocide Scholars [17742]
Intl. Assn. of Genocide Scholars [17742]
Intl. Criminal Court Alliance [5384]
Inyana - League of Rwandan Children and Youth [11474]
Jewish World Watch [17743]
No Peace Without Justice [18269]
Save Darfur Coalition [17744]
Genocide Intervention Network [17739], 1025 Connecticut Ave., Ste. 310, Washington, DC 20036, (202)559-7405
Genocide Watch [17740], PO Box 809, Washington, DC 20044, (703)448-0222
Genocide Watch [17740], PO Box 809, Washington, DC 20044, (703)448-0222
Gensuibaku Kinshi Nihon Kyogikai Gensuikyo [★IO]
Geo and Chevy Club [★21023]
Geo Club [★21023]
Geochemical Soc. [6921], Washington Univ., Earth and Planetary Sciences Dept., One Brookings Dr., CB 1169, St. Louis, MO 63130-4899, (314)935-4131
GeoData Alliance [6534], 11654 Plaza Am. Dr., No. 127, Reston, VA 20190
Geode Rsrc., Conservation, and Development [3720], 308 N 3rd St., Burlington, IA 52601, (319)752-6395
Geodeettinen Laitos [★IO]
Geodetic Soc. of Japan [IO], Tokyo, Japan
Geodetic Surveying; Amer. Assn. for [7485]
GeoForschungsZentrum [IO], Potsdam, Germany
GeoForum [IO], Honefoss, Norway
Geografiska Sallskapet i Finland [★IO]
Geographic Info. Sys. Engineers Soc. [IO], Doha, Qatar
Geographic Soc. of Lima [IO], Lima, Peru
Geographical Assn. of England [IO], Sheffield, United Kingdom
Geographical Org. of Finland [IO], Helsinki, Finland
Geographical Soc. of China [IO], Beijing, People's Republic of China
Geographical Soc. of Ireland [IO], Belfield, Ireland
Geography
Amer. Geographical Soc. [6902]
Assn. of Amer. Geographers [6903]
Intl. Biogeography Soc. [6904]
Natl. Coun. for Geographic Educ. [8211]
Natl. Geographic Soc. [6905]
Soc. of Woman Geographers [6906]
Soc. of Woman Geographers [6906]
GeoHazards Intl. [12571], 200 Town and Country Village, Palo Alto, CA 94301, (650)614-9050
GeoHazards Intl. [12571], 200 Town and Country Village, Palo Alto, CA 94301, (650)614-9050
Geologica Belgica [★IO]
Geological Assn. of Canada [IO], St. John's, NL, Canada
Geological Soc. of Am. [6912], PO Box 9140, Boulder, CO 80301-9140, (303)357-1000
Geological Soc. of Australia [IO], Sydney, Australia
Geological Soc. of China [IO], Beijing, People's Republic of China
Geological Soc. of Denmark [IO], Copenhagen, Denmark
Geological Soc. of France [IO], Paris, France
Geological Soc. of Glasgow [IO], Glasgow, United Kingdom
Geological Soc. of Japan [IO], Tokyo, Japan
Geological Soc. of London [IO], London, United Kingdom
Geological Soc. of Malaysia [IO], Kuala Lumpur, Malaysia
Geological Soc. of Oman [IO], Ruwi, Oman
Geological Soc. of South Africa [IO], Marshalltown, Republic of South Africa
Geological Soc. of Spain [IO], Salamanca, Spain
Geological Soc. of Sweden [IO], Jonkoping, Sweden
Geologiska Foreningen [★IO]

Geologists' Assn. [IO], London, United Kingdom
Geology
Amer. Assn. of Petroleum Geologists [6907]
Amer. Geological Inst. [6908]
Amer. Inst. of Professional Geologists [6909]
Assn. of Amer. State Geologists [6910]
Assn. of Environmental and Engg. Geologists [6911]
Ethiopian Geophysical Union Intl. [6920]
Geological Soc. of Am. [6912]
Geological Soc. of South Africa [14124]
Natl. Assn. of Geoscience Teachers [8212]
Natl. Assn. of State Boards of Geology [6913]
Sigma Gamma Epsilon [23545]
Soc. of Economic Geologists [6914]
Soc. of Independent Professional Earth Scientists [6915]
Geology; Soc. for Sedimentary [7214]
Geomatics Indus. Assn. of Canada [IO], Ottawa, ON, Canada
Geomorfolosko drustvo Slovenije [★IO]
Geomorphological Soc. of Slovenia [IO], Ljubljana, Slovenia
Geophysical Assn. of Ireland [IO], Maynooth, Ireland
George C. Marshall Found. [10664], VMI Parade, PO Box 1600, Lexington, VA 24450, (540)463-7103
George H. Buck Jr., Jazz Found. [21955], 61 French Market Pl., New Orleans, LA 70116, (504)525-5000
George, Henry
Common Ground - U.S.A. [18695]
George Khoury Assn. of Baseball Leagues [22271], 5400 Meramec Bottom Rd., St. Louis, MO 63128, (314)849-8900
George MacDonald Soc. [IO], London, United Kingdom
George Sand Assn. [9366], Alexandra K. Wettlaufer, Treas., Univ. of Texas at Austin, Dept. of French and Italian, 1 Univ. Sta., B7600, Austin, TX 78712
George Sand Soc. - Defunct.
George Smith Patton, Jr. Historical Soc. [★10682]
George Strait Fan Club [23848], PO Box 2119, Hendersonville, TN 37077, (615)824-7176
George Wright Soc. [4262], PO Box 65, Hancock, MI 49930-0065, (906)487-9722
George Wright Soc. [4262], PO Box 65, Hancock, MI 49930-0065, (906)487-9722
Georgia Peanut Commn. [4749], PO Box 967, Tifton, GA 31793, (229)386-3470
Georgia Writers [★10715]
Georgia Writers Assn. [10715], Kennesaw State Univ., English Dept. Bldg., No. 2701, 1000 Chastain Rd., Kennesaw, GA 30144, (770)420-4736
Georgian
Georgian Assn. in the U.S.A. [18998]
Georgian Assn. of Sports Medicine [IO], Tbilisi, Georgia
Georgian Assn. in the U.S.A. [18998], 2300 M St. NW, Ste. 800, Washington, DC 20037, (202)234-2441
Georgian Badminton Fed. [IO], Tbilisi, Georgia
Georgian Bay Elecl. Contractors Assn. [IO], Toronto, ON, Canada
Georgian Chap. of the Assn. of Energy Engineers [IO], Tbilisi, Georgia
Georgian Figure Skating Assn. [IO], Tbilisi, Georgia
Georgian Floorball Assn. [IO], Kutaisi, Georgia
Georgian Gerontology and Geriatrics Soc. [IO], Tbilisi, Georgia
Georgian Medical Assn. [IO], Tbilisi, Georgia
Georgian Natl. Acad. of Sciences [IO], Tbilisi, Georgia
Georgian Natl. Alliance [★18998]
Georgian Natl. DanceSport Fed. [IO], Tbilisi, Georgia
Georgian Paralympic Comm. [IO], Tbilisi, Georgia
Georgian Soc. Against Epilepsy [IO], Tbilisi, Georgia
Georgian Soc. of Cardiology [IO], Tbilisi, Georgia
Georgian Soc. of Paediatric Chemotherapy [IO], Tbilisi, Georgia
Georgian Taekwondo Fed. [IO], Tbilisi, Georgia
Georgian Tennis Fed. [IO], Tbilisi, Georgia
Georgist Registry [★18696]
Geoscience
Amer. Geophysical Union [6916]

Reference to "IO" in place of a book number signifies that the association may be found in the 50th edition of International Organizations.

ASFE **[6917]**
Assn. of Nigerian Petroleum Professionals Abroad **[7235]**
Assn. for Women Geoscientists **[6918]**
Environmental and Engg. Geophysical Soc. **[6919]**
Environmental and Engg. Geophysical Soc. **[6919]**
Ethiopian Geophysical Union Intl. **[6920]**
Fed. of Earth Sci. Info. Partners **[6603]**
Geochemical Soc. **[6921]**
Geophysical Assn. of Ireland **[15667]**
Geoscience Info. Soc. **[6922]**
Geothermal Resources Coun. **[6923]**
IEEE | Geoscience and Remote Sensing Soc. **[6924]**
Intl. Landslide Res. Gp. **[6925]**
Intl. Landslide Res. Gp. **[6925]**
Intl. Soc. for Aeolian Res. **[6926]**
Intl. Soc. of Soil Mechanics and Geotechnical Engg. **[6927]**
Intl. Soc. of Soil Mechanics and Geotechnical Engg. **[6927]**
Meteoritical Soc. **[6928]**
Soc. of Exploration Geophysicists **[6929]**
Geoscience Australia **[IO]**, Canberra, Australia
Geoscience Info. Soc. **[6922]**, PO Box 6881, Radford, VA 24142, (540)831-5703
Geoscience Soc. of New Zealand **[IO]**, Wellington, New Zealand
Geospatial Info. and Tech. Assn. **[6535]**, 14456 E Evans Ave., Aurora, CO 80014, (303)337-0513
Geosynthetics Materials Assn. **[6426]**, 1801 County Rd. B W, Roseville, MN 55113-4061, (651)222-2508
Geosynthetics Soc; Intl. **[6427]**
Geotechnical Soc. of Ireland **[IO]**, Dublin, Ireland
Geothermal Resources Coun. **[6923]**, PO Box 1350, Davis, CA 95617, (530)758-2360
GeoVisions **[8360]**, PO Box 167, Chesterfield, NH 03443, (603)363-4187
Gepipari Tudomanyos Egyesulet **[★IO]**
Geraldine R. Dodge Found. **[13133]**, PO Box 1239, Morristown, NJ 07962, (973)540-8442
Gerda Lissner Found. **[10345]**, 135 E 55th St., 8th Fl., New York, NY 10022, (212)826-6100
GERG - European Gas Res. Gp. **[IO]**, Brussels, Belgium
Geriatric Care Managers; Natl. Assn. of Professional **[15812]**
Geriatric Massage Inst; Day-Break **[15265]**
Geriatric Pharmacy; Commn. for Certification in **[16189]**
Geriatric Psychiatry; Amer. Assn. for **[16322]**
Geriatric Soc. of India **[IO]**, New Delhi, India
German
  Amer. Aid Soc. of German Descendants **[18999]**
  Amer. Aid Soc. of German Descendants **[18999]**
  Amer. Assn. of Teachers of German **[8460]**
  Amer. Coun. on Germany **[19000]**
  Amer. Coun. on Germany **[19000]**
  Amer. Historical Soc. of Germans From Russia **[19001]**
  Amer. Historical Soc. of Germans From Russia **[19001]**
  Amer. Inst. for Contemporary German Stud. **[9634]**
  Amer. Inst. for Contemporary German Stud. **[9634]**
  Delta Phi Alpha **[23546]**
  German-American Natl. Cong. **[19002]**
  German Foods North Am. **[4715]**
  German Soc. of Pennsylvania **[19003]**
  German-Texan Heritage Soc. **[19004]**
  German-Texan Heritage Soc. **[19004]**
  Germans From Russia Heritage Soc. **[19005]**
  Germans From Russia Heritage Soc. **[19005]**
  Goethe-Institut Inter Nationes **[9635]**
  Goethe-Institut Inter Nationes **[9635]**
  Gottscheer Heritage and Genealogy Assn. **[19006]**
  North Amer. Kant Soc. **[10403]**
  Soc. for German-American Stud. **[9636]**
  Soc. for German Idealism **[9637]**
  Steuben Soc. of Am. **[19007]**

Volkswagen Club of Am. **[21193]**
German Academic Exchange Ser. **[8361]**, 871 United Nations Plz., New York, NY 10017, (212)758-3223
German Academic Exchange Ser. **[8361]**, 871 United Nations Plz., New York, NY 10017, (212)758-3223
German Acad. of Language and Poetry **[IO]**, Darmstadt, Germany
German Acad. for Psychoanalysis **[IO]**, Berlin, Germany
German Adult Educ. Assn. **[IO]**, Bonn, Germany
German Aero Club **[IO]**, Braunschweig, Germany
German Aerospace Center **[IO]**, Cologne, Germany
German Aerospace Indus. Assn. **[IO]**, Berlin, Germany
German Agricultural Soc. **[IO]**, Frankfurt, Germany
German Agro Action - Germany **[IO]**, Bonn, Germany
German Alpine Assn. **[IO]**, Munich, Germany
German Amer. Business Assn. - Defunct.
German Amer. Chamber of Commerce **[23364]**, 75 Broad St., 21st Fl., New York, NY 10004-2415, (212)974-8830
German-American Football Assn. **[★22934]**
German-Amer. Information and Education Assn. - Defunct.
German-American Lawyers Assn. **[IO]**, Bonn, Germany
German-American Natl. Cong. **[19002]**, 4740 N Western Ave., Ste. 206, Chicago, IL 60625-2013, (773)275-1100
German Appropriate Tech. Exchange **[IO]**, Eschborn, Germany
German-Armenian Soc. **[IO]**, Enger, Germany
German Asphalt Assn. **[IO]**, Bonn, Germany
German Assn. for Amer. Stud. **[IO]**, Osnabruck, Germany
German Assn. for Asian Stud. **[IO]**, Hamburg, Germany
German Assn. of Biomedical Engg. **[IO]**, Frankfurt am Main, Germany
German Assn. of the Bread and Pastry Indus. **[IO]**, Dusseldorf, Germany
German Assn. of Consulting Engineers **[IO]**, Berlin, Germany
German Assn. of Dietitians **[IO]**, Essen, Germany
German Assn. of Land Surveyors **[IO]**, Wuppertal, Germany
German Assn. of Market and Social Researchers **[IO]**, Berlin, Germany
German Assn. for Materials Res. and Testing **[IO]**, Berlin, Germany
German Assn. for Motor Trades and Repairs **[IO]**, Bonn, Germany
German Assn. for Music Therapy **[IO]**, Berlin, Germany
German Assn. for Personnel Mgt. **[IO]**, Dusseldorf, Germany
German Assn. of Pharmaceutical Medicine **[IO]**, Munich, Germany
German Assn. for Physiotherapy **[IO]**, Cologne, Germany
German Assn. for Railroad-History **[IO]**, Werl, Germany
German Assn. of Self-Employed Midwives **[IO]**, Frankfurt, Germany
German Assn. of Sport Psychology **[IO]**, Kiel, Germany
German Assn. of Surveying **[IO]**, Vogtsburg im Kaiserstuhl, Germany
German Assn. of Tax Advisers **[IO]**, Berlin, Germany
German Assn. for Water, Wastewater and Waste **[IO]**, Hennef, Germany
German Assn. of Women Engineers **[IO]**, Darmstadt, Germany
German Atlantic Assn. **[IO]**, Berlin, Germany
German Atomic Forum **[IO]**, Berlin, Germany
German-Australian Chamber of Indus. and Commerce **[IO]**, Sydney, Australia
German Bar Assn. **[IO]**, Berlin, Germany
German Bible Soc. **[IO]**, Stuttgart, Germany
German - Brazilian Lawyers Assn. **[IO]**, Osnabruck, Germany
German Brewers Union **[IO]**, Berlin, Germany

German-British Chamber of Indus. and Commerce **[IO]**, London, United Kingdom
German Bunsen Soc. for Physical Chemistry **[IO]**, Frankfurt, Germany
German Bus. Aviation Assn. **[IO]**, Berlin, Germany
German Bus. Coun. Qatar **[IO]**, Doha, Qatar
German Cactus Soc. **[IO]**, Pforzheim, Germany
German Cardiac Soc. **[IO]**, Dusseldorf, Germany
German Carpet Res. Inst. **[IO]**, Aachen, Germany
German Cement Works Assn. **[IO]**, Dusseldorf, Germany
German Centre of Gerontology **[IO]**, Berlin, Germany
German Centre Singapore **[IO]**, Singapore, Singapore
German Ceramic Soc. **[IO]**, Cologne, Germany
German Chap. of the ACM **[IO]**, Pforzheim, Germany
German Chem. Soc. **[IO]**, Frankfurt am Main, Germany
German China Assn. **[IO]**, Karlsruhe, Germany
German-Chinese Bus. Assn. **[IO]**, Cologne, Germany
German-Chinese Friendship Assn. **[IO]**, Berlin, Germany
German Civil Ser. Fed. **[IO]**, Berlin, Germany
German Coffee Assn. **[IO]**, Hamburg, Germany
German Colonies Collectors Gp. **[22040]**, PO Box 845, Stevens Point, WI 54481-0845
German Colonies Collectors Gp. **[22040]**, PO Box 845, Stevens Point, WI 54481-0845
German Convention Bur. **[23402]**, 122 E 42nd St., Ste. 2000, New York, NY 10168-0072, (212)661-4582
German Convention Bur. **[IO]**, Frankfurt, Germany
German Cosmetic, Toiletry, Perfumery and Detergent Assn. **[IO]**, Frankfurt, Germany
German Coun. on Foreign Relations **[IO]**, Berlin, Germany
German Coun. for Land Stewardship **[IO]**, Bonn, Germany
German Coun. for Public Relations **[IO]**, Berlin, Germany
German Cricket Fed. **[IO]**, Passau, Germany
German Dairy Assn. **[IO]**, Berlin, Germany
German Dance Sport Fed. **[IO]**, Frankfurt, Germany
German Data Protection Org. **[IO]**, Bonn, Germany
German Dental Assn. **[IO]**, Berlin, Germany
German Dermatological Soc. **[IO]**, Berlin, Germany
German Design Coun. **[IO]**, Frankfurt am Main, Germany
German Development Ser. - Vietnam **[IO]**, Hanoi, Vietnam
German Direct Marketing Assn. **[IO]**, Wiesbaden, Germany
German Directors Guild **[IO]**, Munich, Germany
German Economic Engineers Assn. **[IO]**, Berlin, Germany
German Educ. Union **[IO]**, Frankfurt, Germany
German Educational Res. Assn. **[IO]**, Berlin, Germany
German Elecl. and Electronic Mfrs. Assn. **[IO]**, Frankfurt, Germany
German Fed. Bar **[IO]**, Berlin, Germany
German Fed. for Food Law and Food Sci. **[IO]**, Berlin, Germany
German Fed. of Rural Youth **[IO]**, Berlin, Germany
German Fed. of Sports Medicine and Prevention **[IO]**, Freiburg, Germany
German Floorball Assn. **[IO]**, Dannewerk, Germany
German Foods North Am. **[4715]**, 719 Sixth St. NW, Washington, DC 20001
German Forestry Coun. **[IO]**, Berlin, Germany
German Foundry Assn. **[IO]**, Dusseldorf, Germany
German Franchise Assn. **[IO]**, Berlin, Germany
German Fruit Trade Assn. **[IO]**, Bonn, Germany
German Fur Assn. **[IO]**, Frankfurt, Germany
German Gemmological Assn. **[IO]**, Idar-Oberstein, Germany
German Genealogical Soc. of Am. **[20631]**, Southern California Genealogical Soc., 417 Irving Dr., Burbank, CA 91504-2408, (818)843-7247
German Genealogical Soc. of Am. **[20631]**, Southern California Genealogical Soc., 417 Irving Dr., Burbank, CA 91504-2408, (818)843-7247

A star before a book entry number signifies that the name is not listed separately, but is mentioned within the entry.

German Geological Soc. [IO], Hannover, Germany
German Geophysical Soc. [IO], Potsdam, Germany
German Gun Collectors' Assn. [21342], PO Box 429, Mayfield, UT 84643, (435)979-9723
German Gun Collectors' Assn. [21342], PO Box 429, Mayfield, UT 84643, (435)979-9723
German Historical Inst. [9766], 1607 New Hampshire Ave. NW, Washington, DC 20009-2562, (202)387-3355
German History Soc. [IO], Milton Keynes, United Kingdom
German Holstein Assn. [IO], Bonn, Germany
German Hosp. Fed. [IO], Berlin, Germany
German Hotels and Restaurants Assn. [IO], Berlin, Germany
German Huntington Help [IO], Duisburg, Germany
German Indus. UK [IO], Criccieth, United Kingdom
German Informatics Soc. [IO], Bonn, Germany
German Inst. for Intl. and Security Affairs [IO], Berlin, Germany
German Inst. of Navigation [IO], Bonn, Germany
German Inst. for Polymers [IO], Darmstadt, Germany
German Interdisciplinary Assn. of Critical Care Medicine [IO], Berlin, Germany
German Interior Architects Assn. [IO], Bonn, Germany
German - Japanese Jurists Assn. [IO], Hamburg, Germany
German-Japanese Soc. for Social Sciences [IO], Konstanz, Germany
German Journalists' Fed. [IO], Berlin, Germany
German Language Soc. [IO], Wiesbaden, Germany
German League Against Epilepsy [IO], Giessen, Germany
German Machine Tool Builders' Assn. [IO], Frankfurt, Germany
German Machinery and Plant Mfrs. Assn. - Japan Liaison Off. [IO], Tokyo, Japan
German Marshall Fund of the U.S. [17969], 1744 R St. NW, Washington, DC 20009, (202)683-2650
German Marshall Fund of the U.S. [17969], 1744 R St. NW, Washington, DC 20009, (202)683-2650
German Mathematical Assn. [IO], Berlin, Germany
German Meat Assn. [IO], Bonn, Germany
German Medical Assn. [IO], Berlin, Germany
German Medical Tech. Assn. [IO], Berlin, Germany
German Metal Dealers Assn. [IO], Berlin, Germany
German Meteorological Soc. [IO], Berlin, Germany
German Mineralogical Soc. [IO], Mainz, Germany
German Mining Assn. [IO], Berlin, Germany
German MPS Soc. [IO], Aschaffenburg, Germany
German Museums Assn. [IO], Berlin, Germany
German-Namibian Soc. [IO], Gottingen, Germany
German Natl. Mathematical Soc. [IO], Berlin, Germany
German Natl. Tourist Bd. [3559], 122 E 42nd St., Ste. 2000, New York, NY 10168-0072, (212)661-7200
German Natl. Tourist Off. [3559], 122 E 42nd St., Ste. 2000, New York, NY 10168-0072, (212)661-7200
German Neuroscience Soc. [IO], Berlin, Germany
German Nutrition Soc. [IO], Bonn, Germany
German Olympic Sports Fed. [IO], Frankfurt am Main, Germany
German Ophthalmological Soc. [IO], Munich, Germany
German Org. of Endocrinology [IO], Regenstauf, Germany
German Org. of Nutrition [IO], Bonn, Germany
German Ornithologists' Soc. [IO], Wilhelmshaven, Germany
German Peace Soc. - United War Resisters [IO], Frankfurt, Germany
German PennState Alumni Chap. [IO], Kiel, Germany
German-Peruvian Chamber of Commerce and Indus. [IO], Lima, Peru
German Physical Soc. [IO], Bad Honnef, Germany
German Phytomedical Soc. [IO], Braunschweig, Germany
German Political Sci. Assn. [IO], Osnabruck, Germany
German Prefab. Constr. Assn. [IO], Bad Honnef, Germany

German Printing and Media Indus. Fed. [IO], Wiesbaden, Germany
German Private Equity and Venture Capital Assn. (BVK) [IO], Berlin, Germany
German Professional Women's Assn. [3681], PO Box 476, Lake Orion, MI 48361-0476
German Professional Women's Assn. [3681], PO Box 476, Lake Orion, MI 48361-0476
German Publishers and Booksellers Assn. [IO], Frankfurt am Main, Germany
German Pulp and Paper Assn. [IO], Bonn, Germany
German Res. Assn. - Address unknown since 2011.
German Res. Found. [IO], Bonn, Germany
German Retailers Import Trade Assn. [IO], Cologne, Germany

German Shepherd
  Echo Dogs White Shepherd Rescue [10954]
  German Shepherd Dog Club of Am. I Working Dog Assn. [21569]
  Support Dogs, Inc. [11832]
German Shepherd Dog Club of Am. [21568], Laura Gilbert, Corresponding Sec., 2448 Johnstown Rd., Chesapeake, VA 23322, (757)421-7854
German Shepherd Dog Club of Am. I Working Dog Assn. [21569], Joy Schultz, Recorder/Admin., 72 Oakcrest Ln., Westampton, NJ 08060, (609)526-5418
German Shepherd Dog Club of New England [★21568]
German Shipbuilding and Ocean Indus. Assn. [IO], Hamburg, Germany
German Shipowners' Assn. [IO], Hamburg, Germany
German Shipsupplier Assn. [IO], Hamburg, Germany
German Shoe Indus. Assn. [IO], Offenbach, Germany
German Shorthaired Pointer Club of Am. [21570], 200 Goede Rd., Edgerton, WI 53534, (608)884-4342
German Sleep Soc. [IO], Schwalmstadt, Germany
German Smoking Tobacco Assn. [IO], Bonn, Germany
German Soc. for Aeronautics and Astronautics [IO], Bonn, Germany
German Soc. of Anaesthesiology and Intensive Care Medicine [IO], Nuremberg, Germany
German Soc. of Aviation and Space Medicine [IO], Mannheim, Germany
German Soc. for Biochemistry and Molecular Biology [IO], Frankfurt, Germany
German Soc. for Bog and Peat Res. [IO], Hannover, Germany
German Soc. of Cinematographers [IO], Munich, Germany
German Soc. for Concrete and Constr. Tech. [IO], Berlin, Germany
German Soc. for Disaster Medicine [IO], Munich, Germany
German Soc. for Experimental and Clinical Pharmacology and Toxicology [IO], Dusseldorf, Germany
German Soc. for Fat Sci. [IO], Frankfurt, Germany
German Soc. for Gen. and Visceral Surgery [IO], Berlin, Germany
German Soc. of Gerontology and Geriatrics [IO], Remscheid, Germany
German Soc. of Glass Tech. [IO], Offenbach, Germany
German Soc. for Hematology and Oncology [IO], Berlin, Germany
German Soc. for Horticultural Sci. [IO], Hannover, Germany
German Soc. of Human Genetics [IO], Munich, Germany
German Soc. of Hypertension [IO], Heidelberg, Germany
German Soc. for Info. Sci. and Practice [IO], Frankfurt am Main, Germany
German Soc. for Linguistics [IO], Konstanz, Germany
German Soc. for Marine Res. [IO], Hamburg, Germany
German Soc. for Mining, Metallurgy, Rsrc. and Environmental Tech. [IO], Clausthal-Zellerfeld, Germany
German Soc. of Neurogenetics [IO], Tubingen, Germany

German Soc. for Non-Destructive Testing [IO], Berlin, Germany
German Soc. of Nutrition [IO], Bonn, Germany
German Soc. for Online Res. [IO], Hurth, Germany
German Soc. of Operations Res. [IO], Erkelenz, Germany
German Soc. of Pediatrics and Adolescent Medicine [IO], Berlin, Germany
German Soc. of Pennsylvania [19003], 611 Spring Garden St., Philadelphia, PA 19123-3505, (215)627-2332
German Soc. for Photogrammetry and Remote Sensing [IO], Munster, Germany
German Soc. for Physical Medicine and Rehabilitation [IO], Dresden, Germany
German Soc. of Physiology [IO], Rostock, Germany
German Soc. of Plastic and Reconstructive Surgery [IO], Rotenburg, Germany
German Soc. of Refrigeration and Airconditioning [IO], Hannover, Germany
German Soc. of Reproductive Medicine [IO], Dortmund, Germany
German Soc. of School Music Educators [IO], Mainz, Germany
German Soc. for Sex Res. [IO], Aachen, Germany
German Soc. for Social Sci. Sexuality Res. [IO], Dusseldorf, Germany
German Soc. of Speech, Language, and Voice-Pathology [IO], Lubeck, Germany
German State Archaeologists' Assn. [IO], Bonn, Germany
German Statistical Soc. [IO], Hamburg, Germany
German Steel Constr. Assn. [IO], Dusseldorf, Germany
German Susswarenexportforderung [★IO]
German Sweets Export Assn. [IO], Bonn, Germany
German Teachers' Union [IO], Bonn, Germany
German Tenants' Union [IO], Berlin, Germany
German-Texan Heritage Soc. [19004], 507 E 10th St., PO Box 684171, Austin, TX 78768-4171, (512)482-0927
German-Texan Heritage Soc. [19004], 507 E 10th St., PO Box 684171, Austin, TX 78768-4171, (512)482-0927
German Timber Trade Fed. [IO], Wiesbaden, Germany
German Transpersonal Assn. [IO], Berlin, Germany
German Travel Assn. [IO], Berlin, Germany
German Welding Soc. [IO], Dusseldorf, Germany
German WindEnergy Assn. [IO], Berlin, Germany
German Wine Inst. [IO], Mainz, Germany
German Winegrowers Assn. [IO], Bonn, Germany
German Wirehaired Pointer Club of Am. [21571], Sue Mueller, Treas., W12203-870th Ave., River Falls, WI 54022
German Youth Hostel Assn. [IO], Detmold, Germany
Germanna Found. [★9708]
Germans From Russia Heritage Soc. [19005], 1125 W Turnpike Ave., Bismarck, ND 58501-8115, (701)223-6167
Germans From Russia Heritage Soc. [19005], 1125 W Turnpike Ave., Bismarck, ND 58501-8115, (701)223-6167
Germany
  Hof Reunion Assn. [20349]
  Volkswagen Club of Am. [21193]
Germany Philatelic Soc. [22041], PO Box 6547, Chesterfield, MO 63006-6547
Germany Philatelic Soc. [22041], PO Box 6547, Chesterfield, MO 63006-6547
Gerontological Assn. of Malaysia [IO], Selangor, Malaysia
Gerontological Assn. of Slovenia [IO], Ljubljana, Slovenia
Gerontological Soc. [★14664]
Gerontological Soc. of Am. [14664], 1220 L St. NW, Ste. 901, Washington, DC 20005, (202)842-1275
Gerontological Soc. of the Russian Acad. of Sciences [IO], St. Petersburg, Russia
Gerontological Soc. of Serbia [IO], Belgrade, Serbia
Gerontological Soc. of Singapore [IO], Singapore, Singapore
Gerontology
  Amer. Aging Assn. [14657]
  Amer. Aging Assn. [14657]

Reference to "IO" in place of a book number signifies that the association may be found in the 50th edition of International Organizations.

Amer. Fed. for Aging Res. [14658]
Amer. Found. for Aging Res. [14659]
Amer. Geriatrics Soc. [14660]
Assn. of Directors of Geriatric Academic Programs [14661]
Assn. for Gerontology in Higher Educ. [8213]
Brookdale Found. [14662]
Center for the Stud. of Aging of Albany [10838]
Coun. of Professional Geropsychology Training Programs [14663]
Gerontological Soc. of Am. [14664]
Hea. Promotion Inst. [10845]
Intl. Assn. of Gerontology European Region [5657]
Intl. Psychogeriatric Assn. [14665]
Intl. Psychogeriatric Assn. [14665]
Leadership Coun. of Aging Organizations [10850]
Natl. Assn. of Geriatric Educ. Centers [14666]
Natl. Assn. of Hea. Care Assistants [14667]
Natl. Assn. for Professional Gerontologists [14668]
Natl. Gerontological Nursing Assn. [14669]
Natl. Inst. on Aging [14670]
New England Gerontological Assn. [14671]
Gerontology; The Center for Social [10837]
Gerontolosko Drustvo Srbije [★IO]
Gerontolosko drustvo Slovenije [★IO]
Gerson Inst. [13678], PO Box 161358, San Diego, CA 92176, (619)685-5353
Gesamtverband Deutscher Holzhandel [★IO]
Gesamtverband Deutscher Musikfachgeschafte [★IO]
Gesamtverband der deutschen Textil- und Modeindustrie [★IO]
Geschaftsstelle des Deutscher Sportaztebund [★IO]
Gesellschaft fur deutsche Sprache [★IO]
Gesellschaft fur Aerosolforschung e.V. [★IO]
Gesellschaft fur Arzneipflanzenforschung [★IO]
Gesellschaft fuer Bedrohte Volker [★IO]
Gesellschaft fur Bergbau, Metallurgie, Rohstoff- und Umwelttechnik [★IO]
Gesellschaft fur Bergbau, Metallurgie, Rohstoff-und Umwelttechnik e.V. [★IO]
Gesellschaft fur Biochemie und Molekularbiologie e.V. [★IO]
Gesellschaft fur Chemische Technik und Biotechnologie [★IO]
Gesellschaft fur Deutsch-Chinesische Freundschaft Berlin [★IO]
Gesellschaft Deutscher Chemiker [★IO]
Gesellschaft Deutscher Naturforscher und Arzte [IO], Bad Honnef, Germany
Gesellschaft fur Energieplanung und Systemanalyse [IO], Munster, Germany
Gesellschaft fur Energiewissenschaft und Energiepolitik e.V. [★IO]
Gesellschaft zur Forderung der Literatur aus Afrika, Asien und Lateinamerika [★IO]
Gesellschaft zur Freiwilligen Kontrole von Messe- und Ausstellungszahlen [★IO]
Gesellschaft fuer Informatik [★IO]
Gesellschaft fuer Mukopolysaccharidosen e.V. [★IO]
Gesellschaft fur Neonatologie und Padiatrische Intensivmedizin [★IO]
Gesellschaft fur Oekologie [★IO]
Gesellschaft fur Operations Res. e.V. [★IO]
Gesellschaft fur Selbstspielende Musikinstrumente e.V. [★IO]
Gesellschaft fur Technische Zusammenarbeit [★IO]
Gesellschaft fuer Versuchstierkunde [★IO]
Gesellschaft fur die Volksmusik in der Schweiz [★IO]
Gesellschaft zur Wissenschaftlichen Untersuchung von Parawissenschaften [★IO]
Gesellscraft fur Terminologie and Wissenstransfer [★IO]
GesherCity [19091], Adam Courtney, Dir., 520 8th Ave., 4th Fl., New York, NY 10010, (212)786-5108
Gesneriad Hybridizers Assn. [21796], 1122 E Pike St., PMB 637, Seattle, WA 98122-3916
Gesneriad Soc. [21797], 1122 E Pike St., PMB 637, Seattle, WA 98122-3916
Gesneriad Soc. [21797], 1122 E Pike St., PMB 637, Seattle, WA 98122-3916
Gesselschaft fur bedrohte Sprachen [★IO]

Gestalt Australia and New Zealand [IO], Melbourne, Australia
Gestalt Community [★9832]
Gestalt Therapy; Assn. for the Advancement of [16384]
Get Oil Out! [4792], Environmental Defense Center, Santa Barbara Off., 906 Garden St., Santa Barbara, CA 93101, (805)963-1622
Get Your Guts in Gear [14566], 593 Vanderbilt Ave., PMB 108, Brooklyn, NY 11238, (718)875-2123
Gettysburg Coll. [★18456]
Gettysburg Coll. [★18456]
Gettysburg; Friends of the Natl. Parks at [9687]
Gewerkschaft Erziehung und Wissenschaft [★IO]

Ghana
  Ahoto Partnership for Ghana [15141]
  Ghana Medical Mission [15160]
  Ghana Relief Org. [11289]
  Global Associates for Hea. Development [15161]
  Global Brigades [11588]
  Moringa Community [11610]
Ghana Acad. of Arts and Sciences [IO], Accra, Ghana
Ghana Assn. of Consultants [IO], Accra, Ghana
Ghana Assn. of Physiotherapists [IO], Accra, Ghana
Ghana Athletic Assn. [IO], Accra, Ghana
Ghana Baseball and Softball Assn. [IO], Accra, Ghana
Ghana Chamber of Mines [IO], Accra, Ghana
Ghana Cocoa Marketing Bd. [IO], Accra, Ghana
Ghana Diabetes Assn. [IO], Accra, Ghana
Ghana Employers Assn. [IO], Accra, Ghana
Ghana Export Promotion Coun. [IO], Accra, Ghana
Ghana Geotechnical Soc. [IO], Kumasi, Ghana
Ghana Integrity Initiative [IO], Accra, Ghana
Ghana Medical Assn. [IO], Accra, Ghana
Ghana Medical Mission [15160], 248 McNear Dr., San Rafael, CA 94901
Ghana Natl. Chamber of Commerce and Indus. [IO], Accra, Ghana
Ghana Red Cross Soc. [IO], Accra, Ghana
Ghana Relief Org. [11289], PO Box 1722, Baltimore, MD 21203, (410)486-6832
Ghana Squash Assn. [IO], Accra, Ghana
Ghana Taekwondo Assn. [IO], Accra, Ghana
Ghana Tennis Assn. [IO], Accra, Ghana
Ghana-USA Chamber of Commerce [23365], PO Box 629, Glenwood, IL 60425, (708)331-3277
Ghana-USA Chamber of Commerce [23365], PO Box 629, Glenwood, IL 60425, (708)331-3277
Ghana Wildlife Soc. [IO], Accra, Ghana
Ghaqda Biblika Maltija [★IO]
Ghaqda Maltija Kontra id-Dijabete [★IO]
Ghorfet el Monchekat el Fondokia [★IO]
Ghost Club [IO], Ipswich, United Kingdom
Ghost Res. Soc. [7250], PO Box 205, Oak Lawn, IL 60454-0205, (708)425-5163
Ghost Trackers Club [★7250]
GI Forum [★20772]
GI Joe Collectors' Club [22170], 225 Cattle Baron Parc Dr., Fort Worth, TX 76108, (817)448-9863
Giant Schnauzer Club of Am. [21572], Bill Combs, Membership Chm., 7063 W Arlington Dr., Lakewood, CO 80123, (303)973-2133
Gibraltar Amateur Radio Soc. [IO], Gibraltar, United Kingdom
Gibraltar Assn. of Compliance Officers [IO], Gibraltar, Gibraltar
Gibraltar Badminton Fed. [IO], Gibraltar, Gibraltar
Gibraltar Cat Welfare Soc. [IO], Gibraltar, Gibraltar
Gibraltar Cricket Assn. [IO], Gibraltar, Gibraltar
Gibraltar Dyslexia Support Gp. [IO], Gibraltar, Gibraltar
Gibraltar Fed. of Small Businesses [IO], Gibraltar, Gibraltar
Gibraltar Funds and Investments Assn. [IO], Gibraltar, Gibraltar
Gibraltar Hearing Impaired and Tinnitus Assn. [IO], Gibraltar, Gibraltar
Gibraltar Petanque Assn. [IO], Gibraltar, Gibraltar
Gibraltar Philharmonic Soc. [IO], Gibraltar, Gibraltar
Gibraltar Rhythmic Gymnastics Assn. [IO], Gibraltar, Gibraltar
Gibraltar Squash Assn. [IO], Gibraltar, Gibraltar
Gibraltar Taxi Assn. [IO], Gibraltar, Gibraltar

Gibraltar Tenpin Bowling Assn. [IO], Gibraltar, Gibraltar
Gideon Averill Descendants Org. - Defunct.
The Gideons Intl. [19749], PO Box 140800, Nashville, TN 37214-0800, (615)564-5000
The Gideons Intl. [19749], PO Box 140800, Nashville, TN 37214-0800, (615)564-5000
Gift Associates Interchange Network [3376], ABC-Amega, Inc., 1100 Main St., Buffalo, NY 14209-2356, (716)887-9504
Gift From Within [12712], 16 Cobb Hill Rd., Camden, ME 04843, (207)236-8858
Gift from the Heart Found. [14078], 3860 N. 25th Ave., Schiller Park, IL 60176, (847)671-2711
Gift from the Heart Found. [14078], 3860 N. 25th Ave., Schiller Park, IL 60176, (847)671-2711
Gift and Home Trade Assn. [3161], 2025 E Beltline Ave. SE, Ste. 200, Grand Rapids, MI 49546, (616)949-9104
Gift of Life Intl. [12456], PO Box 650436, Fresh Meadows, NY 11365, (845)546-2104
Gift of Life Intl. [12456], PO Box 650436, Fresh Meadows, NY 11365, (845)546-2104
Gift Sales Manager Assn. [3162], 2537 Grandville Ave., Henderson, NV 89052, (702)361-3955
Gift of Water [13420], 1025 Pine Hill Way, Carmel, IN 46032-7701, (317)371-1656
Gifted
  Amer. Assn. for Gifted Children [8214]
  Amer. Mensa [9638]
  The Assn. for the Gifted [8215]
  Intl. Soc. for Philosophical Enquiry [9639]
  Intl. Soc. for Philosophical Enquiry [9639]
  INTERTEL [9640]
  Mega Soc. [9641]
  Natl. Assn. for Gifted Children [8216]
  Triple Nine Soc. [9642]
Gifted Education; ERIC CH on Disabilities and [★11780]
Gifted Learning Proj. [12424], PO Box 481551, Kansas City, MO 64148-1551, (816)803-4679
Gifts
  Anheuser-Busch Collectors Club [21300]
  Mexican Assn. of Gifts, Decorative Goods and Folk Art Producers [17215]
  Natl. Specialty Gift Assn. [1572]
Gifts In Kind [★12670]
Gifts In Kind Intl. [★12670]
Gifts In Kind of Am. [★12670]
Giftware Associate Interchange Network [★3376]
Giftware Assn. [IO], Birmingham, United Kingdom
Giftware Mfrs. Credit Interchange [★3376]
Gigt Foreningen [★IO]
Gilbert and Sullivan
  Jack Point Preservation Soc. [9501]
Gilbert and Sullivan Soc. [9499], Community Church of New York, 40 E 35th St., New York, NY 10016, (212)757-5804
Gilbert and Sullivan Soc. [IO], Essex, United Kingdom
Gilda Radner Familial Ovarian Cancer Registry [13924], Roswell Park Cancer Inst., Elm and Carlton St., Buffalo, NY 14263-0001, (716)845-4503
Gilda Radner Familial Ovarian Cancer Registry [13924], Roswell Park Cancer Inst., Elm and Carlton St., Buffalo, NY 14263-0001, (716)845-4503
Gilda's Club [13925], 48 Wall St., 11th Fl., New York, NY 10005, (917)305-1200
Gilles de la Tourette Syndrome Assn. [★15636]
Gillespie Clan - Defunct.
Gillie - Gilley Family Org. - Defunct.
Gilligan's Island Fan Club [23919], Ronald A. Turner, VP, 111 Walker Ave., No. 302, Huntsville, AL 35801, (256)535-9536
Gilstrap Family Assn. [20521], 1921 N Harrison, San Angelo, TX 76901-1335, (325)949-0792
Gin Soon Tai Chi Chuan Fed. [22733], 33 Harrison Ave., 2nd Fl., Boston, MA 02111, (617)542-4442
Gin and Vodka Assn. [IO], Salisbury, United Kingdom
Gingerbread [IO], London, United Kingdom
Ginny Doll Club [21691], PO Box 756, Oakdale, CA 95361-0756, (209)848-0300
Ginseng Res. Inst. [★1724]
Ginseng Res. Inst. of Am. [1724], Ginseng Bd. of Wisconsin, 555 N 72nd Ave., Ste. 2, Wausau, WI 54401, (715)845-7300

A star before a book entry number signifies that the name is not listed separately, but is mentioned within the entry.

Giovanni Agnelli Found. **[IO]**, Turin, Italy

Giraffe Club **[18680]**, 30 Brookside Dr., Stratham, NH 03885

Giraffe Heroes Proj. **[9836]**, PO Box 759, Langley, WA 98260, (360)221-7989

Girl Guides Assn. of Cambodia **[IO]**, Phnom Penh, Cambodia

Girl Guides Assn. of Kiribati **[IO]**, Tarawa, Kiribati

Girl Guides Assn. - Malaysia **[IO]**, Kuala Lumpur, Malaysia

Girl Guides Assn. - South Africa **[IO]**, Randburg, Republic of South Africa

Girl Guides Australia - Victoria **[IO]**, South Melbourne, Australia

Girl Guides of Canada **[IO]**, Toronto, ON, Canada

Girl Guides Singapore **[IO]**, Singapore, Singapore

Girl Guides South Australia **[IO]**, Adelaide, Australia

Girl Guides Tasmania **[IO]**, Hobart, Australia

Girl Guiding Scotland **[IO]**, Edinburgh, United Kingdom

Girl Power 2 Cure **[15592]**, 2891 Breakers Ct., Amelia Island, FL 32034, (904)875-4810

Girl Scouting; Natl. Jewish Comm. on **[13025]**

Girl Scouts of the U.S.A. **[13019]**, 420 5th Ave., New York, NY 10018-2798, (212)852-8000

Girlguiding UK **[IO]**, London, United Kingdom

Girls

About-Face **[13448]**

Amer. Legion Auxiliary Girls Nation **[17245]**

Christian Ladies All together Standing against Social Injustice Corp. **[13456]**

Dwa Fanm **[17826]**

Girl Power 2 Cure **[15592]**

Girls Helping Girls **[12118]**

Girls Learn Intl. **[8217]**

Girlstart **[8218]**

Helping Our Teen Girls in Real Life Situations **[12119]**

Intl. Women's Flag Football Assn. **[22589]**

Natl. Campaign to Prevent Teen Pregnancy **[13540]**

Reach Global **[13146]**

Solace Intl. **[13479]**

Women's Alliance for Peace and Human Rights in Afghanistan **[12253]**

Girls and Boys Town **[12947]**, 14100 Crawford St., Boys Town, NE 68010, (402)498-1300

Girls' Brigade Australia **[IO]**, Blacktown, Australia

Girls' Brigade Australia - New South Wales **[IO]**, Toongabbie, Australia

Girls' Brigade Australia - South Australia **[IO]**, Richmond, Australia

Girls' Brigade Australia - Western Australia **[IO]**, Belmont, Australia

Girls' Brigade - England and Wales **[IO]**, Didcot, United Kingdom

Girls' Brigade Intl. Coun. **[IO]**, Glasgow, United Kingdom

Girls' Brigade New Zealand **[IO]**, North Shore City, New Zealand

Girls' Brigade Northern Ireland **[IO]**, Antrim, United Kingdom

Girls' Brigade Queensland **[IO]**, Mansfield, Australia

Girls' Brigade Scotland **[IO]**, Glasgow, United Kingdom

Girls' Brigade Singapore **[IO]**, Singapore, Singapore

Girls' Brigade Victoria **[IO]**, Mitcham, Australia

Girls for a Change **[11290]**, PO Box 1436, San Jose, CA 95109, (408)540-6432

Girls Clubs of Am. **[★13526]**

Girls Educ. Intl. **[9059]**, PO Box 853, Lyons, CO 80540

Girls Educational and Mentoring Services **[18603]**, 298B W 149th St., New York, NY 10039, (212)926-8089

Girls Friendly Soc. - United Kingdom - GFS Platform **[IO]**, London, United Kingdom

Girls' Guild **[★20307]**

Girls Helping Girls **[12118]**, 45945 Sentinel Pl., Fremont, CA 94539, (510)592-4466

Girls Inc. **[13526]**, 120 Wall St., New York, NY 10005-3902, (212)509-2000

Girls Learn Intl. **[8217]**, 252 Seventh Ave., Ste. 3F, New York, NY 10001, (212)707-8577

Girls' Prout **[★18635]**

Girls Rodeo Assn. **[★22851]**

Girls on the Run Intl. **[22863]**, 120 Cottage Pl., Charlotte, NC 28207, (704)376-9817

Girls' Schools Assn. **[IO]**, Leicester, United Kingdom

Girls State **[★17245]**

Girls' Town of Rome **[★13514]**

Girlstart **[8218]**, 1400 W Anderson Ln., Austin, TX 78757, (512)916-4775

Girth and Mirth - Defunct.

Givat Haviva Educational Found. **[18123]**, 114 W 26th St., Ste. 1001, New York, NY 10001, (212)989-9272

Givat Haviva Educational Found. **[18123]**, 114 W 26th St., Ste. 1001, New York, NY 10001, (212)989-9272

Give Children a Choice **[8740]**, PO Box 2298, Matthews, NC 28106

Give Clean Water **[13421]**, PO Box 720953, San Diego, CA 92172-0953, (888)429-6741

Give an Hour **[11088]**, PO Box 5918, Bethesda, MD 20824-5918

Give Kids the World **[★11466]**

Give Kids the World **[★11466]**

Give Kids the World Found. **[★11466]**

Give Kids the World Found. **[★11466]**

Give Kids the World Trust **[★11466]**

Give Kids the World Trust **[★11466]**

Give Kids the World Village **[11466]**, 210 S Bass Rd., Kissimmee, FL 34746-6034, (407)396-1114

Give Kids the World Village **[11466]**, 210 S Bass Rd., Kissimmee, FL 34746-6034, (407)396-1114

Give2TheTroops **[12528]**, 1275 Cromwell Ave., Rocky Hill, CT 06067, (888)876-6775

Give2TheTroops **[12528]**, 1275 Cromwell Ave., Rocky Hill, CT 06067, (888)876-6775

Giving Children Hope **[11291]**, 8332 Commonwealth Ave., Buena Park, CA 90621, (714)523-4454

Giving Children Hope **[11291]**, 8332 Commonwealth Ave., Buena Park, CA 90621, (714)523-4454

Giving Inst. **[1539]**, 303 W Madison St., Ste. 2650, Chicago, IL 60606, (312)981-6794

Giving U.S.A. Found. **[12669]**, 303 W Madison St., Ste. 2650, Chicago, IL 60606-3396, (312)981-6794

Giving Vision **[17076]**, 9663 Santa Monica Blvd., No. 206, Beverly Hills, CA 90210, (310)860-1920

Gladstone Equestrian Assn. **[22680]**, PO Box 469, Gladstone, NJ 07934, (908)453-3332

Glamour Photographers Intl. **[2717]**, PO Box 84374, San Diego, CA 92138, (619)575-0100

Glamour Photographers Intl. **[2717]**, PO Box 84374, San Diego, CA 92138, (619)575-0100

Glasgow Archaeological Soc. **[IO]**, Glasgow, United Kingdom

Glasgow Chamber of Commerce **[IO]**, Glasgow, United Kingdom

Glasgow Mathematical Assn. **[IO]**, Glasgow, United Kingdom

Glasgow Natural History Soc. **[IO]**, Glasgow, United Kingdom

Glasgow Women's Aid **[IO]**, Glasgow, United Kingdom

Glass

Amer. Carnival Glass Assn. **[21828]**

Amer. Cut Glass Assn. **[21829]**

Amer. Natural Soda Ash Corp. **[1573]**

Antique Glass Salt and Sugar Shaker Club **[21304]**

Art Glass Assn. **[1574]**

Art Glass Assn. **[1574]**

Egg Cup Collectors' Corner **[21336]**

Fenton Art Glass Collectors of Am. **[21830]**

Fostoria Glass Collectors **[21831]**

Fostoria Glass Soc. of Am. **[21832]**

Glass Art Soc. **[21833]**

Glass Assn. of North Am. **[1575]**

Glass Mfg. Indus. Coun. **[1576]**

Glass Molders, Pottery, Plastics, and Allied Workers Intl. Union **[23194]**

Heisey Collectors of America/National Heisey Glass Museum **[21834]**

Independent Glass Assn. **[1577]**

Insulating Glass Certification Coun. **[1578]**

Intl. Carnival Glass Assn. **[21835]**

Intl. Carnival Glass Assn. **[21835]**

Natl. Amer. Glass Club **[21836]**

Natl. Cambridge Collectors **[21837]**

Natl. Depression Glass Assn. **[21838]**

Natl. Duncan Glass Soc. **[21839]**

Natl. Fenton Glass Soc. **[21840]**

Natl. Glass Assn. **[1579]**

Natl. Imperial Glass Collectors Soc. **[21841]**

Natl. Milk Glass Collectors Soc. **[21842]**

Protective Glazing Coun. **[1580]**

Retailers of Art Glass and Supplies **[1581]**

Retailers of Art Glass and Supplies **[1581]**

Soc. of Glass and Ceramic Decorated Products **[1582]**

Stained Glass Assn. of Am. **[1583]**

Standing Comm. of the European Glass Indus. **[18877]**

Tiffin Glass Collectors Club **[21843]**

Glass Art Soc. **[21833]**, 6512 23rd Ave. NW, Ste. 329, Seattle, WA 98117, (206)382-1305

Glass Assn. of North Am. **[1575]**, 800 SW Jackson St., Ste. 1500, Topeka, KS 66612-1200, (785)271-0208

Glass Container Mfrs. Inst. **[★880]**

Glass for Europe **[IO]**, Brussels, Belgium

Glass and Glazing Fed. **[IO]**, London, United Kingdom

Glass Inst. **[IO]**, Paris, France

Glass Mfg. Indus. Coun. **[1576]**, 600 N Cleveland Ave., Ste. 210, Westerville, OH 43082, (614)818-9423

Glass Molders, Pottery, Plastics, and Allied Workers Intl. Union **[23194]**, PO Box 607, Media, PA 19063-0607, (610)565-5051

Glass Packaging Inst. **[880]**, 700 N Fairfax St., Ste. 510, Alexandria, VA 22314, (703)684-6359

Glass-Steagall Act Stud. Comm. **[★3206]**

Glass Tempering Assn. **[★1575]**

The Glaucoma Found. **[15959]**, 80 Maiden Ln., Ste. 700, New York, NY 10038, (212)285-0080

Glaucoma Res. Found. **[15960]**, 251 Post St., Ste. 600, San Francisco, CA 94108, (415)986-3162

Glazing Indus. Code Comm. **[564]**, 800 SW Jackson St., Ste. 1500, Topeka, KS 66612-1200, (785)271-0208

Glazounov Soc. - Defunct.

Gleaner Life Insurance Soc. **[19047]**, 5200 W U.S. Hwy. 223, PO Box 1894, Adrian, MI 49221-7894, (800)992-1894

Gleaning for the World **[12839]**, PO Box 645, Concord, VA 24538, (434)993-3600

Glencoe Social Trail Riders **[IO]**, Tarpeena, Australia

Glenkirk **[11791]**, 3504 Commercial Ave., Northbrook, IL 60062, (847)272-5111

Glenmary Res. Center **[19426]**, Glenmary Home Missioners, PO Box 465618, Cincinnati, OH 45246, (513)874-8900

Glenn Miller Birthplace Soc. **[23849]**, 122 W Clark St., PO Box 61, Clarinda, IA 51632, (712)542-2461

Global Action and Information Network - Defunct.

Global Action Intl. **[12840]**, PO Box 131269, Carlsbad, CA 92013, (760)438-3979

Global Action Intl. **[12840]**, PO Box 131269, Carlsbad, CA 92013, (760)438-3979

Global Action to Prevent War **[18168]**, 866 UN Plaza, Ste. 4050, New York, NY 10017, (212)818-1815

Global Action to Prevent War **[18168]**, 866 UN Plaza, Ste. 4050, New York, NY 10017, (212)818-1815

Global Action Proj. **[18825]**, 4 W 37th St., 2nd Fl., New York, NY 10018, (212)594-9577

Global Action Proj. **[18825]**, 4 W 37th St., 2nd Fl., New York, NY 10018, (212)594-9577

Global Action on Widowhood **[18787]**, 3 Newport Rd., Ste. 1, Cambridge, MA 02140, (617)441-8892

Global Advt. Lawyers Alliance **[5660]**, 599 Lexington Ave., 26th Fl., New York, NY 10022, (212)549-0343

Global Advt. Lawyers Alliance **[5660]**, 599 Lexington Ave., 26th Fl., New York, NY 10022, (212)549-0343

Global AIDS Alliance **[13606]**, 1121 14th St. NW, Ste. 200, Washington, DC 20005, (202)789-0432

Global AIDS Interfaith Alliance **[13607]**, PO Box 29110, San Francisco, CA 94129-0110, (415)461-7196

Reference to "IO" in place of a book number signifies that the association may be found in the 50th edition of International Organizations.

Global AIDS Interfaith Alliance **[13607]**, PO Box 29110, San Francisco, CA 94129-0110, (415)461-7196

Global Alliance for Africa **[17150]**, 703 W Monroe St., Chicago, IL 60661, (312)382-0607

Global Alliance Against Traffic in Women **[IO]**, Bangkok, Thailand

Global Alliance of Artists **[9234]**, 1930 N Richmond St., Unit B, Chicago, IL 60647, (312)213-9913

Global Alliance for Community Empowerment **[10811]**, PO Box 12114, Olympia, WA 98508-2114, (360)628-8346

Global Alliance for Incinerator Alternatives **[4982]**, 1958 Univ. Ave., Berkeley, CA 94704, (510)883-9490

Global Alliance for Incinerator Alternatives **[4982]**, 1958 Univ. Ave., Berkeley, CA 94704, (510)883-9490

Global Alliance for Intelligent Arts

Global Alliance for Intelligent Arts - Address unknown since 2011.

Global Alliance for Justice Educ. **[8505]**, Vanderbilt Univ. Law School, 131 21st Ave. S, Nashville, TN 37203-1181

Global Alliance for Justice Educ. **[8505]**, Vanderbilt Univ. Law School, 131 21st Ave. S, Nashville, TN 37203-1181

Global Alliance for Medical Educ. **[8606]**, Celene Chasen, Membership Chair, Baylor Coll. of Medicine, Center for Continuing Medical Educ., Off. of Continuing Medical Educ., 5531 Spellman, Houston, TX 77096, (713)798-4024

Global Alliance for Medical Educ. **[8606]**, Celene Chasen, Membership Chair, Baylor Coll. of Medicine, Center for Continuing Medical Educ., Off. of Continuing Medical Educ., 5531 Spellman, Houston, TX 77096, (713)798-4024

Global Alliance of Performers **[10358]**, 19924 Aurora Ave. N, Ste. 101, Seattle, WA 98133, (206)264-5072

Global Alliance of Performers **[10358]**, 19924 Aurora Ave. N, Ste. 101, Seattle, WA 98133, (206)264-5072

Global Alliance for Preserving the History of WWII in Asia **[20860]**, PO Box 1323, San Carlos, CA 94070-7323

Global Alliance for Preserving the History of WWII in Asia **[20860]**, PO Box 1323, San Carlos, CA 94070-7323

Global Alliance to Prevent Prematurity and Stillbirth **[14105]**, 1100 Olive Way, Ste. 1000, Seattle, WA 98101, (206)884-2777

Global Alliance for Sugar Trade Reform and Liberalisation **[IO]**, Brisbane, Australia

Global Alliance for Women's Hea. **[17126]**, 777 UN Plz., 7th Fl., New York, NY 10017, (212)286-0424

Global Alliance for Women's Hea. **[17126]**, 777 UN Plz., 7th Fl., New York, NY 10017, (212)286-0424

Global Ambassadors for Children **[18249]**, 7399 N Shadeland Ave., No. 116, Indianapolis, IN 46250, (317)814-5318

Global Animal Partnership **[3811]**, PO Box 21484, Washington, DC 20009, (202)540-9880

Global Animal Relief **[3812]**, 2150 Elk Ave., Eugene, OR 97403, (541)505-0743

Global Animal Relief **[3812]**, 2150 Elk Ave., Eugene, OR 97403, (541)505-0743

Global Anti-Incinerator Alliance **[★4982]**

Global Anti-Incinerator Alliance **[★4982]**

Global Applied Disability Res. and Info. Network **[14363]**, Thomas P. Golden, Assoc. Dir., Cornell Univ., ILR School, Employment and Disability Inst., 201 Dolgen Hall, Ithaca, NY 14853-3901, (607)255-2731

Global Applied Disability Res. and Info. Network **[14363]**, Thomas P. Golden, Assoc. Dir., Cornell Univ., ILR School, Employment and Disability Inst., 201 Dolgen Hall, Ithaca, NY 14853-3901, (607)255-2731

Global Aquaculture Alliance **[3823]**, 5661 Telegraph Rd., Ste. 3A, St. Louis, MO 63129, (314)293-5500

Global Aquaculture Alliance **[3823]**, 5661 Telegraph Rd., Ste. 3A, St. Louis, MO 63129, (314)293-5500

Global Associates for Hea. Development **[15161]**, PO Box 790, Freeport, NY 11520, (516)771-1220

Global Associates for Hea. Development **[15161]**, PO Box 790, Freeport, NY 11520, (516)771-1220

Global Assn. for Interpersonal Neurobiology Stud. **[7155]**, PO Box 3605, Santa Monica, CA 90408

Global Assn. for Interpersonal Neurobiology Stud. **[7155]**, PO Box 3605, Santa Monica, CA 90408

Global Assn. of Risk Professionals **[1301]**, 111 Town Square Pl., Ste. 1215, Jersey City, NJ 07310, (201)719-7210

Global Assn. of Risk Professionals **[1301]**, 111 Town Square Pl., Ste. 1215, Jersey City, NJ 07310, (201)719-7210

Global Autism Collaboration **[13793]**, Autism Res. Inst., 4182 Adams Ave., San Diego, CA 92116

Global Autism Proj. **[13794]**, 320 7th Ave., No. 302, Brooklyn, NY 11215

Global Autism Proj. **[13794]**, 320 7th Ave., No. 302, Brooklyn, NY 11215

Global Automakers **[297]**, 1050 K St. NW, Ste. 650, Washington, DC 20001, (202)650-5555

Global Automotive Mgt. Coun. **[298]**, 5305 Plymouth Rd., Ann Arbor, MI 48105, (734)418-2365

Global Biofuels Alliance **[1535]**, 1540 E Lake Rd., Erie, PA 16511, (814)528-9067

Global Brigades **[11588]**, 1099 E Champlain Dr., Ste. A176, Fresno, CA 93720

Global Bus. Coalition on HIV/AIDS **[10880]**, 110 William St., Ste. 1800, New York, NY 10038, (212)584-1600

Global Bus. Coalition on HIV/AIDS, Tuberculosis and Malaria **[10880]**, 110 William St., Ste. 1800, New York, NY 10038, (212)584-1600

Global Bus. and Tech. Assn. **[664]**, PO Box 2686, Huntington Station, NY 11746, (516)876-3408

Global Bus. and Tech. Assn. **[664]**, PO Box 2686, Huntington Station, NY 11746, (516)876-3408

Global Centurion **[11292]**, 2000 Clarendon Blvd., Arlington, VA 22201, (703)276-3000

Global Children **[11293]**, 100 Atlantic Ave., No. 2N, Brooklyn, NY 11201, (917)359-7085

Global Children **[11293]**, 100 Atlantic Ave., No. 2N, Brooklyn, NY 11201, (917)359-7085

Global Children's Org. **[11467]**, 3580 Wilshire Blvd., Ste. 1800, Los Angeles, CA 90010, (310)581-2234

Global China Connection **[8387]**, PO Box 250860, New York, NY 10025

Global Civic Preservation **[12329]**, PO Box 1820, Mableton, GA 30126, (770)217-0717

Global Climate Coalition - Defunct.

Global Communities of Support **[11120]**, 475 Wall St., Princeton, NJ 08540, (609)845-2340

Global Community Initiatives **[11589]**, 12 Parkside Dr., Montpelier, VT 05602, (413)512-1133

Global Coral Reef Alliance **[4069]**, 37 Pleasant St., Cambridge, MA 02139, (617)864-4226

Global Deaf Connection **[14935]**, 1301 E Amer. Blvd., Ste. 109, Minneapolis, MN 55425, (612)724-8565

Global Deaf Connection **[14935]**, 1301 E Amer. Blvd., Ste. 109, Minneapolis, MN 55425, (612)724-8565

Global Development Network **[IO]**, New Delhi, India

Global Economic Outreach **[20047]**, PO Box 12778, Wilmington, NC 28405

Global Economic Outreach **[20047]**, PO Box 12778, Wilmington, NC 28405

Global EcoVillage Network **[★5946]**

Global EcoVillage Network **[★5946]**

Global Ecovillage Network Oceania/Asia **[IO]**, Conondale, Australia

Global Educ. Associates **[17970]**, 475 Riverside Dr., Ste. 1626B, New York, NY 10115, (212)870-3290

Global Educ. Associates **[17970]**, 475 Riverside Dr., Ste. 1626B, New York, NY 10115, (212)870-3290

Global Educ. Partnership - Address unknown since 2010.

Global Emergency Care Collaborative **[15162]**, 2033 W Iowa St., No. 3, Chicago, IL 60622

Global Emergency Relief **[11923]**, 600 Madison Ave., 22nd Fl., New York, NY 10022, (212)213-0213

Global Envelope Alliance **[3349]**, 500 Montgomery St., Ste. 550, Alexandria, VA 22314, (703)739-2200

Global Envelope Alliance **[3349]**, 500 Montgomery St., Ste. 550, Alexandria, VA 22314, (703)739-2200

Global Env. Fac. **[4263]**, 1818 H St. NW, MSN G6-602, Washington, DC 20433, (202)473-0508

Global Environmental Mgt. Initiative **[4329]**, 1155 15th St. NW, Ste. 500, Washington, DC 20005, (202)296-7449

Global Environmental Mgt. Initiative **[4329]**, 1155 15th St. NW, Ste. 500, Washington, DC 20005, (202)296-7449

Global Envision **[17717]**, Mercy Corps, 45 SW Ankeny St., Portland, OR 97204

Global Envision **[17717]**, Mercy Corps, 45 SW Ankeny St., Portland, OR 97204

Global Equity Gauge Alliance **[IO]**, Durban, Republic of South Africa

Global Equity Org. **[1127]**, 1442 E Lincoln Ave., No. 487, Orange, CA 92865, (714)630-2908

Global Equity Org. **[1127]**, 1442 E Lincoln Ave., No. 487, Orange, CA 92865, (714)630-2908

Global Exchange **[17521]**, 2017 Mission St., No. 303, San Francisco, CA 94110, (415)255-7296

Global Exchange **[17521]**, 2017 Mission St., No. 303, San Francisco, CA 94110, (415)255-7296

Global Explorers **[9017]**, 420 S Howes St., Ste. B300, Fort Collins, CO 80521, (877)627-1425

Global Explorers **[9017]**, 420 S Howes St., Ste. B300, Fort Collins, CO 80521, (877)627-1425

Global Fac. for Disaster Reduction and Recovery **[11851]**, 1818 H St. NW, Mailstop H6-601, Washington, DC 20433, (202)458-0268

Global Fac. for Disaster Reduction and Recovery **[11851]**, 1818 H St. NW, Mailstop H6-601, Washington, DC 20433, (202)458-0268

Global Family **[13157]**, 11689 Lowhills Rd., Nevada City, CA 95959, (530)470-9280

Global Family **[13157]**, 11689 Lowhills Rd., Nevada City, CA 95959, (530)470-9280

Global Family Rescue **[13158]**, PO Box 529, Wheaton, IL 60187, (630)220-0101

Global Fed. of Animal Sanctuaries **[10970]**, PO Box 32294, Washington, DC 20007, (928)472-1173

Global Fed. of Animal Sanctuaries **[10970]**, PO Box 32294, Washington, DC 20007, (928)472-1173

Global Flying Hospitals **[14779]**, 4440 PGA Blvd., Ste. 600, Palm Beach Gardens, FL 33410, (855)434-4747

Global Focus Aotearoa **[IO]**, Wellington, New Zealand

Global FoodBanking Network **[12281]**, 203 N La-Salle St., Ste. 1900, Chicago, IL 60601, (312)782-4560

Global Footprint Network **[4207]**, 312 Clay St., Ste. 300, Oakland, CA 94607-3510, (510)839-8879

Global Fund for Women **[17646]**, 222 Sutter St., Ste. 500, San Francisco, CA 94109, (415)248-4800

Global Fund for Women **[17646]**, 222 Sutter St., Ste. 500, San Francisco, CA 94109, (415)248-4800

Global Futures Found. **[★1562]**

Global Gecko Assn. **[4874]**, Charles Powell, II, 2932 Sunburst Dr., San Jose, CA 95111-2264

Global Goods Partners **[12330]**, 115 W 30th St., Ste. 400, New York, NY 10001, (212)461-3647

Global Grassroots **[13497]**, 45 Lyme Rd., Ste. 206, Hanover, NH 03755-1222, (603)643-0400

Global Green U.S.A. **[4264]**, 2218 Main St., 2nd Fl., Santa Monica, CA 90405, (310)581-2700

Global Harmony Found. **[IO]**, Lausanne, Switzerland

Global Healing **[15163]**, 2140 Shattuck Ave., Ste. 203, Berkeley, CA 94704, (510)898-1859

Global Healing **[15163]**, 2140 Shattuck Ave., Ste. 203, Berkeley, CA 94704, (510)898-1859

Global Hea. Action **[15164]**, PO Box 15086, Atlanta, GA 30333, (404)634-5748

Global Hea. Action **[15164]**, PO Box 15086, Atlanta, GA 30333, (404)634-5748

Global Hea. Corps **[15165]**, 5 Penn Plz., 2nd Fl., New York, NY 10001

Global Hea. Coun. **[15166]**, 1111 19th St. NW, Ste. 1120, Washington, DC 20036-3636, (202)833-5900

Global Hea. Coun. **[15166]**, 1111 19th St. NW, Ste. 1120, Washington, DC 20036-3636, (202)833-5900

Global Hea. through Educ., Training and Ser. **[15167]**, 8 N Main St., Ste. 404, Attleboro, MA 02703, (508)226-5091

Global Hea. Informatics Partnership **[15168]**, 4915 St. Elmo Ave., Ste. 402, Bethesda, MD 20814, (301)657-1291

A star before a book entry number signifies that the name is not listed separately, but is mentioned within the entry.

Global Hea. Linkages, Inc. **[15169]**, 10810 Hickory Ridge Rd., Columbia, MD 21044, (410)202-8868

Global Hea. Ministries **[14780]**, 7831 Hickory St. NE, Minneapolis, MN 55432-2500, (763)586-9590

Global Hea. Ministries **[14780]**, 7831 Hickory St. NE, Minneapolis, MN 55432-2500, (763)586-9590

Global Hea. Outreach of the Christian Medical and Dental Soc. **[★19948]**

Global Hea. Outreach of the Christian Medical and Dental Soc. **[★19948]**

Global Hea. Partners **[14781]**, 113 Univ. Pl., 8th Fl., New York, NY 10003, (212)353-9857

Global Hea. Partners **[14781]**, 113 Univ. Pl., 8th Fl., New York, NY 10003, (212)353-9857

Global Hea. Partnerships **[15170]**, PO Box 4395, Albuquerque, NM 87196

Global Hea. Partnerships **[15170]**, PO Box 4395, Albuquerque, NM 87196

Global Hea. Soc. **[15171]**, 28-31 49th St., Astoria, NY 11103, (646)219-5781

Global Hea. Soc. **[15171]**, 28-31 49th St., Astoria, NY 11103, (646)219-5781

Global Hea. Technologies Coalition **[15172]**, PATH, 455 Massachusetts Ave. NW, Ste. 1000, Washington, DC 20001, (202)822-0033

Global Hea. Technologies Coalition **[15172]**, PATH, 455 Massachusetts Ave. NW, Ste. 1000, Washington, DC 20001, (202)822-0033

Global Helps Network **[11530]**, PO Box 1238, Enumclaw, WA 98022

Global Hope Network Intl. **[12841]**, 813 Menendez Ct., Orlando, FL 32801, (407)207-3256

Global Ideas Bank **[IO]**, London, United Kingdom

Global India Venture Capital Assn. **[1302]**, 3000 Sand Hill Rd., Bldg. 4, Ste. 180, Menlo Park, CA 94025, (650)854-3927

Global India Venture Capital Assn. **[1302]**, 3000 Sand Hill Rd., Bldg. 4, Ste. 180, Menlo Park, CA 94025, (650)854-3927

Global Inheritance **[18826]**, 1855 Indus. St., Ste. 613, Los Angeles, CA 90021, (213)626-0061

Global Initiative for the Advancement of Nutritional Therapy **[16851]**, 4426 Hugh Howell Rd., Ste. B-333, Tucker, GA 30084, (770)491-8667

Global Initiative for the Advancement of Nutritional Therapy **[16851]**, 4426 Hugh Howell Rd., Ste. B-333, Tucker, GA 30084, (770)491-8667

Global Initiative on Psychiatry **[IO]**, Hilversum, Netherlands

Global Integrity **[965]**, 1029 Vermont Ave. NW, Ste. 600, Washington, DC 20005, (202)449-4100

Global Integrity **[965]**, 1029 Vermont Ave. NW, Ste. 600, Washington, DC 20005, (202)449-4100

Global Interdependence Center **[18813]**, 3701 Chestnut St., Philadelphia, PA 19104, (215)898-9453

Global Issues Rsrc. Center **[18198]**, Educ. Center Bldg., Rm. 115, 4250 Richmond Rd., Cleveland, OH 44122, (216)987-2224

Global Jewish Assistance and Relief Network **[12236]**, 511 Ave. of the Americas, Ste. 18, New York, NY 10011, (212)868-3636

Global Jewish Assistance and Relief Network **[12236]**, 511 Ave. of the Americas, Ste. 18, New York, NY 10011, (212)868-3636

Global Kids **[8073]**, 137 E 25th St., 2nd Fl., New York, NY 10010, (212)226-0130

Global Lawyers and Physicians **[14708]**, Dept. of Hea. Law, Bioethics and Human Rights, Boston Univ. of Public Hea., 715 Albany St., Boston, MA 02118, (617)638-4626

Global Lawyers and Physicians **[14708]**, Dept. of Hea. Law, Bioethics and Human Rights, Boston Univ. of Public Hea., 715 Albany St., Boston, MA 02118, (617)638-4626

Global Learning **[8404]**, 22 Mary Ann Dr., Brick, NJ 08723, (732)281-8929

Global Literacy Proj. **[8530]**, PO Box 228, New Brunswick, NJ 08903-0228, (908)812-5271

Global Lottery Collectors Soc. **[21343]**, 1532 E 59th Pl., Tulsa, OK 74105-8008

Global Lung Cancer Coalition **[IO]**, Glasgow, United Kingdom

Global Majority **[17406]**, 411 Pacific St., Ste. 318, Monterey, CA 93940, (831)372-5518

Global Majority **[17406]**, 411 Pacific St., Ste. 318, Monterey, CA 93940, (831)372-5518

Global March Against Child Labor **[IO]**, New Delhi, India

Global Market Development Center **[3660]**, 1275 Lake Plaza Dr., Colorado Springs, CO 80906-3583, (719)576-4260

Global Marshall Plan Initiative **[IO]**, Hamburg, Germany

Global Medic Force **[15173]**, 101 W 23rd St., Ste. 179, New York, NY 10011, (866)232-4954

Global Medic Force **[15173]**, 101 W 23rd St., Ste. 179, New York, NY 10011, (866)232-4954

Global Medical Knowledge **[15375]**, PO Box 381184, Cambridge, MA 02238-1184

Global Migration Gp. **[5790]**, UNDP Bur. for Development Policy, 304 E 45th St., 10th Fl., New York, NY 10017

Global Migration Gp. **[5790]**, UNDP Bur. for Development Policy, 304 E 45th St., 10th Fl., New York, NY 10017

Global Mission Ser. **[★13390]**

Global MissionAir **[20170]**, 214 Bel Air Dr., Yakima, WA 98908-3304, (509)966-7398

Global MissionAir **[20170]**, 214 Bel Air Dr., Yakima, WA 98908-3304, (509)966-7398

Global Mobile Entertainers Assn. **[1193]**, PO Box 381, Saratoga Springs, NY 12866, (518)587-3589

Global Mobile Entertainers Assn. **[1193]**, PO Box 381, Saratoga Springs, NY 12866, (518)587-3589

Global Natural Hea. Alliance **[13679]**, 2442 NW Market St., No. 628, Seattle, WA 98107, (970)402-0575

Global Network **[★18199]**

Global Network Against Weapons and Nuclear Power in Space **[18199]**, PO Box 652, Brunswick, ME 04011, (207)443-9502

Global Network for Neglected Tropical Diseases **[14388]**, 2000 Pennsylvania Ave. NW, Ste. 7100, Washington, DC 20006, (202)842-5025

Global Neuro Rescue **[15593]**, Box 956901, Los Angeles, CA 90095, (310)825-5111

Global Neuro Rescue **[15593]**, Box 956901, Los Angeles, CA 90095, (310)825-5111

Global Nomads Gp. **[9078]**, 381 Broadway, 4th Fl., New York, NY 10013, (212)529-0377

Global Nutrition Alliance **[15833]**, 22365 El Toro Rd., No. 338, Lake Forest, CA 92630, (949)630-3472

Global Nutrition Alliance **[15833]**, 22365 El Toro Rd., No. 338, Lake Forest, CA 92630, (949)630-3472

Global Offset and Countertrade Assn. **[2098]**, 818 Connecticut Ave. NW, 12th Fl., Washington, DC 20006, (202)887-9011

Global Options **[18462]**, PO Box 40601, San Francisco, CA 94140, (415)550-1703

Global Options **[18462]**, PO Box 40601, San Francisco, CA 94140, (415)550-1703

Global Org. for Lysosomal Diseases **[IO]**, Chalfont St. Giles, United Kingdom

Global Org. of People of Indian Origin **[19036]**, PO Box 1413, Stamford, CT 06904, (818)708-3885

Global Outreach Mission **[12457]**, PO Box 2010, Buffalo, NY 14231-2010, (716)688-5048

Global Outreach Mission **[12457]**, PO Box 2010, Buffalo, NY 14231-2010, (716)688-5048

Global Parks **[4070]**, 3803 Sulgrave Dr., Alexandria, VA 22309, (703)317-1669

Global Partners in Anesthesia and Surgery **[16814]**, 1600 Divisadero St., San Francisco, CA 94115, (415)729-4727

Global Partners in Anesthesia and Surgery **[16814]**, 1600 Divisadero St., San Francisco, CA 94115, (415)729-4727

Global Partners Running Waters **[11590]**, 13105 Watertown Plank Rd., Elm Grove, WI 53122, (262)787-1010

Global Partnership for Afghanistan **[3716]**, PO Box 1237, New York, NY 10276, (212)735-2080

Global Partnership for Afghanistan **[3716]**, PO Box 1237, New York, NY 10276, (212)735-2080

Global Partnership for Family Hea. **[13608]**, 900 19th St. NW, Ste. 260, Washington, DC 20006, (202)429-0282

Global Peace Initiative of Women **[18250]**, 301 E 57 St., 3rd Fl., New York, NY 10022, (212)593-5877

Global Peace Services **[18251]**, PO Box 27922, Washington, DC 20038-7922, (202)216-9886

Global Pediatric Alliance **[16146]**, PO Box 590264, San Francisco, CA 94159, (415)876-0239

Global Pediatric Alliance **[16146]**, PO Box 590264, San Francisco, CA 94159, (415)876-0239

Global Perioperative Res. Org. - Address unknown since 2011.

Global Perspectives in Educ. **[★8340]**

Global Physicians Corps **[15174]**, PO Box 25772, Los Angeles, CA 90025

Global Planning Educ. Assn. Network **[IO]**, Shanghai, People's Republic of China

Global Policy Forum **[17913]**, 777 UN Plz., Ste. 3D, New York, NY 10017, (212)557-3161

Global Polio Eradication Initiative **[IO]**, Geneva, Switzerland

Global Possibilities **[4930]**, 1955 Mandeville Canyon Rd., Los Angeles, CA 90049, (310)656-1970

Global and Regional Asperger Syndrome Partnership **[15594]**, 666 Broadway, Ste. 830, New York, NY 10012, (888)47-GRASP

Global and Regional Asperger Syndrome Partnership **[15594]**, 666 Broadway, Ste. 830, New York, NY 10012, (888)47-GRASP

Global Res. and Rescue **[5012]**, 300 Queen Anne Ave. N, No. 658, Seattle, WA 98109-4599, (206)284-4717

Global Res. and Rescue **[5012]**, 300 Queen Anne Ave. N, No. 658, Seattle, WA 98109-4599, (206)284-4717

Global Rsrc. Alliance **[3974]**, 945 Oso Rd., Ojai, CA 93023, (805)646-4439

Global Response **[4265]**, PO Box 7490, Boulder, CO 80306-7490, (303)444-0306

Global Response **[4265]**, PO Box 7490, Boulder, CO 80306-7490, (303)444-0306

Global Rights **[17831]**, 1200 18th St. NW, Ste. 602, Washington, DC 20036, (202)822-4600

Global Rights **[17831]**, 1200 18th St. NW, Ste. 602, Washington, DC 20036, (202)822-4600

Global Routes **[9516]**, 1 Short St., Northampton, MA 01060, (413)585-8895

Global Security Inst. **[18200]**, GSB Bldg., Ste. 400, One Belmont Ave., Bala Cynwyd, PA 19004, (610)668-5488

Global Security Inst. **[18200]**, GSB Bldg., Ste. 400, One Belmont Ave., Bala Cynwyd, PA 19004, (610)668-5488

Global Semiconductor Alliance **[1102]**, 12400 Coit Rd., Ste. 650, Dallas, TX 75251, (972)866-7579

Global Semiconductor Alliance **[1102]**, 12400 Coit Rd., Ste. 650, Dallas, TX 75251, (972)866-7579

Global Ser. Corps **[13391]**, 3543 18th St., No. 14, San Francisco, CA 94110, (415)551-0000

Global Ser. Corps **[13391]**, 3543 18th St., No. 14, San Francisco, CA 94110, (415)551-0000

Global Solutions for Infectious Diseases **[15116]**, 830 Dubuque Ave., South San Francisco, CA 94080, (650)228-7900

Global Sourcing Coun. **[2602]**, 750 Third Ave., 11th Fl., New York, NY 10017, (631)398-3366

Global Spatial Data Infrastructure Assn. **[7502]**, Marilyn Gallant, Bus. Mgr., 946 Great Plain Ave., PMB 194, Needham, MA 02492-3030, (508)720-0325

Global Spatial Data Infrastructure Assn. **[7502]**, Marilyn Gallant, Bus. Mgr., 946 Great Plain Ave., PMB 194, Needham, MA 02492-3030, (508)720-0325

Global Sports Alliance USA **[22977]**, 3481 E Michigan St., Tucson, AZ 85714, (520)318-5509

Global Strategies for HIV Prevention **[13609]**, 828 San Pablo Ave., Ste. 260, Albany, CA 94706, (415)451-1814

Global Strategies for HIV Prevention **[13609]**, 828 San Pablo Ave., Ste. 260, Albany, CA 94706, (415)451-1814

Global Stud. Assn. North Am. **[8331]**, 1250 N Wood St., Chicago, IL 60622

Global Stud. Assn. North Am. **[8331]**, 1250 N Wood St., Chicago, IL 60622

Global Stud. Center **[★17733]**

Global Teams **[19709]**, 212 21st St., Ste. 2, Bakersfield, CA 93301, (661)323-1214

Reference to "IO" in place of a book number signifies that the association may be found in the 50th edition of International Organizations.

Global Teams [19709], 212 21st St., Ste. 2, Bakersfield, CA 93301, (661)323-1214

Global Tech. Distribution Coun. [3392], 141 Bay Point Dr. NE, St. Petersburg, FL 33704, (813)412-1148

Global Underwater Explorers [4703], 15 S Main St., High Springs, FL 32643, (386)454-0820

Global Univ. [19575], 1211 S Glenstone Ave., Springfield, MO 65804-0315, (417)862-9533

Global Univ. [19575], 1211 S Glenstone Ave., Springfield, MO 65804-0315, (417)862-9533

Global Urban Development [11591], 1050 K St. NW, Ste. 400, Washington, DC 20001, (202)554-5891

Global Urban Development [11591], 1050 K St. NW, Ste. 400, Washington, DC 20001, (202)554-5891

Global Vaccine Awareness League [14709], 25422 Trabuco Rd., Ste. 105-230, Lake Forest, CA 92630-2797

Global Village Assn. [IO], Macau, Macao

Global Village Inst. [5946], PO Box 90, Summertown, TN 38483-0090, (931)964-4474

Global Village Inst. [5946], PO Box 90, Summertown, TN 38483-0090, (931)964-4474

Global Vision 2020 [17077], PO Box 3332, Easton, MD 21601, (410)822-6170

Global Vision Intl. [IO], St. Albans, United Kingdom

Global Vision for Peace [18252], 5419 Hollywood Blvd., Ste. C208, Los Angeles, CA 90027

Global Visionaries [13134], 2524 16th Ave. S, Rm. 305, Seattle, WA 98144, (206)322-9448

Global Visions [★18614]

Global Volunteer Network [IO], Lower Hutt, New Zealand

Global Volunteers [17971], 375 E Little Canada Rd., St. Paul, MN 55117-1628, (651)407-6100

Global Volunteers [17971], 375 E Little Canada Rd., St. Paul, MN 55117-1628, (651)407-6100

Global Warming Initiatives [4793], 108 Piperwood Dr., Cary, NC 27518, (919)208-7333

Global Warming Initiatives [4793], 108 Piperwood Dr., Cary, NC 27518, (919)208-7333

Global Warming Intl. Center [4266], PO Box 50303, Palo Alto, CA 94303-0303, (630)910-1551

Global Warming Intl. Center [4266], PO Box 50303, Palo Alto, CA 94303-0303, (630)910-1551

Global Water Challenge [4993], 1001 Connecticut Ave. NW, Ste. 925, Washington, DC 20036, (202)457-0960

Global Water Challenge [4993], 1001 Connecticut Ave. NW, Ste. 925, Washington, DC 20036, (202)457-0960

Global Water Partnership, Central Asia and Caucasus [IO], Tashkent, Uzbekistan

Global Wildlife Conservation [5060], PO Box 129, Austin, TX 78767-0129, (512)827-9418

Global Wildlife Resources [5013], PO Box 10248, Bozeman, MT 59719, (406)586-4624

Global Wildlife Resources [5013], PO Box 10248, Bozeman, MT 59719, (406)586-4624

Global Wind Energy Coun. [IO], Brussels, Belgium

Global Witness [IO], London, United Kingdom

Global Workers Justice Alliance [12519], 789 Washington Ave., Brooklyn, NY 11238, (646)351-1160

Global Youth Action Network [18827], 540 Pres. St., 3rd Fl., Brooklyn, NY 11215, (212)661-6111

Global Youth Action Network [18827], 540 Pres. St., 3rd Fl., Brooklyn, NY 11215, (212)661-6111

Global Youth Coalition on HIV/AIDS [10881], 540 Pres. St., 3rd Fl., Brooklyn, NY 11215, (212)661-6111

Global Youth Connect [18828], 668 Aaron Ct., Kingston, NY 12401, (845)657-3273

Global Youth Connect [18828], 668 Aaron Ct., Kingston, NY 12401, (845)657-3273

Global Youth Partnership for Africa [9875], 1101 Pennsylvania Ave. NW, Ste. 601, Washington, DC 20004, (202)756-4601

Global Youth Partnership for Africa [9875], 1101 Pennsylvania Ave. NW, Ste. 601, Washington, DC 20004, (202)756-4601

GlobalPlatform [7503], 1515 Cordilleras Rd., Redwood City, CA 94062

GlobalSecurity.org [18253], 300 N Washington St., Ste. B-100, Alexandria, VA 22314, (703)548-2700

Globe Aware [13392], 6500 E Mockingbird Ln., Ste. 104, Dallas, TX 75214-2497, (214)824-4562

Globe Aware [13392], 6500 E Mockingbird Ln., Ste. 104, Dallas, TX 75214-2497, (214)824-4562

Globe Found. of Canada [IO], Vancouver, BC, Canada

GlobeMed [15175], PO Box 292, Evanston, IL 60204-0292, (847)467-2143

GlobeMed [15175], PO Box 292, Evanston, IL 60204-0292, (847)467-2143

Globetrotters' Club [IO], London, United Kingdom

Globus Relief [12458], 1775 W 1500 S, Salt Lake City, UT 84104-3832, (801)977-0444

Glocal Ventures [12331], 1870 Rufe Snow Dr., Keller, TX 76248, (817)656-5136

Glock Collectors Assn. - Address unknown since 2011.

Glories Happy HATS [13527], PO Box 624, Merrifield, VA 22116-0624, (703)506-1415

Glosa Educ. Org. [IO], Richmond, United Kingdom

Gluckstal Colonies Res. Assn. [9767], 4819 W Seminary Ave., Richmond, VA 23227-3405, (804)262-4174

Glued Laminated Timber Assn. [IO], High Wycombe, United Kingdom

The Glutamate Assn. [1390], PO Box 14266, Washington, DC 20044-4266, (202)783-6135

Glutaric Acidemia; Intl. Org. of [15601]

Gluten Intolerance Gp. [15834], 31214 124th Ave. SE, Auburn, WA 98092, (253)833-6655

Gluten Intolerance Gp. of North Am. [★15834]

Glycerine and Fatty Acid Producers Assn. [★744]

Glycerine and Oleochemicals Assn. [★744]

Glycerine Producers Assn. [★744]

Glycogen Storage Disease; Assn. for [15492]

GM Futurliner [21061], 4521 Majestic Vue, Zeeland, MI 49464, (616)875-3058

GM Futurliner [21061], 4521 Majestic Vue, Zeeland, MI 49464, (616)875-3058

GMB [IO], London, United Kingdom

Gnathology-American Sect; Intl. Acad. of [14288]

GNU Proj. [★6486]

GNU Proj. [★6486]

Go Green Initiative Assn. [8156], PO Box 1604, Pleasanton, CA 94566

GOAL [IO], Dun Laoghaire, Ireland

Goals 2000 Arts Educ. Partnership [★7742]

Goat Veterinary Soc. [IO], Newent, United Kingdom

Goats

    Amer. Kiko Goat Assn. [4497]

    Amer. Nigerian Dwarf Dairy Assn. [4498]

    Colored Angora Goat Breeders Assn. [4499]

    Intl. Boer Goat Assn. [4500]

    Intl. Boer Goat Assn. [4500]

    Intl. Fainting Goat Assn. [4501]

    Intl. Fainting Goat Assn. [4501]

    Intl. Goat Assn. [4502]

    Intl. Goat Assn. [4502]

    Kinder Goat Breeders Assn. [4503]

    Natl. Pygmy Goat Assn. [3795]

    Natl. Toggenburg Club [4504]

    Nigerian Dwarf Goat Assn. [4505]

    North Amer. Packgoat Assn. [4506]

    U.S. Boer Goat Assn. [4507]

Godolphin Soc. [10482], Natl. Museum of Racing and Hall of Fame, 191 Union Ave., Saratoga Springs, NY 12866-3566, (518)584-0400

God's Child Proj. [11294], PO Box 1573, Bismarck, ND 58502, (701)255-7956

God's Kids [11295], 11700 Indus. Ave., Fontana, CA 92337-6934, (877)246-3754

God's Love We Deliver [12150], 166 Ave. of the Americas, New York, NY 10013, (212)294-8100

Godzilla Soc. of North Am. [IO], Steinbach, MB, Canada

Goebel Collectors' Club [★21267]

Goethe Institut [★9635]

Goethe-Institut [★IO]

Goethe Institut [★9635]

Goethe-Institut Hongkong [IO], Hong Kong, People's Republic of China

Goethe-Institut Inter Nationes [9635], 72 Spring St., 11th Fl., New York, NY 10012, (212)439-8700

Goethe-Institut Inter Nationes [9635], 72 Spring St., 11th Fl., New York, NY 10012, (212)439-8700

Goethe Inst. for Promoting the Stud. of the German Language Abroad and for Intl. Cultural Cooperation [IO], Munich, Germany

Goethe Soc. of North Am. [9367], Coll. of Liberal Arts and Sciences, 601 S Morgan St., Chicago, IL 60607, (312)413-7329

Goff/Gough Family Assn. [20522], James Pulliam, 4030 Graces Ln., Decatur, IL 62521

Gold Bondholders Protective Coun. - Defunct.

Gold Inst. - Defunct.

Gold Prospectors Assn. of Am. [22108], 43445 Bus. Park Dr., Ste. 113, Temecula, CA 92590, (951)699-4749

Gold and Silver Wyre Drawers' Company [IO], London, United Kingdom

Gold Star Wives of Am. [20705], PO Box 361986, Birmingham, AL 35236, (888)751-6350

Gold Star Wives of World War II [★20705]

Gold Wing Road Riders Assn. [21928], 21423 N 11th Ave., Phoenix, AZ 85027, (623)581-2500

Golden Glow of Christmas Past [22155], Lillie Ghidiu, 7 Turnbridge Dr., Bridgeton, NJ 08302

"Golden Goal" Public Assn. Osh, KirgizstanIO

Golden Key Intl. Honour Soc. [23559], 1040 Crown Pointe Pkwy., Atlanta, GA 30338, (678)689-2200

Golden Key Natl. Honor Soc. [★23559]

Golden Raspberry Award Found. [21706], PO Box 835, Artesia, CA 90702-0835

Golden Retriever Club of Am. [21573], PO Box 20434, Oklahoma City, OK 73156

Golden Rule Found. [9837], PO Box 658, Camden, ME 04843, (207)236-4104

Golden Rule Found. [9837], PO Box 658, Camden, ME 04843, (207)236-4104

Golden Threads [21418], PO Box 1688, Demorest, GA 30535-1688, (706)776-3959

Golden Threads [21418], PO Box 1688, Demorest, GA 30535-1688, (706)776-3959

Goldfish Soc. of Am. [21726], PO Box 551373, Fort Lauderdale, FL 33355, (954)423-0663

Goldfish Soc. of Am. [21726], PO Box 551373, Fort Lauderdale, FL 33355, (954)423-0663

Goldsmiths' Company [IO], London, United Kingdom

Golf

    Amer. Junior Golf Assn. [22603]

    Amer. Singles Golf Assn. [22604]

    Chinese-American Golf Assn. [22605]

    Coun. of Ivy Gp. Presidents [22975]

    Eastern Amputee Golf Assn. [22606]

    Eastern Amputee Golf Assn. [22606]

    Executive Women's Golf Assn. [22607]

    Golf Coaches Assn. of Am. [22608]

    Golf Course Superintendents Assn. of Ireland [14367]

    Golf Fights Cancer [13926]

    Golf Tournament Assn. of Am. [22609]

    Golf Writers Assn. of Am. [22610]

    Intl. Assn. of Golf Administrators [22611]

    Intl. Assn. of Golf Administrators [22611]

    Intl. Assn. of Golf Tour Operators [1898]

    Intl. Golf Associates [22612]

    Intl. Golf Fed. [22613]

    Intl. Golf Fed. [22613]

    Irish Ladies Golf Union [1764]

    Ladies Professional Golf Assn. [22614]

    Multicultural Golf Assn. of Am. [22615]

    Natl. Advt. Golf Assn. [22616]

    Natl. Assn. of Left-Handed Golfers [22617]

    Natl. Pan-American Junior Golf Assn. [22618]

    Natl. Senior Golf Assn. [22619]

    North Amer. One-Armed Golfer Assn. [22521]

    Polish Amer. Golf Assn. [22620]

    Professional Golf Teachers Assn. of Am. [22621]

    Professional Golfers' Assn. of Am. [22622]

    Professional Putters Assn. [22623]

    Royal Canadian Golf Assn. [22962]

    Salute Military Golf Assn. [22624]

    Southeastern Conf. [23006]

    U.S. Golf Assn. [22625]

    U.S. Golf Teachers Fed. [22626]

    U.S. ProMiniGolf Assn. [22627]

    USGA Green Sect. [22628]

    Western Golf Assn. [22629]

    World Senior Golf Fed. [22630]

    World Senior Golf Fed. [22630]

A star before a book entry number signifies that the name is not listed separately, but is mentioned within the entry.

Golf Assn; Natl. Amputee [22515]

Golf Assn. of the U.S; Miniature [22986]

Golf Club Managers' Assn. [IO], Weston-Super-Mare, United Kingdom

Golf Coaches Assn. of Am. [22608], 1225 W Main St., Ste. 110, Norman, OK 73069, (405)329-4222

Golf Collectors Soc. [21344], PO Box 2386, Florence, OR 97439, (541)991-7313

Golf Collectors Soc. [21344], PO Box 2386, Florence, OR 97439, (541)991-7313

Golf Course Architects; Amer. Soc. of [6186]

Golf Course Builders of Am. [★3330]

Golf Course Builders Assn. [★3330]

Golf Course Builders Assn. of Am. [3330], 727 O St., Lincoln, NE 68508, (402)476-4444

Golf Course Superintendents Assn. of Am. [3331], 1421 Res. Park Dr., Lawrence, KS 66049-3859, (785)841-2240

Golf Course Superintendents Assn. of Ireland [IO], Banbridge, United Kingdom

Golf Fights Cancer [13926], 300 Arnold Palmer Blvd., Norton, MA 02766, (508)549-0214

Golf Fights Cancer [13926], 300 Arnold Palmer Blvd., Norton, MA 02766, (508)549-0214

Golf Range Assn. of Am. [3332], Mr. Steve J. di Costanzo, Founder/Pres., PO Box 240, Georgetown, CT 06829, (203)938-2720

Golf Tournament Assn. of Am. [22609], PO Box 47405, Phoenix, AZ 85068, (602)524-7034

Golf Writers Assn. of Am. [22610], Melanie Hauser, Sec.-Treas., 10210 Greentree Rd., Houston, TX 77042-1232, (713)782-6664

Golfing Union of Ireland [IO], Maynooth, Ireland

Golondrinas Found. [IO], Ibarra, Ecuador

Golvbranschens Riksorganisation [★IO]

Gonja Assn. of North Am.

Gonja Assn. of North Am. - Address unknown since 2011.

Gonstead Clinical Stud. Soc. [14134], 900 17th Ave., Santa Cruz, CA 95062, (888)556-4277

Good Bears of the World [13057], PO Box 13097, Toledo, OH 43613, (419)531-5365

Good Bears of the World [13057], PO Box 13097, Toledo, OH 43613, (419)531-5365

Good Gardeners Assn. [IO], Wotton-under-Edge, United Kingdom

Good Gay Poets - Defunct.

Good Neighbors Intl. [IO], Seoul, Republic of Korea

Good News [★19972]

Good News Jail and Prison Ministry [11714], PO Box 9760, Richmond, VA 23228-0760, (804)553-4090

Good News Jail and Prison Ministry [11714], PO Box 9760, Richmond, VA 23228-0760, (804)553-4090

Good Sam Recreational Vehicle Club [22139], PO Box 6888, Englewood, CO 80155-6888, (800)234-3450

Good Shepherd Volunteers [13393], 25-30 21st Ave., Astoria, NY 11105, (718)943-7488

Good Templars

Natl. Coun. of the U.S., Intl. Org. of Good Templars [19008]

Good360 [12670], 133 Braddock Pl., Ste. 600, Alexandria, VA 22314, (703)836-2121

Goodenow Family Assn. [20523], 163 Landham Rd., Sudbury, MA 01776-3156

Goodguys Rod and Custom Assn. [21062], PO Box 9132, Pleasanton, CA 94566, (925)838-9876

Goods for Good [11296], 180 Varick St., Ste. 1207, New York, NY 10014, (646)963-6076

Goodwill Indus. of Am. [★11792]

Goodwill Indus. of Am. [★11792]

Goodwill Indus. Intl. [11792], 15810 Indianola Dr., Rockville, MD 20855, (301)530-6500

Goodwill Indus. Intl. [11792], 15810 Indianola Dr., Rockville, MD 20855, (301)530-6500

Goodwill Indus. Volunteer Services - Address unknown since 2010.

Goodwill - The Amity Gp. [IO], Hamilton, ON, Canada

Goodwin Family Org. [20524], 39 Lost Trail Rd., Roswell, NM 88201-9509, (505)625-0961

Gordon Inst. for Music Learning [8650], PO Box 126, Buffalo, NY 14231-0121

Gordon Setter Club of Am. [21574], Denise Dunham-Schiele, Membership Chair, 1259 Grace Ct., Downers Grove, IL 60516, (630)971-0861

Goree Inst. [IO], Ile de Goree, Senegal

Gorilla Found. [6123], PO Box 620530, Redwood City, CA 94062, (650)216-6450

Gospel

BCM Intl. [19341]

Catholic Radio Assn. [19406]

Christ Truth Ministries [19346]

Christian Hunters and Anglers Assn. [21279]

Christian Media Assn. [19947]

Evangelical Educ. Soc. [19704]

Full Gospel Bus. Men's Fellowship Intl. [19574]

High School Evangelism Fellowship [19751]

Intl. Org. for Septuagint and Cognate Stud. [19349]

North Am. Christian Creative Assn. [19595]

Pocket Testament League [19352]

Seventh Day Baptist Missionary Soc. [19330]

Soc. of Anglican Missionaries and Senders [20094]

Gospel Assn. for the Blind [17078], PO Box 1162, Bunnell, FL 32110, (386)586-5885

The Gospel Coalition [19576], 2065 Half Day Rd., Deerfield, IL 60015

Gospel Light Intl. [★20048]

Gospel Light Intl. [★20048]

Gospel Literature Intl. [20048], PO Box 4060, Ontario, CA 91761-1003, (909)481-5222

Gospel Literature Intl. [20048], PO Box 4060, Ontario, CA 91761-1003, (909)481-5222

Gospel Missionary Union [★20013]

Gospel Music

North Am. Christian Creative Assn. [19595]

Gospel Music Assn. [10201], PO Box 22697, Nashville, TN 37202, (615)242-0303

Gospel Music Assn. Canada [IO], Calgary, AB, Canada

Gospel Music Workshop of Am. [10202], 3908 W Warren Ave., Detroit, MI 48208, (313)898-6900

Gospel Recordings Network [20049], 41823 Enterprise Cir. N, Ste. 200, Temecula, CA 92590-5682, (951)719-1650

Gospel Truth Assn. - Defunct.

Gospodarska Zbornica Slovenije [★IO]

Gosselin Family Assn. [IO], Ile d'Orleans, QC, Canada

Goteborgs Ornitologiska Forening [★IO]

Gothenburg Ornithological Soc. [IO], Vastra Frolunda, Sweden

Gothic Literature

Bram Stoker Memorial Assn. [9354]

Gotland-Russ Assn. of North Am. [4587], 811 Carpenter Hill Rd., Medford, OR 97501, (541)535-6756

Gottfried-Wilhelm-Leibniz-Gesellschaft [★IO]

Gottscheer Heritage and Genealogy Assn. [19006], PO Box 725, Louisville, CO 80027-0725

Goudy Soc. - Defunct.

Goulbourn Strathbogie Olive Growers Assn. [IO], Euroa, Australia

Gould League [IO], Moorabbin, Australia

Gourd Soc. of Am. [★21771]

Gourmets

Amer. Inst. of Wine and Food [21844]

Confrerie de la Chaine des Rotisseurs, Bailliage des U.S.A. [21845]

Intl. Barbeque Cookers Assn. [21846]

Intl. Chili Soc. [21847]

Intl. Chili Soc. [21847]

Kansas City Barbeque Soc. [21848]

Vinegar Connoisseurs Intl. [21849]

Vinegar Connoisseurs Intl. [21849]

World Alliance of Gourmet Robustas [1584]

World Alliance of Gourmet Robustas [1584]

Governance Inst. [2283], 9685 Via Excelencia, Ste. 100, San Diego, CA 92126, (877)712-8778

Government

African Amer. Fed. Executive Assn. [5504]

Air Mail Pioneers [20879]

Amer. Legion Auxiliary Girls Nation [17245]

Assn. of Governmental Risk Pools [5549]

Assn. of Pacific Island Legislatures [5497]

Assn. of Pacific Island Legislatures [5497]

Assn. of Procurement Technical Asistance Centers [1585]

Canada Employment and Immigration Union [16749]

Center for the Stud. of the Presidency [17246]

Change Bangladesh [17275]

Citizens for Legitimate Govt. [17745]

Citizens United [17746]

Close Up Found. [17249]

Comm. of the Regions [20741]

Congressional Automotive Caucus [17410]

The Conservative Caucus [17420]

The Conservative Caucus Res., Anal. and Educ. Found. [17421]

Digital Govt. Soc. of North Am. [6930]

Digital Govt. Soc. of North Am. [6930]

Fisher Inst. for Medical Res. [17716]

Global Integrity [965]

Govt. Investment Officers Assn. [5611]

Intl. Assn. of Clerks, Recorders, Election Officials and Treasurers [5498]

Intl. Assn. of Clerks, Recorders, Election Officials and Treasurers [5498]

Intl. Professional Partnerships for Sierra Leone [17917]

Natl. Assn. of Minority Govt. Contractors [928]

Natl. Assn. of Regional Councils [5499]

Natl. Comm. for an Effective Cong. [17413]

Natl. Coun. for Intl. Visitors [17979]

Natl. Coun. of State Legislatures I Forum for State Hea. Policy Leadership [17766]

Natl. Governmental Collectors Assn. [5500]

Natl. Org. of Fed. Employees Against Abuse and Retaliation [23206]

Natl. Women's Political Caucus [17669]

Natl. Workforce Assn. [5501]

Partnership for Public Ser. [17331]

Scientists and Engineers for Am. [5314]

U.S. Assn. of Former Members of Cong. [17414]

U.S. Chamber of Commerce [23384]

Worldwide Assurance for Employees of Public Agencies [5502]

Worldwide Assurance for Employees of Public Agencies [5502]

Young America's Found. [17432]

Government Accountability

Center for Public Integrity [17747]

Citizens Against Govt. Waste [17748]

Fund for Constitutional Govt. [17749]

Global Integrity [965]

Govt. Accountability Proj. [17750]

Natl. Legal and Policy Center [17751]

OMB Watch [17752]

Sam Adams Alliance [17753]

Govt. Accountability Proj. [17750], 1612 K St. NW, Ste. 1100, Washington, DC 20006, (202)408-0034

Govt. Contract Mgt. Assn. of Am. [★1587]

Government Contracts

Assn. of Inspectors Gen. [5503]

Assn. of Procurement Technical Asistance Centers [1585]

Coalition for Govt. Procurement [1586]

Natl. Assn. of Minority Govt. Contractors [928]

Natl. Contract Mgt. Assn. [1587]

Government Employees

African Amer. Fed. Executive Assn. [5504]

Air Mail Pioneers [20879]

Amer. Assn. of Port Authorities [5505]

Amer. Assn. of Port Authorities [5505]

Amer. Fed. of Govt. Employees [23195]

Amer. Fed. of State, County and Municipal Employees [23196]

Amer. Foreign Ser. Assn. [23197]

Associates of the Amer. Foreign Ser. Worldwide [23198]

Associates of the Amer. Foreign Ser. Worldwide [23198]

Assn. of Civilian Technicians [23199]

Civil Ser. Employees Assn. [23200]

Civilian Conservation Corps Legacy [19009]

Gays and Lesbians in Foreign Affairs Agencies USA [23201]

Govt. Investment Officers Assn. [5611]

Natl. Assn. of Farm Ser. Agency County Off. Employees [5506]

Reference to "IO" in place of a book number signifies that the association may be found in the 50th edition of International Organizations.

Natl. Assn. of Govt. Employees [23202]
Natl. Assn. of Independent Labor [23203]
Natl. Coun. of Field Labor Locals [23204]
Natl. Fed. of Fed. Employees [23205]
Natl. Org. of Fed. Employees Against Abuse and
Retaliation [23206]
Natl. Org. of Legal Services Workers [23207]
Natl. Treasury Employees Union [23208]
Natl. Women's Political Caucus [17669]
Partnership for Public Ser. [17331]
Soc. of Amer. Indian Govt. Employees [23209]
Govt. Finance Officers Assn. of U.S. and Canada
[5918], 203 N LaSalle St., Ste. 2700, Chicago, IL
60601-1210, (312)977-9700
Govt. Finance Officers Assn. of U.S. and Canada
[5918], 203 N LaSalle St., Ste. 2700, Chicago, IL
60601-1210, (312)977-9700
Govt. Info. Org. [★5324]
Govt. Investment Officers Assn. [5611], 6525 W
Warm Springs Rd., Las Vegas, NV 89118,
(702)255-4767
Govt. Mgt. Info. Sciences [5541], PO Box 27923,
Austin, TX 78755, (512)220-1497
Government Relations
Natl. Soc. of Compliance Professionals [1588]
State Govt. Affairs Coun. [1589]
US-Cuba Reconciliation Initiative [17754]
US-Cuba Reconciliation Initiative [17754]
Women in Govt. Relations [17755]
Women in Govt. Relations LEADER Found.
[17756]
Governmental Accounting Standards Bd. [5181], PO
Box 5116, Norwalk, CT 06856-5116, (203)847-
0700
Governmental Affairs Inst. [★17978]
Governmental Indus. Hygienists; Amer. Conf. of
[15901]
Governmental Refuse Coll. and Disposal Assn.
[★6067]
Governmental Res. Assn. [18463], PO Box 292300,
Birmingham, AL 35229, (205)726-2482
Governor William Bradford Compact - Address
unknown since 2011.
Governors' Conf. [★5999]
Governors Highway Safety Assn. [6031], 444 N
Capitol St. NW, Ste. 722, Washington, DC 20001,
(202)789-0942
Governors' Wind Energy Coalition [6070], 2200
Wilson Blvd., Ste. 102-22, Arlington, VA 22201,
(402)651-2948
Graafinen Teollisuus ry [★IO]
Grace Assn. Pakistan [IO], Islamabad, Pakistan
Grace and Compassion Benedictines [IO], Brighton,
United Kingdom
Grace Contrino Abrams Peace Educ. Found.
[17407], 1900 Biscayne Blvd., Miami, FL 33132,
(305)576-5075
Graduate Bus. Admission Coun. [★8549]
Graduate Bus. Admission Coun. [★8549]
Graduate Mgt. Admission Coun. [8549], 11921
Freedom Dr., Ste. 300, Reston, VA 20190,
(703)668-9600
Graduate Mgt. Admission Coun. [8549], 11921
Freedom Dr., Ste. 300, Reston, VA 20190,
(703)668-9600
Graduate Mgt. Assn. of Australia [IO], Melbourne,
Australia
Graduate Pain Res. Found. [★15373]
Graduate Pain Res. Found. [★15373]
Graduate Record Examinations Bd. [8987],
Educational Testing Ser., PO Box 6000, Princeton,
NJ 08541-6000, (609)771-7670
Graduate Women in Bus. [★686]
Graduation Pledge Alliance [18619], Heidi Gross,
Coor., Bentley Univ., 175 Forest St., Waltham, MA
02452, (781)891-2529
Graduation Pledge Alliance [18619], Heidi Gross,
Coor., Bentley Univ., 175 Forest St., Waltham, MA
02452, (781)891-2529
GRAFIA - Assn. of Professional Graphic Designers
in Finland [IO], Helsinki, Finland
Graham Family Assn. - Defunct.
Graham Found. [242], 4 W Burton Pl., Chicago, IL
60610-1416, (312)787-4071
Graham Owners Club Intl. [21063], 4028 Empire
Creek Cir., Georgetown, CA 95634, (530)333-4105

Grail Movement [★19427]
Grailville [19427], 932 O'Bannonville Rd., Loveland,
OH 45140-9740, (513)683-2340
Grain
Amer. Assn. of Grain Inspection and Weighing
Agencies [1590]
Amer. Celiac Society | Dietary Support Coalition
[15817]
Commodity Markets Coun. [1591]
Distillers Grains Tech. Coun. [1592]
Grain Elevator and Processing Soc. [1593]
Natl. Barley Foods Coun. [1594]
Natl. Barley Growers Assn. [4373]
North Amer. Export Grain Assn. [1595]
North Amer. Export Grain Assn. [1595]
Trans., Elevator and Grain Merchants Assn.
[1596]
U.S. Rice Producers Assn. [4508]
U.S.A. Rice Fed. [1597]
Wheat Foods Coun. [1598]
Grain Elevator and Processing Soc. [1593], 4248
Park Glen Rd., Minneapolis, MN 55416-4758,
(952)928-4640
Grain and Feed Comm. of the EU [IO], Brussels,
Belgium
Grain and Feed Dealers Natl. Assn. [★4374]
Grain and Feed Trade Assn. [IO], London, United
Kingdom
Grain Milling Fed. [IO], Pretoria, Republic of South
Africa
Grains Coun. of Australia [IO], Kingston, Australia
Gram Parsons Found. [23850], 3109 N Ola Ave.,
Tampa, FL 33603, (813)221-0596
Gram Parsons Memorial Found. [★23850]
GRAMMY Found. [10203], 3030 Olympic Blvd.,
Santa Monica, CA 90404, (310)392-3777
Grand Aerie, Fraternal Order of Eagles [18977],
1623 Gateway Cir. S, Grove City, OH 43123,
(614)883-2200
Grand Amer. Road Racing Assn. [22238], 1 Daytona
Blvd., Daytona Beach, FL 32114-1243, (386)310-
6500
Grand Bahama Chamber of Commerce [IO], Free-
port, Bahamas
Grand Bahama YMCA [IO], Freeport, Bahamas
Grand Duchy of Luxembourg Chamber of Com-
merce [IO], Luxembourg, Luxembourg
Grand Intl. Brotherhood of Locomotive Engineers
[★23287]
Grand Intl. Brotherhood of Locomotive Engineers
[★23287]
Grand League of Amer. Horseshoe Pitchers
[★22695]
Grand Lodge Order of the Sons of Hermann in
Texas [19048], PO Box 1941, San Antonio, TX
78297-1941, (210)226-9261
Grand Natl. Archery Soc. [IO], Newport, United
Kingdom
Grand Ole Opry Fan Club [★23880]
Grand Order of Pachyderms [★18386]
Grande Prairie Constr. Assn. [IO], Grande Prairie,
AB, Canada
Grandmothers for Peace [★18201]
Grandmothers for Peace [★18201]
Grandmothers for Peace Intl. [18201], PO Box 1292,
Elk Grove, CA 95759-1292, (916)730-6476
Grandmothers for Peace Intl. [18201], PO Box 1292,
Elk Grove, CA 95759-1292, (916)730-6476
Grandparents
Found. for Grandparenting [12120]
Grandparents as Parents [12121]
Grandparents Rights Org. [12122]
MISS Found. | Alliance of Grandparents, A Sup-
port in Tragedy Intl. [12123]
Grandparents'/Children's Rights - Defunct.
Grandparents as Parents [12121], 22048 Sherman
Way, Ste. 217, Canoga Park, CA 91303-1840,
(818)264-0880
Grandparents Rights Org. [12122], 100 W Long
Lake Rd., Ste. 250, Bloomfield Hills, MI 48304,
(248)646-7191
Grandparents United for Children's Rights - Address
unknown since 2011.
Granotec Chile [IO], Santiago, Chile
Grant-A-Wish Found. [★11449]

Grant Professionals Assn. [12671], 1333
Meadowlark Ln., Ste. 105, Kansas City, KS 66102,
(913)788-3000
Grantmakers in the Arts [12672], 4055 21st Ave. W,
Ste. 100, Seattle, WA 98199-1247, (206)624-2312
Grantmakers for Children and Youth [★12673]
Grantmakers for Children, Youth, and Families
[12673], 8757 Georgia Ave., Ste. 540, Silver
Spring, MD 20910, (301)589-4293
Grantmakers in Hea. [16218], 1100 Connecticut Ave.
NW, Ste. 1200, Washington, DC 20036, (202)452-
8331
Grantmakers Without Borders [12674], 1009 Gen.
Kennedy Ave., No. 2, San Francisco, CA 94129,
(415)264-4370
Grantmakers Without Borders [12674], 1009 Gen.
Kennedy Ave., No. 2, San Francisco, CA 94129,
(415)264-4370
The Grantsmanship Center [1540], PO Box 17220,
Los Angeles, CA 90017, (213)482-9860
Granulomatous Disease Assn; Chronic [14380]
Granulomatous Disease Assn; Chronic [14380]
Graphic Artists Guild [9235], 32 Broadway, Ste.
1114, New York, NY 10004-1612, (212)791-3400
Graphic Artists Guild [9235], 32 Broadway, Ste.
1114, New York, NY 10004-1612, (212)791-3400
Graphic Arts
Advt. Production Club of New York [1599]
Amer. Inst. of Graphic Arts [1600]
Amer. Printing History Assn. [9643]
Art and Creative Materials Inst. [1601]
Benjamin Franklin Educ. Found. [8003]
Binding Indus. Assn. Intl. [1602]
Binding Indus. Assn. Intl. [1602]
Book Mfrs'. Inst. [1603]
California Soc. of Printmakers [1604]
Catalog and Multichannel Marketing Coun. [1605]
Comicbook Artists' Guild [9489]
Communications Workers of Am. | Printing,
Publishing and Media Workers Sector [23210]
Digital Printing and Imaging Assn. [1606]
Digital Watermarking Alliance [6932]
Flexographic Tech. Assn. [1607]
Flexographic Tech. Assn. [1607]
German Convention Bur. [23402]
Graphic Arts Educ. and Res. Found. [1608]
Graphic Arts Employers of Am. [23211]
Graphic Communications Conf. of the Intl.
Brotherhood of Teamsters [23212]
Graphic Communications Coun. [1609]
Gravure Assn. of Am. [1610]
Gravure Educ. Found. [8219]
Heidelberg Digital Imaging Assn. [1611]
IDEAlliance - Intl. Digital Enterprise Alliance
[1612]
IDEAlliance - Intl. Digital Enterprise Alliance
[1612]
Illustrators' Partnership of Am. [9644]
Intl. Assn. of Printing House Craftsmen [1613]
Intl. Assn. of Printing House Craftsmen [1613]
Intl. Confed. for Printing and Allied Indus. [23341]
Intl. Graphic Arts Educ. Assn. [8220]
Intl. Graphic Arts Educ. Assn. [8220]
Intl. Metal Decorators Assn. [1614]
Intl. Publishing Mgt. Assn. [1615]
Intl. Publishing Mgt. Assn. [1615]
Intl. Reprographic Assn. [1616]
Intl. Reprographic Assn. [1616]
Lib. Binding Inst. [1617]
Lib. Binding Inst. [1617]
Natl. Art Materials Trade Assn. [1618]
Natl. Art Materials Trade Assn. [1618]
Natl. Assn. of Litho Clubs [1619]
Natl. Assn. of Printing Ink Mfrs. [1620]
Natl. Assn. for Printing Leadership [1621]
Natl. Assn. of Quick Printers [1622]
Natl. Assn. of Quick Printers [1622]
Natl. Govt. Publishing Assn. [1623]
NPES: Assn. for Suppliers of Printing, Publishing
and Converting Technologies [1624]
Pacific Printing and Imaging Assn. [1625]
Packaging and Label Gravure Assn. Global [1626]
Packaging and Label Gravure Assn. Global [1626]
Printing Brokerage/Buyers Assn. [1627]
Printing Brokerage/Buyers Assn. [1627]

A star before a book entry number signifies that the name is not listed separately, but is mentioned within the entry.

Printing Indus. of Am. [1628]
Professional Org. of Women in the Arts [9315]
Screen Printing Tech. Found. [1629]
Screen Printing Tech. Found. [1629]
Soc. of Amer. Graphic Artists [9645]
Soc. of Typographic Aficionados [1630]
Specialty Graphic Imaging Assn. [1631]
Specialty Graphic Imaging Assn. [1631]
Tamarind Inst. [8221]
Typophiles [9646]
Vesalius Trust [8222]
Waterless Printing Assn. [1632]
Web Offset Assn. [1633]
Xplor Intl. [1634]
Xplor Intl. [1634]
Graphic Arts Coun. of North America - Defunct.
Graphic Arts Educ. and Res. Found. [1608], 1899 Preston White Dr., Reston, VA 20191, (703)264-7200
Graphic Arts Employers of Am. [23211], Printing Indus. of America/Graphic Arts Tech. Found., 200 Deer Run Rd., Sewickley, PA 15143, (412)741-6860
Graphic Arts Intl. Union [★23212]
Graphic Arts Marketing Information Service - Defunct.
Graphic Arts Professionals Educational Found. - Defunct.
Graphic Arts Union Employers of Am. [★23211]
Graphic Communications Assn. [★1612]
Graphic Communications Assn. [★1612]
Graphic Communications Career Center [★1609]
Graphic Communications Conf. of the Intl: Brotherhood of Teamsters [23212], 1900 L St. NW, Ste. 800, Washington, DC 20036, (202)462-1400
Graphic Communications Coun. [1609], 1899 Preston White Dr., Reston, VA 20191-4367, (703)648-1768
Graphic Communications Intl. Union [★23212]
Graphic Design
Amalgamated Printers' Assn. [1635]
Amalgamated Printers' Assn. [1635]
Assn. of Professional Design Firms [1636]
Design Mgt. Inst. [1637]
Digital Signage Assn. [90]
Digital Watermarking Alliance [6932]
Fusion Architecture [6197]
Graphic Arts Employers of Am. [23211]
Natl. Assn. of Photoshop Professionals [1638]
Natl. Assn. of Photoshop Professionals [1638]
Soc. for Environmental Graphic Design [1639]
Soc. of Publication Designers [1640]
Graphics
Amer. Design Drafting Assn. [6931]
Comicbook Artists' Guild [9489]
Digital Signage Assn. [90]
Digital Watermarking Alliance [6932]
Graphic Arts Employers of Am. [23211]
Guild of Natural Sci. Illustrators [6933]
IPA - Assn. of Graphic Solutions Providers [6934]
IPA - Assn. of Graphic Solutions Providers [6934]
Stencilers and Decorative Artists Guild [20972]
Tech. Assn. of the Graphic Arts [6935]
Tech. Assn. of the Graphic Arts [6935]
Type Directors Club [6936]
Graphics Philately Assn. [22042], Bruce L. Johnson, Sec., 115 Raintree Dr., Zionsville, IN 46077-2012
Graphics Preparatory Assn. [★6934]
Graphics Preparatory Assn. [★6934]
Graphology
Amer. Soc. of Professional Graphologists [1641]
Coalition of Handwriting Analysts Intl. [6937]
The Grascals Fan Club [23851], Susie French, Pres., PO Box 148326, Nashville, TN 37214-8326
Grass
Intl. Turf Producers Found. [4509]
Intl. Turf Producers Found. [4509]
Lawn Inst. [4510]
Lawn Inst. [4510]
Neotropical Grassland Conservancy [4112]
O.J. Noer Res. Found. [4511]
Oregon Ryegrass Growers Seed Commn. [4512]
Turfgrass Producers Intl. [4513]
Turfgrass Producers Intl. [4513]
Grassland Heritage Found. [4071], PO Box 394, Shawnee Mission, KS 66201, (785)887-6775

Grassland Soc. of Southern Africa [IO], Hilton, Republic of South Africa
Grassroot Soccer [10882], PO Box 712, Norwich, VT 05055, (802)649-2900
Grassroots Alliance for Community Educ. [7898], PO Box 185, Half Moon Bay, CA 94019, (650)712-0561
Grassroots Artists MovEment [9236], 2427 Morris Ave., 1st Fl., Bronx, NY 10468, (718)690-3393
Grassroots Environmental Educ. [8157], 52 Main St., Port Washington, NY 11050, (516)883-0887
Grassroots Intl. [12332], 179 Boylston St., 4th Fl., Boston, MA 02130, (617)524-1400
Grassroots Intl. [12332], 179 Boylston St., 4th Fl., Boston, MA 02130, (617)524-1400
Grateful Amer. Coin [11089], 15207 Hammock Chase Ct., Odessa, FL 33556, (813)404-2568
Gravely Tractor Club of Am. [22176], PO Box 119, McLean, VA 22101, (610)518-1028
Graves' Disease Found. [★16884]
Graves' Disease Found; Natl. [16884]
Graves Family Assn. [20525], 20 Binney Cir., Wrentham, MA 02093, (508)384-8084
Graves Family Assn. [20525], 20 Binney Cir., Wrentham, MA 02093, (508)384-8084
Gravure Assn. of Am. [1610], PO Box 25617, Rochester, NY 14625, (201)523-6042
Gravure Educ. Found. [8219], PO Box 25617, Rochester, NY 14625, (201)523-6042
Gray is Green: The Natl. Senior Conservation Corps [4072], 26 Broadway, North Haven, CT 06473, (800)684-5889
Gray Iron Res. Inst. [★1836]
Gray Line Sightseeing Assn. [3511], 1835 Gaylord St., Denver, CO 80206, (303)394-6920
Gray Panthers [10844], 1612 K St. NW, Ste. 300, Washington, DC 20006, (202)737-6637
Gray Panthers Proj. Fund [★10844]
Graymoor Ecumenical Inst. [★19655]
Graymoor Ecumenical Inst. [★19655]
Graymoor Ecumenical and Interreligious Inst. [19655], 475 Riverside Dr., Rm. 1960, New York, NY 10115, (212)870-2330
Graymoor Ecumenical and Interreligious Inst. [19655], 475 Riverside Dr., Rm. 1960, New York, NY 10115, (212)870-2330
Grays Harbor Historical Seaport Authority [8552], 712 Hagara St., PO Box 2019, Aberdeen, WA 98520, (360)532-8611
Grayson Found. [★4588]
Grayson-Jockey Club Res. Found. [4588], 821 Corporate Dr., Lexington, KY 40503, (859)224-2850
Great Atlantic Radio Conspiracy - Defunct.
Great Bear Found. [5061], PO Box 9383, Missoula, MT 59807-9383, (406)829-9378
Great Books Found. [9444], 35 E Wacker Dr., Ste. 400, Chicago, IL 60601-2205, (800)222-5870
Great Britain Collectors Club [21345], Larry Rosenblum, Sec.-Treas., 1030 E El Camino Real, PMB 107, Sunnyvale, CA 94087-3759
Great Britain Collectors Club [21345], Larry Rosenblum, Sec.-Treas., 1030 E El Camino Real, PMB 107, Sunnyvale, CA 94087-3759
Great Britain Correspondence Club [★21345]
Great Britain Correspondence Club [★21345]
Great Britain Wheelchair Basketball Assn. [IO], Loughborough, United Kingdom
Great Commn. Alliance [11852], 4700 SW 188th Ave., Southwest Ranches, FL 33332, (954)434-4500
Great Commission Res. Network [19619], Biola Univ., School of Intercultural Stud., 13800 Biola Ave., La Mirada, CA 90639-0001
Great Coun. of U.S. Improved Order of Red Men [19208], 4521 Speight Ave., Waco, TX 76711-1708, (254)756-1221
Great Dads [12607], PO Box 7537, Fairfax Station, VA 22039, (703)830-7500
Great Dane Club of Am. [21575], 2933 Archer Ln., Springfield, OH 45503
Great Lakes
Intl. Shipmasters Assn. [2358]
Great Lakes Booksellers Assn. [★2936]
Great Lakes Colleges Assn. [7880], 535 W William St., Ste. 301, Ann Arbor, MI 48103, (734)661-2350

Great Lakes Commn. [5861], 2805 S Indus. Hwy., Ste. 100, Ann Arbor, MI 48104-6791, (734)971-9135
Great Lakes Dove Assn. [★21212]
Great Lakes Historical Soc. [10056], Inland Seas Maritime Museum, PO Box 435, Vermilion, OH 44089-0435, (440)967-3467
Great Lakes Independent Booksellers Assn. [2936], PO Box 901, Grand Haven, MI 49417, (616)847-2460
Great Lakes Indian Fish and Wildlife Commn. [5062], PO Box 9, Odanah, WI 54861, (715)682-6619
Great Lakes Lighthouse Keepers Assn. [9689], PO Box 219, Mackinaw City, MI 49701-0219, (231)436-5580
Great Lakes Maritime Inst. [10057], PO Box 1990, Dearborn, MI 48121, (313)852-4051
Great Lakes Sport Fishing Coun. [22577], PO Box 297, Elmhurst, IL 60126-0297, (630)941-1351
Great Lakes Sugar Beet Growers Assn. - Defunct.
Great Lakes United [4073], 4380 Main St., Amherst, NY 14226, (716)886-0142
Great Plains
Inst. of the Great Plains [9647]
Great Plains Historical Assn. [★9647]
Great Plains Wheat [★3964]
Great Pyrenees Club of Am. [21576], Kathy Lee, Sec., 285 Meadow Ridge Ln., Boones Mill, VA 24065, (540)334-5213
Great Southern Olive Assn. [IO], Mount Barker, Australia
Great Swamp Res. Inst. - Defunct.
Great War Assn. [10091], 1110 Putnam Blvd., Wallingford, PA 19086, (610)874-3757
Greater Blouse, Skirt and Undergarment Assn. - Address unknown since 2010.
Greater Clothing Contractors Assn. - Defunct.
Greater Ecosystem Alliance [★4247]
Greater London Indus. Archaeology Soc. [IO], Orpington, United Kingdom
Greater Manchester and District Campaign for Nuclear Disarmament [IO], Manchester, United Kingdom
Greater New York Coun. for Foreign Students -English in Action [★17964]
Greater Vancouver Alliance for Arts and Culture [IO], Vancouver, BC, Canada
Greater Vancouver Professional Theatre Alliance [IO], Vancouver, BC, Canada
Greater Yellowstone Coalition [4074], PO Box 1874, Bozeman, MT 59771, (406)586-1593
GreatSchools [7831], 160 Spear St., Ste. 1020, San Francisco, CA 94105, (415)977-0700
Greek
Alpha Epsilon [23516]
Amer. Hellenic Educational Progressive Assn. [19010]
Amer. Hellenic Inst. [23403]
Amer. Sociological Assn. | Honors Prog. [23738]
Beta Beta Beta [23470]
Beta Gamma Sigma [23476]
Beta Phi Mu [23583]
Beta Sigma Kappa [23611]
Chian Fed. [19011]
Daughters of Penelope [19012]
Delta Phi Epsilon Professional Foreign Ser. Sorority [23529]
Delta Sigma Delta [23498]
Evrytania Assn. of Am. [19013]
Gamma Sigma Delta [23463]
Greek Catholic Union of the U.S.A. [19014]
Greek Natl. Tourist Org. [3512]
Hellenic-American Chamber of Commerce [23404]
Hellenic Amer. Natl. Coun. [9648]
Hellenic Amer. Natl. Coun. [9648]
Intl. Org. for Septuagint and Cognate Stud. [19349]
Maids of Athena [19015]
Modern Greek Stud. Assn. [9649]
Modern Greek Stud. Assn. [9649]
Mu Beta Psi [23601]
Natl. Block and Bridle Club [23464]
Natl. Multicultural Greek Coun. [23538]

Reference to "IO" in place of a book number signifies that the association may be found in the 50th edition of International Organizations.

Pan Arcadian Fed. of Am. [19016]
Phi Chi Medical Fraternity [23594]
Sigma Alpha Iota Intl. Music Fraternity [23605]
Soc. of Kastorians Omonoia [19017]
Soc. for the Preservation of the Greek Heritage [9650]
Sons of Pericles [19018]
United Hellenic Voters of Am. [19019]
World Coun. of Hellenes Abroad [19020]
World Coun. of Hellenes Abroad [19020]
Greek Amer. Chamber of Commerce [23366], PO Box 1147, Kearny, NJ 07032
Greek Amer. Chamber of Commerce [23366], PO Box 1147, Kearny, NJ 07032
Greek Animal Rescue [IO], London, United Kingdom
Greek Assn. of Indus. and Processors of Olive Oil [IO], Athens, Greece
Greek Assn. of the Marfan Syndrome [IO], Athens, Greece
Greek Bible Soc. [IO], Athens, Greece
Greek Catholic Union of the U.S.A. [19014], 5400 Tuscarawas Rd., Beaver, PA 15009, (800)722-4428
Greek Collecting Soc. for Literary Works [IO], Athens, Greece
Greek Fed. of Customs Brokers Associations [IO], Piraeus, Greece
Greek Food and Wine Inst. [1391], 34-80 48th St., Long Island City, NY 11101, (718)729-5277
Greek Food and Wine Inst. [1391], 34-80 48th St., Long Island City, NY 11101, (718)729-5277
Greek Hea. Informatics Assn. [IO], Athens, Greece
Greek League Against Epilepsy [IO], Athens, Greece
Greek Multiple Sclerosis Soc. [IO], Thessaloniki, Greece
Greek Natl. Tourist Org. [3512], 305 E 47th St., New York, NY 10017, (212)421-5777
Greek Natl. Tourist Org. [3512], 305 E 47th St., New York, NY 10017, (212)421-5777
Greek Olympic Soc. [22789], 555 N High St., Columbus, OH 43215, (614)224-9020
Greek Olympic Soc. [22789], 555 N High St., Columbus, OH 43215, (614)224-9020
Greek Orthodontic Soc. [IO], Athens, Greece
Greek Orthodox
Greek Orthodox Ladies Philoptochos Soc. [19804]
Greek Orthodox Young Adult League [19805]
Order of Saint Andrew the Apostle [19806]
Saint Photios Found. [19807]
Greek Orthodox Ladies Philoptochos Soc. [19804], 7 W 55th St., Fl. 7, New York, NY 10021-3701, (212)977-7770
Greek Orthodox Young Adult League [19805], 83 St. Basil Rd., Garrison, NY 10524, (646)519-6180
Greek Orthodox Youth of Am. [★19805]
Greek Seed Trade Assn. [IO], Athens, Greece
Greek Squash Rackets Fed. [IO], Athens, Greece
Green Action for Eco-Social Change [IO], Tel Aviv, Israel
Green Actors of West Africa [IO], Freetown, Sierra Leone
Green Advocates Liberia [IO], Monrovia, Liberia
Green for All [17189], 1611 Telegraph Ave., Ste. 600, Oakland, CA 94612, (510)663-6500
Green Am. [957], 1612 K St. NW, Ste. 600, Washington, DC 20006, (202)872-5330
Green Balkans Fed. [IO], Plovdiv, Bulgaria
Green Book of Ireland [IO], Ballsbridge, Ireland
Green Builder Coalition [565], PO Box 7507, Gurnee, IL 60031
Green Building Initiative [566], 2104 SE Morrison, Portland, OR 97214, (503)274-0448
Green Burial Coun. [2534], 550 St. Michaels Dr., Ste. D, Santa Fe, NM 87508, (888)966-3330
Green Bus. Alliance [4267], 925 S Fed. Hwy., Ste. 750, Wachovia Plz., Boca Raton, FL 33432, (561)361-6766
Green Calgary Assn. [IO], Calgary, AB, Canada
Green Circle Program - Defunct.
Green Collar Assn. [1148], PO Box 2093, Washington, DC 20013, (866)262-5735
Green Committees of Correspondence [★18358]
Green Computing Impact Org. [1221], Object Mgt. Gp., 140 Kendrick St., Bldg. A, Ste. 300, Needham, MA 02494, (781)444-0404

Green Cross Intl. [IO], Geneva, Switzerland
Green Cross Pakistan [IO], Lahore, Pakistan
Green Cross Russia [IO], Moscow, Russia
Green Destiny [IO], Hyderabad, India
Green Educ. and Info. Network [★8226]
Green Electronics Coun. [6653], 121 SW Salmon St., Ste. 210, Portland, OR 97204, (503)279-9383
Green Empowerment [3972], 140 SW Yamhill St., Portland, OR 97204, (503)284-5774
Green Empowerment [3972], 140 SW Yamhill St., Portland, OR 97204, (503)284-5774
Green Home Coun. [567], PO Box 51008, Durham, NC 27717-1008, (919)624-7903
Green Hotels Assn. [1748], PO Box 420212, Houston, TX 77242-0212, (713)789-8889
Green Hotels Assn. [1748], PO Box 420212, Houston, TX 77242-0212, (713)789-8889
Green Innovations of Australia [IO], Melbourne, Australia
Green Leaf Natl. Honor Soc. - Address unknown since 2011.
Green Line [IO], Beirut, Lebanon
Green Mech. Coun. [6796], 1701 Pennsylvania Ave. NW, Ste. 300, Washington, DC 20006, (202)461-2203
Green Meeting Indus. Coun. [2449], 8152 SW Hall Blvd., No. 224, Beaverton, OR 97008, (888)450-2098
Green Olive Trade Assn. - Defunct.
Green Org. [IO], Northampton, United Kingdom
Green Parent Assn. [4075], 2601 Westhall Ln., Maitland, FL 32751, (407)493-1372
Green Partners [4177], PO Box 5302, Lakeland, FL 33807
Green Party [★18358]
Green Party of Aotearoa - New Zealand [IO], Wellington, New Zealand
Green Party - Taiwan [IO], Taipei, Taiwan
Green Party of the U.S. [18358], PO Box 57065, Washington, DC 20037, (202)319-7191
Green Reef [IO], San Pedro, Belize
Green Restaurant Assn. [4875], 89 South St., Ste. 802, Boston, MA 02111, (617)737-3344
Green Schools Alliance [8158], Jeffrey A. Smith, Legal Counsel, Cravath, Swaine & Moore LLP, Worldwide Plz., 825 8th Ave., New York, NY 10019
Green Seal [17460], 1001 Connecticut Ave. NW, Ste. 827, Washington, DC 20036-5525, (202)872-6400
Green Spa Network [3056], PO Box 2437, Sebastopol, CA 95473, (800)275-3045
Green Space [IO], Reading, United Kingdom
The Green Standard [4208], 243 Hillcrest Cir., Chapel Hill, NC 27514, (919)968-6516
Green Team Am. [4076], 6300 Westpark Dr., Ste. 210, Houston, TX 77057, (713)334-3000
Green Thumb [★11939]
Green Thumb [★11939]
Green Warriors of Norway [IO], Bergen, Norway
Green World [IO], Sosnovy Bor, Russia
Green World Center [IO], Sutton, QC, Canada
Green Yoga Assn. [5179], 2340 Powell St., No. 141, Emeryville, CA 94608, (415)655-1081
Green Zionist Alliance [4268], PO Box 30006, New York, NY 10011, (347)559-4492
Greenaction for Hea. and Environmental Justice [5511], 703 Market St., Ste. 501, San Francisco, CA 94103, (415)284-5600
Greener Pastures Inst. [12178], PO Box 2916, Orcutt, CA 93457, (800)688-6352
Greenhouse Crisis Found. - Defunct.
Greening Australia [IO], Yarralumla, Australia
Greening Earth Soc. - Defunct.
Greenland Badminton Fed. [IO], Ilulissat, Greenland
Greenland Soc. of Special Educ. [IO], Lahore, Pakistan
Greenlaw Family Assn. [20526], 104 W Upper Ferry Rd., West Trenton, NJ 08628, (609)882-4193
GreenMotion [4227], 5795 S Sandhill Rd., Ste. F, Las Vegas, NV 89120, (310)663-9826
GreenNet [IO], London, United Kingdom
Greenpeace Argentina [IO], Buenos Aires, Argentina
Greenpeace Australia Pacific [IO], Sydney, Australia
Greenpeace Belgium [IO], Brussels, Belgium
Greenpeace Brazil [IO], Sao Paulo, Brazil

Greenpeace Canada [IO], Toronto, ON, Canada
Greenpeace in Central and Eastern Europe [IO], Vienna, Austria
Greenpeace Chile [IO], Santiago, Chile
Greenpeace EU Unit [IO], Brussels, Belgium
Greenpeace France [IO], Paris, France
Greenpeace Intl. [IO], Amsterdam, Netherlands
Greenpeace Japan [IO], Tokyo, Japan
Greenpeace Luxembourg [IO], Esch-sur-Alzette, Luxembourg
Greenpeace Mediterranean [IO], Sliema, Malta
Greenpeace Mexico [IO], Mexico City, Mexico
Greenpeace Netherlands [IO], Amsterdam, Netherlands
Greenpeace New Zealand [IO], Auckland, New Zealand
Greenpeace Nordic [IO], Helsinki, Finland
Greenpeace Russia [IO], Moscow, Russia
Greenpeace Slovakia [IO], Bratislava, Slovakia
Greenpeace Spain [IO], Madrid, Spain
Greenpeace Sweden [IO], Stockholm, Sweden
Greenpeace Switzerland [IO], Zurich, Switzerland
Greenpeace UK [IO], London, United Kingdom
Greenpeace U.S.A. [4269], 702 H St. NW, Washington, DC 20001, (202)462-1177
Greenpeace U.S.A. [4269], 702 H St. NW, Washington, DC 20001, (202)462-1177
Greenpeace in Zentral Osteuropa [★IO]
Greens of Montenegro [IO], Podgorica, Montenegro
Greensward Found. [4077], PO Box 610, New York, NY 10021
Greenway Family Assn. - Defunct.
Greeting Card Assn. [3350], 1133 Westchester Ave., Ste. N136, White Plains, NY 10604-3546, (914)421-3331
Greeting Card Assn. [IO], London, United Kingdom
Grenada
Grenada Bd. of Tourism [23343]
Grenada Assn. of Beekeepers [IO], Grenville, Grenada
Grenada Athletic Assn. [IO], St. George's, Grenada
Grenada Bd. of Tourism [23343], PO Box 1668, Lake Worth, FL 33460, (561)588-8176
Grenada Chamber of Indus. and Commerce [IO], St. George's, Grenada
Grenada Cycling Fed. [IO], St. George's, Grenada
Grenada Diabetes Assn. [IO], St. George's, Grenada
Grenada Draughts Assn. [IO], Chantimelle, Grenada
Grenada Hotel and Tourism Assn. [IO], St. George's, Grenada
Grenada Medical Assn. [IO], St. George's, Grenada
Grenada Red Cross Soc. [IO], St. George's, Grenada
Grenada Relief, Recovery and Reconstruction [IO], St. George's, Grenada
Grenada Tennis Assn. [IO], St. George's, Grenada
Grenada Triathlon Assn. [IO], St. George's, Grenada
Grenada Union of Teachers [IO], St. George's, Grenada
Grey Muzzle Org. [10971], 14460 New Falls of Neuse Rd., Ste. 149-269, Raleigh, NC 27614, (919)529-0309
Grey Nuns - Defunct.
GREY2K U.S.A. [4515], PO Box 442117, Somerville, MA 02144, (617)666-3526
Greyhound
American-European Greyhound Alliance [4514]
American-European Greyhound Alliance [4514]
Galgo Rescue Intl. Network [10969]
GREY2K U.S.A. [4515]
U.S.A. Defenders of Greyhounds [11054]
Greyhound Adoption Center [10972], PO Box 2433, La Mesa, CA 91943-2433, (877)478-8364
Greyhound Awareness League [IO], Glasgow, United Kingdom
Greyhound Club of Am. [21577], Sharon Allert, Sec., 2443 Chardonnay Way, Livermore, CA 94550, (682)518-1056
Greyhound Friends [10973], 167 Saddle Hill Rd., Hopkinton, MA 01748, (508)435-5969
Greyhound Pets of Am. [★10972]
Greyhound Racing Assn. of Am. [22555], 2207 Concord Pike, No. 335, Wilmington, DE 19803, (717)274-3097
Greyhounds in NEED [IO], Wraysbury, United Kingdom

A star before a book entry number signifies that the name is not listed separately, but is mentioned within the entry.

GridWise Alliance **[6727]**, 1155 15th St. NW, Ste. 500, Washington, DC 20005, (202)530-9740

GridWise Architecture Coun. **[7293]**, Pacific Northwest Natl. Lab., PO Box 999, Richland, WA 99352, (509)372-6410

Grief
Hold the Door for Others **[11129]**
MISS Found. | Alliance of Grandparents, A Support in Tragedy Intl. **[12123]**

GriefNet **[13301]**, PO Box 3272, Ann Arbor, MI 48106-3272, (734)761-1960

Grind for Life **[11136]**, 2023 N Atlantic Ave., No. 236, Cocoa Beach, FL 32931, (561)252-3839

Grinding Wheel Inst. **[★2347]**

Grinnell Family Assn. **[20527]**, 10290 N Alder Spring Dr., Oro Valley, AZ 85737, (520)797-3055

Grinzane Cavour Prize Assn. **[IO]**, Turin, Italy

Griswold and Cast Iron Cookware Assn. **[21858]**, 223 Summit Cir., Lakeville, PA 18438

Gritchenko Foundation **[★10621]**

Gritchenko Foundation **[★10621]**

Groberg - Holbrook Genealogical Org. **[20528]**, 1605 S Woodruff Ave., Idaho Falls, ID 83404

Grocery Mfrs. of Am. and Food Products Assn. **[★1392]**

Grocery Mfrs. Assn. **[1392]**, 1305 I St. NW, Ste. 300, Washington, DC 20005, (202)639-5900

Grolier Club **[9445]**, 47 E 60th St., New York, NY 10022, (212)838-6690

Grondkundevereniging van Suid-Afrika **[★IO]**

Gronlands Badminton Forbund **[★IO]**

Grooming Future World Leaders **[13528]**, 950 Eagles Landing Pkwy., Ste. 214, Stockbridge, GA 30281, (770)914-6644

Groove Phi Groove, Social Fellowship **[23670]**, PO Box 8337, Silver Spring, MD 20907

Groovy Mondays **[IO]**, Toronto, ON, Canada

Grosse Pointe War Memorial Assn. **[20789]**, 32 Lake Shore Dr., Grosse Pointe Farms, MI 48236, (313)881-7511

The Grottoes of North Am. **[19129]**, 430 Beecher Rd., Gahanna, OH 43230, (614)933-9193

Ground Water Protection Coun. **[3636]**, 13308 N MacArthur Blvd., Oklahoma City, OK 73142, (405)516-4972

Ground Water Tech. Division of the Natl. Water Well Assn. **[★7603]**

Ground Zero - Defunct.

Ground Zero Resource Center - Defunct.

Grounds for Hea. **[13927]**, 92 S Main St., Waterbury, VT 05676, (802)241-4146

Grounds Management
Natl. Roadside Vegetation Mgt. Assn. **[4516]**
Professional Grounds Mgt. Soc. **[4517]**

Groundwater Found. **[4994]**, PO Box 22558, Lincoln, NE 68542-2558, (402)434-2740

Groundwater Mgt. Caucus **[7599]**, PO Box 905, Colby, KS 67701-0905, (785)462-3915

Groundwater Mgt. Districts Assn. **[4995]**, PO Box 905, Colby, KS 67701-0905, (913)462-3915

Gp. for the Advancement of Psychiatry **[16338]**, PO Box 570218, Dallas, TX 75357-0218, (972)613-0985

Group-Analytic Soc. **[IO]**, London, United Kingdom

Gp. B Strep Assn. **[14079]**, PO Box 16515, Chapel Hill, NC 27516

Gp. for Reference Guide on Costs - Venezuela **[IO]**, Caracas, Venezuela

Gp. of Samanway - Japan **[IO]**, Chiba, Japan

Gp. of Thirty **[1064]**, 1726 M St., Ste. 200, Washington, DC 20036, (202)331-2472

Gp. Underwriters Assn. of Am. **[1962]**, PO Box 118, Weatogue, CT 06089-0118

Gp. of Universities for the Advancement of Vietnamese Abroad **[9035]**, PO Box 208206, New Haven, CT 06520-8206, (203)436-4192

Gp. for the Use of Psychology in History - Defunct.

Gp. of Volunteers of Italian Switzerland **[IO]**, Arbedo-Castione, Switzerland

Groupe Canadien d'Oncologie Urologique **[★IO]**

Groupe Consultatif Actuariel Europeen **[★IO]**

Groupe Consultatif Intl. de Recherche sur le Colza **[★IO]**

Groupe canadien d'etude des parlements **[★IO]**

Groupe d'Etude Intl. du Plomb et du Zinc **[★IO]**

Groupe Europeen d'Administration Publique **[★IO]**

Groupe Europeen Des Experts Immobiliers **[★IO]**

Groupe Europeen des Femmes Diplomees des Universites **[★IO]**

Groupe Europeen de Recherches Gazieres **[★IO]**

Groupe Femmes pour l'Abolition des Mutilations Sexuelles **[★IO]**

Groupe Intl. d'Etudes du Caoutchouc **[★IO]**

Groupe Intl. de Recherches sur la Preservation du Bois **[★IO]**

Groupe de Recherche et d'Echanges Technologiques **[★IO]**

Groupe de Recherche et d'Echanges Technologiques **[★IO]**

Groupe Socialiste au Parlement Europeen **[★IO]**

Groupe Suisse de l'Association Internationale de Droit Penal **[★IO]**

Groupement international des fabricants de revetements muraux **[★IO]**

Groupement des Annonceurs du Maroc **[IO]**, Casablanca, Morocco

Groupement des Associations Meunieres de l'Union Europeenne **[★IO]**

Groupement Belge des Constructeurs de Materiel Aerospatial **[★IO]**

Groupement Europeen des Banques Cooperatives **[★IO]**

Groupement Europeen des Produits Oleochimiques et Associes **[★IO]**

Groupement Europeen des Societies D'Auteurs et Compositeurs **[★IO]**

Groupement des Femmes d'Affaires du Cameroun **[IO]**, Douala, Cameroon

Groupement des Femmes d'Affaires de la Guinee **[IO]**, Conakry, Guinea

Groupement des Indus. Francaises Aeronautiques et Spatiales **[★IO]**

Groupement des Indus. Francaises de l'Optique **[★IO]**

Groupement des Indus. de l'Equipment Electrique, du Controle-Commande et des Services Associes **[★IO]**

Groupement Intl. d'Editeurs Scientifiques, Techniques et Medicaux **[★IO]**

Groupement Intl. d'Etiquetage pour l'Entretien des Textiles **[★IO]**

Groupement Intl. de la Repartition Pharmaceutique **[★IO]**

Groupement Interprofessionnel des Fabricants d'Appareils d'Equipement Menager **[★IO]**

Groupement Pharmaceutique de l'Union Europeene **[★IO]**

Groupo de Estados de Africa, del Caribe y del Pacifico **[★IO]**

Growing Liberia's Children **[11441]**, PO Box 90676, San Diego, CA 92169, (858)539-0954

Growing Planet **[4400]**, 3133 Frontera Way, Ste. 113, Burlingame, CA 94010-5759, (866)476-9873

Growing Planet **[4400]**, 3133 Frontera Way, Ste. 113, Burlingame, CA 94010-5759, (866)476-9873

Growth Energy **[6728]**, 777 N Capitol St. NE, Ste. 805, Washington, DC 20002, (202)545-4000

Growth Found; Human **[16279]**

Grupa Tacaiochta Cuba - Eire **[★IO]**

Grupo de Artistas Latino Americanos - Defunct.

Grupo Civico Etica y Transparencia **[IO]**, Managua, Nicaragua

Grupo de Estudios Ambientales **[★IO]**

Grupo Internacional de Trabajo sobre Asuntos Indigenas **[★IO]**

Grupo Multidisciplinario Para la Atencion a Pacientes y Familiares con Diagnostico de Enfermedad de Huntington **[IO]**, Havana, Cuba

Grupo OFC Guia Referencial de Costos **[★IO]**

Grupo Parlamentar do Partido Social-Democrata **[★IO]**

Grupo Parlamentario InterAmericano Sobre Poblacion y Desarrollo **[★12339]**

Grupo Parlamentario InterAmericano Sobre Poblacion y Desarrollo **[★12339]**

Grupo Portugues da Associacao Internacional de Hidrogeologos **[★IO]**

Grupo Tortura Nunca Mais/RJ **[IO]**, Rio de Janeiro, Brazil

Gruppo Esponenti Italiani **[19075]**, 60 E 42nd St., Ste. 2214, New York, NY 10165, (212)867-2772

Gruppo Italiano Ricercation in Pattern Recognition **[★IO]**

Gruppo Volontari della Svizzera Italiana **[★IO]**

GS1 **[IO]**, Brussels, Belgium

GS1 Argentina **[IO]**, Buenos Aires, Argentina

GS1 Austria **[IO]**, Vienna, Austria

GS1 Belarus **[IO]**, Minsk, Belarus

GS1 Canada **[IO]**, Toronto, ON, Canada

GS1 Chile **[IO]**, Santiago, Chile

GS1 Czech Republic **[IO]**, Prague, Czech Republic

GS1 Denmark **[IO]**, Copenhagen, Denmark

GS1 Hong Kong **[IO]**, Hong Kong, People's Republic of China

GS1 Ireland **[IO]**, Dublin, Ireland

GS1 Macedonia **[IO]**, Skopje, Macedonia

GS1 Malta **[IO]**, Ta'Xbiex, Malta

GS1 Mauritius **[IO]**, Port Louis, Mauritius

GS1 Nederland **[IO]**, Amsterdam, Netherlands

GS1 Philippines **[IO]**, Pasig City, Philippines

GS1 Republica Dominicana **[IO]**, Santo Domingo, Dominican Republic

GS1 South Africa **[IO]**, Craighall, Republic of South Africa

GS1 Tunisia **[IO]**, Tunis, Tunisia

GS1 UK **[IO]**, London, United Kingdom

GS1 Ukraine **[IO]**, Kiev, Ukraine

GS1 Uruguay **[IO]**, Montevideo, Uruguay

GS1 US **[281]**, Princeton Pike Corporate Center, 1009 Lenox Dr., Ste. 202, Lawrenceville, NJ 08648, (609)620-0200

GSM Assn. **[IO]**, London, United Kingdom

GTO Assn. of Am. **[21064]**, PO Box 213, Timnath, CO 80547

Guadalupe Cave Survey **[★7461]**

Guam Bar Assn. **[5755]**, 120 W O'Brien Dr., Guam Judicial Ctr., 2nd Fl., Hagatna, GU 96910, (671)475-3396

Guam Chamber of Commerce **[23340]**, Ada Plaza Center, 173 Aspinall Ave., Ste. 101, Hagatna, GU 96910, (671)472-6311

Guam Chamber of Commerce **[23340]**, Ada Plaza Center, 173 Aspinall Ave., Ste. 101, Hagatna, GU 96910, (671)472-6311

Guam Lytico and Bodig Assn. **[14710]**, PO Box 1458, Hagatna, GU 96932, (671)477-2293

Guam Lytico and Bodig Assn. **[14710]**, PO Box 1458, Hagatna, GU 96932, (671)477-2293

Guam Natl. Olympic Comm. **[22790]**, 715 Rte. 8, Maite, GU 96910-2101, (671)647-4662

Guam Racquetball Fed. **[22830]**, PO Box 315619, Tamuning, GU 96931-5619, (671)472-1819

Guam Racquetball Fed. **[22830]**, PO Box 315619, Tamuning, GU 96931-5619, (671)472-1819

Guam Symphony Soc. **[10204]**, PO Box 4069, Hagatna, GU 96932, (671)477-1959

Guard of Honor of the Immaculate Heart of Mary - Defunct.

Guard Soc. **[1393]**, Food Processing Machinery Assn., 1451 Dolley Madison Blvd., Ste. 200, McLean, VA 22101, (703)761-2600

Guardian Angels **[★11681]**

Guardian Angels **[★11681]**

Guardians
Natl. Guardianship Assn. **[1642]** Guardians Professional Bodyguard Assn.

Guardians of Hydrocephalus Res. Found. **[15595]**, 2618 Ave. Z, Brooklyn, NY 11235-2037, (718)743-4473

Guatemala
God's Child Proj. **[11294]**
Guatemala Human Rights Commn. USA **[17757]**
Lighthouse Sta. **[12736]**
Mike's Angels **[11349]**
Mil Milagros **[11350]**
Miracles in Action **[12740]**
Network in Solidarity with the People of Guatemala **[17758]**
Ninos del Lago **[11370]**
Partner for Surgery **[16818]**
Pueblo a Pueblo **[12124]**
Safe Passage **[11401]**
Threads Weaving Dreams **[12374]**
Wuqu' Kawoq **[15227]**

Guatemala Hea. Rights Support Proj. **[★12789]**

Guatemala Human Rights Commn. USA **[17757]**, 3321 12th St. NE, Washington, DC 20017, (202)529-6599

Reference to "IO" in place of a book number signifies that the association may be found in the 50th edition of International Organizations.

Guatemala League Against Epilepsy **[IO]**, Guatemala City, Guatemala

Guatemalan Banks' Assn. **[IO]**, Guatemala City, Guatemala

Guatemalan Managers' Assn. **[IO]**, Guatemala City, Guatemala

Guatemalan Olympic Comm. **[IO]**, Guatemala City, Guatemala

Guernsey Chamber of Commerce **[IO]**, Guernsey, United Kingdom

Guernsey Indoor Bowling Assn. **[IO]**, Guernsey, United Kingdom

Guest House Accommodation of South Africa **[IO]**, Cape Town, Republic of South Africa

Guide Assn. of Bhutan **[IO]**, Thimpu, Bhutan

Guide Assn. Scotland **[★5054]**

Guide Dog Found. **[★17079]**

Guide Dog Found. for the Blind **[17079]**, 371 E Jericho Tpke., Smithtown, NY 11787-2976, (631)930-9000

Guide Dog Users, Inc. **[17080]**, 14311 Astrodome Dr., Silver Spring, MD 20906-2245, (866)799-8436

Guide Dogs of Am. **[17081]**, 13445 Glenoaks Blvd., Sylmar, CA 91342, (818)362-5834

Guide Dogs for the Blind **[17082]**, PO Box 151200, San Rafael, CA 94915-1200, (415)499-4000

Guide Dogs for the Blind **[17082]**, PO Box 151200, San Rafael, CA 94915-1200, (415)499-4000

Guide Dogs for the Blind Assn. **[IO]**, Reading, United Kingdom

Guide Dogs for the Handicapped, Inc. **[★11762]**

Guides Australia **[IO]**, Strawberry Hills, Australia

Guides Australia - Queensland **[IO]**, Fortitude Valley, Australia

Guides Australia - Western Australia **[IO]**, Perth, Australia

Guides du Canada **[★IO]**

Guides New Zealand **[IO]**, Christchurch, New Zealand

Guides et Scouts d'Europe - France **[IO]**, Chateau Landon, France

Guiding Eyes for the Blind **[17083]**, 611 Granite Springs Rd., Yorktown Heights, NY 10598, (914)245-4024

Guiding Eyes for the Blind **[17083]**, 611 Granite Springs Rd., Yorktown Heights, NY 10598, (914)245-4024

Guiding Light Fan Club **[23920]**, Mindi Schulman, Pres., PO Box 455, Lynbrook, NY 11563-0455

The Guild **[★23272]**

Guild of Agricultural Journalists **[IO]**, Shrewsbury, United Kingdom

Guild of Agricultural Journalists of Ireland **[IO]**, Dublin, Ireland

Guild of Air Pilots and Air Navigators **[IO]**, London, United Kingdom

Guild of Air Traffic Control Officers **[IO]**, Bingham, United Kingdom

Guild of Amer. Luthiers **[2555]**, 8222 S Park Ave., Tacoma, WA 98408, (253)472-7853

Guild of Amer. Luthiers **[2555]**, 8222 S Park Ave., Tacoma, WA 98408, (253)472-7853

Guild of Amer. Papercutters **[21440]**, PO Box 384, Somerset, PA 15501

Guild of Antique Dealers and Restorers **[IO]**, Shrewsbury, United Kingdom

Guild of Architectural Ironmongers **[IO]**, London, United Kingdom

Guild of Aviation Artists **[IO]**, Farnborough, United Kingdom

Guild of Book Workers **[9446]**, 521 5th Ave., New York, NY 10175-0038

Guild of Book Workers **[9446]**, 521 5th Ave., New York, NY 10175-0038

Guild of British Camera Technicians **[IO]**, Greenford, United Kingdom

Guild of Carillonneurs in North America **[10205]**, Tim Sleep, Sec., 28W640 Warrenville Rd., Warrenville, IL 60555-3439

Guild of Carillonneurs in North America **[10205]**, Tim Sleep, Sec., 28W640 Warrenville Rd., Warrenville, IL 60555-3439

Guild of Church Musicians **[IO]**, Bletchingley, United Kingdom

Guild of Drama Adjudicators **[IO]**, Hertford, United Kingdom

Guild of Experienced Motorists **[IO]**, Forest Row, United Kingdom

Guild of Fine Food Retailers **[IO]**, Wincanton, United Kingdom

Guild of Food Writers **[IO]**, Beckenham, United Kingdom

Guild for Human Services **[17084]**, 411 Waverley Oaks Rd., Waltham, MA 02452, (781)893-6000

Guild of Intl. Butler Administrators and Personal Assistants **[IO]**, London, United Kingdom

Guild of Intl. Professional Toastmasters **[IO]**, London, United Kingdom

Guild of Intl. Songwriters and Composers **[IO]**, Penzance, United Kingdom

Guild of Investment and Financial Analysts **[IO]**, Moscow, Russia

Guild of Italian Amer. Actors **[23269]**, Canal St. Sta., PO Box 123, New York, NY 10013-0123, (201)344-3411

Guild of Master Craftsmen **[IO]**, Lewes, United Kingdom

Guild of Motoring Writers **[IO]**, Bournemouth, United Kingdom

Guild of Natural Sci. Illustrators **[6933]**, PO Box 652, Ben Franklin Sta., Washington, DC 20044-0652, (301)309-1514

Guild of Philippine Jewellers, Inc. **[IO]**, Makati City, Philippines

Guild of Prescription Opticians of Am. **[★15985]**

Guild of Press Publishers **[IO]**, Moscow, Russia

Guild of Professional Farriers **[1242]**, PO Box 4541, Midway, KY 40347

Guild of Professional Paperhangers **[★2069]**

Guild of Psychotherapists **[IO]**, London, United Kingdom

Guild of Railway Artists **[IO]**, Minehead, United Kingdom

Guild of Registered Tourist Guides **[IO]**, London, United Kingdom

Guild of St. Vincent **[★19711]**

Guild of St. Vincent **[★19711]**

Guild for Structural Integration **[13680]**, PO Box 1559, Boulder, CO 80306, (303)447-0122

Guild of Taxi Drivers **[★23290]**

Guild of Taxidermists **[IO]**, Stafford, United Kingdom

Guild of TV Cameramen **[IO]**, Devon, United Kingdom

Guild of Temple Musicians **[20125]**, Jeff Marder, VP for Info. Tech., 1305 Remington Rd., Ste. D, Schaumburg, IL 60173-4820

Guild of Travel Mgt. Companies **[IO]**, London, United Kingdom

Guild of Vision Mixers **[IO]**, London, United Kingdom

Guilde Canadienne des Medias **[★IO]**

Guilde Europeenne du Raid **[★IO]**

Guilde de la Marine Marchande du Canada **[★IO]**

GuildHE **[IO]**, London, United Kingdom

Guillain-Barre Syndrome/Chronic Inflammatory Demyelinating Polyneuropathy Found. Intl. **[15596]**, 104 1/2 Forrest Ave., Narberth, PA 19072, (610)667-0131

Guillain-Barre Syndrome/Chronic Inflammatory Demyelinating Polyneuropathy Found. Intl. **[15596]**, 104 1/2 Forrest Ave., Narberth, PA 19072, (610)667-0131

Guillain-Barre Syndrome Found. Intl. **[★15596]**

Guillain-Barre Syndrome Found. Intl. **[★15596]**

Guillian-Barre Syndrome Support Gp. **[★15596]**

Guillian-Barre Syndrome Support Gp. **[★15596]**

Guillian-Barre Syndrome Support Gp. Intl. **[★15596]**

Guillian-Barre Syndrome Support Gp. Intl. **[★15596]**

Guinea Development Found. **[17151]**, 140 W End Ave., Ste. 17G, New York, NY 10023, (212)874-2911

Guinea Development Found. **[17151]**, 140 W End Ave., Ste. 17G, New York, NY 10023, (212)874-2911

Guinea Fowl Breeders Assn. **[3846]**, Phyllis Bender, Sec.-Treas., 4 Coach Ln., Westport, CT 06880

Guinea Fowl Intl. Assn. **[3847]**, 2812 FM 987, Kaufman, TX 75142, (979)773-9100

Guinea Fowl Intl. Assn. **[3847]**, 2812 FM 987, Kaufman, TX 75142, (979)773-9100

Guinea Sports Fed. for Disabled **[IO]**, Conakry, Guinea

Guinean Assn. for the Educ. and Help to Diabetics **[IO]**, Conakry, Guinea

Guitar and Accessories Marketing Assn. **[2556]**, 875 W 181st St., No. 2D, New York, NY 10033, (212)795-3630

Guitar and Accessories Music Marketing Assn. **[★2556]**

Guitar and Accessory Mfrs. Assn. **[★2556]**

Guitar Found. of Am. **[10206]**, PO Box 171269, Austin, TX 78717, (512)761-5597

Guitars For Vets **[11840]**, PO Box 617, Milwaukee, WI 53201, (414)810-4200

Guitars Not Guns **[18169]**, PO Box 3562, Peachtree City, GA 30269, (770)861-2443

Gulf and Caribbean Fisheries Inst. **[4381]**, Univ. of Florida, Picos Rd., Fort Pierce, FL 34946, (561)462-1660

Gulf Coast Allergy Study Group **[★13643]**

Gulf Coast Conservation Assn. **[★4024]**

Gulf Offshore Marine Ser. Assn. **[★2368]**

Gulf Oil Wholesale Marketers Assn. **[★2645]**

Gulf Org. for Indus. Consulting **[IO]**, Doha, Qatar

Gulf Petrochemicals and Chemicals Assn. **[IO]**, Dubai, United Arab Emirates

Gulf Vascular Soc. **[IO]**, Dubai, United Arab Emirates

Gulf Venture Capital Assn. **[IO]**, Manama, Bahrain

Gulf Yachting Assn. **[22339]**, Ken Kleinschrodt, Treas., 4411 Park Rd., Mobile, AL 36605

Gull Wing Gp. Intl. **[21065]**, 776 Cessna Ave., Chico, CA 95928-9571, (530)345-6701

Gull Wing Gp. Intl. **[21065]**, 776 Cessna Ave., Chico, CA 95928-9571, (530)345-6701

Gullwing Gp. **[★21065]**

Gullwing Gp. **[★21065]**

Gun Owners of Am. **[5450]**, 8001 Forbes Pl., Ste. 102, Springfield, VA 22151, (703)321-8585

Gun Owners Found. **[5451]**, 8001 Forbes Pl., Ste. 102, Springfield, VA 22151, (703)321-8585

Gun Trade Assn. **[IO]**, Tewkesbury, United Kingdom

Gungywamp Complex **[★9690]**

Gungywamp Soc. **[9690]**, PO Box 592, Colchester, CT 06415-0592

Gutenberg-Gesellschaft: Internationale Vereinigung fuer Geschichte und Gegenwart der Druckkunst **[★IO]**

Gutenberg Soc.: Intl. Assn. for Past and Present History of the Art of Printing **[IO]**, Mainz, Germany

Guttmacher Inst. **[12034]**, 125 Maiden Ln., 7th Fl., New York, NY 10038, (212)248-1111

Guyana Amateur Powerlifting Fed. **[IO]**, Georgetown, Guyana

Guyana Badminton Assn. **[IO]**, Demerara, Guyana

Guyana Bus. Coalition on HIV/AIDS **[IO]**, Georgetown, Guyana

Guyana Coalition of Citizens with Disability **[IO]**, Georgetown, Guyana

Guyana Lawn Tennis Assn. **[IO]**, Georgetown, Guyana

Guyana Mfg. and Services Assn. **[IO]**, Georgetown, Guyana

Guyana Marine Turtle Conservation Soc. **[IO]**, Georgetown, Guyana

Guyana Red Cross Soc. **[IO]**, Georgetown, Guyana

Guyana Responsible Parenthood Assn. **[IO]**, Georgetown, Guyana

Guyana Squash Assn. **[IO]**, Georgetown, Guyana

Guyana Watch **[IO]**, Georgetown, Guyana

GWEN Project - Defunct.

Gwent Area Welsh Pony and Cob Assn. **[IO]**, Blaenau Gwent, United Kingdom

Gymnasieskolernes Laererforening **[★IO]**

Gymnastics
  Coll. Gymnastics Assn. **[22631]**
  Eastern Intercollegiate Gymnastic League **[22632]**
  Natl. Assn. of Collegiate Gymnastics Coaches/Women **[22633]**
  Natl. Assn. of Women's Gymnastic's Judges **[22634]**
  Natl. Gymnastics Judges Assn. **[22635]**
  USA Gymnastics **[22636]**

Gynaecological Cancer Soc. **[IO]**, Kenmore, Australia

Gynecologic Investigation; Soc. for **[15894]**

Gynecologic Laparoscopists; Amer. Assn. of **[15862]**

Gynecologic Oncologists; Soc. of **[15932]**

A star before a book entry number signifies that the name is not listed separately, but is mentioned within the entry.

Gynecologic Oncology Gp. **[15925]**, 4 Penn Ctr., Ste. 1020, 1600 John F. Kennedy Blvd., Philadelphia, PA 19103, (215)854-0770

Gynecologic Surgery Soc. **[15879]**, 2440 M St. NW, Ste. 801, Washington, DC 20037-1474, (202)293-5205

Gynecological and Obstetrical Soc; Amer. **[15868]**

Gynecologists; Amer. Coll. of Obstetricians and **[15865]**

Gynecologists; Amer. Coll. of Osteopathic Obstetricians and **[15867]**

Gynecology; Amer. Bd. of Obstetrics and **[15863]**

Gynecology and Obstetrics; Assn. of Professors of **[15872]**

Gypsum Assn. **[2504]**, 6525 Belcrest Rd., Ste. 480, Hyattsville, MD 20782, (301)277-8686

Gypsum Products Development Assn. **[IO]**, London, United Kingdom

Gypsy Cob and Drum Horse Assn. **[4589]**, 1812 10th St., Danville, IN 46122, (317)745-6746

Gypsy Lore Soc. **[10515]**, Sheila Salo, Treas., 5607 Greenleaf Rd., Cheverly, MD 20785

Gypsy Lore Soc. **[10515]**, Sheila Salo, Treas., 5607 Greenleaf Rd., Cheverly, MD 20785

Gypsy Lore Soc., North Amer. Chap. **[★10515]**

Gypsy Lore Soc., North Amer. Chap. **[★10515]**

Gypsy Stud. **[IO]**, Paris, France

Gypsy Vanner Horse Soc. **[4590]**, PO Box 65, Waynesfield, OH 45896, (888)520-9777

Gyro Intl. **[13058]**, PO Box 489, Painesville, OH 44077-0489, (440)352-2501

Gyro Intl. **[13058]**, PO Box 489, Painesville, OH 44077-0489, (440)352-2501

H

H2O for Life **[13422]**, 5527 Hugo Rd., White Bear Lake, MN 55110, (651)756-7577

Haagudah Lemilchama Besartan Beyisrael **[★IO]**

Haagudah Letichnun Vepituach Sherutim Lemaan Hazaken Beyisrael **[★IO]**

Haagudah Letoldot Hadoar Shel Eretz Yisrael **[★IO]**

Haagudah Lezechuyot Haezrach Beyisrael **[★IO]**

Haberdashers' Company **[IO]**, London, United Kingdom

Habitat Faunique Canada **[★IO]**

Habitat for Horses **[10974]**, PO Box 213, Hitchcock, TX 77563, (409)935-0277

Habitat para la Humanidad Argentina **[★IO]**

Habitat para la Humanidad de Costa Rica **[★IO]**

Habitat para la Humanidad El Salvador **[★IO]**

Habitat para la Humanidad Guatemala **[★IO]**

Habitat para la Humanidad Mexico **[★IO]**

Habitat para la Humanidad Republica Dominicana **[★IO]**

Habitat para a Humanidade Brasil **[★IO]**

Habitat for Humanity **[★12179]**

Habitat for Humanity **[★12179]**

Habitat for Humanity - Afghanistan **[IO]**, Mazari Sharif, Afghanistan

Habitat for Humanity - Argentina **[IO]**, Buenos Aires, Argentina

Habitat for Humanity - Armenia **[IO]**, Yerevan, Armenia

Habitat for Humanity - Australia **[IO]**, North Sydney, Australia

Habitat for Humanity - Australia Adelaide **[IO]**, Adelaide, Australia

Habitat for Humanity - Bangladesh **[IO]**, Dhaka, Bangladesh

Habitat for Humanity - Belize **[IO]**, Belize City, Belize

Habitat for Humanity - Bermuda **[IO]**, Hamilton, Bermuda

Habitat for Humanity - Bicol **[IO]**, Naga City, Philippines

Habitat for Humanity - Bolivia **[IO]**, Cochabamba, Bolivia

Habitat for Humanity - Botswana **[IO]**, Gaborone, Botswana

Habitat for Humanity - Braga **[IO]**, Braga, Portugal

Habitat for Humanity - Brampton **[IO]**, Brampton, ON, Canada

Habitat for Humanity - Brandon **[IO]**, Brandon, MB, Canada

Habitat for Humanity - Brant **[IO]**, Brantford, ON, Canada

Habitat for Humanity - Brazil **[IO]**, Recife, Brazil

Habitat for Humanity - Brooks **[IO]**, Brooks, AB, Canada

Habitat for Humanity - Bulgaria **[IO]**, Sofia, Bulgaria

Habitat for Humanity - Cabot **[IO]**, St. John's, NL, Canada

Habitat for Humanity - Calgary **[IO]**, Calgary, AB, Canada

Habitat for Humanity - Cambodia **[IO]**, Phnom Penh, Cambodia

Habitat for Humanity - Cameroon **[IO]**, Yaounde, Cameroon

Habitat for Humanity - Camrose Region **[IO]**, Camrose, AB, Canada

Habitat for Humanity - Canada **[IO]**, Waterloo, ON, Canada

Habitat for Humanity - Central Plains **[IO]**, Tarlac City, Philippines

Habitat for Humanity - Chile **[IO]**, Santiago, Chile

Habitat for Humanity - Christchurch **[IO]**, Christchurch, New Zealand

Habitat for Humanity - Colombia **[IO]**, Bogota, Colombia

Habitat for Humanity - Comox Valley **[IO]**, Courtenay, BC, Canada

Habitat for Humanity - Costa Rica **[IO]**, San Jose, Costa Rica

Habitat for Humanity - Cote d'Ivoire **[IO]**, Abidjan, Cote d'Ivoire

Habitat for Humanity - Dominican Republic **[IO]**, Santo Domingo, Dominican Republic

Habitat for Humanity - Dufferin-Caledon **[IO]**, Alton, ON, Canada

Habitat for Humanity - Dunedin **[IO]**, Dunedin, New Zealand

Habitat for Humanity - Durham **[IO]**, Ajax, ON, Canada

Habitat for Humanity - Eastbourne **[IO]**, Eastbourne, United Kingdom

Habitat for Humanity - Ecuador **[IO]**, Quito, Ecuador

Habitat for Humanity - Edmonton **[IO]**, Edmonton, AB, Canada

Habitat for Humanity - Egypt **[IO]**, Cairo, Egypt

Habitat for Humanity - El Salvador **[IO]**, San Salvador, El Salvador

Habitat for Humanity - Ethiopia **[IO]**, Addis Ababa, Ethiopia

Habitat for Humanity - Fiji **[IO]**, Suva, Fiji

Habitat for Humanity - Fredericton Area **[IO]**, Fredericton, NB, Canada

Habitat for Humanity - Gdansk **[IO]**, Gdansk, Poland

Habitat for Humanity - Gen. Santos City **[IO]**, General Santos City, Philippines

Habitat for Humanity - Germany **[IO]**, Cologne, Germany

Habitat for Humanity - Ghana **[IO]**, Accra, Ghana

Habitat for Humanity - Gliwice **[IO]**, Gliwice, Poland

Habitat for Humanity - Great Britain **[IO]**, Banbury, United Kingdom

Habitat for Humanity - Greater Auckland **[IO]**, Auckland, New Zealand

Habitat for Humanity - Greater Kingston and Frontenac **[IO]**, Kingston, ON, Canada

Habitat for Humanity - Greater Metro Manila **[IO]**, Makati City, Philippines

Habitat for Humanity - Greater Vancouver **[IO]**, Vancouver, BC, Canada

Habitat for Humanity - Grey Bruce **[IO]**, Owen Sound, ON, Canada

Habitat for Humanity - Guangdong **[IO]**, Guangzhou, People's Republic of China

Habitat for Humanity - Guangxi **[IO]**, Nanning, People's Republic of China

Habitat for Humanity - Guatemala **[IO]**, Quetzaltenango, Guatemala

Habitat for Humanity - Guyana **[IO]**, Georgetown, Guyana

Habitat for Humanity - Gympie **[IO]**, Gympie, Australia

Habitat for Humanity - Haiti **[IO]**, Petionville, Haiti

Habitat for Humanity - Halifax Regional Municipality **[IO]**, Dartmouth, NS, Canada

Habitat for Humanity - Halton **[IO]**, Burlington, ON, Canada

Habitat for Humanity - Hamilton **[IO]**, Hamilton, ON, Canada

Habitat for Humanity - Honduras **[IO]**, San Pedro Sula, Honduras

Habitat for Humanity - Huronia **[IO]**, Barrie, ON, Canada

Habitat for Humanity - India **[IO]**, Mumbai, India

Habitat for Humanity - Indonesia **[IO]**, Jakarta, Indonesia

Habitat for Humanity Intl. **[12179]**, 121 Habitat St., Americus, GA 31709-3498, (229)924-6935

Habitat for Humanity Intl. **[12179]**, 121 Habitat St., Americus, GA 31709-3498, (229)924-6935

Habitat for Humanity - Invercargill **[IO]**, Invercargill, New Zealand

Habitat for Humanity - Ireland **[IO]**, Dublin, Ireland

Habitat for Humanity - Japan **[IO]**, Tokyo, Japan

Habitat for Humanity - Jordan **[IO]**, Amman, Jordan

Habitat for Humanity - Kamloops **[IO]**, Kamloops, BC, Canada

Habitat for Humanity - Kelowna **[IO]**, Kelowna, BC, Canada

Habitat for Humanity - Kenya **[IO]**, Nairobi, Kenya

Habitat for Humanity - Korea **[IO]**, Seoul, Republic of Korea

Habitat for Humanity - Kyrgyzstan **[IO]**, Bishkek, Kirgizstan

Habitat for Humanity - Lebanon **[IO]**, Beirut, Lebanon

Habitat for Humanity - Lesotho **[IO]**, Maseru, Lesotho

Habitat for Humanity - Lethbridge **[IO]**, Lethbridge, AB, Canada

Habitat for Humanity - London **[IO]**, London, ON, Canada

Habitat for Humanity - Lower North Island **[IO]**, Porirua, New Zealand

Habitat for Humanity - Macedonia **[IO]**, Skopje, Macedonia

Habitat for Humanity - Madagascar **[IO]**, Antananarivo, Madagascar

Habitat for Humanity - Malawi **[IO]**, Blantyre, Malawi

Habitat for Humanity - Malaysia **[IO]**, Kuala Lumpur, Malaysia

Habitat for Humanity - Medicine Hat **[IO]**, Medicine Hat, AB, Canada

Habitat for Humanity - Mexico **[IO]**, Mexico City, Mexico

Habitat for Humanity - Mid-Vancouver Island Soc. **[IO]**, Nanaimo, BC, Canada

Habitat for Humanity - Moncton Area **[IO]**, Moncton, NB, Canada

Habitat for Humanity - Mongolia **[IO]**, Ulan Bator, Mongolia

Habitat for Humanity - Montreal **[IO]**, Montreal, QC, Canada

Habitat for Humanity - Mozambique **[IO]**, Maputo, Mozambique

Habitat for Humanity - Muskoka **[IO]**, Gravenhurst, ON, Canada

Habitat for Humanity - Natl. Capital Region **[IO]**, Ottawa, ON, Canada

Habitat for Humanity - Negros Occidental **[IO]**, Talisay City, Philippines

Habitat for Humanity - Nelson **[IO]**, Nelson, New Zealand

Habitat for Humanity - Nepal **[IO]**, Kathmandu, Nepal

Habitat for Humanity - Netherlands **[IO]**, Haarlem, Netherlands

Habitat for Humanity - New Zealand **[IO]**, Auckland, New Zealand

Habitat for Humanity - Niagara **[IO]**, St. Catharines, ON, Canada

Habitat for Humanity - Nicaragua **[IO]**, Managua, Nicaragua

Habitat for Humanity - Nigeria **[IO]**, Abuja, Nigeria

Habitat for Humanity - Northern Ireland **[IO]**, Belfast, United Kingdom

Habitat for Humanity - Northland **[IO]**, Whangarei, New Zealand

Habitat for Humanity - On the Border **[IO]**, Lloydminster, SK, Canada

Habitat for Humanity - Pakistan **[IO]**, Islamabad, Pakistan

Habitat for Humanity - Panama **[IO]**, Panama City, Panama

Reference to "IO" in place of a book number signifies that the association may be found in the 50th edition of International Organizations.

Habitat for Humanity - Paraguay [IO], Asuncion, Paraguay

Habitat for Humanity - People's Republic of China [IO], Hong Kong, People's Republic of China

Habitat for Humanity - Peterborough and District [IO], Peterborough, ON, Canada

Habitat for Humanity - Philippines [IO], Makati City, Philippines

Habitat for Humanity - Poland [IO], Warsaw, Poland

Habitat for Humanity - Portugal [IO], Braga, Portugal

Habitat for Humanity - Prince Albert [IO], Prince Albert, SK, Canada

Habitat for Humanity - Prince Edward/Hastings [IO], Belleville, ON, Canada

Habitat for Humanity - Prince George Soc. [IO], Prince George, BC, Canada

Habitat for Humanity - Queens [IO], Charlottetown, PE, Canada

Habitat for Humanity - Red Deer Region [IO], Red Deer, AB, Canada

Habitat for Humanity - Regina [IO], Regina, SK, Canada

Habitat for Humanity - Romania [IO], Beius, Romania

Habitat for Humanity - Rotorua [IO], Rotorua, New Zealand

Habitat for Humanity - Russian Fed. [IO], Ulan-Ude, Russia

Habitat for Humanity - Saint John Region [IO], St. John, NB, Canada

Habitat for Humanity - Samoa [IO], Apia, Western Samoa

Habitat for Humanity - Sarnia/Lambton [IO], Sarnia, ON, Canada

Habitat for Humanity - Saskatoon [IO], Saskatoon, SK, Canada

Habitat for Humanity - Sault Ste. Marie and Area [IO], Sault Ste. Marie, ON, Canada

Habitat for Humanity - Senegal [IO], Dakar, Senegal

Habitat for Humanity - Singapore [IO], Singapore, Singapore

Habitat for Humanity - Slovakia [IO], Bratislava, Slovakia

Habitat for Humanity - Solomon Islands [IO], Honiara, Solomon Islands

Habitat for Humanity - South Africa [IO], Newlands, Republic of South Africa

Habitat for Humanity - South Australia [★17131]

Habitat for Humanity - South Peace Soc. [IO], Grande Prairie, AB, Canada

Habitat for Humanity - Sri Lanka [IO], Colombo, Sri Lanka

Habitat for Humanity - Stratford/Perth [IO], Stratford, ON, Canada

Habitat for Humanity - Sudbury District [IO], Sudbury, ON, Canada

Habitat for Humanity - Sunshine Coast [IO], Sechelt, BC, Canada

Habitat for Humanity - Tajikistan [IO], Dushanbe, Tajikistan

Habitat for Humanity - Tanzania [IO], Dar es Salaam, United Republic of Tanzania

Habitat for Humanity - Taranaki [IO], New Plymouth, New Zealand

Habitat for Humanity - Tauranga [IO], Tauranga, New Zealand

Habitat for Humanity - Thailand [IO], Bangkok, Thailand

Habitat for Humanity - The Pas [IO], The Pas, MB, Canada

Habitat for Humanity - Thousand Islands [IO], Brockville, ON, Canada

Habitat for Humanity - Thunder Bay [IO], Thunder Bay, ON, Canada

Habitat for Humanity - Toronto [IO], Toronto, ON, Canada

Habitat for Humanity - Uganda [IO], Kampala, Uganda

Habitat for Humanity - Upper Fraser Valley [IO], Abbotsford, BC, Canada

Habitat for Humanity - Vanuatu [IO], Port Vila, Vanuatu

Habitat for Humanity - Vietnam [IO], Ho Chi Minh City, Vietnam

Habitat for Humanity - Waikato [IO], Hamilton, New Zealand

Habitat for Humanity - Waterloo Region [IO], Waterloo, ON, Canada

Habitat for Humanity - Wellington County [IO], Guelph, ON, Canada

Habitat for Humanity - West Kootenay [IO], Nelson, BC, Canada

Habitat for Humanity - Western Australia [IO], Perth, Australia

Habitat for Humanity - Windsor Essex [IO], Windsor, ON, Canada

Habitat for Humanity - Winnipeg [IO], Winnipeg, MB, Canada

Habitat for Humanity - Wood Buffalo [IO], Fort McMurray, AB, Canada

Habitat for Humanity - York Region [IO], Newmarket, ON, Canada

Habitat for Humanity - Yukon Soc. [IO], Whitehorse, YT, Canada

Habitat for Humanity - Zambia [IO], Lusaka, Zambia

Habitat pour l'humanite Canada [★IO]

Habitat pour L'Humanite - Haiti [★IO]

Habitat pour l'humanite Montreal [★IO]

Habitat pour l'Humanite - Region de la Capitale Nationale [★IO]

Habonim Dror North Am. [19862], 114 W 26th St., Ste. 1004, New York, NY 10001, (212)255-1796

Hachevrah Hayisraelit Lechimia [★IO]

Hadassah, The Women's Zionist Org. of Am. [19863], 50 W 58th St., New York, NY 10019, (212)355-7900

Hadassah, The Women's Zionist Org. of Am. [19863], 50 W 58th St., New York, NY 10019, (212)355-7900

Hadassah WIZO Org. of Canada [IO], Montreal, QC, Canada

Haematology Soc. of Australia and New Zealand [IO], Sydney, Australia

Haemophilia Soc. [IO], London, United Kingdom

Haflinger Assn. of Am. [★4533]

Haflinger Registry North Am. [★4533]

Hagar Cambodia [IO], Phnom Penh, Cambodia

Hagar USA [12237], Town Bank, PO Box 180620, Delafield, WI 53018, (715)514-2294

Hagiography Soc. [20212], PO Box 400770, Charlottesville, VA 22904, (434)924-1393

Hague Acad. of Intl. Law [IO], The Hague, Netherlands

Hague Conf. on Private Intl. Law [IO], The Hague, Netherlands

Hai-Stiftung [★IO]

Haiku Soc. of Am. [10448], PO Box 31, Nassau, NY 12123

Haiku Soc; Yuki Teikei [10458]

Hair

Amer. Bd. of Hair Restoration Surgery [14672]

Amer. Hair Loss Assn. [14673]

Amer. Soc. of Hair Restoration Surgery [14674]

Amer. Soc. of Hair Restoration Surgery [14674]

Children With Hairloss [12125]

Intl. Aesthetic and Laser Assn. [15237]

Intl. Alliance of Hair Restoration Surgeons [14675]

Intl. Soc. of Hair Restoration Surgery [14676]

Natl. Hair Soc. [1643]

North Amer. Hair Res. Soc. [14677]

Hair Loss Coun; Amer. [14317]

Hairdressing Coun. [IO], Croydon, United Kingdom

Hairenik Assn. [18936], 80 Bigelow Ave., Watertown, MA 02472, (617)926-3974

Haiti

1000 Jobs [12713]

All the Children are Children [11182]

Alliance For Relief Mission in Haiti [12799]

Assn. for Haitian Amer. Development [12126]

Assn. of Haitian Professionals [19021]

Brave Intl. [19808]

Clean Water for Haiti [4991]

Forward in Hea. [14777]

Friends for Hea. in Haiti [14778]

Great Commn. Alliance [11852]

Haiti Convention Assn. [12966]

Haiti Cultural Exchange [9517]

Haiti Healthcare Partners [15176]

Haiti Help Med Plus [12127]

Haiti Outreach [11068]

Haiti Works! [12333]

Haitian Amer. Professionals Coalition [11592]

Haitian Art Educ. and Appraisal Soc. [9651]

Haitian Stud. Assn. [17759]

HavServe Volunteer Ser. Network [11069]

Hea. and Educ. Relief Org. [12334]

Help Brings Hope for Haiti [12845]

Hollywood Unites For Haiti [12128]

Hollywood Unites For Haiti [12128]

Hope for Haiti [11595]

Hope for Haiti's Children [11315]

Intl. Coalition for Haiti [11599]

Intl. Org. for Haitian Development [7894]

Little By Little [14802]

Mama Baby Haiti [14107]

Medical Aid to Haiti [12467]

Meds and Food for Kids [11348]

Mission to Haiti [12129]

Mission to Haiti [12129]

Natl. Assn. for the Advancement of Haitian Descendents [19022]

NOVA Hope for Haiti [12474]

People for Haiti [12877]

Rebuilding Haiti Now [12881]

Scattering Resources [12888]

ServeHAITI [11630]

Sustainable Organic Integrated Livelihoods [11645]

Umoja Intl. [12969]

Haiti Convention Assn. [12966], 272 Dunns Mill Rd., No. 254, Bordentown, NJ 08505, (201)532-2374

Haiti Cultural Exchange [9517], 115 S Oxford St., No. 547, Brooklyn, NY 11217, (718)855-8514

Haiti Healthcare Partners [15176], 4607 Lakeview Canyon Ave., No. 640, Westlake Village, CA 91361

Haiti Help Med Plus [12127], 616 E Altamonte Dr., Ste. 100, Altamonte Springs, FL 32701, (407)928-8317

Haiti Outreach [11068], 15119 Minnetonka Blvd., Minnetonka, MN 55345, (612)929-1122

Haiti Philatelic Soc. [22043], 5709 Marble Archway, Alexandria, VA 22315-4013

Haiti Support Network - Address unknown since 2010.

Haiti Survive [★18985]

Haiti Works! [12333], 855 Main St., 5th Fl., Bridgeport, CT 06604, (203)526-3542

Haitian Amer. Assn. Against Cancer [13928], 225 NE 34th St., Ste. 208, Miami, FL 33137, (305)572-1825

Haitian-American Chamber of Commerce and Indus. [IO], Delmas, Haiti

Haitian Amer. Professionals Coalition [11592], 1040 NW 10 Ave., Fort Lauderdale, FL 33311, (305)482-1509

Haitian Amer. Professionals Coalition [11592], 1040 NW 10 Ave., Fort Lauderdale, FL 33311, (305)482-1509

Haitian Art Educ. and Appraisal Soc. [9651], PO Box 182, Gaithersburg, MD 20884, (301)637-4934

Haitian Bible Soc. [IO], Port-au-Prince, Haiti

Haitian Development Fund [★11806]

Haitian Development Fund [★11806]

Haitian Medical Assn. Abroad [★15400]

Haitian Natl. Red Cross Soc. [IO], Port-au-Prince, Haiti

Haitian Stud. Assn. [17759], Univ. of Massachusetts Boston, McCormack Hall, Rm. 2-211, 100 Morrissey Blvd., Boston, MA 02125-3393

Hakluyt Soc. - Australia [IO], Canberra, Australia

Hakluyt Soc. - England [IO], London, United Kingdom

Hales Family History Soc. - Defunct.

Half Saddlebred Registry of Am. [4591], 4083 Iron Works Pkwy., Lexington, KY 40511-8462, (859)259-2742

Halferty Family Registry - Defunct.

Hall of Fame for Great Americans [10665], Bronx Community Coll., 2155 Univ. Ave., Bronx, NY 10453, (718)289-5161

Hallam Assn. - Defunct.

Hallervorden-Spatz Syndrome Assn. [★15625]

Hallgatoi Onkormanyzatok Orszagos Konferenciaja [IO], Budapest, Hungary

Hallmark Soc. [IO], Victoria, BC, Canada

HALO Trust [17401], 1730 Rhode Island Ave. NW, Ste. 403, Washington, DC 20003, (202)331-1266

A star before a book entry number signifies that the name is not listed separately, but is mentioned within the entry.

HALO USA [★17401]
HALO USA [17401], 1730 Rhode Island Ave. NW, Ste. 403, Washington, DC 20003, (202)331-1266
Halogenated Solvents Indus. Alliance [755], 1530 Wilson Blvd., Ste. 690, Arlington, VA 22209, (703)875-0683
HALT [18028], 1612 K St. NW, Ste. 510, Washington, DC 20006-2849, (202)887-8255
HALT - Americans for Legal Reform [★18028]
HALT - Help Abolish Legal Tyranny [★18028]
HALTER, Inc. [16852], PO Box 5885, Katy, TX 77491-5885, (281)861-9138
Hamilton Acoustic Music Club [IO], Hamilton, New Zealand
Hamilton District Soc. of Chefs and Cooks [IO], Hamilton, ON, Canada
Hamilton Natl. Genealogical Soc. [20529], 116 W Vine St., Vicksburg, MI 49097
Hamner Institutes for Hea. Sciences [7571], PO Box 12137, Research Triangle Park, NC 27709-2137, (919)558-1200
HaMoked: Center for the Defence of the Individual [IO], Jerusalem, Israel
Hampshire Conservation Volunteers [IO], Romsey, United Kingdom
Hampton One-Design Class Racing Assn. [22340], 500 E Plume St., Ste. 105, Norfolk, VA 23510-2317, (757)423-3109
Hand
    Amer. Assn. for Hand Surgery [14678]
    Amer. Found. for Surgery of the Hand [14679]
    Amer. Soc. of Hand Therapists [14680]
    Amer. Soc. for Surgery of the Hand [14681]
    Intl. Fed. of Societies for Surgery of the Hand [14682]
    Intl. Fed. of Societies for Surgery of the Hand [14682]
Hand in Hand USA [12842], 710 St. Josephs Dr., Oak Brook, IL 60523, (630)323-2376
Hand in Hand USA [12842], 710 St. Josephs Dr., Oak Brook, IL 60523, (630)323-2376
Hand Knitting Assn. - Defunct.
Hand Tools Inst. [1650], 25 N Broadway, Tarrytown, NY 10591, (914)332-0040
Handball
    U.S. Handball Assn. [22637]
Handball Assn. of Barbados [IO], St. Michael, Barbados
Handball Assn. of Hong Kong, China [IO], Hong Kong, People's Republic of China
Handball Fed. of Azerbaijan [IO], Baku, Azerbaijan
Handball Fed. of Belarus [IO], Minsk, Belarus
Handball Fed. of Bosnia and Herzegovina [IO], Sarajevo, Bosnia-Hercegovina
Handball Ringers of Great Britain [IO], Sheffield, United Kingdom
Handcrafted Soap Makers Guild [21441], PO Box 5103, Portland, OR 97208-5103, (866)900-7627
Handgun Control [★17683]
Handgun Info. Center [★17684]
Handguns
    Armed Females of Am. [17682]
    Natl. Assn. of Arms Shows [21715]
    Natl. Firearms Act Trade and Collectors Assn. [1354]
    Peoples Rights Org. [17319]
Handicap Intl. - Belgium [IO], Brussels, Belgium
Handicap Intl. - Canada [IO], Montreal, QC, Canada
Handicap Intl. - France [IO], Lyon, France
Handicap Intl. - Germany [IO], Munich, Germany
Handicap Intl. - Luxembourg [IO], Luxembourg, Luxembourg
Handicap Intl. - Switzerland [IO], Geneva, Switzerland
Handicap Intl. - UK [IO], London, United Kingdom
Handicap Introductions [★11775]
Handicap Introductions [★11775]
Handicapped
    Acad. of Rehabilitative Audiology [14910]
    Achromatopsia Network [17055]
    Amer. Amputee Soccer Assn. [22932]
    Amer. Assn. of People with Disabilities [11757]
    Amer. Blind Bowling Assn. [22502]
    Amer. Coun. of the Blind [17057]
    Amer. Hosp. Assn., Sect. for Long Term Care and Rehabilitation [15039]

    Amputees in Motion Intl. [11759]
    BlazeSports Am. [22508]
    Blind Sailing Intl. [23109]
    Blind Ser. Assn. [17067]
    Christian Overcomers [11771]
    Deaf and Hard of Hearing Alliance [14929]
    Disability Resources [11776]
    Disabled Amer. Veterans [20412]
    Disabled Amer. Veterans Auxiliary [20413]
    Dogs for the Deaf [14933]
    Extensions for Independence [11786]
    Model Secondary School for the Deaf [14946]
    Natl. Assn. of the Physically Handicapped [11811]
    Natl. Inst. for Rehabilitation Engg. [11817]
    Natl. Order of Trench Rats [20414]
    North Amer. One-Armed Golfer Assn. [22521]
    Rebuilding Together [12200]
    Skating Assn. for the Blind and Handicapped [22901]
    Special Recreation for disABLED Intl. [11831]
    Support Dogs, Inc. [11832]
    Veterans Educ. Proj. [13357]
    World Access for the Blind [17118]
    World T.E.A.M. Sports [22534]
Handicapped; Adventures in Movement for the [16830]
Handicapped Guardians Assn. [IO], Sharjah, United Arab Emirates
Handicapped Scuba Assn. [22511], 1104 El Prado, San Clemente, CA 92672-4637, (949)498-4540
Handicapped Scuba Assn. [22511], 1104 El Prado, San Clemente, CA 92672-4637, (949)498-4540
Handicapped Travel Club [22140], 2660 SE 7th Pl., Homestead, FL 33033, (305)230-0687
Handicaps Welfare Assn. [IO], Singapore, Singapore
Handidactis [IO], Montreal, QC, Canada
Handloom Export Promotion Coun. [IO], Chennai, India
HandReach [11517], 28 Robinwood Ave., Jamaica Plain, MA 02130, (202)213-9267
Hands Across the Mideast Support Alliance [18124], 263 Huntington Ave., No. 315, Boston, MA 02115, (617)266-0080
Hands Across the Mideast Support Alliance [18124], 263 Huntington Ave., No. 315, Boston, MA 02115, (617)266-0080
Hands Across the Water [11297], 159 Independence Dr., Morrisville, PA 19067, (215)375-2020
Hands Across the Water [11297], 159 Independence Dr., Morrisville, PA 19067, (215)375-2020
Hands for Autistic Children of Ethiopia [11121], 621 Bushytail Dr., Frederick, MD 21703, (240)429-8362
HANDS for Cambodia [11593], PO Box 940582, Plano, TX 75094-0582
Hands on Disaster Response [★11846]
Hands to Hearts Intl. [11298], 1125 NW 9th Ave., Ste. 307, Portland, OR 97208-4224, (503)936-5574
Hands for Help Nepal [IO], Kathmandu, Nepal
Hands of Mercy [12157], 163 Minuteman Causeway, Cocoa Beach, FL 32931, (321)799-9445
Hands On USA - Address unknown since 2011.
Hands That Speak [IO], St. Johns, Antigua-Barbuda
Hands and Voices [14936], PO Box 3093, Boulder, CO 80307, (303)492-6283
HandsNet [12581], PO Box 90477, San Jose, CA 95109
HandsOn Network [13394], 600 Means St., Ste. 210, Atlanta, GA 30318, (404)979-2900
Handsplit Red Cedar Shake Assn. [★1500]
Handsplit Red Cedar Shake Assn. [★1500]
Handweavers Guild of Am. [21442], 1255 Buford Hwy., Ste. 211, Suwanee, GA 30024, (678)730-0010
Handwriting Analysts; Amer. Assn. of [10751]
Hanen Centre [IO], Toronto, ON, Canada
Hang Gliding
    U.S. Powered Paragliding Assn. [22796]
Hank Williams Intl. Fan Club [23852], 103 Summit Clr., Daphne, AL 36526, (251)626-1645
Hank Williams Jr. Fan Club [23853], PO Box 1849, Madison, TN 37116, (615)865-8671
Hank Williams, Sr. Intl. Fan Club [★23852]
Hanley-Hazelden Center [★13255]
Hannah's Promise Intl. Aid [12843], PO Box 2102, Boone, NC 28607, (828)668-1434

Hans Christian Andersen Soc. of Copenhagen [IO], Hillerod, Denmark
Hansard Soc. [IO], London, United Kingdom
Hanuman Found. [12208], 223 N Guadalupe St., Box 269, Santa Fe, NM 87501-1850
Hapoel Hamizrachi Women's Org. [★19860]
Hapoel Hamizrachi Women's Org. [★19860]
Happy Hours Brotherhood - Defunct.
Happy Household Pet Cat Club [21251], 14508 Chester Ave., Saratoga, CA 95070, (408)872-0591
Harakat [IO], Kabul, Afghanistan
Harbour Lights Collectors Soc. [21346], PO Box 625, West Kennebunk, ME 04094, (800)365-1219
Hard Fibres Assn. - Defunct.
Hard Hatted Women [3682], 4220 Prospect Ave., Cleveland, OH 44103, (216)861-6500
Hardanger Fiddle Assn. of Am. [10207], PO Box 23046, Minneapolis, MN 55423-0046, (612)568-7448
Harden - Hardin - Harding Family Assn. [20530], 44 Cedar Dr., Sterling, VA 20164, (703)450-4270
Hardware
    Aircraft Locknut Mfrs. Assn. [1644]
    Amer. Hardware Mfrs. Assn. [1645]
    Amer. Ladder Inst. [1646]
    Assoc. Locksmiths of Am. [1647]
    Builders Hardware Mfrs. Assn. [1648]
    Decorative Plumbing and Hardware Assn. [2781]
    Door and Hardware Inst. [1649]
    Door and Hardware Inst. [1649]
    Hand Tools Inst. [1650]
    The Hardware Companies Kollectors Klub [21850]
    Indus. Fasteners Inst. [1651]
    Intl. Magnetics Assn. [1652]
    Intl. Magnetics Assn. [1652]
    Intl. Staple, Nail and Tool Assn. [1653]
    Intl. Staple, Nail and Tool Assn. [1653]
    Lighter Assn. [1654]
    Natl. Fastener Distributors Assn. [1655]
    North Amer. Retail Hardware Assn. [1656]
    Power Tool Inst. [1657]
    Precision Machined Products Assn. [1658]
    Screen Mfrs. Assn. [1659]
    Screen Mfrs. Assn. [1659]
    Security Hardware Distributors Assn. [1660]
    Spring Mfrs. Inst. [1661]
    The Transformer Assn. [1662]
    The Transformer Assn. [1662]
    Valve Mfrs. Assn. of Am. [1663]
    Valve Repair Coun. [1664]
    Wire Fabricators Assn. [1665]
    Wire Fabricators Assn. [1665]
The Hardware Companies Kollectors Klub [21850], Barbara Huhn, Treas., PO Box 285, Pacific, MO 63069-0285, (636)257-2926
Hardware Mfrs. Statistical Assn. [★1648]
Hardwood Coun. [3701], 665 Rodi Rd., Ste. 305, Pittsburgh, PA 15235, (412)244-0440
Hardwood Coun. [3701], 665 Rodi Rd., Ste. 305, Pittsburgh, PA 15235, (412)244-0440
Hardwood Dimension Mfrs. Assn. [★1516]
Hardwood Distributor's Assn. [1507], 2559 S Damen Ave., Chicago, IL 60608, (773)847-7444
Hardwood Export Trade Coun. [★1464]
Hardwood Fed. [1508], 1111 19th St. NW, Ste. 800, Washington, DC 20036, (202)463-2705
Hardwood Mfrs. Assn. [1509], 665 Rodi Rd., Ste. 305, Pittsburgh, PA 15235, (412)244-0440
Hardwood Mfrs. Assn. I Amer. Hardwood Info. Center [3702], 665 Rodi Rd., Ste. 305, Pittsburgh, PA 15235, (412)244-0440
Hardwood Mfrs. Inst. [★1509]
Hardwood Plywood Inst. [★1510]
Hardwood Plywood Mfrs. Assn. [★1510]
Hardwood Plywood and Veneer Assn. [1510], 1825 Michael Faraday Dr., Reston, VA 20190, (703)435-2900
Hardwood Res. Coun. [★1512]
Hardwood Res. Coun. [★1512]
Hardy Fern Found. [4668], PO Box 3797, Federal Way, WA 98063-3797, (253)838-4646
Hardy Plant Soc. [IO], Pershore, United Kingdom
Haribon Found. [IO], Quezon City, Philippines
Harikar Non-Governmental Org. [IO], Duhok, Iraq
Harley Hummer Club [21929], 13 Sylvan Rd., High Bridge, NJ 08829-1716

Reference to "IO" in place of a book number signifies that the association may be found in the 50th edition of International Organizations.

Harley Owners Gp. [21930], PO Box 453, Milwaukee, WI 53201, (414)343-4896

Harm Reduction Coalition [13254], 22 W 27th St., 5th Fl., New York, NY 10001, (212)213-6376

Harm Reduction Coalition [13254], 22 W 27th St., 5th Fl., New York, NY 10001, (212)213-6376

Harmonie Associates [9691], Pennsylvania Historical and Museum Commn., Old Economy Village, 270 16th St., Ambridge, PA 15003-2225, (724)266-4500

Harmony [★IO]

Harmony Found. [IO], Victoria, BC, Canada

Harmony Found. Intl. [10208], 110 7tlf Ave. N, Ste. 200, Nashville, TN 37203-3704, (615)823-5611

Harmony House for Cats [10975], PO Box 18098, Chicago, IL 60618-0098, (773)463-6667

Harness Horse Youth Found. [22652], 16575 Carey Rd., Westfield, IN 46074-8925, (317)867-5877

Harness Racing Communications [★22672]

Harness Racing Museum and Hall of Fame [22653], 240 Main St., Goshen, NY 10924, (845)294-6330

Harness Tracks of Am. [22654], 12025 E Dry Gulch Pl., Tucson, AZ 85749, (520)529-2525

Harp Assn. of Serbia [IO], Belgrade, Serbia

Harriet Beecher Stowe Center [10716], 77 Forest St., Hartford, CT 06105, (860)522-9258

Harriet Beecher Stowe Soc. [10717], Nancy Lusignan Schultz, Treas., Salem State Coll., Dept. of English, 352 Lafayette St., Salem, MA 01970-5333

Harris Tweed Authority [IO], Stornoway, United Kingdom

Harrow Assn. of Disabled People [IO], Harrow, United Kingdom

Harry Connick, Jr. Fan Club [23854], 323 Broadway, Cambridge, MA 02139, (617)354-2736

Harry Connick, Jr. Fan Club [23854], 323 Broadway, Cambridge, MA 02139, (617)354-2736

Harry S. Truman Lib. Inst. for Natl. and Intl. Affairs [10666], 500 W U.S. Hwy. 24, Independence, MO 64050, (816)268-8200

Harry S. Truman Lib. Inst. for Natl. and Intl. Affairs [10666], 500 W U.S. Hwy. 24, Independence, MO 64050, (816)268-8200

Harry S. Truman Scholarship Found. [8192], 712 Jackson Pl. NW, Washington, DC 20006, (202)395-4831

Harry Singer Found. [18464], PO Box 223159, Carmel, CA 93923, (831)625-4223

Harry Stephen Keeler Soc. [9368], 4745 Winton Rd., Cincinnati, OH 45232, (513)591-1226

Harry Stephen Keeler Soc. [9368], 4745 Winton Rd., Cincinnati, OH 45232, (513)591-1226

Hartford Seminary [19832], 77 Sherman St., Hartford, CT 06105-2260, (860)509-9500

Hartford Seminary [19832], 77 Sherman St., Hartford, CT 06105-2260, (860)509-9500

Hartford Whalers Booster Club [23904], PO Box 273, Hartford, CT 06141, (860)956-3839

Harting Family Assn. - Defunct.

Hartlepool Special Needs Support Gp. [IO], Hartlepool, United Kingdom

Hartshorn Family Assn. - Address unknown since 2010.

Hartz Club of Am. [7198], Bob Buckles, Sec.-Treas., 9324 Paramount Blvd., Downey, CA 90240, (562)927-6247

Harvard Alumni Soc. of the UAE [IO], Dubai, United Arab Emirates

Harvard Environmental Law Soc. [5418], Harvard Law School, Pound Hall, 1563 Massachusetts Ave., Cambridge, MA 02138

Harvard Injury Control Res. Center [16927], Harvard School of Public Hea., 677 Huntington Ave., 3rd Fl., Boston, MA 02115, (617)432-3420

Harvest [19986], PO Box 2670, Phoenix, AZ 85002, (602)258-1083

Harvest [19986], PO Box 2670, Phoenix, AZ 85002, (602)258-1083

Harvest Found. [★19986]

Harvest Found. [★19986]

Harvey Cushing Soc. [★15682]

Harvey Cushing Soc. [★15682]

Harvey Soc. [15414], Marie Filbin, PhD, Sec., City Univ. of New York, Hunter Coll., 695 Park Ave., New York, NY 10065, (212)772-5472

Hasbrouck Family Assn. [20531], PO Box 176, New Paltz, NY 12561, (845)255-3223

Hashomer [★19864]

Hashomer Hadati, Bnei Akiva [★19851]

Hashomer Hatzair Socialist Zionist Youth Movement [★19864]

Hashomer Hatzair Zionist Youth Movement [19864], 114 W 26th St., No. 1001, New York, NY 10001-0012, (212)627-2830

Hashomer Hatzair Zionist Youth Org. [★19864]

Haskins Soc. for Viking, Anglo-Saxon, Anglo-Norman, and Angevin History [★10075]

Haskins Soc. for Viking, Anglo-Saxon, Anglo-Norman, and Angevin History [★10075]

HASTI Friends of the Elephants - Defunct.

Hastings Center [11980], 21 Malcolm Gordon Rd., Garrison, NY 10524-4125, (845)424-4040

Hate Free Zone [★17528]

Hathaway Family Assn. [20532], William S. Hathaway, Jr., Pres., 2231 Riverside Ave., Somerset, MA 02726-4104

Haunt Hunters - Defunct.

Haunted Attraction Assn. [1194], Cynthia Prisco, Exec. Dir., 191 Clarksville Rd., Princeton Junction, NJ 08550, (609)799-4900

Hauptverband der Deutschen Schuhindustrie [★IO]

Hauptverband des Osterreichischen Buchhandels [★IO]

Haut Commissariat des Nations Unies pour les Refugies [★IO]

Havana Rabbit Breeders Assn. [4840], N-9487 Walnut Rd., Clintonville, WI 54929, (715)823-5020

Havana Silk Dog Assn. of Am. [21578], Cathy Dilahunty, Treas., 4435 14th St. NE, St. Petersburg, FL 33703

Havergal Brian Soc. [IO], London, United Kingdom

HAVi - Address unknown since 2011.

Haviland Collectors Intl. Found. [21262], PO Box 271383, Fort Collins, CO 80527

HavServe Volunteer Ser. Network [11069], PO Box 4173, Silver Spring, MD 20914

Hawaii Agriculture Res. Center [4936], PO Box 100, Kunia, HI 96759, (808)621-1352

Hawaii Heptachlor Res. and Educ. Found. - Address unknown since 2011.

Hawaiian Intl. Billfish Assn. [★21733]

Hawaiian Intl. Billfish Assn. [★21733]

Hawaiian Intl. Billfish Tournament [21733], PO Box 29638, Honolulu, HI 96820, (808)836-3422

Hawaiian Intl. Billfish Tournament [21733], PO Box 29638, Honolulu, HI 96820, (808)836-3422

Hawaiian Sugar Planters' Assn. [★4936]

Hawk Migration Assn. of North Am. [7199], 51 Pheasant Run, North Granby, CT 06060

Hawk Mountain Sanctuary [5063], 1700 Hawk Mountain Rd., Kempton, PA 19529, (610)756-6961

Hawk and Owl Trust [IO], Taunton, United Kingdom

Hawkes Bay Br. of the Royal Soc. of New Zealand [IO], Napier, New Zealand

Hawkins Assn. [20533], PO Box 2392, Setauket, NY 11733

Hawkwatch Intl. [7200], 2240 S 900 E, Salt Lake City, UT 84106, (801)484-6808

Hawkwatch Intl. [7200], 2240 S 900 E, Salt Lake City, UT 84106, (801)484-6808

Hawley Soc. [★20588]

Hawthorne Soc; Nathaniel [9403]

Haykakan Gradararanayin Asotsiatsia [★IO]

Hazardous Material

Alliance of Hazardous Materials Professionals [4518]

Hazardous Materials Training and Res. Inst. [6938]

Inst. of Hazardous Materials Mgt. [4519]

Intl. Campaign to Ban Landmines [17553]

Intl. Panel on Fissile Materials [18203]

North Amer. Hazardous Materials Mgt. Assn. [4520]

Terra Segura Intl. [17559]

Hazardous Materials Advisory Comm. [★3245]

Hazardous Materials Advisory Coun. [★3245]

Hazardous Materials Training and Res. Inst. [6938], 6301 Kirkwood Blvd. SW, Cedar Rapids, IA 52404, (319)398-5893

Hazardous Wastes

Concerned Citizens for Nuclear Safety [18195]

Hazelden Center for Youth and Families [★13255]

Hazelden Found. [13255], PO Box 11, Center City, MN 55012-0011, (651)213-4200

Hazelden Found. Center [★13255]

Hazelden Renewal Center [★13255]

Hazelnut Coun. [4750], 424 2nd Ave. W, Seattle, WA 98119, (206)270-4639

Hazelnut and Products Exporters Union [IO], Istanbul, Turkey

Hazen Family Assn. - Defunct.

H.C. Andersen-Samfundet i Kobenhavn [★IO]

H.C. Fry Glass Soc. - Address unknown since 2011.

Head Injury

Amer. Combat Veterans of War [20771]

Brain Injury Assn. of Am. [14683]

Headway Ireland - Natl. Assn. for Acquired Brain Injury [4819]

Intl. Brain Injury Assn. [14684]

Natl. Assn. of State Head Injury Administrators [14685]

Head Injury Assn. of Durham Region [IO], Oshawa, ON, Canada

Head Injury Assn. of Fort Erie and District [IO], Fort Erie, ON, Canada

Head Injury Hotline [★16561]

Head Injury Soc. of New Zealand [IO], Hamilton, New Zealand

Head and Neck Soc; Amer. [16083]

Head Start Assn; Natl. [8741]

Headache

Amer. Headache Soc. [14686]

Amer. Headache Soc. l Comm. for Headache Educ. [14687]

Migraine Awareness Gp.: A Natl. Understanding for Migraineurs [14688]

Natl. Headache Found. [14689]

Org. for Understanding Cluster Headaches [14690]

Headache Soc. of Singapore [IO], Singapore, Singapore

HeadCount [17608], 104 W 29th St., 11th Fl., New York, NY 10001

The Headhunters [★5195]

Headmasters' and Headmistresses' Conf. [IO], Leicester, United Kingdom

HQ for Ghost Investigations [★7225]

HQ for Ghost Investigations [★7225]

Headway Ireland - Natl. Assn. for Acquired Brain Injury [IO], Dublin, Ireland

Headway - The Brain Injury Assn. [IO], Nottingham, United Kingdom

Headwest Brain Injury Assn. of WA [IO], Applecross, Australia

Heal the Children [★11468]

Healing Across the Divides [15177], 72 Laurel Dr., Northampton, PA 18067

Healing the Children [11468], PO Box 9065, Spokane, WA 99209-9065, (509)327-4281

Healing the Culture [12930], PO Box 82842, Kenmore, WA 98028, (425)481-6563

Healing the Divide [12238], 75 E 4th St., No. 4416, New York, NY 10003

Healing the Divide [12238], 75 E 4th St., No. 4416, New York, NY 10003

Healing Hands Intl. [13159], 455 McNally Dr., Nashville, TN 37211, (615)832-2000

Healing Hands Intl. [13159], 455 McNally Dr., Nashville, TN 37211, (615)832-2000

Healing Music Org. [15524], PO Box 3731, Santa Cruz, CA 95063, (831)588-7498

Healing Touch Assn. of Canada [IO], Calgary, AB, Canada

Healing Touch Intl. [14782], 445 Union Blvd., Ste. 105, Lakewood, CO 80228, (303)989-7982

Healing Touch Intl. [14782], 445 Union Blvd., Ste. 105, Lakewood, CO 80228, (303)989-7982

Healing Waters Intl. [13423], 534 Commons Dr., Golden, CO 80401, (303)526-7278

Healing Waters Intl. [13423], 534 Commons Dr., Golden, CO 80401, (303)526-7278

HealingWorks [13681], 9300 Colesville Rd., Silver Spring, MD 20901, (301)588-8248

Health

4K for Cancer [13874]

AACTION Autism [13776]

AcademyHealth [14691]

A star before a book entry number signifies that the name is not listed separately, but is mentioned within the entry.

2838

Encyclopedia of Associations, 51st Edition

Reference to "IO" in place of a book number signifies that the association may be found in the 50th edition of International Organizations.

Global Nutrition Alliance [15833]
Global Partners in Anesthesia and Surgery [16814]
Global Partnership for Family Hea. [13608]
Global Pediatric Alliance [16146]
Global Physicians Corps [15174]
Global Solutions for Infectious Diseases [15116]
Global Vaccine Awareness League [14709]
Global Youth Coalition on HIV/AIDS [10881]
GlobeMed [15175]
Globus Relief [12458]
God's Child Proj. [11294]
Golf Fights Cancer [13926]
Grind for Life [11136]
Guam Lytico and Bodig Assn. [14710]
Guam Lytico and Bodig Assn. [14710]
Haiti Healthcare Partners [15176]
HALTER, Inc. [16852]
Healing Across the Divides [15177]
HealingWorks [13681]
Hea. Bridges Intl. [15178]
Hea. Care for Am. Now [17771]
Hea. and Development Intl. [14711]
Hea. and Development Intl. [14711]
Hea. Educ. Coun. [14712]
Hea. and Educ. Relief for Guyana [15179]
Hea. and Educ. Relief Org. [12334]
Hea. Empowering Humanity [14786]
Hea. Horizons Intl. [15180]
Hea. for Humanity [14713]
Hea. Info. Rsrc. Center [14714]
Hea. Justice Collaborative [15181]
Hea. and Life Intl. [14788]
Hea. Promotion Inst. [10845]
Hea. through Walls [15182]
Healthcare Laundry Accreditation Coun. [2192]
HealthCare Volunteer [14790]
HealthShare Intl. [15750]
Healthy Building Network [4330]
Heart Rhythm Soc. [14016]
Helping Autism through Learning and Outreach [13795]
HelpMercy Intl. [14791]
HIMSS Electronic Hea. Record Assn. [15332]
HIS Nets [13588]
Holistic Mentorship Network [14998]
Holistic Pediatric Assn. [13682]
HomeAID for Africa [10812]
Hope Beyond Hope [15185]
Hope Through Healing Hands [15186]
Hope Through Hea. [12385]
HopeLab [15342]
Horizon Intl. Medical Mission [15187]
Hospitals of Hope [15188]
Human Touch Intl. [13589]
Hypospadias and Epispadias Assn. [13842]
Ibis Reproductive Hea. [16585]
Imagery Intl. [15073]
Imagine World Hea. [14715]
Imagine World Hea. [14715]
Impact Carbon [4228]
Integrative Clinics Intl. [14899]
Intercontinental Fed. of Behavioral Optometry [15994]
Intl. Aesthetic and Laser Assn. [15237]
Intl. Alliance for the Prevention of AIDS [13614]
Intl. Alliance of Professional Hypnotists [15089]
Intl. Anesthesia Res. Soc. [13748]
Intl. Assn. for Colon Hydrotherapy [14716]
Intl. Assn. for Colon Hydrotherapy [14716]
Intl. Assn. for Ecology and Hea. [6604]
Intl. Assn. of Healthcare Central Ser. Material Mgt. [15058]
Intl. Assn. of Medical and Therapeutic Specialists [13686]
Intl. Atherosclerosis Soc. [14020]
Intl. Bilingual Nurses Alliance [15755]
Intl. Brain Barriers Soc. [15657]
Intl. Brain Injury Assn. [14684]
Intl. Bronchoesophagological Soc. [13869]
Intl. Coalition for Autism and All Abilities [13796]
Intl. Coun. on Nanotechnology [6430]
Intl. Fed. of Psoriasis Associations [14328]
Intl. Fitness Assn. [16227]
Intl. Genetic Epidemiology Soc. [14514]

Intl. Holistic Practitioner Assn. [13689]
Intl. Medical Alliance [15192]
Intl. Medical Equip. Collaborative [14717]
Intl. Medical Equip. Collaborative [14717]
Intl. Meta-Medicine Assn. [13690]
Intl. Midwife Assistance [15883]
Intl. Pediatric Hypertension Assn. [15076]
Intl. Psoriasis Coun. [14329]
Intl. Skeletal Soc. [16533]
Intl. Smile Power [14221]
Intl. Soc. for Autism Res. [13797]
Intl. Soc. for Bipolar Disorders [13766]
Intl. Soc. for Cardiovascular Translational Res. [14024]
Intl. Soc. of Cardiovascular Ultrasound [14440]
Intl. Soc. for Children with Cancer [13934]
Intl. Soc. for Disease Surveillance [14395]
Intl. Soc. of Gastrointestinal Oncology [14568]
Intl. Soc. for Genetic Eye Diseases and Retino-blastoma [15964]
Intl. Soc. on Metabolic Eye Disease [15966]
Intl. Soc. of Pharmacogenomics [16200]
Intl. Soc. of Regulatory Toxicology and Pharmacology [14718]
Intl. Soc. of Regulatory Toxicology and Pharmacology [14718]
Intl. Soc. for Vaccines [15109]
Intl. Union Against Sexually Transmitted Infec-tions, Regional Off. for North Am. [16656]
Intl. Veterinarians Dedicated to Animal Hea. [17029]
Internet Sexuality Info. Services [8861]
IntraHealth Intl. [14881]
It's My Heart [14028]
Ivory Coast Medical Relief Team [16583]
J. Robert Gladden Orthopaedic Soc. [16037]
Jewish Healthcare Intl. [15194]
Josiah Macy, Jr. Found. [14719]
Journey to Solidarity [14139]
Kidney Care Partners [15551]
Kidney Community Emergency Response Coali-tion [15552]
Leadership Coun. of Aging Organizations [10850]
Let's Talk Pain [16105]
Leukemia and Lymphoma Soc. [13936]
Lily of the Valley Endeavor [10886]
Little By Little [14802]
Lynch Syndrome Intl. [14609]
Malawi Biomedicals Resources [15305]
Mama Baby Haiti [14107]
Managed Care Risk Assn. [1690]
Marijuana Policy Proj. [18086]
Mayan Medical Aid [12466]
MED25 Intl. [14803]
Medical Aid Comm. [15306]
Medical Bridges [15307]
Medical Care Intl. [15196]
Medical Expeditions Intl. [15308]
Medical Mission Gp. [15197]
Medical Records Inst. [15333]
Medical Relief Alliance [12864]
Medical Spa Soc. [14902]
Medicare Rights Center [17764]
Meds and Food for Kids [11348]
Melanoma Awareness [13940]
mHealth Alliance [15198]
Mindful Medicine Worldwide [13693]
Moms Against Mercury [13322]
Multiple Sclerosis Coalition [15609]
Myasthenia Gravis Assn. [17352]
NAMM Found. [10248]
Narcotic Educational Found. of Am. [13267]
Natl. Alliance of Professional Psychology Provid-ers [16411]
Natl. Assn. of Bionutritionists [15839]
Natl. Assn. of Certified Professionals of Equine Therapy [13694]
Natl. Assn. of Community Hea. Centers [14720]
Natl. Assn. for Continuing Educ. [7927]
Natl. Assn. of Female Paramedics [14472]
Natl. Assn. of Hea. Data Organizations [14721]
Natl. Assn. of Hea. Sci. Educ. Partnership [8843]
Natl. Assn. of Hea. Services Executives [14722]
Natl. Assn. of Hea. Unit Coordinators [14723]
Natl. Assn. of Healthcare Transport Mgt. [14724]

Natl. Assn. of Long Term Hospitals [15064]
Natl. Assn. for Males with Eating Disorders [14438]
Natl. Assn. of Residents and Interns [15425]
Natl. Assn. of State Comprehensive Hea. Insur-ance Plans [14861]
Natl. Assn. of Veterans Affairs Chaplains [19527]
Natl. Bus. Coalition on Hea. [14725]
Natl. Center for Farmworker Hea. [14726]
Natl. Coalition of Healthcare Recruiters [15298]
Natl. Coalition of Oncology Nurse Navigators [15778]
Natl. Coalition of Pastors' Spouses [13195]
Natl. Coun. Against Hea. Fraud [17765]
Natl. Coun. of State Legislatures | Forum for State Hea. Policy Leadership [17766]
Natl. Episcopal Hea. Ministries [14727]
Natl. Fibromyalgia and Chronic Pain Assn. [14540]
Natl. Found. for Brain Res. [15666]
Natl. Hea. Coun. [14728]
Natl. Hea. Fed. [14729]
Natl. Hea. Freedom Coalition [14816]
Natl. Hea. Info. Center [14730]
Natl. Hea. Policy Forum [17767]
Natl. Latina Hea. Network [14731]
Natl. Latino Coun. on Alcohol and Tobacco Prevention [12131]
Natl. Melanoma Alliance [13956]
Natl. Org. for Empowering Caregivers [13302]
Natl. Org. of Rheumatology Managers [16621]
Natl. Org. of State Offices of Rural Hea. [16490]
Natl. Transitions of Care Coalition [14821]
Natl. Women's Hea. Alliance [14822]
Naturopathic Medicine for Global Hea. [15536]
Naturopathic Physicians Bd. of Aesthetic Medicine [15537]
Netting Nations [14413]
Network Ethiopia [15199]
Network for the Improvement of World Hea. [15200]
Neuro-Optometric Rehabilitation Assn. Intl. [15559]
Neuroethics Soc. [15679]
Nordic Assn. for Andrology [19743]
North Amer. Clinical Dermatologic Soc. [14337]
North Amer. Pet Hea. Insurance Assn. [14863]
North Amer. Sikh Medical and Dental Assn. [15429]
Nutrition and Educ. Intl. [12586]
Nyaya Hea. [15201]
One Hundred Days [14732]
One World Healthcare USA [14823]
Optometric Glaucoma Soc. [15972]
OrganicAthlete [22232]
Org. for Medical and Psychological Assistance for Children Overseas [14094]
Pan Amer. Hea. Org. [14733]
Pan Amer. Hea. Org. [14733]
Pan Amer. Hea. Org. | Pan Amer. Sanitary Bur. [14734]
Pan Amer. Hea. Org. | Pan Amer. Sanitary Bur. [14734]
Partner for Surgery [16818]
Partners in Hea. [12132]
Partners in Hea. [12132]
Partnership for Prevention [14735]
Patient Privacy Rights [18104]
Patients Against Lymphoma [15257]
People's Medical Soc. [17768]
Peruvian Heart Assn. [14039]
Phi Chi Medical Fraternity [23594]
Philippine Nurses Assn. of Am. [15796]
Physicians Coalition for Injectable Safety [14181]
Physicians Comm. for Responsible Medicine [14736]
Pink Isn't Always Pretty [13969]
Planetree [14737]
Plastic Surgery Found. [14183]
Practice Greenhealth [14506]
Preemptive Love Coalition [14040]
Preimplantation Genetic Diagnosis Intl. Soc. [14656]
Private Duty Homecare Assn. [15015]
Prize4Life [15632]

A star before a book entry number signifies that the name is not listed separately, but is mentioned within the entry.

Professional Football Chiropractic [14143]
Progressive Hea. Partnership [15204]
Proj. HOPE [14738]
Proj. HOPE [14738]
Proj. Kids Worldwide [14095]
Prostate Hea. Educ. Network [13971]
Purine Res. Soc. [15506]
Qigong Alliance Intl. [13701]
Reach Intl. Healthcare and Training [15206]
Regulatory Affairs Professionals Soc. [14739]
Regulatory Affairs Professionals Soc. [14739]
Reiki Educ. [16580]
Reiki Rays of Hope for Caregivers [13707]
Res. for Hea. [15207]
Rock Against Cancer [13975]
Rural Hea. Intl. Non-Profit Org. [15208]
Safety Net Hospitals for Pharmaceutical Access [16213]
San Francisco AIDS Found. [13624]
Save the Patient [14740]
Semmelweis Soc. Intl. [16510]
Ser. for the Love of God [11631]
Sharing Resources Worldwide [15210]
Shelter Animal Reiki Assn. [16581]
Shibumi Intl. Reiki Assn. [16582]
Shine Therapy [15274]
Shout Global Hea. [15211]
Show Me A Cure [13979]
Sigmund Freud Archives [16362]
Silver Age Yoga [17138]
Soc. for the Anal. of African-American Public Hea. Issues [16497]
Soc. for Animal Homeopathy [15023]
Soc. for Clinical and Translational Sci. [14158]
Soc. of Family Planning [14528]
Soc. for Heart Brain Medicine [14046]
Soc. for Heart Valve Disease [14959]
Soc. for the History of Navy Medicine [9808]
Soc. of Nuclear Medicine Technologist Sect. [15697]
Soc. for Orthomolecular Hea. Medicine [13710]
Soc. for Participatory Medicine [14829]
Soc. of Physician Assistants in Rheumatology [16626]
Soc. for the Psychological Stud. of Lesbian, Gay, Bisexual and Transgender Issues [16429]
Soc. for Social Work Leadership in Hea. Care [13226]
Soc. for Worldwide Medical Exchange [15212]
Soft Power Hea. [15213]
South Asian Public Hea. Assn. [16499]
Spa Assn. [3127]
Spinal Hea. Intl. [16706]
Spoons Across Am. [15845]
Sri Lanka Medical Assn. of North Am. [14830]
Stories of Autism [13803]
Stratis Hea. [14741]
S.U.C.C.E.S.S. for Autism [13804]
Support for Intl. Change [15214]
Surfing Medicine Intl. [13712]
Syndromes Without a Name USA [14419]
Together for Kids [15070]
Tourette Syndrome Assn. [15636]
Traditional Chinese Medicine Assn. and Alumni [13714]
Tropical Clinics [15216]
UHAI for Hea. [15217]
Unified for Global Healing [15218]
Unite for HER [13989]
United Methodist Assn. of Hea. and Welfare Ministries [14742]
U.S. Dental Tennis Assn. [23062]
Univ. of Colorado Hea. Sciences Center Alumni Assn. [23547]
Unlocking Autism [13807]
Upenyu [15219]
Uplift Intl. [15220]
US Doctors for Africa [15221]
Venous Disease Coalition [16970]
Venture Strategies for Hea. and Development [14832]
Venture Strategies Innovations [14833]
Veteran's Coalition [20810]
Veterinary Botanical Medicine Assn. [17046]
Vietnamese-American Nurses Assn. [15805]

VietNow Natl. [13358]
Visionary Alternatives [13718]
Vitiligo Support Intl. [14341]
Voluntary Protection Prog. Assn. for Constr. [15910]
Waves of Hea. [15222]
WINGS [12904]
Wireless-Life Sciences Alliance [16829]
Women Against Prostate Cancer [13992]
Women in Balance [17137]
Women for World Hea. [14837]
World Fed. of Athletic Training and Therapy [16722]
World Fed. of Therapeutic Communities [13719]
World Glaucoma Patient Assn. [15979]
World Hea. Ambassador [14838]
World Hea. Clinicians [13630]
World Hea. Imaging, Telemedicine and Informatics Alliance [15224]
World Hea. Services [15226]
World Partners for Development [13210]
World Res. Found. [14743]
World Res. Found. [14743]
World Spine Care [16708]
Wuqu' Kawoq [15227]
Wyman Worldwide Hea. Partners [15228]
ZY Qigong [13722]
Hea. Action Intl. [IO], Amsterdam, Netherlands
Hea. Action Intl. Africa [IO], Nairobi, Kenya
Hea. Action Intl. Asia-Pacific [IO], Colombo, Sri Lanka
Hea. Action Intl. Latin Am. [IO], Lima, Peru
Hea. Assoc. Representatives [★2402]
Health and Beauty Products
    Amer. Hea. and Beauty Aids Inst. [1666]
    Cosmetic Executive Women [1667]
    Cosmetic Indus. Buyers and Suppliers [1668]
    Cosmetic Ingredient Rev. [1669]
    Natl. Hair Soc. [1643]
    Personal Care Prdt. Coun. [1670]
    Shea Yeleen Intl. [1671]
Hea. Bridges Intl. [15178], PO Box 8813, Portland, OR 97207, (503)720-4701
Health Care
    4K for Cancer [13874]
    AACTION Autism [13776]
    ACCESS Hea. Intl. [14744]
    Access Proj. [14745]
    Acupuncture for Veterans [13576]
    Adventist Hea. Intl. [15138]
    African Hea. Now [15139]
    AFT Healthcare [23213]
    Ahoto Partnership for Ghana [15141]
    Aicardi Syndrome Newsl. [14581]
    AIDS Clinical Trials Gp. [13593]
    AIDS Relief Intl. [10873]
    Algerian Amer. Scientists Assn. [7353]
    All Healers Mental Hea. Alliance [15442]
    Alliance for Addiction Solutions [15561]
    Alliance for Advancing Nonprofit Hea. Care [14746]
    Alliance for Biotherapies [16831]
    Alliance of Jamaican and Amer. Humanitarians [11543]
    Alliance for Preventive Hea. [14864]
    Alliance for Rabies Control [14370]
    Alliance for Wellness ROI [16303]
    Alternative Medicine Intl. [13648]
    Amazonas Hope for Hea. [14747]
    Ambassadors for Sustained Hea. [14748]
    Amer. Acad. of Restorative Dentistry [14244]
    Amer. APS Assn. [13808]
    Amer. Assn. of Breast Care Professionals [13858]
    Amer. Assn. of Caregiving Youth [13505]
    Amer. Assn. of Endodontists | Amer. Bd. of Endodontics [14250]
    Amer. Assn. of Nurse Assessment Coordinators [14749]
    Amer. Assn. of Nutritional Consultants [15814]
    Amer. Bd. of Integrative Holistic Medicine [14991]
    Amer. Bd. of Nutrition [15815]
    Amer. Bd. of Oriental Reproductive Medicine [16595]
    Amer. Celiac Disease Alliance [14549]
    Amer. Celiac Society | Dietary Support Coalition [15817]

Amer. Chinese Medical Exchange Soc. [14750]
Amer. Coll. of Community Midwives [15864]
Amer. Coll. of Contingency Planners [14751]
Amer. Coll. of Healthcare Architects [14752]
Amer. Coll. of Healthcare Architects [14752]
Amer. Coll. of Healthcare Info. Administrators [14753]
Amer. Coll. of Physicians [15133]
Amer. Coll. of Veterinary Dermatology [16998]
Amer. Friends of Guinea [15143]
Amer. Herbal Pharmacopoeia [13655]
Amer. Herbalists Guild [14989]
Amer. Hosp. Assn., Sect. for Long Term Care and Rehabilitation [15039]
Amer. Muslim Women Physicians Assn. [16252]
Amer. Nutraceutical Assn. [14754]
Amer. Osteopathic Assn. of Medical Informatics [16065]
Amer. Osteopathic Coll. of Anesthesiologists [13735]
Amer. Paraplegia Soc. [16696]
Amer. Pharmacists Assn. | Acad. of Pharmacy Practice and Mgt. [16176]
Amer. Physician Scientists Assn. [8588]
Amer. Podiatric Medical Students' Assn. [16294]
Amer. Registry of Medical Assistants [15316]
Amer. Soc. for Aesthetic Plastic Surgery [14175]
Amer. Soc. for Clinical Nutrition [15821]
Amer. Soc. of Clinical Radiation Oncology [15918]
Amer. Soc. of Healthcare Publication Editors [14755]
Amer. Soc. of Medication Safety Officers [14869]
Amer. Soc. for Nanomedicine [15398]
Amer. Soc. of Plastic Surgeons | Plastic Surgery Educ. Found. [14178]
Andean Hea. and Development [15145]
Angel Harps [16454]
Answer Africa [14374]
Arise Medical Missions [15146]
Aromatherapy Registration Coun. [13663]
Arthur Vining Davis Foundations [11902]
ASHA Intl. [15448]
Asian Hea. Care Leaders Assn. [15288]
Assn. of Ayurvedic Professionals of North Am. [13664]
Assn. for Behavioral Hea. and Wellness [14756]
Assn. for Benchmarking Hea. Care [1672]
Assn. of Clinicians for the Underserved [14757]
Assn. for Community Affiliated Plans [14758]
Assn. of Healthcare Value Anal. Professionals [14759]
Assn. for Healthcare Volunteer Rsrc. Professionals [13384]
Assn. of Immunization Managers [15100]
Assn. for Integrative Psychology [16389]
Assn. for Medical Ethics [14872]
Assn. for Needle-Free Injection Mfrs. [2330]
Assn. for Network Care [13666]
Assn. for Pelvic Organ Prolapse Support [14760]
Assn. of Physician Assistants in Cardiology [14006]
Assn. of Professors of Cardiology [14008]
Assn. of Prog. Directors in Internal Medicine [15134]
Assn. for Pulmonary and Critical Care Medicine Prog. Directors [14207]
Assn. for Radiological and Imaging Nursing [15739]
Assn. of Standardized Patient Educators [15323]
Assn. for Veterinary Family Practice [17016]
Australian Assn. of Practice Managers [16243]
Autism Allies [13779]
Autism Care and Treatment Today! [13780]
Avenues, Natl. Support Gp. for Arthrogryposis Multiplex Congenita [15573]
Bailey's Team for Autism [13788]
Basic Hea. Intl. [17122]
Be Healthy [13668]
Benign Essential Blepharospasm Res. Found. [15575]
Beverly Found. [10835]
Beyond Hunger [14431]
Binge Eating Disorder Assn. [14432]
Brain Attack Coalition [16729]

Reference to "IO" in place of a book number signifies that the association may be found in the 50th edition of International Organizations.

A star before a book entry number signifies that the name is not listed separately, but is mentioned within the entry.

IntraHealth Intl. [14881]
Iraqi Medical Sciences Assn. [15193]
It's My Heart [14028]
Ivory Coast Medical Relief Team [16583]
J. Robert Gladden Orthopaedic Soc. [16037]
Jewish Healthcare Intl. [15194]
Journey to Solidarity [14139]
Kaiser Family Found. [14800]
Kaiser Family Found. [14800]
Kenya Medical Outreach [12462]
Kidney Care Partners [15551]
Leadership Coun. of Aging Organizations [10850]
Leapfrog Gp. [14801]
Let's Talk Pain [16105]
Leukemia and Lymphoma Soc. [13936]
Lily of the Valley Endeavor [10886]
Little By Little [14802]
Little By Little [14802]
Lynch Syndrome Intl. [14609]
Malawi Biomedicals Resources [15305]
Mama Baby Haiti [14107]
Managed Care Risk Assn. [1690]
Marijuana Policy Proj. [18086]
Mayan Medical Aid [12466]
MED25 Intl. [14803]
Medical Aid Comm. [15306]
Medical Aid to Haiti [12467]
Medical Bridges [15307]
Medical Care Intl. [15196]
Medical Expeditions Intl. [15308]
Medical Mission Gp. [15197]
Medical Outcomes Trust [14804]
Medical Records Inst. [15333]
Medical Relief Alliance [12864]
Medical Relief Intl. [12865]
Medical Spa Soc. [14902]
Medical Wings Intl. [14805]
Medical Wings Intl. [14805]
Medicines for Humanity [14088]
Meds and Food for Kids [11348]
Melanoma Awareness [13940]
mHealth Alliance [15198]
Mindful Medicine Worldwide [13693]
Moms Against Mercury [13322]
Movement Disorder Soc. [14806]
Movement Disorder Soc. [14806]
Multiple Sclerosis Coalition [15609]
Narcotic Educational Found. of Am. [13267]
Natl. Academies of Practice [14807]
Natl. Acad. for State Hea. Policy [14808]
Natl. Alliance of Medicare Set-Aside Professionals [17772]
Natl. Alliance of Professional Psychology Providers [16411]
Natl. Alliance of Wound Care [14809]
Natl. Assembly on School-Based Hea. Care [14810]
Natl. Assn. of Bionutritionists [15839]
Natl. Assn. of Female Paramedics [14472]
Natl. Assn. of Hea. and Educational Facilities Finance Authorities [1673]
Natl. Assn. of Long Term Hospitals [15064]
Natl. Assn. for Males with Eating Disorders [14438]
Natl. Assn. of Residents and Interns [15425]
Natl. Assn. of Specialty Hea. Organizations [14811]
Natl. Assn. for the Support of Long Term Care [14812]
Natl. Assn. of Veterans Affairs Chaplains [19527]
Natl. Center for Assisted Living [14813]
Natl. Certification Coun. for Activity Professionals [1674]
Natl. Coalition on Hea. Care [17773]
Natl. Coalition of Oncology Nurse Navigators [15778]
Natl. Coalition of Pastors' Spouses [13195]
Natl. Coordinating Coun. for Medication Error Reporting and Prevention [14814]
Natl. Coun. on Interpreting in Hea. Care [1675]
Natl. EMS Mgt. Assn. [14476]
Natl. Fibromyalgia and Chronic Pain Assn. [14540]
Natl. Found. for Brain Res. [15666]
Natl. Guideline CH [14815]

Natl. Hea. Freedom Coalition [14816]
Natl. Inst. for Hea. Care Mgt. Res. and Educational Found. [14817]
Natl. Labor Alliance of Hea. Care Coalitions [23215]
Natl. Melanoma Alliance [13956]
Natl. Org. for Empowering Caregivers [13302]
Natl. Org. of Life and Hea. Insurance Guaranty Associations [1676]
Natl. Org. of Rheumatology Managers [16621]
Natl. Org. of State Offices of Rural Hea. [16490]
Natl. PACE Assn. [12133]
Natl. Patient Safety Found. [14818]
Natl. Pressure Ulcer Advisory Panel [14819]
Natl. Quality Forum [14820]
Natl. Transitions of Care Coalition [14821]
Natl. Women's Hea. Alliance [14822]
Naturopathic Medicine for Global Hea. [15536]
Naturopathic Physicians Bd. of Aesthetic Medicine [15537]
Netting Nations [14413]
Network Ethiopia [15199]
Network for the Improvement of World Hea. [15200]
Neuro-Optometric Rehabilitation Assn. Intl. [15559]
Neuroethics Soc. [15679]
Non-Profit Chiropractic Org. [14142]
Norrie Disease Assn. [14415]
North Amer. Clinical Dermatologic Soc. [14337]
North Amer. Pet Hea. Insurance Assn. [14863]
North Amer. Sikh Medical and Dental Assn. [15429]
NOVA Hope for Haiti [12474]
Nyaya Hea. [15201]
Oncology Assn. of Naturopathic Physicians [15539]
One Hundred Days [14732]
One World Healthcare USA [14823]
One World Medical Relief [15202]
Optometric Glaucoma Soc. [15972]
Org. for Medical and Psychological Assistance for Children Overseas [14094]
Partner for Surgery [16818]
Partners for World Hea. [15203]
Partnership for Patient Safety [14824]
Patient Advocate Found. [14825]
Patients Against Lymphoma [15257]
Pediatric Assn. of Naturopathic Physicians [8681]
People's Medical Soc. [17768]
Persons United Limiting Substandards and Errors in Hea. Care [14826]
Peruvian Heart Assn. [14039]
PHI [1677]
Phi Chi Medical Fraternity [23594]
Philippine Nurses Assn. of Am. [15796]
Physicians Coalition for Injectable Safety [14181]
Pink Isn't Always Pretty [13969]
Plastic Surgery Found. [14183]
Power Up Gambia [7441]
Practice Greenhealth [14506]
Preemptive Love Coalition [14040]
Private Duty Homecare Assn. [15015]
Prize4Life [15632]
Professional Football Chiropractic [14143]
Progressive Hea. Partnership [15204]
Proj. Kids Worldwide [14095]
A Promise of Hea. [14827]
Prostate Hea. Educ. Network [13971]
Purine Res. Soc. [15506]
Reach Intl. Healthcare and Training [15206]
Reiki Educ. [16580]
Reiki Rays of Hope for Caregivers [13707]
Res. for Hea. [15207]
Rock Against Cancer [13975]
Rural Hea. Intl. Non-Profit Org. [15208]
Safety Net Hospitals for Pharmaceutical Access [16213]
San Francisco AIDS Found. [13624]
SATELLIFE Global Hea. Info. Network [14828]
SATELLIFE Global Hea. Info. Network [14828]
Save the Patient [14740]
Scleral Lens Educ. Soc. [14168]
Semmelweis Soc. Intl. [16510]
Sharing Resources Worldwide [15210]

Shelter Animal Reiki Assn. [16581]
Shibumi Intl. Reiki Assn. [16582]
Shine Therapy [15274]
Shout Global Hea. [15211]
Show Me A Cure [13979]
Silver Age Yoga [17138]
Small World Found. [16820]
Soc. for Animal Homeopathy [15023]
Soc. for Emotional Well-Being Worldwide [15483]
Soc. for Heart Brain Medicine [14046]
Soc. for Heart Valve Disease [14959]
Soc. of Nuclear Medicine Technologist Sect. [15697]
Soc. for Orthomolecular Hea. Medicine [13710]
Soc. for Participatory Medicine [14829]
Soc. of Physician Assistants in Rheumatology [16626]
Soc. for Social Work Leadership in Hea. Care [13226]
Soc. for Worldwide Medical Exchange [15212]
Soft Power Hea. [15213]
South Asian Public Hea. Assn. [16499]
Spa Assn. [3127]
Spinal Hea. Intl. [16706]
Sri Lanka Medical Assn. of North Am. [14830]
Stories of Autism [13803]
S.U.C.C.E.S.S. for Autism [13804]
Support for Intl. Change [15214]
Surfing Medicine Intl. [13712]
Syndromes Without a Name USA [14419]
Together for Kids [15070]
Touch of Relief [15004]
Tourette Syndrome Assn. [15636]
Traditional Chinese Medicine Assn. and Alumni [13714]
Tropical Clinics [15216]
UHAI for Hea. [15217]
Unified for Global Healing [15218]
Union of Amer. Physicians and Dentists [23216]
Unite for HER [13989]
Universal Hea. Care Action Network [14831]
Unlocking Autism [13807]
Upenyu [15219]
US Doctors for Africa [15221]
Venous Disease Coalition [16970]
Venture Strategies for Hea. and Development [14832]
Venture Strategies for Hea. and Development [14832]
Venture Strategies Innovations [14833]
Veterinary Botanical Medicine Assn. [17046]
Vietnamese-American Nurses Assn. [15805]
VietNow Natl. [13358]
Vitiligo Support Intl. [14341]
Volunteers in Hea. Care [14834]
Waves of Hea. [15222]
Wellstart Intl. [14835]
Wings and Dreams for Kids [14099]
Wireless-Life Sciences Alliance [16829]
Women Against Prostate Cancer [13992]
Women in Balance [17137]
Women in Hea. Care Mgt. [14836]
Women for World Hea. [14837]
Workgroup for Electronic Data Interchange [1678]
World Family Ethiopian Orphans and Medical Care [11432]
World Fed. of Athletic Training and Therapy [16722]
World Glaucoma Patient Assn. [15979]
World Hea. Ambassador [14838]
World Hea. Clinicians [13630]
World Hea. Imaging, Telemedicine and Informatics Alliance [15224]
World Hea. Partners [15225]
World Hea. Services [15226]
World Spine Care [16708]
Wound Healing Soc. [14839]
Wuqu' Kawoq [15227]
Wyman Worldwide Hea. Partners [15228]
ZY Qigong [13722]
Hea. Care for Am. Now [17771], 1825 K St. NW, Ste. 400, Washington, DC 20006, (202)454-6200
Hea. Care Compliance Assn. [14783], 6500 Barrie Rd., Ste. 250, Minneapolis, MN 55435, (952)988-0141

Reference to "IO" in place of a book number signifies that the association may be found in the 50th edition of International Organizations.

Hea. Care Executive Assistants [★64]
Hea. Care Exhibitors Assn. [★1231]
Hea. Care Liability Alliance [★14785]
Health Care Products
Advanced Medical Tech. Assn. [14840]
Amer. Assn. for Homecare [14841]
Amer. Orthotic and Prosthetic Assn. [1679]
Assn. of Needle-Free Injection Mfrs. [2330]
Coalition for Safe Community Needle Disposal [14842]
Contact Lens Mfrs. Assn. [1680]
Contact Lens Mfrs. Assn. [1680]
Contact Lens Soc. of Am. [1681]
Dental Trade Alliance [1682]
Doc to Dock [15302]
Hea. Indus. Distributors Assn. [1683]
Healthcare Mfrs. Mgt. Coun. [14843]
Healthcare Supply Chain Assn. [14844]
Hearing Indus. Assn. [1684]
Independent Medical Distributors Assn. [1685]
Intl. Aloe Sci. Coun. [1686]
Intl. Aloe Sci. Coun. [1686]
Malawi Biomedicals Resources [15305]
Natl. Alliance for the Primary Prevention of Sharps Injuries [16630]
Optical Labs. Assn. [1687]
Optical Labs. Assn. [1687]
Orthopedic Surgical Mfrs. Assn. [1688]
Partnership for Quality Medical Donations [12478]
Pharmaceutical Indus. Labor-Management Assn. [2700]
Scleral Lens Educ. Soc. [14168]
United Natural Products Alliance [14845]
Vision Coun. [1689]
Health Care Resource Mgt. Soc. - Defunct.
Hea. Care Without Harm [14784], 12355 Sunrise Valley Dr., Ste. 680, Reston, VA 20191, (703)860-9790
Hea. Coalition on Liability and Access [14785], PO Box 78096, Washington, DC 20013-9096
Hea. Development Initiative - Rwanda [IO], Kigali, Rwanda
Hea. and Development Intl. [14711], 318 Seth Pl., Rockville, MD 20850, (858)245-2410
Hea. and Development Intl. [14711], 318 Seth Pl., Rockville, MD 20850, (858)245-2410
Hea. Division of Prog. for the Introduction and Adaptation of Contraceptive Tech. [★17197]
Health Education
Alliance for Massage Therapy Educ. [8560]
Amer. Chinese Medical Exchange Soc. [14750]
Amer. Commn. for Accreditation of Reflexology Educ. and Training [7726]
Amer. Coun. for Accredited Certification [4780]
Assn. of Standardized Patient Educators [15323]
Autism Allies [13779]
Bill and Melinda Gates Found. [12134]
Caribbean Hea. Outreach [15149]
Clinic at a Time [15152]HealthDEBRA Intl.
Diabetes Action Res. and Educ. Found. [14347]
Family Hea. Alliance [16584]
Global Hea. through Educ., Training and Ser. [15167]
Global Medic Force [15173]
HANDS for Cambodia [11593]
Hea. Jam [14846]
Helping Autism through Learning and Outreach [13795]
Holistic Mentorship Network [14998]
Honduras Outreach Medical Brigada Relief Effort [15184]
Inter-American Hea. Alliance [14795]
Intl. Assn. of Healthcare Practitioners [8223]
Intl. Healthcare Leadership [14880]
Internet Sexuality Info. Services [8861]
Little By Little [14802]
Medical Mission Gp. [15197]
Medics Without Borders [14469]
Natl. Assn. for Continuing Educ. [7927]
Natl. Assn. of Hea. Educ. Centers [14847]
Natl. Assn. of Hea. Sci. Educ. Partnership [8843]
Natl. Consortium on Hea. Sci. and Tech. Educ. [8224]
NEA Hea. Info. Network [8225]
Non-Profit Chiropractic Org. [14142]

One Hundred Days [14732]
Qigong Alliance Intl. [13701]
Reach Intl. Healthcare and Training [15206]
Save the Patient [14740]
Scleral Lens Educ. Soc. [14168]
Shout Global Hea. [15211]
UHAI for Hea. [15217]
Unified for Global Healing [15218]
Uplift Intl. [15220]
Visionary Alternatives [13718]
Vitiligo Support Intl. [14341]
Waves of Hea. [15222]
Women in Balance [17137]
World Hea. Services [15226]
Hea. Educ. Coun. [14712], 3950 Indus. Blvd., Ste. 600, West Sacramento, CA 95691, (916)556-3344
Hea. Educ. and Life-Skills Proj. Madagascar [IO], Toamasina, Madagascar
Hea. and Educ. Relief for Guyana [15179], 245-07 Francis Lewis Blvd., Rosedale, NY 11422, (347)528-2794
Hea. and Educ. Relief Org. [12334], PO Box 670804, Marietta, GA 30066, (678)494-5595
Hea. and Educ. Relief Org. [12334], PO Box 670804, Marietta, GA 30066, (678)494-5595
Health and Education Resources - Defunct.
Hea. Employers Assn. of British Columbia [IO], Vancouver, BC, Canada
Hea. Empowering Humanity [14786], PO Box 300551, Houston, TX 77230, (888)210-3438
Health and Energy Inst. - Defunct.
Hea. and Environmental Funders Network [11977], 4805 St. Elmo Ave., 2nd Fl., Bethesda, MD 20814, (301)656-7650
Health Food
Intl. Stevia Coun. [1404]
Spoons Across Am. [15845]
Yum-O Org. [12135]
Hea. Food Mfrs'. Assn. [IO], Surrey, United Kingdom
Hea. For All Missions [12459], 9101 W Sahara Ave., Ste. 105-F11, Las Vegas, NV 89117, (702)408-8269
Hea. Global Access Proj. [10883], 429 W 127th St., 2nd Fl., New York, NY 10027, (212)537-0575
Hea. and Healing Ministries [★19950]
Hea. Horizons Intl. [15180], Tufts Univ., Community Health Prog., 112 Packard Ave., Medford, MA 02155, (617)627-4299
Hea. for Humanity [14713], 415 Linden Ave., Ste. B, Wilmette, IL 60091, (847)425-7900
Hea. Indus. Assn. [★14840]
Hea. Indus. Bar Code Coun. [★14220]
Hea. Indus. Bus. Communications Coun. [14220], 2525 E Arizona Biltmore Cir., Ste. 127, Phoenix, AZ 85016, (602)381-1091
Hea. Indus. Distributors Assn. [1683], 310 Montgomery St., Alexandria, VA 22314-1516, (703)549-4432
Hea. Indus. Gp. Purchasing Assn. [★14844]
Hea. Indus. Mfrs. Assn. [★14840]
Hea. Indus. Representatives Assn. [2402], 8 The Meadows, Newnan, GA 30265, (303)756-8115
Hea. Informatics New Zealand [IO], Auckland, New Zealand
Health Information Coun. - Defunct.
Hea. Info. Network [★8225]
Hea. Info. Rsrc. Center [14714], 1850 W Winchester Rd., Ste. 213, Libertyville, IL 60048, (847)816-8660
Health Insurance Assn. of Am. - Defunct.
Hea. Jam [14846], 221 E 122nd St., 5th Fl., New York, NY 10035, (212)722-7987
Hea. Justice Collaborative [15181], 412 Southway, Baltimore, MD 21218, (410)467-4247
Health Law
Amer. Acad. of Psychiatry and the Law [5507]
Amer. Bar Assn. | Commn. on Mental and Physical Disability Law [5508]
Amer. Bar Assn. - Hea. Law Sect. [5509]
Amer. Hea. Lawyers Assn. [5510]
Greenaction for Hea. and Environmental Justice [5511]
Natl. Assn. of Long Term Hospitals [15064]
Natl. Hea. Law Prog. [5512]
Hea. Level Seven [★14787]
Hea. Level Seven Intl. [14787], 3300 Washtenaw Ave., Ste. 227, Ann Arbor, MI 48104, (734)677-7777

Hea. and Life Intl. [14788], PO Box 7822, Fredericksburg, VA 22404, (540)295-2374
Health Media Education - Defunct.
Hea. Ministries [19950], The Lutheran Church-Missouri Synod, 1333 S Kirkwood Rd., St. Louis, MO 63122-7295, (314)996-1380
Hea. Ministries Assn. [20181], PO Box 60042, Dayton, OH 45406, (800)723-4291
Hea. Occupations Students of Am. [8607], 6021 Morriss Rd., Ste. 111, Flower Mound, TX 75028, (972)847-0062
Hea. Optimizing Inst. [14997], PO Box 1233, Del Mar, CA 92014, (858)481-7751
Hea. Oriented Preventive Educ. [IO], Karachi, Pakistan
Hea. Outreach Partners [12520], 405 14th St., Ste. 909, Oakland, CA 94612, (510)268-0091
Hea. Physics Soc. [16277], 1313 Dolley Madison Blvd., Ste. 402, McLean, VA 22101, (703)790-1745
Health Plans
Acad. of Managed Care Providers [14848]
Access to Benefits Coalition [17760]
Alliance of Community Hea. Plans [14849]
Amer. Accreditation Healthcare Commn. [14850]
Amer. Assn. of Preferred Provider Organizations [14851]
America's Hea. Insurance Plans [14852]
Center for Medicare Advocacy [14853]
Coalition for Affordable Hea. Coverage [14854]
Consumer Hea. Educ. Coun. [14855]
Coun. for Affordable Hea. Insurance [14856]
Hea. Care for Am. Now [17771]
Inst. for Hea. Policy Solutions [14857]
ITEM Coalition [14858]
Managed Care Risk Assn. [1690]
Natl. Alliance for Medicaid in Educ. [14859]
Natl. Assn. of Alternative Benefits Consultants [1691]
Natl. Assn. of Medicaid Directors [14860]
Natl. Assn. of State Comprehensive Hea. Insurance Plans [14861]
Natl. Assn. of Vision Care Plans [14862]
North Amer. Pet Hea. Insurance Assn. [14863]HealthWomen in Managed Care
Hea. in Prisons Proj. [IO], London, United Kingdom
Hea. Prdt. Wholesalers' and Mfrs'. Assn. in Finland [IO], Espoo, Finland
Hea. Products Assn. of Southern Africa [IO], Johannesburg, Republic of South Africa
Health Professionals
ACMHA: The Coll. for Behavioral Hea. Leadership [15440]
Acupuncture for Veterans [13576]
Albanian Amer. Medical Soc. [15390]
Algerian Amer. Scientists Assn. [7353]
All Healers Mental Hea. Alliance [15442]
Alliance for Preventive Hea. [14864]
Amer. Abdominal Acupuncture Medical Assn. [13578]
Amer. Acad. of Professional Coders [14865]
Amer. Assn. of Breast Care Professionals [13858]
Amer. Assn. of Clinical Coders and Auditors [14866]
Amer. Assn. of Medical Rev. Officers [14867]
Amer. Assn. of Naturopathic Midwives [15530]
Amer. Assn. of Nutritional Consultants [15814]
Amer. Bd. of Integrative Holistic Medicine [14991]
Amer. Bd. of Nutrition [15815]
Amer. Bd. of Oriental Reproductive Medicine [16595]
Amer. Celiac Society | Dietary Support Coalition [15817]
Amer. Chinese Medical Exchange Soc. [14750]
Amer. Coll. of Community Midwives [15864]
Amer. Coll. of Physicians [15133]
Amer. Hosp. Assn., Sect. for Long Term Care and Rehabilitation [15039]
Amer. Medical Women's Assn. [14868]
Amer. Muslim Women Physicians Assn. [16252]
Amer. Physician Scientists Assn. [8588]
Amer. Psychological Assn. | Division of Independent Practice [16371]
Amer. Soc. for Clinical Nutrition [15821]
Amer. Soc. of Clinical Radiation Oncology [15918]
Amer. Soc. of Medication Safety Officers [14869]

A star before a book entry number signifies that the name is not listed separately, but is mentioned within the entry.

Andean Hea. and Development [15145]
Assn. of Ayurvedic Professionals of North Am. [13664]
Assn. for Catholic Chiropractors [14121]
Assn. of Family Practice Physician Assistants [14870]
Assn. of Hispanic Healthcare Executives [14871]
Assn. for Medical Ethics [14872]
Assn. of Prog. Directors in Internal Medicine [15134]
Assn. of Pulmonary and Critical Care Medicine Prog. Directors [14207]
Assn. for Radiological and Imaging Nursing [15739]
Assn. of Standardized Patient Educators [15323]
Avenues, Natl. Support Gp. for Arthrogryposis Multiplex Congenita [15573]
Benign Essential Blepharospasm Res. Found. [15575]
Cambodian Hea. Professionals Assn. of Am. [14761]
Cancer Support Community [13903]
Caribbean Amer. Medical and Sci. Assn. [14873]
Caribbean Public Hea. Coalition [16482]
Center for Professional Well-Being [14874]
Certification Bd. of Infection Control and Epidemiology [14875]
Certification Bd. for Urologic Nurses and Associates [16944]
Changing Children's Lives [15150]
Child Welfare and Policy and Practice Gp. [11229]
Children's Tumor Found. [15579]
Chinese Amer. Doctors Assn. [16261]
Chinese-American Soc. of Nuclear Medicine [15694]
Chiropractic Diplomatic Corps [14125]
Chiropractic Orthopedists of North Am. [14126]
Coalition of State Rheumatology Organizations [16619]
Commn. for Case Manager Certification [14876]
Community Oncology Alliance [15923]
Consumer Coalition for Quality Hea. Care [14770]
Coun. of Chiropractic Acupuncture [14128]
Coun. on Chiropractic Guidelines and Practice Parameters [14130]
Coun. on Chiropractic Practice [14132]
Coun. of Intl. Neonatal Nurses [15745]
Digital Pathology Assn. [16124]
Direct Care Alliance [1692]
Doctors for United Medical Missions [15155]
Energy Kinesiology Assn. [13674]
Energy Kinesiology Awareness Coun. [13675]
Fed. of Pediatric Organizations [16145]
Forbes Norris MDA/ALS Res. Center [15590]
Genetic Metabolic Dietitians Intl. [15497]
Giving Vision [17076]
Global Associates for Hea. Development [15161]
Global Emergency Care Collaborative [15162]
Global Flying Hospitals [14779]
Global Hea. Partners [14781]
Global Initiative for the Advancement of Nutritional Therapy [16851]
Global Medic Force [15173]
Global Medical Knowledge [15375]
Global Partners in Anesthesia and Surgery [16814]
Global Physicians Corps [15174]
Hea. Professions Network [14877]
HealthCare Volunteer [14790]
HealthShare Intl. [15750]
Heart Rhythm Soc. [14016]
Holistic Mentorship Network [14998]
Holistic Pediatric Assn. [13682]
Ibis Reproductive Hea. [16585]
Imagery Intl. [15073]
Inst. for Diversity in Hea. Mgt. [14878]
Integrative Clinics Intl. [14899]
Intercontinental Fed. of Behavioral Optometry [15994]
Intl. Alliance of Hair Restoration Surgeons [14675]
Intl. Assn. of Healthcare Central Ser. Material Mgt. [15058]
Intl. Assn. of Medical and Therapeutic Specialists [13686]

Intl. Assn. of Sickle Cell Nurses and Physician Assistants [14879]
Intl. Assn. of Sickle Cell Nurses and Physician Assistants [14879]
Intl. Bilingual Nurses Alliance [15755]
Intl. Brain Barriers Soc. [15657]
Intl. Genetic Epidemiology Soc. [14514]
Intl. Healthcare Leadership [14880]
Intl. Healthcare Volunteers [14798]
Intl. Holistic Practitioner Assn. [13689]
Intl. Meta-Medicine Assn. [13690]
Intl. Partnership for Reproductive Hea. [16587]
Intl. Pediatric Hypertension Assn. [15076]
Intl. Soc. for Bipolar Disorders [13766]
Intl. Soc. of Cardiovascular Ultrasound [14440]
Intl. Soc. for Disease Surveillance [14395]
Intl. Soc. of Gastrointestinal Oncology [14568]
Intl. Soc. on Metabolic Eye Disease [15966]
Intl. Soc. of Pharmacogenomics [16200]
IntraHealth Intl. [14881]
Iranian Amer. Psychological Assn. [16406]
Iraqi Medical Sciences Assn. [15193]
J. Robert Gladden Orthopaedic Soc. [16037]
Jewish Healthcare Intl. [15194]
Leadership Coun. of Aging Organizations [10850]
Let's Talk Pain [16105]
Mama Baby Haiti [14107]
Managed Care Risk Assn. [1690]
Medical Expeditions Intl. [15308]
Medics Without Borders [14469]
Natl. Alliance of Professional Psychology Providers [14411]
Natl. Arab Amer. Medical Assn. [14882]
Natl. Assn. of Certified Professionals of Equine Therapy [13694]
Natl. Assn. for Continuing Educ. [7927]
Natl. Assn. of County Behavioral Hea. Directors [14883]
Natl. Assn. of Long Term Hospitals [15064]
Natl. Assn. of Medics and Corpsmen [5219]
Natl. Assn. of Residents and Interns [15425]
Natl. Coalition of Healthcare Recruiters [15298]
Natl. Coalition of Oncology Nurse Navigators [15778]
Natl. Healthcare Collectors Assn. [1693]
Natl. Melanoma Alliance [13956]
Natl. Org. for Empowering Caregivers [13302]
Natl. Org. of Rheumatology Managers [16621]
Natl. Rural Recruitment and Retention Network [14884]
Natl. Soc. of Certified Healthcare Bus. Consultants [14885]
Natl. Transitions of Care Coalition [14821]
Naturopathic Physicians Bd. of Aesthetic Medicine [15537]
Neuro-Optometric Rehabilitation Assn. Intl. [15559]
North Amer. Assn. for Laser Therapy [15238]
North Amer. Sikh Medical and Dental Assn. [15429]
North Amer. Taiwanese Medical Assn. [14886]
Oncology Assn. of Naturopathic Physicians [15539]
One Nurse At A Time [15794]
One World Healthcare USA [14823]
Optometric Glaucoma Soc. [15972]
Pediatric Assn. of Naturopathic Physicians [8681]
Philippine Nurses Assn. of Am. [15796]
Practice Greenhealth [14506]
Preimplantation Genetic Diagnosis Intl. Soc. [14656]
Professional Football Chiropractic [14143]
A Promise of Hea. [14827]
Reiki Rays of Hope for Caregivers [13707]
Res. for Hea. [15207]
Scottsdale Inst. [14887]
Semmelweis Soc. Intl. [16510]
Sino-American Bridge for Educ. and Hea. [9876]
Sino-American Network for Therapeutic Radiology and Oncology [16871]
Soc. for the Anal. of African-American Public Hea. Issues [16497]
Soc. for Emotional Well-Being Worldwide [15483]
Soc. for Heart Brain Medicine [14046]
Soc. of Nuclear Medicine Technologist Sect. [15697]

Soc. for Orthomolecular Hea. Medicine [13710]
Soc. for Participatory Medicine [14829]
Soc. of Physician Assistants in Rheumatology [16626]
Soc. for Worldwide Medical Exchange [15212]
South Asian Public Hea. Assn. [16499]
Tourette Syndrome Assn. [15636]
Traditional Chinese Medicine Assn. and Alumni [13714]
U.S. Dental Tennis Assn. [23062]
US Doctors for Africa [15221]
Vietnamese-American Nurses Assn. [15805]
Wireless-Life Sciences Alliance [16829]
World Fed. of Athletic Training and Therapy [16722]
World Glaucoma Patient Assn. [15979]
Hea. Professions Network [14877], PO Box 112, Shillington, PA 19607-0112, (678)200-2619
Hea. Promotion Inst. [10845], Natl. Coun. on Aging, 1901 L St. NW, 4th Fl., Washington, DC 20036, (202)479-1200
Hea. and Rehabilitative Lib. Services [★9974]
Hea. Res. Bd. [IO], Dublin, Ireland
Hea. Res. Coun. of New Zealand [IO], Auckland, New Zealand
Hea. Res. and Educational Trust [15056], 155 N Wacker, Ste. 400, Chicago, IL 60606, (312)422-2600
Hea. Sci. Communications Assn. [14163], 39 Wedgewood Dr., Ste. A, Jewett City, CT 06351-2420, (860)376-5915
Hea. Sciences Assn. of Alberta [IO], Edmonton, AB, Canada
Hea. Sciences Consortium [★8318]
Health Services
Access to Benefits Coalition [17760]
ACCESS Hea. Intl. [14744]
Acupuncture for Veterans [13576]
Adventist Hea. Intl. [15138]
Ahoto Partnership for Ghana [15141]
Alliance for Preventive Hea. [14864]
Amazonas Hope for Hea. [14747]
Ambassadors for Sustained Hea. [14748]
Amer. APS Assn. [13808]
Amer. Assn. of Caregiving Youth [13505]
Amer. Coll. Hea. Assn. [14888]
Amer. Correctional Hea. Services Assn. [14889]
Amer. Friends of Guinea [15143]
Amer. Intl. Hea. Alliance [14890]
Amer. Intl. Hea. Alliance [14890]
Amer. Medical Gp. Assn. [14891]
Amer. School Hea. Assn. [14892]
Andean Hea. and Development [15145]
Angel Wing Flights [12445]
Arise Medical Missions [15146]
Asian Hea. Care Leaders Assn. [15288]HealthAssoc. Medical Services
Assn. of Asian Pacific Community Hea. Organizations [14893]
Assn. for Benchmarking Hea. Care [1672]
Assn. for Healthcare Volunteer Rsrc. Professionals [13384]
Assn. of Immunization Managers [15100]
Assn. of Nutrition Services Agencies [14894]
Australian Coll. of Hea. Ser. Executives [5646]
Basic Hea. Intl. [17122]
Be Healthy [13668]
Bus. Continuity Planning Workgroup for Healthcare Organizations [14481]
C-Change [13894]
Cambodian Hea. Professionals Assn. of Am. [14761]
Cancer Support Community [13903]
Caribbean Hea. Outreach [15149]
Cats in Crisis [10939]
Changing Children's Lives [15150]
ChildAlive [15151]
Children's Dialysis Intl. [15548]
Children's Intl. Hea. Relief [14067]
Citizens United for Res. in Epilepsy [14518]
Clinic at a Time [15152]
Clinical Directors Network [14895]
Clinicians of the World [15153]
Coalition for Affordable Hea. Coverage [14854]
Coalition to Protect America's Hea. Care [15049]

Reference to "IO" in place of a book number signifies that the association may be found in the 50th edition of International Organizations.

Encyclopedia of Associations, 51st Edition   2845

Common Hope for Hea. [14768]
Community Hea. Intl. [14896]
Doctors in Christ [15303]
Doctors for United Medical Missions [15155]
Dorcas Medical Mission [15156]
Dravet.org [14519]
Engg. World Hea. [15158]
European Assn. for Palliative Care [15473]
FACE AIDS [13602]
Forward in Hea. [14777]
Friends of Hea. [13677]
Friends for Hea. in Haiti [14778]
Friends Women's Assn. [13461]
GAVI Alliance [14897]
Ghana Medical Mission [15160]
Global Emergency Care Collaborative [15162]
Global Flying Hospitals [14779]
Global Hea. Corps [15165]
Global Hea. through Educ., Training and Ser. [15167]
Global Hea. Informatics Partnership [15168]
Global Hea. Linkages, Inc. [15169]
Global Hea. Partnerships [15170]
Global Hea. Soc. [15171]
Global Medic Force [15173]
Global Natural Hea. Alliance [13679]
Global Partnership for Family Hea. [13608]
GlobeMed [15175]
Hea. Bridges Intl. [15178]
Hea. and Educ. Relief for Guyana [15179]
Hea. Empowering Humanity [14786]
Hea. For All Missions [12459]
Hea. Horizons Intl. [15180]
Hea. and Life Intl. [14788]
Hea. Systems Trust - South Africa [675]
Hea. through Walls [15182]
Healthcare Leadership Coun. [14898]
HealthCare Volunteer [14790]
HealthShare Intl. [15750]
HelpMercy Intl. [14791]
Honduras Outreach Medical Brigada Relief Effort [15184]
Hope Beyond Hope [15185]
Hope Through Healing Hands [15186]
Horizon Intl. Medical Mission [15187]
Hospitals of Hope [15188]
Human Touch Intl. [13589]
I Care Grace Intl. [14792]
Integrative Clinics Intl. [14899]
Inter-American Hea. Alliance [14795]
Intl. Hea. and Development Network [15191]
Intl. Healthcare Volunteers [14798]
Intl. Medical Alliance [15192]HealthIntl. Medical Spa Assn.
Intl. Palestinian Cardiac Relief Org. [14021]
Intl. Smile Power [14221]
Intl. Soc. for Urban Hea. [14900]
IntraHealth Intl. [14881]
Jewish Healthcare Intl. [15194]
Lynch Syndrome Intl. [14609]
Malawi Biomedicals Resources [15305]
Mayan Medical Aid [12466]
MED25 Intl. [14803]
Medical Aid Comm. [15306]
Medical Benevolence Found. [14901]
Medical Bridges [15307]
Medical Care Intl. [15196]
Medical Expeditions Intl. [15308]
Medical Mission Gp. [15197]
Medical Relief Intl. [12865]
Medical Spa Soc. [14902]
Medicines for Humanity [14088]
Medics Without Borders [14469]
mHealth Alliance [15198]
Microsoft Hea. Users Gp. [14903]
Mindful Medicine Worldwide [13693]
Mobile Medical Disaster Relief [12472]
Natl. Alliance of Professional Psychology Providers [16411]
Natl. Assn. of Free Clinics [14904]
Natl. Assn. of Private Ambulance Services [584]
Natl. Assn. of State Comprehensive Hea. Insurance Plans [14861]
Natl. Commn. on Correctional Hea. Care [14905]
Natl. Fibromyalgia and Chronic Pain Assn. [14540]

Natl. Hea. Care for the Homeless Coun. [14906]
Natl. Org. for Empowering Caregivers [13302]
Natl. Org. of State Offices of Rural Hea. [16490]
Natl. Transitions of Care Coalition [14821]
Natl. Women's Hea. Alliance [14822]
Netting Nations [14413]
Network for the Improvement of World Hea. [15200]
Non-Profit Chiropractic Org. [14142]
Norrie Disease Assn. [14415]
NOVA Hope for Haiti [12474]
Nyaya Hea. [15201]
One Hundred Days [14732]
One Nurse At A Time [15794]
One World Healthcare USA [14823]
One World Medical Relief [15202]
Partner for Surgery [16818]
Partners for World Hea. [15203]
Partnership for Quality Medical Donations [12478]
Patient Privacy Rights [18104]
Power Up Gambia [7441]
Private Duty Homecare Assn. [15015]
Progressive Hea. Partnership [15204]
Proj. Kids Worldwide [14095]
A Promise of Hea. [14827]
Reach Intl. Healthcare and Training [15206]
Res. for Hea. [15207]
Rural Hea. Intl. Non-Profit Org. [15208]
Save the Patient [14740]
Sharing Resources Worldwide [15210]
Show Me A Cure [13979]
Soc. for Emotional Well-Being Worldwide [15483]
Soc. of Physician Assistants in Rheumatology [16626]
Soft Power Hea. [15213]
Spa Assn. [3127]
Sri Lanka Medical Assn. of North Am. [14830]
Support for Intl. Change [15214]
Trinity Hea. Intl. [14907]
Tropical Clinics [15216]
UHAI for Hea. [15217]
Unified for Global Healing [15218]
Upenyu [15219]
Venture Strategies for Hea. and Development [14832]
Venture Strategies Innovations [14833]
Veteran's Coalition [20810]
Visionary Alternatives [13718]
Waves of Hea. [15222]
Wellness Councils of Am. [14908]
Wings and Dreams for Kids [14099]
Women Against Prostate Cancer [13992]
Women in Balance [17137]
Women for World Hea. [14837]
World Hea. Ambassador [14838]
World Hea. Imaging, Telemedicine and Informatics Alliance [15224]
World Hea. Partners [15225]
World Hea. Services [15226]
World Spine Care [16708]
Wuqu' Kawoq [15227]
Wyman Worldwide Hea. Partners [15228]
Hea. Services Union of Australia [IO], Carlton South, Australia
Hea. Systems Trust - South Africa [IO], Durban, Republic of South Africa
Hea. Volunteers Overseas [12460], 1900 L St. NW, Ste. 310, Washington, DC 20036, (202)296-0928
Hea. Volunteers Overseas [12460], 1900 L St. NW, Ste. 310, Washington, DC 20036, (202)296-0928
Hea. through Walls [15182], 12555 Biscayne Blvd., No. 955, North Miami, FL 33181
Hea. and Welfare Services [★20237]
Hea. Wrights [16486], PO Box 1344, Palo Alto, CA 94302, (650)325-7500
Healthcare Audit Network [★8011]
Healthcare Billing and Mgt. Assn. [15415], 1540 S Coast Hwy., Ste. 203, Laguna Beach, CA 92651, (877)640-4262
Healthcare Caterers Intl. [1394], 406 Surrey Woods Dr., St. Charles, IL 60174, (630)587-6336
HealthCare Chaplaincy [20201], 315 E 62nd St., 4th Fl., New York, NY 10065-7767, (212)644-1111
HealthCare Compliance Packaging Coun. [16192], 2711 Buford Rd., No. 268, Bon Air, VA 23235-2423, (804)338-5778

Healthcare Convention and Exhibitors Assn. [1231], 1100 Johnson Ferry Rd., Ste. 300, Atlanta, GA 30342, (404)252-3663
Healthcare Distribution Mgt. Assn. [16193], 901 N Glebe Rd., Ste. 1000, Arlington, VA 22203, (703)787-0000
Healthcare Educ. Assn. [8024], 2424 Amer. Ln., Madison, WI 53704-3102, (608)441-1054
Healthcare Financial Mgt. Assn. [15258], 2 Westbrook Corporate Ctr., Ste. 700, Westchester, IL 60154, (708)531-9600
Healthcare Financial Mgt. Assn. [IO], Bristol, United Kingdom
Healthcare Financing Study Group - Defunct.
Healthcare Informatics Soc. of Ireland [IO], Dublin, Ireland
Healthcare Info. and Mgt. Systems Soc. [15057], 33 W Monroe St., Ste. 1700, Chicago, IL 60603-5616, (312)664-4467
Healthcare Internal Audit Gp. [★15290]
Healthcare Laundry Accreditation Coun. [2192], PO Box 1805, Frankfort, IL 60423, (815)464-1404
Healthcare Leadership Coun. [14898], 750 9th St. NW, Ste. 500, Washington, DC 20001, (202)452-8700
Healthcare Mfrs. Mgt. Coun. [14843], 1 Rebecca Ln., Savannah, GA 31411, (912)598-1607
Healthcare Mfrs. Marketing Coun. [★14843]
HealthCare Ministries [19809], 521 W Lynn St., Springfield, MO 65802, (417)866-6311
Healthcare People Mgt. Assn. [IO], Richmond, United Kingdom
Healthcare Quality Certification Bd. [13573], PO Box 19604, Lenexa, KS 66285-9604, (913)895-4609
Healthcare Supply Chain Assn. [14844], 2025 M St. NW, Ste. 800, Washington, DC 20036, (202)367-1162
HealthCare Tourism Intl. [14789], 595 Loyola Dr., Los Altos, CA 94024, (310)928-3611
HealthCare Volunteer [14790], 595 Loyola Dr., Los Altos, CA 94024
HealthGrid.US Alliance [13836], 5640 S Ellis Ave., Ste. 405, Chicago, IL 60637, (773)834-8200
Healthlink Worldwide [IO], London, United Kingdom
HealthRight Intl. [12461], 80 Maiden Ln., Ste. 607, New York, NY 10038, (212)226-9890
HealthRight Intl. [12461], 80 Maiden Ln., Ste. 607, New York, NY 10038, (212)226-9890
HealthShare Intl. [15750], 214 W104 St., Ste. 4B, New York, NY 10025, (646)319-3707
HEALTHsports, Inc. [★22524]
HEALTHsports, Inc. [★22524]
Healthy Building Network [4330], 2001 S St. NW, Ste. 570, Washington, DC 20009, (202)741-5717
Healthy Child Healthy World [14080], 12300 Wilshire Blvd., Ste. 320, Los Angeles, CA 90025, (310)820-2030
Healthy House Inst. - Defunct.
Healthy Kids Challenge [14081], 2 West Rd., 210, Dighton, KS 67839, (888)259-6287
Healthy Mothers, Healthy Babies [★15888]
Healthy Schools Network [4339], 110 Maryland Ave. NE, Ste. 505, Washington, DC 20002, (202)543-7555
Healthy Teen Network [12035], 1501 St. Paul St., Ste. 124, Baltimore, MD 21202, (410)685-0410
HEAR Center [14937], 301 E Del Mar Blvd., Pasadena, CA 91101, (626)796-2016
Hear Now [14938], The Starkey Hearing Found., 6700 Washington Ave. S, Eden Prairie, MN 55344-3405, (800)328-8602
Hearing Aid Indus. Conf. [★1684]
Hearing Assn. New Zealand [IO], Palmerston North, New Zealand
Hearing Concern LINK [IO], Eastbourne, United Kingdom
Hearing Dog Prog. [★14954]
Hearing Dog Proj. [★14954]
Hearing Dog Rsrc. Center [★14954]
Hearing Dogs [★14943]
Hearing Dogs [★14943]
Hearing Ear Dog Prog. [★14950]
Hearing Educ. and Awareness for Rockers [16310], 1405 Lyon St., San Francisco, CA 94115, (415)409-3277

A star before a book entry number signifies that the name is not listed separately, but is mentioned within the entry.

Hearing Educ. Through Auditory Res. Found. [★14937]
Hearing Found. of Canada [IO], Toronto, ON, Canada

Hearing Impaired
Abused Deaf Women's Advocacy Services [12136]
Acad. of Doctors of Audiology [14909]
Acad. of Rehabilitative Audiology [14910]
ADARA: Professionals Networking for Excellence in Ser. Delivery with Individuals who are Deaf or Hard of Hearing [14911]HearingAdvisory Coun. for Children with Impaired Hearing
Alexander Graham Bell Assn. for the Deaf and Hard of Hearing [14912]
Alexander Graham Bell Assn. for the Deaf and Hard of Hearing [14912]
Amer. Assn. of the Deaf-Blind [14913]
Amer. Auditory Soc. [14914]
Amer. Hearing Aid Associates [14915]
Amer. Hearing Res. Found. [14916]
Amer. Sign Language Teachers Assn. [14917]
Amer. Soc. for Deaf Children [14918]
Assn. of Adult Musicians with Hearing Loss [14919]
Assn. of Late-Deafened Adults [14920]
Assn. of Medical Professionals with Hearing Losses [14921]
Assn. of Medical Professionals with Hearing Losses [14921]
Better Hearing Inst. [14922]
Center for Hearing and Commun. [14923]
Child Aid [14924]
Child Aid [14924]
Children of Deaf Adults [14925]
Conf. of Educational Administrators of Schools and Programs for the Deaf [14926]
Coun. of Amer. Instructors of the Deaf [14927]
Coun. on Educ. of the Deaf [14928]
Deaf Australia [175]
Deaf Bilingual Coalition [12137]
Deaf Friends Intl. [12138]
Deaf Friends Intl. [12138]
Deaf and Hard of Hearing Alliance [14929]
Deaf Intl. [12139]
Deaf-REACH [14930]
Deaf Seniors of Am. [14931]
Deaf Women United [12140]HearingDeafHear.ie
DeafHope [12141]
Deafness Res. Found. [14932]
Dogs for the Deaf [14933]
DOVE: Advocacy Services for Abused Deaf Women and Children [12142]
Educational Audiology Assn. [14934]
Educational Audiology Assn. [14934]
Global Deaf Connection [14935]
Global Deaf Connection [14935]
Hands and Voices [14936]
HEAR Center [14937]
Hear Now [14938]
Hearing Instrument Mfrs'. Software Assn. [14939]
Hearing Loss Assn. of Am. [14940]
Helen Keller Natl. Center for Deaf-Blind Youths and Adults [14941]
HIKE Fund [14942]
Intl. Catholic Deaf Assn. U.S. Sect. [19435]
Intl. Hearing Dog [14943]
Intl. Hearing Dog [14943]
Intl. Hearing Soc. [14944]
Intl. Hearing Soc. [14944]
Intl. Soc. for Oral Laser Applications [2214]HearingIrish Deaf Soc.
John Tracy Clinic [14945]
Laurent Clerc Natl. Deaf Educ. Center [12143]
Military Audiology Assn. [13775]
Model Secondary School for the Deaf [14946]
Natl. Assn. of the Deaf [14947]
Natl. Captioning Inst. [14948]
Natl. Coalition on Auditory Processing Disorders [14949]
Natl. Educ. for Assistance Dog Services [14950]
Natl. Family Assn. for Deaf-Blind [14951]
Natl. Hearing Conservation Assn. [14952]
Natl. Inst. on Deafness and Other Commun. Disorders Info. CH [14953]

Natl. Ser. Dog Center [14954]
Parents' Sect. of the Alexander Graham Bell Assn. for the Deaf and Hard of Hearing [14955]
Registry of Interpreters for the Deaf [14956]HearingRoyal Inst. for Deaf and Blind Children
Signing Exact English Center for the Advancement of Deaf Children [14957]
Singapore Assn. for the Deaf [16154]
Telecommunications for the Deaf and Hard of Hearing [14958]
U.S.A. Deaf Basketball [22300]
U.S. Flag Football for the Deaf [22530]
Hearing Impaired Kids Endowment Fund [★14942]
Hearing Indus. Assn. [1684], 1444 I St. NW, Ste. 700, Washington, DC 20005, (202)449-1090
Hearing Instrument Mfrs'. Software Assn. [14939], 2600 Eagan Woods Dr., Ste. 460, Eagan, MN 55121, (651)644-2921
Hearing Loss Assn. of Am. [14940], 7910 Woodmont Ave., Ste. 1200, Bethesda, MD 20814, (301)657-2248

Hearing, Speech and
Deaf and Hard of Hearing Alliance [14929]
Intl. Catholic Deaf Assn. U.S. Sect. [19435]
Military Audiology Assn. [13775]
U.S.A. Deaf Basketball [22300]
Hearst Found. [13135], 90 New Montgomery St., Ste. 1212, San Francisco, CA 94105, (415)908-4500
Hearst Memorial Morab Registry [★4641]
Hearst Memorial Morab Registry [★4641]
HEART 9/11: Healing Emergency Aid Response Team 9/11 [11853], 614 Frelinghuysen Ave., Newark, NJ 07114, (862)902-5471
Heart for Africa [11299], PO Box 573, Alpharetta, GA 30009, (678)566-1589
Heart of Africa Mission [★19773]
Heart of Africa Mission [★19773]
Heart of Am. Northwest [18422], 1314 56th St. NE, Ste. 100, Seattle, WA 98105, (206)382-1014
Heart Assn. of Thailand [IO], Bangkok, Thailand
Heart Bandits Amer. Eskimo Dog Rescue [11875], PO Box 4322, Fresno, CA 93744-4322, (559)787-2459
Heart Bandits Amer. Eskimo Dog Rescue [11875], PO Box 4322, Fresno, CA 93744-4322, (559)787-2459
Heart Care Intl. [14014], 139 E Putnam Ave., Greenwich, CT 06830, (203)552-5343
Heart Care Intl. [14014], 139 E Putnam Ave., Greenwich, CT 06830, (203)552-5343

Heart Disease
Heart Rhythm Soc. [14016]
Intl. Palestinian Cardiac Relief Org. [14021]
Peruvian Heart Assn. [14039]
Soc. for Heart Valve Disease [14959]
Heart Failure Soc. of Am. [14015], Cheryl Yano, Exec. Dir., Court Intl. - Ste. 240 S, 2550 Univ. Ave. W, St. Paul, MN 55114, (651)642-1633
Heart Found. of Australia [IO], Deakin, Australia
Heart to Heart Intl. [12844], 401 S Claiborne Rd., Ste. 302, Olathe, KS 66062, (913)764-5200
Heart to Heart Intl. [12844], 401 S Claiborne Rd., Ste. 302, Olathe, KS 66062, (913)764-5200
Heart-Life Assn. [IO], San Marino, San Marino
Heart Rhythm Soc. [14016], 1400 K St. NW, Ste. 500, Washington, DC 20005, (202)464-3400
Heart Rhythm Soc. [14016], 1400 K St. NW, Ste. 500, Washington, DC 20005, (202)464-3400
Heart of Romania's Children Found. [11300], 399 Fairfield Dr., Sanford, FL 32771, (407)323-4656
Heart and Stroke Found. of Canada [IO], Ottawa, ON, Canada
Heart of Texas Country Music Assn. [23855], Mr. Tracy Pitcox, 1701 S Bridge St., Brady, TX 76825, (325)597-1895
Heart Valve Soc. of Am. [14017], PO Box 1365, New York, NY 10021, (212)561-9879
Heart4Kids [11301], 13950 Mansarde Ave., Ste. 186, Herndon, VA 20171, (404)957-9014
Heartbeat [13295], PO Box 16985, Colorado Springs, CO 80935-6985, (719)596-2575
Heartbeat Intl. [12931], 665 E Dublin-Granville Rd., Ste. 440, Columbus, OH 43229-3245, (614)885-7577

Heartbeat Intl. [12931], 665 E Dublin-Granville Rd., Ste. 440, Columbus, OH 43229-3245, (614)885-7577
Heartbeat/Survivors After Suicide [★13295]
Hearth Educ. Found. [★1700]
Hearth, Patio and Barbecue Assn. [1699], 1901 N Moore St., Ste. 600, Arlington, VA 22209, (703)522-0086
Hearth, Patio & Barbecue Assn. [★1699]
Hearth, Patio and Barbecue Found. [1700], 1901 N Moore St., Ste. 600, Arlington, VA 22209, (703)524-8030
Heartland Conservation Soc. [IO], Camberley, United Kingdom
Heartland Inst. [13136], 19 S LaSalle St., Ste. 903, Chicago, IL 60603, (312)377-4000
Hearts Across Romania [11302], 2544 Brookside Dr., Irving, TX 75063, (214)213-9001
Heart's Home USA [19987], 108 St. Edwards St., Brooklyn, NY 11205, (718)522-2922
Hearts for the Hungry [12282], PO Box 10701, Erie, PA 16514, (814)873-1397
Hearts for the Hungry [12282], PO Box 10701, Erie, PA 16514, (814)873-1397
Hearts for Kenya [11070], 1514 Norris Pl., Louisville, KY 40205, (502)459-4582
Hearts and Minds Network [18713], 165 W 105th St., New York, NY 10025, (212)280-0333
Hearts United for Animals [10976], Box 286, Auburn, NE 68305, (402)274-3679
Hearts for Zambia [11303], PO Box 11161, Tacoma, WA 98411, (253)759-9904
HeartStrong [12085], PO Box 2051, Seattle, WA 98111, (206)388-3894
Heat Exchange Inst. [1701], 1300 Sumner Ave., Cleveland, OH 44115-2815, (216)241-7333
HeatGreen Coun. [6113], 3340 Commercial St. SE, Ste. 210, Salem, OR 97302, (503)371-7457
HEATH Rsrc. Center at the Natl. Youth Transitions Center [7972], George Washington Univ., 2134 G St. NW, Washington, DC 20052-0001
Heather Soc. [IO], Wisbech, United Kingdom
Heating Airconditioning and Refrigeration Distributors Intl. [1702], 3455 Mill Run Dr., Ste. 820, Hilliard, OH 43026, (614)345-4328
Heating Airconditioning and Refrigeration Distributors Intl. [1702], 3455 Mill Run Dr., Ste. 820, Hilliard, OH 43026, (614)345-4328

Heating and Cooling
Air Conditioning Contractors of Am. [1694]
Air-Conditioning Heating and Refrigeration Inst. [1695]
Air Diffusion Coun. [1696]
Air Movement and Control Assn. Intl. [1697]
Air Movement and Control Assn. Intl. [1697]
ClimateTalk Alliance [6111]
Evaporative Cooling Inst. [1698]
Hearth, Patio and Barbecue Assn. [1699]
Hearth, Patio and Barbecue Found. [1700]
Heat Exchange Inst. [1701]
HeatGreen Coun. [6113]
Heating Airconditioning and Refrigeration Distributors Intl. [1702]
Heating Airconditioning and Refrigeration Distributors Intl. [1702]
Home Ventilating Inst. [1703]
Indus. Heating Equip. Assn. [1704]
Intl. Air Filtration Certifiers Assn. [1705]
Intl. Assn. for Cold Storage Constr. [1706]
Intl. Assn. for Cold Storage Constr. [1706]
Intl. Assn. of Heat and Frost Insulators and Allied Workers [1707]
Intl. Compressor Remanufacturers Assn. [1708]
Intl. Compressor Remanufacturers Assn. [1708]
Intl. District Energy Assn. [1709]
Intl. District Energy Assn. [1709]
Intl. Ground Source Heat Pump Assn. [1710]
Intl. Ground Source Heat Pump Assn. [1710]
Intl. Inst. of Ammonia Refrigeration [1711]
Intl. Inst. of Ammonia Refrigeration [1711]
Intl. Packaged Ice Assn. [1712]
Masonry Heater Assn. of North Am. [1713]
Mobile Air Conditioning Soc. Worldwide [1714]
Mobile Air Conditioning Soc. Worldwide [1714]
Natl. Air Filtration Assn. [1715]

Reference to "IO" in place of a book number signifies that the association may be found in the 50th edition of International Organizations.

Natl. Environmental Balancing Bur. [1716]
North Amer. Technician Excellence [1717]
Radiant Professionals Alliance [1718]
Refrigeration Ser. Engineers Soc. [1719]
Refrigeration Ser. Engineers Soc. [1719]
Sheet Metal and Air Conditioning Contractors' Natl. Assn. [1720]
Steamfitting Indus. Promotion Fund [1721]
Tubular Exchanger Mfrs. Assn. [1722]
Wholesale Distributors Assn. [2785]
Heating and Piping and Air Conditioning Contractors Natl. Assn. [★924]
Heating and Piping Contractors Natl. Assn. [★924]
Heating, Refrigeration and Air Conditioning Inst. of Canada [IO], Mississauga, ON, Canada
Heating, Ventilating and Air Conditioning Mfrs'. Assn. [IO], Reading, United Kingdom
Heating and Ventilating Contractors' Assn. [IO], London, United Kingdom
Heaven on Earth Soc. for Animals [10977], PO Box 8171, Van Nuys, CA 91409, (818)474-2700
Heavy Duty Mfrs. Assn. [2335], 10 Lab. Dr., PO Box 13966, Research Triangle Park, NC 27709-3966, (919)549-4800
Heavy Duty Mfrs. Assn. I Heavy-Duty Bus. Forum [299], 10 Lab. Dr., PO Box 13966, Research Triangle Park, NC 27709-3966, (919)549-4800
Heavy Duty Representatives Assn. [329], 160 Symphony Way, Elgin, IL 60120, (847)760-0067
Heavy Metal Music
KISS Rocks Fan Club [23869]
Heavy Movable Structures [6375], 1037 Raymond Blvd., One Riverfront Plz., 14th Fl., Newark, NJ 07102, (973)474-5010
Heavy Specialized Carriers Conf. [★3270]
Heavy Specialized Carriers Conf. [★3270]
Heavy Specialized Carriers Sect. - Local Cartage Natl. Conf. [★3270]
Heavy Specialized Carriers Sect. - Local Cartage Natl. Conf. [★3270]
Hebe Haven Yacht Club [IO], Hong Kong, People's Republic of China
Hebe Soc. [IO], Hailsham, United Kingdom
Hebrew Christian Alliance of Am. [★19966]
Hebrew Christian Fellowship [19750], PO Box 177, Dresher, PA 19025-0177, (215)887-3447
Hebrew Free Burial Assn. [19865], 224 W 35th St., Rm. 300, New York, NY 10001, (212)239-1662
Hebrew Free Loan [★19870]
Hebrew Immigrant Aid Soc. [12406], 333 7th Ave., 16th Fl., New York, NY 10001-5019, (212)967-4100
Hebrew Immigrant Aid Soc. [12406], 333 7th Ave., 16th Fl., New York, NY 10001-5019, (212)967-4100
Hebrew Sheltering and Immigrant Aid Soc. [★12406]
Hebrew Sheltering and Immigrant Aid Soc. [★12406]
Hebron USA - Address unknown since 2011.
Hector Kobbekaduwa Agrarian Res. and Training Inst. [IO], Colombo, Sri Lanka
Hedge Fund Assn. [2135], 2875 NE 191st St., Ste. 900, Aventura, FL 33180, (202)478-2000
Hedge Fund Assn. [2135], 2875 NE 191st St., Ste. 900, Aventura, FL 33180, (202)478-2000
Hedge Fund Bus. Operations Assn. [2136], 1350 41st Ave., Ste. 200, Capitola, CA 95010, (831)465-2298
Hedge Funds Care [11143], 70 W 36th St., Ste. 1404, New York, NY 10018, (212)991-9600
Hegel Soc. of Am. [9369], Philosophy Documentation Center, Charlottesville, VA 22906-7147, (804)220-3300
Heidelberg Digital Imaging Assn. [1611], 1 Barney Rd., No. 232, Clifton Park, NY 12065, (518)373-1225
Heifer Intl. [12335], 1 World Ave., Little Rock, AR 72202, (800)422-0474
Heifer Intl. Cambodia [IO], Phnom Penh, Cambodia
Heifer Proj. Intl. [12335], 1 World Ave., Little Rock, AR 72202, (800)422-0474
Heifer Proj. Intl. [3913], 1 World Ave., Little Rock, AR 72202, (800)422-0474
Heifers for Relief [★12335]
Heifers for Relief [★12335]
Heinlein Soc. [9370], 3553 Atlantic Ave., No. 341, Long Beach, CA 90807-5606

Heirs, Inc. [17461], PO Box 292, Villanova, PA 19085, (610)525-4442
Heisey Collectors of America/National Heisey Glass Museum [21834], 169 W Church St., Newark, OH 43055, (740)345-2932
Helen Keller Intl. [17085], 352 Park Ave. S, 12th Fl., New York, NY 10010, (212)532-0544
Helen Keller Intl. [17085], 352 Park Ave. S, 12th Fl., New York, NY 10010, (212)532-0544
Helen Keller Intl. - Asia-Pacific Regional Off. [IO], Phnom Penh, Cambodia
Helen Keller Intl. - Bangladesh [IO], Dhaka, Bangladesh
Helen Keller Intl. - Burkina Faso [IO], Ouagadougou, Burkina Faso
Helen Keller Intl. - Cambodia [IO], Phnom Penh, Cambodia
Helen Keller Intl. - Cameroon [IO], Yaounde, Cameroon
Helen Keller Intl. - China [IO], Guangzhou, People's Republic of China
Helen Keller Intl. - Cote d'Ivoire [IO], Abidjan, Cote d'Ivoire
Helen Keller Intl. - Europe [IO], Paris, France
Helen Keller Intl. - Guinea [IO], Conakry, Guinea
Helen Keller Intl. - Indonesia [IO], Jakarta, Indonesia
Helen Keller Intl. - Mali [IO], Bamako, Mali
Helen Keller Intl. - Mozambique [IO], Maputo, Mozambique
Helen Keller Intl. - Nepal [IO], Kathmandu, Nepal
Helen Keller Intl. - Niger [IO], Niamey, Niger
Helen Keller Intl. - Nigeria [IO], Jos, Nigeria
Helen Keller Intl. - Philippines [IO], Manila, Philippines
Helen Keller Intl. - Sierra Leone [IO], Freetown, Sierra Leone
Helen Keller Intl. - Tanzania [IO], Dar es Salaam, United Republic of Tanzania
Helen Keller Intl. - Vietnam [IO], Hanoi, Vietnam
Helen Keller Natl. Center for Deaf-Blind Youths and Adults [14941], 141 Middle Neck Rd., Sands Point, NY 11050-1218, (516)944-8900
Helen Keller Worldwide [★17085]
Helen Keller Worldwide [★17085]
Helen Suzman Found. [IO], Parktown, Republic of South Africa
Helene Fuld Hea. Trust [15751], Ms. Marianne Caskran, Grants Admin., HSBC Bank USA, 452 Fifth Ave., 13th Fl., New York, NY 10018-2706, (212)525-2418
Heliconia Soc. Intl. [4669], David Lorence, Treas., 3530 Papalina Rd., Kalaheo, HI 96741, (808)332-7324
Heliconia Soc. Intl. [4669], David Lorence, Treas., 3530 Papalina Rd., Kalaheo, HI 96741, (808)332-7324
Helicopter
Combat Helicopter Pilots Assn. [20313]
Pedro Rescue Helicopter Assn. [20316]
Popular Rotorcraft Assn. [20913]
Whirly-Girls - Intl. Women Helicopter Pilots [20923]
Helicopter Assn. of Am. [★136]
Helicopter Assn. of Am. [★136]
Helicopter Assn. Intl. [136], 1635 Prince St., Alexandria, VA 22314-2818, (703)683-4646
Helicopter Assn. Intl. [136], 1635 Prince St., Alexandria, VA 22314-2818, (703)683-4646
Helicopter Assn; Intl. R/C [21903]
Helicopter Club of Great Britain [IO], Banbury, United Kingdom
Helicopter Found. Intl. [137], 1635 Prince St., Alexandria, VA 22314-2818, (703)683-4646
Helicopter Found. Intl. [137], 1635 Prince St., Alexandria, VA 22314-2818, (703)683-4646
Helicopter Loggers Assn. - Defunct.
Helicopter Safety Advisory Conf. [138], BHP Billiton Petroleum, Inc., 1360 Post Oak Blvd., Ste. 150, Houston, TX 77056-3020, (713)499-5452
HELIO Intl. [IO], Paris, France
Helium Soc. [★6582]
Hellenic Advertisers Assn. [IO], Athens, Greece
Hellenic Aerosol Assn. [IO], Athens, Greece
Hellenic Amer. Bankers Assn. [415], PO Box 7244, New York, NY 10150-7201, (212)421-1057

Hellenic-American Chamber of Commerce [23404], 780 3rd Ave., 16 Fl., New York, NY 10017, (212)629-6380
Hellenic Amer. Dental Soc. [14284], PO Box 4803, Oak Brook, IL 60523-4803
Hellenic Amer. Natl. Coun. [9648], 2155 W 80th St., Chicago, IL 60620, (773)994-2222
Hellenic Amer. Natl. Coun. [9648], 2155 W 80th St., Chicago, IL 60620, (773)994-2222
Hellenic Assn. of Dermatology and Venereology [IO], Athens, Greece
Hellenic Assn. of Footwear Mfrs. and Exporters [IO], Neo Psychiko, Greece
Hellenic Assn. of Gerontology and Geriatrics [IO], Athens, Greece
Hellenic Assn. of Pharmaceutical Companies [IO], Athens, Greece
Hellenic Assn. of Professional Cong. Organisers [IO], Athens, Greece
Hellenic Assn. of Travel and Tourist Agencies [IO], Athens, Greece
Hellenic Badminton Fed. [IO], Athens, Greece
Hellenic Billiard Fed. [IO], Athens, Greece
Hellenic Bioscientific Assn. in the USA [7369], PO Box 231134, Boston, MA 02123
Hellenic Cardiological Soc. [IO], Athens, Greece
Hellenic Chamber of Hotels [IO], Athens, Greece
Hellenic Cricket Fed. [IO], Corfu, Greece
Hellenic Fertility and Sterility Soc. [IO], Athens, Greece
Hellenic Found. for European and Foreign Policy [IO], Athens, Greece
Hellenic Geographic Info. Soc. [IO], Athens, Greece
Hellenic Ice Sports Fed. [IO], Athens, Greece
Hellenic League Against Rheumatism [IO], Athens, Greece
Hellenic Olympic Comm. [IO], Athens, Greece
Hellenic Operational Res. Soc. [IO], Athens, Greece
Hellenic Pain Soc. [IO], Athens, Greece
Hellenic Paralympic Comm. [IO], Athens, Greece
Hellenic Professional Yacht Owners Assn. [IO], Piraeus, Greece
Hellenic Radiological Soc. [IO], Athens, Greece
Hellenic Rose Soc. [IO], Piraeus, Greece
Hellenic Soc. for Chemotherapy [IO], Athens, Greece
Hellenic Soc. for Dermatologic Surgery [IO], Athens, Greece
Hellenic Soc. of Hypertension [IO], Athens, Greece
Hellenic Soc. for Infectious Diseases [IO], Athens, Greece
Hellenic Soc. for Microbiology [IO], Athens, Greece
Hellenic Soc. for Photogrammetry and Remote Sensing [IO], Athens, Greece
Hellenic Soc. of Physiology [IO], Athens, Greece
Hellenic Soc. of Rheology [IO], Chania, Greece
Hellenic Soc. for Rheumatology [IO], Athens, Greece
Hellenic Tennis Fed. [IO], Athens, Greece
Hellenic Weightlifting Fed. [IO], Athens, Greece
HELLP Syndrome Soc.
HELLP Syndrome Soc. - Address unknown since 2011.
Hell's Angels Bomb Gp. [★20847]
Helmet Comm., Washington Area Bicyclist Assn. [★12979]
Help the Afghan Children [IO], Kabul, Afghanistan
Help Afghan School Children Org. [IO], Vienna, Austria
Help the Aged [IO], Ottawa, ON, Canada
Help Aid Africa [11594], 1132 Corrie Ln., Walnut Creek, CA 94597
Help Brings Hope for Haiti [12845], 3816 W Morrison Ave., Tampa, FL 33629, (813)832-4244
Help Channel Burundi [IO], Bujumbura, Burundi
Help the Children [12846], PO Box 911607, Los Angeles, CA 90091, (323)980-9870
Help Darfur Now [17741], PO Box 635, Chatham, NJ 07928
Help Darfur Now [17741], PO Box 635, Chatham, NJ 07928
Help Desk Inst. [3235], 102 S Tejon St., Ste. 1200, Colorado Springs, CO 80903, (719)268-0174
Help the Helpless [12303], PO Box 270308, Vadnais Heights, MN 55127, (651)762-8857
Help Hospitalized Veterans [13348], 36585 Penfield Ln., Winchester, CA 92596, (951)926-4500

A star before a book entry number signifies that the name is not listed separately, but is mentioned within the entry.

Help for Incontinent People [★16946]
Help for Incontinent People [★16946]
HELP - Inst. for Body Chemistry [15095], 1139 Heberton St., Pittsburgh, PA 15206, (412)441-2909
Help Liberia Found. [IO], Nawojowa, Poland
HELP Network
HELP Network - Address unknown since 2011.
Help-One Women's Org. [IO], Iganga, Uganda
Help Our Wolves Live - Defunct.
Help and Shelter [IO], Georgetown, Guyana
HELP USA [12158], 5 Hanover Sq., 17th Fl., New York, NY 10004, (212)400-7000
HelpAge Intl. [IO], London, United Kingdom
HelpAge Intl. - Africa Regional Development Centre [IO], Nairobi, Kenya
HelpAge Intl. - Caribbean Regional Development Centre [IO], Kingston, Jamaica
HelpAge Intl. - EU Off. Brussels [IO], Brussels, Belgium
HelpAge Intl. - Latin Am. Regional Development Centre [IO], La Paz, Bolivia
HelpArgentina [IO], Buenos Aires, Argentina
Helpers of God's Precious Infants [18555], The Monastery of the Precious Blood, 5300 Ft. Hamilton Pkwy., Brooklyn, NY 11219
Helpful Soc. [★19148]
Helping Americans Needing Disaster - Address unknown since 2011.
Helping Autism through Learning and Outreach [13795], PO Box 303399, Austin, TX 78703, (512)465-9595
Helping Children Worldwide [11304], 13525 Dulles Tech. Dr., Ste. 103, Herndon, VA 20171, (703)793-9521
Helping Children Worldwide [11304], 13525 Dulles Tech. Dr., Ste. 103, Herndon, VA 20171, (703)793-9521
Helping Hand for Nepal [12847], 2930 Brittany Dr., Anchorage, AK 99504, (907)338-8128
Helping Hands [11305], 2918 Churchill Way, Garland, TX 75044, (972)635-3903
Helping Hands Rescue [10978], 14260 W Newberry Rd., PMB 140, Newberry, FL 32669, (352)281-4358
Helping Hands Rescue [10978], 14260 W Newberry Rd., PMB 140, Newberry, FL 32669, (352)281-4358
Helping Hearts Helping Hands [12730], 7060 Scenic Ridge, Clarkston, MI 48346, (248)660-4507
Helping Honduras Kids [11306], PO Box 111777, Campbell, CA 95011-1777
Helping and Loving Orphans [11307], 2416 2nd Ave. N, Seattle, WA 98109, (206)282-7337
Helping and Loving Orphans [11307], 2416 2nd Ave. N, Seattle, WA 98109, (206)282-7337
Helping Orphans Worldwide [11308], 10736 Jefferson Blvd., Ste. 808, Culver City, CA 90230, (323)337-5466
Helping Orphans Worldwide [11308], 10736 Jefferson Blvd., Ste. 808, Culver City, CA 90230, (323)337-5466
Helping Our Teen Girls in Real Life Situations [12119], 3645 Marketplace Blvd., Ste. 130-190, Atlanta, GA 30344, (404)495-3542
HelpMercy Intl. [14791], Lloyd B. Williams, Chm., 6225 Lorreen Dr., Salt Lake City, UT 84121, (781)866-1645
HelpMercy Intl. [14791], Lloyd B. Williams, Chm., 6225 Lorreen Dr., Salt Lake City, UT 84121, (781)866-1645
Helps Intl. Ministries [20050], 573 Fairview Rd., Asheville, NC 28803, (828)277-3812
Helps Intl. Ministries [20050], 573 Fairview Rd., Asheville, NC 28803, (828)277-3812
HELPSudan [11442], 5255 N Ashland Ave., Chicago, IL 60640
Helsinki Commn. - Baltic Marine Env. Protection Commn. [IO], Helsinki, Finland
Helsinki Found. for Human Rights [IO], Warsaw, Poland
Helsinki Watch [★17836]
Helsinki Watch [★17836]
Helsinska Fundacja Praw Czloweka [★IO]
HELVETAS - Bhutan [IO], Thimphu, Bhutan
Helvetas - Swiss Assn. for Intl. Cooperation [IO], Zurich, Switzerland

Helvetia Philatelic Soc. [★22008]
Helvetia Philatelic Soc. [★22008]
Hematology
    Amer. Soc. of Hematology [14960]
    Amer. Soc. of Pediatric Hematology/Oncology [14961]
    Amer. Thrombosis and Hemostasis Network [14962]
    Aplastic Anemia and MDS Intl. Found. [14963]
    Aplastic Anemia and MDS Intl. Found. [14963]
    Children's Cancer and Blood Found. [14964]
    Coalition for Hemophilia B [14965]
    Cooley's Anemia Found. [14966]
    Hematology/Oncology Pharmacy Assn. [16194]
    Hemophilia Fed. of Am. [14967]
    Histiocytosis Assn. [14968]
    Intl. Soc. for Lab. Hematology [14969]
    Intl. Soc. on Thrombosis and Haemostasis [14970]
    Intl. Soc. on Thrombosis and Haemostasis [14970]
    Irish Haemophilia Soc. [23902]
    Natl. Anemia Action Coun. [14971]
    Natl. Hemophilia Found. [14972]
    Natl. Phlebotomy Assn. [14973]
    Sickle Cell Disease Assn. of Am. [14974]
    Soc. for the Advancement of Blood Mgt. [14975]
    Soc. for the Advancement of Blood Mgt. [14975]
    Soc. for Hematology and Stem Cells [14976]
    Soc. for Hematology and Stem Cells [14976]
Hematology/Oncology Pharmacy Assn. [16194], 4700 W Lake Ave., Glenview, IL 60025, (877)467-2791
Hematopathology; Soc. for [16132]
Hemingway Found. and Soc. [9371], PO Box 2770, Winter Park, FL 32789-4499, (407)691-1706
Hemispheric Cong. of Latin Chambers of Commerce [23367], Latin Chamber of Commerce of U.S.A., 1401 W Flagler St., Miami, FL 33135, (305)642-3870
Hemispheric Cong. of Latin Chambers of Commerce [23367], Latin Chamber of Commerce of U.S.A., 1401 W Flagler St., Miami, FL 33135, (305)642-3870
Hemlock Soc. [★11988]
Hemlock Soc. U.S.A. [★11988]
Hemochromatosis
    Hemochromatosis Info. Soc. [14977]
Hemochromatosis Info. Soc. [14977], 3017 Princeton Dr., Plano, TX 75075, (214)702-2698
Hemophilia Fed. of Am. [14967], 210 7th St. SE, Ste. 200 B, Washington, DC 20003, (202)675-6984
Hemophilia Fed. India [IO], New Delhi, India
Hemophilia Found. [★14972]
Hemophilia Found; Natl. [14972]
Hemp Coun; North Amer. Indus. [6861]
Hemp Indus. Assn. [3441], PO Box 575, Summerland, CA 93067, (707)874-3648
Hemp Indus. Assn. [3441], PO Box 575, Summerland, CA 93067, (707)874-3648
Henlein/Heinlein Family Assn. - Address unknown since 2010.
Henry Clay Memorial Found. [10667], 120 Sycamore Rd., Lexington, KY 40502, (859)266-8581
Henry Doubleday Res. Assn. [IO], Coventry, United Kingdom
Henry George Inst. - New York [18698], 121 E 30th St., New York, NY 10016
Henry Hazlitt Foundation - Defunct.
Henry L. Stimson Center [17897], 1111 19th St. NW, 12th Fl., Washington, DC 20036, (202)223-5956
Henry Luce Found. [11905], 51 Madison Ave., 30th Fl., New York, NY 10010, (212)489-7700
Henry M. Jackson Found. [17598], 1501 Fourth Ave., Ste. 1580, Seattle, WA 98101, (206)682-8565
Henry Nyberg Soc. [21066], 17822 Chicago Ave., Lansing, IL 60438, (708)474-3416
Henry Nyberg Soc. [21066], 17822 Chicago Ave., Lansing, IL 60438, (708)474-3416
Henry Williamson Soc. [IO], Surrey, United Kingdom
Hepatitis C Assn. [14984], 1351 Cooper Rd., Scotch Plains, NJ 07076-2844, (908)769-8479
Hepatitis C Coalition; Natl. [14988]
Hepatitis C Coun. of Victoria [IO], Brunswick, Australia

Hepatitis Found. Intl. [14985], 504 Blick Dr., Silver Spring, MD 20904-2901, (301)622-4200
Hepatitis Found. Intl. [14985], 504 Blick Dr., Silver Spring, MD 20904-2901, (301)622-4200
Hepatology
    Amer. Assn. for the Stud. of Liver Diseases [14978]
    Amer. Hepato-Pancreato-Biliary Assn. [14979]
    Amer. Hepato-Pancreato-Biliary Assn. [14979]
    Amer. Liver Found. [14980]
    Caring Ambassadors Hepatitis C Prog. [14981]
    Children's Liver Assn. for Support Services [14982]
    Frontline Hepatitis Awareness [14983]
    Hepatitis C Assn. [14984]
    Hepatitis Found. Intl. [14985]
    Hepatitis Found. Intl. [14985]
    Natl. Assn. of Hepatitis Task Forces [14986]
    Natl. Hepatitis C Advocacy Coun. [14987]
    Natl. Hepatitis C Coalition [14988]
Heptagonal Games Assn. - Defunct.
Heraldisch-Genealogische Gesellschaft [★IO]
Heraldisk Selskab [★IO]
Heraldry Soc. of England [IO], Guildford, United Kingdom
Heraldry Soc. of Scotland [IO], Edinburgh, United Kingdom
Herb Assn. of South Africa [IO], Johannesburg, Republic of South Africa
Herb Growing and Marketing Network [1725], PO Box 245, Silver Spring, PA 17575-0245, (717)393-3295
Herb Res. Found. [6354], 5589 Arapahoe Ave., Ste. 205, Boulder, CO 80303, (303)449-2265
Herb Soc. [IO], Northampton, United Kingdom
Herb Soc. of Am. [6355], 9019 Kirtland Chardon Rd., Kirtland, OH 44094, (440)256-0514
Herb Soc. of Victoria [IO], Camberwell, Australia
Herb Soc. of Western Australia [IO], Como, Australia
Herbal Medicine Res; Tang Center for [15215]
Herbalife Family Found. [11309], 800 W Olympic Blvd., Ste. 406, Los Angeles, CA 90015, (310)410-9600
Herbalife Family Found. [11309], 800 W Olympic Blvd., Ste. 406, Los Angeles, CA 90015, (310)410-9600
Herbalism
    Veterinary Botanical Medicine Assn. [17046]
Herbert Hoover Birthplace Found. [★10668]
Herbert Hoover Presidential Lib. Assn. [10668], PO Box 696, West Branch, IA 52358, (319)643-5327
Herbert's Standard Plate Number Single Catalogue [★22013]
Herbs
    Alternative Medicine Intl. [13648]
    Amer. Herbal Pharmacopoeia [13655]
    Amer. Herbal Products Assn. [1723]
    Amer. Herbalists Guild [14989]
    Complementary and Alternative Medicine Initiative [13671]
    Flower Essence Soc. [14990]
    Flower Essence Soc. [14990]
    Ginseng Res. Inst. of Am. [1724]
    Herb Growing and Marketing Network [1725]
    Herb Soc. [13816]
    Intl. Herb Assn. [1726]
    Intl. Herb Assn. [1726]
    Intl. Stevia Coun. [1404]
    Veterinary Botanical Medicine Assn. [17046]
Hercules Intl. - Elton John Fan Club [IO], Munich, Germany
Hereditary Disease Found. [15597], 3960 Broadway, 6th Fl., New York, NY 10032, (212)928-2121
Hereditary Order of the Families of the Presidents and First Ladies of Am. [20754], 1716 Bigley Ave., Charleston, WV 25302-3938
Herefords Australia Ltd. [IO], Armidale, Australia
Heritage Canada Found. [IO], Ottawa, ON, Canada
Heritage Conservation Network [★9660]
Heritage Conservation Network [★9660]
Heritage Foods USA [6877], PO Box 198, Brooklyn, NY 11211, (718)389-0985
The Heritage Found. [17718], 214 Massachusetts Ave. NE, Washington, DC 20002-4999, (202)546-4400

Reference to "IO" in place of a book number signifies that the association may be found in the 50th edition of International Organizations.

Heritage Found. [★9693]

Heritage Inst. [19154], PO Box 860, Clinton, WA 98236-0860, (360)341-3020

Heritage Preservation Assn. [17293], PO Box 356, Mansfield, GA 30055-0356, (404)435-5184

Heritage of Pride [12086], 154 Christopher St., Ste. 1D, New York, NY 10014, (212)807-7433

Heritage Railway Assn. [IO], New Romney, United Kingdom

Heritage Rose Found. [21798], PO Box 831414, Richardson, TX 75083

Heritage Roses Gp. [21799], 22 Gypsy Ln., Camarillo, CA 93010-1320

Hermanas de San Jose del Sagrado Corazon [★IO]

Hermandad [17229], PO Box 286269, New York, NY 10128, (347)709-0190

Hermandad [17229], PO Box 286269, New York, NY 10128, (347)709-0190

Hermansky-Pudlak Syndrome Network [14599], 1 South Rd., Oyster Bay, NY 11771-1905, (516)922-3440

Hermansky-Pudlak Syndrome Network [14599], 1 South Rd., Oyster Bay, NY 11771-1905, (516)922-3440

Hernia Soc; Amer. [16798]

Hernia Soc; Amer. [16798]

Hero Initiative [9490], 11301 Olympic Blvd., No. 587, Los Angeles, CA 90064, (818)776-1918

Herocare [13160], 10491 Six Mile Cypress Pkwy., Ste. 204, Fort Myers, FL 33966-6406, (877)437-6411

Heroes of '76 [19130], Natl. Sojourners, Inc., 8301 E Boulevard Dr., Alexandria, VA 22308-1399, (703)765-5000

Hero's Welcome [20348], PO Box 124, Fairview Village, PA 19409-0124, (484)679-1717

Herpes Viruses Assn. [IO], London, United Kingdom

Herpetological Assn. of Africa [IO], Cape Town, Republic of South Africa

Herpetologists' League [6940], Meredith Mahoney, Treas., ISM Res. and Collections Center, 1011 E Ash St., Springfield, IL 62703, (217)785-4843

Herpetology

Amer. Soc. of Ichthyologists and Herpetologists [6939]

Herpetologists' League [6940]

Soc. for the Stud. of Amphibians and Reptiles [6941]

HERS Found. [★15880]

HERS Found. [★15880]

Herstigte Nasionale Party van Suid Afrika [★IO]

Hertfordshire Chamber of Commerce and Indus. [IO], Hatfield, United Kingdom

Heshima Kenya [11310], PO Box 408077, Chicago, IL 60640, (312)714-4038

Heshima Kenya [11310], PO Box 408077, Chicago, IL 60640, (312)714-4038

Hesperian Found. [15183], 1919 Addison St., Ste. 304, Berkeley, CA 94704-1143, (510)845-1447

Hesperian Found. [15183], 1919 Addison St., Ste. 304, Berkeley, CA 94704-1143, (510)845-1447

Het Nederlandse Rodekruis [★IO]

Heterocera Sumatrana Soc. [IO], Gottingen, Germany

Hetrick-Martin Inst. [12087], 2 Astor Pl., New York, NY 10003, (212)674-2400

Hewanorra Musical Soc. [IO], Castries, St. Lucia

H.G. Wells Soc. [IO], Canterbury, United Kingdom

H.H. Franklin Club [21067], Cazenovia Coll., Cazenovia, NY 13035

HHT Found. Intl. [14600], PO Box 329, Monkton, MD 21111, (410)357-9932

HHT Found. Intl. [14600], PO Box 329, Monkton, MD 21111, (410)357-9932

HIAS [★12406]

HIAS [★12406]

Hiawatha Baptist Mission [★19319]

Hickory Handle Assn. - Defunct.

Hid Islenska Bokmenntafelag [★IO]

Hidden Child Foundation [★17783]

Hiep Hoi Doanh Nghiep Phan Mem Viet Nam [★IO]

Higdon Family Assn. [20534], Carolyn Cole, Treas., 4540 Fairway St., Dallas, TX 75219

High Blood Pressure

Intl. Pediatric Hypertension Assn. [15076]

High Coun. for Private Enterprise [IO], Managua, Nicaragua

High Frontier [6086], 2800 Shirlington Rd., Ste. 405, Arlington, VA 22206, (703)671-4111

High Frontier Org. [18678], 500 N Washington St., Alexandria, VA 22314-2314, (703)535-8774

High Performance Building Coun. [6376], 3101 Wilson Blvd., Ste. 900, Arlington, VA 22201, (703)682-1630

High Point Market Authority [1550], 164 S Main St., Ste. 700, High Point, NC 27260, (336)869-1000

High School Band Directors Natl. Assn. [8651], PO Box 886, Fortson, GA 31808, (706)568-0760

High School Evangelism Fellowship [19751], 1 Maple St., Allendale, NJ 07401

High/Scope Educational Res. Found. [7953], 600 N River St., Ypsilanti, MI 48198, (734)485-2000

High Speed Ground Trans. Assn. [7580], 1001 G St. NW, Ste. 400 E, Washington, DC 20001, (202)464-0530

High Speed Rail/Magnetic Levitation Assn. - Defunct.

High Standard Collectors' Assn. [21713], PO Box 1578, Decatur, IL 62525

High Tech Indus. Assn. [IO], Herzliya Pituah, Israel

High Tech. Consortium - Defunct.

High Tech. Crime Investigation Assn. [★5599]

High Tech. Crime Investigation Assn. [★5599]

High Tech. Crime Investigation Assn. Intl. [5599], Carol Hutchings, Exec. Dir., 3288 Goldstone Dr., Roseville, CA 95747, (916)408-1751

High Tech. Crime Investigation Assn. Intl. [5599], Carol Hutchings, Exec. Dir., 3288 Goldstone Dr., Roseville, CA 95747, (916)408-1751

High Twelve Intl. [19131], Bettendorf Masonic Center, 2412 Grand St., Bettendorf, IA 52722, (563)514-3270

High Twelve Intl. [19131], Bettendorf Masonic Center, 2412 Grand St., Bettendorf, IA 52722, (563)514-3270

Higher Coun. for Env. and Natural Resources [IO], Khartoum, Sudan

Higher Education

Alliance for Higher Educ. [8226]

Amer. Assn. of Univ. Women [9051]

Assn. for the Advancement of Sustainability in Higher Educ. [8227]

Assn. for the Advancement of Sustainability in Higher Educ. [8227]

Assn. of Amer. Intl. Colleges and Universities [8389]

Assn. for Consortium Leadership [8228]

Assn. of Public and Land-Grant Universities [7873]

Assn. for the Stud. of Free Institutions [8229]

Assn. for the Stud. of Higher Educ. [8230]

Assn. for Support of Graduate Students [8231]

Assn. of Univ. Leaders for a Sustainable Future [8232]

Assn. of Univ. Leaders for a Sustainable Future [8232]

Center for Advancement of Racial and Ethnic Equity [8627]

Coll. Parents of Am. [8233]

Coll. Summit [8234]HigherConsortium for North Amer. Higher Educ. Collaboration

Coun. for the Advancement of Standards in Higher Educ. [8914]

Coun. of Alumni Marketing and Membership Professionals [2397]

Coun. of Graduate Schools [8235]

Empowering Leadership Alliance [8236]

Higher Educ. Res. and Development Soc. of Australasia [16240]

Hispanic Educational Tech. Services [8973]

IES Abroad [8170]

Intl. Coalition of Lib. Consortia [8522]

Intl. Fed. of Engg. Educ. Societies [8124]

Intl. Org. for Haitian Development [7894]

Intl. Soc. for Comparative Stud. of Chinese and Western Philosophy [8707]

Jesuit Assn. of Student Personnel Administrators [7665]

Mapping Your Future [8237]

Minority Access, Inc. [8631]

Natl. Assn. of Diversity Officers in Higher Educ. [8238]

Natl. Assn. of Peoplecultural Engg. Prog. Advocates [8127]

Natl. Assn. of Scholars [8239]

Natl. Assn. of University-Model Schools [7885]

Natl. Coalition of Independent Scholars [8240]

Natl. Coun. for Continuing Educ. and Training [7928]

Natl. Professional Sci. Master's Assn. [8241]

North Amer. Assn. of Commencement Officers [8242]

Pathways to Coll. Network [8243]

Professional and Organizational Development Network in Higher Educ. [8244]

Professional and Organizational Development Network in Higher Educ. [8244]

Second Nature [8245]

Student Veterans of Am. [9032]

University/Resident Theatre Assn. [9005]

Women Educators [9067]

Higher Educ. Consortium for Urban Affairs [9025], 2233 Univ. Ave. W, Ste. 210, Wright Bldg., St. Paul, MN 55114, (651)646-8832

Higher Educ. Consortium for Urban Affairs [9025], 2233 Univ. Ave. W, Ste. 210, Wright Bldg., St. Paul, MN 55114, (651)646-8832

Higher Educ. Funding Coun. for England [IO], Bristol, United Kingdom

Higher Education Panel - Defunct.

Higher Educ. Res. and Development Soc. of Australasia [IO], Milperra, Australia

Higher Educ. South Africa [IO], Pretoria, Republic of South Africa

Higher Educ. and Training Awards Coun. [IO], Dublin, Ireland

Highland Cattle Soc. [IO], Stirling, United Kingdom

Highland Railway Soc. [IO], Templecombe, United Kingdom

Highlander Class Intl. Assn. [22341], 410 Holiday Rd., Lexington, KY 40502, (859)806-5908

Highpointers Club [22189], PO Box 6364, Sevierville, TN 37864-6364

Highway Loss Data Inst. [1963], 1005 N Glebe Rd., Ste. 700, Arlington, VA 22201, (703)247-1600

Highway Res. Bd. [★7584]

Highway Safety Leaders; Natl. Assn. of Women [12993]

Highways

Citizens for Reliable and Safe Highways [18576]

Natl. Motorists Assn. [13335]

Partnership for Safe Driving [13002]Highways Road Emulsion Assn. Limited

HIKE Fund [14942], 10115 Cherryhill Pl., Spring Hill, FL 34608-7116, (352)688-2579

Hiking

Camping Women [22441]

Hawk Mountain Sanctuary [5063]

New England Trails Conf. [23090]

Tree Climbing USA [21286]

Trekking for Kids [22638]

U.S. Mountain Guides Assn. [22456]

U.S. Ski Mountaineering Assn. [22917]

Hiking Soc; Amer. [23079]

Hilfswerk der Evangelischen Kirchen Schweiz [IO], Zurich, Switzerland

Hillbilly Hits Fan Club [★23855]

Hillel: The Found. for Jewish Campus Life [19866], Charles and Lynn Schusterman Intl. Center, Arthur and Rochelle Belfer Bldg., 800 8th St. NW, Washington, DC 20001-3724, (202)449-6500

HIMAL Assn. [IO], Lalitpur, Nepal

Himalayan Inst. [12209], 952 Bethany Tpke., Honesdale, PA 18431-4194, (570)253-5551

Himalayan Inst. [12209], 952 Bethany Tpke., Honesdale, PA 18431-4194, (570)253-5551

Himalayan Inst. Teachers Association [★12209]

Himalayan Inst. Teachers Association [★12209]

HIMSS Electronic Hea. Record Assn. [15332], 33 W Monroe St., Ste. 1700, Chicago, IL 60603-5616, (312)664-4467

Hinduism

Afghan Hindu Assn. of Am. [19810]

Amer. Hindu Assn. [19811]

Brahman Samaj of North Am. [9652]

Brahman Samaj of North Am. [9652]

Soc. for Hindu-Christian Stud. [20215]

A star before a book entry number signifies that the name is not listed separately, but is mentioned within the entry.

Hindustan Bible Inst. - Address unknown since 2011.

Hineni [9922], 232 W End Ave., New York, NY 10023-3604, (212)496-1660

Hineni [9922], 232 W End Ave., New York, NY 10023-3604, (212)496-1660

Hinman Family Assn. - Address unknown since 2011.

Hip-Hop Assn. [10467], 545 8th Ave., 10th Fl., New York, NY 10018, (718)682-2744

Hip-Hop Summit Youth Coun. [10468], PO Box 300925, Jamaica, NY 11430, (212)316-7639

Hip Soc. [16034], 6300 N River Rd., Ste. 727, Rosemont, IL 60018-4238, (847)698-1638

Hippotherapy Assn; Amer. [16835]

Hippotherapy Assn; Amer. [16835]

Hire Assn. Europe [IO], Solihull, United Kingdom

Hire Indus. Assn. of New Zealand [IO], Auckland, New Zealand

Hirkozlesi es Informatikai Tudomanyos Egyesulet [★IO]

The Hirschfeld Centre [★17849]

The Hirschfeld Centre [★17849]

His Majesty's 10th Regiment of Foot [9116], 61 Ivan St., Lexington, MA 02420-1422, (781)862-2586

HIS Nets [13588], 1017 Elm Ave., Norman, OK 73072, (405)447-2471

Hispanas Organized for Political Equality [17776], 634 S Spring St., Ste. 920, Los Angeles, CA 90014, (213)622-0606

Hispanic

Asociacion para la Educacion Teologica Hispana [9006]

Catholic Assn. of Latino Leaders [19398]

Center for U.S.-Mexican Stud. [17774]

Center for U.S.-Mexican Stud. [17774]

Congressional Hispanic Caucus [17775]

Delta Tau Lambda Sorority [23742]

Feministas Unidas [9653]

Hispanas Organized for Political Equality [17776]

Hispanic Educational Tech. Services [8973]

Hispanic Org. of Latin Actors [9654]

Hispanic Soc. of Am. [9655]

Hispanic Soc. of Am. [9655]

Hispanic Women's Corp. [9656]

Latin Amer. Educational Found. [8246]

Latin Amer. Women's Assn. [13464]

Latino Engineers, Architects and Developers Soc. [7029]

Latinos in Info. Sciences and Tech. Assn. [6983]

League of United Latin Amer. Citizens [19023]

Mexican Amer. Cultural Center [19995]

Mexican Amer. Legal Defense and Educational Fund [17777]

Mexican Amer. Legal Defense and Educational Fund [17777]

Mexican Amer. Opportunity Found. [12144]

Mexican Amer. Unity Coun. [12145]

Mujeres Activas en Letras Y Cambio Social [8247]

Natl. Assn. for Chicana and Chicano Stud. [8248]

Natl. Assn. for Hispanic Elderly [19024]

Natl. Assn. of Hispanic Priests of the USA [19457]

Natl. Assn. of Latino Elected and Appointed Officials [17778]

Natl. Assn. of Latino Fraternal Organizations [18990]

Natl. Community for Latino Leadership [19112]

Natl. Coun. of La Raza [12146]

Natl. Coun. of La Raza [12146]

Natl. Hispana Leadership Inst. [17779]

Natl. Hispanic Found. for the Arts [19025]

Natl. Hispanic Inst. [9657]

Natl. Hispanic Professional Org. [8249]

Natl. Image [19026]

Natl. Org. of Hispanics in Criminal Justice [5513]

Natl. Org. for Mexican Amer. Rights [17780]

Natl. Org. of Professional Hispanic Natural Resources Conservation Ser. Employees [4521]

Natl. Puerto Rican Forum [12147]

Natl. Puro Conjunto Music Assn. [10263]

Natl. Soc. for Hispanic Professionals [695]

Puerto Rican Family Inst. [12148]

Sociedad Honoraria Hispanica [8250]

Spanish Colonial Arts Soc. [9658]

U.S. Conf. of Catholic Bishops | Secretariat for Hispanic Affairs [12149]

U.S. Hispanic Advocacy Assn. [17781]

U.S. Hispanic Chamber of Commerce [23405]

U.S. ICE Hispanic Agents Assn. [5514]

Hispanic Amer. Geriatrics Soc. - Defunct.

Hispanic Amer. Police Command Officers Assn. [5694], PO Box 767, Cibolo, TX 78108, (210)641-1305

Hispanic Assn. of Colleges and Universities [7881], 8415 Datapoint Dr., Ste. 400, San Antonio, TX 78229, (210)692-3805

Hispanic Assn. on Corporate Responsibility [17480], 1444 I St. NW, Ste. 850, Washington, DC 20005, (202)835-9672

Hispanic Coun. for Reform and Educational Options [8025], 8461 Lake Worth Rd., Ste. 245, Lake Worth, FL 33467, (561)340-1408

Hispanic Dental Assn. [14285], 3085 Stevenson Dr., Ste. 200, Springfield, IL 62703, (217)529-6517

Hispanic Educational Tech. Services [8973], PO Box 363255, San Juan, PR 00936-3255, (787)766-1912

Hispanic Elected Local Officials [5846], Natl. League of Cities, 1301 Pennsylvania Ave. NW, Ste. 550, Washington, DC 20004, (202)626-3000

Hispanic Genealogical Soc. [20632], PO Box 231271, Houston, TX 77223-1271

Hispanic Inst. in the U.S. [★9657]

Hispanic Marketing and Commun. Assn. [2403], PO Box 565891, Miami, FL 33256-5891, (305)648-2848

Hispanic Marketing and Commun. Assn. [2403], PO Box 565891, Miami, FL 33256-5891, (305)648-2848

Hispanic Natl. Bar Assn. [5249], 1900 L St. NW, Ste. 700, Washington, DC 20036, (202)223-4777

Hispanic Neuropsychological Soc. [15655], Leo Shea, PhD, Treas., 151 E 31st St., No. 22C, New York, NY 10016

Hispanic Org. of Latin Actors [9654], 107 Suffolk St., Ste. 302, New York, NY 10002, (212)253-1015

Hispanic Org. of Professionals and Executives - Defunct.

Hispanic Policy Development Proj. - Address unknown since 2010.

Hispanic Professional Women's Assn. [3683], 700 12th St. NW, Ste. 700, Washington, DC 20005, (703)880-4831

Hispanic Public Relations Assn. [17345], PO Box 86760, Los Angeles, CA 90086-0760

Hispanic Scholarship Fund [8193], 55 2nd St., Ste. 1500, San Francisco, CA 94105, (415)808-2300

Hispanic-Serving Hea. Professions Schools [8608], Airport Plz. II, 2611 Jefferson Davis Hwy., Ste. 205, Arlington, VA 22202, (703)415-1404

Hispanic Soc. of Am. [9655], 613 W 155th St., New York, NY 10032, (212)926-2234

Hispanic Soc. of Am. [9655], 613 W 155th St., New York, NY 10032, (212)926-2234

Hispanic War Veterans of America - Address unknown since 2011.

Hispanic Women's Corp. [9656], PO Box 20725, Phoenix, AZ 85018-0725, (602)954-7995

Histadruth Ivrith of America - Defunct.

Histiocytosis Assn. [14968], 332 N Broadway, Pitman, NJ 08071, (856)589-6606

Histiocytosis Assn. of Am. [★14968]

Histiocytosis-X Assn. of Am. [★14968]

Histochemical Soc. [6409], PO Box 85630, Univ. Sta., Seattle, WA 98145-1630, (425)329-2610

Historians Against the War [18778], PO Box 442154, Somerville, MA 02144

Historians of Amer. Communism [8257], PO Box 1216, Washington, CT 06793, (860)868-7408

Historians Anonymous - Defunct.

Historians of British Art [9209], Peter Trippi, Pres., 780 Riverside Dr., Ste. 10F, New York, NY 10032

Historians of Eighteenth-Century Art and Architecture - Address unknown since 2011.

Historians Film Comm. [★9599]

Historians of German and Central European Art and Architecture [9588], Rose-Carol Washton Long, Treas., Prog. in Art History, CUNY Graduate Center, 365 Fifth Ave., New York, NY 10016-4309

Historians; Soc. of Ancient Military [10097]

Historic Art's Arthur Szyk Soc. [★9227]

Historic Brass Soc. [10209], 148 W 23rd St., No. 5F, New York, NY 10011, (212)627-3820

Historic Building Inspectors Assn. [9692], PO Box 201, Springtown, PA 18081

Historic Commercial Vehicle Soc. [IO], Tonbridge, United Kingdom

Historic Deerfield [9693], PO Box 321, Deerfield, MA 01342, (413)774-5581

Historic Hawaii Found. [9694], 680 Iwilei Rd., Ste. No. 690, Honolulu, HI 96817, (808)523-2900

Historic House Assn. of Am. [★9717]

Historic Houses Assn. [IO], London, United Kingdom

Historic Motor Sports Assn. [21068], 2029 Verdugo Blvd., No. 1010, Montrose, CA 91020, (818)249-3515

Historic Naval Ships Assn. [10058], PO Box 401, Smithfield, VA 23431-0401, (757)356-9422

Historic Naval Ships Assn. [10058], PO Box 401, Smithfield, VA 23431-0401, (757)356-9422

Historic Naval Ships Assn. of North Am. [★10058]

Historic Naval Ships Assn. of North Am. [★10058]

Historic New England [9695], 141 Cambridge St., Boston, MA 02114, (617)227-3956

Historic Preservation

1965-66 Full Size Chevrolet Club [20980]

Accokeek Found. [9659]

Adventures in Preservation [9660]

Adventures in Preservation [9660]

Advisory Coun. on Historic Preservation [9661]

Amateur Radio Lighthouse Soc. [9662]

Amer. Antiquarian Soc. [9663]

Amer. Friends of St. David's Cathedral [9664]

Amer. Guild of Town Criers [10475]

Amer. Heraldry Soc. [20618]

Amer. Historic Inns [9665]

Amer. Inst. for Conservation of Historic and Artistic Works [9666]

Amer. Inst. for Conservation of Historic and Artistic Works [9666]

Amer. Overseas Schools Historical Soc. [9667]

America's Corvette Club [20996]

APVA Preservation Virginia [9668]

Architectural Heritage Found. [9669]

Assn. for Gravestone Stud. [9670]

Assn. for Heritage Interpretation [4878]

Assn. for Preservation Tech. Intl. [9671]

Assn. for Preservation Tech. Intl. [9671]

Assn. for Professional Basketball Res. [22293]

Assn. for the Protection of Afghan Archaeology [6163]

Atomic Age Alliance [9672]

B-52 Stratofortress Assn. [20331]

Blackburn Family Assn. [20431]

Browning Collectors Assn. [21712]

Burton Island Assn. [20717]

Capitol Hill Restoration Soc. [9673]

Carpenters' Company [9674]

Center for Jewish History [19088]

Cherokee Pilots' Assn. [20887]

Chevrolet Nomad Assn. [21022]

Chrysler Town and Country Owners Registry [21026]

Citroen Quarterly Car Club [21027]

Civil War Dealers and Collectors Assn. [21280]

Civil War Trust [9675]

Cobra Owners Club of Am. [21032]

Combat Helicopter Pilots Assn. [20313]

Communal Stud. Assn. [9676]

Corvair Soc. of Am. [21035]

Coun. of the Alleghenies [9677]

Coun. on America's Military Past [9678]

Country School Assn. of Am. [9679]

Cultural Restoration Tourism Proj. [9680]

Czech Heritage Preservation Soc. [9681]

Death Valley '49ers [9682]

Defense of Place [4039]

DOCOMOMO US [9683]

Erskine Registry [21052]

Eskridge Family Assn. [20513]

Exploring Solutions Past: The Maya Forest Alliance [6168]

F-14 Tomcat Assn. [21201]

Fairchild Club [20895]

Reference to "IO" in place of a book number signifies that the association may be found in the 50th edition of International Organizations.

Ferguson Enthusiasts of North Am. [22174]
First Flight Soc. [20896]
Ford/Fordson Collectors Assn. [22175]
Frank Lloyd Wright Preservation Trust [9684]
French Heritage Soc. [9685]
Friends of Lindenwald [9686]
Friends of the Natl. Parks at Gettysburg [9687]
Future Corvette Owners Assn. [21060]
Gay, Lesbian, Bisexual, Transgender Historical
  Soc. [9688]
Gene Stratton Porter Memorial Soc. [9365]
Great Lakes Lighthouse Keepers Assn. [9689]
Gull Wing Gp. Intl. [21065]
Gungywamp Soc. [9690]
Harmonie Associates [9691]
Historic Building Inspectors Assn. [9692]
Historic Deerfield [9693]
Historic Hawaii Found. [9694]
Historic New England [9695]
Historic Pullman Found. [9696]
Historic Winslow House Assn. [9697]
Historical Soc. of the United Methodist Church
  [9768]
Hollywood Sign Trust [9698]
Hudson-Essex-Terraplane Club [21070]
Hudson Essex Terraplane Historical Soc. [21071]
Hudson River Sloop Clearwater [9699]
Intl. Assn. of Cemetery Preservationists [9700]
Intl. Bird Dog Assn. [20898]
Intl. Catacomb Soc. [9701]
Intl. Catacomb Soc. [9701]
Intl. Coalition of Sites of Conscience [9702]
Intl. Comm. for Documentation of the Intl. Coun.
  of Museums [14497]
Intl. Coun. of Air Shows [20901]
Intl. Coun. on Monuments and Sites I United
  States Natl. Committee [9703]
Intl. Coun. on Monuments and Sites I U.S. Natl.
  Comm. [9703]
Intl. Fire Buff Associates [21708]
Intl. Time Capsule Soc. [9704]
Intl. Time Capsule Soc. [9704]
Jew's Harp Guild [10231]
John Marshall Found. [9705]
Kissel Kar Klub [21088]
Kustom Kemps of Am. [21089]
LandChoices [4089]
Les Amis de Panhard and Deutsch-Bonnet USA
  [21091]
Lincoln Highway Assn. [9706]
Mamie Doud Eisenhower Birthplace Found.
  [9707]
Marmon Club [21098]
Massey Collectors Assn. [22178]
Memorial Found. of the Germanna Colonies in
  Virginia [9708]
Metropolitan Owners Club of North Am. [21105]
Midstates Jeepster Assn. [21107]
Model A Ford Cabriolet Club [21108]
Modern Car Soc. [21114]
Morgan Car Club [21116]
Mount Rushmore Natl. Memorial Soc. [9709]
Natl. Alliance of Highway Beautification Agencies
  [5948]
Natl. Alliance of Preservation Commissions [9710]
Natl. Amusement Park Historical Assn. [20946]
Natl. Assn. for Civil War Brass Music [10251]
Natl. Assn. of Tribal Historic Preservation Officers
  [9711]
Natl. Barn Alliance [9712]
Natl. Center for Preservation Tech. and Training
  [6942]
Natl. Coalition to Save Our Mall [9713]
Natl. Conf. of State Historic Preservation Officers
  [9714]
Natl. Corvette Owners Assn. [21124]
Natl. Day of the Cowboy [9124]
Natl. Historic Route 66 Fed. [9715]
Natl. Mossberg Collectors Assn. [21716]
Natl. Preservation Inst. [9716]
Natl. Trust [19205]
Natl. Trust for Historic Preservation [9717]
Natl. World War II Glider Pilots Assn. [20315]
Navy and Marine Living History Assn. [10094]
Newport Restoration Found. [9718]

Noah Webster House [9719]
North Amer. Araucanian Royalist Soc. [9720]
North Amer. Mini Moke Registry [21137]
North Amer. Voyageur Coun. [9721]
North-South Skirmish Assn. [22885]
Oregon-California Trails Assn. [9722]
Org. of Bricklin Owners [21143]
Philip Boileau Collectors' Soc. [20970]
Plymouth Owners Club [21151]
Police History Soc. [13852]
Popular Rotorcraft Assn. [20913]
Preservation Action [9723]
Preservation Volunteers [9724]
Professional Car Soc. [21155]
Recent Past Preservation Network [6943]
Riva Club USA [21232]
Rodeo Historical Soc. [9125]
Royal Historical Soc. of Queensland [3709]
Royal Oak Found. [9725]HistoricScottish Urban
  Archaeological Trust
Shenandoah Natl. Park Assn. [9726]
Soc. of the Founders and Friends of Norwich,
  Connecticut [9727]
Soc. for the Preservation of Natural History Col-
  lections [9728]
Soc. for the Preservation of Old Mills [9729]
Spohr Soc. of Great Britain [3474]
Statue of Liberty - Ellis Island Found. [9730]
Superstition Mountain Historical Soc. [9126]
Surratt Soc. [9731]
Thomas Jefferson's Poplar Forest [9732]
Touro Synagogue Found. [9733]
Ulster-Scots Soc. of Am. [20664]
United Four-Wheel Drive Associations [21184]
U.S. Life-Saving Ser. Heritage Assn. [9734]
U.S. Lighthouse Soc. [9735]
Veteran Feminists of Am. [17673]
Vintage Garden Tractor Club of Am. [22181]
Vintage Thunderbird Club Intl. [21190]
Volkswagen Club of Am. [21193]
Walden Woods Proj. [9736]
Whirly-Girls - Intl. Women Helicopter Pilots
  [20923]
Wooden Canoe Heritage Assn. [22414]
World Airline Historical Soc. [20924]
Worldwide Camaro Club [21197]
Historic Pullman Found. [9696], 614 E 113th St.,
  Chicago, IL 60628, (773)785-8181
Historic Ships in Baltimore [10059], 301 E Pratt St.,
  Baltimore, MD 21202-3134, (410)539-1797
Historic Winslow House Assn. [9697], 634 Careswell
  St., Marshfield, MA 02050-5623, (781)837-5753
Historical Assn. [IO], London, United Kingdom
Historical Commn., Southern Baptist Convention
  [★19333]
Historical Comm. of the Mennonite Church [★19957]
Historical Diving Soc. [IO], Reigate, United Kingdom
Historical Diving Soc. Canada [IO], North Vancouver,
  BC, Canada
Historical Diving Soc. Germany [IO], Herzogenrath,
  Germany
Historical Diving Soc. Italia [IO], Ravenna, Italy
Historical Diving Soc. Mexico [IO], Mexico City,
  Mexico
Historical Diving Soc. South Africa [IO], Cape Town,
  Republic of South Africa
Historical Diving Soc. U.S.A. [22540], PO Box 2837,
  Santa Maria, CA 93457, (805)934-1660
Historical Farm Assn. [★9797]
Historical Harp Soc. [10210], PO Box 662, Haver-
  town, PA 19083-0662
Historical Manuscripts Commn. [IO], Richmond,
  United Kingdom
Historical Metallurgy Soc. [IO], Gateshead, United
  Kingdom
Historical Model Railway Soc. [IO], Ripley, United
  Kingdom
Historical Radio Soc. of Australia [IO], Mount Waver-
  ley, Australia
Historical Reenactment
  North-South Skirmish Assn. [22885]
Historical Revisionism
  Inst. for Historical Rev. [9737]
Historical Soc. of Early Amer. Decoration [9212], PO
  Box 30, The Farmer's Museum, Cooperstown, NY
  13326, (607)547-5667

Historical Soc. of the Episcopal Church [19710],
  Susan Johnson, Dir. of Operations, PO Box 1749,
  Harlingen, TX 78551, (866)989-5851
Historical Soc. of the Evangelical and Reformed
  Church [★20275]
Historical Soc. of the Evangelical United Brethren
  Church [★10084]
Historical Soc. of Jews from Egypt [9923], PO Box
  230445, Brooklyn, NY 11223
Historical Soc. of the Reformed Church in the U.S.
  [★20275]
Historical Soc. of the United Methodist Church
  [9768], 223 N Emerson St., Mount Prospect, IL
  60056-2509
Historical Soc. of Washington, DC [9769], Mt. Ver-
  non Sq., 801 K St. NW, Washington, DC 20001,
  (202)383-1850
History
  1965-66 Full Size Chevrolet Club [20980]
  Aaron Burr Assn. [10650]
  A.C. Gilbert Heritage Soc. [22168]
  Acad. of Accounting Historians [9738]
  Agricultural History Soc. [9739]
  Ahern Clan Assn. [20420]
  Amer. Acad. of Res. Historians of Medieval Spain
    [9740]
  Amer. Assn. for History and Computing [6944]
  Amer. Assn. for the History of Medicine [9741]
  Amer. Assn. for the History of Nursing [9742]
  Amer. Assn. for State and Local History [9743]
  Amer. Catholic Historical Assn. [9744]
  Amer. Catholic Historical Soc. [9745]
  Amer. Catholic Historical Soc. [9745]
  Amer. Civil War Assn. [9746]
  Amer. Heraldry Soc. [20618]
  Amer. Historical Assn. [9747]
  Amer. History Forum I Civil War Educ. Assn.
    [8251]
  Amer. Journalism Historians Assn. [8252]
  Amer. Numismatic Soc. [21964]
  Amer. Philatelic Res. Lib. [22010]
  Amer. Revolution Round Table [9115]
  Amer. Soc. of Church History [19812]
  Amer. Soc. of Church History [19812]
  Amer. Soc. for Eighteenth-Century Stud. [9748]
  Amer. Soc. for Legal History [9749]
  Amer. Spelean Historical Assn. [9750]
  AMISTAD Am. [8253]
  Ancient Coin Collectors Guild [21967]
  Ancient Coins for Educ. [8685]
  Assn. of Ancient Historians [9751]
  Assn. for the Bibliography of History [9752]
  Assn. of Personal Historians [9753]
  Assn. for Professional Basketball Res. [22293]
  Atomic Age Alliance [9672]
  Baronial Order of Magna Charta [9754]
  Baronial Order of Magna Charta [9754]
  Black Holocaust Soc. [17154]
  Bostonian Soc. [9755]
  British Sundial Soc. [8016]
  Browning Collectors Assn. [21712]
  Burton Island Assn. [20717]
  Bus. History Conf. [9756]
  Carpenters' Company [9674]
  Centennial Legion of Historic Military Commands
    [20743]
  Center for Jewish History [19088]
  Center for Socialist History [9757]
  Charette/Charest Family Assn. [20440]
  Charles Babbage Inst. for the History of Info.
    Tech. [9758]
  Chem. Heritage Found. [9759]
  Cherokee Pilots' Assn. [20887]
  Chess Collectors Intl. [21274]
  Chevrolet Nomad Assn. [21022]
  Chinese Historians in the U.S. [8254]
  Chinese Historians in the U.S. [8254]
  Chrysler Town and Country Owners Registry
    [21026]
  Churchill Soc. London [7713]
  Citroen Quarterly Car Club [21027]
  Civil War Dealers and Collectors Assn. [21280]
  Civil War Token Soc. [21970]
  Clan MacAlpine Soc. [20463]
  Clan MacKinnon Soc. [20470]

A star before a book entry number signifies that the name is not listed separately, but is mentioned within the entry.

Clan McAlister of Am. **[20478]**
Clan Phail Soc. in North America **[20484]**
Cobra Owners Club of Am. **[21032]**
Colonial Coin Collectors Club **[21971]**
Colonial Soc. of Massachusetts **[9760]**
Combat Helicopter Pilots Assn. **[20313]**
Combined Organizations of Numismatic Error Collectors of Am. **[21972]**
Confederate Memorial Literary Soc. **[9761]**
Conf. on Faith and History **[19813]**
Corvair Soc. of Am. **[21035]**
Custer Battlefield Historical and Museum Assn. **[9762]**
Daniel Boone and Frontier Families Res. Assn. **[9763]**
Distinguished Flying Cross Soc. **[20374]**
DOCOMOMO US **[9683]**
Early Slavic Stud. Assn. **[8863]**
Economic History Assn. **[8255]**
Eighteenth-Century Scottish Stud. Soc. **[8256]**
Eighteenth-Century Scottish Stud. Soc. **[8256]**
Erskine Registry **[21052]**
Exploring Solutions Past: The Maya Forest Alliance **[6168]**
F-14 Tomcat Assn. **[21201]**
Facing History and Ourselves Natl. Found. **[9764]**
Facing History and Ourselves Natl. Found. **[9764]**
Finnish Amer. Historical Archives **[9614]**
First Flight Soc. **[20896]**
Flag Res. Center **[10628]**
Ford/Fordson Collectors Assn. **[22175]**
Forest History Soc. **[9765]**
Gene Stratton Porter Memorial Soc. **[9365]**
Gen. Soc. of Mayflower Descendants **[20746]**
German Genealogical Soc. of Am. **[20631]**
German Historical Inst. **[9766]**
German History Soc. **[13953]**
Gluckstal Colonies Res. Assn. **[9767]**
Gull Wing Gp. Intl. **[21065]**
Hagiography Soc. **[20212]**
Henry Williamson Soc. **[1418]**
Historians of Amer. Communism **[8257]**
Historical Soc. of the United Methodist Church **[9768]**
Historical Soc. of Washington, DC **[9769]**
History of Dermatology Soc. **[9770]**
History of Earth Sciences Soc. **[9771]**
History of Economics Soc. **[9772]**
History of Educ. Soc. **[9773]**
History of Sci. Soc. **[9774]**
Hof Reunion Assn. **[20349]**
HOPOS - The Intl. Soc. for the History of Philosophy of Sci. **[8839]**
Hudson-Essex-Terraplane Club **[21070]**
Humanity in Action **[8277]**
Illinois Central Railroad Historical Soc. **[9775]**
Immigration and Ethnic History Soc. **[9776]**
Immigration and Ethnic History Soc. **[9776]**
Indus. Heritage Assn. of Ireland **[14196]**
Inn Sign Soc. **[18564]**
Inst. for Psychohistory **[9777]**
Intl. Assn. for Comparative Mythology **[7133]**
Intl. Assn. for the History of Glass **[9778]**
Intl. Assn. for the History of Glass **[9778]**
Intl. Bank Note Soc. **[21976]**
Intl. Bird Dog Assn. **[20898]**
Intl. Black Writers and Authors **[10721]**
Intl. Coun. of Air Shows **[20901]**
Intl. Fed. of Amer. Homing Pigeon Fanciers **[22097]**
Intl. Fire Buff Associates **[21708]**
Intl. Psychohistorical Assn. **[9779]**
Intl. Psychohistorical Assn. **[9779]**
Intl. Radio Club of Am. **[20937]**
Intl. Soc. for the History, Philosophy, and Social Stud. of Biology **[8258]**
Intl. Soc. for the History, Philosophy, and Social Stud. of Biology **[8258]**
Intl. Soc. for Intellectual History **[9780]**
Intl. Soc. for Intellectual History **[9780]**
Irish Family History Soc. **[14957]**
Jerome K. Jerome Soc. **[3678]**
Jew's Harp Guild **[10231]**
Kissel Kar Klub **[21088]**
Kustom Kemps of Am. **[21089]**

Legacies of War **[8259]**
Legacies of War **[8259]**
Les Amis de Panhard and Deutsch-Bonnet USA **[21091]**
Lewis and Clark Trail Heritage Found. **[9781]**
Liberty Seated Collectors Club **[21979]**
MARHO: The Radical Historians' Org. **[9782]**
Marlowe Soc. **[12077]**
Marmon Club **[21098]**
Massey Collectors Assn. **[22178]**
Metropolitan Owners Club of North Am. **[21105]**
Midstates Jeepster Assn. **[21107]**
Mining History Assn. **[9783]**
Model A Ford Cabriolet Club **[21108]**
Modern Car Soc. **[21114]**
Morgan Car Club **[21116]**
Museum of the Fur Trade **[9784]**
Museum of the Fur Trade **[9784]**
Natl. Amusement Park Historical Assn. **[20946]**
Natl. Capital Historical Museum of Trans. **[9785]**
Natl. Coalition for History **[9786]**
Natl. Corvette Owners Assn. **[21124]**
Natl. Coun. for History Educ. **[8260]**
Natl. Coun. on Public History **[9787]**
Natl. Day of the Cowboy **[9124]**
Natl. History Club **[8261]**
Natl. History Day **[8262]**
Natl. Mossberg Collectors Assn. **[21716]**
Natl. World War II Glider Pilots Assn. **[20315]**
Natural History Network **[7143]**
Navy and Marine Living History Assn. **[10094]**
New Canaan Historical Soc. **[9788]**
Newah Org. of Am. **[11617]**
North Amer. Collectors **[21984]**
North Amer. Mini Moke Registry **[21137]**
North Amer. Radio Archives **[22120]**
North Amer. Soc. for Sport History **[9789]**
North-South Skirmish Assn. **[22885]**
Numismatic Literary Guild **[21986]**
Numismatics Intl. **[21987]**
Omohundro Inst. of Early Amer. History and Culture **[9790]**
Oral History Assn. **[9791]**
Org. of Amer. Historians **[9792]**
Org. of Bricklin Owners **[21143]**
Peace History Soc. **[9793]**
Pearl Harbor History Associates **[9794]**
Pedro Rescue Helicopter Assn. **[20316]**
Phi Alpha Theta **[23548]**
Plymouth Owners Club **[21151]**
Polish-American-Jewish Alliance for Youth Action **[13551]**
Pony Express Historical Assn. **[9795]**
Popular Rotorcraft Assn. **[20913]**
Professional Car Soc. **[21155]**
Public Works Historical Soc. **[9796]**
Quiet Valley Living Historical Farm **[9797]**
Ranching Heritage Assn. **[9798]**
Rider Haggard Soc. **[3802]**
Rossica Soc. of Russian Philately **[22068]**
SATS/EAF Assn. **[20686]**
Scottish Assn. of Family History Societies **[9057]**
Scottish Railway Preservation Soc. **[18504]**
Ships on Stamps Unit **[22074]**
Sir Arthur Sullivan Soc. **[5289]**
Soc. of Architectural Historians **[9799]**
Soc. of Australasian Specialists/Oceania **[22075]**
Soc. of Civil War Historians **[9800]**
Soc. for the Comparative Stud. of Soc. and History **[9801]**
Soc. of Dance History Scholars **[9802]**
Soc. for French Historical Stud. **[9803]**
Soc. for Historians of Amer. Foreign Relations **[9804]**
Soc. for Historians of the Early Amer. Republic **[9805]**
Soc. for the History of Discoveries **[9806]**
Soc. for the History of Discoveries **[9806]**
Soc. for History Educ. **[8263]**
Soc. for History in the Fed. Govt. **[9807]**
Soc. for the History of Navy Medicine **[9808]**
Soc. for the History of Psychology **[7312]**
Soc. for the History of Tech. **[9809]**
Soc. for the Stud. of the Holy Roman Empire **[9810]**

Soc. for Thai Philately **[22079]**
Space Topic Stud. Unit **[22080]**
Stair Soc. **[15334]**
Supreme Court Historical Soc. **[9811]**
Surveyors Historical Soc. **[9812]**HistoryTE Lawrence Soc.
Thomas Lovell Beddoes Soc. **[16020]**
Treasury Historical Assn. **[9813]**
Ulster Folk and Transport Museum **[18581]**
Ulster-Scots Soc. of Am. **[20664]**
United Four-Wheel Drive Associations **[21184]**
U.S. Capitol Historical Soc. **[9814]**
U.S. Mexican Numismatic Assn. **[21996]**
U.S. Natl. Comm. for Byzantine Stud. **[9815]**
USMC Vietnam Tankers Assn. **[20824]**
Veteran Feminists of Am. **[17673]**
Vietnam Era Seabees **[20826]**
Vintage Garden Tractor Club of Am. **[22181]**
Vintage Thunderbird Club Intl. **[21190]**
Volkswagen Club of Am. **[21193]**
Whirly-Girls - Intl. Women Helicopter Pilots **[20923]**
White House Historical Assn. **[9816]**
William Herschel Soc. **[14334]**
Wooden Canoe Heritage Assn. **[22414]**
World Airline Historical Soc. **[20924]**
World History Assn. **[9817]**
World History Assn. **[9817]**
World War Two Stud. Assn. **[9818]**
World War Two Stud. Assn. **[9818]**
Worldwide Camaro Club **[21197]**
History; Amer. Soc. for Environmental **[8139]**
History of Dermatology Soc. **[9770]**, 1760 Market St., No. 301, Philadelphia, PA 19103-4106, (215)563-8333
History of Earth Sciences Soc. **[9771]**, Ramapo Coll. - TAS, 505 Ramapo Valley Rd., Mahwah, NJ 07430, (201)684-7209
History of Economics Soc. **[9772]**, Univ. of New Hampshire, McConnell Hall, 15 Coll. Rd., Durham, NH 03824
History of Educ. Soc. **[9773]**, Univ. of Illinois at Urbana - Champaign, Educational Policy Stud., 360 Educ. Bldg., MC-708, 1310 S 6th St., Champaign, IL 61820, (217)333-2446
History of Sci. Soc. **[9774]**, Univ. of Notre Dame, 440 Geddes Hall, Notre Dame, IN 46556, (574)631-1194
History of Sci. Soc. **[9774]**, Univ. of Notre Dame, 440 Geddes Hall, Notre Dame, IN 46556, (574)631-1194
History of Sci. Soc. of Japan **[IO]**, Tokyo, Japan
History Teachers' Assn. **[★8263]**
History Teachers' Assn. of Australia **[IO]**, Osborne Park, Australia
History Teachers' Assn. of NSW **[IO]**, Annandale, Australia
History Teachers' Assn. of Victoria **[IO]**, Collingwood, Australia
History Teachers' Assn. of Western Australia **[IO]**, Scarborough, Australia
Hitchcock Inst. for Stud. in Amer. Music **[8652]**, Brooklyn Coll. of CUNY, 2900 Bedford Ave., Brooklyn, NY 11210-2889, (718)951-5655
HitchHikers of Am. Intl. **[22141]**, PO Box 180, Osceola, IN 46561, (574)258-0571
HIV/AIDS Prevention Grants Prog. **[10884]**, U.S. Conf. of Mayors, 1620 I St. NW, Washington, DC 20006, (202)861-6707
HIV/AIDS Prog. **[★10884]**
HIV/AIDS Treatment Info. Ser. **[★13597]**
HIV Information Exchange and Support Group - Defunct.
HIV Medicine Assn. **[13610]**, 1300 Wilson Blvd., Ste. 300, Arlington, VA 22209, (703)299-1215
HIV Over Fifty; Natl. Assn. on **[15121]**
HIV Pharmacy Assn. **[IO]**, Langley, United Kingdom
HivNorge **[★IO]**
HivNorway **[IO]**, Oslo, Norway
Hjalparstarf Kirkjunnar **[★IO]**
Hjerneskadeforeningen **[★IO]**
HMI Ministries **[19988]**, PO Box 8451, Grand Rapids, MI 49518-8451, (616)455-5760
The HMO Gp. **[★14849]**
Hmong Natl. Development **[17892]**, 1628 16th St. NW, Ste. 203, Washington, DC 20009, (202)588-1661

Reference to "IO" in place of a book number signifies that the association may be found in the 50th edition of International Organizations.

Hnuti Duha [★IO]
Hnuti Pro zivot CR [★IO]
Hobbies
Collegiate Assn. of Table Top Gamers [21745]
Fed. of Metal Detector and Archaeological Clubs [21851]
First Issues Collectors Club [22038]
Intl. Autograph Dealers Alliance and Collectors Club [21353]
Intl. Bird Dog Assn. [20898]
Intl. Polymer Clay Assn. [21852]
Intl. Scale Soaring Assn. [21904]
Natl. 42 Players Assn. [21750]
Natl. Stamp Dealers Assn. [22060]
Plasticville Collectors Assn. [22100]
Riva Club USA [21232]
Scale Warbird Racing Assn. [21910]
Wagner And Griswold Soc. [21859]
Women in Toys [3479]
Hobby Greenhouse Assn. [21800], 8858 Possum Rd., Worden, IL 62097-1020
Hobby Indus. Assn. [★1728]
Hobby Indus. Assn. of Am. [★1728]
Hobby Mfrs. Assn. [1729], PO Box 315, Butler, NJ 07405, (973)283-9088
Hobby Supplies
Amer. Stamp Dealers Assn. [1727]
Craft and Hobby Assn. [1728]
Hobby Mfrs. Assn. [1729]
Plasticville Collectors Assn. [22100]
Hobie Class Assn. [★22353]
Hobie Class Assn. [★22353]
Hockey
Amer. Collegiate Hockey Assn. [22639]
Amer. Hockey Coaches Assn. [22640]
Amer. Hockey League [22641]
Amer. Hockey League [22641]
Central Collegiate Hockey Assn. [22642]
Eastern Coll. Athletic Conf. [22643]
Eastern Collegiate Hockey Assn. [22644]
Hockey North Am. [22645]
Natl. Collegiate Roller Hockey Assn. [22646]
Natl. Hockey League Booster Clubs [23906]
USA Hockey [22647]
Western Collegiate Hockey Assn. [22648]
Hockey Assn; Amer. Hearing Impaired [22504]
Hockey sur gazon Canada [★IO]
Hockey Canada [IO], Calgary, AB, Canada
Hockey North Am. [22645], PO Box 78, Sterling, VA 20167-0078, (703)430-8100
Hof Reunion Assn. [20349], 232 Green View Dr., Dover, DE 19901-5748
Hogar de Cristo Housing Found. [IO], Santiago, Chile
Hoge Raad voor Diamant [★IO]
Hogg Family Genealogical Soc. - Defunct.
Hoggatt - Hockett Family Assn. - Defunct.
Hohenzollern Soc. - Defunct.
Hoi Chur thap do Viet Nam [★IO]
Hoist Mfrs. Assn. [★1827]
Hoist Mfrs. Inst. [1827], Material Handling Indus. of Am., 8720 Red Oak Blvd., Ste. 201, Charlotte, NC 28217-3992, (704)676-1190
Hold the Door for Others [11129], PO Box 755, Closter, NJ 07624, (888)314-DOOR
Holiday Accommodation Parks Assn. of New Zealand [IO], Paraparaumu, New Zealand
Holiday and Decorative Assn. [1368], PO Box 420244, Dallas, TX 75342-0244, (214)742-2747
Holiday Express [13395], 968 Shrewsbury Ave., Tinton Falls, NJ 07724, (732)544-8010
Holiday Hosp. Proj. [★13396]
Holiday Proj. [13396], 32 Aspen Hill Dr., Fredericksburg, VA 22406, (703)346-8520
Holiday Rambler Recreational Vehicle Club [22142], PO Box 3028, Elkhart, IN 46515, (574)295-9800
Holiday Service [★21853]
Holistic Dental Assn. [14286], 1825 Ponce de Leon Blvd., No. 148, Coral Gables, FL 33134, (305)356-7338
Holistic Dental Assn. Intl. [★14286]
Holistic Life Found. [★12207]
Holistic Mgt. Intl. [4078], 5941 Jefferson St. NE, Ste. B, Albuquerque, NM 87109, (505)842-5252
Holistic Medicine
Amer. Bd. of Integrative Holistic Medicine [14991]

Amer. CranioSacral Therapy Assn. [14992]
Amer. Healing Arts Alliance [14993]
Amer. Holistic Hea. Assn. [14994]
Amer. Holistic Medical Assn. [14995]
Amer. Holistic Nurses' Assn. [14996]
Anahata Intl. [13662]
Hea. Optimizing Inst. [14997]
Holistic Mentorship Network [14998]
Intl. Coll. of Applied Kinesiology U.S.A. [14999]
Intl. Coll. of Applied Kinesiology U.S.A. [14999]
Intl. Holistic Practitioner Assn. [13689]
Kundalini Res. Network [15000]
Life Resources Inst. [15001]
Natl. Assn. for Holistic Aromatherapy [15002]
Therapeutic Touch Intl. Assn. [15003]
Touch of Relief [15004]
World Wide Essence Soc. [15005]
World Wide Essence Soc. [15005]
Yoga Bear [13721]
Zero Balancing Hea. Assn. [15006]
Holistic Mentorship Network [14998], 55 Newton Sparta Rd., Newton, NJ 07860, (973)300-1184
Holistic Moms Network [12608], PO Box 408, Caldwell, NJ 07006, (877)465-6667
Holistic Pediatric Assn. [13682], 220 Fort Salonga Rd., Ste. 101, Northport, NY 11768, (610)565-2360
Holland Historical Trust - Address unknown since 2010.
Holland Lop Rabbit Specialty Club [4841], 2633 Seven Eleven Rd., Chesapeake, VA 23322, (757)421-9607
Holland Soc. of Arts and Sciences [IO], Haarlem, Netherlands
Holland Soc. of New York [20396], 20 W 44th St., 5th Fl., New York, NY 10036, (212)758-1675
Hollingworth Center for Highly Gifted Children - Address unknown since 2011.
Hollow Earth [★12217]
Hollow Earth [★12217]
Holly Soc. of Am. [4969], PO Box 803, 309 Buck St., Millville, NJ 08332-0803, (856)825-4300
Hollywood Chap. of Natl. Acad. of TV Arts and Sciences [★477]
Hollywood Foreign Press Assn. [2829], 646 N Robertson Blvd., West Hollywood, CA 90069, (310)275-3222
Hollywood Radio and TV Soc. [490], 13701 Riverside Dr., Ste. 205, Sherman Oaks, CA 91423, (818)789-1182
Hollywood Sign Trust [9698], PO Box 48361, Los Angeles, CA 90048-9998, (213)300-0108
Hollywood Unites For Haiti [12128], 5338 Hillcrest Dr., Ste. 2, Los Angeles, CA 90043, (323)244-2712
Hollywood Unites For Haiti [12128], 5338 Hillcrest Dr., Ste. 2, Los Angeles, CA 90043, (323)244-2712
Holmes-Greatorex Family Org. - Defunct.
Holocaust
Anne Frank Center U.S.A. [17782]
Anne Frank Center U.S.A. [17782]
Anti-Defamation League [17269]
Anti-Defamation League | Braun Holocaust Inst. [17783]
Assn. of Holocaust Organizations [17784]
Assn. of Holocaust Organizations [17784]
Holocaust Documentation and Educ. Center [17785]
Holocaust Rsrc. Center [17786]
Holocaust Survivors and Friends in Pursuit of Justice [17787]
Jewish Found. for the Righteous [17788]
Jewish Found. for the Righteous [17788]
Natl. Liberty Museum [17789]
Natl. Liberty Museum [17789]
Simon Wiesenthal Center [17790]
Simon Wiesenthal Center [17790]
U.S. Holocaust Memorial Coun. [17791]
Holocaust Centre of Toronto [IO], Toronto, ON, Canada
Holocaust Documentation and Educ. Center [17785], 2031 Harrison St., Hollywood, FL 33020, (954)929-5690
Holocaust Rsrc. Center [17786], Kean Univ. Lib., 2nd Fl., Union, NJ 07083, (908)737-4660
Holocaust Soc; Black [17154]
Holocaust Survivors and Friends in Pursuit of Justice [17787], 184 Washington Ave., Albany, NY 12203-5347, (518)694-9984

Holstein Assn. of Am. [★3914]
Holstein Assn. of Iran [IO], Tehran, Iran
Holstein Assn. U.S.A. [3914], 1 Holstein Pl., Brattleboro, VT 05302-0808, (802)254-4551
Holstein Cattle Breeders' Assn. of the Czech Republic [IO], Prague, Czech Republic
Holstein-Friesian Assn. of Am. [★3914]
Holstein Junior Prog. [3915], Holstein Assn. U.S.A., Inc., 1 Holstein Pl., Brattleboro, VT 05302-0808, (802)254-4551
Holt Adoption Prog. and Holt Children's Services [★11469]
Holt Adoption Prog. and Holt Children's Services [★11469]
Holt Intl. Children's Services [11469], 1195 City View, PO Box 2880, Eugene, OR 97402, (541)687-2202
Holt Intl. Children's Services [11469], 1195 City View, PO Box 2880, Eugene, OR 97402, (541)687-2202
Holy Childhood Assn. [19428], 70 W 36th St., 8th Fl., New York, NY 10018, (212)563-8700
Holy Cross Foreign Mission Soc. [19429], Holy Cross Mission Center, PO Box 543, Notre Dame, IN 46556, (574)631-5477
Holy Face Assn. [19430], PO Box 821, Champlain, NY 12919-0821, (514)747-0357
Holy Face Assn. [IO], Montreal, QC, Canada
Holy Family Cancer Home [★18973]
Holy Land Christian Mission [★20020]
Holy Land Christian Mission [★20020]
Holy Land Christian Mission Intl. [★20020]
Holy Land Christian Mission Intl. [★20020]
Holy Shroud Guild [19431], PO Box 993, Canandaigua, NY 14424, (716)394-2606
Holy Spirit Stud. Centre [IO], Hong Kong, People's Republic of China
Home
Assn. for the Restoration of Church and Home [19613]
Community Associations Inst. [17373]
Escapees [22137]
Green Home Coun. [567]
Interval Intl. [21854]
Leading Builders of Am. [577]
Red Feather Development Gp. [12201]
RV Mfrs'. Clubs Assn. [22146]
The Shelter Alliance [11634]
Home Automation Assn. [★1095]
Home Baking Assn. [1395], 2931 SW Gainsboro Rd., Topeka, KS 66614-4413, (785)478-3283
Home Based Business
Amer. Home Bus. Assn. [1730]
Mothers' Home Bus. Network [1731]
Natl. Assn. of Home Based Businesses [1732]
Solace Intl. [13479]
Home-Based Working Moms [665], PO Box 1628, Spring, TX 77383-1628, (281)757-2207
Home Birth Assn. of Ireland [IO], Athlone, Ireland
Home Builders Inst. [568], 1201 15th St. NW, 6th Fl., Washington, DC 20005, (202)371-0600
Home Care
Amer. Acad. of Home Care Physicians [15007]
God's Love We Deliver [12150]
Home Care Tech. Assn. of Am. [15008]
Hospice Assn. of Am. [15009]
Intl. Assn. for Hospice and Palliative Care [15010]
Intl. Assn. for Hospice and Palliative Care [15010]
Meals on Wheels Assn. of Am. [12151]
Natl. Assn. for Home Care and Hospice [15011]
Natl. Family Caregivers Assn. [15012]
Natl. Private Duty Assn. [15013]
Oley Found. for Home Parenteral and Enteral Nutrition [15014]
Private Duty Homecare Assn. [15015]
World Homecare and Hospice Org. [15016]
World Homecare and Hospice Org. [15016]
Home Care Tech. Assn. of Am. [15008], PO Box 91486, Washington, DC 20090, (202)547-2871
Home Center Inst. - Address unknown since 2010.
Home Counties Welsh Pony and Cob Assn. [IO], Stevenage, United Kingdom
Home Economics
Amer. Assn. of Family and Consumer Sciences [12152]

A star before a book entry number signifies that the name is not listed separately, but is mentioned within the entry.

Intl. Fed. for Home Economics USA [8264]
Intl. Fed. for Home Economics USA [8264]
Kappa Omicron Nu [23549]
Natl. Assn. for Family and Community Educ.
[8265]
Natl. Assn. of Teacher Educators for Family and
Consumer Sciences [8266]
Phi Upsilon Omicron [23550]
Home Economics Educ. Assn. [★8182]
Home Educ. Assn. [IO], Petersham, Australia
Home Energy Rating Systems Coun. - Defunct.
Home Exchange
Homelink Intl. [21853]
Interval Intl. [21854]
Interval Intl. [21854]
Home Fashion Products Assn. [2057], 355
Lexington Ave., Ste. 1500, New York, NY 10017-
6603, (212)297-2122
Home Fashions League [★2064]
Home Fashions League [★2064]
Home Front Campaign [★11448]
Home Front Campaign [★11448]
Home Furnishings Independents Assn. [1551], PO
Box 420807, Dallas, TX 75342, (214)741-7632
Home Healthcare Nurses Assn. [15752], PO Box
91486, Washington, DC 20090, (202)547-7424
Home of Hope [11311], 190 Tobin Clark Dr., Hillsbor-
ough, CA 94010, (650)520-3204
Home Improvement Lenders Assn. - Defunct.
Home Improvement Res. Inst. [1043], 3922 Coconut
Palm Dr., 3rd Fl., Tampa, FL 33619, (813)627-6750
Home Laundering Consultative Coun. [IO], London,
United Kingdom
Home Mfrs. Assn. [★2311]
Home Mfrs. Councils of NAHB [★2311]
Home Off. Life Underwriters Assn. [★1940]
Home Off. Life Underwriters Assn. [★1940]
Home Orchard Soc. [4453], PO Box 230192, Tigard,
OR 97281-0192, (503)293-1468
Home and School Inst. [8026], MegaSkills Educ.
Center, 1500 Massachusetts Ave. NW,
Washington, DC 20005, (202)466-3633
Home School Legal Defense Assn. [8092], PO Box
3000, Purcellville, VA 20134-9000, (540)338-5600
Home School Sports Network [22978], 153 Old
Linen Rd., Linden, VA 22642, (540)631-5683
Home Sewing Assn. - Defunct.
Home-Start North and Mid Beds [IO], Bedford,
United Kingdom
Home Study
Christian Home Educators Assn. of California
[8267]
Distance Educ. and Training Coun. [8268]
Home Stud. Exchange [8269]
Home Stud. Exchange [8269]
Mentalphysics [20190]
Natl. Black Home Educators [8270]
Natl. Challenged Homeschoolers Assoc. Network
[8271]
Natl. Christian Forensics and Communications
Assn. [8272]
Natl. Home Educ. Res. Inst. [8273]
Natl. Home Educ. Res. Inst. [8273]
U.S. Distance Learning Assn. [8274]
Home Stud. Exchange [8269], PO Box 289, Torreon,
NM 87061-0289, (505)847-2909
Home Stud. Exchange [8269], PO Box 289, Torreon,
NM 87061-0289, (505)847-2909
Home for Unwanted and Lost Animals [IO], Milton
Keynes, United Kingdom
Home Ventilating Inst. [1703], 1000 N Rand Rd.,
Ste. 214, Wauconda, IL 60084, (847)416-7257
Home Ventilating Inst. Division of the Air Movement
Control Assn. [★1703]
Home Wine and Beer Trade Assn. [★182]
Home Wine and Beer Trade Assn. [★182]
HomeAID for Africa [10812], 1191 Shady Grove
Way, West Chester, PA 19382, (610)399-0823
HomeFree - U.S.A. [1782], 3401A E W Hwy.,
Hyattsville, MD 20782, (301)891-8400
Homefront Am. [11090], 27375 Paseo La Serna,
San Juan Capistrano, CA 92675, (949)248-9468
Homefront Hugs U.S.A. [13349], 123 Fieldcrest St.,
Ste. 104, Ann Arbor, MI 48103, (734)330-8203
Homeless
Amer. Bar Assn. Commn. on Homelessness and
Poverty [12153]

Amer. Rescue Team Intl. [12154]
Children of the Americas [11234]
Community for Creative Non-Violence [12155]
Family Promise [12156]
Friends of Roman Cats [3859]
Hands of Mercy [12157]
HELP USA [12158]
Homeless Children Intl. [11312]
Inst. for Children, Poverty and Homelessness
[11320]
Manna House of Prayer [12159]
Natl. Alliance to End Homelessness [12160]
Natl. Center for Homeless Educ. [12161]
Natl. Coalition for the Homeless [12162]
Natl. Law Center on Homelessness and Poverty
[12163]
Natl. Rsrc. Center on Homelessness and Mental
Illness [12164]
Natl. Student Campaign Against Hunger and
Homelessness [12286]
NewPlace Intl. [11368]
Picture the Homeless [17792]
Saving Horses, Inc. [12167]
StandUp for Kids [11409]
Homeless Children Intl. [11312], PO Box 416, Re-
idville, SC 29375-0416
Homeless Children Intl. [11312], PO Box 416, Re-
idville, SC 29375-0416
Homeless Children Intl. - Kenya [IO], Nairobi, Kenya
Homeless Children Intl. - United Kingdom [IO], Wor-
thing, United Kingdom
Homelessness Australia [IO], Holt, Australia
Homelessness Info. Exchange [★12162]
Homelink Intl. [21853], 2937 NW 9th Terr., Fort
Lauderdale, FL 33311, (954)566-2687
Homelink International [★21853]
HomeLink Intl. Canada [IO], North Vancouver, BC,
Canada
Homeopathic Coun. for Res. and Education -
Defunct.
Homeopathic Medical Coun. of Canada [IO], Tor-
onto, ON, Canada
Homeopathic Nurses Assn. [15018], Sue Boyle, RN,
Pres., 6286 NE Lincoln Rd. E, Poulsbo, WA
98370, (866)240-0495
Homeopathic Nurses Assn. [15018], Sue Boyle, RN,
Pres., 6286 NE Lincoln Rd. E, Poulsbo, WA
98370, (866)240-0495
Homeopathic Pharmacopoeia of the U.S. [15019],
PO Box 2221, Southeastern, PA 19399-2221
Homeopaths Without Borders [15020], Joe Lillard,
Treas., 260 JR Howvermale Way, Berkeley
Springs, WV 25411, (304)258-2541
Homeopathy
Amer. Inst. of Homeopathy [15017]
Homeopathic Nurses Assn. [15018]
Homeopathic Nurses Assn. [15018]
Homeopathic Pharmacopoeia of the U.S. [15019]
Homeopaths Without Borders [15020]
Natl. Center for Homeopathy [15021]
North Amer. Soc. of Homeopaths [15022]
A Promise of Hea. [14827]
Soc. for Animal Homeopathy [15023]
Homeowners Against Deficient Dwellings [12180],
Paula Schulman, Treas., 22393 N 76th Pl., Scotts-
dale, AZ 85255, (816)560-0030
HomePlug Powerline Alliance [1103], 5200 SW
Macadam Ave., Ste. 470, Portland, OR 97239,
(503)766-2516
Homer Laughlin China Collectors Assn. [21347], PO
Box 721, North Platte, NE 69103-0721
Homer Laughlin China Collectors Assn. [21347], PO
Box 721, North Platte, NE 69103-0721
Homes for Our Troops [20790], 6 Main St., Taunton,
MA 02780, (508)823-3300
Homes for Scotland [IO], Edinburgh, United
Kingdom
Homeworkers Organized for More Employment
[11940], PO Box 10, Orland, ME 04472, (207)469-
7961
Homiletics
Acad. of Homiletics [19814]
Evangelical Homiletics Soc. [19815]
Homoeopathic Medical Assn. [IO], Gravesend,
United Kingdom

Homoeopathic Medical Assn. of India [IO], Ahmeda-
bad, India
Homosexual Info. Center [12088], 8721 Santa
Monica Blvd., Ste. 37, West Hollywood, CA 90069,
(818)527-5442
Homosexuals Anonymous Fellowship Services
[12089], 16506 FM 529 Rd., Houston, TX 77095,
(281)712-2676
Homowo African Arts and Cultures [9094], 7725 N
Fowler Ave., Portland, OR 97217, (503)288-3025
Homowo Found. for African Arts and Cultures
[★9094]
Honda
Intl. CBX Owners Assn. [21931]
Honda Sport Touring Assn. - Address unknown since
2010.
Honduran Agricultural Res. Found. [IO], San Pedro
Sula, Honduras
Honduran Amer. Chamber of Commerce - Teg-
ucigalpa [IO], Tegucigalpa, Honduras
Honduran Assn. of Banking Institutions [IO], Teg-
ucigalpa, Honduras
Honduran Epilepsy Soc. [IO], Tegucigalpa, Honduras
Honduran Mfrs. Assn. [IO], San Pedro Sula,
Honduras
Honduran Private Enterprise Coun. [IO], Teg-
ucigalpa, Honduras
Honduras
Global Brigades [11588]
Honduras Outreach, Inc. [17793]
Honduras Outreach, Inc. [17793]
Honduras Outreach Medical Brigada Relief Effort
[15184]
Primero Agua [13428]
Union MicroFinanza [12964]
Honduras Documentation Center [IO], Tegucigalpa,
Honduras
Honduras Outreach, Inc. [17793], 4105 Briarcliff Rd.
NE, Atlanta, GA 30345, (404)327-5770
Honduras Outreach, Inc. [17793], 4105 Briarcliff Rd.
NE, Atlanta, GA 30345, (404)327-5770
Honduras Outreach Medical Brigada Relief Effort
[15184], West Hosp., 14th Fl., 1200 E Broad St.,
Richmond, VA 23298-0251
Honduras Squash Fed. [IO], Tegucigalpa, Honduras
Honest Ballot Assn. [17609], 27246 Grand Central
Pkwy., Floral Park, NY 11005, (800)541-1851
Honey Assn. [IO], Hamburg, Germany
Hong Chi Assn. [IO], Hong Kong, People's Republic
of China
Hong Kong
Hong Kong Trade Development Coun. [23406]
Hong Kong ACM SIGGRAPH [IO], Hong Kong,
People's Republic of China
Hong Kong Advertisers Assn. [IO], Hong Kong,
People's Republic of China
Hong Kong Aikido Assn. [IO], Hong Kong, People's
Republic of China
Hong Kong Air-Conditioning and Refrigeration Assn.
[IO], Hong Kong, People's Republic of China
Hong Kong Alzheimer's Disease Assn. [IO], Hong
Kong, People's Republic of China
Hong Kong Alzheimer's Disease and Brain Failure
Assn. [★13042]
Hong Kong Amateur Athletic Assn. [IO], Hong Kong,
People's Republic of China
Hong Kong Amateur Karatedo Assn. [IO], Hong
Kong, People's Republic of China
Hong Kong Amateur Radio Transmitting Soc. [IO],
Hong Kong, People's Republic of China
Hong Kong Anti-Cancer Soc. [IO], Hong Kong,
People's Republic of China
Hong Kong Arts Festival Soc. [IO], Hong Kong,
People's Republic of China
Hong Kong Assn. for Applied Linguistics [IO], Hong
Kong, People's Republic of China
Hong Kong Assn. of Banks [IO], Hong Kong,
People's Republic of China
Hong Kong Assn. of Blood Transfusion and Haema-
tology [IO], Hong Kong, People's Republic of
China
Hong Kong Assn. of Certification Labs. [IO], Hong
Kong, People's Republic of China
Hong Kong Assn. for Cmpt. Educ. [IO], Hong Kong,
People's Republic of China

Reference to "IO" in place of a book number signifies that the association may be found in the 50th edition of International Organizations.

Hong Kong Assn. of Critical Care Nurses [IO], Hong Kong, People's Republic of China

Hong Kong Assn. of Dental Surgery Assistants [IO], Hong Kong, People's Republic of China

Hong Kong Assn. of Freight Forwarding and Logistics [IO], Hong Kong, People's Republic of China

Hong Kong Assn. of Gerontology [IO], Hong Kong, People's Republic of China

Hong Kong Assn. of the Pharmaceutical Indus. [IO], Hong Kong, People's Republic of China

Hong Kong Assn. of Property Mgt. Companies [IO], Hong Kong, People's Republic of China

Hong Kong Assn. of Registered Tour Coordinators [IO], Hong Kong, People's Republic of China

Hong Kong Assn. of Rehabilitation Medicine [IO], Hong Kong, People's Republic of China

Hong Kong Assn. of Speech Therapists [IO], Hong Kong, People's Republic of China

Hong Kong Assn. of Sports Medicine and Sports Sci. [IO], Hong Kong, People's Republic of China

Hong Kong Assn. of Textile Bleachers, Dyers, Printers and Finishers [IO], Hong Kong, People's Republic of China

Hong Kong Assn. of Travel Agents [IO], Hong Kong, People's Republic of China

Hong Kong Assn. of Univ. Women [IO], Hong Kong, People's Republic of China

Hong Kong Auto. Assn. [IO], Hong Kong, People's Republic of China

Hong Kong Aviation Club [IO], Hong Kong, People's Republic of China

Hong Kong Badminton Assn. [IO], Hong Kong, People's Republic of China

Hong Kong Bahrain Bus. Assn. [IO], Hong Kong, People's Republic of China

Hong Kong Bar Assn. [IO], Hong Kong, People's Republic of China

Hong Kong Basketball Assn. [IO], Hong Kong, People's Republic of China

Hong Kong Bible Soc. [IO], Hong Kong, People's Republic of China

Hong Kong Bioethics Assn. [IO], Hong Kong, People's Republic of China

Hong Kong Buddhist Assn. [IO], Hong Kong, People's Republic of China

Hong Kong Call Centre Assn. [IO], Hong Kong, People's Republic of China

Hong Kong Cancer Chemotherapy Soc. [IO], Hong Kong, People's Republic of China

Hong Kong Chap. of the ILAE [IO], Hong Kong, People's Republic of China

Hong Kong Chefs Assn. [IO], Hong Kong, People's Republic of China

Hong Kong Chinese Enterprises Assn. [IO], Hong Kong, People's Republic of China

Hong Kong Chinese Textile Mills Assn. [IO], Hong Kong, People's Republic of China

Hong Kong Christian Coun. [IO], Hong Kong, People's Republic of China

Hong Kong Christian Inst. [IO], Hong Kong, People's Republic of China

Hong Kong Christian Ser. [IO], Hong Kong, People's Republic of China

Hong Kong Coalition of AIDS Ser. Organizations [IO], Hong Kong, People's Republic of China

Hong Kong Coll. of Cardiology [IO], Hong Kong, People's Republic of China

Hong Kong Coll. of Hea. Services Executives [IO], Hong Kong, People's Republic of China

Hong Kong Coll. of Obstetricians and Gynaecologists [IO], Hong Kong, People's Republic of China

Hong Kong Coll. of Radiologists [IO], Hong Kong, People's Republic of China

Hong Kong Comm. for UNICEF [IO], Hong Kong, People's Republic of China

Hong Kong Cmpt. Soc. [IO], Hong Kong, People's Republic of China

Hong Kong Confed. of Trade Unions [IO], Hong Kong, People's Republic of China

Hong Kong Constr. Assn. [IO], Hong Kong, People's Republic of China

Hong Kong Coun. of Social Ser. [IO], Hong Kong, People's Republic of China

Hong Kong Cricket Assn. [IO], Hong Kong, People's Republic of China

Hong Kong DanceSport Assn. [IO], Hong Kong, People's Republic of China

Hong Kong Democratic Found. [IO], Hong Kong, People's Republic of China

Hong Kong Dental Assn. [IO], Hong Kong, People's Republic of China

Hong Kong Dental Hygienists' Assn. [IO], Hong Kong, People's Republic of China

Hong Kong Digital Entertainment Assn. [IO], Hong Kong, People's Republic of China

Hong Kong Distance Runners Club [IO], Hong Kong, People's Republic of China

Hong Kong Dragon Boat Assn. [IO], Hong Kong, People's Republic of China

Hong Kong Economic Assn. [IO], Hong Kong, People's Republic of China

Hong Kong Elecl. Contractors' Assn. [IO], Hong Kong, People's Republic of China

Hong Kong Electronic Indus. Assn. [IO], Hong Kong, People's Republic of China

Hong Kong Epidemiological Assn. [IO], Hong Kong, People's Republic of China

Hong Kong Equestrian Fed. [IO], Hong Kong, People's Republic of China

Hong Kong Exchanges and Clearing [IO], Hong Kong, People's Republic of China

Hong Kong Exhibition and Convention Indus. Assn. [IO], Hong Kong, People's Republic of China

Hong Kong Exporters' Assn. [IO], Hong Kong, People's Republic of China

Hong Kong Fashion Designers Assn. [IO], Hong Kong, People's Republic of China

Hong Kong Fed. of Insurers [IO], Hong Kong, People's Republic of China

Hong Kong Fed. of Trade Unions [IO], Hong Kong, People's Republic of China

Hong Kong Franchise Assn. [IO], Hong Kong, People's Republic of China

Hong Kong Fur Fed. [IO], Hong Kong, People's Republic of China

Hong Kong Garment Mfrs. Assn. [IO], Hong Kong, People's Republic of China

Hong Kong Gemstone Mfrs'. Assn. [IO], Hong Kong, People's Republic of China

Hong Kong Gen. Chamber of Commerce [IO], Hong Kong, People's Republic of China

Hong Kong Geotechnical Soc. [IO], Hong Kong, People's Republic of China

Hong Kong Gynaecological Endoscopy Soc. [IO], Hong Kong, People's Republic of China

Hong Kong Hide and Leather Traders' Assn. [IO], Hong Kong, People's Republic of China

Hong Kong Home Economics Assn. [IO], Hong Kong, People's Republic of China

Hong Kong Hotels Assn. [IO], Hong Kong, People's Republic of China

Hong Kong Housing Soc. [IO], Hong Kong, People's Republic of China

Hong Kong Info. Tech. Fed. [IO], Hong Kong, People's Republic of China

Hong Kong Inst. of Accredited Accounting Technicians [IO], Hong Kong, People's Republic of China

Hong Kong Inst. of Architects [IO], Hong Kong, People's Republic of China

Hong Kong Inst. of Certified Public Accountants [IO], Hong Kong, People's Republic of China

Hong Kong Inst. of Chartered Secretaries [IO], Hong Kong, People's Republic of China

Hong Kong Inst. of Human Rsrc. Mgt. [IO], Hong Kong, People's Republic of China

Hong Kong Inst. of Landscape Architects [IO], Hong Kong, People's Republic of China

Hong Kong Inst. of Occupational and Environmental Hygiene [IO], Hong Kong, People's Republic of China

Hong Kong Inst. of Professional Photographers [IO], Hong Kong, People's Republic of China

Hong Kong Inst. of Real Estate [IO], Hong Kong, People's Republic of China

Hong Kong Inst. of Surveyors [IO], Hong Kong, People's Republic of China

Hong Kong Institution of Engineers [IO], Hong Kong, People's Republic of China

Hong Kong Interior Design Assn. [IO], Hong Kong, People's Republic of China

Hong Kong Jade and Stone Mfrs. Assn. [IO], Hong Kong, People's Republic of China

Hong Kong Jewellers' and Goldsmiths' Assn. [IO], Hong Kong, People's Republic of China

Hong Kong Jewellery and Jade Mfrs. Assn. [IO], Hong Kong, People's Republic of China

Hong Kong Jewelry Mfrs. Assn. [IO], Hong Kong, People's Republic of China

Hong Kong Joint Coun. for People with Disabilities [IO], Hong Kong, People's Republic of China

Hong Kong Journalists Assn. [IO], Hong Kong, People's Republic of China

Hong Kong and Kowloon Elec. Trade Assn. [IO], Hong Kong, People's Republic of China

Hong Kong and Kowloon Elecl. Appliances Merchants' Assn. [IO], Hong Kong, People's Republic of China

Hong Kong Ladies Road Runners Club [IO], Hong Kong, People's Republic of China

Hong Kong Lawn Bowls Assn. [IO], Hong Kong, People's Republic of China

Hong Kong Lib. Assn. [IO], Hong Kong, People's Republic of China

Hong Kong Mgt. Assn. [IO], Hong Kong, People's Republic of China

Hong Kong Mathematical Soc. [IO], Hong Kong, People's Republic of China

Hong Kong Medical Assn. [IO], Hong Kong, People's Republic of China

Hong Kong Metal Finishing Soc. [IO], Hong Kong, People's Republic of China

Hong Kong Mountaineering Union [IO], Hong Kong, People's Republic of China

Hong Kong Museum of Medical Sciences Soc. [IO], Hong Kong, People's Republic of China

Hong Kong Netball Assn. [IO], Hong Kong, People's Republic of China

Hong Kong Network on Religion and Peace [IO], Hong Kong, People's Republic of China

Hong Kong - New Zealand Bus. Assn. [IO], Auckland, New Zealand

Hong Kong Occupational Therapy Assn. [IO], Hong Kong, People's Republic of China

Hong Kong Optical Mfrs. Assn. [IO], Hong Kong, People's Republic of China

Hong Kong Orienteering Club [IO], Hong Kong, People's Republic of China

Hong Kong Paediatric Haematology and Oncology Study Group [IO], Hong Kong, People's Republic of China

Hong Kong Paralympic Comm. and Sports Assn. for the Physically Disabled [IO], Hong Kong, People's Republic of China

Hong Kong PHAB Assn. [IO], Hong Kong, People's Republic of China

Hong Kong Pharmacology Soc. [IO], Hong Kong, People's Republic of China

Hong Kong Philharmonic Soc. [IO], Hong Kong, People's Republic of China

Hong Kong Political Sci. Assn. [IO], Hong Kong, People's Republic of China

Hong Kong Printers' Assn. [IO], Hong Kong, People's Republic of China

Hong Kong Productivity Coun. [IO], Hong Kong, People's Republic of China

Hong Kong Psychological Soc. [IO], Hong Kong, People's Republic of China

Hong Kong Public Admin. Assn. [IO], Hong Kong, People's Republic of China

Hong Kong Quality Mgt. Assn. [IO], Hong Kong, People's Republic of China

Hong Kong Red Cross [IO], Hong Kong, People's Republic of China

Hong Kong Reprographic Rights Licensing Soc. [IO], Hong Kong, People's Republic of China

Hong Kong Retail Mgt. Assn. [IO], Hong Kong, People's Republic of China

Hong Kong Sailing Fed. [IO], Hong Kong, People's Republic of China

Hong Kong Schools Music and Speech Assn. [IO], Hong Kong, People's Republic of China

Hong Kong Securities Inst. [IO], Hong Kong, People's Republic of China

Hong Kong Sex Educ. Assn. [IO], Hong Kong, People's Republic of China

A star before a book entry number signifies that the name is not listed separately, but is mentioned within the entry.

Hong Kong Shipowners Assn. [IO], Hong Kong, People's Republic of China
Hong Kong Sinfonietta [IO], Hong Kong, People's Republic of China
Hong Kong Skating Union [IO], Hong Kong, People's Republic of China
Hong Kong Soc. of Certified Prosthetist-Orthotists [IO], Hong Kong, People's Republic of China
Hong Kong Soc. of Clinical Chemistry [IO], Hong Kong, People's Republic of China
Hong Kong Soc. for Colposcopy and Cervical Pathology [IO], Hong Kong, People's Republic of China
Hong Kong Soc. for the Deaf [IO], Hong Kong, People's Republic of China
Hong Kong Soc. of Dermatology and Venereology [IO], Hong Kong, People's Republic of China
Hong Kong Soc. of Digestive Endoscopy [IO], Hong Kong, People's Republic of China
Hong Kong Soc. of Gastroenterology [IO], Hong Kong, People's Republic of China
Hong Kong Soc. of Illustrators [IO], Hong Kong, People's Republic of China
Hong Kong Soc. for Infectious Diseases [IO], Hong Kong, People's Republic of China
Hong Kong Soc. of Medical Genetics [IO], Hong Kong, People's Republic of China
Hong Kong Soc. of Medical Informatics [IO], Hong Kong, People's Republic of China
Hong Kong Soc. for Microbiology and Infection [IO], Hong Kong, People's Republic of China
Hong Kong Soc. of Minimal Access Surgery [IO], Hong Kong, People's Republic of China
Hong Kong Soc. for Multimedia and Image Computing [IO], Hong Kong, People's Republic of China
Hong Kong Soc. of Nephrology [IO], Hong Kong, People's Republic of China
Hong Kong Soc. for Nursing Educ. [IO], Hong Kong, People's Republic of China
Hong Kong Soc. of Oral Implantology [IO], Hong Kong, People's Republic of China
Hong Kong Soc. of Orthodontists [IO], Hong Kong, People's Republic of China
Hong Kong Soc. of Palliative Medicine [IO], Hong Kong, People's Republic of China
Hong Kong Soc. of Professional Optometrists [IO], Hong Kong, People's Republic of China
Hong Kong Soc. for the Protection of Children [IO], Hong Kong, People's Republic of China
Hong Kong Soc. for Quality of Life [IO], Hong Kong, People's Republic of China
Hong Kong Soc. for Rehabilitation [IO], Hong Kong, People's Republic of China
Hong Kong Soc. of Rheumatology [IO], Hong Kong, People's Republic of China
Hong Kong Soc. of Transplantation [IO], Hong Kong, People's Republic of China
Hong Kong Soc. of Wargamers [IO], Hong Kong, People's Republic of China
Hong Kong Softball Assn. [IO], Hong Kong, People's Republic of China
Hong Kong Special Olympics [IO], Hong Kong, People's Republic of China
Hong Kong Sports Photography Assn. [IO], Hong Kong, People's Republic of China
Hong Kong Surgical Laser Assn. [IO], Hong Kong, People's Republic of China
Hong Kong Taekwondo Assn. [IO], Hong Kong, People's Republic of China
Hong Kong Tennis Assn. [IO], Hong Kong, People's Republic of China
Hong Kong Tenpin Bowling Cong. [IO], Hong Kong, People's Republic of China
Hong Kong Thoracic Soc. [IO], Hong Kong, People's Republic of China
Hong Kong Touch and Tag Rugby Assn. [IO], Hong Kong, People's Republic of China
Hong Kong Tourism Bd. [IO], Hong Kong, People's Republic of China
Hong Kong Toys Coun. [IO], Hong Kong, People's Republic of China
Hong Kong Trade Development Coun. [IO], Hong Kong, People's Republic of China
Hong Kong Trade Development Coun. [23406], 219 E 46th St., New York, NY 10017, (212)838-8688

Hong Kong Trade Development Coun. - London Off. [IO], London, United Kingdom
Hong Kong Tuberculosis, Chest and Heart Diseases Assn. [IO], Hong Kong, People's Republic of China
Hong Kong Ultimate Players Assn. [IO], Hong Kong, People's Republic of China
Hong Kong Underwater Assn. [IO], Hong Kong, People's Republic of China
Hong Kong Urological Assn. [IO], Hong Kong, People's Republic of China
Hong Kong Venture Capital Assn. [IO], Hong Kong, People's Republic of China
Hong Kong Veterinary Assn. [IO], Hong Kong, People's Republic of China
Hong Kong Watch Mfrs. Assn. Ltd. [IO], Hong Kong, People's Republic of China
Hong Kong Water Ski Assn. [IO], Hong Kong, People's Republic of China
Hong Kong Women Professionals and Entrepreneurs Assn. [IO], Hong Kong, People's Republic of China
Hong Kong Wushu Union [IO], Hong Kong, People's Republic of China
Hong Kong Youth Hostels Assn. [IO], Hong Kong, People's Republic of China
Honig-Verband [★IO]
Honolulu Japanese Chamber of Commerce [23414], 2454 S Beretania St., Ste. 201, Honolulu, HI 96826, (808)949-5531
Honor Am. [★20612]
Honor the Earth [19155], 2104 Stevens Ave. S, Minneapolis, MN 55404, (612)879-7529

Honor Societies
Alpha Chi [23551]
Alpha Epsilon [23516]
Alpha Kappa Mu [23552]
Alpha Sigma Nu [23553]
Alpha Sigma Nu [23553]
Amer. Sociological Assn. | Honors Prog. [23738]
Assn. of Coll. Honor Societies [23554]
Astronaut Scholars Honor Soc. [23629]
Beta Beta Beta [23470]
Beta Gamma Sigma [23476]
Beta Phi Mu [23583]
Beta Sigma Kappa [23611]
Blue Key Honor Soc. [23555]
Cum Laude Soc. [23556]
Delta Epsilon Sigma [23557]
Delta Phi Epsilon Professional Foreign Ser. Sorority [23529]
Delta Sigma Delta [23498]
Delta Sigma Rho - Tau Kappa Alpha [23754]
Gamma Beta Phi Soc. [23558]
Gamma Sigma Delta [23463]
Golden Key Intl. Honour Soc. [23559]
Intercollegiate Knights [23560]
Kappa Gamma Pi [23561]
Mortar Bd. [23562]
Mu Beta Psi [23601]
Natl. Alpha Lambda Delta [23563]
Natl. Block and Bridle Club [23464]
Natl. Honor Soc. [23564]
Natl. Junior Honor Soc. [23565]
Omicron Delta Kappa Soc. [23566]
Order of the Coif [23567]
Phi Beta Delta [23568]
Phi Chi Medical Fraternity [23594]
Phi Kappa Phi [23569]
Pi Omega Pi [23488]
Pi Sigma Alpha [23622]
Rho Chi - Alpha Beta Chap. [23619]
Sigma Alpha Iota Intl. Music Fraternity [23605]
Sigma Alpha Lambda [23570]
Sigma Sigma Phi [23614]
Sigma Zeta [23633]
Tau Alpha Pi [23524]
Honorable Order of the Blue Goose, Intl. [19049], Terrence M. Maloney, Grand Wielder, 12940 Walnut Rd., Elm Grove, WI 53122, (414)221-0341
Honorable Order of the Blue Goose, Intl. [19049], Terrence M. Maloney, Grand Wielder, 12940 Walnut Rd., Elm Grove, WI 53122, (414)221-0341
Honors Inst. [★23514]
Honors Inst. [★23514]
Honourable Company of Master Mariners [IO], London, United Kingdom

Hoo-Hoo
Hoo-Hoo Intl. [19027]
Hoo-Hoo Intl. [19027], PO Box 118, Gurdon, AR 71743, (870)353-4997
Hood's Texas Brigade Assn. [20384], 605 Pecan Grove Rd., Austin, TX 78704, (512)447-3881
Hoofdbedrijschap Detailhandel [★IO]
Hooved Animal Humane Soc. [10979], 10804 McConnell Rd., Woodstock, IL 60098, (815)337-5563
Hoover Historical Center [20963], Walsh Univ., 1875 E Maple St., North Canton, OH 44720-3331, (330)499-0287
Hoover Institution [★18814]
Hoover Institution on War, Revolution and Peace [18814], Stanford Univ., 434 Galvez Mall, Stanford, CA 94305-6010, (650)723-1754
Hop Growers of Am. [3950], PO Box 1207, Moxee, WA 98936, (509)453-4749
HOPE [IO], Heeslingen-Sassenholz, Germany
Hope Acad. International [★12886]
Hope Acad. International [★12886]
Hope for African Children Initiative [IO], Nairobi, Kenya
Hope After Rape [IO], Kampala, Uganda
HOPE Animal-Assisted Crisis Response [12906], 1292 High St., No. 182, Eugene, OR 97401, (877)467-3597
Hope Beyond Hope [15185], 4230 Harding Rd., Ste. 307, Nashville, TN 37205, (615)292-8299
Hope for the Child [11313], 8315 Emerald Ln., Woodbury, MN 55125, (651)246-0552
Hope for the Child [11313], 8315 Emerald Ln., Woodbury, MN 55125, (651)246-0552
HOPE for Children [IO], Hemel Hempstead, United Kingdom
Hope Development Org. [IO], Faisalabad, Pakistan
Hope Force Intl. [11854], 7065 Moores Ln., Ste. 200, Brentwood, TN 37027, (615)371-1271
Hope Force Intl. [11854], 7065 Moores Ln., Ste. 200, Brentwood, TN 37027, (615)371-1271
Hope and Future for Children in Bolivia [11314], PO Box 4034, Mountain View, CA 94040, (650)962-0137
Hope for Haiti [11595], PO Box 496, Westminster, MD 21158-0496, (410)848-7343
Hope for Haiti's Children [11315], PO Box 936, Sugar Land, TX 77487, (866)314-9330
Hope Imaging [16677], 3800 Bridgeport Way W, No. 501, University Place, WA 98466
HOPE Intl. [13462], 227 Granite Run Dr., Ste. 250, Lancaster, PA 17601, (717)464-3220
Hope Intl. [13462], 227 Granite Run Dr., Ste. 250, Lancaster, PA 17601, (717)464-3220
Hope Intl. Univ. Alumni Assn. [18874], 2500 E Nutwood Ave., Fullerton, CA 92831, (714)879-3901
Hope for Kenya's Kids [11906], PO Box 2883, Winter Haven, FL 33883-2883
Hope for Kenya's Kids [11906], PO Box 2883, Winter Haven, FL 33883-2883
HOPE Qatar [IO], Doha, Qatar
Hope: Rwanda [IO], Baulkham Hills, Australia
Hope of Survivors [13087], PO Box 27, Effingham, IL 62401, (618)983-6434
Hope Through Healing Hands [15186], 2033 Richard Jones Rd., Nashville, TN 37215, (615)386-0045
Hope Through Hea. [12385], PO Box 605, Medway, MA 02053-0605
Hope for Two. The Pregnant With Cancer Network [13929], PO Box 253, Amherst, NY 14226, (800)743-4471
Hope for the Warriors [11091], 1335 Western Blvd., Ste. E, PMB 48, Jacksonville, NC 28546, (910)938-1817
HOPE Worldwide - Afghanistan [IO], Kabul, Afghanistan
HOPE Worldwide - Australia [IO], North Epping, Australia
HOPE Worldwide - Brazil [IO], Sao Paulo, Brazil
HOPE Worldwide - Canada [IO], Toronto, ON, Canada
HOPE Worldwide - Caribbean [IO], Kingston, Jamaica
HOPE Worldwide - Germany [IO], Berlin, Germany
HOPE Worldwide - Indonesia [IO], Jakarta, Indonesia

Reference to "IO" in place of a book number signifies that the association may be found in the 50th edition of International Organizations.

HOPE Worldwide - Malaysia [IO], Kuala Lumpur, Malaysia
HOPE Worldwide - Papua New Guinea [IO], Boroko, Papua New Guinea
HopeLab [15342], 1991 Broadway St., Ste. 136, Redwood City, CA 94063-1957, (650)569-5900
HOPOS - The Intl. Soc. for the History of Philosophy of Sci. [8839], Eric Palmer, Allegheny Coll., Dept. of Philosophy, Meadville, PA 16335
Horace Mann League of the U.S.A. [8772], 560 Rainier Ln., Port Ludlow, WA 98365, (360)437-1186
Horatio Alger Assn. of Distinguished Americans [20375], 99 Canal Center Plz., Ste. 320, Alexandria, VA 22314, (703)684-9444
Horatio Alger Awards Comm. [★20375]
Horatio Alger Newsboy Club [★9372]
Horatio Alger Soc. [9372], PO Box 70361, Richmond, VA 23255
Horizon Community Assn. of Rwanda [IO], Kigali, Rwanda
Horizon Intl. [11316], PO Box 180, Pendleton, IN 46064, (765)778-1016
Horizon Intl. Medical Mission [15187], 111 Lions Gate Rd., Savannah, GA 31419, (912)308-8799
Horizons of Friendship [IO], Cobourg, ON, Canada
Hormone and Pituitary Prog; Natl. [16280]
Horn Relief [IO], Nairobi, Kenya
Horn and Whistle Enthusiasts Gp. [21348], 2 Abell Ave., Ipswich, MA 01938
Horological Inst. [★2155]
Horror Writers of Am. [★10718]
Horror Writers Assn. [10718], 244 5th Ave., Ste. 2767, New York, NY 10001-7604
Horse DrivingHorseDrive Canada
   Equestrian Ministries Intl. [19816]
Horse Lovers United [17795], PO Box 2744, Salisbury, MD 21802-2744, (410)749-3599
Horse Protection League [4592], PO Box 741089, Arvada, CO 80006, (303)216-0141
Horse Racing
   Amer. Cmpt. Barrel Racing Assn. [22649]
   Arabian Jockey Club [22650]
   Barrel Futurities of Am. [22651]
   Harness Horse Youth Found. [22652]
   Harness Racing Museum and Hall of Fame [22653]
   Harness Tracks of Am. [22654]
   Intl. Barrel Racing Assn. [22655]
   Intl. Barrel Racing Assn. [22655]
   Intl. Trotting and Pacing Assn. [22656]
   The Jockey Club [22657]
   Jockeys' Guild [22658]
   Natl. Barrel Horse Assn. [22659]
   Natl. Christian Barrel Racers Assn. [22660]
   Natl. Horsemen's Benevolent and Protective Assn. [12165]
   Natl. Museum of Racing and Hall of Fame [22661]
   Natl. Steeplechase Assn. [22662]
   Natl. Thoroughbred Racing Assn. [22663]
   Oregon Horsemen's Benevolent Protective Assn. [22664]
   Standardbred Owners Assn. [22665]
   Thoroughbred Club of Am. [22666]
   Thoroughbred Owners and Breeders Assn. [22667]
   Thoroughbred Racing Associations [22668]
   Thoroughbred Racing Protective Bur. [22669]
   United Barrel Racing Assn. [22670]
   U.S. Harness Writers' Assn. [2880]
   U.S. Team Penning Assn. [22671]
   U.S. Team Penning Assn. [22671]
   U.S. Trotting Assn. [22672]
   World Championship Cutter and Chariot Racing Assn. [22448]
Horse Racing Ireland [IO], Newbridge, Ireland
Horseback Riding
   Amer. Assn. of Riding Schools [22673]
   Amer. Cutting Horse Assn. [22674]
   Amer. Horse Trials Found. [22675]
   Amer. Junior Rodeo Assn. [22839]
   Amer. Riding Instructors Assn. [22676]
   Back Country Horsemen of Am. [22677]
   Centered Riding [22678]

   CHA - Certified Horsemanship Assn. [22679]
   Equestrian Ministries Intl. [19816]
   Gladstone Equestrian Assn. [22680]
   Harness Horse Youth Found. [22652]
   Horsemanship Safety Assn. [22681]
   InterCollegiate Horse Show Assn. [22682]
   Intl. Jumper Futurity [22683]
   Intl. Side Saddle Org. [22684]
   Natl. Christian Barrel Racers Assn. [22660]
   Natl. Finals Rodeo Comm. [22844]
   Natl. Hunter Jumper Assn. [22685]
   Natl. Versatility Ranch Horse Assn. [22686]
   Trail Riders of Today [22687]
   United Barrel Racing Assn. [22670]
   U.S. Dressage Fed. [22688]
   U.S. Equestrian Fed. [22689]
   U.S. Eventing Assn. [22690]
   U.S. Hunter Jumper Assn. [22691]
   U.S. Pony Clubs [22692]
Horseless Carriage Club of Am. [21069], 5709 Oak Ave., Temple City, CA 91780-2431, (626)287-4222
Horsemanship Safety Assn. [22681], Ted Marthe, 5304 Reeve Rd., Mazomanie, WI 53560, (608)767-2593
Horses
   Akhal-Teke Assn. of Am. [4522]
   Amer. Appaloosa Assn. Worldwide [4523]
   Amer. Appaloosa Assn. Worldwide [4523]
   Amer. Azteca Horse Intl. Assn. [4524]
   Amer. Azteca Horse Intl. Assn. [4524]
   Amer. Bashkir Curly Registry [4525]
   Amer. Buckskin Registry Assn. [4526]
   Amer. Collegiate Horsemen's Assn. [4527]
   Amer. Connemara Pony Soc. [4528]
   Amer. Cream Draft Horse Assn. [4529]
   Amer. Driving Soc. [22693]
   Amer. Drum Horse Assn. [4530]
   Amer. Equestrian Alliance [1733]
   Amer. Equestrian Trade Assn. [4531]
   Amer. Hackney Horse Soc. [4532]
   Amer. Haflinger Registry [4533]
   Amer. Half Quarter Horse Registry [4534]
   Amer. Hanoverian Soc. [4535]
   Amer. Holsteiner Horse Assn. [4536]
   Amer. Horse Coun. [4537]
   Amer. Horse Defense Fund [4538]
   Amer. Horse League [12166]
   Amer. Indian Horse Registry [4539]
   Amer. Junior Paint Horse Assn. [4540]
   Amer. Junior Rodeo Assn. [22839]
   Amer. Kerry Bog Pony Soc. [4541]
   Amer. Kerry Bog Pony Soc. [4541]
   Amer. Miniature Horse Assn. [4542]
   Amer. Morgan Horse Assn. [4543]
   Amer. Mustang and Burro Assn. [4544]
   Amer. Paint Horse Assn. [4545]
   Amer. Part-Blooded Horse Registry [4546]
   Amer. Paso Fino Horse Assn. [4547]
   Amer. Polo Horse Assn. [22812]
   Amer. Quarter Horse Assn. [4548]
   Amer. Quarter Horse Youth Assn. [4549]
   Amer. Quarter Pony Assn. [4550]
   Amer. Ranch Horse Assn. [4551]
   Amer. Saddlebred Horse Assn. [4552]
   Amer. Saddlebred Sporthorse Assn. [4553]
   Amer. Shagya Arabian Verband [4554]
   Amer. Shetland Pony Club I Amer. Miniature Horse Registry [4555]
   Amer. Shire Horse Assn. [4556]
   Amer. Suffolk Horse Assn. [4557]
   Amer. Sulphur Horse Assn. [21855]
   Amer. Sulphur Horse Assn. [21855]
   Amer. Trakehner Assn. [4558]
   Amer. Trakehner Assn. [4558]
   Amer. Trote and Trocha Assn. [4559]
   Amer. Warmblood Registry [4560]
   Amer. Warmblood Soc. [4561]
   Amer. Welara Pony Soc. [4562]
   Amer. Welara Pony Soc. [4562]
   Amer. Youth Horse Coun. [4563]
   Another Chance 4 Horses [10927]
   Appaloosa Horse Club [4564]
   Appaloosa Horse Club [4564]
   Arabian Horse Assn. [4565]
   Arabian Horse Breeders Alliance [4566]

   Arabian Horse Breeders Alliance [4566]
   Arabian Horse Owners Found. [4567]
   Arabian Professional and Amateur Horseman's Assn. [4568]
   Back in the Saddle Horse Adoption [4569]
   Belgian Draft Horse Corp. of Am. [4570]
   Blazer Horse Assn. [4571]
   Bur. of Land Mgt. Natl. Wild Horse and Burro Prog. [4572]
   Canadian Pony Club [1970]
   Caspian Horse Soc. of the Americas [4573]
   Champagne Horse Breeders' and Owners' Assn. [4574]
   Cleveland Bay Horse Soc. of North Am. [4575]
   Clydesdale Breeders of the U.S.A. [4576]
   Colorado Ranger Horse Assn. [4577]
   Curly Sporthorse Intl. [4578]
   Curly Sporthorse Intl. [4578]
   Dales Pony Assn. of North Am. [4579]
   Dales Pony Assn. of North Am. [4579]
   Dales Pony Soc. of Am. [4580]
   Equestrian Ministries Intl. [19816]
   Equine Guided Educ. Assn. [8275]
   Exmoor Pony Assn. Intl. [4581]
   Fell Pony Soc. and Conservancy of the Americas [4582]
   Fell Pony Soc. and Conservancy of the Americas [4582]
   Fell Pony Soc. of North Am. [4583]
   Fell Pony Soc. of North Am. [4583]
   For the Love of Horses [17794]
   Friesian Horse Assn. of North Am. [4584]
   Friesian Horse Assn. of North Am. [4584]
   Front Range Equine Rescue [4585]
   Gaited Horse Intl. Assn. [4586]
   Gotland-Russ Assn. of North Am. [4587]
   Grayson-Jockey Club Res. Found. [4588]
   Gypsy Cob and Drum Horse Assn. [4589]
   Gypsy Vanner Horse Soc. [4590]
   Half Saddlebred Registry of Am. [4591]
   HALTER, Inc. [16852]
   Harness Horse Youth Found. [22652]
   Horse Lovers United [17795]
   Horse Protection League [4592]
   Hungarian Horse Assn. of Am. [4593]
   InterCollegiate Horse Show Assn. [22682]
   Intl. Andalusian and Lusitano Horse Assn. [4594]
   Intl. Andalusian and Lusitano Horse Assn. [4594]
   Intl. Buckskin Horse Assn. [4595]
   Intl. Buckskin Horse Assn. [4595]
   Intl. Colored Appaloosa Assn. [4596]
   Intl. Colored Appaloosa Assn. [4596]
   Intl. Curly Horse Org. [4597]
   Intl. Curly Horse Org. [4597]
   Intl. Friesian Show Horse Assn. [4598]
   Intl. Generic Horse Assn. [4599]
   Intl. Morab Breeders' Assn. [4600]
   Intl. Morab Breeders' Assn. [4600]
   Intl. Morab Registry [4601]
   Intl. Pedigree Assignment and Bloodline Res. Assn. [4602]
   Intl. Pedigree Assignment and Bloodline Res. Assn. [4602]
   Intl. Quarab Horse Assn. [4603]
   Intl. Quarab Horse Assn. [4603]
   Intl. Quarter Pony Assn. [4604]
   Intl. Sport Horses of Color [4605]
   Intl. Sporthorse Registry [4606]
   Intl. Trotting and Pacing Assn. [22656]
   Intl. Warlander Soc. and Registry [4607]
   Intl. Warlander Soc. and Registry [4607]
   Irish Draught Horse Soc. of North Am. [4608]
   Irish Draught Horse Soc. of North Am. [4608]
   Kiger Mesteno Assn. [4609]
   Lipizzan Assn. of North Am. [4610]
   Lippitt Morgan Breeders Assn. [4611]
   Missouri Fox Trotting Horse Breed Assn. [4612]
   Morgan Single-Footing Horse Found. [4613]
   Mountain Pleasure Horse Assn. [4614]
   Natl. Assn. of Certified Professionals of Equine Therapy [13694]
   Natl. Chincoteague Pony Assn. [4615]
   Natl. Christian Barrel Racers Assn. [22660]
   Natl. Cutting Horse Assn. [4616]
   Natl. Finals Rodeo Comm. [22844]

A star before a book entry number signifies that the name is not listed separately, but is mentioned within the entry.

Natl. Morgan Reining Horse Assn. [4617]
Natl. Mustang Assn. [4618]
Natl. Quarter Horse Registry [4619]
Natl. Quarter Pony Assn. [4620]
Natl. Reined Cow Horse Assn. [21856]
Natl. Reining Horse Assn. [4621]
Natl. Reining Horse Assn. [4621]
Natl. Show Horse Registry [4622]
Natl. Snaffle Bit Assn. [4623]
Natl. Spotted Saddle Horse Assn. [4624]
Natl. Versatility Ranch Horse Assn. [22686]
Natl. Walking Horse Assn. [4625]
New Forest Pony Assn. and Registry [4626]
North Amer. Danish Warmblood Assn. [4627]
North Amer. Danish Warmblood Assn. [4627]
North Amer. Dept. of the Royal Warmblood
   Studbook of the Netherlands [4628]
North Amer. Equine Ranching Info. Coun. [1734]
North Amer. Horsemen's Assn. [4629]
North Amer. Model Horse Shows Assn. [21857]
North Amer. Peruvian Horse Assn. [4630]
North Amer. Peruvian Horse Assn. [4630]
North Amer. Shagya-Arabian Soc. [4631]
North Amer. Spotted Draft Horse Assn. [4632]
North Amer. Spotted Draft Horse Assn. [4632]
North Amer. Thoroughbred Soc. [22694]
Norwegian Fjord Horse Registry [4633]
Oldenburg Registry N.A. [4634]
Palomino Horse Assn. [4635]
Palomino Horse Breeders of Am. [4636]
Paso Fino Horse Assn. [4637]
Paso Fino Horse Assn. [4637]
Personal Ponies Ltd. [11822]
Pinto Horse Assn. of Am. [4638]
Pony of the Americas Club [4639]
Pure Puerto Rican Paso Fino Fed. of Am. [4640]
Purebred Morab Horse Association/Registry
   [4641]
Purebred Morab Horse Association/Registry
   [4641]
Racking Horse Breeders' Assn. of Am. [4642]
ReRun [17796]
Rocky Mountain Horse Assn. [4643]
Saving Horses, Inc. [12167]
Show Horse Alliance [4644]
Southwest Spanish Mustang Assn. [4645]
Spanish-Barb Breeders Assn. [4646]
Spanish Mustang Registry [4647]
Spanish-Norman Horse Registry [4648]
Spotted Saddle Horse Breeders' and Exhibitors'
   Assn. [4649]
Standardbred Retirement Found. [4650]
Stolen Horse Intl. [11042]
Swedish Warmblood Assn. of North Am. [4651]
Tennessee Walking Horse Breeders' and Exhibi-
   tors' Assn. [4652]
Tennessee Walking Horse Breeders' and Exhibi-
   tors' Assn. [4652]
Thoroughbred Club of Am. [22666]
Tiger Horse Assn. [4653]
United Barrel Racing Assn. [22670]
United Pegasus Found. [17797]
United Professional Horsemen's Assn. [4654]
U.S. Equine Rescue League [12168]
U.S. Hunter Jumper Assn. [22691]
U.S. Icelandic Horse Cong. [4655]
U.S. Lipizzan Registry [4656]
U.S. Peruvian Horse Assn. [4657]
Unwanted Horse Coalition [11053]
Walkaloosa Horse Assn. [4658]
Walkaloosa Horse Assn. [4658]
Walking Horse Owners' Assn. [4659]
Walking Horse Trainers Assn. [4660]
Welsh Pony and Cob Soc. of Am. [4661]
Western Intl. Walking Horse Assn. [4662]
Western Intl. Walking Horse Assn. [4662]
Western Saddle Clubs Assn. [4663]
World Championship Cutter and Chariot Racing
   Assn. [22448]
Horseshoe Canada Assn. [IO], Saskatoon, SK,
   Canada
Horseshoes
Natl. Horseshoe Pitchers Assn. of Am. [22695]
Horticultural Dealers Assn. [★4675]
Horticultural Res. Inst. [4742], 1000 Vermont Ave.
   NW, Ste. 300, Washington, DC 20005-4914,
   (202)789-2900

Horticultural Trades Assn. [IO], Reading, United
   Kingdom
Horticulture
All-America Rose Selections [4664]
Amer. Clematis Soc. [4665]
Amer. Fern Soc. [6343]
Amer. Penstemon Soc. [21779]
Amer. Public Gardens Assn. [4666]
Assn. of Zoological Horticulture [4667]
Coalition of Organic Landscapers [2179]
The Gardeners of Am. [21794]
Hardy Fern Found. [4668]
Heliconia Soc. Intl. [4669]
Heliconia Soc. Intl. [4669]
Hobby Greenhouse Assn. [21800]
Indoor Gardening Soc. of Am. [21801]
InterAmerican Soc. for Tropical Horticulture [4670]
Intl. Brugmansia and Datura Soc.
   [21738]HorticultureIntl. Cut Flower Growers
   Assn.
Intl. Phalaenopsis Alliance [4671]
Intl. Plant Propagators Soc. [4672]
Intl. Plant Propagators Soc. [4672]
Natl. Garden Bur. [4673]
Natl. Junior Horticultural Assn. [21811]
North Amer. Clivia Soc. [4674]
North Amer. Flowerbulb Wholesalers Assn. [4675]
North Amer. Horticultural Supply Assn. [4676]
North Amer. Lily Soc. [21815]
Org. for Flora Neotropica [6363]
Passiflora Soc. Intl. [4677]
Perennial Plant Assn. [4678]
Plumeria Soc. of Am. [21817]
Tropical Flowering Tree Soc. [4679]
Tropical Flowering Tree Soc. [4679]
Women's Horticultural Assn. [4680]
Horton Family Assn. - Defunct.
Hosei-shi Gakkai [★IO]
Hoshasen Eikyo Kenkyu-sho [★IO]
The Hosiery Assn. [207], 7421 Carmel Executive
   Park, Ste. 200, Charlotte, NC 28226, (704)365-
   0913
Hospice
Acute Long Term Hosp. Assn. [15024]
Children's Hospice Intl. [15025]
Children's Hospice Intl. [15025]
Hospice Educ. Inst. [15026]
Hospice Educ. Inst. [15026]
Hospice Found. of Am. [15027]
Natl. Hospice and Palliative Care Org. [15028]
Natl. Inst. for Jewish Hospice [15029]
Natl. Prison Hospice Assn. [15030]
Hospice Assn. of Am. [15009], 228 Seventh St. SE,
   Washington, DC 20003, (202)546-4759
Hospice Assn. of Ontario [IO], Toronto, ON, Canada
Hospice Educ. Inst. [15026], 3 Unity Sq., PO Box
   98, Machiasport, ME 04655-0098, (207)255-8800
Hospice Educ. Inst. [15026], 3 Unity Sq., PO Box
   98, Machiasport, ME 04655-0098, (207)255-8800
Hospice Found. of Am. [15027], 1710 Rhode Island
   Ave. NW, Ste. 400, Washington, DC 20036,
   (202)457-5811
Hospice New Zealand [IO], Wellington, New Zealand
Hospice Nurses Assn. [★15753]
Hospice and Palliative Medicine; Amer. Acad. of
   [16248]
Hospice and Palliative Nurses Assn. [15753], 1
   Penn Ctr. W, Ste. 229, Pittsburgh, PA 15276,
   (412)787-9301
**HospitalHospitalAmer. Assn. of Eye and Ear
Hospitals**
Amer. Assn. of Healthcare Consultants [15031]
Amer. Assn. of Psychiatric Administrators [15032]
Amer. Coll. of Healthcare Executives [15033]
Amer. Hosp. Assn. [15034]
Amer. Hosp. Assn. | Amer. for the Healthcare
   Environmental [15035]
Amer. Hosp. Assn. | Amer. Soc. for Healthcare
   Engg. [15036]
Amer. Hosp. Assn. | Amer. Soc. for Healthcare
   Environmental Services [15035]
Amer. Hosp. Assn. | Amer. Soc. for Healthcare
   Human Resources Admin. [15037]
Amer. Hosp. Assn. | Assn. for Healthcare Rsrc.
   and Materials Mgt. [15038]

Amer. Hosp. Assn., Sect. for Long Term Care and
   Rehabilitation [15039]
Amer. Hosp. Assn., Sect. for Metropolitan
   Hospitals [15040]
Amer. Hosp. Assn. | Soc. for Healthcare Strategy
   and Market Development [15041]
Amer. Soc. for Healthcare Risk Mgt. [15042]
Amer. Women's Hospitals Ser. Comm. of AMWA
   [15043]
Assn. for Healthcare Foodservice [15044]
Assn. for Healthcare Philanthropy [15045]
Assn. for Healthcare Philanthropy [15045]
Assn. for Healthcare Volunteer Rsrc. Profession-
   als [13384]
Assn. for Hosp. Medical Educ. [15046]
Australian Private Hospitals Assn. [1150]
Catholic Hea. Assn. of the U.S. [15047]
Center to Advance Palliative Care [15048]
Coalition to Protect America's Hea. Care [15049]
Comm. to Reduce Infection Deaths [15050]
Competency and Credentialing Inst. [15051]
Coun. of Teaching Hospitals [15052]
Coun. of Women's and Infants' Specialty
   Hospitals [15053]
Fed. of Amer. Hospitals [15054]
The Floating Hosp. [15055]
Hea. Res. and Educational Trust [15056]
Healthcare Info. and Mgt. Systems Soc. [15057]
Healthcare Laundry Accreditation Coun.
   [2192]HospitalHosp. Org. of Pedagogues in
   Europe
Intl. Assn. of Healthcare Central Ser. Material Mgt.
   [15058]
Intl. Assn. for Healthcare Security and Safety
   [15059]
Intl. Assn. for Healthcare Security and Safety
   [15059]
Joint Commn. [15060]
Natl. Assn. of Children's Hospitals and Related
   Institutions [15061]
Natl. Assn. of Healthcare Access Mgt. [15062]
Natl. Assn. of Hosp. Hospitality Houses [15063]
Natl. Assn. of Long Term Hospitals [15064]
Natl. Assn. of Public Hospitals and Hea. Systems
   [15065]
Natl. Assn. of Urban Hospitals [15066]
Practice Greenhealth [14506]
Safety Net Hospitals for Pharmaceutical Access
   [16213]
Soc. of Hosp. Medicine [15067]
Spirit of Women [15068]
Sustainable Hospitals Proj. [15069]
Together for Kids [15070]
VHA [15071]
Wings and Dreams for Kids [14099]
Hosp. Audiences [10580], 548 Broadway, 3rd Fl.,
   New York, NY 10012, (212)575-7676
Hospital-Based Massage Network [15267], Natural
   Touch Marketing, PO Box 1038, Olympia, WA
   98507-1038, (360)754-9799
Hosp. Caterers Assn. [IO], Wolverhampton, United
   Kingdom
Hosp. Consultants and Specialists Assn. [IO], Bas-
   ingstoke, United Kingdom
Hosp. Financial Mgt. Assn. [★15258]
Hosp. Infection Soc. [IO], London, United Kingdom
Hosp., Institution and Educational Food Ser. Soc.
   [★15828]
Hosp. Mgt. Systems Soc. [★15057]
Hosp. Org. of Pedagogues in Europe [IO], Brussels,
   Belgium
Hosp. Res. and Educational Trust [★15056]
Hospitality Asset Managers Assn. [1749], Stephanie
   Roy, Coor., PO Box 381, North Scituate, MA
   02060, (781)544-7330
Hospitality Assn. of Namibia [IO], Windhoek,
   Namibia
Hospitality Assn. of New Zealand [IO], Wellington,
   New Zealand
Hospitality Comm. for United Nations Delegations
   [17972], PO Box 1201, Grand Central Sta., New
   York, NY 10164, (212)963-8753
Hospitality Financial and Tech. Professionals [1303],
   11709 Boulder Ln., Ste. 110, Austin, TX 78726,
   (512)249-5333

Reference to "IO" in place of a book number signifies that the association may be found in the 50th edition of International Organizations.

Hospitality Financial and Tech. Professionals [1303], 11709 Boulder Ln., Ste. 110, Austin, TX 78726, (512)249-5333
Hospitality Industries
Amer. Hotel and Lodging Assn. [1735]
Amer. Hotel and Lodging Educational Found. [1736]
Asian Amer. Hotel Owners Assn. [1737]
Asian Amer. Hotel Owners Assn. [1737]
Asociacion Mexicana de Hoteles y Moteles [20695]
Assn. of Club Executives [1738]
Assn. for Convention Marketing Executives [1739]
Assn. of Meeting Professionals [1740]
Assn. of Starwood Franchisees and Owners North Am. [1741]
Assn. of Tourist Hotels of the Republic of Argentina [8978]
Assn. for Wedding Professionals Intl. [1742]
Assn. for Wedding Professionals Intl. [1742]
Binational Tourism Alliance [3473]
Brazilian Hotels' Assn. [5757]
Broker Mgt. Coun. [1743]
Convenience Caterers and Food Mfrs. Assn. [1744]
Coun. of Hotel and Restaurant Trainers [1745]
Distinguished Inns of North Am., Select Registry [1746]
Dude Ranchers' Assn. [1747]
Federated Hospitality Assn. of South Africa [21106]
Fed. of Hotel and Restaurant Associations of India [4805]
German Hotels and Restaurants Assn. [14187]
Green Book of Ireland [16861]
Green Hotels Assn. [1748]
Green Hotels Assn. [1748]HospitalityGrenada Hotel and Tourism Assn.
Healthcare Caterers Intl. [1394]
Hospitality Asset Managers Assn. [1749]
Hospitality Inst. of Tech. and Mgt. [1750]
Hospitality Sales and Marketing Assn. Intl. [1751]
Hospitality Sales and Marketing Assn. Intl. [1751]
Hotel Electronic Distribution Network Assn. [1752]
Hotel Tech. Next Generation [1753]
IAHI, the Owners' Assn. [1754]
Innholders' Company [8813]
Intl. Assn. of Conf. Center Administrators [1755]
Intl. Assn. of Conf. Center Administrators [1755]
Intl. Assn. of Holiday Inns [1754]
Intl. Concierge and Lifestyle Mgt. Assn. [1756]
Intl. Coun. on Hotel, Restaurant, and Institutional Educ. [1757]
Intl. Coun. on Hotel, Restaurant, and Institutional Educ. [1757]
Intl. Galapagos Tour Operators Assn. [23454]
Intl. Soc. of Hospitality Purchasers [1758]
Intl. Soc. of Hospitality Purchasers [1758]
Les Clefs d'Or U.S.A. [1759]
Natl. Assn. of Black Hotel Owners, Operators and Developers [1760]
Natl. Assn. of Catering Executives [1761]
Natl. Assn. of Catering Executives [1761]
Natl. Assn. of Pizzeria Operators [1762]
Natl. Black McDonald's Operators Assn. [1763]
Natl. Concierge Assn. [1764]
Natl. Coun. of Chain Restaurants [1765]
Natl. Hotels' and Restaurants' Assn. - Dominican Republic [11983]
Natl. Restaurant Assn. [1766]
Natl. Restaurant Assn. Educational Found. [1767]
Natl. Restaurant Assn. I Multi-Unit Architects, Engineers and Constr. Officers Executive Study Group [1768]
Natl. Restaurant Assn. I Quality Assurance Study Group [1769]
Natl. Ski Areas Assn. [1770]
Professional Assn. of Innkeepers Intl. [1771]
Professional Assn. of Innkeepers Intl. [1771]
Resort Hotel Assn. [1772]
Restaurant Fac. Mgt. Assn. [3091]
Saint Croix Hotel and Tourism Assn. [1773]
Saint Croix Hotel and Tourism Assn. [1773]
St. Maarten Hospitality and Trade Assn. [16685]
Small Luxury Hotels of the World [1774]

Swedish Hotel and Restaurant Assn. [4648]
The Hospitality and Info. Ser. [17973], Meridian Intl. Center, 1630 Crescent Pl. NW, Washington, DC 20009, (202)232-3002
Hospitality Inst. of Tech. and Mgt. [1750], 670 Transfer Rd., Ste. 21A, St. Paul, MN 55114, (651)646-7077
Hospitality Sales and Marketing Assn. [IO], Bendorf, Germany
Hospitality Sales and Marketing Assn. Intl. [1751], 1760 Old Meadow Rd., Ste. 500, McLean, VA 22102, (703)506-3280
Hospitality Sales and Marketing Assn. Intl. [1751], 1760 Old Meadow Rd., Ste. 500, McLean, VA 22102, (703)506-3280
Hospitalized Veterans Writing Proj. [16565], 5920 Nall Ave., Ste. 101, Mission, KS 66202-3456, (913)432-1214
Hospitals of Hope [15188], 3545 N Santa Fe St., Wichita, KS 67219, (316)262-0964
Hospitals of Hope [15188], 3545 N Santa Fe St., Wichita, KS 67219, (316)262-0964
Hostelling Ecuador [IO], Guayaquil, Ecuador
Hostelling Intl. [IO], Welwyn Garden City, United Kingdom
Hostelling Intl. Argentina [IO], Buenos Aires, Argentina
Hostelling Intl. Bolivia [IO], Sucre, Bolivia
Hostelling Intl. Brazil [IO], Rio de Janeiro, Brazil
Hostelling Intl. Canada [IO], Ottawa, ON, Canada
Hostelling Intl. Chile [IO], Santiago, Chile
Hostelling Intl. Colombia [IO], Bogota, Colombia
Hostelling Intl. Iceland [IO], Reykjavik, Iceland
Hostelling Intl. Mexico [IO], Mexico City, Mexico
Hostelling Intl. Northern Island [IO], Belfast, United Kingdom
Hostelling Intl. Norway [IO], Oslo, Norway
Hostelling Intl. Slovenia [IO], Maribor, Slovenia
Hostelling Intl. USA [12766], 8401 Colesville Rd., Ste. 600, Silver Spring, MD 20910, (301)495-1240
Hostelling Intl. USA [12766], 8401 Colesville Rd., Ste. 600, Silver Spring, MD 20910, (301)495-1240
Hot Briquetted Iron Assn. [2471], 624 Matthews-Mint Hill Rd., Ste. 410, Matthews, NC 28105, (704)815-3285
Hot Dip Galvanizers Assn. of Southern Africa [IO], Edenvale, Republic of South Africa
Hotel Assn. of Canada [IO], Ottawa, ON, Canada
Hotel Assn. of Hungary [IO], Budapest, Hungary
Hotel Assn. of India [IO], New Delhi, India
Hotel Brokers Intl. [3013], 1420 NW Vivion Rd., Ste. 111, Kansas City, MO 64118, (816)505-4315
Hotel Brokers Intl. [3013], 1420 NW Vivion Rd., Ste. 111, Kansas City, MO 64118, (816)505-4315
Hotel Electronic Distribution Assn. [★1752]
Hotel Electronic Distribution Network Assn. [1752], 750 Natl. Press Bldg., 529 14th St. NW, Washington, DC 20045, (202)204-8400
Hotel Employees and Restaurant Employees Intl. Union and Union of Needletrades, Indus. and Textile Employees [★23240]
Hotel Management
Hotel Tech. Next Generation [1753]
Hotel Motel Brokers of Am. [★3013]
Hotel Motel Brokers of Am. [★3013]
Hotel and Restaurant Assn. of the Philippines [IO], Makati City, Philippines
Hotel and Restaurant Employees and Bartenders Intl. Union [★23240]
Hotel-, Restaurant- og Turisterhvervets Arbejdsgiver-forening [★IO]
Hotel Tech. Next Generation [1753], 650 E Algon-quin Rd., Ste. 207, Schaumburg, IL 60173, (847)303-5560
Hotels, Restaurants and Cafes in Europe [IO], Brussels, Belgium
Hotot Rabbit Breeders Intl. [4842], 5988 S Mohawk, Ypsilanti, MI 48197
Hotot Rabbit Breeders Intl. [4842], 5988 S Mohawk, Ypsilanti, MI 48197
HOUR Money Network [17378], PO Box 6731, Ithaca, NY 14851, (607)272-3738
House of Boyd Soc. [20535], 1609 Truscott Ct., Roseville, CA 95661
House of Boyd Soc. [20535], 1609 Truscott Ct., Roseville, CA 95661

House Builders Fed. [IO], London, United Kingdom
House Ear Inst. [16686], 2100 W 3rd St., Los Angeles, CA 90057, (213)483-4431
House of Heroes [13350], 4709 Milgen Rd., Columbus, GA 31907-1304, (706)562-1032
House of Hope Soc. [IO], Kingstown, St. Vincent and the Grenadines
House Leadership Fund - Defunct.
House of Marketing [IO], Frederiksberg, Denmark
House of Palestine [10348], 6161 El Cajon Blvd., No. 149, San Diego, CA 92115
House Plan Marketing Assn. [1038], PO Box 225, Gardner, KS 66030, (210)493-7646
House Rabbit Network [10980], PO Box 2602, Woburn, MA 01888-1102, (781)431-1211
House Rabbit Soc. [10981], 148 Broadway, Richmond, CA 94804, (510)970-7575
Houseboat Assn. of America - Defunct.
Household Goods Carriers' Bur. [★3243]
Household Goods Carriers' Bur. [★3243]
Household Goods Forwarders Assn. of Am. [★3249]
Household Goods Forwarders Assn. of Am. [★3249]
Household Hazardous Waste Proj. - Address unknown since 2010.
Housewares
Amer. Brush Mfrs. Assn. [1775]
Cookware Mfrs. Assn. [1776]
Griswold and Cast Iron Cookware Assn. [21858]
Intl. Assn. of Dinnerware Matchers [1777]
Intl. Assn. of Dinnerware Matchers [1777]
Intl. Housewares Assn. [1778]
Intl. Housewares Assn. [1778]
Intl. Housewares Representatives Assn. [1779]
Intl. Housewares Representatives Assn. [1779]
Intl. Sleep Products Assn. [1780]
Intl. Sleep Products Assn. [1780]
Natl. Furniture Bank Assn. [12059]
Wagner And Griswold Soc. [21859]
Housing
African Amer. Alliance for Homeownership [1781]
Amer. Dream Coalition [17264]
Amer. Homeowners Grassroots Alliance [17798]
Amer. Seniors Housing Assn. [12169]
Amer. Sunrise [12170]
Assisted Living Fed. of Am. [12171]
Build Change [12172]
Builders Without Borders [12173]
Builders Without Borders [12173]
Castle Coalition [18403]
Coalition of Landlords, Homeowners and Merchants [18404]
Community Associations Inst. [17373]
Community Economics, Inc. [12174]
Cooperative Housing Found. [12175]
Coun. for Affordable and Rural Housing [12176]
Coun. of Large Public Housing Authorities [5515]
Deaf-REACH [14930]
Efficiency First [4046]
Enterprise Community Partners [12177]
Escapees [22137]
Green Home Coun. [567]
Greener Pastures Inst. [12178]
Habitat for Humanity - Australia Adelaide [17131]
Habitat for Humanity - Bicol [20663]
Habitat for Humanity - Central Plains [18918]
Habitat for Humanity - Fiji [3679]
Habitat for Humanity - Gen. Santos City [23823]
Habitat for Humanity - Greater Auckland [20474]
Habitat for Humanity Intl. [12179]
Habitat for Humanity Intl. [12179]HousingHabitat for Humanity - Malaysia
Habitat for Humanity - Nelson [23770]
Habitat for Humanity - New Zealand [18875]
Habitat for Humanity - Philippines [18892]
Habitat for Humanity - Rotorua [18891]
Habitat for Humanity - Solomon Islands [23813]
Habitat for Humanity - Waikato [20607]
Herocare [13160]
HomeFree - U.S.A. [1782]
Homeowners Against Deficient Dwellings [12180]
House of Heroes [13350]
Housing Assistance Coun. [12181]
Housing Inspection Found. [1916]
Housing Statistics Users Gp. [5516]
Insight Center for Community Economic Development [17578]

A star before a book entry number signifies that the name is not listed separately, but is mentioned within the entry.

Inst. for Community Economics [17380]
Inst. for Responsible Housing Preservation [5517]
Intl. Assn. for Housing Sci. [12182]
Intl. Assn. for Housing Sci. [12182]
Interval Intl. [21854]
Leading Builders of Am. [577]
Natl. Affordable Housing Mgt. Assn. [1783]
Natl. Affordable Housing Network [12183]
Natl. AIDS Housing Coalition [12184]
Natl. Alliance of Community Economic Develop-
   ment Associations [17582]
Natl. Alliance of HUD Tenants [17799]
Natl. Amer. Indian Housing Coun. [5518]
Natl. Assn. of Constr. Contractors Cooperation
   [587]
Natl. Assn. for County Community and Economic
   Development [17384]
Natl. Assn. of Foreclosure Prevention Profession-
   als [2899]
Natl. Assn. of Housing Cooperatives [12185]
Natl. Assn. of Housing Counselors and Agencies
   [1784]
Natl. Assn. of Housing Info. Managers [5519]
Natl. Assn. of Housing and Redevelopment Of-
   ficials [5520]
Natl. Assn. of Local Housing Finance Agencies
   [5521]
Natl. Center for Housing Mgt. [12186]
Natl. Community Development Assn. [17387]
Natl. Coun. on Agricultural Life and Labor Res.
   Fund [12187]
Natl. Coun. of State Housing Agencies [5522]
Natl. Fair Housing Alliance [17800]
Natl. Found. of Manufactured Home Owners
   [12188]
Natl. Housing Conf. [12189]
Natl. Housing Inst. [12190]
Natl. Housing Law Proj. [5523]
Natl. Housing and Rehabilitation Assn. [12191]
Natl. Leased Housing Assn. [12192]
Natl. Low Income Housing Coalition [12193]
Natl. Neighborhood Coalition [17389]
Natl. Org. of African Americans in Housing
   [12194]
Natl. Rsrc. Center on Homelessness and Mental
   Illness [12164]
Natl. Rural Housing Coalition [12195]
Natl. Shared Housing Rsrc. Center [12196]
NeighborWorks Am. [12197]
New Hope Constr. [12198]
Professional Housing Mgt. Assn. [5524]
Public Housing Authorities Directors Assn. [5525]
Real Estate Investment Securities Assn. [1785]
Rebuilding Alliance [12199]
Rebuilding Alliance [12199]
Rebuilding Together [12200]
Red Feather Development Gp. [12201]
RV Mfrs'. Clubs Assn. [22146]
Scottish Churches Housing Action [20385]Hous-
   ingScottish Fed. of Housing Associations
The Shelter Alliance [11634]
Systems Building Res. Alliance [1786]
Tile Partners for Humanity [12202]
Tile Partners for Humanity [12202]
Urban Homesteading Assistance Bd. [12203]
World Orphans [11433]
Housing Assistance Coun. [12181], 1025 Vermont
   Ave. NW, Ste. 606, Washington, DC 20005,
   (202)842-8600
Housing Inspection Found. [1916], 810 N Farrell Dr.,
   Palm Springs, CA 92262, (760)327-5284
Housing Inspection Foundation/Association of Home
   Inspectors [★1916]
Housing Statistics Users Gp. [5516], Natl. Assn. of
   Home Builders, 1201 15th St. NW, Washington,
   DC 20005, (202)266-8441
Housing Works [13611], 57 Willoughby St., 2nd Fl.,
   Brooklyn, NY 11201, (347)473-7400
Housman Soc. [IO], Bromsgrove, United Kingdom
Hovawart Club of North Am. [21579], Utah Felhaber-
   Smith, Membership Dir., 4718 NE 14th Pl.,
   Portland, OR 97211
Hoverclub of Am. [★21860]
Hovercraft
   Hovercraft Club of Am. [21860]HovercraftHover-
      craft Club of Great Britain

Hovercraft Club of Am. [21860], PO Box 908, Foley,
   AL 36536-0908, (251)946-3800
Hovercraft Club of Great Britain [IO], Bolton, United
   Kingdom
Howard Hughes Medical Inst. [15343], 4000 Jones
   Bridge Rd., Chevy Chase, MD 20815-6720,
   (301)215-8500
Howard Hughes Medical Inst. [15343], 4000 Jones
   Bridge Rd., Chevy Chase, MD 20815-6720,
   (301)215-8500
Howard Jarvis Taxpayers Assn. [18686], 621 S
   Westmoreland Ave., Ste. 202, Los Angeles, CA
   90005, (213)384-9656
Howard League for Penal Reform [IO], London,
   United Kingdom
Howth Sea Angling Club [IO], Howth, Ireland
Hoyres Hovedorganisasjon [★IO]
Hoyt Family Assn. - Address unknown since 2011.
HR Policy Assn. [18043], 1100 13th St. NW, Ste.
   850, Washington, DC 20005, (202)789-8670
HR Soc. [IO], Hampshire, United Kingdom
Hrvatska udruga fizioterapeuta [★IO]
Hrvatski orijentacijski savez [★IO]
Hrvatski klizacki savez [★IO]
Hrvatski Atletski Savez [★IO]
Hrvatski Badmintonski Savez [★IO]
Hrvatski Baseball Savez [★IO]
Hrvatski Biciklisticki Savez [★IO]
Hrvatski Crveni Kriz [★IO]
Hrvatski Ferijalni i Hostelski Savez [★IO]
Hrvatski Hokejski Savez [★IO]
Hrvatski Jedrilicarski Savez [★IO]
Hrvatski Kajakaski Savez [★IO]
Hrvatski Nogometni Savez [★IO]
Hrvatski Olimpijski Odbor [★IO]
Hrvatski Rock'n'Roll Savez [★IO]
Hrvatski Sahovski Savez [★IO]
Hrvatski Savez Mladeskih Udruga [★IO]
Hrvatski Savez Slijepih [★IO]
Hrvatski Sportski Plesni Savez [★IO]
Hrvatski Sportski Savez Invalida [★IO]
Hrvatski Squash Savez [★IO]
Hrvatski Strelicarski Savez [★IO]
Hrvatski Taekwondo Savez [★IO]
Hrvatski Teniski Savez [★IO]
Hrvatski Zrakoplovni Savez [★IO]
Hrvatsko fizikalno drustvo [★IO]
Hrvatsko drustvo za medicinsku informatiku [★IO]
Hrvatsko drustvo za zdravstvenu ekologiju [★IO]
Hrvatsko mikroskopijsko drustvo [★IO]
Hrvatsko Drustvo Farmakologa [★IO]
Hrvatsko Drustvo Kemijskih Inzenjera i Tehnologa
   [★IO]
Hrvatsko Drustvo Skladatelja [★IO]
Hrvatsko Drustvo za Zastitu Ptica i Prirode [★IO]
Hrvatsko Entomolosko Drustvo [★IO]
Hrvatsko Farmaceutsko Drustvo [★IO]
Hrvatsko Geotehnicko Drustvo [★IO]
Hrvatsko Kardiolosko Drustvo [★IO]
Hrvatsko Stomatolosko Drustvo [★IO]
HSUS Animal Control Acad. [★10984]
HTML Writers Guild [6536], 119 E Union St., Ste. F,
   Pasadena, CA 91103, (626)449-3709
Hubbell Family Historical Soc. [20536], 4220 Byrum
   Rd., Onondaga, MI 49264-9716
Hubbell Family Historical Soc. [20536], 4220 Byrum
   Rd., Onondaga, MI 49264-9716
Hububat-Bakliyat-Yagli ve Mamuelleri Ihracatcilari
   Birligi [★IO]
Hudson-Essex-Terraplane Club [21070], Charlotte
   Sargent, PO Box 8412, Wichita, KS 67208-0412,
   (316)838-1126
Hudson Essex Terraplane Historical Soc. [21071], 3
   Silver Queen Ct., Park City, UT 84060, (435)657-
   0443
Hudson Family Assn. [20537], 3570 Coco Lake Dr.,
   Coconut Creek, FL 33073
Hudson Inst. [18465], 1015 15th St. NW, 6th Fl.,
   Washington, DC 20005, (202)974-2400
Hudson River Sloop Clearwater [9699], 724 Wolcott
   Ave., Beacon, NY 12508, (845)265-8080
Hudson River Sloop Restoration, Inc. [★9699]
Huettentechnische Vereinigung der Deutschen Glas-
   industrie [★IO]
HUG [★6519]

Hug-A-Tree and Survive - Address unknown since
   2010.
HUG Intl. - HTE Users' Gp. [★6519]
Hug Teva - Defunct.
Hugh O'Brian Youth Found. [★8485]
Hugh O'Brian Youth Leadership [8485], 31255
   Cedar Valley Dr., Ste. 327, Westlake Village, CA
   91362, (818)851-3980
Hughes Medical Inst; Howard [15343]
Hughes Medical Inst; Howard [15343]
Hugs for Our Soldiers [11092], PO Box 532, Vonore,
   TN 37885
Hugs Proj. [11093], 7000 Crossroads Blvd., No.
   1048, Oklahoma City, OK 73149
Huguenot
   Huguenot Historical Soc. [20667]
   Huguenot Soc. of the Founders of Manakin in the
      Colony of Virginia [20668]
   Natl. Huguenot Soc. [20669]
Huguenot Historical Soc. [20667], 18 Broadhead
   Ave., New Paltz, NY 12561-1403, (845)255-1660
Huguenot Soc. of the Founders of Manakin in the
   Colony of Virginia [20668], 981 Huguenot Trail,
   Midlothian, VA 23113, (804)794-5702
Huguenot Soc. of Great Britain and Ireland [IO],
   London, United Kingdom
Huileries de France [IO], Paris, France
Hull and Humber Chamber of Commerce, Indus. and
   Shipping [IO], Hull, United Kingdom
Hull Pottery Assn. [21349], 13199 Rambo Rd.,
   Crooksville, OH 43731, (740)982-2643
Human Anatomy and Physiology Soc. [13732], Sha-
   nan Molnar, Bus. Mgr., PO Box 2945, LaGrange,
   GA 30241-2945, (315)792-5363
Human Appeal Intl. [IO], Manchester, United
   Kingdom
Human Appeal Intl. - United Arab Emirates [IO], Aj-
   man, United Arab Emirates
Human Assistance and Development Intl. [20131],
   PO Box 4598, Culver City, CA 90231-4598,
   (310)642-0006
Human Assistance and Development Intl. [20131],
   PO Box 4598, Culver City, CA 90231-4598,
   (310)642-0006
Human Behavior and Evolution Soc. [6255],
   Gretchen Walker, Univ. of Nebraska, Center for
   Great Plains Stud., 1155 Q St., Lincoln, NE 68588-
   0214
Human Biology Assn. [6300], Indiana Univ., Dept. of
   Anthropology, 130 Student Bldg., 701 E Kirkwood
   Ave., Bloomington, IN 47405, (812)856-4993
Human and Civil Rights Organizations of Am.
   [11524], 10 Chestnut St., Salem, MA 01970-3131,
   (978)744-2608
Human Concern Intl. [IO], Ottawa, ON, Canada
Human Development
   Abriendo Mentes [12950]
   All Our Children Intl. Outreach [11183]
   Amer. Assn. of Human Design Practitioners
      [1036]
   Amer. Creativity Assn. [9819]
   Amer. Men's Stud. Assn. [12204]
   Arica Inst. [9820]
   Arica Inst. [9820]
   Assn. of Camphill Communities [2956]
   Assn. for Transpersonal Psychology [9821]
   Breaking Ground [11552]
   Change Exchange [12205]
   The Change Exchange [12205]
   Christian Action and Relief for Haiti [12820]
   Cultural Survival [9822]
   Cultural Survival [9822]
   Earthstewards Network [12206]
   Earthstewards Network [12206]
   Edurelief [12834]
   Enrichment Educ. [8276]
   Esalen Inst. [9823]
   Feathered Pipe Found. [12207]
   Fields of Growth Intl. [12416]
   Friends of the Children of Angola [11284]
   HandReach [11517]
   Hanuman Found. [12208]
   Himalayan Inst. [12209]
   Himalayan Inst. [12209]
   Human Development and Capability Assn.
      [12210]

Reference to "IO" in place of a book number signifies that the association may be found in the 50th edition of International Organizations.

Encyclopedia of Associations, 51st Edition | 2861

Humanity [6945]
Humanity [6945]
Huna Res. [12211]
Huna Res. [12211]
Imagery Intl. [15073]
Inner Peace Movement [9824]
Inst. of Cultural Affairs [12212]
Inst. of Cultural Affairs Intl. Belgium
[4825]HumanInst. of Cultural Affairs Japan
Inst. for the Development of the Harmonious Human Being [12213]
Inst. of HeartMath [9825]
Inst. for Individual and World Peace [12214]
Inst. for Individual and World Peace [12214]
Inst. for the Stud. of Human Knowledge [9826]
Inst. for Theological Encounter With Sci. and Tech. [12215]
Intl. Assn. for Human Values [12216]
Intl. Children Assistance Network [11323]
Intl. Soc. for a Complete Earth [12217]
Intl. Soc. for a Complete Earth [12217]
Intl. Soc. for Intelligence Res. [7002]
Kids Home Intl. [11334]
Krishnamurti Found. of Am. [12218]
Lama Found. [9827]
Larger Than Life [11341]
Learning Light Found. [9828]
Libraries Without Borders [8519]
Mandala Soc. [12219]
Men's Rsrc. Center [12220]
Natl. Alliance to Nurture the Aged and the Youth [12221]
Natl. Study Group on Chronic Disorganization [9829]
New Road Map Found. [12222]
Orphans Africa [11621]
Quartus Found. for Spiritual Res. [12223]
Rain for the Sahel and Sahara [12359]
Restore Humanity [12362]
Sacred Passage and the Way of Nature Fellowship [12224]
Sacred Passage and the Way of Nature Fellowship [12224]
School of Living [9830]
Seeds For Hope [11861]
Seeds of HOPE Intl. [11403]
Sky of Love [11406]
Soc. for the Stud. of Human Development [6946]
Somatics Soc. [12225]
SustainUS [13559]
Teleos Inst. [12226]
TransWorld Development Initiatives [12262]
Unarius Acad. of Sci. [12227]
Unarius Acad. of Sci. [12227]
UNITED SIKHS [12228]
Venture Scotland [623]
Well-Springs Found. [9831]
Wilbur Hot Springs Hea. Sanctuary [9832]
World Peace One [12229]
World Peace One [12229]
Youth Action Intl. [11436]
Human Development and Capability Assn. [12210], Boston Univ., 67 Bay State Rd., Boston, MA 02215, (617)358-6054
Human Development Rsrc. Coun. [12932], PMB 262, 655 Sugarloaf Pkwy., Ste. 307, Duluth, GA 30097-4934, (770)513-0060
Human Ecology Action League [14502], PO Box 509, Stockbridge, GA 30281, (770)389-4519
Human Engineering
Human Factors and Ergonomics Soc. [6947]
MTM Assn. for Standards and Res. [6948]
Natl. Assn. of Professional Organizers [6949]
Proj. on Tech., Work and Character [6950]
Human Environmental League for Preservation - Nepal [IO], Kathmandu, Nepal
Human Factors and Ergonomics Soc. [6947], PO Box 1369, Santa Monica, CA 90406-1369, (310)394-1811
Human Factors and Ergonomics Soc. of Australia [IO], Baulkham Hills, Australia
Human Factors Soc. [★6947]
Human Friends Org. [IO], Lahore, Pakistan
Human Genetics Soc. of Australasia [IO], Alexandra, Australia

Human Genetics Soc. of Australasia - New South Wales Br. [IO], Waratah, Australia
Human Genetics Soc. of Australasia - Queensland Br. [IO], Herston, Australia
Human Genome Org. [IO], Singapore, Singapore
Human Genome Variation Soc. [IO], Carlton, Australia
Human Growth [★16279]
Human Growth Found. [16279], 997 Glen Cove Ave., Ste. 5, Glen Head, NY 11545, (516)671-4041
Human Life Center - Defunct.
Human Life Found. [12933], 353 Lexington Ave., Ste. 802, New York, NY 10016, (212)685-5210
Human Life Intl. [12934], 4 Family Life Ln., Front Royal, VA 22630, (800)549-5433
Human Life Intl. [12934], 4 Family Life Ln., Front Royal, VA 22630, (800)549-5433
Human Life Intl. - Argentina [IO], Buenos Aires, Argentina
Human Life Intl. - Austria [IO], Vienna, Austria
Human Life Intl. - Belgium [IO], Mechelen, Belgium
Human Life Intl. - Bolivia [IO], Cochabamba, Bolivia
Human Life Intl. - Brazil [IO], Brasilia, Brazil
Human Life Intl. - Cameroon [IO], Douala, Cameroon
Human Life Intl. - Chile [IO], Santiago, Chile
Human Life Intl. - Colombia [IO], Bogota, Colombia
Human Life Intl. - Croatia [IO], Vetovo, Croatia
Human Life Intl. - El Salvador [IO], San Salvador, El Salvador
Human Life Intl. - Germany [IO], Essen, Germany
Human Life Intl. - Hungary [IO], Budapest, Hungary
Human Life Intl. - India [IO], Mumbai, India
Human Life Intl. - Ireland [IO], Dublin, Ireland
Human Life Intl. - Italy [IO], Rome, Italy
Human Life Intl. - Japan [IO], Kochi, Japan
Human Life Intl. - Kenya [IO], Nyeri, Kenya
Human Life Intl. - Latvia [IO], Riga, Latvia
Human Life Intl. - Lithuania [IO], Kaunas, Lithuania
Human Life Intl. - Malaysia [IO], Sarawak, Malaysia
Human Life Intl. - Paraguay [IO], Asuncion, Paraguay
Human Life Intl. - Poland [IO], Gdansk, Poland
Human Life Intl. - Romania [IO], Timisoara, Romania
Human Life Intl. - Singapore [IO], Singapore, Singapore
Human Life Intl. - South Africa [IO], Milnerton, Republic of South Africa
Human Life Intl. - South Korea [IO], Daegu, Republic of Korea
Human Life Intl. - Switzerland [IO], Zug, Switzerland
Human Life Intl. - Tanzania [IO], Dar es Salaam, United Republic of Tanzania
Human Life Intl. - Ukraine [IO], Kiev, Ukraine
Human Life Intl. - Zimbabwe [IO], Harare, Zimbabwe
Human Life Issues
After Death Commun. Res. Found. [15072]
Exit Poverty Empowerment [11067]
Girls Educational and Mentoring Services [18603]
Human Life Found. [12933]
Natl. Pro-Life Alliance [18558]
One More Soul [18561]
Peace of Art [10354]
Sacred Dying Found. [11747]
TeamPact [18631]
Transitions Global [12248]
Vietnamese Alliance to Combat Trafficking [12251]
Human Potential
Assn. for the Development of Human Potential [9833]
Feldenkrais Guild of North Am. [9834]
Feldenkrais Guild of North Am. [9834]
Human Development and Capability Assn. [12210]
Imagery Intl. [15073]
Intl. Imagery Assn. [9835]
Intl. Imagery Assn. [9835]
Human Relations
Giraffe Heroes Proj. [9836]
Golden Rule Found. [9837]
Golden Rule Found. [9837]
Human Development and Capability Assn. [12210]
Human Relations Area Files [9838]

Initiatives of Change [17801]
Initiatives of Change [17801]
Intl. Peace Inst. [17802]
Intl. Peace Inst. [17802]
Lucis Trust [17803]
Lucis Trust [17803]
New Dimensions Radio [17804]
New Dimensions Radio [17804]
World Goodwill U.S.A. [17805]
World Goodwill U.S.A. [17805]
Human Relations Area Files [9838], 755 Prospect St., New Haven, CT 06511-1225, (203)764-9401
Human Relief Org. [IO], Islamabad, Pakistan
Human Rsrc. Certification Inst. [2628], 1800 Duke St., Alexandria, VA 22314, (703)548-3440
Human Rsrc. Development Network [IO], Islamabad, Pakistan
Human Rsrc. Planning Soc. [2284], 401 N Michigan Ave., Ste. 2200, Chicago, IL 60611, (312)321-6805
Human Resources
America's Edge [17599]
Cable and Telecommunications Human Resources Assn. [1787]
Human Resources Outsourcing Assn. [1788]
Natl. Assn. of African Americans in Human Resources [1789]
Natl. Assn. of Professional Background Screeners [1790]
Natl. Coalition of Healthcare Recruiters [15298]
Natl. Org. for Career Credentialing [727]
Recruitment Process Outsourcing Assn. [1791]
SHRM Global Forum [2631]
Work for Progress [12583]
Human Resources Assn. of Calgary [IO], Calgary, AB, Canada
Human Resources Benchmarking Assn. [666], 4606 FM 1960 W, Ste. 250, Houston, TX 77069-9949, (281)440-5044
Human Resources Center [★11751]
Human Resources Outsourcing Assn. [1788], 600 Pennsylvania Ave. NW, Ste. 900, Washington, DC 20004, (202)905-0351
Human Resources Res. Org. [6256], 66 Canal Center Plz., Ste. 700, Alexandria, VA 22314-1591, (703)549-3611
Human Resources Social Welfare Soc. [IO], Charsadda, Pakistan
Human Rights
AAAS Sci. and Human Rights Coalition [17806]
- Advancing Human Rights [17807]
Advocates Intl. [5640]
Africa Network [17808]
African Gender Inst. [4587]
All of Us or None [17256]
Alliance for Human Res. Protection [17809]
Alliance for Intl. Women's Rights [18804]
Amer. Assn. for the Intl. Commn. of Jurists [17810]
Amer. Assn. for the Intl. Commn. of Jurists [17810]
Amer. Civil Rights Union [17263]
Amer. Family Rights Assn. [17622]
Amer. Libyan Freedom Alliance [17513]Human-Amnesty Intl. - Algeria
Amnesty Intl. - Argentina [16567]
Amnesty Intl. - Australia, NSW Br. [16570]Human-Amnesty Intl. - Austria
Amnesty Intl. - Bermuda [13570]
Amnesty Intl. - Chile [3924]
Amnesty Intl. - Cote d'Ivoire [3165]
Amnesty Intl. - Faroe Islands [18320]
Amnesty Intl. - Ireland [8657]
Amnesty Intl. - Malaysia [14188]
Amnesty Intl. - Norway [2137]
Amnesty Intl. - Puerto Rico [17811]
Amnesty Intl. - Puerto Rico [17811]
Amnesty Intl. - Senegal [1197]
Amnesty Intl. - Swiss Sect. [1980]
Amnesty Intl. of the U.S.A. [17812]
Amnesty Intl. of the U.S.A. [17812]
Armed Females of Am. [17682]
Artists for Human Rights [17813]
Artists United for Social Justice [18640]
Asian-American Network Against Abuse of Human Rights [17814]

A star before a book entry number signifies that the name is not listed separately, but is mentioned within the entry.

Asian-American Network Against Abuse of Human Rights [17814]
Atheists For Human Rights [17207]
Atticus Circle [17735]
Bastard Nation: The Adoptee Rights Org. [10782]
Bilateral Safety Corridor Coalition [12230]
Breakthrough [17815]
Burmese Amer. Democratic Alliance [17213]
Canadian Coalition Against the Death Penalty [1968]
Castle Coalition [18403]
Center for Civil and Human Rights [12231]
Center of Concern [17816]
Center of Concern [17816]
Center for Intl. Policy [17817]
Center for Intl. Policy [17817]
Center for Religious Freedom [17818]
Center for Religious Freedom [17818]
Child Protection Intl. [11222]
Citizens Equal Rights Alliance [12232]
Coalition to Abolish Slavery and Trafficking [12233]
Coalition Against Genocide [17738]
Coalition Against Trafficking in Women [17819]
Coalition Against Trafficking in Women [17819]
Coalition for Peace with Justice [18236]
COLAGE [12074]
Comm. of Concerned Scientists [17820]
Comm. on Human Rights [17821]
CorpWatch [17822]
CorpWatch [17822]
Crime Survivors [17487]
Dalit Freedom Network [17823]
Dalit Solidarity [17824]
Darfur Human Rights Org. [17825]
Darfur Human Rights Org. [17825]
Disabled Drummers Assn. [11780]
Discussion Club [17285]
Drishtipat Worldwide [11124]
Dwa Fanm [17826]
EarthRights Intl. [17827]
EarthRights Intl. [17827]
Ensaaf [18641]
European-American Unity and Rights Org. [17288]
Exit Poverty Empowerment [11067]
Facing History and Ourselves Natl. Found. [9764]
Faith Alliance Against Slavery and Trafficking [17289]
Falun Data Info. Center [17828]
FORCES Intl. [17829]
Free Expression Policy Proj. [17290]
Free the Slaves [12234]
Friends of Africa Intl. [17830]
Friends of Africa Intl. [17830]
From Us With Love [12235]
From Us With Love [12235]
Genocide Intervention Network [17739]
Giraffe Club [18680]
Girls Educational and Mentoring Services [18603]
Global Action on Widowhood [18787]
Global Grassroots [13497]
Global Jewish Assistance and Relief Network [12236]
Global Jewish Assistance and Relief Network [12236]
Global Rights [17831]
Global Rights [17831]
Global Youth Connect [18828]
Hagar USA [12237]
Hands Across the Mideast Support Alliance [18124]
Healing the Divide [12238]
Healing the Divide [12238]
Help Darfur Now [17741]
Hope Through Hea. [12385]
Human Rights Advocates [12239]
Human Rights in China [12240]
Human Rights First [17832]
Human Rights First [17832]
Human Rights Rsrc. Center [17833]
Human Rights Watch [17834]
Human Rights Watch [17834]
Human Rights Watch Asia [17835]
Human Rights Watch - Asia [17835]

Human Rights Watch - Helsinki [17836]
Human Rights Watch - Helsinki [17836]
Humanity in Action [8277]
Humanity in Action [8277]
Innocents at Risk [12241]
Insight Arts [9293]
Inst. for Humane Stud. [12242]
Inst. for the Stud. of Genocide [17837]
Inst. for the Stud. of Genocide [17837]
Inst. for the Stud. of Human Rights [17838]
Inter-American Commn. on Human Rights [17839]
Inter-American Commn. on Human Rights [17839]
Intl. Assn. of Former Soviet Political Prisoners and Victims of the Communist Regime [17840]
Intl. Assn. of Former Soviet Political Prisoners and Victims of the Communist Regime [17840]
Intl. Assn. of Official Human Rights Agencies [12243]
Intl. Assn. of Official Human Rights Agencies [12243]
Intl. Center for Transitional Justice [17841]
Intl. Center for Transitional Justice [17841]
Intl. Justice and Human Rights, Natl. Coun. of Churches of Christ USA [12246]
Intl. Justice Mission [12244]
Intl. Justice Mission [12244]
Intl. League for Human Rights [17842]
Intl. League for Human Rights [17842]
Intl. Refugee Rights Initiative [17843]
Intl. Refugee Rights Initiative [17843]
Intl. Women's Rights Action Watch [17844]
Intl. Women's Rights Action Watch [17844]
Invisible Children [17237]
Iran Democratic Union [17845]
Iraqi Human Rights Network [17846]
Iraqi Human Rights Network [17846]
Irish Natl. Caucus [18007]
Jacob Blaustein Inst. for the Advancement of Human Rights [17847]
Jewish World Watch [17743]
Karen Natl. League [18722]
Laogai Res. Found. [17848]
Laogai Res. Found. [17848]
Lebanese Amer. Coun. for Democracy [18069]
Magnus Hirschfeld Center for Human Rights [17849]
Magnus Hirschfeld Center for Human Rights [17849]
Meiklejohn Civil Liberties Inst. [12245]
Middle East Children's Alliance [17850]
Middle East Children's Alliance [17850]
Mind Justice [17851]
Mind Justice [17851]
MindFreedom Intl. [17852]
Mission for Est. of Human Rights in Iran [17853]
Mission for Est. of Human Rights in Iran [17853]
Natl. Advocates for Pregnant Women [17854]
Natl. Coalition of Anti-Violence Programs [18770]
Natl. Coalition of Pro-Democracy Advocates [17526]
Natl. Coming Out Day [12102]
Natl. Coun. of Churches of Christ USA | Intl. Justice and Human Rights [12246]
Natl. Economic and Social Rights Initiative [17855]
Natl. Minorities with Disabilities Coalition [17545]
Natl. Org. of Fed. Employees Against Abuse and Retaliation [23206]
Natl. Org. for Men Against Sexism [17856]
Natl. Org. of Sisters of Color Ending Sexual Assault [13093]
North Korea Freedom Coalition [18035]
Not on Our Watch [17857]
OneWorld United States [17858]
OneWorld U.S. [17858]
Patient Privacy Rights [18104]
People for the Amer. Way [17317]
People's Decade of Human Rights Educ. [17859]
People's Movement for Human Rights Learning [17859]
Physicians for Human Rights [17860]
Physicians for Human Rights [17860]
Picture the Homeless [17792]
Polaris Proj. [17861]
Proj. on Ethnic Relations [17862]

Protection Proj. [12247]
Responsible Endowments Coalition [9082]
Restore Humanity [12362]
Ruckus Soc. [18222]
Save Darfur Coalition [17744]
South Asian Americans Leading Together [18644]
Survivors of Torture Intl. [17863]
Torture Abolition and Survivors Support Coalition Intl. [17864]
Torture Abolition and Survivors Support Coalition Intl. [17864]
Trans Youth Family Allies [12585]
Transitions Global [12248]
UNANIMA Intl. [18645]
uNight [11423]
U.S. Copts Assn. [12249]
U.S. Copts Assn. [12249]
U.S. Off. on Colombia [17956]
U.S.-Tibet Comm. [18726]
Universal Human Rights Network [17865]
Uplift Intl. [15220]
US Human Rights Network [17866]
US Human Rights Network [17866]
Uyghur Amer. Assn. [17867]
Uyghur Amer. Assn. [17867]
Veterans and Military Families for Progress [20815]
Vietnam Human Rights Network [12250]
Vietnam Human Rights Network [12250]
Vietnamese Alliance to Combat Trafficking [12251]
Washington Off. on Latin Am. [18058]
WITNESS [17868]
Women for Afghan Women [12252]
Women for Afghan Women [12252]
Women Watch Afrika [18797]
Women's Alliance for Peace and Human Rights in Afghanistan [12253]
Women's Alliance for Peace and Human Rights in Afghanistan [12253]
Women's Voices Now [18807]
World Org. for Human Rights USA [12254]
World Org. for Human Rights USA [12254]
Youth for Human Rights Intl. [12255]
Youth for Human Rights Intl. [12255]
Human Rights Advocates [12239], PO Box 5675, Berkeley, CA 94705
Human Rights Campaign [12090], 1640 Rhode Island Ave. NW, Washington, DC 20036-3278, (202)628-4160
Human Rights Campaign Fund's Mobilization Proj. [★12090]
Human Rights in China [12240], 350 Fifth Ave., Ste. 3311, New York, NY 10118, (212)239-4495
Human Rights Comm. [IO], Auckland, New Zealand
Human Rights Documentation Exchange [18053], PO Box 2327, Austin, TX 78768, (512)476-9841
Human Rights Documentation Exchange [18053], PO Box 2327, Austin, TX 78768, (512)476-9841
Human Rights Educ. Radio Listener Clubs [IO], Kathmandu, Nepal
Human Rights First [17832], 333 7th Ave., 13th Fl., New York, NY 10001-5108, (212)845-5200
Human Rights First [17832], 333 7th Ave., 13th Fl., New York, NY 10001-5108, (212)845-5200
Human Rights Info. and Documentation Systems Intl. [IO], Versoix, Switzerland
Human Rights Inst. of the Bar of Bordeaux [IO], Bordeaux, France
Human Rights and Intl. Affairs [★12246]
Human Rights and Intl. Affairs [★12246]
Human Rights Internet [IO], Ottawa, ON, Canada
Human Rights Monitor [IO], Tehran, Iran
Human Rights Political Action Comm. - Defunct.
Human Rights and Race Relations Centre [IO], Toronto, ON, Canada
Human Rights Res. and Educ. Centre [IO], Ottawa, ON, Canada
Human Rights Rsrc. Center [17833], Univ. of Minnesota Law School, Mondale Hall, 229 19th Ave. S, Ste. N-120, Minneapolis, MN 55455, (612)626-0041
Human Rights Watch [17834], 350 5th Ave., 34th Fl., New York, NY 10118-3299, (212)290-4700
Human Rights Watch [17834], 350 5th Ave., 34th Fl., New York, NY 10118-3299, (212)290-4700

Reference to "IO" in place of a book number signifies that the association may be found in the 50th edition of International Organizations.

Human Rights Watch Asia [17835], 350 5th Ave., 34th Fl., New York, NY 10118-3299, (212)290-4700
Human Rights Watch - Asia [17835], 350 5th Ave., 34th Fl., New York, NY 10118-3299, (212)290-4700
Human Rights Watch | Children's Rights Div. [11317], 350 5th Ave., 34th Fl., New York, NY 10118, (212)290-4700
Human Rights Watch | Children's Rights Div. [11317], 350 5th Ave., 34th Fl., New York, NY 10118, (212)290-4700
Human Rights Watch - Helsinki [17836], 350 5th Ave., 34th Fl., New York, NY 10118-3299, (212)290-4700
Human Rights Watch - Helsinki [17836], 350 5th Ave., 34th Fl., New York, NY 10118-3299, (212)290-4700
Human Rights for Women [IO], Tubingen, Germany
Human Sciences Res. Coun. [IO], Pretoria, Republic of South Africa
Human Ser. Educ; Coun. for Standards in [8867]
Human Services
1-2-3 Intl. [12573]
1000 Jobs [12713]
Adventrek [12256]
Adventrek [12256]
Afghans4Tomorrow [11541]
African Sky [11542]
AfriHope Intl., Inc. [10806]
Amer. Assn. of Ser. Coordinators [1792]
Amer. Public Human Services Assn. | Natl. Coun. of State Human Ser. Administrators [13171]
Aniz [12257]
Be The Change Intl. [13344]
Because Intl. [12718]
Blessings on Africa [12719]
Breaking Ground [11552]
Care 2 Share [13373]
Care Highway Intl. [12814]
CHAP Intl. [12817]
CHEER for Viet Nam [13374]
Chefs for Humanity [12267]
Choices [12258]
Christian Action and Relief for Haiti [12820]
Compassion First [12827]
Coun. for Zimbabwe [12322]
Deaf Friends Intl. [12138]
Elwyn [12259]
Enable Intl. [13156]
Ethiopian Orphan Relief [11271]
For Victims of War and Poverty [12455]
Friends of the Children of Angola [11284]
Global AIDS Interfaith Alliance [13607]
Hands to Hearts Intl. [11298]
HandsNet [12581]
Helping Hand for Nepal [12847]
Hope Through Hea. [12385]
Human Touch Intl. [13589]
HumaniNet [12848]
Humanitarian Intl. Ser. Gp. [12260]
Humanitarian Travels Intl. [13338]
Intl. Assn. for Human Values [12216]
Irob Relief and Rehabilitation Operations Brotherhood [11986]
Island Aid [11858]
Israel Humanitarian Found. [12393]
Kindness in a Box [11339]
Matanya's Hope [12737]
Mercy Beyond Borders [12738]
Natl. Alliance for Direct Support Professionals [1793]
Natl. Energy Assistance Directors' Assn. [1794]
Neighbors Without Borders [12350]
Nepal SEEDS: Social Educational Environmental Development Services in Nepal [11615]
NextAid [11369]
Not on Our Watch [17857]
Oneworld Works [12354]
Opportunity International-U.S.A. [12261]
Outreach Africa [11386]
Outreach Asia [11116]
Pilgrim Africa [12878]
Read Horn of Africa USA [12360]
Rebuilding Haiti Now [12881]

Relief for Africa [12882]
Rsrc. Development Intl. Cambodia [12361]
RISE-UP From Poverty [12751]
Scattering Resources [12888]
Seeds of HOPE Intl. [11403]
Software and Tech. Vendors' Assn. [819]
TransWorld Development Initiatives [12262]
TransWorld Development Initiatives [12262]
Tusubira - We Have Hope [12755]
United Nations | Vietnam Relief Effort [13372]
U.S.A. Harvest [12298]
Vietnamese Alliance to Combat Trafficking [12251]
Village Focus Intl. [11650]
Village Missions Intl. [11651]
World Action for Humanity [13120]
Worldhealer [12384]
Human Services Assembly; Natl. [13401]
Human Services Assn; Amer. Public [13169]
Human Touch Intl. [13589], PO Box 1549, West Chester, OH 45071, (513)593-1850
Human-Wildlife Conflict Collaboration [5014], 5410 Grosvenor Ln., Ste. 200, Bethesda, MD 20814-2144, (202)986-0067
Human Writes [IO], Colchester, United Kingdom
Humane Farm Animal Care [10982], PO Box 727, Herndon, VA 20172, (703)435-3883
Humane Farming Assn. [10983], PO Box 3577, San Rafael, CA 94912, (415)485-1495
Humane Res. Australia [IO], Malvern, Australia
Humane Slaughter Assn. [IO], Wheathampstead, United Kingdom
Humane Soc. of Dominica [IO], Roseau, Dominica
Humane Soc. Intl. - Australia [IO], Avalon, Australia
Humane Soc. of the U.S. [10984], 2100 L St. NW, Washington, DC 20037, (202)452-1100
Humane Soc. Veterinary Medical Assn. [10985], 2100 L St. NW, Washington, DC 20037, (202)452-1100
Humane Soc. Youth [10986], 67 Norwich Essex Tpke., East Haddam, CT 06423-1736, (860)434-8666
HumanHorizons.Net [IO], Victoria, BC, Canada
HumaniNet [12848], 4068 Ridge Ct., West Linn, OR 97068-8285, (503)957-2960
HumaniNet [12848], 4068 Ridge Ct., West Linn, OR 97068-8285, (503)957-2960
Humanism
Amer. Ethical Union [19817]
Amer. Humanist Assn. [19818]
Aspen Inst. [9839]
Coun. for Secular Humanism [19819]
Coun. for Secular Humanism [19819]
Family of Humanists [9840]
Intl. Fed. for Secular Humanistic Judaism [19820]
Intl. Fed. for Secular Humanistic Judaism [19820]
Secular Student Alliance [17869]
Washington Ethical Soc. [19821]
Humanist Assn. of Ireland [IO], Dublin, Ireland
Humanist Inst. for Cooperation with Developing Countries [IO], The Hague, Netherlands
Humanist Inst. for Development Co-operation [IO], The Hague, Netherlands
Humanistic Education
Assn. for Humanistic Counseling [8278]
Assn. of Waldorf Schools of North Am. [8279]
Assn. of Waldorf Schools of North Am. [8279]
Secular Student Alliance [17869]
Threefold Educational Found. and School [8280]
Humanistisch Instituut voor Ontwikkelingssamen-werking [★IO]
Humanitarian African Relief Org. [12849], 7364 El Cajon Blvd., Ste. 208, San Diego, CA 92115, (619)741-9260
Humanitarian Aid and Development Org. - Yemen [IO], Sana'a, Yemen
Humanitarian Assistance for the Women and Children of Afghanistan [IO], Kabul, Afghanistan
Humanitarian Assn. of Jewish Women [IO], Baku, Azerbaijan
Humanitarian Intl. Ser. Gp. [12260], 870 Commercial Ln., Palmer Lake, CO 80133, (303)662-0845
Humanitarian Law Proj. [18507], Intl. Educ. Development, 8124 W 3rd St., Ste. 105, Los Angeles, CA 90048, (213)999-1037

Humanitarian Law Proj. [18507], Intl. Educ. Development, 8124 W 3rd St., Ste. 105, Los Angeles, CA 90048, (213)999-1037
Humanitarian Resources Intl. [12850], 522 SW 5th Ave., Ste. 1275, Portland, OR 97204, (503)928-7673
Humanitarian Resources Intl. [12850], 522 SW 5th Ave., Ste. 1275, Portland, OR 97204, (503)928-7673
Humanitarian Services for Children of Vietnam [11318], 2965 Spring Lake Rd. SW, Prior Lake, MN 55372, (952)447-3502
Humanitarian Services for Children of Vietnam [11318], 2965 Spring Lake Rd. SW, Prior Lake, MN 55372, (952)447-3502
Humanitarian Travels Intl. [13338], 37940 42nd St. E, Unit 133, Palmdale, CA 93552, (661)285-3889
Humanitarian Travels Intl. [13338], 37940 42nd St. E, Unit 133, Palmdale, CA 93552, (661)285-3889
Humanitas Intl. Human Rights Comm. - Defunct.
Humanities
Amer. Acad. of Arts and Letters [9841]
Amer. Coun. of Learned Societies [9842]
Community Coll. Humanities Assn. [8281]
Consortium of Humanities Centers and Institutes [12263]
Consortium of Humanities Centers and Institutes [12263]
Fed. of State Humanities Councils [9843]
Humanities Educ. and Res. Assn. [8282]
Intl. Assn. for Comparative Mythology [7133]
Natl. Endowment for the Humanities [5526]
Natl. Humanities Alliance [9844]
Natl. Humanities Center [9845]
Natl. Humanities Inst. [8283]
Natl. Soc. of Arts and Letters [9846]
Renaissance Artists and Writers Assn. [9847]
Soc. for the Humanities [9848]
Southern Humanities Coun. [9849]
Woodrow Wilson Intl. Center for Scholars [9850]
Woodrow Wilson Intl. Center for Scholars [9850]
Humanities Educ. and Res. Assn. [8282], PO Box 715, Pacifica, CA 94044
Humanity [6945], 5042 Wilshire Blvd., No. 14334, Los Angeles, CA 90036, (310)916-9676
Humanity [6945], 5042 Wilshire Blvd., No. 14334, Los Angeles, CA 90036, (310)916-9676
; Humanity [6945]
Humanity in Action [8277], 144 E 39th St., New York, NY 10016, (212)828-6874
Humanity in Action [8277], 144 E 39th St., New York, NY 10016, (212)828-6874
Humanity for Children [16147], 3518 Freemont Ave. N, No. 199, Seattle, WA 98103, (866)406-2006
Humanity First USA [11855], 300 E Lombard St., Ste. 840, Baltimore, MD 21202, (877)994-3872
Humanity United in Giving Internationally
Humanity United in Giving Internationally - Address unknown since 2011.
Humans in Crisis Intl. Corp. [12851], 9417 NW 39th Pl., Sunrise, FL 33351, (615)305-5796
Hume Soc. [IO], Akureyri, Iceland
Humility of Mary Ser. [19432], Sister's of the Humility of Mary, PO Box 706, Villa Maria, PA 16155-0706, (724)964-8920
Humility of Mary Ser. [19432], Sister's of the Humility of Mary, PO Box 706, Villa Maria, PA 16155-0706, (724)964-8920
Hummel Collectors Club - Address unknown since 2010.
Hummingbird Monitoring Network [3848], PO Box 115, Patagonia, AZ 85624
Hummingbird Soc. [3849], 6560 Hwy. 179, Ste. 204, Sedona, AZ 86351, (928)284-2251
Humor
Amer. Humor Stud. Assn. [9851]
Burlington Liars Club [21861]
HUMOR Proj. [9852]
Intl. Assn. of People Who Dine Over the Kitchen Sink [21862]
Intl. Banana Club [21863]
Intl. Banana Club [21863]
Intl. Soc. for Humor Stud. [9853]
Intl. Soc. for Humor Stud. [9853]
Man Will Never Fly Memorial Soc. Internationale [21864]

A star before a book entry number signifies that the name is not listed separately, but is mentioned within the entry.

Marx Brotherhood [23808]
Secret Soc. of Happy People [9854]
HUMOR Proj. [9852], 10 Madison Ave., Saratoga
Springs, NY 12866, (518)587-8770
Humperdinck "Goils" [23838]
The Huna Fellowship [★12211]
The Huna Fellowship [★12211]
Huna Forschungsgesellschaft [★IO]
Huna Res. [12211], 126 Camellia Dr., Cape Gi-
rardeau, MO 63703, (573)334-3478
Huna Res. [12211], 126 Camellia Dr., Cape Gi-
rardeau, MO 63703, (573)334-3478
Huna Res. Assn. [IO], Zurich, Switzerland
Hungarian
Amer. Hungarian Educators' Assn. [8284]
Amer. Hungarian Educators' Assn. [8284]
Amer. Hungarian Fed. [19028]
Amer. Hungarian Found. [19029]
Amer. Hungarian Lib. and Historical Soc. [19030]
Hungarian/American Friendship Soc. [19031]
Hungarian Reformed Fed. of Am. [19032]
Hungarian Scouts Assn. [13020]
Hungarian Acad. of Sciences [IO], Budapest,
Hungary
Hungarian ACM Chap. [IO], Szeged, Hungary
Hungarian Advt. Assn. [IO], Budapest, Hungary
Hungarian Aeronautical Assn. [IO], Budaors,
Hungary
Hungarian Agricultural Journalists Assn. [IO], Budap-
est, Hungary
Hungarian Alliance of Reprographic Rights [IO],
Budapest, Hungary
Hungarian Amer. Coalition [17946], 1120 Con-
necticut Ave. NW, Ste. 280, Washington, DC
20036, (202)296-9505
Hungarian Amer. Coalition [17946], 1120 Con-
necticut Ave. NW, Ste. 280, Washington, DC
20036, (202)296-9505
Hungarian/American Friendship Soc. [19031], 17327
W Carmen Dr., Surprise, AZ 85388, (623)398-0452
Hungarian Anatomical Soc. [IO], Pecs, Hungary
Hungarian Assn. of Competition Law [IO], Budapest,
Hungary
Hungarian Assn. of Customs Affairs [IO], Budapest,
Hungary
Hungarian Assn. for Geo-Information [IO], Budapest,
Hungary
Hungarian Assn. of IT Companies [IO], Budapest,
Hungary
Hungarian Assn. of Landscape Architects [IO],
Budapest, Hungary
Hungarian Assn. of Pedodontics and Orthodontics
[IO], Budapest, Hungary
Hungarian Assn. of Rheumatologists [IO], Budapest,
Hungary
Hungarian Badminton Assn. [IO], Budapest,
Hungary
Hungarian Banking Assn. [IO], Budapest, Hungary
Hungarian Bible Soc. [IO], Budapest, Hungary
Hungarian Biophysical Soc. [IO], Budapest, Hungary
Hungarian Bur. for the Protection of Authors' Rights
[IO], Budapest, Hungary
Hungarian Chap. of the ILAE [IO], Budapest,
Hungary
Hungarian Chem. Indus. Assn. [IO], Budapest,
Hungary
Hungarian Chem. Soc. [IO], Budapest, Hungary
Hungarian Cost Engg. Club [IO], Budapest, Hungary
Hungarian Dancesport Assn. [IO], Budapest,
Hungary
Hungarian Dermatological Soc. [IO], Budapest,
Hungary
Hungarian Economic Assn. [IO], Budapest, Hungary
Hungarian Fed. of Forestry and Wood Indus. [IO],
Budapest, Hungary
Hungarian Floorball Fed. [IO], Budapest, Hungary
Hungarian Franchise Assn. [IO], Budapest, Hungary
Hungarian Freedom Fighters Fed. U.S.A. - Address
unknown since 2010.
Hungarian Geological Soc. [IO], Budapest, Hungary
Hungarian Horse Assn. [★4593]
Hungarian Horse Assn. of Am. [4593], HC 71, Box
108, Anselmo, NE 68813, (308)749-2411
Hungarian Hospice Assn. [IO], Budapest, Hungary
Hungarian Hydrological Soc. [IO], Budapest,
Hungary

Hungarian Lancia Delta Fan Club [IO], Szigetszent-
miklos, Hungary
Hungarian Marketing Assn. [IO], Budapest, Hungary
Hungarian Mining and Metallurgical Soc. [IO],
Budapest, Hungary
Hungarian Multiple Sclerosis Soc. [IO], Szekesfeher-
var, Hungary
Hungarian Natl. Baseball and Softball Fed. [IO],
Budapest, Hungary
Hungarian Natl. Skating Fed. [IO], Budapest,
Hungary
Hungarian Natl. Tourist Off. [IO], Budapest, Hungary
Hungarian Olympic Comm. [IO], Budapest, Hungary
Hungarian Operational Res. Soc. [IO], Budapest,
Hungary
Hungarian Osteoporosis Patients Assn. [IO], Budap-
est, Hungary
Hungarian Pain Soc. [IO], Budapest, Hungary
Hungarian Paralympic Comm. [IO], Budapest,
Hungary
Hungarian Physiological Soc. [IO], Budapest,
Hungary
Hungarian Psychological Assn. [IO], Budapest,
Hungary
Hungarian Publishers and Booksellers Assn. [IO],
Budapest, Hungary
Hungarian Pumi Club of Am. [21580], 24185 Beaver
Dam Dr., Seaford, DE 19973, (302)628-0216
Hungarian Real Estate Assn. [IO], Budapest,
Hungary
Hungarian Red Cross [★IO]
Hungarian Reformed Fed. of Am. [19032], 2001
Massachusetts Ave. NW, Washington, DC 20036-
1011, (202)328-2630
Hungarian Schoolsport Fed. [IO], Budapest,
Hungary
Hungarian Sci. Soc. for Building [IO], Budapest,
Hungary
Hungarian Sci. Soc. of Energy Economics [IO],
Budapest, Hungary
Hungarian Scouts Assn. [13020], 2850 State Rte. 23
N, Newfoundland, NJ 07435-1443, (973)208-0450
Hungarian Soc. for Chemotherapy [IO], Budapest,
Hungary
Hungarian Soc. of Hypertension [IO], Budapest,
Hungary
Hungarian Soc. for Microscopy [IO], Budapest,
Hungary
Hungarian Soc. for Osteoporosis and Osteoarthrol-
ogy [IO], Budapest, Hungary
Hungarian Soc. of Psychosomatic Obstetrics and
Gynaecology [IO], Debrecen, Hungary
Hungarian Soc. of Sports Medicine [IO], Budapest,
Hungary
Hungarian Soc. of Surveying, Mapping and Remote
Sensing [IO], Budapest, Hungary
Hungarian Soc. of Textile Tech. and Sci. [IO],
Budapest, Hungary
Hungarian Squash Assn. [IO], Budapest, Hungary
Hungarian Taekwondo Fed. [IO], Budapest, Hungary
Hungarian Tenants Assn. [IO], Budapest, Hungary
Hungarian-U.S. Bus. Coun. [667], Chamber of Com-
merce of the U.S., 1615 H St. NW, Washington,
DC 20062-2000, (202)659-6000
Hungarian-U.S. Bus. Coun. [667], Chamber of Com-
merce of the U.S., 1615 H St. NW, Washington,
DC 20062-2000, (202)659-6000
Hungarian Venture Capital and Private Equity Assn.
[IO], Budapest, Hungary
Hungarian Water Ski and Wakeboard Fed. [IO],
Budapest, Hungary
Hungarian Yachting Assn. [IO], Budapest, Hungary
Hungary
Hungarian Scouts Assn. [13020]
Hunger
Aid for the World [12715]
Alliance to End Hunger [12264]
Amer. Outreach to Ethiopia [12265]
Artists Striving to End Poverty [12716]
Beyond Hunger [14431]
Bread for the World [17870]
Bread for the World [17870]
Canadian Feed The Children [3608]
Challah for Hunger [12266]
Challah for Hunger [12266]

Chefs for Humanity [12267]
Chefs for Humanity [12267]
Community Food Security Coalition [12268]
Community Food Security Coalition [12268]
The Dinner Garden [12269]
Educational Concerns for Hunger Org. [12270]
Educational Concerns for Hunger Org. [12270]
End Childhood Hunger [12271]
End Hunger Network [17871]
Feed My Hungry Children [11274]
Feeding Am. [12272]
Feeding Hungry Children Intl. [12273]
Feeding Hungry Children Intl. [12273]
Fight Against Hunger Org. [12274]
Food-Aid [12275]
Food-Aid [12275]
Food for the Hungry [12276]
Food Providers of Am. [12277]
Food Res. and Action Center [12278]
Freedom from Hunger [12279]
From Hunger to Harvest [12280]
From Hunger to Harvest [12280]
Global FoodBanking Network [12281]
Hearts for the Hungry [12282]
Hearts for the Hungry [12282]
Hearts for Kenya [11070]
The Hunger Proj. [17872]
The Hunger Proj. [17872]
Inst. for Food and Development Policy [17873]
Inst. for Food and Development Policy [17873]
Intl. Crisis Aid [12854]
Intl. Food Policy Res. Inst. [17874]
Intl. Food Policy Res. Inst. [17874]
Kids Against Hunger [12283]
MAZON [12284]
MAZON [12284]
Meals on Wheels Assn. of Am. [12151]
Move For Hunger [12285]
Natl. Assn. of Ser. Dogs [11876]
Natl. Student Campaign Against Hunger and
Homelessness [12286]
Partnership to Cut Hunger and Poverty in Africa
[12746]
Physicians Against World Hunger [12287]
Physicians Against World Hunger [12287]
Presbyterian Hunger Prog. [12288]
RESULTS [17875]
RESULTS [17875]
rock CAN roll [12289]
Rotarian Action Gp. for the Alleviation of Hunger
and Malnutrition [12290]
Rotarian Action Gp. for the Alleviation of Hunger
and Malnutrition [12290]
Senior Gleaners [12291]
Share Our Strength [12292]
Simple Hope [12891]
Soc. of St. Andrew [12293]
Stop Hunger Now [12294]
Stop Hunger Now [12294]
Teens Fighting Hunger [12295]
Touching Hearts [10817]
Trees for Life [12296]
Trees for Life [12296]
U.S. Natl. Comm. for World Food Day [12297]
U.S. Natl. Comm. for World Food Day [12297]
U.S.A. Harvest [12298]
Why Hunger [17876]
Why Hunger [17876]
World Food Prog. USA [12299]
World Hunger Educ. Ser. [17877]
World Hunger Educ. Ser. [17877]
Hunger Prog. Comm. of the United Presbyterian
Church of the U.S.A. in 1981 [★12288]
The Hunger Proj. [17872], 5 Union Sq. W, New
York, NY 10003, (212)251-9100
The Hunger Proj. [17872], 5 Union Sq. W, New
York, NY 10003, (212)251-9100
Hunt Saboteurs Assn. [IO], London, United Kingdom
Hunter Archaeological Soc. [IO], Sheffield, United
Kingdom
Hunter Educ. Assn. [★22698]
Hunter Educ. Assn. [★22698]
Hunter Olive Assn. [IO], Narrabeen, Australia
Hunterian Soc. [IO], London, United Kingdom
Hunters Helping Hunters [21865], Mike Bell, VP/Dir.
of Assistance, 509 Joyner Rd., Waynesboro, GA
30830-5836

Reference to "IO" in place of a book number signifies that the association may be found in the 50th edition of International Organizations.

Hunting
Amer. Coon Hunters Assn. [22696]
Bluetick Breeders of Am. [21527]
Browning Collectors Assn. [21712]
Christian Hunters and Anglers Assn. [21279]
Fur Free Alliance [10968]
Hunters Helping Hunters [21865]
Hunting Assn. of Ireland [4357]
Intl. Bowhunting Org. [22697]
Intl. Bowhunting Org. [22697]
Intl. Hunter Educ. Assn. [22698]
Intl. Hunter Educ. Assn. [22698]
Masters of Foxhounds Assn. of Am. [22699]
Natl. Alliance for the Development of Archery [22222]
Natl. Archery Assn. of the U.S. [22223]
North Amer. Bowhunting Coalition [21866]
North Amer. Hunting Club [22700]
North-South Skirmish Assn. [22885]
Self-Guided Hunting Assn. [21867]
United Beagle Gundog Fed. [21661]
U.S. Sportsmen's Alliance [22701]
World Wide Assn. of Treasure Seekers [22109]
Hunting Assn. of Ireland [IO], Kilmallock, Ireland
Hunting Dogs
Bluetick Breeders of Am. [21527]
Club de l'Epagneul Breton of the U.S. [21541]
North Amer. Teckel Club [21622]
United Beagle Gundog Fed. [21661]
U.S. Complete Shooting Dog Assn. [21668]
Hunting Retriever Club [21581], PO Box 210, Alexandria, LA 71309, (318)446-0075
Huntington Assn. of Russia [IO], Moscow, Russia
Huntington Assn. of Slovenia [IO], Vrhnika, Slovenia
Huntington Assn. of South Africa [IO], Cape Town, Republic of South Africa
Huntington Disease Assn. [IO], Liverpool, United Kingdom
Huntington Disease Assn. - Canterbury, New Zealand [IO], Christchurch, New Zealand
Huntington Disease Care and Cure Soc. of Pakistan [IO], Peshawar, Pakistan
Huntington Disease Found. of Am. [★15598]
Huntington Disease Soc. of Colombia [IO], Juan de Acosta, Colombia
Huntington Espoir [IO], Cuvry, France
Huntington Foreningen I Sverige [IO], Stockholm, Sweden
Huntington Liga [IO], Bierbeek, Belgium
Huntington Self Support Gp. Malta [IO], Floriana, Malta
Huntington Soc. of Canada [IO], Kitchener, ON, Canada
Huntington United Gp. South Africa [IO], Johannesburg, Republic of South Africa
Huntington's Disease Assn. of Ireland [IO], Dublin, Ireland
Huntington's Disease Soc. of Am. [15598], 505 8th Ave., Ste. 902, New York, NY 10018, (212)242-1968
Huntington's Org. [IO], Gurgaon, India
Hurlingham Polo Assn. [IO], Faringdon, United Kingdom
Hurst/Olds Club of Am. [21072], Tara Worsham, Membership Coor., 3098 S Point Pleasant Rd., Decatur, IL 62521
Huset Markedsforing [★IO]
Hyacinth Control Soc. [★6350]
Hyderabad Race Club [IO], Hyderabad, India
Hydraulic Inst. [1828], 6 Campus Dr., 1st Fl. N, Parsippany, NJ 07054-4406, (973)267-9700
Hydrauliikka-ja Pneumatiikkayhdistys r.y. [★IO]
Hydrocephalus Assn. [15599], 870 Market St., Ste. 705, San Francisco, CA 94102, (415)732-7040
Hydrocephalus Found; Natl. [14409]
Hydrocephalus Res. Found. - Defunct.
Hydrocephalus Res. Found; Guardians of [15595]
Hydrogen 2000 [6729], 11684 Ventura Blvd., No. 5108, Studio City, CA 91604, (303)530-0336
Hydrogen Assn; Amer. [6689]
Hydrogen Assn. and U.S. Fuel Cell Coun; Natl. [★7368]
The Hydrographic Soc. of Am. [7487], 451 Hungerford Dr., Ste. 119-360, Rockville, MD 20850
Hydrology; Amer. Inst. of [7594]

Hydroponic Merchants Assn. [★4496]
Hydropower Assn; Natl. [6740]
Hygiene; Amer. Bd. of Indus. [15899]
Hygienists; Amer. Conf. of Governmental Indus. [15901]
Hygienists' Assn; Amer. Dental [14263]
Hygienists' Assn; Natl. Dental [14303]
Hymn Soc. of Am. [★20126]
Hymn Soc. of Great Britain and Ireland [IO], Lancaster, United Kingdom
Hymn Soc. in the U.S. and Canada [20126], Baptist Theological Seminary at Richmond, 3400 Brook Rd., Richmond, VA 23227-4536, (804)204-1226
Hyperbaric Medical Soc; Undersea and [16935]
Hyperbaric Medicine
Intl. Hyperbarics Assn. [15074]
Hyperoxaluria Found; Oxalosis and [15556]
Hypertension
Amer. Soc. of Hypertension [15075]
Amer. Soc. of Hypertension [15075]Hypertension-HELLP Syndrome Soc.
Intl. Pediatric Hypertension Assn. [15076]
Intl. Pediatric Hypertension Assn. [15076]
Intl. Soc. on Hypertension in Blacks [15077]
Intl. Soc. on Hypertension in Blacks [15077]
Natl. Hypertension Assn. [15078]
Pulmonary Hypertension Assn. [15079]
Hypertension Coun. [★14712]
Hyperthermia Assn. of the U.S; Malignant [14611]
Hypertrophic Cardiomyopathy Assn. [14018], PO Box 306, Hibernia, NJ 07842, (973)983-7429
Hypertrophic Cardiomyopathy Assn. [14018], PO Box 306, Hibernia, NJ 07842, (973)983-7429
Hyphenate Lobby [★17335]
Hypnosis
Amer. Acad. of Medical Hypnoanalysts [15080]
Amer. Alliance of Hypnotists [15081]
Amer. Assn. of Professional Hypnotherapists [15082]
Amer. Bd. of Hypnotherapy [15083]
Amer. Bd. of Psychological Hypnosis [15084]
Amer. Coun. of Hypnotist Examiners [15085]
Amer. Guild of Hypnotherapists [15086]
Amer. Hypnosis Assn. [15087]
Amer. Psychological Assn. I Soc. of Psychological Hypnosis [16380]
Amer. Soc. of Clinical Hypnosis [15088]
Intl. Alliance of Professional Hypnotists [15089]
Intl. Assn. of Counselors and Therapists [15090]
Intl. Assn. of Counselors and Therapists [15090]
Intl. Medical and Dental Hypnotherapy Assn. [15091]
Intl. Medical and Dental Hypnotherapy Assn. [15091]
Natl. Bd. for Certified Clinical Hypnotherapists [15092]
Natl. Guild of Hypnotists [15093]
Soc. for Clinical and Experimental Hypnosis [15094]
Hypnosis Educational Coun. Intl. [★15093]
Hypnotherapy Assn. [IO], Chorley, United Kingdom
Hypnotists Examining Coun. [★15085]
Hypoglycemia
HELP - Inst. for Body Chemistry [15095]
Hypoglycemia Assn. - Defunct.
Hypoparathyroidism Assn. [14491], PO Box 2258, Idaho Falls, ID 83403, (208)524-3857
Hypoparathyroidism Assn. [14491], PO Box 2258, Idaho Falls, ID 83403, (208)524-3857
Hypospadias and Epispadias Assn. [13842], 240 W 44th St., Ste. 2, New York, NY 10036, (212)382-3471
Hyresgasternas Riksforbund [★IO]
Hysterectomy Educational Resources and Services Found. [15880], 422 Bryn Mawr Ave., Bala Cynwyd, PA 19004, (610)667-7757
Hysterectomy Educational Resources and Services Found. [15880], 422 Bryn Mawr Ave., Bala Cynwyd, PA 19004, (610)667-7757 .

I

I Am Your Child Found. [★12614]
I CAN [IO], London, United Kingdom
I-CAR [★357]

I Care Grace Intl. [14792], 400 Riverside Ave., Charlottesville, VA 22902, (434)973-6889
I Create - Address unknown since 2010.
I Have a Dream Found. [13529], 330 7th Ave., 20th Fl., New York, NY 10001, (212)293-5480
I Seek a Transsexual Female and Intros - Defunct.
IAB Partners - Address unknown since 2011.
IADT, The Intl. Assn. for Document Technologies [★3354]
IAHI, the Owners' Assn. [1754], 3 Ravinia Dr., Ste. 100, Atlanta, GA 30346, (770)604-5555
IAMCO [IO], Grand Cayman, Cayman Islands
IANA [★3514]
IARF - Europe and the Middle East [IO], De Bilt, Netherlands
IARF - Philippines [IO], Dumaguete City, Philippines
IARF - South Asia [IO], Pathanamthitta, India
Ibero-American Fed. of Acoustics [IO], Lisbon, Portugal
Ibero-American Fed. of Exchanges [IO], Buenos Aires, Argentina
Ibero-American Inst. of Aeronautic and Space Law and Commercial Aviation [IO], Madrid, Spain
Ibero-American Univ. Assn. for Postgraduate Universities [IO], Salamanca, Spain
Ibero-Latin Amer. Coll. of Dermatology [IO], Buenos Aires, Argentina
Ibero-Latin Amer. Fed. of Plastic Surgery [IO], Quito, Ecuador
Iberoamerican Assn. of Educational TV [IO], Madrid, Spain
Iberoamerican Cultural Exchange Program - Defunct.
Ibis Reproductive Hea. [16585], 17 Dunster St., Ste. 201, Cambridge, MA 02138, (617)349-0040
IbnSina Afghanistan [IO], Kabul, Afghanistan
Ibsen Soc. of Am. [9373], Prof. Arne Lunde, Treas., Scandinavian Sect., UCLA, 212 Royce Hall, Los Angeles, CA 90095
Ibsen Soc. of Am. [9373], Prof. Arne Lunde, Treas., Scandinavian Sect., UCLA, 212 Royce Hall, Los Angeles, CA 90095
ICA - Australia [IO], Highgate, Australia
ICA Bunka Jigyo Kyokai Japan [★IO]
ICA Gender Equality Comm. [IO], Geneva, Switzerland
ICA Gp. [1137], 1 Harvard St., Ste. 200, Brookline, MA 02445, (617)232-8765
ICC - Austria [IO], Vienna, Austria
ICC Belgique-Belgie [★IO]
ICC - Ceska Republika [★IO]
ICC Commercial Crime Services [IO], London, United Kingdom
ICC Counterfeiting Intelligence Bur. [IO], London, United Kingdom
ICC - Finland [IO], Helsinki, Finland
ICC Intl. Maritime Bur. [IO], London, United Kingdom
ICC Nederland [★IO]
ICC - Polska [IO], Bydgoszcz, Poland
ICC - Russia [IO], Moscow, Russia
ICC Suomi [★IO]
Ice Cream
Assn. of Ice Cream and Related Products Mfrs. [8979]
Ice Cream Alliance [IO], Derby, United Kingdom
Ice Hockey UK [IO], Romford, United Kingdom
Ice Screamers [21350], PO Box 465, Warrington, PA 18976, (215)343-2676
Ice Skating Assn. of India [IO], New Delhi, India
Ice Skating Australia [IO], North Strathfield, Australia
Ice Skating Inst. [3278], 6000 Custer Rd., Bldg. 9, Plano, TX 75023, (972)735-8800
Ice Skating Inst. [3278], 6000 Custer Rd., Bldg. 9, Plano, TX 75023, (972)735-8800
Ice Skating Inst. of Am. [★3278]
Ice Skating Inst. of Am. [★3278]
Ice Speed Skating New Zealand [IO], Christchurch, New Zealand
Iceberg Athletic Club - Defunct.
Iceland Assn. of Women Entrepreneurs FKA [IO], Reykjavik, Iceland
Iceland Chamber of Commerce [IO], Reykjavik, Iceland
Iceland Music Info. Centre [IO], Reykjavik, Iceland
Iceland Squash Comm. [IO], Reykjavik, Iceland

A star before a book entry number signifies that the name is not listed separately, but is mentioned within the entry.

Icelandic Amateur Theatre Assn. [IO], Reykjavik, Iceland
The Icelandic Aquaculture Assn. [IO], Reykjavik, Iceland
Icelandic Assn. of the Deaf [IO], Reykjavik, Iceland
Icelandic Athletic Fed. [IO], Reykjavik, Iceland
Icelandic Auto. Assn. [IO], Reykjavik, Iceland
Icelandic Bible Soc. [IO], Reykjavik, Iceland
Icelandic Cardiac Soc. [IO], Reykjavik, Iceland
Icelandic Centre for Res. [IO], Reykjavik, Iceland
Icelandic Church Aid [IO], Reykjavik, Iceland
Icelandic Comm. for UNICEF [IO], Reykjavik, Iceland
Icelandic Dance Sport Fed. [IO], Reykjavik, Iceland
Icelandic Geotechnical Soc. [IO], Reykjavik, Iceland
Icelandic Heart Assn. [IO], Reykjavik, Iceland
Icelandic League against Rheumatism - Gigtarfelag Islands [IO], Reykjavik, Iceland
Icelandic Literary Soc. [IO], Reykjavik, Iceland
Icelandic Medical Assn. [IO], Kopavogur, Iceland
Icelandic Mountain Bike Club [IO], Reykjavik, Iceland
Icelandic Natl. Gp. of IFPI [IO], Seltjarnarnes, Iceland
Icelandic Nurses' Assn. [IO], Reykjavik, Iceland
Icelandic Orthodontic Soc. [IO], Reykjavik, Iceland
Icelandic Pre-School Teachers Union [IO], Reykjavik, Iceland
Icelandic Publishers' Assn. [IO], Reykjavik, Iceland
Icelandic Radio Amateurs [IO], Reykjavik, Iceland
Icelandic Red Cross [IO], Reykjavik, Iceland
Icelandic Sailing Assn. [IO], Reykjavik, Iceland
Icelandic Sheepdog Assn. of Am. [21582], Peg Johnson, Membership Sec., 8314 20th Ave. NW, Seattle, WA 98117
Icelandic Skating Assn. [IO], Reykjavik, Iceland
Icelandic Ski Assn. [IO], Akureyri, Iceland
Icelandic Soc. for Info. Processing [IO], Reykjavik, Iceland
Icelandic Teachers' Union [IO], Reykjavik, Iceland
Icelandic Tennis Assn. [IO], Reykjavik, Iceland
Icelandic Weightlifting Fed. [IO], Reykjavik, Iceland
ICHCA Intl. Limited [IO], Romford, United Kingdom
Ichthyologists and Herpetologists; Amer. Soc. of [6939]
Ichthyology
   Amer. Fisheries Soc. [6951]
   Amer. Fisheries Soc. [6951]
   Amer. Inst. of Fishery Res. Biologists [6952]
   Fed. of Amer. Aquarium Societies [6953]
   Intl. Assn. of Astacology [6954]
   Intl. Assn. of Astacology [6954]
   North Amer. Native Fishes Assn. [6955]
   North Amer. Native Fishes Assn. [6955]
   Pacific Ocean Res. Found. [6956]
Ichthyosis and Related Skin Types; Found. for [14326]
ICIA - Defunct.
ICOM Energy Assn. [IO], Kenilworth, United Kingdom
ICOMOS Canada [IO], Ottawa, ON, Canada
ICOMOS Documentation Centre [★9703]
ICOMOS Documentation Centre [★9703]
ICRA [11920], Family Online Safety Inst., 624 Ninth St. NW, Ste. 222, Washington, DC 20001, (202)729-4037
ICRA [11920], Family Online Safety Inst., 624 Ninth St. NW, Ste. 222, Washington, DC 20001, (202)729-4037
Ida P. Rolf Found. for Structural Integration [★13708]
Idaho Potato Commn. [4454], 661 S Rivershore Ln., Ste. 230, Eagle, ID 83616, (208)334-2350
Idaho Potato and Onion Commn. [★4454]
IDB Family Assn. - Address unknown since 2010.
IDEA Hea. and Fitness Assn. [16226], 10455 Pacific Center Ct., San Diego, CA 92121, (858)535-8979
IDEA: Intl. Dance Exercise Assn. [★16226]
IDEA: The Assn. for Fitness Professionals [★16226]
Idea, The Hea. & Fitness Source [★16226]
IDEA, The Hea. and Fitness Source [★16226]
Idealist and Action Without Borders [★17726]
Idealist and Action Without Borders [★17726]
Idealist Intl. - Defunct.
Idealist.org; Action Without Borders/ [17726]

IDEAlliance - Intl. Digital Enterprise Alliance [1612], 1421 Prince St., Ste. 230, Alexandria, VA 22314-2805, (703)837-1070
IDEAlliance - Intl. Digital Enterprise Alliance [1612], 1421 Prince St., Ste. 230, Alexandria, VA 22314-2805, (703)837-1070
IdeasAmerica [1149], 162 S Vista, Auburn Hills, MI 48326-1447, (248)961-2674
IDEEA Inc. [★1233]
IDEEA Inc. [★1233]
Ident-A-Pet [★11044]
Identity Theft Rsrc. Center [18071], PO Box 26833, San Diego, CA 92196, (858)693-7935
Idoma Assn. USA [19176], PO Box 7211342, Houston, TX 77272-1342
IDRA - Intl. Disaster Recovery Assn. [★7544]
IDRA - Intl. Disaster Recovery Assn. [★7544]
I.E. Canada [IO], Toronto, ON, Canada
iEARN [8027], 475 Riverside Dr., Ste. 450, New York, NY 10115, (212)870-2693
IEEE | Aerospace and Electronics Systems Soc. [6654], Robert Lyons, Jr., Exec. VP, 1701 NW 85th Terr., Plantation, FL 33322-5544, (571)220-9257
IEEE | Antennas and Propagation Soc. [6655], Univ. of Arizona, Meinel Bldg., Rm. 623, Tucson, AZ 85745, (520)626-8183
IEEE | Broadcast Tech. Soc. [7538], Lisa Weisser, Sr. Admin., 445 Hoes Ln., Piscataway, NJ 08854, (732)562-5345
IEEE | Circuits and Systems Soc. [6656], 445 Hoes Ln., Piscataway, NJ 08854, (732)465-5821
IEEE | Communications Soc. [7539], 3 Park Ave., 17th Fl., New York, NY 10016, (212)705-8900
IEEE Components, Hybrids, and Mfg. Tech. Soc. [★6657]
IEEE | Components, Packaging, and Mfg. Tech. Soc. [6657], PO Box 1331, Piscataway, NJ 08855-1331, (732)562-5529
IEEE | Cmpt. Soc. [6451], 2001 L St. NW, Ste. 700, Washington, DC 20036-4910, (202)371-0101
IEEE | Consumer Electronics Soc. [6658], Charlotte Kobert, Admin., 4115 Clendenning Rd., Gibsonia, PA 15044, (724)612-1060
IEEE | Control Systems Soc. [6797], Northeastern Univ., Dept. Elecl. & Cmpt. Engg., 360 Huntington Ave., Ste. 440 DA, Boston, MA 02115, (617)737-5364
IEEE | Dielectrics and Elecl. Insulation Soc. [6641], Auburn Univ., Elecl. and Cmpt. Engg., 200 Broun Hall, Auburn, AL 36849-5201, (334)844-1822
IEEE Elecl. Insulation Soc. [★6641]
IEEE | Electromagnetic Compatibility Soc. [6659], 445 Hoes Ln., PO Box 6804, Piscataway, NJ 08855-6802
IEEE | Electron Devices Soc. [6660], IEEE Operations Center, 445 Hoes Ln., Piscataway, NJ 08854, (732)562-3926
IEEE Engg. Mgt. Soc. - Address unknown since 2011.
IEEE | Engg. in Medicine and Biology Soc. [6328], 445 Hoes Ln., Piscataway, NJ 08854, (732)981-3433
IEEE Engg. in Medicine and Biology Soc. [6328], 445 Hoes Ln., Piscataway, NJ 08854, (732)981-3433
IEEE | Geoscience and Remote Sensing Soc. [6924], 104 Bldg. 007 BARC-W, Beltsville, MD 20705, (301)504-8511
IEEE | Indus. Electronics Soc. [6661], Univ. of Arkansas, Bell Engg. Center, Rm. 4183, Fayetteville, AR 72701, (479)575-6011
IEEE Indus. Electronics Soc. [6661], Univ. of Arkansas, Bell Engg. Center, Rm. 4183, Fayetteville, AR 72701, (479)575-6011
IEEE | Indus. Applications Soc. [6962], Lynda Bernstein, Admin., 445 Hoes Ln., Piscataway, NJ 08854, (732)465-6627
IEEE Info. Theory Gp. - Address unknown since 2011.
IEEE | Instrumentation and Measurement Soc. [6998], 9513 Old Court Rd., Windsor Mill, MD 21244-1028, (410)521-6849
IEEE Lasers and Electro-Optics Soc. [★6663]
IEEE Lasers and Electro-Optics Soc. [★6663]
IEEE | Magnetics Soc. [6662], 445 Hoes Ln., PO Box 459, Piscataway, NJ 08855-0459, (908)981-0060

IEEE Neural Networks Coun. [★6791]
IEEE | Nuclear and Plasma Sciences Soc. [7165], Defense Nuclear Fac. Safety Bd., 625 Indiana Ave. NW, Ste. 700, Washington, DC 20004, (202)694-7090
IEEE | Oceanic Engg. Soc. [7181], 411 Country Club Dr., Picayune, MS 39466, (601)798-0277
IEEE | Photonics Soc. [6663], 445 Hoes Ln., Piscataway, NJ 08854-1331, (732)562-3891
IEEE Photonics Soc. [6663], 445 Hoes Ln., Piscataway, NJ 08854-1331, (732)562-3891
IEEE Power Electronics Coun. [★6664]
IEEE | Power Electronics Soc. [6664], Ms. Donna Florek, Sr. Admin., 445 Hoes Ln., Piscataway, NJ 08855, (732)465-6480
IEEE | Power and Energy Soc. [6642], 445 Hoes Ln., Piscataway, NJ 08854-1331, (732)562-3883
IEEE Power Engg. Soc. [★6642]
IEEE | Professional Commun. Soc. [6665], PO Box 6804, Piscataway, NJ 08854-6804, (732)981-0060
IEEE | Reliability Soc. [6666], 3 Park Ave., 17th Fl., New York, NY 10016-5997, (212)419-7900
IEEE | Robotics and Automation Soc. [7343], Prof. Kevin M. Lynch, Sec., 2145 Sheridan Rd., Evanston, IL 60208-0834, (847)467-5451
IEEE | Signal Processing Soc. [6079], 445 Hoes Ln., Piscataway, NJ 08854-4141, (732)562-3888
IEEE | Soc. on Social Implications of Tech. [7504], Univ. of Connecticut, 1 Univ. Pl., Stamford, CT 06901-2315, (203)251-8431
IEEE Solid-State Circuits Coun. [★6643]
IEEE | Solid-State Circuits Soc. [6643], 445 Hoes Ln., Piscataway, NJ 08855-1331, (732)981-3400
IEEE Sonics and Ultrasonics Soc. [★6080]
IEEE | Systems, Man, and Cybernetics Soc. [6452], 3 Park Ave., 17th Fl., New York, NY 10016-5997, (212)419-7900
IEEE | Ultrasonics, Ferroelectrics, and Frequency Control Soc. [6080], IEEE Operations Center, 445 Hoes Ln., Piscataway, NJ 08854-4141, (732)981-0060
IEEE | Vehicular Tech. Soc. [6667], 3 Park Ave., 17th Fl., New York, NY 10016-5997, (212)419-7900
Iemanya Oceanica [5064], 23293 Ventura Blvd., Woodland Hills, CA 91364, (818)224-4250
IES Abroad [8170], 33 N LaSalle St., 15th Fl., Chicago, IL 60602-2602, (312)944-1750
IES Abroad [8170], 33 N LaSalle St., 15th Fl., Chicago, IL 60602-2602, (312)944-1750
IETF [★15600]
IETF [★15600]
IFA Aquaculture [IO], Bluebell, Ireland
IFCA Intl. [19620], PO Box 810, Grandville, MI 49468-0810, (616)531-1840
IFDC [3756], PO Box 2040, Muscle Shoals, AL 35662, (256)381-6600
IFO Institut fur Wirtschaftsforschung [★IO]
IFO Inst. for Economic Res. [IO], Munich, Germany
IFPA Film and Video Communicators [★1259]
IFPA Film and Video Communicators [★1259]
IFRA [IO], Darmstadt, Germany
IFS Nepal Children Welfare Prog. [IO], Kathmandu, Nepal
IGAF Worldwide [29], 3235 Satellite Blvd., Bldg. 400, Ste. 300, Duluth, GA 30096, (678)417-7730
Igbere Progressive Assn. Intl. [12576], PO Box 540814, Houston, TX 77254, (713)773-4887
IHRA World Championship Series [★22244]
IIE/Europe [IO], Budapest, Hungary
IIEC-Asia [IO], Bangkok, Thailand
IISRP [★3132]
Ijaw Natl. Alliance of the Americas [12577], PO Box 24435, Brooklyn, NY 11202-4435
Ikatan Ahli Ilmu Faal Indonesia [★IO]
Ikatan Nasional Konsultan Indonesia [★IO]
Ikatan Sarjana Wanita Indonesia [IO], Jakarta, Indonesia
Ikatan Sekretaris Indonesia [IO], Cimahi, Indonesia
Ikebana Intl. [IO], Tokyo, Japan
Iklimlendirme Sogutma Klima Imalatcilari Dernegi [★IO]
Il Circalo Italiano [★23655]
ILEIA: Centre for Info. on Low External Input and Sustainable Agriculture [IO], Amersfoort, Netherlands

Reference to "IO" in place of a book number signifies that the association may be found in the 50th edition of International Organizations.

Illinois Central Railroad Historical Soc. [9775], PO Box 288, Paxton, IL 60957

Illuminating and Allied Glassware Mfrs. Assn. - Defunct.

Illuminating Engg. Res. Inst. [★7033]

Illuminating Engg. Soc. of North Am. [7031], 120 Wall St., 17th Fl., New York, NY 10005-4001, (212)248-5000

Illusion Theater [11888], 528 Hennepin Ave., Ste. 704, Minneapolis, MN 55403, (612)339-4944

Illustrators' Partnership of Am. [9644], 845 Moraine St., Marshfield, MA 02050, (781)837-9152

ILO Decent Work Tech. Support Team and Country Off. for Central and Eastern Europe (DWT/CO - Budapest) [IO], Budapest, Hungary

IMAGE Soc. [6453], PO Box 6221, Chandler, AZ 85246-6221

Imagery Intl. [15073], 1574 Coburg Rd., No. 555, Eugene, OR 97401-4802, (514)938-6131

Imagine Canada [IO], Toronto, ON, Canada

Imagine World Hea. [14715], 105 E Dolphin Blvd., Ponte Vedra Beach, FL 32082-1714, (904)285-0240

Imaging Media
  DICOM Standards Comm. [6957]
  Intl. Visual Sociology Assn. [7428]

Imaging; North Amer. Soc. for Cardiovascular [14036]

Imaging; North Amer. Soc. for Cardiovascular [14036]

Imaging Supplies Coalition [5569], 1435 E Venice Ave., No. 104, MBN 249, Venice, FL 34292, (941)961-7897

IMAGO - European Fed. of Cinematographers [IO], London, United Kingdom

Imam Mahdi Assn. of Marjaeya [20132], 835 Mason St., Dearborn, MI 48124, (313)303-9280

IMDR [★4693]

Immigrant Genealogical Soc. [20633], PO Box 7369, Burbank, CA 91510-7369, (818)848-3122

Immigrant Lib. [★20633]

Immigrant Women Services Ottawa [IO], Ottawa, ON, Canada

Immigration
  African Fed., Inc. [17900]
  Amer. Civic Assn. [12300]
  Amer. Fund for Czech and Slovak Relief [12771]
  Amer. Immigration Control Found. [17878]
  Amer. Immigration Coun. [5527]
  Amer. Immigration Lawyers Assn. [5528]
  Americans for Immigration Control [17879]
  Assn. for New Canadians [20439]
  Assn. for Refugee Ser. Professionals [12301]
  Catholic Legal Immigration Network [19822]
  Center for Equal Opportunity [9855]
  Center for Immigration Stud. [17880]
  Emerald Isle Immigration Center [17881]
  Emerald Isle Immigration Center [17881]
  Fed. for Amer. Immigration Reform [17882]
  Immigration Voice [5529]
  Iranian Alliances Across Borders [19069]
  Legal Immigrant Assn. [5530]
  Liberty's Promise [5531]
  Natl. Immigration Forum [17883]
  Natl. Immigration Law Center [17884]
  Natl. Immigration Proj. l Natl. Lawyers Guild [5532]
  Natl. Network for Immigrant and Refugee Rights [17885]
  Population Rsrc. Center [12708]
  Salvadoran Amer. Natl. Network [18979]
  U.S. Border Control [17886]

Immigration Advisory Ser. [IO], London, United Kingdom

Immigration Equality [12091], 40 Exchange Pl., 17th Fl., New York, NY 10005, (212)714-2904

Immigration and Ethnic History Soc. [9776], Cheryl Greenberg, Treas., Trinity Coll., Dept. of History, 300 Summit St., Hartford, CT 06106

Immigration and History Soc. [★9776]

Immigration and Refugee Services of Am. - Address unknown since 2010.

Immigration Voice [5529], 3561 Homestead Rd., No. 375, Santa Clara, CA 95051-5161, (202)386-6250

Immortalist Soc. [6583], 24355 Sorrentino Ct., Clinton Township, MI 48035, (586)791-5961

Immune Deficiency Found. [15106], 40 W Chesapeake Ave., Ste. 308, Towson, MD 21204, (410)321-6647

Immunization Action Coalition [15107], 1573 Selby Ave., Ste. 234, St. Paul, MN 55104, (651)647-9009

Immunogenetics; Amer. Soc. for Histocompatibility and [15099]

Immunologists; Amer. Assn. of Veterinary [16985]

Immunology
  Amer. Assn. of Immunologists [15096]
  Amer. Autoimmune Related Diseases Assn. [15097]
  Amer. Immunization Registry Assn. [15098]
  Amer. Soc. for Histocompatibility and Immunogenetics [15099]
  Assn. of Immunization Managers [15100]
  Assn. of Medical Lab. Immunologists [15101]
  Childhood Influenza Immunization Coalition [15102]
  Clinical Immunology Soc. [15103]Immunology-European Soc. for Immunodeficiencies
  European Soc. of Reproductive and Development Immunology [778]
  Evans Syndrome Res. and Support Gp. [15104]
  Evans Syndrome Res. and Support Gp. [15104]
  Fed. of Clinical Immunology Societies [15105]
  GAVI Alliance [14897]
  Immune Deficiency Found. [15106]
  Immunization Action Coalition [15107]
  Intl. Complement Soc. [15108]
  Intl. Complement Soc. [15108]
  Intl. Soc. for Vaccines [15109]
  Jeffrey Modell Found. [15110]
  Natl. Network for Immunization Info. [15111]
  Soc. for Mucosal Immunology [15112]
  Soc. for Mucosal Immunology [15112]
  ThinkTwice Global Vaccine Inst. [15113]

Immunology; Amer. Bd. of Allergy and [13634]

Immunology of Diabetes Soc. [14351], Matt De Vol, Sr. Dir. of Finance, La Jolla Inst. of Allergy & Immunology, 9420 Athena Cir., La Jolla, CA 92037

Immunology of Diabetes Soc. [14351], Matt De Vol, Sr. Dir. of Finance, La Jolla Inst. of Allergy & Immunology, 9420 Athena Cir., La Jolla, CA 92037

Impact Alliance [12336], 1350 Connecticut Ave. NW, Ste. 1100, Washington, DC 20036, (202)742-5774

Impact Carbon [4228], 182 2nd St., Ste. 400, San Francisco, CA 94105, (415)968-9087

Impact Carbon [4228], 182 2nd St., Ste. 400, San Francisco, CA 94105, (415)968-9087

Impact First Intl. [IO], Toronto, ON, Canada

Impact Sports Intl. [22979], 301 Gallman Rd., Inman, SC 29349, (864)278-8006

ImpactLives [9491], PO Box 2548, Maple Grove, MN 55311, (763)515-0470

ImpactLives [9491], PO Box 2548, Maple Grove, MN 55311, (763)515-0470

Imperial Coun. of the Ancient Arabic Order of the Nobles of the Mystic Shrine for North Am. [19132], Shriners Intl. HQ, 2900 Rocky Point Dr., Tampa, FL 33607-1460, (813)281-0300

Imperial Glass Collectors Soc. [★21841]

Imperial Soc. of Teachers of Dancing [IO], London, United Kingdom

Implements
  Cast Iron Seat Collectors Assn. [21868]
  Mid-West Tool Collectors Assn. [21869]
  Natl. Reamer Collectors Assn. [21870]
  Potomac Antique Tools and Indus. Assn. [21871]
  World Atlatl Assn. [21872]
  World Atlatl Assn. [21872]

Imported Car Gp. [★297]

Imported Car Gp. [★297]

Imported Hardwood Plywood Assn. [★1469]

Imported Hardwood Plywood Assn. [★1469]

Imported Hardwood Plywood Assn. of Am. [★1469]

Imported Hardwood Plywood Assn. of Am. [★1469]

Imported Hardwood Products Assn. [★1469]

Imported Hardwood Products Assn. [★1469]

Imported Tyre Mfrs'. Assn. [IO], London, United Kingdom

Importers Chamber of Argentine Republic [IO], Buenos Aires, Argentina

Importers and Exporters Assn. of Taipei [IO], Taipei, Taiwan

Impuls - Vorming, Training en Procesbeheer [IO], Aarschot, Belgium

IMS Forum [7540], 211 Summit Pl., No. 292, Silverthorne, CO 80498, (970)262-6100

IMS Forum [7540], 211 Summit Pl., No. 292, Silverthorne, CO 80498, (970)262-6100

IMZ Intl. Music Media Centre [IO], Vienna, Austria

IMZ Internationales Musik Medienzentrum [★IO]

In Coun. on Hotel, Restaurant and Institutional Educ. [★1757]

In Coun. on Hotel, Restaurant and Institutional Educ. [★1757]

In Defense of Animals [10987], 3010 Kerner Blvd., San Rafael, CA 94901, (415)448-0048

In Kind Canada [IO], Toronto, ON, Canada

In Legal Color [5844], 207 E Ohio St., Ste. 383, Chicago, IL 60611-3238, (312)895-4980

In Our Own Quiet Way [13424], 110 S Main St., Lindon, UT 84042, (801)669-7583

In-Plant Mgt. Assn. [★1615]

In-Plant Mgt. Assn. [★1615]

Incentive Fed. [2404], 6619 Goldsboro Rd., Falls Church, VA 22042, (703)848-7588

Incentive Mfrs. and Representatives Alliance [2318], 1601 N Bond St., Ste. 303, Naperville, IL 60563, (630)369-7786

Incest Anonymous; Survivors of [13102]

Incest Natl. Network; Rape, Abuse and [12758]

Incest Survivors Anonymous [13088], PO Box 17245, Long Beach, CA 90807-7245, (562)428-5599

INCITE! Women of Color Against Violence [18769], PO Box 226, Redmond, WA 98073, (484)932-3166

Inclusion Intl. [IO], London, United Kingdom

Inclusion Ireland [IO], Dublin, Ireland

Inclusive Soc. Pakistan [IO], Karachi, Pakistan

INCODA - Defunct.

Incontinentia Pigmenti Intl. Found. [14601], Susanne Bross Emmerich, Exec. Dir., 30 E 72nd St., New York, NY 10021, (212)452-1231

Incorporated Assn. of Organists [IO], Newcastle upon Tyne, United Kingdom

Incorporated Soc. of British Advertisers [IO], London, United Kingdom

Incorporated Soc. of Irish/American Lawyers [5661], Meghan Kennedy Riordan, 2nd VP, 40 N Main St., Ste. 435, Mount Clemens, MI 48043, (586)468-2940

Incorporated Soc. of Musicians [IO], London, United Kingdom

Incorporated Soc. of Organ Builders - England [IO], Hebden Bridge, United Kingdom

INDA, Assn. of the Nonwoven Fabrics Indus. [3442], PO Box 1288, Cary, NC 27512-1288, (919)233-1210

Indego Africa Proj. [10813], 507 Archwood Trail, Houston, TX 77007, (713)568-1842

Indenlandsk Somandsmission [★IO]

INDENT, Dutch Dental Assn. [IO], Zoetermeer, Netherlands

Independence Dogs - Defunct.

Independence Inst. [17294], 13952 Denver W Pkwy., Ste. 400, Golden, CO 80401, (303)279-6536

Independence Seaport Museum [20759], Penn's Landing, 211 S Columbus Blvd., Philadelphia, PA 19106, (215)413-8655

Independent Armored Car Operators Assn. [3248], 8000 Res. Forest Dr., Ste. 115-155, The Woodlands, TX 77382-1504, (281)292-8208

Independent Arts and Media [9179], PO Box 420442, San Francisco, CA 94142, (415)738-4975

Independent Assn. of German Dentists [IO], Bonn, Germany

Independent Assn. of Preparatory Schools [IO], Leamington Spa, United Kingdom

Independent Assn. of Publishers' Employees [23285], 5 Schalks Crossing Rd., Ste. 220, Plainsboro, NJ 08536, (609)275-6020

Independent Assn. of Questioned Document Examiners [5484], Paul H. McDonald, Pres./Seminar Chm., 968 Main St., Bolton, MA 01740, (978)779-0388

Independent Automotive Damage Appraisers Assn. [231], PO Box 12291, Columbus, GA 31917-2291, (800)369-4232

A star before a book entry number signifies that the name is not listed separately, but is mentioned within the entry.

Independent Automotive Ser. Assn. [★353]

Independent Bakers Assn. [392], PO Box 3731, Washington, DC 20007, (202)333-8190

Independent Bankers Assn. of Am. [★416]

Independent Battery Mfrs. Assn. - Defunct.

Independent Bd. for Presbyterian Foreign Missions [20156], PO Box 1346, Blue Bell, PA 19422-0435, (610)279-0952

Independent Book Publishers Assn. [2937], 627 Aviation Way, Manhattan Beach, CA 90266, (310)372-2732

Independent Bus. Alliance [★3280]

Independent Charities of Am. [1541], 1100 Larkspur Landing Cir., Ste. 340, Larkspur, CA 94939, (415)924-1108

Independent Coll. Funds of Am. [★8288]

Independent Community Bankers of Am. [416], 1615 L St. NW, Ste. 900, Washington, DC 20036, (202)659-8111

Independent Community Consultants - Defunct.

Independent Cmpt. Consultants Assn. - Defunct.

Independent Contractors of Australia [IO], Watsonia, Australia

Independent Curators Incorporated [★9180]

Independent Curators Incorporated [★9180]

Independent Curators Intl. [9180], 799 Broadway, Ste. 205, New York, NY 10003, (212)254-8200

Independent Curators Intl. [9180], 799 Broadway, Ste. 205, New York, NY 10003, (212)254-8200

Independent Data Communications Mfrs. Assn. - Defunct.

Independent Diplomat [17898], 137 2nd Ave., 2nd Fl., New York, NY 10003, (212)594-8295

Independent Educ. Union of Australia [IO], Deakin West, Australia

Independent Educational Consultants Assn. [8028], 3251 Old Lee Hwy., Ste. 510, Fairfax, VA 22030-1504, (703)591-4850

Independent Educational Counselors Assn. [★8028]

Independent Elecl. Contractors [913], 4401 Ford Ave., Ste. 1100, Alexandria, VA 22302-1432, (703)549-7351

Independent Feature Proj. [1256], 68 Jay St., Rm. 425, Brooklyn, NY 11201, (212)465-8200

Independent Fed. of Chinese Students and Scholars

Independent Fed. of Chinese Students and Scholars - Address unknown since 2011.

Independent Film and TV Alliance [1257], 10850 Wilshire Blvd., 9th Fl., Los Angeles, CA 90024-4321, (310)446-1000

Independent Financial Brokers of Canada [IO], Mississauga, ON, Canada

Independent Footwear Retailers' Assn. [IO], Banbury, United Kingdom

Independent Free Papers of Am. [2938], 107 Hemlock Dr., Rio Grande, NJ 08242, (609)408-8000

Independent Fundamental Churches of Am. [★19620]

Independent Fundamental Churches of Am. [★19620]

Independent Glass Assn. [1577], 354 Westlind Rd., Syracuse, NY 13219, (315)706-9172

Independent Hermetic Rebuilders Assn. [★1708]

Independent Hermetic Rebuilders Assn. [★1708]

The Independent Inst. [18466], 100 Swan Way, Ste. 200, Oakland, CA 94621-1459, (510)632-1366

Independent Insurance Agents of Am. [★1964]

Independent Insurance Agents and Brokers of Am. [1964], 127 S Peyton St., Alexandria, VA 22314, (800)221-7917

Independent Jewelers Org. [2161], 25 Seir Hill Rd., Norwalk, CT 06850, (203)846-4215

Independent Labs. Inst. [2177], 1050 17th St. NW, Ste. 1000, Washington, DC 20006, (202)887-5872

Independent Lab. Distributors Assn. [3175], PO Box 1464, Fairplay, CO 80440, (719)836-9091

Independent Liquid Terminals Assn. [★3620]

Independent Literary Agents Assn. [★161]

Independent Living Canada [IO], Ottawa, ON, Canada

Independent Lubricant Mfrs. Assn. [2652], 400 N Columbus St., Ste. 201, Alexandria, VA 22314-2264, (703)684-5574

Independent Lubricant Mfrs. Assn. [2652], 400 N Columbus St., Ste. 201, Alexandria, VA 22314-2264, (703)684-5574

Independent Media Arts Alliance [IO], Montreal, QC, Canada

Independent Media Arts Preservation [10072], Lehman Coll., Lief Lib. 201, 250 Bedford Park Blvd. W, Bronx, NY 10468

Independent Medical Distributors Assn. [1685], 5204 Fairmount Ave., Downers Grove, IL 60515, (630)655-9280

Independent Midwives UK [IO], Abingdon, United Kingdom

Independent Music Companies Assn. [IO], Brussels, Belgium

Independent Music New Zealand [IO], Auckland, New Zealand

Independent Music Retailers Assn. - Address unknown since 2011.

Independent Natural Gas Assn. of Am. [★4489]

Independent Off. Products and Furniture Dealers Assn. [1552], 301 N Fairfax St., Ste. 200, Alexandria, VA 22314, (800)542-6672

Independent Oil Compounders Assn. [★2652]

Independent Oil Compounders Assn. [★2652]

Independent Online Booksellers Assn. [467], 216 Richard Burbydge, Williamsburg, VA 23185, (757)229-4808

Independent Order of B'nai B'rith [★19849]

Independent Order of B'nai B'rith [★19849]

Independent Order of Foresters [IO], Toronto, ON, Canada

Independent Order of Odd Fellows [19181], 422 Trade St., Winston-Salem, NC 27101, (336)725-5955

Independent Order of Svithiod [19217], 5518 W Lawrence Ave., Chicago, IL 60630, (773)736-1191

Independent Order of Vikings [19050], 5250 S Sixth St., PO Box 5147, Springfield, IL 62705-5147, (877)241-6006

Independent Organic Inspectors Assn. [4761], PO Box 6, Broadus, MT 59317-0006, (406)436-2031

Independent Pet and Animal Trans. Assn. Intl. [2678], 745 Winding Trail, Holly Lake Ranch, TX 75765, (903)769-2267

Independent Petroleum Assn. of Am. [2653], 1201 15th St. NW, Ste. 300, Washington, DC 20005, (202)857-4722

Independent Photo Imagers [2718], 2518 Anthem Village Dr., Ste. 100, Henderson, NV 89052, (702)617-1141

Independent Pilots Assn. [23152], 3607 Fern Valley Rd., Louisville, KY 40219, (502)410-8700

Independent Press Assn. [IO], Chisinau, Moldova

Independent Press Assn. - Defunct.

Independent Print Indus. Assn. [IO], Stafford, United Kingdom

Independent Professional Representatives Org. [276], 34157 W 9 Mile Rd., Farmington Hills, MI 48335, (248)474-0522

Independent Professional Seedsmen Assn. [3757], PO Box 241312, Omaha, NE 68124-5312, (402)991-3550

Independent Progressive Politics Network [18620], PO Box 1041, Bloomfield, NJ 07003, (973)338-5398

Independent Property Managers' Assn. [IO], Christchurch, New Zealand

Independent Psychiatric Assn. of Russia [IO], Moscow, Russia

Independent Publishers Guild [IO], Whitland, United Kingdom

Independent Res. Libraries Assn. [9987], PO Box 7311, Richmond, VA 23221-0311, (804)342-9656

Independent Scholars of Asia - Defunct.

Independent Schools

Amer. Assn. of Presidents of Independent Colleges and Universities [8285]

Center for Spiritual and Ethical Educ. [8286]

Coun. of Independent Colleges [8287]

Found. for Independent Higher Educ. [8288]

Independent Schools Assn. of the Central States [8289]

Natl. Assn. of Independent Colleges and Universities [8290]

Natl. Assn. of Independent Schools [8291]

Independent Schools Assn. of the Central States [8289], 1165 N Clark St., Ste. 311, Chicago, IL 60610, (312)255-1244

Independent Schools Assn. of Southern Africa [IO], Houghton, Republic of South Africa

Independent Schools Coun. [IO], London, United Kingdom

Independent Schools Coun. of Australia [IO], Deakin West, Australia

Independent Schools Coun. Info. Ser. [IO], London, United Kingdom

Independent Schools Educ. Bd. [★8291]

Independent Schools Talent Search Prog. [★8077]

Independent Sector [12675], 1602 L St. NW, Ste. 900, Washington, DC 20036, (202)467-6100

Independent Telephone Assn. of Am. [★3604]

Independent TV Assn. [IO], London, United Kingdom

Independent Terminal Operators Assn. - Address unknown since 2010.

Independent Textile Rental Assn. [3443], PO Box 190, Hogansville, GA 30230, (800)477-7843

Independent Textile Rental Assn. [3443], PO Box 190, Hogansville, GA 30230, (800)477-7843

Independent Theatre Coun. [IO], London, United Kingdom

Independent Time and Labor Mgt. Assn. [3464], Michael Hoover, Sec.-Treas., 2049 Stout Dr., Ste. A-1, Warminster, PA 18974, (215)443-8720

Independent Travel Agencies of America Assn. - Defunct.

Independent Turf and Ornamental Distributors Assn. [2180], 174 Crestview Dr., Bellefonte, PA 16823-8516, (717)243-7677

Independent Univ., Washington-Paris-Moscow [★8343]

Independent Univ., Washington-Paris-Moscow [★8343]

Independent Visually Impaired Enterprisers [17086], 2201 Limerick Dr., Tallahassee, FL 32309, (850)906-9821

Independent Wire Producers Assn. [★1804]

Independent Women's Forum [18345], 1875 I St. NW, Ste. 500, Washington, DC 20006, (202)857-5201

Independent Workers Assn. - Defunct.

Independent Workers Union [IO], Cork, Ireland

Indexing Soc. of Canada [IO], Toronto, ON, Canada

India

Amer. Hindu Assn. [19811]

Assn. of Ayurvedic Professionals of North Am. [13664]

Assn. of Kannada Kootas of Am. [19035]

Child Vikaas Intl. [11161]

Ensaaf [18641]

Friends of Christ in India [19823]

Global Helps Network [11530]

Global India Venture Capital Assn. [1302]

India Development Ser. [18571]

India Partners [17887]

Intl. Alumni Assn. of Shri Mahavir Jain Vidyalaya [19219]

Jagannath Org. for Global Awareness [20213]

Sikh Sports Assn. of the U.S.A. [22894]

Two Cents of Hope [8292]

India Amer. Cultural Assn. [9857], 1281 Cooper Lake Rd. SE, Smyrna, GA 30082, (770)436-3719

India Amer. Cultural Assn. [9857], 1281 Cooper Lake Rd. SE, Smyrna, GA 30082, (770)436-3719

India Club Maldives [IO], Male, Maldives

India Development Ser. [18571], PO Box 980, Chicago, IL 60690, (708)524-2041

India Development Ser. [18571], PO Box 980, Chicago, IL 60690, (708)524-2041

India Literacy Proj. [8531], PO Box 361143, Milpitas, CA 95035-9998

India Literacy Proj. [8531], PO Box 361143, Milpitas, CA 95035-9998

The India Mission [★20023]

The India Mission [★20023]

India Partners [17887], PO Box 5470, Eugene, OR 97405-0470, (541)683-0696

India Semiconductor Assn. [IO], Bangalore, India

India Stud. Circle for Philately [22044], PO Box 7326, Washington, DC 20044, (202)564-6876

India Trade Promotion Org. [IO], New Delhi, India

Indian

Amer. Inst. of Indian Stud. [8293]

Amer. Org. for the Development of Bihar [12302]

Reference to "IO" in place of a book number signifies that the association may be found in the 50th edition of International Organizations.

Encyclopedia of Associations, 51st Edition

2869

Assn. of Indian Muslims of Am. [19033]
Assn. of Indians in Am. [19034]
Assn. of Kannada Kootas of Am. [19035]
Bihar Assn. of North Am. [9856]
Bihar Assn. of North Am. [9856]
GAVI Alliance [14897]
Global Org. of People of Indian Origin [19036]
Help the Helpless [12303]
India Amer. Cultural Assn. [9857]
Indian Amer. Muslim Coun. [17888]
Indicorps [12304]
Intl. Alumni Assn. of Shri Mahavir Jain Vidyalaya [19219]
Jagannath Org. for Global Awareness [20213]
Leuva Patidar Samaj of USA [9858]
Milan Cultural Assn. [9859]
Natl. Fed. of Indian Amer. Associations [19037]
Network of Indian Professionals [19038]
North Amer. Sikh Medical and Dental Assn. [15429]
Old Sleepy Eye Collectors' Club of Am. [21268]
Pratham U.S.A. [12305]
Punjabi-American Cultural Assn. [9860]
Sikh Coun. on Religion and Educ. [20241]
Sikh Sports Assn. of the U.S.A. [22894]
Soc. for Indian Philosophy and Religion [9861]
United Indian Missions Intl. [20102]
U.S. Indian Amer. Chamber of Commerce [23407]
Uttaranchal Assn. of North Am. [9862]
World Malayalee Coun. [19039]
Indian Acad. of Neurology - Clinical Neurophysiology [IO], New Delhi, India
Indian Acad. of Sciences [IO], Bangalore, India
Indian Adult Educ. Assn. [IO], New Delhi, India
Indian Amer. Forum for Political Educ. [18381], 259 Amherst Ave., Colonia, NJ 07067, (781)861-6797
Indian Amer. Muslim Coun. [17888], 6321 W Dempster St., Ste. 295, Morton Grove, IL 60053-2848, (800)839-7270
Indian Arts and Crafts Assn. [10328], 4010 Carlisle Blvd. NE, Ste. C, Albuquerque, NM 87107, (505)265-9149
Indian Assn. of Amusement Parks and Indus. [IO], Mumbai, India
Indian Assn. of Cardiovascular Thoracic Anaesthesiologists [IO], New Delhi, India
Indian Assn. for the Cultivation of Sci. [IO], Calcutta, India
Indian Assn. of Dermatologists, Venereologists and Leprologists Maharashtra Br. [IO], Mumbai, India
Indian Assn. of Gastrointestinal Endosurgeons [IO], Coimbatore, India
Indian Assn. of Physiotherapists [IO], Mumbai, India
Indian Assn. of Secretaries and Administrative Professionals [IO], Mumbai, India
Indian Assn. of Social Sci. Institutions [IO], New Delhi, India
Indian Assn. of Sports Medicine [IO], New Delhi, India
Indian Assn. of Surgical Oncology [IO], New Delhi, India
Indian Banks' Assn. [IO], Mumbai, India
Indian Biophysical Soc. [IO], Mumbai, India
Indian Bus. and Professional Coun., Dubai [IO], Dubai, United Arab Emirates
Indian Cancer Soc. [IO], Mumbai, India
Indian Chamber of Commerce - Calcutta [IO], Calcutta, India
Indian Chamber of Commerce Hong Kong [IO], Hong Kong, People's Republic of China
Indian Chap. of Intl. Hepato Pancreato Biliary Assn. [IO], Mumbai, India
Indian Chem. Coun. [IO], Mumbai, India
Indian Chem. Soc. [IO], Calcutta, India
Indian Children's Fund Australia [IO], Sydney, Australia
Indian Coun. of Agricultural Res. [IO], New Delhi, India
Indian Coun. for Cultural Relations [IO], New Delhi, India
Indian Coun. of Medical Res. [IO], New Delhi, India
Indian Coun. of Social Sci. Res. [IO], New Delhi, India
Indian Dairy Assn. [IO], New Delhi, India
Indian Defense League of Am. [19156], PO Box 305, Niagara Falls, NY 14302

Indian Dental Assn. [IO], Mumbai, India
Indian Dental Assn. U.S.A. [14287], 140 Tulip Ave., Floral Park, NY 11001, (718)639-0192
Indian Diamond and Colorstone Assn. [2162], 56 W 45th St., Ste. 705, New York, NY 10036, (212)921-4488
Indian Drug Mfrs'. Assn. [IO], Mumbai, India
Indian Economic Assn. [IO], Patna, India
Indian Educators Fed. [★8676]
Indian Elecl. and Electronics Mfrs. Assn. [IO], Mumbai, India
Indian Epilepsy Soc. [IO], New Delhi, India
Indian Fed. of Tenants Coun. [IO], Calcutta, India
Indian Footwear Components Mfrs. Assn. [IO], Noida, India
Indian Geotechnical Soc. [IO], New Delhi, India
Indian Inst. of Architects [IO], Mumbai, India
Indian Inst. of Materials Mgt. [IO], Mumbai, India
Indian Inst. of Metals [IO], Calcutta, India
Indian Inst. of Packaging [IO], Mumbai, India
Indian Jute Mills Assn. [IO], Calcutta, India
Indian Law Inst. [IO], New Delhi, India
Indian Law Rsrc. Center [18152], 602 N Ewing St., Helena, MT 59601, (406)449-2006
Indian Medical Assn. [IO], New Delhi, India
Indian Medical Assn. - Bangalore Br. [IO], Bangalore, India
Indian Medical Assn. - Chandigarh [IO], Chandigarh, India
Indian Merchants' Chamber [IO], Mumbai, India
Indian Motion Picture Producers' Assn. [IO], Mumbai, India
Indian Music Indus. [IO], Mumbai, India
Indian Muslim Council-U.S.A. [★17888]
Indian Muslim Relief and Charities [12852], 1000 San Antonio Rd., Ste. 101, Palo Alto, CA 94303, (650)856-0440
Indian Muslim Relief and Charities [12852], 1000 San Antonio Rd., Ste. 101, Palo Alto, CA 94303, (650)856-0440
Indian Natl. Sci. Acad. [IO], New Delhi, India
Indian Natl. Shipowners' Assn. [IO], Mumbai, India
Indian Natl. Trade Union Cong. [IO], New Delhi, India
Indian Navy Found. [IO], New Delhi, India
Indian Newspaper Soc. [IO], New Delhi, India
Indian and Northern Affairs Canada [IO], Ottawa, ON, Canada
Indian Ocean Commn. [IO], Quatre Bornes, Mauritius
Indian Oilseed and Produce Export Promotion Coun. [IO], Mumbai, India
Indian Olympic Assn. [IO], New Delhi, India
Indian Peptide Soc. [IO], New Delhi, India
Indian Pest Control Assn. [IO], New Delhi, India
Indian Pharmaceutical Assn. [IO], Mumbai, India
Indian Pharmacological Soc. [IO], Hyderabad, India
Indian Physics Assn. [IO], Mumbai, India
Indian Phytopathological Soc. [IO], New Delhi, India
Indian Plumbing Assn. [IO], New Delhi, India
Indian Polyurethane Assn. [IO], Chennai, India
Indian Red Cross Soc. [IO], New Delhi, India
Indian Refractory Makers Assn. [IO], Calcutta, India
Indian Rheumatology Assn. [IO], Hyderabad, India
Indian Ritual Object Repatriation Found; Amer. [18149]
Indian Rubber Mfrs. Res. Assn. [IO], Thane, India
Indian Sci. Cong. Assn. [IO], Calcutta, India
Indian Silk Export Promotion Coun. [IO], Mumbai, India
Indian Soc. of Advertisers [IO], Mumbai, India
Indian Soc. of Agricultural Economics [IO], Mumbai, India
Indian Soc. for Antimicrobial Chemotherapy [IO], New Delhi, India
Indian Soc. for Assisted Reproduction [IO], Mumbai, India
Indian Soc. of Cinematographers [IO], Thiruvananthapuram, India
Indian Soc. of Critical Care Medicine [IO], Mumbai, India
Indian Soc. of Geomatics [IO], Ahmedabad, India
Indian Soc. for Mathematical Modelling and Cmpt. Simulation [IO], Kanpur, India
Indian Soc. of Nephrology [IO], Chandigarh, India

Indian Soc. of Neuroradiology [IO], New Delhi, India
Indian Soc. for Parenteral and Enteral Nutrition [IO], Chennai, India
Indian Soc. of Psychosomatic Obstetrics and Gynaecology [IO], Linkoping, Sweden
Indian Soc. of Soil Sci. [IO], New Delhi, India
Indian Soc. for Trenchless Tech. [IO], New Delhi, India
Indian Soc. of Vascular and Interventional Radiology [IO], New Delhi, India
Indian Space Res. Org. [IO], Bangalore, India
Indian Spina Bifida Assn. [IO], Jaipur, India
Indian Stainless Steel Development Assn. [IO], Gurgaon, India
Indian Steam Railway Soc. [IO], New Delhi, India
Indian Sugar Mills Assn. [IO], New Delhi, India
Indian Tea Assn. [IO], Calcutta, India
Indian Textile Accessories and Machinery Mfrs'. Assn. [IO], Mumbai, India
Indian Trade Promotion Org. [IO], New Delhi, India
Indian Unit for Pattern Recognition and Artificial Intelligence [IO], Calcutta, India
Indian Venture Capital Assn. [IO], New Delhi, India
Indian Wind Energy Assn. [IO], New Delhi, India
Indian Women's Assn. [IO], Singapore, Singapore
Indian Youth of Am. [12561], PO Box 2786, Sioux City, IA 51106, (712)252-3230
Indiana Limestone Inst. of Am. [3362], 400 Stone City Bank Bldg., Bedford, IN 47421, (812)275-4426
Indiana State Univ. Alumni Assn. [18875], Indiana State Univ., 30 N 5th St., Terre Haute, IN 47807, (812)237-3707
Indians Into Medicine [8609], UNDSMHS, Rm. 2101, 501 N Columbia Rd., Stop 9037, Grand Forks, ND 58202-9037, (701)777-3037
Indicorps [12304], 3418 Hwy. 6 S, Ste. B, No. 309, Houston, TX 77082, (281)617-1057
Indify [13530], 3418 Hwy. 6 S, Ste. B, No. 309, Houston, TX 77082
Indigenous Communications Assn. - Defunct.
Indigenous Diabetes Educ. Alliance [14352], 2612 Forest Pl., Rapid City, SD 57701, (605)430-6479
Indigenous Environmental Network [4320], PO Box 485, Bemidji, MN 56619, (218)751-4967

Indigenous Peoples
1-2-3 Intl. [12573]
Afoakom-USA [9863]
Afoakom-USA [9863]
Assn. of Kannada Kootas of Am. [19035]
ATAYAL [9864]
Australian Inst. of Aboriginal and Torres Strait Islander Stud. [14688]
Center for World Indigenous Stud. [17889]
Center for World Indigenous Stud. [17889]
First Peoples Worldwide [9865]
First Peoples Worldwide [9865]
For Mother Earth [17890]
Fourth World Documentation Proj. [17891]
Fourth World Documentation Proj. [17891]
HealthShare Intl. [15750]
Hmong Natl. Development [17892]
Indian Defense League of Am. [19156]
Indigenous Peoples Coun. on Biocolonialism [12306]
Intl. Indian Treaty Coun. [17893]
Intl. Indian Treaty Coun. [17893]
Journey to the Heart [9866]
Karen Natl. League [18722]
Lakota Student Alliance [19158]
Mayan Medical Aid [12466]
Natl. Aboriginal Islander Skills Development Assn. [362]
Natl. Org. for Manyu Advancement [18840]
Native Amer. Leadership Alliance [20147]
Native Cultural Alliance [4290]
Native Movement [19166]
Native Public Media [18098]
Ngwa Natl. Assn. USA [19040]
Pueblo a Pueblo [12124]
Pushback Network [18491]
Saq' Be': Org. for Mayan and Indigenous Spiritual Bodies [9867]
Threads Weaving Dreams [12374]
Urhobo Natl. Assn. of North Am. [19178]
World Malayalee Coun. [19039]

A star before a book entry number signifies that the name is not listed separately, but is mentioned within the entry.

World Sound Healing Org. [12640]
Indigenous Peoples Coun. on Biocolonialism [12306], PO Box 72, Nixon, NV 89424, (775)574-0248
Indigo Threads [11596], PO Box 401, La Quinta, CA 92247, (760)564-2679
Indo-American Arts Coun. [9292], 517 E 87th St., Ste. 1B, New York, NY 10128, (212)594-3685
Indo-American Arts Coun. [9292], 517 E 87th St., Ste. 1B, New York, NY 10128, (212)594-3685
Indo-American Chamber of Commerce [IO], Mumbai, India
Indo-American Soc. of Interventional Cardiology
Indo-American Soc. of Interventional Cardiology - Address unknown since 2011.
Indo-Burma Pioneer Mission [★20015]
Indo-Burma Pioneer Mission [★20015]
Indo-French Chamber of Commerce and Indus. [IO], Mumbai, India
Indo-German Chamber of Commerce [IO], Mumbai, India
Indo Madagascar Chamber of Commerce [IO], Antananarivo, Madagascar
Indo-Pacific Conservation Alliance [4079], 1525 Bernice St., Honolulu, HI 96817, (808)848-4124
Indo-Pacific Prehistory Assn. [IO], Canberra, Australia

Indochina
 Amer. Fund for Czech and Slovak Relief [12771]
Indochina Center - Defunct.
Indochina Refugee Action Center [★12790]
Indochina Rsrc. Action Center [★12790]

Indonesia
 Alliance for Tompotika Conservation [3985]
 Amer. Indonesian Chamber of Commerce [23408]
 Indo-Pacific Conservation Alliance [4079]IndonesiaSoc. for Indonesian-Americans
Indonesia Archery Assn. [IO], Jakarta, Indonesia
Indonesia Human Rights Campaign [IO], Thornton Heath, United Kingdom
Indonesia Relief - USA [11856], 2297 Emerald Heights Ct., Reston, VA 20191
Indonesia Sailing Fed. [IO], Jakarta, Indonesia
Indonesia Skateboarding Assn. [IO], Bandung, Indonesia
Indonesian Assn. of Advt. Agencies [IO], Jakarta, Indonesia
Indonesian Assn. for Sports Hea. [IO], Jakarta, Indonesia
Indonesian Chamber of Commerce and Indus. [IO], Jakarta, Indonesia
Indonesian Dancesport Assn. [IO], Jakarta, Indonesia
Indonesian Furniture Indus. and Handicraft Assn. [IO], Jakarta, Indonesia
Indonesian Gas Assn. [IO], Jakarta, Indonesia
Indonesian Heart Assn. [IO], Jakarta, Indonesia
Indonesian ICT Soc. [IO], Jakarta, Indonesia
Indonesian Internet Ser. Provider Assn. [IO], Jakarta, Indonesia
Indonesian Osteoporosis Soc. [IO], Jakarta, Indonesia
Indonesian Physiological Soc. [IO], Surabaya, Indonesia
Indonesian Physiotherapists Assn. [IO], Jakarta, Indonesia
Indonesian Planned Parenthood Assn. [IO], Jakarta, Indonesia
Indonesian Red Cross Soc. [IO], Jakarta, Indonesia
Indonesian Soc. Against Epilepsy [IO], Bandung, Indonesia
Indonesian Soc. for Chemotherapy [IO], Jakarta, Indonesia
Indonesian Soc. for Clinical Neurophysiology [IO], Jakarta, Indonesia
Indonesian Soc. of Dermatology and Venereology [IO], Jakarta, Indonesia
Indonesian Soc. of Digestive Endoscopy [IO], Jakarta, Indonesia
Indonesian Soc. for Geotechnical Engg. [IO], Jakarta, Indonesia
Indonesian Taekwondo Assn. [IO], Jakarta, Indonesia
Indonesian Tennis Assn. [IO], Jakarta, Indonesia
Indoor Air Quality Assn. [4794], 12339 Carroll Ave., Rockville, MD 20852, (301)231-8388

Indoor Gardening Soc. of Am. [21801], 505 Elmhood Ave., No. 4H, Brooklyn, NY 11230, (718)377-0743
Indoor Light Gardening Soc. of Am. [★21801]
Indoor Tennis Assn. [★2743]
Indoor Tennis Assn. [★2743]
Indore Mgt. Assn. [IO], Indore, India
The Indus Entrepreneurs Dubai [IO], Dubai, United Arab Emirates
Indus Women Leaders [18065], 236 W Portal Ave., No. 473, San Francisco, CA 94127
Industria Nacional de Autopartes [★IO]
Indus. Accident Prevention Assn. [IO], Mississauga, ON, Canada
Indus. Areas Found. [17379], 637 S Dearborn St., 1st fl., Chicago, IL 60610, (312)245-9211
Indus. Asset Mgt. Coun. [3014], 6625 The Corners Pkwy., Ste. 200, Norcross, GA 30092, (770)325-3461
Industrial Assn. of Juvenile Apparel Mfrs. - Defunct.
Indus. Assn. of Macau [IO], Macau, Macao
Indus. Auctioneers Assn. [269], 3213 Ayr Ln., Dresher, PA 19025, (215)366-5450
Indus. Audio-Visual Assn. [★274]
Indus. Bag and Cover Assn. [★2607]
Indus. Biotechnology Assn. [★457]
Indus. Cleaning Machine Mfrs'. Assn. [IO], London, United Kingdom
Indus. Commun. Coun. [★807]
Indus. Communications Assn. [★3411]
Indus. Communications Assn. [★3411]
Indus. Cooperative Assn. [★1137]

Industrial Design
 Alliance for Sustainable Built Environments [517]
 Assn. of Women Indus. Designers [6958]
 Assn. of Women Indus. Designers [6958]
 Green Builder Coalition [565]
 Green Building Initiative [566]
 Indus. Designers Soc. of Am. [6959]
Indus. Design Educ. Assn. [★6959]
Indus. Designers Inst. [★6959]
Indus. Designers Soc. of Am. [6959], 45195 Bus. Ct., Ste. 250, Dulles, VA 20166-6717, (703)707-6000

Industrial Development
 Assn. of Defense Communities [5533]
 ClimateTalk Alliance [6111]
 Intl. Economic Development Coun. [5534]
 Intl. Economic Development Coun. [5534]
 Natl. Wind Watch [18788]
Indus. Development Bd. of Ceylon [IO], Moratuwa, Sri Lanka
Indus. Diamond Assn. [1829], PO Box 29460, Columbus, OH 43229, (614)797-2265
Indus. Diamond Assn. of Am. [★1829]
Indus. Diamond Assn. of Japan [IO], Tokyo, Japan
Indus. Distribution Assn. [★1830]

Industrial Education
 Assn. for Skilled and Tech. Sciences [8294]
 Assn. for sTEm Teacher Educ. [8295]
 Assn. of Tech., Mgt. and Applied Engg. [8296]
 Coun. on Tech. Teacher Educ. [8297]
 European Consortium of Innovative Universities [20949]
 Intl. Tech. Educ. Assn. I Coun. on Tech. Teacher Educ. [8297]
 SkillsUSA [8298]
 Tech. Student Assn. [8299]
 WoodLINKS USA [8300]
 WoodLINKS USA [8300]
Indus. Energy Consumers of Am. [1169], 1155 15th St. NW, Ste. 500, Washington, DC 20005, (202)223-1661

Industrial Engineering
 Assn. for Operations Mgt. [6960]
 Assn. for Operations Mgt. [6960]
 Completion Engg. Assn. [6961]
 IEEE I Indus. Applications Soc. [6962]
 Miles Value Found. [6963]
 SAVE Intl. [6964]
 SAVE Intl. [6964]
 SOLE - The Intl. Soc. of Logistics [6965]
 SOLE - The Intl. Soc. of Logistics [6965]

Industrial Equipment
 Abrasive Engg. Soc. [1795]
 Abrasive Engg. Soc. [1795]

 Amer. Bearing Mfrs. Assn. [1796]
 Amer. Boiler Mfrs. Assn. [1797]
 Amer. Chain Assn. [1798]
 Amer. Gear Mfrs. Assn. [1799]
 Amer. Gear Mfrs. Assn. [1799]
 Amer. Machine Tool Distributors' Assn. [1800]
 Amer. Mold Builders Assn. [1801]
 Amer. Textile Machinery Assn. [1802]
 Amer. Wire Cloth Inst. [1803]
 Amer. Wire Producers Assn. [1804]
 Antique Caterpillar Machinery Owners Club [21878]
 Antique Small Engine Collectors Club [21702]
 Assoc. Equip. Distributors [1805]
 Assoc. Wire Rope Fabricators [1806]
 Assn. of Equip. Mgt. Professionals [1807]
 Assn. of Equip. Mgt. Professionals [1807]
 Assn. of Ingersoll-Rand Distributors [1808]
 Assn. of Suppliers to the Paper Indus. [1809]
 Assn. of Vacuum Equip. Mfrs. [1810]
 Assn. of Vacuum Equip. Mfrs. [1810]
 Automated Storage/Retrieval Systems [1811]
 Automatic Guided Vehicle Systems Sect. of the Material Handling Inst. [1812]
 Bearing Specialists Assn. [1813]
 Casting Indus. Suppliers Assn. [1814]
 Compressed Air and Gas Inst. [1815]
 Contractors Pump Bur. [1816]
 Converting Equip. Mfrs. Assn. [1817]
 Conveyor Equip. Mfrs. Assn. [1818]
 Coun. of Indus. Boiler Owners [1819]
 Crane Mfrs. Assn. of Am. [1820]
 Energy Storage Coun. [6722]
 European Confed. of Iron and Steel Indus. [11828]
 Fabricators and Mfrs. Assn. Intl. [1821]
 Fabricators and Mfrs. Assn. Intl. [1821]
 Fluid Controls Inst. [1822]
 Fluid Sealing Assn. [1823]
 FPDA Motion and Control Network [1824]
 Gases and Welding Distributors Assn. [1825]
 Gasket Fabricators Assn. [1826]
 Hoist Mfrs. Inst. [1827]
 Hydraulic Inst. [1828]
 Indus. Auctioneers Assn. [269]
 Indus. Diamond Assn. [1829]
 Indus. Supply Assn. [1830]
 Intl. Assn. of Diecutting and Diemaking [1831]
 Intl. Assn. of Diecutting and Diemaking [1831]
 Intl. Assn. of Elevator Consultants [1832]
 Intl. Coun. for Machinery Lubrication [7034]
 Intl. Glove Assn. [1833]
 Intl. Glove Assn. [1833]
 Intl. Soc. for Concrete Pavements [574]
 Intl. Special Tooling and Machining Assn. [1834]
 Intl. Special Tooling and Machining Assn. [1834]
 Investment Casting Inst. [1835]
 Investment Casting Inst. [1835]
 Iron Casting Res. Inst. [1836]
 Loading Dock Equip. Mfrs. [1837]
 Machine Knife Assn. [1838]
 Machinery Dealers Natl. Assn. [1839]
 Machinery Dealers Natl. Assn. [1839]
 Mfrs. of Aerial Devices and Digger-Derricks Coun. [1840]
 Mfrs. Standardization Soc. of the Valve and Fittings Indus. [1841]
 Mfrs. Standardization Soc. of the Valve and Fittings Indus. [1841]
 Mfrs. of Telescoping and Articulated Cranes Coun. [1842]
 MAPI [1843]
 Material Handling Equip. Distributors Assn. [1844]
 Material Handling Indus. of Am. [1845]
 Material Handling Inst. of Amer., Lift Mfrs. Prdt. Sect. [1846]
 Materials Handling Indus. of Am. I Electrification and Controls Mfrs. Assn. [1847]
 Mech. Power Transmission Assn. [1848]
 Metal Treating Inst. [2481]
 Millwright Gp. [23221]
 Monorail Mfrs. Assn. [1849]
 Natl. Assn. of Hose and Accessories Distribution [1850]
 Natl. Elevator Indus., Inc. [1851]

Reference to "IO" in place of a book number signifies that the association may be found in the 50th edition of International Organizations.

Natl. Fluid Power Assn. [1852]
Natl. Fluid Power Assn. [1852]
Natl. Indus. Belting Assn. [1853]
Natl. Pavement Contractors Assn. [595]
Non-Ferrous Founders' Soc. [1854]
North Amer. Die Casting Assn. [1855]
North Amer. Punch Mfrs. Assn. [1856]
Powder Actuated Tool Mfrs'. Inst. [1857]
Power Crane and Shovel Assn. [1858]
Power-Motion Tech. Representatives Assn. [1859]
Power Transmission Distributors Assn. [1860]
Power Transmission Distributors Assn. [1860]
Pressure Vessel Mfrs. Assn. [1861]
Pressure Washer Mfrs. Assn. [1862]
Process Equip. Mfrs. Assn. [1863]
Rack Mfrs. Inst. [1864]
Rack Mfrs. Inst. [1864]
Resistance Welding Mfg. Alliance [1865]
Secondary Materials and Recycled Textiles [1866]
Secondary Materials and Recycled Textiles [1866]
Sewn Products Equip. and Suppliers of the
   Americas [1867]
Soc. of Professional Rope Access Technicians
   [1868]
Specialty Tools and Fasteners Distributors Assn.
   [1869]
Steel Founders' Soc. of Am. [1870]
Steel Founders' Soc. of Am. [1870]
Storage Equip. Mfrs. Assn. [1871]
Supplier Excellence Alliance [1872]
Surface Mount Tech. Assn. [1873]
Tooling, Mfg. and Technologies Assn. [1874]
Unified Abrasives Mfrs'. Assn. - Grain Comm.
   [1875]
Unified Abrasives Mfrs'. Assn. - Superabrasives
   Div. [1876]
U.S. Cutting Tool Inst. [1877]
Water and Wastewater Equip. Mfrs. Assn. [1878]
Web Sling and Tie Down Assn. [1879]
Wood Machinery Mfrs. of Am. [1880]
Woodworking Machinery Indus. Assn. [1881]
Woven Wire Products Assn. [1882]
Indus. Fabrics Assn. Intl. [3444], 1801 County Rd. B
   W, Roseville, MN 55113-4061, (651)222-2508
Indus. Fabrics Assn. Intl. [3444], 1801 County Rd. B
   W, Roseville, MN 55113-4061, (651)222-2508
Indus. Fasteners Inst. [1651], 6363 Oak Tree Blvd.,
   Independence, OH 44131, (216)241-1482
Indus. Fiber Soc. [★6860]
Indus. Forestry Assn. [★1473]
Indus. Found. of Am. [1150], 179 Enterprise Pkwy.,
   Ste. 102, Boerne, TX 78006, (830)249-7899
Indus. Furnace Mfrs. Assn. [★1704]
Indus. Gas Cleaning Inst. [★2786]
Indus. Heating Equip. Assn. [1704], 5040 Old Taylor
   Mill, PMB No. 13, Taylor Mill, KY 41015, (859)356-
   1575
Indus. Heritage Assn. of Ireland [IO], Dublin, Ireland
Indus. Hydraulics Training Assn. [★6865]
Indus. Insurers' Conf. [★1990]
Indus. Mgt. Soc. [★6799]
Industrial Mathematics Soc. - Defunct.
Indus. Methods Soc. [★2304]
Indus. Minerals Assn. - North Am. [2505], 2011
   Pennsylvania Ave. NW, Ste. 301, Washington, DC
   20006, (202)457-0200
Indus. Minerals Assn. - North Am. [2505], 2011
   Pennsylvania Ave. NW, Ste. 301, Washington, DC
   20006, (202)457-0200
Indus. Network [★2597]
Indus. Perforators Assn. [2472], 6737 W Washington
   St., Milwaukee, WI 53214, (414)389-8618
Industrial Photographers of New Jersey - Defunct.
Indus. Relations Res. Assn. [★23236]
Indus. Res. Inst. [7329], 2200 Clarendon Blvd., Ste.
   1102, Arlington, VA 22201, (703)647-2580
Indus. Safety Equip. Assn. [★3143]
Indus. Safety Equip. Assn. [★3143]
Indus. Sanitation Mgt. Assn. [★2246]
Industrial Security
ASIS Intl. [1883]
ASIS Intl. [1883]
Assn. of Certified Fraud Examiners [1884]
Assn. of Certified Fraud Examiners [1884]
Assn. of Certified Fraud Specialists [1885]

Bus. Espionage Controls and Countermeasures
   Assn. [1886]
Bus. Espionage Controls and Countermeasures
   Assn. [1886]
Communications Fraud Control Assn. [1887]
Communications Fraud Control Assn. [1887]
Cmpt. Security Inst. [1888]
Energy Security Coun. [1889]
Info. Systems Security Assn. [1890]
Info. Systems Security Assn. [1890]
NCMS - Soc. of Indus. Security Professionals
   [1891]
Transported Asset Protection Assn. [7396]
Indus. Soc. [IO], Santiago, Chile
Indus. Stapling Mfrs. Inst. [★1653]
Indus. Stapling Mfrs. Inst. [★1653]
Indus. Stapling and Nailing Tech. Assn. [★1653]
Indus. Stapling and Nailing Tech. Assn. [★1653]
Indus. Supply Assn. [1830], 100 N 20th St., 4th Fl.,
   Philadelphia, PA 19103, (215)320-3862
Indus. Supply and Machinery Mfrs. Assn. [★1830]
Indus. Supply Mfrs. Assn. [★1830]
Indus. Telecommunications Assn. [★3407]
Indus. TV Soc. [★1262]
Indus. TV Soc. [★1262]
Indus. Truck Assn. [330], 1750 K St. NW, Ste. 460,
   Washington, DC 20006, (202)296-9880
Industrial Union Dept. (of AFL-CIO) - Defunct.
Indus. Unit Heater Assn. [★1697]
Indus. Unit Heater Assn. [★1697]
Indus. Wire Cloth Inst. [★1803]
Industrial Workers
AFL-CIO [23217]
Australian Mfg. Workers' Union [2680]
Indus. Workers of the World [23218]
Indus. Workers of the World [23218]
Intl. Union of Elevator Constructors [23219]
Intl. Union of Elevator Constructors [23219]
Intl. Union of Indus. and Independent Workers
   [23312]
Machinists Non-Partisan Political League [23220]
Millwright Gp. [23221]
Natl. Org. of Indus. Trade Unions [23222]
Voluntary Protection Prog. Assn. for Constr.
   [15910]
Indus. Workers of the World [23218], PO Box
   180195, Chicago, IL 60618, (773)857-1090
Indus. Workers of the World [23218], PO Box
   180195, Chicago, IL 60618, (773)857-1090
Indus. Workers of the World Starbucks Workers
   Union [23311], 44-61 11th St., 3rd Fl., Long Island
   City, NY 11101, (612)598-6205
Industrialists' Assn. of Panama [IO], Panama City,
   Panama
Industrie Mondiale de l'Automedication Responsable
   [★IO]
Industrieverband Heimtierbedarf [★IO]
Industrieverband Korperpflege-und Waschmittel e.V.
   [★IO]
Industrievereinigung Chemiefaser [★IO]
Indus. Bar Code Alliance [★282]
Indus. Coun. for Electronic Equip. Recycling [IO],
   London, United Kingdom
Indus. Coun. for Packaging and the Env. [IO], Read-
   ing, United Kingdom
Indus. Coun. for Tangible Assets [3378], PO Box
   1365, Severna Park, MD 21146-8365, (410)626-
   7005
Indus. Film Producers Assn. [★1259]
Indus. Film Producers Assn. [★1259]
Indus. and Investment NSW Rural Women's
   Network [IO], Orange, Australia
Industry Planning Coun. - Defunct.
Indus. Tech. Facilitator [IO], Aberdeen, United
   Kingdom
Indus. for Turnaround [IO], London, United Kingdom
Infact [★18197]
Infact [★18197]
Infancy Intl. [14113], PO Box 180461, Delafield, WI
   53018, (310)295-4255
Infant Death Syndrome Inst; Amer. Sudden [16759]
Infant Feeding Action Coalition - Canada [IO], Tor-
   onto, ON, Canada
Infant Massage USA [15268], 7481 Huntsman Blvd.,
   Ste. 635, Springfield, VA 22153, (703)455-3455

Infant and Nursery Products Assn. of Australia [IO],
   Boronia, Australia
Infante Sano - Address unknown since 2010.
Infants
Children with AIDS Proj. of Am. [10783]
Fed. of Pediatric Organizations [16145]
Geneva Infant Feeding Assn. [12108]
Global Alliance to Prevent Prematurity and
   Stillbirth [14105]
Global Neuro Rescue [15593]
Intl. Baby Food Action Network - Africa [16250]
Intl. Baby Food Action Network - Asia [15692]
Intl. Baby Food Action Network - Brazil [14544]
Intl. Baby Food Action Network - Latin Am.
   [16794]
La Leche League Intl. [11480]
Mama Baby Haiti [14107]
One More Soul [18561]
Infants', Children's and Girls' Sportswear and Coat
   Assn. - Defunct.
INFARMA - Employers' Union of Innovative
   Pharmaceutical Companies [IO], Warsaw, Poland
Infection Control Assn. Australian Capital Territory
   [IO], Garran, Australia
Infection Control Assn. New South Wales [IO], Croy-
   don, Australia
Infection Control Assn. of Singapore [IO], Singapore,
   Singapore
Infection Control Assn. of South Australia [IO], North
   Adelaide, Australia
Infection Control Assn. of Western Australia [IO],
   Claremont, Australia
Infection Control and Epidemiology; Certification Bd.
   of [14875]
Infection Control Nurses' Assn. [IO], Bathgate,
   United Kingdom
Infection Control Practitioners Assn. of Queensland
   [IO], Buranda, Australia
Infectionists Sci. Soc. of Republic Belarus [IO],
   Vitebsk, Belarus
Infectious Disease Soc. of the Netherlands [IO],
   Bilthoven, Netherlands
Infectious Diseases
AIDS-Free World [13594]
Amer. Sepsis Alliance [15114]
Assn. for Professionals in Infection Control and
   Epidemiology [15115]
Blood: Water Mission [10809]
Childhood Influenza Immunization Coalition
   [15102]
Frontline Hepatitis Awareness [14983]
Global Medic Force [15173]
Global Solutions for Infectious Diseases [15116]
Global Youth Coalition on HIV/AIDS [10881]
Infectious Diseases Soc. of Am. [15117]
Infectious Diseases Soc. of Am. Emerging Infec-
   tions Network [15118]
Intl. Alliance for the Prevention of AIDS [13614]
Intl. Leptospirosis Soc. [15119]
Intl. Leptospirosis Soc. [15119]
Intl. Soc. for Infectious Diseases [15120]
Intl. Soc. for Infectious Diseases [15120]
Intl. Soc. for Vaccines [15109]
Lily of the Valley Endeavor [10886]
Natl. Assn. on HIV Over Fifty [15121]
Natl. Found. for Infectious Diseases [15122]
Parents of Kids with Infectious Diseases [15123]
Pediatric Infectious Diseases Soc. [15124]
Pediatric Infectious Diseases Soc. [15124]
Time for Lyme [15125]
Infectious Diseases Gp. of Pakistan Paediatric Assn.
   [IO], Lahore, Pakistan
Infectious Diseases Soc. of Am. [15117], 1300
   Wilson Blvd., Ste. 300, Arlington, VA 22209,
   (703)299-0200
Infectious Diseases Soc. of Am. Emerging Infections
   Network [15118], Susan Beekmann, RN, Prog.
   Coor., Univ. of Iowa, Carver Coll. of Medicine, SW
   34 JGH, 200 Hawkins Dr., Iowa City, IA 52242,
   (319)384-8622
Infectious Diseases Soc. of Pakistan [IO], Karachi,
   Pakistan
Infertility Assn; Resolve, The Natl. [14535]
Infertility Awareness Assn. of Canada [IO], Montreal,
   QC, Canada

A star before a book entry number signifies that the name is not listed separately, but is mentioned within the entry.

Infertility Info. Dissemination; Intl. Coun. on [14533]
Infertility Info. Dissemination; Intl. Coun. on [14533]
Infertility Network Exchange; Natl. [12612]
Infertility Network UK [IO], Bexhill-on-Sea, United Kingdom
InfiniBand Trade Assn. [6454], 3855 SW 153rd Dr., Beaverton, OR 97006, (503)619-0565
Inflammation Res. Assn. [14389], 10300 Campus Point Dr., San Diego, CA 92121, (858)638-8572
Inflammatory Skin Disease Inst. [14390], PO Box 1074, Newport News, VA 23601, (757)223-0795
Inflatable Advt. Dealers Assn. [92], PO Box 502, Tipp City, OH 45371, (937)405-5943
Inflight Food Ser. Assn. [★1445]
Inflight Food Ser. Assn. [★1445]
InfoComm Intl. [277], 11242 Waples Mill Rd., Ste. 200, Fairfax, VA 22030, (703)273-7200
InfoComm Intl. [277], 11242 Waples Mill Rd., Ste. 200, Fairfax, VA 22030, (703)273-7200
INFORM [18647], 318 W 39th St., 5th Fl., New York, NY 10018, (212)361-2400
Informatics
  Amer. Osteopathic Assn. of Medical Informatics [16065]
  Cooperative Assn. for Internet Data Anal. [7007]
  Intl. Assn. of Info. Tech. Asset Managers [1892]
  Intl. Assn. of Info. Tech. Asset Managers [1892]
  Intl. Soc. for Computational Biology [1893]
  Intl. Soc. for Computational Biology [1893]
Informatikai Vallalkozasok Szovetsege [★IO]
Info. for Action [IO], Perth, Australia
Info. Centre on Southern Africa [IO], Bonn, Germany
Info. and Communications Tech. Coun. [IO], Ottawa, ON, Canada
Info. and Communications Tech. Ireland [IO], Dublin, Ireland
Info. and Communications Tech. Soc. of Trinidad and Tobago [IO], Port of Spain, Trinidad and Tobago
Info. Div., Taipei Economic and Cultural Off. in New York [★9480]
The Information Exchange - Defunct.
Info. Film Producers of Am. [★1259]
Info. Film Producers of Am. [★1259]
Information Industry Liaison Comm. - Defunct.
Info. Indus. South Africa [IO], Midrand, Republic of South Africa
Information Management
  Accessibility Interoperability Alliance [6966]
  AIIM - The Enterprise Content Mgt. Assn. [1894]
  Alliance of Info. and Referral Systems [6967]
  Alliance of Info. and Referral Systems [6967]
  Amer. Booksellers Found. for Free Expression [17727]
  Amer. Coll. of Healthcare Info. Administrators [14753]
  Amer. Coun. for Tech. [5535]
  Amer. Lib. Assn. - Public Info. Off. [10476]
  Amer. Osteopathic Assn. of Medical Informatics [16065]
  Amer. Soc. of Access Professionals [5536]
  Amer. Soc. for Info. Sci. and Tech. [6968]
  ARMA Intl. - The Assn. of Info. Mgt. Professionals [1895]
  ARMA Intl. - The Assn. of Info. Mgt. Professionals [1895]
  Assn. of Certified Green Tech. Auditors [6692]
  Assn. for Configuration and Data Mgt. [6969]
  Assn. for Fed. Info. Resources Mgt. [5537]
  Assn. of Independent Info. Professionals [1896]
  Assn. of Independent Info. Professionals [1896]InformationAssn. of Info. and Dissemination Centers
  Assn. of Medical Directors of Info. Systems [15126]
  Assn. of Public Data Users [6970]
  Broadband Forum [1897]
  Canadian IT Law Assn. [17157]
  Chinese Info. and Networking Assn. [6971]
  Coalition for Networked Info. [6972]
  Coll. of Healthcare Info. Mgt. Executives [1898]
  Connect Worldwide [6510]
  Coun. of Professional Associations on Fed. Statistics [5538]
  Customers of SirsiDynix User Gp. Inc. [6973]

Cyber Security Indus. Alliance [6974]
Data Mgt. Assn. Intl. [6975]
Data Mgt. Assn. Intl. [6975]
Document Security Alliance [5539]
Edutechnia [6976]
Electronic Document Systems Found. [1899]
Electronic Privacy Info. Center [6977]
European Fed. for Medical Informatics [15981]
Fed. Consumer Info. Center Prog. [5540]
Global Tech. Distribution Coun. [3392]
Govt. Mgt. Info. Sciences [5541]
HIMSS Electronic Hea. Record Assn. [15332]
ICRA [11920]
Info. Resources Mgt. Assn. [1900]
Info. Resources Mgt. Assn. [1900]
Inst. of Certified Records Managers [1901]
Intl. Assn. of Chiefs of Police I Law Enforcement Info. Mgt. Sect. [5542]
Intl. Assn. for Cmpt. and Info. Sci. [6456]
Intl. Assn. for Info. and Data Quality [6978]
Intl. Assn. of Privacy Professionals [1902]
Intl. Assn. of Privacy Professionals [1902]
Intl. DB2 Users Gp. [6592]
Intl. Records Mgt. Trust [22135]
Intl. Soc. for Ethics and Info. Tech. [6979]
Intl. Soc. of Info. Fusion [6980]
Intl. Soc. of Info. Fusion [6980]
IT Ser. Mgt. Forum USA [6981]
Ithaka [6982]
Knowledge Mgt. Professional Soc. [1903]
Latinos in Info. Sciences and Tech. Assn. [6983]
Medical Records Inst. [15333]
Meta-Data Professional Org. [6984]
MSPAlliance [6547]
Natl. Assn. of Govt. Archives and Records Administrators [5543]
Natl. Assn. for Info. Destruction [1904]
Natl. Assn. for Info. Destruction [1904]
Natl. Assn. for Public Hea. Info. Tech. [6985]
Natl. Assn. of State Chief Info. Officers [5544]
Natl. Fed. of Abstracting and Info. Services [6986]
Natl. Fed. of Abstracting and Info. Services [6986]
Natl. Freedom of Info. Coalition [18437]
Natl. Info. Standards Org. [6987]
Natl. MIS User Gp. [6988]
Natl. Public Records Res. Assn. [1905]
NiUG Intl. [6989]
Nuclear Info. Tech. Strategic Leadership [7170]
ODF Alliance [6990]
ODF Alliance [6990]
Open DeviceNet Vendor Assn. [6492]
The Open Gp. [1906]
Panel on World Data Centers [6991]
Panel on World Data Centers [6991]
PRISM Intl. [1907]
PRISM Intl. [1907]
SCSI Trade Assn. [1908]
SEARCH - The Natl. Consortium for Justice Info. and Statistics [11734]
Soc. of Competitive Intelligence Professionals [6993]
Software and Tech. Vendors' Assn. [819]
Special Interest Gp. on Info. Retrieval [6992]
Strategic and Competitive Intelligence Professionals [6993]
Supply-Chain Coun. [1909]
Supply-Chain Coun. [1909]
Tech. Councils of North Am. [6994]
Tech. Councils of North Am. [6994]
Urban and Regional Info. Systems Assn. [6995]
Usability Professionals' Assn. [1910]
Usability Professionals' Assn. [1910]
World Org. of Webmasters [1911]
World Org. of Webmasters [1911]
Zangle Natl. Users' Gp. [6996]
Information Processing
  Assn. for Educ. in Healthcare Info. Tech. [15369]
  Cyber Security Indus. Alliance [6974]
  Intl. DB2 Users Gp. [6592]
  Intl. Soc. for Ethics and Info. Tech. [6979]
  Irish Internet Assn. [5626]
  Latinos in Info. Sciences and Tech. Assn. [6983]
  ODF Alliance [6990]
  Open DeviceNet Vendor Assn. [6492]
Info. Processing Soc. of Japan [IO], Tokyo, Japan

Info. Rsrc. Mgt. Assn. of Canada [IO], Toronto, ON, Canada
Info. Resources Mgt. Assn. [1900], 701 E Chocolate Ave., Ste. 200, Hershey, PA 17033-1240, (717)533-8845
Info. Resources Mgt. Assn. [1900], 701 E Chocolate Ave., Ste. 200, Hershey, PA 17033-1240, (717)533-8845
Info. for School and Coll. Governors [IO], Gerrards Cross, United Kingdom
Info. Sci. and Automation Div. [★9992]
Info. Services on Latin Am. [18054], PO Box 6103, Albany, CA 94706, (510)996-2318
Info. Storage Indus. Consortium [6538], 12396 World Trade Dr., Ste. 201, San Diego, CA 92128, (858)279-7230
Info. Systems Audit and Control Assn. and Found. [67], 3701 Algonquin Rd., Ste. 1010, Rolling Meadows, IL 60008, (847)253-1545
Info. Systems Audit and Control Assn. and Found. [67], 3701 Algonquin Rd., Ste. 1010, Rolling Meadows, IL 60008, (847)253-1545
Info. Systems Audit and Control Assn. and Found. Singapore [IO], Singapore, Singapore
Info. Systems Mgt. Benchmarking Consortium [668], 4606 FM 1960 W, Ste. 250, Houston, TX 77069-9949, (281)440-5044
Info. Systems Security Assn. [1890], 9220 SW Barbur Blvd., No. 119-333, Portland, OR 97219, (206)388-4584
Info. Systems Security Assn. [1890], 9220 SW Barbur Blvd., No. 119-333, Portland, OR 97219, (206)388-4584
Info. Systems Security Assn. Brussels-European Chap. [IO], Brussels, Belgium
Info. Systems Security Assn. - Netherlands Chap. [IO], Badhoevedorp, Netherlands
Info. Technologies Credit Union Assn. - Address unknown since 2010.
Info. Tech. Alliance [7042], 23940 N 73rd Pl., Scottsdale, AZ 85255, (480)515-2003
Info. Tech. Assn. of Canada [IO], Mississauga, ON, Canada
Info. Tech. Assn. of Grenada [IO], St. George's, Grenada
Info. Tech. Assn. of Jordan [IO], Amman, Jordan
Info. Tech. Assn. of South Africa [IO], Halfway House, Republic of South Africa
Info. Tech. Contract and Recruitment Assn. [IO], Melbourne, Australia
Info. Tech. Indus. Coun. [6539], 1101 K St. NW, Ste. 610, Washington, DC 20005, (202)737-8888
Info. Tech. Mgt. Assn. Singapore [IO], Singapore, Singapore
Info. Tech. Professionals Assn. of Am. - Address unknown since 2011.
Info. Tech. Providers Assn. of Guyana [IO], Georgetown, Guyana
Information Technology Resellers Assn. - Defunct.
Info. Tech. Services Marketing Assn. [2405], Lexington Off. Park, 420 Bedford St., Ste. 110, Lexington, MA 02420, (781)862-8500
Info. Tech. Soc. [IO], Frankfurt, Germany
Info. and Telecommunications Technologies Gp. of Electronic Indus. Assn. [★3422]
Informationsstelle Sudliches Afrika [★IO]
Informed Consent [★11520]
Informed Consent [★11520]
Informed Families Educ. Center I Natl. Family Partnership [13256], 2490 Coral Way, Ste. 501, Miami, FL 33145, (305)856-4886
Infoshare Intl.
Infoshare Intl. - Address unknown since 2011.
InfraGard Natl. Members Alliance [5968], Eagle Crest Bldg., 225 N Humphreys Blvd., Ste. 3000, Memphis, TN 38120-2107, (901)747-4300
Infrared Data Assn. [6591], PO Box 3883, Walnut Creek, CA 94598, (925)943-6546
Infrared Data Assn. [6591], PO Box 3883, Walnut Creek, CA 94598, (925)943-6546
The Infrastructure Security Partnership [3212], 607 Prince St., Alexandria, VA 22314-3117, (703)549-3800
Infusion Nurses Soc. [16853], 315 Norwood Park S, Norwood, MA 02062, (781)440-9408

Reference to "IO" in place of a book number signifies that the association may be found in the 50th edition of International Organizations.

Ingalls Wilder Memorial Soc; Laura [9391]
Ingenieurs Canada [★IO]
Ingenieurs Sans Frontieres [★IO]
Ingeniorforeningen i Danmark [★IO]
Ingenjorsforbundet [★IO]
Inglewood and Region Olive Co-operative [IO], Inglewood, Australia
Inhalation Therapy Assn. [★16834]
Inhlangano Yezokusakaza Eningizimu Afrika [★IO]
Initiative for Development and Cooperation - Montenegro [IO], Podgorica, Montenegro
Initiative for Global Development [12731], 1215 4th Ave., Ste. 650, Seattle, WA 98161, (206)373-7150
Initiativen der Veranderung [★IO]
Initiatives of Change [17801], 2201 W Broad St., Ste. 200, Richmond, VA 23220, (804)358-1764
Initiatives of Change [17801], 2201 W Broad St., Ste. 200, Richmond, VA 23220, (804)358-1764
Initiatives of Change - Switzerland [IO], Lucerne, Switzerland
Initiators - Defunct.
InJAz Bahrain [IO], Manama, Bahrain
Injury Control Center [★16927]
Injury Control Res. Center [★16927]
Injury Control Res. Center; Harvard [16927]
Injury Prevention Res. Center; Univ. of Iowa [7347]
Inkjet Cartridge Recycling Assn. - Defunct.
Inland Bird Banding Assn. [7201], 1833 S Winfield Dr., Tiffin, OH 44883
Inland Intl. Trade Assn. - Defunct.
Inland Lake Yachting Assn. [22342], PO Box 311, Fontana, WI 53125, (262)203-7721
Inland Marine Underwriters Assn. [1965], 14 Wall St., 8th Fl., New York, NY 10005, (212)233-0550
Inland Press Assn. [2939], 701 Lee St., Ste. 925, Des Plaines, IL 60016, (847)795-0380
Inland Rivers Ports and Terminals [2379], 316 Bd. of Trade Pl., New Orleans, LA 70130, (504)585-0715
Inland Seas Educ. Assn. [2356], 100 Dame St., Suttons Bay, MI 49682, (231)271-3077
Inland Waterways Advisory Coun. [IO], London, United Kingdom
Inland Waterways Assn. of England [IO], Chesham, United Kingdom
Inland Waterways Assn. of Ireland [IO], Dublin, Ireland
Inlandboatman's Union of the Pacific [2380], 1711 W Nickerson St., Ste. D, Seattle, WA 98119, (206)284-6001
Inliners Intl. [21073], Jean Weigt, Membership Chair, 14 E Main St., Winters, CA 95694, (530)795-0224
Inliners Intl. [21073], Jean Weigt, Membership Chair, 14 E Main St., Winters, CA 95694, (530)795-0224
INMED Partnerships for Children [15189], 20110 Ashbrook Pl., Ste. 260, Ashburn, VA 20147, (703)729-4951
INMED Partnerships for Children [15189], 20110 Ashbrook Pl., Ste. 260, Ashburn, VA 20147, (703)729-4951
Inn Sign Soc. [IO], Wolverhampton, United Kingdom
Inner Circle of Advocates [5773], Mark S. Davis, Pres., 400 Davis Levin Livingston Pl., 851 Fort St., Honolulu, HI 96813, (808)524-7500
Inner Light Found. [7330], PO Box 750265, Petaluma, CA 94975, (707)765-2200
Inner Peace Movement [9824], PO Box 681757, San Antonio, TX 78268, (877)475-7792
Inner Wheel New Zealand [IO], Auckland, New Zealand
Innes Clan Soc. [20538], 8351 Lekcin Ln., Concrete, WA 98237
Innes Clan Soc. [20538], 8351 Lekcin Ln., Concrete, WA 98237
Innholders' Company [IO], London, United Kingdom
Innocence in Danger - U.S.A. [11319], 200 Chambers St., Ste. 27A, New York, NY 10007, (866)552-7840
Innocence in Danger U.S.A. [11319], 200 Chambers St., Ste. 27A, New York, NY 10007, (866)552-7840
Innocence Proj. [5372], 40 Worth St., Ste. 701, New York, NY 10013, (212)364-5340
Innocents at Risk [12241], 1101 30th St. NW, Ste. 500, Washington, DC 20007, (202)625-4338
Innovation
    Bus. Retention and Expansion Intl. [1055]

ClimateTalk Alliance [6111]
    Innovation: Africa [6114]
    Innovation Network [1912]
    Innovations for Poverty Action [17190]
    mHealth Alliance [15198]
    Natl. Collegiate Inventors and Innovators Alliance [6997]
    Water Innovations Alliance [7614]
Innovation: Africa [6114], 520 8th Ave., 4th Fl., New York, NY 10018, (212)710-6430
Innovation Mgt. Assn. of Canada [IO], Ottawa, ON, Canada
Innovation Network [1912], 8200 Kroll Way, No. 72, Bakersfield, CA 93311, (870)656-4141
Innovation Norway - U.S. [23368], 655 3rd Ave., Rm. 1810, New York, NY 10017-9111, (212)885-9700
Innovation Norway - United States [23368], 655 3rd Ave., Rm. 1810, New York, NY 10017-9111, (212)885-9700
Innovations in Civic Participation [17253], 1776 Massachusetts Ave. NW, Ste. 201, Washington, DC 20036, (202)775-0290
Innovations in Civic Participation [17253], 1776 Massachusetts Ave. NW, Ste. 201, Washington, DC 20036, (202)775-0290
Innovations for Poverty Action [17190], 101 Whitney Ave., New Haven, CT 06510, (203)772-2216
Innovations et Reseaux pour le Developpement [★IO]
Innovative Support to Emergencies Diseases and Disasters [11857], 480 S California Ave., Ste. 104, Palo Alto, CA 94306, (650)326-5000
Innovative Support to Emergencies Diseases and Disasters [11857], 480 S California Ave., Ste. 104, Palo Alto, CA 94306, (650)326-5000
Innovators and Entrepreneurs Assn. [IO], Singapore, Singapore
Inorganic Feed Phosphates/CEFIC Sector Gp. [IO], Brussels, Belgium
INROADS [8486], 10 S Broadway, Ste. 300, St. Louis, MO 63102, (314)241-7488
INSA, The Intl. Ser. Assn. for Hea. [★15164]
INSA, The Intl. Ser. Assn. for Hea. [★15164]
Insect Screening Weavers Assn. - Defunct.
Insects
    Bee Native [3839]
    Black Entomologists [6840]
    The Intl. Lepidoptera Survey [6845]
    Natl. Entomology Scent Detection Canine Assn. [2633]
    Overseas Chinese Entomologists Assn. [6849]
INSEE Info Ser. [IO], Paris, France
InsideOut Intl. - Address unknown since 2011.
Insight Arts [9293], 6934 N Glenwood Ave., No. 2C, Chicago, IL 60626, (773)338-5933
Insight Center for Community Economic Development [17578], 2201 Broadway, Ste. 815, Oakland, CA 94612-3024, (510)251-2600
Insititut Bank-Bank Malaysia [★IO]
Inslee Family Assn. - Defunct.
Insol Intl. [IO], London, United Kingdom
Insolvency
    Insolvency Practitioners Assn. of Australia [10338]
Insolvency Practitioners Assn. [IO], London, United Kingdom
Insolvency Practitioners Assn. of Australia [IO], Sydney, Australia
Inspectors
    Amer. Inst. of Inspectors [1913]
    Assn. of Constr. Inspectors [1914]
    Examination Bd. of Professional Home Inspectors [1915]
    Healthcare Laundry Accreditation Coun. [2192]
    Housing Inspection Found. [1916]
    Intl. Assn. of Bedding and Furniture Law Officials [5545]
    Intl. Assn. of Independent Private Sector Inspectors Gen. [5546]
    Intl. Fed. of Inspection Agencies-Americas Comm. [1917]
    Natl. Assn. of Certified Home Inspectors [1918]
    Natl. Assn. of Certified Home Inspectors [1918]
    Natl. Assn. of Home Inspectors [1919]
    Natl. Bd. of Boiler and Pressure Vessel Inspectors [5547]

Inspiration Ministries [11793], N2270 State Rd. 67, Walworth, WI 53184, (262)275-6131
Inspiration through the Written Word - Defunct.
Institiuid Ceimice Na hEireann [★IO]
Institue Goree [★IO]
Institusi Jurutera, Malaysia [★IO]
Institut de recherche en politiques publiques [★IO]
Institut international du developpement durable [★IO]
Institut canadien du droit des ressources [★IO]
L'Institut canadien de recherches avancees [★IO]
L'Institut canadien pour la resolution des conflits [★IO]
Institut canadien de la construction en acier [★IO]
Institut Aeronautique et Spatial du Canada [★IO]
Institut Africain de Developpement Economique et de Planification [★IO]
Institut Africain Intl. [★IO]
Institut fur Afrika-Kunde [★IO]
Institut Americain Universitaire [★8391]
Institut Americain Universitaire [★8391]
Institut agree de la logistique et des transports Amerique du Nord [★IO]
Institut de Biologie Physico-Chimique [IO], Paris, France
L'Institut de chimie du Canada [★IO]
Institut professionel de la fonction publique du Canada [★IO]
L'Institut Canadien [★IO]
Institut Canadien des Actuaires [★IO]
Institut Canadien d Admin. de la Justice [★IO]
Institut Canadien du Beton Prefabrique et Precontraint [★IO]
Institut Canadien des Comptables Agrees [★IO]
Institut Canadien des Condominiums [★IO]
Institut Canadien de Conservation [★IO]
L'Institut Canadien du Credit [★IO]
Institut Canadien De La Sante Animale [★IO]
L'Institut Canadien d'Etudes Strategiques [★IO]
Institut Canadien d'Etudes Ukrainiennes [★IO]
Institut Canadien des Economistes en Constr. [★IO]
Institut Canadien des Engrais [★IO]
Institut Canadien des Experts en Evaluation d'Enterprises [★IO]
Institut Canadien du Film [★IO]
Institut Canadien de Gestion [★IO]
Institut Canadien de l'immeuble [★IO]
Institut Canadien des Ingenieurs [★IO]
Institut Canadien des Inspecteurs en Sante Publique [★IO]
Institut Canadien de l'Energie [★IO]
Institut Canadien du Marketing [★IO]
Institut Canadien de Planification Finaniere [★IO]
L'Institut Canadien de Plomberie et de Chauffage [★IO]
Institut Canadien des Professionels de la Logistiques [★IO]
Institut Canadien de la Recherche sur la Condition Physique et le Mode de Vie [★IO]
Institut Canadien de Recherches sur les femmes [★IO]
Institut Canadien de Recherches sur le Judaisme [★IO]
Institut Canadien de Relations avec les Investisseurs [★IO]
Institut Canadien de la Retraite et des Avantages Sociaux [★IO]
Institut Canadien de la Sante Infantile [★IO]
L'Institut Canadien de Sci. et Technologie Alimentaires [★IO]
Institut Canadien du Sucre [★IO]
Institut Canadien du Tapis [★IO]
Institut Canadien des Technologies Scenographiques [★IO]
Institut Canadien des Textiles [★IO]
Institut Canadien du Trafic et du Transport [★IO]
Institut Canadien des Urbanistes [★IO]
Institut Canadien des Valeurs Mobilieres [★IO]
Institut Canadiens des Conseillers en Voyages [★IO]
Institut C.D. Howe [★IO]
Institut du Chrysotile [★IO]
L'Institut d'administration publique du Canada [★IO]
Institut Des Fonds D'Investissement Du Canada [★IO]

A star before a book entry number signifies that the name is not listed separately, but is mentioned within the entry.

2874

Encyclopedia of Associations, 51st Edition

Institut d'Estudis Catalans [★IO]
Institut d'Europe pour la Prevention du Crime et la Lutte Contre la Delinquance Affile a l'Organisation des Nations Unies [★IO]
Institut d'Histoire de l'Amerique Francaise [IO], Montreal, QC, Canada
Institut d'Histoire de l'Amerique Francaise [★IO]
Institut canadien d'information sur la sante [★IO]
Institut de Droit Intl. [★IO]
Institut des Droits de l'Homme du Barreau de Bordeaux [★IO]
Institut fur Europaische Politik [★IO]
Institut Europeen du Cuivre [★IO]
Institut Europeen d'Administration Publique [★IO]
Institut Europeen d'Education et de Politique Sociale [★IO]
Institut Europeen des Itineraires Culturels [★IO]
Institut Europeen de Recherches et d'Etudes Superieures en Mgt. [★IO]
Institut Feuerverzinken [★IO]
Institut Forestier du Canada [★IO]
Institut de la Fourrure du Canada [★IO]
Institut Francais d'Histoire Sociale [★IO]
Institut Francais du Petrole [★IO]
Institut Francais de Pondichery [★IO]
Institut Francais des Relations Internationales [★IO]
Institut Intl. du Canada pour le Grain [★IO]
Institut Intl. des Communications [★IO]
Institut Intl. d'Agriculture Tropicale [★IO]
Institut Intl. d'Aluminium [★IO]
Institut Intl. d'Anthropologie [★IO]
Institut Intl. d'Etudes Sociales [★IO]
Institut Intl. d'Etudes Strategiques [★IO]
Institut Intl. de Droit Humanitaire [★IO]
Institut Intl. des Droits de l'Homme [★IO]
Institut Intl. de Finances Publiques [★IO]
Institut Intl. du Froid [★IO]
Institut Intl. pour l'Analyse des Systemes Appliques [★IO]
Institut Intl. de l'Ocean [★IO]
Institut Intl. de l'Ombusdman [★IO]
Institut Intl. pour l'Unification du Droit Prive [★IO]
Institut Intl. du Manganese [★IO]
Institut Intl. de Planification de l'Education [★IO]
Institut Intl. de la Potasse [★IO]
Institut Intl. de Promotion et de Prestige [★IO]
Institut Intl. de Recherches Betteravieres [★IO]
Institut Intl. des Sciences Administratives [★IO]
Institut Intl. des Sciences Humaines Integrales [★IO]
Institut Intl. de la Soudure [★IO]
Institut Intl. de Statistique [★IO]
Institut Internationale du Theatre [★IO]
L'institut canadien du droit et de la politique en l'environnement [★IO]
L'Institut de l'euro [★IO]
Institut de l'Horticulture [★IO]
Institut de l'UNESCO pour l'apprentissage tout au long de la vie.[★IO]
Institut za Medunarodne Odnose [★IO]
Institut canadien des mines, Metallurgie et Petrole [★IO]
Institut du Monde Arabe [★IO]
Institut fuer Naehtechnik [IO], Monchengladbach, Germany
L'Institut Natl. Canadien pour les Aveugles [★IO]
L'Institut Natl. de Recherche en Informatique et en Automatique [★IO]
Institut des Nations Unies pour la Formation et la Recherche [★IO]
L'Institut Nord-Sud [★IO]
Institut Pan-Africain pour le Developpement - Afrique de l'Ouest-Sahel [★IO]
Institut Panos Afrique de l'Ouest [★IO]
Institut Pierre Richet [IO], Bouake, Cote d'Ivoire
Institut de Radioprotection du Canada [★IO]
Institut de Recherche des Nations Unies pour le Developpement Social [★IO]
Institut de Recherches et d'Etudes sur le Monde Arabe et Musulman [★IO]
Institut de Recherches et d'Etudes Publicitaires [★IO]
Institut des Reviseurs d'Entreprises - Luxembourg [IO], Luxembourg, Luxembourg
Institut Royal d'Architecture du Canada [★IO]
Institut Royal des Relations Internationale [★IO]

Institut Ruder Boskovic [★IO]
Institut des Sciences de l'Environnement [★IO]
Institut fur Seeverkehrswirtschaft und Logistik [★IO]
Institut fur Sportwissenschaft [★IO]
Institut pour une Synthese Planetaire [★IO]
Institut Tal-Gurnalisti Maltin [★IO]
Institut Tropical Suisse [★IO]
Institut du Verre [★IO]
Institut der Wirtschaftspruefer in Deutschland e.V. [IO]
Inst. for 21st Century Stud. [★17733]
Inst. of Acoustics [IO], St. Albans, United Kingdom
Inst. of Actuaries of Australia [IO], Sydney, Australia
Inst. of Actuaries - United Kingdom [IO], London, United Kingdom
Inst. of Administrative Mgt. [IO], London, United Kingdom
Inst. for Adoption Info. [10790], 409 Dewey St., Bennington, VT 05201, (802)442-2845
Inst. for Advanced Judaic Stud. [IO], Toronto, ON, Canada
Inst. of Advanced Motorists [IO], London, United Kingdom
Inst. for Advanced Pastoral Stud. [★19674]
Inst. for Advanced Res. in Asian Sci. and Medicine [★15215]
Inst. for Advanced Res. in Asian Sci. and Medicine [★15215]
Inst. for the Advanced Stud. of Black Family Life and Culture [9101], 1012 Linden St., Oakland, CA 94607, (510)836-3705
Inst. for Advanced Stud. in Rational Psychotherapy [★16444]
Inst. for the Advancement of Criminal Justice [★13274]
Inst. for the Advancement of Hawaiian Affairs - Address unknown since 2011.
Inst. for the Advancement of Human Behavior [13815], 4370 Alpine Rd., Ste. 209, Portola Valley, CA 94028, (650)851-8411
Inst. for the Advancement of Journalism [IO], Houghton, Republic of South Africa
Inst. for the Advancement of Philosophy for Children [10380], Montclair State Univ., Univ. Hall 2151, Montclair, NJ 07043, (973)655-4278
Inst. for the Advancement of Philosophy for Children [10380], Montclair State Univ., Univ. Hall 2151, Montclair, NJ 07043, (973)655-4278
Inst. of Advt. Practitioners in Ireland [IO], Dublin, Ireland
Inst. of Advt. Stud. and Res. [IO], Paris, France
Inst. for Aerobics Res. [★16223]
Inst. for Aerobics Res. [★16223]
Inst. of the Aerospace Sciences [★6082]
Inst. of African Affairs [IO], Hamburg, Germany
Inst. of Agricultural Secretaries and Administrators [IO], Kenilworth, United Kingdom
Inst. for Agriculture and Trade Policy [17168], 2105 1st Ave. S, Minneapolis, MN 55404, (612)870-0453
Inst. for Alternative Futures [6888], 100 N Pitt St., Ste. 235, Alexandria, VA 22314-3134, (703)684-5880
Inst. for Alternative Futures [6888], 100 N Pitt St., Ste. 235, Alexandria, VA 22314-3134, (703)684-5880
Inst. for Amer. Church Growth [★20220]
Inst. of Amer. Indian Arts [10329], 83 Avan Nu Po Rd., Santa Fe, NM 87508, (505)424-2300
Inst. for Amer. Indian Stud. [6169], PO Box 1260, Washington, CT 06793-0260, (860)868-0518
Inst. of Amer. Meat Packers [★2431]
Inst. for Amer. Strategy [★18588]
Inst. for Amer. Universities [8391], 531 E Roosevelt Rd., Ste. 101, Wheaton, IL 60187, (800)221-2051
Inst. for Amer. Universities [8391], 531 E Roosevelt Rd., Ste. 101, Wheaton, IL 60187, (800)221-2051
Inst. for Amer. Values [12010], 1841 Broadway, Ste. 211, New York, NY 10023, (212)246-3942
Inst. for America's Future [18382], 1825 K St. NW, Ste. 400, Washington, DC 20006, (202)955-5665
Inst. of Andean Stud. [9130], PO Box 9307, Berkeley, CA 94709, (510)222-6284
Inst. of Andean Stud. [9130], PO Box 9307, Berkeley, CA 94709, (510)222-6284
Inst. for Animal Hea. [IO], Newbury, United Kingdom

Inst. of Animal Tech. [IO], Oxford, United Kingdom
Inst. of Apostolic Oblates [19433], 205 S Pine Dr., Fullerton, CA 92833, (714)956-1020
Inst. of Archaeo-Metallurgical Stud. [IO], London, United Kingdom
Inst. of Art Stud. [IO], Sofia, Bulgaria
Inst. for Art and Urban Resources [★9316]
Inst. of Asian Res. [IO], Vancouver, BC, Canada
Inst. of Asian Stud. [★7757]
Inst. of Asian Stud. [★7757]
Inst. of Assn. Mgt. [IO], Welwyn Garden City, United Kingdom
Inst. of Assn. Mgt. Companies [★261]
Inst. of Assn. Mgt. Companies [★261]
Inst. of Athletic Motivation [★22818]
Inst. of Australian Geographers [IO], Hobart, Australia
Inst. of Automotive Engineer Assessors [IO], Lichfield, United Kingdom
Inst. of Automotive Mech. Engineers [IO], Auburn, Australia
Inst. of Bankers in Ireland [IO], Dublin, Ireland
Inst. of Bankers Malaysia [IO], Kuala Lumpur, Malaysia
Inst. of Bankers in South Africa [IO], Marshalltown, Republic of South Africa
Inst. of Bankers of Zimbabwe [IO], Harare, Zimbabwe
Inst. in Basic Life Principles [13531], Box 1, Oak Brook, IL 60522-3001, (630)323-9800
Inst. in Basic Youth Conflicts [★13531]
Inst. for Behavioral Healthcare [★13815]
Inst. for Better Packaging [★2609]
Inst. for Biblical Res. [19348], 1635 E Kramer St., Mesa, AZ 85203
Inst. of Biomedical Sci. [IO], London, United Kingdom
Inst. for Briquetting and Agglomeration - Defunct.
Inst. of British Foundrymen [IO], West Midlands, United Kingdom
Inst. of Bus. Appraisers [232], PO Box 17410, Plantation, FL 33318, (954)584-1144
Inst. of Bus. Consulting [IO], London, United Kingdom
Inst. of Bus. Designers, Coun. for Fed. Interior Designers [★2065]
Inst. for Bus. and Home Safety [1966], 4775 E Fowler Ave., Tampa, FL 33617, (813)286-3400
Inst. for Cancer Prevention - Defunct.
Inst. of Career Guidance [IO], Stourbridge, United Kingdom
Inst. of Caribbean Stud. [12337], 917 Sixth St. NW, Washington, DC 20001, (202)638-0460
Inst. of Caribbean Stud. [12337], 917 Sixth St. NW, Washington, DC 20001, (202)638-0460
Inst. of Carpenters [IO], London, United Kingdom
Inst. of Cast Metals Engineers [IO], West Bromwich, United Kingdom
Inst. of Catalan Stud. [IO], Barcelona, Spain
Inst. for Certification of Computing Professionals [7906], 2400 E Devon Ave., Ste. 281, Des Plaines, IL 60018, (847)299-4227
Inst. for the Certification of Engg. Technicians [★6814]
Inst. of Certified Bus. Counselors [669], 18831 Willamette Dr., West Linn, OR 97068, (877)422-2674
Inst. of Certified Financial Planners [★1298]
Inst. of Certified Financial Planners [★1298]
Inst. for Certified Investment Mgt. Consultants [★2138]
Inst. for Certified Investment Mgt. Consultants [★2138]
Inst. for Certified Investment Mgt. Consultants - Defunct.
Inst. of Certified Professional Managers [2285], James Madison Univ., MSC 5504, Harrisonburg, VA 22807, (540)568-3247
Inst. of Certified Professional Managers [2285], James Madison Univ., MSC 5504, Harrisonburg, VA 22807, (540)568-3247
Inst. of Certified Records Managers [1901], 403 E Taft Rd., North Syracuse, NY 13212, (315)234-1904
Inst. of Certified Travel Agents [★3579]
Inst. of Chartered Accountants in Australia [IO], Sydney, Australia

Reference to "IO" in place of a book number signifies that the association may be found in the 50th edition of International Organizations.

Inst. of Chartered Accountants in England and Wales [IO], London, United Kingdom

Inst. of Chartered Accountants of Guyana [IO], Georgetown, Guyana

Inst. of Chartered Accountants of India [IO], New Delhi, India

Inst. of Chartered Accountants in Ireland [IO], Belfast, United Kingdom

Inst. of Chartered Accountants of New Zealand [IO], Wellington, New Zealand

Inst. of Chartered Accountants of Nigeria [IO], Lagos, Nigeria

Inst. of Chartered Accountants of Scotland [IO], Edinburgh, United Kingdom

Inst. of Chartered Accountants of Zimbabwe [IO], Harare, Zimbabwe

Inst. of Chartered Financial Analysts [★2133]

Inst. of Chartered Financial Analysts [★2133]

Inst. of Chartered Financial Analysts of India [IO], Hyderabad, India

Inst. of Chartered Foresters [IO], Edinburgh, United Kingdom

Inst. of Chartered Secretaries and Administrators - Canada [IO], Ottawa, ON, Canada

Inst. of Chartered Secretaries and Administrators - United Kingdom [IO], London, United Kingdom

Inst. of Chartered Secretaries and Administrators - Zimbabwe [IO], Harare, Zimbabwe

Inst. of Chartered Shipbrokers - England [IO], London, United Kingdom

Inst. for Chem. Educ. [7820], Univ. of Wisconsin-Madison, Dept. of Chemistry, 1101 Univ. Ave., Madison, WI 53706-1396, (608)262-3033

Inst. of Chemistry of Ireland [IO], Dublin, Ireland

Inst. for Childhood Resources - Address unknown since 2010.

Inst. for Children, Poverty and Homelessness [11320], 44 Cooper St., New York, NY 10003, (212)358-8086

Inst. of Chinese Culture [9479], 10550 Westoffice Dr., Houston, TX 77042, (713)339-1992

Inst. of Chiropodists and Podiatrists [IO], Southport, United Kingdom

Inst. of Civil Protection and Emergency Mgt. [IO], Eastleigh, United Kingdom

Inst. of Clean Air Companies [2786], 1730 M St. NW, Ste. 206, Washington, DC 20036, (202)457-0911

Inst. of Clerks of Works and Constr. Inspectorate of Great Britain [IO], Peterborough, United Kingdom

Inst. of Clinical Res. [IO], Bourne End, United Kingdom

Inst. for Coll. and Univ. Administrators [★8482]

Inst. for Commercial Forestry Res. [IO], Scottsville, Republic of South Africa

Inst. of Commercial Mgt. [IO], Ringwood, United Kingdom

Inst. of Commonwealth Stud. [IO], London, United Kingdom

Inst. of Commun. Agencies [IO], Toronto, ON, Canada

Inst. for Community Economics [17380], 1101 30th St. NW, Ste. 400, Washington, DC 20007-3708, (202)333-8931

Inst. for Complementary and Natural Medicine [IO], London, United Kingdom

Inst. for Cmpt. Capacity Mgt. - Defunct.

Inst. for Computers in Jewish Life [8313], 2750 W Pratt Blvd., Chicago, IL 60645, (312)533-4240

Inst. of Concrete Tech. [IO], Camberley, United Kingdom

Inst. for Conservation Leadership [4270], 6930 Carroll Ave., Ste. 1050, Takoma Park, MD 20912, (301)270-2900

Inst. for Constitutional Res. - Defunct.

Inst. of Consumer Affairs [IO], London, United Kingdom

Inst. of Consumer Financial Educ. [8186], PO Box 34070, San Diego, CA 92163-4070, (619)239-1401

Inst. of Contemporary Arts [IO], London, United Kingdom

Inst. for Contemporary Stud. [18467], 815 Harbour Way S, Ste. 17, Richmond, CA 94802, (510)234-6270

Inst. for Control Therapy, Reality Therapy, and Quality Mgt. [★16475]

Inst. for the Cooperative Stud. of Intl. Sea-food Markets [★1360]

Inst. for the Cooperative Stud. of Intl. Sea-food Markets [★1360]

Inst. of Corrosion [IO], Leighton Buzzard, United Kingdom

Inst. of Cost Anal. [★1327]

Inst. for Counter-Terrorism [IO], Herzliya, Israel

Inst. for Creation Res. [20221], 1806 Royal Ln., Dallas, TX 75229, (214)615-8300

Inst. of Credit Mgt. [IO], South Luffenham, United Kingdom

Inst. of Cultural Affairs [12212], 4750 N Sheridan Rd., Chicago, IL 60640, (773)769-6363

Inst. of Cultural Affairs Australia [IO], Highgate Hill, Australia

Inst. of Cultural Affairs Brazil [IO], Rio de Janeiro, Brazil

Inst. of Cultural Affairs Chile [IO], Santiago, Chile

Inst. of Cultural Affairs Cote D'Ivoire [IO], Abidjan, Cote d'Ivoire

Inst. of Cultural Affairs Egypt [IO], Cairo, Egypt

Inst. of Cultural Affairs Ghana [IO], Accra, Ghana

Inst. of Cultural Affairs Guatemala [IO], Guatemala City, Guatemala

Inst. of Cultural Affairs India [IO], Pune, India

Inst. of Cultural Affairs Intl. Belgium [IO], Brussels, Belgium

Inst. of Cultural Affairs Japan [IO], Tokyo, Japan

Inst. of Cultural Affairs Kenya [IO], Nairobi, Kenya

Inst. of Cultural Affairs Malaysia [IO], Kuala Lumpur, Malaysia

Inst. of Cultural Affairs Middle East and North Africa [IO], Cairo, Egypt

Inst. of Cultural Affairs Nepal [IO], Kathmandu, Nepal

Inst. of Cultural Affairs Netherlands [IO], Amsterdam, Netherlands

Inst. of Cultural Affairs Nigeria [IO], Lagos, Nigeria

Inst. of Cultural Affairs Peru [IO], Lima, Peru

Inst. of Cultural Affairs Tanzania [IO], Moshi, United Republic of Tanzania

Inst. of Cultural Affairs Uganda [IO], Kyambogo, Uganda

Inst. of Cultural Affairs United Kingdom [IO], Manchester, United Kingdom

Inst. of Cultural Affairs Zambia [IO], Lusaka, Zambia

Inst. of Cultural Affairs Zimbabwe [IO], Harare, Zimbabwe

Inst. of Current World Affairs [18815], 4545 42nd St. NW, Ste. 311, Washington, DC 20016-4623, (202)364-4068

Inst. of Current World Affairs [18815], 4545 42nd St. NW, Ste. 311, Washington, DC 20016-4623, (202)364-4068

Inst. of Decontamination Sciences [IO], Bathgate, United Kingdom

Inst. for Defense Analyses [5969], 4850 Mark Center Dr., Alexandria, VA 22311-1882, (703)845-2000

Inst. for Defense and Disarmament Stud. - Address unknown since 2011.

Inst. for Delphinid Res. [★7041]

Inst. for Democracy in Eastern Europe [17566], 1718 M St. NW, No. 147, Washington, DC 20036, (202)466-7105

Inst. for Democracy in Eastern Europe [17566], 1718 M St. NW, No. 147, Washington, DC 20036, (202)466-7105

Inst. for Democratic Educ. [★17269]

Inst. of Designers in Ireland [IO], Dublin, Ireland

Inst. d'Etudes de Securite [★IO]

Inst. of Developing Economies, Japan External Trade Org. [IO], Chiba, Japan

Inst. for Development Anthropology - Defunct.

Inst. for the Development of the Harmonious Human Being [12213], PO Box 370, Nevada City, CA 95959, (530)271-2239

Inst. for Development Policy and Mgt. [IO], Manchester, United Kingdom

Inst. for Development Res. [★7692]

Inst. for Development Res. [★7692]

Inst. of Development Stud. [IO], Brighton, United Kingdom

Inst. for Development Training [★15164]

Inst. for Development Training [★15164]

Inst. of Directors - England [IO], London, United Kingdom

Inst. of Directors in Ireland [IO], Dublin, Ireland

Inst. of Directors - Zimbabwe [IO], Harare, Zimbabwe

Inst. for Diversity in Hea. Mgt. [14878], 155 N Wacker Dr., Chicago, IL 60606, (312)422-2630

Inst. of Domestic Heating and Environmental Engineers [IO], Southampton, United Kingdom

Inst. for a Drug-Free Workplace [13257], 10701 Parkridge Blvd., Ste. 300, Reston, VA 20191, (703)391-7222

Inst. of Early Amer. History and Culture [★9790]

Inst. for Earth Educ. [8144], Cedar Cove, PO Box 115, Greenville, WV 24945-0115, (304)832-6404

Inst. for Earth Educ. [8144], Cedar Cove, PO Box 115, Greenville, WV 24945-0115, (304)832-6404

Inst. for East West Stud. [★17896]

Inst. for East West Stud. [★17896]

Inst. of Eastern Culture [IO], Tokyo, Japan

Inst. of Ecology and Environmental Mgt. [IO], Winchester, United Kingdom

Inst. of Economic Affairs [IO], London, United Kingdom

Inst. for Economic Anal. [6620], 262 Harvard St., Apt. 12, Cambridge, MA 02139, (617)864-9933

Inst. of Economics, Inst. for Govt. Res. [★18443]

Inst. of Ecotechnics [IO], London, United Kingdom

Inst. for Ecumenical Res. [IO], Strasbourg, France

Inst. for Educ. in Peace and Justice [★18254]

Inst. for Educational Innovation [★8020]

Inst. for Educational Leadership [8029], 4455 Connecticut Ave. NW, Ste. 310, Washington, DC 20008, (202)822-8405

Inst. of Elecl. and Electronics Engineers - Nigerian Sect. [IO], Port Harcourt, Nigeria

Inst. of Elecl. and Electronics Engineers USA [6798], 2001 L St. NW, Ste. 700, Washington, DC 20036-4910, (202)785-0017

Inst. of Elecl. Engineers of Japan [IO], Tokyo, Japan

Inst. of Electronics, Info. and Commun. Engineers [IO], Tokyo, Japan

Inst. of Employment Rights [IO], Liverpool, United Kingdom

Inst. for Energy and Environmental Res. [6730], 6935 Laurel Ave., Ste. 201, Takoma Park, MD 20912, (301)270-5500

Inst. of Environmental Engineers [★7331]

Inst. of Environmental Sciences [★7331]

Inst. of Environmental Sciences and Tech. [7331], 2340 S Arlington Heights Rd., Ste. 100, Arlington Heights, IL 60005-4516, (847)981-0100

Inst. of Environmental Sciences and Tech. [7331], 2340 S Arlington Heights Rd., Ste. 100, Arlington Heights, IL 60005-4516, (847)981-0100

Inst. of Ergonomics and Human Factors [IO], Loughborough, United Kingdom

Institute for Esperanto in Commerce and Industry [★9583]

Inst. of Estuarine and Coastal Stud. [IO], Hull, United Kingdom

Inst. of European and Asian Stud. [★7757]

Inst. of European and Asian Stud. [★7757]

Inst. for European Environmental Policy [IO], London, United Kingdom

Inst. for European Politics [IO], Berlin, Germany

Inst. for European Stud. [★7757]

Inst. for European Stud. [★8170]

Inst. for European Stud. [★7757]

Inst. for European Stud. [★8170]

Inst. of Explosives Engineers [IO], Swindon, United Kingdom

Inst. of Export [IO], Peterborough, United Kingdom

Inst. for Expressive Anal. [16461], 150 E 84th St., Ste. 2P, New York, NY 10028, (212)463-0758

Inst. of Farm Brokers [★3043]

Inst. for Female Alternative Medicine [16596], 6815 Noble Ave., Ste. 410, Van Nuys, CA 91405, (818)997-5000

Inst. of Field Archaeologists [IO], Reading, United Kingdom

Inst. of Finance Professionals New Zealand [IO], Wellington, New Zealand

Inst. of Financial Accountants [IO], Sevenoaks, United Kingdom

A star before a book entry number signifies that the name is not listed separately, but is mentioned within the entry.

Inst. for Financial Crime Prevention [★1884]
Inst. for Financial Crime Prevention [★1884]
The Inst. of Financial Operations [6512], 16 East Colonial Dr., Orland, FL 32803, (407)351-3322
Inst. of Financial Planning [IO], Bristol, United Kingdom
Inst. for Fiscal Stud. [IO], London, United Kingdom
Inst. of Fisheries Mgt. [IO], Nottingham, United Kingdom
Inst. for Fluitronics Education - Defunct.
Inst. de la Fondation D'Acupuncture du Canada [★IO]
Inst. for Food and Development Policy [17873], 398 60th St., Oakland, CA 94618, (510)654-4400
Inst. for Food and Development Policy [17873], 398 60th St., Oakland, CA 94618, (510)654-4400
Inst. for Food Safety and Hea. [1396], 6502 S Archer Rd., Summit, IL 60501-1957, (708)563-1576
Inst. of Food Sci. and Tech. - UK [IO], London, United Kingdom
Inst. of Food Technologists [6878], 525 W Van Buren St., Ste. 1000, Chicago, IL 60607, (312)782-8424
Inst. of Foreign Bankers [★417]
Inst. of Foreign Bankers [★417]
Inst. for Foreign Policy Anal. [17703], Central Plz. Bldg., 10th Fl., 675 Massachusetts Ave., Cambridge, MA 02139-3309, (617)492-2116
Inst. of Fundraising [IO], London, United Kingdom
Inst. for the Future [6889], 124 Univ. Ave., 2nd Fl., Palo Alto, CA 94301, (650)854-6322
Inst. for the Future [6889], 124 Univ. Ave., 2nd Fl., Palo Alto, CA 94301, (650)854-6322
Inst. of Gas Tech. [★4488]
Inst. of Gen. Semantics [10531], 3000 A Landers St., Fort Worth, TX 76107, (817)922-9950
Inst. of Gen. Semantics [10531], 3000 A Landers St., Fort Worth, TX 76107, (817)922-9950
Inst. of Geologists of Ireland [IO], Dublin, Ireland
Inst. of Gerontology [IO], London, United Kingdom
Inst. for Global Communications [7541], PO Box 29047, San Francisco, CA 94129-0047
Inst. for Global Communications [7541], PO Box 29047, San Francisco, CA 94129-0047
Inst. on Global Drug Policy [13258], Drug Free Am. Found., Inc., 5999 Central Ave., Ste. 301, St. Petersburg, FL 33704-2744, (727)828-0211
Inst. on Global Drug Policy [13258], Drug Free Am. Found., Inc., 5999 Central Ave., Ste. 301, St. Petersburg, FL 33704-2744, (727)828-0211
Inst. of Global Env. and Soc. [4271], 4041 Powder Mill Rd., Ste. 302, Beltsville, MD 20705-3106, (301)595-7000
Inst. of Global Env. and Soc. [4271], 4041 Powder Mill Rd., Ste. 302, Beltsville, MD 20705-3106, (301)595-7000
Inst. for Global Ethics [6852], PO Box 39, Rockland, ME 04841-0039, (207)594-6658
Inst. for Global Ethics [6852], PO Box 39, Rockland, ME 04841-0039, (207)594-6658
Inst. for Global Labour and Human Rights [17230], 5 Gateway Center, 6th Fl., Pittsburgh, PA 15222, (412)562-2406
Inst. of the Great Plains [9647], PO Box 68, Lawton, OK 73502, (580)581-3460
Inst. of Grocery Distribution [IO], Watford, United Kingdom
Inst. of Groundsmanship [IO], Milton Keynes, United Kingdom
Inst. of Gp. Anal. [IO], London, United Kingdom
Inst. of Hazardous Materials Mgt. [4519], 11900 Parklawn Dr., Ste. 450, Rockville, MD 20852-2624, (301)984-8969
Inst. for Hea. Policy Solutions [14857], 1444 Eye St. NW, Ste. 900, Washington, DC 20005, (202)789-1491
Inst. for Hea. and Productivity Mgt. [2286], 17470 N Pacesetter Way, Scottsdale, AZ 85255, (480)305-2100
Inst. for Hea. and Productivity Mgt. [2286], 17470 N Pacesetter Way, Scottsdale, AZ 85255, (480)305-2100
Inst. of Hea. Promotion and Educ. [IO], Manchester, United Kingdom

Inst. of Health Studies - Address unknown since 2011.
Inst. of Healthcare Engg. and Estate Mgt. [IO], Portsmouth, United Kingdom
Inst. for Healthcare Improvement [14793], 20 Univ. Rd., 7th Fl., Cambridge, MA 02138, (617)301-4800
Inst. of Healthcare Mgt. - United Kingdom [IO], London, United Kingdom
Inst. of HeartMath [9825], 14700 W Park Ave., Boulder Creek, CA 95006, (831)338-8500
Inst. of Heraldic and Genealogical Stud. [IO], Canterbury, United Kingdom
Inst. for Highway Incorporated Engineers [IO], London, United Kingdom
Inst. for Historical Rev. [9737], PO Box 2739, Newport Beach, CA 92659, (714)593-9725
Inst. of Home Office Underwriters - Defunct.
Inst. of Horticulture [IO], Enfield, United Kingdom
Inst. on Hosp. and Community Psychiatry [★16332]
Inst. of Hospitality [IO], Sutton, United Kingdom
Inst. of Human Origins [6854], Arizona State Univ., PO Box 874101, Tempe, AZ 85287-4101, (480)727-6580
Inst. for Human Rights - Defunct.
Inst. for Humane Stud. [12242], George Mason Univ., 3301 N Fairfax Dr., Ste. 440, Arlington, VA 22201, (703)993-4880
Inst. for Humanist Stud. [★19818]
Inst. of Incorporated Public Accountants [IO], Naas, Ireland
Inst. for Independent Education - Defunct.
Inst. for Individual and World Peace [12214], 3500 W Adams Blvd., Los Angeles, CA 90018, (323)328-1905
Inst. for Individual and World Peace [12214], 3500 W Adams Blvd., Los Angeles, CA 90018, (323)328-1905
Inst. of Indus. Engineers [6799], 3577 Parkway Ln., Ste. 200, Norcross, GA 30092, (770)449-0460
Inst. of Indus. Engineers Hong Kong [IO], Hong Kong, People's Republic of China
Inst. of Indus. Engineers Ireland [IO], Dublin, Ireland
Inst. of Inspection, Cleaning and Restoration Certification [2058], 2715 E Mill Plain Blvd., Vancouver, WA 98661, (360)693-5675
Inst. of Insurance Brokers [IO], Higham Ferrers, United Kingdom
Inst. for the Integration of Latin Am. and the Caribbean [IO], Buenos Aires, Argentina
Inst. for Interconnecting and Packaging Electronic Circuits [★1106]
Inst. for Intercultural Stud. - Defunct.
Inst. on Interdenominational Stud. [★19680]
Inst. of Internal Auditors [30], 247 Maitland Ave., Altamonte Springs, FL 32701-4907, (407)937-1100
Inst. of Internal Auditors [30], 247 Maitland Ave., Altamonte Springs, FL 32701-4907, (407)937-1100
Inst. of Internal Auditors - Australia [IO], Sydney, Australia
Inst. of Internal Auditors - Hong Kong [IO], Hong Kong, People's Republic of China
Inst. of Internal Auditors - UK and Ireland [IO], London, United Kingdom
Inst. of Internal Commun. [IO], Milton Keynes, United Kingdom
Inst. of Intl. Bankers [417], 299 Park Ave., 17th Fl., New York, NY 10171, (212)421-1611
Inst. of Intl. Bankers [417], 299 Park Ave., 17th Fl., New York, NY 10171, (212)421-1611
Inst. of Intl. Container Lessors [881], 1990 M St. NW, Ste. 650, Washington, DC 20036-3417, (202)223-9800
Inst. of Intl. Container Lessors [881], 1990 M St. NW, Ste. 650, Washington, DC 20036-3417, (202)223-9800
Inst. for Intl. Cooperation and Development [12338], PO Box 520, Williamstown, MA 01267, (413)441-5126
Inst. for Intl. Cooperation and Development [12338], PO Box 520, Williamstown, MA 01267, (413)441-5126
Inst. for Intl. Economic Co-operation [IO], Milan, Italy
Inst. of Intl. Educ. [8362], 809 United Nations Plz., New York, NY 10017-3580, (212)883-8200
Inst. of Intl. Educ. [8362], 809 United Nations Plz., New York, NY 10017-3580, (212)883-8200

Inst. of Intl. Educ. - China [IO], Hong Kong, People's Republic of China
Inst. of Intl. Educ. - Egypt [IO], Cairo, Egypt
Inst. of Intl. Educ. - India [IO], New Delhi, India
Inst. of Intl. Educ. - Latin Am. [IO], Mexico City, Mexico
Inst. of Intl. Educ. - Russia [IO], Moscow, Russia
Inst. of Intl. Educ. - Southeast Asia [IO], Bangkok, Thailand
Inst. for the Intl. Educ. of Students [7757], 33 N LaSalle St., 15th Fl., Chicago, IL 60602-2602, (312)944-1750
Inst. for the Intl. Educ. of Students [7757], 33 N LaSalle St., 15th Fl., Chicago, IL 60602-2602, (312)944-1750
Inst. of Intl. Educ. - Ukraine [IO], Kiev, Ukraine
Inst. of Intl. Finance [418], 1333 H St. NW, Ste. 800E, Washington, DC 20005-4770, (202)857-3600
Inst. of Intl. Finance [418], 1333 H St. NW, Ste. 800E, Washington, DC 20005-4770, (202)857-3600
Inst. for Intl. and Foreign Trade Law [★5588]
Inst. for Intl. and Foreign Trade Law [★5588]
Inst. for Intl. Govt. [★17711]
Inst. for Intl. Govt. [★17711]
Inst. for Intl. Human Resources [★2631]
Inst. for Intl. Human Resources [★2631]
Inst. of Intl. Law [IO], Geneva, Switzerland
Inst. of Intl. Licensing Practitioners [IO], Milton Keynes, United Kingdom
Inst. for Intl. Order [★17711]
Inst. for Intl. Order [★17711]
Inst. for Intl. Peace Stud; Joan B. Kroc [18261]
Inst. for Intl. Peace Stud; Joan B. Kroc [18261]
Inst. for Intl. Policy [★17817]
Inst. for Intl. Policy [★17817]
Inst. for Intl. Political Stud. [IO], Milan, Italy
Inst. for Intl. Relations [IO], Zagreb, Croatia
Inst. of Intl. Relations Prague [IO], Prague, Czech Republic
Inst. of Intl. Trade of Ireland [IO], Dublin, Ireland
Inst. of Inventors [IO], London, United Kingdom
Inst. of the Ironworking Indus. - Address unknown since 2011.
Inst. for Jewish-Christian Relations - Defunct.
Inst. for Jewish Medical Ethics [19867], Lisa Kampner Hebrew Acad., 645 14th Ave., San Francisco, CA 94118, (415)752-7333
Inst. for Jewish Policy Res. [IO], London, United Kingdom
Institute for Jewish Studies [★19889]
Inst. of Judicial Admin. [5622], Torrey L. Whitman, Exec. Dir., New York Univ. School of Law, Wilf Hall, 139 MacDougal St., Rm. 116, New York, NY 10012, (212)998-6149
Inst. for Justice [5662], 901 N Glebe Rd., Ste. 900, Arlington, VA 22203, (703)682-9320
Inst. of Labor and Indus. Relations [23235], Univ. of Michigan, Victor Vaughan Bldg., 1111 E Catherine St., Ann Arbor, MI 48109-2054, (734)763-3116
Inst. for Lab. Animal Res. [13762], 500 Fifth St. NW, Washington, DC 20001, (202)334-2590
Inst. of Lab. Animal Resources [★13762]
Inst. of Landscape Architects of South Africa [IO], Ferndale, Republic of South Africa
Inst. of Leadership and Mgt. [IO], Lichfield, United Kingdom
Inst. for Learning Technologies [8107], Teachers Coll. - Columbia Univ., 525 W 120th St., New York, NY 10027-6605, (212)678-4007
Inst. of Legal Cashiers and Administrators [IO], Kent, United Kingdom
Inst. of Legal Executives [IO], Kempston, United Kingdom
Inst. of Legal Executives Victoria [IO], Burwood, Australia
Institute for Legislative Action [★22108]
Inst. for Liberty and Community - Defunct.
Inst. for Liberty and Justice [★17282]
Inst. of Lithuanian Stud. [10053], 5600 S Claremont Ave., Chicago, IL 60636-1039, (773)434-4545
Inst. for Local Self-Reliance [11597], 2001 S St. NW, Ste. 570, Washington, DC 20009, (202)898-1610
Inst. of Makers of Explosives [1239], 1120 19th St. NW, Ste. 310, Washington, DC 20036-3605, (202)429-9280

Reference to "IO" in place of a book number signifies that the association may be found in the 50th edition of International Organizations.

Inst. of Maltese Journalists [IO], Valletta, Malta

Inst. of Mgt. [IO], London, United Kingdom

Inst. of Mgt. Accountants [31], 10 Paragon Dr., Ste. 1, Montvale, NJ 07645-1774, (201)573-9000

Inst. of Mgt. Accountants, Cost Mgt. Gp. [2287], 10 Paragon Dr., Montvale, NJ 07645-1773, (201)573-9000

Inst. of Mgt. Consultants [IO], Surrey Hills, Australia

Inst. of Mgt. Consultants and Advisers [IO], Dublin, Ireland

Inst. of Mgt. Consultants USA [2288], 2025 M St. NW, Ste. 800, Washington, DC 20036-3309, (202)367-1134

Inst. for the Mgt. of Info. Systems [IO], Orpington, United Kingdom

The Inst. of Mgt. Sciences [★2289]

The Inst. of Mgt. Sciences [★2289]

Inst. of Mgt. Services [IO], Lichfield, United Kingdom

Inst. for Mfg. [IO], Cambridge, United Kingdom

Inst. of Marine Engg., Sci. and Tech. [IO], London, United Kingdom

Inst. of Marketing Mgt. Graduate School of Marketing [IO], Auckland Park, Republic of South Africa

Inst. of Masters of Wine [IO], London, United Kingdom

Inst. of Materials Engg. Australasia [IO], North Melbourne, Australia

Inst. of Materials, Minerals, and Mining [IO], London, United Kingdom

Inst. of Mathematical Statistics [7475], PO Box 22718, Beachwood, OH 44122, (216)295-2340

Inst. of Mathematics and its Applications [IO], Essex, United Kingdom

Inst. of Measurement and Control [IO], London, United Kingdom

Inst. of Measurement and Control of New Zealand [IO], Auckland, New Zealand

Inst. for Mediation and Conflict Resolution [5206], 384 E 149th St., Ste. 330, Bronx, NY 10455, (718)585-1190

Inst. for Medical Quality [16507], 221 Main St., Ste. 210, San Francisco, CA 94105, (415)882-5151

Inst. for Medical Record Economics [★15333]

Inst. of Medicine [15416], 500 5th St. NW, Washington, DC 20001, (202)334-2352

Inst. for Mental Hea. Initiatives - Address unknown since 2011.

Inst. of Mental Physics [★20190]

Inst. of Metal Finishing [IO], Birmingham, United Kingdom

Inst. of Mine Surveyors of South Africa [IO], Marshalltown, Republic of South Africa

Inst. for Molecular Mfg. [7044], 555 Bryant St., Ste. 354, Palo Alto, CA 94301, (650)917-1120

Inst. of the Motor Indus. [IO], Hertford, United Kingdom

Inst. of Municipal Engg. of Southern Africa [IO], Westville, Republic of South Africa

Inst. of Musical Instrument Tech. [IO], Croydon, United Kingdom

Inst. of Natl. Affairs [IO], Port Moresby, Papua New Guinea

Inst. of Nautical Archaeology [6170], PO Drawer HG, College Station, TX 77841-5137, (979)845-6694

Inst. of Nautical Archaeology [6170], PO Drawer HG, College Station, TX 77841-5137, (979)845-6694

Inst. of Navigation [7150], 8551 Rixlew Ln., Ste. 360, Manassas, VA 20109, (703)366-2723

Inst. of Near Eastern and African Stud. [8030], PO Box 425125, Cambridge, MA 02142, (617)864-6327

Inst. of Near Eastern and African Stud. [8030], PO Box 425125, Cambridge, MA 02142, (617)864-6327

Inst. for a New Middle East Policy - Defunct.

Inst. of Newspaper Controllers and Finance Officers [★1312]

Inst. of Newspaper Controllers and Finance Officers [★1312]

Inst. of Noetic Sciences [10541], 101 San Antonio Rd., Petaluma, CA 94952, (707)775-3500

Inst. of Noise Control Engg. [7162], 9100 Purdue Rd., Ste. 200, Indianapolis, IN 46268, (317)735-4063

Inst. of Nuclear Materials Mgt. [7166], 111 Deer Lake Rd., Ste. 100, Deerfield, IL 60015, (847)480-9573

Inst. of Nuclear Power Operations [7175], 700 Galleria Pkwy. SE, Ste. 100, Atlanta, GA 30339-5943

Inst. for Numerical Computation and Anal. [IO], Dublin, Ireland

Inst. of Nutrition of Central Am. and Panama [IO], Guatemala City, Guatemala

Inst. for Objectivist Stud. [★10408]

Inst. of Occupational Medicine [IO], Edinburgh, United Kingdom

Inst. of Operations Mgt. [IO], Corby, United Kingdom

Inst. for Operations Res. and the Mgt. Sciences [2289], 7240 Parkway. Dr., Ste. 300, Hanover, MD 21076-1310, (443)757-3500

Inst. for Operations Res. and the Mgt. Sciences [2289], 7240 Parkway. Dr., Ste. 300, Hanover, MD 21076-1310, (443)757-3500

Inst. of Ophthalmology [IO], London, United Kingdom

Inst. of Outdoor Drama [10581], East Carolina Univ., Coll. of Fine Arts and Commun., 310 Erwin Bldg., Greenville, NC 27858-4353, (252)328-5363

Inst. for Outdoor Learning [IO], Cumbria, United Kingdom

Inst. of Packaging Professionals [7208], 1833 Centre Point Cir., Ste. 123, Naperville, IL 60563, (630)544-5050

Inst. of Packaging - South Africa [IO], Pinegowrie, Republic of South Africa

Inst. for Palestine Stud. [9140], 3501 M St. NW, Washington, DC 20007, (202)342-3990

Inst. for Palestine Stud. [9140], 3501 M St. NW, Washington, DC 20007, (202)342-3990

Inst. of Paper [IO], Chertsey, United Kingdom

Inst. of Paper Chemistry [★7217]

Inst. of Paper Chemistry [★7217]

Inst. of Paper Sci. and Tech. [7217], 500 10th St. NW, Atlanta, GA 30332-0620, (404)894-5700

Inst. of Paper Sci. and Tech. [7217], 500 10th St. NW, Atlanta, GA 30332-0620, (404)894-5700

Inst. of Pastoral Care [★19668]

Inst. of Patentees and Inventors [IO], London, United Kingdom

Inst. of Payroll Professionals [IO], Solihull, United Kingdom

Inst. for Peace and Justice [18254], 475 E Lockwood Ave., St. Louis, MO 63119, (314)918-2630

Inst. of People Mgt. [IO], Randburg, Republic of South Africa

Inst. for People's Educ. and Action [8031], 73 Willow St., Florence, MA 01062, (413)585-8755

Inst. of Personal Image Consultants - Defunct.

Inst. of Pharmacy Mgt. Intl. [IO], Glasgow, United Kingdom

Inst. for Philosophy and Public Policy [18468], George Mason Univ., Robinson Hall B, Rm. 465, 4400 Univ. Dr., 3F1, Fairfax, VA 22030, (703)993-1290

Inst. of Photographic Tech. [IO], Melbourne, Australia

Inst. of Physics [IO], London, United Kingdom

Inst. of Physics [7266], Inst. of Physics Publishing, The Public Ledger Bldg., 150 S Independence Mall W, Ste. 929, Philadelphia, PA 19106

Inst. of Physics and Engg. in Medicine [IO], York, United Kingdom

Inst. of Physics, Singapore [IO], Singapore, Singapore

Inst. for Planetary Synthesis - Switzerland [IO], Geneva, Switzerland

Inst. of Plumbing - Australia [IO], Marmion, Australia

Inst. of Policy Anal. and Res. [IO], Nairobi, Kenya

Inst. of Policy and Legal Stud. [IO], Tirana, Albania

Inst. for Policy Stud. [18469], 1112 16th St. NW, Ste. 600, Washington, DC 20036, (202)234-9382

Inst. for Policy Stud. [18469], 1112 16th St. NW, Ste. 600, Washington, DC 20036, (202)234-9382

Inst. for Polyacrylate Absorbents [756], 1850 M St. NW, Ste. 700, Washington, DC 20036-5810, (202)721-4154

Inst. for Polyacrylate Absorbents [756], 1850 M St. NW, Ste. 700, Washington, DC 20036-5810, (202)721-4154

Institute for Polynesian Studies [★10465]

Institute for Polynesian Studies [★10465]

Inst. for Practical Idealism [★8409]

Inst. for Practical Idealism [★8409]

Inst. of Practitioners in Advt. [IO], London, United Kingdom

Inst. for Prevention and Control of Violence and Extremism [★17320]

Inst. of Printed Circuits [★1106]

Inst. of Professional Administrators [IO], London, United Kingdom

Inst. of Professional Engg. Technologists [IO], Randburg, Republic of South Africa

Inst. of Professional Environmental Practice [4272], 600 Forbes Ave., 339 Fisher Hall, Pittsburgh, PA 15282, (412)396-4094

Inst. of Professional Environmental Practice [4272], 600 Forbes Ave., 339 Fisher Hall, Pittsburgh, PA 15282, (412)396-4094

Inst. of Professional Soil Scientists [IO], Cranfield, United Kingdom

Inst. for Professionals in Taxation [6010], 600 Northpark Town Center, 1200 Abernathy Rd., Ste. L-2, Atlanta, GA 30328-1040, (404)240-2300

Inst. of Property Taxation [★6010]

Inst. for Prospective Technological Stud. [IO], Seville, Spain

Inst. for the Protection of Lesbian and Gay Youth [★12087]

Inst. of Psychiatry [IO], London, United Kingdom

Inst. for Psychohistory [9777], 140 Riverside Dr., New York, NY 10024-2605, (212)799-2294

Inst. of Psychosexual Medicine [IO], London, United Kingdom

Inst. for Public Accuracy [18470], 65 9th St., Ste. 3, San Francisco, CA 94103, (415)552-5378

Inst. of Public Admin. [IO], Dublin, Ireland

Inst. of Public Admin. Australia [IO], Brisbane, Australia

Inst. of Public Admin. of Canada [IO], Toronto, ON, Canada

Inst. of Public Admin. USA [5906], 411 Lafayette St., Ste. 303, New York, NY 10003-7032, (212)992-9898

Inst. of Public Admin. USA [5906], 411 Lafayette St., Ste. 303, New York, NY 10003-7032, (212)992-9898

Inst. of Public Affairs [IO], Melbourne, Australia

Inst. of Public Auditors in Germany [IO], Dusseldorf, Germany

Inst. of Public Loss Assessors [IO], Bushey, United Kingdom

Inst. for Public Relations [8765], PO Box 118400, Gainesville, FL 32611-8400, (352)392-0280

Inst. for Public Relations Res. and Educ. [★8765]

Inst. of Public Utilities [3596], Michigan State Univ., W157 Owen Graduate Hall, East Lansing, MI 48825-1109, (517)355-1876

Inst. of Public Works Engg. Australia [IO], Sydney, Australia

Inst. of Purchasing and Supply of Hong Kong [IO], Hong Kong, People's Republic of China

Inst. of Quarrying - Australia [IO], Blakehurst, Australia

Inst. of Quarrying - England [IO], Nottingham, United Kingdom

Inst. of Quarrying - Hong Kong Br. [IO], Hong Kong, People's Republic of China

Inst. of Quarrying - Southern Africa [IO], Gallo Manor, Republic of South Africa

Inst. of Race Relations [IO], London, United Kingdom

Inst. for Rational-Emotive Therapy [★16444]

Inst. for Rational Living [★16444]

Inst. of Real Estate Mgt. [3015], 430 N Michigan Ave., Chicago, IL 60611, (312)329-6000

Inst. for Reality Therapy [★16475]

Inst. for Reduction of Crime [★8818]

Inst. of Refrigeration [IO], Carshalton, United Kingdom

Inst. for Regional and Intl. Stud.

Inst. for Regional and Intl. Stud. - Address unknown since 2011.

Inst. on Religion in an Age of Sci. [20234], 744 DuBois Dr., Baton Rouge, LA 70808

Inst. on Religion and Democracy [17522], 1023 15th St. NW, Ste. 601, Washington, DC 20005-2601, (202)682-4131

A star before a book entry number signifies that the name is not listed separately, but is mentioned within the entry.

Inst. for Religious and Social Stud. [★19680]

Inst. for Reproductive Hea. [★16596]

Institute for Res. in Modern History of Poland [★10460]

Institute for Res. in Modern History of Poland [★10460]

Inst. for Res. on Public Policy [IO], Montreal, QC, Canada

Institute for Res. in Social Sci. [★10622]

Institute for Res. in Social Sci. [★10622]

Inst. for Res. and Stud. of the Arab and Muslim World [IO], Aix-en-Provence, France

Inst. for Rsrc. and Security Stud. [18471], 27 Ellsworth Ave., Cambridge, MA 02139, (617)491-5177

Inst. for Responsible Housing Preservation [5517], 401 9th St. NW, Ste. 900, Washington, DC 20004, (202)585-8739

Inst. for Retired Professionals [12917], New School Univ., 66 W 12th St., Rm. 502, New York, NY 10011, (212)229-5682

Inst. for Retirement Stud. [★7922]

Inst. of Revenues, Rating and Valuation [IO], London, United Kingdom

Inst. of Risk Mgt. [IO], London, United Kingdom

Inst. of Risk Mgt. [★2043]

Inst. of Road Safety Officers [IO], Horrow, United Kingdom

Inst. of Roofing [IO], London, United Kingdom

Inst. of Roofing and Waterproofing Consultants - Defunct.

Inst. for Safe Medication Practices [14794], 200 Lakeside Dr., Ste. 200, Horsham, PA 19044-2321, (215)947-7797

Inst. of Sales and Marketing Mgt. [IO], Luton, United Kingdom

Inst. of Sanitation Mgt. [★2246]

Inst. for Sci. and Intl. Security [18584], 236 Massachusetts Ave. NE, Ste. 305, Washington, DC 20002, (202)547-3633

Inst. for Sci. and Intl. Security [18584], 236 Massachusetts Ave. NE, Ste. 305, Washington, DC 20002, (202)547-3633

Inst. of Sci. and Tech. [IO], Sheffield, United Kingdom

Inst. of Sci. and Tech. Communicators [IO], Croydon, United Kingdom

Inst. of Scrap Iron and Steel [★3637]

Inst. of Scrap Iron and Steel [★3637]

Inst. of Scrap Recycling Indus. [3637], 1615 L St. NW, Ste. 600, Washington, DC 20036-5610, (202)662-8500

Inst. of Scrap Recycling Indus. [3637], 1615 L St. NW, Ste. 600, Washington, DC 20036-5610, (202)662-8500

Inst. for Security Stud. [IO], Pretoria, Republic of South Africa

Inst. of Sheet Metal Engg. [IO], Wolverhampton, United Kingdom

Inst. of Shipping Economics and Logistics [IO], Bremen, Germany

Inst. of Shortening and Edible Oils [2584], 1319 F St. NW, Ste. 600, Washington, DC 20004, (202)783-7960

Inst. of Shortening Mfrs. [★2584]

Inst. of Signage Res. [★1078]

Inst. of Signage Res. [★1078]

Inst. of Singles Dynamics [19989], PO Box 27222, Overland Park, KS 66225-7222, (816)763-9401

Inst. of Small Enterprise and Development [IO], Kochi, India

Inst. for Social Res. [7414], Univ. of Michigan, PO Box 1248, Ann Arbor, MI 48106-1248, (734)764-8354

Inst. for Social Res. | Prog. for Res. on Black Americans [6105], PO Box 1248, Ann Arbor, MI 48106-1248, (734)763-0045

Inst. of Social Stud. Trust [IO], New Delhi, India

Inst. of Soc., Ethics, and the Life Sciences [★11980]

Inst. for SocioEconomic Stud. [18472], 10 New King St., White Plains, NY 10604-1204, (914)686-7112

Inst. for Soil, Climate and Water [IO], Pretoria, Republic of South Africa

Inst. for Southern Stud. [9120], PO Box 531, Durham, NC 27702, (919)419-8311

Inst. for Soviet Amer. Relations [★17996]

Inst. for Space and Security Stud. [18202], 1494 Patriot Dr., Melbourne, FL 32940, (321)752-5955

Inst. of Speculative Philosophy [IO], Ottawa, ON, Canada

Inst. for Sport, Parks and Leisure [IO], Reading, United Kingdom

Inst. of Sport and Recreation Mgt. [IO], Loughborough, United Kingdom

Inst. of Spring Tech. [IO], Sheffield, United Kingdom

Inst. of Statehood and Democracy [IO], Kiev, Ukraine

Inst. of Store Planners [★3124]

Inst. of Store Planners [★3124]

Inst. for Stud. in Amer. Music [★8652]

Inst. for the Stud. of Antisocial Behavior in Youth [IO], Oakville, ON, Canada

Inst. for the Stud. of Athletic Motivation [★22818]

Inst. for the Stud. of Athletic Motivation and Inst. of Athletic Motivation [★22818]

Inst. for the Stud. of Genocide [17837], John Jay Coll. of Criminal Justice, 899 10th Ave., Rm. 325, New York, NY 10019

Inst. for the Stud. of Genocide [17837], John Jay Coll. of Criminal Justice, 899 10th Ave., Rm. 325, New York, NY 10019

Inst. for the Stud. of Human Ideas on Ultimate Reality and Meaning [IO], Calgary, AB, Canada

Inst. for the Stud. of Human Knowledge [9826], PO Box 176, Los Altos, CA 94023, (650)948-9428

Inst. for the Stud. of Human Rights [17838], Columbia Univ., Mail Code 3365, New York, NY 10027, (212)854-2479

Inst. for the Stud. of Labor and Economic Crisis [★18462]

Inst. for the Stud. of Labor and Economic Crisis [★18462]

Inst. for the Stud. of Man [6142], 1133 13th St. NW, Ste. C-2, Washington, DC 20005, (202)371-2700

Inst. for the Study of Matrimonial Laws - Defunct.

Inst. for the Stud. of Traditional Amer. Indian Arts - Defunct.

Inst. for the Stud. and Treatment of Pain [IO], Vancouver, BC, Canada

Inst. for Supply Mgt. [2971], PO Box 22160, Tempe, AZ 85285-2160, (480)752-6276

Inst. for Sustainable Communities [11598], 535 Stone Cutters Way, Montpelier, VT 05602, (802)229-2900

Inst. for Sustainable Communities [11598], 535 Stone Cutters Way, Montpelier, VT 05602, (802)229-2900

Inst. of Systems, Control and Info. Engineers [IO], Kyoto, Japan

Inst. of Tax Consultants [6011], 7500 212th SW, Ste. 205, Edmonds, WA 98026-7617, (425)774-3521

Inst. on Taxation and Economic Policy [17592], Washington Off., 1616 P St. NW, Ste. 200, Washington, DC 20036, (202)299-1066

Inst. of Tech. and Polytechnics of New Zealand [IO], Wellington, New Zealand

Inst. of Temporary Services [★1142]

Inst. of Textiles and Clothing [IO], Hong Kong, People's Republic of China

Inst. for Theological Encounter With Sci. and Tech. [12215], 20 Archbishop May Dr., Ste. 3400A, St. Louis, MO 63119, (314)792-7220

Inst. of Totally Useless Skills - Address unknown since 2010.

Inst. of Trade Mark Attorneys [IO], Croydon, United Kingdom

Inst. for Traditional Medicine and Preventive Hea. Care [13683], 2017 SE Hawthorne Blvd., Portland, OR 97214, (503)233-4907

Inst. for Traditional Medicine and Preventive Hea. Care [13683], 2017 SE Hawthorne Blvd., Portland, OR 97214, (503)233-4907

Inst. of Traffic Engineers [★7581]

Inst. of Traffic Engineers [★7581]

Inst. of Training Professionals [IO], Hong Kong, People's Republic of China

Inst. of Transactional Anal. [IO], Cambridge, United Kingdom

Inst. for the Transfer of Tech. to Educ. [8314], Natl. School Boards Assn., 1680 Duke St., Alexandria, VA 22314, (703)838-6722

Inst. of Translation and Interpreting [IO], Milton Keynes, United Kingdom

Inst. of Transport Admin. [IO], Westoning, United Kingdom

Inst. of Transport Economics [IO], Oslo, Norway

Inst. for Trans. and Development Policy [17914], 9 E 19th St., 7th Fl., New York, NY 10003, (212)629-8001

Inst. for Trans. and Development Policy [17914], 9 E 19th St., 7th Fl., New York, NY 10003, (212)629-8001

Inst. of Trans. Engineers [7581], 1627 Eye St. NW, Ste. 600, Washington, DC 20006, (202)785-0060

Inst. of Trans. Engineers [7581], 1627 Eye St. NW, Ste. 600, Washington, DC 20006, (202)785-0060

Inst. of Travel and Tourism [IO], Ware, United Kingdom

Inst. for Tribal Environmental Professionals [19157], PO Box 15004, Flagstaff, AZ 86011, (928)523-9555

Inst. of Trichologists [IO], London, United Kingdom

Inst. of Turkish Stud. [10617], Georgetown Univ., ICC Box 571033, Washington, DC 20057-1033, (202)687-0295

Inst. for UFO Contactee Studies - Defunct.

Inst. for Univ. Cooperation [IO], Rome, Italy

Inst. for Urban Design [6198], 17 W 17th St., 7th Fl., New York, NY 10011, (212)366-0780

Inst. of Urban Life - Defunct.

Inst. of Vehicle Recovery [IO], West Drayton, United Kingdom

Inst. for Vietnamese Music [10211], 2005 Willow Ridge Cir., Kent, OH 44240

Inst. for Vietnamese Music [10211], 2005 Willow Ridge Cir., Kent, OH 44240

Inst. of Vitreous Enamellers [IO], Cannock, United Kingdom

Inst. of Water [IO], Gateshead, United Kingdom

Inst. of Welfare [IO], Stourbridge, United Kingdom

Inst. on Women and Tech. [★12697]

Inst. on Women and Tech. [★12697]

Inst. of Women Today [17647], 7315 S Yale Ave., Chicago, IL 60621, (773)651-8372

Inst. for Women in Trades, Tech. and Sci. [3684], 1150 Ballena Blvd., Ste. 102, Alameda, CA 94501-3696, (510)749-0200

Inst. for Women's Policy Res. [17648], 1200 18th St. NW, Ste. 301, Washington, DC 20036, (202)785-5100

Inst. for Women's Stud. in the Arab World [IO], Beirut, Lebanon

Inst. of Wood Sci. [IO], London, United Kingdom

Inst. of World Affairs [8407], 1928 Beulah Rd., Vienna, VA 22182, (202)744-7755

Inst. of World Affairs [★8407]

Inst. of World Affairs [8407], 1928 Beulah Rd., Vienna, VA 22182, (202)744-7755

Inst. for World Economics of the Hungarian Acad. of Sciences [IO], Budapest, Hungary

Inst. for World Order [★17711]

Inst. for World Order [★17711]

Institutes for the Achievement of Human Potential [11470], 8801 Stenton Ave., Wyndmoor, PA 19038, (215)233-2050

Insts. for Behavior Resources - Defunct.

Institutes for Org. Mgt. [★23384]

Instituti Per Studimet Publike Dhe Ligjore [★IO]

Institution of Agricultural Engineers [IO], Bedford, United Kingdom

Institution of Analysts and Programmers [IO], London, United Kingdom

Institution of Certificated Mech. and Elecl. Engineers, South Africa [IO], Bruma, Republic of South Africa

Institution of Chem. Engineers [IO], Rugby, United Kingdom

Institution of Civil Engineers [IO], London, United Kingdom

Institution of Diagnostic Engineers [IO], Wakefield, United Kingdom

Institution of Diesel and Gas Turbine Engineers [IO], Bedford, United Kingdom

Institution of Economic Development [IO], Northampton, United Kingdom

Institution of Electronics and Telecommunication Engineers [IO], New Delhi, India

Reference to "IO" in place of a book number signifies that the association may be found in the 50th edition of International Organizations.

Institution of Engg. Designers [IO], Westbury, United Kingdom
Institution of Engg. and Tech. [IO], Stevenage, United Kingdom
Institution of Engineers Australia/Engineers Australia [IO], Barton, Australia
Institution of Engineers - India [IO], Calcutta, India
Institution of Engineers - Malaysia [IO], Petaling Jaya, Malaysia
Institution of Engineers - Pakistan [IO], Karachi, Pakistan
Institution of Engineers - Sri Lanka [IO], Colombo, Sri Lanka
Institution of Environmental Sciences [IO], London, United Kingdom
Institution of Fire Engineers - England [IO], Moreton-in-Marsh, United Kingdom
Institution of Fire Engineers in South Africa [IO], Houghton, Republic of South Africa
Institution of Gas Engineers and Managers [IO], Kegworth, United Kingdom
Institution of Lighting Engineers [IO], Rugby, United Kingdom
Institution of Mech. Engineers [IO], London, United Kingdom
Institution of Occupational Safety and Hea. [IO], Wigston, United Kingdom
Institution of Professional Engineers New Zealand [IO], Wellington, New Zealand
Institution of Railway Signal Engineers [IO], London, United Kingdom
Institution of Structural Engineers [IO], London, United Kingdom
Institution of Surveyors, Australia [IO], Deakin, Australia
Institutional Food Editorial Coun. [★2832]
Institutional Food Editorial Coun. [★2832]
Institutional Food Mfrs. of Am. [★1401]
Institutional Food Mfrs. of Am. [★1401]
Institutional Food Mfrs. Assn. [★1401]
Institutional Food Mfrs. Assn. [★1401]
Institutional Food-Service Mfrs. Assn. [★1401]
Institutional Food-Service Mfrs. Assn. [★1401]
Institutional Locksmiths' Assn. [1047], PO Box 9560, Naperville, IL 60567-9560
Institutional and Municipal Parking Cong. [★2626]
Institutional and Municipal Parking Cong. [★2626]
Instituto Argentino del Envase [★IO]
Instituto de Assuntos Culturais - Brasil [★IO]
Instituto de Asuntos Culturales [★IO]
Instituto de Asuntos Culturales [★IO]
Instituto Boliviano de Comercio Exterior [★IO]
Instituto Brasileiro de Economia [★IO]
Instituto Brasileiro de Informacao em Ciencia e Tecnologia [★IO]
Instituto Centroamericano de la Salud [★IO]
Instituto Colombiano de Productores de Cemento [★IO]
Instituto de Desarrollo y Medio Ambiente [★IO]
Instituto de las Espanas [★9657]
Instituto Forestal Latinoamericano [★IO]
Instituto Geografico Militar - Chile [★IO]
Instituto Historico e Geografico Brasileiro [★IO]
Instituto Humanista para la Cooperacion con los Paises en Desarrollo [★IO]
Instituto Iberoamericano de Derecho Aeronautico y del Espacio y de la Aviacion Comercial [★IO]
Instituto para la Integracion de Am. Latina y el Caribe [★IO]
Instituto Interamericano de Cooperacion para la Agricultura [★IO]
Instituto Interamericano de Cooperacion para la Agricultura - Guyana [★IO]
Instituto Interamericano de Cooperacion para la Agricultura - Paraguay [★IO]
Instituto Interamericano de Cooperacion para la Agricultura - St. Lucia [★IO]
Instituto Interamericano de Cooperacion para la Agricultura - Dominican Republic [★IO]
Instituto Interamericano de Cooperacion para la Agriculture - Grenada [★IO]
Instituto Interamericano de Derechos Humanos [★IO]
Instituto Interamericano de Derechos Humanos - Programa Mujer y Derechos Humanos [IO], San Jose, Costa Rica

Instituto Interamericano de Estadistica [★IO]
Instituto Interamericano del Nino [★IO]
Instituto Latino-Americano de Estudos Avancados [★IO]
Instituto Latinoamericano de Derecho Tributario [★IO]
Instituto Latinoamericano del Fierro y el Acero [★IO]
Instituto Latinoamericano de Investigaciones Sociales [★IO]
Instituto di Medicina Pa Deporte di Aruba [IO], San Nicolas, Aruba
Instituto de la Mujer [★IO]
Instituto Nacional de Estadistica [★IO]
Instituto Nacional Hispano de Liturgia [19434], PO Box 18, Washington, DC 20064, (202)319-6450
Instituto Nacional de Liturgia Para Hispanos [★19434]
Instituto Nacional de Metrologia, Normalizacao e Qualidade Indus. [★IO]
Instituto Nacional de las Mujeres [IO], San Jose, Costa Rica
Instituto Nacional de Vitivinicultura [★IO]
Instituto de Nutricion de Centro Am. y Panama [★IO]
Instituto Panamericano de Geografia e Historia [★IO]
Instituto Panamericano de Ingenieria Naval [★IO]
Instituto Papelero Espanol [★IO]
Instituto Peruano de Educacion en Derechos Humanos y la Paz [★IO]
Instituto Peruano de Paternidad Responsible [IO], Lima, Peru
Instituto Portuguez da Voz [★IO]
Instituto Textil de Chile [★IO]
Instituto da Vinha e do Vinho [★IO]
Instituto do Vinho do Porto [★IO]
Instituut vir Gediplomeerde Werktuigkundige en Elektegniese Ingenieurs, Suid-Afrika [★IO]
Instituut van Landskapargitekte van Suid Afrika [★IO]
Instream Flow Coun. [4080], North Carolina Wildlife Resources Commn., 645 Hatchery Rd., Marion, NC 28752, (828)652-4360
Instructional Materials Reference Center [★17062]

Instructional Media
ACUTA: The Assn. for Communications Tech. Professionals in Higher Educ. [8301]
Agency for Instructional Tech. [8302]
Assn. of Amer. Univ. Presses [8303]
Assn. for Educational Communications and Tech. [8304]
Center for Teaching About China [8305]
Cmpt. Assisted Language Instruction Consortium [8306]
Cmpt. Assisted Language Instruction Consortium [8306]
Consortium of Coll. and Univ. Media Centers [8307]
Consortium for School Networking [8308]
Educ., Training and Res. Associates [8309]
EDUCAUSE [8310]
EPIE Inst. [8311]
French Amer. Cultural Exchange [8312]
Inst. for Computers in Jewish Life [8313]
Inst. for the Transfer of Tech. to Educ. [8314]
Instructional Systems Assn. [8315]
Instructional Tech. Coun. [8316]
Instructional Tech. Coun. [8316]
Manpower Educ. Inst. [8317]
Natl. Assn. for Health Science Educ. Partnerships [8318]
Natl. Info. Center for Educational Media [8319]
Soc. for Applied Learning Tech. [8320]
Univ. and Coll. Designers Assn. [8321]
Univ. and Coll. Designers Assn. [8321]
Instructional Systems Assn. [8315], 12427 Hedges Run Dr., No. 120, Lake Ridge, VA 22192, (703)730-2838

Instructional Technology
Reasoning Mind [8569]
Instructional Tech. Coun. [8316], 1 Dupont Cir. NW, Ste. 360, Washington, DC 20036-1130, (202)293-3110
Instructional Tech. Coun. [8316], 1 Dupont Cir. NW, Ste. 360, Washington, DC 20036-1130, (202)293-3110

Instructional Telecommunications Consortium [★8316]
Instructional Telecommunications Consortium [★8316]
Instructional Telecommunications Coun. [★8316]
Instructional Telecommunications Coun. [★8316]
Instrument Contracting and Engg. Assn. [914], Nick Theisen, Exec. Dir., 4312 Rochard Ln., Fort Mill, SC 29707-5851, (704)905-0319
Instrument Soc. of Am. [★6999]
Instrument Soc. of Am. [★6999]
Instrumentation
IEEE | Instrumentation and Measurement Soc. [6998]
Instrumentation Testing Assn. [1920]
Instrumentation Testing Assn. [1920]
Intl. Soc. of Automation [6999]
Intl. Soc. of Automation [6999]
Natl. Assn. for Civil War Brass Music [10251]
Instrumentation Testing Assn. [1920], 2481 Del Prado Blvd. N, No. 301, Ste. 107, Cape Coral, FL 33909, (702)568-1445
Instrumentation Testing Assn. [1920], 2481 Del Prado Blvd. N, No. 301, Ste. 107, Cape Coral, FL 33909, (702)568-1445
Insulated Cable Engineers Assn. [6800], PO Box 1568, Carrollton, GA 30112, (770)830-0369
Insulated Power Cable Engineers Assn. [★6800]
Insulated Render and Cladding Assn. [IO], London, United Kingdom
Insulating Concrete Form Assn. [828], PO Box 3470, Crofton, MD 21114, (847)657-9730
Insulating Glass Certification Coun. [1578], PO Box 730, Sackets Harbor, NY 13685, (315)646-2234
Insulating Glass Mfrs. Alliance [IO], Ottawa, ON, Canada
Insulation Contractors Assn. of Am. [915], 1321 Duke St., Ste. 303, Alexandria, VA 22314, (703)739-0356
Insulation Distributor Contractors Natl. Assn. [★938]
Insulin for Life Australia [IO], Ballarat, Australia
Insulindependence [14353], Peter H. Nerothin, Pres./Founder, 7770 Regents Rd., No. 113390, San Diego, CA 92122-1967, (888)912-3837
Insurance
ACORD [1921]
ACORD [1921]
Actuarial Soc. of South Africa [7207]
Alliance of Claims Assistance Professionals [1922]
Amer. Acad. of Actuaries [1923]
Amer. Assn. of Crop Insurers [1924]
Amer. Assn. of Dental Consultants [1925]
Amer. Assn. of Insurance Services [1926]
Amer. Assn. for Long-Term Care Insurance [1927]
Amer. Assn. of Managing Gen. Agents [1928]
Amer. Assn. of State Compensation Insurance Funds [1929]
Amer. Assn. of State Compensation Insurance Funds [1929]
Amer. Coun. of Life Insurers [1930]
Amer. Foreign Ser. Protective Assn. [19041]
Amer. Fraternal Alliance [19042]
Amer. Fraternal Union [19043]
SC 29707-5851, (704)905-0319
Amer. Inst. for CPCU [1931]
Amer. Inst. of Marine Underwriters [1932]
Amer. Insurance Assn. [1933]
Amer. Insurance Marketing and Sales Soc. [1934]
Amer. Nuclear Insurers [1935]
Amer. Risk and Insurance Assn. [8322]
Artisans Order of Mutual Protection [19044]
Assn. for Advanced Life Underwriting [1936]
Assn. of Average Adjusters of the U.S. [1937]
Assn. of Defense Trial Attorneys [5548]
Assn. of Finance and Insurance Professionals [1938]
Assn. of Financial Guaranty Insurers [1939]
Assn. of Governmental Risk Pools [5549]
Assn. of Home Off. Underwriters [1940]
Assn. of Home Off. Underwriters [1940]
Assn. of Life Insurance Counsel [5550]
Assn. of Lloyd's Members [22495]
Assn. of Online Insurance Agents [1941]
Assn. of Policy Market Makers [19093]
Assn. of Professional Insurance Women [1942]

A star before a book entry number signifies that the name is not listed separately, but is mentioned within the entry.

Aviation Insurance Assn. [1943]
Bank Insurance and Securities Assn. [1944]
Blue Cross and Blue Shield Assn. [15127]
Canadian Bar Insurance Assn. [14499]
Captive Insurance Companies Assn. [1945]
Casualty Actuarial Soc. [1946]
Claims Support Professional Assn. [1947]
Coalition for Affordable Hea. Coverage [14854]
Coalition Against Insurance Fraud [1948]
Coalition to Insure Against Terrorism [1949]
Comm. of Annuity Insurers [1950]
Conf. of Consulting Actuaries [1951]
Consumer Credit Indus. Assn. [1952]
Coun. of Insurance Agents and Brokers [1953]
Coun. of Insurance Agents and Brokers [1953]
CPCU Soc. [1954]
Crop Insurance Professionals Assn. [1955]
Crop Insurance and Reinsurance Bur. [1956]
Degree of Honor Protective Assn. [19045]
Direct Marketing Insurance and Financial Services
   Coun. [1957]
Eastern Claims Conf. [1958]
Environmental Risk Resources Assn. [4260]
Equitable Reserve Assn. [19046]
Estonian Insurance Assn. [19090]
Fed. of Defense and Corporate Counsel [5551]
Fire Mark Circle of the Americas [21707]
Foreign Credit Insurance Assn. [1959]
Fraternal Field Managers' Assn. [1960]
GAMA Intl. [1961]
GAMA Intl. [1961]
Gamma Iota Sigma [23571]
Gamma Iota Sigma [23571]
Gen. Insurance Assn. of Singapore [23324]
Gleaner Life Insurance Soc. [19047]
Grand Lodge Order of the Sons of Hermann in
   Texas [19048]
Gp. Underwriters Assn. of Am. [1962]
Highway Loss Data Inst. [1963]
Honorable Order of the Blue Goose, Intl. [19049]
Honorable Order of the Blue Goose, Intl. [19049]
Independent Insurance Agents and Brokers of
   Am. [1964]
Independent Order of Vikings [19050]
Inland Marine Underwriters Assn. [1965]
Inst. for Bus. and Home Safety [1966]
Insurance Accounting and Systems Assn. [1967]
Insurance Accounting and Systems Assn. [1967]
Insurance Assn. of the Caribbean [18470]
Insurance Brokers and Agents of the West [1968]
Insurance Consumer Affairs Exchange [1969]
Insurance Coun. of Australia [21687]
Insurance Data Mgt. Assn. [1970]
Insurance Info. Inst. [1971]
Insurance Inst. of Am. [1972]
Insurance Loss Control Assn. [1973]
Insurance Marketing and Communications Assn.
   [1974]
Insurance Marketplace Standards Assn. [1975]
Insurance Media Assn. [1976]
Insurance Regulatory Examiners Soc. [1977]
Insurance Res. Coun. [1978]
Insurance Soc. of New York [1979]
Insurers' Company [23535]
Intermediaries and Reinsurance Underwriters
   Assn. [1980]
Intl. Assn. of Black Actuaries [1981]
Intl. Assn. of Black Actuaries [1981]
Intl. Assn. of Insurance Fraud Agencies [5552]
Intl. Assn. of Insurance Fraud Agencies [5552]
Intl. Assn. for Insurance Law in the U.S. [5553]
Intl. Assn. for Insurance Law in the U.S. [5553]
Intl. Assn. of Insurance Receivers [1982]
Intl. Assn. of Insurance Receivers [1982]
Intl. Assn. of Special Investigation Units [1983]
Intl. Assn. of Special Investigation Units [1983]
Intl. Claim Assn. [1984]
Intl. Claim Assn. [1984]
Intl. Cooperative and Mutual Insurance Federa-
   tion/Regional Assn. for The Americas [1985]
Intl. Insurance Soc. [1986]
Intl. Insurance Soc. [1986]
Intersure - Singer Nelson Charlmers [1987]
Liability Insurance Res. Bur. [1988]
Life Insurance Settlement Assn. [1989]

Life Insurers Coun. [1990]
Life Underwriter Training Coun. [8323]
LIMRA Intl. [1991]
LIMRA Intl. [1991]
LOMA [1992]
LOMA [1992]
Loss Executives Assn. [1993]
Loyal Christian Benefit Assn. [19051]
Luso-American Fraternal Soc. [19052]
Luso-American Life Insurance Soc. [19053]
Managed Care Risk Assn. [1690]
Mass Marketing Insurance Inst. [1994]
MIB Gp. [15128]
Million Dollar Round Table [1995]
Mortgage Insurance Companies of Am. [1996]
Natl. African-American Insurance Assn. [1997]
Natl. Alliance of Gen. Agents [1998]
Natl. Alliance for Insurance Educ. and Res. [1999]
Natl. Assn. of Catastrophe Adjusters [2000]
Natl. Assn. of Dental Plans [15129]
Natl. Assn. of Fire Investigators [2001]
Natl. Assn. for Fixed Annuities [2002]
Natl. Assn. of Fraternal Insurance Counsellors
   [2003]
Natl. Assn. of Hea. Underwriters [2004]
Natl. Assn. of Independent Insurance Adjusters
   [2005]
Natl. Assn. of Independent Insurance Auditors and
   Engineers [2006]
Natl. Assn. of Independent Life Brokerage Agen-
   cies [2007]
Natl. Assn. of Insurance Commissioners [5554]
Natl. Assn. of Insurance and Financial Advisors
   [2008]
Natl. Assn. of Insurance Women Intl. [2009]
Natl. Assn. of Mutual Insurance Companies
   [2010]
Natl. Assn. of Professional Allstate Agents [2011]
Natl. Assn. of Professional Insurance Agents
   [2012]
Natl. Assn. of Professional Surplus Lines Offices
   [2013]
Natl. Assn. of Public Insurance Adjusters [2014]
Natl. Assn. of State Comprehensive Hea. Insur-
   ance Plans [14861]
Natl. Assn. of State Farm Agents [2015]
Natl. Assn. of Surety Bond Producers [2016]
Natl. Assn. of Unemployment Insurance Appellate
   Boards [5555]
Natl. Chamber of Insurance Businesses [21337]
Natl. Conf. of Insurance Legislators [5556]
Natl. Coun. on Compensation Insurance [2017]
Natl. Coun. of Self-Insurers [2018]
Natl. Crop Insurance Services [2019]
Natl. Hea. Care Anti-Fraud Assn. [15130]
Natl. InStar Users Gp. [7000]
Natl. Insurance Crime Bur. [2020]
Natl. Org. of Injured Workers [23319]
Natl. Risk Retention Assn. [2021]
Natl. Soc. of Insurance Premium Auditors [2022]
Natl. Soc. of Professional Insurance Investigators
   [2023]
Natl. Truck and Heavy Equip. Claims Coun.
   [2024]
Nationwide Insurance Independent Contractors
   Assn. [2025]
North Amer. Bar-Related Title Insurers [2026]
North Amer. Pet Hea. Insurance Assn. [14863]
Order of United Commercial Travelers of Am.
   [19054]
Organized Flying Adjusters [2027]
Physician Insurers Assn. of Am. [15131]
Police and Firemen's Insurance Assn. [19055]
Professional Insurance Marketing Assn. [2028]
Professional Liability Underwriting Soc. [2029]
Professional Liability Underwriting Soc. [2029]
Professional Risk Managers' Intl. Assn. [2030]
Property Casualty Insurers Assn. of Am. [2031]
Property Loss Res. Bur. [2032]
Public Agency Risk Managers Assn. [5557]
Public Risk Mgt. Assn. [5558]
Reinsurance Assn. of Am. [2033]
Risk and Insurance Mgt. Soc. [2034]
Royal Neighbors of Am. [19056]
Securities and Insurance Licensing Assn. [2035]

Security Anal. and Risk Mgt. Assn. [3227]
Self-Insurance Inst. of Am. [2036]
Shipowners Claims Bur. [2037]
Societe Culinaire Philanthropique [19057]
Soc. of Actuaries [2038]
Soc. of Certified Insurance Counselors [8324]
Soc. of Financial Ser. Professionals [2039]
Soc. of Financial Ser. Professionals [2039]
Soc. of Insurance Res. [2040]
Soc. of Insurance Trainers and Educators [8325]
Soc. of Registered Professional Adjusters [2041]
Soc. of Registered Professional Adjusters [2041]
Soc. for Risk Anal. [2042]
Soc. of Risk Mgt. Consultants [2043]
South African Insurance Assn. [22923]
SPJST [19058]
Supreme Coun. of the Royal Arcanum [19059]
Surety and Fidelity Assn. of Am. [2044]
Teachers Insurance and Annuity Assn. [8326]
TechAssure Assn. [2045]
Travelers Protective Assn. of Am. [19060]
U.S. Letter Carriers Mutual Benefit Assn. [19061]
Univ. Risk Mgt. and Insurance Assn. [8327]
Vasa Order of Am. [19062]
Vasa Order of Am. [19062]
Venezuelan Chamber of Insurance Companies
   [4313]
Water Quality Insurance Syndicate [2046]
William Penn Assn. [19063]
Woman's Life Insurance Soc. [19064]
Women in Insurance and Financial Services
   [2047]
Women in Insurance and Financial Services
   [2047]
Workers Compensation Insurance Organizations
   [2048]
Workmen's Benefit Fund of the U.S.A. [19065]
Workmen's Circle [19066]
WSA Fraternal Life [19067]
Insurance Accounting and Statistical Assn. [★1967]
Insurance Accounting and Statistical Assn. [★1967]
Insurance Accounting and Systems Assn. [1967],
   PO Box 51340, Durham, NC 27717-1340,
   (919)489-0991
Insurance Accounting and Systems Assn. [1967],
   PO Box 51340, Durham, NC 27717-1340,
   (919)489-0991
Insurance Advt. Conf. [★1974]
Insurance Assn. of the Caribbean [IO], St. Michael,
   Barbados
Insurance Assn. of Cyprus [IO], Nicosia, Cyprus
Insurance Brokers and Agents of the West [1968],
   7041 Koll Center Pkwy., Ste. 290, Pleasanton, CA
   94566-3128, (925)426-3310
Insurance Brokers Assn. of Canada [IO], Toronto,
   ON, Canada
Insurance Bur. of Canada [IO], Toronto, ON, Canada
Insurance Company Educ. Directors Soc. [★8325]
Insurance Consultants Soc. [★2043]
Insurance Consumer Affairs Exchange [1969], PO
   Box 746, Lake Zurich, IL 60047, (847)991-8454
Insurance Coun. of Australia [IO], Sydney, Australia
Insurance Coun. of New Zealand [IO], Wellington,
   New Zealand
Insurance Crime Prevention Inst. [★2020]
Insurance Data Mgt. Assn. [1970], 545 Washington
   Blvd., Jersey City, NJ 07310-1686, (201)469-3069
Insurance and Financial Communicators Assn. [IO],
   Cambridge, ON, Canada
Insurance Fund; United Furniture Workers [23193]
Insurance Info. Inst. [1971], 110 William St., New
   York, NY 10038, (212)346-5500
Insurance Inst. of Am. [1972], 720 Providence Rd.,
   Ste. 100, Malvern, PA 19355-3433, (800)644-2101
Insurance Inst. for Highway Safety [12985], 1005 N
   Glebe Rd., Ste. 800, Arlington, VA 22201,
   (703)247-1500
Insurance Inst. of Hong Kong [IO], Hong Kong,
   People's Republic of China
Insurance Inst. of India [IO], Mumbai, India
Insurance Inst. of Ireland [IO], Dublin, Ireland
Insurance Inst. of London [IO], London, United
   Kingdom
Insurance Inst. for Property Loss Reduction [★1966]
Insurance Loss Control Assn. [1973], 118 Treetops
   Dr., Lancaster, PA 17601-1790, (717)898-9056

Reference to "IO" in place of a book number signifies that the association may be found in the 50th edition of International Organizations.

Insurance Managers Assn. of Cayman [IO], Grand Cayman, Cayman Islands

Insurance Marketing and Communications Assn. [1974], 4916 Point Fosdick Dr. NW, No. 180, Gig Harbor, WA 98335, (206)219-9811

Insurance Marketplace Standards Assn. [1975], 4550 Montgomery Ave., Ste. 700N, Bethesda, MD 20814, (240)744-3030

Insurance Media Assn. [1976], 9221 Ravenna Rd., Ste. D8, Twinsburg, OH 44087, (330)425-8399

Insurance Plans; America's Hea. [14852]

Insurance Regulatory Examiners Soc. [1977], 1821 Univ. Ave. W, Ste. S256, St. Paul, MN 55104, (651)917-6250

Insurance Res. Coun. [1978], 718 Providence Rd., Malvern, PA 19355-0725, (610)644-2212

Insurance Soc. of New York [1979], St. John's Univ., 8000 Utopia Pkwy., Jamaica, NY 11439, (718)990-6653

Insurance Workers Intl. Union [★23191]

Insurers' Company [IO], London, United Kingdom

INTACT Educational Found. [★11520]

INTACT Educational Found. [★11520]

Integrated Bus. Communications Alliance [282], 81 Cottage St., Doylestown, PA 18901, (215)489-1722

Integrated Mfg. Tech. Initiative [7045], 10535 Hardin Valley Rd., Knoxville, TN 37932, (865)862-5668

Integrated Media Assn. [491], 740 Bismark Rd. NE, Atlanta, GA 30324, (845)876-2577

Integrated Plant Protection Center [3758], Oregon State Univ., Dept. of Environmental and Molecular Toxicology, 2040 Cordley Hall, Corvallis, OR 97331, (541)737-3541

Integrated Waste Services Assn. [★4981]

Integration
Fund for an OPEN Soc. [17894]

Integrative Clinics Intl. [14899], 3871 Piedmont Ave., No. 34, Oakland, CA 94611

Integrity: Arts and Culture Assn. [9181], PO Box 6491, Rock Island, IL 61204-6491, (309)716-9854

Integrity USA [19793], 620 Park Ave., No. 311, Rochester, NY 14607-2943, (585)360-4512

Intellect [IO], London, United Kingdom

Intellectual Disability Rights Ser. [IO], Redfern, Australia

Intellectual Property
Amer. Intellectual Property Law Assn. [5559]
Amer. Soc. of Composers, Authors and Publishers [5560]
Assn. of Patent Law Firms [5885]
Assn. of Univ. Tech. Managers [5561]
Bus. Software Alliance [5562]
Center for Social and Legal Res. [5563]
Center for Social and Legal Res. [5563]
Coalition Against Counterfeiting and Piracy [5564]
Coalition for Intellectual Property Rights [5565]
Copyright Alliance [5566]
Copyright Clearance Center [5567]
Copyright Soc. of the U.S.A. [5568]
Embroidery Software Protection Coalition [2049]
Imaging Supplies Coalition [5569]
Imaging Supplies Coalition [5569]
Intellectual Property Owners Assn. [5570]
Intl. Intellectual Property Assn. [5571]
Intl. Intellectual Property Assn. [5571]
Intl. Licensing Indus. Merchandisers' Assn. [5572]
Intl. Licensing Indus. Merchandisers' Assn. [5572]
Intl. Trademark Assn. [5573]
Intl. Trademark Assn. [5573]
Inventors Workshop Intl. [5574]
Inventors Workshop Intl. [5574]
IP Justice [5575]
Licensing Executives Soc. [5576]
Los Angeles Copyright Soc. [5577]
Patent Off. Professional Assn. [5578]
Patent and Trademark Off. Soc. [5579]
Public Interest Intellectual Property Advisors [5580]
Software and Info. Indus. Assn. [5581]
Songwriters Guild of Am. [5582]
Visual Artists and Galleries Assn. [5583]

Intellectual Property Owners [★5570]

Intellectual Property Owners Assn. [5570], 1501 M St. NW, Ste. 1150, Washington, DC 20005, (202)507-4500

Intelligence
Intl. Assn. for Intelligence Educ. [8328]
Intl. High IQ Soc. [19068]
Intl. High IQ Soc. [19068]
Intl. Intelligence Ethics Assn. [7001]
Intl. Soc. for Intelligence Res. [7002]
Natl. Counter Intelligence Corps Assn. [20670]

Intelligence Proj. - Address unknown since 2010.

Intelligent Building Gp. [IO], London, United Kingdom

Intelligent Buildings Inst. - Defunct.

Intelligent Systems Sci. Soc. of Iran [IO], Mashhad, Iran

Intelligent Transport Systems - Arab [IO], London, United Kingdom

Intelligent Transport Systems - Australia [IO], Port Melbourne, Australia

Intelligent Transport Systems - Japan [IO], Tokyo, Japan

Intelligent Transport Systems - Singapore [IO], Singapore, Singapore

Intelligent Transport Systems - South Africa [IO], Gauteng, Republic of South Africa

Intelligent Transport Systems - United Kingdom [IO], London, United Kingdom

Intelligent Trans. Soc. of Am. [3513], 1100 17th St. NW, Ste. 1200, Washington, DC 20036, (202)484-4847

Intensive Care Soc. [IO], London, United Kingdom

Inter-African Coffee Org. [IO], Abidjan, Cote d'Ivoire

Inter-American Assn. of Intellectual Property [IO], Montevideo, Uruguay

Inter-American Assn. of Sanitary Engg. [★7348]

Inter-American Assn. of Sanitary Engg. [★7348]

Inter-American Assn. of Sanitary Engg. and Env. [★7348]

Inter-American Assn. of Sanitary Engg. and Env. [★7348]

Inter-American Assn. of Sanitary Engg. and Environmental Sciences [★7348]

Inter-American Assn. of Sanitary Engg. and Environmental Sciences [★7348]

Inter-American Assn. of Sanitary Engineers [★7348]

Inter-American Assn. of Sanitary Engineers [★7348]

Inter-American Assn. of Sanitary and Environmental Engg. [★7348]

Inter-American Assn. of Sanitary and Environmental Engg. [★7348]

Inter-American Bar Assn. [5663], 1211 Connecticut Ave. NW, Ste. 202, Washington, DC 20036, (202)466-5944

Inter-American Bar Assn. [5663], 1211 Connecticut Ave. NW, Ste. 202, Washington, DC 20036, (202)466-5944

Inter-American Children's Inst. [IO], Montevideo, Uruguay

Inter-American Commercial Arbitration Commn. - Address unknown since 2011.

Inter-American Commn. on Human Rights [17839], 1889 F St. NW, Washington, DC 20006, (202)458-6002

Inter-American Commn. on Human Rights [17839], 1889 F St. NW, Washington, DC 20006, (202)458-6002

Inter-American Commn. of Women [17649], Org. of Amer. States, 17th St. and Constitution Ave. NW, Washington, DC 20006, (202)458-3000

Inter-American Commn. of Women [17649], Org. of Amer. States, 17th St. and Constitution Ave. NW, Washington, DC 20006, (202)458-3000

Inter-American Conductive Educ. Assn. [8884], PO Box 3169, Toms River, NJ 08756-3169, (732)797-2566

Inter-American Conductive Educ. Assn. [8884], PO Box 3169, Toms River, NJ 08756-3169, (732)797-2566

Inter-American Confed. for Catholic Educ. [IO], Bogota, Colombia

Inter-American Conf. of Ministers of Labor of the OAS [17523], Org. of Amer. States, 1889 F St. NW, 7th Fl., Washington, DC 20006, (202)458-3567

Inter-American Conf. of Ministers of Labor of the OAS [17523], Org. of Amer. States, 1889 F St. NW, 7th Fl., Washington, DC 20006, (202)458-3567

Inter-American Conf. of Social Security [IO], Mexico City, Mexico

Inter-Amer. Coun. for Education, Science and Culture - Defunct.

Inter-American Defense Bd. [17504], 2600 NW 16th St., Washington, DC 20441, (202)939-6041

Inter-American Defense Bd. [17504], 2600 NW 16th St., Washington, DC 20441, (202)939-6041

Inter-American Development Bank [17579], 1300 New York Ave. NW, Washington, DC 20577, (202)623-1000

Inter-American Development Bank [17579], 1300 New York Ave. NW, Washington, DC 20577, (202)623-1000

Inter-American Elecl. Commun. Commn. [★3409]

Inter-American Elecl. Commun. Commn. [★3409]

Inter-American Found. [18572], 901 N Stuart St., 10th Fl., Balston, Arlington, VA 22203-1821, (703)306-4301

Inter-American Found. [18572], 901 N Stuart St., 10th Fl., Balston, Arlington, VA 22203-1821, (703)306-4301

Inter-American Hea. Alliance [14795], 2301 Vanderbilt Pl., PMB 351804, Nashville, TN 37235, (703)725-9320

Inter-American Inst. for Cooperation on Agriculture - Costa Rica [IO], San Jose, Costa Rica

Inter-American Inst. for Cooperation on Agriculture - Dominican Republic [IO], Santo Domingo, Dominican Republic

Inter-American Inst. for Cooperation on Agriculture - Grenada [IO], St. George's, Grenada

Inter-American Inst. for Cooperation on Agriculture - Guyana [IO], Georgetown, Guyana

Inter-American Inst. for Cooperation on Agriculture - Paraguay [IO], Asuncion, Paraguay

Inter-American Inst. for Cooperation on Agriculture - St. Lucia [IO], Castries, St. Lucia

Inter-American Inst. for Global Change Res. [IO], Sao Jose dos Campos, Brazil

Inter-American Inst. of Human Rights [IO], San Jose, Costa Rica

Inter-American Org. for Higher Educ. [IO], Quebec, QC, Canada

Inter-American Parliamentary Gp. on Population and Development [12339], 845 3rd Ave., 6th Fl., New York, NY 10022, (646)240-4053

Inter-American Parliamentary Gp. on Population and Development [12339], 845 3rd Ave., 6th Fl., New York, NY 10022, (646)240-4053

Inter Amer. Press Assn. [17346], Jules Dubois Bldg., 1801 SW 3rd Ave., Miami, FL 33129, (305)634-2465

Inter Amer. Press Assn. [17346], Jules Dubois Bldg., 1801 SW 3rd Ave., Miami, FL 33129, (305)634-2465

Inter-American Res. and Documentation Centre on Vocational Training [IO], Montevideo, Uruguay

Inter-American School Ser. [★8395]

Inter-American School Ser. [★8395]

Inter-American Soc. of Cardiology [IO], Mexico City, Mexico

Inter-American Statistical Inst. [IO], Panama City, Panama

Inter-Amer. Task Force on Alcohol and Other Substnace Abuse Issues [★13243]

Inter-American Telecommunication Commn. [3409], 1889 F St. NW, Washington, DC 20006, (202)458-3004

Inter-American Telecommunication Commn. [3409], 1889 F St. NW, Washington, DC 20006, (202)458-3004

Inter-American Telecommunication Conf. [★3409]

Inter-American Telecommunication Conf. [★3409]

Inter-American Tropical Tuna Commn. [5454], 8604 La Jolla Shores Dr., La Jolla, CA 92037-1508, (858)546-7100

Inter-American Tropical Tuna Commn. [5454], 8604 La Jolla Shores Dr., La Jolla, CA 92037-1508, (858)546-7100

Inter-Association Task Force on Alcohol Issues [★13243]

Inter-Association Task Force on Campus Alcohol and Other Substance Abuse Issues [★13243]

Inter-collegiate Men's Chorus, A Natl. Assn. of Male Choruses [★10212]

A star before a book entry number signifies that the name is not listed separately, but is mentioned within the entry.

Inter-collegiate Men's Chorus, A Natl. Assn. of Male Choruses [★10212]

Inter-Faith Community Services [12732], 3370 S Irving St., Englewood, CO 80110-1816, (303)789-0501

Inter-Faith Task Force [★12732]

Inter-Faith Task Force for Community Services [★12732]

Inter-Galactic Spacecraft UFO Intercontinental Res. and Analytic Network - Defunct.

Inter-Governmental Philatelic Corp. [22045], 161 Helen St., South Plainfield, NJ 07080, (908)548-8088

Inter-Industry Conf. on Auto Collision Repair [357], 5125 Trillium Blvd., Hoffman Estates, IL 60192-3600, (847)590-1198

Inter-Industry Farm Elec. Utilization Coun. [★6753]

Inter-Lake Yachting Assn. [22343], Allen Ashley, Sec., 2200 Grand Blvd., Monroe, MI 48162

Inter-National Assn. of Bus., Indus. and Rehabilitation [11794], PO Box 15242, Washington, DC 20003, (202)543-6353

Inter-Pacific Bar Assn. [IO], Tokyo, Japan

Inter Pares [IO], Ottawa, ON, Canada

Inter-Parliamentary Consultative Coun. of Benelux [IO], Brussels, Belgium

Inter-Parliamehtary Union [IO], Geneva, Switzerland

Inter Press Ser. Intl. Assn. [IO], Rome, Italy

Inter-Society Color Coun. [6434], 11491 Sunset Hills Rd., Reston, VA 20190, (703)318-0263

Inter-Society Color Coun. [6434], 11491 Sunset Hills Rd., Reston, VA 20190, (703)318-0263

Inter-Society Cytology Coun. [★14214]

Inter-Society for the Electronic Arts [IO], Amsterdam, Netherlands

Inter-Union Commn. on Solar Terrestrial Physics [★7272]

Inter-Union Commn. on Solar Terrestrial Physics [★7272]

Inter-University Comm. on the Superior Student [★8050]

Inter-University Consortium for Political and Social Res. [7288], Univ. of Michigan Inst. for Social Res., PO Box 1248, Ann Arbor, MI 48106-1248, (734)647-5000

Inter-University Coun. for East Africa [IO], Kampala, Uganda

Inter-University Prog. for Latino Res. [18984], Univ. of Notre Dame, Inst. for Latino Stud., 230 McKenna Hall, PO Box 764, Notre Dame, IN 46556-5685, (574)631-3481

Inter-University Seminar on Armed Forces and Soc. [5807], Loyola Univ. Chicago, Political Sci. Dept., 1032 W Sheridan Rd., Chicago, IL 60660, (773)508-2930

Inter Varsity Christian Fellowship [20051], PO Box 7895, Madison, WI 53707-7895, (608)274-9001

Inter Varsity Missions Fellowship [★20051]

Interact Worldwide [IO], London, United Kingdom

InterAction [12340], 1400 16th St. NW, Ste. 210, Washington, DC 20036, (202)667-8227

InterAction [12340], 1400 16th St. NW, Ste. 210, Washington, DC 20036, (202)667-8227

Interaction Design Assn. [6599], PO Box 2833, Westport, CT 06880

Interaction Design Assn. [6599], PO Box 2833, Westport, CT 06880

Interactive Advt. Bur. [93], 116 E 27th St., 7th Fl., New York, NY 10016, (212)380-4700

Interactive Advt. Bur. [93], 116 E 27th St., 7th Fl., New York, NY 10016, (212)380-4700

Interactive Advt. Bur. - Europe [IO], Brussels, Belgium

Interactive Audio Special Interest Gp. [2557], MIDI Mfrs. Assn., PO Box 3173, La Habra, CA 90632-3173, (714)736-9774

Interactive Digital Software Assn. [★6485]

Interactive Entertainment Assn. of Australia [IO], Eveleigh, Australia

Interactive Gaming Coun. [IO], Vancouver, BC, Canada

Interactive Media Entertainment and Gaming Assn. [7008], 2325 Dulles Corner Blvd., Ste. 500, Herndon, VA 20171, (703)788-6845

Interactive Multimedia Assn. - Defunct.

Interactive TV Assn. [★3400]

Interactive Travel Services Assn. [3560], Natl. Press Bldg., 529 14th St. NW, Ste. 750, Washington, DC 20045, (202)955-0089

Interagency Coalition on AIDS and Development [IO], Ottawa, ON, Canada

Interagency Coun. on Info. Resources in Nursing [9988], Richard J. Barry, MSLS, Amer. Nurses Assn. Lib., 8515 Georgia Ave., Ste. 400, Silver Spring, MD 20910-3492, (301)628-5143

Interamerican Accounting Assn. [32], 275 Fountainebleau Blvd., Ste. 245, Miami, FL 33172, (305)225-1991

Interamerican Accounting Assn. [32], 275 Fountainebleau Blvd., Ste. 245, Miami, FL 33172, (305)225-1991

Interamerican Accounting Conf. [★32]

Interamerican Assn. for Environmental Defense [4331], Earthjustice, 426 17th St., 6th Fl., Oakland, CA 94612, (510)550-6753

Interamerican Assn. for Environmental Defense [4331], Earthjustice, 426 17th St., 6th Fl., Oakland, CA 94612, (510)550-6753

Interamerican Coll. of Physicians and Surgeons [16264], 233 Broadway, Ste. 954, New York, NY 10279, (866)291-7544

Interamerican Coll. of Physicians and Surgeons [16264], 233 Broadway, Ste. 954, New York, NY 10279, (866)291-7544

Interamerican Fed. of Touring and Auto. Clubs [IO], Buenos Aires, Argentina

Interamerican Heart Cardiology Found. [★14019]

InterAmerican Heart Found. [14019], 7272 Greenville Ave., Dallas, TX 75231-4596, (214)706-1301

InterAmerican Soc. for Tropical Horticulture [4670], Fairchild Tropical Garden, 11935 SW Old Cutler Rd., Miami, FL 33156

InterAmerican Travel Agents Soc. - Address unknown since 2011.

Intercambio de Casas [★21853]

Intercede Intl. [IO], Fort Erie, ON, Canada

Intercessors for Am. [19577], PO Box 915, Purcellville, VA 20134, (540)317-2070

Interchangeable Virtual Instruments [★6545]

The InterChurch Center [19656], 475 Riverside Dr., New York, NY 10115-0002, (212)870-2200

Interchurch Medical Assistance [19951], PO Box 429, New Windsor, MD 21776, (410)635-8720

Interchurch Medical Assistance [19951], PO Box 429, New Windsor, MD 21776, (410)635-8720

Interchurch Org. for Development Cooperation [IO], Utrecht, Netherlands

Intercoiffure Am. [968], Maryanne McCormack, Membership Chair, 1303 Campbell Rd., Houston, TX 77055, (713)984-8800

InterCol London [IO], London, United Kingdom

Intercollegiate Assn. of Amateur Athletes of Am. [22990], Eastern Coll. Athletic Conf., PO Box 3, Centerville, MA 02632, (508)771-5060

Intercollegiate Broadcasting Sys. [7774], 367 Windsor Hwy., New Windsor, NY 12553-7900, (845)565-0003

Intercollegiate Fencing Assn. [22564], Eastern Coll. Athletic Conf., 1311 Craigville Beach Rd., Centerville, MA 02632, (508)771-5060

InterCollegiate Horse Show Assn. [22682], 8125 Verbeck Dr., Manlius, NY 13104

Intercollegiate Ice Hockey Assn. [★22643]

Intercollegiate Knights [23560], PO Box 7264, Provo, UT 84602-7264, (801)489-0458

Intercollegiate Men's Choruses, An Intl. Assn. of Male Choruses [10212], Washington Men's Camerata, The Univ. of Virginia Glee Club, 1503 S St. NW, Washington, DC 20009, (202)364-1064

Intercollegiate Men's Choruses, An Intl. Assn. of Male Choruses [10212], Washington Men's Camerata, The Univ. of Virginia Glee Club, 1503 S St. NW, Washington, DC 20009, (202)364-1064

Intercollegiate Musical Coun., A Natl. Assn. of Male Choruses [★10212]

Intercollegiate Musical Coun., A Natl. Assn. of Male Choruses [★10212]

InterCollegiate Outing Club Assn. [23085], Don Wade, Direct Mail Chair, 35-41 72 St., Jackson Heights, NY 11372

Intercollegiate Rowing Assn. [22856], Eastern Coll. Athletic Conf., 1311 Craigville Beach Rd., Centerville, MA 02632-4129, (508)771-5060

Intercollegiate Soc. of Individualists [★17425]

Intercollegiate Stud. Inst. [17425], 3901 Centerville Rd., Wilmington, DE 19807-1938, (302)652-4600

Intercollegiate Taiwanese Amer. Students Assn. [19252], PO Box 5703, Evanston, IL 60204

InterCollegiate Tennis Assn. [23055], 174 Tamarack Cir., Skillman, NJ 08558-2021, (609)497-6920

Intercollegiate Tennis Coaches Assn. [★23055]

Intercollegiate Women's Lacrosse Coaches Assn. [22714], Gothard Lane, Exec. Dir., PO Box 1124, Grand Lake, CO 80447, (443)951-9611

InterConnection [11664], 3415 Stone Way N, Seattle, WA 98103, (206)633-1517

Intercontainer-Interfrigo [IO], Basel, Switzerland

Intercontinental Church Soc. [IO], Warwick, United Kingdom

Intercontinental Fed. of Behavioral Optometry [15994], Robert Williams, Exec. Dir., 1921 E Carnegie Ave., Ste. 3L, Santa Ana, CA 92705

Intercontinental Fed. of Behavioral Optometry [15994], Robert Williams, Exec. Dir., 1921 E Carnegie Ave., Ste. 3L, Santa Ana, CA 92705

Intercooperation Kyrgyzstan [IO], Bishkek, Kirgizstan

Intercultural

Assn. for Africanist Anthropology [6133]

Australia-Britain Soc. [4518]InterculturalBritish Coun. Canada

Champa Cultural Preservation Assn. of USA [10636]

Delta Sigma Chi Sorority [23741]

Haiti Cultural Exchange [9517]

Intercultural Alliance of Artists and Scholars [9237]

Interracial-InterCultural Pride [12013]

My Travel Bug [9018]

Nepali Amer. Friendship Assn. [19172]

New Zealand Ireland Assn. [15984]

Ngwa Natl. Assn. USA [19040]

North Amer. Taiwan Stud. Assn. [8938]

Saq' Be': Org. for Mayan and Indigenous Spiritual Bodies [9867]

Turkish Amer. Alliance for Fairness [19260]

WICUDA-USA [9095]

Intercultural Alliance of Artists and Scholars [9237], PO Box 4378, New York, NY 10163-4378

Intercultural Cancer Coun. [13930], 1 Baylor Plz., Houston, TX 77030-3411, (713)798-5424

Intercultural Cancer Coun. [13930], 1 Baylor Plz., Houston, TX 77030-3411, (713)798-5424

Intercultural Development Res. Assn. [7769], 5815 Callaghan Rd., Ste. 101, San Antonio, TX 78228-1102, (210)444-1710

Intercultural Development Res. Assn. [7769], 5815 Callaghan Rd., Ste. 101, San Antonio, TX 78228-1102, (210)444-1710

Intercultural Studies

Assn. for Africanist Anthropology [6133]

Intl. Soc. for the Stud. of Religion, Nature and Culture [8329]

Interracial-InterCultural Pride [12013]InterculturalNatl. Assn. for Multicultural Educ.

Saq' Be': Org. for Mayan and Indigenous Spiritual Bodies [9867]

Interdenominational Foreign Mission Assn. of North Am. [★20033]

Interdenominational Foreign Missions Assn. [★20033]

Interdisciplinary Biblical Res. Inst. [19677], PO Box 423, 512 Oaklyn, Harleysville, PA 19438, (215)256-0725

Interdisciplinary Education

Intl. Soc. of the Arts, Mathematics, and Architecture [7003]

Interdisciplinary Environmental Assn. [4321], Dept. of History, Stetson Univ., Deland, FL 32724, (386)822-7541

Interdisciplinary Environmental Assn. [4321], Dept. of History, Stetson Univ., Deland, FL 32724, (386)822-7541

Interdisciplinary Studies

Assn. for Integrative Stud. [9868]

Reference to "IO" in place of a book number signifies that the association may be found in the 50th edition of International Organizations.

Assn. for the Stud. of Law, Culture and the
Humanities [8330]
BIO IT Coalition [6333]
Educational Center for Applied Ekistics [9869]
Global Stud. Assn. North Am. [8331]
Global Stud. Assn. North Am. [8331]
Intl. Soc. of the Arts, Mathematics, and
Architecture [7003]
Intl. Soc. of Trace Element Biogeochemistry
[7004]
Paleoanthropology Soc. [7211]
Salzburg Global Seminar [9870]
Soc. for Cross-Cultural Res. [9871]
Soc. of Educators and Scholars [9872]
Soc. of Educators and Scholars [9872]
Soc. for the Stud. of Human Development [6946]
Vision Sciences Soc. [7394]
Interested Veterans of the Central City [★20794]
InterEuropean Comission en Eglise et Ecole [★IO]
InterEuropean Commn. on Church and School [IO],
Oslo, Norway
InterExchange [8363], 161 6th Ave., New York, NY
10013, (212)924-0446
InterExchange [8363], 161 6th Ave., New York, NY
10013, (212)924-0446
Interfaith
Abrahamic Alliance Intl. [19824]
Global Family Rescue [13158]
Interfaith Worker Justice [19825]
Monks Without Borders [19826]
Muslim Women's Coalition [20136]
Sikh Coun. on Religion and Educ. [20241]
Interfaith Alliance [20182], 1212 New York Ave. NW,
Ste. 1250, Washington, DC 20005, (202)238-3300
Interfaith Center on Corporate Responsibility
[17481], 475 Riverside Dr., Ste. 1842, New York,
NY 10115, (212)870-2295
Interfaith Church of Metaphysics [20247], 163 Moon
Valley Rd., Windyville, MO 65783, (417)345-8411
Interfaith Comm. on Social Responsibility in Invest-
ments [★17481]
Interfaith Encounter Assn. [IO], Jerusalem, Israel
Interfaith Worker Justice [19825], 1020 W Bryn
Mawr Ave., 4th Fl., Chicago, IL 60660, (773)728-
8400
Interfaith Working Group - Address unknown since
2011.
Interferon and Cytokine Res; Intl. Soc. for [15345]
Interferon and Cytokine Res; Intl. Soc. for [15345]
Interferry [IO], Victoria, BC, Canada
InterFuture [8408], PO Box 282, State House Sta.,
Boston, MA 02133, (617)573-8267
InterFuture [8408], PO Box 282, State House Sta.,
Boston, MA 02133, (617)573-8267
Intergovernmental Authority on Development [IO],
Djibouti, Djibouti
Intergovernmental Comm. of the Universal Copyright
Convention [IO], Paris, France
Intergovernmental Comm. on Urban and Regional
Res. [IO], Toronto, ON, Canada
Intergovernmental Gp. on Meat and Dairy Products
[IO], Rome, Italy
Intergovernmental Hea. Policy Proj. [★17766]
Intergovernmental Oceanographic Commn. [IO],
Paris, France
Intergovernmental Org. for Intl. Carriage by Rail [IO],
Bern, Switzerland
Intergovernmental Panel on Climate Change [IO],
Geneva, Switzerland
Intergovernmental Renewable Energy Org. [6731],
United Nations Dag Hammarskjold Centre, No.
20050, 884 2nd Ave., New York, NY 10017,
(212)647-7000
Interhelp [18621], PO Box 111, Greenwich, NY
12834, (518)475-1929
Interhelp [18621], PO Box 111, Greenwich, NY
12834, (518)475-1929
Interhostel - Address unknown since 2011.
Interights, the Intl. Centre for the Legal Protection of
Human Rights [IO], London, United Kingdom
Interim Mgt. Assn. [IO], London, United Kingdom
InterIntel - Address unknown since 2011.
Interior Design
Amer. Floorcovering Alliance [2050]
Amer. Soc. of Interior Designers [2051]

Assn. for Contract Textiles [3437]
Assn. of Univ. Interior Designers [2052]
Carpet Cushion Coun. [2053]
Carpet and Rug Inst. [2054]
Certified Interior Decorators Intl. [2055]
Certified Interior Decorators Intl. [2055]
Coun. for Interior Design Accreditation [8332]
Coun. for Qualification of Residential Interior
Designers [2056]
Decorative Plumbing and Hardware Assn. [2781]
Home Fashion Products Assn. [2057]
Inst. of Inspection, Cleaning and Restoration
Certification [2058]
Interior Design Educators Coun. [8333]
Interior Design Soc. [2059]
Interior Redesign Indus. Specialists [2060]
Intl. Assn. of Home Staging Professionals [2061]
Intl. Assn. of Home Staging Professionals [2061]
Intl. Assn. of Lighting Designers [2062]
Intl. Assn. of Lighting Designers [2062]
Intl. Design Guild [2063]
Intl. Design Guild [2063]
Intl. Furnishings and Design Assn. [2064]
Intl. Furnishings and Design Assn. [2064]
Intl. Interior Design Assn. [2065]
Intl. Interior Design Assn. [2065]
Kitchen Cabinet Mfrs. Assn. [2066]
Natl. Candle Assn. [2067]
Natl. Coun. for Interior Design Qualification [2068]
Natl. Coun. for Interior Design Qualification [2068]
Natl. Guild of Professional Paperhangers [2069]
Natl. Kitchen and Bath Assn. [2070]
Oriental Rug Importers Assn. [2071]
Oriental Rug Retailers of Am. [2072]
Paint and Decorating Retailers Assn. [2073]
Paint and Decorating Retailers Assn. [2073]
Professional Decorative Painters Assn. [2614]
Scottish Decorators Fed. [19543]
Set Decorators Soc. of Am. [2074]
Wallcoverings Assn. [2075]
Window Covering Mfrs. Assn. [2076]
Window Coverings Assn. of Am. [2077]
Workroom Assn. of Am. [2078]
Interior Design Educators Coun. [8333], 9100 Pur-
due Rd., Ste. 200, Indianapolis, IN 46268,
(317)328-4437
Interior Design Soc. [2059], 164 S Main St., Fl. 8,
High Point, NC 27260, (336)884-4437
Interior Redesign Indus. Specialists [2060], 1100-H
Brandywine Blvd., Zanesville, OH 43701-7303,
(740)450-1330
Interkerkelijke Organisatie voor Ontwikkelingssamen-
werking [★IO]
Interlac - Address unknown since 2010.
Interlake Sailing Class Assn. [22344], Ron Gall,
Sec.-Treas., 2022 Glencove Dr., Toledo, OH
43609-1945, (419)356-7296
Interlingua Inst. - Defunct.
Interlink Rural Info. Ser. [IO], Nairobi, Kenya
Interlochen Center for the Arts [9294], PO Box 199,
Interlochen, MI 49643-0199, (231)276-7472
Interlochen Center for the Arts [9294], PO Box 199,
Interlochen, MI 49643-0199, (231)276-7472
Interlocking Concrete Pavement Inst. [829], 13921
Park Center Rd., Ste. 270, Herndon, VA 20171,
(703)657-6900
Interlocking Concrete Pavement Inst. [829], 13921
Park Center Rd., Ste. 270, Herndon, VA 20171,
(703)657-6900
Intermarket Agency Network [2406], 5307 S 92nd
St., Hales Corners, WI 53130, (414)425-8800
Intermarket Agency Network [2406], 5307 S 92nd
St., Hales Corners, WI 53130, (414)425-8800
Intermarket Assn. of Advt. Agencies [★2406]
Intermarket Assn. of Advt. Agencies [★2406]
Intermed Intl. [15190], 125-28 Queens Blvd., Ste.
538, Kew Gardens, NY 11415, (212)327-4940
Intermed Intl. [15190], 125-28 Queens Blvd., Ste.
538, Kew Gardens, NY 11415, (212)327-4940
Intermedia [★12246]
Intermedia [IO], Islamabad, Pakistan
Intermedia [★12246]
Intermediaries and Reinsurance Underwriters Assn.
[1980], 971 Rte. 202 N, Branchburg, NJ 08876,
(908)203-0211

Intermediate Tech. Development Gp. - Peru [IO],
Lima, Peru
Intermission [★11827]
Intermission [★11827]
Intermodal Assn. of North Am. [3514], 11785 Belts-
ville Dr., Ste. 1100, Calverton, MD 20705-4049,
(301)982-3400
Intermountain Forest Assn. - Address unknown since
2011.
Intermountain Veterinary Medical Assn. [★17052]
Intermuseum Conservation Assn. [10120], 2915
Detroit Ave., Cleveland, OH 44113, (216)658-8700
Internacia Esperanto Instituto [★IO]
Internacia Ligo de Esperantistaj Instruistoj [★IO]
Internacional de la Educacion, Oficina Regional para
Americana Latina [★IO]
Internacional Socialista [★IO]
Internal Admin. Textbook Prog. [★8997]
Internal Combustion Engine Inst. [★1181]
Internal Medicine
Alliance for Academic Internal Medicine [8334]
Amer. Bd. of Internal Medicine [15132]
Amer. Coll. of Physicians [15133]
Assn. of Prog. Directors in Internal Medicine
[15134]
Assn. of Pulmonary and Critical Care Medicine
Prog. Directors [14207]
Assn. of Specialty Professors [8335]
Assn. of Specialty Professors [8335]
Clerkship Directors in Internal Medicine [15135]
Clerkship Directors in Internal Medicine [15135]
Natl. MedPeds Residents' Assn. [15136]
Soc. of Gen. Internal Medicine [15137]
Internal Medicine Overseas [★16044]
Internal Medicine Overseas [★16044]
Internamerican Accounting Conf. [★32]
Internasjonal Kvinneliga for Fred og Frihet [★IO]
Internatinaal Juridisch Instituut [★IO]
Internationale Arbeitsorganisation Vertretung in Deut-
schland [★IO]
Internationaal Instituut voor Sociale Geschiedenis
[★IO]
Intl. 5.5 Class Assn. [IO], The Hague, Netherlands
Intl. 190SL Gp. [21074], 258 E Paul Revere Dr.,
Chesterton, IN 46304-9370, (219)926-3216
Intl. 190SL Lone Gp., Inc. [★21074]
Intl. 210 Assn. [22345], Greg Sullivan, Treas., 59
Water St., Hingham, MA 02043, (781)749-6436
Intl. 505 Yacht Racing Assn., Amer. Sect. [22346],
401 Washington Ave., Ste. 803, Towson, MD
21204, (757)897-2127
Intl. ABBA Fan Club [IO], Roosendaal, Netherlands
Intl. Abstinence Assn. - Address unknown since
2011.
Intl. Acad. of Aquatic Art [23039], 803 E Washington
Blvd., Lombard, IL 60148
Intl. Acad. of Architecture - Bulgaria [IO], Sofia,
Bulgaria
Intl. Acad. of Astronautics [IO], Paris, France
Intl. Acad. of Aviation and Space Medicine [IO],
Brossard, QC, Canada
Intl. Acad. of Ceramics [IO], Geneva, Switzerland
Intl. Acad. for Child Brain Development [15656],
Institutes for the Achievement of Human Potential,
8801 Stenton Ave., Wyndmoor, PA 19038,
(215)233-2050
Intl. Acad. for Child Brain Development [15656],
Institutes for the Achievement of Human Potential,
8801 Stenton Ave., Wyndmoor, PA 19038,
(215)233-2050
Intl. Acad. of Comparative Law [IO], Paris, France
Intl. Acad. of Compounding Pharmacists [16195],
4638 Riverstone Blvd., Missouri City, TX 77459,
(281)933-8400
Intl. Acad. of Cosmetic Dermatology [14327], Ms.
Sandy Silverstein, Exec. Sec., 602 Merion Ave.,
Havertown, PA 19083, (610)668-1170
Intl. Acad. of Cosmetic Dermatology [14327], Ms.
Sandy Silverstein, Exec. Sec., 602 Merion Ave.,
Havertown, PA 19083, (610)668-1170
Intl. Acad. of Cosmetic Surgery [IO], Rome, Italy
Intl. Acad. of Cytology [IO], Freiburg, Germany
Intl. Acad. of Gnathology-American Sect. [14288],
Michael A. Mansueto, Sec.-Treas., 40 Villa Verde,
San Antonio, TX 78230, (210)567-3644

A star before a book entry number signifies that the name is not listed separately, but is mentioned within the entry.

Intl. Acad. of Law and Mental Hea. **[IO]**, Montreal, QC, Canada

Intl. Acad. of Legal Medicine **[IO]**, Coimbra, Portugal

Intl. Acad. of Linguistic Law **[IO]**, Montreal, QC, Canada

Intl. Acad. of Mgt. **[IO]**, Barcelona, Spain

Intl. Acad. of Matrimonial Lawyers **[IO]**, Essex, United Kingdom

Intl. Acad. of Myodontics - Address unknown since 2010.

Intl. Acad. of Nutrition and Preventative Medicine **[★15835]**

Intl. Acad. of Nutrition and Preventative Medicine **[★15835]**

Intl. Acad. of Nutritional Consultants **[★15814]**

Intl. Acad. of Olympic Chiropractic Officers **[14135]**, 546 Broad Ave., Englewood, NJ 07631, (201)569-1444

Intl. Acad. of Olympic Chiropractic Officers **[14135]**, 546 Broad Ave., Englewood, NJ 07631, (201)569-1444

Intl. Acad. of Opticianry **[★15983]**

Intl. Acad. of Oral Medicine and Toxicology **[14289]**, 8297 Champions Gate Blvd., No. 193, Champions Gate, FL 33896, (863)420-6373

Intl. Acad. of Oral Medicine and Toxicology **[14289]**, 8297 Champions Gate Blvd., No. 193, Champions Gate, FL 33896, (863)420-6373

Intl. Acad. of Orthodontics **[★14291]**

Intl. Acad. of Orthodontics **[★14291]**

Intl. Acad. of Osteopathy **[IO]**, Alkmaar, Netherlands

Intl. Acad. of Pathology **[16125]**, WRAMC, Bldg. 54, Rm. N-1610, 14th St. and Alaska Ave. NW, Washington, DC 20306-6000, (202)782-2503

Intl. Acad. of Pathology **[16125]**, WRAMC, Bldg. 54, Rm. N-1610, 14th St. and Alaska Ave. NW, Washington, DC 20306-6000, (202)782-2503

Intl. Acad. of Periodontology **[IO]**, Mumbai, India

Intl. Acad. of Podiatric Medicine - Defunct.

Intl. Acad. of Preventive Medicine **[★15835]**

Intl. Acad. of Preventive Medicine **[★15835]**

Intl. Acad. of Proctology - Defunct.

Intl. Acad. for Production Engg. **[IO]**, Paris, France

Intl. Acad. for Quality **[7317]**, PO Box 3005, 600 N Plankinton Ave., Milwaukee, WI 53201, (414)272-8575

Intl. Acad. for Quality **[7317]**, PO Box 3005, 600 N Plankinton Ave., Milwaukee, WI 53201, (414)272-8575

Intl. Acad. at Santa Barbara - Defunct.

Intl. Acad. of Sciences **[IO]**, Turin, Italy

Intl. Acad. of TV Arts and Sciences **[492]**, 888 7th Ave., 5th Fl., New York, NY 10106, (212)489-6969

Intl. Acad. of TV Arts and Sciences **[492]**, 888 7th Ave., 5th Fl., New York, NY 10106, (212)489-6969

Intl. Acad. of Toxicological Risk Assessment **[★4287]**

Intl. Acad. of Toxicological Risk Assessment **[★4287]**

Intl. Acad. of Trial Lawyers **[5250]**, 5841 Cedar Lake Rd., Ste. 204, Minneapolis, MN 55416-5657, (952)546-2364

Intl. Acad. of Trial Lawyers **[5250]**, 5841 Cedar Lake Rd., Ste. 204, Minneapolis, MN 55416-5657, (952)546-2364

Intl. Acad. of Twirling Teachers - Defunct.

Intl. Accidental War Info. Sharing Proj. **[★18270]**

Intl. Accidental War Info. Sharing Proj. **[★18270]**

Intl. Accounting Standards Bd. **[IO]**, London, United Kingdom

Intl. Accounts Payable Professionals **[33]**, PO Box 590373, Orlando, FL 32859-0373, (407)351-3322

Intl. Acetylene Assn. **[★1569]**

Intl. Action **[13425]**, 819 L St. SE, Washington, DC 20003, (202)488-0735

Intl. Action Center **[18137]**, Solidarity Center, 55 W 17th St., Ste. 5C, New York, NY 10011, (212)633-6646

Intl. Action Center **[18137]**, Solidarity Center, 55 W 17th St., Ste. 5C, New York, NY 10011, (212)633-6646

Intl. Action Network on Small Arms **[IO]**, London, United Kingdom

Intl. Actuarial Assn. **[IO]**, Ottawa, ON, Canada

Intl. Acupuncture Assn. of Physical Therapists **[IO]**, Timaru, New Zealand

Intl. Adam Smith Soc. **[10381]**, Prof. Ryan Patrick Hanley, Pres., Marquette Univ., Dept. of Political Sci., PO Box 1881, Milwaukee, WI 53201-1881, (414)288-6842

Intl. Adhesions Soc. **[16100]**, 6757 Arapaho Rd., Ste. 711, No. 238, Dallas, TX 75248, (972)931-5596

Intl. Adhesions Soc. **[16100]**, 6757 Arapaho Rd., Ste. 711, No. 238, Dallas, TX 75248, (972)931-5596

Intl. Adoption Assn. - Ireland **[IO]**, Dublin, Ireland

Intl. Advt. Assn.

Intl. Advt. Assn. - Address unknown since 2011.

Intl. Advt. Festival **[IO]**, London, United Kingdom

Intl. Advisory Coun. for Homosexual Men and Women in Alcoholics Anonymous **[★13291]**

Intl. Aerobatic Club **[22211]**, EAA Aviation Center, PO Box 3086, Oshkosh, WI 54903-3086, (920)426-4800

Intl. Aeronauts League **[21203]**, PO Box 200931, Austin, TX 78720-0931, (512)740-2506

Intl. Aesthetic and Laser Assn. **[15237]**, 4830 W Kennedy Blvd., Ste. 440, Tampa, FL 33609-2548, (813)286-8100

International Affairs

  African Fed., Inc. **[17900]**

  Assn. of Public and Land Grant Universities I Commn. on Intl. Programs **[17903]**

  Bosniak Amer. Advisory Coun. for Bosnia and Herzegovina **[17895]**

  Carnegie Coun. for Ethics in Intl. Affairs **[19827]**

  Carnegie Coun. on Ethics and Intl. Affairs **[19827]**

  Coalition for a Realistic Foreign Policy **[17698]**

  Commn. of the Churches on Intl. Affairs **[19828]**

  Commn. of the Churches on Intl. Affairs **[19828]**

  Conflict Solutions Intl. **[17405]**

  EastWest Inst. **[17896]**

  EastWest Inst. **[17896]**

  Friends of Mali **[18246]**

  Friends of Taiwan Intl. **[17945]**

  Global Migration Gp. **[5790]**

  Henry L. Stimson Center **[17897]**

  High Frontier Org. **[18678]**

  Idoma Assn. USA **[19176]**

  Independent Diplomat **[17898]**

  Intl. Assn. of Space Entrepreneurs **[139]**

  Intl. Coun. for Middle East Stud. **[18125]**

  Intl. Forum on Globalization **[17899]**

  Intl. Forum on Globalization **[17899]**

  Irish Amer. Unity Conf. **[18009]**

  Just Vision **[17409]**

  Minority Peace Corps Assn. **[18307]**

  Natl. Jewish Democratic Coun. **[18387]**

  Natl. Security and Law Soc. **[5970]**

  New Rules for Global Finance Coalition **[17584]**

  Prevent Nuclear Terrorism Org. **[18718]**

  United Burundian-American Community Assn. **[17953]**

  U.S. Off. on Colombia **[17956]**

  U.S. Women and Cuba Collaboration **[17957]**

  US-Azerbaijan Coun. **[17958]**

  Win Without War **[18178]**

  World Growth **[2079]**

Intl. African Inst. **[IO]**, London, United Kingdom

Intl. Afro-American Museum **[★9100]**

Intl. Afro-American Museum **[★9100]**

Intl. Afro-American Museum Comm. **[★9100]**

Intl. Afro-American Museum Comm. **[★9100]**

Intl. Agency for the Prevention of Blindness **[IO]**, London, United Kingdom

Intl. Agency for Res. on Cancer **[IO]**, Lyon, France

Intl. Agriculture Development Ser. **[★17171]**

Intl. Agriculture Development Ser. **[★17171]**

Intl. Agro Alliance **[4940]**, 173 NW 89th St., Miami, FL 33150, (877)292-3921

Intl. Aid **[12853]**, 17011 Hickory St., Spring Lake, MI 49456-9712, (616)846-7490

Intl. Aid **[12853]**, 17011 Hickory St., Spring Lake, MI 49456-9712, (616)846-7490

Intl. Aid for Korean Animals **[10988]**, PO Box 20600, Oakland, CA 94620-0600, (510)271-6795

Intl. Aid Services **[IO]**, Vallingby, Sweden

Intl. Aid Serving Kids **[11321]**, 1135 N 650 E, Orem, UT 84097

Intl. Aid Serving Kids **[11321]**, 1135 N 650 E, Orem, UT 84097

Intl. AIDS Soc. - Switzerland **[IO]**, Geneva, Switzerland

Intl. AIDS Soc. USA **[13612]**, 425 California St., Ste. 1450, San Francisco, CA 94104-2120, (415)544-9400

Intl. AIDS Soc. USA **[13612]**, 425 California St., Ste. 1450, San Francisco, CA 94104-2120, (415)544-9400

Intl. AIDS Vaccine Initiative **[13613]**, New York HQ, 125 Broad St., 9th Fl., New York, NY 10004, (212)847-1111

Intl. AIDS Vaccine Initiative **[13613]**, New York HQ, 125 Broad St., 9th Fl., New York, NY 10004, (212)847-1111

Intl. Aikido Assn. **[22218]**, PO Box 4528, Dallas, TX 75208, (214)943-7530

The Intl. Air Cargo Assn. **[3515]**, PO Box 661510, Miami, FL 33266-1510, (786)265-7011

The Intl. Air Cargo Assn. **[3515]**, PO Box 661510, Miami, FL 33266-1510, (786)265-7011

Intl. Air Carrier Assn. **[IO]**, Brussels, Belgium

Intl. Air Filtration Certifiers Assn. **[1705]**, 129 S Gallatin, Liberty, MO 64068, (888)679-1904

Intl. Air Rail Org. **[IO]**, London, United Kingdom

Intl. Air Transport Assn. - Argentina **[IO]**, Buenos Aires, Argentina

Intl. Air Transport Assn. - Australia **[IO]**, Sydney, Australia

Intl. Air Transport Assn. - Austria **[IO]**, Vienna, Austria

Intl. Air Transport Assn. - Bolivia **[IO]**, La Paz, Bolivia

Intl. Air Transport Assn. - Brazil **[IO]**, Sao Paulo, Brazil

Intl. Air Transport Assn. - Canada **[IO]**, Montreal, QC, Canada

Intl. Air Transport Assn. - Chile **[IO]**, Santiago, Chile

Intl. Air Transport Assn. - Colombia **[IO]**, Bogota, Colombia

Intl. Air Transport Assn. - Costa Rica **[IO]**, San Jose, Costa Rica

Intl. Air Transport Assn. - Ecuador **[IO]**, Quito, Ecuador

Intl. Air Transport Assn. - Egypt **[IO]**, Heliopolis, Egypt

Intl. Air Transport Assn. - El Salvador **[IO]**, San Salvador, El Salvador

Intl. Air Transport Assn. - India **[IO]**, Mumbai, India

Intl. Air Transport Assn. - Indonesia **[IO]**, Jakarta, Indonesia

Intl. Air Transport Assn. - Israel **[IO]**, Tel Aviv, Israel

Intl. Air Transport Assn. - Japan **[IO]**, Tokyo, Japan

Intl. Air Transport Assn. - Jordan **[IO]**, Amman, Jordan

Intl. Air Transport Assn. - Kenya **[IO]**, Nairobi, Kenya

Intl. Air Transport Assn. - Korea **[IO]**, Seoul, Republic of Korea

Intl. Air Transport Assn. - Malaysia **[IO]**, Kuala Lumpur, Malaysia

Intl. Air Transport Assn. - Mexico **[IO]**, Mexico City, Mexico

Intl. Air Transport Assn. - New Zealand **[IO]**, Auckland, New Zealand

Intl. Air Transport Assn. - Philippines **[IO]**, Makati City, Philippines

Intl. Air Transport Assn. - Poland **[IO]**, Warsaw, Poland

Intl. Air Transport Assn. - Portugal **[IO]**, Lisbon, Portugal

Intl. Air Transport Assn. - Romania **[IO]**, Bucharest, Romania

Intl. Air Transport Assn. - Russia **[IO]**, Moscow, Russia

Intl. Air Transport Assn. - Saudi Arabia **[IO]**, Jeddah, Saudi Arabia

Intl. Air Transport Assn. - Singapore **[IO]**, Singapore, Singapore

Intl. Air Transport Assn. - Slovenia **[IO]**, Ljubljana, Slovenia

Intl. Air Transport Assn. - South Africa **[IO]**, Sandton, Republic of South Africa

Intl. Air Transport Assn. - Spain **[IO]**, Madrid, Spain

Intl. Air Transport Assn. - Sweden **[IO]**, Solna, Sweden

Intl. Air Transport Assn. - Switzerland **[IO]**, Geneva, Switzerland

Intl. Air Transport Assn. - Taiwan **[IO]**, Taipei, Taiwan

Intl. Air Transport Assn. - Thailand **[IO]**, Bangkok, Thailand

Intl. Air Transport Assn. - Trinidad and Tobago **[IO]**, Port of Spain, Trinidad and Tobago

Reference to "IO" in place of a book number signifies that the association may be found in the 50th edition of International Organizations.

Intl. Air Transport Assn. - Turkey [IO], Istanbul, Turkey

Intl. Air Transport Assn. - Uruguay [IO], Buenos Aires, Argentina

Intl. Air Transport Assn. - Venezuela [IO], Caracas, Venezuela

Intl. Airline Passengers Assn. [22190], PO Box 700188, Dallas, TX 75370-0188, (972)404-9980

Intl. Airline Passengers Assn. [22190], PO Box 700188, Dallas, TX 75370-0188, (972)404-9980

Intl. Airline Passengers Assn. - London [IO], Croydon, United Kingdom

Intl. Al Jolson Soc. [23856], Tom Nestor, Treas., 1709 Billingshurst Ct., Orlando, FL 32825, (888)456-5766

Intl. Alliance of ALS/MND Associations [IO], Northampton, United Kingdom

The Intl. Alliance, An Assn. of Executive and Professional Women [★670]

The Intl. Alliance, An Assn. of Executive and Professional Women [★670]

Intl. Alliance for Animal Therapy and Healing [13765], Maryann Frisbee, Prog. Mgr., PO Box 1255, Winters, CA 95694, (530)795-5040

Intl. Alliance for Animal Therapy and Healing [13765], Maryann Frisbee, Prog. Mgr., PO Box 1255, Winters, CA 95694, (530)795-5040

Intl. Alliance of Avaya Users [3410], 401 N Michigan Ave., Chicago, IL 60611, (312)321-5126

Intl. Alliance for Child and Adolescent Mental Hea. and Schools [15455], Educ. Development Center, Inc., Hea. and Human Development Programs, 55 Chapel St., Newton, MA 02458-1060

Intl. Alliance for Child and Adolescent Mental Hea. and Schools [15455], Educ. Development Center, Inc., Hea. and Human Development Programs, 55 Chapel St., Newton, MA 02458-1060

Intl. Alliance of Composers [10213], Chris Merritt, Exec. Dir., 9701 Clearwater Dr., Knoxville, TN 37923, (877)294-0912

Intl. Alliance of Equestrian Journalists [IO], Aurora, ON, Canada

Intl. Alliance of Furnishing Publications - Address unknown since 2011.

Intl. Alliance of Hair Restoration Surgeons [14675], Paul J. McAndrews, MD, Sr. Medical Advisor, 435 N Roxbury Dr., No. 204, Beverly Hills, CA 90210, (877)424-7362

Intl. Alliance of Holistic Lawyers - Defunct.

Intl. Alliance of Indigenous and Tribal Peoples of Tropical Forests [IO], Panama City, Panama

Intl. Alliance of Iranian Students - Address unknown since 2011.

Intl. Alliance of Law Firms [IO], London, United Kingdom

Intl. Alliance of Messianic Congregations and Synagogues [19963], PO Box 1570, Havertown, PA 19083, (215)452-5590

Intl. Alliance of Messianic Congregations and Synagogues [19963], PO Box 1570, Havertown, PA 19083, (215)452-5590

Intl. Alliance of Patients' Organizations [IO], London, United Kingdom

Intl. Alliance for the Prevention of AIDS [13614], 1747 W Devonshire Ave., Phoenix, AZ 85015

Intl. Alliance of Professional Hypnotists [15089], 8852 SR 3001, Laceyville, PA 18623-9417, (570)869-1021

Intl. Alliance in Ser. and Educ.

Intl. Alliance in Ser. and Educ. - Address unknown since 2011.

Intl. Alliance for Sustainable Agriculture [★4345]

Intl. Alliance of Theatrical Stage Employees, Motion Picture Technicians, Artists and Allied Crafts of the U.S. and Canada [★23270]

Intl. Alliance of Theatrical Stage Employees, Motion Picture Technicians, Artists and Allied Crafts of the U.S. and Canada [★23270]

Intl. Alliance of Theatrical Stage Employees, Motion Picture Technicians, Artists and Allied Crafts of the U.S., U.S. Territories and Canada [★23270]

Intl. Alliance of Theatrical Stage Employees, Motion Picture Technicians, Artists and Allied Crafts of the U.S., U.S. Territories and Canada [★23270]

Intl. Alliance of Theatrical Stage Employees, Moving Picture Technicians, Artists and Allied Crafts of the U.S., Its Territories and Canada [23270], 1430 Broadway, 20th Fl., New York, NY 10018, (212)730-1770

Intl. Alliance of Theatrical Stage Employees, Moving Picture Technicians, Artists and Allied Crafts of the U.S., Its Territories and Canada [23270], 1430 Broadway, 20th Fl., New York, NY 10018, (212)730-1770

Intl. Alliance of Women [IO], Nambucca Heads, Australia

The Intl. Alliance for Women [670], 1760 Old Meadow Rd., Ste. 500, McLean, VA 22102, (866)533-8429

The Intl. Alliance for Women [670], 1760 Old Meadow Rd., Ste. 500, McLean, VA 22102, (866)533-8429

Intl. Alliance for Women in Music [10214], Deborah Hayes, Membership Chair, 3290 Darley Ave., Boulder, CO 80305-6412

Intl. Alliance for Women in Music [10214], Deborah Hayes, Membership Chair, 3290 Darley Ave., Boulder, CO 80305-6412

Intl. Alliance for Youth Sports [23138], 2050 Vista Pkwy., West Palm Beach, FL 33411, (561)684-1141

Intl. Allied Printing Trades Assn. - Address unknown since 2011.

Intl. Aloe Sci. Coun. [1686], 8630 Fenton St., Ste. 918, Silver Spring, MD 20910, (301)588-2420

Intl. Aloe Sci. Coun. [1686], 8630 Fenton St., Ste. 918, Silver Spring, MD 20910, (301)588-2420

Intl. Aluminium Inst. [IO], London, United Kingdom

Intl. Alumni Assn. of Shri Mahavir Jain Vidyalaya [19219], 1119 Flanders St., Garner, NC 27529, (919)283-4232

Intl. Alumni Assn. of Shri Mahavir Jain Vidyalaya [19219], 1119 Flanders St., Garner, NC 27529, (919)283-4232

Intl. Amateur-Professional Photoelectric Photometry [6229], 4229 Franklin Rd., Nashville, TN 37204, (615)383-4630

Intl. Amateur-Professional Photoelectric Photometry [6229], 4229 Franklin Rd., Nashville, TN 37204, (615)383-4630

Intl. Amateur Radio Union [20936], PO Box 310905, Newington, CT 06131-0905, (860)594-0200

Intl. Amateur Swimming Fed. [IO], Lausanne, Switzerland

Intl. Amateur Theatre Assn. [IO], Tallinn, Estonia

Intl. and Amer. Associations of Clinical Nutritionists [15835], 15280 Addison Rd., Ste. 130, Addison, TX 75001, (972)407-9089

Intl. and Amer. Associations of Clinical Nutritionists [15835], 15280 Addison Rd., Ste. 130, Addison, TX 75001, (972)407-9089

Intl. Amer. Saddlebred Pleasure Horse Assn. [★4552]

Intl. Amphicar Owners Club [21075], Ina Cabanas, Treas., 11 Pemberton St., Pemberton, NJ 08068-1111

Intl. Amusement and Leisure Defense Assn. [3057], PO Box 4563, Louisville, KY 40204, (502)473-0956

Intl. Andalusian and Lusitano Horse Assn. [4594], 101 Carnoustie N, No. 200, Birmingham, AL 35242, (205)995-8900

Intl. Andalusian and Lusitano Horse Assn. [4594], 101 Carnoustie N, No. 200, Birmingham, AL 35242, (205)995-8900

Intl. Anesthesia Res. Soc. [13748], 100 Pine St., Ste. 230, San Francisco, CA 94111, (415)296-6900

Intl. Anesthesia Res. Soc. [13748], 100 Pine St., Ste. 230, San Francisco, CA 94111, (415)296-6900

Intl. Animal Rescue - UK [IO], Uckfield, United Kingdom

Intl. Animated Film Assn. [IO], Zagreb, Croatia

Intl. Animated Film Assn. - Canada [IO], St. Laurent, QC, Canada

Intl. Animated Film Soc., ASIFA - Hollywood [1258], 2114 W Burbank Blvd., Burbank, CA 91506, (818)842-8330

Intl. Animated Film Soc. - Hollywood [★1258]

Intl. A.N.S.W.E.R. - Act Now to Stop War and End Racism [18255], 617 Florida Ave. NW, Lower Level, Washington, DC 20001, (202)265-1948

Intl. A.N.S.W.E.R. - Act Now to Stop War and End Racism [18255], 617 Florida Ave. NW, Lower Level, Washington, DC 20001, (202)265-1948

Intl. Anti-Euthanasia Task Force [★11990]

Intl. Anticounterfeiting Coalition [17462], 1730 M St. NW, Ste. 1020, Washington, DC 20036, (202)223-6667

Intl. Anticounterfeiting Coalition [17462], 1730 M St. NW, Ste. 1020, Washington, DC 20036, (202)223-6667

Intl. Apparel Fed. [IO], Zeist, Netherlands

Intl. Apple Assn. [★4478]

Intl. Apple Inst. [★4478]

Intl. Archery Fed. [IO], Lausanne, Switzerland

Intl. Arctic Sci. Comm. [IO], Potsdam, Germany

Intl. Arid Lands Consortium [4273], 1955 E 6th St., Tucson, AZ 85719, (520)626-0329

Intl. Arid Lands Consortium [4273], 1955 E 6th St., Tucson, AZ 85719, (520)626-0329

Intl. Aroid Soc. [21802], PO Box 43-1852, South Miami, FL 33143

Intl. Aroid Soc. [21802], PO Box 43-1852, South Miami, FL 33143

Intl. Aromatherapy and Aromatic Medicine Assn. [IO], Burwood, Australia

Intl. Aromatherapy and Herb Assn. [13684], 3541 W Acapulco Ln., Phoenix, AZ 85053, (602)938-4439

Intl. Aromatherapy and Herb Assn. [13684], 3541 W Acapulco Ln., Phoenix, AZ 85053, (602)938-4439

Intl. Art and Architecture Res. Assn. [IO], Tehran, Iran

Intl. Arthroscopy Assn. [★16036]

Intl. Arthroscopy Assn. [★16036]

Intl. Arthurian Soc., North Amer. Br. [10041], 211 Castro St., Norman, OK 73069

Intl. Arthurian Soc., North Amer. Br. [10041], 211 Castro St., Norman, OK 73069

Intl. Artificial Intelligence in Educ. Soc. [IO], Amsterdam, Netherlands

Intl. Artist Managers' Assn. [IO], London, United Kingdom

Intl. Arts and Artists [9295], 9 Hillyer Ct. NW, Washington, DC 20008, (202)338-0680

Intl. Arts and Artists [9295], 9 Hillyer Ct. NW, Washington, DC 20008, (202)338-0680

Intl. Asclepiad Soc. [IO], Wighton, United Kingdom

Intl. Assembly for Collegiate Bus. Educ. [7791], PO Box 3960, Olathe, KS 66063, (913)631-3009

Intl. Assembly for Collegiate Bus. Educ. [7791], PO Box 3960, Olathe, KS 66063, (913)631-3009

Intl. Assembly of Grocery Mfrs. Associations [★1397]

Intl. Assembly of Grocery Mfrs. Associations [★1397]

Intl. Assn. of Accident and Hea. Underwriters [★2004]

Intl. Assn. of Accident Reconstruction Specialists [2195], Bill Brandt, Treas., PO Box 534, Grand Ledge, MI 48837-0534, (517)622-3135

Intl. Assn. of Accident Reconstruction Specialists [2195], Bill Brandt, Treas., PO Box 534, Grand Ledge, MI 48837-0534, (517)622-3135

Intl. Assn. of Addictions and Offender Counselors [11674], Rider Univ., Dept. of Graduate Educ., Leadership, and Counseling, Memorial 202, 2083 Lawrenceville Rd., Lawrenceville, NJ 08648, (800)347-6647

Intl. Assn. of Addictions and Offender Counselors [11674], Rider Univ., Dept. of Graduate Educ., Leadership, and Counseling, Memorial 202, 2083 Lawrenceville Rd., Lawrenceville, NJ 08648, (800)347-6647

Intl. Assn. for Adolescent Hea. [IO], Montreal, QC, Canada

Intl. Assn. for the Advancement of Steam Power [7480], Box 106, Sacramento, CA 95821, (916)483-4249

Intl. Assn. for the Advancement of Teaching and Res. in Intellectual Property [IO], Munich, Germany

Intl. Assn. of African-American Music [10215], PO Box 382, Gladwyne, PA 19035, (610)664-8292

Intl. Assn. of African-American Music [10215], PO Box 382, Gladwyne, PA 19035, (610)664-8292

Intl. Assn. Against Painful Experiments on Animals [IO], Hayling Island, United Kingdom

Intl. Assn. of Agricultural Economists [6621], 555 E Wells St., Ste. 1100, Milwaukee, WI 53202, (414)918-3199

Intl. Assn. of Agricultural Economists [6621], 555 E Wells St., Ste. 1100, Milwaukee, WI 53202, (414)918-3199

A star before a book entry number signifies that the name is not listed separately, but is mentioned within the entry.

Intl. Assn. of Agricultural Medicine and Rural Hea. [IO], Saku, Japan

Intl. Assn. of Agricultural Museums [IO], Roznov pod Radhostem, Czech Republic

Intl. Assn. of Agricultural Production Insurers [IO], Zurich, Switzerland

Intl. Assn. of Air Travel Couriers

Intl. Assn. of Air Travel Couriers - UK [IO], Chepstow, United Kingdom

Intl. Assn. of Airline Internal Auditors [IO], Dubai, United Arab Emirates

Intl. Assn. of Airport Duty Free Stores [3105], 2025 M St. NW, Ste. 800, Washington, DC 20036-3309, (202)367-1184

Intl. Assn. of Airport and Seaport Police [IO], London, United Kingdom

Intl. Assn. of Allergology [★13644]

Intl. Assn. of Allergology and Clinical Immunology [★13644]

Intl. Assn. of ALS/MND Associations [★11897]

Intl. Assn. for Ambulatory Surgery [IO], Kornwestheim, Germany

Intl. Assn. of Amusement Parks [★1195]

Intl. Assn. of Amusement Parks & Attractions [★1186]

Intl. Assn. of Amusement Parks and Attractions [1195], 1448 Duke St., Alexandria, VA 22314, (703)836-4800

Intl. Assn. for Analytical Psychology [IO], Zurich, Switzerland

Intl. Assn. of Animal Behavior Consultants [7636], 565 Callery Rd., Cranberry Township, PA 16066

Intl. Assn. of Animal Massage and Bodywork [15269], 3347 McGregor Ln., Toledo, OH 43623, (419)464-8922

Intl. Assn. of Antarctica Tour Operators [3561], Steve Wellmeier, Exec. Dir., 11 S Angell St., Box 302, Providence, RI 02906, (401)272-2152

Intl. Assn. of Anti-Corruption Authorities [IO], Beijing, People's Republic of China

Intl. Assn. of Applied Control Theory [6257], PO Box 1046, Carrboro, NC 27510, (800)441-3604

Intl. Assn. of Applied Linguistics [IO], Erfurt, Germany

Intl. Assn. of Applied Psychology [IO], Madrid, Spain

Intl. Assn. of Approved Basketball Officials [22295], PO Box 355, Carlisle, PA 17013-0344, (717)713-8129

Intl. Assn. for Aquatic Animal Medicine [17025], Cindy P. Driscoll, DVM, Membership Chair, Maryland Dept. of Natural Resources, 904 S Morris St., Oxford, MD 21654, (410)226-5193

Intl. Assn. of Aquatic and Marine Sci. Libraries and Info. Centers [9989], Hatfield Marine Sci. Center, Oregon State Univ., 2030 S Marine Sci. Dr., Newport, OR 97365, (541)867-0249

Intl. Assn. of Architectural Photographers [2719], 2901 136th St. NW, Gig Harbor, WA 98332-9111, (877)845-4783

Intl. Assn. of Arson Investigators [5440], 2111 Baldwin Ave., Ste. 203, Crofton, MD 21114, (410)451-3473

Intl. Assn. for Art, Creativity and Therapy [IO], Basel, Switzerland

Intl. Assn. of Art Critics - Canada Sect. [IO], Toronto, ON, Canada

Intl. Assn. of Art Critics - France [IO], Paris, France

Intl. Assn. of Art Critics - Germany [IO], Berlin, Germany

Intl. Assn. of Art Critics - Hong Kong [IO], Hong Kong, People's Republic of China

Intl. Assn. of Art Critics - Ireland [IO], Dublin, Ireland

Intl. Assn. of Art Critics - Taiwan [IO], Changhua City, Taiwan

Intl. Assn. of Art Critics - U.S. Sect. [9296], London Terrace Stn., PO Box 20533, New York, NY 10011

Intl. Assn. for Artificial Intelligence and Law [6455], 286 Selby Ln., Atherton, CA 94027, (650)368-1297

Intl. Assn. of Arts and Cultural Mgt. [IO], Montreal, QC, Canada

Intl. Assn. of Asian Crime Investigators [5363], PO Box 1327, Marina, CA 93933, (831)901-4595

Intl. Assn. of Asian Stud. [7761], PO Box 6670, Scarborough, ME 04070-6670, (207)839-8004

Intl. Assn. of Assay Offices [IO], London, United Kingdom

Intl. Assn. of Assembly Managers [★2441]

Intl. Assn. of Assessing Officers [6012], 314 W 10th St., Kansas City, MO 64105-1616, (816)701-8100

Intl. Assn. of Assistance Dog Partners [14364], Dana Spears, PO Box 638, Sterling Heights, MI 48311, (586)826-3938

Intl. Assn. of Assn. Mgt. Companies [★261]

Intl. Assn. for Assyriology [IO], Leiden, Netherlands

Intl. Assn. of Astacology [6954], Antonio Garza de Yta, Sec., Auburn Univ., Dept. of Fisheries and Allied Aquaculture, 203 Swingle Hall, Auburn University, AL 36849-5419, (334)844-4786

Intl. Assn. of Asthmology [IO], Amorebieta-Etxano, Spain

Intl. Assn. of Athletics Federations [IO], Monaco, Monaco

Intl. Assn. of Attorneys and Executives in Corporate Real Estate [3016], Lisa V. Carreras, Exec. VP/Dir., 20106 S Sycamore Dr., Frankfort, IL 60423, (815)464-6019

Intl. Assn. of Attunement Practitioners [13685], PO Box 28574, Kansas City, MO 64188

Intl. Assn. of Audio Info. Services [17087], Lori Kesinger, Membership Chair, Kansas Audio-Reader Network, PO Box 847, Lawrence, KS 66044, (800)280-5325

Intl. Assn. of Audio Visual Communicators [1259], The CINDY Competitions, PO Box 270779, Flower Mound, TX 75027, (469)464-4180

Intl. Assn. of Auditorium Managers [★2441]

Intl. Assn. Auto Theft Investigators [5695], PO Box 223, Clinton, NY 13323-0223, (315)853-1913

Intl. Assn. of Avian Trainers and Educators [21217], 15001 Margaux Dr., Clermont, FL 34714, (678)778-2373

Intl. Assn. of Baptist Colleges and Universities [9012], 8120 Sawyer Brown Rd., Ste. 108, Nashville, TN 37221-1410, (615)673-1896

Intl. Assn. for Bear Res. and Mgt. [5065], Univ. of Tennessee, USGS-SAFL, 274 Ellington Hall, Knoxville, TN 37996, (865)974-0200

Intl. Assn. of Bedding and Furniture Law Officials [5545], Dept. of Consumer Protection, 165 Capitol Ave., Hartford, CT 06106, (860)713-6123

Intl. Assn. of Biblical Counselors [19634], 11500 Sheridan Blvd., Westminster, CO 80020, (303)469-4222

Intl. Assn. of Bioethics [IO], Quezon City, Philippines

Intl. Assn. for Biological and Medical Res. [15344], Tsute Chen, The Forsyth Inst., 140 Fenway, Boston, MA 02120

Intl. Assn. for Biological Oceanography [IO], Rondebosch, Republic of South Africa

Intl. Assn. of Biological Technicians [IO], Neuilly-sur-Marne, France

Intl. Assn. for Biologicals [IO], Geneva, Switzerland

Intl. Assn. of Black Actuaries [1981], PO Box 369, Windsor, CT 06095, (860)219-9534

Intl. Assn. of Black Actuaries [1981], PO Box 369, Windsor, CT 06095, (860)219-9534

Intl. Assn. of Black Professional Fire Fighters [5441], 1020 N Taylor Ave., St. Louis, MO 63113, (513)763-9312

Intl. Assn. of Black Professional Fire Fighters [5441], 1020 N Taylor Ave., St. Louis, MO 63113, (513)763-9312

Intl. Assn. of Black Yoga Teachers - Defunct.

Intl. Assn. of Bloodstain Pattern Analysts [5364], 12139 E Makohoh Trail, Tucson, AZ 85749-8179, (520)760-6620

Intl. Assn. of Blue Print and Allied Indus. [★1616]

Intl. Assn. of Boards of Examiners in Optometry [★15991]

Intl. Assn. of Bomb Technicians and Investigators [6859], 1120 Intl. Pkwy., Ste. 129, Goldvein, VA 22720-0160, (540)752-4533

Intl. Assn. of Book-Keepers [IO], West Malling, United Kingdom

Intl. Assn. of Bowling Equipment Specialists [569], N.A.I.R, 5806 W 127th St., Alsip, IL 60803, (708)371-8237

Intl. Assn. for Bridge Maintenance and Safety [6369], Prof. Dan M. Frangopol, Pres., Lehigh Univ., ATLSS Ctr., 117 ATLSS Dr., Bethlehem, PA 18015-4728, (610)758-6103

Intl. Assn. for Bridge and Structural Engg. [IO], Zurich, Switzerland

Intl. Assn. of Bridge, Structural, Ornamental and Reinforcing Iron Workers [23254], 1750 New York Ave. NW, Ste. 400, Washington, DC 20006, (202)383-4800

Intl. Assn. of Broadcast Meteorology [IO], Wexford, Ireland

Intl. Assn. of Broadcast Monitors [493], 7604 Big Bend Blvd., Ste. D, St. Louis, MO 63119, (314)646-7984

Intl. Assn. of Broadcasting Mfrs. [IO], Reading, United Kingdom

Intl. Assn. of Buddhist Stud. [IO], Lausanne, Switzerland

Intl. Assn. of Building Companions [IO], Ludwigshafen am Rhein, Germany

Intl. Assn. of Building Services Contractors [IO], Munich, Germany

Intl. Assn. of Bus. Communicators [809], 601 Montgomery St., Ste. 1900, San Francisco, CA 94111, (415)544-4700

Intl. Assn. of Bus. Communicators British Colombia [IO], Vancouver, BC, Canada

Intl. Assn. of Bus. Communicators Calgary [IO], Calgary, AB, Canada

Intl. Assn. of Bus. Communicators Hong Kong [IO], Hong Kong, People's Republic of China

Intl. Assn. of Bus. Communicators Malaysia Chap. [IO], Petaling Jaya, Malaysia

Intl. Assn. of Bus. Communicators Newfoundland and Labrador [IO], St. John's, NL, Canada

Intl. Assn. of Bus. Communicators Ottawa [IO], Ottawa, ON, Canada

Intl. Assn. of Bus. Communicators Philippines [IO], Makati City, Philippines

Intl. Assn. of Bus. Communicators Polar Chap. [IO], Yellowknife, NT, Canada

Intl. Assn. of Bus. Communicators Regina [IO], Regina, SK, Canada

Intl. Assn. for Bus. Organizations - Address unknown since 2010.

Intl. Assn. of Butterfly Exhibitions [1232], Cockerell Butterfly Center, Houston Museum of Natural Sci., 5555 Hermann Park Dr., Houston, TX 77030, (713)639-4742

Intl. Assn. for Campus Law Enforcement Administrators [8817], 342 N Main St., West Hartford, CT 06117-2507, (860)586-7517

Intl. Assn. of Cancer Registries [IO], Lyon, France

Intl. Assn. of Canine Professionals [4189], PO Box 560156, Montverde, FL 34756-0156, (407)469-2008

Intl. Assn. of Career Consulting Firms - Defunct.

Intl. Assn. of Caribbean Organizations [11140], PO Box 671393, Marietta, GA 30066

Intl. Assn. of Cemetery Preservationists [9700], PO Box 10312, Daytona Beach, FL 32120-0312

Intl. Assn. for Cereal Sci. and Tech. [IO], Vienna, Austria

Intl. Assn. of Certified Surveillance Professionals [3213], 4333 Bell Rd., Apt. No. 1210, Newburgh, IN 47630, (812)472-1744

Intl. Assn. of Certified Thermographers [7565], 106 S Railroad Ave., Ste. 3, Ashland, VA 23005, (866)417-3949

Intl. Assn. of CFOs and Corporate Treasurers China [IO], Hong Kong, People's Republic of China

Intl. Assn. of Chain Stores [★3101]

Intl. Assn. of Character Cities

Intl. Assn. of Charities [IO], Louvain-la-Neuve, Belgium

Intl. Assn. of Chiefs of Police [5696], 515 N Washington St., Alexandria, VA 22314-2344, (703)836-6767

Intl. Assn. of Chiefs of Police | Law Enforcement Info. Mgt. Sect. [5542], 515 N Washington St., Alexandria, VA 22314-2357, (703)836-6767

Intl. Assn. for Child and Adolescent Psychiatry and Allied Professions [IO], Stockholm, Sweden

Intl. Assn. for Child and Adolescent Psychiatry and Allied Professions Germany [IO], Ibadan, Nigeria

Intl. Assn. for China Planning [18315], Jianling Li, Univ. of Texas at Arlington, School of Urban and Public Affairs, 501 Univ. Hall, 601 S Nedderman Dr., Arlington, TX 76010, (512)471-0139

Reference to "IO" in place of a book number signifies that the association may be found in the 50th edition of International Organizations.

Intl. Assn. of Chinese Linguistics [7025], Univ. of Arizona, PO Box 210105, Tucson, AZ 85721-0105

Intl. Assn. for Chinese Mgt. Res. [2290], Univ. of Colorado, 419 UCB, Boulder, CO 80309, (316)978-6788

Intl. Assn. of Christian Chaplains [19520], 5804 Babcock Rd., PMB 189, San Antonio, TX 78240-2134, (210)696-7313

Intl. Assn. for Chronic Fatigue Syndrome [14391], 27 N Wacker Dr., Ste. 416, Chicago, IL 60606, (847)258-7248

Intl. Assn. of Cities and Ports [IO], Le Havre, France

Intl. Assn. for Citizenship Social and Economics Educ. [IO], Glasgow, United Kingdom

Intl. Assn. of Civil Aviation Chaplains [IO], Nice, France

Intl. Assn. of Civil Engg. Students [IO], Wuppertal, Germany

Intl. Assn. of Clan MacInnes [20539], Eric MacGinnis Perry, Membership Dir., 14 Jakes Ln., Dexter, ME 04930-2194, (207)924-6565

Intl. Assn. for Classical Archaeology [IO], Rome, Italy

Intl. Assn. of Classification Societies [IO], London, United Kingdom

Intl. Assn. of Clerks, Recorders, Election Officials and Treasurers [5498], 2400 Augusta Dr., Ste. 250, Houston, TX 77057, (800)890-7368

Intl. Assn. of Clothing Designers [★215]

Intl. Assn. of Clothing Designers and Executives

Intl. Assn. for Cognitive Psychotherapy [16462], Amer. Inst. for Cognitive Therapy, 136 E 57th St., Ste. 1101, New York, NY 10022, (212)308-2440

Intl. Assn. for Cold Storage Constr. [1706], 1500 King St., Ste. 201, Alexandria, VA 22314, (703)373-4300

Intl. Assn. of Cold Storage Contractors [★1706]

Intl. Assn. of Coll. and Univ. Security Directors [★8817]

Intl. Assn. of Colloid and Interface Scientists [IO], Wageningen, Netherlands

Intl. Assn. for Colon Hydrotherapy [14716], PO Box 461285, San Antonio, TX 78246-1285, (210)366-2888

Intl. Assn. of Colon Therapy [16315], PO Box 461285, San Antonio, TX 78246-1285, (210)366-2888

Intl. Assn. of Color Mfrs. [800], 1620 I St. NW, Ste. 925, Washington, DC 20006, (202)293-5800

Intl. Assn. of Commercial Collectors [1033], 4040 W 70th St., Minneapolis, MN 55435, (952)925-0760

Intl. Assn. for Comparative Mythology [7133], Sanskrit Dept., 1 Bow St., 3rd Fl., Cambridge, MA 02138, (617)496-2990

Intl. Assn. for Comparative Res. on Leukemia and Related Diseases [15926], 1216 James Cancer Hosp., 300 W 10th Ave., Columbus, OH 43210, (614)293-7518

Intl. Assn. for Computational Mechanics [IO], Barcelona, Spain

International Assn. of Computational Mechanics [★7080]

Intl. Assn. for Cmpt. and Info. Sci. [6456], 735 Meadowbrook Dr., Mount Pleasant, MI 48858, (989)774-1175

Intl. Assn. for Cmpt. Info. Systems [7907], Richard McCarthy, VP, Quinnipiac Univ., School of Bus., 275 Mt. Carmel Ave., Hamden, CT 06518

Intl. Assn. of Cmpt. Investigative Specialists [7908], PO Box 2411, Leesburg, VA 20177, (304)915-0555

Intl. Assn. for Computing in Educ. [★7909]

Intl. Assn. of Concrete Repair Specialists [★830]

Intl. Assn. of Conf. Center Administrators [1755], 6832 Milan Dr., Lincoln, NE 68526, (402)202-1973

Intl. Assn. of Conf. Centers [2440], 243 N Lindbergh Blvd., St. Louis, MO 63141, (314)993-8575

Intl. Assn. of Conf. Interpreters [IO], Geneva, Switzerland

Intl. Assn. of Conf. Translators [IO], Geneva, Switzerland

Intl. Assn. for Consumer Law [IO], Helsinki, Finland

Intl. Assn. of Contact Lens Educators [IO], Sydney, Australia

Intl. Assn. for Continuing Educ. and Training [7925], 1760 Old Meadow Rd., Ste. 500, McLean, VA 22102, (703)506-3275

Intl. Assn. for Contract and Commercial Mgt. [716], 90 Grove St., Ridgefield, CT 06877, (203)431-8741

Intl. Assn. of Convention and Visitor Bureaus [★2447]

Intl. Assn. of Cooking Professionals [★1444]

Intl. Assn. of Cooking Schools [★1444]

Intl. Assn. of Coroners and Medical Examiners [15328], 1704 Pinto Ln., Las Vegas, NV 89106, (702)455-3210

Intl. Assn. of Corporate Entertainment Producers [1196], PO Box 9826, Wilmington, DE 19809, (302)765-3945

Intl. Assn. for Corporate and Professional Recruitment [1151], 327 N Palm Dr., Ste. 201, Beverly Hills, CA 90210, (310)550-0304

Intl. Assn. of Corporate and Professional Resources [★1151]

Intl. Assn. for Corporate Real Estate Executives [★3006]

Intl. Assn. for Correctional and Forensic Psychology [11715], Mr. David Randall, Sec.-Treas., PO Box 7642, Wilmington, NC 28406

Intl. Assn. of Correctional Training Personnel [11716], PO Box 473254, Aurora, CO 80047, (719)738-9969

Intl. Assn. of Counseling Services [7943], 101 S Whiting St., Ste. 211, Alexandria, VA 22304, (703)823-9840

Intl. Assn. of Counselors and Therapists [15090], 8852 SR 3001, Laceyville, PA 18623, (570)869-1021

Intl. Assn. for Counterterrorism and Security Professionals [18714], PO Box 100688, Arlington, VA 22210, (201)224-0588

Intl. Assn. for Creative Dance [9549], 103 Princeton Ave., Providence, RI 02907, (401)521-0546

Intl. Assn. of Credit Cards [★5600]

Intl. Assn. of Credit Portfolio Managers [991], 360 Madison Ave., 17th Fl., New York, NY 10017-7111, (646)289-5430

Intl. Assn. of Crime Analysts [5387], 9218 Metcalf Ave., No. 364, Overland Park, KS 66212, (800)609-3419

Intl. Assn. of Crime Writers, North Amer. Br. [10719], PO Box 8674, New York, NY 10116-8674

Intl. Assn. for Criminal Identification [★5485]

Intl. Assn. for Critical Realism [IO], Tromso, Norway

Intl. Assn. for Cross-Cultural Psychology [IO], Hong Kong, People's Republic of China

Intl. Assn. of Cross-Reference Dir. Publishers [2940], 684 W Baltimore St., Detroit, MI 48202-2902, (313)874-0570

Intl. Assn. for Cryptologic Res. [6586], Shai Halevi, Membership Sec., IBM T. J. Watson Res. Center, 19 Skyline Dr., Hawthorne, NY 10532, (914)768-7653

Intl. Assn. of Culinary Professionals [1444], 1100 Johnson Ferry Rd., Ste. 300, Atlanta, GA 30342, (404)252-3663

Intl. Assn. of Culinary Professionals Found. [★7946]

Intl. Assn. of Currency Affairs [419], PO Box 821, Colleyville, TX 76034, (778)998-5723

Intl. Assn. for Dairy and Milk Inspectors [★5462]

Intl. Assn. for Dairy and Milk Inspectors [★5462]

Intl. Assn. for Dance Medicine and Sci. [15417], 1214 Univ. of Oregon, Dept. of Dance, Eugene, OR 97403-1214, (541)465-1763

Intl. Assn. of Defense Counsel [5251], 303 W Madison, Ste. 925, Chicago, IL 60606, (312)368-1494

Intl. Assn. for Dental Res. [14290], 1619 Duke St., Alexandria, VA 22314-3406, (703)548-0066

Intl. Assn. of Dental Students [IO], Ferney-Voltaire, France

Intl. Assn. of Dental Traumatology [IO], Reykjavik, Iceland

Intl. Assn. of Dento-Maxillo-Facial Radiology - Defunct.

Intl. Assn. of Dept. Stores [IO], Paris, France

Intl. Assn. for Dialogue Anal. [7026], Northeastern Illinois Univ., 5500 N St. Louis Ave., Chicago, IL 60625

Intl. Assn. of Diecutting and Diemaking [1831], 651 W Terra Cotta Ave., Ste. 132, Crystal Lake, IL 60014, (815)455-7519

Intl. Assn. of Dinnerware Matchers [1777], Richard Goldberg, 67 Beverly Rd., Hawthorne, NJ 07506, (800)252-6655

Intl. Assn. of Directional Drilling [7238], 525 Sam Houston Pkwy. E, Ste. 525, Houston, TX 77060, (281)931-8811

Intl. Assn. for Disability and Oral Hea. - Sweden [IO], Wentworthville, Australia

Intl. Assn. of Dive Rescue Specialists [2215], PO Box 877, Vero Beach, FL 32961, (970)482-1562

Intl. Assn. of Dredging Companies [IO], The Hague, Netherlands

Intl. Assn. of Drilling Contractors [2654], PO Box 4287, Houston, TX 77210-4287, (713)292-1945

Intl. Assn. of Dry Cargo Shipowners [IO], London, United Kingdom

Intl. Assn. of Duncan Certified Ceramic Teachers [21263], 510 Salem St., Risingsun, OH 43457, (419)457-7281

Intl. Assn. of Dutch Stud. [IO], Woubrugge, Netherlands

Intl. Assn. for Earthquake Engg. [IO], Tokyo, Japan

Intl. Assn. of Eating Disorders Professionals [14435], PO Box 1295, Pekin, IL 61555-1295, (309)346-3341

Intl. Assn. for Ecology [IO], Seoul, Republic of Korea

Intl. Assn. for Ecology and Hea. [6604], 460 W 34th St., 17th Fl., New York, NY 10001, (212)380-4460

Intl. Assn. for Educational Assessment [IO], Arnhem, Netherlands

Intl. Assn. of Educators [8114], 1971 S Orchard St., Urbana, IL 61801

Intl. Assn. of Educators for World Peace USA [18256], PO Box 3282, Mastin Lake Sta., Huntsville, AL 35810-0282, (256)534-5501

Intl. Assn. of Egyptologists [IO], Mainz, Germany

Intl. Assn. of Elecl. Inspectors [1075], PO Box 830848, Richardson, TX 75083-0848, (972)235-1455

Intl. Assn. of Elecl. Inspectors - Japan Chap. [IO], Tokyo, Japan

Intl. Assn. of Elecl. Inspectors - Korea Chap. [IO], Seoul, Republic of Korea

Intl. Assn. of Elecl. Inspectors - Mexico Chap. [IO], Coyoacan, Mexico

Intl. Assn. of Elecl. Inspectors - Saudi Arabia Chap. [IO], Ras Tanura, Saudi Arabia

Intl. Assn. of Elecl. Leagues [★1077]

Intl. Assn. of Electronics Recyclers [★1107]

Intl. Assn. of Elevator Consultants [1832], 15600 NE 8th St., Ste. B1, PMB 153, Bellevue, WA 98008, (425)732-3328

Intl. Assn. Emergency Managers [5307], 201 Park Washington Ct., Falls Church, VA 22046-4527, (703)538-1795

Intl. Assn. of Empirical Aesthetics [IO], Rome, Italy

Intl. Assn. of Employment Web Sites [1152], 2052 Shippan Ave., Stamford, CT 06902, (203)964-1888

Intl. Assn. of EMTs and Paramedics [23186], 159 Burgin Pkwy., Quincy, MA 02169, (617)376-0220

Intl. Assn. of Endocrine Surgeons [IO], Sydney, Australia

Intl. Assn. for Energy Economics [6732], 28790 Chagrin Blvd., Ste. 350, Cleveland, OH 44122-4630, (216)464-5365

Intl. Assn. for Energy Economics - Austria [IO], Vienna, Austria

Intl. Assn. for Energy Economics - Canada [IO], Edmonton, AB, Canada

Intl. Assn. for Energy Economics - Czech Republic [IO], Prague, Czech Republic

Intl. Assn. for Energy Economics - Denmark [IO], Frederiksberg, Denmark

Intl. Assn. for Energy Economics - Finland [IO], Espoo, Finland

Intl. Assn. for Energy Economics - France [IO], Rueil-Malmaison, France

Intl. Assn. for Energy Economics - Germany [IO], Berlin, Germany

Intl. Assn. for Energy Economics - Japan [IO], Tokyo, Japan

Intl. Assn. for Energy Economics - Korea [IO], Seoul, Republic of Korea

Intl. Assn. for Energy Economics - Latvia [IO], Riga, Latvia

A star before a book entry number signifies that the name is not listed separately, but is mentioned within the entry.

Intl. Assn. for Energy Economics - Lithuania [IO], Kaunas, Lithuania

Intl. Assn. for Energy Economics - Mexico [IO], Mexico City, Mexico

Intl. Assn. for Energy Economics - Spain [IO], Gijon, Spain

Intl. Assn. for Energy Economics - Switzerland [IO], Zurich, Switzerland

Intl. Assn. for Energy Economics - Taiwan [IO], Taipei, Taiwan

Intl. Assn. of Energy Economists [★6732]

Intl. Assn. of Energy Economists [★6732]

Intl. Assn. for Engg. Geology and the Env. [IO], Subiaco, Australia

Intl. Assn. for Enterostomal Therapy [★15807]

Intl. Assn. for Enterostomal Therapy [★15807]

Intl. Assn. of Entertainment Lawyers - France [IO], London, United Kingdom

Intl. Assn. of Entertainment Lawyers - United Kingdom [IO], London, United Kingdom

Intl. Assn. of Environmental Analytical Chemistry [IO], Allschwil, Switzerland

Intl. Assn. of Environmental Mutagen Societies [6301], 1821 Michael Faraday Dr., Ste. 300, Reston, VA 20190, (703)438-3103

Intl. Assn. of Environmental Mutagen Societies [6301], 1821 Michael Faraday Dr., Ste. 300, Reston, VA 20190, (703)438-3103

Intl. Assn. for Environmental Philosophy [10382], Rochester Inst. of Tech., Dept. of Philosophy, Rochester, NY 14623-5604

Intl. Assn. for the Evaluation of Educational Achievement [IO], Amsterdam, Netherlands

Intl. Assn. for the Exchange of Students for Tech. Experience [IO], Banbridge, United Kingdom

Intl. Assn. for the Exchange of Students for Tech. Experience [★8347]

Intl. Assn. for the Exchange of Students for Tech. Experience Argentina [IO], Buenos Aires, Argentina

Intl. Assn. for the Exchange of Students for Tech. Experience - Armenia [IO], Yerevan, Armenia

Intl. Assn. for the Exchange of Students for Tech. Experience - Australia [IO], Hawthorn, Australia

Intl. Assn. for the Exchange of Students for Tech. Experience - Austria [IO], Vienna, Austria

Intl. Assn. for the Exchange of Students for Tech. Experience Belarus [IO], Minsk, Belarus

Intl. Assn. for the Exchange of Students for Tech. Experience Belgium [IO], Gent, Belgium

Intl. Assn. for the Exchange of Students for Tech. Experience Bosnia and Herzegovina [IO], Banja Luka, Bosnia-Hercegovina

Intl. Assn. for the Exchange of Students for Tech. Experience Botswana [IO], Gaborone, Botswana

Intl. Assn. for the Exchange of Students for Tech. Experience Brazil [IO], Sao Paulo, Brazil

Intl. Assn. for the Exchange of Students for Tech. Experience - Bulgaria [IO], Plovdiv, Bulgaria

Intl. Assn. for the Exchange of Students for Tech. Experience - Canada [IO], Kingston, ON, Canada

Intl. Assn. for the Exchange of Students for Tech. Experience China [IO], Shanghai, People's Republic of China

Intl. Assn. for the Exchange of Students for Tech. Experience Columbia [IO], Ibague, Colombia

Intl. Assn. for the Exchange of Students for Tech. Experience - Croatia [IO], Zagreb, Croatia

Intl. Assn. for the Exchange of Students for Tech. Experience - Cyprus [IO], Nicosia, Cyprus

Intl. Assn. for the Exchange of Students for Tech. Experience - Czech Republic [IO], Prague, Czech Republic

Intl. Assn. for the Exchange of Students for Tech. Experience - Denmark [IO], Lyngby, Denmark

Intl. Assn. for the Exchange of Students for Tech. Experience Ecuador [IO], Quito, Ecuador

Intl. Assn. for the Exchange of Students for Tech. Experience - Egypt [IO], Giza, Egypt

Intl. Assn. for the Exchange of Students for Tech. Experience - Estonia [IO], Tallinn, Estonia

Intl. Assn. for the Exchange of Students for Tech. Experience Finland [IO], Helsinki, Finland

Intl. Assn. for the Exchange of Students for Tech. Experience - France [IO], Paris, France

Intl. Assn. for the Exchange of Students for Tech. Experience Germany [IO], Bonn, Germany

Intl. Assn. for the Exchange of Students for Tech. Experience Ghana [IO], Kumasi, Ghana

Intl. Assn. for the Exchange of Students for Tech. Experience Greece [IO], Athens, Greece

Intl. Assn. for the Exchange of Students for Tech. Experience Hungary [IO], Budapest, Hungary

Intl. Assn. for the Exchange of Students for Tech. Experience Iceland [IO], Reykjavik, Iceland

Intl. Assn. for the Exchange of Students for Tech. Experience India [IO], Coimbatore, India

Intl. Assn. for the Exchange of Students for Tech. Experience - Iran [IO], Tehran, Iran

Intl. Assn. for the Exchange of Students for Tech. Experience Israel [IO], Haifa, Israel

Intl. Assn. for the Exchange of Students for Tech. Experience Italy [IO], Milan, Italy

Intl. Assn. for the Exchange of Students for Tech. Experience Japan [IO], Tokyo, Japan

Intl. Assn. for the Exchange of Students for Tech. Experience Jordan [IO], Amman, Jordan

Intl. Assn. for the Exchange of Students for Tech. Experience Kazakhstan [IO], Almaty, Kazakhstan

Intl. Assn. for the Exchange of Students for Tech. Experience - Kenya [IO], Nairobi, Kenya

Intl. Assn. for the Exchange of Students for Tech. Experience - Latvia [IO], Riga, Latvia

Intl. Assn. for the Exchange of Students for Tech. Experience - Lebanon [IO], Beirut, Lebanon

Intl. Assn. for the Exchange of Students for Tech. Experience - Lithuania [IO], Kaunas, Lithuania

Intl. Assn. for the Exchange of Students for Tech. Experience - Luxembourg [IO], Luxembourg, Luxembourg

Intl. Assn. for the Exchange of Students for Tech. Experience - Macao [IO], Macau, Macao

Intl. Assn. for the Exchange of Students for Tech. Experience - Macedonia [IO], Skopje, Macedonia

Intl. Assn. for the Exchange of Students for Tech. Experience - Malta [IO], Msida, Malta

Intl. Assn. for the Exchange of Students for Tech. Experience - Mexico [IO], Queretaro, Mexico

Intl. Assn. for the Exchange of Students for Tech. Experience - Mongolia [IO], Ulan Bator, Mongolia

Intl. Assn. for the Exchange of Students for Tech. Experience - Norway [IO], Trondheim, Norway

Intl. Assn. for the Exchange of Students for Tech. Experience - Oman [IO], Muscat, Oman

Intl. Assn. for the Exchange of Students for Tech. Experience - Pakistan [IO], Karachi, Pakistan

Intl. Assn. for the Exchange of Students for Tech. Experience - Panama [IO], Panama City, Panama

Intl. Assn. for the Exchange of Students for Tech. Experience - Peru [IO], Piura, Peru

Intl. Assn. for the Exchange of Students for Tech. Experience - Poland [IO], Warsaw, Poland

Intl. Assn. for the Exchange of Students for Tech. Experience - Portugal [IO], Lisbon, Portugal

Intl. Assn. for the Exchange of Students for Tech. Experience - Romania [IO], Bucharest, Romania

Intl. Assn. for the Exchange of Students for Tech. Experience - Russia [IO], Moscow, Russia

Intl. Assn. for the Exchange of Students for Tech. Experience - Sierra Leone [IO], Freetown, Sierra Leone

Intl. Assn. for the Exchange of Students for Tech. Experience - Slovakia [IO], Bratislava, Slovakia

Intl. Assn. for the Exchange of Students for Tech. Experience - Slovenia [IO], Ljubljana, Slovenia

Intl. Assn. for the Exchange of Students for Tech. Experience - South Africa [IO], Pretoria, Republic of South Africa

Intl. Assn. for the Exchange of Students for Tech. Experience - Spain [IO], Valencia, Spain

Intl. Assn. for the Exchange of Students for Tech. Experience - Sri Lanka [IO], Moratuwa, Sri Lanka

Intl. Assn. for the Exchange of Students for Tech. Experience - Sweden [IO], Stockholm, Sweden

Intl. Assn. for the Exchange of Students for Tech. Experience - Switzerland [IO], Zurich, Switzerland

Intl. Assn. for the Exchange of Students for Tech. Experience - Syria [IO], Damascus, Syrian Arab Republic

Intl. Assn. for the Exchange of Students for Tech. Experience - Tajikistan [IO], Dushanbe, Tajikistan

Intl. Assn. for the Exchange of Students for Tech. Experience - Thailand [IO], Bangkok, Thailand

Intl. Assn. for the Exchange of Students for Tech. Experience - Tunisia [IO], Tunis, Tunisia

Intl. Assn. for the Exchange of Students for Tech. Experience - Turkey [IO], Istanbul, Turkey

Intl. Assn. for the Exchange of Students for Tech. Experience - Ukraine [IO], Kiev, Ukraine

Intl. Assn. for the Exchange of Students for Tech. Experience - United Arab Emirates [IO], Sharjah, United Arab Emirates

Intl. Assn. for the Exchange of Students for Tech. Experience - United Kingdom [IO], London, United Kingdom

Intl. Assn. for the Exchange of Students for Tech. Experience (U.S.) [★8347]

Intl. Assn. for the Exchange of Students for Tech. Experience - Uruguay [IO], Montevideo, Uruguay

Intl. Assn. for the Exchange of Students for Tech. Experience - Uzbekistan [IO], Tashkent, Uzbekistan

Intl. Assn. for the Exchange of Students for Tech. Experience [8918], 10400 Little Patuxent Pkwy., Ste. 250, Columbia, MD 21044-3519, (410)997-3069

Intl. Assn. for the Exchange of Students for Tech. Experience [8918], 10400 Little Patuxent Pkwy., Ste. 250, Columbia, MD 21044-3519, (410)997-3069

Intl. Assn. for Exhibition Mgt. [2450], 12700 Park Central Dr., Ste. 308, Dallas, TX 75251, (972)458-8002

Intl. Assn. of Exhibitions and Events [2450], 12700 Park Central Dr., Ste. 308, Dallas, TX 75251, (972)458-8002

Intl. Assn. of Facilitators [2895], 14985 Glazier Ave., Ste. 550, St. Paul, MN 55124, (952)891-3541

Intl. Assn. of Facilitators [2895], 14985 Glazier Ave., Ste. 550, St. Paul, MN 55124, (952)891-3541

Intl. Assn. of Factory Inspectors [★5635]

Intl. Assn. of Fairs and Expositions [2451], PO Box 985, Springfield, MO 65801, (417)862-5771

Intl. Assn. of Fairs and Expositions [2451], PO Box 985, Springfield, MO 65801, (417)862-5771

Intl. Assn. for the Fantastic in the Arts [10520], PO Box 3701, Youngstown, OH 44513

Intl. Assn. for Feminist Economics - Europe [IO], Amsterdam, Netherlands

Intl. Assn. for Feminist Economics U.S.A. [6622], Univ. of Nebraska-Lincoln, Dept. of Agricultural Economics, 208A Filley Hall, East Campus, Lincoln, NE 68583-0922, (402)472-3372

Intl. Assn. for Feminist Economics U.S.A. [6622], Univ. of Nebraska-Lincoln, Dept. of Agricultural Economics, 208A Filley Hall, East Campus, Lincoln, NE 68583-0922, (402)472-3372

Intl. Assn. of Film and TV Schools [IO], Brussels, Belgium

Intl. Assn. of Financial Crimes [★5600]

Intl. Assn. of Financial Crimes [★5600]

Intl. Assn. of Financial Crimes Investigators [5600], 1020 Suncast Ln., Ste. 102, El Dorado Hills, CA 95762, (916)939-5000

Intl. Assn. of Financial Crimes Investigators [5600], 1020 Suncast Ln., Ste. 102, El Dorado Hills, CA 95762, (916)939-5000

Intl. Assn. of Financial Engineers [1304], 347 5th Ave., Ste. 703, New York, NY 10016, (646)736-0705

Intl. Assn. of Financial Engineers [1304], 347 5th Ave., Ste. 703, New York, NY 10016, (646)736-0705

Intl. Assn. of Financial Executives Institutes [IO], Makati City, Philippines

Intl. Assn. for Financial Planning [★1298]

Intl. Assn. for Financial Planning [★1298]

Intl. Assn. of Fire Chiefs [5442], 4025 Fair Ridge Dr., Ste. 300, Fairfax, VA 22033-2868, (703)273-0911

Intl. Assn. of Fire Chiefs [5442], 4025 Fair Ridge Dr., Ste. 300, Fairfax, VA 22033-2868, (703)273-0911

Intl. Assn. of Fire Fighters [23188], 1750 New York Ave. NW, Ste. 300, Washington, DC 20006, (202)737-8484

Intl. Assn. for Fire Safety Sci.

Intl. Assn. for Fire Safety Sci. - Address unknown since 2010.

Intl. Assn. of Fish and Wildlife Agencies [★4004]

Reference to "IO" in place of a book number signifies that the association may be found in the 50th edition of International Organizations.

Intl. Assn. of Fish and Wildlife Agencies [★4004]

Intl. Assn. of Flight and Critical Care Paramedics [14468], 4835 Riveredge Cove, Snellville, GA 30039, (770)979-6372

Intl. Assn. of Flight Paramedics [★14468]

Intl. Assn. of Fly Fishing Veterinarians [21734], Dr. Jack Quick, Sec.-Treas., 6420 E Placita Zacatecas, Tucson, AZ 85750, (517)349-0454

Intl. Assn. of Food Indus. Suppliers [★1020]

Intl. Assn. of Food Indus. Suppliers [★1020]

Intl. Assn. of Food Indus. Suppliers and Food Processing Machinery Assn. [★1020]

Intl. Assn. of Food Indus. Suppliers and Food Processing Machinery Assn. [★1020]

Intl. Assn. for Food Protection [5462], 6200 Aurora Ave., Ste. 200W, Des Moines, IA 50322-2864, (515)276-3344

Intl. Assn. for Food Protection [5462], 6200 Aurora Ave., Ste. 200W, Des Moines, IA 50322-2864, (515)276-3344

Intl. Assn. of Forensic Nurses [15754], 1517 Ritchie Hwy., Ste. 208, Arnold, MD 21012, (410)626-7805

Intl. Assn. of Forensic Nurses [15754], 1517 Ritchie Hwy., Ste. 208, Arnold, MD 21012, (410)626-7805

Intl. Assn. for Forensic Psychotherapy [IO], London, United Kingdom

Intl. Assn. of Forensic and Security Metrology [7465], 3416 Primm Ln., Birmingham, AL 35216, (205)823-6106

The Intl. Assn. of Forensic Toxicologists [IO], Gent, Belgium

Intl. Assn. of Former Soviet Political Prisoners and Victims of the Communist Regime [17840], 1310 Ave. R, Ste. 6-F, Brooklyn, NY 11229, (718)339-4563

Intl. Assn. of Former Soviet Political Prisoners and Victims of the Communist Regime [17840], 1310 Ave. R, Ste. 6-F, Brooklyn, NY 11229, (718)339-4563

Intl. Assn. of Found. Drilling [★894]

Intl. Assn. of Found. Drilling [★894]

Intl. Assn. of French Language Archives [IO], Quebec, QC, Canada

Intl. Assn. of French Language Demographers [IO], Paris, France

Intl. Assn. of French Language Sociologists [IO], Toulouse, France

Intl. Assn. of French-Speaking Directors of Educational Institutions [IO], Montreal, QC, Canada

Intl. Assn. of Game, Fish, and Conservation Commissioners [★4004]

Intl. Assn. of Game, Fish, and Conservation Commissioners [★4004]

Intl. Assn. of Gay/Lesbian Country Western Dance Clubs [9550], PMB 107, 5543 Edmondson Pike, Nashville, TN 37211

Intl. Assn. of Gay/Lesbian Country Western Dance Clubs [9550], PMB 107, 5543 Edmondson Pike, Nashville, TN 37211

Intl. Assn. of Gay and Lesbian Martial Artists [22734], PO Box 590601, San Francisco, CA 94159-0601, (610)940-1434

Intl. Assn. of Gay and Lesbian Martial Artists [22734], PO Box 590601, San Francisco, CA 94159-0601, (610)940-1434

Intl. Assn. of Gay Square Dance Clubs [9551], PO Box 9176, Denver, CO 80209-0176

Intl. Assn. of Gay Square Dance Clubs [9551], PO Box 9176, Denver, CO 80209-0176

Intl. Assn. on the Genesis of Ore Deposits [IO], Oslo, Norway

Intl. Assn. of Genocide Scholars [17742], PO Box 809, Washington, DC 20044

Intl. Assn. of Genocide Scholars [17742], PO Box 809, Washington, DC 20044

Intl. Assn. of Geochemistry [IO], Pinawa, MB, Canada

Intl. Assn. of Geodesy [IO], Munich, Germany

Intl. Assn. of Geomagnetism and Aeronomy [IO], Copenhagen, Denmark

Intl. Assn. of Geomorphologists [IO], Wellington, New Zealand

Intl. Assn. of Geophysical Contractors [2655], 1225 N Loop West, Ste. 220, Houston, TX 77008-1761, (713)957-8080

Intl. Assn. of Geophysical Contractors [2655], 1225 N Loop West, Ste. 220, Houston, TX 77008-1761, (713)957-8080

Intl. Assn. of Geosynthetic Installers [916], PO Box 18012, St. Paul, MN 55118, (651)554-1895

Intl. Assn. of Geosynthetic Installers [916], PO Box 18012, St. Paul, MN 55118, (651)554-1895

Intl. Assn. of Gerontology European Region [IO], Ostend, Belgium

Intl. Assn. of Gerontology and Geriatrics [IO], Toulouse, France

Intl. Assn. of Golf Administrators [22611], 1974 Sproul Rd., Ste. 400, Broomall, PA 19008, (610)687-2340

Intl. Assn. of Golf Administrators [22611], 1974 Sproul Rd., Ste. 400, Broomall, PA 19008, (610)687-2340

Intl. Assn. of Golf Tour Operators [IO], London, United Kingdom

Intl. Assn. of Governmental Labor Officials [★5635]

Intl. Assn. for Great Lakes Res. [7022], 4840 S State Rd., Ann Arbor, MI 48108, (734)665-5303

Intl. Assn. for Great Lakes Res. [7022], 4840 S State Rd., Ann Arbor, MI 48108, (734)665-5303

Intl. Assn. for Greek Philosophy [IO], Alimos, Greece

Intl. Assn. for Gp. Psychotherapy and Gp. Processes [IO], Sao Paulo, Brazil

Intl. Assn. of Gyro Clubs [★13058]

Intl. Assn. of Gyro Clubs [★13058]

Intl. Assn. of Hand Papermakers and Paper Artists [IO], Mainburg, Germany

Intl. Assn. for Handicapped Divers [IO], Meppel, Netherlands

Intl. Assn. of Haunted Attractions [1194], Cynthia Prisco, Exec. Dir., 191 Clarksville Rd., Princeton Junction, NJ 08550, (609)799-4900

Intl. Assn. of Hea. Underwriters [★2004]

Intl. Assn. of Healthcare Central Ser. Material Mgt. [15058], 213 W Inst. Place, Ste. 307, Chicago, IL 60610, (312)440-0078

Intl. Assn. of Healthcare Practitioners [8223], 11211 Prosperity Farms Rd., Ste. 325D, Palm Beach Gardens, FL 33410, (561)622-8273

Intl. Assn. of Healthcare Practitioners [14796], 11211 Prosperity Farms Rd., Ste. D-325, Palm Beach Gardens, FL 33410, (561)622-4334

Intl. Assn. of Healthcare Practitioners [14796], 11211 Prosperity Farms Rd., Ste. D-325, Palm Beach Gardens, FL 33410, (561)622-4334

Intl. Assn. for Healthcare Security and Safety [15059], PO Box 5038, Glendale Heights, IL 60139, (630)529-3913

Intl. Assn. for Healthcare Security and Safety [15059], PO Box 5038, Glendale Heights, IL 60139, (630)529-3913

Intl. Assn. of Heat and Frost Insulators and Allied Workers [1707], 9602 Martin Luther King, Jr. Hwy., Lanham, MD 20706, (301)731-9101

Intl. Assn. of Heat and Frost Insulators and Asbestos Workers [★1707]

Intl. Assn. of Hispanic Meeting Professionals [2452], 2600 S Shore Blvd., Ste. 300, League City, TX 77573, (281)245-3330

Intl. Assn. of Hispanic Meeting Professionals [2452], 2600 S Shore Blvd., Ste. 300, League City, TX 77573, (281)245-3330

Intl. Assn. of Hispanists [IO], Mexico City, Mexico

Intl. Assn. for the History of Glass [9778], Corning Museum of Glass, 1 Museum Way, Corning, NY 14830

Intl. Assn. for the History of Glass [9778], Corning Museum of Glass, 1 Museum Way, Corning, NY 14830

Intl. Assn. for the History of Religions [IO], Odense, Denmark

Intl. Assn. of Holiday Inns [1754], 3 Ravinia Dr., Ste. 100, Atlanta, GA 30346, (770)604-5555

Intl. Assn. of Holiday Inns [★1754]

Intl. Assn. of Home Staging Professionals [2061], 2420 Sand Creek Rd. C-1, No. 263, Brentwood, CA 94513, (800)392-7161

Intl. Assn. of Home Staging Professionals [2061], 2420 Sand Creek Rd. C-1, No. 263, Brentwood, CA 94513, (800)392-7161

Intl. Assn. of Homes and Services for the Ageing [10846], 2519 Connecticut Ave. NW, Washington, DC 20008, (202)508-9468

Intl. Assn. of Homes and Services for the Ageing [10846], 2519 Connecticut Ave. NW, Washington, DC 20008, (202)508-9468

Intl. Assn. of Horticultural Producers [IO], Zoetermeer, Netherlands

Intl. Assn. for Hospice and Palliative Care [15010], 5535 Memorial Dr., Ste. F, PMB 509, Houston, TX 77007, (936)321-9846

Intl. Assn. for Hospice and Palliative Care [15010], 5535 Memorial Dr., Ste. F, PMB 509, Houston, TX 77007, (936)321-9846

Intl. Assn. for Hosp. Security [★15059]

Intl. Assn. for Hosp. Security [★15059]

Intl. Assn. of Hospitality Accountants [★1303]

Intl. Assn. of Hospitality Accountants [★1303]

Intl. Assn. for Housing Sci. [12182], PO Box 340254, Coral Gables, FL 33134

Intl. Assn. for Housing Sci. [12182], PO Box 340254, Coral Gables, FL 33134

Intl. Assn. of Human-Animal Interaction Organizations [16854], Delta Soc., 875 124th Ave. NE, Ste. 101, Bellevue, WA 98005-2531, (425)679-5511

Intl. Assn. of Human-Animal Interaction Organizations [16854], Delta Soc., 875 124th Ave. NE, Ste. 101, Bellevue, WA 98005-2531, (425)679-5511

Intl. Assn. of Human Biologists [IO], Zagreb, Croatia

Intl. Assn. for Human Caring [14797], 801 E Park Dr., Ste. 100, Harrisburg, PA 17111, (717)703-0033

Intl. Assn. for Human Caring [14797], 801 E Park Dr., Ste. 100, Harrisburg, PA 17111, (717)703-0033

Intl. Assn. for Human Rsrc. Info. Mgt. [68], PO Box 1086, Burlington, MA 01803, (781)791-9488

Intl. Assn. for Human Rsrc. Info. Mgt. [68], PO Box 1086, Burlington, MA 01803, (781)791-9488

Intl. Assn. for Human Values [12216], 2401 15th St. NW, Washington, DC 20009, (202)558-0231

Intl. Assn. for Hungarian Stud. [IO], Budapest, Hungary

Intl. Assn. of Hydraulic Engg. and Res. [IO], Madrid, Spain

Intl. Assn. for Hydrogen Energy [6733], 5794 SW 40 St., No. 303, Miami, FL 33155, (877)839-7126

Intl. Assn. for Hydrogen Energy [6733], 5794 SW 40 St., No. 303, Miami, FL 33155, (877)839-7126

Intl. Assn. of Hydrogeologists - Argentina [IO], Santa Rosa, Argentina

Intl. Assn. of Hydrogeologists - Australia [IO], Cloisters Square, Australia

Intl. Assn. of Hydrogeologists - Belgium [IO], Brussels, Belgium

Intl. Assn. of Hydrogeologists - Canada [IO], Antigonish, NS, Canada

Intl. Assn. of Hydrogeologists - Chile [IO], Santiago, Chile

Intl. Assn. of Hydrogeologists - China [IO], Beijing, People's Republic of China

Intl. Assn. of Hydrogeologists - Columbia [IO], Bogota, Colombia

Intl. Assn. of Hydrogeologists - Croatia [IO], Zagreb, Croatia

Intl. Assn. of Hydrogeologists - Egypt [IO], Cairo, Egypt

Intl. Assn. of Hydrogeologists - France [IO], Orleans, France

Intl. Assn. of Hydrogeologists - Georgia [IO], Tbilisi, Georgia

Intl. Assn. of Hydrogeologists - Germany [IO], Hannover, Germany

Intl. Assn. of Hydrogeologists - Ireland [IO], Dublin, Ireland

Intl. Assn. of Hydrogeologists - Italy [IO], Cagliari, Italy

Intl. Assn. of Hydrogeologists - Japan [IO], Chiba, Japan

Intl. Assn. of Hydrogeologists - Mexico [IO], Coyoacan, Mexico

Intl. Assn. of Hydrogeologists - Morocco [IO], Agadir, Morocco

Intl. Assn. of Hydrogeologists - Netherlands [IO], Utrecht, Netherlands

Intl. Assn. of Hydrogeologists - Northern Territory [IO], Darwin, Australia

Intl. Assn. of Hydrogeologists - Peru [IO], Lima, Peru

Intl. Assn. of Hydrogeologists - Poland [IO], Krakow, Poland

A star before a book entry number signifies that the name is not listed separately, but is mentioned within the entry.

Intl. Assn. of Hydrogeologists - Republic of Korea [IO], Daejeon, Republic of Korea

Intl. Assn. of Hydrogeologists - Romania [IO], Bucharest, Romania

Intl. Assn. of Hydrogeologists - Slovakia [IO], Bratislava, Slovakia

Intl. Assn. of Hydrogeologists - Slovenia [IO], Ljubljana, Slovenia

Intl. Assn. of Hydrogeologists - Spain [IO], Barcelona, Spain

Intl. Assn. of Hydrogeologists - United Kingdom [IO], Reading, United Kingdom

Intl. Assn. of Hydrogeologists - Western Australia [IO], Cloisters Square, Australia

Intl. Assn. of Hydrological Sciences [IO], Paris, France

Intl. Assn. for Hydromagnetic Phenomena and Applications [IO], Dresden, Germany

Intl. Assn. of Hygienic Physicians [15528], 4620 Euclid Blvd., Youngstown, OH 44512, (330)788-0526

Intl. Assn. of Hygienic Physicians [15528], 4620 Euclid Blvd., Youngstown, OH 44512, (330)788-0526

Intl. Assn. of Ice Cream Distributors and Vendors [3611], 5024-R Campbell Blvd., Baltimore, MD 21236, (410)931-8100

International Assn. of Ice Cream Vendors [★3611]

Intl. Assn. of Ice Cream Vendors [3611], 5024-R Campbell Blvd., Baltimore, MD 21236, (410)931-8100

Intl. Assn. for Identification [5485], 2131 Hollywood Blvd., Ste. 403, Hollywood, FL 33020, (954)589-0628

Intl. Assn. for Identification [5485], 2131 Hollywood Blvd., Ste. 403, Hollywood, FL 33020, (954)589-0628

Intl. Assn. for Identification - Great Britain [IO], London, United Kingdom

Intl. Assn. for Identification - Russia [IO], Moscow, Russia

Intl. Assn. for Identification - Switzerland [IO], Lausanne, Switzerland

Intl. Assn. for Impact Assessment [7505], 1330 23rd St. S, Ste. C, Fargo, ND 58103, (701)297-7908

Intl. Assn. for Impact Assessment [7505], 1330 23rd St. S, Ste. C, Fargo, ND 58103, (701)297-7908

Intl. Assn. of Independent Info. Brokers [★1896]

Intl. Assn. of Independent Info. Brokers [★1896]

Intl. Assn. of Independent Private Sector Inspectors Gen. [5546], PO Box 5017, New York, NY 10185, (888)70I-PSIG

Intl. Assn. of Independent Tanker Owners [IO], Oslo, Norway

Intl. Assn. of Individual Psychology [IO], Reggio Emilia, Italy

Intl. Assn. of Indus. Accident Boards and Commissions [5399], 5610 Medical Cir., Ste. 24, Madison, WI 53719-1295, (608)663-6355

Intl. Assn. of Indus. Accident Boards and Commissions [5399], 5610 Medical Cir., Ste. 24, Madison, WI 53719-1295, (608)663-6355

Intl. Assn. of Infant Massage [15270], PO Box 6370, Ventura, CA 93006, (805)644-8524

Intl. Assn. of Infant Massage [15270], PO Box 6370, Ventura, CA 93006, (805)644-8524

Intl. Assn. of Infant Massage Instructors [★15270]

Intl. Assn. of Infant Massage Instructors [★15270]

Intl. Assn. for Infant Mental Hea. [★16349]

Intl. Assn. for Infant Mental Hea. [★16349]

Intl. Assn. for Info. and Data Quality [6978], 19239 N Dale Mabry Hwy., No. 137, Lutz, FL 33548, (813)343-2163

Intl. Assn. of Info. Tech. Asset Managers [1892], 1137 State Rte. 43, Mogadore, OH 44260-9678, (330)628-3012

Intl. Assn. of Info. Tech. Asset Managers [1892], 1137 State Rte. 43, Mogadore, OH 44260-9678, (330)628-3012

Intl. Assn. of Insurance Counsel [★5251]

Intl. Assn. of Insurance Counsel [★5251]

Intl. Assn. of Insurance Fraud Agencies [5552], PO Box 10018, Kansas City, MO 64171, (816)756-5285

Intl. Assn. of Insurance Fraud Agencies [5552], PO Box 10018, Kansas City, MO 64171, (816)756-5285

Intl. Assn. for Insurance Law in the U.S. [5553], PO Box 9001, Mount Vernon, NY 10552, (914)966-3180

Intl. Assn. for Insurance Law in the U.S. [5553], PO Box 9001, Mount Vernon, NY 10552, (914)966-3180

Intl. Assn. for Insurance Law, U.S. Chap. [★5553]

Intl. Assn. for Insurance Law, U.S. Chap. [★5553]

Intl. Assn. of Insurance Receivers [1982], 3626 E Tremont Ave., Ste. 203, Throggs Neck, NY 10465, (718)892-0228

Intl. Assn. of Insurance Receivers [1982], 3626 E Tremont Ave., Ste. 203, Throggs Neck, NY 10465, (718)892-0228

Intl. Assn. of Integrative Coaches - Address unknown since 2010.

Intl. Assn. for Intelligence Educ. [8328], Michelle Henderson, PO Box 10508, Erie, PA 16514, (814)824-3121

Intl. Assn. of Interaction Design [IO], Paris, France

Intl. Assn. of Investigative Locksmiths [3214], PO Box 342, Arcola, IL 61910, (410)982-6530

Intl. Assn. of Investigative Locksmiths [3214], PO Box 342, Arcola, IL 61910, (410)982-6530

Intl. Assn. for Jazz Educ. [8653], PO Box 70213, San Diego, CA 92167-1213, (619)223-2069

Intl. Assn. for Jazz Educ. [8653], PO Box 70213, San Diego, CA 92167-1213, (619)223-2069

Intl. Assn. of Jazz Educators [★8653]

Intl. Assn. of Jazz Educators [★8653]

Intl. Assn. of Jazz Record Collectors [21956], PO Box 524, Brookfield, IL 60513-0524

Intl. Assn. of Jazz Record Collectors [21956], PO Box 524, Brookfield, IL 60513-0524

Intl. Assn. of Jesuit Bus. Schools [7793], 4001 W McNichols Rd., Detroit, MI 48221, (313)993-1219

Intl. Assn. of Jesuit Bus. Schools [7793], 4001 W McNichols Rd., Detroit, MI 48221, (313)993-1219

Intl. Assn. of Jewish Genealogical Societies [20634], Paul Silverstone, Treas., PO Box 3624, Cherry Hill, NJ 08034-0556

Intl. Assn. of Jewish Genealogical Societies [20634], Paul Silverstone, Treas., PO Box 3624, Cherry Hill, NJ 08034-0556

Intl. Assn. of Jewish Lawyers and Jurists [IO], Tel Aviv, Israel

Intl. Assn. of Jewish Vocational Services [9044], 1845 Walnut St., Ste. 640, Philadelphia, PA 19103, (215)854-0233

Intl. Assn. of Jewish Vocational Services [9044], 1845 Walnut St., Ste. 640, Philadelphia, PA 19103, (215)854-0233

Intl. Assn. of Jim Beam Bottle and Specialties Clubs [21235], 2965 Waubesa Ave., Madison, WI 53711-5964, (608)663-9661

Intl. Assn. of Jim Beam Bottle and Specialties Clubs [21235], 2965 Waubesa Ave., Madison, WI 53711-5964, (608)663-9661

Intl. Assn. of Judges [IO], Rome, Italy

Intl. Assn. for Jungian Stud. [IO], London, United Kingdom

Intl. Assn. for K-12 Online Learning [7719], 1934 Old Gallows Rd., Ste. 350, Vienna, VA 22182-4040, (703)752-6216

Intl. Assn. for K-12 Online Learning [7719], 1934 Old Gallows Rd., Ste. 350, Vienna, VA 22182-4040, (703)752-6216

Intl. Assn. of Labour History Institutions [IO], Amsterdam, Netherlands

Intl. Assn. of Labour Inspection [IO], Strassen, Luxembourg

Intl. Assn. for Landscape Ecology I U.S. Regional Assn. [4209], Portland State Univ., PO Box 751, Portland, OR 97207, (503)725-2494

Intl. Assn. of Language Centres [IO], Canterbury, United Kingdom

Intl. Assn. for Language Learning Tech. [IO], Victoria, BC, Canada

Intl. Assn. of Laryngectomees [11795], 925B Peachtree St. NE, Ste. 316, Atlanta, GA 30309, (866)425-3678

Intl. Assn. of Laryngectomees [11795], 925B Peachtree St. NE, Ste. 316, Atlanta, GA 30309, (866)425-3678

Intl. Assn. of Law Enforcement Firearms Instructors [5698], 25 Country Club Rd., Ste. 707, Gilford, NH 03249-6977, (603)524-8787

Intl. Assn. of Law Enforcement Firearms Instructors [5698], 25 Country Club Rd., Ste. 707, Gilford, NH 03249-6977, (603)524-8787

Intl. Assn. of Law Enforcement Intelligence Analysts [5601], PO Box 13857, Richmond, VA 23225

Intl. Assn. of Law Enforcement Intelligence Analysts [5601], PO Box 13857, Richmond, VA 23225

Intl. Assn. of Law Enforcement Planners [5373], PO Box 11437, Torrance, CA 90510-1437, (310)225-5148

Intl. Assn. of Law Enforcement Planners [5373], PO Box 11437, Torrance, CA 90510-1437, (310)225-5148

Intl. Assn. of Law, Ethics and Sci. [IO], Paris, France

Intl. Assn. of Law Schools [8506], 1201 Connecticut Ave. NW, Ste. 800, Washington, DC 20036-2717, (202)296-8851

Intl. Assn. of Law Schools [8506], 1201 Connecticut Ave. NW, Ste. 800, Washington, DC 20036-2717, (202)296-8851

Intl. Assn. of Lawyers [IO], Paris, France

Intl. Assn. of Lawyers Against Nuclear Arms [IO], Berlin, Germany

Intl. Assn. for Learning Alternatives [7720], 112103 Haering Cir., Chaska, MN 55318, (612)716-5620

Intl. Assn. for Learning Alternatives [7720], 112103 Haering Cir., Chaska, MN 55318, (612)716-5620

Intl. Assn. of Lemon Law Administrators [5291], Ms. Pauline Liese, Pres., Dept. of Motor Vehicles, 120 State St., Montpelier, VT 05603, (802)828-2943

Intl. Assn. of Lesbian and Gay Judges

Intl. Assn. of Lesbian and Gay Judges - Address unknown since 2011.

Intl. Assn. of Lesbian/Gay Pride Coordinators [★12094]

Intl. Assn. of Lesbian/Gay Pride Coordinators [★12094]

Intl. Assn. for Lichenology [IO], Nottingham, United Kingdom

Intl. Assn. of Lighting Designers [2062], Merchandise Mart, Ste. 9-104, Chicago, IL 60654, (312)527-3677

Intl. Assn. of Lighting Designers [2062], Merchandise Mart, Ste. 9-104, Chicago, IL 60654, (312)527-3677

Intl. Assn. of Lighting Mgt. Companies [2218], E Grand Off. Park, 100 E Grand Ave., Ste. 330, Des Moines, IA 50309-1835, (515)243-2360

Intl. Assn. of Lighting Mgt. Companies [2218], E Grand Off. Park, 100 E Grand Ave., Ste. 330, Des Moines, IA 50309-1835, (515)243-2360

Intl. Assn. of Lions Clubs [★13065]

Intl. Assn. of Lions Clubs [★13065]

Intl. Assn. of Literary Critics [IO], Paris, France

Intl. Assn. of Logopedics and Phoniatrics [IO], Ulrum, Netherlands

Intl. Assn. of Machinists [★23153]

Intl. Assn. of Machinists and Aerospace Workers [23153], 9000 Machinists Pl., Upper Marlboro, MD 20772-2687, (301)967-4500

International Assn. of Mgt; Assn. of Management/ [6251]

International Assn. of Mgt; Assn. of Management/ [6251]

Intl. Assn. for the Mgt. of Tech. [7506], PO Box 248294, Coral Gables, FL 33124, (305)284-2344

Intl. Assn. of Marine Aids to Navigation and Lighthouse Authorities [IO], St.-Germain-en-Laye, France

Intl. Assn. for Marine Electronics Companies [IO], London, United Kingdom

Intl. Assn. of Marine Investigators [2357], 711 Medford Ctr., No. 419, Medford, OR 97504, (541)776-8601

Intl. Assn. of Marine Investigators [2357], 711 Medford Ctr., No. 419, Medford, OR 97504, (541)776-8601

Intl. Assn. of Marine-Related Institutions [IO], Qingdao, People's Republic of China

Intl. Assn. of Marine Sciences Libraries and Info. Centers [★9989]

Intl. Assn. of Marine Sciences Libraries and Info. Centers [★9989]

Intl. Assn. of Maritime Institutions [IO], South Shields, United Kingdom

Reference to "IO" in place of a book number signifies that the association may be found in the 50th edition of International Organizations.

Intl. Assn. for Marriage and Family Counselors [11675], Texas A&M Univ. - Corpus Christi, Coll. of Educ., 6300 Ocean Dr., Corpus Christi, TX 78412, (361)825-2307

Intl. Assn. for Marriage and Family Counselors [11675], Texas A&M Univ. - Corpus Christi, Coll. of Educ., 6300 Ocean Dr., Corpus Christi, TX 78412, (361)825-2307

Intl. Assn. for Maternal and Neonatal Hea. [IO], Basel, Switzerland

Intl. Assn. for Mathematical Geosciences [IO], Kingston, ON, Canada

Intl. Assn. of Mathematical Physics [IO], Prague, Czech Republic

Intl. Assn. of Mathematical Sciences [IO], Osaka, Japan

Intl. Assn. for Mathematics and Computers in Simulation [6457], Rutgers Univ. - Bush Campus, Dept. of Cmpt. Sci., Hill Center, Brett Rd., New Brunswick, NJ 08903, (732)445-2081

Intl. Assn. for Mathematics and Computers in Simulation [6457], Rutgers Univ. - Bush Campus, Dept. of Cmpt. Sci., Hill Center, Brett Rd., New Brunswick, NJ 08903, (732)445-2081

Intl. Assn. of Mayors Responsible for Capital Cities or Metropolises Partially or Entirely French-Speaking [IO], Paris, France

Intl. Assn. on Mechanization of Field Experiments [IO], St. Petersburg, Russia

Intl. Assn. for Media and Commun. Res. [IO], London, United Kingdom

Intl. Assn. for Media and Communications Res. [IO], London, United Kingdom

Intl. Assn. for Media and History [IO], Amsterdam, Netherlands

Intl. Assn. of Media Tie-in Writers [10720], PO Box 8212, Calabasas, CA 91372

Intl. Assn. of Media Tie-in Writers [10720], PO Box 8212, Calabasas, CA 91372

Intl. Assn. for Medical Assistance to Travellers [13339], 1623 Military Rd., No. 279, Niagara Falls, NY 14304-1745, (716)754-4883

Intl. Assn. for Medical Assistance to Travellers [13339], 1623 Military Rd., No. 279, Niagara Falls, NY 14304-1745, (716)754-4883

Intl. Assn. for Medical Assistance to Travellers - Canada [IO], Guelph, ON, Canada

Intl. Assn. for Medical Assistance to Travellers - New Zealand [IO], Christchurch, New Zealand

Intl. Assn. for Medical Assistance to Travellers Switzerland [IO], Zurich, Switzerland

Intl. Assn. of Medical Equip. Remarketers [★15376]

Intl. Assn. of Medical Equip. Remarketers [★15376]

Intl. Assn. of Medical Equip. Remarketers and Servicers [15376], Robert J. Kerwin, Gen. Counsel, 101 Huntington Ave., Ste. 500, Boston, MA 02199, (617)218-2000

Intl. Assn. of Medical Equip. Remarketers and Servicers [15376], Robert J. Kerwin, Gen. Counsel, 101 Huntington Ave., Ste. 500, Boston, MA 02199, (617)218-2000

Intl. Assn. of Medical Intuitives [15418], Rich Crystal Wolfe, Treas., PO Box 30752, Spokane, WA 99223-3021, (509)389-7290

Intl. Assn. of Medical Intuitives [15418], Rich Crystal Wolfe, Treas., PO Box 30752, Spokane, WA 99223-3021, (509)389-7290

Intl. Assn. of Medical Museums [★16125]

Intl. Assn. of Medical Museums [★16125]

Intl. Assn. of Medical Sci. Educators [15324], 3473 US Rte. 60 E, Huntington, WV 25705, (304)733-1270

Intl. Assn. of Medical Sci. Educators [15324], 3473 US Rte. 60 E, Huntington, WV 25705, (304)733-1270

Intl. Assn. of Medical and Therapeutic Specialists [13686], 125 S Wilke, Ste. 101, Arlington Heights, IL 60005, (847)760-5000

Intl. Assn. of Medicine and Biology of Env. [IO], Paris, France

Intl. Assn. for Mediterranean Forests [IO], Marseille, France

Intl. Assn. of Meiobenthologists [IO], Gent, Belgium

Intl. Assn. Merger and Acquisition Consultants [★671]

Intl. Assn. Merger and Acquisition Consultants [★671]

Intl. Assn. of Merger and Acquisition Professionals [671], 6000 Cattleridge Dr., Ste. 300, Sarasota, FL 34232, (941)378-5500

Intl. Assn. of Merger and Acquisition Professionals [671], 6000 Cattleridge Dr., Ste. 300, Sarasota, FL 34232, (941)378-5500

Intl. Assn. of Meteorology and Atmospheric Sciences [IO], Wessling, Germany

Intl. Assn. of Microsoft Certified Partners [IO], Markham, ON, Canada

Intl. Assn. of Microsoft Certified Partners [★6487]

Intl. Assn. of Microsoft Channel Partners [6487], 401 N Michigan Ave., Ste. 2200, Chicago, IL 60611, (312)321-6801

Intl. Assn. of Military Flight Surgeon-Pilots

Intl. Assn. of Military Flight Surgeon-Pilots - Address unknown since 2011.

Intl. Assn. of Milk Control Agencies [5463], New York Dept. of Agriculture and Markets, 10 B Airline Dr., Albany, NY 12235, (518)457-5731

Intl. Assn. of Milk Control Agencies [5463], New York Dept. of Agriculture and Markets, 10 B Airline Dr., Albany, NY 12235, (518)457-5731

Intl. Assn. of Milk, Food and Environmental Sanitarians [★5462]

Intl. Assn. of Milk, Food and Environmental Sanitarians [★5462]

Intl. Assn. of Milk and Food Sanitarians [★5462]

Intl. Assn. of Milk and Food Sanitarians [★5462]

Intl. Assn. of Milk Sanitarians [★5462]

Intl. Assn. of Milk Sanitarians [★5462]

Intl. Assn. of Ministers Wives and Ministers Widows [19657], 105 River Knoll, Macon, GA 31211, (478)743-5126

Intl. Assn. of Ministers Wives and Ministers Widows [19657], 105 River Knoll, Macon, GA 31211, (478)743-5126

Intl. Assn. for Mission Stud. [IO], Oxford, United Kingdom

Intl. Assn. of Missionary Aviation [20052], PO Box 5612, Tucson, AZ 85703-0612, (520)908-7122

Intl. Assn. of Movers [3249], 5904 Richmond Hwy., Ste. 404, Alexandria, VA 22303-1864, (703)317-9950

Intl. Assn. of Movers [3249], 5904 Richmond Hwy., Ste. 404, Alexandria, VA 22303-1864, (703)317-9950

Intl. Assn. of Music Info. Centres [IO], Brussels, Belgium

Intl. Assn. of Music Libraries, Archives and Documentation Centres [IO], Goteborg, Sweden

Intl. Assn. of Music Libraries, Archives and Documentation Centres - Australia Br. [IO], Sydney, Australia

Intl. Assn. of Music Libraries, Archives and Documentation Centres - New Zealand Br. [IO], Wellington, New Zealand

Intl. Assn. of Music Libraries, Archives and Documentation Centres - United Kingdom and Ireland [IO], Manchester, United Kingdom

Intl. Assn. of Nanotechnology [7507], 49000 Milmont Dr., Fremont, CA 94538, (408)280-6222

Intl. Assn. of Nanotechnology [7507], 49000 Milmont Dr., Fremont, CA 94538, (408)280-6222

Intl. Assn. of Native Amer. Stud. [8677], NAAAS and Affiliates, PO Box 6670, Scarborough, ME 04070-6670, (207)839-8004

Intl. Assn. for Natural Gas Vehicles [IO], Auckland, New Zealand

Intl. Assn. of Natural Rsrc. Pilots [3836], Larry Gepfert, Treas., 222 Seven Oaks Rd., Glenwood Springs, CO 81601, (970)618-9483

Intl. Assn. of Natural Rsrc. Pilots [3836], Larry Gepfert, Treas., 222 Seven Oaks Rd., Glenwood Springs, CO 81601, (970)618-9483

Intl. Assn. for Near-Death Stud. [7251], 2741 Campus Walk Ave., Bldg. 500, Durham, NC 27705-8878, (919)383-7940

Intl. Assn. for Near-Death Stud. [7251], 2741 Campus Walk Ave., Bldg. 500, Durham, NC 27705-8878, (919)383-7940

Intl. Assn. for Neo-Latin Stud. [IO], Copenhagen, Denmark

Intl. Assn. for Neuro-Linguistic Programming [★16464]

Intl. Assn. of Neuro-Linguistic Programming [★16464]

Intl. Assn. for Neuro-Linguistic Programming [★16464]

Intl. Assn. of Neuro-Linguistic Programming [★16464]

Intl. Assn. of Nitrox and Tech. Divers [22541], 2124 NE 123rd St., Ste. 210, North Miami, FL 33181-2939, (786)704-9722

Intl. Assn. for Obsidian Stud. [6171], Univ. of Washington, Dept. of Anthropology, Box 353100, Seattle, WA 98195-3100

Intl. Assn. for Obsidian Stud. [6171], Univ. of Washington, Dept. of Anthropology, Box 353100, Seattle, WA 98195-3100

Intl. Assn. of Official Human Rights Agencies [12243], 444 N Capitol St. NW, Ste. 536, Washington, DC 20001, (202)624-5410

Intl. Assn. of Official Human Rights Agencies [12243], 444 N Capitol St. NW, Ste. 536, Washington, DC 20001, (202)624-5410

Intl. Assn. for Official Statistics [IO], The Hague, Netherlands

Intl. Assn. of Open Systems Professionals [★6520]

Intl. Assn. of Open Systems Professionals [★6520]

Intl. Assn. of Operative Millers [2501], 10100 W 87th St., Ste. 306, Overland Park, KS 66212, (913)338-3377

Intl. Assn. of Operative Millers [2501], 10100 W 87th St., Ste. 306, Overland Park, KS 66212, (913)338-3377

Intl. Assn. of Oral and Maxillofacial Surgeons [16006], 17W220 22nd St., Ste. 420, Oakbrook Terrace, IL 60181, (630)833-0945

Intl. Assn. of Oral and Maxillofacial Surgeons [16006], 17W220 22nd St., Ste. 420, Oakbrook Terrace, IL 60181, (630)833-0945

Intl. Assn. of Oral Pathologists [IO], Heidelberg, Australia

Intl. Assn. for Organ Donation [16906], PO Box 545, Dearborn, MI 48121, (313)745-2379

Intl. Assn. for Organ Donation [16906], PO Box 545, Dearborn, MI 48121, (313)745-2379

Intl. Assn. of Orofacial Myology [16126], Emily Clayton, Exec. Coor., 2000 NE 42nd Ave., PMB 295, Portland, OR 97213-1305, (503)280-0614

Intl. Assn. of Orofacial Myology [16126], Emily Clayton, Exec. Coor., 2000 NE 42nd Ave., PMB 295, Portland, OR 97213-1305, (503)280-0614

Intl. Assn. for Orthodontics [14291], 750 N Lincoln Memorial Dr., Ste. 422, Milwaukee, WI 53202, (414)272-2757

Intl. Assn. for Orthodontics [14291], 750 N Lincoln Memorial Dr., Ste. 422, Milwaukee, WI 53202, (414)272-2757

Intl. Assn. of Outsourcing Professionals [2603], 2600 South Rd., Ste. 44-240, Poughkeepsie, NY 12601, (845)452-0600

Intl. Assn. of Outsourcing Professionals [2603], 2600 South Rd., Ste. 44-240, Poughkeepsie, NY 12601, (845)452-0600

Intl. Assn. of Paediatric Dentistry [IO], Ferney-Voltaire, France

Intl. Assn. for Pain and Chem. Dependency [16101], 101 Washington St., Morrisville, PA 19067, (800)661-5767

Intl. Assn. of Panoramic Photographers [2720], Full Circle Ltd., 33 E 21st St., Baltimore, MD 21218, (410)528-1868

Intl. Assn. of Panoramic Photographers [2720], Full Circle Ltd., 33 E 21st St., Baltimore, MD 21218, (410)528-1868

Intl. Assn. of Paper Historians [IO], Gladbach, Germany

Intl. Assn. of Papyrologists [IO], Brussels, Belgium

Intl. Assn. for Paratuberculosis [17026], 112 Barnview Rd., Kennett Square, PA 19348, (610)444-5800

Intl. Assn. for Paratuberculosis [17026], 112 Barnview Rd., Kennett Square, PA 19348, (610)444-5800

Intl. Assn. of Parents of the Deaf [★14918]

Intl. Assn. of Pastel Societies [9182], PO Box 46107, Rio Rancho, NM 87174, (505)294-7752

A star before a book entry number signifies that the name is not listed separately, but is mentioned within the entry.

Intl. Assn. of Pastel Societies [9182], PO Box 46107, Rio Rancho, NM 87174, (505)294-7752

Intl. Assn. for Patristic Stud. [IO], Durham, United Kingdom

Intl. Assn. for Pattern Recognition [IO], Hamamatsu, Japan

Intl. Assn. of Pedodontics - Defunct.

Intl. Assn. for Penal Law [IO], Bordeaux, France

Intl. Assn. of Penal Law - Austria [IO], Bordeaux, France

Intl. Assn. of Penal Law - Switzerland [IO], Zurich, Switzerland

Intl. Assn. of People Who Dine Over the Kitchen Sink [21862], PO Box 221413, Sacramento, CA 95822

Intl. Assn. of Personnel in Employment Security [★5400]

Intl. Assn. of Personnel in Employment Security [★5400]

Intl. Assn. for Personnel Women [★2630]

Intl. Assn. of Pet Cemeteries and Crematories [2679], 4991 Peachtree Rd., Atlanta, GA 30341, (800)952-5541

Intl. Assn. of Pet Cemeteries and Crematories [2679], 4991 Peachtree Rd., Atlanta, GA 30341, (800)952-5541

Intl. Assn. of Philatelic Experts [IO], Innsbruck, Austria

Intl. Assn. for Philosophy of Law and Social Philosophy, Amer. Sect. - Defunct.

Intl. Assn. for Philosophy and Literature [10383], Prof. Hugh J. Silverman, Exec. Dir., Stony Brook Univ., Philosophy Dept., Stony Brook, NY 11794-3750, (631)331-4598

Intl. Assn. for Philosophy and Literature [★10432]

Intl. Assn. for Philosophy and Literature [★10392]

Intl. Assn. for Philosophy and Literature [★10392]

Intl. Assn. for Philosophy and Literature [10383], Prof. Hugh J. Silverman, Exec. Dir., Stony Brook Univ., Philosophy Dept., Stony Brook, NY 11794-3750, (631)331-4598

Intl. Assn. of Philosophy and Literature [★10432]

Intl. Assn. of Photoplatemakers [★6934]

Intl. Assn. of Photoplatemakers [★6934]

Intl. Assn. of Physical Activity [★10838]

Intl. Assn. of Physical Educ. and Sport for Girls and Women - Address unknown since 2010.

Intl. Assn. of Physicians in AIDS Care [16265], 123 W Madison St., Ste. 1704, Chicago, IL 60602-4613, (312)795-4930

Intl. Assn. of Physicians in AIDS Care [16265], 123 W Madison St., Ste. 1704, Chicago, IL 60602-4613, (312)795-4930

Intl. Assn. of Physics Students [IO], Mulhouse, France

Intl. Assn. of Piano Builders and Technicians [2558], Piano Technicians Guild, 4444 Forest Ave., Kansas City, KS 66106, (913)432-9975

Intl. Assn. of Piano Builders and Technicians [2558], Piano Technicians Guild, 4444 Forest Ave., Kansas City, KS 66106, (913)432-9975

Intl. Assn. of Pipe Smokers Clubs [22099], Paul T. Spaniola, Chm., 647 S Saginaw St., Flint, MI 48502

Intl. Assn. of Pipe Smokers Clubs [22099], Paul T. Spaniola, Chm., 647 S Saginaw St., Flint, MI 48502

Intl. Assn. for the Plant Protection Sciences [3759], 6517 S 19th St., Lincoln, NE 68512, (402)805-4748

Intl. Assn. for the Plant Protection Sciences [3759], 6517 S 19th St., Lincoln, NE 68512, (402)805-4748

Intl. Assn. for Plant Taxonomy [IO], Vienna, Austria

Intl. Assn. of Plastics Distribution [2769], 6734 W 121st St., Overland Park, KS 66209, (913)345-1005

Intl. Assn. of Plastics Distribution [2769], 6734 W 121st St., Overland Park, KS 66209, (913)345-1005

Intl. Assn. of Plastics Distributors [★2769]

Intl. Assn. of Plastics Distributors [★2769]

Intl. Assn. of Plumbing and Mech. Officials [5301], 4755 E Philadelphia St., Ontario, CA 91761, (909)472-4100

Intl. Assn. of Plumbing and Mech. Officials [5301], 4755 E Philadelphia St., Ontario, CA 91761, (909)472-4100

Intl. Assn. of Police Professors [★11698]

Intl. Assn. of Political Consultants [IO], Krefeld, Germany

Intl. Assn. of Ports and Harbors [IO], Tokyo, Japan

Intl. Assn. of Practising Accountants [IO], Farnham, United Kingdom

Intl. Assn. for Presentation Professionals - Defunct.

Intl. Assn. of Printing House Craftsmen [1613], PO Box 2549, Maple Grove, MN 55311-7549, (763)560-1620

Intl. Assn. of Printing House Craftsmen [1613], PO Box 2549, Maple Grove, MN 55311-7549, (763)560-1620

Intl. Assn. of Privacy Professionals [1902], 75 Rochester Ave., Ste. 4; Portsmouth, NH 03801, (603)427-9200

Intl. Assn. of Privacy Professionals [1902], 75 Rochester Ave., Ste. 4, Portsmouth, NH 03801, (603)427-9200

Intl. Assn. Private Investigators [★2124]

Intl. Assn. for Prdt. Development [2887], 28 Adams Hill Rd., Gloucester, MA 01930-1304, (978)281-8478

Intl. Assn. for Prdt. Development [2887], 28 Adams Hill Rd., Gloucester, MA 01930-1304, (978)281-8478

Intl. Assn. for Professional Art Advisors [249], 433 Third St., Ste. 3, Brooklyn, NY 11215, (718)788-1425

Intl. Assn. of Professional Bureaucrats - Address unknown since 2010.

Intl. Assn. of Professional and Bus. Women in Bulgaria [IO], Sofia, Bulgaria

Intl. Assn. of Professional Cong. Organizers [IO], Freshwater, United Kingdom

Intl. Assn. of Professional Event Photographers [★2736]

Intl. Assn. of Professional Event Photographers [★2736]

Intl. Assn. of Professional Natural Hygienists [★15528]

Intl. Assn. of Professional Natural Hygienists [★15528]

Intl. Assn. of Professional Numismatists [IO], Brussels, Belgium

Intl. Assn. of Professional Security Consultants [3215], 575 Market St., Ste. 2125, San Francisco, CA 94105, (415)536-0288

Intl. Assn. of Professional Security Consultants [3215], 575 Market St., Ste. 2125, San Francisco, CA 94105, (415)536-0288

Intl. Assn. for the Promotion of Cooperation with Scientists from the New Independent States of the Former Soviet Union [IO], Brussels, Belgium

Intl. Assn. for the Properties of Steam [★5983]

Intl. Assn. for the Properties of Steam [★5983]

Intl. Assn. for the Properties of Water and Steam [5983], 2616 Chelsea Dr., Charlotte, NC 28209

Intl. Assn. for the Properties of Water and Steam [5983], 2616 Chelsea Dr., Charlotte, NC 28209

Intl. Assn. of Property Crime Investigators [5602], 10685-B Hazelhurst Dr., No. 1503, Houston, TX 77043, (206)426-1689

Intl. Assn. for Property and Evidence [5699], 903 N San Fernando Blvd., Ste. 4, Burbank, CA 91504-4327, (818)846-2926

Intl. Assn. for Property and Evidence [5699], 903 N San Fernando Blvd., Ste. 4, Burbank, CA 91504-4327, (818)846-2926

Intl. Assn. of Prosecutors [IO], The Hague, Netherlands

Intl. Assn. for the Protection of Intellectual Property [IO], Zurich, Switzerland

Intl. Assn. for Protein Structure Anal. and Proteomics [6270], Brookhaven Natl. Lab., 50 Bell Ave., Upton, NY 11973-5000

Intl. Assn. of Protocol Consultants [865], PO Box 6150, McLean, VA 22106-6150

Intl. Assn. of Protocol Consultants [865], PO Box 6150, McLean, VA 22106-6150

Intl. Assn. for Psychoanalytic Self Psychology [16400], 3670 Clairemont Dr., Ste. 10, San Diego, CA 92117, (858)270-3503

Intl. Assn. of Psychosocial Rehabilitation Services [★16577]

Intl. Assn. of Psychosocial Rehabilitation Services [★16577]

Intl. Assn. of Public Employment Services [★5400]

Intl. Assn. of Public Employment Services [★5400]

Intl. Assn. for Public Participation Practitioners [5947], 13762 Colorado Blvd., Ste. 124, PMB 54, Thornton, CO 80602, (303)254-5642

Intl. Assn. for Public Participation Practitioners [5947], 13762 Colorado Blvd., Ste. 124, PMB 54, Thornton, CO 80602, (303)254-5642

Intl. Assn. of Public Transport [IO], Brussels, Belgium

Intl. Assn. of Public Works Officials [★5944]

Intl. Assn. of Pupil Personnel Workers [★8082]

Intl. Assn. of Pupil Personnel Workers [★8082]

Intl. Assn. of Qualified Financial Planners [1340], PO Box 7007, Beverly Hills, CA 90212-7007, (877)346-3037

Intl. Assn. of Quality Circles [★7319]

Intl. Assn. of Quality Technicians in the Automotive Industry - Address unknown since 2010.

Intl. Assn. for Radio, Telecommunications and Electromagnetics [7542], 840 Queen St., New Bern, NC 28560, (252)672-0200

Intl. Assn. of Radiopharmacology [IO], Edmonton, AB, Canada

Intl. Assn. of Railway Operations Res. [IO], Delft, Netherlands

Intl. Assn. of Rebekah Assemblies, IOOF [19182], 422 Trade St., Winston-Salem, NC 27101, (336)725-6037

Intl. Assn. of Rebekah Assemblies, IOOF [19182], 422 Trade St., Winston-Salem, NC 27101, (336)725-6037

Intl. Assn. of Reentry [17484], PO Box 14125, Columbus, OH 43214-0125

Intl. Assn. of Reentry [17484], PO Box 14125, Columbus, OH 43214-0125

Intl. Assn. of Refrigerated Warehouses [3619], 1500 King St., Ste. 201, Alexandria, VA 22314, (703)373-4300

Intl. Assn. of Refrigerated Warehouses [3619], 1500 King St., Ste. 201, Alexandria, VA 22314, (703)373-4300

Intl. Assn. of Registered Financial Consultants [1305], PO Box 42506, 2507 N Verity Pkwy., Middletown, OH 45042-0506, (513)424-6395

Intl. Assn. of Registered Financial Consultants [1305], PO Box 42506, 2507 N Verity Pkwy., Middletown, OH 45042-0506, (513)424-6395

Intl. Assn. for Regression Res. and Therapies [16855], PO Box 20151, Riverside, CA 92516, (951)784-1570

Intl. Assn. of Rehabilitation Facilities [★16557]

Intl. Assn. of Rehabilitation Professionals [16566], 1926 Waukegan Rd., Ste. 1, Glenview, IL 60025, (847)657-6964

Intl. Assn. of Reiki Professionals [13687], PO Box 6182, Nashua, NH 03063-6182, (603)881-8838

Intl. Assn. of Reiki Professionals [13687], PO Box 6182, Nashua, NH 03063-6182, (603)881-8838

Intl. Assn. for Relational Psychoanalysis and Psychotherapy [16357], 799 Broadway, Ste. 305, New York, NY 10003, (212)669-6123

Intl. Assn. for Relational Psychoanalysis and Psychotherapy [16357], 799 Broadway, Ste. 305, New York, NY 10003, (212)669-6123

Intl. Assn. for Relationship Res. [7332], Christopher R. Agnew, Dept. of Psychological Sciences, Purdue Univ., 703 Third St., West Lafayette, IN 47907-2081

Intl. Assn. for Religion and Parapsychology [IO], Tokyo, Japan

Intl. Assn. for Religious Freedom [IO], London, United Kingdom

Intl. Assn. for Religious Freedom - Japan [IO], Osaka, Japan

Intl. Assn. of Religious Sci. Churches [★20183]

Intl. Assn. of Religious Sci. Churches [★20183]

Intl. Assn. for Res. on Epstein Barr Virus and Assoc. Diseases [IO], Birmingham, United Kingdom

Intl. Assn. for Res. in Income and Wealth [17139], Periodicals Ser. Company, 11 Main St., Germantown, NY 12526, (518)537-4700

Reference to "IO" in place of a book number signifies that the association may be found in the 50th edition of International Organizations.

Intl. Assn. for Res. in Income and Wealth **[17139]**, Periodicals Ser. Company, 11 Main St., Germantown, NY 12526, (518)537-4700

Intl. Assn. for Res. on Service-Learning and Community Engagement **[7899]**, Tulane Univ. Center for Public Ser., Alcee Fortier Hall, 6823 St. Charles Ave., New Orleans, LA 70118, (504)862-3366

Intl. Assn. for Res. in Vietnamese Music **[★10211]**

Intl. Assn. for Res. in Vietnamese Music **[★10211]**

Intl. Assn. of Reservation Executives **[3475]**, PO Box 45484, Omaha, NE 68145, (877)458-3494

Intl. Assn. of Reservation Executives **[3475]**, PO Box 45484, Omaha, NE 68145, (877)458-3494

Intl. Assn. of Residential and Community Alternative **[★11717]**

Intl. Assn. of Residential and Community Alternative **[★11717]**

Intl. Assn. for the Retractable Awning Industry - Address unknown since 2010.

Intl. Assn. for the Rhine Ships Register **[IO]**, Rotterdam, Netherlands

Intl. Assn. of Rotary Clubs **[★13074]**

Intl. Assn. of Rotary Clubs **[★13074]**

Intl. Assn. of Round Dance Teachers **[9552]**, 176 S Cole Rd., Boise, ID 83709-0932, (208)377-1232

Intl. Assn. of Round Dance Teachers **[9552]**, 176 S Cole Rd., Boise, ID 83709-0932, (208)377-1232

Intl. Assn. of R.S. Prussia Collectors **[21351]**, PO Box 624, Mayfield, KY 42066

Intl. Assn. of Sanskrit Stud. **[IO]**, Edinburgh, United Kingdom

Intl. Assn. of School Librarianship **[IO]**, Zillmere, Australia

Intl. Assn. of School Security Directors **[★8820]**

Intl. Assn. of Schools and Institutes of Admin. **[IO]**, Brussels, Belgium

Intl. Assn. of Schools of Social Work **[IO]**, Hong Kong, People's Republic of China

Intl. Assn. of Sci. Parks **[IO]**, Malaga, Spain

Intl. Assn. of Sci. and Tech. for Development **[IO]**, Calgary, AB, Canada

Intl. Assn. of Sci. Experts in Tourism **[IO]**, St. Gallen, Switzerland

Intl. Assn. for the Sci. Stud. of Intellectual Disabilities **[IO]**, Canterbury, United Kingdom

Intl. Assn. for the Sci. Stud. of Intellectual Disabilities - Ireland **[IO]**, Canterbury, United Kingdom

Intl. Assn. of Sci., Tech. and Medical Publishers **[IO]**, The Hague, Netherlands

Intl. Assn. of Security and Investigative Regulators **[2122]**, PO Box 93, Waterloo, IA 50704, (888)354-2747

Intl. Assn. of Sedimentologists **[IO]**, Copenhagen, Denmark

Intl. Assn. of Seismology and Physics of the Earth's Interior **[7399]**, Prof. Thorne Lay, Univ. of California - Santa Cruz, Earth & Planetary Sci. Dept., Earth & Marine Sci. Bldg., Santa Cruz, CA 95064, (831)459-3164

Intl. Assn. of Seismology and Physics of the Earth's Interior **[7399]**, Prof. Thorne Lay, Univ. of California - Santa Cruz, Earth & Planetary Sci. Dept., Earth & Marine Sci. Bldg., Santa Cruz, CA 95064, (831)459-3164

Intl. Assn. for Semiotic Stud. **[IO]**, Vienna, Austria

Intl. Assn. of Ser. Evaluators **[2978]**, 225 N Delaware St., Indianapolis, IN 46204, (800)582-8281

Intl. Assn. of Ser. Evaluators **[2978]**, 225 N Delaware St., Indianapolis, IN 46204, (800)582-8281

Intl. Assn. of Severe Weather Specialists - Defunct.

Intl. Assn. for Shell and Spatial Structures **[IO]**, Madrid, Spain

Intl. Assn. of Sickle Cell Nurses and Physician Assistants **[14879]**, Jane Hennessy, MPH, Treas., 2530 Chicago Ave. S, Ste. 175, Minneapolis, MN 55404, (612)813-6998

Intl. Assn. of Sickle Cell Nurses and Physician Assistants **[14879]**, Jane Hennessy, MPH, Treas., 2530 Chicago Ave. S, Ste. 175, Minneapolis, MN 55404, (612)813-6998

Intl. Assn. of Siderographers - Defunct.

Intl. Assn. of Silver Art Collectors **[21352]**, PO Box 3987, Clarksville, TN 37043

Intl. Assn. of Silver Bar Collectors **[★21352]**

Intl. Assn. of Skateboard Companies **[22833]**, 22431 Antonio Pkwy., Ste. B160-412, Rancho Santa Margarita, CA 92688, (949)455-1112

Intl. Assn. of Skateboard Companies **[22833]**, 22431 Antonio Pkwy., Ste. B160-412, Rancho Santa Margarita, CA 92688, (949)455-1112

Intl. Assn. for Soaps, Detergents and Maintenance Products **[IO]**, Brussels, Belgium

Intl. Assn. for Soc. and Natural Resources **[4735]**, Penn State, Dept. of Agricultural Economics and Rural Sociology, 114 Armsby Bldg., University Park, PA 16802, (814)863-8643

Intl. Assn. for Soc. and Natural Resources **[4735]**, Penn State, Dept. of Agricultural Economics and Rural Sociology, 114 Armsby Bldg., University Park, PA 16802, (814)863-8643

Intl. Assn. of Software Architects **[6488]**, 11044 Res. Blvd., Ste. B-400, Austin, TX 78759-5246, (512)637-4272

Intl. Assn. of Software Architects **[6488]**, 11044 Res. Blvd., Ste. B-400, Austin, TX 78759-5246, (512)637-4272

Intl. Assn. of Sound and Audiovisual Archives **[IO]**, Auckland Park, Republic of South Africa

Intl. Assn. of Space Entrepreneurs **[139]**, 16 First Ave., Nyack, NY 10960

Intl. Assn. of Space Entrepreneurs **[139]**, 16 First Ave., Nyack, NY 10960

Intl. Assn. of Speakers Bureaus **[10479]**, 3933 S McClintock Dr., Ste. 505, Tempe, AZ 85282, (480)839-1423

Intl. Assn. of Speakers Bureaus **[10479]**, 3933 S McClintock Dr., Ste. 505, Tempe, AZ 85282, (480)839-1423

Intl. Assn. of Special Investigation Units **[1983]**, PO Box 26, Manchester, MD 21102-0026, (443)507-6500

Intl. Assn. of Sport Kinetics **[IO]**, Warsaw, Poland

Intl. Assn. for Sports Info. **[IO]**, Barcelona, Spain

Intl. Assn. for Sports and Leisure Facilities **[IO]**, Cologne, Germany

Intl. Assn. of Sports Museums and Halls of Fame **[★22984]**

Intl. Assn. for Sports Surface Sciences **[IO]**, Eschenz, Switzerland

Intl. Assn. for Statistical Computing **[IO]**, The Hague, Netherlands

Intl. Assn. for Statistical Educ. **[IO]**, The Hague, Netherlands

Intl. Assn. of Structural Integrators **[13688]**, 7044 S 13th St., Oak Creek, WI 53154, (414)908-4947

Intl. Assn. for Structural Mechanics in Reactor Tech. **[7508]**, Bonnie Diaz, Center for Nuclear Power Plants Structures, Equip and Piping, North Carolina State Univ., Campus Box 7908, Raleigh, NC 27695-7908, (919)515-5277

Intl. Assn. of Structural Movers **[3250]**, PO Box 2637, Lexington, SC 29071-2637, (803)951-9304

Intl. Assn. of Students in Agriculture and Related Sciences **[IO]**, Heverlee, Belgium

Intl. Assn. of Students in Agriculture and Related Sciences - France **[IO]**, Nancy, France

Intl. Assn. of Students in Agriculture and Related Sciences - Greece **[IO]**, Athens, Greece

Intl. Assn. of Students in Agriculture and Related Sciences - Hungary **[IO]**, Mosonmagyarovar, Hungary

Intl. Assn. of Students in Agriculture and Related Sciences - Poland **[IO]**, Warsaw, Poland

Intl. Assn. of Students in Agriculture and Related Sciences - Switzerland **[IO]**, Zurich, Switzerland

Intl. Assn. of Students in Agriculture and Related Sciences - Ukraine **[IO]**, Kiev, Ukraine

Intl. Assn. of Students in Agriculture and Related Sciences - Uzbekistan **[IO]**, Tashkent, Uzbekistan

Intl. Assn. of Students in Agriculture and Related Sciences - Vila Real **[IO]**, Vila Real, Portugal

Intl. Assn. of Students in Economics and Bus. Management—United States **[7782]**

Intl. Assn. of Students in Economics and Bus. Management—United States **[7782]**

Intl. Assn. for the Stud. of Ancient Mosaics **[IO]**, Paris, France

Intl. Assn. for the Stud. of Clays **[IO]**, Rio de Janeiro, Brazil

Intl. Assn. for the Stud. of the Commons **[4081]**, PO Box 26170, Greensboro, NC 27402-6170, (336)256-0520

Intl. Assn. for the Stud. of the Commons **[4081]**, PO Box 26170, Greensboro, NC 27402-6170, (336)256-0520

Intl. Assn. for the Stud. of Dreams **[16666]**, 1672 Univ. Ave., Berkeley, CA 94703, (209)724-0889

Intl. Assn. for the Stud. of Forced Migration **[IO]**, Oxford, United Kingdom

Intl. Assn. for the Stud. of Fossil Cnidaria and Porifera **[IO]**, Sosnowiec, Poland

Intl. Assn. for the Stud. of German Politics **[IO]**, Brighton, United Kingdom

Intl. Assn. for the Stud. of Insurance Economics **[IO]**, Geneva, Switzerland

Intl. Assn. for the Stud. of Irish Literatures **[10042]**, Univ. of Missouri, Dept. of English, 5100 Rockhill Rd., Kansas City, MO 64110

Intl. Assn. for the Stud. of Irish Literatures **[10042]**, Univ. of Missouri, Dept. of English, 5100 Rockhill Rd., Kansas City, MO 64110

Intl. Assn. for the Stud. of the Liver **[IO]**, Munich, Germany

Intl. Assn. for the Stud. of Lung Cancer **[13931]**, 12801 E 17th Ave., Aurora, CO 80045, (303)724-4499

Intl. Assn. for the Stud. of Maritime Mission **[IO]**, York, United Kingdom

Intl. Assn. for the Stud. of Obesity **[IO]**, London, United Kingdom

Intl. Assn. for the Stud. of Organized Crime **[11686]**, John Jay Coll. of Criminal Justice, Dept. of Law, Police Sci. and Criminal Justice Admin., 899 Tenth Ave., No. 422-17, New York, NY 10019, (212)237-8249

Intl. Assn. for the Stud. of Organized Crime **[11686]**, John Jay Coll. of Criminal Justice, Dept. of Law, Police Sci. and Criminal Justice Admin., 899 Tenth Ave., No. 422-17, New York, NY 10019, (212)237-8249

Intl. Assn. for the Stud. of Pain **[16102]**, 111 Queen Anne Ave. N, Ste. 501, Seattle, WA 98109-4955, (206)283-0311

Intl. Assn. for the Stud. of Pain **[16102]**, 111 Queen Anne Ave. N, Ste. 501, Seattle, WA 98109-4955, (206)283-0311

Intl. Assn. for the Stud. of Popular Music **[IO]**, Grahamstown, Republic of South Africa

Intl. Assn. of Sublimation Printers - Defunct.

Intl. Assn. of Sufism **[19833]**, 14 Commercial Blvd., Ste. 101, Novato, CA 94949, (415)382-7834

Intl. Assn. for Suicide Prevention **[IO]**, Gondrin, France

Intl. Assn. of Supreme Administrative Jurisdictions **[IO]**, Paris, France

Intl. Assn. of Survey Statisticians **[IO]**, Libourne, France

Intl. Assn. for Teachers of Chinese to Speakers of Other Languages **[7844]**, 9 E Loockerman St., Ste. 3A, Dover, DE 19901

Intl. Assn. of Teachers of Czech **[9529]**, Univ. of Texas, PO Box 7217, Austin, TX 78713

Intl. Assn. of Teachers of Czech **[9529]**, Univ. of Texas, PO Box 7217, Austin, TX 78713

Intl. Assn. of Teachers of English as a Foreign Language **[IO]**, Kent, United Kingdom

Intl. Assn. of Teachers of Russian Language and Literature **[IO]**, Moscow, Russia

Intl. Assn. of Technological Univ. Libraries **[IO]**, Dublin, Ireland

Intl. Assn. for Textile Care Labelling **[IO]**, Clichy, France

Intl. Assn. of Theatre for Children and Young People **[IO]**, Zagreb, Croatia

Intl. Assn. of Theatre Critics **[IO]**, Seoul, Republic of Korea

Intl. Assn. of Theoretical and Applied Limnology **[★7023]**

Intl. Assn. of Theoretical and Applied Limnology **[★7023]**

Intl. Assn. of Therapeutic Drug Monitoring and Clinical Toxicology **[IO]**, Kingston, ON, Canada

Intl. Assn. for Time Use Res. **[IO]**, Oxford, United Kingdom

A star before a book entry number signifies that the name is not listed separately, but is mentioned within the entry.

Intl. Assn. of Torch Clubs [10474], 11712C Jefferson Ave., No. 246, Newport News, VA 23606, (757)926-5368

Intl. Assn. of Tour Managers [IO], London, United Kingdom

Intl. Assn. of Tour Managers - Central Europe [IO], Lucerne, Switzerland

Intl. Assn. of Tour Managers - France [IO], London, United Kingdom

Intl. Assn. of Tour Managers - Israel [IO], Tel Aviv, Israel

Intl. Assn. of Tour Managers - Italy [IO], Rome, Italy

Intl. Assn. of Tour Managers - North Amer. Region [3562], 24 Blevins Rd., Kerhonkson, NY 12446-1302, (212)208-6800

Intl. Assn. of Tour Managers - North Amer. Region [3562], 24 Blevins Rd., Kerhonkson, NY 12446-1302, (212)208-6800

Intl. Assn. of Tour Managers - Pacific [IO], Sydney, Australia

Intl. Assn. of Tour Managers - Spain [IO], London, United Kingdom

Intl. Assn. of Tour Managers - Taiwan [IO], Taipei, Taiwan

Intl. Assn. of Trade Exchanges [★3485]

Intl. Assn. of Trade Exchanges [★3485]

Intl. Assn. of Traffic and Safety Sciences [IO], Tokyo, Japan

Intl. Assn. of Trauma Counseling [★11671]

Intl. Assn. of Trauma Counseling [★11671]

Intl. Assn. of Travel Exhibitors - Defunct.

Intl. Assn. of Travel Journalists - Defunct.

Intl. Assn. for the Treatment of Sexual Offenders [IO], Vienna, Austria

Intl. Assn. of Trichologists [IO], Sydney, Australia

Intl. Assn. for Truancy and Dropout Prevention [8082], Henrietta Pryor, Sec., 10602 Holly Springs, Houston, TX 77042, (713)802-4745

Intl. Assn. for Truancy and Dropout Prevention [8082], Henrietta Pryor, Sec., 10602 Holly Springs, Houston, TX 77042, (713)802-4745

Intl. Assn. of Undercover Officers [5700], 142 Banks Dr., Brunswick, GA 31523, (800)876-5943

Intl. Assn. of Undercover Officers [5700], 142 Banks Dr., Brunswick, GA 31523, (800)876-5943

Intl. Assn. of Universities [IO], Paris, France

Intl. Assn. of Univ. Professors of English [IO], Mex, Switzerland

Intl. Assn. of Univ. Res. Parks [★8791]

Intl. Assn. for Urban Climate [IO], Singapore, Singapore

Intl. Assn. of Used Equip. Dealers [2770], 214 Edgewood Dr., Ste. 100, Wilmington, DE 19809, (302)765-3571

Intl. Assn. of Used Equip. Dealers [2770], 214 Edgewood Dr., Ste. 100, Wilmington, DE 19809, (302)765-3571

Intl. Assn. for Vegetation Sci. [IO], Renkum, Netherlands

Intl. Assn. for Vehicle Sys. Dynamics [IO], Prague, Czech Republic

Intl. Assn. of Venue Managers [2441], 635 Fritz Dr., Ste. 100, Coppell, TX 75019-4442, (972)906-7441

Intl. Assn. of Voice Identification [★5485]

Intl. Assn. of Voice Identification [★5485]

Intl. Assn. of Volcanology and Chemistry of the Earth's Interior [IO], Barcelona, Spain

Intl. Assn. for Volunteer Effort [13397], 805 15th St. NW, Ste. 100, Washington, DC 20005, (202)628-4360

Intl. Assn. for Volunteer Effort [13397], 805 15th St. NW, Ste. 100, Washington, DC 20005, (202)628-4360

Intl. Assn. for Volunteer Effort - Belarus [IO], Minsk, Belarus

Intl. Assn. for Volunteer Effort - Bolivia [IO], Santa Cruz, Bolivia

Intl. Assn. for Volunteer Effort - Botswana [IO], Gaborone, Botswana

Intl. Assn. for Volunteer Effort - Brazil [IO], Rio de Janeiro, Brazil

Intl. Assn. for Volunteer Effort - Colombia [IO], Bogota, Colombia

Intl. Assn. for Volunteer Effort - Cyprus [IO], Nicosia, Cyprus

Intl. Assn. for Volunteer Effort - Czech Republic [IO], Prague, Czech Republic

Intl. Assn. for Volunteer Effort - Ecuador [IO], Quito, Ecuador

Intl. Assn. for Volunteer Effort - France [IO], Paris, France

Intl. Assn. for Volunteer Effort - Greece [IO], Athens, Greece

Intl. Assn. for Volunteer Effort - Hong Kong [IO], Hong Kong, People's Republic of China

Intl. Assn. for Volunteer Effort - India [IO], New Delhi, India

Intl. Assn. for Volunteer Effort - Korea [IO], Seoul, Republic of Korea

Intl. Assn. for Volunteer Effort - Liberia [IO], Monrovia, Liberia

Intl. Assn. for Volunteer Effort - Nigeria [IO], Lagos, Nigeria

Intl. Assn. for Volunteer Effort - Russia [IO], Moscow, Russia

Intl. Assn. for Volunteer Effort - Sierra Leone [IO], Freetown, Sierra Leone

Intl. Assn. for Volunteer Effort - Slovenia [IO], Ljubljana, Slovenia

Intl. Assn. for Volunteer Effort - Switzerland [IO], Geneva, Switzerland

Intl. Assn. for Volunteer Effort - Uruguay [IO], Montevideo, Uruguay

Intl. Assn. of Wagner Societies [IO], Hannover, Germany

Intl. Assn. of Water Polo Referees [IO], Rome, Italy

Intl. Assn. of Waterworks in the Rhine Basin Area [IO], Cologne, Germany

Intl. Assn. of Webmasters and Designers

Intl. Assn. of Webmasters and Designers - Address unknown since 2011.

Intl. Assn. of Wildland Fire [4401], 1418 Washburn St., Missoula, MT 59801, (406)531-8264

Intl. Assn. of Wildland Fire [4401], 1418 Washburn St., Missoula, MT 59801, (406)531-8264

Intl. Assn. of Wiping Cloth Mfrs. [★1866]

Intl. Assn. of Wiping Cloth Mfrs. [★1866]

Intl. Assn. of Women Chefs and Restaurateurs [★739]

Intl. Assn. for Women of Color Day [17650], 3325 Northrop Ave., Sacramento, CA 95864, (916)483-9804

Intl. Assn. for Women of Color Day [17650], 3325 Northrop Ave., Sacramento, CA 95864, (916)483-9804

Intl. Assn. of Women in Family Enterprises [3289], 1906 Vista Del Lago Dr., No. L-119, Valley Springs, CA 95252, (209)772-9200

Intl. Assn. of Women in Fire and Emergency Services [5443], 4025 Fair Ridge Dr., Ste. 300, Fairfax, VA 22033, (703)896-4858

Intl. Assn. of Women Judges [5623], 1850 M St. NW, Ste. 350, Washington, DC 20036, (202)223-4455

Intl. Assn. of Women Ministers [20287], 579 Main St., Stroudsburg, PA 18360

Intl. Assn. of Women Ministers [20287], 579 Main St., Stroudsburg, PA 18360

Intl. Assn. of Women Police [IO], London, United Kingdom

Intl. Assn. for Women's Mental Hea. [15456], 8213 Lakenheath Way, Potomac, MD 20854, (301)983-6282

Intl. Assn. of Wood Anatomists [IO], Leiden, Netherlands

Intl. Assn. of Wool Textile Labs. [IO], Huddersfield, United Kingdom

Intl. Assn. of Word and Image Stud. [8796], Univ. of Pennsylvania, Germanic Languages and Literatures, 745 Williams Hall, Philadelphia, PA 19104-6305, (215)898-7334

Intl. Assn. of Word and Image Stud. [8796], Univ. of Pennsylvania, Germanic Languages and Literatures, 745 Williams Hall, Philadelphia, PA 19104-6305, (215)898-7334

Intl. Assn. of Workforce Professionals [5400], 1801 Louisville Rd., Frankfort, KY 40601, (502)223-4459

Intl. Assn. of Workforce Professionals [5400], 1801 Louisville Rd., Frankfort, KY 40601, (502)223-4459

Intl. Assn. for World Englishes [9578], Larry E. Smith, 45-301 Akimala Pl., No. 1070, Kaneohe, HI 96744

Intl. Assn. of Young Lawyers [IO], Brussels, Belgium

Intl. Assn. of Youth and Family Judges and Magistrates [IO], Vienna, Austria

Intl. Astrobiology Soc. [IO], Florence, Italy

Intl. Astronautical Fed. [IO], Paris, France

Intl. Astronomical Union [IO], Paris, France

Intl. Atherosclerosis Soc. [14020], 6535 Fannin St., MS A-601, Houston, TX 77030, (713)797-0401

Intl. Athletic Found. [IO], Monaco, Monaco

Intl. Atlantic Economic Soc. [6623], Intl. Tower, Peachtree Ctr., 229 Peachtree St. NE, Ste. 650, Atlanta, GA 30303, (404)965-1555

Intl. Atlantic Economic Soc. [6623], Intl. Tower, Peachtree Ctr., 229 Peachtree St. NE, Ste. 650, Atlanta, GA 30303, (404)965-1555

Intl. Atomic Energy Agency [IO], Vienna, Austria

Intl. Audiotex Regulators Network [IO], Dusseldorf, Germany

Intl. Autistic Res. Org. [IO], Croydon, United Kingdom

Intl. Auto Sound Challenge Assn. [1104], 2200 S Ridgewood Ave., South Daytona, FL 32119, (386)322-1551

Intl. Autograph Dealers Alliance and Collectors Club [21353], 11435 Lake Shore Dr., Hollywood, FL 33026

Intl. Auto. Fed. [IO], Paris, France

Intl. Automotive Remarketers Alliance [300], PO Box 431, Mount Arlington, NJ 07856, (973)398-2774

Intl. Automotive Remarketers Alliance [300], PO Box 431, Mount Arlington, NJ 07856, (973)398-2774

Intl. Automotive Technicians' Network [301], PO Box 1599, Brea, CA 92822, (714)257-1335

Intl. Avaya Users Gp. [3410], 401 N Michigan Ave., Chicago, IL 60611, (312)321-5126

Intl. Aviation Ground Support Assn. [377], 201 Park Washington Ct., Falls Church, VA 22046-4527, (703)533-0251

Intl. Aviation Ground Support Assn. [377], 201 Park Washington Ct., Falls Church, VA 22046-4527, (703)533-0251

Intl. Aviation Theft Bur. [★375]

Intl. Aviation Womens Assn. [378], PO Box 1088, Edgewater, MD 21037, (410)571-1990

Intl. Aviation Womens Assn. [378], PO Box 1088, Edgewater, MD 21037, (410)571-1990

Intl. Aviculturists Soc. [3850], PO Box 280383, Memphis, TN 38618, (910)872-7612

Intl. Aviculturists Soc. [3850], PO Box 280383, Memphis, TN 38618, (910)872-7612

Intl. B-24 Liberator Club [20861], PO Box 1479, Tehachapi, CA 93581, (661)822-4809

Intl. B-24 Liberator Club [20861], PO Box 1479, Tehachapi, CA 93581, (661)822-4809

Intl. Baby Food Action Network - Africa [IO], Mbabane, Swaziland

Intl. Baby Food Action Network - Asia [IO], Pitampura, India

Intl. Baby Food Action Network - Brazil [IO], Jundiai, Brazil

Intl. Baby Food Action Network - Latin Am. [IO], San Jose, Costa Rica

Intl. Baccalaureate Org. [IO], Geneva, Switzerland

Intl. Backpackers Assn. [★23079]

Intl. Banana Club [21863], 14012 Siesta Dr., Apple Valley, CA 92307, (760)242-6724

Intl. Banana Club [21863], 14012 Siesta Dr., Apple Valley, CA 92307, (760)242-6724

Intl. Bank Note Soc. [21976], Roger Urce, Gen. Sec., PO Box 289, St. James, NY 11780-0289

Intl. Bank for Reconstruction and Development [17915], 1818 H St. NW, Washington, DC 20433, (202)473-1000

Intl. Bank for Reconstruction and Development [17915], 1818 H St. NW, Washington, DC 20433, (202)473-1000

Intl. Bankers Forum [IO], Frankfurt am Main, Germany

Intl. Banking, Economics and Finance Assn. [6624], Fed. Reserve Bank of Dallas, Dallas, TX 75201, (214)922-5055

Intl. Banknotes Soc. - England [IO], London, United Kingdom

Intl. Bar Assn. [IO], London, United Kingdom

Intl. Barbeque Cookers Assn. [21846], PO Box 12, Godley, TX 76044, (817)389-2214

Reference to "IO" in place of a book number signifies that the association may be found in the 50th edition of International Organizations.

Intl. Barrel Racing Assn. [22655], PO Box 91298, Louisville, KY 40291, (502)239-4000

Intl. Barrel Racing Assn. [22655], PO Box 91298, Louisville, KY 40291, (502)239-4000

Intl. Barter Alliance USA [440], 7801 W Rosedale Dr., Homosassa, FL 34448-2965, (727)489-2634

Intl. Baseball Fed. [IO], Lausanne, Switzerland

Intl. Basketball Fed. [IO], Geneva, Switzerland

Intl. BBSing and Electronic Communications Corp. - Address unknown since 2011.

Intl. Bear Assn. [★5065]

Intl. Bear Assn. [★5065]

Intl. Bee Res. Assn. [IO], Cardiff, United Kingdom

Intl. Beefalo Breeders Registry [★3776]

Intl. Beefalo Breeders Registry [★3776]

Intl. Behavioral Neuroscience Soc. [15677], Marianne Van Wagner, Exec. Coor., 8181 Tezel Rd., No. 10269, San Antonio, TX 78250, (830)796-9393

Intl. Behavioral Neuroscience Soc. [15677], Marianne Van Wagner, Exec. Coor., 8181 Tezel Rd., No. 10269, San Antonio, TX 78250, (830)796-9393

Intl. Behavioural and Neural Genetics Soc. [IO], London, United Kingdom

Intl. Benchrest Shooters [22875], 1231 Sheldon Hill Rd., Springville, PA 18844, (570)965-2505

The Intl. Bengal Breeders' Assn. [3860], 11290 N Dixie Hwy., Bonnieville, KY 42713, (270)531-7966

The Intl. Bengal Breeders' Assn. [3860], 11290 N Dixie Hwy., Bonnieville, KY 42713, (270)531-7966

The Intl. Bengal Cat Soc. [3861], PO Box 1894, Lake Dallas, TX 75065-1894

The Intl. Bengal Cat Soc. [3861], PO Box 1894, Lake Dallas, TX 75065-1894

Intl. Berkeley Soc. [10384], Texas A and M Univ., Dept. of Philosophy, College Station, TX 77843

Intl. Betta Cong. [21727], Steve Van Camp, Membership Chm./Sec., 923 Wadsworth St., Syracuse, NY 13208, (315)454-4792

Intl. Betta Cong. [21727], Steve Van Camp, Membership Chm./Sec., 923 Wadsworth St., Syracuse, NY 13208, (315)454-4792

Intl. Beverage Dispensing Equip. Assn. [446], 3837 Naylors Ln., Baltimore, MD 21208, (410)602-0616

Intl. Beverage Dispensing Equip. Assn. [446], 3837 Naylors Ln., Baltimore, MD 21208, (410)602-0616

Intl. Beverage Packaging Assn. - Defunct.

Intl. Biathlon Union [IO], Salzburg, Austria

Intl. Bible Soc. [19345], 1820 Jet Stream Dr., Colorado Springs, CO 80921, (719)488-9200

Intl. Bicycle Fund [13334], 4887 Columbia Dr. S, Seattle, WA 98108-1919, (206)767-0848

Intl. Bicycle Fund [13334], 4887 Columbia Dr. S, Seattle, WA 98108-1919, (206)767-0848

Intl. Biliary Assn. [★14979]

Intl. Biliary Assn. [★14979]

Intl. Bilingual Nurses Alliance [15755], PO Box 540745, Grand Prairie, TX 75054-0745

Intl. Bioacoustics Coun. [IO], London, United Kingdom

Intl. Biochar Initiative [6115], 640 Brook Run Dr., Westerville, OH 43081

Intl. Biochar Initiative [6115], 640 Brook Run Dr., Westerville, OH 43081

Intl. Biodeterioration and Biodegradation Soc. [IO], Northwich, United Kingdom

Intl. BioExploration Soc. [8180], Dr. Slavik Dushenkov, 59 Dudley Rd., Foran Hall, New Brunswick, NJ 08901-8520, (212)208-2584

Intl. Biogeography Soc. [6904], Field Museum, Chicago, IL

Intl. BioIron Soc. [15517], Two Woodfield Lake, 1100 E Woodfield Rd., Ste. 520, Schaumburg, IL 60173, (847)517-7225

Intl. BioIron Soc. [15517], Two Woodfield Lake, 1100 E Woodfield Rd., Ste. 520, Schaumburg, IL 60173, (847)517-7225

Intl. Biometric Identification Assn. [7509], 919 18th St. NW, Washington, DC 20006, (202)587-4855

Intl. Biometric Soc. [7476], 1444 I St. NW, Ste. 700, Washington, DC 20005, (202)712-9049

Intl. Biometric Soc. [7476], 1444 I St. NW, Ste. 700, Washington, DC 20005, (202)712-9049

Intl. Biometric Soc., Eastern North Amer. Region [7477], 12100 Sunset Hills Rd., Ste. 130, Reston, VA 20190, (703)437-4377

Intl. Biometric Soc., Western North Amer. Region [7478], 1730 Minor Ave., Ste. 1900, Cancer Res. and Biostatistics, Seattle, WA 98101-1468

Intl. Biometric Soc., Western North Amer. Region [7478], 1730 Minor Ave., Ste. 1900, Cancer Res. and Biostatistics, Seattle, WA 98101-1468

Intl. Biopharmaceutical Assn. [16196], PMB 143, 11521 N FM 620, No. 250, Austin, TX 78726, (713)366-8062

Intl. Biopharmaceutical Assn. [16196], PMB 143, 11521 N FM 620, No. 250, Austin, TX 78726, (713)366-8062

Intl. Bird Beer Label Assn. [20929], PO Box 2551, Homer, AK 99603

Intl. Bird Beer Label Assn. [20929], PO Box 2551, Homer, AK 99603

Intl. Bird Dog Assn. [20898], 1845 Port Stanhope Pl., Newport Beach, CA 92660

Intl. Bird Rescue Res. Center [5066], San Francisco Oiled Wildlife Care and Educ. Center, 4369 Cordelia Rd., Fairfield, CA 94534, (707)207-0380

Intl. Bird Rescue Res. Center [5066], San Francisco Oiled Wildlife Care and Educ. Center, 4369 Cordelia Rd., Fairfield, CA 94534, (707)207-0380

Intl. Bird Strike Comm. [IO], The Hague, Netherlands

Intl. Black Women's Cong. [17651], 645 Church St., Ste. 200, Norfolk, VA 23510, (757)625-0500

Intl. Black Women's Cong. [17651], 645 Church St., Ste. 200, Norfolk, VA 23510, (757)625-0500

Intl. Black Writers [10721], PO Box 43576, Los Angeles, CA 90043, (213)964-3721

Intl. Black Writers and Authors [10721], PO Box 43576, Los Angeles, CA 90043, (213)964-3721

Intl. Black Writers Conf. [★10721]

Intl. Black Writers Conf. [★10721]

Intl. Blind Sports Fed. [IO], Ankara, Turkey

Intl. Blind Sports Fed. Europe [IO], Olival Basto, Portugal

Intl. Blind Sports Fed. Oceania [IO], Auckland, New Zealand

Intl. Blogging and New Media Assn. - Address unknown since 2010.

Intl. Blue Crescent Relief and Development Found. [IO], Istanbul, Turkey

Intl. Blue Jay Class Assn. [22347], 12 Sandpiper Point Rd., Old Lyme, CT 06371, (860)434-5125

Intl. Blue Jay Class Assn. [22347], 12 Sandpiper Point Rd., Old Lyme, CT 06371, (860)434-5125

Intl. Bluegrass Music Assn. [10216], 2 Music Cir. S, Ste. 100, Nashville, TN 37203, (615)256-3222

Intl. Bluegrass Music Assn. [10216], 2 Music Cir. S, Ste. 100, Nashville, TN 37203, (615)256-3222

Intl. Bd. on Books for Young People [IO], Basel, Switzerland

Intl. Bd. on Books for Young People - Dutch Sect. [IO], Amsterdam, Netherlands

Intl. Bd. on Books for Young People - Serbian Natl. Sect. [IO], Belgrade, Serbia

International Bd. of Electrologist Certification [★14445]

Intl. Bd. of Jewish Missions [19752], PO Box 1386, Hixson, TN 37343, (423)876-8150

Intl. Bd. of Jewish Missions [19752], PO Box 1386, Hixson, TN 37343, (423)876-8150

Intl. Bd. of Lactation Consultant Examiners [13863], 6402 Arlington Blvd., Ste. 350, Falls Church, VA 22042, (703)560-7330

Intl. Bd. of Lactation Consultant Examiners [13863], 6402 Arlington Blvd., Ste. 350, Falls Church, VA 22042, (703)560-7330

Intl. Bd. for Regression Therapy [16856], 3702 Mt. Diablo Blvd., Lafayette, CA 94549, (925)283-3941

Intl. Bd. for Regression Therapy [16856], 3702 Mt. Diablo Blvd., Lafayette, CA 94549, (925)283-3941

Intl. Bd. of Standards and Practices for Certified Financial Planners [★1338]

Intl. Bobath Alumni Assn. [★15668]

Intl. Boer Goat Assn. [4500], PO Box 1045, Whitewright, TX 75491, (903)364-5735

Intl. Boer Goat Assn. [4500], PO Box 1045, Whitewright, TX 75491, (903)364-5735

Intl. Boethius Soc. [10385], Noel Harold Kaylor, Jr., Exec. Dir., Troy Univ., Dept. of English, Troy, AL 36082

Intl. Bond and Share Soc. [21354], 116 Parklane Dr., San Antonio, TX 78212, (650)773-4125

Intl. Bone Marrow Transplant Registry [★13857]

Intl. Bone Marrow Transplant Registry [★13857]

Intl. Book Bank [8364], 4000 Buena Vista Ave., Baltimore, MD 21211, (410)362-0334

Intl. Book Bank [8364], 4000 Buena Vista Ave., Baltimore, MD 21211, (410)362-0334

Intl. Book Proj. [8365], 1440 Delaware Ave., Lexington, KY 40505, (859)254-6771

Intl. Book Proj. [8365], 1440 Delaware Ave., Lexington, KY 40505, (859)254-6771

Intl. Booksellers Fed. [IO], Brussels, Belgium

Intl. Borzoi Coun. [21583], 752 River Rd., Ewing, NJ 08628-3303, (609)883-4743

Intl. Borzoi Coun. [21583], 752 River Rd., Ewing, NJ 08628-3303, (609)883-4743

Intl. Bossons Collectors Soc. [21355], 8316 Woodlake Pl., Tampa, FL 33615-1728, (813)885-2038

Intl. Bottled Water Assn. [447], 1700 Diagonal Rd., Ste. 650, Alexandria, VA 22314, (703)683-5213

Intl. Bottled Water Assn. [447], 1700 Diagonal Rd., Ste. 650, Alexandria, VA 22314, (703)683-5213

Intl. Boundaries Res. Unit [IO], Durham, United Kingdom

International Bowhunter Educ. Program [★22224]

Intl. Bowhunting Org. [22697], PO Box 398, Vermilion, OH 44089, (440)967-2137

Intl. Bowhunting Org. [22697], PO Box 398, Vermilion, OH 44089, (440)967-2137

Intl. Bowling Fed. [IO], Singapore, Singapore

Intl. Bowling Pro Shop and Instructors Assn. [468], PO Box 6574, Arlington, TX 76005-6574, (817)649-0079

Intl. Boxing Fed. [22434], 899 Mountain Ave., Ste. 2C, Springfield, NJ 07081, (973)564-8046

Intl. Boxing Fed. [22434], 899 Mountain Ave., Ste. 2C, Springfield, NJ 07081, (973)564-8046

Intl. Boxing Hall of Fame Museum [22435], 1 Hall of Fame Dr., Canastota, NY 13032, (315)697-7095

Intl. Boys' Schools Coalition [8032], 700 Rte. 22, Pawling, NY 12564, (207)841-7441

Intl. Boys' Schools Coalition [8032], 700 Rte. 22, Pawling, NY 12564, (207)841-7441

Intl. Braford Assn. [★3942]

Intl. Brain Barriers Soc. [15657], Lester R. Drewes, UM - Medical School Duluth, 251 SMed, 1035 Univ. Dr., Duluth, MN 55812, (218)726-7925

Intl. Brain Educ. Assn. [15678], 866 United Nations Plz., Ste. 479, New York, NY 10017, (212)319-0848

Intl. Brain Injury Assn. [14684], PO Box 1804, Alexandria, VA 22313, (703)960-6500

Intl. Brain Res. Org. [IO], Paris, France

Intl. Brain Tumour Alliance [IO], Tadworth, United Kingdom

Intl. Brangus Breeders Assn. [3916], 5750 Epsilon, San Antonio, TX 78249, (210)696-4343

Intl. Brecht Soc. [9374], Webster Univ., 470 E Lockwood, St. Louis, MO 63119, (314)968-6900

Intl. Brecht Soc. [9374], Webster Univ., 470 E Lockwood, St. Louis, MO 63119, (314)968-6900

Intl. Brick Collectors' Assn. [21356], 3141 S Fork Rd., Cody, WY 82414-8009, (307)587-5061

Intl. Bridal Mfrs. Assn. [472], 118 W 20th St., 3rd Fl., New York, NY 10011-3627, (646)638-9600

Intl. Bridge Press Assn. [IO], Sliema, Malta

Intl. Bridge, Tunnel and Turnpike Assn. [6032], 1146 19th St. NW, Ste. 600, Washington, DC 20036-3725, (202)659-4620

Intl. Bridge, Tunnel and Turnpike Assn. [6032], 1146 19th St. NW, Ste. 600, Washington, DC 20036-3725, (202)659-4620

Intl. Bridges to Justice [IO], Geneva, Switzerland

Intl. Bronchoesophagological Soc. [13869], Mayo Clinic Arizona, 13400 E Shea Blvd., Scottsdale, AZ 85259, (480)301-9692

Intl. Bronchoesophagological Soc. [13869], Mayo Clinic Arizona, 13400 E Shea Blvd., Scottsdale, AZ 85259, (480)301-9692

Intl. Brotherhood of Boilermakers I Stove, Furnace, Energy and Allied Appliance Workers Div. [23144], 1504 E Franklin St., Ste. 101, Chapel Hill, NC 27514, (919)967-3652

Intl. Brotherhood of Boilermakers [★23144]

A star before a book entry number signifies that the name is not listed separately, but is mentioned within the entry.

Intl. Brotherhood of Boilermakers, Iron Ship Builders, Blacksmiths, Forgers and Helpers [23159], 753 State Ave., Ste. 570, Kansas City, KS 66101, (913)371-2640

Intl. Brotherhood of DuPont Workers [23171], PO Box 10, Waynesboro, VA 22980

Intl. Brotherhood of Elecl. Workers [23183], 900 Seventh St. NW, Washington, DC 20001, (202)833-7000

Intl. Brotherhood of Locomotive Engineers [★23287]

Intl. Brotherhood of Locomotive Engineers [★23287]

Intl. Brotherhood of Magicians [21879], Sindie Richison, 13 Point W Blvd., St. Charles, MO 63301, (636)724-2400

Intl. Brotherhood of Magicians [21879], Sindie Richison, 13 Point W Blvd., St. Charles, MO 63301, (636)724-2400

Intl. Brotherhood of Motorcycle Campers [22779], PO Box 375, Helper, UT 84526, (805)278-9244

Intl. Brotherhood of Motorcycle Campers [22779], PO Box 375, Helper, UT 84526, (805)278-9244

Intl. Brotherhood of Painters and Allied Trades [★11941]

Intl. Brotherhood of Painters and Allied Trades [★11941]

Intl. Brotherhood of Police Officers [23241], 159 Burgin Pkwy., Quincy, MA 02169, (617)376-0220

Intl. Brotherhood of Pottery and Allied Workers [★23194]

Intl. Brotherhood of Stationary Firemen [★23189]

Intl. Brotherhood of Teamsers I Brewery and Soft Drink Workers Conf. [23158], 25 Louisiana Ave. NW, Washington, DC 20001, (202)624-6800

Intl. Brotherhood of Teamsters [23301], 25 Louisiana Ave. NW, Washington, DC 20001, (202)624-6800

Intl. Brotherhood of Teamsters [★23212]

Intl. Brotherhood of Teamsters, Chauffeurs, Stablemen and Helpers of Am. [★23301]

Intl. Brugmansia and Datura Soc. [21738], PO Box 121236, Clermont, FL 34712-1236

Intl. Buckskin Horse Assn. [4595], PO Box 268, Shelby, IN 46377, (219)552-1013

Intl. Buckskin Horse Assn. [4595], PO Box 268, Shelby, IN 46377, (219)552-1013

Intl. Buckskin Horse Registry [★4595]

Intl. Buckskin Horse Registry [★4595]

Intl. Budget Partnership [34], 820 1st St. NE, Ste. 510, Washington, DC 20002, (202)408-1080

Intl. Budget Proj. of the Center on Budget and Policy Priorities [★34]

Intl. Budget Proj. of the Center on Budget and Policy Priorities [34], 820 1st St. NE, Ste. 510, Washington, DC 20002, (202)408-1080

Intl. Builders Exchange Executives [917], 4047 Naco Perrin, Ste. 201a, San Antonio, TX 78217, (204)783-4334

Intl. Builders Exchange Executives [917], 4047 Naco Perrin, Ste. 201a, San Antonio, TX 78217, (204)783-4334

Intl. Building Performance Simulation Assn. [6377], Lawrence Berkeley Natl. Lab., Environmental Energy Technologies Div., One Cyclotron Rd., Berkeley, CA 94720

Intl. Building Performance Simulation Assn. [6377], Lawrence Berkeley Natl. Lab., Environmental Energy Technologies Div., One Cyclotron Rd., Berkeley, CA 94720

Intl. Bulb Soc. [6356], PO Box 336, Sanger, CA 93657-0336

Intl. Bulb Soc. [6356], PO Box 336, Sanger, CA 93657-0336

Intl. Bunker Indus. Assn. [IO], Southampton, United Kingdom

Intl. Bur. of Educ. [IO], Geneva, Switzerland

Intl. Bur. for Epilepsy [IO], Dublin, Ireland

Intl. Bur. of Fiscal Documentation [IO], Amsterdam, Netherlands

Intl. Bur. for Precast Concrete [IO], Brussels, Belgium

Intl. Bur. of Social Tourism [IO], Brussels, Belgium

Intl. Bur. for the Standardization of Man-Made Fibres [IO], Brussels, Belgium

Intl. Bur. of Weights and Measures [IO], Sevres, France

Intl. Bus. Aviation Coun. [IO], Montreal, QC, Canada

Intl. Bus. Brokers Assn. [3017], 401 N Michigan Ave., Ste. 2200, Chicago, IL 60611-4267, (888)686-4222

Intl. Bus. Brokers Assn. [3017], 401 N Michigan Ave., Ste. 2200, Chicago, IL 60611-4267, (888)686-4222

Intl. Bus. Chamber Cambodia [IO], Phnom Penh, Cambodia

Intl. Bus. Club of Cambodia [IO], Phnom Penh, Cambodia

Intl. Bus. Coun. [★2083]

Intl. Bus. Coun. [IO], Bishkek, Kirgizstan

Intl. Bus. Coun. [★2083]

Intl. Bus. Coun. Midamerica [★2083]

Intl. Bus. Coun. Midamerica [★2083]

Intl. Bus. Law Consortium [IO], Salzburg, Austria

Intl. Butterfly Breeders Assn. [3858], Max Sandberg, Treas., 5040 Savannah River Way, Unit 204, Orlando, FL 32839, (407)309-6545

Intl. Butterfly Breeders Assn. [3858], Max Sandberg, Treas., 5040 Savannah River Way, Unit 204, Orlando, FL 32839, (407)309-6545

Intl. Cable Protection Comm. [IO], Lymington, United Kingdom

Intl. Cablemakers' Fed. [IO], Vienna, Austria

Intl. Cadmium Assn. [IO], Brussels, Belgium

Intl. Cadmium Assn. - Belgium [IO], Brussels, Belgium

Intl. Call Center Benchmarking Consortium [672], The Benchmarking Network, 4606 FM 1960 W, Ste. 250, Houston, TX 77069-9949, (281)440-5044

Intl. Camaro Club - Address unknown since 2010.

Intl. Camellia Soc. [IO], Waiuku, New Zealand

Intl. Campaign to Ban Landmines [17553], US Campaign to Ban Landmines, Handicap Intl., 6930 Carroll Ave., Ste. 240, Takoma Park, MD 20912, (301)891-2138

Intl. Campaign to Ban Landmines [17553], US Campaign to Ban Landmines, Handicap Intl., 6930 Carroll Ave., Ste. 240, Takoma Park, MD 20912, (301)891-2138

Intl. Campaign to Free Geronimo ji jaga Pratt - Defunct.

Intl. Campaign for Tibet [18723], 1825 Jefferson Pl. NW, Washington, DC 20036, (202)785-1515

Intl. Campaign for Tibet [18723], 1825 Jefferson Pl. NW, Washington, DC 20036, (202)785-1515

Intl. Canoe Fed. [IO], Lausanne, Switzerland

Intl. Canopy Network [6302], 2103 Harrison Ave. NW, PMB 612, Olympia, WA 98502-2607, (360)866-6788

Intl. Canopy Network [6302], 2103 Harrison Ave. NW, PMB 612, Olympia, WA 98502-2607, (360)866-6788

Intl. Capital Market Assn. [IO], Zurich, Switzerland

Intl. Card Mfrs. Assn. [2771], 191 Clarksville Rd., Princeton Junction, NJ 08550, (609)799-4900

Intl. Card Mfrs. Assn. [2771], 191 Clarksville Rd., Princeton Junction, NJ 08550, (609)799-4900

Intl. Cardiology Found. [★14019]

Intl. Cargo Gear Bur. [5777], 321 W 44th St., New York, NY 10036, (212)757-2011

Intl. Cargo Gear Bur. [5777], 321 W 44th St., New York, NY 10036, (212)757-2011

Intl. Cargo Security Coun. [3216], 3 Church Cir., No. 292, Annapolis, MD 21401, (410)571-7913

Intl. Carnival Glass Assn. [21835], Box 306, Mentone, IN 46539, (574)353-7678

Intl. Carnival Glass Assn. [21835], Box 306, Mentone, IN 46539, (574)353-7678

Intl. Carnivorous Plant Soc. [21803], 1564-A Fitzgerald Dr., PMB 322, Pinole, CA 94564-2229

Intl. Carnivorous Plant Soc. [21803], 1564-A Fitzgerald Dr., PMB 322, Pinole, CA 94564-2229

Intl. Cartographic Assn. [IO], Newcastle upon Tyne, United Kingdom

Intl. Carwash Assn. [358], 401 N Michigan Ave., Ste. 2200, Chicago, IL 60611, (888)422-8422

Intl. Carwash Assn. [358], 401 N Michigan Ave., Ste. 2200, Chicago, IL 60611, (888)422-8422

Intl. Cast Polymer Assn. [570], 1010 N Glebe Rd., Ste. 450, Arlington, VA 22201, (703)525-0320

Intl. Cast Polymer Assn. [570], 1010 N Glebe Rd., Ste. 450, Arlington, VA 22201, (703)525-0320

Intl. Castor Oil Assn. [2585], 24 Burton Ave., Woodmere, NY 11598

Intl. Castor Oil Assn. [2585], 24 Burton Ave., Woodmere, NY 11598

The Intl. Cat Assn. [21252], PO Box 2684, Harlingen, TX 78551, (956)428-8046

The Intl. Cat Assn. [21252], PO Box 2684, Harlingen, TX 78551, (956)428-8046

Intl. Catacomb Soc. [9701], 21 Cummings Park, Ste. 220, Woburn, MA 01801, (781)729-1150

Intl. Catacomb Soc. [9701], 21 Cummings Park, Ste. 220, Woburn, MA 01801, (781)729-1150

Intl. Catalina 27/270 Assn. [22348], 2963 Mt. View Ct., Cameron Park, CA 95682, (530)677-6229

Intl. Catalina 27 Assn. [★22348]

Intl. Catalina 400 Assn. [22349], PO Box 9840, Fayetteville, AR 72703

Intl. Catholic Child Bur. [IO], Paris, France

Intl. Catholic Child Bur. - Switzerland [IO], Geneva, Switzerland

Intl. Catholic Deaf Assn. U.S. Sect. [19435], 7202 Buchanan St., Landover Hills, MD 20784-2236, (301)429-0697

Intl. Catholic Migration Commn. - Switzerland [IO], Geneva, Switzerland

Intl. Catholic Rural Assn. [IO], Vatican City, Vatican City

Intl. Catholic Stewardship Coun. [19436], 1275 K St. NW, Ste. 880, Washington, DC 20005-4077, (202)289-1093

Intl. Catholic Stewardship Coun. [19436], 1275 K St. NW, Ste. 880, Washington, DC 20005-4077, (202)289-1093

Intl. Catholic Union of the Press [IO], Geneva, Switzerland

Intl. CBX Owners Assn. [21931], PO Box 546, Knox, PA 16232, (717)697-5559

Intl. CBX Owners Assn. [21931], PO Box 546, Knox, PA 16232, (717)697-5559

Intl. Cell Death Soc. [14216], Zahra Zakeri, PhD, Queens Coll. of CUNY, 65-30 Kissena Blvd., Flushing, NY 11367, (718)997-3417

Intl. Cell Death Soc. [14216], Zahra Zakeri, PhD, Queens Coll. of CUNY, 65-30 Kissena Blvd., Flushing, NY 11367, (718)997-3417

Intl. Cell Res. Org. [IO], Paris, France

Intl. Cellular Medicine Soc. [14649], PO Box 4423, Salem, OR 97302

Intl. Cemetery, Cremation and Funeral Assn. [2535], 107 Carpenter Dr., Ste. 100, Sterling, VA 20164, (703)391-8400

Intl. Cemetery, Cremation and Funeral Assn. [2535], 107 Carpenter Dr., Ste. 100, Sterling, VA 20164, (703)391-8400

Intl. Cemetery and Funeral Assn. [★2535]

Intl. Cemetery and Funeral Assn. [★2535]

Intl. Cemetery Supply Assn. [★2536]

Intl. Cemetery Supply Assn. [★2536]

Intl. Center for Agricultural Res. in the Dry Areas [IO], Aleppo, Syrian Arab Republic

Intl. Center for Alcohol Policies [184], 1519 New Hampshire Ave. NW, Washington, DC 20036, (202)986-1159

Intl. Center for Alcohol Policies [184], 1519 New Hampshire Ave. NW, Washington, DC 20036, (202)986-1159

Intl. Center for Assault Prevention [11889], 107 Gilbreth Pkwy., Ste. 200, Mullica Hill, NJ 08062, (856)582-7000

Intl. Center for Attitudinal Healing [★15451]

Intl. Center for Attitudinal Healing [★15451]

Intl. Center for Comparative Criminology [IO], Montreal, QC, Canada

Intl. Center for Earth Tides [IO], Faaa, French Polynesia

Intl. Center for Economic Policy Stud. [★18433]

Intl. Center for Fabry Disease [16771], Mt. Sinai School of Medicine, One Gustav I. Levy Pl., New York, NY 10029-6574, (212)241-6506

Intl. Center for Fabry Disease [16771], Mt. Sinai School of Medicine, One Gustav I. Levy Pl., New York, NY 10029-6574, (212)241-6506

Intl. Center for Holocaust Stud. [★17783]

Intl. Center for Jefferson Stud. [★8736]

Intl. Center for Jefferson Stud; Robert H. Smith [8736]

Intl. Center for Job's Daughters [★19133]

Reference to "IO" in place of a book number signifies that the association may be found in the 50th edition of International Organizations.

Intl. Center for Job's Daughters [★19133]

Intl. Center for Journalists [2830], 1616 H St. NW, 3rd Fl., Washington, DC 20006, (202)737-3700

Intl. Center for Journalists [2830], 1616 H St. NW, 3rd Fl., Washington, DC 20006, (202)737-3700

Intl. Center of Medieval Art [10076], The Cloisters, Ft. Tryon Park, New York, NY 10040, (212)928-1146

Intl. Center of Medieval Art [10076], The Cloisters, Ft. Tryon Park, New York, NY 10040, (212)928-1146

Intl. Center for Monetary and Banking Stud. [IO], Geneva, Switzerland

Intl. Center in New York [17974], 50 W 23rd St., 7th Fl., New York, NY 10010-5205, (212)255-9555

Intl. Center in New York [17974], 50 W 23rd St., 7th Fl., New York, NY 10010-5205, (212)255-9555

Intl. Center for Not-for-Profit Law [5664], 1126 16th St. NW, Ste. 400, Washington, DC 20036, (202)452-8600

Intl. Center for Not-for-Profit Law [5664], 1126 16th St. NW, Ste. 400, Washington, DC 20036, (202)452-8600

Intl. Center of Photography [8710], 1114 Ave. of the Americas, 43rd St., New York, NY 10036, (212)857-0000

Intl. Center of Photography [8710], 1114 Ave. of the Americas, 43rd St., New York, NY 10036, (212)857-0000

Intl. Center for Promotion of Enterprises [IO], Ljubljana, Slovenia

Intl. Center for Reiki Training [22153], 21421 Hilltop St., Unit 28, Southfield, MI 48034, (248)948-8112

Intl. Center for Reiki Training [22153], 21421 Hilltop St., Unit 28, Southfield, MI 48034, (248)948-8112

Intl. Center of Res. and Info. on the Public, Social and Cooperative Economy [IO], Liege, Belgium

Intl. Center for Res. on Women [17652], 1120 20th St. NW, Ste. 500 N, Washington, DC 20036, (202)797-0007

Intl. Center for Res. on Women [17652], 1120 20th St. NW, Ste. 500 N, Washington, DC 20036, (202)797-0007

Intl. Center for Social Gerontology [★10837]

An Intl. Center for Soil Fertility and Agricultural Development [★3756]

An Intl. Center for Soil Fertility and Agricultural Development [★3756]

Intl. Center for the Solution of Environmental Problems [4274], 5120 Woodway Dr., Ste. 8009, Houston, TX 77056-1788, (713)527-8711

Intl. Center for the Solution of Environmental Problems [4274], 5120 Woodway Dr., Ste. 8009, Houston, TX 77056-1788, (713)527-8711

Intl. Center for Spirit at Work [20248], 36 Sylvan Hills Rd., East Haven, CT 06513, (203)467-9084

Intl. Center for Spirit at Work [20248], 36 Sylvan Hills Rd., East Haven, CT 06513, (203)467-9084

Intl. Center for the Stud. of Psychiatry and Psychology

Intl. Center for the Stud. of Psychiatry and Psychology - Address unknown since 2010.

Intl. Center for Transitional Justice [17841], 5 Hanover Sq., 24th Fl., New York, NY 10004, (917)637-3800

Intl. Center for Transitional Justice [17841], 5 Hanover Sq., 24th Fl., New York, NY 10004, (917)637-3800

International Center for Youth Studies [★13514]

Intl. Centers for Spiritual Living [20183], PO Box 2152, Spokane, WA 99210-2152, (509)624-7000

Intl. Centers for Spiritual Living [20183], PO Box 2152, Spokane, WA 99210-2152, (509)624-7000

Intl. Centre for Advanced Mediterranean Agronomic Stud. [IO], Paris, France

Intl. Centre for Agricultural Educ. [IO], Bern, Switzerland

Intl. Centre for Criminal Law Reform and Criminal Justice Policy [IO], Vancouver, BC, Canada

Intl. Centre for Ethnic Stud. [IO], Colombo, Sri Lanka

Intl. Centre of Films for Children and Young People [IO], Tehran, Iran

Intl. Centre for Genetic Engg. and Biotechnology [IO], Trieste, Italy

Intl. Centre of Graphic Arts [IO], Ljubljana, Slovenia

Intl. Centre for Heat and Mass Transfer [IO], Ankara, Turkey

Intl. Centre for Human Rights and Democratic Development [IO], Montreal, QC, Canada

Intl. Centre of Insect Physiology and Ecology [IO], Nairobi, Kenya

Intl. Centre for Integrated Mountain Development [IO], Kathmandu, Nepal

Intl. Centre for Island Tech. [IO], Stromness, United Kingdom

Intl. Centre for Local Credit [IO], Paris, France

Intl. Centre for Mech. Sciences [IO], Udine, Italy

Intl. Centre for Pure and Applied Mathematics [IO], Nice, France

Intl. Centre for Res. and Stud. on Tourism [IO], Aix-en-Provence, France

Intl. Centre for Settlement of Investment Disputes [5207], 1818 H St. NW, Washington, DC 20433, (202)458-1534

Intl. Centre for Settlement of Investment Disputes [5207], 1818 H St. NW, Washington, DC 20433, (202)458-1534

Intl. Centre for Sports History and Culture [IO], Leicester, United Kingdom

Intl. Centre for the Stud. of the Preservation and Restoration of Cultural Property [IO], Rome, Italy

Intl. Centre for Training and Exchanges in the Geosciences [IO], Orleans, France

Intl. Centre for Tropical Agriculture [IO], Cali, Colombia

Intl. Certified Floorcovering Installers Assn. [918], 2400 E Truman Rd., Kansas City, MO 64127, (816)231-4646

Intl. Certified Floorcovering Installers Assn. [918], 2400 E Truman Rd., Kansas City, MO 64127, (816)231-4646

Intl. Cesarean Awareness Network [15881], PO Box 98, Savage, MN 55378, (800)686-ICAN

Intl. Cesarean Awareness Network [15881], PO Box 98, Savage, MN 55378, (800)686-ICAN

Intl. Cessna 120/140 Assn. [20899], PO Box 830092, Richardson, TX 75083-0092

Intl. Cessna 120/140 Assn. [20899], PO Box 830092, Richardson, TX 75083-0092

The Intl. Cessna 170 Assn. [20900], 22 Vista View Ln., Cody, WY 82414-9606, (307)587-6397

Intl. Chain Salon Assn. [★969]

Intl. Chain Salon Assn. [★969]

Intl. Chamber of Commerce - Austria [IO], Vienna, Austria

Intl. Chamber of Commerce - Belgium [IO], Brussels, Belgium

Intl. Chamber of Commerce - Czech Republic [IO], Prague, Czech Republic

Intl. Chamber of Commerce - Deutschland [IO], Berlin, Germany

Intl. Chamber of Commerce - Finland [IO], Helsinki, Finland

Intl. Chamber of Commerce - France [IO], Paris, France

Intl. Chamber of Commerce - Georgia [IO], Tbilisi, Georgia

Intl. Chamber of Commerce - Hellas [IO], Athens, Greece

Intl. Chamber of Commerce - Hrvatska [IO], Zagreb, Croatia

Intl. Chamber of Commerce - Hungary [IO], Budapest, Hungary

Intl. Chamber of Commerce - Iran [IO], Tehran, Iran

Intl. Chamber of Commerce - Italia [IO], Rome, Italy

Intl. Chamber of Commerce - Lithuania [IO], Vilnius, Lithuania

Intl. Chamber of Commerce - Luxembourg [IO], Luxembourg, Luxembourg

Intl. Chamber of Commerce - Madagascar [IO], Antananarivo, Madagascar

Intl. Chamber of Commerce - Netherlands [IO], The Hague, Netherlands

Intl. Chamber of Commerce - Pakistan [IO], Karachi, Pakistan

Intl. Chamber of Commerce - Panama [IO], Panama City, Panama

Intl. Chamber of Commerce - Qatar [IO], Doha, Qatar

Intl. Chamber of Commerce - Syria [IO], Damascus, Syrian Arab Republic

Intl. Chamber of Commerce - Togo [IO], Lome, Togo

Intl. Chamber of Commerce - UK [IO], London, United Kingdom

Intl. Chamber of Commerce - United Arab Emirates [IO], Dubai, United Arab Emirates

Intl. Chamber of Commerce - USA [23369], U.S. Coun. for Intl. Bus., 1212 Ave. of the Americas, New York, NY 10036-1689, (212)354-4480

Intl. Chamber of Commerce - USA [23369], U.S. Coun. for Intl. Bus., 1212 Ave. of the Americas, New York, NY 10036-1689, (212)354-4480

Intl. Chamber of Shipping [IO], London, United Kingdom

Intl. Charollaise Assn. [★3881]

Intl. Charollaise Assn. [★3881]

Intl. Cheerleading Found. - Defunct.

Intl. Cheese Coun. of Canada [IO], Toronto, ON, Canada

Intl. Cheese and Deli Assn. [★1398]

Intl. Cheese and Deli Assn. [★1398]

Intl. Cheese and Deli Seminar [★1398]

Intl. Cheese and Deli Seminar [★1398]

Intl. Chem. Workers Union [★23191]

Intl. Child Amputee Network [11796], PO Box 514, Abilene, TX 79604-0514

Intl. Child Amputee Network [11796], PO Box 514, Abilene, TX 79604-0514

Intl. Child Care - Canada [IO], Markham, ON, Canada

Intl. Child Care U.S.A. [11471], 240 W Michigan, Kalamazoo, MI 49007, (269)382-9960

Intl. Child Care U.S.A. [11471], 240 W Michigan, Kalamazoo, MI 49007, (269)382-9960

Intl. Child Empowerment Network [11472], 8605-B Engleside Off. Park Dr., Alexandria, VA 22309, (571)332-1179

Intl. Child Hea. Found. [★14061]

Intl. Child Hea. Found. [★14061]

Intl. Child Neurology Assn. [IO], Uppsala, Sweden

Intl. Child Rsrc. Inst. [11322], 1581 LeRoy Ave., Berkeley, CA 94708, (510)644-1000

Intl. Child Rsrc. Inst. [11322], 1581 LeRoy Ave., Berkeley, CA 94708, (510)644-1000

Intl. Childbirth Educ. Assn. [15882], 1500 Sunday Dr., Ste. 102, Raleigh, NC 27607, (919)863-9487

Intl. Childbirth Educ. Assn. [15882], 1500 Sunday Dr., Ste. 102, Raleigh, NC 27607, (919)863-9487

Intl. Children Assistance Network [11323], PO Box 5863, Santa Clara, CA 95056, (408)509-8788

Intl. Children's Alliance - Address unknown since 2011.

Intl. Children's Anophthalmia Network [17088], Center for Developmental Medicine and Genetics, 5501 Old York Rd., Genetics, Levy 2 W, Philadelphia, PA 19141, (800)580-4226

Intl. Children's Anophthalmia Network [17088], Center for Developmental Medicine and Genetics, 5501 Old York Rd., Genetics, Levy 2 W, Philadelphia, PA 19141, (800)580-4226

Intl. Chili Soc. [21847], PO Box 1027, San Juan Capistrano, CA 92693, (949)496-2651

Intl. Chili Soc. [21847], PO Box 1027, San Juan Capistrano, CA 92693, (949)496-2651

Intl. Chinese Boxing Assn. [22436], 3308 Preston Rd., Ste. 350-356, Plano, TX 75093

Intl. Chinese Boxing Assn. [22436], 3308 Preston Rd., Ste. 350-356, Plano, TX 75093

Intl. Chinese Snuff Bottle Soc. [21236], 2601 N Charles St., Baltimore, MD 21218, (410)467-9400

Intl. Chiropractic Pediatric Assn. [14136], 327 N Middletown Rd., Media, PA 19063, (610)565-2360

Intl. Chiropractic Pediatric Assn. [14136], 327 N Middletown Rd., Media, PA 19063, (610)565-2360

Intl. Chiropractors Assn. [14137], 6400 Arlington Blvd., Ste. 800, Falls Church, VA 22042, (703)528-5000

Intl. Chiropractors Assn. [14137], 6400 Arlington Blvd., Ste. 800, Falls Church, VA 22042, (703)528-5000

Intl. Choral Network [IO], Marktoberdorf, Germany

Intl. Christian Accrediting Assn. [7646], 2448 E 81st St., Tulsa, OK 74137, (918)493-8880

Intl. Christian Accrediting Assn. [7646], 2448 E 81st St., Tulsa, OK 74137, (918)493-8880

Intl. Christian Concern [19578], 2020 Pennsylvania Ave. NW, No. 941, Washington, DC 20006-1846, (301)585-5915

A star before a book entry number signifies that the name is not listed separately, but is mentioned within the entry.

Intl. Christian Concern [**19578**], 2020 Pennsylvania Ave. NW, No. 941, Washington, DC 20006-1846, (301)585-5915

Intl. Christian Cycling Club U.S.A. [**22478**], PO Box 441757, Aurora, CO 80044-1757, (720)870-3707

Intl. Christian Cycling Club U.S.A. [**22478**], PO Box 441757, Aurora, CO 80044-1757, (720)870-3707

Intl. Christian Dance Fellowship [**IO**], Lane Cove, Australia

Intl. Christian Education Assn. - Defunct.

Intl. Christian Ser. for Peace [**IO**], Neuwied, Germany

Intl. Christian Stud. Assn. [**19579**], 1065 Pine Bluff Dr., Pasadena, CA 91107

Intl. Christian Stud. Assn. [**19579**], 1065 Pine Bluff Dr., Pasadena, CA 91107

Intl. Christian Technologists Assn. [**19990**], 5555 Erindale Dr., Ste. 205, Colorado Springs, CO 80918-6965, (719)785-0120

Intl. Christian Technologists Assn. [**19990**], 5555 Erindale Dr., Ste. 205, Colorado Springs, CO 80918-6965, (719)785-0120

Intl. Christian Union of Bus. Executives [**IO**], Paris, France

Intl. Christian Women's Fellowship [**★20288**]

Intl. Christian Women's Fellowship [**★20288**]

Intl. Chromium Development Assn. [**IO**], Paris, France

Intl. Church of Metaphysics [**★20247**]

Intl. Churchill Soc. - Canada [**IO**], Markham, ON, Canada

Intl. Churchill Soc. - U.S. [**★10657**]

Intl. Cinema Tech. Assn. [**1260**], 770 Broadway, 7th Fl., New York, NY 10003-9522, (212)493-4097

Intl. Cinema Tech. Assn. [**1260**], 770 Broadway, 7th Fl., New York, NY 10003-9522, (212)493-4097

Intl. Circle for the Promotion of Creation [**IO**], Bafoussam, Cameroon

Intl. Circulation Managers Assn. [**★2953**]

Intl. City/County Mgt. Assn. [**5847**], 777 N Capitol St. NE, Ste. 500, Washington, DC 20002-4201, (202)289-4262

Intl. City/County Mgt. Assn. [**5847**], 777 N Capitol St. NE, Ste. 500, Washington, DC 20002-4201, (202)289-4262

Intl. City Mgt. Assn. [**★5847**]

Intl. City Mgt. Assn. [**★5847**]

Intl. City Managers' Assn. [**★5847**]

Intl. City Managers' Assn. [**★5847**]

Intl. Civil Aviation Org. [**IO**], Montreal, QC, Canada

Intl. Civil Aviation Org. Asia Pacific Off. [**IO**], Bangkok, Thailand

Intl. Civil Aviation Org. Eastern and Southern African Off. [**IO**], Nairobi, Kenya

Intl. Civil Defence Org. [**IO**], Geneva, Switzerland

Intl. Civil Ser. Commn. [**23259**], 2 United Nations Plz., 10th Fl., New York, NY 10017, (212)963-5465

Intl. Civil Ser. Commn. [**23259**], 2 United Nations Plz., 10th Fl., New York, NY 10017, (212)963-5465

Intl. Claim Assn. [**1984**], 1155 15th St. NW, Ste. 500, Washington, DC 20005, (202)452-0143

Intl. Claim Assn. [**1984**], 1155 15th St. NW, Ste. 500, Washington, DC 20005, (202)452-0143

Intl. Clarinet Assn. [**10217**], PO Box 237, Longmont, CO 80502, (405)651-6064

Intl. Clarinet Assn. [**10217**], PO Box 237, Longmont, CO 80502, (405)651-6064

Intl. Clarinet Soc. [**★10217**]

Intl. Clarinet Society/Clarinetwork Intl. [**★10217**]

Intl. Classified Media Assn. [**IO**], Amsterdam, Netherlands

Intl. Cleaning Companies Assn. [**IO**], Moscow, Russia

Intl. Clematis Soc. [**IO**], Waltham Cross, United Kingdom

Intl. Clergy Coun. - Defunct.

Intl. Cliff Richard Movement [**IO**], Amsterdam, Netherlands

Intl. Climatology Assn. [**IO**], Rennes, France

Intl. Clinical Epidemiology Network [**14513**], 1420 Walnut St., Ste. 411, Philadelphia, PA 19102-4003, (215)735-8170

Intl. Clinical Phonetics and Linguistics Assn. [**10026**], Nicole Mueller, Univ. of Louisiana at Lafayette, Dept. of Communicative Disorders, PO Box 43107, Lafayette, LA 70504-3170

Intl. Clinical Phonetics and Linguistics Assn. [**10026**], Nicole Mueller, Univ. of Louisiana at Lafayette, Dept. of Communicative Disorders, PO Box 43107, Lafayette, LA 70504-3170

Intl. Clubmakers' Guild [**3310**], 95 Washington St., Ste. 104-335, Canton, MA 02021

Intl. Co-operative Alliance - Switzerland [**IO**], Geneva, Switzerland

Intl. Coach Fed. [**22459**], 2365 Harrodsburg Rd., Ste. A325, Lexington, KY 40504, (859)219-3580

Intl. Coach Fed. [**22459**], 2365 Harrodsburg Rd., Ste. A325, Lexington, KY 40504, (859)219-3580

Intl. Coach Fed. - Australasian Region [**IO**], Kariong, Australia

Intl. Coalition for Addiction Stud. Educ. [**8934**], PO Box 224, Vermillion, SD 57069-0224, (480)517-8522

Intl. Coalition for the Advancement of Fibromyalgia/CFIDS Treatment - Address unknown since 2011.

Intl. Coalition of Apostles [**19991**], PO Box 164217, Fort Worth, TX 76161, (817)232-5815

Intl. Coalition for Autism and All Abilities [**13796**], 200 Crestwood Plz., St. Louis, MO 63126

Intl. Coalition for Genital Integrity [**11519**], 1970 N River Rd., West Lafayette, IN 47906, (765)497-0150

Intl. Coalition for Genital Integrity [**11519**], 1970 N River Rd., West Lafayette, IN 47906, (765)497-0150

Intl. Coalition for Haiti [**11599**], 4 S Orange Ave., Ste. 261, South Orange, NJ 07079, (877)774-8416

Intl. Coalition for Haiti [**11599**], 4 S Orange Ave., Ste. 261, South Orange, NJ 07079, (877)774-8416

Intl. Coalition of Lib. Consortia [**8522**], Tom Sanville, 1438 W Peachtree St. NW, Ste. 200, Atlanta, GA 30309, (404)592-4873

Intl. Coalition of Lib. Consortia [**8522**], Tom Sanville, 1438 W Peachtree St. NW, Ste. 200, Atlanta, GA 30309, (404)592-4873

Intl. Coalition for Religious Freedom [**18519**], 7245 Hanover Pkwy., Ste. A, Greenbelt, MD 20770, (301)789-1589

Intl. Coalition for Religious Freedom [**18519**], 7245 Hanover Pkwy., Ste. A, Greenbelt, MD 20770, (301)789-1589

Intl. Coalition for the Responsibility to Protect [**18498**], World Federalist Movement, Inst. for Global Policy, 708 3rd Ave., 24th Fl., New York, NY 10017, (212)599-1320

Intl. Coalition of Sites of Conscience [**9702**], 333 7th Ave., 14th Fl., New York, NY 10001-5108, (646)755-6180

Intl. Coalition for Sustainable Production and Consumption [**17381**], Integrative Strategies Forum, PO Box 7458, Silver Spring, MD 20907, (301)588-5550

Intl. Coalition for Sustainable Production and Consumption [**17381**], Integrative Strategies Forum, PO Box 7458, Silver Spring, MD 20907, (301)588-5550

Intl. Cocoa Org. [**IO**], London, United Kingdom

Intl. Code Coun. [**5302**], 500 New Jersey Ave. NW, 6th Fl., Washington, DC 20001-2070, (202)370-1800

Intl. Code Coun. [**5302**], 500 New Jersey Ave. NW, 6th Fl., Washington, DC 20001-2070, (202)370-1800

Intl. Coenzyme Q10 Assn. [**IO**], Ancona, Italy

Intl. Coffee Org. [**IO**], London, United Kingdom

Intl. Coil Winding Assn. [**★1072**]

Intl. Coleman Collectors Club [**21357**], 10 S Main St., Mont Vernon, NH 03057-1620

Intl. Coll. of Angiology [**16960**], 161 Morin Dr., Jay, VT 05859-9283, (802)988-4065

Intl. Coll. of Angiology [**16960**], 161 Morin Dr., Jay, VT 05859-9283, (802)988-4065

Intl. Coll. of Applied Kinesiology U.S.A. [**14999**], 6405 Metcalf Ave., Ste. 503, Shawnee Mission, KS 66202-3929, (913)384-5336

Intl. Coll. of Applied Kinesiology U.S.A. [**14999**], 6405 Metcalf Ave., Ste. 503, Shawnee Mission, KS 66202-3929, (913)384-5336

Intl. Coll. of Applied Nutrition [**★15835**]

Intl. Coll. of Applied Nutrition [**★15835**]

Intl. Coll. of Cranio-Mandibular Orthopedics [**16035**], 619 N 35th St., Ste. 307, Seattle, WA 98103, (206)633-4355

Intl. Coll. of Cranio-Mandibular Orthopedics [**16035**], 619 N 35th St., Ste. 307, Seattle, WA 98103, (206)633-4355

Intl. Coll. of Dentists [**14292**], 1010 Rockville Pike, Ste. 510, Rockville, MD 20852-1482, (240)403-7246

Intl. Coll. of Dentists [**14292**], 1010 Rockville Pike, Ste. 510, Rockville, MD 20852-1482, (240)403-7246

Intl. Coll. for Hea. Cooperation in Developing Countries Italy [**IO**], Padua, Italy

Intl. Coll. of Nuclear Medicine Physicians [**IO**], Mexico City, Mexico

Intl. Coll. of Oral Implantologists [**★14294**]

Intl. Coll. of Oral Implantologists [**★14294**]

Intl. Coll. of Prosthodontists [**14293**], 4425 Cass St., Ste. A, San Diego, CA 92109-4015, (858)270-1814

Intl. Coll. of Prosthodontists [**14293**], 4425 Cass St., Ste. A, San Diego, CA 92109-4015, (858)270-1814

Intl. Coll. of Surgeons [**16815**], 1516 N Lake Shore Dr., Chicago, IL 60610, (312)642-3555

Intl. Coll. of Surgeons [**16815**], 1516 N Lake Shore Dr., Chicago, IL 60610, (312)642-3555

Intl. Collegiate Licensing Assn. [**2407**], NACDA, PO Box 16428, Cleveland, OH 44116, (440)892-4000

Intl. Color Consortium [**801**], 1899 Preston White Dr., Reston, VA 20191, (703)264-7200

Intl. Colored Appaloosa Assn. [**4596**], PO Box 99, Shipshewana, IN 46565, (574)238-4280

Intl. Colored Appaloosa Assn. [**4596**], PO Box 99, Shipshewana, IN 46565, (574)238-4280

Intl. Colored Gemstone Assn. [**3363**], 36 W 44th St., Ste. 914, New York, NY 10036, (212)620-0900

Intl. Colored Gemstone Assn. [**3363**], 36 W 44th St., Ste. 914, New York, NY 10036, (212)620-0900

Intl. Colour Assn. [**IO**], Alexandria, Australia

Intl. Commn. of Agricultural Engg. [**IO**], Tsukuba, Japan

Intl. Commn. for Agricultural and Food Indus. [**IO**], Paris, France

Intl. Commn. for Alpine Rescue [**IO**], Marthalen, Switzerland

Intl. Commn. on Biological Effects of Noise [**IO**], London, United Kingdom

Intl. Commn. of Catholic Prison Pastoral Care [**IO**], Zeist, Netherlands

Intl. Commn. on Civil Status [**IO**], Strasbourg, France

Intl. Commn. for the Conservation of Atlantic Tunas [**IO**], Madrid, Spain

Intl. Commn. on Glass [**IO**], Paris, France

Intl. Commn. for Historical Demography [**IO**], Paris, France

Intl. Commn. on the History of the Geological Sciences [**IO**], Burnside, Australia

Intl. Commn. on the History of Mathematics [**IO**], Saragossa, Spain

Intl. Commn. for the History of Representative and Parliamentary Institutions [**IO**], Brasilia, Brazil

Intl. Commn. for the History of Towns [**IO**], Kiel, Germany

Intl. Commn. on Illumination [**IO**], Vienna, Austria

Intl. Commn. on Illumination, U.S. Natl. Comm. [**7032**], Thomas M. Lemons, Pres., 7 Pond St., Salem, MA 01970, (781)771-7242

Intl. Commn. on Irrigation and Drainage [**IO**], New Delhi, India

Intl. Commn. on Irrigation and Drainage - England [**IO**], London, United Kingdom

Intl. Commn. of Jurists - Canadian Sect. [**IO**], Ottawa, ON, Canada

Intl. Commn. of Jurists - Switzerland [**IO**], Geneva, Switzerland

Intl. Commn. on Large Dams [**IO**], Paris, France

Intl. Commn. on Mathematical Instruction [**IO**], Coimbra, Portugal

Intl. Commn. on Microbiological Specifications for Foods [**IO**], Sharnbrook, United Kingdom

Intl. Commn. on Missing Persons [**IO**], Sarajevo, Bosnia-Hercegovina

Intl. Commn. on Occupational Hea. [**IO**], Rome, Italy

Intl. Commn. for Optics [**IO**], Madrid, Spain

Intl. Commn. of the Palaeozoic Microflora [**IO**], Llandudno, United Kingdom

Intl. Commn. of Peace [**17408**], 20669 Martinez St., Woodland Hills, CA 91364

Reference to "IO" in place of a book number signifies that the association may be found in the 50th edition of International Organizations.

Intl. Commn. on Physics Educ. [IO], New Delhi, India

Intl. Commn. for Protection Against Environmental Mutagens and Carcinogens - Defunct.

Intl. Commn. for the Protection of Alpine Regions [IO], Schaan, Liechtenstein

Intl. Commn. for the Protection of the Rhine [IO], Koblenz, Germany

Intl. Commn. on Radiation Units and Measurements [7321], 7910 Woodmont Ave., Ste. 400, Bethesda, MD 20814-3076, (301)657-2652

Intl. Commn. on Radiation Units and Measurements [7321], 7910 Woodmont Ave., Ste. 400, Bethesda, MD 20814-3076, (301)657-2652

Intl. Commn. on Radiological Units [★7321]

Intl. Commn. on Radiological Units [★7321]

Intl. Commn. on Radiological Units and Measurements [★7321]

Intl. Commn. on Radiological Units and Measurements [★7321]

Intl. Commn. for Uniform Methods of Sugar Anal. [IO], Peterborough, United Kingdom

Intl. Commn. on Zoological Nomenclature [IO], London, United Kingdom

Intl. Comm. Against Racism - Defunct.

Intl. Comm. for Animal Recording [IO], Rome, Italy

Intl. Comm. for the Children of Chechnya [11324], PO Box 381305, Cambridge, MA 02238

Intl. Comm. for the Children of Chechnya [11324], PO Box 381305, Cambridge, MA 02238

Intl. Comm. for Coal and Organic Petrology [IO], Utrecht, Netherlands

Intl. Comm. for the Defense of the Breton Language, U.S. Branch [9454], Lois Kuter, Sec.-Treas./Ed., 169 Greenwood Ave., B-4, Jenkintown, PA 19046, (215)886-6361

Intl. Comm. for the Defense of the Breton Language, U.S. Br. [9454], Lois Kuter, Sec.-Treas./Ed., 169 Greenwood Ave., B-4, Jenkintown, PA 19046, (215)886-6361

Intl. Comm. for the Defense of Salman Rushdie and His Publishers - Defunct.

Intl. Comm. for Documentation of the Intl. Coun. of Museums [IO], Marburg, Germany

Intl. Comm. on Economic and Applied Microbiology - Defunct.

Intl. Comm. on English in the Liturgy - Defunct.

Intl. Comm. for Historical Metrology [IO], Lille, France

Intl. Comm. of Historical Sciences [IO], Montreal, QC, Canada

Intl. Comm. for the History of the Second World War [IO], Paris, France

Intl. Comm. for the History of Tech. [IO], Bochum, Germany

Intl. Comm. for the Indigenous Peoples of the Americas [IO], Zurich, Switzerland

InterNational Comm. for Info. Tech. Standards [7510], Info. Tech. Indus. Coun., 1250 Eye St. NW, Ste. 200, Washington, DC 20005-5977, (202)737-8888

Intl. Comm. for Life, Disability and Hea. Insurance Medicine [IO], Vienna, Austria

Intl. Comm. for Mental Hygiene [★15486]

Intl. Comm. for Mental Hygiene [★15486]

Intl. Comm. on Microbial Biology - Defunct.

Intl. Comm. of Military Medicine [IO], Brussels, Belgium

Intl. Comm. of Plastics in Agriculture [IO], Madrid, Spain

Intl. Comm. to Preserve Catacombs in Italy [★9701]

Intl. Comm. to Preserve Catacombs in Italy [★9701]

Intl. Comm. for Radiological Units [★7321]

Intl. Comm. for Radiological Units [★7321]

Intl. Comm. of the Red Cross - Armenia [IO], Yerevan, Armenia

Intl. Comm. of the Red Cross - Azerbaijan [IO], Baku, Azerbaijan

Intl. Comm. of the Red Cross - Switzerland [IO], Geneva, Switzerland

Intl. Comm. for the Rescue of KAL 007 Survivors [18547], 34 Blackbird St., Edwards, CA 93523, (661)475-4079

Intl. Comm. on Seafarer's Welfare [IO], Watford, United Kingdom

Intl. Comm. for Social Sci. Info. and Documentation [IO], Buenos Aires, Argentina

Intl. Comm. of Sports for the Deaf [22512], 528 Trail Ave., Frederick, MD 21701

Intl. Comm. of Sports for the Deaf [22512], 528 Trail Ave., Frederick, MD 21701

Intl. Comm. on Ultra-High Intensity Lasers [7027], PO Box 808, Livermore, CA 94551, (925)423-8486

Intl. Comm. on Ultra-High Intensity Lasers [7027], PO Box 808, Livermore, CA 94551, (925)423-8486

Intl. Comm. for World Day of Prayer [★20294]

Intl. Comm. for World Day of Prayer [★20294]

Intl. Communal Stud. Assn. [IO], Ramat Efal, Israel

Intl. Commun. Assn. [3411], 1500 21st St. NW, Washington, DC 20036, (202)955-1444

Intl. Commun. Assn. [3411], 1500 21st St. NW, Washington, DC 20036, (202)955-1444

Intl. Communications Agency Network [810], PO Box 490, Rollinsville, CO 80474-0490, (303)258-9511

Intl. Communications Agency Network [810], PO Box 490, Rollinsville, CO 80474-0490, (303)258-9511

Intl. Communications Consultancy Org. [IO], Hilversum, Netherlands

Intl. Communications Indus. Assn. [★277]

Intl. Communications Indus. Assn. [★277]

Intl. Community Corrections Assn. [11717], 8701 Georgia Ave., Ste. 402, Silver Spring, MD 20910, (301)585-6090

Intl. Community Corrections Assn. [11717], 8701 Georgia Ave., Ste. 402, Silver Spring, MD 20910, (301)585-6090

Intl. Community Services - Yemen [IO], Sana'a, Yemen

Intl. Comparative Literature Assn. - Address unknown since 2010.

Intl. Complement Soc. [15108], Dr. Andrea Tenner, 3205 McGaugh Hall, Irvine, CA 92697, (949)824-3268

Intl. Complement Soc. [15108], Dr. Andrea Tenner, 3205 McGaugh Hall, Irvine, CA 92697, (949)824-3268

Intl. Compressor Remanufacturers Assn. [1708], 1505 Carthage Rd., Lumberton, NC 28358, (910)301-7060

Intl. Compressor Remanufacturers Assn. [1708], 1505 Carthage Rd., Lumberton, NC 28358, (910)301-7060

Intl. Cmpt. Games Assn. [IO], London, United Kingdom

Intl. Cmpt. Music Assn. [2559], 1819 Polk St., Ste. 330, San Francisco, CA 94109

Intl. Cmpt. Music Assn. [2559], 1819 Polk St., Ste. 330, San Francisco, CA 94109

Intl. Computer Users Groups Assn. - Defunct.

Intl. Computing Centre [IO], Geneva, Switzerland

Intl. Concerns for Children - Defunct.

Intl. Concierge and Errand Assn. [★1756]

Intl. Concierge and Lifestyle Mgt. Assn. [1756], 3650 Rogers Rd., No. 328, Wake Forest, NC 27587, (804)368-1667

Intl. Concrete Repair Inst. [830], 10600 W Higgins Rd., Ste. 607, Rosemont, IL 60018, (847)827-0830

Intl. Concrete Repair Inst. [830], 10600 W Higgins Rd., Ste. 607, Rosemont, IL 60018, (847)827-0830

Intl. Confectionery Assn. [IO], Brussels, Belgium

Intl. Confed. of Accordionists [IO], Ikaalinen, Finland

Intl. Confed. of Agricultural Credit [IO], Zurich, Switzerland

Intl. Confed. of Architectural Museums [IO], Rotterdam, Netherlands

Intl. Confed. of Art Dealers - Austria [IO], Vienna, Austria

Intl. Confed. of Associations for Pluralism in Economics [6625], Prof. Martha A. Starr, Acting Exec. Dir., Amer. Univ., Dept. of Economics, 4400 Massachusetts Ave., Washington, DC 20016

Intl. Confed. for Electroacoustic Music [IO], Bourges, France

Intl. Confed. of European Beet Growers [IO], Paris, France

Intl. Confed. of Mfrs. of Furnishing Fabrics [IO], Wuppertal, Germany

Intl. Confed. of Meat and Meat Processing Indus. [IO], Brussels, Belgium

Intl. Confed. of Midwives [IO], The Hague, Netherlands

Intl. Confed. of Paper and Bd. Converters in Europe [IO], Brussels, Belgium

Intl. Confed. of Popular Banks [IO], Brussels, Belgium

Intl. Confed. for Printing and Allied Indus. [IO], Brussels, Belgium

Intl. Confed. of Societies of Authors and Composers [IO], Neuilly-sur-Seine, France

Intl. Confed. for Thermal Anal. and Calorimetry [IO], Sao Carlos, Brazil

Intl. Conf. of Agricultural Economists [★6621]

Intl. Conf. of Agricultural Economists [★6621]

Intl. Conf. of Funeral Ser. Examining Boards of the U.S. [5845], 1885 Shelby Ln., Fayetteville, AR 72704, (479)442-7076

Intl. Conf. of Labour and Social History [IO], Vienna, Austria

Intl. Conf. of Police Chaplains [19521], PO Box 5590, Destin, FL 32540-5590, (850)654-9736

Intl. Conf. of Police Chaplains [19521], PO Box 5590, Destin, FL 32540-5590, (850)654-9736

Intl. Conf. for the Stud. of Political Thought [7289], Prof. Sharon Snowiss, Sec.-Treas., Pitzer Coll., Dept. of Political Sci., 1050 N Mills Ave., Claremont, CA 91711, (909)607-3178

Intl. Conf. of Symphony and Opera Musicians [10218], 1609 Tammany Dr., Nashville, TN 37206, (919)833-8720

Intl. Conf. of Symphony and Opera Musicians [10218], 1609 Tammany Dr., Nashville, TN 37206, (919)833-8720

Intl. Conf. of Weekly Newspaper Editors [★2836]

Intl. Conf. of Weekly Newspaper Editors [★2836]

Intl. Cong. and Convention Assn. [IO], Amsterdam, Netherlands

International Cong. for the History of Discoveries [★9806]

International Cong. for the History of Discoveries [★9806]

Intl. Cong. of Maritime Museums [10121], 329 High St., Mystic, CT 06355

Intl. Cong. of Maritime Museums [10121], 329 High St., Mystic, CT 06355

Intl. Cong. of Oral Implantologists [14294], 248 Lorraine Ave., Upper Montclair, NJ 07043, (973)783-6300

Intl. Cong. of Oral Implantologists [14294], 248 Lorraine Ave., Upper Montclair, NJ 07043, (973)783-6300

Intl. Consortium for Emergency Contraception [12036], Family Care Intl., 588 Broadway, Ste. 503, New York, NY 10012, (212)941-5300

Intl. Consortium for Emergency Contraception [12036], Family Care Intl., 588 Broadway, Ste. 503, New York, NY 10012, (212)941-5300

Intl. Consortium on Governmental Financial Mgt. [1306], PO Box 1077, St. Michaels, MD 21663, (410)745-8570

Intl. Consortium on Governmental Financial Mgt. [1306], PO Box 1077, St. Michaels, MD 21663, (410)745-8570

Intl. Consultants and Contractors Assn. of Iran [IO], Tehran, Iran

Intl. Consultative Res. Gp. on Rapeseed [IO], Paris, France

Intl. Consumer Prdt. Hea. and Safety Org. [2888], 7044 S 13th St., Oak Creek, WI 53154, (414)908-4930

Intl. Consumer Prdt. Hea. and Safety Org. [2888], 7044 S 13th St., Oak Creek, WI 53154, (414)908-4930

Intl. Contact Center Benchmarking Consortium [672], The Benchmarking Network, 4606 FM 1960 W, Ste. 250, Houston, TX 77069-9949, (281)440-5044

Intl. Contact Dermatitis Res. Gp. [IO], Brussels, Belgium

Intl. Contemporary Music Exchange - Defunct.

Intl. Continence Soc. [IO], Bristol, United Kingdom

Intl. Conure Assn. [21218], PO Box 70123, Las Vegas, NV 89170

Intl. Conure Assn. [21218], PO Box 70123, Las Vegas, NV 89170

Intl. Convention of Faith, Churches and Ministers [★19580]

A star before a book entry number signifies that the name is not listed separately, but is mentioned within the entry.

Intl. Convention of Faith, Churches and Ministers [★19580]
Intl. Convention of Faith Ministries [19580], 5500 Woodland Park Blvd., Arlington, TX 76013, (817)451-9620
Intl. Convention of Faith Ministries [19580], 5500 Woodland Park Blvd., Arlington, TX 76013, (817)451-9620
International Cooperation
  African Fed., Inc. [17900]
  African Fed., Inc. [17900]
  Amer. Brazilian Cultural Exchange [9513]
  Amer. MidEast Leadership Network [17934]
  Assn. for Peace and Understanding in the Middle East [18117]
  Assn. of Thai Professionals in Am. and Canada [19255]
  Building Bridges: Middle East-US [8385]InternationalBus. for Economic Security, Tourism and Trade
  Chinese Amer. Cooperation Coun. [9873]
  Empower Peace [18241]
  Friends of Taiwan Intl. [17945]
  Global China Connection [8387]
  Global Peace Initiative of Women [18250]
  Intergovernmental Renewable Energy Org. [6731]
  Intl. Assn. of Space Entrepreneurs [139]
  Ishmael and Isaac [18126]
  Laotian Amer. Soc. [19102]
  Peace Boat US [8695]
  Syrian-American Relations Coun. [17951]
  Thai U.S.A. Assn. [19256]
  Ugandan Amer. Partnership Org. [12307]
  Ugandan Amer. Partnership Org. [12307]
  Ugandan North Amer. Assn. [18841]
  United Burundian-American Community Assn. [17953]
  United Nations [18747]
  U.S.-Japan Coun. [17955]
  U.S. Off. on Colombia [17956]
  U.S. Women and Cuba Collaboration [17957]
  Win Without War [18178]
  World Growth [2079]
  World Growth [2079]
Intl. Cooperation Coun. [★17987]
Intl. Cooperation Coun. [★17987]
Intl. Cooperation for Development and Solidarity [IO], Brussels, Belgium
Intl. Cooperative Development Assn. [★4174]
Intl. Cooperative Development Assn. [★4174]
Intl. Cooperative and Mutual Insurance Fed. [IO], Bowdon, United Kingdom
Intl. Cooperative and Mutual Insurance Federation/ Regional Assn. for The Americas [1985], 8400 Westpark Dr., 2nd Fl., McLean, VA 22102, (703)245-8077
Intl. Coordinating Comm. on Solid State Sensors and Actuators Res. [6668], Univ. of California, Berkeley Sensor and Actuator Center, 483 Cory Hall, No. 1774, Berkeley, CA 94720-1774, (510)643-5663
Intl. Coordinating Comm. on Solid State Sensors and Actuators Res. [6668], Univ. of California, Berkeley Sensor and Actuator Center, 483 Cory Hall, No. 1774, Berkeley, CA 94720-1774, (510)643-5663
Intl. Coordinating Comm. on Solid State Transducers Res. [★6668]
Intl. Coordinating Comm. on Solid State Transducers Res. [★6668]
Intl. Coordinating Coun. of Aerospace Indus. Associations [140], 1000 Wilson Blvd., Ste. 1700, Arlington, VA 22209-3901
Intl. Coordinating Coun. of Aerospace Indus. Associations [140], 1000 Wilson Blvd., Ste. 1700, Arlington, VA 22209-3901
Intl. Coordination Coun. of Educational Institutions Alumni [IO], Moscow, Russia
Intl. Copper Assn. [7094], 260 Madison Ave., 16th Fl., New York, NY 10016-2401, (212)251-7240
Intl. Copper Assn. [7094], 260 Madison Ave., 16th Fl., New York, NY 10016-2401, (212)251-7240
Intl. Copper Res. Assn. [★7094]
Intl. Copper Res. Assn. [★7094]
Intl. Cops for Christ [19581], PO Box 444, Liverpool, PA 17045, (717)329-0470

Intl. Copyright Information Center - Defunct.
Intl. Coronelli Soc. for the Stud. of Globes [IO], Vienna, Austria
Intl. Corrections and Prisons Assn. [IO], Edinburgh, United Kingdom
Intl. Correspondence Inst. [★19575]
Intl. Correspondence Inst. [★19575]
Intl. Corrosion Coun. [IO], Madrid, Spain
Intl. Corrugated Case Assn. [882], 25 NW Point Blvd., Ste. 510, Elk Grove Village, IL 60007, (847)364-9600
Intl. Corrugated Case Assn. [882], 25 NW Point Blvd., Ste. 510, Elk Grove Village, IL 60007, (847)364-9600
Intl. Corrugated Packaging Found. [12676], 113 S West St., Alexandria, VA 22314, (703)549-8580
Intl. Corrugated Packaging Found. [12676], 113 S West St., Alexandria, VA 22314, (703)549-8580
Intl. Cost Engg. Coun. [IO], Deakin West, Australia
Intl. Cotton Advisory Comm. [3951], 1629 K St. NW, Ste. 702, Washington, DC 20006-1636, (202)463-6660
Intl. Cotton Advisory Comm. [3951], 1629 K St. NW, Ste. 702, Washington, DC 20006-1636, (202)463-6660
Intl. Coun. of Academies of Engg. and Technological Sciences [8840], 3601 N Peary St., Arlington, VA 22207, (703)527-5782
Intl. Coun. of Academies of Engg. and Technological Sciences [8840], 3601 N Peary St., Arlington, VA 22207, (703)527-5782
Intl. Coun. for Adult Educ. [IO], Montevideo, Uruguay
Intl. Coun. of the Aeronautical Sciences [IO], Stockholm, Sweden
Intl. Coun. of African Museums [IO], Nairobi, Kenya
Intl. Coun. of Air Shows [20901], 750 Miller Dr. SE, Ste. F3, Leesburg, VA 20175, (703)779-8510
Intl. Coun. of Air Shows [20901], 750 Miller Dr. SE, Ste. F3, Leesburg, VA 20175, (703)779-8510
Intl. Coun. of Aircraft Owner and Pilot Associations [141], 421 Aviation Way, Frederick, MD 21701, (301)695-2220
Intl. Coun. of Aircraft Owner and Pilot Associations [141], 421 Aviation Way, Frederick, MD 21701, (301)695-2220
Intl. Coun. on Alcohol and Addictions [IO], Lausanne, Switzerland
Intl. Coun. on Alcohol, Drugs and Traffic Safety [16740], 2901 Baxter Rd., Ann Arbor, MI 48109-2150, (734)764-6504
Intl. Coun. on Alcohol, Drugs and Traffic Safety [16740], 2901 Baxter Rd., Ann Arbor, MI 48109-2150, (734)764-6504
Intl. Coun. for Applied Mineralogy [IO], Hannover, Germany
Intl. Coun. for Archaeozoology [IO], Sheffield, United Kingdom
Intl. Coun. on Archives [IO], Paris, France
Intl. Coun. of Associations for Sci. Educ. [IO], Tartu, Estonia
Intl. Coun. for Bird Preservation [★5023]
Intl. Coun. of Bottled Water Associations [IO], Richmond Hill, ON, Canada
Intl. Coun. for Canadian Stud. [IO], Ottawa, ON, Canada
Intl. Coun. for Caring Communities [5328], 24 Central Park S, New York, NY 10019, (212)688-4321
Intl. Coun. for Central and East European Stud. [IO], Berlin, Germany
Intl. Coun. of Christians and Jews [IO], Heppenheim, Germany
Intl. Coun. on Clean Trans. [3516], 1225 Eye St. NW, Ste. 1000, Washington, DC 20005, (202)534-1600
Intl. Coun. of Community Churches [19621], 21116 Washington Pkwy., Frankfort, IL 60423, (815)464-5690
Intl. Coun. for Computer Communication - Defunct.
Intl. Coun. for Computers in Educ. [★7909]
Intl. Coun. for the Control of Iodine Deficiency Disorders - Australia [IO], Westmead, Australia
Intl. Coun. on Disability - Defunct.
Intl. Coun. on Educ. for Teaching [8948], 1000 Capitol Dr., Wheeling, IL 60090-7201, (847)947-5881

Intl. Coun. of Employers of Bricklayers and Allied Craftworkers [23252], PO Box 21462, Washington, DC 20009, (202)457-9040
Intl. Coun. for Engg. and Tech. [IO], Paris, France
Intl. Coun. of Environmental Law [IO], Bonn, Germany
Intl. Coun. for the Exploration of the Sea [IO], Copenhagen, Denmark
Intl. Coun. of Fine Arts Deans [7748], PO Box 110168, Bradenton, FL 34211, (941)753-0080
Intl. Coun. of the French Language [IO], Paris, France
Intl. Coun. of Graphic Design Associations [IO], Montreal, QC, Canada
Intl. Coun. of Grocery Mfr. Associations [1397], 1350 I St. NW, Ste. 300, Washington, DC 20005, (202)337-9400
Intl. Coun. for Hea., Physical Educ., Recreation, Sport, and Dance [8716], 1900 Assn. Dr., Reston, VA 20191-1598, (703)476-3486
Intl. Coun. of Hides, Skins and Leather Traders Associations [IO], Beijing, People's Republic of China
Intl. Coun. on Hotel, Restaurant, and Institutional Educ. [1757], 2810 N Parham Rd., Ste. 230, Richmond, VA 23294, (804)346-4800
Intl. Coun. for the Improvement of Reading and Instruction [★8780]
Intl. Coun. of Indus. Editors [★809]
Intl. Coun. on Infertility Info. Dissemination [14533], PO Box 6836, Arlington, VA 22206, (703)379-9178
Intl. Coun. of Iranian Christians [19582], PO Box 25607, Colorado Springs, CO 80936, (719)596-0010
Intl. Coun. of Jewish Women [IO], Tzur Hadassah, Israel
Intl. Coun. of Kinetography Laban [9553], Valerie Williams, Treas., 2801 Northwest Blvd., Columbus, OH 43221
Intl. Coun. on Korean Stud. [8450], 14641 Lee Hwy., Ste. 208, Centreville, VA 20121-5822, (703)266-3245
Intl. Coun. on Large Elec. Systems [IO], Paris, France
Intl. Coun. for the Life Sciences [7370], 4245 N Fairfax Dr., Ste. 625, Arlington, VA 22203, (202)659-8058
Intl. Coun. for Local Environmental Initiatives [IO], Toronto, ON, Canada
Intl. Coun. for Machinery Lubrication [7034], 1943 W Concorde Cir., Broken Arrow, OK 74012, (918)742-2950
Intl. Coun. of Marine Indus. Associations [IO], Egham, United Kingdom
Intl. Coun. on Materials Educ. [8033], 3940 North Elm St., Denton, TX 76207, (940)565-3262
Intl. Coun. for Middle East Stud. [18125], 1055 Thomas Jefferson St. NW, Ste. M100, Washington, DC 20009, (202)315-8680
Intl. Coun. on Mining and Metals [IO], London, United Kingdom
Intl. Coun. on Monuments and Sites [IO], Paris, France
Intl. Coun. on Monuments and Sites I United States Natl. Committee [9703], 401 F St. NW, Ste. 331, Washington, DC 20001, (202)842-1866
Intl. Coun. of the Museum of Modern Art [9183], 11 W 53rd St., New York, NY 10019, (212)708-9400
Intl. Coun. of Museums [IO], Paris, France
Intl. Coun. of Museums, U.S. Natl. Comm. [10122], 1575 Eye St. NW, Ste. 400, Washington, DC 20005, (202)289-9132
Intl. Coun. on Nanotechnology [6430], PO Box 1892, Houston, TX 77251, (713)348-8210
Intl. Coun. - Natl. Acad. of TV Arts and Sciences [★492]
Intl. Coun. of Nurses [IO], Geneva, Switzerland
Intl. Coun. for Open and Distance Educ. [IO], Oslo, Norway
Intl. Coun. of Ophthalmology [15961], 945 Green St., San Francisco, CA 94133, (415)409-8410
Intl. Coun. of Organizations for Folklore Festivals and Folk Art [IO], Paris, France
Intl. Coun. for Philosophy and Humanistic Stud. [IO], Paris, France
Intl. Coun. for Physical Activity and Fitness Res. [IO], Kwadlangezwa, Republic of South Africa

Reference to "IO" in place of a book number signifies that the association may be found in the 50th edition of International Organizations.

Intl. Coun. of Psychologists - Defunct.

Intl. Coun. for Quality Function Deployment [2889], 1140 Morehead Ct., Ann Arbor, MI 48103-6181, (734)995-0847

Intl. Coun. of Reflexologists [IO], Durban, Republic of South Africa

Intl. Coun. for Res. and Innovation in Building and Constr. [IO], Rotterdam, Netherlands

Intl. Coun. for Sci. and Tech. Info. [IO], Paris, France

Intl. Coun. of Seamen's Agencies [★13029]

Intl. Coun. of Shopping Centers [3106], 1221 Ave. of the Americas, 41st Fl., New York, NY 10020-1099, (646)728-3800

Intl. Coun. for Small Bus. [3290], GWU School of Bus., 2201 G St. NW, Funger Hall, Ste. 315, Washington, DC 20052

Intl. Coun. on Social Welfare - Canada [IO], Utrecht, Netherlands

Intl. Coun. of Societies of Indus. Design [IO], Montreal, QC, Canada

Intl. Coun. of Sport Sci. and Physical Educ. [IO], Berlin, Germany

Intl. Coun. on Systems Engg. [6801], 7670 Opportunity Rd., Ste. 220, San Diego, CA 92111-2222, (858)541-1725

Intl. Coun. on Systems Engg. - South Africa [IO], Highveld Park, Republic of South Africa

Intl. Coun. of Tanners [IO], Northampton, United Kingdom

Intl. Coun. for Tech. Commun. [IO], Kuesnacht, Switzerland

Intl. Coun. of Toy Indus. [3477], 1115 Broadway, Ste. 400, New York, NY 10010, (212)675-1141

Intl. Coun. of Voluntary Agencies [IO], Geneva, Switzerland

Intl. Coun. of Women [IO], Paris, France

Intl. Counselor Exchange Program [8366], 38 W 88th St., New York, NY 10024, (212)787-7706

Intl. Counter-Terrorism Officers Assn. [18715], PO Box 580009, Flushing, NY 11358, (212)564-5048

Intl. Courtly Literature Soc. [10043], Michelle Szkilnik, Univ. of Notre Dame, 343 O'Shaughnessy Hall, Notre Dame, IN 46556

Intl. Crane Found. [5067], E-11376 Shady Ln. Rd., PO Box 447, Baraboo, WI 53913-0447, (608)356-9462

Intl. Craniofacial Foundations [★14193]

Intl. Craniopathic Soc. [★14144]

Intl. Credit Assn. - Defunct.

Intl. Credit Insurance and Surety Assn. [IO], Amsterdam, Netherlands

Intl. Cremation Fed. [IO], The Hague, Netherlands

Intl. Crime Free Assn. [5365], PO Box 1146, Higley, AZ 85236

Intl. Criminal Court Alliance [5384], 11835 W Olympic Blvd., Ste. 1090, Los Angeles, CA 90064, (310)473-0777

Intl. Criminal Police Org. - Interpol [IO], Lyon, France

Intl. Crisis Aid [12854], PO Box 510167, St. Louis, MO 63151-0167, (314)487-1400

Intl. Crisis Gp., Washington Off. [17402], 1629 K St. NW, Ste. 450, Washington, DC 20006, (202)785-1601

Intl. Critical Incident Stress Found. [16725], 3290 Pine Orchard Ln., Ste. 106, Ellicott City, MD 21042, (410)750-9600

Intl. Crop Improvement Assn. [★5189]

Intl. Crosby Circle [23857], 5608 N 34th St., Arlington, VA 22207, (703)241-5608

Intl. Cruise Victims [18759], 704 228th Ave. NE, PMB 525, Sammamish, WA 98074, (425)753-7711

Intl. Cryogenic Materials Conf. [6584], 917 Front St., Ste. 220, Louisville, CO 80027, (303)499-2299

Intl. Cuemakers Assn. [456], 444 Flint Hill Rd., Aragon, GA 30104, (770)684-7004

Intl. Culinary Tourism Assn. [737], 4110 SE Hawthorne Blvd., Ste. 440, Portland, OR 97214, (503)750-7200

Intl. Cultic Stud. Assn. [19640], PO Box 2265, Bonita Springs, FL 34133, (239)514-3081

Intl. Cultural Youth Exchange [IO], Arhus, Denmark

Intl. Cultural Youth Exchange - Bolivia [IO], La Paz, Bolivia

Intl. Cultural Youth Exchange - Colombia [IO], Bogota, Colombia

Intl. Cultural Youth Exchange - Denmark [IO], Arhus, Denmark

Intl. Cultural Youth Exchange - Ghana [IO], Accra, Ghana

Intl. Cultural Youth Exchange - Japan [IO], Tokyo, Japan

Intl. Cultural Youth Exchange - Kenya [IO], Nairobi, Kenya

Intl. Cultural Youth Exchange - New Zealand [IO], Papamoa, New Zealand

Intl. Cultural Youth Exchange - Nigeria [IO], Lagos, Nigeria

Intl. Cultural Youth Exchange - South Korea [IO], Seoul, Republic of Korea

Intl. Cultural Youth Exchange - Switzerland [IO], Bern, Switzerland

Intl. Cultural Youth Exchange - Taiwan [IO], Tainan, Taiwan

Intl. Cultural Youth Exchange - United Kingdom [IO], London, United Kingdom

Intl. Curly Horse Org. [4597], HC 31 Box 102A, Williamsburg, NM 87942, (575)740-4159

Intl. Curly Horse Org. [4597], HC 31 Box 102A, Williamsburg, NM 87942, (575)740-4159

Intl. Customer Ser. Assn. [3236], 1110 South Ave., Ste. No. 50, Staten Island, NY 10314, (374)273-1303

Intl. Customs Tariffs Bur. [IO], Brussels, Belgium

Intl. Cut Flower Growers Assn.

Intl. Cut Flower Growers Assn. - Defunct.

Intl. Cut Stone Quarrymen's Assn. [★3360]

Intl. Cycling Union [IO], Aigle, Switzerland

Intl. Cystic Fibrosis-Mucoviscidosis Assn. [IO], Valencia, Spain

Intl. Dairy-Deli-Bakery Assn. [1398], PO Box 5528, Madison, WI 53705-0528, (608)310-5000

Intl. Dairy-Deli-Bakery Assn. [1398], PO Box 5528, Madison, WI 53705-0528, (608)310-5000

Intl. Dairy Fed. [IO], Brussels, Belgium

Intl. Dairy Fed. - Canadian Natl. Comm. [IO], Ottawa, ON, Canada

Intl. Dairy Foods Assn. [1021], 1250 H St. NW, Ste. 900, Washington, DC 20005, (202)737-4332

Intl. Dairy Foods Assn. [1021], 1250 H St. NW, Ste. 900, Washington, DC 20005, (202)737-4332

Intl. Dams Newsl. [★7602]

Intl. Dams Newsl. [★7602]

Intl. Dance Coun. [IO], Paris, France

Intl. Dance Sport Fed. [IO], Sant Cugat del Valles, Spain

Intl. Dance Teachers' Assn. [IO], Brighton, United Kingdom

Intl. Dark-Sky Assn. [6230], 3225 N 1st Ave., Tucson, AZ 85719-2103, (520)293-3198

Intl. Dark-Sky Assn. [6230], 3225 N 1st Ave., Tucson, AZ 85719-2103, (520)293-3198

Intl. DB2 Users Gp. [6592], 401 N Michigan Ave., Chicago, IL 60611-4267, (312)321-6881

Intl. Debate Educ. Assn. [18671], 900 State St., Salem, OR 97301, (212)548-0185

Intl. Defenders of Animals [10989], PO Box 5634, Weybosset Hill Sta., Providence, RI 02903-0634, (401)461-1922

Intl. Defenders of Animals [10989], PO Box 5634, Weybosset Hill Sta., Providence, RI 02903-0634, (401)461-1922

Intl. Defense Equip. Exhibitors Assn. [1233], 6233 Nelway Dr., McLean, VA 22101, (703)760-0762

Intl. Defense Equip. Exhibitors Assn. [1233], 6233 Nelway Dr., McLean, VA 22101, (703)760-0762

Intl. Defensive Pistol Assn. [22876], 2232 CR 719, Berryville, AR 72616, (870)545-3886

Intl. Defensive Pistol Assn. [22876], 2232 CR 719, Berryville, AR 72616, (870)545-3886

Intl. Democrat Union [IO], Oslo, Norway

Intl. Desalination Assn. [7600], PO Box 387, Topsfield, MA 01983, (978)887-0410

Intl. Desalination Assn. [7600], PO Box 387, Topsfield, MA 01983, (978)887-0410

Intl. Desalination and Environmental Assn. [★7600]

Intl. Desalination and Environmental Assn. [★7600]

Intl. Desert Lynx Cat Assn. [3862], PO Box 511, Selma, OR 97538

Intl. Desert Lynx Cat Assn. [3862], PO Box 511, Selma, OR 97538

Intl. Design Center Berlin [IO], Berlin, Germany

Intl. Design Guild [2063], 670 Commercial St., Manchester, NH 03101, (800)205-4345

Intl. Design Guild [2063], 670 Commercial St., Manchester, NH 03101, (800)205-4345

International Development

Accountability in Intl. Development [12308]

Accountability in Intl. Development [12308]

Africa Am. Crisis Assistance Network [12797]

AfriHope Intl., Inc. [10806]

Agri-Energy Roundtable [17901]

Agri-Energy Roundtable [17901]

Aid to Artisans [12309]

All One People [10808]

Alliance of Small Island States [17902]

Alliance of Small Island States [17902]

Alliance for Southern African Progress [12310]

Alliance for Southern African Progress [12310]

Amer. Comm. for KEEP [12311]

AmeriGhana [12312]

AmeriGhana [12312]

Armenian Intl. Women's Assn. [13451]

Ashoka: Innovators for the Public [12313]

Ashoka: Innovators for the Public [12313]

Assn. for Haitian Amer. Development [12126]

Assn. of Haitian Professionals [19021]

Assn. for India's Development [12314]

Assn. for India's Development [12314]

Assn. of Public and Land Grant Universities I Commn. on Intl. Programs [17903]

Assn. of Public and Land Grant Universities I Commn. on Intl. Programs [17903]

Assn. of Thai Professionals in Am. and Canada [19255]

Assn. on Third World Affairs [17904]

Assn. on Third World Affairs [17904]

Assn. of Third World Stud. [17905]

Assn. of Third World Stud. [17905]

Be The Change Intl. [13344]

BERWA [12315]

Beyond Borders [12316]

Blood: Water Mission [10809]

Bodomase Development Assn. USA [11551]

Bosniak Amer. Advisory Coun. for Bosnia and Herzegovina [17895]

Brave Intl. [19808]

BuildingBlocks Intl. [11666]

Burma Relief Network [12813]

Care 2 Share [13373]

Caribbean-Central Amer. Action [12317]

Caribbean-Central Amer. Action [12317]

CDC Development Solutions [17906]

Centre for Development and Population Activities [12318]

CHEER for Viet Nam [13374]

ChildFund Intl. [11231]

Children of the Nations Intl. [11237]

China Connection [12319]

China Connection [12319]

Christian Reformed World Relief Comm. [12320]

Christian Reformed World Relief Comm. [12320]

Citizens Development Corps [17906]

Claretian Volunteers and Lay Missionaries [19413]

Consultative Gp. to Assist the Poor [17907]

Consultative Gp. to Assist the Poor [17907]

Consultative Gp. on Intl. Agricultural Res. [12321]

Consultative Gp. on Intl. Agricultural Res. [12321]

Coun. for Zimbabwe [12322]

Coun. for Zimbabwe [12322]

Counterpart Intl. [12323]

Counterpart Intl. [12323]

Counterpart - U.S. Off. [17908]

Counterpart - U.S. Off. [17908]

Darfur Peace and Development Org. [12324]

Darfur Peace and Development Org. [12324]

Development Gp. for Alternative Policies [17909]

Development Gp. for Alternative Policies [17909]

Digital Divide Data [7005]

Drishtipat Worldwide [11124]

East Meets West Found. [17910]

East Meets West Found. [17910]

Egyptians Relief Assn. [11577]

Emerging Humanity [12325]

Emerging Humanity [12325]

A star before a book entry number signifies that the name is not listed separately, but is mentioned within the entry.

Reference to "IO" in place of a book number signifies that the association may be found in the 50th edition of International Organizations.

Intl. Documentary Found. [★1261]
Intl. Documentary Found. [★1261]
Intl. Dodge Ball Fed. [22981], 3451A Washington Ave., Gulfport, MS 39507, (347)640-4323
Intl. Doll Makers Assn. [21692], 9101 Hwy. 231, Panama City, FL 32404, (850)753-3135
Intl. Doll Makers Assn. [21692], 9101 Hwy. 231, Panama City, FL 32404, (850)753-3135
Intl. Doll Makers Assn. - Internationals [★21692]
Intl. Doll Makers Assn. - Internationals [★21692]
Intl. Door Assn. [571], PO Box 246, West Milton, OH 45383-0246, (937)698-8042
Intl. Door Assn. [571], PO Box 246, West Milton, OH 45383-0246, (937)698-8042
Intl. Dostoevsky Soc. [IO], Geneva, Switzerland
Intl. Double Reed Soc. [10219], Norma R. Hooks, Exec. Sec.-Treas., 2423 Lawndale Rd., Finksburg, MD 21048-1401, (410)871-0658
Intl. Double Reed Soc. [10219], Norma R. Hooks, Exec. Sec.-Treas., 2423 Lawndale Rd., Finksburg, MD 21048-1401, (410)871-0658
Intl. DOVE Assn. [IO], Olds, AB, Canada
Intl. Downtown Assn. [673], 1025 Thomas Jefferson St. NW, Ste. 500W, Washington, DC 20007, (202)393-6801
Intl. Downtown Assn. [673], 1025 Thomas Jefferson St. NW, Ste. 500W, Washington, DC 20007, (202)393-6801
Intl. Downtown Executives Assn. [★673]
Intl. Downtown Executives Assn. [★673]
Intl. Dragon Boat Assn. - Defunct.
Intl. Drilling Fed. [★935]
Intl. Drilling Fed. [★935]
Intl. Drip Irrigation Assn. [★170]
Intl. Drip Irrigation Assn. [★170]
Intl. Drug Strategy Inst. [★13258]
Intl. Drug Strategy Inst. [★13258]
Intl. Dwarf Fruit Tree Assn. [★4970]
Intl. Dwarf Fruit Tree Assn. [★4970]
Intl. Dyslexia Assn. [14428], 40 York Rd., 4th Fl., Baltimore, MD 21204-5243, (410)296-0232
Intl. Dyslexia Assn. [14428], 40 York Rd., 4th Fl., Baltimore, MD 21204-5243, (410)296-0232
Intl. E-22 Class Assn. [★22351]
Intl. E-22 Class Assn. [★22351]
Intl. E-Learning Assn. [7721], 304 Park Ave. S, 11th Fl., New York, NY 10010
Intl. Earthlight Alliance [7105], PO Box 620198, Redwood City, CA 94062
Intl. Ecology Inst. [IO], Oldendorf, Germany
Intl. Ecology Soc. - Defunct.
Intl. Economic Alliance [1065], 1 Mifflin Pl., Ste. 400, Cambridge, MA 02138, (617)418-1971
Intl. Economic Assn. [IO], Paris, France
Intl. Economic Development Coun. [5534], 734 15th St. NW, Ste. 900, Washington, DC 20005, (202)223-7800
Intl. Economic Development Coun. [5534], 734 15th St. NW, Ste. 900, Washington, DC 20005, (202)223-7800
Intl. Economic History Assn. [IO], Tubingen, Germany
Intl. Economics and Finance Soc. [6626], Prof. Keith E. Maskus, Pres.-Elect, Univ. of Colorado-Boulder, Dept. of Economics, UCB 256, Boulder, CO 80302, (303)492-7588
The Intl. Ecotourism Soc. [3476], PO Box 96503, Washington, DC 20090-6503, (202)506-5033
The Intl. Ecotourism Soc. [3476], PO Box 96503, Washington, DC 20090-6503, (202)506-5033
Intl. ECP Therapists Assn. [16857], PO Box 1043, Syosset, NY 14791, (800)376-3321
Intl. Edsel Club [21076], PO Box 233, Sully, IA 50251-0233
Intl. Education Assn. - Defunct.
Intl. Educ. Res. Found. [8392], PO Box 3665, Culver City, CA 90231-3665, (310)258-9451
Intl. Educ. Res. Found. [8392], PO Box 3665, Culver City, CA 90231-3665, (310)258-9451
Intl. Educ. and Rsrc. Network [8027], 475 Riverside Dr., Ste. 450, New York, NY 10115, (212)870-2693
Intl. Educ. and Resource Network [★8027]
Intl. Educ. and Rsrc. Network - Egypt [IO], Cairo, Egypt
Intl. Educ. and Rsrc. Network - Suriname [IO], Paramaribo, Suriname

Intl. Educ. and Rsrc. Network - Trinidad and Tobago [IO], Port of Spain, Trinidad and Tobago
The Intl. Educator [8393], PO Box 513, Cummaquid, MA 02637, (508)790-1990
Intl. Educator's Inst. [★8393]
Intl. Educator's Inst. [8393], PO Box 513, Cummaquid, MA 02637, (508)790-1990
Intl. EECP Therapists Assn. [16857], PO Box 1043, Syosset, NY 14791, (800)376-3321
Intl. Egg Commn. [IO], London, United Kingdom
Intl. Elecl. Testing Assn. [1076], 3050 Old Centre Ave., Ste. 102, Portage, MI 49024, (269)488-6382
Intl. Elecl. Testing Assn. [1076], 3050 Old Centre Ave., Ste. 102, Portage, MI 49024, (269)488-6382
Intl. Electronics Mfg. Initiative [7046], 2214 Rock Hill Rd., Ste. 110, Herndon, VA 20170-4214, (703)834-0330
Intl. Electrophoresis Soc. [★6639]
Intl. Electrotechnical Commn. [IO], Geneva, Switzerland
Intl. Elvis Presley Fan Club Hong Kong [IO], Hong Kong, People's Republic of China
Intl. Embryo Transfer Soc. [17027], 2441 Village Green Pl., Champaign, IL 61822, (217)398-4697
Intl. Embryo Transfer Soc. [17027], 2441 Village Green Pl., Champaign, IL 61822, (217)398-4697
Intl. Enamellers Inst. [IO], Milan, Italy
Intl. Endotoxin and Innate Immunity Soc. [7572], Alan S. Cross, MD, Pres., Univ. of Maryland, Baltimore School of Medicine, Center for Vaccine Development, 685 W Baltimore St., Baftimore, MD 21201, (410)706-5328
Intl. Endotoxin and Innate Immunity Soc. [7572], Alan S. Cross, MD, Pres., Univ. of Maryland, Baltimore School of Medicine, Center for Vaccine Development, 685 W Baltimore St., Baltimore, MD 21201, (410)706-5328
Intl. Energy Agency [IO], Paris, France
Intl. Energy Conservation Environmental Protection Assn. [IO], Beijing, People's Republic of China
Intl. Energy Credit Assn. [1307], 1500 Commerce Pkwy., Ste. C, Mount Laurel, NJ 08054, (856)380-6849
Intl. Energy Credit Assn. [1307], 1500 Commerce Pkwy., Ste. C, Mount Laurel, NJ 08054, (856)380-6849
Intl. Energy Found. [IO], Okotoks, AB, Canada
Intl. Engg. Consortium [6669], 233 Wacker Dr., Ste. 8400, Chicago, IL 60606-5114, (312)283-8457
Intl. Engg. Consortium [6669], 233 Wacker Dr., Ste. 8400, Chicago, IL 60606-5114, (312)283-8457
Intl. Enneagram Assn. [16161], 4010 Executive Park Dr., Ste. 100, Cincinnati, OH 45241, (513)232-5054
Intl. Enneagram Assn. [16161], 4010 Executive Park Dr., Ste. 100, Cincinnati, OH 45241, (513)232-5054
Intl. Enterprise Singapore [IO], Singapore, Singapore
Intl. Entertainment Buyers Assn. [1197], 9 Music Sq. W, Nashville, TN 37203, (615)251-9000
Intl. Epidemiological Assn. [IO], Alexandria, Egypt
Intl. Ergonomics Assn. [IO], Hsinchu, Taiwan
Intl. Erosion Control Assn. [4082], 3401 Quebec St., Ste. 3500, Denver, CO 80207, (303)640-7554
Intl. Erosion Control Assn. [4082], 3401 Quebec St., Ste. 3500, Denver, CO 80207, (303)640-7554
Intl. Erosion Control Assn. - Iberoamerican [IO], Buenos Aires, Argentina
Intl. Erosion Control Assn. - Malaysia [IO], Kuala Lumpur, Malaysia
Intl. Erosion Control Assn. - South Africa [IO], Pretoria, Republic of South Africa
Intl. Esperanto Inst. [IO], The Hague, Netherlands
Intl. Essential Tremor Found. [15600], PO Box 14005, Lenexa, KS 66285-4005, (913)341-3880
Intl. Essential Tremor Found. [15600], PO Box 14005, Lenexa, KS 66285-4005, (913)341-3880
Intl. Etchells Class Assn. [22351], Sherri Campbell, Exec. Sec., 2812 Canon St., San Diego, CA 92106, (619)222-0252
Intl. Etchells Class Assn. [22351], Sherri Campbell, Exec. Sec., 2812 Canon St., San Diego, CA 92106, (619)222-0252
International Exchange
    AFS Intercultural Programs [8336]

AHA Intl. [8337]
AHA Intl. [8337]
Alliance for Intl. Educational and Cultural Exchange [8338]
Alliance for Intl. Educational and Cultural Exchange [8338]
Amer. Coun. for Intl. Stud. [8339]
Amer. Coun. for Intl. Stud. [8339]
Amer. Egyptian Cooperation Found. [17931]
Amer. Egyptian Cooperation Found. [17931]
Amer. Forum for Global Educ. [8340]
Amer. Home Life Intl. [8341]
Amer. Home Life Intl. [8341]
Amer. Intercultural Student Exchange [8342]
Amer. Turkish Friendship Coun. [17937]
Amer. Univ. in Moscow [8343]
Amer. Univ. in Moscow [8343]
Asian Amer. Curriculum Proj. [8344]
Asian Amer. Curriculum Proj. [8344]
ASPECT Found. [8345]
ASSE Intl. Student Exchange Programs [8346]
ASSE Intl. Student Exchange Programs [8346]
Assn. for Intl. Practical Training [8347]
Assn. for Intl. Practical Training [8347]
Assn. for World Travel Exchange [8366]
Au Pair in Am. [8348]
Brazilian Stud. Assn. [8349]
Brazilian Stud. Assn. [8349]
British Amer. Educational Found. [8350]
British Universities North Am. Club [8351]
Center for Citizen Initiatives [17960]
Center for Global Educ. [8406]
Community Colleges for Intl. Development [8352]
Community Colleges for Intl. Development [8352]
Coun. for Amer. Students in Intl. Negotiations [8386]
Coun. on Intl. Educational Exchange USA [8353]
Coun. on Intl. Educational Exchange USA [8353]
Coun. for Intl. Exchange of Scholars l Institute of Intl. Educ. [8354]
Coun. for Intl. Exchange of Scholars l Inst. of Intl. Educ. [8354]
Coun. on Standards for Intl. Educational Travel [8355]
Coun. on Standards for Intl. Educational Travel [8355]
Crosscurrents Intl. Inst. [17961]
East-West Center [17962]
Edu-Culture Intl. [8356]
EF Found. for Foreign Stud. [8357]
EF Found. for Foreign Stud. [8357]
Found. for Intl. Cooperation [8358]
Found. for Intl. Cooperation [8358]
French-American Found. [17965]
Friends of Togo [17966]
Friendship Ambassadors Found. [17967]
Friendship Force Intl. [17968]
Fulbright Assn. [8359]
Fulbright Assn. [8359]
GeoVisions [8360]
German Academic Exchange Ser. [8361]
German Academic Exchange Ser. [8361]
German Marshall Fund of the U.S. [17969]
Global Educ. Associates [17970]
Global Volunteers [17971]
Inst. of Intl. Educ. [8362]
Inst. of Intl. Educ. [8362]
Inst. of World Affairs [8407]
InterExchange [8363]
InterExchange [8363]
InterFuture [8408]
Intl. Book Bank [8364]
Intl. Book Bank [8364]
Intl. Book Proj. [8365]
Intl. Book Proj. [8365]
Intl. Center in New York [17974]
Intl. Counselor Exchange Program [8366]
Intl. Healthy Cities Found. [13345]
Intl. Multiracial Shared Cultural Org. [17975]
Intl. Res. and Exchanges Bd. [8367]
Intl. Res. and Exchanges Bd. [8367]International-ISAR: Resources for Environmental Activists
Japan-America Student Conf. [8368]
Japan Center for Intl. Exchange USA [17976]
Legacy Intl. [8409]

A star before a book entry number signifies that the name is not listed separately, but is mentioned within the entry.

Lisle Intercultural [8369]
Lisle Intercultural [8369]
Meridian Intl. Center [17977]
NACEL Open Door [8370]
Natl. Coun. for Intl. Visitors [17979]
Natl. Jewish Democratic Coun. [18387]
Natl. Registration Center for Stud. Abroad [8371]
Natl. Registration Center for Stud. Abroad [8371]
One to World [8372]
OneWorld Now! [8929]
Our Developing World [17981]
Overseas Young Chinese Forum [7845]
Palestine Center [8373]
People to People Ambassador Prog. [17982]
People to People Intl. [17983]
Perhaps Kids Meeting Kids Can Make a Difference [17984]
Prog. of Academic Exchange [8374]
Proj. Harmony [8375]
Scandinavian Seminar [8376]
Sister Cities Intl. [17985]
Soc. for Intercultural Educ., Training and Res. U.S.A. [8410]
U.S.-China Educ. Found. [8377]
U.S.-Japan Coun. [17955]
U.S. Servas [17986]
Unity-and-Diversity World Coun. [17987]
Volunteers for Peace [17990]
Working Capital for Community Needs [17991]
World Artists Experiences [9325]
World Bamboo Org. [4738]
World Heritage [8378]
World Learning [8379]
World Learning Visitor Exchange Prog. [17992]
World Neighbors [17993]
World Peace Found. [17994]
World Pen Pals [8380]
Yale-China Assn. [8381]
YMCA Intl. Camp Counselor Prog. [8382]
Youth For Understanding USA [8383]
Intl. Exchange Assn. [★8338]
Intl. Exchange Center [IO], Riga, Latvia
Intl. Exchangors Assn. - Defunct.
Intl. Executive Housekeepers Assn. [2247], 1001 Eastwind Dr., Ste. 301, Westerville, OH 43081-3361, (614)895-7166
Intl. Executive Ser. Corps [674], 1900 M St. NW, Ste. 500, Washington, DC 20036, (202)589-2600
Intl. Exer-Safety Assn. [★16224]
Intl. Exhibition Logistics Associates [IO], Berkhamsted, United Kingdom
Intl. Exhibitions Bur. [IO], Paris, France
Intl. Exhibitions Found. [★9164]
Intl. Exhibitors Assn. [★1238]
Intl. Experiential Marketing Assn. [2408], 550 15th St., Ste. 31, San Francisco, CA 94103, (415)355-1586
Intl. Experimental Aerospace Soc. [6087], 14870 Granada Ave., No. 316, Apple Valley, MN 55124, (952)583-2587
Intl. Expressive Arts Therapy Assn. [13773], PO Box 320399, San Francisco, CA 94132-0399, (415)522-8959
Intl. Eye Found. [15962], 10801 Connecticut Ave., Kensington, MD 20895, (240)290-0263
Intl. Fabricare Inst. [★2191]
Intl. Fac. Mgt. Assn. [2901], 1 E Greenway Plz., Ste. 1100, Houston, TX 77046-0104, (713)623-4362
Intl. Fac. Mgt. Assn. - Toronto Chap. [IO], Toronto, ON, Canada
Intl. Factoring Assn. [1308], 2665 Shell Beach Rd., Ste. 3, Pismo Beach, CA 93449-1778, (805)773-0011
Intl. Fainting Goat Assn. [4501], 1039 State Rte. 168, Darlington, PA 16115, (724)843-2084
Intl. Fan Club Org. [23858], PO Box 40328, Nashville, TN 37204-0328, (615)371-9596
Intl. Fancy Guppy Assn. - Address unknown since 2010.
Intl. Fantasy Gaming Soc. [21748], PO Box 36555, Cincinnati, OH 45236, (303)443-1012
Intl. Farm Mgt. Assn. [IO], Cambridge, United Kingdom
Intl. Fed. of Accountants [35], 545 5th Ave., 14th Fl., New York, NY 10017, (212)286-9344

Intl. Fed. of Action by Christians for the Abolition of Torture [IO], Paris, France
Intl. Fed. of Actors [IO], Brussels, Belgium
Intl. Fed. of Advt. Agencies [★810]
Intl. Fed. of Aestheticians [IO], Brussels, Belgium
Intl. Fed. on Ageing [IO], Toronto, ON, Canada
Intl. Fed. of Agricultural Journalists [IO], Duiven, Netherlands
Intl. Fed. of Agricultural Producers [IO], Paris, France
Intl. Fed. of Air Line Pilots Associations [IO], Chertsey, United Kingdom
Intl. Fed. of Air Traffic Controllers' Associations [IO], Montreal, QC, Canada
Intl. Fed. of Air Traffic Safety Electronics Assn. [IO], Steenokkerzeel, Belgium
Intl. Fed. of Airworthiness [IO], East Grinstead, United Kingdom
Intl. Fed. of Amer. Football [IO], La Courneuve, France
Intl. Fed. of Amer. Homing Pigeon Fanciers [22097], Val Matteucci, Sec.-Treas., PO Box 374, Hicksville, NY 11802, (516)794-3612
Intl. Fed. of Anti-Leprosy Associations [IO], London, United Kingdom
Intl. Fed. of Arts Councils and Culture Agencies [IO], Strawberry Hills, Australia
Intl. Fed. of Asian and Western Pacific Contractors' Associations [IO], Pasig City, Philippines
Intl. Fed. of Assoc. Wrestling Styles [IO], Vevey, Switzerland
Intl. Fed. of Assn. Football [IO], Zurich, Switzerland
Intl. Fed. of Associations of Pharmaceutical Physicians [IO], Woerden, Netherlands
Intl. Fed. of Audit Bureaux of Circulations [IO], Petaling Jaya, Malaysia
Intl. Fed. of Automatic Control - Canada [IO], Gatineau, QC, Canada
Intl. Fed. of Automatic Control - Hungary [IO], Budapest, Hungary
Intl. Fed. of Auto. Experts [IO], Brussels, Belgium
Intl. Fed. of Automotive Aftermarket Distributors [IO], Brussels, Belgium
Intl. Fed. of Automotive Engg. Societies [IO], London, United Kingdom
Intl. Fed. of Basque Pelota [IO], Pamplona, Spain
Intl. Fed. of Beekeepers' Associations [IO], Rome, Italy
Intl. Fed. of Bike Messenger Associations
Intl. Fed. of Biomedical Lab. Sci. [IO], Hamilton, ON, Canada
Intl. Fed. of Black Prides [12092], 1806 Vernon St. NW, Ste. 200, Washington, DC 20009, (202)347-0555
Intl. Fed. of Blood Donor Organizations [IO], Frederiksberg, Denmark
Intl. Fed. of the Blue Cross [IO], Bern, Switzerland
Intl. Fed. of Boat Show Organisers [IO], Woking, United Kingdom
Intl. Fed. of Bodybuilders and Fitness [IO], Montreal, QC, Canada
Intl. Fed. of Camping and Caravanning [IO], Brussels, Belgium
Intl. Fed. of Catholic Medical Associations [IO], Vatican City, Vatican City
Intl. Fed. of Catholic Parochial Youth Communities [IO], Antwerp, Belgium
Intl. Fed. of Catholic Universities [IO], Paris, France
Intl. Fed. of Cell Biology [6303], Marshall Univ. School of Medicine, 1542 Spring Valley Dr., Huntington, WV 25704-9388, (304)696-7339
Intl. Fed. for Cervical Pathology and Colposcopy [IO], Dublin, Ireland
Intl. Fed. of Chem., Energy, Mine and Gen. Workers' Unions [IO], Geneva, Switzerland
Intl. Fed. of Chiropractors and Organizations [14138], 2276 Wassergass Rd., Hellertown, PA 18055, (239)597-6099
Intl. Fed. for Choral Music [IO], Louvigny, France
Intl. Fed. of Clinical Chemistry and Lab. Medicine [IO], Milan, Italy
Intl. Fed. of Clinical Neurophysiology [IO], Vancouver, BC, Canada
Intl. Fed. of Competitive Eating [22982], 18 E 41st St., 15th Fl., New York, NY 10017, (212)352-8651

Intl. Fed. of Consular Corps and Associations [IO], Brussels, Belgium
Intl. Fed. of Consulting Engineers [IO], Geneva, Switzerland
Intl. Fed. of Cosmopolitan Clubs [★13056]
Intl. Fed. of Customs Brokers Associations [IO], Ottawa, ON, Canada
Intl. Fed. of Denturists [IO], Winnipeg, MB, Canada
Intl. Fed. of Employees in Public Ser. [IO], Brussels, Belgium
Intl. Fed. of Engg. Educ. Societies [8124], Amer. Soc. for Engg. Educ., 1818 N St. NW, Ste. 600, Washington, DC 20036-2476, (202)331-3511
Intl. Fed. for Equestrian Sports [IO], Lausanne, Switzerland
Intl. Fed. of Essential Oils and Aroma Trades [IO], London, United Kingdom
Intl. Fed. of Esthetic Dentistry [IO], Taubate, Brazil
Intl. Fed. of Esthetic Dentistry [14295], 3420 Fostoria Way, Ste. G202, San Ramon, CA 94583, (925)901-0262
Intl. Fed. of Exhibition and Event Services [IO], Brussels, Belgium
Intl. Fed. of Family Associations of Missing Persons from Armed Conflicts [12544], PO Box 6888, Rockford, IL 61125
Intl. Fed. of Festival Organizations [1198], 4230 Stansbury Ave., Ste. 105, Sherman Oaks, CA 91423, (818)789-7596
Intl. Fed. of Film Archives [IO], Brussels, Belgium
Intl. Fed. of Film Producers Associations [IO], Paris, France
Intl. Fed. of Foot and Ankle Societies [16298], 6300 N River Rd., Ste. 510, Rosemont, IL 60018, (847)698-4654
Intl. Fed. of Freight Forwarders Associations [IO], Glattbrugg, Switzerland
Intl. Fed. of Fruit Juice Producers [IO], Paris, France
Intl. Fed. of Gynecology and Obstetrics [IO], London, United Kingdom
Intl. Fed. of Hard of Hearing People [IO], Stockholm, Sweden
Intl. Fed. of Hard of Hearing Young People [IO], Ljubljana, Slovenia
Intl. Fed. of Hardware and Housewares Associations [IO], Kidderminster, United Kingdom
Intl. Fed. of Hea. Plans [IO], London, United Kingdom
Intl. Fed. for Heat Treatment and Surface Engg. [IO], London, United Kingdom
Intl. Fed. for High Rise Structures [IO], Bangalore, India
Intl. Fed. for Home Economics USA [8264], 402 N Randolph St., Macomb, IL 61455-2960
Intl. Fed. of Horseracing Authorities [IO], Boulogne, France
Intl. Fed. for Housing and Planning [IO], The Hague, Netherlands
Intl. Fed. of Hydrographic Societies [IO], Plymouth, United Kingdom
Intl. Fed. of Indus. Energy Consumers [IO], Brussels, Belgium
Intl. Fed. of Infection Control [IO], Portadown, United Kingdom
Intl. Fed. for Info. Processing [IO], Laxenburg, Austria
Intl. Fed. of Inspection Agencies-Americas Comm. [1917], 3942 N Upland St., Arlington, VA 22207, (703)533-9539
Intl. Fed. of Interior Architects/Designers [IO], Singapore, Singapore
Intl. Fed. of Intl. Furniture Removers [IO], Brussels, Belgium
Intl. Fed. of Inventors' Associations [IO], Budapest, Hungary
Intl. Fed. of Iranian Refugees [IO], Eindhoven, Netherlands
Intl. Fed. of Journalists [IO], Brussels, Belgium
Intl. Fed. of Kennel Clubs [IO], Thuin, Belgium
Intl. Fed. of Landscape Architects [IO], Christchurch, New Zealand
Intl. Fed. of Leather Guilds [2199], 2264 Logan Dr., New Palestine, IN 46163, (317)861-9711
Intl. Fed. of Liberal and Radical Youth [IO], London, United Kingdom

Reference to "IO" in place of a book number signifies that the association may be found in the 50th edition of International Organizations.

Intl. Fed. of Lib. Associations and Institutions [IO], The Hague, Netherlands

Intl. Fed. of the Little Bros. of the Poor [IO], Paris, France

Intl. Fed. for Manual/Musculoskeletal Medicine [IO], Warsage, Belgium

Intl. Fed. of Mfrs. of Gummed Paper [IO], Hoofddorp, Netherlands

Intl. Fed. of Marfan Syndrome Organizations [14602], Natl. Marfan Found., 22 Manhasset Ave., Port Washington, NY 11050

Intl. Fed. for Medical and Biological Engg. [IO], Singapore, Singapore

Intl. Fed. of Medical Students' Associations [IO], Ferney-Voltaire, France

Intl. Fed. of Messianic Jews [19964], PO Box 271708, Tampa, FL 33688

Intl. Fed. for Modern Languages and Literatures [IO], Umea, Sweden

Intl. Fed. of the Movements of Modern School [IO], Coyoacan, Mexico

Intl. Fed. of Municipal Engg. [IO], London, United Kingdom

Intl. Fed. of Musicians [IO], Paris, France

Intl. Fed. of Nematology Societies [IO], Richmond, BC, Canada

Intl. Fed. of Netball Associations [IO], Manchester, United Kingdom

Intl. Fed. of Nonlinear Analysts [7371], Florida Inst. of Tech., 150 W Univ. Blvd., Melbourne, FL 32901, (321)674-7412

Intl. Fed. of Ophthalmological Societies [15961], 945 Green St., San Francisco, CA 94133, (415)409-8410

Intl. Fed. of Organic Agriculture Movements [IO], Bonn, Germany

Intl. Fed. of Oto-Rhino-Laryngological Societies [IO], Leiden, Netherlands

Intl. Fed. of Park and Recreation Admin. [IO], Reading, United Kingdom

Intl. Fed. of Pediatric and Adolescent Gynecology [IO], Athens, Greece

Intl. Fed. of the Periodical Press [IO], London, United Kingdom

Intl. Fed. of Persons with Physical Disability [IO], Vac, Hungary

Intl. Fed. of Petanque and Provencal Games [IO], Marseille, France

Intl. Fed. of Petroleum and Chemical Workers - Defunct.

Intl. Fed. of Pharmaceutical Mfrs. and Associations [IO], Geneva, Switzerland

Intl. Fed. of Pharmaceutical Wholesalers [2695], 10569 Crestwood Dr., Manassas, VA 20109, (703)331-3714

Intl. Fed. of Philosophical Societies [10386], William L. McBride, Pres., Purdue Univ., Dept. of Philosophy, 100 N Univ. St., West Lafayette, IN 47907-2098, (765)494-4285

Intl. Fed. of the Phonographic Indus. - Chile [IO], Santiago, Chile

Intl. Fed. of the Phonographic Indus. - Czech Republic [IO], Prague, Czech Republic

Intl. Fed. of the Phonographic Indus. - Denmark [IO], Copenhagen, Denmark

Intl. Fed. of the Phonographic Indus. - England [IO], London, United Kingdom

Intl. Fed. of the Phonographic Indus. - Finland [IO], Helsinki, Finland

Intl. Fed. of the Phonographic Indus. - Germany [IO], Berlin, Germany

Intl. Fed. of the Phonographic Indus. - Hong Kong [IO], Hong Kong, People's Republic of China

Intl. Fed. of the Phonographic Indus. - Israel [IO], Ramat Gan, Israel

Intl. Fed. of the Phonographic Indus. - Jamaica [IO], Kingston, Jamaica

Intl. Fed. of the Phonographic Indus. - Nigeria [IO], Lagos, Nigeria

Intl. Fed. of the Phonographic Indus. - Slovak Republic [IO], Bratislava, Slovakia

Intl. Fed. of the Phonographic Indus. - Sweden [IO], Stockholm, Sweden

Intl. Fed. of the Phonographic Indus. - Switzerland [IO], Zurich, Switzerland

Intl. Fed. of Photographic Art [IO], Paris, France

Intl. Fed. for Physical Educ. [IO], Foz do Iguacu, Brazil

Intl. Fed. of Postcard Dealers [22104], PO Box 399, Neosho, MO 64850

Intl. Fed. of Postcard Dealers [22104], PO Box 399, Neosho, MO 64850

Intl. Fed. of Professional Aromatherapists [IO], Hinckley, United Kingdom

Intl. Fed. of Professional and Tech. Engineers [6802], 501 3rd St. NW, Ste. 701, Washington, DC 20001, (202)239-4880

Intl. Fed. of Psoriasis Associations [14328], 6600 SW 92nd, Ste. 300, Portland, OR 97223-7195, (503)244-7404

Intl. Fed. of Psoriasis Associations [14328], 6600 SW 92nd, Ste. 300, Portland, OR 97223-7195, (503)244-7404

Intl. Fed. for Psychoanalytic Educ. [8760], PO Box 961, Culver City, CA 90232-0961, (310)694-3463

Intl. Fed. for Psychoanalytic Educ. [★8760]

Intl. Fed. of Psychoanalytic Societies [IO], Mexico City, Mexico

Intl. Fed. of Purchasing and Supply Mgt. [IO], Aarau, Austria

Intl. Fed. of Rabbis [19868], 5600 Wisconsin Ave., No. 1107, Chevy Chase, MD 20815

Intl. Fed. of Rabbis [19868], 5600 Wisconsin Ave., No. 1107, Chevy Chase, MD 20815

Intl. Fed. of Ragtime - Defunct.

Intl. Fed. of Red Cross and Red Crescent Societies [IO], Geneva, Switzerland

Intl. Fed. of Red Cross and Red Crescent Societies - Vietnam [IO], Hanoi, Vietnam

Intl. Fed. of Registered Equine Massage Therapists [IO], St. Thomas, ON, Canada

Intl. Fed. of Reproduction Rights Org. [IO], Brussels, Belgium

Intl. Fed. for Res. in Women's History [IO], Sheffield, United Kingdom

Intl. Fed. of Robotics [IO], Frankfurt, Germany

Intl. Fed. of Rock Art Organizations [IO], Caulfield South, Australia

Intl. Fed. for the Roofing Trade [IO], Marburg, Germany

Intl. Fed. of Rowing Associations [IO], Lausanne, Switzerland

Intl. Fed. of Rural Adult Catholic Movements [IO], Assesse, Belgium

Intl. Fed. of Secular Humanistic Jews [★19820]

Intl. Fed. of Secular Humanistic Jews [★19820]

Intl. Fed. for Secular Humanistic Judaism [19820], 1777 T St. NW, Washington, DC 20009, (202)248-4880

Intl. Fed. for Secular Humanistic Judaism [19820], 1777 T St. NW, Washington, DC 20009, (202)248-4880

Intl. Fed. for Secular Humanistic Judaism [★19820]

Intl. Fed. of Shipmasters' Associations [IO], London, United Kingdom

Intl. Fed. of Sleddog Sports [22556], Sally O'Sullivan Bair, Sec. Gen., 8554 Gateway Cir., Monticello, MN 55362, (763)295-5465

Intl. Fed. of Social Workers [IO], Bern, Switzerland

Intl. Fed. of the Societies of Classical Stud. [IO], Neuchatel, Switzerland

Intl. Fed. of Societies of Cosmetic Chemists [IO], Luton, United Kingdom

Intl. Fed. of Societies of Electron Microscopy [★7114]

Intl. Fed. of Societies of Electron Microscopy [★7114]

Intl. Fed. of Societies for Microscopy [7114], Prof. C. Barry Carter, Pres., Univ. of Connecticut, Dept. of Chem., Materials and Biomolecular Engg., 191 Auditorium Rd., Unit 3222, Storrs Mansfield, CT 06269-3222, (860)486-4020

Intl. Fed. of Societies for Microscopy [7114], Prof. C. Barry Carter, Pres., Univ. of Connecticut, Dept. of Chem., Materials and Biomolecular Engg., 191 Auditorium Rd., Unit 3222, Storrs Mansfield, CT 06269-3222, (860)486-4020

Intl. Fed. of Societies for Surgery of the Hand [14682], Duke Univ. Medical Center, PO Box 2912, Durham, NC 27710

Intl. Fed. of Societies for Surgery of the Hand [14682], Duke Univ. Medical Center, PO Box 2912, Durham, NC 27710

Intl. Fed. of Sound Hunters [IO], Bern, Switzerland

Intl. Fed. for Spina Bifida and Hydrocephalus [IO], Brussels, Belgium

Intl. Fed. of Spine Assns. - Defunct.

Intl. Fed. of Sports Chiropractic [IO], Lausanne, Switzerland

Intl. Fed. of Sports Medicine [IO], Rome, Italy

Intl. Fed. of Stamp Dealers' Associations [IO], Zurich, Switzerland

Intl. Fed. of Standards Users [IO], Geneva, Switzerland

Intl. Fed. of Surgical Colleges [IO], Dublin, Ireland

Intl. Fed. of Surveyors [IO], Copenhagen, Denmark

Intl. Fed. for Systems Res. [IO], Vienna, Austria

Intl. Fed. of Teachers of Eurhythmics [IO], Geneva, Switzerland

Intl. Fed. of Teachers of French [IO], Sevres, France

Intl. Fed. for the Teaching of English [IO], Winnipeg, MB, Canada

Intl. Fed. of Thanatologists Assn. [IO], Hilversum, Netherlands

Intl. Fed. for Theatre Res. [IO], Lancaster, United Kingdom

Intl. Fed. of Trade Unions of Transport Workers [IO], Brussels, Belgium

Intl. Fed. of Training Centers for the Promotion of Progressive Educ. [IO], Paris, France

Intl. Fed. of Training and Development Organizations [IO], New Delhi, India

Intl. Fed. of Translators [IO], Montreal, QC, Canada

Intl. Fed. of Univ. Women - Switzerland [IO], Geneva, Switzerland

Intl. Fed. of Vexillological Associations [10629], 504 Branard St., Houston, TX 77006-5018, (713)529-2545

Intl. Fed. of Vexillological Associations [10629], 504 Branard St., Houston, TX 77006-5018, (713)529-2545

Intl. Fed. of Wines and Spirits [IO], Paris, France

Intl. Fed. of Women's Travel Organizations [IO], Torremolinos, Spain

Intl. Feed Indus. Fed. [IO], Cheltenham, United Kingdom

Intl. Fellowship of Christians and Jews [20184], 30 N La Salle St., Ste. 2600, Chicago, IL 60602-3356, (312)641-7200

Intl. Fellowship of Christians and Jews [20184], 30 N La Salle St., Ste. 2600, Chicago, IL 60602-3356, (312)641-7200

Intl. Fellowship of Evangelical Students [IO], Oxford, United Kingdom

Intl. Fellowship of Fishing Rotarians [21735], 7600 NE 137 Pl., Citra, FL 32113, (352)236-4504

Intl. Fellowship of Fishing Rotarians [21735], 7600 NE 137 Pl., Citra, FL 32113, (352)236-4504

Intl. Fellowship of Reconciliation - Austria [IO], Vienna, Austria

Intl. Fellowship of Reconciliation - Bangladesh [IO], Dhaka, Bangladesh

Intl. Fellowship of Reconciliation - Belgium [IO], Brussels, Belgium

Intl. Fellowship of Reconciliation - England [IO], Oxford, United Kingdom

Intl. Fellowship of Reconciliation - France [IO], Paris, France

Intl. Fellowship of Reconciliation - Germany [IO], Minden, Germany

Intl. Fellowship of Reconciliation - India [IO], Trivandrum, India

Intl. Fellowship of Reconciliation - Italy [IO], Turin, Italy

Intl. Fellowship of Reconciliation - Japan [IO], Tokyo, Japan

Intl. Fellowship of Reconciliation - Madagascar [IO], Antananarivo, Madagascar

Intl. Fellowship of Reconciliation - Netherlands [IO], Alkmaar, Netherlands

Intl. Fellowship of Reconciliation - Norway [IO], Oslo, Norway

Intl. Fellowship of Reconciliation - Sweden [IO], Sundbyberg, Sweden

Intl. Fellowship of Reconciliation - Uganda [IO], Kampala, Uganda

A star before a book entry number signifies that the name is not listed separately, but is mentioned within the entry.

Intl. Fellowship of Reconciliation - Wales [IO], Caernarfon, United Kingdom

Intl. Fellowship of Reconciliation - Zimbabwe [IO], Harare, Zimbabwe

Intl. Fellowship Soc. [★1348]

Intl. Female Boxers Assn. [22437], 701 N Green Valley Pkwy., Ste. 200, Henderson, NV 89074, (310)428-1403

Intl. Feminist Approaches to Bioethics [11981], 5 Riverpointe Rd., Hastings-on-Hudson, NY 10706, (914)674-0122

Intl. Feminist Approaches to Bioethics [11981], 5 Riverpointe Rd., Hastings-on-Hudson, NY 10706, (914)674-0122

Intl. Fence Indus. Assn. [★840]

Intl. Fence Indus. Assn. [★840]

Intl. Feng Shui Guild [9573], 705 B SE Melody Ln., Ste. 166, Lee's Summit, MO 64063, (816)246-1898

Intl. Feng Shui Guild [9573], 705 B SE Melody Ln., Ste. 166, Lee's Summit, MO 64063, (816)246-1898

Intl. Fertiliser Soc. - England [IO], York, United Kingdom

Intl. Fertility Res. Prog. [★12033]

Intl. Fertility Res. Prog. [★12033]

Intl. Fertilizer Development Center - USA [★3756]

Intl. Fertilizer Development Center - USA [★3756]

Intl. Fertilizer Indus. Assn. [IO], Paris, France

Intl. Festivals Assn. [★1199]

Intl. Festivals Assn. [★1199]

Intl. Festivals and Events Assn. [1199], 2603 Eastover Terr., Boise, ID 83706, (208)433-0950

Intl. Festivals and Events Assn. [1199], 2603 Eastover Terr., Boise, ID 83706, (208)433-0950

Intl. Fibrodysplasia Ossificans Progressiva Assn. [14603], PO Box 196217, Winter Springs, FL 32719-6217, (407)365-4194

Intl. Fiction Rev. [IO], Fredericton, NB, Canada

Intl. Fight'n Rooster Cutlery Club [21874], 140 Public Sq., Lebanon, TN 37087, (615)444-8070

Intl. Fight'n Rooster Cutlery Club [21874], 140 Public Sq., Lebanon, TN 37087, (615)444-8070

Intl. Film Seminars [9604], 6 E 39th St., 12th Fl., New York, NY 10016, (212)448-0457

Intl. Film Seminars [9604], 6 E 39th St., 12th Fl., New York, NY 10016, (212)448-0457

Intl. Finance Corp. [17580], 2121 Pennsylvania Ave. NW, Washington, DC 20433, (202)473-1000

Intl. Finance Corp. [17580], 2121 Pennsylvania Ave. NW, Washington, DC 20433, (202)473-1000

Intl. Financial Services Assn. [420], 9 Sylvan Way, Ste. 130, Parsippany, NJ 07054-3817, (973)656-1900

Intl. Fine Print Dealers Assn. [254], 250 W 26th St., Ste. 405, New York, NY 10001, (212)674-6095

Intl. Fine Print Dealers Assn. [254], 250 W 26th St., Ste. 405, New York, NY 10001, (212)674-6095

Intl. Finn Assn. [IO], Pezilla-la-Riviere, France

Intl. Finn Assn. - Antigua [IO], English Harbour, Antigua-Barbuda

Intl. Finn Assn. - Australia [IO], East Fremantle, Australia

Intl. Finn Assn. - Austria [IO], Gmunden, Austria

Intl. Finn Assn. - Belarus [IO], Minsk, Belarus

Intl. Finn Assn. - Belgium [IO], Lokeren, Belgium

Intl. Finn Assn. - Bermuda [IO], Pembroke, Bermuda

Intl. Finn Assn. - Brazil [IO], Sao Paulo, Brazil

Intl. Finn Assn. - Canada [IO], Milton, ON, Canada

Intl. Finn Assn. - Costa Rica [IO], San Jose, Costa Rica

Intl. Finn Assn. - Croatia [IO], Split, Croatia

Intl. Finn Assn. - Czech Republic [IO], Prague, Czech Republic

Intl. Finn Assn. - Denmark [IO], Ishoj, Denmark

Intl. Finn Assn. - Estonia [IO], Parnu, Estonia

Intl. Finn Assn. - Finland [IO], Espoo, Finland

Intl. Finn Assn. - France [IO], Nantes, France

Intl. Finn Assn. - Germany [IO], Emden, Germany

Intl. Finn Assn. - Greece [IO], Athens, Greece

Intl. Finn Assn. - Hong Kong [IO], Hong Kong, People's Republic of China

Intl. Finn Assn. - Hungary [IO], Budapest, Hungary

Intl. Finn Assn. - Iceland [IO], Hafnarfjorour, Iceland

Intl. Finn Assn. - India [IO], Mumbai, India

Intl. Finn Assn. - Japan [IO], Tokyo, Japan

Intl. Finn Assn. - Lithuania [IO], Kaunas, Lithuania

Intl. Finn Assn. - Mexico [IO], Guadalajara, Mexico

Intl. Finn Assn. - Monaco [IO], Monaco, Monaco

Intl. Finn Assn. - Netherlands [IO], Amsterdam, Netherlands

Intl. Finn Assn. - New Zealand [IO], Auckland, New Zealand

Intl. Finn Assn. - Philippines [IO], Quezon City, Philippines

Intl. Finn Assn. - Poland [IO], Olsztyn, Poland

Intl. Finn Assn. - Portugal [IO], Lisbon, Portugal

Intl. Finn Assn. - Romania [IO], Constanta, Romania

Intl. Finn Assn. - Russia [IO], Moscow, Russia

Intl. Finn Assn. - Slovakia [IO], Senec, Slovakia

Intl. Finn Assn. - Slovenia [IO], Koper, Slovenia

Intl. Finn Assn. - South Africa [IO], Cape Town, Republic of South Africa

Intl. Finn Assn. - Spain [IO], Cartagena, Spain

Intl. Finn Assn. - Switzerland [IO], Bern, Switzerland

Intl. Finn Assn. - Thailand [IO], Bangkok, Thailand

Intl. Finn Assn. - Turkey [IO], Istanbul, Turkey

Intl. Finn Assn. - Ukraine [IO], Yuzhny, Ukraine

Intl. Finn Assn. - Zimbabwe [IO], Harare, Zimbabwe

Intl. Fire Buff Associates [21708], 11017 N Redwood Tree Ct., Mequon, WI 53092

Intl. Fire Chiefs' Assn. of Asia [IO], Tokyo, Japan

Intl. Fire Marshals Assn. [5444], 1 Batterymarch Park, Quincy, MA 02169-7471, (617)984-7424

Intl. Fire Marshals Assn. [5444], 1 Batterymarch Park, Quincy, MA 02169-7471, (617)984-7424

Intl. Fire Photographers Assn. [2721], 15 Sherrin Rd., Chestnut Hill, MA 02467

Intl. Fire Photographers Assn. [2721], 15 Sherrin Rd., Chestnut Hill, MA 02467

Intl. Fire Ser. Training Assn. [8966], 930 N Willis, Stillwater, OK 74078, (405)744-5723

Intl. Fire Ser. Training Assn. [8966], 930 N Willis, Stillwater, OK 74078, (405)744-5723

Intl. FireStop Coun. [6862], 17209 Bradgate Ave., Cleveland, OH 44111, (877)241-3769

Intl. FireStop Coun. [6862], 17209 Bradgate Ave., Cleveland, OH 44111, (877)241-3769

Intl. Fiscal Assn. [IO], Rotterdam, Netherlands

Intl. Fiscal Assn. - Australia [IO], Sydney, Australia

Intl. Fiscal Assn. - Belgium [IO], Brussels, Belgium

Intl. Fiscal Assn. - Brazil [IO], Rio de Janeiro, Brazil

Intl. Fiscal Assn. - Canada Br. [IO], Kingston, ON, Canada

Intl. Fiscal Assn. - China [IO], Shanghai, People's Republic of China

Intl. Fiscal Assn. - Colombia [IO], Bogota, Colombia

Intl. Fiscal Assn. - Cyprus [IO], Limassol, Cyprus

Intl. Fiscal Assn. - Czech Republic [IO], Prague, Czech Republic

Intl. Fiscal Assn. - Egypt [IO], Cairo, Egypt

Intl. Fiscal Assn. - Estonia [IO], Tartu, Estonia

Intl. Fiscal Assn. - Finland [IO], Helsinki, Finland

Intl. Fiscal Assn. - France [IO], Paris, France

Intl. Fiscal Assn. - Germany [IO], Bonn, Germany

Intl. Fiscal Assn. - Greece [IO], Athens, Greece

Intl. Fiscal Assn. - Hong Kong [IO], Hong Kong, People's Republic of China

Intl. Fiscal Assn. - Hungary [IO], Budapest, Hungary

Intl. Fiscal Assn. - Indonesia [IO], Jakarta, Indonesia

Intl. Fiscal Assn. - Ireland [IO], Dublin, Ireland

Intl. Fiscal Assn. - Israel [IO], Tel Aviv, Israel

Intl. Fiscal Assn. - Italy [IO], Rome, Italy

Intl. Fiscal Assn. - Japan [IO], Tokyo, Japan

Intl. Fiscal Assn. - Luxembourg [IO], Luxembourg, Luxembourg

Intl. Fiscal Assn. - Malaysia [IO], Kuala Lumpur, Malaysia

Intl. Fiscal Assn. - Malta [IO], Valletta, Malta

Intl. Fiscal Assn. - Mauritius [IO], Port Louis, Mauritius

Intl. Fiscal Assn. - Poland [IO], Warsaw, Poland

Intl. Fiscal Assn. - Russia [IO], Moscow, Russia

Intl. Fiscal Assn. - Singapore [IO], Singapore, Singapore

Intl. Fiscal Assn. - Spain [IO], Pamplona, Spain

Intl. Fiscal Assn. - United Arab Emirates [IO], Dubai, United Arab Emirates

Intl. Fiscal Assn. - Uruguay [IO], Montevideo, Uruguay

Intl. Fishmeal and Fish Oil Org. [IO], St. Albans, United Kingdom

Intl. Fitness Assn. [16227], 12472 Lake Underhill Rd., No. 341, Orlando, FL 32828, (407)579-8610

Intl. Fitness Professionals Assn. [16228], 14509 Univ. Point Pl., Tampa, FL 33613, (813)979-1925

Intl. Flattie Yacht Racing Assn. [★22338]

Intl. Flight Services Assn. [1445], 1100 Johnson Ferry Rd., Ste. 300, Atlanta, GA 30342, (404)252-3663

Intl. Flight Services Assn. [1445], 1100 Johnson Ferry Rd., Ste. 300, Atlanta, GA 30342, (404)252-3663

Intl. Floorball Fed. [IO], Helsinki, Finland

Intl. Florist Org. [IO], Ede, Netherlands

Intl. Fluid Power Soc. [6865], PO Box 1420, Cherry Hill, NJ 08034-0054, (856)489-8983

Intl. Fly Fishing Assn. [IO], Perth, United Kingdom

Intl. Flying Dutchman Class Assn. of the U.S. [22352], Jonathan Clapp, Sec.-Treas., PO Box 223, Amherst, MA 01004-0223, (978)660-4497

Intl. Flying Dutchman Class Assn. of the U.S. [22352], Jonathan Clapp, Sec.-Treas., PO Box 223, Amherst, MA 01004-0223, (978)660-4497

Intl. Flying Farmers [4353], PO Box 309, Mansfield, IL 61854, (217)489-9300

Intl. Flying Farmers [4353], PO Box 309, Mansfield, IL 61854, (217)489-9300

Intl. Folk Dance Found. [★9314]

Intl. Food and Agribusiness Mgt. Assn. [1399], PO Box 14145, College Station, TX 77841-4145, (979)845-2118

Intl. Food and Agribusiness Mgt. Assn. [1399], PO Box 14145, College Station, TX 77841-4145, (979)845-2118

Intl. Food Info. Coun. [1400], 1100 Connecticut Ave. NW, Ste. 430, Washington, DC 20036, (202)296-6540

Intl. Food Info. Ser. [IO], Reading, United Kingdom

Intl. Food Policy Res. Inst. [17874], 2033 K St. NW, Washington, DC 20006-1002, (202)862-5600

Intl. Food Policy Res. Inst. [17874], 2033 K St. NW, Washington, DC 20006-1002, (202)862-5600

Intl. Food Safety Coun. - Address unknown since 2010.

Intl. Food Ser. Executive's Assn. [1446], 4955 Miller St., Ste. 107, Wheat Ridge, CO 80033, (800)893-5499

Intl. Food Ser. Executive's Assn. [1446], 4955 Miller St., Ste. 107, Wheat Ridge, CO 80033, (800)893-5499

Intl. Food, Wine and Travel Writers Assn. [2831], 1142 S Diamond Bar Blvd., No. 177, Diamond Bar, CA 91765-2203, (909)860-6914

Intl. Food, Wine and Travel Writers Assn. [2831], 1142 S Diamond Bar Blvd., No. 177, Diamond Bar, CA 91765-2203, (909)860-6914

Intl. Foodservice Distributors Assn. [1447], 1410 Spring Hill Rd., No. 210, McLean, VA 22102, (703)532-9400

Intl. Foodservice Distributors Assn. [1447], 1410 Spring Hill Rd., No. 210, McLean, VA 22102, (703)532-9400

Intl. Foodservice Editorial Coun. [2832], PO Box 491, Hyde Park, NY 12538-0491, (845)229-6973

Intl. Foodservice Editorial Coun. [2832], PO Box 491, Hyde Park, NY 12538-0491, (845)229-6973

Intl. Foodservice Mfrs. Assn. [1401], 2 Prudential Plz., 180 N Stetson Ave., Ste. 4400, Chicago, IL 60601, (312)540-4400

Intl. Foodservice Mfrs. Assn. [1401], 2 Prudential Plz., 180 N Stetson Ave., Ste. 4400, Chicago, IL 60601, (312)540-4400

Intl. Foodservice Mfrs. Assn. I Intl. Gold and Silver Plate Soc. [18941], 2 Prudential Plz., 180 N Stetson Ave., Ste. 4400, Chicago, IL 60601-6766, (312)540-4400

Intl. Footprint Assn. [5701], PO Box 1652, Walnut, CA 91788-1652, (877)432-3668

Intl. FOP Assn. [★14603]

Intl. Forensic Entomology Detection Canine Assn. [5489], 1913 Hooper Ave., Toms River, NJ 08753, (732)255-1649

Intl. Formalwear Assn. [208], 244 E Main St., Galesburg, IL 61401, (309)721-5450

Intl. Formalwear Assn. [208], 244 E Main St., Galesburg, IL 61401, (309)721-5450

Reference to "IO" in place of a book number signifies that the association may be found in the 50th edition of International Organizations.

Intl. Fortean Org. **[7252]**, PO Box 50088, Baltimore, MD 21211, (443)564-2158

Intl. Fortean Org. **[7252]**, PO Box 50088, Baltimore, MD 21211, (443)564-2158

Intl. Forum of Alan's - Defunct.

Intl. Forum on Globalization **[17899]**, 1009 Gen. Kennedy Ave., No. 2, San Francisco, CA 94129, (415)561-7650

Intl. Forum on Globalization **[17899]**, 1009 Gen. Kennedy Ave., No. 2, San Francisco, CA 94129, (415)561-7650

Intl. Forum for Psychoanalytic Educ. **[8760]**, PO Box 961, Culver City, CA 90232-0961, (310)694-3463

Intl. Found. **[12344]**, PO Box 69, Brookfield, WI 53008-0069, (888)334-3327

Intl. Found. **[12344]**, PO Box 69, Brookfield, WI 53008-0069, (888)334-3327

Intl. Found. for Art Res. **[9184]**, 500 5th Ave., Ste. 935, New York, NY 10110, (212)391-6234

Intl. Found. for Art Res. **[9184]**, 500 5th Ave., Ste. 935, New York, NY 10110, (212)391-6234

Intl. Found. of Bio-Magnetics

Intl. Found. of Bio-Magnetics - Address unknown since 2011.

Intl. Found. for the Conservation of Wildlife **[IO]**, Paris, France

Intl. Found. for Dermatology **[IO]**, London, United Kingdom

Intl. Found. for Election Systems **[17610]**, 1101 15th St. NW, 3rd Fl., Washington, DC 20005, (202)350-6700

Intl. Found. for Electoral Systems **[★17610]**

Intl. Found. of Employee Benefit Plans **[1128]**, PO Box 69, Brookfield, WI 53008-0069, (262)786-6700

Intl. Found. of Employee Benefit Plans **[1128]**, PO Box 69, Brookfield, WI 53008-0069, (262)786-6700

Intl. Found. for Ethical Res. **[10990]**, 53 W Jackson Blvd., Ste. 1552, Chicago, IL 60604, (312)427-6025

Intl. Found. for Ethical Res. **[10990]**, 53 W Jackson Blvd., Ste. 1552, Chicago, IL 60604, (312)427-6025

Intl. Found. for Functional Gastrointestinal Disorders **[14567]**, PO Box 170864, Milwaukee, WI 53217, (414)964-1799

Intl. Found. for Functional Gastrointestinal Disorders **[14567]**, PO Box 170864, Milwaukee, WI 53217, (414)964-1799

Intl. Found. for Gender Educ. **[13105]**, PO Box 540229, Waltham, MA 02454, (781)899-2212

Intl. Found. of the High-Altitude Res. Stations Jungfraujoch and Gornergrat **[IO]**, Bern, Switzerland

Intl. Found. for Music Res. **[★10248]**

Intl. Found. for Protection Officers **[3217]**, PO Box 771329, Naples, FL 34107-1329, (239)430-0534

Intl. Found. for Protection Officers **[3217]**, PO Box 771329, Naples, FL 34107-1329, (239)430-0534

Intl. Found. for Telemetering **[7553]**, 5665 Oberlin Dr., Ste. 200, San Diego, CA 92121, (858)225-4164

Intl. Found. for Telemetering **[7553]**, 5665 Oberlin Dr., Ste. 200, San Diego, CA 92121, (858)225-4164

Intl. Found. for Terror Act Victims **[12970]**, 1300 Indus. Blvd., Ste. 204, Southampton, PA 18966, (321)213-0198

Intl. Found. for Terror Act Victims **[12970]**, 1300 Indus. Blvd., Ste. 204, Southampton, PA 18966, (321)213-0198

Intl. Fragrance Assn. **[IO]**, Brussels, Belgium

Intl. Franchise Assn. **[1528]**, 1501 K St. NW, Ste. 350, Washington, DC 20005, (202)628-8000

Intl. Franchise Assn. **[1528]**, 1501 K St. NW, Ste. 350, Washington, DC 20005, (202)628-8000

Intl. Frankenstein Soc. - Address unknown since 2010.

Intl. Fraternity of Lambda Alpha **[★23505]**

Intl. Freedom of Expression Exchange CH **[IO]**, Toronto, ON, Canada

Intl. Freedom Found. **[17426]**, 200 G St. NE, Ste. 300, Washington, DC 20002-4328, (202)546-5788

Intl. Freedom to Publish Comm.

Intl. Freedom to Publish Comm. - Defunct.

Intl. Freeze-Dry Floral Assn. - Defunct.

Intl. French Brittany Club of Am. **[21584]**, 870 Barren Valley Rd., Chuckey, TN 37641

Intl. French Brittany Club of Am. **[21584]**, 870 Barren Valley Rd., Chuckey, TN 37641

Intl. Friends of the London Lib.

Intl. Friends of the London Lib. - Defunct.

Intl. Friends of Nature **[IO]**, Vienna, Austria

Intl. Friesian Show Horse Assn. **[4598]**, PO Box 535, Santa Ynez, CA 93460, (805)448-3027

Intl. Fruit Tree Assn. **[4970]**, Rick Dungey, Exec. Dir., 16020 Swingley Ridge Rd., Ste. 300, Chesterfield, MO 63017, (636)449-5083

Intl. Fruit Tree Assn. **[4970]**, Rick Dungey, Exec. Dir., 16020 Swingley Ridge Rd., Ste. 300, Chesterfield, MO 63017, (636)449-5083

Intl. Function Point Users Gp. **[675]**, 191 Clarksville Rd., Princeton Junction, NJ 08550, (609)799-4900

Intl. Functional Elecl. Stimulation Soc. **[15658]**, 1854 Los Encinos Ave., Glendale, CA 91208-2240

Intl. Functional Elecl. Stimulation Soc. **[15658]**, 1854 Los Encinos Ave., Glendale, CA 91208-2240

Intl. Fund for Agricultural Development - Italy **[IO]**, Rome, Italy

Intl. Fund for Animal Welfare **[10991]**, 290 Summer St., Yarmouth Port, MA 02675-0193, (508)744-2000

Intl. Fund for Animal Welfare **[10991]**, 290 Summer St., Yarmouth Port, MA 02675-0193, (508)744-2000

Intl. Fund for Concerned Photography **[★8710]**

Intl. Fund for Concerned Photography **[★8710]**

Intl. Fur Trade Fed. **[IO]**, Weybridge, United Kingdom

Intl. Furnishings and Design Assn. **[2064]**, 150 S Warner Rd., Ste. 156, King of Prussia, PA 19406, (610)535-6422

Intl. Furnishings and Design Assn. **[2064]**, 150 S Warner Rd., Ste. 156, King of Prussia, PA 19406, (610)535-6422

Intl. Furniture Rental Assn. **[1553]**, 5229 Coll. Hill Rd., Woodstock, VT 05091

Intl. Furniture Rental Assn. **[1553]**, 5229 Coll. Hill Rd., Woodstock, VT 05091

Intl. Furniture and Trans. Logistics Coun. **[3251]**, 282 N Ridge Rd., Brooklyn, MI 49230, (517)467-9355

Intl. Furniture Trans. and Logistics Coun. **[3251]**, 282 N Ridge Rd., Brooklyn, MI 49230, (517)467-9355

Intl. G. G. Drayton Assn. - Defunct.

Intl. Galapagos Tour Operators Assn. **[23454]**, PO Box 1713, Lolo, MT 59847

Intl. Galapagos Tour Operators Assn. **[23454]**, PO Box 1713, Lolo, MT 59847

Intl. Galdos Assn. - Defunct.

Intl. Game Developers Assn. **[6459]**, 19 Mantua Rd., Mount Royal, NJ 08061, (856)423-2990

Intl. Game Developers Assn. **[6459]**, 19 Mantua Rd., Mount Royal, NJ 08061, (856)423-2990

Intl. Game Fish Assn. **[22578]**, IGFA Fishing Hall of Fame and Museum, 300 Gulf Stream Way, Dania Beach, FL 33004, (954)927-2628

Intl. Garden Club - Address unknown since 2010.

Intl. Gas Turbine Inst. **[★6782]**

Intl. Gas Turbine Inst. **[★6782]**

Intl. Gas Union **[IO]**, Oslo, Norway

Intl. Gay Bowling Org. **[22424]**, PO Box 30722, Charlotte, NC 28230-0722

Intl. Gay Figure Skating Union **[22895]**, PO Box 945, New York, NY 10116

Intl. Gay and Lesbian Aquatics **[23040]**, 7423 Hollywood Blvd., Los Angeles, CA 90046-2819

Intl. Gay and Lesbian Football Assn. **[22936]**, 723 ML King Jr. Way, Seattle, WA 98122

Intl. Gay and Lesbian Human Rights Commn. **[12093]**, 80 Maiden Ln., Ste. 1505, New York, NY 10038, (212)430-6054

Intl. Gay and Lesbian Human Rights Commn. **[12093]**, 80 Maiden Ln., Ste. 1505, New York, NY 10038, (212)430-6054

Intl. Gay and Lesbian Travel Assn. **[3563]**, 1201 NE 26th St., Ste. 103, Fort Lauderdale, FL 33305, (954)630-1637

Intl. Gay Rodeo Assn. **[22840]**, PO Box 460504, Aurora, CO 80046-0504

Intl. Gay Rodeo Assn. **[22840]**, PO Box 460504, Aurora, CO 80046-0504

Intl. Gender and Trade Network - Central Asia **[IO]**, Tashkent, Uzbekistan

Intl. Gen. Produce Assn. **[IO]**, London, United Kingdom

Intl. Generic Horse Assn. **[4599]**, PO Box 6778, San Pedro, CA 90734-6778

Intl. Genetic Epidemiology Soc. **[14514]**, Dept. of Epidemiology, Unit 1340, PO Box 301439, Houston, TX 77230-1439, (713)794-1594

Intl. Genetic Epidemiology Soc. **[14514]**, Dept. of Epidemiology, Unit 1340, PO Box 301439, Houston, TX 77230-1439, (713)794-1594

Intl. Genetic Resources Programme **[★3747]**

Intl. Genetic Resources Programme **[★3747]**

Intl. Genetics Fed. **[IO]**, Tubingen, Germany

Intl. Geographical Union **[IO]**, Seoul, Republic of Korea

Intl. Geographical Union - Commn. on Geographical Educ. **[IO]**, Hamilton, New Zealand

Intl. Geosphere-Biosphere Programme **[IO]**, Stockholm, Sweden

Intl. Geosynthetics Soc. **[6427]**, 1934 Commerce Lane, Ste. 4, Jupiter, FL 33458, (561)768-9489

Intl. Geosynthetics Soc. **[6427]**, 1934 Commerce Lane, Ste. 4, Jupiter, FL 33458, (561)768-9489

Intl. Geosynthetics Soc. - Brazilian Chap. **[IO]**, Sao Jose dos Campos, Brazil

Intl. Geosynthetics Soc. - Chinese Chap. **[IO]**, Shanghai, People's Republic of China

Intl. Geosynthetics Soc. - Indian Chap. **[IO]**, New Delhi, India

Intl. Geosynthetics Soc. - Turkish Chap. **[IO]**, Istanbul, Turkey

Intl. Geothermal Assn. **[IO]**, Reykjavik, Iceland

Intl. German Coolie Soc. and Registry **[21585]**, 1139 LCR 454, Groesbeck, TX 76642, (903)390-0300

Intl. Glaciological Soc. **[IO]**, Cambridge, United Kingdom

Intl. Glaucoma Assn. **[IO]**, Ashford, United Kingdom

Intl. Gloster Breeders Assn. **[21219]**, Regina McCarthy, Sec.-Treas., 58 Joanne Dr., Hanson, MA 02341, (781)294-0340

Intl. Glove Assn. **[1833]**, PO Box 146, Brookville, PA 15825, (814)328-5208

Intl. Glove Assn. **[1833]**, PO Box 146, Brookville, PA 15825, (814)328-5208

Intl. Goat Assn. **[4502]**, 1 World Ave., Little Rock, AR 72202, (501)454-1641

Intl. Goat Assn. **[4502]**, 1 World Ave., Little Rock, AR 72202, (501)454-1641

Intl. Golf Associates **[22612]**, 1040 Genter St., No. 103, La Jolla, CA 92037-5550, (858)546-4737

Intl. Golf Assn. **[★22612]**

Intl. Golf Fed. **[22613]**, PO Box 708, Far Hills, NJ 07931-0708, (908)234-2300

Intl. Golf Fed. **[22613]**, PO Box 708, Far Hills, NJ 07931-0708, (908)234-2300

Intl. Gottfried Wilhelm Leibniz Soc. **[IO]**, Hannover, Germany

International Grail Movement **[★19427]**

Intl. Grains Coun. **[IO]**, London, United Kingdom

Intl. Graphic Arts Educ. Assn. **[8220]**, 1899 Preston White Dr., Reston, VA 20191-4367, (703)758-0595

Intl. Graphic Arts Educ. Assn. **[8220]**, 1899 Preston White Dr., Reston, VA 20191-4367, (703)758-0595

Intl. Graphoanalysis Soc. **[10755]**, 842 5th Ave., New Kensington, PA 15068, (724)472-9701

Intl. Graphoanalysis Soc. **[10755]**, 842 5th Ave., New Kensington, PA 15068, (724)472-9701

Intl. Graphonomics Soc. **[IO]**, Fisciano, Italy

Intl. Gravity Bur. **[IO]**, Toulouse, France

Intl. Gravity Sports Assn. **[22983]**, PO Box 933, Larkspur, CA 94977, (951)532-6378

Intl. Gravity Sports Assn. **[22983]**, PO Box 933, Larkspur, CA 94977, (951)532-6378

Intl. Green Energy Coun. **[6116]**, 1701 Pennsylvania Ave. NW, Ste. 300, Washington, DC 20006, (202)349-7138

Intl. Grooving and Grinding Assn. **[831]**, 12573 Rte. 9W, West Coxsackie, NY 12192, (518)731-7450

Intl. Grooving and Grinding Assn. **[831]**, 12573 Rte. 9W, West Coxsackie, NY 12192, (518)731-7450

Intl. Ground Source Heat Pump Assn. **[1710]**, 374 Cordell S, Stillwater, OK 74078-8018, (405)744-5175

Intl. Ground Source Heat Pump Assn. **[1710]**, 374 Cordell S, Stillwater, OK 74078-8018, (405)744-5175

A star before a book entry number signifies that the name is not listed separately, but is mentioned within the entry.

Intl. Gp. of Accounting Firms [★29]

Intl. Gp. of Accounting Firms [29], 3235 Satellite Blvd., Bldg. 400, Ste. 300, Duluth, GA 30096, (678)417-7730

Intl. Gp. of Agencies and Bureaus [★10479]

Intl. Gp. of Agencies and Bureaus [★10479]

Intl. Guards Union of Am. [23294], 420 Hardwicke Dr., Knoxville, TN 37923

Intl. Guiding Eyes [★17081]

Intl. Guild of Artists [IO], Ilkley, United Kingdom

Intl. Guild of Candle Artisans [21443], PO Box 321, Kechi, KS 67067

Intl. Guild of Candle Artisans [21443], PO Box 321, Kechi, KS 67067

Intl. Guild of Glass Artists [255], 4735 Waverly Ln., Jacksonville, FL 32210, (904)236-6684

Intl. Guild of Glass Artists [255], 4735 Waverly Ln., Jacksonville, FL 32210, (904)236-6684

Intl. Guild of Knot Tyers [IO], Wirral, United Kingdom

Intl. Guild of Lamp Researchers - Address unknown since 2011.

Intl. Guild of Lay Ministers and Acolytes [★19711]

Intl. Guild of Lay Ministers and Acolytes [★19711]

Intl. Guild of Miniature Artisans [21444], PO Box 629, Freedom, CA 95019-0629, (831)724-7974

Intl. Guild of Miniature Artisans [21444], PO Box 629, Freedom, CA 95019-0629, (831)724-7974

Intl. Guild of Musicians in Dance [23271], Univ. of Illinois at Urbana-Champaign, 302 E John St., Ste. 202, Champaign, IL 61820

Intl. Guild of Musicians in Dance [23271], Univ. of Illinois at Urbana-Champaign, 302 E John St., Ste. 202, Champaign, IL 61820

Intl. Guild of Professional Consultants and Coaches

Intl. Guild of Professional Consultants and Coaches - Address unknown since 2011.

Intl. Guild of Realism [9297], 4400 N Scottsdale Rd., No. 9539, Scottsdale, AZ 85251

Intl. Guild of Symphony, Opera and Ballet Musicians [23272], 12724 19th Ave. NE, Seattle, WA 98125

Intl. Gustav Mahler Soc. [IO], Vienna, Austria

Intl. Gymnastic Fed. [IO], Lausanne, Switzerland

Intl. H Boat Class Assn. - Defunct.

Intl. HACCP Alliance [4809], 120 Rosethal Ctr., 2471 TAMU, College Station, TX 77843-2471, (979)862-3643

Intl. Hajji Baba Soc. [9185], Kelvin Webb, Treas., 1105 D St. SE, Washington, DC 20003

Intl. Hajji Baba Soc. [9185], Kelvin Webb, Treas., 1105 D St. SE, Washington, DC 20003

Intl. Halfway House Assn. [★11717]

Intl. Halfway House Assn. [★11717]

Intl. Hand Protection Assn. [★1833]

Intl. Hand Protection Assn. [★1833]

Intl. Handball Fed. [IO], Basel, Switzerland

Intl. Handgun Metallic Silhouette Assn. [22877], Lorene Thompson, PO Box 95690, South Jordan, UT 84095-5690, (801)733-8423

Intl. Handgun Metallic Silhouette Assn. [22877], Lorene Thompson, PO Box 95690, South Jordan, UT 84095-5690, (801)733-8423

Intl. Handicappers' Net - Defunct.

Intl. Harbour Masters' Assn. [IO], Fareham, United Kingdom

Intl. Hard Anodizing Assn. [2473], PO Box 579, Moorestown, NJ 08057-0579, (856)234-0330

Intl. Hard Anodizing Assn. [2473], PO Box 579, Moorestown, NJ 08057-0579, (856)234-0330

Intl. Hardware Distributors Assn. - Defunct.

Intl. Hardwood Products Assn. [★1469]

Intl. Hardwood Products Assn. [★1469]

Intl. Harm Reduction Assn. [IO], London, United Kingdom

Intl. Harvester Collectors [22177], PO Box 35, Dublin, IN 47335-0035, (765)478-6179

Intl. Hazard Control Manager Certification Bd. [★3138]

Intl. Headache Soc. [IO], London, United Kingdom

International Health

  ACCESS Hea. Intl. [14744]

  Adventist Hea. Intl. [15138]

  Adventist Hea. Intl. [15138]

  African Hea. Now [15139]

  African Hea. Now [15139]

  African Medical and Res. Found. [15140]

African Medical and Res. Found. [15140]

Ahoto Partnership for Ghana [15141]

AIDS-Free World [13594]

Amazonas Hope for Hea. [14747]

Ambassadors for Sustained Hea. [14748]

Amer. Chinese Medical Exchange Soc. [14750]

Amer. Coll. of Intl. Physicians [15142]

Amer. Coll. of Intl. Physicians [15142]

Amer. Friends of Guinea [15143]

Amer. Medical Resources Found. [15144]

Amer. Medical Resources Found. [15144]

Amer. Women's Hospitals Ser. Comm. of AMWA [15043]

AmeriGhana [12312]

Andean Hea. and Development [15145]

Answer Africa [14374]

Arise Medical Missions [15146]

ASHA Intl. [15448]

Assn. of Muslim Hea. Professionals [15147]

Assn. for Pelvic Organ Prolapse Support [14760]

Basic Hea. Intl. [17122]

BIO Ventures for Global Hea. [15148]

BIO Ventures for Global Hea. [15148]

Cambodian Hea. Professionals Assn. of Am. [14761]

Caribbean Hea. Outreach [15149]

Caribbean Public Hea. Coalition [16482]

Changing Children's Lives [15150]

Changing Children's Lives [15150]

ChildAlive [15151]

ChildFund Intl. [11231]

Children's Intl. Hea. Relief [14067]

A Child's Right [13415]

Childspring Intl. [14070]

Clinic at a Time [15152]

Clinicians of the World [15153]

Coalition for Healthy India [15154]

Community Hea. Intl. [14896]

Doctors for United Medical Missions [15155]

Dorcas Medical Mission [15156]

Egyptians Relief Assn. [11577]

Emofra Africa [15157]

Empowering the Poor [12326]

Engg. World Hea. [15158]

FACE AIDS [13602]

Flying Doctors of Am. [12454]

Forward in Hea. [14777]

Found. for the Support of Intl. Medical Training [15159]

Found. for the Support of Intl. Medical Training [15159]

Friends for Hea. in Haiti [14778]

Ghana Medical Mission [15160]

Global Associates for Hea. Development [15161]

Global Associates for Hea. Development [15161]

Global Emergency Care Collaborative [15162]

Global Flying Hospitals [14779]

Global Healing [15163]

Global Healing [15163]

Global Hea. Action [15164]

Global Hea. Action [15164]

Global Hea. Corps [15165]

Global Hea. Coun. [15166]

Global Hea. Coun. [15166]

Global Hea. through Educ., Training and Ser. [15167]

Global Hea. Informatics Partnership [15168]

Global Hea. Linkages, Inc. [15169]

Global Hea. Ministries [14780]

Global Hea. Partners [14781]

Global Hea. Partners [14781]

Global Hea. Partnerships [15170]

Global Hea. Partnerships [15170]

Global Hea. Soc. [15171]

Global Hea. Soc. [15171]

Global Hea. Technologies Coalition [15172]

Global Hea. Technologies Coalition [15172]

Global Medic Force [15173]

Global Medic Force [15173]

Global Natural Hea. Alliance [13679]

Global Network for Neglected Tropical Diseases [14388]

Global Nutrition Alliance [15833]

Global Partners in Anesthesia and Surgery [16814]

Global Partnership for Family Hea. [13608]

Global Physicians Corps [15174]

Global Solutions for Infectious Diseases [15116]

Global Vision 2020 [17077]

GlobeMed [15175]

GlobeMed [15175]

God's Child Proj. [11294]

Haiti Healthcare Partners [15176]

Healing Across the Divides [15177]

Hea. Bridges Intl. [15178]

Hea. and Educ. Relief for Guyana [15179]

Hea. and Educ. Relief Org. [12334]

Hea. Empowering Humanity [14786]

Hea. Horizons Intl. [15180]

Hea. Justice Collaborative [15181]

Hea. and Life Intl. [14788]

Hea. through Walls [15182]

Hesperian Found. [15183]

Hesperian Found. [15183]

Honduras Outreach Medical Brigada Relief Effort [15184]

Hope Beyond Hope [15185]

Hope Through Healing Hands [15186]

Hope Through Hea. [12385]

Horizon Intl. Medical Mission [15187]

Hospitals of Hope [15188]

Hospitals of Hope [15188]

I Care Grace Intl. [14792]

INMED Partnerships for Children [15189]

INMED Partnerships for Children [15189]

Inter-American Hea. Alliance [14795]

Intermed Intl. [15190]

Intermed Intl. [15190]

Intl. Assn. for Women's Mental Hea. [15456]

Intl. Hea. and Development Network [15191]

Intl. Healthcare Leadership [14880]

Intl. Healthcare Volunteers [14798]

Intl. Medical Alliance [15192]

Intl. Midwife Assistance [15883]

Intl. Palestinian Cardiac Relief Org. [14021]

Intl. Partnership for Reproductive Hea. [16587]

Intl. Smile Power [14221]

IntraHealth Intl. [14881]

Iraqi Medical Sciences Assn. [15193]

Iraqi Medical Sciences Assn. [15193]

Jewish Healthcare Intl. [15194]

Jewish Healthcare Intl. [15194]

Lily of the Valley Endeavor [10886]

Lynch Syndrome Intl. [14609]

Mayan Medical Aid [12466]

MED25 Intl. [14803]

Medical Aid Comm. [15306]

Medical Care Development Intl. [15195]

Medical Care Intl. [15196]

Medical Mission Gp. [15197]

Medics Without Borders [14469]

mHealth Alliance [15198]

Natl. Student Campaign Against Hunger and Homelessness [12286]

Naturopathic Medicine for Global Hea. [15536]

Network Ethiopia [15199]

Network for the Improvement of World Hea. [15200]

Network for the Improvement of World Hea. [15200]

Nutrition and Educ. Intl. [12586]

Nyaya Hea. [15201]

Nyaya Hea. [15201]

One World Healthcare USA [14823]

One World Medical Relief [15202]

One World Medical Relief [15202]

Partner for Surgery [16818]

Partners for World Hea. [15203]

Progressive Hea. Partnership [15204]

Proj. Concern Intl. [15205]

Proj. Concern Intl. [15205]

Reach Intl. Healthcare and Training [15206]

Res. for Hea. [15207]

Res. for Hea. [15207]

Rural Hea. Intl. Non-Profit Org. [15208]

SHARED, Inc. [15209]

Sharing Resources Worldwide [15210]

Shout Global Hea. [15211]

Soc. for Emotional Well-Being Worldwide [15483]

Soc. for Worldwide Medical Exchange [15212]

Reference to "IO" in place of a book number signifies that the association may be found in the 50th edition of International Organizations.

Soc. for Worldwide Medical Exchange [15212]
Soft Power Hea. [15213]
South Asian Public Hea. Assn. [16499]
Spinal Hea. Intl. [16706]
Support for Intl. Change [15214]
SURGE [13431]
Tang Center for Herbal Medicine Res. [15215]
Tang Center for Herbal Medicine Res. [15215]
Thirst Relief Intl. [13432]
Tropical Clinics [15216]
UHAI for Hea. [15217]
Unified for Global Healing [15218]
Universities Allied for Essential Medicines [8384]
Upenyu [15219]
Uplift Intl. [15220]
US Doctors for Africa [15221]
US Doctors for Africa [15221]
Waves of Hea. [15222]
Wired Intl. [15223]
Women for World Hea. [14837]
World Against AIDS [12386]
World Against AIDS [12386]
World Fed. of Therapeutic Communities [13719]
World Hea. Ambassador [14838]
World Hea. Clinicians [13630]
World Hea. Imaging, Telemedicine and Informatics
 Alliance [15224]
World Hea. Partners [15225]
World Hea. Services [15226]
World Spine Care [16708]
Wuqu' Kawoq [15227]
Wyman Worldwide Hea. Partners [15228]
Intl. Hea. and Development Network [15191], PO
 Box 7488, Springfield, IL 62791
Intl. Hea. Org., India [IO], Patna, India
Intl. Hea., Racquet and Sportsclub Assn. [2743],
 Seaport Ctr., 70 Fargo St., Boston, MA 02210,
 (617)951-0055
Intl. Hea., Racquet and Sportsclub Assn. [2743],
 Seaport Ctr., 70 Fargo St., Boston, MA 02210,
 (617)951-0055
Intl. Healthcare Leadership [14880], Columbia Univ.
 Medical Center, 3959 Broadway, 8 N, New York,
 NY 10032, (212)305-5475
Intl. Healthcare Volunteers [14798], PO Box 8231,
 Trenton, NJ 08650, (609)259-8807
Intl. Healthy Cities Found. [13345], 2054 Univ. Ave.,
 Ste. 300, Berkeley, CA 94704, (510)314-8300
Intl. Healthy Cities Found. [13345], 2054 Univ. Ave.,
 Ste. 300, Berkeley, CA 94704, (510)314-8300
Intl. Hearing Dog [14943], 5901 E 89th Ave., Hend-
 erson, CO 80640, (303)287-3277
Intl. Hearing Dog [14943], 5901 E 89th Ave., Hend-
 erson, CO 80640, (303)287-3277
Intl. Hearing Soc. [14944], 16880 Middlebelt Rd.,
 Ste. 4, Livonia, MI 48154-3374, (734)522-7200
Intl. Hearing Soc. [14944], 16880 Middlebelt Rd.,
 Ste. 4, Livonia, MI 48154-3374, (734)522-7200
Intl. Heart Hea. Soc. [IO], Burnaby, BC, Canada
International Heart and Lung Transplantation
 Registry [★16909]
International Heart and Lung Transplantation
 Registry [★16909]
Intl. Hebrew Christian Alliance [★19753]
Intl. Hebrew Christian Alliance [★19753]
Intl. Hedgehog Assn. [10992], PO Box 1060, Divide,
 CO 80814
Intl. Hedgehog Assn. [10992], PO Box 1060, Divide,
 CO 80814
Intl. Hedgehog Club [★10992]
Intl. Hedgehog Club [★10992]
Intl. Hedgehog Fanciers Soc. [★10992]
Intl. Hedgehog Fanciers Soc. [★10992]
Intl. Heinrich Schutz Soc. [IO], Kassel, Germany
Intl. Helicopter Found. [★137]
Intl. Helicopter Found. [★137]
Intl. Helsinki Fed. for Human Rights [IO], Vienna,
 Austria
Intl. Hepato-Biliary Pancreatic Assn. [★14979]
Intl. Hepato-Biliary Pancreatic Assn. [★14979]
Intl. Hepato-Pancreato-Biliary Assn. [★14979]
Intl. Hepato-Pancreato-Biliary Assn. [★14979]
Intl. Herb Assn. [1726], PO Box 5667, Jacksonville,
 FL 32247-5667, (904)614-7745
Intl. Herb Assn. [1726], PO Box 5667, Jacksonville,
 FL 32247-5667, (904)614-7745

Intl. Herb Growers and Marketers Assn. [★1726]
Intl. Herb Growers and Marketers Assn. [★1726]
Intl. High Five Soc. - Defunct.
Intl. High IQ Soc. [19068], PO Box 3882, New York,
 NY 10163
Intl. High IQ Soc. [19068], PO Box 3882, New York,
 NY 10163
Intl. Hobie Class Assn. [22353], Lori Mohney, VP,
 2812 E Shore Dr., Portage, MI 49002, (269)327-
 4565
Intl. Hobie Class Assn. [22353], Lori Mohney, VP,
 2812 E Shore Dr., Portage, MI 49002, (269)327-
 4565
Intl. Hockey Fed. [IO], Lausanne, Switzerland
Intl. Holistic Practitioner Assn. [13689], PO Box 684,
 Gainesville, VA 20156-0684, (571)766-1430
Intl. Hologram Mfrs. Assn. [IO], Sunbury-on-Thames,
 United Kingdom
International Home Exchange [★21853]
Intl. Home Furnishings Marketing Assn. [★1550]
Intl. Home Furnishings Representatives Assn.
 [1554], PO Box 670, High Point, NC 27261,
 (336)889-3920
Intl. Home Furnishings Representatives Assn.
 [1554], PO Box 670, High Point, NC 27261,
 (336)889-3920
Intl. Homeopathic Medical League [IO], Berlin,
 Germany
Intl. Homicide Investigators Assn. [5603], 10711
 Spotsylvania Ave., Fredericksburg, VA 22408,
 (877)843-4442
Intl. Homicide Investigators Assn. [5603], 10711
 Spotsylvania Ave., Fredericksburg, VA 22408,
 (877)843-4442
Intl. Horn Soc. [10220], PO Box 630158, Lanai City,
 HI 96763-0158, (808)565-7273
Intl. Horn Soc. [10220], PO Box 630158, Lanai City,
 HI 96763-0158, (808)565-7273
Intl. Hosp. Fed. [IO], Ferney-Voltaire, France
Intl. Hospitality Info. Tech. Assn. [7511], 4505
 Maryland Pkwy., Box 456021, Las Vegas, NV
 89154-6021, (702)895-5811
Intl. Hot Rod Assn. [22244], 9 1/2 E Main St., Nor-
 walk, OH 44857, (419)663-6666
Intl. Hotel and Restaurant Assn. [IO], Geneva,
 Switzerland
Intl. House - World Trade Center [★2091]
Intl. House - World Trade Center [★2091]
Intl. Housewares Assn. [1778], 6400 Shafer Ct., Ste.
 650, Rosemont, IL 60018, (847)292-4200
Intl. Housewares Assn. [1778], 6400 Shafer Ct., Ste.
 650, Rosemont, IL 60018, (847)292-4200
Intl. Housewares Representatives Assn. [1779],
 1755 Lake Cook Rd., No. 118, Highland Park, IL
 60035, (847)748-8269
Intl. Housewares Representatives Assn. [1779],
 1755 Lake Cook Rd., No. 118, Highland Park, IL
 60035, (847)748-8269
Intl. Human Powered Vehicle Assn. [7582], PO Box
 357, Cutten, CA 95534-0357, (877)333-1029
Intl. Human Powered Vehicle Assn. [7582], PO Box
 357, Cutten, CA 95534-0357, (877)333-1029
Intl. Human Rights Assn. of Amer. Minorities [IO],
 Nanaimo, BC, Canada
Intl. Human Rights Law Gp. [★17831]
Intl. Human Rights Law Gp. [★17831]
Intl. Human Rights Observer [IO], Islamabad,
 Pakistan
Intl. Humanist and Ethical Union [IO], London,
 United Kingdom
Intl. Humanitarian City [IO], Dubai, United Arab
 Emirates
Intl. Humic Substances Soc. [7372], Natl. Soil Tilth
 Lab., 2110 Univ. Blvd., Ames, IA 50011-3120,
 (515)294-8412
Intl. Humic Substances Soc. [7372], Natl. Soil Tilth
 Lab., 2110 Univ. Blvd., Ames, IA 50011-3120,
 (515)294-8412
Intl. Hunter Educ. Assn. [22698], 2727 W 92nd Ave.,
 Ste. 103, Federal Heights, CO 80260, (303)430-
 7233
Intl. Hunter Educ. Assn. [22698], 2727 W 92nd Ave.,
 Ste. 103, Federal Heights, CO 80260, (303)430-
 7233
Intl. Huntington Assn. [IO], The Hague, Netherlands

Intl. Huntington Assn. - Chile [IO], Santiago, Chile
Intl. Huntington Assn. - Ecuador [IO], Quito, Ecuador
Intl. Huntington Assn. - Egypt [IO], Giza, Egypt
Intl. Huntington Assn. - Hungary [IO], Szeged,
 Hungary
Intl. Huntington Assn. - Korea [IO], Seoul, Republic
 of Korea
Intl. Huntington Assn. - Oman [IO], Muscat, Oman
Intl. Huntington Assn. - Paraguay [IO], Asuncion,
 Paraguay
Intl. Huntington Assn. - Peru [IO], Lima, Peru
Intl. Huntington Assn. - Uruguay [IO], Montevideo,
 Uruguay
Intl. Huntington Assn. - Zimbabwe [IO], Bulawayo,
 Zimbabwe
Intl. Husserl and Phenomenological Res. Soc.
 [10387], World Phenomenology Inst., 1 Ivy Pointe
 Way, Hanover, NH 03755, (802)295-3487
Intl. Husserl and Phenomenological Res. Soc.
 [10387], World Phenomenology Inst., 1 Ivy Pointe
 Way, Hanover, NH 03755, (802)295-3487
Intl. Hustle Dance Assn. [9554], PO Box 11655,
 Philadelphia, PA 19116
Intl. Hydrofoil Soc. [22354], PO Box 51, Cabin John,
 MD 20818
Intl. Hydrofoil Soc. [22354], PO Box 51, Cabin John,
 MD 20818
Intl. Hydrographic Bur. [IO], Monte Carlo, Monaco
Intl. Hyperbarics Assn. [15074], 15810 E Gale Ave.,
 No. 178, Hacienda Heights, CA 91745, (323)888-
 1591
Intl. Hyperhidrosis Soc. [14492], 2560 Township Rd.,
 Ste. B, Quakertown, PA 18951, (610)346-6008
Intl. Hyperhidrosis Soc. [14492], 2560 Township Rd.,
 Ste. B, Quakertown, PA 18951, (610)346-6008
Intl. Hypnological Assn. [★15093]
Intl. Ice Hockey Fed. [IO], Zurich, Switzerland
Intl. Imagery Assn. [9835], Leslie J. Dagnall, Dir. of
 Training, 18 Edgeclif Terr., Yonkers, NY 10705,
 (914)476-0781
Intl. Imagery Assn. [9835], Leslie J. Dagnall, Dir. of
 Training, 18 Edgeclif Terr., Yonkers, NY 10705,
 (914)476-0781
Intl. Imaging Indus. Assn. [2722], Virtual, Inc., 401
 Edgewater Pl., Ste. 600, Wakefield, MA 01880,
 (914)285-4933
Intl. Imaging Indus. Assn. [2722], Virtual, Inc., 401
 Edgewater Pl., Ste. 600, Wakefield, MA 01880,
 (914)285-4933
Intl. Independence Inst. [★17380]
Intl. Indian Treaty Coun. [17893], 2940 16th St., Ste.
 305, San Francisco, CA 94103-3664, (415)641-
 4482
Intl. Indian Treaty Coun. [17893], 2940 16th St., Ste.
 305, San Francisco, CA 94103-3664, (415)641-
 4482
Intl. Indus. Photographers Assn. [IO], Rotterdam,
 Netherlands
Intl. Indus. Relations Assn. [IO], Geneva,
 Switzerland
Intl. Indus. TV Assn. [★1262]
Intl. Indus. TV Assn. [★1262]
Intl. Inflight Food Ser. Assn. [★1445]
Intl. Inflight Food Ser. Assn. [★1445]
Intl. Informatiecentrum en Archief voor de Vrouwen-
 beweging [★IO]
Intl. Info. Centre and Archives for the Women's
 Movement [IO], Amsterdam, Netherlands
Intl. Info. Centre for Terminology [IO], Vienna,
 Austria
Intl. Info. Systems Security Certification Consortium
 [6540], 1964 Gallows Rd., Ste. 210, Vienna, VA
 22182, (703)891-6781
Intl. Info. Systems Security Certification Consortium
 [6540], 1964 Gallows Rd., Ste. 210, Vienna, VA
 22182, (703)891-6781
Intl. Initiative to End Child Labor [★11325]
Intl. Initiative on Exploitative Child Labor [11325],
 1016 S Wayne St., Ste. 702, Arlington, VA 22204,
 (703)920-0435
Intl. Initiative on Exploitative Child Labor [11325],
 1016 S Wayne St., Ste. 702, Arlington, VA 22204,
 (703)920-0435
Intl. Inline Skating Assn. - Defunct.
Intl. Input-Output Assn. [IO], Vienna, Austria

A star before a book entry number signifies that the name is not listed separately, but is mentioned within the entry.

Intl. Inst. of Administrative Sciences **[IO]**, Brussels, Belgium

Intl. Inst. on Ageing, United Nations - Malta **[IO]**, Valletta, Malta

Intl. Inst. of Ammonia Refrigeration **[1711]**, 1001 N Fairfax St., Ste. 503, Alexandria, VA 22314, (703)312-4200

Intl. Inst. of Ammonia Refrigeration **[1711]**, 1001 N Fairfax St., Ste. 503, Alexandria, VA 22314, (703)312-4200

Intl. Inst. of Anthropology **[IO]**, Paris, France

Intl. Inst. for Applied Systems Anal. **[IO]**, Laxenburg, Austria

Intl. Inst. for Baubiologie and Ecology **[4210]**, PO Box 16313, Clearwater, FL 33766-6313, (866)960-0333

Intl. Inst. for Beet Res. **[IO]**, Gottingen, Germany

Intl. Inst. for Bioenergetic Anal. **[IO]**, Zurich, Switzerland

Intl. Inst. of Biophysics **[IO]**, Neuss, Germany

Intl. Inst. of Carpet and Upholstery Certification **[★2058]**

Intl. Inst. of Catechetics and Pastoral Stud. **[IO]**, Brussels, Belgium

Intl. Inst. of Central Asia Biodiversity **[IO]**, Tashkent, Uzbekistan

Intl. Inst. for Children's Literature and Reading Res. **[IO]**, Vienna, Austria

Intl. Inst. of Communications **[IO]**, London, United Kingdom

Intl. Inst. of Concern for Public Hea. **[IO]**, Toronto, ON, Canada

Intl. Inst. of Conf. Mgt. **[★2445]**

Intl. Inst. of Conf. Mgt. **[★2445]**

Intl. Inst. of Connector and Interconnection Tech. **[6670]**, 3000 Lakeside Dr., Ste. 308N, Bannockburn, IL 60015, (847)739-0352

Intl. Inst. of Connector and Interconnection Tech. **[6670]**, 3000 Lakeside Dr., Ste. 308N, Bannockburn, IL 60015, (847)739-0352

Intl. Inst. for Conservation of Historic and Artistic Works **[IO]**, London, United Kingdom

Intl. Inst. for Conservation of Historic and Artistic Works—American Gp. **[9666]**

Intl. Inst. for Conservation of Historic and Artistic Works—American Gp. **[9666]**

Intl. Inst. of Convention Mgt. **[★2445]**

Intl. Inst. of Convention Mgt. **[★2445]**

Intl. Inst. of Educational Planning **[IO]**, Paris, France

Intl. Inst. of Embryology **[★9341]**

Intl. Inst. of Energy Conservation **[6734]**, 10005 Leamoore Ln., No. 100, Vienna, VA 22181, (703)281-7263

Intl. Inst. of Energy Conservation **[6734]**, 10005 Leamoore Ln., No. 100, Vienna, VA 22181, (703)281-7263

Intl. Inst. for Env. and Development **[IO]**, London, United Kingdom

Intl. Inst. for Ethnic Gp. Rights and Regionalism **[IO]**, Munich, Germany

Intl. Inst. for Field-Being **[8706]**, Fairfield Univ., IIFB N Benson Rd., Fairfield, CT 06824-5195, (203)254-4000

Intl. Inst. of Fisheries Economics and Trade **[1360]**, Oregon State Univ., Dept. of Agricultural and Rsrc. Economics, Corvallis, OR 97331-3601, (541)737-1439

Intl. Inst. of Fisheries Economics and Trade **[1360]**, Oregon State Univ., Dept. of Agricultural and Rsrc. Economics, Corvallis, OR 97331-3601, (541)737-1439

Intl. Inst. of Forecasters **[6890]**, 53 Tesla Ave., Medford, MA 02155, (781)234-4077

Intl. Inst. of Forecasters **[6890]**, 53 Tesla Ave., Medford, MA 02155, (781)234-4077

Intl. Inst. for Geo-Information Sci. and Earth Observation **[IO]**, Enschede, Netherlands

International Inst. for Hearing Instruments Stud. **[★14944]**

International Inst. for Hearing Instruments Stud. **[★14944]**

Intl. Inst. of Human Rights **[IO]**, Strasbourg, France

Intl. Inst. of Humanitarian Law **[IO]**, Sanremo, Italy

Intl. Inst. of Iberoamerican Literature **[10044]**, Univ. of Pittsburgh, 1312 Cathedral of Learning, Pittsburgh, PA 15260, (412)624-3359

Intl. Inst. of Iberoamerican Literature **[10044]**, Univ. of Pittsburgh, 1312 Cathedral of Learning, Pittsburgh, PA 15260, (412)624-3359

Intl. Inst. of Integral Human Sciences **[IO]**, Montreal, QC, Canada

Intl. Inst. of Investment and Merchant Banking - Defunct.

Intl. Inst. of Islamic Thought **[9891]**, 500 Grove St., Ste. 200, Herndon, VA 20170, (703)471-1133

Intl. Inst. of Islamic Thought **[9891]**, 500 Grove St., Ste. 200, Herndon, VA 20170, (703)471-1133

Intl. Inst. of Islamic Thought and Civilization **[IO]**, Kuala Lumpur, Malaysia

Intl. Inst. for Labour Stud. **[IO]**, Geneva, Switzerland

Intl. Inst. for Land Reclamation and Improvement **[IO]**, Wageningen, Netherlands

Intl. Inst. for Ligurian Stud. **[IO]**, Bordighera, Italy

Intl. Inst. for Mgt. Development **[IO]**, Lausanne, Switzerland

Intl. Inst. of Municipal Clerks **[5848]**, 8331 Utica Ave., Ste. 200, Rancho Cucamonga, CA 91730, (909)944-4162

Intl. Inst. of Municipal Clerks **[5848]**, 8331 Utica Ave., Ste. 200, Rancho Cucamonga, CA 91730, (909)944-4162

Intl. Inst. of Peace Stud. and Global Philosophy **[IO]**, Powys, United Kingdom

Intl. Inst. of Photographic Arts **[2723]**, 1690 Frontage Rd., Chula Vista, CA 91911, (619)628-1466

Intl. Inst. of Photographic Arts **[2723]**, 1690 Frontage Rd., Chula Vista, CA 91911, (619)628-1466

Intl. Inst. for Promotion and Prestige **[IO]**, Geneva, Switzerland

Intl. Inst. of Public Finance **[IO]**, Munich, Germany

Intl. Inst. of Reflexology **[IO]**, Sheffield, United Kingdom

Intl. Inst. of Reflexology **[16858]**, PO Box 12642, St. Petersburg, FL 33733-2642, (727)343-4811

Intl. Inst. of Reflexology **[16858]**, PO Box 12642, St. Petersburg, FL 33733-2642, (727)343-4811

Intl. Inst. of Refrigeration **[IO]**, Paris, France

Intl. Inst. of Risk and Safety Mgt. **[IO]**, London, United Kingdom

Intl. Inst. of Rural Reconstruction U.S. Chap. **[12956]**, 40 Exchange Pl., Ste. 1205, New York, NY 10005, (212)880-9147

Intl. Inst. of Rural Reconstruction U.S. Chap. **[12956]**, 40 Exchange Pl., Ste. 1205, New York, NY 10005, (212)880-9147

Intl. Inst. for the Sci. of Sintering **[IO]**, Belgrade, Serbia

Intl. Inst. of Seismology and Earthquake Engg. **[IO]**, Tsukuba, Japan

Intl. Inst. of Social History **[IO]**, Amsterdam, Netherlands

Intl. Inst. of Space Law **[IO]**, Paris, France

Intl. Inst. for Strategic Stud. **[IO]**, London, United Kingdom

Intl. Inst. for Strategic Stud. US **[18423]**, 1850 K St. NW, Ste. 300, Washington, DC 20006, (202)659-1490

Intl. Inst. for Strategic Stud. US **[18423]**, 1850 K St. NW, Ste. 300, Washington, DC 20006, (202)659-1490

Intl. Inst. for the String Bass **[★10223]**

Intl. Inst. for the String Bass **[★10223]**

Intl. Inst. for Sustainable Development **[IO]**, Winnipeg, MB, Canada

Intl. Inst. of Synthetic Rubber Producers **[3132]**, 2077 S Gessner Rd., Ste. 133, Houston, TX 77063, (713)783-7511

Intl. Inst. of Synthetic Rubber Producers **[3132]**, 2077 S Gessner Rd., Ste. 133, Houston, TX 77063, (713)783-7511

Intl. Inst. of Tropical Agriculture **[IO]**, Ibadan, Nigeria

Intl. Inst. of Tropical Agriculture - United Kingdom **[IO]**, Croydon, United Kingdom

Intl. Inst. for the Unification of Private Law **[IO]**, Rome, Italy

Intl. Inst. for the Visually Impaired **[★17066]**

Intl. Inst. of Welding **[IO]**, Villepinte, France

Intl. Insurance Coun. - Defunct.

Intl. Insurance Seminars **[★1986]**

Intl. Insurance Seminars **[★1986]**

Intl. Insurance Soc. **[1986]**, 101 Murray St., New York, NY 10007-2165, (212)815-9291

Intl. Insurance Soc. **[1986]**, 101 Murray St., New York, NY 10007-2165, (212)815-9291

Intl. Integrative Psychotherapy Assn. **[16463]**, PO Box 131, Newtown Square, PA 19073, (610)293-1063

Intl. Intellectual Property Assn. **[5571]**, 2101 L St. NW, Ste. 1000, Washington, DC 20037, (202)833-4198

Intl. Intellectual Property Assn. **[5571]**, 2101 L St. NW, Ste. 1000, Washington, DC 20037, (202)833-4198

Intl. Intelligence Ethics Assn. **[7001]**, PO Box 8474, Washington, DC 20032-8474

Intl. Intelligence Network **[3218]**, PO Box 350, Gladwyne, PA 19035, (610)520-9222

Intl. Intelligence Network **[3218]**, PO Box 350, Gladwyne, PA 19035, (610)520-9222

Intl. Intelligent Buildings Assn. - Defunct.

Intl. Interior Design Assn. **[2065]**, 222 Merchandise Mart, Ste. 567, Chicago, IL 60654, (312)467-1950

Intl. Interior Design Assn. **[2065]**, 222 Merchandise Mart, Ste. 567, Chicago, IL 60654, (312)467-1950

Intl. Internet Leather Crafters' Guild **[2200]**, Pat Hay, Treas., PO Box 98, Cary, MS 39054

Intl. Internet Leather Crafters' Guild **[2200]**, Pat Hay, Treas., PO Box 98, Cary, MS 39054

Intl. Internet Marketing Assn. **[IO]**, Vancouver, BC, Canada

Intl. Intradiscal Therapy Soc.

Intl. Intradiscal Therapy Soc. - Address unknown since 2011.

Intl. Inventor's Assn. - Defunct.

Intl. Iridology Practitioners Assn. **[15963]**, 2101 Magnolia Ave. S, Ste. 100-A, Birmingham, AL 35205, (205)226-3522

Intl. Iridology Practitioners Assn. **[15963]**, 2101 Magnolia Ave. S, Ste. 100-A, Birmingham, AL 35205, (205)226-3522

Intl. Iridology Res. Assn. **[★15963]**

Intl. Iridology Res. Assn. **[★15963]**

Intl. ISBN Agency **[IO]**, London, United Kingdom

Intl. Islamic Charitable Org. - Defunct.

Intl. Islamic News Agency **[IO]**, Jeddah, Saudi Arabia

Intl. Isotope Soc. **[6271]**, Perkin Elmer Life Sciences, 549 Albany St., Boston, MA 02118, (617)350-9435

Intl. Isotope Soc. **[6271]**, Perkin Elmer Life Sciences, 549 Albany St., Boston, MA 02118, (617)350-9435

Intl. J/22 Class Assn. **[22355]**, 12900 Lake Ave., No. 2001, Lakewood, OH 44107

Intl. J/22 Class Assn. **[22355]**, 12900 Lake Ave., No. 2001, Lakewood, OH 44107

Intl. Jack Benny Fan Club **[23797]**, PO Box 11288, Piedmont, CA 94611

Intl. Janitorial Cleaning Services Assn. **[2248]**, 2011 Oak St., Wyandotte, MI 48192, (734)252-6189

Intl. Jelly and Preserve Assn. **[1402]**, 5775 Peachtree-Dunwoody Rd., Ste. 500-G, Atlanta, GA 30342, (404)252-3663

Intl. Jelly and Preserve Assn. **[1402]**, 5775 Peachtree-Dunwoody Rd., Ste. 500-G, Atlanta, GA 30342, (404)252-3663

Intl. Jet Ski Boating Assn. **[★23116]**

Intl. Jet Ski Boating Assn. **[★23116]**

Intl. Jet Sports Boating Assn. and Amer. Watercraft Assn. **[23116]**, 330 Purissima St., Ste. C, Half Moon Bay, CA 94019, (714)751-8695

Intl. Jet Sports Boating Assn. and Amer. Watercraft Assn. **[23116]**, 330 Purissima St., Ste. C, Half Moon Bay, CA 94019, (714)751-8695

Intl. Jewelry Workers Union **[★23296]**

Intl. Jewelry Workers Union **[★23296]**

Intl. John Steinbeck Soc. - Defunct.

Intl. Joint Commn. **[4736]**, 2000 L St. NW, Ste. 615, Washington, DC 20440, (202)736-9024

Intl. Joint Commn. **[4736]**, 2000 L St. NW, Ste. 615, Washington, DC 20440, (202)736-9024

Intl. Joint Painting, Decorating and Drywall Apprenticeship and Manpower Training Fund **[★11941]**

Intl. Joint Painting, Decorating and Drywall Apprenticeship and Manpower Training Fund **[★11941]**

Intl. Joseph A. Schumpeter Soc. **[IO]**, Augsburg, Germany

Intl. Joseph Disease Found. - Defunct.

Reference to "IO" in place of a book number signifies that the association may be found in the 50th edition of International Organizations.

Intl. Judo Fed. [IO], Budapest, Hungary

Intl. Jugglers' Assn. [22707], PO Box 7307, Austin, TX 78713-7307, (570)645-3463

Intl. Jumper Futurity [22683], PO Box 1445, Georgetown, KY 40324, (502)535-6787

Intl. Junior Brangus Breeders Assn. [3917], 5750 Epsilon Dr., San Antonio, TX 78249, (210)696-4343

Intl. Junior Brangus Breeders Assn. [3917], 5750 Epsilon Dr., San Antonio, TX 78249, (210)696-4343

Intl. Justice and Human Rights, Natl. Coun. of Churches of Christ USA [12246], Justice and Advocacy Commn., 475 Riverside Dr., Ste. 880, New York, NY 10115, (212)870-2048

Intl. Justice Mission [12244], PO Box 58147, Washington, DC 20037-8147, (703)465-5495

Intl. Justice Mission [12244], PO Box 58147, Washington, DC 20037-8147, (703)465-5495

Intl. Kart Fed. [22711], 1609 S Grove Ave., Ste. 105, Ontario, CA 91761, (909)923-4999

Intl. Kart Fed. [22711], 1609 S Grove Ave., Ste. 105, Ontario, CA 91761, (909)923-4999

Intl. KCI [★13061]

Intl. KCI [★13061]

Intl. Kennel Club of Chicago [21586], 6222 W North Ave., Chicago, IL 60639, (773)237-5100

Intl. Kindergarten Union [★7825]

Intl. Kindergarten Union [★7825]

Intl. King Midget Car Club [21077], Teresa Harris, Sec., 5198 Happy Hollow Rd., Nelsonville, OH 45764, (740)591-0084

Intl. Kirlian Res. Assn. - Defunct.

Intl. Kitchen Exhaust Cleaning Assn. [1350], 100 N 20th St., Ste. 400, Philadelphia, PA 19103, (215)564-3484

Intl. Kodaly Soc. [IO], Budapest, Hungary

Intl. Kolping Soc. [IO], Cologne, Germany

Intl. Korfball Fed. [IO], Zeist, Netherlands

Intl. Labor Press of Am. [★2911]

Intl. Labor Press Assn. [★2911]

Intl. Labor Rights Educ. and Res. Fund [★18044]

Intl. Labor Rights Educ. and Res. Fund [★18044]

Intl. Labor Rights Forum [18044], 1634 I St. NW, No. 1001, Washington, DC 20006, (202)347-4100

Intl. Labor Rights Forum [18044], 1634 I St. NW, No. 1001, Washington, DC 20006, (202)347-4100

Intl. Labor Rights Fund [★18044]

Intl. Labor Rights Fund [★18044]

Intl. Labor and Working Class History Study Group - Defunct.

Intl. Labour Org. [IO], Geneva, Switzerland

Intl. Labour Org. Ankara [IO], Ankara, Turkey

Intl. Labour Org. Beijing Off. [IO], Beijing, People's Republic of China

Intl. Labour Org. Cairo Off. [IO], Cairo, Egypt

Intl. Labour Org. Caribbean Off. [IO], Port of Spain, Trinidad and Tobago

Intl. Labour Org. Jakarta Off. [IO], Jakarta, Indonesia

Intl. Labour Org. Off. for the European Union and the Benelux countries [IO], Brussels, Belgium

Intl. Labour Org. Off. in Germany: ILO-Berlin [IO], Berlin, Germany

Intl. Labour Org. Off. for Italy and San Marino [IO], Rome, Italy

Intl. Labour Org. Off. for the United Kingdom and Republic of Ireland [IO], London, United Kingdom

Intl. Labour Org. Regional Off. for Africa [IO], Abidjan, Cote d'Ivoire

Intl. Labour Org. Regional Off. for the Arab States [IO], Beirut, Lebanon

Intl. Labour Org. Regional Off. for Asia and the Pacific [IO], Bangkok, Thailand

Intl. Labour Org. Subregional Off. for East Asia [IO], Bangkok, Thailand

Intl. Labour Org. Subregional Off. for Eastern Europe and Central Asia [IO], Moscow, Russia

Intl. Labour Org. Subregional Off. for South Asia [IO], New Delhi, India

Intl. Labour Org. Subregional Off. for South-East Asia and the Pacific [IO], Makati City, Philippines

Intl. Labour Org. Subregional Off. for Southern Africa [IO], Harare, Zimbabwe

Intl. Labour Org. Suva Off. [IO], Suva, Fiji

Intl. Lactation Consultant Assn. [11473], 2501 Aerial Center Pkwy., Ste. 103, Morrisville, NC 27560, (919)861-5577

Intl. Lactation Consultant Assn. [11473], 2501 Aerial Center Pkwy., Ste. 103, Morrisville, NC 27560, (919)861-5577

Intl. Lama Registry [20952], PO Box 8, Kalispell, MT 59903, (406)755-3438

Intl. Lama Registry [20952], PO Box 8, Kalispell, MT 59903, (406)755-3438

Intl. Landslide Res. Gp. [6925], 4377 Newland Heights Dr., Rocklin, CA 95765

Intl. Landslide Res. Gp. [6925], 4377 Newland Heights Dr., Rocklin, CA 95765

Intl. Laser Class Assn. - North Amer. Region [22356], One Design Mgt., 2812 Canon St., San Diego, CA 92106, (619)222-0252

Intl. Laser Display Assn. [1200], 7062 Edgeworth Dr., Orlando, FL 32819, (407)797-7654

Intl. Laser Display Assn. [1200], 7062 Edgeworth Dr., Orlando, FL 32819, (407)797-7654

Intl. Laser Tag Assn. [21749], 5351 E Thompson Rd., Ste. 236, Indianapolis, IN 46237, (317)786-9755

Intl. Latino Film Soc. [9946], 984 Folsom St., San Francisco, CA 94107, (415)513-5308

Intl. Latino Gang Investigator's Assn. [5604], PO Box 1148, Gig Harbor, WA 98335

Intl. Latino Gang Investigator's Assn. [5604], PO Box 1148, Gig Harbor, WA 98335

International Law

Amer. Bar Assn. Sect. of Intl. Law [5584]

Amer. Bar Assn. Sect. of Intl. Law [5584]

Amer. Foreign Law Assn. [5585]

Amer. Non-Governmental Organizations Coalition for the Intl. Criminal Court [17488]

Amer. Soc. of Comparative Law [5586]

Amer. Soc. of Intl. Law [5587]

Amer. Soc. of Intl. Law [5587]

Canadian Coun. on Intl. Law [5679]

Daisy Alliance [18239]

Intl. Law Inst. [5588]

Intl. Law Inst. [5588]

Intl. Law Students Assn. [5589]

Intl. Law Students Assn. [5589]

Intl. Legal Defense Counsel [5590]

Intl. Legal Defense Counsel [5590]

Win Without War [18178]

World Assn. of Lawyers [5591]

World Assn. of Lawyers [5591]

World Bus. Associates [5592]

World Bus. Associates [5592]

World Jurist Assn. [5593]

World Jurist Assn. [5593]

Intl. Law Assn. [IO], London, United Kingdom

Intl. Law Assn., German Br. [IO], Frankfurt, Germany

Intl. Law Assn., Indian Br. [IO], New Delhi, India

Intl. Law Assn., Japan Br. [IO], Tokyo, Japan

Intl. Law Assn., Korean Br. [IO], Seoul, Republic of Korea

Intl. Law Assn., Swedish Br. [IO], Stockholm, Sweden

Intl. Law Assn., Swiss Br. [IO], Zurich, Switzerland

Intl. Law Enforcement Educators and Trainers Assn. [5702], 1972 Gail Lynne Dr., Burlington, WI 53105, (262)767-1406

Intl. Law Enforcement Educators and Trainers Assn. [5702], 1972 Gail Lynne Dr., Burlington, WI 53105, (262)767-1406

Intl. Law Inst. [5588], The Foundry Bldg., 1055 Thomas Jefferson St. NW, Washington, DC 20007, (202)247-6006

Intl. Law Inst. [5588], The Foundry Bldg., 1055 Thomas Jefferson St. NW, Washington, DC 20007, (202)247-6006

Intl. Law Students Assn. [5589], 25 E Jackson Blvd., Ste. 518, Chicago, IL 60604, (312)362-5025

Intl. Law Students Assn. [5589], 25 E Jackson Blvd., Ste. 518, Chicago, IL 60604, (312)362-5025

Intl. Lawrence Durrell Soc. [9375], Paul H. Lorenz, Sec.-Treas., 3201 S Beech St., No. 40, Pine Bluff, AR 71603, (870)575-8618

Intl. Lawrence Durrell Soc. [9375], Paul H. Lorenz, Sec.-Treas., 3201 S Beech St., No. 40, Pine Bluff, AR 71603, (870)575-8618

Intl. Lawyers in Alcoholics Anonymous [13260], 17216 Saticoy St., Ste. 211, Van Nuys, CA 91406, (818)343-2189

Intl. Lead Assn. [IO], London, United Kingdom

Intl. Lead Zinc Res. Org. [7095], 1822 NC Hwy. 54 E, Ste. 120, Durham, NC 27713-3210, (919)361-4647

Intl. Lead Zinc Res. Org. [7095], 1822 NC Hwy. 54 E, Ste. 120, Durham, NC 27713-3210, (919)361-4647

Intl. Lead and Zinc Study Group [IO], Lisbon, Portugal

Intl. League Against Epilepsy [IO], Brussels, Belgium

Intl. League Against Epilepsy of United Kingdom [IO], London, United Kingdom

Intl. League of Antiquarian Booksellers [3107], Tom Congalton, VP., 35 W Maple Ave., Merchantville, NJ 08109-5141, (856)665-2284

Intl. League of Antiquarian Booksellers [3107], Tom Congalton, VP., 35 W Maple Ave., Merchantville, NJ 08109-5141, (856)665-2284

Intl. League of Associations for Rheumatology [IO], Leiden, Netherlands

Intl. League for Competition Law [IO], Lausanne, Switzerland

Intl. League of Competition Law, Austria [IO], Vienna, Austria

Intl. League of Competition Law, Brazil [IO], Rio de Janeiro, Brazil

Intl. League for Competition Law, Czech Republic [IO], Prague, Czech Republic

Intl. League for Competition Law, Japan [IO], Tokyo, Japan

Intl. League for Competition Law, Nordic Countries [IO], Stockholm, Sweden

Intl. League of Conservation Photographers [4777], 2011 Crystal Dr., Ste. 500, Arlington, VA 22202, (703)341-2821

Intl. League of Conservation Photographers [4777], 2011 Crystal Dr., Ste. 500, Arlington, VA 22202, (703)341-2821

Intl. League of Elecl. Associations [1077], 39 Harmon Rd., Churchville, NY 14428, (585)538-6350

Intl. League of Elecl. Associations [1077], 39 Harmon Rd., Churchville, NY 14428, (585)538-6350

Intl. League of Esperantist Teachers [IO], The Hague, Netherlands

Intl. League for Human Rights [17842], 352 7th Ave., Ste. 1234, New York, NY 10001, (212)661-0480

Intl. League for Human Rights [17842], 352 7th Ave., Ste. 1234, New York, NY 10001, (212)661-0480

Intl. League of Non-Religious and Atheists [IO], Hagen, Germany

Intl. League of Professional Baseball Clubs [22272], 55 S High St., Ste. 202, Dublin, OH 43017, (614)791-9300

Intl. League for the Repatriation of Russian Jews - Defunct.

Intl. League for the Rights of Man [★17842]

Intl. League for the Rights of Man [★17842]

Intl. Legal Defense Counsel [5590], 405 Lexington Ave., 26th Fl., New York, NY 10174, (888)534-9106

Intl. Legal Defense Counsel [5590], 405 Lexington Ave., 26th Fl., New York, NY 10174, (888)534-9106

Intl. Legal Inst. [IO], The Hague, Netherlands

International Legion of Intelligence [★9640]

The Intl. Lepidoptera Survey [6845], PO Box 1124, Herndon, VA 20172

Intl. Leptospirosis Soc. [15119], Prof. Joseph Vinetz, Sec., Univ. of California San Diego School of Medicine, Div. of Infectious Diseases, 9500 Gilman Dr., La Jolla, CA 92093-0640, (858)822-4469

Intl. Leptospirosis Soc. [15119], Prof. Joseph Vinetz, Sec., Univ. of California San Diego School of Medicine, Div. of Infectious Diseases, 9500 Gilman Dr., La Jolla, CA 92093-0640, (858)822-4469

Intl. Lesbian and Gay Assn. [IO], Brussels, Belgium

Intl. Lexical Functional Grammar Assn. [8471], Univ. at Albany, State Univ. of New York, Dept. of Anthropology, Arts and Sciences Bldg., Rm. 237, 1400 Washington Ave., Albany, NY 12222, (518)442-4700

Intl. Lexical Functional Grammar Assn. [8471], Univ. at Albany, State Univ. of New York, Dept. of Anthropology, Arts and Sciences Bldg., Rm. 237, 1400 Washington Ave., Albany, NY 12222, (518)442-4700

A star before a book entry number signifies that the name is not listed separately, but is mentioned within the entry.

Intl. Liaison of Lay Volunteers in Mission (U.S. Catholic Network of Lay Mission Programs) [★19405]

Intl. Liaison U.S. Catholic Coordinating Center for Lay Missioners [★19405]

Intl. Liaison, U.S. Catholic Coordinating Center for Lay Volunteer Ministries [★19405]

Intl. Liaison for Volunteer Ser. [★19405]

Intl. Licensing Indus. Merchandisers' Assn. [5572], 350 5th Ave., Ste. 4019, New York, NY 10118, (212)244-1944

Intl. Licensing Indus. Merchandisers' Assn. [5572], 350 5th Ave., Ste. 4019, New York, NY 10118, (212)244-1944

Intl. Life Saving Fed. [IO], Leuven, Belgium

Intl. Life Sciences Inst., European Br. [IO], Brussels, Belgium

Intl. Life Sciences Inst. - North Am. [15836], 1156 15th St. NW, Ste. 200, Washington, DC 20005, (202)659-0074

Intl. Life Sciences Inst. - North Am. [15836], 1156 15th St. NW, Ste. 200, Washington, DC 20005, (202)659-0074

Intl. Life Sciences Inst. - Nutrition Found. [★15836]

Intl. Life Sciences Inst. - Nutrition Found. [★15836]

Intl. Lightning Class Assn. [22357], 7625 S Yampa St., Centennial, CO 80016, (303)325-5886

Intl. Lightning Class Assn. [22357], 7625 S Yampa St., Centennial, CO 80016, (303)325-5886

Intl. Lignin Inst. [IO], Lausanne, Switzerland

Intl. Lilac Soc. [21804], Karen McCauley, Treas./ Interim Membership Sec., 325 W 82nd St., Chaska, MN 55318, (952)443-3703

Intl. Lilac Soc. [21804], Karen McCauley, Treas./ Interim Membership Sec., 325 W 82nd St., Chaska, MN 55318, (952)443-3703

Intl. Linear Algebra Soc. [7073], Pacific Lutheran Univ., Dept. of Mathematics, Tacoma, WA 98447

Intl. Linear Algebra Soc. [7073], Pacific Lutheran Univ., Dept. of Mathematics, Tacoma, WA 98447

Intl. Linen Promotion Commn. - Defunct.

Intl. Liquid Crystal Soc. [6589], Prof. Samuel Sprunt, Treas., Kent State Univ., Dept. of Physics, Kent, OH 44242-0001, (330)672-2682

Intl. Liquid Crystal Soc. [6589], Prof. Samuel Sprunt, Treas., Kent State Univ., Dept. of Physics, Kent, OH 44242-0001, (330)672-2682

Intl. Liquid Terminals Assn. [3620], 1005 N Glebe Rd., Ste. 600, Arlington, VA 22201, (703)875-2011

Intl. Listening Assn. [8034], PO Box 164, Belle Plaine, MN 56011-0164, (952)594-5697

Intl. Listening Assn. [8034], PO Box 164, Belle Plaine, MN 56011-0164, (952)594-5697

Intl. Liver Transplantation Soc. [16907], 15000 Commerce Pkwy., Ste. C, Mount Laurel, NJ 08054, (856)439-0500

Intl. Liver Transplantation Soc. [16907], 15000 Commerce Pkwy., Ste. C, Mount Laurel, NJ 08054, (856)439-0500

Intl. Livestock Brand Conf. [★4691]

Intl. Livestock Brand and Theft Conf. [★4691]

Intl. Livestock Identification Assn. [4691], 4701 Marion St., Ste. 201, Denver, CO 80216, (303)294-0895

Intl. Livestock Identification and Theft Investigators Assn. [★4691]

Intl. Livestock Investigators Assn. [4692], Dept. of Livestock, PO Box 202001, Public Information Center, Helena, MT 59620-2001, (406)444-9431

Intl. Livestock Investigators Assn. [4692], Dept. of Livestock, PO Box 202001, Public Information Center, Helena, MT 59620-2001, (406)444-9431

Intl. Livestock Res. Inst. - Kenya [IO], Nairobi, Kenya

Intl. Llama Assn. - Defunct.

Intl. Log Rolling Assn. - Address unknown since 2011.

Intl. Longshore and Warehouse Union [23247], 1188 Franklin St., 4th Fl., San Francisco, CA 94109, (415)775-0533

Intl. Longshore and Warehouse Union [23247], 1188 Franklin St., 4th Fl., San Francisco, CA 94109, (415)775-0533

Intl. Longshoremen's Assn. [23248], 5000 W Side Ave., North Bergen, NJ 07047, (212)425-1200

Intl. Longshoremen's and Warehousemen's Union [★23247]

Intl. Longshoremen's and Warehousemen's Union [★23247]

Intl. Loran Assn. [7151], 741 Cathedral Pointe Ln., Santa Barbara, CA 93111, (805)967-8649

Intl. Loran Assn. [7151], 741 Cathedral Pointe Ln., Santa Barbara, CA 93111, (805)967-8649

Intl. Luge Fed. [IO], Berchtesgaden, Germany

Intl. Lunar Observatory Assn. [6231], 65-1230 Mamalahoa Hwy., Ste. D20, Kamuela, HI 96743, (808)885-3474

Intl. Lutheran Laymen's League [19925], 660 Mason Ridge Center, St. Louis, MO 63141, (314)317-4100

Intl. Lutheran Laymen's League [19925], 660 Mason Ridge Center, St. Louis, MO 63141, (314)317-4100

Intl. Lutheran Women's Missionary League [★19936]

Intl. Lyme and Assoc. Diseases Soc. [14393], PO Box 341461, Bethesda, MD 20827-1461, (301)263-1080

Intl. Lyme and Assoc. Diseases Soc. [14393], PO Box 341461, Bethesda, MD 20827-1461, (301)263-1080

Intl. Machine Quilters Assn. [21445], PO Box 419, Higginsville, MO 64037, (800)980-9505

Intl. Magnesium Assn. [2474], 1000 N Rand Rd., Ste. 214, Wauconda, IL 60084, (847)526-2010

Intl. Magnesium Assn. [2474], 1000 N Rand Rd., Ste. 214, Wauconda, IL 60084, (847)526-2010

Intl. Magnetics Assn. [1652], 8 S Michigan Ave., Ste. 1000, Chicago, IL 60603, (312)456-5590

Intl. Magnetics Assn. [1652], 8 S Michigan Ave., Ste. 1000, Chicago, IL 60603, (312)456-5590

Intl. Mail Art Network - Defunct.

Intl. Mailers Union [★23210]

Intl. Maillard Reaction Soc. [6410], Wolstein Bldg., 2103 Cornell Rd., Rm. 5127, Cleveland, OH 44106, (216)368-2930

Intl. Maine-Anjou Assn. [★3887]

Intl. Maintenance Inst. [2249], PO Box 751896, Houston, TX 77275, (281)481-0869

Intl. Maintenance Inst. [2249], PO Box 751896, Houston, TX 77275, (281)481-0869

Intl. Maize and Wheat Improvement Center [IO], Mexico City, Mexico

Intl. Maledicta Soc. [10027], PO Box 14123, Santa Rosa, CA 95402-6123, (707)795-8178

Intl. Maledicta Soc. [10027], PO Box 14123, Santa Rosa, CA 95402-6123, (707)795-8178

Intl. Mammalian Genome Soc. [6900], Darla Miller, Univ. of North Carolina at Chapel Hill, Dept. of Genetics, 5047 Genetic Medicine Bldg., CB No. 7264, Chapel Hill, NC 27599, (919)843-6471

Intl. Mgt. Coun. of the YMCA [★2299]

Intl. Mgt. Coun. of the YMCA - Defunct.

Intl. Mgt. Development Assn. [676], PO Box 216, Hummelstown, PA 17036, (717)566-3054

Intl. Mgt. Development Assn. [676], PO Box 216, Hummelstown, PA 17036, (717)566-3054

Intl. Manganese Inst. [IO], Paris, France

Intl. Map Collectors' Soc. [IO], Newton Abbot, United Kingdom

Intl. Map Dealers Assn. [★6380]

Intl. Map Dealers Assn. [★6380]

Intl. Map Trade Assn. [6380], Mr. Sanford J. Hill, Exec. Dir., 23052 Alicia Pkwy., Ste. H-602, Mission Viejo, CA 92692-1661, (949)458-8200

Intl. Map Trade Assn. [6380], Mr. Sanford J. Hill, Exec. Dir., 23052 Alicia Pkwy., Ste. H-602, Mission Viejo, CA 92692-1661, (949)458-8200

Intl. Maple Syrup Inst. [1403], 387 County Rd., Woodstock, CT 06281, (860)974-1235

Intl. Maple Syrup Inst. [1403], 387 County Rd., Woodstock, CT 06281, (860)974-1235

Intl. Marie de France Soc. [8733], Matthieu Boyd, Pres., Harvard Univ., Dept. of Celtic Languages and Literatures, Barker Center, 12 Quincy St., Cambridge, MA 02138

Intl. Marina Inst. [★2377]

Intl. Marina Inst. [★2377]

Intl. Marine Animal Trainers Assn. [3805], 1200 S Lake Shore Dr., Chicago, IL 60605, (312)692-3193

Intl. Marine Animal Trainers Assn. [3805], 1200 S Lake Shore Dr., Chicago, IL 60605, (312)692-3193

Intl. Marine Contractors Assn. [IO], London, United Kingdom

Intl. Marine Minerals Soc. [4704], Univ. of Hawaii, 1000 Pope Rd., MSB 303, Honolulu, HI 96822, (808)956-6036

Intl. Marine Minerals Soc. [4704], Univ. of Hawaii, 1000 Pope Rd., MSB 303, Honolulu, HI 96822, (808)956-6036

Intl. Maritime Comm. [IO], Antwerp, Belgium

Intl. Maritime Hea. Assn. [IO], Antwerp, Belgium

Intl. Maritime Indus. Forum [IO], London, United Kingdom

Intl. Maritime Org. [IO], London, United Kingdom

Intl. Maritime Pilots' Assn. [IO], London, United Kingdom

Intl. Maritime Rescue Fed. [IO], Poole, United Kingdom

Intl. Maritime Satellite Org. [IO], London, United Kingdom

Intl. Marketing Inst. - Defunct.

Intl. Marking and Identification Assn. [3351], PO Box 49649, Charlotte, NC 28277, (704)847-0064

Intl. Marking and Identification Assn. [3351], PO Box 49649, Charlotte, NC 28277, (704)847-0064

Intl. Masonry Inst. [919], The James Brice House, 42 East St., Annapolis, MD 21401, (410)280-1305

Intl. Masonry Inst. [919], The James Brice House, 42 East St., Annapolis, MD 21401, (410)280-1305

Intl. Masonry Soc. [IO], Whyteleafe, United Kingdom

Intl. Massage Assn. [15271], PO Box 421, Warrenton, VA 20188-0421, (800)776-6268

Intl. Massage Assn. [15271], PO Box 421, Warrenton, VA 20188-0421, (800)776-6268

Intl. Masters of Gaming Law [5495], Melissa Lurie, Exec. Dir., 3288 St. Vincent Pl., Boulder, CO 80301, (303)449-9955

Intl. Match Safe Assn. [21358], PO Box 4212, Bartonville, IL 61607-4212

Intl. Material Mgt. Soc. [★7064]

Intl. Material Mgt. Soc. [★7064]

Intl. Mathematical Union [IO], Berlin, Germany

Intl. Matrix Gp. [★7073]

Intl. Matrix Gp. [★7073]

Intl. MC Class Sailboat Racing Assn. [★22369]

Intl. Measurement Confed. [IO], Budapest, Hungary

Intl. Meat Secretariat [IO], Paris, France

Intl. Medical Alliance [15192], PO Box 2727, Rancho Mirage, CA 92270, (760)485-8963

Intl. Medical Cooperation Comm. [IO], Copenhagen, Denmark

Intl. Medical Corps [12855], 1919 Santa Monica Blvd., Ste. 400, Santa Monica, CA 90404, (310)826-7800

Intl. Medical Corps [12855], 1919 Santa Monica Blvd., Ste. 400, Santa Monica, CA 90404, (310)826-7800

Intl. Medical and Dental Hypnotherapy Assn. [15091], 8852 SR 3001, Laceyville, PA 18623, (570)869-1021

Intl. Medical and Dental Hypnotherapy Assn. [15091], 8852 SR 3001, Laceyville, PA 18623, (570)869-1021

Intl. Medical Equip. Collaborative [14717], 1600 Osgood St., North Andover, MA 01845, (978)557-5510

Intl. Medical Equip. Collaborative [14717], 1600 Osgood St., North Andover, MA 01845, (978)557-5510

Intl. Medical Hea. Org. [14799], 2381 Hylan Blvd., Ste. 13B, Staten Island, NY 10306, (347)601-1364

Intl. Medical Informatics Assn. [IO], Geneva, Switzerland

Intl. Medical Relief Fund/Salvadoran Medical Relief Fund - Defunct.

Intl. Medical and Res. Found. [★15140]

Intl. Medical and Res. Found. [★15140]

Intl. Medical Services for Hea. [★15189]

Intl. Medical Services for Hea. [★15189]

Intl. Medical Soc. for Bio-Physical Info. - Therapy Assn. [IO], Freiburg, Germany

Intl. Medical Spa Assn.

Intl. Medical Spa Assn. - Address unknown since 2011.

Intl. Medical Volunteers Assn. [15304], PO Box 205, Woodville, MA 01784, (508)435-7377

Reference to "IO" in place of a book number signifies that the association may be found in the 50th edition of International Organizations.

Intl. Medical Volunteers Assn. **[15304]**, PO Box 205, Woodville, MA 01784, (508)435-7377

Intl. Meeting in Community Ser. **[IO]**, Stuttgart, Germany

Intl. Memorialization Supply Assn. **[2536]**, PO Box 425, West Bend, WI 53095, (800)375-0335

Intl. Memorialization Supply Assn. **[2536]**, PO Box 425, West Bend, WI 53095, (800)375-0335

Intl. Meniere Fed. **[IO]**, Vilvoorde, Belgium

Intl. Menopause Soc. **[IO]**, Lancaster, United Kingdom

Intl. Mental Game Coaching Assn. **[22460]**, PO Box 8151, San Jose, CA 95155, (408)294-2776

Intl. Mentoring Network Org. **[11139]**, 766 E 560 N, No. 206, Provo, UT 84606, (801)361-9942

Intl. Mentoring Network Org. **[11139]**, 766 E 560 N, No. 206, Provo, UT 84606, (801)361-9942

Intl. Mercury Owners Assn. **[21078]**, PO Box 1245, Northbrook, IL 60065-1245, (847)997-8624

Intl. Messianic Jewish Alliance **[19753]**, 5480 Baltimore Dr., Ste. 203, La Mesa, CA 91942-2015, (619)464-9793

Intl. Messianic Jewish Alliance **[19753]**, 5480 Baltimore Dr., Ste. 203, La Mesa, CA 91942-2015, (619)464-9793

Intl. Meta-Medicine Assn. **[13690]**, 578 Washington Blvd., No. 716, Venice, CA 90292-5442, (310)928-6638

Intl. Metal Decorators Assn. **[1614]**, 9574 Deereco Rd., Timonium, MD 21093, (410)252-5205

Intl. Metalworkers' Fed. **[IO]**, Geneva, Switzerland

Intl. Meteor Org. **[IO]**, Hove, Belgium

Intl. Meteorite Collectors Assn. **[22159]**, Mr. Norbert Classen, Pres., 115 Maple Ave. N, Lehigh Acres, FL 33936-6482

Intl. Methodist Historical Soc. **[★19979]**

Intl. Methodist Historical Soc. **[★19979]**

Intl. Methodist Historical Union **[★19979]**

Intl. Methodist Historical Union **[★19979]**

Intl. Microelectric and Packing Soc. **[★6671]**

Intl. Microelectric and Packing Soc. **[★6671]**

Intl. Microelectronic and Packaging Soc. **[6671]**, 611 2nd St. NE, Washington, DC 20002-4909, (202)548-4001

Intl. Microelectronic and Packaging Soc. **[6671]**, 611 2nd St. NE, Washington, DC 20002-4909, (202)548-4001

Intl. Microwave Power Inst. **[7118]**, PO Box 1140, Mechanicsville, VA 23111, (804)559-6667

Intl. Microwave Power Inst. **[7118]**, PO Box 1140, Mechanicsville, VA 23111, (804)559-6667

Intl. Midas Dealers Assn. **[359]**, 4831 Las Virgenes Rd., Ste. 159, Calabasas, CA 91302, (888)916-4111

Intl. Midas Dealers Assn. **[359]**, 4831 Las Virgenes Rd., Ste. 159, Calabasas, CA 91302, (888)916-4111

Intl. Midwife Assistance **[15883]**, PO Box 916, Boulder, CO 80306-0916, (303)588-1663

Intl. Military Community Executives Assn. **[2498]**, PO Box 91356, Austin, TX 78709-1356, (512)814-6232

Intl. Military Community Executives Assn. **[2498]**, PO Box 91356, Austin, TX 78709-1356, (512)814-6232

Intl. Military Sports Coun. **[IO]**, Brussels, Belgium

Intl. Milk Dealers Assn. **[★1022]**

Intl. Milk Dealers Assn. **[★1022]**

Intl. Mine Water Assn. **[IO]**, Sydney, NS, Canada

Intl. Mineralogical Assn. **[IO]**, Nancy, France

Intl. Miniature Aircraft Assn. **[22130]**, 1223 Weatherford Dr., King, NC 27021, (336)985-3983

Intl. Miniature Cattle Breeders Soc. and Registry **[3918]**, 25204 156th Ave. SE, Covington, WA 98042, (253)631-1911

Intl. Miniature Donkey Registry **[4693]** PO Box 982, Cripple Creek, CO 80813, (719)689-2904

Intl. Miniature Donkey Registry **[4693]**, PO Box 982, Cripple Creek, CO 80813, (719)689-2904

Intl. Miniature Horse Registry **[★4542]**

Intl. Miniature Zebu Assn. **[3919]**, 3571 Hwy. 20, Crawford, NE 69339, (308)665-1431

Intl. Minilab Assn. - Defunct.

Intl. Mission Bd. **[20053]**, PO Box 6767, Richmond, VA 23230-0767, (800)999-3113

Intl. Mission Bd. **[20053]**, PO Box 6767, Richmond, VA 23230-0767, (800)999-3113

Intl. Missions **[★20023]**

Intl. Missions **[★20023]**

Intl. Mobile Air Conditioning Assn. - Defunct.

Intl. Mobile Satellite Org. **[IO]**, London, United Kingdom

Intl. Mobjack Assn. **[22358]**, 3720 Blue Heron Ln., West Point, VA 23181, (804)843-2682

Intl. Mobjack Assn. **[22358]**, 3720 Blue Heron Ln., West Point, VA 23181, (804)843-2682

Intl. Model Power Boat Assn. **[21901]**, 515 Winifred Ave., Lansing, MI 48917, (517)321-6230

Intl. Model Power Boat Assn. **[21901]**, 515 Winifred Ave., Lansing, MI 48917, (517)321-6230

Intl. Modena Club **[22098]**, 10032 Goodrich Rd., Bloomington, MN 55437-2413

Intl. Modern Arnis Fed. Philippines **[IO]**, Mandaluyong City, Philippines

Intl. Modern Hapkido Fed. **[22735]**, 210 Homestead Dr., Roaring Brook Township, PA 18444, (570)842-1558

Intl. Molded Fibre Assn. **[2618]**, 1425 W Mequon Rd., Ste. C, Mequon, WI 53092, (414)527-4829

Intl. Molded Fibre Assn. **[2618]**, 1425 W Mequon Rd., Ste. C, Mequon, WI 53092, (414)527-4829

Intl. Molded Pulp Environmental Packaging Assn. **[★2618]**

Intl. Molded Pulp Environmental Packaging Assn. **[★2618]**

Intl. Molders' and Allied Workers' Union **[★23194]**

The Intl. Molinological Soc. **[IO]**, Vaihingen an der Enz, Germany

Intl. Molybdenum Assn. **[IO]**, London, United Kingdom

Intl. Molyneux Family Assn. **[20540]**, PO Box 10306, Bainbridge Island, WA 98110, (206)842-0565

Intl. MOMS Club - Defunct.

Intl. Monetary Fund **[17581]**, 700 19th St. NW, Washington, DC 20431, (202)623-7000

Intl. Monetary Fund **[17581]**, 700 19th St. NW, Washington, DC 20431, (202)623-7000

Intl. Montessori Accreditation Coun. **[8634]**, 8115 Fenton St., No. 304, Silver Spring, MD 20910, (301)589-1127

Intl. Montessori Accreditation Coun. **[8634]**, 8115 Fenton St., No. 304, Silver Spring, MD 20910, (301)589-1127

Intl. Montessori Assn. **[IO]**, Amsterdam, Netherlands

Intl. Montessori Soc. **[8635]**, 9525 Georgia Ave., No. 200, Silver Spring, MD 20910, (301)589-1127

Intl. Montessori Soc. **[8635]**, 9525 Georgia Ave., No. 200, Silver Spring, MD 20910, (301)589-1127

Intl. Morab Breeders' Assn. **[4600]**, 24 Bauneg Beg Rd., Sanford, ME 04073, (866)667-2246

Intl. Morab Breeders' Assn. **[4600]**, 24 Bauneg Beg Rd., Sanford, ME 04073, (866)667-2246

Intl. Morab Registry **[4601]**, Intl. Morab Breeders Assn., 24 Bauneg Beg Rd., Sanford, ME 04073, (866)667-2246

Intl. Motor Contest Assn. **[22245]**, PO Box 921, Vinton, IA 52349, (319)472-2201

Intl. Motor Press Assn. **[2833]**, PO Box 146, Harrington Park, NJ 07640, (201)750-3533

Intl. Motor Press Assn. **[2833]**, PO Box 146, Harrington Park, NJ 07640, (201)750-3533

Intl. Motor Sports Assn. **[22246]**, 1394 Broadway Ave., Braselton, GA 30517, (706)658-2120

Intl. Motor Vehicle Inspection Comm. **[IO]**, Brussels, Belgium

Intl. Motorcycling Fed. **[IO]**, Mies, Switzerland

Intl. Mountain Bicycling Assn. **[22479]**, PO Box 7578, Boulder, CO 80306, (303)545-9011

Intl. Mountain Bicycling Assn. **[22479]**, PO Box 7578, Boulder, CO 80306, (303)545-9011

Intl. Mountain Soc. - Defunct.

Intl. Movement Against All Forms of Discrimination and Racism **[IO]**, Tokyo, Japan

Intl. Movement of Catholic Agricultural and Rural Youth **[IO]**, Brussels, Belgium

Intl. Movement of Catholic Students - African Secretariat **[IO]**, Nairobi, Kenya

Intl. Movement of Catholic Students - Pax Romana **[IO]**, Paris, France

Intl. Movement Towards Educational Change **[IO]**, Oslo, Norway

Intl. MS Support Found. - Defunct.

Intl. Multiracial Shared Cultural Org. **[17975]**, 4 Park Ave., New York, NY 10163, (212)532-5449

Intl. Multiracial Shared Cultural Org. **[17975]**, 4 Park Ave., New York, NY 10163, (212)532-5449

Intl. Municipal Lawyers Assn. **[5252]**, 7910 Woodmont Ave., Ste. 1440, Bethesda, MD 20814, (202)466-5424

Intl. Municipal Lawyers Assn. **[5252]**, 7910 Woodmont Ave., Ste. 1440, Bethesda, MD 20814, (202)466-5424

Intl. Municipal Parking Cong. **[★2626]**

Intl. Municipal Parking Cong. **[★2626]**

Intl. Municipal Signal Assn. **[5964]**, PO Box 539, Newark, NY 14513-0539, (315)331-2182

Intl. Municipal Signal Assn. **[5964]**, PO Box 539, Newark, NY 14513-0539, (315)331-2182

Intl. Musculoskeletal Laser Soc. **[IO]**, Oldham, United Kingdom

Intl. Museum Theatre Alliance

Intl. Museum Theatre Alliance - Address unknown since 2011.

Intl. Music Coun. **[IO]**, Paris, France

Intl. Music and Media Centre **[IO]**, Vienna, Austria

Intl. Musicological Soc. **[IO]**, Basel, Switzerland

Intl. Mustang Bullitt Owners Club **[21079]**, PO Box 376, Springboro, OH 45066

Intl. Mustang Club **[★5070]**

Intl. Mustang Club **[★5070]**

Intl. Mycological Assn. **[7129]**, Prof. J. Taylor, Pres., Univ. of California, Dept. of Plant and Microbial Biology, 111 Koshland Hall, Berkeley, CA 94720

Intl. Mycological Assn. **[7129]**, Prof. J. Taylor, Pres., Univ. of California, Dept. of Plant and Microbial Biology, 111 Koshland Hall, Berkeley, CA 94720

Intl. Myeloma Found. **[13932]**, 12650 Riverside Dr., Ste. 206, North Hollywood, CA 91607-3421, (818)487-7455

Intl. Myeloma Found. **[13932]**, 12650 Riverside Dr., Ste. 206, North Hollywood, CA 91607-3421, (818)487-7455

Intl. MYOPAIN Soc. **[16103]**, PO Box 690402, San Antonio, TX 78269, (210)401-7224

Intl. Myotonic Dystrophy Org. **[14604]**, PO Box 1121, Sunland, CA 91041-1121, (818)951-2311

Intl. Mystery Shopping Alliance **[3108]**, 210 Crossways Park Dr., Woodbury, NY 11797, (516)576-1188

Intl. Nanny Assn. **[11151]**, PO Box 1299, Hyannis, MA 02601, (713)526-2670

Intl. Nanny Assn. **[11151]**, PO Box 1299, Hyannis, MA 02601, (713)526-2670

Intl. Nanocasting Assn.

Intl. Nanocasting Assn. - Address unknown since 2011.

Intl. Naples Sabot Assn. **[22359]**, PO Box 265, Balboa Island, CA 92662, (858)530-2541

Intl. Narcotic Enforcement Officers Assn. **[5464]**, PO Box 2938, Glenville, NY 12325-0938, (518)280-2347

Intl. Narcotic Enforcement Officers Assn. **[5464]**, PO Box 2938, Glenville, NY 12325-0938, (518)280-2347

Intl. Narcotics Control Bd. **[IO]**, Vienna, Austria

Intl. Narcotics Interdiction Assn. **[5465]**, 11683 La Colina Rd., San Diego, CA 92131, (858)271-4407

Intl. Narcotics Interdiction Assn. **[5465]**, 11683 La Colina Rd., San Diego, CA 92131, (858)271-4407

Intl. Native Amer. Flute Assn. **[10221]**, 3351 Mintonville Point Dr., Suffolk, VA 23435, (757)538-0468

Intl. Native Amer. Flute Assn. **[10221]**, 3351 Mintonville Point Dr., Suffolk, VA 23435, (757)538-0468

Intl. Natural Bodybuilding and Fitness Fed. **[22418]**, PO Box 4, Pocono Lake, PA 18347

Intl. Natural Bodybuilding and Fitness Fed. **[22418]**, PO Box 4, Pocono Lake, PA 18347

Intl. Naturist Fed. **[IO]**, Horsching, Austria

Intl. Naval Res. Org. **[10092]**, 5905 Reinwood Dr., Toledo, OH 43613-5605, (419)472-1331

Intl. Naval Res. Org. **[10092]**, 5905 Reinwood Dr., Toledo, OH 43613-5605, (419)472-1331

Intl. Navigation Assn. - Belgium **[IO]**, Brussels, Belgium

Intl. Navigation Assn. - USA - Defunct.

Intl. .NET Assn. **[6489]**, PO Box 6713, Bellevue, WA 98008-0713

A star before a book entry number signifies that the name is not listed separately, but is mentioned within the entry.

Intl. Network of Alternative Financial Institution [IO], Dakar, Senegal

Intl. Network for the Availability of Sci. Publications [IO], Oxford, United Kingdom

Intl. Network of Boutique Law Firms [5253], 75 Rockefeller Plz., 18th Flr., New York, NY 10019, (866)758-0317

Intl. Network of Boutique Law Firms [5253], 75 Rockefeller Plz., 18th Flr., New York, NY 10019, (866)758-0317

Intl. Network for Cancer Treatment and Res. [IO], Brussels, Belgium

Intl. Network of Children's Ministry [19583], PO Box 190, Castle Rock, CO 80104, (800)324-4543

Intl. Network of Children's Ministry [19583], PO Box 190, Castle Rock, CO 80104, (800)324-4543

Intl. Network for Contemporary Iraqi Artists [IO], London, United Kingdom

Intl. Network of Engineers and Scientists Against Proliferation [IO], Darmstadt, Germany

Intl. Network of Engineers and Scientists for Global Responsibility [IO], Berlin, Germany

Intl. Network on Family Poultry Development [IO], Rome, Italy

Intl. Network of Liberal Women [IO], London, United Kingdom

Intl. Network on Participatory Irrigation Mgt. [7016], 333 1/2 Pennsylvania Ave. SE, 3rd Fl., Washington, DC 20003, (202)546-7005

Intl. Network on Participatory Irrigation Mgt. [7016], 333 1/2 Pennsylvania Ave. SE, 3rd Fl., Washington, DC 20003, (202)546-7005

Intl. Network of Performing and Visual Arts Schools [★7741]

Intl. Network of Performing and Visual Arts Schools [★7741]

Intl. Network on Personal Meaning [IO], Toronto, ON, Canada

Intl. Network for the Prevention of Elder Abuse [IO], Vancouver, BC, Canada

Intl. Network of Prison Ministries [19992], Box 227475, Dallas, TX 75222

Intl. Network of Prison Ministries [19992], Box 227475, Dallas, TX 75222

Intl. Network for Religion and Animals - Defunct.

Intl. Network for Social Network Anal. [7415], Univ. of South Florida, Dept. of Sociology, 4202 E Fowler Ave., CPR 107, Tampa, FL 33620-5550, (813)974-7288

Intl. Network for Social Network Anal. [7415], Univ. of South Florida, Dept. of Sociology, 4202 E Fowler Ave., CPR 107, Tampa, FL 33620-5550, (813)974-7288

Intl. Network of Somewhere in Time Enthusiasts [23806], 8110 S Verdev Dr., Oak Creek, WI 53154, (708)579-3749

Intl. Network of Somewhere in Time Enthusiasts [23806], 8110 S Verdev Dr., Oak Creek, WI 53154, (708)579-3749

Intl. Network for Sustainable Energy [IQ], Hjortshoj, Denmark

Intl. Network for Terminology [IO], Vienna, Austria

Intl. Network of Women in Tech. [★7534]

Intl. Network of Women in Tech. [★7534]

Intl. Neural Network Soc. [15659], 2424 Amer. Ln., Madison, WI 53704, (608)443-2461

Intl. Neural Network Soc. [15659], 2424 Amer. Ln., Madison, WI 53704, (608)443-2461

Intl. Neuro-Linguistic Programming Assn. [16464], 42 Spruce Ridge, Rte. 9P, Saratoga Springs, NY 12866, (518)587-3478

Intl. Neuro-Linguistic Programming Assn. [16464], 42 Spruce Ridge, Rte. 9P, Saratoga Springs, NY 12866, (518)587-3478

Intl. Neuro-Linguistic Programming Trainers Assn. [16465], Wyatt L. Woodsmall, PhD, Founder/Dir., 1201 Delta Glen Ct., Vienna, VA 22182, (703)757-7945

Intl. Neuroendocrine Fed. [IO], Paris, France

Intl. Neuromodulation Soc. [15660], 2000 Van Ness Ave., Ste. 402, San Francisco, CA 94109, (415)683-3237

Intl. Neuromodulation Soc. [15660], 2000 Van Ness Ave., Ste. 402, San Francisco, CA 94109, (415)683-3237

Intl. Neuropsychiatric Assn. [IO], Randwick, Australia

Intl. Neuropsychological Soc. [15661], 700 Ackerman Rd., Ste. 625, Columbus, OH 43202, (614)263-4200

Intl. Neuropsychological Soc. [15661], 700 Ackerman Rd., Ste. 625, Columbus, OH 43202, (614)263-4200

Intl. Neurotoxicology Assn. [7573], Dr. Donald Fox, Univ. of Houston, Coll. of Optometry, 505 J Davis Armistead Bldg., Houston, TX 77204-2020, (713)743-1964

Intl. New Thought Alliance [10388], 5003 E Broadway Rd., Mesa, AZ 85206, (480)830-1074

Intl. News Ser. [★2879]

Intl. News Ser. [★2879]

Intl. Newsmedia Marketing Assn. [2941], PO Box 740186, Dallas, TX 75374, (214)373-9111

Intl. Newsmedia Marketing Assn. [2941], PO Box 740186, Dallas, TX 75374, (214)373-9111

Intl. Newspaper Advt. and Marketing Executives [★2953]

Intl. Newspaper Gp. [2834], 64 Spyglass Dr., Jackson, NJ 08527, (732)833-8004

Intl. Newspaper Marketing Assn. [★2941]

International Newspaper Marketing Assn. [★2941]

Intl. Newspaper Promotion Assn. [★2941]

Intl. Newspaper Promotion Assn. [★2941]

Intl. NGO Forum on Indonesian Development - Indonesia [IO], Jakarta, Indonesia

Intl. NGO Training and Res. Centre [IO], Oxford, United Kingdom

Intl. Nick Tate Club [IO], Birmingham, United Kingdom

Intl. Nippon Collectors Club [21264], 8 Geoley Ct., Thurmont, MD 21788

Intl. Nippon Collectors Club [21264], 8 Geoley Ct., Thurmont, MD 21788

Intl. Non-Violence and Vegetarian Soc. - Defunct.

Intl. Nonwovens and Disposables Assn. [★3442]

Intl. Norton Owners' Assn. [21932], Tari Norum, Sec./Ed., 276 Butterworth Ln., Langhorne, PA 19047, (215)741-0110

Intl. Norton Owners' Assn. [21932], Tari Norum, Sec./Ed., 276 Butterworth Ln., Langhorne, PA 19047, (215)741-0110

Intl. Nubian Breeders Assn. [3790], Caroline Lawson, Sec.-Treas., 5124 FM 1940, Franklin, TX 77856, (979)828-4158

Intl. Nubian Breeders Assn. [3790], Caroline Lawson, Sec.-Treas., 5124 FM 1940, Franklin, TX 77856, (979)828-4158

Intl. Nuclear Law Assn. [IO], Brussels, Belgium

Intl. Numismatic Commn. [IO], Vienna, Austria

Intl. Nurses Anonymous

Intl. Nurses Anonymous - Address unknown since 2011.

Intl. Nurses Soc. on Addictions [15756], PO Box 14846, Lenexa, KS 66285, (913)895-4621

Intl. Nurses Soc. on Addictions [15756], PO Box 14846, Lenexa, KS 66285, (913)895-4621

Intl. Nursing Assn. for Clinical Simulation and Learning [15757],

Intl. Nursing Assn. for Clinical Simulation and Learning [15757],

Intl. Nursing Coalition for Mass Casualty Educ. [★15770]

Intl. Nursing Services Assn. [★15164]

Intl. Nursing Services Assn. [★15164]

Intl. Oak Soc. [4971], 299 Pond Dr., Monterey, TN 38574

Intl. Oak Soc. [4971], 299 Pond Dr., Monterey, TN 38574

Intl. Occultation Timing Assn. [6232], 2505 Jeannes Trail, Edmond, OK 73012

Intl. Occultation Timing Assn. [6232], 2505 Jeannes Trail, Edmond, OK 73012

Intl. OCD Found. [15457], PO Box 961029, Boston, MA 02196, (617)973-5801

Intl. Ocean Inst. [IO], Gzira, Malta

Intl. Ocular Inflammation Soc. [IO], Alicante, Spain

Intl. Off. for Water [IO], Paris, France

Intl. Oil Pollution Compensation Funds [IO], London, United Kingdom

Intl. Oil Scouts Assn. [2656], PO Box 940310, Houston, TX 77094-7310, (713)420-6257

Intl. Oil Scouts Assn. [2656], PO Box 940310, Houston, TX 77094-7310, (713)420-6257

Intl. Okinawa Kobudo Assn. - Address unknown since 2011.

Intl. Old Lacers, Inc. [21446], Barbara Saltern, Membership Chair, 662 Luther Ln., Nazareth, PA 18064

Intl. Old Lacers, Inc. [21446], Barbara Saltern, Membership Chair, 662 Luther Ln., Nazareth, PA 18064

Intl. Oleander Soc. [21805], PO Box 3431, Galveston, TX 77552-0431, (409)762-9334

Intl. Oleander Soc. [21805], PO Box 3431, Galveston, TX 77552-0431, (409)762-9334

Intl. Olive Oil Coun. [IO], Madrid, Spain

Intl. Olympic Comm. [IO], Lausanne, Switzerland

Intl. Ombudsman Assn. [677], 390 Amwell Rd., Ste. 403, Hillsborough, NJ 08844, (908)359-0246

Intl. Ombudsman Inst. [IO], Vienna, Austria

Intl. Opticians Assn. [IO], London, United Kingdom

Intl. Oracle Users Gp. [6513], 401 N Michigan Ave., 22nd Fl., Chicago, IL 60611-4267, (312)245-1579

Intl. Oracle Users Gp. [6513], 401 N Michigan Ave., 22nd Fl., Chicago, IL 60611-4267, (312)245-1579

Intl. Oracle Users Gp. - Americas [★6513]

Intl. Oracle Users Gp. - Americas [★6513]

Intl. Order of Alhambra [18953], 4200 Leeds Ave., Baltimore, MD 21229, (410)242-0660

Intl. Order of the Alhambra [★18953]

Intl. Order of Alhambra [18953], 4200 Leeds Ave., Baltimore, MD 21229, (410)242-0660

Intl. Order of the Alhambra [★18953]

Intl. Order of E.A.R.S. [10543], PO Box 17141, Louisville, KY 40217, (502)245-0643

Intl. Order of E.A.R.S. [10543], PO Box 17141, Louisville, KY 40217, (502)245-0643

Intl. Order of the Golden Rule [2537], 3520 Executive Center Dr., Ste. 300, Austin, TX 78731, (512)334-5504

Intl. Order of the Golden Rule [2537], 3520 Executive Center Dr., Ste. 300, Austin, TX 78731, (512)334-5504

Intl. Order of Hoo-Hoo [★19027]

Intl. Order of Job's Daughters, Supreme Guardian Coun. [★19133]

Intl. Order of Job's Daughters, Supreme Guardian Coun. [★19133]

Intl. Order of the King's Daughters and Sons [19584], PO Box 1017, Chautauqua, NY 14722-1017, (716)357-4951

Intl. Order of the King's Daughters and Sons [19584], PO Box 1017, Chautauqua, NY 14722-1017, (716)357-4951

Intl. Order of Runeberg [9616], 6094 Myrtle Ave., Eureka, CA 95503, (707)445-2364

Intl. Order of Runeberg [9616], 6094 Myrtle Ave., Eureka, CA 95503, (707)445-2364

Intl. Order of Saint Luke the Physician [20185], PO Box 780909, San Antonio, TX 78278-0909, (210)492-5222

Intl. Order of Saint Luke the Physician [20185], PO Box 780909, San Antonio, TX 78278-0909, (210)492-5222

Intl. Order of St. Vincent [19711], 126 Coming St., Charleston, SC 29403, (843)722-7345

Intl. Order of St. Vincent [19711], 126 Coming St., Charleston, SC 29403, (843)722-7345

Intl. Organ Festival at St. Albans [IO], St. Albans, United Kingdom

Intl. Org. of Aluminum Aerosol Container Mfrs. [IO], Dusseldorf, Germany

Intl. Org. for Biotechnology and Bioengineering [IO], Kenmore, Australia

Intl. Org. for the Elimination of All Forms of Racial Discrimination [IO], Geneva, Switzerland

Intl. Org. of Motor Vehicle Mfrs. [IO], Paris, France

Intl. Org. for the Ornamental Plants Indus. [IO], Noordwijk, Netherlands

Intl. Org. for the Transition of Professional Dancers [IO], Lausanne, Switzerland

Intl. Org. of Vine and Wine [IO], Paris, France

Intl. Org. for Adolescents [11326], Shelby French, Exec. Dir., 4305 N Lincoln Ave., Ste. K, Chicago, IL 60618, (773)404-8831

Intl. Org. for Adolescents [11326], Shelby French, Exec. Dir., 4305 N Lincoln Ave., Ste. K, Chicago, IL 60618, (773)404-8831

Reference to "IO" in place of a book number signifies that the association may be found in the 50th edition of International Organizations.

Intl. Org. of Asian Crime Investigators and Specialists [5366], PO Box 612, North Scituate, MA 02060

Intl. Org. for Biological Control of Noxious Animals and Plants [IO], Wageningen, Netherlands

Intl. Org. of Black Security Executives [3219], PO Box 1471, San Mateo, CA 94401, (888)884-6273

Intl. Org. of Chinese Physicist and Astronomers [7267], Sun-Yiu Fung, Treas., PO Box 8743, Newport Beach, CA 92658, (949)721-8812

Intl. Org. of Citrus Virologists [6357], Univ. of California, Dept. of Plant Pathology, Riverside, CA 92521

Intl. Org. of Citrus Virologists [6357], Univ. of California, Dept. of Plant Pathology, Riverside, CA 92521

Intl. Org. of Consumers Unions - USA - Defunct.

Intl. Org. for the Elimination of All Forms of Racial Discrimination [IO], Geneva, Switzerland

Intl. Org. of the Flavor Indus. [IO], Geneva, Switzerland

Intl. Org. for Forensic Odonto-Stomatology [IO], Oslo, Norway

Intl. Org. of Glutaric Acidemia [15601], 9638 Rte. 22 Hwy., Blairsville, PA 15717, (724)459-0179

Intl. Org. of Glutaric Acidemia [15601], 9638 Rte. 22 Hwy., Blairsville, PA 15717, (724)459-0179

Intl. Org. for Haitian Development [7894], 1425 K St. NW, Ste. 350, Washington, DC 20005, (305)735-3242

Intl. Org. of Legal Metrology [IO], Paris, France

Intl. Org. for Migration - Abidjan, Cote d'Ivoire [IO], Abidjan, Cote d'Ivoire

Intl. Org. for Migration - Abuja, Nigeria [IO], Abuja, Nigeria

Intl. Org. for Migration - Accra, Ghana [IO], Accra, Ghana

Intl. Org. for Migration - Addis Ababa, Ethiopia [IO], Addis Ababa, Ethiopia

Intl. Org. for Migration - Amman, Jordan [IO], Amman, Jordan

Intl. Org. for Migration - Armenia [IO], Yerevan, Armenia

Intl. Org. for Migration - Ashgabat, Turkmenistan [IO], Ashgabat, Turkmenistan

Intl. Org. for Migration - Athens, Greece [IO], Athens, Greece

Intl. Org. for Migration - Austria [IO], Vienna, Austria

Intl. Org. for Migration - Azerbaijan [IO], Baku, Azerbaijan

Intl. Org. for Migration - Bamako, Mali [IO], Bamako, Mali

Intl. Org. for Migration - Belgium [IO], Brussels, Belgium

Intl. Org. for Migration - Bosnia and Herzegovina [IO], Sarajevo, Bosnia-Hercegovina

Intl. Org. for Migration - Bratislava, Slovakia [IO], Bratislava, Slovakia

Intl. Org. for Migration - Bucharest, Romania [IO], Bucharest, Romania

Intl. Org. for Migration - Budapest, Hungary [IO], Budapest, Hungary

Intl. Org. for Migration - Cambodia [IO], Phnom Penh, Cambodia

Intl. Org. for Migration - Canberra, Australia [IO], Canberra, Australia

Intl. Org. for Migration - China [IO], Hong Kong, People's Republic of China

Intl. Org. for Migration - Colombia [IO], Bogota, Colombia

Intl. Org. for Migration - Colombo, Sri Lanka [IO], Colombo, Sri Lanka

Intl. Org. for Migration - Conakry, Guinea [IO], Conakry, Guinea

Intl. Org. for Migration - Costa Rica [IO], San Pedro, Costa Rica

Intl. Org. for Migration - Dar es Salaam, Tanzania [IO], Dar es Salaam, United Republic of Tanzania

Intl. Org. for Migration - Dhaka, Bangladesh [IO], Dhaka, Bangladesh

Intl. Org. for Migration - Dublin, Ireland [IO], Dublin, Ireland

Intl. Org. for Migration - Dushanbe [IO], Dushanbe, Tajikistan

Intl. Org. for Migration - Freetown, Sierra Leone [IO], Freetown, Sierra Leone

Intl. Org. for Migration - Germany [IO], Berlin, Germany

Intl. Org. for Migration - Guatemala [IO], Guatemala City, Guatemala

Intl. Org. for Migration - Harare, Zimbabwe [IO], Harare, Zimbabwe

Intl. Org. for Migration - Islamabad, Pakistan [IO], Islamabad, Pakistan

Intl. Org. for Migration - Istanbul, Turkey [IO], Ankara, Turkey

Intl. Org. for Migration - Jakarta, Indonesia [IO], Jakarta, Indonesia

Intl. Org. for Migration - Kabul, Afghanistan [IO], Kabul, Afghanistan

Intl. Org. for Migration - Kampala, Uganda [IO], Kampala, Uganda

Intl. Org. for Migration - Kazakhstan [IO], Astana, Kazakhstan

Intl. Org. for Migration - Khartoum, Sudan [IO], Khartoum, Sudan

Intl. Org. for Migration - Kiev, Ukraine [IO], Kiev, Ukraine

Intl. Org. for Migration - Kingston, Jamaica [IO], Kingston, Jamaica

Intl. Org. for Migration - Kinshasa, Democratic Republic of the Congo [IO], Brazzaville, Republic of the Congo

Intl. Org. for Migration - Kyrgyz Republic [IO], Bishkek, Kirgizstan

Intl. Org. for Migration - La Paz, Bolivia [IO], La Paz, Bolivia

Intl. Org. for Migration - Lima, Peru [IO], Lima, Peru

Intl. Org. for Migration - Lisbon, Portugal [IO], Lisbon, Portugal

Intl. Org. for Migration - Ljubljana [IO], Ljubljana, Slovenia

Intl. Org. for Migration - Luanda, Angola [IO], Luanda, Angola

Intl. Org. for Migration - Lusaka, Zambia [IO], Lusaka, Zambia

Intl. Org. for Migration - Madrid, Spain [IO], Madrid, Spain

Intl. Org. for Migration - Managua, Nicaragua [IO], Managua, Nicaragua

Intl. Org. for Migration - Mexico [IO], Mexico City, Mexico

Intl. Org. for Migration - Minsk, Belarus [IO], Minsk, Belarus

Intl. Org. for Migration - Moldova [IO], Chisinau, Moldova

Intl. Org. for Migration - Moscow, Russia [IO], Moscow, Russia

Intl. Org. for Migration - Nairobi, Kenya [IO], Nairobi, Kenya

Intl. Org. for Migration - Netherlands [IO], The Hague, Netherlands

Intl. Org. for Migration - Norway [IO], Oslo, Norway

Intl. Org. for Migration - Paris, France [IO], Paris, France

Intl. Org. for Migration - Philippines [IO], Makati City, Philippines

Intl. Org. for Migration - Port au Prince, Haiti [IO], Port-au-Prince, Haiti

Intl. Org. for Migration - Prague, Czech Republic [IO], Prague, Czech Republic

Intl. Org. for Migration - Quito, Ecuador [IO], Quito, Ecuador

Intl. Org. for Migration - Regional Off. for the Baltic and Nordic States [IO], Helsinki, Finland

Intl. Org. for Migration - Riga, Latvia [IO], Riga, Latvia

Intl. Org. for Migration - Rome, Italy [IO], Rome, Italy

Intl. Org. for Migration - San Salvador, El Salvador [IO], San Salvador, El Salvador

Intl. Org. for Migration - Santiago, Chile [IO], Santiago, Chile

Intl. Org. for Migration - Santo Domingo, Dominican Republic [IO], Santo Domingo, Dominican Republic

Intl. Org. for Migration - Seoul, Republic of Korea [IO], Seoul, Republic of Korea

Intl. Org. for Migration - Skopje [IO], Skopje, Macedonia

Intl. Org. for Migration - Sofia, Bulgaria [IO], Sofia, Bulgaria

Intl. Org. for Migration - Southern Africa [IO], Pretoria, Republic of South Africa

Intl. Org. for Migration - Switzerland [IO], Geneva, Switzerland

Intl. Org. for Migration - Tallinn, Estonia [IO], Tallinn, Estonia

Intl. Org. for Migration - Tbilisi, Georgia [IO], Tbilisi, Georgia

Intl. Org. for Migration - Tegucigalpa, Honduras [IO], Tegucigalpa, Honduras

Intl. Org. for Migration - Tehran, Iran [IO], Tehran, Iran

Intl. Org. for Migration - Thailand [IO], Bangkok, Thailand

Intl. Org. for Migration - Tirana, Albania [IO], Tirana, Albania

Intl. Org. for Migration - Tokyo, Japan [IO], Tokyo, Japan

Intl. Org. for Migration - Tunis, Tunisia [IO], Tunis, Tunisia

Intl. Org. for Migration - United Kingdom [IO], London, United Kingdom

Intl. Org. for Migration - Vietnam [IO], Hanoi, Vietnam

Intl. Org. for Migration - Vilnius, Lithuania [IO], Vilnius, Lithuania

Intl. Org. for Migration - Warsaw, Poland [IO], Warsaw, Poland

Intl. Org. for Migration - Zagreb, Croatia [IO], Zagreb, Croatia

Intl. Org. of Multiple Sclerosis Nurses [15758], 359 Main St., Ste. A, Hackensack, NJ 07601, (201)487-1050

Intl. Org. of Multiple Sclerosis Nurses [15758], 359 Main St., Ste. A, Hackensack, NJ 07601, (201)487-1050

Intl. Org. for Mycoplasmology [6304], Dr. Mitchell F. Balish, Treas., 80 Pearson Hall, Oxford, OH 45056, (513)528-0167

Intl. Org. for Mycoplasmology [6304], Dr. Mitchell F. Balish, Treas., 80 Pearson Hall, Oxford, OH 45056, (513)528-0167

Intl. Org. for Peace, Care and Relief [IO], Tripoli, Libyan Arab Jamahiriya

Intl. Org. of Plant Biosystematists [6358], Peter C. Hoch, PhD, Treas., Missouri Botanical Garden, PO Box 299, St. Louis, MO 63166-0299

Intl. Org. of Plant Biosystematists [6358], Peter C. Hoch, PhD, Treas., Missouri Botanical Garden, PO Box 299, St. Louis, MO 63166-0299

Intl. Org. of Scenographers, Theatre Architects, and Technicians [IO], Taipei, Taiwan

Intl. Org. for Sci. and Tech. Educ. [IO], Ashwood, Republic of South Africa

Intl. Org. of Securities Commissions [IO], Madrid, Spain

Intl. Org. for Septuagint and Cognate Stud. [19349], PO Box 275, Winona Lake, IN 46590-0275

Intl. Org. for Septuagint and Cognate Stud. [19349], PO Box 275, Winona Lake, IN 46590-0275

Intl. Org. on Shape Memory and Superelastic Technologies [7096], Sarina Pastoric, Member Ser. Center, 9639 Kinsman Rd., Novelty, OH 44073, (440)338-5151

Intl. Org. on Shape Memory and Superelastic Technologies [7096], Sarina Pastoric, Member Ser. Center, 9639 Kinsman Rd., Novelty, OH 44073, (440)338-5151

Intl. Org. of Space Communications [IO], Moscow, Russia

Intl. Org. for Standardization [IO], Geneva, Switzerland

Intl. Org. for Succulent Plant Stud. [IO], Sherborne, United Kingdom

Intl. Org. of Supreme Audit Institutions [IO], Vienna, Austria

Intl. Org. for Victim Assistance [13364], 32465 NE Old Parrett Mountain Rd., Newberg, OR 97132, (503)554-1552

Intl. Org. for Women and Development [16586], PO Box 616, Rockville Centre, NY 11571-0616

Intl. Org. of Women Pilots [★151]

Intl. Org. of Women Pilots [★151]

Intl. Orienteering Fed. [IO], Helsinki, Finland

Intl. Oromo Youth Assn.

A star before a book entry number signifies that the name is not listed separately, but is mentioned within the entry.

Intl. Oromo Youth Assn. - Address unknown since 2011.
Intl. Orphan Care [11327], PO Box 3397, Laguna Hills, CA 92654, (949)939-1712
Intl. Orphans, Inc. [★11232]
Intl. Orthodox Christian Charities [19585], PO Box 630225, Baltimore, MD 21263-0225, (410)243-9820
Intl. Orthodox Christian Charities [19585], PO Box 630225, Baltimore, MD 21263-0225, (410)243-9820
Intl. Orthoptic Assn. [IO], London, United Kingdom
The Intl. Osprey Found. [5068], PO Box 250, Sanibel, FL 33957-0250
The Intl. Osprey Found. [5068], PO Box 250, Sanibel, FL 33957-0250
Intl. Ostomy Assn. [IO], Toronto, ON, Canada
Intl. Otter Survival Fund [IO], Broadford, United Kingdom
Intl. Oxygen Mfrs. Assn. [1571], 1025 Thomas Jefferson St. NW, Ste. 500 E, Washington, DC 20007, (202)521-9300
Intl. Oxygen Mfrs. Assn. [1571], 1025 Thomas Jefferson St. NW, Ste. 500 E, Washington, DC 20007, (202)521-9300
Intl. Ozone Assn. [6893], PO Box 28873, Scottsdale, AZ 85255, (480)529-3787
Intl. Ozone Assn. [6893], PO Box 28873, Scottsdale, AZ 85255, (480)529-3787
Intl. Ozone Assn. - EA3G [IO], Poitiers, France
Intl. Ozone Inst. [★6893]
Intl. Ozone Inst. [★6893]
Intl. Pacific Halibut Commn. [5455], 2320 W Commodore Way, Ste. 300, Seattle, WA 98199-1287, (206)634-1838
Intl. Pacific Halibut Commn. [5455], 2320 W Commodore Way, Ste. 300, Seattle, WA 98199-1287, (206)634-1838
Intl. Packaged Ice Assn. [1712], PO Box 1199, Tampa, FL 33601-1199, (813)258-1690
Intl. Packet Communications Consortium [★7540]
Intl. Packet Communications Consortium [★7540]
Intl. Paddle Assn. [★22832]
Intl. Paddle Rackets Assn. [★22832]
Intl. Palestinian Cardiac Relief Org. [14021], Palestine Children's Relief Fund, PO Box 1926, Kent, OH 44240, (330)678-2645
Intl. Palestinian Cardiac Relief Org. [14021], Palestine Children's Relief Fund, PO Box 1926, Kent, OH 44240, (330)678-2645
Intl. Palm Soc. [6359], Liz Stansfeld, 9300 Sandstone St., Austin, TX 78737, (512)301-2744
Intl. Palm Soc. [6359], Liz Stansfeld, 9300 Sandstone St., Austin, TX 78737, (512)301-2744
Intl. Palmtherapy Assn. [16859], 16161 Ventura Blvd., Encino, CA 91436, (818)905-7761
Intl. Palmtherapy Assn. [16859], 16161 Ventura Blvd., Encino, CA 91436, (818)905-7761
Intl. Panel on Fissile Materials [18203], Princeton Univ., 221 Nassau St., 2nd Fl., Princeton, NJ 08542, (609)258-4677
Intl. Panel on Fissile Materials [18203], Princeton Univ., 221 Nassau St., 2nd Fl., Princeton, NJ 08542, (609)258-4677
Intl. Paneuropean Union [IO], Munich, Germany
Intl. Paperweight Soc. [22004], 761 Chestnut St., Santa Cruz, CA 95060, (408)427-1177
Intl. Paralegal Mgt. Assn. [5665], PO Box 659, Avondale Estates, GA 30002-0659, (404)292-4762
Intl. Paralegal Mgt. Assn. [5665], PO Box 659, Avondale Estates, GA 30002-0659, (404)292-4762
Intl. Paralympic Comm. [IO], Bonn, Germany
Intl. Parents' Org. [★14955]
Intl. Parking Inst. [2626], PO Box 7167, Fredericksburg, VA 22404, (540)371-7535
Intl. Parking Inst. [2626], PO Box 7167, Fredericksburg, VA 22404, (540)371-7535
Intl. Parrotlet Soc. [21220], PO Box 2446, Aptos, CA 95003-2446, (831)688-5560
Intl. Parrotlet Soc. [21220], PO Box 2446, Aptos, CA 95003-2446, (831)688-5560
Intl. Partners [12345], 1320 Fenwick Ln., Ste. 400, Silver Spring, MD 20910, (301)318-2545
Intl. Partnership for Critical Markers of Disease [14022], 24 Frank Lloyd Wright Dr., Ste. H1200, Ann Arbor, MI 48105, (734)930-4400

Intl. Partnership for Microbicides [13615], 8401 Colesville Rd., Ste. 200, Silver Spring, MD 20910, (301)608-2221
Intl. Partnership for Microbicides [13615], 8401 Colesville Rd., Ste. 200, Silver Spring, MD 20910, (301)608-2221
Intl. Partnership for Reproductive Hea. [16587], PO Box 510, Chesterton, IN 46304
Intl. Passenger Ship Assn. [★3557]
Intl. Patent and Trademark Assn. [★5571]
Intl. Patent and Trademark Assn. [★5571]
Intl. Patient Assn. for Primary Immunodeficiencies [IO], Cornwall, United Kingdom
Intl. Peace Acad. [★17802]
Intl. Peace Acad. [★17802]
Intl. Peace Bur. [IO], Geneva, Switzerland
Intl. Peace Inst. [17802], 777 United Nations Plz., New York, NY 10017-3521, (212)687-4300
Intl. Peace Inst. [17802], 777 United Nations Plz., New York, NY 10017-3521, (212)687-4300
Intl. Peace Lantern Exchange Project - Defunct.
Intl. Peace Operations Assn. [★18257]
Intl. Peace Operations Assn. [18257], 1634 I St. NW, Ste. 800, Washington, DC 20006, (202)464-0721
International Peace Scholarship Fund [★9063]
International Peace Scholarship Fund [★9063]
Intl. Peat Soc. [IO], Jyvaskyla, Finland
Intl. Pectin Producers Assn. [IO], Neuenburg, Germany
Intl. Pediatric Endosurgery Gp. [16148], 11300 W Olympic Blvd., Ste. 600, Los Angeles, CA 90064, (310)437-0553
Intl. Pediatric Endosurgery Gp. [16148], 11300 W Olympic Blvd., Ste. 600, Los Angeles, CA 90064, (310)437-0553
Intl. Pediatric Hypertension Assn. [15076], Cincinnati Children's Hosp. Medical Center, 3333 Burnet Ave., MLC 7002, Cincinnati, OH 45229, (513)636-8265
Intl. Pediatric Hypertension Assn. [15076], Cincinnati Children's Hosp. Medical Center, 3333 Burnet Ave., MLC 7002, Cincinnati, OH 45229, (513)636-8265
Intl. Pediatric Nephrology Assn. [15550], Gen. Clinical Res. Center, 10833 Le Conte Ave., 27-066 CHS, Los Angeles, CA 90095-1697, (310)206-9295
Intl. Pediatric Nephrology Assn. [15550], Gen. Clinical Res. Center, 10833 Le Conte Ave., 27-066 CHS, Los Angeles, CA 90095-1697, (310)206-9295
Intl. Pediatric Transplant Assn. [16908], 15000 Commerce Pkwy., Ste. C, Mount Laurel, NJ 08054, (856)439-0500
Intl. Pediatric Transplant Assn. [16908], 15000 Commerce Pkwy., Ste. C, Mount Laurel, NJ 08054, (856)439-0500
Intl. Pedigree Assignment and Bloodline Res. Assn. [4602], 321 N Martha St., Lombard, IL 60148
Intl. Pedigree Assignment and Bloodline Res. Assn. [4602], 321 N Martha St., Lombard, IL 60148
Intl. Pelvic Pain Soc. [16104], 2 Woodfield Lake, 1100 E Woodfield Rd., Ste. 520, Schaumburg, IL 60173, (847)517-8712
Intl. Pelvic Pain Soc. [16104], 2 Woodfield Lake, 1100 E Woodfield Rd., Ste. 520, Schaumburg, IL 60173, (847)517-8712
Intl. Pemphigus and Pemphigoid Found. [14394], 2701 Cottage Way, No. 16, Sacramento, CA 95825, (916)922-1298
Intl. Pen Assn. - Address unknown since 2010.
Intl. P.E.N. - England [IO], London, United Kingdom
Intl. Pen Friends [21419], Lorrin Lee, Agent, 500 Univ. Ave., Ste. 2415, Honolulu, HI 96826, (808)949-5000
Intl. Pen Friends - Australia [IO], Paynesville, Australia
Intl. Pen Pal Support Group Network for Chronic Dizziness and Balance Disorders - Defunct.
Intl. P.E.N. - Scottish Centre [IO], Edinburgh, United Kingdom
Intl. PEN - U.S.A West [★10731]
Intl. P.E.N. Women Writers' Comm. [IO], Gardenvale, Australia
Intl. PEN Writers Assn. [IO], London, United Kingdom

Intl. Penguin Class Dinghy Assn. [22360], Charles Krafft, Treas., 8300 Waverly Rd., Owings, MD 20736
Intl. Penguin Class Dinghy Assn. [22360], Charles Krafft, Treas., 8300 Waverly Rd., Owings, MD 20736
Intl. Penpal Club [IO], Mumbai, India
Intl. Peoplemedia Telecommunications Consortium [7543], 2400 Camino Ramon, Ste. 375, San Ramon, CA 94583, (925)275-6600
Intl. Peoplemedia Telecommunications Consortium [7543], 2400 Camino Ramon, Ste. 375, San Ramon, CA 94583, (925)275-6600
Intl. People's Democratic Uhuru Movement [17524], 1245 18th Ave. S, St. Petersburg, FL 33705
Intl. People's Democratic Uhuru Movement [17524], 1245 18th Ave. S, St. Petersburg, FL 33705
Intl. People's Sports - U.S.A. [★22965]
Intl. Pepper Community [IO], Jakarta, Indonesia
Intl. Percy Grainger Soc. [9500], 7 Cromwell Pl., White Plains, NY 10601, (914)843-4784
Intl. Percy Grainger Soc. [9500], 7 Cromwell Pl., White Plains, NY 10601, (914)843-4784
Intl. Performing Arts for Youth [10359], 1616 Walnut St., Ste. 1800, Philadelphia, PA 19103, (267)690-1325
Intl. Perfume Bottle Assn. [21359], PO Box 425, Pennington, NJ 08534
Intl. Perfume Bottle Assn. [21359], PO Box 425, Pennington, NJ 08534
Intl. Perfume and Scent Bottle Collectors Assn. [★21359]
Intl. Perfume and Scent Bottle Collectors Assn. [★21359]
Intl. Permafrost Assn. - Argentina [IO], Mendoza, Argentina
Intl. Permafrost Assn. - Austria [IO], Graz, Austria
Intl. Permafrost Assn. - Belgium [IO], Gent, Belgium
Intl. Permafrost Assn. - Canada [IO], Ottawa, ON, Canada
Intl. Permafrost Assn. - China [IO], Lanzhou, People's Republic of China
Intl. Permafrost Assn. - Finland [IO], Helsinki, Finland
Intl. Permafrost Assn. - France [IO], Orsay, France
Intl. Permafrost Assn. - Japan [IO], Ibaraki, Japan
Intl. Permafrost Assn. - Kazakhstan [IO], Almaty, Kazakhstan
Intl. Permafrost Assn. - Mongolia [IO], Ulan Bator, Mongolia
Intl. Permafrost Assn. - Netherlands [IO], Amsterdam, Netherlands
Intl. Permafrost Assn. - Norway [IO], Potsdam, Germany
Intl. Permafrost Assn. - Poland [IO], Lublin, Poland
Intl. Permafrost Assn. - Russia [IO], Tyumen, Russia
Intl. Permafrost Assn. - Spain [IO], Valladolid, Spain
Intl. Permafrost Assn. - Sweden [IO], Lund, Sweden
Intl. Permafrost Assn. - United Kingdom [IO], Brighton, United Kingdom
Intl. Personnel Mgt. Assn. [1153], 1617 Duke St., Alexandria, VA 22314, (703)549-7100
Intl. Personnel Mgt. Assn. - Canada [IO], Ottawa, ON, Canada
Intl. Peruvian Paso Horse Assn. [★4630]
Intl. Peruvian Paso Horse Assn. [★4630]
Intl. Petroleum Credit Assn. [★1307]
Intl. Petroleum Credit Assn. [★1307]
Intl. Petroleum Indus. Environmental Conservation Assn. [IO], London, United Kingdom
Intl. Petula Clark Soc. [IO], Ramsgate, United Kingdom
Intl. Phalaenopsis Alliance [4671], Lynn Fuller, Membership Sec., 1401 Pennsylvania Ave., No. 1604, Wilmington, DE 19806, (302)594-0765
Intl. Pharmaceutical Excipients Coun. [★2696]
Intl. Pharmaceutical Excipients Coun. [★2696]
Intl. Pharmaceutical Excipients Coun. of the Americas [2696], 1655 N Ft. Myer Dr., Ste. 700, Arlington, VA 22209, (703)875-2127
Intl. Pharmaceutical Excipients Coun. of the Americas [2696], 1655 N Ft. Myer Dr., Ste. 700, Arlington, VA 22209, (703)875-2127
Intl. Pharmaceutical Fed. [IO], The Hague, Netherlands

Reference to "IO" in place of a book number signifies that the association may be found in the 50th edition of International Organizations.

Intl. Pharmaceutical Students' Fed. **[IO]**, The Hague, Netherlands

Intl. Philatelic Fed. **[IO]**, Zurich, Switzerland

Intl. Philosophers for the Prevention of Nuclear Omnicide **[18204]**, Prof. Howard Friedman, Exec. Dir., 124 Clay St., Thomaston, CT 06787

Intl. Philosophers for the Prevention of Nuclear Omnicide **[18204]**, Prof. Howard Friedman, Exec. Dir., 124 Clay St., Thomaston, CT 06787

Intl. Phonetic Assn. **[IO]**, Thessaloniki, Greece

Intl. Photodynamic Assn. **[IO]**, Tokyo, Japan

Intl. Photographic Historical Org. **[10439]**, PO Box 16074, San Francisco, CA 94116, (415)681-4356

Intl. Photographic Historical Org. **[10439]**, PO Box 16074, San Francisco, CA 94116, (415)681-4356

Intl. Phototherapy Assn. **[IO]**, Vancouver, BC, Canada

Intl. Photovoltaic Equip. Assn. **[1170]**, PO Box 771507, Orlando, FL 32877, (407)856-9100

Intl. Physical Fitness Assn. **[3333]**, 415 W Court St., Flint, MI 48503, (810)239-2166

Intl. Physical Fitness Assn. **[3333]**, 415 W Court St., Flint, MI 48503, (810)239-2166

Intl. Physicians Commn. **[★17579]**

Intl. Physicians for the Prevention of Nuclear War **[18205]**, 66-70 Union Sq., No. 204, Somerville, MA 02143, (617)440-1733

Intl. Physicians for the Prevention of Nuclear War **[18205]**, 66-70 Union Sq., No. 204, Somerville, MA 02143, (617)440-1733

Intl. Piano Guild

Intl. Piano Guild - Address unknown since 2011.

Intl. Pietenpol Assn. **[20902]**, PO Box 127, Blakesburg, IA 52536, (515)938-2773

Intl. Pipeline and Offshore Contractors Assn. **[IO]**, Geneva, Switzerland

Intl. Planetarium Soc. **[6233]**, Imiloa Astronomy Center of Hawaii, 600 Imiloa Pl., Hilo, HI 96720, (808)969-9735

Intl. Planetarium Soc. **[6233]**, Imiloa Astronomy Center of Hawaii, 600 Imiloa Pl., Hilo, HI 96720, (808)969-9735

Intl. Planned Parenthood Fed. - Africa Regional Off. **[IO]**, Nairobi, Kenya

Intl. Planned Parenthood Fed. - East and South East Asia and Oceania Regional Off. **[IO]**, Kuala Lumpur, Malaysia

Intl. Planned Parenthood Fed. - European Network **[IO]**, Brussels, Belgium

Intl. Planned Parenthood Fed. - United Kingdom **[IO]**, London, United Kingdom

Intl. Planned Parenthood Fed., Western Hemisphere Region **[12037]**, 120 Wall St., 9th Fl., New York, NY 10005, (212)248-6400

Intl. Planned Parenthood Fed., Western Hemisphere Region **[12037]**, 120 Wall St., 9th Fl., New York, NY 10005, (212)248-6400

Intl. Planning History Soc. **[IO]**, Helsinki, Finland

Intl. Plant Biotech Network - Defunct.

Intl. Plant Nutrition Inst. I Potash and Phosphate Inst. **[572]**, 655 Engineering Dr., Ste. 110, Norcross, GA 30092-2837, (770)447-0335

Intl. Plant Propagators Soc. **[4672]**, 4 Hawthorn Ct., Carlisle, PA 17015

Intl. Plant Propagators Soc. **[4672]**, 4 Hawthorn Ct., Carlisle, PA 17015

Intl. Plasma Fractionation Assn. **[IO]**, Amsterdam, Netherlands

Intl. Plastic Modelers Society/United States Br. **[21902]**, PO Box 2475, North Canton, OH 44720-0475, (330)477-6622

Intl. Plato Soc. **[IO]**, Yokohama, Japan

Intl. Play Equip. Mfrs. Assn. **[2778]**, 4305 N 6th St., Ste. A, Harrisburg, PA 17110, (717)238-1744

Intl. Play Equip. Mfrs. Assn. **[2778]**, 4305 N 6th St., Ste. A, Harrisburg, PA 17110, (717)238-1744

Intl. Playground Contractors Assn. **[920]**, PO Box 2364, Salt Lake City, UT 84110-2364, (888)908-9519

Intl. Playground Contractors Assn. **[920]**, PO Box 2364, Salt Lake City, UT 84110-2364, (888)908-9519

Intl. Plutarch Soc. **[10389]**, Utah State Univ., Dept. of History, 0710 Old Main Hill, Logan, UT 84322-0710, (435)797-1298

Intl. Poetry Forum **[10449]**, 3333 5th Ave., Pittsburgh, PA 15213, (412)578-6244

Intl. Poetry Forum **[10449]**, 3333 5th Ave., Pittsburgh, PA 15213, (412)578-6244

Intl. Police Assn. **[IO]**, Nottingham, United Kingdom

Intl. Police and Fire Chaplain's Assn. **[19522]**, 9393 Pardee Rd., Taylor, MI 48180, (313)291-2571

Intl. Police Mountain Bike Assn. **[5703]**, 583 Frederick Rd., Ste. 5B, Baltimore, MD 21228, (410)744-2400

Intl. Police Work Dog Assn. **[5704]**, PO Box 7455, Greenwood, IN 46142, (317)882-9191

Intl. Police Work Dog Assn. **[5704]**, PO Box 7455, Greenwood, IN 46142, (317)882-9191

Intl. Polio Network **[★11823]**

Intl. Polio Network **[★11823]**

Intl. Political Sci. Assn. **[IO]**, Montreal, QC, Canada

Intl. Polka Assn. **[10222]**, 4608 S Archer Ave., Chicago, IL 60632-2932, (800)TOP-OLKA

Intl. Polka Assn. **[10222]**, 4608 S Archer Ave., Chicago, IL 60632-2932, (800)TOP-OLKA

Intl. Polymer Clay Assn. **[21852]**, 1350 Beverly Rd., Ste. 115-345, McLean, VA 22101

Intl. Pompe Assn. **[IO]**, Baarn, Netherlands

Intl. Popcorn Assn. **[★1451]**

Intl. Positive Psychology Assn. **[16401]**, 19 Mantua Rd., Mount Royal, NJ 08061, (856)423-2862

Intl. Possibilities Unlimited **[18642]**, Metro Plaza II, 8403 Colesville Rd., Silver Spring, MD 20910, (301)562-0883

Intl. Possibilities Unlimited **[18642]**, Metro Plaza II, 8403 Colesville Rd., Silver Spring, MD 20910, (301)562-0883

Intl. Post Polio Support Org. **[16301]**, 2252 Table Rock Rd., No. 40, Medford, OR 97501, (541)772-1102

Intl. Post Polio Support Org. **[16301]**, 2252 Table Rock Rd., No. 40, Medford, OR 97501, (541)772-1102

Intl. Postal Stationery Soc. **[★22087]**

Intl. Pot and Kettle Clubs - Defunct.

Intl. Potash Inst. **[IO]**, Horgen, Switzerland

Intl. Potato Center **[IO]**, Lima, Peru

Intl. Powered Access Fed. **[IO]**, Crooklands, United Kingdom

Intl. Practical Shooting Confed. Australia **[IO]**, Highbury, Australia

Intl. Prader-Willi Syndrome Org. **[IO]**, Costozza, Italy

Intl. Pragmatics Assn. **[IO]**, Antwerp, Belgium

Intl. Precancel Club **[★22067]**

Intl. Precious Metals Inst. **[7097]**, 5101 N 12th Ave., Ste. C, Pensacola, FL 32504, (850)476-1156

Intl. Precious Metals Inst. **[7097]**, 5101 N 12th Ave., Ste. C, Pensacola, FL 32504, (850)476-1156

Intl. Premature Ovarian Failure Assn. **[15884]**, PO Box 23643, Alexandria, VA 22304, (703)913-4787

Intl. Premature Ovarian Failure Assn. **[15884]**, PO Box 23643, Alexandria, VA 22304, (703)913-4787

Intl. Premium Cigar and Pipe Retailers **[3109]**, 4 Bradley Park Ct., Ste. 2-H, Columbus, GA 31904-3637, (706)494-1143

Intl. Prepress Assn. **[★6934]**

Intl. Prepress Assn. **[★6934]**

Intl. Press Inst. **[IO]**, Vienna, Austria

Intl. Press Telecommunications Coun. **[IO]**, London, United Kingdom

Intl. Primate Protection League **[10993]**, PO Box 766, Summerville, SC 29484-0766, (843)871-2280

Intl. Primate Protection League **[10993]**, PO Box 766, Summerville, SC 29484-0766, (843)871-2280

Intl. Primatological Soc. **[6143]**, Nancy Caine, Gen. Sec., California State Univ. San Marcos, San Marcos, CA 92096, (760)750-4145

Intl. Primatological Soc. **[6143]**, Nancy Caine, Gen. Sec., California State Univ. San Marcos, San Marcos, CA 92096, (760)750-4145

Intl. Print Triennial Soc. - Krakow **[IO]**, Krakow, Poland

Intl. Printing and Graphics Communications Union **[★23212]**

Intl. Prison Ministry **[11718]**, PO Box 2868, Costa Mesa, CA 92628-2868, (800)527-1212

Intl. Prison Ministry **[11718]**, PO Box 2868, Costa Mesa, CA 92628-2868, (800)527-1212

Intl. Prisoners Aid Assn. - Defunct.

Intl. Private Practitioners Assn. **[IO]**, Worcester, United Kingdom

Intl. Produce Fed. - Defunct.

Intl. Prdt. Safety Mgt. Certification Bd. **[★3139]**

Intl. Production Planning and Scheduling Assn. **[2336]**, PO Box 5031, Incline Village, NV 89450, (775)833-3922

Intl. Production Planning and Scheduling Assn. **[2336]**, PO Box 5031, Incline Village, NV 89450, (775)833-3922

Intl. Professional Groomers **[2680]**, 123 Manley Ave., Greensboro, NC 27401, (336)852-9867

Intl. Professional Partnerships for Sierra Leone **[17917]**, 2042 Swans Neck Way, Reston, VA 20191-4030, (202)390-5375

Intl. Professional Pond Contractors Assn. **[236]**, 4045 N Arnold Mill Rd., Woodstock, GA 30188, (770)592-9790

Intl. Professional Rodeo Assn. **[22841]**, PO Box 83377, Oklahoma City, OK 73148, (405)235-6540

Intl. Professional Security Assn. - England **[IO]**, London, United Kingdom

Intl. Professional Surrogates Assn. **[16648]**, 3428 Motor Ave., Los Angeles, CA 90034, (310)836-1662

Intl. Professional Surrogates Assn. **[16648]**, 3428 Motor Ave., Los Angeles, CA 90034, (310)836-1662

Intl. Prog. Off. **[★17903]**

Intl. Prog. Off. **[★17903]**

Intl. Programme on Chem. Safety **[IO]**, Geneva, Switzerland

Intl. Programs and Stud. Off. **[★17903]**

Intl. Programs and Stud. Off. **[★17903]**

Intl. Progress Org. **[IO]**, Vienna, Austria

Intl. Progressive Educ. **[8074]**, 501 Westminster Ave., Fulton, MO 65251

Intl. Proj. Mgt. Assn. **[IO]**, Nijkerk, Netherlands

Intl. Proteolysis Soc. **[6272]**, Wayne State Univ. School of Medicine, Scott Hall, Rm. 6304, 540 E Canfield, Detroit, MI 48201, (313)577-0514

Intl. Proteolysis Soc. **[6272]**, Wayne State Univ. School of Medicine, Scott Hall, Rm. 6304, 540 E Canfield, Detroit, MI 48201, (313)577-0514

Intl. Psoriasis Coun. **[14329]**, 2626 Cole Ave., Ste. 400, Dallas, TX 75204, (214)369-0406

Intl. Psycho-Oncology Soc. **[13933]**, 154 Hansen Rd., Ste. 201, Charlottesville, VA 22911, (434)293-5350

Intl. Psycho-Oncology Soc. **[13933]**, 154 Hansen Rd., Ste. 201, Charlottesville, VA 22911, (434)293-5350

Intl. Psychoanalytical Assn. **[IO]**, London, United Kingdom

Intl. Psychogeriatric Assn. **[14665]**, 550 Frontage Rd., Ste. 3759, Northfield, IL 60093, (847)501-3310

Intl. Psychogeriatric Assn. **[14665]**, 550 Frontage Rd., Ste. 3759, Northfield, IL 60093, (847)501-3310

Intl. Psychohistorical Assn. **[9779]**, 266 Monroe Ave., Wyckoff, NJ 07481-1915

Intl. Psychohistorical Assn. **[9779]**, 266 Monroe Ave., Wyckoff, NJ 07481-1915

Intl. Public Debate Assn. **[8777]**, Box 3460, Monticello, AR 71656

Intl. Public Debate Assn. **[8777]**, Box 3460, Monticello, AR 71656

Intl. Public Mgt. Assn. for Human Resources **[1153]**, 1617 Duke St., Alexandria, VA 22314, (703)549-7100

Intl. Public Relations Assn. **[IO]**, Dorking, United Kingdom

The Intl. Publication Planning Assn. **[2942]**, 1350 41st Ave., Ste. 200, Capitola, CA 95010, (831)465-2298

The Intl. Publication Planning Assn. **[2942]**, 1350 41st Ave., Ste. 200, Capitola, CA 95010, (831)465-2298

Intl. Publishers Assn. **[IO]**, Geneva, Switzerland

Intl. Publishing Mgt. Assn. **[1615]**, 105 S Jefferson, Ste. B-4, Kearney, MO 64060, (816)902-4762

Intl. Publishing Mgt. Assn. **[1615]**, 105 S Jefferson, Ste. B-4, Kearney, MO 64060, (816)902-4762

Intl. Pugwash **[★17403]**

A star before a book entry number signifies that the name is not listed separately, but is mentioned within the entry.

Intl. Pugwash [★17403]

Intl. Pulse Trade and Indus. Confed. [IO], Paris, France

Intl. Qajar Stud. Assn. [9881], PO Box 31107, Santa Barbara, CA 93130, (805)687-1148

Intl. Quantitative Linguistics Assn. [IO], Graz, Austria

Intl. Quantum Structure Assn. [IO], Brussels, Belgium

Intl. Quarab Horse Assn. [4603], PO Box 263, Hopkins, MI 49328-0263, (269)672-9175

Intl. Quarab Horse Assn. [4603], PO Box 263, Hopkins, MI 49328-0263, (269)672-9175

Intl. Quarter Horse Registry [★4619]

Intl. Quarter Pony Assn. [4604], PO Box 230, Lyles, TN 37098, (931)996-3987

Intl. Quilt Assn. [21447], 7660 Woodway, Ste. 550, Houston, TX 77063, (713)781-6882

Intl. R/C Helicopter Assn. [21903], 5161 E Memorial Dr., Muncie, IN 47302-9050, (765)287-1256

Intl. Racquet Sports Assn. [★2743]

Intl. Racquet Sports Assn. [★2743]

Intl. Racquetball Assn. [★22832]

Intl. Racquetball Fed. [22831], 1631 Mesa Ave., Colorado Springs, CO 80906, (719)477-6934

Intl. Racquetball Fed. [22831], 1631 Mesa Ave., Colorado Springs, CO 80906, (719)477-6934

Intl. Radiation Protection Assn. [IO], Fontenay-aux-Roses, France

Intl. Radiator Standards Assn. [★19657]

Intl. Radiator Standards Assn. [★19657]

Intl. Radio Club of Am. [20937], PO Box 60241, Lafayette, LA 70596

Intl. Radio and TV Soc. [★494]

Intl. Radio and TV Soc. Found. [494], 420 Lexington Ave., Ste. 1601, New York, NY 10170, (212)867-6650

Intl. RadioSurgery Assn. [16514], PO Box 5186, Harrisburg, PA 17110, (717)260-9808

Intl. RadioSurgery Assn. [16514], PO Box 5186, Harrisburg, PA 17110, (717)260-9808

Intl. Rafting Fed. [22837], Mr. Mark Joffe, Treas., 2647 S Flower St., Lakewood, CO 80227, (303)989-7194

Intl. Raiffeisen Union [IO], Bonn, Germany

Intl. Rail Transport Comm. [IO], Bern, Switzerland

Intl. Rainwater Catchment Systems Assn. [7601], Dr. Brett Martinson, Treas., UH-CTAHR-NREM, 875 Komohana St., Hilo, HI 96720

Intl. Rainwater Catchment Systems Assn. [7601], Dr. Brett Martinson, Treas., UH-CTAHR-NREM, 875 Komohana St., Hilo, HI 96720

Intl. Randonneurs - Defunct.

Intl. Ranger Fed. [IO], Mount Beauty, Australia

Intl. Ray Price Fan Club [★23884]

Intl. Rayon and Synthetic Fibres Comm. [IO], Brussels, Belgium

Intl. Reading Assn. [8780], PO Box 8139, Newark, DE 19714-8139, (302)731-1600

Intl. Reading Assn. [8780], PO Box 8139, Newark, DE 19714-8139, (302)731-1600

Intl. Real Estate Fed. - France [IO], Paris, France

Intl. Real Estate Inst. [3018], PO Box 879, Palm Springs, CA 92263, (760)327-5284

Intl. Real Estate Inst. [3018], PO Box 879, Palm Springs, CA 92263, (760)327-5284

Intl. Rebecca West Soc. [10722], Long Island Univ., English Dept., 1 Univ. Plz., Brooklyn, NY 11201-5372, (718)488-1098

Intl. Reciprocal Trade Assn. [3485], 524 Middle St., Portsmouth, VA 23704, (757)393-2292

Intl. Reciprocal Trade Assn. [3485], 524 Middle St., Portsmouth, VA 23704, (757)393-2292

Intl. Recording Media Assn. [★1254]

Intl. Recording Media Assn. [★1254]

Intl. Records Mgt. Trust [IO], London, United Kingdom

Intl. Recreational Go-Kart Assn. [1201], 1113 Belle Pl., Fort Worth, TX 76107, (817)738-3344

Intl. Recreational Go-Kart Assn. [1201], 1113 Belle Pl., Fort Worth, TX 76107, (817)738-3344

Intl. Refugee Rights Initiative [17843], 866 United Nations Plz., Ste. 4018, New York, NY 10017, (212)453-5853

Intl. Refugee Rights Initiative [17843], 866 United Nations Plz., Ste. 4018, New York, NY 10017, (212)453-5853

Intl. Regional Magazine Assn. [2943], Andrew Jackson, Exec. Dir., PO Box 252, Montpelier, VT 05601-0252, (802)522-6531

Intl. Regional Org. of Plant Protection and Animal Hea. [IO], San Salvador, El Salvador

Intl. Registry for Religious-Wo/men-Artists - Defunct.

Intl. Rehabilitation Coun. for Torture Victims [IO], Copenhagen, Denmark

International Relations

Africa News Ser. [17144]

African Fed., Inc. [17900]

Amer. Bahraini Friendship Soc. [17932]

Amer. Brazilian Cultural Exchange [9513]

Amer. Ditchley Found. [17933]

Amer. MidEast Leadership Network [17934]

Amer. Sovereignty Task Force [17935]

Amer. Task Force on Palestine [17936]

Amer. Turkish Friendship Coun. [17937]

Armenian Amer. Chamber of Commerce [23352]

Assn. of Concerned African Scholars [17147]

Assn. for Haitian Amer. Development [12126]

Australian Amer. Assn. [7548]

Bridges of Understanding [17938]

Bridging Nations [17939]

Bridging Nations [17939]

Building Bridges: Middle East-US [8385]

Bus. Coun. for Intl. Understanding [17940]

Bus. Coun. for Intl. Understanding [17940]

Carnegie Endowment for Intl. Peace [17941]

Carnegie Endowment for Intl. Peace [17941]

Center for War/Peace Stud. [17942]

CHEER for Viet Nam [13374]

Citizens Network for Foreign Affairs [17943]InternationalCoalition for Amer. Leadership Abroad

Coalition for a Realistic Foreign Policy [17698]

Conflict Solutions Intl. [17405]

Coun. for Amer. Students in Intl. Negotiations [8386]

Croatian Amer. Assn. [17944]

Croatian Amer. Assn. [17944]

Cyprus-US Chamber of Commerce [23360]

Dutch Soc. for Intl. Affairs [3240]

Egyptian Student Assn. in North America [8917]

Friends of Taiwan Intl. [17945]

Friends of Tent of Nations North Am. [12629]

Global China Connection [8387]

Global Migration Gp. [5790]

Global Options [18462]

Global Youth Partnership for Africa [9875]

Global Youth Partnership for Africa [9875]

Haiti Cultural Exchange [9517]

The Hospitality and Info. Ser. [17973]

Hungarian Amer. Coalition [17946]

Hungarian Amer. Coalition [17946]

Impact Sports Intl. [22979]

ImpactLives [9491]

Intl. Coun. for Middle East Stud. [18125]

Iran Policy Comm. [17998]

Iraqi Amer. Chamber of Commerce and Indus. [23370]

Just Vision [17409]

Krochet Kids Intl. [12735]

Laotian Amer. Soc. [19102]

Meridian Intl. Center [17977]

Middle East Peace Dialogue Network [12515]

Middle Powers Initiative [17554]

Natl. Coun. for Intl. Visitors [17979]

Natl. Democratic Inst. for Intl. Affairs [17947]

Natl. Democratic Inst. for Intl. Affairs [17947]

Natl. Jewish Democratic Coun. [18387]

Newah Org. of Am. [11617]

Open Soc. Inst. [17948]

Open Soc. Inst. [17948]

Pakistan Chamber of Commerce USA [23435]

Peace Boat US [8695]

Polish-American-Jewish Alliance for Youth Action [13551]

Proj. South: Inst. for the Elimination of Poverty and Genocide [17949]

Proj. South: Inst. for the Elimination of Poverty and Genocide [17949]

Sino-American Bridge for Educ. and Hea. [9876]

South African USA Chamber of Commerce [23379]

Sovereignty Intl. [17950]

Sovereignty Intl. [17950]

Syrian-American Relations Coun. [17951]

Syrian-American Relations Coun. [17951]

Thai U.S.A. Assn. [19256]

ThinkImpact [12373]

Trilateral Commn. [17952]

Trilateral Commn. [17952]

Turkish-American Chamber of Commerce and Indus. [23455]

Turkish Coalition U.S.A. Political Action Comm. [18340]

Ugandan North Amer. Assn. [18841]

United Burundian-American Community Assn. [17953]

United Nations I Vietnam Relief Effort [13372]

U.S. Assn. for the Univ. for Peace [18294]

U.S.-China Exchange Assn. [17954]

U.S. Fed. for Middle East Peace [18295]

U.S.-Japan Coun. [17955]

U.S. Off. on Colombia [17956]

U.S. Off. on Colombia [17956]

U.S.-U.A.E. Bus. Coun. [2115]

U.S. Women and Cuba Collaboration [17957]

US-Azerbaijan Coun. [17958]

US-Azerbaijan Coun. [17958]InternationalWashington Inst. of Foreign Affairs

Weatherhead Center for Intl. Affairs [17959]

Weatherhead Center for Intl. Affairs [17959]

Win Without War [18178]

World Artists Experiences [9325]

World Fed. of Therapeutic Communities [13719]

World Growth [2079]

Intl. Relief Assn. [★12783]

Intl. Relief and Development [11600], 1621 N Kent St., 4th Fl., Arlington, VA 22209, (703)248-0161

Intl. Relief and Development [11600], 1621 N Kent St., 4th Fl., Arlington, VA 22209, (703)248-0161

Intl. Relief Friendship Found. [13190], 216 Barrytown Rd., Barrytown, NY 12507, (917)319-6802

Intl. Relief Friendship Found. [13190], 216 Barrytown Rd., Barrytown, NY 12507, (917)319-6802

Intl. Relief Teams [12856], 4560 Alvarado Canyon Rd., Ste. 2G, San Diego, CA 92120, (619)284-7979

Intl. Relief Teams [12856], 4560 Alvarado Canyon Rd., Ste. 2G, San Diego, CA 92120, (619)284-7979

Intl. Religious Liberty Assn. [18520], Carol Rasmussen, Exec. Asst., 12501 Old Columbia Pike, Silver Spring, MD 20904, (301)680-6686

Intl. Religious Liberty Assn. [18520], Carol Rasmussen, Exec. Asst., 12501 Old Columbia Pike, Silver Spring, MD 20904, (301)680-6686

Intl. Remote Viewing Assn. [7304], PO Box 381, East Windsor Hill, CT 06028, (860)882-1210

Intl. Reprographic Assn. [1616], 401 N Michigan Ave., Chicago, IL 60611, (312)673-4805

Intl. Reprographic Assn. [1616], 401 N Michigan Ave., Chicago, IL 60611, (312)673-4805

Intl. Reprographic Blueprint Assn. [★1616]

Intl. Reprographic Blueprint Assn. [★1616]

Intl. Republican Inst. USA [17525], 1225 Eye St. NW, Ste. 700, Washington, DC 20005, (202)408-9450

Intl. Republican Inst. USA [17525], 1225 Eye St. NW, Ste. 700, Washington, DC 20005, (202)408-9450

Intl. Rescue Comm. I Spanish Refugee Aid [12782], 122 E 42nd St., New York, NY 10168-1289, (212)551-3000

Intl. Rescue Comm. USA [12783], 122 E 42nd St., New York, NY 10168-1289, (212)551-3000

Intl. Rescue Comm. USA [12783], 122 E 42nd St., New York, NY 10168-1289, (212)551-3000

Intl. Rescue and Emergency Care Assn. [14452], PO Box 431000, Minneapolis, MN 55443, (763)391-8519

Intl. Rescue and Emergency Care Assn. [14452], PO Box 431000, Minneapolis, MN 55443, (763)391-8519

Intl. Rescue and First Aid Assn. [★14452]

Intl. Rescue and First Aid Assn. [★14452]

Intl. Res. and Exchanges Bd. [8367], 2121 K St. NW, Ste. 700, Washington, DC 20037, (202)628-8188

Reference to "IO" in place of a book number signifies that the association may be found in the 50th edition of International Organizations.

Intl. Res. and Exchanges Bd. [8367], 2121 K St. NW, Ste. 700, Washington, DC 20037, (202)628-8188

Intl. Res. Gp. on Wood Protection [IO], Stockholm, Sweden

Intl. Res. Inst. for Media, Commun. and Cultural Development [IO], Vienna, Austria

Intl. Res. Soc. for Children's Literature [IO], Burwood, Australia

Intl. Res. Training Center on Erosion and Sedimentation [IO], Beijing, People's Republic of China

Intl. Resources Gp. [5308], 1211 Connecticut Ave. NW, Ste. 700, Washington, DC 20036, (202)289-0100

Intl. Resources Gp. [5308], 1211 Connecticut Ave. NW, Ste. 700, Washington, DC 20036, (202)289-0100

Intl. Rett Syndrome Found. [15602], 4600 Devitt Dr., Cincinnati, OH 45246, (513)874-3020

Intl. Rett Syndrome Found. [15602], 4600 Devitt Dr., Cincinnati, OH 45246, (513)874-3020

Intl. Rett's Syndrome Assn. [★15602]

Intl. Rett's Syndrome Assn. [★15602]

Intl. RFID Bus. Assn. [283], 5 W 37th St., 5th Ave., 9th Fl., New York, NY 10018, (610)357-0990

Intl. Rice Commn. [IO], Rome, Italy

Intl. Rice Res. Inst. [IO], Manila, Philippines

Intl. Right of Way Assn. [5958], 19210 S Vermont Ave., Bldg. A, Ste. 100, Gardena, CA 90248, (310)538-0233

Intl. Right of Way Assn. [5958], 19210 S Vermont Ave., Bldg. A, Ste. 100, Gardena, CA 90248, (310)538-0233

Intl. Rivers [7602], 2150 Allston Way, Ste. 300, Berkeley, CA 94704-1378, (510)848-1155

Intl. Rivers [7602], 2150 Allston Way, Ste. 300, Berkeley, CA 94704-1378, (510)848-1155

Intl. Road Fed. [3517], Madison Pl., 500 Montgomery St., 5th Fl., Alexandria, VA 22314-1565, (703)535-1001

Intl. Road Fed. [3517], Madison Pl., 500 Montgomery St., 5th Fl., Alexandria, VA 22314-1565, (703)535-1001

Intl. Road Safety Org. [IO], Amersfoort, Netherlands

Intl. Road Transport Union [IO], Geneva, Switzerland

Intl. Rodeo Assn. [★22841]

Intl. Romani Writers' Assn. [IO], Helsinki, Finland

Intl. Rope Skipping Org. [★22853]

Intl. Rose O'Neill Club [★21693]

Intl. Rose O'Neill Club [★21693]

Intl. Rose O'Neill Club Found. [21693], Ron Songer, 2nd VP, 2013 Ridgeway Dr., Denison, IA 51442

Intl. Rose O'Neill Club Found. [21693], Ron Songer, 2nd VP, 2013 Ridgeway Dr., Denison, IA 51442

Intl. Rubber Conf. Org. [IO], Frankfurt, Germany

Intl. Rubber Study Group [IO], Singapore, Singapore

Intl. Rural Development Off. [★17903]

Intl. Rural Development Off. [★17903]

Intl. Rural Sociology Assn. [7427], David O. Hansen, RSS, Sec.-Treas., Ohio State Univ., Intl. Prog. for Agriculture, 2120 Fyffe Rd., Columbus, OH 43085, (614)292-7252

Intl. Rural Sociology Assn. [7427], David O. Hansen, RSS, Sec.-Treas., Ohio State Univ., Intl. Prog. for Agriculture, 2120 Fyffe Rd., Columbus, OH 43085, (614)292-7252

Intl. Safe Transit Assn. [3252], 1400 Abbott Rd., Ste. 160, East Lansing, MI 48823-1900, (517)333-3437

Intl. Safe Transit Assn. [3252], 1400 Abbott Rd., Ste. 160, East Lansing, MI 48823-1900, (517)333-3437

Intl. Safety Equip. Assn. [3143], 1901 N Moore St., Arlington, VA 22209-1762, (703)525-1695

Intl. Safety Equip. Assn. [3143], 1901 N Moore St., Arlington, VA 22209-1762, (703)525-1695

Intl. Sailing Fed. [IO], Southampton, United Kingdom

Intl. Sailing Schools Assn. [IO], Derby, United Kingdom

Intl. SalonSpa Bus. Network [969], 207 E Ohio St., No. 361, Chicago, IL 60611, (866)444-ICSA

Intl. SalonSpa Bus. Network [969], 207 E Ohio St., No. 361, Chicago, IL 60611, (866)444-ICSA

Intl. Salvage Union [IO], London, United Kingdom

Intl. Sand Collectors Soc. [21360], PO Box 117, North Haven, CT 06473-0117, (203)239-5488

Intl. Sanitary Supply Assn. [2250], 7373 N Lincoln Ave., Lincolnwood, IL 60712-1799, (847)982-0800

Intl. Sanitary Supply Assn. [2250], 7373 N Lincoln Ave., Lincolnwood, IL 60712-1799, (847)982-0800

Intl. Save the Pun Found. [IO], Toronto, ON, Canada

Intl. Saw and Knife Assn. [2176], Paul Muscat, Sec., Skarpaz Tooling Systems Inc., Oak Park, IL 60304, (425)454-7627

Intl. Saw and Knife Assn. [2176], Paul Muscat, Sec., Skarpaz Tooling Systems Inc., Oak Park, IL 60304, (425)454-7627

Intl. Scale Soaring Assn. [21904], Rick Briggs, Treas./Webmaster, 3015 Volk Ave., Long Beach, CA 90808, (562)421-4864

Intl. Scale Soaring Assn. [21904], Rick Briggs, Treas./Webmaster, 3015 Volk Ave., Long Beach, CA 90808, (562)421-4864

Intl. Schizophrenia Found. [IO], Toronto, ON, Canada

Intl. School Psychology Assn. [IO], Amsterdam, Netherlands

International Schools

Assn. for the Advancement of Intl. Educ. [8388]

Assn. for the Advancement of Intl. Educ. [8388]

Assn. of Amer. Intl. Colleges and Universities [8389]

Assn. of Amer. Intl. Colleges and Universities [8389]

Assn. of Amer. Schools in South Am. [8390]

Inst. for Amer. Universities [8391]

Inst. for Amer. Universities [8391]

Intl. Educ. Res. Found. [8392]

Intl. Educ. Res. Found. [8392]

The Intl. Educator [8393]

Intl. Educator's Inst. [8393]

Intl. Schools Assn. [8394]

Intl. Schools Assn. [8394]

Intl. Schools Services [8395]

Intl. Schools Services [8395]

Network of Intl. Christian Schools [7857]

United Bd. for Christian Higher Educ. in Asia [8396]

United Bd. for Christian Higher Educ. in Asia [8396]

Intl. Schools Assn. [8394], 10333 Diego Dr. S, Boca Raton, FL 33428, (561)883-3854

Intl. Schools Assn. [8394], 10333 Diego Dr. S, Boca Raton, FL 33428, (561)883-3854

Intl. Schools Assn. of Thailand [IO], Pak Kret, Thailand

Intl. Schools Found. [★8395]

Intl. Schools Found. [★8395]

Intl. Schools Services [8395], PO Box 5910, Princeton, NJ 08543, (609)452-0990

Intl. Schools Services [8395], PO Box 5910, Princeton, NJ 08543, (609)452-0990

Intl. Sci. Writers Assn. [2835], Mr. James Cornell, Pres., 6666 N Mesa View Dr., Tucson, AZ 85718, (520)529-6835

Intl. Sci. Writers Assn. [2835], Mr. James Cornell, Pres., 6666 N Mesa View Dr., Tucson, AZ 85718, (520)529-6835

Intl. Sci. Assn. for Probiotics and Prebiotics [7176], 502 Mace Blvd., Ste. 12, Davis, CA 95618, (530)753-0681

Intl. Sci. Assn. for World Economy and World Economics [IO], Berlin, Germany

Intl. Scleroderma Fed. [★16636]

Intl. Scleroderma Network [16634], 7455 France Ave. S, No. 266, Edina, MN 55435, (952)583-5735

Intl. Scleroderma Network [16634], 7455 France Ave. S, No. 266, Edina, MN 55435, (952)583-5735

Intl. Scouting Collectors Assn. [21361], Tod Johnson, PO Box 10008, South Lake Tahoe, CA 96158

Intl. Sculpture Center [10528], 19 Fairgrounds Rd., Ste. B, Hamilton, NJ 08619-3447, (609)689-1051

Intl. Seafood Sustainability Assn. [1361], PO Box 11110, McLean, VA 22102, (703)752-8897

Intl. SeaKeepers Soc. [4705], 355 Alhambra Cir., Ste. 1100, Coral Gables, FL 33134, (786)221-0600

Intl. SeaKeepers Soc. [4705], 355 Alhambra Cir., Ste. 1100, Coral Gables, FL 33134, (786)221-0600

Intl. Sealing Distributors Assn. [3661], 105 Eastern Ave., Ste. 104, Annapolis, MD 21403, (410)940-6344

Intl. Seapost Cover Club [★22051]

Intl. Seapost Cover Club [★22051]

Intl. Seaweed Assn. [IO], St. John, NB, Canada

Intl. Sect. of the Natl. Coun. on Family Relations [12011], 1201 W River Pkwy., Ste. 200, Minneapolis, MN 55454, (763)781-9331

Intl. Sect. of the Natl. Coun. on Family Relations [12011], 1201 W River Pkwy., Ste. 200, Minneapolis, MN 55454, (763)781-9331

Intl. Security Mgt. Assn. [3220], PO Box 623, Buffalo, IA 52728, (563)381-4008

Intl. Security Mgt. Assn. [3220], PO Box 623, Buffalo, IA 52728, (563)381-4008

Intl. Security, Trust and Privacy Alliance

Intl. Security, Trust and Privacy Alliance - Address unknown since 2011.

Intl. Seed Fed. [IO], Nyon, Switzerland

Intl. Seed Testing Assn. [IO], Bassersdorf, Switzerland

Intl. Seismological Centre [IO], Thatcham, United Kingdom

Intl. Senior Lawyers Proj. [5254], 31 W 52nd St., 9th Fl., New York, NY 10019, (212)880-5836

Intl. Senior Lawyers Proj. [5254], 31 W 52nd St., 9th Fl., New York, NY 10019, (212)880-5836

Intl. Senior Softball Assn. [22952], 9401 East St., Manassas, VA 20110, (571)436-9704

Intl. Senior Softball Assn. [22952], 9401 East St., Manassas, VA 20110, (571)436-9704

Intl. Seppala Assn. [21587], 3255 Bullock Rd., Brown City, MI 48416

Intl. Ser. for the Acquisition of Agri-biotech Applications [3760], Ms. Patricia Meenen, Admin. Mgr., Cornell Univ., 417 Bradfield Hall, Ithaca, NY 14853, (607)255-1724

Intl. Ser. for the Acquisition of Agri-biotech Applications [3760], Ms. Patricia Meenen, Admin. Mgr., Cornell Univ., 417 Bradfield Hall, Ithaca, NY 14853, (607)255-1724

Intl. Ser. for Human Rights - Switzerland [IO], Geneva, Switzerland

Intl. Service Robot Assn. - Defunct.

Intl. Seven-Star Mantis Style Lee Kam Wing Martial Art Assn. USA [22736], Ortiz Chinese Boxing Acad., 148-B Middle Neck Rd., Great Neck, NY 11021, (516)972-1670

Intl. Sex Worker Found. for Art, Culture and Educ. [13106], 8801 Cedros Ave., No. 7, Panorama City, CA 91402-2249, (818)892-2029

Intl. SGML/XML Users' Gp. [IO], Swindon, United Kingdom

Intl. Shade Tree Conf. [★4972]

Intl. Shade Tree Conf. [★4972]

Intl. Shaolin Kenpo Assn. [22737], 69 Washington St., Daly City, CA 94014, (650)755-8996

Intl. Shaolin Kenpo Assn. [22737], 69 Washington St., Daly City, CA 94014, (650)755-8996

Intl. Sharps Injury Prevention Soc. [16629], 3756 Elk Vista Ln., South Jordan, UT 84095, (801)896-8131

Intl. Sharps Injury Prevention Soc. [16629], 3756 Elk Vista Ln., South Jordan, UT 84095, (801)896-8131

Intl. Sheep Dog Soc. [IO], Bedford, United Kingdom

Intl. Ship Elecl. and Engg. Ser. Assn. [IO], Ware, United Kingdom

Intl. Ship Managers Assn. [IO], Monaco, Monaco

Intl. Ship Suppliers and Services Assn. [IO], London, United Kingdom

Intl. Shipmasters Assn. [2358], 514 Jaycox Rd., Avon Lake, OH 44012-2219, (440)933-4376

Intl. Shipmasters Assn. [2358], 514 Jaycox Rd., Avon Lake, OH 44012-2219, (440)933-4376

Intl. Shipmasters Assn. of the Great Lakes [★2358]

Intl. Shipmasters Assn. of the Great Lakes [★2358]

Intl. Shipping Fed. [IO], London, United Kingdom

Intl. Ships-In-Bottles Assn. [★21911]

Intl. Shooting Sport Fed. [IO], Munich, Germany

Intl. Show Caves Assn. [IO], Ancona, Italy

Intl. Shrine Clown Assn. [21289], PO Box 102, Marine, IL 62061-0102, (618)887-4544

Intl. Shrine Clown Assn. [21289], PO Box 102, Marine, IL 62061-0102, (618)887-4544

Intl. Shuffleboard Assn. [22892], 390 Santa Fe Trail, North Fort Myers, FL 33917, (239)543-1235

Intl. Shuffleboard Assn. [22892], 390 Santa Fe Trail, North Fort Myers, FL 33917, (239)543-1235

A star before a book entry number signifies that the name is not listed separately, but is mentioned within the entry.

Intl. Side Saddle Org. **[22684]**, PO Box 161, Stevensville, MD 21666-0161, (918)685-0072

Intl. Side-Saddle Org. and World Sidesaddle Fed., Inc. **[★22684]**

Intl. Sign Assn. **[1078]**, 1001 N Fairfax St., Ste. 301, Alexandria, VA 22314, (703)836-4012

Intl. Sign Assn. **[1078]**, 1001 N Fairfax St., Ste. 301, Alexandria, VA 22314, (703)836-4012

Intl. Silo Assn. **[169]**, E106 Church Rd., Luxemburg, WI 54217, (920)655-3301

Intl. Silo Assn. **[169]**, E106 Church Rd., Luxemburg, WI 54217, (920)655-3301

Intl. Simulation and Gaming Assn. **[8208]**, George Washington Univ., School of Bus. and Public Mgt., Monroe Hall, Washington, DC 20052, (202)994-4930

Intl. Simulation and Gaming Assn. **[8208]**, George Washington Univ., School of Bus. and Public Mgt., Monroe Hall, Washington, DC 20052, (202)994-4930

Intl. Sivananda Yoga Vedanta Center **[IO]**, Val Morin, QC, Canada

Intl. Size Acceptance Assn. **[12588]**, PO Box 82126, Austin, TX 78758, (206)600-3089

Intl. Size Acceptance Assn. **[12588]**, PO Box 82126, Austin, TX 78758, (206)600-3089

Intl. Skating Union **[IO]**, Lausanne, Switzerland

Intl. Skeletal Soc. **[16533]**, 1100 E Woodfield Rd., Ste. 520, Schaumburg, IL 60173, (847)264-5915

Intl. Skeletal Soc. **[16533]**, 1100 E Woodfield Rd., Ste. 520, Schaumburg, IL 60173, (847)264-5915

Intl. Ski Dancing Assn. **[22909]**, 22 Fountain Dr., Westerly, RI 02891, (401)596-8009

Intl. Ski Fed. **[IO]**, Oberhofen, Switzerland

Intl. Skiing History Assn. **[10533]**, PO Box 191, Ishpeming, MI 49849, (906)486-4202

Intl. Skiing History Assn. **[10533]**, PO Box 191, Ishpeming, MI 49849, (906)486-4202

Intl. Skin Care Nursing Gp. **[IO]**, London, United Kingdom

Intl. Sled Dog Racing Assn. **[22557]**, 22702 Rebel Rd., Merrifield, MN 56465, (218)765-4297

Intl. Sled Dog Racing Assn. **[22557]**, 22702 Rebel Rd., Merrifield, MN 56465, (218)765-4297

Intl. Sleep Products Assn. **[1780]**, 501 Wythe St., Alexandria, VA 22314-1917, (703)683-8371

Intl. Sleep Products Assn. **[1780]**, 501 Wythe St., Alexandria, VA 22314-1917, (703)683-8371

Intl. Slurry Seal Assn. **[★573]**

Intl. Slurry Seal Assn. **[★573]**

Intl. Slurry Surfacing Assn. **[573]**, 3 Church Cir., PMB 250, Annapolis, MD 21401, (410)267-0023

Intl. Slurry Surfacing Assn. **[573]**, 3 Church Cir., PMB 250, Annapolis, MD 21401, (410)267-0023

Intl. Smile Power **[14221]**, 704-228th Ave. NE, No. 204, Sammamish, WA 98074, (206)715-6322

Intl. Snow Leopard Trust **[5069]**, 4649 Sunnyside Ave. N, Ste. 325, Seattle, WA 98103, (206)632-2421

Intl. Snow Leopard Trust **[5069]**, 4649 Sunnyside Ave. N, Ste. 325, Seattle, WA 98103, (206)632-2421

Intl. Snowmobile Mfrs. Assn. **[3065]**, 1640 Haslett Rd., Ste. 170, Haslett, MI 48840, (517)339-7788

Intl. Snowmobile Mfrs. Assn. **[3065]**, 1640 Haslett Rd., Ste. 170, Haslett, MI 48840, (517)339-7788

Intl. Social Affiliation of Women Airline Pilots **[★143]**

Intl. Social Affiliation of Women Airline Pilots **[★143]**

Intl. Social Sci. Coun. **[IO]**, Paris, France

Intl. Social Security Assn. **[IO]**, Geneva, Switzerland

Intl. Social Ser. **[IO]**, Geneva, Switzerland

Intl. Social Ser., Amer. Br. **[★12526]**

Intl. Social Ser., Amer. Br. **[★12526]**

Intl. Social Ser. - Australian Br. **[IO]**, Melbourne, Australia

Intl. Social Ser. - Hong Kong **[IO]**, Hong Kong, People's Republic of China

Intl. Social Ser. - Japan **[IO]**, Tokyo, Japan

Intl. Social Ser., U.S.A. Br. **[12526]**, 200 E Lexington St., Ste. 1700, Baltimore, MD 21202, (443)451-1200

Intl. Social Ser., U.S.A. Br. **[12526]**, 200 E Lexington St., Ste. 1700, Baltimore, MD 21202, (443)451-1200

Intl. Soc. of Acoustic Remote Sensing of the Atmosphere and Oceans **[IO]**, Cambridge, United Kingdom

Intl. Soc. for Adaptive Behavior **[6258]**, Prof. Herb Roitblat, VP, Univ. of Hawaii at Manoa, Dept. of Psychology, 2430 Campus Rd., Honolulu, HI 96822, (808)956-6727

Intl. Soc. for Adaptive Behavior **[6258]**, Prof. Herb Roitblat, VP, Univ. of Hawaii at Manoa, Dept. of Psychology, 2430 Campus Rd., Honolulu, HI 96822, (808)956-6727

Intl. Soc. for Adolescent Psychiatry and Psychology **[16339]**, Frances Bell, PO Box 570218, Dallas, TX 75357, (972)686-6166

Intl. Soc. for Adolescent Psychiatry and Psychology **[16339]**, Frances Bell, PO Box 570218, Dallas, TX 75357, (972)686-6166

Intl. Soc. for Adult Congenital Cardiac Disease **[★14023]**

Intl. Soc. for Adult Congenital Cardiac Disease **[★14023]**

Intl. Soc. for Adult Congenital Heart Disease **[14023]**, 1500 Sunday Dr., Ste. 102, Raleigh, NC 27607, (919)861-5578

Intl. Soc. for Adult Congenital Heart Disease **[14023]**, 1500 Sunday Dr., Ste. 102, Raleigh, NC 27607, (919)861-5578

Intl. Soc. for Advancement of Cytometry **[6305]**, 9650 Rockville Pike, Bethesda, MD 20814-3998, (301)634-7435

Intl. Soc. for Aeolian Res. **[6926]**, 3810 4th St., Lubbock, TX 79415-3397, (806)723-5240

Intl. Soc. for Aerosols in Medicine **[IO]**, Gemunden, Germany

Intl. Soc. of African Scientists **[7373]**, PO Box 9209, Wilmington, DE 19809

Intl. Soc. of African Scientists **[7373]**, PO Box 9209, Wilmington, DE 19809

Intl. Soc. for Aging and Physical Activity **[13590]**, Wojtek Chodzko-Zajko, PhD, Pres., Univ. of Illinois at Urbana-Champaign, Dept. of Kinesiology, Louise Freer Hall, 906 S Goodwin Ave., Urbana, IL 61801, (217)244-0823

Intl. Soc. for Aging and Physical Activity **[13590]**, Wojtek Chodzko-Zajko, PhD, Pres., Univ. of Illinois at Urbana-Champaign, Dept. of Kinesiology, Louise Freer Hall, 906 S Goodwin Ave., Urbana, IL 61801, (217)244-0823

Intl. Soc. for Agricultural Safety and Hea. **[12986]**, Nancy Hetzel, Treas., 895 Smith Rd., Charles Town, WV 25414, (304)728-0011

Intl. Soc. of Air Safety Investigators **[12987]**, 107 E Holly Ave., Ste. 11, Sterling, VA 20164, (703)430-9668

Intl. Soc. of Air Safety Investigators **[12987]**, 107 E Holly Ave., Ste. 11, Sterling, VA 20164, (703)430-9668

Intl. Soc. for Alstrom Syndrome Families **[★14586]**

Intl. Soc. for Alstrom Syndrome Families **[★14586]**

Intl. Soc. for Alternative and Augmentative Commun. - Finland **[IO]**, Tampere, Finland

Intl. Soc. for Anaesthetic Pharmacology **[13749]**, 6737 W Washington St., Ste. 1300, Milwaukee, WI 53214, (414)755-6296

Intl. Soc. for Anaesthetic Pharmacology **[13749]**, 6737 W Washington St., Ste. 1300, Milwaukee, WI 53214, (414)755-6296

Intl. Soc. for Analytical Cytology **[★6305]**

Intl. Soc. for Analytical Cytology **[6305]**, 9650 Rockville Pike, Bethesda, MD 20814-3998, (301)634-7435

Intl. Soc. of Andrology **[IO]**, Florence, Italy

Intl. Soc. of Anglo-Saxonists **[8133]**, Rutgers Univ., Dept. of Engg., 510 George St., New Brunswick, NJ 08901-1167

Intl. Soc. of Anglo-Saxonists **[8133]**, Rutgers Univ., Dept. of Engg., 510 George St., New Brunswick, NJ 08901-1167

Intl. Soc. for Animal Genetics **[IO]**, Jouy-en-Josas, France

Intl. Soc. of Animal License Collectors - Address unknown since 2010.

Intl. Soc. for Animal Rights **[10994]**, PO Box F, Clarks Summit, PA 18411, (570)586-2200

Intl. Soc. for Animal Rights **[10994]**, PO Box F, Clarks Summit, PA 18411, (570)586-2200

Intl. Soc. for Anthrozoology **[IO]**, Cambridge, United Kingdom

Intl. Soc. of Antique Scale Collectors **[21362]**, 3616 Noakes St., Los Angeles, CA 90023, (323)263-6878

Intl. Soc. of Antique Scale Collectors **[21362]**, 3616 Noakes St., Los Angeles, CA 90023, (323)263-6878

Intl. Soc. for Applied Ethology **[IO]**, Lelystad, Netherlands

Intl. Soc. of Applied Intelligence **[6211]**, Texas State Univ., San Marcos, Dept. of Cmpt. Sci., 601 Univ. Dr., San Marcos, TX 78666-4616, (512)245-8050

Intl. Soc. of Applied Intelligence **[6211]**, Texas State Univ., San Marcos, Dept. of Cmpt. Sci., 601 Univ. Dr., San Marcos, TX 78666-4616, (512)245-8050

Intl. Soc. of Appraisers **[233]**, 303 W Madison St., Ste. 2650, Chicago, IL 60606, (312)981-6778

Intl. Soc. of Appraisers **[233]**, 303 W Madison St., Ste. 2650, Chicago, IL 60606, (312)981-6778

Intl. Soc. of Arachnology **[IO]**, Berlin, Germany

Intl. Soc. of Arboriculture **[4972]**, PO Box 3129, Champaign, IL 61826-3129, (217)355-9411

Intl. Soc. of Arboriculture **[4972]**, PO Box 3129, Champaign, IL 61826-3129, (217)355-9411

Intl. Soc. of Arboriculture - United Kingdom and Ireland **[IO]**, Wednesbury, United Kingdom

Intl. Soc. of Arthroscopy, Knee Surgery and Orthopaedic Sports Medicine **[16036]**, 2678 Bishop Dr., Ste. 250, San Ramon, CA 94583-2338, (925)807-1197

Intl. Soc. of Arthroscopy, Knee Surgery and Orthopaedic Sports Medicine **[16036]**, 2678 Bishop Dr., Ste. 250, San Ramon, CA 94583-2338, (925)807-1197

Intl. Soc. of Artificial Life **[6306]**, Reed Coll., 3203 SE Woodstock Blvd., Portland, OR 97202-8199, (503)788-6697

Intl. Soc. of Artificial Life **[6306]**, Reed Coll., 3203 SE Woodstock Blvd., Portland, OR 97202-8199, (503)788-6697

Intl. Soc. of the Arts, Mathematics, and Architecture **[7003]**, Nat Friedman, Founder/Ed., Univ. at Albany, 1400 Washington Ave., Albany, NY 12222

Intl. Soc. for the Arts, Sciences and Tech; Leonardo, The **[9330]**

Intl. Soc. for the Arts, Sciences and Tech; Leonardo, The **[9330]**

Intl. Soc. for Astrological Res. **[6219]**, PO Box 38613, Los Angeles, CA 90038, (805)525-0461

Intl. Soc. for Astrological Res. **[6219]**, PO Box 38613, Los Angeles, CA 90038, (805)525-0461

Intl. Soc. for Augmentative and Alternative Commun. **[IO]**, Toronto, ON, Canada

Intl. Soc. for Autism Res. **[13797]**, 342 N Main St., West Hartford, CT 06117-2507, (860)586-7575

Intl. Soc. of Automation **[6999]**, 67 Alexander Dr., PO Box 12277, Research Triangle Park, NC 27709, (919)549-8411

Intl. Soc. of Automation **[6999]**, 67 Alexander Dr., PO Box 12277, Research Triangle Park, NC 27709, (919)549-8411

Intl. Soc. for Aviation Photography **[2724]**, N4752 Valley Rd., Luxemburg, WI 54217

Intl. Soc. for Ayurveda and Hea. **[13691]**, PO Box 271737, West Hartford, CT 06127-1737, (860)561-4857

Intl. Soc. of Barristers **[6044]**, Univ. of Michigan Law School, 802 Legal Res. Bldg., Ann Arbor, MI 48109-1215, (734)763-0165

Intl. Soc. of Barristers **[6044]**, Univ. of Michigan Law School, 802 Legal Res. Bldg., Ann Arbor, MI 48109-1215, (734)763-0165

Intl. Soc. of Bassists **[10223]**, 14070 Proton Rd., Ste. 100, LB 9, Dallas, TX 75244, (972)233-9107

Intl. Soc. of Bassists **[10223]**, 14070 Proton Rd., Ste. 100, LB 9, Dallas, TX 75244, (972)233-9107

Intl. Soc. for Bayesian Anal. **[7074]**, Prof. Michael I. Jordan, Pres., Univ. of California, Statistics Dept., 427 Evans Hall, No. 3860, Berkeley, CA 94720-1767, (510)643-0991

Intl. Soc. for Bayesian Anal. **[7074]**, Prof. Michael I. Jordan, Pres., Univ. of California, Statistics Dept., 427 Evans Hall, No. 3860, Berkeley, CA 94720-1767, (510)643-0991

Intl. Soc. of Behavioral Medicine **[IO]**, Ulm, Germany

Intl. Soc. for Behavioral Nutrition and Physical Activity **[13826]**, Univ. of Texas, 313 E 12th St., Ste. 220, Minneapolis, MN 55455, (512)482-6168

Reference to "IO" in place of a book number signifies that the association may be found in the 50th edition of International Organizations.

Intl. Soc. for Behavioral Nutrition and Physical Activity [13826], Univ. of Texas, 313 E 12th St., Ste. 220, Minneapolis, MN 55455, (512)482-6168

Intl. Soc. of Beverage Technologists [448], 14070 Proton Rd., Ste. 100, LB 9, Dallas, TX 75244-3601, (972)233-9107

Intl. Soc. of Beverage Technologists [448], 14070 Proton Rd., Ste. 100, LB 9, Dallas, TX 75244-3601, (972)233-9107

Intl. Soc. of Bible Collectors [19350], PO Box 26654, Minneapolis, MN 55426

Intl. Soc. of Bible Collectors [19350], PO Box 26654, Minneapolis, MN 55426

Intl. Soc. of Bioethics [IO], Gijon, Spain

Intl. Soc. for Biological and Environmental Repositories [6307], 9650 Rockville Pike, Bethesda, MD 20814-3993, (301)634-7949

Intl. Soc. for Biological and Environmental Repositories [6307], 9650 Rockville Pike, Bethesda, MD 20814-3993, (301)634-7949

Intl. Soc. for Biological Therapy of Cancer [★13982]

Intl. Soc. for Biological Therapy of Cancer [13982], 555 E Wells St., Ste. 1100, Milwaukee, WI 53202-3823, (414)271-2456

Intl. Soc. for Bioluminescence and Chemiluminescence [7374], PO Box 45192, Madison, WI 53744, (608)274-4330

Intl. Soc. for Bioluminescence and Chemiluminescence [7374], PO Box 45192, Madison, WI 53744, (608)274-4330

Intl. Soc. of Biomechanics [IO], Wollongong, Australia

Intl. Soc. of Biomechanics in Sports [IO], Limerick, Ireland

Intl. Soc. for Biomedical Res. on Alcoholism [16741], PO Box 202332, Denver, CO 80220-8332, (303)355-6420

Intl. Soc. for Biomedical Res. on Alcoholism [16741], PO Box 202332, Denver, CO 80220-8332, (303)355-6420

Intl. Soc. for Biophysics and Imaging of the Skin [IO], Schenefeld, Germany

Intl. Soc. for Biosafety Res. [6308], Univ. of California, Batchelor Hall 3110, Riverside, CA 92521-0124

Intl. Soc. for Biosafety Res. [6308], Univ. of California, Batchelor Hall 3110, Riverside, CA 92521-0124

Intl. Soc. for Bipolar Disorders [13766], PO Box 7168, Pittsburgh, PA 15213, (412)802-6940

Intl. Soc. of Blood Transfusion [IO], Amsterdam, Netherlands

Intl. Soc. for Brachial Plexus and Peripheral Nerve Injury [15662], 2201 W Holcombe Blvd., Ste. 225, Houston, TX 77030, (713)592-9900

Intl. Soc. for British Genealogy and Family History [20635], PO Box 350459, Westminster, CO 80035-0459, (303)422-9371

Intl. Soc. for British Genealogy and Family History [20635], PO Box 350459, Westminster, CO 80035-0459, (303)422-9371

Intl. Soc. for Burn Injuries [13872], 2172 US Hwy. 181 S, Floresville, TX 78114

Intl. Soc. for Burn Injuries [13872], 2172 US Hwy. 181 S, Floresville, TX 78114

Intl. Soc. of Bus. Astrologers [IO], Bronshoj, Denmark

Intl. Soc. for Bus. Educ. [7794], 2411 Lebanon Rd., Pendleton, SC 29670

Intl. Soc. for Bus. Educ. [7794], 2411 Lebanon Rd., Pendleton, SC 29670

Intl. Soc. for Cardiovascular Translational Res. [14024], 5580 La Jolla Blvd., Ste. 605, La Jolla, CA 92037, (858)774-0206

Intl. Soc. for Cardiovascular Translational Res. [14024], 5580 La Jolla Blvd., Ste. 605, La Jolla, CA 92037, (858)774-0206

Intl. Soc. of Cardiovascular Ultrasound [14440], PO Box 323, Gardendale, AL 35071, (205)934-8256

Intl. Soc. of Caricature Artists [1202], 922 W Dayton St., Ferndale, MI 48220, (248)336-8536

Intl. Soc. for Cell Biology [★6303]

Intl. Soc. for Cell Biology [★6303]

Intl. Soc. of Certified Electronics Technicians [1105], 3608 Pershing Ave., Fort Worth, TX 76107-4527, (817)921-9101

Intl. Soc. of Certified Electronics Technicians [1105], 3608 Pershing Ave., Fort Worth, TX 76107-4527, (817)921-9101

Intl. Soc. of Certified Employee Benefit Specialists [1129], PO Box 209, Brookfield, WI 53008-0209, (262)786-8771

Intl. Soc. of Certified Employee Benefit Specialists [1129], PO Box 209, Brookfield, WI 53008-0209, (262)786-8771

Intl. Soc. of Chem. Ecology [6273], Dr. Kenneth Haynes, Treas., Univ. of Kentucky, Dept. of Entomology, Lexington, KY 40546, (859)257-1618

Intl. Soc. of Chem. Ecology [6273], Dr. Kenneth Haynes, Treas., Univ. of Kentucky, Dept. of Entomology, Lexington, KY 40546, (859)257-1618

Intl. Soc. of Chemotherapy [IO], Aberdeen, United Kingdom

Intl. Soc. for Children with Cancer [13934], 16808 Armstrong Ave., Ste. 170, Irvine, CA 92606, (949)679-9911

Intl. Soc. for Chronobiology [6309], Univ. of Texas, Medical Br., Dept. of Neuroscience and Cell Biology, Galveston, TX 77555-1069, (409)772-1294

Intl. Soc. for Chronobiology [6309], Univ. of Texas, Medical Br., Dept. of Neuroscience and Cell Biology, Galveston, TX 77555-1069, (409)772-1294

Intl. Soc. of Citriculture [4455], Univ. of California, Dept. of Botany and Plant Sciences, Riverside, CA 92521-0124

Intl. Soc. of Citriculture [4455], Univ. of California, Dept. of Botany and Plant Sciences, Riverside, CA 92521-0124

Intl. Soc. of City and Regional Planners [IO], The Hague, Netherlands

Intl. Soc. of Cleaning Technicians [★2260]

Intl. Soc. for Clinical Biostatistics [IO], Birkerod, Denmark

Intl. Soc. for Clinical Densitometry [16054], 306 Indus. Park Rd., Ste. 208, Middletown, CT 06457, (860)259-1000

Intl. Soc. for Clinical Densitometry [16054], 306 Indus. Park Rd., Ste. 208, Middletown, CT 06457, (860)259-1000

Intl. Soc. for Clinical Electrophysiology of Vision [IO], Glasgow, United Kingdom

Intl. Soc. for Clinical Haemorheology [IO], Amsterdam, Netherlands

Intl. Soc. for Coating Sci. and Tech. [6431], Corning Inc., 1 Sci. Center Dr., Corning, NY 14831, (607)974-9730

Intl. Soc. for Coating Sci. and Tech. [6431], Corning Inc., 1 Sci. Center Dr., Corning, NY 14831, (607)974-9730

Intl. Soc. of Commodity Sci. and Tech. [IO], Vienna, Austria

Intl. Soc. for Community Development - Defunct.

Intl. Soc. of Comparative Adult Educ. [IO], Tubingen, Germany

Intl. Soc. for Comparative Psychology [16402], Wayne State Univ., Dept. of Psychology, 71 W Waren, Detroit, MI 48202, (313)577-2813

Intl. Soc. for Comparative Psychology [16402], Wayne State Univ., Dept. of Psychology, 71 W Waren, Detroit, MI 48202, (313)577-2813

Intl. Soc. for Comparative Stud. of Chinese and Western Philosophy [8707], Prof. Hagop Sarkissian, Sec.-Treas., Box B5/295, New York, NY 10010

Intl. Soc. for the Comparative Stud. of Civilizations [7416], Betsy Drummer, Treas., Western Michigan Univ., Haworth Coll. of Bus., Kalamazoo, MI 49008, (269)387-5710

Intl. Soc. for the Comparative Stud. of Civilizations [7416], Betsy Drummer, Treas., Western Michigan Univ., Haworth Coll. of Bus., Kalamazoo, MI 49008, (269)387-5710

Intl. Soc. for Complementary Medicine Res. [13692], 109 S Observatory St., Ann Arbor, MI 48109-2029, (734)763-7379

Intl. Soc. for Complementary Medicine Res. [13692], 109 S Observatory St., Ann Arbor, MI 48109-2029, (734)763-7379

Intl. Soc. for a Complete Earth [12217], PO Box 277, Lawai, HI 96765, (866)649-3477

Intl. Soc. for a Complete Earth [12217], PO Box 277, Lawai, HI 96765, (866)649-3477

Intl. Soc. for Computational Biology [1893], UCSD, 9500 Gilman Dr., MC 0505, La Jolla, CA 92093-0505, (858)534-0852

Intl. Soc. for Computational Biology [1893], UCSD, 9500 Gilman Dr., MC 0505, La Jolla, CA 92093-0505, (858)534-0852

Intl. Soc. for Computerized Electrocardiology [14025], 11495 Emmanuel Way, No. 518, Solomons, MD 20688-3031, (301)855-1004

Intl. Soc. for Computerized Electrocardiology [14025], 11495 Emmanuel Way, No. 518, Solomons, MD 20688-3031, (301)855-1004

Intl. Soc. for Computers and Their Applications [6541], 975 Walnut St., Ste. 132, Cary, NC 27511-4216, (919)467-5559

Intl. Soc. for Concrete Pavements [574], 7085 Highland Creek Dr., Bridgeville, PA 15017, (412)221-8450

Intl. Soc. for Contemporary Music - Netherlands [IO], Amsterdam, Netherlands

Intl. Soc. for Contemporary Music USA [10224], 609 Warren St., Brooklyn, NY 11217, (718)442-5225

Intl. Soc. for Contemporary Music USA [10224], 609 Warren St., Brooklyn, NY 11217, (718)442-5225

Intl. Soc. of Cosmetic and Laser Surgeons

Intl. Soc. of Cosmetic and Laser Surgeons - Address unknown since 2011.

Intl. Soc. of Cosmetogynecology [14180], 350 Kennedy Blvd., Bayonne, NJ 07002, (201)436-8025

Intl. Soc. for Cow Protection [10995], RD 1, Box 322A, Moundsville, WV 26041, (304)843-1658

Intl. Soc. for Cow Protection [10995], RD 1, Box 322A, Moundsville, WV 26041, (304)843-1658

Intl. Soc. of Crime Prevention Practitioners [11687], PO Box 476, Simpsonville, SC 29681, (864)884-8466

Intl. Soc. of Crime Prevention Practitioners [11687], PO Box 476, Simpsonville, SC 29681, (864)884-8466

Intl. Soc. of Criminology [IO], Paris, France

Intl. Soc. for Crippled Children [★16575]

Intl. Soc. for Crippled Children [★16575]

Intl. Soc. of Cryosurgery [IO], Trieste, Italy

Intl. Soc. for Cultural and Activity Res. [IO], Frankston, Australia

Intl. Soc. Daughters of Utah Pioneers [20748], 300 N Main St., Salt Lake City, UT 84103-1699, (801)532-6479

Intl. Soc. Daughters of Utah Pioneers [20748], 300 N Main St., Salt Lake City, UT 84103-1699, (801)532-6479

Intl. Soc. of Dermatology [14330], 2323 N State St., No. 30, Bunnell, FL 32110, (386)437-4405

Intl. Soc. of Dermatology [14330], 2323 N State St., No. 30, Bunnell, FL 32110, (386)437-4405

Intl. Soc. of Dermatology: Tropical, Geographic, and Ecologic [★14330]

Intl. Soc. of Dermatology: Tropical, Geographic, and Ecologic [★14330]

Intl. Soc. of Developmental Biologists [IO], Kobe, Japan

Intl. Soc. for Developmental Neuroscience [IO], Vancouver, BC, Canada

Intl. Soc. for Developmental Psychobiology [16403], 8181 Tezel Rd., No. 10269, San Antonio, TX 78250, (830)796-9393

Intl. Soc. for Developmental Psychobiology [16403], 8181 Tezel Rd., No. 10269, San Antonio, TX 78250, (830)796-9393

Intl. Soc. for Dialogical Sci. [7305], Prof. Vincent W. Hevern, PhD, Le Moyne Coll., Psychology Dept., 1419 Salt Springs Rd., Syracuse, NY 13214

Intl. Soc. for Dialogical Sci. [7305], Prof. Vincent W. Hevern, PhD, Le Moyne Coll., Psychology Dept., 1419 Salt Springs Rd., Syracuse, NY 13214

Intl. Soc. of Difference Equations [7075], Trinity Univ., Dept. of Mathematics, Marrs-McLean Sci. Bldg., Rm. 115-D, One Trinity Pl., San Antonio, TX 78212-7200, (210)999-8246

Intl. Soc. of Difference Equations [7075], Trinity Univ., Dept. of Mathematics, Marrs-McLean Sci. Bldg., Rm. 115-D, One Trinity Pl., San Antonio, TX 78212-7200, (210)999-8246

Intl. Soc. of Differentiation [6310], Jennifer Shultz, Admin. Off., PO Box 55, Higganum, CT 06441, (860)554-5300

A star before a book entry number signifies that the name is not listed separately, but is mentioned within the entry.

Intl. Soc. of Differentiation [6310], Jennifer Shultz, Admin. Off., PO Box 55, Higganum, CT 06441, (860)554-5300

Intl. Soc. for Digital Earth [IO], Beijing, People's Republic of China

Intl. Soc. for Disease Surveillance [14395], 26 Lincoln St., No. 3, Brighton, MA 02135, (617)779-0880

Intl. Soc. for Disease Surveillance [14395], 26 Lincoln St., No. 3, Brighton, MA 02135, (617)779-0880

Intl. Soc. of Doctors for the Env. [IO], Basel, Switzerland

Intl. Soc. of Doctors for the Env. - Germany [IO], Bremen, Germany

Intl. Soc. of Dynamic Games [IO], Espoo, Finland

Intl. Soc. for Ecological Economics [1066], Anne C. Aitken, Managing Dir., 15 River St., No. 204, Boston, MA 02108

Intl. Soc. for Ecological Economics [1066], Anne C. Aitken, Managing Dir., 15 River St., No. 204, Boston, MA 02108

Intl. Soc. for Ecological Modelling [4211], PMB 255, 550 M Ritchie Hwy., Severna Park, MD 21146

Intl. Soc. for Ecological Modelling [4211], PMB 255, 550 M Ritchie Hwy., Severna Park, MD 21146

Intl. Soc. for Ecological Psychology [7306], William M. Mace, Dept. of Psychology, 300 Summit St., Hartford, CT 06106-3100, (860)297-2343

Intl. Soc. for Ecological Psychology [7306], William M. Mace, Dept. of Psychology, 300 Summit St., Hartford, CT 06106-3100, (860)297-2343

Intl. Soc. for Ecology and Culture [IO], Darlington, United Kingdom

Intl. Soc. for Educ. Through Art - Netherlands [IO], Arnhem, Netherlands

Intl. Soc. for Educational Planning [8730], 2903 Ashlawn Dr., Blacksburg, VA 24060-8101, (540)951-2051

Intl. Soc. for Educational Planning [8730], 2903 Ashlawn Dr., Blacksburg, VA 24060-8101, (540)951-2051

Intl. Soc. for Educative Communities [IO], Frankfurt, Germany

Intl. Soc. for Eighteenth-Century Stud. [IO], Oxford, United Kingdom

Intl. Soc. of Electrocardiology [IO], Linden, Netherlands

Intl. Soc. of Electrochemistry [IO], Lausanne, Switzerland

Intl. Soc. for Electrophysiology and Kinesiology [IO], Potchefstroom, Republic of South Africa

Intl. Soc. for Endangered Cats [IO], Calgary, AB, Canada

Intl. Soc. for Endocrinology [IO], Birmingham, United Kingdom

Intl. Soc. of Endovascular Specialists [16961], 1928 E Highland Ave., Ste. F104-605, Phoenix, AZ 85016, (602)650-1334

Intl. Soc. of Endovascular Specialists [16961], 1928 E Highland Ave., Ste. F104-605, Phoenix, AZ 85016, (602)650-1334

Intl. Soc. for Engg. Educ. [IO], Baden, Austria

Intl. Soc. of Environmental Botanists [IO], Lucknow, India

Intl. Soc. for Environmental Ethics [4275], Colorado Coll., Dept. of Philosophy, 14 E Cache La Poudre St., Colorado Springs, CO 80903, (719)227-8331

Intl. Soc. for Environmental Ethics [4275], Colorado Coll., Dept. of Philosophy, 14 E Cache La Poudre St., Colorado Springs, CO 80903, (719)227-8331

Intl. Soc. of Environmental Forensics [6882], 150 Fearing St., Ste. 21, Amherst, MA 01002, (413)549-5170

Intl. Soc. of Environmental Forensics [6882], 150 Fearing St., Ste. 21, Amherst, MA 01002, (413)549-5170

Intl. Soc. for Environmental Toxicology and Cancer - Defunct.

Intl. Soc. for Ethics and Info. Tech. [6979], Philosophy Documentation Center, PO Box 7147, Charlottesville, VA 22906-7147

Intl. Soc. of Exercise and Immunology [IO], Copenhagen, Denmark

Intl. Soc. for Experimental Cytology [★6303]

Intl. Soc. for Experimental Cytology [★6303]

Intl. Soc. of Explosives Engineers [6803], 30325 Bainbridge Rd., Cleveland, OH 44139, (440)349-4400

Intl. Soc. of Explosives Engineers [6803], 30325 Bainbridge Rd., Cleveland, OH 44139, (440)349-4400

Intl. Soc. of Facilities Executives [2251], INSITE, 200 Corporate Pl., Ste. 6B, Peabody, MA 01960-3840, (978)536-0100

Intl. Soc. for Fat Res. [7186], Amer. Oil Chemists' Soc., PO Box 17190, Urbana, IL 61803-7190, (217)359-2344

Intl. Soc. for Fat Res. [7186], Amer. Oil Chemists' Soc., PO Box 17190, Urbana, IL 61803-7190, (217)359-2344

Intl. Soc. of Filipinos in Finance and Accounting [36], 801 S Grand Ave., Ste. 400, Los Angeles, CA 90017, (800)375-2689

Intl. Soc. of Financiers [1309], 64 Brookside Dr., Hendersonville, NC 28792, (828)393-8908

Intl. Soc. of Financiers [1309], 64 Brookside Dr., Hendersonville, NC 28792, (828)393-8908

Intl. Soc. for Fire Ser. Instructors [5445], 14001C St. Germain Dr., Ste. 128, Centreville, VA 20121, (800)435-0005

Intl. Soc. for Fire Ser. Instructors [5445], 14001C St. Germain Dr., Ste. 128, Centreville, VA 20121, (800)435-0005

Intl. Soc. of First Responders

Intl. Soc. of First Responders - Address unknown since 2011.

Intl. Soc. for Fluoride Res. [IO], Dunedin, New Zealand

Intl. Soc. for Folk Harpers and Craftsmen [10225], Alice Williams, Sec., 1614 Pittman Dr., Missoula, MT 59803, (406)542-1976

Intl. Soc. for Folk Harpers and Craftsmen [10225], Alice Williams, Sec., 1614 Pittman Dr., Missoula, MT 59803, (406)542-1976

Intl. Soc. for Folk Narrative Res. [IO], Gottingen, Germany

Intl. Soc. For Apheresis [IO], Otsu, Japan

Intl. Soc. for Forensic Genetics [IO], Cologne, Germany

Intl. Soc. of Friendship and Good Will [9584], 3119 Lassiter St., Durham, NC 27707-3888

Intl. Soc. of Friendship and Good Will [9584], 3119 Lassiter St., Durham, NC 27707-3888

Intl. Soc. of Gastroenterological Carcinogenesis [IO], Hiroshima, Japan

Intl. Soc. of Gastrointestinal Oncology [14568], 200 Broadhollow Rd., Ste. 207, Melville, NY 11747, (631)390-8390

Intl. Soc. on Gen. Relativity and Gravitation [IO], London, United Kingdom

Intl. Soc. for Genetic Eye Diseases and Retinoblastoma [15964], Elias I. Traboulsi, MD, Exec. VP, 9500 Euclid Ave., I32, Cleveland, OH 44195, (216)444-4363

Intl. Soc. for Geographical and Epidemiological Ophthalmology [IO], Moshi, United Republic of Tanzania

Intl. Soc. for Gesture Stud. [6435], Susan Goldin Meadow, Pres., Univ. of Chicago, Dept. of Psychology, 5848 S Univ. Ave., Chicago, IL 60637

Intl. Soc. for Gesture Stud. [6435], Susan Goldin Meadow, Pres., Univ. of Chicago, Dept. of Psychology, 5848 S Univ. Ave., Chicago, IL 60637

Intl. Soc. of Glass Beadmakers [9298], 85 E Gay St., Ste. 707, Columbus, OH 43215, (614)222-2243

Intl. Soc. of Glass Beadmakers [9298], 85 E Gay St., Ste. 707, Columbus, OH 43215, (614)222-2243

Intl. Soc. for Gynaecologic Endoscopy [IO], Morphett Vale, Australia

Intl. Soc. of Haematology - European and African Div. [IO], Ankara, Turkey

Intl. Soc. of Hair Restoration Surgery [14676], 303 W State St., Geneva, IL 60134, (630)262-5399

Intl. Soc. for Heart and Lung Transplantation [16909], 14673 Midway Rd., Ste. 200, Addison, TX 75001, (972)490-9495

Intl. Soc. for Heart and Lung Transplantation [16909], 14673 Midway Rd., Ste. 200, Addison, TX 75001, (972)490-9495

Intl. Soc. for Heart Res. [IO], London, United Kingdom

Intl. Soc. for Heart Transplantation [★16909]

Intl. Soc. for Heart Transplantation [★16909]

Intl. Soc. of Heterocyclic Chemistry [IO], Shanghai, People's Republic of China

Intl. Soc. for Hildegard Von Bingen Stud. [10669], K. Christian McGuire, Treas., 787 Iowa Ave. W, St. Paul, MN 55117, (651)487-6357

Intl. Soc. for Hildegard Von Bingen Stud. [10669], K. Christian McGuire, Treas., 787 Iowa Ave. W, St. Paul, MN 55117, (651)487-6357

Intl. Soc. for History Didactics [IO], Bubenreuth, Germany

Intl. Soc. for the History of Ideas - Defunct.

Intl. Soc. for the History of Islamic Medicine [IO], Manama, Bahrain

Intl. Soc. for the History of the Neurosciences [7156], Sherry R. Ginn, Sec., Rowan-Cabarrus Community Coll., 1531 Trinity Church Rd., Concord, NC 28027, (704)216-3799

Intl. Soc. for the History of the Neurosciences [7156], Sherry R. Ginn, Sec., Rowan-Cabarrus Community Coll., 1531 Trinity Church Rd., Concord, NC 28027, (704)216-3799

Intl. Soc. for the History of Pharmacy [IO], Eschborn, Germany

Intl. Soc. for the History of Philosophy of Sci; HOPOS - The [8839]

Intl. Soc. for the History, Philosophy, and Social Stud. of Biology [8258], UC Davis, Dept. of Philosophy, 1 Shields Ave., Davis, CA 95616, (530)752-8987

Intl. Soc. for the History, Philosophy, and Social Stud. of Biology [8258], UC Davis, Dept. of Philosophy, 1 Shields Ave., Davis, CA 95616, (530)752-8987

Intl. Soc. for the History of Physical Educ. and Sport [IO], Vancouver, BC, Canada

Intl. Soc. for the History of Rhetoric [10511], Dr. Stephen McKenna, Sec. Gen., The Catholic Univ. of Am., Dept. of Media Stud., Washington, DC 20064, (202)319-5488

Intl. Soc. for the History of Rhetoric [10511], Dr. Stephen McKenna, Sec. Gen., The Catholic Univ. of Am., Dept. of Media Stud., Washington, DC 20064, (202)319-5488

Intl. Soc. for HIV/AIDS Education and Prevention - Defunct.

Intl. Soc. for Horticultural Sci. [IO], Leuven, Belgium

Intl. Soc. of Hospitality Consultants [866], 411 6th St. S, No. 204, Naples, FL 34102, (239)436-3915

Intl. Soc. of Hospitality Consultants [866], 411 6th St. S, No. 204, Naples, FL 34102, (239)436-3915

Intl. Soc. of Hospitality Purchasers [1758], 6205 Blue Lagoon Dr., Ste. 300, Miami, FL 33126, (305)421-6900

Intl. Soc. of Hospitality Purchasers [1758], 6205 Blue Lagoon Dr., Ste. 300, Miami, FL 33126, (305)421-6900

Intl. Soc. for Human and Animal Mycology [IO], Nijmegen, Netherlands

Intl. Soc. for Human Ethology [6259], Dori LeCroy, Treas., 175 King St., Charleston, SC 29401

Intl. Soc. for Human Ethology [6259], Dori LeCroy, Treas., 175 King St., Charleston, SC 29401

Intl. Soc. for Human Rights - Germany [IO], Frankfurt am Main, Germany

Intl. Soc. for Humor Stud. [9853], Martin D. Lampert, PhD, Exec. Sec., Holy Names Univ., Psychology Dept., 3500 Mountain Blvd., Oakland, CA 94619-1627, (510)436-1532

Intl. Soc. for Humor Stud. [9853], Martin D. Lampert, PhD, Exec. Sec., Holy Names Univ., Psychology Dept., 3500 Mountain Blvd., Oakland, CA 94619-1627, (510)436-1532

Intl. Soc. for Hyaluronan Sciences [6274], 725 River Rd., Ste. 205, Edgewater, NJ 07020, (201)945-5885

Intl. Soc. for Hybrid Microelectronics [★6671]

Intl. Soc. for Hybrid Microelectronics [★6671]

Intl. Soc. on Hypertension in Blacks [15077], 157 Summit View Dr., McDonough, GA 30253, (770)898-7910

Intl. Soc. on Hypertension in Blacks [15077], 157 Summit View Dr., McDonough, GA 30253, (770)898-7910

Reference to "IO" in place of a book number signifies that the association may be found in the 50th edition of International Organizations.

Intl. Soc. of Hypertension - United Kingdom [IO], Hampton Hill, United Kingdom

Intl. Soc. of Hypnosis [IO], Rome, Italy

Intl. Soc. for IGF Res. [6851], Box 1055, New York, NY 10029, (212)241-6306

Intl. Soc. for IGF Res. [6851], Box 1055, New York, NY 10029, (212)241-6306

Intl. Soc. for Imaging in the Eye [★15948]

Intl. Soc. for Improvised Music [10226], PO Box 1603, Ann Arbor, MI 48106, (734)926-9403

Intl. Soc. for Individual Liberty [18078], 237 Kearny St., No. 120, San Francisco, CA 94108-4502, (415)859-5174

Intl. Soc. for Individual Liberty [18078], 237 Kearny St., No. 120, San Francisco, CA 94108-4502, (415)859-5174

Intl. Soc. for Indus. Ecology [4276], Yale School of Forestry and Environmental Stud., Yale Univ., 195 Prospect St., New Haven, CT 06511-2189, (203)432-6953

Intl. Soc. for Indus. Ecology [4276], Yale School of Forestry and Environmental Stud., Yale Univ., 195 Prospect St., New Haven, CT 06511-2189, (203)432-6953

Intl. Soc. for Infectious Diseases [15120], 9 Babcock St., Unit 3, Brookline, MA 02446, (617)277-0551

Intl. Soc. for Infectious Diseases [15120], 9 Babcock St., Unit 3, Brookline, MA 02446, (617)277-0551

Intl. Soc. of Infectious Diseases and Human Infertility [★16598]

Intl. Soc. of Infectious Diseases and Human Infertility [★16598]

Intl. Soc. of Info. Fusion [6980], Yaakov Bar-Shalom, VP Publications, Univ. of Connecticut, 371 Fairfield Rd., Storrs, CT 06269-2157, (860)486-4823

Intl. Soc. of Info. Fusion [6980], Yaakov Bar-Shalom, VP Publications, Univ. of Connecticut, 371 Fairfield Rd., Storrs, CT 06269-2157, (860)486-4823

Intl. Soc. of Integral Psychoanalysis [IO], Sao Paulo, Brazil

Intl. Soc. for Intellectual History [9780], Mr. Steven Lestition, PhD, Membership Sec., Mathey Coll., B41 Holder Hall, Princeton, NJ 08544, (609)258-3317

Intl. Soc. for Intellectual History [9780], Mr. Steven Lestition, PhD, Membership Sec., Mathey Coll., B41 Holder Hall, Princeton, NJ 08544, (609)258-3317

Intl. Soc. for Intelligence Res. [7002], 2001 Killarney Dr., Bellevue, WA 98004, (216)368-2681

Intl. Soc. for the Interaction of Mechanics and Mathematics [IO], Trento, Italy

Intl. Soc. for Intercultural Educ., Training and Res. [★8410]

Intl. Soc. for Intercultural Educ., Training and Res. [★8410]

Intl. Soc. for Interferon and Cytokine Res. [15345], Fed. of Amer. Societies for Experimental Biology, 9650 Rockville Pike, Bethesda, MD 20814-3999, (301)634-7250

Intl. Soc. for Interferon and Cytokine Res. [15345], Fed. of Amer. Societies for Experimental Biology, 9650 Rockville Pike, Bethesda, MD 20814-3999, (301)634-7250

Intl. Soc. of Interior Designer [★2065]

Intl. Soc. of Internal Medicine [IO], Bern, Switzerland

Intl. Soc. for Interpersonal Acceptance and Rejection - Address unknown since 2010.

Intl. Soc. of Introduction Services - Defunct.

Intl. Soc. for Iranian Culture [9882], 220 Madison Ave., Ste. 11G, New York, NY 10016, (212)679-6410

Intl. Soc. for Iranian Culture [9882], 220 Madison Ave., Ste. 11G, New York, NY 10016, (212)679-6410

Intl. Soc. of Iraqi Scientists [7375], 3800 Woodward Ave., Ste. 808, Detroit, MI 48201, (313)577-2048

Intl. Soc. of Iraqi Scientists [7375], 3800 Woodward Ave., Ste. 808, Detroit, MI 48201, (313)577-2048

Intl. Soc. for Islamic Legal Stud. [8414], Peri Bearman, Sec.-Treas., PO Box 669, Groton, MA 01450

Intl. Soc. for Islamic Legal Stud. [8414], Peri Bearman, Sec.-Treas., PO Box 669, Groton, MA 01450

Intl. Soc. of the Knee [★16036]

Intl. Soc. of the Knee [★16036]

Intl. Soc. for Knowledge Org. [IO], Bonn, Germany

Intl. Soc. for Krishna Consciousness - Address unknown since 2010.

Intl. Soc. for Lab. Hematology [14969], SPLtrak, 5250 Old Orchard Rd., Ste. 300, Skokie, IL 60077, (847)983-3519

Intl. Soc. for Labour and Social Security Law [IO], Geneva, Switzerland

Intl. Soc. for Language Stud. [9939], 8374 Market St., Ste. 202, Lakewood Ranch, FL 34202-5137, (888)475-7121

Intl. Soc. for Language Stud. [9939], 8374 Market St., Ste. 202, Lakewood Ranch, FL 34202-5137, (888)475-7121

Intl. Soc. for Law and Tech. [5666], Dr. Mohamed Hamza, Sec.-Treas., 1811 W Katella Ave., No. 101, Anaheim, CA 92804, (714)778-3230

Intl. Soc. for Law and Tech. [5666], Dr. Mohamed Hamza, Sec.-Treas., 1811 W Katella Ave., No. 101, Anaheim, CA 92804, (714)778-3230

Intl. Soc. of Limnology [7023], Denise L. Johnson, Bus. Coor., Univ. of North Carolina at Chapel Hill, GSGPH, ESE, CB 7431, No. 148 Rosenau Hall, 135 Dauer Dr., Chapel Hill, NC 27599-7431, (336)376-9362

Intl. Soc. of Limnology [7023], Denise L. Johnson, Bus. Coor., Univ. of North Carolina at Chapel Hill, GSGPH, ESE, CB 7431, No. 148 Rosenau Hall, 135 Dauer Dr., Chapel Hill, NC 27599-7431, (336)376-9362

Intl. Soc. for Liturgical Stud. and Renewal [★19666]

Intl. Soc. for Liturgical Stud. and Renewal [★19666]

Intl. Soc. of Livestock Husbandry [IO], Bubendorf, Switzerland

Intl. Soc. for Low Vision Res. and Rehabilitation [15965], Lorna Frazier-Lindsey, Admin., PO Box 1185, Urbanna, VA 23175

Intl. Soc. of Lymphology [15253], M.H. Witte, MD, Sec. Gen., Univ. of Arizona, Coll. of Medicine, Dept. of Surgery, PO Box 245200, Tucson, AZ 85724-5200, (520)626-6118

Intl. Soc. of Lymphology [15253], M.H. Witte, MD, Sec. Gen., Univ. of Arizona, Coll. of Medicine, Dept. of Surgery, PO Box 245200, Tucson, AZ 85724-5200, (520)626-6118

Intl. Soc. of Lyophilization - Freeze Drying [6335], 917 Lexington Way, Waunakee, WI 53597, (608)577-6790

Intl. Soc. for Magnetic Resonance in Medicine [16534], 2030 Addison St., 7th Fl., Berkeley, CA 94704, (510)841-1899

Intl. Soc. for Magnetic Resonance in Medicine [16534], 2030 Addison St., 7th Fl., Berkeley, CA 94704, (510)841-1899

Intl. Soc. for Magnetic Resonance in Medicine - British Chap. [IO], Sutton, United Kingdom

Intl. Soc. for Magnetic Resonance in Medicine - German Chap. [IO], Erlangen, Germany

Intl. Soc. of Managing and Tech. Editors [2944], 1107 Mantua Pike, Ste. 701, No. 122, Mantua, NJ 08051, (856)292-8512

Intl. Soc. for Mangrove Ecosystems [IO], Okinawa, Japan

Intl. Soc. for Mannosidosis and Related Diseases [14605], 3921 Country Club Dr., Lakewood, CA 90712

Intl. Soc. for Mannosidosis and Related Diseases [14605], 3921 Country Club Dr., Lakewood, CA 90712

Intl. Soc. of Medical Hydrology and Climatology [IO], Budapest, Hungary

Intl. Soc. for Medical and Psychological Hypnosis [IO], Milan, Italy

Intl. Soc. for Medical Publication Professionals [16503], PO Box 2523, Briarcliff Manor, NY 10510, (914)945-0507

Intl. Soc. for Medical Publication Professionals [16503], PO Box 2523, Briarcliff Manor, NY 10510, (914)945-0507

Intl. Soc. of Meeting Planners [2453], 810 N Farrell Dr., Palm Springs, CA 92262, (760)327-5284

Intl. Soc. of Meeting Planners [2453], 810 N Farrell Dr., Palm Springs, CA 92262, (760)327-5284

Intl. Soc. for Mental Hea. Online [15458], Paddy Kennington, PhD, Sec.-Treas., 388 Chester St. SE, Marietta, GA 30060-2086, (888)875-3570

Intl. Soc. for Mental Hea. Online [15458], Paddy Kennington, PhD, Sec.-Treas., 388 Chester St. SE, Marietta, GA 30060-2086, (888)875-3570

Intl. Soc. on Metabolic Eye Disease [15966], 1125 Park Ave., New York, NY 10128

Intl. Soc. on Metabolic Eye Disease [15966], 1125 Park Ave., New York, NY 10128

Intl. Soc. for Microbial Ecology - Netherlands [IO], Heteren, Netherlands

Intl. Soc. for Military Law and Law of War [IO], Brussels, Belgium

Intl. Soc. of Mine Safety Professionals [15518], PO Box 772, Jasper, GA 30143, (706)253-3675

Intl. Soc. of Mine Safety Professionals [15518], PO Box 772, Jasper, GA 30143, (706)253-3675

Intl. Soc. for Minimal Intervention in Spinal Surgery [16701], 1001 Newbury Rd., Newbury Park, CA 91320

Intl. Soc. for Minimally Invasive Cardiac Surgery [★14026]

Intl. Soc. for Minimally Invasive Cardiac Surgery [★14026]

Intl. Soc. for Minimally Invasive Cardiothoracic Surgery [14026], 500 Cummings Ctr., Ste. 4550, Beverly, MA 01915, (978)927-8330

Intl. Soc. for Minimally Invasive Cardiothoracic Surgery [14026], 500 Cummings Ctr., Ste. 4550, Beverly, MA 01915, (978)927-8330

Intl. Soc. for Molecular Plant Microbe Interactions [6360], 3340 Pilot Knob Rd., St. Paul, MN 55121, (651)454-7250

Intl. Soc. for Molecular Plant Microbe Interactions [6360], 3340 Pilot Knob Rd., St. Paul, MN 55121, (651)454-7250

Intl. Soc. of Motor Control [7157], Penn State Univ., Dept. of Kinesiology, 29 Recreation Bldg., University Park, PA 16802

Intl. Soc. of Motor Control [7157], Penn State Univ., Dept. of Kinesiology, 29 Recreation Bldg., University Park, PA 16802

Intl. Soc. for Mountain Medicine [15419], PO Box 31142, Colorado Springs, CO 80931

Intl. Soc. for Mountain Medicine [15419], PO Box 31142, Colorado Springs, CO 80931

Intl. Soc. for Mushroom Sci. [IO], Pretoria, Republic of South Africa

Intl. Soc. for Music Educ. - Australia [IO], Nedlands, Australia

Intl. Soc. for Music and Educ. - Germany [IO], Bramsche, Germany

Intl. Soc. for Music in Medicine [IO], Ludenscheid, Germany

Intl. Soc. for Nanoscale Sci., Computation and Engg. [7376],

Intl. Soc. for Nanoscale Sci., Computation and Engg. [7376],

Intl. Soc. for Neoplatonic Stud. [10390], Univ. of Iowa, Dept. of Classics, 210 Jefferson Bldg., Iowa City, IA 52242, (319)335-0288

Intl. Soc. for Neoplatonic Stud. [10390], Univ. of Iowa, Dept. of Classics, 210 Jefferson Bldg., Iowa City, IA 52242, (319)335-0288

Intl. Soc. of Nephrology [IO], Brussels, Belgium

Intl. Soc. of Neuro-Semantics [16642], PO Box 8, Clifton, CO 81520-0008, (970)523-7877

Intl. Soc. of Neuro-Semantics [16642], PO Box 8, Clifton, CO 81520-0008, (970)523-7877

Intl. Soc. for Neurochemistry [IO], Melbourne, Australia

Intl. Soc. for Neurofeedback and Res. [15663], 1925 Francisco Blvd. E, No. 12, San Rafael, CA 94901, (415)485-1344

Intl. Soc. for Neurofeedback and Res. [15663], 1925 Francisco Blvd. E, No. 12, San Rafael, CA 94901, (415)485-1344

Intl. Soc. for Neuroimmunomodulation [15664], PO Box 41269, Arlington, VA 22204-8269

Intl. Soc. for Neuroimmunomodulation [15664], PO Box 41269, Arlington, VA 22204-8269

Intl. Soc. for Neuronal Regulation [★15663]

Intl. Soc. for Neuronal Regulation [★15663]

Intl. Soc. of Neuropathology [IO], Bristol, United Kingdom

Intl. Soc. of NeuroVirology [15665], Temple Univ. School of Medicine, 3500 N Broad St., Rm. 740 MERB, Philadelphia, PA 19140, (215)707-9788

A star before a book entry number signifies that the name is not listed separately, but is mentioned within the entry.

Intl. Soc. of NeuroVirology [15665], Temple Univ. School of Medicine, 3500 N Broad St., Rm. 740 MERB, Philadelphia, PA 19140, (215)707-9788

Intl. Soc. of Nurses in Cancer Care [IO], Vancouver, BC, Canada

Intl. Soc. of Nurses in Genetics [14650], 461 Cochran Rd., Box 246, Pittsburgh, PA 15228, (412)344-1414

Intl. Soc. of Nurses in Genetics [14650], 461 Cochran Rd., Box 246, Pittsburgh, PA 15228, (412)344-1414

Intl. Soc. of Offshore and Polar Engineers [6804], PO Box 189, Cupertino, CA 95015-0189, (650)254-1871

Intl. Soc. of Offshore and Polar Engineers [6804], PO Box 189, Cupertino, CA 95015-0189, (650)254-1871

Intl. Soc. of Olympic Historians [IO], Fochteloo, Netherlands

Intl. Soc. for Oncodevelopmental Biology and Medicine [IO], Munich, Germany

Intl. Soc. of Oncology Pharmacy Practitioners [16197], Ross Davidson, 305 W Country Dr., Duluth, GA 30097-5906, (678)584-9661

Intl. Soc. of Oncology Pharmacy Practitioners [16197], Ross Davidson, 305 W Country Dr., Duluth, GA 30097-5906, (678)584-9661

The Intl. Soc. for Optical Engg. [★7190]

The Intl. Soc. for Optical Engg. [★7190]

Intl. Soc. on Optics Within Life Sciences [IO], Munster, Germany

Intl. Soc. for Oral Laser Applications [IO], Vienna, Austria

Intl. Soc. for Oral Literatures of Africa [IO], Pretoria, Republic of South Africa

Intl. Soc. of Organbuilders [IO], Lidingo, Sweden

Intl. Soc. for Organization Development [2596], 11234 Walnut Ridge Rd., Chesterland, OH 44026, (440)729-7419

Intl. Soc. of Oriental Medicine [IO], Seoul, Republic of Korea

Intl. Soc. for Orthomolecular Medicine [IO], Toronto, ON, Canada

Intl. Soc. of Orthopaedic Surgery and Traumatology [IO], Brussels, Belgium

Intl. Soc. of Paediatric Oncology [IO], Eindhoven, Netherlands

Intl. Soc. for Panetics [18622], PO Box 142, College Park, MD 20741

Intl. Soc. for Panetics [18622], PO Box 142, College Park, MD 20741

Intl. Soc. of Parametric Analysts [6460], 527 Maple Ave. E, Ste. 301, Vienna, VA 22180, (703)938-5090

Intl. Soc. of Parametric Analysts [6460], 527 Maple Ave. E, Ste. 301, Vienna, VA 22180, (703)938-5090

Intl. Soc. for Paranormal Res. [2625], 4712 Admiralty Way, No. 541, Marina del Rey, CA 90292, (323)644-8866

Intl. Soc. for Paranormal Res. [2625], 4712 Admiralty Way, No. 541, Marina del Rey, CA 90292, (323)644-8866

Intl. Soc. for Pathophysiology [IO], Beijing, People's Republic of China

Intl. Soc. for Pediatric and Adolescent Diabetes [IO], Berlin, Germany

Intl. Soc. for Performance Improvement [8988], 1400 Spring St., Ste. 260, Silver Spring, MD 20910, (301)587-8570

Intl. Soc. for Performance Improvement [8988], 1400 Spring St., Ste. 260, Silver Spring, MD 20910, (301)587-8570

Intl. Soc. for Performance Improvement - Argentina [IO], Buenos Aires, Argentina

Intl. Soc. for Performance Improvement - Europe [IO], Walldorf, Germany

Intl. Soc. for Performance Improvement - Israel [IO], Haifa, Israel

Intl. Soc. for Performance Improvement - Japan [IO], Tokyo, Japan

Intl. Soc. for Performance Improvement - Melbourne [IO], St. Kilda, Australia

Intl. Soc. for Performance Improvement - Mexico [IO], Ciudad Obregon, Mexico

Intl. Soc. for Performance Improvement - Nigeria [IO], Lagos, Nigeria

Intl. Soc. for Performance Improvement - South Africa [IO], Johannesburg, Republic of South Africa

Intl. Soc. for Performance Improvement - Sydney [IO], Sydney, Australia

Intl. Soc. for the Performing Arts [9299], 630 9th Ave., Ste. 213, New York, NY 10036-4752, (212)206-8490

Intl. Soc. for the Performing Arts [9299], 630 9th Ave., Ste. 213, New York, NY 10036-4752, (212)206-8490

Intl. Soc. of Performing Arts Administrators [★9299]

Intl. Soc. of Performing Arts Administrators [★9299]

Intl. Soc. for the Performing Arts Found. [9300], 630 9th Ave., Ste. 213, New York, NY 10036-4752, (212)206-8490

Intl. Soc. for the Performing Arts Found. [9300], 630 9th Ave., Ste. 213, New York, NY 10036-4752, (212)206-8490

Intl. Soc. for Peritoneal Dialysis [IO], Milton, ON, Canada

Intl. Soc. for Pharmaceutical Engg. [7244], 600 N Westshore Blvd., Ste. 900, Tampa, FL 33609, (813)960-2105

Intl. Soc. for Pharmaceutical Engg. [7244], 600 N Westshore Blvd., Ste. 900, Tampa, FL 33609, (813)960-2105

Intl. Soc. of Pharmaceutical Engineers [★7244]

Intl. Soc. of Pharmaceutical Engineers [★7244]

Intl. Soc. for Pharmacoeconomics and Outcomes Res. [16198], 3100 Princeton Pike, Bldg. 3, Ste. E, Lawrenceville, NJ 08648, (609)219-0773

Intl. Soc. for Pharmacoeconomics and Outcomes Res. [16198], 3100 Princeton Pike, Bldg. 3, Ste. E, Lawrenceville, NJ 08648, (609)219-0773

Intl. Soc. for Pharmacoeconomics and Outcomes Res. Pakistan Chap. [IO], Karachi, Pakistan

Intl. Soc. for Pharmacoepidemiology [16199], 5272 River Rd., Ste. 630, Bethesda, MD 20816, (301)718-6500

Intl. Soc. for Pharmacoepidemiology [16199], 5272 River Rd., Ste. 630, Bethesda, MD 20816, (301)718-6500

Intl. Soc. of Pharmacogenomics [16200], Prof. Julio Licinio, Coor., UCLA Gonda Center, Rm. 3357A, 695 Charles Young Dr. S, Los Angeles, CA 90095-1761, (310)206-6207

Intl. Soc. for Phenomenological Stud. [10391], Prof. William Blattner, Dir., Georgetown Univ., Dept. of Philosophy, 240 New North Bldg., Washington, DC 20057-1133, (202)687-4528

Intl. Soc. for Phenomenological Stud. [10391], Prof. William Blattner, Dir., Georgetown Univ., Dept. of Philosophy, 240 New North Bldg., Washington, DC 20057-1133, (202)687-4528

Intl. Soc. of Phenomenology, Aesthetics, and the Fine Arts [9301], The World Phenomenology Inst., 1 Ivy Pointe Way, Hanover, NH 03755

Intl. Soc. of Phenomenology, Aesthetics, and the Fine Arts [9301], The World Phenomenology Inst., 1 Ivy Pointe Way, Hanover, NH 03755

Intl. Soc. for Phenomenology and the Human Sciences [★10393]

Intl. Soc. for Phenomenology and the Human Sciences [★10393]

Intl. Soc. for Phenomenology and Literature [10392], World Phenomenology Inst., 1 Ivy Pointe Way, Hanover, NH 03755

Intl. Soc. for Phenomenology and Literature [10392], World Phenomenology Inst., 1 Ivy Pointe Way, Hanover, NH 03755

Intl. Soc. for Phenomenology and the Sciences of Life [10393], World Phenomenology Inst., 1 Ivy Pointe Way, Hanover, NH 03755

Intl. Soc. for Phenomenology and the Sciences of Life [10393], World Phenomenology Inst., 1 Ivy Pointe Way, Hanover, NH 03755

Intl. Soc. for Philosophical Enquiry [9639], 700 Terrace Heights, No. 60, Winona, MN 55987

Intl. Soc. for Philosophical Enquiry [9639], 700 Terrace Heights, No. 60, Winona, MN 55987

Intl. Soc. for the Philosophy of Chemistry [IO], Bradford, United Kingdom

Intl. Soc. of Phonetic Sciences [IO], Budapest, Hungary

Intl. Soc. for Photogrammetry and Remote Sensing [IO], Beijing, People's Republic of China

Intl. Soc. for Photosynthesis Res. [IO], Weston Creek, Australia

Intl. Soc. for Phylogenetic Nomenclature [6901], T. Michael Keesey, Treas., PO Box 9630, Glendale, CA 91226-0630

Intl. Soc. for Phylogenetic Nomenclature [6901], T. Michael Keesey, Treas., PO Box 9630, Glendale, CA 91226-0630

Intl. Soc. of Physical and Rehabilitation Medicine [IO], Assenede, Belgium

Intl. Soc. of Planetarium Educators [★6233]

Intl. Soc. of Planetarium Educators [★6233]

Intl. Soc. for Plant Molecular Biology

Intl. Soc. for Plant Molecular Biology - Address unknown since 2011.

Intl. Soc. of Plant Morphologists [IO], New Delhi, India

Intl. Soc. for Plant Pathology [IO], Jamison, Australia

Intl. Soc. for Plasmid Biology and other Mobile Genetic Elements [7111], Richard P. Novick, Pres., SKI 2 Admin., 540 First Ave., New York, NY 10016, (212)263-6290

Intl. Soc. for Plastination [16127], Prof. Carlos A.C. Baptista, PhD, Pres., Univ. of Toledo, Colorado of Medicine, Dept. of Neurosciences, 3035 Arlington Ave., Toledo, OH 43614-2591, (419)383-4283

Intl. Soc. for Plastination [16127], Prof. Carlos A.C. Baptista, PhD, Pres., Univ. of Toledo, Colorado of Medicine, Dept. of Neurosciences, 3035 Arlington Ave., Toledo, OH 43614-2591, (419)383-4283

Intl. Soc. of Podiatric Laser Surgery - Defunct.

Intl. Soc. of Political Psychology [16404], ISPP Central Off., Virginia Commonwealth Univ., 919 W Franklin St., Richmond, VA 23284-3061, (804)828-1989

Intl. Soc. of Political Psychology [16404], ISPP Central Off., Virginia Commonwealth Univ., 919 W Franklin St., Richmond, VA 23284-3061, (804)828-1989

Intl. Soc. of Prenatal and Perinatal Psychology and Medicine [IO], Heidelberg, Germany

Intl. Soc. for Presence Res. [7333], Matthew Lombard, Pres., Temple Univ., Media Interface and Network Design Lab., Dept. of Broadcasting, Telecommunications, and Mass Media, Philadelphia, PA 19122

Intl. Soc. for Preservation of the Tropical Rainforest [4857], 3302 N Burton Ave., Rosemead, CA 91770, (626)572-0233

Intl. Soc. for Preservation of the Tropical Rainforest [4857], 3302 N Burton Ave., Rosemead, CA 91770, (626)572-0233

Intl. Soc. for Prevention of Child Abuse and Neglect [11328], PO Box 809343, West Chicago, IL 60185, (303)864-5222

Intl. Soc. for Prevention of Child Abuse and Neglect [11328], PO Box 809343, West Chicago, IL 60185, (303)864-5222

Intl. Soc. for Preventive Oncology - Address unknown since 2010.

Intl. Soc. of Primerus Law Firms [5255], 171 Monroe Ave. NW, Ste. 750, Grand Rapids, MI 49503, (616)454-9939

Intl. Soc. of Primerus Law Firms [5255], 171 Monroe Ave. NW, Ste. 750, Grand Rapids, MI 49503, (616)454-9939

Intl. Soc. for Productivity Enhancement [6805], CERA Inst., PO Box 60650, Irvine, CA 92602, (714)396-9424

Intl. Soc. for Productivity Enhancement [6805], CERA Inst., PO Box 60650, Irvine, CA 92602, (714)396-9424

Intl. Soc. for Professional Hypnosis - Defunct.

Intl. Soc. of Professional Trackers [3494], 445 Laguna Rd., Rohnert Park, CA 94928, (707)338-4760

Intl. Soc. for Prosthetics and Orthotics [IO], Brussels, Belgium

Intl. Soc. for Prosthetics and Orthotics - United Kingdom [IO], Glasgow, United Kingdom

Intl. Soc. for the Protection of Mustangs and Burros [5070], PO Box 55, Lantry, SD 57636-0055, (605)964-6866

Intl. Soc. for the Protection of Mustangs and Burros [5070], PO Box 55, Lantry, SD 57636-0055, (605)964-6866

Reference to "IO" in place of a book number signifies that the association may be found in the 50th edition of International Organizations.

Intl. Soc. of Protistologists [7637], Harriett Smith-Somerville, Univ. of Alabama, Dept. of Biological Sciences, Box 870344, Tuscaloosa, AL 35487, (205)348-1830

Intl. Soc. of Protozoologists [IO], Liverpool, United Kingdom

Intl. Soc. of Psychiatric Consultation Liaison Nurses - Defunct.

Intl. Soc. of Psychiatric Genetics [14651], 5034 Thoroughbred Ln., Ste. A, Brentwood, TN 37027, (615)649-3086

Intl. Soc. of Psychiatric Genetics [14651], 5034 Thoroughbred Ln., Ste. A, Brentwood, TN 37027, (615)649-3086

Intl. Soc. of Psychiatric-Mental Hea. Nurses [15759], 2424 Amer. Ln., Madison, WI 53704-3102, (608)443-2463

Intl. Soc. of Psychiatric-Mental Hea. Nurses [15759], 2424 Amer. Ln., Madison, WI 53704-3102, (608)443-2463

Intl. Soc. for the Psychological Treatments of the Schizophrenias and Other Psychoses U.S.A. [15459], PO Box 491, Narberth, PA 19072, (610)308-4744

Intl. Soc. for the Psychological Treatments of the Schizophrenias and Other Psychoses U.S.A. [15459], PO Box 491, Narberth, PA 19072, (610)308-4744

Intl. Soc. of Psychoneuroendocrinology [15346], Mt. Sinai School of Medicine, Psychiatry Dept. 116/A, Bronx, NY 10468

Intl. Soc. of Psychoneuroendocrinology [15346], Mt. Sinai School of Medicine, Psychiatry Dept. 116/A, Bronx, NY 10468

Intl. Soc. for the Psychopathology of Expression and Art Therapy [IO], Pau, France

Intl. Soc. for Psychophysics [IO], Freiburg im Breisgau, Germany

Intl. Soc. of Psychosomatic Obstetrics and Gynaecology [IO], Linkoping, Sweden

Intl. Soc. for Quality Electronic Design [6600], PO Box 607, Los Altos, CA 94023, (408)573-0100

Intl. Soc. for Quality in Healthcare [IO], Dublin, Ireland

Intl. Soc. for Quality of Life Res. [6260], 555 E Wells St., Ste. 1100, Milwaukee, WI 53202, (414)918-9797

Intl. Soc. for Quality-of-Life Stud. [7768], 1800 Kraft Dr., Ste. 111, Blacksburg, VA 24060-6370

Intl. Soc. for Quality-of-Life Stud. [7768], 1800 Kraft Dr., Ste. 111, Blacksburg, VA 24060-6370

Intl. Soc. of Radiographers and Radiological Technologists [IO], Cardiff, United Kingdom

Intl. Soc. of Radiolabeled Blood Elements [13850], Chief Division of Nuclear Medicine, Long Island Jewish Medical Center, 270-05 76th Ave., New Hyde Park, NY 11040

Intl. Soc. of Radiolabeled Blood Elements [13850], Chief Division of Nuclear Medicine, Long Island Jewish Medical Center, 270-05 76th Ave., New Hyde Park, NY 11040

Intl. Soc. of Radiology [16535], 7910 Woodmont Ave., Ste. 400, Bethesda, MD 20814, (301)657-2652

Intl. Soc. of Radiology [16535], 7910 Woodmont Ave., Ste. 400, Bethesda, MD 20814, (301)657-2652

Intl. Soc. for Range Mgt. [★4863]

Intl. Soc. for Reef Stud. [4277], Univ. of Hawaii at Manoa, Kewalo Marine Lab., 41 Ahui St., Honolulu, HI 96813

Intl. Soc. for Reef Stud. [IO], Burnaby, BC, Canada

Intl. Soc. for Reef Stud. [4277], Univ. of Hawaii at Manoa, Kewalo Marine Lab., 41 Ahui St., Honolulu, HI 96813

Intl. Soc. of Regulatory Toxicology and Pharmacology [14718], 6546 Belleview Dr., Columbia, MD 21046-1054, (410)992-9083

Intl. Soc. of Regulatory Toxicology and Pharmacology [14718], 6546 Belleview Dr., Columbia, MD 21046-1054, (410)992-9083

Intl. Soc. for Rehabilitation of the Disabled [★16575]

Intl. Soc. for Rehabilitation of the Disabled [★16575]

Intl. Soc. for Res. on Aggression [6261], The Univ. of Iowa, Dept. of Psychology, 11 Seashore Hall E, Iowa City, IA 52240

Intl. Soc. for Res. on Aggression [6261], The Univ. of Iowa, Dept. of Psychology, 11 Seashore Hall E, Iowa City, IA 52240

Intl. Soc. for Res. in Healthcare Financial Mgt. - Address unknown since 2011.

Intl. Soc. for Res. in Human Milk and Lactation [13864], Shelley McGuire, PhD, Sec.-Treas., Washington State Univ., School of Biological Sciences, Pullman, WA 99164, (509)335-3896

Intl. Soc. for Res. in Human Milk and Lactation [13864], Shelley McGuire, PhD, Sec.-Treas., Washington State Univ., School of Biological Sciences, Pullman, WA 99164, (509)335-3896

Intl. Soc. for Res. on Impulsivity [16340], Univ. of Texas at Houston, 1941 East Rd., Ste. 1306, Houston, TX 77054, (713)486-2796

Intl. Soc. for Res. on Impulsivity [16340], Univ. of Texas at Houston, 1941 East Rd., Ste. 1306, Houston, TX 77054, (713)486-2796

Intl. Soc. for Res. in Stereoencephalotomy [★15690]

Intl. Soc. for Res. in Stereoencephalotomy [★15690]

Intl. Soc. for Res. in Stereoencephalotomy, Amer. Br. [★15684]

Intl. Soc. for Res. in Stereoencephalotomy, Amer. Br. [★15684]

Intl. Soc. of Restaurant Assn. Executives [★3087]

Intl. Soc. of Restaurant Assn. Executives [3087], 5024-R Campbell Blvd., Baltimore, MD 21236-5943, (410)931-8100

Intl. Soc. for Retirement and Life Planning - Defunct.

Intl. Soc. for Rock Mechanics [IO], Lisbon, Portugal

Intl. Soc. of the Rorschach and Projective Methods [IO], Stockholm, Sweden

Intl. Soc. of Rotary Blood Pumps [14027], Dr. T. Motomura, Asst. Sec., 1 Baylor Plz., Stop BCM390, Houston, TX 77030, (713)798-8439

Intl. Soc. for the Scholarship of Teaching and Learning [8809], Viterbo Univ., 900 Viterbo Dr., La Crosse, WI 54601, (608)796-3080

Intl. Soc. for the Scholarship of Teaching and Learning [8809], Viterbo Univ., 900 Viterbo Dr., La Crosse, WI 54601, (608)796-3080

Intl. Soc. of Scientist-Artists [★9330]

Intl. Soc. of Scientist-Artists [★9330]

Intl. Soc. for Scientometrics and Informetrics [IO], Leuven, Belgium

Intl. Soc. for Self and Identity [7307], Camille Johnson, San Jose State Univ., Coll. of Bus., 1 Washington Sq., San Jose, CA 95112-3613, (408)924-3416

Intl. Soc. for Self and Identity [7307], Camille Johnson, San Jose State Univ., Coll. of Bus., 1 Washington Sq., San Jose, CA 95112-3613, (408)924-3416

Intl. Soc. for Sexual Medicine [IO], Wormerveer, Netherlands

Intl. Soc. of Six Sigma Professionals [7295], PO Box 26775, Scottsdale, AZ 85255, (602)363-8309

Intl. Soc. of Six Sigma Professionals [7295], PO Box 26775, Scottsdale, AZ 85255, (602)363-8309

Intl. Soc. of Social Defence [IO], Milan, Italy

Intl. Soc. for the Social Stud. [8865], PO Box 161250, Orlando, FL 32816-1250

Intl. Soc. for the Sociology of Religion [IO], Leuven, Belgium

Intl. Soc. for Soil Mechanics and Geotechnical Engg. [IO], London, United Kingdom

Intl. Soc. of Soil Mechanics and Geotechnical Engg. [6927], Geo-Institute of the ASCE, 1801 Alexander Bell Dr., Reston, VA 20191-4400, (703)295-6015

Intl. Soc. of Soil Mechanics and Geotechnical Engg. [6927], Geo-Institute of the ASCE, 1801 Alexander Bell Dr., Reston, VA 20191-4400, (703)295-6015

Intl. Soc. of Speakers, Authors and Consultants - Defunct.

Intl. Soc. for Spelaeological Art [IO], Kidderminster, United Kingdom

Intl. Soc. of Sports Nutrition [15837], Maelu Fleck, Exec. Dir., 600 Pembrook Dr., Woodland Park, CO 80863, (866)740-4776

Intl. Soc. of Sports Nutrition [15837], Maelu Fleck, Exec. Dir., 600 Pembrook Dr., Woodland Park, CO 80863, (866)740-4776

Intl. Soc. of Sports Psychology [16405], Traci Statler, VP, 800 N State Coll. Blvd., Fullerton, CA 92831-3547, (657)278-8554

Intl. Soc. of Sports Psychology [16405], Traci Statler, VP, 800 N State Coll. Blvd., Fullerton, CA 92831-3547, (657)278-8554

Intl. Soc. for Stem Cell Res. [14652], 111 Deer Lake Rd., Ste. 100, Deerfield, IL 60015, (847)509-1944

Intl. Soc. for Stem Cell Res. [14652], 111 Deer Lake Rd., Ste. 100, Deerfield, IL 60015, (847)509-1944

Intl. Soc. for Stereology [IO], Arhus, Denmark

Intl. Soc. for Structural Hea. Monitoring of Intelligent Infrastructure [6428], Drexel Intelligent Infrastructure and Trans. Safety Inst., 3001 Market St., Ste. 50, Philadelphia, PA 19104, (215)895-6135

Intl. Soc. for Structural Hea. Monitoring of Intelligent Infrastructure [6428], Drexel Intelligent Infrastructure and Trans. Safety Inst., 3001 Market St., Ste. 50, Philadelphia, PA 19104, (215)895-6135

Intl. Soc. for the Stud. of Behavioural Development [IO], Helsinki, Finland

Intl. Soc. for the Stud. of Dissociation [★15460]

Intl. Soc. for the Stud. of Dissociation [★15460]

Intl. Soc. for the Study of Expressionism - Defunct.

Intl. Soc. for the Stud. of Ghosts and Apparitions [7225], Penthouse N, 29 Washington Sq. W, New York, NY 10011-9180

Intl. Soc. for the Stud. of Ghosts and Apparitions [7225], Penthouse N, 29 Washington Sq. W, New York, NY 10011-9180

Intl. Soc. for the Stud. of Human Ideas on Ultimate Reality and Meaning [IO], Pickering, ON, Canada

Intl. Soc. for the Stud. of Hypertension in Pregnancy [IO], Groningen, Netherlands

Intl. Soc. for the Stud. of the Lumbar Spine [IO], Goteborg, Sweden

Intl. Soc. for the Stud. of Medieval Philosophy [IO], Freiburg, Germany

Intl. Soc. for the Stud. of Multiple Personalities and Dissociation [★15460]

Intl. Soc. for the Stud. of Multiple Personalities and Dissociation [★15460]

Intl. Soc. for the Stud. of Pilgrimage Art [9186], Univ. of West Georgia, Art Dept., 324 Humanities Hall, Carrollton, GA 30118, (770)836-4532

Intl. Soc. for the Stud. of Pilgrimage Art [9186], Univ. of West Georgia, Art Dept., 324 Humanities Hall, Carrollton, GA 30118, (770)836-4532

Intl. Soc. for the Stud. of Religion, Nature and Culture [8329], PO Box 117410, Gainesville, FL 32611, (352)392-1625

Intl. Soc. for the Stud. of Subtle Energies and Energy Medicine [14166], 2770 Arapaho Rd., Ste. 132, Lafayette, CO 80026, (303)425-4625

Intl. Soc. for the Stud. of Subtle Energies and Energy Medicine [14166], 2770 Arapaho Rd., Ste. 132, Lafayette, CO 80026, (303)425-4625

Intl. Soc. for the Stud. of Tension in Performance [IO], Middlesex, United Kingdom

Intl. Soc. for the Stud. of Time [10612], Jo Alyson Parker, Ed., St. Joseph's Univ., English Dept., 5600 City Ave., Philadelphia, PA 19131-1395

Intl. Soc. for the Stud. of Time [10612], Jo Alyson Parker, Ed., St. Joseph's Univ., English Dept., 5600 City Ave., Philadelphia, PA 19131-1395

Intl. Soc. for the Stud. of Trauma and Dissociation [15460], 8400 Westpark Dr., 2nd Fl., McLean, VA 22102, (703)610-9037

Intl. Soc. for the Stud. of Trauma and Dissociation [15460], 8400 Westpark Dr., 2nd Fl., McLean, VA 22102, (703)610-9037

Intl. Soc. for the Stud. of Vascular Anomalies [15603], Box 0316, San Francisco, CA 94143, (415)353-7880

Intl. Soc. for the Stud. of Women's Sexual Hea. [16649], Two Woodfield Lake, 1100 E Woodfield Rd., Ste. 520, Schaumburg, IL 60173, (847)517-7225

Intl. Soc. for the Stud. of Women's Sexual Hea. [16649], Two Woodfield Lake, 1100 E Woodfield Rd., Ste. 520, Schaumburg, IL 60173, (847)517-7225

Intl. Soc. of Sugar Cane Technologists [IO], Mount Edgecombe, Republic of South Africa

Intl. Soc. of Surgery [IO], Lupsingen, Switzerland

Intl. Soc. of Sustainability Professionals [4340], 2515 NE 17th Ave., Ste. 300, Portland, OR 97212, (503)284-9132

A star before a book entry number signifies that the name is not listed separately, but is mentioned within the entry.

Intl. Soc. for Systematic and Comparative Musicology [IO], Hamburg, Germany

Intl. Soc. for the Systems Sciences [IO], York, United Kingdom

Intl. Soc. for Tech. in Educ. [7909], 180 W8th Ave., Ste. 300, Eugene, OR 97401-2916, (541)302-3777

Intl. Soc. for Tech. in Educ. [7909], 180 W8th Ave., Ste. 300, Eugene, OR 97401-2916, (541)302-3777

Intl. Soc. for Telemedicine and eHealth [IO], Regensburg, Germany

Intl. Soc. for Theoretical Chem. Physics [IO], Uppsala, Sweden

Intl. Soc. for Third-Sector Res. [12595], 559 Wyman Park Bldg., 3400 N Charles St., Baltimore, MD 21218-2688, (410)516-4678

Intl. Soc. for Third-Sector Res. [12595], 559 Wyman Park Bldg., 3400 N Charles St., Baltimore, MD 21218-2688, (410)516-4678

Intl. Soc. on Thrombosis and Haemostasis [14970], 610 Jones Ferry Rd., Ste. 205, Carrboro, NC 27510, (919)929-3807

Intl. Soc. on Thrombosis and Haemostasis [14970], 610 Jones Ferry Rd., Ste. 205, Carrboro, NC 27510, (919)929-3807

Intl. Soc. on Toxinology [IO], North Adelaide, Australia

Intl. Soc. of Trace Element Biogeochemistry [7004], Louisiana State Univ., Sturgis Hall, Baton Rouge, LA 70803

Intl. Soc. of Transport Aircraft Trading [142], 401 N Michigan Ave., Ste. 2200, Chicago, IL 60611, (312)321-5169

Intl. Soc. of Transport Aircraft Trading [142], 401 N Michigan Ave., Ste. 2200, Chicago, IL 60611, (312)321-5169

Intl. Soc. for Traumatic Stress Stud. [16726], 111 Deer Lake Rd., Ste. 100, Deerfield, IL 60015, (847)480-9028

Intl. Soc. for Traumatic Stress Stud. [16726], 111 Deer Lake Rd., Ste. 100, Deerfield, IL 60015, (847)480-9028

Intl. Soc. of Travel Medicine [15420], 315 W Ponce de Leon Ave., Ste. 245, Decatur, GA 30030, (404)373-8282

Intl. Soc. of Travel Medicine [15420], 315 W Ponce de Leon Ave., Ste. 245, Decatur, GA 30030, (404)373-8282

Intl. Soc. of Travel and Tourism Educators [3564], 23220 Edgewater, St. Clair Shores, MI 48082-2037, (586)294-0208

Intl. Soc. of Travel and Tourism Educators [3564], 23220 Edgewater, St. Clair Shores, MI 48082-2037, (586)294-0208

Intl. Soc. for Trenchless Tech. [IO], London, United Kingdom

Intl. Soc. of Tropical Dermatology [★14330]

Intl. Soc. of Tropical Dermatology [★14330]

Intl. Soc. of Tropical Foresters [4402], 5400 Grosvenor Ln., Bethesda, MD 20814, (301)530-4514

Intl. Soc. of Tropical Foresters [4402], 5400 Grosvenor Ln., Bethesda, MD 20814, (301)530-4514

Intl. Soc. for Tropical Root Crops [IO], Chatham, United Kingdom

Intl. Soc. for Twin Stud. [IO], Brisbane, Australia

Intl. Soc. of Typographic Designers [IO], Taunton, United Kingdom

Intl. Soc. on Ultrasonic Diagnostics in Ophthalmology [IO], Naples, Italy

Intl. Soc. of Ultrasound in Obstetrics and Gynecology [IO], London, United Kingdom

Intl. Soc. for Urban Hea. [14900], Alex Rothman, Coor., New York Acad. of Medicine, Center for Urban Epidemiologic Stud., 1216 Fifth Ave., New York, NY 10029, (212)822-7387

Intl. Soc. for Utilitarian Stud. [IO], London, United Kingdom

Intl. Soc. for Vaccines [15109], Univ. of Massachusetts Medical School, 354 Plantation St., LRB 304, Worcester, MA 01605, (508)856-6791

Intl. Soc. for Vascular Surgery [16816], 11 Scott Dr., Smithtown, NY 11787, (631)979-3780

Intl. Soc. for Vascular Surgery [16816], 11 Scott Dr., Smithtown, NY 11787, (631)979-3780

Intl. Soc. of Veterinary Dermatopathology [17028], 623 Woodlawn Ave., Venice, CA 90291

Intl. Soc. of Veterinary Dermatopathology [17028], 623 Woodlawn Ave., Venice, CA 90291

Intl. Soc. of Wang Users - Defunct.

Intl. Soc. of Weekly Newspaper Editors [2836], Missouri Southern State Univ., Inst. of Intl. Stud., 3950 E Newman Rd., Joplin, MO 64801-1595, (417)659-4442

Intl. Soc. of Weekly Newspaper Editors [2836], Missouri Southern State Univ., Inst. of Intl. Stud., 3950 E Newman Rd., Joplin, MO 64801-1595, (417)659-4442

Intl. Soc. of Weighing and Measurement [3656], 9707 Key West Ave., Ste. 100, Rockville, MD 20850, (301)258-1115

Intl. Soc. of Weighing and Measurement [3656], 9707 Key West Ave., Ste. 100, Rockville, MD 20850, (301)258-1115

Intl. Soc. for the Welfare of Cripples [★16575]

Intl. Soc. for the Welfare of Cripples [★16575]

Intl. Soc. of Women Airline Pilots [143], 723 S Casino Center Blvd., 2nd Fl., Las Vegas, NV 89101-6716

Intl. Soc. of Women Airline Pilots [143], 723 S Casino Center Blvd., 2nd Fl., Las Vegas, NV 89101-6716

Intl. Soc. for Work Options - Defunct.

Intl. Soc. of Worldwide Stamp Collectors [22046], PO Box 580, Whittier, CA 90608

Intl. Soc. of Worldwide Stamp Collectors [22046], PO Box 580, Whittier, CA 90608

Intl. Soc. of Young Filipino Accountants [★36]

Intl. Soc. of Zoological Sciences [IO], Beijing, People's Republic of China

Intl. Sociological Assn. [IO], Madrid, Spain

Intl. Softball Fed. [22953], 1900 S Park Rd., Plant City, FL 33563-8113, (813)864-0100

Intl. Softball Fed. [22953], 1900 S Park Rd., Plant City, FL 33563-8113, (813)864-0100

Intl. Soil Reference and Info. Centre [IO], Wageningen, Netherlands

Intl. Solar Energy Soc. [IO], Freiburg, Germany

Intl. Solid Surface Fabricators Assn. [★2337]

Intl. Solid Surface Fabricators Assn. [★2337]

Intl. Solid Waste Assn. [IO], Vienna, Austria

Intl. Solidarity Found. [IO], Helsinki, Finland

Intl. Songwriters Assn. [IO], Limerick, Ireland

Intl. Songwriters Guild [2560], 5108 Louvre Ave., Orlando, FL 32812-1028, (407)851-5328

Intl. Sonoran Desert Alliance [4278], 401 W Esperanza, Ajo, AZ 85321, (520)387-6823

Intl. Sonoran Desert Alliance [4278], 401 W Esperanza, Ajo, AZ 85321, (520)387-6823

Intl. Soundex Reunion Registry [10791], PO Box 371179, Las Vegas, NV 89137, (775)882-7755

Intl. Soundex Reunion Registry [10791], PO Box 371179, Las Vegas, NV 89137, (775)882-7755

Intl. Spa Assn. [3058], 2365 Harrodsburg Rd., Ste. A325, Lexington, KY 40504, (859)226-4326

Intl. Spa Assn. [3058], 2365 Harrodsburg Rd., Ste. A325, Lexington, KY 40504, (859)226-4326

Intl. Space Exploration and Colonization Company [6088], PO Box 60885, Fairbanks, AK 99706-0885, (907)488-1001

Intl. Space Exploration and Colonization Company [6088], PO Box 60885, Fairbanks, AK 99706-0885, (907)488-1001

Intl. Space Sci. Inst. [IO], Bern, Switzerland

Intl. Special Events Soc. [1203], 401 N Michigan Ave., Ste. 2200, Chicago, IL 60611-4267, (312)321-6853

Intl. Special Events Soc. [1203], 401 N Michigan Ave., Ste. 2200, Chicago, IL 60611-4267, (312)321-6853

Intl. Special Tooling Assn. [★1834]

Intl. Special Tooling Assn. [★1834]

Intl. Special Tooling and Machining Assn. [1834], Mr. Dave Tilstone, VP, 9300 Livingston Rd., Fort Washington, MD 20744, (301)248-6862

Intl. Special Tooling and Machining Assn. [1834], Mr. Dave Tilstone, VP, 9300 Livingston Rd., Fort Washington, MD 20744, (301)248-6862

Intl. Speech Commun. Assn. [IO], Baixas, France

Intl. Spenser Soc. [9376], Prof. Sheila Cavanagh, Ed., Emory Univ., 302 Callaway N, 537 Kilgo Cir., Atlanta, GA 30322, (404)727-7916

Intl. Spin Fishing Assn. [★22578]

Intl. Spinal Cord Soc. [IO], Aylesbury, United Kingdom

Intl. Spinal Development and Res. Found.

Intl. Spinal Development and Res. Found. - Address unknown since 2011.

Intl. Spinal Injection Soc. [★16702]

Intl. Spinal Res. Trust [IO], Guildford, United Kingdom

Intl. Spine Intervention Soc. [16702], 161 Mitchell Blvd., Ste. 103, San Rafael, CA 94903, (415)457-4747

Intl. Sport Horses of Color [4605], PO Box 1710, Cottage Grove, OR 97424-0068, (541)836-3000

Intl. Sport Press Assn. [IO], Lausanne, Switzerland

Intl. Sport Show Producers Assn. [1234], PO Box 480084, Denver, CO 80248-0084, (303)892-6966

Intl. Sporthorse Registry [4606], 517 DeKalb Ave., Sycamore, IL 60178, (815)899-7803

Intl. Sports Engg. Assn. [IO], Sheffield, United Kingdom

Intl. Sports Fed. for People with Intellectual Disability [IO], Wakefield, United Kingdom

Intl. Sports Heritage Assn. [22984], PO Box 2384, Florence, OR 97439, (541)991-7315

Intl. Sprout Growers Assn. [3732], 733A Bald Hill Rd., Warwick, RI 02886, (508)657-4742

Intl. Sprout Growers Assn. [3732], 733A Bald Hill Rd., Warwick, RI 02886, (508)657-4742

Intl. Stability Operations Assn. [18257], 1634 I St. NW, Ste. 800, Washington, DC 20006, (202)464-0721

Intl. Stamp Mfrs. Assn. [★3351]

Intl. Stamp Mfrs. Assn. [★3351]

International Standards

Albanian-American Trade and Development Assn. [23409]

Albanian-American Trade and Development Assn. [23409]

Coun. for Intl. Tax Educ. [2080]

Coun. for Intl. Tax Educ. [2080]

FCIB-NACM Corp. [2081]

FCIB-NACM Corp. [2081]

Fed. of Intl. Trade Associations [2082]

Fed. of Intl. Trade Associations [2082]

Freshfel Europe [20506]

Intl. Trade Club of Chicago [2083]

Intl. Trade Club of Chicago [2083]

Iranian Trade Assn. [2084]

Iranian Trade Assn. [2084]

Moroccan Amer. Bus. Coun. [2085]

Moroccan Amer. Bus. Coun. [2085]

Natl. Coun. on Intl. Trade Development [2086]

Natl. Coun. on Intl. Trade Development [2086]

Natl. Foreign Trade Coun. [2087]

Natl. Foreign Trade Coun. [2087]

Soc. of Intl. Bus. Fellows [2088]

Soc. of Intl. Bus. Fellows [2088]

U.S. Russia Bus. Coun. [2089]

U.S. Russia Bus. Coun. [2089]

U.S.-Taiwan Bus. Coun. [2090]

U.S.-Taiwan Bus. Coun. [2090]

World Trade Center of New Orleans [2091]

World Trade Center of New Orleans [2091]

Intl. Standing Comm. of the Intl. Cong. on Animal Reproduction [IO], Sydney, Australia

Intl. Staple, Nail and Tool Assn. [1653], 512 W Burlington Ave., Ste. 203, La Grange, IL 60525-2245, (708)482-8138

Intl. Staple, Nail and Tool Assn. [1653], 512 W Burlington Ave., Ste. 203, La Grange, IL 60525-2245, (708)482-8138

Intl. Star Class Yacht Racing Assn. [22361], 914 Bay Ridge Rd., Ste. 220, Annapolis, MD 21403, (443)458-5733

Intl. Star Class Yacht Racing Assn. [22361], 914 Bay Ridge Rd., Ste. 220, Annapolis, MD 21403, (443)458-5733

Intl. Star Riders Assn. [21933], 848 N Rainbow Blvd., No. 793, Las Vegas, NV 89107

Intl. Stationary Steam Engine Soc.

Intl. Stationary Steam Engine Soc. - Address unknown since 2011.

Intl. Statistical Inst. [IO], The Hague, Netherlands

Intl. Steel Guitar Convention [10227], 9535 Midland Blvd., St. Louis, MO 63114-3314, (314)427-7794

Reference to "IO" in place of a book number signifies that the association may be found in the 50th edition of International Organizations.

Intl. Steel Guitar Convention [10227], 9535 Midland Blvd., St. Louis, MO 63114-3314, (314)427-7794

Intl. Steel Trade Assn. [IO], London, United Kingdom

Intl. Step by Step Assn. [IO], Amsterdam, Netherlands

Intl. Stevia Coun. [1404], 750 Natl. Press Bldg., 529 14th St. NW, Washington, DC 20045, (202)591-2467

Intl. Stewards and Caterers Assn. [★1446]

Intl. Stewards and Caterers Assn. [★1446]

Intl. Stillbirth Alliance [14106], PO Box 46757, Kansas City, MO 64188

Intl. Stillbirth Alliance [14106], PO Box 46757, Kansas City, MO 64188

Intl. Strategic Stud. Assn. [17505], PO Box 320608, Alexandria, VA 22320, (703)548-1070

Intl. Strategic Stud. Assn. [17505], PO Box 320608, Alexandria, VA 22320, (703)548-1070

Intl. Street and Evangelism Ministries Assn. - Defunct.

Intl. Stress Mgt. Assn. - India [IO], Hyderabad, India

Intl. Stress Mgt. Assn. UK [IO], Bristol, United Kingdom

Intl. String Figure Assn. [21448], PO Box 5134, Pasadena, CA 91117, (626)398-1057

Intl. String Figure Assn. [21448], PO Box 5134, Pasadena, CA 91117, (626)398-1057

Intl. Student Pugwash [★18819]

Intl. Student Visitors Ser. [★8363]

Intl. Student Visitors Ser. [★8363]

Intl. Student Week Ilmenau [IO], Ilmenau, Germany

Intl. Students, Inc. [19754], PO Box C, Colorado Springs, CO 80901, (719)576-2700

Intl. Students, Inc. [19754], PO Box C, Colorado Springs, CO 80901, (719)576-2700

International Studies

Amer. Assn. for Ukrainian Stud. [8397]

Amer. Assn. for Ukrainian Stud. [8397]

Amer. Inst. for Foreign Stud. [8398]

Amer. Inst. for Foreign Stud. Found. [8399]

Assn. for Borderlands Stud. [8400]

Assn. for Borderlands Stud. [8400]

Assn. of Professional Schools of Intl. Affairs [8401]

Assn. of Professional Schools of Intl. Affairs [8401]

Central Eurasian Stud. Soc. [9877]

Central Eurasian Stud. Soc. [9877]

Comparative and Intl. Educ. Soc. [8402]

Comparative and Intl. Educ. Soc. [8402]

Cordell Hull Found. for Intl. Educ. [8403]

Cordell Hull Found. for Intl. Educ. [8403]

Global Learning [8404]

Intl. Stud. Assn. [9878]

Intl. Stud. Assn. [9878]

Island Resources Found. [9879]

Natl. Model United Nations [8405]

Intl. Stud. Assn. [9878], Univ. of Arizona, 324 Social Sciences Bldg., Tucson, AZ 85721, (520)621-7715

Intl. Stud. Assn. [9878], Univ. of Arizona, 324 Social Sciences Bldg., Tucson, AZ 85721, (520)621-7715

Intl. Stud. Assn. for Teachers and Teaching [IO], Reading, United Kingdom

Intl. Submariners Association-USA [20678], 7178 Prairie Ridge Rd., Prescott Valley, AZ 86315-9043, (928)772-0275

Intl. Substance Abuse and Addiction Coalition [IO], Reading, United Kingdom

Intl. Sufi Movement [IO], The Hague, Netherlands

Intl. Sugar Org. [IO], London, United Kingdom

Intl. Sugar Trade Coalition [3367], 1054 31st St. NW, Ste. 300, Washington, DC 20007, (202)333-4000

Intl. Sugar Trade Coalition [3367], 1054 31st St. NW, Ste. 300, Washington, DC 20007, (202)333-4000

Intl. Sumo Fed. [IO], Tokyo, Japan

Intl. Sunfish Class Assn. [22362], PO Box 300128, Waterford, MI 48330-0128, (248)673-2750

Intl. Sunfish Class Assn. [22362], PO Box 300128, Waterford, MI 48330-0128, (248)673-2750

Intl. Sunflower Assn. [IO], Paris, France

Intl. Sungja-Do Assn. [22738], 137 Timberlake Dr., Florence, SC 29501, (843)968-8178

Intl. Sunshine Soc. - Defunct.

Intl. Surface Fabricators Assn. [2337], 165 N 1330 W, No. A3, Orem, UT 84057, (801)341-7360

Intl. Surface Fabricators Assn. [2337], 165 N 1330 W, No. A3, Orem, UT 84057, (801)341-7360

Intl. Surfing Assn. [23034], 5580 La Jolla Blvd., No. 145, La Jolla, CA 92037, (858)551-8580

Intl. Survey Lib. Assn. - Defunct.

Intl. Sustainability Coun. [4212], 35246 US Hwy. 19 N, No. 299, Palm Harbor, FL 34684, (518)859-5370

Intl. Sustainability Coun. [4212], 35246 US Hwy. 19 N, No. 299, Palm Harbor, FL 34684, (518)859-5370

Intl. Swaps and Derivatives Assn. [2137], 360 Madison Ave., 16th Fl., New York, NY 10017, (212)901-6000

Intl. Sweeteners Assn. [IO], Brussels, Belgium

Intl. Swift Assn. [★20919]

Intl. Swimming Hall of Fame [23041], 1 Hall of Fame Dr., Fort Lauderdale, FL 33316, (954)462-6536

Intl. Swimming Hall of Fame [23041], 1 Hall of Fame Dr., Fort Lauderdale, FL 33316, (954)462-6536

Intl. Swizzle Stick Collectors Assn. [21363], PO Box 5205, Bellingham, WA 98227-5205, (604)936-7636

Intl. Swizzle Stick Collectors Assn. [21363], PO Box 5205, Bellingham, WA 98227-5205, (604)936-7636

Intl. Sybil Jason Fan Club - Address unknown since 2011.

Intl. Symbiosis Soc. [18623], 6505 NE 65th St., Seattle, WA 98115

Intl. Symbiosis Soc. [18623], 6505 NE 65th St., Seattle, WA 98115

Intl. Sys. Safety Soc. [3144], PO Box 70, Unionville, VA 22567-0070, (540)854-8630

Intl. Systems Dealers Assn. [★2579]

Intl. Systems Security Engg. Assn. [6806], 13873 Park Center Rd., Ste. 200, Herndon, VA 20171

Intl. Systems Security Engg. Assn. [6806], 13873 Park Center Rd., Ste. 200, Herndon, VA 20171

Intl. Table Tennis Fed. [IO], Lausanne, Switzerland

Intl. Tamil Tech. Professionals' Org. [12346], 3106 Pepita Ct., San Jose, CA 95132

Intl. Tank Container Org. [IO], Surbiton, United Kingdom

Intl. Tanker Owners Pollution Fed. [IO], London, United Kingdom

Intl. Tap Assn. [9555], PO Box 150574, Austin, TX 78715, (303)443-7989

Intl. Tape Assn. [★1254]

Intl. Tape Assn. [★1254]

Intl. Tape/Disc Assn. [★1254]

Intl. Tape/Disc Assn. [★1254]

Intl. Task Force on Euthanasia and Assisted Suicide [11990], PO Box 760, Steubenville, OH 43952, (740)282-3810

Intl. Task Force for the Rural Poor [IO], Moradabad, India

Intl. Tax Planning Assn. [IO], Jersey, United Kingdom

Intl. Taxicab Assn. [★3537]

Intl. Taxicab Assn. [★3537]

Intl. Taxicab and Livery Assn. [★3537]

Intl. Taxicab and Livery Assn. [★3537]

Intl. Tea Comm. [IO], London, United Kingdom

Intl. Tech. Tropical Timber Assn. [IO], Paris, France

Intl. Tech. Educ. Assn. - Coun. for Supervisors [★8968]

Intl. Tech. Educ. Assn. - Coun. for Supervisors [★8968]

Intl. Tech. Educ. Assn. | Coun. on Tech. Teacher Educ. [8297], 1914 Assn. Dr., Reston, VA 20191-1539, (703)860-2100

Intl. Tech. and Engineering Educ. Assn. [8967], 1914 Assn. Dr., Ste. 201, Reston, VA 20191-1539, (703)860-2100

Intl. Tech. and Engg. Educators Assn. [8967], 1914 Assn. Dr., Ste. 201, Reston, VA 20191-1539, (703)860-2100

Intl. Tech. and Engg. Educators Assn. | Coun. for Supervision and Leadership [8968], Maryland Dept. of Educ., 200 W Baltimore St., Baltimore, MD 21201, (410)767-0177

Intl. Tech. and Engg. Educators Assn. - Coun. for Supervision and Leadership [8968], Maryland Dept. of Educ., 200 W Baltimore St., Baltimore, MD 21201, (410)767-0177

Intl. Tech. Inst.

Intl. Tech. Inst. - Address unknown since 2011.

Intl. Tech. Law Assn. [5323], 401 Edgewater Pl., Ste. 600, Wakefield, MA 01880, (781)876-8877

Intl. Tele-Education - Defunct.

Intl. Telecommunication Union [IO], Geneva, Switzerland

Intl. (Telecommunications) Disaster Recovery Assn. [7544], BWT Associates, PO No. 4515, Shrewsbury, MA 01545, (508)845-6000

Intl. (Telecommunications) Disaster Recovery Assn. [7544], BWT Associates, PO No. 4515, Shrewsbury, MA 01545, (508)845-6000

Intl. Telecommunications Satellite Org. [7545], 3400 Intl. Dr. NW, Washington, DC 20008-3006, (202)243-5096

Intl. Telecommunications Satellite Org. [7545], 3400 Intl. Dr. NW, Washington, DC 20008-3006, (202)243-5096

Intl. Telecommunications Soc. [3412], Leland W. Schmidt, Treas./Finance Comm. Chm., 33 Alpine Dr., Gilford, NH 03249, (603)293-4094

Intl. Telecommunications Soc. [3412], Leland W. Schmidt, Treas./Finance Comm. Chm., 33 Alpine Dr., Gilford, NH 03249, (603)293-4094

Intl. Telecommunications Users Gp. [IO], Driebergen, Netherlands

Intl. TV Assn. [★1262]

Intl. TV Assn. [★1262]

Intl. TV Assn. Deutschland [IO], Frankfurt, Germany

Intl. TV Assn. - Japan [IO], Tokyo, Japan

Intl. Telework Assn. and Coun. [3413], 14040 N Northsight Blvd., Scottsdale, AZ 85260, (877)951-9191

Intl. Telework Assn. and Coun. [3413], 14040 N Northsight Blvd., Scottsdale, AZ 85260, (877)951-9191

Intl. Tennis Fed. [IO], London, United Kingdom

Intl. Tennis Hall of Fame [23056], 194 Bellevue Ave., Newport, RI 02840, (401)849-3990

Intl. Tennis Hall of Fame [23056], 194 Bellevue Ave., Newport, RI 02840, (401)849-3990

Intl. Test and Evaluation Assn. [7559], 4400 Fair Lakes Ct., Ste. 104, Fairfax, VA 22033-3801, (703)631-6220

Intl. Test and Evaluation Assn. [7559], 4400 Fair Lakes Ct., Ste. 104, Fairfax, VA 22033-3801, (703)631-6220

Intl. Texas Longhorn Assn. [3920], PO Box 2610, Glen Rose, TX 76043, (254)898-0157

Intl. Texas Longhorn Assn. [3920], PO Box 2610, Glen Rose, TX 76043, (254)898-0157

Intl. Textile and Apparel Assn. [3445], PO Box 70687, Knoxville, TN 37938-0687, (865)992-1535

Intl. Textile and Apparel Assn. [3445], PO Box 70687, Knoxville, TN 37938-0687, (865)992-1535

Intl. Textile, Garment and Leather Workers' Fed. [IO], Brussels, Belgium

Intl. Textile Mfrs. Fed. [IO], Zurich, Switzerland

Intl. Textile Market Assn. [3446], PO Box 1208, High Point, NC 27261, (336)885-6842

Intl. Thai Therapists Assn. [15272], 4715 Bruton Rd., Plant City, FL 33565, (706)358-8646

Intl. Thai Therapists Assn. [15272], 4715 Bruton Rd., Plant City, FL 33565, (706)358-8646

Intl. Theatre Equip. Assn. [★1260]

Intl. Theatre Equip. Assn. [★1260]

Intl. Theatre Inst. - France [IO], Paris, France

Intl. Theatre Inst. - Switzerland [IO], Basel, Switzerland

Intl. Theatre Inst. of the U.S. - Defunct.

Intl. Theodore Dreiser Soc. [9377], Roark Mulligan, Sec.-Treas., Christopher Newport Univ., Dept. of English, Newport News, VA 23606

Intl. Theodore Dreiser Soc. [9377], Roark Mulligan, Sec.-Treas., Christopher Newport Univ., Dept. of English, Newport News, VA 23606

Intl. Thermal Storage Advisory Coun. - Defunct.

Intl. Thermionic Soc. - Defunct.

Intl. Thermoelectric Soc. [IO], Nagoya, Japan

Intl. Thespian Soc. [★9001]

Intl. Third World Legal Stud. Assn. - Defunct.

Intl. Thomas Merton Soc. [9378], 4537 Melvina, Chicago, IL 60630, (479)521-5001

Intl. Thomas Merton Soc. [9378], 4537 Melvina, Chicago, IL 60630, (479)521-5001

A star before a book entry number signifies that the name is not listed separately, but is mentioned within the entry.

Intl. Thriller Writers [10723], PO Box 311, Eureka, CA 95502

Intl. Thriller Writers [10723], PO Box 311, Eureka, CA 95502

Intl. Thunderbird Assn. [★22363]

Intl. Thunderbird Class Assn. [22363], PO Box 1033, Mercer Island, WA 98040-1033, (425)430-7290

Intl. Thunderbird Club [21080], 6213 Harley Rd., Middletown, MD 21769, (301)371-3108

Intl. Thunderbird Club [21080], 6213 Harley Rd., Middletown, MD 21769, (301)371-3108

Intl. Ticketing Assn. [1204], One Coll. Park, 8910 Purdue Rd., Ste. 480, Indianapolis, IN 46268, (212)629-4036

Intl. Ticketing Assn. [1204], One Coll. Park, 8910 Purdue Rd., Ste. 480, Indianapolis, IN 46268, (212)629-4036

Intl. Time Capsule Soc. [9704], Oglethorpe Univ., 4484 Peachtree Rd. NE, Atlanta, GA 30319, (404)261-1441

Intl. Time Capsule Soc. [9704], Oglethorpe Univ., 4484 Peachtree Rd. NE, Atlanta, GA 30319, (404)261-1441

Intl. Tire and Rubber Assn. [★3465]

Intl. Tit Soc. - Defunct.

Intl. Titanium Assn. [2475], 2655 W Midway Blvd., Ste. 300, Broomfield, CO 80020-7187, (303)404-2221

Intl. Titanium Assn. [2475], 2655 W Midway Blvd., Ste. 300, Broomfield, CO 80020-7187, (303)404-2221

Intl. Tobacco Growers Assn. [IO], Castelo Branco, Portugal

Intl. Touring Alliance [IO], Geneva, Switzerland

Intl. Tourism Stud. Assn. [IO], Beijing, People's Republic of China

Intl. Tourism Trade Fairs Assn. [IO], Richmond, United Kingdom

Intl. Toy Libraries Assn. [IO], Gauteng, Republic of South Africa

Intl. Trachoma Initiative [17089], 325 Swanton Way, Decatur, GA 30030, (404)371-0466

Intl. Trachoma Initiative [17089], 325 Swanton Way, Decatur, GA 30030, (404)371-0466

Intl. Tracing Ser. [IO], Bad Arolsen, Germany

International Trade

America-Georgia Bus. Coun. [2092]

Amer. Assn. of Exporters and Importers [2093]

Amer. Importers Assn. [2094]

Armenian Amer. Chamber of Commerce [23352]

Australian New Zealand - Amer. Chambers of Commerce [23339]

Bus. Assn. Italy Am. [2095]

Canada-United States Bus. Assn. [2096]

ChristianTrade Assn. Intl. [19561]

Emergency Comm. for Amer. Trade [2097]

Global Offset and Countertrade Assn. [2098]

Iraqi Amer. Chamber of Commerce and Indus. [23370]

Joint Indus. Gp. [2099]

Latin Am. Trade Coalition [2187]

Mauritius-U.S. Bus. Assn. [2100]

Natl. Assn. of Export Companies [2101]

Natl. Assn. of Foreign-Trade Zones [2102]

Natl. Customs Brokers and Forwarders Assn. of Am. [2103]

North America-Mongolia Bus. Coun. [2104]

North Amer. Importers Assn. [2105]

Pakistan Chamber of Commerce USA [23435]

Small Bus. Exporters Assn. of the U.S. [2106]

South African USA Chamber of Commerce [23379]

Swiss-American Bus. Coun. [2107]

Turkish-American Chamber of Commerce and Indus. [23455]

U.S.-Algeria Bus. Coun. [2108]

U.S.-Bahrain Bus. Coun. [2109]

U.S.-China Bus. Coun. [2110]

U.S.-Cuba Trade Assn. [2111]

U.S. Indian Amer. Chamber of Commerce [23407]

U.S.-Kazakhstan Bus. Assn. [2112]

U.S. New Zealand Coun. [2113]

U.S.-Saudi Arabian Bus. Coun. [2114]

U.S.-U.A.E. Bus. Coun. [2115]

World Growth [2079]

Intl. Trade Assn. - Defunct.

Intl. Trade Centre [IO], Geneva, Switzerland

Intl. Trade Club of Chicago [2083], 134 N LaSalle St., Ste. 1300, Chicago, IL 60602, (312)368-9197

Intl. Trade Club of Chicago [2083], 134 N LaSalle St., Ste. 1300, Chicago, IL 60602, (312)368-9197

Intl. Trade Commn. Trial Lawyers Assn. [★6045]

Intl. Trade Mart [★2091]

Intl. Trade Mart [★2091]

Intl. Trade Union Confed. [IO], Brussels, Belgium

Intl. Trade Union Confed. - African Regional Org. [IO], Nairobi, Kenya

Intl. Trademark Assn. [5573], 655 3rd Ave., 10th Fl., New York, NY 10017-5617, (212)642-1700

Intl. Trademark Assn. [5573], 655 3rd Ave., 10th Fl., New York, NY 10017-5617, (212)642-1700

Intl. Traditional Country Music Fan Club - Address unknown since 2011.

Intl. Traditional Karate Fed. [22739], 1930 Wilshire Blvd., Ste. 503, Los Angeles, CA 90057-3603, (213)483-8262

Intl. Traditional Karate Fed. [22739], 1930 Wilshire Blvd., Ste. 503, Los Angeles, CA 90057-3603, (213)483-8262

Intl. Training and Simulation Alliance [6461], 2111 Wilson Blvd., Ste. 400, Arlington, VA 22201-3061, (703)247-9471

Intl. Training and Simulation Alliance [6461], 2111 Wilson Blvd., Ste. 400, Arlington, VA 22201-3061, (703)247-9471

Intl. Transactional Anal. Assn. [16341], 2843 Hopyard Rd., Ste. 155, Pleasanton, CA 94588, (925)600-8110

Intl. Transactional Anal. Assn. [16341], 2843 Hopyard Rd., Ste. 155, Pleasanton, CA 94588, (925)600-8110

Intl. Transplant Coordinators Soc. [IO], Leuven, Belgium

Intl. Transplant Nurses Soc. [15760], 1739 E Carson St., PO Box 351, Pittsburgh, PA 15203-1700, (412)343-4867

Intl. Transplant Nurses Soc. [15760], 1739 E Carson St., PO Box 351, Pittsburgh, PA 15203-1700, (412)343-4867

Intl. Transport Forum [IO], Paris, France

Intl. Transport Workers' Fed. [IO], London, United Kingdom

Intl. Trans. Mgt. Assn. [6033], PO Box 62654, Houston, TX 77205, (713)343-0889

Intl. Trans. Mgt. Assn. [6033], PO Box 62654, Houston, TX 77205, (713)343-0889

Intl. Trauma Anesthesia and Critical Care Soc. [13750], PO Box 4826, Baltimore, MD 21211

Intl. Trauma Anesthesia and Critical Care Soc. [13750], PO Box 4826, Baltimore, MD 21211

Intl. Travel Catering Assn. [IO], Godalming, United Kingdom

Intl. Tree Found. [IO], Crawley Down, United Kingdom

Intl. Tree Nut Coun. [IO], Reus, Spain

Intl. Tremor Found. [★15600]

Intl. Tremor Found. [★15600]

Intl. Triathlon Union [IO], North Vancouver, BC, Canada

Intl. Trombone Assn. [IO], Coventry, United Kingdom

Intl. Trotting and Pacing Assn. [22656], 5140 County Rd. 56, Auburn, IN 46706, (260)337-5808

Intl. Truck Parts Assn. [331], 1720-10 Ave. S, Ste. 4, PMB 199, Great Falls, MT 59405, (866)346-5692

Intl. Truck Parts Assn. [331], 1720-10 Ave. S, Ste. 4, PMB 199, Great Falls, MT 59405, (866)346-5692

Intl. Trumpet Guild [10228], Dixie Burress, Treas., PO Box 2688, Davenport, IA 52809-2688

Intl. Trumpet Guild [10228], Dixie Burress, Treas., PO Box 2688, Davenport, IA 52809-2688

Intl. Tsunami Info. Center [7400], 737 Bishop St., Ste. 2200, Honolulu, HI 96813, (808)532-6423

Intl. Tsunami Info. Center [7400], 737 Bishop St., Ste. 2200, Honolulu, HI 96813, (808)532-6423

Intl. Tuba-Euphonium Assn. [10229], PO Box 50867, Kalamazoo, MI 49005, (888)331-4832

Intl. Tuba-Euphonium Assn. [10229], PO Box 50867, Kalamazoo, MI 49005, (888)331-4832

Intl. Tube Assn. [IO], Leamington Spa, United Kingdom

Intl. Tungsten Indus. Assn. [IO], London, United Kingdom

Intl. Tunnelling Assn. [IO], Lausanne, Switzerland

Intl. Turf Producers Found. [4509], Turfgrass Producers Intl., 2 E Main St., East Dundee, IL 60118, (847)649-5555

Intl. Turf Producers Found. [4509], Turfgrass Producers Intl., 2 E Main St., East Dundee, IL 60118, (847)649-5555

Intl. Typographical Union [★23210]

Intl. Tyre, Rubber, and Plastics Fed. [IO], Birmingham, United Kingdom

Intl. UFO Museum and Res. Center at Roswell, New Mexico [7253], 114 N Main St., Roswell, NM 88203, (800)822-3545

Intl. UFO Museum and Res. Center at Roswell, New Mexico [7253], 114 N Main St., Roswell, NM 88203, (800)822-3545

Intl. Ultraviolet Assn. [6735], 1718 M St. NW, No. 276, Washington, DC 20036, (202)422-2445

International Understanding

Amer. Turkish Friendship Coun. [17937]

Assn. of Nepalis in the Americas [19171]

Center for Citizen Initiatives [17960]

Center for Global Educ. [8406]

Conflict Solutions Intl. [17405]

Crosscurrents Intl. Inst. [17961]

East-West Center [17962]

Educators for Social Responsibility [17963]

English in Action [17964]

French-American Found. [17965]

Friends of Mali [18246]

Friends of Togo [17966]

Friendship Ambassadors Found. [17967]

Friendship Force Intl. [17968]

German Marshall Fund of the U.S. [17969]

Global Ambassadors for Children [18249]

Global Educ. Associates [17970]

Global Volunteers [17971]

Hospitality Comm. for United Nations Delegations [17972]

The Hospitality and Info. Ser. [17973]

Inst. of World Affairs [8407]

InterFuture [8408]

Intl. Center in New York [17974]

Intl. Coun. for Middle East Stud. [18125]

Intl. Multiracial Shared Cultural Org. [17975]

Japan Center for Intl. Exchange USA [17976]

Just Vision [17409]

Kiwanis Intl. [13062]

Laotian Amer. Soc. [19102]

Legacy Intl. [8409]

Meridian Intl. Center [17977]

Meridian Intl. Center Programming Div. [17978]

Natl. Coun. for Intl. Visitors [17979]

Natl. Jewish Democratic Coun. [18387]

Org. for Intl. Cooperation [17980]

Our Developing World [17981]

People to People Ambassador Prog. [17982]

People to People Intl. [17983]

Perhaps Kids Meeting Kids Can Make a Difference [17984]

Polish-American-Jewish Alliance for Youth Action [13551]

Sister Cities Intl. [17985]

Soc. for Intercultural Educ., Training and Res. U.S.A. [8410]

Thai U.S.A. Assn. [19256]

Ugandan North Amer. Assn. [18841]

UNANIMA Intl. [18645]

U.S. Assn. for the Univ. for Peace [18294]

U.S. Fed. for Middle East Peace [18295]

U.S. Servas [17986]

U.S. Women and Cuba Collaboration [17957]

Unity-and-Diversity World Coun. [17987]

US-Azerbaijan Coun. [17958]

Venceremos Brigade [17988]

Veterans for Am. [17989]

Volunteers for Peace [17990]

Working Capital for Community Needs [17991]

World Learning Visitor Exchange Prog. [17992]

World Neighbors [17993]

World Peace Found. [17994]

Intl. Underwater Spearfishing Assn. [22579], 2515 NW 29th Dr., Boca Raton, FL 33434

Reference to "IO" in place of a book number signifies that the association may be found in the 50th edition of International Organizations.

Intl. Underwater Spearfishing Assn. **[22579]**, 2515 NW 29th Dr., Boca Raton, FL 33434

Intl. Underwriting Assn. of London **[IO]**, London, United Kingdom

Intl. Unicycling Fed. **[22480]**, PO Box 2082, Spring Valley, CA 91979

Intl. Union Against Cancer **[IO]**, Geneva, Switzerland

Intl. Union Against Sexually Transmitted Infections, Regional Off. for North Am. **[16656]**, Harborview Medical Center, 325 9th Ave., Box 359931, Seattle, WA 98104, (206)744-3679

Intl. Union Against Sexually Transmitted Infections, Regional Off. for North Am. **[16656]**, Harborview Medical Center, 325 9th Ave., Box 359931, Seattle, WA 98104, (206)744-3679

Intl. Union Against Sexually Transmitted Infections - United Kingdom **[IO]**, Southampton, United Kingdom

Intl. Union Against Tuberculosis and Lung Disease **[IO]**, Paris, France

Intl. Union Against the Venereal Diseases and the Treponematoses, Regional Off. for North Am. **[★16656]**

Intl. Union Against the Venereal Diseases and the Treponematoses, Regional Off. for North Am. **[★16656]**

Intl. Union of Air Pollution Prevention and Environmental Protection Associations **[IO]**, Burgess Hill, United Kingdom

Intl. Union of Angiology **[IO]**, Rome, Italy

Intl. Union of Anthropological and Ethnological Sciences **[IO]**, Leiden, Netherlands

Intl. Union of Architects **[IO]**, Paris, France

Intl. Union of Aviation Insurers **[IO]**, London, United Kingdom

Intl. Union of Biochemistry and Molecular Biology **[IO]**, Calgary, AB, Canada

Intl. Union of Biological Sciences **[IO]**, Orsay, France

Intl. Union of Bricklayers and Allied Craftsmen **[★23164]**

Intl. Union of Bricklayers and Allied Craftworkers **[23164]**, 620 F St. NW, Washington, DC 20004, (202)783-3788

Intl. Union of Building Centres **[IO]**, Helsinki, Finland

Intl. Union for Conservation of Nature **[IO]**, Gland, Switzerland

Intl. Union for Conservation of Nature and Natural Resources - Botswana **[IO]**, Gaborone, Botswana

Intl. Union for the Conservation of Nature and Natural Resources U.S. **[4083]**, 1630 Connecticut Ave. NW, 3rd Fl., Washington, DC 20009, (202)387-4826

Intl. Union for the Conservation of Nature and Natural Resources U.S. **[4083]**, 1630 Connecticut Ave. NW, 3rd Fl., Washington, DC 20009, (202)387-4826

Intl. Union for Conservation of Nature and Natural Resources - Vietnam **[IO]**, Hanoi, Vietnam

Intl. Union for Conservation of Nature and Natural Resources - Zambia **[IO]**, Lusaka, Zambia

Intl. Union for the Conservation of Nature's Primate Specialist Group - Defunct.

Intl. Union of Credit and Investment Insurers/The Berne Union **[IO]**, London, United Kingdom

Intl. Union of Crystallography **[IO]**, Chester, United Kingdom

Intl. Union of District 50, Allied and Tech. Workers of the U.S. and Canada **[★23256]**

Intl. Union of Elecl., Radio and Machine Workers **[★23184]**

Intl. Union for Electricity Applications **[IO]**, Puteaux, France

Intl. Union of Electronic, Elecl., Salaried, Machine, and Furniture Workers **[23184]**, 501 Third St. NW, Washington, DC 20001, (937)294-9764

Intl. Union of Electronic, Elecl., Tech., Salaried, Machine, and Furniture Workers **[★23184]**

Intl. Union of Elevator Constructors **[23219]**, 7154 Columbia Gateway Dr., Columbia, MD 21046, (410)953-6150

Intl. Union of Elevator Constructors **[23219]**, 7154 Columbia Gateway Dr., Columbia, MD 21046, (410)953-6150

Intl. Union of Food, Agricultural, Hotel, Restaurant, Catering, Tobacco, and Allied Workers' Associations **[IO]**, Petit-Lancy, Switzerland

Intl. Union of Food Sci. and Tech. **[IO]**, Oakville, ON, Canada

Intl. Union of Forest Res. Organizations **[IO]**, Vienna, Austria

Intl. Union of Francophone Press **[IO]**, Paris, France

Intl. Union of Geological Sciences **[IO]**, Ottawa, ON, Canada

Intl. Union of Gospel Missions **[★13174]**

Intl. Union of Gospel Missions **[★13174]**

Intl. Union of Guides and Scouts of Europe **[IO]**, Chateau Landon, France

Intl. Union for Hea. Promotion and Educ. **[IO]**, St.-Denis, France

Intl. Union for Housing Finance **[IO]**, Brussels, Belgium

Intl. Union of Immunological Societies **[IO]**, Vienna, Austria

Intl. Union of Indus. and Independent Workers **[23312]**, 145 Brooks Glen, Roswell, GA 30075, (678)725-1001

Intl. Union of Indus. and Independent Workers **[23312]**, 145 Brooks Glen, Roswell, GA 30075, (678)725-1001

Intl. Union of Labs. and Experts in Constr. Materials, Systems and Structures **[IO]**, Bagneux, France

Intl. Union for Land Value Taxation and Free Trade **[IO]**, London, United Kingdom

Intl. Union of Marine Insurance **[IO]**, Zurich, Switzerland

Intl. Union of Microbiological Societies **[IO]**, Utrecht, Netherlands

Intl. Union of Mine, Mill and Smelter Workers **[★23256]**

Intl. Union of Operating Engineers **[23165]**, 1125 17th St. NW, Washington, DC 20036, (202)429-9100

Intl. Union of Painters and Allied Trades **[23262]**, 7234 Parkway Dr., Hanover, MD 21076, (410)564-5900

Intl. Union of Painters and Allied Trades | Joint Apprenticeship and Training Fund **[11941]**, 1750 New York Ave. NW, Washington, DC 20006, (202)637-0700

Intl. Union of Painters and Allied Trades | Joint Apprenticeship and Training Fund **[11941]**, 1750 New York Ave. NW, Washington, DC 20006, (202)637-0700

Intl. Union for Physical and Engg. Sciences in Medicine **[IO]**, Stockholm, Sweden

Intl. Union of Physiological Sciences **[IO]**, Oxford, United Kingdom

Intl. Union of Police Associations **[23242]**, 1549 Ringling Blvd., Ste. 600, Sarasota, FL 34236, (941)487-2560

Intl. Union of Private Wagons **[IO]**, Brussels, Belgium

Intl. Union of Professional Drivers **[IO]**, Murten, Switzerland

Intl. Union for the Protection of New Varieties of Plants **[IO]**, Geneva, Switzerland

Intl. Union of Psychological Sci. **[IO]**, Ottawa, ON, Canada

Intl. Union for Pure and Applied Biophysics **[IO]**, Sydney, Australia

Intl. Union of Pure and Applied Chemistry **[6411]**, PO Box 13757, Research Triangle Park, NC 27709-3757, (919)485-8700

Intl. Union of Pure and Applied Chemistry **[6411]**, PO Box 13757, Research Triangle Park, NC 27709-3757, (919)485-8700

Intl. Union of Pure and Applied Physics **[IO]**, Tsukuba, Japan

Intl. Union for Quaternary Res. **[IO]**, Dublin, Ireland

Intl. Union of Radio Sci. **[IO]**, Gent, Belgium

Intl. Union of Radio Sci., U.S. Natl. Comm. **[7546]**, Yahya Rahmat-Samii, Chm., Univ. of California at Los Angeles, Elecl. Engg. Dept., 6731K Boelter Hall, Los Angeles, CA 90095-1594, (310)206-2275

Intl. Union of Radioecology **[IO]**, St.-Paul-les-Durance, France

Intl. Union of Railways **[IO]**, Paris, France

Intl. Union for the Sci. Stud. of Population **[IO]**, Paris, France

Intl. Union, Security, Police and Fire Professionals of Am. **[23295]**, 25510 Kelly Rd., Roseville, MI 48066, (586)772-7250

Intl. Union, Security, Police and Fire Professionals of Am. **[23295]**, 25510 Kelly Rd., Roseville, MI 48066, (586)772-7250

Intl. Union of Sex Workers **[IO]**, London, United Kingdom

Intl. Union of Shoe Indus. Technicians **[IO]**, Elda, Spain

Intl. Union of Societies of Foresters - Defunct.

Intl. Union of Soil Sciences **[IO]**, Reading, United Kingdom

Intl. Union of Speleology **[IO]**, Prague, Czech Republic

Intl. Union of Students **[IO]**, Prague, Czech Republic

Intl. Union for the Stud. of Social Insects **[6846]**, 105 Northway Rd., Greenbelt, MD 20770, (301)504-5143

Intl. Union for the Stud. of Social Insects **[6846]**, 105 Northway Rd., Greenbelt, MD 20770, (301)504-5143

Intl. Union of Tech. Associations and Organizations **[IO]**, Paris, France

Intl. Union of Tenants **[IO]**, Stockholm, Sweden

Intl. Union of Theoretical and Applied Mechanics **[IO]**, Eindhoven, Netherlands

Intl. Union, United Auto., Aerospace and Agricultural Implement Workers of Am. **[23145]**, 8000 E Jefferson Ave., Solidarity House, Detroit, MI 48214, (313)926-5000

Intl. Union, United Auto., Aircraft, and Agricultural Implement Workers of Am. **[★23145]**

Intl. Union of United Brewery, Flour, Cereal, Soft Drink and Distillery Workers of Am. **[★23158]**

Intl. Union United Mine Workers of Am. **[★23257]**

Intl. Union United Plant Guard Workers of Am. **[★23295]**

Intl. Union United Plant Guard Workers of Am. **[★23295]**

Intl. Union, United Welders **[★23165]**

Intl. Union for Vacuum Sci., Technique and Applications **[IO]**, Chester, United Kingdom

Intl. Univ. Sports Fed. **[IO]**, Brussels, Belgium

Intl. Urban Development Assn. **[IO]**, The Hague, Netherlands

Intl. Utilities Revenue Protection Assn. **[6052]**, Southern Company, 1769 Sands Pl., Marietta, GA 30067, (770)618-5123

Intl. Utilities Revenue Protection Assn. **[6052]**, Southern Company, 1769 Sands Pl., Marietta, GA 30067, (770)618-5123

Intl. VAR Assn. - Defunct.

Intl. Vaulting Club

Intl. Vaulting Club - Address unknown since 2010.

Intl. Vegetarian Union **[IO]**, Altrincham, United Kingdom

International Ventilator Users Network **[★11823]**

Intl. Venture Capital Inst. - Defunct.

Intl. Veterinarians Dedicated to Animal Hea. **[17029]**, PO Box 20246, Boulder, CO 80308-3246

Intl. Veterinary Acupuncture Soc. **[17030]**, 1730 S Coll. Ave., Ste. 301, Fort Collins, CO 80525, (970)266-0666

Intl. Veterinary Acupuncture Soc. **[17030]**, 1730 S Coll. Ave., Ste. 301, Fort Collins, CO 80525, (970)266-0666

Intl. Veterinary Students' Assn. **[IO]**, Frederiksberg, Denmark

Intl. Veterinary Ultrasound Soc. **[17031]**, PO Box 930275, Verona, WI 53593

Intl. Veterinary Ultrasound Soc. **[17031]**, PO Box 930275, Verona, WI 53593

Intl. Video Fed. **[IO]**, Brussels, Belgium

Intl. Vintage Poster Dealers Assn. **[94]**, PO Box 501, New York, NY 10113-0501

Intl. Vintage Poster Dealers Assn. **[94]**, PO Box 501, New York, NY 10113-0501

Intl. Viola Soc. **[IO]**, Auckland, New Zealand

Intl. Virginia Woolf Soc. **[9379]**, Dept. of English, Adjordan Hall, 3800 Lindell Blvd., St. Louis, MO 63108, (314)977-3003

Intl. Virginia Woolf Soc. **[9379]**, Dept. of English, Adjordan Hall, 3800 Lindell Blvd., St. Louis, MO 63108, (314)977-3003

Intl. Virtual Assistants Assn. **[69]**, 375 N Stephanie St., Ste. 1411, Henderson, NV 89014, (702)583-4970

A star before a book entry number signifies that the name is not listed separately, but is mentioned within the entry.

International Visitors Program [★17978]

Intl. Visual Communications Assn. [IO], London, United Kingdom

Intl. Visual Literacy Assn. [8035], Karen Kaminski, Exec. Treas., Colorado State Univ., 213 Educ., Fort Collins, CO 80526

Intl. Visual Literacy Assn. [8035], Karen Kaminski, Exec. Treas., Colorado State Univ., 213 Educ., Fort Collins, CO 80526

Intl. Visual Sociology Assn. [7428], Dee Britton, Treas., 126 Redfield Ave., Fayetteville, NY 13066

Intl. Vladimir Nabokov Soc. [9380], Zoran Kuzmanovich, Pres./Ed., Davidson Coll., English Dept., Davidson, NC 28036

Intl. Vladimir Nabokov Soc. [9380], Zoran Kuzmanovich, Pres./Ed., Davidson Coll., English Dept., Davidson, NC 28036

Intl. Vocational Educ. and Training Assn. [9045], 186 Wedgewood Dr., Mahtomedi, MN 55115, (651)770-6719

Intl. Vocational Educ. and Training Assn. [9045], 186 Wedgewood Dr., Mahtomedi, MN 55115, (651)770-6719

Intl. Volleyball Fed. - Switzerland [IO], Lausanne, Switzerland

Intl. Voluntary Ser. [IO], Edinburgh, United Kingdom

Intl. Voluntary Ser. [★13405]

Intl. Voluntary Ser. [★13405]

Intl. Volunteer Org. for Women, Educ. and Development [IO], Rome, Italy

Intl. Volunteer Prog. [13398], 7106 Sayre Dr., Oakland, CA 94611, (415)477-3667

Intl. Volunteer Prog. [13398], 7106 Sayre Dr., Oakland, CA 94611, (415)477-3667

Intl. Volunteer Programs Assn. [13399], PO Box 287049, New York, NY 10128, (646)505-8209

Intl. Volunteer Programs Assn. [13399], PO Box 287049, New York, NY 10128, (646)505-8209

Intl. Volunteers for Development [IO], Rome, Italy

Intl. Wallcovering Mfrs. Assn. [IO], Brussels, Belgium

Intl. Warehouse Logistics Assn. [3621], 2800 S River Rd., Ste. 260, Des Plaines, IL 60018-6003, (847)813-4699

Intl. Warehouse Logistics Assn. [3621], 2800 S River Rd., Ste. 260, Des Plaines, IL 60018-6003, (847)813-4699

Intl. Warlander Soc. and Registry [4607], 12218 26th Ave. NE, Tulalip, WA 98271

Intl. Warlander Soc. and Registry [4607], 12218 26th Ave. NE, Tulalip, WA 98271

Intl. Watch Collectors Soc. [22165], 257 Adams Ln., Hewlett, NY 11557, (516)295-2516

Intl. Watch Fob Assn. [22166], 601 Patriot Pl., Holmen, WI 54636, (608)385-7237

Intl. Watch Fob Assn. [22166], 601 Patriot Pl., Holmen, WI 54636, (608)385-7237

Intl. Water Assn. [IO], London, United Kingdom

Intl. Water History Assn. [IO], Bergen, Norway

Intl. Water Level Coalition [5004], PO Box 316, Clayton, NY 13624

Intl. Water Lily Soc. [★21806]

Intl. Water Lily Soc. [★21806]

Intl. Water Mgt. Inst. [IO], Colombo, Sri Lanka

Intl. Waterlily and Water Gardening Soc. [21806], 7443 Buffalo Rd., Churchville, NY 14428, (585)293-9144

Intl. Waterlily and Water Gardening Soc. [21806], 7443 Buffalo Rd., Churchville, NY 14428, (585)293-9144

Intl. Waterski and Wakeboard Fed. [IO], Unterageri, Switzerland

Intl. Webcasting Assn.

Intl. Webcasting Assn. - Address unknown since 2011.

Intl. Webmasters Assn. [6542], 119 E Union St., Ste. F, Pasadena, CA 91103, (626)449-3709

Intl. Webmasters Assn. [6542], 119 E Union St., Ste. F, Pasadena, CA 91103, (626)449-3709

Intl. Weed Sci. Soc. [3742], Univ. of Arkansas, Dept. of Crop, Soil, and Environmental Sciences, 1366 W Altheimer Dr., Fayetteville, AR 72704, (479)575-3984

Intl. Weed Sci. Soc. [3742], Univ. of Arkansas, Dept. of Crop, Soil, and Environmental Sciences, 1366 W Altheimer Dr., Fayetteville, AR 72704, (479)575-3984

Intl. Weightlifting Fed. [IO], Budapest, Hungary

Intl. Well Control Forum [IO], Montrose, United Kingdom

Intl. Western Music Assn. [★10312]

Intl. Whaling Commn. [IO], Cambridge, United Kingdom

Intl. Wheat Gluten Assn. [1405], 9300 Metcalf Ave., Ste. 300, Overland Park, KS 66212-6319, (913)381-8180

Intl. Wheat Gluten Assn. [1405], 9300 Metcalf Ave., Ste. 300, Overland Park, KS 66212-6319, (913)381-8180

Intl. Wheelchair and Amputee Sports Fed. [IO], Aylesbury, United Kingdom

Intl. Wheelchair Aviators [20903], 923 W Sherwood Blvd., Big Bear City, CA 92314, (951)529-2644

Intl. Wheelchair Aviators [20903], 923 W Sherwood Blvd., Big Bear City, CA 92314, (951)529-2644

Intl. Wild Waterfowl Assn. [5071], 1111 Hillsboro Cove Cir., Webster, NY 14580

Intl. Wild Waterfowl Assn. [5071], 1111 Hillsboro Cove Cir., Webster, NY 14580

Intl. Wildfowl Carvers Assn. [21449], 194 Summerside Dr., Centralia, WA 98531, (360)736-1082

Intl. Wildfowl Carvers Assn. [21449], 194 Summerside Dr., Centralia, WA 98531, (360)736-1082

Intl. Wildlife Rehabilitation Coun. [5072], PO Box 3197, Eugene, OR 97403, (408)876-6153

Intl. Wildlife Rehabilitation Coun. [5072], PO Box 3197, Eugene, OR 97403, (408)876-6153

Intl. Willow Collectors [21364], 2408 46th St., Des Moines, IA 50310

Intl. Willow Collectors [21364], 2408 46th St., Des Moines, IA 50310

Intl. Window Cleaning Assn. [2252], 400 Admiral Blvd., Kansas City, MO 64106, (816)471-4922

Intl. Window Cleaning Assn. [2252], 400 Admiral Blvd., Kansas City, MO 64106, (816)471-4922

Intl. Window Film Assn. [575], PO Box 3871, Martinsville, VA 24115-3871, (276)666-4932

Intl. Window Film Assn. [575], PO Box 3871, Martinsville, VA 24115-3871, (276)666-4932

Intl. Wine and Food Soc. - London [IO], London, United Kingdom

Intl. Wire and Machinery Assn. [IO], Leamington Spa, United Kingdom

Intl. Wizard of Oz Club [9381], PO Box 2657, Alameda, CA 94501

Intl. Wizard of Oz Club [9381], PO Box 2657, Alameda, CA 94501

Intl. Women Fly Fishers [21736], Rebecca Blair, 6404 Lagunitas Ave., El Cerrito, CA 94530

Intl. Women Fly Fishers [21736], Rebecca Blair, 6404 Lagunitas Ave., El Cerrito, CA 94530

Intl. Women's Anthropology Conf. [6144], New York Univ., Anthropology Dept., 25 Waverly Pl., New York, NY 10003, (212)998-8550

Intl. Women's Anthropology Conf. [6144], New York Univ., Anthropology Dept., 25 Waverly Pl., New York, NY 10003, (212)998-8550

Intl. Women's Coffee Alliance [11601], J.Ganes Consulting, LLC, 6 Old Katonah Dr., Katonah, NY 10536, (914)232-1362

Intl. Women's Coffee Alliance [11601], J.Ganes Consulting, LLC, 6 Old Katonah Dr., Katonah, NY 10536, (914)232-1362

Intl. Women's Fishing Assn. [22580], PO Box 21066, Fort Lauderdale, FL 33335-1066

Intl. Women's Fishing Assn. [22580], PO Box 21066, Fort Lauderdale, FL 33335-1066

Intl. Women's Flag Football Assn. [22589], 25 A 7th Ave., Key West, FL 33040, (305)293-9315

Intl. Women's Forum [13463], 2120 L St. NW, Ste. 460, Washington, DC 20037, (202)387-1010

Intl. Women's Forum [13463], 2120 L St. NW, Ste. 460, Washington, DC 20037, (202)387-1010

Intl. Women's Hea. Coalition [17127], 333 7th Ave., 6th Fl., New York, NY 10001, (212)979-8500

Intl. Women's Hea. Coalition [17127], 333 7th Ave., 6th Fl., New York, NY 10001, (212)979-8500

Intl. Women's Media Found. [3685], 1625 K St. NW, Ste. 1275, Washington, DC 20006, (202)496-1992

Intl. Women's Media Found. [3685], 1625 K St. NW, Ste. 1275, Washington, DC 20006, (202)496-1992

Intl. Women's Rights Action Watch [17844], Univ. of Minnesota, 229-19th Ave. S, Minneapolis, MN 55455, (612)625-4985

Intl. Women's Rights Action Watch [17844], Univ. of Minnesota, 229-19th Ave. S, Minneapolis, MN 55455, (612)625-4985

Intl. Women's Tribune Centre/Women, Ink - Defunct.

Intl. Women's Writing Guild [10724], PO Box 810, Gracie Sta., New York, NY 10028-0082, (212)737-7536

Intl. Women's Writing Guild [10724], PO Box 810, Gracie Sta., New York, NY 10028-0082, (212)737-7536

Intl. Wood Collectors Soc. [22203], 2300 W Rangeline Rd., Greencastle, IN 46135-7875, (765)653-6483

Intl. Wood Products Assn. [1469], 4214 King St., Alexandria, VA 22302, (703)820-6696

Intl. Wood Products Assn. [1469], 4214 King St., Alexandria, VA 22302, (703)820-6696

Intl. Wooden Bow Tie Club [209], 24B Rosemary Ln., Middlefield, CT 06455, (860)349-9328

Intl. Wool Textile Org. [IO], Brussels, Belgium

Intl. Work Gp. for Indigenous Affairs [IO], Copenhagen, Denmark

Intl. Workcamp Org. [IO], Seoul, Republic of Korea

Intl. Workcamps Morocco [IO], Marrakech, Morocco

Intl. World Games Assn. [IO], Hoensbroek, Netherlands

Intl. World Wide Web Conf. Steering Comm. [IO], Hong Kong, People's Republic of China

Intl. Wrought Copper Coun. [IO], London, United Kingdom

Intl. X-Ray Unit Comm. [★7321]

Intl. X-Ray Unit Comm. [★7321]

Intl. Yak Assn. [4694], PO Box 27, Hillside, CO 81232, (719)942-4181

Intl. Yak Assn. [4694], PO Box 27, Hillside, CO 81232, (719)942-4181

Intl. Yang Style Tai Chi Chuan Assn. [22740], PO Box 786, Bothell, WA 98041, (425)869-1185

Intl. Yang Style Tai Chi Chuan Assn. [22740], PO Box 786, Bothell, WA 98041, (425)869-1185

Intl. YMCA [★8382]InternationalIntl. Yoga Soc. 20302

Intl. Yoga Teachers' Assn. [IO], Sydney, Australia

Intl. Young Catholic Students [IO], Paris, France

Intl. Young Christian Workers - Belgium [IO], Brussels, Belgium

Intl. Young Democrat Union [IO], London, United Kingdom

Intl. Youth Assn. [IO], Tallinn, Estonia

Intl. Youth Conditioning Assn. [23139], PO Box 1539, Elizabethtown, KY 42702, (888)366-4922

Intl. Youth Found. [13532], 32 South St., Ste. 500, Baltimore, MD 21202, (410)951-1500

Intl. Youth Found. [13532], 32 South St., Ste. 500, Baltimore, MD 21202, (410)951-1500

Intl. Youth Lib. [IO], Munich, Germany

Intl. Zen Assn. [IO], Paris, France

Intl. Zinc Assn. - America [2476], 1750 K St. NW, Ste. 700, Washington, DC 20006, (202)223-2478

Intl. Zinc Assn. - Belgium [IO], Brussels, Belgium

Intl. Zinc Assn. - Europe [IO], Brussels, Belgium

Internationale Arbeitsgemeinschaft der Papier historiker [★IO]

Internationale Arbeitsgemeinschaft der Wasserwerke im Rheineinzugsgebiet [★IO]

Internationale Arzte-Gesellschaft fur Biophysikalische Informations - Therapie e.V. [★IO]

Internationale Begegnung in Gemeinschaftsdiensten [★IO]

Internationale des Coiffures de Dames [★968]

Internationale Coronelli-Gesellschaft fuer Globenkunde [★IO]

Internationale Democrate Chretienne [★IO]

Internationale Federation des Dachdeckerhandwerks e.V. [★IO]

Internationale Federation Vexillologischer Gesellschaften [★10629]

Internationale Federation Vexillologischer Gesellschaften [★10629]

Internationale Frauenliga fur Frieden und Freiheit [★IO]

Internationale Gesellschaft fur die Geschichte der Pharmazie [★IO]

Internationale Gesellschaft fur Geschichtsdidaktik [★IO]

Reference to "IO" in place of a book number signifies that the association may be found in the 50th edition of International Organizations.

Encyclopedia of Associations, 51st Edition

2931

Internationale Gesellschaft fur Ingenieurpadagogik [★IO]
Internationale Gesellschaft fur Menschenrechte [★IO]
Internationale Gesellschaft fur Musik in der Medizin [★IO]
Internationale Gesellschaft fur Musikwissenschaft [★IO]
Internationale Gesellschaft fur Nutztierhaltung [★IO]
Internationale Gesellschaft fur Warenwissenschaft und Technologie [★IO]
Internationale Gesselschaft Fur Kunst, Gestaltung Und Therapie [★IO]
Internationale Gustav Mahler Gesellschaft [★IO]
Internationale Hegel-Gesellschaft [IO], Berlin, Germany
Internationale Hegel-Vereinigung [IO], Heidelberg, Germany
Internationale Heinrich Schutz-Gesellschaft [★IO]
Internationale Jugendbibliothek [★IO]
Internationale Kolpingwerk [★IO]
Internationale Kommission fur Alpines Rettungswesen [★IO]
Internationale Kommission fur Geschichte der Geologischen Wissenschaften [★IO]
Internationale Kommission zum Schutz des Rheins [★IO]
Internationale de l'Education [★IO]
Internationale Liberale [★IO]
Internationale Messtechnische Konfoderation [★IO]
Internationale Organisatie voor Migratie in Nederland [★IO]
Internationale Org. fur Sukkulenten-Forschung [★IO]
Internationale Orientierungslauf Foderation [★IO]
Internationale Paneuropa Union [★IO]
Internationale Raiffeisen Union [★IO]
Internationale des Resistants a la Guerre [★IO]
Internationale Sektion der IVSS fur die Verhutung von Arbeitsunfallen und Berufskrankheiten durch Elektrizitat-Gas-Fernwarme-Wasser [★IO]
Internationale des Services Publics [★IO]
Internationale Socialiste des Femmes [★IO]
Internationale Studiengemeinschaft fur Pranatale und Perinatale Psychologie und Medizin [★IO]
Internationale Tagung der Historikerinnen der Arbeiter-und anderer sozialer Bewegungen [★IO]
Internationale Terminologienetz [★IO]
Internationale Union der Lebensmittel, Landwirtschafts, Hotel, Restaurant, Cafe und Genussmittelarbeiter-Gewerkschaften [★IO]
Internationale Vereinigung fur Bruckenbau und Hochbau [★IO]
Internationale Vereinigung der Schall-und Audiovisuellen Archv. [★IO]
Internationale Vereinigung fur Schul-und Berufsberatung [★IO]
Internationale Vereinigung Sport- und Freizeiteinrichtungen [★IO]
Internationale Vereinigung van Telecommunicatiegebruikers [★IO]
Internationale Vereinigung fur Vegetationskunde [★IO]
Internationale Vereniging voor Neerlandistiek [★IO]
Internationale Versohnungsbund [★IO]
Internationale Vredesbrigades Belgie [★IO]
Internationalen Rat der Christen und Juden [★IO]
Internationalen Wissenschaftlichen Vereinigung Weltwirtschaft und Weltpolitik, e.V. [★IO]
Internationaler Arbeitskreis fur Musik [★IO]
Internationaler Arbeitskreis Systematische und Vergleichende Musikwissenschaft [★IO]
Internationaler Bauorden [★IO]
Internationaler Bund der Konfessionslosen und Atheisten [★IO]
Internationaler Christlicher Friedensdienst [★IO]
Internationaler Draht- und Maschinenverband [★IO]
Internationaler Kunstkritikerverband Sektion Deutschland [★IO]
Internationaler Suchdienst [★IO]
Internationaler Verband des Erwerbsgartenbaues [★IO]
Internationaler Versohnungsbund - Osterreichischer Zweig [★IO]
Internationales Design Zentrum Berlin [★IO]
Internationales Forschungsinstitut fur Medien, Kommunikation und Kulturelle Entwicklung [★IO]

Internationales Institut fur Jugendliteratur und Leseforschung [★IO]
Internationales Institut fur Nationalitatenrecht und Regionalismus [★IO]
Internationales Katholisches Missionswerk [★IO]
Internationales Komitte fur die Indianer Amerikas [★IO]
Internationales Musik Medienzentrum [★IO]
Internationales Theater-Institut, Zentrum Schweiz [★IO]
Internationalle Gesellschaft fur Erzieherische Hilfen [★IO]
Internationella Kvinnoforbundet for Fred och Frihet [★IO]

Internet
Advanced Media Workflow Assn. [3386]
Anti-Child Pornography Org. [12710]
Coalition Against Domain Name Abuse [7006]
Consumer Web Watch [17455]
Cooperative Assn. for Internet Data Anal. [7007]
CyberAngels [12387]
Enough Is Enough [17995]
Ethernet Alliance [7499]
InCommon [6537]
Interactive Media Entertainment and Gaming Assn. [7008]
InterConnection [11664]InternetIntl. Assn. of Webmasters and Designers
Internet Commerce Assn. [2116]
Internet Keep Safe Coalition [17996]
Internet Merchants Assn. [2117]
Internet Sexuality Info. Services [8861]
Natl. Coalition for Telecommunications Educ. and Learning [8981]
Online Trust Alliance [6550]
Pro vs. GI Joe [21762]
SailMail Assn. [6679]
SavetheInternet.com Coalition [17997]
Top Level Domain Assn. [2118]
Virtual Private Network Consortium [2119]
Virtual Private Network Consortium [2119]
VON Coalition [2120]
Web Analytics Assn. [7009]

Internet Advt. Bur. [IO], London, United Kingdom
Internet Alliance [678], Tammy Cota, Exec. Dir., 1615 L St. NW, Ste. 1100, Washington, DC 20036-5624, (202)861-2407
Internet Alliance [678], Tammy Cota, Exec. Dir., 1615 L St. NW, Ste. 1100, Washington, DC 20036-5624, (202)861-2407
Internet Assn. Japan [IO], Tokyo, Japan
Internet Bus. Alliance [3396], PO Box 11518, Seattle, WA 98110-5518
Internet Business Assn. Intl. - Defunct.
Internet Commerce Assn. [2116], 161 First St., 4th Fl., Cambridge, MA 02142
Internet Content Rating Assn. [★11920]
Internet Content Rating Assn. [★11920]
Internet Corp. for Assigned Names and Numbers [6543], 4676 Admiralty Way, Ste. 330, Marina del Rey, CA 90292, (310)823-9358
Internet Fraud Watch; National Fraud Information Center/ [17467]
Internet Indus. Assn. [IO], Manuka, Australia
Internet Indus. Assn; U.S. [6521]
Internet Infidels [10394], PO Box 142, Colorado Springs, CO 80901-0142, (877)501-5113
Internet Keep Safe Coalition [17996], 1401 K St. NW, Ste. 600, Washington, DC 20005, (202)587-5583
Internet Local Advt. and Commerce Assn. [★678]
Internet Local Advt. and Commerce Assn. [★678]
Internet Local Advertising and Commerce Assn. - Defunct.
Internet Merchants Assn. [2117], 11792 Osprey Pointe Cir., Wellington, FL 33449, (561)615-1461
Internet and Mobile Assn. of India [IO], Mumbai, India
Internet Professional Assn. [IO], Hong Kong, People's Republic of China
Internet Ser. Providers Assn. [IO], Parklands, Republic of South Africa
Internet Ser. Providers Assn. of Bangladesh [IO], Dhaka, Bangladesh
Internet Ser. Providers Assn. of India [IO], New Delhi, India

Internet Sexuality Info. Services [8861], 409 13th St., 14th Fl., Oakland, CA 94612-2607, (510)835-9400
Internet Soc. [6544], 1775 Wiehle Ave., Ste. 201, Reston, VA 20190-5158, (703)439-2120
Internet Soc. [6544], 1775 Wiehle Ave., Ste. 201, Reston, VA 20190-5158, (703)439-2120
Internet Soc. of Australia [IO], Sydney, Australia
Internet Soc. of China [IO], Beijing, People's Republic of China
Internet Soc. Nederland [IO], The Hague, Netherlands
Internet Soc. of New Zealand [IO], Wellington, New Zealand
Internet Software Consortium [★6490]
Internet Streaming Media Alliance - Address unknown since 2010.
Internet Systems Consortium [6490], 950 Charter St., Redwood City, CA 94063, (650)423-1300
Internet Telephony Services Providers' Assn. [IO], London, United Kingdom
Internews Network [18090], PO Box 4448, Arcata, CA 95518-4448, (707)826-2030
Internews Network [18090], PO Box 4448, Arcata, CA 95518-4448, (707)826-2030
InterNICHE [IO], Leicester, United Kingdom
Interns for Peace - Address unknown since 2010.
Interoffice Basketball League [IO], Belize City, Belize
INTERPAVE [IO], Leicester, United Kingdom
Interplast [14185], 857 Maude Ave., Mountain View, CA 94043, (650)962-0123
Interplast [★14185]
INTERPRED - World Trade Center Sofia [IO], Sofia, Bulgaria
Interpretation Mgt. Institute [★7142]
InterPride [12094], PO Box 66071, Houston, TX 77266-6071
InterPride [12094], PO Box 66071, Houston, TX 77266-6071
Interprofessional Fostering of Ophthalmic Care for Underserved Sectors [17090], 24914 Kuykendahl Rd., Ste. D, Tomball, TX 77375-3381, (281)398-7525

Interracial
Interracial Family Circle [12012]
Interracial-InterCultural Pride [12013]

Interracial Family Circle [12012], 4923 E Chalk Point Rd., West River, MD 20778
Interracial-InterCultural Pride [12013], PO Box 11811, Berkeley, CA 94712-2811, (510)759-8550
Interregional Assn. for Clinical Microbiology and Antimicrobial Chemotherapy [IO], Smolensk, Russia
Interreligious Found. for Community Org. [11656], 418 W 145th St., New York, NY 10031, (212)926-5757
Interreligious and Intl. Fed. for World Peace [★18298]
Interreligious and Intl. Fed. for World Peace [★18298]
Interrogator Translator Teams Assn; Marine Corps [19123]
Interscience Res. Inst. [★13704]
Intersections [IO], Pago Pago, American Samoa
InterServe U.S.A. [20054], PO Box 418, Upper Darby, PA 19082-0418, (800)809-4440
InterServe U.S.A. [20054], PO Box 418, Upper Darby, PA 19082-0418, (800)809-4440
Interservice Sports Comm. [★5799]
Interservice Sports Coun. [★5799]
Intersex Soc. of North Am.
Intersex Soc. of North Am. - Defunct.
Intersocietal Commn. for the Accreditation of Vascular Labs. [16962], 6021 Univ. Blvd., Ste. 500, Ellicott City, MD 21043, (800)838-2110
Intersociety Commn. for Heart Disease Resources [★14002]
Intersociety Comm. on Pathology Info. [★16128]
Intersociety Coun. for Pathology Info. [16128], 9650 Rockville Pike, Bethesda, MD 20814-3993, (301)634-7200
Interspecies [7010], 301 Hidden Meadows Ln., Friday Harbor, WA 98250
Interspecies [7010], 301 Hidden Meadows Ln., Friday Harbor, WA 98250

A star before a book entry number signifies that the name is not listed separately, but is mentioned within the entry.

Interspecies Commun. [★7010]
Interspecies Commun. [★7010]
Interspecies Communication
  Interspecies [7010]
  Interspecies [7010]
Interstate Club [20904], PO Box 127, Blakesburg, IA 52536
Interstate Compact for Education [★8019]
Interstate Conf. of Employment Security Agencies [★5401]
Interstate Conf. of Unemployment Compensation Agencies [★5401]
Interstate Conf. on Water Policy [★5862]
Interstate Cotton Seed Crushers' Assn. [★2587]
Interstate Coun. on Water Policy [5862], 51 Monroe St., Ste. PE-08A, Rockville, MD 20850, (301)984-1908
Interstate Dental Assn. [★14301]
Interstate Migrant Educ. Coun. [12521], 1 Massachusetts Ave., Ste. 700, Washington, DC 20001, (202)336-7078
Interstate Migrant Educ. Task Force [★12521]
Interstate Mining Compact Commn. [5840], 445-A Carlisle Dr., Herndon, VA 20170, (703)709-8654
Interstate Natural Gas Assn. of Am. [4489], 20 F St. NW, Ste. 450, Washington, DC 20001, (202)216-5900
Interstate Oil Compact Commn. [★5405]
Interstate Oil and Gas Compact Commn. [5405], PO Box 53127, Oklahoma City, OK 73152-3127, (405)525-3556
Interstate Postgraduate Medical Assn. of North Am. [14525], PO Box 5474, Madison, WI 53705, (608)231-9045
Interstate Producers Livestock Assn. [★4725]
Interstate Renewable Energy Coun. [6736], PO Box 1156, Latham, NY 12110-0079, (518)458-6059
Interstate Rodeo Assn. [★22841]
Interstate Towing Assn. - Defunct.
Interstate Trolley Club of New York [★10493]
Interstitial Cystitis Assn. [16945], 100 Park Ave., Ste. 108A, Rockville, MD 20850, (800)435-7422
Intersure [★1987]
Intersure - Singer Nelson Charlmers [1987], PO Box 16, Teaneck, NJ 07666, (201)837-1100
INTERTECT [★5308]
INTERTECT [★5308]
INTERTEL [9640], PO Box 5518, Douglasville, GA 30154, (678)838-7979
Intertribal Bison Cooperative [4729], 2497 W Chicago St., Rapid City, SD 57702, (605)394-9730
Intertribal Deaf Coun. [10330], PO Box 181, Clayton, DE 19938, (971)239-5697
Interuniversity Consortium for Political Res. [★7288]
Interval Intl. [21854], PO Box 431920, Miami, FL 33243-1920, (305)666-1884
Interval Intl. [21854], PO Box 431920, Miami, FL 33243-1920, (305)666-1884
InterVarsity Link [8919], PO Box 7895, Madison, WI 53707-7895, (608)274-9001
InterVarsity Link [8919], PO Box 7895, Madison, WI 53707-7895, (608)274-9001
Intervenor Org. of Ontario [IO], Toronto, ON, Canada
Intervention and Coiled Tubing Assn. [7276], PO Box 1082, Montgomery, TX 77356, (936)520-1549
Interweave Continental: Unitarian Universalists for Lesbian, Gay, Bisexual and Transgender Concerns [19794], 45 State St., No. 380, Montpelier, VT 05602
Intimate Apparel Mfrs. Assn. - Defunct.
Intimate Apparel Square Club [12052], 326 Field Rd., Clinton Corners, NY 12514, (845)758-5752
Into Your Hands [12967], PO Box 3981, Evergreen, CO 80437, (720)810-2837
InTouch Networks - Address unknown since 2010.
IntraHealth Intl. [14881], 6340 Quadrangle Dr., Ste. 200, Chapel Hill, NC 27517, (919)313-9100
Intravenous Nurses Soc. [★16853]
Intrax Cultural Exchange [8203], 600 California St., 10th Fl., San Francisco, CA 94108, (415)434-1221
Intrax Cultural Exchange [8203], 600 California St., 10th Fl., San Francisco, CA 94108, (415)434-1221
Inuit Art Found. [IO], Ottawa, ON, Canada
Inuit Circumpolar Coun. - Greenland [IO], Nuuk, Greenland

Inuit Issittormiut Siunnersuisoqatigiifiat [★IO]
Invasive Species Specialist Gp. [IO], Auckland, New Zealand
Invention Marketing Inst. [★7012]
Inventors
  Amer. Soc. of Inventors [7011]
  Intl. Fed. of Inventors' Associations [20224]
  Inventors Assistance League [7012]
  Inventors Workshop Intl. [5574]
  Natl. Cong. of Inventors Organizations [7013]
  Natl. Inventors Found. [7014]
  United Inventors Assn. of the U.S.A. [7015]
Inventors Assistance League [7012], 1053 Colorado Blvd., Ste. G1, Los Angeles, CA 90041, (818)246-6542
Inventors Workshop Intl. [5574], PO Box 285, Santa Barbara, CA 93102-0285, (805)879-1729
Inventors Workshop Intl. [5574], PO Box 285, Santa Barbara, CA 93102-0285, (805)879-1729
Inventrepreneurs' Forum - Defunct.
Inverell and District Olive Growers Assn. [IO], Inverell, Australia
InvesteringsForeningsRadet [★IO]
Investigation
  Assn. of Certified Background Investigators [5594]
  Assn. of Christian Investigators [5595]
  Assn. of Former Agents of the U.S. Secret Ser. [5596]
  Assn. of Former Intelligence Officers [5597]
  Assn. of Former Intelligence Officers [5597]
  Coun. of Intl. Investigators [2121]
  Coun. of Intl. Investigators [2121]
  Fed. Law Enforcement Officers Assn. [5598]
  High Tech. Crime Investigation Assn. Intl. [5599]
  High Tech. Crime Investigation Assn. Intl. [5599]
  InfraGard Natl. Members Alliance [5968]
  Intl. Assn. of Financial Crimes Investigators [5600]
  Intl. Assn. of Financial Crimes Investigators [5600]
  Intl. Assn. of Independent Private Sector Inspectors Gen. [5546]
  Intl. Assn. of Law Enforcement Intelligence Analysts [5601]
  Intl. Assn. of Law Enforcement Intelligence Analysts [5601]
  Intl. Assn. of Property Crime Investigators [5602]
  Intl. Assn. of Security and Investigative Regulators [2122]
  Intl. Forensic Entomology Detection Canine Assn. [5489]
  Intl. Homicide Investigators Assn. [5603]
  Intl. Homicide Investigators Assn. [5603]
  Intl. Intelligence Ethics Assn. [7001]
  Intl. Latino Gang Investigator's Assn. [5604]
  Intl. Latino Gang Investigator's Assn. [5604]
  ION [2123]
  Natl. Assn. of Investigative Specialists [2124]
  Natl. Assn. of Legal Investigators [5605]
  Natl. Assn. of Legal Search Consultants [2125]
  Natl. Assn. of Property Recovery Investigators [5606]
  Natl. Assn. of Property Recovery Investigators [5606]
  Natl. Assn. of Traffic Accident Reconstructionists and Investigators [5607]
  Natl. Defender Investigator Assn. [5608]
  Natl. Military Intelligence Assn. [5609]
  Professional Soc. of Forensic Mapping [5490]
  Soc. of Professional Investigators [5610]
  World Investigators Network [2126]
  World Investigators Network [2126]
Investigative Open Network [★2123]
Investigative Reporters and Editors [2837], Missouri School of Journalism, 141 Neff Annex, Columbia, MO 65211, (573)882-2042
Investigative Reporters and Editors [2837], Missouri School of Journalism, 141 Neff Annex, Columbia, MO 65211, (573)882-2042
Investigators Anywhere Rsrc. Line [★2123]
Investment Adviser Assn. [3199], 1050 17th St. NW, Ste. 725, Washington, DC 20036-5514, (202)293-4222
Investment Bankers Assn. of Am. [★3206]
Investment Bankers Conf. [★3198]
Investment Casting Inst. [1835], 136 Summit Ave., Montvale, NJ 07645-1720, (201)573-9770

Investment Casting Inst. [1835], 136 Summit Ave., Montvale, NJ 07645-1720, (201)573-9770
Investment Company Inst. [3200], 1401 H St. NW, Ste. 1200, Washington, DC 20005, (202)326-5800
Investment Counsel Assn. of Am. [★3199]
Investment Educ. Inst. [8187], PO Box 220, Royal Oak, MI 48068, (248)583-6242
Investment and Financial Services Assn. [IO], Sydney, Australia
Investment Funds Inst. of Canada [IO], Toronto, ON, Canada
Investment Mgt. Assn. [IO], London, United Kingdom
Investment Mgt. Assn. of Singapore [IO], Singapore, Singapore
Investment Mgt. Consultants Assn. [2138], 5619 DTC Pkwy., Ste. 500, Greenwood Village, CO 80111, (303)770-3377
Investment Mgt. Consultants Assn. [2138], 5619 DTC Pkwy., Ste. 500, Greenwood Village, CO 80111, (303)770-3377
Investment Partnership Prog. [★2139]
Investment Prog. Assn. [2139], PO Box 480, Ellicott City, MD 21041-0480, (212)812-9799
Investment Recovery Assn. [3369], 638 W 39th St., Kansas City, MO 64111-2910, (816)561-5323
Investment Savings and Insurance Assn. [IO], Wellington, New Zealand
Investment Trusts Assn. [IO], Tokyo, Japan
Investments
  Alternative Investments Compliance Assn. [2127]
  Amer. Assn. of Professional Tech. Analysts [3387]
  Angel Capital Assn. [2128]
  Armenian Amer. Chamber of Commerce [23352]
  Assn. of Asian Amer. Investment Managers [2129]
  Assn. of Foreign Investors in Real Estate [2130]
  Assn. of Foreign Investors in Real Estate [2130]
  Assn. of Investment Mgt. Sales Executives [2131]
  Brazil-U.S. Bus. Coun. [23354]
  Brazilian Govt. Trade Bur. of the Consulate Gen. of Brazil in New York [23335]
  British Trade Off. at Consulate-General [23336]
  Center for Venture Res. [2132]
  CFA Inst. [2133]
  CFA Inst. [2133]
  Chartered Alternative Investment Analyst Assn. [2134]
  Financial Publishers Assn. [2934]
  Global Grassroots [13497]
  Global India Venture Capital Assn. [1302]
  Govt. Investment Officers Assn. [5611]
  Hedge Fund Assn. [2135]
  Hedge Fund Assn. [2135]
  Hedge Fund Bus. Operations Assn. [2136]
  Indus. Asset Mgt. Coun. [3014]
  Intl. Assn. of Space Entrepreneurs [139]
  Intl. Swaps and Derivatives Assn. [2137]
  Investment Mgt. Consultants Assn. [2138]
  Investment Mgt. Consultants Assn. [2138]
  Investment Prog. Assn. [2139]
  Investorside Res. Assn. [2140]
  Iraqi Amer. Chamber of Commerce and Indus. [23370]InvestmentsIrish Assn. of Investment Managers
  Korean Amer. Soc. of Entrepreneurs [718]
  Managed Funds Assn. [23410]
  Middle East Investment Initiative [1313]
  Natl. Assn. of Govt. Defined Contribution Administrators [2141]
  Natl. Assn. of Investment Professionals [2142]
  Natl. Assn. of Investors Corp. [2143]
  Natl. Assn. of Publicly Traded Partnerships [2144]
  Natl. Coalition for Capital [1058]
  Natl. Coun. of Real Estate Investment Fiduciaries [2145]
  Natl. Investment Company Ser. Assn. [2146]
  Natl. Investor Relations Inst. [2147]
  Natl. Real Estate Investors Assn. [2148]
  Natl. United States-Arab Chamber of Commerce [23374]
  Natl. Venture Capital Assn. [2149]
  Pakistan Chamber of Commerce USA [23435]
  Professional Assn. for Investment Communications Resources [2150]
  Romanian-U.S. Bus. Coun. [23438]
  South African USA Chamber of Commerce [23379]

Reference to "IO" in place of a book number signifies that the association may be found in the 50th edition of International Organizations.

Encyclopedia of Associations, 51st Edition   **2933**

Stable Value Investment Assn. [2151]
Swedish Trade Coun. [3489]
Turkish-American Chamber of Commerce and Indus. [23455]
Investor Relations Soc. [IO], London, United Kingdom
Investorside Res. Assn. [2140], Argus Res., 61 Broadway, Ste. 1700, New York, NY 10006, (877)834-4777
Invisible Children [17237], 1620 5th Ave., Ste. 400, San Diego, CA 92101, (619)562-2799
Involvement and Participation Assn. [IO], London, United Kingdom
Inyana - League of Rwandan Children and Youth [11474], 230 Sunset Ridge, Rocky Hill, CT 06067
IOCALUM [23086], 597 State Hwy. 162, Sprakers, NY 12166-4008, (518)673-3212
ION [2123], 4548 Jones Rd., Oak Harbor, WA 98277, (360)279-8343
IoP: The Packaging Soc. [IO], Grantham, United Kingdom
Iota Lambda Sigma [23758], 607 Parkway W, Oregon, OH 43616, (419)693-6860
Iota Phi Lambda [23482], 1761 S St. NW, Ste. LL3, Washington, DC 20009, (202)462-4628
Iota Sigma Pi [23490], Angelo State Univ., Dept. of Chemistry & Biochemistry, Cavness Sci. Bldg., Rm. 204B, San Angelo, TX 76909-0892, (325)486-6662
Iowa Mountaineers - Defunct.
Iowa Wesleyan Coll. Alumni Assn. [18876], 601 N Main St., Mount Pleasant, IA 52641, (800)582-2383
IP Fed. [IO], London, United Kingdom
IP Justice [5575], 1192 Haight St., San Francisco, CA 94117, (415)553-6261
The IPA Assn. of Am. [16266], 2350 Saddlesprings Dr., Milton, GA 30004, (510)967-7305
IPA - Assn. of Graphic Solutions Providers [6934], 7200 France Ave. S, Ste. 223, Edina, MN 55435, (952)896-1908
IPA - Assn. of Graphic Solutions Providers [6934], 7200 France Ave. S, Ste. 223, Edina, MN 55435, (952)896-1908
Ipas [16588], PO Box 5027, Chapel Hill, NC 27514, (919)967-7052
IPC - Assn. Connecting Electronics Indus. [1106], 3000 Lakeside Dr., 309 S, Bannockburn, IL 60015, (847)615-7100
IPREX - Address unknown since 2010.
IPS - Inter Press Ser. Intl. Assn. [IO], Rome, Italy
Iqbal Acad. Pakistan [IO], Lahore, Pakistan
IQNet Assn. - Intl. Certification Network [IO], Bern, Switzerland
Iracambi Rainforest Conservation and Res. Center [IO], Rosario da Limeira, Brazil
Irakiska Riksforbundet i Sverige [★IO]
Iran
Assn. of Professors and Scholars of Iranian Heritage [8411]
Iran Democratic Union [17845]
Iran Policy Comm. [17998]
Iranian Amer. Psychological Assn. [16406]
United Against Nuclear Iran [18218]
Iran Advt. Agencies Assn. [IO], Tehran, Iran
Iran and Belgium Chamber of Commerce and Indus. [IO], Tehran, Iran
Iran Blind Learned and Univ. Students Scientific-Cultural Soc. [IO], Tehran, Iran
Iran Composites Assn. [IO], Tehran, Iran
Iran Democratic Union [17845], PO Box 61551, Potomac, MD 20859-1551, (202)618-1438
Iran Freedom Found. [18001], PO Box 34422, Bethesda, MD 20827, (301)215-6677
Iran Freedom Found. [18001], PO Box 34422, Bethesda, MD 20827, (301)215-6677
Iran Interior Mission [★20023]
Iran Interior Mission [★20023]
Iran Lead and Zinc Indus. and Mines Assn. [IO], Tehran, Iran
Iran Logistics Soc. [IO], Tehran, Iran
Iran Nanotechnology Initiative Coun. [IO], Tehran, Iran
Iran-Netherlands Bus. Coun. [IO], Tehran, Iran
Iran Policy Comm. [17998], 3700 Massachusetts Ave. NW, Ste. 507, Washington, DC 20016, (202)333-7346

Iran Proj. Mgt. Assn. [IO], Tehran, Iran
Iran School Sport Fed. [IO], Tehran, Iran
Iran Soc. of Biophysical Chemistry [IO], Tehran, Iran
Iran Sport for All Fed. [IO], Tehran, Iran
Iran Squash Fed. [IO], Tehran, Iran
Iran Taekwondo Union [IO], Tehran, Iran
Iran Traditional Karate and Kobudo Assn. [IO], Tehran, Iran
Iran Vehicle Mfrs'. Assn. [IO], Tehran, Iran
Iranian
30 Years After [17999]
30 Years After [17999]
Amer. Inst. of Iranian Stud. [9880]
Amer. Inst. of Iranian Stud. [9880]
Amer. Iranian Coun. [18000]
Assn. of Professors and Scholars of Iranian Heritage [8411]
Assn. for the Stud. of Persianate Societies [8412]
Intl. Qajar Stud. Assn. [9881]
Intl. Soc. for Iranian Culture [9882]
Intl. Soc. for Iranian Culture [9882]
Intl. Soc. for Iranian Culture [9882]
Iran Freedom Found. [18001]
Iran Freedom Found. [18001]
Iran Policy Comm. [17998]
Iranian Alliances Across Borders [19069]
Iranian Amer. Psychological Assn. [16406]
Natl. Coalition of Pro-Democracy Advocates [17526]
Natl. Iranian Amer. Coun. [19070]
Public Affairs of Iranian Americans [18002]
Soc. of Iranian Architects and Planners [6206]
Iranian Accounting Assn. [IO], Tehran, Iran
Iranian Alliances Across Borders [19069], PO Box 20429, New York, NY 10009
Iranian Amer. Bar Assn. [5256], 1025 Connecticut Ave. NW, Ste. 1012, Washington, DC 20036, (202)828-1217
Iranian Amer. Medical Assn. [15421], PO Box 8218, Haledon, NJ 07538, (973)595-8888
Iranian Amer. Psychological Assn. [16406], 3580 Wilshire Blvd., Ste. 2000, Los Angeles, CA 90010, (213)381-1250
Iranian Assn. of Clinical Lab. Doctors [IO], Tehran, Iran
Iranian Assn. for Energy Economics [IO], Tehran, Iran
Iranian Assn. of Gastroenterology and Hepatology [IO], Tehran, Iran
Iranian Assn. of Medical, Dental and Lab Equip. Mfrs. [IO], Tehran, Iran
Iranian Assn. of Tech. Designers and Stage Executants of Cinema [IO], Tehran, Iran
Iranian Assn. of Water and Wastewater Experts [IO], Tehran, Iran
Iranian Blood Transfusion Org. [IO], Tehran, Iran
Iranian Bus. Coun. - Dubai [IO], Dubai, United Arab Emirates
Iranian Ceramic Soc. [IO], Tehran, Iran
Iranian Cheetah Soc. [IO], Tehran, Iran
Iranian Chemists' Assn. of the Amer. Chem. Soc. [6412], 35 Meadowbrook Ln., Woodbury, CT 06798, (203)573-3220
Iranian Counseling Assn. [IO], Tehran, Iran
Iranian Documentary Filmmakers Assn. [IO], Tehran, Iran
Iranian Earthquake Engg. Assn. [IO], Tehran, Iran
Iranian Geotechnical Subcomm. [IO], Tehran, Iran
Iranian Graphic Designers Soc. [IO], Tehran, Iran
Iranian Heart Assn. [IO], Tehran, Iran
Iranian Homeopathic Assn. [IO], Tehran, Iran
Iranian Institutional Investors Assn. [IO], Tehran, Iran
Iranian Intl. Stud. Assn. [IO], Tehran, Iran
Iranian Lighting Mfrs. Assn. [IO], Tehran, Iran
Iranian Medical Informatics Assn. [IO], Tehran, Iran
Iranian Medical Laser Assn. [IO], Tehran, Iran
Iranian Medical Lib. and Info. Sci. Assn. [IO], Tehran, Iran
Iranian Muslim Assn. of North Am. [20133], 3376 Motor Ave., Los Angeles, CA 90034, (310)202-8181
Iranian Muslim Assn. of North Am. [20133], 3376 Motor Ave., Los Angeles, CA 90034, (310)202-8181
Iranian Neurological Soc. [IO], Tehran, Iran

Iranian Pain Soc. [IO], Tehran, Iran
Iranian Physiotherapy Assn. [IO], Tehran, Iran
Iranian Privatization Org. [IO], Tehran, Iran
Iranian Proteomics Soc. [IO], Karaj, Iran
Iranian Red Crescent [IO], Tehran, Iran
Iranian Refugees' Alliance [12784], Cooper Sta., PO Box 316, New York, NY 10276-0316, (212)260-7460
Iranian Refugees' Alliance [12784], Cooper Sta., PO Box 316, New York, NY 10276-0316, (212)260-7460
Iranian Soc. of Clinical Cytology [IO], Isfahan, Iran
Iranian Soc. of Colposcopy and Cervical Pathology [IO], Tehran, Iran
Iranian Soc. of Consulting Engineers [IO], Tehran, Iran
Iranian Soc. of Environmentalists [IO], Tehran, Iran
Iranian Soc. of Fertility and Sterility [IO], Tehran, Iran
Iranian Soc. for Green Mgt. [IO], Tehran, Iran
Iranian Soc. for Indus. and Applied Mathematics [IO], Tehran, Iran
Iranian Soc. of Pediatric Cardiology [IO], Tehran, Iran
Iranian Soc. of Pediatric Surgeons [IO], Tehran, Iran
Iranian Soc. of Physiology and Pharmacology [IO], Tehran, Iran
Iranian Soc. for Quality [IO], Tehran, Iran
Iranian Soc. of Toxicology [IO], Tehran, Iran
Iranian Statistical Soc. [IO], Tehran, Iran
Iranian Taekwondo Assn. [IO], Tehran, Iran
Iranian Tour Operators Assn. [IO], Tehran, Iran
Iranian Trade Assn. [2084], PO Box 927743, San Diego, CA 92192, (619)368-6790
Iranian Trade Assn. [2084], PO Box 927743, San Diego, CA 92192, (619)368-6790
Iranian Tunnelling Assn. [IO], Tehran, Iran
Iran's Assn. of Flour Producers [IO], Tehran, Iran
Iraq
Educ. for Peace in Iraq Center [18003]
Environmentalists Against War [18777]
Generation Iraq [12388]
Iraq Action Coalition [18004]
Iraq Action Coalition [18004]
Iraqi Amer. Chamber of Commerce and Indus. [23370]
Iraqi Christian Relief Coun. [12857]
Iraqi Human Rights Network [17846]
Iraqi Medical Sciences Assn. [15193]
JumpStart Intl. [11605]
Musical Missions of Peace [10352]
Natl. Org. of Iraqi Christians [12630]
Preemptive Love Coalition [14040]
Win Without War [18178]
Iraq Action Coalition [18004], 7309 Haymarket Ln., Raleigh, NC 27615
Iraq Action Coalition [18004], 7309 Haymarket Ln., Raleigh, NC 27615
Iraq and Afghanistan Veterans of Am. [20791], 292 Madison Ave., 10th Fl., New York, NY 10017, (212)982-9699
Iraq Occupation Focus [IO], London, United Kingdom
Iraq Soc. Against Epilepsy [IO], Baghdad, Iraq
Iraq Veterans Against the War [20842], PO Box 3565, New York, NY 10008-3561, (646)723-0989
Iraqi Amateur Athletic Fed. [IO], Baghdad, Iraq
Iraqi Amateur Radio Soc. [IO], Baghdad, Iraq
Iraqi Amer. Chamber of Commerce and Indus. [23370], 15265 Maturin Dr., No. 184, San Diego, CA 92127, (858)613-9215
Iraqi Amer. Chamber of Commerce and Indus. [23370], 15265 Maturin Dr., No. 184, San Diego, CA 92127, (858)613-9215
Iraqi Artists Assn. [9238], PO Box 1011, Hazel Park, MI 48030
Iraqi Assn. [IO], London, United Kingdom
Iraqi Badminton Fed. [IO], Baghdad, Iraq
Iraqi Christian Relief Coun. [12857], PO Box 3021, Glenview, IL 60025, (847)401-8846
Iraqi Fertility Soc. [IO], Baghdad, Iraq
Iraqi Human Rights Network [17846], 23902 Ann Arbor Trail, Dearborn Heights, MI 48127, (313)730-0821
Iraqi Human Rights Network [17846], 23902 Ann Arbor Trail, Dearborn Heights, MI 48127, (313)730-0821

A star before a book entry number signifies that the name is not listed separately, but is mentioned within the entry.

Iraqi Medical Assn. [IO], Baghdad, Iraq
Iraqi Medical Sciences Assn. [15193], PO Box 1154, Libertyville, IL 60048
Iraqi Medical Sciences Assn. [15193], PO Box 1154, Libertyville, IL 60048
Iraqi Natl. Paralympic Comm. [IO], Baghdad, Iraq
Iraqi Powerlifting Fed. [IO], Baghdad, Iraq
Iraqi Red Crescent Soc. [IO], Baghdad, Iraq
Iraqi Reproductive Hea. and Family Planning Assn. [IO], Baghdad, Iraq
Iraqi Taekwondo Fed. [IO], Baghdad, Iraq
Iraqi Tennis Fed. [IO], Baghdad, Iraq
Iraqi Widows Org. [IO], Al Diwaniyah, Iraq
IRC Centre Intl. de l'Eau et l'Assainissement [★IO]
IRC Intl. Water and Sanitation Centre [IO], The Hague, Netherlands
IRCDA/SDA [★6556]
Ireland
   Amer. Ireland Fund [18005]
   Amer. Ireland Fund [18005]
   Doors of Hope [18006]
   Doors of Hope [18006]
   Irish Natl. Caucus [18007]
   Irish Natl. Caucus [18007]
   Irish Northern Aid [18008]
   Ulster-Scots Soc. of Am. [20664]
Ireland Chamber of Commerce U.S.A. [23371], Larry Handeli, Exec. Dir., 556 Central Ave., New Providence, NJ 07974, (908)286-1300
Ireland Chamber of Commerce U.S.A. [23371], Larry Handeli, Exec. Dir., 556 Central Ave., New Providence, NJ 07974, (908)286-1300
Ireland China Assn. [IO], Dublin, Ireland
Ireland Japan Assn. [IO], Dublin, Ireland
IRG Ltd. [★5308]
IRG Ltd. [★5308]
Iridology Practitioners Assn; Intl. [15963]
Iridology Practitioners Assn; Intl. [15963]
Iris Films [★10640]
Iris Films/Iris Feminist Collective [10640], 2600 Tenth St., Ste. 607, Berkeley, CA 94710, (510)845-5414
Irish
   Amer. Conf. for Irish Stud. [9883]
   Amer. Conf. for Irish Stud. [9883]
   Amer. Irish Historical Soc. [9884]
   Ancient Order of Hibernians in Am. [19071]
   Clan MacCarthy Soc. [20464]
   Irish Amer. Cultural Inst. [9885]
   Irish Amer. Partnership [9886]
   Irish Amer. Partnership [9886]
   Irish Amer. Unity Conf. [18009]
   Irish Amer. Unity Conf. [18009]
   Irish Arts Center [9887]
   Mensa I Irish Special Interest Gp. [9888]
   North Amer. Irish Dance Fed. [9563]
   Royal Soc. of Antiquaries of Ireland [6073]
   Soc. of the Friendly Sons of St. Patrick in the City of New York [19072]
   Ulster-Scots Soc. of Am. [20664]
Irish Aikido Fed. [IO], Dublin, Ireland
Irish Airmail Soc. [IO], Bray, Ireland
Irish Amateur Rowing Union [IO], Dublin, Ireland
Irish Amateur Weightlifting Assn. [IO], Dublin, Ireland
Irish Amer. Cultural Inst. [9885], 1 Lackawanna Pl., Morristown, NJ 07960, (973)605-1991
Irish Amer. Partnership [9886], 33 Broad St., Boston, MA 02109, (617)723-2707
Irish Amer. Partnership [9886], 33 Broad St., Boston, MA 02109, (617)723-2707
Irish Amer. Unity Conf. [18009], PO Box 55573, Washington, DC 20040, (800)947-4282
Irish Amer. Unity Conf. [18009], PO Box 55573, Washington, DC 20040, (800)947-4282
The Irish Ancestral Res. Assn. [18997], Dept. W, 2120 Commonwealth Ave., Auburndale, MA 02466-1909
The Irish Ancestral Res. Assn. [18997], Dept. W, 2120 Commonwealth Ave., Auburndale, MA 02466-1909
Irish Angus Cattle Soc. [IO], Carrick-On-Shannon, Ireland
Irish Anti-Vivisection Soc. [IO], Greystones, Ireland
Irish Antique Dealers Assn. [IO], Dublin, Ireland
Irish Arts Center [9887], 553 W 51st St., New York, NY 10019, (212)757-3318

Irish Assn. for Amer. Stud. [IO], Kilmeague, Ireland
Irish Assn. for Counselling and Psychotherapy [IO], Bray, Ireland
Irish Assn. of Creative Arts Therapists [IO], Dublin, Ireland
Irish Assn. of Dermatologists [IO], Dublin, Ireland
Irish Assn. for Economic Geology [IO], Kilkenny, Ireland
Irish Assn. of Investment Managers [IO], Dublin, Ireland
Irish Assn. for Nurses in Oncology [IO], Dublin, Ireland
Irish Assn. of Pastoral Care in Educ. [IO], Dublin, Ireland
Irish Assn. of Pension Funds [IO], Dublin, Ireland
Irish Assn. of Physicists in Medicine [IO], Dublin, Ireland
Irish Assn. of Social Workers [IO], Dublin, Ireland
Irish Assn. for Spina Bifida and Hydrocephalus [IO], Dublin, Ireland
Irish Assn. of Suicidology [IO], Ballsbridge, Ireland
Irish Assn. of Teachers in Special Educ. [IO], Dublin, Ireland
Irish Astronomical Assn. [IO], Glengormley, Ireland
Irish Auctioneers' and Valuers' Inst. [IO], Dublin, Ireland
Irish Australian Chamber of Commerce [IO], Melbourne, Australia
Irish Banking Fed. [IO], Dublin, Ireland
Irish Biblical Assn. [IO], Dublin, Ireland
Irish Bioenergy Assn. [IO], Waterford, Ireland
Irish Blacks Assn. [3921], 25377 Weld County Rd. 17, Johnstown, CO 80534, (970)587-2252
Irish Blue Cross [IO], Dublin, Ireland
Irish Brokers Assn. [IO], Dublin, Ireland
Irish Bus. and Employers Confed. [IO], Dublin, Ireland
Irish Campaign for Nuclear Disarmament [IO], Dublin, Ireland
Irish Cancer Soc. [IO], Dublin, Ireland
Irish Canoe Union [IO], Dublin, Ireland
Irish Cardiac Soc. [IO], Dublin, Ireland
Irish Cattle and Sheep Farmers Assn. [IO], Portlaoise, Ireland
Irish Centre for European Law [IO], Dublin, Ireland
Irish Chamber of Shipping [IO], Dublin, Ireland
Irish Christmas Tree Growers [IO], Dublin, Ireland
Irish Cmpt. Soc. [IO], Dublin, Ireland
Irish Cong. of Trade Unions [IO], Dublin, Ireland
Irish Copyright Licensing Agency [IO], Dublin, Ireland
Irish Cosmetics, Detergent and Allied Products Assn. [IO], Dublin, Ireland
Irish Coun. for Civil Liberties [IO], Dublin, Ireland
Irish Creamery Milk Suppliers' Assn. [IO], Limerick, Ireland
Irish Cultural Society - Defunct.
Irish Curling Assn. [IO], Blessington, Ireland
Irish Dairy Bd. [IO], Dublin, Ireland
Irish Deaf Soc. [IO], Dublin, Ireland
Irish Dental Assn. [IO], Dublin, Ireland
Irish Direct Marketing Assn. [IO], Dublin, Ireland
Irish Doctors Environmental Assn. [IO], Bandon, Ireland
Irish Draught Horse Soc. [IO], Ballinrobe, Ireland
Irish Draught Horse Soc. of North Am. [4608], Rachel Cox, Info. Off., HC65 Box 45, Pleasant Mount, PA 18453-9605, (866)434-7621
Irish Draught Horse Soc. of North Am. [4608], Rachel Cox, Info. Off., HC65 Box 45, Pleasant Mount, PA 18453-9605, (866)434-7621
Irish Economic Assn. [IO], Belfield, Ireland
Irish Engg. Enterprises Fed. [IO], Dublin, Ireland
Irish Epilepsy League [IO], Dublin, Ireland
Irish Ergonomics Soc. [IO], Limerick, Ireland
Irish Exporters Assn. [IO], Dublin, Ireland
Irish Family History Forum [20636], PO Box 67, Plainview, NY 11803-0067
Irish Family History Soc. [★20638]
Irish Family History Soc. [IO], Naas, Ireland
Irish Family Jour. [★20637]
Irish Family Jour. [★20637]
Irish Family Names Soc. - Defunct.
Irish Family Planning Assn. [IO], Dublin, Ireland
Irish Farmers' Assn. [IO], Bluebell, Ireland

Irish Fed. of Univ. Teachers [IO], Dublin, Ireland
Irish Fed. of Univ. Women [IO], Dublin, Ireland
Irish Fish Producers Org. [IO], Dublin, Ireland
Irish Foster Care Assn. [IO], Dublin, Ireland
Irish Fragile X Soc. [IO], Dublin, Ireland
Irish Franchise Assn. [IO], Dublin, Ireland
Irish Funds Indus. Assn. [IO], Dublin, Ireland
Irish Genealogical Found. [20637], PO Box 7575, Kansas City, MO 64116
Irish Genealogical Found. [20637], PO Box 7575, Kansas City, MO 64116
Irish Genealogical Res. Soc. [IO], Rainham, United Kingdom
Irish Genealogical Soc. Intl. [20638], 1185 Concord St. N, Ste. 218, South St. Paul, MN 55075
Irish Georgian Soc. [IO], Dublin, Ireland
Irish Gerontological Soc. [IO], Dublin, Ireland
Irish Girl Guides [IO], Dublin, Ireland
Irish Graduates Assn. of Singapore [IO], Singapore, Singapore
Irish Grain and Feed Assn. [IO], Portlaoise, Ireland
Irish Greyhound Bd. [IO], Limerick, Ireland
Irish Guide Dogs for the Blind [IO], Cork, Ireland
Irish Haemophilia Soc. [IO], Dublin, Ireland
Irish Handball Coun. [IO], Dublin, Ireland
Irish Hard of Hearing Assn. [IO], Dublin, Ireland
Irish Hardware and Building Materials Assn. [IO], Dublin, Ireland
Irish Heritage [IO], Manchester, United Kingdom
Irish Holstein Friesian Assn. [IO], Clonakilty, Ireland
Irish Home Builders Assn. [IO], Dublin, Ireland
Irish Hosp. Consultants Assn. [IO], Dublin, Ireland
Irish Hospitality Inst. [IO], Dublin, Ireland
Irish Hotels Fed. [IO], Dublin, Ireland
Irish Immigration Reform Movement [★17881]
Irish Immigration Reform Movement [★17881]
Irish Inst. of Credit Mgt. [IO], Dublin, Ireland
Irish Inst. of Training and Development [IO], Naas, Ireland
Irish Insurance Fed. [IO], Dublin, Ireland
Irish Intl. Freight Assn. [IO], Dublin, Ireland
Irish Internet Assn. [IO], Dublin, Ireland
Irish Jet Sport Assn. [IO], Newtownards, United Kingdom
Irish Kidney Assn. [IO], Dublin, Ireland
Irish Labour Party [IO], Dublin, Ireland
Irish Ladies Golf Union [IO], Dublin, Ireland
Irish Landscape Inst. [IO], Dublin, Ireland
Irish LP Gas Assn. [IO], Drogheda, Ireland
Irish Mgt. Inst. [IO], Dublin, Ireland
Irish Marine Fed. [IO], Dublin, Ireland
Irish Mathematical Soc. [IO], Dublin, Ireland
Irish Medical Devices Assn. [IO], Dublin, Ireland
Irish Medical Org. [IO], Dublin, Ireland
Irish Meteorological Soc. [IO], Dublin, Ireland
Irish Mining and Quarrying Soc. [IO], Belfield, Ireland
Irish Missionary Union [IO], Dublin, Ireland
Irish Moiled Cattle Soc. [IO], Dorchester, United Kingdom
Irish Motor Neurone Disease Assn. [IO], Dublin, Ireland
Irish Music Rights Org. [IO], Dublin, Ireland
Irish Natl. Caucus [18007], PO Box 15128, Washington, DC 20003-0849, (202)544-0568
Irish Natl. Caucus [18007], PO Box 15128, Washington, DC 20003-0849, (202)544-0568
Irish Natl. Teachers' Org. [IO], Dublin, Ireland
Irish Northern Aid [18008], 20 Wilsey Sq., Ridgewood, NJ 07450-3793, (212)736-1916
Irish Nutrition and Dietetic Inst. [IO], Dun Laoghaire, Ireland
Irish Offshore Operators' Assn. [IO], Dublin, Ireland
Irish Organic Farmers and Growers Assn. [IO], Newtownforbes, Ireland
Irish Org. for Geographic Info. [IO], Naas, Ireland
Irish Orienteering Assn. [IO], Dublin, Ireland
Irish Pain Soc. [IO], Dublin, Ireland
Irish Pattern Recognition and Classification Soc. [IO], Coleraine, United Kingdom
Irish Payment Services Org. [IO], Dun Laoghaire, Ireland
Irish Peatland Conservation Coun. [IO], Rathangan, Ireland
Irish Pharmaceutical Healthcare Assn. [IO], Dublin, Ireland

Reference to "IO" in place of a book number signifies that the association may be found in the 50th edition of International Organizations.

Irish Playwrights and Screenwriters Guild [IO], Dublin, Ireland
Irish Productivity Centre [IO], Dublin, Ireland
Irish Quaternary Assn. [IO], Maynooth, Ireland
Irish Radio Transmitters Soc. [IO], Dublin, Ireland
Irish Railway Record Soc. [IO], Dublin, Ireland
Irish Raynaud's and Scleroderma Soc. [IO], Dublin, Ireland
Irish Recorded Music Assn. [IO], Dun Laoghaire, Ireland
Irish Refugee Coun. [IO], Dublin, Ireland
Irish Road Haulage Assn. [IO], Clonee, Ireland
Irish Rugby Football Union [IO], Dublin, Ireland
Irish Rugby Union Players Assn. [IO], Dublin, Ireland
Irish Sailing Assn. [IO], Dun Laoghaire, Ireland
Irish Salmon Growers' Assn. [IO], Dublin, Ireland
Irish Schoolsport Fed. [IO], Dublin, Ireland
Irish Security Indus. Assn. [IO], Dublin, Ireland
Irish Setter Club of Am. [21588], Mrs. Debra Davis, Pres., 3372 Breezewood Ct., Ortonville, MI 48462, (248)627-3729
Irish Small and Medium Enterprises Assn. [IO], Dublin, Ireland
Irish Soc. for Archives [IO], Dublin, Ireland
Irish Soc. for Autism [IO], Dublin, Ireland
Irish Soc. of Chartered Physiotherapists [IO], Dublin, Ireland
Irish Soc. for Disability and Oral Hea. [IO], Ballymun, Ireland
Irish Soc. of Homeopaths [IO], Dublin, Ireland
Irish Soc. of Human Genetics [IO], Dublin, Ireland
Irish Soc. of Occupational Medicine [IO], Dublin, Ireland
Irish Soc. of Periodontology [IO], Galway, Ireland
Irish Soc. for the Prevention of Cruelty to Animals [IO], Longford, Ireland
Irish Soc. for Quality and Safety in Healthcare [IO], Dublin, Ireland
Irish Soc. for Rheumatology [IO], Dublin, Ireland
Irish Soc. of Surveying, Photogrammetry and Remote Sensing [IO], Dublin, Ireland
Irish South and West Fish Producers Org. [IO], Castletownbere, Ireland
Irish Sports Coun. [IO], Dublin, Ireland
Irish Squash [IO], Dublin, Ireland
Irish Stammering Assn. [IO], Dublin, Ireland
Irish Sudden Infant Death Assn. [IO], Dublin, Ireland
Irish Taekwondo Union [IO], Dublin, Ireland
Irish Taxation Inst. [IO], Dublin, Ireland
Irish Terrier Club of Am. [21589], 97 Brooklyn Tpke., Windham, CT 06280-2003, (860)465-9185
Irish Texts Soc. [IO], London, United Kingdom
Irish Timber Growers' Assn. [IO], Dublin, Ireland
Irish Tour Operators Assn. [IO], Bray, Ireland
Irish Tourist Indus. Confed. [IO], Dublin, Ireland
Irish Travel Agents Assn. [IO], Dublin, Ireland
Irish United Nations Veterans Assn. [IO], Dublin, Ireland
Irish Visual Artists' Rights Org. [IO], Dublin, Ireland
Irish Vocational Educ. Assn. [IO], Dublin, Ireland
Irish Water Spaniel Club of Am. [21590], PO Box 1409, Bothell, WA 98041, (425)486-9205
Irish Waterski Fed. [IO], Cork, Ireland
Irish Wheelchair Assn. [IO], Dublin, Ireland
Irish Wind Energy Assn. [IO], Naas, Ireland
Irish Wolfhound Club of Am. [21591], 7155 County Rd. 26, Maple Plain, MN 55359, (763)479-1638
Irish Woodturners' Guild [IO], Dublin, Ireland
Irish Youth Found. [IO], Dublin, Ireland
Irish Youth Hostel Assn. [IO], Dublin, Ireland
IRM Services - Defunct.
Irob Relief and Rehabilitation Operations Brotherhood [11986], PO Box 4448, Washington, DC 20017, (202)722-5430
Iron Casting Res. Inst. [1836], 2802 Fisher Rd., Columbus, OH 43204, (614)275-4201
Iron Overload Diseases Assn. [15498], 525 Mayflower Rd., West Palm Beach, FL 33405, (561)586-8246
Iron Overload Diseases Assn. [15498], 525 Mayflower Rd., West Palm Beach, FL 33405, (561)586-8246
Iron and Steel Division of the Metallurgical Soc. of AIME [★7091]
Iron and Steel Inst. of Japan [IO], Tokyo, Japan

Iron and Steel Soc. [★7091]
Ironmongers' Company [IO], London, United Kingdom
Iroquois Stud. Assn. [10331], 28 Zevan Rd., Johnson City, NY 13790, (607)729-0016

Irrigation
Intl. Network on Participatory Irrigation Mgt. [7016]
Intl. Network on Participatory Irrigation Mgt. [7016]
Irrigation Water Mgt. Soc. [5005]
Irrigation Assn. [170], 6540 Arlington Blvd., Falls Church, VA 22042-6638, (703)536-7080
Irrigation Assn. [170], 6540 Arlington Blvd., Falls Church, VA 22042-6638, (703)536-7080
Irrigation Australia Limited [IO], Sydney, Australia
Irrigation Water Mgt. Soc. [5005], 2008 Sycamore Dr., Eagle Mountain, UT 84005, (509)981-6441
Irritable Bowel Info. and Support Assn. [IO], Mt. Ommaney, Australia
IRSA, The Assn. of Quality Clubs [★2743]
IRSA, The Assn. of Quality Clubs [★2743]
I.S. Financial Mgt. Assn. [★1310]
Isabel Hampton Robb Memorial Fund [★15788]
ISAR: CH on Grassroots in Eurasia [★17996]
ISAR: Initiative for Social Action and Renewal in Eurasia [★17996]
ISAR: Resources for Environmental Activists
ISAR: Resources for Environmental Activists - Defunct.
ISBE Employers of Am. [★3287]
ISCO Careerscope [IO], Camberley, United Kingdom
ISDA - Assn. of Storage and Retrieval Professionals [2579], 750 Holiday Dr., Bldg. 9, Ste. 500, Pittsburgh, PA 15220, (877)921-3501
ISDA - The Off. Systems Cooperative [★2579]
Ishmael and Isaac [18126], One Bratenahl Pl., Ste. 1302, Bratenahl, OH 44108, (216)233-7333
Isis Internacional [IO], Santiago, Chile
Isis International-Manila [IO], Quezon City, Philippines
ISIS - Women's Intl. Cross-Cultural Exchange [IO], Kampala, Uganda

Islam
Assn. of Islamic Charitable Projects [19830]
Comm. for Crescent Observation Intl. [9890]
Fiqh Coun. of North Am. [19831]
Intl. Soc. for Islamic Legal Stud. [8414]
Middle East Inst. [18129]
Muslim Amer. Soc. [20135]
Universal Muslim Assn. of Am. [20137]

Islamic
Amer. Druze Soc. [19829]
Amer. Soc. for Muslim Advancement [9889]
Assn. of Islamic Charitable Projects [19830]
Comm. for Crescent Observation Intl. [9890]
Comm. for Crescent Observation Intl. [9890]
Coun. on American-Islamic Relations [19073]
Coun. on Islamic Educ. [8413]
Egyptian Student Assn. in North America [8917]
Fiqh Coun. of North Am. [19831]
Hartford Seminary [19832]
Hartford Seminary [19832]
Intl. Assn. of Sufism [19833]
Intl. Inst. of Islamic Thought [9891]
Intl. Inst. of Islamic Thought [9891]
Intl. Soc. for Iranian Culture [9882]
Intl. Soc. for Islamic Legal Stud. [8414]
Intl. Soc. for Islamic Legal Stud. [8414]
Islamic Assembly of North Am. [19834]
Islamic Assembly of North Am. [19834]
Islamic Center of Am. [19835]
Islamic Info. Center of Am. [19836]
Islamic Res. Found. Intl. [8415]
Islamic Res. Found. Intl. [8415]
Islamic Schools League of Am. [8416]
Islamic Soc. of North Am. [9892]
Islamic Texts Soc. [14563]
Lahore Ahmadiyya Movement for the Propagation of Islam - Canada [20446]
Muslim Alliance in North America [19147]
Muslim Amer. Soc. [20135]
Muslim Ummah of North Am. [9893]
North Amer. Islamic Trust [9894]
Universal Muslim Assn. of Am. [20137]

Islamic Acad. of Sciences [IO], Amman, Jordan
Islamic Assembly of North Am. [19834], 3588 Plymouth Rd., PMB 270, Ann Arbor, MI 48105, (734)528-0006
Islamic Assembly of North Am. [19834], 3588 Plymouth Rd., PMB 270, Ann Arbor, MI 48105, (734)528-0006
Islamic Center of Am. [19835], 19500 Ford Rd., Dearborn, MI 48128-2404, (313)593-0000
Islamic Centre for Development of Trade [IO], Casablanca, Morocco
Islamic Circle of North Am. [20134], 166-26 89th Ave., Jamaica, NY 11432, (718)658-1199
Islamic Development Bank [IO], Jeddah, Saudi Arabia
Islamic Development Org. [IO], Tehran, Iran
Islamic Educational, Sci., and Cultural Org. [IO], Rabat, Morocco
Islamic Food and Nutrition Coun. of Am. [1406], 777 Busse Hwy., Park Ridge, IL 60068, (847)993-0034
Islamic Food and Nutrition Coun. of Am. [1406], 777 Busse Hwy., Park Ridge, IL 60068, (847)993-0034
Islamic Info. Center of Am. [19836], PO Box 4052, Des Plaines, IL 60016, (847)541-8141
Islamic Medical Assn. [★16267]
Islamic Medical Assn. of North Am. [16267], 101 W 22nd St., Ste. 106, Lombard, IL 60148, (630)932-0000
Islamic Org. for Medical Sciences [IO], Sulaibekhat, Kuwait
Islamic Relief U.S.A. [12858], PO Box 22250, Alexandria, VA 22304, (703)370-7202
Islamic Relief U.S.A. [12858], PO Box 22250, Alexandria, VA 22304, (703)370-7202
Islamic Res. Found. for Advancement of Knowledge [★8415]
Islamic Res. Found. for Advancement of Knowledge [★8415]
Islamic Res. Found. Intl. [8415], 7102 W Shefford Ln., Louisville, KY 40242-6462, (502)287-6262
Islamic Res. Found. Intl. [8415], 7102 W Shefford Ln., Louisville, KY 40242-6462, (502)287-6262
Islamic Schools League of Am. [8416], PO Box 795, Okemos, MI 48805-0795, (517)303-3905
Islamic Soc. of the Cayman Islands [IO], George Town, Cayman Islands
Islamic Soc. of North Am. [9892], PO Box 38, Plainfield, IN 46168, (317)839-8157
Islamic Soc. of North Am. Fiqh Comm. [★19831]
Islamic States Broadcasting Org. [IO], Jeddah, Saudi Arabia
Islamic Texts Soc. [IO], Cambridge, United Kingdom
Islamic Univ. of Tech. [IO], Gazipur, Bangladesh
Islamic Writers Alliance [10318], Linda D. Delgado, Dir., PO Box 27503, Tempe, AZ 85285
Island Aid [11858], 450 Taraval St., No. 110, San Francisco, CA 94116, (415)272-9100
Island Conservation [4084], 100 Shaffer Rd., Santa Cruz, CA 95060, (831)359-4787
Island Conservation Soc. [IO], Victoria, Seychelles
Island Dolphin Care [11797], Island Dolphin Care Ctr., 150 Lorelane Pl., Key Largo, FL 33037, (305)451-5884
Island Resources Found. [9879], 1718 P St. NW, Ste. T-4, Washington, DC 20036, (202)265-9712
Islandsdeild Amnesty Intl. [★IO]
Isle of Man Chamber of Commerce [IO], Douglas, United Kingdom
Isle of Wight Chamber of Commerce [IO], Newport, United Kingdom
Islensk Tonverkamistod [★IO]
Islenski Fjallahjolaklubburinn [★IO]
Islenskir Radioamatorar [★IO]
Iso and Bizzarrini Owners Club [21081], 2025 Drake Dr., Oakland, CA 94611
ISPOR, Chinese Medical Dr. Assn. - Pharmacoeconomics Chap. [IO], Shanghai, People's Republic of China

Israel
All4Israel [12389]
All4Israel [12389]
Amer. Comm. for Shaare Zedek Hosp. in Jerusalem [12390]
Amer. Comm. for Shaare Zedek Hosp. in Jerusalem [12390]

A star before a book entry number signifies that the name is not listed separately, but is mentioned within the entry.

Amer. Friends of Magen David Adom **[12801]**
Amer. Physicians Fellowship for Medicine in Israel **[12391]**
Amer. Physicians and Friends for Medicine in Israel **[12391]**
Amer. Veterans of Israel **[20671]**
Americans for Peace Now **[18010]**
Americans for Peace Now **[18010]**
Anti-Defamation League **[17269]**
Central Rabbinical Cong. of the U.S.A. and Canada **[19854]**
Christians' Israel Public Action Campaign **[18011]**
Christians' Israel Public Action Campaign **[18011]**
Coalition for Peace with Justice **[18236]**
Emunah of Am. **[12392]**
Friends of Israel Disabled Veterans **[20672]**
Fuel for Truth **[18608]**
Green Zionist Alliance **[4268]**
Israel Humanitarian Found. **[12393]**
Israel Humanitarian Found. **[12393]**
The Israel Proj. **[18012]**
Israel Ser. Org. **[12394]**
Kibbutz Prog. Center **[18013]**
Maccabi USA/Sports for Israel **[22985]**IsraelMeals4Israel
Natl. Jewish Democratic Coun. **[18387]**
NAVAH **[13311]**
New Israel Fund **[18014]**
PEF Israel Endowment Funds **[12395]**
PEF Israel Endowment Funds **[12395]**
StandWithUs **[18015]**
Volunteers for Israel **[18016]**
Volunteers for Israel **[18016]**
Israel Acad. of Sciences and Humanities **[IO]**, Jerusalem, Israel
Israel Aliyah Center - Address unknown since 2010.
Israel-American Chamber of Commerce and Indus. **[IO]**, Tel Aviv, Israel
Israel; Amer. Jewish League for **[19842]**
Israel; Americans for a Safe **[18116]**
Israel; Americans for a Safe **[18116]**
Israel Antiquities Authority **[IO]**, Tel Aviv, Israel
Israel Assn. of Baseball **[IO]**, Tel Aviv, Israel
Israel Assn. for Computational Methods in Mechanics **[IO]**, Haifa, Israel
Israel Assn. for Cmpt. Vision and Pattern Recognition **[IO]**, Haifa, Israel
Israel Assn. for Ethiopian Jews **[IO]**, Jerusalem, Israel
Israel Assn. of Illustrators **[IO]**, Tel Aviv, Israel
Israel Assn. for Info. Systems **[IO]**, Ramat Hasharon, Israel
Israel Assn. of Univ. Women **[IO]**, Jerusalem, Israel
Israel Badminton Assn. **[IO]**, Even Yehuda, Israel
Israel Cancer Assn. **[IO]**, Givatayim, Israel
Israel Chem. Soc. **[IO]**, Ramat Gan, Israel
Israel Dance Sport Assn. **[IO]**, Ashdod, Israel
Israel Democracy Inst. **[IO]**, Jerusalem, Israel
Israel Emergency Alliance **[★18015]**
Israel Flying Disc Assn. **[IO]**, Herzliya, Israel
Israel Genealogical Soc. **[IO]**, Kiryat Gat, Israel
Israel Geological Soc. **[IO]**, Jerusalem, Israel
Israel Heart Soc. **[IO]**, Ramat Gan, Israel
Israel Histadrut Found. **[★12393]**
Israel Histadrut Found. **[★12393]**
Israel Hotel Assn. **[IO]**, Tel Aviv, Israel
Israel Hotel Managers Assn. **[IO]**, Tel Aviv, Israel
Israel Humanitarian Found. **[12393]**, 2 W 46th St., Ste. 1500, New York, NY 10036, (212)683-5676
Israel Humanitarian Found. **[12393]**, 2 W 46th St., Ste. 1500, New York, NY 10036, (212)683-5676
Israel Hypertension Soc. **[IO]**, Jerusalem, Israel
Israel Ice Skating Fed. **[IO]**, Metula, Israel
Israel Internet Assn. **[IO]**, Petah Tikva, Israel
Israel Jewelry Mfrs. Assn. **[IO]**, Kfar Saba, Israel
Israel; Machne **[12411]**
Israel Mathematical Union **[IO]**, Rehovot, Israel
Israel Medical Assn. **[IO]**, Ramat Gan, Israel
Israel Mobile Commun. Assn. **[IO]**, Tel Aviv, Israel
Israel Music Inst. **[IO]**, Tel Aviv, Israel
Israel Musicological Soc. **[IO]**, Jerusalem, Israel
Israel; Natl. Coun. of Young **[19889]**
Israel Pain Assn. **[IO]**, Tel HaShomer, Israel
Israel/Palestine Center for Res. and Info. **[IO]**, Jerusalem, Israel

Israel-Palestine Philatelic Soc. of Am. **[★22078]**
Israel Physical Soc. **[IO]**, Jerusalem, Israel
The Israel Proj. **[18012]**, 2020 K St. NW, Ste. 7600, Washington, DC 20006, (202)857-6644
Israel Psoriasis Assn. **[IO]**, Tel Aviv, Israel
Israel Public Affairs Comm; Amer. **[18114]**
Israel Ser. Org. **[12394]**, 151 Oxford Rd., New Rochelle, NY 10804, (917)620-4771
Israel Shippers' Coun. **[IO]**, Haifa, Israel
Israel Soc. for Biochemistry and Molecular Biology **[IO]**, Ramat Efal, Israel
Israel Soc. of Dermatology and Venereology **[IO]**, Tel Aviv, Israel
The Israel Soc. for Developmental Biology **[IO]**, Haifa, Israel
Israel Soc. for Microbiology **[IO]**, Tel Aviv, Israel
Israel Soc. for Microscopy **[IO]**, Haifa, Israel
Israel Soc. for Neuroscience **[IO]**, Rishon LeZion, Israel
Israel Soc. for Physiology and Pharmacology **[IO]**, Tel Aviv, Israel
Israel Soc. for Quality **[IO]**, Ness Ziona, Israel
Israel Soc. of Sports Medicine **[IO]**, Jerusalem, Israel
Israel Sports Assn. for the Disabled **[IO]**, Tel Aviv, Israel
Israel Squash Rackets Assn. **[IO]**, Ra'anana, Israel
Israel Taekwondo Fed. **[IO]**, Jerusalem, Israel
Israel Tennis Assn. **[IO]**, Tel Aviv, Israel
Israel Translators Assn. **[IO]**, Tel Aviv, Israel
Israel Vacuum Soc. **[IO]**, Haifa, Israel
Israel Veterinary Medical Assn. **[IO]**, Ra'anana, Israel
Israel Women's Network **[IO]**, Ramat Gan, Israel
Israel Yachting Assn. **[IO]**, Tel Aviv, Israel
Israel Youth Hostels Assn. **[IO]**, Jerusalem, Israel
Israeli
America-Israel Cultural Found. **[9895]**
America-Israel Cultural Found. **[9895]**
America-Israel Friendship League **[9896]**
Amer. Associates Ben-Gurion Univ. of the Negev **[8417]**
Amer. Communities Helping Israel **[12396]**
Amer. Friends of Magen David Adom **[12801]**
Amer. Friends of Tel Aviv Univ. **[8418]**
Amer. Friends of The Hebrew Univ. **[8419]**
Amer. Technion Soc. **[8420]**
Amer. Technion Soc. **[8420]**
Friends of Bezalel Acad. of Arts **[9897]**
Healing Across the Divides **[15177]**
Jewish Heart for Africa **[10822]**
Just Vision **[17409]**
Maccabi USA/Sports for Israel **[22985]**
Ohr Torah Institutions of Israel **[8421]**
Unity Coalition for Israel **[8422]**
Unity Coalition for Israel **[8422]**
Israeli Assn. for Aerosol Res. **[IO]**, Haifa, Israel
Israeli Assn. of Automatic Control **[IO]**, Haifa, Israel
Israeli Assn. of Creative and Expressive Therapies **[IO]**, Jerusalem, Israel
Israeli Assn. of Gastroenterology and Hepatology **[IO]**, Beersheba, Israel
Israeli Assn. of Grid Technologies **[IO]**, Herzliya, Israel
Israeli Assn. for Immigrant Children **[IO]**, Rehovot, Israel
Israeli Assn. for Medical Informatics **[IO]**, Tel Aviv, Israel
Israeli Assn. of Physical Therapists **[IO]**, Tel Aviv, Israel
Israeli Assn. for Psychoanalytic Psychotherapy **[IO]**, Herzliya, Israel
Israeli Athletic Assn. **[IO]**, Tel Aviv, Israel
Israeli Chap. of the ILAE **[IO]**, Tel Aviv, Israel
Israeli Comm. Against House Demolitions - USA **[18258]**, PO Box 2565, Chapel Hill, NC 27515, (919)277-0632
Israeli Coun. for Israeli-Palestinian Peace **[IO]**, Holon, Israel
Israeli Dance Inst. **[9556]**, JCRC, Ste. 700, 70 W 36th St., New York, NY 10018, (212)983-4806
Israeli Draughts Fed. **[IO]**, Rehovot, Israel
Israeli Family Planning Assn. **[IO]**, Tel Aviv, Israel
Israeli Feldenkrais Qualified Practitioners Assn. **[IO]**, Tel Aviv, Israel

Israeli Org. of Occupational Therapy **[IO]**, Tel Aviv, Israel
Israeli Soc. for Bioinformatics and Computational Biology **[IO]**, Haifa, Israel
Israeli Soc. of Gene and Cell Therapy **[IO]**, Jerusalem, Israel
Israeli Soc. for Infectious Diseases **[IO]**, Petah Tikva, Israel
Israeli Soc. of Photogrammetry and Remote Sensing **[IO]**, Tel Aviv, Israel
Israeli Soc. of Plant Sciences **[IO]**, Jerusalem, Israel
Israeli Soc. of Psychosomatic Obstetrics and Gynaecology **[IO]**, Tel Aviv, Israel
Israeli Soc. for Res. and Treatment of Obesity **[IO]**, Beersheba, Israel
Israeli Support Gp. for HD Families **[IO]**, Gedera, Israel
ISREC Found. **[IO]**, Epalinges, Switzerland
ISRI **[1107]**, 1615 L St. NW, Ste. 600, Washington, DC 20036-5664, (202)662-8500
ISRI **[1107]**, 1615 L St. NW, Ste. 600, Washington, DC 20036-5664, (202)662-8500
ISSA Sect. on the Prevention of Occupational Risks Due to Electricity-Gas-Long-Distance Heating-Water **[IO]**, Cologne, Germany
ISSHII Assn. **[★415]**
ISSN Intl. Centre **[IO]**, Paris, France
The Issue Exchange **[★2291]**
Issue Mgt. Coun. **[2291]**, 207 Loudoun St. SE, Leesburg, VA 20175-3115, (703)777-8450
Istanbul Chamber of Commerce **[IO]**, Istanbul, Turkey
Istanbul Found. for Culture and Arts **[IO]**, Istanbul, Turkey
Istanbul Kultur Sanat Vakfi **[★IO]**
Istanbul Ticaret Odasi **[★IO]**
ISTD Dance Examinations Bd. **[IO]**, London, United Kingdom
Istituto Cooperazione Economica Internazionale **[★IO]**
Istituto per la Cooperazione Universitaria **[★IO]**
Istituto Internazionale di Studi Liguri **[★IO]**
Istituto Internazionale Suore di Santa Marcellina **[IO]**, Milan, Italy
Istituto Italiano Alimenti Surgelati **[★IO]**
Istituto Italiano degli Attuari **[★IO]**
Istituto Italiano di Cultura **[9899]**, 686 Park Ave., New York, NY 10021-5009, (212)879-4242
Istituto Italiano Imballaggio **[★IO]**
Istituto Italiano della Saldatura **[★IO]**
Istituto Italo-Latino Americano **[★IO]**
Istituto Nazionale di Studi Romani **[IO]**, Rome, Italy
Istituto Paolo VI: Centro Internazionale di Studi e Documentazione **[★IO]**
Istituto Paolo VI: Intl. Centre for Stud. and Documentation **[IO]**, Brescia, Italy
Istituto Secolare Piccole Apostole della Carita **[★IO]**
Istituto Siciliano di Bioetica **[★IO]**
Istituto per gli Studi di Politica Internazionale **[★IO]**
IT Assn. of Bhutan **[IO]**, Thimphu, Bhutan
IT-Brancheforeningen **[★IO]**
I.T. Financial Mgt. Assn. **[1310]**, PO Box 30188, Santa Barbara, CA 93130, (805)687-7390
IT Indus. Assn. **[IO]**, Copenhagen, Denmark
IT Ser. Mgt. Forum USA **[6981]**, 150 E Colorado Blvd., Ste. 215, Pasadena, CA 91105, (626)449-3300
ITA - Intl. Assn. of Magnetic and Optical Media Mfrs. and Related Indus. **[★1254]**
ITA - Intl. Assn. of Magnetic and Optical Media Mfrs. and Related Indus. **[★1254]**
Italia Camera Di Commercio Internazionale **[★IO]**
Italian
Amer. Assn. of Teachers of Italian **[8461]**
Amer. Comm. on Italian Migration **[19074]**
Amer. Italian Historical Assn. **[9898]**
Amer. Italian Historical Assn. **[9898]**
Gruppo Esponenti Italiani **[19075]**
Istituto Italiano di Cultura **[9899]**
Italian-American Chamber of Commerce **[23411]**
Italian Amer. Cultural Soc. **[19076]**
Italian Catholic Fed. Central Coun. **[19077]**
Italian Folk Art Fed. of Am. **[9900]**
Italian Genealogical Soc. of Am. **[9901]**
Italian Historical Soc. of Am. **[9902]**

Reference to "IO" in place of a book number signifies that the association may be found in the 50th edition of International Organizations.

Italian Historical Soc. of Am. [9902]
Italic Inst. of Am. [9903]
Italy-America Chamber of Commerce [23412]
Maserati Info. Exchange [21100]
Natl. Italian Amer. Found. [19078]
Natl. Italian Amer. Found. [19078]
Natl. Org. of Italian-American Women [19079]
Order Sons of Italy in Am. [19080]
Soc. for Italian Historical Stud. [9904]
Unico Natl. [19081]
Italian ACM SIGCHI [IO], Padua, Italy
Italian Actors Union [★23269]
Italian Amer. Alliance for Bus. and Tech. [679], 74 W
Long Lake Rd., Ste. 204, Bloomfield Hills, MI
48304, (248)227-6143
Italian-American Chamber of Commerce [23411],
500 N Michigan Ave., Ste. 506, Chicago, IL 60611,
(312)553-9137
Italian Amer. Cultural Soc. [19076], 43843 Romeo
Plank Rd., Clinton Township, MI 48038, (586)228-
3030
Italian Amer. Found. [★19078]
Italian Amer. Found. [★19078]
Italian Amer. Librarians Caucus - Defunct.
Italian Assn. for Advanced Documentation [IO],
Rome, Italy
Italian Assn. of Cost Mgt. [IO], Milan, Italy
Italian Assn. of Energy Economists [IO], Rome, Italy
Italian Assn. of Fasteners Mfrs. [IO], Milan, Italy
Italian Assn. for the Fight against Parkinson's
Disease, Extrapyramidal Disorders and Dementia
[IO], Rome, Italy
Italian Assn. of Friends of Raoul Follereau [IO],
Bologna, Italy
Italian Assn. for Hydrogen and Fuel Cells [IO], Milan,
Italy
Italian Assn. of Indus. Producers, Exporters and
Importers of Wine, Spirits, Syrups and Vinegars
[IO], Rome, Italy
Italian Assn. for Inflammatory Bowel Diseases [IO],
Milan, Italy
Italian Assn. for Info. Systems [IO], Rome, Italy
Italian Assn. for Japanese Stud. [IO], Venice, Italy
Italian Assn. of Leather and Leather Substitute Mfrs.
[IO], Milan, Italy
Italian Assn. of Mfg. and Trading Companies in Fluid
Power Equip. and Components [IO], Milan, Italy
Italian Assn. of Medical Physics [IO], Gazzada, Italy
Italian Assn. for Metallurgy [IO], Milan, Italy
Italian Assn. of Milk and Cheese Producers [IO], Mi-
lan, Italy
Italian Assn. of Osteoporosis Patients [IO], Florence,
Italy
Italian Assn. for Pattern Recognition [IO], Pozzuoli,
Italy
Italian Assn. of Pediatric Hematology and Oncology
[IO], Bologna, Italy
Italian Assn. of Precision Moulds, Dies and Tooling
Mfrs. [IO], Milan, Italy
Italian Assn. of Sporting Goods Mfrs. [IO], Treviso,
Italy
Italian Atlantic Comm. [IO], Rome, Italy
Italian Automotive Ser. Equip. Mfrs. Assn. [IO],
Bologna, Italy
Italian Booksellers' Assn. [IO], Rome, Italy
Italian Bus. Coun. Qatar [IO], Doha, Qatar
Italian Catholic Fed. Central Coun. [19077], 8393
Capwell Dr., Ste. 110, Oakland, CA 94621,
(510)633-9058
Italian Cement Assn. [IO], Rome, Italy
Italian Center of Solidarity [IO], Rome, Italy
Italian Chamber of Commerce and Indus. in
Australia - SA [IO], Adelaide, Australia
Italian Chamber of Commerce and Indus. in Queens-
land [IO], Fortitude Valley, Australia
Italian Chamber of Commerce and Indus. for the UK
[IO], London, United Kingdom
Italian Chem. Soc. [IO], Rome, Italy
Italian Confed. of Retailers, Commerce, Tourism and
Ser. [IO], Rome, Italy
Italian Cooperatives Assn. [IO], Rome, Italy
Italian Cricket Fed. [IO], Turin, Italy
Italian Cultural Inst. [★9899]
Italian Dance Sport Fed. [IO], Rome, Italy
Italian Dental Indus. Assn. [IO], Milan, Italy

Italian Elecl. and Electronics Assn. [IO], Milan, Italy
Italian Fed. of the Chem. Indus. [IO], Milan, Italy
Italian Fed. of Goldsmiths, Jewelry and Silver Retail-
ers and Wholesalers [IO], Rome, Italy
Italian Fed. of Tour Operators and Travel Agencies
[IO], Rome, Italy
Italian Fed. of Univ. Women [IO], Cava Manara, Italy
Italian Fed. of Urban Cyclists and Bicycle Tourism
[IO], Mestre, Italy
Italian Fed. of the YMCA [IO], Rome, Italy
Italian Folk Art Fed. of Am. [9900], PO Box 3185,
Fort Lee, NJ 07024, (800)601-6888
Italian Food Indus. Fed. [IO], Rome, Italy
Italian Franchising Assn. [IO], Milan, Italy
Italian Frozen Food Inst. [IO], Rome, Italy
Italian Garage Equip. Mfrs. Assn. [IO], Bologna, Italy
Italian Genealogical Gp. [20639], PO Box 626, Be-
thpage, NY 11714-0626
Italian Genealogical Soc. of Am. [9901], PO Box
3572, Peabody, MA 01961-3572
Italian Geological Soc. [IO], Rome, Italy
Italian Greyhound Club of Am. [21592], Lilian
Barber, 35648 Menifee Rd., Murrieta, CA 92563,
(951)679-5084
Italian Historical Soc. of Am. [9902], 410 Park Ave.,
Ste. 1530, New York, NY 10022
Italian Historical Soc. of Am. [9902], 410 Park Ave.,
Ste. 1530, New York, NY 10022
Italian Independent Record Producers' Assn. [IO],
Milan, Italy
Italian Indus. Assn. for Aerospace Systems and
Defence [IO], Rome, Italy
Italian Inst. of Actuaries [IO], Rome, Italy
Italian Inst. of Packaging [IO], Milan, Italy
Italian Inst. of Welding [IO], Genoa, Italy
Italian-Latin Amer. Inst. [IO], Rome, Italy
Italian League Against Epilepsy [IO], Rome, Italy
Italian League Against Hypertension [IO], Milan, Italy
Italian Lib. Assn. [IO], Rome, Italy
Italian Mathematical Union [IO], Bologna, Italy
Italian Meteorological Soc. [IO], Bussoleno, Italy
Italian Moebius Syndrome Assn. [IO], Muggio, Italy
Italian Natl. Assn. of Insurance Adjusters [IO], Rome,
Italy
Italian Neuroscience Soc. [IO], Turin, Italy
Italian Newspaper Publishers' Assn. [IO], Rome,
Italy
Italian Paralympic Comm. [IO], Rome, Italy
Italian Pasta Makers' Union [IO], Rome, Italy
Italian PEN Club [IO], Milan, Italy
Italian Pharmacists' Fed. [IO], Rome, Italy
Italian Physical Soc. [IO], Bologna, Italy
Italian Private Equity and Venture Capital Assn. [IO],
Milan, Italy
Italian Publishers Assn. [IO], Milan, Italy
Italian Remote Sensing Assn. [IO], Turin, Italy
Italian Rice Millers Assn. [IO], Pavia, Italy
Italian Sailing Fed. [IO], Genoa, Italy
Italian Soc. of Agriculture Genetics [IO], Portici, Italy
Italian Soc. of Anatomy [IO], Rome, Italy
Italian Soc. of Biophysics [IO], Naples, Italy
Italian Soc. of Chemotherapy [IO], Florence, Italy
Italian Soc. of Dermatology [IO], Brescia, Italy
Italian Soc. of Digestive Endoscopy [IO], Naples,
Italy
Italian Soc. of Ecology [IO], Parma, Italy
Italian Soc. for Endoscopic Surgery and New
Technologies [IO], Rome, Italy
Italian Soc. for Environmental Geology [IO], Rome,
Italy
Italian Soc. of Fertility, Sterility and Reproductive
Medicine [IO], Cattolica, Italy
Italian Soc. of Gerontology and Geriatrics [IO], Flo-
rence, Italy
Italian Soc. for Hosp. Pharmacy [IO], Milan, Italy
Italian Soc. of Internal Medicine [IO], Rome, Italy
Italian Soc. for Intl. Org. [IO], Rome, Italy
Italian Soc. for Microscopical Sciences [IO], Rome,
Italy
Italian Soc. of Pediatric Endocrinology and Diabetol-
ogy [IO], Milan, Italy
Italian Soc. of Pharmacology [IO], Milan, Italy
Italian Soc. for Plant Pathology [IO], Reggio di Cala-
bria, Italy
Italian Soc. of Psychosomatic Obstetrics and Gynae-
cology [IO], Modena, Italy

Italian Soc. of Radiology [IO], Milan, Italy
Italian Soc. of Surgical and Oncological Dermatology
[IO], Rome, Italy
Italian Soc. for Therapeutic Psychosynthesis [IO],
Florence, Italy
Italian Soc. of Toxicology [IO], Milan, Italy
Italian Sports Medicine Fed. [IO], Rome, Italy
Italian Squash Fed. [IO], Riccione, Italy
Italian Stainless Steel Development Assn. [IO], Mi-
lan, Italy
Italian Tchoukball Fed. [IO], Varese, Italy
Italian Tile Center [★576]
Italian Tobacconists' Fed. [IO], Rome, Italy
Italian Trade Commn. [576], 33 E 67th St., New
York, NY 10021-5949, (212)980-1500
Italian Unihockey and Floorball Assn. [IO], Rodano,
Italy
Italian Union of the Blind [IO], Rome, Italy
Italian Vacuum Assn. [IO], Milan, Italy
Italian Vending Machines' Assn. [IO], Milan, Italy
Italian Wine and Food Inst. [1407], PO Box 789,
New York, NY 10150-0789, (212)867-4111
Italic Inst. of Am. [9903], PO Box 818, Floral Park,
NY 11001, (516)488-7400
Italic Stud. Inst. [★9903]
Italy
  Boys' Towns of Italy [13514]
  Maserati Info. Exchange [21100]
Italy-America Chamber of Commerce [23412], 730
5th Ave., Ste. 600, New York, NY 10019, (212)459-
0044
Italy Medical Informatics Soc. [IO], Rome, Italy
ITAP Intl. Alliance [717], 4 Terry Dr., Ste. 5, New-
town, PA 18940, (215)860-5640
ITC Trial Lawyers Assn. [6045], PO Box 6186,
Benjamin Franklin Sta., Washington, DC 20044-
6186, (202)429-3770
ITC/USA/2003 [★7553]
ITEM Coalition [14858], 1875 Eye St. NW, 12th Fl.,
Washington, DC 20006, (202)349-4260
Ithaka [6982], 151 E 61st St., New York, NY 10065,
(212)500-2600
ITRI Innovation [IO], St. Albans, United Kingdom
It's My Heart [14028], 1775 St. James Pl., Ste. 130,
Houston, TX 77056, (713)334-4244
ITS The Assn. of Imaging Technology and Sound -
Defunct.
Ittleson Found. [13137], 15 E 67th St., New York,
NY 10065, (212)794-2008
IUCN: Centre for Mediterranean Cooperation of the
World Conservation Union [IO], Campanillas,
Spain
IUCN: Environmental Law Programme - Germany
[IO], Bonn, Germany
IUCN: World Conservation Union - Bangladesh [IO],
Dhaka, Bangladesh
IUCN: World Conservation Union - Botswana [IO],
Gaborone, Botswana
IUCN: World Conservation Union - Cambodia [IO],
Phnom Penh, Cambodia
IUCN: World Conservation Union - China [IO],
Beijing, People's Republic of China
IUCN: World Conservation Union - Congo [IO],
Brazzaville, Republic of the Congo
IUCN: World Conservation Union - Guinea - Bissau
[IO], Bissau, Guinea-Bissau
IUCN: World Conservation Union - Kenya [IO],
Nairobi, Kenya
IUCN: World Conservation Union - Lao People's
Democratic Republic [IO], Vientiane, Lao People's
Democratic Republic
IUCN: World Conservation Union - Mali [IO], Ba-
mako, Mali
IUCN: World Conservation Union - Mozambique
[IO], Maputo, Mozambique
IUCN: World Conservation Union - Nepal [IO], Lalit-
pur, Nepal
IUCN: World Conservation Union - Niger [IO], Kano,
Niger
IUCN: World Conservation Union - Pakistan [IO],
Karachi, Pakistan
IUCN: World Conservation Union - Protected Area
Mgt. and Wildlife Conservation Proj. Wildlife Dept.
[IO], Accra, Ghana
IUCN: World Conservation Union Regional Off. for
Europe [IO], Brussels, Belgium

A star before a book entry number signifies that the name is not listed separately, but is mentioned within the entry.

IUCN: World Conservation Union - Russia [IO], Moscow, Russia

IUCN: World Conservation Union - Senegal [IO], Dakar, Senegal

IUCN: World Conservation Union - Sri Lanka [IO], Colombo, Sri Lanka

IUCN: World Conservation Union - Tanzania [IO], Dar es Salaam, United Republic of Tanzania

IUCN: World Conservation Union - Thailand [IO], Bangkok, Thailand

IUCN: World Conservation Union - Uganda [IO], Kampala, Uganda

IUCN: World Conservation Union - Vietnam [IO], Hanoi, Vietnam

IVAS [★17030]

IVAS [★17030]

IVH Parents - Defunct.

IVI Found. [6545], PO Box 1016, Niwot, CO 80544-1016, (303)652-2585

Ivory Coast Medical Relief Team [16583], 14817 Linden Ave. N, Shoreline, WA 98133

Ivory Coast Medical Relief Team [16583], 14817 Linden Ave. N, Shoreline, WA 98133

Ivory Coast Soc. of Dermatology and Venereology [IO], Abidjan, Cote d'Ivoire

Ivory Family Assn. - Defunct.

Ivy League [★22975]

Iyengar Yoga Natl. Assn. of the U.S; B.K.S. [23137]

Izaak Walton League of Am. [4085], 707 Conservation Ln., Gaithersburg, MD 20878, (301)548-0150

Izaak Walton League of Am. Endowment [4086], Shirley A. Freeman, Exec. Sec., 106 Maple Cir., Waverly, IA 50677-4383, (319)352-2435

J

J/24 Class Assn. [★22402]

J/80 Class Assn. [22364], 814 Lockearn St., Los Angeles, CA 90049, (310)633-6236

J. Allen Rynek Center for UFO Stud. [7254], PO Box 31335, Chicago, IL 60631, (773)271-3611

J. Robert Gladden Orthopaedic Soc. [16037], 6300 N River Rd., Ste. 727, Rosemont, IL 60018, (847)698-1633

Jaan Tonisson Inst. [IO], Tallinn, Estonia

Jaan Tonissoni Instituut [★IO]

Jack and Jill of Am. [11475], 1930 17th St. NW, Washington, DC 20009, (202)667-7010

Jack and Jill of Am. Found. [11476], 1930 17th St. NW, Washington, DC 20009, (202)232-5290

Jack Knight Air Mail Soc. [22047], PO Box 1239, Elgin, IL 60121-1239

Jack Knight Air Mail Soc. [22047], PO Box 1239, Elgin, IL 60121-1239

Jack London Foundation [★9382]

Jack London Res. Center [9382], PO Box 337, Glen Ellen, CA 95442, (707)996-2888

Jack Point Preservation Soc. [9501], PO Box 179, New Ellenton, SC 29809, (803)652-3492

Jack Russell Terrier Assn. of Am. [★21629]

Jack Russell Terrier Club of Am. [21593], PO Box 4527, Lutherville, MD 21094-4527, (410)561-3655

Jackie Chan Charitable Found. [IO], Hong Kong, People's Republic of China

Jackie Chan and Friends [IO], Gladesville, Australia

Jackie Chan Intl. Fan Club, Japan [IO], Tokyo, Japan

Jackie Chan UK Fan Club [IO], Bath, United Kingdom

Jackie Robinson Found. [13533], One Hudson Sq., 75 Varick St., 2nd Fl., New York, NY 10013-1917, (212)290-8600

Jackson Orthopaedic Soc; Ruth [16047]

Jackson State Univ. Natl. Alumni Assn. [18877], PO Box 17820, Jackson, MS 39217, (601)979-2281

Jacob Blaustein Inst. for the Advancement of Human Rights [17847], Amer. Jewish Comm., PO Box 705, New York, NY 10150, (212)751-4000

Jacob Hochstetler Family Assn. [20541], 1102 S 13th St., Goshen, IN 46526, (574)533-7819

Jacob Sheep Breeders Assn. [4909], 83136 Rattlesnake Rd., Dexter, OR 97431, (541)747-6149

Jacob Sheep Soc. [IO], Warwick, United Kingdom

Jacob Wetterling Found. [★11329]

Jacob Wetterling Rsrc. Center [11329], 2314 Univ. Ave. W, Ste. 14, St. Paul, MN 55114-1863, (651)714-4673

Jacques Timothe Boucher Sieur de Montbrun Heritage Soc. [20397], Peggy Binkley, Treas., 4009 Ivy Dr., Nashville, TN 37216

Jaffa Inst. [IO], Jaffa, Israel

Jagannath Org. for Global Awareness [20213], PO Box 94, Clarksville, MD 21029, (410)531-7445

Jaguar Clubs of North Am. [21082], Nancy Rath, 234 Buckland Trace, Louisville, KY 40245, (502)244-1672

Jaguar Clubs of North Am. [21082], Nancy Rath, 234 Buckland Trace, Louisville, KY 40245, (502)244-1672

Jama'at Ahmadiyyah [★IO]

Jamaica

Blue Mountain Proj. [12397]

Coalition of Jamaican Organizations [9905]

Friends of Jamaica USA [11285]

Jamaica Impact [12398]

Jamaica Tourist Bd. [23413]

Jamaica Unite [11602]

Love and Hope Ministries Intl. [12399]

Jamaica Agricultural Soc. [IO], Kingston, Jamaica

Jamaica Amateur Athletic Assn. [IO], Kingston, Jamaica

Jamaica Assn. of Administrative Professionals [IO], Kingston, Jamaica

Jamaica Assn. of Villas and Apartments [IO], St. Mary, Jamaica

Jamaica Bankers' Assn. [IO], Kingston, Jamaica

Jamaica Baseball Assn. [IO], Kingston, Jamaica

Jamaica Cancer Soc. [IO], Kingston, Jamaica

Jamaica Exporters Assn. [IO], Kingston, Jamaica

Jamaica Hotel and Tourist Assn. [IO], Kingston, Jamaica

Jamaica Impact [12398], PO Box 3794, New York, NY 10163, (212)459-4390

Jamaica Mfrs'. Assn. [IO], Kingston, Jamaica

Jamaica Olympic Assn. [IO], Kingston, Jamaica

Jamaica Physiotherapy Assn. [IO], Kingston, Jamaica

Jamaica Red Cross [IO], Kingston, Jamaica

Jamaica Squash Assn. [IO], Kingston, Jamaica

Jamaica Taekwondo Fed. [IO], Kingston, Jamaica

Jamaica Teachers' Assn. [IO], Kingston, Jamaica

Jamaica Tourist Bd. [23413], 5201 Blue Lagoon Dr., Ste. 670, Miami, FL 33126, (305)665-0557

Jamaica Unite [11602], 3613 NW 194th Terr., Miami Gardens, FL 33056, (954)353-7032

Jamaica USA Chamber of Commerce [23372], 4770 Biscayne Blvd., Ste. 1050, Miami, FL 33137, (305)576-7888

Jamaica USA Chamber of Commerce [23372], 4770 Biscayne Blvd., Ste. 1050, Miami, FL 33137, (305)576-7888

Jamaica Yachting Assn. [IO], Kingston, Jamaica

Jamaican Airline Pilots' Assn. [IO], Kingston, Jamaica

Jamaican Assn. for the Deaf [IO], Kingston, Jamaica

Jamaican Chap. of ILAE [IO], Kingston, Jamaica

Jamaicans For Justice [IO], Kingston, Jamaica

James A. Michener Soc. [9383], 2736 S Clayton St., Denver, CO 80210-6444, (303)756-9352

James Beard Found. [10670], 167 W 12th St., New York, NY 10011, (212)675-4984

James Bond Intl. Fan Club [IO], York, United Kingdom

James Ewing Soc. [★15934]

James Jones Literary Soc. [10725], PO Box 68, Robinson, IL 62454

James Joyce Soc. [9384], Stephen Pantani, Treas., 80 E Hartsdale Ave., No. 414, Hartsdale, NY 10530

James K. Polk Memorial Assn. [10671], PO Box 741, Columbia, TN 38402, (931)388-2354

James Madison Found. [★18458]

James Monroe Memorial Found. [10672], 1009 Bainbridge St., Richmond, VA 23224, (804)231-1827

James Renwick Alliance [9187], 4405 E West Hwy., Ste. 510, Bethesda, MD 20814, (301)907-3888

James Robison Evangelistic Assn. [★19759]

James Robison Life Intl. [★19759]

Jamestown Found. [17567], 1111 16th St. NW, Ste. No. 320, Washington, DC 20036, (202)483-8888

Jamestown Found. [17567], 1111 16th St. NW, Ste. No. 320, Washington, DC 20036, (202)483-8888

Jamestowne Soc. [20398], PO Box 6845, Richmond, VA 23230, (804)353-1226

Jamii Moja [11603], 10110 NW Ash St., Portland, OR 97229, (503)989-1932

Jana Jae Fan Club [23859], PO Box 35726, Tulsa, OK 74153, (918)786-8896

Jane Addams Peace Assn. [18259], 777 United Nations Plz., 6th Fl., New York, NY 10017, (212)682-8830

Jane Addams Peace Assn. [18259], 777 United Nations Plz., 6th Fl., New York, NY 10017, (212)682-8830

Jane Austen Soc. of North Am. [9385], Bobbie Gay, Membership Sec., 7230 N San Blas Dr., Tucson, AZ 85704, (800)836-3911

Jane Austen Soc. of North Am. [9385], Bobbie Gay, Membership Sec., 7230 N San Blas Dr., Tucson, AZ 85704, (800)836-3911

Jane Austen Soc. of the United Kingdom [IO], Havant, United Kingdom

Jane Goodall Inst. for Wildlife Res., Educ., and Conservation [5073], 4245 N Fairfax Dr., Ste. 600, Arlington, VA 22203, (703)682-9220

JANET [IO], Didcot, United Kingdom

Japan

All Japan Ju-Jitsu Intl. Fed. [22720]

High School Evangelism Fellowship [19751]

Honolulu Japanese Chamber of Commerce [23414]

Japan Convention Bur. [23415]

Japan External Trade Org. [23416]

Japan Natl. Tourist Org. [23417]

Japan Stud. Assn. [9906]

U.S.-Japan Bus. Coun. [23418]

U.S.-Japan Coun. [17955]

U.S./Japan Cultural Trade Network [9519]

Japan Academic Assn. for Copyright Clearance [IO], Tokyo, Japan

Japan Advertisers Assn. [IO], Tokyo, Japan

Japan Advt. Agencies Assn. [IO], Tokyo, Japan

Japan Aeronautic Assn. [IO], Tokyo, Japan

Japan Agricultural Journalists Assn. [IO], Tokyo, Japan

Japan Aikido Assn. U.S.A. [★22752]

Japan Aluminium Assn. [IO], Tokyo, Japan

Japan Amateur Radio League [IO], Tokyo, Japan

Japan-America Soc. of Washington, D.C. [9907], 1819 L St. NW, 1B Level, Washington, DC 20036, (202)833-2210

Japan-America Soc. of Washington, D.C. [9907], 1819 L St. NW, 1B Level, Washington, DC 20036, (202)833-2210

Japan-America Student Conf. [8368], Intl. Student Conferences, 1150 18th St. NW, Ste. LL2, Washington, DC 20036, (202)289-9088

Japan Analytical Instruments Mfrs. Assn. [IO], Tokyo, Japan

Japan Ankylosing Spondylitis Club [IO], Tokyo, Japan

Japan Art Assn. [IO], Tokyo, Japan

Japan Art History Forum [9210], Univ. of Hawaii at Manoã, Dept. of Art and Art History, 2535 McCarthy Mall, Honolulu, HI 96822, (808)956-8033

Japan Asian Assn. and Asian Friendship Soc. [IO], Osaka, Japan

Japan Assn. of Adult Orthodontics [IO], Tokyo, Japan

Japan Assn. for African Stud. [IO], Kyoto, Japan

Japan Assn. of Athletics Federations [IO], Tokyo, Japan

Japan Assn. of Coll. English Teachers [IO], Tokyo, Japan

Japan Assn. of Corporate Executives [IO], Tokyo, Japan

Japan Assn. of Graphic Arts Tech. [IO], Tokyo, Japan

Japan Assn. for Intl. Chem. Info. [IO], Tokyo, Japan

Japan Assn. for Intl. Collaboration of Agriculture and Forestry [IO], Tokyo, Japan

Japan Assn. for Intl. Horse Racing [IO], Tokyo, Japan

Reference to "IO" in place of a book number signifies that the association may be found in the 50th edition of International Organizations.

Encyclopedia of Associations, 51st Edition

2939

Japan Assn. for Language Teaching **[IO]**, Tokyo, Japan

Japan Assn. of Legal Philosophy **[IO]**, Tokyo, Japan

Japan Assn. for Medical Informatics **[IO]**, Tokyo, Japan

Japan Assn. of New Bus. Incubation Org. **[IO]**, Tokyo, Japan

Japan Assn. for Philosophy of Sci. **[IO]**, Tokyo, Japan

Japan Assn. for Quaternary Res. **[IO]**, Tokyo, Japan

Japan Assn. for Trade with Russia and Central-Eastern Europe **[IO]**, Tokyo, Japan

Japan Assn. of Travel Agents **[IO]**, Tokyo, Japan

Japan Atherosclerosis Soc. **[IO]**, Tokyo, Japan

Japan Audio Soc. **[IO]**, Tokyo, Japan

Japan Audio Visual Educ. Assn. **[IO]**, Tokyo, Japan

Japan Auto Parts Indus. Assn. **[IO]**, Tokyo, Japan

Japan Auto. Fed. **[IO]**, Tokyo, Japan

Japan Auto. Importers Assn. **[IO]**, Tokyo, Japan

Japan Auto. Mfrs. Assn. **[IO]**, Tokyo, Japan

Japan Auto. Mfrs. Assn., Washington Off. **[332]**, 1050 17th St. NW, Ste. 410, Washington, DC 20036, (202)296-8537

Japan Auto. Tyre Mfrs. Assn. **[IO]**, Tokyo, Japan

Japan Automotive Products' Assn. **[IO]**, Tokyo, Japan

Japan Automotive Ser. Equip. Assn. **[IO]**, Tokyo, Japan

Japan Bamboo Soc. **[IO]**, Kyoto, Japan

Japan Bearing Indus. Assn. **[IO]**, Tokyo, Japan

Japan Biscuit Assn. **[IO]**, Tokyo, Japan

Japan Boating Indus. Assn. **[IO]**, Tokyo, Japan

Japan Book Publishers Assn. **[IO]**, Tokyo, Japan

Japan Bus. Aviation Assn. **[IO]**, Tokyo, Japan

Japan Bus. Fed. **[IO]**, Tokyo, Japan

Japan Bus. Machine and Info. Sys. Indus. Assn. **[IO]**, Tokyo, Japan

Japan Cartographers Assn. **[IO]**, Tokyo, Japan

Japan Center for Intl. Exchange **[IO]**, Tokyo, Japan

Japan Center for Intl. Exchange USA **[17976]**, 274 Madison Ave., Ste. 1102, New York, NY 10016, (212)679-4130

Japan Center for Intl. Exchange USA **[17976]**, 274 Madison Ave., Ste. 1102, New York, NY 10016, (212)679-4130

Japan Chap. of Intl. Geosynthetics Soc. **[IO]**, Saitama, Japan

Japan Chem. Fibers Assn. **[IO]**, Tokyo, Japan

Japan Chem. Indus. Assn. **[IO]**, Tokyo, Japan

Japan Clock and Watch Assn. **[IO]**, Tokyo, Japan

Japan Coal Energy Center **[IO]**, Tokyo, Japan

Japan Commercial Arbitration Assn. **[IO]**, Tokyo, Japan

Japan Constr. Mechanization Assn. **[IO]**, Tokyo, Japan

Japan Convention Bur. **[23415]**, 1 Rockefeller Plz., Ste. 1250, New York, NY 10020, (212)757-5641

Japan Copper Development Assn. **[IO]**, Tokyo, Japan

Japan Cotton Traders Assn. **[IO]**, Osaka, Japan

Japan Coun. Against A and H Bombs **[IO]**, Tokyo, Japan

Japan Craft Beer Assn. **[IO]**, Ashiya, Japan

Japan Cricket Assn. **[IO]**, Tokyo, Japan

Japan Customs Brokers Assn. **[IO]**, Tokyo, Japan

Japan Dam Found. **[IO]**, Tokyo, Japan

Japan DanceSport Fed. **[IO]**, Tokyo, Japan

Japan Die and Mold Indus. Assn. **[IO]**, Tokyo, Japan

Japan Direct Marketing Assn. **[IO]**, Tokyo, Japan

Japan Donor Family Club **[IO]**, Tokyo, Japan

Japan Economic Inst. of America - Defunct.

Japan Economic Policy Assn. **[IO]**, Tokyo, Japan

Japan Elec. Lamp Mfrs. Assn. **[IO]**, Tokyo, Japan

Japan Elec. Measuring Instruments Mfrs'. Assn. **[IO]**, Tokyo, Japan

Japan Elecl. Mfrs. Assn. **[IO]**, Tokyo, Japan

Japan Electronic Data Interchange Coun. **[IO]**, Tokyo, Japan

Japan Electronic Products Importers Assn. **[IO]**, Tokyo, Japan

Japan Electronics and Info. Tech. Indus. Assn. **[IO]**, Tokyo, Japan

Japan Electronics Show Assn. **[IO]**, Tokyo, Japan

Japan Embedded Systems Tech. Assn. **[IO]**, Tokyo, Japan

Japan EMDR Assn. **[IO]**, Hyogo, Japan

Japan Environmental Mgt. Assn. for Indus. **[IO]**, Tokyo, Japan

Japan Epilepsy Soc. **[IO]**, Hirosaki, Japan

Japan Evangelical Lutheran Church **[IO]**, Tokyo, Japan

Japan Explosives Soc. **[IO]**, Tokyo, Japan

Japan External Trade Org. **[IO]**, Tokyo, Japan

Japan External Trade Org. **[23416]**, 1221 Ave. of the Americas, McGraw Hill Bldg., 42nd Fl., New York, NY 10020, (212)997-0400

Japan Farm Machinery Mfrs. Assn. **[IO]**, Tokyo, Japan

Japan Fashion Color Assn. **[IO]**, Tokyo, Japan

Japan Fed. of Bar Associations **[IO]**, Tokyo, Japan

Japan Fed. of Composers **[IO]**, Tokyo, Japan

Japan Fed. of Ser. and Distributive Workers Unions **[IO]**, Tokyo, Japan

Japan Fed. of Telecommunications, Electronic Info. and Allied Workers **[IO]**, Tokyo, Japan

Japan Fisheries Assn. **[IO]**, Tokyo, Japan

Japan Floorball Assn. **[IO]**, Saitama, Japan

Japan Fluid Power Assn. **[IO]**, Tokyo, Japan

Japan Flying Disc Assn. **[IO]**, Tokyo, Japan

Japan Foreign Trade Coun. **[IO]**, Tokyo, Japan

Japan Forest Tech. Assn. **[IO]**, Tokyo, Japan

Japan Found. **[9908]**, New York Off., 152 W 57th St., 17th Fl., New York, NY 10019, (212)489-0299

Japan Gas Assn. **[IO]**, Tokyo, Japan

Japan Gastroenterological Endoscopy Soc. **[IO]**, Tokyo, Japan

Japan Gear Mfrs. Assn. **[IO]**, Tokyo, Japan

Japan Gerontological Soc. **[IO]**, Tokyo, Japan

Japan Golf Goods Assn. **[IO]**, Tokyo, Japan

Japan Heterocerists' Soc. **[IO]**, Chiba, Japan

Japan Image and Info. Mgt. Assn. **[IO]**, Tokyo, Japan

Japan Indus. Design Promotion Org. **[IO]**, Tokyo, Japan

Japan Indus. Designers' Assn. **[IO]**, Tokyo, Japan

Japan Indus. Mgt. Assn. **[IO]**, Tokyo, Japan

Japan Indus. Safety and Hea. Assn. **[IO]**, Tokyo, Japan

Japan Indus. Assn. of Radiological Systems **[IO]**, Tokyo, Japan

Japan Info. Access Proj. **[9909]**, 1730 Rhode Island Ave. NW, Ste. 414, Washington, DC 20036-3100, (202)822-6040

Japan Info. Access Proj. **[9909]**, 1730 Rhode Island Ave. NW, Ste. 414, Washington, DC 20036-3100, (202)822-6040

Japan Info. Tech. Services Indus. Assn. **[IO]**, Tokyo, Japan

Japan Inst. of Intl. Affairs **[IO]**, Tokyo, Japan

Japan Inst. of Invention and Innovation **[IO]**, Tokyo, Japan

Japan Inst. of Metals **[IO]**, Sendai, Japan

Japan Inst. of Navigation **[IO]**, Tokyo, Japan

Japan Intl. Center for the Rights of the Child **[IO]**, Osaka, Japan

Japan Intl. Christian Univ. Found. **[19678]**, 475 Riverside Dr., Ste. 439, New York, NY 10115-0439, (212)870-3386

Japan Intl. Christian Univ. Found. **[19678]**, 475 Riverside Dr., Ste. 439, New York, NY 10115-0439, (212)870-3386

Japan Intl. Food and Aquaculture Soc. **[IO]**, Moriya, Japan

Japan Intl. Food for the Hungry **[IO]**, Osaka, Japan

Japan Intl. League of Artists **[IO]**, Tokyo, Japan

Japan Intl. Volunteer Center **[IO]**, Tokyo, Japan

Japan Iron and Steel Fed. **[IO]**, Tokyo, Japan

Japan Karate-Do Org. **[22741]**, 3545 Midway Dr., Ste. C, San Diego, CA 92110-4922, (619)223-7405

Japan Karate-Dō Org. **[22741]**, 3545 Midway Dr., Ste. C, San Diego, CA 92110-4922, (619)223-7405

Japan Legal History Assn. **[IO]**, Kyoto, Japan

Japan Lib. Assn. **[IO]**, Tokyo, Japan

Japan Linen, Ramie and Jute Spinners' Assn. **[IO]**, Tokyo, Japan

Japan Machine Tool Builders' Assn. **[IO]**, Tokyo, Japan

Japan Machine Tool Importers' Assn. **[IO]**, Tokyo, Japan

Japan Machinery Center for Trade and Investment **[IO]**, Tokyo, Japan

Japan Machinery Fed. **[IO]**, Tokyo, Japan

Japan Magazine Advt. Assn. **[IO]**, Tokyo, Japan

Japan Maillard Reaction Soc. **[IO]**, Nishinomiya, Japan

Japan Mgt. Assn. **[IO]**, Tokyo, Japan

Japan Marketing Assn. **[IO]**, Tokyo, Japan

Japan Marketing Res. Assn. **[IO]**, Tokyo, Japan

Japan Medical Assn. **[IO]**, Tokyo, Japan

Japan Natl. Assembly of Disabled People's Intl. **[IO]**, Tokyo, Japan

Japan Natl. Tourist Assn. **[★23417]**

Japan Natl. Tourist Org. **[23417]**, 11 W 42nd St., 19th Fl., New York, NY 10036, (212)757-5640

Japan Natl. Tourist Org. **[IO]**, Tokyo, Japan

Japan Neuroendocrine Soc. **[IO]**, Kyoto, Japan

Japan Neuroscience Soc. **[IO]**, Tokyo, Japan

Japan Neurosurgical Soc. **[IO]**, Tokyo, Japan

Japan Newspaper Publishers and Editors Assn. **[IO]**, Tokyo, Japan

Japan Oil Chemists' Soc. **[IO]**, Tokyo, Japan

Japan Optical Measuring Instrument Mfrs'. Assn. **[IO]**, Tokyo, Japan

Japan Organ Transplant Network **[IO]**, Tokyo, Japan

Japan Overseas Christian Medical Cooperative Ser. **[IO]**, Tokyo, Japan

Japan Overseas Rolling Stock Assn. **[IO]**, Tokyo, Japan

Japan Paint Mfrs. Assn. **[IO]**, Tokyo, Japan

Japan Paper Exporters' Assn. **[IO]**, Tokyo, Japan

Japan Paper Importers' Assn. **[IO]**, Tokyo, Japan

Japan Pearl Exporters' Assn. **[IO]**, Kobe, Japan

Japan Pediatric Soc. **[IO]**, Tokyo, Japan

Japan Petroleum Development Assn. **[IO]**, Tokyo, Japan

Japan Pharmaceutical Mfrs'. Assn. **[IO]**, Tokyo, Japan

Japan Philatelic Soc. **[IO]**, Tokyo, Japan

Japan Powder Metallurgy Assn. **[IO]**, Tokyo, Japan

Japan Printing Machinery Mfrs'. Assn. **[IO]**, Tokyo, Japan

Japan Productivity Center **[IO]**, Tokyo, Japan

Japan Proj. **[★9909]**

Japan Proj. **[★9909]**

Japan Public Hea. Assn. **[IO]**, Tokyo, Japan

Japan Racing Assn. **[IO]**, Tokyo, Japan

Japan Radiation Res. Soc. **[IO]**, Chiba, Japan

Japan Radiological Soc. **[IO]**, Tokyo, Japan

Japan Railway Engineers Assn. **[IO]**, Tokyo, Japan

Japan Railway Trade Unions Confed. **[IO]**, Tokyo, Japan

Japan Refrigeration and Air Conditioning Indus. Assn. **[IO]**, Tokyo, Japan

Japan Road Contractors Assn. **[IO]**, Tokyo, Japan

Japan Robot Assn. **[IO]**, Tokyo, Japan

Japan Rose Soc. **[IO]**, Tokyo, Japan

Japan Rubber Mfrs. Assn. **[IO]**, Minato, Japan

Japan Sailing Fed. **[IO]**, Tokyo, Japan

Japan Sci. and Tech. Agency **[IO]**, Saitama, Japan

Japan Scientists' Assn. **[IO]**, Tokyo, Japan

Japan Secretaries Assn. **[IO]**, Tokyo, Japan

Japan Securities Dealers' Assn. **[IO]**, Tokyo, Japan

Japan Seed Trade Assn. **[IO]**, Tokyo, Japan

Japan Sewing Machinery Mfrs. Assn. **[IO]**, Tokyo, Japan

Japan Sheep Casing Importers' Assn. **[IO]**, Tokyo, Japan

Japan Ship Exporters' Assn. **[IO]**, Tokyo, Japan

Japan Shotokan Karate Assn. of Iran **[IO]**, Tehran, Iran

Japan Skating Fed. **[IO]**, Tokyo, Japan

Japan Smoking Articles Corporate Assn. **[IO]**, Tokyo, Japan

Japan Soap and Detergent Assn. **[IO]**, Tokyo, Japan

Japan Soc. **[9910]**, 333 E 47th St., New York, NY 10017, (212)832-1155

Japan Soc. **[9910]**, 333 E 47th St., New York, NY 10017, (212)832-1155

Japan Soc. for Analytical Chemistry **[IO]**, Tokyo, Japan

Japan Soc. of Applied Physics **[IO]**, Tokyo, Japan

Japan Soc. for Bioscience, Biotechnology and Agro-chemistry **[IO]**, Tokyo, Japan

Japan Soc. of Blood Transfusion **[IO]**, Tokyo, Japan

Japan Soc. of Civil Engineers **[IO]**, Tokyo, Japan

Japan Soc. of Clinical Oncology **[IO]**, Kyoto, Japan

A star before a book entry number signifies that the name is not listed separately, but is mentioned within the entry.

Japan Soc. of Cost and Proj. Engineers [IO], Kanagawa, Japan
Japan Soc. of Indus. Machinery Mfrs. [IO], Tokyo, Japan
Japan Soc. of Lib. and Info. Sci. [IO], Tsukuba, Japan
Japan Soc. of Materials Sci. [IO], Kyoto, Japan
Japan Soc. of Mech. Engineers [IO], Tokyo, Japan
Japan Soc. of Microgravity Application [IO], Tokyo, Japan
Japan Soc. of Nuclear and Radiochemical Sciences [IO], Osaka, Japan
Japan Soc. of Obstetrics and Gynecology [IO], Tokyo, Japan
Japan Soc. of Photogrammetry and Remote Sensing [IO], Tokyo, Japan
Japan Soc. of Political Economy [IO], Tokyo, Japan
Japan Soc. for the Promotion of Machine Indus. [IO], Tokyo, Japan
Japan Soc. for the Promotion of Sci. [IO], Tokyo, Japan
Japan Soc. of Refrigerating and Air Conditioning Engineers [IO], Tokyo, Japan
Japan Soc. for Reproductive Medicine [IO], Akita, Japan
Japan Soc. of Risk Mgt. for Preventive Medicine [IO], Tokyo, Japan
Japan Soc. for Southeast Asian History [IO], Toyohashi, Japan
Japan Soc. - United Kingdom [IO], London, United Kingdom
Japan Sociological Soc. [IO], Tokyo, Japan
Japan Soft Drink Assn. [IO], Tokyo, Japan
Japan Special Libraries Assn. [IO], Tokyo, Japan
Japan Spinners' Assn. [IO], Osaka, Japan
Japan Squash Assn. [IO], Tokyo, Japan
Japan Statistical Soc. [IO], Tokyo, Japan
Japan Stud. Assn. [9906], Ohio Wesleyan Univ., Dept. of Sociology/Anthropology, 61 S Sandusky St., Delaware, OH 43015
Japan Surgical Soc. [IO], Tokyo, Japan
Japan for Sustainability [IO], Kanagawa, Japan
Japan Table Tennis Assn. [IO], Tokyo, Japan
Japan Telework Assn. [IO], Tokyo, Japan
Japan Textile Finishers' Assn. [IO], Tokyo, Japan
Japan Touch Assn. [IO], Tokyo, Japan
Japan Toy Assn. [IO], Tokyo, Japan
Japan-U.S. Bus. Alliance - Defunct.
Japan UNIX Soc. [IO], Tokyo, Japan
Japan Valve Mfrs'. Assn. [IO], Tokyo, Japan
Japan Vending Machine Mfrs. Assn. [IO], Tokyo, Japan
Japan Video Software Assn. [IO], Tokyo, Japan
Japan Watch Importers' Assn. [IO], Tokyo, Japan
Japan Weather Assn. [IO], Tokyo, Japan
Japan Whaling Assn. [IO], Tokyo, Japan
Japan Wines and Spirits Importers' Assn. [IO], Tokyo, Japan
Japan Wood Res. Soc. [IO], Tokyo, Japan
Japan Youth Hostels [IO], Tokyo, Japan
Japanese
  Aikido Assn. of Am. [22216]
  All Japan Ju-Jitsu Intl. Fed. [22720]
  Austrian-Japan Soc. for Sci. and Art [6913]
  British Assn. for Japanese Stud. [10204]
  Italian Assn. for Japanese Stud. [4592]
  Japan-America Soc. of Washington, D.C. [9907]
  Japan-America Soc. of Washington, D.C. [9907]
  Japan Found. [9908]
  Japan Info. Access Proj. [9909]
  Japan Info. Access Proj. [9909]
  Japan Soc. [9910]
  Japan Soc. [9910]
  Japan Stud. Assn. [9906]
  Japanese Amer. Citizens League [19082]
  Japanese Amer. Living Legacy [9911]
  Japanese Chamber of Commerce and Indus. of Hawaii [23419]
  Japanese Chamber of Commerce and Indus. of New York [23420]
  Japanese Natl. Honor Soc. [23572]
  Natl. Assn. of Japan-America Societies [19083]
  Natl. Japanese Amer. Historical Soc. [9912]
  Netherlands Assn. for Japanese Stud. [16433]
  Nippon Club [19084]

  Reiki Educ. [16580]
  Shibumi Intl. Reiki Assn. [16582]
  U.S./Japan Cultural Trade Network [9519]
  Urasenke Tea Ceremony Soc. [9913]
Japanese Amer. Citizens League [19082], 1765 Sutter St., San Francisco, CA 94115, (415)345-1075
Japanese Amer. Curriculum Proj. [★8344]
Japanese Amer. Curriculum Proj. [★8344]
Japanese Amer. Living Legacy [9911], 800 N State Coll. Blvd., RGC 8, Fullerton, CA 92831, (657)278-4483
Japanese Amer. Soc. for Legal Studies - Defunct.
Japanese Amer. Veterans Assn. [20792], Dave Buto, 4226 Holborn Ave., Annandale, VA 22003, (703)503-3431
Japanese Animation Soc. [IO], Leicester, United Kingdom
Japanese Assn. for Acute Medicine [IO], Tokyo, Japan
Japanese Assn. for Amer. Stud. [IO], Tokyo, Japan
Japanese Assn. for Behavior Anal. [IO], Osaka, Japan
Japanese Assn. of Chiropractors [IO], Tokyo, Japan
Japanese Assn. for Death Stud. and Bereavement Support [IO], Tokyo, Japan
Japanese Assn. on Disability and Difficulty [IO], Tokyo, Japan
Japanese Assn. of Healthcare Info. Systems Indus. [IO], Tokyo, Japan
Japanese Assn. for Infectious Diseases [IO], Tokyo, Japan
Japanese Assn. of Mathematical Sciences [★18140]
Japanese Assn. of Mineralogists, Petrologists and Economic Geologists [IO], Sendai, Japan
Japanese Assn. of Occupational Therapists [IO], Tokyo, Japan
Japanese Assn. for Petroleum Tech. [IO], Tokyo, Japan
Japanese Assn. of Real Estate Appraisal [IO], Tokyo, Japan
Japanese Assn. of Rural Medicine [IO], Tokyo, Japan
Japanese Assn. for Semiotic Stud. [IO], Tokyo, Japan
Japanese Assn. of Speech-Language-Hearing Therapists [IO], Tokyo, Japan
Japanese Assn. of Univ. Women [IO], Tokyo, Japan
Japanese Assn. for Women in Sport [IO], Otsu, Japan
Japanese Bankers Assn. [IO], Tokyo, Japan
Japanese Biochemical Soc. [IO], Tokyo, Japan
Japanese Chamber of Commerce and Indus. of Hawaii [23419], 714 Kanoelehua Ave., Hilo, HI 96720, (808)934-0177
Japanese Chamber of Commerce and Indus. of New York [23420], 145 W 57th St., New York, NY 10019, (212)246-8001
Japanese Chamber of Commerce of New York [★23420]
Japanese Chin Club of Am. [21594], Patricia Gerberich, Treas., PO Box 920898, Houston, TX 77292
Japanese Circulation Soc. [IO], Kyoto, Japan
Japanese Communist Party [IO], Tokyo, Japan
Japanese Confed. of Port and Transport Workers' Unions [IO], Tokyo, Japan
Japanese Consumers' Co-operative Union [IO], Tokyo, Japan
Japanese Dermatological Assn. [IO], Tokyo, Japan
Japanese Fed. of Pulp and Paper Workers' Unions [IO], Tokyo, Japan
Japanese Geotechnical Soc. [IO], Tokyo, Japan
Japanese Huntington's Disease Network [IO], Nagano, Japan
Japanese Inst. of Certified Public Accountants [IO], Tokyo, Japan
Japanese Marine Equip. Assn. [IO], Tokyo, Japan
Japanese Midwives' Assn. [IO], Tokyo, Japan
Japanese Natl. Honor Soc. [23572], PO Box 3719, Boulder, CO 80307-3719
Japanese NGO Center for Intl. Cooperation [IO], Tokyo, Japan
Japanese Nursing Assn. [IO], Tokyo, Japan
Japanese Olympic Comm. [IO], Tokyo, Japan
Japanese Ophthalmological Soc. [IO], Tokyo, Japan

Japanese Organic Inspectors Assn. [IO], Tokyo, Japan
Japanese Org. for Intl. Cooperation in Family Planning [IO], Tokyo, Japan
Japanese Orthodontic Soc. [IO], Niigata, Japan
Japanese Orthopaedic Assn. [IO], Tokyo, Japan
Japanese Peptide Soc. [IO], Minoh, Japan
Japanese Pharmacological Soc. [IO], Tokyo, Japan
Japanese Physical Therapy Assn. [IO], Tokyo, Japan
Japanese Red Cross Soc. [IO], Tokyo, Japan
Japanese Rubber Workers' Union Confed. [IO], Tokyo, Japan
Japanese Shipowners' Assn. [IO], Tokyo, Japan
Japanese Shipowners Assn. - United Kingdom [IO], London, United Kingdom
Japanese Soc. of Adlerian Psychology [IO], Osaka, Japan
Japanese Soc. of Agricultural Machinery [IO], Saitama, Japan
Japanese Soc. of Allergology [IO], Tokyo, Japan
Japanese Soc. of Anesthesiologists [IO], Kobe, Japan
Japanese Soc. of Animal Sci. [IO], Tokyo, Japan
Japanese Soc. of Applied Entomology and Zoology [IO], Tokyo, Japan
Japanese Soc. of Applied Glycoscience [IO], Tokyo, Japan
Japanese Soc. for Bioinformatics [IO], Tokyo, Japan
Japanese Soc. of Breeding [IO], Kyoto, Japan
Japanese Soc. of Certified Pension Actuaries [IO], Tokyo, Japan
Japanese Soc. for Chemotherapy [IO], Tokyo, Japan
Japanese Soc. of Cinematographers [IO], Tokyo, Japan
Japanese Soc. of Clinical Neurophysiology [IO], Tokyo, Japan
Japanese Soc. of Computational Statistics [IO], Tokyo, Japan
Japanese Soc. for Dental Hea. [IO], Tokyo, Japan
Japanese Soc. of Developmental Biologists [IO], Kobe, Japan
Japanese Soc. for Dialysis Therapy [IO], Tokyo, Japan
Japanese Soc. of Fisheries Sci. [IO], Tokyo, Japan
Japanese Soc. of Hematology [IO], Kyoto, Japan
Japanese Soc. of Hypertension [IO], Tokyo, Japan
Japanese Soc. of Internal Medicine [IO], Tokyo, Japan
Japanese Soc. of Legal Medicine [IO], Tokyo, Japan
Japanese Soc. of Limnology [IO], Tokyo, Japan
Japanese Soc. of Medical Imaging Tech. [IO], Tokyo, Japan
Japanese Soc. of Microscopy [IO], Tokyo, Japan
Japanese Soc. of Nephrology [IO], Tokyo, Japan
Japanese Soc. of Neurology [IO], Tokyo, Japan
Japanese Soc. of Nuclear Medicine [IO], Tokyo, Japan
Japanese Soc. of Pathology [IO], Tokyo, Japan
Japanese Soc. of Plant Physiologists [IO], Kyoto, Japan
Japanese Soc. for Plant Systematics [IO], Kyoto, Japan
Japanese Soc. of Psychiatry and Neurology [IO], Tokyo, Japan
Japanese Soc. of Radiological Tech. [IO], Kyoto, Japan
Japanese Soc. of Snow and Ice [IO], Tokyo, Japan
Japanese Soc. of Social Psychology [IO], Tokyo, Japan
Japanese Soc. of Soil Sci. and Plant Nutrition [IO], Tokyo, Japan
Japanese Soc. of Tribologists [IO], Tokyo, Japan
Japanese Soc. of Tropical Medicine [IO], Nagasaki, Japan
Japanese Soc. of Veterinary Sci. [IO], Tokyo, Japan
Japanese Spaniel Club of Am. [★21594]
Japanese Standards Assn. [IO], Tokyo, Japan
Japanese Sword Soc. of the U.S. [20965], PO Box 5216, Albuquerque, NM 87181
Japanese Sword Soc. of the U.S. [20965], PO Box 5216, Albuquerque, NM 87181
Japanese Tenants Assn. [IO], Tokyo, Japan
Japanese Urological Assn. [IO], Tokyo, Japan
JARC [12503], 30301 Northwestern Hwy., Ste. 100, Farmington Hills, MI 48334, (248)538-6611

Reference to "IO" in place of a book number signifies that the association may be found in the 50th edition of International Organizations.

Jardine Clan Soc. of Canada [IO], Lindsay, ON, Canada
Jargon Press [★9621]
Jargon Soc. [9621], PO Box 15458, Winston-Salem, NC 27113
Jathika Pusthakala Ha Pralekhana Seva Mandalaya [★IO]
Jaw Joints and Allied Musculo-Skeletal Disorders Found. [16038], 790 Boylston St., Ste. 17-G, Boston, MA 02199, (617)266-2550
Jaycees Intl. [★13059]
Jaycees Intl. [★13059]
Jayco Jafari Intl. Travel Club [★22143]
Jayco Travel Club [22143], 58800 Executive Dr., Mishawaka, IN 46544, (574)258-0571
Jazz
    Amer. Fed. of Jazz Societies [9914]
    Assn. for the Advancement of Creative Musicians [10162]
    Intl. Assn. for Jazz Educ. [8653]
    JazzReach [9915]
Jazz Interactions - Defunct.
Jazz Journalists Assn. [2838], Gene Marlowe, Treas., 235 Adams St., 7A, Brooklyn, NY 11201
Jazz Journalists Assn. [2838], Gene Marlowe, Treas., 235 Adams St., 7A, Brooklyn, NY 11201
Jazz World Soc. - Address unknown since 2010.
Jazzmobile [10230], 154 W 127th St., 2nd Fl., New York, NY 10027, (212)866-4900
JazzReach [9915], 45 Main St., Ste. 728, Brooklyn, NY 11201, (718)625-5188
JBI Intl. - Jewish Braille Inst. of Am. [17091], 110 E 30th St., New York, NY 10016, (212)889-2525
JBI Intl. - Jewish Braille Inst. of Am. [17091], 110 E 30th St., New York, NY 10016, (212)889-2525
JCC Assn. [★12408]
JCI Auckland [IO], Auckland, New Zealand
JCI Belgium [IO], Brussels, Belgium
JCI Cameroon [IO], Douala, Cameroon
JCI Dublin [IO], Dublin, Ireland
Jean Piaget Soc. [★16407]
Jean Piaget Soc.: Soc. for the Stud. of Knowledge and Development [16407], Univ. of Minnesota, Inst. of Child Development, Minneapolis, MN 55455, (612)625-5957
Jeanette MacDonald Intl. Fan Club [23771], 1617 SW Indian Trail, Topeka, KS 66604-1951
Jeannie Seely's Circle of Friends [23860], 1128 Mayors Dr., Sevierville, TN 37862
JEDEC [1108], 3103 N 10th St., Ste. 240-S, Arlington, VA 22201-2107, (703)907-7540
Jednota Ceskych Matematiku a Fyziku [★IO]
Jeena [11798], 1510 Centre Pointe Dr., Milpitas, CA 95035, (408)957-0481
Jeff Carson Intl. Fan Club [23861], PO Box 1332, Franklin, TN 37065, (615)321-5080
Jefferson Davis Assn. [10673], Papers of Jefferson Davis, Rice Univ., MS 43, PO Box 1892, Houston, TX 77251-1892, (713)348-4990
Jefferson Found. [17439], 809 Quail St., Bldg. No. 1, Lakewood, CO 80215, (303)982-2210
Jefferson Legacy Found. [8735], PO Box 76, Ripton, VT 05766-0076, (802)388-7676
Jefferson's Poplar Forest; Thomas [9732]
Jeffrey Modell Found. [15110], 780 3rd Ave., New York, NY 10017, (212)819-0200
Jennifer Trust for Spinal Muscular Atrophy [IO], Stratford-upon-Avon, United Kingdom
Jensen Healey Preservation Soc. [21083], 4 Estrade Ln., Foothill Ranch, CA 92610
Jeofizik Muhendisleri Odasi [★IO]
Jernkontoret [★IO]
Jerome K. Jerome Soc. [IO], Newport, United Kingdom
Jerry B. Jenkins Christian Writers Guild [20295], 5525 N Union Blvd., Ste. 200, Colorado Springs, CO 80918, (719)495-5177
Jerry Jeff Walker Fan Club [23862], Tried and True Music, PO Box 39, Austin, TX 78767, (512)477-0036
Jersey Chamber of Commerce and Indus. [IO], Jersey, United Kingdom
Jersey Touch Assn. [IO], Jersey, United Kingdom
Jerusalem Institutions for the Blind [★17093]
Jerusalem Institutions for the Blind [★17093]

Jerusalem Intl. YMCA [IO], Jerusalem, Israel
Jerusalem Media and Communications Centre [IO], East Jerusalem, Israel
Jesse Stuart Found. [9386], PO Box 669, Ashland, KY 41105, (606)326-1667
Jessie Ball duPont Fund [12677], 1 Independent Dr., Ste. 1400, Jacksonville, FL 32202-0511, (904)353-0890
Jesuit Assn. of Student Personnel Administrators [7665], 2500 California Plz., Omaha, NE 68178, (402)280-2717
Jesuit Conf. [19437], 1616 P St. NW, Ste. 300, Washington, DC 20036-1408, (202)462-0400
Jesuit Educational Assn. [★7816]
Jesuit Educational Assn. [★7814]
Jesuit Missions [★19437]
Jesuit Refugee Ser. Italy [IO], Rome, Italy
Jesuit Refugee Service/U.S.A. [12785], 1016 16th St. NW, Ste. 500, Washington, DC 20036, (202)462-0400
Jesuit Refugee Service/U.S.A. [12785], 1016 16th St. NW, Ste. 500, Washington, DC 20036, (202)462-0400
Jesuit Res. Coun. of Am. [★7814]
Jesuit Secondary Educ. Assn. [7816], 1016 16th St. NW, Ste. 200, Washington, DC 20036, (202)667-3888
Jesuit Seismological Assn. - Defunct.
Jesuit Volunteer Corps: Northwest [19438], PO Box 3928, Portland, OR 97208-3928, (503)335-8202
Jesuits
    Jesuit Assn. of Student Personnel Administrators [7665]
Jesuits in Communication in the U.S. - Defunct.
Jesus to the Communist World [★20105]
Jesus to the Iron Curtain [★20105]
Jet 14 Class Assn. [22365], 6176 Winding Creek Ln., North Olmsted, OH 44070, (440)716-1859
Jet Sports Boating Assn. of Serbia and Montenegro [IO], Belgrade, Serbia
Jet Sports Racing Assn. of Great Britain [IO], Bradford, United Kingdom
Jeune Chambre Economique Francaise [IO], Paris, France
Jeune Chambre Economique de Madagascar [IO], Antananarivo, Madagascar
Jeune Chambre Economique du Mali [★IO]
Jeune Chambre Economique Suisse [★IO]
Jeune Chambre Intl. Canada [★IO]
Jeune Chambre Internationale - Togo [IO], Lome, Togo
Jeunesse Canada Monde [★IO]
Jeunesse des Chantiers Marocains [★IO]
Jeunesse Etudiante Catholique Internationale [★IO]
Jeunesse Ouvriere Chretienne Internationale [★IO]
Jeunesse en Reconstruction du Monde en Destruction [★IO]
Jeunesses Musicales Deutschland [★IO]
Jeunesses Musicales Intl. [IO], Brussels, Belgium
Jeunesses Musicales de Suisse [IO], Geneva, Switzerland
Jewel Heart [19368], 1129 Oak Valley Dr., Ann Arbor, MI 48108, (734)994-3387
Jewelers of Am. [2163], 52 Vanderbilt Ave., 19th Fl., New York, NY 10017-3827, (646)658-0246
Jewelers Bd. of Trade [2164], 95 Jefferson Blvd., Warwick, RI 02888-1046, (401)467-0055
Jewelers' Security Alliance [2165], 6 E 45th St., New York, NY 10017, (800)537-0067
Jewelers Security Alliance of the U.S. [★2165]
Jewelers Shipping Assn. [2166], 125 Carlsbad St., Cranston, RI 02920, (401)943-6020
Jewelers Vigilance Comm. [2167], 25 W 45th St., Ste. 1406, New York, NY 10036, (212)997-2002
Jewellers Assn. of Australia [IO], Sydney, Australia
Jewellers Vigilance Canada [IO], Toronto, ON, Canada
Jewellers and Watchmakers of New Zealand [IO], Christchurch, New Zealand
Jewellery and Allied Indus. Training Coun. [IO], Birmingham, United Kingdom
Jewellery Distributors' Assn. of the United Kingdom [IO], Birmingham, United Kingdom
Jewelry
    Accredited Gemologists Assn. [2152]

Amer. Gem Soc. [2153]
Amer. Gem Trade Assn. [2154]
Amer. Soc. of Jewelry Historians [9916]
Amer. Soc. of Jewelry Historians [9916]
Amer. Watchmakers-Clockmakers Inst. [2155]
Diamond Coun. of Am. [2156]
Diamond Dealers Club [2157]
Diamond Mfrs. and Importers Assn. of Am. [2158]
Gem and Lapidary Dealers Assn. [2159]
Gemological Inst. of Am. [2160]
Gemological Inst. of Am. Alumni Assn. [19085]
Gemological Inst. of Am. Alumni Assn. [19085]
Green Zionist Alliance [4268]
Independent Jewelers Org. [2161]
Indian Diamond and Colorstone Assn. [2162]
Jewelers of Am. [2163]
Jewelers Bd. of Trade [2164]
Jewelers' Security Alliance [2165]
Jewelers Shipping Assn. [2166]
Jewelers Vigilance Comm. [2167]
Jewelry Info. Center [2168]
Leading Jewelers of the World [2169]
Leading Jewelers of the World [2169]
Mfg. Jewelers and Suppliers of Am. [2170]
Natl. Assn. of Goldsmiths [2480]
Natl. Assn. of Jewelry Appraisers [2171]
Natural Color Diamond Assn. [2172]
Palladium Alliance Intl. [2489]
U.S. Faceters Guild [6590]
Women's Jewelry Assn. [2173]
Jewelry Indus. Coun. [★2168]
Jewelry Indus. Distributors Assn. - Address unknown since 2010.
Jewelry Info. Center [2168], 52 Vanderbilt Ave., 19th Fl., New York, NY 10017, (646)658-0246
Jewish
30 Years After [17999]
92nd St. Y [12400]
Abrahamic Alliance Intl. [19824]
Ameinu [19086]
Amer. Bd. of Rabbis - Vaad Harabonim of Am. [19837]
Amer. Conf. of Cantors [19838]
Amer. Coun. for Judaism [19839]
Amer. Jewish Comm. [19840]
Amer. Jewish Cong. [19841]
Amer. Jewish Historical Soc. [9917]
Amer. Jewish Joint Distribution Comm. [12401]
Amer. Jewish Joint Distribution Comm. [12401]
Amer. Jewish League for Israel [19842]
Amer. Jewish Soc. for Ser. [12402]
Amer. Sephardi Fed. [19843]
Amer. Soc. for Jewish Heritage in Poland [9918]
Amer. Soc. for Jewish Heritage in Poland [9918]
Amer. Zionist Movement [19844]
Americans for Peace Now [18010]
AMIT [19845]
Anti-Defamation League [17269]JewishARZA - Canada
Assn. of Humanistic Rabbis [19846]
Assn. of Jewish Family and Children's Agencies [12403]
Assn. for Jewish Stud. [8423]
Assn. for Jewish Stud. [8423]
Assn. for Religion and Intellectual Life [19669]
Assn. for the Social Sci. Stud. of Jewry [8424]
Assn. for the Social Sci. Stud. of Jewry [8424]JewishAUFBAU Trust
AZRA/World Union for Progressive Judaism North Am. [19847]
AZRA/World Union for Progressive Judaism North Am. [19847]
Beth Din of Am. [19848]
The Blue Card [12404]
B'nai B'rith Intl. [19849]
B'nai B'rith Intl. [19849]
B'nai B'rith International's Center for Jewish Identity [8425]
B'nai B'rith International's Center for Jewish Identity [8425]
B'nai B'rith Youth Org. [19850]
Bnai Zion Found. [19087]
Bnei Akiva of the U.S. and Canada [19851]
Canadian Inst. for Jewish Res. [23453]
Cantors Assembly [19852]

A star before a book entry number signifies that the name is not listed separately, but is mentioned within the entry.

Cantors Assembly [19852]
Center for Christian/Jewish Understanding [19650]
Center for Jewish Community Stud. [18017]
Center for Jewish History [19088]
Central Agency for Jewish Educ. [19089]
Central Conf. of Amer. Rabbis [19853]
Central Conf. of Amer. Rabbis [19853]
Central Rabbinical Cong. of the U.S.A. and Canada [19854]
Chabad Lubavitch [19855]
CLAL - The Natl. Jewish Center for Learning and Leadership [19856]
Coalition on the Env. and Jewish Life [19857]
Conf. on Jewish Material Claims Against Germany [12405]
Conf. of Presidents of Major Amer. Jewish Organizations [19858]
Congregation Shema Yisrael [19859]
Cong. for Jewish Culture [9919]
Cong. of Secular Jewish Organizations [9920]
Eleanor Leff Jewish Women's Rsrc. Center [9921]
Emunah Women of Am. [19860]
Emunah Women of Am. [19860]
European Assn. for Jewish Stud. [20452]
Fed. of Jewish Men's Clubs [19861]
Found. for the Advancement of Sephardic Stud. and Culture [19090]
GesherCity [19091]
Habonim Dror North Am. [19862]
Hadassah, The Women's Zionist Org. of Am. [19863]
Hadassah, The Women's Zionist Org. of Am. [19863]
Hashomer Hatzair Zionist Youth Movement [19864]
Hebrew Free Burial Assn. [19865]
Hebrew Immigrant Aid Soc. [12406]
Hebrew Immigrant Aid Soc. [12406]
Hillel: The Found. for Jewish Campus Life [19866]
Hineni [9922]
Hineni [9922]
Historical Soc. of Jews from Egypt [9923]
Inst. for Jewish Medical Ethics [19867]
Intl. Fed. of Rabbis [19868]
Intl. Fed. of Rabbis [19868]
Intl. Org. for Septuagint and Cognate Stud. [19349]
Jewish Chautauqua Soc. [19869]
Jewish Communal Ser. Assn. of North Am. [12407]
Jewish Communal Ser. Assn. of North Am. [12407]
Jewish Community Centers Assn. of North Am. [12408]
Jewish Coun. for Public Affairs [12409]
Jewish Defense Org. [18018]
Jewish Educ. Ser. of North Am. [8426]
Jewish Educators Assembly [8427]
Jewish Educators Assembly [8427]
Jewish Federations of North Am. [12410]
Jewish Free Loan Assn. [19870]
Jewish Healthcare Intl. [15194]
Jewish Heart for Africa [10822]
Jewish Labor Comm. [18019]
Jewish Lawyers Guild [19871]
Jewish Natl. Fund [19872]
Jewish Orthodox Feminist Alliance [19873]
Jewish Prisoner Services Intl. [19874]
Jewish Publication Soc. [9924]
Jewish Reconstructionist Fed. [19875]
Jewish Student Press Ser. [8428]
Jewish Telegraphic Agency [18020]
Jewish Telegraphic Agency [18020]
Jewish Voice for Peace [19092]
Jewish Women Intl. [19876]
Jewish Women Intl. [19876]
Jews for Animal Rights [10996]
Jews for Judaism [20186]
Jews for Morality [19877]
JOY for Our Youth [11330]
Kolel Chibas Jerusalem [19878]
League for Yiddish [19879]
Leo Baeck Inst. [9925]
Leo Baeck Inst. [9925]

Lubavitch Youth Org. [19880]
Maccabi USA/Sports for Israel [22985]
Machne Israel [12411]
Marcus Center of the Amer. Jewish Archives [9926]
Masada/Maccabi Israel Summer Programs [19881]
Memorial Found. for Jewish Culture [9927]
Memorial Found. for Jewish Culture [9927]
Men of Reform Judaism [19882]
MERCAZ USA [19883]
MERCAZ USA [19883]
Na'amat U.S.A. [19884]
Natl. Assn. of Jewish Chaplains [19526]
Natl. Assn. of Professors of Hebrew [8429]
Natl. Assn. of Temple Administrators [19885]
Natl. Assn. of Temple Educators [19886]
Natl. Assn. of Temple Educators [19886]
Natl. Center for Jewish Healing [9928]
Natl. Comm. for the Furtherance of Jewish Educ. [8430]
Natl. Conf. of Shomrim Societies [12412]
Natl. Conf. of Synagogue Youth [19887]
Natl. Coun. of Jewish Women [19888]
Natl. Coun. of Young Israel [19889]
Natl. Coun. of Young Israel | Young Israel Coun. of Rabbis [19890]
Natl. Havurah Comm. [19891]
Natl. Jewish Democratic Coun. [18387]
Natl. Ramah Commn. [8431]
Natl. Ramah Commn. [8431]
Natl. Yiddish Book Center [9929]
North Amer. Conf. on Ethiopian Jewry [18021]
North Amer. Conf. on Ethiopian Jewry [18021]
North Amer. Fed. of Temple Youth [19093]
OK Kosher Certification [19892]
ORT Am. [12413]
ORT Am. [12413]
Orthodox Union [19893]
Polish-American-Jewish Alliance for Youth Action [13551]
Proj. Genesis [8432]
Rabbinical Assembly [19894]
Rabbinical Assembly [19894]
Rabbinical Coun. of Am. [19895]
Reconstructionist Rabbinical Assn. [19896]
Reform Jewish Appeal [19897]
Reform Judaism [19898]
Religious Action Center of Reform Judaism [18022]
Religious Action Center of Reform Judaism [18022]
Remnant Of Israel [19770]
Schechter Day School Network [8433]
Shomrim Soc. [12414]
Soc. for the Advancement of Judaism [19899]
Soc. for Humanistic Judaism [19900]
Soc. for Humanistic Judaism [19900]
Soc. of Jewish Ethics [19901]
Soc. of Jewish Sci. [19902]
Tzivos Hashem [9930]
Union for Reform Judaism [19903]
Union for Reform Judaism | Commn. on Outreach and Synagogue Community [19904]
Union for Traditional Judaism [19905]
United Synagogue of Conservative Judaism [19906]
United Synagogue of Conservative Judaism [19906]
United Synagogue Youth [19907]
Universal Torah Registry [19908]
Volunteers for Israel [18016]
Women of Reform Judaism [19909]
Women's League for Conservative Judaism [19910]
World Coun. of Conservative/Masorti Synagogues [19911]
World Coun. of Conservative/Masorti Synagogues [19911]
World Jewish Cong., Amer. Sect. [18023]
World Jewish Cong., Amer. Sect. [18023]
World Org. for Jews From Arab Countries [18024]
YIVO Inst. for Jewish Res. [9931]
YIVO Inst. for Jewish Res. [9931]
Young Judaea [19912]

Yugntruf - Youth for Yiddish [9932]
Yugntruf - Youth for Yiddish [9932]
Zionist Org. of Am. [19913]
Jewish Alcoholics, Chemically Dependent Persons and Significant Others [13261], 135 W 50th St., 6th Fl., New York, NY 10020, (212)397-4197
Jewish Alcoholics, Chemically Dependent Persons and Significant Others [13261], 135 W 50th St., 6th Fl., New York, NY 10020, (212)397-4197
Jewish Assn. of Residential Care [★12503]
Jewish Assn. for Retarded Citizens [★12503]
Jewish Assn. for Services for the Aged [10847], 132 W 31st St., 15th Fl., New York, NY 10001, (212)273-5272
Jewish Book Coun. [9447], 520 8th Ave., 4th Fl., New York, NY 10018, (212)201-2920
Jewish Book Coun. of the Jewish Community Center Assn. of North Am. [★9447]
Jewish Braille Inst. of Am. [★17091]
Jewish Braille Inst. of Am. [★17091]
Jewish Chaplains Coun; JWB [19523]
Jewish Chautauqua Soc. [19869], 633 3rd Ave., New York, NY 10017, (212)650-4100
Jewish Children's Adoption Network [10792], PO Box 147016, Denver, CO 80214-7016, (303)573-8113
Jewish Comm. on the Middle East [18127], PO Box 18367, Washington, DC 20036, (202)362-5266
Jewish Comm. on the Middle East [18127], PO Box 18367, Washington, DC 20036, (202)362-5266
Jewish Communal Ser. Assn. of North Am. [12407], 25 Broadway, Ste. 1700, New York, NY 10004, (212)532-0167
Jewish Communal Ser. Assn. of North Am. [12407], 25 Broadway, Ste. 1700, New York, NY 10004, (212)532-0167
Jewish Community Centers Assn. of North Am. [12408], 520 8th Ave., New York, NY 10018, (212)532-4949
Jewish Community of Estonia [IO], Tallinn, Estonia
Jewish Coun. for Public Affairs [12409], PO Box 1415, New York, NY 10156-1415, (212)684-6950
Jewish Defense Org. [18018], PO Box 646, FDR Sta., New York, NY 10150, (212)252-3383
Jewish Educ. Ser. of North Am. [8426], 318 W 39th St., 5th Fl., New York, NY 10018, (212)284-6950
Jewish Educators Assembly [8427], PO Box 413, Cedarhurst, NY 11516, (516)569-2537
Jewish Educators Assembly [8427], PO Box 413, Cedarhurst, NY 11516, (516)569-2537
Jewish Federations of North Am. [12410], PO Box 157, New York, NY 10268, (212)284-6500
Jewish Film; Natl. Center for [9606]
The Jewish Found. for Christian Rescue [★17788]
The Jewish Found. for Christian Rescue [★17788]
Jewish Found. for the Righteous [17788], 305 7th Ave., 19th Fl., New York, NY 10001-6008, (212)727-9955
Jewish Found. for the Righteous [17788], 305 7th Ave., 19th Fl., New York, NY 10001-6008, (212)727-9955
Jewish Free Loan Assn. [19870], 6505 Wilshire Blvd., Ste. 715, Los Angeles, CA 90048, (323)761-8830
Jewish Fund for Justice [12733], New York Off., 330 7th Ave., Fl. 19, New York, NY 10001-5010, (212)213-2113
Jewish Funeral Directors of Am. [2538], 385 Craig Ct., Deerfield, IL 60015, (847)607-9156
Jewish Genealogical Soc. [20640], PO Box 6398, New York, NY 10249, (212)294-8326
Jewish Guild for the Blind [17092], 15 W 65th St., New York, NY 10023, (212)769-6200
Jewish Healing Center [★9928]
Jewish Healthcare Intl. [15194], The Selig Center, 1440 Spring St. NW, Atlanta, GA 30309-2832, (678)222-3722
Jewish Healthcare Intl. [15194], The Selig Center, 1440 Spring St. NW, Atlanta, GA 30309-2832, (678)222-3722
Jewish Heart for Africa [10822], 520 8th Ave., 4th Fl., New York, NY 10018, (212)710-6426
Jewish Historical Soc. of England [IO], London, United Kingdom
Jewish Inst. for Natl. Security Affairs [17506], 1779 Massachusetts Ave. NW, Ste. 515, Washington, DC 20036, (202)667-3900

Reference to "IO" in place of a book number signifies that the association may be found in the 50th edition of International Organizations.

Jewish Inst. for Natl. Security Affairs [17506], 1779 Massachusetts Ave. NW, Ste. 515, Washington, DC 20036, (202)667-3900

Jewish Labor Comm. [18019], 25 E 21st St., New York, NY 10010, (212)477-0707

Jewish Lawyers Guild [19871], 1 Battery Plz., 4th Fl., New York, NY 10022, (212)422-1200

Jewish Librarians Assn. [★9967]

Jewish Librarians Assn. [★9967]

Jewish Lib. Assn. [★9967]

Jewish Lib. Assn. [★9967]

Jewish Loan Fund [★19870]

Jewish Museums; Coun. of Amer. [10117]

Jewish Natl. Fund [19872], 42 E 69th St., New York, NY 10021, (212)879-9305

Jewish Occupational Coun. [★9044]

Jewish Occupational Coun. [★9044]

Jewish Orthodox Feminist Alliance [19873], 520 8th Ave., 4th Fl., New York, NY 10018, (212)679-8500

Jewish Peace Fellowship [18260], PO Box 271, Nyack, NY 10960-0271, (845)358-4601

Jewish Peace Lobby [17704], PO Box 7778, Silver Spring, MD 20907, (301)589-8764

Jewish Peace Lobby [17704], PO Box 7778, Silver Spring, MD 20907, (301)589-8764

Jewish Perspective; A Messianic [19968]

Jewish Prisoner Services Intl. [19874], PO Box 85840, Seattle, WA 98145-1840, (206)985-0577

Jewish Publication Soc. [9924], 2100 Arch St., 2nd Fl., Philadelphia, PA 19103-4599, (215)832-0608

Jewish Publication Soc. of Am. [★9924]

Jewish Reconstructionist Fed. [19875], 101 Greenwood Ave., Ste. 430, Jenkintown, PA 19046, (215)885-5601

Jewish Reconstructionist Found. [★19875]

Jewish Socialists Gp. [IO], London, United Kingdom

Jewish Storytelling Coalition [10544], 63 Gould Rd., Waban, MA 02468, (617)244-2884

Jewish Student Editorial Projects [★8428]

Jewish Student Press Ser. [8428], 125 Maiden Ln., 8th Fl., New York, NY 10038, (212)675-1168

Jewish Telegraphic Agency [18020], 330 7th Ave., 17th Fl., New York, NY 10001, (212)643-1890

Jewish Telegraphic Agency [18020], 330 7th Ave., 17th Fl., New York, NY 10001, (212)643-1890

Jewish Vegetarians [★10624]

Jewish Vegetarians of North Am. [10624], 49 Patton Dr., Newport News, VA 23606-1744

Jewish Voice for Peace [19092], 1611 Telegraph Ave., Ste. 550, Oakland, CA 94612, (510)465-1777

Jewish War Veterans of Canada [IO], Downsview, ON, Canada

Jewish War Veterans of the U.S.A. [20793], 1811 R St. NW, Washington, DC 20009, (202)265-6280

Jewish War Veterans of the U.S.A. I Natl. Ladies Auxiliary [20706], 1811 R St. NW, Washington, DC 20009-1603, (202)265-6280

Jewish War Veterans, U.S.A. Natl. Memorial [★20799]

Jewish Women Intl. [19876], 2000 M St. NW, Ste. 720, Washington, DC 20036, (202)857-1300

Jewish Women Intl. [19876], 2000 M St. NW, Ste. 720, Washington, DC 20036, (202)857-1300

Jewish Women Intl. of Canada [IO], Toronto, ON, Canada

Jewish Women's Rsrc. Center [★9921]

Jewish World Watch [17743], 5551 Balboa Blvd., Encino, CA 91316, (818)501-1836

Jews Against the Occupation - Address unknown since 2011.

Jews for Animal Rights [10996], 255 Humphrey St., Marblehead, MA 01945, (781)631-7601

Jew's Harp Guild [10231], 69954 Hidden Valley Ln., Cove, OR 97824

Jews for Jesus [19965], 60 Haight St., San Francisco, CA 94102-5802, (415)864-2600

Jews for Jesus [19965], 60 Haight St., San Francisco, CA 94102-5802, (415)864-2600

Jews for Judaism [20186], Rabbi Bentzion Kravitz, Dir., PO Box 351235, Los Angeles, CA 90035-1235, (310)556-3344

Jews for Judaism [20186], Rabbi Bentzion Kravitz, Dir., PO Box 351235, Los Angeles, CA 90035-1235, (310)556-3344

Jews for Morality [19877], Gravesend Sta., PO Box 262, Brooklyn, NY 11223, (206)350-2622

Jews for the Preservation of Firearms Ownership [17295], PO Box 270143, Hartford, WI 53027, (262)673-9745

JIAP [★9909]

JIAP [★9909]

JICA Alumni Assn. of Bhutan [IO], Thimphu, Bhutan

JILA [7268], Univ. of Colorado, 440 UCB, Boulder, CO 80309-0440, (303)492-7789

Jim Smith Soc. [19242], 256 Lake Meade Dr., East Berlin, PA 17316

Jim Smith Soc. [19242], 256 Lake Meade Dr., East Berlin, PA 17316

Jin Shin Do Found. for Bodymind Acupressure [16015], PO Box 416, Idyllwild, CA 92549, (951)659-5707

Jin Shin Do Found. for Bodymind Acupressure [16015], PO Box 416, Idyllwild, CA 92549, (951)659-5707

J.N. "Ding" Darling Found. - Defunct.

Joan B. Kroc Inst. for Intl. Peace Stud. [18261], Univ. of Notre Dame, Intl. Stud., 100 Hesburgh Ctr., Notre Dame, IN 46556-5677, (574)631-6970

Joan B. Kroc Inst. for Intl. Peace Stud. [18261], Univ. of Notre Dame, Intl. Stud., 100 Hesburgh Ctr., Notre Dame, IN 46556-5677, (574)631-6970

Joaquim Nabuco Found. [IO], Recife, Brazil

Job Accommodation Network [11799], PO Box 6080, Morgantown, WV 26506-6080, (304)293-7186

A Job is a Right Campaign [11942], PO Box 06053, Milwaukee, WI 53206, (414)374-1034

Jobs for America's Graduates [11943], 1729 King St., Ste. 100, Alexandria, VA 22314, (703)684-9479

Job's Daughters [★19133]

Job's Daughters [★19133]

Job's Daughters Intl. [19133], Susan M. Goolsby, Exec. Mgr., 233 W 6th St., Papillion, NE 68046-2210, (402)592-7987

Job's Daughters Intl. [19133], Susan M. Goolsby, Exec. Mgr., 233 W 6th St., Papillion, NE 68046-2210, (402)592-7987

Jobs for the Future [11944], 88 Broad St., Boston, MA 02110, (617)728-4446

Jobs With Justice [18808], 1325 Massachusetts Ave. NW, Ste. 200, Washington, DC 20005, (202)393-1044

The Jockey Club [22657], 821 Corporate Dr., Lexington, KY 40503, (859)224-2700

Jockey Club [IO], London, United Kingdom

Jockey Club Argentina [IO], Buenos Aires, Argentina

Jockey Club of Canada [IO], Etobicoke, ON, Canada

Jockey Club Ceske Republiky [★IO]

Jockey Club Czech Republic [IO], Prague, Czech Republic

Jockey Club Res. Found. [★4588]

Jockey Club Royal de Belgique [IO], Brussels, Belgium

Jockey Club of Turkey [IO], Istanbul, Turkey

Jockey Clube de Macau [★IO]

Jockey's Community Fund and Guild [★22658]

Jockeys' Guild [22658], 103 Wind Haven Dr., Ste. 200, Nicholasville, KY 40356, (859)523-5625

Jodo Shinshu Buddhist Temples of Canada [IO], Richmond, BC, Canada

Johannes Schwalm Historical Assn. [20641], PO Box 127, Scotland, PA 17254-0127

John A. Hartford Found. [10848], 55 E 59th St., 16th Fl., New York, NY 10022-1713, (212)832-7788

John Berry's Fan Club [23863], 1720 Epps Bridge Rd., Ste. 108, Athens, GA 30606, (615)297-7002

John Birch Soc. [17427], PO Box 8040, Appleton, WI 54912, (920)749-3780

John Brown Anti-Klan Comm. - Defunct.

John Burroughs Assn. [7140], 15 W 77th St., New York, NY 10024, (212)769-5169

John Burroughs Memorial Assn. [★7140]

John Clare Soc. [IO], Ely, United Kingdom

John Clough Genealogical Soc. [20542], 21 Lowell Rd., Pembroke, MA 02359

John and Elizabeth Curtis/Curtiss Soc. [★20499]

John Ericsson Soc. [10674], 5 E 48th St., New York, NY 10017, (845)735-1567

John F. Kennedy Lib. Found. [9990], Columbia Point, Boston, MA 02125, (617)514-1550

John Gary Intl. Fan Club [23864], 7 Briarwood Cir., Richardson, TX 75080

John Gary Intl. Fan Club [23864], 7 Briarwood Cir., Richardson, TX 75080

John Gary Memorial Fan Club [★23864]

John Gary Memorial Fan Club [★23864]

John Gray Intl. Fan Club [★23864]

John Gray Intl. Fan Club [★23864]

John Hall and Mary Bates Family Org. - Defunct.

John Hampden Soc. [IO], High Wycombe, United Kingdom

John Howard Assn. [11719], 375 E Chicago Ave., Ste. 529, Chicago, IL 60611, (312)503-6300

John Innes Mfrs. Assn. [IO], Reading, United Kingdom

John Libby Family Assn. [20543], 195 Deacon Haynes Rd., Concord, MA 01742, (978)369-6250

John Marshall Found. [9705], Lynn Brackenridge, Exec. Dir., 209 W Franklin St., Richmond, VA 23220, (804)775-0861

John Milton Soc. for the Blind - USA - Defunct.

John More Assn. [20544], Judith Erikson, Treas., 188 Bay Shore Dr., Plymouth, MA 02360

John Pelham Historical Assn. [10675], Bill Gilmore, Treas., 210 Old Gabblettville Rd., West Point, GA 31833

John Reich Collectors Soc. [21977], PO Box 135, Harrison, OH 45030-0135

John Roger Found. [★12214]

John Roger Found. [★12214]

John S. and James L. Knight Found. [12415], 200 S Biscayne Blvd., Ste. 3300, Miami, FL 33131-2349, (305)908-2600

John T. Conner Center for East/West Reconciliation - Defunct.

John Templeton Found. [20187], 300 Conshohocken State Rd., Ste. 500, West Conshohocken, PA 19428, (610)941-2828

John Tracy Clinic [14945], 806 W Adams Blvd., Los Angeles, CA 90007-2505, (213)748-5481

John Von Neumann Cmpt. Soc. - Hungary [IO], Budapest, Hungary

John and Walter Cusick Family Assn. - Defunct.

Johnnie Ray Intl. Fan Club [23865], 220 S 8th St., 4th Fl., Eunice, LA 70535

Johnny Adams Blues Org. - Address unknown since 2010.

Johnny Benson Fan Club [23791], 3128 Bird, Grand Rapids, MI 49525

Johns Hopkins Center for Alternatives to Animal Testing [10997], 615 N Wolfe St., Baltimore, MD 21205, (410)614-4990

Johnson Soc. - Lichfield [IO], Lichfield, United Kingdom

Johnson Soc. of London [IO], London, United Kingdom

Johnston(e) Clan in Am. [★20460]

Johnston(e) Clan in Am. [★20460]

Joho-Shori Gakkai [★IO]

Join Hands Day [11604], 1301 W 22nd St., Ste. 700, Oak Brook, IL 60523, (630)522-6322

Joiners' and Ceilers' Company [IO], Woking, United Kingdom

Joint Assn. of Classical Teachers [IO], London, United Kingdom

Joint Baltic Amer. Comm. [★17209]

Joint Baltic Amer. Comm. [★17209]

Joint Baltic Amer. Natl. Comm. [17209], 400 Hurley Ave., Rockville, MD 20850-3121, (301)340-1954

Joint Baltic Amer. Natl. Comm. [17209], 400 Hurley Ave., Rockville, MD 20850-3121, (301)340-1954

Joint Center for Political and Economic Stud. [7290], 1090 Vermont Ave. NW, Ste. 1100, Washington, DC 20005-4928, (202)789-3500

Joint Center for Political Stud. [★7290]

Joint Commn. [15060], 1 Renaissance Blvd., Oak-brook Terrace, IL 60181-4294, (630)792-5000

Joint Commn. on Accreditation of Healthcare Organizations [★15060]

Joint Commn. on Accreditation of Hospitals [★15060]

Joint Commn. on Allied Hea. Personnel in Ophthalmology [15967], 2025 Woodlane Dr., St. Paul, MN 55125-2998, (651)731-2944

Joint Commn. on Competitive Safeguards and the Medical Aspects of Sports [★16719]

Joint Commn. on Sports Medicine and Sci. [16719], 2952 Stemmons Fwy., Ste. 200, Dallas, TX 75247, (214)637-6282

A star before a book entry number signifies that the name is not listed separately, but is mentioned within the entry.

Joint Comm. on Careers in Nursing [★15781]
Joint Comm. on Grassland Farming [★4862]
Joint Comm. on Mortuary Educ. [★2526]
Joint Comm. of Schools of Journalism [★8434]
Joint Comm. of the States [5197], Natl. Alcohol Beverage Control Assn., 4401 Ford Ave., Ste. 700, Alexandria, VA 22302-1473, (703)578-4200
Joint Comm. of the States to Stud. Alcohol Beverage Laws [★5197]
Joint Comm. on Tall Buildings [★6196]
Joint Comm. on Tall Buildings [★6196]
Joint Coun. of Allergy, Asthma and Immunology [13641], 50 N Brockway, Ste. 3-3, Palatine, IL 60067, (847)934-1918
Joint Coun. in Economic Educ. [★7987]
Joint Coun. on Intl. Children's Services [10793], 117 S St. Asaph St., Alexandria, VA 22314, (703)535-8045
Joint Coun. on Intl. Children's Services [10793], 117 S St. Asaph St., Alexandria, VA 22314, (703)535-8045
Joint Coun. of Socio Economics of Allergy [★13641]
Joint Coun. for the Welfare of Immigrants [IO], London, United Kingdom
Joint Cultural Appeal - Defunct.
Joint Distribution Comm. [★12401]
Joint Distribution Comm. [★12401]
Joint Distribution Comm. for Relief of Jewish War Sufferers [★12401]
Joint Distribution Comm. for Relief of Jewish War Sufferers [★12401]
Joint Educational Development - Defunct.
Joint Electron Device Engg. Coun. [★1108]
Joint FAO-WHO Codex Alimentarius Commn. [IO], Rome, Italy
Joint Indus. Bd. of the Elecl. Indus. [921], 158-11 Harry Van Arsdale Jr. Ave., Flushing, NY 11365, (718)591-2000
Joint Indus. Gp. [2099], 111 Rockville Pike, Ste. 410, Rockville, MD 20850, (202)466-5490
Joint Info. Systems Comm. [IO], Bristol, United Kingdom
Joint Inst. for Nuclear Res. [IO], Dubna, Russia
Joint Labor Mgt. Comm. of the Retail Food Indus. [23190], 2153 Wealthy St. SE, UPS Box 324 E, Grand Rapids, MI 49506, (800)304-5540
Joint Maritime Cong. [★5788]
Joint Natl. Comm. for Languages [9940], 4646 40th St. NW, Ste. 310, Washington, DC 20016, (202)966-8477
Joint Nature Conservation Comm. [IO], Peterborough, United Kingdom
Joint Radio Co. [IO], London, United Kingdom
Joint Rev. Commn. for the Ophthalmic Medical Personnel [★8579]
Joint Rev. Comm. on Educ. in Diagnostic Medical Sonography [8581], 6021 Univ. Blvd., Ste. 500, Ellicott City, MD 21043, (443)973-3251
Joint Rev. Comm. on Educ. in Radiologic Tech. [8582], 20 N Wacker Dr., Ste. 2850, Chicago, IL 60606-3182, (312)704-5300
Joint Rev. Comm. on Educ. for the Surgical Technologist [★15361]
Joint Rev. Comm. on Educational Programs for the EMT-Paramedic [★8578]
Joint Rev. Comm. on Educational Programs for Physician's Assistants [★16234]
Joint Rev. Comm. for the Ophthalmic Medical Asst. [★8579]
Joint Rev. Comm. for Ophthalmic Medical Personnel [★8579]
Joint Rev. Comm. for Respiratory Therapy Educ. [★16845]
Joint Rev. on Educational Programs for Physician Assistants [★16234]
Joint Univ. Coun. [IO], Nottingham, United Kingdom
Joint Users of Siemens Technologies U.S. - Address unknown since 2011.
Joint Venture: Silicon Valley Network [7512], 100 W San Fernando St., Ste. 310, San Jose, CA 95113-1820, (408)298-9330
Jon-Erik Hexum Fan Club [23772], 32 Lee Ave., St. Louis, MO 63136
Jones/NCTI [495], 9697 E Mineral Ave., Centennial, CO 80112, (303)797-9393

Jongerenwerkgroep voor Sterrenkunde [★IO]
Joni and Friends [11800], PO Box 3333, Agoura Hills, CA 91376-3333, (818)707-5664
Joni James Intl. Fan Club [23803], PO Box 7207, Westchester, IL 60154-7207
Jorbrugsakademikernes Forbund [★IO]
Jordan
  Jordan Info. Bur. [23421]
Jordan Athletic Fed. [IO], Amman, Jordan
Jordan Badminton Fed. [IO], Amman, Jordan
Jordan Exporters and Producers Assn. of Fruit and Vegetables [IO], Amman, Jordan
Jordan Hotel Assn. [IO], Amman, Jordan
Jordan Info. Bur. [23421], 3504 Intl. Dr. NW, Washington, DC 20008, (202)265-1606
Jordan Insurance Fed. [IO], Amman, Jordan
Jordan Red Crescent [IO], Amman, Jordan
Jordan Register - Address unknown since 2010.
Jordan Squash Fed. [IO], Amman, Jordan
Jordan Tennis Fed. [IO], Amman, Jordan
Jordanian Assn. for Family Planning and Protection [IO], Amman, Jordan
Jordanian Astronomical Soc. [IO], Amman, Jordan
Jordanian Chap. of Epilepsy [IO], Amman, Jordan
Jordanian Chem. Soc. [IO], Amman, Jordan
Jordanian Natl. Comm. for Women [IO], Amman, Jordan
Jordanian Osteoporosis Prevention Soc. [IO], Amman, Jordan
Jordanian Physiotherapy Soc. [IO], Amman, Jordan
Jordanian Soc. for Fertility and Genetics [IO], Amman, Jordan
Jordanian Soc. of Gastroenterology [IO], Amman, Jordan
Jordanian Soc. for Occupational Therapy [IO], Amman, Jordan
Jose Carreras Club Vienna [IO], Vienna, Austria
Jose Carreras Intl. Leukaemia Found. [IO], Barcelona, Spain
Joseph Campbell Found. [8949], PO Box 36, San Anselmo, CA 94979-0036, (800)330-6984
Joseph Conrad Soc. of Am. [9387], Chapman Univ., Dept. of English and Comparative Literature, 1 Univ. Dr., Orange, CA 92866
Joseph Drown Found. [11907], 1999 Ave. of the Stars, Ste. 2330, Los Angeles, CA 90067, (310)277-4488
Joseph and Edna Josephson Inst. of Ethics [11982], 9841 Airport Blvd., Ste. 300, Los Angeles, CA 90045-5415, (310)846-4800
Joseph P. Kennedy, Jr. Found. [12504], 1133 19th St. NW, 12th Fl., Washington, DC 20036-3604, (202)393-1250
Joseph P. and Rose F. Kennedy Inst. of Ethics [11983], Georgetown Univ., Healy Hall, 4th Fl., Washington, DC 20057-1212, (202)687-8099
Josephine Porter Inst. for Applied Bio-Dynamics [3743], PO Box 133, Woolwine, VA 24185, (276)930-2463
Joshua Slocum Soc. Intl. [22366], 15 Codfish Hill Rd. Extension, Bethel, CT 06801, (203)790-6616
Josiah Macy, Jr. Found. [14719], 44 E 64th St., New York, NY 10065-7306, (212)486-2424
Josiah Royce Soc. [10395], Vanderbilt Univ., Dept. of Philosophy, 111 Furman Hall, Nashville, TN 37240, (516)659-2779
Joslin Clinic [★14354]
Joslin Diabetes Center [14354], 1 Joslin Pl., Boston, MA 02215, (617)732-2400
Joslin Diabetes Found. [★14354]
Joubert Syndrome Found. [★14606]
Joubert Syndrome Found. and Related Cerebellar Disorders [14606], 414 Hungerford Dr., Ste. 252, Rockville, MD 20850, (614)864-1362
Joubert Syndrome Parents in Touch Network [★14606]
Journalism
  Accrediting Coun. on Educ. in Journalism and Mass Communications [8434]
  Africa News Ser. [17144]
  Amer. Philatelic Soc. Writers Unit [22012]
  Amer. Press Inst. [8435]
  Assoc. Collegiate Press [8436]
  Assn. for Educ. in Journalism and Mass Commun. [8437]

  Carol Burnett Fund for Responsible Journalism [8438]
  Coll. Media Advisers [8439]
  Collegiate Network [8440]
  Community Coll. Journalism Assn. [8441]
  Dow Jones Newspaper Fund [8442]
  Football Writers Assn. of Am. [22588]
  Golf Writers Assn. of Am. [22610]
  John S. and James L. Knight Found. [12415]
  Journalism Assn. of Community Colleges [8443]
  Journalism Educ. Assn. [8444]
  Kappa Tau Alpha [23573]
  Natl. Agricultural Communicators of Tomorrow [8445]
  Natl. Assn. of Independent Writers and Editors [2844]
  Natl. Journalism Center [17721]
  New Am. Media [18099]
  Nieman Found. for Journalism at Harvard [8446]
  Peace in Focus [18275]
  Quill and Scroll Soc. [23574]
  Scripps Howard Found. [8447]
  Sigma Delta Chi Found. [23575]
  Silent Images [13148]
  Soc. of Environmental Journalists [8448]
  Student Press Law Center [17358]
  Thomas Nast Soc. [9208]
  United Amateur Press Assn. of Am. [22107]
  Washington Journalism Center [8449]
Journalism Assn. of Community Colleges [8443], PO Box 163509, Sacramento, CA 95816, (562)652-9435
Journalism Assn. of Junior Colleges [★8443]
Journalism Educ. Assn. [8444], Kansas State Univ., 103 Kedzie Hall, Manhattan, KS 66506-1505, (785)532-5532
Journalistes Canadiens pour la Liberte d'Expression [★IO]
Journalists
  Amer. Philatelic Soc. Writers Unit [22012]
  Auto. Journalists Assn. of Canada [22674]JournalistsBritish Assn. of Journalists
  European Journalism Centre [17042]
  European Journalism Training Assn. [2859]
  Football Writers Assn. of Am. [22588]
  Foreign Press Assn. [2828]
  Golf Writers Assn. of Am. [22610]
  Intl. Alliance of Equestrian Journalists [21738]
  Outer Critics Circle [10597]
  Silent Images [13148]JournalistsSoc. for Editors and Proofreaders
  Student Press Law Center [17358]
Journey to the Heart [9866], 10828 Whitburn St., Culver City, CA 90230, (800)540-0471
Journey to Solidarity [14139], 301 Cottage Grove Ave. SE, Cedar Rapids, IA 52403, (888)860-9263
Journey Toward Sustainability [8159], 6585 Gatehouse Ct. NW, Concord, NC 28027, (704)641-7223
Journeying [IO], Saffron Walden, United Kingdom
Journeys Within Our Community [IO], Siem Reap, Cambodia
Jousting
  Natl. Jousting Assn. [22702]
Jove Cambra de Barcelona [★IO]
Jove Cambra De Girona [★IO]
Jove Cambra De Terrassa [★IO]
Jove Cambra D'empresaris de Barcelona [★IO]
Jove Cambra Internacional Igualada [★IO]
Jove Cambra de Lleida [★IO]
Jove Cambra de Manresa [★IO]
Jove Cambra de Reus [★IO]
Jove Cambra de Sabadell [★IO]
Jove Cambra de Tarragona [★IO]
Joves Cambres de Catalunya [IO], Barcelona, Spain
Jowett Car Club [IO], Essex, United Kingdom
JOY for Our Youth [11330], 1805 Swarthmore Ave., Lakewood, NJ 08701, (866)GIV-EJOY
Joy Proj. [14436], PO Box 16488, St. Paul, MN 55116
Joyce Soc; James [9384]
Jozef Pilsudski Inst. of Am. for Res. in the Modern History of Poland [10460], 180 2nd Ave., New York, NY 10003-5778, (212)505-9077
Jozef Pilsudski Inst. of Am. for Res. in the Modern History of Poland [10460], 180 2nd Ave., New York, NY 10003-5778, (212)505-9077 ·

Reference to "IO" in place of a book number signifies that the association may be found in the 50th edition of International Organizations.

Jubilee Action - UK **[IO]**, Guildford, United Kingdom
Jubilee Res. **[IO]**, London, United Kingdom
Jubilee U.S.A. Network **[17681]**, 212 E Capitol St. NE, Washington, DC 20003, (202)783-3566
Jubilee U.S.A. Network **[17681]**, 212 E Capitol St. NE, Washington, DC 20003, (202)783-3566
Judge Advocates Assn. **[5808]**, Theresa Kauffman, Exec. Dir., 5958 Oakland Park Dr., Burke, VA 22015, (703)474-7691
Judge David L. Bazelon Center for Mental Hea. Law **[17296]**, 1101 15th St. NW, Ste. 1212, Washington, DC 20005, (202)467-5730
The Judge GTO Intl. **[21084]**, 114 Prince George Dr., Hampton, VA 23669, (757)838-2059
Judicial Reform
　Center for Judicial Accountability **[18025]**
　Criminal Justice Policy Found. **[18026]**
　Fully Informed Jury Assn. **[18027]**
　HALT **[18028]**
　Lawyers for Civil Justice **[18029]**
　Natl. Judicial Educ. Prog. **[18030]**
Judicial Selection Proj. **[★5932]**
Judiciary
　Amer. Judges Assn. **[5612]**
　Amer. Judicature Soc. **[5613]**
　Assn. of Administrative Law Judges **[5614]**
　Assn. of Reporters of Judicial Decisions **[5615]**
　Conf. of Chief Justices **[5616]**
　Coun. for Court Excellence **[5617]**
　Equal Justice Works **[5618]**
　Fed. Administrative Law Judges Conf. **[5619]**
　Federalist Soc. for Law and Public Policy Stud. **[5620]**
　Fund for Modern Courts **[5621]**
　Inst. of Judicial Admin. **[5622]**JudiciaryIntl. Assn. of Lesbian and Gay Judges
　Intl. Assn. of Women Judges **[5623]**
　Natl. Alliance for Family Court Justice **[5624]**
　Natl. Alliance for Family Court Justice **[5624]**
　Natl. Amer. Indian Court Judges Assn. **[5625]**
　Natl. Assn. of Appellate Court Attorneys **[5260]**
　Natl. Assn. of Hearing Officials **[5626]**
　Natl. Assn. of Women Judges **[5627]**
　Natl. Center for State Courts **[5628]**
　Natl. Conf. of Bankruptcy Judges **[5629]**
　Natl. Conf. of Fed. Trial Judges **[5630]**
　Natl. Conf. of Specialized Court Judges **[5631]**
　Natl. Coun. of Juvenile and Family Court Judges **[5632]**
　Natl. Judges Assn. **[5633]**
　Natl. Judicial Coll. **[5634]**
Judkins Family Assn. **[20545]**, 1538 NW 60th St., Seattle, WA 98107-2328
Judo
　Amer. Judo and Jujitsu Fed. **[22703]**
　U.S. Judo **[22704]**
　U.S. Judo Assn. **[22705]**
　U.S. Judo Fed. **[22706]**
　World Martial Arts Assn. **[22771]**
Judo Black Belt Fed. of the U.S.A. **[★22706]**
Judo Scotland **[IO]**, Newbridge, United Kingdom
Juggling
　Intl. Jugglers' Assn. **[22707]**
　World Juggling Fed. **[22708]**
Jugoslovensko udruzenje za plasticnu, rekonstruktivnu i estetsku hirurgiju **[★IO]**
Juice Products Assn. **[449]**, 750 Natl. Press Bldg., 529 14th St. NW, Washington, DC 20045, (202)785-3232
Julian Jaynes Soc. **[16408]**, PO Box 778153, Henderson, NV 89077-8153
Julius E. Farr Family Org. - Defunct.
JumpStart Coalition for Personal Financial Literacy **[8188]**, 919 18th St. NW, Ste. 300, Washington, DC 20006, (202)466-8610
JumpStart Intl. **[11605]**, PO Box 868, Decatur, GA 30031, (404)607-8153
June 4th Found. **[17241]**, 733 15th St. NW, Ste. 700, Washington, DC 20005, (202)347-0017
June 4th Found. **[★17240]**
Junge Liberalen Bonn **[IO]**, Bonn, Germany
Junge Wirtschaft Osterreich **[★IO]**
Junior Achievement **[7795]**, 1 Educ. Way, Colorado Springs, CO 80906, (719)540-8000
Junior Achievement **[7795]**, 1 Educ. Way, Colorado Springs, CO 80906, (719)540-8000

Junior Achievement of Canada **[IO]**, Toronto, ON, Canada
Junior Achievement China **[IO]**, Beijing, People's Republic of China
Junior Achievement Ireland **[IO]**, Monkstown, Ireland
Junior Achievement Russia **[IO]**, Moscow, Russia
Junior Achievement Tajikistan **[IO]**, Khujand, Tajikistan
Junior Activities Dept. of the Amer. Angus Assn. **[★3925]**
Junior Amer. Citizens **[9117]**, 1776 D St. NW, Washington, DC 20006-5303, (202)628-1776
Junior Art Club **[IO]**, Accra, Ghana
Junior Beta Club **[★23636]**
Junior Chamber Austria **[IO]**, Vienna, Austria
Junior Chamber Barcelona **[IO]**, Barcelona, Spain
Junior Chamber Empresaris de Barcelona **[IO]**, Barcelona, Spain
Junior Chamber Germany **[IO]**, Berlin, Germany
Junior Chamber Girona **[IO]**, Girona, Spain
Junior Chamber Igualada **[IO]**, Igualada, Spain
Junior Chamber Intl. **[13059]**, 15645 Olive Blvd., Chesterfield, MO 63017, (636)449-3100
Junior Chamber Intl. **[13059]**, 15645 Olive Blvd., Chesterfield, MO 63017, (636)449-3100
Junior Chamber Intl. Australia **[IO]**, Montmorency, Australia
Junior Chamber Intl. Bangladesh **[IO]**, Dhaka, Bangladesh
Junior Chamber Intl. Benin **[IO]**, Cotonou, Benin
Junior Chamber Intl. Bolivia **[IO]**, Cochabamba, Bolivia
Junior Chamber Intl. Botswana **[IO]**, Gaborone, Botswana
Junior Chamber Intl. Brasil **[IO]**, Curitiba, Brazil
Junior Chamber Intl. Burkina **[IO]**, Ouagadougou, Burkina Faso
Junior Chamber Intl. Canada **[IO]**, Toronto, ON, Canada
Junior Chamber Intl. Colombia **[IO]**, Bogota, Colombia
Junior Chamber Intl. Denmark **[IO]**, Copenhagen, Denmark
Junior Chamber Intl. of Dominican Republic **[IO]**, Santo Domingo, Dominican Republic
Junior Chamber Intl. Ecuador **[IO]**, Guayaquil, Ecuador
Junior Chamber Intl. Estonia **[IO]**, Tallinn, Estonia
Junior Chamber Intl. Finland **[IO]**, Helsinki, Finland
Junior Chamber Intl. Gabon **[IO]**, Port-Gentil, Gabon
Junior Chamber Intl. Greece **[IO]**, Piraeus, Greece
Junior Chamber Intl. Hong Kong **[IO]**, Hong Kong, People's Republic of China
Junior Chamber Intl. Hungary **[IO]**, Budapest, Hungary
Junior Chamber Intl. Indonesia **[IO]**, Jakarta, Indonesia
Junior Chamber Intl. Ireland **[IO]**, Dublin, Ireland
Junior Chamber Intl. Island **[IO]**, Reykjavik, Iceland
Junior Chamber Intl. Japan **[IO]**, Tokyo, Japan
Junior Chamber Intl. Jordan **[IO]**, Amman, Jordan
Junior Chamber Intl. Korea **[IO]**, Seoul, Republic of Korea
Junior Chamber Intl. Latvia **[IO]**, Riga, Latvia
Junior Chamber Intl. Limerick **[IO]**, Limerick, Ireland
Junior Chamber Intl. Lithuania **[IO]**, Vilnius, Lithuania
Junior Chamber Intl. Lleida **[IO]**, Lleida, Spain
Junior Chamber Intl. Malaysia **[IO]**, Kuala Lumpur, Malaysia
Junior Chamber Intl. Mali **[IO]**, Bamako, Mali
Junior Chamber Intl. Mexico **[IO]**, Mexico City, Mexico
Junior Chamber Intl. New Zealand **[IO]**, Wellington, New Zealand
Junior Chamber Intl. Nigeria **[IO]**, Lagos, Nigeria
Junior Chamber Intl. Pakistan **[IO]**, Karachi, Pakistan
Junior Chamber Intl. Peru **[IO]**, Lima, Peru
Junior Chamber Intl. Philippines **[IO]**, Quezon City, Philippines
Junior Chamber Intl. South Africa **[IO]**, Pretoria, Republic of South Africa
Junior Chamber Intl. Sweden **[IO]**, Stockholm, Sweden
Junior Chamber Intl. The Netherlands **[IO]**, De Rijp, Netherlands

Junior Chamber Intl. Tunisie **[IO]**, Tunis, Tunisia
Junior Chamber Intl. Turkey **[IO]**, Istanbul, Turkey
Junior Chamber Intl. Ukraine **[IO]**, Kiev, Ukraine
Junior Chamber Intl. United Kingdom **[IO]**, Grantham, United Kingdom
Junior Chamber Intl. of Venezuela **[IO]**, Valencia, Venezuela
Junior Chamber Intl. Waterford **[IO]**, Waterford, Ireland
Junior Chamber Italiana **[IO]**, Varese, Italy
Junior Chamber Manresa **[IO]**, Manresa, Spain
Junior Chamber Namibia **[IO]**, Windhoek, Namibia
Junior Chamber Nepal **[IO]**, Kathmandu, Nepal
Junior Chamber Poland **[IO]**, Cieszyn, Poland
Junior Chamber Reus **[IO]**, Reus, Spain
Junior Chamber Romania **[IO]**, Bucharest, Romania
Junior Chamber Sabadell **[IO]**, Sabadell, Spain
Junior Chamber Serbia **[IO]**, Subotica, Serbia
Junior Chamber Singapore **[IO]**, Singapore, Singapore
Junior Chamber Switzerland **[IO]**, Glarus, Switzerland
Junior Chamber Tarragona **[IO]**, Tarragona, Spain
Junior Chamber Terrassa **[IO]**, Terrassa, Spain
Junior Chamber Zimbabwe **[IO]**, Harare, Zimbabwe
Junior Chaplain's Corps **[★19625]**
Junior Classical League **[★7865]**
Junior Coll. Journalism Assn. **[★8441]**
Junior Engg. Tech. Soc. **[8125]**, 1420 King St., Ste. 405, Alexandria, VA 22314, (703)548-5387
Junior Engg. Training for Schools **[★8125]**
Junior Hadassah **[★19912]**
Junior Hollywood Radio and TV Soc. **[496]**, 13701 Riverside Dr., Ste. 205, Sherman Oaks, CA 91423
Junior Knights of Peter Claver **[18954]**, 1825 Orleans Ave., New Orleans, LA 70116-2825, (504)821-4425
Junior Lodge, Independent Order of Odd Fellows **[19183]**, Sovereign Grand Lodge Off., 422 Trade St., Winston-Salem, NC 27101, (336)725-5955
Junior Optimist Clubs **[★13060]**
Junior Optimist Clubs **[★13060]**
Junior Optimist Octagon Intl. **[13060]**, 4494 Lindell Blvd., St. Louis, MO 63108, (314)371-6000
Junior Optimist Octagon Intl. **[13060]**, 4494 Lindell Blvd., St. Louis, MO 63108, (314)371-6000
Junior Order, Knights of Pythias **[19095]**, Supreme Lodge Knights of Pythias, 59 Coddington St., Ste. 202, Quincy, MA 02169-4510, (617)472-8800
Junior Panel Outdoor Advt. Assn. **[★91]**
Junior Shag Assn. **[9557]**, Ron Alexander, 1141 Bate Harvey Rd., Clover, SC 29710, (910)582-0048
Junior State of Am. **[8487]**, 800 D Claremont St., Ste. 202, San Mateo, CA 94402, (650)347-1600
Junior Statesmen of Am. **[★8487]**
Junior Statesmen Found. **[8488]**, 800 S Claremont St., Ste. 202, San Mateo, CA 94402, (650)347-1600
Junior Wireless Club, Limited **[★22121]**
Junkins Family Assn. **[20546]**, 9 Springside Ct., Yardley, PA 19067, (215)295-4279
Junta Internacional de Fiscalizacion de Estupefacientes **[★IO]**
Juridisk Radgivning for Kvinner **[★IO]**
Jussi Bjorling Soc. U.S.A. **[9239]**, 3337 Conservancy Ln., Middleton, WI 53562, (608)836-6911
Just Detention Intl. **[11720]**, 3325 Wilshire Blvd., Ste. 340, Los Angeles, CA 90010, (213)384-1400
Just One Break **[11801]**, 570 Seventh Ave., New York, NY 10018, (212)785-7300
Just for Openers **[21365]**, PO Box 64, Chapel Hill, NC 27514, (919)824-3046
Just Plain Folks Music Org. **[2561]**, 5327 Kit Dr., Indianapolis, IN 46237
Just Think **[18829]**, 539 Bryant St., Ste. 301, San Francisco, CA 94107, (415)734-9100
Just Transition Alliance **[23227]**, 2810 Camino Del Rio S, Ste. 116, San Diego, CA 92108, (619)573-4934
Just Transition Alliance **[23227]**, 2810 Camino Del Rio S, Ste. 116, San Diego, CA 92108, (619)573-4934
Just Vision **[17409]**, 1616 P St. NW, Ste. 340, Washington, DC 20036, (202)232-6821
Justice for Children Intl. **[★11344]**

A star before a book entry number signifies that the name is not listed separately, but is mentioned within the entry.

Justice for Children Intl. [★11344]
Justice Inc. [17490], 6047 Tyvola Glen Cir., Charlotte, NC 28217, (800)965-0387
Justice and Peace Commn. of the Hong Kong Catholic Diocese [IO], Hong Kong, People's Republic of China
Justice Res. and Statistics Assn. [11721], 777 N Capitol St. NE, Ste. 801, Washington, DC 20002, (202)842-9330
Justice Stud. Assn. [13122], Mohawk Valley Community Coll., Social Science/Criminal Justice Dept., Utica, NY 13501, (315)792-5653
Justice for Veteran Victims of the Veterans Administration - Defunct.
Justice Without Borders [5756], PO Box 2400, Madison, WI 53701-2400
Justice Without Borders [5756], PO Box 2400, Madison, WI 53701-2400
Justices' Clerks' Soc. [IO], Liverpool, United Kingdom
Jute Carpet Backing Coun. and Burlap and Jute Assn. - Address unknown since 2010.
Jute Mfrs. Development Coun. [IO], Calcutta, India

Juvenile
Amer. Specialty Toy Retailing Assn. [2174]
Amer. Youth Work Center [13508]
Australian Toy Assn. [9788]
Juvenile Products Mfrs. Assn. [2175]
Kollaboration [13534]
Robert F. Kennedy Center for Justice and Human Rights [13555]
Women in Toys [3479]

Juvenile Delinquency
Amer. Youth Work Center [13508]
Robert F. Kennedy Center for Justice and Human Rights [13555]

Juvenile Diabetes Found. [★14355]
Juvenile Diabetes Found. [★14355]
Juvenile Diabetes Res. Found. [IO], St. Leonards, Australia
Juvenile Diabetes Res. Found. - Hellas [IO], Athens, Greece
Juvenile Diabetes Res. Found. Intl. [14355], 26 Broadway, 14th Fl., New York, NY 10004, (800)533-CURE
Juvenile Diabetes Res. Found. Intl. [14355], 26 Broadway, 14th Fl., New York, NY 10004, (800)533-CURE
Juvenile Products Mfrs. Assn. [2175], 15000 Commerce Pkwy., Ste. C, Mount Laurel, NJ 08054, (856)638-0420
Juvenile Scleroderma Network [16635], 1204 W 13th St., San Pedro, CA 90731, (310)519-9511
Juventude Social-Democratica [IO], Lisbon, Portugal
JWB [★12408]
JWB Jewish Book Coun. [★9447]
JWB Jewish Chaplains Coun. [19523], 520 8th Ave., New York, NY 10018-6507, (212)532-4949

K

K-W and Area Right to Life Assn. [IO], Kitchener, ON, Canada
KaBOOM! [12695], 4455 Connecticut Ave. NW, Ste. B100, Washington, DC 20008, (202)659-0215
Kafka Soc. of Am. and Jour. [9388], 160 E 65th St., No. 2C, New York, NY 10021, (212)744-0821
Kafka Soc. of Am. and Jour. [9388], 160 E 65th St., No. 2C, New York, NY 10021, (212)744-0821
Kagaku Gijyutsu Shinko Kiko [★IO]
Kagaku Kisoron Gakkai [★IO]
Kageno Worldwide [11606], 261 Broadway, No. 10D, New York, NY 10007, (212)227-0509
Kaigai Consulting Kigyo Kyokai [★IO]
Kaiser-Darrin Owners Roster [21085], 734 Antram Rd., Somerset, PA 15501-8856, (814)445-6135
Kaiser Family Found. [14800], 2400 Sand Hill Rd., Menlo Park, CA 94025, (650)854-9400
Kaiser Family Found. [14800], 2400 Sand Hill Rd., Menlo Park, CA 94025, (650)854-9400
Kaiser-Frazer Owners Club Intl. [21086], PO Box 424, Thomasville, AL 36784, (334)636-5873
Kaiser-Frazer Owners Club Intl. [21086], PO Box 424, Thomasville, AL 36784, (334)636-5873
Kaiser-Frazer Owners Clubs of Am. [★21086]

Kaiser-Frazer Owners Clubs of Am. [★21086]
Kalabaw-No-Kai [IO], Yokohama, Japan
Kalatalouden Keskusliitto [★IO]
Kaleidoscope Theatre Productions Soc. [IO], Victoria, BC, Canada
Kamer van Koophandel Amsterdam [★IO]
Kamer van Koophandel en Fabrieken [★IO]
Kamer van Koophandel The Haag [★IO]
KampGround Owners Assn. [3059], 3416 Primm Ln., Birmingham, AL 35216, (205)824-0022
Kamut Assn. of North Am. [3952], PO Box 4903, Missoula, MT 59806, (406)251-9418
Kanada Esperanto-Asocio [★IO]
Kanata Cross Country Ski Club [IO], Kanata, ON, Canada
Kanazawa Goodwill Guide Network [IO], Kanazawa, Japan
Kansainvalinen Romanikirjailijaliitto [★IO]
Kansainvalinen Solidaarisuussaatio [★IO]
Kansas City Barbeque Soc. [21848], 11514 Hickman Mills Dr., Kansas City, MO 64134, (816)765-5891
Kansas City Bd. of Trade [3967], 4800 Main St., Ste. 303, Kansas City, MO 64112, (816)753-7500
Kansas Wheat Improvement Assn. Hard Winter Wheat Quality Coun. [★3966]
Kappa Alpha [★23673]
Kappa Alpha Order [23671], PO Box 1865, Lexington, VA 24450, (540)463-1865
Kappa Alpha Psi Fraternity [23672], 2322-24 N Broad St., Philadelphia, PA 19132, (215)228-7184
Kappa Alpha Psi Fraternity [23672], 2322-24 N Broad St., Philadelphia, PA 19132, (215)228-7184
Kappa Alpha Soc. [23673], 3109 N Triphammer Rd., Lansing, NY 14882, (917)913-5542
Kappa Alpha Theta [23725], 8740 Founders Rd., Indianapolis, IN 46268, (317)876-1870
Kappa Delta [23726], 3205 Players Ln., Memphis, TN 38125-8897, (901)748-1897
Kappa Delta Epsilon [23511], 5627 Bull Run, Pinson, AL 35126, (205)854-9755
Kappa Delta Epsilon Sorority [★23511]
Kappa Delta Pi [23512], 3707 Woodview Trace, Indianapolis, IN 46268-1158, (317)871-4900
Kappa Delta Rho [23674], 331 S Main St., Greensburg, PA 15601-3111, (724)838-7100
Kappa Delta Rho Found. [★23674]
Kappa Eta Kappa - Address unknown since 2010.
Kappa Gamma Pi [23561], 10215 Chardon Rd., Chardon, OH 44024-9700, (440)286-3764
Kappa Gamma Pi Natl. Off. [★23561]
Kappa Kappa Gamma [23727], PO Box 38, Columbus, OH 43216-0038, (614)228-6515
Kappa Kappa Iota [★23513]
Kappa Kappa Psi [23600], PO Box 849, Stillwater, OK 74076-0849, (800)543-6505
Kappa Mu Epsilon [23587], 732 N Washington St., Alexandria, VA 22314, (660)543-8929
Kappa Omicron Nu [23549], 4990 Northwind Dr., Ste. 140, East Lansing, MI 48823-5031, (517)351-8335
Kappa Omicron Phi [★23549]
Kappa Phi Gamma Sorority [23746], 7 Lynch Rd., Wayne, PA 19087
Kappa Pi Intl. Honorary Art Fraternity [23467], 400 S Bolivar Ave., Cleveland, MS 38732-3745, (662)846-4729
Kappa Pi Intl. Honorary Art Fraternity [23467], 400 S Bolivar Ave., Cleveland, MS 38732-3745, (662)846-4729
Kappa Psi [23616], 2060 N Collins Blvd., Ste. 128, Richardson, TX 75080, (972)479-1879
Kappa Psi Kappa Fraternity [23535], PO Box 773, Philadelphia, PA 19105
Kappa Sigma [23675], PO Box 5066, Charlottesville, VA 22905-5066, (434)295-3193
Kappa Sigma Alpha Epsilon [★23520]
Kappa Sigma Kappa [★23706]
Kappa Tau Alpha [23573], Univ. of Missouri, School of Journalism, Columbia, MO 65211-1200, (573)882-7685
Karachi ACM Chap. [IO], Karachi, Pakistan
Karakul Fur Sheep Registry [★4893]
Karaoke Intl. Sing-Along Assn. - Defunct.

Karate
Amer. Kenpo Karate Intl. [22709]

USA Natl. Karate-do Fed. [22710]
World Martial Arts Assn. [22771]

Karen Horney Clinic [16358], 329 E 62nd St., New York, NY 10021, (212)838-4333
Karen Horney Psychoanalytic Clinic [★16358]
Karen Natl. League [18722], PO Box 320518, San Francisco, CA 94132-0518
Karg-Elert Archv. [IO], Church Stretton, United Kingdom
Karl Jaspers Soc. of North Am. [10396], Boston Univ., 145 Bay State Rd., Boston, MA 02215, (508)240-6709
Karl Kuebel Found. for Child and Family [IO], Bensheim, Germany
Karl Kuebel Stiftung fuer Kind und Familie [★IO]
Karmann Ghia Club of North Am. [21087], 4200 Park Blvd., No. 151, Oakland, CA 94602, (510)717-6942
Karmann Ghia Club of North Am. [21087], 4200 Park Blvd., No. 151, Oakland, CA 94602, (510)717-6942
Kart Marketing Assn. of America - Defunct.

Kart Racing
Intl. Kart Fed. [22711]
Intl. Kart Fed. [22711]

Kartografiska Sallskapet [★IO]
Karuna Trust [IO], London, United Kingdom
Kas Hastaliklari Dernegi [★IO]
Kasaragod Assn. Bahrain [IO], Manama, Bahrain
Kasese Wildlife Conservation Awareness Org. [5074], PO Box 10664, Portland, OR 97296
Kasese Wildlife Conservation Awareness Org. [5074], PO Box 10664, Portland, OR 97296
Katalysis Found. [★17231]
Katalysis Found. [★17231]
Katalysis North/South Development Partnership [★17231]
Katalysis North/South Development Partnership [★17231]
Katalysis Partnership [17231], Katalysis Bootstrap Fund, 3601 Pacific Ave., Stockton, CA 95211, (209)644-6245
Katalysis Partnership [17231], Katalysis Bootstrap Fund, 3601 Pacific Ave., Stockton, CA 95211, (209)644-6245
Katanning Shire Coun. [IO], Katanning, Australia
Kate Smith Commemorative Soc. [23866], PO Box 242, Syracuse, NY 13214-0242
Kate Smith Commemorative Soc. [23866], PO Box 242, Syracuse, NY 13214-0242
Kate Smith/God Bless Am. Found. [★23866]
Kate Smith/God Bless Am. Found. [★23866]
Kate's Voice [8764], PO Box 365, Sudbury, MA 01776, (978)440-9913
Kathmandu Environmental Educ. Proj. - Nepal [IO], Kathmandu, Nepal
Katholiek Vormingswerk van Landelijke Vrouwen [IO], Leuven, Belgium
Katholische Bibelfoederation [★IO]
Katholischer Deutscher Frauenbund [★IO]
Kathy Mattea Fan Club - Address unknown since 2011.
Katipunang Manggagawang Pilipino [★IO]
Kauffman Center for Entrepreneurial Leadership [680], 4801 Rockhill Rd., Kansas City, MO 64110, (816)932-1000
Kaunihera mo te Whakapakari Ao Whanul [★IO]
Kaupan Keskusliitto [★IO]
Kavak Ve Hizli Gelisen Orman Agaclari Arastirma Enstitusu [★IO]
Kay Boyle Soc. [10726], Columbia Coll., Dept. of English, 1301 Columbia Coll. Dr., Columbia, SC 29203
Kazak fiziologtardyn uiymy [★IO]
Kazakh Physiology Soc. [IO], Almaty, Kazakhstan
Kazakhistanian Assn. of Sports Medicine [IO], Almaty, Kazakhstan
Kazakhstan Assn. Inst. of Non-Proliferation [IO], Almaty, Kazakhstan
Kazakhstan Badminton Fed. [IO], Almaty, Kazakhstan
Kazakhstan Geotechnical Soc. [IO], Astana, Kazakhstan
Kazakhstan Natl. League Against Epilepsy [IO], Almaty, Kazakhstan

---

Reference to "IO" in place of a book number signifies that the association may be found in the 50th edition of International Organizations.

Kazakhstan Sailing Fed. [IO], Almaty, Kazakhstan

Kazakhstan Tennis Fed. [IO], Astana, Kazakhstan

KDK [★22146]

Keats-Shelley Assn. of Am. [9389], 476 5th Ave., New York Public Lib., Rm. 226, New York, NY 10018

Keep Am. Beautiful [4279], 1010 Washington Blvd., Stamford, CT 06901-2202, (203)659-3000

Keep Britain Tidy [IO], Wigan, United Kingdom

Keep Fit Assn. [IO], Horsham, United Kingdom

Keep Tahoe Blue [★4091]

Keepers of the Waters [4996], 1415 SE Tacoma St., Portland, OR 97202, (503)234-6642

Keepers of the Waters [4996], 1415 SE Tacoma St., Portland, OR 97202, (503)234-6642

Keeping Track [5075], PO Box 444, Huntington, VT 05462, (802)434-7000

Keeshond Club of Am. [21595], Judi James, Corresponding Sec., 1265 Summer St. NE, Salem, OR 97301

Kehot Publications Society [★19855]

Keidanren Nature Conservation Fund [IO], Tokyo, Japan

Keisoku Jidouseigyo Gakkai [★IO]

Keizai Doyukai [★IO]

Keizai Riron Gakkai [★IO]

Kelley's Kobras [★20324]

Kelly Lang Fan Club [23867], 59 Blue Ridge Trace, Hendersonville, TN 37075, (615)333-7235

Kelsey Kindred of Am. [20547], 37 Ackerman St., Salem, NH 03079, (603)893-6814

Kemianteollisuus [★IO]

Kemisk Forening [★IO]

Kemisk-Tekniska Leverantoerfoerbundet [★IO]

Kempe Center for the Prevention and Treatment of Child Abuse and Neglect [11331], 13123 E 16th Ave., B390, Aurora, CO 80045, (303)864-5300

Kempe Children's Center [★11331]

Kempe Natl. Center for the Prevention and Treatment of Child Abuse and Neglect [★11331]

Kennarasamband Islands [★IO]

Kennedy Center Alliance for Arts Educ. Network [7749], John F. Kennedy Center for the Performing Arts, 2700 F St. NW, Washington, DC 20566, (202)416-8817

Kennedy Lib. Found; John F. [9990]

Kennedy's Disease Assn. [15604], PO Box 1105, Coarsegold, CA 93614-1105, (559)658-5950

Kennedy's Disease Assn. [15604], PO Box 1105, Coarsegold, CA 93614-1105, (559)658-5950

Kennel Club [IO], Aylesbury, United Kingdom

Kennel Club Boliviano [IO], La Paz, Bolivia

Kenny Chesney Fan Club [23868], PO Box 880, Crozet, VA 22932

Kenpo Karate Intl. [★22709]

Kent State Univ. Alumni Assn. [18878], Williamson Alumni Center, PO Box 5190, Kent, OH 44242-0001, (330)672-5368

Kent Waldrep Intl. Spinal Cord Res. Found. [★16700]

Kenya AIDS Intervention/Prevention Proj. Gp. [IO], Kakamega, Kenya

Kenya Assn. of Hotelkeepers and Caterers [IO], Nairobi, Kenya

Kenya Assn. of Mfrs. [IO], Nairobi, Kenya

Kenya Assn. of Tour Operators [IO], Nairobi, Kenya

Kenya Badminton Assn. [IO], Nairobi, Kenya

Kenya Bur. of Standards [IO], Nairobi, Kenya

Kenya Diabetes Assn. [IO], Nairobi, Kenya

Kenya Disabled Development Soc. [IO], Nairobi, Kenya

Kenya Female Advisory Org. [IO], Kisumu, Kenya

Kenya Hypertension League [IO], Nairobi, Kenya

Kenya Inst. of Mgt. [IO], Nairobi, Kenya

Kenya Junior Chamber [IO], Nairobi, Kenya

Kenya Lawn Tennis Assn. [IO], Nairobi, Kenya

Kenya Medical Assn. [IO], Nairobi, Kenya

Kenya Medical Outreach [12462], 4355 Suwanee Dam Rd., Ste. 100, Suwanee, GA 30024, (678)858-3380

Kenya Natl. Acad. of Sciences [IO], Nairobi, Kenya

Kenya Occupational Therapists Assn. [IO], Nairobi, Kenya

Kenya Red Cross Soc. [IO], Nairobi, Kenya

Kenya Scouts Assn. [IO], Nairobi, Kenya

Kenya Soc. for Epilepsy [IO], Nairobi, Kenya

Kenya Soc. of Physiotherapists [IO], Nairobi, Kenya

Kenya Squash Rackets Assn. [IO], Nairobi, Kenya

Kenya Taekwondo Assn. [IO], Nairobi, Kenya

Kenya Yachting Assn. [IO], Nairobi, Kenya

Kenya Youth Hostels Assn. [IO], Nairobi, Kenya

Kenyan Americans Community Org. [10823], PO Box 1701, Duluth, GA 30096, (404)219-2098

Kenyan Geotechnical Soc. [IO], Nairobi, Kenya

Kenyan Physiological Soc. [IO], Nairobi, Kenya

Kenyan Publishers Assn. [IO], Nairobi, Kenya

Kenyan Sect. of the Intl. Commn. of Jurists [IO], Nairobi, Kenya

Keramos - Address unknown since 2011.

Keren Kayemeth Leisrael [★19872]

Keren Or [17093], 350 7th Ave., Ste. 701, New York, NY 10001, (212)279-4070

Keren Or [17093], 350 7th Ave., Ste. 701, New York, NY 10001, (212)279-4070

Keresztyen Ifjusagi Egyesulet [★IO]

Kerntechnischer Ausschuss [★IO]

Kerr Family Assn. of North Am. [20548], 7980 Ridgewood Rd., Goodlettsville, TN 37072-9461

Kerr Family Assn. of North Am. [20548], 7980 Ridgewood Rd., Goodlettsville, TN 37072-9461

Kershner Family Assn. - Address unknown since 2010.

Kesatuan Guru-Guru Melayu Singapura [★IO]

Keuka Coll. Alumni Assn. [18879], Off. of Alumni and Family Relations, 141 Central Ave., Ball 122, Keuka Park, NY 14478, (315)279-5238

Key Club Intl. [13061], 3636 Woodview Trace, Indianapolis, IN 46268-3196, (317)875-8755

Key Club Intl. [13061], 3636 Woodview Trace, Indianapolis, IN 46268-3196, (317)875-8755

The Keystone Center [7513], 1628 St. John Rd., Keystone, CO 80435, (970)513-5800

Keystone Center for Continuing Educ. [★7513]

Keystone Conservation [5076], PO Box 6733, Bozeman, MT 59771, (406)587-3389

KEZA [210], PO Box 681381, Franklin, TN 37068-1381

Khadarlis for Sierra Leone [11607], 99 Acad. Ave., Providence, RI 02908, (401)454-6916

Khmer Amateur Athletic Assn. [IO], Phnom Penh, Cambodia

Khmer Assn. for Development [IO], Phnom Penh, Cambodia

Khmer HIV/AIDS NGO Alliance [IO], Phnom Penh, Cambodia

Khmer Weightlifting Fed. [IO], Phnom Penh, Cambodia

Khmer Youth and Social Development [IO], Phnom Penh, Cambodia

Khwarzimic Sci. Soc. [IO], Lahore, Pakistan

Kibbutz Indus. Assn. [IO], Tel Aviv, Israel

Kibbutz Prog. Center [18013], 114 W 26th St., Ste. 1004, New York, NY 10001, (212)462-2764

Kickboxing Fed. of Uzbekistan [IO], Tashkent, Uzbekistan

KickStart Intl. [12734], 2435 Polk St., Ste. 20, San Francisco, CA 94109, (415)346-4820

Kidlinks World [11332], PO Box 628283, Middleton, WI 53562, (608)658-1171

Kidney

Children's Dialysis Intl. [15548]

Kidney Cancer Assn. [13935], 1234 Sherman Ave., Ste. 203, Evanston, IL 60202-1375, (847)332-1051

Kidney Cancer UK [IO], Uttoxeter, United Kingdom

Kidney Care Partners [15551], Susan Murdock, 2550 M St. NW, Washington, DC 20037, (703)830-9192

Kidney Community Emergency Response Coalition [15552], 5201 W Kennedy Blvd., Ste. 900, Tampa, FL 33609, (813)383-1530

Kidney Found; Natl. [15554]

Kidney Fund; Amer. [15542]

Kidney Patients; Amer. Assn. of [15541]

Kidney Transplant/Dialysis Assn. [16910], PO Box 51362 GMF, Boston, MA 02205-1362, (781)641-4000

Kidpower Teenpower Fullpower Intl. [12988], PO Box 1212, Santa Cruz, CA 95061, (831)426-4407

Kidpower Teenpower Fullpower Intl. [12988], PO Box 1212, Santa Cruz, CA 95061, (831)426-4407

Kids Against Hunger [12283], 5401 Boone Ave. N, New Hope, MN 55428, (763)257-0202

Kids Against Junk Food - Defunct.

Kids with Cameras [12694], 122 Main St., Salt Lake City, UT 84101, (646)213-1333

Kids and Cars [18577], 2913 W 113th St., Leawood, KS 66211, (913)327-0013

Kids for a Clean Env. [4280], PO Box 158254, Nashville, TN 37215, (615)331-7381

KIDS COUNT [11333], The Annie E. Casey Found., 701 St. Paul St., Baltimore, MD 21202, (410)547-6600

Kids to the Cup - Defunct.

Kids Ecology Corps [4322], 1350 E Sunrise Blvd., Fort Lauderdale, FL 33304-2815, (954)524-0366

Kids Enjoy Exercise Now [21474], 1301 K St. NW, Ste. 600, Washington, DC 20005, (866)903-5336

Kids First Coalition - Address unknown since 2011.

Kids First Parent Assn. of Canada [IO], Edmonton, AB, Canada

Kids in Flight [14082], PO Box 5234, Willowick, OH 44095-0234

Kids with Food Allergies [★13642]

Kids with Food Allergies Found. [13642], 73 Old Dublin Pike, Ste. 10, No. 163, Doylestown, PA 18901, (215)230-5394

Kids Fund - Address unknown since 2010.

Kids Home Intl. [11334], 2309 Plymouth Ave. N, Minneapolis, MN 55411

Kids at Hope [11477], 2400 W Dunlap Ave., Ste. 135, Phoenix, AZ 85021, (602)674-0026

Kids In Danger [11335], 116 W Illinois St., Ste. 5E, Chicago, IL 60654, (312)595-0649

Kids Konnected [11478], 26071 Merit Cir., Ste. 103, Laguna Hills, CA 92653, (949)582-5443

Kids Korps USA [13400], 2210 Encinitas Blvd., Ste. N, Encinitas, CA 92024, (760)452-2676

Kids Kottage Found. [IO], Edmonton, AB, Canada

Kids Making a Difference [3813], 1527 W State Hwy. 114, Ste. 500, No. 106, Grapevine, TX 76051

Kids Meeting Kids [★17984]

Kids Meeting Kids [★17984]

Kids Need Both Parents [17623], PO Box 6481, Portland, OR 97228-6481, (503)727-3686

Kids for Peace [18262], 3303 James Dr., Carlsbad, CA 92008, (760)730-3320

Kids for Saving Earth [8145], 37955 Bridge Rd., North Branch, MN 55056, (763)559-1234

Kids Together [11802], PO Box 574, Quakertown, PA 18951

Kids Universe, Inc. [8075], Janeczka Eberhart, CFO, PO Box 465552, Lawrenceville, GA 30042, (404)348-4184

Kids With A Cause [11336], 10736 Jefferson Blvd., No. 401, Culver City, CA 90230-4933, (310)614-7711

Kids With Heart Natl. Assn. for Children's Heart Disorders [14029], PO Box 12504, Green Bay, WI 54307-2504, (920)498-0058

Kids Without Borders [11337], PO Box 24, Bellevue, WA 98009-0024, (425)836-5354

Kids Without Borders [11337], PO Box 24, Bellevue, WA 98009-0024, (425)836-5354

Kidsave Intl. [10794], 100 Corporate Pointe, Ste. 380, Culver City, CA 90230, (310)642-7283

Kidsave Intl. [10794], 100 Corporate Pointe, Ste. 380, Culver City, CA 90230, (310)642-7283

KIDSCOPE [11137], 2045 Peachtree Rd., Ste. 150, Atlanta, GA 30309, (404)892-1437

KidsPeace [11338], 4085 Independence Dr., Schnecksville, PA 18078-2574, (800)257-3223

Kidwell Family Assn. - Defunct.

Kiger Mesteno Assn. [4609], 11124 NE Halsey St., Ste. 591, Portland, OR 97220

Kill Devil Hills Memorial Assn. [★20896]

Kilts Family Assn. [20549], 141 Hudson Ave., Chatham, NY 12037, (518)392-4544

Kilvert Soc. [IO], Bristol, United Kingdom

Kin Canada [IO], Cambridge, ON, Canada

Kinder Goat Breeders Assn. [4503], PO Box 4, Miami, MO 65344-0004

Kinder- und Jugendfilmzentrum in Deutschland [★IO]

Kindernothilfe e.V. [IO], Duisburg, Germany

Kindernothilfe Osterreich [★IO]

A star before a book entry number signifies that the name is not listed separately, but is mentioned within the entry.

2948

Encyclopedia of Associations, 51st Edition

KinderUSA **[11479]**, PO Box 224846, Dallas, TX 75222, (972)664-1991
Kindness in a Box **[11339]**, 5955 Grayling View Ct., Villa Ridge, MO 63089
Kindness in a Box **[11339]**, 5955 Grayling View Ct., Villa Ridge, MO 63089
Kinesiology and Physical Educ; Amer. Acad. of **[★8717]**
Kinesiotherapy Assn; Amer. **[16556]**
King Baudouin Found. **[IO]**, Brussels, Belgium
King, Jr. Center for Nonviolent Social Change; Martin Luther **[18170]**
Kingdom Chamber of Commerce **[23392]**, 383 N Kings Highway, Ste. 201, Cherry Hill, NJ 08034, (856)414-0818
King's Garden **[★13184]**
Kingston Hard of Hearing Club **[IO]**, Kingston, ON, Canada
Kinship Circle **[10998]**, 7380 Kingsbury Blvd., St. Louis, MO 63130, (314)863-9445
KioskCom Professional Soc. - Address unknown since 2010.
Kipling Soc. **[IO]**, London, United Kingdom
Kiribati Athletics Assn. **[IO]**, Tarawa, Kiribati
Kiribati Cmpt. and Internet Soc. **[IO]**, Tarawa, Kiribati
Kiribati Judo Assn. **[IO]**, Bairiki, Kiribati
Kiribati Natl. Olympic Comm. **[IO]**, Tarawa, Kiribati
Kiribati Red Cross Soc. **[IO]**, Tarawa, Kiribati
Kiribati Tennis Assn. **[IO]**, Tarawa, Kiribati
Kiribati and Tungaru Assn. **[IO]**, Bristol, United Kingdom
Kiribati Weightlifting Fed. **[IO]**, Tarawa, Kiribati
Kirjakauppaliitto **[★IO]**
Kirkon Ulkomaanapu **[★IO]**
KISS Rocks Fan Club **[23869]**, 15 Maple Rd., Briarcliff Manor, NY 10510
KISS Rocks Fan Club **[23869]**, 15 Maple Rd., Briarcliff Manor, NY 10510
Kissel Kar Klub **[21088]**, Wisconsin Automotive Museum, 147 N. Rural St., Hartford, WI 53027, (262)673-7999
Kitchen, Bathroom, Bedroom Specialists Assn. **[IO]**, Mansfield, United Kingdom
Kitchen Cabinet Mfrs. Assn. **[2066]**, 1899 Preston White Dr., Reston, VA 20191-5435, (703)264-1690
Kitchen Gardeners Intl. **[9628]**, 3 Powderhorn Dr., Scarborough, ME 04074, (207)956-0606
Kitchen Gardeners Intl. **[9628]**, 3 Powderhorn Dr., Scarborough, ME 04074, (207)956-0606
Kite Flying
 Amer. Kitefliers Assn. **[22712]**
Kite Trade Assn. Intl. **[3311]**, PO Box 443, Otis, OR 97368, (541)994-9647
Kite Trade Assn. Intl. **[3311]**, PO Box 443, Otis, OR 97368, (541)994-9647
Kitty Wells Appreciation Soc. **[★23870]**
Kitty Wells-Johnny Wright-Bobby Wright Intl. Fan Club **[23870]**, PO Box 1189, Madison, TN 37116, (615)865-1900
Kitty Wells/Johnny Wright Fan Club **[★23870]**
Kituo cha Elimuya Demokrasia kwa Wanawake **[★IO]**
Kiviteollisuusliitto ry **[★IO]**
Kiwanis Club of Te Awamutu **[IO]**, Hamilton, New Zealand
Kiwanis Intl. **[13062]**, 3636 Woodview Trace, Indianapolis, IN 46268-3196, (317)875-8755
Kiwanis Intl. **[13062]**, 3636 Woodview Trace, Indianapolis, IN 46268-3196, (317)875-8755
Kjaerulf Family Assn. **[20550]**, 358 S Bentley Ave., Los Angeles, CA 90049-3219, (310)472-9206
Kjottbransjens Landsforbund **[★IO]**
Klassieke Vereniging van Suid-Afrika **[★IO]**
Klinefelter Syndrome and Associates **[16772]**, PO Box 461047, Aurora, CO 80046-1047, (303)400-9040
Klinefelter Syndrome Info. and Support; Amer. Assn. for **[14694]**
Klingenstein Third Generation Found. **[14083]**, 787 Seventh Ave., 6th Fl., New York, NY 10019-6016, (212)492-6179
Klippel-Trenaunay Support Gp. **[13843]**, 5404 Dundee Rd., Edina, MN 55436, (952)925-2596
Klondike Visitors Assn. **[IO]**, Dawson City, YT, Canada

Klub Hateufah Leisrael **[★IO]**
Klub Inteligencji Katolickiej **[★IO]**
Knattspyrnusamband Islands **[★IO]**
KNH Austria **[IO]**, Vienna, Austria
Knife Collectors Club **[21875]**, 2900 S 26th St., U.S. 540 Exit 81, Rogers, AR 72758-8571, (479)631-0130
Knifemakers' Guild **[21450]**, 2914 Winters Ln., La Grange, KY 40031, (502)222-1397
Knight Bros. Found. **[★12415]**
Knights of Columbus **[18955]**, 1 Columbus Plz., New Haven, CT 06510, (203)752-4000
Knights of Columbus **[18955]**, 1 Columbus Plz., New Haven, CT 06510, (203)752-4000
Knights of Dunamis **[★13023]**
Knights of Equity - Address unknown since 2010.
Knights of the Hook **[★23560]**
Knights of the Immaculata Movement **[★19451]**
Knights of the Ku Klux Klan **[18782]**, PO Box 2222, Harrison, AR 72601, (870)427-3414
Knights and Ladies of Sta. Peter Claver **[★18956]**
Knights of Life Motorcycle Club **[12989]**, PO Box 533, Morristown, NJ 07963
Knights of Peter Claver **[18956]**, 1825 Orleans Ave., New Orleans, LA 70116, (504)821-4225
Knights of Pythias
 Dramatic Order Knights of Khorassan **[19094]**
 Junior Order, Knights of Pythias **[19095]**
 Supreme Lodge Knights of Pythias **[19096]**
 Supreme Temple Order Pythian Sisters **[19097]**
Knights of Saint Andrew **[★19806]**
Knights of Saint John Intl. **[18957]**, 89 S Pine Ave., Albany, NY 12208-2214, (518)453-5675
Knights of Saint John Intl. **[18957]**, 89 S Pine Ave., Albany, NY 12208-2214, (518)453-5675
Knights Templar, Grand Encampment, U.S.A. **[19134]**, 5909 W Loop S, Ste. 495, Bellaire, TX 77401-2402, (713)349-8700
Knights of the White Cross **[★19180]**
Knights of the White Cross **[★19180]**
Knightsbridge Intl. **[12859]**, PO Box 4394, West Hills, CA 91308-4394, (818)372-6902
Knitted Textile Assn. **[★3451]**
The Knitting Guild of Am. **[★21451]**
The Knitting Guild Assn. **[21451]**, 1100-H Brandywine Blvd., Zanesville, OH 43701-7303, (740)452-4541
Knitting Indus'. Fed. **[IO]**, Leicester, United Kingdom
Knitwear Employers Assn. - Defunct.
Knives
 Case Collectors Club **[21873]**
 Intl. Fight'n Rooster Cutlery Club **[21874]**
 Intl. Fight'n Rooster Cutlery Club **[21874]**
 Intl. Saw and Knife Assn. **[2176]**
 Intl. Saw and Knife Assn. **[2176]**
 Knife Collectors Club **[21875]**
 Natl. Knife Collectors Assn. **[21876]**
Knowbility **[11803]**, 3925 W Braker Ln., 3rd Fl., Austin, TX 78759, (512)305-0310
Knowledge Alliance **[8797]**, 1 Saint Matthew's Ct. NW, Washington, DC 20036, (202)518-0847
Knowledge Ecology Intl. **[7514]**, 1621 Connecticut Ave. NW, No. 500, Washington, DC 20009, (202)332-2670
Knowledge for Iraqi Woman Soc. **[IO]**, Baghdad, Iraq
Knowledge Mgt. Professional Soc. **[1903]**, PO Box 846, Severn, MD 21144-0846, (757)460-6500
Knowles/Knoles/Noles Family Assn. **[20642]**, 133 Acadian Ln., Mandeville, LA 70471-1789, (985)845-4688
Kobe YMCA Cross Cultural Center **[IO]**, Kobe, Japan
Kodbranchens Faellesraad **[★IO]**
Koepel van Christelijke Werknemersorganisaties **[IO]**, Brussels, Belgium
Koinonia Caritas **[IO]**, Nicosia, Cyprus
Koinonia Found. **[19658]**, 6037 Franconia Rd., Alexandria, VA 22310, (703)971-1991
Kokoomuksen Nuorten Liitto **[★IO]**
Koko.org **[★6123]**
Kokuren Josei Kaihatsu Kikin Nihon Kokunai Iinkai **[★IO]**
Kokusai Jishin Kogaku-kai **[★IO]**
Kokusai Kanko Shinko-kai **[★IO]**

Kokusai Koryu Kikin **[★9908]**
Kokusai Kotsu Anzen Gakkai **[★IO]**
Kokusai Kowan Kyokai **[★IO]**
Kokusai Kyoryoku BGO Center **[★IO]**
Kokusai Yoshoku Sangyo Kai **[★IO]**
Kolel Chibas Jerusalem **[19878]**, 4802-A 12th Ave., Brooklyn, NY 11219, (718)633-7112
Kollaboration **[13534]**, 1100 S Flower St., No. 3160, Los Angeles, CA 90015
Kologh Naba **[IO]**, Ouagadougou, Burkina Faso
Kommission der Kirchen fur Migranten in Europa **[★IO]**
Kommission fur Musikforschung der Osterreichischen Akademie der Wissenschaften **[★IO]**
Kommission Reinhaltung der Luft im VDI und DIN - Normenausschuss **[★IO]**
Kommunalberatung - Unternehmensberatung fur Wirtschaft und Verwaltung **[★IO]**
Komondor Club of Am. **[21596]**, 159 Beville Rd., Chehalis, WA 98532, (360)245-3464
Komoradanoych poradcu CR **[★IO]**
Kongelig Dansk Aeroklub **[★IO]**
Kongelige Danske Geografiske Selskab **[★IO]**
Kongelige Danske Landhusholdningsselskab **[★IO]**
Kongelige Danske Videnskabernes Selskab **[★IO]**
Koninklijk Belgisch Genootschap voor Numismatiek **[★IO]**
Koninklijk Belgisch Yachting Verbond **[★IO]**
Koninklijk Instituut van Ingenieurs **[★IO]**
Koninklijk Instituut voor den Tropen **[★IO]**
Koninklijk Nederlands Aardrijkskundig Genootschap **[★IO]**
Koninklijk Nederlands Korfbalverbond **[★IO]**
Koninklijke Academie voor Nederlandse Taal-en Letterkunde **[★IO]**
Koninklijke Belgische Baseball en Softball Federatie **[IO]**, Evere, Belgium
Koninklijke Belgische Vereniging der Elektrotechnici **[★IO]**
Koninklijke Boekverkopersbond **[★IO]**
Koninklijke Hollandsche Maatschappij der Wetenschappen **[★IO]**
Koninklijke Landbouwkundige Vereniging **[★IO]**
Koninklijke Nederlandsche Maatschappij tot bevordering der Geneeskunst **[★IO]**
Koninklijke Nederlandse Akademie van Wetenschappen **[★IO]**
Koninklijke Nederlandse Atletiek Unie **[IO]**, Arnhem, Netherlands
Koninklijke Nederlandse Cricket Bond **[★IO]**
Koninklijke Nederlandse Lawn Tennis Bond **[IO]**, Amersfoort, Netherlands
Koninklijke Nederlandse Toonkunstenaars Vereniging **[★IO]**
Koninklijke Nederlandse Vereniging voor de Koffiehandel **[IO]**, Rijswijk, Netherlands
Koninklijke Nederlandse Vereniging Voor Luchtvaart **[★IO]**
Koninklijke Vereniging voor Nederlandse Muziekgeschiedenis **[★IO]**
Koninklijke Vereniging van Nederlandse Reders **[★IO]**
Koninklijke Vereniging van Nederlandse Wijnhandelaren **[★IO]**
Konoinklijke Nederlandse Chemische Vereniging **[★IO]**
Konrad Adenauer Found. - Germany **[IO]**, St. Augustin, Germany
Konrad Adenauer Found. - South Africa **[IO]**, Johannesburg, Republic of South Africa
Konrad Adenauer Found. - Zimbabwe **[IO]**, Harare, Zimbabwe
Konrad Adenauer Stiftung **[★IO]**
Konrad-Adenauer Stiftung **[★IO]**
Konservativ Ungdom **[★IO]**
Konservative Folkepartis **[★IO]**
Kopenhagen Fur **[IO]**, Glostrup, Denmark
KOPIKEN **[IO]**, Nairobi, Kenya
KOPINOR **[IO]**, Oslo, Norway
KOPIOSTO **[IO]**, Helsinki, Finland
KOPIPOL **[IO]**, Kielce, Poland
Korea
 Intl. Aid for Korean Animals **[10988]**
 Korea Stamp Soc. **[22048]**
 Korean Amer. Soc. of Entrepreneurs **[718]**

Reference to "IO" in place of a book number signifies that the association may be found in the 50th edition of International Organizations.

Korea ACM SIGCHI **[IO]**, Seoul, Republic of Korea
Korea Agro-Fisheries Trade Corp. **[IO]**, Seoul, Republic of Korea
Korea-America Commerce and Indus. Assn. **[★23422]**
Korea Auto Indus. Cooperative Assn. **[IO]**, Seoul, Republic of Korea
Korea Auto. Mfrs'. Assn. **[IO]**, Seoul, Republic of Korea
Korea Certified Investment Analysts Assn. **[IO]**, Seoul, Republic of Korea
Korea Chamber of Commerce and Indus. **[IO]**, Seoul, Republic of Korea
Korea Chem. Fibers Assn. **[IO]**, Seoul, Republic of Korea
Korea Die and Mold Indus. Cooperative **[IO]**, Seoul, Republic of Korea
Korea Economic Inst. **[18031]**, 1800 K St. NW, Ste. 1010, Washington, DC 20006, (202)464-1982
Korea Economic Inst. of Am. **[★18031]**
Korea Elecl. Contractors' Assn. **[IO]**, Seoul, Republic of Korea
Korea Elecl. Mfrs'. Cooperative **[IO]**, Seongnam, Republic of Korea
Korea Electronic Indus. Cooperative **[IO]**, Seoul, Republic of Korea
Korea Employers Fed. **[IO]**, Seoul, Republic of Korea
Korea Fed. of Advt. Associations **[IO]**, Seoul, Republic of Korea
Korea Fed. of Banks **[IO]**, Seoul, Republic of Korea
Korea Fed. of Small and Medium Bus. **[IO]**, Seoul, Republic of Korea
Korea Fed. of Textile Indus. **[IO]**, Seoul, Republic of Korea
Korea Floorball Fed. **[IO]**, Seoul, Republic of Korea
Korea Food for the Hungry Intl. **[IO]**, Seoul, Republic of Korea
Korea Found. **[IO]**, Seoul, Republic of Korea
Korea Indus. Safety Assn. **[IO]**, Seoul, Republic of Korea
Korea Info. Tech. Network **[6462]**, 3003 N 1st St., San Jose, CA 95134, (408)232-5475
Korea Info. Tech. Network **[6462]**, 3003 N 1st St., San Jose, CA 95134, (408)232-5475
Korea Intl. Freight Forwarders Assn. **[IO]**, Seoul, Republic of Korea
Korea Iron and Steel Assn. **[IO]**, Seoul, Republic of Korea
Korea Life Insurance Assn. **[IO]**, Seoul, Republic of Korea
Korea Machine Tool Mfrs'. Assn. **[IO]**, Seoul, Republic of Korea
Korea Musical Instrument Indus. Assn. **[IO]**, Seoul, Republic of Korea
Korea Non-Life Insurance Assn. **[IO]**, Seoul, Republic of Korea
Korea Orienteering Fed. **[IO]**, Seoul, Republic of Korea
Korea Paper Mfrs'. Assn. **[IO]**, Seoul, Republic of Korea
Korea Petrochemical Indus. Assn. **[IO]**, Seoul, Republic of Korea
Korea Polio Found. **[IO]**, Seoul, Republic of Korea
Korea Racing Assn. **[IO]**, Gwacheon, Republic of Korea
Korea Shipbuilders' Assn. **[IO]**, Seoul, Republic of Korea
Korea Skating Union **[IO]**, Seoul, Republic of Korea
The Korea Soc. **[23422]**, 950 3rd Ave., 8th Fl., New York, NY 10022, (212)759-7525
Korea Squash Fed. **[IO]**, Seoul, Republic of Korea
Korea Stamp Soc. **[22048]**, John E. Talmage, Jr., Sec.-Treas., PO Box 6889, Oak Ridge, TN 37831
Korea Stationery Indus. Cooperative **[IO]**, Seoul, Republic of Korea
Korea Taekwondo Assn. **[IO]**, Seoul, Republic of Korea
Korea Tennis Assn. **[IO]**, Seoul, Republic of Korea
Korea Trade Promotion Corp. **[IO]**, Seoul, Republic of Korea
Korea Veterans Assn. of Canada **[IO]**, London, ON, Canada
Korea Welfare Found. **[IO]**, Seoul, Republic of Korea
Korean
Assn. for Korean Music Res. **[10165]**

Intercollegiate Taiwanese Amer. Students Assn. **[19252]**
Intl. Aid for Korean Animals **[10988]**
Intl. Coun. on Korean Stud. **[8450]**
Korea Economic Inst. **[18031]**
The Korea Soc. **[23422]**
Korea Stamp Soc. **[22048]**
Korean Amer. Citizens League **[18032]**
Korean Amer. Coalition **[19098]**
Korean Amer. League for Civic Action **[18033]**
Korean Amer. Soc. of Entrepreneurs **[718]**
Korean Amer. Voters' Coun. **[18034]**
North Korea Freedom Coalition **[18035]**
Soc. of Korean-American Scholars **[8451]**
World Hapkido Assn. **[22767]**
World Kouk Sun Do Soc. **[9933]**
World Kouk Sun Do Soc. **[9933]**
Korean Acad. of Psychotherapists **[IO]**, Seoul, Republic of Korea
Korean Amateur Radio League **[IO]**, Seoul, Republic of Korea
Korean Amer. Citizens League **[18032]**, PO Box 3512, Portland, OR 97208
Korean Amer. Coalition **[19098]**, 3540 Wilshire Blvd., Ste. 911, Los Angeles, CA 90005, (213)365-5999
Korean Amer. League for Civic Action **[18033]**, 149 W 24th St., 6th Fl., New York, NY 10011, (212)633-2000
Korean Amer. Medical Assn. **[15422]**, 420 Lexington Ave., Ste. 2546, New York, NY 10170, (646)783-6097
Korean-American Medical Assn. of Am. **[★15422]**
Korean-American Scientists and Engineers Assn. **[6807]**, 1952 Gallows Rd., Ste. 300, Vienna, VA 22182, (703)748-1221
Korean Amer. Sharing Movement **[12860]**, 7004 Little River Tpke., Ste. O, Annandale, VA 22003, (703)867-0846
Korean Amer. Soc. of Entrepreneurs **[718]**, 2882 Sand Hill Rd., Ste. 100, Menlo Park, CA 94025
Korean Amer. Voters' Coun. **[18034]**, 35-20 147th St., No. 2D, Flushing, NY 11354, (718)961-4117
Korean Assn. of Orthodontics **[IO]**, Seoul, Republic of Korea
Korean Assn. of Univ. Women **[IO]**, Seoul, Republic of Korea
Korean Athletics Fed. **[IO]**, Seoul, Republic of Korea
Korean Baseball Assn. **[IO]**, Seoul, Republic of Korea
Korean Chamber of Commerce in Hong Kong **[IO]**, Hong Kong, People's Republic of China
Korean Chem. Soc. **[IO]**, Seoul, Republic of Korea
Korean Customs Brokers Assn. **[IO]**, Seoul, Republic of Korea
Korean Dermatological Assn. **[IO]**, Seoul, Republic of Korea
Korean Economic Assn. **[IO]**, Seoul, Republic of Korea
Korean EMDR Assn. **[IO]**, Seoul, Republic of Korea
Korean Epilepsy Soc. **[IO]**, Daegu, Republic of Korea
Korean Fed. of DanceSport **[IO]**, Seoul, Republic of Korea
Korean Footwear Indus. Assn. **[IO]**, Seoul, Republic of Korea
Korean Foster Care Assn. **[IO]**, Seoul, Republic of Korea
Korean Geotechnical Soc. **[IO]**, Seoul, Republic of Korea
Korean Inst. of Intl. Stud. **[IO]**, Seoul, Republic of Korea
Korean Inst. of Landscape Architecture **[IO]**, Seoul, Republic of Korea
Korean Inst. for Women and Politics **[IO]**, Seoul, Republic of Korea
Korean Medical Assn. **[IO]**, Seoul, Republic of Korea
Korean Natl. Commn. for UNESCO **[IO]**, Seoul, Republic of Korea
Korean Nuclear Soc. **[IO]**, Daejeon, Republic of Korea
Korean Olympic Comm. **[IO]**, Seoul, Republic of Korea
Korean Operations Res. and Mgt. Sci. Soc. **[IO]**, Seoul, Republic of Korea
Korean Paralympic Comm. **[IO]**, Seoul, Republic of Korea

Korean Physical Therapy Assn. **[IO]**, Seoul, Republic of Korea
Korean Physiological Soc. **[IO]**, Seoul, Republic of Korea
Korean Red Cross **[IO]**, Seoul, Republic of Korea
Korean Sailing Fed. **[IO]**, Seoul, Republic of Korea
Korean Scientists and Engineers Assn. in Am. **[★6807]**
Korean Soc. of Anesthesiologists **[IO]**, Seoul, Republic of Korea
Korean Soc. for the Cerebral Palsied **[IO]**, Seoul, Republic of Korea
Korean Soc. for Chemotherapy **[IO]**, Seoul, Republic of Korea
Korean Soc. of Circulation **[IO]**, Seoul, Republic of Korea
Korean Soc. of Electron Microscopy **[IO]**, Seoul, Republic of Korea
Korean Soc. of Gastrointestinal Endoscopy **[IO]**, Seoul, Republic of Korea
Korean Soc. of Hypertension **[IO]**, Seoul, Republic of Korea
Korean Soc. of Pharmacology **[IO]**, Seoul, Republic of Korea
Korean Soc. of Radiology **[IO]**, Seoul, Republic of Korea
Korean Soc. of Remote Sensing **[IO]**, Seoul, Republic of Korea
Korean Soc. of Soil Sci. and Fertilizer **[IO]**, Suwon, Republic of Korea
Korean Soc. of Surveying, Geodesy, Photogrammetry and Cartography **[IO]**, Seoul, Republic of Korea
Korean Standards Assn. **[IO]**, Seoul, Republic of Korea
Korean War
2nd Infantry Div., Korean War Veterans Alliance **[20673]**
2nd Infantry Div., Korean War Veterans Alliance **[20673]**
Chosin Few **[20674]**
Chosin Few **[20674]**
Korean War Veterans Assn. **[20675]**
Korean War Veterans Assn. **[20675]**
Mosquito Assn. **[20328]**
Korean War Proj. **[6057]**, PO Box 180190, Dallas, TX 75218-0190, (214)320-0342
Korean War Veterans Assn. **[20675]**, PO Box 407, Charleston, IL 61920-0407, (217)345-4414
Korean War Veterans Assn. **[20675]**, PO Box 407, Charleston, IL 61920-0407, (217)345-4414
Korean Water Ski and Wakeboard Assn. **[IO]**, Seoul, Republic of Korea
Korean Women Entrepreneurs Assn. **[IO]**, Seoul, Republic of Korea
Korean Women Workers Associations **[IO]**, Seoul, Republic of Korea
Korean Women's Inst. **[IO]**, Seoul, Republic of Korea
Korruptsioonivaba Eesti **[★IO]**
Kosciuszko Found. **[10461]**, 15 E 65th St., New York, NY 10021-6595, (212)734-2130
Kosciuszko Found. **[10461]**, 15 E 65th St., New York, NY 10021-6595, (212)734-2130
Kosovo
Amer. Coun. for Kosovo **[18036]**
Intl. Progressive Educ. **[8074]**
Kost och Naring- en branchforening inom Ledarna **[★IO]**
Kosuto Kougaku Ken'Kyusho **[★IO]**
Kott och Chark Foretagen **[★IO]**
Kotzebue Area Hea. Corp. **[★12562]**
Kotzebue Area Hea. Corp. **[★12562]**
Kowloon Chamber of Commerce **[IO]**, Hong Kong, People's Republic of China
Kozvetlen Ertekesitok Szovetsege **[★IO]**
Krajowa Izba Gospodarcza **[★IO]**
Kreis Katholischer Frauen im Heliand-Bund **[IO]**, Frankfurt, Germany
Kresge Found. **[13138]**, 3215 W Big Beaver Rd., Troy, MI 48084, (248)643-9630
Kresge Found. **[13138]**, 3215 W Big Beaver Rd., Troy, MI 48084, (248)643-9630
Kring voor Toegeporte Fysioch Geografie **[★IO]**
Krishnamurti Found. of Am. **[12218]**, PO Box 1560, Ojai, CA 93024, (805)646-2726

A star before a book entry number signifies that the name is not listed separately, but is mentioned within the entry.

Kristelige Foreninger av Unge Vinner [★IO]
Kristelijke Werknemersbeweging [IO], Brussels, Belgium
Kristna Fredsrorelsen [★IO]
Kroc Inst. for Intl. Peace Stud; Joan B. [18261]
Krochet Kids Intl. [12735], 1630 Superior Ave., Unit C, Costa Mesa, CA 92627
Kroeber Anthropological Soc. [6145], Univ. of California, Berkeley, Dept. of Anthropology, 232 Kroeber Hall, Berkeley, CA 94720-3710, (510)642-6932
Krousar Thmey [IO], Paris, France
Krystonia Collector's Club [21366], 125 W Ellsworth Rd., Ann Arbor, MI 48108, (734)332-8773
KS and Associates [★16772]
Ku Klux Klan; Knights of the [18782]
Kuki-Chowa Eisei Kogakkai [★IO]
Kultana Orchids [IO], Bangkok, Thailand
Kultura Centro Esperantista [★IO]
Kulturradet [★IO]
Kumitat Olimpiku Malta [★IO]
Kumiteollisuus ry [★IO]
Kump Family Assn. [20551], 7783 S 4950 W, West Jordan, UT 84084-5516
Kump Family Org. [★20551]
Kumpulan Kebudayaan Malaysia [★IO]
Kundalini Res. Network [15000], PO Box 541166, Cincinnati, OH 45254
Kungl. Vetenskapsakademien [★IO]
Kungliga Fysiografiska Sallskapet [★IO]
Kungliga Vitterhets Historie och Antikvitets Akademien [★IO]
Kunzang Palyul Choling [19369], PO Box 88, Poolesville, MD 20837, (301)710-6259
Kupenda for the Children [11340], PO Box 473, Hampton, NH 03843, (410)456-2311
Kuratorium fur die Tagungen der Nobelpreistrager [★IO]
Kurdish
  Amer. Kurdish Info. Network [18037]
  Amer. Kurdish Info. Network [18037]
  Kurdish Heritage Found. of Am. [19099]
  Kurdish Heritage Found. of Am. [19099]
Kurdish Heritage Found. of Am. [19099], 345 Park Pl., Brooklyn, NY 11238, (718)783-7930
Kurdish Heritage Found. of Am. [19099], 345 Park Pl., Brooklyn, NY 11238, (718)783-7930
Kurdish Human Rights Proj. [IO], London, United Kingdom
Kurk Sanayicileri ve Is Adamlari Dernegi [★IO]
Kurt-Godel-Gesellschaft [★IO]
Kurt Goedel Soc. [IO], Vienna, Austria
Kurt Weill Found. for Music [10232], 7 E 20th St., New York, NY 10003-1106, (212)505-5240
Kurt Weill Found. for Music [10232], 7 E 20th St., New York, NY 10003-1106, (212)505-5240
Kustom Kemps of Am. [21089], 26 Main St., Cassville, MO 65625-9400, (417)847-2940
Kustoms of Am. [22116], 4427 Ginger Dr., Gastonia, NC 28056, (704)865-4433
Kuvasz Club of Am. [21597], Penelope Johns, Membership Sec., 8620 Louise Ave., Northridge, CA 91325-3418
Kuwait Amateur Radio Soc. [IO], Safat, Kuwait
Kuwait Assn. of Athletics Fed. [IO], Safat, Kuwait
Kuwait Badminton Fed. [IO], Hawalli, Kuwait
Kuwait Boxing and Weightlifting Assn. [IO], Hawalli, Kuwait
Kuwait Chamber of Commerce and Indus. [IO], Safat, Kuwait
Kuwait Jet Ski Fed. [IO], Safat, Kuwait
Kuwait Journalists Assn. [IO], Safat, Kuwait
Kuwait Judo and Taekwondo Fed. [IO], Safat, Kuwait
Kuwait Medical Assn. [IO], Safat, Kuwait
Kuwait Natl. Commn. for Educ., Sci. and Culture [IO], Safat, Kuwait
Kuwait Olympic Comm. [IO], Safat, Kuwait
Kuwait Red Crescent Soc. [IO], Safat, Kuwait
Kuwait Soc. of Dermatologists [IO], Khaldiya, Kuwait
Kuwait Sports Medicine Assn. [IO], Safat, Kuwait
Kuwait Squash Fed. [IO], Sabah Al-Salem, Kuwait
Kuwait Tennis Fed. [IO], Hawalli, Kuwait
Kvindernes Internationale Liga for Fred og Frihed [★IO]

KVINFO - Danish Centre for Info. on Women and Gender [IO], Copenhagen, Denmark
Kvinnliga Akademikers Forening [★IO]
Kyosiga Community Christians Assn. for Development [IO], Kampala, Uganda
Kypriaki Aerathlitiki Omospondia [★IO]
Kypriakos Syndesmos Biomichanion Endysis [★IO]
Kyrghyz Natl. Badminton Fed. [IO], Bishkek, Kirgizstan
Kyrgyz Adult Educ. Assn. [IO], Bishkek, Kirgizstan
Kyrgyz Alpine Club [IO], Bishkek, Kirgizstan
Kyrgyz Assn. of Japanese Language Teachers [IO], Bishkek, Kirgizstan
Kyrgyz Assn. of Tour Operators [IO], Bishkek, Kirgizstan
Kyrgyz Community Based Tourism Assn. [IO], Bishkek, Kirgizstan
Kyrgyz League Against Epilepsy [IO], Bishkek, Kirgizstan
Kyrgyz Parliamentarians Against Corruption [IO], Bishkek, Kirgizstan
Kyrgyz Res. and Educ. Network Assn. [IO], Bishkek, Kirgizstan
Kyrgyzstan Taekwondo Assn. [IO], Bishkek, Kirgizstan
Kyrgyzstan Tennis Fed. [IO], Bishkek, Kirgizstan
Kythe [IO], Quezon City, Philippines

L

L5 Soc. [★6090]
La federation humaniste europeenne [★IO]
La Asociacion Internacional de Fibrosis Quistica (Mucoviscidosis) [★IO]
La Asociacion Pro-Bienestar de la Familia Colombia [IO], Bogota, Colombia
La Camara De Comercio Americana En Espana [★IO]
La societe des comptables professionnels du Canada [★IO]
La Chambre Canadienne Allemande de l'Industrie et du Commerce [★IO]
La Chambre de Commerce du Canada [★IO]
La Chambre de Commerce Canada - Grande Bretagne [★IO]
La Cle d'la Baie en Huronie [★IO]
La Communaute Baha'ie du Canada [★IO]
La Conseil Canadien des Ministres de l'Environnement [★IO]
La Corp. Canadienne des Retraites Interesses [★IO]
La Croix Rouge Monegasque [★IO]
La Federacion Dominicana de Badminton [IO], Santo Domingo, Dominican Republic
La Fed. Canadienne de Bridge [★IO]
La Fed. Canado-Arabe [★IO]
La Fed. des associations europeennes d'ecrivains [★IO]
La Fed. Internationale des Chambres Syndicales des Negociants en Timbres-Poste [★IO]
La Fed. des Societes Canadiennes d'Assistance aux Animaux [★IO]
La Fed. de Tir du Canada [★IO]
La Fondation des ecrivains canadiens [★IO]
La Fondation Canadienne MedicAlert [★IO]
La Fondation Canadienne de Recherche en Publicite [★IO]
La Fondation Canado Palestinienne du Quebec [★IO]
La Fondation Heritage pour Haiti [★IO]
La Fondation des Mines Terrestres du Canada [★IO]
La Guilde Canadienne des Realisateurs [★IO]
La Leche League [IO], Montreal, QC, Canada
La Leche League Intl. [11480], PO Box 4079, Schaumburg, IL 60168-4079, (847)519-7730
La Leche League Intl. [11480], PO Box 4079, Schaumburg, IL 60168-4079, (847)519-7730
La Leche League of New Zealand [IO], Porirua, New Zealand
La Ligue Canadienne des Compositeurs [★IO]
La Ligue des Familles [★IO]
La Prevention Routiere Internationale [★IO]
La Raza Natl. Bar Assn. [★5249]
La Raza; Natl. Coun. of [12146]
La Raza Natl. Lawyers Assn. [★5249]

La Raza Unida Party [18359], PO Box 40376, Albuquerque, NM 87196
La Sertoma Intl. [13063], 4095 Upham Rd., Kettering, OH 45429, (937)534-1410
La Sertoma Intl. [13063], 4095 Upham Rd., Kettering, OH 45429, (937)534-1410
La Societe canadienne des etudes mesopotamiennes [★IO]
La Societe des sculpteurs du Canada [★IO]
La Societe Canadienne D' Histoire de L'Eglise Catholique [★IO]
La Societe Canadienne d'Addison [★IO]
La Societe Canadienne De La Douleur [★IO]
La Societe Canadienne d'Etudes Ethniques [★IO]
La Societe Canadienne des Eleveurs de Moutons [★IO]
La Societe Canadienne de Genie Agroalimentaire et de Bioingenierie [★IO]
La Societe Canadienne de l'Ouie [★IO]
La Societe Canadienne de Neurophysiologie Clinique [★IO]
La Societe Canadienne de Physiologie [★IO]
La Societe Canadienne Pour la Recherche Nautique [★IO]
La Societe Canadienne de Sante Internationale [★IO]
La Societe Canadienne de Sciences de la Nutrition [★IO]
La Societe Canadienne de Sociologie [★IO]
La Societe Canadienne de Texels [★IO]
La Societe d'histoire nationale du Canada [★IO]
La Societe de Genetique du Canada [★IO]
La Societe Geographique Royale du Canada [★IO]
La Societe Guernesiaise [IO], Guernsey, United Kingdom
La Societe canadienne des eleveurs de bovins Highland [★IO]
La Societe pour l'etude de l'architecture au Canada [★IO]
La Societe Opimian [★IO]
La Societe de Philosophie Exacte [★10421]
La Societe de Philosophie Exacte [★10421]
La Societe de Protection des Infirmies et infirmiers du Canada [★IO]
La Societe Royale de Philatelie du Canada [★IO]
La Voix des Enfants [★IO]
Laakarin Sosiaalinen Vastuu [★IO]
Laban/Bartenieff Inst. of Movement Stud. [9558], 520 8th Ave., Rm. 304, New York, NY 10018, (212)643-8888
Laban Guild [IO], Basingstoke, United Kingdom
Laban Inst. of Movement Stud. [★9558]
Label Printing Indus. of Am. [3352], 200 Deer Run Rd., Sewickley, PA 15143, (412)741-6860
Labor
AED Natl. Inst. for Work and Learning [18038]
AFL-CIO I Dept. Professional Employees [23223]
Amer. Assn. of Classified School Employees [23177]
Amer. Rights at Work [18039]
America's Edge [17599]
Asian Pacific Amer. Labor Alliance [23224]
Assn. of Minor League Umpires [22266]
Bakery, Confectionery, Tobacco Workers and Grain Millers Intl. Union [23225]
California Public Employee Relations Prog. [18040]
Center for Labor and Community Res. [18041]
Center for Labor Res. and Educ. [8452]
Child Labor Coalition [11220]
Concerned Educators Against Forced Unionism [18042]
Directors Guild of Am. [23187]
Eugene V. Debs Found. [9934]
Fed. of Employers and Workers of Am. [1147]
Gen. Ser. Employees Union Local 73 [23226]
Graphic Arts Employers of Am. [23211]
HR Policy Assn. [18043]
Intl. Brotherhood of DuPont Workers [23171]
Intl. Brotherhood of Teamsers I Brewery and Soft Drink Workers Conf. [23158]
Intl. Guild of Symphony, Opera and Ballet Musicians [23272]
Intl. Initiative on Exploitative Child Labor [11325]
Intl. Labor Rights Forum [18044]

Intl. Labor Rights Forum [18044]
Intl. Union of Electronic, Elecl., Salaried, Machine, and Furniture Workers [23184]
Intl. Union of Indus. and Independent Workers [23312]
Joint Labor Mgt. Comm. of the Retail Food Indus. [23190]
Just Transition Alliance [23227]
Just Transition Alliance [23227]
Labor Coun. for Latin Amer. Advancement [23228]
Labor Res. Assn. [23239]
Lithuanian Labour Fed. [16786]
Machinists Non-Partisan Political League [23220]
Millwright Gp. [23221]
Natl. Assn. Broadcast Employees and Technicians | Communications. Workers of Am. [23162]
Natl. Assn. of Governmental Labor Officials [5635]
Natl. Day Laborer Organizing Network [23229]
Natl. Mobilization Against Sweatshops [18045]
Natl. Public Employer Labor Relations Assn. [5636]
Professional Airways Systems Specialists [23155]
Public Ser. Res. Coun. [18046]
Ser. Workers United [23230]
Soc. of Fed. Labor and Employee Relations Professionals [5637]
SweatFree Communities [23231]
Trans. Communications Intl. Union [23290]
Trans. Communications Union | Brotherhood Railway Carmen Div. [23291]
United Assn. of Journeymen and Apprentices of the Plumbing, Pipe Fitting, Sprinkler Fitting Indus. of the U.S. and Canada [23277]
United Assn. for Labor Educ. [8453]
United Brotherhood of Carpenters and Joiners of Am. [23169]
United Nations Staff Union [23261]
U.S. Labor Educ. in the Americas Proj. [18047]
U.S. Labor Educ. in the Americas Proj. [18047]
Wal-Mart Workers for Change [23232]
Youth for Intl. Socialism [18663]
The Labor Center [★8452]
Labor Coun. for Latin Amer. Advancement [23228], 815 16th St. NW, 4th Fl., Washington, DC 20006, (202)508-6919
Labor Educ. and Res. Proj. [★23237]
Labor and Employment Relations Assn. [23236], Univ. of Illinois, 121 Labor and Employment Relations Bldg., 504 E Armory Ave., Champaign, IL 61820, (217)333-0072
Labor Heritage Found. [9302], 815 16th St. NW, Washington, DC 20006, (202)639-6204
Labor Inst. of Public Affairs - Defunct.
Labor Management
Amer. Assn. of Classified School Employees [23177]
Assn. of Minor League Umpires [22266]
Directors Guild of Am. [23187]
Graphic Arts Employers of Am. [23211]
Intl. Brotherhood of DuPont Workers [23171]
Intl. Brotherhood of Teamsers | Brewery and Soft Drink Workers Conf. [23158]
Intl. Guild of Symphony, Opera and Ballet Musicians [23272]
Intl. Union of Electronic, Elecl., Salaried, Machine, and Furniture Workers [23184]
Intl. Union of Indus. and Independent Workers [23312]
Joint Labor Mgt. Comm. of the Retail Food Indus. [23190]
Labor Res. Assn. [23239]
Machinists Non-Partisan Political League [23220]
Millwright Gp. [23221]
Natl. Assn. Broadcast Employees and Technicians | Communications Workers of Am. [23162]
Professional Airways Systems Specialists [23155]
Trans. Communications Intl. Union [23290]
Trans. Communications Union | Brotherhood Railway Carmen Div. [23291]
United Assn. of Journeymen and Apprentices of the Plumbing, Pipe Fitting, Sprinkler Fitting Indus. of the U.S. and Canada [23277]
United Brotherhood of Carpenters and Joiners of Am. [23169]
United Nations Staff Union [23261]

Labor-Mgt. Relations Service of the U.S. Conf. of Mayors - Defunct.
Labor Notes [23237], 7435 Michigan Ave., Detroit, MI 48210, (313)842-6262
Labor Policy Assn. [★18043]
Labor Proj. for Working Families [23238], 2521 Channing Way, No. 5555, Berkeley, CA 94720, (510)643-7088
Labor Reform
Center on Natl. Labor Policy [18048]
Natl. Right to Work Comm. [18049]
Natl. Right to Work Legal Defense and Educ. Found. [18050]
Labor Res. Assn. [23239], Jeannine Rudolph, 80 Broad St., Ste. 705, New York, NY 10004, (212)714-1677
Labor Studies
Amer. Assn. of Classified School Employees [23177]
Assn. of Labor Relations Agencies [23233]
Assn. of Labor Relations Agencies [23233]
Assn. for Union Democracy [23234]
Directors Guild of Am. [23187]
Graphic Arts Employers of Am. [23211]
Inst. of Labor and Indus. Relations [23235]
Intl. Brotherhood of DuPont Workers [23171]
Intl. Brotherhood of Teamsers | Brewery and Soft Drink Workers Conf. [23158]
Intl. Guild of Symphony, Opera and Ballet Musicians [23272]
Intl. Union of Electronic, Elecl., Salaried, Machine, and Furniture Workers [23184]
Joint Labor Mgt. Comm. of the Retail Food Indus. [23190]
Labor and Employment Relations Assn. [23236]
Labor Notes [23237]
Labor Proj. for Working Families [23238]
Labor Res. Assn. [23239]
Labor and Working Class History Assn. [8454]
Machinists Non-Partisan Political League [23220]
Millwright Gp. [23221]
Natl. Assn. Broadcast Employees and Technicians | Communications Workers of Am. [23162]
Professional Airways Systems Specialists [23155]
Trans. Communications Intl. Union [23290]
Trans. Communications Union | Brotherhood Railway Carmen Div. [23291]
United Assn. of Journeymen and Apprentices of the Plumbing, Pipe Fitting, Sprinkler Fitting Indus. of the U.S. and Canada [23277]
United Brotherhood of Carpenters and Joiners of Am. [23169]
United Nations Staff Union [23261]
Working Class Stud. Assn. [8455]
Labor Union Cong. of Quebec [IO], Montreal, QC, Canada
Labor Unions
Amer. Assn. of Classified School Employees [23177]
Assn. of Minor League Umpires [22266]
Directors Guild of Am. [23187]
Graphic Arts Employers of Am. [23211]
Intl. Assn. of Heat and Frost Insulators and Allied Workers [1707]
Intl. Brotherhood of DuPont Workers [23171]
Intl. Brotherhood of Teamsers | Brewery and Soft Drink Workers Conf. [23158]
Intl. Guild of Symphony, Opera and Ballet Musicians [23272]
Intl. Union of Electronic, Elecl., Salaried, Machine, and Furniture Workers [23184]
Intl. Union of Indus. and Independent Workers [23312]
Joint Labor Mgt. Comm. of the Retail Food Indus. [23190]
Labor Res. Assn. [23239]
Machinists Non-Partisan Political League [23220]
Millwright Gp. [23221]
Natl. Assn. Broadcast Employees and Technicians | Communications Workers of Am. [23162]
Professional Airways Systems Specialists [23155]
Trans. Communications Intl. Union [23290]
Trans. Communications Union | Brotherhood Railway Carmen Div. [23291]
Unite Here [23240]

United Assn. of Journeymen and Apprentices of the Plumbing, Pipe Fitting, Sprinkler Fitting Indus. of the U.S. and Canada [23277]
United Brotherhood of Carpenters and Joiners of Am. [23169]
United Nations Staff Union [23261]
Labor and Working Class History Assn. [8454], Abby Goldman, Exec. Admin., Duke Univ., Stanford Indus., Box 90239, Durham, NC 27708-0239, (919)688-5134
Labor Zionist Alliance [★19086]
Laboratoires des Assureurs de Canada [★IO]
Laboratory
Addgene [7110]
Amer. Assn. of Bioanalysts [15229]
Amer. Assn. for Lab. Accreditation [7017]
Amer. Assn. for Lab. Animal Sci. [13757]
Amer. Assn. of Physician Offices and Labs. [15230]
Amer. Bd. of Bioanalysis [7018]
Amer. Clinical Lab. Assn. [15231]
Amer. Coun. of Independent Labs. [7019]
Amer. Soc. for Clinical Lab. Sci. [15232]
Assn. of Biomolecular Rsrc. Facilities [7020]
Assn. of Lab. Managers [7021]
Clinical Lab. Mgt. Assn. [15233]
Clinical and Lab. Standards Inst. [15234]
Clinical and Lab. Standards Inst. [15234]
Forbes Norris MDA/ALS Res. Center [15590]
Independent Labs. Inst. [2177]
Inst. for Chem. Educ. [7820]
Intl. Soc. for Plasmid Biology and other Mobile Genetic Elements [7111]
North Amer. Specialized Coagulation Lab. Assn. [15235]
North Amer. Specialized Coagulation Lab. Assn. [15235]
Lab. Animal Mgt. Assn. [13763], 7500 Flying Cloud Dr., Ste. 900, Eden Prairie, MN 55344, (952)253-6235
Lab. Animal Managers Assn. [★13763]
Lab. Animal Sci. Assn. [IO], Hull, United Kingdom
Lab. Diagnosticians; Amer. Assn. of Veterinary [16986]
Lab. Products Assn. [3176], PO Box 428, Fairfax, VA 22038, (703)836-1360
Laborers' Intl. Union of North Am. [23166], 905 16th St. NW, Washington, DC 20006, (202)737-8320
Laborers' Intl. Union of North Am. [23166], 905 16th St. NW, Washington, DC 20006, (202)737-8320
Labour Party - Britain [IO], Newcastle upon Tyne, United Kingdom
Labour Women's Coun. [IO], Wellington, New Zealand
Labour Women's Network [IO], Leeds, United Kingdom
Labrador Retriever Club [★21612]
Lace Guild [IO], Stourbridge, United Kingdom
Lackey Family Assn. - Defunct.
Laconia Sled Dog Club [★22558]
Lacrosse
Canadian Lacrosse Assn. [13509]
Coun. of Ivy Gp. Presidents [22975]
Fed. of Intl. Lacrosse [22713]
Fields of Growth Intl. [12416]
Intercollegiate Women's Lacrosse Coaches Assn. [22714]
Men's Collegiate Lacrosse Assn. [22715]
Southeastern Conf. [23006]
U.S. Intercollegiate Lacrosse Assn. [22716]
U.S. Lacrosse [22717]
U.S. Lacrosse Assn., Women's Div. [22718]
The Lacrosse Found. [★22717]
Lacrosse Players Assn; Professional [23299]
Lactation; Intl. Soc. for Res. in Human Milk and [13864]
Lactation; Intl. Soc. for Res. in Human Milk and [13864]
Ladder Assn. [IO], Glasgow, United Kingdom
Ladies Auxiliary of the Military Order of the Purple Heart U.S.A. [20376], 19138 Bedford Dr., Oregon City, OR 97045, (503)657-7085
Ladies Catholic Benevolent Assn. [★19051]
Ladies of Charity of the U.S.A. [13191], Natl. Ser. Center, 100 N Jefferson Ave., St. Louis, MO 63103, (314)881-6017

A star before a book entry number signifies that the name is not listed separately, but is mentioned within the entry.

Ladies' Golf Union [IO], St. Andrews, United Kingdom

Ladies of the Grand Army of the Republic [20385], 21733 W 56th St., Shawnee, KS 66218, (913)422-4953

Ladies' Hermitage Assn. [10676], 4580 Rachel's Ln., Hermitage, TN 37076, (615)889-2941

Ladies Kennel Assn. of Am. [21598], Terri Cude, Corresponding Sec., 77 Bleecker St., No. 302, New York, NY 10012, (212)673-3208

Ladies Oriental Shrine of North Am. [19135], 1111 E 54th St., Ste. 111, Indianapolis, IN 46220

Ladies Professional Golf Assn. [22614], 100 Intl. Golf Dr., Daytona Beach, FL 32124-1092, (386)274-6200

Lady Bird Johnson Wildflower Center [6361], 4801 La Crosse Ave., Austin, TX 78739, (512)232-0100

Ladyslipper [10641], PO Box 3124, Durham, NC 27715, (919)383-8773

Laekemedelsindustrifoereningen [★IO]

Lahore Ahmadiyya Movement for the Propagation of Islam - Canada [IO], Toronto, ON, Canada

Lahore Ahmadiyya Movement for the Propagation of Islam - Pakistan [IO], Lahore, Pakistan

Laity
Natl. Assn. for Lay Ministry [19914]
Natl. Bible Assn. [19915]
Natl. Center for the Laity [19916]

Laity for Life [19439], PO Box 111478, Naples, FL 34108, (239)352-6333

Lakare for Miljon [★IO]

Lakasberlok es Lakok Egyesulete [★IO]

Lake Carriers' Assn. [2381], 20325 Center Ridge Rd., Ste. 720, Rocky River, OH 44116, (440)333-4444

Lakemedelsindustriforeningen [★IO]

Lakes
Intl. Assn. for Great Lakes Res. [7022]
Intl. Assn. for Great Lakes Res. [7022]
Intl. Soc. of Limnology [7023]
Intl. Soc. of Limnology [7023]
Intl. Water Level Coalition [5004]
League to Save Lake Tahoe [4091]
North Amer. Lake Mgt. Soc. [7024]

Lakes Region Sled Dog Club [22558], Peter Colbath, Treas., PO Box 341, Laconia, NH 03247-0382, (603)524-4314

Lakota Student Alliance [19158], PO Box 225, Kyle, SD 57752, (605)867-1507

Lalmba Assn. [12861], 7685 Quartz St., Arvada, CO 80007, (303)420-1810

Lalmba Assn. [12861], 7685 Quartz St., Arvada, CO 80007, (303)420-1810

LAM Found. [14396], 4015 Executive Park Dr., Ste. 320, Cincinnati, OH 45241, (513)777-6889

LAM Treatment Alliance [16610], 64 Church St., 2nd Fl., Cambridge, MA 02138, (617)460-7339

Lama Found. [9827], PO Box 240, San Cristobal, NM 87564, (505)586-1269

Lamaze Intl. [15885], 2025 M St. NW, Ste. 800, Washington, DC 20036-3309, (202)367-1128

Lamaze Intl. [15885], 2025 M St. NW, Ste. 800, Washington, DC 20036-3309, (202)367-1128

Lamb Comm. - Defunct.

Lambda Alpha [23465], Ball State Univ., Dept. of Anthropology, Muncie, IN 47306, (765)285-1575

Lambda Alpha Epsilon [★11703]

Lambda Alpha Intl. [23505], 1821 Univ. Ave. W, Ste. S256, St. Paul, MN 55104, (651)917-6257

Lambda Chi Alpha [23676], 8741 Founders Rd., Indianapolis, IN 46268-1389, (317)872-8000

Lambda Iota Tau - Address unknown since 2010.

Lambda Kappa Sigma [23617], PO Box 570, Muskego, WI 53150, (800)557-1913

Lambda Legal Defense and Educ. Fund [12095], 120 Wall St., Ste. 1500, New York, NY 10005-3904, (212)809-8585

Lambda Omicron Gamma Medical Soc. - Defunct.

Lambda Pi Alumni Assn. [23536], PO Box 1133, Chico, CA 95927, (707)738-5971

Lambda Psi Delta Sorority [23747], PO Box 260128, Hartford, CT 06106

Lambda Theta Phi [23537], 181 New Rd., Ste. 304, Parsippany, NJ 07054, (866)425-2623

Lamborghini Club Am. [21090], PO Box 701963, Plymouth, MI 48170, (734)216-4455

The Lambs [10582], 3 W 51st St., New York, NY 10019, (212)586-0306

Laminating Materials Assn. [★1503]

Laminating Materials Assn. [★1503]

Laminators Safety Glass Assn. [★1575]

Lamp of Hope Proj. [17218], PO Box 305, League City, TX 77574-0305

Lamps
Aladdin Knights of the Mystic Light [21877]

Lancashire Welsh Pony and Cob Assn. [IO], Manchester, United Kingdom

Lancaster District Chamber of Commerce, Trade and Indus. [IO], Lancaster, United Kingdom

Lancaster Mennonite Historical Soc. [20643], 2215 Millstream Rd., Lancaster, PA 17602-1499, (717)393-9745

Lancaster Mennonite Historical Soc. [20643], 2215 Millstream Rd., Lancaster, PA 17602-1499, (717)393-9745

Lancaster Railway and Locomotive Historical Soc. [★10493]

Lancia Club Belgio [IO], Dilbeek, Belgium

Lancia Club Deutschland [IO], Stuttgart, Germany

Lancia Club Finland [IO], Laihia, Finland

Lancia Club France [IO], Paris, France

Lancia Club Japan [IO], Tokyo, Japan

Lancia Club Nederland [IO], Zandvoort, Netherlands

Lancia Club Suisse [IO], Feuerthalen, Switzerland

Lancia Club Vincenzo [IO], Mullheim, Germany

Lancia Motor Club [IO], Southport, United Kingdom

Lancia Motor Club New South Wales [IO], Northbridge, Australia

Lancisti Norvegesi [IO], Oslo, Norway

Land Control
Land Loss Fund [12417]
Lincoln Inst. of Land Policy [5638]

Land Improvement Contractors of Am. [4087], 3080 Ogden Ave., Ste. 300, Lisle, IL 60532, (630)548-1984

The Land Inst. [4354], 2440 E Water Well Rd., Salina, KS 67401, (785)823-5376

Land Loss Fund [12417], PO Box 61, Tillery, NC 27887, (252)826-3017

Land Mobile Communications Coun. [3414], 8484 Westpark Dr., Ste. 630, McLean, VA 22102-5117, (703)528-5115

Land Rights [★5901]

Land Rover Owner Austria [IO], Willendorf, Austria

Land Trust Alliance [4088], 1660 L St. NW, Ste. 1100, Washington, DC 20036, (202)638-4725

Land Trust Exchange [★4088]

Landau Network - Centry Volta [IO], Como, Italy

LandboUngdom [★IO]

LandChoices [4089], PO Box 181, Milford, MI 48381, (248)685-0483

Landex - The Assn. for Land Based Colleges [IO], Nantwich, United Kingdom

Landing Craft Infantry Natl. Assn. [★20807]

Landscape Architects; Amer. Soc. of [6187]

Landscape Architecture Found. [6199], 818 18th St. NW, Ste. 810, Washington, DC 20006, (202)331-7070

Landscape Artists Intl. [9240], Karl Eric Leitzel Studio, 155 Murray School Ln., Spring Mills, PA 16875, (814)422-8461

Landscape Artists Intl. [9240], Karl Eric Leitzel Studio, 155 Murray School Ln., Spring Mills, PA 16875, (814)422-8461

Landscape Assn. of Westfalen-Lippe [IO], Munster, Germany

Landscape Indus. Assn. Singapore [IO], Singapore, Singapore

Landscape Inst. [IO], London, United Kingdom

Landscape Res. Gp. [IO], Sheffield, United Kingdom

Landscaping
Assn. of Professional Landscape Designers [2178]
Assn. of Professional Landscape Designers [2178]
Assn. of Synthetic Grass Installers [534]
Coalition of Organic Landscapers [2179]
Coun. of Educators in Landscape Architecture [8456]
Ecological Landscaping Assn. [4681]
Ecological Landscaping Assn. [4681]

European Found. for Landscape Architecture [10739]

Independent Turf and Ornamental Distributors Assn. [2180]

Natl. Assn. of Pond Professionals [237]

Natl. Pavement Contractors Assn. [595]

New York State Turf and Landscape Assn. [2181]

Northeastern Weed Sci. Soc. [4682]

Overseas Chinese Landscape Architects Assn. [2182]

Professional Landcare Network [2183]

Proj. EverGreen [4683]

Sports Turf Managers Assn. [2184]

Sports Turf Managers Assn. [2184]

Turf and Ornamental Communicators Assn. [2185]

Landschaftsverband Westfalen-Lippe [★IO]

Landsforeningen for Huntington's Sykdom [IO], Kristiansand, Norway

Landsforeningen for Marfan Syndrom [★IO]

Landslaget Fysisk Fostring I Skolen [IO], Tonsberg, Norway

Landsorganisationen i Danmark [★IO]

Landsradet for Sveriges Ungdomsorganisationer [★IO]

Landssamband KFUM [★IO]

Landstuhl Hosp. Care Proj. [12463], 29 Greenleaf Terr., Stafford, VA 22556

Langbrugsraadet [★IO]

Langston Hughes Soc. [9390], City Coll. of New York/CUNY, English Dept., 160 Convent Ave., New York, NY 10031

Language
Acad. of Rehabilitative Audiology [14910]
Alpha Mu Gamma Natl. [23576]
Amer. Assn. of Teachers of Arabic [8457]
Amer. Assn. of Teachers of Esperanto [8458]
Amer. Assn. of Teachers of Esperanto [8458]
Amer. Assn. of Teachers of French [8459]
Amer. Assn. of Teachers of German [8460]
Amer. Assn. of Teachers of Italian [8461]
Amer. Assn. of Teachers of Italian [8461]
Amer. Assn. of Teachers of Slavic and East European Languages [8462]
Amer. Assn. of Teachers of Spanish and Portuguese [8463]
Amer. Assn. of Teachers of Spanish and Portuguese [8463]
Amer. Classical League [8464]
Amer. Coun. on the Teaching of Foreign Languages [8465]
Amer. Dialect Soc. [10022]
Amer. Philological Assn. [9935]
Assembly for the Teaching of English Grammar [8466]
Assn. for the Advancement of Documentation Sciences and Techniques [12240]
Assn. of Departments of Foreign Languages [8467]
Assn. of Language Companies [2186]
Assn. of Teachers of Japanese [8468]
Assyrian Academic Soc. [9936]
Assyriari Academic Soc. [9936]
Bhojpuri Assn. of North Am. [9937]
Bhojpuri Assn. of North Am. [9937]
Coll. Language Assn. [8469]
Corporate Speech Pathology Network [3303]
Coun. of Teachers of Southeast Asian Languages [7756]
Deaf and Hard of Hearing Alliance [14929]
Dogs for the Deaf [14933]
Endangered Language Fund [9938]
English-Speaking Union of the U.S. [19100]
ERIC CH on Languages and Linguistics [8470]
Esperanto-USA [9583]
European Language Coun. [16214]
Intl. Assn. of Chinese Linguistics [7025]
Intl. Assn. of Chinese Linguistics [7025]
Intl. Assn. for Dialogue Anal. [7026]
Intl. Assn. for Dialogue Anal. [7026]
Intl. Assn. for Teachers of Chinese to Speakers of Other Languages [7844]
Intl. Lexical Functional Grammar Assn. [8471]
Intl. Lexical Functional Grammar Assn. [8471]
Intl. Soc. for Language Stud. [9939]

Reference to "IO" in place of a book number signifies that the association may be found in the 50th edition of International Organizations.

Intl. Soc. for Language Stud. [9939]
Joint Natl. Comm. for Languages [9940]
Language Materials Proj. [8472]
Less Commonly Taught Languages Proj. [8473]
Logical Language Gp. [9941]
Media Access Gp. [12418]
Model Secondary School for the Deaf [14946]
Modern Language Assn. of Am. [8474]
Modern Language Assn. of Am. [8474]
Natl. Alliance to Save Native Languages [9942]
Natl. Assn. of Self-Instructional Language
Programs [8475]
Natl. Coun. for Languages and Intl. Stud. [9943]
Natl. Coun. for Languages and Intl. Stud. [9943]
Natl. Coun. of Less Commonly Taught Languages
[8476]
Natl. Coun. of Less Commonly Taught Languages
[8476]
Natl. Coun. of State Supervisor of Foreign
Languages [8477]
Natl. Foreign Language Center [8478]
North Amer. Assn. for Celtic Language Teachers
[8479]
North Amer. Christian Foreign Language Assn.
[8480]
Northeast Conf. on the Teaching of Foreign
Languages [8481]
Phi Sigma Iota [23577]
Rhetoric Soc. of Am. [10512]
Soc. for the Stud. of Indigenous Languages of the
Americas [9944]
Soc. for the Stud. of Indigenous Languages of the
Americas [9944]
Swedish Translators in North America [10615]
WordTheatre [10550]
Language Materials Proj. [8472], Univ. of California,
1337 Rolfe Hall, Box 951487, Los Angeles, CA
90095-1487, (310)267-4720
Lansforeningen mod Huntingtons Chorea [★IO]
Lantbrukarnas Riksfoerbund [★IO]
Lao Amateur Athletic Assn. [IO], Vientiane, Lao
People's Democratic Republic
Lao Badminton Fed. [IO], Vientiane, Lao People's
Democratic Republic
Lao Medical Assn. [IO], Vientiane, Lao People's
Democratic Republic
Lao Natl. Chamber of Commerce and Indus. [IO],
Vientiane, Lao People's Democratic Republic
Lao Taekwondo Fed. [IO], Vientiane, Lao People's
Democratic Republic
Lao Tennis Fed. [IO], Vientiane, Lao People's
Democratic Republic
Laogai Res. Found. [17848], 1734 20th St. NW,
Washington, DC 20009, (202)408-8300
Laogai Res. Found. [17848], 1734 20th St. NW,
Washington, DC 20009, (202)408-8300
Laotian
Laotian Amer. Natl. Alliance [19101]
Laotian Amer. Soc. [19102]
Laotian Amer. Soc. [19102]
Laotian Amer. Natl. Alliance [19101], 1628 16th St.
NW, Washington, DC 20009, (202)370-7841
Laotian Amer. Soc. [19102], PO Box 48432, Atlanta,
GA 30362
Laotian Amer. Soc. [19102], PO Box 48432, Atlanta,
GA 30362
LaPerm Soc. of Am. [21253], Sandy Brew, Treas.,
4403 Old Buckingham Rd., Powhatan, VA 23139,
(505)753-6005
Laptops for the Wounded [11526], Kathy Drouin, VP,
607 Charlestown Rd., Acworth, NH 03601,
(860)463-2885
Lararforbundet [★IO]
Lararnas Riksforbund [★IO]
Large Public Power Coun. [5406], 300 N
Washington St., Ste. 405, Alexandria, VA 22314,
(703)740-1700
Largely Positive [15854], PO Box 170223,
Milwaukee, WI 53217-8021, (414)299-9295
Larger Than Life [11341], 54-15 35th St., Long
Island City, NY 11101, (888)644-4040
Larry Jones Evangelistic Assn. [★12837]
Larry Jones Evangelistic Assn. [★12837]
Larry Jones Intl. Ministries [★12837]
Larry Jones Intl. Ministries [★12837]

Laryngological Assn; Amer. [16084]
Laryngological, Rhinological and Otological Soc;
Amer. [16085]
Lasallian Volunteers [20055], Hecker Ctr., Ste. 300,
3025 Fourth St. NE, Washington, DC 20017,
(202)529-0047
Laser Indus. Assn. [★7028]
Laser Inst. of Am. [7028], 13501 Ingenuity Dr., Ste.
128, Orlando, FL 32826, (407)380-1553
Laser Medicine
Amer. Soc. for Laser Medicine and Surgery
[15236]
Intl. Aesthetic and Laser Assn. [15237]
North Amer. Assn. for Laser Therapy [15238]
Lasers
Intl. Aesthetic and Laser Assn. [15237]
Intl. Comm. on Ultra-High Intensity Lasers [7027]
Intl. Comm. on Ultra-High Intensity Lasers [7027]
Laser Inst. of Am. [7028]
North Amer. Assn. for Laser Therapy [15238]
Lasher Family Assn. [20552], PO Box 1194, King-
ston, NY 12402, (845)339-5279
LASPAU: Academic and Professional Programs for
the Americas [7882], 25 Mt. Auburn St.,
Cambridge, MA 02138-6095, (617)495-5255
LASPAU: Academic and Professional Programs for
the Americas [7882], 25 Mt. Auburn St.,
Cambridge, MA 02138-6095, (617)495-5255
l'Association des fournisseurs de produits sanitaires
[★IO]
Last Acts Partnership - Defunct.
Last Chance for Animals [10999], 8033 Sunset
Blvd., No. 835, Los Angeles, CA 90046, (310)271-
6096
Last Chance Corral [11000], 5350 US-33 S, Athens,
OH 45701, (740)594-4336
Last Chance Forever [5077], PO Box 460993, San
Antonio, TX 78246-0993, (210)499-4080
Last Harvest [★12935]
Last Harvest Ministries [12935], PO Box 462192,
Garland, TX 75046-2192, (214)703-0505
Lastensuojelun Keskusliitto [★IO]
Late Model Smoothie Div. [★21089]
LATET - Israeli Humanitarian Aid Org. [IO], Tel Aviv,
Israel
Latex Allergy Assn; Amer. [13636]
Latham Found. [11001], Latham Plaza Bldg., 1826
Clement Ave., Alameda, CA 94501, (510)521-0920
Latin
Hemispheric Cong. of Latin Chambers of Com-
merce [23367]
Latin Amer. Women's Assn. [13464]
Natl. Junior Classical League [7865]
Natl. Senior Classical League [7866]
Latin America
Assn. of Amer. Chambers of Commerce in Latin
Am. [23423]
Basic Hea. Intl. [17122]
Comm. on US/Latin Amer. Relations [19103]
Community Action on Latin Am. [18051]
Community Action on Latin Am. [18051]
Conf. on Latin Amer. History [9945]
Coun. of the Americas [23424]
Delta Tau Lambda Sorority [23742]
Fellowship of Reconciliation Task Force on Latin
Am. and Caribbean [18052]
Fellowship of Reconciliation Task Force on Latin
Am. and Caribbean [18052]
HealthShare Intl. [15750]
Hemispheric Cong. of Latin Chambers of Com-
merce [23367]
Human Rights Documentation Exchange [18053]
Human Rights Documentation Exchange [18053]
Info. Services on Latin Am. [18054]
Intl. Latino Film Soc. [9946]
Latin Am. Data Base [18055]
Latin Am. Data Base [18055]
Latin Am. Trade Coalition [2187]
Latin Am. Working Group [18056]
Latin Am. Working Group [18056]
Latin Amer. Stud. Assn. [9947]
Latin Amer. Stud. Assn. [9947]
Latin Chamber of Commerce of U.S.A. [23425]
The Latino Coalition [9948]
Latino Engineers, Architects and Developers Soc.
[7029]

Natl. Latina Bus. Women Assn. [2188]
Natl. Latina/Latino Law Student Assn. [18057]
Natl. Latino Peace Officers Assn. [19104]
Panamerican Cultural Circle [9949]
Panamerican Cultural Circle [9949]
Permacultura Am. Latina [4684]
Pro Mujer [13475]
Soc. of Anglican Missionaries and Senders
[20094]
Strategies for Intl. Development [12372]
Tinker Found. [9950]
Tinker Found. [9950]
Tomas Rivera Policy Inst. [19105]
Washington Off. on Latin Am. [18058]
Washington Off. on Latin Am. [18058]
William C. Velasquez Inst. [19106]
Latin Am. Data Base [18055], 1 Univ. of New
Mexico, MSC 02 1690, Albuquerque, NM 87131-
0001, (505)277-6839
Latin Am. Data Base [18055], 1 Univ. of New
Mexico, MSC 02 1690, Albuquerque, NM 87131-
0001, (505)277-6839
Latin Am. Gender and Trade Network [IO], Montev-
ideo, Uruguay
Latin Am. Mission [20056], PO Box 527900, Miami,
FL 33152-7900, (305)884-8400
Latin Am. Mission [20056], PO Box 527900, Miami,
FL 33152-7900, (305)884-8400
Latin Am. Parents Assn. [10795], PO Box 339-340,
Brooklyn, NY 11234, (718)236-8689
Latin Am. Trade Coalition [2187], 1615 H St. NW,
Washington, DC 20062-0001, (202)463-5880
Latin Am. Wind Energy Assn. - U.S. [7622], 9418
FM 2920 Rd., Tomball, TX 77375, (281)710-7456
Latin Am. Working Group [18056], 424 C St. NE,
Washington, DC 20002, (202)546-7010
Latin Am. Working Group [18056], 424 C St. NE,
Washington, DC 20002, (202)546-7010
Latin Am. Working Group Educ. Fund [★18056]
Latin Am. Working Group Educ. Fund [★18056]
Latin American
Assn. of Latino Administrators and
Superintendents [7661]
Before Columbus Found. [10036]
Catholic Assn. of Latino Leaders [19398]
Children Beyond Our Borders [17235]
Delta Tau Lambda Sorority [23742]
Global Hea. Partners [14781]
Global Pediatric Alliance [16146]
Hemispheric Cong. of Latin Chambers of Com-
merce [23367]
Hispanas Organized for Political Equality [17776]
Latin Amer. Women's Assn. [13464]
Latinos in Info. Sciences and Tech. Assn. [6983]
Mexican Amer. Cultural Center [19995]
Natl. Community for Latino Leadership [19112]
Natl. Soc. for Hispanic Professionals [695]
Pro Mujer [13475]
Soc. of Anglican Missionaries and Senders
[20094]
Latin Amer. Acad. of Sciences [IO], Caracas,
Venezuela
Latin Amer. Advancement; Labor Coun. for [23228]
Latin Amer. Aeronautical Assn. [379], 5100 S Collins
St., Arlington Airport, Arlington, TX 76018,
(817)284-0431
Latin Amer. Aeronautical Assn. [379], 5100 S Collins
St., Arlington Airport, Arlington, TX 76018,
(817)284-0431
Latin Amer. Anthropology Gp. [★6154]
Latin Amer. Anthropology Gp. [★6154]
Latin Amer. Art Song Alliance [10233], 1116 N Fran-
klin Ave., Normal, IL 61761
Latin Amer. Assn. of Communications Researchers
[IO], La Paz, Bolivia
Latin Amer. Assn. of Development Financing Institu-
tions [IO], Lima, Peru
Latin Amer. Assn. of Development Organizations
[IO], San Jose, Costa Rica
Latin Amer. Assn. of Natl. Academies of Medicine -
Defunct.
Latin Amer. Banking Fed. [IO], Bogota, Colombia
Latin Amer. Blind Union - Uruguay [IO], Panama
City, Panama
Latin Amer. Botanical Assn. [IO], La Serena, Chile

A star before a book entry number signifies that the name is not listed separately, but is mentioned within the entry.

Latin Amer. Brewers Assn. [IO], San Antonio de Los Altos, Venezuela

Latin Amer. and Caribbean Comm. for the Defense of Women's Rights [IO], Lima, Peru

Latin Amer. and Caribbean Demographic Centre [IO], Santiago, Chile

Latin Amer. and Caribbean Economic Assn. [IO], Bogota, Colombia

Latin Amer. and Caribbean Economic Sys. [IO], Caracas, Venezuela

Latin Amer. and Caribbean Solidarity Assn. [★18159]

Latin Amer. and Caribbean Solidarity Assn. [★18159]

Latin Amer. and Caribbean Women's Hea. Network [IO], Santiago, Chile

Latin Amer. Center of Physics [IO], Rio de Janeiro, Brazil

Latin Amer. Center of Social Ecology [IO], Montevideo, Uruguay

Latin Amer. Centre for Development Admin. [IO], Caracas, Venezuela

Latin Amer. Coun. of Churches [IO], Quito, Ecuador

Latin Amer. Diabetes Assn. [IO], Celaya, Mexico

Latin Amer. Educational Found. [8246], 561 Santa Fe Dr., Denver, CO 80204, (303)446-0541

Latin Amer. Energy Org. [IO], Quito, Ecuador

Latin Amer. Evangelistic Campaign [★20056]

Latin Amer. Evangelistic Campaign [★20056]

Latin Amer. Fed. of Associations for Relatives of the Detained-Disappeared [IO], Caracas, Venezuela

Latin Amer. Fed. of the Pharmaceutical Indus. [IO], Mexico City, Mexico

Latin Amer. Forestry Inst. [IO], Merida, Venezuela

Latin Amer. Info. Agency [IO], Quito, Ecuador

Latin Amer. Inst. for Advanced Stud. [IO], Porto Alegre, Brazil

Latin Amer. Inst. for Social Res. [IO], Quito, Ecuador

Latin Amer. Iron and Steel Inst. [IO], Santiago, Chile

Latin Amer. Notaphilic Soc. [★21978]

Latin Amer. Paper Money Soc. [21978], 6602 Cambria Terr., Elkridge, MD 21075

Latin Amer. Petrochemical Assn. [IO], Buenos Aires, Argentina

Latin Amer. Phytopathology Assn. [IO], San Nicolas de los Garza, Mexico

Latin Amer. Railway Assn. [IO], Buenos Aires, Argentina

Latin Amer. Scholarship Prog. of Amer. Universities [★7882]

Latin Amer. Scholarship Prog. of Amer. Universities [★7882]

Latin Amer. Soc. for Interventional Cardiology [IO], Buenos Aires, Argentina

Latin Amer. Soc. of Nephrology and Hypertension [IO], Mexico City, Mexico

Latin Amer. Stud. Assn. [9947], Univ. of Pittsburgh, 416 Bellefield Hall, Pittsburgh, PA 15260, (412)648-7929

Latin Amer. Stud. Assn. [9947], Univ. of Pittsburgh, 416 Bellefield Hall, Pittsburgh, PA 15260, (412)648-7929

Latin Amer. Tax Law Inst. [IO], Montevideo, Uruguay

Latin Amer. Venture Capital Assn. [1311], 589 8th Ave., 18th Fl., New York, NY 10018, (646)315-6735

Latin Amer. Women's Assn. [13464], 7810 Ballantyne Commons Pkwy., Ste. 300, Charlotte, NC 28277, (704)552-1003

Latin Bus. Assn. [681], 120 S San Pedro St., Ste. 530, Los Angeles, CA 90012, (213)628-8510

Latin Chamber of Commerce [★23425]

Latin Chamber of Commerce of U.S.A. [23425], 1401 W Flagler St., Miami, FL 33135, (305)642-3870

Latin Liturgy Assn. [19440], Mr. James F. Pauer, Pres., PO Box 16517, Rocky River, OH 44116

Latin Mass Soc. [IO], London, United Kingdom

Latinas and Latinos for Social Change [18159], PO Box 1279, Cambridge, MA 02238, (617)290-5614

Latinas and Latinos for Social Change [18159], PO Box 1279, Cambridge, MA 02238, (617)290-5614

Latino Center on Aging [10849], 1133 Broadway, Ste. 708, New York, NY 10010, (212)330-8120

Latino Center on Aging [10849], 1133 Broadway, Ste. 708, New York, NY 10010, (212)330-8120

The Latino Coalition [9948], 18881 Von Karman Ave., 6th Fl., Irvine, CA 92612, (949)546-0476

Latino Engineers, Architects and Developers Soc. [7029], PO Box 226722, Los Angeles, CA 90022, (213)353-9438

Latino Gerontological Center [★10849]

Latino Gerontological Center [★10849]

Latino Issues Forum - Address unknown since 2011.

Latino Nutrition Coalition [15838], Oldways, 266 Beacon St., 1st Fl., Boston, MA 02116, (617)421-5500

Latino Org. for Liver Awareness - Defunct.

Latinos in Info. Sciences and Tech. Assn. [6983], 251 Ft. Washington Ave., Ste. 53, New York, NY 10032, (678)620-3173

Latter Day Saints

Assn. of Mormon Counselors and Psychotherapists [16457]

Dialogue Found. [19917]

Mormon History Assn. [19918]

Latvia Sports Medicine Assn. [IO], Riga, Latvia

Latvian

Amer. Latvian Assn. [19107]

Latvian Acad. of Sciences [IO], Riga, Latvia

Latvian Art Directors Club [IO], Riga, Latvia

Latvian Assn. of Consulting Engineers [IO], Riga, Latvia

Latvian Assn. of Gastrointestinal Endoscopy [IO], Riga, Latvia

Latvian Assn. of Language Teachers [IO], Riga, Latvia

Latvian Assn. of Occupational Therapists [IO], Riga, Latvia

Latvian Assn. of Rheumatologists [IO], Riga, Latvia

Latvian Assn. for the Stud. of Pain [IO], Riga, Latvia

Latvian Assn. of Univ. Women [IO], Salaspils, Latvia

Latvian Athletic Fed. [IO], Riga, Latvia

Latvian Authorized Auto. Dealers' Assn. [IO], Riga, Latvia

Latvian Badminton Fed. [IO], Riga, Latvia

Latvian Bible Soc. [IO], Riga, Latvia

Latvian Biochemical Soc. [IO], Riga, Latvia

Latvian Canadian Cultural Centre [IO], Toronto, ON, Canada

Latvian Chamber of Commerce and Indus. [IO], Riga, Latvia

Latvian Dancesport Fed. [IO], Riga, Latvia

Latvian Floorball Union [IO], Riga, Latvia

Latvian Flying Disc Fed. [IO], Ogre, Latvia

Latvian Football Fed. [IO], Riga, Latvia

Latvian Fund for Nature [IO], Riga, Latvia

Latvian League Against Epilepsy [IO], Riga, Latvia

Latvian Multiple Sclerosis Assn. [IO], Riga, Latvia

Latvian Natl. Found. [IO], Stockholm, Sweden

Latvian Ornithological Soc. [IO], Riga, Latvia

Latvian Paralympic Comm. [IO], Riga, Latvia

Latvian Peat Producer's Assn. [IO], Riga, Latvia

Latvian Physical Soc. [IO], Riga, Latvia

Latvian Physicians Assn. [IO], Riga, Latvia

Latvian Physiological Soc. [IO], Riga, Latvia

Latvian Physiotherapists Assn. [IO], Riga, Latvia

Latvian Press Publishers Assn. [IO], Riga, Latvia

Latvian Publishers' Assn. [IO], Riga, Latvia

Latvian Red Cross [IO], Riga, Latvia

Latvian Rheumatic Assn. [IO], Riga, Latvia

Latvian Schoolsport Fed. [IO], Riga, Latvia

Latvian Social Democratic Workers' Party [IO], Riga, Latvia

Latvian Soc. of Cardiology [IO], Riga, Latvia

Latvian Soc. for Electron Microscopy [IO], Riga, Latvia

Latvian Soc. of Geodesy and Photogrammetry [IO], Riga, Latvia

Latvian Soc. of Osteoporosis [IO], Riga, Latvia

Latvian Soc. of Pharmacology [IO], Riga, Latvia

Latvian Squash Fed. [IO], Riga, Latvia

Latvian Taekwondo Fed. [IO], Riga, Latvia

Latvian Tennis Union [IO], Jurmala, Latvia

Latvian Traders' Assn. [IO], Riga, Latvia

Latvian Venture Capital and Private Equity Assn. [IO], Riga, Latvia

Latvia's Assn. for Family Planning and Sexual Hea. Assn. "Papardes zieds" Riga, LatviaIO

Latviesu Nacionalais Fonds [★IO]

Latvijas Badmintona Federacija [★IO]

Latvijas Bibeles biedriba [★IO]

Latvijas Dabas Fonds [★IO]

Latvijas Farmakologijas Biedriba [★IO]

Latvijas Fizikas Biedriba [★IO]

Latvijas Florbola Savieniba [★IO]

Latvijas Frisbija Federacija [★IO]

Latvijas Futbola Federacija [★IO]

Latvijas Gimenes Planosanas un Seksualas Veselibas Asociacija "Papardes zieds" [IO]

Latvijas Gramatizdeveju Asociacija [★IO]

Latvijas Inzenierkonsultantu Asociacija [★IO]

Latvijas Komercbanku Asociacija [★IO]

Latvijas Multiplas Sklerozes Asociacijas [★IO]

Latvijas Ornitologijas Biedriba [★IO]

Latvijas Pilnvaroto Autotirgotaju Asociacija [★IO]

Latvijas Preses Izdeveju Asociacija [★IO]

Latvijas Riska Kapitala Asociacija [★IO]

Latvijas Sapju Izpetes Biedriba [★IO]

Latvijas Skvosa Federacija [★IO]

Latvijas Socialdemokratiska Stradnieku Partija [★IO]

Latvijas Sports Deju Federacija [★IO]

Latvijas Studentu apvieniba [★IO]

Latvijas Tirdzniecibas Un Rupniecibas Kamera [★IO]

Latvijas Tirgotaju Asociacija [★IO]

Latvijas Valodu Skolotaju Asociacija [★IO]

Latvijas Vieglatletikas Savieniba [★IO]

Latvijas Zinatnu Akademija [★IO]

Laubach Literacy Intl. [★8538]

Laubach Literacy Intl. [★8538]

Laughter Therapy [16860], PO Box 827, Monterey, CA 93942

Laundry

Assn. for Linen Mgt. [2189]

Coin Laundry Assn. [2190]

Drycleaning and Laundry Inst. Intl. [2191]

Drycleaning and Laundry Inst. Intl. [2191]

Healthcare Laundry Accreditation Coun. [2192]

Multi-Housing Laundry Assn. [2193]

Textile Care Allied Trades Assn. [2194]

Laundry and Cleaners Allied Trades Assn. [★2194]

Laundry and Dry Cleaners Machinery Mfrs. Assn. [★2194]

Laura Ingalls Wilder Memorial Soc. [9391], PO Box 426, De Smet, SD 57231, (605)854-3383

Laurence-Moon-Bardet-Biedl Syndrome Network [14607], PO Box 9103, Surprise, AZ 85374, (623)523-1484

Laurence-Moon-Biedl Syndrome Network [★14607]

Laurent Clerc Natl. Deaf Educ. Center [12143], 800 Florida Ave. NE, Washington, DC 20002, (202)651-5051

Law

AAUW Legal Advocacy Fund [5639]

Acad. of Criminal Justice Sciences [11698]

ACLU | Natl. Prison Proj. [11699]

Advocates Intl. [5640]

Advocates Intl. [5640]

Alliance of Guardian Angels [11681]

Alliance of Legal Document Asst. Professionals [5751]

Amer. Bar Assn. Center on Children and the Law [11186]

Amer. Bar Assn. | Commn. on Law and Aging [5641]

Amer. Bar Assn. Criminal Justice Sect. [5642]

Amer. Bar Assn. | Natl. Conf. of Bar Foundations [5643]

Amer. Bar Found. [5644]

Amer. Catholic Lawyers Assn. [5645]

Amer. Coll. of Environmental Lawyers [5410]

Amer. Coll. of Tax Counsel [5646]

Amer. Law and Economics Assn. [5647]

Amer. Law Inst. [5648]

Amer. Non-Governmental Organizations Coalition for the Intl. Criminal Court [17488]

Amer. attorneys in good standing. seeks to improve the administration of civil and criminal justice, and the availability of legal services to the public. Assn. | Amer. Lawyers Auxiliary [5233]

Amer. Tort Reform Assn. [5649]

Amer. Veterinary Medical Law Assn. [5650]

Animal Law Coalition [10915]

Asian Amer. Justice Center [5651]

Asian Law Caucus [5652]

Reference to "IO" in place of a book number signifies that the association may be found in the 50th edition of International Organizations.

A star before a book entry number signifies that the name is not listed separately, but is mentioned within the entry.

Law and Soc. Assn. [5667], Univ. of Massachusetts, 217 Draper Hall, 40 Campus Center Way, Amherst, MA 01003-9244, (413)545-4617

Law and Soc. Assn. [5667], Univ. of Massachusetts, 217 Draper Hall, 40 Campus Center Way, Amherst, MA 01003-9244, (413)545-4617

Law Soc. of England [IO], London, United Kingdom

Law Soc. of Hong Kong [IO], Hong Kong, People's Republic of China

Law Soc. of Ireland [IO], Dublin, Ireland

Law Soc. of Maldives [IO], Male, Maldives

Law Soc. of Northern Ireland [IO], Belfast, United Kingdom

Law Soc. of Scotland [IO], Edinburgh, United Kingdom

Law Soc. of Singapore [IO], Singapore, Singapore

Law Soc. of South Africa [IO], Pretoria, Republic of South Africa

Law and Soc. Trust [IO], Colombo, Sri Lanka

Law Students' Assn. of Bermuda [IO], Hamilton, Bermuda

Law Students for Choice [★18524]

Law Students for Reproductive Justice [18524], 1730 Franklin St., Ste. 212, Oakland, CA 94612, (510)622-8134

Lawn Bowls Assn. of Alberta [IO], Edmonton, AB, Canada

Lawn and Garden Dealers Assn. [1568], 5616 S 122nd East Ave., Ste. N, Tulsa, OK 74146, (800)752-5296

Lawn and Garden Marketing and Distribution Assn. - Defunct.

Lawn Inst. [4510], 2 E Main St., East Dundee, IL 60118, (847)649-5555

Lawn Inst. [4510], 2 E Main St., East Dundee, IL 60118, (847)649-5555

Lawn Mower Inst. [★1184]

Lawn Tennis Assn. [IO], London, United Kingdom

Lawn Tennis Assn. of Malawi [IO], Blantyre, Malawi

Lawn Tennis Assn. of Thailand [IO], Nonthaburi, Thailand

Lawrence Technological Univ. Alumni Assn. [18880], 21000 W 10 Mile Rd., Southfield, MI 48075-1058, (248)204-2309

Lawton Collector's Guild [21694], PO Box 1227, Hilmar, CA 95324, (209)632-3655

Lawyer-Pilots Assn. [★5293]

Lawyer-Pilots Bar Assn. [5293], PO Box 1510, Edgewater, MD 21037, (410)571-1750

Lawyers Alliance for Nuclear Arms Control [★18206]

Lawyers Alliance for Nuclear Arms Control [★18206]

Lawyers Alliance for World Security [18206], Center for Defense Info., 1779 Massachusetts Ave. NW, Ste. 615, Washington, DC 20036-2109, (202)332-0600

Lawyers Alliance for World Security [18206], Center for Defense Info., 1779 Massachusetts Ave. NW, Ste. 615, Washington, DC 20036-2109, (202)332-0600

Lawyers Assoc. Worldwide [5257], 2823 McKenzie Point Rd., Wayzata, MN 55391, (952)404-1546

Lawyers Assoc. Worldwide [5257], 2823 McKenzie Point Rd., Wayzata, MN 55391, (952)404-1546

Lawyers for Children Am. [5757], 151 Farmington Ave. RW61, Hartford, CT 06156, (860)273-0441

Lawyers for Civil Justice [18029], 1140 Connecticut Ave. NW, Ste. 503, Washington, DC 20036, (202)429-0045

Lawyers' Comm. for Civil Rights Under Law [5758], 1401 New York Ave. NW, Ste. 400, Washington, DC 20005, (202)662-8600

Lawyers Comm. for Human Rights [★17832]

Lawyers Comm. for Human Rights [★17832]

Lawyers Comm. for Intl. Human Rights [★17832]

Lawyers Comm. for Intl. Human Rights [★17832]

Lawyers' Comm. on Nuclear Policy [18207], 866 UN Pl., Ste. 4050, New York, NY 10017, (212)818-1861

Lawyers for an Independent Judiciary - Defunct.

Lawyers for One Am. [5759], 4136 Redwood Hwy., Ste. 9, San Rafael, CA 94903, (415)479-3636

Lawyers and Physicians; Global [14708]

Lawyers and Physicians; Global [14708]

Lawyers Without Borders [18072], 750 Main St., Hartford, CT 06103, (860)541-2288

Lawyers Without Borders [18072], 750 Main St., Hartford, CT 06103, (860)541-2288

Lay Carmelite Order of the Blessed Virgin Mary [19441], 8501 Bailey Rd., Darien, IL 60561-8417, (630)969-5050

Lay Carmelites [★19441]

Lay Mission-Helpers Assn. [19442], 3435 Wilshire Blvd., Ste. 1940, Los Angeles, CA 90010, (213)368-1870

Lay Mission-Helpers Assn. [19442], 3435 Wilshire Blvd., Ste. 1940, Los Angeles, CA 90010, (213)368-1870

The Layman Tithing Company [★20267]

Layman Tithing Found. [★20267]

Laymen's Home Missionary Movement [19755], 1156 St. Matthews Rd., Chester Springs, PA 19425-2700, (610)827-7665

Laymen's Home Missionary Movement [19755], 1156 St. Matthews Rd., Chester Springs, PA 19425-2700, (610)827-7665

Laymen's Movement for a Christian World [★20260]

Laymen's Natl. Bible Assn. [★19915]

Laymen's Natl. Bible Comm. [★19915]

L.C. Smith Collectors Assn. [21714], 1322 Bay Ave., Mantoloking, NJ 08738

LCD TV Assn. [3431], 16055 SW Walker Rd., Ste. 264, Beaverton, OR 97006, (215)206-6506

LDS Bus. Coll. Alumni Assn. [18881], 1140 E South Temple, Salt Lake City, UT 84111, (801)524-8100

Le Bur. Canadien de Soudage [★IO]

Le Bur. Hydrographique Intl. [★IO]

Le Bur. Regional UICN pour l'Afrique de l'Ouest [IO], Ouagadougou, Burkina Faso

Le Centre Parlementaire [★IO]

Le Centre de Recherches pour le Developpement Intl. [★IO]

Le Club BMW du Canada [★IO]

Le Coll. Royal Canadien des Organistes [★IO]

Le Coll. Royal des Medecins et Chirurgiens du Canada [★IO]

Le Comite international pour la documentation du Conseil international des musees [★IO]

Le Conseil Africain pour l'Enseignement de la Commun. [★IO]

Le Conseil des Arts du Canada [★IO]

Le Conseil Atlantique du Canada [★IO]

Le Conseil Canadien des Administrateurs de Ecoles Montessori [★IO]

Le Conseil Canadien des Arpenteurs-Geometres [★IO]

Le Conseil Canadien de la Readaptation et du Travail [★IO]

Le Conseil Canadiene des distributeurs de vehicules hors route [★IO]

Le Conseil canadien de l'agrement des programmes de pharmacie [★IO]

Le Conseil canadien pour l'avancement de l'education [★IO]

Le Forum Train European [★IO]

Le Front Des Artistes Canadiens [★IO]

Le Groupe Canadien de Recherche en Geomorphologie [★IO]

Le Havre World Trade Center [IO], Le Havre, France

Le Paradis Des Orchidees [IO], Laval, QC, Canada

Le Reseau Canadien pour la Sante des Femmes [★IO]

Le Syndicat Canadien de la Fonction Publique [★IO]

LE TRIPTYQUE [IO], Paris, France

Lea-Francis Owners' Club [IO], Abingdon, United Kingdom

LEAD - Afrique Francophone [IO], Dakar, Senegal

LEAD - Canada [IO], Ormstown, QC, Canada

LEAD - China [IO], Beijing, People's Republic of China

LEAD - CIS [IO], Moscow, Russia

Lead Contractors Assn. [IO], East Grinstead, United Kingdom

LEAD - Indonesia [IO], Jakarta, Indonesia

Lead Industries Assn. - Defunct.

LEAD Intl.: Leadership for Env. and Development [IO], London, United Kingdom

LEAD Intl. - United Kingdom [IO], London, United Kingdom

LEAD - Mexico [IO], Mexico City, Mexico

LEAD - Nigeria [IO], Lagos, Nigeria

LEAD - Pakistan [IO], Islamabad, Pakistan

Lead Sheet Assn. [IO], Tonbridge, United Kingdom

LEAD - Southern and Eastern Africa [IO], Zomba, Malawi

LEAD - Togo [IO], Lome, Togo

Lead-Zinc Producers [★2487]

Lead-Zinc Producers Comm. [★2487]

The Leader [★2533]

Leader Dog League for the Blind [★17094]

Leader Dog League for the Blind [★17094]

Leader Dogs for the Blind [17094], 1039 S Rochester Rd., Rochester Hills, MI 48307, (248)651-9011

Leader Dogs for the Blind [17094], 1039 S Rochester Rd., Rochester Hills, MI 48307, (248)651-9011

Leadership

Alliance for Regional Stewardship [18060]

Amer. Coun. on Educ. | Center for Intl. Initiatives [8482]

Amer. Coun. of Young Political Leaders [18061]

Amer. Coun. of Young Political Leaders [18061]

Amer. Leadership Forum [18062]

Arab Amer. Leadership Coun. [18063]

Assn. of Leadership Educators [8483]

Beatitudes Soc. [19540]

Black Leadership Forum [18844]

Catholic Assn. of Latino Leaders [19398]

Center for Visionary Leadership [18064]

CEO Netweavers [962]

Destination ImagiNation [8697]

Fund for Amer. Stud. [8484]

Fund for Amer. Stud. [8484]

Global Youth Partnership for Africa [9875]

Grooming Future World Leaders [13528]

Hugh O'Brian Youth Leadership [8485]

Indus Women Leaders [18065]

INROADS [8486]

Intl. Org. for Haitian Development [7894]

Junior State of Am. [8487]

Junior Statesmen Found. [8488]

Leadership Am. [8489]

Leadership Inst. [8490]

Natl. Assn. of Latina Leaders [2196]

Natl. Community for Latino Leadership [19112]

Natl. Inst. for Leadership Development [2197]

Natl. Title I Assn. [7677]

Natl. Youth Leadership Coun. [8491]

Native Amer. Leadership Alliance [20147]

Native Movement [19166]

Network 20/20 [18066]

New Leaders for New Schools [8492]

Nonprofit Leadership Alliance [8493]

Partnership for Public Ser. [17331]

Presidential Classroom [8494]

Presidential Prayer Team [19919]

RandomKid [13554]

Rising Leaders [18067]

Shuttleworth Leadership Soc. Intl. [8495]

Student African Amer. Brotherhood [19288]

SustainUS [13559]

ThinkImpact [12373]

University-Community Partnership for Social Action Res. [7895]

Leadership Am. [8489], 3800 Parry Ave., Dallas, TX 75226, (214)647-6105

Leadership Conf. on Civil Rights [17297], 1629 K St. NW, 10th Fl., Washington, DC 20006-1602, (202)466-3311

Leadership Conf. Educ. Fund [7864], 1629 K St. NW, Fl. 10, Washington, DC 20006-1602, (202)466-3311

Leadership Conf. of Women Religious [19443], 8808 Cameron St., Silver Spring, MD 20910-4152, (301)588-4955

Leadership Conf. of Women Religious of the U.S.A. [★19443]

Leadership Coun. of Aging Organizations [10850], 2519 Connecticut Ave. NW, Washington, DC 20008, (202)783-2242

Leadership Coun. on Child Abuse and Interpersonal Violence [11890], 6501 N Charles St., Baltimore, MD 21204-6819

Leadership Coun. for Mental Hea., Justice and the Media [★11890]

Reference to "IO" in place of a book number signifies that the association may be found in the 50th edition of International Organizations.

Encyclopedia of Associations, 51st Edition

2957

Leadership Couns. of America - Defunct.

Leadership Development Network [17382], 1244 Hillside Oaks Dr., La Vernia, TX 78121-4734, (210)313-8000

Leadership Educ. for Asian Pacifics [9339], 327 E 2nd St., Ste. 226, Los Angeles, CA 90012, (213)485-1422

Leadership for Energy Automated Processing [1171], Mary Dortenzio, Treas., Glencore, 301 Tresser Blvd., Stamford, CT 06901, (203)846-1300

Leadership Enterprise for a Diverse Am. [8920], 501 Seventh Ave., 7th Fl., New York, NY 10018, (212)672-9750

Leadership Inst. [8490], 1101 N Highland St., Arlington, VA 22201, (703)247-2000

Leadership to Keep Children Alcohol Free [13262], 2933 Lower Bellbrook Rd., Spring Valley, OH 45370, (207)729-1911

Leadership Training
Natl. Community for Latino Leadership [19112]

Leading Builders of Am. [577], 1455 Pennsylvania Ave. NW, Ste. 400, Washington, DC 20004, (202)621-1815

Leading Edge Alliance [37], 621 Cedar St., St. Charles, IL 60174, (630)513-9814

Leading Jewelers of the World [2169], 500 7th Ave., Ste. 12B, New York, NY 10018, (212)398-6401

Leading Jewelers of the World [2169], 500 7th Ave., Ste. 12B, New York, NY 10018, (212)398-6401

Leading Spas of Canada [IO], Sooke, BC, Canada

LeadingAge [10851], 2519 Connecticut Ave. NW, Washington, DC 20008-1520, (202)783-2242

Leaf Tobacco Exporters Assn. - Defunct.

Leafy Greens Coun. [4456], 33 Pheasant Ln., St. Paul, MN 55127, (651)484-7270

LEAGUE [12096], 208 S Akard, Ste. 810.08, Dallas, TX 75202

League Against Cruel Sports [IO], Godalming, United Kingdom

League Against Epilepsy of Republic Macedonia [IO], Skopje, Macedonia

League of Amer. Bicyclists [22481], 1612 K St. NW, Ste. 800, Washington, DC 20006-2850, (202)822-1333

League of Amer. Orchestras [10234], 33 W 60th St., 5th Fl., New York, NY 10023, (212)262-5161

League of Amer. Theatres and Producers [★10572]

League of Amer. Wheelmen [★22481]

League of Amer. Wheelmen/Bicycle U.S.A. [★22481]

League of Canadian Poets [IO], Toronto, ON, Canada

League of Composers - Intl. Soc. for Contemporary Music, U.S. Sect. [★10224]

League of Composers - Intl. Soc. for Contemporary Music, U.S. Sect. [★10224]

League of Conservation Voters [18346], 1920 L St. NW, Ste. 800, Washington, DC 20036, (202)785-8683

League for Earth and Animal Protection [4090], 21781 Ventura Blvd., Ste. 633, Woodland Hills, CA 91364, (818)346-5280

League of European Res. Universities [IO], Leuven, Belgium

League for the Exchange of Commonwealth Teachers [IO], Reading, United Kingdom

League of Families [IO], Brussels, Belgium

League of Federal Recreation Assns. - Defunct.

League of Finnish-American Societies [IO], Helsinki, Finland

League of Free Nations Assn. [★17700]

League of Free Nations Assn. [★17700]

League for the Hard of Hearing [★14923]

League of Historic Amer. Theatres [10583], 2105 Laurel Bush Rd., Ste. 200, Bel Air, MD 21015, (443)640-1058

League of Homeowners' Associations - Habitat [IO], Bucharest, Romania

League of IBM Employees Credit Unions [★1000]

League for Innovation in the Community Coll. [7892], 4505 E Chandler Blvd., Ste. 250, Phoenix, AZ 85048, (480)705-8200

League/ISCM [★10224]

League/ISCM [★10224]

League of Jewish Women [IO], London, United Kingdom

League of Lefthanders - Defunct.

League of New York Theatres [★10572]

League of New York Theatres and Producers [★10572]

League of Private Property Owners [★5901]

League of Private Property Voters - Address unknown since 2011.

League of Professional Sys. Administrators [6546], PO Box 5161, Trenton, NJ 08638, (202)567-7201

League of Professional Sys. Administrators [6546], PO Box 5161, Trenton, NJ 08638, (202)567-7201

League for Programming Freedom [7299], 60 Thoreau St., No. 299, Concord, MA 01742-2411

League of Resident Theatres [10584], 1501 Broadway, Ste. 2401, New York, NY 10036, (212)944-1501

League of Revolutionaries for a New Am. [18335], PO Box 477113, Chicago, IL 60647, (773)486-0028

League for the Revolutionary Party [18656], PO Box 1936, Murray Hill Sta., New York, NY 10156, (212)330-9017

League of Rural Voters Educ. Proj. [★17168]

League of St. Dymphna [19444], Natl. Shrine of St. Dymphna, PO Box 4, Massillon, OH 44648-0004, (330)833-8478

League to Save Lake Tahoe [4091], 2608 Lake Tahoe Blvd., South Lake Tahoe, CA 96150, (530)541-5388

League of the South [17298], PO Box 760, Killen, AL 35645, (256)757-6789

League of Ukrainian Catholics of Am. [19261], Dr. Michael Labuda, Membership Dir., 14 Prince St., Plains, PA 18705-1211

League of Ukranian Canadian Women [IO], Toronto, ON, Canada

League of United Latin Amer. Citizens [19023], 2000 L St. NW, Ste. 610, Washington, DC 20036, (202)833-6130

League of Winant Volunteers [★13409]

League of Winant Volunteers [★13409]

League of Women Voters Educ. Fund [18473], 1730 M St. NW, Ste. 1000, Washington, DC 20036-4508, (202)429-1965

League of Women Voters of the U.S. [18383], 1730 M St. NW, Ste. 1000, Washington, DC 20036-4570, (202)429-1965

League of World War I Aviation Historians [20905], 16820 25th Ave. N, Plymouth, MN 55447

League of World War I Aviation Historians [20905], 16820 25th Ave. N, Plymouth, MN 55447

League for Yiddish [19879], 64 Fulton St., Ste. 1101, New York, NY 10038, (212)889-0380

League of Young Voters [18384], 310 Atlantic Ave., 2nd Fl., Brooklyn, NY 11201, (347)464-8683

Leapfrog Gp. [14801], Acad. Hea., 1150 17th St. NW, Ste. 600, Washington, DC 20036, (202)292-6713

Learn to Care [IO], Birmingham, United Kingdom

Learning Ally [17095], 20 Roszel Rd., Princeton, NJ 08540, (609)452-0606

Learning and Development Kenya [IO], Nakuru, Kenya

Learning Disabilities Assn. of Alberta [IO], Edmonton, AB, Canada

Learning Disabilities Assn. of Alberta - Calgary Chap. [IO], Calgary, AB, Canada

Learning Disabilities Assn. of Alberta - Edmonton Chap. [IO], Edmonton, AB, Canada

Learning Disabilities Assn. of Alberta - Red Deer Chap. [IO], Red Deer, AB, Canada

Learning Disabilities Assn. of Am. [12425], 4156 Lib. Rd., Pittsburgh, PA 15234-1349, (412)341-1515

Learning Disabilities Assn. of Canada [IO], Ottawa, ON, Canada

Learning Disabilities Assn. of Halton [IO], Burlington, ON, Canada

Learning Disabilities Assn. of Kingston [IO], Kingston, ON, Canada

Learning Disabilities Assn. of Kitchener - Waterloo [IO], Kitchener, ON, Canada

Learning Disabilities Assn. of Lambton County [IO], Sarnia, ON, Canada

Learning Disabilities Assn. - London Region [IO], London, ON, Canada

Learning Disabilities Assn. of Manitoba [IO], Winnipeg, MB, Canada

Learning Disabilities Assn. - Mississauga Chap. [IO], Mississauga, ON, Canada

Learning Disabilities Assn. of New Brunswick [IO], Fredericton, NB, Canada

Learning Disabilities Assn. of Newfoundland and Labrador [IO], St. John's, NL, Canada

Learning Disabilities Assn. - North Peel Chap. [IO], Brampton, ON, Canada

Learning Disabilities Assn. of Nova Scotia [IO], Dartmouth, NS, Canada

Learning Disabilities Assn. of the NWT [IO], Yellowknife, NT, Canada

Learning Disabilities Assn. of Ontario [IO], Toronto, ON, Canada

Learning Disabilities Assn. of Ontario - Durham Region [IO], Pickering, ON, Canada

Learning Disabilities Assn. of Ontario - Niagara Chap. [IO], St. Catharines, ON, Canada

Learning Disabilities Assn. of Ontario - Thunder Bay Chap. [IO], Thunder Bay, ON, Canada

Learning Disabilities Assn. of Ottawa - Carleton [IO], Ottawa, ON, Canada

Learning Disabilities Assn. of PEI [IO], Charlottetown, PE, Canada

Learning Disabilities Assn. of Peterborough [IO], Peterborough, ON, Canada

Learning Disabilities Assn. of Quebec [IO], Montreal, QC, Canada

Learning Disabilities Assn. of Quebec - Laval Sect. [IO], Laval, QC, Canada

Learning Disabilities Assn. of Saskatchewan [IO], Saskatoon, SK, Canada

Learning Disabilities Assn. of Saskatchewan - Prince Albert Br. [IO], Prince Albert, SK, Canada

Learning Disabilities Assn. of Saskatchewan - Regina Br. [IO], Regina, SK, Canada

Learning Disabilities Assn. of Sault Ste. Marie [IO], Sault Ste. Marie, ON, Canada

Learning Disabilities Assn. of Simcoe County [IO], Barrie, ON, Canada

Learning Disabilities Assn. - South Vancouver Island Chap. [IO], Victoria, BC, Canada

Learning Disabilities Assn. of Sudbury [IO], Sudbury, ON, Canada

Learning Disabilities Assn. of Toronto District [IO], Toronto, ON, Canada

Learning Disabilities Assn. of Vancouver [IO], Vancouver, BC, Canada

Learning Disabilities Assn. of York Region [IO], Richmond Hill, ON, Canada

Learning Disabilities Assn. of Yukon Territory [IO], Whitehorse, YT, Canada

Learning Disabled
AACTION Autism [13776]
Academic Language Therapy Assn. [12420]
Assn. for Children with Down Syndrome [12496]
Coun. for Learning Disabilities [12421]
DAD: Drums and Disabilities [12422]
Friends of LADDERS [12423]
Gifted Learning Proj. [12424]
Learning Disabilities Assn. of Am. [12425]
Natl. Assn. for the Educ. of African Amer. Children with Learning Disabilities [12426]
Natl. Center for Learning Disabilities [12427]
Natl. Fed. of Arch Clubs [563]
Nonverbal Learning Disorders Assn. [15239]
Nonverbal Learning Disorders Assn. [15239]

Learning First Alliance [8036], 4455 Connecticut Ave., Ste. 310, Washington, DC 20008, (202)296-5220

Learning Light Found. [9828], 1212 E Lincoln Ave., Anaheim, CA 92805-4249, (714)533-2311

Learning is Necessary to Care [★12496]

Learning Resources Network [7926], PO Box 9, River Falls, WI 54022, (715)426-9777

Learning Round Table [9991], Denver Public Lib., 10 W 14th Avenue Pkwy., Denver, CO 80204, (720)865-2071

Learning and Teaching Scotland [IO], Glasgow, United Kingdom

LearnServe Intl. [8828], PO Box 6203, Washington, DC 20015, (202)370-1865

LearnWell Resources [13161], PO Box 1178, Folsom, CA 95763, (916)984-7437

A star before a book entry number signifies that the name is not listed separately, but is mentioned within the entry.

Leasing Assn. of Pakistan **[IO]**, Karachi, Pakistan
Leather
    Amer. Saddle Makers Assn. **[2198]**
    Australian Plaiters and Whipmakers Assn. **[5889]**
    Intl. Fed. of Leather Guilds **[2199]**
    Intl. Internet Leather Crafters' Guild **[2200]**
    Intl. Internet Leather Crafters' Guild **[2200]**
    Leather Apparel Assn. **[2201]**
    Leather Indus. of Am. **[2202]**
    Leathercraft Guild **[2203]**
    Natl. Luggage Dealers Assn. **[2204]**
    Saddle, Harness and Allied Trades Assn. **[2205]**
    Skinners' Company **[8161]**
    Soc. of Leather Technologists and Chemists
      South African Sect. **[18930]**
    Sponge and Chamois Inst. **[2206]**
    U.S. Hide, Skin and Leather Assn. **[2207]**
Leather Apparel Assn. **[2201]**, 4705 Center Blvd.,
    Ste. 806, Long Island City, NY 11109, (718)606-
    0767
Leather Garment Mfrs'. Assn. **[IO]**, Istanbul, Turkey
Leather Indus. of Am. **[2202]**, 3050 K St. NW, Ste.
    400, Washington, DC 20007, (202)342-8497
Leather Indus. Assn. **[IO]**, Vienna, Austria
Leather and Shoe Res. Assn. of New Zealand **[IO]**,
    Palmerston North, New Zealand
Leather Workers Intl. Union **[★23141]**
Leathercraft Guild **[2203]**, PO Box 4603, Ontario, CA
    91761-0823, (909)983-9544
Leatherhead Food Intl. **[IO]**, Leatherhead, United
    Kingdom
Leatherneck Assn. **[★5779]**
Lebanese
    AlKoura League **[12428]**
    Amer. Lebanese Coalition **[18068]**
    Amer. Task Force for Lebanon **[19113]**
    Lebanese Amer. Coun. for Democracy **[18069]**
    U.S. Comm. for a Free Lebanon **[18070]**
Lebanese Aikido Fed. **[IO]**, Beirut, Lebanon
Lebanese Amer. Coun. for Democracy **[18069]**,
    South Bldg., Ste. 900, 601 Pennsylvania Ave. NW,
    Washington, DC 20004, (202)220-3039
Lebanese Assn. of Certified Public Accountants **[IO]**,
    Beirut, Lebanon
Lebanese Coun. to Resist Violence Against Women
    [IO], Beirut, Lebanon
Lebanese Dermatological Soc. **[IO]**, Beirut, Lebanon
Lebanese Economic Assn. **[IO]**, Beirut, Lebanon
Lebanese Hypertension League **[IO]**, Beirut,
    Lebanon
Lebanese Info. Center **[18128]**, 4900 Leesburg Pike,
    Ste. 203, Alexandria, VA 22302, (703)578-4214
Lebanese Info. Center **[18128]**, 4900 Leesburg Pike,
    Ste. 203, Alexandria, VA 22302, (703)578-4214
Lebanese League Against Epilepsy **[IO]**, Beirut,
    Lebanon
Lebanese Medical Association **[★15394]**
Lebanese Olympic Comm. **[IO]**, Beirut, Lebanon
Lebanese Orthodontic Soc. **[IO]**, Beirut, Lebanon
Lebanese Osteoporosis Prevention Soc. **[IO]**, Beirut,
    Lebanon
Lebanese Ostomy Assn. **[IO]**, Keserwan, Lebanon
Lebanese Soc. of Gastroenterology **[IO]**, Beirut,
    Lebanon
Lebanese Soc. for Infectious Diseases **[IO]**, Beirut,
    Lebanon
Lebanese Soc. of Rheumatology **[IO]**, Beirut,
    Lebanon
Lebanese Soc. for the Stud. of Pain **[IO]**, Beirut,
    Lebanon
Lebanese Squash Fed. **[IO]**, Beirut, Lebanon
Lebanese Transparency Assn. **[IO]**, Baabda,
    Lebanon
Lederer Found. **[★19756]**
Lederer Messianic Ministries **[19756]**, Messianic
    Jewish Communications, 6120 Day Long Ln.,
    Clarksville, MD 21029, (410)531-6644
Ledernes Hovedeorganisation **[IO]**, Copenhagen,
    Denmark
Leeds Chamber of Commerce **[IO]**, Leeds, United
    Kingdom
Leeds Philosophical and Literary Soc. **[IO]**, Leeds,
    United Kingdom
Left-Handers
    Natl. Assn. of Left-Handed Golfers **[22617]**

A Leg To Stand On **[12600]**, 267 5th Ave., Ste. 800,
    New York, NY 10016, (212)683-8805
Lega Italiana contro l'Epilessia **[★IO]**
Lega Italiana per la Lotta contro la Malattia di Par-
    kinson, le Sindromi Extrapiramidali e le Demenze
    [★IO]
Lega Italiana Osteoporosi **[IO]**, Milan, Italy
Legacies of War **[8259]**, 1628 16th St. NW, 3rd Fl.,
    Washington, DC 20009, (202)965-1785
Legacies of War **[8259]**, 1628 16th St. NW, 3rd Fl.,
    Washington, DC 20009, (202)965-1785
LEGACY - Defunct.
Legacy Intl. **[8409]**, 1020 Legacy Dr., Bedford, VA
    24523, (540)297-5982
Legacy Intl. **[8409]**, 1020 Legacy Dr., Bedford, VA
    24523, (540)297-5982
Legal
    Acad. of Criminal Justice Sciences **[11698]**
    ACLU | Natl. Prison Proj. **[11699]**
    Alliance of Legal Document Asst. Professionals
      [5751]
    Amer. Assn. of Legal Nurse Consultants **[15240]**
    Amer. Assn. of Nurse Attorneys **[15241]**
    Amer. Bar Assn. Center on Children and the Law
      [11186]
    Amer. Coll. of Environmental Lawyers **[5410]**
    Amer. Coll. of Legal Medicine **[15242]**
    Amer. Conservative Union **[17418]**
    Amer. Hosp. Assn. | Soc. for Healthcare
      Consumer Advocacy **[15243]**
    Amer. Legal Finance Assn. **[1279]**
    Amer. Soc. of Digital Forensics and eDiscovery
      [6883]
    Amer. Soc. of Law, Medicine and Ethics **[15244]**
    Amer. Soc. for Pharmacy Law **[15245]**
    Animal Law Coalition **[10915]**
    Assn. of Patent Law Firms **[5885]**
    Assn. of State Correctional Administrators **[11706]**
    Center for Stud. in Criminal Justice **[11707]**
    Children's Healthcare is a Legal Duty **[15246]**
    Clarity **[5746]**
    Coun. on Litigation Mgt. **[5747]**
    EarthRights Intl. **[17827]**
    HALT **[18028]**
    In Legal Color **[5844]**
    Insight Center for Community Economic Develop-
      ment **[17578]**
    Intl. Amusement and Leisure Defense Assn.
      [3057]
    Intl. Assn. for Correctional and Forensic Psychol-
      ogy **[11715]**
    Intl. Assn. of Independent Private Sector Inspec-
      tors Gen. **[5546]**
    Intl. Masters of Gaming Law **[5495]**
    Intl. Soc. for Islamic Legal Stud. **[8414]**
    Judge David L. Bazelon Center for Mental Hea.
      Law **[17296]**
    Justice Inc. **[17490]**
    A Matter of Justice Coalition **[5748]**
    NALS **[5749]**
    Natl. Alliance for Family Court Justice **[5624]**
    Natl. Assn. of Appellate Court Attorneys **[5260]**
    Natl. Legal Sanctuary for Community Advance-
      ment **[5750]**
    Natl. Security and Law Soc. **[5970]**
    North Amer. South Asian Bar Assn. **[5678]**
    North Amer. South Asian Law Student Assn.
      [8511]
    Personal Injury Lawyers Marketing and Mgt. Assn.
      [268]
    Professional Mediation Assn. **[5211]**
    Public Interest Intellectual Property Advisors
      [5580]
    Renaissance Lawyer Soc. **[5281]**
    Sport and Recreation Law Assn. **[23022]**
    Total Practice Mgt. Assn. **[5287]**
Legal Advice for Women **[IO]**, Oslo, Norway
Legal Aid
    Immigration Voice **[5529]**
    Natl. Domestic Violence Hotline **[11894]**
    Natl. Org. of Fed. Employees Against Abuse and
      Retaliation **[23206]**
    WildCat Conservation Legal Aid Soc. **[5016]**
    WITNESS **[17868]**
Legal Aid of Cambodia **[IO]**, Phnom Penh,
    Cambodia

Legal Aid Org. of Afghanistan **[IO]**, Kabul,
    Afghanistan
Legal Asst. Mgt. Assn. **[★5665]**
Legal Asst. Mgt. Assn. **[★5665]**
Legal Eagles **[★5293]**
Legal Education
    Acad. of Criminal Justice Sciences **[11698]**
    Acad. of Legal Stud. in Bus. **[8496]**
    Acad. of Legal Stud. in Bus. **[8496]**
    Amer. Assn. for Paralegal Educ. **[8497]**
    Amer. Bar Assn. - Law Student Div. **[8498]**
    Assn. of Amer. Law Schools **[8499]**
    Assn. of Amer. Law Schools | Sect. on Sexual
      Orientation and Gender Identity Issues **[8500]**
    Assn. for Continuing Legal Educ. **[8501]**
    Clinical Legal Educ. Assn. **[8502]**
    Coun. on Legal Educ. Opportunity **[8503]**
    Earl Warren Legal Training Prog. **[8504]**
    Global Alliance for Justice Educ. **[8505]**
    Global Alliance for Justice Educ. **[8505]**
    In Legal Color **[5844]**
    Intl. Assn. of Law Schools **[8506]**
    Intl. Assn. of Law Schools **[8506]**
    Intl. Soc. for Islamic Legal Stud. **[8414]**
    Law School Admission Coun. **[8507]**
    Law School Admission Coun. **[8507]**
    Natl. Assn. for Law Placement **[8508]**
    Natl. Black Law Students Assn. **[8509]**
    Natl. Native Amer. Law Students Assn. **[8510]**
    North Amer. South Asian Bar Assn. **[5678]**
    North Amer. South Asian Law Student Assn.
      [8511]
    North Amer. South Asian Law Student Assn.
      [8511]
    Phi Delta Phi Intl. Legal Fraternity **[23581]**
    Phi Delta Phi Intl. Legal Fraternity **[23581]**
    Practising Law Inst. **[8512]**
    Renaissance Lawyer Soc. **[5281]**
Legal Immigrant Assn. **[5530]**, PO Box 2082, Santa
    Clara, CA 95055, (800)556-7065
Legal Marketing Assn. **[2409]**, 401 N Michigan Ave.,
    22th Fl., Chicago, IL 60611-6610, (312)321-6898
Legal Marketing Assn. **[2409]**, 401 N Michigan Ave.,
    22th Fl., Chicago, IL 60611-6610, (312)321-6898
Legal Momentum **[★17653]**
Legal Momentum: Advancing Women's Rights
    [17653], 395 Hudson St., 5th Fl., New York, NY
    10014, (212)925-6635
Legal Resources Centre **[IO]**, Johannesburg,
    Republic of South Africa
Legal Resources Found. - Zambia **[IO]**, Lusaka,
    Zambia
Legal Resources Found. - Zimbabwe **[IO]**, Harare,
    Zimbabwe
Legal Rights and Natural Resources Center -
    Kasama sa Kalikasan **[IO]**, Quezon City, Philip-
    pines
Legal Sales and Services Org. **[5760]**, 92 State St.,
    9th Fl., Boston, MA 02109, (617)726-1500
Legal Secretaries, Inc. **[★72]**
Legal Secretaries, Inc. **[★72]**
Legal Secretaries Intl. **[70]**, 2302 Fannin St., Ste.
    500, Houston, TX 77002-9136, (409)797-3206
Legal Secretaries Intl. **[70]**, 2302 Fannin St., Ste.
    500, Houston, TX 77002-9136, (409)797-3206
Legal Services
    Acad. of Criminal Justice Sciences **[11698]**
    ACLU | Natl. Prison Proj. **[11699]**
    Alliance of Legal Document Asst. Professionals
      [5751]
    Amer. Guild of Court Videographers **[5752]**
    Amer. Legal Finance Assn. **[1279]**
    Amer. Prepaid Legal Services Inst. **[5753]**
    Assn. of Patent Law Firms **[5885]**
    Assn. of State Correctional Administrators **[11706]**
    Center for Stud. in Criminal Justice **[11707]**
    Coalition of Landlords, Homeowners and
      Merchants **[18404]**
    Farmers' Legal Action Gp. **[5754]**
    Guam Bar Assn. **[5755]**
    Identity Theft Rsrc. Center **[18071]**
    Immigration Voice **[5529]**
    Intl. Amusement and Leisure Defense Assn.
      [3057]
    Intl. Assn. for Correctional and Forensic Psychol-
      ogy **[11715]**

Reference to "IO" in place of a book number signifies that the association may be found in the 50th edition of International Organizations.

Intl. Bus. Law Consortium [13245]
Judge David L. Bazelon Center for Mental Hea. Law [17296]
Justice Without Borders [5756]
Justice Without Borders [5756]
Lawyers for Children Am. [5757]
Lawyers' Comm. for Civil Rights Under Law [5758]
Lawyers for One Am. [5759]
Lawyers Without Borders [18072]
Lawyers Without Borders [18072]
Legal Sales and Services Org. [5760]
Legal Services for Children [12429]
Legal Services for the Elderly [12430]
Migrant Legal Action Prog. [12431]
Natl. Acad. of Elder Law Attorneys [5761]
Natl. Assn. of Appellate Court Attorneys [5260]
Natl. Assn. of Foreclosure Prevention Professionals [2899]
Natl. Center on Poverty Law [5762]
Natl. Law Center on Homelessness and Poverty [12163]
Natl. Legal Aid and Defender Assn. [5763]
Natl. Structured Settlements Trade Assn. [5764]
Personal Injury Lawyers Marketing and Mgt. Assn. [268]
Pretrial Justice Inst. [5765]
Public Interest Intellectual Property Advisors [5580]
Renaissance Lawyer Soc. [5281]
Soc. for Advanced Legal Stud. [15476]
St. Law [5766]
Sylvia Rivera Law Proj. [18730]
Volunteer Lawyers for the Arts [5767]
Western Center on Law and Poverty [5768]
Legal Services for Children [12429], 1254 Market St., 3rd Fl., San Francisco, CA 94102, (415)863-3762
Legal Services for the Elderly [12430], 5 Wabon St., Augusta, ME 04330, (207)621-0087
Legal Services for the Elderly Poor [★12430]
Legal Services Staff Assn. [★23207]
Legal Software Suppliers Assn. [IO], Grantham, United Kingdom
Legal Support Ser; Refugee [★18053]
Legal Tech. Insider [IO], Harleston, United Kingdom
Legambiente [IO], Rome, Italy
Legambiente Campania [IO], Naples, Italy
Legambiente Ecopolis, Turin [IO], Turin, Italy
Legatus [19445], 5072 Annunciation Cir., Ste. 202, Ave Maria, FL 34142, (239)435-3852
Legemiddel Industri Foreningen [★IO]
Legemiddelindustriforeningen [★IO]
Legion Royale Canadienne [★IO]
Legion of Valor of the U.S.A. [20377], 4706 Calle Reina, Santa Barbara, CA 93110-2018, (703)627-0294
Legion of Young Polish Women [19188], PO Box 56-110, Chicago, IL 60656
Legislative Coun. [★4722]
Legislative Coun. for Photogrammetry [★7260]
Legislative Reform
Coalition for Tax Fairness [18694]
HALT [18028]
MOMSTELL [13265]
Natl. Order of Women Legislators [5769]
Twelve Lights League [18073]
Legitimerade Sjukgymnasters Riksforbund [★IO]
Leicestershire Chamber of Commerce and Indus. [IO], Leicester, United Kingdom
Leieboerforeningen [★IO]
Leieboerforeningen Bergen [★IO]
Leif Ericson Soc. Intl. [★10677]
Leif Ericson Viking Ship [10677], PO Box 393, Swarthmore, PA 19081-0393, (410)275-8516
Leinster Soc. of Chartered Accountants [IO], Dublin, Ireland
Leisure and Outdoor Furniture Assn. [IO], Chichester, United Kingdom
Leisure Stud. Assn. [IO], Eastbourne, United Kingdom
Lejernes Landsorganisation [★IO]
Lelio Basso Intl. Found. for the Rights and Liberation of Peoples [IO], Rome, Italy
Lembaga Getah Malaysia [★IO]

Lembaga Koko Malaysia [★IO]
Lembaga Lada Malaysia [★IO]
Lembaga Perindustrian Nanas Malaysia [★IO]
Lemon Administrative Comm. - Defunct.
Lending
Amer. Financial Services Assn. [2208]
Commercial Finance Assn. [2209]
Commercial Finance Assn. [2209]
Credit Builders Alliance [990]
Natl. Aircraft Finance Assn. [2210]
Natl. Assn. of Development Companies [2211]
Natl. Assn. of Govt. Guaranteed Lenders [5770]
Natl. Assn. of Mortgage Processors [428]
Natl. Found. for Credit Counseling [2212]
Natl. Pawnbrokers Assn. [2213]
Natl. Reverse Mortgage Lenders Assn. [2214]
Lenten Desert Experience [★18209]
Lentz Peace Res. Assn. - Address unknown since 2010.
Leo Baeck Inst. [9925], 15 W 16th St., New York, NY 10011-6301, (212)744-6400
Leo Baeck Inst. [9925], 15 W 16th St., New York, NY 10011-6301, (212)744-6400
Leo Clubs [★13065]
Leonard Cheshire Intl. [IO], London, United Kingdom
Leonard Peltier Defense Comm. [17507], PO Box 474701, Des Moines, IA 50947-0001
Leonard Peltier Defense Comm. [17507], PO Box 474701, Des Moines, IA 50947-0001
Leonard Wood Memorial - Amer. Leprosy Found. [15248], 1 ALM Way, Greenville, SC 29601, (877)241-1736
Leonard Wood Memorial for the Eradication of Leprosy [★15248]
Leonard Wood Memorial for the Eradication of Leprosy [★15248]
Leonardo, The Intl. Soc. for the Arts, Sciences and Tech. [9330], 211 Sutter St., Ste. 501, San Francisco, CA 94108, (415)391-1110
Leonardo, The Intl. Soc. for the Arts, Sciences and Tech. [9330], 211 Sutter St., Ste. 501, San Francisco, CA 94108, (415)391-1110
Leonardo da Vinci Soc. - Defunct.
Leopold Stokowski Club [9502], 3900 SE 33 Ave., Ocala, FL 34480
Leopold Stokowski Soc. [IO], Deal, United Kingdom
Leopold Stokowski Soc. of Am. [★9502]
Lepidoptera Res. Found. - Defunct.
Lepidopterological Soc. of Finland [IO], Helsinki, Finland
Lepidopterology
North Amer. Butterfly Assn. [7030]
LEPRA - England [IO], Colchester, United Kingdom
Lepra Soc. [IO], Secunderabad, India
Leprosy
Amer. Leprosy Missions [15247]
Amer. Leprosy Missions [15247]
Amer. Leprosy Missions | Leonard Wood Memorial [15248]
Damien-Dutton Soc. for Leprosy Aid [15249]
Leonard Wood Memorial - Amer. Leprosy Found. [15248]
Leprosy Relief Assn. [IO], Colchester, United Kingdom
Les amis canadiens de la birmanie [★IO]
Les Amis de Cliff Richard and The Shadows [IO], Vif, France
Les Amis d'Escoffier Soc. of New York [1408], 787 Ridgewood Rd., Millburn, NJ 07041, (212)414-5820
Les Amis d'Escoffier Soc. of New York [1408], 787 Ridgewood Rd., Millburn, NJ 07041, (212)414-5820
Les Amis du Louvre [★IO]
Les Amis de Panhard and Deutsch-Bonnet USA [21091], 7992 Oak Creek Dr., Reno, NV 89511-1065, (775)853-8452
Les Amis de la Terre - France [★IO]
Les Anciens Combattants Juifs du Canada [★IO]
Les Anciens Combattants de l'Armee, de la Marine et des Forces Aeriennes Au Canada [★IO]
Les Choeurs de l'Union Europeenne [★IO]
Les Clefs d'Or U.S.A. [1759], 68 Laurie Ave., Boston, MA 02132, (617)469-5397
Les Dames d'Escoffier Intl. [1010], PO Box 4961, Louisville, KY 40204, (502)456-1851

Les Dietetistes du Canada [★IO]
Les Eleveurs de Dindon du Canada [★IO]
Les Femmes d'Entreprises Mondiales [★IO]
Les Grands Freres Grandes Soeurs du Canada [★IO]
Les Humains Associes [★IO]
Les Meres contre L'alcool au volant [★IO]
LES Osterreich [★IO]
Les Producteurs D'Ceufs du Canada [★IO]
Les Unions d'Agents et Organizateurs de Voyages en Europe [★IO]
Lesbian Bisexual Gay Coalition [★12075]
Lesbian and Gay Assoc. Engineers and Scientists [★7379]
Lesbian and Gay Band Assn. [10235], PO Box 14172, San Francisco, CA 94114-0172
Lesbian and Gay Bands of Am. [★10235]
Lesbian, Gay and Bisexual Returned Peace Corps Volunteers [★18306]
Lesbian, Gay, Bisexual and Transgender concerns; More Light Presbyterians for [19798]
Lesbian, Gay, Bisexual and Transgender U.S. Peace Corps Alumni [18306], PO Box 14332, San Francisco, CA 94114-4332, (800)424-8580
Lesbian and Gay Christian Movement [IO], London, United Kingdom
Lesbian and Gay Immigration Rights Task Force [★12091]
Lesbian Hea. Fund [14578], Gay and Lesbian Medical Assn., 1326 18th St. NW, Ste. 22, Washington, DC 20036, (202)600-8037
Lesbian Hea. Fund [14578], Gay and Lesbian Medical Assn., 1326 18th St. NW, Ste. 22, Washington, DC 20036, (202)600-8037
Lesbian Herstory Archives [★10642]
Lesbian Herstory Archives [★10642]
Lesbian Herstory Educational Found. [10642], PO Box 1258, New York, NY 10116, (718)768-3953
Lesbian Herstory Educational Found. [10642], PO Box 1258, New York, NY 10116, (718)768-3953
Lesbian Rsrc. Center [12097], 2214 S Jackson St., Seattle, WA 98144, (206)322-3953
Lesbian Rights Proj. [★12100]
Leschetizky Assn. [10236], 37-21 90th St., Apt. 2R, Jackson Heights, NY 11372
Lesley Gore Intl. Fan Club [23871], PO Box 1548, Ocean Pines, MD 21811, (410)208-6369
Leslie Charleson Fan Club [23773], 4151 Prospect Ave., Los Angeles, CA 90027, (323)671-4583
Leslie-Lohman Gay Art Found. [9188], 26 Wooster St., New York, NY 10013, (212)431-2609
Lesotho Amateur Athletics Assn. [IO], Maseru, Lesotho
Lesotho Badminton Assn. [IO], Maseru, Lesotho
Lesotho Coun. of Non-Governmental Organizations [IO], Maseru, Lesotho
Lesotho Cycling Assn. [IO], Maseru, Lesotho
Lesotho Democracy Programme [IO], Maseru, Lesotho
Lesotho Football Assn. [IO], Maseru, Lesotho
Lesotho Lawn Tennis Assn. [IO], Maseru, Lesotho
Lesotho Natl. Coun. of Women [IO], Maseru, Lesotho
Lesotho Natl. Fed. of Organizations of the Disabled [IO], Maseru, Lesotho
Lesotho Natl. Netball Assn. [IO], Maseru, Lesotho
Lesotho Natl. Olympic Comm. [IO], Maseru, Lesotho
Lesotho Red Cross Soc. [IO], Maseru, Lesotho
Lesotho Squash Assn. [IO], Maseru, Lesotho
Lesotho Taekwondo Assn. [IO], Maseru, Lesotho
Lesotho Weightlifting Fed. [IO], Maseru, Lesotho
Less Commonly Taught Languages Proj. [8473], Center for Advanced Res. on Language Acquisition, 140 Univ. Intl. Center, 331 17th Ave. SE, Minneapolis, MN 55414, (612)626-8600
Lessing Soc. - Address unknown since 2010.
Letelier-Moffitt Memorial Fund for Human Rights - Address unknown since 2010.
Let's Face It USA [14200], Univ. of Michigan, School of Dentistry, Dentistry Lib., 1011 N Univ. Ave., Ann Arbor, MI 48109-1078
Let's Face It USA [14200], Univ. of Michigan, School of Dentistry, Dentistry Lib., 1011 N Univ. Ave., Ann Arbor, MI 48109-1078
Let's Talk Pain [16105], Amer. Pain Found., 201 N Charles St., Ste. 710, Baltimore, MD 21201-4111, (888)615-7246

A star before a book entry number signifies that the name is not listed separately, but is mentioned within the entry.

Letzebuerger Chreschtleche Gewerkschafts-Bond [★IO]

Leukaemia CARE [IO], Worcester, United Kingdom

Leukemia
  Children's Cancer and Blood Found. [14964]
  Leukemia and Lymphoma Soc. [13936]

Leukemia Found; Friends of the Jose Carreras Intl.

Leukemia and Lymphoma Soc. [13936], 1311 Mamaroneck Ave., Ste. 310, White Plains, NY 10605, (914)949-5213

Leukemia Res. Assn; Children's [13907]

Leukemia Soc. of Am. [★13936]

Leukodystrophy Found; United [15641]

Leukodystrophy Found; United [15641]

Leuva Patidar Samaj of USA [9858], 716 Sweetwater Cir., Old Hickory, TN 37138, (615)712-6999

Lewa Wildlife Conservancy (U.S.A.) [5078], 40 Marin View Ave., Mill Valley, CA 94941, (657)206-5392

Lewis Carroll Soc. [IO], London, United Kingdom

Lewis Carroll Soc. of North Am. [9392], Clare Imholtz, Sec., 11935 Beltsville Dr., Beltsville, MD 20705

Lewis and Clark Trail Heritage Found. [9781], PO Box 3434, Great Falls, MT 59403-3434, (406)454-1234

Lewis D. and John J. Gilbert, Corporate Democracy - Defunct.

Lewy Body Dementia Assn. [15605], 912 Killian Hill Rd. SW, Ste. 202C, Lilburn, GA 30047, (404)935-6444

Lewy Body Dementia Assn. [15605], 912 Killian Hill Rd. SW, Ste. 202C, Lilburn, GA 30047, (404)935-6444

Lex Mundi [5258], 2100 W Loop S, Ste. 1000, Houston, TX 77027, (713)626-9393

Lex Mundi [5258], 2100 W Loop S, Ste. 1000, Houston, TX 77027, (713)626-9393

Lexington Gp. in Trans. History [10490], Don L. Hofsommer, Treas./Ed., St. Cloud State Univ., Dept. of History, St. Cloud, MN 56301, (320)308-4906

Liability
  Amer. Bd. of Professional Liability Attorneys [5771]
  Defense Res. Inst. [5772]
  Inner Circle of Advocates [5773]
  Natl. Assn. of Forensic Economics [5774]

Liability Insurance Res. Bur. [1988], 3025 Highland Pkwy., Ste. 800, Downers Grove, IL 60515-1291, (630)724-2250

Liaison Comm. on Continuing Medical Educ. [★15389]

Liaison Comm. on Graduate Medical Educ. [★7642]

Liaison Coun. on Certification for the Surgical Technologist [★13574]

Liaison Endorsement Comm. [★14478]

Liaison Gp. for Intl. Educational Exchange [★8338]

Liaison Gp. for Intl. Educational Exchange [★8338]

Liaison Off. of the European Ceramic Indus. [IO], Brussels, Belgium

Libel Defense Rsrc. Center [★5668]

Liberal Arts
  Amer. Acad. for Liberal Educ. [8513]
  Assn. for Core Texts and Courses [8514]
  Assn. for Core Texts and Courses [8514]
  Assn. for Gen. and Liberal Stud. [8515]
  Assn. of Graduate Liberal Stud. Programs [8516]
  Phi Sigma Pi Natl. Honor Fraternity [23582]

Liberal Democratic Party of Japan [IO], Tokyo, Japan

Liberal Intl. [IO], London, United Kingdom

Liberal Party of Australia [IO], Kingston, Australia

Liberal Party of Canada [IO], Ottawa, ON, Canada

Liberal Party of Norway [IO], Oslo, Norway

Liberal Religious Educ. Directors Assn. [★20268]

Liberal Religious Educators Assn. [20268], 220 Main St., Northampton, MA 01060-3105, (413)584-1390

Liberal Studies
  Assn. for Core Texts and Courses [8514]
  Modernist Stud. Assn. [8517]

Liberal Youth [IO], London, United Kingdom

Liberalism
  Americans for Democratic Action [18074]
  Found. for the Stud. of Independent Social Ideas [18075]

Liberator Club [★20861]

Liberator Club [★20861]

Liberia
  Assn. of Liberian Engineers USA [6786]
  Children's Welfare Intl. [11253]
  Liberian Anti Poverty Assn. [11071]
  Relief Liberia Intl. [12884]

Liberia Agency for Community Empowerment [IO], Monrovia, Liberia

Liberia Assn. of Psychosocial Services [IO], Monrovia, Liberia

Liberia Chamber of Commerce [IO], Monrovia, Liberia

Liberia Cmpt. Rehabilitating Soc. [IO], Monrovia, Liberia

Liberia Dujar Assn. [IO], Stockholm, Sweden

Liberia Natl. Law Enforcement Assn. [IO], Monrovia, Liberia

Liberia Taekwondo Fed. [IO], Monrovia, Liberia

Liberia Tennis Assn. [IO], Monrovia, Liberia

Liberia Track and Field Fed. [IO], Monrovia, Liberia

Liberian Anti Poverty Assn. [11071], 5507 Whitby Ave., Philadelphia, PA 19143-4014

Liberian Anti Poverty Assn. [11071], 5507 Whitby Ave., Philadelphia, PA 19143-4014

Liberian History Educ. and Development [IO], Monrovia, Liberia

Liberian Red Cross Soc. [IO], Monrovia, Liberia

Liberian Shipowners' Coun. [2382], 99 Park Ave., Ste. 1700, New York, NY 10016, (212)973-3896

Liberian Shipowners' Coun. [2382], 99 Park Ave., Ste. 1700, New York, NY 10016, (212)973-3896

Libertarian Alliance [IO], London, United Kingdom

Libertarian Futurist Soc. [18079], 650 Castro St., Ste. 120-433, Mountain View, CA 94041

Libertarian Intl. [★18078]

Libertarian Intl. [★18078]

Libertarian Nation Found. [5775], 335 Mulberry St., Raleigh, NC 27604

Libertarian Natl. Comm. [18360], 2600 Virginia Ave. NW, Ste. 200, Washington, DC 20037, (202)333-0008

Libertarian Party [★18360]

Libertarian SIG [10397], Amer. Mensa, 1229 Corporate Dr. W, Arlington, TX 76006-6103, (817)607-0060

Libertarianism
  Advocates for Self-Government [18076]
  Assn. of Libertarian Feminists [18077]
  Intl. Soc. for Individual Liberty [18078]
  Intl. Soc. for Individual Liberty [18078]
  Libertarian Futurist Soc. [18079]
  Libertarian Nation Found. [5775]
  Libertarians for Life [18080]
  World Libertarian Order [18081]
  Young Americans for Liberty [18836]

Libertarians for Life [18080], 13424 Hathaway Dr., Wheaton, Silver Spring, MD 20906, (301)460-4141

Liberty [IO], London, United Kingdom

Liberty Godparent Home [12936], PO Box 4199, Lynchburg, VA 24502, (434)845-3466

Liberty Godparent Ministry [★12936]

Liberty Lobby - Defunct.

Liberty Museum and Educ. Center [★17789]

Liberty Museum and Educ. Center [★17789]

Liberty Seated Collectors Club [21979], Leonard Augsburger, Sec.-Treas., PO Box 261, Wellington, OH 44090

Liberty Services - Address unknown since 2011.

Liberty's Promise [5531], 1010 Pendleton St., Alexandria, VA 22314-1837, (703)549-9950

LibertyTree [17428], 100 Swan Way, Oakland, CA 94621-1428, (800)927-8733

LibertyTree Network [★17428]

Librarians Assn. of Malaysia [IO], Kuala Lumpur, Malaysia

Libraries
  Amer. Assn. of Law Libraries [9951]
  Amer. Assn. of School Librarians [9952]
  Amer. Friends of the Vatican Lib. [9953]
  Amer. Indian Lib. Assn. [9954]
  Amer. Lib. Assn. [9955]
  Amer. Lib. Assn. | Alternatives Media Task Force [9956]
  Amer. Lib. Assn. | Gay, Lesbian, Bisexual and Transgendered Roundtable [9633]

Amer. Lib. Assn. - Public Info. Off. [10476]

Amer. Soc. for Indexing [9957]

Amer. Theological Lib. Assn. [9958]

AMIGOS Lib. Services [9959]

APLIC [9960]

APLIC [9960]

Archivists and Librarians in the History of the Hea. Sciences [9961]

Art Libraries Soc. of North Am. [13770]

Asia/Pacific Amer. Librarians Assn. [9962]

Asian Pacific Amer. Librarians Assn. [9962]

Assn. of Architecture School Librarians [9963]

Assn. of Caribbean Univ., Res. and Institutional Libraries [9964]

Assn. of Caribbean Univ., Res. and Institutional Libraries [9964]

Assn. of Christian Librarians [9965]

Assn. of Christian Librarians [9965]

Assn. of Coll. and Res. Libraries [9966]

Assn. of Jewish Libraries [9967]

Assn. of Jewish Libraries [9967]

Assn. for Lib. Collections and Tech. Services [9968]

Assn. for Lib. Ser. to Children [9969]

Assn. of Lib. Trustees, Advocates, Friends and Foundations [9970]

Assn. for Recorded Sound Collections [9971]

Assn. for Recorded Sound Collections [9971]

Assn. of Res. Libraries [9972]

Assn. of Seventh-Day Adventist Librarians [9973]

Assn. of Specialized and Cooperative Lib. Agencies [9974]

Assn. of Vision Sci. Librarians [9975]

Athenaeum of Philadelphia [9976]

Atmospheric Sci. Librarians Intl. [8518]

Beta Phi Mu [23583]

Black Caucus of the Amer. Lib. Assn. [9977]

Catholic Lib. Assn. [9978]

Center for Res. Libraries [9979]

Chief Officers of State Lib. Agencies [9980]

Church and Synagogue Lib. Assn. [9981]

Comm. on Res. Materials on Southeast Asia [9982]

Comm. on Res. Materials on Southeast Asia [9982]

Coun. on Botanical and Horticultural Libraries [9983]

Coun. on Botanical and Horticultural Libraries [9983]

Coun. on Lib. and Info. Resources [9984]

Evangelical Church Lib. Assn. [9985]

Fed. Lib. and Info. Center Comm. [9986]

Independent Res. Libraries Assn. [9987]

Interagency Coun. on Info. Resources in Nursing [9988]

Intl. Assn. of Aquatic and Marine Sci. Libraries and Info. Centers [9989]

Intl. Assn. of Aquatic and Marine Sci. Libraries and Info. Centers [9989]LibrariesIntl. Assn. of Music Libraries, Archives and Documentation Centres - Australia Br. LibrariesIntl. Friends of the London Lib.

John F. Kennedy Lib. Found. [9990]

Learning Round Table [9991]

Libraries Without Borders [8519]

Lib. and Info. Tech. Assn. [9992]

Lib. Leadership and Mgt. Assn. [9993]

Major Orchestra Librarians' Assn. [9994]

Medical Lib. Assn. [9995]

Middle East Librarians Assn. [9996]

Middle East Librarians Assn. [9996]

Music Lib. Assn. [9997]

Natl. Church Lib. Assn. [9998]

Natural Resources Info. Coun. [9999]

Natural Resources Info. Coun. [9999]

North Amer. Coordinating Coun. on Japanese Lib. Resources [10000]

North Amer. Coordinating Coun. on Japanese Lib. Resources [10000]

North Amer. Serials Interest Gp. [10001]

Off. for Intellectual Freedom [10002]

Online Audiovisual Catalogers [10003]

Polar Libraries Colloquy [10004]

Polar Libraries Colloquy [10004]

Progressive Librarians Guild [10005]

Reference to "IO" in place of a book number signifies that the association may be found in the 50th edition of International Organizations.

Public Lib. Assn. **[10006]**
Public Lib. of Sci. **[10007]**
Reference and User Services Assn. of Amer. Lib. Assn. **[10008]**
REFORMA: Natl. Assn. to Promote Lib. Services to the Spanish-Speaking **[10009]**
Schomburg Center for Res. in Black Culture **[9105]**
Seminar on the Acquisition of Latin Amer. Lib. Materials **[10010]**
Seminar on the Acquisition of Latin Amer. Lib. Materials **[10010]**
Social Responsibilities Round Table of the Amer. Lib. Assn. **[10011]**
Soc. of School Librarians Intl. **[10012]**
Soc. of School Librarians Intl. **[10012]**
Special Libraries Assn. **[10013]**
Special Libraries Assn. **[10013]**
Spirituality and Practice **[7929]**
Substance Abuse Librarians and Info. Specialists **[10014]**
Substance Abuse Librarians and Info. Specialists **[10014]**
Theatre Lib. Assn. **[10015]**
U.S. Book Exchange **[10016]**
Urban Libraries Coun. **[10017]**
Western Assn. of Map Libraries **[10018]**
Young Adult Lib. Services Assn. **[10019]**
Libraries for the Future - Defunct.
Libraries Without Borders **[8519]**, 50 Hazel Rd., Berkeley, NY 94705, (917)204-5375
Lib. Admin. Division of ALA **[★9993]**
Lib. Admin. and Mgt. Assn. **[★9993]**
Lib. Assn. of Austria **[IO]**, Vienna, Austria
Lib. Assn. of Ireland **[IO]**, Dublin, Ireland
Lib. Assn. of Singapore **[IO]**, Singapore, Singapore
Lib. Binding Inst. **[1617]**, 4440 PGA Blvd., Ste. 600, Palm Beach Gardens, FL 33410, (561)745-6821
Lib. Binding Inst. **[1617]**, 4440 PGA Blvd., Ste. 600, Palm Beach Gardens, FL 33410, (561)745-6821
Lib. and Info. Assn. of New Zealand Aotearoa **[IO]**, Wellington, New Zealand
Lib. and Info. Assn. of South Africa **[IO]**, Pretoria, Republic of South Africa
Lib. and Info. Res. Gp. **[IO]**, London, United Kingdom
Lib. and Info. Tech. Assn. **[9992]**, Amer. Lib. Assn., 50 E Huron St., Chicago, IL 60611-2795, (312)280-4268
Lib. Leadership and Mgt. Assn. **[9993]**, 50 E Huron St., Chicago, IL 60611-2729, (312)280-5032
Lib. of Presidential Papers **[★17246]**
Library Science
Assn. for Lib. and Info. Sci. Educ. **[8520]**
Beta Phi Mu **[23583]**
Beta Phi Mu **[23583]**
Coun. on Library-Media Technicians **[8521]**
Intl. Coalition of Lib. Consortia **[8522]**
Intl. Coalition of Lib. Consortia **[8522]**
Learning Round Table **[9991]**
Libya Amateur Athletic Fed. **[IO]**, Tripoli, Libyan Arab Jamahiriya
Libyan
Amer. Libyan Freedom Alliance **[17513]**
Libyan Arab Tennis and Squash Fed. **[IO]**, Tripoli, Libyan Arab Jamahiriya
Libyan Arabian Horse Breeders Soc. **[IO]**, Tripoli, Libyan Arab Jamahiriya
Libyan Assn. Against Cancer **[IO]**, Sabratha, Libyan Arab Jamahiriya
Libyan Cardiac Soc. **[IO]**, Tripoli, Libyan Arab Jamahiriya
Libyan Corrosion Soc. **[IO]**, Benghazi, Libyan Arab Jamahiriya
Libyan Fed. of Sports for Disabled **[IO]**, Tripoli, Libyan Arab Jamahiriya
Libyan Red Crescent **[IO]**, Benghazi, Libyan Arab Jamahiriya
Libyan Sailing Fed. **[IO]**, Tripoli, Libyan Arab Jamahiriya
Libyan Soc. of Gastroenterology and Hepatology **[IO]**, Tripoli, Libyan Arab Jamahiriya
Libyan Taekwondo Fed. **[IO]**, Tripoli, Libyan Arab Jamahiriya
Licensed Beverage Indus. **[★180]**

Licensed Beverage Information Coun. - Defunct.
Licensed Merchandisers' Assn. **[★5572]**
Licensed Merchandisers' Assn. **[★5572]**
Licensed Taxi Drivers Assn. **[IO]**, London, United Kingdom
Licensed Vintners' Assn. **[IO]**, Dublin, Ireland
Licensing
Natl. Assn. for Regulatory Admin. **[15250]**
Natl. Org. for Career Credentialing **[727]**
Women in Toys **[3479]**
Licensing Assn; Intl. Collegiate **[2407]**
Licensing Executives Soc. **[5576]**, 1800 Diagonal Rd., Ste. 280, Alexandria, VA 22314, (703)836-3106
Licensing Executives Soc. Andean Community **[IO]**, Caracas, Venezuela
Licensing Executives Soc. Arab Countries **[IO]**, Amman, Jordan
Licensing Executives Soc. Argentina **[IO]**, Buenos Aires, Argentina
Licensing Executives Soc. of Australia and New Zealand **[IO]**, Pakenham Upper, Australia
Licensing Executives Soc. Austria **[IO]**, Vienna, Austria
Licensing Executives Soc. Benelux **[IO]**, Wijk bij Durstede, Netherlands
Licensing Executives Soc. Brazil **[IO]**, Rio de Janeiro, Brazil
Licensing Executives Soc. Britain and Ireland **[IO]**, East Kilbride, United Kingdom
Licensing Executives Soc. China **[IO]**, Beijing, People's Republic of China
Licensing Executives Soc. France **[IO]**, Paris, France
Licensing Executives Soc. Germany **[IO]**, Hamburg, Germany
Licensing Executives Soc. Hungary **[IO]**, Budapest, Hungary
Licensing Executives Soc. India **[IO]**, New Delhi, India
Licensing Executives Soc. Italy **[IO]**, Milan, Italy
Licensing Executives Soc. Japan **[IO]**, Tokyo, Japan
Licensing Executives Soc. Korea **[IO]**, Seoul, Republic of Korea
Licensing Executives Soc. Malaysia **[IO]**, Kuala Lumpur, Malaysia
Licensing Executives Soc. Mexico **[IO]**, Mexico City, Mexico
Licensing Executives Soc. Philippines **[IO]**, Makati City, Philippines
Licensing Executives Soc. Poland **[IO]**, Wroclaw, Poland
Licensing Executives Soc. Russia **[IO]**, Moscow, Russia
Licensing Executives Soc. Scandinavia **[IO]**, Malmo, Sweden
Licensing Executives Soc. Singapore **[IO]**, Singapore, Singapore
Licensing Executives Soc. Switzerland **[IO]**, Zurich, Switzerland
Licensing Indus. Assn. **[★5572]**
Licensing Indus. Assn. **[★5572]**
LICU **[1000]**, 1 Credit Union Plz., 24 McKinley Ave., Endicott, NY 13760, (607)754-7900
; LICU **[1000]**
Lido 14 Class Assn. **[22367]**, PO Box 1252, Newport Beach, CA 92663, (714)437-1370
Liechtenstein Assn. of Professional Trustees **[IO]**, Vaduz, Liechtenstein
Liechtenstein Bankers Assn. **[IO]**, Vaduz, Liechtenstein
Liechtenstein Chamber of Lawyers **[IO]**, Schaan, Liechtenstein
Liechtenstein Chap. of the Assn. for Info. Systems **[IO]**, Vaduz, Liechtenstein
Liechtenstein Floorball Assn. **[IO]**, Schaan, Liechtenstein
Liechtenstein Investment Fund Assn. **[IO]**, Vaduz, Liechtenstein
Liechtenstein Olympic Sports Assn. **[IO]**, Schaan, Liechtenstein
Liechtenstein Soc. of Investment Professionals **[IO]**, Vaduz, Liechtenstein
Liechtenstein Squash Rackets Assn. **[IO]**, Vaduz, Liechtenstein

Liechtenstein Unihockey Verband **[★IO]**
Liechtensteiner Tanzsportverband **[IO]**, Schaan, Liechtenstein
Liechtensteiner Tennisverband **[IO]**, Triesen, Liechtenstein
Liechtensteinische Treuhandervereinigung **[★IO]**
Liechtensteinischer Anlagefondsverband **[★IO]**
Liechtensteinischer Bankenverband **[★IO]**
Liechtensteinischer Hangegleiter Verband **[IO]**, Vaduz, Liechtenstein
Liechtensteinischer Olympischer Sportverband **[★IO]**
Liederkranz Found. **[10237]**, 6 E 87th St., New York, NY 10128, (212)534-0880
Lietuviu kataliku spaudos draugija **[★19117]**
Lietuvos bibliotekininku draugija **[★IO]**
Lietuvos parolimpinis komitetas **[★IO]**
Lietuvos literaturos verteju sajunga **[★IO]**
Lietuvos tautinis olimpinis komitetas **[★IO]**
Lietuvos Aeroklubas **[★IO]**
Lietuvos Aprangos ir Tekstiles Imoniu Asociacija **[★IO]**
Lietuvos Artrito Asociacija **[★IO]**
Lietuvos Badmintono Federacija **[★IO]**
Lietuvos Banku Asociacija **[★IO]**
Lietuvos Beisbolo Asociacija **[★IO]**
Lietuvos Biblijos skaitymos draugija **[★IO]**
Lietuvos Biblijos Draugija **[★IO]**
Lietuvos Buriuotoju Sajunga **[★IO]**
Lietuvos Darbo Federacija **[★IO]**
Lietuvos Duju Asociacija **[★IO]**
Lietuvos Energetikos Institutas **[★IO]**
Lietuvos Greitojo Ciuozimo Asociacija **[★IO]**
Lietuvos Gydytoju Sajunga **[★IO]**
Lietuvos Hipertenzijos Draugija **[★IO]**
Lietuvos Kompiuterininku Sajunga **[★IO]**
Lietuvos Kompozitoriu Sajunga **[★IO]**
Lietuvos Laivu Statytoju ir Remontininku Asociacija **[★IO]**
Lietuvos Lengvosios Atletikos Federacija **[★IO]**
Lietuvos Mesiniu Galviju Augintoju ir Gerintoju Asociacija **[★IO]**
Lietuvos Mokslu Akademija **[★IO]**
Lietuvos Nekilnojamojo Turto Pletros Asociacija **[★IO]**
Lietuvos Orientavimosi Sporto Federacija **[★IO]**
Lietuvos Pakuotoju Asociacija **[★IO]**
Lietuvos Pramonininku Konfederacija **[★IO]**
Lietuvos prekybos, pramones ir amatu rumu asociacija **[★IO]**
Lietuvos Projektavimo Imoniu Asociacija **[★IO]**
Lietuvos Radijo Megeju Draugija **[★IO]**
Lietuvos Raudonojo Kryzius **[★IO]**
Lietuvos Respublikos Odontologu Rumai **[★IO]**
Lietuvos Sirdies Asociacija **[★IO]**
Lietuvos Spaustuvininku Asociacija **[★IO]**
Lietuvos Sportiniu Sokiu Federacija **[★IO]**
Lietuvos Taekwondo Federija **[★IO]**
Lietuvos Teniso Sajunga **[★IO]**
Lietuvos Universitetu Moteru Asociacija **[IO]**, Kaunas, Lithuania
Lietuvos Vejo Energetiku Asociacija **[★IO]**
Lietuvos Verslo Konfederacija **[★IO]**
Lietuvos Zaliuju Judejimas **[★IO]**
LIFE **[IO]**, Leamington Spa, United Kingdom
Life in Abundance Intl. **[10814]**, 1605 E Elizabeth St., Ste. 1069, Pasadena, CA 91104, (626)213-2203
Life Acad. **[IO]**, Guildford, United Kingdom
Life Action Ministries **[★19757]**
Life Action Revival Ministries **[19757]**, PO Box 31, Buchanan, MI 49107-0031, (269)697-8600
Life After Exoneration Prog. **[17491]**, 760 Wildcat Canyon, Berkeley, CA 94708, (510)292-6010
Life Coalition Intl.
Life Coalition Intl. - Address unknown since 2011.
Life Decisions Intl. **[12937]**, PO Box 439, Front Royal, VA 22630, (540)631-0380
Life Decisions Intl. **[12937]**, PO Box 439, Front Royal, VA 22630, (540)631-0380
Life and Hope Assn. **[IO]**, Siem Reap, Cambodia
Life Insurance Agency Mgt. Assn. **[★1991]**
Life Insurance Agency Mgt. Assn. **[★1991]**
Life Insurance Assn. of Japan **[IO]**, Tokyo, Japan
Life Insurance Assn. - Singapore **[IO]**, Singapore, Singapore

A star before a book entry number signifies that the name is not listed separately, but is mentioned within the entry.

Life Insurance Marketing and Res. Assn. [★1991]
Life Insurance Marketing and Res. Assn. [★1991]
Life Insurance Sales Res. Bur. [★1991]
Life Insurance Sales Res. Bur. [★1991]
Life Insurance Settlement Assn. [1989], 1011 E Colonial Dr., Ste. 500, Orlando, FL 32803, (407)894-3797
Life Insurers Coun. [1990], 2300 Windy Ridge Pkwy., Ste. 600, Atlanta, GA 30339-8443, (770)951-1770
Life and Liberty for Women [10767], PO Box 271778, Fort Collins, CO 80527-1778, (970)217-7577
Life in Messiah Intl. [19758], PO Box 5470, Lansing, IL 60438-5470, (708)418-0020
Life in Messiah Intl. [19758], PO Box 5470, Lansing, IL 60438-5470, (708)418-0020
LIFE Ministries [19795], 250 Meadow Ln., Conestoga, PA 17516, (717)871-0540
Life Off. Mgt. Assn. [★1992]
Life Off. Mgt. Assn. [★1992]
Life Outreach Intl. [19759], PO Box 982000, Fort Worth, TX 76182-8000, (817)267-4211
Life Raft Gp. [13937], 155 Rte. 46 W, Ste. 202, Wayne, NJ 07470, (973)837-9092
Life for Relief and Development [12862], 17300 W 10 Mile Rd., Southfield, MI 48075, (248)424-7493
Life for Relief and Development [12862], 17300 W 10 Mile Rd., Southfield, MI 48075, (248)424-7493
Life Resources Inst. [15001], 116 High St., Ashland, OR 97520, (541)482-1289
Life Services for the Handicapped [★11779]
The Life Story People [★9753]
Life Underwriter Training Coun. [8323], 7625 Wisconsin Ave., Bethesda, MD 20814, (610)526-1000
Life Underwriters Assn. of Hong Kong [IO], Hong Kong, People's Republic of China
LifeBanc [14424], 4775 Richmond Rd., Cleveland, OH 44128-5919, (216)752-5433
LIFEbeat [10885], 676A 9th Ave., Ste. 111, New York, NY 10036, (212)459-2590
Lifeboat Found. [18667], 1638 Esmeralda Ave., Minden, NV 89423-4009, (775)972-0180
Lifeforce Found. [IO], Vancouver, BC, Canada
Lifelong Fitness Alliance [23070], 2682 Middlefield Rd., Ste. Z, Redwood City, CA 94063, (650)361-8282
Lifesaver; Oper. [13001]

Lifesaving
Intl. Assn. of Dive Rescue Specialists [2215]
Surf Life Saving Australia [5817]

Lifesaving Assn; U.S. [12912]
LifeSharers [16911], 6509 Cornwall Dr., Nashville, TN 37205, (888)674-2688
Lifespan Resources [10852], PO Box 995, New Albany, IN 47151-0995, (812)948-8330
Lifespire [12505], Empire State Bldg., 350 5th Ave., Ste. 301, New York, NY 10118, (212)741-0100
LifeWind Intl. [19993], PO Box 1302, Salida, CA 95368, (209)543-7500
LifeWind Intl. [19993], PO Box 1302, Salida, CA 95368, (209)543-7500
LIFT [11072], 800 7th St. NW, Ste. 300, Washington, DC 20001, (202)289-1151
Lift Disability Network [11804], PO Box 770607, Winter Garden, FL 34777, (407)228-8343
Lift Disability Network [11804], PO Box 770607, Winter Garden, FL 34777, (407)228-8343
Lift and Escalator Indus. Assn. [IO], London, United Kingdom
Lifting Equip. Engineers Assn. [IO], Huntingdon, United Kingdom
Liga Argentina Contra la Tuberculosis [IO], Buenos Aires, Argentina
Liga Asociatiilor de Proprietari - Habitat [★IO]
Liga Brasileira de Epilepsia [★IO]
Liga Colombiana Contra la Epilepsia [★IO]
Liga Colombiana de Lucha Contra La Osteoporosis [★IO]
Liga Espanola Contra La Epilepsia [★IO]
Liga Internacional de Mujeres pro Paz y Libertad - Costa Rica [★IO]
Liga Intl. [12464], 19671 Lucaya Ct., Apple Valley, CA 92308, (909)875-6300

Liga Intl. [12464], 19671 Lucaya Ct., Apple Valley, CA 92308, (909)875-6300
Liga Intl. de Mujeres por la Paz y la Libertad - Colombia [★IO]
Liga Medicorum Homeopathica Internationalis [★IO]
Liga Portuguesa Contra as Doencas Reumaticas [IO], Lisbon, Portugal
Liga Portuguesa Contra a Epilepsia [★IO]
Liga Reumatologica Espanola [IO], Madrid, Spain
Liga Uruguaya Contra La Epilepsia [★IO]
Ligeia Assn. pour le Renouvellement de la Culture Artistique Europeenne [IO], Paris, France
Light Aircraft Assn. [IO], Brackley, United Kingdom
Light of Cambodian Children [11342], 181 Market St., Lowell, MA 01852
Light Elec. Vehicle Assn. [3518], PO Box 286, Orono, ME 04473
Light Millennium [17299], 87-82 115th St., Richmond Hill, NY 11418, (718)846-5776
Light Music Soc. [IO], Clitheroe, United Kingdom
Light to the Nations [IO], Jerusalem, Israel
Light Rail Transit Assn. [IO], Welling, United Kingdom
Light Truck Accessory Alliance [333], Specialty Equip. Market Assn., PO Box 4910, Diamond Bar, CA 91765, (909)396-0289
Light on Yoga Italia [IO], Florence, Italy
Light of Yoga Soc. [★10760]
Lighter Assn. [1654], 1701 Pennsylvania Ave. NW, Ste. 300, Washington, DC 20006, (202)253-4347
Lightform Intl. Filipino Photographers Guild [IO], Dubai, United Arab Emirates
LightHawk [4092], PO Box 653, Lander, WY 82520, (307)332-3242
Lighthouse Intl. [17096], 111 E 59th St., New York, NY 10022-1202, (212)821-9200
Lighthouse Intl. [17096], 111 E 59th St., New York, NY 10022-1202, (212)821-9200
Lighthouse Keepers Assn. [★9689]
Lighthouse Keepers Assn; Great Lakes [9689]
Lighthouse Soc; U.S. [9735]
Lighthouse Sta. [12736], 2215 Canton St., Apt. 121, Dallas, TX 75201, (214)676-9999

Lighting
Aladdin Knights of the Mystic Light [21877]
Amer. Lighting Assn. [2216]
Assn. of Outdoor Lighting Professionals [2217]
China Assn. of the Lighting Indus. [14429]
Fairy Lamp Club [21337]
Fifty Lanterns Intl. [7439]
Illuminating Engg. Soc. of North Am. [7031]
Intl. Assn. of Lighting Mgt. Companies [2218]
Intl. Assn. of Lighting Mgt. Companies [2218]
Intl. Commn. on Illumination, U.S. Natl. Comm. [7032]
Lighting Controls Assn. [2219]
Lighting Res. Off. [7033]
Natl. Assn. of Independent Lighting Distributors [2220]
Natl. Coun. on Qualifications for the Lighting Professions [2221]
Natl. Lighting Bur. [2222]
Natl. Lighting Bur. [2222]
Professional Lighting and Sign Mgt. Companies of Am. [2223]
Rushlight Club [10020]

Lighting Assn. [IO], Telford, United Kingdom
Lighting Controls Assn. [2219], NEMA, 1300 N 17th St., Ste. 1752, Rosslyn, VA 22209, (703)841-3200
Lighting Indus. Fed. [IO], London, United Kingdom
Lighting Res. Inst. [★7033]
Lighting Res. Off. [7033], Elec. Power Res. Inst., 942 Corridor Park Blvd., Knoxville, TN 37932, (865)218-8015
Lighting Union [IO], Paris, France
Lightmongers' Company [IO], London, United Kingdom
Lightning Protection Inst. [3145], PO Box 99, Maryville, MO 64468, (804)314-8955
Lightning Strike and Elec. Shock Survivors Intl. [14441], PO Box 1156, Jacksonville, NC 28541-1156, (910)346-4708
Lightning Strike and Elec. Shock Survivors Intl. [14441], PO Box 1156, Jacksonville, NC 28541-1156, (910)346-4708

Lightning Strike and Elec. Shock Victims [★14441]
Lightning Strike and Elec. Shock Victims [★14441]
Ligue des Associations Sportives Estudiantes Luxembourgeoises [IO], Strassen, Luxembourg
Ligue pour le bien-etre de l'enfance du Canada [★IO]
Ligue des Cadets de l'Air du Canada [★IO]
Ligue des Cadets de l'Armee du Canada [★IO]
Ligue Cardiologique Belge [★IO]
Ligue Europeene de Cooperation Economique [★IO]
Ligue Europeenne Contre le Rhumatisme [★IO]
Ligue Francaise contre la Sclerose En Plaques [IO], Paris, France
Ligue Huntington Francophone Belge [IO], Liege, Belgium
Ligue Internationale du Droit de la concurrence [★IO]
Ligue Internationale du Droit de la concurrence [★IO]
Ligue Internationale du Droit de la Concurrence [★IO]
Ligue Internationale de Femmes pour la Paix et la Liberte [★IO]
Ligue Internationale de Femmes pour la Paix et la Liberte [★IO]
Ligue La Leche [★IO]
Ligue pour la Lecture de la Bible - Brazzaville [IO], Brazzaville, Republic of the Congo
Ligue pour la Lecture de la Bible - Burkina Faso [IO], Ouagadougou, Burkina Faso
Ligue pour la Lecture de la Bible Cameroun [★IO]
Ligue pour la Lecture de la Bible Congo [★IO]
Ligue pour la Lecture de la Bible - Cote d'Ivoire [IO], Abidjan, Cote d'Ivoire
Ligue pour la Lecture de la Bible - Guinea [IO], Conakry, Guinea
Ligue pour la Lecture de la Bible - Madagascar [IO], Antananarivo, Madagascar
Ligue pour la Lecture de la Bible Rwanda [★IO]
Ligue pour la Lecture de la Bible Togo [★IO]
Ligue canadienne contre l'epilepsie [★IO]
Ligue Monarchiste du Canada [★IO]
Ligue Nationale Belge de la Sclerose en Plaques [IO], Brussels, Belgium
Ligue des Pays du Commonwealth [★IO]
Ligue Trotskyste du Canada [★IO]
Lily of the Valley Endeavor [10886], PO Box 1007, Agoura Hills, CA 91376-1007, (805)277-1827
Lima Chamber of Commerce [IO], Lima, Peru
Limbless Assn. [IO], London, United Kingdom
Lime, Gypsum, and Allied Workers Div; Cement, [23175]
Limerick Chamber of Commerce [IO], Limerick, Ireland
Limnology and Oceanography; Amer. Soc. of [7177]
Limnology and Oceanography; Amer. Soc. of [★7177]
Limnology Soc. of Am. [★7177]
Limnology Soc. of Am. [★7177]
LIMRA Europe [IO], Rickmansworth, United Kingdom
LIMRA Intl. [1991], 300 Day Hill Rd., Windsor, CT 06095, (860)688-3358
LIMRA Intl. [1991], 300 Day Hill Rd., Windsor, CT 06095, (860)688-3358
Lincoln Assn; Abraham [10651]
Lincoln Centennial Assn. [★10651]
Lincoln Continental Owners Club [★21092]
Lincoln and Continental Owners Club [21092], PO Box 1715, Maple Grove, MN 55311-6715, (763)420-7829
Lincoln Highway Assn. [9706], PO Box 308, Franklin Grove, IL 61031, (815)456-3030
Lincoln Inst. of Land Policy [5638], 113 Brattle St., Cambridge, MA 02138, (617)661-3016
Lincoln Inst. for Res. and Educ. [17156], PO Box 254, Great Falls, VA 22066, (703)759-4278
Lincoln Univ. Alumni Assn. [18882], Lincoln Univ., Memorial Hall, 818 Chestnut St., Jefferson City, MO 65102-0029, (573)681-5570
Lincoln Zephyr Owner's Club [21093], 25609 N Forrest Rd., Ste. 10, Rio Verde, AZ 85263
Lincolnshire Chamber of Commerce and Indus. [IO], Lincoln, United Kingdom
Linda Davis Fan Club [23872], Linda Davis, Inc., PO Box 767, Hermitage, TN 37076, (615)566-6639

Reference to "IO" in place of a book number signifies that the association may be found in the 50th edition of International Organizations.

Linda Gray's Official Fan Club [23774], PO Box 5064, Sherman Oaks, CA 91403

Lindbergh Memorial Fund [★4240]

Lindesmith Center [★17286]

Lindesmith Center - Defunct.

Lindsay Wagner's Official Fan Club [23775], PO Box 5002, Sherman Oaks, CA 91413

Line Dance Assn. of Australia [IO], Kerrimuir, Australia

Line Dance Soc. Singapore [IO], Singapore, Singapore

Linen and Lace Paper Inst. [★1041]

Linen Supply Assn. of Am. [★3083]

Lingerie Indus. Coun. [★199]

Lingue New Caledonia Athletic [IO], Noumea, New Caledonia

Linguistic Assn. of Canada and the U.S. [10028], Brooklyn Coll., English Dept., 2900 Bedford Ave., Brooklyn, NY 11210-2889

Linguistic Assn. of Canada and the U.S. [10028], Brooklyn Coll., English Dept., 2900 Bedford Ave., Brooklyn, NY 11210-2889

Linguistic Assn. of Finland [IO], Helsinki, Finland

Linguistic Data Consortium [2224], 3600 Market St., Ste. 810, Philadelphia, PA 19104-2653, (215)898-0464

Linguistic Data Consortium [2224], 3600 Market St., Ste. 810, Philadelphia, PA 19104-2653, (215)898-0464

Linguistic Institute [★10029]

Linguistic Institute [★10029]

Linguistic Soc. of Am. [10029], 1325 18th St. NW, Ste. 211, Washington, DC 20036-6501, (202)835-1714

Linguistic Soc. of Am. [10029], 1325 18th St. NW, Ste. 211, Washington, DC 20036-6501, (202)835-1714

Linguistic Soc. of Europe [IO], Lancaster, United Kingdom

Linguistic Soc. of Hong Kong [IO], Hong Kong, People's Republic of China

Linguistic Soc. of New Zealand [IO], Christchurch, New Zealand

Linguistic Soc. of Southern Africa [IO], Bloemfontein, Republic of South Africa

Linguistics

Amer. Assn. for Applied Linguistics [10021]

Amer. Dialect Soc. [10022]LinguisticsAmer. Soc. of Geolinguistics

Assn. for Computational Linguistics [10023]

Assn. for Computational Linguistics [10023]

Center for Applied Linguistics [10024]

Coun. of Teachers of Southeast Asian Languages [7756]

Elvish Linguistic Fellowship [10025]

Elvish Linguistic Fellowship [10025]

Intl. Clinical Phonetics and Linguistics Assn. [10026]

Intl. Clinical Phonetics and Linguistics Assn. [10026]

Intl. Maledicta Soc. [10027]

Intl. Maledicta Soc. [10027]

Linguistic Assn. of Canada and the U.S. [10028]

Linguistic Assn. of Canada and the U.S. [10028]

Linguistic Data Consortium [2224]

Linguistic Data Consortium [2224]

Linguistic Soc. of Am. [10029]

Linguistic Soc. of Am. [10029]

Linguistics Assn. of Great Britain [IO], Cambridge, United Kingdom

Linguistics; ERIC CH on Languages and [8470]

Link Found. [7536], Binghamton Univ. Found., PO Box 6005, Binghamton, NY 13902-6005

Links Found. [13064], 1200 Massachusetts Ave. NW, Washington, DC 20005-4501, (202)842-8686

Linnean Soc. of London [IO], London, United Kingdom

Linseed Castor Seed Assn. of New York [★2585]

Linseed Castor Seed Assn. of New York [★2585]

l'Institut Canadien de la Tole d'Acier pour le Batiment [★IO]

Linus Pauling Inst. of Science and Medicine - Defunct.

Lionel Collectors Club of Am. [21889], 4315 Saint Andrews St., Howell, MI 48843-7469, (248)709-4137

Lionel Railroader Club [21890], 26750 23rd Mile Rd., Chesterfield, MI 48051-1956, (586)949-4100

Lions Club Paradise Seychelles [IO], Victoria, Seychelles

Lions Clubs Intl. [13065], 300 W 22nd St., Oak Brook, IL 60523-8842, (630)571-5466

Lions Clubs Intl. [13065], 300 W 22nd St., Oak Brook, IL 60523-8842, (630)571-5466

Lions Intl. [★13065]

Lions Intl. [★13065]

Lions-Quest [7968], PO Box 304, Annapolis Junction, MD 20701-0304, (800)446-2700

Lions-Quest Programs [★7968]

Lipid Nurse Task Force [★15797]

Lipizzan Assn. of North Am. [4610], PO Box 1133, Anderson, IN 46015-1133, (765)215-6798

Lippitt Morgan Breeders Assn. [4611], 620 Millers Falls Rd., Northfield, MA 01360, (413)498-5553

Liquefied Petroleum Gas Assn. [★4491]

Liquid Water [13426], 96 Speedwell Ave., Morristown, NJ 07960, (973)615-1583

Liquor Hospitality and Miscellaneous Union [IO], Haymarket, Australia

Liquor Merchants Assn. of Australia [IO], Chatswood, Australia

Lisbon Acad. of Sciences [IO], Lisbon, Portugal

Lisle Fellowship [★8369]

Lisle Fellowship [★8369]

Lisle Inc. [★8369]

Lisle Inc. [★8369]

Lisle Intercultural [8369], 900 County Rd. 269, Leander, TX 78641, (800)477-1538

Lisle Intercultural [8369], 900 County Rd. 269, Leander, TX 78641, (800)477-1538

Lissencephaly Network [15606], 10408 Bitterroot Ct., Fort Wayne, IN 46804, (260)432-4310

Lissencephaly Network [15606], 10408 Bitterroot Ct., Fort Wayne, IN 46804, (260)432-4310

Lissner Found; Gerda [10345]

Listin Diario [IO], Santo Domingo, Dominican Republic

Liszt Ferenc Soc., Budapest [IO], Budapest, Hungary

Liszt Soc; Amer. [9497]

LITA, Soc. of Authors [IO], Bratislava, Slovakia

Literacy

ABLE: Assn. for Better Living and Educ. Intl. [11537]

Abriendo Mentes [12950]

Amer. Literacy Coun. [8523]

Australian Literacy Educators' Assn. [22132]

Barbara Bush Found. for Family Literacy [8524]

Basic Educ. Coalition [8525]

Building Educated Leaders for Life [8526]

Children of Tanzania [11065]

Children's Literacy Initiative [8527]

Christian Literacy Associates [8528]

Christian Literacy Associates [8528]

Culturatti Kids Resource Network [9074]

Family Literacy Alliance [18082]

First Book [8529]

Global Literacy Proj. [8530]

Haiti Convention Assn. [12966]

India Literacy Proj. [8531]

India Literacy Proj. [8531]

Literacy and Evangelism Intl. [8532]

Literacy and Evangelism Intl. [8532]

Literacy USA [8533]

Natl. Center for Family Literacy [8534]

Natl. Coalition for Literacy [8535]

Natl. Jewish Coalition for Literacy [8536]

Native Amer. Coalition for Healthy Alternatives [12567]

One World Educ. [8928]

PlanetRead [8537]

PlanetRead [8537]

ProLiteracy Worldwide [8538]

ProLiteracy Worldwide [8538]

Rolling Readers [12432]

Talking Page Literacy Org. [8539]

Literacy and Community Ser. of local clubs [★13050]

Literacy and Community Ser. of local clubs [★13050]

Literacy and Evangelism Intl. [8532], 1800 S Jackson Ave., Tulsa, OK 74107-1897, (918)585-3826

Literacy and Evangelism Intl. [8532], 1800 S Jackson Ave., Tulsa, OK 74107-1897, (918)585-3826

Literacy Intl. [★8532]

Literacy Intl. [★8532]

Literacy Res. Assn. [8781], 7044 S 13th St., Oak Creek, WI 53154, (414)908-4924

Literacy USA [8533], 1612 K St. NW, Ste. 300, Washington, DC 20006

Literacy Volunteers [★8538]

Literacy Volunteers [★8538]

Literacy Volunteers of Am. [★8538]

Literacy Volunteers of Am. [★8538]

Literary and Artistic Assn. Canada [IO], Montreal, QC, Canada

Literary Managers and Dramaturgs of the Americas [10585], PO Box 36, New York, NY 10129, (800)680-2148

Literary Press Gp. of Canada [IO], Toronto, ON, Canada

Literary Translators' Assn. of Canada [IO], Montreal, QC, Canada

Literature

African Amer. Literature and Culture Soc. [10030]

Amer. Comparative Literature Assn. [10031]

Amer. Friends of the Hakluyt Soc. [10032]

Amer. Literature Assn. [10033]

Amer. Soc. for Aesthetics [9270]

Assn. of Literary Scholars, Critics, and Writers [10034]

Assn. for the Stud. of Amer. Indian Literatures [10322]

Assn. for the Stud. of Literature and Env. [10035]

Before Columbus Found. [10036]

Center for the Book [10037]

Children's Literature Assn. [10038]

Conf. on Christianity and Literature [10039]

Conf. on Coll. Composition and Commun. [8132]

Coun. on Natl. Literatures [10040]

Culturatti Kids Resource Network [9074]

Intercultural Alliance of Artists and Scholars [9237]

Intl. Arthurian Soc., North Amer. Br. [10041]

Intl. Arthurian Soc., North Amer. Br. [10041]

Intl. Assn. for Comparative Mythology [7133]

Intl. Assn. for the Stud. of Irish Literatures [10042]

Intl. Assn. for the Stud. of Irish Literatures [10042]

Intl. Courtly Literature Soc. [10043]

Intl. Courtly Literature Soc. [10043]

Intl. Inst. of Iberoamerican Literature [10044]

Intl. Inst. of Iberoamerican Literature [10044]

James Jones Literary Soc. [10725]

Margery Allingham Soc. [15786]

Mythopoeic Soc. [10045]

Mythopoeic Soc. [10045]

New Chaucer Soc. [8540]

Philolexian Soc. [10046]

Philomathean Soc. of the Univ. of Pennsylvania [10047]

Sedgwick Soc. [10738]

Soc. for the Stud. of Midwestern Literature [10048]

Soc. for the Stud. of Southern Literature [10049]

Soc. for Textual Scholarship [10050]

Swedish Translators in North America [10615]

Vietnamese Nom Preservation Found. [10051]

Vietnamese Nom Preservation Found. [10051]

Western Literature Assn. [10052]

WordTheatre [10550]

Worldcraft Circle of Native Writers' and Storytellers [19170]

Lithographers and Printers Natl. Assn. [★1628]

Lithuanian

Amer. Professional Partnership for Lithuanian Educ. [8541]

Inst. of Lithuanian Stud. [10053]

Lithuanian-American Community [19114]

Lithuanian Amer. Coun. [19115]

Lithuanian Catholic Alliance [19116]

Lithuanian Catholic Press Soc. [19117]

Lithuanian Natl. Found. [18083]

Lithuanian Natl. Found. [18083]

Lithuanian Res. and Stud. Center I Inst. of Lithuanian Stud. [10053]

Lituanus Found. [10054]

A star before a book entry number signifies that the name is not listed separately, but is mentioned within the entry.

Lithuanian Acad. of Sciences [IO], Vilnius, Lithuania

Lithuanian Alliance of Am. - Address unknown since 2010.

Lithuanian Amateur Radio Soc. [IO], Vilnius, Lithuania

Lithuanian-American Bar Assn. [5259], 221 N Main St., Ste. 300, Ann Arbor, MI 48104, (734)222-0088

Lithuanian-American Bar Assn. [5259], 221 N Main St., Ste. 300, Ann Arbor, MI 48104, (734)222-0088

Lithuanian Amer. Bus. Coun. - Address unknown since 2010.

Lithuanian-American Community [19114], 2715 E Allegheny Ave., Philadelphia, PA 19134, (800)625-1170

Lithuanian-American Community of the U.S. [★19114]

Lithuanian Amer. Coun. [19115], 6500 S Pulaski Rd., Ste. 200, Chicago, IL 60629, (773)735-6677

Lithuanian Apparel and Textile Indus. Assn. [IO], Vilnius, Lithuania

Lithuanian Arthritis Assn. [IO], Vilnius, Lithuania

Lithuanian Assn. of Beef Cattle Breeders and Improvers [IO], Kaunas, Lithuania

Lithuanian Assn. of Consulting Companies [IO], Vilnius, Lithuania

Lithuanian Assn. of Literary Translators [IO], Vilnius, Lithuania

Lithuanian Athletic Fed. [IO], Vilnius, Lithuania

Lithuanian Badminton Fed. [IO], Vilnius, Lithuania

Lithuanian Baseball Assn. [IO], Vilnius, Lithuania

Lithuanian Catholic Alliance [19116], Ladies Pennsylvania Slovak Catholic Union, 71 S Washington St., Wilkes-Barre, PA 18701, (570)823-3513

Lithuanian Catholic Alliance of Am. [★19116]

Lithuanian Catholic Press Soc. [19117], 4545 W 63rd St., Chicago, IL 60629, (773)585-9500

Lithuanian Catholic Religious Aid [19446], 64-25 Perry Ave., Maspeth, NY 11378-2411, (718)326-5202

Lithuanian Composers' Union [IO], Vilnius, Lithuania

Lithuanian Cmpt. Soc. [IO], Vilnius, Lithuania

Lithuanian Confed. of Industrialists [IO], Vilnius, Lithuania

Lithuanian Dancesport Fed. [IO], Vilnius, Lithuania

Lithuanian Draughts Fed. [IO], Vilnius, Lithuania

Lithuanian Flying Disc Fed. [IO], Vilnius, Lithuania

Lithuanian Gas Assn. [IO], Vilnius, Lithuania

Lithuanian Geotechnical Soc. [IO], Vilnius, Lithuania

Lithuanian Green Movement [IO], Kaunas, Lithuania

Lithuanian Heart Assn. [IO], Vilnius, Lithuania

Lithuanian Hypertension League [IO], Vilnius, Lithuania

Lithuanian Kinezitherapy Assn. [IO], Kaunas, Lithuania

Lithuanian Labour Fed. [IO], Vilnius, Lithuania

Lithuanian Librarians' Assn. [IO], Vilnius, Lithuania

Lithuanian Medical Assn. [IO], Vilnius, Lithuania

Lithuanian Natl. Found. [18083], 307 W 30th St., New York, NY 10001-2703, (212)868-5860

Lithuanian Natl. Found. [18083], 307 W 30th St., New York, NY 10001-2703, (212)868-5860

Lithuanian Orienteering Fed. [IO], Vilnius, Lithuania

Lithuanian Packaging Assn. [IO], Kaunas, Lithuania

Lithuanian Paralympic Comm. [IO], Vilnius, Lithuania

Lithuanian Physiological Soc. [IO], Kaunas, Lithuania

Lithuanian Printers' Assn. [IO], Vilnius, Lithuania

Lithuanian Real Estate Development Assn. [IO], Vilnius, Lithuania

Lithuanian Red Cross Soc. [IO], Vilnius, Lithuania

Lithuanian Republic Chamber of Odontologists [IO], Vilnius, Lithuania

Lithuanian Res. and Stud. Center I Inst. of Lithuanian Stud. [10053], 5600 S Claremont Ave., Chicago, IL 60636-1039, (773)434-4545

Lithuanian Rheumatologists Assn. [IO], Vilnius, Lithuania

Lithuanian Roads Assn. [IO], Vilnius, Lithuania

Lithuanian Skating Fed. [IO], Kaunas, Lithuania

Lithuanian Soc. of Cardiology [IO], Kaunas, Lithuania

Lithuanian Soc. of Gastrointestinal Endoscopy [IO], Kaunas, Lithuania

Lithuanian Soc. of Palliative Care [IO], Kaunas, Lithuania

Lithuanian Speed Skating Assn. [IO], Vilnius, Lithuania

Lithuanian Sports Medicine Assn. [IO], Vilnius, Lithuania

Lithuanian Squash Fed. [IO], Vilnius, Lithuania

Lithuanian Stuttering Problem Club [IO], Vilnius, Lithuania

Lithuanian Taekwondo Fed. [IO], Vilnius, Lithuania

Lithuanian Tennis Assn. [IO], Vilnius, Lithuania

Lithuanian-U.S. Bus. Coun.

Lithuanian-U.S. Bus. Coun. - Address unknown since 2011.

Lithuanian Weightlifting Fed. [IO], Vilnius, Lithuania

Lithuanian Wind Energy Assn. [IO], Klaipeda, Lithuania

Lithuanian Yachting Union [IO], Vilnius, Lithuania

Little Big Horn Associates [★10678]

Little Bigger League [★22268]

Little Bighorn History Alliance [10678], PO Box 1752, Niceville, FL 32588

Little Britches Rodeo [★22847]

Little Bros. - Friends of the Elderly [10853], 28 E Jackson Blvd., Ste. 405, Chicago, IL 60604, (312)829-3055

Little Bros. of the Poor [★10853]

Little By Little [14802], PO Box 934, Glenview, IL 60025-0934

Little By Little [14802], PO Box 934, Glenview, IL 60025-0934

Little City Found. [12506], 1760 W Algonquin Rd., Palatine, IL 60067-4799, (847)358-5510

Little Company of Mary Generalate [IO], London, United Kingdom

Little Flower Soc. [★19498]

Little Hearts [14084], PO Box 171, Cromwell, CT 06416, (860)635-0006

Little League Baseball [★22273]

Little League Baseball and Softball [22273], PO Box 3485, Williamsport, PA 17701-0485, (570)326-1921

Little League Found. [22274], 539 U.S. Rte. 15 Hwy., PO Box 3485, Williamsport, PA 17701-0485, (570)326-1921

Little Mouse Club

Little Mouse Club - Address unknown since 2011.

Little People of Am. [13116], 250 El Camino Real, Ste. 201, Tustin, CA 92780, (714)368-3689

Little Sisters of the Assumption - France [IO], Paris, France

Little Sisters of Jesus [IO], Rome, Italy

Little Theatre Guild of Great Britain [IO], Bishop Auckland, United Kingdom

Littlefield CH and Info. Exchange [★20553]

Littlefield Family Newsl. [20553], PO Box 912, Ogunquit, ME 03907-0912

Lituanus Found. [10054], 47 W Polk St., Ste. 100-300, Chicago, IL 60605

Liturgical Conf. [19659], PO Box 31, Evanston, IL 60204, (800)354-1420

Liturgical Conf. [19659], PO Box 31, Evanston, IL 60204, (800)354-1420

Litzenberger-Litzenberg Assn. [20554], 3233 Simberlan Dr., San Jose, CA 95148-3128, (408)270-7227

Live Oak Soc. [4403], 3609 Purdue Dr., Metairie, LA 70003

Live Performance Australia [IO], Melbourne, Australia

Liveaboard Assn. of Maldives [IO], Male, Maldives

Liver Diseases; Amer. Assn. for the Stud. of [14978]

Liver Found; Amer. [14980]

Liverpool Chamber of Commerce and Indus. [IO], Liverpool, United Kingdom

Livestock

Alpacas Without Borders [3773]

Amer. Emu Assn. [4685]

Amer. Grassfed Assn. [4686]

Amer. Kiko Goat Assn. [4497]

Amer. Livestock Breeds Conservancy [4687]

Amer. Royal Assn. [4688]

Amer. Water Buffalo Assn. [4689]

Amer. Water Buffalo Assn. [4689]

ARCA: Amer. Romeldale/CVM Assn. [4903]

Food Animal Concerns Trust [4690]

Global Animal Partnership [3811]

Intl. HACCP Alliance [4809]

Intl. Livestock Identification Assn. [4691]

Intl. Livestock Investigators Assn. [4692]

Intl. Livestock Investigators Assn. [4692]

Intl. Miniature Donkey Registry [4693]

Intl. Miniature Donkey Registry [4693]

Intl. Yak Assn. [4694]

Intl. Yak Assn. [4694]

Miniature and Novelty Sheep Breeders Assn. and Registry [4910]

Natl. Assn. of Animal Breeders [4695]

Natl. Inst. for Animal Agriculture [4696]

Natl. Miniature Donkey Assn. [4697]

Painted Desert Sheep Soc. [4921]

Professional Rabbit Meat Assn. [4853]

Public Lands Coun. [4824]

Soays of Am. [4922]

Livestock Auctioneers' Assn. [IO], Carlisle, United Kingdom

Livestock Conservation, Inc. [★4696]

Livestock Conservation Inst. [★4696]

Livestock Marketing Assn. [4716], 10510 NW Ambassador Dr., Kansas City, MO 64153, (816)891-0502

Livestock Publications Coun. [2945], 910 Currie St., Fort Worth, TX 76107, (817)336-1130

The Living Bank [14425], PO Box 6725, Houston, TX 77265-6725, (713)528-2971

The Living Bank [★14425]

The Living Bank Intl. [14425], PO Box 6725, Houston, TX 77265-6725, (713)528-2971

Living Bibles Intl. [★19345]

Living Bibles Intl. [★19345]

Living Church Found. [19712], PO Box 514036, Milwaukee, WI 53203-3436, (414)276-5420

Living/Dying Proj. [13316], PO Box 357, Fairfax, CA 94978-0357, (415)456-3915

Living in Freedom Eternally [★19795]

Living Streets [IO], London, United Kingdom

Living Waters Org. [11608], PO Box 640, Union, NJ 07083, (908)967-8578

Livres Canada Books [IO], Ottawa, ON, Canada

Lizzie High Soc. - Address unknown since 2011.

Llama Assn. of North Am. [3791], 1800 S Obenchain Rd., Eagle Point, OR 97524, (541)830-5262

Llama RescueNet - Address unknown since 2011.

LLGAF [★9188]

Lloyd Shaw Found. [7960], Ruth Ann Knapp, Membership Chair, 2124 Passolt St., Saginaw, MI 48603

LMBBS Network [★14607]

LO-TCO Bistandsnamnd [★IO]

LO-TCO Secretariat of Intl. Trade Union Development Cooperation [IO], Stockholm, Sweden

Loading Dock Equip. Mfrs. [1837], 8720 Red Oak Blvd., Ste. 201, Charlotte, NC 28217, (704)676-1190

Loan Syndications and Trading Assn. [421], 366 Madison Ave., 15th Fl., New York, NY 10017, (212)880-3000

Loan Syndications and Trading Assn. [421], 366 Madison Ave., 15th Fl., New York, NY 10017, (212)880-3000

Lobby Europeen des Femmes [★IO]

Local Action [IO], Khartoum, Sudan

Local Authorities Coordinators of Regulatory Services [IO], London, United Kingdom

Local Authorities Res. and Intelligence Assn. [IO], Warrington, United Kingdom

Local Authority Caterers Assn. [IO], Woking, United Kingdom

Local Authority Recycling Advisory Comm. [IO], Knighton, United Kingdom

Local Govt. Center [★5855]

Local Independent Charities of Am. [12678], Natl. HQ, 1100 Larkspur Landing, Ste. 340, Larkspur, CA 94939, (800)876-0413

Local Initiatives Support Corp. [17383], 501 7th Ave., New York, NY 10018-5903, (212)455-9800

Local Officials' Admin. Network [★23025]

Local Online Marketing Assn. [2410], 250 Cliff Rd., Southern Pines, NC 28387, (910)695-1280

Localization Indus. Standards Assn. [IO], Romainmotier-Envy, Switzerland

Location Managers Guild of Am. [2292], 8033 Sunset Blvd., Ste. 1017, West Hollywood, CA 90046, (310)967-2007

Reference to "IO" in place of a book number signifies that the association may be found in the 50th edition of International Organizations.

Lock Museum of Am. [21452], 230 Main St., Rte. 6, PO Box 104, Terryville, CT 06786-0104, (860)589-6359

Locks of Love [14085], 234 Southern Blvd., West Palm Beach, FL 33405-2701, (561)833-7332

Locomotive and Carriage Institution [IO], Middlesex, United Kingdom

Log Cabin Fed. [★18529]

Log Cabin Republicans [18529], 1050 Connecticut Ave. NW, Ste. 400, Washington, DC 20036-5339, (202)360-4445

Log Home Builders Assn. of North Am. [922], 14241 NE Woodinville-Duvall Rd., Ste. 345, Woodinville, WA 98072-8564, (360)794-4469

Log House Assn. of North Am. [★922]

Log House Builder's Assn. of North Am. [★922]

Logan Community Resources [11805], 2505 E Jefferson Blvd., South Bend, IN 46615, (574)289-4831

Logical Language Gp. [9941], 2904 Beau Ln., Fairfax, VA 22031, (703)385-0273

Logistics Officer Assn. [2499], PO Box 2264, Arlington, VA 22202, (703)693-8995

Logistics Officer Assn. [2499], PO Box 2264, Arlington, VA 22202, (703)693-8995

Logistics and Transport New Zealand [IO], Auckland, New Zealand

LOGOI [19679], 14540 SW 136 St., Ste. 200, Miami, FL 33186, (305)232-5880

LOGOI [19679], 14540 SW 136 St., Ste. 200, Miami, FL 33186, (305)232-5880

Lohman Gay Art Found; Leslie- [9188]

Lois Intl. [★19243]

Lois Intl. [★19243]

Lois Link Intl. - USA [19243], Lois Widly, Chair, 11155 Meads Ave., Orange, CA 92869

Lois Link Intl. - USA [19243], Lois Widly, Chair, 11155 Meads Ave., Orange, CA 92869

Lollard Soc. [20188], Texas Christian Univ., Dept. of English, Box 297270, Fort Worth, TX 76129

Lollard Soc. [20188], Texas Christian Univ., Dept. of English, Box 297270, Fort Worth, TX 76129

LOMA [1992], 2300 Windy Ridge Pkwy., Ste. 600, Atlanta, GA 30339-8443, (770)951-1770

LOMA [1992], 2300 Windy Ridge Pkwy., Ste. 600, Atlanta, GA 30339-8443, (770)951-1770

London Assn. of Primal Psychotherapists [IO], London, United Kingdom

London Chamber of Commerce and Indus. [IO], London, United Kingdom

London Councils [IO], London, United Kingdom

London Intl. Financial Futures and Options Exchange [IO], London, United Kingdom

London Mathematical Soc. [IO], London, United Kingdom

London and Middlesex Archaeological Soc. [IO], London, United Kingdom

London Natural History Soc. [IO], London, United Kingdom

London Record Soc. [IO], Exeter, United Kingdom

London Region Campaign for Nuclear Disarmament [IO], London, United Kingdom

London Soc. [IO], London, United Kingdom

London Swing Dance Soc. [IO], Middlesex, United Kingdom

London Topographical Soc. [IO], Dorchester, United Kingdom

London Transport Users Comm. [IO], London, United Kingdom

London Underground Railway Soc. [IO], London, United Kingdom

London Vintage Taxi Assn. [IO], Uxbridge, United Kingdom

London Vintage Taxi Assn. - Amer. Sect. [21094], PO Box 445, Windham, NH 03087-0445, (603)893-8919

Londonderry Chamber of Commerce [IO], Londonderry, United Kingdom

Lone Ranger Fan Club [23921], PO Box 1253, Salisbury, MD 21802

Lonergan Philosophical Soc. [10398], Loyola Marymount Univ., Dept. of Philosophy, 1 LMU Dr., Ste. 3600, Los Angeles, CA 90045-2659

Lonergan Philosophical Soc. [10398], Loyola Marymount Univ., Dept. of Philosophy, 1 LMU Dr., Ste. 3600, Los Angeles, CA 90045-2659

Loners on Wheels [22144], 1795 O Kelley Rd. SE, Deming, NM 88030, (575)544-7303

Lonestar Fatherhood Initiative [★18107]

Long Distance Love [★21417]

Long Distance Walkers Assn. [IO], Ulverston, United Kingdom

Long Island Soc. of Anesthetists [★13737]

Long Island Univ. - Southampton Coll. Alumni Assn. [18883], 720 Northern Blvd., Brookville, NY 11548-1300, (516)299-4052

Long Staple Yarn Assn. [★3436]

Long Way Home [11073], 13444 Janwood Ln., Dallas, TX 75234, (936)275-7807

Longhorn Cattle Soc. [IO], Stoneleigh, United Kingdom

Longshore and Warehouse Union; Intl. [23247]

Longshore and Warehouse Union; Intl. [23247]

Longshoremen's Assn; Intl. [23248]

Longwave Club of Am. [20938], 45 Wildflower Rd., Levittown, PA 19057

LonMark Intl. [3372], 550 Meridian Ave., San Jose, CA 95126, (408)938-5266

LonMark Interoperability Assn. [★3372]

Loops for Lupus - Defunct.

Lop Rabbit Club of Am. [4843], 6599 Sergeant Rd., Sodus, NY 14551, (315)576-3448

Lord's Day Alliance of the U.S. [20230], PO Box 941745, Atlanta, GA 31145-0745, (404)693-5530

Lord's Day Observance Soc. [★18437]

Lorrie Morgan Intl. Fan Club [23873], 1625 Broadway, Ste. 500, Nashville, TN 37203, (615)724-1818

Los Algarrobos - Asociacion Civil para el Desarrollo Sustentable [★IO]

Los Algarrobos - Assn. for Sustainable Development [IO], Cordoba, Argentina

Los Amigos [★23654]

Los Angeles Advt. Agencies Assn. [★109]

Los Angeles Copyright Soc. [5577], Michael Perlstein, Sec., 1875 Century Park E, Ste. 1450, Los Angeles, CA 90067

Los Angeles Found. of Otology [★16686]

Los Angeles Kings Booster Club [23905], 555 N Nash St., El Segundo, CA 90245

Los Californianos [20380], PO Box 600522, San Diego, CA 92160-0522

Los Ninos [12522], 717 3rd Ave., Chula Vista, CA 91910, (619)426-9110

Loss Adjusters Assn. of Japan [IO], Tokyo, Japan

Loss Executives Assn. [1993], PO Box 37, Tenafly, NJ 07670, (201)569-3346

Lost in Space Fannish Alliance [23922], PO Box 510442, St. Louis, MO 63151-0442, (314)416-4071

Lotteries

North Amer. Assn. of State and Provincial Lotteries [5776]

North Amer. Assn. of State and Provincial Lotteries [5776]

Lotteries Coun. [IO], Shrewsbury, United Kingdom

Lottery Collectors Soc. [★21343]

Lotus [★21095]

Lotus Lantern Intl. Buddhist Center [IO], Seoul, Republic of Korea

Lotus, Ltd. [21095], PO Box L, College Park, MD 20741, (301)982-4054

Lotus Outreach [13162], PO Box 620222, San Diego, CA 92162-0222, (760)290-7190

Lou Christie Intl. Fan Club [23874], PO Box 260172, St. Louis, MO 63126

Louis Finkelstein Inst. for Religious and Social Stud. [19680], Jewish Theological Seminary, 3080 Broadway, New York, NY 10027, (212)678-8000

Louis and Harold Price Found. [13192], 1371 Hecla Dr., Ste. B-1, Louisville, CO 80027-2318, (303)665-9201

Louisa May Alcott Memorial Assn. [9393], PO Box 343, Concord, MA 01742-0343, (978)369-4118

Louise Brooks Soc. [23776], 1518 Church St., San Francisco, CA 94131-2018

Louise Brooks Soc. [23776], 1518 Church St., San Francisco, CA 94131-2018

Louisiana Sugar Planters Assn., Amer. Cane Growers Assn. and [★4933]

Love in Action [19635], PO Box 343418, Bartlett, TN 38184, (901)751-2468

The Love Alliance [17365], PO Box 111431, Palm Bay, FL 32911-1431, (321)989-0349

Love and Hope Ministries Intl. [12399], 1 East Ave., Coram, NY 11727, (631)828-4062

Love Humanity [IO], Nargol, India

Love on a Leash - The Found. for Pet Provided Therapy [16861], PO Box 4115, Oceanside, CA 92052-4115, (760)740-2326

Love Our Children USA [11343], 220 E 57th St., 9th Fl., Ste. G, New York, NY 10022, (212)629-2099

Love Proj. [★12226]

Love Token Soc. [21980], PO Box 2351, Denham Springs, LA 70727, (225)664-0718

Love Yourself Stop the Violence - Address unknown since 2011.

Love146 [11344], PO Box 8266, New Haven, CT 06530, (203)772-4420

Love146 [11344], PO Box 8266, New Haven, CT 06530, (203)772-4420

Loved Ones and Drivers Support [13342], PO Box 544, Plover, WI 54467-0544

LOVEfords [21096], 2484 W Genesee Tpke., Camillus, NY 13031-9610, (315)672-5548

Loving Hands for the Needy [11345], PO Box 243456, Boynton Beach, FL 33424, (561)283-3599

Loving More [13107], PO Box 1658, Loveland, CO 80539, (303)543-7540

LOVW [★21853]

Low Impact Living Initiative [IO], Winslow, United Kingdom

Low Income Housing Info. Ser. [★12193]

Low Power Radio Assn. [IO], Zaventem, Belgium

Lowe Syndrome Assn. [14608], PO Box 864346, Plano, TX 75086-4346, (972)733-1338

Lowell Celebrates Kerouac! [9394], PO Box 1111, Lowell, MA 01853-1111, (603)883-3141

Loyal Christian Benefit Assn. [19051], PO Box 13005, Erie, PA 16514-1305, (814)453-4331

Loyal Escorts of the Green Garter [20679], Charles Ables, Sec.-Treas., 4940 Park Dr., Carlsbad, CA 92008

Loyola Extension Services [IO], Trivandrum, India

LPG Australia [IO], Canberra, Australia

LS ESSI, Inc. [★14441]

LS ESSI, Inc. [★14441]

LSM Natl. Assn. [★20734]

LTD Shippers Assn. [3486], 1230 Pottstown Pike, Ste. 6, Glenmoore, PA 19343, (610)458-3636

LTD Shippers Assn. [3486], 1230 Pottstown Pike, Ste. 6, Glenmoore, PA 19343, (610)458-3636

LTN - Defunct.

Lubavitch Movement [★19855]

Lubavitch Youth Org. [19880], 770 Eastern Pkwy., Brooklyn, NY 11213-3409, (718)953-1000

Lubricants

Deep Draft Lubricant Assn. [2225]

Intl. Coun. for Machinery Lubrication [7034]

Intl. Coun. for Machinery Lubrication [7034]

Lucio Fan Club [23875], 315 Cypress Glen Dr., Mount Juliet, TN 37122-3083

Lucis Trust [17803], 120 Wall St., 24th Fl., New York, NY 10005, (212)292-0707

Lucis Trust [17803], 120 Wall St., 24th Fl., New York, NY 10005, (212)292-0707

Lucy Stone League [17654], Syracuse Univ., 401 Hall of Languages, Syracuse, NY 13224

Lucy Stone League [17654], Syracuse Univ., 401 Hall of Languages, Syracuse, NY 13224

Ludwick Family Found. [12053], PO Box 1796, Glendora, CA 91740, (626)852-0092

Ludwig Boltzman Gesellschaft - Osterreichische Vereinigung zur Forderung der Wissenschaftlichen Forschung [★IO]

Ludwig Boltzmann Assn. - Austrian Soc. for the Promotion of Sci. Res. [IO], Vienna, Austria

Lufftfororenings- och klimatsekretariatet [★IO]

Luge

U.S. Luge Assn. [22719]

Luggage

Travel Goods Assn. [2226]

Luis Palau Assn. [19760], PO Box 50, Portland, OR 97207, (503)614-1500

Luis Palau Assn. [19760], PO Box 50, Portland, OR 97207, (503)614-1500

Luis Palau Evangelistic Assn. [★19760]

A star before a book entry number signifies that the name is not listed separately, but is mentioned within the entry.

Luis Palau Evangelistic Assn. [★19760]
Luis Palau Evangelistic Team [★19760]
Luis Palau Evangelistic Team [★19760]
LULAC Natl. Educational Ser. Centers [8037], 133 19th St. NW, Ste. 1000, Washington, DC 20036, (202)835-9646
Lumber and Building Materials Assn. of Ontario [IO], Mississauga, ON, Canada
Lumen Vitae - Centre Intl. d'Etudes de la Formation Religieuse [★IO]
Lumunos [19660], PO Box 307, Marlborough, NH 03455-0307, (603)876-4121
Lunds Botaniska Forening [★IO]
Lung Assn; Amer. [16604]
Lung Assn. of Zurich [IO], Zurich, Switzerland
Lung Cancer Alliance [13938], PO Box 630972, Baltimore, MD 21263-0972, (202)463-2080
Lungenliga Zurich [★IO]
l'Union Catholique Internationale de la Presse [★IO]
Luontaistuotealan Tukkukauppiaiden Liitto ry [★IO]
Luovan Saveltaiteen Edistamissaatio [★IO]
Lupus Assn. of NSW [IO], North Ryde, Australia
Lupus Assn. Singapore [IO], Singapore, Singapore
Lupus Erythematosus
Alliance for Lupus Res. [15251]
Alliance for Lupus Res. [15251]
Lupus Found. of Am. [15252]
Lupus Found. of Am. [15252], 2000 L St. NW, Ste. 410, Washington, DC 20036-4952, (202)349-1155
Luscombe Assn. [★20906]
Luscombe Endowment [20906], 2487 S Gilbert Rd., Ste. 106, PMB 113, Gilbert, AZ 85295, (480)650-0883
Lusitano Breed Soc. of Great Britain [IO], Pontyclun, United Kingdom
Luso-American Educ. Found. [10470], PO Box 2967, Dublin, CA 94568, (925)828-3883
Luso-American Fraternal Fed. [19052], 7080 Donlon Way, Ste. 200, Dublin, CA 94568, (925)828-4884
Luso-American Fraternal Fed. Scholarship Comm. [★10470]
Luso-American Life Insurance Soc. [19053], 7080 Donlon Way, Ste. 200, Dublin, CA 94568, (925)828-4884
Lute Soc. [IO], Guildford, United Kingdom
Lute Soc. of Am. [10238], Garald Farnham, Treas., 255 W 98th St., No. 5C, New York, NY 10025-7282
Lutheran
African Amer. Lutheran Assn. [19920]
Amer. Lutheran Publicity Bur. [19921]
Assn. of Lutheran Secondary Schools [8542]
Concordia Deaconess Conf. [19922]
Concordia Historical Inst. [19923]
Disability Ministries [19924]
Evangelical Lutheran Educ. Assn. [8543]
Intl. Lutheran Laymen's League [19925]
Intl. Lutheran Laymen's League [19925]
Lutheran Deaconess Assn. [19926]
Lutheran Deaconess Conf. [19927]
Lutheran Deaf Mission [19928]
Lutheran Deaf Mission Soc. [19928]
Lutheran Educ. Assn. [8544]
Lutheran Educ. Assn. [8544]
Lutheran Educational Conf. of North Am. [8545]
Lutheran Girl Pioneers [19929]
Lutheran Historical Conf. [19930]
Lutheran Human Relations Assn. [19931]
Lutheran Men in Mission [19932]
Lutheran Services in Am. [19933]
Lutheran Student Movement - U.S.A. [19934]
Lutheran Volunteer Corps [19935]
Lutheran Women's Missionary League [19936]
Lutheran World Relief [19937]
Lutheran World Relief [19937]
Natl. Assn. of Lutheran Interim Pastors [19938]
Natl. Lutheran Outdoors Ministry Assn. [19939]
Seafarers and Intl. House [19940]
Thrivent Financial for Lutherans [19941]
Wheat Ridge Ministries [19942]
WordAlone Ministries [19943]
World Mission Prayer League [19944]
World Mission Prayer League [19944]
Youth Ministry [19945]
Lutheran Benevolent Assn. - Defunct.

Lutheran Bible Translators [19351], PO Box 2050, 303 N Lake St., Aurora, IL 60507-2050, (630)897-0660
Lutheran Bible Translators of Canada [IO], Kitchener, ON, Canada
Lutheran Braille Evangelism Assn. [17097], 1740 Eugene St., White Bear Lake, MN 55110-3312, (651)426-0469
Lutheran Braille Evangelism Assn. [17097], 1740 Eugene St., White Bear Lake, MN 55110-3312, (651)426-0469
Lutheran Braille Workers [17098], PO Box 5000, Yucaipa, CA 92399, (909)795-8977
Lutheran Braille Workers [17098], PO Box 5000, Yucaipa, CA 92399, (909)795-8977
Lutheran Brotherhood Found. [★19941]
Lutheran Church in Am. [★19922]
Lutheran Church Lib. Assn. [★9998]
Lutheran Coun. in the U.S.A. [★19668]
Lutheran Deaconess Assn. [19926], 1304 LaPorte Ave., Valparaiso, IN 46383, (219)464-6925
Lutheran Deaconess Conf. [19927], 1304 LaPorte Ave., Valparaiso, IN 46383, (219)464-6925
Lutheran Deaf Mission [19928], 9907 Sappington Rd., St. Louis, MO 63128, (989)400-9404
Lutheran Deaf Mission Soc. [19928], 9907 Sappington Rd., St. Louis, MO 63128, (989)400-9404
Lutheran Educ. Assn. [8544], 7400 Augusta St., River Forest, IL 60305, (708)209-3343
Lutheran Educ. Assn. [8544], 7400 Augusta St., River Forest, IL 60305, (708)209-3343
Lutheran Educational Conf. of North Am. [8545], 2601 S Minnesota Ave., No. 105, Sioux Falls, SD 57105, (605)271-9894
Lutheran Fraternities of Am. - Address unknown since 2010.
Lutheran Girl Pioneers [19929], 1611 Caledonia St., La Crosse, WI 54603, (608)781-5232
Lutheran Historical Conf. [19930], Marvin A. Huggins, Membership Sec., 5732 White Pine Dr., St. Louis, MO 63129-2936, (314)505-7921
Lutheran Human Relations Assn. [19931], 1821 N 16th St., Milwaukee, WI 53205, (414)536-0585
Lutheran Human Relations Assn. of Am. [★19931]
Lutheran Immigration and Refugee Ser. [12786], 700 Light St., Baltimore, MD 21230, (410)230-2700
Lutheran Immigration and Refugee Ser. [12786], 700 Light St., Baltimore, MD 21230, (410)230-2700
Lutheran Immigration Ser. [★12786]
Lutheran Immigration Ser. [★12786]
Lutheran Laymen's League [★19925]
Lutheran Laymen's League [★19925]
Lutheran Laymen's League of Canada [IO], Kitchener, ON, Canada
Lutheran Men in Mission [19932], Evangelical Lutheran Church in Am., 8765 W Higgins Rd., Chicago, IL 60631, (800)638-3522
Lutheran Outdoors Ministry Assn. [★19939]
Lutheran Peace Fellowship [18263], 1710 11th Ave., Seattle, WA 98122-2420, (206)720-0313
Lutheran Seaman's Center [★19940]
Lutheran Services in Am. [19933], 700 Light St., Baltimore, MD 21230-3850, (410)230-2702
Lutheran Soc. for Worship, Music and the Arts [★19659]
Lutheran Soc. for Worship, Music and the Arts [★19659]
Lutheran Student Assn. of Am. [★19934]
Lutheran Student Movement - U.S.A. [19934], 8765 W Higgins Rd., Chicago, IL 60631-4194, (773)380-2852
Lutheran Volunteer Corps [19935], 1226 Vermont Ave. NW, Washington, DC 20005, (202)387-3222
Lutheran Women's Missionary League [19936], PO Box 411993, St. Louis, MO 63141-1993, (800)252-5965
Lutheran World Fed. [IO], Geneva, Switzerland
Lutheran World Fed. - U.S.A. Natl. Comm. - Defunct.
Lutheran World Relief [19937], 700 Light St., Baltimore, MD 21230, (410)230-2800
Lutheran World Relief [19937], 700 Light St., Baltimore, MD 21230, (410)230-2800
Lutheran World Ser. - India [IO], Calcutta, India
Lutheran Youth Fellowship [★19945]
Lutherans Concerned for Gay People [★19796]

Lutherans Concerned/North Am. [19796], PO Box 4707, St. Paul, MN 55104-0707, (651)665-0861
Lutherans For Life [12938], 1120 S G Ave., Nevada, IA 50201-2774, (515)382-2077
Lutherans for Life - Australia [IO], Adelaide, Australia
Luxembourg
Luxembourg Amer. Chamber of Commerce [23426]
Luxembourg Amateur Dance Fed. [IO], Hauctharage, Luxembourg
Luxembourg Amer. Chamber of Commerce [23426], 17 Beekman Pl., New York, NY 10022, (212)888-6701
Luxembourg Badminton Fed. [IO], Luxembourg, Luxembourg
Luxembourg Bankers' Assn. [IO], Luxembourg, Luxembourg
Luxembourg Baseball Fed. [IO], Dudelange, Luxembourg
Luxembourg Confed. of Christian Trade Unions [IO], Luxembourg, Luxembourg
Luxembourg Cricket Fed. [IO], Luxembourg, Luxembourg
Luxembourg Dietetic Assn. [IO], Walferdange, Luxembourg
Luxembourg Fed. of Hospitals [IO], Bertrange, Luxembourg
Luxembourg Fed. of Hotels, Restaurants and Coffee Shops [IO], Luxembourg, Luxembourg
Luxembourg Naturalist Soc. [IO], Luxembourg, Luxembourg
Luxembourg-Nicaragua Solidarity Assn. [IO], Luxembourg, Luxembourg
Luxembourg Org. for Reproduction Rights [IO], Luxembourg, Luxembourg
Luxembourg Socialist Workers' Party [IO], Luxembourg, Luxembourg
Luxembourg Soc. for Contemporary Music [IO], Luxembourg, Luxembourg
Luxembourg Soc. of Gastroenterology and Digestive Endoscopy [IO], Luxembourg, Luxembourg
Luxembourg Water Ski Fed. [IO], Strassen, Luxembourg
Luxembourg Youth Hostels Assn. [IO], Luxembourg, Luxembourg
Luxemburger Gesellschaft fur Neue Musik [★IO]
Luz Social Services [13263], 2797 N Introspect Dr., Tucson, AZ 85745, (520)882-6216
Lydia - A Women's Cooperative Interchange - Defunct.
Lyman Boat Owners Assn. [22368], PO Box 40052, Cleveland, OH 44140, (440)954-4005
Lyme Borreliosis Found. [★14398]
Lyme Disease Assn. [14397], PO Box 1438, Jackson, NJ 08527, (888)366-6611
Lyme Disease Found. [14398], PO Box 332, Tolland, CT 06084-0332, (860)870-0070
Lyme Disease Found; Amer. [14371]
Lymphatic Res. Found. [15254], 40 Garvies Point Rd., Glen Cove, NY 11542, (516)625-9675
Lymphedema Network; Natl. [15255]
Lymphology
Intl. Soc. of Lymphology [15253]
Intl. Soc. of Lymphology [15253]
Lymphatic Res. Found. [15254]
Natl. Lymphedema Network [15255]
North Amer. Vodder Assn. of Lymphatic Therapy [15256]
North Amer. Vodder Assn. of Lymphatic Therapy [15256]
Patients Against Lymphoma [15257]
Lymphoma Assn. [IO], Aylesbury, United Kingdom
Lymphoma Res. Found. [13939], 115 Broadway, Ste. 1301, New York, NY 10006, (212)349-2910
Lymphoma Res. Found. of Am. [★13939]
Lymphoma Soc; Leukemia and [13936]
Lymphovenous Canada [IO], Toronto, ON, Canada
Lynch Syndrome Intl. [14609], PO Box 5456, Vacaville, CA 95688, (707)689-5089
Lyre Assn. of North Am. [21957], Samantha Embrey, Treas., PO Box 96, Piney River, VA 22964, (434)277-8180
Lyre Assn. of North America-Esther Centers [★21957]
Lysosomal Diseases New Zealand [IO], Lower Hutt, New Zealand

Reference to "IO" in place of a book number signifies that the association may be found in the 50th edition of International Organizations.

M

Maan ystavat [★IO]

Ma'an Development Center [IO], Jerusalem, Israel

MAAP Services for Autism and Asperger Syndrome [15607], PO Box 524, Crown Point, IN 46308, (219)662-1311

Maasai Assn. [10824], PO Box 868, Medina, WA 98039

MAAWS for Global Welfare [12347], 64-17 Broadway, 2nd Fl., Woodside, NY 11377, (718)478-1045

Macao Chamber of Commerce [IO], Macau, Macao

Macao Fed. of Intl. Chongguang Qigong Assn. [IO], Hong Kong, People's Republic of China

Macao Trademark Assn. [IO], Macau, Macao

Macao Voices [IO], Macau, Macao

Macao Youth Symphony Orchestra [IO], Macau, Macao

Macau Air Freight Forwarding Logistics Assn. [IO], Macau, Macao

Macau Band Directors Assn. [IO], Macau, Macao

Macau Child Development Assn. [IO], Taipa, Macao

Macau Convention and Exhibition Assn. [IO], Macau, Macao

Macau DanceSport Fed. [IO], Macau, Macao

Macau Gaming Res. Assn. [IO], Macau, Macao

Macau Human Resources Mgt. Assn. [IO], Macau, Macao

Macau Importers and Exporters Assn. [IO], Macau, Macao

Macau Intl. Courier Assn. [IO], Macau, Macao

Macau-Italy Assn. [IO], Macau, Macao

Macau Jockey Club [IO], Taipa, Macao

Macau Junior Chamber China [IO], Macau, Macao

Macau MBA Assn. [IO], Macau, Macao

Macau Professional Golfers' Assn. [IO], Macau, Macao

Macau SAR Kendo Associations Union [IO], Macau, Macao

Macau Soc. of Registered Accountants [IO], Macau, Macao

Macau Sports Medicine Assn. [IO], Macau, Macao

Macau Tourist Guide Assn. [IO], Macau, Macao

Macau Weightlifting Assn. [IO], Macau, Macao

Macbride Museum Soc. [IO], Whitehorse, YT, Canada

Maccabi USA/Sports for Israel [22985], 1926 Arch St., No. 4R, Philadelphia, PA 19103, (215)561-6900

Macclesfield Chamber of Commerce and Enterprise [IO], Macclesfield, United Kingdom

Macedonia Taekwondo Fed. [IO], Skopje, Macedonia

Macedonian

Macedonian Amer. Friendship Assn. [19118]
Macedonian Arts Coun. [10055]
Macedonian Arts Coun. [10055]
Macedonian Outreach [19946]
Macedonian Outreach [19946]
Macedonian Patriotic Org. of U.S. and Canada [19119]
Macedonian Patriotic Org. of U.S. and Canada [19119]

Macedonian Amer. Friendship Assn. [19118], 57 Jefferson Ave., Columbus, OH 43215, (614)668-9656

Macedonian Arts Coun. [10055], 380 Rector Pl., Ste. 21E, New York, NY 10280, (212)799-0009

Macedonian Arts Coun. [10055], 380 Rector Pl., Ste. 21E, New York, NY 10280, (212)799-0009

Macedonian Assn. Against Rheumatism [IO], Skopje, Macedonia

Macedonian Assn. of Info. Tech. [IO], Skopje, Macedonia

Macedonian Dance Assn. [IO], Skopje, Macedonia

Macedonian Dermatovenerologic Soc. [IO], Skopje, Macedonia

Macedonian Geotechnical Soc. [IO], Skopje, Macedonia

Macedonian Medical Assn. [IO], Skopje, Macedonia

Macedonian Olympic Comm. [IO], Skopje, Macedonia

Macedonian Outreach [19946], PO Box 398, Danville, CA 94526-0398, (925)820-4107

Macedonian Outreach [19946], PO Box 398, Danville, CA 94526-0398, (925)820-4107

Macedonian Patriotic Org. of U.S. and Canada [19119], 124 W Wayne St., Fort Wayne, IN 46802, (260)422-5900

Macedonian Patriotic Org. of U.S. and Canada [19119], 124 W Wayne St., Fort Wayne, IN 46802, (260)422-5900

Macedonian School Sport Fed. [IO], Skopje, Macedonia

Macedonian Tennis Fed. [IO], Skopje, Macedonia

Machine Cancel Soc. [22049], 3097 Frobisher Ave., Dublin, OH 43017-1652

Machine Knife Assn. [1838], 30200 Detroit Rd., Cleveland, OH 44145-1967, (440)899-0010

Machine Knife Mfrs. Assn. [★1838]

Machinery

Antique Caterpillar Machinery Owners Club [21878]
Antique Small Engine Collectors Club [21702]
Indus. Auctioneers Assn. [269]
Intl. Coun. for Machinery Lubrication [7034]
Intl. Union of Electronic, Elecl., Salaried, Machine, and Furniture Workers [23184]
Machinists Non-Partisan Political League [23220]

Machinery and Allied Products Inst. [★1843]

Machinery Dealers Natl. Assn. [1839], 315 S Patrick St., Alexandria, VA 22314, (703)836-9300

Machinery Dealers Natl. Assn. [1839], 315 S Patrick St., Alexandria, VA 22314, (703)836-9300

Machinery Info. Mgt. Open Systems Alliance [2338], 204 Marina Dr., Ste. 100, Tuscaloosa, AL 35406, (949)625-8616

Machinists Non-Partisan Political League [23220], 9000 Machinists Pl., Upper Marlboro, MD 20772-2687, (301)967-4500

Machinists Vise Assn. [★1650]

Machne Israel [12411], 770 Eastern Pkwy., Brooklyn, NY 11213, (718)774-4000

Mackenzie Inst. [IO], Toronto, ON, Canada

Maclellan Found. [20189], 820 Broad St., Ste. 300, Chattanooga, TN 37402, (423)755-1366

Maclellan Found. [20189], 820 Broad St., Ste. 300, Chattanooga, TN 37402, (423)755-1366

Macra Na Feirme [IO], Dublin, Ireland

Macrocosm USA [2946], PO Box 185, Cambria, CA 93428, (805)927-2515

MacThomas North Am. [20555], PO Box 16549, Dublin, GA 31040

Macular Degeneration Found. [17099], PO Box 531313, Henderson, NV 89053, (888)633-3937

Macular Disease Soc. [IO], Andover, United Kingdom

Macular Diseases; Assn. for [15945]

Madagascar Wildlife Conservation [IO], Antananarivo, Madagascar

Madison Proj. [5957], PO Box 15179, Washington, DC 20003

The Madison Proj. [8564], Graduate School of Educ., James Madison Univ., 800 S Main St., Harrisonburg, VA 22807

Madonna House Apostolate [IO], Combermere, ON, Canada

MADRE [12465], 121 W 27th St., Ste. 301, New York, NY 10001, (212)627-0444

Madrid Chamber of Commerce and Indus. [IO], Madrid, Spain

Magazine Printers Sect. - Defunct.

Magazine Publishers of Am. [2947], 810 7th Ave., 24th Fl., New York, NY 10019, (212)872-3700

Magazine Publishers Assn. [★2947]

Magazine Publishers' Assn. - Brazil [IO], Sao Paulo, Brazil

Magazine Publishers' Assn. of New Zealand [IO], Auckland, New Zealand

Magazine Publishers of Australia [IO], Sydney, Australia

Magazines

Argentine Magazine Publishers' Assn. [1594]
The Christian Sci. Publishing Soc. [2927]
Football Writers Assn. of Am. [22588]
Golf Writers Assn. of Am. [22610]
United Amateur Press Assn. of Am. [22107]

Magazines Canada [IO], Toronto, ON, Canada

Magazines Ireland [IO], Dublin, Ireland

Magic

Intl. Brotherhood of Magicians [21879]

Intl. Brotherhood of Magicians [21879]
Magicians Without Borders [21880]
Magicians Without Borders [21880]
Soc. of Amer. Magicians [21881]

Magic Bus, India [IO], Mumbai, India

Magic Circle [IO], London, United Kingdom

MAGIC Found. [14086], 6645 W North Ave., Oak Park, IL 60302, (708)383-0808

MAGIC Found. for Children's Growth [★14086]

Magic Johnson Found. [13193], 9100 Wilshire Blvd., Ste. 700 E, Beverly Hills, CA 90212, (310)246-4400

Magic Lantern Soc. of the U.S. and Canada [20961], Ron Easterday, Sec.-Treas., 1380 Lena Pl. NE, Poulsbo, WA 98370-6307, (360)394-8223

The Magic Penny, Inc. [IO], Freetown, Sierra Leone

Magic Youth Intl. - Address unknown since 2010.

Magicians Without Borders [21880], 100 Geary Rd., Lincoln, VT 05443, (802)453-5425

Magicians Without Borders [21880], 100 Geary Rd., Lincoln, VT 05443, (802)453-5425

Magis Americas [12968], U.S.A. Jesuit Conf., 1016 16th NW, Ste. 400, Washington, DC 20036, (202)462-0400

Magistrates' Assn. of England and Wales [IO], London, United Kingdom

Magnesium Assn. [★2474]

Magnesium Assn. [★2474]

Magnetic Materials Producers Assn. [★1652]

Magnetic Materials Producers Assn. [★1652]

Magnetic Resonance Managers Soc. [16536], Lori Nicolay, Sec., St. Luke's Imaging Center, 4321 Washington St., Ste. 1400, Kansas City, MO 64111, (816)561-5858

Magnetic Resonance Soc; Clinical [14155]

Magnetic Resonance; Soc. of Computed Body Tomography and [16541]

Magnetic Resonance Technologists; Sect. for [15384]

Magnificent 13 [★11681]

Magnificent 13 [★11681]

The Magnolia Soc. [★6362]

Magnolia Soc. Intl. [6362], 3000 Henneberry Rd., Jamesville, NY 13078, (315)677-7813

Magnum Memorabilia [23923], 438 Leroy St., Ferndale, MI 48220

Magnus Hirschfeld Center for Human Rights [17849], Crosswicks House, PO Box 1974, Bloomfield, NJ 07003-1974, (862)823-1767

Magnus Hirschfeld Center for Human Rights [17849], Crosswicks House, PO Box 1974, Bloomfield, NJ 07003-1974, (862)823-1767

Magyar Bankszovetseg [★IO]

Magyar Biofizikai Tarsasag [★IO]

Magyar Csalad - es Novedelmi Tudomanyos Tarsasag [★IO]

Magyar Dermatologiai Tarsulat [★IO]

Magyar Ensz Tarsasag [★IO]

Magyar Fallabda (Squash) Szovetseg [★IO]

Magyar Feltalalok Egyesuletenek [★IO]

Magyar Floorball Szovetseg [★IO]

Magyar Franchise Szovetseg [★IO]

Magyar Geofizikusok Egyesulete [★IO]

Magyar Gepjarmuipari Szovetseg [★IO]

Magyar Hanglemezkiadok Szovetsege [★IO]

Magyar Hidrologiai Tarsasag [★IO]

Magyar Ingatlanszovetseg [★IO]

Magyar Kockazati es Magantoke Egyesulet [★IO]

Magyar Konyvtarosok Egyesulete [★IO]

Magyar Kozgazdasagi Tarsasag [★IO]

Magyar Marketing Szovetseg [★IO]

Magyar Mezogazdasag [★IO]

Magyar Onteszeti Szovetseg [★IO]

Magyar Orszagos Baseball es Softball Szovetseg [★IO]

Magyar Orvostudomanyi Tarsasagok es Egyesuletek Szovetsege [★IO]

Magyar Paralimpiai Bizottsg [★IO]

Magyar Pszichologiai Tarsasag [★IO]

Magyar Reklamszovetseg [★IO]

Magyar Reprografiai Szovetseg [★IO]

Magyar Repulo Szovetseg [★IO]

Magyar Szakszervezetek Orszagos Szovettsege [★IO]

Magyar Szallodaszovetseg [★IO]

A star before a book entry number signifies that the name is not listed separately, but is mentioned within the entry.

Magyar Taekwon-Do Szovetseg [★IO]
Magyar Tanacsado Mernokok es Epiteszek Szovetsege [★IO]
Magyar TancSport Szakszovetseg [★IO]
Magyar Tenisz Szovetseg [IO], Budapest, Hungary
Magyar Termeszetvedok Szovetsege [★IO]
Magyar Termeszetvedok Szovetsege [★IO]
Magyar Tollaslabda Szovetseg [★IO]
Magyar Tudomanyos Akademia Vilaggazdasagi Kutatointezet [★IO]
Magyar Vamugyi Szovetseg [★IO]
Magyar Vas- Es Acelipari Egyesules [★IO]
Magyar Vegyipari Szovetseg [★IO]
Magyar Versenyjogi Egyesulet [★IO]
Magyar Victorlas Szovetseg [★IO]
Magyar Voroskereszt [IO], Budapest, Hungary
Magyarhoni Foldtani Tarsulat [★IO]
Magyarorszag Nemzetkozi Csereprogram Alapitvany [★IO]
Magyarorszagi Fajdalom Tarsasag [★IO]
Magyarorszagi Kiallitas-es Vasarszervezok Szovetsege [★IO]
Mai Wah Soc. [9340], PO Box 404, Butte, MT 59703, (406)723-3231
Mai Wah Soc. [9340], PO Box 404, Butte, MT 59703, (406)723-3231
Maids of Athena [19015], AHEPA HQ, 1909 Q St. NW, Ste. 500, Washington, DC 20009, (202)232-6300
Maids of Athens [★19015]
Mail
41pounds.org [4232]
Air Mail Pioneers [20879]
Airforwarders Assn. [2227]
Alliance of Nonprofit Mailers [2228]
Amer. Philatelic Res. Lib. [22010]
Amer. Philatelic Soc. Writers Unit [22012]
Amer. Topical Assn. [22016]
Assoc. Collectors of El Salvador [22020]
Assoc. Mail and Parcel Centers [2229]
Assn. of Alternate Postal Systems [2230]
Assn. of Mailing, Shipping and Off. Automation Specialists [2231]
Assn. for Postal Commerce [2232]
Brazil Philatelic Assn. [22022]
Citizens' Stamp Advisory Comm. [22029]
Collectors of Religion on Stamps [22032]
Confederate Stamp Alliance [22033]
Cover Collectors Circuit Club [22034]
EcoLogical Mail Coalition [4698]
Errors, Freaks and Oddities Collectors' Club [22037]
First Issues Collectors Club [22038]
France and Colonies Philatelic Soc. [22039]
Intl. Fed. of Amer. Homing Pigeon Fanciers [22097]
Intl. Soc. of Worldwide Stamp Collectors [22046]
Jack Knight Air Mail Soc. [22047]
Korea Stamp Soc. [22048]
Mail Systems Mgt. Assn. [2233]
Mailers Coun. [2234]
Mailer's Postmark Permit Club [22050]
Meter Stamp Soc. [22053]
Mexico Elmhurst Philatelic Soc. Intl. [22055]
Natl. Assn. of Presort Mailers [2235]
Natl. Star Route Mail Contractors Assn. [2236]
Parcel Shippers Assn. [2237]
Red Tag News Publications Assn. [2238]
Rossica Soc. of Russian Philately [22068]
SailMail Assn. [6679]
Ships on Stamps Unit [22074]
Soc. of Australasian Specialists/Oceania [22075]
Soc. for Thai Philately [22079]
Space Topic Stud. Unit [22080]
Wreck and Crash Mail Soc. [22093]
Mail Advt. Ser. Assn. Intl. [★95]
Mail Order Traders' Assn. [IO], London, United Kingdom
Mail Systems Mgt. Assn. [2233], PO Box 1145, North Riverside, IL 60546-0545, (708)442-8589
Mail Users' Assn. [IO], Emsworth, United Kingdom
Mailers Coun. [2234], Jim O'Brien, 2001 Jefferson Davis Hwy., Ste. 1004, Arlington, VA 22202-3617, (212)522-3036
Mailer's Postmark Permit Club [22050], Scott A. Shaulis, Pres., 3955 Hickory Hill Rd., Murrysville, PA 15668

Mailing and Fulfillment Ser. Assn. [95], 1421 Prince St., Ste. 410, Alexandria, VA 22314-2806, (703)836-9200
Mailorder Gardening Assn. [★3102]
Main St. Proj. [★17393]
Maine-Anjou Soc. [★3887]
Maine Folklife Center [9622], 5773 S Stevens Hall, Rm. 112B, Orono, ME 04469-5773, (207)581-1891
Maine Lobstermen's Assn. [3183], 21 Western Ave., Ste. 1, Kennebunk, ME 04043, (207)967-4555
Maine Sardine Coun. - Defunct.
Maine Sardine Packers Assn. - Defunct.
Mainland Miniature Horse Club [IO], Kaiapoi, New Zealand
Mainostajien Liitto [★IO]
Mainstream Media Proj. [18503], 854 9th St., Ste. B, Arcata, CA 95521, (707)826-9111
Mainstream Media Proj. [18503], 854 9th St., Ste. B, Arcata, CA 95521, (707)826-9111
Mainstream Republicans of Washington [18530], PO Box 15144, Tumwater, WA 98511
Maintenance
Amer. Homeowners Assn. [2239]
Assn. of Residential Cleaning Services Intl. [2240]
Assn. of United Window Cleaners [2241]
Building Ser. Contractors Assn. Intl. [2242]
Building Ser. Contractors Assn. Intl. [2242]
Chimney Safety Inst. of Am. [2243]
Cleaning Equip. Trade Assn. [2244]
Cleaning Equip. Trade Assn. [2244]
Cleaning Mgt. Inst. [2245]
Environmental Mgt. Assn. [2246]
Healthcare Laundry Accreditation Coun. [2192]
Intl. Assn. for Bridge Maintenance and Safety [6369]
Intl. Executive Housekeepers Assn. [2247]
Intl. Executive Housekeepers Assn. [2247]
Intl. Janitorial Cleaning Services Assn. [2248]
Intl. Maintenance Inst. [2249]
Intl. Maintenance Inst. [2249]
Intl. Sanitary Supply Assn. [2250]
Intl. Sanitary Supply Assn. [2250]
Intl. Soc. of Facilities Executives [2251]
Intl. Window Cleaning Assn. [2252]
Intl. Window Cleaning Assn. [2252]
Master Window Cleaners of Am. [2253]
Natl. Air Duct Cleaners Assn. [2254]
Natl. Chimney Sweep Guild [2255]
North Amer. Power Sweeping Assn. [2256]
Power Washers of North Am. [2257]
Power Washers of North Am. [2257]
Restoration Indus. Assn. [2258]
Sanitary Supply Wholesaling Assn. [2259]
Soc. of Cleaning and Restoration Technicians [2260]
Soc. for Maintenance and Reliability Professionals [2261]
United Assn. of Mobile Contract Cleaners [2262]
The Maintenance Coun. of the Amer. Trucking Associations [★3505]
Maitri [13465], 234 E Gish Rd., Ste. 200, San Jose, CA 95112, (408)436-8393
Maize Assn. of Australia [IO], Finley, Australia
Majlis Belia Malaysia [★IO]
Majlis Kanser Nasional [★IO]
Majlis Olimpik Malaysia [★IO]
Majlis Wanita Negara Brunei Darussalam [★IO]
Majolica Intl. Soc. [21265], PMB 103, 1275 1st Ave., New York, NY 10021
Majolica Intl. Soc. [21265], PMB 103, 1275 1st Ave., New York, NY 10021
Major Aspects of Growth in Children Found. [★14086]
Major Energy Users Coun. [IO], London, United Kingdom
Major League Baseball [22275], 75 9th Ave., 5th Fl., New York, NY 10011, (512)434-1542
Major League Baseball Players Alumni Assn. [22276], 1631 Mesa Ave., Ste. D, Colorado Springs, CO 80906-2956, (719)477-1870
Major League Baseball Players Assn. [23156], 12 E 49th St., 24th Fl., New York, NY 10017-8207, (212)826-0808
Major League Umpires Assn. - Defunct.
Major Orchestra Librarians' Assn. [9994], 1530 Locust St., Philadelphia, PA 19102

Makassed Found. of Am.
Makassed Found. of Am. - Address unknown since 2011.
Makassed Philanthropic Islamic Assn. [IO], Beirut, Lebanon
Makatab Tarighat OveyssiShahmaghsoudi [20249], PO Box 3620, Washington, DC 20027, (800)820-2180
Make-A-Wish Found. of Am. [11481], 4742 N 24th St., Ste. 400, Phoenix, AZ 85016, (602)230-9900
Make a Child Smile [11482], PO Box 422, Minneola, FL 34755
Make Early Diagnosis to Prevent Early Death [14610], Univ. of Utah, School of Medicine, 420 Chipeta Way, Rm. 1160, Salt Lake City, UT 84108
Make Early Diagnosis to Prevent Early Death [14610], Univ. of Utah, School of Medicine, 420 Chipeta Way, Rm. 1160, Salt Lake City, UT 84108
Makeni Ecumenical Centre [IO], Lusaka, Zambia
Makina Muehendisleri Odasi [★IO]
Making Music [IO], London, United Kingdom
Malacological Soc. of Japan [IO], Tokyo, Japan
Malacological Soc. of London [IO], Kent, United Kingdom
Malacological Soc. of the Philippines [IO], Quezon City, Philippines
Malacology
Amer. Malacological Soc. [7035]
Malacological Soc. of London [19825]
Natl. Shellfisheries Assn. [7036]
Natl. Shellfisheries Assn. [7036]
Western Soc. of Malacologists [7037]
Malagasy Bible Soc. [IO], Antananarivo, Madagascar
Malagasy Fed. of Taekwondo [IO], Antananarivo, Madagascar
Malagasy Red Cross Soc. [IO], Antananarivo, Madagascar
Malama Intl. [11346], PO Box 429, Avon, CT 06001, (860)409-0775
Malaria No More [14399], 432 Park Ave. S, 14th Fl., New York, NY 10016, (212)792-7929
Malawi Assn. of Christian Support [IO], Canterbury, United Kingdom
Malawi Biomedicals Resources [15305], 12829 Carousel Ct., Upper Marlboro, MD 20772, (301)574-1736
Malawi Biomedicals Resources [15305], 12829 Carousel Ct., Upper Marlboro, MD 20772, (301)574-1736
Malawi Children's Mission [11347], PO Box 313, Redwood City, CA 94064
Malawi Proj. [10815], Richard Stephens, VP, 3314 Van Tassel Dr., Indianapolis, IN 46240
Malawi Proj. [10815], Richard Stephens, VP, 3314 Van Tassel Dr., Indianapolis, IN 46240
Malawi Red Cross Soc. [IO], Lilongwe, Malawi
Malay Chamber of Commerce Malaysia [IO], Kuala Lumpur, Malaysia
Malay for Natl. Consciousness Movement [IO], Penang, Malaysia
Malayalee Engineers Assn. in North America [6808], 6807 Fieldstone Dr., Burr Ridge, IL 60527, (630)851-1690
Malaysia
Malaysia Tourism Promotion Bd. [23427]
Malaysia Amateur Athletic Union [IO], Kuala Lumpur, Malaysia
Malaysia Budget Hotel Assn. [IO], Kuala Lumpur, Malaysia
Malaysia Mold and Die Assn. [IO], Kuala Lumpur, Malaysia
Malaysia Occupational Therapists Assn. [IO], Kuala Lumpur, Malaysia
Malaysia Retailers' Assn. [IO], Selangor, Malaysia
Malaysia South-South Assn. [IO], Kuala Lumpur, Malaysia
Malaysia Taekwondo Assn. [IO], Kuala Lumpur, Malaysia
Malaysia Tourism Promotion Bd. [IO], Kuala Lumpur, Malaysia
Malaysia Tourism Promotion Bd. [23427], 818 W 7th St., Ste. 970, Los Angeles, CA 90017-3431, (213)689-9702
Malaysia Tourist Info. Center [★23427]
Malaysian AIDS Coun. [IO], Kuala Lumpur, Malaysia

Reference to "IO" in place of a book number signifies that the association may be found in the 50th edition of International Organizations.

Encyclopedia of Associations, 51st Edition   **2969**

Malaysian Airlines Pilots' Assn. [IO], Selangor, Malaysia

Malaysian Amateur Radio Transmitter's Soc. [IO], Kuala Lumpur, Malaysia

Malaysian Assoc. Indian Chambers of Commerce and Indus. [IO], Kuala Lumpur, Malaysia

Malaysian Assn. for the Blind [IO], Kuala Lumpur, Malaysia

Malaysian Assn. of Clinical Biochemists [IO], Kuala Lumpur, Malaysia

Malaysian Assn. in France [IO], Paris, France

Malaysian Assn. of Hotels [IO], Kuala Lumpur, Malaysia

Malaysian Assn. Myanmar [IO], Yangon, Myanmar

Malaysian Assn. of the Netherlands [IO], Rotterdam, Netherlands

Malaysian Assn. of Professional Secretaries and Administrators [IO], Kuala Lumpur, Malaysia

Malaysian Assn. of Risk and Insurance Mgt. [IO], Petaling Jaya, Malaysia

Malaysian Assn. of Speech Language and Hearing [IO], Selangor, Malaysia

Malaysian Assn. of Tour and Travel Agents [IO], Kuala Lumpur, Malaysia

Malaysian Automotive Components and Parts Mfrs. Assn. [IO], Kuala Lumpur, Malaysia

Malaysian Automotive Tyre Mfrs. Indus. Gp. [IO], Kuala Lumpur, Malaysia

Malaysian Bar Coun. [IO], Kuala Lumpur, Malaysia

Malaysian Br. of the Royal Asiatic Soc. [IO], Kuala Lumpur, Malaysia

Malaysian Bus. Coun. of Cambodia [IO], Phnom Penh, Cambodia

Malaysian Chamber of Mines [IO], Kuala Lumpur, Malaysia

Malaysian Chinese Assn. [IO], Kuala Lumpur, Malaysia

Malaysian Cocoa Bd. [IO], Kota Kinabalu, Malaysia

Malaysian Cosmetics and Toiletries Indus. Gp. [IO], Kuala Lumpur, Malaysia

Malaysian Cricket Assn. [IO], Puchong, Malaysia

Malaysian Cultural Gp. [IO], Kuala Lumpur, Malaysia

Malaysian Danish Assn. [IO], Frederiksberg, Denmark

Malaysian Dental Assn. [IO], Kuala Lumpur, Malaysia

Malaysian Dietitians Assn. [IO], Petaling Jaya, Malaysia

Malaysian Economic Assn. [IO], Kuala Lumpur, Malaysia

Malaysian Employers' Fed. [IO], Petaling Jaya, Malaysia

Malaysian Floorball Assn. [IO], Petaling Jaya, Malaysia

Malaysian Food Mfg. Gp. [IO], Kuala Lumpur, Malaysia

Malaysian Franchise Assn. [IO], Kuala Lumpur, Malaysia

Malaysian Gas Assn. [IO], Kuala Lumpur, Malaysia

Malaysian Golf Assn. [IO], Kuala Lumpur, Malaysia

Malaysian Inst. of Architects [IO], Kuala Lumpur, Malaysia

Malaysian Inst. of Certified Public Accountants [IO], Kuala Lumpur, Malaysia

Malaysian Inst. of Chartered Secretaries and Administrators [IO], Kuala Lumpur, Malaysia

Malaysian Intl. Chamber of Commerce and Indus. [IO], Kuala Lumpur, Malaysia

Malaysian Iron and Steel Indus. Fed. [IO], Shah Alam, Malaysia

Malaysian Medical Assn. [IO], Kuala Lumpur, Malaysia

Malaysian Menopause Soc. [IO], Petaling Jaya, Malaysia

Malaysian Natl. Cmpt. Confed. [IO], Petaling Jaya, Malaysia

Malaysian Nature Soc. [IO], Kuala Lumpur, Malaysia

Malaysian Nuclear Soc. [IO], Kajang, Malaysia

Malaysian Org. of Pharmaceutical Indus. [IO], Petaling Jaya, Malaysia

Malaysian Osteoporosis Soc. [IO], Selangor, Malaysia

Malaysian Palm Oil Assn. [IO], Kuala Lumpur, Malaysia

Malaysian Pepper Bd. [IO], Sarawak, Malaysia

Malaysian Physiotherapy Assn. [IO], Kuala Lumpur, Malaysia

Malaysian Pineapple Indus. Bd. [IO], Johor Bahru, Malaysia

Malaysian Plastic Mfrs. Assn. [IO], Petaling Jaya, Malaysia

Malaysian Printers' Assn. [IO], Kuala Lumpur, Malaysia

Malaysian Red Crescent Soc. [IO], Kuala Lumpur, Malaysia

Malaysian Rubber Bd. [IO], Kuala Lumpur, Malaysia

Malaysian Rubber Glove Mfrs'. Assn. [IO], Petaling Jaya, Malaysia

Malaysian Sci. Assn. [IO], Petaling Jaya, Malaysia

Malaysian Senior Scientists' Assn. [IO], Petaling Jaya, Malaysia

Malaysian Soc. of Allergy and Immunology [IO], Kuala Lumpur, Malaysia

Malaysian Soc. of Anaesthesiologists [IO], Kuala Lumpur, Malaysia

Malaysian Soc. of Gastroenterology and Hepatology [IO], Kuala Lumpur, Malaysia

Malaysian Soc. of Infectious Diseases and Chemotherapy [IO], Kuala Lumpur, Malaysia

Malaysian Soc. of Nephrology [IO], Kuala Lumpur, Malaysia

Malaysian Soc. of Pharmacology and Physiology [IO], Shah Alam, Malaysia

Malaysian Soc. for Quality in Hea. [IO], Kuala Lumpur, Malaysia

Malaysian Soc. of Radiographers [IO], Kuala Lumpur, Malaysia

Malaysian Soc. of Transplantation [IO], Kuala Lumpur, Malaysia

Malaysian Textile Mfrs'. Assn. [IO], Kuala Lumpur, Malaysia

Malaysian Timber Coun. [IO], Kuala Lumpur, Malaysia

Malaysian Timber Indus. Bd. [IO], Kuala Lumpur, Malaysia

Malaysian Venture Capital Assn. [IO], Kuala Lumpur, Malaysia

Malaysian Youth Coun. [IO], Kuala Lumpur, Malaysia

Maldives Assn. of Constr. Indus. [IO], Male, Maldives

Maldives Basketball Assn. [IO], Male, Maldives

Maldives Body Building and Fitness Assn. [IO], Male, Maldives

Maldives Natl. Chamber of Commerce and Indus. [IO], Male, Maldives

Maldives Photographers Assn. [IO], Male, Maldives

Maldives Surfing Assn. [IO], Male, Maldives

Maldivian Democracy Network [IO], Male, Maldives

Maldivian Medical Assn. [IO], Male, Maldives

Male Liberation Found. [18106], 701 NE 67th St., Miami, FL 33138, (305)756-6249

MaleSurvivor: The Natl. Org. Against Male Sexual Victimization [13089], 5505 Connecticut Ave. NW, PMB 103, Washington, DC 20015-2601, (800)738-4181

Mali Assistance Proj. [10816], 950 Yellow Pine Ave., Boulder, CO 80304, (303)449-1774

Mali Fed. of Sport for the Disabled [IO], Bamako, Mali

Mali Red Cross [IO], Bamako, Mali

Malian Found. [IO], Crows Nest, Australia

Malignant Hyperthermia Assn. of the U.S. [14611], PO Box 1069, Sherburne, NY 13460, (607)674-7901

Malleable Chain Mfrs. Inst. [★1798]

Malone Soc. [IO], London, United Kingdom

Malt Anal. Standardization Comm. [★6396]

Malt Anal. Standardization Comm. [★6396]

Malta Amateur Athletic Assn. [IO], Marsa, Malta

Malta Amateur Radio League [IO], Valletta, Malta

Malta Assn. of Occupational Therapists [IO], Pieta, Malta

Malta Assn. of Physiotherapists [IO], Msida, Malta

Malta Assn. of Women in Bus. [IO], Naxxar, Malta

Malta Bible Soc. [IO], Floriana, Malta

Malta Chamber of Commerce and Enterprise [IO], Valletta, Malta

Malta Cricket Assn. [IO], Marsa, Malta

Malta Dancesport Assn. [IO], Paola, Malta

Malta Employers' Assn. [IO], Valletta, Malta

Malta Feline Guardians Club [IO], Attard, Malta

Malta Football Assn. [IO], Ta' Qali, Malta

Malta Handball Assn. [IO], Gzira, Malta

Malta Hotels and Restaurants Assn. [IO], San Gwann, Malta

Malta Labour Party [IO], Hamrun, Malta

Malta Lib. and Info. Assn. [IO], Msida, Malta

Malta Red Cross [IO], Valletta, Malta

Malta Squash [IO], Naxxar, Malta

Malta Tennis Fed. [IO], Sliema, Malta

Malta Tourism Authority [IO], Valletta, Malta

Malta Union of Teachers [IO], Valletta, Malta

Malta Veterinary Assn. [IO], Gzira, Malta

Malta Weightlifting Assn. [IO], Marsascala, Malta

Malta Workers' Union [IO], Floriana, Malta

Maltese Assn. of Dermatology and Venereology [IO], San Gwann, Malta

Maltese Assn. of Gerontology and Geriatrics [IO], Msida, Malta

Maltese Diabetes Assn. [IO], Valletta, Malta

Maltese Olympic Comm. [IO], Gzira, Malta

Malteurs de France [★IO]

Malting Barley Improvement Assn. [★3948]

Maltsters Assn. of Great Britain [IO], Newark, United Kingdom

Mama Baby Haiti [14107], PO Box 657, Newberg, OR 97132

Mama Baby Haiti [14107], PO Box 657, Newberg, OR 97132

Mama Hope [11609], 582 Market St., Ste. 709, San Francisco, CA 94104, (415)686-6954

Mamburao-U.S.A. Assn. [10365], PO Box 17616, Beverly Hills, CA 90209-5616, (310)286-2482

Mamie Doud Eisenhower Birthplace Found. [9707], 709 Carroll St., Boone, IA 50036, (515)432-1907

Mammal Soc. [IO], Southampton, United Kingdom

Mammalogy
    Amer. Cetacean Soc. [7038]
    Amer. Soc. of Mammalogists [7039]
    Center for Whale Res. [7040]
    Dolphin Res. Center [7041]
    Intl. Mammalian Genome Soc. [6900]

Mamselle Sorority [★13112]

Man and the Biosphere Programme [IO], Paris, France

Man from U.N.C.L.E.
    Man from U.N.C.L.E. Fan Club [23924]

Man from U.N.C.L.E. Fan Club [23924], PO Box 1733, Oshkosh, WI 54903

Man Watchers [★21853]

Man Will Never Fly Memorial Soc. Internationale [21864], 103 Caribbean Ave., Virginia Beach, VA 23451-4716

MANA, A Natl. Latina Org. [17655], 1146 19th St. NW, Ste. 700, Washington, DC 20036, (202)833-0060

Managed Care Risk Assn. [1690], 6900 Wedgewood Rd. N, Ste. 150, Maple Grove, MN 55311, (804)672-4430

Managed Funds Assn. [23410], 600 14th St. NW, Ste. 900, Washington, DC 20005, (202)730-2600

Management
    Acad. of Mgt. [8546]
    Amer. Mgt. Assn. [2263]
    Amer. Mgt. Assn. [2263]
    Amer. Mgt. Assn. I Oper. Enterprise [8547]
    Amer. Soc. for the Advancement of Proj. Mgt. [2264]
    Amer. Soc. for the Advancement of Proj. Mgt. [2264]
    APQC [2265]
    Assn. of AE Bus. Leaders [2266]
    Assn. of Bus. Process Mgt. Professionals [2267]
    Assn. of Certified Adizes Practitioners Intl. [2268]
    Assn. of Certified Adizes Practitioners Intl. [2268]
    Assn. of Governmental Risk Pools [5549]
    Assn. of Internal Mgt. Consultants [2269]
    Assn. of Internal Mgt. Consultants [2269]
    Assn. of Latino Administrators and Superintendents [7661]
    Assn. of Mgt. Consulting Firms [2270]
    Assn. of Productivity Specialists [2271]
    Assn. of Productivity Specialists [2271]
    Assn. of Proposal Mgt. Professionals [2272]
    Assn. for Strategic Alliance Professionals [2273]

A star before a book entry number signifies that the name is not listed separately, but is mentioned within the entry.

Assn. for Strategic Alliance Professionals [2273]
Bd. of Certified Prdt. Safety Mgt. [3139]
Bus. Architects Assn. [2595]
Center for Creative Leadership [2274]
Center for Creative Leadership [2274]
Center for Mgt. Effectiveness [2275]
Central Asian Found. for Mgt. Development [5337]
Coll. of Performance Mgt. [2276]
Coll. of Performance Mgt. [2276]
Community Managers Intl. Assn. [2277]
Consortium for Graduate Stud. in Mgt. [8548]
Constr. Mgt. Assn. of Am. [2278]
Corporate Responsibility Officers Assn. [963]
Corporate Social Responsibility Assn. [964]
Customer Relationship Mgt. Assn. [869]
Emergency Mgt. Professional Org. for Women's Enrichment [2279]
Employers Gp. [2280]
European Fac. Mgt. Network [15507]
European Operations Mgt. Assn. [9248]
Executives Without Borders [60]
Financial Executives Res. Found. [2281]
Financial Managers Soc. [2282]
Gift Sales Manager Assn. [3162]
Global Automotive Mgt. Coun. [298]
Governance Inst. [2283]
Graduate Mgt. Admission Coun. [8549]
Graduate Mgt. Admission Coun. [8549]
Healthcare Financial Mgt. Assn. [15258]
Human Rsrc. Planning Soc. [2284]
Indus. Asset Mgt. Coun. [3014]
Info. Tech. Alliance [7042]
Inst. of Certified Professional Managers [2285]
Inst. of Certified Professional Managers [2285]
Inst. for Hea. and Productivity Mgt. [2286]
Inst. for Hea. and Productivity Mgt. [2286]
Inst. of Mgt. Accountants, Cost Mgt. Gp. [2287]
Inst. of Mgt. Consultants USA [2288]
Inst. for Operations Res. and the Mgt. Sciences [2289]
Inst. for Operations Res. and the Mgt. Sciences [2289]
Intl. Assn. for Chinese Mgt. Res. [2290]
Intl. Soc. of Facilities Executives [2251]
Issue Mgt. Coun. [2291]
Location Managers Guild of Am. [2292]
MRA [2293]
Natl. Assn. of Corporate Directors [2294]
Natl. Assn. of Elecl. Distributors I Natl. Educ. and Res. Found. [2295]
Natl. Assn. for Moisture Mgt. [1223]
Natl. Assn. of Senior Move Managers [2296]
Natl. Conf. of Executives of the Arc [2297]
Natl. Grants Mgt. Assn. [2298]
Natl. Mgt. Assn. [2299]
Natl. Petroleum Mgt. Assn. [2663]
Org. Design Forum [2300]
Org. Design Forum [2300]
Personal Injury Lawyers Marketing and Mgt. Assn. [268]
Prdt. Development and Mgt. Assn. [2301]
Production Managers Assn. [2293]
Production and Operations Mgt. Soc. [2302]
Production and Operations Mgt. Soc. [2302]
Professional Lighting and Sign Mgt. Companies of Am. [2223]
Proj. Mgt. Inst. [2303]
Proj. Mgt. Inst. [2303]
Restaurant Fac. Mgt. Assn. [3091]
Security Anal. and Risk Mgt. Assn. [3227]
Sigma Iota Epsilon [23584]
Soc. for Advancement of Mgt. [2304]
Soc. for Info. Mgt. [2305]
Total Practice Mgt. Assn. [5287]
Turnaround Mgt. Assn. [2306]
Women in Mgt. [2307]
Women Organizing for Change in Agriculture and NRM [3769]
Workflow Mgt. Coalition [2308]
Mgt. Assistance Gp. [12596], 1629 K St. NW, Ste. 300, Washington, DC 20006, (202)659-1963
Mgt. Assn. for Private Photogrammetric Surveyors [7260], 1856 Old Reston Ave., Ste. 205, Reston, VA 20190, (703)787-6996

Mgt. Company for Amer. Poultry U.S.A. [★4806]
Mgt. Company for Amer. Poultry U.S.A. [★4806]
Mgt. Consultancies Assn. [IO], London, United Kingdom
Mgt. Educ. Alliance [7796], 300 Cumnock Hall, Boston, MA 02163, (617)495-6494
Mgt. Info. Systems Gp. - Address unknown since 2011.
Mgt. Sci. Soc. of Ireland [IO], Dublin, Ireland
Mgt. Soc. for Healthcare Professionals [IO], Hong Kong, People's Republic of China
Managers
  Assn. of Dermatology Administrators and Managers [14323]
  BuildingBlocks Intl. [11666]
  CEO Netweavers [962]
  Gift Sales Manager Assn. [3162]
  Global Automotive Mgt. Coun. [298]Managers-Guatemalan Managers' Assn.
  Inst. of People Mgt. [10929]
Mananga Centre for Regional Integration and Mgt. Development [IO], Mbabane, Swaziland
Manchester Chamber of Commerce and Indus. [IO], Manchester, United Kingdom
Manchester Geological Assn. [IO], Northwich, United Kingdom
Mandala Soc. [12219], PO Box 1233, Del Mar, CA 92014, (858)481-7751
Mandate Trade Union [IO], Dublin, Ireland
M&M's Collectors Club [21367], 612 Head of River Rd., Chesapeake, VA 23322
Mangalore Cultural Assn. [IO], Doha, Qatar
Manhattan Bowery Corp. [★13285]
Manhattan Inst. for Policy Res. [18433], 52 Vanderbilt Ave., New York, NY 10017, (212)599-7000
Mani Tese [★IO]
Manic Depressive and Depressive Assn. [★15452]
Maniilaq Assn. [12562], PO Box 256, Kotzebue, AK 99752, (907)442-7660
Manitoba 4-H [IO], Brandon, MB, Canada
Manitoba Amateur Boxing Assn. [IO], Winnipeg, MB, Canada
Manitoba Brain Injury Assn. [IO], Winnipeg, MB, Canada
Manitoba Cricket Assn. [IO], Winnipeg, MB, Canada
Manitoba Psychological Soc. [IO], Winnipeg, MB, Canada
Manitoba Wheelchair Sports Assn. [IO], Winnipeg, MB, Canada
ManKind Proj. [13043], 801 N Brand Blvd., Ste. 550, Glendale, CA 91203, (800)870-4611
Manna House of Prayer [12159], PO Box 675, Concordia, KS 66901, (785)243-4428
Mannerheim League for Child Welfare [IO], Helsinki, Finland
Mannerheimin Lastensuojeluliitto [★IO]
Mannosidosis and Related Diseases; Intl. Soc. for [14605]
Mannosidosis and Related Diseases; Intl. Soc. for [14605]
Mano A Mano: Mexican Culture Without Borders [10085], 126 St. Felix St., Brooklyn, NY 11217, (212)587-3070
Manorial Soc. of Great Britain [IO], London, United Kingdom
Manpower Educ. Inst. [8317], 715 Ladd Rd., Bronx, NY 10471-1203, (718)548-4200
The Manpower Inst. [★18038]
MANU - Societe d'Ornithologie de Polynesie [★IO]
Manufactured Housing
  Manufactured Housing Inst. [2309]
  Metal Building Contractors and Erectors Assn. [2310]
  Natl. Assn. of Home Builders I Building Systems Coun. [2311]
  Natl. Assn. of Home Builders I Log Homes Coun. [2312]
  Natl. Assn. of Home Builders I Modular Building Systems Coun. [2313]
  Natl. Assn. of Home Builders I Panelized Building Systems Coun. [2314]
  Western Manufactured Housing Communities Assn. [2315]
Manufactured Housing Assn. for Regulatory Reform - Address unknown since 2010.

Manufactured Housing Inst. [2309], 2111 Wilson Blvd., Ste. 100, Arlington, VA 22201, (703)558-0400
Manufactured Housing Res. Alliance [★1786]
Manufactured Imports Promotion Org. [IO], Tokyo, Japan
Mfrs. of Aerial Devices and Digger-Derricks Coun. [1840], 6737 W Washington St., Ste. 2400, Milwaukee, WI 53214-5647, (414)272-0943
Mfrs'. Agents' Assn. of Great Britain and Ireland [IO], Harpenden, United Kingdom
Mfrs. Agents for Food Ser. Indus. [★1440]
Mfrs'. Agents for the Foodservice Indus. [1440], 1199 Euclid Ave., Atlanta, GA 30307, (404)214-9474
Mfrs'. Agents Natl. Assn. [2319], 16 A Journey, Ste. 200, Aliso Viejo, CA 92656-3317, (949)859-4040
Mfrs. Alliance [★1843]
Mfrs. Alliance for Productivity and Innovation [★1843]
Mfrs. Div., Natl. Assn. of Amusement Parks [★1187]
Mfrs. Div., Natl. Assn. of Amusement Parks [★1187]
Mfrs. of Educational and Commercial Stationery European Assn. [IO], Paris, France
Mfrs. of Emission Controls Assn. [2787], 2020 N 14th St., Ste. 220, Arlington, VA 22201, (202)296-4797
Mfrs. of Illumination Products - Defunct.
Mfrs. Members of the Natl. Warm Air Heating and Air Conditioning Assn. [★1695]
Mfrs. Radio Frequency Advisory Comm. [★498]
Manufacturers Representatives
  Assn. of Independent Manufacturers'/Representatives [2316]
  Equip. Marketing and Distribution Assn. [2317]
  Incentive Mfrs. and Representatives Alliance [2318]
  Mfrs'. Agents Natl. Assn. [2319]
  Mfrs. Representatives Educational Res. Found. [2320]
  Mech. Equip. Mfrs. Representatives Assn. [2321]
  NAGMR [2322]
  Natl. Mobility Equip. Dealers Assn. [2323]
  Natl. Mobility Equip. Dealers Assn. [2323]
  United Assn. Mfrs'. Representatives [2324]
Mfrs. Representatives of Am. [1042], 1111 Jupiter Rd., Ste. 204D, Plano, TX 75074, (972)422-0428
Mfrs. Representatives Educational Res. Found. [2320], 8329 Cole St., Arvada, CO 80005, (303)463-1801
Mfrs. Standardization Soc. of the Valve and Fittings Indus. [1841], 127 Park St. NE, Vienna, VA 22180-4602, (703)281-6613
Mfrs. Standardization Soc. of the Valve and Fittings Indus. [1841], 127 Park St. NE, Vienna, VA 22180-4602, (703)281-6613
Mfrs. of Telescoping and Articulated Cranes Coun. [1842], Assn. of Equip. Mfrs., 6737 W Washington St., Ste. 2400, Milwaukee, WI 53214-5647, (414)272-0943
Manufacturiers et Exportateurs du Canada [★IO]
Manufacturing
  911 Indus. Alliance [804]
  Alliance for Amer. Mfg. [2325]
  Alliance of Supplier Diversity Professionals [2969]
  Amer. Indus. Extension Alliance [2326]
  Amer. Mfg. Trade Action Coalition [2327]
  Amer. Small Mfrs. Coalition [2328]
  Assn. for Mfg. Excellence [2329]
  Assn. for Mfg. Excellence [2329]
  Assn. for Mfg. Tech. [7043]
  Assn. of Needle-Free Injection Mfrs. [2330]
  Aviation Suppliers Assn. [2331]
  Barbados Mfrs'. Assn. [1609]
  Battery Recycling Assn. of North Am. [3071]
  CAMUS Intl. [2332]
  CAMUS Intl. [2332]
  Consortium for Advanced Mgt. Intl. [2333]
  Consortium for Advanced Mfg. Intl. [2333]
  Door and Access Systems Mfrs. Assn. Intl. [2334]
  Door and Access Systems Mfrs. Assn. Intl. [2334]
  European Assn. of Flexible Polyurethane Foam Blocks Mfrs. [9068]
  European Liaison Comm. of Machine Tool Importers [8234]

Reference to "IO" in place of a book number signifies that the association may be found in the 50th edition of International Organizations.

Fed. of Norwegian Indus. [21120]
Gasket Cutters Assn. [13315]
Global Envelope Alliance [3349]
Guyana Mfg. and Services Assn. [12076]
Heavy Duty Mfrs. Assn. [2335]
Indus. Energy Consumers of Am. [1169]
Inst. for Molecular Mfg. [7044]
Integrated Mfg. Tech. Initiative [7045]
Intl. Bridal Mfrs. Assn. [472]
Intl. Electronics Mfg. Initiative [7046]
Intl. Photovoltaic Equip. Assn. [1170]
Intl. Production Planning and Scheduling Assn. [2336]
Intl. Production Planning and Scheduling Assn. [2336]
Intl. Soc. for Quality Electronic Design [6600]
Intl. Sugar Trade Coalition [3367]
Intl. Surface Fabricators Assn. [2337]
Intl. Surface Fabricators Assn. [2337]
Ladder Assn. [14751]
Machinery Info. Mgt. Open Systems Alliance [2338]
MIDI Mfrs. Assn. [2339]
Natl. Assn. of Mfrs. [2340]
Natl. Assn. of Mfrs. Coun. of Mfg. Associations [2341]
Natl. Coun. for Advanced Mfg. [2342]
Parachute Indus. Assn. [2623]
Pump Indus. Australia [50]
Rapid Technologies and Additive Mfg. Community [7047]
The Remanufacturing Inst. [2343]
The Remanufacturing Inst. [2343]
Retailers of Art Glass and Supplies [1581]
Schiffli Embroidery Mfrs. Promotion Fund [3453]
SEAMS Assn. [2344]
Soc. of Mfg. Emgineers | Composites Mfg. Tech Gp. [2345]
Soc. of Mfg. Engineers [7048]
Soc. of Mfg. Engineers | Composites Mfg. Tech Gp. [2345]
Soc. of Mfg. Engineers | North Amer. Mfg. Res. Institution [7049]
Tooling and Mfg. Assn. [2346]
Transmission Rebuilders Network Intl. [341]
Trinidad and Tobago Mfrs. Assn. [5978]
Unified Abrasives Mfrs'. Assn. [2347]
United Kingdom Indus. Vision Assn. [19581]
United Kingdom Spring Mfrs. Assn. [12929]
U.S. Coun. for Automotive Res. [6245]
Wind Energy Mfrs. Assn. [3667]
Women in Toys [3479]
WoodLINKS USA [8300]
Mfg. Enterprise Solutions Assn. Intl. [7491], 107 S Southgate Dr., Chandler, AZ 85226, (480)893-6883
Mfg. Enterprise Solutions Assn. Intl. [7491], 107 S Southgate Dr., Chandler, AZ 85226, (480)893-6883
Mfg. Jewelers and Silversmiths of Am. [★2170]
Mfg. Jewelers and Suppliers of Am. [2170], 57 John L. Dietsch Sq., Attleboro Falls, MA 02763, (401)274-3840
Mfg. Perfumers Assn. of the U.S. [★1670]
Mfg. Skill Standards Coun. [7466], 1410 King St., Alexandria, VA 22314, (703)739-9000
Mfg. Technologies Assn. [IO], London, United Kingdom
Manuscript Soc. [21368], 14003 Rampart Ct., Baton Rouge, LA 70810, (908)459-0155
Manushi for Sustainable Development [IO], Kathmandu, Nepal
Manx
North Amer. Manx Assn. [19120]
North Amer. Manx Assn. [19120]
MAP Intl. [19952], 4700 Glynco Pkwy., Brunswick, GA 31525-6800, (912)265-6010
MAP Intl. [19952], 4700 Glynco Pkwy., Brunswick, GA 31525-6800, (912)265-6010
MAP Intl. - Eastern Africa Off. [IO], Nairobi, Kenya
MAP Intl. - Latin Am. Off. [IO], Quito, Ecuador
Map Online Users Group - Defunct.
Mapendo Intl. [12863], 689 Massachusetts Ave., 2nd Fl., Cambridge, MA 02139, (617)864-7800
Mapendo Intl. [12863], 689 Massachusetts Ave., 2nd Fl., Cambridge, MA 02139, (617)864-7800
MAPI [1843], 1600 Wilson Blvd., 11th Fl., Arlington, VA 22209-2594, (703)841-9000

Maple Flooring Mfrs. Assn. [578], 111 Deer Lake Rd., Ste. 100, Deerfield, IL 60015, (847)480-9138
Maple Flooring Mfrs. Assn. [578], 111 Deer Lake Rd., Ste. 100, Deerfield, IL 60015, (847)480-9138
Maple Syrup Urine Disease Family Support Gp. [15499], Dave Bulcher, Treas., 82 Ravine Rd., Columbus, OH 43085, (740)548-4475
Mapping Sciences Inst., Australia [IO], East Perth, Australia
Mapping Your Future [8237], PO Box 5176, Round Rock, TX 78683, (940)497-0741
Maranatha Volunteers Intl. [19761], 990 Reserve Dr., Ste. 100, Roseville, CA 95678, (916)774-7700
Maranatha Volunteers Intl. [19761], 990 Reserve Dr., Ste. 100, Roseville, CA 95678, (916)774-7700
Marangopoulos Found. for Human Rights [IO], Athens, Greece
Maraschino Cherry and Glace Fruit Processors - Defunct.
Marathon Skating Intl. [22896], PO Box 89, Norwich, VT 05055, (802)649-3939
Marble Inst. of Am. [3364], 28901 Clemens Rd., Ste. 100, Cleveland, OH 44145-1166, (440)250-9222
Marble Inst. of Am. [3364], 28901 Clemens Rd., Ste. 100, Cleveland, OH 44145-1166, (440)250-9222
Marce Soc. [IO], St. Albans, United Kingdom
March of Dimes Found. [13844], 1275 Mamaroneck Ave., White Plains, NY 10605, (914)997-4488
March for Life [★18556]
March for Life Educ. and Defense Fund [18556], PO Box 90300, Washington, DC 20090-0300, (202)543-3377
Marching Bands of Am. [★10167]
Marching New Zealand [IO], Nelson, New Zealand
Marco Polo Club - Defunct.
Marcus Center of the Amer. Jewish Archives [9926], 3101 Clifton Ave., Cincinnati, OH 45220, (513)221-1875
Maremma Sheepdog Club of Am. [21599], 6211 Lake Gulch Rd., Castle Rock, CO 80104, (720)733-3618
Marfan Argentina [IO], Buenos Aires, Argentina
Marfan Assn. UK [IO], Fleet, United Kingdom
Marfan Brasil [IO], Sao Luis, Brazil
Marfan Hilfe Deutschland e.V. [IO], Eutin, Germany
Marga Inst., Centre for Development Stud. [IO], Colombo, Sri Lanka
Margarine and Spreads Assn. [IO], London, United Kingdom
Margery Allingham Soc. [IO], Amersham, United Kingdom
MARHO: The Radical Historians' Org. [9782], Tamiment Lib., 70 Washington Sq. S, New York, NY 10012, (212)998-2632
Maria Mitchell Assn. [6234], 4 Vestal St., Nantucket, MA 02554, (508)228-9198
Mariana Islands Nature Alliance [IO], Saipan, Northern Mariana Islands
Mariana Islands Water Operator Assn. [IO], Saipan, Northern Mariana Islands
Mariannhill Mission Soc. [19447], 23715 Ann Arbor Trail, Dearborn Heights, MI 48127, (313)561-7140
Marie Curie Cancer Care [IO], London, United Kingdom
Marie Stopes Intl. - United Kingdom [IO], London, United Kingdom
Marie Stopes Intl. - Vietnam [IO], Hanoi, Vietnam
Marie Stopes Soc. Pakistan [IO], Karachi, Pakistan
Marijuana
Amer. Alliance for Medical Cannabis [15259]
Americans for Safe Access [15260]
Compassionate Coalition [18084]
Do It Now Found. [13248]
Friends and Families of Cannabis Consumers [18085]
Marijuana Policy Proj. [18086]
Narcotic Educational Found. of Am. [13267]
November Coalition [18681]
Marijuana Anonymous World Services [13044], PO Box 2912, Van Nuys, CA 91404, (800)766-6779
Marijuana Laws; Natl. Org. for the Reform of [17311]
Marijuana Policy Proj. [18086], 236 Massachusetts Ave. NE, Ste. 400, Washington, DC 20002, (202)462-5747
Marin Self-Publishers Assn. [★2924]

Marin Small-Publishers Assn. [★2924]
Marina Operators Assn. of Am. - Defunct.
MARINALG Intl., World Assn. of Seaweed Processors [IO], Brussels, Belgium
Marine
AFL-CIO | Intl. Org. of Masters, Mates and Pilots [23245]
AFL-CIO | Maritime Trades Dept. [23246]
Aircraft Carrier Indus. Base Coalition [1034]
Alliance of Marine Mammal Parks and Aquariums [4699]
Alliance of Marine Mammal Parks and Aquariums [4699]
Amer. Boat Builders and Repairers Assn. [2348]
Amer. Boat and Yacht Coun. [2349]
Amer. Littoral Soc. Northeast Region [7050]
Amer. Marinelife Dealers Assn. [4700]
Amer. Maritime Safety [2350]
Amer. Reef Coalition [3993]
Amer. Soc. of Naval Engineers [7051]
Amer. Waterways Operators [2351]
Assn. of Certified Marine Surveyors [2352]
Assn. for Marine Exploration [4701]
Assn. of Marine Technicians [2353]
Australian Coral Reef Soc. [15321]
Blue Dolphin Alliance [4702]
Canadian Centre for Marine Communications [316]
Cetos Res. Org. [4199]
Coastal and Estuarine Res. Fed. [7052]
Coun. of Amer. Master Mariners [2354]
Deep Draft Lubricant Assn. [2225]
Dredging Contractors of Am. [2355]
European Soc. for Oceanists [8996]
Global Underwater Explorers [4703]
Great Lakes Historical Soc. [10056]
Great Lakes Maritime Inst. [10057]
Historic Naval Ships Assn. [10058]
Historic Naval Ships Assn. [10058]
Historic Ships in Baltimore [10059]
Iemanya Oceanica [5064]
Inland Seas Educ. Assn. [2356]
Intl. Assn. of Marine Investigators [2357]
Intl. Assn. of Marine Investigators [2357]
Intl. Bunker Indus. Assn. [7948]
Intl. Cargo Gear Bur. [5777]
Intl. Cargo Gear Bur. [5777]
Intl. Longshore and Warehouse Union [23247]
Intl. Longshore and Warehouse Union [23247]
Intl. Longshoremen's Assn. [23248]
Intl. Marine Minerals Soc. [4704]
Intl. Marine Minerals Soc. [4704]
Intl. SeaKeepers Soc. [4705]
Intl. SeaKeepers Soc. [4705]
Intl. Shipmasters Assn. [2358]
Intl. Shipmasters Assn. [2358]
Intl. Submariners Association-USA [20678]
LTD. Shippers Assn. [3486]
Marine Animal Rescue Soc. [4093]
Marine Bd. [7053]
Marine Corps Veterans Assn. [20683]
Marine Mammal Conservancy [5079]
Marine Retailers Assn. of Am. [2359]
Marine Soc. of the City of New York [2360]
Marine Tech. Soc. [7054]
MarineBio Conservation Soc. [4714]
Marines Helping Marines [12433]
Montford Point Marine Assn. [5810]
Mystic Seaport [10060]
Natl. Aquarium Soc. [10061]
Natl. Assn. of Charterboat Operators [2361]
Natl. Assn. of Marine Labs. [7055]
Natl. Assn. of Marine Services [2362]
Natl. Assn. of Marine Surveyors [7056]
Natl. Marine Charter Assn. [2384]
Natl. Marine Distributors Assn. [2363]
Natl. Marine Educators Assn. [8550]
Natl. Marine Electronics Assn. [2364]
Natl. Marine Mfrs. Assn. [2365]
Natl. Marine Representatives Assn. [2366]
Natl. Oceanic Soc. [4102]
North Amer. Soc. for Oceanic History [10062]
North Amer. Soc. for Oceanic History [10062]
Northwest Marine Trade Assn. [2367]
Ocean Conservation Res. [4116]

A star before a book entry number signifies that the name is not listed separately, but is mentioned within the entry.

Ocean Renewable Energy Coalition [6747]
Oceanic Preservation Soc. [4119]
Offshore Marine Ser. Assn. [2368]
Oikonos [4213]
Pacific Coast Marine Firemen, Oilers, Watertenders and Wipers Assn. [23249]
Pacific Marine Mammal Center [5103]
PACON Intl. [4706]
PACON Intl. [4706]
Passenger Vessel Assn. [2369]
Penobscot Marine Museum [10063]
Reef Check [4707]
Reef Check [4707]
Reef Relief [4708]
Reef Relief [4708]
ReefGuardian Intl. [4709]
ReefGuardian Intl. [4709]
Sailors' Union of the Pacific [23250]
SATS/EAF Assn. [20686]
Sea Educ. Assn. [8551]
Sea Grant Assn. [7057]
Seafarers' Intl. Union of North Am. [23251]
SeaWeb [4710]
Shipbuilders Coun. of Am. [2370]
Sirenian Intl. [4711]
Sirenian Intl. [4711]
Soc. for Marine Mammalogy [4712]
South St. Seaport Museum [10064]
State of the World's Sea Turtles [5134]
Sustainable Fisheries Partnership [3830]
Titanic Historical Soc. [10065]
Titanic Historical Soc. [10065]
Titanic Intl. Soc. [10066]
Titanic Intl. Soc. [10066]
Turtle Island Restoration Network [4156]
Turtle Survival Alliance [5140]
U.S. Aquaculture Soc. [3831]
U.S. Marine Safety Assn. [5778]
U.S. Maritime Alliance [2371]
U.S. Naval Sailing Assn. [20727]
U.S. Navy Beach Jumpers Assn. [20728]
USMC Vietnam Tankers Assn. [20824]
USS St. Louis CL-49 Assn. [10067]
Vietnam Era Seabees [20826]
Water Planet USA [4713]
Water Planet USA [4713]
West Gulf Maritime Assn. [2372]
Western Dredging Assn. [2373]
Whaling Museum Soc. [10068]
Women's Aquatic Network [7058]
World Fed. for Coral Reef Conservation [4169]
World Org. of Dredging Associations [2374]
World Org. of Dredging Associations [2374]
World Whale Police [5018]
Yacht Brokers Assn. of Am. [2375]
Marine Animal Rescue Soc. [4093], PO Box 833356, Miami, FL 33283, (305)546-1111
Marine Aquarium Coun. [3824], PO Box 90370, Los Angeles, CA 90009, (808)550-8217
Marine Aquarium Coun. [3824], PO Box 90370, Los Angeles, CA 90009, (808)550-8217
Marine Aquarium Coun. - Indonesia [IO], Bali, Indonesia
Marine Aquarium Societies of North Am. [3825], PO Box 105603, Atlanta, GA 30348-5603
Marine Assn. of the British Virgin Islands [IO], Tortola, British Virgin Islands
Marine Biological Assn. of the United Kingdom [IO], Plymouth, United Kingdom
Marine Biology
  Amer. Elasmobranch Soc. [7059]
  Aquatic Animal Life Support Operators [7060]
  Cetos Res. Org. [4199]
  MarineBio Conservation Soc. [4714]
  Ocean Soc. [7183]
  Pacific Marine Mammal Center [5103]
  Shark Res. Inst. [7061]
  Shark Res. Inst. [7061]
  Soc. for Marine Mammalogy [4712]
  U.S. Aquaculture Soc. [3831]
  World Fed. for Coral Reef Conservation [4169]
  World Whale Police [5018]
Marine Bd. [7053], Natl. Academies, 500 5th St. NW, Washington, DC 20001, (202)334-2934
Marine Connection [IO], London, United Kingdom

Marine Conservation Soc. [IO], Ross-on-Wye, United Kingdom
Marine Cooks and Stewards Union [★23251]
Marine Corps
  1st Marine Div. Assn. [20676]
  Devil Pups [20677]
  Intl. Submariners Association-USA [20678]
  Loyal Escorts of the Green Garter [20679]
  Marine Corps Assn. [5779]
  Marine Corps Aviation Assn. [5780]
  Marine Corps Aviation Reconnaissance Assn. [5781]
  Marine Corps CounterIntelligence Assn. [19121]
  Marine Corps Cryptologic Assn. [20680]
  Marine Corps Engineer Assn. [5782]
  Marine Corps Heritage Found. [10069]
  Marine Corps Intelligence Assn. [19122]
  Marine Corps Interrogator Translator Teams Assn. [19123]
  Marine Corps League [5783]
  Marine Corps League Auxiliary [20681]
  Marine Corps Mustang Assn. [20682]
  Marine Corps Reserve Assn. [5784]
  Marine Corps Veterans Assn. [20683]
  Marine Embassy Guard Assn. [20684]
  MarineParents.com [12434]
  Marines Helping Marines [12433]
  Military Order of the Devil Dog Fleas [20685]
  Mothers of Military Support [12529]
  Never Forget Our Fallen [11095]
  Oper. Paperback [11100]
  SATS/EAF Assn. [20686]
  Second Marine Div. Assn. [20687]
  Sixth Marine Div. Assn. [20868]
  Support Our Troops [11110]
  U.S. Marine Corps Scout/Sniper Assn. [20688]
  U.S. Naval Sailing Assn. [20727]
  U.S. Navy Beach Jumpers Assn. [20728]
  USMC Vietnam Tankers Assn. [20824]
  Vietnam Era Seabees [20826]
  Women Marines Assn. [20689]
Marine Corps Assn. [5779], 715 Broadway St., Quantico, VA 22134, (703)640-6161
Marine Corps Aviation Assn. [5780], PO Box 296, Quantico, VA 22134, (703)630-1903
Marine Corps Aviation Reconnaissance Assn. [5781], Terry Miner, Sec.-Treas., 4734 Grand Ridge Ct., Las Vegas, NV 89147, (702)253-9953
Marine Corps CounterIntelligence Assn. [19121], PO Box 19125, Washington, DC 20036-9125.
Marine Corps Cryptologic Assn. [20680], 4486 Sandalwood St., Napa, CA 94558-1766, (877)856-9562
Marine Corps Engineer Assn. [5782], PO Box 322, Ashville, NY 14710, (716)763-5655
Marine Corps Heritage Found. [10069], 3800 Fettler Park Dr., Ste. 104, Dumfries, VA 22025, (703)640-7965
Marine Corps Historical Found. [★10069]
Marine Corps Intelligence Assn. [19122], PO Box 1028, Quantico, VA 22134-1028
Marine Corps Interrogator Translator Teams Assn. [19123], 1900 S Ocean Blvd., Apt. 14L, Pompano Beach, FL 33062-8030
Marine Corps League [5783], PO Box 3070, Merrifield, VA 22116-3070, (703)207-9588
Marine Corps League Auxiliary [20681], 8626 Lee Hwy., Ste. 207, Fairfax, VA 22031-2135, (703)207-0626
Marine Corps Mustang Assn. [20682], Bunker 127, Mountain City, GA 30562, (866)937-6262
Marine Corps Recruiters Assn. - Address unknown since 2010.
Marine Corps Reserve Assn. [5784], 8626 Lee Hwy., Fairfax, VA 22031-2135, (703)289-1204
Marine Corps Reserve Officers' Assn. [★5784]
Marine Corps Toys for Tots Found. [★11483]
Marine Corps Veterans Assn. [20683], PO Box 214183, Sacramento, CA 95821-0183, (916)486-4050
Marine Embassy Guard Assn. [20684], PO Box 6226, Wausau, WI 54402-6226, (715)693-4750
Marine Engine Mfrs. Assn. [★2365]
Marine Engineers' Beneficial Assn. [7087], 444 N Capitol St., Ste. 800, Washington, DC 20001, (202)638-5355

Marine Firemen, Oilers and Watertenders of the Pacific [★23249]
Marine Firemen's Union [★23249]
Marine Fish Conservation Network [4094], 600 Pennsylvania Ave. SE, Ste. 210, Washington, DC 20003, (202)543-5509
Marine Industries
  Amer. Bur. of Shipping [2376]
  Assn. of Marina Indus. [2377]
  Assn. of Marina Indus. [2377]
  Assn. of Ship Brokers and Agents U.S.A. [2378]
  European Maritime Pilots' Assn. [7271]
  Inland Rivers Ports and Terminals [2379]
  Inlandboatman's Union of the Pacific [2380]
  Lake Carriers' Assn. [2381]
  Liberian Shipowners' Coun. [2382]
  Liberian Shipowners' Coun. [2382]
  Marine Machinery Assn. [2383]
  Natl. Marine Charter Assn. [2384]
  World Ocean Coun. [5009]
Marine Indus. Assn. of St. Lucia [IO], Castries, St. Lucia
Marine Machinery Assn. [2383], 8665 Sudley Rd., Ste. 270, Manassas, VA 20110-4588, (703)791-4800
Marine Mammal Conservancy [5079], PO Box 1625, Key Largo, FL 33037, (305)451-4774
Marine Mammal Conservation Fund [★4115]
Marine Mammal Conservation Fund [★4115]
Marine Mammal Stranding Center [5080], PO Box 773, 3625 Brigantine Blvd., Brigantine, NJ 08203, (609)266-0538
Marine Medical Mission [★20076]
Marine Retailers Assn. of Am. [2359], PO Box 725, Boca Grande, FL 33921, (941)964-2534
Marine Sci. Libraries Assn. [★9989]
Marine Sci. Libraries Assn. [★9989]
Marine Soc. [IO], London, United Kingdom
Marine Soc. of the City of New York [2360], 17 Battery Pl., Ste. 714, New York, NY 10004, (212)425-0448
Marine Soc. and Sea Cadets [IO], London, United Kingdom
Marine Stewardship Coun. [IO], London, United Kingdom
Marine Stewardship Coun. [4877], 2110 N Pacific St., Ste. 102, Seattle, WA 98103, (206)691-0188
Marine Tech. Soc. [7054], 5565 Sterrett Pl., Ste. 108, Columbia, MD 21044, (410)884-5330
Marine Toys for Tots Found. [11483], 18251 Quantico Gateway Dr., Triangle, VA 22172, (703)640-9433
MarineBio Conservation Soc. [4714], PO Box 235273, Encinitas, CA 92023, (713)248-2576
MarineParents.com [12434], PO Box 1115, Columbia, MO 65205, (573)303-5500
Marines Helping Marines [12433], PO Box 141, Westminster, MD 21158, (443)465-1406
Mario Santo Domingo Found. [IO], Barranquilla, Colombia
Mariological Soc. of Am. [19448], Univ. of Dayton, The Marian Lib., Dayton, OH 45469-1390, (937)229-4294
Mariposa Folk Found. [IO], Orillia, ON, Canada
Mariposa In The Schools [IO], Toronto, ON, Canada
Marist Bros. of the Schools [IO], Rome, Italy
Marist Volunteer Program - Defunct.
Maritime
  Amer. Power Boat Assn. [22316]
  Blind Sailing Intl. [23109]
  Center for Seafarers' Rights [5785]
  Force 5 Class Assn. [22336]
  Geary 18 Intl. Yacht Racing Assn. [22338]
  Grays Harbor Historical Seaport Authority [8552]
  Highlander Class Intl. Assn. [22341]
  Intl. Hobie Class Assn. [22353]
  Intl. Submariners Association-USA [20678]
  Natl. Butterfly Assn. [22371]
  Professional Windsurfers Assn. [22385]
  SailMail Assn. [6679]
  Ships on Stamps Unit [22074]
  Soc. for the History of Navy Medicine [9808]
  U.S. A-Class Catamaran Assn. [22400]
  U.S. Albacore Assn. [22401]
  U.S. Naval Sailing Assn. [20727]

Reference to "IO" in place of a book number signifies that the association may be found in the 50th edition of International Organizations.

U.S. Navy Beach Jumpers Assn. [20728]
U.S. Power Squadrons [22405]
U.S. Wayfarer Assn. [22410]
Women's Intl. Shipping and Trading Assn. [3276]
Maritime Assn. of the Port of New York [★3253]
Maritime Assn. of the Port of New York and New
Jersey [3253], 17 Battery Pl., Ste. 913, New York,
NY 10004, (212)425-5704
Maritime Fiddlers Assn. [IO], Wolfville, NS, Canada
Maritime Info. Assn. [IO], London, United Kingdom
Maritime Inst. of Tech. and Graduate Stud. [★23245]
Maritime Law
Center for Seafarers' Rights [5785]
Law of the Sea Inst. [5786]
Maritime Law Assn. of the U.S. [5787]
Maritime Law Assn. of the U.S. [5787], 80 Pine St.,
New York, NY 10005-1759, (212)425-1900
Maritime Museums; Coun. of Amer. [10118]
Maritime Postmark Soc. [22051], PO Box 497, Wads-
worth, OH 44282
Maritime Postmark Soc. [22051], PO Box 497, Wads-
worth, OH 44282
Maritime Trans. Res. Bd. [★7053]
Maritime Union of Australia [IO], Sydney, Australia
Maritime Union of New Zealand [IO], Wellington,
New Zealand
Mark Twain Assn. of New York [★9396]
Mark Twain Boyhood Home Associates [9395], 120
N Main St., Hannibal, MO 63401, (573)221-9010
Mark Twain Circle of New York [9396], Salwen Bus.
Communications, 156 5th Ave., Ste. 517, New
York, NY 10010-7002, (212)242-5546
Mark Twain Home Found. [9397], 120 N Main St.,
Hannibal, MO 63401, (573)221-9010
Mark Twain House and Museum [9398], 351 Farm-
ington Ave., Hartford, CT 06105-4401, (860)247-
0998
Mark Twain Memorial [★9398]
Mark Twain Res. Found. - Address unknown since
2011.
Market Development Advisory Comm. [IO], Kent
Town, Australia
Market Res. Soc. of New Zealand [IO], North Shore
City, New Zealand
Market Res. Soc. of the United Kingdom [IO],
London, United Kingdom
Marketing
ABA Marketing Network [2385]
Acad. of Marketing Sci. [8553]
Accountants Motivational Marketing Org. [2]Mar-
ketingAlliance of Intl. Market Res. Institutes
Amer. Assn. of Inside Sales Professionals [3156]
Amer. Collegiate Retailing Assn. [8554]
Amer. Marketing Assn. [2386]
Amer. Teleservices Assn. [2387]
Argentine Marketing Assn. [19833]
Assn. for Accounting Marketing [2388]
Assn. of Dir. Marketing [2389]
Assn. of Entertainment Marketing Agencies [1189]
Assn. of Equip. Mfrs. I AEM Marketing Coun.
[2390]
Assn. of Independent Creative Editors [2811]
Assn. of Needle-Free Injection Mfrs. [2330]
Assn. of Procurement Technical Asistance
Centers [1585]
Assn. for Rehabilitation Marketing and Sales
[2391]
Australian Direct Marketing Assn. [18497]
Black Fashion Designers Assn. [1037]
Brazilian Direct Selling Assn. [17278]
British Promotional Merchandise Assn. [13192]
Bus. Marketing Assn. [2392]
Bus. Marketing Assn. [2392]
Calendar Marketing Assn. [2393]
Catalog and Multichannel Marketing Coun. [1605]
CCNG Intl. [2394]
Circulation Coun. of DMA [2395]
Corporate Event Marketing Assn. [2396]
Coun. of Alumni Marketing and Membership
Professionals [2397]
CPExchange [7062]
CUES Financial Suppliers Forum [2398]
Diagnostic Marketing Assn. [2399]
Digital Signage Assn. [90]
Direct Marketing Assn. [2400]

Direct Marketing Educational Found. [8555]
Distributive Educ. Clubs of Am. [8556]
EcoLogical Mail Coalition [4698]
Electronic Retailing Assn. [2401]
Electronic Retailing Assn. [2401]
Farmers Market Coalition [3731]
German Foods North Am. [4715]
Hea. Indus. Representatives Assn. [2402]
Hispanic Marketing and Commun. Assn. [2403]
Hispanic Marketing and Commun. Assn. [2403]
House Plan Marketing Assn. [1038]
Incentive Fed. [2404]
Info. Tech. Services Marketing Assn. [2405]
Intermarket Agency Network [2406]
Intermarket Agency Network [2406]
Intl. Assn. of Butterfly Exhibitions [1232]
Intl. Collegiate Licensing Assn. [2407]
Intl. Experiential Marketing Assn. [2408]
Intl. Experiential Marketing Assn. [2408]
LCD TV Assn. [3431]
Legal Marketing Assn. [2409]
Legal Marketing Assn. [2409]
Livestock Marketing Assn. [4716]
Local Online Marketing Assn. [2410]
Marketing Educ. Assn. [8557]
Marketing Executives Networking Gp. [2411]
Marketing Res. Assn. [2412]
Marketing Sci. Inst. [2413]
Marketing Soc. of Kenya [455]
Materials Marketing Associates [2414]
Mexican Assn. of Marketing and Public Opinion
Res. Agencies [14394]
Mexican Market Res. and Opinion Polls Assn.
[17160]
Mu Kappa Tau [23585]
Multi-Level Marketing Intl. Assn. [2415]
Multi-Level Marketing Intl. Assn. [2415]
Mystery Shopping Providers Assn. [2416]
Natl. Alliance of Market Developers [2417]
Natl. Assn. of African Americans for Positive
Imagery [17157]
Natl. Assn. of Pharmaceutical Representatives
[2697]
Natl. Assn. of Produce Market Managers [4717]
Natl. Cattlemen's Beef Assn. [4718]
National Fraud Information Center/Internet Fraud
Watch [17467]
Natl. Livestock Producers Assn. [4719]
Natl. Mail Order Assn. [2418]
Natl. Marine Charter Assn. [2384]
Natl. Org. for Diversity in Sales and Marketing
[2419]
Natl. Watermelon Assn. [4462]
Newspaper Target Marketing Coalition [2576]
North Amer. Agricultural Marketing Officials [4720]
North Amer. Farmers' Direct Marketing Assn.
[4721]
Organic Trade Assn. [4722]
Paper and Plastic Representatives Mgt. Coun.
[2420]
Pi Sigma Epsilon [23586]
Private Label Mfrs. Assn. [2421]
Produce Marketing Assn. [4723]
Produce Marketing Assn. [4723]
Producers Livestock Marketing Assn. [4724]
Professional Rabbit Meat Assn. [4853]
Promotion Marketing Assn. [2422]
Renewable Energy Markets Assn. [1176]
Retail Energy Supply Assn. [1177]
Rising Tide Capital [1060]
Search Engine Marketing Professional Org.
[2423]
Soc. for Marketing Professional Services [2424]
Strategic Account Mgt. Assn. [2425]
Strategic Account Mgt. Assn. [2425]
Turkish Assn. of Marketing and Public Opinion
Researchers [11734]
United Producers, Inc. [4725]
Word of Mouth Marketing Assn. [2426]
Marketing and Advt. Global Network [96], 1017
Perry Hwy., Ste. 5, Pittsburgh, PA 15237,
(412)366-6850
Marketing and Advt. Global Network [96], 1017
Perry Hwy., Ste. 5, Pittsburgh, PA 15237,
(412)366-6850

Marketing Agencies Assn. Worldwide [3163], 89
Woodland Cir., Minneapolis, MN 55424, (952)922-
0130
Marketing Agencies Assn. Worldwide [3163], 89
Woodland Cir., Minneapolis, MN 55424, (952)922-
0130
Marketing Agents for Food Ser. Indus. [★1440]
Marketing Assn. of Pakistan [IO], Karachi, Pakistan
Marketing Assn. of Thailand [IO], Bangkok, Thailand
Marketing and Distributive Educ. Assn. [★8557]
Marketing Educ. Assn. [8557], PO Box 27473,
Tempe, AZ 85285-7473, (602)750-6735
Marketing Ethnic Faculty Assn. - Address unknown
since 2011.
Marketing Executives Networking Gp. [2411], 3
Anchorage Ln., Old Saybrook, CT 06475
Marketing Mgt. Coun. [★3007]
Marketing Mgt. Coun. [★3007]
Marketing Res. Assn. [2412], 110 Natl. Dr., 2nd Fl.,
Glastonbury, CT 06033-1212, (860)682-1000
Marketing Res. Trade Assn. [★2412]
Marketing Sci. Inst. [2413], 1000 Massachusetts
Ave., Cambridge, MA 02138-5396, (617)491-2060
Marketing Soc. of Ireland [IO], Bray, Ireland
Marketing Soc. of Kenya [IO], Nairobi, Kenya
Marketing Soc. - United Kingdom [IO], Teddington,
United Kingdom
Markham Prayer Card Apostolate - Defunct.
Marking Device Assn. [★3351]
Marking Device Assn. [★3351]
Marking Device Assn. Intl. [★3351]
Marking Device Assn. Intl. [★3351]
Markkinointiviestinnan Toismistojen Liitto [★IO]
Markle Found. [6436], 10 Rockefeller Plz., 16th Fl.,
New York, NY 10020-1903, (212)713-7600
Marklin Digital Special Interest Gp. [21891], PO Box
510559, New Berlin, WI 53151-0559, (262)784-
8854
Marky Cattle Assn. [3922], PO Box 198, Walton, KS
67151-0198, (620)837-3303
Marley Family Assn. [20556], Michael D. Frost, PhD,
Archivist, 5964 Overhill Rd., Mission Hills, KS
66208, (913)262-0448
Marlin Auto Club [21097], 7580 Old Dayton Rd.,
Dayton, OH 45427, (812)246-9920
Marlowe Soc. [IO], Teddington, United Kingdom
Marlowe Soc. of Am. [9399], 823 N Midland St.,
Little Rock, AR 72205
Marmon Club [21098], PO Box 530759, Miami
Shores, FL 33153-0759, (717)350-6665
MARQUES - Assn. of European Trademark Owners
[IO], Leicester, United Kingdom
Marquette Univ. Alumni Assn. [18884], Marquette
Univ., PO Box 1881, Milwaukee, WI 53201-1881,
(414)288-7441
Marriage
Alliance for Marriage [12435]
Alternatives to Marriage Proj. [18087]
Alternatives to Marriage Proj. [18087]
Amer. Assn. of Wedding Planners [2427]
Amer. Professional Wedding Photographers Assn.
[2710]
Assn. of Certified Professional Wedding Consult-
ants [2428]
Assn. for Couples in Marriage Enrichment [12436]
Christian Family Life [12001]
Commn. on Accreditation for Marriage and Family
Therapy Educ. [8558]
Loved Ones and Drivers Support [13342]
Marriage Equality U.S.A. [12437]
Natl. Marriage Encounter [12438]
Natl. Org. for Marriage [12439]MarriageNorthern
Ireland Mixed Marriage Assn.
Secretariat for Family, Laity, Women, and Youth
[12020]
Stepfamily Found. [12021]
Straight Spouse Network [12440]
Union for Reform Judaism I Commn. on Outreach
and Synagogue Community [19904]
Wedding Indus. Professionals Assn. [475]
Worldwide Marriage Encounter [12441]
Worldwide Marriage Encounter [12441]
Marriage Care [IO], London, United Kingdom
Marriage Equality U.S.A. [12437], 4096 Piedmont
Ave., Ste. 257, Oakland, CA 94611, (510)496-2700

A star before a book entry number signifies that the name is not listed separately, but is mentioned within the entry.

Marrow Donor Prog; Natl. [14426]
Marrow Donor Prog; Natl. [14426]
Mars Soc. [IO], Edinburgh, United Kingdom
Mars Soc. [7452], 11111 W 8th Ave., Unit A, Lakewood, CO 80215, (303)980-0890
Marshall Coll. Fund; Thurgood [7705]
Marshall Islands Athletics [IO], Majuro, Marshall Islands
Marshall Islands Judo Assn. [IO], Majuro, Marshall Islands
Marshall Islands Natl. Olympic Comm. [IO], Majuro, Marshall Islands
Marshall Islands Tennis Fed. [IO], Majuro, Marshall Islands
Marshall Islands Weightlifting Fed. [IO], Majuro, Marshall Islands
Martha Org. [IO], Helsinki, Finland
Martial Arts
  Aikido Assn. of Am. [22216]
  All Japan Ju-Jitsu Intl. Fed. [22720]
  Amer. Amateur Karate Fed. [22721]
  Amer. Kempo-Karate Assn. [22722]
  Amer. Sambo Assn. [22723]
  Amer. Teachers Assn. of the Martial Arts [22724]
  Amer. Wu Shu Soc. [22725]
  Amer. Wu Shu Soc. [22725]
  Amer. Yangjia Michuan Taijiquan Assn. [22726]
  Assn. for Renaissance Martial Arts [8559]
  Assn. for Renaissance Martial Arts [8559]
  Assn. of Women Martial Arts Instructors [22727]
  Chen Qingzhou Martial Arts Assn., USA [22728]
  Choy Lee Fut Martial Arts Fed. of Am. [22729]
  Christian Jujitsu Assn. [22730]
  Combat Martial Art Practitioners Assn. [22731]
  European Taekwondo Union [2074]
  Feminist Karate Union [22732]
  Gin Soon Tai Chi Chuan Fed. [22733]
  Intl. Assn. of Gay and Lesbian Martial Artists [22734]
  Intl. Assn. of Gay and Lesbian Martial Artists [22734]
  Intl. Chinese Boxing Assn. [22436]
  Intl. Disabled Self-Defense Assn. [13032]
  Intl. Modern Hapkido Fed. [22735]
  Intl. Seven-Star Mantis Style Lee Kam Wing Martial Art Assn. USA [22736]
  Intl. Shaolin Kenpo Assn. [22737]
  Intl. Shaolin Kenpo Assn. [22737]
  Intl. Sungja-Do Assn. [22738]
  Intl. Traditional Karate Fed. [22739]
  Intl. Traditional Karate Fed. [22739]
  Intl. Yang Style Tai Chi Chuan Assn. [22740]
  Intl. Yang Style Tai Chi Chuan Assn. [22740]
  Japan Karate-Do Org. [22741]
  Japan Karate-Do Org. [22741]
  Martial Arts Indus. Assn. [2429]
  Martial Arts Indus. Assn. [2429]
  Martial Arts Intl. Fed. [22742]
  Martial Arts Intl. Fed. [22742]
  Martial Arts Teachers' Assn. [22743]
  Martial Arts U.S.A. [22744]
  Natl. Assn. of Professional Martial Artists [22745]
  Natl. Coun. for Taekwondo Masters Certification [22746]
  Natl. Team Cheng Martial Arts Assn. [22747]
  Natl. Women's Martial Arts Fed. [22748]Martial-North Am. Wu(Hao) Taiji Fed.
  Pan Amer. Taekwondo Union [22749]
  Pan Amer. Taekwondo Union [22749]
  Patience T'ai Chi Assn. [22750]
  Shudokan Martial Arts Assn. [22751]
  Special Military Active Retired Travel Club [20690]
  Special Military Active Retired Travel Club [20690]
  Tomiki Aikido of the Americas [22752]
  Traditional Tae Kwon Do Chung Do Assn. [22753]
  Triangle Martial Arts Assn. [22754]
  U.S.A. Wushu-Kungfu Fed. [22755]
  U.S. Cheng Ming Martial Arts Assn. [22756]
  U.S. Hapki Hae [22757]
  U.S. Isshinryu Karate Assn. [22758]
  U.S. Kuo Shu Fed. [22759]
  U.S. Martial Arts Assn. [22760]
  U.S. Martial Arts Assn. [22760]
  U.S. Muay Thai Assn. [22761]
  U.S. Sport Jujitsu Assn. [22762]

  U.S. Taekwondo Union [22763]
  U.S. War Dogs Assn. [20691]
  U.S. Yudo Assn. [22764]
  Universal Martial Arts Brotherhood [22765]
  Universal Martial Arts Brotherhood [22765]
  U.S.A. Karate Fed. [22766]
  USA Natl. Karate-do Fed. [22710]
  World Hapkido Assn. [22767]
  World Head of Family Sokeship Coun. [22768]
  World Jeet Kune Do Fed. [22769]
  The World Kuoshu Fed. [22770]
  World Martial Arts Assn. [22771]
  World Modern Arnis Alliance [22772]
  World Mudo Fed. [22773]
  World Traditional Karate Org. [22774]
  World Traditional Karate Org. [22774]
  Zen-do Kai Martial Arts [22775]
Martial Arts Assn. of Maldives [IO], Male, Maldives
Martial Arts Indus. Assn. [2429], 1000 Century Blvd., Oklahoma City, OK 73110, (866)626-6226
Martial Arts Indus. Assn. [IO], Kenthurst, Australia
Martial Arts Indus. Assn. [2429], 1000 Century Blvd., Oklahoma City, OK 73110, (866)626-6226
Martial Arts Intl. Fed. [22742], 1850 Columbia Pike, Ste. No. 612, Arlington, VA 22204, (703)920-1590
Martial Arts Intl. Fed. [22742], 1850 Columbia Pike, Ste. No. 612, Arlington, VA 22204, (703)920-1590
Martial Arts Teachers' Assn. [22743], 800 S Gulfview Blvd., Ste. 804, Clearwater Beach, FL 33767
Martial Arts U.S.A. [22744], 1619 Fairway Dr. SW, Jacksonville, AL 36265, (256)782-5078
Martin Luther King, Jr. Center for Nonviolent Social Change [18170], 449 Auburn Ave. NE, Atlanta, GA 30312, (404)526-8900
Martin Luther King, Jr. Center for Social Change [★18170]
Martina McBride Fan Club [23876], PO Box 291627, Nashville, TN 37229-1627
Martinique Billfish Assn. [IO], Fort-de-France, Martinique
Marttaliitto [★IO]
Marx Brotherhood [23808], 335 Fieldstone Dr., New Hope, PA 18938-1012
Marx Bros. Stud. Unit [★23808]
Marxism
  Marxism and Philosophy Assn. [10070]
  Youth for Intl. Socialism [18663]
Marxism and Philosophy Assn. [10070], Drexel Univ., Dept. of English and Philosophy, 3141 Chestnut St., 5030 MacAlister Hall, Philadelphia, PA 19104, (215)895-1353
Marxist-Leninist Party of the U.S.A. - Defunct.
Mary Swords Debaillon Louisiana Iris Soc. [★21822]
Marycrest Intl. Univ. Alumni Assn. - Defunct.
Maryheart Crusaders [19449], 22 Button St., Meriden, CT 06450, (203)238-9735
MaryKnoll Associate Lay Missioners [★20057]
MaryKnoll Associate Lay Missioners [★20057]
Maryknoll Fathers and Bros. [19450], PO Box 304, Maryknoll, NY 10545-0304, (914)941-7590
Maryknoll Fathers and Bros. [19450], PO Box 304, Maryknoll, NY 10545-0304, (914)941-7590
Maryknoll Lay Missioners [20057], PO Box 307, Maryknoll, NY 10545-0307, (914)762-6364
Maryknoll Lay Missioners [20057], PO Box 307, Maryknoll, NY 10545-0307, (914)762-6364
Maryknoll Mission Family [★19450]
Maryknoll Mission Family [★19450]
Maryknoll Priests, Bros., and Priest and Brother Associates [★19450]
Maryknoll Priests, Bros., and Priest and Brother Associates [★19450]
Maryknoll Sisters of Saint Dominic [20058], PO Box 311, Maryknoll, NY 10545-0311, (914)941-7575
Maryland Suicide Found. [★13294]
Maryland Truck Stop Found. [★3120]
Masada/Maccabi Israel Summer Programs [19881], 520 8th Ave., New York, NY 10018, (212)532-4949
The Maserati Club [21099], 325 Walden Ave., Harriman, TN 37748, (865)882-9230
The Maserati Club [21099], 325 Walden Ave., Harriman, TN 37748, (865)882-9230
Maserati Club of Am. [★21099]
Maserati Club of Am. [★21099]
Maserati Info. Exchange [21100], 1620 Indus. Dr. SW, Ste. F, Auburn, WA 98001-6555, (253)833-2598

Maserati Owners Club of North Am. [★21099]
Maserati Owners Club of North Am. [★21099]
Mason Contractors Assn. of Am. [923], 1481 Merchant Dr., Algonquin, IL 60102, (224)678-9709
Masonic Ser. Assn. of North Am. [19136], 8120 Fenton St., Ste. 203, Silver Spring, MD 20910-4785, (301)588-4010
Masonic Services Assn. of the U.S. [★19136]
Masonry
  Intl. Coun. of Employers of Bricklayers and Allied Craftworkers [23252]
Masonry Heater Assn. of North Am. [1713], 2180 S Flying Q Ln., Tucson, AZ 85713, (520)883-0191
Masonry Indus. Comm. [★919]
Masonry Indus. Comm. [★919]
Masonry Res. Found. [★919]
Masonry Res. Found. [★919]
The Masonry Soc. [6576], 3970 Broadway, Ste. 201-D, Boulder, CO 80304-1135, (303)939-9700
The Masonry Soc. [6576], 3970 Broadway, Ste. 201-D, Boulder, CO 80304-1135, (303)939-9700
Masons
  Ancient Accepted Scottish Rite of Free-Masonry, Northern Masonic Jurisdiction I Supreme Coun. [19124]
  Ancient and Accepted Scottish Rite of Free Masonry, Southern Jurisdiction I Supreme Coun. 33rd Degree [19125]
  Ancient Egyptian Arabic Order Nobles of the Mystic Shrine [19126]
  Gen. Grand Chap., Order of the Eastern Star [19127]
  Gen. Grand Chap., Order of the Eastern Star [19127]
  Gen. Grand Chap. of Royal Arch Masons Intl. [19128]
  Gen. Grand Chap. of Royal Arch Masons Intl. [19128]
  The Grottoes of North Am. [19129]
  Heroes of '76 [19130]
  High Twelve Intl. [19131]
  High Twelve Intl. [19131]
  Imperial Coun. of the Ancient Arabic Order of the Nobles of the Mystic Shrine for North Am. [19132]
  Job's Daughters Intl. [19133]
  Job's Daughters Intl. [19133]
  Knights Templar, Grand Encampment, U.S.A. [19134]
  Ladies Oriental Shrine of North Am. [19135]
  Masonic Ser. Assn. of North Am. [19136]
  Modern Free and Accepted Masons of the World [19137]
  Modern Free and Accepted Masons of the World [19137]
  Natl. Sojourners [19138]
  Philalethes Soc. [19139]
  Red Cross of Constantine I United Grand Imperial Coun. [19140]
  Royal Order of Scotland [19141]
  Tall Cedars of Lebanon of North Am. [19142]
  Universal Masonic Brotherhood [19143]
Masons' Company [IO], London, United Kingdom
The Masquers [10586], PO Box 71037, Richmond, CA 94807, (510)232-3888
Mass Communications; Accrediting Coun. on Educ. in Journalism and [8434]
Mass Finishing Job Shops Assn. [1347], 808 13th St., East Moline, IL 61244-1628, (309)755-1101
Mass Marketing Insurance Inst. [1994], 14 W 3rd St., Ste. 200, Kansas City, MO 64105, (816)221-7575
Mass Merchandising Res. Found. [★3125]
Mass Retailing Inst. [★3125]
Massachusetts Bay Railroad Enthusiasts [10491], PO Box 4245, Andover, MA 01810-0814, (617)489-5277
Massachusetts Catholic Order of Foresters [★18946]
Massachusetts Center for Renaissance Stud. [10507], Univ. of Massachusetts, Dept. of English, Center for Renaissance Stud., PO Box 2300, Amherst, MA 01004, (413)577-3600
Massachusetts Center for Renaissance Stud. [10507], Univ. of Massachusetts, Dept. of English, Center for Renaissance Stud., PO Box 2300, Amherst, MA 01004, (413)577-3600

Reference to "IO" in place of a book number signifies that the association may be found in the 50th edition of International Organizations.

Encyclopedia of Associations, 51st Edition   **2975**

Massachusetts Soc. of Examining Physicians [★15244]

Massachusetts Soc. of Law and Medicine [★15244]

Massage
Alliance for Massage Therapy Educ. [8560]
Amer. Massage Therapy Assn. [15261]
Amer. Medical Massage Assn. [15262]
Amer. Org. for Bodywork Therapies of Asia [15263]
Assoc. Bodywork and Massage Professionals [15264]
Day-Break Geriatric Massage Inst. [15265]
Emergency Response Massage Intl. [15266]
Father Josef's Method of Reflexology [13676]
Hospital-Based Massage Network [15267]
Infant Massage USA [15268]
Intl. Assn. of Animal Massage and Bodywork [15269]
Intl. Assn. of Animal Massage and Bodywork [15269]
Intl. Assn. of Infant Massage [15270]
Intl. Assn. of Infant Massage [15270]
Intl. Massage Assn. [15271]
Intl. Massage Assn. [15271]
Intl. Thai Therapists Assn. [15272]
Intl. Thai Therapists Assn. [15272]
Medical Spa Soc. [14902]
Natl. Certification Bd. for Therapeutic Massage and Bodywork [15273]
Shine Therapy [15274]
Spa Assn. [3127]
Thai Healing Alliance Intl. [15275]
Touch of Relief [15004]

Massage Therapists; Natl. Assn. of Nurse [15768]

Massage Therapy Assn. [IO], Kenilworth, Republic of South Africa

Massenet Soc. - Defunct.

Massey Collectors Assn. [22178], 53231 213th St., Lake Crystal, MN 56055, (507)381-1429

Master Brewers Assn. of Am. [★450]

Master Brewers Assn. of Am. [★450]

Master Brewers Assn. of the Americas [450], 3340 Pilot Knob Rd., St. Paul, MN 55121-2097, (651)454-7250

Master Brewers Assn. of the Americas [450], 3340 Pilot Knob Rd., St. Paul, MN 55121-2097, (651)454-7250

Master Builders Assn. - Australian Capital Territory [IO], Canberra, Australia

Master Builders Assn. - Malaysia [IO], Kuala Lumpur, Malaysia

Master Builders Assn. - New South Wales [IO], Forest Lodge, Australia

Master Builders Assn. - South Australia [IO], Adelaide, Australia

Master Builders Assn. - Tasmania [IO], Hobart, Australia

Master Builders Assn. - Victoria [IO], Melbourne, Australia

Master Builders Assn. - Western Australia [IO], West Perth, Australia

Master Builders Australia [IO], Yarralumla, Australia

Master Builders South Africa [IO], Halfway House, Republic of South Africa

Master Carvers Assn. [IO], Leighton Buzzard, United Kingdom

Master Drawings Assn. [9189], 225 Madison Ave., New York, NY 10016, (212)590-0369

Master Locksmiths Assn. [IO], Daventry, United Kingdom

Master Painters Australia - Western Australian Assn. [IO], Maylands, Australia

Master Photo Dealers' and Finishers' Assn. [★2730]
Master Photo Dealers' and Finishers' Assn. [★2730]
Master Photo Finishers and Dealers Assn. [★2730]
Master Photo Finishers and Dealers Assn. [★2730]

Master Photographers Assn. [IO], Darlington, United Kingdom

Master Plumbers and Mech. Services Assn. of Australia [IO], West Melbourne, Australia

Master Weavers Inst. - Defunct.

Master Window Cleaners of Am. [2253], 1220G Airport Fwy., No. 561, Bedford, TX 76022

Masters of Foxhounds Assn. of Am. [22699], PO Box 363, Millwood, VA 22646, (540)955-5680

Master's Men of the Free Will Baptist Church [★19323]

Master's Men of the Natl. Assn. of Free Will Baptists [19323], PO Box 5002, Antioch, TN 37011-5002, (615)760-6142

Masters Swimming Comm. of the AAU [★23044]

Mastic Asphalt Coun. [IO], Hastings, United Kingdom

Mastiff and Bullmastiff Club in France [IO], Chassagny, France

Mastiff Club of Am. [21600], Jodi LoBambard, Membership Sec., 189 Miranda Ln., Roxboro, NC 27574, (585)594-5354

The Mastocytosis Soc. [14400], PO Box 731, Brenham, TX 77834-0731

Masyarakat Telematika Indonesia [★IO]

Matagiri Sri Aurobindo Center [★20301]

Matanya's Hope [12737], PO Box 562, Homewood, IL 60430

Matanya's Hope [12737], PO Box 562, Homewood, IL 60430

MATCH Intl. Centre [IO], Ottawa, ON, Canada

Matchbox U.S.A. [21369], 62 Saw Mill Rd., Durham, CT 06422, (860)349-1655

Matchcover
Rathkamp Matchcover Soc. [21882]

Material Handling Accessory Mfrs., Production Sect. of the Material Handling Indus. [★1847]

Material Handling Equip. Distributors Assn. [1844], 201 U.S. Hwy. 45, Vernon Hills, IL 60061-2398, (847)680-3500

Material Handling Indus. [★1845]

Material Handling Indus. of Am. [1845], 8720 Red Oak Blvd., Ste. 201, Charlotte, NC 28217-3992, (704)676-1190

Material Handling Inst. [★1845]

Material Handling Inst. of Amer., Lift Mfrs. Prdt. Sect. [1846], 8720 Red Oak Blvd., Ste. 201, Charlotte, NC 28217-3996, (704)676-1190

Materials
Asphalt Interlayer Assn. [525]
CR Found. [14277]
Fed. of Materials Societies [7063]
Materials Handling Indus. of Am. I Electrification and Controls Mfrs. Assn. [1847]
Materials Handling and Mgt. Soc. [7064]
Materials Handling and Mgt. Soc. [7064]
Materials Res. Soc. [7065]
Natl. Materials Advisory Bd. [7066]
Palladium Alliance Intl. [2489]
Soc. for the Advancement of Material and Process Engg. [7067]

Materials Advisory Bd. [★7066]

Materials Engg. Institute [★7090]

Materials Engg. Institute [★7090]

Materials Handling Engineers Assn. [IO], Ely, United Kingdom

Materials Handling Indus. of Am. I Electrification and Controls Mfrs. Assn. [1847], 8720 Red Oak Blvd., Ste. 201, Charlotte, NC 28217-3992, (704)676-1190

Materials Handling and Mgt. Soc. [7064], 8720 Red Oak Blvd., Ste. 201, Charlotte, NC 28217, (704)676-1190

Materials Handling and Mgt. Soc. [7064], 8720 Red Oak Blvd., Ste. 201, Charlotte, NC 28217, (704)676-1190

Materials Marketing Associates [2414], 136 S Kewee St., Dayton, OH 45402, (937)222-1024

Materials and Methods Standards Assn. [579], 4125 LaPalma Ave., No. 250, Anaheim, CA 92807

Materials Properties Coun. [7098], PO Box 1942, New York, NY 10113-1941, (216)658-3847

Materials Res. Soc. [7065], 506 Keystone Dr., Warrendale, PA 15086-7573, (724)779-3003

Materials Tech. Inst. [757], 1215 Fern Ridge Pkwy., Ste. 206, St. Louis, MO 63141-4408, (314)576-7712

Materials Tech. Inst. of the Chem. Process Indus. [★757]

Maternal Life Intl. [16589], 1154 Steele St., Butte, MT 59701-2136, (406)782-9132

Maternal Life Intl. [16589], 1154 Steele St., Butte, MT 59701-2136, (406)782-9132

Maternity Center Assn. [★15875]

Maternity Coalition [IO], Blackburn, Australia

Math for Am. [8565], 160 5th Ave., 8th Fl., New York, NY 10010, (646)437-0904

Math/Science Network [★8563]

Mathematical Assn. [IO], Leicester, United Kingdom

Mathematical Assn. of Am. [7076], 1529 18th St. NW, Washington, DC 20036-1358, (202)387-5200

Mathematical Soc. of Japan [IO], Tokyo, Japan

Mathematical Stud. Unit [22052], Estelle A. Buccino, Sec.-Treas., 830 W 40th St., Apt. 803, Baltimore, MD 21211

Mathematical Union of Argentina [IO], Buenos Aires, Argentina

Mathematics
Amer. Mathematical Assn. of Two-Year Colleges [8561]
Amer. Mathematical Soc. [7068]
Assn. for Computing Machinery I Special Interest Gp. for Symbolic and Algebraic Manipulation [7069]
Assn. of State Supervisor of Mathematics [8562]
Assn. for Symbolic Logic [7070]
Assn. for Symbolic Logic [7070]
Assn. for Women in Mathematics [7071]
Canadian Mathematical Soc. [4250]
Comm. of Presidents of Statistical Societies [7473]
Conf. Bd. of the Mathematical Sciences [7072]
Euler Soc. [10071]
EYH Network [8563]
HOPOS - The Intl. Soc. for the History of Philosophy of Sci. [8839]
Intl. Assn. of Mathematical Sciences [18140]
Intl. Linear Algebra Soc. [7073]
Intl. Linear Algebra Soc. [7073]
Intl. Soc. of the Arts, Mathematics, and Architecture [7003]
Intl. Soc. for Bayesian Anal. [7074]
Intl. Soc. for Bayesian Anal. [7074]
Intl. Soc. of Difference Equations [7075]
Intl. Soc. of Difference Equations [7075]
Israel Mathematical Union [783]
Kappa Mu Epsilon [23587]
The Madison Proj. [8564]
Math for Am. [8565]
Mathematical Assn. of Am. [7076]
Mu Alpha Theta [23588]
Natl. Assn. of Math Circles [8566]
Natl. Coun. of Supervisors of Mathematics [8567]
Natl. Coun. of Teachers of Mathematics [8568]
Pi Mu Epsilon [23589]
Reasoning Mind [8569]
Sigma Zeta [23633]
Soc. for Indus. and Applied Mathematics [7077]
Soc. for Natural Philosophy [7078]
Women and Mathematics Educ. [8570]
World Sci. and Engg. Acad. and Soc. [6837]

Mathematics Assn. of Pakistan [IO], Karachi, Pakistan

Mathematics Assn; School Sci. and [8851]

Mathematics Assn; School Sci. and [8851]

Matkailun Edistamiskeskus [★IO]

Matrix Biology Soc. of Australia and New Zealand [IO], Balnarring, Australia

Matrix Found. [18793], 400 N Washington St., Ste. 300, Alexandria, VA 22314

A Matter of Justice Coalition [5748], PO Box 1209, Dahlgren, VA 22448-1209, (540)663-0486

Mature Outlook - Defunct.

Mauneluk Assn. [★12562]

Mauritanian Red Crescent [IO], Nouakchott, Mauritania

Mauritius Amateur Radio Soc. [IO], Quatre Bornes, Mauritius

Mauritius Assn. of Quantity Surveyors [IO], Quatre Bornes, Mauritius

Mauritius Badminton Assn. [IO], Rose Hill, Mauritius

Mauritius Chamber of Commerce and Indus. [IO], Port Louis, Mauritius

Mauritius Employers' Fed. [IO], Ebene City, Mauritius

Mauritius Red Cross Soc. [IO], Curepipe, Mauritius

Mauritius Squash Rackets Assn. [IO], Quatre Bornes, Mauritius

Mauritius Taekwondo Assn. [IO], Port Louis, Mauritius

A star before a book entry number signifies that the name is not listed separately, but is mentioned within the entry.

Mauritius Tennis Fed. [IO], Phoenix, Mauritius
Mauritius Turf Club [IO], Port Louis, Mauritius
Mauritius-U.S. Bus. Assn. [2100], 1054 31st St. NW, Ste. 540, Washington, DC 20007, (202)965-4000
Mauritius Yachting Assn. [IO], Port Louis, Mauritius
Mautner Proj. for Lesbian Hea. [14579], 1875 Connecticut Ave. NW, Ste. 710, Washington, DC 20009, (202)332-5536
Mautner Proj. for Lesbians with Cancer [★14579]
Maverick/Comet Club Intl. [21101], Seth Roberts, Coor., 1815 Kildaire Farm R, Cary, NC 27518, (919)645-3131
Max-Eyth-Gesselschaft Agrartechnik im VDI [★IO]
Max-Eyth Soc. for Agricultural Engg. of the VDI [IO], Dusseldorf, Germany
Maxillofacial Prosthetics; Amer. Acad. of [14238]
Maxillofacial Surgeons; Amer. Assn. of Oral and [16002]
Maxillofacial Surgeons; Amer. Coll. of Oral and [16004]
Maxillofacial Surgery; Amer. Bd. of Oral and [16003]
May I Speak Freely Media [18091], 27 Cambridge Terr., Cambridge, MA 02140
Mayan and Indigenous Spiritual Bodies; Saq' Be': Org. for [9867]
Mayan Medical Aid [12466], 6988 Pinehaven Rd., Oakland, CA 94611-1018
Maybee Soc. [20557], 154 Wolverine Way, Scotts Valley, CA 95066
Mayflower Descendants; Gen. Soc. of [20746]
Mayflower Descendants; Gen. Soc. of [20746]
Mayflower Soc. [★20746]
Mayflower Soc. [★20746]
Maynard Bernstein Resource Center on Cults - Defunct.
Mayonnaise and Salad Dressing Inst. [★1377]
Mayonnaise and Salad Dressing Mfrs. Assn. [★1377]
Mazda Club [21102], PO Box 11238, Chicago, IL 60611, (773)769-6262
MAZON [12284], 10495 Santa Monica Blvd., Ste. 100, Los Angeles, CA 90025, (310)442-0020
MAZON [12284], 10495 Santa Monica Blvd., Ste. 100, Los Angeles, CA 90025, (310)442-0020
MBIRA [10239], PO Box 7863, Berkeley, CA 94707-0863, (510)548-6053
Mbong Found., Intl. [IO], Mexico City, Mexico
MC Sailing Assn. [22369], PO Box 250, Lewis Center, OH 43035-0250, (740)549-4700
MCAD Family Support Gp. [★15496]
MCAD Family Support Gp. [★15496]
McAdams Historical Soc. [20558], 711 17th Ave. N, Surfside Beach, SC 29575, (818)789-1086
McAlpin(e) Family Assn. - Defunct.
McCoy Pottery Collectors' Soc. [21266], 420 Quail Run Cir., Fountain Inn, SC 29644
McCullough/McCulloch Clan Soc. - Defunct.
McDonald's Collectors Club [21370], Joyce Losonsky, 168 Fieldcrest Ln., Ephrata, PA 17522
McDonald's Hispanic Operators Assn. [3090], Ronald McDonald House Charities, 1 Kroc Dr., Oak Brook, IL 60523, (630)623-7048
McGrath Family Assn. - Defunct.
McLaughlin Buick Club of Canada [IO], Sutton, ON, Canada
McLibel Support Campaign - UK [IO], London, United Kingdom
McLibel Support Campaign - U.S.A. - Defunct.
MDA/ALS Res. Center; Forbes Norris [15590]
MDS Indus. Assn. [★3427]
MDS Indus. Assn. [★3427]
Meader Family Assn. [20559], 158 Ashdown Rd., Ballston Lake, NY 12019, (518)399-5013
Meals for Millions Found. [★12279]
Meals for Millions/Freedom from Hunger Found. [★12279]
Meals-on-Wheels America - Defunct.
Meals on Wheels Assn. of Am. [12151], 203 S Union St., Alexandria, VA 22314-3355, (703)548-5558
Meals4Israel
Meals4Israel - Address unknown since 2011.
Meaningful Media [12442], 10825 Washington Blvd., Culver City, CA 90232, (310)876-3686
Measurement, Control, and Automation Assn. [3177], PO Box 3698, Williamsburg, VA 23187-3698, (757)258-3100

Meat
Amer. Assn. of Meat Processors [2430]
Amer. Meat Inst. [2431]
Intl. HACCP Alliance [4809]
Intl. Yak Assn. [4694]
Meat Bd. of Namibia [12607]
Meat Importers Coun. of Am. [2432]
Natl. Meat Assn. [2433]
North Amer. Meat Processors Assn. [2434]
North Amer. Meat Processors Assn. [2434]
Professional Rabbit Meat Assn. [4853]
U.S. Meat Export Fed. [2435]
U.S. Meat Export Fed. [2435]
Meat Bd. [IO], Zoetermeer, Netherlands
Meat Bd. of Namibia [IO], Windhoek, Namibia
Meat Importers' Coun. [★2432]
Meat Importers Coun. of Am. [2432], 1901 Ft. Myer Dr., Ste. 1110, Arlington, VA 22209, (703)522-1910
Meat Indus'. Assn. [IO], Rozzano, Italy
Meat and Livestock Australia [IO], North Sydney, Australia
Meat Loaf UK Fanclub [IO], Cheadle Hulme, United Kingdom
Meat Processing Indus. Assn. of Spain [IO], Madrid, Spain
Meat and Wool New Zealand [IO], Wellington, New Zealand
Mech. Bank Collectors of Am. [21204], PO Box 13323, Pittsburgh, PA 15242
Mech. Bank Collectors of Rhode Island [★21204]
Mech. Contractors Assn. of Am. [924], 1385 Piccard Dr., Rockville, MD 20850-4340, (301)869-5800
Mech. Contractors Assn. of Canada [IO], Ottawa, ON, Canada
Mech. Equip. Mfrs. Representatives Assn. [2321], 11 W Mt. Vernon Pl., Baltimore, MD 21201, (410)793-0202
Mech. and Metal Trades Confed. [IO], Paisley, United Kingdom
Mech. Packing Assn. [★1823]
Mech. Power Transmission Assn. [1848], 6724 Lone Oak Blvd., Naples, FL 34109, (239)514-3441
Mech. Power Transmission Equip. Distributors Assn. [★1860]
Mech. Power Transmission Equip. Distributors Assn. [★1860]
Mechanics
Amer. Soc. of Mech. Engineers [7079]
Assn. of Chairmen of Departments of Mechanics [8571]
U.S. Assn. for Computational Mechanics [7080]
U.S. Natl. Comm. on Theoretical and Applied Mechanics [7081]
Vibration Inst. [7082]
Mechanics Educational Soc. of America - Defunct.
Mechanics and Tradesmen of the City of New York; Gen. Soc. of [8965]
MED25 Intl. [14803], PO Box 1459, Mercer Island, WA 98040, (206)779-0655
MEDACT [IO], London, United Kingdom
Medal Collectors of Am. [21981], Barry Tayman, Treas., 3115 Nestling Pine Ct., Ellicott City, MD 21042
Medal of Honor Historical Soc. - Defunct.
Medal of Honor Legion [★20377]
Medau Movement [IO], Horsham, United Kingdom
Medecins pour la survie mondiale [★IO]
Medecins en Faveur de l'Environnement [★IO]
Medecins du Monde UK [IO], London, United Kingdom
Medecins Sans Frontieres [★12833]
Medecins Sans Frontieres [★IO]
Medecins Sans Frontieres [★IO]
Medecins Sans Frontieres [★12833]
Medecins Sans Frontieres - Australia [★IO]
Medecins Sans Frontieres - Hong Kong [IO], Hong Kong, People's Republic of China
Medecins Sans Frontieres - UAE [IO], Abu Dhabi, United Arab Emirates
Medecins Sans Frontieres - UK [IO], London, United Kingdom
Media
About-Face [13448]
Action Coalition for Media Educ. [18088]
Advanced Media Workflow Assn. [3386]

Africa News Ser. [17144]
Am. Abroad Media [18089]
Amer. Coun. on Consumer Interests [17442]
Amer. Family Assn. [17334]
Amer. Lib. Assn. - Public Info. Off. [10476]
Assn. for Computing Machinery | Special Interest Group on MultiMedia [6528]
Assn. for Downloadable Media [2436]
Assn. for Interactive Marketing [3400]
Baseball Writers Assn. of Am. [2814]
Beyondmedia Educ. [8572]
Breakthrough [17815]
Christian Media Assn. [19947]
The Christian Sci. Publishing Soc. [2927]
DigitalEve [7083]
DVD Assn. [7084]
European Multimedia Forum [8078]
Free Expression Policy Proj. [17290]
Independent Arts and Media [9179]
Independent Media Arts Preservation [10072]
Interactive Media Entertainment and Gaming Assn. [7008]
Intl. Assn. of Audio Visual Communicators [1259]
Intl. Digital Media Arts Assn. [7085]
Intl. Newspaper Gp. [2834]MediaIntl. Webcasting Assn.
Internews Network [18090]
Internews Network [18090]
Just Vision [17409]
Mainstream Media Proj. [18503]
May I Speak Freely Media [18091]
Meaningful Media [12442]
Media Action Grassroots Network [18092]
Media Action Network for Asian Americans [18093]
Media and Democracy Coalition [18094]
Media Ecology Assn. [8573]
Media Guilds Intl. [2437]
Media Res. Center [12443]
MediaChannel.org [18095]
MediaGlobal [12348]
Mobile Voter [18096]
Natl. Assn. of Media Brokers [3024]
Natl. Assn. for Media Literacy Educ. [8574]
Natl. Assn. of Media and Tech. Centers [2438]
Natl. Radio Proj. [18097]
Native Public Media [18098]
New Am. Media [18099]
Newspaper Target Marketing Coalition [2576]
OURMedia Network [18100]
Pacific Islanders in Communications [10073]
POWER UP: Professional Org. of Women in Entertainment Reaching UP! [17737]
Professional Outdoor Media Assn. [2439]
Prometheus Radio Proj. [18101]
Public Educ. Center [18425]
Public Media Found. [18102]
Public Radio Capital [10483]
Red Tag News Publications Assn. [2238]
Sci. Commun. Network [4726]
Soliya [18833]
We Interrupt This Message [18103]
Where Peace Lives [10355]
Wildlife Media [5155]MediaWorld Media Assn.
Media Access Gp. [12418], 1 Guest St., Boston, MA 02135, (617)300-3600
Media Access Proj. [17347], 1625 K St. NW, Ste. 1000, Washington, DC 20006, (202)232-4300
Media Action Grassroots Network [18092], Center for Media Justice, 436 14th St., 5th Fl., Oakland, CA 94612, (510)698-3800
Media Action Network for Asian Americans [18093], PO Box 11105, Burbank, CA 91510, (213)486-4433
Media Action Res. Center - Defunct.
Media-Advertising Partnership for a Drug-Free Am. [★13281]
Media Alliance [17348], 1904 Franklin St., Ste. 500, Oakland, CA 94612, (510)832-9000
Media Associates Intl. [19724], 351 S Main Pl., Ste. 230, Carol Stream, IL 60188-2455, (630)260-9063
Media Associates Intl. [19724], 351 S Main Pl., Ste. 230, Carol Stream, IL 60188-2455, (630)260-9063
Media Centre; IMZ Intl. Music [IO]
Media Coalition [17300], 19 Fulton St., Rm. 407, New York, NY 10038, (212)587-4025

Reference to "IO" in place of a book number signifies that the association may be found in the 50th edition of International Organizations.

Media Coalition/Americans for Constitutional Freedom [★17300]

Media Communications Assn. - Denmark [IO], Copenhagen, Denmark

Media Communications Assn. Intl. [1262], PO Box 5135, Madison, WI 53705-0135, (888)899-6224

Media Communications Assn. Intl. [1262], PO Box 5135, Madison, WI 53705-0135, (888)899-6224

Media and Democracy Coalition [18094], 1705 Desales St. NW, 5th Fl., Washington, DC 20036, (202)331-4090

Media Ecology Assn. [8573], Paul Soukup, Treas., Santa Clara Univ., Commun. Dept., 500 El Camino Real, Santa Clara, CA 95053, (408)554-4022

Media and Educational Technology Unit of the Amer. Assn. for Adult and Continuing Education - Defunct.

Media, Entertainment and Arts Alliance [IO], Strawberry Hills, Australia

Media Fellowship Intl. [19762], PO Box 82685, Kenmore, WA 98028, (425)488-3965

Media Fellowship Intl. [19762], PO Box 82685, Kenmore, WA 98028, (425)488-3965

Media Financial Mgt. Assn. [1312], 550 W Frontage Rd., Ste. 3600, Northfield, IL 60093, (847)716-7000

Media Financial Mgt. Assn. [1312], 550 W Frontage Rd., Ste. 3600, Northfield, IL 60093, (847)716-7000

Media Guilds-Intl. [2437], 10020 Benjamin Nicholas Pl., No. 103, Las Vegas, NV 89144, (702)878-4959

Media Human Resources Assn.

Media Human Resources Assn. - Address unknown since 2010.

The Media Inst. [17349], 2300 Clarendon Blvd., Ste. 602, Arlington, VA 22201-3398, (703)243-5700

Media Inst. of Southern Africa - Namibia [IO], Windhoek, Namibia

Media Inst. of Southern Africa - South Africa [IO], Johannesburg, Republic of South Africa

Media Inst. of Southern Africa - Tanzania [IO], Dar es Salaam, United Republic of Tanzania

Media Inst. of Southern Africa - Zambia [IO], Lusaka, Zambia

Media Law Rsrc. Center [5668], North Tower, 20th Fl., 520 Eighth Ave., New York, NY 10018, (212)337-0200

Media in Ministry Assn. [19994], 2549 Newbolt Dr., Orlando, FL 32817, (407)678-0159

Media Network - Defunct.

Media Rating Coun. [497], 420 Lexington Ave., Ste. 343, New York, NY 10170, (212)972-0300

Media Res. Center [12443], 325 S Patrick St., Alexandria, VA 22314-3580, (703)683-9733

Media Support Partnership Afghanistan [IO], Kabul, Afghanistan

Media Watch [17350], PO Box 618, Santa Cruz, CA 95061-0618, (831)423-6355

Media Watch [17350], PO Box 618, Santa Cruz, CA 95061-0618, (831)423-6355

MediaChannel.org [18095], 575 8th Ave., New York, NY 10018, (212)246-0202

MediaGlobal [12348], 7 Whitney Pl., Princeton Junction, NJ 08550, (609)529-6129

MediaGlobal [12348], 7 Whitney Pl., Princeton Junction, NJ 08550, (609)529-6129

Median Iris Soc. [21807], 682 Huntley Heights, Ballwin, MO 63021-5878, (636)256-3927

Mediation Familiale Canada [★IO]

Mediators Inst. Ireland [IO], Dublin, Ireland

Mediators Without Borders [5208], 4450 Arapahoe Ave., Ste. 100, Boulder, CO 80303, (877)268-5337

Mediawatch - UK [IO], Ashford, United Kingdom

Medicaid/SCHIP Dental Assn. [14296], 4411 Connecticut Ave. NW, Apt. 302, Washington, DC 20008, (508)322-0557

Medical

African Hea. Now [15139]

Aicardi Syndrome Newsl. [14581]

AIDS Clinical Trials Gp. [13593]

Alliance for Preventive Hea. [14864]

Amer. Acad. of Restorative Dentistry [14244]

Amer. Assn. of Endodontists | Amer. Bd. of Endodontics [14250]

Amer. Assn. of Nutritional Consultants [15814]

Amer. Bd. of Nutrition [15815]

Amer. Celiac Society | Dietary Support Coalition [15817]

Amer. Coll. of Community Midwives [15864]

Amer. Coll. of Physicians [15133]

Amer. Coll. of Veterinary Dermatology [16998]

Amer. Herbalists Guild [14989]

Amer. Hosp. Assn., Sect. for Long Term Care and Rehabilitation [15039]

Amer. Muslim Women Physicians Assn. [16252]

Amer. Osteopathic Coll. of Anesthesiologists [13735]

Amer. Paraplegia Soc. [16696]

Amer. Pharmacists Assn. | Acad. of Pharmacy Practice and Mgt. [16176]

Amer. Physician Scientists Assn. [8588]

Amer. Podiatric Medical Students' Assn. [16294]

Amer. Registry of Medical Assistants [15316]

Amer. Soc. for Aesthetic Plastic Surgery [14175]

Amer. Soc. for Clinical Nutrition [15821]

Amer. Soc. of Medication Safety Officers [14869]

Amer. Soc. of Plastic Surgeons | Plastic Surgery Educ. Found. [14178]

Assn. of Biomedical Communications Directors [14161]

Assn. of Needle-Free Injection Mfrs. [2330]

Assn. of Professors of Cardiology [14008]

Assn. of Prog. Directors in Internal Medicine [15134]

Assn. for Radiological and Imaging Nursing [15739]

Avenues, Natl. Support Gp. for Arthrogryposis Multiplex·Congenita [15573]

Benign Essential Blepharospasm Res. Found. [15575]

Cancer Support Community [13903]

Certification Bd. for Urologic Nurses and Associates [16944]

Chemotherapy Found. [15922]

Children's Cancer and Blood Found. [14964]

Children's Tumor Found. [15579]

Chinese Amer. Doctors Assn. [16261]

Chinese-American Soc. of Nuclear Medicine [15694]

Coalition for Tactical Medicine [15907]

Digital Pathology Assn. [16124]

Encephalitis Global [14384]

Environmental Res. Found. [13638]

Extensions for Independence [11786]

Fed. of Pediatric Organizations [16145]

Forbes Norris MDA/ALS Res. Center [15590]

Frontline Hepatitis Awareness [14983]

Global Neuro Rescue [15593]

Hea. Info. Rsrc. Center [14714]

Heart Rhythm Soc. [14016]

Intl. Anesthesia Res. Soc. [13748]

Intl. Assn. of Healthcare Central Ser. Material Mgt. [15058]

Intl. Assn. of Medical and Therapeutic Specialists [13686]

Intl. Atherosclerosis Soc. [14020]

Intl. Bronchoesophagological Soc. [13869]

Intl. Cellular Medicine Soc. [14649]

Intl. Fed. of Psoriasis Associations [14328]

Intl. Genetic Epidemiology Soc. [14514]

Intl. Pediatric Hypertension Assn. [15076]

Intl. Skeletal Soc. [16533]

Intl. Soc. for Cardiovascular Translational Res. [14024]

Intl. Soc. of Gastrointestinal Oncology [14568]

Intl. Soc. on Metabolic Eye Disease [15966]

Intl. Union Against Sexually Transmitted Infections, Regional Off. for North Am. [16656]

Iraqi Medical Sciences Assn. [15193]

Ivory Coast Medical Relief Team [16583]

Leukemia and Lymphoma Soc. [13936]

Marijuana Policy Proj. [18086]

Medical Records Inst. [15333]

Medical Spa Soc. [14902]

Natl. Alliance for the Primary Prevention of Sharps Injuries [16630]

Natl. Assn. of Female Paramedics [14472]

Natl. Assn. of Residents and Interns [15425]

Natl. Found. for Brain Res. [15666]

Neuro-Optometric Rehabilitation Assn. Intl. [15559]

North Amer. Assn. for Laser Therapy [15238]

North Amer. Clinical Dermatologic Soc. [14337]

North Amer. Sikh Medical and Dental Assn. [15429]

Oligonucleotide Therapeutics Soc. [16866]

Partnership for Quality Medical Donations [12478]

Peruvian Heart Assn. [14039]

Phi Chi Medical Fraternity [23594]

Philippine Nurses Assn. of Am. [15796]

Plastic Surgery Found. [14183]

Preimplantation Genetic Diagnosis Intl. Soc. [14656]

Purine Res. Soc. [15506]

Safety Net Hospitals for Pharmaceutical Access [16213]

San Francisco AIDS Found. [13624]

Semmelweis Soc. Intl. [16510]

Sino-American Network for Therapeutic Radiology and Oncology [16871]

Soc. of Nuclear Medicine Technologist Sect. [15697]

Soc. for Participatory Medicine [14829]

Soc. for Worldwide Medical Exchange [15212]

Tissue Engg. Intl. and Regenerative Medicine Soc. [13835]

Tourette Syndrome Assn. [15636]

Tropical Clinics [15216]

US Doctors for Africa [15221]

Veterinary Botanical Medicine Assn. [17046]

Medical Accreditation

Amer. Commn. for Accreditation of Reflexology Educ. and Training [7726]

Amer. Medical Assn. | Coun. on Medical Educ. [8575]

Amer. Medical Assn. | Liaison Comm. on Medical Educ. [8576]

Commn. on Accreditation of Allied Hea. Educ. Programs [8577]

Comm. on Accreditation for Educational Programs for the EMS Professions [8578]

Comm. on Accreditation of Ophthalmic Medical Programs [8579]

Coun. on Accreditation of Nurse Anesthesia Educational Programs [8580]

Councils on Chiropractic Educ. Intl. [7849]

Joint Rev. Comm. on Educ. in Diagnostic Medical Sonography [8581]

Joint Rev. Comm. on Educ. in Radiologic Tech. [8582]

Medical AdministrationMedicalAcad. for Intl. Hea. Stud.

ACMHA: The Coll. for Behavioral Hea. Leadership [15440]

Amer. Acad. of Medical Administrators [15276]

Amer. Acad. of Medical Administrators Res. and Educational Found. [15277]

Amer. Assn. of Healthcare Administrative Mgt. [15278]

Amer. Assn. of Integrated Healthcare Delivery Systems [15279]

Amer. Assn. of Medical Audit Specialists [15280]

Amer. Case Mgt. Assn. [15281]

Amer. Coll. of Cardiovascular Administrators [15282]

Amer. Coll. of Medical Practice Executives [15283]

Amer. Coll. of Oncology Administrators [15284]

Amer. Coll. of Physician Executives [15285]

Amer. Medical Billing Assn. [15286]

Amer. Soc. of Ophthalmic Administrators [15287]

Asian Hea. Care Leaders Assn. [15288]

Asian Hea. Care Leaders Assn. [15288]

Assn. of Biomedical Communications Directors [14161]

Assn. of Dermatology Administrators and Managers [14323]

Assn. of Family Medicine Residency Directors [15289]

Assn. of Healthcare Internal Auditors [15290]

Assn. for Long Term Care Financial Managers [15291]

Assn. of Otolaryngology Administrators [15292]

Assn. of Professors of Cardiology [14008]

Assn. of Prog. Directors in Internal Medicine [15134]

A star before a book entry number signifies that the name is not listed separately, but is mentioned within the entry.

Assn. of Pulmonary and Critical Care Medicine
 Prog. Directors [14207]
Case Mgt. Soc. of Am. [15293]
Case Mgt. Soc. of Am. [15293]
Medical Gp. Mgt. Assn. [15294]
NAMDRC [15295]
Natl. Assn. for Healthcare Recruitment [15296]
Natl. Assn. Medical Staff Services [15297]
Natl. Coalition of Healthcare Recruiters [15298]
Natl. Renal Administrators Assn. [15299]
Professional Assn. of Hea. Care Off. Mgt. [15300]
Radiology Bus. Mgt. Assn. [15301]

Medical Aid
Adventist Hea. Intl. [15138]
African Hea. Now [15139]
AIDS Relief Intl. [10873]
Alternative Medicine Intl. [13648]
Amazonas Hope for Hea. [14747]
Amer. Acad. of Urgent Care Medicine [13726]
AmeriGhana [12312]
Angel Flight West [12444]
Angel Wing Flights [12445]
Arise Medical Missions [15146]
Assist Intl. [12446]
Assist Intl. [12446]
Blessings Intl. [12447]
Blessings Intl. [12447]
Burma Relief Network [12813]
Cambodian Amer. Mobile Clinic [14110]
Cambodian Hea. Professionals Assn. of Am.
 [14761]
Catholic Medical Mission Bd. [12448]
Catholic Medical Mission Bd. [12448]
Chemists Without Borders [12449]
Children's Intl. Hea. Relief [14067]
Children's Medical Mission of Haiti [11247]
Childspring Intl. [14070]
CHOSEN [12450]
Clinicians of the World [15153]
Coalition for Tactical Medicine [15907]
Common Hope for Hea. [14768]
Community Hea. Intl. [14896]
Direct Relief Intl. [12451]
Direct Relief Intl. [12451]
Doc to Dock [15302]
DOCARE Intl. [12452]
DOCARE Intl., N.F.P. [12452]
Dr. to Dr. [12453]
Dr. to Dr. [12453]
Doctors in Christ [15303]
Doctors for United Medical Missions [15155]
Doctors Without Borders USA [12833]
Dorcas Medical Mission [15156]
Engg. World Hea. [15158]
Flying Doctors of Am. [12454]
Flying Doctors of Am. [12454]
For Victims of War and Poverty [12455]
For Victims of War and Poverty [12455]
Forward in Hea. [14777]
Friends for Hea. in Haiti [14778]
Friends of Nutre Hogar [14112]
Gift of Life Intl. [12456]
Gift of Life Intl. [12456]
Global Flying Hospitals [14779]
Global Hea. Partners [14781]
Global Hea. Partnerships [15170]
Global Hea. Soc. [15171]
Global Neuro Rescue [15593]
Global Outreach Mission [12457]
Global Outreach Mission [12457]
Global Vision 2020 [17077]
Globus Relief [12458]
God's Child Proj. [11294]
Hand in Hand USA [12842]
Hannah's Promise Intl. Aid [12843]
Hea. Empowering Humanity [14786]
Hea. For All Missions [12459]
Hea. Volunteers Overseas [12460]
Hea. Volunteers Overseas [12460]
Hea. through Walls [15182]
HealthRight Intl. [12461]
HealthRight Intl. [12461]
HelpMercy Intl. [14791]
Honduras Outreach Medical Brigada Relief Effort
 [15184]

Hope Beyond Hope [15185]
Horizon Intl. Medical Mission [15187]
Hospitals of Hope [15188]
Humanity for Children [16147]
I Care Grace Intl. [14792]
Integrative Clinics Intl. [14899]
Intl. Crisis Aid [12854]
Intl. Development Missions [12342]
Intl. Hea. and Development Network [15191]
Intl. Medical Alliance [15192]
Intl. Medical Volunteers Assn. [15304]
Intl. Medical Volunteers Assn. [15304]
Intl. Palestinian Cardiac Relief Org. [14021]
Israel Humanitarian Found. [12393]
Ivory Coast Medical Relief Team [16583]
Journey to Solidarity [14139]
Kenya Medical Outreach [12462]
Landstuhl Hosp. Care Proj. [12463]
Liga Intl. [12464]
Liga Intl. [12464]
MADRE [12465]
Malawi Biomedicals Resources [15305]
Malawi Biomedicals Resources [15305]
Mama Baby Haiti [14107]
Marines Helping Marines [12433]
Mayan Medical Aid [12466]
Medical Aid Comm. [15306]
Medical Aid to Haiti [12467]
Medical Bridges [15307]
Medical Care Intl. [15196]
Medical Expeditions Intl. [15308]
Medical Expeditions Intl. [15308]
Medical Missions for Children [14087]
Medical Relief Alliance [12864]
Medical Relief Intl. [12865]
Medicine for Mali [12468]
Medicines for Humanity [14088]
Medics Without Borders [14469]
MediSend Intl. [12469]
MediSend Intl. [12469]
Meds and Food for Kids [11348]
MedShare Intl. [12470]
MedShare Intl. [12470]
Mercy Ships Intl. Operations Center [15309]
Mercy Ships Intl. Operations Center [15309]
Mindful Medicine Worldwide [13693]
Mission Doctors Assn. [12471]
Mission Doctors Assn. [12471]
Mobile Medical Disaster Relief [12472]
Natl. Assn. of Female Paramedics [14472]
NeedyMeds [15310]
New Eyes for the Needy [12473]
New Reality Intl. [12743]
NOVA Hope for Haiti [12474]
One Nurse At A Time [15794]
One World Healthcare USA [14823]
One World Medical Relief [15202]
Oper. Rainbow [15311]
Oper. Smile [12475]
Oper. Smile [12475]
Oper. U.S.A. [12476]
Org. for Medical and Psychological Assistance for
 Children Overseas [14094]
Pan Amer. Hea. and Educ. Found. [12477]
Pan Amer. Hea. and Educ. Found. [12477]
Partner for Surgery [16818]
Partners for World Hea. [15203]
Partnership for Quality Medical Donations [12478]
Partnership for Quality Medical Donations [12478]
Physicians for Peace [15312]
Physicians for Peace [15312]
Proj.: Hearts and Minds [12479]
Reach Across [20084]
Recovered Medical Equip. for the Developing
 World [15313]
Recovered Medical Equip. for the Developing
 World [15313]
Refugee Relief Intl. [12480]
Refugee Relief Intl. [12480]
Sharing Resources Worldwide [15210]
SHIP Aid: Shipping Humanitarian Aid to
 Impoverished People [12889]
Small World Found. [16820]
Somali Medical and Supplies Relief Org. [12893]
Sri Lanka Medical Assn. of North Am. [14830]

Task Force for Child Survival and Development
 [12481]
Tropical Clinics [15216]
United Amputee Services Assn. [15314]
Venture Strategies for Hea. and Development
 [14832]
VOSH Intl. [12482]
VOSH Intl. [12482]
Women for World Hea. [14837]
World Family Ethiopian Orphans and Medical
 Care [11432]
World Hea. Ambassador [14838]
World Medical Relief [12483]
World Medical Relief [12483]
Medical Aid Comm. [15306], 59 Windsor Rd.,
 Brookline, MA 02445-1334, (617)739-2638
Medical Aid for El Salvador - Defunct.
Medical Aid to Haiti [12467], 80 S Main St., West
 Hartford, CT 06107, (860)760-7009
Medical Ambassadors Intl. [★19993]
Medical Ambassadors Intl. [★19993]
Medical Assistance Programs [★19952]
Medical Assistance Programs [★19952]

Medical Assistants
Amer. Assn. of Medical Assistants [15315]
Amer. Registry of Medical Assistants [15316]
Amer. Soc. of Anesthesia Technologists and
 Technicians [15317]
Assn. for Healthcare Documentation Integrity
 [15318]
Global Hea. Soc. [15171]

Medical Assn; Amer. Holistic Veterinary [17006]
Medical Assn; Amer. Veterinary [17010]
Medical Assn. of the Bahamas [IO], Nassau,
 Bahamas
Medical Assn. in Brunei [IO], Bandar Seri Begawan,
 Brunei Darussalam
Medical Assn. of Jamaica [IO], Kingston, Jamaica
Medical Assn. of Malta [IO], Gzira, Malta
Medical Assn; Natl. Arab Amer. [14882]
Medical Assn. for Prevention of War - Australia [IO],
 Carlton, Australia
Medical Assn. of South East Asian Nations [IO], Sin-
 gapore, Singapore
Medical Assn. of Turkey [IO], Ankara, Turkey
Medical Banking Proj. - Address unknown since
 2011.
Medical Benevolence Found. [14901], 10707
 Corporate Dr., Ste. 220, Stafford, TX 77477-4095,
 (281)201-2043
Medical Boards; Fed. of Podiatric [16297]
Medical Bridges [15307], PO Box 300245, Houston,
 TX 77230-0245, (713)748-8131
Medical Care Development Intl. [15195], 8401
 Colesville Rd., Ste. 425, Silver Spring, MD 20910,
 (301)562-1920
Medical Care Intl. [15196], PO Box 69, New Hope,
 PA 18938
Medical Coun. of India [IO], New Delhi, India
Medical Defence Malaysia [IO], Kuala Lumpur,
 Malaysia
Medical Defence Union [IO], London, United
 Kingdom
Medical Dental Hosp. Bus. Associates [38], 350
 Poplar Ave., Elmhurst, IL 60126, (630)941-8100
Medical Dermatology Soc. [14331], 526 Superior
 Ave. E, Ste. 540, Cleveland, OH 44114, (216)579-
 9300
Medical Device Mfrs. Assn. [3178], 1350 I St. NW,
 Ste. 540, Washington, DC 20005, (202)354-7171

Medical Education
Acad. of Pharmaceutical Physicians and
 Investigators [20083]
Alliance for Continuing Medical Educ. [8584]
Alliance of Independent Academic Medical
 Centers [15319]
Alliance for Massage Therapy Educ. [8560]
Amer. Acad. of Medical Mgt. [15320]
Amer. Acad. of Urgent Care Medicine [13726]
Amer. Assn. of Colleges of Nursing [8585]
Amer. Chinese Medical Exchange Soc. [14750]
Amer. Medical Assn. Found. [8586]
Amer. Medical Student Assn. [8587]
Amer. Physician Scientists Assn. [8588]
Amer. Soc. for Bioethics and Humanities [8589]

Reference to "IO" in place of a book number signifies that the association may be found in the 50th edition of International Organizations.

Assn. of Amer. Medical Colleges [8590]
Assn. of Amer. Medical Colleges-Women in Medicine. Prog. [8591]
Assn. of Black Nursing Faculty [8592]
Assn. for Medical Educ. and Res. in Substance Abuse [8593]
Assn. of Minority Hea. Professions Schools [8594]
Assn. of Native Amer. Medical Students [15321]
Assn. of Pediatric Prog. Directors [8595]
Assn. of Professors of Medicine [8596]
Assn. of Prog. Directors in Internal Medicine [15134]
Assn. of Prog. Directors in Radiology [15322]
Assn. of Psychology Postdoctoral and Internship Centers [8597]
Assn. of Schools of Allied Hea. Professions [8598]
Assn. of Standardized Patient Educators [15323]
Assn. for Surgical Educ. [8599]
Assn. for Surgical Educ. [8599]
Assn. of Univ. Programs in Hea. Admin. [8600]MedicalBoston Intl. Found. for Medical Education/Exchange
Chiropractic Diplomatic Corps [14125]
Coalition of Natl. Hea. Educ. Organizations [8601]
Commn. on Collegiate Nursing Educ. [8602]
Comprehensive Hea. Educ. Found. [8603]
Coun. for Acupuncture Res. and Educ. [13580]
Coun. on Medical Student Educ. in Pediatrics [8604]
Councils on Chiropractic Educ. Intl. [7849]
Found. for the Advancement of Chiropractic Educ. [8605]
Global Alliance for Medical Educ. [8606]
Global Alliance for Medical Educ. [8606]
Global Medical Knowledge [15375]
Hea. Occupations Students of Am. [8607]
Hispanic-Serving Hea. Professions Schools [8608]
Indians Into Medicine [8609]
Intl. Assn. of Medical Sci. Educators [15324]
Intl. Assn. of Medical Sci. Educators [15324]
Medical Educ. Cooperation with Cuba [15325]
Natl. Assn. of Advisors for the Hea. Professions [8610]
Natl. Assn. for Continuing Educ. [7927]
Natl. Assn. of EMS Educators [8611]
Natl. Assn. of EMS Educators [8611]
Natl. Assn. of Medical Minority Educators [8612]
Natl. Assn. for Practical Nurse Educ. and Ser. [8613]
Natl. Medical Fellowships [8614]
Natl. Resident Matching Prog. [8615]
Natl. Student Nurses' Assn. [8616]
Naturopathic Medical Student Assn. [15535]
Phi Delta Epsilon Medical Fraternity [23590]
Phi Delta Epsilon Medical Fraternity [23590]
Salvadoran Amer. Medical Soc. [15326]
Salvadoran Amer. Medical Soc. [15326]
Save the Patient [14740]
Soc. for Academic Continuing Medical Educ. [8617]
Soc. for Academic Continuing Medical Educ. [8617]
Student Natl. Medical Assn. [8618]
Universities Allied for Essential Medicines [8384]
Medical Educ; Accreditation Coun. for Continuing [15389]
Medical Educ. Cooperation with Cuba [15325], PO Box 361449, Decatur, GA 30036, (678)904-8092
Medical Educ. for South African Blacks - Defunct.
Medical Equip. and Tech. Assn. [15377], 220 S Bus. Park Dr., Ste. A-1, Oostburg, WI 53070
Medical Examiners
Amer. Bd. of Independent Medical Examiners [15327]
Amer. Bd. of Independent Medical Examiners [15327]
Intl. Assn. of Coroners and Medical Examiners [15328]
Intl. Assn. of Coroners and Medical Examiners [15328]
Natl. Assn. of Medical Examiners [15329]
Natl. Bd. of Medical Examiners [15330]
Medical Exhibitors Assn. [★1231]

Medical Expeditions Intl. [15308], 1235 N Decatur Rd. NE, Atlanta, GA 30306, (404)892-6672
Medical Expeditions Intl. [15308], 1235 N Decatur Rd. NE, Atlanta, GA 30306, (404)892-6672
Medical Fitness Assn. [16229], 1905 Huguenot Rd., Ste. 203, Richmond, VA 23235-8026, (804)897-5701
Medical Found. for AIDS and Sexual Hea. [IO], London, United Kingdom
Medical Gp. Mgt. Assn. [15294], 104 Inverness Terr. E, Englewood, CO 80112-5306, (303)799-1111
Medical Gp. Missions of the Christian Medical and Dental Soc. [★19948]
Medical Gp. Missions of the Christian Medical and Dental Soc. [★19948]
Medical Identification
Action Against Medical Accidents [8116]MedicalEuropean Medical Students' Assn.
Medical Image Computing and Cmpt. Assisted Intervention Soc. [IO], London, ON, Canada
Medical Image Perception Soc. [15378], CREOL, Univ. Central Florida, 4000 Central Florida Blvd., Orlando, FL 32816-2700, (407)823-6870
Medical Info. Bur. [★15128]
Medical Journalists' Assn. [IO], London, United Kingdom
Medical Lab. Technologists Assn. of Pakistan [IO], Punjab, Pakistan
Medical Letter [16201], 145 Huguenot St., Ste. 312, New Rochelle, NY 10801, (914)235-0500
Medical Lib. Assn. [9995], 65 E Wacker Pl., Ste. 1900, Chicago, IL 60601-7246, (312)419-9094
Medical Mission Gp. [15197], 134 Grove St., Pearl River, NY 10965, (845)920-9001
Medical Mission Sisters [20059], 8400 Pine Rd., Philadelphia, PA 19111, (215)742-6100
Medical Mission Sisters [20059], 8400 Pine Rd., Philadelphia, PA 19111, (215)742-6100
Medical Missions for Children [14087], 10-G Roessler Rd., Ste. 500, Woburn, MA 01801, (508)697-5821
Medical Missions Response [19953], PO Box 57011, Oklahoma City, OK 73157-7011, (866)667-8996
Medical Missions Response [19953], PO Box 57011, Oklahoma City, OK 73157-7011, (866)667-8996
Medical Mycological Soc. of the Americas [15525], Ms. Annette W. Fothergill, MA, Sec.-Treas., Univ. of Texas, Fungus Tech. Lab., Hea. Sci. Center, 7703 Floyd Curl Dr., San Antonio, TX 78229, (210)567-6074
Medical Officers of Schools Assn. [IO], Sevenoaks, United Kingdom
Medical Outcomes Trust [14804], Darmouth Medical School, Dept. of Community and Family Medicine, HB 7250, Hanover, NH 03755
Medical Pharmaceutical Info. Assn. [IO], Almaty, Kazakhstan
Medical Protection Soc. [IO], London, United Kingdom
Medical Records
Alliance for Wellness ROI [16303]
Amer. Hea. Info. Mgt. Assn. [15331]
HIMSS Electronic Hea. Record Assn. [15332]
Hong Kong Soc. of Medical Informatics [22677]
Medical Records Inst. [15333]
Medical Transcription Indus. Assn. [15334]
Patient Privacy Rights [18104]
Medical Records Inst. [15333], 425 Boylston St., Boston, MA 02116-3315, (617)964-3923
Medical Reform
Incontinentia Pigmenti Intl. Found. [14601]
Medical Rehabilitation Center for Torture Victims [IO], Athens, Greece
Medical Relief Alliance [12864], 244 5th Ave., Ste. B293, New York, NY 10001, (212)252-2102
Medical Relief Alliance [12864], 244 5th Ave., Ste. B293, New York, NY 10001, (212)252-2102
Medical Relief Intl. [12865], 12316 134th Ct. NE, Redmond, WA 98052, (425)284-2630
Medical Research
Acad. of Surgical Res. [15335]
Amer. Acad. of Urgent Care Medicine [13726]
Amer. Hea. Assistance Found. [15336]
Amer. Pharmacists Assn. I Acad. of Pharmacy Practice and Mgt. [16176]

Amer. Soc. for Clinical Nutrition [15821]
Applied Res. Ethics Natl. Assn. [15337]
Australian Soc. for Medical Res. [1337]
Avenues, Natl. Support Gp. for Arthrogryposis Multiplex Congenita [15573]
Benign Essential Blepharospasm Res. Found. [15575]
CancerClimber Assn. [13904]
Children's Tumor Found. [15579]
Chinese Amer. Soc. Of Anesthesiology [13745]
Citizens United for Res. in Epilepsy [14518]
City of Hope [15338]
Coalition for the Advancement of Medical Res. [15339]
Cornea Res. Found. of Am. [15340]
Diabetes Action Res. and Educ. Found. [14347]
Dysphagia Res. Soc. [14383]
Environmental Res. Found. [13638]
Esther A. and Joseph Klingenstein Fund [15341]
Heart Rhythm Soc. [14016]
HopeLab [15342]
Howard Hughes Medical Inst. [15343]
Howard Hughes Medical Inst. [15343]
Intl. Assn. for Biological and Medical Res. [15344]
Intl. Atherosclerosis Soc. [14020]
Intl. Brain Barriers Soc. [15657]
Intl. Genetic Epidemiology Soc. [14514]
Intl. Psoriasis Coun. [14329]
Intl. Soc. for Autism Res. [13797]
Intl. Soc. for Cardiovascular Translational Res. [14024]
Intl. Soc. for Interferon and Cytokine Res. [15345]
Intl. Soc. for Interferon and Cytokine Res. [15345]
Intl. Soc. for Low Vision Res. and Rehabilitation [15965]
Intl. Soc. on Metabolic Eye Disease [15966]
Intl. Soc. of Psychoneuroendocrinology [15346]
Intl. Soc. of Psychoneuroendocrinology [15346]
Intl. Soc. for Vaccines [15109]
Medical Res. Modernization Comm. [15347]
Natl. Found. for Brain Res. [15666]
Natl. Melanoma Alliance [13956]
NCI Alliance for Nanotechnology in Cancer [15348]
Optometric Glaucoma Soc. [15972]
PanAmerican Soc. for Pigment Cell Res. [15349]
Peruvian Heart Assn. [14039]
Prize4Life [15632]
Purine Res. Soc. [15506]
Res.! Am. [15350]
Res. for Hea. [15207]
RGK Found. [15351]
Soc. for Clinical and Translational Sci. [14158]
Soc. for Translational Oncology [15935]
Student Soc. for Stem Cell Res. [15352]
Student Soc. for Stem Cell Res. [15352]
Surfing Medicine Intl. [13712]
Tenovus Scotland [23796]
Tissue Engg. Intl. and Regenerative Medicine Soc. [13835]
Tourette Syndrome Assn. [15636]
Universities Allied for Essential Medicines [8384]
W.M. Keck Found. [15353]
Medical Res. Modernization Comm. [15347], 3200 Morley Rd., Shaker Heights, OH 44122, (216)283-6702
Medical Res. Soc. [IO], Cambridge, United Kingdom
Medical Soc. Executives Assn. [★15392]
Medical Software Indus. Assn. [IO], Newcastle, Australia
Medical Spa Soc. [14902], 60 E 56th St., 2nd Fl., New York, NY 10022, (212)688-5882
Medical Specialties
Amer. Assn. of Medical Dosimetrists [15354]
Amer. Bd. of Medical Specialties [15355]
Amer. Osteopathic Coll. of Anesthesiologists [13735]
Amer. Soc. of Ocularists [15356]
Caribbean Amer. Medical and Sci. Assn. [14873]
Certification Bd. for Sterile Processing and Distribution [15357]
Children's Cancer and Blood Found. [14964]
Coalition of State Rheumatology Organizations [16619]
Coun. of Medical Specialty Societies [15358]

A star before a book entry number signifies that the name is not listed separately, but is mentioned within the entry.

Digital Pathology Assn. [16124]
Intl. Alliance of Hair Restoration Surgeons [14675]
Intl. Anesthesia Res. Soc. [13748]
Intl. Skeletal Soc. [16533]
Intl. Soc. for Vaccines [15109]
Let's Talk Pain [16105]
NIDCD: Natl. Temporal Bone, Hearing and Balance Pathology Rsrc. Registry [15359]
Periodic Paralysis Assn. [15360]
Semmelweis Soc. Intl. [16510]
Soc. of Nuclear Medicine Technologist Sect. [15697]
Soc. for Worldwide Medical Exchange [15212]
Medical and Sports Music Inst. of America - Defunct.
Medical Students' Assn. of Rwanda [IO], Butare, Rwanda
Medical Students for Choice [16590], PO Box 40188, Philadelphia, PA 19106, (215)625-0800
Medical-Surgical Mfrs. Assn. [★14840]
Medical Teams Intl. [12866], PO Box 10, Portland, OR 97207-0010, (503)624-1000
Medical Teams Intl. [12866], PO Box 10, Portland, OR 97207-0010, (503)624-1000
Medical Technology
Accreditation Rev. Coun. on Educ. in Surgical Tech. and Surgical Assisting [15361]
Accrediting Bur. of Hea. Educ. Schools [15362]
Amer. Acad. of Anti-Aging Medicine [15363]
Amer. Medical Technologists [15364]
Amer. Registry of Radiologic Technologists [15365]
Amer. Soc. of Extra-Corporeal Tech. [15366]
Amer. Soc. for Mohs Histotechnology [15367]
Amer. Soc. of Radiologic Technologists [15368]
Assn. for Educ. in Healthcare Info. Tech. [15369]
Assn. of Surgical Technologists [15370]
Bd. of Registered Polysomnographic Technologists [15371]
Chinese-American Soc. of Nuclear Medicine [15694]
CuresNow [15372]
Digital Pathology Assn. [16124]
ECRI Inst. [15373]
ECRI Inst. [15373]
Engg. World Hea. [15158]
European Chinese Soc. for Clinical Magnetic Resonance [5427]
Extensions for Independence [11786]
Found. for Informed Medical Decision Making [15374]
Global Medical Knowledge [15375]
Intl. Aesthetic and Laser Assn. [15237]
Intl. Assn. of Medical Equip. Remarketers and Servicers [15376]
Intl. Assn. of Medical Equip. Remarketers and Servicers [15376]
Medical Equip. and Tech. Assn. [15377]
Medical Image Perception Soc. [15378]
Natl. Accrediting Agency for Clinical Lab. Sciences [15379]
Natl. Alliance for the Primary Prevention of Sharps Injuries [16630]
Natl. Assn. of Orthopaedic Technologists [15380]
Natl. Coalition for Assistive and Rehab Tech. [15381]
Natl. Inst. of Electromedical Info. [15382]
Natl. Soc. for HistoTechnology [15383]
Neuro-Optometric Rehabilitation Assn. Intl. [15559]
North Amer. Assn. for Laser Therapy [15238]
Sect. for Magnetic Resonance Technologists [15384]
Sino-American Network for Therapeutic Radiology and Oncology [16871]
Soc. for Cardiovascular Magnetic Resonance [15385]
Soc. for Cardiovascular Magnetic Resonance [15385]
Soc. for Simulation in Healthcare [15386]
Soc. for Simulation in Healthcare [15386]
Soc. for Whole Body Autoradiography [15387]
Universities Allied for Essential Medicines [8384]
World Hea. Imaging, Telemedicine and Informatics Alliance [15224]
Medical Tech. Assn. of Australia [IO], North Sydney, Australia

Medical Tourism Assn. [15423], 10130 Northlake Blvd., Ste. 214-315, West Palm Beach, FL 33412, (561)791-2000
Medical Transcription Indus. Alliance [★15334]
Medical Transcription Indus. Assn. [15334], 4230 Kiernan Ave., Ste. 130, Modesto, CA 95356, (209)527-9620
Medical Wings Intl. [14805], PO Box 610542, Dallas, TX 75261, (817)800-0080
Medical Wings Intl. [14805], PO Box 610542, Dallas, TX 75261, (817)800-0080
Medical Women's Fed. [IO], London, United Kingdom
Medical Women's Intl. Assn. [IO], Burnaby, BC, Canada
MedicAlert Found. Intl. [14453], 2323 Colorado Ave., Turlock, CA 95382, (888)633-4298
MedicAlert Found. Intl. [14453], 2323 Colorado Ave., Turlock, CA 95382, (888)633-4298
Medically Induced Trauma Support Services [16928], 830 Boylston St., Ste. 206, Chestnut Hill, MA 02467, (617)232-0090
Medicare Advocacy; Center for [14853]
Medicare Beneficiaries Defense Fund [★17764]
Medicare Rights Center [17764], North Wing, 3rd Fl., 520 8th Ave., New York, NY 10018, (212)869-3850
Medicine
Acad. of Molecular Imaging [15388]
Accreditation Coun. for Continuing Medical Educ. [15389]
Albanian Amer. Medical Soc. [15390]
Alliance for Biotherapies [16831]
Alpha Epsilon Delta [23591]
Alpha Omega Alpha Honor Medical Soc. [23592]
Amer. Abdominal Acupuncture Medical Assn. [13578]
Amer. Assn. of Integrative Medicine [15391]
Amer. Assn. of Medical Soc. Executives [15392]
Amer. Assn. of Nutritional Consultants [15814]
Amer. Bd. of Integrative Holistic Medicine [14991]
Amer. Bd. of Nutrition [15815]
Amer. Bd. of Oriental Reproductive Medicine [16595]
Amer. Celiac Society | Dietary Support Coalition [15817]
Amer. Coll. of Emergency Physicians | Amer. Assn. of Women Emergency Physicians [14460]
Amer. Coll. of Physicians [15133]
Amer. Herbal Pharmacopoeia [13655]
Amer. Herbalists Guild [14989]
Amer. Hosp. Assn., Sect. for Long Term Care and Rehabilitation [15039]
Amer. Integrative Medical Assn. [15393]
Amer. Lebanese Medical Assn. [15394]
Amer. Medical Assn. [15395]
Amer. Medical Assn. Alliance [15396]
Amer. Osler Soc. [15397]
Amer. Pharmacists Assn. | Acad. of Pharmacy Practice and Mgt. [16176]
Amer. Physician Scientists Assn. [8588]
Amer. Soc. for Clinical Nutrition [15821]
Amer. Soc. for Nanomedicine [15398]
Americans for Free Choice in Medicine [15399]
Assn. of Ayurvedic Professionals of North Am. [13664]
Assn. of Haitian Physicians Abroad [15400]
Assn. of Immunization Managers [15100]
Assn. for Integrative Hea. Care Practitioners [15401]
Assn. of Medical Device Reprocessors [15402]
Assn. for Palliative Medicine of Great Britain and Ireland [14068]
Assn. of Prog. Directors in Internal Medicine [15134]
Assn. of Pulmonary and Critical Care Medicine Prog. Directors [14207]
Assyrian Medical Soc. [15403]
Assyrian Medical Soc. [15403]
Auxiliary to the Natl. Medical Assn. [15404]
Avenues, Natl. Support Gp. for Arthrogryposis Multiplex Congenita [15573]
Bangladesh Medical Assn. of North Am. [15405]
Benign Essential Blepharospasm Res. Found. [15575]

Berufsverband der Pharmaberater [223]
British Assn. for Performing Arts Medicine [8015]
Burmese Medical Assn. of North Am. [15406]
Children's Tumor Found. [15579]
Chinese Amer. Medical Soc. [15407]
Chinese-American Soc. of Nuclear Medicine [15694]
Christian Medical and Dental Associations [19948]
Christian Medical and Dental Associations [19948]
Coalition for Tactical Medicine [15907]
COLA [15408]
Community Acupuncture Network [13579]
Complementary and Alternative Medicine Initiative [13671]
Consortium for Conservation Medicine [15409]
Consortium for Conservation Medicine [15409]
Coun. for Healing [13672]
Doc to Dock [15302]
Doctors in Christ [15303]
Energy Kinesiology Assn. [13674]
Energy Kinesiology Awareness Coun. [13675]
Evidenced-Based Veterinary Medicine Assn. [17024]
Fed. of Chinese Amer. and Chinese Canadian Medical Societies [15410]
Fed. of Chinese Amer. and Chinese Canadian Medical Societies [15410]
Fed. of State Medical Boards of the U.S. [15411]
Fed. of State Medical Boards of the U.S. [15411]
Fellowship of Associates of Medical Evangelism [19949]
Forbes Norris MDA/ALS Res. Center [15590]
Found. for Innovation in Medicine [15412]
Friends of the Natl. Lib. of Medicine [15413]
Global Initiative for the Advancement of Nutritional Therapy [16851]
Global Solutions for Infectious Diseases [15116]
Harvey Soc. [15414]
Hea. Ministries [19950]
Healthcare Billing and Mgt. Assn. [15415]
Heart Rhythm Soc. [14016]
HopeLab [15342]
Inst. of Medicine [15416]
Interchurch Medical Assistance [19951]
Interchurch Medical Assistance [19951]
Intl. Alliance of Professional Hypnotists [15089]
Intl. Assn. for Dance Medicine and Sci. [15417]
Intl. Assn. of Healthcare Central Ser. Material Mgt. [15058]
Intl. Assn. of Medical Intuitives [15418]
Intl. Assn. of Medical Intuitives [15418]
Intl. Assn. of Medical and Therapeutic Specialists [13686]
Intl. Cellular Medicine Soc. [14649]
Intl. Meta-Medicine Assn. [13690]
Intl. Soc. for Autism Res. [13797]
Intl. Soc. for Ayurveda and Hea. [13691]
Intl. Soc. for Cardiovascular Translational Res. [14024]
Intl. Soc. on Metabolic Eye Disease [15966]
Intl. Soc. for Mountain Medicine [15419]
Intl. Soc. for Mountain Medicine [15419]
Intl. Soc. for Orthomolecular Medicine [6554]
Intl. Soc. of Pharmacogenomics [16200]
Intl. Soc. for the Stud. of the Lumbar Spine [12261]
Intl. Soc. of Travel Medicine [15420]
Intl. Soc. of Travel Medicine [15420]
Intl. Veterinarians Dedicated to Animal Hea. [17029]
Iranian Amer. Medical Assn. [15421]
Iraqi Medical Sciences Assn. [15193]
J. Robert Gladden Orthopaedic Soc. [16037]
Journey to Solidarity [14139]
Kidney Care Partners [15551]
Korean Amer. Medical Assn. [15422]
MAP Intl. [19952]
MAP Intl. [19952]
Medical Missions Response [19953]
Medical Missions Response [19953]
Medical Tourism Assn. [15423]
Medicine in Action [15424]
Mindful Medicine Worldwide [13693]
Natl. Alliance for the Primary Prevention of Sharps Injuries [16630]

Reference to "IO" in place of a book number signifies that the association may be found in the 50th edition of International Organizations.

Natl. Assn. of Pharmaceutical Representatives [2697]
Natl. Assn. of Residents and Interns [15425]
Natl. Hispanic Medical Assn. [15426]
Natl. Medical Assn. [15427]
Naturopathic Physicians Bd. of Aesthetic Medicine [15537]
Network for Continuing Medical Educ. [15428]
Neuroethics Soc. [15679]
New Zealand Medical Assn. [20295]
Nordic Telemedicine Assn. [22149]
North Amer. Assn. for Laser Therapy [15238]
North Amer. Sikh Medical and Dental Assn. [15429]
North Amer. Sikh Medical and Dental Assn. [15429]
Partnership for Quality Medical Donations [12478]
Personalized Medicine Coalition [15430]
Pharmaceutical Indus. Labor-Management Assn. [2700]
Phi Alpha Sigma [23593]
Phi Chi Medical Fraternity [23594]
Phi Rho Sigma Medical Soc. [23595]
Philippine Nurses Assn. of Am. [15796]
Physician Hospitals of Am. [15431]
Preimplantation Genetic Diagnosis Intl. Soc. [14656]
Prize4Life [15632]
Renewable Energy for Medicine and Educ. [6749]
Russian Amer. Medical Assn. [15432]
Russian Amer. Medical Assn. [15432]
Safety Net Hospitals for Pharmaceutical Access [16213]
Scottish Soc. of the History of Medicine [14883]
Soc. for Clinical and Translational Sci. [14158]
Soc. for Executive Leadership in Academic Medicine Intl. [15433]
Soc. for Executive Leadership in Academic Medicine Intl. [15433]
Soc. for Heart Brain Medicine [14046]
Soc. for the History of Navy Medicine [9808]
Soc. for Medical Decision Making [15434]
Soc. for Molecular Imaging [15435]
Soc. for Molecular Imaging [15435]
Soc. of Nuclear Medicine Technologist Sect. [15697]
Soc. for Participatory Medicine [14829]
Soc. for Translational Oncology [15935]
Surfer's Medical Assn. [15436]
Surfing Medicine Intl. [13712]
TECH, Tech. Exchange for Christian Healthcare [19954]
Tissue Engg. Intl. and Regenerative Medicine Soc. [13835]
Tourette Syndrome Assn. [15636]
Traditional Chinese Medicine Assn. and Alumni [13714]
Ukrainian Medical Assn. of North Am. [15437]
Universities Allied for Essential Medicines [8384]
Univ. of Colorado Hea. Sciences Center Alumni Assn. [23547]
Vietnamese Medical Assn. of the U.S.A. [15438]
Vietnamese Medical Assn. of the U.S.A. [15438]
Wilderness Medical Soc. [15439]
World Medical Mission [19955]
World Medical Mission [19955]
ZY Qigong [13722]
Medicine in Action [15424], 8101 Skyline Blvd., Oakland, CA 94611, (510)339-7579
Medicine for Mali [12468], 4605 80th Pl., Urbandale, IA 50322
Medicine for Peace [18434], 2732 Unicorn Ln. NW, Washington, DC 20015, (202)441-4545
Medicine for Peace [18434], 2732 Unicorn Ln. NW, Washington, DC 20015, (202)441-4545
Medicine in the Public Interest - Defunct.
Medicines Australia [IO], Deakin, Australia
Medicines for Humanity [14088], 800 Hingham St., Ste. 1800, Rockland, MA 02370, (781)982-0274
Medics Without Borders [14469], PO Box 35, Woodbridge, VA 22194, (703)268-4774
Medicus Mundi Intl. [IO], Basel, Switzerland
Mediebedriftenes Landsforening [★IO]
Medienplanung fur Entwicklungslander, Mittel und Osteuropa [★IO]

Medieval
Center for Medieval and Renaissance Stud. [10074]
Charles Homer Haskins Soc. [10075]
Charles Homer Haskins Soc. [10075]
Hagiography Soc. [20212]
Intl. Center of Medieval Art [10076]
Intl. Center of Medieval Art [10076]
Medieval Acad. of Am. [10077]
The Medieval Acad. of Am., Centers and Regional Associations [10078]
Soc. for Creative Anachronism [10079]
Soc. for Medieval and Renaissance Philosophy [10080]
Medieval Acad. of Am. [10077], 104 Mt. Auburn St., 5th Fl., Cambridge, MA 02138, (617)491-1622
The Medieval Acad. of Am., Centers and Regional Associations [10078], 104 Mt. Auburn St., 5th Fl., Cambridge, MA 02138-5019, (617)491-1622
Mediothek Afghanistan [IO], Kabul, Afghanistan
MediSend Intl. [12469], 9244 Markville Dr., Dallas, TX 75243, (214)575-5006
MediSend Intl. [12469], 9244 Markville Dr., Dallas, TX 75243, (214)575-5006
Medisinsk teknisk forening [★IO]
Meditation
Amer. Buddhist Stud. Center [19358]
Anahata Intl. [13662]
Breathecure [13669]
Buddhist Churches of Am. Fed. of Buddhist Women's Associations [19359]
Cambridge Buddhist Assn. [19363]
Dharma Drum Mountain Buddhist Assn. [19364]
Dharma Realm Buddhist Assn. [19365]
Found. of Human Understanding [10081]
Hanuman Found. [12208]
Mentalphysics [20190]
Natl. Neigong Res. Soc. [10082]
Theosophical Book Assn. for the Blind [20264]
Yoga Bear [13721]
Mediterranean
Mediterranean Stud. Assn. [10083]
Mediterranean Assn. to Save the Sea Turtles - Greece [IO], Athens, Greece
Mediterranean Assn. to Save the Sea Turtles - United Kingdom [IO], London, United Kingdom
Mediterranean Editors and Translators [IO], Barcelona, Spain
Mediterranean Soc. of Chemotherapy [IO], Athens, Greece
Mediterranean Stud. Assn. [10083], Box 79351, North Dartmouth, MA 02747, (508)979-8687
Mednarodni Graficni Likovni Center [★IO]
MedPed [★14610]
MedPed [★14610]
Meds and Food for Kids [11348], 4488 Forest Park Ave., Ste. 230, St. Louis, MO 63108, (314)420-1634
Meds and Food for Kids [11348], 4488 Forest Park Ave., Ste. 230, St. Louis, MO 63108, (314)420-1634
MedShare Intl. [12470], 3240 Clifton Springs Rd., Decatur, GA 30034, (770)323-5858
MedShare Intl. [12470], 3240 Clifton Springs Rd., Decatur, GA 30034, (770)323-5858
Medugorje Center - Defunct.
Meduxnekeag River Assn. [IO], Woodstock, NB, Canada
Medzinarodna federacia fonografickeho priemyslu Narodna skupina slovenskej republiky [★IO]
Meet A Mum Assn. [IO], Norton Radstock, United Kingdom
Meeting and Events Australia [IO], North Sydney, Australia
Meeting Places
Intl. Assn. of Assembly Managers [2441]
Intl. Assn. of Conf. Centers [2440]
Intl. Assn. of Conf. Centers [2440]
Intl. Assn. of Venue Managers [2441]
Natl. Convention Assn. [2456]
Meeting Planners
Alliance of Meeting Mgt. Companies [2442]
Assn. of Collegiate Conf. and Events Directors Intl. [2443]
Assn. of Collegiate Conf. and Events Directors Intl. [2443]

Assn. for Convention Operations Mgt. [2444]
Assn. for Convention Operations Mgt. [2444]
Connected Intl. Meeting Professionals Assn. [2445]
Connected Intl. Meeting Professionals Assn. [2445]
Coun. of Protocol Executives [2446]
Destination Marketing Assn. Intl. [2447]
Destination Marketing Assn. Intl. [2447]
Exposition Ser. Contractors Assn. [2448]
Green Meeting Indus. Coun. [2449]
Intl. Assn. for Exhibition Mgt. [2450]
Intl. Assn. of Exhibitions and Events [2450]
Intl. Assn. of Fairs and Expositions [2451]
Intl. Assn. of Fairs and Expositions [2451]
Intl. Assn. of Hispanic Meeting Professionals [2452]
Intl. Assn. of Hispanic Meeting Professionals [2452]
Intl. Soc. of Meeting Planners [2453]
Intl. Soc. of Meeting Planners [2453]
Meeting Professionals Intl. [2454]
Meeting Professionals Intl. [2454]
Natl. Coalition of Black Meeting Planners [2455]
Natl. Convention Assn. [2456]
Professional Convention Mgt. Assn. [2457]
Religious Conf. Mgt. Assn. [2458]
Religious Conf. Mgt. Assn. [2458]
Soc. of Govt. Meeting Professionals [2459]
Meeting Planners Intl. [★2454]
Meeting Planners Intl. [★2454]
Meeting Professionals Intl. [2454], 3030 Lyndon B. Johnson Fwy., Ste. 1700, Dallas, TX 75234-2759, (972)702-3000
Meeting Professionals Intl. [2454], 3030 Lyndon B. Johnson Fwy., Ste. 1700, Dallas, TX 75234-2759, (972)702-3000
Meetings and Events Australia - Australian Capital Territory Br. [IO], Sydney, Australia
Meetings and Events Australia - New South Wales Br. [IO], North Sydney, Australia
Meetings and Events Australia - Northern Territory Br. [IO], North Sydney, Australia
Meetings and Events Australia - Queensland Br. [IO], Sydney, Australia
Meetings and Events Australia - Tasmania Br. [IO], Sydney, Australia
Meetings and Events Australia - Victoria Br. [IO], Melbourne, Australia
Meetings and Events Australia - Western Australia Br. [IO], North Sydney, Australia
Mega Soc. [9641], 13155 Wimberly Sq., No. 284, San Diego, CA 92128
Meginfelag Ahugaleikara Feroya [★IO]
Meiklejohn Civil Liberties Inst. [12245], PO Box 673, Berkeley, CA 94701-0673, (510)848-0599
Mejeriforeningen [★IO]
Mekong River Commn. [IO], Vientiane, Lao People's Democratic Republic
The Mel Gablers [★8995]
Mel Tillis Fan Club [23877], Mel Tellis Enterprise, PO Box 305, Silver Springs, FL 34489
Mel Tillis Fan Club [23877], Mel Tellis Enterprise, PO Box 305, Silver Springs, FL 34489
Melanoma Awareness [13940], 3320 Minnesota Ln., Plymouth, MN 55447, (763)553-1746
Melanoma Res. Found. [13941], 1411 K St. NW, Ste. 500, Washington, DC 20005, (202)347-9675
Melbourne ACM SIGGRAPH [IO], Parkville, Australia
Melbourne Argonauts Queer Rowing Club [IO], Melbourne, Australia
Melbourne Nordic Ski Club [IO], Camberwell, Australia
Melbourne Trail Horse Riders Club [IO], Melbourne, Australia
Mellemfolkeligt Samvirke [★IO]
Melodious Accord [10240], 96 Middle Rd., Hawley, MA 01339, (413)339-8508
Melos Inst. [265], 1071 Yosemite Dr., Pacifica, CA 94044, (650)355-4094
Melpomene Inst. [17128], 550 Rice St., Ste. 104, St. Paul, MN 55103, (651)789-0140
Melpomene Inst. for Women's Hea. Res. [★17128]
Melungeon Heritage Assn. [18921], PO Box 1253, Danville, VA 24543

A star before a book entry number signifies that the name is not listed separately, but is mentioned within the entry.

Melvil Dui Marching and Chowder Assn. - Defunct.
Melville Soc. [9400], Gerard McGowan, Treas., Dept. of English and Philosophy, Bldg. 607, Cullum Rd., West Point, NY 10996
MEMA Info. Services Coun. [★71]
MEMA Tech. Coun. [71], 10 Lab. Dr., Research Triangle Park, NC 27709, (919)406-8830
Members Prime Club - Defunct.

Membrane Science
North Amer. Membrane Soc. [7086]
Membrane Soc. of Japan [IO], Tokyo, Japan
Memorial Found. of the Germanna Colonies in Virginia [9708], PO Box 279, Locust Grove, VA 22508-0279, (540)423-1700
Memorial Found. for Jewish Culture [9927], 50 Broadway, 34th Fl., New York, NY 10004-1690, (212)425-6606
Memorial Found. for Jewish Culture [9927], 50 Broadway, 34th Fl., New York, NY 10004-1690, (212)425-6606
Memories of Elvis Fan Club [IO], Auckland, New Zealand
Memphis Cotton Exchange [3968], 65 Union Ave., Memphis, TN 38103, (901)531-7826

Men
Natl. Assn. for Males with Eating Disorders [14438]
Natl. Compadres Network [12484]
Natl. Practitioners Network for Fathers and Families [12018]
Phi Sigma Nu Native Amer. Fraternity [23685]
Prostate Hea. Educ. Network [13971]
Psi Sigma Phi Multicultural Fraternity [23638]
Student African Amer. Brotherhood [19288]
Women in Fatherhood, Inc. [13151]
Men Against Breast Cancer [13942], PO Box 150, Adamstown, MD 21710-0150, (866)547-6222
Men Against Destruction - Defending Against Drugs and Social Disorder [13264], PO Box 22704, Alexandria, VA 22304, (904)781-0905
Men of the Church Coun. [★20162]
Men/Fathers Hotline [★18107]
Men and Fathers Rsrc. Center [18107], LoneStar Fatherhood Initiative, 807 Brazos St., Ste. 315, Austin, TX 78701-2508, (512)472-3237
Men of Goodwill [★17805]
Men of Goodwill [★17805]
Men for Missions Intl. [20060], PO Box A, Greenwood, IN 46142-6599, (317)881-6752
Men for Missions Intl. [20060], PO Box A, Greenwood, IN 46142-6599, (317)881-6752
Men of Reform Judaism [19882], 633 3rd Ave., New York, NY 10017, (212)650-4100
Men Stopping Violence [18171], 2785 Lawrenceville Hwy., Ste. 112, Decatur, GA 30033, (404)270-9894
MENC: The Natl. Assn. for Music Educ. [8654], 1806 Robert Fulton Dr., Reston, VA 20191, (703)860-4000
Mencken Soc. [9401], PO Box 16218, Baltimore, MD 21210
MEND - Mothers Embracing Nuclear Disarmament - Defunct.
Mended Hearts Club [★14030]
Mended Hearts, Inc. [14030], 8150 N Central Expy., Dallas, TX 75206, (214)296-9252
Mending Kids Intl. [14089], 4100 W Alameda Ave., Ste. 103, Burbank, CA 91505, (818)843-6363
Mendoza Hall of Fame - Defunct.
Meningitis Angels [14401], PO Box 448, Porter, TX 77365, (281)572-1998
Meningitis Assn; Natl. [14410]

Mennonite
Canadian Conf. of Mennonite Brethren Churches [14804]
Mennonite Central Comm. [19956]
Mennonite Central Comm. [19956]
Mennonite Church USA Historical Comm. [19957]
Mennonite Economic Development Associates [19958]
Mennonite Educ. Agency [19959]
Mennonite Voluntary Ser. [19960]
Mennonite Women U.S.A. [19961]
Rosedale Mennonite Missions [19962]
Rosedale Mennonite Missions [19962]
Mennonite Assn. of Retired Persons [12918], 23 Homestead Dr., Lancaster, PA 17602, (717)201-8391

Mennonite Bd. of Educ. [★19959]
Mennonite Central Comm. [19956], 21 S 12th St., PO Box 500, Akron, PA 17501-0500, (717)859-1151
Mennonite Central Comm. [19956], 21 S 12th St., PO Box 500, Akron, PA 17501-0500, (717)859-1151
Mennonite Central Comm. Overseas Peace Off. [18264], 21 S 12th St., PO Box 500, Akron, PA 17501-0500, (717)859-1151
Mennonite Central Comm. Overseas Peace Off. [18264], 21 S 12th St., PO Box 500, Akron, PA 17501-0500, (717)859-1151
Mennonite Church USA Historical Comm. [19957], 1700 S Main St., Goshen, IN 46526, (574)523-3080
Mennonite Disaster Ser. [12867], 583 Airport Rd., Lititz, PA 17543, (717)735-3536
Mennonite Disaster Ser. [12867], 583 Airport Rd., Lititz, PA 17543, (717)735-3536
Mennonite Economic Development Associates [IO], Waterloo, ON, Canada
Mennonite Economic Development Associates [19958], 32C E Roseville Rd., Lancaster, PA 17601-3861, (717)560-6546
Mennonite Educ. Agency [19959], 63846 County Rd. 35, Ste. 1, Goshen, IN 46528-9621, (574)642-3164
Mennonite Health Assn. - Defunct.
Mennonite Indus. and Bus. Assn. [★19958]
Mennonite Voluntary Ser. [19960], PO Box 347, Newton, KS 67114-0347, (574)523-3000
Mennonite Women U.S.A. [19961], 718 Main St., Newton, KS 67114-1819, (316)281-4396
Menopause Soc; North Amer. [15890]
Men's Clothing Mfrs. Assn. [IO], Montreal, QC, Canada
Men's Collegiate Lacrosse Assn. [22715], PO Box 93531, Atlanta, GA 30377
Men's Educational Support Assn. [IO], Calgary, AB, Canada
Men's Garden Clubs of Am. [★21794]
Men's Hea. Network - Address unknown since 2010.
Men's Intl. Peace Exchange [18265], 612 Kenney Ln., Brookhaven, PA 19015-1422
Men's Intl. Peace Exchange [18265], 612 Kenney Ln., Brookhaven, PA 19015-1422
Men's Rsrc. Center [12220], 12 SE 14th Ave., Portland, OR 97214, (503)235-3433
Men's Resources Hot Line [★18109]

Men's Rights
Amer. Union of Men [18105]
Male Liberation Found. [18106]
Men and Fathers Rsrc. Center [18107]
Natl. Center for Men [18108]
Natl. Coalition for Men [18109]
Natl. Org. for Men [18110]
US Human Rights Network [17866]
Men's Rights Agency of Australia [IO], Waterford West, Australia
Mensa; Amer. [9638]
Mensa, the High IQ Soc. [★9638]
Mensa Intl. [IO], Wolverhampton, United Kingdom
Mensa I Irish Special Interest Gp. [9888], Box 230, Rte. 2, Valley City, ND 58072
Mensa South Africa [IO], Pinegowrie, Republic of South Africa

Menswear
YMA Fashion Scholarship Fund [216]
Mental Disability Legal Rsrc. Center [★5508]
Mental Disability Rights Intl. [12507], 1156 15th St. NW, Ste. 1001, Washington, DC 20005, (202)296-0800
Mental Disability Rights Intl. [12507], 1156 15th St. NW, Ste. 1001, Washington, DC 20005, (202)296-0800

Mental Health
AACTION Autism [13776]
ACMHA: The Coll. for Behavioral Hea. Leadership [15440]
Active Minds [15441]
Aging with Autism [13777]
All Healers Mental Hea. Alliance [15442]
Amer. Asperger's Assn. [15564]
Amer. Assn. of Anger Mgt. Providers [15443]
Amer. Combat Veterans of War [20771]

Amer. Mental Hea. Alliance [15444]
Amer. Mental Hea. Counselors Assn. [15445]
Amer. Psychological Assn. I Division of Independent Practice [16371]
Amer. Psychological Assn. I Soc. of Psychological Hypnosis [16380]
Annapolis Coalition on the Behavioral Hea. Workforce [15446]
Ardent Lion Soc. [11659]
Armenian Amer. Soc. for Stud. on Stress and Genocide [15447]
Art Therapy Connection [13772]
ASHA Intl. [15448]
Assn. for Advanced Training in the Behavioral Sciences [8761]MentalAssn. for Convulsive Therapy
Assn. for Integrative Psychology [16389]
Autism Care and Treatment Today! [13780]
Autism Community of Africa [11119]
Binge Eating Disorder Assn. [14432]
Black Mental Hea. Alliance [15449]
Center for the Stud. of Aging of Albany [10838]
Clowns Without Borders [11524]
Cognitive Development Soc. [13825]
Comm. for Truth in Psychiatry [15450]
CorStone [15451]
CorStone [15451]
Coun. on Accreditation [13182]
Coun. of Professional Geropsychology Training Programs [14663]
Deaf-REACH [14930]
Depression and Bipolar Support Alliance [15452]
Double Trouble in Recovery [12485]
Emotions Anonymous Intl. Ser. Center [12486]
Emotions Anonymous Intl. Ser. Center [12486]
Families for Depression Awareness [15453]
Fed. of Families for Children's Mental Hea. [12487]
Feldenkrais Guild of North Am. [9834]
Freedom From Fear [15454]
Give an Hour [11088]
Global Autism Collaboration [13793]
Hea. Promotion Inst. [10845]
Imagery Intl. [15073]
Intl. Alliance for Child and Adolescent Mental Hea. and Schools [15455]
Intl. Alliance for Child and Adolescent Mental Hea. and Schools [15455]
Intl. Assn. for Women's Mental Hea. [15456]
Intl. Brain Barriers Soc. [15657]
Intl. OCD Found. [15457]
Intl. Positive Psychology Assn. [16401]
Intl. Soc. for Bipolar Disorders [13766]
Intl. Soc. for Mental Hea. Online [15458]
Intl. Soc. for Mental Hea. Online [15458]
Intl. Soc. for the Psychological Treatments of the Schizophrenias and Other Psychoses U.S.A. [15459]
Intl. Soc. for the Psychological Treatments of the Schizophrenias and Other Psychoses U.S.A. [15459]
Intl. Soc. for the Stud. of Trauma and Dissociation [15460]
Intl. Soc. for the Stud. of Trauma and Dissociation [15460]
Iranian Amer. Psychological Assn. [16406]
Judge David L. Bazelon Center for Mental Hea. Law [17296]
ManKind Proj. [13043]
Marijuana Policy Proj. [18086]
Mental Hea. Am. [15461]
Mental Hea. Ireland [21270]
Mental Hea. Workers Without Borders [15462]
Mental Hea. Workers Without Borders [15462]
Milestones Autism Org. [13798]
NADD - An Assn. for Persons with Developmental Disabilities and Mental Hea. Needs [12488]
NAMM Found. [10248]
Narcotic Educational Found. of Am. [13267]
NARSAD: The Brain and Behavior Res. Fund [15463]
Natl. Alliance on Mental Illness [15464]
Natl. Alliance of Professional Psychology Providers [16411]
Natl. Anger Mgt. Assn. [15465]

Reference to "IO" in place of a book number signifies that the association may be found in the 50th edition of International Organizations.

Natl. Asian Amer. Pacific Islander Mental Hea. Assn. [15466]
Natl. Assn. of Certified Professionals of Equine Therapy [13694]
Natl. Assn. for Males with Eating Disorders [14438]
Natl. Assn. of Mental Hea. Planning and Advisory Councils [15467]
Natl. Assn. of Peer Specialists [15468]
Natl. Assn. for Rural Mental Hea. [15469]
Natl. Assn. for Self Esteem [15470]
Natl. Assn. of State Mental Hea. Prog. Directors [15471]
Natl. Center for Amer. Indian and Alaska Native Mental Hea. Res. [15472]
Natl. Coalition of Mental Hea. Professionals and Consumers [15473]
Natl. Coun. for Community Behavioral Healthcare [15474]
Natl. Educ. Alliance for Borderline Personality Disorder [15475]
Natl. Inst. of Mental Hea. [15476]
Natl. Latino Behavioral Hea. Assn. [15477]
Natl. Mental Hea. Consumers' Self-Help CH [12489]
Natl. Rsrc. Center on Homelessness and Mental Illness [12164]
Natl. Stigma CH [15478]
Network Against Coercive Psychiatry [12490]
North Amer. Soc. for Childhood Onset Schizophrenia [15479]
Obsessive-Compulsive Anonymous [12491]
Org. for Medical and Psychological Assistance for Children Overseas [14094]
PRS, Inc. [15480]
Sandtray Network [16361]
Schizophrenia Intl. Res. Soc. [15481]
Schizophrenia Intl. Res. Soc. [15481]
Schizophrenia Ireland [14391]
Schizophrenia Soc. of Canada [21694]
Selective Mutism Found. [15482]
Sidran Inst. for Traumatic Stress Educ. and Advocacy [12492]
Sigmund Freud Archives [16362]
Soc. for Emotional Well-Being Worldwide [15483]
Soc. for the Psychological Stud. of Lesbian, Gay, Bisexual and Transgender Issues [16429]
Soul Friends [16873]
Stop Calling It Autism! [13802]MentalSuicide and Mental Hea. Assn. Intl.
Suicide Prevention Intl. [13299]
Talk About Curing Autism [13805]
Treatment and Res. Advancements Assn. for Personality Disorder [15484]
Trichotillomania Learning Center [15485]
Unlocking Autism [13807]
World Fed. for Mental Hea. [15486]
World Fed. for Mental Hea. [15486]
Youth Taking Charge [12493]
Mental Hea. Am. [15461], 2000 N Beauregard St., 6th Fl., Alexandria, VA 22311, (703)684-7722
Mental Hea. Assn. [★15461]
Mental Hea. Assn. NSW [IO], East Sydney, Australia
Mental Hea. Assn. Queensland [IO], Brisbane, Australia
Mental Hea. Coalition of South Australia [IO], Adelaide, Australia
Mental Hea. Corporations of Am. [13816], 1876-A Eider Ct., Tallahassee, FL 32308, (850)942-4900
Mental Hea. Coun. of Australia [IO], Canberra, Australia
Mental Hea. Found. [IO], London, United Kingdom
Mental Hea. Ireland [IO], Dublin, Ireland
Mental Hea. Law Proj. [★17296]
Mental Health Materials Center - Defunct.
Mental Health Policy Resource Center - Defunct.
Mental Hea. Workers Without Borders [15462], Martin Gittelman, 100 W 94th St., New York, NY 10025
Mental Hea. Workers Without Borders [15462], Martin Gittelman, 100 W 94th St., New York, NY 10025
Mental Illness Found. - Defunct.
Mental and Physical Disability Legal Res. Services and Databases [★5508]

Mental Res. Inst. [13817], 555 Middlefield Rd., Palo Alto, CA 94301, (650)321-3055
Mental Retardation Assn. of America - Defunct.
Mentally Disabled
AACTION Autism [13776]
Action for Autism [16028]
Aging with Autism [13777]
Aicardi Syndrome Newsl. [14581]
Alliance for Full Participation [11754]
Amer. Asperger's Assn. [15564]
Amer. Assn. on Intellectual and Developmental Disabilities [15487]
Amer. Bd. of Disability Analysts [16553]
Amer. Network of Community Options and Resources [12494]
Arc of the U.S. [12495]
Assn. for Children with Down Syndrome [12496]
Assn. for the Help of Retarded Children [15488]
Assn. of Univ. Centers on Disabilities [12497]
Autism Community of Africa [11119]
Best Buddies Intl. [12498]
Best Buddies Intl. [12498]
Bethesda Lutheran Homes and Services [12499]
Center for Family Support [12500]
Coun. on Quality and Leadership [12501]
Coun. on Quality and Leadership [12501]
Empower the Children [11268]
Families with Autism Spectrum Disorders [13790]
Fed. for Children with Special Needs [12502]
Global Communities of Support [11120]
Gospel Assn. for the Blind [17078]
HALTER, Inc. [16852]
Hands for Autistic Children of Ethiopia [11121]
JARC [12503]
Joseph P. Kennedy, Jr. Found. [12504]
Lifespire [12505]
Little City Found. [12506]
Mental Disability Rights Intl. [12507]
Mental Disability Rights Intl. [12507]
Milestones Autism Org. [13798]
Natl. Assn. of Councils on Developmental Disabilities [12508]
Natl. Assn. of Qualified Developmental Disability Professionals [15489]
Natl. Assn. of State Directors of Developmental Disabilities Services [12509]
Natl. Down Syndrome Cong. [12510]
Natl. Down Syndrome Soc. [15490]
New Avenues to Independence [12511]
Parents Of Autistic Children [13801]
Pilot Parents of Southern Arizona [12512]
Stop Calling It Autism! [13802]
Talk About Curing Autism [13805]
Unlocking Autism [13807]
VOR [12513]
YAI Network [12514]
Mentalphysics [20190], PO Box 1000, Joshua Tree, CA 92252, (760)365-8371
Mercado Global [3686], 20 Mitchell Dr., New Haven, CT 06511, (203)772-4292
MERCAZ USA [19883], 820 Second Ave., 10th Fl., New York, NY 10017-4504, (212)533-2061
MERCAZ USA [19883], 820 Second Ave., 10th Fl., New York, NY 10017-4504, (212)533-2061
Mercedes-Benz Club of Am. [21103], 1907 Lelaray St., Colorado Springs, CO 80909-2872, (719)633-6427
Mercedes-Benz M-100 Owner's Gp. [21104], 910 Suellen Dr., Reading, PA 19605
Mercers' Company [IO], London, United Kingdom
Merchant Marine
Amer. Maritime Cong. [5788]
Chamber of Shipping of Am. [5789]
Marine Engineers' Beneficial Assn. [7087]
Merchant Risk Coun. [1052], 2400 N 45th St., Ste. 15, Seattle, WA 98103, (206)364-2789
Merchant Tailors and Designers Assn. of Am. [★204]
Merchant Taylors' Company [IO], London, United Kingdom
Merchants' Exchange of St. Louis - Defunct.
Merchants and Mfrs. Assn. [★2280]
Merchants Payment Coalition [12913], 325 7th St. NW, Ste. 1100, Washington, DC 20004
Merck Family Fund [4281], 95 Eliot St., Ste. 2, Milton, MA 02186, (617)696-3580

Mercury
Moms Against Mercury [13322]
Mercury Policy Proj. [18729], 1420 North St., Montpelier, VT 05602, (802)223-9000
Mercy Beyond Borders [12738], 1885 De La Cruz Blvd., Ste. 101, Santa Clara, CA 95050, (650)815-1554
Mercy Corps [★17919]
Mercy Corps [12739], Dept. W, PO Box 2669, Portland, OR 97208-2669, (800)292-3355
Mercy Corps [★17919]
Mercy Corps [12739], Dept. W, PO Box 2669, Portland, OR 97208-2669, (800)292-3355
Mercy For Animals [11002], 3712 N Broadway St., Ste. 560, Chicago, IL 60613, (866)632-6446
Mercy Intl. Hea. Services [★14907]
MERCY Malaysia [IO], Kuala Lumpur, Malaysia
Mercy Medical Airlift - Defunct.
Mercy Ships Intl. Operations Center [15309], PO Box 2020, Garden Valley, TX 75771-2020, (903)939-7000
Mercy Ships Intl. Operations Center [15309], PO Box 2020, Garden Valley, TX 75771-2020, (903)939-7000
Mercy Universal [IO], Greenford, United Kingdom
Mercy - U.S.A. for Aid and Development [12868], 44450 Pinetree Dr., Ste. 201, Plymouth, MI 48170-3869, (734)454-0011
Mercy - U.S.A. for Aid and Development [12868], 44450 Pinetree Dr., Ste. 201, Plymouth, MI 48170-3869, (734)454-0011
Meretz U.S.A. [18266], 114 W 26th St., No. 1002, New York, NY 10001, (212)242-4500
Meridian House Found. [★17977]
Meridian House Found. [★17977]
Meridian House Intl. [★17977]
Meridian House Intl. [★17977]
Meridian Intl. Center [17977], 1630 Crescent Pl. NW, Washington, DC 20009, (202)667-6800
Meridian Intl. Center [17977], 1630 Crescent Pl. NW, Washington, DC 20009, (202)667-6800
Meridian Intl. Center Programming Div. [17978], 1630 Crescent Pl. NW, Washington, DC 20009, (202)667-6800
Merit Contractors Assn. [IO], Edmonton, AB, Canada
Merle Thorpe, Jr. Found. [★18122]
Merle Thorpe, Jr. Found. [★18122]
Merleau-Ponty Circle [10399], Univ. of Rhode Island, Dept. of Philosophy, 170 Chafee Social Sci. Center, 10 Chafee Rd., Kingston, RI 02881, (401)874-4790
Merrill's Marauders Assn. [20862], 13033 Azalea Dr., Seneca, SC 29678-4508
Merseyside Campaign for Nuclear Disarmament [IO], Liverpool, United Kingdom
Mesoamerican Ecotourism Alliance [4964], 4076 Crystal Ct., Boulder, CO 80304, (303)440-3362
Mesothelioma Applied Res. Found. [14402], 1317 King St., Alexandria, VA 22314, (805)563-8400
Message! Products [18648], PO Box 700, Edgewood, MD 21040-0700, (800)243-2565
Messenger Courier Assn. of Am. [3254], 750 Natl. Press Bldg., 529 14th St. NW, Washington, DC 20045, (202)785-3298
Messengers of Christ-Lutheran Bible Translators [★19351]
Messianic Jewish Alliance of Am. [19966], PO Box 274, Springfield, PA 19064, (610)338-0451
Messianic Jewish Movement Intl. [19967], PO Box 41071, Phoenix, AZ 85080-1071, (480)786-6564
Messianic Jewish Movement Intl. [19967], PO Box 41071, Phoenix, AZ 85080-1071, (480)786-6564
A Messianic Jewish Perspective [19968], 60 Haight St., San Francisco, CA 94102, (415)864-2600
Messianic Judaism
Intl. Alliance of Messianic Congregations and Synagogues [19963]
Intl. Alliance of Messianic Congregations and Synagogues [19963]
Intl. Fed. of Messianic Jews [19964]
Intl. Fed. of Messianic Jews [19964]
Jews for Jesus [19965]
Jews for Jesus [19965]
Messianic Jewish Alliance of Am. [19966]
Messianic Jewish Movement Intl. [19967]

A star before a book entry number signifies that the name is not listed separately, but is mentioned within the entry.

Messianic Jewish Movement Intl. [19967]
A Messianic Jewish Perspective [19968]
Messies Anonymous [13045], 10525 NW 146th Pl.,
Alachua, FL 32615-5723
Meta-Data Professional Org. [6984], PO Box
170445, Boston, MA 02117, (973)379-7212
Metaalunie, Nederlandse Organisatie van Onderne-
mers in het Midden- en Kleinbedrijf in de Metaal
[★IO]
Metaalunie, Netherlands Org. for Small- and
Medium-Sized Enterprises in the Metal Indus. [IO],
Nieuwegein, Netherlands
Metabolic Dietary Disorder Assn. [IO], Croydon,
Australia
**Metabolic DisordersMetabolicAlbinism World Al-
liance**
Amer. Bd. of Nutrition [15815]
Amer. Porphyria Found. [15491]
Assn. for Glycogen Storage Disease [15492]
Children's PKU Network [15493]
Cystinosis Found. [15494]
Cystinosis Res. Network [15495]
FOD Family Support Gp. [15496]
FOD Family Support Gp. [15496]
Genetic Metabolic Dietitians Intl. [15497]
Intl. Soc. on Metabolic Eye Disease [15966]
Iron Overload Diseases Assn. [15498]
Iron Overload Diseases Assn. [15498]
Maple Syrup Urine Disease Family Support Gp.
[15499]
Natl. Gaucher Found. [15500]
Natl. MPS Soc. [15501]
Natl. Niemann Pick Disease Found. [15502]
Natl. Org. for Albinism and Hypopigmentation
[15503]
Paget Found. for Paget's Disease of Bone and
Related Disorders [15504]
Parents of Galactosemic Children [15505]
Purine Res. Soc. [15506]
Syndrome X Assn. [15507]
Wilson's Disease Assn. Intl. [15508]
Metafore - Address unknown since 2011.
Metal
AFL-CIO | Metal Trades Dept. [23253]
Aluminum Assn. [2460]
Aluminum Extruders Coun. [2461]
Amer. Copper Coun. [2462]
Amer. Inst. for Intl. Steel [2463]
Amer. Inst. for Intl. Steel [2463]
Amer. Iron and Steel Inst. [2464]
Assn. of Steel Distributors [2465]
Cemented Carbide Producers Assn. [2466]
Cold Finished Steel Bar Inst. [2467]
Cool Metal Roofing Coalition [550]
Copper and Brass Servicenter Assn. [2468]
Copper Development Assn. [18409]
European Metallizers Assn. [16131]
Foil Stamping and Embossing Assn. [2469]
Forging Indus. Assn. [2470]
Hot Briquetted Iron Assn. [2471]
Indus. Perforators Assn. [2472]
Intl. Assn. of Bridge, Structural, Ornamental and
Reinforcing Iron Workers [23254]
Intl. Hard Anodizing Assn. [2473]
Intl. Hard Anodizing Assn. [2473]
Intl. Magnesium Assn. [2474]
Intl. Magnesium Assn. [2474]
Intl. Titanium Assn. [2475]
Intl. Titanium Assn. [2475]
Intl. Zinc Assn. - America [2476]
Metal Injection Molding Assn. [2477]
Metal Powder Indus. Fed. [2478]
Metal Powder Producers Assn. [2479]
Metal Roofing Alliance [2480]
Metal Treating Inst. [2481]
Metal Treating Inst. [2481]
Metals Ser. Center Inst. [2482]
Natl. Assn. of Architectural Metal Mfrs. [2483]
Natl. Assn. of Graphic and Prdt. Identification
Mfrs. [2484]
Natl. Assn. of Hose and Accessories Distribution
[1850]
Natl. Inst. of Steel Detailing [2485]
Natl. Inst. of Steel Detailing [2485]
Natl. Ornamental and Miscellaneous Metals Assn.
[2486]

Natl. Union of Metalworkers of South Africa
[18732]
Non-Ferrous Metals Producers Comm. [2487]
North Amer. Steel Alliance [2488]
Palladium Alliance Intl. [2489]
Photo-Chemical Machining Inst. [2490]
Photo-Chemical Machining Inst. [2490]
Precision Metalforming Assn. [2491]
Sheet Metal Workers' Intl. Assn. [23255]
Silver Inst. [2492]
Silver Users Assn. [2493]
Specialty Steel Indus. of North Am. [2494]
Steel Framing Alliance [2495]
Steel Framing Alliance [2495]
Steel Mfrs. Assn. [2496]
United Steelworkers of Am. [23256]
Vanadium Producers and Reclaimers Assn.
[2497]
Metal Boat Soc. [462], 721 Marine Dr., Bellingham,
WA 98225, (425)485-2100
Metal Building Contractors and Erectors Assn.
[2310], PO Box 499, Shawnee Mission, KS 66201,
(913)432-3800
Metal Building Dealers Assn. [★2310]
Metal Building Mfrs. Assn. [580], 1300 Sumner Ave.,
Cleveland, OH 44115-2851, (216)241-7333
Metal Buildings Inst. [7776], Ray Barbieri, Pres.-
Elect, 588 Winsted Rd., Torrington, CT 06790,
(860)496-7503
Metal Constr. Assn. [581], 4700 W Lake Ave., Glen-
view, IL 60025-1485, (847)375-4718
Metal Cookware Mfrs. Assn. [★1776]
Metal Cutting Knife Assn. [★1838]
Metal Cutting Tool Inst. [★1877]
Metal Etching and Fabricating Assn. [★2484]
Metal Fabricating Inst. - Defunct.
Metal Finishing Suppliers' Assn., Natl. Assn. of Metal
Finishers and Amer. Electroplaters and Surface
Finishers Soc. [★1348]
Metal Framing Mfrs. Assn. [582], 401 N Michigan
Ave., Chicago, IL 60611-4267, (312)644-6610
Metal Injection Molding Assn. [2477], Metal Powder
Indus. Fed., 105 Coll. Rd. E, Princeton, NJ 08540-
6692, (609)452-7700
Metal Ladder Mfrs. Assn. - Defunct.
Metal Packaging Mfrs. Assn. [IO], Wokingham,
United Kingdom
Metal Polishers, Buffers, Platers and Allied Workers
Intl. Union [★23159]
Metal Powder Assn. [★2478]
Metal Powder Indus. Fed. [2478], 105 Coll. Rd. E,
Princeton, NJ 08540-6692, (609)452-7700
Metal Powder Producers Assn. [2479], Metal
Powder Inst. Fed., 105 Coll. Rd. E, Princeton, NJ
08540-6692, (609)452-7700
Metal Properties Coun. [★7098]
Metal Roofing Alliance [2480], E 4142 Hwy. 302,
Belfair, WA 98528, (360)275-6164
Metal Treating Inst. [2481], 504 Osceola Ave.,
Jacksonville Beach, FL 32250-3222, (904)249-
0448
Metal Treating Inst. [2481], 504 Osceola Ave.,
Jacksonville Beach, FL 32250-3222, (904)249-
0448
Metalforming Machinery Makers' Assn. [IO], Hook
Norton, United Kingdom
Metallurgic and Metal Mech. Indus'. Assn. [IO], San-
tiago, Chile
The Metallurgical Soc. [★7099]
Metallurgical Soc. of Am; Mining and [7126]
Metallurgistes Unis d'Amerique [★IO]
Metallurgy
Amer. Bur. of Metal Statistics [7088]
APMI Intl. [7089]
APMI Intl. [7089]
Argentine Chamber of the Aluminum, Metals and
Related Indus. [8107]
Argentine Metallurgical Indus'. Assn. [11566]
ASM Intl. [7090]
ASM Intl. [7090]
Assn. for Iron and Steel Tech. [7091]
Australian Die Casting Assn. [2980]
Cold Finished Steel Bar Inst. [2467]
Ductile Iron Soc. [7092]
Forging Indus. Educational and Res. Found.
[7093]

Intl. Copper Assn. [7094]
Intl. Copper Assn. [7094]
Intl. Lead Zinc Res. Org. [7095]
Intl. Lead Zinc Res. Org. [7095]
Intl. Org. on Shape Memory and Superelastic
Technologies [7096]
Intl. Org. on Shape Memory and Superelastic
Technologies [7096]
Intl. Precious Metals Inst. [7097]
Intl. Precious Metals Inst. [7097]
Materials Properties Coun. [7098]
Metal Treating Inst. [2481]
Minerals, Metals, and Materials Soc. [7099]
Natl. Inst. for Metalworking Skills [7100]
Palladium Alliance Intl. [2489]
Soc. of Carbide and Tool Engineers [7101]
Wire Assn. Intl. [7102]
Wire Assn. Intl. [7102]
Metals
Cold Finished Steel Bar Inst. [2467]
Metal Treating Inst. [2481]
Welders Without Borders [7619]
Metals Ser. Center Inst. [2482], 4201 Euclid Ave.,
Rolling Meadows, IL 60008-2025, (847)485-3000
Metamorphic Assn. [IO], Hastings, United Kingdom
Metanoia Ministries [19636], PO Box 448,
Washington, NH 03280, (603)495-0035
Metaphysical Soc. of Am. [10400], Univ. of Alabam-
aHuntsville, Dept. of Philosophy, Huntsville, AL
35899, (205)895-6555
Metapsychic Investigations and Sci. Res. Soc. [IO],
Istanbul, Turkey
Meteoritical Soc. [6928], 3635 Concorde Pkwy., Ste.
500, Chantilly, VA 20151-1125, (703)652-9953
Meteorological Soc. of New Zealand [IO], Welling-
ton, New Zealand
Meteorology
Amer. Assn. of State Climatologists [7103]
Amer. Meteorological Soc. [7104]
Inst. of Global Env. and Soc. [4271]
Intl. Earthlight Alliance [7105]
Intl. Soc. for Aeolian Res. [6926]
Natl. Weather Assn. [7106]
North Amer. Meteor Network [7107]
North Amer. Meteor Network [7107]
PlanetQuest [6235]
Univ. Corp. for Atmospheric Res. [7108]
Weather Modification Assn. [7109]
Meter-Slogan Associates [★22053]
Meter Stamp Soc. [22053], PO Box 16278, Tucson,
AZ 85732-6278
Methacrylate Producers Assn. [758], 17260 Vannes
Ct., Hamilton, VA 20158, (540)751-2093
Methanol Inst. [6894], 124 S West St., Ste. 203,
Alexandria, VA 22314, (703)248-3636
Methodist
Black Methodists for Church Renewal [19969]
Center for the Evangelical United Brethren
Heritage [19719]
Christian Methodist Episcopal Church | Women's
Missionary Coun. [19970]
Fellowship of United Methodists in Music and
Worship Arts [19971]
Forum for Scriptural Christianity [19972]
Gen. Commn. on Archives and History of the
United Methodist Church [10084]
Historical Soc. of the United Methodist Church
[9768]
Methodist Fed. for Social Action [19973]
The Mission Soc. [19974]
Reconciling Ministries Network [19799]
United Methodist Church | Gen. Bd. of Church
and Soc. [19975]
United Methodist Comm. on Relief [19976]
United Methodist Comm. on Relief [19976]
United Methodist Youth Org. [19977]Methodist-
World Fed. of Methodist and Uniting Church
Women - USA
World Methodist Coun. [19978]
World Methodist Coun. [19978]
World Methodist Historical Soc. [19979]
World Methodist Historical Soc. [19979]
Methodist Assn. of Hea. and Welfare Ministries;
United [14742]
Methodist Church of New Zealand [IO],
Christchurch, New Zealand

Reference to "IO" in place of a book number signifies that the association may be found in the 50th edition of International Organizations.

Methodist Comm. for Overseas Relief [★19976]
Methodist Comm. for Overseas Relief [★19976]
Methodist Coun. on Youth Ministry [★19977]
Methodist Fed. for Social Action [19973], 212 E Capitol St. NE, Washington, DC 20003, (202)546-8806
Methodist Fed. for Social Ser. [★19973]
Methodist Historical Union [★19979]
Methodist Historical Union [★19979]
Methodist Women in Ireland [IO], Belfast, United Kingdom
Methods Time Measurements Assn. for Standards and Res. [★6948]
Metopera [★10241]
Metric Assn. [★7470]
Metro Ethernet Forum [7515], 6033 W Century Blvd., Ste. 830, Los Angeles, CA 90045, (310)642-2800
Metro Ethernet Forum [7515], 6033 W Century Blvd., Ste. 830, Los Angeles, CA 90045, (310)642-2800
Metro Intl. Prog. Services of New York [★8372]
Metrology Soc. of Australia [IO], Lindfield, Australia
Metrology Soc. of Thailand [IO], Bangkok, Thailand
Metropolitan Air Post Soc. [22054], 7 Evelyn Terr., Wayne, NJ 07470-3446
Metropolitan Air Post Soc. [22054], 7 Evelyn Terr., Wayne, NJ 07470-3446
Metropolitan Airmail Cover Club [★22054]
Metropolitan Airmail Cover Club [★22054]
Metropolitan Assn. of Urban Designers and Environmental Planners - Defunct.
Metropolitan Community Church [★19797]
Metropolitan Community Churches [19797], PO Box 1374, Abilene, TX 79604, (310)360-8640
Metropolitan Microchemical Soc. [★6394]
Metropolitan Opera Assn. [10241], Lincoln Center, New York, NY 10023, (212)799-3100
Metropolitan Opera Guild [10242], 70 Lincoln Center Plz., New York, NY 10023, (212)769-7000
Metropolitan Owners' Club [IO], Pulborough, United Kingdom
Metropolitan Owners Club of North Am. [21105], 6530 Shenandoah Dr., Lincoln, NE 68510, (402)430-6380
Metropolitan Tree Improvement Alliance [4973], Michigan State Univ., Dept. of Horticulture, East Lansing, MI 48824-1325
Metropolitan YMCA Singapore [IO], Singapore, Singapore
Mexican Acad. of Dermatology [IO], Mexico City, Mexico
Mexican Acad. of Sciences [IO], Tlalpan, Mexico
Mexican Advt. Agencies' Assn. [IO], Mexico City, Mexico
Mexican Amer. Cultural Center [19995], PO Box 28185, San Antonio, TX 78228, (210)732-2156
Mexican-American Engg. Soc. [★6827]
Mexican Amer. Grocers Assn. - Address unknown since 2011.
Mexican Amer. Legal Defense and Educational Fund [17777], 634 S Spring St., Los Angeles, CA 90014, (213)629-2512
Mexican Amer. Legal Defense and Educational Fund [17777], 634 S Spring St., Los Angeles, CA 90014, (213)629-2512
Mexican Amer. Opportunity Found. [12144], 401 N Garfield Ave., Montebello, CA 90640, (323)890-9600
Mexican Amer. Unity Coun. [12145], 2300 W Commerce St., Ste. 200, San Antonio, TX 78207, (210)978-0500
Mexican Amer. Women's Natl. Assn. [★17655]
Mexican Article Numbering Assn. [IO], Mexico City, Mexico
Mexican Assn. of Car Dealers [IO], Mexico City, Mexico
Mexican Assn. for Cmpt. Vision, Neurocomputing and Robotics [IO], Guadalajara, Mexico
Mexican Assn. of Fair, Exhibition, and Convention Professionals [IO], Mexico City, Mexico
Mexican Assn. of Gifts, Decorative Goods and Folk Art Producers [IO], Mexico City, Mexico
Mexican Assn. of Indus. Parks [IO], Mexico City, Mexico

Mexican Assn. of Machinery Distributors [IO], Mexico City, Mexico
Mexican Assn. of Marketing and Public Opinion Res. Agencies [IO], Mexico City, Mexico
Mexican Assn. of Restaurants [IO], Mexico City, Mexico
Mexican Automotive Assn. [IO], Mexico City, Mexico
Mexican Chamber of the Constr. Indus. [IO], Mexico City, Mexico
Mexican Commn. for the Defense and Promotion of Human Rights [IO], Mexico City, Mexico
Mexican Found. for Family Planning [IO], Mexico City, Mexico
Mexican Govt. Tourism Off. [★23428]
Mexican League Against Epilepsy [IO], Mexico City, Mexico
Mexican Market Res. and Opinion Polls Assn. [IO], Mexico City, Mexico
Mexican Olympic Comm. [IO], Lomas de Sotelo, Mexico
Mexican Pharmaceutical Assn. [IO], Mexico City, Mexico
Mexican Professional Assn. of Conf. Interpreters [IO], Cuauhtemoc, Mexico
Mexican Soc. of Dermatologic Surgery and Oncology [IO], Mexico City, Mexico
Mexican Soc. of Dermatology [IO], Mexico City, Mexico
Mexican Soc. of Economic, Financial and Cost Engg. [IO], Mexico City, Mexico
Mexican Soc. for the History of Sci. and Tech. [IO], Mexico City, Mexico
Mexican Soc. on Mechatronics [IO], Queretaro, Mexico
Mexican Soc. of Psychology [IO], Mexico City, Mexico

Mexican War
Descendants of Mexican War Veterans [20692]
Mexico
Mano A Mano: Mexican Culture Without Borders [10085]
Mexico Elmhurst Philatelic Soc. Intl. [22055]
Mexico Tourism Bd. [23428]
U.S. Mexican Numismatic Assn. [21996]
Mexico ACM SIGCHI [IO], Morelia, Mexico
Mexico Apparel Chamber [IO], Mexico City, Mexico
Mexico Elmhurst Philatelic Soc. Intl. [22055], 5881 W 75th St., Los Angeles, CA 90045
Mexico Elmhurst Philatelic Soc. Intl. [22055], 5881 W 75th St., Los Angeles, CA 90045
Mexico/Monterrey Chap. of the Assn. of Energy Engineers [IO], Monterrey, Mexico
Mexico Tourism Bd. [23428], 400 Madison Ave., Ste. 11C, New York, NY 10017, (212)308-2110
Mezogazdasagi Szovetkezok es Termelok Orszagos Szovetsege [★IO]
MFM Publishing [★12885]
MG Car Club [IO], Abingdon, United Kingdom
MG Drivers Club of North Am. [21106], 18 George's Pl., Clinton, NJ 08809-1334, (908)713-6251
MG Octagon Car Club [IO], Rugeley, United Kingdom
MG Vintage Racers [22117], 55 Belden Rd., Burlington, CT 06013
MHE Coalition [14612], 6783 York Rd., Apt. No. 104, Parma Heights, OH 44130, (440)842-8817
mHealth Alliance [15198], 1800 Massachusetts Ave. NW, Ste. 400, Washington, DC 20036, (202)887-9040
M.I. Hummel Club [21267], Goebel Plz., PO Box 11, Pennington, NJ 08534-0011, (609)737-8700
MIB Gp. [15128], 50 Braintree Hill Park, Ste. 400, Braintree, MA 02184-8734, (781)751-6000
Michael Crawford Intl. Fan Assn. [23777], 2272 Colorado Blvd., PMB No. 1367, Los Angeles, CA 90041
Michael E. DeBakey Intl. Cardiovascular Soc. [★14031]
Michael E. DeBakey Intl. Cardiovascular Soc. [★14031]
Michael E. DeBakey Intl. Surgical Soc. [14031], Kenneth L. Mattox, MD, Sec.-Treas., 1 Baylor Plz., Houston, TX 77030, (713)798-4557
Michael E. DeBakey Intl. Surgical Soc. [14031], Kenneth L. Mattox, MD, Sec.-Treas., 1 Baylor Plz., Houston, TX 77030, (713)798-4557

Michael Fund (Intl. Found. for Genetic Res.) [14613], 4371 Northern Pike, Monroeville, PA 15146-2837, (412)374-0111
Michael Fund (Intl. Found. for Genetic Res.) [14613], 4371 Northern Pike, Monroeville, PA 15146-2837, (412)374-0111
Michael Jackson Fan Club [23878], PO Box 181275, Corpus Christi, TX 78480
Michael Jackson Fan Club 3 Generations [IO], Neuchatel, Switzerland
Michael Oakeshott Assn. [10401], Prof. Timothy Fuller, Colorado Coll., Political Sciences Dept., 14 E Cache La Poudre St., Colorado Springs, CO 80903, (719)389-6583
Michele Lee Fan Club [★23778]
Michele Lee Fan Club/Michele Lee Online [23778], Peter Roth, Pres., 4000 Warner Blvd., Burbank, CA 91522
Michener Soc; James A. [9383]
Michigan Apple Comm. [4457], 13105 Schavey Rd., Ste. 2, DeWitt, MI 48820, (517)669-8353
Michigan Tooling Assn. [★1874]
Mickey Mantle Found. - Defunct.
Micro and Anophthalmic Childrens Soc. [IO], Holyhead, United Kingdom
Micro Indus. Development Assistance and Services [IO], Dhaka, Bangladesh
Microanalysis Soc. [7115], Univ. of Michigan, Electron Microbeam Anal. Lab., North Campus, 417 SRB, 2455 Hayward St., Ann Arbor, MI 48109-2143, (734)936-3352
Microbeam Anal. Soc. [★7115]
Microbiology
Addgene [7110]
Comm. on the Status of Women in Microbiology [6297]
Intl. Soc. for Plasmid Biology and other Mobile Genetic Elements [7111]
Israel Soc. for Microbiology [19529]
Puerto Rico Soc. of Microbiologists [7112]
Microbiology; Amer. Acad. of [6282]
Microbiology; Amer. Acad. of [6282]
Microbiology; Waksman Found. for [6324]
Microcar and Minicar Club - Defunct.
Microcirculatory Soc. [16963], Dr. Anatoliy Gashev, Membership Chair, Texas A&M Univ. Sys. Hea. Sci. Center, Coll. of Medicine, Dept. of Medical Physiology, Temple, TX 76504, (254)742-7147
Microcomputer Software Assn. - of ADAPSO [★6499]
Microfinance Investment Support Fac. for Afghanistan [IO], Kabul, Afghanistan
Microlight Assn. of South Africa [IO], Germiston, Republic of South Africa
Micronesia Inst. - Defunct.
Micronesia Red Cross [IO], Kolonia, Federated States of Micronesia
Microneurography Soc. - Defunct.
Microscopical Soc. of Canada [IO], Lethbridge, AB, Canada
Microscopical Soc. of Ireland [IO], Dublin, Ireland
Microscopy
Amer. Microscopical Soc. [7113]
Intl. Fed. of Societies for Microscopy [7114]
Intl. Fed. of Societies for Microscopy [7114]
Microanalysis Soc. [7115]
Microscopy Soc. of Am. [7116]
New York Microscopical Soc. [7117]
Optical Imaging Assn. [4727]
Microscopy New Zealand [IO], Auckland, New Zealand
Microscopy Soc. of Am. [7116], 12100 Sunset Hills Rd., Ste. 130, Reston, VA 20190, (703)234-4115
Microscopy Soc. Singapore [IO], Singapore, Singapore
Microscopy Soc. of Southern Africa [IO], Pretoria, Republic of South Africa
Microsoft Hea. Users Gp. [14903], 12601 Fair Lakes Cir., Fairfax, VA 22033
Microsurgery; Amer. Soc. forReconstructive [16802]
Microsurgery; Amer. Soc. for Reconstructive [16802]
Microwave Communications Assn. [★3427]
Microwave Communications Assn. [★3427]
Microwave Technologies Assn. [IO], Isle of Wight, United Kingdom

A star before a book entry number signifies that the name is not listed separately, but is mentioned within the entry.

Microwaves
Intl. Microwave Power Inst. [7118]
Intl. Microwave Power Inst. [7118]
Mid-America Buddhist Assn. [19370], 299 Heger Ln., Augusta, MO 63332-1445, (636)482-4037
Mid-America Coun. on Intl. Banking [★420]
Mid-American Greek Coun. Assn. [★23531]
Mid-American Res. Lib. [★18587]
Mid-Atlantic Equity Consortium [8038], 5272 River Rd., Ste. 340, Bethesda, MD 20816, (301)657-7741
Mid Atlantic Fiber Assn. [256], Dave Banks, Membership Chm., 509 3rd St., Delanco, NJ 08075, (757)258-8632
Mid-Atlantic Radical Historians Org. [★9782]
Mid-Atlantic States Assn. of Avian Veterinarians [17032], Memorial Bldg., Ste. 291, 610 N Main St., Blacksburg, VA 24060-3311, (540)951-2559
Mid-Continent Oil and Gas Assn. [★2673]
Mid-Continent Railway Historical Soc. [22126], PO Box 358, North Freedom, WI 53951, (608)522-4261
Mid-Peninsula Conversion Proj. [★17547]
Mid Somerset Campaign for Nuclear Disarmament [IO], Shepton Mallet, United Kingdom
Mid-West Tool Collectors Assn. [21869], LeRoy E. Witzel, Treas., PO Box 355, Humboldt, IA 50548-0355
Mid-West Truckers Assn. [3519], 2727 N Dirksen Pkwy., Springfield, IL 62702, (217)525-0310
Midamerica Commodity Exchange - Defunct.
Middle Atlantic Planetarium Soc. [8841], John Meader, PO Box 302, Fairfield, ME 04937, (207)453-7668
Middle Atlantic Water Polo Conf. [★23112]
Middle East
America-Israel Coun. for Israeli-Palestinian Peace [18111]
America-MidEast Educational and Training Services [18112]
America-MidEast Educational and Training Services [18112]
Amer. Educational Trust [18113]
Amer. Israel Public Affairs Comm. [18114]
Amer. MidEast Leadership Network [17934]
Americans for Middle East Understanding [18115]
Americans for Middle East Understanding [18115]
Americans for a Safe Israel [18116]
Americans for a Safe Israel [18116]
Arab Palestine Assn. [18553]
Assn. for Peace and Understanding in the Middle East [18117]
Assn. for Peace and Understanding in the Middle East [18117]
Assn. for the Stud. of the Middle East and Africa [8619]
Assn. for the Stud. of the Middle East and Africa [8619]
Bethlehem Assn. [18118]
Bridges of Understanding [17938]
Building Bridges: Middle East-US [8385]
Catholic Near East Welfare Assn. [18119]
Catholic Near East Welfare Assn. [18119]
Comm. for Accuracy in Middle East Reporting in Am. [18120]
Comm. for Accuracy in Middle East Reporting in Am. [18120]
Facts and Logic About the Middle East [18121]
Found. for Middle East Peace [18122]
Found. for Middle East Peace [18122]
Givat Haviva Educational Found. [18123]
Givat Haviva Educational Found. [18123]
Hands Across the Mideast Support Alliance [18124]
Hands Across the Mideast Support Alliance [18124]
Intl. Coun. for Middle East Stud. [18125]
Intl. Soc. for Iranian Culture [9882]
Iraqi Human Rights Network [17846]
Ishmael and Isaac [18126]
Jewish Comm. on the Middle East [18127]
Jewish Comm. on the Middle East [18127]
Lebanese Amer. Coun. for Democracy [18069]
Lebanese Info. Center [18128]
Lebanese Info. Center [18128]

Middle East Info. Network [19144]
Middle East Info. Network [19144]
Middle East Inst. [18129]
Middle East Inst. [18129]
Middle East Investment Initiative [1313]
Middle East Peace Dialogue Network [12515]
Middle East Peace Dialogue Network [12515]
Middle East Policy Coun. [18130]
Middle East Policy Coun. [18130]
Middle East Res. and Info. Proj. [18131]
Middle East Res. and Info. Proj. [18131]
Middle East Stud. Assn. of North Am. [18132]
Middle East Stud. Assn. of North Am. [18132]
Natl. Coun. on U.S.-Arab Relations [18133]
Natl. Coun. on U.S.-Arab Relations [18133]
Near East Found. [18134]
Near East Found. [18134]
Save Yemen's Flora and Fauna [4140]
Scholars for Peace in the Middle East [18135]
Scholars for Peace in the Middle East [18135]
Syrian-American Relations Coun. [17951]
Syrian Stud. Assn. [8620]
Tomorrow's Youth Org. [13562]
United People in Christ [19980]
U.S. Fed. for Middle East Peace [18295]
Women and the Env. Org. [4323]
Middle East Assn. [IO], London, United Kingdom
Middle East Bus. Aviation Assn. [IO], Dubai, United Arab Emirates
Middle East Children's Alliance [17850], 1101 8th St., Ste. 100, Berkeley, CA 94710, (510)548-0542
Middle East Children's Alliance [17850], 1101 8th St., Ste. 100, Berkeley, CA 94710, (510)548-0542
Middle East Coun. of Amer. Chambers of Commerce [IO], Riyadh, Saudi Arabia
Middle East Coun. of Shopping Centres [IO], Dubai, United Arab Emirates
Middle East Duty Free Assn. [IO], Dubai, United Arab Emirates
Middle East Fac. Mgt. Assn. [IO], Dubai, United Arab Emirates
Middle East Info. Network [19144], 197 Fairmount Ave., Unit 2, Boston, MA 02136
Middle East Info. Network [19144], 197 Fairmount Ave., Unit 2, Boston, MA 02136
Middle East Inst. [18129], 1761 N St. NW, Washington, DC 20036-2882, (202)785-1141
Middle East Inst. [18129], 1761 N St. NW, Washington, DC 20036-2882, (202)785-1141
Middle East Investment Initiative [1313], 500 Eighth St. NW, Washington, DC 20004, (202)741-6283
Middle East Librarians Assn. [9996], Harvard Univ., Widener Lib., Rm. 5, 1 Harvard Yard, Cambridge, MA 02138, (617)496-3001
Middle East Librarians Assn. [9996], Harvard Univ., Widener Lib., Rm. 5, 1 Harvard Yard, Cambridge, MA 02138, (617)496-3001
Middle East Nonviolence and Democracy [IO], Jerusalem, Israel
Middle East Peace Dialogue Network [12515], 200 Country Club Pkwy., Mount Laurel, NJ 08054, (856)768-0938
Middle East Peace Dialogue Network [12515], 200 Country Club Pkwy., Mount Laurel, NJ 08054, (856)768-0938
Middle East Policy Coun. [18130], 1730 M St. NW, Ste. 512, Washington, DC 20036, (202)296-6767
Middle East Policy Coun. [18130], 1730 M St. NW, Ste. 512, Washington, DC 20036, (202)296-6767
Middle East Project [★18176]
Middle East Project [★18176]
Middle East Res. and Info. Proj. [18131], 1344 T St. NW, No. 1, Washington, DC 20005, (202)223-3677
Middle East Res. and Info. Proj. [18131], 1344 T St. NW, No. 1, Washington, DC 20005, (202)223-3677
Middle East Stud. Assn. of North Am. [18132], Univ. of Arizona, 1219 N Santa Rita Ave., Tucson, AZ 85721, (520)621-5850
Middle East Stud. Assn. of North Am. [18132], Univ. of Arizona, 1219 N Santa Rita Ave., Tucson, AZ 85721, (520)621-5850
Middle Eastern Dance Assn. of New Zealand [IO], Wellington, New Zealand
Middle Powers Initiative [17554], 866 United Nations Plz., Ste. 4050, New York, NY 10017, (646)289-5170

Middle Schools
Natl. Middle Level Sci. Teachers' Assn. [8848]
Natl. Middle School Assn. [8621]
One World Educ. [8928]
OneWorld Now! [8929]
Middle States Assn. of Colleges and Schools [8039], 3624 Market St., Philadelphia, PA 19104-2680, (215)662-5600
Middle States Assn. of Colleges and Secondary Schools [★8039]
MIDI Mfrs. Assn. [2339], PO Box 3173, La Habra, CA 90632-3173
Midori Found. [★7750]
Midori and Friends [7750], 352 7th Ave., Ste. 301, New York, NY 10001, (212)767-1300
Midsouth Indemnity Assn. and Asian Amer. Hotel Owners Assn. [★1737]
Midsouth Indemnity Assn. and Asian Amer. Hotel Owners Assn. [★1737]
Midstates Jeepster Assn. [21107], 7721 Howick Rd., Celina, OH 45822
Midtown Churches Community Assn. [★12159]
Midtown Intl. Center [★17974]
Midtown Intl. Center [★17974]
Midwest Acad. [11531], 27 E Monroe, 11th Fl., Chicago, IL 60603, (312)427-2304
Midwest Archives Conf. [9144], 4440 PGA Blvd., Ste. 600, Palm Beach Gardens, FL 33410
Midwest Benthological Soc. [★4220]
Midwest Benthological Soc. [★4220]
Midwest Center for Labor Res. [★18041]
Midwest Collegiate Ski Assn. [★22918]
Midwest Compensation Assn. [★1162]
Midwest Compensation Assn. [★1162]
Midwest Decoy Collectors Assn. [21371], 6 E Scott St., No. 3, Chicago, IL 60610, (312)337-7957
Midwest Equip. Dealers Assn. [3733], 5330 Wall St., Ste. 100, Madison, WI 53718, (608)240-4700
Midwest Feed Mfrs. Assn. [★4370]
Midwest Free Community Papers [2948], PO Box 1350, Iowa City, IA 52244-1350, (319)341-4352
Midwest Interlibrary Center [★9979]
Midwest Middle School Assn. [★8621]
Midwest Migrant Hea. Info. Off. [★12523]
Midwest Old Settlers and Threshers Assn. [9213], 405 E Threshers Rd., Mount Pleasant, IA 52641, (319)385-8937
Midwest Olive Assn. [IO], Dongara, Australia
Midwest Org. Development Network [★2596]
Midwest Org. Development Network [★2596]
Midwest Rugby Football Union [★22861]
Midwest Ski Representatives Assn. [★3334]
Midwest Stock Exchange [★3194]
Midwest Sunbeam Registry - Address unknown since 2010.
Midwest Treaty Network [19159], PO Box 43, Oneida, WI 54155, (920)496-5360
Midwest UFO Network [★7255]
Midwest Winter Ski Representative Assn. [★3334]
Midwest Winter Sports Representatives Assn. [3334], Gayle Snyder, PO Box 76, Hazelhurst, WI 54531, (715)358-6262
Midwestern Advt. Agency Network [★96]
Midwestern Advt. Agency Network [★96]
Midwestern Assn. for Behavior Anal. [★6248]
Midwestern Celiac Sprue Assn. [★14558]
Midwestern Fast-Draw Assn. [★22891]
Midwestern Psychological Assn. [16409], Dr. Brian Cronk, Missouri Western State Univ., Dept. of Psychology, 4525 Downs Dr., St. Joseph, MO 64507, (816)271-4394
Midwifery Assn. of Pakistan [IO], Karachi, Pakistan
Midwifery; Citizens for [14104]
Midwifery Educ. Accreditation Coun. [7823], PO Box 984, La Conner, WA 98257, (360)466-2080
Midwives Alliance of North Am. [15886], 611 Pennsylvania Ave. SE, No. 1700, Washington, DC 20003-4303, (888)923-6262
Midwives; Amer. Coll. of Nurse- [15719]
Midwives Info. and Rsrc. Ser. [IO], Bristol, United Kingdom
MIE Corp. [★21100]
Mietervereinigung Osterreichs [IO], Vienna, Austria
Migraine Action [IO], Leicester, United Kingdom
Migraine Assn. of Ireland [IO], Dublin, Ireland

Reference to "IO" in place of a book number signifies that the association may be found in the 50th edition of International Organizations.

Migraine Awareness Gp.: A Natl. Understanding for
Migraineurs [14688], 100 N Union St., Ste. B,
Alexandria, VA 22314, (703)349-1929
Migrant Dropout Reconnection Program - Defunct.
Migrant Hea. Promotion [12523], 224 W Michigan
Ave., Saline, MI 48176, (734)944-0244
Migrant Legal Action Prog. [12431], 1001 Con-
necticut Ave. NW, Ste. 915, Washington, DC
20036, (202)775-7780
Migrant Ministry [★12525]
Migrant Workers
Andolan - Organizing South Asian Workers
[12516]
Assn. of Farmworker Opportunity Programs
[12517]
Farmworker Justice Fund [12518]
Global Workers Justice Alliance [12519]
Hea. Outreach Partners [12520]
Intl. Bilingual Nurses Alliance [15755]
Interstate Migrant Educ. Coun. [12521]
Los Ninos [12522]
Migrant Hea. Promotion [12523]
Natl. Assn. of State Directors of Migrant Educ.
[12524]
Natl. Farm Worker Ministry [12525]
Migration
Center for Migration Stud. of New York [10086]
Center for Migration Stud. of New York [10086]
Global Migration Gp. [5790]
Global Migration Gp. [5790]
Intl. Refugee Rights Initiative [17843]
Intl. Social Ser., U.S.A. Br. [12526]
Intl. Social Ser., U.S.A. Br. [12526]
Migration Dept. of the Amer. Jewish Joint Distribution
Comm. [★12406]
Migration Dept. of the Amer. Jewish Joint Distribution
Comm. [★12406]
Migration and Refugee Services [★12792]
Mikciojimo Problemu Klubas [★IO]
Mike's Angels [11349], 2090 Dunwoody Club Dr.,
Ste. 106-120, Atlanta, GA 30350-5424, (770)396-
7858
Mil Milagros [11350], 400 Atlantic Ave., Boston, MA
02110, (617)330-7382
Mil Milagros [11350], 400 Atlantic Ave., Boston, MA
02110, (617)330-7382
Milan Cultural Assn. [9859], 75 Ruff Cir., Glaston-
bury, CT 06033, (860)657-4271
Milan Cultural Assn. [9859], 75 Ruff Cir., Glaston-
bury, CT 06033, (860)657-4271
Milano ACM SIGGRAPH Professional Chap. [IO],
Milan, Italy
Milano Chamber of Commerce [IO], Milan, Italy
Miles Ahead [★18673]
Miles Merwin Assn. [20560], 8416 Power Dr.,
Oscoda, MI 48750-2016, (989)739-9394
Miles Value Found. [6963], 5505 Connecticut Ave.
NW, No. 149, Washington, DC 20015-2601,
(202)253-5550
Milestone Car Soc. - Address unknown since 2010.
Milestones Autism Org. [13798], 23880 Commerce
Park, Ste. 2, Beachwood, OH 44122, (216)464-
7600
Military
29th Infantry Div. Assn. [20353]
80th Fighter Squadron Headhunters' Assn. [5195]
129th Alumni and Heritage Assn. [19270]
146th Alumni Assn. [7727]
Adjutants Gen. Assn. of the U.S. [5791]
Air Force Assn. [5792]
Air Force Sergeants Assn. [5793]
Aircraft Carrier Indus. Base Coalition [1034]
Amer. Combat Veterans of War [20771]
Amer. Logistics Assn. [5794]
Amer. Military Soc. [5795]
Amer. Retirees Assn. [20693]
Amer. Soc. of Military Comptrollers [5796]
Amer. Soc. of Military Insignia Collectors [21883]
Amer. Veterans for Equal Rights [12067]
Armed Forces Communications and Electronics
Assn. [5797]
Armed Forces Communications and Electronics
Assn. [5797]
Armed Forces Hostess Assn. [5798]
Armed Forces Sports [5799]

Army Aviation Assn. of Am. [5800]
Army Cadet League of Canada [16962]
Army Nurse Corps Assn. [15509]
Arnold Air Soc. [23596]
Assn. of Amer. Military Uniform Collectors [21884]
Assn. for Counselors and Educators in Govt.
[11669]
Assn. of Graduates [8622]
Assn. of Military Colleges and Schools of the U.S.
[8623]
Assn. of Military Surgeons of the U.S. [15510]
Assn. of NROTC Colleges and Universities [8624]
Assn. of the U.S. Army [5801]
B-52 Stratofortress Assn. [20331]
Bus. Leaders for Sensible Priorities [18414]
Catholic War Veterans Auxiliary of the U.S.A.
[20704]
Catholic War Veterans of the U.S.A. [20781]
Cell Phones for Soldiers [11086]
Centennial Legion of Historic Military Commands
[20743]
Center on Conscience and War [17560]
Center for Strategic and Budgetary Assessments
[18136]
Central Comm. for Conscientious Objectors
[17561]
Chief Warrant and Warrant Officers Assn. I U.S.
Coast Guard [5802]
Citizen Soldier [5803]
Civil Affairs Assn. [5804]
Civil Affairs Assn. [5804]
Civil War Token Soc. [21970]
Coalition for Tactical Medicine [15907]
Combat Helicopter Pilots Assn. [20313]
Company of Military Historians [21885]
Defense Advisory Comm. on Women in the
Services [5805]
Disabled Amer. Veterans [20412]
Disabled Amer. Veterans Auxiliary [20413]
Distinguished Flying Cross Soc. [20374]
Enlisted Assn. of Natl. Guard of the U.S. [5806]
Escort Carrier Sailors and Airmen Assn. [20694]
For the Fallen [12531]
Freedom is Not Free [12527]
Freedom is Not Free [12527]
Give an Hour [11088]
Give2TheTroops [12528]
Give2TheTroops [12528]
GlobalSecurity.org [18253]
HealingWorks [13681]
Hof Reunion Assn. [20349]
House of Heroes [13350]
Inter-University Seminar on Armed Forces and
Soc. [5807]
Intl. Action Center [18137]
Intl. Action Center [18137]
Intl. Bird Dog Assn. [20898]
Intl. Coun. of Air Shows [20901]
Intl. Military Community Executives Assn. [2498]
Intl. Military Community Executives Assn. [2498]
Judge Advocates Assn. [5808]
Logistics Officer Assn. [2499]
Logistics Officer Assn. [2499]
Marine Corps Veterans Assn. [20683]
Military Impacted Schools Assn. [8625]
Military Law Task Force [5809]
Military Order of the Devil Dog Fleas [20685]
Military Order of the Loyal Legion of the U.S.
[20386]
Military Order of the Purple Heart of the U.S.A.
[20378]
Military Order of the Stars and Bars [20387]
Military Toxics Proj. [4728]
Military Vehicle Preservation Assn. [21886]
Military, Veterans and Patriotic Ser. Organizations
of Am. [20695]
Military Writers Soc. of Am. [22207]
Montford Point Marine Assn. [5810]
Mothers of Military Support [12529]
Natl. Assn. for Civil War Brass Music [10251]
Natl. Assn. of Medics and Corpsmen [5219]
Natl. Assn. of State Military Rsrc. Managers
[5811]
Natl. Assn. for Uniformed Services [5812]
Natl. Comm. for Employer Support of the Guard
and Reserve [5813]

Natl. Defense Indus. Assn. [5814]
Natl. Defense Trans. Assn. [5815]
Natl. Guard Assn. of the U.S. [5816]
Natl. Guard Executive Directors Assn. [5817]
Natl. Naval Officers Assn. [5818]
Natl. Order of Trench Rats [20414]
Natl. Soc. of Pershing Rifles [23597]
Natl. Soc. of Scabbard and Blade [23598]
Natl. Soc. of Women Descendants of the Ancient
and Honorable Artillery Company [20403]
Natl. World War II Glider Pilots Assn. [20315]
Naval Civilian Managers Assn. [5819]
Naval Enlisted Reserve Assn. [5820]
Naval Intelligence Professionals [5821]
Naval Reserve Assn. [5822]
Naval Sea Cadet Corps [5823]
Navy Club of the U.S.A. [5824]
Navy Club of the U.S.A. Auxiliary [5825]
Navy League of the U.S. [5826]
Navy League of the U.S. [5826]
Never Forget Our Fallen [11095]
Nine Lives Associates [3224]
Non Commissioned Officers Assn. of the U.S.A.
[5827]
North-South Skirmish Assn. [22885]
Oper. Hug-A-Hero [12533]
Oper. Interdependence [12530]
Oper. Paperback [11100]
Orders and Medals Soc. of Am. [21887]
Orders and Medals Soc. of Am. [21887]
Our Military Kids [12534]
Pro vs. GI Joe [21762]
Professional Loadmaster Assn. [5828]
Proj. on Govt. Oversight [18138]
Reserve Officers Assn. of the U.S. [5829]
Retired Activities Br. [5830]
Salute Military Golf Assn. [22624]
SATS/EAF Assn. [20686]
Save-A-Vet [11036]
Soc. of the 3rd Infantry Div. [20696]
Soc. of Air Force Physicians [15511]
Soc. of Amer. Military Engineers [6823]
Soc. of the Ark and the Dove [20407]
Soc. of the Fifth Div. [20697]
Soc. of Medical Consultants to the Armed Forces
[15512]
Soc. of Military Orthopaedic Surgeons [15513]
Soc. of Military Otolaryngologists - Head and
Neck Surgeons [15514]
A Soldier's Wish List [11108]
Stars for Stripes [20417]
State Guard Assn. of the U.S. [5831]
Step Up 4 Vets [13354]
Support Our Troops [11110]
Tailhook Assn. [5832]
Troops Out Now Coalition [18292]
Uniformed Services Acad. of Family Physicians
[15515]
U.S. Armor Assn. [5833]
U.S. Army Warrant Officers Assn. [5834]
U.S. Marine Corps Motor Transport Assn. [2500]
U.S. Marine Corps Scout/Sniper Assn. [20688]
U.S. Marine Raider Assn. [5835]
U.S. Naval Inst. [5836]
U.S. Navy Beach Jumpers Assn. [20728]
United We Serve [20712]
USAF Medical Ser. Corps Assn. [15516]
USMC Vietnam Tankers Assn. [20824]
Veterans Assn. of Am. [20809]
Veterans and Military Families for Progress
[20815]
Veterans2Work [20818]
Vietnam Dustoff Assn. [20836]
Vietnam Era Seabees [20826]
Women Against Military Madness [18139]
Wounded Warrior Proj. [20822]
Military Aid - Address unknown since 2011.
Military Audiology Assn. [13775], 1720 Republic Rd.,
Silver Spring, MD 20902-3357
Military Aviation Preservation Soc. [9087], MAPS Air
Museum, 2260 Intl. Pkwy., North Canton, OH
44720, (330)896-6332
Military Benefit Assn. [18928], PO Box 221110,
Chantilly, VA 20153-1110, (703)968-6200
Military Benefits
Laptops for the Wounded [11526]

A star before a book entry number signifies that the name is not listed separately, but is mentioned within the entry.

Our Military Kids [12534]
U.S. Marine Corps Scout/Sniper Assn. [20688]
Military Chaplains Assn. of the U.S.A. [19524], PO Box 7056, Arlington, VA 22207-7056, (703)533-5890
Military Child Educ. Coalition [8626], PO Box 2519, Harker Heights, TX 76548-2519, (254)953-1923
Military Child Educ. Coalition [8626], PO Box 2519, Harker Heights, TX 76548-2519, (254)953-1923
Military Equipment
Laptops for the Wounded [11526]
Military Families
Amer. Combat Veterans of War [20771]
Amer. Gold Star Mothers [20698]
Amer. Legion Auxiliary [20699]
Amer. Military Family [20700]
Amer. War Mothers [20701]
Ancient and Honorable Artillery Company of Massachusetts [20702]
Assn. for Counselors and Educators in Govt. [11669]
Blue Star Mothers of Am. [20703]
Catholic War Veterans Auxiliary of the U.S.A. [20704]
Catholic War Veterans of the U.S.A. [20781]
Disabled Amer. Veterans [20412]
Disabled Amer. Veterans Auxiliary [20413]
For the Fallen [12531]
Give an Hour [11088]
Gold Star Wives of Am. [20705]
House of Heroes [13350]
Jewish War Veterans of the U.S.A. | Natl. Ladies Auxiliary [20706]
Military Child Educ. Coalition [8626]
Military Child Educ. Coalition [8626]
Military Order of the Loyal Legion of the U.S. [20386]
Mothers of Military Support [12529]
Natl. Military Family Assn. [20707]
Never Forget Our Fallen [11095]
ONE Freedom [20708]
Oper. Homefront [12532]
Oper. Hug-A-Hero [12533]
Oper. Interdependence [12530]
Our Military Kids [12534]
Silver Star Families of Am. [12535]
Soc. of Military Widows [20709]
A Soldier's Wish List [11108]
Sons of the Amer. Legion [20710]
Sons and Daughters In Touch [20711]
Step Up 4 Vets [13354]
U.S. Marine Corps Scout/Sniper Assn. [20688]
United We Serve [20712]
Veterans Assn. of Am. [20809]
Veterans of Foreign Wars of the U.S. | Ladies Auxiliary [20814]
Veterans and Military Families for Progress [20815]
World War II War Brides Assn. [20713]
World War II War Brides Assn. [20713]
Military Families Speak Out [18779], 525 S 4th St., Ste. 477, Philadelphia, PA 19147-1582, (267)324-3042
Military Fellowship; Christian [19555]
Military Food and Packaging Systems; Res. and Development Associates for [6879]
Military Geographic Inst. [IO], Santiago, Chile
Military Govt. Assn. [★5804]
Military Govt. Assn. [★5804]
Military Heraldry Soc. [IO], Dover, United Kingdom
Military Historical Soc. of Australia [IO], Garran, Australia
Military History
80th Fighter Squadron Headhunters' Assn. [5195]
146th Alumni Assn. [7727]
Air Force Historical Found. [10087]
Amer. Soc. of Military Insignia Collectors [21883]
Army Historical Found. [10088]
B-52 Stratofortress Assn. [20331]
Catholic War Veterans Auxiliary of the U.S.A. [20704]
Catholic War Veterans of the U.S.A. [20781]
Centennial Legion of Historic Military Commands [20743]
Civil War Dealers and Collectors Assn. [21280]

Civil War Token Soc. [21970]
Coast Defense Study Group [10089]
Combat Helicopter Pilots Assn. [20313]
De Re Militari: The Soc. for Medieval Military History [10090]
Disabled Amer. Veterans [20412]
Disabled Amer. Veterans Auxiliary [20413]
Distinguished Flying Cross Soc. [20374]
Great War Assn. [10091]
Hof Reunion Assn. [20349]
Intl. Naval Res. Org. [10092]
Intl. Naval Res. Org. [10092]
Military Order of the Loyal Legion of the U.S. [20386]
Military Order of the Purple Heart of the U.S.A. [20378]
Military Order of the Stars and Bars [20387]
Natl. Assn. for Civil War Brass Music [10251]
Natl. Order of Trench Rats [20414]
Natl. Soc. of Women Descendants of the Ancient and Honorable Artillery Company [20403]
Naval Historical Found. [10093]
Navy and Marine Living History Assn. [10094]
North-South Skirmish Assn. [22885]
Order of the Indian Wars [10095]
SATS/EAF Assn. [20686]
Sharkhunters Intl. [10096]
Sharkhunters Intl. [10096]
Soc. of Ancient Military Historians [10097]
Soc. of the Ark and the Dove [20407]
Soc. for Military History [10098]
Ulysses S. Grant Assn. [10695]
U.S. Cavalry Assn. and Memorial Res. Lib. [10099]
U.S. Navy Beach Jumpers Assn. [20728]
USMC Vietnam Tankers Assn. [20824]
Vietnam Era Seabees [20826]
Western Front Assn. - U.S. Br. [10100]
Military History Soc. of Ireland [IO], Dublin, Ireland
Military Impacted Schools Assn. [8625], 1600 Hwy. 370, Bellevue, NE 68005, (402)293-4005
Military Intelligence Corps Assn. [5218], PO Box 13020, Fort Huachuca, AZ 85670-3020, (520)227-3894
Military Law
Amer. Veterans for Equal Rights [12067]
Servicemembers Legal Defense Network [5837]
Military Law Task Force [5809], 730 N 1st St., San Jose, CA 95122, (619)463-2369
Military Officers Assn. of Am. [20740], 201 N Washington St., Alexandria, VA 22314-2537, (703)549-2311
Military Operations Res. Soc. [7187], 1703 N Beauregard St., Ste. 450, Alexandria, VA 22311, (703)933-9070
Military Order of the Carabao [20745], The Army and Navy Club, Farragut Sq., 901 17th St. NW, Washington, DC 20006-2503, (301)621-9480
Military Order of the Devil Dog Fleas [20685], 125 Grist Mill Loop, Georgetown, TX 78626-9437, (512)819-9688
Military Order of the Loyal Legion of the U.S. [20386], 4209 Santa Clara Dr., Holt, MI 48842-1868, (517)694-9394
Military Order of the Purple Heart of the U.S.A. [20378], 5413-A, B and C Backlick Rd., Springfield, VA 22151-3915, (703)354-2140
Military Order of the Stars and Bars [20387], PO Box 1700, White House, TN 37188-1700, (877)790-6672
Military Order of the World Wars [20874], 435 N Lee St., Alexandria, VA 22314, (703)683-4911
Military Order of the World Wars [20874], 435 N Lee St., Alexandria, VA 22314, (703)683-4911
Military Police
CID Agents Assn. [20714]
Military Police Regimental Assn. [20715]
Retired Military Police Assn. [20716]
Military Police Assn. [★20715]
Military Police Regimental Assn. [20715], PO Box 2182, Fort Leonard Wood, MO 65473, (573)329-6772
Military Postal History Soc. [22056], Ed Dubin, VP, PO Box 586, Belleville, MI 48112
Military Railway Service Veterans - Defunct.

Military Reporters and Editors [5895], Medill School of Journalism, 1325 G St. NW, Ste. 730, Washington, DC 20005, (202)661-0141
Military Space [11094], 3111 E ParkRidge Dr., Nampa, ID 83687, (208)936-0235
Military Spouses for Change - Address unknown since 2011.
Military Toxics Proj. [4728], PO Box 558, Lewiston, ME 04243, (207)783-5091
Military Vehicle Collectors Club [★21886]
Military Vehicle Preservation Assn. [21886], PO Box 520378, Independence, MO 64052, (816)833-6872
Military, Veterans and Patriotic Ser. Organizations of Am. [20695], 1100 Larkspur Landing Cir., Ste. 340, Larkspur, CA 94939-1880, (800)626-6526
Military Writers Soc. of Am. [22207], PO Box 264, Bridgeville, PA 15017
Militia Immaculata [★19451]
Militia of the Immaculata Movement [19451], 1600 W Park Ave., Libertyville, IL 60048, (847)367-7800
Miljoforbundet Jordens Vanner [★IO]
Milk Indus. Center [IO], Buenos Aires, Argentina
Milk Indus. Found. [1022], Intl. Dairy Foods Assn., 1250 H St. NW, Ste. 900, Washington, DC 20005, (202)737-4332
Milk Indus. Found. [1022], Intl. Dairy Foods Assn., 1250 H St. NW, Ste. 900, Washington, DC 20005, (202)737-4332
Millennium Campus Network [17191], 1330 Beacon St., Ste. 249, Brookline, MA 02446
Millennium Inst. [17733], 1634 Eye St. NW, Ste. 300, Washington, DC 20006, (202)383-6200
Millennium Promise [11074], 432 Park Ave. S, 13th Fl., New York, NY 10016, (212)584-5710
Millennium Promise [11074], 432 Park Ave. S, 13th Fl., New York, NY 10016, (212)584-5710
Millennium Water Alliance [13427], 1980 Post Oak Blvd., Ste. 800, Houston, TX 77056, (803)547-6541
Millennium Wildlife Sciences [5015], PO Box 2504, Vincentown, NJ 08088, (609)268-2878
Millers
Intl. Assn. of Operative Millers [2501]
Intl. Assn. of Operative Millers [2501]
North Amer. Millers' Assn. [2502]
Rice Millers' Assn. [2503]
Millers' Natl. Fed. [★2502]
Million Dollar Round Table [1995], 325 W Touhy Ave., Park Ridge, IL 60068-4265, (847)692-6378
Million Mom March - Address unknown since 2011.
Mills
Assn. of Coffee Mill Enthusiasts [21306]
Soc. for the Preservation of Old Mills [9729]
Millwork Cost Bur. [★522]
Millwright Gp. [23221], Specialized Carriers and Rigging Assn., 2750 Prosperity Ave., Ste. 620, Fairfax, VA 22031-4312, (703)698-0291
Milo's Bali Orchids [IO], Denpasar, Indonesia
Milton H. Erickson Found. [16466], 3606 N 24th St., Phoenix, AZ 85016, (602)956-6196
Milton Keynes and North Buckinghamshire Chamber of Commerce [IO], Milton Keynes, United Kingdom
Milton S. Eisenhower Found. [11688], 1875 Connecticut Ave. NW, Ste. 410, Washington, DC 20009, (202)234-8104
Milton Soc. of Am. [9402], Duquesne Univ., English Dept., Pittsburgh, PA 15282
Minato Intl. Assn. [IO], Tokyo, Japan
Mind Development Association/U.S. Psi Squad - Address unknown since 2010.
Mind Justice [17851], 915 Zaragoza St., Davis, CA 95618, (530)758-1626
Mind Justice [17851], 915 Zaragoza St., Davis, CA 95618, (530)758-1626
Mind - Natl. Assn. for Mental Hea. [IO], London, United Kingdom
Mind Sci. Found. [7226], 117 W El Prado Dr., San Antonio, TX 78212, (210)821-6094
Mind Sport Assn. of Pakistan [IO], Karachi, Pakistan
MindFreedom Intl. [17852], PO Box 11284, Eugene, OR 97440, (541)345-9106
Mindful Medicine Worldwide [13693], 1458 W Highland Ave., Ste. 3B, Chicago, IL 60660, (847)351-0272
Mindful Medicine Worldwide [13693], 1458 W Highland Ave., Ste. 3B, Chicago, IL 60660, (847)351-0272

Reference to "IO" in place of a book number signifies that the association may be found in the 50th edition of International Organizations.

Mine Safety Inst. of Am. [5841], 319 Painterville Rd., Hunker, PA 15639, (724)925-5150

Mine Warfare Assn. [18596], Ms. Suzanne Wyatt, DMC Companies, 484B Washington St., MB 340, Monterey, CA 93940, (831)373-0508

Mineral Indus. Consultants Assn. [IO], Carlton, Australia

Mineral Indus. Res. Org. [IO], Birmingham, United Kingdom

Mineral Info. Inst. [7123], 12999 E Adam Aircraft Cir., Englewood, CO 80112-4167, (303)948-4236

Mineral Insulation Mfrs. Assn. [★604]

Mineral Policy Center [★5839]

Mineral Products Assn. [IO], London, United Kingdom

Mineralogical Assn. of Canada [IO], Quebec, QC, Canada

Mineralogical Assn. of South Africa [IO], Helderkruin, Republic of South Africa

Mineralogical Soc. [IO], Twickenham, United Kingdom

Mineralogical Soc. of Denmark [IO], Copenhagen, Denmark

Mineralogical Soc. of Egypt [IO], Cairo, Egypt

Mineralogical Soc. of Finland [IO], Helsinki, Finland

Mineralogical Soc. of Korea [IO], Seoul, Republic of Korea

Mineralogical Soc. of Poland [IO], Krakow, Poland

Mineralogical Soc. of Slovakia [IO], Bratislava, Slovakia

Mineralogiese Assosiasie van Suid Afrika [★IO]

Mineralogy
  Amer. Fed. of Mineralogical Societies [7119]
  Canadian Micro Mineral Assn. [11982]
  Circum-Pacific Coun. for Energy and Mineral Resources [7120]
  Circum-Pacific Coun. for Energy and Mineral Resources [7120]
  Clay Minerals Soc. [7121]
  Fluorescent Mineral Soc. [7122]
  Fluorescent Mineral Soc. [7122]
  Mineral Info. Inst. [7123]
  Soc. of Mineral Analysts [7124]

Mineralolwirtschaftsverband e.V. [★IO]

Minerals
  Gypsum Assn. [2504]
  Indus. Minerals Assn. - North Am. [2505]
  Indus. Minerals Assn. - North Am. [2505]
  Intl. BioIron Soc. [15517]
  Intl. BioIron Soc. [15517]
  Natl. Indus. Sand Assn. [2506]
  Salt Inst. [2507]
  Sorptive Minerals Inst. [2508]
  World Gold Coun. [2509]
  World Gold Coun. [2509]

Minerals Coun. of Australia [IO], Kingston, Australia

Minerals Engg. Soc. [IO], Worksop, United Kingdom

Minerals, Metals, and Materials Soc. [7099], 184 Thorn Hill Rd., Warrendale, PA 15086-7514, (724)776-9000

Minga [11351], PO Box 610004, Newton, MA 02461, (617)584-1305

Mingalar Myanmar [IO], Yangon, Myanmar

Mini-Basketball England [IO], Northampton, United Kingdom

Mini Lop Rabbit Club of Am. [4844], PO Box 17, Pittsburg, KS 66762, (417)842-3317

Miniature Armoured Fighting Vehicle Assn. [IO], Crewe, United Kingdom

Miniature Arms Collectors/Makers Soc. [20966], Carmen Gianforte, Membership Chm., 664 Francisco Rd. NW, Georgetown, TN 37336, (423)559-1546

Miniature Arms Collectors/Makers Soc. [20966], Carmen Gianforte, Membership Chm., 664 Francisco Rd. NW, Georgetown, TN 37336, (423)559-1546

Miniature Arms Soc. [★20966]

Miniature Arms Soc. [★20966]

Miniature Australian Shepherd Club of Am. [21601], PO Box 248, Roanoke, IN 46783

Miniature Book Soc. [9448], 702 Rosecrans St., San Diego, CA 92106-3013

Miniature Book Soc. [9448], 702 Rosecrans St., San Diego, CA 92106-3013

Miniature Bull Terrier Club of Am. [21602], Kathy Flaugh, Membership Chair, 9224 Kinlock Dr., Indianapolis, IN 46256-2242, (317)849-0929

Miniature Donkey Registry of the U.S. [★3781]

Miniature Golf Assn. of the U.S. [22986], 1113 Belle Pl., Fort Worth, TX 76107, (817)738-5522

Miniature Hereford Breeders Assn. [3923], 60885 Salt Creek Rd., Collbran, CO 81624

Miniature Hereford Breeders Assn. [3923], 60885 Salt Creek Rd., Collbran, CO 81624

Miniature Horse Assn. of Australia [IO], Drouin, Australia

Miniature Horse Club of Southland [IO], Invercargill, New Zealand

Miniature Motorsports Racing Assn. [22239], PO Box 50906, Bowling Green, KY 42102-4206, (270)784-8231

Miniature and Novelty Sheep Breeders Assn. and Registry [4910], 113 Blake Rd., Toledo, WA 98591, (360)864-6116

Miniature Piano Enthusiast Club [21372], 633 Pennsylvania Ave., Hagerstown, MD 21740, (301)797-7675

Miniature Pinscher Club of Am. [21603], Judy Stout-Reynolds, Treas., 5375 SW Oak Ridge Rd., Lake Oswego, OR 97035

Miniatures Industry Assn. of America - Defunct.

Mining
  Amer. Inst. of Mining, Metallurgical, and Petroleum Engineers [7125]
  Amer. Soc. of Mining and Reclamation [5838]
  China Clay Producers Assn. [2510]
  Colorado Mining Assn. [2511]
  Copper Development Assn. [2512]
  Earthworks [5839]
  Equip. Managers Coun. of Am. [845]
  European Assn. of Mining Indus., Metals Ores and Indus. Minerals [402]
  Inst. of Mine Surveyors of South Africa [22995]
  Intl. Soc. of Mine Safety Professionals [15518]
  Intl. Soc. of Mine Safety Professionals [15518]
  Interstate Mining Compact Commn. [5840]
  Mine Safety Inst. of Am. [5841]
  Mining Elecl. Maintenance and Safety Assn. [2513]
  Mining Found. of the Southwest [2514]
  Mining Inst. of Scotland [14765]
  Mining and Metallurgical Soc. of Am. [7126]
  Natl. Assn. of State Land Reclamationists [5842]
  Natl. Mine Rescue Assn. [7127]
  Northwest Mining Assn. [2515]
  Perlite Inst. [2516]
  Proj. Underground [18140]
  Soc. for Mining, Metallurgy, and Exploration [7128]
  South African Inst. of Mining and Metallurgy [13717]
  United Mine Workers of Am. [23257]
  U.S. Mine Rescue Assn. [12536]
  U.S. Mine Rescue Assn. [12536]
  Women in Mining [2517]
  World Wide Assn. of Treasure Seekers [22109]

Mining Assn. of Canada [IO], Ottawa, ON, Canada

Mining Br., Amer. Inst. of Mining, Metallurgical and Petroleum Engineers [★7128]

Mining Club [★19239]

Mining Club of the Southwest [★2514]

Mining Elecl. Maintenance and Safety Assn. [2513], Bill Collins, Sec.-Treas., PO Box 7163, Lakeland, FL 33807

Mining Found. of the Southwest [2514], PO Box 42317, Tucson, AZ 85733, (520)577-7519

Mining History Assn. [9783], PO Box 552, Sedalia, CO 80135

Mining Inst. of Scotland [IO], Dunfermline, United Kingdom

Mining and Metallurgical Soc. of Am. [7126], PO Box 810, Boulder, CO 80306-0810, (303)444-6032

Mining and Reclamation Coun. [★785]

Ministry
  Acad. of Parish Clergy [19981]
  Administrative Personnel Assn. of the Presbyterian Church [19609]
  ASGM [19339]
  Assn. of Christian Truckers [19982]
  Assn. of Presbyterian Church Educators [19612]
  Assn. of Reformed Baptist Churches of Am. [19309]
  Aurora Ministries [19983]
  Bros. and Sisters in Christ [19541]
  Canadian Coun. of Christian Charities [15727]
  Catholic Campus Ministry Assn. [19399]
  Christ for the City Intl. [19984]
  Christ for the City Intl. [19984]
  Christian Aid Ministries [18570]
  Christian Community Development Assn. [19985]
  Confessing Synod Ministries [20242]
  Divine Sci. Ministers Assn. [19645]
  Episcopal Women's Caucus [19702]
  Equestrian Ministries Intl. [19816]
  First Fruit [19747]
  The Gospel Coalition [19576]
  Harvest [19986]
  Harvest [19986]
  Heart's Home USA [19987]
  HMI Ministries [19988]
  Inst. of Singles Dynamics [19989]
  Intl. Assn. of Christian Chaplains [19520]
  Intl. Assn. of Missionary Aviation [20052]
  Intl. Christian Technologists Assn. [19990]
  Intl. Christian Technologists Assn. [19990]
  Intl. Coalition of Apostles [19991]
  Intl. Network of Prison Ministries [19992]
  Intl. Network of Prison Ministries [19992]
  LifeWind Intl. [19993]
  LifeWind Intl. [19993]
  Media in Ministry Assn. [19994]
  Mexican Amer. Cultural Center [19995]
  Ministry Architecture [6200]
  Mission: Moving Mountains [19996]
  Mission: Moving Mountains [19996]
  Natl. Assn. of Catholic Family Life Ministers [19997]
  Natl. Assn. of Catholic Youth Ministry Leaders [19455]
  Natl. Assn. of Family Ministries [19998]
  Natl. Assn. of Hispanic Priests of the USA [19457]
  New Life Intl. Alliance [19999]
  Pocket Testament League [19352]
  Samaritan's Purse [20000]
  Soc. for the Increase of the Ministry [20001]
  Wesleyan/Holiness Women Clergy [20002]
  Wesleyan/Holiness Women Clergy [20002]
  World Hope Intl. [20003]
  World Hope Intl. [20003]

Ministry Architecture [6200], 1904 S Union Pl., Lakewood, CO 80228, (720)937-9664

Ministry of Hotels and Tourism [IO], Yangon, Myanmar

Ministry with Persons with Disabilities [★19924]

Minneapolis Grain Exchange [3969], 400 S 4th St., 130 Grain Exchange Bldg., Minneapolis, MN 55415, (612)321-7101

Minnesota Beer Wholesalers Assn. [185], Campbell Mithun Tower, 222 S Ninth St., Ste. 3150, Minneapolis, MN 55402, (612)604-4400

A Minor Consideration [11676], 15003 S Denker Ave., Gardena, CA 90247

Minor League Baseball [★22280]

Minor Metals Trade Assn. [IO], London, United Kingdom

Minorities
  1-2-3 Intl. [12573]
  30 Years After [17999]
  African Amer. Art Song Alliance [10134]
  African Amer. Environmentalist Assn. [4234]
  African Amer. Fed. Executive Assn. [5504]
  African Amer. Women in Cinema Org. [9592]
  African Cultural Alliance of North Am. [10818]
  Amer. Muslim Alliance [18142]
  Asian Hea. Care Leaders Assn. [15288]
  Asian Pacific Americans for Progress [17205]
  Assn. of African Amer. Financial Advisors [1334]
  Assn. for Haitian Amer. Development [12126]
  Assn. of Kannada Kootas of Am. [19035]
  Assn. of Latino Administrators and Superintendents [7661]
  Assn. of Liberian Engineers USA [6786]
  Assn. of Nepalis in the Americas [19171]
  Before Columbus Found. [10036]
  Black Entomologists [6840]
  Black World Found. [9093]
  Bridge Kids Intl. [13515]

A star before a book entry number signifies that the name is not listed separately, but is mentioned within the entry.

Catholic Assn. of Latino Leaders [19398]
Center for Advancement of Racial and Ethnic Equity [8627]
Champa Cultural Preservation Assn. of USA [10636]
Coalition to Promote Minority Hea. [15853]
Coun. of Supplier Diversity Professionals [715]
Darfur Human Rights Org. [17825]
Delta Tau Lambda Sorority [23742]
Dialogue on Diversity [8628]
Episcopal Women's Caucus [19702]
European-American Unity and Rights Org. [17288]
Filipina Women's Network [18792]
GesherCity [19091]
Global Alliance for Community Empowerment [10811]
Hispanas Organized for Political Equality [17776]
Humanity in Action [8277]
Idoma Assn. USA [19176]
Igbere Progressive Assn. Intl. [12576]
In Legal Color [5844]
Intl. Alumni Assn. of Shri Mahavir Jain Vidyalaya [19219]
Intl. Soc. of Filipinos in Finance and Accounting [36]
Iranian Alliances Across Borders [19069]
J. Robert Gladden Orthopaedic Soc. [16037]
Kappa Phi Gamma Sorority [23746]
Karen Natl. League [18722]
Korean Amer. Soc. of Entrepreneurs [718]
Laotian Amer. Soc. [19102]
Latin Amer. Women's Assn. [13464]
The Latino Coalition [9948]
Latino Engineers, Architects and Developers Soc. [7029]
Latinos in Info. Sciences and Tech. Assn. [6983]
Minority Access, Inc. [8631]
Minority Peace Corps Assn. [18307]
Muslim Alliance in North America [19147]
Muslim Amer. Soc. [20135]
Natl. Alliance for Filipino Concerns [17200]
Natl. Assn. of Hispanic Priests of the USA [19457]
Natl. Assn. of Minority Govt. Contractors [928]
Natl. Assn. of Peoplecultural Engg. Prog. Advocates [8127]
Natl. Coalition of Pro-Democracy Advocates [17526]
Natl. Community for Latino Leadership [19112]
Natl. Cong. of Black Women [5843]
Natl. Coun. of Minorities in Energy [1173]
Natl. Latina Bus. Women Assn. [2188]
Natl. Latina/Latino Law Student Assn. [18057]
Natl. Minorities with Disabilities Coalition [17545]
Natl. Org. for African-American Women [10829]
Natl. Org. of Hispanics in Criminal Justice [5513]
Natl. Org. for Manyu Advancement [18840]
Natl. Org. of Sisters of Color Ending Sexual Assault [13093]
Natl. Soc. for Hispanic Professionals [695]
Native Amer. Coalition for Healthy Alternatives [12567]
Native Amer. Leadership Alliance [20147]
Native Movement [19166]
Native Public Media [18098]
Nepali Amer. Friendship Assn. [19172]
New Am. Media [18099]
Ngwa Natl. Assn. USA [19040]
North Amer. South Asian Bar Assn. [5678]
North Amer. South Asian Law Student Assn. [8511]
Nubian United Benevolent Intl. Assn. [12787]
Peace in Focus [18275]
Polish Amer. Golf Assn. [22620]
Pueblo a Pueblo [12124]
Pushback Network [18491]
Red Feather Development Gp. [12201]
Salvadoran Amer. Natl. Network [18979]
Sikh Sports Assn. of the U.S.A. [22894]
Soc. for the Anal. of African-American Public Hea. Issues [16497]
Soc. of Iranian Architects and Planners [6206]
South Asian Amer. Voting Youth [18392]
Student African Amer. Brotherhood [19288]
Sylvia Rivera Law Proj. [18730]

Thai U.S.A. Assn. [19256]
Turkish Amer. Alliance for Fairness [19260]
Ugbajo Itsekiri U.S.A. [19145]
Ulster-Scots Soc. of Am. [20664]
Union of North Amer. Vietnamese Students Assn. [19275]
UNITED SIKHS [12228]
Unreserved Amer. Indian Fashion and Art Alliance [9134]
Urhobo Natl. Assn. of North Am. [19178]
WICUDA-USA [9095]
Women of Yemen Assn. [11080]
Women and Youth Supporting Each Other [9069]
World Malayalee Coun. [19039]
Minorities in Agriculture, Natural Resources and Related Sciences [3761], PO Box 79506, Atlanta, GA 30357, (404)347-2975
Minority Access, Inc. [8631], 5214 Baltimore Ave., Hyattsville, MD 20781-2044, (301)779-7100
Minority Business
Airport Minority Advisory Coun. [2518]
Diversity Info. Resources [2519]
Executive Leadership Coun. [2520]
Minority Bus. Enterprise Legal Defense and Educ. Fund [2521]
Natl. Assn. of Investment Companies [2522]
Natl. Assn. of Minority Auto. Dealers [2523]
Natl. Coun. of Minorities in Energy [1173]
Natl. Minority Bus. Coun. [2524]
Natl. Minority Supplier Development Coun. [2525]
Minority Bus. Enterprise Legal Defense and Educ. Fund [2521], 1100 Mercantile Ln., Ste. 115-A, Largo, MD 20774, (301)583-4648
Minority Corporate Counsel Assn. [5346], 1111 Pennsylvania Ave. NW, Washington, DC 20004, (202)739-5901
Minority Engg. Educ. Effort [★8126]
Minority Golf Assn. of Am. [★22615]
Minority Peace Corps Assn. [18307], Stone Mountain, GA 30087, (404)966-0018
Minority Rights Gp. Intl. [IO], London, United Kingdom
Minority Student Achievement Network [8167], Wisconsin Center for Educ. Res., 695 Educ. Sciences Bldg., 1025 W Johnson St., Madison, WI 53706, (608)263-4260
Minority Students
Center for Advancement of Racial and Ethnic Equity | Amer. Coun. on Educ. [8629]
Excelencia in Educ. [8630]
In Legal Color [5844]
Intl. Alumni Assn. of Shri Mahavir Jain Vidyalaya [19219]
Minority Access, Inc. [8631]
Natl. Latina/Latino Law Student Assn. [18057]
North Amer. South Asian Law Student Assn. [8511]
Student African Amer. Brotherhood [19288]
Union of North Amer. Vietnamese Students Assn. [19275]
Minsaki Katende Found. [IO], Kampala, Uganda
Minuteman Civil Defense Corps - Defunct.
Mir Pace Intl. [12869], 1173 Nantasket Ave., C-6, Hull, MA 02045, (781)925-0090
Mir Pace Intl. [12869], 1173 Nantasket Ave., C-6, Hull, MA 02045, (781)925-0090
MIRA [IO], Nuneaton, United Kingdom
Miracle Corners of the World [13535], 166 Madison Ave., 5th Fl., New York, NY 10016, (212)453-5811
Miracle Diapers [★11749]
Miracle Flights for Kids [14454], 2764 N Green Valley Pkwy., No. 115, Henderson, NV 89014-2120, (702)261-0494
Miracles in Action [12740], 241 Countryside Dr., Naples, FL 34104, (239)348-0815
Miracles of Hope Network [11352], 12064 Ulrich Rd., Losantville, IN 47354, (765)381-1112
Miracles of Hope Network [11352], 12064 Ulrich Rd., Losantville, IN 47354, (765)381-1112
Miscarriage
Miscarriage Assn. of Ireland [929]
Miscarriage Assn. [IO], Wakefield, United Kingdom
Miscarriage Assn. of Ireland [IO], Dublin, Ireland
Miscarriage Infant Death and Stillbirth Support Gp. [16773], 1001 Kenney Way, Bridgewater, NJ 08807, (908)231-8358

Miso Music Portugal [IO], Cascais, Portugal
Miss Am. Org. [21416], 222 New Rd., Ste. 700, Linwood, NJ 08221, (609)653-8700
MISS Found. | Alliance of Grandparents, A Support in Tragedy Intl. [12123], PO Box 5333, Peoria, AZ 85385, (623)979-1000
Missao Para o Interior da Africa [★IO]
Missile Defense Advocacy Alliance [17508], 515 King St., Ste. 320, Alexandria, VA 22314, (703)299-0060
Missing Children
Assn. of Missing and Exploited Children's Organizations [12537]
Assn. of Missing and Exploited Children's Organizations [12537]
The Child Connection [12538]
The Child Connection [12538]
Child Watch of North Am. [11225]
Comm. for Missing Children [12539]
Comm. for Missing Children [12539]
Missing Children in Am. [11353]
Polly Klaas Found. [12540]
Take Root [12541]
Missing Children in Am. [11353], 17 Giera Ct., Parlin, NJ 08859, (888)556-4774
Missing Children Center - Defunct.
Missing Children...HELP Center - Defunct. Missing-Missing and Exploited Children; Commn. on [11256]
Missing and Exploited Children; Natl. Center for [11359]
Missing-in-Action
Natl. League of Families of Amer. Prisoners and Missing in Southeast Asia [18141]
Natl. League of Families of Amer. Prisoners and Missing in Southeast Asia [18141]
VietNow Natl. [13358]
Missing Persons
Amer. Assn. for Lost Children [12542]
Child Watch of North Am. [11225]
Doe Network [12543]
Doe Network [12543]
Intl. Fed. of Family Associations of Missing Persons from Armed Conflicts [12544]
Intl. Fed. of Family Associations of Missing Persons from Armed Conflicts [12544]
One Missing Link [12545]
Outpost for Hope [12546]
Missing Pet Partnership [12650], PO Box 3085, Federal Way, WA 98063, (253)529-3999
Mission
Advent Christian Gen. Conf. [19287]
Africa Inland Mission Intl. [20004]
Africa Inland Mission Intl. [20004]
Agricultural Missions, Inc. [20005]
Amer. Missionary Fellowship [20006]
Amer. Soc. of Missiology [20007]
AMG Intl. [20008]
AMG Intl. [20008]
ARISE Intl. Mission [20009]
ARISE Intl. Mission [20009]
ASGM [19339]
Associate Missionaries of the Assumption [20010]
Associate Missionaries of the Assumption [20010]
Assn. of North Amer. Missions [20011]
Assn. of Professors of Mission [20012]
Assn. of Reformed Baptist Churches of Am. [19309]
Avant Ministries [20013]
Baptist Mid-Missions [19314]
BCM Intl. [19341]
Bethany Intl. Missions [20014]
Bethany Intl. Missions [20014]
Bibles For The World [20015]
Bibles For The World [20015]
Brethren in Christ World Missions [20016]
Brethren in Christ World Missions [20016]
Cabrini Mission Corps [20017]
CAM Intl. [20018]
CAM Intl. [20018]
Catholic Campus Ministry Assn. [19399]
Catholic Central Union of Am. | Central Bur. [19400]
Catholic Comm. of Appalachia [20019]
Catholic Radio Assn. [19406]

Reference to "IO" in place of a book number signifies that the association may be found in the 50th edition of International Organizations.

Children Intl. [20020]
Children Intl. [20020]
Chinese Christian Mission [20021]
CHOSEN [12450]
Christ for the Nations [20022]
Christ for the Nations [20022]
Christ Truth Ministries [19346]
CHRISTAR [20023]
CHRISTAR [20023]
Christian Aid Mission [20024]
Christian Aid Mission [20024]
Christian Literature and Bible Center [20025]
Christian Literature and Bible Center [20025]
Christian Mission for the Deaf [20026]
Christian Missionary Fellowship [20027]
Christian Missionary Fellowship [20027]
Christian Missions in Many Lands [20028]
Christian Pilots Assn. [20029]
Christians for Peace in El Salvador [20030]
Church of God World Missions [20031]
Church of God World Missions [20031]Mission-
    Church Planting Intl.
Claretian Volunteers and Lay Missionaries
    [19413]
Coalition on the Env. and Jewish Life [19857]
Crosier Missions [20032]
Crosier Missions [20032]
CrossGlobal Link [20033]
CrossWorld [20034]
CrossWorld [20034]
A Cup of Water Intl. [20282]
Danish Missionary Coun. [431]
Domestic/Foreign Missionary Soc. of the
    Protestal Episcopal Church [20035]
Domestic/Foreign Missionary Soc. of the
    Protestant Episcopal Church [20035]
Dominican Mission Found. [20036]
Dominican Volunteers USA [20037]
EAPE/Campolo Ministries - Evangelical Assn. for
    the Promotion of Educ. [20038]
EAPE/Campolo Ministries - Evangelical Assn. for
    the Promotion of Educ. [20038]
The Evangelical Alliance Mission [20039]
Evangelical Educ. Soc. [19704]
Evangelical Free Church of Am. [20040]
Evangelical Free Church of Am. [20040]
Evangelical Missiological Soc. [20041]
Evangelistic Faith Missions [20042]
Evangelistic Faith Missions [20042]
Evangelize China Fellowship [20043]
Evangelize China Fellowship [20043]
Fellowship Intl. Mission [20044]
Fellowship Intl. Mission [20044]
Fellowship of Missions [20045]
Found. of Compassionate Amer. Samaritans
    [20046]
Found. of Compassionate Amer. Samaritans
    [20046]
Global Economic Outreach [20047]
Global Economic Outreach [20047]
Global Teams [19709]
Gospel Literature Intl. [20048]
Gospel Literature Intl. [20048]
Gospel Recordings Network [20049]
Heart's Home USA [19987]
Helps Intl. Ministries [20050]
Helps Intl. Ministries [20050]
Holy Childhood Assn. [19428]
Inter Varsity Christian Fellowship [20051]
Intl. Assn. of Missionary Aviation [20052]
Intl. Catholic Deaf Assn. U.S. Sect. [19435]
Intl. Mission Bd. [20053]
Intl. Mission Bd. [20053]
InterServe U.S.A. [20054]
InterServe U.S.A. [20054]
Knightsbridge Intl. [12859]
Lasallian Volunteers [20055]
Latin Am. Mission [20056]
Latin Am. Mission [20056]
Mariannhill Mission Soc. [19447]
Maryknoll Lay Missioners [20057]
Maryknoll Lay Missioners [20057]
Maryknoll Sisters of Saint Dominic [20058]
Medical Mission Sisters [20059]
Medical Mission Sisters [20059]

Men for Missions Intl. [20060]
Men for Missions Intl. [20060]
Mission Aviation Fellowship [20061]
The Mission Exchange [20062]
Mission Services Assn. [20063]
Mission Soc. of the Mother of God of Boronyavo
    [20191]
Mission Training Intl. [20064]
Mission Training Intl. [20064]
Missionary Church [20065]
Missionary Church [20065]
Missionary Gospel Fellowship [20066]
Missionary Sisters of St. Peter Claver [20067]
Missionary Sisters of the Soc. of Mary [20068]
Missionary Soc. of Saint Paul the Apostle [19454]
Missionary TECH Team [20069]
Moody Bible Inst. [20070]
Mustard Seed Found. [20071]
Nazarene Missions Intl. [20072]
Nazarene Missions Intl. [20072]
New Hope Intl. [20073]
New Hope Intl. [20073]
New Tribes Mission [20074]
New Tribes Mission [20074]
New Wineskins Missionary Network [20075]
North Am. Indigenous Ministries [20076]
Nuestros Pequenos Hermanos Intl. [20077]
O.C. Intl. [20078]
O.C. Intl. [20078]
OMF Intl. U.S.A. [20079]
OMF Intl. U.S.A. [20079]
OMS Intl. [20080]
OMS Intl. [20080]
Paraclete [20081]
Pocket Testament League [19352]
Presbyterian Frontier Fellowship [20082]
Prison Mission Assn. [20083]
Reach Across [20084]
Reach Across [20084]
Response-Ability [20085]
Romanian Missionary Soc. [20086]
St. Anthony's Guild [20087]
St. Vincent Pallotti Center for Apostolic Develop-
    ment [20088]
Salesian Missioners [20089]
Salesian Missioners [20089]
Samaritans Intl. [20090]
Samaritans Intl. [20090]
Seventh Day Baptist Missionary Soc. [19330]
Sharing of Ministries Abroad U.S.A. [20091]
Slavic Gospel Assn. [20092]
Slavic Gospel Assn. [20092]
SMA Lay Missionaries [20093]
Small World Found. [16820]
Soc. of Anglican Missionaries and Senders
    [20094]
Soc. of the Companions of the Holy Cross
    [19716]
South Am. Mission [20095]
Spanish World Ministries [20096]
Spanish World Ministries [20096]
Sports Ambassadors [20097]
STEER [20098]
STEER [20098]
Teen Missions Intl. [20099]
Teen Missions Intl. [20099]
Trans World Radio [20100]
Trans World Radio [20100]
Transport for Christ, Intl. [20101]
Transport for Christ, Intl. [20101]
Triratna Buddhist Community [19374]
United Indian Missions Intl. [20102]
United Indian Missions, Intl. [20102]
United World Mission [20103]
United World Mission [20103]
Voice of China and Asia Missionary Soc. [20104]
Voice of China and Asia Missionary Soc. [20104]
Voice of the Martyrs [20105]
The Way Intl. [20106]
The Way Intl. [20106]
World for Christ Crusade [20107]
World for Christ Crusade [20107]
World Gospel Mission [20108]
World Gospel Mission [20108]
World Impact [20109]

World Impact [20109]
World Salt Found. [20110]
World Salt Found. [20110]
World Team [20111]
World Team [20111]
World Vision [20112]
World-Wide Missions [20113]
World-Wide Missions [20113]
World Witness, Foreign Mission Bd. of the Associ-
    ate Reformed Presbyterian Church [20114]
World Witness, Foreign Mission Bd. of the Associ-
    ate Reformed Presbyterian Church [20114]
Xaverian Missionaries of the U.S. [20115]
Xaverian Missionaries of the U.S. [20115]
Youth With a Mission [20116]
Mission Am. Coalition [19586], PO Box 13930, Palm
    Desert, CA 92255, (760)200-2707
Mission to the Americas [★19324]
Mission to the Americas [★19324]
Mission Aviation Fellowship [20061], PO Box 47,
    Nampa, ID 83653, (208)498-0800
Mission Builders Intl. [19587], PO Box 406, Lake-
    side, MT 59922, (406)844-2683
Mission Cataract USA [17100], 1233 E Brandywine
    Ln., PMB 211, Fresno, CA 93720, (800)343-7265
Mission Doctors Assn. [12471], 3435 Wilshire Blvd.,
    Ste. 1940, Los Angeles, CA 90010, (213)368-1872
Mission Doctors Assn. [12471], 3435 Wilshire Blvd.,
    Ste. 1940, Los Angeles, CA 90010, (213)368-1872
Mission for Est. of Human Rights in Iran [17853],
    PO Box 2037, Palos Verdes Peninsula, CA 90274,
    (310)377-4590
Mission for Est. of Human Rights in Iran [17853],
    PO Box 2037, Palos Verdes Peninsula, CA 90274,
    (310)377-4590
The Mission Exchange [20062], 655 Village Sq. Dr.,
    Ste. A, Stone Mountain, GA 30083, (770)457-6677
Mission to Haiti [12129], PO Box 523157, Miami, FL
    33152-3157, (305)823-7516
Mission to Haiti [12129], PO Box 523157, Miami, FL
    33152-3157, (305)823-7516
Mission Inst. [★20058]
Mission of Mercy [12741], PO Box 62600, Colorado
    Springs, CO 80962, (719)481-0400
Mission of Mercy [12741], PO Box 62600, Colorado
    Springs, CO 80962, (719)481-0400
Mission: Moving Mountains [19996], PO Box 6000,
    Colorado Springs, CO 80934, (719)594-2727
Mission: Moving Mountains [19996], PO Box 6000,
    Colorado Springs, CO 80934, (719)594-2727
Mission Sans Frontieres [★IO]
Mission to Seafarers [IO], London, United Kingdom
Mission Services Assn. [20063], 2004 E Magnolia
    Ave., Knoxville, TN 37917, (865)525-7010
The Mission Soc. [19974], 6234 Crooked Creek Rd.,
    Norcross, GA 30092-3106, (770)446-1381
Mission Society; American Advent [★19287]
Mission Soc. of the Mother of God of Boronyavo
    [20191], 1838 Palomas Dr. NE, Albuquerque, NM
    87110, (505)256-5350
Mission Training Intl. [20064], PO Box 1220, Palmer
    Lake, CO 80133, (719)487-0111
Mission Training Intl. [20064], PO Box 1220, Palmer
    Lake, CO 80133, (719)487-0111
Mission Vie et Famillie [★IO]
Mission des Volontaires Contre la Pauvrete [★IO]
Mission of Volunteers to Combat Poverty [IO], Lome,
    Togo
Mission Without Borders - Australia [IO], Auburn,
    Australia
Mission Without Borders - Canada [IO], Abbotsford,
    BC, Canada
Mission Without Borders - South Africa [IO], Orange
    Grove, Republic of South Africa
Mission Without Borders - United Kingdom [IO],
    London, United Kingdom
Mission: Wolf [5081], PO Box 1211, Westcliffe, CO
    81252, (719)859-2157
Mission to the World [20157], 1600 N Brown Rd.,
    Lawrenceville, GA 30043-8141, (678)823-0004
Mission to the World [20157], 1600 N Brown Rd.,
    Lawrenceville, GA 30043-8141, (678)823-0004
Missionaries of Africa - Defunct.
Missionary Church [20065], PO Box 9127, Fort
    Wayne, IN 46899-9127, (260)747-2027

A star before a book entry number signifies that the name is not listed separately, but is mentioned within the entry.

Missionary Church [20065], PO Box 9127, Fort Wayne, IN 46899-9127, (260)747-2027
Missionary Church Assn. [★20065]
Missionary Church Assn. [★20065]
Missionary Church Historical Soc. - Address unknown since 2010.
Missionary Dentists [★12457]
Missionary Dentists [★12457]
Missionary Engg. [★20061]
Missionary Gospel Fellowship [20066], PO Box 1535, Turlock, CA 95381-1535, (209)634-8575
Missionary Internship [★20064]
Missionary Internship [★20064]
Missionary Sisters of the Holy Rosary [19452], 741 Polo Rd., Bryn Mawr, PA 19010-3825, (610)520-1974
Missionary Sisters of Our Lady of the Holy Rosary [19452], 741 Polo Rd., Bryn Mawr, PA 19010-3825, (610)520-1974
Missionary Sisters of the Precious Blood [IO], Rome, Italy
Missionary Sisters of Saint Peter Claver [IO], Toronto, ON, Canada
Missionary Sisters of St. Peter Claver [20067], PO Box 401, Chesterfield, MO 63006-0401, (314)434-8084
Missionary Sisters of the Soc. of Mary [20068], 349 Grove St., Waltham, MA 02453, (781)891-5736
Missionary Soc. of Saint Columban [19453], PO Box 10, St. Columbans, NE 68056, (402)291-1920
Missionary Soc. of Saint Columban [IO], Navan, Ireland
Missionary Soc. of Saint Paul the Apostle [19454], 3015 4th St. NE, Washington, DC 20017-1102, (202)269-2521
Missionary TECH Team [20069], 25 FRJ Dr., Longview, TX 75602-4703, (903)757-4530
Missionary Union of the Clergy in U.S.A. [★19486]
Missione Bethleem Immense [★IO]
Missions Catholiques au Canada [★IO]
Missions Door [19324], 2530 Washington St., Denver, CO 80205-3142, (303)308-1818
Missions Door [19324], 2530 Washington St., Denver, CO 80205-3142, (303)308-1818
Missions Intl. [19763], PO Box 93235, Southlake, TX 76092-3235, (817)410-7399
Missions Intl. [19763], PO Box 93235, Southlake, TX 76092-3235, (817)410-7399
Mississippi Valley Historical Assn. [★9792]
Mississippi Valley Medical Editors' Assn. [★2798]
Missouri Fox Trotting Horse Breed Assn. [4612], PO Box 1027, Ava, MO 65608-1027, (417)683-2468
Mita Soc. for Lib. and Info. Sci. [IO], Tokyo, Japan
Mitochondria Res. Soc. [14403], Prof. Keshav K. Singh, PhD, Founder, Roswell Park Cancer Inst., Dept. of Cancer Genetics, BLSC Bldg., Rm. 3-316, Elm and Carlton St., Buffalo, NY 14263, (716)845-8017
Mitochondria Res. Soc. [14403], Prof. Keshav K. Singh, PhD, Founder, Roswell Park Cancer Inst., Dept. of Cancer Genetics, BLSC Bldg., Rm. 3-316, Elm and Carlton St., Buffalo, NY 14263, (716)845-8017
Mitochondrial Disease Found; United [16612]
Mitochondrial Medicine Soc. [14217], Children's Specialists of San Diego, 3020 Children's Way - MC 5064, San Diego, CA 92123-4282, (858)576-1700
Mitochondrial Medicine Soc. [14217], Children's Specialists of San Diego, 3020 Children's Way - MC 5064, San Diego, CA 92123-4282, (858)576-1700
Mixed Harmony Barbershop Quartet Assn. [10243], PO Box 1209, Aptos, CA 95001
Mizrachi Palestine Fund - Defunct.
Mizrachi Women's Org. of Amer. [★19845]
Mlup Baitong [IO], Phnom Penh, Cambodia
Mobile Air Conditioning Soc. [★1714]
Mobile Air Conditioning Soc. [★1714]
Mobile Air Conditioning Soc. Worldwide [1714], PO Box 88, Lansdale, PA 19446, (215)631-7020
Mobile Air Conditioning Soc. Worldwide [1714], PO Box 88, Lansdale, PA 19446, (215)631-7020
Mobile Communications
  Cell Phones for Soldiers [11086]

  Recycling for Charities [4871]
Mobile Data Assn. [IO], Sleaford, United Kingdom
Mobile Enhancement Retailers Assn. [3110], 85 Flagship Dr., Ste. F, North Andover, MA 01845, (978)867-6759
Mobile Home Mfrs. Assn. [★2309]
Mobile Home Owners Fed. [★12188]
Mobile Homes
  Teton Club Intl. [21888]
  Teton Club Intl. [21888]
Mobile Indus. Caterers' Assn. [★1744]
Mobile Mfrs. Forum [IO], Brussels, Belgium
Mobile Marketing Assn. [97], 8 W 38th St., Ste. 200, New York, NY 10018, (646)257-4515
Mobile Marketing Assn. [97], 8 W 38th St., Ste. 200, New York, NY 10018, (646)257-4515
Mobile Medical Disaster Relief [12472], 5409 Maryland Way, Ste. 119, Brentwood, TN 37027, (615)833-3002
Mobile Modular Off. Assn. [★2580]
Mobile Operators Assn. [IO], London, United Kingdom
Mobile Post Off. Soc. [22057], PO Box 427, Marstons Mills, MA 02648-0427, (508)428-9132
Mobile Riverine Force Assn. [20832], 106 Belleview Dr. NE, Conover, NC 28613, (828)464-7228
Mobile Satellite Users Assn. [7350], 1350 Beverly Rd., Ste. 115-341, McLean, VA 22101, (650)839-0376
Mobile Self-Storage Assn. [3622], 2001 Jefferson Davis Hwy., Ste. 1004, Arlington, VA 22202, (703)416-0060
Mobile Voter [18096], 44 Elsie St., San Francisco, CA 94110
Mobility Intl. USA [11806], 132 E Broadway, Ste. 343, Eugene, OR 97401, (541)343-1284
Mobility Intl. USA [11806], 132 E Broadway, Ste. 343, Eugene, OR 97401, (541)343-1284
Mobilization Against AIDS [10887], 429 W 127th St., 2nd Fl., New York, NY 10027, (212)537-0575
Moby Dick Acad. - Defunct.
Mocha Moms [13466], PO Box 1995, Upper Marlboro, MD 20773
Modaraba Assn. of Pakistan [IO], Karachi, Pakistan
Model A 68-B Cabriolet Club [★21108]
Model A Ford Cabriolet Club [21108], PO Box 1487, Conroe, TX 77305, (936)441-8209
Model A Ford Club of Am. [21109], 250 S Cypress St., La Habra, CA 90631-5515, (562)697-2712
Model A Ford Found. [21110], PO Box 95151, Nonantum, MA 02495-0151
Model A Restorers Club [21111], 6721 Merriman Rd., Garden City, MI 48135, (734)427-9050
Model A Restorers Club of Southern California [★21109]
Model Aeronautical Assn. of Australia [IO], West Pennant Hills, Australia
Model Aeronautical Assn. of Queensland [IO], Annandale, Australia
Model Indus. Assn. [★1728]
Model Missile Assn. [★21905]
Model Secondary School for the Deaf [14946], Gallaudet Univ., 800 Florida Ave. NE, Washington, DC 20002, (202)651-5031
Model T Ford Club of Am. [21112], PO Box 126, Centerville, IN 47330-0126, (765)855-5248
Model T Ford Club Intl. [21113], PO Box 355, Hudson, NC 28638-0355, (828)728-5758
Model T Ford Club Intl. [21113], PO Box 355, Hudson, NC 28638-0355, (828)728-5758
Model Trains
  Lionel Collectors Club of Am. [21889]
  Lionel Railroader Club [21890]
  Marklin Digital Special Interest Gp. [21891]
  Natl. Model Railroad Assn. [21892]
  Teen Assn. of Model Railroaders [21893]
  Toy Train Collectors Soc. [21894]
  Toy Train Operating Soc. [21895]
  Train Collectors Assn. [21896]
  Train Collectors Assn. [21896]
  Youth in Model Railroading [21897]
Modellfluggruppe Liechtenstein [IO], Schaan, Liechtenstein
Models
  1/87 Vehicle Club [21898]

  Air Mail Pioneers [20879]
  Amer. Model Yachting Assn. [21899]
  Circus Model Builders, Intl. [21900]
  Circus Model Builders Intl. [21900]
  First Flight Soc. [20896]
  Intl. Coun. of Air Shows [20901]
  Intl. Model Power Boat Assn. [21901]
  Intl. Model Power Boat Assn. [21901]
  Intl. Plastic Modelers Society/United States Br. [21902]
  Intl. R/C Helicopter Assn. [21903]
  Intl. Scale Soaring Assn. [21904]
  Intl. Scale Soaring Assn. [21904]
  Natl. Assn. of Rocketry [21905]
  Natl. Assn. of Scale Aeromodelers [21906]
  Natl. Assn. of Scale Aeromodelers [21906]
  Natl. World War II Glider Pilots Assn. [20315]
  Navy Carrier Soc. [21907]
  North Amer. Model Boat Assn. [21908]
  North Amer. Model Boat Assn. [21908]
  Popular Rotorcraft Assn. [20913]
  Scale Ship Modelers Assn. of North Am. [21909]
  Scale Warbird Racing Assn. [21910]
  Ships-in-Bottles Assn. of Am. [21911]
  Toy Train Collectors Soc. [21894]
  U.S. Scale Masters Assn. [21912]
  Unlimited Scale Racing Assn. [21913]
  Whirly-Girls - Intl. Women Helicopter Pilots [20923]
  World Airline Historical Soc. [20924]
  World Miniature Warbird Assn. [21914]
  Youth in Model Railroading [21897]
The Models Guild - Defunct.
Moderata Ungdomsforbundet [IO], Stockholm, Sweden
Moderate Party [IO], Stockholm, Sweden
Moderaterna [★IO]
Moderation Mgt. [16742], 22 W 27th St., 5th Fl., New York, NY 10001, (212)871-0974
Modern Car Soc. [21114], Rolls-Royce Owners' Club, 191 Hempt Rd., Mechanicsburg, PA 17055
Modern Churchpeople's Union [IO], Liverpool, United Kingdom
Modern Free and Accepted Masons of the World [19137], PO Box 1072, Columbus, GA 31902, (706)322-3326
Modern Free and Accepted Masons of the World [19137], PO Box 1072, Columbus, GA 31902, (706)322-3326
Modern Greek Stud. Assn. [9649], Prof. S. Victor Papacosma, Exec. Dir., PO Box 945, Brunswick, ME 04011, (207)406-2567
Modern Greek Stud. Assn. [9649], Prof. S. Victor Papacosma, Exec. Dir., PO Box 945, Brunswick, ME 04011, (207)406-2567
Modern Humanities Res. Assn. [IO], London, United Kingdom
Modern Language Assn. of Am. [8474], 26 Broadway, 3rd Fl., New York, NY 10004-1789, (646)576-5000
Modern Language Assn. of Am. [8474], 26 Broadway, 3rd Fl., New York, NY 10004-1789, (646)576-5000
Modern Music Masters [★10305]
Modern Pentathlon Assn. of Great Britain [IO], Bath, United Kingdom
Modern Poetry Assn. [★10452]
Modern Poetry Assn. [★10452]
Modern Woodmen of Am. [19284], PO Box 2005, Rock Island, IL 61204-2005, (800)447-9811
Modernising and Activating Women's Role in Economic Development [IO], Damascus, Syrian Arab Republic
Modernist Stud. Assn. [8517], Karen Tiefenwerth, Admin. Mgr., Johns Hopkins Univ., Dept. of English, 3400 N Charles St., Gilman Hall, Rm. 14, Baltimore, MD 21218, (800)548-1784
Modernized Chinese Medicine Intl. Assn. [IO], Hong Kong, People's Republic of China
Modular Building Inst. [2580], 944 Glenwood Sta. Ln., Ste. 204, Charlottesville, VA 22901-1480, (434)296-3288
Modular and Portable Building Assn. [IO], Caersws, United Kingdom
Mohair Coun. of Am. [3792], 233 W Twohig Ave., San Angelo, TX 76903, (325)655-3161

Reference to "IO" in place of a book number signifies that the association may be found in the 50th edition of International Organizations.

Moisture Seekers [★16625]
Moisture Seekers [★16625]
Moldavian League Against Epilepsy [IO], Chisinau, Moldova
Moldavian League Against Rheumatic Diseases [IO], Chisinau, Moldova
Moldavian Soc. of Cardiology [IO], Chisinau, Moldova
Moldavian Squash Fed. [IO], Chisinau, Moldova
Moldova Dance Sport Fed. [IO], Chisinau, Moldova
Moldova Republic Tennis Fed. [IO], Chisinau, Moldova
Molecular Biology; Amer. Soc. for Biochemistry and [6268]
Molecular Imaging; Acad. of [15388]
Molecular Mfg; Inst. for [7044]
Molecular Pathology; Assn. for [16119]
The Moles [19244], 577 Chestnut Ridge Rd., Woodcliff Lake, NJ 07677, (201)930-1923
Molestation
　MaleSurvivor: The Natl. Org. Against Male Sexual Victimization [13089]
Molluscan Shellfish Inst. - Address unknown since 2010.
Mommies Network - Address unknown since 2011.
Moms Against Mercury [13322], 55 Carson's Trail, Leicester, NC 28748, (828)776-0082
Moms Against Poverty [12742], PO Box 4212, Burlingame, CA 94011, (650)271-7178
Moms in Touch Intl. [20289], PO Box 1120, Poway, CA 92074-1120, (858)486-4065
Moms in Touch Intl. [20289], PO Box 1120, Poway, CA 92074-1120, (858)486-4065
MOMSTELL [13265], PO Box 450, Mechanicsburg, PA 17055
Monaco DanceSport Assn. Stade Louis II [IO], Monaco, Monaco
Monaco Red Cross [IO], Monaco, Monaco
Monaco Sci. Center [IO], Monte Carlo, Monaco
Monaghan Photographic Soc. [IO], Monaghan, Ireland
Monarchist League of Canada [IO], Oakville, ON, Canada
Monarchy
　Amer. Heraldry Soc. [20618]
Monash Dance Sport [IO], Clayton, Australia
Monbukagakusho Alumni Assn. of Pakistan [IO], Islamabad, Pakistan
Mondiale ORT [★IO]
Monegasque Tennis Fed. [IO], Monaco, Monaco
Monell Found; Ambrose [13124]
Money Advice Scotland [IO], Glasgow, United Kingdom
Money Mgt. Intl. [12044], 14141 SW Freeway, Ste. 1000, Sugar Land, TX 77478-3494, (866)889-9347
Mongolia Soc. [10102], Indiana Univ., 322 Goodbody Hall, 1011 E 3rd St., Bloomington, IN 47405-7005, (812)855-4078
Mongolian
　Arts Coun. of Mongolia-US [10101]
　Edurelief [12834]
　Mongolia Soc. [10102]
Mongolian Acad. of Sciences [IO], Ulan Bator, Mongolia
Mongolian Advt. Assn. [IO], Ulan Bator, Mongolia
Mongolian Assn. of Free and Independent Publishers [IO], Ulan Bator, Mongolia
Mongolian Assn. of Univ. Women [IO], Ulan Bator, Mongolia
Mongolian Athletic Fed. [IO], Ulan Bator, Mongolia
Mongolian Badminton Assn. [IO], Erdenet, Mongolia
Mongolian Dancesport Assn. [IO], Ulan Bator, Mongolia
Mongolian Epilepsy Soc. [IO], Ulan Bator, Mongolia
Mongolian Family Welfare Assn. [IO], Ulan Bator, Mongolia
Mongolian Fed. of Draughts [IO], Ulan Bator, Mongolia
Mongolian Junior Chamber [IO], Ulan Bator, Mongolia
Mongolian Natl. Soc. for Photogrammetry and Remote Sensing [IO], Ulan Bator, Mongolia
Mongolian Red Cross Soc. [IO], Ulan Bator, Mongolia
Mongolian Squash Fed. [IO], Ulan Bator, Mongolia

Mongolian Taekwondo Fed. [IO], Ulan Bator, Mongolia
Mongolian Tennis Assn. [IO], Ulan Bator, Mongolia
Mongolian Volunteers Assn. [IO], Ulan Bator, Mongolia
Mongolian Women Lawyers Assn. [IO], Ulan Bator, Mongolia
Mongoliin Deed Bolobsroltoi Emegteichuudiin Holboo [★IO]
Monkees
　Purple Flower Gang [23883]
Monks Without Borders [19826], 1750 Grant St., Eugene, OR 97402, (562)448-2012
Monland Restoration Coun. [17214], 6505 Decatur Rd., Fort Wayne, IN 46816, (260)441-0549
Monocoupe Club [20907], 1218 Kingstowne Pl., St. Charles, MO 63304
Monorail Mfrs. Assn. [1849], 8720 Red Oak Blvd., Ste. 201, Charlotte, NC 28217, (704)676-1190
The Monorail Soc. [22183], 36193 Carnation Way, Fremont, CA 94536-2641
The Monroe Inst. [7158], 365 Roberts Mountain Rd., Faber, VA 22938-2318, (434)361-1252
Monroe Inst. of Applied Sciences [★7158]
Monster Truck Racing Assn. [22825], Brenda Noelke, Sec.-Treas., 947 Crider Ln., Union, MO 63084, (636)234-6162
Monster Truck Racing Assn. [22825], Brenda Noelke, Sec.-Treas., 947 Crider Ln., Union, MO 63084, (636)234-6162
Montadale Sheep Breeders Assn. [4911], 3321 Piney Creek Dr., Elkhorn, NE 68022-4422, (402)884-7555
Montana Coun. for Indian Educ. [★8675]
Montana Outfitters and Dude Ranchers Assn. [★23087]
Montana Outfitters and Guides Assn. [23087], 5 Microwave Hill Rd., Montana City, MT 59634, (406)449-3578
Monte Jade Sci. and Tech. Assn. [7516], Lilly Chung, 2870 Zanker Rd., Ste. 140, San Jose, CA 95134, (408)428-0388
Montenegrin Assn. Against AIDS [IO], Podgorica, Montenegro
Montenegrin Assn. of Am. - Address unknown since 2011.
Montenegrin Assn. of Craft, Small and Medium Enterprises [IO], Podgorica, Montenegro
Montenegrin Assn. of Snowsport Instructors [IO], Podgorica, Montenegro
Montenegrin Cancer Soc. [IO], Podgorica, Montenegro
Montenegrin Employers Fed. [IO], Podgorica, Montenegro
Montenegrin Hotel Assn. [IO], Petrovac, Montenegro
Montenegrin P.E.N. Centre [IO], Cetinje, Montenegro
Montenegro Golf Assn. [IO], Niksic, Montenegro
Montenegro Tourism Assn. [IO], Budva, Montenegro
Monterey County Vintners and Growers Assn. [5168], PO Box 1793, Monterey, CA 93942-1793, (831)375-9400
Monterey Wine Country Assn. [★5168]
Montessori
　Amer. Montessori Soc. [8632]
　Assn. Montessori International USA [8633]
　Canadian Coun. of Montessori Administrators [5669]
　Intl. Montessori Accreditation Coun. [8634]
　Intl. Montessori Accreditation Coun. [8634]
　Intl. Montessori Soc. [8635]
　Intl. Montessori Soc. [8635]
　Montessori Educational Programs Intl. [8636]
　Montessori Educational Programs Intl. [8636]
Montessori Accreditation Coun. for Teacher Educ. [8040], 313 2nd St. SE, Ste. 112, Charlottesville, VA 22902, (434)202-7793
Montessori Accreditation Coun. for Teacher Educ. [8040], 313 2nd St. SE, Ste. 112, Charlottesville, VA 22902, (434)202-7793
Montessori Assn. of New Zealand [IO], Nelson, New Zealand
Montessori Educational Programs Intl. [8636], PO Box 6, Smithville, IN 47458, (812)824-6366
Montessori Educational Programs Intl. [8636], PO Box 6, Smithville, IN 47458, (812)824-6366

Montessori Inst. of Am. [8041], 23807 98th Ave. S, Kent, WA 98031, (253)859-2262
Montford Point Marine Assn. [5810], PO Box 1070, Sharon Hill, PA 19079
Montreat Coll. Alumni Assn. [18885], PO Box 1267, Montreat, NC 28757, (828)669-8012
Montserrat Amateur Radio Soc. [IO], Plymouth, Montserrat
Montserrat Animal Protection Soc. [IO], Brades, Montserrat
Montserrat Hospitality Assn. [IO], Brades, Montserrat
Montserrat Progressive Soc. of New York [19280], The Montserrat Bldg., 207 W 137th St., New York, NY 10030-2425, (212)283-3346
Monument Builders of Am. [★2539]
Monument Builders of Canada [★2539]
Monument Builders of North Am. [2539], 136 S Keowee St., Dayton, OH 45402, (800)233-4472
Monumental Brass Soc. [IO], Suffolk, United Kingdom
Moody Bible Inst. [20070], 820 N LaSalle Blvd., Chicago, IL 60610, (312)329-4000
Moody Literature Ministries [★20070]
Moody Literature Mission [★20070]
Moon Soc. [7453], PO Box 940825, Plano, TX 75094-0825
Mooncircles [20250], 397 Arnos St., Talent, OR 97540-9610
Moore River Olive Assn. [IO], Perth, Australia
Moore Stephens North Am. [39], Park 80 West, Plaza II, Ste. 200, Saddle Brook, NJ 07663, (201)291-2660
Moose Intl. [18989], 155 S Intl. Dr., Mooseheart, IL 60539-1169, (630)966-2209
Moose Intl. [18989], 155 S Intl. Dr., Mooseheart, IL 60539-1169, (630)966-2209
Morab Community Network [★4600]
Morab Community Network [★4600]
The Morab Registry [★4601]
Moral Alternatives [★17317]
Moral Re-Armament [★17801]
Moral Re-Armament [★17801]
Morality in Media [18399], 475 Riverside Dr., Ste. 1264, New York, NY 10115, (212)870-3222
Moravian
　Moravian Historical Soc. [20117]
Moravian Historical Soc. [20117], 214 E Center St., Nazareth, PA 18064, (610)759-5070
Moravian Music Found. [10244], 457 S Church St., Winston Salem, NC 27101, (336)725-0651
Mordechai Bernstein Literary Prizes Assn. [IO], Tel Aviv, Israel
More Game Birds in Am. [★5047]
More Light Presbyterians for Lesbian, Gay, Bisexual and Transgender concerns [19798], PMB 246, 4737 County Rd. 101, Minnetonka, MN 55345-2634, (505)820-7082
Morgan 3/4 Gp. [21115], PO Box 1208, Ridgefield, CT 06877, (917)880-2962
Morgan Car Club [21116], Lisa Shriver, 45070 Brae Terr., Ashburn, VA 20147
Morgan Family Club - Address unknown since 2011.
Morgan Horse Club [★4543]
Morgan Memorial and Cooperative Indus. and Stores [★11792]
Morgan Memorial and Cooperative Indus. and Stores [★11792]
Morgan Owners Gp. [★21115]
Morgan Plus Four Club [21117], 5073 Melbourne Dr., Cypress, CA 90630, (714)828-3127
Morgan Single-Footing Horse Found. [4613], 650 E 1070 N, Richfield, UT 84701, (435)896-6824
Morgan Sports Car Club [IO], Petersfield, United Kingdom
Morgan Three-Wheeler Club [IO], Worcester, United Kingdom
Moringa Community [11610], 242 N Limerick Rd., Schwenksville, PA 19473, (610)287-7802
Moringa Community [11610], 242 N Limerick Rd., Schwenksville, PA 19473, (610)287-7802
Mormon History Assn. [19918], 10 W 100 S, Ste. 610, Salt Lake City, UT 84101, (801)521-6565
Morning Bird Social Welfare Org. [IO], Sylhet, Bangladesh
Morningside House [★10831]

A star before a book entry number signifies that the name is not listed separately, but is mentioned within the entry.

Mornington Peninsula Olive Assn. [IO], Red Hill South, Australia

Moroccan Amer. Bus. Coun. [2085], 1085 Commonwealth Ave., Ste. 194, Boston, MA 02215, (508)230-9943

Moroccan Amer. Bus. Coun. [2085], 1085 Commonwealth Ave., Ste. 194, Boston, MA 02215, (508)230-9943

Moroccan-American Soc. for Life Sciences [7141], PO Box 324, Dunn Loring, VA 22027-0324, (202)413-6025

Moroccan-American Soc. for Life Sciences [7141], PO Box 324, Dunn Loring, VA 22027-0324, (202)413-6025

Moroccan Exporters' Assn. [IO], Casablanca, Morocco

Moroccan Red Crescent [IO], Rabat, Morocco

Moroccan Soc. of Chemotherapy [IO], Casablanca, Morocco

Moroccan Soc. of Dermatology [IO], Rabat, Morocco

Moroccan Soc. of Fertility and Contraception [IO], Casablanca, Morocco

Moroccan Soc. for Rheumatology [IO], Rabat, Morocco

Morocco
Friends of Morocco [19146]
Friends of Morocco [19146]
Moroccan-American Soc. for Life Sciences [7141]

Morocco Mfrs. Natl. Assn. [★2202]

Morris Animal Found. [11003], 10200 E Girard Ave., Ste. B430, Denver, CO 80231, (303)790-2345

Morris Animal Found. [11003], 10200 E Girard Ave., Ste. B430, Denver, CO 80231, (303)790-2345

Morris Cerullo World Evangelism [19764], PO Box 85277, San Diego, CA 92186-5277, (858)277-2200

Morris Cerullo World Evangelism [19764], PO Box 85277, San Diego, CA 92186-5277, (858)277-2200

Morris Fed. [IO], Suffolk, United Kingdom

Morris-Jumel Mansion [10679], 65 Jumel Terr., New York, NY 10032, (212)923-8008

Morris Plan Bankers Assn. [★407]

Morris Pratt Inst. Assn. [20142], 11811 Watertown Plank Rd., Milwaukee, WI 53226-3342, (414)774-2994

Morris Register [IO], Earley, United Kingdom

Morrocan League Against Epilepsy [IO], Rabat, Morocco

Morse Soc. [20644], PO Box 984, Lakeland, FL 33802

Morse Telegraph Club [22161], 5301 Neville Ct., Alexandria, VA 22310, (703)971-4095

Mortality
Nutrition and Educ. Intl. [12586]

Mortar Bd. [23562], 1200 Chambers Rd., Ste. 201, Columbus, OH 43212, (614)488-4094

Mortar Indus. Assn. [IO], London, United Kingdom

Mortar Mfrs. Standards Assn. [★579]

Mortgage Bankers Assn. [422], 1717 Rhode Island Ave. NW, Ste. 400, Washington, DC 20036, (202)557-2700

Mortgage Bankers Assn. of Am. [★422]

Mortgage and Finance Assn. of Australia [IO], Neutral Bay, Australia

Mortgage Insurance Companies of Am. [1996], 1425 K St. NW, Ste. 210, Washington, DC 20005, (202)682-2683

Mortuary Science
Amer. Bd. of Funeral Ser. Educ. [2526]
Intl. Conf. of Funeral Ser. Examining Boards of the U.S. [5845]

Mortuary Services
Amer. Inst. of Commemorative Art [2527]
Amer. Soc. of Embalmers [2528]
Casket and Funeral Supply Assn. of Am. [2529]
Catholic Cemetery Conf. [2530]
Cremation Assn. of North Am. [2531]
Federated Funeral Directors of Am. [2532]
Funeral Consumers Alliance [2533]
Green Burial Coun. [2534]
Intl. Cemetery, Cremation and Funeral Assn. [2535]
Intl. Cemetery, Cremation and Funeral Assn. [2535]
Intl. Fed. of Thanatologists Assn. [4721]
Intl. Memorialization Supply Assn. [2536]

Intl. Memorialization Supply Assn. [2536]
Intl. Order of the Golden Rule [2537]
Intl. Order of the Golden Rule [2537]
Jewish Funeral Directors of Am. [2538]
Monument Builders of North Am. [2539]
Natl. Concrete Burial Vault Assn. [2540]
Natl. Funeral Directors Assn. [2541]
Natl. Funeral Directors and Morticians Assn. [2542]
Preferred Funeral Directors Intl. [2543]
Preferred Funeral Directors Intl. [2543]
Selected Independent Funeral Homes [2544]

Mosaic Assn. of Australia and New Zealand [IO], Rozelle, Australia

Mosaism
United Israel World Union [20118]
United Israel World Union [20118]

Moscow ACM SIGMOD [IO], Moscow, Russia

Moscow Intl. Bus. Assn. [IO], Moscow, Russia

Moses Collins Family Org. - Defunct.

Moslem Mosque - Defunct.

Mosquito Assn. [20328], Dick Souza, Dir.-at-Large, 79 Bradstreet Ave., Lowell, MA 01851-4120, (978)453-3887

Mosquito Control Assn. of Australia [IO], Gold Coast, Australia

Mosquito Historical Found. [★20328]

Motel Brokers Assn. of Am. [★3013]

Motel Brokers Assn. of Am. [★3013]

Mothers' Access to Careers at Home - Defunct.

Mothers Acting Up [13467], PO Box 1244, Boulder, CO 80306, (303)474-1286

Mothers Against Drunk Drivers [★12990]

Mothers Against Drunk Driving [12990], 511 E John Carpenter Fwy., Ste. 700, Irving, TX 75062, (214)744-6233

Mothers Against Drunk Driving - Canada [IO], Oakville, ON, Canada

Mothers Against Misuse and Abuse [16743], 5217 SE 28th Ave., Portland, OR 97202, (503)233-4202

Mothers Against Munchausen Syndrome by Proxy Allegations [14090], 1407 Ranch Dr., Senatobia, MS 38668

Mothers Against Sexual Abuse [13090], 404 Wilson St., Union, SC 29379

Mothers Against Sexual Predators At Large [13091], PO Box 606, Bonner, MT 59823, (406)244-5923

Mothers Against War - Address unknown since 2011.

Mothers And More [11945], PO Box 31, Elmhurst, IL 60126, (630)941-3553

Mothers Anonymous [★11388]

Mothers Arms [13033], 4757 E Greenway Rd., 107B No. 124, Phoenix, AZ 85032, (800)464-4840

Mothers of Asthmatics [★16602]

Mothers' Center Development Proj. [★12609]

Mothers and Fathers Aligned Saving Kids [17238], 2566-70 Nostrand Ave., Brooklyn, NY 11210, (718)758-0400

Mothers at Home [★12606]

Mothers' Home Bus. Network [1731], PO Box 423, East Meadow, NY 11554

Mothers-in-Law Club Intl. - Defunct.

Mothers Matter - Defunct.

Mothers of Military Support [12529], 1105 D 15th Ave., No. 111, Longview, WA 98632, (360)430-3597

Mothers of Murdered Youth [11484], PO Box 17516, Colorado Springs, CO 80935, (719)231-8234

Mothers of the Plaza de Mayo [IO], Buenos Aires, Argentina

Mother's Right Found. [IO], Moscow, Russia

Mothers Supporting Daughters with Breast Cancer [13943], 25235 Fox Chase Dr., Chestertown, MD 21620, (410)778-1982

Mothers' Union - England [IO], London, United Kingdom

Mothers United for Moral Support [★16774]

Mothers' Voices [13616], 150 W Flagler St., Ste. 2825, Miami, FL 33130, (305)347-5467

Mothers Without Borders [11354], 125 E Main St., Ste. 402, American Fork, UT 84003, (801)607-5641

Mothers Without Borders [11354], 125 E Main St., Ste. 402, American Fork, UT 84003, (801)607-5641

Motion Picture
African Amer. Women in Cinema Org. [9592]
Intl. Assn. of Audio Visual Communicators [1259]
Stuntwomen's Assn. of Motion Pictures [1268]

Motion Picture Assn. of Am. [1263], 15301 Ventura Blvd., Bldg. E, Sherman Oaks, CA 91403-5585, (818)995-6600

Motion Picture Assn. of Bhutan [IO], Thimphu, Bhutan

Motion Picture Pilots Assn. [380], 7435 Valjean Ave., Van Nuys, CA 91406, (818)947-5454

Motion Picture Producers and Distributors of Am. [★1263]

Motion Picture Relief Fund [★11971]

Motion Picture Sound Editors [1264], 10061 Riverside Dr., PMB 751, Toluca Lake, CA 91602-2560, (818)506-7731

Motion Picture and TV Engineers; Soc. of [6828]

Motion Picture and TV Fund [11971], 23388 Mulholland Dr., Woodland Hills, CA 91364, (818)876-1050

Motion Picture Theatre Associations of Canada [IO], Toronto, ON, Canada

Motor Bus Division of Amer. Auto. Assn. [★3500]

Motor Bus Soc. [21118], PO Box 261, Paramus, NJ 07653-0261

Motor Bus Soc. [21118], PO Box 261, Paramus, NJ 07653-0261

Motor Carrier Lawyers Assn. [★6040]

Motor and Equip. Mfrs. Assn. [334], PO Box 13966, Research Triangle Park, NC 27709-3966, (919)549-4800

Motor and Equip. Mfrs. Assn. [334], PO Box 13966, Research Triangle Park, NC 27709-3966, (919)549-4800

Motor Freight Carriers Assn. [★3540]

Motor Indus. Assn. [IO], Auckland, New Zealand

Motor Maids [22780], 44 W Poinsetta Ave., Toledo, OH 43612

Motor Maids of Am. [★22780]

Motor Neurone Disease Assn. of New Zealand [IO], Auckland, New Zealand

Motor Neurone Disease Assn. of NSW [IO], Gladesville, Australia

Motor Neurone Disease Assn. of Queensland [IO], Brisbane, Australia

Motor Neurone Disease Assn. of South Africa [IO], Western Cape, Republic of South Africa

Motor Neurone Disease Assn. of South Australia [IO], Adelaide, Australia

Motor Neurone Disease Assn. of the United Kingdom [IO], Northampton, United Kingdom

Motor Neurone Disease Assn. of Western Australia [IO], Nedlands, Australia

Motor Neurone Disease Australia [IO], Gladesville, Australia

Motor Neurone Disease Res. Inst. of Australia [IO], Gladesville, Australia

Motor Schools Assn. of Great Britain [IO], Stockport, United Kingdom

Motor Sports Assn. [IO], Colnbrook, United Kingdom

Motor Trades Assn. of Australia [IO], Kingston, Australia

Motor Vehicle Dismantlers' Assn. of Great Britain [IO], Lichfield, United Kingdom

Motorbranschens Riksfoerbund [★IO]

Motorcycle
All-American Indian Motorcycle Club [21915]
Amer. Fed. of Motorcyclists [21916]
Amer. Historic Racing Motorcycle Assn. [21917]
Amer. Motorcycle Heritage Found. [22776]
Amer. Motorcyclist Assn. [22777]
Amer. Voyager Assn. [21918]
Amer. Voyager Assn. [21918]
Antique Motorcycle Club of Am. [21919]
Antique Motorcycle Club of Am. [21919]
Ariel Motorcycle Club North Am. [21920]
Assn. of Recovering Motorcyclists [13236]
Blue Knights Intl. Law Enforcement Motorcycle Club [21921]
Blue Knights Intl. Law Enforcement Motorcycle Club [21921]
BMW Motorcycle Owners of Am. [21922]
BMW Riders Assn. Intl. [21923]
British Biker Cooperative [21924]

Reference to "IO" in place of a book number signifies that the association may be found in the 50th edition of International Organizations.

Christian Motorcyclists Assn. [21925]
Combat Veterans Motorcycle Assn. [21926]
Continental Motorsport Club [22778]
Cushman Club of Am. [21927]
Downed Bikers Assn. [12547]
Gold Wing Road Riders Assn. [21928]
Harley Hummer Club [21929]
Harley Owners Gp. [21930]
Intl. Brotherhood of Motorcycle Campers [22779]
Intl. Brotherhood of Motorcycle Campers [22779]
Intl. CBX Owners Assn. [21931]
Intl. CBX Owners Assn. [21931]
Intl. Norton Owners' Assn. [21932]
Intl. Norton Owners' Assn. [21932]
Intl. Star Riders Assn. [21933]
Light Elec. Vehicle Assn. [3518]
Motor Maids [22780]
Motorcycle Events Assn. [21934]
Motorcycle Indus. Coun. [2545]
Motorcycle Riders Found. [21935]
Motorcycle Safety Found. [3146]
Motorcycle Touring Assn. [22781]
Ride to Work [21936]
Riders for Hea. [15519]
Riders for Justice [21937]
Triumph Intl. Owners Club [21938]
Triumph Intl. Owners Club [21938]
United Sidecar Assn. [21939]
U.S. Classic Racing Assn. [21940]
Velocette Owners Club of North Am. [21941]
Vespa Club of Am. [21942]
Vintage BMW Motorcycle Owners [21943]
Vintage Motor Bike Club [21944]
Virago Owners Club [21945]
WERA Motorcycle Roadracing [22782]
White Plate Flat Trackers Assn. [22783]
Women On Wheels Motorcycle Assn. [22784]
Women in the Wind [21946]
Women's Motorcyclist Found. [21947]
Yamaha 650 Soc. [21948]
Yamaha 650 Soc. [21948]
Motorcycle and Allied Trades Assn. [★2545]
Motorcycle Events Assn. [21934], 3221 Tyrone Blvd.
N, St. Petersburg, FL 33710, (727)343-1049
Motorcycle Indus. Assn. [IO], Coventry, United
Kingdom
Motorcycle Indus. Coun. [2545], 2 Jenner St., Ste.
150, Irvine, CA 92618-3806, (949)727-4211
Motorcycle Indus. Coun. Safety and Educ. Found.
[★3146]
Motorcycle Indus. in Europe [IO], Brussels, Belgium
Motorcycle Retailers Assn. [IO], Rugby, United
Kingdom
Motorcycle Riders Found. [21935], 236 Mas-
sachusetts Ave. NE, Ste. 510, Washington, DC
20002-4980, (202)546-0983
Motorcycle Safety Found. [3146], 2 Jenner St., Ste.
150, Irvine, CA 92618-3806, (949)727-3227
Motorcycle, Scooter and Allied Trades Assn.
[★2545]
Motorcycle Touring Assn. [22781], 1441 Ugugu Dr.,
Brevard, NC 28712, (828)483-4534
Motorcycle Touring Soc. [★22781]
Motorist Info. and Services Assn. [13340], 1500
Liberty St. SE, Ste. 150, Salem, OR 97302,
(503)373-0864
Motorsport Assn. of Pakistan [IO], Karachi, Pakistan
Motorsport Indus. Assn. [IO], Stoneleigh, United
Kingdom
Motree Family Assn. - Defunct.
Moulding and Millwork Producers Assn. [583], 507
1st St., Woodland, CA 95695, (530)661-9591
Mt. Diablo Peace Center [18267], 55 Eckley Ln.,
Walnut Creek, CA 94596, (925)933-7850
Mt. Marty Coll. Alumni Assn. [18886], 1105 W 8th
St., Yankton, SD 57078, (605)668-1292
Mount Rushmore Natl. Memorial Soc. [9709], 13000
Hwy. 244, Bldg. 31, Ste. 1, Keystone, SD 57751-
0268, (605)574-2523
Mount Rushmore Soc. [★9709]
Mount Vernon Estate and Gardens [★10680]
Mount Vernon Ladies' Assn. [10680], PO Box 110,
Mount Vernon, VA 22121, (703)780-2000
Mount Vernon Ladies' Assn. of the Union [★10680]
Mountain Bike Orienteering Australia [IO], Mitchell,
Australia

Mountain and Glacier Protection Org. [IO], Islama-
bad, Pakistan
The Mountain Inst. [9623], 3000 Connecticut Ave.
NW, Ste. 101, Washington, DC 20008, (202)234-
4050
Mountain Lion Found. [5082], PO Box 1896,
Sacramento, CA 95812, (916)442-2666
Mountain Lion Preservation Found. [★5082]
Mountain Pleasure Horse Assn. [4614], PO Box 33,
Wellington, KY 40387, (606)768-3847
Mountain Press Res. Center [20645], PO Box 400,
Signal Mountain, TN 37377-0400, (423)886-6369
Mountain Rescue Assn. [12907], PO Box 880868,
San Diego, CA 92168-0868, (858)229-4295
Mountain States Genetics Found. [14653], 8129 W
Fremont Ave., Littleton, CO 80128, (303)978-0125
Mountaineering Coun. of Ireland [★3675]
Mountaineering Coun. of Scotland [IO], Perth,
United Kingdom
Mountaineering Ireland [IO], Dublin, Ireland
Mountaineers [23088], 7700 Sand Point Way NE,
Seattle, WA 98115, (206)521-6000
Mountains and Plains Independent Booksellers
Assn. [682], 8020 Springhare Dr., Park City, UT
84098, (435)649-6079
Mounted Games Across Am. [22987], Susan Melvin,
Sec., 1950 Centerville Rd., Anderson, SC 29625,
(864)617-0237
Mounted Games Assn. of Ireland [IO], Naas, Ireland
Mouse
Amer. Fancy Rat and Mouse Assn. [21949]
Rat Assistance and Teaching Soc. [21950]
Rat Fan Club [21951]
Rat and Mouse Club of Am. [21952]
Mouvement Chretien pour la Paix [★IO]
Mouvement Chretien Pour L'Evangelisation, Le
Counseling Et La Reconciliation [★IO]
Mouvement Contre le Racisme et pour l'Amitie Entre
les Peuples [★IO]
Mouvement Ecologique [★IO]
Mouvement des Entreprises de France [★IO]
Mouvement Francais pour le Planning Familial [IO],
Paris, France
Mouvement Intl. de la Jeunesse Agricole et Rurale
Catholique [★IO]
Mouvement Intl. de la Reconciliation [★IO]
Mouvement Mondial des Meres [★IO]
Mouvement Mondial des Travailleurs Chretiens
[★IO]
Mouvement du Nid [IO], Clichy, France
Mouvement de Saintete Biblique [★IO]
Mouvement Soufi Intl. [★IO]
Movable Book Soc. [21233], PO Box 9190, Salt
Lake City, UT 84109, (801)277-6700
Move Am. Forward [18716], PO Box 1497,
Sacramento, CA 95812, (916)441-6197
Move For Hunger [12285], 1930 Heck Ave.,
Neptune, NJ 07753, (732)774-0521
MOVE Intl.: Mobility Opportunities Via Educ. U.S.A.
[11807], City Centre, 1300 17th St., Bakersfield,
CA 93301-4504, (800)397-6683
MOVE Intl.: Mobility Opportunities Via Educ. U.S.A.
[11807], City Centre, 1300 17th St., Bakersfield,
CA 93301-4504, (800)397-6683
Movement Against Racism and for Friendship
Between Peoples [IO], Paris, France
Movement for a Better World - Defunct.
Movement for Compassionate Living the Vegan Way
[IO], Swansea, United Kingdom
Movement Disorder Soc. [14806], 555 E Wells St.,
Ste. 1100, Milwaukee, WI 53202-3823, (414)276-
2145
Movement Disorder Soc. [14806], 555 E Wells St.,
Ste. 1100, Milwaukee, WI 53202-3823, (414)276-
2145
Movement of French Businesses [IO], Paris, France
Movie Makers Guild - Defunct.
Moviment ghall-Ambjent [★IO]
Movimento dei Focolari [★IO]
Movimiento Internacional de Estudiantes Catolicos -
Pax Romana [★IO]
Mozambique Chamber of Commerce [IO], Maputo,
Mozambique
Mozambique News Agency [IO], Brighton, United
Kingdom

Mozambique Red Cross Soc. [IO], Maputo, Mozam-
bique
Mozart Soc. of Am. [9503], 389 Main St., Ste. 202,
Malden, MA 02148, (781)397-8870
MPLS and Frame Relay Alliance - Defunct.
MPS Australia [IO], Sydney, Australia
MPS Austria [IO], Breitenbach, Austria
MPS Best Care Limited [★IO]
MPS Soc. [★15501]
Mr. Holland's Opus Found. [8655], 4370 Tujunga
Ave., Ste. 330, Studio City, CA 91604, (818)762-
4328
MRA [2293], PO Box 911, Pewaukee, WI 53072-
0911, (262)523-9090
MRA - The Mgt. Assn. [★2293]
MRFAC [498], 899-A Harrison St. SE, Leesburg, VA
20175, (703)669-0320
MS ActionAid - Denmark [IO], Copenhagen,
Denmark
MS - Danish Assn. for Intl. Co-operation [IO], Dar es
Salaam, United Republic of Tanzania
MS Felag Islands [★IO]
MS-Forbundet [★IO]
Ms. Found. for Women [17656], 12 MetroTech
Center, 26th Fl., Brooklyn, NY 11201, (212)742-
2300
MS Nepal: Danish Assn. for Intl. Cooperation [IO],
Kathmandu, Nepal
MS Soc. of Iceland [IO], Reykjavik, Iceland
MS-Training Centre for Development Cooperation
[IO], Arusha, United Republic of Tanzania
MSG
The Glutamate Assn. [1390]
MSPAlliance [6547], 1354 E Ave., No. R376, Chico,
CA 95926, (530)891-1340
MSPCA-Angell [11004], 350 S Huntington Ave.,
Boston, MA 02130, (617)522-7400
MSUD Family Support Gp. [★15499]
MSV - Ennio Morricone Soc. [IO], Alkmaar,
Netherlands
MTM Assn. for Standards and Res. [6948], 1111 E
Touhy Ave., Des Plaines, IL 60018, (847)299-1111
Mu Alpha Theta [23588], Univ. of Oklahoma, 601
Elm Ave., Rm. 1102, Norman, OK 73019-3103,
(405)325-4489
Mu Beta Psi [23601], Megan Roble, Ed., 1211 Ben
Avon St., Indiana, PA 15701
Mu Kappa Tau [23585], Univ. of Wisconsin-Madison,
Grainger Hall, 975 Univ. Ave., Madison, WI 53706
Mu Phi Epsilon [★23602]
Mu Phi Epsilon Intl. [23602], 4705 N Sonora Ave.,
Ste. 114, Fresno, CA 93722-3947, (559)277-1898
MU-YAP Baglantili Hak Sahibi Fonogram Yapimcilari
Meslek Birligi [★IO]
MU-YAP Turkish Phonographic Indus. Soc. [IO],
Istanbul, Turkey
Muay Thai Assn; U.S. [22761]
Mucopolysaccharidoses
Canadian Soc. for Mucopolysaccharide and
Related Diseases [22828]
Muhyiddin Ibn Arabi Soc. [20251], PO Box 45,
Berkeley, CA 94701-0045
Mujeres Activas en Letras Y Cambio Social [8247],
1404 66th St., Berkeley, CA 94702
Mukono Multi-Purpose Youth Org. [IO], Kampala,
Uganda
Mulch and Soil Coun. [1511], 10210 Leatherleaf Ct.,
Manassas, VA 20111-4245, (703)257-0111
Multi-Bank Data Processing Org. [★63]
Multi-Faith Gp. for Healthcare Chaplaincy [IO], Salis-
bury, United Kingdom
Multi-Housing Laundry Assn. [2193], 1500 Sunday
Dr., Ste. 102, Raleigh, NC 27607, (919)861-5579
Multi-Level Marketing Intl. Assn. [2415], 119 Stan-
ford Ct., Irvine, CA 92612, (949)854-0484
Multi-Level Marketing Intl. Assn. [2415], 119 Stan-
ford Ct., Irvine, CA 92612, (949)854-0484
Multicore Assn. [6463], Markus Levy, Pres., PO Box
4854, El Dorado Hills, CA 95762, (530)672-9113
Multicultural
Delta Gamma Pi Multicultural Sorority [23739]
Delta Sigma Chi Sorority [23741]
Kappa Phi Gamma Sorority [23746]
Lambda Psi Delta Sorority [23747]
Natl. Multicultural Greek Coun. [23538]

A star before a book entry number signifies that the name is not listed separately, but is mentioned within the entry.

Phi Sigma Nu Native Amer. Fraternity [23685]
Psi Sigma Phi Multicultural Fraternity [23638]
Zeta Chi Phi Multicultural Sorority [23752]
Multicultural Foodservice and Hospitality Alliance [1448], 1144 Narragansett Blvd., Providence, RI 02905, (401)461-6342
Multicultural Forum of the Amer. Soc. for Training and Development - Defunct.
Multicultural Golf Assn. of Am. [22615], PO Box 1081, Westhampton Beach, NY 11978-7081, (631)288-8255
Multicultural Inst. of the Intl. Counseling Center [★11679]
Multidisciplinary Assn. for Psychedelic Stud. [16202], 309 Cedar St., No. 2323, Santa Cruz, CA 95060, (831)429-6362
MultiFunction Products Assn. [2581], 1010 Old Chase Ave., Bldg. B, El Cajon, CA 92020, (619)447-3246
Multinational Assn. of Supportive Care in Cancer [13944], Linda S. Elting, Sec., 1515 Holcombe Blvd., Unit 447, Houston, TX 77030, (713)745-5984
Multinational Exchange for Sustainable Agriculture [4941], 2362 Bancroft Way, No. 202, Berkeley, CA 94704, (510)654-8858
Multipel Sklerose Forbundet I Norge [IO], Oslo, Norway
Multiple Assn. Mgt. Inst. [★261]
Multiple Assn. Mgt. Inst. [★261]
Multiple Birth
Center for the Stud. of Multiple Birth [15520]
Natl. Org. of Mothers of Twins Clubs [12548]
The Triplet Connection [12549]
Twinless Twins Support Gp. Intl. [12550]
Twinless Twins Support Gp. Intl. [12550]
Twins Found. [12551]
Multiple Births Canada [IO], Wasaga Beach, ON, Canada
Multiple Myeloma Res. Found. [13945], 383 Main Ave., 5th Fl., Norwalk, CT 06851, (203)229-0464
Multiple Sclerosis Assn. of Am. [15608], 706 Haddonfield Rd., Cherry Hill, NJ 08002-2652, (856)488-4500
Multiple Sclerosis Australia [IO], Lidcombe, Australia
Multiple Sclerosis Coalition [15609], 706 Haddonfield Rd., Cherry Hill, NJ 08002, (800)532-7667
Multiple Sclerosis Found. [15610], 6520 N Andrews Ave., Fort Lauderdale, FL 33309-2130, (954)776-6805
Multiple Sclerosis Intl. Fed. [IO], London, United Kingdom
Multiple Sclerosis Soc. of Canada [IO], Toronto, ON, Canada
Multiple Sclerosis Soc. of India [IO], Mumbai, India
Multiple Sclerosis Soc. of Ireland [IO], Dublin, Ireland
Multiple Sclerosis Soc. of Malta [IO], B'Kara, Malta
Multiple Sclerosis Soc; Natl. [15619]
Multiple Sclerosis Soc. of New Zealand [IO], Wellington, New Zealand
Multiple Sclerosis Soc. of the United Kingdom [IO], London, United Kingdom
Multiple Sclerosis Soc. of Zimbabwe [IO], Harare, Zimbabwe
Multiple Sclerosis South Africa [IO], London, United Kingdom
Multiple V-Belt Drive and Mech. Power Transmission Assn. [★1848]
MultiService Assn. [IO], Newark, United Kingdom
MultiService Forum [811], 48377 Fremont Blvd., Ste. 117, Fremont, CA 94538, (510)492-4050
Multiservice Switching Forum [★811]
Multisport Assn. of Russia [IO], Moscow, Russia
MultiState Tax Commn. [6013], 444 N Capitol St. NW, Ste. 425, Washington, DC 20001-1512, (202)624-8699
MUMS Natl. Parent-to-Parent Network [16774], 150 Custer Ct., Green Bay, WI 54301-1243, (920)336-5333
Munchausen Syndrome by Proxy Allegations; Mothers Against [14090]
Mundo Negro [★IO]
Municipal Arborists and Urban Foresters Soc. [★4414]

Municipal Consulting - Inst. for Org. and Economic Consulting [IO], Herne, Germany
Municipal Environmental Assn. - Defunct.
Municipal Finance Officers Assn. of U.S. and Canada [★5918]
Municipal Finance Officers Assn. of U.S. and Canada [★5918]
Municipal Government
Equip. Managers Coun. of Am. [845]
Hispanic Elected Local Officials [5846]
Intl. City/County Mgt. Assn. [5847]
Intl. City/County Mgt. Assn. [5847]
Intl. Inst. of Municipal Clerks [5848]
Intl. Inst. of Municipal Clerks [5848]
Natl. Assn. of Local Govt. Environmental Professionals [5849]
Natl. Assn. of Towns and Townships [5850]
Natl. Black Caucus of Local Elected Officials [5851]
Natl. Civic League [5852]
Natl. Conf. of Black Mayors [5853]
Natl. League of Cities [5854]
Reason Found. [5855]
U.S. Conf. of Mayors [5856]
Women in Govt. [5857]
Women in Govt. [5857]
Women in Municipal Govt. [5858]
Municipal Treasurers Assn. of the U.S. and Canada [★5917]
Municipal Waste Assn. [IO], Guelph, ON, Canada
Municipal Waste Mgt. Assn. [6066], 1620 Eye St. NW, Ste. 300, Washington, DC 20006, (202)861-6775
Muotikaupan Liitto [★IO]
Muoviyhdistys [★IO]
Murder Victims' Families Against the Death Penalty [★17219]
Murder Victims' Families for Reconciliation [17219], 2100 M St. NW, Ste. 170-296, Washington, DC 20037, (877)896-4702
Murray Clan Soc. North Am. [20561], 37 Blanchard Rd., Cambridge, MA 02138-1010
Muscular Dystrophy Assn. [15611], 3300 E Sunrise Dr., Tucson, AZ 85718, (520)529-2000
Muscular Dystrophy Assn. [IO], Auckland, New Zealand
Muscular Dystrophy Assn. Singapore [IO], Singapore, Singapore
Muscular Dystrophy Canada [IO], Toronto, ON, Canada
Muscular Dystrophy Ireland [IO], Dublin, Ireland
Musculo-Skeletal Disorders Found; Jaw Joints and Allied [16038]
Musculoskeletal Disorders
Bd. of Specialty Societies [15521]
Musculoskeletal Tumor Soc. [15522]
TMJ and Orofacial Pain Soc. of Am. [15523]
Musculoskeletal and Skin Diseases Info. CH; Natl. Inst. of Arthritis and [16620]
Musculoskeletal Tumor Soc. [15522], PO Box 320062, Alexandria, VA 22320, (703)548-2112
Musculoskeletal Ultrasound Soc. [16934], 3588 Plymouth Rd., No. 249, Ann Arbor, MI 48105, (734)973-7462
Musculoskeletal Ultrasound Soc. [16934], 3588 Plymouth Rd., No. 249, Ann Arbor, MI 48105, (734)973-7462
Musee canadien de la nature [★IO]
Museum of African Amer. History [★9100]
Museum of African Amer. History [★9100]
Museum of African Amer. History [9102], 14 Beacon St., Ste. 719, Boston, MA 02108, (617)725-0022
Museum of Amer. Finance [10123], 48 Wall St., New York, NY 10005, (212)908-4110
Museum of Amer. Financial History [★10123]
Museum Assn. of the Amer. Frontier [★9784]
Museum Assn. of the Amer. Frontier [★9784]
Museum Cmpt. Network [IO], Calgary, AB, Canada
Museum Educ. Roundtable [10124], PO Box 15727, Washington, DC 20003, (202)547-8378
Museum of the Fur Trade [9784], 6321 Hwy. 20, Chadron, NE 69337, (308)432-3843
Museum of the Fur Trade [9784], 6321 Hwy. 20, Chadron, NE 69337, (308)432-3843
Museum of Independent Telephony [★22162]

Museum Store Assn. [3111], 4100 E Mississippi Ave., Ste. 800, Denver, CO 80246-3055, (303)504-9223
Museum of Transport [★10502]
Museum Trustee Assn. [10125], 1776 I St. NW, 9th Fl., Washington, DC 20006, (202)756-4832
Museum Trustee Comm. for Res. and Development [★10125]
Museum and White House of the Confederacy [★9761]
Museums
African Amer. Museum [10103]
African Amer. Museum [10103]
African Amer. Museums Assn. [10104]
Amer. Anthropological Assn. I Coun. for Museum Anthropology [10105]
Amer. Assn. for Museum Volunteers [10106]
Amer. Assn. of Museums [10107]
Amer. Friends of the Israel Museum [10108]
Amer. Friends of the Natl. Gallery of Australia [10109]
Assn. of Academic Museums and Galleries [10110]
Assn. of Art Museum Curators [10111]
Assn. of Art Museum Curators [10111]
Assn. of Art Museum Directors [10112]
Assn. of Children's Museums [10113]
Assn. for Living History, Farm and Agricultural Museums [10114]
Assn. of Sci. Museum Directors [10115]
Assn. of Science-Technology Centers [10116]
Canadian Art Museum Directors' Org. [12748]
Coun. of Amer. Jewish Museums [10117]
Coun. of Amer. Maritime Museums [10118]
Edna Hibel Soc. [10119]
Intermuseum Conservation Assn. [10120]
Intl. Cong. of Maritime Museums [10121]
Intl. Cong. of Maritime Museums [10121]
Intl. Coun. of Museums, U.S. Natl. Comm. [10122]MuseumsIntl. Museum Theatre Alliance
Museum of Amer. Finance [10123]
Museum Educ. Roundtable [10124]
Museum Trustee Assn. [10125]
Natl. Assn. of Auto. Museums [10126]
Natl. Automotive and Truck Museum of U.S. [10127]
San Francisco Maritime Natl. Park Assn. [10128]
Small Museum Assn. [10129]
Volunteer Committees of Art Museums of Canada and the U.S. [10130]
Wyckoff House and Assn. [10131]
Museums Assn. - England [IO], London, United Kingdom
Museums Australia [IO], Civic Square, Australia
Mushroom Coun. [4458], 2880 Zanker Rd., Ste. 203, San Jose, CA 95134, (408)432-7210
Music
Acad. of Country Music [10132]
Accordionists and Teachers Guild, Intl. [8637]
Accordionists and Teachers Guild, Intl. [8637]
ACMP - The Chamber Music Network [10133]
ACMP - The Chamber Music Network [10133]
African Amer. Art Song Alliance [10134]
Air Distribution Inst. [2546]
Air Supply Fan Club [23809]
Alabama Fan Club [23810]
Alan Jackson Fan Club [23811]
Alliance for Canadian New Music Proj. [468]
Always Patsy Cline World Wide Fan Org. [23812]
Am. Sings! [10135]
Amer. Acad. of Teachers of Singing [8638]
Amer. Accordion Musicological Soc. [10136]
Amer. Accordionists' Assn. [10137]
Amer. Bandmasters Assn. [10138]
Amer. Brahms Soc. [9494]
Amer. Children of SCORE [10139]
Amer. Choral Directors Assn. [10140]
Amer. Coll. of Musicians [8639]
Amer. Composers Alliance [10141]
Amer. Disc Jockey Assn. [2547]
Amer. Festival of Microtonal Music [10142]
Amer. Flute Guild [10143]
Amer. Guild of English Handbell Ringers [10144]
Amer. Guild of Music [10145]
Amer. Guild of Organists [10146]

Reference to "IO" in place of a book number signifies that the association may be found in the 50th edition of International Organizations.

Amer. Harp Soc. [10147]
Amer. Inst. of Musical Stud. [8640]
Amer. Inst. of Musical Stud. [8640]
Amer. Inst. of Organbuilders [2548]
Amer. Inst. for Verdi Stud. [10148]
Amer. Matthay Assn. [8641]
Amer. Music Center [10149]
Amer. Music Educator's Repair Assn. [2549]
Amer. Musical Instrument Soc. [10150]
Amer. Musicological Soc. [10151]
Amer. Nyckelharpa Assn. [10152]
Amer. Nyckelharpa Assn. [10152]
Amer. Orff-Schulwerk Assn. [10153]
Amer. Pianists Assn. [21953]
Amer. Recorder Soc. [10154]
Amer. School Band Directors' Assn. [8642]
Amer. Soc. of Appraisers [2550]
Amer. Soc. for Jewish Music [10155]
Amer. Soc. of Music Arrangers and Composers
  [10156]
Amer. String Teachers Assn. [8643]
Amer. Theatre Organ Soc. [10157]
Amer. Viola Soc. [10158]
Americana Music Assn. [10159]
Amy Beth Fan Club [23813]
Angel Harps [16454]
Art Greenhaw Official Intl. Fan Club [23814]
Asian Amer. Music Soc. [10160]
Asiatic Philharmonia Soc. [10161]
Asiatic Philharmonia Soc. [10161]
Asleep at the Wheel Fan Club [23815]
Assoc. Pipe Organ Builders of Am. [2551]
Assn. for the Advancement of Creative Musicians
  [10162]
Assn. of Anglican Musicians [20119]
Assn. of Cajun Music Enthusiasts [10163]
Assn. of Concert Bands [10164]
Assn. of Independent Music Publishers [2552]
Assn. for Korean Music Res. [10165]
Assn. for Korean Music Res. [10165]
Assn. of Music Producers [2553]
Assn. for Tech. in Music Instruction [8644]
Austin Cody's Official Intl. Fan Club [23816]
Australian Music Retailers Assn. [13566]
Balalaika and Domra Assn. of Am. [10166]
Bands of Am. [10167]
Beach Boys Fan Club [23817]
Better World Chorus [12552]
Better World Chorus [12552]
Billy "Crash" Craddock Fan Club [23818]
The Blues Found. [10168]
Blues Heaven Found. [10169]
British Trombone Soc. [16542]
Brooks and Dunn Fan Club [23819]
Caledonian Found. USA [10170]
Caledonian Found. USA [10170]
Carousel Organ Assn. of Am. [21954]
CAS Forum of the Violin Soc. of Am. [10171]
Center for Contemporary Opera [10172]
Chamber Music Am. [10173]
Charity Music [12553]
Charles Ives Soc. [10174]
Charley Pride Fan Club [23820]
Chet Atkins Appreciation Soc. [23821]
Chicago Fan Club [23822]
Chicago True Advocates [23823]
Chopin Found. of the U.S. [10175]
Choristers Guild [20120]
Chorus Am. [10176]
Chris LeDoux Intl. Fan Club [23824]
Chris Young Fan Club [23825]
Christian Instrumentalists and Directors Assn.
  [20121]
Church Music Assn. of Am. [20122]
Church Music Publishers Assn. [20123]
Classical Music Lovers' Exchange [10177]
Cliff Richard Fan Club of Am. [23826]
Cobbett Assn. for Chamber Music Res. [10178]
Coll. Band Directors Natl. Assn. [8645]
Coll. Music Soc. [8646]
Company of Fifers and Drummers [10179]
Conductors Guild [10180]
Connie Francis Intl. Fan Club [23827]
Contemporary A Cappella Soc. of Am. [10181]
Coun. for Res. in Music Educ. [8647]

Coun. for Res. in Music Educ. [8647]
Country Legends Assn. [10182]
Country Music Assn. [10183]
Country Music Found. [10184]
Country Music Showcase Intl. [10185]
Cowsills Fan Club [23828]
Creative Music Found. [10186]
Creative Musicians Coalition [2554]
Dart Music Intl. [10187]
David Allan Coe Fan Club [23829]
Del Shannon Appreciation Soc. [23830]
Delbert McClinton Intl. Fan Club [23831]
Delta Omicron [23599]
Diamond Rio Fan Club [23832]
Dinah Shore Fan Club [23833]
Disabled Drummers Assn. [11780]
Diverse Emerging Music Org. [10188]
Donna Fargo Intl. Fan Club [23834]
Donny Osmond Intl. Network [23835]
Doors Collectors Club [23836]
Drinker Lib. of Choral Music [10189]
Drum Corps Intl. [10190]
Drum Corps Intl. [10190]
The Duke Ellington Soc. [10191]
Early Childhood Music and Movement Assn.
  [12554]
Early Music Am. [8648]
Early Music Network [10192]
Eddy Raven Fan Club [23837]
Educ. Through Music [8649]
Electronic Music Found. [10193]
Engelbert's "Goils" [23838]
Engel's Angels in Humperdinck Heaven Fan Club
  [23839]
Engel's Angels in Humperdinck Heaven Fan Club
  [23839]
Ernst Bacon Soc. [10194]
European Amer. Musical Alliance [10195]
Face the Music Fan Club [23840]
Fellowship of Amer. Baptist Musicians [20124]
Film Music Soc. [10196]
Fischoff Natl. Chamber Music Assn. [10197]
Florence Ballard Fan Club [23841]
Florence Ballard Fan Club [23841]
Fretted Instrument Guild of Am. [10198]
Friends of the Cassidys [23842]
Friends of Josh Groban Fan Club [23843]
Friends of Paul Overstreet [23844]
Future of Music Coalition [10199]
Gary Morris Fan Club [23845]
Gay and Lesbian Assn. of Choruses [10200]
Gene Pitney Intl. Fan Club [23846]
Gene Summers Intl. Fan Club [23847]
Gene Summers Intl. Fan Club [23847]
George H. Buck Jr., Jazz Found. [21955]
George Strait Fan Club [23848]
Glenn Miller Birthplace Soc. [23849]
Gordon Inst. for Music Learning [8650]
Gospel Music Assn. [10201]
Gospel Music Workshop of Am. [10202]
Gram Parsons Found. [23850]
GRAMMY Found. [10203]
The Grascals Fan Club [23851]
Guam Symphony Soc. [10204]
Guild of Amer. Luthiers [2555]
Guild of Amer. Luthiers [2555]
Guild of Carillonneurs in North America [10205]
Guild of Carillonneurs in North America [10205]
Guild of Temple Musicians [20125]
Guitar and Accessories Marketing Assn. [2556]
Guitar Found. of Am. [10206]
Guitars For Vets [11840]
Hank Williams Intl. Fan Club [23852]
Hank Williams Jr. Fan Club [23853]
Hardanger Fiddle Assn. of Am. [10207]
Harmony Found. Intl. [10208]
Harry Connick, Jr. Fan Club [23854]
Harry Connick, Jr. Fan Club [23854]
Healing Music Org. [15524]
Heart of Texas Country Music Assn. [23855]
High School Band Directors Natl. Assn. [8651]
Historic Brass Soc. [10209]
Historical Harp Soc. [10210]
Hitchcock Inst. for Stud. in Amer. Music [8652]
Hong Kong Sinfonietta [18911]

Hymn Soc. of Great Britain and Ireland [10869]
Hymn Soc. in the U.S. and Canada [20126]
Inst. for Vietnamese Music [10211]
Inst. for Vietnamese Music [10211]
Interactive Audio Special Interest Gp. [2557]
Intercollegiate Men's Choruses, An Intl. Assn. of
  Male Choruses [10212]
Intercollegiate Men's Choruses, An Intl. Assn. of
  Male Choruses [10212]
Intl. Al Jolson Soc. [23856]
Intl. Alliance of Composers [10213]
Intl. Alliance for Women in Music [10214]
Intl. Alliance for Women in Music [10214]
Intl. Assn. of African-American Music [10215]
Intl. Assn. of African-American Music [10215]
Intl. Assn. for Jazz Educ. [8653]
Intl. Assn. for Jazz Educ. [8653]
Intl. Assn. of Jazz Record Collectors [21956]
Intl. Assn. of Jazz Record Collectors [21956]
Intl. Assn. of Music Info. Centres [21749]
Intl. Assn. of Piano Builders and Technicians
  [2558]
Intl. Assn. of Piano Builders and Technicians
  [2558]
Intl. Bluegrass Music Assn. [10216]
Intl. Bluegrass Music Assn. [10216]
Intl. Clarinet Assn. [10217]
Intl. Clarinet Assn. [10217]
Intl. Cmpt. Music Assn. [2559]
Intl. Cmpt. Music Assn. [2559]
Intl. Conf. of Symphony and Opera Musicians
  [10218]
Intl. Conf. of Symphony and Opera Musicians
  [10218]
Intl. Crosby Circle [23857]
Intl. Double Reed Soc. [10219]
Intl. Double Reed Soc. [10219]
Intl. Fan Club Org. [23858]
Intl. Fan Club Org. [23858]
Intl. Guild of Musicians in Dance [23271]
Intl. Horn Soc. [10220]
Intl. Horn Soc. [10220]
Intl. Native Amer. Flute Assn. [10221]
Intl. Native Amer. Flute Assn. [10221]MusicIntl.
  Piano Guild
Intl. Polka Assn. [10222]
Intl. Polka Assn. [10222]
Intl. Soc. of Bassists [10223]
Intl. Soc. of Bassists [10223]
Intl. Soc. for Contemporary Music USA [10224]
Intl. Soc. for Contemporary Music USA [10224]
Intl. Soc. of Folk Harpers and Craftsmen [10225]
Intl. Soc. of Folk Harpers and Craftsmen [10225]
Intl. Soc. for Improvised Music [10226]
Intl. Soc. for Music Educ. - Australia [18842]
Intl. Songwriters Guild [2560]
Intl. Steel Guitar Convention [10227]
Intl. Steel Guitar Convention [10227]
Intl. Trumpet Guild [10228]
Intl. Trumpet Guild [10228]
Intl. Tuba-Euphonium Assn. [10229]
Intl. Tuba-Euphonium Assn. [10229]
Jana Jae Fan Club [23859]
Jazzmobile [10230]
Jeannie Seely's Circle of Friends [23860]
Jeff Carson Intl. Fan Club [23861]
Jerry Jeff Walker Fan Club [23862]
Jew's Harp Guild [10231]
John Berry's Fan Club [23863]
John Gary Intl. Fan Club [23864]
John Gary Intl. Fan Club [23864]
Johnnie Ray Intl. Fan Club [23865]
Just Plain Folks Music Org. [2561]
Kappa Kappa Psi [23600]
Kate Smith Commemorative Soc. [23866]
Kate Smith Commemorative Soc. [23866]
Kate's Voice [8764]
Kelly Lang Fan Club [23867]
Kenny Chesney Fan Club [23868]
KISS Rocks Fan Club [23869]
KISS Rocks Fan Club [23869]
Kitty Wells-Johnny Wright-Bobby Wright Intl. Fan
  Club [23870]
Kurt Weill Found. for Music [10232]
Kurt Weill Found. for Music [10232]

A star before a book entry number signifies that the name is not listed separately, but is mentioned within the entry.

Latin Amer. Art Song Alliance [10233]
League of Amer. Orchestras [10234]
Lesbian and Gay Band Assn. [10235]
Leschetizky Assn. [10236]
Lesley Gore Intl. Fan Club [23871]
Liederkranz Found. [10237]
Linda Davis Fan Club [23872]
Lorrie Morgan Intl. Fan Club [23873]
Lou Christie Intl. Fan Club [23874]
Lucio Fan Club [23875]
Lute Soc. of Am. [10238]
Lyre Assn. of North Am. [21957]
Martina McBride Fan Club [23876]
MBIRA [10239]
Mel Tillis Fan Club [23877]
Mel Tillis Fan Club [23877]
Melodious Accord [10240]
MENC: The Natl. Assn. for Music Educ. [8654]
Metropolitan Opera Assn. [10241]
Metropolitan Opera Guild [10242]
Michael Jackson Fan Club [23878]
Mixed Harmony Barbershop Quartet Assn.
    [10243]
Moravian Music Found. [10244]
Mr. Holland's Opus Found. [8655]
Mu Beta Psi [23601]
Mu Phi Epsilon Intl. [23602]
Music Critics Assn. of North Am. [10245]
Music Distributors Assn. [2562]
Music EdVentures [8656]
Music and Entertainment Indus. Educators Assn.
    [8657]
Music Performance Fund [10246]
Music Publishers' Assn. of the U.S. [2563]
Music Teachers Natl. Assn. [8658]
Music Therapy for Healing [16467]
Music for Troops [12555]
Musical Box Soc. Intl. [21958]
Musical Box Soc. Intl. [21958]
Musical Instrument Technicians Assn., Intl. [2564]
Musical Instrument Technicians Assn., Intl. [2564]
Musical Missions of Peace [10352]
Musicians Found. [10247]
Musicians for Harmony [10353]
NAMM Found. [10248]
NAMM - The Intl. Music Products Assn. [2565]
Nashville Songwriters Assn. Intl. [10249]
Nashville Songwriters Assn. Intl. [10249]
Natl. Acad. of Recording Arts and Sciences
    [10505]
Natl. Alliance for Musical Theatre [10250]
Natl. Assn. for Civil War Brass Music [10251]
Natl. Assn. of Coll. Wind and Percussion Instruc-
    tors [8659]
Natl. Assn. of Composers U.S.A. [10252]
Natl. Assn. of Negro Musicians [10253]
Natl. Assn. of Pastoral Musicians [8660]
Natl. Assn. of Professional Band Instrument
    Repair Technicians [2566]
Natl. Assn. of Rhythm and Blues Dee Jay's
    [10254]
Natl. Assn. of School Music Dealers [2567]
Natl. Assn. of Schools of Music [8661]
Natl. Assn. for the Stud. and Performance of
    African-American Music [8662]
Natl. Assn. of Teachers of Singing [8663]
Natl. Band Assn. [10255]
Natl. Catholic Band Assn. [10256]
Natl. Christian Choir [20127]
Natl. Fed. of Music Clubs [10257]
Natl. Flute Assn. [10258]
Natl. Forum of Greek Orthodox Church Musicians
    [20128]
Natl. Guild of Piano Teachers [8664]
Natl. High School Band Directors Hall of Fame
    [8665]
Natl. Music Coun. [10259]
Natl. Music Publishers' Assn. [2568]
Natl. Oldtime Fiddlers' Assn. [10260]
Natl. Opera Assn. [10261]
Natl. Orchestral Assn. [10262]
Natl. Piano Found. [8666]
Natl. Puro Conjunto Music Assn. [10263]
Natl. Puro Conjunto Music Assn. [10263]
Natl. Symphony Orchestra Assn. [10264]

Natl. Traditional Country Music Assn. [10265]
New Horizons Intl. Music Assn. [10266]
New Violin Family Assn. [10267]
New Wilderness Found. [10268]
New Zealand Accordion Assn. [18868]
NFHS Music Assn. [8667]
North Am. Christian Creative Assn. [19595]
North Amer. Brass Band Assn. [10269]
North Amer. British Music Stud. Assn. [10270]
North Amer. British Music Stud. Assn. [10270]
North Amer. Dhrupad Assn. [10271]
North Amer. Dhrupad Assn. [10271]
North Amer. Guild of Change Ringers [10272]
North Amer. Saxophone Alliance [10273]
Oak Ridge Boys Intl. Fan Club [23879]
Official Fan Club of the Grand Ole Opry [23880]
OPERA Am. [10274]
Opera Found. [10275]
Oper. Happy Note [12556]
Organ CH LLC [10276]
Organ Historical Soc. [10277]
Org. of Amer. Kodaly Educators [8668]
Other Minds [10278]
Pam Tillis Fan Club [23881]
Patti Page Appreciation Soc. [23882]
Patti Page Appreciation Soc. [23882]
Pedal Steel Guitar Assn. [10279]
Percussion Marketing Coun. [2569]
Percussion Marketing Coun. [2569]
Percussive Arts Soc. [10280]
Phi Beta Mu [23603]
Phi Beta Mu [23603]
Phi Mu Alpha Sinfonia Fraternity and Found. Natl.
    HQ [23604]
Piano Mfrs. Assn. Intl. [2570]
Piano Mfrs. Assn. Intl. [2570]
Piano Technicians Guild [2571]
Polish Singers Alliance of Am. [10281]
Polish Singers Alliance of Am. [10281]
Positive Music Assn. [10282]
Presbyterian Assn. of Musicians [20129]
Professional Women Singers Assn. [10283]
Purple Flower Gang [23883]
Ray Price Intl. Fan Club [23884]
Reed Organ Soc. [10284]
REG - The Intl. Roger Waters Fan Club [23885]
Retail Print Music Dealers Assn. [2572]
Reverb [4130]
Rick's Loyal Supporters [23886]
Ricky Skaggs Intl. Fan Club [23887]
Rock Against Cancer [13975]
rock CAN roll [12289]
Ronny and the Daytonas Fan Club [23888]
Roy Rogers - Dale Evans Collectors Assn.
    [23889]
Royal Scottish Acad. of Music and Drama [1772]
Sammy Kershaw Fan Club [23890]
Sci. Songwriters' Assn. [10285]
Sci. Songwriters' Assn. [10285]
Scott Joplin Intl. Ragtime Found. [10286]
Scott Joplin Intl. Ragtime Found. [10286]
Scottish Harp Soc. of Am. [10287]
Scriabin Soc. of Am. [10288]
Shon Branham Fan Club [23891]
Sigma Alpha Iota Intl. Music Fraternity [23605]
Soc. for Amer. Music [10289]
Soc. for Asian Music [10290]
Soc. for Asian Music [10290]
Soc. for Eighteenth-Century Music [10291]
Soc. for Electro-Acoustic Music in the U.S.
    [10292]
Soc. for Ethnomusicology [10293]
Soc. for Music Perception and Cognition [10294]
Soc. for Music Teacher Educ. [8669]
Soc. for Music Theory [10295]
Soc. for Music Theory [10295]
Soc. of Pi Kappa Lambda [23606]
Soc. for the Preservation and Advancement of the
    Harmonica [10296]
Soc. for the Preservation and Advancement of the
    Harmonica [10296]
Soc. for the Preservation and Encouragement of
    Barber Shop Quartet Singing in Am. [10297]
Soc. for Seventeenth-Century Music [10298]
Soc. of Singers [12557]

SoundExchange [2573]
Southeastern Composers' League [10299]
Southeastern Historical Keyboard Soc. [21959]
Southwest Bluegrass Assn. [10300]
Sphinx Org. [10301]
Surfun: The Official Jan and Dean Fan Club
    [23892]
Suzuki Assn. of the Americas [8670]
Suzy Bogguss Fan Club [23893]
Sweet Adelines Intl. [10302]
Sweet Adelines Intl. [10302]
Tamburitza Assn. of Am. [10303]
Tamizdat [9518]
Tau Beta Sigma [23607]
Tech. Inst. for Music Educators [8671]MusicTex
    Ritter Fan Club
T.G. Sheppard Intl. Fan Club [23894]
Theatre Organ Soc. Intl. [10304]
Three Dog Night Fan Club [23895]
Tom Jones "Tom Terrific" Fan Club [23896]
TRI-M Music Honor Soc. [10305]
Trisha Yearwood Fan Club [23897]
The Unconservatory [10306]
Unitarian Universalist Musicians' Network [20130]
United Catholic Music and Video Assn. [19506]
United in Gp. Harmony Assn. [10307]
Viola d'Amore Soc. of Am. [10308]
Viola da Gamba Soc. of Am. [10309]
Violin Soc. of Am. [10310]
Wagner Soc. of New York [10311]
Western Music Assn. [10312]
Wolfpack Fan Club [23898]
Women Band Directors Intl. [8672]
Women Band Directors Intl. [8672]
World Folk Music Assn. [10313]
World Folk Music Assn. [10313]
World Piano Competition [10314]
Young Concert Artists [10315]
Music Assn. of Korea [IO], Seoul, Republic of Korea
Music BC [IO], Vancouver, BC, Canada
Music Centre Slovakia [IO], Bratislava, Slovakia
Music Critics Assn. [★10245]
Music Critics Assn. of North Am. [10245], 722 Du-
    laney Valley Rd., No. 259, Baltimore, MD 21204,
    (410)435-3881
Music Distributors Assn. [2562], 14070 Proton Rd.,
    Ste. 100, LB 9, Dallas, TX 75244-3601, (972)233-
    9107
Music Educ. Coun. [IO], Altrincham, United Kingdom
Music Educators Natl. Conf. [★8654]
Music EdVentures [8656], Tony Williamson, 20 NE
    68th Ave., Portland, OR 97213, (503)254-3286
Music and Entertainment Indus. Educators Assn.
    [8657], Ms. Angela Breedon, Admin. Asst., 1900
    Belmont Blvd., Nashville, TN 37212-3758,
    (615)460-6946
Music Indus. Assn. of Canada [IO], Toronto, ON,
    Canada
Music Indus. Assn. - England [IO], Surrey, United
    Kingdom
Music Industry Conf. - Defunct.
Music Info. Centre Norway [IO], Oslo, Norway
Music Lib. Assn. [9997], 8551 Res. Way, Ste. 180,
    Middleton, WI 53562-3567, (608)836-5825
Music Managers Forum [IO], London, United
    Kingdom
Music Masters' and Mistresses' Assn. [IO],
    Cambridge, United Kingdom
Music Network [IO], Dublin, Ireland
Music Operators of Am. [★1188]
Music Performance Fund [10246], 1040 Ave. of the
    Americas, 18th Fl., New York, NY 10018,
    (212)391-3950
Music Performance Trust Funds [★10246]
Music Producers Guild [IO], London, United
    Kingdom
Music Publishers Assn. [IO], London, United
    Kingdom
Music Publishers' Assn. of the U.S. [2563], 243 5th
    Ave., Ste. 236, New York, NY 10016, (212)327-
    4044
Music Publishers Protective Assn. [★2568]
Music Supervisors Natl. Conf. [★8654]
Music Teachers Natl. Assn. [8658], 441 Vine St.,
    Ste. 3100, Cincinnati, OH 45202-3004, (513)421-
    1420

Reference to "IO" in place of a book number signifies that the association may be found in the 50th edition of International Organizations.

Music Therapy Assn. of British Columbia **[IO]**, North Vancouver, BC, Canada
Music Therapy for Healing **[16467]**, 6688 Nolensville Rd., Ste. 111, No. 165, Brentwood, TN 37027, (615)216-0589
Music for Troops **[12555]**, PO Box 295, Lyon Station, PA 19536
Music Video Production Assn. **[3050]**, Beth Sadler, Sony Pictures Studios, 10202 W Washington Blvd., Cohn Bldg., Culver City, CA 90232, (310)244-6964
Music Women Intl. - Defunct.
Musica Nostra et Vostra, Natl. Corp. of America - Defunct.
Musical Box Hobbyists **[★21958]**
Musical Box Hobbyists **[★21958]**
Musical Box Soc. of Great Britain **[IO]**, Welwyn, United Kingdom
Musical Box Soc. Intl. **[21958]**, PO Box 10196, Springfield, MO 65808-0196
Musical Box Soc. Intl. **[21958]**, PO Box 10196, Springfield, MO 65808-0196
Musical Dog Sport Assn. **[22546]**, PO Box 143, Bozeman, MT 59771-0143
Musical Heritage Soc. **[10504]**, 1710 Hwy. 35, Oakhurst, NJ 07755, (732)531-7003
Musical Instrument Technicians Assn., Intl. **[2564]**, 376 Old Woodbury Rd., Southbury, CT 06488
Musical Instrument Technicians Assn., Intl. **[2564]**, 376 Old Woodbury Rd., Southbury, CT 06488
Musical Missions of Peace **[10352]**, 2700 Winding Trail Dr., Boulder, CO 80304, (303)898-6125
Musicians
　African Amer. Art Song Alliance **[10134]**
　Art Greenhaw Official Intl. Fan Club **[23814]**
　Chris Young Fan Club **[23825]**
　Classical Music Lovers' Exchange **[10177]**
　Diverse Emerging Music Org. **[10188]**
　The Grascals Fan Club **[23851]**
　Intl. Crosby Circle **[23857]**
　Intl. Guild of Musicians in Dance **[23271]**
　Jeannie Seely's Circle of Friends **[23860]**
　Jew's Harp Guild **[10231]**
　Johnnie Ray Intl. Fan Club **[23865]**
　Michael Jackson Fan Club **[23878]**
　Mu Beta Psi **[23601]**
　Music Therapy for Healing **[16467]**
　Musical Missions of Peace **[10352]**
　Musicians for Harmony **[10353]**
　Natl. Puro Conjunto Music Assn. **[10263]**
　North Am. Christian Creative Assn. **[19595]**
　Reverb **[4130]**
　Sigma Alpha Iota Intl. Music Fraternity **[23605]**
　Tamizdat **[9518]**
Musicians' Assistance Prog. - Address unknown since 2011.
Musicians Found. **[10247]**, 875 6th Ave., Ste. 2303, New York, NY 10001, (212)239-9137
Musicians for Harmony **[10353]**, 345 E 93rd St., Ste. 12B, New York, NY 10128, (212)996-8010
Musicians Natl. Hot Line Assn. - Defunct.
Musicians Union **[IO]**, London, United Kingdom
Musicians Without Borders **[IO]**, Alkmaar, Netherlands
Musiciens Amateurs du Canada **[★IO]**
Musicological Soc. of Australia **[IO]**, Canberra, Australia
Musicological Soc. of Japan **[IO]**, Tokyo, Japan
Musikkinformasjonssenteret **[★IO]**
Muskelsvindfonden **[IO]**, Arhus, Denmark
Muskies Inc. **[3826]**, 1509 Stahl Rd., Sheboygan, WI 53081-8894, (262)641-8771
Muskoka and District Chefs Assn. **[IO]**, Orillia, ON, Canada
Muslim
　Abrahamic Alliance Intl. **[19824]**
　Amer. Muslim Alliance **[18142]**
　Amer. Muslim Women Physicians Assn. **[16252]**
　Amer. Muslims Intent on Learning and Activism **[10316]**
　Assn. for Religion and Intellectual Life **[19669]**
　Collections and Stories of Amer. Muslims **[10317]**
　Free Muslims Coalition **[18143]**
　Free Muslims Coalition **[18143]**
　Human Assistance and Development Intl. **[20131]**
　Human Assistance and Development Intl. **[20131]**

　Imam Mahdi Assn. of Marjaeya **[20132]**
　Iranian Muslim Assn. of North Am. **[20133]**
　Iranian Muslim Assn. of North Am. **[20133]**
　Islamic Circle of North Am. **[20134]**
　Islamic Writers Alliance **[10318]**
　Muslim Alliance in North America **[19147]**
　Muslim Amer. Soc. **[20135]**
　Muslim Public Affairs Coun. **[18144]**
　Muslim Women's Coalition **[20136]**
　Reach Across **[20084]**
　Soliya **[18833]**
　Universal Muslim Assn. of Am. **[20137]**
Muslim Alliance in North America **[19147]**, PO Box 910375, Lexington, KY 40591, (859)296-0206
Muslim Amer. Soc. **[20135]**, 1325 G St. NW, Ste. 500, Washington, DC 20005, (202)552-7414
Muslim Assn. of Britain **[IO]**, Wembley, United Kingdom
Muslim Public Affairs Coun. **[18144]**, 3010 Wilshire Blvd., No. 217, Los Angeles, CA 90010-1103, (202)547-7701
Muslim Students Assn. of the U.S. and Canada **[8921]**, PO Box 13930, Fairlawn, OH 44334
Muslim Students Assn. of the U.S. and Canada **[8921]**, PO Box 13930, Fairlawn, OH 44334
Muslim Ummah of North Am. **[9893]**, PO Box 80411, Brooklyn, NY 11208, (718)277-7900
Muslim Women's Coalition **[20136]**, 1283 Hwy. 27, Somerset, NJ 08873, (732)545-8833
Muslim Women's Natl. Network of Australia **[IO]**, Granville, Australia
Muslim World League **[IO]**, Makkah, Saudi Arabia
Muslim Writers Guild - Defunct.
Mustang Club of Am. **[21119]**, 4051 Barrancas Ave., PMB 102, Pensacola, FL 32507, (850)438-0626
Mustang II Network **[21120]**, 115 McDonald Dr., Houghton Lake, MI 48629, (313)653-1516
The Mustard Seed **[★20071]**
Mustard Seed Found. **[20071]**, 7115 Leesburg Pike, Ste. 304, Falls Church, VA 22043, (703)524-5620
Muszaki Koltsegtervez Klub **[★IO]**
MUTA **[IO]**, London, United Kingdom
Mutagen Soc; Environmental **[6298]**
Mutual Advancement and Reconciliation in Soc. **[IO]**, Sheikhupura, Pakistan
Mutual Advt. Agency Network **[★96]**
Mutual Advt. Agency Network **[★96]**
Mutual Aid
　Artists' Fellowship **[19148]**
　Fed. Employee Educ. and Assistance Fund **[19149]**
　Riot Relief Fund **[19150]**
Mutual Aircraft Conf. **[★1926]**
Mutual Benefit and Aid Soc. **[★19065]**
Mutual Benefit Dept. of the Order of Railroad Telegraphers **[★19286]**
Mutual Fund Educ. Alliance **[3201]**, 100 NW Englewood Rd., Ste. 130, Kansas City, MO 64118, (816)454-9422
Mutual Israelite Assn. - Argentina **[IO]**, Buenos Aires, Argentina
Mutual Loss Res. Bur. **[★2032]**
Mutual Marine Conf. **[★1926]**
Mutual UFO Network **[7255]**, 2619 11th St. Rd., Greeley, CO 80634, (970)352-5319
Muzzaki es Termeszettudomanyi Egyesuletek Szovetsege **[★IO]**
Muzzle Loaders Assn. of Great Britain **[IO]**, Warwick, United Kingdom
My Good Deed **[13310]**, 19000 MacArthur Blvd., Irvine, CA 92612, (949)233-0050
My Own Bus., Inc. **[7797]**, 13181 Crossroads Pkwy. N, Ste. 190, City of Industry, CA 91746, (562)463-1800
My Travel Bug **[9018]**, 60 Elm St., Westerly, RI 02891
My Travel Bug **[9018]**, 60 Elm St., Westerly, RI 02891
Myanmar Assn. of Japan Alumni **[IO]**, Yangon, Myanmar
Myanmar Badminton Fed. **[IO]**, Yangon, Myanmar
Myanmar Bus. Coalition on AIDS **[IO]**, Yangon, Myanmar
Myanmar Cmpt. Professionals Assn. **[IO]**, Yangon, Myanmar

Myanmar Customs Brokers Assn. **[IO]**, Yangon, Myanmar
Myanmar Egress **[IO]**, Yangon, Myanmar
Myanmar Engg. Soc. **[IO]**, Yangon, Myanmar
Myanmar Forest Products and Timber Merchants Assn. **[IO]**, Yangon, Myanmar
Myanmar Geosciences Soc. **[IO]**, Yangon, Myanmar
Myanmar Hotelier Assn. **[IO]**, Yangon, Myanmar
Myanmar Intl. Freight Forwarders' Assn. **[IO]**, Yangon, Myanmar
Myanmar Maternal and Child Welfare Assn. **[IO]**, Yangon, Myanmar
Myanmar Medical Assn. **[IO]**, Yangon, Myanmar
Myanmar Overseas Seafarers Assn. **[IO]**, Yangon, Myanmar
Myanmar Pharmaceutical and Medical Equip. Entrepreneurs' Assn. **[IO]**, Yangon, Myanmar
Myanmar Physically Handicapped Assn. **[IO]**, Yangon, Myanmar
Myanmar Red Cross Soc. **[IO]**, Yangon, Myanmar
Myanmar Seamen Employment Assn. **[IO]**, Yangon, Myanmar
Myanmar Taekwondo Fed. **[IO]**, Yangon, Myanmar
Myanmar Track and Field Fed. **[IO]**, Yangon, Myanmar
Myanmar Weightlifting Fed. **[IO]**, Yangon, Myanmar
Myanmar Women's Affairs Fed. **[IO]**, Yangon, Myanmar
Myanmar Yachting Fed. **[IO]**, Yangon, Myanmar
Myasthenia Gravis Assn. **[IO]**, Derby, United Kingdom
Myasthenia Gravis Found. **[★15612]**
Myasthenia Gravis Found. of Am. **[15612]**, 355 Lexington Ave., 15th Fl., New York, NY 10017, (212)297-2156
MYCCI **[IO]**, Huddersfield, United Kingdom
Mycenaean Commn. **[IO]**, Vienna, Austria
Mycological Sect., Botanical Soc. of Am. **[★7130]**
Mycological Sect., Botanical Soc. of Am. **[★7130]**
Mycological Soc. of Am. **[7130]**, PO Box 7065, Lawrence, KS 66044-7065, (785)843-1235
Mycological Soc. of Am. **[7130]**, PO Box 7065, Lawrence, KS 66044-7065, (785)843-1235
Mycological Soc. of Japan **[IO]**, Tsukuba, Japan
Mycological Soc. of New Caledonia **[IO]**, Noumea, New Caledonia
Mycology
　Intl. Mycological Assn. **[7129]**
　Intl. Mycological Assn. **[7129]**
　Medical Mycological Soc. of the Americas **[15525]**
　Mycological Soc. of Am. **[7130]**
　Mycological Soc. of Am. **[7130]**MycologyNetherlands Mycological Soc.
　North Amer. Mycological Assn. **[7131]**
　North Amer. Truffling Soc. **[7132]**
Myelitis Assn; Transverse **[15637]**
Myelitis Assn; Transverse **[15637]**
Myeloma Res. Found; Multiple **[13945]**
Mykenische Kommission **[★IO]**
Myopia Intl. Res. Found. - Defunct.
The Myositis Assn. **[15613]**, 1737 King St., Ste. 600, Alexandria, VA 22314, (703)299-4850
Myositis Assn. of Am. **[★15613]**
Myotubular Myopathy Rsrc. Gp. **[16775]**, 2602 Quaker Dr., Texas City, TX 77590, (409)945-8569
Mysore Resettlement and Development Agency **[IO]**, Bangalore, India
Mystery Readers Intl. **[23805]**, PO Box 8116, Berkeley, CA 94707-8116, (510)845-3600
Mystery Shopping Providers Assn. **[2416]**, 4230 LBJ Freeway, Ste. 414, Dallas, TX 75244
Mystery Shopping Providers Assn. - Europe **[IO]**, The Hague, Netherlands
Mystery Writers of Am. **[10727]**, 1140 Broadway, Ste. 1507, New York, NY 10001, (212)888-8171
Mystic Seaport **[10060]**, PO Box 6000, Mystic, CT 06355-0990, (860)572-0711
Mystic Seaport Museum **[★10060]**
Mystic Valley Railway Soc. **[10492]**, PO Box 365486, Hyde Park, MA 02136-0009, (617)361-4445
Mysticism
　Astara **[20138]**
　Earthspirit Community **[20139]**
　Found. for Shamanic Stud. **[20140]**

A star before a book entry number signifies that the name is not listed separately, but is mentioned within the entry.

Peyote Way Church of God [20141]
Mythology
Intl. Assn. for Comparative Mythology [7133]
Mythopoeic Linguistic Fellowship [★10025]
Mythopoeic Linguistic Fellowship [★10025]
Mythopoeic Soc. [10045], PO Box 6707, Altadena, CA 91003
Mythopoeic Soc. [10045], PO Box 6707, Altadena, CA 91003
Myvesta - Defunct.

N

NAACCR [★13960]
NAACOG Certification Corp. [★15776]
NAACP [17301], 4805 Mt. Hope Dr., Baltimore, MD 21215, (410)580-5777
NAACP [★17301]
NAACP | Legal Defense and Educational Fund [17302], 99 Hudson St., Ste. 1600, New York, NY 10013, (212)965-2200
NAACP Natl. Housing Corp. [★17301]
NAADAC: The Assn. for Addiction Professionals [16744], 1001 N Fairfax St., Ste. 201, Alexandria, VA 22314, (703)741-7686
NA'AMAT Canada [IO], Montreal, QC, Canada
NA'AMAT Pioneras [IO], Buenos Aires, Argentina
Na'amat U.S.A. [19884], 505 8th Ave., Ste. 2302, New York, NY 10118, (212)563-5222
NABAC, The Assn. for Bank Audit, Control and Oper. [★403]
NAC - Environmental Info. Assn. [★558]
NACCA Bar Assn. [★6041]
NACE Intl. [★6809]
NACE Intl. [★6809]
NACE Intl. - Brazil Sect. [IO], Rio de Janeiro, Brazil
NACE Intl. - Chile Sect. [IO], Santiago, Chile
NACE Intl. - Colombia Sect. [IO], Barranquilla, Colombia
NACE Intl. - India Sect. [IO], Mumbai, India
NACE Intl. - Israel Sect. [IO], Haifa, Israel
NACE Intl. - Italian Sect. [IO], Milan, Italy
NACE Intl. - Kuwait Sect. [IO], Safat, Kuwait
NACE Intl. - Mainland China Sect. [IO], Beijing, People's Republic of China
NACE Intl. - Mexico Sect. [IO], Mexico City, Mexico
NACE Intl. - Montreal Sect. [IO], Montreal, QC, Canada
NACE Intl. - Oman Sect. [IO], Muscat, Oman
NACE Intl. - Pakistan Sect. [IO], Lahore, Pakistan
NACE Intl. - Peru Sect. [IO], Lima, Peru
NACE Intl. - Qatar Sect. [IO], Doha, Qatar
NACE Intl. - Saskatchewan Sect. [IO], Saskatoon, SK, Canada
NACE Intl. - Saudi Arabia Sect. [IO], Dhahran, Saudi Arabia
NACE Intl. - Singapore Sect. [IO], Singapore, Singapore
NACE Intl.: The Corrosion Soc. [6809], 1440 S Creek Dr., Houston, TX 77084-4906, (281)228-6200
NACE Intl.: The Corrosion Soc. [6809], 1440 S Creek Dr., Houston, TX 77084-4906, (281)228-6200
NACE Intl. - Toronto Sect. [IO], Toronto, ON, Canada
NACE Intl. - Trinidad and Tobago Sect. [IO], Gasparillo, Trinidad and Tobago
NACE Intl. - United Arab Emirates Sect. [IO], Dubai, United Arab Emirates
NACE Intl. - United Kingdom Sect. [IO], London, United Kingdom
NACE Intl. - West Asia/Africa Region [IO], Dhahran, Saudi Arabia
NACEL Open Door [8370], 380 Jackson St., Ste. 200, St. Paul, MN 55101, (651)686-0080
NACHA: The Electronic Payments Assn. [423], 13450 Sunrise Valley Dr., Ste. 100, Herndon, VA 20171, (703)561-1100
Nacionalno Turisticne Zdruzenje [★IO]
Naciones Unidas sobre el Cambio Climatico [★IO]
NACM North Central [★1300]
NACORE Intl. [★3006]
NACORE Intl. [★3006]
Nacro [IO], London, United Kingdom

NADD - An Assn. for Persons with Developmental Disabilities and Mental Hea. Needs [12488], 132 Fair St., Kingston, NY 12401-4802, (845)331-4336
NAE World Relief Commn. [★19727]
NAE World Relief Commn. [★19727]
NAEM [4282], 1612 K St. NW, Ste. 1002, Washington, DC 20006-2843, (202)986-6616
NAEM - Natl. Assn. for Environmental Mgt. [★4282]
Naeringslivets Hovedorganisasjon [★IO]
N.A.F. Intl. A.M.B.A. [IO], Copenhagen, Denmark
NAFA Fleet Mgt. Assn. [302], 125 Village Blvd., Ste. 200, Princeton Forrestal Village, Princeton, NJ 08540, (609)720-0882
NAFSA: Assn. of Intl. Educators [8204], 1307 New York Ave. NW, 8th Fl., Washington, DC 20005-4701, (202)737-3699
NAFSA: Association of Intl. Educators [8204], 1307 New York Ave. NW, 8th Fl., Washington, DC 20005-4701, (202)737-3699
Nager and Miller Syndromes; Found. for [14598]
NAGMR [2322], 16A Journey, Ste. 200, Aliso Viejo, CA 92656, (949)859-4040
NAGMR Consumer Products Broker [★2322]
NAGMR Consumer Products Sales Agencies [★2322]
Nail Patella Syndrome Worldwide [14614], 14980 Stream Valley Ct., Haymarket, VA 20169
Nail Patella Syndrome Worldwide [14614], 14980 Stream Valley Ct., Haymarket, VA 20169
NAIOP - The Assn. for Commercial Real Estate [★3022]
Naisjarjestojen Keskusliitto - Kvinnoorganisationernas Centralforbund Ry [★IO]
Naismith Memorial Basketball Hall of Fame [22296], 1000 W Columbus Ave., Springfield, MA 01105, (413)781-6500
Naissances Multiples [★IO]
Nakovammaisten Keskusliitto [★IO]
NALGAP: The Assn. of Lesbian, Gay, Bisexual, and Transgender Addiction Professionals and Their Allies [13266], 1001 N Fairfax St., Ste. 201, Alexandria, VA 22314
NALS [5749], 8159 E 41st St., Tulsa, OK 74145, (918)582-5188
NAMBA Intl. [★21908]
NAMBA Intl. [★21908]
NAMDRC [15295], 8618 Westwood Center Dr., Ste. 210, Vienna, VA 22182-2222, (703)752-4359
NAMDRC: Physician Advocacy for Excellence in the Delivery of Pulmonary and Critical Care [★15295]
Names Proj. [★13617]
Names Proj. Found. | AIDS Memorial Quilt [13617], 204 14th St. NW, Atlanta, GA 30318-5304, (404)688-5500
NAMI [★15464]
Namibia Agricultural Union [IO], Windhoek, Namibia
Namibia Assn. of Occupational Therapists [IO], Windhoek, Namibia
Namibia Baseball Assn. [IO], Windhoek, Namibia
Namibia Inst. of Architects [IO], Windhoek, Namibia
Namibia Nature Found. [IO], Windhoek, Namibia
Namibia Red Cross [IO], Windhoek, Namibia
Namibia Sailing Assn. [IO], Windhoek, Namibia
Namibia Sports Fed. of the Disabled [IO], Windhoek, Namibia
Namibia Tennis Assn. [IO], Windhoek, Namibia
Namibian Economic Policy Res. Unit [IO], Windhoek, Namibia
Namibian Env. and Wildlife Soc. [IO], Windhoek, Namibia
Namibian Natl. Olympic Comm. [IO], Windhoek, Namibia
Namibian Soc. of Physiotherapy [IO], Windhoek, Namibia
Namibian Squash Assn. [IO], Windhoek, Namibia
Namlo Intl. [12349], 4105 E Florida Ave., Ste. 200, Denver, CO 80222, (303)399-3649
NAMM Found. [10248], 5790 Armada Dr., Carlsbad, CA 92008, (760)438-8001
NAMM - The Intl. Music Products Assn. [2565], 5790 Armada Dr., Carlsbad, CA 92008, (760)438-8001
Nanaimo Brain Injury Soc. [IO], Nanaimo, BC, Canada
NANDA Intl. [15761], PO Box 157, Kaukauna, WI 54130-0157, (920)344-8670

NANDA Intl. [15761], PO Box 157, Kaukauna, WI 54130-0157, (920)344-8670
Nanmin Wo Tasukeru Kai [★IO]
NanoBusiness Alliance [7517], 8045 Lamon Ave., Skokie, IL 60077, (312)224-8319
Nanoose Conversion Campaign [IO], Vancouver, BC, Canada
Nanzan Inst. for Religion and Culture [IO], Nagoya, Japan
Napa Valley Grape Growers Assn. [★5169]
Napa Valley Grapegrowers [5169], 1795 3rd St., Napa, CA 94559-2803, (707)944-8311
Napa Valley Vintners Assn. [5170], PO Box 141, St. Helena, CA 94574, (707)963-3388
Napa Valley Wine Lib. Assn. [22199], PO Box 328, St. Helena, CA 94574-0328, (707)963-5145
NAPE, Inc. [★14332]
Naples Sabot One—Design Assn. [22359]
Napoleon
Napoleonic Age Philatelists [22058]
Napoleonic Age Philatelists [22058], 7513 Clayton Dr., Oklahoma City, OK 73132-5636, (405)721-0044
Napoleonic Assn. [IO], Wokingham, United Kingdom
Napoleonic Historical Soc. [10681], 6000A W Irving Park Rd., Chicago, IL 60634, (773)794-1804
Napoleonic Soc. [★10681]
Napoleonic Soc. of Am. [★10681]
Naprapathic Educ. and Res. Foundation [★15526]
Naprapathy
Amer. Naprapathic Assn. [15526]
NAQP Cmpt. Users Gp. [6514], PrintImage Intl., 2250 E Devon Ave., Ste. 245, Des Plaines, IL 60018, (847)298-8680
NARA: The Assn. of Property and Fixed Charge Receivers [IO], Oldham, United Kingdom
NARAL Pro-Choice Am. [18525], 1156 15th St. NW, Ste. 700, Washington, DC 20005, (202)973-3000
Narcolepsy Assn. United Kingdom [IO], Penicuik, United Kingdom
Narcolepsy Network [16667], 110 Ripple Ln., North Kingstown, RI 02852, (401)667-2523
Narcotic Educational Found. of Am. [13267], 28245 Ave. Crocker, Ste. 230, Santa Clarita, CA 91355-1201, (661)775-6960
Narcoticos Anonimos de Argentina [IO], Buenos Aires, Argentina
Narcoticos Anonimos Region Mexico [★IO]
Narcotics Anonymous [13268], World Ser. Off., PO Box 9999, Van Nuys, CA 91409, (818)773-9999
Narcotics Anonymous [13268], World Ser. Off., PO Box 9999, Van Nuys, CA 91409, (818)773-9999
Narcotics Anonymous Berlin [IO], Berlin, Germany
Narcotics Anonymous British Columbia Region [IO], Vancouver, BC, Canada
Narcotics Anonymous Gebeit Berlin [★IO]
Narcotics Anonymous Hamilton Area [IO], Hamilton, ON, Canada
Narcotics Anonymous Ireland [IO], Dublin, Ireland
Narcotics Anonymous Malta [IO], St. Julian's, Malta
Narcotics Anonymous Mexico Region [IO], Mexico City, Mexico
Narcotics Anonymous Omrade Sor Servicekomite [★IO]
Narcotics Anonymous Polish Region [IO], Torun, Poland
Narcotics Anonymous Southern Area Ser. Comm. [IO], Kristiansand, Norway
Narcotics Anonymous UK Region [IO], London, United Kingdom
NARGON: The Grocery Retailers' Asscociation [IO], Wellington, New Zealand
Narika [13468], PO Box 14014, Berkeley, CA 94712, (510)444-6068
Narodna Asociacia Realitnych Kancelarii Slovenska [★IO]
Narramore Christian Found. [19588], 250 W Colorado Blvd., Ste. 200, Arcadia, CA 91007, (626)821-8400
Narrow Fabrics Inst. [3447], 1801 County Rd. B W, Roseville, MN 55113-4061, (651)222-6920
Narrow Fabrics Inst. [3447], 1801 County Rd. B W, Roseville, MN 55113-4061, (651)222-6920
NARSAD: The Brain and Behavior Res. Fund [15463], 60 Cutter Mill Rd., Ste. 404, Great Neck, NY 11021, (516)829-0091

Reference to "IO" in place of a book number signifies that the association may be found in the 50th edition of International Organizations.

NARTE Inc. [★7542]

NARTS - The Assn. of Resale Professionals [3112], PO Box 80707, St. Clair Shores, MI 48080-5707, (586)294-6700

NASBA - The Assn. of Sys. Builders and Integrators [3373], 15280 NW Central Dr., Ste. 220, Portland, OR 97229, (503)828-1924

NASBITE Intl. [7798], Cleveland State Univ., Glbal Bus. Center, 2121 Euclid Ave., BU 327, Cleveland, OH 44115-2214, (216)802-3381

NASBITE Intl. [7798], Cleveland State Univ., Glbal Bus. Center, 2121 Euclid Ave., BU 327, Cleveland, OH 44115-2214, (216)802-3381

NASCA, Inc [★13108]

NASCA, Inc [★13108]

NASCA Intl. [13108], PO Box 7128, Buena Park, CA 90622-7128, (714)828-8174

NASCA Intl. [13108], PO Box 7128, Buena Park, CA 90622-7128, (714)828-8174

NASEN [IO], Tamworth, United Kingdom

Nash Car Club of Am. [21121], 1N274 Prairie Ave., Glen Ellyn, IL 60137

Nashville Songwriters Assn. [★10249]

Nashville Songwriters Assn. [★10249]

Nashville Songwriters Assn. Intl. [10249], 1710 Roy Acuff Pl., Nashville, TN 37203, (615)256-3354

Nashville Songwriters Assn. Intl. [10249], 1710 Roy Acuff Pl., Nashville, TN 37203, (615)256-3354

Nashwaak Watershed Assn. Inc. [IO], Fredericton, NB, Canada

Nasionale Wolkwekersvereeniging van Suid-Afrika [★IO]

NASIRE [★5544]

Nasjonalforeningen for Folkehelsen [★IO]

NaSPA [6515], 7044 S 13th St., Oak Creek, WI 53154, (414)908-4945

NaSPA, Inc. [★6515]

NASPA - Student Affairs Administrators in Higher Educ. [7666], 111 K St. NE, 10th Fl., Washington, DC 20002, (202)265-7500

NASSCO [3597], 11521 Cronridge Dr., Ste. J, Owings Mills, MD 21117, (410)486-3500

NASSTRAC [3255], 9382 Oak Ave., Waconia, MN 55387, (952)442-8850

Natal Sharks Bd. [IO], Durban, Republic of South Africa

Nathan Cummings Found. [13139], 475 10th Ave., 14th Fl., New York, NY 10018-9715, (212)787-7300

Nathan W. Ackerman Family Inst. [★11992]

Nathaniel Hawthorne Soc. [9403], Mr. Leland S. Person, Treas., Univ. of Cincinnati, Dept. of English, Cincinnati, OH 45221-0069, (513)556-5924

Nation Inst. [18474], Taya Kitman, Exec. Dir., 116 E 16th St., 8th Fl., New York, NY 10003, (212)822-0250

Nationaal Verbond der Kristelijke Arbeidersvrouwenbeweging [IO], Brussels, Belgium

Natl. 4-H Coun. [13536], 7100 Connecticut Ave., Chevy Chase, MD 20815, (301)961-2801

Natl. 4th Infantry Ivy Div. Assn. [20365], Don Kelby, Exec. Dir., PO Box 1914, St. Peters, MO 63376-0035, (314)606-1969

Natl. 42 Players Assn. [21750], David Roberts, Treas., 215 Sunday Cir., Fredericksburg, TX 78624, (830)990-0123

Natl. AAU Taekwondo Union of the U.S.A. [★22763]

Natl. Abandoned Infants Assistance Rsrc. Center [11485], Univ. of California, Berkeley, 1950 Addison St., Ste. 104, No. 7402, Berkeley, CA 94720-7402, (510)643-8390

Natl. Ability Center [22513], PO Box 682799, Park City, UT 84068, (435)649-3991

Natl. Aboriginal Achievement Found. [IO], Ohsweken, ON, Canada

Natl. Aboriginal Capital Corp. Assn. [IO], Ottawa, ON, Canada

Natl. Aboriginal Hea. Org. [IO], Ottawa, ON, Canada

Natl. Aboriginal Islander Skills Development Assn. [IO], Kariong, Australia

Natl. Aboriginal Lands Managers Assn. [IO], Curve Lake, ON, Canada

Natl. Abortion Coun. [★10768]

Natl. Abortion Fed. [10768], 1660 L St. NW, Ste. 450, Washington, DC 20036, (202)667-5881

Natl. Abortion and Reproductive Action League [★18525]

Natl. Abortion Rights Action League [★18525]

Natl. Abstinence Educ. Assn. [8862], 1701 Pennsylvania Ave. NW, Ste. 300, Washington, DC 20006, (202)248-5420

Natl. Academic Advising Assn. [7944], Kansas State Univ., 2323 Anderson Ave., Ste. 225, Manhattan, KS 66502-2912, (785)532-5717

Natl. Academic Advising Assn. [7944], Kansas State Univ., 2323 Anderson Ave., Ste. 225, Manhattan, KS 66502-2912, (785)532-5717

Natl. Academies of Emergency Dispatch [14484], 139 E South Temple, Ste. 200, Salt Lake City, UT 84111, (801)359-6916

Natl. Academies of Practice [14807], The Center for Community Solutions, 1501 Euclid Ave., Ste. 310, Cleveland, OH 44115-2108, (216)781-2944

Natl. Acad. of Amer. Scholars [8108], PO Box 750356, Las Vegas, NV 89136, (702)233-5049

Natl. Acad. of Arbitrators [5209], 1 N Main St., Ste. 412, Cortland, NY 13045; (607)756-8363

Natl. Acad. of Building Inspection Engineers [584], PO Box 860, Shelter Island, NY 11964, (631)749-8870

Natl. Acad. of Clinical Biochemistry [13829], Amer. Assn. for Clinical Chemistry, 1850 K St. NW, Ste. 625, Washington, DC 20006, (202)857-0717

Natl. Acad. of Counselors and Family Therapists [★11994]

Natl. Acad. of Educ. [8042], 500 5th St. NW, Washington, DC 20001, (202)334-2341

Natl. Acad. of Elder Law Attorneys [5761], 1577 Spring Hill Rd., Ste. 220, Vienna, VA 22182, (703)942-5711

Natl. Acad. of Emergency Medical Dispatch [★14484]

Natl. Acad. of Engg. [6810], 500 5th St. NW, Washington, DC 20001, (202)334-3200

Natl. Acad. of Exact, Physical and Natural Sciences [IO], Buenos Aires, Argentina

Natl. Acad. of Geography [IO], Buenos Aires, Argentina

Natl. Acad. of History [IO], Buenos Aires, Argentina

Natl. Acad. of Kinesiology [8717], PO Box 5076, Champaign, IL 61825-5076, (217)403-7545

Natl. Acad. of Music, Dance and Drama [IO], New Delhi, India

Natl. Acad. of Needlearts [21453], 1 Riverbanks Ct., Greer, SC 29651

Natl. Acad. of Needlearts [21453], 1 Riverbanks Ct., Greer, SC 29651

Natl. Acad. of Neuropsychology [16410], 7555 E Hampden Ave., Ste. 525, Denver, CO 80231, (303)691-3694

National Acad. for Nuclear Training [★7175]

Natl. Acad. of Opticianry [15983], 8401 Corporate Dr., Ste. 605, Landover, MD 20785, (800)229-4828

Natl. Acad. of Popular Music - Address unknown since 2010.

Natl. Acad. of Public Admin. [5907], 900 7th St. NW, Ste. 600, Washington, DC 20001, (202)347-3190

Natl. Acad. of Public Admin. [5907], 900 7th St. NW, Ste. 600, Washington, DC 20001, (202)347-3190

Natl. Acad. of Recording Arts and Sciences [10505], 3402 Pico Blvd., Santa Monica, CA 90405, (310)392-3777

Natl. Acad. of Sciences [7377], 500 5th St. NW, Washington, DC 20001, (202)334-2000

Natl. Acad. of Sciences of Armenia [IO], Yerevan, Armenia

Natl. Acad. of Sciences of Belarus [IO], Minsk, Belarus

Natl. Acad. of Sciences of Bolivia [IO], La Paz, Bolivia

Natl. Acad. of Sciences of the Republic of Korea [IO], Seoul, Republic of Korea

Natl. Acad. of Social Insurance [18650], 1776 Massachusetts Ave. NW, Ste. 400, Washington, DC 20036, (202)452-8097

Natl. Acad. of Songwriters [★5582]

Natl. Acad. of Songwriters - Defunct.

Natl. Acad. for State Hea. Policy [14808], 10 Free St., 2nd Fl., Portland, ME 04101, (207)874-6524

Natl. Acad. of Surgery [IO], Paris, France

Natl. Acad. for Teaching and Learning About Aging [10854], PO Box 310919, Denton, TX 76203-0919, (940)565-3450

Natl. Acad. of TV Arts and Sciences [499], 1697 Broadway, Ste. 1001, New York, NY 10019, (212)586-8424

Natl. Acad. of TV Journalists [2839], PO Box 31, Salisbury, MD 21803, (410)548-5343

Natl. Acad. of Visual Instruction [★8304]

National Acad. for Voluntarism [★12056]

Natl. Acad. of Western Art - Defunct.

Natl. Account Mgt. Assn. [★2425]

Natl. Account Mgt. Assn. [★2425]

Natl. Account Marketing Assn. [★2425]

Natl. Account Marketing Assn. [★2425]

Natl. Accountability Gp. [IO], Freetown, Sierra Leone

Natl. Accounting and Finance Coun. [40], 950 N Glebe Rd., Ste. 210, Arlington, VA 22203-4181, (703)838-1915

Natl. Accreditation Commn. for Schools and Colleges of Acupuncture and Oriental Medicine [★16009]

Natl. Accreditation Coun. for Agencies Serving the Blind and Visually Handicapped [★17101]

Natl. Accreditation Coun. for Agencies Serving the Blind and Visually Impaired [17101], Blind & Visually Impaired Services Accreditation, 7017 Pearl Rd., Middleburg Heights, OH 44130, (440)545-1601

Natl. Accreditation Coun. for Environmental Hea. Sci. and Protection [★14505]

Natl. Accrediting Agency for Clinical Lab. Sciences [15379], 5600 N River Rd., Ste. 720, Rosemont, IL 60018-5119, (773)714-8880

Natl. Accrediting Commn. of Cosmetology Arts and Sciences [7647], 4401 Ford Ave., Ste. 1300, Alexandria, VA 22302, (703)600-7600

Natl. Accrediting Commn. for Cosmetology Schools [★7647]

Natl. Acoustical Contractors Assn. [★905]

Natl. Acrylic Painters' Assn. [IO], Wallasey, United Kingdom

Natl. Action Coun. for Minorities in Engg. [8126], 440 Hamilton Ave., Ste. 302, White Plains, NY 10601-1813, (914)539-4010

Natl. Action Forum for Midlife and Older Women - Defunct.

Natl. Action Network [17303], 106 W 145th St., New York, NY 10039, (212)690-3070

Natl. Action Org. [13469], 336 Bon Air Ctr., Ste. 124, Greenbrae, CA 94904-3017, (415)464-1324

Natl. Active and Retired Fed. Employees Assn. [5433], 606 N Washington St., Alexandria, VA 22314, (703)838-7760

Natl. Acupuncture Detoxification Assn. [16745], PO Box 1655, Columbia, MO 65205-1655, (573)777-9955

Natl. Acupuncture Detoxification Assn. [16745], PO Box 1655, Columbia, MO 65205-1655, (573)777-9955

Natl. Addison's Disease Found. [★14493]

Natl. Adoption Center [10796], 1500 Walnut St., Ste. 701, Philadelphia, PA 19102, (215)735-9988

Natl. Adrenal Diseases Found. [14493], 505 Northern Blvd., Great Neck, NY 11021, (516)487-4992

Natl. Adult Baseball Assn. [22277], 3609 S Wadsworth Blvd., Ste. 135, Lakewood, CO 80235, (303)639-9955

Natl. Adult Day Services Assn. [10855], 1421 E Broad St., Ste. 425, Fuquay Varina, NC 27526, (877)745-1440

Natl. Adult Educ. Honor Soc. [7690], PO Box 76571, Highland Heights, KY 41076, (859)685-8559

Natl. Adult Educ. Professional Development Consortium [7691], 444 N Capitol St. NW, Ste. 422, Washington, DC 20001, (202)624-5250

Natl. Advt. Assn. - Mexico [IO], Mexico City, Mexico

Natl. Advt. Assn. - Venezuela [IO], Caracas, Venezuela

Natl. Advt. Div. Coun. of Better Bus. Bureaus [98], 70 W 36th St., 13th Fl., New York, NY 10018, (212)705-0120

Natl. Advt. Golf Assn. [22616], 207 Chestnut Oaks Cir., Simpsonville, SC 29681

A star before a book entry number signifies that the name is not listed separately, but is mentioned within the entry.

Natl. Advt. Network, Inc. [★2922]

Natl. Advt. Network, Inc. [★2922]

Natl. Advt. Newspaper Assn. [★2967]

Natl. Advt. Rev. Bd. [99], 70 W 36th St., 13th Fl., New York, NY 10018, (212)705-0114

Natl. Advisory Comm. on Scouting with Special Needs - Defunct.

Natl. Advisory Coun. on the Employment of Women [IO], Wellington, New Zealand

Natl. Advisory Coun. for Minorities in Engg. [★8126]

Natl. Advocacy Coalition on Extractives [IO], Freetown, Sierra Leone

Natl. Advocates for Pregnant Women [17854], 15 W 36th St., Ste. 901, New York, NY 10018, (212)255-9252

Natl. Aerial Applicators Assn. [★3837]

Natl. Aerial Applicators Assn. [★3837]

Natl. Aero Club of Ireland [IO], Dublin, Ireland

Natl. Aeronautic Assn. [144], 1 Reagan Natl. Airport, Hangar 7, Ste. 202, Washington, DC 20001-6015, (703)416-4888

Natl. Aeronautic Assn. of the U.S.A. [★144]

Natl. Aeronca Assn. [20908], 304 Adda St., Roberts, IL 60962-8049

Natl. Affordable Housing Mgt. Assn. [1783], 400 N Columbus St., Ste. 203, Alexandria, VA 22314, (703)683-8630

Natl. Affordable Housing Network [12183], PO Box 632, Butte, MT 59702, (406)782-8145

Natl. African Amer. Drug Policy Coalition [13269], Howard Univ., Center for Drug Abuse Res., 2900 Van Ness St. NW, Ste. 400, Washington, DC 20008, (202)806-8600

Natl. African-American Insurance Assn. [1997], 1718 M St. NW, Box No. 1110, Washington, DC 20036, (866)566-2242

Natl. African-American RV'ers Assn. [22145], 614 Chipney Ave., Charlotte, NC 28205, (704)333-3070

Natl. AfterSchool Assn. [11152], 8400 Westpark Dr., Ste. 200, McLean, VA 22102, (703)610-9026

Natl. Aggregates Assn. [★3366]

Natl. Agri-Marketing Assn. [100], 11020 King St., Ste. 205, Overland Park, KS 66210, (913)491-6500

Natl. AgriChemical Retailers Assn. [★3092]

Natl. Agricultural Advt. and Marketing Assn. [★100]

Natl. Agricultural Aviation Assn. [3837], 1005 E St. SE, Washington, DC 20003-2847, (202)546-5722

Natl. Agricultural Aviation Assn. [3837], 1005 E St. SE, Washington, DC 20003-2847, (202)546-5722

Natl. Agricultural Chemicals Assn. [★753]

Natl. Agricultural Communicators of Tomorrow [8445], Univ. of Arkansas, AGRI 205, Fayetteville, AR 72701, (479)575-5650

Natl. Agricultural Marketing Officials [★4720]

Natl. AIDS CH [★13601]

Natl. AIDS Comm. - Mexico [IO], Mexico City, Mexico

Natl. AIDS Control Org. [IO], New Delhi, India

Natl. AIDS Housing Coalition [12184], 727 15th St. NW, 6th Fl., Washington, DC 20005, (202)347-0333

Natl. AIDS Info. CH [★13601]

Natl. AIDS Res. Found. [★13603]

Natl. AIDS Treatment Advocacy Proj. [13618], 580 Broadway, Ste. 1010, New York, NY 10012, (212)219-0106

Natl. AIDS Treatment Advocacy Proj. [13618], 580 Broadway, Ste. 1010, New York, NY 10012, (212)219-0106

Natl. AIDS Trust [IO], London, United Kingdom

Natl. Air Carrier Assn. [145], 1000 Wilson Blvd., Ste. 1700, Arlington, VA 22209, (703)358-8060

Natl. Air Disaster Alliance [11123], 2020 Pennsylvania Ave., No. 315, Washington, DC 20006-1846, (888)444-6232

Natl. Air Duct Cleaners Assn. [2254], 1518 K St. NW, Ste. 503, Washington, DC 20005, (202)737-2926

Natl. Air Filtration Assn. [1715], PO Box 68639, Virginia Beach, VA 23471, (757)313-7400

Natl. Air-Racing Gp. [22212], 1932 Mahan, Richland, WA 99352-2121, (509)946-5690

Natl. Air Traffic Controllers Assn. [23154], 1325 Massachusetts Ave. NW, Washington, DC 20005, (202)628-5451

Natl. Air Transport Coordinating Comm. [★128]

Natl. Air Trans. Assn. [146], 4226 King St., Alexandria, VA 22302, (703)845-9000

Natl. Air Trans. Conferences [★146]

Natl. Aircraft Appraisers Assn. [147], 7 W Square Lake Rd., Bloomfield Hills, MI 48302, (248)758-2333

Natl. Aircraft Finance Assn. [2210], PO Box 1570, Edgewater, MD 21037, (410)571-1740

Natl. Aircraft Resale Assn. [148], PO Box 3860, Grapevine, TX 76099, (402)475-2611

Natl. Alarm Assn. of Am. [3221], PO Box 3409, Dayton, OH 45401, (800)283-6285

Natl. Albanian Amer. Coun. [18847], 1133 20th St. NW, Ste. 210, Washington, DC 20036, (202)466-6900

Natl. Alcohol Beverage Control Assn. [★5197]

Natl. Alcohol Beverage Control Assn. [5198], 4401 Ford Ave., Ste. 700, Alexandria, VA 22302-1473, (703)578-4200

Natl. Alcohol Tax Coalition [★17175]

Natl. Aldrich Family Assn. - Address unknown since 2011.

Natl. Alfalfa Alliance [★4372]

Natl. Alfalfa and Forage Alliance [4372], 4630 Churchill St., No. 1, St. Paul, MN 55126, (651)484-3888

Natl. Algae Assn. [6117], 4747 Res. Forest Dr., Ste. 180, The Woodlands, TX 77381, (936)321-1125

Natl. Allergy and Asthma Network [★16602]

Natl. Alliance [18783], PO Box 90, Hillsboro, WV 24946, (304)653-2091

Natl. Alliance for Accessible Golf [22514], 1733 King St., Alexandria, VA 22314, (703)299-4296

Natl. Alliance for Advanced Tech. Batteries [441], 122 S Michigan Ave., Ste. 1700, Chicago, IL 60603, (312)588-0477

Natl. Alliance of Advocates for Buprenorphine Treatment [16746], PO Box 333, Farmington, CT 06034

Natl. Alliance Against Christian Discrimination [19589], PO Box 62685, Colorado Springs, CO 80962

Natl. Alliance Against Racist and Political Repression [17304], 1325 S Wabash Ave., Ste. 105, Chicago, IL 60605, (312)939-2750

Natl. Alliance of Black Interpreters [3497], PO Box 77372, Washington, DC 20013-7372, (877)NAOBI-87

Natl. Alliance of Black School Educators [8950], 310 Pennsylvania Ave. SE, Washington, DC 20003, (202)608-6310

Natl. Alliance of Black School Superintendents [★8950]

Natl. Alliance for Breastfeeding Advocacy [13865], 9684 Oak Hill Dr., Ellicott City, MD 21042-6321

Natl. Alliance of Burmese Breeders [3863], PO Box 100038, Cudahy, WI 53110

Natl. Alliance of Cardiovascular Technologists [★13997]

Natl. Alliance for Caregiving [12014], 4720 Montgomery Ln., 2nd Fl., Bethesda, MD 20814

Natl. Alliance for Civic Educ. [7861], Inst. for Philosophy and Public Policy, Maryland School of Public Affairs, 3111 Van Munching, College Park, MD 20742

Natl. Alliance of Clean Energy Bus. Incubators [1172], 1617 Cole Blvd., Golden, CO 80401-3393, (303)275-4152

Natl. Alliance of Community Economic Development Associations [17582], 1020 16th St. NW, Ste. 305, Washington, DC 20036, (202)659-7701

Natl. Alliance of Concurrent Enrollment Partnerships [7883], Adam I. Lowe, Exec. Sec., 126 Mallette St., Chapel Hill, NC 27516, (919)593-5205

Natl. Alliance of Covenanting Congregations [IO], North Vancouver, BC, Canada

Natl. Alliance of Craftsmen Associations [11611], 816 Camaron St., Ste. 212, San Antonio, TX 78212, (210)271-9100

Natl. Alliance Daughters of Veterans [★20383]

Natl. Alliance for the Development of Archery [22222], PO Box 249, Newberry, FL 32669, (352)472-2388

Natl. Alliance for Direct Support Professionals [1793], PO Box 13447, Minneapolis, MN 55414, (612)624-7650

Natl. Alliance for Drug Endangered Children [13270], 9101 Harlan St., Ste. 245, Westminster, CO 80031, (303)317-5855

Natl. Alliance to End Homelessness [12160], 1518 K St. NW, Ste. 410, Washington, DC 20005, (202)638-1526

Natl. Alliance for Eye and Vision Res. [17102], 1801 Rockville Pike, Ste. 400, Rockville, MD 20852, (240)221-2905

Natl. Alliance for Fair Contracting [23167], 905 16th St. NW, 4th Fl., Washington, DC 20006, (866)523-6232

Natl. Alliance of Families for the Return of America's Missing Servicemen [20756], Janella A. Rose, 2528 Poly Dr., Billings, MT 59102-1442

Natl. Alliance for Family Court Justice [5624], 4309 Greenberry Ln., Annandale, VA 22003, (703)658-2308

Natl. Alliance for Family Court Justice [5624], 4309 Greenberry Ln., Annandale, VA 22003, (703)658-2308

Natl. Alliance for Family Life [★11994]

Natl. Alliance for Filipino Concerns [17200], 40-21 69th St., Woodside, NY 11377, (718)565-8862

Natl. Alliance for Food Safety and Security [1409], Dept. of Poultry Sci., PO Box 313, Fleetwood, NC 28626, (336)877-1059

Natl. Alliance of Forest Owners [4404], 122 C St. NW, Ste. 630, Washington, DC 20001, (202)747-0759

Natl. Alliance of Gang Investigators Associations [5367], PO Box 782, Elkhorn, NE 68022, (402)510-8581

Natl. Alliance of Gen. Agents [1998], Tri-State Gen. Insurance Agency, PO Box 4072, Salisbury, MD 21803, (800)556-7894

Natl. Alliance for Grieving Children [11486], The Center for Grieving Children, 555 Forest Ave., Portland, ME 04104, (207)775-5216

Natl. Alliance for Hea. Info. Tech. - Defunct.

Natl. Alliance of Highway Beautification Agencies [5948], PO Box 191, Columbia, SC 29202

Natl. Alliance for Hispanic Hea. [13194], 1501 16th St. NW, Washington, DC 20036, (202)387-5000

Natl. Alliance of HUD Tenants [17799], 42 Seaverns Ave., Boston, MA 02130, (617)267-9564

Natl. Alliance of Independent Crop Consultants [3721], 349 E Nolley Dr., Collierville, TN 38017, (901)861-0511

Natl. Alliance for Infusion Therapy - Address unknown since 2010.

Natl. Alliance for Insurance Educ. and Res. [1999], PO Box 27027, Austin, TX 78755-2027, (800)633-2165

Natl. Alliance of Market Developers [2417], 620 Sheridan Ave., Plainfield, NJ 07060, (908)561-4062

Natl. Alliance for Media Arts and Culture [9303], 145 9th St., Ste. 102, San Francisco, CA 94103, (415)431-1391

Natl. Alliance for Medicaid in Educ. [14859], Steven Wright, Treas., 1 Eagles Glen, Clifton Park, NY 12065, (518)486-4887

Natl. Alliance of Medicare Set-Aside Professionals [17772], 341 N Maitland Ave., Ste. 130, Maitland, FL 32751, (407)647-8839

Natl. Alliance for Medication Assisted Recovery [16747], 435 2nd Ave., New York, NY 10010, (212)595-6262

Natl. Alliance for Medication Assisted Recovery [16747], 435 2nd Ave., New York, NY 10010, (212)595-6262

Natl. Alliance on Mental Illness [15464], 3803 N Fairfax Dr., Ste. 100, Arlington, VA 22203-5860, (703)524-7600

Natl. Alliance for the Mentally Ill [★15464]

Natl. Alliance of Methadone Advocates [★16747]

Natl. Alliance of Methadone Advocates [★16747]

Natl. Alliance for Model State Drug Laws [5390], 215 Lincoln Ave., Ste. 201, Santa Fe, NM 87501, (703)836-6100

Natl. Alliance for Musical Theatre [10250], 520 8th Ave., Ste. 301, New York, NY 10018, (212)714-6668

Natl. Alliance to Nurture the Aged and the Youth [12221], 659 NE 125th St., North Miami, FL 33161-5503, (305)981-3232

Reference to "IO" in place of a book number signifies that the association may be found in the 50th edition of International Organizations.

Natl. Alliance for Oral Hea. - Defunct.

Natl. Alliance of Police, Security and Corrections Organizations - Address unknown since 2011.

Natl. Alliance of Postal Employees [★23279]

Natl. Alliance of Postal and Fed. Employees [23279], 1628 11th St. NW, Washington, DC 20001, (202)939-6325

Natl. Alliance of Preservation Commissions [9710], PO Box 1605, Athens, GA 30602, (706)542-4731

Natl. Alliance for the Primary Prevention of Sharps Injuries [16630], 126 Main St., PO Box 10, Milner, GA 30257, (770)358-7860

Natl. Alliance of Professional and Executive Women's Networks [★670]

Natl. Alliance of Professional and Executive Women's Networks [★670]

Natl. Alliance of Professional Psychology Providers [16411], PO Box 6263, Garden Grove, CA 92846-6263, (714)927-4439

Natl. Alliance for Public Charter Schools [8773], 1101 15th St. NW, Ste. 1010, Washington, DC 20005, (202)289-2700

Natl. Alliance for Public Trust - Address unknown since 2011.

National Alliance Res. Academy [★8324]

Natl. Alliance for Res. on Schizophrenia and Depression [★15463]

Natl. Alliance for Safe Schools [8818], PO Box 335, Slanesville, WV 25444-0335, (304)496-8100

Natl. Alliance to Save Native Languages [9942], 1455 Pennsylvania Ave. NW, Washington, DC 20004, (206)430-4638

Natl. Alliance for Secondary Educ. and Transition [8855], Univ. of Minnesota, Inst. on Community Integration, 150 Pillsbury Dr. SE, 6 Pattee Hall, Minneapolis, MN 55455, (612)624-1143

Natl. Alliance of Sentencing Advocates and Mitigation Specialists [5374], 1140 Connecticut Ave. NW, Ste. 900, Washington, DC 20036, (202)452-0620

Natl. Alliance for Spiritual Growth - Defunct.

Natl. Alliance of State Pharmacy Associations [16203], 2530 Professional Rd., Ste. 202, Richmond, VA 23235, (804)285-4431

Natl. Alliance of State Sci. and Mathematics Coalitions [8842], 2200 Wilson Blvd., Ste. 102-166, Arlington, VA 22201-3324, (703)516-5973

Natl. Alliance of State and Territorial AIDS Directors [10888], 444 N Capitol St. NW, Ste. 339, Washington, DC 20001, (202)434-8090

Natl. Alliance of Statewide Preservation Organizations [★9694]

Natl. Alliance for Thrombosis and Thrombophilia [14032], 120 White Plains Rd., Ste. 100, Tarrytown, NY 10591, (914)220-5040

Natl. Alliance of Vietnamese Amer. Ser. Agencies [19272], 7223 Lee Hwy., Ste. 301, Falls Church, VA 22046, (703)241-7190

Natl. Alliance for Worker and Employer Rights - Address unknown since 2010.

Natl. Alliance of Wound Care [14809], 5464 N Port Washington Rd., No. 134, Glendale, WI 53217, (877)922-6292

Natl. Alliance for Youth Sports [22461], 2050 Vista Pkwy., West Palm Beach, FL 33411, (561)684-1141

Natl. Aloe Sci. Coun. [★1686]

Natl. Aloe Sci. Coun. [★1686]

Natl. Alopecia Areata Found. [16633], 14 Mitchell Blvd., San Rafael, CA 94903, (415)472-3780

Natl. Alpha Lambda Delta [23563], PO Box 4403, Macon, GA 31208-4403, (800)9ALPHA-1

Natl. ALS Found. [★15569]

Natl. Alternative Educ. Assn. [7722], 3707 Watson Rd., Greenwood, AR 72936

Natl. Alumni Coun. of the UNCF [★18904]

Natl. Amateur Athletic Assn. of Trinidad and Tobago [IO], Port of Spain, Trinidad and Tobago

Natl. Amateur Baseball Fed. [22278], Charles M. Blackburn, Jr., Exec. Dir., PO Box 705, Bowie, MD 20715, (410)721-4727

Natl. Amateur Body Builders Assn. U.S.A. [22419], PO Box 531, Bronx, NY 10469, (718)882-6413

Natl. Amateur Dodgeball Assn. [22253], 1223 W Sharon Ln., Schaumburg, IL 60193, (847)985-2120

Natl. Amateur Press Assn. [22106], 6507 Westland Dr., Knoxville, TN 37919, (865)584-9222

Natl. Amateur Retriever Club [21604], Retriever Field Trial News Inc., 4379 S Howell Ave., Ste. 17, Milwaukee, WI 53207-5053, (414)481-2760

Natl. AMBUCS [11808], PO Box 5127, High Point, NC 27262, (800)838-1845

Natl. Amer. Arab Nurses Assn. [15762], PO Box 43, Dearborn Heights, MI 48127, (313)680-5049

Natl. Amer. Eskimo Dog Assn. [21605], Sally Bedow, Treas., 1978 School Rd., Port Lavaca, TX 77979, (361)655-8042

Natl. Amer. Glass Club [21836], PO Box 24, Elkland, PA 16920

Natl. Amer. Indian Court Judges Assn. [5625], 1535 W 15th St., Lawrence, KS 66045, (785)864-4753

Natl. Amer. Indian Housing Coun. [5518], 900 2nd St. NE, Ste. 107, Washington, DC 20002, (202)789-1754

Natl. Amer. Legion Press Assn. [20334], PO Box 334, West Seneca, NY 14224-0334, (716)675-0560

Natl. Amer. Pit Bull Terrier Assn. [21606], 12825 Settlers Trail Ct., Charlotte, NC 28278, (704)267-9407

Natl. Amer. Semi-Professional Baseball Assn. [22279], 2609 Vista View Dr., Evansville, IN 47711, (812)430-2725

National-American Wholesale Lumber Assn. [★1471]

Natl. Amputation Found. [11809], 40 Church St., Malverne, NY 11565, (516)887-3600

Natl. Amputee Golf Assn. [22515], 11 Walnut Hill Rd., Amherst, NH 03031-1713, (603)672-6444

Natl. Amputee Skiers Assn. [★22510]

Natl. Amusement Park Historical Assn. [20946], PO Box 871, Lombard, IL 60148-0871

Natl. Anemia Action Coun. [14971], 555 E Wells St., Ste. 1100, Milwaukee, WI 53202, (414)225-0138

Natl. Anger Mgt. Assn. [15465], 2753 Broadway, Ste. 395, New York, NY 10025, (646)485-5116

Natl. Angora Rabbit Breeders Club [4845], 909 Hwy. E, Silex, MO 63377, (573)384-5866

Natl. Animal Control Assn. [11005], PO Box 480851, Kansas City, MO 64148-0851, (913)768-1319

Natl. Animal Interest Alliance [11006], PO Box 66579, Portland, OR 97290, (503)761-8962

Natl. Animal Supplement Coun. [3806], PO Box 2568, Valley Center, CA 92082, (760)751-3360

Natl. Animal Welfare Trust [IO], Watford, United Kingdom

Natl. Ankylosing Spondylitis Soc. [IO], Richmond, United Kingdom

Natl. Anti-Hunger Coalition - Defunct.

Natl. Anti-Vivisection Soc. [11007], 53 W Jackson Blvd., Ste. 1552, Chicago, IL 60604, (312)427-6065

Natl. Anti-Vivisection Soc. [IO], London, United Kingdom

Natl. Antique and Art Dealers Assn. of Am. [257], 220 E 57th St., New York, NY 10022, (212)826-9707

Natl. Antique Doll Dealers Assn. [21695], PO Box 462, Natick, MA 01760-0005, (508)545-1424

Natl. Antique Doll Dealers Assn. [21695], PO Box 462, Natick, MA 01760-0005, (508)545-1424

Natl. Antique Oldsmobile Club [21122], 121 N Railroad St., Myerstown, PA 17067

Natl. Antique Tractor Pullers Assn. [22179], Curtis Rink, Co-Sec., 3124 N Maize Rd., Wichita, KS 67205, (316)622-8083

Natl. Anxiety Center [18436], 28 W 3rd St., Ste. 1321, South Orange, NJ 07079, (973)763-6392

Natl. Apartment Assn. [3019], 4300 Wilson Blvd., Ste. 400, Arlington, VA 22203, (703)518-6141

Natl. Apartment Owners Assn. [★3019]

Natl. Aphasia Assn. [13768], 350 Seventh Ave., Ste. 902, New York, NY 10001, (800)922-4622

Natl. Apostolate for Inclusion Ministry [19765], PO Box 218, Riverdale, MD 20738-0218, (301)577-1130

Natl. Apostolate for the Mentally Retarded [★19765]

Natl. Apostolate with Mentally Retarded Persons [★19765]

Natl. Apostolate with People with Mental Retardation [★19765]

Natl. Appaloosa Pony [★4639]

Natl. Apple Inst. [★4478]

Natl. AppleWorks Users Group - Defunct.

Natl. Appliance Parts Suppliers Assn. [219], 4015 W Marshall Ave., Longview, TX 75604

Natl. Appliance Ser. Assn. [220], PO Box 2514, Kokomo, IN 46904, (765)453-1820

Natl. Aquaculture Assn. [3827], PO Box 1647, Pine Bluff, AR 71613, (870)850-7900

Natl. Aquaculture Assn. of Guyana [IO], Georgetown, Guyana

Natl. Aquarium Soc. [10061], U.S. Department of Commerce Bldg., Rm. B-077, 14th St. and Constitution Ave. NW, Washington, DC 20230, (202)482-2825

Natl. Arab Amer. Journalists Assn. [2840], PO Box 2127, Orland Park, IL 60462

Natl. Arab Amer. Medical Assn. [14882], 801 S Adams Rd., Ste. 208, Birmingham, MI 48009, (248)646-3661

Natl. Arborist Assn. [★4976]

Natl. Arborist Assn. [★4976]

Natl. Archery Assn. of the U.S. [22223], 1 Olympic Plz., Colorado Springs, CO 80909-5778, (719)866-4576

Natl. Architectural Accrediting Bd. [7736], 1735 New York Ave. NW, Washington, DC 20006, (202)783-2007

Natl. Armored Car Assn. [3256], 9532 Stevebrook Rd., Fairfax, VA 22032, (703)426-1976

Natl. Art Educ. Assn. [7751], 1806 Robert Fulton Dr., Ste. 300, Reston, VA 20191, (703)860-8000

Natl. Art Exhibitions by the Mentally Ill [9304], PO Box 350891, Miami, FL 33135, (954)922-8692

Natl. Art Materials Trade Assn. [1618], 20200 Zion Ave., Cornelius, NC 28031, (704)892-6244

Natl. Art Materials Trade Assn. [1618], 20200 Zion Ave., Cornelius, NC 28031, (704)892-6244

Natl. Art Museum of Sport [9190], Univ. Pl. - IUPUI, 850 W Michigan St., Indianapolis, IN 46202, (317)274-3627

Natl. Arthritis and Musculoskeletal and Skin Diseases Info. CH [★16620]

Natl. Arts Coun. - Seychelles [IO], Mahe, Seychelles

Natl. Arts Coun. of Zambia [IO], Lusaka, Zambia

Natl. Arts Found. [IO], Buenos Aires, Argentina

Natl. Arts Found. - Address unknown since 2010.

Natl. Arts Stabilization Fund - Defunct.

Natl. Asbestos Coun. [★558]

Natl. Ash Assn. [★3629]

Natl. Asian Amer. Pacific Islander Mental Hea. Assn. [15466], 1215 19th St., Ste. A, Denver, CO 80202, (303)298-7910

Natl. Asian Amer. Soc. of Accountants [★11]

Natl. Asian Amer. Telecommunications Assn. [★17336]

Natl. Asian Pacific Amer. Bar Assn. [5669], 1612 K St. NW, Ste. 1400, Washington, DC 20006, (202)775-9555

Natl. Asian Pacific Amer. Families Against Substance Abuse [13271], 340 E 2nd St., Ste. 409, Los Angeles, CA 90012, (213)625-5795

Natl. Asian Pacific Amer. Legal Consortium [★5651]

Natl. Asian Pacific Center on Aging [10856], 1511 3rd Ave., Ste. 914, Seattle, WA 98101, (206)624-1221

Natl. Asian Peace Officers' Assn. [5709], PO Box 71551, Oakland, CA 94612

Natl. Asian Women's Hea. Org. [17129], 4900 Hopyard Rd., Ste. 100, Pleasanton, CA 94588, (925)468-4120

Natl. Asian Women's Hea. Org. [17129], 4900 Hopyard Rd., Ste. 100, Pleasanton, CA 94588, (925)468-4120

Natl. Asphalt Pavement Assn. [585], 5100 Forbes Blvd., Lanham, MD 20706, (301)731-4748

Natl. Assembly of Chief Livestock Hea. Officials [★17045]

Natl. Assembly of Community Arts Agencies [★9271]

Natl. Assembly of Disabled People [IO], Lae, Papua New Guinea

Natl. Assembly of Hea. and Human Ser. Organizations [★13401]

Natl. Assembly of Local Arts Agencies [★9271]

Natl. Assembly of Natl. Hea. and Social Welfare Organizations [★13401]

Natl. Assembly of Natl. Voluntary Hea. and Social Welfare Organizations [★13401]

A star before a book entry number signifies that the name is not listed separately, but is mentioned within the entry.

Natl. Assembly of Religious Bros. [★19490]

Natl. Assembly of Rollerbladers - Defunct.

Natl. Assembly on School-Based Hea. Care [14810], 1010 Vermont Ave. NW, Ste. 600, Washington, DC 20005, (202)638-5872

Natl. Assembly for Social Policy and Development [★13401]

Natl. Assembly of State Arts Agencies [9305], 1029 Vermont Ave. NW, 2nd Fl., Washington, DC 20005, (202)347-6352

Natl. Assembly of Women [IO], Cullercoats, United Kingdom

Natl. Assessment of Educational Progress [8989], 1990 K St. NW, Rm. 8095, Washington, DC 20006, (202)502-7321

Natl. Assessment of Educational Progress, The Nation's Rpt. Card [★8989]

Natl. Assistance League [★13052]

Natl. Assistance Mgt. Assn. [★2298]

Natl. Assoc. CPA Firms [41], 136 S Keowee St., Dayton, OH 45402, (937)222-1024

Natl. Assoc. Marine Suppliers [★2362]

Natl. Assn. of Abortion Facilities [★10768]

Natl. Assn. of Academic Advisors [★7945]

Natl. Assn. of Academic Advisors for Athletics [7945], NCSU Campus Box 8509, Raleigh, NC 27695, (919)513-1007

Natl. Assn. of Academies of Sci. [7378], Mary E. Burke, Sec., Acad. of Sci. of St. Louis, 5050 Oakland Ave., St. Louis, MO 63110, (314)533-8082

Natl. Assn. of Accident and Hea. Underwriters [★2004]

Natl. Assn. of Accompanists and Coaches - Defunct.

Natl. Assn. of Accountants [★31]

Natl. Assn. of Accountants and Auditors of Uzbekistan [IO], Tashkent, Uzbekistan

Natl. Assn. of Accountants in Insolvencies [★14]

Natl. Assn. of ADA Coordinators [11810], PO Box 958, Rancho Mirage, CA 92270, (888)679-7227

Natl. Assn. of Addiction Treatment Providers [13272], 313 W Liberty St., Ste. 129, Lancaster, PA 17603-2748, (717)392-8480

Natl. Assn. of Administrators of State and Fed. Educ. Programs [★7670]

Natl. Assn. of Adult Educ. [IO], Dublin, Ireland

Natl. Assn. for Adult Educ. in Haiti [IO], Port-au-Prince, Haiti

Natl. Assn. for Adults with Special Learning Needs [7973], 1143 Tidewater Ct., Westerville, OH 43082, (888)562-2756

Natl. Assn. to Advance Fat Acceptance [12589], PO Box 22510, Oakland, CA 94609, (916)558-6880

Natl. Assn. for the Advancement of Black Amers. in Vocational Education - Defunct.

Natl. Assn. for the Advancement of Caring Teachers [8951], Sindi D. Wasserman, Founder/Pres., PO Box 1282, Chino, CA 91708, (909)680-1347

Natl. Assn. for the Advancement of Colored People [★17301]

Natl. Assn. for the Advancement of Haitian Descendents [19022], 74 Trinity Pl., Wall St., New York, NY 10006, (212)203-0016

Natl. Assn. for the Advancement of Humane Educ. [★10986]

Natl. Assn. for the Advancement of Orthotics and Prosthetics [16052], 1501 M St. NW, 7th Fl., Washington, DC 20005-1700, (202)624-0064

Natl. Assn. for the Advancement of Psychoanalysis [16359], 80 8th Ave., Ste. 1501, New York, NY 10011-7158, (212)741-0515

Natl. Assn. for the Advancement of Psychoanalysis [16359], 80 8th Ave., Ste. 1501, New York, NY 10011-7158, (212)741-0515

Natl. Assn. for the Advancement of Psychoanalysis and the Amer. Bd. for Accreditation in Psychoanalysis [★16359]

Natl. Assn. for the Advancement of Psychoanalysis and the Amer. Bd. for Accreditation in Psychoanalysis [★16359]

Natl. Assn. of Advisors for the Hea. Professions [8610], PO Box 1518, Champaign, IL 61824-1518, (217)355-0063

Natl. Assn. of Affordable Housing Lenders [424], 1667 K St., Ste. 210, Washington, DC 20006, (202)293-9850

Natl. Assn. of African Amer. Stud. [7704], PO Box 6670, Scarborough, ME 04070-6670, (207)839-8004

Natl. Assn. of African Americans in Human Resources [1789], PO Box 311395, Atlanta, GA 31131

Natl. Assn. of African Americans for Positive Imagery [17157], 1231 N Broad St., Philadelphia, PA 19122, (215)235-6488

Natl. Assn. of African Palm Growers [IO], Quito, Ecuador

Natl. Assn. Agricultural Contractors [IO], Peterborough, United Kingdom

Natl. Assn. of Agricultural Educators [7711], Univ. of Kentucky, 300 Garrigus Bldg., Lexington, KY 40546-0215, (859)257-2224

Natl. Assn. of Agricultural Produce Trading Companies [IO], Mexico City, Mexico

Natl. Assn. of Agriculture Employees [5190], 9080 Torrey Rd., Willis, MI 48191, (734)942-9005

Natl. Assn. to Aid Fat Americans [★12589]

Natl. Assn. of Air Medical Commun. Specialists [13585], PO Box 19240, Topeka, KS 66619, (877)396-2227

Natl. Assn. of Air Natl. Guard Health Technicians - Defunct.

Natl. Assn. of Air Traffic Specialists - Address unknown since 2010.

Natl. Assn. on Alcohol, Drugs and Disability [16748], 2165 Bunker Hill Dr., San Mateo, CA 94402-3801, (650)578-8047

Natl. Assn. of Alcoholic Beverage Importers [★186]

Natl. Assn. of Alcoholism and Drug Abuse Counselors [★16744]

Natl. Assn. of Alcoholism Treatment Programs [★13272]

Natl. Assn. of Alternative Benefits Consultants [1691], 435 Pennsylvania Ave., Glen Ellyn, IL 60137, (800)627-0552

Natl. Assn. for Alternative Certification [8115], PO Box 5750, Washington, DC 20016, (202)277-3600

Natl. Assn. of Amateur Oarsmen [★22859]

Natl. Assn. for Ambulatory Care Medicine [★13727]

Natl. Assn. for Ambulatory Urgent Care [13727], 18870 Rutledge Rd., Wayzata, MN 55391

Natl. Assn. of Amer. Bus. Clubs [★13051]

Natl. Assn. of the Amer. People - Address unknown since 2010.

Natl. Assn. of Amusement Parks [★1195]

Natl. Assn. of Amusement Parks [★1195]

Natl. Assn. of Amusement Parks, Pools, and Beaches [★1195]

Natl. Assn. of Amusement Parks, Pools and Beaches [★1195]

Natl. Assn. of Amusement Ride Safety Officials [1205], PO Box 638, Brandon, FL 33509-0638, (813)661-2779

Natl. Assn. of Animal Breeders [4695], PO Box 1033, Columbia, MO 65205, (573)445-4406

Natl. Assn. of Anorexia Nervosa and Assoc. Disorders [14437], PO Box 640, Naperville, IL 60566, (630)577-1333

Natl. Assn. of Apnea Professionals - Defunct.

Natl. Assn. of Appellate Court Attorneys [5260], Mary Ellen Donaghy, Exec. Dir., Univ. of Richmond Law School, 28 Westhampton Way, University of Richmond, VA 23173, (804)289-8204

Natl. Assn. of Appointment Secretaries [★8699]

Natl. Assn. of Architectural Metal Mfrs. [2483], 800 Roosevelt Rd., Bldg. C, Ste. 312, Glen Ellyn, IL 60137, (630)942-6591

Natl. Assn. of Area Agencies on Aging [10857], 1730 Rhode Island Ave. NW, Ste. 1200, Washington, DC 20036, (202)872-0888

Natl. Assn. for Areas of Outstanding Natural Beauty [IO], Northleach, United Kingdom

Natl. Assn. for Armenian Stud. and Res. [9149], 395 Concord Ave., Belmont, MA 02478, (617)489-1610

Natl. Assn. of Arms Shows [21715], PO Box 290, Kaysville, UT 84037-0290, (801)544-9125

Natl. Assn. of Artificial Breeders [★4695]

Natl. Assn. of Artists and Crafters - Address unknown since 2011.

Natl. Assn. of Asian Amer. Law Enforcement Commanders [5710], PO Box 420496, San Francisco, CA 94142-0496

Natl. Assn. of Asian Amer. Professionals [9341], PO Box 354, Uwchland, PA 19480, (215)715-3046

Natl. Assn. of Asian-Pacific Amer. Deacons [20202], 7031 Kenmare Dr., Bloomington, MN 55438, (952)942-6288

Natl. Assn. for Asian and Pacific Amer. Educ. [7758], PO Box 3471, Palos Verdes Peninsula, CA 90274, (818)677-6853

Natl. Assn. of Assessing Officers [★6012]

Natl. Assn. of Assessing Officers [★6012]

Natl. Assn. of Asst. U.S. Attorneys [5261], 12427 Hedges Run Dr., Ste. 104, Lake Ridge, VA 22192, (800)455-5661

Natl. Assn. of Athletic Development Directors [22988], 1 Champions Dr., Ste. 200, Columbia, MO 65211, (573)884-6428

Natl. Assn. of ATM ISOs and Operators [425], 8601 Dunwoody Pl., Ste. 106, Atlanta, GA 30350, (770)755-5945

Natl. Assn. of Atomic Veterans [13351], 11214 Sageland, Houston, TX 77089, (281)481-1357

Natl. Assn. of Attorneys Gen. [5991], 2030 M St. NW, 8th Fl., Washington, DC 20036-3306, (202)326-6000

Natl. Assn. of Auto. Dealers [IO], Mexico City, Mexico

Natl. Assn. of Auto. Mfrs. of South Africa [IO], Pretoria, Republic of South Africa

Natl. Assn. of Auto. Museums [10126], PO Box 271, Auburn, IN 46706, (260)925-1444

Natl. Assn. of Automotive Component and Allied Mfrs. [IO], Edenvale, Republic of South Africa

Natl. Assn. of Automotive Dealers, Repair Outlets and Component Retailers [IO], Madrid, Spain

Natl. Assn. of Avon Clubs [★21373]

Natl. Assn. of Avon Collectors [21373], PO Box 7006, Kansas City, MO 64113

Natl. Assn. of Baby Boomer Women [13470], 9672 W US Hwy. 20, Galena, IL 61036, (877)-BOOMERZ

Natl. Assn. of Bail Enforcement Agents [5296], PO Box 129, Falls Church, VA 22040-0129, (703)534-4211

Natl. Assn. of Bail Insurance Companies [★383]

Natl. Assn. of Bakery Products [IO], Mexico City, Mexico

Natl. Assn. of Bakery Sanitarians [★2246]

Natl. Assn. for Bank Auditors and Controllers [★403]

Natl. Assn. for Bank Cost Anal. [★400]

Natl. Assn. for Bank, Cost, and Mgt. Accounting [★400]

Natl. Assn. of Bank Servicers [★63]

Natl. Assn. of Bank Women [★414]

Natl. Assn. of Bank Women [★414]

Natl. Assn. of Bankruptcy Trustees [5319], 1 Windsor Cove, Ste. 305, Columbia, SC 29223, (803)252-5646

Natl. Assn. of Baptist Professors of Religion [9013], Anderson Coll., PO Box 1123, Anderson, SC 29621

Natl. Assn. of Bar Executives [5670], 321 N Clark St., Chicago, IL 60654, (312)988-6008

Natl. Assn. of Barber Boards [★970]

Natl. Assn. of Barber Boards of Am. [970], 2703 Pine St., Arkadelphia, AR 71923, (501)682-2806

Natl. Assn. of Barber Styling Schools - Defunct.

Natl. Assn. of Bariatric Nurses [15855], East Carolina Univ., Coll. of Nursing, 2111 Hea. Sciences Bldg., Greenville, NC 27858, (252)744-6379

Natl. Assn. of Basketball Coaches [22297], 1111 Main St., Ste. 1000, Kansas City, MO 64105-2136, (816)878-6222

Natl. Assn. of Basketball Coaches of the U.S. [★22297]

Natl. Assn. of Bedding Mfrs. [★1780]

Natl. Assn. of Bedding Mfrs. [★1780]

Natl. Assn. for Beginning Teachers [8952], 2505 Anthem Village Dr., Ste. 301, Henderson, NV 89052, (888)246-0189

Natl. Assn. of Bench and Bar Spouses [5262], Roberta Bell, Financial Sec., 245 Farragut St. NW, Washington, DC 20011, (202)291-4946

Natl. Assn. of Benefits and Work Incentive Specialists [1130], 12009 Shallot St., Orlando, FL 32837, (407)859-7767

Natl. Assn. of Beverage Importers [186], Natl. Press Bldg., 529 14th St. NW, Ste. 1183, Washington, DC 20045, (202)393-6224

Natl. Assn. of Beverage Retailers [★174]

Natl. Assn. of Biblical Instructors [★7993]

Natl. Assn. of Bicycle and Sports Retailers [IO], Stockholm, Sweden

Natl. Assn. for Bilingual Educ. [7770], 8701 Georgia Ave., Ste. 611, Silver Spring, MD 20910, (240)450-3700

Natl. Assn. of Biology Teachers [7771], 1313 Dolley Madison Blvd., Ste. 402, McLean, VA 22101, (703)264-9696

Natl. Assn. for Biomedical Res. [13764], 818 Connecticut Ave. NW, Ste. 900, Washington, DC 20006, (202)857-0540

Natl. Assn. of Bionutritionists [15839], Emily Tarleton, Sec.-Treas., UCB CTRC, FAHC, Gen. Clinical Res. Center, MCHV Campus Baird 726, 111 Colchester Ave., Burlington, VT 05104

Natl. Assn. of Black Accountants [42], 7474 Greenway Center Dr., Ste. 1120, Greenbelt, MD 20770, (301)474-6222

Natl. Assn. of Black County Officials [5348], 1090 Vermont Ave. NW, Ste. 1290, Washington, DC 20005, (202)350-6696

Natl. Assn. of Black Female Executives in Music and Entertainment [1206], 59 Maiden Ln., 27th Fl., New York, NY 10038, (212)424-9568

Natl. Assn. of Black Hospitality Professionals - Defunct.

Natl. Assn. of Black Hotel Owners, Operators and Developers [1760], 3520 W Broward Blvd., Ste. 119, Fort Lauderdale, FL 33312, (954)797-7102

Natl. Assn. of Black Journalists [2841], Univ. of Maryland, 1100 Knight Hall, Ste. 3100, College Park, MD 20742, (301)445-7100

Natl. Assn. of Black Law Enforcement Officers [5711], PO Box 1182, Newark, NJ 07102, (401)465-9152

Natl. Assn. of Black Owned Broadcasters [500], 1201 Connecticut Ave. NW, Ste. 200, Washington, DC 20036, (202)463-8970

Natl. Assn. of Black Scuba Divers [23122], PO Box 91630, Washington, DC 20090-1630, (800)521-NABS

Natl. Assn. of Black Social Workers [13220], 2305 Martin Luther King Ave. SE, Washington, DC 20020-5813, (202)678-4570

Natl. Assn. of Black Storytellers [10545], PO Box 67722, Baltimore, MD 21215, (410)947-1117

Natl. Assn. of Black Telecommunications Professionals - Address unknown since 2011.

Natl. Assn. for Black Veterans [20794], PO Box 11432, Milwaukee, WI 53211, (877)622-8387

Natl. Assn. of Black Women in Constr. [848], 1910 NW 105 Ave., Pembroke Pines, FL 33026

Natl. Assn. of Blacks in Criminal Justice [11722], 1801 Fayetteville St., Durham, NC 27707-3129, (919)683-1801

Natl. Assn. of Blessed Billionaires [7799], Presbyterian Church of Mt. Vernon, 199 N Columbus Ave., Mount Vernon, NY 10553, (914)633-4417

Natl. Assn. for the Blind, India [IO], Mumbai, India

Natl. Assn. of Blind Merchants [3616], 1837 S Nevada Ave., PMB 243, Colorado Springs, CO 80905, (719)527-0488

Natl. Assn. of Blind Teachers [8953], Amer. Coun. of the Blind, 2200 Wilson Blvd., Ste. 650, Arlington, VA 22201, (202)467-5081

Natl. Assn. of Boards of Barbers Examiners of Am. [★970]

Natl. Assn. of Boards, Commissions, and Councils of Catholic Educ. [★7815]

Natl. Assn. of Boards of Educ. [★7815]

Natl. Assn. of Boards of Examiners of Long Term Care Administrators [15811], 1444 I St. NW, No. 700, Washington, DC 20005-6542, (202)712-9040

Natl. Assn. of Boards of Examiners of Nursing Home Administrators [★15811]

Natl. Assn. of Boards of Pharmacy [16204], 1600 Feehanville Dr., Mount Prospect, IL 60056, (847)391-4406

Natl. Assn. of Boat Mfrs. - Defunct.

Natl. Assn. of Bond Lawyers [5671], 601 13th St. NW, Ste. 800 S, Washington, DC 20005, (202)503-3300

Natl. Assn. of Book Editors [IO], Montreal, QC, Canada

Natl. Assn. of Breweriana Advt. [21374], 340 E Ashland Ave., Mount Zion, IL 62549-1275

Natl. Assn. of Brick Distributors [★536]

Natl. Assn. of British and Irish Millers [IO], London, United Kingdom

Natl. Assn. Broadcast Employees and Technicians l Communications Workers of Am. [23162], 501 3rd St. NW, Washington, DC 20001-2797, (202)434-1100

Natl. Assn. of Broadcasters [501], 1771 N St. NW, Washington, DC 20036, (202)429-5300

Natl. Assn. of Broadcasters of South Africa [IO], Craighall, Republic of South Africa

Natl. Assn. of Building Cooperatives Soc. [IO], Dublin, Ireland

Natl. Assn. of Building Mfrs. [★2311]

Natl. Assn. of Building Owners and Managers [★3004]

Natl. Assn. of Building Owners and Managers [★3004]

Natl. Assn. of Building Ser. Contractors [★2242]

Natl. Assn. of Building Ser. Contractors [★2242]

Natl. Assn. of Bur. of Animal Indus. Veterinarians [★17033]

Natl. Assn. of Bus. Brokers [★3024]

Natl. Assn. of Bus. Consultants - Defunct.

Natl. Assn. for Bus. Economics [6627], 1233 20th St. NW, No. 505, Washington, DC 20036, (202)463-6223

Natl. Assn. of Bus. Economists [★6627]

Natl. Assn. of Bus. and Educational Radio [★3416]

Natl. Assn. of Bus. and Educational Radio and Assn. of Communications Technicians [★3416]

Natl. Assn. for Bus. Organizations [3291], 5432 Price Ave., Baltimore, MD 21215, (410)367-5309

Natl. Assn. of Bus. Political Action Committees [18336], 101 Constitution Ave. NW, Ste. L-110, Washington, DC 20001, (202)341-3780

Natl. Assn. for Bus. Teacher Educ. [7800], Natl. Bus. Educ. Assn., 1914 Assn. Dr., Reston, VA 20191-1596, (703)860-8300

Natl. Assn. of Bus. Women of Tajikistan [IO], Khujand, Tajikistan

Natl. Assn. of Buyers' Agents [303], PO Box 513, Kentfield, CA 94914, (415)721-7741

Natl. Assn. of Call Centers [812], 100 S 22nd Ave., Hattiesburg, MS 39401, (601)447-8300

Natl. Assn. for Campus Activities [8906], 13 Harbison Way, Columbia, SC 29212-3401, (803)732-6222

Natl. Assn. of Campus Card Users [3374], 9201 N 25th Ave., Ste. 188, Phoenix, AZ 85021, (602)395-8989

Natl. Assn. of Canadians of Origins in India [IO], Ottawa, ON, Canada

Natl. Assn. for Cancer Awareness [IO], Muscat, Oman

Natl. Assn. of Car Mfrs. [IO], Turin, Italy

Natl. Assn. of Career Colleges [IO], Brantford, ON, Canada

Natl. Assn. of Casino Party Operators [1207], PO Box 5626, South San Francisco, CA 94083, (888)922-0777

Natl. Assn. of Casino and Theme Party Operators [★1207]

Natl. Assn. of Casualty and Surety Agents [★1953]

Natl. Assn. of Casualty and Surety Agents [★1953]

Natl. Assn. of Casualty and Surety Executives - Defunct.

Natl. Assn. of Catastrophe Adjusters [2000], PO Box 821864, North Richland Hills, TX 76182, (817)498-3466

Natl. Assn. of Catering Butchers [IO], London, United Kingdom

Natl. Assn. of Catering Executives [1761], 9891 Broken Land Pkwy., Ste. 301, Columbia, MD 21046, (410)290-5410

Natl. Assn. of Catering Executives [1761], 9891 Broken Land Pkwy., Ste. 301, Columbia, MD 21046, (410)290-5410

Natl. Assn. of Catholic Chaplains [19525], 4915 S Howell Ave., Ste. 501, Milwaukee, WI 53207, (414)483-4898

Natl. Assn. of Catholic Diocesan Family Life Ministers [★19997]

Natl. Assn. of Catholic Diocesan Lesbian and Gay Ministries [★19786]

Natl. Assn. of Catholic Family Life Ministers [19997], 300 Coll. Park, Dayton, OH 45469-2512, (937)431-5443

Natl. Assn. of Catholic Nurses - U.S.A. [15763], PO Box 3016, Lisle, IL 60532-8016

Natl. Assn. of Catholic School Teachers [7817], 1700 Sansom St., Ste. 903, Philadelphia, PA 19103, (800)99N-ACST

Natl. Assn. of Catholic Youth Ministry Leaders [19455], 415 Michigan Ave. NE, Ste. 40, Washington, DC 20017, (202)636-3825

Natl. Assn. for Cave Diving [23103], PO Box 14492, Gainesville, FL 32604, (386)497-3494

Natl. Assn. of Cellular Agents [★3428]

Natl. Assn. of Cement Users [★6570]

Natl. Assn. of Cemeteries [★2535]

Natl. Assn. of Cemeteries [★2535]

Natl. Assn. of Centers for Urgent Treatment [★13727]

Natl. Assn. of Certified Fraud Examiners [★1884]

Natl. Assn. of Certified Fraud Examiners [★1884]

Natl. Assn. of Certified Home Inspectors [1918], 1750 30th St., Boulder, CO 80301, (303)502-6214

Natl. Assn. of Certified Home Inspectors [1918], 1750 30th St., Boulder, CO 80301, (303)502-6214

Natl. Assn. of Certified Professional Midwives [15887], 243 Banning Rd., Putney, VT 05346

Natl. Assn. of Certified Professionals of Equine Therapy [13694], 711 W 17th St., No. A8, Costa Mesa, CA 92627, (949)646-8010

Natl. Assn. of Certified Public Bookkeepers [43], 162 W Baer Creek Dr., Kaysville, UT 84037, (866)444-9989

Natl. Assn. of Certified Valuation Analysts [44], 1111 Brickyard Rd., Ste. 200, Salt Lake City, UT 84106-5401, (801)486-0600

Natl. Assn. of Certified Valuators and Analysts [44], 1111 Brickyard Rd., Ste. 200, Salt Lake City, UT 84106-5401, (801)486-0600

Natl. Assn. of Chain Drug Stores [16205], 413 N Lee St., Alexandria, VA 22314, (703)549-3001

Natl. Assn. of Chamber Ambassadors [23373], PO Box 1198, Seminole, TX 79360, (800)411-6222

Natl. Assn. of Chap. 13 Trustees [★5319]

Natl. Assn. of Charter School Authorizers [8043], 105 W Adams St., Ste. 3500, Chicago, IL 60603-6253, (312)376-2300

Natl. Assn. of Charterboat Operators [2361], PO Box 2990, Orange Beach, AL 36561, (251)981-5136

Natl. Assn. of Chem. Distributors [759], 1555 Wilson Blvd., Ste. 700, Arlington, VA 22209, (703)527-6223

Natl. Assn. of Chewing Gum Mfrs. - Defunct.

Natl. Assn. for Chicana and Chicano Stud. [8248], PO Box 720052, San Jose, CA 95172-0052, (408)924-5310

Natl. Assn. for Chicano Stud. [★8248]

Natl. Assn. of Chiefs of Police [5712], 6350 Horizon Dr., Titusville, FL 32780, (321)264-0911

Natl. Assn. of Chiefs of Police [★5696]

Natl. Assn. of Chiefs of Police [★5696]

Natl. Assn. of Child Advocates [★11426]

Natl. Assn. of Child Care Professionals [11153], PO Box 90723, Austin, TX 78709, (512)301-5557

Natl. Assn. of Child Care Rsrc. and Referral Agencies [11154], 1515 N Courthouse Rd., 11th Fl., Arlington, VA 22201, (703)341-4100

Natl. Assn. of Childbearing Centers [★15861]

Natl. Assn. for Children of Alcoholics [13273], 10920 Connecticut Ave., Ste. 100, Kensington, MD 20895, (301)468-0985

Natl. Assn. of Children with Arthritis [IO], Lisbon, Portugal

Natl. Assn. for Children's Behavioral Hea. [16342], 1025 Connecticut Ave. NW, Ste. 1012, Washington, DC 20036-3536, (202)857-9735

Natl. Assn. of Children's Hospitals and Related Institutions [15061], 401 Wythe St., Alexandria, VA 22314-1915, (703)684-1355

A star before a book entry number signifies that the name is not listed separately, but is mentioned within the entry.

Natl. Assn. of Chimney Engineers [IO], Lincoln, United Kingdom

Natl. Assn. of Chimney Sweeps [IO], Stone, United Kingdom

Natl. Assn. of Chiropodists [★16293]

Natl. Assn. for Chiropractic Medicine - Address unknown since 2010.

Natl. Assn. of Choirs [IO], Nottingham, United Kingdom

Natl. Assn. of Christian Child and Family Agencies [19590], PO Box 727, Hillsville, VA 24343, (276)236-5578

Natl. Assn. of Christian Financial Consultants [1341], 1055 Maitland Center Commons Blvd., Maitland, FL 32751, (407)644-9793

Natl. Assn. of Christian Singles - Defunct.

Natl. Assn. of Christians in Social Work [★13225]

Natl. Assn. of Church Bus. Admin. [20203], 100 N Central Expy., Ste. 914, Richardson, TX 75080-5326, (972)699-7555

Natl. Assn. of Church Bus. Administrators [★20203]

Natl. Assn. of Church Design Builders [586], 1000 Ballpark Way, Ste. 306, Arlington, TX 76011, (817)200-2622

Natl. Assn. of Church Facilities Managers [20204], Ms. Victoria Hardy, Wentworth Inst. of Tech., Dept. of Design and Facilities, 550 Huntington Ave., Boston, MA 02115, (616)956-9377

Natl. Assn. of Church Food Ser. [1449], PO Box 43694, Birmingham, AL 35243, (205)970-5176

Natl. Assn. of Church Personnel Administrators [20205], 100 E 8th St., Cincinnati, OH 45202, (513)421-3134

Natl. Assn. of the Cigar Indus. [IO], Bonn, Germany

Natl. Assn. of Citizens Advice Bureaux [IO], London, United Kingdom

Natl. Assn. Citizens on Patrol [12991], PO Box 727, Corona, CA 92878-0727, (951)898-8551

Natl. Assn. of Citrus Juice Processors [★449]

Natl. Assn. for Civil War Brass Music [10251], 124 Maiden Choice Ln., Baltimore, MD 21228, (410)744-7708

Natl. Assn. for Civilian Oversight of Law Enforcement [5713], 638 E Vermont St., Indianapolis, IN 46202, (866)462-2653

Natl. Assn. of Claimants Compensation Attorneys [★6041]

Natl. Assn. of Clean Air Agencies [5419], 444 N Capitol St. NW, Ste. 307, Washington, DC 20001, (202)624-7864

Natl. Assn. of Clean Water Agencies [5949], 1816 Jefferson Pl. NW, Washington, DC 20036-2505, (202)833-2672

Natl. Assn. of Clergy Hypnotherapists [★15093]

Natl. Assn. of Clergy Hypnotherapists - Defunct.

Natl. Assn. of Clinical Managers [★15294]

Natl. Assn. of Clinical Nurse Specialists [15764], 100 N 20th St., Ste. 400, Philadelphia, PA 19103, (215)320-3881

Natl. Assn. of Clothing Designers [★215]

Natl. Assn. of Clothing Mfrs. [IO], Lisbon, Portugal

Natl. Assn. of Cocoa Exporters [IO], Guayaquil, Ecuador

Natl. Assn. of the Coffee Indus. - Mexico [IO], Mexico City, Mexico

Natl. Assn. of Cognitive-Behavioral Therapists [16440], PO Box 2195, Weirton, WV 26062, (800)853-1135

Natl. Assn. of Coin Laundry Equip. Operators [★2193]

Natl. Assn. of Cold Storage Contractors [★1706]

Natl. Assn. of Cold Storage Contractors [★1706]

Natl. Assn. of Cold Storage Insulation Contractors [★1706]

Natl. Assn. of Cold Storage Insulation Contractors [★1706]

Natl. Assn. of Colitis and Crohn's Disease [IO], St. Albans, United Kingdom

Natl. Assn. for Coll. Admission Counseling [7684], 1050 N Highland St., Ste. 400, Arlington, VA 22201-2197, (703)836-2222

Natl. Assn. of Coll. Admission Counselors [★7684]

Natl. Assn. of Coll. Admissions Counselors [★7684]

Natl. Assn. of Coll. Automotive Teachers [★7763]

Natl. Assn. of Coll. Auxiliary Services [3170], PO Box 5546, Charlottesville, VA 22905-5546, (434)245-8425

Natl. Assn. of Coll. Stores [3113], 500 E Lorain St., Oberlin, OH 44074, (800)622-7498

Natl. Assn. of Coll. Teachers of Agriculture [★7716]

Natl. Assn. of Coll. and Univ. Attorneys [5396], 1 Dupont Cir., Ste. 620, Washington, DC 20036, (202)833-8390

Natl. Assn. of Coll. and Univ. Bus. Officers [7667], 1110 Vermont Ave. NW, Ste. 800, Washington, DC 20005, (202)861-2500

National Assn. of Coll. and Univ. Chaplains and Directors of Religious Life [★8905]

Natl. Assn. of Coll. and Univ. Food Services [1450], 2525 Jolly Rd., Ste. 280, Okemos, MI 48864-3680, (517)332-2494

Natl. Assn. of Coll. and Univ. Mail Services [2790], PO Box 270367, Fort Collins, CO 80527-0367, (877)NAC-UMS1

Natl. Assn. of Coll. and Univ. Security Directors [★8817]

Natl. Assn. of Coll. and Univ. Security Directors [★8817]

Natl. Assn. of Coll. and Univ. Summer Sessions [★8935]

Natl. Assn. of Coll. and Univ. Summer Sessions [★8935]

Natl. Assn. of Coll. Wind and Percussion Instructors [8659], Dr. Richard K. Weerts, Exec. Sec.-Treas., 308 Hillcrest Dr., Kirksville, MO 63501

Natl. Assn. of Coll. Women [★9060]

Natl. Assn. of Colleges and Departments of Educ. [★8940]

Natl. Assn. of Colleges and Employers [8727], 62 Highland Ave., Bethlehem, PA 18017-9481, (610)868-1421

Natl. Assn. of Colleges and Teachers of Agriculture [★7716]

Natl. Assn. of Collegiate Directors of Athletics [22989], 24651 Detroit Rd., Westlake, OH 44145, (440)892-4000

Natl. Assn. of Collegiate Gymnastics Coaches/Women [22633], Stanford Univ., Arrillaga Family Sports Center, Stanford, CA 94305-6150, (650)724-0457

Natl. Assn. of Collegiate Marketing Administrators [22990], 24651 Detroit Rd., Westlake, OH 44145, (440)892-4000

Natl. Assn. of Collegiate Women Athletics Administrators [8718], 2000 Baltimore Ave., Ste. 100, Kansas City, MO 64108, (816)389-8200

Natl. Assn. of Colored Women's Clubs [13066], 1601 R St. NW, Washington, DC 20009, (202)667-4080

Natl. Assn. of Comics Art Educators [7887], 1581 W Northwest Blvd., Winston-Salem, NC 27104-4312

Natl. Assn. of Commercial Broadcasters in Japan [IO], Tokyo, Japan

Natl. Assn. of Commercial Finance Brokers [IO], Exeter, United Kingdom

Natl. Assn. of Commissioned Travel Agents [3565], 1101 King St., Ste. 200, Alexandria, VA 22314, (703)739-6826

Natl. Assn. of Commissioners, Secretaries and Directors of Agriculture [★5192]

Natl. Assn. of Commissions for Women [17657], 401 N Washington St., Ste. 100, Rockville, MD 20850-1737, (240)777-8308

Natl. Assn. of Commun. Systems Engineers [6437], PO Box 92, Castle Rock, CO 80104, (720)269-4777

Natl. Assn. of Community Action Agencies [★12723]

Natl. Assn. for Community Coll. Entrepreneurship [7801], Laura Wolpert, Dir., Bldg. 101-R, 1 Fed. St., Springfield, MA 01105, (413)306-3131

Natl. Assn. of Community Coll. Teacher Educ. Programs [8954], 2411 W 14th St., Tempe, AZ 85281, (480)731-8760

Natl. Assn. of Community Development Extension Professionals [11612], PO Box 68721, Grand Rapids, MI 49516, (616)301-1011

Natl. Assn. of Community Development Loan Funds [★17390]

Natl. Assn. of Community Hea. Centers [14720], 7200 Wisconsin Ave., Ste. 210, Bethesda, MD 20814, (301)347-0400

Natl. Assn. for Community Leadership [★11622]

Natl. Assn. of Community Leadership Organizations [★11622]

Natl. Assn. for Community Mediation [5210], 1959 S Power Rd., Ste. 103-279, Mesa, AZ 85206-4398, (602)633-4213

Natl. Assn. of Competitive Mounted Orienteering [22794], 4309 Laura St. NW, Comstock Park, MI 49321, (616)784-1645

Natl. Assn. of Competitive Mounted Orienteering [22794], 4309 Laura St. NW, Comstock Park, MI 49321, (616)784-1645

Natl. Assn. for Composers and Conductors [★10252]

Natl. Assn. of Composers U.S.A. [10252], PO Box 49256, Barrington Sta., Los Angeles, CA 90049, (818)709-8534

Natl. Assn. of Cmpt. Consulting Businesses Canada [IO], Kanata, ON, Canada

Natl. Assn. of Cmpt. Database Consultant Businesses [★868]

Natl. Assn. of Computerized Tax Processors [6014], Jamie Stiles, 235 E Palmer St., Franklin, NC 28734, (828)524-8020

Natl. Assn. of Concerned Veterans - Defunct.

Natl. Assn. of Concessionaires [1451], 35 E Wacker Dr., Ste. 1816, Chicago, IL 60601, (312)236-3858

Natl. Assn. of Condo Hotel Owners - Address unknown since 2011.

Natl. Assn. of Congregational Christian Churches [19628], PO Box 288, Oak Creek, WI 53154-0288, (414)764-1620

Natl. Assn. of Conservation Districts [4095], 509 Capitol Ct. NE, Washington, DC 20002-4937, (202)547-6223

Natl. Assn. of Constr. Contractors Cooperation [587], 7447 Holmes Rd., Ste. 300, Kansas City, MO 64131, (816)442-8680

Natl. Assn. of Consulting Engineers of Slovenia [IO], Ljubljana, Slovenia

Natl. Assn. of Consumer Advocates [17463], 1730 Rhode Island Ave. NW, Ste. 710, Washington, DC 20036, (202)452-1989

Natl. Assn. of Consumer Agency Administrators [5341], PO Box 40542, Nashville, TN 37204, (615)498-1563

Natl. Assn. of Consumer Agency Administrators [5341], PO Box 40542, Nashville, TN 37204, (615)498-1563

Natl. Assn. of Consumer Bankruptcy Attorneys [5263], 2300 M St., Ste. 800, Washington, DC 20037, (216)491-6770

Natl. Assn. of Consumer Bankruptcy Attorneys [5263], 2300 M St., Ste. 800, Washington, DC 20037, (216)491-6770

Natl. Assn. of Consumer Credit Administrators [5342], PO Box 20871, Columbus, OH 43220-0871, (614)326-1165

Natl. Assn. of Consumer Shows [1235], 147 SE 102nd Ave., Portland, OR 97216, (503)253-0832

Natl. Assn. of Container Distributors [883], 1833 Center Point Cir., Ste. 123, Naperville, IL 60563, (630)544-5052

Natl. Assn. for Continence [16946], PO Box 1019, Charleston, SC 29402-1019, (843)377-0900

Natl. Assn. for Continence [16946], PO Box 1019, Charleston, SC 29402-1019, (843)377-0900

Natl. Assn. for Continuing Educ. [7927], 7860 Peters Rd., Ste. F111, Plantation, FL 33324, (954)723-0057

Natl. Assn. of Convenience Stores [3114], 1600 Duke St., Alexandria, VA 22314, (703)684-3600

Natl. Assn. of Convenience Stores [3114], 1600 Duke St., Alexandria, VA 22314, (703)684-3600

Natl. Assn. of Coordinators of State Programs for the Mentally Retarded [★12509]

Natl. Assn. for Core Curriculum - Defunct.

Natl. Assn. for Corporate Art Mgt. [★249]

Natl. Assn. for Corporate Art Mgt. [★249]

Natl. Assn. of Corporate Directors [2294], Two Lafayette Ctr., 1133 21st St. NW, Ste. 700, Washington, DC 20036, (202)775-0509

Natl. Assn. of Corporate and Professional Recruiters [★1151]

Natl. Assn. of Corporate and Professional Recruiters [★1151]

Reference to "IO" in place of a book number signifies that the association may be found in the 50th edition of International Organizations.

Natl. Assn. of Corporate Real Estate Executives [★3006]

Natl. Assn. of Corporate Real Estate Executives [★3006]

Natl. Assn. of Corporate Treasurers [1314], 12100 Sunset Hills Rd., Ste. 130, Reston, VA 20190, (703)437-4377

Natl. Assn. of Corp. Schools [★2263]

Natl. Assn. of Corp. Schools [★2263]

Natl. Assn. of Corrosion Engineers [★6809]

Natl. Assn. of Corrosion Engineers [★6809]

Natl. Assn. of Cost Accountants [★31]

Natl. Assn. of Cotton Cloth Glove Mfrs. [★1833]

Natl. Assn. of Cotton Cloth Glove Mfrs. [★1833]

Natl. Assn. of Cotton Mfrs. [★3451]

Natl. Assn. of Councils on Developmental Disabilities [12508], 1660 L St. NW, Ste. 700, Washington, DC 20036, (202)506-5813

Natl. Assn. of Counsel for Children [11487], Janis McCubbrey, Membership Dir., 13123 E 16th Ave. B390, Aurora, CO 80045, (303)864-5324

Natl. Assn. of Counsellors, Hypnotherapists and Psychotherapists [IO], Cambridge, United Kingdom

Natl. Assn. of Counselors - Address unknown since 2010.

Natl. Assn. of Counties [5349], 25 Massachusetts Ave. NW, Washington, DC 20001, (202)393-6226

Natl. Assn. of County 4-H Club Agents [★13537]

Natl. Assn. of County Administrators - Defunct.

Natl. Assn. of County Aging Programs - Address unknown since 2011.

Natl. Assn. of County Agricultural Agents [5191], 6584 W Duroc Rd., Maroa, IL 61756, (217)794-3700

Natl. Assn. of County Behavioral Hea. Directors [14883], 25 Massachusetts Ave., Ste. 500, Washington, DC 20001, (202)661-8816

Natl. Assn. of County and City Hea. Officials [5929], 1100 17th St. NW, 7th Fl., Washington, DC 20036, (202)783-5550

Natl. Assn. of County Civil Attorneys - Address unknown since 2010.

Natl. Assn. of County Club Agents [★13537]

Natl. Assn. of County Collectors, Treasurers and Finance Officers [5919], PO Box 421, Carthage, MO 64836, (417)237-1062

Natl. Assn. of County Community Development Directors [★17384]

Natl. Assn. for County Community and Economic Development [17384], 2025 M St. NW, Ste. 800, Washington,.DC 20036-3309, (202)367-1149

Natl. Assn. of County of Employment and Training Administrators [★5349]

Natl. Assn. of County Engineers [6811], 25 Massachusetts Ave. NW, Ste. 580, Washington, DC 20001-1430, (202)393-5041

Natl. Assn. of County Hea. Officers [★5929]

Natl. Assn. of County Hea. Officials [★5929]

Natl. Assn. of County Human Services Administrators [★5349]

Natl. Assn. of County Info. Officers [5350], Tom Goodman, Public Affairs Dir., 25 Massachusetts Ave. NW, Washington, DC 20001, (202)393-6226

Natl. Assn. of County Off. Employees [★5506]

Natl. Assn. of County Officials [★5349]

Natl. Assn. of County Park and Recreation Officials [5875], 16 W 284-97th St., Burr Ridge, IL 60527

Natl. Assn. of County Planners [5329], 440 1st St. NW, 8th Fl., Washington, DC 20001, (202)661-8807

Natl. Assn. of County Planning Directors [★5329]

Natl. Assn. of County and Prosecuting Attorneys [★5272]

Natl. Assn. of County Recorders and Clerks [★5351]

Natl. Assn. of County Recorders, Election Officials, and Clerks [5351], 2501 Aerial Center Pkwy., Ste. 103, Morrisville, NC 27560, (919)459-2080

Natl. Assn. of County Surveyors [5352], R. Charles Pearson, Sec.-Treas., County Surveyor, Clackamas County, 150 Beavercreek Rd., No. 319, Oregon City, OR 97045, (503)742-4499

Natl. Assn. of County Training and Employment Professionals [★5349]

Natl. Assn. of County Treasurers and Finance Officers [★5919]

Natl. Assn. of County Veterans Ser. Officers [20795], LeSueur County Veteran Services, 88 S Park Ave., Le Center, MN 56057-1600

Natl. Assn. of County Welfare Directors [★5349]

Natl. Assn. for Court Admin. [★5355]

Natl. Assn. for Court Admin. [★5355]

Natl. Assn. for Court Mgt. [5355], Natl. Center for State Courts, 300 Newport Ave., Williamsburg, VA 23185-4147, (757)259-1841

Natl. Assn. for Court Mgt. [5355], Natl. Center for State Courts, 300 Newport Ave., Williamsburg, VA 23185-4147, (757)259-1841

Natl. Assn. for the Craniofacially Handicapped [★14197]

Natl. Assn. of Credential Evaluation Services [8172], PO Box 3665, Culver City, CA 90231-3665, (310)258-9451

Natl. Assn. of Credit Mgt. [1315], 8840 Columbia 100 Pkwy., Columbia, MD 21045-2158, (410)740-5560

Natl. Assn. of Credit Mgt. North Central [★1300]

Natl. Assn. of Credit Union Chairmen [1001], PO Box 160, Del Mar, CA 92014, (858)792-3883

Natl. Assn. of Credit Union Presidents [★1001]

Natl. Assn. of Credit Union Services Organizations [1002], 3419 Via Lido, PMB 135, Newport Beach, CA 92663, (949)645-5296

Natl. Assn. of Credit Union Supervisory and Auditing Committees [1003], PO Box 160, Del Mar, CA 92014, (800)287-5949

Natl. Assn. of Crime Victim Compensation Boards [13365], PO Box 16003, Alexandria, VA 22302, (703)780-3200

Natl. Assn. for Crime Victims Rights - Defunct.

Natl. Assn. of Criminal Defense Lawyers [5385], 1660 L St. NW, 12th Fl., Washington, DC 20036, (202)872-8600

Natl. Assn. of Crop Insurance Agents [★1955]

Natl. Assn. of Cruise Only Agencies [★3566]

Natl. Assn. of Cruise-Oriented Agencies [3566], 7378 Atlantic Blvd., No. 115, Margate, FL 33063, (305)663-5626

Natl. Assn. of Cuban Economists [IO], Havana, Cuba

Natl. Assn. of Cultured Marble Mfrs. [★570]

Natl. Assn. of Cultured Marble Mfrs. [★570]

Natl. Assn. of Cytologists [IO], Bristol, United Kingdom

Natl. Assn. of the Deaf [14947], 8630 Fenton St., Ste. 820, Silver Spring, MD 20910-3819, (301)587-1788

Natl. Assn. for Deaf People [★1300]

Natl. Assn. of Deafened People [IO], Amersham, United Kingdom

Natl. Assn. of Dealer Counsel [304], 1155 15th St. NW, Ste. 500, Washington, DC 20005, (202)293-1454

Natl. Assn. of Dealers in Antiques - Defunct.

Natl. Assn. of Deans and Advisers of Men [★7666]

Natl. Assn. of Deans and Directors of Schools of Social Work [8871], Vitali Chamov, Prog. Coor., 1701 Duke St., Ste. 200, Alexandria, VA 22314, (703)683-8080

Natl. Assn. of Decorative Fabric Distributors [3448], 1 Windsor Cove, Ste. 305, Columbia, SC 29223-1833, (803)252-5646

Natl. Assn. of Decorative and Fine Arts Societies [IO], London, United Kingdom

Natl. Assn. of Defense Lawyers in Criminal Cases [★5385]

Natl. Assn. of Demolition Contractors [★934]

Natl. Assn. of Dental Examiners [★14247]

Natl. Assn. of Dental Labs. [14297], 325 John Knox Rd., No. L103, Tallahassee, FL 32303, (850)205-5626

Natl. Assn. of Dental Plans [15129], 12700 Park Central Dr., Ste. 400, Dallas, TX 75251, (972)458-6998

Natl. Assn. of Development Companies [2211], 6764 Old McLean Village Dr., McLean, VA 22101, (703)748-2575

Natl. Assn. of Development Organizations [5330], 400 N Capitol St. NW, Ste. 390, Washington, DC 20001, (202)624-7806

Natl. Assn. of Development Organizations Res. Found. [17385], 400 N Capitol St. NW, Ste. 390, Washington, DC 20001, (202)624-7806

Natl. Assn. of Developmental Disabilities Councils [★12508]

Natl. Assn. for Developmental Educ. [7969], 500 N Estrella Pkwy., Ste. B2, PMB 412, Goodyear, AZ 85338, (877)233-9455

Natl. Assn. of Diaconate Directors [19456], 7625 N High St., Columbus, OH 43235, (614)985-2276

Natl. Assn. of Diaper Services - Defunct.

Natl. Assn. of Diemakers and Diecutters [★1831]

Natl. Assn. of Diemakers and Diecutters [★1831]

Natl. Assn. for the Diffusion of Fertilizers [IO], Sao Paulo, Brazil

Natl. Assn. of Diocesan Ecumenical Officers [★19649]

Natl. Assn. of Direct Sellers [★1537]

Natl. Assn. of Direct Selling Companies [★3157]

Natl. Assn. of Directors and Administrators [★14720]

Natl. Assn. of Directors of Nursing Admin. in Long Term Care [15765], Reed Hartman Tower, 11353 Reed Hartman Hwy., Ste. 210, Cincinnati, OH 45241, (513)791-3679

Natl. Assn. of Disability Examiners [14165], 1599 Green St., No. 303, San Francisco, CA 94123, (510)622-3385

Natl. Assn. of Disability Representatives [18651], 1615 L St. NW, Ste. 650, Washington, DC 20036, (202)822-2155

Natl. Assn. of Disabled Bus. Women of Uzbekistan [IO], Tashkent, Uzbekistan

Natl. Assn. of Display Indus. - Address unknown since 2010.

Natl. Assn. of Distance Educ. and Open Learning in South Africa [IO], Braamfontein, Republic of South Africa

Natl. Assn. of Distributive Educ. Local Supervisors [★8557]

Natl. Assn. for Distributive Educ. Teachers [★8557]

Natl. Assn. of Diversified Mfrs. Representatives [★2322]

Natl. Assn. of Diversity Officers in Higher Educ. [8238], 4440 PGA Blvd., Ste. 600, Palm Beach Gardens, FL 33410, (561)472-8479

Natl. Assn. of Div. Order Analysts [2657], PO Box 6845, Edmond, OK 73083, (432)685-4374

Natl. Assn. of Document Examiners [5486], Linda James, CDE, Pres., PO Box 867226, Plano, TX 75086, (972)612-2232

Natl. Assn. of Dog Obedience Instructors [21607], PO Box 1439, Socorro, NM 87801, (505)850-5957

Natl. Assn. of Domestic Elecl. Appliance Mfrs. [IO], Madrid, Spain

Natl. Assn. for Drama Therapy [16468], 44365 Premier Plz., Ste. 220, Ashburn, VA 20147, (571)333-2991

Natl. Assn. of Dramatic and Speech Arts [10587], 504 Coll. Dr., Albany, GA 31705, (229)430-4840

Natl. Assn. of Dredging Contractors [★2355]

Natl. Assn. on Drug Abuse Problems [13274], 355 Lexington Ave., New York, NY 10017, (212)986-1170

Natl. Assn. of Drug Court Professionals [6004], 1029 N Royal St., Ste. 201, Alexandria, VA 22314, (703)575-9400

Natl. Assn. of Drug Court Professionals [6004], 1029 N Royal St., Ste. 201, Alexandria, VA 22314, (703)575-9400

Natl. Assn. of Drug Diversion Investigators [5714], 1810 York Rd., No. 435, Lutherville, MD 21093, (410)321-4600

Natl. Assn. of Drug Mfrs. Representatives [★2322]

Natl. Assn. for the Dually Diagnosed [★12488]

Natl. Assn. for the Dually Diagnosed [14365], 132 Fair St., Kingston, NY 12401, (845)331-4336

Natl. Assn. of Early Childhood Teacher Educators [8955], Anne Dorsey, 1082 Witt Rd., Cincinnati, OH 45255

Natl. Assn. of Ecumenical and Interreligious Staff [19661], PO Box 95949, Seattle, WA 98145, (206)625-9790

Natl. Assn. of Ecumenical Staff [★19661]

Natl. Assn. of the Edible Oils and Fats Indus. [IO], Mexico City, Mexico

Natl. Assn. for the Educ. and Advancement of Cambodian, Laotian, and Vietnamese Americans [19273], Univ. of Hawai'i, Dept. of Indo-Pacific Languages & Literatures, Spalding Hall 255, 2540 Maile Way, Honolulu, HI 96822

A star before a book entry number signifies that the name is not listed separately, but is mentioned within the entry.

Natl. Assn. for the Educ. of African Amer. Children with Learning Disabilities [12426], PO Box 9521, Columbus, OH 43209, (614)237-6021

Natl. Assn. for the Educ. of Young Children [7832], PO Box 97156, Washington, DC 20090-7156, (202)232-8777

Natl. Assn. of Educational Buyers [★7669]

Natl. Assn. for Educational Guidance for Adults [IO], Wiltshire, United Kingdom

Natl. Assn. of Educational Negotiators [★23182]

Natl. Assn. of Educational Off. Personnel [★7668]

Natl. Assn. of Educational Off. Professionals [7668], PO Box 12619, Wichita, KS 67277-2619, (316)942-4822

Natl. Assn. of Educational Procurement [7669], 5523 Res. Park Dr., Ste. 340, Baltimore, MD 21228, (443)543-5540

Natl. Assn. of Educational Secretaries [★7668]

Natl. Assn. of Elec. Companies [★3593]

Natl. Assn. of Elec. Companies [★3593]

Natl. Assn. of Elecl. Distributors [1079], 1181 Corporate Lake Dr., St. Louis, MO 63132, (314)991-9000

Natl. Assn. of Elecl. Distributors l Natl. Educ. and Res. Found. [2295], 1181 Corporate Lake Dr., St. Louis, MO 63132, (314)991-9000

Natl. Assn. of Elementary School Principals [8749], 1615 Duke St., Alexandria, VA 22314, (703)684-3345

Natl. Assn. of Elevator Contractors [925], 1298 Wellbrook Cir., Conyers, GA 30012, (770)760-9660

Natl. Assn. of Elevator Safety Authorities Intl. - Defunct.

Natl. Assn. of Emergency Medical Technicians [14470], PO Box 1400, Clinton, MS 39060-1400, (601)924-7744

Natl. Assn. of Emergency Medical Technicians [14470], PO Box 1400, Clinton, MS 39060-1400, (601)924-7744

Natl. Assn. of Emergency Vehicle Technicians - Address unknown since 2010.

Natl. Assn. for Employee Recognition [★17613]

Natl. Assn. of Employees of Collectors of Internal Revenue [★23208]

Natl. Assn. of Employers on Health Care Action - Defunct.

Natl. Assn. of Employment Agencies [★1156]

Natl. Assn. of Employment Managers [★2263]

Natl. Assn. of Employment Managers [★2263]

Natl. Assn. of EMS Educators [8611], 250 Mt. Lebanon Blvd., Ste. 209, Pittsburgh, PA 15234, (412)343-4775

Natl. Assn. of EMS Educators [8611], 250 Mt. Lebanon Blvd., Ste. 209, Pittsburgh, PA 15234, (412)343-4775

Natl. Assn. of EMS Physicians [14471], PO Box 19570, Lenexa, KS 66285, (913)895-4611

Natl. Assn. of Energy Ser. Companies [6737], 1615 M St. NW, Ste. 800, Washington, DC 20036-3224, (202)822-0950

Natl. Assn. of Engine and Boat Mfrs. [★2365]

Natl. Assn. of Engineering Companies - Defunct.

Natl. Assn. of Enrolled Agents [6015], 1120 Connecticut Ave. NW, Ste. 460, Washington, DC 20036-3953, (202)822-6232

Natl. Assn. of Entrepreneurial Parents - Address unknown since 2010.

Natl. Assn. for Environmental Educ. [IO], Walsall, United Kingdom

Natl. Assn. of Environmental Law Societies [5420], Dan Worth, 22 Oakview Terr., Boston, MA 02130

Natl. Assn. for Environmental Mgt. [★4282]

Natl. Assn. of Environmental Professionals [4283], PO Box 460, Collingswood, NJ 08108, (856)283-7816

Natl. Assn. for Episcopal Christian Educ. Directors [7856], 1406 Univ. Dr., Hammond, LA 70401

Natl. Assn. of Episcopal Schools [8163], 815 2nd Ave., Ste. 819, New York, NY 10017-4594, (212)716-6134

Natl. Assn. for Equal Educational Opportunities - Defunct.

Natl. Assn. for Equal Opportunity in Higher Educ. [7884], 209 Third St. SE, Washington, DC 20003, (202)552-3300

Natl. Assn. of Equip. Leasing Brokers [3079], 455 S Fourth St., Ste. 650, Louisville, KY 40202, (800)996-2352

Natl. Assn. of Equity Source Banks [426], 5432 Price Ave., Baltimore, MD 21215, (410)367-5309

Natl. Assn. of ESOP Companies [★1136]

Natl. Assn. of Estate Agents [IO], Warwick, United Kingdom

Natl. Assn. of Estate Planners and Councils [1342], 1120 Chester Ave., Ste. 470, Cleveland, OH 44114, (866)226-2224

Natl. Assn. of Estate Planning Councils [★1342]

Natl. Assn. for Ethnic Stud. [9586], Colorado State Univ., Dept. of Ethnic Stud., 1790 Campus Delivery, Fort Collins, CO 80523-1790

Natl. Assn. of Evangelicals [19766], PO Box 23269, Washington, DC 20026-3269, (202)789-1011

Natl. Assn. of Evangelicals [19725], PO Box 23269, Washington, DC 20026, (202)789-1011

Natl. Assn. for the Exchange of Indus. Resources [8089], 560 McClure St., Galesburg, IL 61401, (309)343-0704

Natl. Assn. of Exclusive Buyer Agents [18504], 1481 N Eliseo C. Felix Jr. Way, Ste. 223, Avondale, AZ 85323, (623)932-0098

Natl. Assn. of Executive Recruiters [1154], 1 E Wacker Dr., Ste. 2600, Chicago, IL 60601, (847)885-1453

Natl. Assn. of Executive Secretaries [★62]

Natl. Assn. of Executive Secretaries and Administrative Assistants [★62]

Natl. Assn. of Exotic Pest Plant Councils [4774], Univ. of Georgia, Center for Invasive Species and Ecosystem Hea., PO Box 748, Tifton, GA 31793, (229)386-3298

Natl. Assn. of Export Companies [2101], PO Box 3949, Grand Central Sta., New York, NY 10163, (877)291-4901

Natl. Assn. of Exposition Managers [★2450]

Natl. Assn. of Exposition Managers [★2450]

Natl. Assn. of Extension 4-H Agents [13537], 20423 State Rd. 7, Ste. F6-491, Boca Raton, FL 33498, (561)477-8100

Natl. Assn. of Extension Home Economists [★5344]

Natl. Assn. of Exterminators and Fumigators [★2634]

Natl. Assn. of Exterminators and Fumigators [★2634]

Natl. Assn. for Families and Addiction Res. and Education - Defunct.

Natl. Assn. for Family Child Care [12024], 1743 W Alexander St., Salt Lake City, UT 84119, (801)886-2322

Natl. Assn. for Family and Community Educ. [8265], 73 Cavalier Blvd., Ste. 106, Florence, KY 41042, (877)712-4477

Natl. Assn. of Family Ministries [19998], Carri Taylor, Treas., 13919-B N May Ave., No. 198, Oklahoma City, OK 73134

Natl. Assn. of Fan Mfrs. [★1697]

Natl. Assn. of Fan Mfrs. [★1697]

Natl. Assn. of Farm Broadcasters [★502]

Natl. Assn. of Farm Broadcasting [502], PO Box 500, Platte City, MO 64079, (816)431-4032

Natl. Assn. of Farm Bus. Anal. Specialists [165], PO Box 467, Camp Point, IL 62320, (217)593-7233

Natl. Assn. of Farm Ser. Agency County Off. Employees [5506], 11238 W 22000 Rd., Fontana, KS 66026, (913)294-3751

Natl. Assn. of Farmers' Market Nutrition Programs [4355], PO Box 9080, Alexandria, VA 22304, (703)837-0451

Natl. Assn. of Farriers, Blacksmiths and Agricultural Engineers [IO], Kenilworth, United Kingdom

Natl. Assn. of Fed. Credit Unions [1004], 3138 10th St. N, Arlington, VA 22201-2149, (703)522-4770

Natl. Assn. of Fed. Defenders [5375], PO Box 22223, Nashville, TN 37202

Natl. Assn. of Fed. Educ. Prog. Administrators [7670], Rick Carder, Pres., 125 David Dr., Sutter Creek, CA 95685, (916)669-5102

Natl. Assn. of Fed. Prog. Administrators [★7670]

Natl. Assn. of Fed. Veterinarians [17033], 1910 Sunderland Pl. NW, Washington, DC 20036-1608, (202)223-4878

Natl. Assn. of Federally Impacted Schools [8101], 444 N Capitol St. NW, Ste. 419, Washington, DC 20001, (202)624-5455

Natl. Assn. of Fellowships Advisors [8810], Alicia Hayes, Sec., Univ. of California, Berkeley, Scholarship Connection, 301 Campbell Hall, No. 2922, Berkeley, CA 94720-2922

Natl. Assn. for Female Executives [683], PO Box 3052, Langhorne, PA 19047, (800)927-6233

Natl. Assn. of Female Paramedics [14472], PO Box 1133, Orlando, FL 32802, (407)932-2839

Natl. Assn. of Field Training Officers [5715], Sgt. Kimber Williams, Pres., 2554 Ordinance Rd., Santa Rosa, CA 95403, (707)579-7760

Natl. Assn. of Finance Institutions [IO], Madrid, Spain

Natl. Assn. of Financial and Estate Planning [1316], 515 E 4500 S, No. G-200, Salt Lake City, UT 84107, (800)454-2649

Natl. Assn. of Financial Services [IO], Berlin, Germany

Natl. Assn. of Fine Art Dealers [★247]

Natl. Assn. of Fire Equip. Distributors [3147], 122 S Michigan Ave., Ste. 1040, Chicago, IL 60603, (312)461-9600

Natl. Assn. of Fire Investigators [2001], 857 Tallevast Rd., Sarasota, FL 34243, (941)359-2800

Natl. Assn. of Firearms Retailers [1353], 11 Mile Hill Rd., Newtown, CT 06470, (203)426-1320

Natl. Assn. of Fisheries Commissioners [★7036]

Natl. Assn. of Fisheries Commissioners [★7036]

Natl. Assn. for Fixed Annuities [2002], 2300 E Kensington Blvd., Milwaukee, WI 53211, (414)332-9306

Natl. Assn. of Flavors and Food-Ingredient Systems [1410], 3301 Rte. 66, Bldg. C, Ste. 205, Neptune, NJ 07753, (732)922-3218

Natl. Assn. of Fleet Administrators [★302]

Natl. Assn. of Fleet Resale Dealers [360], 2521 Brown Blvd., Arlington, TX 76006, (817)649-5858

Natl. Assn. of Fleet Tug Sailors [20720], 221 Buland Dr., Castle Rock, WA 98611, (800)293-3587

Natl. Assn. of Flight Instructors [149], 730 Grand St., Allegan, MI 49010, (866)806-6156

Natl. Assn. of Flood and Storm Water Mgt. Agencies [5863], 1333 H St. NW, West Tower, 10th Fl., Washington, DC 20005, (202)289-8625

Natl. Assn. of Floor Covering Distributors [★602]

Natl. Assn. of Flour Distributors [1411], G. Timothy Dove, Exec. Sec., 5350 Woodland Pl., Canfield, OH 44406, (330)718-6563

Natl. Assn. of Flower Arrangement Societies [IO], London, United Kingdom

Natl. Assn. of Food Chains [★3104]

Natl. Assn. of Food and Dairy Equip. Mfrs. [★1020]

Natl. Assn. of Food and Dairy Equip. Mfrs. [★1020]

Natl. Assn. of Food Equip. Mfrs. [★1441]

Natl. Assn. of Food Indus. [IO], Paris, France

Natl. Assn. of Food Products Retailers and Mfrs. [IO], Lisbon, Portugal

Natl. Assn. of Foreclosure Prevention Professionals [2899], 5505 Connecticut Ave. NW, No. 287, Washington, DC 20015, (800)989-9329

Natl. Assn. of Foreign Medical Graduates [★15142]

Natl. Assn. of Foreign Medical Graduates [★15142]

Natl. Assn. of Foreign Student Advisors [★8204]

Natl. Assn. of Foreign Student Advisors [★8204]

Natl. Assn. for Foreign Student Affairs [★8204]

Natl. Assn. for Foreign Student Affairs [★8204]

Natl. Assn. of Foreign-Trade Zones [2102], 1001 Connecticut Ave. NW, Ste. 350, Washington, DC 20036, (202)331-1950

Natl. Assn. of Foremen [★2299]

Natl. Assn. of Forensic Accountants [45], 6451 N Fed. Hwy., Ste. 121, Fort Lauderdale, FL 33308, (800)523-3680

Natl. Assn. of Forensic Counselors [5376], PO Box 8827, Fort Wayne, IN 46898-8827, (260)426-7234

Natl. Assn. of Forensic Economics [5774], PO Box 394, Mount Union, PA 17066, (814)542-3253

Natl. Assn. of Forensic Economists [★5774]

Natl. Assn. of Forest Indus. [IO], Deakin West, Australia

Natl. Assn. of Form 1099 Filers - Address unknown since 2010.

Natl. Assn. of Former Foster Care Children of Am. [11355], 5505 5th St. NW, Washington, DC 20011, (202)291-1603

Reference to "IO" in place of a book number signifies that the association may be found in the 50th edition of International Organizations.

Natl. Assn. of Fraternal Insurance Counsellors [2003], 211 Canal Rd., Waterloo, WI 53594, (866)478-3880

Natl. Assn. of Free Clinics [14904], Nicole D. Lamoureux, Exec. Dir., 1800 Diagonal Rd., Ste. 600, Alexandria, VA 22314, (703)647-7427

Natl. Assn. of Free Will Baptists [19325], 5233 Mt. View Rd., Antioch, TN 37013-2306, (615)731-6812

Natl. Assn. of Freestanding Emergency Centers [★13727]

Natl. Assn. of Frozen Food Packers [★1371]

Natl. Assn. of Fruits, Flavors and Syrups [★1410]

Natl. Assn. of Fugitive Investigators - Address unknown since 2011.

Natl. Assn. of Funeral Directors [IO], Solihull, United Kingdom

Natl. Assn. of Furniture Mfrs. [★1543]

Natl. Assn. of Future Doctors of Audiology - Defunct.

Natl. Assn. of Gambling Regulatory Agencies [★5494]

Natl. Assn. for Gambling Stud. [IO], Prahran, Australia

Natl. Assn. of Game Commissioners and Wardens [★4004]

Natl. Assn. of Game Commissioners and Wardens [★4004]

Natl. Assn. of Garage Door Mfrs. - Defunct.

Natl. Assn. of Gardeners [★4517]

Natl. Assn. of Gay Alcoholism Professionals [★13266]

Natl. Assn. Gen. Merchandise Representatives Consumer Prdt. Brokers [★2322]

Natl. Assn. of Gen. Practitioner Veterinarians [IO], Frankfurt, Germany

Natl. Assn. of Geoscience Teachers [8212], 1 N Coll. St., Northfield, MN 55057, (507)222-7096

Natl. Assn. of Geriatric Educ. Centers [14666], 1695 NW 9th Ave., Ste. 3208 (D-101), Miami, FL 33136, (305)355-9123

Natl. Assn. of Geriatric Nursing Assistants [★14667]

Natl. Assn. of German Bus. Consultants [IO], Bonn, Germany

Natl. Assn. of the German Cement Indus. [IO], Berlin, Germany

Natl. Assn. of the German Food Indus. [IO], Berlin, Germany

Natl. Assn. of the German Gravel and Sand Indus. [IO], Duisburg, Germany

Natl. Assn. of German Non-Alcoholic Beverage Indus. [IO], Berlin, Germany

Natl. Assn. of German Stamp Dealers [IO], Cologne, Germany

Natl. Assn. of the German Tallow and Lard Indus. [IO], Bonn, Germany

Natl. Assn. of German Tobacco Wholesalers and Vending Machine Installers [IO], Cologne, Germany

Natl. Assn. for Gifted Children [IO], Milton Keynes, United Kingdom

Natl. Assn. for Gifted Children [8216], 1331 H St. NW, Ste. 1001, Washington, DC 20005, (202)785-4268

Natl. Assn. of Girl Scout Executives [★13017]

Natl. Assn. of Girls Clubs [★13539]

Natl. Assn. for Girls and Women in Sport [8719], 1900 Assn. Dr., Reston, VA 20191-1598, (703)476-3452

Natl. Assn. of the Glass Indus. [IO], Dusseldorf, Germany

Natl. Assn. of Glass Mfrs. [IO], Rome, Italy

Natl. Assn. of Goldsmiths [IO], London, United Kingdom

Natl. Assn. of Goodwill Indus. [★11792]

Natl. Assn. of Goodwill Indus. [★11792]

Natl. Assn. of Govt. Archives and Records Administrators [5543], 1450 Western Ave., Ste. 101, Albany, NY 12203, (518)694-8472

Natl. Assn. of Govt. Communicators [5324], 201 Park Washington Ct., Falls Church, VA 22046-4527, (703)538-1787

Natl. Assn. of Govt. Deferred Compensation Administrators [★2141]

Natl. Assn. of Govt. Defined Contribution Administrators [2141], 201 E Main St., Ste. 1405, Lexington, KY 40507, (859)514-9161

Natl. Assn. of Govt. Employees [23202], 159 Burgin Pkwy., Quincy, MA 02169, (617)376-0220

Natl. Assn. of Govt. Guaranteed Lenders [5770], 215 E 9th Ave., Stillwater, OK 74074, (405)377-4022

Natl. Assn. for Govt. Training and Development [2629], 156 Whispering Winds Dr., Lexington, SC 29072, (803)397-8468

Natl. Assn. of Govt. Webmasters [6548], 86 Woodstone Rd., Rockaway, NJ 07866, (973)594-6249

Natl. Assn. of Governmental Labor Officials [5635], PO Box 29609, Atlanta, GA 30359, (404)679-1795

Natl. Assn. of Governor's Councils on Physical Fitness and Sport [★16230]

Natl. Assn. of Governors' Highway Safety Representatives [★6031]

Natl. Assn. of Graduate Admissions Professionals [7685], PO Box 14605, Lenexa, KS 66285-4605, (913)895-4616

Natl. Assn. of Graduate-Professional Students [8922], PO Box 96503, Washington, DC 20090-6503, (202)643-8043

Natl. Assn. of Graphic and Prdt. Identification Mfrs. [2484], 1300 Sumner Ave., Cleveland, OH 44115-2851, (216)241-7333

Natl. Assn. of Greeting Card Publishers [★3350]

Natl. Assn. of Gun and Knife Shows [★17280]

Natl. Assn. for Gun Rights [17305], PO Box 7002, Fredericksburg, VA 22404, (877)405-4570

Natl. Assn. for the Habilitation of the Mentally Handicapped in Israel [IO], Tel Aviv, Israel

Natl. Assn. of Head Teachers [IO], Haywards Heath, United Kingdom

Natl. Assn. of Hea. Care Assistants [14667], 501 E 15th St., Joplin, MO 64804, (800)784-6049

Natl. Assn. of Hea. Data Organizations [14721], 448 E 400 S, Ste. 301, Salt Lake City, UT 84111, (801)532-2299

Natl. Assn. of Hea. Educ. Centers [14847], 1533 N River Center Dr., Milwaukee, WI 53212-3913, (414)390-2188

Natl. Assn. of Hea. and Educational Facilities Finance Authorities [1673], 701 Pennsylvania Ave. NW, No. 900, Washington, DC 20004, (202)434-7311

Natl. Assn. for Hea. and Fitness [16230], Be Active New York State, 65 Niagara Sq., Rm. 607, Buffalo, NY 14202, (716)851-4052

Natl. Assn. of Hea. Sci. Educ. Partnership [8843], Duquesne Univ., 222 Mellon Hall, Pittsburgh, PA 15282, (412)855-4043

Natl. Assn. for Health Science Educ. Partnerships [8318], Duquesne Univ., 222 Mellon Hall, Pittsburgh, PA 15282, (412)855-4043

Natl. Assn. of Hea. Services Executives [14722], 1050 Connecticut Ave. NW, 10th Fl., Washington, DC 20036, (202)772-1030

Natl. Assn. of Hea. Underwriters [2004], 2000 N 14th St., Ste. 450, Arlington, VA 22201, (703)276-0220

Natl. Assn. of Hea. Unit Clerks-Coordinators [★14723]

Natl. Assn. of Hea. Unit Coordinators [14723], 1947 Madron Rd., Rockford, IL 61107-1716, (815)633-4351

Natl. Assn. of Hea. and Welfare Ministries of The United Methodist Church [★14742]

Natl. Assn. of Healthcare Access Mgt. [15062], 2025 M St. NW, Ste. 800, Washington, DC 20036-2422, (202)367-1125

Natl. Assn. for Healthcare Quality [16508], 4700 W Lake Ave., Glenview, IL 60025, (847)375-4720

Natl. Assn. of Healthcare Recruiters [★15296]

Natl. Assn. for Healthcare Recruitment [15296], 2501 Aerial Center Pkwy., Ste. 103, Morrisville, NC 27560, (919)459-2167

Natl. Assn. of Healthcare Transport Mgt. [14724], Cathleen Thom, VP, PO Box 409, Twin Falls, ID 83303, (208)737-2929

Natl. Assn. of Hearing Officials [5626], PO Box 4999, Midlothian, VA 23112, (701)328-3260

Natl. Assn. for Hearing and Speech Action [★16682]

Natl. Assn. of Hearing and Speech Agencies [★16682]

Natl. Assn. of Hepatitis Task Forces [14986], PO Box 66, Miller, NE 68858, (308)457-2641

Natl. Assn. of High School Teachers of Journalism [★8444]

Natl. Assn. for Hispanic Elderly [19024], 234 E Colorado Blvd., Ste. 300, Pasadena, CA 91101, (626)564-1988

Natl. Assn. of Hispanic Fed. Executives [5434], PO Box 23270, Washington, DC 20026, (202)315-3942

Natl. Assn. of Hispanic Firefighters [5446], 1220 L St. NW, Ste. 100-199, Washington, DC 20005, (877)342-6243

Natl. Assn. of Hispanic Journalists [2842], 1050 Connecticut Ave. NW, 10th Fl., Washington, DC 20036-5334, (202)662-7145

Natl. Assn. of Hispanic and Latino Stud. [9587], Natl. Assn. of African Amer. Studies and Affiliates, PO Box 6670, Scarborough, ME 04070-6670, (207)839-8004

Natl. Assn. of Hispanic Nurses [15766], 1455 Pennsylvania Ave. NW, Ste. 400, Washington, DC 20004, (202)387-2477

Natl. Assn. of Hispanic Priests of the USA [19457], PO Box 2279, Brownsville, TX 78522-2279

Natl. Assn. of Hispanic Publications [2949], 529 14th St. NW, Ste. 1126, Washington, DC 20045, (202)662-7250

Natl. Assn. of Hispanic Real Estate Professionals [3020], 5414 Oberlin Dr., Ste. 230, San Diego, CA 92121, (858)622-9046

Natl. Assn. of Hispanic-Serving Hea. Professions Schools [★8608]

Natl. Assn. on HIV Over Fifty [15121], 23 Miner St., Boston, MA 02215-3318, (617)233-7107

Natl. Assn. for Holistic Aromatherapy [15002], PO Box 1868, Banner Elk, NC 28604, (828)898-6161

Natl. Assn. of the Holy Name Soc. [19458], Cleveland Cosom, Dir., PO Box 12012, Baltimore, MD 21281-2012, (410)325-1523

Natl. Assn. of Home Based Businesses [1732], 5432 Price Ave., Baltimore, MD 21215, (410)367-5308

Natl. Assn. of Home Builders [926], 1201 15th St. NW, Washington, DC 20005, (202)266-8200

Natl. Assn. of Home Builders I Building Systems Coun. [2311], 1201 15th St. NW, Washington, DC 20005, (202)266-8200

Natl. Assn. of Home Builders I Leading Suppliers Coun. [588], 1201 15th St. NW, Washington, DC 20005-2800, (202)266-8200

Natl. Assn. of Home Builders I Log Homes Coun. [2312], 1201 15th St. NW, Washington, DC 20005, (800)368-5242

Natl. Assn. of Home Builders I Modular Building Systems Coun. [2313], 1201 15th St. NW, Washington, DC 20005, (202)266-8200

Natl. Assn. of Home Builders I Panelized Building Systems Coun. [2314], 1201 15th St. NW, Washington, DC 20005, (202)266-8200

Natl. Assn. of Home Builders of the U.S. [★926]

Natl. Assn. for Home Care and Hospice [15011], 228 7th St. SE, Washington, DC 20003, (202)547-7424

Natl. Assn. of Home Delivered and Congregate Meal Providers [★12151]

Natl. Assn. of Home Inspectors [1919], 4248 Park Glen Rd., Minneapolis, MN 55416, (952)928-4641

Natl. Assn. of Home Mfrs. [★2311]

Natl. Assn. of Home and Workshop Writers [2843], PO Box 12, Baker, NV 89311, (866)457-2582

Natl. Assn. of Homes for Boys [★13542]

Natl. Assn. of Homes for Children [★11993]

Natl. Assn. of Homes for Children [★11993]

Natl. Assn. of Homes and Services for Children [★11993]

Natl. Assn. of Homes and Services for Children [★11993]

Natl. Assn. of Horseshoe and Quoit Pitchers [★22695]

Natl. Assn. of Hose and Accessories Distribution [1850], 105 Eastern Ave., Ste. 104, Annapolis, MD 21403, (410)940-6350

Natl. Assn. of Hosiery Mfrs. [★207]

Natl. Assn. of Hosp. Admitting Managers [★15062]

Natl. Assn. for Hosp. Development [★15045]

Natl. Assn. for Hosp. Development [★15045]

Natl. Assn. of Hosp. Fire Officers [IO], Cardiff, United Kingdom

A star before a book entry number signifies that the name is not listed separately, but is mentioned within the entry.

Natl. Assn. of Hosp. Hospitality Houses [15063], PO Box 1439, Gresham, OR 97030, (800)542-9730

Natl. Assn. of Hotel Accountants [★1303]

Natl. Assn. of Hotel Accountants [★1303]

Natl. Assn. of the Hotel Indus. [IO], Casablanca, Morocco

Natl. Assn. of Hotel and Motel Accountants [★1303]

Natl. Assn. of Hotel and Motel Accountants [★1303]

Natl. Assn. of Hotel and Restaurant Meat Purveyors [★2434]

Natl. Assn. of Hotel and Restaurant Meat Purveyors [★2434]

Natl. Assn. of Housing Cooperatives [12185], 1444 I St. NW, Ste. 700, Washington, DC 20005-6542, (202)737-0797

Natl. Assn. of Housing Counselors and Agencies [1784], PO Box 91873, Lafayette, LA 70509-1873

Natl. Assn. of Housing Info. Managers [5519], 134 S 13th St., Ste. 701, Lincoln, NE 68508, (402)476-9424

Natl. Assn. of Housing Officials [★5520]

Natl. Assn. of Housing and Redevelopment Officials [5520], PO Box 90487, Washington, DC 20090, (202)289-3500

Natl. Assn. for Humane and Environmental Educ. [★10986]

Natl. Assn. for Humanities Educ. - Address unknown since 2010.

Natl. Assn. of the Ice Indus. [★1712]

Natl. Assn. of Importers and Exporters [IO], Mexico City, Mexico

Natl. Assn. for an Inclusive Priesthood [★19418]

Natl. Assn. of Independent Artists [9241], Cynthia Davis, 3155 Buck Island Rd., Charlottesville, VA 22902, (734)761-5698

Natl. Assn. of Independent Colleges and Universities [8290], 1025 Connecticut Ave. NW, Ste. 700, Washington, DC 20036, (202)785-8866

Natl. Assn. of Independent Fee Appraisers [234], 401 N Michigan Ave., Ste. 2200, Chicago, IL 60611, (312)321-6830

Natl. Assn. of Independent Insurance Adjusters [2005], PO Box 807, Geneva, IL 60134, (630)208-5002

Natl. Assn. of Independent Insurance Auditors and Engineers [2006], PO Box 794, Clifton Park, NY 12065, (800)232-2342

Natl. Assn. of Independent Insurers [★2031]

National Assn. of Independent Insurers Safety Association [★12985]

Natl. Assn. of Independent Labor [23203], One City Center, Ste. 300, 11815 Fountain Way, Newport News, VA 23606, (757)926-5216

Natl. Assn. of Independent Life Brokerage Agencies [2007], 11325 Random Hills Rd., Ste. 110, Fairfax, VA 22030, (703)383-3081

Natl. Assn. of Independent Lighting Distributors [2220], 2207 Elmwood Ave., Buffalo, NY 14216-1009, (716)875-3670

Natl. Assn. for Independent Living - Defunct.

Natl. Assn. of Independent Lubes [★351]

Natl. Assn. of Independent Mass-Media in Tajikistan [IO], Dushanbe, Tajikistan

Natl. Assn. of Independent Nurses - Address unknown since 2011.

Natl. Assn. of Independent Public Finance Advisors [1343], PO Box 304, Montgomery, IL 60538-0304, (630)896-1292

Natl. Assn. of Independent Publishers Representatives [2950], 111 E 14th St., PMB 157, New York, NY 10003-4103, (646)414-2993

Natl. Assn. of Independent Real Estate Brokers [3021], 7102 Mardyke Ln., Indianapolis, IN 46226, (317)549-1709

National Assn. of Independent Resurfacers [★569]

Natl. Assn. of Independent Schools [8291], 1620 L St. NW, Ste. 1100, Washington, DC 20036-5695, (202)973-9700

Natl. Assn. of Independent Tire Dealers [★3465]

Natl. Assn. of Independent Writers and Editors [2844], PO Box 549, Ashland, VA 23005, (804)767-5961

Natl. Assn. of Indian Affairs [★18150]

Natl. Assn. for Indiana Limestone [★3362]

Natl. Assn. of Indonesian Consultants [IO], Jakarta, Indonesia

Natl. Assn. of Indus. and Off. Parks [★3022]

Natl. Assn. of Indus. and Off. Properties [3022], 2201 Cooperative Way, Ste. 300, Herndon, VA 20171-3034, (703)904-7100

Natl. Assn. of Indus. Parks [★3022]

Natl. Assn. of Indus. Security Companies [IO], Sofia, Bulgaria

Natl. Assn. of Indus. Teacher Educators [★8295]

Natl. Assn. of Indus. Teacher Trainers [★8295]

Natl. Assn. of Indus. and Tech. Teacher Educators [★8295]

Natl. Assn. of Indus. Tech. [★8296]

Natl. Assn. for Info. Destruction [1904], 1951 W Camelback Rd., Ste. 350, Phoenix, AZ 85015, (602)788-6243

Natl. Assn. for Info. Destruction [1904], 1951 W Camelback Rd., Ste. 350, Phoenix, AZ 85015, (602)788-6243

Natl. Assn. of Inpatient Physicians [★15067]

Natl. Assn. Insecticide and Disinfectant Mfrs. [★752]

Natl. Assn. of Installation Developers [★5533]

Natl. Assn. of Institutional Laundry Managers [★2189]

Natl. Assn. of Institutional Linen Mgt. [★2189]

Natl. Assn. of Insurance Agents [★1964]

Natl. Assn. of Insurance Commissioners [5554], 2301 McGee St., Ste. 800, Kansas City, MO 64108-2662, (816)842-3600

Natl. Assn. of Insurance and Financial Advisors [2008], 2901 Telestar Ct., Falls Church, VA 22042-1205, (703)770-8100

Natl. Assn. of Insurance Women [★2009]

Natl. Assn. of Insurance Women Intl. [2009], 9343 E 95th Ct. S, Tulsa, OK 74133, (918)294-3700

Natl. Assn. for Interactive Services [★678]

Natl. Assn. for Interactive Services [★678]

Natl. Assn. of Intercollegiate Athletics [22991], 1200 Grand Blvd., Kansas City, MO 64106, (816)595-8000

Natl. Assn. of Intercollegiate Basketball [★22991]

Natl. Assn. of Interdisciplinary Ethnic Stud. [★9586]

Natl. Assn. of Interdisciplinary Stud. for Native Amer., Black, Chicano, Puerto Rican, Asian Americans [★9586]

Natl. Assn. of Internal Revenue Employees [★23208]

Natl. Assn. of Internet Ser. Providers of Romania [IO], Bucharest, Romania

Natl. Assn. for Interpretation [7142], PO Box 2246, Fort Collins, CO 80522, (970)484-8283

Natl. Assn. of Investigative Specialists [2124], PO Box 82148, Austin, TX 78708, (512)719-3595

Natl. Assn. of the Investment Advisory Publishers [★2966]

Natl. Assn. of the Investment Advisory Publishers [★2966]

Natl. Assn. of Investment Clubs [★2143]

Natl. Assn. of Investment Companies [2522], 1300 Pennsylvania Ave. NW, Ste. 700, Washington, DC 20004, (202)204-3001

Natl. Assn. of Investment Companies [★3200]

Natl. Assn. of Investment Professionals [2142], 12664 Emmer Pl., Ste. 201, St. Paul, MN 55124, (952)322-4322

Natl. Assn. of Investors Corp. [2143], PO Box 220, Royal Oak, MI 48068, (248)583-6242

Natl. Assn. of Italian Footwear Mfrs. [IO], Milan, Italy

Natl. Assn. of Japan-America Societies [19083], 1819 L St. NW, Ste. 200, Washington, DC 20036, (202)429-5545

Natl. Assn. of Jazz Educators [★8653]

Natl. Assn. of Jazz Educators [★8653]

Natl. Assn. of Jewelry Appraisers [2171], PO Box 18, Rego Park, NY 11374-0018, (718)896-1536

Natl. Assn. of Jewish Chaplains [19526], 901 Rte. 10, Whippany, NJ 07981-1156, (973)929-3168

Natl. Assn. of Jewish Homes for the Aged [★10834]

Natl. Assn. of Jewish Vocational Services [★9044]

Natl. Assn. of Jewish Vocational Services [★9044]

Natl. Assn. of Jim Beam Bottle and Specialties Clubs [★21235]

Natl. Assn. of Jim Beam Bottle and Specialties Clubs [★21235]

Natl. Assn. of Journalism Directors [★8444]

Natl. Assn. of Judiciary Interpreters and Translators [5356], 1707 L St. NW, Ste. 570, Washington, DC 20036, (202)293-0342

Natl. Assn. of Junior Auxiliaries [13067], PO Box 1873, Greenville, MS 38702-1873, (662)332-3000

Natl. Assn. for Justice Info. Systems [5377], 101 E Wilson, 8th Fl., PO Box 7844, Madison, WI 53707-7844, (608)261-6614

Natl. Assn. of Juvenile Correctional Agencies - Defunct.

Natl. Assn. of Karate and Martial Arts Schools [IO], Herne Bay, United Kingdom

Natl. Assn. of Korean Americans [17306], 3883 Plaza Dr., Fairfax, VA 22030, (703)267-2388

Natl. Assn. of Labour Banks [IO], Tokyo, Japan

Natl. Assn. of Ladies' Circles of Great Britain and Ireland [IO], Birmingham, United Kingdom

Natl. Assn. of Land Title Examiners and Abstractors [3023], 7490 Eagle Rd., Waite Hill, OH 44094

Natl. Assn. of Language Advisers [IO], Lancashire, United Kingdom

Natl. Assn. of Laryngectomee Clubs [IO], London, United Kingdom

Natl. Assn. of Latina Leaders [2196], 1230 6th Ave., Ste. 700, New York, NY 10020

Natl. Assn. of Latino Appointed Democratic Officials [★17778]

Natl. Assn. of Latino Arts and Culture [9306], 1208 Buena Vista St., San Antonio, TX 78207, (210)432-3982

Natl. Assn. of Latino Elected and Appointed Officials [17778], 1122 W Washington Blvd., 3rd Fl., Los Angeles, CA 90015-3316, (213)747-7606

Natl. Assn. of Latino Fraternal Organizations [18990], PO Box 27322, Tempe, AZ 85285-7322

Natl. Assn. of Latino Independent Producers [1265], PO Box 1247, Santa Monica, CA 90406, (310)395-8880

Natl. Assn. of the Launderette Indus. [IO], Berkshire, United Kingdom

Natl. Assn. of Law Firm Marketing Administrators [★2409]

Natl. Assn. of Law Firm Marketing Administrators [★2409]

Natl. Assn. for Law Placement [8508], 1220 19th St. NW, Ste. 401, Washington, DC 20036-2405, (202)835-1001

Natl. Assn. for Lay Ministry [19914], 6896 Laurel St. NW, Washington, DC 20012, (202)291-4100

Natl. Assn. of Lay Ministry Coordinators [★19914]

Natl. Assn. of Leagues, Umpires and Scorers - Defunct.

Natl. Assn. of Left-Handed Golfers [22617], PO Box 640, Leland, NC 28451, (910)383-0339

Natl. Assn. of Legal Assistants [5871], 1516 S Boston, Ste. 200, Tulsa, OK 74119, (918)587-6828

Natl. Assn. of Legal Document Preparers - Address unknown since 2010.

Natl. Assn. of Legal Fee Anal. [5672], 35 E Wacker Dr., Ste. 922, Chicago, IL 60601, (312)854-7157

Natl. Assn. of Legal Investigators [5605], 235 N Pine St., Lansing, MI 48933, (517)702-9835

Natl. Assn. of Legal Search Consultants [2125], 1525 N Park Dr., Ste. 102, Weston, FL 33326, (954)349-8081

Natl. Assn. of Legal Secretaries Intl. [72], 8159 E 41st St., Tulsa, OK 74145-3312, (918)582-5188

Natl. Assn. of Legal Secretaries Intl. [72], 8159 E 41st St., Tulsa, OK 74145-3312, (918)582-5188

Natl. Assn. for Legal Support of Alternative Schools [7723], PO Box 2823, Santa Fe, NM 87504, (505)474-0300

Natl. Assn. of Legal Vendors - Defunct.

Natl. Assn. of Lesbian/Gay Addiction Professionals [★13266]

Natl. Assn. of Lesbian/Gay Alcoholism Professionals [★13266]

Natl. Assn. of Lesbian, Gay, Bisexual and Transgender Community Centers [★11661]

Natl. Assn. of Letter Carriers [★23280]

Natl. Assn. of Letter Carriers of the U.S.A. [23280], 100 Indiana Ave. NW, Washington, DC 20001-2144, (202)393-4695

Natl. Assn. of Licensed Paralegals [IO], London, United Kingdom

Natl. Assn. of Licensed Practical Nurses [★8613]

Natl. Assn. of Life Underwriters [★2008]

Natl. Assn. for Literature Development [IO], Ilkley, United Kingdom

Reference to "IO" in place of a book number signifies that the association may be found in the 50th edition of International Organizations.

Natl. Assn. of Litho Clubs [1619], 3268 N 147th Ln., Goodyear, AZ 85395, (650)339-4007

Natl. Assn. of Lively Families - Address unknown since 2011.

Natl. Assn. of Livestock Trailer Mfrs. [★335]

Natl. Assn. of Local Boards of Hea. [16487], 1840 E Gypsy Lane Rd., Bowling Green, OH 43402, (419)353-7714

Natl. Assn. of Local Councils [IO], London, United Kingdom

Natl. Assn. of Local Govt. Auditors [★5183]

Natl. Assn. of Local Govt. Environmental Professionals [5849], 1333 New Hampshire Ave. NW, 2nd Fl., Washington, DC 20036, (202)879-4014

Natl. Assn. of Local Housing Finance Agencies [5521], 2025 M St. NW, Ste. 800, Washington, DC 20036-3309, (202)367-1197

Natl. Assn. of Location Analysts and Negotiators [★3006]

Natl. Assn. of Location Analysts and Negotiators [★3006]

Natl. Assn. of Locum Tenens Org. [16268], 222 S Westmonte Dr., Ste. 101, Altamonte Springs, FL 32714, (407)774-7880

Natl. Assn. of Long Term Hospitals [15064], Karen Hinen, 342 N Main St., West Hartford, CT 06117, (860)586-7579

Natl. Assn. of Lutheran Interim Pastors [19938], PO Box 4416, Bethlehem, PA 18018-0416, (610)866-1931

Natl. Assn. of Magazine Publishers [★2947]

Natl. Assn. of Mail Ser. Pharmacies [★16211]

Natl. Assn. of Major Mail Users [IO], Scarborough, ON, Canada

Natl. Assn. for Males with Eating Disorders [14438], 118 Palm Dr., No. 11, Naples, FL 34112, (239)775-1145

Natl. Assn. of Managed Care Physicians [16269], 4435 Waterfront Dr., Ste. 101, Glen Allen, VA 23058, (804)527-1905

Natl. Assn. of Mgt. and Tech. Assistance Centers [★9047]

Natl. Assn. of Mfrs. [2340], 1331 Pennsylvania Ave. NW, Ste. 600, Washington, DC 20004-1790, (202)637-3000

Natl. Assn. of Mfrs. [★498]

Natl. Assn. of Mfrs. Coun. of Mfg. Associations [2341], 1331 Pennsylvania Ave. NW, Ste. 600, Washington, DC 20004-1790, (202)637-3000

Natl. Assn. of Mfrs. and Installers of Security Systems [IO], Brucken, Germany

Natl. Assn. of Manufacturing Opticians - Defunct.

Natl. Assn. of Marble Dealers [★3364]

Natl. Assn. of Marble Dealers [★3364]

Natl. Assn. of Margarine Mfrs. [2586], 750 Natl. Press Bldg., 529 14th St. NW, Washington, DC 20045, (202)785-3232

Natl. Assn. of Marine Labs. [7055], Mr. Ivar Babb, Univ. of Connecticut, Northeast Underwater Res. Tech. and Educ. Center, 1080 Shennecossett Rd., Groton, CT 06340, (912)598-2400

Natl. Assn. of Marine Services [2362], 5458 Wagon Master Dr., Colorado Springs, CO 80917, (719)573-5946

Natl. Assn. of Marine Surveyors [7056], PO Box 9306, Chesapeake, VA 23321-9306, (757)638-9638

Natl. Assn. of Market Developers [★2417]

Natl. Assn. of Marketing Officials [★4720]

Natl. Assn. of Marketing Teachers [★2386]

Natl. Assn. of Master Appraisers - Defunct.

Natl. Assn. of Master Bakers - England [IO], Ware, United Kingdom

Natl. Assn. of Master Plumbers [★946]

Natl. Assn. of Master Steam and Hot Water Fitters [★924]

Natl. Assn. of Math Circles [8566], Mathematical Sciences Res. Inst., 17 Gauss Way, Berkeley, CA 94720, (510)642-0143

National Assn. of Mathematicians [★7072]

Natl. Assn. of Mathematics Advisers [IO], Gloucestershire, United Kingdom

Natl. Assn. of Meal Programs [★12151]

Natl. Assn. of Meat Purveyors [★2434]

Natl. Assn. of Meat Purveyors [★2434]

Natl. Assn. of Media Brokers [3024], 2910 Electra Dr., Colorado Springs, CO 80906-1073, (719)630-3111

Natl. Assn. for Media Literacy Educ. [8574], 10 Lauren Hill Dr., Cherry Hill, NJ 08003, (888)775-2652

Natl. Assn. of Media and Tech. Centers [2438], PO Box 9844, Cedar Rapids, IA 52409-9844, (319)654-0608

Natl. Assn. of Media Women - Defunct.

Natl. Assn. of Medicaid Directors [14860], 444 N Capitol St., No. 309, Washington, DC 20001, (202)403-8620

Natl. Assn. for Medical Direction of Respiratory Care [★15295]

Natl. Assn. of Medical Examiners [15329], 31479 Arrow Ln., Marceline, MO 64658, (660)734-1891

Natl. Assn. of Medical Minority Educators [8612], 1101 Pennsylvania Ave., NW, Ste. 600, Washington, DC 20004, (202)756-5036

Natl. Assn. Medical Staff Services [15297], 2025 M St. NW, Ste. 800, Washington, DC 20036, (202)367-1196

Natl. Assn. of Medics and Corpsmen [5219], PO Box 594, Colville, WA 99114-0594

Natl. Assn. of Melkite Youth [19591], 140 Mitchell St., Manchester, NH 03103, (603)623-8944

Natl. Assn. of Memoir Writers - Address unknown since 2010.

Natl. Assn. of Memorial Masons [IO], Rugby, United Kingdom

National Assn. of Men's Sportswear Buyers - Address unknown since 2010.

Natl. Assn. for Mental Hea. [★15461]

Natl. Assn. of Mental Hea. Planning and Advisory Councils [15467], 2000 N Beauregard St., 6th Fl., Alexandria, VA 22311, (703)797-2595

Natl. Assn. of Metal Cans, Packagings and Closures Mfrs. [IO], Clichy, France

Natl. Assn. of Metal Name Plate Mfrs. [★2484]

Natl. Assn. of Military Schools [★8623]

Natl. Assn. of Milk Bottle Collectors [21375], 18 Pond Pl., Cos Cob, CT 06807, (203)544-8079

Natl. Assn. of Milk Control Boards of Am. [★5463]

Natl. Assn. of Milk Control Boards of Am. [★5463]

Natl. Assn. of Miniature Enthusiasts [21376], PO Box 69, Carmel, IN 46082-0069, (317)571-8094

Natl. Assn. of Mining History Organisations [IO], Matlock, United Kingdom

Natl. Assn. of Ministers' Wives [★19657]

Natl. Assn. of Ministers' Wives [★19657]

Natl. Assn. of Ministers Wives and Ministers' Widows [★19657]

Natl. Assn. of Ministers Wives and Ministers' Widows [★19657]

Natl. Assn. of Minorities in Communications [★813]

Natl. Assn. of Minority Auto. Dealers [2523], 8201 Corporate Dr., Ste. 550, Lanham, MD 20785, (301)306-1614

Natl. Assn. of Minority Contractors [927], The Ronald Reagan House Off. Bldg., Ste. 700, 1300 Pennsylvania Ave. NW, Washington, DC 20004, (202)204-3093

Natl. Assn. of Minority Engg. Prog. Administrators [★8127]

Natl. Assn. of Minority Govt. Contractors [928], PO Box 44609, Washington, DC 20026, (202)510-6431

Natl. Assn. of Minority and Women Owned Law Firms [5264], 735 N Water St., Ste. 1205, Milwaukee, WI 53202, (414)277-1139

Natl. Assn. of Mobile Entertainers [1208], PO Box 144, Willow Grove, PA 19090, (215)658-1193

Natl. Assn. for Moisture Mgt. [1223], 76 D St., Hull, MA 02045, (781)925-0354

Natl. Assn. of Mold Professionals [1224], 3130 Old Farm Ln., Ste. 1, Commerce Township, MI 48390, (248)669-5673

Natl. Assn. of Mortgage Brokers [427], 7900 Westpark Dr., Ste. T309, McLean, VA 22102, (703)342-5900

Natl. Assn. of Mortgage Processors [428], 1250 Connecticut Ave. NW, Ste. 200, Washington, DC 20036, (202)261-6505

Natl. Assn. of Mothers' Centers [12609], 1740 Old Jericho Tpke., Jericho, NY 11753, (516)939-MOMS

Natl. Assn. of Motor Bus Operators [★3500]

Natl. Assn. of Motor Bus Owners [★3500]

Natl. Assn. for Multi-Ethnicity in Communications [813], 320 W 37th St., 8th Fl., New York, NY 10018, (212)594-5985

Natl. Assn. for Multicultural Educ.

Natl. Assn. for Multicultural Educ. - Address unknown since 2011.

Natl. Assn. of Multicultural Media Executives - Address unknown since 2011.

Natl. Assn. of Municipal Judges [★5612]

Natl. Assn. of Music Educators [IO], Matlock, United Kingdom

Natl. Assn. of Music Executives in State Universities - Defunct.

Natl. Assn. of Music Merchants [★2565]

Natl. Assn. for Music Therapy [★16451]

Natl. Assn. of Musical Merchandise Mfrs. [★2556]

Natl. Assn. of Musical Merchandise Wholesalers [★2562]

Natl. Assn. of Mutual Insurance Agents [★2012]

Natl. Assn. of Mutual Insurance Companies [2010], 3601 Vincennes Rd., Indianapolis, IN 46268, (317)875-5250

Natl. Assn. of Myofascial Trigger Point Therapists [16862], Lois Morford, Treas., 88 Union Ave., Pittsburgh, PA 15205

Natl. Assn. of Nameplate Mfrs. [★2484]

Natl. Assn. for Nanny Care - Defunct.

Natl. Assn. for Native Amer. Children of Alcoholics [11356], White Bison, Inc., 6145 Lehman Dr., Ste. 200, Colorado Springs, CO 80918, (719)548-1000

Natl. Assn. of Native Amer. Stud. [8678], PO Box 6670, Scarborough, ME 04070-6670, (207)839-8004

Natl. Assn. of Negro Bus. and Professional Women's Clubs [13068], 1806 New Hampshire Ave. NW, Washington, DC 20009, (202)483-4206

Natl. Assn. of Negro Musicians [10253], PO Box 43053, Chicago, IL 60643, (773)568-3818

Natl. Assn. of Neighborhood Hea. Centers [★14720]

Natl. Assn. for Neighborhood Schools - Address unknown since 2010.

Natl. Assn. of Neighborhoods [11532], 1300 Pennsylvania Ave. NW, Ste. 700, Washington, DC 20004, (202)332-7766

Natl. Assn. of Neonatal Nurses [15767], 4700 W Lake Ave., Glenview, IL 60025-1468, (847)375-3660

Natl. Assn. of Nephrology Technicians/Technologists [15553], PO Box 2307, Dayton, OH 45401-2307, (937)586-3705

Natl. Assn. of Nephrology Technologists [★15553]

Natl. Assn. of Non-Custodial Moms [12610], PO Box 21054, Columbus, OH 43221

Natl. Assn. of Norwegian Architects [IO], Oslo, Norway

Natl. Assn. of Nurse Massage Therapists [15768], PO Box 232, West Milton, OH 45383, (937)698-4128

Natl. Assn. of Nurse Practitioners in Reproductive Hea. [★15769]

Natl. Assn. of Nurse Practitioners in Women's Hea. [15769], 505 C St. NE, Washington, DC 20002, (202)543-9693

Natl. Assn. of Nurse Recruiters [★15296]

Natl. Assn. for Nursery Educ. [★7832]

Natl. Assn. of Nutrition and Aging Services Programs [15840], 1612 K St. NW, Ste. 400, Washington, DC 20006, (202)682-6899

Natl. Assn. of OEW Contractors [929], Joe Cudney, Sec., Parsons, 3577 Parkway Ln., Ste. 100, Norcross, GA 30092, (678)969-2344

Natl. Assn. of Official Prison Visitors [IO], Westcliff-on-Sea, United Kingdom

Natl. Assn. of Oil Equip. Jobbers [★2665]

Natl. Assn. of Oil Equip. Jobbers [★2665]

Natl. Assn. of Older Worker Employment Services - Defunct.

Natl. Assn. for Olmsted Parks [5331], 1111 16th St. NW, Ste. 310, Washington, DC 20036, (202)223-9113

Natl. Assn. of Oncology Social Workers [★13214]

Natl. Assn. of Optical Goods Mfrs. [IO], Milan, Italy

Natl. Assn. of Ornamental Metal Mfrs. [★2483]

A star before a book entry number signifies that the name is not listed separately, but is mentioned within the entry.

Natl. Assn. of Orthopaedic Nurses [15770], 401 N Michigan Ave., Ste. 2200, Chicago, IL 60611, (678)341-6789

Natl. Assn. of Orthopaedic Technologists [15380], 8365 Keystone Crossing, Ste. 107, Indianapolis, IN 46240, (317)205-9484

Natl. Assn. of OTC Pharmaceutical Products [IO], Madrid, Spain

Natl. Assn. of Ovulation Method Instructors UK [IO], Crawley, United Kingdom

Natl. Assn. of the Ovulation Method of Ireland [IO], Dublin, Ireland

Natl. Assn. of Paper Merchants [IO], Nottingham, United Kingdom

Natl. Assn. of Paperstock Women [2619], PO Box 826, Williamsville, NY 14221

Natl. Assn. of Parents with Children in Special Educ. [8885], 1431 W South Fork Dr., Phoenix, AZ 85045, (800)754-4421

Natl. Assn. for Parents of Children With Visual Impairments [17103], PO Box 317, Watertown, MA 02471, (617)972-7441

Natl. Assn. of Parents and Friends of Mentally Retarded Children [★12495]

Natl. Assn. for Parents of the Visually Impaired [★17103]

Natl. Assn. of Parish Catechetical Directors [19681], Natl. Catholic Educational Assn., 1005 N Glebe Rd., Ste. 525, Arlington, VA 22201, (202)337-6232

Natl. Assn. of Parish Coordinators/Directors of Religious Educ. [★19681]

Natl. Assn. of Parliamentarians [10351], 213 S Main St., Independence, MO 64050-3850, (816)833-3892

Natl. Assn. of Parliamentarians [10351], 213 S Main St., Independence, MO 64050-3850, (816)833-3892

Natl. Assn. of Part-Time and Temporary Employees [1155], 5800 Barton, Ste. 201, PO Box 3805, Shawnee, KS 66203, (913)962-7740

Natl. Assn. of the Partners of the Alliance [★17183]

Natl. Assn. of the Partners of the Alliance [★17183]

Natl. Assn. of Partners in Education - Defunct.

Natl. Assn. of Passenger Vessel Owners [★2369]

Natl. Assn. of Passport and Visa Services [3567], 1417 Highland Dr., Silver Spring, MD 20910, (301)650-2321

Natl. Assn. for Pastoral Care in Educ. [IO], Coventry, United Kingdom

Natl. Assn. of Pastoral Musicians [8660], 962 Wayne Ave., Ste. 210, Silver Spring, MD 20910-4461, (240)247-3000

Natl. Assn. of Patent Practitioners [5886], PO Box 231184, San Diego, CA 92193, (800)216-9588

Natl. Assn. of Patients on Hemodialysis [★15541]

Natl. Assn. of Patients on Hemodialysis and Transplantation [★15541]

Natl. Assn. of Pediatric Nurse Practitioners [15771], 20 Brace Rd., Ste. 200, Cherry Hill, NJ 08034-2634, (856)857-9700

Natl. Assn. of Peer Program Professionals [11677], PO Box 10627, Kansas City, MO 64188-0627, (877)314-7337

Natl. Assn. of Peer Programs [★11677]

Natl. Assn. of Peer Specialists [15468], 755 Alta Dale Ave. SE, Ada, MI 49301, (616)773-8866

Natl. Assn. of Pension Consultants and Administrators [★17477]

Natl. Assn. of Pension Funds [IO], London, United Kingdom

Natl. Assn. of People with AIDS [13619], 8401 Colesville Rd., Ste. 505, Silver Spring, MD 20910, (240)247-0880

Natl. Assn. of People Living With HIV/AIDS [IO], Sydney, Australia

Natl. Assn. of Peoplecultural Engg. Prog. Advocates [8127], 341 N Maitland Ave., Ste. 130, Maitland, FL 32751-4761, (407)647-8839

Natl. Assn. of Peoplecultural Rehabilitation Concerns [16567], Off. of Rehabilitation and Disability Stud., Michigan State Univ., 459 Erickson Hall, East Lansing, MI 48824

Natl. Assn. of Percussion Teachers [IO], Basingstoke, United Kingdom

Natl. Assn. Performing Arts Managers and Agent [★164]

Natl. Assn. of Periodical Publishers [★2947]

Natl. Assn. of Permanent Diaconate Directors [★19456]

Natl. Assn. of Personal Financial Advisors [1344], 3250 N Arlington Heights Rd., Ste. 109, Arlington Heights, IL 60004, (847)483-5400

Natl. Assn. of Personnel Consultants [★1156]

Natl. Assn. of Personnel Services [1156], 131 Prominence Ct., Ste. 130, Dawsonville, GA 30534, (706)531-0060

Natl. Assn. of Personnel Workers [★7672]

Natl. Assn. of Pet Cemeteries [★2679]

Natl. Assn. of Pet Cemeteries [★2679]

Natl. Assn. for PET Container Resources [3638], PO Box 1327, Sonoma, CA 95476, (707)996-4207

Natl. Assn. of Pet Sitters [★2681]

Natl. Assn. of the Pharmaceutical Indus. - Italy [IO], Rome, Italy

Natl. Assn. of the Pharmaceutical Indus. - Spain [IO], Madrid, Spain

Natl. Assn. of Pharmaceutical Representatives [2697], 2020 Pennsylvania Ave. NW, Ste. 5050, Washington, DC 20006, (800)913-0701

Natl. Assn. of the Phonographic Indus. [IO], Berlin, Germany

Natl. Assn. of Photographic Equip. Technicians [2725], PMA - The Worldwide Community of Imaging Associations, 3000 Picture Pl., Jackson, MI 49201, (517)788-8100

Natl. Assn. of Photographic Mfrs. [★2722]

Natl. Assn. of Photographic Mfrs. [★2722]

Natl. Assn. of Photoshop Professionals [1638], 333 Douglas Rd. E, Oldsmar, FL 34677, (813)433-5005

Natl. Assn. of Photoshop Professionals [1638], 333 Douglas Rd. E, Oldsmar, FL 34677, (813)433-5005

Natl. Assn. of Physical Administrators of Universities and Colleges [★8087]

Natl. Assn. of Physical Administrators of Universities and Colleges [★8087]

Natl. Assn. of the Physically Handicapped [11811], 1375 Dewitt Dr., Akron, OH 44313, (330)724-1994

Natl. Assn. of Physician Assistants [16237], 2375 E Tropicana Ave., Ste. 8, No. 213, Las Vegas, NV 89119-6563, (702)939-4788

Natl. Assn. of Physician Recruiters [16270], 222 S Westmonte Dr., Ste. 101, Altamonte Springs, FL 32714, (407)774-7880

Natl. Assn. of Physicians for the Env. - Defunct.

Natl. Assn. of Piano Tuners [★2571]

Natl. Assn. of Pipe Coating Applicators [789], 1000 Louisiana St., Ste. 3400, Houston, TX 77002, (713)276-5306

Natl. Assn. of Pipe Coating Applicators [789], 1000 Louisiana St., Ste. 3400, Houston, TX 77002, (713)276-5306

Natl. Assn. of Pipe Fabricators [2749], 2887 Goat Creek Rd., Box 242, Kerrville, TX 78028, (888)798-1924

Natl. Assn. of Pizzeria Operators [1762], 908 S 8th St., Ste. 200, Louisville, KY 40203, (502)736-9500

Natl. Assn. of Placement Personnel Officers [★8699]

Natl. Assn. of Planning Councils [18316], 11118 Ferndale Rd., Dallas, TX 75238, (214)341-3657

Natl. Assn. for Plastic Container Recovery [★3638]

Natl. Assn. of Plastics Distributors [★2769]

Natl. Assn. of Plastics Distributors [★2769]

Natl. Assn. of Plumbing Contractors [★946]

Natl. Assn. of Plumbing-Heating-Cooling Contractors [★946]

Natl. Assn. for Poetry Therapy [16469], Nessa McCasey, Admin., 3365 Wildridge Dr. NE, Grand Rapids, MI 49525, (616)363-6352

Natl. Assn. of Police Athletic Leagues [13538], 658 W Indiantown Rd., Ste. 201, Jupiter, FL 33458, (561)745-5535

Natl. Assn. of Police Organizations [5716], 317 S Patrick St., Alexandria, VA 22314-3501, (703)549-0775

Natl. Assn. of Pond Professionals [237], PO Box 369, Epworth, GA 30541, (706)258-3534

Natl. Assn. of Popcorn Mfrs. [★1451]

Natl. Assn. of Post Off. and Postal Trans. Ser. Mail Handlers, Watchmen and Messengers [★23283]

Natl. Assn. of Postal Supervisors [23281], 1727 King St., Ste. 400, Alexandria, VA 22314-2700, (703)836-9660

Natl. Assn. of Postmasters of the U.S. [5891], 8 Herbert St., Alexandria, VA 22305-2600, (703)683-9027

Natl. Assn. of Power Engineers [7294], 1 Springfield St., Chicopee, MA 01013, (413)592-6273

Natl. Assn. for Practical Nurse Educ. and Ser. [8613], 1940 Duke St., Ste. 200, Alexandria, VA 22314, (703)933-1003

Natl. Assn. Practical Refrigerating Engineers [★6820]

Natl. Assn. for the Practice of Anthropology [6146], Amer. Anthropological Assn., 2200 Wilson Blvd., Ste. 600, Arlington, VA 22201, (703)528-1902

Natl. Assn. for Pre-Paid Funeral Plans [IO], Solihull, United Kingdom

Natl. Assn. for Premenstrual Syndrome [IO], Kent, United Kingdom

Natl. Assn. of Presbyterian Scouters [13021], Programs of Religious Activities with Youth, 11123 S Towne Sq., Ste. B, St. Louis, MO 63123, (609)214-3162

Natl. Assn. for the Preservation and Perpetuation of Storytelling [★10546]

Natl. Assn. of Preserved Vegetable Indus. [IO], Naples, Italy

Natl. Assn. of Presort Mailers [2235], 1195 Mace Rd., Annapolis, MD 21403-4330, (877)620-6276

Natl. Assn. of Press Agencies [IO], Liverpool, United Kingdom

Natl. Assn. to Prevent Sexual Abuse of Children [13092], 2324 Univ. Ave. W, Ste. 105, St. Paul, MN 55114, (651)714-4673

Natl. Assn. for the Prevention of Addiction to Narcotics [★13274]

Natl. Assn. of Priest Pilots [19459], Rev. Mel Hemann, Treas., 127 Kaspend Pl., Cedar Falls, IA 50613-1683, (319)266-3889

Natl. Assn. of Primary Care [IO], London, United Kingdom

Natl. Assn. for Primary Educ. [IO], Northampton, United Kingdom

Natl. Assn. of Principals of Schools for Girls [8750], 23490 Caraway Lakes Dr., Bonita Springs, FL 34135-8441, (239)947-6196

Natl. Assn. of Printers and Lithographers [★1621]

Natl. Assn. of Printing Ink Makers [★1620]

Natl. Assn. of Printing Ink Mfrs. [1620], 581 Main St., Ste. 520, Woodbridge, NJ 07095-1144, (732)855-1525

Natl. Assn. for Printing Leadership [1621], 75 W Century Rd., Ste. 100, Paramus, NJ 07652-1408, (201)634-9600

Natl. Assn. of Private Ambulance Services [IO], Peterborough, United Kingdom

Natl. Assn. of Private Catholic and Independent Schools [7648], 2640 3rd Ave., Sacramento, CA 95818, (916)451-4963

Natl. Assn. of Private Enterprise [IO], San Salvador, El Salvador

Natl. Assn. of Private Geriatric Care Managers [★15812]

Natl. Assn. of Private Indus. Councils [★11946]

Natl. Assn. of Private Psychiatric Hospitals [★16343]

Natl. Assn. of Private Residential Facilities for the Mentally Retarded [★12494]

Natl. Assn. of Private Residential Resources [★12494]

Natl. Assn. of Private Schools for Exceptional Children [★8886]

Natl. Assn. of Private Special Educ. Centers [8886], 601 Pennsylvania Ave. NW, Ste. 900, South Bldg., Washington, DC 20004, (202)434-8225

Natl. Assn. of Pro America - Defunct.

Natl. Assn. of Pro-Life Nurses [16628], PO Box 8236, Hot Springs Village, AR 71910-8236, (501)984-5530

Natl. Assn. of Probation Executives [5378], Ms. Christie Davidson, Exec. Dir., Sam Houston State Univ., Correctional Mgt. Inst. of Texas, George J. Beto Criminal Justice Center, Huntsville, TX 77341-2296, (936)294-3757

Natl. Assn. of Probation Officers [IO], London, United Kingdom

Natl. Assn. of Produce Market Managers [4717], PO Box 291284, Columbia, SC 29229, (803)333-9421

Reference to "IO" in place of a book number signifies that the association may be found in the 50th edition of International Organizations.

Natl. Assn. of Prdt. Fund Raisers [★1537]

Natl. Assn. of Professional Accident Reconstruction Specialists [5965], PO Box 866, Farmington, NH 03835, (603)32-3267

Natl. Assn. of Professional Accident Reconstructionists [★5965]

Natl. Assn. of Professional Allstate Agents [2011], PO Box 7666, Gulfport, MS 39506, (877)627-2248

Natl. Assn. of Professional Asian Amer. Women [684], 304 Oak Knoll Terr., Rockville, MD 20850, (301)785-8585

Natl. Assn. of Professional Background Screeners [1790], 2501 Aerial Center Pkwy., Ste. 103, Morrisville, NC 27560, (919)459-2082

Natl. Assn. of Professional Band Instrument Repair Technicians [2566], PO Box 51, Normal, IL 61761, (309)452-4257

Natl. Assn. of Professional Baseball Leagues [22280], PO Box A, St. Petersburg, FL 33731, (727)822-6937

Natl. Assn. of Professional Canine Handlers [5717], 3441 Filbert St., Wayne, MI 48184, (734)506-8690

Natl. Assn. of Professional Contracts Administrators [★1587]

Natl. Assn. for Professional Development Schools [8829], Jason Kinsey, Admin., Univ. of South Carolina, Coll. of Educ., Wardlaw 252, Columbia, SC 29208, (803)777-1515

Natl. Assn. of Professional Employer Organizations [1157], 707 N St. Asaph St., Alexandria, VA 22314, (703)836-0466

Natl. Assn. of Professional Geriatric Care Managers [15812], 3275 W Ina Rd., Ste. 130, Tucson, AZ 85741-2198, (520)881-8008

Natl. Assn. for Professional Gerontologists [14668], PO Box 1209, Los Altos, CA 94023, (650)947-9132

Natl. Assn. for Professional Inspectors and Testers [IO], Mansfield, United Kingdom

Natl. Assn. of Professional Insurance Agents [2012], 400 N Washington St., Alexandria, VA 22314, (703)836-9340

Natl. Assn. of Professional Martial Artists [22745], 5601 116th Ave. N, Clearwater, FL 33760, (727)540-0500

Natl. Assn. of Professional Mortgage Women [429], PO Box 451718, Garland, TX 75045, (800)827-3034

Natl. Assn. of Professional Organizers [6949], 15000 Commerce Pkwy., Ste. C, Mount Laurel, NJ 08054, (856)380-6828

Natl. Assn. of Professional Pet Sitters [2681], 15000 Commerce Pkwy., Ste. C, Mount Laurel, NJ 08054, (856)439-0324

Natl. Assn. of Professional Process Servers [5897], PO Box 4547, Portland, OR 97208-4547, (503)222-4180

Natl. Assn. for Professional Saleswomen - Defunct.

Natl. Assn. of Professional Surplus Lines Offices [2013], 200 NE 54th St., No. 200, Kansas City, MO 64118, (816)741-3910

Natl. Assn. of Professionals in Energy Conservation [★6693]

Natl. Assn. of Professionals in Energy Conservation [★6693]

Natl. Assn. of Professionals with Language Impairment in Children [IO], Addlestone, United Kingdom

Natl. Assn. of Professors of Christian Educ. [★7858]

Natl. Assn. of Professors of Hebrew [8429], Univ. of Wisconsin-Madison, 1346 Van Hise Hall, 1220 Linden Dr., Madison, WI 53706-1558, (608)262-2997

Natl. Assn. for Proficiency Testing [7560], 901 Twelve Oaks Center Dr., Ste. 920, Wayzata, MN 55391, (952)303-6126

Natl. Assn. for Promotional and Advt. Allowances [★110]

Natl. Assn. of Property and Casualty Reinsurers [★2033]

Natl. Assn. of Property Inspectors - Address unknown since 2010.

Natl. Assn. of Property Owners - Defunct.

Natl. Assn. of Property Recovery Investigators [5606], 5715 Will Clayton Pkwy., No. 1503, Humble, TX 77338, (386)479-5329

Natl. Assn. of Property Recovery Investigators [5606], 5715 Will Clayton Pkwy., No. 1503, Humble, TX 77338, (386)479-5329

Natl. Assn. of Property Tax Representatives - Transportation, Energy and Communications - Defunct.

Natl. Assn. to Protect Children [11357], PO Box 27599, Knoxville, TN 37927, (865)525-0901

Natl. Assn. of Protection and Advocacy Systems [★11815]

Natl. Assn. for Proton Therapy [15927], 1301 Highland Dr., Silver Spring, MD 20910, (301)587-6100

Natl. Assn. of Prudential Retirees and Vested Terminators, Inc. - Address unknown since 2010.

Natl. Assn. for Pseudoxanthoma Elasticum [14332], 8760 Manchester Rd., St. Louis, MO 63144-2724, (314)962-0100

Natl. Assn. of Psychiatric Hea. Systems [16343], 900 17th St., Ste. 420, Washington, DC 20006-2507, (202)393-6700

Natl. Assn. of Psychiatric Survivors - Defunct.

Natl. Assn. of Psychiatric Treatment Centers for Children [★16342]

Natl. Assn. of Psychometrists [16412], Stephanie Hotltan, Membership Chair, Neuropsychology Clinic, 3100 N Dries Ln., Ste. 203, Peoria, IL 61604

Natl. Assn. of Public Affairs Networks [17212], 21 Oak St., Ste. 605, Hartford, CT 06106, (860)246-1553

Natl. Assn. of Public Auto Auctions [270], PO Box 41368, Raleigh, NC 27629, (919)876-0687

Natl. Assn. of Public Child Welfare Administrators [11358], 1133 19th St. NW, Ste. 400, Washington, DC 20036, (202)682-0100

Natl. Assn. for Public Continuing Adult Educ. [★7920]

Natl. Assn. of Public Golf Clubs [IO], Redditch, United Kingdom

Natl. Assn. for Public Hea. Info. Tech. [6985], 624 N Broadway, Rm. 325, Baltimore, MD 21205

Natl. Assn. for Public Hea. Statistics and Info. Systems [5930], 962 Wayne Ave., Ste. 701, Silver Spring, MD 20910, (301)563-6001

Natl. Assn. of Public Hospitals [★15065]

Natl. Assn. of Public Hospitals and Hea. Systems [15065], 1301 Pennsylvania Ave. NW, Ste. 950, Washington, DC 20004, (202)585-0100

Natl. Assn. of Public Insurance Adjusters [2014], 21165 Whitfield Pl., No. 105, Potomac Falls, VA 20165, (703)433-9217

Natl. Assn. for Public Interest Law [★5618]

Natl. Assn. of Public and Private Employer Negotiators and Administrators - Defunct.

Natl. Assn. of Public Relations Counsel [★2908]

Natl. Assn. of Public Sector Equal Opportunity Officers - Address unknown since 2010.

Natl. Assn. of Public TV Stations [★483]

Natl. Assn. of Publicly Funded Truck Driving Schools [3520], Tina Frindt, Treas., Northampton Community Coll., 1900 Corporate Center Dr. E, Tobyhanna, PA 18466, (217)641-4914

Natl. Assn. of Publicly Traded Partnerships [2144], 1940 Duke St., Ste. 200, Alexandria, VA 22314, (703)518-4185

Natl. Assn. for Publishers' Representatives [2951], 1901 N Roselle Rd., Ste. 920, Schaumburg, IL 60195, (847)885-2410

Natl. Assn. of Puerto Rican Hispanic Social Workers [13221], PO Box 651, Brentwood, NY 11717, (631)864-1536

Natl. Assn. of Punch Mfrs. [★1856]

Natl. Assn. of Pupil Personnel Administrators [★7671]

Natl. Assn. of Pupil Services Administrators [7671], PO Box 113, Williamsport, PA 17701, (570)323-2050

Natl. Assn. for Pupil Trans. [6034], 1840 Western Ave., Albany, NY 12203-4624, (518)452-3611

Natl. Assn. of Purchasing Agents [★2971]

Natl. Assn. of Purchasing Card Professionals [2972], Lynn Berglund, Admin. Mgr., 12701 Whitewater Dr., Ste. 280, Minnetonka, MN 55343, (952)546-1880

Natl. Assn. of Purchasing Mgt. [★2971]

Natl. Assn. of Purchasing Mgt. [★2482]

Natl. Assn. of Purchasing and Payables [2973], Larry Kreider, Co-Chm., 1570 Doxee Terr., Marco Island, FL 34145, (239)393-2220

Natl. Assn. of Qualified Developmental Disability Professionals [15489], 2081 Calistoga Dr., Ste. 1S, New Lenox, IL 60451, (815)485-4781

Natl. Assn. of Qualified Mental Retardation Professionals [★15489]

Natl. Assn. of Quality Assurance Professionals [★16508]

Natl. Assn. Quick Printers [★1622]

Natl. Assn. of Quick Printers [1622], 2250 E Devon Ave., Ste. 245, Des Plaines, IL 60018, (847)298-8680

Natl. Assn. of Quick Printers [1622], 2250 E Devon Ave., Ste. 245, Des Plaines, IL 60018, (847)298-8680

Natl. Assn. Quick Printers [★1622]

Natl. Assn. of Radio Farm Directors [★502]

Natl. Assn. of Radio News Directors [★511]

Natl. Assn. of Radio Reading Services [★17087]

Natl. Assn. of Radio Reading Services [★17087]

Natl. Assn. of Radio and Telecommunications Engineers [★7542]

Natl. Assn. of Radio Telephone Systems [★3416]

Natl. Assn. of Radio Telephone Systems [★3416]

Natl. Assn. of Radio and TV Broadcasters [★501]

Natl. Assn. of Rail Shippers [★3529]

Natl. Assn. of Rail Shippers Advisory Boards [★3529]

Natl. Assn. of Railroad Enthusiasts [★10491]

Natl. Assn. of Railroad Passengers [2989], 505 Capitol Ct. NE, Ste. 300, Washington, DC 20002, (202)408-8362

Natl. Assn. of Railroad Tie Producers [★2995]

Natl. Assn. of Railroad Trial Counsel [6035], 1430 E Missouri Ave., Ste. B200, Phoenix, AZ 85014, (602)265-2700

Natl. Assn. of Railway Bus. Women [2990], 621 Lippincott Ave., Riverton, NJ 08077

Natl. Assn. of Railway Commissioners [★6053]

Natl. Assn. of Railway and Utilities Commissioners [★6053]

Natl. Assn. Rainbow Div. Veterans [★20876]

Natl. Assn. of Real Estate Appraisers [235], PO Box 879, Palm Springs, CA 92263, (760)327-5284

Natl. Assn. of Real Estate Boards [★3030]

Natl. Assn. of Real Estate Brokers [3025], 5504 Brentwood Stair Rd., Fort Worth, TX 76112, (817)446-7715

National Assn. of Real Estate Buyer Brokers - Address unknown since 2010.

Natl. Assn. of Real Estate Companies [3026], 216 W Jackson Blvd., Ste. 625, Chicago, IL 60606, (312)263-1755

Natl. Assn. of Real Estate Consultants [3027], 2758 W River Dr., Lenore, ID 83541, (208)746-7963

Natl. Assn. of Real Estate Editors [2845], 1003 NW 6th Terr., Boca Raton, FL 33486-3455, (561)391-3599

Natl. Assn. of Real Estate Exchanges [★3030]

Natl. Assn. of Real Estate Investment Funds [★3029]

Natl. Assn. of Real Estate Investment Managers [3028], 900 7th St. NW, Ste. 960, Washington, DC 20001, (202)789-4373

Natl. Assn. of Real Estate Investment Trusts [3029], 1875 I St. NW, Ste. 600, Washington, DC 20006-5413, (202)739-9400

Natl. Assn. of Real Estate License Law Officials [★5956]

Natl. Assn. of Real Estate License Law Officials [★5956]

Natl. Assn. of Real Estate Offices of Slovakia [IO], Bratislava, Slovakia

Natl. Assn. of Realtors [3030], 430 N Michigan Ave., Chicago, IL 60611-4087, (800)874-6500

Natl. Assn. of Record Merchandisers [★3051]

Natl. Assn. of Recording Merchandisers [3051], 9 Eves Dr., Ste. 120, Marlton, NJ 08053, (856)596-2221

Natl. Assn. of Recreation Rsrc. Planners [5876], PO Box 221, Marienville, PA 16239, (814)927-8212

Natl. Assn. Recycling Indus. [★3637]

Natl. Assn. Recycling Indus. [★3637]

Natl. Assn. of Regional Councils [5499], 777 N Capitol St. NE, Ste. 305, Washington, DC 20002, (202)986-1032

A star before a book entry number signifies that the name is not listed separately, but is mentioned within the entry.

Natl. Assn. of Regional Game Councils [IO], Dublin, Ireland

Natl. Assn. of Regional Media Centers - Address unknown since 2010.

Natl. Assn. of Registered Nursing Homes [★14696]

Natl. Assn. for Regulatory Admin. [15250], Ms. Pauline Koch, Exec. Dir., 910 Glen Falls Ct., Newark, DE 19711, (302)234-4152

Natl. Assn. of Regulatory Utility Commissioners [6053], 1101 Vermont Ave. NW, Ste. 200, Washington, DC 20005-3553, (202)898-2200

Natl. Assn. of Rehabilitation Facilities [★16557]

Natl. Assn. for Rehabilitation Leadership [16568], Natl. Rehabilitation Assn., 633 S Washington St., Alexandria, VA 22314, (703)836-0850

Natl. Assn. of Rehabilitation Professionals in the Private Sector [★16566]

Natl. Assn. of Rehabilitation Providers and Agencies [16569], 701 8th St. NW, Ste. 500, Washington, DC 20001, (866)839-7710

Natl. Assn. of Rehabilitation Support Staff - Address unknown since 2011.

Natl. Assn. of Reinforcing Steel Contractors [930], PO Box 280, Fairfax, VA 22038, (703)591-1870

Natl. Assn. of Relay Mfrs. [★1085]

Natl. Assn. of Religious Bros. [★19490]

Natl. Assn. for Remedia/Developmental Stud. in Postsecondary Educ. [★7969]

Natl. Assn. for Remedial Teachers [★8780]

Natl. Assn. for Remedial Teachers [★8780]

Natl. Assn. of the Remodeling Indus. [589], 780 Lee St., Ste. 200, Des Plaines, IL 60016, (847)298-9200

Natl. Assn. for Remotely Piloted Vehicles [★7341]

Natl. Assn. for Remotely Piloted Vehicles [★7341]

Natl. Assn. for Repeal of Abortion Laws [★18525]

Natl. Assn. for Res. in Sci. Teaching [8844], 12100 Sunset Hills Rd., Ste. 130, Reston, VA 20190-3221, (703)234-4138

Natl. Assn. for Res. and Therapy of Homosexuality [14580], 16633 Ventura Blvd., Ste. 1340, Encino, CA 91436-1801, (818)789-4440

Natl. Assn. for the Res. and Treatment of Homosexuality [★14580]

Natl. Assn. of Residential Property Managers [2902], 638 Independence Pkwy., Ste. 100, Chesapeake, VA 23320, (800)782-3452

Natl. Assn. of Residents and Interns [15425], Hillsboro Executive Center N, 350 Fairway Dr., Ste. 200, Deerfield Beach, FL 33441-1834, (800)221-2168

Natl. Assn. of Rsrc. Conservation and Development Councils [4096], 444 N Capitol St. NW, Ste. 345, Washington, DC 20001, (202)434-4780

Natl. Assn. of Responsible Loan Officers - Address unknown since 2011.

Natl. Assn. of Retail Coll. Attorneys [5265], 601 Pennsylvania Ave. NW, Ste. 900 S, Washington, DC 20004, (202)861-0706

Natl. Assn. of Retail Druggists [★16206]

Natl. Assn. of Retail Grocers of Australia [IO], Hurstville, Australia

Natl. Assn. of Retail Grocers of the U.S. [★3117]

Natl. Assn. of Retail Ice Cream Mfrs. [★1024]

Natl. Assn. for Retail Marketing Services [3115], 2417 Post Rd., Stevens Point, WI 54481, (715)342-0948

Natl. Assn. for Retail Merchandising Services [★3115]

Natl. Assn. of Retailers' Co-operatives [IO], Rome, Italy

Natl. Assn. of Retailers and Wholesalers of Dairy Products [IO], Milan, Italy

Natl. Assn. for Retarded Children [★12495]

Natl. Assn. for Retarded Citizens [★12495]

Natl. Assn. of Retired Civil Employees [★5433]

Natl. Assn. of Retired Fed. Employees [★5433]

National Assn. of Retired and Veteran Railway Employees - Defunct.

Natl. Assn. of Reunion Managers [2896], PO Box 335428, North Las Vegas, NV 89033, (800)654-2776

Natl. Assn. of Reversionary Property Owners [18405], 227 Bellevue Way NE, Ste. 719, Bellevue, WA 98004, (425)646-8812

Natl. Assn. of Rev. Appraisers and Mortgage Underwriters [3031], 810 N Farrell Dr., Palm Springs, CA 92262, (760)327-5284

Natl. Assn. of Rhythm and Blues Dee Jay's [10254], Rock Hall, Sec., PO Box 11118, Southport, NC 28461, (910)279-3217

Natl. Assn. for Rights Protection and Advocacy [17307], Box 855, Huntsville, AL 35804, (205)464-9933

Natl. Assn. of Rocketry [21905], PO Box 407, Marion, IA 52302, (800)262-4872

Natl. Assn. of Rotary Clubs [★13074]

Natl. Assn. of Rotary Clubs [★13074]

Natl. Assn. of Royalty Owners [2658], 15 W 6th St., Ste. 2626, Tulsa, OK 74119, (918)794-1660

Natl. Assn. of Rural Hea. Clinics [16488], 2 E Main St., Fremont, MI 49412, (866)306-1961

Natl. Assn. of Rural Landowners [18406], PO Box 1031, Issaquah, WA 98027, (425)837-5365

Natl. Assn. for Rural Mental Hea. [15469], 300 33rd Ave. S, Ste. 101, Waite Park, MN 56387, (320)202-1820

Natl. Assn. of RV Parks and Campgrounds [3060], 9085 E Mineral Cir., Ste. 200, Centennial, CO 80112, (303)681-0401

Natl. Assn. of Sailing Instructors and Sailing Schools - Defunct.

Natl. Assn. of Sales Managers [★2263]

Natl. Assn. of Sales Managers [★2263]

Natl. Assn. of Sales Professionals [3164], 555 Friendly St., Livonia, MI 48152, (866)365-1520

Natl. Assn. of Sanitarians [★14504]

Natl. Assn. of Saw Shops [★2176]

Natl. Assn. of Saw Shops [★2176]

Natl. Assn. of Scale Aeromodelers [21906], 3903 Whispering Creek Ln., Delaware, OH 43015

Natl. Assn. of Scale Aeromodelers [21906], 3903 Whispering Creek Ln., Delaware, OH 43015

Natl. Assn. of Scale Mfrs. [★3657]

Natl. Assn. of Scholars [8239], 1 Airport Pl., Ste. 7, Princeton, NJ 08540-1532, (609)683-7878

Natl. Assn. of School Accounting and Bus. Officials of Public Schools [★7662]

Natl. Assn. of School Accounting and Bus. Officials of Public Schools [★7662]

Natl. Assn. of School Accounting Officers [★7662]

Natl. Assn. of School Accounting Officers [★7662]

Natl. Assn. of School Building Officials [★7662]

Natl. Assn. of School Building Officials [★7662]

Natl. Assn. of School Bus Contract Operators [★3526]

Natl. Assn. of School Bus. Officials [★7662]

Natl. Assn. of School Bus. Officials [★7662]

Natl. Assn. of School Music Dealers [2567], 14070 Proton Rd., Ste. 100, Dallas, TX 75244-3601, (972)233-9107

Natl. Assn. of School Nurses [15772], 8484 Georgia Ave., Ste. 420, Silver Spring, MD 20910, (240)821-1130

Natl. Assn. of School Psychologists [16413], 4340 E West Hwy., Ste. 402, Bethesda, MD 20814, (301)657-0270

Natl. Assn. of School Rsrc. Officers [8819], 2020 Valleydale Rd., Ste. 207A, Hoover, AL 35244, (205)281-5521

Natl. Assn. of School Safety and Law Enforcement Officers [8820], PO Box 210079, Milwaukee, WI 53221, (315)529-4858

Natl. Assn. of School Secretaries [★7668]

Natl. Assn. of School Security Directors [★8820]

Natl. Assn. of School Social Workers [★13222]

Natl. Assn. of School Superintendents [★7651]

Natl. Assn. of Schoolmasters and Union of Women Teachers [IO], Birmingham, United Kingdom

Natl. Assn. of Schools of Art [★7752]

Natl. Assn. of Schools of Art and Design [7752], 11250 Roger Bacon Dr., Ste. 21, Reston, VA 20190-5248, (703)437-0700

Natl. Assn. of Schools of Dance [7961], 11250 Roger Bacon Dr., Ste. 21, Reston, VA 20190-5248, (703)437-0700

Natl. Assn. of Schools of Design [★7752]

Natl. Assn. of Schools of Music [8661], 11250 Roger Bacon Dr., Ste. 21, Reston, VA 20190-5248, (703)437-0700

Natl. Assn. of Schools of Public Affairs and Admin. [5908], 1029 Vermont Ave. NW, Ste. 1100, Washington, DC 20005-3517, (202)628-8965

Natl. Assn. of Schools of Theatre [9002], 11250 Roger Bacon Dr., Ste. 21, Reston, VA 20190-5248, (703)437-0700

Natl. Assn. of Sci. Writers [2846], PO Box 7905, Berkeley, CA 94707, (510)647-9500

Natl. Assn. of Sci. Writers [2846], PO Box 7905, Berkeley, CA 94707, (510)647-9500

Natl. Assn. of Sci. Materials Managers [3179], Ohio State Univ. at Marion, 330 Morrill Hall, 1465 Mt. Vernon Ave., Marion, OH 43302, (740)725-6319

Natl. Assn. of Screening Agencies [★3034]

Natl. Assn. for Search and Rescue [12908], PO Box 232020, Centreville, VA 20120-2020, (703)222-6277

Natl. Assn. of Search and Rescue Coordinators [★12908]

Natl. Assn. of Secondary School Principals [8751], 1904 Assn. Dr., Reston, VA 20191-1537, (703)860-0200

Natl. Assn. of Secretaries of State [5992], Hall of States, 444 N Capitol St. NW, Ste. 401, Washington, DC 20001-1557, (202)624-3525

Natl. Assn. of Securities and Commercial Law Attorneys [★5320]

Natl. Assn. of Securities Commissioners [★3205]

Natl. Assn. of Securities Dealers [★3198]

Natl. Assn. of Securities Professionals [3202], 727 15th St., NW, Ste. 750, Washington, DC 20005, (202)371-5535

Natl. Assn. of Security Companies [3222], 444 N Capitol St. NW, Ste. 345, Washington, DC 20001, (202)347-3257

Natl. Assn. of Security and Data Vaults [★1907]

Natl. Assn. of Security and Data Vaults [★1907]

Natl. Assn. for the Self-Employed [3292], PO Box 241, Annapolis Junction, MD 20701-0241, (800)232-6273

Natl. Assn. for Self Esteem [15470], PO Box 597, Fulton, MD 20759-0597

Natl. Assn. of Self-Instructional Language Programs [8475], Univ. of Arizona, 1717 E Speedway Blvd., Ste. 3312, Tucson, AZ 85721-0151, (520)626-5258

Natl. Assn. of Self-Service and Dept. Stores [IO], Mexico City, Mexico

Natl. Assn. of Senior Move Managers [2296], PO Box 209, Hinsdale, IL 60522, (877)606-2766

Natl. Assn. of Sentencing Advocates [★5374]

Natl. Assn. of Ser. and Conservation Corps [★13519]

National Assn. of Service Dealers - Address unknown since 2010.

Natl. Assn. of Ser. Dogs [11876], PO Box 1515, Newport Beach, CA 92659-0515, (888)669-6273

Natl. Assn. of Ser. Managers [3237], PO Box 250796, Milwaukee, WI 53225, (414)466-6060

Natl. Assn. of Service Merchandising - Defunct.

Natl. Assn. of Ser. Providers in Private Rehabilitation [16570], Natl. Rehabilitation Assn., 633 S Washington St., Alexandria, VA 22314, (703)836-0850

Natl. Assn. of Settlement Purchasers [1317], Earl Nesbitt, Contact, 15851 Dallas Pkwy., Ste. 800, Addison, TX 75001, (972)371-2411

Natl. Assn. of Seventh-day Adventist Dentists [14298], PO Box 101, Loma Linda, CA 92354, (909)558-8187

Natl. Assn. of Sewer Ser. Companies [★3597]

Natl. Assn. of Shareholder and Consumer Attorneys [5320], 1 Pennsylvania Plz., 49th Fl., New York, NY 10119, (212)946-9312

Natl. Assn. of Shell Marketers [2659], PO Box 658, Garrisonville, VA 22463-0658, (703)582-8478

Natl. Assn. of Shellfish Commissioners [★7036]

Natl. Assn. of Shellfish Commissioners [★7036]

Natl. Assn. of Sheltered Workshops and Homebound Programs [★16557]

Natl. Assn. of Shippers Advisory Boards [★3529]

Natl. Assn. of Shoe Chain Stores [★1458]

Natl. Assn. of Shooting Ranges - Address unknown since 2010.

Natl. Assn. of Shooting Sports Athletes [22878], 2103 Wheaton Dr., Richardson, TX 75081

Reference to "IO" in place of a book number signifies that the association may be found in the 50th edition of International Organizations.

Natl. Assn. of Shopfitters **[IO]**, Warlingham, United Kingdom

Natl. Assn. for Shoplifting Prevention **[13046]**, 225 Broadhollow Rd., Ste. 400E, Melville, NY 11747, (631)923-2737

Natl. Assn. of Shortwave Broadcasters **[503]**, 10400 NW 240th St., Okeechobee, FL 34972, (863)763-0281

Natl. Assn. of Show Trucks **[3521]**, 23227 Freedom Ave., Ste. 7, Port Charlotte, FL 33980, (734)604-3242

Natl. Assn. for Sick Child Daycare **[11155]**, 1716 5th Ave. N, Birmingham, AL 35203, (205)324-8447

Natl. Assn. for Sickle Cell Disease **[★14974]**

Natl. Assn. of Sign Supply Distributors **[3662]**, 5024-R Campbell Blvd., Baltimore, MD 21236-5943, (410)931-8100

Natl. Assn. of Silo Mfrs. **[★169]**

Natl. Assn. of Silo Mfrs. **[★169]**

Natl. Assn. of Single People **[13118]**, 4570 Campus Dr., Newport Beach, CA 92660, (714)756-1000

Natl. Assn. for Single Sex Public Educ. **[8774]**, 64 E Uwchlan Ave., No. 259, Exton, PA 19341-1203, (610)296-2821

Natl. Assn. of the Sixth Infantry Div. **[20366]**, Thomas E. Price, 317 Court St. NE, Ste. 203, Salem, OR 97301, (503)363-7334

Natl. Assn. of the Sixth Infantry/Motorized Div. **[★20366]**

Natl. Assn. of Small Bus. Contractors **[931]**, 1200 G St. NW, Ste. 800, Washington, DC 20005, (888)861-9290

Natl. Assn. of Small Bus. Fed. Contractors - Address unknown since 2010.

Natl. Assn. of Small Bus. Intl. Trade Educators **[★7798]**

Natl. Assn. of Small Bus. Intl. Trade Educators **[★7798]**

Natl. Assn. of Small Bus. Investment Companies **[3293]**, 1100 H St. NW, Ste. 610, Washington, DC 20005, (202)628-5055

Natl. Assn. of Small Loan Supervisors **[★5342]**

Natl. Assn. for Small Schools **[IO]**, Banbury, United Kingdom

Natl. Assn. of Smaller Communities **[★5850]**

Natl. Assn. of Social Workers **[13222]**, 750 1st St. NE, Ste. 700, Washington, DC 20002-4241, (202)408-8600

Natl. Assn. of Social Workers Comm. on Lesbian and Gay Issues **[★12098]**

Natl. Assn. of Social Workers Natl. Comm. on Lesbian, Gay and Bisexual Issues **[12098]**, 750 First St. NE, Ste. 700, Washington, DC 20002-4241, (202)408-8600

Natl. Assn. of Social Workers- Natl. Comm. on Lesbian and Gay Issues **[★12098]**

Natl. Assn. of Societies for Care of the Handicapped **[IO]**, Harare, Zimbabwe

Natl. Assn. of Software and Ser. Companies **[IO]**, New Delhi, India

Natl. Assn. of Soil Conservation Districts **[★4095]**

Natl. Assn. of Soil and Water Conservation Districts **[★4095]**

Natl. Assn. of Somali Sci. and Environmental Journalists **[IO]**, Mogadishu, Somalia

Natl. Assn. of Spanish Speaking-Spanish Surnamed Nurses **[★15766]**

Natl. Assn. of Special Educ. Teachers **[8887]**, 1250 Connecticut Ave. NW, Ste. 200, Washington, DC 20036, (800)754-4421

Natl. Assn. for the Specialty Food Trade **[1412]**, 136 Madison Ave., 12th Fl., New York, NY 10016, (212)482-6440

Natl. Assn. of Specialty Hea. Organizations **[14811]**, 222 S First St., Ste. 303, Louisville, KY 40202, (502)403-1122

Natl. Assn. for Sport and Physical Educ. **[8720]**, 1900 Assn. Dr., Reston, VA 20191-1598, (703)476-3410

Natl. Assn. of Sporting Goods Wholesalers **[3312]**, 1833 Centre Point Cir., Stem 123, Naperville, IL 60563, (630)596-9006

Natl. Assn. of Sports Commissions **[23023]**, 9916 Carver Rd., Ste. 100, Cincinnati, OH 45242, (513)281-3888

Natl. Assn. of Sports Nutrition **[15841]**, 7710 Balboa Ave., Ste. 311, San Diego, CA 92111, (858)694-0317

Natl. Assn. of Sports Officials **[23024]**, 2017 Lathrop Ave., Racine, WI 53405, (262)632-5448

Natl. Assn. of Sports Officials - Organizations Network **[23025]**, 2017 Lathrop Ave., Racine, WI 53405, (262)632-5448

Natl. Assn. of State 911 Administrators **[7547]**, North Carolina Off. of Info. Tech., 3810 Mitchell Cir., New Bern, NC 28562, (919)754-2942

Natl. Assn. of State Administrators and Supervisor of Private Schools **[8755]**, PO Box 025250, Miami, FL 33102-5250

Natl. Assn. State Agencies for Surplus Property **[5898]**, 1924 S 10 - 1/2 St., Springfield, IL 62703, (217)785-6903

Natl. Assn. of State Alcohol and Drug Abuse Directors **[13275]**, 1025 Connecticut Ave. NW, Ste. 605, Washington, DC 20036, (202)293-0090

Natl. Assn. of State Approving Agencies **[6058]**, PO Box 19432, Springfield, IL 62794-9432, (217)782-7838

Natl. Assn. of State Aquaculture Coordinators **[3828]**, Joseph Myers, PO Box 330, Trenton, NJ 08625, (609)984-2502

Natl. Assn. of State Archaeologists **[6172]**, Arthur E. Spiess, Sec.-Treas., Maine Historic Preservation Commn., 65 State House Sta., Augusta, ME 04333-0065, (207)287-2132

Natl. Assn. of State Archives and Records Administrators **[★5543]**

Natl. Assn. of State Auditors, Comptrollers, and Treasurers **[5920]**, 449 Lewis Hargett Cir., Ste. 290, Lexington, KY 40503-3669, (859)276-1147

Natl. Assn. of State Aviation Officials **[5294]**, Washington Natl. Airport, Hangar 7, Ste. 218, Washington, DC 20001, (703)417-1880

Natl. Assn. of State-Based Child Advocacy Organizations **[★11426]**

Natl. Assn. of State Beer Assn. Secretaries **[★185]**

Natl. Assn. of State Boards of Accountancy **[5182]**, 150 4th Ave. N, Ste. 700, Nashville, TN 37219-2417, (615)880-4200

Natl. Assn. of State Boards of Educ. **[8815]**, 2121 Crystal Dr., Ste. 350, Arlington, VA 22202, (703)684-4000

Natl. Assn. of State Boards of Geology **[6913]**, PO Box 11591, Columbia, SC 29211-1591, (803)739-5676

Natl. Assn. of State Boating Law Administrators **[5299]**, 1500 Leestown Rd., Ste. 330, Lexington, KY 40511, (859)225-9487

Natl. Assn. of State Budget Officers **[5921]**, Hall of the States Bldg., 444 N Capitol St. NW, Ste. 642, Washington, DC 20001-1511, (202)624-5382

Natl. Assn. of State Catholic Conf. Directors **[19460]**, Mr. Edward E. Dolejsi, Exec. Dir., 1119 K St., 2nd Fl., Sacramento, CA 95814, (916)443-4851

Natl. Assn. of State Charity Officials **[5491]**, 815 Olive St., St. Louis, MO 63101

Natl. Assn. of State Chief Administrators **[5993]**, PO Box 11910, Lexington, KY 40578-1910, (859)244-8181

Natl. Assn. of State Chief Info. Officers **[5544]**, AMR Mgt. Services, 201 E Main St., Ste. 1405, Lexington, KY 40507, (859)514-9166

Natl. Assn. of State Civil Defense Directors **[★5398]**

Natl. Assn. for State Community Services Programs **[5994]**, 444 N Capitol St. NW, Ste. 846, Washington, DC 20001, (202)624-5866

Natl. Assn. of State Comprehensive Hea. Insurance Plans **[14861]**, 33 E Main St., Ste. 230, Madison, WI 53703, (608)441-5777

Natl. Assn. of State Conservation Agencies **[4097]**, 3903 Cook St., Alexandria, VA 22311, (703)399-5594

Natl. Assn. of State Contractors Licensing Agencies **[932]**, 23309 N 17th Dr., Bldg. 1, Unit 10, Phoenix, AZ 85027, (623)587-9354

Natl. Assn. of State Controlled Substances Authorities **[5391]**, 72 Brook St., Quincy, MA 02170, (617)472-0520

Natl. Assn. of State Credit Union Supervisor **[5362]**, 1655 N Ft. Myer Dr., Ste. 300, Arlington, VA 22209, (703)528-8351

Natl. Assn. of State Departments of Agriculture **[5192]**, 1156 15th St. NW, Ste. 1020, Washington, DC 20005, (202)296-9680

Natl. Assn. of State Directors of Admin. and Gen. Ser. Officers **[★5993]**

Natl. Assn. of State Directors of Career Tech. Educ. Consortium **[9046]**, 8484 Georgia Ave., Ste. 320, Silver Spring, MD 20910, (301)588-9630

Natl. Assn. of State Directors of Developmental Disabilities Services **[12509]**, 113 Oronoco St., Alexandria, VA 22314, (703)683-4202

Natl. Assn. of State Directors for Disaster Preparedness **[★5398]**

Natl. Assn. of State Directors of Migrant Educ. **[12524]**, 1001 Connecticut Ave. NW, Ste. 915, Washington, DC 20036

Natl. Assn. of State Directors of Special Educ. **[8888]**, 1800 Diagonal Rd., Ste. 320, Alexandria, VA 22314, (703)519-3800

Natl. Assn. of State Directors of Teacher Educ. and Certification **[8956]**, 1225 Providence Rd., PMB 116, Whitinsville, MA 01588, (508)380-1202

Natl. Assn. of State Directors of Veterans Affairs **[6059]**, Linda Schwartz, Pres., 107 S West St., No. 570, Alexandria, VA 22314

Natl. Assn. of State Directors of Vocational Tech. Educ. Consortium **[★9046]**

Natl. Assn. of State Drug Abuse Prog. Coordinators **[★13275]**

Natl. Assn. for State Economic Opportunity Off. Directors **[★5994]**

Natl. Assn. of State Election Directors **[1067]**, 12543 Westella Dr., Ste. 100, Houston, TX 77077-3929, (281)752-6200

Natl. Assn. of State EMS Officials **[14473]**, 201 Park Washington Ct., Falls Church, VA 22046-4527, (703)538-1799

Natl. Assn. of State Energy Officials **[5407]**, 1414 Prince St., Ste. 200, Alexandria, VA 22314, (703)299-8800

Natl. Assn. of State Facilities Administrators **[5909]**, PO Box 11910, Lexington, KY 40578-1910, (859)244-8181

Natl. Assn. of State Farm Agents **[2015]**, 8015 Corporate Dr., Ste. A, Baltimore, MD 21236, (410)931-3332

Natl. Assn. of State Fire Marshals **[5447]**, 1319 F St. NW, Ste. 301, Washington, DC 20004, (202)737-1226

Natl. Assn. of State Foresters **[4405]**, 444 N Capitol St. NW, Ste. 540, Washington, DC 20001, (202)624-5415

Natl. Assn. of State Head Injury Administrators **[14685]**, PO Box 878, Waitsfield, VT 05673, (802)498-3349

Natl. Assn. of State Info. Rsrc. Executives **[★5544]**

Natl. Assn. for State Info. Systems **[★5544]**

Natl. Assn. of State Land Reclamationists **[5842]**, Anna Harrington, Southern Illinois Univ., Coal Res. Center, Carbondale, IL 62901-4623, (618)536-5521

Natl. Assn. of State and Local Equity Funds **[1318]**, 1970 Broadway, Ste. 250, Oakland, CA 94612, (510)444-1101

Natl. Assn. of State Lotteries **[★5776]**

Natl. Assn. of State Lotteries **[★5776]**

Natl. Assn. of State Medicaid Directors **[★14860]**

Natl. Assn. of State Mental Hea. Prog. Directors **[15471]**, 66 Canal Center Plz., Ste. 302, Alexandria, VA 22314, (703)739-9333

Natl. Assn. of State Military Rsrc. Managers **[5811]**, Shawn Fitzgerald, Pres., 1300 Military Rd., Lincoln, NE 68510, (402)309-7140

Natl. Assn. of State Motorcycle Safety Administrators **[5966]**, Ms. Ruth Wilson, PO Box 2708, Littleton, CO 80161, (303)797-2318

Natl. Assn. of State Park Directors **[5877]**, 8829 Woodyhill Rd., Raleigh, NC 27613, (919)676-8365

Natl. Assn. of State Personnel Executives **[5995]**, PO Box 11910, Lexington, KY 40578-1910, (859)244-8182

Natl. Assn. of State Procurement Officials **[5950]**, 201 E Main St., Ste. 1405, Lexington, KY 40507-2004, (859)514-9159

Natl. Assn. of State Public Hea. Veterinarians **[★16981]**

A star before a book entry number signifies that the name is not listed separately, but is mentioned within the entry.

Natl. Assn. of State Purchasing Officials [★5950]

Natl. Assn. of State Racing Commissioners [★5952]

Natl. Assn. of State Racing Commissioners [★5952]

Natl. Assn. of State Recreation Planners [★5876]

Natl. Assn. of State Retirement Administrators [5310], PO Box 14117, Baton Rouge, LA 70898, (225)757-7452

Natl. Assn. of State Savings and Loan Supervisors [★397]

Natl. Assn. of State School Nurse Consultants [15773], Marjorie Cole, Membership Chair, 1848 Elmira Ct., St. Louis, MO 63146

Natl. Assn. of State Sentencing Commissions [5379], Meredith Farrar-Owens, Pres./Deputy Dir., Virginia Criminal Sentencing Commn., 100 N 9th St., Richmond, VA 23219, (804)371-7626

Natl. Assn. of State Social Security Administrators [★5973]

Natl. Assn. of State Supervisors of Distributive Educ. [★8557]

Natl. Assn. of State Tech. Directors [6022], 2760 Res. Park Dr., Lexington, KY 40511-8482, (859)244-8187

Natl. Assn. of State Telecommunications Directors [★6022]

Natl. Assn. of State and Territorial Public Hea. Veterinarians [★16981]

Natl. Assn. of State Textbook Administrators [★8997]

Natl. Assn. of State Textbook Administrators [8996], Marcie Buckle, Pres., PO Box 94064, Baton Rouge, LA 70804-9064

Natl. Assn. of State Textbook Directors [★8997]

Natl. Assn. of State Treasurers [5922], PO Box 11910, Lexington, KY 40578-1910, (859)244-8175

Natl. Assn. of State United for Aging and Disabilities [10858], 1201 15th St. NW, Ste. 350, Washington, DC 20005, (202)898-2578

Natl. Assn. of State Units on Aging [★10858]

Natl. Assn. of State Universities and Public Land-Grant Colleges [★7873]

Natl. Assn. of State Utility Consumer Advocates [6054], 8380 Colesville Rd., Ste. 101, Silver Spring, MD 20910-6267, (301)589-6313

Natl. Assn. of State Veterans Homes [13352], 3416 Columbus Ave., Sandusky, OH 44870-5598, (419)625-2454

Natl. Assn. of State Workforce Agencies [5401], 444 N Capitol St. NW, Ste. 142, Washington, DC 20001, (202)434-8020

Natl. Assn. of Stationery Mfrs. [IO], Milan, Italy

Natl. Assn. of Steam and Fluid Specialty Mfrs. [★1822]

Natl. Assn. of Steel Pipe Distributors [2750], 1501 E Mockingbird Ln., Ste. 307, Victoria, TX 77904, (361)574-7878

Natl. Assn. of Steel Stockholders [IO], Birmingham, United Kingdom

Natl. Assn. for Stock Car Auto Racing [22247], PO Box 2875, Daytona Beach, FL 32120, (386)681-5977

Natl. Assn. of Stock Plan Professionals [1345], PO Box 21639, Concord, CA 94521-0639, (925)685-9271

Natl. Assn. of Stockholders and Traders in Iron and Steel, Non-Ferrous Metals, Ferros and Non-Ferros Scrap [IO], Milan, Italy

Natl. Assn. to Stop Guardian Abuse [11919], PO Box 886, Mount Prospect, IL 60056

Natl. Assn. of Store Fixture Mfrs. [★533]

Natl. Assn. of Storm Chasers and Spotters [7616], Weatherstock Inc., PO Box 31808, Tucson, AZ 85751

Natl. Assn. of St. Entertainers [IO], Brighton, United Kingdom

Natl. Assn. of St. Schools [★9083]

Natl. Assn. of St. Vendors of India [IO], Patna, India

Natl. Assn. of Student Activity Advisers - Defunct.

Natl. Assn. of Student Affairs Professionals [7672], Tennessee State Univ., 3500 John A. Merritt Blvd., Nashville, TN 37209-1500, (615)969-5361

Natl. Assn. of Student Anthropologists - Address unknown since 2011.

Natl. Assn. of Student Councils [8923], 1904 Assn. Dr., Reston, VA 20191-1537, (703)860-0200

Natl. Assn. of Student Employment Administrators [★8728]

Natl. Assn. of Student Employment Services [IO], Liverpool, United Kingdom

Natl. Assn. of Student Financial Aid Administrators [8102], 1101 Connecticut Ave. NW, Ste. 1100, Washington, DC 20036-4312, (202)785-0453

Natl. Assn. of Student Loan Administrators - Address unknown since 2010.

Natl. Assn. of Student Personnel Administrators [★7666]

Natl. Assn. of Students Against Violence Everywhere [18172], 322 Chapanoke Rd., Ste. 110, Raleigh, NC 27603, (919)661-7800

Natl. Assn. of Students Against Violence Everywhere [18172], 322 Chapanoke Rd., Ste. 110, Raleigh, NC 27603, (919)661-7800

Natl. Assn. for the Stud. and Performance of African-American Music [8662], Martha Cistrunk Brown, Treas., 809 E Gladwick St., Carson, CA 90746

Natl. Assn. for the Stud. and Prevention of Tuberculosis [★16604]

Natl. Assn. for the Stud. of Snow and Avalanches [IO], Grenoble, France

Natl. Assn. of Subacute and Post-Acute Care - Address unknown since 2010.

Natl. Assn. of Subrogation Professionals [2897], 3 Robinson Plz., Ste. 130, 6600 Steubenville Pike, Pittsburgh, PA 15205, (412)706-8000

Natl. Assn. of Suggestion Systems [★1149]

Natl. Assn. of Suggestion Systems [★1149]

Natl. Assn. of Summer Sessions [★8935]

Natl. Assn. of Summer Sessions [★8935]

Natl. Assn. of Superintendents of U.S. Naval Shore Establishments - Address unknown since 2011.

Natl. Assn. of Supermarkets and Related Businesses [IO], Caracas, Venezuela

Natl. Assn. of Supervisor of Agricultural Educ. [7712], 300 Garrigus Bldg., Lexington, KY 40546-0215, (859)257-2224

Natl. Assn. of Supervisor of Bus. Educ. [7802], Colorado Community Coll. Sys., 9101 E Lowry Blvd., Denver, CO 80230, (720)858-2746

Natl. Assn. of Supervisors [★5432]

Natl. Assn. of Supervisors of Bus. and Off. Educ. [★7802]

Natl. Assn. of Supervisors, Dept. of Defense [★5432]

Natl. Assn. of Supervisors, Fed. Govt. [★5432]

Natl. Assn. of Supervisors of State Banks [★5298]

Natl. Assn. of Supervisors of Student Training [★8945]

Natl. Assn. of Supervisors and Teachers of High School Journalism [★8444]

Natl. Assn. of Suppliers for the Footwear and Leather Indus. [IO], Leon, Mexico

Natl. Assn. for the Support of Long Term Care [14812], 1321 Duke St., Ste. 304, Alexandria, VA 22314, (703)549-8500

Natl. Assn. of Surety Bond Producers [2016], 1140 19th St., Ste. 800, Washington, DC 20036-5104, (202)686-3700

Natl. Assn. for Surface Finishing [1348], 1155 15th St. NW, Ste. 500, Washington, DC 20005, (202)457-8404

Natl. Assn. of Surrogate Mothers - Defunct.

Natl. Assn. for Sustainable Agriculture Australia [IO], Stirling, Australia

Natl. Assn. of Swedish Architects [IO], Stockholm, Sweden

Natl. Assn. of Tanners [★2202]

Natl. Assn. of Tax Administrators [★6008]

Natl. Assn. of Tax Advisors [IO], Berlin, Germany

Natl. Assn. of Tax Consultants [6016], 321 W 13th Ave., Eugene, OR 97401, (541)298-2829

Natl. Assn. of Tax Practitioners [★6017]

Natl. Assn. of Tax Professionals [6017], PO Box 8002, Appleton, WI 54914-8002, (800)558-3402

Natl. Assn. of Taxicab Owners [★3537]

Natl. Assn. of Taxicab Owners [★3537]

Natl. Assn. of Teacher Educ. Institutions of Metropolitan Districts [★8940]

Natl. Assn. of Teacher Educators for Family and Consumer Sciences [8266], Western Kentucky Univ., 1906 Coll. Heights Blvd., No. 11037, Bowling Green, KY 41201-1037, (270)745-3997

Natl. Assn. of Teacher Educators for Home Economics [★8266]

Natl. Assn. of Teacher Educators for Vocational Home Economics [★8266]

Natl. Assn. of Teachers of Singing [8663], 9957 Moorings Dr., Ste. 401, Jacksonville, FL 32257, (904)992-9101

Natl. Assn. for the Teaching of English [IO], Sheffield, United Kingdom

Natl. Assn. for Teaching English and other Community Languages to Adults [IO], Birmingham, United Kingdom

Natl. Assn. for Tech Prep Leadership [8974], Cindy Powell, Treas., 6101 Grayson Dr., Denison, TX 75020, (903)463-8648

Natl. Assn. of Telecommunications Officers and Advisors [6023], 2121 Eisenhower Ave., Ste. 401, Alexandria, VA 22314, (703)519-8035

Natl. Assn. for Telematics for Transport and Safety [IO], Rome, Italy

Natl. Assn. of TV and Electronic Servicers of Am. [★1110]

Natl. Assn. of TV Prog. Executives [504], 5757 Wilshire Blvd., Penthouse 10, Los Angeles, CA 90036-3681, (310)453-4440

Natl. Assn. of TV Prog. Executives [504], 5757 Wilshire Blvd., Penthouse 10, Los Angeles, CA 90036-3681, (310)453-4440

Natl. Assn. of Television-Radio Farm Directors [★502]

Natl. Assn. of Temple Administrators [19885], PO Box 936, Ridgefield, WA 98642, (360)887-0464

Natl. Assn. of Temple Educators [19886], 633 3rd Ave., New York, NY 10017-6778, (212)452-6510

Natl. Assn. of Temple Educators [19886], 633 3rd Ave., New York, NY 10017-6778, (212)452-6510

Natl. Assn. of Temple Secretaries [★19885]

Natl. Assn. of Temporary Services [★1142]

Natl. Assn. of Temporary and Staffing Services [★1142]

Natl. Assn. of Tenants' Organisations [IO], Dublin, Ireland

Natl. Assn. for the Terminally Ill - Address unknown since 2010.

Natl. Assn. of Test Directors [8990], 445 W Amelia St., Orlando, FL 32801-1129, (407)317-3201

Natl. Assn. of Texaco Consignees [★2659]

Natl. Assn. of Texaco and Shell Marketers [★2659]

Natl. Assn. of Texaco Wholesalers [★2659]

Natl. Assn. of Textile Machinery Mfrs. [★1802]

Natl. Assn. of The Bahamas [11141], PO Box 162039, Miami, FL 33116, (954)888-1113

Natl. Assn. of Theatre Owners [1209], 750 1st St. NE, Ste. 1130, Washington, DC 20002, (202)962-0054

Natl. Assn. of Theatre Owners [1209], 750 1st St. NE, Ste. 1130, Washington, DC 20002, (202)962-0054

Natl. Assn. of Therapeutic Schools and Programs [13818], 5272 River Rd., Ste. 600, Bethesda, MD 20816, (301)986-8770

Natl. Assn. of Therapeutic Wilderness Camping [22444], PO Box 593, Davis, WV 26260

Natl. Assn. of Ticket Brokers [1210], 214 N Hale St., Wheaton, IL 60187, (630)510-4594

Natl. Assn. of Timetable Collectors [22184], PO Box 446, Georgetown, TX 78627-0446

Natl. Assn. of Tire and Renovating Plants Distributors [IO], Mexico City, Mexico

Natl. Assn. of Tire Specialists [IO], Bologna, Italy

Natl. Assn. of Tobacco Outlets [3468], 15560 Boulder Pointe Rd., Minneapolis, MN 55437, (866)869-8888

Natl. Assn. of Tower Erectors [6378], 8 2nd St. SE, Watertown, SD 57201-3624, (605)882-5865

Natl. Assn. of Town Watch [11689], PO Box 303, Wynnewood, PA 19096, (610)649-7055

Natl. Assn. of Towns and Townships [5850], 1130 Connecticut Ave. NW, Ste. 300, Washington, DC 20036, (202)454-3954

Natl. Assn. of Trade Exchanges [3487], 10151 IH 35 N, San Antonio, TX 78233, (617)763-3311

Natl. Assn. for Trade and Indus. Educ. and Natl. Assn. of State Supervisors for Trade and Indus. Educ. [★8294]

Natl. Assn. of Trade Press Publishers [IO], Milan, Italy

Reference to "IO" in place of a book number signifies that the association may be found in the 50th edition of International Organizations.

Natl. Assn. of Trade and Tech. Schools and the Assn. of Independent Colleges and Schools [★9041]

Natl. Assn. of Traffic Accident Reconstructionists and Investigators [5607], PO Box 2588, West Chester, PA 19382, (610)696-1919

Natl. Assn. of Trailer Mfrs. [335], 1320 SW Topeka Blvd., Topeka, KS 66612-1817, (785)272-4433

Natl. Assn. of Travel Agents Singapore [IO], Singapore, Singapore

Natl. Assn. of Triads [12992], 1450 Duke St., Alexandria, VA 22314, (703)836-7827

Natl. Assn. of Trial Court Administrators [★5355]

Natl. Assn. of Trial Court Administrators [★5355]

Natl. Assn. of Tribal Historic Preservation Officers [9711], PO Box 19189, Washington, DC 20036-9189, (202)628-8476

Natl. Assn. of Truck Stop Operators [★3119]

Natl. Assn. for Tutoring [★9022]

Natl. Assn. of Unclaimed Property Administrators [5899], NAST, PO Box 11910, Lexington, KY 40578-1910, (859)244-8150

Natl. Assn. of Underwater Instructors [23104], PO Box 89789, Tampa, FL 33689-0413, (813)628-6284

Natl. Assn. of Unemployment Insurance Appellate Boards [5555], Stephen Wilson, Treas., 850 E Madison St., Springfield, IL 62702, (770)994-2220

Natl. Assn. of Uniform Mfrs. and Distributors [211], 336 W 37th St., Ste. 370, New York, NY 10018, (212)736-3010

Natl. Assn. for Uniformed Services [5812], 5535 Hempstead Way, Springfield, VA 22151-4094, (703)750-1342

Natl. Assn. for Uniformed Services Retirees [★5812]

Natl. Assn. of Univ. Fisheries and Wildlife Programs [8146], Oregon State Univ., Dept. of Fisheries & Wildlife, 104 Nash Hall, Corvallis, OR 97331-3803, (541)737-2910

Natl. Assn. of University-Model Schools [7885], 103 N 1st St., Midlothian, TX 76065, (972)525-7005

Natl. Assn. of Univ. Women [9060], 1001 E St. SE, Washington, DC 20003, (202)547-3967

Natl. Assn. of Univ. Women Moldova [IO], Balti, Moldova

Natl. Assn. of Upholstery Fabric Distributors [★3448]

Natl. Assn. of Urban Bankers [★438]

Natl. Assn. of Urban Debate Leagues [8892], 332 S Michigan Ave., Ste. 500, Chicago, IL 60604, (312)427-0175

Natl. Assn. of Urban Flood Mgt. Agencies [★5863]

Natl. Assn. of Urban Hospitals [15066], 21351 Gentry Dr., Ste. 210, Sterling, VA 20166, (703)444-0989

Natl. Assn. of Utilization Rev. Coordinators [★16508]

Natl. Assn. of Van Pool Operators [★13331]

Natl. Assn. of Van Pool Operators [★13331]

Natl. Assn. of the Van Valkenburg Family [20562], PO Box 9536, Newark, DE 19714

Natl. Assn. for Variable Annuities - Address unknown since 2010.

Natl. Assn. of Vascular Access Networks [★16958]

Natl. Assn. of Vertical Trans. Professionals [★1832]

Natl. Assn. of Veterans Affairs Chaplains [19527], Chaplain Stephen Brandow, Pres., PO Box 69004, Alexandria, LA 71306, (318)473-0010

Natl. Assn. of Veterans Affairs Physicians and Dentists [16271], PO Box 15418, Arlington, VA 22215-0418, (866)836-3520

Natl. Assn. of Veterans Prog. Administrators [20796], 2020 Pennsylvania Ave. NW, Ste. 1975, Washington, DC 20006-1846, (517)483-1932

Natl. Assn. of Veterans' Res. and Educ. Foundations [6060], 5480 Wisconsin Ave., Ste. 214, Chevy Chase, MD 20815, (301)656-5005

Natl. Assn. for Veterinary Acupuncture - Defunct.

Natl. Assn. of Veterinary Technicians in Am. [17034], 1666 K St. NW, Ste. 260, Washington, DC 20006-1260, (703)740-8737

Natl. Assn. of Victim Ser. Professionals in Corrections [13366], Erin Gaffney, Treas., 999 Barretts Mill Rd., West Concord, MA 01742, (978)369-3618

Natl. Assn. of Video Distributors - Address unknown since 2010.

Natl. Assn. for Vietnamese Amer. Educ. [★19273]

Natl. Assn. of Vietnamese Nurses - Address unknown since 2011.

Natl. Assn. of Village Councils [IO], Belmopan, Belize

Natl. Assn. of Vision Care Plans [14862], 222 S First St., Ste. 330, Louisville, KY 40202, (502)403-1122

Natl. Assn. of Vision Professionals [15968], 1775 Church St. NW, Washington, DC 20036, (202)234-1010

Natl. Assn. of Vision Prog. Consultants [★15968]

Natl. Assn. for the Visual Arts [IO], Potts Point, Australia

Natl. Assn. of Visual Educ. Dealers [★277]

Natl. Assn. of Visual Educ. Dealers [★277]

Natl. Assn. for Visually Handicapped [★17096]

Natl. Assn. for Visually Handicapped [★17096]

Natl. Assn. of Vocational Educ. Special Needs Personnel - Defunct.

Natl. Assn. for Voluntary and Community Action [IO], Sheffield, United Kingdom

Natl. Assn. of Volunteer Programs in Local Govt. [6064], 25 Massachusetts Ave. NW, Washington, DC 20001

Natl. Assn. of Wastewater Transporters [3639], 336 Chestnut Ln., Ambler, PA 19002-1001, (215)643-6798

Natl. Assn. of Watch and Clock Collectors [22167], 514 Poplar St., Columbia, PA 17512-2124, (717)684-8261

Natl. Assn. of Water Companies [3649], 2001 L St. NW, Ste. 850, Washington, DC 20036, (202)833-8383

Natl. Assn. of Water Inst. Directors [★7605]

Natl. Assn. of Waterproofing and Structural Repair Contractors [590], 8015 Corporate Dr., Ste. A, Baltimore, MD 21236, (410)931-3332

Natl. Assn. of Webmasters [★1911]

Natl. Assn. of Webmasters [★1911]

Natl. Assn. of Wheat Growers [3953], 415 2nd St. NE, Ste. 300, Washington, DC 20002-4993, (202)547-7800

Natl. Assn. of Wheat Weavers [21454], 46 Ophir Ave., Lincoln, IL 62656, (217)732-1957

Natl. Assn. of Wheat Weavers [21454], 46 Ophir Ave., Lincoln, IL 62656, (217)732-1957

Natl. Assn. of Wholesale Butchers and Meat Merchants [IO], Bonn, Germany

Natl. Assn. of Wholesale Independent Distributors [★3346]

Natl. Assn. of Wholesaler-Distributors [3663], 1325 G St. NW, Ste. 1000, Washington, DC 20005, (202)872-0885

Natl. Assn. of Wholesalers [★3663]

Natl. Assn. of WIC Directors [★5976]

Natl. Assn. of Widows - England [IO], Coventry, United Kingdom

Natl. Assn. of Women Artists [9242], 80 5th Ave., Ste. 1405, New York, NY 10011, (212)675-1616

Natl. Assn. of Women Bus. Owners [685], 601 Pennsylvania Ave. NW, South Bldg., Ste. 900, Washington, DC 20004, (800)556-2926

Natl. Assn. of Women in Constr. [933], 327 S Adams St., Fort Worth, TX 76104, (817)877-5551

Natl. Assn. of Women in Constr. [933], 327 S Adams St., Fort Worth, TX 76104, (817)877-5551

Natl. Assn. of Women in Constr. - Australia [IO], Melbourne, Australia

Natl. Assn. for Women in Education - Defunct.

Natl. Assn. of Women Highway Safety Leaders [12993], 21780 CR 3, Lindon, CO 80740, (719)768-3266

Natl. Assn. of Women Judges [5627], 1341 Connecticut Ave. NW, Ste. 4.2, Washington, DC 20036, (202)393-0222

Natl. Assn. of Women and the Law [IO], Gloucester, ON, Canada

Natl. Assn. of Women Law Enforcement Executives [5718], 160 Lawrenceville-Pennington Rd., Ste. 16-115, Lawrenceville, NJ 08648, (973)975-6146

Natl. Assn. of Women Lawyers [5266], Amer. Bar Center, MS 15.2, 321 N Clark St., Chicago, IL 60654, (312)988-6186

Natl. Assn. of Women MBAs [686], Rice Univ., PO Box 2932, Houston, TX 77251-2932

Natl. Assn. of Women Organizations in Uganda [IO], Kampala, Uganda

Natl. Assn. of Women Pharmacists [IO], Kirk Ella, United Kingdom

Natl. Assn. of Women Writers [★10739]

Natl. Assn. of Women's Gymnastic's Judges [22634], Betty Sroufe, Sec.-Treas., 2096 Rolling Hills Blvd., Fairfield, OH 45014-3732, (513)829-5671

Natl. Assn. of Women's Yellow Pages [★3698]

Natl. Assn. of Woodworkers New Zealand [IO], Tauranga, New Zealand

Natl. Assn. of Wool Producers [IO], Covilha, Portugal

Natl. Assn. on Work and the Coll. Student [★8728]

Natl. Assn. of Workforce Boards [11946], 1133 19th St. NW, Ste. 400, Washington, DC 20036, (202)857-7900

Natl. Assn. of Workforce Development Professionals [11947], 1133 19th St. NW, 4th Fl., Washington, DC 20036-3623, (202)589-1790

Natl. Assn. of Working Seniors - Address unknown since 2011.

Natl. Assn. of Writers in Educ. [IO], York, United Kingdom

Natl. Assn. of Writing Instrument Distributors [★3346]

Natl. Assn. for Year-Round Educ. [8044], PO Box 711386, San Diego, CA 92171-1386, (619)276-5296

Natl. Assn. of Young Asian Professionals [★9341]

Natl. Assn. of Youth in Agriculture [IO], Roseau, Dominica

Natl. Assn. of Youth Clubs [13539], Natl. Assn. of Colored Women's Clubs, 1601 R St. NW, Washington, DC 20009, (202)667-4080

Natl. Assn. of Youth Courts [18830], PO Box 10875, Tallahassee, FL 32302

Natl. Assn. for Youth Drama [IO], Dublin, Ireland

Natl. Assn. of Youth Orchestras [IO], Edinburgh, United Kingdom

Natl. Assn. of Youth Theatres [IO], Darlington, United Kingdom

Natl. Associations of Canoe Liveries and Outfitters [★3316]

Natl. Astrological Lib. [★6213]

Natl. Ataxia Found. [15614], 2600 Fernbrook Ln., No. 119, Minneapolis, MN 55447, (763)553-0020

Natl. Athletic Trainers' Assn. [23095], 2952 Stemmons Fwy., No. 200, Dallas, TX 75247-6196, (214)637-6282

Natl. Athletics Assn. of Zimbabwe [IO], Gweru, Zimbabwe

Natl. Auctioneers Assn. [271], 8880 Ballentine St., Overland Park, KS 66214, (913)541-8084

Natl. Audio-Visual Assn. [★277]

Natl. Audio-Visual Assn. [★277]

Natl. Audubon Soc. [4098], 225 Varick St., 7th Fl., New York, NY 10014, (212)979-3000

Natl. Auricula and Primula Soc. [IO], Loughborough, United Kingdom

Natl. Auricula and Primula Soc. Midland and West Sect. [IO], Loughborough, United Kingdom

Natl. Australia Day Coun. [IO], Parkes, Australia

Natl. Autism Assn. [13799], 20 Alice Agnew Dr., Attleboro Falls, MA 02763, (877)622-2884

Natl. Autism Hotline [★13785]

Natl. Autism Soc. of Malaysia [IO], Kuala Lumpur, Malaysia

Natl. Autism Soc. of Sweden [IO], Stockholm, Sweden

Natl. Autistic Soc. [IO], London, United Kingdom

Natl. Auto Auction Assn. [272], 5320 Spectrum Dr., Ste. D, Frederick, MD 21703, (301)696-0400

Natl. Auto Body Coun. [305], 191 Clarksville Rd., Princeton Junction, NJ 08550, (888)667-7433

Natl. Auto and Flat Glass Dealers Assn. [★1579]

Natl. Auto and Truck Wreckers Assn. [★3632]

Natl. Auto Wreckers Assn. [★3632]

Natl. Automated CH Assn. [★423]

Natl. Automatic Laundry and Cleaning Coun. [★2190]

Natl. Automatic Merchandising Assn. [3612], 20 N Wacker Dr., Ste. 3500, Chicago, IL 60606-3102, (312)346-0370

Natl. Automatic Pistol Collectors Assn. [20967], PO Box 15738, St. Louis, MO 63163, (314)638-6505

Natl. Automatic Sprinkler Assn. [★3148]

Natl. Automatic Sprinkler and Fire Control Assn. [★3148]

A star before a book entry number signifies that the name is not listed separately, but is mentioned within the entry.

Natl. Auto. Dealers Assn. **[361]**, 8400 Westpark Dr., McLean, VA 22102, (703)821-7000

Natl. Automobile Education Assn. - Defunct.

Natl. Auto. Theft Bur. **[★2020]**

Natl. Automotive Finance Assn. **[362]**, 7250 Parkway Dr., Ste. 510, Hanover, MD 21076-1343, (410)712-4036

Natl. Automotive Radiator Ser. Assn. **[363]**, 3000 Village Run Rd., Ste. 103, No. 221, Wexford, PA 15090-6315, (412)847-5747

Natl. Automotive Technicians Educ. Found. **[7762]**, 101 Blue Seal Dr., Ste. 101, Leesburg, VA 20175, (703)669-6650

Natl. Automotive and Truck Museum of U.S. **[10127]**, 1000 Gordon M. Buehrig Pl., Auburn, IN 46706, (260)925-9100

Natl. Autosound Challenge Assn. **[★1104]**

Natl. Autumn Leaf Collectors Club **[21377]**, Dianna Kowallis, 2nd VP, PO Box 318, Riverside, CA 92508-6039

Natl. Aviation Club - Defunct.

Natl. Aviation and Space Educ. Alliance **[7764]**, 23 Nutmeg Dr., Enfield, CT 06082, (505)774-0029

Natl. Aviation Trades Assn. **[★146]**

Natl. Ayurvedic Medical Assn. **[13695]**, 620 Cabrillo Ave., Santa Cruz, CA 95065, (800)669-8914

Natl. Badminton Fed. of Russia **[IO]**, Moscow, Russia

Natl. Ballroom and Entertainment Assn. **[1211]**, 2799 Locust Rd., Decorah, IA 52101-7600, (563)382-3871

Natl. Ballroom Operators Assn. **[★1211]**

Natl. Band Assn. **[10255]**, PO Box 25136, Baton Rouge, LA 70894, (225)578-2259

Natl. Band and Choral Directors Hall of Fame **[★8665]**

Natl. Bankers Assn. **[430]**, 1513 P St. NW, Washington, DC 20005, (202)588-5432

Natl. Baptist Convention **[★19326]**

Natl. Baptist Convention U.S.A. **[19326]**, World Center HQ, 1700 Baptist World Center Dr., Nashville, TN 37207, (615)228-6292

Natl. Baptist Educational Convention **[★19326]**

Natl. Bar Assn. **[5267]**, 1225 11th St. NW, Washington, DC 20001, (202)842-3900

Natl. Barbecue Assn. **[1413]**, 455 S Fourth St., Ste. 650, Louisville, KY 40202, (888)909-2121

Natl. Bark Producers Assn. **[★1511]**

Natl. Bark and Soil Producers Assn. **[★1511]**

Natl. Barley Foods Coun. **[1594]**, 2702 W Sunset Blvd., Spokane, WA 99224, (509)456-2481

Natl. Barley Growers Assn. **[4373]**, Idaho Grain Producers Assn., 821 W State St., Boise, ID 83702, (208)345-0706

Natl. Barn Alliance **[9712]**, 9526 Locust Hill Dr., Great Falls, VA 22066

Natl. Barrel and Drum Assn. **[★888]**

Natl. Barrel Horse Assn. **[22659]**, PO Box 1988, Augusta, GA 30903-1988, (706)722-7223

Natl. Barristers' Wives **[★5262]**

Natl. Baseball Cong. **[22281]**, 300 S Sycamore, Wichita, KS 67213, (316)264-6887

Natl. Baseball Fed. **[★22278]**

Natl. Baseball Hall of Fame and Museum **[22282]**, 25 Main St., Cooperstown, NY 13326, (607)547-7200

Natl. Basketball Assn. **[22298]**, 645 5th Ave., 10th Fl., New York, NY 10022, (212)407-8000

Natl. Basketball Assn. of Afghanistan **[IO]**, Kabul, Afghanistan

Natl. Basketball Athletic Trainers Assn. **[22299]**, 400 Colony Sq., Ste. 1750, Atlanta, GA 30361, (404)892-8919

Natl. Basketball Players Assn. **[23298]**, 310 Lenox Ave., New York, NY 10027, (212)655-0880

Natl. Basketball Trainers Assn. **[★22299]**

Natl. Basketry Org. **[21455]**, PO Box 277, Brasstown, NC 28902, (828)837-1280

Natl. Bass Anglers Assn. **[22581]**, 2532 Barber Rd., Hastings, MI 49058, (269)838-9482

Natl. Baton Twirling Assn. **[★22305]**

Natl. Baton Twirling Assn. Intl. **[22305]**, PO Box 266, Janesville, WI 53547, (608)754-2238

Natl. Battery Mfrs. Assn. **[★323]**

Natl. Battery Mfrs. Assn. **[★323]**

Natl. Beagle Club of Am. **[21608]**, Ms. Sharon L. Clark, Asst. Treas., 133 New Harrison Bridge Rd., Simpsonville, SC 29860, (864)862-2537

Natl. Beauty and Barber Mfrs. Assn. **[★975]**

Natl. Beauty Culturists' League **[971]**, 25 Logan Cir. NW, Washington, DC 20005-3725, (202)332-2695

Natl. Beauty Salon Chain Assn. **[★969]**

Natl. Beauty Salon Chain Assn. **[★969]**

Natl. Bed Fed. **[IO]**, Skipton, United Kingdom

Natl. Beef Coun. **[★4718]**

Natl. Beekeepers Assn. of New Zealand **[IO]**, Wellington, New Zealand

Natl. Beep Baseball Assn. **[22516]**, 3444 Limerick Ln. NE, Rochester, MN 55906, (507)208-8383

Natl. Beer Wholesalers Assn. **[187]**, 1101 King St., Ste. 600, Alexandria, VA 22314-2944, (703)683-4300

Natl. Beer Wholesalers' Assn. of Am. **[★187]**

Natl. Begonia Soc. **[IO]**, Oakham, United Kingdom

Natl. Bench Rest Shooters Assn. **[22879]**, 2835 Guilford Ln., Oklahoma City, OK 73120-4404, (405)842-9585

Natl. Beta Club **[23636]**, 151 Beta Club Way, Spartanburg, SC 29306-3012, (800)845-8281

Natl. Better Bus. Bur. **[★17445]**

Natl. Better Bus. Bur. **[★17445]**

Natl. Beverage Dispensing Equip. Assn. **[★446]**

Natl. Beverage Dispensing Equip. Assn. **[★446]**

Natl. Bible Assn. **[19915]**, 405 Lexington Ave., 26th Fl., New York, NY 10174, (212)907-6427

Natl. Bicycle Dealers Assn. **[3313]**, 3176 Pullman St., No. 117, Costa Mesa, CA 92626, (949)722-6909

Natl. Bicycle League **[22482]**, 1000 Creekside Plz., Ste. 300, Gahanna, OH 43230, (614)416-7680

Natl. Bicycle Tour Directors Assn. **[22483]**, PO Box 155, Lanesboro, MN 55949, (507)467-3321

Natl. Biodiesel Bd. **[1536]**, PO Box 104898, Jefferson City, MO 65110, (573)635-3893

Natl. Biographical Assn. - Defunct.

Natl. Biographysics Conf. **[★6331]**

Natl. Biosolids Partnership **[4795]**, 601 Wythe St., Alexandria, VA 22314, (703)684-2400

Natl. Biplane Assn. **[20909]**, PO Box 470350, Tulsa, OK 74147-0350, (918)665-0755

Natl. Bird Dog Challenge Assn. **[21609]**, 32 County Rd. 30 SW, Montrose, MN 55363, (612)812-0628

Natl. Birman Fanciers **[21254]**, 7 Cornwall Ct., Hamburg, NJ 07419-1359

Natl. Birth Defects Prevention Network **[13845]**, 14781 Memorial Dr., No. 1561, Houston, TX 77079, (404)498-3918

Natl. Bison Assn. **[3793]**, 8690 Wolff Ct., No. 200, Westminster, CO 80031, (303)292-2833

Natl. Bituminous Concrete Assn. **[★585]**

Natl. Black Alcoholism and Addiction Coun. **[13276]**, 1500 Golden Valley Rd., Minneapolis, MN 55411, (877)NBAC-ORG

Natl. Black Alcoholism Coun. **[★13276]**

Natl. Black Assn. for Speech-Language and Hearing **[16687]**, 700 McKnight Park Dr., Pittsburgh, PA 15237, (412)366-1177

Natl. Black Bridal Assn. **[473]**, 68 Abbond Ct., Plainfield, NJ 07063, (888)299-2250

Natl. Black Bus. Coun. **[687]**, 600 Corporate Pointe, Ste. 1010, Culver City, CA 90230, (310)585-6222

Natl. Black Catholic Clergy Caucus **[19461]**, 2815 Forbes Dr., Montgomery, AL 36110, (404)226-8170

Natl. Black Catholic Cong. **[19462]**, 320 Cathedral St., Baltimore, MD 21201, (410)547-8496

Natl. Black Caucus of Local Elected Officials **[5851]**, Natl. League of Cities, 1301 Pennsylvania Ave. Nw, Ste. 550, Washington, DC 20004, (202)626-3100

Natl. Black Caucus of State Legislators **[5996]**, 444 N Capitol St. NW, Ste. 622, Washington, DC 20001, (202)624-5457

Natl. Black Chamber of Commerce **[23341]**, 1350 Connecticut Ave. NW, Ste. 405, Washington, DC 20036, (202)466-6888

Natl. Black Child Development Inst. **[11164]**, 1313 L St. NW, Ste. 110, Washington, DC 20005-4110, (202)833-2220

Natl. Black Coalition of Fed. Aviation Employees **[5295]**, PO Box 845; Hampton, GA 30228, (888)311-1622

Natl. Black Consumers Union **[IO]**, Johannesburg, Republic of South Africa

Natl. Black Deaf Advocates **[11812]**, Sharon White, Sec., PO Box 32, Frankfort, KY 40602

Natl. Black Environmental Justice Network **[4284]**, PO Box 15845, Washington, DC 20003, (202)265-4919

Natl. Black Farmers Assn. **[12042]**, 68 Wind Rd., Baskerville, VA 23915, (804)691-8528

Natl. Black Gay Men's Advocacy Coalition **[12099]**, 3636 Georgia Ave. NW, Washington, DC 20010, (202)455-8441

Natl. Black Graduate Student Assn. **[18846]**, 2400 6th St. NW, Washington, DC 20059, (800)471-4102

Natl. Black Herstory Task Force **[10643]**, PO Box 55021, Atlanta, GA 30308, (404)749-6994

Natl. Black Home Educators **[8270]**, 13434 Plank Rd., PMB 110, Baker, LA 70714, (225)778-0169

Natl. Black Home Educators Rsrc. Assn. **[★8270]**

Natl. Black Justice Coalition **[18643]**, 1638 R St. NW, Ste. 300, Washington, DC 20009, (202)319-1552

Natl. Black Law Students Assn. **[8509]**, 1225 11th St. NW, Washington, DC 20001-4217, (202)618-2572

Natl. Black Leadership Initiative on Cancer **[13946]**, Robin Mitchell, Res. Specialist, 2121 W Taylor St., Chicago, IL 60612, (312)996-8046

Natl. Black MBA Assn. **[7803]**, 180 N Michigan Ave., Ste. 1400, Chicago, IL 60601, (312)236-2622

Natl. Black McDonald's Operators Assn. **[1763]**, PO Box 820668, South Florida, FL 33082-0668, (954)389-4487

Natl. Black Meeting Planners Coalition **[★2455]**

Natl. Black Music Caucus of the Music Educators Natl. Conf. **[★8662]**

Natl. Black Nurses Assn. **[15774]**, 8630 Fenton St., Ste. 330, Silver Spring, MD 20910-3803, (301)589-3200

Natl. Black Owned Broadcasters Assn. **[★500]**

Natl. Black Police Assn. **[5719]**, 3100 Main St., No. 256, Dallas, TX 75226

Natl. Black Police Assn. - UK **[IO]**, Wakefield, United Kingdom

Natl. Black Programming Consortium **[9460]**, 68 E 131st St., 7th Fl., New York, NY 10037, (212)234-8200

Natl. Black Public Relations Soc. **[2907]**, 14636 Runnymede St., Van Nuys, CA 91405, (888)976-0005

Natl. Black Republican Assn. **[18531]**, 4594 Chase Oaks Dr., Sarasota, FL 34241-9183, (866)905-6701

Natl. Black Sisters' Conf. **[19463]**, 3027 4th St. NE, Washington, DC 20017, (202)529-9250

Natl. Black State Troopers Coalition **[5720]**, PO Box 66464, Baton Rouge, LA 70896, (337)247-5361

Natl. Black United Fed. of Charities **[17158]**, 40 Clinton St., 5th Fl., Newark, NJ 07102, (973)643-3767

Natl. Black United Fund **[12597]**, 40 Clinton St., Newark, NJ 07102, (973)643-5122

Natl. Black Women's Hea. Proj. **[★17123]**

Natl. Blacksmiths and Weldors Assn. **[461]**, Jim Holman, Info. Off., PO Box 123, Arnold, NE 69120, (308)848-2913

Natl. Blind Children's Soc. **[IO]**, Birmingham, United Kingdom

National Blindness Info. Center **[★17107]**

Natl. Block and Bridle Club **[23464]**, Joel V. Yelich, IFAS - Dept. of Animal Sciences, Univ. of Florida, PO Box 110910, Gainesville, FL 32611-0910, (352)392-7560

Natl. Blonde D'Aquitaine Found. **[★3868]**

Natl. Blood Found. **[13851]**, 8101 Glenbrook Rd., Bethesda, MD 20814-2749, (301)215-6552

Natl. Bd. of Boiler and Pressure Vessel Inspectors **[5547]**, 1055 Crupper Ave., Columbus, OH 43229-1183, (614)888-8320

Natl. Bd. for Cardiopulmonary Credentialing **[★14010]**

Natl. Bd. for Cardiopulmonary Credentialing **[★14010]**

Natl. Bd. for Cardiovascular and Pulmonary Credentialing **[★14010]**

Natl. Bd. for Cardiovascular and Pulmonary Credentialing [★14010]

Natl. Bd. of Cardiovascular Tech. [★14010]

Natl. Bd. of Cardiovascular Tech. [★14010]

Natl. Bd. for Certification in Dental Lab. Tech. [14299], 325 John Knox Rd., No. L103, Tallahassee, FL 32303, (850)205-5627

Natl. Bd. for Certification in Occupational Therapy [16863], 12 S Summit Ave., Ste. 100, Gaithersburg, MD 20877-4150, (301)990-7979

Natl. Bd. for Certification of Orthopaedic Technologists [16039], 4736 Onondaga Blvd., No. 166, Syracuse, NY 13219, (866)466-2268

Natl. on Certification and Recertification of Nurse Anesthetists [15775], 222 S Prospect Ave., Park Ridge, IL 60068, (866)894-3908

Natl. Bd. for Certified Clinical Hypnotherapists [15092], 1110 Fidler Ln., Ste. 1218, Silver Spring, MD 20910, (301)608-0123

Natl. Bd. for Certified Counselors [★11678]

Natl. Bd. for Certified Counselors and Affiliates [11678], 3 Terrace Way, Greensboro, NC 27403-3660, (336)547-0607

Natl. Bd. of Chiropractic Examiners [14140], 901 54th Ave., Greeley, CO 80634, (800)964-6223

National Bd. Examination Comm. [★16988]

Natl. Bd. of Examiners in Optometry [15995], 200 S Coll. St., No. 1920, Charlotte, NC 28202, (704)332-9565

Natl. Bd. of Examiners for Osteopathic Physicians and Surgeons [★16077]

Natl. Bd. of the Fac. Mgt. Assn. of Australia [IO], Melbourne, Australia

Natl. Bd. of Fire Underwriters [★1933]

Natl. Bd. of Hypnosis Educ. & Certification [★15093]

Natl. Bd. of Medical Examiners [15330], 3750 Market St., Philadelphia, PA 19104-3102, (215)590-9500

Natl. Bd. of Osteopathic Medical Examiners [16077], 8765 W Higgins Rd., Ste. 200, Chicago, IL 60631-4174, (773)714-0622

Natl. Bd. of Pediatric Nurse Practitioners and Associates [★15795]

Natl. Bd. of Podiatric Medical Examiners [16299], PO Box 510, Bellefonte, PA 16823, (814)357-0487

Natl. Bd. of Podiatry Examiners [★16299]

Natl. Bd. for Professional Teaching Standards [8957], 1525 Wilson Blvd., Ste. 500, Arlington, VA 22209, (703)465-2700

Natl. Bd. for Respiratory Care [16864], 18000 W 105th St., Olathe, KS 66061-7543, (913)895-4900

Natl. Bd. for Respiratory Therapy [★16864]

Natl. Bd. for the Retail Trade [IO], The Hague, Netherlands

Natl. Bd. of Rev. of Motion Pictures [9605], 40 W 37th St., Ste. 501, New York, NY 10018, (212)465-9166

Natl. Bd. of Surgical Tech. and Surgical Assisting [13574], 6 W Dry Creek Cir., Ste. 100, Littleton, CO 80120, (800)707-0057

Natl. Bd. of Trial Advocacy [6046], 200 Stonewall Blvd., Ste. 1, Wrentham, MA 02093-2210, (508)384-6565

Natl. Boating Fed. [22370], PO Box 4111, Annapolis, MD 21403-4111

Natl. Bobsled Fed. [★22926]

Natl. Bone Marrow Donor Registry [★14426]

Natl. Bone Marrow Donor Registry [★14426]

Natl. Bone Marrow Transplant Link [16912], 20411 W 12 Mile Rd., Ste. 108, Southfield, MI 48076, (248)358-1886

Natl. Book Critics Circle [9449], 160 Varick St., 11th Fl., New York, NY 10013

Natl. Book Development Coun. of Singapore [IO], Singapore, Singapore

Natl. Book Trust India [IO], New Delhi, India

Natl. Border Patrol Coun. [23243], PO Box 678, Campo, CA 91906, (619)478-5145

Natl. Bottlers Assn. [★442]

Natl. Bottlers Protective Assn. [★442]

Natl. Bowhunter Educ. Found. [22224], PO Box 180757, Fort Smith, AR 72918, (479)649-9036

The Natl. Bowling Assn. [22425], 9944 Reading Rd., Cincinnati, OH 45241-3106, (513)769-1985

Natl. Bowling Coun. - Defunct.

Natl. Bowling Pro Shop and Instructors Assn. [★468]

Natl. Bowling Writer's Assn. [★2816]

Natl. Braille Assn. [17104], 95 Allens Creek Rd., Bldg. 1, Ste. 202, Rochester, NY 14618, (585)427-8260

Natl. Braille Club [★17104]

Natl. Braille Press [17105], 88 St. Stephen St., Boston, MA 02115, (617)266-6160

Natl. Brain Tumor Soc. [14404], 124 Watertown St., Ste. 2D, Watertown, MA 02472, (617)924-9997

Natl. Breast Cancer Coalition [13947], 1101 17th St. NW, Ste. 1300, Washington, DC 20036, (202)296-7477

Natl. Breast and Ovarian Cancer Centre [IO], Strawberry Hills, Australia

Natl. Breast and Ovarian Cancer Coalition [★13948]

Natl. Breast and Ovarian Cancer Connection [13948], 7688 Colonial Beach Rd., Pasadena, MD 21122, (443)822-5125

Natl. Breeders and Fanciers Assn. [★4835]

Natl. Bridal Ser. [474], 1004 W Thompson St., Ste. 205, Richmond, VA 23230, (804)342-0055

Natl. Broadcast Editorial Assn. [★2848]

Natl. Broadcasting Soc. - Alpha Epsilon Rho [23472], PO Box 4206, Chesterfield, MO 63006, (636)536-1943

Natl. Broiler Assn. [★4810]

Natl. Broiler Coun. [★4810]

Natl. Brotherhood of Skiers [22910], 1525 E 53rd St., Ste. 418, Chicago, IL 60615, (773)955-4100

Natl. Brownfield Assn. [2905], 1250 S Grove Ave., Ste. 200, Barrington, IL 60010, (224)567-6790

Natl. Bucking Bull Assn. [22842], PO Box 867, Canton, TX 75103, (903)848-4150

Natl. Buffalo Assn. [★3793]

Natl. Builders' Hardware Assn. [★1649]

Natl. Builders' Hardware Assn. [★1649]

Natl. Building Granite Quarries Assn. [3365], 1220 L St. NW, Ste. 100-167, Washington, DC 20005, (800)557-2848

Natl. Building Material Distributors Assn. [★603]

Natl. Building Museum [6201], 401 F St. NW, Washington, DC 20001, (202)272-2448

Natl. Bulk Vendors Assn. [3613], 3240 E Union Hills Dr., Ste. 129, Phoenix, AZ 85050, (888)NBV-AUSA

Natl. Bur. of Certified Consultants - Address unknown since 2010.

Natl. Bur. of Document Examiners - Defunct.

Natl. Bur. of Economic Res. [6628], 1050 Massachusetts Ave., Cambridge, MA 02138, (617)868-3900

Natl. Burglar and Fire Alarm Assn. [★3211]

Natl. Burlap Bag Dealers Assn. [★893]

Natl. Bus Traffic Assn. [3522], 111 K St. NE, 9th Fl., Washington, DC 20002, (202)898-2700

Natl. Bus. Aircraft Assn. [★150]

Natl. Bus. Assn. [3294], PO Box 700728, Dallas, TX 75370, (972)458-0900

Natl. Bus. Aviation Assn. [150], 1200 18th St. NW, Ste. 400, Washington, DC 20036-2527, (202)783-9000

Natl. Bus. Circulation Assn. [★2952]

Natl. Bus. Coalition on Hea. [14725], 1015 18th St. NW, Ste. 730, Washington, DC 20036, (202)775-9300

Natl. Bus. and Disability Coun. [11948], 201 I.U. Willets Rd., Albertson, NY 11507, (516)465-1516

Natl. Bus. Educ. Assn. [7804], 1914 Assn. Dr., Reston, VA 20191-1596, (703)860-8300

Natl. Bus. Forms Assn. [★3354]

Natl. Bus. Incubation Assn. [688], 20 E Circle Dr., No. 37198, Athens, OH 45701-3571, (740)593-4331

Natl. Bus. Initiative [IO], Auckland Park, Republic of South Africa

Natl. Bus. Officers Assn. [7779], 900 19th St. NW, Ste. 200, Washington, DC 20006, (202)407-7140

Natl. Bus. Publications [★2914]

Natl. Bus. Teachers Assn. [★7804]

Natl. Bus. Travel Assn. [3568], 110 N Royal St., 4th Fl., Alexandria, VA 22314, (703)684-0836

Natl. Butterfly Assn. [22371], Windwards Boatworks, WS302 Bend Rd., Princeton, NJ 54968, (608)575-8033

Natl. Button Soc. [21378], Susan Porter, Sec., 1564 Wilson Rd., Ramona, CA 92065-3539, (760)789-4133

Natl. Buy-Black Campaign [★2519]

Natl. C Scow Sailing Assn. [22372], PO Box 473, Pewaukee, WI 53072

Natl. C Scow Sailing Assn. [22372], PO Box 473, Pewaukee, WI 53072

Natl. Cable and Telecommunications Assn. [505], 25 Massachusetts Ave. NW, Ste. 100, Washington, DC 20001-1413, (202)222-2300

Natl. Cable TV Assn. [★505]

Natl. Cable TV Assn. [IO], Mexico City, Mexico

Natl. Cable TV Cooperative [725], 11200 Corporate Ave., Lenexa, KS 66219-1392, (913)599-5900

Natl. Cage Bird Show [21221], John Muscato, Sec., 2725 Midland Dr., Naperville, IL 60564, (630)305-9043

Natl. Cambridge Collectors [21837], PO Box 416, Cambridge, OH 43725-0416, (740)432-4245

Natl. Camp Assn. [22445], PO Box 5371, New York, NY 10185-5371, (212)645-0653

Natl. Campaign for Freedom of Expression - Defunct.

Natl. Campaign for a Peace Tax Fund [18699], 2121 Decatur Pl. NW, Washington, DC 20008, (202)483-3751

Natl. Campaign to Prevent Teen Pregnancy [13540], 1776 Massachusetts Ave. NW, Ste. 200, Washington, DC 20036, (202)478-8500

Natl. Campaign for Radioactive Waste Safety - Address unknown since 2010.

Natl. Campaign for Real Nursery Educ. [IO], London, United Kingdom

Natl. Campaign for a World Peace Tax Fund [★18699]

Natl. Campers and Hikers Assn. [★22443]

Natl. Campground Owners Assn. [★3060]

Natl. Camping Assn. [★22445]

Natl. Campus Ministry Assn. [19682], 13339 Bolingbrook Ln., Charlotte, NC 28273-9055, (704)588-0183

Natl. Cancer Care Found. [★13896]

Natl. Cancer Center [15928], 88 Sunnyside Blvd., Ste. 307, Plainview, NY 11803-1518, (516)349-0610

Natl. Cancer Coun. [IO], Kuala Lumpur, Malaysia

Natl. Cancer Cytology Center [★15928]

Natl. Cancer Found. [★13896]

National Cancer Inst. [★15914]

Natl. Cancer Registrars Assn. [15929], 1340 Braddock Pl., Ste. 203, Alexandria, VA 22314, (703)299-6640

Natl. Candle Assn. [2067], 529 14th St. NW, Ste. 750, Washington, DC 20045, (202)393-2210

Natl. Canine Defence League [★20979]

Natl. Canvas Goods Mfrs. Assn. [★3444]

Natl. Canvas Goods Mfrs. Assn. [★3444]

Natl. Capital Historical Museum of Trans. [9785],

Natl. Capital Trolley Museum, 1313 Bonifant Rd., Colesville, MD 20905-5955, (301)384-6088

Natl. Capital Lyme and Tick-Borne Disease Assn. [14405], PO Box 8211, McLean, VA 22106-8211, (703)821-8833

National Capital Trolley Museum [★9785]

Natl. Captioning Inst. [14948], 3725 Concorde Pkwy., Ste. 100, Chantilly, VA 20151, (703)917-7600

Natl. Caravan Coun. [IO], Aldershot, United Kingdom

Natl. Career Development Assn. [11949], 305 N Beech Cir., Broken Arrow, OK 74012, (918)663-7060

Natl. Career Pathways Network [8109], PO Box 21689, Waco, TX 76702-1689, (254)772-5095

Natl. Cargo Bur. [3257], 17 Battery Pl., Ste. 1232, New York, NY 10004-1110, (212)785-8300

Natl. Caricaturist Network [★1202]

Natl. Carnival Bands Assn. of Trinidad and Tobago [IO], Port of Spain, Trinidad and Tobago

Natl. Carousel Assn. [21241], Norma Pankratz, Exec. Sec., PO Box 382, Burlington, CO 80807

Natl. Carousel Roundtable [★21241]

Natl. Cartoonists Soc. [9243], 341 N Maitland Ave., Ste. 130, Maitland, FL 32751, (407)647-8839

Natl. CASA Assn. [★11364]

Natl. Casket Retailers Assn. - Address unknown since 2011.

Natl. Cast Iron Implement Seat Collectors [★21868]

A star before a book entry number signifies that the name is not listed separately, but is mentioned within the entry.

Natl. Cat Protection Soc. [11008], 6904 W Coast Hwy., Newport Beach, CA 92663-1306, (949)650-1232

Natl. Cathedral Assn. [19662], 3101 Wisconsin Ave. NW, Washington, DC 20016-5098, (202)537-6200

Natl. Catholic AIDS Network [13620], 1400 W Devon Ave., No. 502, Chicago, IL 60660, (773)508-7080

Natl. Catholic Band Assn. [10256], Villanova Univ., 800 E Lancaster Ave., Villanova, PA 19085

Natl. Catholic Bandmasters' Assn. [★10256]

Natl. Catholic Cemetery Conf. [★2530]

Natl. Catholic Coll. Admission Assn. [19464], PO Box 267, New Albany, OH 43054, (614)633-5444

Natl. Catholic Comm. on Scouting [13022], PO Box 152079, Irving, TX 75015-2079, (972)580-2114

Natl. Catholic Conf. on Family Life [★12020]

Natl. Catholic Conf. for Interracial Justice [17308], The White House, 1600 Pennsylvania Ave. NW, Washington, DC 20500, (202)456-1414

Natl. Catholic Conf. for Total Stewardship [19465], 3408 Waterlily Ct., No. 104, Palm Beach Gardens, FL 33410, (561)248-9431

Natl. Catholic Coun. on Alcoholism and Related Drug Problems [13277], 1601 Joslyn Rd., Lake Orion, MI 48360, (248)391-4445

Natl. Catholic Coun. on Alcoholism and Related Drug Problems [13277], 1601 Joslyn Rd., Lake Orion, MI 48360, (248)391-4445

Natl. Catholic Development Conf. [19466], 86 Front St., Hempstead, NY 11550-3617, (516)481-6000

Natl. Catholic Educational Assn. [7818], 1005 N Glebe Rd., Ste. 525, Arlington, VA 22201, (202)337-6232

Natl. Catholic Educational Exhibitors [1236], 2621 Dryden Rd., Dayton, OH 45439

Natl. Catholic Forensic League [8893], Mount Mercy Acad., 88 Red Jacket Pkwy., Buffalo, NY 14220

Natl. Catholic Guidance Conf. [★7940]

Natl. Catholic Music Educators Assn. [★8660]

Natl. Catholic News Ser. [★2817]

Natl. Catholic Off. for the Deaf [19467], 7202 Buchanan St., Landover Hills, MD 20784, (301)577-1684

Natl. Catholic Off. for Persons With Disabilities [★19468]

Natl. Catholic Partnership on Disability [19468], 415 Michigan Ave. NE, Ste. 95, Washington, DC 20017-4501, (202)529-2933

Natl. Catholic Rural Life Conf. [19469], 4625 Beaver Ave., Des Moines, IA 50310-2145, (515)270-2634

Natl. Catholic Rural Life Conf. [19469], 4625 Beaver Ave., Des Moines, IA 50310-2145, (515)270-2634

Natl. Catholic Soc. for Animal Welfare [★10994]

Natl. Catholic Soc. for Animal Welfare [★10994]

Natl. Catholic Soc. of Foresters [18958], 320 S School St., Mount Prospect, IL 60056-3334, (800)344-6273

Natl. Catholic Stewardship Coun. [★19436]

Natl. Catholic Stewardship Coun. [★19436]

Natl. Cattlemen's Beef Assn. [4718], 9110 E Nichols Ave., Ste. 300, Centennial, CO 80112, (303)694-0305

Natl. Caucus and Center on Black Aged [10859], 1220 L St. NW, Ste. 800, Washington, DC 20005, (202)637-8400

Natl. Caucus of Gay and Lesbian Counselors [★12069]

Natl. Caves Assn. [1212], PO Box 280, Park City, KY 42160, (270)749-2228

Natl. Center of Afro-American Artists [9103], 300 Walnut Ave., Boston, MA 02119, (617)442-8614

Natl. Center for Amer. Indian and Alaska Native Mental Hea. Res. [15472], Centers for Amer. Indian and Alaska Native Hea., Univ. of Colorado - Denver, School of Public Hea., Nighthorse Campbell Native Hea. Bldg., PO Box 6508, Aurora, CO 80045-0508, (303)724-1414

Natl. Center for Amer. Indian Enterprise Development [12563], 953 E Juanita Ave., Mesa, AZ 85204, (480)545-1298

Natl. Center for Appropriate Tech. [17194], PO Box 3838, Butte, MT 59702, (406)494-4572

Natl. Center on Arts and the Aging - Defunct.

Natl. Center for Assisted Living [14813], 1201 L St. NW, Washington, DC 20005, (202)842-4444

National Center for Atmospheric Research [★7381]

Natl. Center for Automated Information Res. - Defunct.

Natl. Center for Bicycling and Walking [22484], 1612 K St. NW, Ste. 802, Washington, DC 20006, (202)223-3621

National Center for Child Abuse Prevention Research [★11392]

National Center for Child Abuse Prevention Research [★11392]

Natl. Center for Children in Poverty [11488], 215 W 125th St., 3rd Fl., New York, NY 10027, (646)284-9600

Natl. Center for Clinical Infant Programs [★14053]

Natl. Center for Community Educ. - Address unknown since 2010.

Natl. Center for Complementary and Alternative Medicine [13696], PO Box 7923, Gaithersburg, MD 20898-7923, (301)519-3153

Natl. Center for Constitutional Stud. [17440], 37777 W Juniper Rd., Malta, ID 83342, (208)645-2625

Natl. Center for Constr. Educ. and Res. [17719], 3600 NW 43rd St., Bldg. G, Gainesville, FL 32606, (352)334-0911

Natl. Center for the Diaconate [★19692]

Natl. Center for Disability Services [★11751]

Natl. Center for the Dissemination of Disability Res. [14366], SEDL, 4700 Mueller Blvd., Austin, TX 78723-3081, (512)476-6861

Natl. Center on Educ. and the Economy [8045], 2000 Pennsylvania Ave. NW, Washington, DC 20006, (202)379-1800

Natl. Center for Educ. in Maternal and Child Hea. [14091], Georgetown Univ., PO Box 571272, Washington, DC 20057-1272, (202)784-9770

Natl. Center for Educ. Statistics [8046], 1990 K St. NW, Washington, DC 20006, (202)502-7300

Natl. Center on Elder Abuse [11891], Center for Community Res. and Services, Univ. of Delaware, 297 Graham Hall, Newark, DE 19716, (302)831-3525

Natl. Center for Employee Ownership [1138], 1736 Franklin St., 8th Fl., Oakland, CA 94612, (510)208-1300

Natl. Center on Employment of the Deaf [★11954]

Natl. Center for Environmental Hea. Strategies [14503], Mary Lamielle, Exec. Dir., 1100 Rural Ave., Voorhees, NJ 08043, (856)429-5358

National Center for ESL Literacy Education [★10024]

Natl. Center for the Exploration of Human Potential [★14997]

Natl. Center for Fair and Open Testing [8991], 15 Court Sq., Ste. 820, Boston, MA 02108, (857)350-8207

Natl. Center for Family Literacy [8534], 325 W Main St., Ste. 300, Louisville, KY 40202-4237, (502)584-1133

Natl. Center for Farmworker Hea. [14726], 1770 FM 967, Buda, TX 78610, (512)312-2700

Natl. Center for Fathering [18225], PO Box 413888, Kansas City, MO 64141, (800)593-DADS

Natl. Center for Fathering [18225], PO Box 413888, Kansas City, MO 64141, (800)593-DADS

Natl. Center for Financial Educ. [★8186]

Natl. Center for Food Safety and Tech. [★1396]

Natl. Center For Advanced Technologies [7518], 1000 Wilson Blvd., Ste. 1700, Arlington, VA 22209-3901, (703)358-1000

Natl. Center for Hea. Educ. - Address unknown since 2011.

Natl. Center for Hea. Promotion and Aging [★10845]

Natl. Center for Hearing Dog Info. [★14954]

Natl. Center for Higher Educ. Mgt. Systems [7673], 3035 Center Green Dr., Ste. 150, Boulder, CO 80301-2205, (303)497-0301

Natl. Center for Home Equity Conversion - Address unknown since 2011.

Natl. Center for Homeless Educ. [12161], PO Box 5367, Greensboro, NC 27435, (336)315-7453

Natl. Center for Homeopathy [15021], 101 S Whiting St., Ste. 16, Alexandria, VA 22304, (703)548-7790

Natl. Center for Housing Mgt. [12186], 12021 Sunset Hills Rd., Ste. 210, Reston, VA 20190, (703)435-9393

Natl. Center for Immigrants' Rights [★17884]

Natl. Center for Immigrants' Rights [★17884]

Natl. Center for Improving Sci. Educ. [8845], Senta A. Raizen, Dir., 1350 Connecticut Ave. NW, Ste. 1050, Washington, DC 20036-1709, (202)429-9728

Natl. Center for Infants, Toddlers and Families [★14053]

Natl. Center on Institutions and Alternatives [11723], 7222 Ambassador Rd., Baltimore, MD 21244, (443)780-1300

Natl. Center for Jewish Film [9606], Brandeis Univ., Lown 102 MS053, Waltham, MA 02454, (781)899-7044

Natl. Center for Jewish Healing [9928], 135 W 50th St., 6th Fl., New York, NY 10020, (212)632-4500

Natl. Center for Juvenile Justice [11724], 3700 S Water St., Ste. 200, Pittsburgh, PA 15203, (412)227-6950

Natl. Center for the Laity [19916], PO Box 291102, Chicago, IL 60629

Natl. Center for Law and Economic Justice [5943], 275 7th Ave., Ste. 1506, New York, NY 10001, (212)633-6967

Natl. Center for Learning Disabilities [12427], 381 Park Ave. S, Ste. 1401, New York, NY 10016, (212)545-7510

Natl. Center for Lesbian Rights [12100], 870 Market St., Ste. 370, San Francisco, CA 94102, (415)392-6257

Natl. Center for Men [18108], PO Box 531, Coram, NY 11727, (613)476-2115

Natl. Center for Missing and Exploited Children [11359], Charles B. Wang Intl. Children's Bldg., 699 Prince St., Alexandria, VA 22314-3175, (703)224-2150

Natl. Center for Montessori Educ. and Amer. Montessori Soc. [★8632]

Natl. Center for Municipal Development - Defunct.

Natl. Center for Neighborhood Enterprise [★17370]

Natl. Center for Nonprofit Boards [★12592]

Natl. Center for Nonprofit Enterprise [12582], 205 S Patrick St., Alexandria, VA 22314, (703)548-7978

Natl. Center for Policy Anal. [18475], Dallas HQ, 12770 Coit Rd., Ste. 800, Dallas, TX 75251-1339, (972)386-6272

Natl. Center for Posttraumatic Stress Disorder [16727], U.S. U.S. Department of Veterans Affairs, 215 N Main St., White River Junction, VT 05009, (802)296-5132

Natl. Center on Poverty Law [5762], 50 E Washington St., Ste. 500, Chicago, IL 60602, (312)263-3830

Natl. Center for Preservation Tech. and Training [6942], 645 Univ. Pkwy., Natchitoches, LA 71457, (318)356-7444

Natl. Center for Prosecution of Child Abuse [11360], 44 Canal Center Plz., Ste. 110, Alexandria, VA 22314, (703)549-9222

Natl. Center for Public Policy Res. [18476], 501 Capitol Ct. NE, Washington, DC 20002, (202)543-4110

Natl. Center for Public Ser. Internship Programs [★8177]

Natl. Center for Res. on Evaluation, Standards, and Student Testing [8047], UCLA CSE, GSE and IS Bldg., 3rd Fl., 300 Charles E. Young Dr. N, Mailbox 951522, Los Angeles, CA 90095-1522, (310)206-1532

Natl. Center for Res. in Vocational Educ. [★9043]

Natl. Center for Sci. Educ. [8846], 420 40th St., Ste. 2, Oakland, CA 94609-2509, (510)601-7203

Natl. Center for Social Policy and Practice [★13222]

Natl. Center for State Courts [5628], 300 Newport Ave., Williamsburg, VA 23185-4147, (757)259-1816

Natl. Center for State Courts I Conf. of State Court Administrators [5357], 300 Newport Ave., Williamsburg, VA 23185, (800)877-1233

Natl. Center for Student Leadership [8924], 2718 Dryden Dr., Madison, WI 53704-3086, (608)227-8111

Natl. Center for the Stud. of Collective Bargaining in Higher Educ. [★23173]

Natl. Center for the Stud. of Collective Bargaining in Higher Educ. and the Professions [23173], 425 E 25th St., Box 615, New York, NY 10010-2547, (212)481-7550

Reference to "IO" in place of a book number signifies that the association may be found in the 50th edition of International Organizations.

Natl. Center for the Stud. of Corporal Punishment and Alternatives [7975], Temple Univ., 253 Ritter Annex, Philadelphia, PA 19122, (215)204-6091

Natl. Center for Stuttering - Address unknown since 2011.

Natl. Center for Tobacco-Free Kids [16673], 1400 Eye St. NW, Ste. 1200, Washington, DC 20005, (202)296-5469

Natl. Center for Urban Ethnic Affairs - Address unknown since 2011.

Natl. Center for Victims of Crime [13367], 2000 M St. NW, Ste. 480, Washington, DC 20036, (202)467-8700

Natl. Center for Voice and Speech [16688], 136 S Main St., Ste. 320, Salt Lake City, UT 84101-1623, (801)596-2012

Natl. Center on Women and Family Law - Defunct.

Natl. Center for Women and Policing [5721], 433 S Beverly Dr., Beverly Hills, CA 90212, (310)556-2526

Natl. Center for the Workplace - Defunct.

National Center for Youth with Disabilities - Defunct.

Natl. Center for Youth Law [5424], 405 14th St., 15th Fl., Oakland, CA 94612, (510)835-8098

Natl. Centre for Audiology [IO], London, ON, Canada

Natl. Centre for Missing Children [IO], Indore, India

Natl. Centre for the Performing Arts [IO], Mumbai, India

Natl. Centre for Res. [IO], Khartoum, Sudan

Natl. Centre for Trade Info. [IO], New Delhi, India

Natl. Ceramic Dealers Assn. [★1728]

Natl. Ceramic Mfrs. Assn. [★1728]

Natl. Ceramic Teachers Assn. [★1728]

Natl. Certification Bd. for Diabetes Educators [14356], 330 E Algonquin Rd., Ste. 4, Arlington Heights, IL 60005, (847)228-9795

Natl. Certification Bd. of Pediatric Nurse Practitioners and Nurses [★15795]

Natl. Certification Bd. Perioperative Nursing [★15051]

Natl. Certification Bd. for Therapeutic Massage and Bodywork [15273], 1901 S Meyers Rd., Ste. 240, Oakbrook Terrace, IL 60181, (630)627-8000

Natl. Certification Commn. for Acupuncture and Oriental Medicine [16016], 76 S Laura St., Ste. 1290, Jacksonville, FL 32202, (904)598-1005

National Certification Commn. in Chemistry and Chem. Engg. [★6392]

Natl. Certification Corp. for the Obstetric, Gynecologic and Neonatal Nursing Specialties [15776], PO Box 11082, Chicago, IL 60611-0082, (312)951-0207

Natl. Certification Coun. for Activity Professionals [1674], PO Box 62589, Virginia Beach, VA 23466, (757)552-0653

Natl. Certified Pipe Welding Bur. [2751], 1385 Piccard Dr., Rockville, MD 20850, (301)869-5800

Natl. Cervical Cancer Coalition [13949], 6520 Platt Ave., No. 693, West Hills, CA 91307, (818)992-4242

Natl. Cesky Terrier Club of Am. - Defunct.

Natl. CFIDS Found. [15615], 103 Aletha Rd., Needham, MA 02492, (781)449-3535

Natl. Challenged Homeschoolers Assoc. Network [8271], PO Box 310, Moyie Springs, ID 83845, (208)267-6246

Natl. Chamber of Agriculture and Agro-Industry [IO], San Jose, Costa Rica

Natl. Chamber of Commerce - Algeria [IO], Algiers, Algeria

Natl. Chamber of Commerce - Bolivia [IO], La Paz, Bolivia

Natl. Chamber of Commerce and Indus. of Malaysia [IO], Kuala Lumpur, Malaysia

Natl. Chamber of Commerce and Ser. of Uruguay [IO], Montevideo, Uruguay

Natl. Chamber of Commerce of Sri Lanka [IO], Colombo, Sri Lanka

Natl. Chamber of Consultancy Businesses [IO], Mexico City, Mexico

Natl. Chamber of Elec. Manufactures [IO], Mexico City, Mexico

Natl. Chamber of the Fish Indus. [IO], Mexico City, Mexico

Natl. Chamber Found. [18477], 1615 H St. NW, Washington, DC 20062-2000, (202)463-5500

Natl. Chamber of Insurance Businesses [IO], San Jose, Costa Rica

Natl. Chamber Litigation Center [5935], 1615 H St. NW, Washington, DC 20062-2000, (202)463-5337

Natl. Chamber of Mfrs. [IO], Mexico City, Mexico

Natl. Chamber of the Mexican Publishing Indus. [IO], Mexico City, Mexico

Natl. Chamber of Milk Producers [IO], San Jose, Costa Rica

Natl. Chamber of the Perfume and Cosmetics, Toiletries and Hygiene Prdt. [IO], Mexico City, Mexico

Natl. Chamber of the Pharmaceutical Indus. [IO], Mexico City, Mexico

Natl. Chamber of Radio and TV Indus. [IO], Mexico City, Mexico

Natl. Chamber of the Restaurant and Food Seasoning Indus. [★18416]

Natl. Chamber of the Restaurant and Seasoned Food Indus. [IO], Mexico City, Mexico

Natl. Chamber of Sugar Confectionery Mfrs. [IO], Paris, France

Natl. Championship Racing Assn. [22826], 7700 N Broadway, Wichita, KS 67219, (316)755-1781

Natl. Chaplains Assn. [19625], PO Box 6418, Kingsport, TN 37663-1418, (423)574-1485

Natl. Chap. of Canada IODE [IO], Toronto, ON, Canada

Natl. Charities Info. Bur. [★17445]

Natl. Charities Info. Bur. [★17445]

Natl. Checker Assn. [★21740]

Natl. Checker Assn. [★21740]

Natl. Cheese Inst. [1023], Intl. Dairy Foods Assn., 1250 H St. Nw, Ste. 900, Washington, DC 20005-3952, (202)737-4332

Natl. Cheese Seminar [★1398]

Natl. Cheese Seminar [★1398]

Natl. Chem. Credit Assn. [1319], 1100 Main St., Buffalo, NY 14209-2308, (716)887-9547

Natl. Chem. Indus. Assn. [IO], Mexico City, Mexico

Natl. Cherry Growers and Indus. Found. [4459], 2667 Reed Rd., Hood River, OR 97031, (541)386-5761

Natl. Chevy Assn. [21123], 947 Arcade St., St. Paul, MN 55106-3850, (651)778-9522

Natl. Chicken Coun. [4810], 1015 15th St. NW, Ste. 930, Washington, DC 20005-2622, (202)296-2622

Natl. Chief Petty Officers' Assn. [20721], Marjorie L. Hays, Treas., 1014 Ronald Dr., Corpus Christi, TX 78412-3548, (361)991-2383

Natl. Chiefs of Police Union [★5696]

Natl. Chiefs of Police Union [★5696]

Natl. Child Abuse Defense and Rsrc. Center [13368], PO Box 638, Holland, OH 43528, (419)865-0513

Natl. Child Care Assn. [11156], 1325 G St. NW, Ste. 500, Washington, DC 20005, (800)543-7161

Natl. Child Labor Comm. [13541], 1501 Broadway, Ste. 1908, New York, NY 10036, (212)840-1801

Natl. Child Support Enforcement Assn. [5425], 1760 Old Meadow Rd., Ste. 500, McLean, VA 22102, (703)506-2880

Natl. Child Traumatic Stress Network [16929], NC-CTS - Univ. of California, Los Angeles, 11150 W Olympic Blvd., Ste. 650, Los Angeles, CA 90064, (310)235-2633

Natl. Childbirth Trust [IO], London, United Kingdom

Natl. Childminding Assn. [IO], Bromley, United Kingdom

Natl. Children's Alliance [11361], 516 C St. NE, Washington, DC 20002, (202)548-0090

Natl. Children's Bur. [IO], London, United Kingdom

Natl. Children's Cancer Soc. [13950], 1 S Memorial Dr., Ste. 800, St. Louis, MO 63102, (314)241-1600

Natl. Children's Eye Care Found. [★15955]

Natl. Children's Nurseries Assn. [IO], Dublin, Ireland

Natl. Childrenswear Assn. [IO], London, United Kingdom

Natl. Chimney Sweep Guild [2255], 2155 Commercial Dr., Plainfield, IN 46168, (317)837-1500

Natl. Chincoteague Pony Assn. [4615], 2595 Jensen Rd., Bellingham, WA 98226, (360)671-8338

Natl. Chinese Honor Soc. [23492], PO Box 249, Barre, MA 01005

Natl. Chiropractic Assn. [★14116]

Natl. Chocolate and Confectionery Producers' Assn. [IO], Mexico City, Mexico

Natl. Christ Child Soc. [19470], 4340 E West Hwy., Ste. 202, Bethesda, MD 20814, (301)718-0220

Natl. Christian Barrel Racers Assn. [22660], 3531 W Topeka Dr., Glendale, AZ 85308, (623)879-9288

Natl. Christian Choir [20127], 17B Firstfield Rd., Ste. 108, Gaithersburg, MD 20878, (301)670-6331

Natl. Christian Coll. Athletic Assn. [22992], 302 W Washington St., Greenville, SC 29601-1919, (864)250-1199

Natl. Christian Coun. in Japan [IO], Tokyo, Japan

Natl. Christian Education Assn. - Defunct.

Natl. Christian Forensics and Communications Assn. [8272], PO Box 212, Mountlake Terrace, WA 98043-0212, (205)500-0081

Natl. Christian Life Community of the U.S.A. [19471], 3601 Lindell Blvd., St. Louis, MO 63108-3301, (314)977-7370

Natl. Christian Network [★12935]

Natl. Christian School Educ. Assn. [★7851]

Natl. Christian School Educ. Assn. [★7851]

Natl. Christmas Tree Assn. [4974], 16020 Swingley Ridge Rd., Ste. 300, Chesterfield, MO 63017, (636)449-5070

Natl. Christmas Tree Growers Assn. [★4974]

Natl. Chronic Care Consortium - Defunct.

Natl. Chronic Epstein-Barr Virus Assn. [★14406]

Natl. Chronic Fatigue Syndrome Assn. [★14406]

Natl. Chronic Fatigue Syndrome and Fibromyalgia Assn. [14406], PO Box 18426, Kansas City, MO 64133-8426, (816)737-1343

Natl. Chrysanthemum Soc. [21808], 10107 Homar Pond Dr., Fairfax Station, VA 22039-1650, (703)978-7981

Natl. Chrysanthemum Soc. [IO], Blyth, United Kingdom

Natl. Church Conf. of the Blind [13379], PO Box 196, Grover, CO 80729-0196, (970)895-2352

Natl. Church Goods Assn. [3073], 800 Roosevelt Rd., Bldg. C, Ste. 312, Glen Ellyn, IL 60137, (630)942-6599

Natl. Church Lib. Assn. [9998], 275 S 3rd St., Ste. 204, Stillwater, MN 55082, (651)430-0770

National Circus Acad. [★9486]

Natl. Circus Fund [★9485]

Natl. Circus Preservation Soc. [9485], Cheryl Deptula, Exec. Sec.-Treas., 2704 Marshall Ave., Lorain, OH 44052

Natl. Circus Proj. [9486], 56 Lion Ln., Westbury, NY 11590, (516)334-2123

Natl. Citizens Coalition for Nursing Home Reform [★17465]

Natl. Citizens Comm. for Food and Shelter [★12160]

Natl. Citizens Comm. for the Right to Keep and Bear Arms [★17280]

Natl. Citizens Police Acad. Assn. [5722], Lt. Richard Powers, Pres., 701 W Sample St., South Bend, IN 46601, (574)235-9402

Natl. Civic Coun. [IO], North Melbourne, Australia

Natl. Civic League [5852], 1889 York St., Denver, CO 80206, (303)571-4343

Natl. Civil Liberties Legal Found. - Defunct.

Natl. Class E Scow Assn. [22373], Lon Schoor, Sec.-Treas., PO Box 3022, Madison, WI 53704-0022, (608)347-1480

Natl. Classification Mgt. Soc. [★1891]

Natl. Classified Network [★2938]

Natl. Clay Pipe Inst. [2752], PO Box 759, Lake Geneva, WI 53147, (262)248-9094

Natl. Clay Pipe Mfrs. [★2752]

Natl. CH for Alcohol and Drug Info. [16749], PO Box 2345, Rockville, MD 20847-2345, (301)468-2600

Natl. CH for Bilingual Educ. [★8048]

Natl. CH on Child Abuse and Neglect Info. and Natl. Adoption Info. CH [★11226]

Natl. CH for Commuter Programs [8925], Northeastern State Univ., 3100 E New Orleans St., Broken Arrow, OK 74014, (918)449-6200

Natl. CH for English Language Acquisition and Language Instruction Educational Programs [8048], 2011 Eye St. NW, Ste. 300, Washington, DC 20006, (202)467-0867

Natl. CH for Legal Services [★5762]

Natl. CH on Licensure, Enforcement, and Regulation [★5986]

A star before a book entry number signifies that the name is not listed separately, but is mentioned within the entry.

National CH for Professions in Special Education [★11788]

National CH for Professions in Special Education [★8879]

National CH for Professions in Special Education [★11788]

Natl. Clergy Conf. on Alcoholism [★13277]

Natl. Clergy Conf. on Alcoholism [★13277]

Natl. Clergy Coun. on Alcoholism and Related Drug Problems [★13277]

Natl. Clergy Coun. on Alcoholism and Related Drug Problems [★13277]

Natl. Client Protection Org. [5673], 1325 4th Ave., Ste. 600, Seattle, WA 98101-2539, (206)727-8232

Natl. Client Protection Org. [5673], 1325 4th Ave., Ste. 600, Seattle, WA 98101-2539, (206)727-8232

National Climatic Data Center [★4286]

Natl. Clogging Org. [9559], 2986 Mill Park Ct., Dacula, GA 30019, (678)889-4355

Natl. Club Assn. [777], 1201 15th St., Ste. 450, Washington, DC 20005, (202)822-9822

Natl. Club Baseball Assn. [22283], 850 Ridge Ave., Ste. 301, Pittsburgh, PA 15212, (412)321-8440

Natl. Club Indus. Assn. of Am. [1213], 1090 Vermont Ave. NW, Ste. 910, Washington, DC 20005, (866)266-6526

Natl. Club Indus. Assn. of Am. [1213], 1090 Vermont Ave. NW, Ste. 910, Washington, DC 20005, (866)266-6526

Natl. Club Sports Assn. - Defunct.

Natl. Coal Assn. [★785]

Natl. Coal Trans. Assn. [784], 4 W Meadow Lark Ln., Ste. 100, Littleton, CO 80127-5718, (303)979-2798

Natl. Coalition of 100 Black Women [17658], 1925 Adam C. Powell Jr. Blvd., Ste. 1L, New York, NY 10026, (212)222-5660

Natl. Coalition to Abolish Corporal Punishment in Schools [7976], 155 W Main St., No. 1603, Columbus, OH 43215, (614)221-8829

Natl. Coalition to Abolish the Death Penalty [17220], 1705 DeSales St. NW, 5th Fl., Washington, DC 20036, (202)331-4090

Natl. Coalition for Advanced Mfg. [★2342]

Natl. Coalition of Advanced Tech. Centers [8975], 33607 Seneca Dr., Cleveland, OH 44139, (708)326-2509

Natl. Coalition of Advanced Tech. Centers [8975], 33607 Seneca Dr., Cleveland, OH 44139, (708)326-2509

Natl. Coalition for the Advancement of Drug Free Athletics - Address unknown since 2011.

Natl. Coalition Against Censorship [17226], 19 Fulton St., Ste. 407, New York, NY 10038, (212)807-6222

Natl. Coalition Against the Death Penalty [★17220]

Natl. Coalition Against Domestic Violence [11892], 1 Broadway, Ste. 210B, Denver, CO 80203, (303)839-1852

Natl. Coalition Against Legalized Gambling [★12065]

Natl. Coalition Against the Misuse of Pesticides [★13321]

Natl. Coalition Against Pornography [★18400]

Natl. Coalition Against Sexual Assault - Defunct.

Natl. Coalition Against Violent Athletes [22231], PO Box 620453, Littleton, CO 80162, (303)524-9853

Natl. Coalition of Alternative Community Schools [7724], PO Box 1451, Ypsilanti, MI 48198, (734)483-7040

Natl. Coalition of Anti-Deportation Campaigns [IO], Birmingham, United Kingdom

Natl. Coalition of Anti-Violence Programs [18770], 240 W 35th St., Ste. 200, New York, NY 10001, (212)714-1184

Natl. Coalition of Arts Therapy Associations [★16470]

Natl. Coalition for Asian Pacific Amer. Community Development [11613], 1628 16th St. NW, 4th Fl., Washington, DC 20009, (202)223-2442

Natl. Coalition for Assistive and Rehab Tech. [15381], 161 Huxley Dr., Buffalo, NY 14226, (716)839-9728

Natl. Coalition on Auditory Processing Disorders [14949], PO Box 494, Rockville Centre, NY 11571-0494

Natl. Coalition for Aviation Educ. [7765], Virginia U.S. Department of of Aviation, 5702 Gulfstream Rd., Richmond, VA 23250-2422

Natl. Coalition to Ban Handguns [★17686]

Natl. Coalition on Black Civic Participation [18385], 1050 Connecticut Ave. NW, Ste. 1000, Washington, DC 20036, (202)659-4929

Natl. Coalition of Black Meeting Planners [2455], 4401 Huntchase Dr., Bowie, MD 20720, (301)860-0200

Natl. Coalition on Black Voter Participation [★18385]

Natl. Coalition of Blacks for Reparations in Am. [17159], PO Box 90604, Washington, DC 20090, (202)291-8400

Natl. Coalition Building Inst. [17386], 1120 Connecticut Ave. NW, Ste. 450, Washington, DC 20036-3965, (202)785-9400

Natl. Coalition for Campus Child Care [★11157]

Natl. Coalition for Campus Children's Centers [11157], 950 Glenn Dr., Ste. 150, Folsom, CA 95630, (877)736-6222

Natl. Coalition for Cancer Survivorship [13951], 1010 Wayne Ave., Ste. 770, Silver Spring, MD 20910, (301)650-9127

Natl. Coalition for Capital [1058], 1010 Wisconsin Ave. NW, Ste. 205, Washington, DC 20007, (202)337-1661

Natl. Coalition for Child Protection Reform [11362], 53 Skyhill Rd., Ste. 202, Alexandria, VA 22314-4997, (703)212-2006

Natl. Coalition for Children's Centers [★11157]

Natl. Coalition for Consumer Educ. [17464], Natl. Consumers League, 1701 K St. NW, Ste. 1200, Washington, DC 20006, (202)835-3323

Natl. Coalition of Creative Arts Therapies Associations [16470], 8455 Colesville Rd., Ste. 1000, Silver Spring, MD 20910

Natl. Coalition for Dialogue and Deliberation [8778], Sandy Heierbacher, Co-Founder/Dir., 114 W Springville Rd., Boiling Springs, PA 17007, (717)243-5144

Natl. Coalition for Disability Rights - Address unknown since 2011.

Natl. Coalition for Electronics Educ. [8118], Carla Hurtubise, ETA Intl., 5 Depot St., Greencastle, IN 46135, (800)288-3824

Natl. Coalition to End Racism in America's Child Care System - Defunct.

Natl. Coalition of Estheticians, Manufacturers/ Distributors and Associations [972], 484 Spring Ave., Ridgewood, NJ 07450, (201)670-4100

Natl. Coalition of Ethnic Minority Nurse Associations [15777], 6101 W Centinela Ave., Ste. 378, Culver City, CA 90230, (310)258-9515

Natl. Coalition for Food and Agricultural Res. [3744], 2441 Village Green Pl., Champaign, IL 61822, (217)356-3182

Natl. Coalition of Girls' Schools [8049], 50 Leonard St., Ste. 2C, Belmont, MA 02478, (617)489-0013

Natl. Coalition for Haitian Rights - Address unknown since 2010.

Natl. Coalition on Hea. Care [17773], 1120 G St. NW, Ste. 810, Washington, DC 20005, (202)638-7151

Natl. Coalition for Hea. Professional Educ. in Genetics [14654], 2360 W Joppa Rd., Ste. 320, Lutherville, MD 21093, (410)583-0600

Natl. Coalition of Healthcare Recruiters [15298], 1742 N Willow Woods Dr., Apt. D, Anaheim, CA 92807, (714)463-4450

Natl. Coalition for a Healthy Am. [15856], 304 Tequesta Dr., Ste. 200, Tequesta, FL 33469, (877)843-2358

Natl. Coalition of Hispanic Hea. and Human Services Organizations [★13194]

Natl. Coalition for History [9786], Lee White, Exec. Dir., 400 A St. SE, Washington, DC 20003, (202)544-2422

Natl. Coalition for the Homeless [12162], 2201 P St. NW, Washington, DC 20037-1033, (202)462-4822

Natl. Coalition for Homeless Veterans [20797], 333 1/2 Pennsylvania Ave. SE, Washington, DC 20003-1148, (202)546-1969

Natl. Coalition of Independent Living Programs [★11813]

Natl. Coalition of Independent Scholars [8240], PO Box 19302, Jonesboro, AR 72403

Natl. Coalition for LGBT Hea. [12101], 1325 Massachusetts Ave. NW, Ste. 705, Washington, DC 20005, (202)558-6828

Natl. Coalition for Literacy [8535], PO Box 2932, Washington, DC 20013-2932

Natl. Coalition for Marine Conservation [4099], 4 Royal St. SE, Leesburg, VA 20175, (703)777-0037

Natl. Coalition for Men [18109], 932 C St., Ste. B, San Diego, CA 92101, (888)223-1280

Natl. Coalition of Men's Ministries [★19592]

Natl. Coalition of Mental Hea. Professionals and Consumers [15473], PO Box 438, Commack, NY 11725, (631)979-5307

Natl. Coalition of Ministries to Men [19592], 180 Wilshire Blvd., Casselberry, FL 32707, (407)472-2188

Natl. Coalition of Oncology Nurse Navigators [15778], PO Box 1688, Rockville, MD 20849-1688, (888)451-8995

Natl. Coalition of Pastors' Spouses [13195], 950 Mt. Moriah Rd., Ste. 201, Memphis, TN 38117, (901)517-6537

Natl. Coalition of Patriotic Amers. - Defunct.

Natl. Coalition of Pharmaceutical Distributors [2703], 20101 NE 16th Pl., Miami, FL 33179, (305)690-4233

Natl. Coalition to Preserve Scenic Beauty [★4303]

Natl. Coalition of Pro-Democracy Advocates [17526], 2020 Pennsylvania Ave. NW, Ste. 235, Washington, DC 20006, (202)595-1823

Natl. Coalition for Promoting Physical Activity [22806], 1100 H St. NW, Ste. 510, Washington, DC 20005, (202)454-7521

Natl. Coalition for the Protection of Children and Families [★18400]

Natl. Coalition for Public School Options [8775], PO Box 3230, Arlington, VA 22203-0230, (866)558-2874

Natl. Coalition for Quality Colorectal Cancer Screening and Care [13952], 612 Third St., Ste. 4A, Annapolis, MD 21403, (410)777-5310

Natl. Coalition on Rural Aging - Address unknown since 2010.

Natl. Coalition to Save Our Mall [9713], PO Box 4709, Rockville, MD 20849, (301)340-3938

Natl. Coalition for Sex Equity in Educ. [★8164]

Natl. Coalition for Sexual Freedom [18604], 822 Guilford Ave., Box 127, Baltimore, MD 21202-3707, (410)539-4824

Natl. Coalition of STD Directors [16657], 1029 Vermont Ave. NW, Ste. 500, Washington, DC 20005

Natl. Coalition for Tech. in Educ. and Training [8976], Meetings and Events of Distinction, LLC, 2724 Kenwood Ave., Alexandria, VA 22302, (703)626-1266

Natl. Coalition for Telecommunications Educ. and Learning [8981], 6021 S Syracuse Way, Ste. 213, Greenwood Village, CO 80111

Natl. Coalition on TV Violence - Defunct.

Natl. Coalition of Title I/Chapter 1 Parents - Address unknown since 2010.

Natl. Coalition for Women and Girls in Educ. [9061], Amer. Assn. of Univ. Women, 1111 16th St. NW, Washington, DC 20036, (202)785-7793

Natl. Cochlear Implant Users Assn. [IO], Dorchester, United Kingdom

Natl. Cockatiel Soc. [21222], Sherri Lewis, Membership Sec., PO Box 1114, Troy, VA 22974

Natl. Coffee Assn. of U.S.A. [451], 45 Broadway, Ste. 1140, New York, NY 10006, (212)766-4007

Natl. Coffee Ser. Assn. [★3612]

Natl. Coil Coating Assn. [790], 1300 Sumner Ave., Cleveland, OH 44115, (216)241-7333

Natl. Collaboration for Youth [★13401]

Natl. Collaboration for Youth [11363], 1319 F St. NW, Ste. 402, Washington, DC 20004-1112, (202)347-2080

Natl. Collective of Rape Crisis and Related Groups of Aotearoa [IO], Auckland, New Zealand

Natl. Collectors Assn. of Die Doubling [21982], PO Box 15, Lykens, PA 17048-0015, (717)453-9530

Natl. Coll. for Criminal Defense [★5386]

Reference to "IO" in place of a book number signifies that the association may be found in the 50th edition of International Organizations.

Natl. Coll. of District Attorneys - Address unknown
since 2010.
Natl. Coll. of Hypnosis and Psychotherapy [IO],
Loughborough, United Kingdom
Natl. Coll. of the State Judiciary [★5634]
Natl. Coll. of State Trial Judges [★5634]
Natl. Collegiate Assn. for Res. of Principles - Ad-
dress unknown since 2010.
Natl. Collegiate Athletic Assn. [22993], PO Box
6222, Indianapolis, IN 46206-6222, (317)917-6222
Natl. Collegiate Athletic Assn. of Wrestling Coaches
and Officials [★23132]
Natl. Collegiate Baseball Writers Assn. [2847], Conf.
USA, 5201 N O'Connor Blvd., Ste. 300, Irving, TX
75039, (214)774-1351
Natl. Collegiate Cross Country Coaches Assn.
[★22868]
Natl. Collegiate EMS Found. [14474], PO Box 93,
West Sand Lake, NY 12196, (208)728-7342
Natl. Collegiate Honors Coun. [8050], Univ. of
Nebraska-Lincoln, 1100 Neihardt Residence Ctr.,
540 N 16th St., Lincoln, NE 68588-0627, (402)472-
9150
Natl. Collegiate Honors Soc. for Anthropology
[★23465]
Natl. Collegiate Inventors and Innovators Alliance
[6997], 100 Venture Way, 3rd Fl., Hadley, MA
01035, (413)587-2172
Natl. Collegiate Licensing Assn. [★2407]
Natl. Collegiate Paintball Assn. [22799], 530 E South
Ave., Chippewa Falls, WI 54729, (612)605-8323
Natl. Collegiate Players - Defunct.
Natl. Collegiate Roller Hockey Assn. [22646], 4733
Torrance Blvd., No. 618, Torrance, CA 90503,
(310)753-7285
Natl. Collegiate Ski Assn. [★22918]
Natl. Collegiate Table Tennis Assn. [23049], 2322
5th St., No. 204, Santa Monica, CA 90405
Natl. Collegiate Tennis Coaches Assn. [★23055]
Natl. Collegiate Water Ski Assn. [23117], 1251 Holy
Cow Rd., Polk City, FL 33868-8200, (863)324-4341
Natl. Color-Bred Assn. [21223], Doyle Johnson,
Treas./Bands and Awards Sec., 5111 S Meridian
Ave., No. 268, Wichita, KS 67217
Natl. Colored Women's League [★13066]
Natl. Coming Out Day [12102], Human Rights
Campaign, 1640 Rhode Island Ave., Washington,
DC 20036-3278, (202)628-4160
Natl. Commercial Finance Assn. [★2209]
Natl. Commercial Finance Assn. [★2209]
Natl. Commercial Finance Conf. [★2209]
Natl. Commercial Finance Conf. [★2209]
Natl. Commn. for the Certification of Acupuncturists
[★16016]
Natl. Commn. for the Certification of Crane Opera-
tors [849], 2750 Prosperity Ave., Ste. 505, Fairfax,
VA 22031, (703)560-2391
Natl. Commn. on Certification of Physician As-
sistants [16238], 12000 Findley Rd., Ste. 100,
Johns Creek, GA 30097, (678)417-8100
Natl. Commn. on Certification of Physician's As-
sistants [★16238]
Natl. Commn. for Cooperative Educ. [7934], 360
Huntington Ave., 384CP, Boston, MA 02115-5096,
(617)373-3770
Natl. Commn. on Correctional Hea. Care [14905],
1145 W Diversey Pkwy., Chicago, IL 60614,
(773)880-1460
Natl. Commn. for Culture and the Arts [IO], Manila,
Philippines
Natl. Commn. on Nuclear Safety and Safeguards
[IO], Mexico City, Mexico
Natl. Commn. on the Public Service - Defunct.
Natl. Commn. on Working Women - Defunct.
Natl. Comm. on Accounting [★40]
Natl. Comm. for Adoption [★10797]
Natl. Comm. Against Fluoridation [★14729]
Natl. Comm. on Aging of Natl. Social Welfare As-
sembly [★10861]
Natl. Comm. on Alcoholism [★13278]
Natl. Comm. for Amateur Baseball [★22291]
Natl. Comm. on Amer. Foreign Policy [17705], 320
Park Ave., 8th Fl., New York, NY 10022-6815,
(212)224-1120
Natl. Comm. on Amer. Foreign Policy [17705], 320
Park Ave., 8th Fl., New York, NY 10022-6815,
(212)224-1120

Natl. Comm. for Amish Religious Freedom [19290],
15343 Susanna Cir., Livonia, MI 48154, (734)464-
3908
Natl. Comm. for Clinical Lab. Standards [★15234]
Natl. Comm. for Clinical Lab. Standards [★15234]
Natl. Comm. of Communications Supervisors
[★3411]
Natl. Comm. of Communications Supervisors
[★3411]
Natl. Comm. in Deafness and Other Commun.
Disorders [★14953]
Natl. Comm. for Educ. on Alcoholism [★13278]
Natl. Comm. for an Effective Cong. [17413], 160 E
89th St., No. 9B, New York, NY 10128, (212)987-
8900
Natl. Comm. for Employer Support of the Guard and
Reserve [5813], 1555 Wilson Blvd., Ste. 200,
Arlington, VA 22209-2405, (703)696-1386
Natl. Comm. for Fair Divorce and Alimony Laws
[★18110]
Natl. Comm. of the Fed. Ser. Campaign for Natl.
Hea. Agencies [★12051]
Natl. Comm. on Foundations and Trusts for Com-
munity Welfare [★12593]
Natl. Comm. for the Furtherance of Jewish Educ.
[8430], 824 Eastern Pkwy., Brooklyn, NY 11213,
(718)735-0200
Natl. Comm. for a Human Life Amendment [18557],
1500 Massachusetts Ave. NW, Ste. 24,
Washington, DC 20005, (202)393-0703
Natl. Comm. for the Improvement of Nursing
Services [★15781]
Natl. Comm. for Latin and Greek [9487], Amy Som-
mer, Treas., 2320 S Univ. Blvd., Apt. 201, Denver,
CO 80210
Natl. Comm. for Medical Res. Ethics [IO], Oslo,
Norway
Natl. Comm. for Mental Hygiene [★15461]
Natl. Comm. for Motor Fleet Supervisor Training and
Certification [★7981]
Natl. Comm. on Pay Equity [17659], 555 New
Jersey Ave. NW, Washington, DC 20001-2029,
(703)920-2010
Natl. Comm. on Planned Giving [★1542]
Natl. Comm. to Preserve Social Security [★18652]
Natl. Comm. to Preserve Social Security and
Medicare [18652], 10 G St. NE, Ste. 600,
Washington, DC 20002-4215, (202)216-0420
Natl. Comm. for the Prevention of Blindness
[★17112]
Natl. Comm. for the Prevention of Elder Abuse
[10860], 1612 K St. NW, Washington, DC 20006,
(202)682-4140
Natl. Comm. on Property Insurance [★1966]
Natl. Comm. on Public Polls [★18397]
Natl. Comm. for Quality Assurance [16509], 1100
13th St. NW, Ste. 1000, Washington, DC 20005,
(202)955-3500
Natl. Comm. on Radiation Protection [★5954]
Natl. Comm. on Radiation Protection and Measure-
ments [★5954]
Natl. Comm. for Recording for the Blind [★17095]
Natl. Comm. Relations Advisory Coun. [★12409]
Natl. Comm. to Reopen the Rosenberg Case
[17309], 339 Lafayette St., Ste. 203, New York, NY
10012-2725, (212)533-1015
Natl. Comm. for Responsive Philanthropy [12679],
1331 H St. NW, Ste. 200, Washington, DC 20005,
(202)387-9177
Natl. Comm. to Restore Internal Security - Defunct.
Natl. Comm. for Small Bus. Mgt. Development
[★3290]
Natl. Comm. for Small Bus. Mgt. Development
[★3290]
Natl. Comm. on the Treatment of Intractable Pain -
Defunct.
Natl. Comm. on Uniform Traffic Accidents Statistics
[★13010]
Natl. Comm. on Uniform Traffic Laws and
Ordinances [6025], 107 S West St., No. 110,
Alexandria, VA 22314-2824, (800)807-5290
Natl. Comm. on United States-China Relations
[17242], 71 W 23rd St., Ste. 1901, New York, NY
10010-4102, (212)645-9677
Natl. Comm. on United States-China Relations
[17242], 71 W 23rd St., Ste. 1901, New York, NY
10010-4102, (212)645-9677

Natl. Comm. for Utilities Radio [★3425]
Natl. Comm. for Women in Public Admin. [★5912]
Natl. Comm. of YMCAs of China [IO], Shanghai,
People's Republic of China
Natl. Comm. of the Young Women's Christian As-
sociation of China [IO], Shanghai, People's
Republic of China
Natl. Commun. Assn. [8894], 1765 N St. NW,
Washington, DC 20036, (202)464-4622
Natl. Commun. Coun. for Human Services [★2908]
Natl. Communications Network for the Elimination of
Violence Against Women [★11892]
Natl. Community Action Agency Directors Assn.
[★12723]
Natl. Community Action Agency Executive Directors
Assn. [★12723]
Natl. Community Action Found. [11533], 1 Mas-
sachusetts Ave. NW, Ste. 310, Washington, DC
20001, (202)842-2092
Natl. Community Capital Assn. [★17390]
Natl. Community Development Assn. [17387], 522
21st St. NW, No. 120, Washington, DC 20006-
5059, (202)293-7587
Natl. Community Educ. Assn. [7900], 3929 Old Lee
Hwy., No. 91-A, Fairfax, VA 22030-2401, (703)359-
8973
Natl. Community Land Trust Center [★17380]
Natl. Community for Latino Leadership [19112],
1701 K St. NW, Ste. 301, Washington, DC 20006,
(202)257-4419
Natl. Community Mental Healthcare Coun. [★15474]
Natl. Community Pharmacists Assn. [16206], 100
Daingerfield Rd., Alexandria, VA 22314, (703)683-
8200
National Community Pharmacists Assn. Foundation
[★16206]
Natl. Community Reinvestment Coalition [17388],
727 15th St. NW, Ste. 900, Washington, DC
20005, (202)628-8866
Natl. Community School Educ. Assn. [★7900]
Natl. Community Tax Coalition [18700], Center for
Economic Progress, 29 E Madison St., Ste. 900,
Chicago, IL 60602, (312)252-0280
Natl. Community TV Assn. [★505]
Natl. Compadres Network [12484], PO Box 1228,
Santa Clara, CA 95052-1228, (213)325-1699
Natl. Comprehensive Cancer Network [13953], 275
Commerce Dr., Ste. 300, Fort Washington, PA
19034, (215)690-0300
Natl. Cmpt. Graphics Assn. [★6441]
Natl. Cmpt. Graphics Assn. [★6441]
Natl. Concierge Assn. [1764], 2920 Idaho Ave. N,
Minneapolis, MN 55427, (612)317-2932
Natl. Concrete Burial Vault Assn. [2540], PO Box
917525, Longwood, FL 32791-7525, (407)788-
1996
Natl. Concrete Contractors Assn. [★895]
Natl. Concrete Masonry Assn. [832], 13750 Sunrise
Valley Dr., Herndon, VA 20171-4662, (703)713-
1900
Natl. Confectioners Assn. of the U.S. [1414], 1101
30th St. NW, Ste. 200, Washington, DC 20007,
(202)534-1440
Natl. Confectionery Sales Assn. [3116], 10225 Berea
Rd., Ste. B, Cleveland, OH 44102, (216)631-8200
Natl. Confectionery Sales Assn. of Am. [★3116]
Natl. Confed. of Bakers [IO], Paris, France
Natl. Confed. of Commerce [IO], Rio de Janeiro,
Brazil
Natl. Confed. of Hungarian Trade Unions [IO],
Budapest, Hungary
Natl. Confed. of Ice Cream Producers [IO], Paris,
France
Natl. Confed. of Workers in Educ. [IO], Brasilia,
Brazil
Natl. Conf. on the Advancement of Res. - Defunct.
Natl. Conf. of Appellate Court Clerks [5358], 450 E
St. NW, Rm. 103, Washington, DC 20442,
(202)761-1448
Natl. Conf. of Bankruptcy Judges [5629], 241 Aris-
tides Dr., Irmo, SC 29063, (803)749-4115
Natl. Conf. of Bar Examiners [5674], 302 S Bedford
St., Madison, WI 53703-3622, (608)280-8550
Natl. Conf. of Bar Executives [★5670]
Natl. Conf. of Bar Foundations [5643], Div. for Bar
Services, 321 N Clark St., Ste. 2000, Chicago, IL
60654, (312)988-5344

A star before a book entry number signifies that the name is not listed separately, but is mentioned within the entry.

Natl. Conf. of Bar Presidents [5268], Div. for Bar Services, 321 N Clark St., 20th Fl., Chicago, IL 60654, (312)988-5345

Natl. Conf. of Bar-Related Title Insurers [★2026]

Natl. Conf. of Bar Secretaries [★5670]

Natl. Conf. of Black Lawyers [5269], PO Box 998, New York, NY 10024, (866)266-5091

Natl. Conf. of Black Lawyers [5269], PO Box 998, New York, NY 10024, (866)266-5091

Natl. Conf. of Black Mayors [5853], The 191 Bldg., 191 Peachtree St. NE, Ste. 849, Atlanta, GA 30303, (404)765-6444

Natl. Conf. for Catechetical Leaders [★19683]

Natl. Conf. for Catechetical Leadership [19683], 125 Michigan Ave. NE, Washington, DC 20017, (202)884-9753

Natl. Conf. of Catholic Airport Chaplains [19528], PO Box 66353, Chicago, IL 60666-0353, (773)686-2636

Natl. Conf. of Catholic Charities [★13176]

Natl. Conf. of Catholic Guidance Councils [★7940]

Natl. Conf. on Citizenship [17251], 1875 K St. NW, 5th Fl., Washington, DC 20006, (202)729-8038

Natl. Conf. on City Planning [★5326]

Natl. Conf. of Commercial Receivable Companies [★2209]

Natl. Conf. of Commercial Receivable Companies [★2209]

Natl. Conf. of Commissioners on Uniform State Laws [5997], 111 N Wabash Ave., Ste. 1010, Chicago, IL 60602-1917, (312)450-6600

Natl. Conf. of Court Administrative Officers [★5357]

Natl. Conf. of CPA Practitioners [46], 22 Jericho Tpke., Ste. 110, Mineola, NY 11501, (516)333-8282

Natl. Conf. on Developmental Disabilities [★12508]

Natl. Conf. of Diocesan Guidance Councils [★7940]

Natl. Conf. of Directors of Religious Educ. [★19683]

Natl. Conf. of Editorial Writers [2848], 3899 N Front St., Harrisburg, PA 17110, (717)703-3015

Natl. Conf. of Executives of the Arc [2297], 1660 L St. NW, Ste. 301, Washington, DC 20036, (225)927-0855

Natl. Conf. of Executives of Higher Educ. Loan Plans [★8103]

Natl. Conf. of Family Relations [★12015]

Natl. Conf. of Fed. Trial Judges [5630], Amer. Bar Assn., Judicial Div., 321 N Clark St., 19th Fl., Chicago, IL 60654, (800)238-2667

Natl. Conf. of Firemen and Oilers [23189], 1023 15th St. NW, 10th Fl., Washington, DC 20005-2602, (202)962-0981

Natl. Conf. on Fluid Power [6866], 3333 N Mayfair Rd., Ste. 211, Milwaukee, WI 53222-3219, (414)778-3344

Natl. Conf. of Governmental Indus. Hygienists [★15901]

Natl. Conf. of Insurance Legislators [5556], 385 Jordan Rd., Troy, NY 12180, (518)687-0178

Natl. Conf. on Interstate Milk Shipments [4182], 585 County Farm Rd., Monticello, IL 61856, (217)762-2656

Natl. Conf. of Jewish Communal Ser. [★12407]

Natl. Conf. of Jewish Communal Ser. [★12407]

Natl. Conf. of Lieutenant Governors [★6000]

Natl. Conf. of Local Environmental Hea. Administrators [16489], 1010 S Third St., Dayton, WA 99328, (509)382-2181

Natl. Conf. on Ministry to the Armed Forces - Defunct.

Natl. Conf. on Peacemaking and Conflict Resolution - Address unknown since 2011.

Natl. Conf. of Personal Managers [163], PO Box 50008, Henderson, NV 89016, (702)837-1170

Natl. Conf. on Public Employee Retirement Systems [5311], 444 N Capitol St. NW, Ste. 630, Washington, DC 20001-1512, (877)202-5706

Natl. Conf. of Puerto Rican Women [17660], 1220 L St. NW, Ste. 100-177, Washington, DC 20005-4018, (215)546-0988

Natl. Conf. of Real Estate Editors [★2845]

Natl. Conf. of Religious Vocation Directors [★19478]

Natl. Conf. of Schools of Design [★7752]

Natl. Conf. of Shomrim Societies [12412], PO Box 598, Knickerbocker Sta., New York, NY 10002

Natl. Conf. on Soviet Jewry [★17568]

Natl. Conf. on Soviet Jewry [★17568]

Natl. Conf. of Special Court Judges [★5631]

Natl. Conf. of Specialized Court Judges [5631], ABA Judicial Div., 321 N Clark St., 19th Fl., Chicago, IL 60654-7598, (312)988-5705

Natl. Conf. of Standards Labs. [★7467]

Natl. Conf. of Standards Labs. [★7467]

Natl. Conf. of State Court Administrators [★5357]

Natl. Conf. of State Criminal Justice Planning Administrators [★11726]

Natl. Conf. of State Fleet Administrators [6036], 301 W High St., Rm. 760, Jefferson City, MO 65101, (405)744-7938

Natl. Conf. of State Gen. Ser. Officers [★5993]

Natl. Conf. of State Historic Preservation Officers [9714], Hall of States, Ste. 342, 444 N Capitol St. NW, Washington, DC 20001-1512, (202)624-5465

Natl. Conf. of State Legislative Leaders [★5998]

Natl. Conf. of State Legislatures [5998], 7700 E First Pl., Denver, CO 80230-7143, (303)364-7700

Natl. Conf. of State Liquor Administrators [★5197]

Natl. Conf. of State Liquor Administrators [5199], PO Box 95046, Lincoln, NE 68509, (402)471-2571

Natl. Conf. on State Parks [★5880]

Natl. Conf. of State Pharmaceutical Assn. Secretaries [★16203]

Natl. Conf. of State Social Security Administrators [5973], Social Security Admin., 61 Forsyth St. SW, Ste. 22T64, Atlanta, GA 30303, (404)562-1324

Natl. Conf. of State Societies - Address unknown since 2011.

Natl. Conf. of State Trans. Specialists [6037], Mark Breiner, Treas., Nebraska Public Ser. Commn., PO Box 94927, Lincoln, NE 68509-4927, (402)471-0226

Natl. Conf. of States on Building Codes and Standards [5303], 505 Huntmar Park Dr., Ste. 210, Herndon, VA 20170, (703)437-0100

Natl. Conf. on St. and Highway Safety [★6025]

Natl. Conf. on Student Leadership [★8924]

Natl. Conf. on Student Services [★8924]

Natl. Conf. of Synagogue Youth [19887], 11 Broadway, New York, NY 10004, (212)613-8233

National Conf. on Trusteeship [★7659]

Natl. Conf. on Uniform Reciprocal Enforcement of Support [★5425]

Natl. Conf. on Weights and Measures [5984], 1135 M St., Ste. 110, Lincoln, NE 68508, (402)434-4880

Natl. Conf. of Women's Bar Associations [5270], PO Box 82366, Portland, OR 97282-0366, (503)775-4396

Natl. Conferences on Undergraduate Res. [8798], Montana State Univ., 318 Montana Hall, Bozeman, MT 59717, (406)994-6057

Natl. Congenital Port Wine Stain Found. - Defunct.

Natl. Cong. of Amer. Indians [18153], 1516 P St. NW, Washington, DC 20005, (202)466-7767

Natl. Cong. of Black Women [5843], 1251 4th St. SW, Washington, DC 20024, (202)678-6788

Natl. Cong. of Colored Parents and Teachers [★8691]

Natl. Cong. for Community Economic Development - Defunct.

Natl. Cong. of Inventors Organizations [7013], 8306 Wilshire Blvd., Ste. 391, Beverly Hills, CA 90211, (800)458-5624

Natl. Cong. of Mothers [★8691]

Natl. Cong. of Mothers and Parent-Teachers Associations [★8691]

Natl. Cong. of Neighborhood Women - Defunct.

Natl. Cong. of Parents and Teachers [★8691]

Natl. Cong. of Petroleum Retailers [★2669]

Natl. Cong. on Surveying and Mapping [★7486]

Natl. Cong. of Vietnamese Americans [19274], 6433 Northanna Dr., Springfield, VA 22150, (703)971-9178

Natl. Conservation District Employees Assn. [23313], Rich Duesterhaus, Exec. Dir., 509 Capitol Ct. NE, Washington, DC 20002-4937, (202)547-6223

Natl. Consortium of Breast Centers [13860], PO Box 1334, Warsaw, IN 46581-1334, (574)267-8058

Natl. Consortium for Computer-Based Music Instruction [★8644]

Natl. Consortium of Deaf-Blindness [17106], Western Oregon Univ., Teaching Res. Inst., 345 N Monmouth Ave., Monmouth, OR 97361, (800)438-9376

Natl. Consortium for Graduate Degrees for Minorities in Engg. [★8128]

Natl. Consortium for Graduate Degrees for Minorities in Engg. and Sci. [8128], 1430 Duke St., Alexandria, VA 22314, (703)562-3646

Natl. Consortium for Graduate Degrees for Minorities in Sci. and Engg. [★8128]

Natl. Consortium on Hea. Sci. and Tech. Educ. [8224], 2410 Woodlake Dr., Okemos, MI 48864-3997, (517)347-3332

Natl. Consortium of the Rubber Indus. [IO], Madrid, Spain

Natl. Constables Assn. [5723], 16 Stonybrook Dr., Levittown, PA 19055-2217, (215)547-6400

Natl. Consultation on Pornography and Obscenity [★18400]

Natl. Consumer Bd. for Stuttering - Defunct.

Natl. Consumer Finance Assn. [★2208]

Natl. Consumer Forum [IO], Johannesburg, Republic of South Africa

Natl. Consumer Law Center [5343], 7 Winthrop Sq., Boston, MA 02110-1245, (617)542-8010

Natl. Consumer Voice for Quality Long-Term Care [17465], 1001 Connecticut Ave. NW, Ste. 425, Washington, DC 20036, (202)332-2275

Natl. Consumer's Assn. of Swaziland [IO], Mbabane, Swaziland

Natl. Consumers Coun. [★13337]

Natl. Consumers League [17466], 1701 K St. NW, Ste. 1200, Washington, DC 20006, (202)835-3323

Natl. Contact Lens Examiners [15996], 6506 Loisdale Rd., Ste. 209, Springfield, VA 22150, (703)719-5800

Natl. Contract Mgt. Assn. [1587], 21740 Beaumeade Cir., Ste. 125, Ashburn, VA 20147, (571)382-0082

Natl. Convenience Store Advisory Gp. - Address unknown since 2011.

Natl. Convenience Store Distributors Assn. [IO], Laval, QC, Canada

Natl. Convention Assn. [2456], 1560 Broadway, 46th St., Times Sq., New York, NY 10036-1518, (212)555-8665

Natl. Convention of Insurance Commissioners [★5554]

Natl. Cooperative Bus. Assn. [958], 1401 New York Ave. NW, Ste. 1100, Washington, DC 20005, (202)638-6222

Natl. Cooperative Grocers Assn. [959], 14 S Linn St., Iowa City, IA 52240, (319)466-9029

Natl. Cooperative Milk Producers Fed. [★4185]

Natl. Cooperatives [★4176]

Natl. Coordinating Comm. for Multi-employer Plans [1131], 815 16th St. NW, Washington, DC 20006, (202)737-5315

Natl. Coordinating Comm. for the Promotion of History [★9786]

Natl. Coordinating Coun. on Emergency Mgt. [★5307]

Natl. Coordinating Coun. on Emergency Mgt. [★5307]

Natl. Coordinating Coun. for Medication Error Reporting and Prevention [14814], 7272 Wisconsin Ave., Bethesda, MD 20814, (301)664-8796

Natl. Coordinating Off. for Latin and Greek [★9487]

Natl. Corn Growers Assn. [3954], 632 Cepi Dr., Chesterfield, MO 63005-1221, (636)733-9004

Natl. Corporate Cash Mgt. Assn. [★1283]

National Corporate Leadership Program [★12056]

Natl. Corporate Theatre Fund [10588], 505 8th Ave., Ste. 2303, New York, NY 10018, (212)750-6895

Natl. Correctional Indus. Assn. [11725], 1202 N Charles St., Baltimore, MD 21201, (410)230-3972

Natl. Correctional Recreational Assn. - Defunct.

Natl. Corrugated Metal Pipe Assn. [★2753]

Natl. Corrugated Steel Pipe Assn. [2753], 14070 Proton Rd., Ste. 100, LB 9, Dallas, TX 75244, (972)850-1907

Natl. Corvette Owners Assn. [21124], 900 S Washington St., Ste. G-13, Falls Church, VA 22046, (703)533-7222

Natl. Corvette Restorers Soc. [21125], 6291 Day Rd., Cincinnati, OH 45252-1334, (513)385-8526

Natl. Cosmetology Assn. - Address unknown since 2010.

Natl. Costumers Assn. [212], 121 N Bosart Ave., Indianapolis, IN 46201, (317)351-1940

Reference to "IO" in place of a book number signifies that the association may be found in the 50th edition of International Organizations.

Natl. Cotton Batting Inst. [982], 4322 Bloombury St., Southaven, MS 38672, (662)449-0000

Natl. Cotton Coun. of Am. [983], PO Box 2995, Cordova, TN 38088-2995, (901)274-9030

Natl. Cotton Ginners' Assn. [984], PO Box 2995, Cordova, TN 38088-2995, (901)274-9030

Natl. Cottonseed Products Assn. [2587], 866 Willow Tree Cir., Cordova, TN 38018-4234, (901)682-0800

Natl. Coun. for Accreditation of Teacher Educ. [7649], 2010 Massachusetts Ave. NW, Ste. 500, Washington, DC 20036, (202)466-7496

Natl. Coun. of Acoustical Consultants [591], 9100 Purdue Rd., Ste. 200, Indianapolis, IN 46268, (317)328-0642

Natl. Coun. of Acupuncture Schools and Colleges [★16012]

Natl. Coun. for Adoption [10797], 225 N Washington St., Alexandria, VA 22314, (703)299-6633

Natl. Coun. for Advanced Mfg. [2342], 2025 M St. NW, Ste. 800, Washington, DC 20036, (202)367-1178

Natl. Coun. for the Advancement of Educ. Writing [★2826]

Natl. Coun. Against Hea. Fraud [17765], PO Box 600793, Newton, MA 02460, (617)332-3063

Natl. Coun. on Ageing [IO], Belmopan, Belize

Natl. Coun. on Aging [10861], 1901 L St. NW, 4th Fl., Washington, DC 20036, (202)479-1200

Natl. Coun. on the Aging | Natl. Inst. of Senior Centers [10862], 1901 L St. NW, 4th Fl., Washington, DC 20036, (202)479-1200

Natl. Coun. for Agricultural Educ. [7713], 1410 King St., Ste. 400, Alexandria, VA 22314, (703)838-5882

Natl. Coun. of Agricultural Employers [3722], 8233 Old Courthouse Rd., Ste. 200, Vienna, VA 22182, (703)790-9039

Natl. Coun. on Agricultural Life and Labor Res. Fund [12187], 363 Saulsbury Rd., Dover, DE 19904, (302)678-9400

Natl. Coun. for Air and Stream Improvement [4406], PO Box 13318, Research Triangle Park, NC 27709-3318, (919)941-6400

Natl. Coun. on Alcoholism [★13278]

Natl. Coun. on Alcoholism and Drug Dependence [13278], 244 E 58th St., 4th Fl., New York, NY 10022, (212)269-7797

Natl. Coun. on Alternative Health Care Policy - Defunct.

Natl. Coun. of Amer. Baptist Women [★19305]

Natl. Coun. of Amer. Importers [★2093]

Natl. Coun. of Amer. Shipbuilders [★2370]

Natl. Coun. of Applied Economic Res. [IO], New Delhi, India

Natl. Coun. of Architectural Registration Boards [5214], 1801 K St. NW, Ste. 700-K, Washington, DC 20006-1310, (202)783-6500

Natl. Coun. of Architectural Registration Boards [5214], 1801 K St. NW, Ste. 700-K, Washington, DC 20006-1310, (202)783-6500

Natl. Coun. on Art in Jewish Life - Defunct.

Natl. Coun. of Asian Amer. Bus. Associations [719], 475 N Whisman Rd., Ste. 200, Mountain View, CA 94043, (650)303-6164

Natl. Coun. of Asian Indian Organizations in North America [★19037]

Natl. Coun. of Asian Pacific Americans [17206], 6930 Carroll Ave., Ste. 506, Takoma Park, MD 20912, (301)270-1855

Natl. Coun. of BIA Educators [★8676]

Natl. Coun. on Bible Curriculum in Public Schools [20214], PO Box 9743, Greensboro, NC 27429, (336)272-3799

Natl. Coun. for the Blind of Ireland [IO], Drumcondra, Ireland

Natl. Coun. of Brown Swiss Cattle Breeders of Australia [IO], Tocumwal, Australia

Natl. Coun. for Bus. Educ. [★7804]

Natl. Coun. of Catholic Men - Defunct.

Natl. Coun. of Catholic Women [19472], 200 N Glebe Rd., Ste. 725, Arlington, VA 22203, (703)224-0990

Natl. Coun. for Cement and Building Materials [IO], Ballabgarh, India

Natl. Coun. of Certified Dementia Practitioners [15616], 103 Valley View Trail, Sparta, NJ 07871, (877)729-5191

Natl. Coun. of Chain Restaurants [1765], 325 7th St. NW, Ste. 1100, Washington, DC 20004, (202)783-7971

Natl. Coun. of Chief State School Officers [★8014]

Natl. Coun. on Child Abuse and Family Violence [11893], 1025 Connecticut Ave. NW, Ste. 1000, Washington, DC 20036, (202)429-6695

Natl. Coun. for Children's Rights [★11864]

Natl. Coun. of Chiropractic Hosp. and Sanitaria [★14116]

Natl. Coun. of Chiropractic Roentgenologists [★16532]

Natl. Coun. of Churches [19622], 475 Riverside Dr., Ste. 800, New York, NY 10115, (212)870-2228

Natl. Coun. of Churches [★19684]

Natl. Coun. of Churches [★19663]

Natl. Coun. of Churches of Christ in the U.S.A. [19663], 475 Riverside Dr., Ste. 880, New York, NY 10115, (212)870-2228

Natl. Coun. of Churches of Christ USA | Intl. Justice and Human Rights [12246], Justice and Advocacy Commn., 475 Riverside Dr., Ste. 880, New York, NY 10115, (212)870-2048

Natl. Coun. of Churches, Educ. and Leadership Ministries Commn. [19684], 475 Riverside Dr., 8th Fl., New York, NY 10115-0500, (212)870-2267

Natl. Coun. of Churches, Ministries in Christian Educ. [★19684]

Natl. Coun. of Churches U.S.A. | Commun. Commn. [19356], 475 Riverside Dr., Ste. 700, New York, NY 10115, (212)870-2497

Natl. Coun. of Coll. Publications Advisers [★8439]

Natl. Coun. of Commercial Plant Breeders [4881], 1701 Duke St., Ste. 275, Alexandria, VA 22314, (703)837-8140

Natl. Coun. for Community Behavioral Healthcare [15474], 1701 K St. NW, Ste. 400, Washington, DC 20006, (202)684-7457

Natl. Coun. of Community Churches [★19621]

Natl. Coun. of Community Churches [★19621]

Natl. Coun. of Community Churches [★19621]

Natl. Coun. on Community Foundations [★12593]

Natl. Coun. of Community Hospitals - Defunct.

Natl. Coun. on Community Mental Hea. Centers [★15474]

Natl. Coun. for Community Relations [★8766]

Natl. Coun. on Community Services and Continuing Educ. [★7928]

Natl. Coun. for Community Services to Intl. Visitors [★17979]

Natl. Coun. for Community Services to Intl. Visitors [★17979]

Natl. Coun. of Community World Affairs Organizations [★18820]

Natl. Coun. of Community World Affairs Organizations [★18820]

Natl. Coun. on Compensation Insurance [2017], 901 Peninsula Corporate Cir., Boca Raton, FL 33487, (561)893-1000

Natl. Coun. on Compulsive Gambling [★12064]

Natl. Coun. for the Conservation of Plants and Gardens [IO], Guildford, United Kingdom

Natl. Coun. for Continuing Educ. and Training [7928], PO Box 162551, Austin, TX 78716-2551, (512)306-8686

Natl. Coun. to Control Handguns [★17683]

Natl. Coun. of Corvette Clubs [21126], Larry Morrison, VP of Membership, 492 Meadowlark Way, Clifton, CO 81520-8811

Natl. Coun. of County Assn. Executives [5353], 25 Massachusetts Ave. NW, Ste. 500, Washington, DC 20001, (202)942-4242

Natl. Coun. on Crime and Delinquency [11690], 1970 Broadway, Ste. 500, Oakland, CA 94612, (510)208-0500

Natl. Coun. of Dance Teacher Organizations [★7962]

Natl. Coun. of Dance Teachers Organizations [★22494]

Natl. Coun. of Development Commun. [IO], Varanasi, India

Natl. Coun. for Drama Training [IO], London, United Kingdom

Natl. Coun. on Economic Educ. [7987], 122 E 42nd St., Ste. 2600, New York, NY 10168, (212)730-7007

Natl. Coun. on Educ. for the Ceramic Arts [21456], 77 Erie Village Sq., Ste. 280, Erie, CO 80516-6996, (303)828-2811

Natl. Coun. of Educ. Providers [8083], Mr. J.C. Huizenga, Chm., 618 Kenmoor Ave. SE, Ste. 120, Grand Rapids, MI 49546, (616)957-9060

Natl. Coun. of Educational Opportunity Associations [★8080]

Natl. Coun. of Educational Res. and Training [IO], New Delhi, India

Natl. Coun. of Elected County Executives - Defunct.

Natl. Coun. for Elementary Sci. [★8837]

Natl. Coun. for Elementary Sci. [★8837]

Natl. Coun. of Engg. Examiners [★6812]

Natl. Coun. on Ethics in Human Res. [IO], Ottawa, ON, Canada

Natl. Coun. for Eurasian and East European Res. [10535], PO Box 353650, Seattle, WA 98195, (206)829-2445

Natl. Coun. of Examiners for Engg. and Surveying [6812], PO Box 1686, Clemson, SC 29633-1686, (864)654-6824

Natl. Coun. of Exchangors [3032], PO Box 668, Morro Bay, CA 93443-0668, (800)324-1031

Natl. Coun. on Family Relations [12015], 1201 W River Pkwy., Ste. 200, Minneapolis, MN 55454-1115; (763)781-9331

Natl. Coun. on Family Relations, Family and Hea. Sect. [14526], 290D McNeal Hall, 1985 Buford Ave., St. Paul, MN 55108-6140, (612)624-1208

Natl. Coun. on Family Relations Family Therapy Sect. [★16849]

Natl. Coun. on Family Relations Feminism and Family Stud. Sect. [★12016]

Natl. Coun. on Family Relations | Feminism and Family Stud. Sect. [12016], 1201 W River Pkwy., Ste. 200, Minneapolis, MN 55454, (763)781-9331

Natl. Coun. on Family Relations | Religion and Family Life Sect. [12017], 1201 W River Pkwy., Ste. 200, Minneapolis, MN 55454, (763)781-9331

Natl. Coun. on Family Relations | Religion and Family Life Sect. [12017], 1201 W River Pkwy., Ste. 200, Minneapolis, MN 55454, (763)781-9331

Natl. Coun. of Farmer Cooperatives [4175], 50 F St. NW, Ste. 900, Washington, DC 20001, (202)626-8700

Natl. Coun. of Field Labor Locals [23204], 8 N 3rd St., Rm. 207, Lafayette, IN 47901, (765)423-2152

Natl. Coun. on Fireworks Safety [11991], 1701 Pennsylvania Ave. NW, Ste. 300, Washington, DC 20006

Natl. Coun. on Foreign Language and Intl. Stud. [★8340]

Natl. Coun. for GeoCosmic Res. [6579], 531 Main St., No. 1612, New York, NY 10044, (212)838-6247

Natl. Coun. for Geographic Educ. [8211], 1145 17th St. NW, Rm. 7620, Washington, DC 20036, (202)857-7695

Natl. Coun. of Geography Teachers [★8211]

Natl. Coun. on Governmental Accounting [★5181]

Natl. Coun. for Graduate Entrepreneurship [IO], Birmingham, United Kingdom

Natl. Coun. of Hea. Centers [★14696]

Natl. Coun. on Health Laboratory Services - Defunct.

Natl. Coun. of Higher Educ. Loan Programs [8103], 1100 Connecticut Ave. NW, Ste. 1200, Washington, DC 20036-4110, (202)822-2106

Natl. Coun. for Historic Sites and Buildings [★9717]

Natl. Coun. for History Educ. [8260], 7100 Baltimore Ave., Ste. 510, College Park, MD 20740, (440)835-1776

Natl. Coun. on Hotel and Restaurant Educ. [★1757]

Natl. Coun. on Hotel and Restaurant Educ. [★1757]

Natl. Coun. of the Housing Indus. [★588]

Natl. Coun. of Independent Colleges and Universities [★8290]

Natl. Coun. on Independent Living [11813], 1710 Rhode Island Ave. NW, 5th Fl., Washington, DC 20036, (202)207-0334

Natl. Coun. of Independent Schools [★8291]

Natl. Coun. for Industrial Defense - Defunct.

Natl. Coun. of Innovation, Sci. and Tech. [IO], Montevideo, Uruguay

Natl. Coun. on Intellectual Disability [IO], Mawson, Australia

A star before a book entry number signifies that the name is not listed separately, but is mentioned within the entry.

Natl. Coun. for Interior Design Qualification [2068], 1602 L St. NW, Ste. 200, Washington, DC 20036-2581, (202)721-0220

Natl. Coun. for Interior Design Qualification [2068], 1602 L St. NW, Ste. 200, Washington, DC 20036-2581, (202)721-0220

Natl. Coun. for Intl. Hea. [★15166]

Natl. Coun. for Intl. Hea. [★15166]

Natl. Coun. on Intl. Trade Development [2086], 1707 L St. NW, Ste. 570, Washington, DC 20036, (202)872-9280

Natl. Coun. on Intl. Trade Development [2086], 1707 L St. NW, Ste. 570, Washington, DC 20036, (202)872-9280

Natl. Coun. for Intl. Visitors [17979], 1420 K St. NW, Ste. 800, Washington, DC 20005, (202)842-1414

Natl. Coun. for Intl. Visitors [17979], 1420 K St. NW, Ste. 800, Washington, DC 20005, (202)842-1414

Natl. Coun. on Interpreting in Hea. Care [1675], 5505 Connecticut Ave. NW, No. 119, Washington, DC 20015-2601, (202)596-2436

Natl. Coun. of Investigation and Security Services [3223], 7501 Sparrows Point Blvd., Baltimore, MD 21219-1927, (800)445-8408

Natl. Coun. of Japanese Language Teachers [8958], PO Box 3719, Boulder, CO 80307-3719

Natl. Coun. of Jewish Women [19888], 475 Riverside Dr., Ste. 250, New York, NY 10115, (212)645-4048

Natl. Coun. of Jewish Women in Australia [IO], Caulfield Junction, Australia

Natl. Coun. of Juvenile Court Judges [★5632]

Natl. Coun. of Juvenile and Family Court Judges [5632], PO Box 8970, Reno, NV 89507, (775)784-6012

Natl. Coun. of La Raza [12146], Raul Yzaguirre Bldg., 1126 16th St. NW, Washington, DC 20036, (202)785-1670

Natl. Coun. of La Raza [12146], Raul Yzaguirre Bldg., 1126 16th St. NW, Washington, DC 20036, (202)785-1670

Natl. Coun. for Languages and Intl. Stud. [9943], 4646 40th St. NW, Ste. 310, Washington, DC 20016, (202)966-8477

Natl. Coun. for Languages and Intl. Stud. [9943], 4646 40th St. NW, Ste. 310, Washington, DC 20016, (202)966-8477

Natl. Coun. of Lawyer Disciplinary Boards [5271], PO Box 12426, Austin, TX 78711

Natl. Coun. of Less Commonly Taught Languages [8476], Natl. African Language Rsrc. Ctr., 4231 Humanities Bldg., 455 N Park St., Madison, WI 53706, (608)265-7905

Natl. Coun. of Less Commonly Taught Languages [8476], Natl. African Language Rsrc. Ctr., 4231 Humanities Bldg., 455 N Park St., Madison, WI 53706, (608)265-7905

Natl. Coun. of Maori Nurses [IO], Tauranga, New Zealand

Natl. Coun. for Marketing and Public Relations [8766], PO Box 336039, Greeley, CO 80633, (970)330-0771

Natl. Coun. on Measurement in Educ. [8992], 2424 Amer. Ln., Madison, WI 53704, (608)443-2487

Natl. Coun. on Measurements Used in Educ. [★8992]

Natl. Coun. of Minorities in Energy [1173], PO Box 65783, Washington, DC 20035, (866)663-9045

Natl. Coun. on Minority Educ. in Transplantation - Address unknown since 2011.

Natl. Coun. of Negro Women [17661], 633 Pennsylvania Ave. NW, Washington, DC 20004, (202)737-0120

Natl. Coun. of Nepal YMCA's [IO], Kathmandu, Nepal

Natl. Coun. of Nonprofit Associations [★266]

Natl. Coun. of Nonprofits [266], 1101 Vermont Ave. NW, Ste. 1002, Washington, DC 20005, (202)962-0322

Natl. Coun. for Occupational Educ. [★8116]

Natl. Coun. of Organizations of Less Commonly Taught Languages [★8476]

Natl. Coun. of Organizations of Less Commonly Taught Languages [★8476]

Natl. Coun. on Paint Disposition [4765], PO Box 74, East Brunswick, NJ 08816, (732)309-2022

Natl. Coun. for Palliative Care [IO], London, United Kingdom

Natl. Coun. on Patient Info. and Educ. [16207], 200-A Monroe St., Ste. 212, Rockville, MD 20850-4448, (301)340-3940

Natl. Coun. on Pet Population Stud. and Policy [6124], PO Box 131488, Ann Arbor, MI 48113-1488

Natl. Coun. on Philanthropy [★12675]

Natl. Coun. of Physical Distribution Mgt. [★3658]

Natl. Coun. of Postal Credit Unions [1005], PO Box 160, Del Mar, CA 92014-0160, (858)792-3883

Natl. Coun. for Prescription Drug Programs [16208], 9240 E Raintree Dr., Scottsdale, AZ 85260-7518, (480)477-1000

Natl. Coun. of Preservation Executives - Defunct.

Natl. Coun. of Primary Educ. [★7825]

Natl. Coun. of Primary Educ. [★7825]

Natl. Coun. of Private Enterprises - Dominican Republic [IO], Panama City, Panama

Natl. Coun. of Private Enterprises - Panama [IO], Panama City, Panama

Natl. Coun. for Private School Accreditation [7650], PO Box 13686, Seattle, WA 98198-1010

Natl. Coun. on Problem Gambling [12064], 730 11th St. NW, Ste. 601, Washington, DC 20001, (202)547-9204

Natl. Coun. for the Professional Development of Nursing and Midwifery [IO], Dublin, Ireland

Natl. Coun. on Public History [9787], 327 Cavanaugh Hall - IUPUI, 425 Univ. Blvd., Indianapolis, IN 46202, (317)274-2716

Natl. Coun. on Public Polls [18397], 1425 Broad St., Ste. 7, Clifton, NJ 07013, (973)857-8500

Natl. Coun. for Public-Private Partnerships [17720], 2000 14th St. N, Ste. 480, Arlington, VA 22201, (703)469-2233

Natl. Coun. on Qualifications for the Lighting Professions [2221], PO Box 142729, Austin, TX 78714-2729, (512)973-0042

Natl. Coun. on Radiation Protection and Measurements [5954], 7910 Woodmont Ave., Ste. 400, Bethesda, MD 20814-3076, (301)657-2652

Natl. Coun. on Real Estate Investment Fiduciaries [2145], 2 Prudential Plz., 180 N Stetson Ave., Ste. 2515, Chicago, IL 60601, (312)819-5890

Natl. Coun. on Rehabilitation Educ. [16571], 497 N Clovis Ave., Ste. 202, Clovis, CA 93611, (559)906-0787

Natl. Coun. for Reliable Hea. Info. [★17765]

Natl. Coun. on Religion in Higher Educ. [★19687]

Natl. Coun. for Res. on Women [17662], 11 Hanover Sq., 24th Fl., New York, NY 10005, (212)785-7335

Natl. Coun. of Resistance of Iran [IO], London, United Kingdom

Natl. Coun. of Returned Peace Corps Volunteers [★18308]

Natl. Coun. of Salesmen's Orgs. - Defunct.

Natl. Coun. on Schoolhouse Constr. [★8088]

Natl. Coun. on Schoolhouse Constr. [★8088]

Natl. Coun. for Sci. and the Env. [4285], 1101 17th St. NW, Ste. 250, Washington, DC 20036, (202)530-5810

Natl. Coun. for Sci. Res. - Lebanon [IO], Beirut, Lebanon

Natl. Coun. of Sci. and Technological Development [IO], Brasilia, Brazil

Natl. Coun. of Seamen's Agencies [★13029]

Natl. Coun. of Seamen's Agencies [★13029]

Natl. Coun. of Secondary School Athletic Directors - Address unknown since 2011.

Natl. Coun. of Self-Insurers [2018], 1253 Springfield Ave., PMB 345, New Providence, NJ 07974, (908)665-2152

Natl. Coun. of Senior Citizens - Defunct.

Natl. Coun. for Skill Standards in Graphic Communications - Address unknown since 2011.

Natl. Coun. on Skin Cancer Prevention [13954], 1776 Eye St. NW, Ste. 900, Mount Airy, MD 21771, (301)801-4422

Natl. Coun. of Social Security Mgt. Associations [5974], 418 C St. NE, Washington, DC 20002, (202)547-8530

Natl. Coun. of Social Ser. [IO], Singapore, Singapore

Natl. Coun. for the Social Stud. [8866], 8555 16th St., Ste. 500, Silver Spring, MD 20910, (301)588-1800

Natl. Coun. for Soviet and East European Res. [★10535]

Natl. Coun. for Spirit Safety and Educ. [22451], PO Box 311192, Enterprise, AL 36331-1192, (334)347-4688

Natl. Coun. of State Boards of Engg. Examiners [★6812]

Natl. Coun. of State Boards of Nursing [15779], 111 E Wacker Dr., Ste. 2900, Chicago, IL 60601, (312)525-3600

Natl. Coun. of State Directors of Community Colleges [7893], 1 Dupont Cir. NW, Ste. 410, Washington, DC 20036, (202)728-0200

Natl. Coun. of State Educ. Associations - Address unknown since 2010.

Natl. Coun. of State Garden Clubs [★21809]

Natl. Coun. of State Housing Agencies [5522], 444 N Capitol St. NW, Ste. 438, Washington, DC 20001, (202)624-7710

Natl. Coun. of State Legislatures | Forum for State Hea. Policy Leadership [17766], 444 N Capitol St. NW, Ste. 515, Washington, DC 20001, (202)624-5400

Natl. Coun. of State Pharmaceutical Assn. [★16203]

Natl. Coun. of State Pharmacy Assn. Executives [★16203]

Natl. Coun. of State Public Welfare Administrators [★13171]

Natl. Coun. of State School Boards Assn. [★8816]

Natl. Coun. of State Self-Insurers' Associations [★2018]

Natl. Coun. of State Sociological Associations [7429], Xiao-qing Wang, Pres., Cottey Coll., 1000 W Austin, Nevada, MO 64772

Natl. Coun. of State Supervisor of Foreign Languages [8477], Ryan Wertz, Treas., 1265 Millington Ct., Columbus, OH 43235

Natl. Coun. of State Tourism Directors [23449], 1100 New York Ave. NW, Ste. 450, Washington, DC 20005-3934, (202)408-8422

Natl. Coun. of State Travel Directors [★23449]

Natl. Coun. on Strength and Fitness [23096], PO Box 163908, Miami, FL 33116, (305)668-8705

Natl. Coun. of Structural Engineers Associations [6813], 645 N Michigan Ave., Ste. 540, Chicago, IL 60611, (312)649-4600

Natl. Coun. on Student Development [8907], PO Box 3948, Parker, CO 80134, (866)972-0717

Natl. Coun. of Supervisors of Mathematics [8567], 6000 E Evans Ave., Ste. 3-205, Denver, CO 80222-5423, (303)758-9611

Natl. Coun. for Support of Disability Issues - Address unknown since 2011.

Natl. Coun. of Swedish Youth Organisations [IO], Stockholm, Sweden

Natl. Coun. of Synthetic Fuels Production [★4487]

Natl. Coun. of Synthetic Fuels Production [★4487]

Natl. Coun. for Taekwondo Masters Certification [22746], 501 W Glenoaks Blvd., No. 336, Glendale, CA 91202, (213)503-3302

Natl. Coun. of Tanzania YMCA [IO], Moshi, United Republic of Tanzania

Natl. Coun. on Teacher Quality [8959], 1420 New York Ave. NW, Ste. 800, Washington, DC 20005, (202)393-0020

Natl. Coun. on Teacher Retirement [23180], 7600 Greenhaven Dr., Ste. 302, Sacramento, CA 95831, (916)394-2075

Natl. Coun. of Teachers of English [8134], 1111 Kenyon Rd., Urbana, IL 61801-1096, (217)328-3870

Natl. Coun. of Teachers of English | Conf. on English Educ. [8135], 1111 W Kenyon Rd., Urbana, IL 61801-1096, (217)328-3870

Natl. Coun. of Teachers of Mathematics [8568], 1906 Assn. Dr., Reston, VA 20191-1502, (703)620-9840

Natl. Coun. for Telephone Ministries [★19632]

Natl. Coun. of Textile Organizations [3449], 910 17th St. NW, Ste. 1020, Washington, DC 20006, (202)822-8028

Natl. Coun. for Therapeutic Recreation Certification [16865], 7 Elmwood Dr., New City, NY 10956, (845)639-1439

Natl. Coun. for Torah Education - Defunct.

Reference to "IO" in place of a book number signifies that the association may be found in the 50th edition of International Organizations.

Natl. Coun. for the Traditional Arts [9624], 1320 Fenwick Ln., Ste. 200, Silver Spring, MD 20910, (301)565-0654

Natl. Coun. for the Training of Journalists [IO], Saffron Walden, United Kingdom

Natl. Coun. for Uniform Interest Compensation [★423]

Natl. Coun. of United Presbyterian Men [★20162]

Natl. Coun. on U.S.-Arab Relations [18133], 1730 M St. NW, Ste. 503, Washington, DC 20036, (202)293-6466

Natl. Coun. on U.S.-Arab Relations [18133], 1730 M St. NW, Ste. 503, Washington, DC 20036, (202)293-6466

Natl. Coun. of the U.S., Intl. Org. of Good Templars [19008], PO Box 202238, Minneapolis, MN 55420-2238, (952)210-0382

Natl. Coun. of Univ. Res. Administrators [8799], 1225 19th St. NW, Ste. 850, Washington, DC 20036-2453, (202)466-3894

Natl. Coun. of Urban Indian Hea. [15527], 924 Pennsylvania Ave. SE, Washington, DC 20003, (202)544-0344

Natl. Coun. for US-China Trade [★2110]

Natl. Coun. of Voluntary Organisations [IO], Grand Cayman, Cayman Islands

Natl. Coun. for Voluntary Organisations [IO], London, United Kingdom

Natl. Coun. of Woman of Malta [IO], Blata I-Bajda, Malta

Natl. Coun. of Women of Australia [IO], Deakin, Australia

Natl. Coun. of Women of Canada [IO], Ottawa, ON, Canada

Natl. Coun. of Women of Finland [IO], Helsinki, Finland

Natl. Coun. of Women of Kenya [IO], Nairobi, Kenya

Natl. Coun. of Women of New Zealand [IO], Wellington, New Zealand

Natl. Coun. of Women of Switzerland [IO], Bern, Switzerland

Natl. Coun. of Women of Thailand [IO], Bangkok, Thailand

Natl. Coun. on Women's Hea. [17130], 1300 York Ave., New York, NY 10065-4805, (212)746-6967

Natl. Coun. of Women's Organizations [17663], 714 G St. SE, Washington, DC 20003, (202)293-4505

Natl. Coun. for Workforce Educ. [8116], 1050 Larrabee Ave., No. 104-308, Bellingham, WA 98225

Natl. Coun. on Workmen's Compensation Insurance [★2017]

Natl. Coun. of World Affairs Organizations [★18820]

Natl. Coun. of World Affairs Organizations [★18820]

Natl. Coun. for a World Peace Tax Fund [★18699]

Natl. Coun. of Writing Prog. Administrators [★9073]

Natl. Coun. of YMCA's of Australia [IO], South Melbourne, Australia

Natl. Coun. of YMCA's of Bangladesh [IO], Dhaka, Bangladesh

Natl. Coun. of YMCA's of Ghana [IO], Accra, Ghana

Natl. Coun. of YMCA's of Greece [IO], Athens, Greece

Natl. Coun. of YMCA's of Guyana [IO], Linden, Guyana

Natl. Coun. of YMCA's of Jamaica [IO], Kingston, Jamaica

Natl. Coun. of YMCA's of Japan [IO], Tokyo, Japan

Natl. Coun. of YMCA's of Liberia [IO], Monrovia, Liberia

Natl. Coun. of YMCA's of Malaysia [IO], Kuala Lumpur, Malaysia

Natl. Coun. of YMCA's of Malta [IO], Valletta, Malta

Natl. Coun. of YMCA's of Myanmar [IO], Yangon, Myanmar

Natl. Coun. of YMCA's of New Zealand [IO], Wellington, New Zealand

Natl. Coun. of YMCA's of Nigeria [IO], Lagos, Nigeria

Natl. Coun. of YMCA's of Pakistan [IO], Lahore, Pakistan

Natl. Coun. of YMCA's of Papua New Guinea [IO], Lae, Papua New Guinea

Natl. Coun. of YMCA's of Sri Lanka [IO], Colombo, Sri Lanka

Natl. Coun. of YMCA's of Sudan [IO], Khartoum, Sudan

Natl. Coun. of YMCA's of Zambia [IO], Lusaka, Zambia

Natl. Coun. of YMCA's of Zimbabwe [IO], Harare, Zimbabwe

Natl. Coun. of Young Israel [19889], 111 John St., Ste. 450, New York, NY 10038, (212)929-1525

Natl. Coun. of Young Israel | Young Israel Coun. of Rabbis [19890], 111 John St., Ste. 450, New York, NY 10038, (212)929-1525

Natl. Coun. of Youth Organizations in Korea [IO], Seoul, Republic of Korea

Natl. Coun. of Youth Sports [22994], 7185 SE Seagate Ln., Stuart, FL 34997, (772)781-1452

Natl. Counter Intelligence Corps Assn. [20670], David Bianchi, 72 Main St., Princeton, MA 01541, (215)232-3451

Natl. Country Ham Assn. [1415], PO Box 948, Conover, NC 28613-0948, (828)466-2760

Natl. Courier Assn. [IO], Pudsey, United Kingdom

Natl. Court Appointed Special Advocate Assn. [11364], 100 W Harrison St., North Tower, Ste. 500, Seattle, WA 98119, (206)270-0072

Natl. Court Clubs Assn. [★2743]

Natl. Court Clubs Assn. [★2743]

Natl. Court Reporters Assn. [5359], 8224 Old Courthouse Rd., Vienna, VA 22182-3808, (703)556-6272

Natl. Cowboy Hall of Fame and Western Heritage Center [★9123]

Natl. Cowboy Symposium and Celebration | Amer. Cowboy Culture Assn. [9122], PO Box 6638, Lubbock, TX 79493, (806)798-7825

Natl. Cowboy and Western Heritage Museum [9123], 1700 NE 63rd St., Oklahoma City, OK 73111, (405)478-2250

Natl. CPA Gp. [★16]

Natl. CPA Gp. [★16]

Natl. CPA Hea. Care Advisors Assn. [13570], 624 Grassmere Park Dr., Ste. 15, Nashville, TN 37211, (615)377-3392

Natl. Creameries Assn. [★4185]

Natl. Credentialing Agency for Lab. Personnel - Address unknown since 2010.

Natl. Credit Reporting Assn. [992], 125 E Lake St., Ste. 200, Bloomingdale, IL 60108, (630)539-1525

Natl. Credit Union Mgt. Assn. [1006], PO Box 333, Cumming, GA 30028, (404)255-6828

Natl. Crime Prevention Coun. [11691], 2001 Jefferson Davis Hwy., Ste. 901, Arlington, VA 22202-4801, (202)466-6272

Natl. Crime Prevention Inst. [11692], Univ. of Louisville, 206 McCandless Hall, Louisville, KY 40292, (502)852-8577

Natl. Crime Victim Bar Assn. [6063], 2000 M St. NW, Ste. 480, Washington, DC 20036, (202)467-8753

Natl. Criminal Defense Coll. [5386], Mercer Law School, 343 Orange St., Macon, GA 31207, (478)746-4151

Natl. Criminal Enforcement Assn. [5724], 8491 Hosp. Dr., No. 316, Douglasville, GA 30134, (770)573-2728

Natl. Criminal Justice Assn. [11726], 720 7th St. NW, 3rd Fl., Washington, DC 20001, (202)628-8550

Natl. Cristina Found. [11814], 500 W Putnam Ave., Greenwich, CT 06830, (203)863-9100

Natl. Cristina Found. [11814], 500 W Putnam Ave., Greenwich, CT 06830, (203)863-9100

Natl. Critics Inst. [★10596]

Natl. Croatian Soc. [★18967]

Natl. Crop Insurance Assn. [★2019]

Natl. Crop Insurance Services [2019], 8900 Indian Creek Pkwy., Ste. 600, Overland Park, KS 66210-1567, (913)685-2767

Natl. Crossbowmen of the U.S.A., Inc. [★22225]

The Natl. Crossbowmen of the U.S.A. [22225], Patricia Copley, Sec.-Treas., 38 B Ave., Richwood, WV 26261, (304)846-6420

Natl. Crushed Stone Assn. [★3366]

Natl. Cued Speech Assn. [16689], PO Box 10159, Rochester, NY 14610, (315)789-1608

Natl. Cursillo Movement [19473], PO Box 799, Jarrell, TX 76537, (512)746-2020

Natl. Customs Brokers Assn. of Liberia [IO], Monrovia, Liberia

Natl. Customs Brokers and Forwarders Assn. of Am. [2103], 1200 18th St. NW, No. 901, Washington, DC 20036, (202)466-0222

Natl. Customs Ser. Assn. [★23208]

Natl. Cutting Horse Assn. [4616], 260 Bailey Ave., Fort Worth, TX 76107-1862, (817)244-6188

Natl. Cyber-Forensics and Training Alliance [6884], 2000 Tech. Dr., Ste. 450, Pittsburgh, PA 15219, (412)802-8000

Natl. Cyber Security Alliance [7395], Michael Kaiser, Exec. Dir., 1101 Pennsylvania Ave. NW, Ste. 600, Washington, DC 20004, (202)463-0013

Natl. Cylinder Grinders Assn. [★319]

Natl. Cylinder Grinders Assn. [★319]

Natl. CYO Fed. [★19476]

Natl. Cystic Fibrosis Res. Found. [★16607]

Natl. Dairy Coun. [★1019]

Natl. Dairy Coun. [4183], 10255 W Higgins Rd., Ste. 900, Rosemont, IL 60018, (312)240-2880

Natl. Dairy Coun. [IO], Dublin, Ireland

Natl. Dairy Herd Improvement Assn. [3924], PO Box 930399, Verona, WI 53593-0399, (608)848-6455

Natl. Dairy Shrine [4184], PO Box 725, Denmark, WI 54208, (920)863-6333

Natl. Dance Assn. [9560], 1900 Assn. Dr., Reston, VA 20191, (703)476-3400

Natl. Dance Coun. of Am. [7962], Eleanor Wiblin, Registrar, PO Box 22018, Provo, UT 84602-2018, (801)422-8124

Natl. Dance Educ. Assn. [22493], 8609 Second Ave., Ste. 203-B, Silver Spring, MD 20910, (301)585-2880

Natl. Dance Guild [★9534]

Natl. Dance Inst. [7963], 217 W 147th St., New York, NY 10039, (212)226-0083

Natl. Dance Teacher's Assn. [22494], 2309 E Atlantic Blvd., Pompano Beach, FL 33062, (954)782-7760

Natl. Dance Teachers Guild [★9534]

Natl. DanceSport Fed. of Greece [IO], Piraeus, Greece

Natl. Day of the Cowboy [9124], PO Box 25298, Prescott Valley, AZ 86312-5298, (928)759-0951

Natl. Day Laborer Organizing Network [23229], 675 S Park View St., Ste. B, Los Angeles, CA 90057, (213)380-2783

Natl. Day Nurseries Assn. [IO], Huddersfield, United Kingdom

Natl. Deaf Children's Soc. [IO], London, United Kingdom

Natl. Deaf Women's Bowling Assn. [22517], Jane Jacobson, Sec.-Treas., 3314 64th St., Urbandale, IA 50322

Natl. Debt Assn. of China [IO], Beijing, People's Republic of China

Natl. Debt Repayment Found. - Defunct.

Natl. Decorating Products Assn. [★2073]

Natl. Decorating Products Assn. [★2073]

Natl. Defender Investigator Assn. [5608], Beverly Davidson, Exec. Sec., 460 Smith St., Ste. K, Middletown, CT 06457, (860)635-5533

Natl. Defense Coun. Found. - Defunct.

Natl. Defense Found. [★20415]

Natl. Defense Indus. Assn. [5814], 2111 Wilson Blvd., Ste. 400, Arlington, VA 22201-3061, (703)522-1820

Natl. Defense Preparedness Assn. [★5814]

Natl. Defense Trans. Assn. [5815], 50 S Pickett St., Ste. 220, Alexandria, VA 22304-7296, (703)751-5011

Natl. Defined Contribution Coun. - Defunct.

Natl. Democratic Club [17539], 30 Ivy St. SE, Washington, DC 20003, (202)543-2035

Natl. Democratic Forum [★18447]

Natl. Democratic Inst. [★17947]

Natl. Democratic Inst. [★17947]

Natl. Democratic Inst. for Intl. Affairs [17947], 455 Massachusetts Ave. NW, 8th Fl., Washington, DC 20001, (202)728-5500

Natl. Democratic Inst. for Intl. Affairs [17947], 455 Massachusetts Ave. NW, 8th Fl., Washington, DC 20001, (202)728-5500

Natl. Demolition Assn. [934], 16 N Franklin St., Ste. 203, Doylestown, PA 18901-3536, (215)348-4949

Natl. Demolition Derby Assn. - Defunct.

Natl. Demonstration Water Proj. [★7610]

Natl. Dental Assistants Assn. [14300], Natl. Dental Assn., 3517 16th St. NW, Washington, DC 20010, (202)588-1697

A star before a book entry number signifies that the name is not listed separately, but is mentioned within the entry.

Natl. Dental Assn. [★14262]

Natl. Dental Assn. [14301], 3517 16th St. NW, Washington, DC 20010, (202)588-1697

Natl. Dental EDI Coun. [14302], 4225 W Glendale Ave., Ste. E104, Phoenix, AZ 85051-8153, (602)266-7740

Natl. Dental Hygiene Honor Soc. [★23501]

Natl. Dental Hygienists' Assn. [14303], PO Box 22463, Tampa, FL 33622, (800)234-1096

Natl. Denturist Assn. [14304], PO Box 308, Towanda, PA 18848, (888)599-7958

Natl. Depression Glass Assn. [21838], PO Box 8264, Wichita, KS 67208-0264

Natl. Depressive and Manic Depressive Assn. [★15452]

Natl. Derby Rallies [22930], 6644 Switzer Ln., Shawnee, KS 66203, (913)962-6360

Natl. DeSoto Club [21127], 1323 W Beach Rd., Oak Harbor, WA 98277, (360)720-2465

Natl. Development Coun. [17583], 708 Third Ave., Ste. 710, New York, NY 10017, (212)682-1106

Natl. Diabetes Info. CH [14357], 1 Info. Way, Bethesda, MD 20892, (800)860-8747

Natl. Dietary Foods Assn. [★3121]

Natl. Digestive Diseases Educ. and Info. CH [★14569]

Natl. Digestive Diseases Info. CH [14569], 2 Info. Way, Bethesda, MD 20892-3570, (800)891-5389

Natl. Dimension Mfrs. Assn. [★1516]

Natl. Diocesan Press [★19699]

Natl. Directors of Educational Res. [★8790]

Natl. Directory Publishing Assn. - Defunct.

Natl. Disability Rights Network [11815], 900 2nd St. NE, Ste. 211, Washington, DC 20002, (202)408-9514

Natl. Disability Services [IO], Deakin West, Australia

Natl. Disability Sports Alliance - Address unknown since 2011.

Natl. Disabled Law Officers Assn. - Defunct.

Natl. Disabled Police Assn. [IO], Ashford, United Kingdom

Natl. Disaster Search Dog Found. [12909], 501 E Ojai Ave., Ojai, CA 93023, (888)459-4376

Natl. Disease Clusters Alliance [14407], PO Box 44081, Tucson, AZ 85733-4081, (877)676-6322

Natl. Dissemination Assn. [8051], Max McConkey, Exec. Dir., 4732 N Oracle Rd., Ste. 217, Tucson, AZ 85705, (602)888-2838

Natl. Dissemination Center for Children with Disabilities [11816], 1825 Connecticut Ave. NW, Ste. 700, Washington, DC 20009, (202)884-8200

National Distinguished Principals Program [★8749]

Natl. Distribution Union [IO], Auckland, New Zealand

Natl. Distributors Assn. of Constr. Equip. [★1805]

Natl. District Attorneys Assn. [5272], 44 Canal Center Plz., Ste. 110, Alexandria, VA 22314, (703)549-9222

Natl. District Attorneys Assn. Found. [★5272]

Natl. District Heating Assn. [★1709]

Natl. District Heating Assn. [★1709]

Natl. Dog Groomers Assn. of Am. [2682], PO Box 101, Clark, PA 16113-0101, (724)962-2711

Natl. Dog Registry [11009], PO Box 51105, Mesa, AZ 85208, (800)NDR-DOGS

Natl. Dog Warden Assn. [IO], Gloucester, United Kingdom

Natl. Doll and Toy Collectors [★21700]

National Dome Coun. - Address unknown since 2010.

Natl. Domestic Violence Hotline [11894], PO Box 161810, Austin, TX 78716, (512)794-1133

Natl. Door Mfrs. Assn. [★635]

Natl. Down Syndrome Cong. [12510], 1370 Center Dr., Ste. 102, Atlanta, GA 30338, (770)604-9500

Natl. Down Syndrome Soc. [15490], 666 Broadway, 8th Fl., New York, NY 10012, (800)221-4602

Natl. Down's Syndrome Cong. [★12510]

Natl. Dried Fruit Trade Assn. [IO], Essex, United Kingdom

Natl. Drilling Assn. [935], 1545 W 130th St., Ste. A2, Hinckley, OH 44233, (877)632-4748

Natl. Drilling Assn. [935], 1545 W 130th St., Ste. A2, Hinckley, OH 44233, (877)632-4748

Natl. Drilling Contractors Assn. [★935]

Natl. Drilling Contractors Assn. [★935]

Natl. Dropout Prevention Center/Network [8084], Clemson Univ., 209 Martin St., Clemson, SC 29631-1555, (864)656-2599

Natl. Drowning Prevention Alliance [12994], Kristin Goffman, Exec. Dir., PO Box 1641, Idyllwild, CA 92549, (951)659-8600

Natl. Drug Enforcement Officers Assn. [5725], DEA Acad., Off. of Training/TRDS, PO Box 1475, Quantico, VA 22134-1475

Natl. Drug Strategy Network [17310], Criminal Justice Policy Found., 8730 Georgia Ave., Ste. 400, Silver Spring, MD 20910, (301)589-6020

Natl. Dry Bean Coun. [★4479]

Natl. Duck Stamp Collectors Soc. [22059], PO Box 43, Harleysville, PA 19438-0043

Natl. Duckpin Bowling Cong. [22426], Sue Burucker, Exec. Dir./Sec., 4991 Fairview Ave., Linthicum, MD 21090, (410)636-2695

Natl. Duncan Glass Soc. [21839], PO Box 965, Washington, PA 15301, (724)225-9950

Natl. Dysautonomia Res. Found. [14408], PO Box 301, Red Wing, MN 55066-0301, (651)327-0367

Natl. Eagle Scout Assn. [13023], Boy Scouts of Am., 1325 W Walnut Hill Ln., PO Box 152079, Irving, TX 75015-2079, (972)580-2183

Natl. Early Amer. Glass Club [★21836]

Natl. Earth Sci. Teachers Assn. [8847], PO Box 20854, Boulder, CO 80308, (720)328-5350

Natl. Easter Seal Soc. [★11784]

Natl. Eating Disorder Info. Centre [IO], Toronto, ON, Canada

Natl. Eating Disorders Assn. [14439], 603 Stewart St., Ste. 803, Seattle, WA 98101, (206)382-3587

Natl. Eating Disorders Org. [★14439]

Natl. Economic Assn. [6629], Spelman Coll., 350 Spelman Ln., Box 167, Atlanta, GA 30314

Natl. Economic Development and Law Center [★17578]

Natl. Economic and Social Rights Initiative [17855], 90 John St., Ste. 308, New York, NY 10038, (212)253-1710

Natl. Economists Club [6630], PO Box 19281, Washington, DC 20036, (703)493-8824

Natl. Eczema Assn. [14333], 4460 Redwood Hwy., Ste. 16-D, San Rafael, CA 94903-1953, (415)499-3474

Natl. Eczema Assn. for Sci. and Educ. [★14333]

Natl. Eczema Soc. [IO], London, United Kingdom

Natl. Editorial Assn. [★2852]

Natl. Educ. Alliance for Borderline Personality Disorder [15475], PO Box 974, Rye, NY 10580

Natl. Educ. for Assistance Dog Services [14950], PO Box 213, West Boylston, MA 01583, (978)422-9064

Natl. Educ. Assn. [23181], 1201 16th St. NW, Washington, DC 20036-3290, (202)833-4000

Natl. Educ. Assn. I Natl. Coun. of Urban Educ. Associations [9029], 1201 16th St. NW, Ste. 410, Washington, DC 20036, (202)833-4000

Natl. Educ. Fed. [IO], Bucharest, Romania

Natl. Educ., Hea. and Allied Workers' Union [IO], Johannesburg, Republic of South Africa

Natl. Educ. Knowledge Indus. Assn. [★8797]

Natl. Educational Assn. of Disabled Students [IO], Ottawa, ON, Canada

Natl. Educational Telecommunications Assn. [8090], PO Box 50008, Columbia, SC 29250, (803)799-5517

Natl. Educational TV [★9459]

Natl. Educators Fellowship [★19672]

Natl. Educators Fellowship [★19672]

Natl. Elec. Drag Racing Assn. [22559], 3200 Dutton Ave., No. 220, Santa Rosa, CA 95407

Natl. Elec. Reliability Coun. [★1083]

Natl. Elec. Sign Assn. [★1078]

Natl. Elec. Sign Assn. [★1078]

Natl. Elec. Wholesalers Assn. [★1079]

Natl. Elecl. and Communications Assn. [IO], St. Leonards, Australia

Natl. Elecl. Contractors Assn. [936], 3 Bethesda Metro Ctr., Ste. 1100, Bethesda, MD 20814, (301)657-3110

Natl. Elecl. Engg. Dept. Heads Assn. [★6793]

Natl. Elecl. Mfrs. Assn. [1080], 1300 N 17th St., Ste. 1752, Rosslyn, VA 22209, (703)841-3200

Natl. Elecl. Mfrs. Assn. [1080], 1300 N 17th St., Ste. 1752, Rosslyn, VA 22209, (703)841-3200

Natl. Elecl. Mfrs. Representatives Assn. [1081], 28 Deer St., Ste. 302, Portsmouth, NH 03801, (914)524-8650

Natl. Elecl. Testing Assn. [★1076]

Natl. Elecl. Testing Assn. [★1076]

Natl. Electrolysis Org. [★14446]

Natl. Electronic Associations [★1110]

Natl. Electronic Billers Alliance - Address unknown since 2010.

Natl. Electronic Distributors Assn. [1109], 1111 Alderman Dr., Ste. 400, Alpharetta, GA 30005, (678)393-9990

Natl. Electronic Ser. Dealers Assn. [★1110]

Natl. Electronics Conf. [★6669]

Natl. Electronics Conf. [★6669]

Natl. Electronics Mfg. Initiative [★7046]

Natl. Electronics Ser. Dealers Assn. [1110], 3608 Pershing Ave., Fort Worth, TX 76107-4527, (817)921-9061

Natl. Elementary Schools Press Assn. [8747], PO Box 870172, Tuscaloosa, AL 35487, (205)348-2772

Natl. Elevator Indus., Inc. [1851], 1677 County Rte. 64, PO Box 838, Salem, NY 12865-0838, (518)854-3100

Natl. Elevator Mfg. Indus. [★1851]

Natl. Emergency Civil Liberties Comm. [★17273]

Natl. Emergency Dept. Nurses Assn. [★14467]

Natl. Emergency Mgt. Assn. [5398], PO Box 11910, Lexington, KY 40578, (859)244-8000

Natl. Emergency Medicine Assn. [14475], PO Box 1039, Edgewood, MD 21040, (443)922-7533

Natl. Emergency Number Assn. [14455], 1700 Diagonal Rd., Ste. 500, Alexandria, VA 22314, (202)618-6369

Natl. Emphysema Found. [14033], 128 East Ave., Norwalk, CT 06851, (203)866-5000

Natl. Employee Rights Inst. [★11925]

Natl. Employee Services and Recreation Assn. [★12765]

Natl. Employment Assn. [★1156]

Natl. Employment Bd. [★1156]

Natl. Employment Counseling Assn. [11950], 6836 Bee Cave Rd., Ste. 260, Austin, TX 78746, (800)347-6647

Natl. Employment Law Proj. [11951], 75 Maiden Ln., Ste. 601, New York, NY 10038, (212)285-3025

Natl. Employment Lawyers Assn. [5273], 417 Montgomery St., 4th Fl., San Francisco, CA 94104, (415)296-7629

Natl. Employment Services Assn. [IO], South Melbourne, Australia

Natl. EMS Mgt. Assn. [14476], 679 Encinitas Blvd., Ste. 211, Encinitas, CA 92024, (760)632-7375

Natl. EMS Pilots Assn. [14456], PO Box 2128, Layton, UT 84041-9128, (877)668-0430

Natl. Endangered Species Act Reform Coalition [5421], 1050 Thomas Jefferson St., 7th Fl., Washington, DC 20007, (202)333-7481

Natl. Endowment for the Animals [11010], 660 S 40th St., Boulder, CO 80305, (720)252-8449

Natl. Endowment for the Arts [9307], 1100 Pennsylvania Ave. NW, Washington, DC 20004, (202)682-5400

Natl. Endowment for the Christian Arts - Address unknown since 2011.

Natl. Endowment for Democracy [17527], 1025 F St. NW, Ste. 800, Washington, DC 20004, (202)293-9700

Natl. Endowment for the Humanities [5526], 1100 Pennsylvania Ave. NW, Washington, DC 20506, (202)606-8400

Natl. Energy Assistance Directors' Assn. [1794], Mark Wolfe, Exec. Dir., 1232 31st St. NW, Washington, DC 20007, (202)237-5199

Natl. Energy Educ. Day Proj. [★17617]

Natl. Energy Educ. Development Proj. [17617], 8408 Kao Cir., Manassas, VA 20110, (703)257-1117

Natl. Energy Found. [8147], 4516 S 700 E, Ste. 100, Salt Lake City, UT 84107, (801)908-5800

Natl. Energy Found. [IO], Milton Keynes, United Kingdom

Natl. Energy Mgt. Inst. [6738], 601 N Fairfax St., Ste. 240, Alexandria, VA 22314, (703)739-7100

Reference to "IO" in place of a book number signifies that the association may be found in the 50th edition of International Organizations.

Encyclopedia of Associations, 51st Edition   3029

Natl. Energy Marketers Assn. [1174], 3333 K St. NW, Ste. 110, Washington, DC 20007, (202)333-3288

Natl. Energy Marketers Assn. [1174], 3333 K St. NW, Ste. 110, Washington, DC 20007, (202)333-3288

Natl. Energy Services Assn. [6739], 6430 FM 1960 W, No. 213, Houston, TX 77069, (713)856-6525

Natl. Engg. Consortium [★6669]

Natl. Engg. Consortium [★6669]

Natl. Engg. Coun. for Guidance [★8125]

Natl. Entertainment and Campus Activities Assn. [★8906]

Natl. Entertainment Conf. [★8906]

Natl. Enthronement Center [19474], PO Box 111, Fairhaven, MA 02719-0111, (508)999-2680

Natl. Entlebucher Mountain Dog Assn. [21610], Jami Lockhart, Membership Chm., 637 Seneca Dr., South Lake Tahoe, CA 96150

Natl. Entomology Scent Detection Canine Assn. [2633], PO Box 3840, Seminole, FL 33775

Natl. Enuresis Soc. [★15554]

Natl. Environmental Balancing Bur. [1716], 8575 Grovemont Cir., Gaithersburg, MD 20877, (301)977-3698

Natl. Environmental Coalition of Native Americans [4730], Claremore Veterans Center, PO Box 988, Claremore, OK 74018, (918)342-3041

Natl. Environmental Educ. Found. [8160], 4301 Connecticut Ave. NW, Ste. 160, Washington, DC 20008, (202)833-2933

Natl. Environmental Educ. and Training Found. [★8160]

Natl. Environmental Hea. Assn. [14504], 720 S Colorado Blvd., Ste. 1000-N, Denver, CO 80246-1926, (303)756-9090

Natl. Environmental Hea. Sci. and Protection Accreditation Coun. [14505], 8620 Roosevelt Way NE, Ste. A, Seattle, WA 98115, (206)522-5272

Natl. Environmental, Safety and Hea. Training Assn. [4796], 2700 N Central Ave., Ste. 900, Phoenix, AZ 85004-1147, (602)956-6099

Natl. Environmental, Safety and Hea. Training Assn. [4796], 2700 N Central Ave., Ste. 900, Phoenix, AZ 85004-1147, (602)956-6099

Natl. Environmental Satellite, Data, and Info. Ser. [4286], 1335 E West Hwy., SSMC1, 8th Fl., Silver Spring, MD 20910, (301)713-3578

Natl. Environmental Societies Trust [IO], Kingston, Jamaica

Natl. Environmental Systems Contractors Assn. [★1694]

Natl. Environmental Training Assn. [★4796]

Natl. Environmental Training Assn. [★4796]

Natl. Environmental Trust - Defunct.

Natl. Eosinophilia-Myalgia Syndrome Network [16894], 155 Delaware Ave., Lexington, OH 44904-1212, (419)884-7120

Natl. Episcopal AIDS Coalition [10889], 6050 N Meridian St., Indianapolis, IN 46208, (317)534-0480

Natl. Episcopal Coalition on Alcohol and Drugs [★13287]

Natl. Episcopal Hea. Ministries [14727], 6050 N Meridian St., Indianapolis, IN 46208, (317)253-1277

Natl. Episcopal Scouters Assn. [13024], PO Box 6574, High Point, NC 27262, (336)869-6890

Natl. Equipment Servicing Dealers Assn. - Defunct.

Natl. Erectors Assn. [★904]

Natl. Estimating Soc. [★1327]

Natl. Ethanol Vehicle Coalition [4490], 3216 Emerald Ln., Ste. C, Jefferson City, MO 65109, (573)635-8445

Natl. Ethiopian Cycling Fed. [IO], Addis Ababa, Ethiopia

Natl. Ethnic Coalition of Organizations [18985], 232 Madison Ave., Ste. 900, New York, NY 10016-2901, (212)755-1492

Natl. Evangelization Teams [19475], 110 Crusader Ave. W, West St. Paul, MN 55118-4427, (651)450-6833

Natl. Even Start Assn. - Defunct.

Natl. Examining Bd. of Ocularists [15969], 625 1st Ave., Ste. 220, Coralville, IA 52241-2101, (319)339-1125

Natl. Exchange Carrier Assn. [3598], 80 S Jefferson Rd., Whippany, NJ 07981-1009, (800)228-8597

Natl. Exchange Club [13069], 3050 Central Ave., Toledo, OH 43606-1700, (419)535-3232

Natl. Exchange Club Found. [11365], 3050 Central Ave., Toledo, OH 43606-1700, (419)535-3232

Natl. Exchange Club Found. for the Prevention of Child Abuse [★11365]

Natl. Execution Alert Network [★17220]

Natl. Executive Housekeepers Assn. [★2247]

Natl. Executive Housekeepers Assn. [★2247]

Natl. Executive Ser. Corps [689], 55 W 39th St., 12th Fl., New York, NY 10018, (212)269-1234

Natl. Exercise Trainers Assn. [22208], 5955 Golden Valley Rd., Ste. 240, Minneapolis, MN 55422-4472, (763)545-2505

Natl. Extension Assn. of Family and Consumer Sciences [5344], 14070 Proton Rd., Ste. 100, Dallas, TX 75244, (972)371-2570

Natl. Extension Assn. of Family and Consumer Services [★5344]

Natl. Extension Homemakers Coun. [★8265]

Natl. Fac. Mgt. Assn. [★2901]

Natl. Fac. Mgt. Assn. [★2901]

Natl. Fair Access Coalition on Testing [7561], 3 Terrace Way, Greensboro, NC 27403-3660, (336)547-0607

Natl. Fair Housing Alliance [17800], 1101 Vermont Ave. NW, Ste. 710, Washington, DC 20005, (202)898-1661

Natl. Families in Action [13279], PO Box 133136, Atlanta, GA 30333-3136, (404)248-9676

Natl. Family Assn. for Deaf-Blind [14951], 141 Middle Neck Rd., Sands Point, NY 11050, (800)255-0411

Natl. Family Caregivers Assn. [15012], 10400 Connecticut Ave., Ste. 500, Kensington, MD 20895-3944, (301)942-6430

Natl. Family Farm Coalition [17169], 110 Maryland Ave. NE, Ste. 307, Washington, DC 20002, (202)543-5675

Natl. Family Planning Forum [★12038]

Natl. Family Planning and Reproductive Hea. Assn. [12038], 1627 K St. NW, 12th Fl., Washington, DC 20006, (202)293-3114

Natl. Fantasy Fan Club for Disneyana Enthusiasts [★23792]

Natl. Fantasy Fan Fed. [10521], 25549 Byron St., San Bernardino, CA 92404-6403

Natl. Farm-City Comm. [★4356]

Natl. Farm-City Coun. [4356], PO Box 6825, Reading, PA 19610, (877)611-8161

Natl. Farm and Power Equip. Dealers Assn. [★172]

Natl. Farm and Ranch Bus. Mgt. Educ. Assn. [4357], 1123 S Main St., Rugby, ND 58368, (701)776-5095

Natl. Farm Worker Ministry [12525], 438 N Skinker Blvd., St. Louis, MO 63130, (314)726-6470

Natl. Farm Workers Assn. [★23143]

Natl. Farmers' Fed. [IO], Kingston, Australia

Natl. Farmers Org. [4358], PO Box 2508, Ames, IA 50010-2000, (800)247-2110

Natl. Farmers Union [4359], 200 F St. NW, Ste. 300, Washington, DC 20001, (202)554-1600

Natl. Farmers' Union - Canada [IO], Saskatoon, SK, Canada

Natl. Farmers' Union - England [IO], Stoneleigh, United Kingdom

Natl. Fashion Accessories Assn. [213], Fashion Accessories Shippers' Assn., 137 W 25th St., 3rd Fl., New York, NY 10001, (212)947-3424

Natl. Fastdance Assn. [9561], 3371 Debussy Rd., Jacksonville, FL 32277, (904)744-2424

Natl. Fastener Distributors Assn. [1655], 401 N Michigan Ave., Chicago, IL 60611, (312)527-6671

Natl. Fastpitch Coaches Assn. [22995], 100 G T Thames Dr., Ste. D, Starkville, MS 39759, (662)320-2155

Natl. Fatherhood Initiative [17624], 20410 Observation Dr., Ste. 107, Germantown, MD 20876, (301)948-0599

Natl. Father's Day/Mother's Day Coun. [18669], 37 W 39th St., Ste. 1102, New York, NY 10018, (212)594-5977

Natl. Fed. of Abstracting and Indexing Services [★6986]

Natl. Fed. of Abstracting and Indexing Services [★6986]

Natl. Fed. of Abstracting and Info. Services [6986], 1518 Walnut St., Ste. 1004, Philadelphia, PA 19102-3403, (215)893-1561

Natl. Fed. of Abstracting and Info. Services [6986], 1518 Walnut St., Ste. 1004, Philadelphia, PA 19102-3403, (215)893-1561

Natl. Fed. of Advt. Agencies [IO], Madrid, Spain

Natl. Fed. of Afro-American Women [★13066]

Natl. Fed. of Agricultural Cooperative Associations [IO], Tokyo, Japan

Natl. Fed. of Agricultural Cooperators and Producers [IO], Budapest, Hungary

Natl. Fed. of Arch Clubs [IO], Dublin, Ireland

Natl. Fed. of Asian Indian Organizations in Am. [★19037]

Natl. Fed. of Australia-Japan Societies [IO], Royal Exchange, Australia

Natl. Fed. of Beekeepers Associations [★3815]

Natl. Fed. for Biblio/Poetry Therapy [16471], 1625 Mid Valley Dr., No. 1, Ste. 126, Steamboat Springs, CO 80487

Natl. Fed. of the Blind [17107], 200 E Wells St., Baltimore, MD 21230, (410)659-9314

Natl. Fed. of Buddhist Women's Associations [★19359]

Natl. Fed. of Builders [IO], Crawley, United Kingdom

Natl. Fed. of Catholic Physicians Guilds [★16260]

Natl. Fed. for Catholic Youth Ministry [19476], 415 Michigan Ave. NE, Ste. 40, Washington, DC 20017-4503, (202)636-3825

Natl. Fed. of Cemetery Friends [IO], South Croydon, United Kingdom

Natl. Fed. of Clinical Social Workers [★13217]

Natl. Fed. Coaches Assn. [★22465]

Natl. Fed. of Coffee Growers of Colombia [IO], Bogota, Colombia

Natl. Fed. of Coll. and Univ. Bus. Officers Associations [★7667]

Natl. Fed. of Community Broadcasters [506], 1970 Broadway, Ste. 1000, Oakland, CA 94612, (510)451-8200

Natl. Fed. of Community Development Credit Unions [1007], 39 Broadway, Ste. 2140, New York, NY 10006-3063, (212)809-1850

Natl. Fed. of Credit Guarantee Corporations [IO], Tokyo, Japan

Natl. Fed. of Croatian Americans [9511], 2401 Res. Blvd., Ste. 115, Rockville, MD 20850, (301)208-6650

Natl. Fed. of Dairy Cooperatives [IO], Paris, France

Natl. Fed. of the Dairy Indus. [IO], Paris, France

Natl. Fed. of Dairy Producers [IO], Paris, France

Natl. Fed. for Decency [★17334]

Natl. Fed. of Democratic Women [17540], 1420 Primrose Rd. NW, Washington, DC 20012, (202)429-9393

Natl. Fed. of Demolition Contractors [IO], Hemel Hempstead, United Kingdom

Natl. Fed. of Diocesan Catholic Youth Councils [★19476]

Natl. Fed. of the Disabled Nepal [IO], Kathmandu, Nepal

Natl. Fed. of Disabled Persons Associations [IO], Budapest, Hungary

Natl. Fed. of Edible Oil Traders [IO], Rome, Italy

Natl. Fed. of Electrotechnical and Electronic Indus. [IO], Milan, Italy

Natl. Fed. of Enterprise Agencies [IO], Bedford, United Kingdom

Natl. Fed. of Fed. Employees [23205], 805 15th St. NW, Ste. 500, Washington, DC 20005, (202)216-4420

Natl. Fed. of Filipino Amer. Associations [10366], 1322 18th St. NW, Washington, DC 20036-1803

Natl. Fed. of Fish Friers [IO], Leeds, United Kingdom

Natl. Fed. of Fishermen's Organisations [IO], York, United Kingdom

Natl. Fed. of Fishing Companies [IO], Rome, Italy

Natl. Fed. of Fishmongers [IO], Colchester, United Kingdom

Natl. Fed. of Flemish Giant Breeders [★4846]

Natl. Fed. of Flemish Giant Rabbit Breeders [4846], 7587 W Cromwell Rd., Ligonier, IN 46767

A star before a book entry number signifies that the name is not listed separately, but is mentioned within the entry.

Natl. Fed. of French Hairdressers [IO], Paris, France
Natl. Fed. of Furniture Traders [IO], Milan, Italy
Natl. Fed. of Goldsmiths [IO], Milan, Italy
Natl. Fed. of Grain Cooperatives [★4175]
Natl. Fed. of Grange Mutual Insurance Companies - Defunct.
Natl. Fed. of Hispanics in Communications - Defunct.
Natl. Fed. of Housestaff Orgs. - Defunct.
Natl. Fed. of Humane Societies [11011], 808 Cottage St. SW, Vienna, VA 22180-6355, (703)242-3675
Natl. Fed. of Independent Unions [23314], 1166 S 11th St., Philadelphia, PA 19147, (215)336-3300
Natl. Fed. of Indian Amer. Associations [19037], 319 Summit Hall Rd., Gaithersburg, MD 20877, (301)926-3013
Natl. Fed. Interscholastic Music Assn. [★8667]
Natl. Fed. Interscholastic Officials Assn. [★23026]
Natl. Fed. Interscholastic Speech and Debate Assn. [★8898]
Natl. Fed. Interscholastic Spirit Assn. [★22466]
National Fed. Interscholastic Spirit Association [★22996]
Natl. Fed. of Italian Perfume Retailers [IO], Milan, Italy
Natl. Fed. of Jewish Men's Clubs [★19861]
Natl. Fed. of Licensed Practical Nurses [15780], 111 W Main St., Ste. 100, Garner, NC 27529, (919)779-0046
Natl. Fed. of Local Cable Programmers [★17333]
Natl. Fed. of Meat and Food Traders [IO], Tunbridge Wells, United Kingdom
Natl. Fed. of Mobile Home Owners [★12188]
Natl. Fed. of Municipal Analysts [47], Lisa Good, Exec. Dir., PO Box 14893, Pittsburgh, PA 15234-0893, (412)341-4898
Natl. Fed. Music Adjudicator Assn. [★8667]
Natl. Fed. of Music Clubs [10257], 1646 Smith Valley Rd., Greenwood, IN 46142, (317)882-4003
Natl. Fed. of Nonprofits [★264]
Natl. Fed. Officials Assn. [★23026]
Natl. Fed. of Opticianry Schools [15984], Randall L. Smith, Exec. Mgr., 2800 Springport Rd., Jackson, MI 49202, (517)990-6945
Natl. Fed. of Pachyderm Clubs [18386], 1555 Kisker Rd., Ste. 150, St. Charles, MO 63304, (888)467-2249
Natl. Fed. of Paralegal Associations [5872], PO Box 2016, Edmonds, WA 98020, (425)967-0045
Natl. Fed. of Parents for Drug-Free Youth [★13256]
Natl. Fed. of Plus Areas of Great Britain [IO], Sutton Coldfield, United Kingdom
Natl. Fed. of Preserved Vegetable Indus. Associations [IO], Madrid, Spain
Natl. Fed. of Press Women [2849], PO Box 5556, Arlington, VA 22205, (703)812-9487
Natl. Fed. of Priests' Councils [19477], 333 N Michigan Ave., Ste. 1205, Chicago, IL 60601-4002, (312)442-9700
Natl. Fed. of Professional Bullriders [22843], 2222 Hwy. F, Mansfield, MO 65704, (417)924-3591
Natl. Fed. of Professional Trainers [23097], PO Box 4579, Lafayette, IN 47903-4579, (765)471-4514
Natl. Fed. of Professors [IO], Lisbon, Portugal
Natl. Fed. of Republican Women [18532], 124 N Alfred St., Alexandria, VA 22314, (703)548-9688
Natl. Fed. of Retail Newsagents [IO], London, United Kingdom
Natl. Fed. of Roofing Contractors [IO], London, United Kingdom
Natl. Fed. of Sci. Abstracting and Indexing Services [★6986]
Natl. Fed. of Sci. Abstracting and Indexing Services [★6986]
Natl. Fed. of Seed Potato Growers [IO], Beaurains, France
Natl. Fed. of Services for Unmarried Parents and Their Children [IO], Dublin, Ireland
Natl. Fed. of Settlements [★11648]
Natl. Fed. of Settlements and Neighborhood Centers [★11648]
Natl. Fed. of Shoe Traders [IO], Trieste, Italy
Natl. Fed. of Societies for Clinical Social Work [★13217]

Natl. Fed. of Specialized Press [IO], Paris, France
Natl. Fed. for Specialty Nursing Orgs. - Defunct.
Natl. Fed. of State High School Associations [22996], PO Box 690, Indianapolis, IN 46206, (317)972-6900
Natl. Fed. of State High School Athletic Associations [★22996]
Natl. Fed. of State Humanities Councils [★9843]
Natl. Fed. of State Poetry Societies [10450], 18 S Rembert St., Memphis, TN 38104
Natl. Fed. of SubPostmasters [IO], Shoreham-by-Sea, United Kingdom
Natl. Fed. TARGET Program - Defunct.
Natl. Fed. of Temple Brotherhoods [★19882]
Natl. Fed. of Temple Sisterhoods [★19909]
Natl. Fed. of Terrazzo, Marble and Mosaic Specialists [IO], London, United Kingdom
Natl. Fed. of Tire Retailers [IO], Bologna, Italy
Natl. Fed. of Tourist Guide Associations USA [23450], Esther Banike, CTG, Pres., 1127 Central Ave., Downers Grove, IL 60516
Natl. Fed. of the Travel and Tourism Indus. [IO], Rome, Italy
Natl. Fed. of UNESCO Associations in Japan [IO], Tokyo, Japan
Natl. Fed. of Vegetable Producers [IO], Paris, France
Natl. Fed. of Wholesale Distributors of Elec. Materials [IO], Milan, Italy
Natl. Fed. of Women's Institutes [IO], London, United Kingdom
Natl. Fed. of Women's Republican Clubs [★18532]
Natl. Fed. of Young Farmers' Clubs [IO], Kenilworth, United Kingdom
Natl. Feed Ingredients Assn. [★4370]
Natl. Feeder Pig Marketing Assn. - Defunct.
Natl. Fellowship of Child Care Executives [13542], PO Box 1195, Somerset, PA 15501
Natl. Fellowship of Grace Brethren Ministries [★19355]
Natl. Fellowship of Methodist Musicians [★19971]
Natl. Fencing Coaches Assn. of Am. [★22566]
Natl. Fenestration Rating Coun. [592], 6305 Ivy Ln., Ste. 140, Greenbelt, MD 20770, (301)589-1776
Natl. Fenton Glass Soc. [21840], PO Box 4008, Marietta, OH 45750, (740)374-3345
Natl. Ferret Welfare Soc. [IO], Kingsbridge, United Kingdom
Natl. Fertilizer Solutions Assn. [★3092]
Natl. FFA [★7714]
Natl. FFA [★7714]
National FFA Alumni Assn. [★7714]
National FFA Alumni Assn. [★7714]
Natl. FFA Org. [7714], PO Box 68960, Indianapolis, IN 46268-0960, (317)802-6060
Natl. FFA Org. [7714], PO Box 68960, Indianapolis, IN 46268-0960, (317)802-6060
Natl. Fibre Can and Tube Assn. [★875]
Natl. Fibre Can and Tube Assn. [★875]
Natl. Fibromyalgia Assn. [14539], 2121 S Towne Centre Pl., Ste. 300, Anaheim, CA 92806, (714)921-0150
Natl. Fibromyalgia Awareness Campaign [★14539]
Natl. Fibromyalgia and Chronic Pain Assn. [14540], 31 Fed. Ave., Logan, UT 84321
Natl. Fibromyalgia Partnership [14541], PO Box 2355, Centreville, VA 20122, (866)725-4404
Natl. Fibromyalgia Res. Assn. [15617], PO Box 500, Salem, OR 97308, (503)315-7257
Natl. Field Archery Assn. [22226], 800 Archery Ln., Yankton, SD 57078, (605)260-9279
Natl. Field Archery Soc. [IO], Nottingham, United Kingdom
Natl. Field Hockey Coaches Assn. [22567], PO Box 13289, Chandler, AZ 85248, (480)895-5751
Natl. Field Selling Assn. [3165], 100 N 20th St., 4th Fl., Philadelphia, PA 19103-1443, (215)564-1627
Natl. Film Bd. of Canada [IO], Montreal, QC, Canada
Natl. Finals Rodeo Commn. [★22844]
Natl. Finals Rodeo Comm. [22844], 101 Pro Rodeo Dr., Colorado Springs, CO 80919, (719)593-8840
Natl. Finance Adjusters [431], PO Box 3855, Baltimore, MD 21217, (410)728-2400
Natl. Financial Institutions' Assn. [IO], Bogota, Colombia

Natl. Finch Soc. [★21224]
Natl. Finch and Softbill Soc. [21224], Ms. Rebecca Mikel, Exec. Sec., 13779 US 12 E, Union, MI 49130, (269)641-7209
Natl. Fire Indus. Assn. [IO], Werribee, Australia
Natl. Fire Protection Assn. [12995], 1 Batterymarch Park, Quincy, MA 02169-7471, (617)770-3000
Natl. Fire Sprinkler Assn. [3148], 40 Jon Barrett Rd., Patterson, NY 12563, (845)878-4200
Natl. Firearms Act Trade and Collectors Assn. [1354], 20603 Big Wells Dr., Katy, TX 77449-6269, (281)492-8288
Natl. Firebird Club [★21128]
Natl. Firebird and Trans Am Club [21128], PO Box 11238, Chicago, IL 60611, (773)769-6262
Natl. Fireplace Assn. [IO], High Wycombe, United Kingdom
Natl. Fireproofing Contractors Assn. [1351], PO Box 1571, Westford, MA 01886, (866)250-4111
Natl. Fireworks Assn. [1240], Nancy Blogin, Sec., 8224 NW Bradford Ct., Kansas City, MO 64151, (816)505-3589
National Fish Meal and Oil Assn. - Address unknown since 2010.
Natl. Fisheries Education and Res. Found. - Defunct.
Natl. Fisheries Inst. [3184], 7918 Jones Br. Dr., Ste. 700, McLean, VA 22102, (703)752-8880
Natl. Fishing Lure Collectors Club [21379], Colby Sorrells, Sec.-Treas., PO Box 509, Mansfield, TX 76063-0509, (817)473-6748
Natl. Fitness Therapy Assn. - Address unknown since 2010.
Natl. Flag Day Found. [20612], PO Box 55, Waubeka, WI 53021-0055, (262)692-9111
Natl. Flag Found. [10630], Flag Plz., 1275 Bedford Ave., Pittsburgh, PA 15219, (412)261-1776
Natl. Flexible Packaging Assn. [★2607]
Natl. Flight Nurses Assn. [★15700]
Natl. Flight Paramedics Assn. [★14468]
Natl. Flood Determination Assn. [4732], PO Box 82642, Austin, TX 78708-2642, (512)977-3007
Natl. Floor Covering Assn. [IO], Mississauga, ON, Canada
Natl. Floor Safety Inst. [3149], PO Box 92607, Southlake, TX 76092, (817)749-1700
Natl. Florist Assn. - Defunct.
Natl. Flossing Coun. [14305], 533 4th St. SE, Washington, DC 20003, (202)544-0711
Natl. Fluid Power Assn. [1852], 3333 N Mayfair Rd., Ste. 211, Milwaukee, WI 53222-3219, (414)778-3344
Natl. Fluid Power Assn. [1852], 3333 N Mayfair Rd., Ste. 211, Milwaukee, WI 53222-3219, (414)778-3344
Natl. Flute Assn. [10258], 26951 Ruether Ave., Ste. H, Santa Clarita, CA 91351, (661)713-6013
Natl. Flying Farmers Assn. [★4353]
Natl. Flying Farmers Assn. [★4353]
Natl. Folk Festival Assn. [★9624]
Natl. Food and Conservation Through Swine - Defunct.
Natl. Food and Energy Coun. [★6753]
Natl. Food Service Assn. - Defunct.
Natl. Food Ser. Mgt. Inst. [1452], Univ. of Mississippi, 6 Jeanette Philips Dr., PO Drawer 188, University, MS 38677-0188, (662)915-7658
Natl. Foodservice Marketing Associates [★3160]
Natl. Foodservice Marketing Associates [★3160]
National Football Conf. [★22591]
Natl. Football Found. and Coll. Hall of Fame [22590], 433 E Las Colinas Blvd., Ste. 1130, Irving, TX 75039, (972)556-1000
Natl. Football League [22591], 280 Park Ave., New York, NY 10017
Natl. Football League Alumni [22592], 1 Washington Park, 1 Washington St., 14th Fl., Newark, NJ 07102, (973)718-7350
Natl. Football League Alumni, Inc. [★22592]
Natl. Football Shrine and Hall of Fame [★22590]
Natl. Footwear Assn. of Russia [IO], Moscow, Russia
Natl. Foreign Language Center [8478], PO Box 93, College Park, MD 20741, (301)405-9828
Natl. Foreign Trade Coun. [2087], 1625 K St. NW, Ste. 200, Washington, DC 20006, (202)887-0278

Reference to "IO" in place of a book number signifies that the association may be found in the 50th edition of International Organizations.

Natl. Foreign Trade Coun. **[2087]**, 1625 K St. NW, Ste. 200, Washington, DC 20006, (202)887-0278

Natl. Forensic Assn. **[8895]**, Prof. Larry Schnoor, Pres., 107 Agency Rd., Mankato, MN 56001-5053, (507)387-3010

Natl. Forensic Center **[5487]**, Natl. Dir. of Expert Witnesses, PO Box 270529, San Diego, CA 92198-2529, (800)735-6660

Natl. Forensic League **[8896]**, PO Box 38, Ripon, WI 54971, (920)748-6206

Natl. Forest Found. **[4100]**, Bldg. 27, Ste. 3, Ft. Missoula Rd., Missoula, MT 59804, (406)542-2805

Natl. Forest Protection Alliance - Address unknown since 2011.

Natl. Forest Recreation Assn. **[3061]**, PO Box 488, Woodlake, CA 93286, (559)564-2365

Natl. Forum for the Advancement of Aquatics - Defunct.

Natl. Forum API **[IO]**, Plovdiv, Bulgaria

Natl. Forum for Black Public Administrators **[5910]**, 777 N Capitol St. NE, Ste. 807, Washington, DC 20002, (202)408-9300

Natl. Forum of Greek Orthodox Church Musicians **[20128]**, 3814 Regents Cir., Bloomington, IN 47401, (812)339-3142

Natl. Forum for Hea. Care Quality Measurement and Reporting **[★14820]**

Natl. Foster Care Coalition **[11366]**, 605 N Carolina Ave. SE, Unit No. 2, Washington, DC 20003, (202)280-2039

Natl. Foster Parent Assn. **[12611]**, 2021 E Hennepin Ave., Ste. 320, Minneapolis, MN 55413-1865, (253)853-4000

Natl. Found. for Advancement in the Arts **[9308]**, 777 Brickell Ave., Ste. 370, Miami, FL 33131, (305)377-1140

Natl. Found. for Australian Women **[IO]**, Sydney, Australia

Natl. Found. for Brain Res. **[15666]**, BrainNet.org, PO Box 390, Solomons, MD 20688, (202)250-3845

Natl. Found. for Cancer Res. **[15930]**, 4600 E West Hwy., Ste. 525, Bethesda, MD 20814, (301)654-1250

Natl. Found. for Cancer Res. **[15930]**, 4600 E West Hwy., Ste. 525, Bethesda, MD 20814, (301)654-1250

Natl. Found. for Credit Counseling **[2212]**, 2000 M St. NW, Ste. 505, Washington, DC 20036, (800)388-2227

Natl. Found. of Dentistry for the Handicapped **[★14280]**

Natl. Found. for Ectodermal Dysplasias **[14615]**, 410 E Main St., PO Box 114, Mascoutah, IL 62258, (618)566-2020

Natl. Found. for Educational Res. **[IO]**, Slough, United Kingdom

Natl. Found. for Facial Reconstruction **[14201]**, 317 E 34th St., Rm. 901, New York, NY 10016, (212)263-6656

Natl. Found. of Hea., Welfare and Pension Plans **[★1128]**

Natl. Found. of Hea., Welfare and Pension Plans **[★1128]**

Natl. Found. of Hea., Welfare and Pension Plans, Trustees and Administrators **[★1128]**

Natl. Found. of Hea., Welfare and Pension Plans, Trustees and Administrators **[★1128]**

Natl. Found. for History of Chemistry **[★9759]**

Natl. Found. for Ileitis and Colitis **[★14559]**

Natl. Found. for the Improvement of Educ. **[★8052]**

Natl. Found. of Indian Engineers **[IO]**, New Delhi, India

Natl. Found. for Infantile Paralysis **[★13844]**

Natl. Found. for Infectious Diseases **[15122]**, 4733 Bethesda Ave., Ste. 750, Bethesda, MD 20814-5278, (301)656-0003

Natl. Found. for Jewish Genetic Diseases - Defunct.

Natl. Found. of Manufactured Home Owners **[12188]**, John Sisker, 80 Huntington St., No. 266, Huntington Beach, CA 92648-5343, (714)536-3850

Natl. Found. - March of Dimes **[★13844]**

Natl. Found. for Non-Invasive Diagnostics - Defunct.

Natl. Found. for Peroneal Muscular Atrophy **[★15577]**

Natl. Found. for Teaching Entrepreneurship **[7805]**, 120 Wall St., 18th Fl., New York, NY 10005, (212)232-3333

Natl. Found. for Transplants **[16913]**, 5350 Poplar Ave., Ste. 430, Memphis, TN 38119, (901)684-1697

Natl. Found. for Unemployment Compensation and Workers Compensation **[5402]**, 910 17th St., Ste. 315, Washington, DC 20006, (202)223-8902

Natl. Found. for Wholistic Medicine - Defunct.

Natl. Found. for Women Bus. Owners **[★3678]**

Natl. Found. for Women Legislators **[6073]**, 910 16th St., Ste. 100, Washington, DC 20006, (202)293-3040

Natl. Fragile X Found. **[14616]**, PO Box 37, Walnut Creek, CA 94597, (925)938-9300

Natl. Frame Builders Assn. **[937]**, 4700 W Lake Ave., Glenview, IL 60025, (800)557-6957

Natl. Franchise Assn. **[★1529]**

Natl. Franchise Assn. **[★1529]**

Natl. Franchisee Assn. **[1529]**, 1701 Barrett Lakes Blvd. NW, Ste. 180, Kennesaw, GA 30144, (678)797-5160

Natl. Franchisee Assn. **[1529]**, 1701 Barrett Lakes Blvd. NW, Ste. 180, Kennesaw, GA 30144, (678)797-5160

Natl. Fraternal Cong. **[★19042]**

Natl. Fraternal Cong. of Am. **[★19042]**

Natl. Fraternity of Student Musicians - Address unknown since 2011.

National Fraud Information Center/Internet Fraud Watch **[17467]**, Natl. Consumers League, 1701 K St. NW, Ste. 1200, Washington, DC 20006, (202)835-3323

Natl. Freedom Fund for Librarians **[★17225]**

Natl. Freedom of Info. Coalition **[18437]**, Univ. of Missouri-Columbia, Journalism Inst., 101 Reynolds, Columbia, MO 65211, (573)882-4856

Natl. Freight Transportation Assn. - Defunct.

Natl. French Honor Soc. **[★23544]**

Natl. Frozen Food Assn. **[★1417]**

Natl. Frozen Food Distributors Assn. **[★1417]**

Natl. Frozen Food Locker Assn. **[★2430]**

Natl. Frozen Food Locker Inst. **[★2430]**

Natl. Frozen Pizza Inst. **[1416]**, 2000 Corporate Ridge, Ste. 1000, McLean, VA 22102, (703)821-0770

Natl. Frozen and Refrigerated Foods Assn. **[1417]**, PO Box 6069, Harrisburg, PA 17112, (717)657-8601

Natl. Fruit and Syrup Mfrs. Assn. **[★1410]**

Natl. Fund for Minority Engg. Students **[★8126]**

Natl. Funeral Directors Assn. **[2541]**, 13625 Bishop's Dr., Brookfield, WI 53005-6607, (262)789-1880

Natl. Funeral Directors and Morticians Assn. **[2542]**, 6290 Shannon Pkwy., Union City, GA 30291, (404)286-6740

Natl. Furniture Bank Assn. **[12059]**, PO Box 2902, Decatur, GA 30031, (877)373-2835

Natl. Furniture Traffic Conf. **[★3251]**

Natl. Furniture Traffic Conf. **[★3251]**

Natl. Futures Assn. **[1564]**, 300 S Riverside Plz., No. 1800, Chicago, IL 60606-6615, (312)781-1300

Natl. Gaming Coun. **[★8209]**

Natl. Garden Bur. **[4673]**, 1311 Butterfield Rd., Ste. 310, Downers Grove, IL 60515-5625

Natl. Garden Clubs **[21809]**, 4401 Magnolia Ave., St. Louis, MO 63110, (314)776-7574

Natl. Gardening Assn. **[21810]**, 1100 Dorset St., South Burlington, VT 05403, (802)863-5251

Natl. Gardens Scheme **[IO]**, Guildford, United Kingdom

Natl. Gastroenterological Assn. **[★14550]**

Natl. Gaucher Found. **[15500]**, 2227 Idlewood Rd., Ste. 6, Tucker, GA 30084, (800)504-3189

Natl. Gay and Lesbian Chamber of Commerce **[23401]**, 729 15th St. NW, 9th Fl., Washington, DC 20005, (202)234-9181

Natl. Gay and Lesbian Task Force **[12103]**, 1325 Massachusetts Ave. NW, Ste. 600, Washington, DC 20005, (202)393-5177

Natl. Gay Pilot's Assn. **[381]**, PO Box 1652, San Jose, CA 95109, (214)336-0873

Natl. Gay Task Force **[★12103]**

Natl. Genealogical Soc. **[20646]**, 3108 Columbia Pike, Ste. 300, Arlington, VA 22204-4370, (703)525-0050

Natl. Geographic Soc. **[6905]**, PO Box 98199, Washington, DC 20090-8199, (813)979-6845

National Geographic Soc. Geography Educ. Prog. **[★6905]**

National Geophysical Data Center **[★4286]**

Natl. Gerontological Nursing Assn. **[14669]**, 3493 Lansdowne Dr., Ste. 2, Lexington, KY 40517, (859)977-7453

Natl. Ghost Ranch Found. **[20158]**, Ghost Ranch Educ. and Retreat Center, HC77, Box 11, Abiquiu, NM 87510, (505)685-4333

Natl. Glass Assn. **[1579]**, 1945 Old Gallows Rd., Ste. 750, Vienna, VA 22182, (703)442-4890

Natl. Glass Clubs Affl. **[★21832]**

Natl. Glass Dealers Assn. **[★1579]**

Natl. Glaucoma Trust and The Glaucoma Found. **[★15959]**

Natl. Gliding Assn. **[★22213]**

Natl. Goalie War Assn. **[22937]**, PO Box 105, Shrewsbury, PA 17361, (717)659-3344

Natl. Golf Clubs' Advisory Assn. **[IO]**, Worcester, United Kingdom

Natl. Golf Course Owners Assn. **[3335]**, 291 Seven Farms Dr., Charleston, SC 29492, (843)881-9956

Natl. Golf Found. **[3336]**, 1150 S U.S. Hwy. 1, Ste. 401, Jupiter, FL 33477, (561)744-6006

Natl. Govt. Publishing Assn. **[1623]**, 629 N Main St., Hattiesburg, MS 39401, (601)582-3330

Natl. Governmental Collectors Assn. **[5500]**, PO Box 3012, Conroe, TX 77305, (832)296-4602

Natl. Governors Assn. **[5999]**, Hall of States, 444 N Capitol St., Ste. 267, Washington, DC 20001-1512, (202)624-5300

Natl. Governors' Conf. **[★5999]**

Natl. Grain and Feed Assn. **[4374]**, 1250 I St. NW, Ste. 1003, Washington, DC 20005, (202)289-0873

Natl. Grain Sorghum Producers **[★3955]**

Natl. Grain Trade Coun. **[★1591]**

Natl. Grand Lodge, Intl. Order of Good Templars **[★19008]**

Natl. Grange **[4360]**, 1616 H St. NW, Washington, DC 20006, (202)628-3507

Natl. Graniteware Soc. **[21380]**, PO Box 123, Amana, IA 52203

Natl. Grants Mgt. Assn. **[2298]**, 2100 M St. NW, Ste. 170, Washington, DC 20037, (703)648-9023

Natl. Graphic Artists Guild **[★9235]**

Natl. Graphic Artists Guild **[★9235]**

Natl. Graphic Arts Educ. Assn. **[★8220]**

Natl. Graphic Arts Educ. Assn. **[★8220]**

Natl. Graphic Arts Guild **[★8220]**

Natl. Graphic Arts Guild **[★8220]**

Natl. Grassroots Peace Network - The Natl. Network to End the War Against Iraq - Defunct.

Natl. Graves Assn. **[IO]**, Dublin, Ireland

Natl. Graves' Disease Found. **[16884]**, 400 Intl. Dr., Williamsville, NY 14221, (716)631-2310

Natl. Greenhouse Mfrs. Assn. **[171]**, 4305 N Sixth St., Ste. A, Harrisburg, PA 17110, (717)238-4530

Natl. Greenkeeping Superintendents Assn. **[★3331]**

Natl. Greyhound Adoption Prog. **[11012]**, 10901 Dutton Rd., Philadelphia, PA 19154, (215)331-7918

Natl. Greyhound Assn. **[21611]**, PO Box 543, Abilene, KS 67410, (785)263-4660

Natl. Grigsby Family Soc. **[20563]**, David Bushey, 10478 Courtney, Fairfax, VA 22030

Natl. Grocers Assn. **[3117]**, 1005 N Glebe Rd., Ste. 250, Arlington, VA 22201-5758, (703)516-0700

Natl. Ground Water Assn. **[3650]**, 601 Dempsey Rd., Westerville, OH 43081-8978, (614)898-7791

Natl. Ground Water Assn. **[3650]**, 601 Dempsey Rd., Westerville, OH 43081-8978, (614)898-7791

Natl. Groundwater Assn. l Assn. of Ground Water Scientists and Engineers **[7603]**, 601 Dempsey Rd., Westerville, OH 43081-8978, (614)898-7791

Natl. Group Rides and Designated Drivers - Defunct.

Natl. Guard Assn. of the U.S. **[5816]**, 1 Massachusetts Ave. NW, Washington, DC 20001, (202)789-0031

Natl. Guard Civilian Employees Assn. **[★23199]**

Natl. Guard Executive Directors Assn. **[5817]**, 3706 Crawford Ave., Austin, TX 78731, (512)454-7300

Natl. Guardianship Assn. **[1642]**, 174 Crestview Dr., Bellefonte, PA 16823, (877)326-5992

Natl. Guideline CH **[14815]**, ECRI Inst., 5200 Butler Pike, Plymouth Meeting, PA 19462

Natl. Guild of Catholic Psychiatrists - Defunct.

A star before a book entry number signifies that the name is not listed separately, but is mentioned within the entry.

Natl. Guild for Community Arts Educ. **[7753]**, 520 8th Ave., Ste. 302, New York, NY 10018, (212)268-3337

Natl. Guild of Community Music Schools **[★7753]**

Natl. Guild of Community Schools of the Arts **[★7753]**

Natl. Guild of Decoupeurs **[21457]**, 1017 Pucker St., Stowe, VT 05672, (802)253-3903

Natl. Guild of Hypnotists **[15093]**, PO Box 308, Merrimack, NH 03054, (603)429-9438

Natl. Guild of Master Craftsmen **[IO]**, Dublin, Ireland

Natl. Guild of Piano Teachers **[8664]**, Amer. Coll. of Musicians, PO Box 1807, Austin, TX 78767, (512)478-5775

Natl. Guild of Professional Paperhangers **[2069]**, 136 S Keowee St., Dayton, OH 45402, (937)222-6477

Natl. Gulf War Rsrc. Center **[20798]**, 2611 SW 17th St., Topeka, KS 66604, (785)221-0162

Natl. Gulf War Rsrc. Center **[20798]**, 2611 SW 17th St., Topeka, KS 66604, (785)221-0162

Natl. Gym Assn. **[22807]**, PO Box 970579, Coconut Creek, FL 33097-0579, (954)344-8410

Natl. Gymanfa GANU Assn. of U.S. and Canada **[★19279]**

Natl. Gymanfa GANU Assn. of U.S. and Canada **[★19279]**

Natl. Gymnastics Judges Assn. **[22635]**, 2302 Sand Point, Champaign, IL 61822, (217)359-4866

Natl. Gypsy Moth Coun. **[★4775]**

Natl. Gypsy Moth Mgt. Bd. **[4775]**, Northeastern Center for Forest Hea. Res., 51 Mill Pond Rd., Hamden, CT 06514, (203)230-4321

Natl. Hacky Sack Footbag Players Assn. **[★23019]**

Natl. Hacky Sack Footbag Players Assn. **[★23019]**

Natl. Hair Soc. **[1643]**, 39252 Winchester Rd., No. 107-383, Murrieta, CA 92563, (951)256-4385

Natl. Hair Sys. Culture League **[★971]**

Natl. Hairdressers' Fed. **[IO]**, Bedford, United Kingdom

Natl. Handbag Assn. **[★213]**

Natl. Handicapped Sports **[★22510]**

Natl. Handicapped Sports and Recreation Assn. **[★22510]**

Natl. Hardwood Lumber Assn. **[1512]**, PO Box 34518, Memphis, TN 38184-0518, (901)377-1818

Natl. Hardwood Lumber Assn. **[1512]**, PO Box 34518, Memphis, TN 38184-0518, (901)377-1818

Natl. Harmonica League **[IO]**, Maidenhead, United Kingdom

Natl. Harry Benjamin Gender Dysphoria Assn. **[★13113]**

Natl. Harry Benjamin Gender Dysphoria Assn. **[★13113]**

Natl. Havurah Comm. **[19891]**, 7135 Germantown Ave., 2nd Fl., Philadelphia, PA 19119-1842, (215)248-1335

Natl. Havurah Coordinating Comm. **[★19891]**

Natl. Hay Assn. **[4375]**, 151 Treasure Island Causeway, No. 2, St. Petersburg, FL 33706, (727)367-9702

Natl. Head Injury Found. **[★14683]**

Natl. Head Start Assn. **[8741]**, 1651 Prince St., Alexandria, VA 22314, (703)739-0875

National Head Start Directors Association **[★8741]**

National Head Start Friends Association **[★8741]**

National Head Start Parent Association **[★8741]**

National Head Start Staff Association **[★8741]**

Natl. Headache Found. **[14689]**, 820 N Orleans St., Ste. 411, Chicago, IL 60610, (312)274-2650

Natl. Hea. Agencies Comm. for the Combined Fed. Campaign **[★12051]**

Natl. Hea. Alliance Against Obesity - Address unknown since 2010.

Natl. Hea. Assn. **[15529]**, PO Box 30630, Tampa, FL 33630, (813)961-6100

Natl. Hea. Care Anti-Fraud Assn. **[15130]**, 1201 New York Ave. NW, Ste. 1120, Washington, DC 20005-6100, (202)659-5955

Natl. Hea. Care Found. for the Deaf **[★14930]**

Natl. Hea. Care for the Homeless Coun. **[14906]**, PO Box 60427, Nashville, TN 37206-0427, (615)226-2292

Natl. Hea. Coun. **[14728]**, 1730 M St. NW, Ste. 500, Washington, DC 20036, (202)785-3910

Natl. Hea. Fed. **[14729]**, PO Box 688, Monrovia, CA 91017, (626)357-2181

Natl. Hea. Freedom Coalition **[14816]**, 2136 Ford Pkwy., St. Paul, MN 55116, (507)663-9018

Natl. Hea. Info. Center **[14730]**, PO Box 1133, Washington, DC 20013-1133, (301)565-4167

Natl. Hea. Info. CH **[★14730]**

Natl. Hea. Law Prog. **[5512]**, 2639 S La Cienega Blvd., Los Angeles, CA 90034-2675, (310)204-6010

Natl. Health Lawyers Assn. - Defunct.

Natl. Hea. and Medical Res. Coun. **[IO]**, Canberra, Australia

Natl. Hea. Policy Forum **[17767]**, 2131 K St. NW, Ste. 500, Washington, DC 20037, (202)872-1390

Natl. Hea. Ser. Consultants Assn. **[★15399]**

Natl. Healthcare Collectors Assn. **[1693]**, 1502 Williamson Rd. NE, Ste. 100, Roanoke, VA 24012, (888)698-8022

Natl. Healthcare Cost & Quality Assn. - Defunct.

Natl. Healthy Mothers, Healthy Babies Coalition **[15888]**, 2000 N Beauregard St., 6th Fl., Alexandria, VA 22311, (703)837-4792

Natl. Healthy Start Assn. **[15889]**, 1411 K St. NW, Ste. 1350, Washington, DC 20005, (202)296-2195

Natl. Hearing Aid Soc. **[★14944]**

Natl. Hearing Aid Soc. **[★14944]**

Natl. Hearing Conservation Assn. **[14952]**, 3030 W 81st Ave., Westminster, CO 80031, (303)224-9022

Natl. Heart Assn. of Malaysia **[IO]**, Kuala Lumpur, Malaysia

Natl. Heart Coun. **[14034]**, Natl. Emergency Medicine Assn., PO Box 1039, Edgewood, MD 21040, (443)922-7533

Natl. Heart Forum **[IO]**, London, United Kingdom

Natl. Heart Res. **[★14034]**

Natl. Heart Savers Assn. **[14035]**, Am. Heart Assn., 7272 Greenville Ave., Dallas, TX 75231, (800)242-8721

Natl. Heartburn Alliance - Address unknown since 2011.

Natl. Hedgelaying Soc. **[IO]**, Toddington, United Kingdom

Natl. Hemophilia Found. **[14972]**, 116 W 32nd St., 11th Fl., New York, NY 10001, (212)328-3700

Natl. Hepatitis C Advocacy Coun. **[14987]**, Michael Carden, 221 Ainslie St., Brooklyn, NY 11211

Natl. Hepatitis C Coalition **[14988]**, PO Box 5058, Hemet, CA 92544, (951)766-8238

Natl. Herbalists Assn. of Australia **[IO]**, Concord West, Australia

Natl. Hereford Hog Record Assn. **[4949]**, 826 140th St., Aledo, IL 61231, (309)299-5122

Natl. Hide Assn. **[★2207]**

Natl. High School Alliance **[8856]**, Inst. for Educational Leadership, 4455 Connecticut Ave. NW, Ste. 310, Washington, DC 20008, (202)822-8405

Natl. High School Athletic Coaches Assn. **[22462]**, Jerome Garry, PO Box 5921, Rochester, MN 55903

Natl. High School Band and Choral Directors Hall of Fame **[★8665]**

Natl. High School Band Directors Hall of Fame **[8665]**, 400 E Agency St., Roberta, GA 31078

Natl. High School Band Inst. **[★8665]**

Natl. High School Baseball Coaches Assn. **[22284]**, PO Box 12843, Tempe, AZ 85284, (602)615-0571

Natl. High School Golf Coaches Assn. **[22463]**, 6740 Antioch Rd., Ste. 250, Merriam, KS 66204-1393, (913)236-8311

Natl. High School and Junior Coll. Mathematics Club **[★23588]**

Natl. High School Rodeo Assn. **[22845]**, 12011 Tejon St., Ste. 900, Denver, CO 80234, (303)452-0820

Natl. Higher Education Conf. on Students of Color - Defunct.

Natl. Highway Post Off. Soc. **[★22057]**

Natl. Hispana Leadership Inst. **[17779]**, 1601 N Kent St., Ste. 803, Arlington, VA 22209, (703)527-6007

Natl. Hispanic Bus. Assn. - Address unknown since 2011.

Natl. Hispanic Corporate Coun. **[690]**, 1050 Connecticut Ave. NW, Fl. 10, Washington, DC 20036-5334, (202)772-1100

Natl. Hispanic Coun. on Aging **[10863]**, 734 15th St. NW, Ste. 1050, Washington, DC 20005, (202)347-9733

Natl. Hispanic Found. for the Arts **[19025]**, 1010 Wisconsin Ave. NW, Ste. 650, Washington, DC 20007-3676, (202)293-8330

Natl. Hispanic Inst. **[9657]**, PO Box 220, Maxwell, TX 78656-0020, (512)357-6137

Natl. Hispanic Media Coalition **[17351]**, 55 S Grand Ave., Pasadena, CA 91105, (626)792-6462

Natl. Hispanic Medical Assn. **[15426]**, 1411 K St. NW, Ste. 1100, Washington, DC 20005, (202)628-5895

Natl. Hispanic Professional Org. **[8249]**, PO Box 41780, Austin, TX 78704, (512)662-0249

Natl. Historic Communal Societies Assn. **[★9676]**

Natl. Historic Route 66 Fed. **[9715]**, Dept. WS, PO Box 1848, Lake Arrowhead, CA 92352-1848, (909)336-6131

Natl. Historical Fire Found. **[21709]**, Hall of Flame Museum, 6101 E Van Buren St., Phoenix, AZ 85008-3421, (602)275-3473

Natl. History Club **[8261]**, The Concord Rev., Inc., 730 Boston Post Rd., Ste. 24, Sudbury, MA 01776, (800)331-5007

Natl. History Day **[8262]**, Univ. of Maryland, 0119 Cecil Hall, College Park, MD 20742, (301)314-9739

Natl. HIV Nurses Assn. **[IO]**, London, United Kingdom

Natl. Hockey League Booster Clubs **[23906]**, PO Box 805, St. Louis, MO 63188

Natl. Hockey League Players' Assn. **[IO]**, Toronto, ON, Canada

Natl. Home Demonstration Agents' Assn. **[★5344]**

Natl. Home Demonstration Coun. **[★8265]**

Natl. Home Educ. Res. Inst. **[8273]**, PO Box 13939, Salem, OR 97309, (503)364-1490

Natl. Home Educ. Res. Inst. **[8273]**, PO Box 13939, Salem, OR 97309, (503)364-1490

Natl. Home Fashions League **[★2064]**

Natl. Home Fashions League **[★2064]**

Natl. Home Furnishings Assn. **[1555]**, 3910 Tinsley Dr., Ste. 101, High Point, NC 27265-3610, (336)886-6100

Natl. Home Furnishings Assn. **[1555]**, 3910 Tinsley Dr., Ste. 101, High Point, NC 27265-3610, (336)886-6100

Natl. Home Furnishings Representatives Assn. **[★1554]**

Natl. Home Furnishings Representatives Assn. **[★1554]**

Natl. Home Improvement Coun. **[★589]**

Natl. Home Improvement Coun. **[IO]**, London, United Kingdom

Natl. Home Infusion Assn. - Address unknown since 2011.

Natl. Home Missions Fellowship **[★20011]**

Natl. Home Oxygen Patients Assn. **[14548]**, 8618 Westwood Center Dr., Ste. 210, Vienna, VA 22182-2222, (703)752-4353

Natl. Home Stud. Coun. **[★8268]**

Natl. Homeschool Assn. - Defunct.

Natl. Honey Bd. **[1418]**, 11409 Bus. Park Cir., Ste. 210, Firestone, CO 80504, (303)776-2337

Natl. Honey Packers and Dealers Assn. **[1419]**, 3301 Rte. 66, Ste. 205, Bldg. C, Neptune, NJ 07753, (732)922-3008

Natl. Honor Soc. **[23564]**, 1904 Assn. Dr., Reston, VA 20191-1537, (703)860-0200

Natl. Honor Soc. of Sports Medicine **[16720]**, PO Box 6061-271, Sherman Oaks, CA 91413, (641)715-3900

Natl. Hook-Up of Black Women **[17664]**, 1809 E 71st St., Ste. 205, Chicago, IL 60649-2000, (773)667-7061

Natl. Hormone and Pituitary Prog. **[16280]**, Harbor - UCLA Medical Center, 1000 W Carson St., Torrance, CA 90509, (310)222-3537

Natl. Horse Protection League - Address unknown since 2011.

Natl. Horse Show Commn. - Address unknown since 2011.

Natl. Horsemen's Benevolent and Protective Assn. **[12165]**, 870 Corporate Dr., Ste. 300, Lexington, KY 40503-5419, (859)259-0451

Reference to "IO" in place of a book number signifies that the association may be found in the 50th edition of International Organizations.

Natl. Horseracing [IO], Budapest, Hungary

Natl. Horseracing Authority of Southern Africa [IO], Johannesburg, Republic of South Africa

Natl. Horseshoe Pitchers Assn. of Am. [22695], Dick Hansen, Sec.-Treas., 3085 S 76th St., Franksville, WI 53126, (262)835-9108

Natl. HOSA [★8607]

Natl. Hospice Org. [★15028]

Natl. Hospice and Palliative Care Org. [15028], 1731 King St., Ste. 100, Alexandria, VA 22314, (703)837-1500

Natl. Hospice Regatta Alliance [22374], PO Box 1054, McLean, VA 22101

Natl. Hospitality Mgt. Club [IO], Sofia, Bulgaria

Natl. Hot Rod Assn. [22248], 2035 Financial Way, Glendora, CA 91741, (626)914-4761

Natl. Hotels' and Restaurants' Assn. - Dominican Republic [IO], Santo Domingo, Dominican Republic

Natl. House-Building Coun. [IO], Amersham, United Kingdom

Natl. House Buyers Assn. [IO], Kuala Lumpur, Malaysia

Natl. Household Hazardous Waste Forum [IO], Leeds, United Kingdom

Natl. Housewares Mfrs. Assn. [★1778]

Natl. Housewares Mfrs. Assn. [★1778]

Natl. Housewives' League of America for Economic Security - Defunct.

Natl. Housing Center Coun. [★588]

Natl. Housing Conf. [12189], 1900 M St. NW, Ste. 200, Washington, DC 20036, (202)466-2121

Natl. Housing Endowment [593], 1201 15th St. NW, Washington, DC 20005, (800)368-5242

Natl. Housing Inst. [12190], 60 S Fullerton Ave., No. 206, Montclair, NJ 07042, (973)509-1600

Natl. Housing Law Proj. [5523], 703 Market St., Ste. 2000, San Francisco, CA 94103, (415)546-7000

Natl. Housing Rehabilitation Assn. [★12191]

Natl. Housing and Rehabilitation Assn. [12191], 1400 16th St. NW, Ste. 420, Washington, DC 20036-2244, (202)939-1750

Natl. Huguenot Soc. [20669], 7340 Blanco Rd., Ste. 104, San Antonio, TX 78216, (210)366-9995

Natl. Human Resources Assn. [2630], PO Box 7326, Nashua, NH 03060-7326, (866)523-4417

Natl. Human Services Assembly [13401], 1319 F St. NW, Ste. 402, Washington, DC 20004, (202)347-2080

Natl. Humane Educ. Soc. [11013], PO Box 340, Charles Town, WV 25414-0340, (304)725-0506

Natl. Humanities Alliance [9844], 21 Dupont Cir. NW, Ste. 800, Washington, DC 20036, (202)296-4994

Natl. Humanities Center [9845], PO Box 12256, Research Triangle Park, NC 27709-2256, (919)549-0661

Natl. Humanities Inst. [8283], PO Box 1387, Bowie, MD 20718-1387, (301)464-4277

Natl. Hunter Jumper Assn. [22685], PO Box 11635, Lexington, KY 40576, (434)979-0675

Natl. Huntington's Disease Assn. [★15598]

Natl. Hydrocephalus Found. [14409], 12413 Centralia Rd., Lakewood, CA 90715-1623, (562)924-6666

Natl. Hydrogen Assn. and U.S. Fuel Cell Coun. [★7368]

Natl. Hydrologic Warning Coun. [7604], 2480 W 26th Ave., Ste. 156-B, Denver, CO 80211-5304, (303)455-6277

Natl. Hydropower Assn. [6740], 25 Massachusetts Ave. NW, Ste. 450, Washington, DC 20001, (202)682-1700

Natl. Hypertension Assn. [15078], 324 E 30th St., New York, NY 10016, (212)889-3557

Natl. Ice Assn. [★1712]

Natl. Ice Carving Assn. [9191], PO Box 3593, Oak Brook, IL 60522-3593, (630)871-8431

Natl. Ice Cream Retailers Assn. [1024], 1028 W Devon Ave., Elk Grove Village, IL 60007, (847)301-7500

Natl. Ice Cream and Yogurt Retailers Assn. [★1024]

Natl. Ice Skating Assn. of the United Kingdom [IO], Nottingham, United Kingdom

Natl. Ichthyosis Found. [★14326]

Natl. Identification Prog. for the Advancement in Higher Educ. Admin. [★9054]

Natl. Illumination Comm. of Great Britain [IO], Salisbury, United Kingdom

Natl. Image [19026], PO Box 1368, Bonita, CA 91908, (858)495-7407

Natl. Immigration Forum [17883], 50 F St. NW, Ste. 300, Washington, DC 20001, (202)347-0040

Natl. Immigration Forum [17883], 50 F St. NW, Ste. 300, Washington, DC 20001, (202)347-0040

Natl. Immigration Law Center [17884], 3435 Wilshire Blvd., Ste. 2850, Los Angeles, CA 90010, (213)639-3900

Natl. Immigration Law Center [17884], 3435 Wilshire Blvd., Ste. 2850, Los Angeles, CA 90010, (213)639-3900

Natl. Immigration Proj. | Natl. Lawyers Guild [5532], 14 Beacon St., Ste. 602, Boston, MA 02108, (617)227-9727

Natl. Immigration Refugee Citizenship Forum [★17883]

Natl. Immigration Refugee Citizenship Forum [★17883]

Natl. Impala Assn. [21129], 5400 43rd Ave. S, Minneapolis, MN 55417, (612)727-2404

Natl. Imperial Glass Collectors Soc. [21841], PO Box 534, Bellaire, OH 43906

Natl. Incontinentia Pigmenti Found. [★14601]

Natl. Incontinentia Pigmenti Found. [★14601]

Natl. Inconvenienced Sportsmen's Assn. [★22510]

Natl. Independent Auto. Dealers Assn. [364], 2521 Brown Blvd., Arlington, TX 76006, (817)640-3838

Natl. Independent Bank Equip. Suppliers Assn. [★412]

Natl. Independent Bank Equip. and Systems Assn. [★412]

Natl. Independent Concessionaires Assn. [1453], PO Box 89429, Tampa, FL 33689, (727)346-9302

Natl. Independent Dairy-Food Assn. - Defunct.

Natl. Independent Energy Producers [★6714]

Natl. Independent Flag Dealers Assn. [1364], 214 N Hale St., Wheaton, IL 60187, (630)510-4574

Natl. Independent Poultry and Food Distributors Assn. [★1421]

Natl. Independent Telephone Assn. [★3604]

Natl. Independent Union Coun. [★23314]

Natl. Indian AIDS Hotline [★10890]

Natl. Indian Bus. Assn. [691], 1730 Rhode Island Ave., NW Ste. 1008, Washington, DC 20036, (202)223-3766

Natl. Indian Child Care Assn. [12564], PO Box 2146, Tahlequah, OK 74465, (918)453-5051

Natl. Indian Child Welfare Assn. [19160], 5100 SW Macadam Ave., Ste. 300, Portland, OR 97239, (503)222-4044

Natl. Indian Coun. on Aging [10864], PO Box 21070, Albuquerque, NM 87154, (505)292-2001

Natl. Indian Counselors Assn. - Defunct.

Natl. Indian Educ. Assn. [8679], 110 Maryland Ave. NE, Ste. 104, Washington, DC 20002, (202)544-7290

Natl. Indian Gaming Assn. [5493], 224 2nd St. SE, Washington, DC 20003, (202)546-7711

Natl. Indian Hea. Bd. [12565], 926 Pennsylvania Ave. SE, Washington, DC 20003, (202)507-4070

Natl. Indian Justice Center [19161], 5250 Aero Dr., Santa Rosa, CA 95403, (707)579-5507

Natl. Indian Youth Coun. [10332], Norman Ration, Exec. Dir., 318 Elm St. SE, Albuquerque, NM 87102, (505)247-2251

Natl. Indoor Tennis Assn. [★2743]

Natl. Indoor Tennis Assn. [★2743]

Natl. Indoor Track Meet Directors Assn. - Defunct.

Natl. Indus. Advertisers Assn. [★2392]

Natl. Indus. Advertisers Assn. [★2392]

Natl. Indus. Belting Assn. [1853], 6737 W Washington St., Ste. 1300, Milwaukee, WI 53214, (414)389-8606

Natl. Indus. Coalition [IO], Moscow, Russia

Natl. Indus. Conf. Bd. [★6618]

Natl. Indus. Conf. Bd. [★6618]

Natl. Industrial Glove Distributors Assn. - Defunct.

Natl. Indus. Leather Assn. [★1853]

Natl. Indus. Property Mgt. Assn. [★2903]

Natl. Indus. Recreation Assn. [★12765]

Natl. Indus. Sand Assn. [2506], 2011 Pennsylvania Ave., Ste. 301, Washington, DC 20006, (202)457-0200

Natl. Indus. Ser. Assn. [★1069]

Natl. Indus. Ser. Assn. [★1069]

Natl. Indus. TV Assn. [★1262]

Natl. Indus. TV Assn. [★1262]

Natl. Indus. Traffic League [★3523]

Natl. Indus. Trans. League [3523], 1700 N Moore St., Ste. 1900, Arlington, VA 22209, (703)524-5011

Natl. Industrial Zoning Comm. - Defunct.

Natl. Indus. for the Blind [17108], 1310 Braddock Pl., Alexandria, VA 22314-1691, (703)310-0500

Natl. Indus. for the Severely Handicapped [★11820]

Natl. Indus. Assn. [IO], Tegucigalpa, Honduras

Natl. Indy 500 Collectors Club [21130], PO Box 24105, Speedway, IN 46224

Natl. Infant Torticollis Assn. - Address unknown since 2011.

Natl. Infertility Network Exchange [12612], PO Box 204, East Meadow, NY 11554, (516)794-5772

Natl. Infomercial Marketing Assn. [★2401]

Natl. Infomercial Marketing Assn. [★2401]

Natl. Info. Center for Children and Youth with Disabilities [★11816]

Natl. Info. Center for Children and Youth with Handicaps [★11816]

Natl. Information Center on Deafness - Defunct.

Natl. Info. Center for Educational Media [8319], PO Box 8640, Albuquerque, NM 87198-8640, (800)926-8328

Natl. Info. Center for the Handicapped [★11816]

Natl. Info. Center for Handicapped Children and Youth [★11816]

Natl. Info. CH for Infants with Disabilities and Life-Threatening Conditions - Defunct.

Natl. Info. and Communications Tech. Indus. Alliance [IO], Canberra, Australia

Natl. Info. Officers Assn. [5942], PO Box 10125, Knoxville, TN 37939, (865)389-8736

Natl. Info. Ser. for Earthquake Engg. [7401], Univ. of California, Berkeley, 1301 S 46th St., RFS 453, Richmond, CA 94804-4698, (510)665-3419

Natl. Info. Standards Org. [6987], 1 N Charles St., Ste. 1905, Baltimore, MD 21201, (301)654-2512

Natl. Info. Standards Org. - Z39 [★6987]

Natl. Ingredient Marketing Specialists [★1422]

Natl. Inhalant Prevention Coalition [16750], 318 Lindsay St., Chattanooga, TN 37403, (423)265-4662

Natl. Inholders Assn. [★5901]

Natl. Initiative for Children's Healthcare Quality [14092], 30 Winter St., 6th Fl., Boston, MA 02108, (617)391-2700

Natl. Initiative for a Networked Cultural Heritage [9524], 21 Dupont Cir. NW, Washington, DC 20036, (202)296-5346

Natl. Inspection Coun. for Elecl. Installation Contracting [IO], Dunstable, United Kingdom

Natl. InStar Users Gp. [7000], PO Box 35718, Richmond, VA 23235, (804)276-1300

Natl. Institut voor de Statistiek - Institut Natl. de Statistique [★IO]

Natl. Inst. of Adult Continuing Educ. [IO], Leicester, United Kingdom

Natl. Inst. Against Prejudice and Violence [★17320]

Natl. Inst. on Age, Work and Retirement. - Defunct.

Natl. Inst. on Aging [14670], Bldg. 31, Rm. 5C27, 31 Center Dr., MSC 2292, Bethesda, MD 20892, (301)496-1752

Natl. Inst. of Agricultural Botany [IO], Cambridge, United Kingdom

Natl. Inst. of Amer. Doll Artists [21696], 109 Ladder Hill North, Weston, CT 06883, (203)557-3169

Natl. Inst. for Animal Agriculture [4696], 13570 Meadowgrass Dr., Ste. 201, Colorado Springs, CO 80921, (719)538-8843

Natl. Inst. for Applied Behavioral Sci. [★8178]

Natl. Inst. for Applied Behavioral Sci. [★8178]

Natl. Inst. for Architectural Educ. [★7737]

Natl. Inst. of Arthritis and Musculoskeletal and Skin Diseases Info. CH [16620], Natl. Institutes of Hea., 1 AMS Cir., Bethesda, MD 20892-3675, (301)495-4484

Natl. Inst. for Automotive Ser. Excellence [365], 101 Blue Seal Dr. SE, Ste. 101, Leesburg, VA 20175, (703)669-6600

Natl. Inst. of Bank Mgt. [IO], Pune, India

A star before a book entry number signifies that the name is not listed separately, but is mentioned within the entry.

Natl. Inst. for Biological Standards and Control [IO], Potters Bar, United Kingdom

Natl. Inst. of Building Sciences [6577], 1090 Vermont Ave. NW, Ste. 700, Washington, DC 20005-4905, (202)289-7800

Natl. Inst. for Campus Ministries [★19669]

Natl. Inst. of Carpet and Floorlayers [IO], Nottingham, United Kingdom

Natl. Inst. of Ceramic Engineers [6383], 2840 Windrush Ln., Roswell, GA 30076, (770)891-2212

Natl. Inst. for Certification in Engg. Technologies [6814], 1420 King St., Alexandria, VA 22314-2794, (703)548-1518

Natl. Inst. for the Certification of Healthcare Sterile Processing and Distribution Personnel [★15357]

Natl. Inst. for Chem. Stud. [13323], 3200 Kanawha Tpke., South Charleston, WV 25303, (800)611-2296

Natl. Inst. of Child Hea. and Human Development [★14074]

Natl. Inst. for Citizen Educ. in the Law [★5766]

Natl. Inst. for the Clinical Application of Behavioral Medicine [13819], PO Box 523, Mansfield Center, CT 06250, (860)456-1153

Natl. Inst. on Community-Based Long-Term Care [10865], Natl. Coun. on Aging, 1901 I St. NW, 4th Fl., Washington, DC 20036, (202)479-1200

Natl. Inst. for Compilation and Translation [IO], Taipei, Taiwan

Natl. Inst. of Credit [★1315]

Natl. Inst. on Deafness and Other Commun. Disorders Info. CH [14953], 1 Commun. Ave., Bethesda, MD 20892-3456, (800)241-1044

Natl. Inst. of Dental and Craniofacial Res. [14306], 31 Center Dr., Rm. 5B-55, MSC 2190, Bethesda, MD 20892, (301)496-4261

Natl. Inst. for Dispute Resolution - Defunct.

Natl. Inst. on Drug Abuse [6005], Natl. Institutes of Hea., 6001 Executive Blvd., Rm. 5213, Bethesda, MD 20892, (301)443-1124

Natl. Inst. of Drycleaning [★2191]

Natl. Inst. of Drycleaning [★2191]

Natl. Inst. of Economic and Social Res. [IO], London, United Kingdom

Natl. Inst. of Electromedical Info. [15382], PO Box 4633, Bayside, NY 11360-4633, (718)849-1044

Natl. Inst. of Farm and Land Brokers [★3043]

Natl. Inst. for Farm Safety [★12986]

Natl. Inst. for Farm Safety [12986], Nancy Hetzel, Treas., 895 Smith Rd., Charles Town, WV 25414, (304)728-0011

Natl. Inst. for the Foodservice Indus. [★1767]

Natl. Inst. of Governmental Purchasing [5951], 151 Spring St., Herndon, VA 20170, (703)736-8900

Natl. Inst. of Governmental Purchasing [5951], 151 Spring St., Herndon, VA 20170, (703)736-8900

Natl. Inst. for Hea. Care Mgt. Res. and Educational Found. [14817], 1225 19th St. NW, Ste. 710, Washington, DC 20036, (202)296-4426

Natl. Inst. of Hispanic Liturgy [★19434]

Natl. Inst. on the Holocaust [★17789]

Natl. Inst. on the Holocaust [★17789]

Natl. Inst. of Independent Colleges and Universities [★8290]

Natl. Inst. for Jewish Hospice [15029], 732 Univ. St., Valley Stream, NY 11581, (516)791-9888

Natl. Inst. for Leadership Development [2197], 1202 W Thomas Rd., Phoenix, AZ 85013, (602)285-7495

Natl. Inst. of Locker and Freezer Provisioners [★2430]

Natl. Inst. for Materials Sci. [IO], Ibaraki, Japan

Natl. Inst. of Medical Herbalists [IO], Exeter, United Kingdom

Natl. Inst. of Mental Hea. [15476], 6001 Executive Blvd., Rm. 8184, MSC 9663, Bethesda, MD 20892-9663, (301)443-4513

Natl. Inst. for Metalworking Skills [7100], 10565 Fairfax Blvd., Ste. 203, Fairfax, VA 22030, (703)352-4971

Natl. Inst. of Metrology, Standardization and Indus. Quality [IO], Rio de Janeiro, Brazil

Natl. Inst. of Neurological Disorders and Stroke [15618], PO Box 5801, Bethesda, MD 20824, (301)496-5751

Natl. Inst. of Oilseed Products [2588], 750 Natl. Press Bldg., 529 14th St. NW, Washington, DC 20045, (202)591-2461

Natl. Inst. of Oilseed Products [2588], 750 Natl. Press Bldg., 529 14th St. NW, Washington, DC 20045, (202)591-2461

Natl. Inst. of Ophthalmology [IO], Pune, India

Natl. Inst. on Out-of-School Time [11165], Wellesley Centers for Women, 106 Central St., Wellesley, MA 02481, (781)283-2547

Natl. Inst. of Packaging, Handling and Logistics Engineers [7209], 177 Fairsom Ct., Lewisburg, PA 17837-6844, (570)523-6475

Natl. Inst. of Pension Administrators [1132], 401 N Michigan Ave., Ste. 2200, Chicago, IL 60611, (800)999-6472

Natl. Inst. of Public Admin. [★5906]

Natl. Inst. of Public Admin. [★5906]

Natl. Inst. for Public Policy [18478], 9302 Lee Hwy., Ste. 750, Fairfax, VA 22031, (703)293-9181

Natl. Inst. of Red Orange Canaries and All Other Cage Birds - Address unknown since 2010.

Natl. Inst. for Rehabilitation Engg. [11817], PO Box T, Hewitt, NJ 07421, (973)853-6585

Natl. Inst. for Res. in Cmpt. Sci. and Control [IO], Le Chesnay, France

National Inst. of Safety and Health [★8838]

Natl. Inst. for Sci., Law and Public Policy [3745], 1400 16th St. NW, Ste. 101, Washington, DC 20036, (202)462-8800

Natl. Inst. of Senior Housing - Address unknown since 2010.

Natl. Inst. for State Credit Union Examination [★5362]

Natl. Inst. of Statistical Sciences [7479], PO Box 14006, 19 T.W. Alexander Dr., Research Triangle Park, NC 27709-4006, (919)685-9300

Natl. Inst. of Steel Detailing [2485], 1810 Catalina Ct., Livermore, CA 94550, (925)294-9626

Natl. Inst. of Steel Detailing [2485], 1810 Catalina Ct., Livermore, CA 94550, (925)294-9626

Natl. Inst. of Transplantation [16914], 2200 W 3rd St., Ste. 100, Los Angeles, CA 90057, (213)413-2779

Natl. Inst. for Trial Advocacy [6047], 1685 38th St., Ste. 200, Boulder, CO 80301, (800)225-6482

Natl. Inst. for Women of Color [★17650]

Natl. Inst. for Women of Color [★17650]

Natl. Inst. of Wood Kitchen Cabinets [★2066]

Natl. Institutes for Water Resources [7605], Idaho Water Resources Res. Inst., 322 E Front St., Ste. 242, Boise, ID 83702, (208)332-4422

Natl. Institutional Food Distributors Assn. [★1433]

Natl. Institutional Res. Forum [★8729]

Natl. Institutional Teacher Placement Assn. [★8726]

Natl. Instructional TV Lib. [★8302]

Natl. Insulation and Abatement Contractors Assn. [★938]

Natl. Insulation Assn. [938], 12100 Sunset Hills Rd., Ste. 330, Reston, VA 20190, (703)464-6422

Natl. Insulation Assn. [IO], Leighton Buzzard, United Kingdom

Natl. Insulation Contractors Assn. [★938]

Natl. Insulator Assn. [21701], PO Box 188, Providence, UT 84332

Natl. Insulin Resistance Coun. [16311], 5414 MD 188, Bethesda, MD 20814, (301)652-3111

Natl. Insurance Brokers Assn. - Defunct.

Natl. Insurance Buyers Assn. [★2034]

Natl. Insurance Crime Bur. [2020], 1111 E Touhy Ave., Ste. 400, Des Plaines, IL 60018, (847)544-7160

National Insurance Educ. Scholarship Program [★8324]

Natl. Integrated and Development Assn. - Pakistan [IO], Besham, Pakistan

Natl. Intelligence Study Center - Defunct.

Natl. Inter-religious Conf. on Peace [★18304]

Natl. Inter-religious Conf. on Peace [★18304]

Natl. InterAssociation Comm. on Internships [★8615]

Natl. InterCollegiate Flying Assn. [20910], PO Box 15081, Monroe, LA 71207, (318)325-6156

Natl. Intercollegiate Flying Club [★20910]

Natl. InterCollegiate Rodeo Assn. [22846], 2033 Walla Walla Ave., Walla Walla, WA 99362, (509)529-4402

Natl. Intercollegiate Running Club Assn. [22864], 121 N Coll. Ave., Bloomington, IN 47404, (812)822-0327

Natl. Intercollegiate Soccer Officials Assn. [22938], 1030 Ohio Ave., Cape May, NJ 08204

Natl. Interfaith Coalition on Aging - Address unknown since 2010.

Natl. Interfaith Comm. for Worker Justice [★19825]

Natl. Interfaith Hospitality Network [★12156]

Natl. Interfraternity Conf. [★23542]

Natl. Interfraternity Found. [★23541]

Natl. Intern Matching Prog. [★8615]

Natl. Intern and Resident Matching Prog. [★8615]

National/International Safe Transit Assn. [★3252]

National/International Safe Transit Assn. [★3252]

Natl. Interprofessional Off. of Cognac [IO], Cognac, France

Natl. Interprofessional Off. of Fruit, Vegetables and Horticulture [IO], Montreuil, France

Natl. Interprofessional Off. of Wine [IO], Montreuil-sous-Bois, France

Natl. Interreligious Ser. Bd. for Conscientious Objectors [★17560]

Natl. Interreligious Ser. Bd. for Conscientious Objectors [★17560]

Natl. Interscholastic Athletic Administrators Assn. [8721], 9100 Keystone Crossing, Ste. 650, Indianapolis, IN 46240, (317)587-1450

Natl. InterScholastic Swimming Coaches Assn. of Am. [23042], 29 Fairview Ave., Great Neck, NY 11023-1206

Natl. - Interstate Coun. of State Boards of Cosmetology [973], 7622 Briarwood Cir., Little Rock, AR 72205, (501)227-8262

Natl. Intramural Assn. [★22997]

Natl. Intramural-Recreational Sports Assn. [22997], 4185 SW Res. Way, Corvallis, OR 97333-1067, (541)766-8211

Natl. Introducing Brokers Assn. [1565], 55 W Monroe St., Ste. 3600, Chicago, IL 60603, (312)977-0598

Natl. Inventors Found. [7014], Inventors Assistance League, 1053 Colorado Blvd., Ste. G1, Los Angeles, CA 90041, (818)246-6542

Natl. Investigation Comm. on Aerial Phenomena [★7254]

Natl. Investigations Comm. on Unidentified Flying Objects [7256], 9101 Topanga Canyon Blvd., No. 209, Chatsworth, CA 91311-5763, (818)882-0039

Natl. Investigations Comm. on Unidentified Flying Objects [7256], 9101 Topanga Canyon Blvd., No. 209, Chatsworth, CA 91311-5763, (818)882-0039

Natl. Investment Banking Assn. [432], PO Box 6625, Athens, GA 30604, (706)208-9620

Natl. Investment Company Ser. Assn. [2146], 8400 Westpark Dr., 2nd Fl., McLean, VA 22102, (508)485-1500

Natl. Investor Relations Inst. [2147], 8020 Towers Crescent Dr., Ste. 250, Vienna, VA 22182, (703)506-3570

Natl. Iranian Amer. Coun. [19070], 1411 K St. NW, Ste. 600, Washington, DC 20005, (202)386-6325

Natl. Iridology Res. Assn. [★15963]

Natl. Iridology Res. Assn. [★15963]

Natl. Irish Safety Org. [IO], Dublin, Ireland

Natl. Issues Forums [★18479]

Natl. Issues Forums Inst. [18479], 100 Commons Rd., Dayton, OH 45459-2777, (937)434-7300

Natl. IST of Municipal Law Officers [★5252]

Natl. IST of Municipal Law Officers [★5252]

Natl. Italian Amer. Bar Assn. [5675], PO Box 510500, Milwaukee, WI 53203-0093, (414)271-7776

Natl. Italian Amer. Found. [19078], 1860 19th St. NW, Washington, DC 20009, (202)387-0600

Natl. Italian Amer. Found. [19078], 1860 19th St. NW, Washington, DC 20009, (202)387-0600

Natl. Jail Assn. [★11704]

Natl. Jail Managers Assn. [★11704]

Natl. Japanese Amer. Historical Soc. [9912], 1684 Post St., San Francisco, CA 94115, (415)921-5007

Natl. Jersey Wooly Rabbit Club [4847], 309 S St. Paul, Sioux Falls, SD 57103, (810)637-1537

Natl. Jersey Wooly Rabbit Club [4847], 309 S St. Paul, Sioux Falls, SD 57103, (810)637-1537

Reference to "IO" in place of a book number signifies that the association may be found in the 50th edition of International Organizations.

Natl. Jewish Center for Learning and Leadership; CLAL - The [19856]

Natl. Jewish Coalition [★18537]

Natl. Jewish Coalition for Literacy [8536], 134 Beach St., No. 2A, Boston, MA 02111, (617)423-0063

Natl. Jewish Comm. on Girl Scouting [13025], 33 Central Dr., Bronxville, NY 10708-4603, (914)738-3986

Natl. Jewish Comm. on Scouting [13026], Keith Walton, Advisor, PO Box 152079, Irving, TX 75015-2091, (972)580-2151

Natl. Jewish Democratic Coun. [18387], PO Box 65683, Washington, DC 20035, (202)216-9060

Natl. Jewish Girl Scout Comm. of the Synagogue Coun. of Am. [★13025]

Natl. Jewish Medical and Res. Center - Address unknown since 2010.

Natl. Jewish Welfare Bd. [★12408]

Natl. Job Corps Alumni Assn. - Address unknown since 2011.

Natl. Jogging Assn. [★22803]

Natl. Joint Painting, Decorating, and Drywall Apprenticeship and Training Comm. [★11941]

Natl. Joint Painting, Decorating, and Drywall Apprenticeship and Training Comm. [★11941]

Natl. Journalism Center [17721], 529 14th St. NW, Ste. 937, Washington, DC 20045, (202)628-1490

Natl. Jousting Assn. [22702], PO Box 14, Mount Solon, VA 22843, (434)983-2989

Natl. Judges Assn. [5633], PO Box 325, Glendale, OR 97442, (541)832-2101

Natl. Judicial Coll. [5634], Judicial Coll. Bldg., MS 358, Reno, NV 89557, (775)784-6747

Natl. Judicial Educ. Prog. [18030], Legal Momentum, 395 Hudson St., New York, NY 10014, (212)925-6635

Natl. Judicial Educ. Prog. to Promote Equality for Women and Men in the Courts [★18030]

National Judo Hall of Fame [★22705]

Natl. Juice Products Assn. and Processed Apples Inst. [★449]

Natl. Juneteenth Observance Found. [17160], PO Box 269, Belzoni, MS 39038, (662)247-3364

Natl. Junior Angus Assn. [3925], 3201 Frederick Ave., St. Joseph, MO 64506, (816)383-5100

Natl. Junior Baseball League [22285], 4 White Spruce Ln., Hauppauge, NY 11788, (631)582-5191

Natl. Junior Classical League [7865], Miami Univ., 422 Wells Mill Dr., Oxford, OH 45056, (513)529-7741

Natl. Junior Coll. Athletic Assn. [22998], 1631 Mesa Ave., Ste. B, Colorado Springs, CO 80906, (719)590-9788

Natl. Junior Hereford Assn. [3926], Amer. Hereford Assn., PO Box 014059, Kansas City, MO 64101, (816)842-3757

Natl. Junior Honor Soc. [23565], 1904 Assn. Dr., Reston, VA 20191-1537, (703)860-0200

Natl. Junior Horticultural Assn. [21811], 15 Railroad Ave., Homer City, PA 15748-1378, (724)479-3254

Natl. Junior Santa Gertrudis Assn. [3927], PO Box 1257, Kingsville, TX 78364, (361)592-9357

Natl. Junior Swine Assn. [4950], PO Box 2417, West Lafayette, IN 47996-2417, (765)463-3594

Natl. Junior Vegetable Growers Assn. [★21811]

Natl. Juvenile Court Services Assn. [5426], Univ. of Nevada, Mail Stop 311, Reno, NV 89557, (888)367-7552

Natl. Juvenile Detention Assn. - Address unknown since 2010.

Natl. Kappa Kappa Iota [23513], 1875 E 15th St., Tulsa, OK 74104-4610, (918)744-0389

Natl. Karting Assn. [IO], Colchester, United Kingdom

Natl. Kidney Disease Found. [★15554]

Natl. Kidney Found. [15554], 30 E 33rd St., New York, NY 10016-5337, (212)889-2210

Natl. Kidney and Urologic Diseases Info. CH [16947], 3 Info. Way, Bethesda, MD 20892-3580, (800)891-5390

Natl. Kindergarten Alliance [8742], Winona State Univ., 228 Gildemeister Hall, Winona, MN 55987

Natl. Kitchen and Bath Assn. [2070], 687 Willow Grove St., Hackettstown, NJ 07840, (908)852-0033

Natl. Kitchen Cabinet Assn. [★2066]

Natl. Knife Collectors Assn. [21876], PO Box 21070, Chattanooga, TN 37424-0070, (423)240-3371

Natl. Kraut Packers Assn. - Defunct.

Natl. Labor Alliance of Hea. Care Coalitions [23215], PO Box 231443, Hartford, CT 06123, (860)249-6100

Natl. Labor Comm. [★17230]

Natl. Labor Comm. [17230], 5 Gateway Center, 6th Fl., Pittsburgh, PA 15222, (412)562-2406

Natl. Labor Comm. in Support of Democracy and Human Rights in El Salvador [★17230]

Natl. Labor Comm. in Support of Democracy and Human Rights in El Salvador [★17230]

Natl. Labor Comm. in Support of Worker and Human Rights in Central Am. [★17230]

Natl. Labor Comm. in Support of Worker and Human Rights in Central Am. [★17230]

Natl. Labrador Retriever Club [21612], 1121 Crystal Springs Rd., Two Rivers, WI 54241, (920)794-7858

Natl. Lamb Feeders Assn. [4912], 1270 Chemeketa St. NE, Salem, OR 97301-4145, (503)364-5462

Natl. LambdaRail [7519], PO Box 1610, Cypress, CA 90630

Natl. Land Title Reclamation Assn. - Defunct.

Natl. Land Use Planning Commn. [IO], Dar es Salaam, United Republic of Tanzania

Natl. Landlords Assn. [IO], London, United Kingdom

Natl. Latina Bus. Women Assn. [2188], 1740 W Katella Ave., Ste. Q, Orange, CA 92867, (714)724-7762

Natl. Latina Hea. Network [14731], 7720 Wisconsin Ave., Ste. 212, Bethesda, MD 20814, (301)664-9466

Natl. Latina/Latino Law Student Assn. [18057], PO Box 27104, Albuquerque, NM 87125, (888)544-6013

Natl. Latinas Caucus - Defunct.

Natl. Latino Alliance for the Elimination of Domestic Violence [11895], PO Box 7886, Albuquerque, NM 87194, (505)224-9080

Natl. Latino Behavioral Hea. Assn. [15477], 6555 Robin St., Cochiti Lake, NM 87083, (505)980-5156

Natl. Latino Coun. on Alcohol and Tobacco Prevention [12131], 250 5th Ave., Ste. 403, New York, NY 10001

Natl. Latino Officers Assn. [5676], PO Box 02-0120, Brooklyn, NY 11201, (866)579-5809

Natl. Latino Peace Officers Assn. [19104], PO Box 23159, Santa Ana, CA 92711-3159, (800)206-8380

Natl. Laundry Allied Trades Assn. [★2194]

Natl. Law Center for Children and Families [5427], 211 N Union St., Ste. 100, Alexandria, VA 22314, (703)548-5522

Natl. Law Center on Homelessness and Poverty [12163], 1411 K St. NW, Ste. 1400, Washington, DC 20005, (202)638-2535

Natl. Law Enforcement Officers Memorial Fund [5726], 901 E St. NW, Ste. 100, Washington, DC 20004-2025, (202)737-3400

Natl. Law Firm Marketing Assn. [★2409]

Natl. Law Firm Marketing Assn. [★2409]

Natl. Lawyers Assn. [5274], 44 Cook St., Ste. 100, Denver, CO 80206, (303)398-7030

Natl. Lawyers Club - Defunct.

Natl. Lawyers Guild [5275], 132 Nassau St., Rm. 922, New York, NY 10038, (212)679-5100

Natl. Lawyers Wines [★5233]

National Leadership Development Program [★23514]

National Leadership Development Program [★23514]

Natl. League of Amer. Pen Women [9309], Pen Arts Bldg., 1300 17th St. NW, Washington, DC 20036-1973, (202)785-1997

Natl. League of Cities [5854], 1301 Pennsylvania Ave. NW, Ste. 550, Washington, DC 20004-1747, (202)626-3100

Natl. League for the Control of Cardiovascular Disease [IO], Rabat, Morocco

Natl. League of Disabled Voters - Defunct.

Natl. League of Families of Amer. Prisoners and Missing in Southeast Asia [18141], 5673 Columbia Pike, Ste. 100, Falls Church, VA 22041, (703)465-7432

Natl. League of Families of Amer. Prisoners and Missing in Southeast Asia [18141], 5673 Columbia Pike, Ste. 100, Falls Church, VA 22041, (703)465-7432

Natl. League of Masonic Clubs - Address unknown since 2011.

Natl. League for Nursing [15781], 61 Broadway, 33rd Fl., New York, NY 10006, (212)363-5555

Natl. League of Nursing Educ. [★15781]

Natl. League of Postmasters of the U.S. [23282], 1 Beltway Ctr., 5904 Richmond Hwy., Ste. 500, Alexandria, VA 22303-1864, (703)329-4550

Natl. League of POW/MIA Families [★18141]

Natl. League of POW/MIA Families [★18141]

Natl. League of Professional Baseball Clubs - Defunct.

Natl. League to Promote School Attendance [★8082]

Natl. League to Promote School Attendance [★8082]

Natl. League of Spanish Speaking Elected Officials [★5846]

Natl. League of Wholesale Fresh Fruit and Vegetable Distributors [★4476]

Natl. League of Women Voters [★18383]

Natl. Leased Housing Assn. [12192], 1900 L St. NW, Ste. 300, Washington, DC 20036, (202)785-8888

Natl. Leather Assn. [★13109]

Natl. Leather Assn. - Intl. [13109], PO Box 423, Blacklick, OH 43004-0423, (780)454-1992

Natl. Leather Coun. [IO], Paris, France

Natl. Leather and Shoe Finders Assn. [★1461]

Natl. Legal Aid and Defender Assn. [5763], 1140 Connecticut Ave. NW, Ste. 900, Washington, DC 20036, (202)452-0620

Natl. Legal Found. [5936], PO Box 64427, Virginia Beach, VA 23467-4427, (757)463-6133

Natl. Legal and Policy Center [17751], 107 Park Washington Ct., Falls Church, VA 22046, (703)237-1970

Natl. Legal Rsrc. Center for Child Advocacy and Protection [★11186]

Natl. Legal Sanctuary for Community Advancement [5750], 444 DeHaro St., Ste. 205, San Francisco, CA 94107, (415)553-7100

Natl. Legal Video Assn. - Address unknown since 2011.

Natl. Legislative Conf. [★5998]

Natl. Legislative Coun. for the Disabled and Senior Citizens of the Democratic Party - Defunct.

Natl. Lesbian and Gay Journalists Assn. [2850], 1420 K St. NW, Ste. 910, Washington, DC 20005, (202)588-9888

Natl. Lesbian and Gay Law Assn. [★5276]

Natl. Lesbian and Gay Lawyers Assn. [★5276]

Natl. Leukemia Assn. [★13907]

Natl. LGBT Bar Assn. [5276], 1301 K St. NW, Ste. 1100 E Tower, Washington, DC 20005, (202)637-6384

Natl. Liberty Museum [17789], 321 Chestnut St., Philadelphia, PA 19106, (215)925-2800

Natl. Liberty Museum [17789], 321 Chestnut St., Philadelphia, PA 19106, (215)925-2800

Natl. Librarians Assn. - Defunct.

Natl. Lib. and Documentation Services Bd. [IO], Colombo, Sri Lanka

Natl. Lib. of Uganda [IO], Kampala, Uganda

Natl. Licensed Beverage Assn. [★174]

Natl. Licensed Beverage Assn. - Defunct.

Natl. Lieutenant Governors Assn. [6000], 75 Cavalier Blvd., Ste. 226, Florence, KY 41042-5168, (859)283-1400

Natl. Life Center [12939], 686 N Broad St., Woodbury, NJ 08096, (856)848-1819

Natl. Life Share Found. - Defunct.

Natl. Lighting Bur. [2222], 8811 Colesville Rd., Ste. G106, Silver Spring, MD 20910, (301)587-9572

Natl. Lighting Bur. [2222], 8811 Colesville Rd., Ste. G106, Silver Spring, MD 20910, (301)587-9572

Natl. Lilac Rabbit Club of Am. [4848], N 3650 Oak Ridge Rd., Waupaca, WI 54981

Natl. Lime Assn. [760], 200 N Glebe Rd., Ste. 800, Arlington, VA 22203, (703)243-5463

Natl. Limestone Inst. [★3366]

Natl. Limousine Assn. [3524], 49 S Maple Ave., Marlton, NJ 08053, (856)596-3344

Natl. Lincoln Civil War Coun. [★10660]

Natl. Lincoln Sheep Breeders' Assn. [4913], 15603 173rd Ave., Milo, IA 50166-8940, (641)942-6402

A star before a book entry number signifies that the name is not listed separately, but is mentioned within the entry.

Natl. Lipid Assn. [13830], 6816 Southpoint Pkwy., Ste. 1000, Jacksonville, FL 32216, (904)998-0854

Natl. Liquor Law Enforcement Assn. [5727], 11720 Beltsville Dr., Ste. 900, Calverton, MD 20705-3111, (301)755-2795

Natl. Liquor Stores Assn. [★174]

Natl. Litigation Support Services Assn. [IO], Mississauga, ON, Canada

Natl. Little Britches Rodeo Assn. [22847], 5050 Edison Ave., Ste. 105, Colorado Springs, CO 80915, (719)389-0333

Natl. Little Coll. Athletic Assn. [★23012]

Natl. Live Stock Marketing Assn. [★4719]

Natl. Live Stock and Meat Bd. [★4718]

Natl. Livestock Brand Conf. [★4691]

Natl. Livestock Dealers Assn. [★4716]

Natl. Livestock Loss Prevention Bd. [★4696]

Natl. Livestock Producers Assn. [4719], 13570 Meadowgrass Dr., Ste. 201, Colorado Springs, CO 80921, (719)538-8843

Natl. Livestock Sanitary Comm. [★4696]

Natl. Local Tech. Assistance Prog. Assn. [13196], Illinois Dept. of Trans., 2300 S Dirksen Pkwy., Rm. 205, Springfield, IL 62764, (217)785-5048

Natl. Locksmith Suppliers Assn. [★1660]

Natl. Low Income Housing Coalition [12193], 727 15th St. NW, 6th Fl., Washington, DC 20005, (202)662-1530

Natl. LP-Gas Coun. [★4491]

Natl. LSM Assn. [★20734]

Natl. Lubricating Grease Inst. [2660], 4635 Wyandotte St., Ste. 202, Kansas City, MO 64112-1509, (816)931-9480

Natl. Luggage Dealers Assn. [2204], 1817 Elmdale Ave., Glenview, IL 60026, (847)998-6869

Natl. Lum and Abner Soc. [22119], Tim Hollis, Sec., 81 Sharon Blvd., Dora, AL 35062, (205)674-0101

Natl. Lumber and Building Material Dealers Assn. [1513], 2025 M St. NW, Ste. 800, Washington, DC 20036-3309, (202)367-1169

Natl. Lumber Exporters Assn. [★1464]

Natl. Lung Cancer Partnership [13955], 222 N Midvale Blvd., Ste. 6, Madison, WI 53705, (608)233-7905

Natl. Lutheran Educ. Conf. [★8545]

Natl. Lutheran Outdoors Ministry Assn. [19939], PO Box 1672, Tahlequah, OK 74465, (918)458-0704

Natl. Lymphedema Network [15255], 1611 Telegraph Ave., Ste. 1111, Latham Sq., Oakland, CA 94612-2138, (510)208-3200

Natl. Macaroni Mfrs. Assn. [★1420]

Natl. Machine Accountants Assn. [★7904]

Natl. Machine Embellishment Instructors and Artists - Defunct.

Natl. Machine Tool Builders' Assn. [★7043]

Natl. Mah Jongg League [21751], 250 W 57th St., New York, NY 10107, (212)246-3052

Natl. Mail Order Assn. [2418], 2807 Polk St. NE, Minneapolis, MN 55418-2954, (612)788-1673

Natl. Major Gang Task Force [5380], PO Box 3689, Pueblo, CO 81005, (719)226-4915

Natl. Malaria Soc. [★16932]

Natl. Male Nurse Assn. [★15705]

Natl. Maliks Assn. [IO], Kabul, Afghanistan

Natl. Mgt. Assn. [2299], 2210 Arbor Blvd., Dayton, OH 45439, (937)294-0421

Natl. Manpower Inst. [★18038]

Natl. Manufactured Housing Fed. [★2309]

Natl. Marfan Found. [16887], 22 Manhasset Ave., Port Washington, NY 11050-2023, (516)883-8712

Natl. Marine Bankers Assn. [433], 231 S LaSalle St., Ste. 2050, Chicago, IL 60604, (312)946-6260

Natl. Marine Charter Assn. [2384], 105 Eastern Ave., Ste. 101, Annapolis, MD 21403, (800)745-6094

Natl. Marine Distributors Assn. [2363], 37 Pratt St., Essex, CT 06426, (860)767-7898

Natl. Marine Educ. Assn. [★8550]

Natl. Marine Educators Assn. [8550], PO Box 1470, Ocean Springs, MS 39566-1470, (228)896-9182

Natl. Marine Electronics Assn. [2364], 7 Riggs Ave., Severna Park, MD 21146, (410)975-9425

Natl. Marine Mfrs. Assn. [2365], 231 S LaSalle, Ste. 2050, Chicago, IL 60604, (312)946-6200

Natl. Marine Representatives Assn. [2366], PO Box 360, Gurnee, IL 60031, (847)662-3167

Natl. Maritime Museum Assn. [★10128]

Natl. Market Traders' Fed. [IO], Barnsley, United Kingdom

Natl. Marriage Encounter [12438], 3922 77th St., Urbandale, IA 50322, (515)278-8458

Natl. Marrow Donor Prog. [14426], 3001 Broadway St. NE, Ste. 100, Minneapolis, MN 55413-1753, (612)627-5800

Natl. Marrow Donor Prog. [14426], 3001 Broadway St. NE, Ste. 100, Minneapolis, MN 55413-1753, (612)627-5800

Natl. Mass Retailing Inst. [★3125]

Natl. Mastitis Coun. [★17035]

Natl. Materials Advisory Bd. [7066], The Natl. Academies, 500 5th St. NW, Washington, DC 20001-2736, (202)334-3505

National Materials Properties Data Network [★7098]

Natl. Maternal and Child Health Clearinghouse - Defunct.

Natl. Meat Assn. [★2431]

Natl. Meat Assn. [2433], 1970 Broadway, Ste. 825, Oakland, CA 94612, (510)763-1533

Natl. Mech. Trade Coun. [★900]

Natl. Medic-Card Systems - Defunct.

Natl. Medical Assn. [15427], 8403 Colesville Rd., Ste. 920, Silver Spring, MD 20910, (202)347-1895

Natl. Medical and Dental Assn. [19189], 9412 Acad. Rd., Philadelphia, PA 19114

Natl. Medical Fellowships [8614], 347 Fifth Ave., Ste. 510, New York, NY 10016, (212)483-8880

Natl. MedPeds Residents' Assn. [15136], Cheryl Dempsey, Exec. Asst., Tulane Univ. School of Medicine, 1430 Tulane Ave., SL-37, New Orleans, LA 70112, (504)988-6689

Natl. Melanoma Alliance [13956], 411 Walnut St., No. 3213, Green Cove Springs, FL 32043, (877)877-1594

Natl. Memorial Inst. for the Prevention of Terrorism [18717], 621 N Robinson Ave., 4th Fl., Oklahoma City, OK 73102-6203, (405)278-6300

Natl. Meningitis Assn. [14410], PO Box 725165, Atlanta, GA 31139, (866)366-3662

Natl. Men's Rsrc. Center - Address unknown since 2011.

Natl. Mental Hea. Assn. [★15461]

Natl. Mental Hea. Consumers' Self-Help CH [12489], 1211 Chestnut St., Ste. 1207, Philadelphia, PA 19107, (215)751-1810

Natl. Mental Hea. Found. [★15461]

Natl. Merchants' Fed. [IO], Bogota, Colombia

Natl. Metal Decorators Assn. [★1614]

Natl. Microfilm Assn. [★1894]

Natl. Micrographics Assn. [★1894]

Natl. Midas Dealers Assn. [★359]

Natl. Midas Dealers Assn. [★359]

Natl. Middle Level Sci. Teachers' Assn. [8848], 548 N Linden St., Marshall, MI 49068

Natl. Middle School Assn. [8621], 4151 Executive Pkwy., Ste. 300, Westerville, OH 43081, (614)895-4730

Natl. Migraine Found. [★14689]

Natl. Migrant Referral Proj. [★14726]

Natl. Migrant Workers Coun. [★12523]

Natl. Military Family Assn. [20707], 2500 N Van Dorn St., Ste. 102, Alexandria, VA 22302-1601, (703)931-6632

Natl. Military Fish and Wildlife Assn. [5083], 32 Old Orchard Ln., Warrenton, VA 20186, (540)349-9662

Natl. Military Intelligence Assn. [5609], 256 Morris Creek Rd., Cullen, VA 23934, (434)542-5929

Natl. Military Wives Assn. [★20707]

Natl. Milk Glass Collectors Soc. [21842], 1466 St., Rte. 292 S, Zanesfield, OH 43360, (937)666-5011

Natl. Milk Producers Fed. [4185], 2101 Wilson Blvd., Ste. 400, Arlington, VA 22201, (703)243-6111

Natl. Mine Rescue Assn. [7127], Wayne Duerr, Cochrans Mill Rd., Pittsburgh, PA 15236

Natl. Mineral Feed Assn. [★4370]

Natl. Mini Rex Rabbit Club [4849], Jennifer Whaley, Sec.-Treas., PO Box 712499, Santee, CA 92072, (619)933-6505

Natl. Mini Rex Rabbit Club [4849], Jennifer Whaley, Sec.-Treas., PO Box 712499, Santee, CA 92072, (619)933-6505

Natl. Miniature Donkey Assn. [4697], 6450 Dewey Rd., Rome, NY 13440, (315)336-0154

Natl. Mining Assn. [785], 101 Constitution Ave. NW, Ste. 500 E, Washington, DC 20001-2133, (202)463-2600

Natl. Mining, Petroleum and Energy Soc. [IO], Lima, Peru

Natl. Minorities with Disabilities Coalition [17545], 1213 Wyndhurst Dr., Plainsboro, NJ 08536

Natl. Minority AIDS Coun. [13621], 1931 13th St. NW, Washington, DC 20009-4432, (202)483-6622

Natl. Minority Bus. Campaign [★2519]

Natl. Minority Bus. Coun. [2524], 120 Broadway, 19th Fl., New York, NY 10271, (212)693-5050

Natl. Minority Bus. Directories [★2519]

Natl. Minority Purchasing Coun. [★2525]

Natl. Minority Supplier Development Coun. [2525], 1359 Broadway, 10th Fl., New York, NY 10018, (212)944-2430

Natl. MIS User Gp. [6988], 101 S Eisenhower Dr., Beckley, WV 25801, (304)256-7140

Natl. Mitigation Banking Assn. [4101], 1155 15th St. NW, Ste. 500, Washington, DC 20005, (202)457-8409

Natl. Mobile/Manufactured Home Owners Found. [★12188]

Natl. Mobile Radio Sys. [★3416]

Natl. Mobile Radio Sys. [★3416]

Natl. Mobility Equip. Dealers Assn. [2323], 3327 W Bearss Ave., Tampa, FL 33618, (813)264-2697

Natl. Mobility Equip. Dealers Assn. [2323], 3327 W Bearss Ave., Tampa, FL 33618, (813)264-2697

Natl. Mobilization Against AIDS [★10887]

Natl. Mobilization Against Sweatshops [18045], PO Box 130293, New York, NY 10013-0995, (718)625-9091

Natl. Model Cities Community Development Directors Assn. [★17387]

Natl. Model Cities Directors Assn. [★17387]

Natl. Model Railroad Assn. [21892], 4121 Cromwell Rd., Chattanooga, TN 37421-2119, (423)892-2846

Natl. Model United Nations [8405], 2945 44th Ave. S, Ste. 600, Minneapolis, MN 55406, (612)353-5649

Natl. Mole Day Found. [6413], PO Box 602, Millersport, OH 43046, (740)928-8455

Natl. Money Transmitters Assn. [1320], 12 Welwyn Rd., Ste. C, Great Neck, NY 11021, (516)829-2742

Natl. Monte Carlo Owners Assn. [21131], 204 Shelby Dr., Greensburg, PA 15601-4974, (724)853-1460

Natl. Morgan Cutting and Stock Horse Assn. - Defunct.

Natl. Morgan Reining Horse Assn. [4617], 7701 Olivas Ln., Vacaville, CA 95688, (707)448-0247

Natl. Mossberg Collectors Assn. [21716], PO Box 487, Festus, MO 63028, (636)937-6401

Natl. Motor Bus Assn. [★21118]

Natl. Motor Bus Assn. [★21118]

Natl. Motor Bus Division of Amer. Auto. Assn. [★3500]

Natl. Motor Freight Traffic Assn. [3258], 1001 N Fairfax St., Ste. 600, Alexandria, VA 22314, (703)838-1810

Natl. Motor Vehicle Assn. [IO], Porto, Portugal

Natl. Motorists Assn. [13335], 402 W 2nd St., Waunakee, WI 53597-1342, (608)849-6000

Natl. Motorists Assn. Australia [IO], Clayfield, Australia

Natl. Moving and Storage Assn. [★3243]

Natl. Moving and Storage Assn. [★3243]

Natl. Moving and Storage Assn. - Defunct.

Natl. MPS Soc. [15501], PO Box 14686, Durham, NC 27709-4686, (919)806-0101

Natl. Multi Housing Coun. [3033], 1850 M St. NW, Ste. 540, Washington, DC 20036-5803, (202)974-2300

Natl. Multicultural Greek Coun. [23538], PO Box 25632, Newark, NJ 07101

Natl. MultiCultural Inst. [11679], 1666 K St. NW, Ste. 440, Washington, DC 20006-1242, (202)483-0700

Natl. Multifamily Resident Info. Coun. [3034], 3337 Duke St., Alexandria, VA 22314, (703)370-7436

Natl. Multiple Sclerosis Soc. [15619], 733 3rd Ave., 3rd Fl., New York, NY 10017, (212)986-3240

Natl. Municipal League [★5852]

Natl. Museum of Amer. Jewish Military History [20799], 1811 R St. NW, Washington, DC 20009, (202)265-6280

Reference to "IO" in place of a book number signifies that the association may be found in the 50th edition of International Organizations.

Natl. Museum of Racing and Hall of Fame [22661], 191 Union Ave., Saratoga Springs, NY 12866-3566, (518)584-0400

Natl. Museum of Transport [★10502]

Natl. Music Camp [★9294]

Natl. Music Camp [★9294]

Natl. Music Coun. [10259], 425 Park St., Montclair, NJ 07043

Natl. Music Coun. of The United Kingdom [IO], London, United Kingdom

Natl. Music Publishers' Assn. [2568], 101 Constitution Ave. NW, Ste. 705 E, Washington, DC 20001, (202)742-4375

Natl. Music Theater Network [10589], PO Box 2639, New York, NY 10108, (212)664-0979

Natl. Musicamp Assn. of Zimbabwe [IO], Harare, Zimbabwe

Natl. Mustang Assn. [4618], PO Box 1367, Cedar City, UT 84721, (888)867-8662

Natl. Muzzle Loading Rifle Assn. [22880], PO Box 67, Friendship, IN 47021, (812)667-5131

Natl. Narcotic Detector Dog Assn. [5728], 379 CR 105, Carthage, TX 75633, (888)289-0070

Natl. Narcotic Enforcement Officers Assn. [★5464]

Natl. Narcotic Enforcement Officers Assn. [★5464]

Natl. Native Amer. AIDS Prevention Center [10890], 720 S Colorado Blvd., Ste. 650-S, Denver, CO 80246, (720)382-2244

Natl. Native Amer. Cooperative [10333], Carole J. Garcia, Intl. Rep., PO Box 27626, Tucson, AZ 85726-7626, (520)622-4900

Natl. Native Amer. Law Enforcement Assn. [5729], PO Box 171, Washington, DC 20044, (202)204-3065

Natl. Native Amer. Law Students Assn. [8510], UCLA School of Law, 2L, Los Angeles, CA 90095

Natl. Native Amer. Veterans Assn. [20800], 3903 County Rd. 382, San Antonio, TX 78253

Natl. Naval Officers Assn. [5818], PO Box 10871, Alexandria, VA 22310-0871, (703)231-8554

Natl. Necrotizing Fasciitis Found. [16776], 2731 Porter St. SW, Grand Rapids, MI 49519, (616)261-2538

The Natl. Needle Arts Assn. [3450], 1100-H Brandywine Blvd., Zanesville, OH 43701-7303, (740)455-6773

The Natl. Needlework Assn. [★3450]

Natl. Negro Bankers Assn. [★430]

Natl. Negro Funeral Directors and Morticians Assn. [★2542]

Natl. Neighborhood Coalition [17389], 1221 Connecticut Ave. NW, 2nd Fl., Washington, DC 20036, (202)429-0790

Natl. Neigong Res. Soc. [10082], 325M Sharon Park Dr., No. 729, Menlo Park, CA 94025

Natl. Nephrosis Found. [★15554]

Natl. Network [★12948]

Natl. Network of Abortion Funds [10769], PO Box 170280, Boston, MA 02117, (800)772-9100

Natl. Network of Commercial Real Estate Women [★3011]

Natl. Network for Curriculum Coordination in Vocational and Technical Education - Defunct.

Natl. Network to End Domestic Violence [11896], 2001 S St. NW, Ste. 400, Washington, DC 20009, (202)543-5566

Natl. Network to End Violence Against Immigrant Women [13471], Family Violehce Prevention Fund, 383 Rhode Island St., Ste. 304, San Francisco, CA 94103, (415)252-8900

Natl. Network of Episcopal Clergy Associations [19713], Rev. Michael R. Link, 11844 Orense Dr., Las Vegas, NV 89138

Natl. Network of Estate Planning Attorneys [5277], 3500 DePauw Blvd., Ste. 2090, Indianapolis, IN 46268, (800)638-8681

Natl. Network of Forest Practitioners [4407], 8 N Court St., Ste. 411, Athens, OH 45701, (740)593-8733

Natl. Network for Immigrant and Refugee Rights [17885], 310 8th St., Ste. 303, Oakland, CA 94607-4253, (510)465-1984

Natl. Network for Immunization Info. [15111], 301 Univ. Blvd., Galveston, TX 77555, (409)772-0199

Natl. Network for Social Work Managers [13223], Special Ser. for Groups, 605 W Olympic Blvd., Ste. 600, Los Angeles, CA 90015, (213)553-1870

Natl. Network for Women Leaders [★9054]

National Network of Women's Caucuses and Committees in the Disciplinary and Professional Associations [★17662]

Natl. Network of Women's Funds [★13492]

Natl. Network for Youth [12948], 741 8th St. SE, Washington, DC 20003, (202)783-7949

Natl. Network of Youth Ministries [20306], PO Box 501748, San Diego, CA 92150-1748, (858)451-1111

Natl. Neurofibromatosis Found. [★15579]

Natl. Neurotrauma Soc. [15667], 5745 SW 75 St., No. 197, Gainesville, FL 32608, (352)213-8656

Natl. New Deal Preservation Assn. [10360], PO Box 602, Santa Fe, NM 87504-0602, (505)473-3985

National New England Lead Burning Assn. - Address unknown since 2010.

Natl. New Play Network [10590], 641 D St. NW, Washington, DC 20004, (202)312-5270

Natl. Newman Chaplains Assn. [★19399]

Natl. News Bur. [2851], PO Box 43039, Philadelphia, PA 19129, (215)849-9016

Natl. Newspaper Assn. [2852], PO Box 7540, Columbia, MO 65205-7540, (573)777-4980

Natl. Newspapers of Ireland [IO], Dublin, Ireland

Natl. Niemann Pick Disease Found. [15502], PO Box 49, 401 Madison Ave., Ste. B, Fort Atkinson, WI 53538, (920)563-0930

Natl. Nitrogen Solutions Assn. [★3092]

Natl. No-Nukes Prison Support Collective [18208], PO Box 43383, Tucson, AZ 85733, (520)323-8697

Natl. No-Nukes Prison Support Collective [18208], PO Box 43383, Tucson, AZ 85733, (520)323-8697

Natl. Nostalgic Nova [21132], PO Box 2344, York, PA 17405, (717)252-4192

Natl. Notary Assn. [5868], PO Box 2402, 9350 DeSoto Ave., Chatsworth, CA 91313-2402, (800)876-6827

Natl. Nubian Club [★3790]

Natl. Nubian Club [★3790]

Natl. Nurses in Bus. Assn. [692], PO Box 561081, Rockledge, FL 32956-1081, (321)633-4610

Natl. Nurses Soc. on Addictions [★15756]

Natl. Nurses Soc. on Addictions [★15756]

Natl. Nurses Soc. on Alcoholism [★15756]

Natl. Nurses Soc. on Alcoholism [★15756]

Natl. Nursing Accrediting Ser. [★15781]

Natl. Nursing Staff Development Org. [15782], 401 N Michigan Ave., Ste. 2200, Chicago, IL 60611, (312)673-5135

Natl. Nutritional Foods Assn. [★3121]

Natl. Oak Flooring Mfrs. Assn. [★600]

Natl. Ocean Indus. Assn. [7182], 1120 G St. NW, Ste. 900, Washington, DC 20005, (202)347-6900

Natl. Oceanic Soc. [4102], 17300 Red Hill Ave., Ste. 280, Irvine, CA 92614, (949)500-5451

National Oceanographic Data Center [★4286]

Natl. Oceanography Assn. [★7182]

Natl. Odd Shoe Exchange [11818], PO Box 1120, Chandler, AZ 85244-1120, (480)892-3484

Natl. Odd Shoe Exchange [11818], PO Box 1120, Chandler, AZ 85244-1120, (480)892-3484

Natl. Off-Road Bicycling Assn. [★22489]

Natl. Off. Machine Dealers Assn. [★2577]

Natl. Off. Products Alliance [3353], 301 N Fairfax St., Ste. 200, Alexandria, VA 22314, (800)542-6672

Natl. Off. for the Rights of the Indigent [★17302]

Natl. Office for Social Responsibility - Defunct.

Natl. Office Systems Assn. - Defunct.

Natl. Offshore Coun. [★22375]

Natl. Offshore Dept. [22375], U.S. Sailing Assn., PO Box 1260, Portsmouth, RI 02871-0907, (401)683-0800

Natl. Oil and Acrylic Painters' Soc. [9192], PO Box 676, Osage Beach, MO 65065-0676, (573)348-1764

Natl. Oil Recyclers Assn. [2661], 5965 Amber Ridge Rd., Haymarket, VA 20169, (703)753-4277

Natl. Oil Scouts and Landmen's Assn. [★2656]

Natl. Oil Scouts and Landmen's Assn. [★2656]

Natl. Oilseed Processors Assn. [2589], 1300 L St. NW, Ste. 1020, Washington, DC 20005-4168, (202)842-0463

Natl. Old Lacers [★21446]

Natl. Old Lacers [★21446]

Natl. Old Timers Auto Racing Club - Address unknown since 2011.

Natl. Oldtime Fiddlers' Assn. [10260], Natl. Oldtime Fiddlers' Contest and Festival, PO Box 447, Weiser, ID 83672, (208)414-0255

Natl. Oleander Soc. [★21805]

Natl. Oleander Soc. [★21805]

Natl. Olympic Comm. of Armenia [IO], Yerevan, Armenia

Natl. Olympic Comm. of Azerbaijan [IO], Baku, Azerbaijan

Natl. Olympic Comm. of Iraq [IO], Baghdad, Iraq

Natl. Olympic Comm. of the Islamic Republic of Iran [IO], Tehran, Iran

Natl. Olympic Comm. of Lithuania [IO], Vilnius, Lithuania

Natl. Olympic Comm. of the Republic of Belarus [IO], Minsk, Belarus

Natl. Olympic Comm. of the Republic of Kazakhstan [IO], Almaty, Kazakhstan

Natl. Olympic Comm. of Solomon Islands [IO], Honiara, Solomon Islands

Natl. Olympic Comm. and Sports Confed. of Denmark [IO], Brondby, Denmark

Natl. Olympic Comm. of Turkey [IO], Istanbul, Turkey

Natl. Olympic Comm. of Ukraine [IO], Kiev, Ukraine

Natl. One Coat Stucco Assn. [594], PO Box 121325, Arlington, TX 76012, (817)461-3351

Natl. One Design Racing Assn. [22376], Jolly Booth, Sec.-Treas., 1225 E Bronson St., South Bend, IN 46615

Natl. Onion Assn. [4460], 822 7th St., Ste. 510, Greeley, CO 80631-3941, (970)353-5895

Natl. Onsite Wastewater Recycling Assn. [4983], 601 Wythe St., Alexandria, VA 22314, (800)966-2942

Natl. Opera Assn. [10261], Robert Hansen, Exec. Dir., PO Box 60869, Canyon, TX 79016-0869, (806)651-2857

Natl. Operatic and Dramatic Assn. [IO], Peterborough, United Kingdom

Natl. Operating Comm. on Standards for Athletic Equip. [3150], 11020 King St., Ste. 215, Overland Park, KS 66210, (913)888-1340

Natl. Opossum Soc. [11014], PO Box 21197, Catonsville, MD 21228, (410)233-1102

National Optical Astronomy Observatory [★7381]

Natl. Optometric Assn. [15997], PO Box 198959, Chicago, IL 60619-8959, (877)394-2020

Natl. Optometric Soc. for Developmental Vision Care [★15993]

Natl. Oral Hea. Info. CH [14307], 1 NOHIC Way, Bethesda, MD 20892-3500, (866)232-4528

Natl. Orange Juice Assn. [★449]

Natl. Orchestral Assn. [10262], PO Box 7016, New York, NY 10150-7016, (212)208-4691

Natl. Order of Battlefield Commissions - Defunct.

Natl. Order of the Blue and Gray - Defunct.

Natl. Order of Trench Rats [20414], PO Box 1068, Kingston, PA 18704-0068, (570)714-2554

Natl. Order of Women Legislators [5769], 910 16th St., Ste. 100, Washington, DC 20006, (202)293-3040

Natl. Org. for Motor Retail Trade and Repairs [IO], Stockholm, Sweden

Natl. Org. of Adolescent Pregnancy and Parenting [★12035]

Natl. Org. on Adolescent Pregnancy, Parenting and Prevention [★12035]

Natl. Org. for Advancement of Associate Degree Nursing [★15783]

Natl. Org. for African-American Women [10829], PO Box 29579, Washington, DC 20017, (202)529-5508

Natl. Org. of African Americans in Housing [12194], 601 13th St. NW, 11th Fl., Washington, DC 20001-4382, (202)534-1792

Natl. Org. for Albinism and Hypopigmentation [15503], PO Box 959, East Hampstead, NH 03826-0959, (603)887-2310

Natl. Org. of Alternative Programs [16631], PO Box 10703, Austin, TX 78766, (512)377-9382

Natl. Org. for Associate Degree Nursing [15783], 7794 Grow Dr., Pensacola, FL 32514, (850)484-6948

A star before a book entry number signifies that the name is not listed separately, but is mentioned within the entry.

Natl. Org. of Bar Counsel [**5677**], 110 E Main St., Madison, WI 53703, (608)267-8915

Natl. Org. of Black Architects [★**6202**]

Natl. Org. of Black Chemists and Chem. Engineers [★**6414**]

Natl. Org. of Black County Officials [★**5348**]

Natl. Org. of Black Law Enforcement Executives [**5730**], 4609-F Pinecrest Off. Park Dr., Alexandria, VA 22312-1442, (703)658-1529

Natl. Org. of Blacks in Govt. [**5312**], 3005 Georgia Ave. NW, Washington, DC 20001-3807, (202)667-3280

Natl. Org. for Career Credentialing [**727**], 1133 May St., Lansing, MI 48906, (804)310-2552

Natl. Org. Caring for Kids - Defunct.

Natl. Org. for Changing Men [★**17856**]

Natl. Org. of Circumcision Info. Rsrc. Centers [**11520**], PO Box 2512, San Anselmo, CA 94979-2512, (415)488-9883

Natl. Org. of Circumcision Info. Rsrc. Centers [**11520**], PO Box 2512, San Anselmo, CA 94979-2512, (415)488-9883

Natl. Org. for Competency Assurance - Address unknown since 2010.

Natl. Org. for Continuing Educ. of Roman Catholic Clergy [**19685**], 333 N Michigan Ave., Ste. 1205, Chicago, IL 60601, (312)781-9450

Natl. Org. on Disability [**11819**], 1625 K St. NW, Ste. 802, Washington, DC 20006, (202)293-5960

Natl. Org. on Disability [**11819**], 1625 K St. NW, Ste. 802, Washington, DC 20006, (202)293-5960

Natl. Org. for Disorders of the Corpus Callosum [**15620**], PMB 363, 18032-C Lemon Dr., Yorba Linda, CA 92886, (714)747-0063

Natl. Org. for Diversity in Sales and Marketing [**2419**], PO Box 99640, Raleigh, NC 27624, (800)691-6380

Natl. Org. of Downsized Employees - Defunct.

Natl. Org. for Drug-Induced Disorders - Address unknown since 2011.

Natl. Org. for Empowering Caregivers [**13302**], 425 W 23rd St., Ste. 9B, New York, NY 10011, (212)807-1204

Natl. Org. for Empowering Caregivers [**13302**], 425 W 23rd St., Ste. 9B, New York, NY 10011, (212)807-1204

Natl. Org. of Episcopalians for Life [★**12923**]

Natl. Org. of Fed. Employees Against Abuse and Retaliation [**23206**], 11645 Sutphin Blvd., Jamaica, NY 11434-1526, (917)567-2660

Natl. Org. on Fetal Alcohol Syndrome [**16751**], 1200 Eton Ct. NW, 3rd Fl., Washington, DC 20007, (202)785-4585

Natl. Org. For River Sports [★**22838**]

Natl. Org. of Forensic Social Work [**8205**], 460 Smith St., Ste. K, Middletown, CT 06457, (860)613-0254

Natl. Org. of Gay and Lesbian Scientists and Tech. Professionals [**7379**], PO Box 91803, Pasadena, CA 91109, (626)791-7689

Natl. Org. to Halt the Abuse and Routine Mutilation of Males [**11521**], PO Box 460795, San Francisco, CA 94146, (415)826-9351

Natl. Org. of Hispanics in Criminal Justice [**5513**], PO Box 452614, Kissimmee, FL 34745, (505)876-8201

Natl. Org. for Human Ser. Educ. [★**8868**]

Natl. Org. for Human Ser. Educators [★**8868**]

Natl. Org. for Human Services [**8868**], 5341 Old Hwy. 5, Ste. 206, No. 214, Woodstock, GA 30188, (770)924-8899

Natl. Org. of Immigrants and Visible Minority Women of Canada [**IO**], Ottawa, ON, Canada

Natl. Org. of Indus. Trade Unions [**23222**], 148-06 Hillside Ave., Jamaica, NY 11435, (718)291-3434

Natl. Org. of Injured Workers [**23319**], 640 Bailey Rd., Ste. 129, Pittsburg, CA 94565, (925)235-1115

Natl. Org. of Iraqi Christians [**12630**], PO Box 833, Hazel Park, MI 48030, (586)939-2554

Natl. Org. of Italian-American Women [**19079**], 25 W 43rd St., 10th Fl., New York, NY 10036, (212)642-2003

Natl. Org. on Legal Problems of Educ. [★**5395**]

Natl. Org. on Legal Problems of Educ. [★**5395**]

Natl. Org. of Legal Services Workers [**23207**], 256 W 38th St., Ste. 705, New York, NY 10018, (212)228-0992

Natl. Org. for Lesbians of Size [**12104**], PO Box 5475, Oakland, CA 94605, (888)831-2139

Natl. Org. of Life and Hea. Insurance Guaranty Associations [**1676**], 13873 Park Center Rd., Ste. 329, Herndon, VA 20171, (703)481-5206

Natl. Org. on Male Sexual Victimization [★**13089**]

Natl. Org. for Manyu Advancement [**18840**], PO Box 66992, Phoenix, AZ 85082, (602)561-4800

Natl. Org. for Marriage [**12439**], 20 Nassau St., Ste. 242, Princeton, NJ 08542, (609)688-0450

Natl. Org. for Men [**18110**], Warren Farrel, 30 Besey St., New York, NY 10007, (415)459-6343

Natl. Org. for Men Against Sexism [**17856**], PO Box 455, Louisville, CO 80027-0455, (303)666-7043

Natl. Org. for Mentally Ill Children [★**15461**]

Natl. Org. for Mexican Amer. Rights [**17780**], PO Box 681205, San Antonio, TX 78268-1205, (210)520-1831

Natl. Org. of Minority Architects [**6202**], Howard Univ., Coll. of Engg., Architecture and Cmpt. Sciences, School of Architecture and Design, 2366 Sixth St. NW, Rm. 100, Washington, DC 20059, (202)686-2780

Natl. Org. of Mothers of Twins Clubs [**12548**], 2000 Mallory Ln., Ste. 130-600, Franklin, TN 37067-8231, (248)231-4480

Natl. Org. of Nurse Practitioners Faculties [**15784**], 900 19th St. NW, Ste. 200B, Washington, DC 20006, (202)289-8044

Natl. Org. of Nurses with Disabilities [**15785**], 1640 W Roosevelt Rd., Rm. 736, Chicago, IL 60608, (312)413-4097

Natl. Org. of Parents of Blind Children [**17109**], 1800 Johnson St., Baltimore, MD 21230-4998, (410)659-9314

Natl. Org. for People of Color Against Suicide [**13296**], PO Box 75571, Washington, DC 20013, (202)549-6039

Natl. Org. for the Professional Advancement of Black Chemists and Chem. Engineers [**6414**], PO Box 77040, Washington, DC 20013, (240)228-1763

Natl. Org. of Professional Hispanic Natural Resources Conservation Ser. Employees [**4521**], Rosabeth Garcia-Sais, Treas., 24 La Loma Ln., Belen, NM 87002, (505)761-4411

Natl. Org. for Public Hea. Nursing [★**15781**]

Natl. Org. for Rare Disorders [**14411**], PO Box 1968, Danbury, CT 06813-1968, (203)744-0100

Natl. Org. for Raw Materials [**17170**], 680 E 5 Point Hwy., Charlotte, MI 48813, (517)543-0111

Natl. Org. for the Reform of Marijuana Laws [**17311**], 1600 K St. NW, Ste. 501, Washington, DC 20006-2832, (202)483-5500

Natl. Org. of Remediators and Mold Inspectors [**1225**], 22174 Prats Rd., Abita Springs, LA 70420, (877)251-2296

Natl. Org. of Responsible Animal Owners - Defunct.

Natl. Org. of Restoring Men [**11522**], 3205 Northwood Dr., Ste. 209, Concord, CA 94520-4506, (925)827-4077

Natl. Org. of Restoring Men - UK [**IO**], Stone, United Kingdom

Natl. Org. of Rheumatology Managers [**16621**], 1121 Military Cutoff Rd., No. 337, Wilmington, NC 28405, (910)256-9898

Natl. Org. for Rivers [**22838**], 212 W Cheyenne Mountain Blvd., Colorado Springs, CO 80906-3712, (719)579-8759

Natl. Org. of Short Statured Adults [**13117**], PO Box 1187, New York, NY 10008-1187, (888)667-7239

Natl. Org. of Single Mothers [**13119**], PO Box 68, Midland, NC 28107

Natl. Org. of Sisters of Color Ending Sexual Assault [**13093**], PO Box 625, Canton, CT 06019, (860)693-2031

Natl. Org. of Social Security Claimants' Representatives [**18653**], 560 Sylvan Ave., Englewood Cliffs, NJ 07632, (201)567-4228

Natl. Org. of State Offices of Rural Hea. [**16490**], 44648 Mound Rd., No. 114, Sterling Heights, MI 48314, (586)739-9940

Natl. Org. Taunting Safety and Fairness Everywhere - Address unknown since 2010.

Natl. Org. of Test, Res., and Training Reactors [**7167**], Jeanine Holbrook, Oak Ridge Natl. Laboratory, One Bethel Valley Rd., Oak Ridge, TN 37831-6249, (865)241-7600

Natl. Org. of Travelers Aid Societies [★**13205**]

Natl. Org. of Travelers Aid Societies [★**13205**]

Natl. Org. of Tutoring and Mentoring Centers [★**9022**]

Natl. Org. of Vascular Anomalies [**16964**], PO Box 38216, Greensboro, NC 27438

Natl. Org. of Veterans' Advocates [**6061**], 1425 K St. NW, Ste. 350, Washington, DC 20005-3514, (304)413-0838

Natl. Org. for Victim Assistance [**13369**], 510 King St., Ste. 424, Alexandria, VA 22314, (703)535-6682

Natl. Org. for Women [**17665**], 1100 H St. NW, 3rd Fl., Washington, DC 20005, (202)628-8669

Natl. Org. for Women's Shelters and Young Women's Shelters in Sweden [**IO**], Stockholm, Sweden

Natl. Organizations for Youth Safety [**13543**], 7371 Atlas Walk Way, No. 109, Gainesville, VA 20155, (828)367-6697

Natl. Organizers Alliance [**13153**], PO Box 60708, Washington, DC 20039, (301)270-0640

Natl. Orientation Directors Assn. [**7674**], Univ. of Minnesota, 1313 5th St. SE, Mail Unit 72, Minneapolis, MN 55414, (612)627-0150

Natl. Orientation Directors Conf. [★**7674**]

Natl. Ornamental Glass Mfrs. Assn. [★**1583**]

Natl. Ornamental Iron Mfrs. Assn. [★**2486**]

Natl. Ornamental Metal Mfrs. Assn. [★**2486**]

Natl. Ornamental and Miscellaneous Metals Assn. [**2486**], 805 S Glynn St., Ste. 127, No. 311, Fayetteville, GA 30214, (888)516-8585

Natl. Orphan Train Complex [**20647**], PO Box 322, Concordia, KS 66901, (785)243-4471

Natl. ORT League - Defunct.

Natl. Osteopathic Found. [★**16073**]

Natl. Osteopathic Women Physician's Assn. [**23613**], ATSU - Kirksville Coll. of Osteophatic Medicine, 800 W Jefferson St., Kirksville, MO 63501

Natl. Osteoporosis Found. [**16040**], 1150 17th St. NW, Ste. 850, Washington, DC 20036-4641, (202)223-2226

Natl. Osteoporosis Patient Soc. Austria [**IO**], Graz, Austria

Natl. Osteoporosis Soc. [**IO**], Bath, United Kingdom

Natl. Outdoor Events Assn. [**IO**], Wells, United Kingdom

Natl. Outdoor Showmen's Assn. [★**1195**]

Natl. Outdoor Showmen's Assn. [★**1195**]

Natl. Outerwear and Sportswear Assn. [★**199**]

Natl. Ovarian Cancer Assn. [**IO**], Toronto, ON, Canada

Natl. Ovarian Cancer Coalition [**13957**], 2501 Oak Lawn Ave., Ste. 435, Dallas, TX 75219, (973)944-0719

Natl. PACE Assn. [**12133**], 801 N Fairfax St., Ste. 309, Alexandria, VA 22314, (703)535-1565

Natl. Pacific/Asian Rsrc. Center on Aging [★**10856**]

Natl. Paddleball Assn. [**22254**], 7642 Kingston Dr., Portage, MI 49002, (269)779-6615

Natl. Paideia Center [**8110**], 140 Friday Center Dr., Chapel Hill, NC 27517, (919)962-3128

Natl. Pain Educ. Coun. - Address unknown since 2011.

Natl. Paint and Coatings Assn. and FED of Societies for Coatings Tech. [★**2613**]

Natl. Paint and Ink Mfrs'. Assn. [**IO**], Mexico City, Mexico

Natl. Paint, Oil and Varnish Assn. [★**2613**]

Natl. Paint, Varnish and Lacquer Assn. [★**2613**]

Natl. Painting, Decorating, and Drywall Apprenticeship and Manpower Training Fund [★**11941**]

Natl. Painting, Decorating, and Drywall Apprenticeship and Manpower Training Fund [★**11941**]

Natl. PAL [★**13538**]

Natl. Palliative Care Nursing Org. [**IO**], Eltham, Australia

Natl. Palm Oil Growers' Fed. [**IO**], Bogota, Colombia

Natl. Pan-American Junior Golf Assn. [**22618**], Natl. Pan-American Golf Assn., PO Box 7211, Corpus Christi, TX 78467-7211, (903)569-2638

Natl. Pan-Hellenic Coun. [**23539**], 3951 Snapfinger Pkwy., Ste. 218, Decatur, GA 30035, (404)592-6145

Natl. Panhellenic Conf. [**23540**], 3901 W 86th St., Ste. 398, Indianapolis, IN 46268, (317)872-3185

Reference to "IO" in place of a book number signifies that the association may be found in the 50th edition of International Organizations.

Natl. Panhellenic Conf. | Natl. Panhellenic Editors Conf. **[23508]**, 3901 W 86th St., Ste. 398, Indianapolis, IN 46268, (317)872-3185

Natl. Paper Trade Assn. **[★2620]**

Natl. Parachute Jumpers-Riggers Assn. **[★22800]**

Natl. Paralegal Assn. **[5873]**, Box 406, Solebury, PA 18963, (215)297-8333

Natl. Paralympic Comm. Germany **[IO]**, Duisburg, Germany

Natl. Paralympic Comm. Islamic Republic of Iran **[IO]**, Tehran, Iran

Natl. Paraplegia Found. **[★16703]**

Natl. Parent Info. Network - Defunct.

Natl. Parents and Siblings Alliance **[IO]**, Dublin, Ireland

Natl. Park Found. **[5878]**, 1201 Eye St. NW, Ste. 550B, Washington, DC 20005, (202)354-6460

Natl. Park Hospitality Assn. **[1214]**, 1225 New York Ave. NW, Ste. 450, Washington, DC 20005, (202)682-9530

Natl. Park Trust **[4768]**, 401 E Jefferson St., Ste. 102, Rockville, MD 20850, (301)279-PARK

Natl. Park Trust Fund Bd. **[★5878]**

Natl. Parking Assn. **[2627]**, 1112 16th St. NW, Ste. 840, Washington, DC 20036, (202)296-4336

Natl. Parkinson Found. **[15621]**, 1501 NW 9th Ave., Bob Hope Rd., Miami, FL 33136-1494, (305)243-6666

National Parkinson Institute **[★15621]**

Natl. Parks Assn. **[★5879]**

Natl. Parks Conservation Assn. **[5879]**, 1300 19th St. NW, Ste. 300, Washington, DC 20036, (202)223-6722

Natl. Parks and Conservation Assn. **[★5879]**

Natl. Parks Inholders Assn. **[★5901]**

Natl. Parliamentary Debate Assn. **[8897]**, Prof. Brent Northup, Treas., Carroll Coll., 1601 N Benton Ave., Helena, MT 59625, (406)447-5400

Natl. Parrot Sanctuary **[IO]**, Friskney, United Kingdom

Natl. Particleboard Assn. **[★1503]**

Natl. Particleboard Assn. **[★1503]**

Natl. Partnership for Community Leadership **[11663]**, 2728 Sherman Ave., Washington, DC 20001-5409, (202)234-6725

Natl. Partnership for Women and Families **[17666]**, 1875 Connecticut Ave. NW, Ste. 650, Washington, DC 20009, (202)986-2600

Natl. Passenger Traffic Assn. **[★3568]**

Natl. Pasta Assn. **[1420]**, 750 Natl. Press Bldg., 529 14th St. NW, Washington, DC 20045, (202)637-5888

Natl. Patient Safety Found. **[14818]**, 268 Summer St., 6th Fl., Boston, MA 02210, (617)391-9900

Natl. Pavement Contractors Assn. **[595]**, PO Box 57, Mineral Wells, TX 76068-0057, (940)327-8041

Natl. Paving Brick Assn. **[★536]**

Natl. Pawnbrokers Assn. **[2213]**, PO Box 508, Keller, TX 76244, (817)337-8830

Natl. Pawnbrokers Assn. **[IO]**, Reading, United Kingdom

Natl. Payphone Assn. **[★3399]**

Natl. Peace Acad. Campaign **[★18268]**

Natl. Peace Acad. Found. **[★18268]**

Natl. Peace Acad. Fund **[★18268]**

Natl. Peace Corps Assn. **[18308]**, 1900 L St. NW, Ste. 404, Washington, DC 20036, (202)293-7728

Natl. Peace Day Celebrations - Defunct.

Natl. Peace Found. **[18268]**, PO Box 232, Brevard, NC 28712, (888)616-1186

Natl. Peace Inst. Found. **[★18268]**

Natl. Peach Partners - Address unknown since 2011.

Natl. Peanut Buying Points Assn. **[4751]**, PO Box 314, 115 W 2nd St., Tifton, GA 31793, (229)386-1716

Natl. Peanut Coun. **[★4745]**

Natl. Peanut Festival Assn. **[4752]**, 5622 Hwy. 231 S, Dothan, AL 36301, (334)793-4323

Natl. Pearson Yacht Owners Assn. - Address unknown since 2011.

Natl. Pecan Marketing Coun. - Defunct.

Natl. Pecan Shellers Assn. **[4753]**, 1100 Johnson Ferry Rd., Ste. 300, Atlanta, GA 30342, (404)252-3663

Natl. Pediatric and Family HIV Rsrc. Center - Defunct.

Natl. Pediatrics AIDS Network **[16149]**, PO Box 1032, Boulder, CO 80306

Natl. Pediculosis Assn. **[16491]**, 1005 Boylston St., Ste. 343, Newton, MA 02461, (617)905-0176

Natl. Pedigreed Livestock Coun. **[3794]**, Zane Akins, Sec.-Treas., 177 Palermo Pl., The Villages, FL 32159, (352)259-6005

Natl. Peer Helpers Assn. **[★11677]**

Natl. Pemphigus Found. **[★14394]**

Natl. People's Action **[11534]**, 810 N Milwaukee Ave., Chicago, IL 60642, (312)243-3035

Natl. Performance Network **[10591]**, PO Box 56698, New Orleans, LA 70156-6698, (504)595-8008

Natl. Perinatal Assn. **[16157]**, 457 State St., Binghamton, NY 13901, (888)971-3295

Natl. Perinatal Info. Center **[16158]**, 225 Chapman St., Ste. 200, Providence, RI 02905, (401)274-0650

Natl. Perishable Logistics Assn. - Defunct.

Natl. Personnel Assn. **[★2263]**

Natl. Personnel Assn. **[★2263]**

Natl. Pest Control Assn. **[★2634]**

Natl. Pest Control Assn. **[★2634]**

Natl. Pest Mgt. Assn. Intl. **[2634]**, 10460 N St., Fairfax, VA 22030, (703)352-6762

Natl. Pest Mgt. Assn. Intl. **[2634]**, 10460 N St., Fairfax, VA 22030, (703)352-6762

Natl. Pest Technicians Assn. **[IO]**, Nottingham, United Kingdom

Natl. Pesticide Info. Center **[13324]**, Oregon State Univ., 333 Weniger Hall, Corvallis, OR 97331-6502, (800)858-7378

Natl. Pesticide Info. CH **[★13324]**

Natl. Pesticide Telecommunications Network **[★13324]**

Natl. Pet Alliance **[11015]**, PO Box 53385, San Jose, CA 95153, (408)363-0700

Natl. Pet Dealers and Breeders Assn. - Defunct.

Natl. Petrochemical and Refiners Assn. **[2662]**, 1667 K St. NW, Ste. 700, Washington, DC 20006, (202)457-0480

Natl. Petroleum Assn. **[★2662]**

Natl. Petroleum Coun. **[5408]**, 1625 K St. NW, Ste. 600, Washington, DC 20006, (202)393-6100

Natl. Petroleum Mgt. Assn. **[2663]**, 4222 Fortuna Center Plz., No. 641, Dumfries, VA 22025, (703)583-1206

Natl. Petroleum Refiners Assn. **[★2662]**

Natl. Pharmaceutical Alliance **[★2694]**

Natl. Pharmaceutical Assn. **[16209]**, 107 Kilmayne Dr., Ste. C, Cary, NC 27511, (877)215-2091

Natl. Pharmaceutical Coun. **[2698]**, 1894 Preston White Dr., Reston, VA 20191-5433, (703)620-6390

Natl. Pharmacies' Assn. **[IO]**, Lisbon, Portugal

Natl. Pharmacy Assn. **[IO]**, St. Albans, United Kingdom

Natl. Pharmacy Technician Assn. **[16210]**, PO Box 683148, Houston, TX 77268, (888)247-8700

Natl. Philatelic Soc. **[IO]**, London, United Kingdom

Natl. Phlebotomy Assn. **[14973]**, 1901 Brightseat Rd., Landover, MD 20785, (301)386-4200

Natl. Phobics Soc. **[★190]**

Natl. Photographic Dealers Assn. **[★2730]**

Natl. Photographic Dealers Assn. **[★2730]**

Natl. Physicians Alliance **[16272]**, 888 16th St. NW, Ste. 800, Washington, DC 20006, (202)420-7896

Natl. Piano Found. **[8666]**, 14070 Proton Rd., Ste. 100, LB9, Dallas, TX 75244, (972)233-9107

Natl. Piano Mfrs. Assn. of Am. **[★2570]**

Natl. Piano Mfrs. Assn. of Am. **[★2570]**

Natl. Pickle Packers Assn. **[★1425]**

Natl. Pickle Packers Assn. **[★1425]**

Natl. Piers Soc. **[IO]**, London, United Kingdom

Natl. Pigeon Assn. **[21225]**, Ed Pointer, Co-Sec., PO Box 950088, Oklahoma City, OK 73195-0088, (405)604-8792

Natl. Pipeline Reform Coalition - Defunct.

Natl. Pitching Assn. **[22286]**, PO Box 2350, Del Mar, CA 92014, (858)549-2800

Natl. Pituitary Agency **[★16280]**

Natl. Plant Bd. **[5193]**, Aurelio Posadas, Exec. Sec., PO Box 847, Elk Grove, CA 95759, (916)709-3484

Natl. Plant Food Inst. **[★1245]**

Natl. Plasterers Coun. **[2762]**, 4344 Laura St., Port Charlotte, FL 33980, (941)766-0634

Natl. Plastics Indus. Assn. **[IO]**, Mexico City, Mexico

Natl. Pocket Billiard Assn. - Defunct.

Natl. Podiatric Medical Assn. **[16300]**, 1706 E 87th St., Chicago, IL 60617, (773)374-5300

Natl. Podiatry Assn. **[★16300]**

Natl. Poetry Day Comm. - Defunct.

Natl. Poetry Found. **[10451]**, Univ. of Maine, 5752 Neville Hall, Rm. 400, Orono, ME 04469-5752, (207)581-3814

Natl. Police Accountability Proj. **[5731]**, 14 Beacon St., Ste. 701, Boston, MA 02108, (617)227-6015

Natl. Police Athletic League **[★13538]**

Natl. Police Bloodhound Assn. **[5732]**, Coby Webb, Treas., 38540 Alva Dr., Cherry Valley, CA 92223

Natl. Police Canine Assn. **[5733]**, PO Box 538, Waddell, AZ 85355, (713)562-7371

Natl. Police Constables Assn. **[★5723]**

Natl. Police and Fire Fighters Assn. **[★5686]**

Natl. Police Officers Assn. of Am. - Address unknown since 2010.

Natl. Political Cong. of Black Women **[★5843]**

Natl. Pollution Prevention Roundtable **[4797]**, 50 F St. NW, Ste. 350, Washington, DC 20001, (202)299-9701

Natl. Polymer Clay Guild **[★21852]**

Natl. Pony Soc. **[IO]**, Alton, United Kingdom

Natl. Pop Can Collectors **[21381]**, 1082 S 46th St., West Des Moines, IA 50266

Natl. Pork Coun. Women **[★4951]**

Natl. Pork Producers Coun. **[4951]**, 122 C St. NW, Ste. 875, Washington, DC 20001, (202)347-3600

Natl. Post Off. Mail Handlers, Watchmen, Messengers, and Gp. Leaders **[★23283]**

Natl. Postal Forum **[5892]**, 3998 Fair Ridge Dr., Ste. 150, Fairfax, VA 22033-2907, (703)218-5015

Natl. Postal Mail Handlers Union **[23283]**, 1101 Connecticut Ave. NW, Ste. 500, Washington, DC 20036-4325, (202)833-9095

Natl. Postdoctoral Assn. **[8800]**, 1200 New York Ave. NW, Ste. 635, Washington, DC 20005, (202)326-6424

Natl. Postsecondary Agricultural Student Org. **[7715]**, AgrowKnowledge Ctr., PO Box 2068, Cedar Rapids, IA 52406, (208)670-3704

The Natl. Potato Bd. **[★4480]**

Natl. Potato Chip Inst. **[★1430]**

Natl. Potato Coun. **[4461]**, 1300 L St. NW, No. 910, Washington, DC 20005, (202)682-9456

Natl. Potato Promotion Bd. **[★4480]**

Natl. Potter Syndrome Forum **[16777]**, 8221 Township Rd. 323, Holmesville, OH 44633, (330)279-4374

Natl. Poultry and Food Distributors Assn. **[1421]**, 2014 Osborne Rd., St. Marys, GA 31558, (678)850-9311

Natl. Poultry Union **[IO]**, Rome, Italy

Natl. PR1ME User Group - Defunct.

Natl. Practitioners Network for Fathers and Families **[12018]**, 1003 K St. NW, Ste. 565, Washington, DC 20001, (202)737-6680

Natl. Precast Concrete Assn. **[833]**, 1320 City Center Dr., Ste. 200, Carmel, IN 46032, (317)571-9500

Natl. Precast Concrete Assn. Australia **[IO]**, Adelaide, Australia

Natl. Premium Mfrs. Representatives **[★2318]**

Natl. Preservation Inst. **[9716]**, PO Box 1702, Alexandria, VA 22313, (703)765-0100

Natl. Preservers Assn. **[★1402]**

Natl. Preservers Assn. **[★1402]**

Natl. Press Club **[2853]**, Natl. Press Bldg., 529 14th St. NW, 13th Fl., Washington, DC 20045, (202)662-7500

Natl. Press Found. **[2854]**, 1211 Connecticut Ave. NW, Ste. 310, Washington, DC 20036, (202)663-7280

Natl. Press Photographers Assn. **[2726]**, 3200 Croasdaile Dr., Ste. 306, Durham, NC 27705-2588, (919)383-7246

Natl. Pressure Ulcer Advisory Panel **[14819]**, 1025 Thomas Jefferson St. NW, Ste. 500 E, Washington, DC 20007, (202)521-6789

Natl. Printing Equip. Assn. **[★1624]**

Natl. Printing Equip. and Supply Assn. **[★1624]**

Natl. Priorities Proj. **[17625]**, 243 King St., Ste. 109, Northampton, MA 01060, (413)584-9556

A star before a book entry number signifies that the name is not listed separately, but is mentioned within the entry.

Natl. Prison Assn. [★11702]

Natl. Prison Hospice Assn. [15030], 11 S Angell St., No. 303, Providence, RI 02906

Natl. Private Duty Assn. [15013], 941 E 86th St., Ste. 270, Indianapolis, IN 46240, (317)663-3637

Natl. Private Truck Coun. [3525], 950 N Glebe Rd., Ste. 530, Arlington, VA 22203-4183, (703)683-1300

Natl. Private Trucking Assn. [★3525]

Natl. Pro-Life Alliance [18558], 4521 Windsor Arms Ct., Annandale, VA 22003, (703)321-9200

Natl. Pro-Life Religious Coun. [18559], PO Box 61838, Staten Island, NY 10306, (718)980-4400

Natl. Probation Assn. [★11690]

Natl. Probation and Parole Assn. [★11690]

Natl. Productivity and Competitiveness Coun. [IO], Ebene City, Mauritius

Natl. Productivity Coun. [IO], New Delhi, India

Natl. Professional Anglers' Assn. [22582], 8410 Curve Rd., Forestville, WI 54213, (920)856-6151

Natl. Professional Colorists of Am. [★2709]

Natl. Professional Honorary Agricultural Educ. Fraternity [★23460]

Natl. Professional Sci. Master's Assn. [8241], 100 Inst. Rd., Worcester, MA 01609, (508)831-4996

Natl. Prog. for Playground Safety [18578], Univ. of Northern Iowa, Human Performance Ctr. 103, Cedar Falls, IA 50614-0618, (800)554-PLAY

Natl. Propane Gas Assn. [4491], 1899 L St. NW, Ste. 350, Washington, DC 20036-4623, (202)466-7200

Natl. Property Mgt. Assn. [2903], 28100 U.S. Hwy. 19 N, Ste. 400, Clearwater, FL 33761, (727)736-3788

Natl. Prostate Cancer Coalition [★13995]

Natl. Psoriasis Found. [★14328]

Natl. Psoriasis Found. [★14328]

Natl. Psoriasis Found. USA [14334], 6600 SW 92nd Ave., Ste. 300, Portland, OR 97223-7195, (503)244-7404

Natl. Psychological Assn. for Psychoanalysis [16360], 40 W 13th St., New York, NY 10011-7891, (212)924-7440

Natl. PTA [8691], 1250 N Pitt St., Alexandria, VA 22314, (703)518-1200

Natl. Public Employer Labor Relations Assn. [5636], 1012 S Coast Hwy., Ste. M, Oceanside, CA 92054, (760)433-1686

Natl. Public Housing Conf. [★12189]

Natl. Public Parks Tennis Assn. [23057], 1800 W Old Shakopee Rd., Bloomington, MN 55431, (952)563-8886

Natl. Public Radio [9461], 635 Massachusetts Ave. NW, Washington, DC 20001, (202)513-2000

Natl. Public Records Res. Assn. [1905], 2501 Aerial Center Pkwy., Ste. 103, Morrisville, NC 27560, (919)459-2078

Natl. Public Safety Telecommunications Coun. [3415], 8191 Southpark Ln., No. 205, Littleton, CO 80120, (866)807-4755

Natl. Public School ABC Prog. [★8077]

Natl. Publishers Assn. [★2947]

Natl. Puerto Rican Coalition [18501], 1444 I St. NW, Ste. 800, Washington, DC 20005, (202)223-3915

Natl. Puerto Rican Coalition [18501], 1444 I St. NW, Ste. 800, Washington, DC 20005, (202)223-3915

Natl. Puerto Rican Forum [12147], Promesa, 1776 Clay Ave., Bronx, NY 10457, (718)299-1100

Natl. Purchasing Inst. [2974], PO Box 370192, Las Vegas, NV 89137-0192, (702)989-8095

Natl. Puro Conjunto Music Assn. [10263], 9200 Lockwood Springs Rd., Manor, TX 78653, (512)835-5886

Natl. Puro Conjunto Music Assn. [10263], 9200 Lockwood Springs Rd., Manor, TX 78653, (512)835-5886

Natl. Puzzlers' League [21752], Joseph J. Adamski, Treas., 2507 Almar St., Jenison, MI 49428

Natl. Pygmy Goat Assn. [3795], 1932 149th Ave. SE, Snohomish, WA 98290, (425)334-6506

Natl. Pyrotechnic Distributors Assn. [★2976]

Natl. Qigong Chi Kung Assn. [13697], PO Box 270065, St. Paul, MN 55127, (888)815-1893

Natl. Quality Forum [14820], 601 13th St. NW, Ste. 500 N, Washington, DC 20005, (202)783-1300

Natl. Quality Forum and Natl. Comm. for Quality Hea. Care [★14820]

Natl. Quality Inst. [IO], Toronto, ON, Canada

Natl. Quarter Horse Registry [4619], 1497 S Staghorn, Toquerville, UT 84774, (435)559-2069

Natl. Quarter Pony Assn. [4620], PO Box 171, Melrose, OH 45861, (419)594-2968

Natl. Quilting Assn. [21458], PO Box 12190, Columbus, OH 43212-0190, (614)488-8520

Natl. Radiator Core Mfg. Credit Assn. [★1300]

Natl. Radiator Mfg. Credit Assn. [★1300]

Natl. Radio Broadcasters Assn. [★501]

Natl. Radio Parts Distributors [★1109]

Natl. Radio Proj. [18097], 1714 Franklin St., No. 100-251, Oakland, CA 94612, (510)251-1332

Natl. Railroad Constr. and Maintenance Assn. [2991], 500 New Jersey Ave. NW, Ste. 400, Washington, DC 20001, (202)715-2920

Natl. Railway Historical Soc. [10493], 100 N 20th St., Ste. 400, Philadelphia, PA 19103, (215)557-6606

Natl. Ramah Commn. [8431], 3080 Broadway, New York, NY 10027, (212)678-8881

Natl. Ramah Commn. [8431], 3080 Broadway, New York, NY 10027, (212)678-8881

Natl. Rare Blood Club - Defunct.

Natl. Reading Conf. [★8781]

Natl. Ready Mixed Concrete Assn. [834], 900 Spring St., Silver Spring, MD 20910, (301)587-1400

Natl. Real Estate Investors Assn. [2148], 525 W 5th St., Ste. 101, Covington, KY 41011, (859)292-7342

Natl. Reamer Collectors Assn. [21870], 8019 W 45th Pl., Lyons, IL 60534-1812, (708)447-6978

Natl. Reciprocal and Family Support Enforcement Assn. [★5425]

Natl. Reclamation Assn. [★7607]

Natl. Records Mgt. Coun. - Defunct.

Natl. Recovery and Collection Assn. - Defunct.

Natl. Recreation Assn. of Japan [IO], Tokyo, Japan

Natl. Recreation and Park Assn. [5880], 22377 Belmont Ridge Rd., Ashburn, VA 20148-4501, (703)858-0784

Natl. Recycling Coalition [3640], 1220 L St. NW, Ste. 100-155, Washington, DC 20005, (202)618-2107

Natl. Red Cherry Inst. [★4444]

Natl. Reform Assn. - Address unknown since 2010.

Natl. Refrigeration Contractors Assn. - Defunct.

Natl. Regap Network - Address unknown since 2011.

Natl. Register of Hea. Ser. Providers in Psychology [16414], 1120 G St. NW, Ste. 330, Washington, DC 20005, (202)783-7663

Natl. Register of Hypnotherapists and Psychotherapists [IO], Nelson, United Kingdom

Natl. Register of Personal Trainers [IO], Sywell, United Kingdom

Natl. Register of Warranted Builders [IO], London, United Kingdom

Natl. Registration Center for Stud. Abroad [8371], PO Box 1393, Milwaukee, WI 53201, (414)278-0631

Natl. Registration Center for Stud. Abroad [8371], PO Box 1393, Milwaukee, WI 53201, (414)278-0631

Natl. Registry of Certified Chemists [6415], 927 S Walter Reed Dr., No. 11, Arlington, VA 22204, (703)979-9001

Natl. Registry in Clinical Chemistry [★6415]

Natl. Registry of Emergency Medical Technicians [14477], Rocco V. Morando Bldg., 6610 Busch Blvd., PO Box 29233, Columbus, OH 43229, (614)888-4484

Natl. Registry of Environmental Professionals [4287], PO Box 2099, Glenview, IL 60025, (847)724-6631

Natl. Registry of Environmental Professionals [4287], PO Box 2099, Glenview, IL 60025, (847)724-6631

National Registry of Microbiologists [★6282]

National Registry of Microbiologists [★6282]

Natl. Registry of Professional Interpreters and Translators for the Deaf [★14956]

Natl. Registry of Willys - Knight Automobiles [★21195]

Natl. Registry of Willys - Knight Automobiles [★21195]

Natl. Rehabilitation Admin. Assn. [★16568]

Natl. Rehabilitation Assn. [16572], 633 S Washington St., Alexandria, VA 22314, (703)836-0850

Natl. Rehabilitation Counseling Assn. [16573], PO Box 4480, Manassas, VA 20108, (703)361-2077

Natl. Rehabilitation Info. Center [16574], 8201 Corporate Dr., Ste. 600, Landover, MD 20785, (301)459-5900

Natl. Reined Cow Horse Assn. [21856], 13181 U.S. Hwy. 177, Byars, OK 74831, (580)759-4949

Natl. Reining Horse Assn. [4621], 3000 NW 10th St., Oklahoma City, OK 73107-5302, (405)946-7400

Natl. Reining Horse Assn. [4621], 3000 NW 10th St., Oklahoma City, OK 73107-5302, (405)946-7400

Natl. Relief Network [12870], PO Box 125, Greenville, MI 48838-0125, (616)225-2525

Natl. Religious Affairs Assn. [19638], PO Box 77075, Washington, DC 20013-8075

Natl. Religious Broadcasters [19357], 9510 Tech. Dr., Manassas, VA 20110, (703)330-7000

Natl. Religious Broadcasters [19357], 9510 Tech. Dr., Manassas, VA 20110, (703)330-7000

Natl. Religious Liberty Assn. [★18520]

Natl. Religious Liberty Assn. [★18520]

Natl. Religious Publicity Coun. [★20168]

Natl. Religious Vocation Conf. [19478], 5401 S Cornell Ave., Ste. 207, Chicago, IL 60615-5664, (773)363-5454

Natl. Remodelers Assn. [★589]

Natl. Remotivation Therapy Org. - Address unknown since 2010.

Natl. Renal Administrators Assn. [15299], 100 N 20th St., 4th Fl., Philadelphia, PA 19103, (215)320-4655

Natl. Renderers Assn. [2590], 801 N Fairfax St., Ste. 205, Alexandria, VA 22314, (703)683-0155

Natl. Renewables Cooperative Org. [6741], 4140 W 99th St., Carmel, IN 46032-7731, (317)344-7900

Natl. Rental Housing Coun. [★3033]

Natl. Rental Ser. Assn. [★3076]

Natl. Republican Club of Capitol Hill [18533], 300 1st St. SE, Washington, DC 20003, (202)484-4590

Natl. Republican Congressional Comm. [18534], 320 1st St. SE, Washington, DC 20003, (202)479-7000

Natl. Republican Inst. for Intl. Affairs [★17525]

Natl. Republican Inst. for Intl. Affairs [★17525]

Natl. Republican Senatorial Comm. [18535], Ronald Reagan Republican Center, 425 2nd St. NE, Washington, DC 20002, (202)675-6000

Natl. Res. Coun. [7380], Natl. Acad. of Sciences, 500 5th St. NW, Washington, DC 20001, (202)334-2000

Natl. Res. Coun. [IO], Rome, Italy

Natl. Res. Coun. of Canada [IO], Ottawa, ON, Canada

Natl. Res. Coun. of the Philippines [IO], Taguig, Philippines

Natl. Res. Council's Inst. for Res. in Constr. [IO], Ottawa, ON, Canada

Natl. Res. Found. [IO], Pretoria, Republic of South Africa

Natl. Resident Matching Prog. [8615], 2450 N St. NW, Washington, DC 20037-1127, (202)828-0566

Natl. Residential Appraisers Inst. [3035], 2001 Cooper Foster Park Rd., Amherst, OH 44001, (440)282-7925

Natl. Rsrc. Center for Hea. and Safety in Child Care [★11158]

Natl. Rsrc. Center for Hea. and Safety in Child Care and Early Educ. [11158], Univ. of Colorado Coll. of Nursing, Campus Mail Stop F541, 13120 E 19th Ave., Aurora, CO 80045-0508, (303)724-0654

Natl. Rsrc. Center on Homelessness and Mental Illness [12164], Homelessness Rsrc. Center, 200 Reservoir St., Ste. 202, Needham, MA 02494, (617)467-6014

Natl. Rsrc. Center for Paraprofessionals in Educ. and Related Services [8889], Utah State Univ., 6526 Old Main Hill, Logan, UT 84322-6526, (435)797-7272

Natl. Rsrc. Center for Youth Services [11367], 4502 E 41st St., Bldg. 4W, Tulsa, OK 74135-2512, (918)660-3700

Natl. Resource Network - Defunct.

Natl. Restaurant Assn. [1766], 1200 17th St. NW, Washington, DC 20036, (202)331-5900

Natl. Restaurant Assn. Educational Found. [1767], 175 W Jackson Blvd., Ste. 1500, Chicago, IL 60604-2702, (312)715-1010

Reference to "IO" in place of a book number signifies that the association may be found in the 50th edition of International Organizations.

Natl. Restaurant Assn. | Multi-Unit Architects, Engineers and Constr. Officers Executive Study Group [1768], 1200 17th St. NW, Washington, DC 20036, (202)973-3678

Natl. Restaurant Assn. | Quality Assurance Study Group [1769], 1200 17th St. NW, Washington, DC 20036, (202)331-5900

Natl. Restaurant Assn. Risk and Safety Managers - Defunct.

Natl. Resume Writers' Assn. [3706], 1050 E Ray Rd., No. A5, 195, Chandler, AZ 85225, (602)788-3121

Natl. Resume Writers' Assn. [3706], 1050 E Ray Rd., No. A5, 195, Chandler, AZ 85225, (602)788-3121

Natl. Retail Farm Equip. Assn. [★172]

Natl. Retail Fed. [3118], 325 7th St. NW, Ste. 1100, Washington, DC 20004, (202)783-7971

Natl. Retail Furniture Assn. [★1555]

Natl. Retail Furniture Assn. [★1555]

Natl. Retail Grocers Secretaries Assn. [★3103]

Natl. Retail Hardware Assn. [★1656]

Natl. Retail Hobby Stores Assn. [693], 214 N Hale St., Wheaton, IL 60187, (630)510-4596

Natl. Retail Hobby Stores Assn. [693], 214 N Hale St., Wheaton, IL 60187, (630)510-4596

Natl. Retail Liquor Package Stores Assn. [★174]

Natl. Retail Lumber Dealers Assn. [★1513]

Natl. Retail Merchants Assn. [★3118]

Natl. Retail Sales Tax Alliance - Address unknown since 2011.

Natl. Retail Tenants Assn. [3080], 60 Shaker Rd., East Longmeadow, MA 01028-2760, (413)525-4565

Natl. Retired Teachers Assn. [8801], Amer. Assn. of Retired Persons, 601 E St. NW, Washington, DC 20049, (202)434-3525

Natl. Retriever Club [22547], 4379 S Howell Ave., Ste. 17, Milwaukee, WI 53207-5053, (414)481-2760

Natl. Reverse Mortgage Lenders Assn. [2214], 1400 16th St. NW, Ste. 420, Washington, DC 20036, (202)939-1760

Natl. Rex Rabbit Club [4850], PO Box 1465, Cave Junction, OR 97523, (541)592-4865

Natl. Reye's Syndrome Found. [16615], PO Box 829, Bryan, OH 43506, (419)924-9000

Natl. Rheumatoid Arthritis Soc. [IO], Maidenhead, United Kingdom

Natl. Rice Growers' Assn. [IO], Bogota, Colombia

Natl. Rice Producers' Assn. [IO], Lisbon, Portugal

Natl. Rifle Assn. of Am. [22881], 11250 Waples Mill Rd., Fairfax, VA 22030, (703)267-1600

Natl. Rifle Assn. of New Zealand [IO], Upper Hutt, New Zealand

Natl. Rifle Assn. of the United Kingdom [IO], Brookwood, United Kingdom

Natl. Rifle and Pistol Assn. of Ireland [IO], Blackrock, Ireland

Natl. Right to Life Comm. [12940], 512 10th St. NW, Washington, DC 20004, (202)626-8800

Natl. Right to Life Educational Trust Fund [18560], 512 10th St. NW, Washington, DC 20004, (202)626-8800

Natl. Right to Read Found. [8782], PO Box 560, Strasburg, VA 22657, (540)465-2349

Natl. Right to Work Comm. [18049], 8001 Braddock Rd., Ste. 500, Springfield, VA 22160, (703)321-9820

Natl. Right to Work Found. [★18050]

Natl. Right to Work Legal Defense and Educ. Found. [18050], 8001 Braddock Rd., Springfield, VA 22160, (703)321-8510

Natl. Right to Work Legal Defense Found. [★18050]

Natl. Risk Retention Assn. [2021], 2214 Rock Hill Rd., Ste. 315, Herndon, VA 20170, (703)297-0059

Natl. Road Carriers [IO], Auckland, New Zealand

Natl. Road Runners Club [★22866]

Natl. Road Transport Assn. [IO], Rome, Italy

Natl. Roadside Vegetation Mgt. Assn. [4516], 5616 Lynchburg Cir., Hueytown, AL 35023, (205)491-7574

Natl. Rocket Club [★6089]

Natl. Roof Certification and Inspection Assn. [596], 2232 E Wilson Ave., Orange, CA 92867, (888)687-7663

Natl. Roof Deck Contractors Assn. - Defunct.

Natl. Roofing Contractors Assn. [939], 10255 W Higgins Rd., Ste. 600, Rosemont, IL 60018-5607, (847)299-9070

Natl. Roofing Educ. Found. [★7918]

Natl. Roofing Found. [7918], The Roofing Indus. Alliance for Progress, 10255 W Higgins Rd., Ste. 600, Rosemont, IL 60018-5607, (847)299-9070

Natl. Rosacea Soc. [14335], 196 James St., Barrington, IL 60010, (888)662-5874

Natl. Rose O'Neill Club [★21693]

Natl. Rose O'Neill Club [★21693]

Natl. Roundtable of State P2 Programs [★4797]

Natl. Rowing Found. [22857], 67 Mystic Rd., North Stonington, CT 06359, (860)535-0634

Natl. Runaway Switchboard [12949], 3080 N Lincoln Ave., Chicago, IL 60657, (773)880-9860

Natl. Rural Economic Developers Assn. [18573], 100 E Grand Ave., Ste. 330, Des Moines, IA 50309, (515)284-1421

Natl. Rural Educ. Advocacy Coalition [8804], Amer. Assn. of School Administrators, 22 S 22nd St., Harrisburg, PA 17104, (717)236-7180

Natl. Rural Educ. Assn. [8805], Purdue Univ., Beering Hall of Liberal Arts and Educ., 100 N Univ. St., West Lafayette, IN 47907-2098, (765)494-0086

Natl. Rural Elec. Cooperative Assn. [1082], 4301 Wilson Blvd., Arlington, VA 22203, (703)907-5500

Natl. Rural Elec. Cooperative Assn. [1082], 4301 Wilson Blvd., Arlington, VA 22203, (703)907-5500

Natl. Rural Hea. Assn. [16492], Administrative Off., 521 E 63rd St., Kansas City, MO 64110-3329, (816)756-3140

Natl. Rural Hea. Care Assn. [★16492]

Natl. Rural Housing Coalition [12195], 1331 G St. NW, 10th Fl., Washington, DC 20005, (202)393-5229

Natl. Rural Letter Carriers' Assn. [23284], 1630 Duke St., Alexandria, VA 22314-3465, (703)684-5545

Natl. Rural Recruitment and Retention Network [14884], 2004 King St., La Crosse, WI 54601, (608)782-0660

Natl. Rural Utilities Cooperative Finance Corp. [1321], 2201 Cooperative Way, Herndon, VA 20171, (703)709-6700

Natl. Rural Water Assn. [12957], 2915 S 13th St., Duncan, OK 73533, (580)252-0629

Natl. Russell Collectors Assn. [21382], 561 29th St. NW, Massillon, OH 44647, (330)875-6022

Natl. Saanen Breeders Assn. [3796], Lisa Shepard, Sec.-Treas., PO Box 916, Santa Cruz, NM 87567, (505)689-1371

Natl. Saanen Club [★3796]

Natl. Safe Boating Comm. [★12996]

Natl. Safe Boating Coun. [12996], PO Box 509, Bristow, VA 20136, (703)361-4294

Natl. Safe Boating Week Comm. [★12996]

Natl. Safe Kids Campaign [★11400]

Natl. Safe Skies Alliance [18733], 110 McGhee Tyson Blvd., Ste. 201, Alcoa, TN 37701, (865)970-0515

Natl. Safe Transit Assn. [★3252]

Natl. Safe Transit Assn. [★3252]

Natl. Safe Transit Comm. [★3252]

Natl. Safe Transit Comm. [★3252]

Natl. Safety Coun. [12997], 1121 Spring Lake Dr., Itasca, IL 60143-3201, (630)285-1121

Natl. Safety Coun. of Australia [IO], Glen Waverley, Australia

Natl. Safety Coun. of Singapore [IO], Singapore, Singapore

Natl. Safety Mgt. Soc. [12998], PO Box 4460, Walnut Creek, CA 94596-0460, (800)321-2910

Natl. Sanitary Supply Assn. [★2250]

Natl. Sanitary Supply Assn. [★2250]

Natl. Sanitation Found. [★16493]

Natl. Sanitation Found. [★16493]

Natl. Sash and Door Jobbers Assn. [★531]

Natl. Save the Family Farm Coalition [★17169]

Natl. Scale Men's Assn. [★3656]

Natl. Scale Men's Assn. [★3656]

Natl. Scholarship Providers Assn. [8811], 2222 14th St., Boulder, CO 80302, (303)442-2524

Natl. Scholarship Providers Assn. [8811], 2222 14th St., Boulder, CO 80302, (303)442-2524

Natl. Scholastic Press Assn. [8748], Univ. of Minnesota, 2221 Univ. Ave. SE, Ste. 121, Minneapolis, MN 55414-3074, (612)625-8335

Natl. Scholastic Surfing Assn. [23035], PO Box 495, Huntington Beach, CA 92648, (714)378-0899

Natl. School-Age Care Alliance [★11152]

Natl. School Boards Assn. [8816], 1680 Duke St., Alexandria, VA 22314-3493, (703)838-6722

Natl. School Development Coun. - Address unknown since 2010.

Natl. School Orchestra Assn. [★8643]

Natl. School Plant Mgt. Assn. [7675], John Noel, Exec. Sec.-Treas., PO Box 8010, Lexington, KY 40533, (859)296-1343

Natl. School Public Relations Assn. [8767], 15948 Derwood Rd., Rockville, MD 20855-2123, (301)519-0496

Natl. School Safety Center [8821], 141 Duesenberg Dr., Ste. 7B, Westlake Village, CA 91362, (805)373-9977

Natl. School Sailing Assn. [IO], Cambridge, United Kingdom

Natl. School Ser. Inst. [★3171]

Natl. School Supply and Equip. Assn. [3171], 8380 Colesville Rd., Ste. 250, Silver Spring, MD 20910, (301)495-0240

Natl. School Trans. Assn. [3526], 113 S West St., 4th Fl., Alexandria, VA 22314, (800)222-NSTA

Natl. Schools Comm. for Economic Educ. [7988], 250 E 73rd St., Ste. 12G, New York, NY 10021-8641, (212)535-9534

Natl. Sci. Coun. of Taiwan [IO], Taipei, Taiwan

Natl. Sci. Educ. Leadership Assn. [8849], 1219 N 54 St., Omaha, NE 68132, (402)561-0176

Natl. Sci. Found. [7381], 4201 Wilson Blvd., Arlington, VA 22230, (703)292-5111

Natl. Sci. Supervisors Assn. [★8849]

Natl. Sci. Teachers Assn. [8850], 1840 Wilson Blvd., Arlington, VA 22201-3000, (703)243-7100

Natl. Sci. and Tech. Educ. Partnership [13140], 2500 Wilson Blvd., Ste. 210, Arlington, VA 22201-3834, (703)907-7400

Natl. Sci. Coun. on the Developing Child [14052], Harvard Univ., 50 Church St., 4th Fl., Cambridge, MA 02138, (617)496-0578

Natl. Scoliosis Found. [16639], 5 Cabot Pl., Stoughton, MA 02072-4624, (800)673-6922

Natl. Scouts Assn. of Panama [IO], Panama City, Panama

Natl. Scrabble Assn. [21753], PO Box 700, Greenport, NY 11944, (631)477-0033

Natl. Screw Machine Products Assn. [★1658]

Natl. Sculpture Soc. [10529], ANS, 75 Varick St., 11th Fl., New York, NY 10017, (212)764-5645

National Sea Grant Program [★7057]

Natl. Seafood Educators [3185], PO Box 60006, Seattle, WA 98160, (206)546-6410

Natl. Search Dog Alliance [12910], 1302 Waugh Dr., No. 121, Houston, TX 77019, (360)808-0894

Natl. Secular Soc. [IO], London, United Kingdom

Natl. Security Indus. Assn. [★5814]

Natl. Security Inspectorate [IO], Maidenhead, United Kingdom

Natl. Security and Law Soc. [5970], 4801 Massachusetts Ave. NW, Washington, DC 20016, (202)274-4000

Natl. Security Traders Assn. [★3208]

Natl. Security Whistleblowers Coalition [18597], PO Box 320518, Alexandria, VA 22320

Natl. Selected Morticians [★2544]

Natl. Self-Help CH - Address unknown since 2010.

Natl. Senior Citizens Law Center [10866], 1444 Eye St. NW, Ste. 1100, Washington, DC 20005, (202)289-6976

Natl. Senior Classical League [7866], 250 Spring Mill Rd., Villanova, PA 19085, (856)287-5179

Natl. Senior Games Assn. [22808], PO Box 82059, Baton Rouge, LA 70884-2059, (225)766-6316

Natl. Senior Golf Assn. [22619], 200 Perrine Rd., Ste. 201, Old Bridge, NJ 08857-2842, (800)282-6772

Natl. Senior Sports Assn. - Defunct.

Natl. Senior Women's Tennis Assn. [23058], PO Box 7115, West Palm Beach, FL 33405

Natl. Ser. Agencies [★12048]

A star before a book entry number signifies that the name is not listed separately, but is mentioned within the entry.

Natl. Ser. Bd. for Religious Objectors [★17560]

Natl. Ser. Bd. for Religious Objectors [★17560]

Natl. Ser. Committee/Chariscenter USA [19479], PO Box 628, Locust Grove, VA 22508-0628, (540)972-0225

Natl. Ser. Dog Center [14954], Delta Soc., 875 124th Ave. NW, Ste. 101, Bellevue, WA 98005, (425)679-5500

Natl. Service-Learning CH [8830], 4 Carbonero Way, Scotts Valley, CA 95066, (831)461-0205

Natl. Service-Learning Partnership [8857], Acad. for Educational Development, 1825 Connecticut Ave. NW, Ste. 800, Washington, DC 20009-5721, (202)884-8356

Natl. Ser. Org. - COSA [★13082]

Natl. Ser. Org. - COSA [★13082]

Natl. Ser. to Regional Councils [★5499]

Natl. Settlement Purchasers Assn. [★1317]

Natl. Sewerage Assn. [IO], New Malden, United Kingdom

Natl. Sexual Violence Rsrc. Center [13094], 123 N Enola Dr., Enola, PA 17025, (717)909-0710

Natl. Shade Tree Evaluation [★4972]

Natl. Shade Tree Evaluation [★4972]

Natl. Shared Housing Rsrc. Center [12196], 321 E 25th, Baltimore, MD 21218, (410)366-8362

Natl. Shaving Mug Collectors Assn. [21383], 366 Lake Shore Dr., Hewitt, NJ 07421

Natl. Sheep Assn. [IO], Malvern, United Kingdom

Natl. Shelley China Club [21384], 591 W 67th Ave., Anchorage, AK 99518-1555

Natl. Shellfisheries Assn. [7036], Dr. Sandra Shumway, Ed., Univ. of Connecticut, Dept. of Marine Sciences, 1080 Shennecossett Rd., Groton, CT 06340, (860)405-9282

Natl. Shellfisheries Assn. [7036], Dr. Sandra Shumway, Ed., Univ. of Connecticut, Dept. of Marine Sciences, 1080 Shennecossett Rd., Groton, CT 06340, (860)405-9282

Natl. Sheriffs' Assn. [5734], 1450 Duke St., Alexandria, VA 22314-3490, (703)836-7827

Natl. Shiba Club of Am. [21613], Nick Marinos, Corresponding Sec., 1070 Lonesome Trail, Driftwood, TX 78619

Natl. Shippers Strategic Trans. Coun. [3259], 9382 Oak Ave., Waconia, MN 55387, (952)442-8850

Natl. Shipyard Assn. [★2370]

Natl. Shoe Retailers Assn. [1459], 3037 W Ina Rd., Tucson, AZ 85741, (800)673-8446

Natl. Shooting Sports Found. [22882], Flintlock Ridge Off. Ctr., 11 Mile Hill Rd., Newtown, CT 06470-2359, (203)426-1320

Natl. Shorthand Reporters Assn. [★5359]

Natl. Show Horse Registry [4622], PO Box 862, Lewisburg, OH 45338, (937)962-4336

Natl. Show Pig Assn. - Address unknown since 2011.

Natl. Shrine to the Jewish War Dead [★20799]

Natl. Shrine of St. Elizabeth Ann Seton [19480], 333 S Seton Ave., Emmitsburg, MD 21727-9297, (301)447-6606

Natl. SIDS/Infant Death Rsrc. Center [★16762]

Natl. Silo Assn. [★169]

Natl. Silo Assn. [★169]

Natl. Silver-Haired Cong. - Defunct.

Natl. Silver Rabbit Club [4851], 1030 SW KK Hwy., Holden, MO 64040, (816)732-6208

Natl. Single Parent Coalition [★12623]

Natl. Sisters Vocation Conf. [★19478]

Natl. Sjogren's Syndrome Assn. [16622], PO Box 22066, Beachwood, OH 44122, (216)292-3866

Natl. Skeet Shooting Assn. [22883], 5931 Roft Rd., San Antonio, TX 78253, (210)688-3371

Natl. Ski Areas Assn. [1770], 133 S Van Gordon St., Ste. 300, Lakewood, CO 80228, (303)987-1111

Natl. Ski Assn. of Am. [★22918]

Natl. Ski Coun. Fed. [22911], 4 Green Rd., Mine Hill, NJ 07803-2908, (973)598-1005

Natl. Ski Patrol Sys. [22912], 133 S Van Gordon St., Ste. 100, Lakewood, CO 80228, (303)988-1111

Natl. Ski Retailers Asso. [★3314]

Natl. Ski and Snowboard Retailers Assn. [3314], 1601 Feehanville Dr., Ste. 300, Mount Prospect, IL 60056-6035, (847)391-9825

Natl. Ski Touring Assn. [★23079]

Natl. Ski Touring Operators' Assn. [★3327]

Natl. Skills Coalition [11952], 1730 Rhode Island Ave. NW, Ste. 712, Washington, DC 20036, (202)223-8991

Natl. Skin Cancer Found. [★13981]

Natl. Slag Assn. [597], PO Box 1197, Pleasant Grove, UT 84062, (801)785-4535

Natl. Sleep Found. [16668], 1010 N Glebe Rd., Ste. 310, Arlington, VA 22201, (703)243-1697

Natl. Slovak Soc. of the U.S.A. [19231], 351 Valley Brook Rd., McMurray, PA 15317-3337, (724)731-0094

Natl. Small-Bore Rifle Assn. [IO], Woking, United Kingdom

Natl. Small Bus. Assn. [3295], 1156 15th St. NW, Ste. 1100, Washington, DC 20005, (202)293-8830

Natl. Small Coll. Athletic Assn. [★23012]

Natl. Small Shipments Traffic Conf. [★3259]

Natl. Small Shipments Traffic Conf. [★3255]

Natl. Smokejumper Assn. [5448], 160 Clay St., Custer, SD 57730, (605)786-6808

Natl. Snaffle Bit Assn. [4623], 4203 Grove Ave., Gurnee, IL 60031, (847)623-6722

Natl. Snow Indus. Assn. [IO], Westmount, QC, Canada

Natl. Soaring Found. - Address unknown since 2011.

Natl. Soccer Coaches Assn. of Am. [22939], 800 Ann Ave., Kansas City, KS 66101, (913)362-1747

Natl. Social Sci. Honor Soc. [★23709]

Natl. Social Sci. Honor Soc. [★23709]

Natl. Social Welfare Assembly [★13401]

Natl. Social Work Coun. [★13401]

Natl. Socialist Amer. Workers Freedom Movement [★18784]

Natl. Socialist Amer. Workers Freedom Movement [★18784]

Natl. Socialist Movement [18784], PO Box 13768, Detroit, MI 48213, (651)659-6307

Natl. Socialist Movement [18784], PO Box 13768, Detroit, MI 48213, (651)659-6307

Natl. Socialist White Americans Party [★18781]

Natl. Socialist White Americans Party [★18781]

Natl. Socialist White People's Party [★18786]

Natl. Socialist White People's Party [★18786]

Natl. Soc. of Accountants [48], 1010 N Fairfax St., Alexandria, VA 22314, (703)549-6400

Natl. Soc. of Accountants for Cooperatives [49], 136 S Keowee St., Dayton, OH 45402, (937)222-6707

Natl. Soc. of Allied and Independent Funeral Directors [IO], Sawbridgeworth, United Kingdom

Natl. Soc. of Allotment and Leisure Gardeners [IO], Corby, United Kingdom

Natl. Soc. for Amer. Indian Elderly [19162], 200 E Filmore St., No. 151, Phoenix, AZ 85004, (602)424-0542

Natl. Soc. of Appraiser Specialists - Address unknown since 2011.

Natl. Soc. of Architectural Engineers [★6185]

Natl. Soc. of Architectural Engineers [★6185]

Natl. Soc. of Artists [9244], PO Box 1885, Dickinson, TX 77539-1885, (281)337-4232

Natl. Soc. of Arts and Letters [9846], 4227 46th St. NW, Washington, DC 20016, (202)363-5443

Natl. Soc. for Autistic Children [★13786]

Natl. Soc. of Black Engineers [6815], 205 Daingerfield Rd., Alexandria, VA 22314, (703)549-2207

Natl. Soc. of Black Physicists [7269], 1100 N Glebe Rd., Ste. 1010, Arlington, VA 22201, (703)536-4207

Natl. Soc. of Cardiology of the Former Yugoslav Republic of Macedonia [IO], Skopje, Macedonia

Natl. Soc. of Cardiopulmonary Technologists [★13997]

Natl. Soc. for Cardiopulmonary Tech. [★13997]

Natl. Soc. for Cardiovascular Tech. [★13997]

Natl. Soc. of Certified Healthcare Bus. Consultants [14885], 12100 Sunset Hills Rd., Ste. 130, Reston, VA 20190, (703)234-4099

Natl. Soc. of Chemotherapy of the Russian Fed. [IO], Moscow, Russia

Natl. Soc. of the Children of the Amer. Revolution [20338], 1776 D St. NW, Rm. 224, Washington, DC 20006-5303, (202)638-3153

Natl. Soc. of Coll. Teachers of Educ. [★8061]

Natl. Soc. of Collegiate Scholars [8812], 11 Dupont Cir. NW, Ste. 650, Washington, DC 20036, (202)265-9000

Natl. Soc. of the Colonial Dames of Am. [20399], 2715 Que St. NW, Washington, DC 20007-3071, (202)337-2288

Natl. Soc. Colonial Dames XVII Century [20400], 1300 New Hampshire Ave. NW, Washington, DC 20036-1502, (202)293-1700

Natl. Soc. of Compliance Professionals [1588], 22 Kent Rd., Cornwall Bridge, CT 06754, (860)672-0843

Natl. Soc. of Conservationists [IO], Budapest, Hungary

Natl. Soc. of Consulting Soil Scientists [4926], PO Box 1219, Sandpoint, ID 83864, (208)263-9391

Natl. Soc. of Controllers and Financial Officers of Savings Institutions [★2282]

Natl. Soc., Daughters of the Amer. Colonists [20401], 2205 Massachusetts Ave. NW, Washington, DC 20008, (202)667-3076

Natl. Soc., Daughters of the Amer. Revolution [20339], 1776 D St. NW, Washington, DC 20006-5303, (202)628-1776

Natl. Soc., Daughters of the British Empire in the U.S.A. [18965], 245 E 40th St., New York, NY 10017, (646)220-2309

Natl. Soc. Daughters of Utah Pioneers [★20748]

Natl. Soc. Daughters of Utah Pioneers [★20748]

Natl. Soc. for Educ. in Art and Design [IO], Corsham, United Kingdom

Natl. Soc. of Environmental Consultants - Address unknown since 2011.

Natl. Soc. for Epilepsy [IO], Aylesbury, United Kingdom

Natl. Soc. for Experiential Educ. [8177], Talley Mgt. Gp., Inc., 19 Mantua Rd., Mount Royal, NJ 08061, (856)423-3427

Natl. Soc. of Fund Raisers [★12049]

Natl. Soc. of Fund Raising Executives [★12049]

Natl. Soc. of Genetic Counselors [14655], 401 N Michigan Ave., Chicago, IL 60611, (312)321-6834

Natl. Soc. for Graphology [10756], 250 W 57th St., Ste. 1228A, New York, NY 10107-1221, (212)265-1148

Natl. Soc. of Guide Dog Users [★17080]

Natl. Soc. of High School Scholars [8813], 1936 N Druid Hills Rd., Atlanta, GA 30319, (404)235-5500

Natl. Soc. of Hispanic MBAs [694], 1303 Walnut Hill Ln., Ste. 100, Irving, TX 75038, (214)596-9338

Natl. Soc. of Hispanic Physicists [7270], Dr. Jesus Pando, Treas., DePaul Univ., Dept. of Physics, 2219 N Kenmore Ave., Chicago, IL 60614-3504

Natl. Soc. for Hispanic Professionals [695], 1835 NE Miami Gardens Dr., No. 313, Miami, FL 33179

Natl. Soc. for HistoTechnology [15383], 10320 Little Patuxent Pkwy., Ste. 804, Columbia, MD 21044, (443)535-4060

Natl. Soc. of Insurance Premium Auditors [2022], PO Box 936, Columbus, OH 43216-0936, (888)846-7472

Natl. Soc. for Internships and Experiential Educ. [★8177]

Natl. Soc. of Leadership and Success [8926], 50 Harrison St., Ste. 308, Hoboken, NJ 07030, (201)222-6544

Natl. Soc. of Live Stock Record Associations [★3794]

Natl. Soc. of Madison Family Descendants [20648], 1180 Peachtree St., Ste. 1700, Atlanta, GA 30309, (404)572-4714

Natl. Soc. of Master Thatchers [IO], Thame, United Kingdom

Natl. Soc. for Medical Res. [★13764]

Natl. Soc. of Mural Painters [9245], 450 W 31st St., 7th Fl., New York, NY 10001, (212)244-2800

Natl. Soc. of Newspaper Columnists [2855], PO Box 411532, San Francisco, CA 94141, (415)488-6762

Natl. Soc. of Painters in Casein and Acrylic [9246], 5513 Jaclyn Ln., Bethlehem, PA 18017

Natl. Soc. of Patient Representation and Consumer Affairs of the Amer. Hosp. Assn. [★15243]

Natl. Soc. of Patient Representatives of the Amer. Hosp. Assn. [★15243]

Natl. Soc. of Penal Info. [★11728]

Natl. Soc. for Performance and Instruction [★8988]

Natl. Soc. for Performance and Instruction [★8988]

Natl. Soc. of Pershing Rifles [23597], PO Box 25057, Baton Rouge, LA 70894

Reference to "IO" in place of a book number signifies that the association may be found in the 50th edition of International Organizations.

Natl. Soc. of Persons with dissAbilities [IO], Kingstown, St. Vincent and the Grenadines

Natl. Soc. of Pharmaceutical Sales Trainers [★3168]

Natl. Soc. for Phenylketonuria [IO], London, United Kingdom

Natl. Soc. to Prevent Blindness [★17112]

Natl. Soc. for the Prevention of Blindness [★17112]

Natl. Soc. for the Prevention of Cruelty to Children [IO], London, United Kingdom

Natl. Soc. of Professional Engineers [6816], 1420 King St., Alexandria, VA 22314-2794, (703)684-2800

Natl. Soc. of Professional Insurance Investigators [2023], PO Box 88, Delaware, OH 43015, (888)677-4498

Natl. Soc. of Professional Surveyors [7488], 6 Montgomery Village Ave., Ste. 403, Gaithersburg, MD 20879-3557, (240)632-9716

Natl. Soc. for Programmed Instruction [★8988]

Natl. Soc. for Programmed Instruction [★8988]

Natl. Soc. for the Promotion of Occupational Therapy [★16837]

Natl. Soc. of Public Accountants [★48]

Natl. Soc. for Pulmonary Tech. [★13997]

Natl. Soc. for Res. into Allergy [IO], Hinckley, United Kingdom

Natl. Soc. of Saint Vincent de Paul - Malaysia [IO], Kuala Lumpur, Malaysia

Natl. Soc. of Sales Training Executives [★3166]

Natl. Soc. of Scabbard and Blade [23598], 1018 S Lewis St., Stillwater, OK 74074-4622, (405)377-4279

Natl. Soc., Sons of the Amer. Colonists [20402], 7501 W 101th St., No. 204, Minneapolis, MN 55438-2521, (952)261-6937

Natl. Soc., Sons of the Amer. Revolution [20340], 1000 S 4th St., Louisville, KY 40203, (502)589-1776

Natl. Soc. Sons and Daughters of the Pilgrims - Defunct.

Natl. Soc. of the Sons of Utah Pioneers [20749], 3301 E 2920 S, Salt Lake City, UT 84109, (801)484-4441

Natl. Soc. of State Legislators [★5998]

Natl. Soc. for the Stud. of Commun. [★3411]

Natl. Soc. for the Stud. of Commun. [★3411]

Natl. Soc. for the Stud. of Educ. - Defunct.

Natl. Soc. of Tole and Decorative Painters [★21467]

Natl. Soc., U.S. Daughters of 1812 [20841], 1461 Rhode Island Ave. NW, Washington, DC 20005-5402, (202)745-1812

Natl. Soc. for Vision and Perception Training [★15993]

Natl. Soc. for Vocational Educ. [★9039]

Natl. Soc. of Women Descendants of the Ancient and Honorable Artillery Company [20403], Kathy Deegan, Treas., 1524 Victoria Farms Ln., Vienna, VA 22182, (703)759-6445

Natl. Soda Dispensing Equip. Assn. [★446]

Natl. Soda Dispensing Equip. Assn. [★446]

Natl. Soft Drink Assn. [★442]

Natl. Soft Drink Mfrs'. Assn. [IO], Madrid, Spain

Natl. Soft Wheat Assn. [★2502]

Natl. Softball Assn. [22954], PO Box 7, Nicholasville, KY 40340, (859)887-4114

Natl. Sojourners [19138], 8301 E Boulevard Dr., Alexandria, VA 22308-1399, (703)765-5000

Natl. Solid Waste Assn. of India [IO], Mumbai, India

Natl. Solid Wastes Mgt. Assn. [3260], 4301 Connecticut Ave. NW, Ste. 300, Washington, DC 20008-2304, (202)244-4700

Natl. Sorghum Producers [3955], 4201 N Interstate 27, Lubbock, TX 79403, (806)749-3478

Natl. Sorority of Phi Delta Kappa - Address unknown since 2011.

Natl. Sound and Communications Assn. [★1111]

Natl. South Asian Bar Assn. [★5678]

National Sovereignty

Armenian Revolutionary Fed. [18145]

Armenian Revolutionary Fed. [18145]

Armenian Youth Fed. [18146]

Natl. Soy Ink Info. Center - Defunct.

Natl. Soybean Processors Assn. [★2589]

Natl. Spa and Pool Inst. [★3054]

Natl. Spa and Pool Inst. [★3054]

Natl. Space Club [6089], 204 E St. NE, Washington, DC 20002, (202)547-0060

Natl. Space Inst. [★6090]

Natl. Space Soc. [6090], 115 15th St. NW, Ste. 500, Washington, DC 20005, (202)429-1600

Natl. Space Soc. of Australia [IO], Sydney, Australia

Natl. Spasmodic Dysphonia Assn. [15622], 300 Park Blvd., Ste. 415, Itasca, IL 60143, (800)795-6732

Natl. Spasmodic Torticollis Assn. [15623], 9920 Talbert Ave., Fountain Valley, CA 92708, (714)378-9837

Natl. Speakers Assn. [10480], 1500 S Priest Dr., Tempe, AZ 85281, (480)968-2552

Natl. Speakers Assn. of Australia [IO], Kingscliff, Australia

Natl. Speakers Assn. of New Zealand [IO], Auckland, New Zealand

Natl. Special Educ. Info. Center [★11816]

Natl. Special Needs Network [★14367]

Natl. Special Needs Network Found. [14367], 4613 N Univ. Dr., No. 242, Coral Springs, FL 33067, (561)447-4152

Natl. Specialist Contractors Coun. [IO], London, United Kingdom

Natl. Specialty Beverage Retailers Marketing Assn. - Defunct.

Natl. Specialty Gift Assn. [1572], 7238 Bucks Ford Dr., Riverview, FL 33578, (813)374-1777

Natl. Speleological Soc. [7462], 2813 Cave Ave., Huntsville, AL 35810-4431, (256)852-1300

Natl. Spinach Assn. [★4456]

Natl. Spinal Cord Injury Assn. [16703], 75-20 Astoria Blvd., Ste. 120, East Elmhurst, NY 11370, (718)512-0010

Natl. Spinal Cord Injury Found. [★16703]

The Natl. Spiritual Alliance [20143], PO Box 88, Lake Pleasant, MA 01347

Natl. Spiritual Assembly of the Baha'is of India [IO], New Delhi, India

Natl. Spiritual Assembly of the Baha'is of New Zealand [IO], Auckland, New Zealand

Natl. Spiritual Assembly of the Baha'is of the U.S. [20192], 1233 Central St., Evanston, IL 60201, (847)733-3400

Natl. Spiritual Assembly of the Baha'is of the U.S. and Canada [★20192]

National Spiritualist

Morris Pratt Inst. Assn. [20142]

The Natl. Spiritual Alliance [20143]

Natl. Spiritualist Assn. of Churches [20144]

Natl. Spiritualist Assn. of Churches I Healers League [20145]

Natl. Spiritualist Teachers Club [20146]

Natl. Spiritualist Assn. of Churches [20144], PO Box 217, Lily Dale, NY 14752, (716)595-2000

Natl. Spiritualist Assn. of Churches I Healers League [20145], PO Box 217, Lily Dale, NY 14752, (716)595-2000

Natl. Spiritualist Teachers Club [20146], Natl. Spiritualist Assn. of Churches, PO Box 217, Lily Dale, NY 14752, (716)595-2000

Natl. Sport Fed. of Baseball and Softball of the Republic of Moldova [IO], Chisinau, Moldova

Natl. Sporting Clays Assn. [22884], 5931 Roft Rd., San Antonio, TX 78253, (210)688-3371

Natl. Sporting Goods Assn. [3315], 1601 Feehanville Dr., Ste. 300, Mount Prospect, IL 60056, (800)815-5422

Natl. Sportscasters and Sportswriters Assn. [2856], PO Box 1545, Salisbury, NC 28145, (704)633-4275

Natl. Spotted Poland China Record [★4952]

Natl. Spotted Saddle Horse Assn. [4624], PO Box 898, Murfreesboro, TN 37133-0898, (615)890-2864

Natl. Spotted Swine Record [4952], PO Box 9758, Peoria, IL 61612-9758, (309)693-1804

Natl. Spray Equipment Mfrs. Assn. - Defunct.

Natl. Square Dance Convention [9562], 8538 Lotticks Corner Rd., SE, Elizabeth, IN 47117, (812)969-2307

Natl. Staff Development Coun. [7676], 504 S Locust St., Oxford, OH 45056, (513)523-6029

Natl. Staff Development and Training Assn. [13197], PO Box 112, Merced, CA 95341-0112, (209)385-3000

Natl. Staff Leasing Assn. [★1157]

Natl. Stamp Dealers Assn. [22060], 2916 NW Bucklin Hill Rd., No. 136, Silverdale, WA 98383-8514, (800)875-6633

National Standard Plumbing Code Committee - Address unknown since 2010.

Natl. Standards Authority of Ireland [IO], Dublin, Ireland

Natl. Star Route Mail Carriers Assn. [★2236]

Natl. Star Route Mail Contractors Assn. [2236], 324 E Capitol St., Washington, DC 20003-3897, (202)543-1661

Natl. Starwind/Spindrift Class Assn. [22377], PO Box 21262, Columbus, OH 43221

Natl. State Printing Assn. [★1623]

Natl. State Publishing Assn. [★1623]

Natl. States Geographic Info. Coun. [6549], 2105 Laurel Bush Rd., Ste. 200, Bel Air, MD 21015, (443)640-1075

Natl. Statistical Onion Assn. [★4460]

Natl. Statistics Inst. [IO], Madrid, Spain

Natl. Steam Specialty Club [★1822]

Natl. Steel Bridge Alliance [6370], Roger E. Ferch, Exec. Dir., 1 E Wacker Dr., Ste. 700, Chicago, IL 60601-1802, (312)670-2400

Natl. Steel Door and Frame Assn. [★2483]

Natl. Steel Producers Assn. [★2496]

Natl. Steeplechase Assn. [22662], 400 Fair Hill Dr., Elkton, MD 21921, (410)392-0700

Natl. Steeplechase and Hunt Assn. [★22662]

Natl. Steinbeck Center [9404], 1 Main St., Salinas, CA 93901, (831)796-3833

Natl. Stereoscopic Assn. [10440], PO Box 86708, Portland, OR 97286, (503)771-4440

Natl. Stigma CH [15478], 245 8th Ave., No. 213, New York, NY 10011, (212)255-4411

Natl. Stinson Club [20911], Intl. Stinson Club, PO Box 3311, San Jose, CA 95157-3311, (408)272-8120

Natl. Stone Assn. [★3366]

Natl. Stone, Sand and Gravel Assn. [3366], 1605 King St., Alexandria, VA 22314-2726, (703)525-8788

Natl. Storage Indus. Consortium [★6538]

Natl. Storm Shelter Assn. [3654], PO Box 41023, Lubbock, TX 79409, (806)742-6772

Natl. Storytelling Assn. [★10546]

Natl. Storytelling Network [10546], PO Box 795, Jonesborough, TN 37659, (423)913-8201

Natl. Strategy Info. Center [17509], 1730 Rhode Island Ave. NW, Ste. 500, Washington, DC 20036-3117, (202)429-0129

Natl. St. Law Inst. [★5766]

Natl. St. Rod Assn. [21133], 4030 Park Ave., Memphis, TN 38111, (901)452-4030

Natl. Strength Coaches Assn. [★23098]

Natl. Strength and Conditioning Assn. [23098], 1885 Bob Johnson Dr., Colorado Springs, CO 80906, (719)632-6722

Natl. Stroke Assn. [16731], 9707 E Easter Ln., Ste. B, Centennial, CO 80112, (303)649-9299

Natl. Stroke Assn. of Malaysia [IO], Petaling Jaya, Malaysia

Natl. Structured Settlements Trade Assn. [5764], 1100 New York Ave. NW, Ste. 750W, Washington, DC 20005, (202)289-4004

Natl. Student Assistance Assn. - Address unknown since 2011.

Natl. Student Campaign Against Hunger [★12286]

Natl. Student Campaign Against Hunger and Homelessness [12286], 328 S Jefferson St., Ste. 620, Chicago, IL 60661, (312)544-4436

Natl. Student Educational Fund [★8933]

Natl. Student Employment Assn. [8728], 715 Northill Dr., Richardson, TX 75080, (972)690-8772

Natl. Student Exchange [8908], 4656 W Jefferson Blvd., Ste. 140, Fort Wayne, IN 46804, (260)436-2634

Natl. Student Lobby [★8932]

Natl. Student Nurses' Assn. [8616], 45 Main St., Ste. 606, Brooklyn, NY 11201, (718)210-0705

Natl. Student Safety Prog. [18579], Highway Safety Services, 1434 Trim Tree Rd., Indiana, PA 15701, (877)485-7172

Natl. Student Speech and Hearing Assn. [★16690]

A star before a book entry number signifies that the name is not listed separately, but is mentioned within the entry.

Natl. Student Speech Language Hearing Assn. **[16690]**, 2200 Res. Blvd., No. 450, Rockville, MD 20850, (800)498-2071

Natl. Student Union of Macedonia **[IO]**, Skopje, Macedonia

Natl. Study Group on Chronic Disorganization **[9829]**, 1693 S Hanley Rd., St. Louis, MO 63144, (314)416-2236

Natl. Stud. of School Evaluation - Address unknown since 2010.

Natl. Stuttering Assn. **[16691]**, 119 W 40th St., 14th Fl., New York, NY 10018, (212)944-4050

Natl. Submetering and Utility Allocation Assn. **[★3608]**

Natl. Sudden Infant Death Syndrome CH **[★16762]**

Natl. Sudden Infant Death Syndrome Found. **[★16761]**

Natl. Sudden and Unexpected Infant/Child Death and Pregnancy Loss Rsrc. Center **[16762]**, 2115 Wisconsin Ave. NW, Ste. 601, Washington, DC 20007-2265, (202)687-7466

Natl. Sunflower Assn. **[3956]**, 2401 46th Ave. SE, Ste. 206, Mandan, ND 58554-4829, (701)328-5100

Natl. Sunroom Assn. **[598]**, 1300 Sumner Ave., Cleveland, OH 44115-2851, (216)241-7333

Natl. Suppliers to Food Processors Assn. - Defunct.

Natl. Surf Life Saving Assn. of Am. **[★12912]**

Natl. Surf Schools and Instructors Assn. **[23036]**, PO Box 550, Chesapeake Beach, MD 20732, (240)464-3301

Natl. Surgical Asst. Assn. **[16817]**, 2615 Amesbury Rd., Winston-Salem, NC 27103, (336)768-4443

Natl. Sustainable Agriculture Coalition **[4942]**, 110 Maryland Ave. NE, Washington, DC 20002, (202)547-5754

Natl. Sweet Sorghum Producers and Processors Assn. **[3957]**, PO Box 1356, Cookeville, TN 38503-1356, (931)644-7764

Natl. Swim School Assn. **[★23045]**

Natl. Swimming Pool Found. **[3062]**, 4775 Granby Cir., Colorado Springs, CO 80919-3131, (719)540-9119

Natl. Swimming Pool Inst. **[★3054]**

Natl. Swimming Pool Inst. **[★3054]**

Natl. Swine Growers Coun. **[★4951]**

Natl. Swine Improvement Fed. **[4953]**, Univ. of Tennessee, Dept. of Animal Sci., 102 McCord Hall, 2640 Morgan Circle Dr., Knoxville, TN 37996-4588, (865)974-7238

Natl. Swine Registry **[4954]**, 2639 Yeager Rd., West Lafayette, IN 47906, (765)463-3594

Natl. Swine Registry I United Duroc Swine Registry **[4955]**, 2639 Yeager Rd., West Lafayette, IN 47996-2417, (765)463-3594

Natl. Symphony Orchestra Assn. **[10264]**, John F. kennedy Center for the Performing Arts, 2700 F St. NW, Washington, DC 20566, (202)416-8310

Natl. Systems Contractors Assn. **[1111]**, 3950 River Ridge Dr. NE, Cedar Rapids, IA 52402, (319)366-6722

Natl. Systems Programmers Assn. **[★6515]**

Natl. Systems Programmers Assn. **[★6515]**

Natl. Tactical Officers Assn. **[5735]**, PO Box 797, Doylestown, PA 18901, (215)230-7616

Natl. Tank Truck Carriers **[3261]**, 950 N Glebe Rd., Ste. 520, Arlington, VA 22203, (703)838-1960

Natl. Tattoo Assn. **[10557]**, 485 Bus. Park Ln., Allentown, PA 18109-9120, (610)433-7261

Natl. Tattoo Assn. **[10557]**, 485 Bus. Park Ln., Allentown, PA 18109-9120, (610)433-7261

Natl. Tattoo Club of the World **[★10557]**

Natl. Tattoo Club of the World **[★10557]**

Natl. Tax Assn. **[6018]**, 725 15th St. NW, No. 600, Washington, DC 20005-2109, (202)737-3325

Natl. Tax-Limitation Comm. **[18701]**, 1700 Eureka Rd., Ste. 150A, Roseville, CA 95661, (916)786-9400

Natl. Taxi Assn. **[IO]**, Carlisle, United Kingdom

Natl. Taxidermists Assn. **[3384]**, 108 Br. Dr., Slidell, LA 70461-1912, (985)641-4682

Natl. Taxpayers Union **[18702]**, 108 N Alfred St., Alexandria, VA 22314, (703)683-5700

Natl. Tay-Sachs and Allied Diseases Assn. **[15624]**, 2001 Beacon St., Ste. 204, Boston, MA 02135, (617)277-4463

Natl. Tay-Sachs and Allied Diseases Assn. **[15624]**, 2001 Beacon St., Ste. 204, Boston, MA 02135, (617)277-4463

Natl. Tay-Sachs Assn. **[★15624]**

Natl. Tay-Sachs Assn. **[★15624]**

Natl. Teachers Assn. **[★23181]**

Natl. Teachers' Union **[IO]**, Luxembourg, Luxembourg

Natl. Teaching-Family Assn. **[★12022]**

Natl. Team Cheng Martial Arts Assn. **[22747]**, 2269 Garrett Rd., Drexel Hill, PA 19026, (610)622-5260

Natl. Tech Prep Network **[★8109]**

Natl. Tech. Assn. **[7520]**, 2705 Bladensburg Rd. NE, Washington, DC 20018, (202)575-4NTA

Natl. Tech. Honor Soc. **[23759]**, PO Box 1336, Flat Rock, NC 28731, (828)698-8011

Natl. Teen Age Republicans **[18536]**, PO Box 2128, Manassas, VA 20108, (703)368-4220

Natl. Teen Anglers **[21737]**, 1177 Bayshore Dr., No. 207, Fort Pierce, FL 34949, (772)519-0482

Natl. Teen Challenge **[★20308]**

Natl. Teen Challenge **[★20308]**

Natl. Teens for Life **[12941]**, 512 10th St. NW, Washington, DC 20004, (202)626-8833

Natl. Telecommunications Cooperative Assn. **[3599]**, 4121 Wilson Blvd., Ste. 1000, Arlington, VA 22203, (703)351-2000

Natl. TeleMedia Coun. **[9462]**, 1922 Univ. Ave., Madison, WI 53726, (608)218-1182

Natl. Telephone Cooperative Assn. **[★3599]**

Natl. Temporal Bone Banks Prog. of The DRF **[★15359]**

Natl. Temporal Bone, Hearing and Balance Pathology Registry **[★15359]**

Natl. Temporal Bone, Hearing and Balance Pathology Rsrc. Registry **[★15359]**

Natl. Temporal Bone, Hearing and Balance Pathology Rsrc. Registry; NIDCD: **[15359]**

Natl. Temporal Bone Registry **[★15359]**

Natl. Tennis Acad. **[★23063]**

Natl. Tennis Assn. **[★2743]**

Natl. Tennis Assn. **[★2743]**

Natl. Tennis Educational Found. **[★23056]**

Natl. Tennis Educational Found. **[★23056]**

Natl. Tennis Fed. of Republic of Tajikistan **[IO]**, Dushanbe, Tajikistan

Natl. Tennis Found. and Hall of Fame **[★23056]**

Natl. Tennis Found. and Hall of Fame **[★23056]**

Natl. Tertiary Educ. Union **[IO]**, Melbourne, Australia

Natl. Textile Assn. **[3451]**, 6 Beacon St., Ste. 1125, Boston, MA 02108-3812, (617)542-8220

Natl. Textile Assn. I Wool Mfrs. Coun. **[3452]**, 6 Beacon St., Ste. 1125, Boston, MA 02108-3812, (617)542-8220

Natl. Textile Rsrc. and Res. Center **[★21453]**

Natl. Textile Rsrc. and Res. Center **[★21453]**

Natl. Thanksgiving Commn. **[★18670]**

Natl. Thanksgiving Commn. **[★18670]**

Natl. Theatre Conf. **[10592]**, Penn State Theatre, 103 Arts Bldg., University Park, PA 16802, (814)685-7586

Natl. Theatre Inst. **[★9003]**

Natl. Theatre Workshop of the Handicapped **[10593]**, 535 Greenwich St., New York, NY 10013, (212)206-7789

Natl. Therapeutic Recreation Soc. - Address unknown since 2010.

Natl. Thespian Soc. **[★9001]**

Natl. Thoroughbred Racing Assn. **[22663]**, 2525 Harrodsburg Rd., Ste. 400, Lexington, KY 40504, (859)245-6872

Natl. Threshers Assn. **[9214]**, 22343 Lemoyne Rd., Luckey, OH 43443, (419)833-6371

Natl. Throws Coaches Assn. **[22464]**, PO Box 14114, Palm Desert, CA 92255-4114, (760)779-9148

Natl. Tile Contractors Assn. **[940]**, PO Box 13629, Jackson, MS 39236, (601)939-2071

Natl. Tile Roofing Mfrs. Assn. **[★629]**

Natl. Time Equip. Assn. **[★3464]**

Natl. Tire Dealers and Retreaders Assn. **[★3465]**

Natl. Title I Assn. **[7677]**, 1200 G St. NW, Ste. 800, PMB 8287, Washington, DC 20005, (571)480-9970

Natl. Toggenburg Club **[4504]**, 2100 Painted Desert Dr., Winslow, AZ 86047, (928)289-4868

Natl. Token Collectors Assn. **[21983]**, Jerry Adams, Sec., 1425 Cat Mountain Trail, Keller, TX 76248, (817)581-6804

Natl. Tool and Die Mfrs. Assn. **[★1834]**

Natl. Tool and Die Mfrs. Assn. **[★1834]**

Natl. Tool, Die and Precision Machining Assn. **[★1834]**

Natl. Tool, Die and Precision Machining Assn. **[★1834]**

Natl. Toothpick Holder Collectors' Soc. **[21385]**, PO Box 852, Archer City, TX 76351

Natl. Tots and Teens **[13544]**, 16555 Wyoming Ave., Detroit, MI 48221, (313)863-1705

Natl. Tour Assn. **[3569]**, 101 Prosperous Pl., Ste. 350, Lexington, KY 40509, (859)226-4444

Natl. Tour Brokers Assn. **[★3569]**

Natl. Tourism Org. of Serbia **[IO]**, Belgrade, Serbia

Natl. Town Builders' Assn. **[599]**, 3220 N St. NW, No. 238, Washington, DC 20007, (202)333-1902

Natl. Toy Fox Terrier Assn. **[21614]**, 22481 Bohn Rd., Belleville, MI 48111, (734)652-5184

Natl. Tractor Pullers Assn. **[23073]**, 6155-B Huntley Rd., Columbus, OH 43229, (614)436-1761

Natl. Trade Circulation Found., Inc. **[2952]**, JoAnn Binz, PO Box 515, Swiftwater, PA 18370-0515, (570)839-2708

Natl. Trade Press Assn. **[IO]**, Milan, Italy

Natl. Trade Show Exhibitors Assn. **[★1238]**

Natl. Trades Union Cong. **[IO]**, Singapore, Singapore

Natl. Traditional Country Music Assn. **[10265]**, PO Box 492, Anita, IA 50020, (712)762-4363

Natl. Traditional Music Assn. **[★10265]**

Natl. Traditionalist Caucus **[17429]**, PO Box 971, New York, NY 10116, (212)685-4689

Natl. Traffic Incident Mgt. Coalition **[13330]**, 4802 Sheboygan Ave., Madison, WI 53705-2927, (608)266-0459

National Traffic System **[★20931]**

Natl. Trailer Dealers Assn. **[3527]**, 9864 E Grand River Ave., Ste. 110, PO Box 290, Brighton, MI 48116, (810)229-5960

Natl. Trails Coun. **[★23080]**

Natl. Trainers Fed. **[IO]**, Hungerford, United Kingdom

Natl. Training Coun. of the Marshall Islands **[IO]**, Majuro, Marshall Islands

Natl. Training and Info. Center - Address unknown since 2010.

Natl. Training Labs. **[★8178]**

Natl. Training Labs. **[★8178]**

Natl. Training Lab. in Gp. Development **[★8178]**

Natl. Training Lab. in Gp. Development **[★8178]**

Natl. Training and Simulation Assn. **[6464]**, 2111 Wilson Blvd., Ste. 400, Arlington, VA 22201-3061, (703)247-9471

Natl. Training Systems Assn. **[★5814]**

Natl. Transit Benefit Assn. **[6038]**, PO Box 25, Clifton, VA 20124, (703)222-9373

Natl. Transitions of Care Coalition **[14821]**, 6301 Ranch Dr., Little Rock, AR 72223-4623, (501)225-2229

Natl. Translator Assn. **[507]**, 5611 Kendall Ct., Ste. 2, Arvada, CO 80002, (303)465-5742

Natl. Translator LPTV Assn. **[★507]**

Natl. Transplant Soc. **[16915]**, 3149 Dundee Rd., Ste. 314, Northbrook, IL 60062

Natl. Transsexual - Transvestite Feminization Union - Defunct.

Natl. Trappers Assn. **[4963]**, 2815 Washington Ave., Bedford, IN 47421, (812)277-9670

Natl. Treasury Employees Union **[23208]**, 1750 H St. NW, Washington, DC 20006-4600, (202)572-5500

Natl. Treatment Consortium for Alcohol and Other Drugs - Defunct.

Natl. Tree Soc. **[4288]**, PO Box 10808, Bakersfield, CA 93389, (805)589-6912

Natl. Tribal Child Support Assn. **[11489]**, PO Box 1423, Tahlequah, OK 74465-1423, (918)453-5380

Natl. Tribal Development Assn. **[19163]**, Box 1080, Box Elder, MT 59521-9722, (406)395-4095

Natl. Tribal Environmental Coun. **[18154]**, 4520 Montgomery Blvd. NE, Ste. 3, Albuquerque, NM 87109, (505)242-2175

Natl. Trotting Assn. **[★22672]**

Natl. Truck Equip. Assn. **[336]**, 37400 Hills Tech Dr., Farmington Hills, MI 48331-3414, (248)489-7090

Natl. Truck and Heavy Equip. Claims Coun. [2024], PO Box 27, Wolfeboro Falls, NH 03896-0027, (603)569-8910

Natl. Truck Leasing Sys. [3081], 1S450 Summit Ave., Ste. 300, Oakbrook Terrace, IL 60181-3990, (630)925-7710

Natl. Truck Tank Assn. [★892]

Natl. Truck Tank and Trailer Tank Inst. [★892]

Natl. Truckers Assn. [3528], 3131 Turtle Creek Blvd., Ste. 1120, Dallas, TX 75219, (800)823-8454

Natl. Trust [IO], Warrington, United Kingdom

Natl. Trust of Australia [IO], Civic Square, Australia

Natl. Trust for the Cayman Islands [IO], Grand Cayman, Cayman Islands

Natl. Trust, Central Volunteering Team [IO], Swindon, United Kingdom

Natl. Trust for the Development of African Amer. Men [17161], 672 13th St., Oakland, CA 94612

Natl. Trust for Historic Preservation [9717], 1785 Massachusetts Ave. NW, Washington, DC 20036-2117, (202)588-6000

Natl. Trust for Ireland [IO], Dublin, Ireland

Natl. Trust Main St. Center [17393], 1785 Massachusetts Ave. NW, Washington, DC 20036-2117, (202)588-6000

Natl. Trust for Scotland [IO], Edinburgh, United Kingdom

Natl. Tuberculosis Assn. [★16604]

Natl. Tuberculosis Controllers Assn. [14412], 2452 Spring Rd. SE, Smyrna, GA 30080, (678)503-0503

Natl. Tuberculosis and Respiratory Disease Assn. [★16604]

Natl. Tuberous Sclerosis Assn. [★15639]

Natl. Tumor Registrars Assn. [★15929]

Natl. Tunis Sheep Registry, Inc. [4914], 15603 173rd Ave., Milo, IA 50166, (641)942-6402

Natl. Turf Writers Assn. [2857], 3920 Grassy Creek Dr., Lexington, KY 40514

Natl. Turkey Fed. [4811], 1225 New York Ave., Ste. 400, Washington, DC 20005, (202)898-0100

Natl. Tutoring Assn. [9022], PO Box 6840, Lakeland, FL 33807-6840, (863)529-5206

Natl. Typewriter and Off. Machine Dealers Assn. [★2577]

Natl. Tyre Distributors Assn. [IO], Aylesbury, United Kingdom

Natl. UNESCO Club for Sci. Expeditions [IO], Sofia, Bulgaria

Natl. Union of Automotive Distributors [IO], Rome, Italy

Natl. Union of Disabled Persons of Uganda [IO], Kampala, Uganda

Natl. Union of Israel Students [IO], Tel Aviv, Israel

Natl. Union of Journalists - England [IO], London, United Kingdom

Natl. Union of Journalists India [IO], New Delhi, India

Natl. Union of Law Enforcement Associations [23244], 7700 Authur Dr., McCalla, AL 35111, (757)630-0202

Natl. Union of the Leather Indus. [IO], Milan, Italy

Natl. Union of Metalworkers of South Africa [IO], Excom, Republic of South Africa

Natl. Union of Mine Workers [IO], Johannesburg, Republic of South Africa

Natl. Union of Mineworkers - United Kingdom [IO], Barnsley, United Kingdom

Natl. Union of Pharmacies [IO], Paris, France

Natl. Union of Phonographic Publishing [IO], Paris, France

Natl. Union of Public and Gen. Employees [IO], Nepean, ON, Canada

Natl. Union of Publishing [IO], Paris, France

Natl. Union of Rail, Maritime and Transport Workers [IO], London, United Kingdom

Natl. Union of School Workers [IO], Rome, Italy

Natl. Union of Students - Australia [IO], Carlton South, Australia

Natl. Union of Students - United Kingdom [IO], London, United Kingdom

Natl. Union of Teachers in Sweden [IO], Stockholm, Sweden

Natl. Union of the Teaching Profession [IO], Kuala Lumpur, Malaysia

Natl. Union of Tenants of Nigeria [IO], Port Harcourt, Nigeria

Natl. Union of Tourism Hospitality [IO], Neuilly-sur-Seine, France

Natl. Union of Tourism and Outdoor Associations [IO], Paris, France

Natl. Union of Tunisian Women [IO], Tunis, Tunisia

Natl. Union of Workers [IO], North Melbourne, Australia

Natl. United Church Ushers Assn. [★20277]

Natl. United Church Ushers Assn. of Am. [20277], PO Box 363863, North Las Vegas, NV 89036-7863, (718)789-6764

Natl. United States-Arab Chamber of Commerce [23374], 1023 15th St. NW, Ste. 400, Washington, DC 20005, (202)289-5920

National UNITY Council [★10337]

Natl. Univ. Continuing Educ. Assn. [★7930]

Natl. Univ. Continuing Educ. Assn. [★7930]

Natl. Univ. Extension Assn. [★7930]

Natl. Univ. Extension Assn. [★7930]

Natl. Upper Cervical Chiropractic Assn. [14141], 1500 Sunday Dr., Ste. 102, Raleigh, NC 27607, (919)573-5443

Natl. Urban Alliance for Effective Educ. [9030], 33 Queens St., Ste. 100, Syosset, NY 11791, (516)802-4192

Natl. Urban Fellows [18756], 102 W 38th St., Ste. 700, New York, NY 10018, (212)730-1700

Natl. Urban Indian Family Coalition [12566], Box 99100, Discovery Park, Seattle, WA 98199, (206)829-2229

Natl. Urban League [17312], 120 Wall St., New York, NY 10005, (212)558-5300

Natl. Urban/Rural Fellos [★18756]

Natl. Urban Squash and Educ. Assn. [23028], 795 Columbus Ave., Roxbury Crossing, MA 02120, (617)373-7375

Natl. Urban Tech. Center [7521], 80 Maiden Ln., Ste. 606, New York, NY 10038, (212)528-7355

Natl. Used Car Dealers Assn. [★364]

Natl. Utilities Diversity Coun. [3600], 1017 L St., Sacramento, CA 95814, (916)752-4386

Natl. Utility Contractors Assn. [941], 11350 Random Hills Rd., Arlington, VA 22203-1627, (703)358-9300

Natl. Utility Contractors Assn. l Clean Water Coun. [4997], 3925 Chain Bridge Rd., Ste. 301, Fairfax, VA 22030, (703)358-9300

Natl. Utility Locating Contractors Assn. [942], 1501 Shirkey Ave., Richmond, MO 64085

Natl. Utility Locating Contractors Assn. [942], 1501 Shirkey Ave., Richmond, MO 64085

Natl. Utility Training and Safety Educ. Assn. [3601], 1024 Steamboat Run, Newburgh, IN 47630, (812)508-1305

Natl. Vaccine Info. Center [14093], 407 Church St., Ste. H, Vienna, VA 22180, (703)938-0342

Natl. Valentine Collectors' Assn. [21386], PO Box 647, Franklin Lakes, NJ 07417

Natl. Valuers Assn. of Cambodia [IO], Phnom Penh, Cambodia

Natl. Vegetable Soc. [IO], Dundee, United Kingdom

Natl. Vehicle Leasing Assn. [3082], 7250 Pkwy. Dr., Ste. 510, Hanover, MD 21076, (410)782-2342

Natl. Vendors Assn. [★3613]

Natl. Venture Capital Assn. [2149], 1655 N Ft. Myer Dr., Ste. 850, Arlington, VA 22209, (703)524-2549

Natl. Verbatim Reporters Assn. [3707], 629 N Main St., Hattiesburg, MS 39401, (601)582-4345

Natl. Versatility Ranch Horse Assn. [22686], 590 Hwy. 105, Box 150, Monument, CO 80132, (719)487-9014

Natl. Veteran-Owned Bus. Assn. [3615], 429 Mill St., Coraopolis, PA 15108, (412)424-0164

Natl. Veterans Legal Services Prog. [20801], PO Box 65762, Washington, DC 20035, (202)265-8305

Natl. Veterans Services Fund [13353], PO Box 2465, Darien, CT 06820-0465, (800)521-0198

Natl. Viatical Assn. - Defunct.

Natl. Victims' Constitutional Amendment Partnership [18760], 789 Sherman St., Ste. 670, Denver, CO 80203, (303)832-1522

Natl. Vietnam and Gulf War Veterans Coalition [18763], 2020 Pennsylvania Ave., No. 961, Washington, DC 20006

Natl. Vietnam Veterans Coalition [★18763]

Natl. Viewers and Listeners Assn. [★15730]

Natl. Vintage Tractor and Engine Club [IO], Retford, United Kingdom

Natl. Viticulture Inst. [IO], Mendoza, Argentina

Natl. Vitiligo Found. [14336], PO Box 23226, Cincinnati, OH 45223, (513)541-3903

Natl. Vocational Agricultural Teachers Assn. [★7711]

Natl. Vocational Guidance Assn. [★11949]

Natl. Vocational-Technical Honor Soc. [★23759]

Natl. Voices [IO], London, United Kingdom

Natl. Voluntary Hea. Agencies [★12051]

Natl. Voluntary Organizations Active in Disaster [12871], 1501 Lee Hwy., Ste. 206, Arlington, VA 22209-1109, (703)778-5088

Natl. Voluntary Orgs. for Independent Living for the Aging - Defunct.

Natl. Volunteer Fire Coun. [5449], 7852 Walker Dr., Ste. 450, Greenbelt, MD 20770, (202)887-5700

Natl. Vulvodynia Assn. [17131], PO Box 4491, Silver Spring, MD 20914-4491, (301)299-0775

Natl. Walking Horse Assn. [4625], 4059 Iron Works Pkwy., Ste. 4, Lexington, KY 40511, (859)252-6942

Natl. Wallpaper Wholesalers Assn. [★2075]

Natl. War Tax Resistance Coordinating Comm. [18703], PO Box 150553, Brooklyn, NY 11215, (718)768-3420

Natl. Warm Air Heating and Air Conditioning Assn. [★1694]

Natl. Water Center [7606], 5473 Hwy. 23N, Eureka Springs, AR 72631

Natl. Water Company Conf. [★3649]

Natl. Water Resources Assn. [7607], 3800 N Fairfax Dr., Ste. 4, Arlington, VA 22203, (703)524-1544

Natl. Water Safety Cong. [12999], PO Box 1632, Mentor, OH 44061, (440)209-9805

Natl. Water Safety Cong. [12999], PO Box 1632, Mentor, OH 44061, (440)209-9805

Natl. Water Supply Improvement Assn. [★7595]

Natl. Water Supply Improvement Assn. [★7595]

Natl. Water Well Assn. [★3650]

Natl. Water Well Assn. [★3650]

Natl. Waterbed Retailers Assn. [★1556]

Natl. Watercolor Soc. [9193], 915 S Pacific Ave., San Pedro, CA 90731, (310)831-1099

Natl. Waterfowl Alliance, Waterfowl U.S.A. [★4159]

Natl. Waterfowl Coun. - Defunct.

Natl. Watermelon Assn. [4462], 5129 S Lakeland Dr. Ste. 1, Lakeland, FL 33813, (813)619-7575

Natl. Watershed Cong. - Defunct.

Natl. Waterways Conf. [3262], 4650 Washington Blvd., No. 608, Arlington, VA 22201, (703)243-4090

Natl. Weather Assn. [7106], 228 W Millbrook Rd., Raleigh, NC 27609-4304, (919)845-7121

Natl. Weather Ser. Employees Org. [6069], 601 Pennsylvania Ave. NW, Ste. 900, Washington, DC 20004, (202)907-3036

Natl. Weightlifting Fed. of Georgia [IO], Tbilisi, Georgia

Natl. Welding Supply Assn. [★1825]

Natl. Well Spouse Found. [★16785]

Natl. Wellness Inst. [16312], PO Box 827, Stevens Point, WI 54481-0827, (715)342-2969

Natl. Wellness Inst. [16312], PO Box 827, Stevens Point, WI 54481-0827, (715)342-2969

Natl. Welsh-American Found. [19278], 24 Essex Rd., Scotch Plains, NJ 07076-0247, (908)889-4942

Natl. Wetlands Coalition - Address unknown since 2010.

Natl. Wheelchair Athletic Assn. [★22533]

Natl. Wheelchair Basketball Assn. [22518], 1130 Elkton St., Ste. C, Colorado Springs, CO 80907, (719)266-4082

Natl. Wheelchair Poolplayer Assn. [22519], Bob Calderon, Sec., 9757 Mt. Lompoc Ct., Las Vegas, NV 89178-7511, (702)437-6792

Natl. Wheelchair Poolplayer Assn. [22519], Bob Calderon, Sec., 9757 Mt. Lompoc Ct., Las Vegas, NV 89178-7511, (702)437-6792

Natl. Wheelchair Softball Assn. [22520], 13414 Paul St., Omaha, NE 68154, (402)305-5020

Natl. Whistleblower Center [13000], 3238 P St. NW, Washington, DC 20007, (202)342-1903

Natl. Wholesale Druggists' Assn. [★16193]

Natl. Wholesale Frozen Food Distributors Assn. [★1417]

A star before a book entry number signifies that the name is not listed separately, but is mentioned within the entry.

Natl. Wholesale Furniture Salesmen's Assn. [★1554]

Natl. Wholesale Furniture Salesmen's Assn. [★1554]

Natl. Wholesale Lumber Dealers Assn. [★1471]

Natl. Wholesale Lumber Distributing Yard Assn. [★1507]

Natl. WIC Assn. [5976], 2001 S St. NW, Ste. 580, Washington, DC 20009, (202)232-5492

Natl. Wild Turkey Fed. [5084], PO Box 530, Edgefield, SC 29824-0530, (803)637-3106

Natl. Wildfire Suppression Assn. [4408], PO Box 330, Lyons, OR 97358, (503)769-2291

Natl. Wildlife Control Operators Assn. [5085], PO Box 402, Neotsu, OR 97364, (541)994-8900

Natl. Wildlife Fed. [4103], 11100 Wildlife Center Dr., Reston, VA 20190-5362, (703)438-6000

Natl. Wildlife Fed. Corporate Conservation Coun. - Defunct.

Natl. Wildlife Refuge Assn. [5086], 1250 Connecticut Ave. NW, Ste. 600, Washington, DC 20036, (202)292-2402

Natl. Wildlife Rehabilitators Assn. [5087], 2625 Clearwater Rd., Ste. 110, St. Cloud, MN 56301, (320)230-9920

Natl. Wind Watch [18788], PO Box 293, Rowe, MA 01367

Natl. Windshield Repair Assn. [366], PO Box 569, Garrisonville, VA 22463, (540)720-7484

Natl. Wine Trade Fed. [IO], Milan, Italy

Natl. Wolfdog Alliance [21615], PO Box 2757, Loves Park, IL 61132-2757

Natl. Woman's Christian Temperance Union [13309], Frances Williard Memorial Lib. Archives, 1730 Chicago Ave., Evanston, IL 60201-4585, (847)864-1322

Natl. Woman's Missionary Soc. of the Church of God [★19615]

Natl. Woman's Party [17667], Sewall-Belmont House & Museum, 144 Constitution Ave. NE, Washington, DC 20002-5608, (202)546-1210

Natl. Woman's Suffrage Assn. [★18473]

Natl. Women in Agriculture Assn. [3762], 1701 N Martin Luther King Ave., Oklahoma City, OK 73119, (405)424-4623

Natl. Women Law Students Assn. - Address unknown since 2011.

Natl. Women's Assn. of Allied Beverage Indus. [★194]

Natl. Women's Assn. of Allied Beverage Indus. [★194]

Natl. Women's Bus. Coun. [3687], 409 3rd St. SW, Ste. 210, Washington, DC 20024, (202)205-3850

Natl. Women's Coun. of Ireland [IO], Dublin, Ireland

Natl. Women's Coun. of the New Zealand Coun. of Trade Unions [IO], Wellington, New Zealand

Natl. Women's Employment Proj. [★17626]

Natl. Women's Forum [★13463]

Natl. Women's Forum [★13463]

Natl. Women's Hall of Fame [20379], PO Box 335, Seneca Falls, NY 13148, (315)568-8060

Natl. Women's Hea. Alliance [14822], 200 W 57th St., Ste. 402, New York, NY 10019, (212)425-5566

Natl. Women's Hea. Coalition [★17127]

Natl. Women's Hea. Coalition [★17127]

Natl. Women's Hea. Network [17132], 1413 K St. NW, 4th Fl., Washington, DC 20005, (202)682-2640

Natl. Women's Hea. Rsrc. Center [17133], 157 Broad St., Ste. 106, Red Bank, NJ 07701, (732)530-3425

Natl. Women's History Proj. [10644], 3440 Airway Dr., Ste. F, Santa Rosa, CA 95403, (707)636-2888

Natl. Women's History Week Proj. [★10644]

Natl. Women's Justice Coalition [IO], Canberra, Australia

Natl. Women's Law Center [17668], 11 Dupont Cir. NW, Ste. 800, Washington, DC 20036, (202)588-5180

Natl. Women's League of the United Synagogue of Am. [★19910]

Natl. Women's Martial Arts Fed. [22748], 14525 SW Millikan Way, No. 19350, Beaverton, OR 97005-2343, (206)339-5251

Natl. Women's Neckwear and Scarf Assn. - Defunct.

Natl. Women's Political Caucus [17669], PO Box 50476, Washington, DC 20091, (202)785-1100

Natl. Women's Register [IO], Norwich, United Kingdom

Natl. Women's Rowing Assn. [★22859]

Natl. Women's Sailing Assn. [22378], 1 Esquire Dr., Peabody, MA 01960, (401)682-2064

Natl. Women's Stud. Assn. [9062], Univ. of Maryland, 7100 Baltimore Ave., Ste. 203, College Park, MD 20740, (301)403-0407

Natl. Wood Carvers Assn. [21459], PO Box 43218, Cincinnati, OH 45243, (513)561-0627

Natl. Wood Carvers Assn. [21459], PO Box 43218, Cincinnati, OH 45243, (513)561-0627

Natl. Wood Flooring Assn. [600], 111 Chesterfield Indus. Blvd., Chesterfield, MO 63005, (800)422-4556

Natl. Wood Window and Door Assn. [★635]

Natl. Wooden Box Assn. [★884]

Natl. Wooden Pallet and Container Assn. [884], 1421 Prince St., Ste. 340, Alexandria, VA 22314-2805, (703)519-6104

Natl. Wooden Pallet Mfrs. Assn. [★884]

Natl. Woodland Owners Assn. [4409], 374 Maple Ave. E, Ste. 310, Vienna, VA 22180, (703)255-2700

Natl. Woodwork Mfrs. Assn. [★635]

Natl. Wool Growers Assn. [★4900]

Natl. Wool Growers' Assn. of South Africa [IO], Port Elizabeth, Republic of South Africa

Natl. Wool Marketing Corp. - Defunct.

Natl. Workforce Assn. [5501], One Massachusetts Ave. NW, Ste. 310, Washington, DC 20001, (202)842-4004

Natl. World War II Glider Pilots Assn. [20315], 4037 Ringdove Way, Roanoke, TX 76262, (719)338-6487

Natl. Wrestling Coaches Assn. [23132], PO Box 254, Manheim, PA 17545-0254, (717)653-8009

Natl. Write Your Congressman [18388], PO Box 830308, Richardson, TX 75083-0308, (214)342-0299

Natl. Write Your Congressman Club [★18388]

Natl. Writers Assn. [2858], 10940 S Parker Rd., No. 508, Parker, CO 80134, (303)841-0246

Natl. Writers Union [23320], 256 W 38th St., Ste. 703, New York, NY 10018, (212)254-0279

Natl. Writing Proj. [9075], Univ. of California, 2105 Bancroft Way, No. 1042, Berkeley, CA 94720, (510)642-0963

Natl. Yellow Pages Ser. Assn. [★2968]

Natl. Yiddish Book Center [9929], Harry and Jeanette Weinberg Bldg., 1021 West St., Amherst, MA 01002-3375, (413)256-4900

Natl. Yiddish Book Exchange [★9929]

Natl. Yogurt Assn. [1025], 2000 Corporate Ridge, Ste. 1000, McLean, VA 22102, (703)821-0770

Natl. Young Farmer Educational Assn. [4361], PO Box 20326, Montgomery, AL 36120, (334)213-3276

Natl. Youth Advocacy Coalition - Defunct.

Natl. Youth Agency [IO], Leicester, United Kingdom

Natl. Youth Alliance [★18783]

Natl. Youth Coun. of Ireland [IO], Dublin, Ireland

Natl. Youth Court Center - Defunct.

Natl. Youth Employment Coalition [13545], 1836 Jefferson Pl. NW, Washington, DC 20036, (202)659-1064

Natl. Youth Leadership Coun. [8491], 1667 Snelling Ave. N, Ste. D300, St. Paul, MN 55108, (651)631-3672

Natl. Youth Ministry Org. [★19977]

Natl. Youth Orchestra Assn. of Canada [IO], Toronto, ON, Canada

Natl. Youth Rights Assn. [18831], 1101 15th St. NW, Ste. 200, Washington, DC 20005, (202)296-2992

Natl. Youth Sports Coaches Assn. [★22461]

Natl. Youth Sports Found. for the Prevention of Athletic Injuries [★16721]

Natl. Youth Sports Safety Found. [16721], 1 Beacon St., Ste. 3333, Boston, MA 02108, (617)367-6677

NationaLease [★3081]

Nationalist Movement; The [18785]

The Nationalist Movement [18785], PO Box 2000, Learned, MS 39154, (601)885-2288

Nationalist Observer - Defunct.

Nationals [IO], Kingston, Australia

Nation's Rpt. Card [★8989]

Nations Unies Commn. Economique pour l'Afrique [★IO]

Nationwide Caterers Assn. [IO], Solihull, United Kingdom

Nationwide Insurance Independent Contractors Assn. [2025], 2001 Jefferson Davis Hwy., Ste. 104, Arlington, VA 22202-3617, (703)416-4422

Native American

Affiliated Tribes of Northwest Indians [19151]

All Indian Pueblo Coun. [18147]

Amer. Indian Culture Res. Center [10319]

Amer. Indian Heritage Found. [10320]

Amer. Indian Higher Educ. Consortium [8673]

Amer. Indian Inst. [10321]

Amer. Indian Movement [18148]

Amer. Indian Ritual Object Repatriation Found. [18149]

Amer. Indian Youth Running Strong [12558]

Americans for Indian Opportunity [12559]

Assn. on Amer. Indian Affairs [18150]

Assn. of Community Tribal Schools [8674]

Assn. for the Stud. of Amer. Indian Literatures [10322]

Before Columbus Found. [10036]

Black Indians and Intertribal Native Amer. Assn. [19152]

Cherokee Natl. Historical Soc. [10323]

Comanche Language and Cultural Preservation Comm. [10324]

Consortia of Administrators for Native Amer. Rehabilitation [19153]

Coun. of Energy Rsrc. Tribes [18151]

Coun. for Indian Educ. [8675]

Crazy Horse Memorial Found. [10325]

Cultural Conservancy [10326]

Fed. of Indian Ser. Employees [8676]

First Nations Development Inst. [12560]

For Mother Earth [17890]

Gathering of Nations [10327]

Heritage Inst. [19154]

Honor the Earth [19155]

Indian Arts and Crafts Assn. [10328]

Indian Defense League of Am. [19156]

Indian Law Rsrc. Center [18152]

Indian Youth of Am. [12561]

Inst. of Amer. Indian Arts [10329]

Inst. for Tribal Environmental Professionals [19157]

Intl. Assn. of Native Amer. Stud. [8677]

Intertribal Bison Cooperative [4729]

Intertribal Deaf Coun. [10330]

Iroquois Stud. Assn. [10331]

Lakota Student Alliance [19158]

Maniilaq Assn. [12562]

Midwest Treaty Network [19159]

Natl. Assn. of Native Amer. Stud. [8678]

Natl. Assn. of The Bahamas [11141]

Natl. Center for Amer. Indian Enterprise Development [12563]

Natl. Cong. of Amer. Indians [18153]

Natl. Coun. of Urban Indian Hea. [15527]

Natl. Environmental Coalition of Native Americans [4730]

Natl. Indian Child Care Assn. [12564]

Natl. Indian Child Welfare Assn. [19160]

Natl. Indian Educ. Assn. [8679]

Natl. Indian Hea. Bd. [12565]

Natl. Indian Justice Center [19161]

Natl. Indian Youth Coun. [10332]

Natl. Native Amer. Cooperative [10333]

Natl. Native Amer. Law Students Assn. [8510]

Natl. Soc. for Amer. Indian Elderly [19162]

Natl. Tribal Development Assn. [19163]

Natl. Tribal Environmental Coun. [18154]

Natl. Urban Indian Family Coalition [12566]

Native Amer. Bus. Alliance [19164]

Native Amer. Coalition for Healthy Alternatives [12567]

Native Amer. Community Bd. [12568]

Native Amer. Indian Info. and Trade Center [23429]

Native Amer. Leadership Alliance [20147]

Native Amer. Recreation and Sport Inst. [22785]

Native Amer. Rights Fund [18155]

Native Amer. Sports Coun. [22786]

Reference to "IO" in place of a book number signifies that the association may be found in the 50th edition of International Organizations.

Native Elder Hea. Care Rsrc. Center **[19165]**
Native Movement **[19166]**
Native Public Media **[18098]**
North Am. Native Amer. Info. and Trade Center **[10334]**
North Amer. Alliance for the Advancement of Native Peoples **[12569]**
North Amer. Alliance for the Advancement of Native Peoples **[12569]**
Old Sleepy Eye Collectors' Club of Am. **[21268]**
Oyate **[19167]**
Pan Amer. Indian Assn. **[10335]**
Phi Sigma Nu Native Amer. Fraternity **[23685]**
Red Earth **[19168]**
Red Feather Development Gp. **[12201]**
Redbirds Vision **[19169]**
Seventh Generation Fund for Indian Development **[18156]**
Tribal Preservation Prog. **[10336]**
United Indian Missions Intl. **[20102]**
United Indians of All Tribes Found. **[18157]**
United Natl. Indian Tribal Youth **[10337]**
United South and Eastern Tribes **[12570]**
Unreserved Amer. Indian Fashion and Art Alliance **[9134]**
White Bison **[10338]**
Worldcraft Circle of Native Writers' and Storytellers **[19170]**
Native Amer. Art Stud. Assn. **[7740]**, Peabody Essex Museum, E India Sq., Salem, MA 01970
Native Amer. Bus. Alliance **[19164]**, 23400 Michigan Ave., Ste. 503, Dearborn, MI 48124, (248)988-9344
Native Amer. Cancer Res. **[13958]**, 3110 S Wadsworth, Ste. 103, Denver, CO 80227, (303)975-2449
Native Amer. Coalition for Healthy Alternatives **[12567]**, 2843 Samco Rd., Unit T, Rapid City, SD 57702, (605)716-3568
Native Amer. Community Bd. **[12568]**, PO Box 572, Lake Andes, SD 57356-0572, (605)487-7072
Native Amer. Contractors Assn. **[943]**, 1514 P St. NW, Ste. 2, Washington, DC 20005, (202)758-2676
Native Amer. Environmental Protection Coalition **[4104]**, EDGE-SCI Bldg., 27368 Via Industria, Ste. 105, Temecula, CA 92590, (951)296-5595
Native Amer. Fatherhood and Families Assn. **[12613]**, 123 N Centennial Way, Ste. 150, Mesa, AZ 85201, (480)833-5007
Native Amer. Finance Officers Assn. **[1322]**, PO Box 50637, Phoenix, AZ 85076-0637, (602)330-9208
Native Amer. Fish and Wildlife Soc. **[4289]**, 8333 Greenwood Blvd., Ste. 260; Denver, CO 80221, (303)466-1725
Native Amer. Fitness Coun. **[16231]**, PO Box K, Flagstaff, AZ 86002, (928)774-3048
Native Amer. Heritage Found. **[★10320]**
Native Amer. Indian Info. and Trade Center **[23429]**, PO Box 27626, Tucson, AZ 85726-7626, (520)622-4900
Native Amer. Journalists Assn. **[2859]**, Univ. of Oklahoma, Gaylord Coll., 395 W Lindsey St., Norman, OK 73019, (405)325-9008
Native Amer. Law Students Assn. **[★8510]**
Native Amer. Leadership Alliance **[20147]**, 3600 New York Ave. NE, 3rd Fl., Washington, DC 20002, (202)841-9061
Native Amer. Medical Students; Assn. of **[15321]**
Native Amer. Press Assn. **[★2859]**
Native Amer. Public Broadcasting Consortium **[★9463]**
Native Amer. Public Telecommunications **[9463]**, 1800 N 33rd St., Lincoln, NE 68503, (402)472-3522
Native Amer. Recreation and Sport Inst. **[22785]**, 116 W Osage St., Greenfield, IN 46140, (317)462-4245
Native Amer. Rights Fund **[18155]**, 1506 Broadway, Boulder, CO 80302, (303)447-8760
Native Amer. Scholarship Fund **[★8190]**
Native Amer. Sports Coun. **[22786]**, 1235 Lake Plaza Dr., Ste. 221, Colorado Springs, CO 80906, (719)632-5282
Native Amer. TV **[10558]**, PO Box 1754, Williamsburg, VA 23187

Native Amer. Water Assn. **[3651]**, 1662 Hwy. 395, Ste. 212, Minden, NV 89423, (775)782-6636
Native Amer. Women's Hea. Educ. Rsrc. Center **[17134]**, PO Box 572, Lake Andes, SD 57356-0572, (605)487-7072
Native Amer. Women's Hea. Educ. Rsrc. Center **[17134]**, PO Box 572, Lake Andes, SD 57356-0572, (605)487-7072
Native Americans in Philanthropy **[12680]**, 2801 21st Ave. S, Ste. 132 D, Minneapolis, MN 55407, (612)724-8798
Native Americans in Sci; Soc. for Advancement of Chicanos and **[7387]**
Native Cultural Alliance **[4290]**, PO Box 104, Marion, CT 06444-0104
Native Daughters of the Golden West **[18943]**, 543 Baker St., San Francisco, CA 94117, (415)563-9091
Native Elder Hea. Care Rsrc. Center **[19165]**, Mailstop F800, 13055 E 17th Ave., Aurora, CO 80045-0508, (303)724-1452
Native Financial Educ. Coalition **[8201]**, 1010 9th St., Ste. 3, Rapid City, SD 57701, (605)342-3770
Native Fish Australia **[IO]**, Doncaster, Australia
Native Fish Soc. **[5088]**, 221 Molalla Ave., Ste. 100, Oregon City, OR 97045, (503)496-0807
Native Forest Coun. **[4105]**, PO Box 2190, Eugene, OR 97402, (541)688-2600
Native Forest Network **[4106]**, PO Box 8251, Missoula, MT 59807, (406)542-7343
Native Forest Network Australia **[IO]**, Deloraine, Australia
Native Habitat Org. - Address unknown since 2010.
Native Movement **[19166]**, PO Box 896, Flagstaff, AZ 86002, (928)213-9063
Native Public Media **[18098]**, PO Box 3955, Flagstaff, AZ 86003, (904)471-6843
Native Seeds/SEARCH **[4107]**, Administrative Offices and Seed Bank, 3584 E River Rd., Tucson, AZ 85718-8849, (520)622-0830
Native Seeds/Southwestern Endangered Arid-Land Rsrc. CH **[★4107]**
Native Sons of the Golden State **[★18962]**
Native Sons of the Golden West **[18944]**, 414 Mason St., Ste. 300, San Francisco, CA 94102, (800)337-1875
Native Tourism Alliance - Address unknown since 2011.
Native Women's Assn. of Canada **[IO]**, Ottawa, ON, Canada
Native Workplace **[10896]**, 4415 Garnett Ave., Ste. A, Austin, TX 78745, (512)462-9056
Native Writers' Circle of the Americas **[★19170]**
NATO Consultation, Command and Control Agency **[IO]**, Brussels, Belgium
NATO Parliamentary Assembly **[IO]**, Brussels, Belgium
NATSO **[3119]**, 1737 King St., Ste. 200, Alexandria, VA 22314, (703)549-2100
NATSO Found. **[3120]**, 1737 King St., Ste. 200, Alexandria, VA 22314, (703)549-2100
NATSO, Representing the Travel Plaza and Truckstop Indus. **[★3119]**
Natur og Ungdom **[★IO]**
Natural Area Coun. - Defunct.
Natural Areas Assn. **[4108]**, PO Box 1504, Bend, OR 97709, (541)317-0199
Natural Building Network **[601]**, PO Box 4120, Portland, OR 97208, (541)345-1174
Natural Color Diamond Assn. **[2172]**, 52 Vanderbilt, 19th Fl., New York, NY 10017, (212)644-9747
Natural Colored Wool Growers Assn. **[4915]**, PO Box 406, New Palestine, IN 46163, (317)681-4765
Natural Colored Wool Growers Assn. **[4915]**, PO Box 406, New Palestine, IN 46163, (317)681-4765
Natural Cork Quality Coun. **[★1505]**
Natural Disasters
  Am. Continental 2000 **[11847]**
  Disaster Mgt. Alliance **[11850]**
  Floodplain Mgt. Assn. **[4731]**
  GeoHazards Intl. **[12571]**
  GeoHazards Intl. **[12571]**
  Global Fac. for Disaster Reduction and Recovery **[11851]**
  Indonesia Relief - USA **[11856]**

  Innovative Support to Emergencies Diseases and Disasters **[11857]**
  Natl. Flood Determination Assn. **[4732]**
  Natural Hazards Res. and Applications Info. Center **[7134]**
  Psychology Beyond Borders **[11860]**
  World Assn. of Natural Disaster Awareness and Assistance **[12572]**
Natural Doctors Intl. **[15534]**, 29672 Zuma Bay Way, Malibu, CA 90265
Natural Dyes Intl. **[7982]**, Box 21912, El Prado, NM 87529, (800)665-9786
Natural England **[IO]**, Sheffield, United Kingdom
Natural Fertility New Zealand **[IO]**, Wellington, New Zealand
Natural Fibers Gp. **[21705]**, 549 Bluebird Trail, Blounts Creek, NC 27814, (252)322-4646
Natural Fitness Trainers Assn. **[22809]**, PO Box 49874, Athens, GA 30606-9998, (706)254-2798
Natural Gas Processors Assn. **[★2650]**
Natural Gas Processors Supplier's Assn. **[★2651]**
Natural Gas Supply Assn. **[4492]**, 1620 Eye St. NW, Ste. 700, Washington, DC 20006, (202)326-9300
Natural Gas Supply Comm. **[★4492]**
Natural Gas Vehicle for Am. **[6242]**, 400 N Capitol St. NW, Washington, DC 20001, (202)824-7366
Natural Gas Vehicle Assn. **[★6242]**
Natural Gas Vehicle Coalition **[★6242]**
Natural Gasoline Assn. of Am. **[★2650]**
Natural Gasoline Supply Men's Assn. **[★2651]**
Natural Hazards Res. and Applications Info. Center **[7134]**, Univ. of Colorado, 483 UCB, Boulder, CO 80309-0482, (303)492-6818
Natural History Network **[7143]**, PO Box 11363, Prescott, AZ 86304, (928)350-2219
Natural Hygiene
  Intl. Assn. of Hygienic Physicians **[15528]**
  Intl. Assn. of Hygienic Physicians **[15528]**
  Natl. Hea. Assn. **[15529]**
Natural Product Broker Assn. - Defunct.
Natural Products Assn. **[3121]**, 1773 T St. NW, Washington, DC 20009, (202)223-0101
Natural Products Marketing Coun. **[IO]**, Truro, NS, Canada
Natural Resources
  Advanced Conservation Strategies **[3979]**
  Africa Environmental Watch **[3980]**
  African Amer. Environmentalist Assn. **[4234]**
  Agua Muisne **[13411]**
  Alliance for Global Conservation **[3983]**
  Alliance for Green Heat **[6682]**
  Alliance for Renewable Energy **[6683]**
  Alliance for Tompotika Conservation **[3985]**
  Alternative Medicine Intl. **[13648]**
  Amer. Biogas Coun. **[6109]**
  Amer. Energy Alliance **[17614]**
  Amer. Reef Coalition **[3993]**
  Amer. Wilderness Coalition **[5010]**
  Anglers for Conservation **[4000]**
  Assn. of Metropolitan Water Agencies **[5859]**
  Audubon Intl. **[4008]**
  Audubon Lifestyles **[4196]**
  Avoided Deforestation Partners **[4390]**
  Biomass Thermal Energy Coun. **[6697]**
  Bioneers **[4733]**
  BlueVoice.org **[4013]**
  Children and Nature Network **[4241]**
  Citizens for Affordable Energy **[6701]**
  Citizens' Alliance for Responsible Energy **[6702]**
  Clean Water Am. Alliance **[4988]**
  Coalition of Natl. Park Ser. Retirees **[4766]**
  Community Forestry Intl. **[4391]**
  Community Water Solutions **[13417]**
  Complementary and Alternative Medicine Initiative **[13671]**
  The Conservation Campaign **[17416]**
  Conservation Leaders Network **[4734]**
  Conservation through Poverty Alleviation Intl. **[4030]**
  Consumer Energy Alliance **[6708]**
  Cork Forest Conservation Alliance **[4036]**
  Defense of Place **[4039]**
  Eco-Life Concepts **[4318]**
  Ecological Res. and Development Gp. **[4045]**
  Elephants Without Borders **[5011]**

A star before a book entry number signifies that the name is not listed separately, but is mentioned within the entry.

Energy Action Coalition [6717]
Energy Conservation Org. [8120]
Energy Extraction Technologies [6718]
Energy and Mineral Law Found. [5860]
Environmental Entrepreneurs [4050]
Experience Intl. [4054]
FishWise [1359]
Focus the Nation [17616]
Forest Partners Intl. [4395]
Forest Planters Intl. [4396]
Friends of the Osa [4063]
GAIA Movement USA [4066]
Give Clean Water [13421]
Global Parks [4070]
Global Rsrc. Alliance [3974]
Great Lakes Commn. [5861]
Green Yoga Assn. [5179]
GreenMotion [4227]
Growing Planet [4400]
HeatGreen Coun. [6113]
Iemanya Oceanica [5064]
Indo-Pacific Conservation Alliance [4079]
Intl. Assn. for Environmental Philosophy [10382]
Intl. Assn. for Soc. and Natural Resources [4735]
Intl. Assn. for Soc. and Natural Resources [4735]
Intl. Biochar Initiative [6115]
Intl. DME Assn. [3770]
Intl. Green Energy Coun. [6116]
Intl. Joint Commn. [4736]
Intl. Joint Commn. [4736]
Intl. Water Level Coalition [5004]
Interstate Coun. on Water Policy [5862]
Journey Toward Sustainability [8159]
Kids Ecology Corps [4322]
LandChoices [4089]
Millennium Water Alliance [13427]
Natl. Assn. of Flood and Storm Water Mgt. Agencies [5863]
Natl. Oceanic Soc. [4102]
Natl. Org. of Professional Hispanic Natural Resources Conservation Ser. Employees [4521]
Natl. Renewables Cooperative Org. [6741]
Natl. Wildlife Fed. [4103]
Nature Abounds [4291]
Nature's Voice Our Choice [4998]
Neotropical Grassland Conservancy [4112]
New Energy Indus. Assn. for Asia and the Pacific [6742]
New Generation Energy [6743]
Ocean Champions [17417]
Ocean Conservation Res. [4116]
Ocean Renewable Energy Coalition [6747]
Oceanic Preservation Soc. [4119]
Orchid Conservation Alliance [4120]
OurEarth.org [4121]
Pacific Islands Conservation Res. Assn. [4123]
Paso Pacifico [4125]
Population Rsrc. Center [12708]
Public Lands Coun. [4824]
Rainforest Partnership [4859]
Renewable Energy Markets Assn. [1176]
Renewable Energy Resources [6750]
Rights and Resources Initiative [4412]
Rivers Without Borders [4134]
Rocky Mountain Inst. [4737]
Rocky Mountain Mineral Law Found. [5864]
Rocky Mountain Mineral Law Found. [5864]
Safe Water Network [13429]
Save the Rain [13430]
Save Yemen's Flora and Fauna [4140]
Solar for Peace [7447]
Sustainable Smiles [4876]
Thirst Relief Intl. [13432]
Tropical Forest Gp. [4153]
Turtle Island Restoration Network [4156]
U.S. Aquaculture Soc. [3831]
U.S. Offshore Wind Collaborative [7623]
U.S. Water and Power [6121]
US-China Green Energy Coun. [6760]
Vision Earth Soc. [4223]
Water 1st Intl. [13433]
Water to Thrive [13439]
Water for Waslala [13440]
Wild Gift [5146]

Wilderness Intl. [4160]
Wind Energy Mfrs. Assn. [3667]
Wind Energy Works! [7625]
Women Organizing for Change in Agriculture and NRM [3769]
Wonderful World of Wildlife [5157]
World Bamboo Org. [4738]
World Bamboo Org. [4738]
World Fed. for Coral Reef Conservation [4169]
World Ocean Coun. [5009]
Natural Resources Defense Coun. [4109], 40 W 20th St., New York, NY 10011, (212)727-2700
Natural Resources Info. Coun. [9999], Univ. of North Texas, Discovery Park Lib., 1155 Union Cir., No. 305190, Denton, TX 76203-5017, (940)369-6437
Natural Resources Info. Coun. [9999], Univ. of North Texas, Discovery Park Lib., 1155 Union Cir., No. 305190, Denton, TX 76203-5017, (940)369-6437
Natural Rights Center [★5946]
Natural Rights Center [★5946]
Natural Sci. Collections Alliance [6311], 1313 Dolley Madison Blvd., Ste. 402, McLean, VA 22101, (703)790-1745
Natural Sci. for Youth Found. - Defunct.

Natural Sciences
Acad. of Natural Sciences [7135]
Acad. of Natural Sciences [7135]
Amer. Museum of Natural History [7136]
Amer. Quaternary Assn. [7137]
Amer. Soc. of Naturalists [7138]
Big Bend Natural History Assn. [7139]
Birmingham Natural History Soc. [5651]
Coalition on the Public Understanding of Sci. [7365]
European Nature Heritage Fund [18169]
Fed. of Earth Sci. Info. Partners [6603]
HOPOS - The Intl. Soc. for the History of Philosophy of Sci. [8839]
Intl. Assn. for Ecology and Hea. [6604]
Intl. Assn. for Environmental Philosophy [10382]
The Intl. Lepidoptera Survey [6845]
Intl. Lunar Observatory Assn. [6231]
John Burroughs Assn. [7140]
Moroccan-American Soc. for Life Sciences [7141]
Moroccan-American Soc. for Life Sciences [7141]
Natl. Assn. for Interpretation [7142]
Natural History Network [7143]
Radiochemistry Soc. [6418]
Soc. of Herbarium Curators [6368]
Soc. for Northwestern Vertebrate Biology [7144]
Western Natl. Parks Assn. [7145]
Western Soc. of Naturalists [7146]
World Corrosion Org. [4178]
Yosemite Conservancy [7147]
Natural Trails and Waters Coalition [4823], PO Box 7516, Missoula, MT 59807, (406)543-9551
Nature Abounds [4291], PO Box 241, Clearfield, PA 16830
Nature Canada [IO], Ottawa, ON, Canada
Nature Connection [11016], PO Box 155, Concord, MA 01742, (978)369-2585
Nature Conservancy [4110], 4245 N Fairfax Dr., Ste. 100, Arlington, VA 22203-1606, (703)841-5300
Nature and Culture Intl. [4111], 1400 Maiden Ln., Del Mar, CA 92014, (858)259-0374
Nature Healing Nature [11614], 514 Byrne St., Houston, TX 77009, (832)423-8425
Nature Kenya: the East Africa Natural History Soc. [IO], Nairobi, Kenya
Nature Saskatchewan [IO], Regina, SK, Canada
Nature Seychelles [IO], Victoria, Seychelles
Nature and Youth [IO], Oslo, Norway
Nature's Voice Our Choice [4998], 1940 Duke St. Ste. 200, Alexandria, VA 22314, (202)360-8373
Naturfreunde Osterreich [★IO]
The Naturist Soc. [10343], PO Box 132, Oshkosh, WI 54903, (920)426-5009
The Naturists [★10343]
Naturopathic Medical Student Assn. [15535], 2828 Naito Pkwy., Ste. 401, Portland, OR 97201, (503)334-4153
Naturopathic Medicine for Global Hea. [15536], 37 Mulberry Row, Princeton, NJ 08540, (609)310-1340
Naturopathic Physicians Bd. of Aesthetic Medicine [15537], PO Box 13100, Prescott, AZ 86304, (602)430-0744

Naturopaths Intl. [15538], 114 N San Francisco St., Ste. 12, Flagstaff, AZ 86001, (928)214-8793
Naturopathy
Amer. Assn. of Naturopathic Midwives [15530]
Amer. Assn. of Naturopathic Physicians [15531]
Amer. Naturopathic Medical Assn. [15532]
Assn. of Accredited Naturopathic Medical Colleges [8680]
Assn. of Accredited Naturopathic Medical Colleges [8680]
Assn. of Natural Medicine Pharmacists [15533]
Canadian Coll. of Naturopathic Medicine [1999]
Mama Baby Haiti [14107]
Natural Doctors Intl. [15534]
Naturopathic Medical Student Assn. [15535]
Naturopathic Medicine for Global Hea. [15536]
Naturopathic Physicians Bd. of Aesthetic Medicine [15537]
Naturopaths Intl. [15538]
Oncology Assn. of Naturopathic Physicians [15539]
Pediatric Assn. of Naturopathic Physicians [8681]
NAUCRATES [IO], Cori, Italy
Nauru Amateur Athletic Assn. [IO], Nauru, Nauru
Nauru Badminton Assn. [IO], Aiwo, Nauru
Nauru Judo Assn. [IO], Aiwo, Nauru
Nauru Olympic Comm. [IO], Nauru, Nauru
Nauru Tennis Assn. [IO], Aiwo, Nauru
Nauru Volleyball Assn. [IO], Yaren, Nauru
Nauru Weightlifting Fed. [IO], Nauru, Nauru
Nautical Archaeology Soc. [IO], Portsmouth, United Kingdom
Nautical Inst. [IO], London, United Kingdom
Nautical Res. Guild [22379], 31 Water St., Ste. 7, Cuba, NY 14727, (585)968-8111
Nautical Res. Guild [22379], 31 Water St., Ste. 7, Cuba, NY 14727, (585)968-8111
Nautilus Inst. [18598], Univ. of San Francisco, 2130 Fulton St., K 180A, San Francisco, CA 94117, (415)422-5523
Nautilus Inst. [18598], Univ. of San Francisco, 2130 Fulton St., K 180A, San Francisco, CA 94117, (415)422-5523
Nautilus Intl. [IO], London, United Kingdom
NAVAH [13311], 616 Corporate Way, Ste. 2 - 4560, Valley Cottage, NY 10989-2050, (718)689-1493
Navajo-Churro Sheep Assn. [4916], PO Box 1994, El Prado, NM 87529, (575)751-3767
Navajo Code Talkers Assn. [20863], PO Box 1266, Window Rock, AZ 86515-1266, (520)871-5468
Navajo Gospel Crusade [★20102]
Navajo Gospel Crusade [★20102]
Naval Airship Assn. [6091], Peter F. Brouwer, Sec.-Treas., 1950 SW Cycle St., Port St. Lucie, FL 34953-1778, (772)871-9379
Naval Aviation Museum Found. [★6091]
Naval Civilian Administrators Assn. [★5819]
Naval Civilian Managers Assn. [5819], 9170 2nd St., Ste. 120, Norfolk, VA 23511-2393, (757)502-4481
Naval Commandery of Am. [★20722]
Naval Engineering
Personal Submersibles Org. [7148]
Soc. of Naval Architects and Marine Engineers [7149]
Naval Enlisted Reserve Assn. [5820], 6703 Farragut Ave., Falls Church, VA 22042-2189, (703)534-1329
Naval Historical Collectors and Res. Assn. [IO], North Walsham, United Kingdom
Naval Historical Found. [10093], 1306 Dahlgren Ave. SE, Washington Navy Yard, Washington, DC 20374-5055, (202)678-4333
Naval Historical Soc. of Australia [IO], Garden Island, Australia
Naval Intelligence Professionals [5821], PO Box 11579, Burke, VA 22009-1579, (703)250-6765
Naval Legion of the U.S. [★20722]
Naval Officers' Assn. of Canada [IO], Kanata, ON, Canada
Naval Order of the U.S. [20722], PO Box 2714, Merrifield, VA 22116-2714, (904)221-0923
Naval Records Club [★10092]
Naval Records Club [★10092]
Naval Res. Lab. - Seafloor Geosciences Div. - Address unknown since 2010.
Naval Reserve Assn. [5822], 1619 King St., Alexandria, VA 22314-2793, (703)548-5800

Reference to "IO" in place of a book number signifies that the association may be found in the 50th edition of International Organizations.

Naval Reserve Officers Assn. [★5829]

Naval Sea Cadet Corps [5823], 2300 Wilson Blvd., Ste. 200, Arlington, VA 22201, (703)243-6910

Naval Ships Assn; Historic [10058]

Naval Ships Assn; Historic [10058]

Naval Submarine League [17510], PO Box 1146, Annandale, VA 22003, (703)256-0891

Navigation

Inst. of Navigation [7150]

Intl. Loran Assn. [7151]

Intl. Loran Assn. [7151]

The Navigators [19593], PO Box 6000, Colorado Springs, CO 80934-6000, (719)598-1212

Navy

AE/AEO Sailors Assn. [5865]

Aircraft Carrier Indus. Base Coalition [1034]

All Navy Women's Natl. Alliance [5866]

Burton Island Assn. [20717]

Fleet Reserve Assn. [20718]

Force Recon Assn. [20719]

Marine Corps Veterans Assn. [20683]

Natl. Assn. of Fleet Tug Sailors [20720]

Natl. Chief Petty Officers' Assn. [20721]

Naval Civilian Managers Assn. [5819]

Naval Order of the U.S. [20722]

Navy and Marine Living History Assn. [10094]

Navy Records Soc. [3698]

Navy Seabee Veterans of Am. [20723]

Oper. Paperback [11100]

Patrol Craft Sailors Assn. [20724]

Salisbury Sound Assn. [20725]

Soc. for the History of Navy Medicine [9808]

Support Our Troops [11110]

Tin Can Sailors - The Natl. Assn. of Destroyer Veterans [20726]

U.S. Naval Sailing Assn. [20727]

U.S. Navy Beach Jumpers Assn. [20728]

U.S. Navy Memorial Found. [20729]

USMC Vietnam Tankers Assn. [20824]

USS BB-42 Idaho Assn. [20730]

USS Intrepid Assn. of Former Crew Members [20731]

U.S.S. LCI Natl. Assn. [20807]

USS Leyte CV32 Assn. [20732]

USS Liberty Veterans Assn. [20733]

USS LSM-LSMR Assn. [20734]

USS Nimitz CVN-68 Assn. [20735]

USS North Carolina Battleship Assn. [20870]

USS Pyro AE-1 and AE-24 Assn. [20736]

USS Wisconsin Assn. [20737]

Veteran's Assn. of the USS Iowa [20738]

Vietnam Era Seabees [20826]

WAVES Natl. [20739]

Navy Anesthesia Soc. [13751], Naval Medical Center, Dept. of Anesthesiology, San Diego, CA 92134-5000, (619)532-8943

Navy Carrier Soc. [21907], 225 W Orchid Ln., Phoenix, AZ 85021

Navy Club of the U.S.A. [5824], 6243 S 150 W, Lafayette, IN 47909-8909, (765)586-2500

Navy Club of the U.S.A. Auxiliary [5825], 6243 S 150 W, Lafayette, IN 47909-8909, (765)586-2500

Navy League Cadet Corps. [★5823]

Navy League of the U.S. [5826], 2300 Wilson Blvd., Ste. 200, Arlington, VA 22201-3308, (703)528-1775

Navy League of the U.S. [5826], 2300 Wilson Blvd., Ste. 200, Arlington, VA 22201-3308, (703)528-1775

Navy-Marine Corps Relief Soc. [18929], 875 N Randolph St., Ste. 225, Arlington, VA 22203, (703)696-4904

Navy and Marine Living History Assn. [10094], 422 Clay St., Erlanger, KY 41018-1466

Navy Nurse Corps Assn. [15786], PO Box 5983, Virginia Beach, VA 23471, (757)490-5738

Navy Records Soc. [IO], Pangbourne, United Kingdom

Navy Relief Soc. [★18929]

Navy Seabee Veterans of Am. [20723], 555 Fairview Ave., Creve Coeur, IL 61610-3237, (309)699-7344

NAW Inst. for Distribution Excellence [3664], 1325 G St. NW, Ste. 1000, Washington, DC 20005, (202)872-0885

NAWE: Advancing Women in Higher Education - Defunct.

Nazarene Compassionate Ministries Intl. [19594], 17001 Prairie Star Pkwy., Lenexa, KS 66220, (913)768-4808

Nazarene Compassionate Ministries Intl. [19594], 17001 Prairie Star Pkwy., Lenexa, KS 66220, (913)768-4808

Nazarene Foreign Missionary Soc. [★20072]

Nazarene Foreign Missionary Soc. [★20072]

Nazarene Missions Intl. [20072], 17001 Prairie Star Pkwy., Lenexa, KS 66220, (913)577-2970

Nazarene Missions Intl. [20072], 17001 Prairie Star Pkwy., Lenexa, KS 66220, (913)577-2970

Nazarene World Mission Soc. [★20072]

Nazarene World Mission Soc. [★20072]

Nazarene World Missionary Soc. [★20072]

Nazarene World Missionary Soc. [★20072]

NBIA Disorders Assn. [15625], 2082 Monaco Ct., El Cajon, CA 92019-4235, (619)588-2315

NBLC Dutch Assn. of Public Libraries [IO], The Hague, Netherlands

NCAA Golf Coaches Assn. [★22608]

NCCLS: The Clinical Lab. Standards Org. [★15234]

NCCLS: The Clinical Lab. Standards Org. [★15234]

NCI Alliance for Nanotechnology in Cancer [15348], Natl. Cancer Inst., Bldg. 31, Rm. 10A52, 31 Center Dr., MSC 2580, Bethesda, MD 20892-2580, (301)451-8983

NCMS - Soc. of Indus. Security Professionals [1891], 994 Old Eagle School Rd., Ste. 1019, Wayne, PA 19087-1866, (610)971-4856

NCO Assn. [★5827]

NCPG [★1542]

NCSJ: Advocates on Behalf of Jews in Russia, Ukraine, the Baltic States and Eurasia [17568], 2020 K St. NW, Ste. 7800, Washington, DC 20006, (202)898-2500

NCSJ: Advocates on Behalf of Jews in Russia, Ukraine, the Baltic States and Eurasia [17568], 2020 K St. NW, Ste. 7800, Washington, DC 20006, (202)898-2500

NCSL Intl. [7467], 2995 Wilderness Pl., Ste. 107, Boulder, CO 80301-5404, (303)440-3339

NCSL Intl. [7467], 2995 Wilderness Pl., Ste. 107, Boulder, CO 80301-5404, (303)440-3339 ·

NDEITA - Natl. Dance Exercise Instructors Training Assn. [★22208]

NEA Bricklin Club [★21014]

NEA Found. [8052], 1201 16th St. NW, Washington, DC 20036-3207, (202)822-7840

NEA Found. for the Improvement of Educ. [★8052]

NEA Hea. Info. Network [8225], 1201 16th St. NW, Ste. 216, Washington, DC 20036, (202)822-7570

NEA Higher Educ. Coun. [★23181]

Near East Archaeological Soc. [6173], Andrews Univ., Horn Archaeological Museum, Berrien Springs, MI 49104, (269)471-3273

Near East Archaeological Soc. [6173], Andrews Univ., Horn Archaeological Museum, Berrien Springs, MI 49104, (269)471-3273

Near East Found. [18134], 430-432 Crouse Hinds Hall, 900 S Crouse Ave., Syracuse, NY 13244-2130, (315)428-8670

Near East Found. [18134], 430-432 Crouse Hinds Hall, 900 S Crouse Ave., Syracuse, NY 13244-2130, (315)428-8670

Near East Relief [★18134]

Near East Relief [★18134]

Near Field Commun. Forum [6438], 401 Edgewater Pl., Ste. 600, Wakefield, MA 01880, (781)876-6239

Nebraska Christian Coll. Alumni Assn. [18887], 12550 S 114th St., Papillion, NE 68046, (402)935-9400

Nederlands Antilliaans Olympisch Comite [★IO]

Nederlands Antilliaanse Atletiek Unie [IO], Curacao, Netherlands Antilles

Nederlands Atoomforum [★IO]

Nederlands Bijbelgenootschap [★IO]

Nederlands Centrum voor Inheemse Volken [★IO]

Nederlands akoestisch Genootschap [★IO]

Nederlands Genootschap van Abortusartsen [★IO]

Nederlands Genootschap voor Internationale Zaken [★IO]

Nederlands Genootschap voor Japanse Studien [★IO]

Nederlands Helsinki Comite [★IO]

Nederland's Instituut voor Navigatie [★IO]

Nederlands Instituut voor Zuidelijk Afrika [★IO]

Nederlands Juristen Comite voor de Mensenrechten [★IO]

Nederlands Nationaal Comite van de Internationale Zuivelbond [★IO]

Nederlands Normalisatie-instituut [★IO]

Nederlands Olympisch Comite [★IO]

Nederlands Textielinstituut [★IO]

Nederlands Uitgeversverbond [★IO]

Nederlands Verbond van de Groothandel [★IO]

Nederlandsch Economisch-Historisch Archief [★IO]

Nederlandsche Maatschappij tot Bevordering des Tandheelkunde [★IO]

Nederlandsche Maatschappij voor Nijverheid en Handel [★IO]

Nederlandse Algemene Danssport Bond [IO], Enschede, Netherlands

Nederlandse Badminton Bond [IO], Nieuwegein, Netherlands

Nederlandse Bakkerij Centrum [★IO]

Nederlandse Beroepsvereniging Tolken Gebarentaal [★IO]

Nederlandse vereniging voor Biomaterialen en Tissue Engg. [★IO]

Nederlandse Biotechnologische Vereniging [★IO]

Nederlandse Bond van Handelaren in Vee [★IO]

Nederlandse Cosmetica Vereniging [★IO]

Nederlandse Culturele Aikikai Federatie [IO], Amsterdam, Netherlands

Nederlandse Franchise Vereniging [★IO]

Nederlandse Frisbee Bond [★IO]

Nederlandse vereniging Frisdranken, Waters, Sappen [★IO]

Nederlandse Fruittelers Organisatie [★IO]

Nederlandse Juweliers- en Uurwerkenbranche [★IO]

Nederlandse Kring voor Joodse Genealogie [★IO]

Nederlandse Mycologische Vereniging [★IO]

Nederlandse Natuurkundige Vereniging [★IO]

Nederlandse Organisatie voor Internationale Ontwikkelingssamenwerking [★IO]

Nederlandse Organisatie voor Internationale Samenwerking in het Hoger Onderwijs [★IO]

Nederlandse Organisatie voor toegepast-Natuurwetenschappelijk onderzoek [★IO]

Nederlandse Patienten Consumenten Federatie [★IO]

Nederlandse Stichting Voor Kostentechniek [★IO]

Nederlandse Taalunie [★IO]

Nederlandse Triathlon Bond [IO], Nieuwegein, Netherlands

Nederlandse Vereiniging voor Psychiatrie [★IO]

Nederlandse Vereniging voor Addison en Cushing Patienten [★IO]

Nederlandse Vereniging Algemene Toelevering [★IO]

Nederlandse Vereniging voor Calcium en Botstofwisseling [★IO]

Nederlandse Vereniging voor Cardiologie [★IO]

Nederlandse Vereniging van Dietisten [★IO]

Nederlandse Vereniging voor Endocrinologie [★IO]

Nederlandse Vereniging voor Fysiologie [★IO]

Nederlandse Vereniging voor Fysiologie [★IO]

Nederlandse Vereniging van Journalisten [★IO]

Nederlandse Vereniging voor Kwaliteit en Zorg [★IO]

Nederlandse Vereniging voor Microscopie [★IO]

Nederlandse Vereniging van Producenten en Importeurs van Beeld- en Geluidsdragers [★IO]

Nederlandse Vereniging voor Psychiatrische Verpleegkunde [★IO]

Nederlandse Vereniging voor Reumatologie [★IO]

Nederlandse Vereniging Techniek in de Landbouw [★IO]

Nederlandse Vereniging voor Tuin en Landschapsarchitektuur [★IO]

Nederlandse Vereniging Van Huisvrouwen [IO], Amersfoort, Netherlands

Nederlandse Vereniging Voor Farmacologie [★IO]

Nederlandse Vereniging Voor Gerontologie [★IO]

Nederlandse Vereniging Voor Vrouwenbelangen [★IO]

Nederlandse Vereniging voor Weer- en Sterrenkunde [IO], Utrecht, Netherlands

Nederlandse Vereniging van Zeepfabrikanten [★IO]

Nederlandse Vrouwen Raad [★IO]

Nederlandse Woonbond [★IO]

Nederlanse Floorball en Unihockey Bond [★IO]

Need Proj. [★17617]

A star before a book entry number signifies that the name is not listed separately, but is mentioned within the entry.

Needlework
Amer. Bunka Embroidery Assn. [21960]
Crochet Guild of Am. [21961]
Krochet Kids Intl. [12735]
Rwanda Knits [11626]
Spinning and Weaving Assn. [3456]
Needlework Guild of Am. [★13070]
Needmor Fund [13141], 42 S St. Clair St., Toledo, OH 43604, (419)255-5560
NeedyMeds [15310], PO Box 219, Gloucester, MA 01931, (978)865-4115
Negative Population Growth [12699], 2861 Duke St., Ste. 36, Alexandria, VA 22314, (703)370-9510
Negro Airmen Intl. [6092], PO Box 23911, Savannah, GA 31403, (912)232-7524
Negro Leagues Baseball Museum [22287], 1616 E 18th St., Kansas City, MO 64108-1610, (816)221-1920
Negro Natl. Bowling Assn. [★22425]
NEHRP Coalition [7402], 101 Constitution Ave. NW, Ste. 375 E, Washington, DC 20001, (202)789-7850
Neighbor to Neighbor [17232], 1550 Blue Spruce Dr., Fort Collins, CO 80524, (970)484-7498
Neighbor to Neighbor [17232], 1550 Blue Spruce Dr., Fort Collins, CO 80524, (970)484-7498
Neighborhood Arts Programs Natl. Org. Comm. [★9264]
Neighborhood Coalition [★17389]
Neighborhood Funders Gp. [12681], 1301 Connecticut Ave. NW, Ste. 500, Washington, DC 20036, (202)833-4690
Neighborhood Prevention Network [★13274]
Neighborhood Reinvestment Corp. [★12197]
Neighbors Without Borders [12350], PO Box 6392, San Rafael, CA 94903, (415)479-1740
Neighbors of Woodcraft [★19286]
NeighborWorks Am. [12197], 1325 G St. NW, Ste. 800, Washington, DC 20005-3100, (202)220-2300
NEIGHBOURS [IO], London, United Kingdom
Nematological Soc. of Southern Africa [IO], Potchefstroom, Republic of South Africa
Nematologiese Vereniging van Suidelike Afrika [★IO]
Nematology
Soc. of Nematologists [7152]
Nemzeti Loverseny [★IO]
Nemzetkozi Adoszakertok Magyarorszagi Tarsasaga [★IO]
Neonatal Death; Aiding Mothers and Fathers Experiencing [11744]
Neotropical Grassland Conservancy [4112], 6274 Heathcliff Dr., Carmichael, CA 95608, (916)967-3223
Neotropical Grassland Conservancy [4112], 6274 Heathcliff Dr., Carmichael, CA 95608, (916)967-3223
Nepal Acad. of Sci. and Tech. [IO], Kathmandu, Nepal
Nepal Airsport Assn. [IO], Kathmandu, Nepal
Nepal Amateur Athletics Assn. [IO], Kathmandu, Nepal
Nepal Assn. of Tour and Travel Agents [IO], Kathmandu, Nepal
Nepal Assn. of Univ. Women [IO], Kathmandu, Nepal
Nepal Badminton Assn. [IO], Kathmandu, Nepal
Nepal Bible Soc. [IO], Kathmandu, Nepal
Nepal Chamber of Commerce [IO], Kathmandu, Nepal
Nepal Dental Assn. [IO], Lalitpur, Nepal
Nepal Epilepsy Soc. [IO], Kathmandu, Nepal
Nepal Geotechnical Soc. [IO], Kathmandu, Nepal
Nepal Medical Assn. [IO], Kathmandu, Nepal
Nepal Olympic Comm. [IO], Kathmandu, Nepal
Nepal Physiotheraphy Assn. [IO], Kathmandu, Nepal
Nepal Press Inst. [IO], Kathmandu, Nepal
Nepal Red Cross Soc. [IO], Kathmandu, Nepal
Nepal Reliance Org. [IO], Kathmandu, Nepal
Nepal Remote Sensing and Photogrammetric Soc. [IO], Kathmandu, Nepal
Nepal SEEDS: Social Educational Environmental Development Services in Nepal [11615], 800 Kansas St., San Francisco, CA 94107, (415)813-3331
Nepal Squash Rackets Assn. [IO], Kathmandu, Nepal

Nepal Stationery and Educational Materials Indus. Assn. [IO], Kathmandu, Nepal
Nepal Stud. Assn. [★8682]
Nepal Stud. Assn. [★8682]
Nepal Taekwondo Assn. [IO], Kathmandu, Nepal
Nepal and Tibet Philatelic Stud. Circle [22061], Mr. Richard M. Hanchett, Ed., 6 Rainbow Ct., Warwick, RI 02889-1118, (401)738-0466
Nepal Weight Lifting Assn. [IO], Kathmandu, Nepal
NepalAama [7833], PO Box 1565, Simi Valley, CA 93062
Nepalese
Assn. of Nepal and Himalayan Stud. [8682]
Assn. of Nepal and Himalayan Stud. [8682]
Assn. of Nepalis in the Americas [19171]
Assn. of Nepalis in the Americas [19171]
Community Members Interested [11569]
Educate the Children [11461]
NepalAama [7833]
Nepali Amer. Friendship Assn. [19172]
Newah Org. of Am. [11617]
NRN Natl. Coordination Coun. of U.S. [19173]
Nyaya Hea. [15201]
One Earth Designs [4293]
Nepalese Americas Coun. [★19173]
Nepali Amer. Friendship Assn. [19172], 318 Cheyenne Trail, Madison, WI 53705, (608)663-6556
Nephrology
Alliance for Paired Donation [15540]
Amer. Assn. of Kidney Patients [15541]
Amer. Kidney Fund [15542]
Amer. Nephrology Nurses' Assn. [15543]
Amer. Soc. of Diagnostic and Interventional Nephrology [15544]
Amer. Soc. of Nephrology [15545]
Amer. Soc. of Pediatric Nephrology [15546]
Bd. of Nephrology Examiners Nursing and Tech. [15547]
Children's Dialysis Intl. [15548]
Dialysis Patient Citizens [15549]
Intl. Pediatric Nephrology Assn. [15550]
Intl. Pediatric Nephrology Assn. [15550]
Irish Kidney Assn. [23900]
Kidney Care Partners [15551]
Kidney Community Emergency Response Coalition [15552]
Natl. Assn. of Nephrology Technicians/Technologists [15553]
Natl. Kidney Found. [15554]
North Amer. Soc. for Dialysis and Transplantation [15555]
Oxalosis and Hyperoxaluria Found. [15556]
Renal Physicians Assn. [15557]
Renal Support Network [15558]
Nepisiguit Salmon Assn. [IO], Bathurst, NB, Canada
Nesbitt/Nisbet Soc.: A Worldwide Clan Soc. [20564], 5930 Creekside Ln., Hoschton, GA 30548-8232
Nesbitt/Nisbet Soc.: A Worldwide Clan Soc. [20564], 5930 Creekside Ln., Hoschton, GA 30548-8232
NET Ministries, Inc. [★19475]
NetAction - Address unknown since 2011.
NetAid - Address unknown since 2011.
Netball
Caribbean Amer. Netball Assn. [22787]
U.S.A. Netball Assn. [22788]
Netball New Zealand [IO], Auckland, New Zealand
NetGALA [★18888]
Netherland Amer. Stud. Assn. [IO], Middelburg, Netherlands
Netherlands
Netherlands Bd. of Tourism and Conventions [23430]
Netherlands Chamber of Commerce in the U.S. [23431]
Netherlands ACM SIGCHI [IO], Amsterdam, Netherlands
Netherlands Aerospace Gp. [IO], Zoetermeer, Netherlands
Netherlands Antilles
Bonaire Govt. Tourist Off. [23432]
Curacao Convention Bureau/Tourist Bd. [23433]
Netherlands Antilles Hockey Assn. [IO], Curacao, Netherlands Antilles
Netherlands Antilles Olympic Comm. [IO], Curacao, Netherlands Antilles

Netherlands Antilles Tennis Fed. [IO], Curacao, Netherlands Antilles
Netherlands Assn. of Intl. Dutch Contractors [IO], Zoetermeer, Netherlands
Netherlands Assn. for Japanese Stud. [IO], Leiden, Netherlands
Netherlands Assn. of Journalists [IO], Amsterdam, Netherlands
Netherlands Assn. for Landscape Architecture [IO], Amsterdam, Netherlands
Netherlands Assn. for Lib., Info. and Knowledge Professionals [IO], Amersfoort, Netherlands
Netherlands Assn. of Sports Medicine [IO], Bilthoven, Netherlands
Netherlands Assn. for Women's Interests, Women's Work and Equal Citizenship [IO], The Hague, Netherlands
Netherlands Atlantic Assn. [IO], The Hague, Netherlands
Netherlands Atomic Forum [IO], Petten, Netherlands
Netherlands Bible Soc. [IO], Haarlem, Netherlands
Netherlands Bio-Energy Assn. [IO], Arnhem, Netherlands
Netherlands Biotechnological Soc. [IO], Vlaardingen, Netherlands
Netherlands Bd. of Tourism [★23430]
Netherlands Bd. of Tourism and Conventions [23430], 215 Park Ave. S, Ste. 2005, New York, NY 10003, (212)370-7360
Netherlands Bd. of Tourism and Conventions [IO], Leidschendam, Netherlands
Netherlands British Chamber of Commerce [IO], London, United Kingdom
Netherlands Centre Alternatives to Animal Use [IO], Utrecht, Netherlands
Netherlands Centre for Indigenous Peoples [IO], Amsterdam, Netherlands
Netherlands Chamber of Commerce Australia [IO], Melbourne, Australia
Netherlands Chamber of Commerce in the U.S. [23431], 267 5th Ave., Ste. 908, New York, NY 10016, (212)265-6460
Netherlands Comm. of Jurists for Human Rights [IO], Leiden, Netherlands
Netherlands Convention Bur. [★23430]
Netherlands Convention and Visitors Bur. [★23430]
Netherlands Coun. of Women [IO], The Hague, Netherlands
Netherlands Defence Mfrs. Assn. [IO], The Hague, Netherlands
Netherlands Development Org. [IO], The Hague, Netherlands
Netherlands Development Org. - Burkina Faso [IO], Ouagadougou, Burkina Faso
Netherlands Development Org. - Cameroon [IO], Yaounde, Cameroon
Netherlands Development Org. - Mali [IO], Bamako, Mali
Netherlands Dietetic Assn. [IO], Houten, Netherlands
Netherlands Economic History Archv. [IO], Amsterdam, Netherlands
Netherlands Economic Inst. [IO], Rotterdam, Netherlands
Netherlands Floorball and Unihockey Assn. [IO], Nieuwegein, Netherlands
Netherlands Franchise Assn. [IO], Hilversum, Netherlands
Netherlands Helsinki Comm. [IO], The Hague, Netherlands
Netherlands Inst. of Navigation [IO], Rotterdam, Netherlands
Netherlands Inst. for Southern Africa [IO], Amsterdam, Netherlands
Netherlands Inst. for Space Res. [IO], Utrecht, Netherlands
Netherlands Mycological Soc. [IO], Utrecht, Netherlands
Netherlands Natl. Comm. of the Intl. Dairy Fed. [IO], Zoetermeer, Netherlands
Netherlands Olympic Comm. [IO], Arnhem, Netherlands
Netherlands Org. for Hea. Res. and Development [IO], The Hague, Netherlands
Netherlands Org. for Applied Sci. Res. [IO], Delft, Netherlands

Reference to "IO" in place of a book number signifies that the association may be found in the 50th edition of International Organizations.

Netherlands Org. for Intl. Cooperation in Higher Educ. [IO], The Hague, Netherlands

Netherlands Org. for Intl. Development Cooperation [IO], The Hague, Netherlands

Netherlands Paralympic Comm. [IO], Arnhem, Netherlands

Netherlands Physical Soc. [IO], Amsterdam, Netherlands

Netherlands Psychiatric Assn. [IO], Utrecht, Netherlands

Netherlands Red Cross Soc. [IO], The Hague, Netherlands

Netherlands' Shipbuilding Indus. Assn. [IO], Zoetermeer, Netherlands

Netherlands Soc. of Agricultural Engineers [IO], Wageningen, Netherlands

Netherlands Soc. of Cardiology [IO], Utrecht, Netherlands

Netherlands Soc. for Endocrinology [IO], Groningen, Netherlands

Netherlands Soc. for English Stud. [IO], Amsterdam, Netherlands

Netherlands Soc. of Gerontology [IO], Dronten, Netherlands

Netherlands Soc. for Indus. and Trade [IO], The Hague, Netherlands

Netherlands Soc. for Jewish Genealogy [IO], Amsterdam, Netherlands

Netherlands Soc. for Nature and Env. [IO], Utrecht, Netherlands

Netherlands Soc. of Parents with Nepalese Children [IO], Diemen, Netherlands

Netherlands Soc. for Statistics and Operations Res. [IO], Barendrecht, Netherlands

Netherlands Standardization Inst. [IO], Delft, Netherlands

Netherlands Wholesale and Intl. Trade Fed. [IO], The Hague, Netherlands

NetHope [12872], 10615 Judicial Dr., Ste. 402, Fairfax, VA 22030, (703)388-2845

Netting Nations [14413], 7119 W Sunset Blvd., Ste. 317, Los Angeles, CA 90046

Netting Nations [14413], 7119 W Sunset Blvd., Ste. 317, Los Angeles, CA 90046

NetWare Users Intl. [★3393]

NetWare Users Intl. [★3393]

NETWORK [★18624]

NETWORK [8053], 136 Fenno Dr., Rowley, MA 01969-1004, (978)948-7764

Network [IO], Durham, United Kingdom

Network 20/20 [18066], 850 7th Ave., Ste. 1101, New York, NY 10019, (212)582-1870

NETWORK, A Natl. Catholic Social Justice Lobby [18624], 25 E St. NW, Ste. 200, Washington, DC 20001-1630, (202)347-9797

Network Against Coercive Psychiatry [12490], 172 W 79th St., No. 2E, New York, NY 10024, (212)560-7288

Network Alliance of Congregations Caring for Earth - Address unknown since 2011.

Network Branded Prepaid Card Assn. [1323], 110 Chestnut Ridge Rd., Ste. 111, Montvale, NJ 07645-1706, (201)746-0725

Network of Conservation Educators and Practitioners [4113], Amer. Museum of Natural History, Center for Biodiversity and Conservation, Central Park West, 79th St., New York, NY 10024, (212)769-5742

Network for Continuing Medical Educ. [15428], 1 Harmon Plz., Secaucus, NJ 07094, (201)867-3550

Network for Educ. and Academic Rights [IO], London, United Kingdom

Network of Educators on the Americas [★8111]

Network of Employers for Traffic Safety [18580], 344 Maple Ave. W, No. 357, Vienna, VA 22180, (703)273-6005

Network Ethiopia [15199], 2401 Virginia Ave. NW, Washington, DC 20037, (202)835-8383

Network of European Agricultural Tropically and Subtropically Oriented Universities and Sci. Complexes Related with Agricultural Development [IO], Prague, Czech Republic

Network of European Foundations for Innovative Cooperation [IO], Brussels, Belgium

Network on Feminist Approaches to Bioethics [★11981]

Network on Feminist Approaches to Bioethics [★11981]

Network of Gay and Lesbian Alumni/ae Associations [18888], PO Box 53188, Washington, DC 20009

Network of Govt. Lib. and Info. Specialists [IO], London, United Kingdom

Network for the Improvement of World Hea. [15200], PO Box 18716, Washington, DC 20036

Network for the Improvement of World Hea. [15200], PO Box 18716, Washington, DC 20036

Network of Indian Professionals [19038], PO Box 06362, Chicago, IL 60606, (312)952-0254

Network of Ingredient Marketing Specialists [1422], PO Box 681864, Marietta, GA 30068-0032, (770)971-8116

Network of Innovative Schools [★8053]

Network Intl. [★13518]

Network of Intl. Christian Schools [7857], 3790 Goodman Rd. E, Southaven, MS 38672, (662)892-4300

Network of Iranian Amer. Soc. [13546], 14252 Culver Dr., No. 406, Irvine, CA 92604

Network Myanmar [IO], Guildford, United Kingdom

Network Professional Assn. [6465], 1401 Hermes Ln., San Diego, CA 92154, (888)672-6720

Network of Single Adult Leaders - Defunct.

Network in Solidarity with the People of Guatemala [17758], 436 14th St., Ste. 409, Oakland, CA 94612, (510)238-8400

Network and Systems Professionals Assn. [★6515]

Network and Systems Professionals Assn. [6515], 7044 S 13th St., Oak Creek, WI 53154, (414)908-4945

Network of Trial Law Firms [5278], 303 S Broadway, Ste. 222, Tarrytown, NY 10591, (914)332-4400

Network of Trial Law Firms [5278], 303 S Broadway, Ste. 222, Tarrytown, NY 10591, (914)332-4400

Network Women in Development Europe [IO], Brussels, Belgium

Networkers' Soc. of Pakistan [IO], Karachi, Pakistan

Networking

Benchmarking Network [2574]

Caucus-Association of High Tech Procurement Professionals [7153]

CEO Netweavers [962]

Clean Tech. and Sustainable Indus. Org. [3856]

GesherCity [19091]

Global Sourcing Coun. [2602]

Intl. Assn. of Space Entrepreneurs [139]

Natl. Soc. for Hispanic Professionals [695]

RandomKid [13554]

Rising Tide Capital [1060]

SailMail Assn. [6679]

Neumann Janos Szamitogep-tudomanyi Tarsasag [★IO]

Neuro-Developmental Treatment Assn. [15668], 1540 S Coast Hwy., Ste. 203, Laguna Beach, CA 92651, (800)869-9295

Neuro-Ophthalmology

Neuro-Optometric Rehabilitation Assn. Intl. [15559]

Neuro-Optometric Rehabilitation Assn. Intl. [15559]

Neuro-Optometric Rehabilitation Assn. Intl. [15559], Robert A. Williams, Exec. Dir., 1921 E Carnegie Ave., Ste. 3L, Santa Ana, CA 92705, (949)250-8070

Neuro-Optometric Rehabilitation Assn. Intl. [15559], Robert A. Williams, Exec. Dir., 1921 E Carnegie Ave., Ste. 3L, Santa Ana, CA 92705, (949)250-8070

Neurobehavioral Teratology Soc. [15626], Lori Driscoll, PhD, Sec., Colorado Coll., Dept. of Psychology, 14 E Cache La Poudre, Colorado Springs, CO 80903, (719)227-8201

Neuroblastoma Children's Cancer Soc. [13959], PO Box 957672, Hoffman Estates, IL 60195, (847)605-1245

Neurochemistry; Amer. Soc. for [7154]

Neurocritical Care Soc. [14208], 5841 Cedar Lake Rd., Ste. 204, Minneapolis, MN 55416, (952)646-2034

Neurocritical Care Soc. [14208], 5841 Cedar Lake Rd., Ste. 204, Minneapolis, MN 55416, (952)646-2034

Neuroendocrinology; Intl. Soc. of Psycho [15346]

Neuroethics Soc. [15679], PO Box 34252, Bethesda, MD 20827, (703)261-9233

Neurofibromatosis [14617], PO Box 66884, Chicago, IL 60666, (800)942-6825

Neurofibromatosis Assn. of Australia [IO], Lindfield, Australia

Neurofibromatosis Assn. of Ireland [IO], Dublin, Ireland

Neurofibromatosis Assn. of the United Kingdom [IO], Kingston Upon Thames, United Kingdom

Neuroimaging; Amer. Soc. of [16525]

Neuroleptic Malignant Syndrome Info. Ser. [15627], PO Box 1069, Sherburne, NY 13460-1069, (607)674-7920

Neuroleptic Malignant Syndrome Info. Ser. [15627], PO Box 1069, Sherburne, NY 13460-1069, (607)674-7920

Neurological Coun. of Western Australia [IO], Nedlands, Australia

Neurological Disorders

Accelerated Cure Proj. for Multiple Sclerosis [15560]

Alliance for Addiction Solutions [15561]NeurologicalALS Diagnostic Support Gp.

ALS Support Gp. - Belgium [20148]

Amer. Acad. for Cerebral Palsy and Developmental Medicine [15562]

Amer. Acad. of Hea. Care Providers in the Addictive Disorders [15563]

Amer. Asperger's Assn. [15564]

Amer. Assn. of Neuromuscular and Electrodiagnostic Medicine [15565]

Amer. Brain Coalition [15566]

Amer. Parkinson Disease Assn. [15567]

Amer. Syringomyelia and Chiari Alliance Proj. [15568]

Amyotrophic Lateral Sclerosis Assn. [15569]

Amyotrophic Lateral Sclerosis Soc. of Canada [16922]

Angioma Alliance [15570]

Angioma Alliance [15570]

Asociacion Espanola de Esclerosis Lateral Amiotrofica [13877]

Associacao Brasileira de Esclerose Multipla [4755]

Assn. for Frontotemporal Degeneration [15571]

Assn. de la Suisse Romande et Italienne Contre les Myopathies [10431]

Associazione Italian Sclerosi Laterale Amiotrofica [18729]

Attention Deficit Disorder Assn. [15572]

Autism Allies [13779]

Autism Care and Treatment Today! [13780]

Autism Ser. Dogs of Am. [13784]

Avenues, Natl. Support Gp. for Arthrogryposis Multiplex Congenita [15573]

Batten Disease Support and Res. Assn. [15574]

Benign Essential Blepharospasm Res. Found. [15575]

Brain Attack Coalition [16729]

Care4Dystonia [15576]

Charcot-Marie-Tooth Assn. [15577]

Children and Adults With Attention Deficit/Hyperactivity Disorder [15578]

Children's Tumor Found. [15579]

Coalition for SafeMinds [15580]

Commun. Independence for the Neurologically Impaired [15581]

Cyprus Multiple Sclerosis Assn. [4468]

Czech Multiple Sclerosis Soc. [1011]

Danish Multiple Sclerosis Soc. [738]

Dementia Advocacy and Support Network Intl. [15582]

Dementia Advocacy and Support Network Intl. [15582]

Deutsche Gesellschaft fur Muskelkranke [19170]

Deutsche Multiple Sklerose Gesellschaft Bundesverband E.V. [3945]

Dravet.org [14519]

Dysautonomia Found. [15583]

Dysautonomia Youth Network of Am. [15584]

Dyspraxia Assn. of Ireland [17398]

Dyspraxia USA [15585]

Dystonia Medical Res. Found. [15586]

A star before a book entry number signifies that the name is not listed separately, but is mentioned within the entry.

Esclerosis Multiple Argentina [4183]
Facial Pain Assn. [15587]
Families with Autism Spectrum Disorders [13790]
Families of S.M.A. [15588]
Fibromuscular Dysplasia Soc. of Am. [15589]
Finnish MS Soc. [1707]
Forbes Norris MDA/ALS Res. Center [15590]
FSH Soc. [15591]
Generation Rescue [13792]
Girl Power 2 Cure [15592]
Global Autism Collaboration [13793]
Global Neuro Rescue [15593]
Global Neuro Rescue [15593]
Global and Regional Asperger Syndrome Partnership [15594]
Global and Regional Asperger Syndrome Partnership [15594]NeurologicalGreek Multiple Sclerosis Soc.
Guardians of Hydrocephalus Res. Found. [15595]
Guillain-Barre Syndrome/Chronic Inflammatory Demyelinating Polyneuropathy Found. Intl. [15596]
Guillain-Barre Syndrome/Chronic Inflammatory Demyelinating Polyneuropathy Found. Intl. [15596]
Hereditary Disease Found. [15597]
Hungarian Multiple Sclerosis Soc. [18415]
Huntington's Disease Assn. of Ireland [2867]
Huntington's Disease Soc. of Am. [15598]
Hydrocephalus Assn. [15599]
Intl. Alliance of ALS/MND Associations [11897]
Intl. Brain Barriers Soc. [15657]
Intl. Brain Injury Assn. [14684]
Intl. Coalition for Autism and All Abilities [13796]
Intl. Essential Tremor Found. [15600]
Intl. Essential Tremor Found. [15600]
Intl. Org. of Glutaric Acidemia [15601]
Intl. Org. of Glutaric Acidemia [15601]
Intl. Rett Syndrome Found. [15602]
Intl. Rett Syndrome Found. [15602]
Intl. Soc. for the Stud. of Vascular Anomalies [15603]
Jeena [11798]
Kennedy's Disease Assn. [15604]
Kennedy's Disease Assn. [15604]
Latvian Multiple Sclerosis Assn. [6135]
Lewy Body Dementia Assn. [15605]
Lewy Body Dementia Assn. [15605]
Ligue Francaise contre la Sclerose En Plaques [11752]
Ligue Nationale Belge de la Sclerose en Plaques [4458]
Lissencephaly Network [15606]
Lissencephaly Network [15606]
MAAP Services for Autism and Asperger Syndrome [15607]
MS Soc. of Iceland [18412]NeurologicalMultipel Sklerose Forbundet I Norge
Multiple Sclerosis Assn. of Am. [15608]
Multiple Sclerosis Coalition [15609]
Multiple Sclerosis Found. [15610]
Multiple Sclerosis Soc. of Canada [23924]
Multiple Sclerosis Soc. of India [17530]
Multiple Sclerosis Soc. of Ireland [8601]
Multiple Sclerosis South Africa [23262]
Muscular Dystrophy Assn. [15611]
Muscular Dystrophy Ireland [16168]
Myasthenia Gravis Found. of Am. [15612]
The Myositis Assn. [15613]
Narcolepsy Assn. United Kingdom [1739]
Natl. Ataxia Found. [15614]
Natl. CFIDS Found. [15615]
Natl. Coun. of Certified Dementia Practitioners [15616]
Natl. Fibromyalgia Res. Assn. [15617]
Natl. Found. for Brain Res. [15666]
Natl. Inst. of Neurological Disorders and Stroke [15618]
Natl. Multiple Sclerosis Soc. [15619]
Natl. Org. for Disorders of the Corpus Callosum [15620]
Natl. Parkinson Found. [15621]
Natl. Spasmodic Dysphonia Assn. [15622]
Natl. Spasmodic Torticollis Assn. [15623]
Natl. Tay-Sachs and Allied Diseases Assn. [15624]

Natl. Tay-Sachs and Allied Diseases Assn. [15624]
NBIA Disorders Assn. [15625]
Neurobehavioral Teratology Soc. [15626]
Neuroleptic Malignant Syndrome Info. Ser. [15627]
Neuroleptic Malignant Syndrome Info. Ser. [15627]
Neurologiskt Handikappades Riksforbund [8930]
Parents of Infants and Children with Kernicterus [15628]
Parkinson Alliance [15629]
Parkinson's Disease Found. [15630]NeurologicalParkinson's Disease Soc. of the United Kingdom
Pediatric Neurotransmitter Disease Assn. [15631]
Portuguesa Multiple Sclerosis Soc. [17397]
Prize4Life [15632]
Purine Res. Soc. [15506]
Reflex Sympathetic Dystrophy Syndrome Assn. of Am. [15633]
Shy Drager Syndrome/Multiple Sys. Atrophy Support Gp. [15634]
Slovak Multiple Sclerosis Soc. [18420]
Spanish Assn. of Multiple Sclerosis [18328]
Stop Calling It Autism! [13802]
Stories of Autism [13803]
Sturge-Weber Found. [15635]
S.U.C.C.E.S.S. for Autism [13804]
Tourette Syndrome Assn. [15636]
Transverse Myelitis Assn. [15637]
Transverse Myelitis Assn. [15637]
Tremor Action Network [15638]
Tremor Action Network [15638]
Tuberous Sclerosis Alliance [15639]
United Cerebral Palsy Associations [15640]
United Leukodystrophy Found. [15641]
United Leukodystrophy Found. [15641]
World Fed. of Neurology Res. Gp. on Motor Neuron Diseases [15642]
World Fed. of Neurology Res. Gp. on Motor Neuron Diseases/Amyotropic Lateral Sclerosis [15642]
Yugoslav MND Assn. [3751]
Zdruzenje Multiple Sklerose Slovenie [17644]
Neurological Surgeons; Amer. Assn. of [15682]
Neurological Surgeons; Amer. Assn. of [15682]
Neurologiskt Handikappades Riksforbund [★IO]
Neurologiskt Handikappades Riksforbund [IO], Stockholm, Sweden

Neurology
Amer. Acad. of Clinical Neuropsychology [15643]
Amer. Acad. of Neurology [15644]
Amer. Neurological Assn. [15645]
Amer. Soc. for Experimental Neuro Therapeutics [15646]
Amer. Soc. for Neural Therapy and Repair [15647]
Amer. Soc. of Neurophysiological Monitoring [15648]
Amer. Soc. of Neurorehabilitation [15649]
Amer. Synesthesia Assn. [15650]
Assn. for Comprehensive NeuroTherapy [15651]
Assn. for Network Care [13666]
Avenues, Natl. Support Gp. for Arthrogryposis Multiplex Congenita [15573]
Benign Essential Blepharospasm Res. Found. [15575]
Cajal Club [15652]
Child Neurology Soc. [15653]
Children's Tumor Found. [15579]
Dana Alliance for Brain Initiatives [15654]NeurologyEuropean Fed. of Neurological Societies
Forbes Norris MDA/ALS Res. Center [15590]
Global Neuro Rescue [15593]
Hispanic Neuropsychological Soc. [15655]
Intl. Acad. for Child Brain Development [15656]
Intl. Acad. for Child Brain Development [15656]
Intl. Brain Barriers Soc. [15657]
Intl. Brain Injury Assn. [14684]
Intl. Functional Elecl. Stimulation Soc. [15658]
Intl. Functional Elecl. Stimulation Soc. [15658]
Intl. Neural Network Soc. [15659]
Intl. Neural Network Soc. [15659]
Intl. Neuromodulation Soc. [15660]

Intl. Neuromodulation Soc. [15660]
Intl. Neuropsychological Soc. [15661]
Intl. Neuropsychological Soc. [15661]
Intl. Soc. for Brachial Plexus and Peripheral Nerve Injury [15662]
Intl. Soc. for Neurofeedback and Res. [15663]
Intl. Soc. for Neurofeedback and Res. [15663]
Intl. Soc. for Neuroimmunomodulation [15664]
Intl. Soc. for Neuroimmunomodulation [15664]
Intl. Soc. of NeuroVirology [15665]
Intl. Soc. of NeuroVirology [15665]
Lissencephaly Network [15606]
Multiple Sclerosis Coalition [15609]
Natl. Found. for Brain Res. [15666]
Natl. Neurotrauma Soc. [15667]
Neuro-Developmental Treatment Assn. [15668]
The Neuropathy Assn. [15669]
Neurotechnology Indus. Org. [15670]
North Amer. Skull Base Soc. [15671]
North Amer. Spine Soc. [15672]
North Amer. Spine Soc. [15672]
Prize4Life [15632]
Purine Res. Soc. [15506]
Soc. for Heart Brain Medicine [14046]
Spine Arthroplasty Soc. [15688]
Tourette Syndrome Assn. [15636]
United Brachial Plexus Network [15673]
United Brachial Plexus Network [15673]
United Coun. for Neurological Subspecialties [15674]
Neurology; Amer. Bd. of Psychiatry and [16325]
Neuroma Assn; Acoustic [16080]
Neuromodulation Soc; Intl. [15660]
Neuromodulation Soc; Intl. [15660]
Neuromodulation Soc; North Amer. [16106]
Neuromuscular Diseases Assn. of Romania [IO], Arad, Romania
Neuromuscular and Electrodiagnostic Medicine; Amer. Assn. of [15565]
Neuropathologists; Amer. Assn. of [16110]
The Neuropathy Assn. [15669], 60 E 42 St., Ste. 942, New York, NY 10165, (212)692-0662
Neuropsychiatric Assn; Amer. [16328]
Neuropsychiatric Res. Soc. [★16337]
Neuropsychology; Amer. Acad. of Clinical [15643]
Neuropsychopharmacology; Amer. Coll. of [16173]
Neuroradiology; Amer. Soc. of [16526]

Neuroscience
Amer. Autonomic Soc. [15675]
Amer. Soc. for Neurochemistry [7154]
Assn. for Network Care [13666]
Austrian Neuroscience Assn. [14670]
Cognitive Neuroscience Soc. [15676]
Cognitive Neuroscience Soc. [15676]
Danish Soc. for Neuroscience [20783]
Fed. of European Neuroscience Societies - Milan [4605]
German Neuroscience Soc. [11338]
Global Assn. for Interpersonal Neurobiology Stud. [7155]
Global Assn. for Interpersonal Neurobiology Stud. [7155]
Intl. Behavioral Neuroscience Soc. [15677]
Intl. Behavioral Neuroscience Soc. [15677]
Intl. Brain Educ. Assn. [15678]
Intl. Soc. for the History of the Neurosciences [7156]
Intl. Soc. for the History of the Neurosciences [7156]
Intl. Soc. of Motor Control [7157]
Intl. Soc. of Motor Control [7157]
Israel Soc. for Neuroscience [3853]
The Monroe Inst. [7158]
Neuroethics Soc. [15679]
Neurotech Network [15680]
Norwegian Neuroscience Soc. [22115]
Org. for Human Brain Mapping [7159]
Soc. for Neuroscience [7160]
Spine Arthroplasty Soc. [15688]
Vision Sciences Soc. [7394]
Whitehall Found. [7161]
Neuroscience Nursing; Amer. Bd. of [15715]
Neurosurgery
Amer. Acad. of Neurological and Orthopaedic Surgeons [15681]

Reference to "IO" in place of a book number signifies that the association may be found in the 50th edition of International Organizations.

Amer. Assn. of Neurological Surgeons [15682]
Amer. Assn. of Neurological Surgeons [15682]
Amer. Bd. of Neurological Surgery [15683]
Amer. Soc. for Stereotactic and Functional Neuro-
surgery [15684]
Amer. Soc. for Stereotactic and Functional Neuro-
surgery [15684]
Cong. of Neurological Surgeons [15685]
Cong. of Neurological Surgeons [15685]Neurosurg-
eryNeurosurgery Intl.
Soc. of Neurological Surgeons [15686]
Soc. for Neuroscience in Anesthesiology and Criti-
cal Care [15687]
Spine Arthroplasty Soc. [15688]
Women in Neurosurgery [15689]
World Soc. for Stereotactic and Functional Neuro-
surgery [15690]
World Soc. for Stereotactic and Functional Neuro-
surgery [15690]
Neurosurgery Intl.
Neurosurgery Intl. - Address unknown since 2010.
Neurosurgical Assn. of Malaysia [IO], Kuala Lumpur,
Malaysia
Neurosurgical Nurses [★15715]
Neurosurgical Physician Assistants; Assn. of [16236]
Neurosurgical Soc. of Australasia [IO], Melbourne,
Australia
Neurotech Network [15680], PO Box 27386, Tampa,
FL 33623, (727)321-0150
Neurotechnology Indus. Org. [15670], 315 30th St.,
San Francisco, CA 94131, (415)341-0193
Neurotology Soc; Amer. [16681]
Neurowissenschaftliche Gesellschaft e.V. [★IO]
Neutron Scattering Soc. of Am. [7271], Jaime A.
Fernandez-Baca, Membership Sec., Neutron Scat-
tering Sci. Div., Oak Ridge Natl. Lab., Oak Ridge,
TN 37831-6393, (865)576-8659
Neutropenia Support Assn., Inc. [IO], Winnipeg, MB,
Canada
Nevada Assn. Race and Sports Book Operators -
Defunct.
Nevada Desert Experience [18209], 1420 W Bartlett
Ave., Las Vegas, NV 89106-2226, (702)646-4814
Never Again Campaign
Never Again Campaign - Address unknown since
2011.
Never Again Rwanda [IO], Kigali, Rwanda
Never Forget Our Fallen [11095], PO Box 695,
Roseville, CA 95661, (916)223-6816
Never More War [IO], Tarm, Denmark
Nevil Inst. for Rehabilitation and Ser. [★17063]
Nevil Shute Soc. - Defunct.
Nevis Historical and Conservation Soc. [IO],
Charlestown, St. Kitts and Nevis
Nevis Island Cultural Center of the U.S. - Defunct.
Nevus Network [16778], The Congenital Nevus Sup-
port Gp., PO Box 305, West Salem, OH 44287,
(419)853-4525
Nevus Network [16778], The Congenital Nevus Sup-
port Gp., PO Box 305, West Salem, OH 44287,
(419)853-4525
Nevus Outreach [14414], 600 SE Delaware Ave.,
Ste. 200, Bartlesville, OK 74003, (918)331-0595
New Afghanistan Women Assn. [IO], Kabul,
Afghanistan
New Age [★10852]
New Age
Coalition of Visionary Resources [2575]
New Age Citizen [17313], PO Box 419, Dearborn
Heights, MI 48127, (313)704-0021
New Age Patriot [★17313]
New Age World Religious and Scientific Res. Found.
- Defunct.
New Am. Alliance [1059], 8150 N Central Expy., Ste.
1625, Dallas, TX 75206, (214)466-6410
New Am. Found. [18480], 1899 L St., NW, Ste. 400,
Washington, DC 20036, (202)986-2700
New Am. Media [18099], 275 9th St., 3rd Fl., San
Francisco, CA 94103, (415)503-4170
New Am. Movement [★18654]
New Art Dealers Alliance [9194], 55 Chrystie St. Ste.
310, New York, NY 10002, (212)594-0883
New Avenues to Independence [12511], 17608 Eu-
clid Ave., Cleveland, OH 44112-1216, (216)481-
1909

New Brunswick Coun. of the Atlantic Salmon Fed.
[IO], Fredericton, NB, Canada
New Brunswick Fed. of Woodlot Owners [IO], Fre-
dericton, NB, Canada
New Brunswick Inst. of Agrologists [IO], Fredericton,
NB, Canada
New Brunswick Wheelchair Sports Assn. [IO], St.
John, NB, Canada
New Brunswick Wildlife Fed. [IO], St. Leonard, NB,
Canada
New Buildings Inst. [5304], PO Box 2349, White
Salmon, WA 98672, (509)493-4468
New Caledonia Rugby Union [IO], Noumea, New
Caledonia
New Caledonia Weightlifting Fed. [IO], Noumea,
New Caledonia
New Canaan Historical Soc. [9788], 13 Oenoke
Ridge, New Canaan, CT 06840, (203)966-1776
New Chaucer Soc. [8540], Washington Univ., One
Bookings Dr., St. Louis, MO 63130, (314)935-4407
New Civilization Network - Address unknown since
2011.
New Democratic Dimensions [17541], 152 Madison
Ave., Ste. 804, New York, NY 10016-5424,
(212)481-7251
New Democratic Party of Canada [IO], Ottawa, ON,
Canada
New Dimensions Found. [★17804]
New Dimensions Found. [★17804]
New Dimensions Radio [17804], PO Box 569,
Ukiah, CA 95482, (707)468-5215
New Dimensions Radio [17804], PO Box 569,
Ukiah, CA 95482, (707)468-5215
New Dramatists [10594], 424 W 44th St., New York,
NY 10036, (212)757-6960
New Dramatists Comm. [★10594]
New Ecology, Inc. [11616], 15 Court Sq., Ste. 420,
Boston, MA 02108, (617)557-1700
New Economics Found. [IO], London, United
Kingdom
New Economics Inst. [17195], 140 Jug End Rd.,
Great Barrington, MA 01230, (413)528-1737
New Edinburgh Folk Club [IO], Dunedin, New
Zealand
New El Salvador Today [★17604]
New El Salvador Today [★17604]
New Energy Indus. Assn. for Asia and the Pacific
[6742], 2055 Junction Ave., Ste. 225, San Jose,
CA 95131, (408)434-1993
New England Antiquities Res. Assn. [6174], 94
Cross Point Rd., Edgecomb, ME 04556, (207)882-
9425
New England Assistance Dog Prog. [★14950]
New England Assistance Dog Ser. [★14950]
New England Assn. of Colleges and Secondary
Schools [★8054]
New England Assn. of Graduate Admissions Profes-
sionals [★7685]
New England Assn. of Schools and Colleges [8054],
209 Burlington Rd., Ste. 201, Bedford, MA 01730-
1433, (781)271-0022
New England Assn. of Soldiers of the War of 1812
[★20840]
New England Camping Assn. [★22446]
New England Family Campers Assn. [★22446]
New England Fisheries Development Assn. -
Defunct.
New England Gerontological Assn. [14671], 1 Cutts
Rd., Durham, NH 03824-3102, (603)868-5757
New England Historic Genealogical Soc. [20649],
101 Newbury St., Boston, MA 02116, (617)536-
5740
New England Kiln Drying Assn. [1470], William B.
Smith, Exec. Sec., Suny Coll. of Environmental
Sci. and Forestry, 1 Forestry Dr., Syracuse, NY
13210, (315)470-6832
New England Knitted Outerwear Assn. [★20439]
New England Knitted Outerwear Mfrs. Assn.
[★20439]
New England Knitwear and Sportswear Assn. -
Defunct.
New England M.G. T Register Limited [21134], PO
Box 1028, Ridgefield, CT 06877-9028, (203)438-
2796
New England Order of Protection [★19286]

New England Rainwear Mfrs. Assn. [★199]
New England Rubber Club [★3133]
New England Theatre Conf. [10595], 215 Knob Hill
Dr., Hamden, CT 06518, (617)851-8535
New England Trail Rider Assn. [23089], PO Box
469, Collinsville, CT 06022, (860)693-9111
New England Trails Conf. [23090], PO Box 550,
Charlestown, NH 03603, (603)543-1700
New England Wild Flower Preservation Soc.
[★4114]
New England Wild Flower Soc. [4114], 180 Hemen-
way Rd., Framingham, MA 01701, (508)877-7630
New English Art Club [IO], London, United Kingdom
New Env. Assn. [4292], 1200 Euclid Ave., Syracuse,
NY 13210, (315)446-8009
New Eyes for the Needy [12473], 549 Millburn Ave.,
Short Hills, NJ 07078, (973)376-4903
New Family for Development [IO], Bujumbura, Bu-
rundi
New Farmers of Am. [★7714]
New Farmers of Am. [★7714]
New Flemish Alliance [IO], Brussels, Belgium
New Forest Pony Assn. [★4626]
New Forest Pony Assn. and Registry [4626], Lucille
Guilbault, VP, PO Box 206, Pascoag, RI 02859-
0206, (401)568-8238
New Forest Pony Breeding and Cattle Soc. [IO],
Bransgore, United Kingdom
New Forests Fund [★12351]
New Forests Proj. [12351], 737 8th St. SE, Ste. 202,
Washington, DC 20003, (202)464-9386
New Frontiers Hea. Force [12873], 11380 66th St.
N, Ste. 139, Largo, FL 33773, (727)447-3555
New Fuels Alliance [6885], 101 Tremont St., Ste.
700, Boston, MA 02108, (617)275-8215
New Generation Energy [6743], 98 N Washington
St., Ste. 305, Boston, MA 02114, (617)624-3688
New Homemakers of Am. [★8181]
New Hope Constr. [12198], PO Box 1186, Hender-
sonville, TN 37077, (615)822-0111
New Hope Found. [13280], PO Box 66, Marlboro,
NJ 07746, (732)946-3030
New Hope Intl. [20073], PO Box 25490, Colorado
Springs, CO 80936, (719)577-4450
New Hope Intl. [20073], PO Box 25490, Colorado
Springs, CO 80936, (719)577-4450
New Hope Ministries [★20073]
New Hope Ministries [★20073]
New Horizons Intl. Music Assn. [10266], Shirley
Michaels, Ed., 1975 28th Ave., No. 18, Greeley,
CO 80634, (970)301-4585
New Israel Fund [18014], 2100 M St. NW, Ste. 619,
Washington, DC 20037, (202)842-0900
New Jersey Devils Fan Club [★23903]
New Jetsons Fan Club [23925], PO Box 02222,
Detroit, MI 48202
New Komeito [IO], Tokyo, Japan
New Leaders for New Schools [8492], 30 W 26th
St., 2nd Fl., New York, NY 10010, (646)792-1070
New Life Intl. Alliance [19999], PO Box 135, Ned-
row, NY 13120, (315)469-1106
New Mgt. Era [IO], Tirana, Albania
New Media Development Assn. [IO], Tokyo, Japan
New Order [18786], Box 270486, Milwaukee, WI
53227
New Order [18786], Box 270486, Milwaukee, WI
53227
New Orleans Bd. of Trade [3970], 316 Bd. of Trade
Pl., New Orleans, LA 70130, (504)262-0412
New Orleans Produce Exchange [★3970]
New Parents Network [8692], PO Box 64237,
Tucson, AZ 85728-4237, (520)461-6806
New Party [★18368]
New Political Sci. [★7287]
New Producers Alliance [IO], London, United
Kingdom
New Reality Intl. [12743], 1420 Roosevelt Ave., Ste.
7, Mount Vernon, WA 98273, (360)830-6741
New Right Watch [★18771]
New Road Map Found. [12222], PO Box 1363, Lan-
gley, WA 98260
New Rules for Global Finance Coalition [17584],
1717 Massachusetts Ave. NW, Ste. 801,
Washington, DC 20036, (202)247-7486
New South Wales Assn. for Youth Hea. [IO], Camp-
erdown, Australia

A star before a book entry number signifies that the name is not listed separately, but is mentioned within the entry.

New South Wales Dental Therapists' Assn. **[IO]**, Sydney, Australia

New South Wales Farmers' Assn. **[IO]**, Sydney, Australia

New South Wales Secondary Principals Assn. **[IO]**, Narara, Australia

New South Wales Women's Bowling Assn. **[IO]**, Sydney, Australia

New Transport for Christ **[★20101]**

New Transport for Christ **[★20101]**

New Tribes Mission **[20074]**, 1000 E 1st St., Sanford, FL 32771-1441, (407)323-3430

New Tribes Mission **[20074]**, 1000 E 1st St., Sanford, FL 32771-1441, (407)323-3430

New Violin Family Assn. **[10267]**, 701 3rd St., Encinitas, CA 92024, (760)632-0554

New Water Supply Coalition **[7608]**, 1750 H St. NW, Ste. 600, Washington, DC 20006, (202)737-0700

New Ways to Work **[11953]**, 103 Morris St., Ste. A, Sebastopol, CA 95472, (707)824-4000

New Wilderness Found. **[10268]**, Charles Morrow Production, LLC, 307 Seventh Ave., Ste. 1402, New York, NY 10001, (646)912-7990

New Wineskins Missionary Network **[20075]**, PO Box 278, Ambridge, PA 15003, (724)266-2810

New World Club - Defunct.

New World Hope Org. **[IO]**, Islamabad, Pakistan

New World Soc. - Defunct.

New York Acad. of Sciences **[7382]**, 7 World Trade Ctr., 250 Greenwich St., 40th Fl., New York, NY 10007-2157, (212)298-8600

New York Assn. of Wine Producers **[★5171]**

New York Bible Soc. **[★19345]**

New York Bible Soc. **[★19345]**

New York Bible Soc. Intl. **[★19345]**

New York Bible Soc. Intl. **[★19345]**

New York Center for Independent Publishing - Address unknown since 2011.

New York Children's Aid Soc. **[★20647]**

New York City Intl. Bible Soc. **[★19345]**

New York City Intl. Bible Soc. **[★19345]**

New York City Medical Soc. on Alcoholism **[★16736]**

New York C.S. Lewis Soc. **[9405]**, 84-23 77th Ave., Glendale, NY 11385-7706

New York Customs Brokers Assn. **[★2103]**

New York Fertility Inst. **[★14532]**

New York Fertility Res. Found. **[★14532]**

New York Financial Writers' Assn. **[2860]**, PO Box 338, Ridgewood, NJ 07451-0338, (201)612-0100

New York Foreign Freight Forwarders and Brokers Assn. **[★3263]**

New York Genealogical and Biographical Soc. **[20650]**, 36 W 44th St., 7th Fl., New York, NY 10036-8105, (212)755-8532

New York Guild for the Jewish Blind **[★17092]**

New York Islanders Booster Club **[23907]**, PO Box 502, Hicksville, NY 11802-0502, (631)547-6942

New York Mathematical Soc. **[★7068]**

New York Microscopical Soc. **[7117]**, 1 Prospect Village Plz., Clifton, NJ 07013, (973)470-8733

New York Mounters Assn. - Defunct.

New York/New Jersey Foreign Freight Forwarders and Brokers Assn. **[3263]**, PO Box 8217, Red Bank, NJ 07701, (732)741-1936

New York-New Jersey Sect. of the Microchemical Soc. **[★6394]**

New York Newspaper Women's Club **[★2862]**

New York Raincoat Mfrs. Assn. - Defunct.

New York Rainforest Alliance **[★4127]**

New York Rainforest Alliance **[★4127]**

New York Rangers Fan Club **[23908]**, GPO Box 8713, New York, NY 10116-8713

New York Road Runners Club **[22865]**, 9 E 89th St., New York, NY 10128, (212)860-4455

New York Shipping Assn. **[3264]**, 333 Thornall St., Ste. 3A, Edison, NJ 08837, (732)452-7800

New York Soc. of Anesthetists **[★13737]**

New York Soc. of Security Analysts **[3203]**, 1540 Broadway, Ste. 1010, New York, NY 10036-2714, (212)541-4530

New York State Assn. of Ser. Stations **[★367]**

New York State Assn. of Ser. Stations and Repair Shops **[367]**, 6 Walker Way, Albany, NY 12205, (518)452-4367

New York State Comm. for the Prevention of Blindness **[★17112]**

New York State Turf and Landscape Assn. **[2181]**, 1 Prospect Ave., White Plains, NY 10607, (914)993-9455

New York State Wine Grape Growers **[★5171]**

New York Stock Exchange **[3204]**, 11 Wall St., New York, NY 10005, (212)656-3000

New York Stock Transfer Assn. **[★3207]**

New York Triathlon Club **[23099]**, PO Box 50, Saugerties, NY 12477-0050, (845)247-0271

New York Turtle and Tortoise Soc. **[5089]**, PO Box 878, Orange, NJ 07051-0878

New York Wine Coun. **[★5171]**

New York Wine/Grape Found. **[5171]**, 800 S Main St., Ste. 200, Canandaigua, NY 14424-2213, (585)394-3620

New York Women in Communications, Inc. Found. **[814]**, 355 Lexington Ave., 15th Fl., New York, NY 10017-6603, (212)297-2133

New York Women's League for Animals **[★10917]**

New York Workshop in Nonviolence **[★18177]**

New York Zoological Soc. **[★4162]**

New Zealand

Australian New Zealand - Amer. Chambers of Commerce **[23339]**

New Zealand Tourism Bd. **[23434]**

Soc. of Australasian Specialists/Oceania **[22075]**

New Zealand Acad. of Fine Arts **[IO]**, Wellington, New Zealand

New Zealand Accordion Assn. **[IO]**, Auckland, New Zealand

New Zealand ACM SIGCHI **[IO]**, Hamilton, New Zealand

New Zealand Aikido Fed. **[IO]**, Auckland, New Zealand

New Zealand Air Line Pilots' Assn. **[IO]**, Manukau City, New Zealand

New Zealand Antique Dealers Assn. **[IO]**, Rotorua, New Zealand

New Zealand Aotearoa Adolescent Hea. and Development **[IO]**, Wellington, New Zealand

New Zealand Archaeological Assn. **[IO]**, Dunedin, New Zealand

New Zealand Asian Stud. Soc. **[IO]**, Wellington, New Zealand

New Zealand Assn. for Comparative Law **[IO]**, Wellington, New Zealand

New Zealand Assn. of Credit Unions **[IO]**, Auckland, New Zealand

New Zealand Assn. for Environmental Educ. **[IO]**, Wellington, New Zealand

New Zealand Assn. of Events Professionals **[IO]**, Christchurch, New Zealand

New Zealand Assn. of Gerontology **[IO]**, Wellington, New Zealand

New Zealand Assn. for Gifted Children **[IO]**, Auckland, New Zealand

New Zealand Assn. of Optometrists **[IO]**, Wellington, New Zealand

New Zealand Assn. of Orthodontics **[IO]**, Christchurch, New Zealand

New Zealand Assn. for Psychological Type **[IO]**, Napier, New Zealand

New Zealand Assn. of Radio Transmitters **[IO]**, Upper Hutt, New Zealand

New Zealand Assn. of Rationalists and Humanists **[IO]**, Auckland, New Zealand

New Zealand Assn. of Rsrc. Mgt. **[IO]**, Hamilton East, New Zealand

New Zealand Assn. of Sci. Educators **[IO]**, Nelson, New Zealand

New Zealand Assn. of Scientists **[IO]**, Wellington, New Zealand

New Zealand Assn. for the Teaching of English **[IO]**, Christchurch, New Zealand

New Zealand Assn. for Training and Development **[IO]**, Lower Hutt, New Zealand

New Zealand Audiological Soc. **[IO]**, Auckland, New Zealand

New Zealand Auto. Assn. **[IO]**, Auckland, New Zealand

New Zealand Avocado Growers Assn. **[IO]**, Tauranga, New Zealand

New Zealand Badminton Fed. **[IO]**, Wellington, New Zealand

New Zealand Bankers' Assn. **[IO]**, Wellington, New Zealand

New Zealand Baptist Missionary Soc. **[IO]**, Penrose, New Zealand

New Zealand Baseball Fed. **[IO]**, Auckland, New Zealand

New Zealand Bonsai Assn. **[IO]**, Dunedin, New Zealand

New Zealand Book Coun. **[IO]**, Wellington, New Zealand

New Zealand Buick Enthusiasts **[IO]**, Christchurch, New Zealand

New Zealand Building Trades Union **[IO]**, Christchurch, New Zealand

New Zealand Bus. Coun. for Sustainable Development **[IO]**, Auckland, New Zealand

New Zealand Cartographic Soc. **[IO]**, Auckland, New Zealand

New Zealand Chambers of Commerce and Indus. **[IO]**, Wellington, New Zealand

New Zealand Chefs Assn. **[IO]**, Auckland, New Zealand

New Zealand Chem. Indus. Coun. **[IO]**, Wellington, New Zealand

New Zealand Childcare Assn. **[IO]**, Wellington, New Zealand

New Zealand Christian Counsellors Assn. **[IO]**, Auckland, New Zealand

New Zealand Coastal Soc. **[IO]**, Hamilton, New Zealand

New Zealand Coll. of Midwives **[IO]**, Christchurch, New Zealand

New Zealand Comm. for the Sci. Investigation of Claims of the Paranormal **[IO]**, Christchurch, New Zealand

New Zealand Community Newspapers Assn. **[IO]**, Ashburton, New Zealand

New Zealand Cmpt. Soc. **[IO]**, Wellington, New Zealand

New Zealand Continence Assn. **[IO]**, Drury, New Zealand

New Zealand Coun. of Christian Social Services **[IO]**, Wellington, New Zealand

New Zealand Coun. for Educational Res. **[IO]**, Wellington, New Zealand

New Zealand Coun. of Trade Unions **[IO]**, Wellington, New Zealand

New Zealand Croquet Coun. **[IO]**, Wellington, New Zealand

New Zealand Dairy Goat Breeders Assn. **[IO]**, Gisborne, New Zealand

New Zealand Dairy Workers' Union **[IO]**, Hamilton, New Zealand

New Zealand Dancesport Assn. **[IO]**, Auckland, New Zealand

New Zealand Deer Farmers' Assn. **[IO]**, Wellington, New Zealand

New Zealand Democratic Party **[IO]**, Invercargill, New Zealand

New Zealand Dental Assn. **[IO]**, Auckland, New Zealand

New Zealand Dental Hygienists Assn. **[IO]**, Christchurch, New Zealand

New Zealand Dental Therapists' Assn. **[IO]**, Auckland, New Zealand

New Zealand Dermatological Soc. **[IO]**, Auckland, New Zealand

New Zealand Dietetic Assn. **[IO]**, Wellington, New Zealand

New Zealand Down Syndrome Assn. **[IO]**, Auckland, New Zealand

New Zealand Ecological Soc. **[IO]**, Christchurch, New Zealand

New Zealand Educational Inst. **[IO]**, Wellington, New Zealand

New Zealand Educational Inst. - Women's Network **[IO]**, Wellington, New Zealand

New Zealand Engg., Printing and Mfg. Union **[IO]**, Wellington, New Zealand

New Zealand Ergonomics Soc. **[IO]**, Palmerston North, New Zealand

New Zealand Fed. of Ethnic Councils **[IO]**, Wellington, New Zealand

New Zealand Fed. of Graduate Women **[IO]**, North Shore City, New Zealand

New Zealand Ferret Protection and Welfare Soc. **[IO]**, Auckland, New Zealand

---

Reference to "IO" in place of a book number signifies that the association may be found in the 50th edition of International Organizations.

New Zealand Film Commn. [IO], Wellington, New Zealand

New Zealand First [IO], North Shore City, New Zealand

New Zealand Fishing Industry Bd. - Defunct.

New Zealand Flower Exporters Assn. [IO], Pukekohe, New Zealand

New Zealand Flying Disc Assn. [IO], Christchurch, New Zealand

New Zealand Forest Owners Assn. [IO], Wellington, New Zealand

New Zealand Freshwater Sciences Soc. [IO], Christchurch, New Zealand

New Zealand Fruitgrowers' Fed. [IO], Wellington, New Zealand

New Zealand Geographical Soc. [IO], Auckland, New Zealand

New Zealand Geotechnical Soc. [IO], Wellington, New Zealand

New Zealand Gift Trade Assn. [IO], Auckland, New Zealand

New Zealand Golf [IO], North Shore City, New Zealand

New Zealand Green Building Coun. [IO], Auckland, New Zealand

New Zealand Guidelines Gp. [IO], Wellington, New Zealand

New Zealand Guild of Agricultural Journalists and Communicators [IO], Wellington, New Zealand

New Zealand Guild of Storytellers [IO], Invercargill, New Zealand

New Zealand Heavy Engg. Res. Assn. [IO], Manukau City, New Zealand

New Zealand Historic Places Trust [IO], Wellington, New Zealand

New Zealand Historical Assn. [IO], Hamilton, New Zealand

New Zealand Holstein Friesian Assn. [IO], Hamilton, New Zealand

New Zealand Hydrological Soc. [IO], Wellington, New Zealand

New Zealand Ice Cream Mfrs'. Assn. [IO], Wellington, New Zealand

New Zealand Ice Skating Assn. [IO], Dunedin, New Zealand

New Zealand Inst. of Agricultural and Horticultural Sci. [IO], Auckland, New Zealand

New Zealand Inst. of Architects [IO], Auckland, New Zealand

New Zealand Inst. of Chemistry [IO], Christchurch, New Zealand

New Zealand Inst. of Economic Res. [IO], Wellington, New Zealand

New Zealand Inst. of Food Sci. and Tech. [IO], Palmerston North, New Zealand

New Zealand Inst. of Forestry [IO], Wellington, New Zealand

New Zealand Inst. of Intl. Affairs [IO], Wellington, New Zealand

New Zealand Inst. of Landscape Architects [IO], Wellington, New Zealand

New Zealand Inst. of Mgt. [IO], Wellington, New Zealand

New Zealand Inst. of Medical Radiation Tech. [IO], Auckland, New Zealand

New Zealand Inst. of Physics [IO], Lower Hutt, New Zealand

New Zealand Inst. of Quantity Surveyors [IO], Wellington, New Zealand

New Zealand Inst. of Travel and Tourism [IO], Wellington, New Zealand

New Zealand Ireland Assn. [IO], Ashford, Ireland

New Zealand Juice and Beverage Assn. [IO], Auckland, New Zealand

New Zealand Kennel Club [IO], Porirua, New Zealand

New Zealand Labour Party [IO], Wellington, New Zealand

New Zealand Law Soc. [IO], Wellington, New Zealand

New Zealand Maori Arts and Crafts Inst. [IO], Rotorua, New Zealand

New Zealand Marine Sciences Soc. [IO], Christchurch, New Zealand

New Zealand Marketing Assn. [IO], Auckland, New Zealand

New Zealand Masonry Trades Registration Bd. [IO], Wellington, New Zealand

New Zealand Mathematical Soc. [IO], Christchurch, New Zealand

New Zealand Medical Assn. [IO], Wellington, New Zealand

New Zealand Merchant Ser. Guild [IO], Wellington, New Zealand

New Zealand Microbiological Soc. [IO], Mosgiel, New Zealand

New Zealand Miniature Horse Assn. [IO], Invercargill, New Zealand

New Zealand Model Railway Guild [IO], Waitakere, New Zealand

New Zealand Mortgage Brokers Assn. [IO], Auckland, New Zealand

New Zealand Mounted Games Assn. [IO], Carterton, New Zealand

New Zealand Natl. Party [IO], Wellington, New Zealand

New Zealand Native Freshwater Fish Soc. [IO], Auckland, New Zealand

New Zealand Natural Medicine Assn. [IO], Auckland, New Zealand

New Zealand Naturist Fed. [IO], Wellington, New Zealand

New Zealand Nga Herenga Tatai o AFS [★IO]

New Zealand Nurses Org. [IO], Wellington, New Zealand

New Zealand Olympic Comm. [IO], Wellington, New Zealand

New Zealand Orienteering Fed. [IO], Pukekohe, New Zealand

New Zealand Pacific Bus. Coun. [IO], Auckland, New Zealand

New Zealand Pain Soc. [IO], Wellington, New Zealand

New Zealand Plant Protection Soc. [IO], Christchurch, New Zealand

New Zealand Playcentre Fed. [IO], Hamilton, New Zealand

New Zealand Police Assn. [IO], Wellington, New Zealand

New Zealand Pork Indus. Bd. [IO], Wellington, New Zealand

New Zealand Press Assn. [IO], Wellington, New Zealand

New Zealand Press Coun. [IO], Wellington, New Zealand

New Zealand Professional Firefighters Union [IO], Lower Hutt, New Zealand

New Zealand Professional Fishing Guides Assn. [IO], Gisborne, New Zealand

New Zealand Property Investors Fed. [IO], Bishopdale, New Zealand

New Zealand Psychological Soc. [IO], Wellington, New Zealand

New Zealand Public Ser. Assn. [IO], Wellington, New Zealand

New Zealand Railway and Locomotive Soc. [IO], Wellington, New Zealand

New Zealand Recreation Assn. [IO], Wellington, New Zealand

New Zealand Red Cross [IO], Wellington, New Zealand

New Zealand Resident Doctors' Assn. [IO], Auckland, New Zealand

New Zealand Retailers Assn. [IO], Wellington, New Zealand

New Zealand Rodeo Cowboys Assn. [IO], Manukau City, New Zealand

New Zealand Rugby Players Assn. [IO], Auckland, New Zealand

New Zealand Seafood Indus. Coun. [IO], Wellington, New Zealand

New Zealand Secondary Schools Sports Coun. [IO], Oakura, New Zealand

New Zealand Shipping Fed. [IO], Wellington, New Zealand

New Zealand Sign Language Teachers Assn. [IO], Auckland, New Zealand

New Zealand Snowsports Coun. [IO], Wellington, New Zealand

New Zealand Soc. of Animal Production [IO], Hamilton, New Zealand

New Zealand Soc. of Authors [IO], Auckland, New Zealand

New Zealand Soc. of Diversional Therapists [IO], Christchurch, New Zealand

New Zealand Soc. for Earthquake Engg. [IO], Wellington, New Zealand

New Zealand Soc. of Gastroenterology [IO], Wellington, New Zealand

New Zealand Soc. of Genealogists [IO], Auckland, New Zealand

New Zealand Soc. of Genealogists - Auckland Br. [IO], Auckland, New Zealand

New Zealand Soc. of Genealogists - Cambridge Br. [IO], Cambridge, New Zealand

New Zealand Soc. of Genealogists - Coromandel [IO], Coromandel, New Zealand

New Zealand Soc. of Genealogists - Far North [IO], Kaitaia, New Zealand

New Zealand Soc. of Genealogists - Hamilton Br. [IO], Hamilton, New Zealand

New Zealand Soc. of Genealogists - Hibiscus Coast Br. [IO], Orewa, New Zealand

New Zealand Soc. of Genealogists - Howick Br. [IO], Manukau City, New Zealand

New Zealand Soc. of Genealogists - Lake Taupo Br. [IO], Taupo, New Zealand

New Zealand Soc. of Genealogists - Matamata Br. [IO], Tirau, New Zealand

New Zealand Soc. of Genealogists - North Shore Br. [IO], North Shore City, New Zealand

New Zealand Soc. of Genealogists - Northern Wairoa Br. [IO], Dargaville, New Zealand

New Zealand Soc. of Genealogists - Onehunga Br. [IO], Auckland, New Zealand

New Zealand Soc. of Genealogists - Papakura Br. [IO], Papakura, New Zealand

New Zealand Soc. of Genealogists - Rotorua Br. [IO], Rotorua, New Zealand

New Zealand Soc. of Genealogists - St. Johns Br. [IO], Auckland, New Zealand

New Zealand Soc. of Genealogists - Tauranga Br. [IO], Tauranga, New Zealand

New Zealand Soc. of Genealogists - Waitakere Br. [IO], Waitakere, New Zealand

New Zealand Soc. of Genealogists - Wanganui Br. [IO], Wanganui, New Zealand

New Zealand Soc. of Genealogists - Wellsford Br. [IO], Wellsford, New Zealand

New Zealand Soc. of Genealogists - Whakatane Br. [IO], Whakatane, New Zealand

New Zealand Soc. for Music Therapy [IO], Wellington, New Zealand

New Zealand Soc. of Physiotherapists [IO], Wellington, New Zealand

New Zealand Soc. of Plant Biologists [IO], Hamilton, New Zealand

New Zealand Soc. of Soil Sci. [IO], Christchurch, New Zealand

New Zealand Soc. for Sustainability Engg. and Sci. [IO], Auckland, New Zealand

New Zealand Soc. of Translators and Interpreters [IO], Auckland, New Zealand

New Zealand Specialist Cheesemakers Assn. [IO], Auckland, New Zealand

New Zealand Stainless Steel Development Assn. [IO], Manukau City, New Zealand

New Zealand Statistical Assn. [IO], Wellington, New Zealand

New Zealand Taxi Fed. [IO], Wellington, New Zealand

New Zealand Theatre Fed. [IO], Palmerston North, New Zealand

New Zealand Thoroughbred Racing [IO], Wellington, New Zealand

New Zealand Timber Indus. Fed. [IO], Wellington, New Zealand

New Zealand Touch Assn. [IO], Petone, New Zealand

New Zealand Tourism Bd. [23434], 501 Santa Monica Blvd., Ste. 300, Santa Monica, CA 90401, (310)395-7480

New Zealand Tourist and Publicity Off. [★23434]

New Zealand Trade and Enterprise [IO], Auckland, New Zealand

New Zealand Vegetarian Soc. [IO], Auckland, New Zealand

A star before a book entry number signifies that the name is not listed separately, but is mentioned within the entry.

New Zealand Veterinary Assn. **[IO]**, Wellington, New Zealand

New Zealand Water Ski Racing Assn. **[IO]**, Auckland, New Zealand

New Zealand Wind Energy Assn. **[IO]**, Wellington, New Zealand

New Zealand Writers Guild **[IO]**, Auckland, New Zealand

New Zealand's Biotech Indus. Org. **[IO]**, Wellington, New Zealand

Newah Org. of Am. **[11617]**, 16182 Eable Beak Cir., Woodbridge, VA 22191, (703)999-6476

Newborns in Need **[11438]**, 3323 Transou Rd., Pfafftown, NC 27040, (336)469-8953

Newcastle Cycleways Movement **[IO]**, New Lambton, Australia

Newcastle Master Builders Assn. **[IO]**, Broadmeadow, Australia

Newcomen Soc. for the Stud. of the History of Engg. and Tech. **[IO]**, London, United Kingdom

Newcomen Soc. of the U.S. - Defunct.

Newfoundland Brain Injury Assn. **[IO]**, St. John's, NL, Canada

Newfoundland Club of Am. **[21616]**, Mary Lou Cuddy, Membership Chair, 1155 Raymond Rd., Ballston Spa, NY 12020-3719, (518)885-5030

Newfoundland and Labrador Assn. of Social Workers **[IO]**, St. John's, NL, Canada

Newfoundland and Labrador Palliative Care Assn. **[IO]**, St. John's, NL, Canada

NewPlace Intl. **[11368]**, PO Box 130189, Boston, MA 02113, (413)629-9777

Newport Inst. for Ethics, Law and Public Policy - Address unknown since 2011.

Newport Restoration Found. **[9718]**, 51 Touro St., Newport, RI 02840, (401)849-7300

News Brunswick Advisory Coun. on the Status of Women **[IO]**, Fredericton, NB, Canada

News and Letters Comm. **[18657]**, 228 S Wabash, Ste. 230, Chicago, IL 60604, (312)431-8242

Newsl. Assn. **[★2966]**

Newsl. Assn. **[★2966]**

Newsl. Assn. of Am. **[★2966]**

Newsl. Assn. of Am. **[★2966]**

Newsl. and Electronic Publishers Assn. **[★2966]**

Newsl. and Electronic Publishers Assn. **[★2966]**

Newsl. Publishers Assn. **[★2966]**

Newsl. Publishers Assn. **[★2966]**

Newspaper Advt. Bur. **[★2953]**

Newspaper Advt. Co-Op Network **[★2953]**

Newspaper Assn. of Am. **[2953]**, 4401 Wilson Blvd., Ste. 900, Arlington, VA 22203-1867, (571)366-1000

Newspaper Assn. Managers **[2861]**, PO Box 458, Essex, MA 01929, (978)210-6832

Newspaper Assn. of Mongolia **[IO]**, Ulan Bator, Mongolia

Newspaper Collectors Soc. of Am. - Address unknown since 2010.

Newspaper Conf. **[IO]**, London, United Kingdom

Newspaper Food Editors and Writers Assn. **[★2809]**

Newspaper Food Editors and Writers Assn. **[★2809]**

Newspaper Fund **[★8442]**

The Newspaper Guild **[23258]**, 501 3rd St. NW, 6th Fl., Washington, DC 20001-2760, (202)434-7177

Newspaper Personnel Relations Assn. **[★2718]**

Newspaper Promotion Assn. **[★2941]**

Newspaper Promotion Assn. **[★2941]**

Newspaper Publishers' Assn. of New Zealand **[IO]**, Wellington, New Zealand

Newspaper Res. Coun. **[★2953]**

Newspaper Soc. **[IO]**, London, United Kingdom

Newspaper Soc. of Sri Lanka **[IO]**, Colombo, Sri Lanka

Newspaper Target Marketing Coalition **[2576]**, 2969 Blackwood Rd., Decatur, GA 30033, (202)386-6357

Newspaper Women's Club of New York **[★2862]**

Newspapers

   Africa News Ser. **[17144]**

   Brazilian Assn. of Media Companies Representatives **[14867]**

   Ecuadorian Assn. of Newspaper Publishers **[13823]**

   Football Writers Assn. of Am. **[22588]**

   Golf Writers Assn. of Am. **[22610]**

Intl. Newspaper Gp. **[2834]**

The Newspaper Guild **[23258]**

Newspaper Target Marketing Coalition **[2576]**

Norwegian Media Businesses' Assn. **[22116]**

Print Media South Africa **[1386]**

Red Tag News Publications Assn. **[2238]**

Newswomen's Club of New York **[2862]**, 15 Gramercy Park S, New York, NY 10003-1705, (212)777-1610

NewTithing Gp. **[18727]**, Webster Systems, LLC, 1 Maritime Plz., Ste. 1400, San Francisco, CA 94111, (415)733-9722

Next Generation Connect **[IO]**, Kigali, Rwanda

NextAid **[11369]**, 3666 Westwood Blvd., Ste. 202, Los Angeles, CA 90034

NextAid **[11369]**, 3666 Westwood Blvd., Ste. 202, Los Angeles, CA 90034

NextGen Energy Coun. - Address unknown since 2010.

NEXUS - Intl. Broadcasting Assn. **[IO]**, Milan, Italy

NF Assn. **[★1509]**

NFHS Coaches Assn. **[22465]**, Natl. Fed. of State High Schools, PO Box 690, Indianapolis, IN 46206, (317)972-6900

NFHS Music Assn. **[8667]**, PO Box 690, Indianapolis, IN 46206, (317)972-6900

NFHS Officials Assn. **[23026]**, PO Box 690, Indianapolis, IN 46206, (317)972-6900

NFHS Speech, Debate and Theatre Assn. **[8898]**, PO Box 690, Indianapolis, IN 46206, (317)972-6900

NFHS Spirit Assn. **[22466]**, Natl. Fed. of State High School Associations, PO Box 690, Indianapolis, IN 46206-0690, (317)972-6900

NFSH The Healing Trust **[IO]**, Northampton, United Kingdom

NGA **[13070]**, 822 Veterans Way, Warminster, PA 18974, (215)682-9183

Nga Kaikorero Purakau O Aotearoa **[★IO]**

Nga Whare Takiura o Aotearoa **[★IO]**

Nga Whiitiki Whanau Ahuru Mowai o Aotearoa **[★IO]**

NgaKohine Whakamahiri o Aotecroa **[★IO]**

NGLTF Policy Inst. **[★12103]**

NGO Comm. on Disarmament **[★17555]**

NGO Comm. on Disarmament **[★17555]**

NGO Comm. on Disarmament, Peace and Security **[17555]**, 777 UN Plz., Ste. 3-B, New York, NY 10017, (212)687-5340

NGO Comm. on Disarmament, Peace and Security **[17555]**, 777 UN Plz., Ste. 3-B, New York, NY 10017, (212)687-5340

NGO Coordination for Development **[IO]**, Madrid, Spain

Ngwa Natl. Assn. USA **[19040]**, 1333A N Ave., PMB No. 540, New Rochelle, NY 10804, (914)275-3887

NHS Blood and Transplant **[IO]**, Bristol, United Kingdom

NHS Consultants Assn. **[IO]**, Oxon, United Kingdom

Niagara Inst. **[IO]**, Niagara-on-the-Lake, ON, Canada

NIBA - The Belting Assn. **[★1853]**

Nicaragua

   1-2-3 Intl. **[12573]**

   Amigos for Christ **[12574]**

   Bikes Not Bombs **[18158]**

   Bikes Not Bombs **[18158]**

   Latinas and Latinos for Social Change **[18159]**

   Latinas and Latinos for Social Change **[18159]**

   Planting Hope **[11622]**

   Quest for Peace **[18160]**

   Quest for Peace **[18160]**

   ViviendasLeon **[12575]**

   Water for Waslala **[13440]**

   Witness for Peace **[18161]**

   Witness for Peace **[18161]**

Nicaragua Chap. of the ILAE **[IO]**, Managua, Nicaragua

Nicaragua-Honduras Educ. Proj. **[★8406]**

Nicaragua-Honduras Educ. Proj. **[★8406]**

Nicaragua Solidarity Campaign **[IO]**, London, United Kingdom

Nicaraguan Information Center - Defunct.

Nichidoku-Shakaikagaku-Gakkai **[★IO]**

Nichiren Buddhist Assn. of Am. **[19371]**, PO Box 622641, Orlando, FL 32862-2641

Nichiren Shoshu Soka Gakkai of Am. **[★19372]**

Nichiren Shoshu Soka Gakkai of Am. **[★19372]**

Nickel Inst. - North Am. **[IO]**, Toronto, ON, Canada

Nickel Inst. - UK **[IO]**, Birmingham, United Kingdom

Nicotine Anonymous World Services **[13047]**, 6333 E Mockingbird Ln., Ste. 147-817, Dallas, TX 75214, (415)750-0328

Nicotine Anonymous World Services **[13047]**, 6333 E Mockingbird Ln., Ste. 147-817, Dallas, TX 75214, (415)750-0328

NICRO Women's Support Centre **[IO]**, Cape Town, Republic of South Africa

NIDAA **[IO]**, Khartoum, Sudan

NIDCAP Fed. Intl. **[14114]**, Children's Hosp. Boston, Neurobehavioral Infant and Child Stud., Enders Pediatric Res. Bldg., EN107, 320 Longwood Ave., Boston, MA 02115

NIDCD: Natl. Temporal Bone, Hearing and Balance Pathology Rsrc. Registry **[15359]**, Massachusetts Eye & Ear Infirmary, 243 Charles St., Boston, MA 02114-3096, (617)573-3711

Nieman Found. for Journalism **[★8446]**

Nieman Found. for Journalism at Harvard **[8446]**, Harvard Univ., Walter Lippmann House, 1 Francis Ave., Cambridge, MA 02138, (617)495-2237

Nietzsche Soc. - Address unknown since 2010.

Nieuw-Vlaamse Alliantie **[★IO]**

Niger Delta Women for Justice **[IO]**, Port Harcourt, Nigeria

Niger Junior Chamber **[IO]**, Niamey, Niger

Nigeria Assn. of Univ. Women **[IO]**, Awka, Nigeria

Nigeria Employers' Consultative Assn. **[IO]**, Lagos, Nigeria

Nigeria Scripture Union **[IO]**, Ibadan, Nigeria

Nigeria Taekwondo Fed. **[IO]**, Lagos, Nigeria

Nigerian

   Assn. of Nigerian Petroleum Professionals Abroad **[7235]**

   Eduwatch **[8683]**

   Egbe Omo Yoruba: Natl. Assn. of Yoruba Descendants in North America **[19174]**

   Egbe Omo Yoruba: Natl. Assn. of Yoruba Descendants in North America **[19174]**

   Friends of Nigeria **[19175]**

   Friends of Nigeria **[19175]**

   Idoma Assn. USA **[19176]**

   Igbere Progressive Assn. Intl. **[12576]**

   Ijaw Natl. Alliance of the Americas **[12577]**

   Ijaw Natl. Alliance of the Americas **[12577]**

   Ngwa Natl. Assn. USA **[19040]**

   Nigerian Women Leadership Coun. Intl. **[12578]**

   Nigerian Women Leadership Coun. Intl. **[12578]**

   Ogbaru Natl. Assn. **[12579]**

   Ogwashi-Uku Assn., USA **[19177]**

   Ogwashi-Uku Assn., USA **[19177]**

   Urhobo Natl. Assn. of North Am. **[19178]**

   Zumunta Assn. USA **[19179]**

Nigerian Assn. of Chambers of Commerce, Indus., Mines, and Agriculture **[IO]**, Lagos, Nigeria

Nigerian Assn. of Occupational Therapists **[IO]**, Lagos, Nigeria

Nigerian Assn. of Pharmacists and Pharmaceutical Scientists in the Americas **[2704]**, 1761 Tennessee Ave., Cincinnati, OH 45229, (513)641-3300

Nigerian Assn. of Sports Medicine **[IO]**, Lagos, Nigeria

Nigerian Baseball and Softball Assn. **[IO]**, Lagos, Nigeria

Nigerian Dwarf Goat Assn. **[4505]**, PO Box 97, Pahrump, NV 89041, (928)445-3423

Nigerian Economic Soc. **[IO]**, Ibadan, Nigeria

Nigerian Fertility Soc. **[IO]**, Lagos, Nigeria

Nigerian Gas Assn. **[IO]**, Lagos, Nigeria

Nigerian Geotechnical Assn. **[IO]**, Port Harcourt, Nigeria

Nigerian Hypertension Soc. **[IO]**, Benin City, Nigeria

Nigerian Lawyers Assn. **[5279]**, 321 Broadway, 3rd Fl., New York, NY 10007, (212)566-9926

Nigerian Medical Assn. **[IO]**, Abuja, Nigeria

Nigerian School Sports Fed. **[IO]**, Osogbo, Nigeria

Nigerian Social Workers Assn. **[13224]**, PO Box 3295, New York, NY 10008-3295, (646)460-2324

Nigerian Soc. of Engineers **[IO]**, Abuja, Nigeria

Nigerian Soc. for Photogrammetry and Remote Sensing **[IO]**, Lagos, Nigeria

Nigerian Squash Rackets Assn. **[IO]**, Lagos, Nigeria

Reference to "IO" in place of a book number signifies that the association may be found in the 50th edition of International Organizations.

Nigerian Weightlifting Fed. [IO], Lagos, Nigeria
Nigerian Women Leadership Coun. Intl. [12578], 6523 Hwy. 85, Ste. 105, Riverdale, GA 30274, (678)777-3322
Nigerian Women Leadership Coun. Intl. [12578], 6523 Hwy. 85, Ste. 105, Riverdale, GA 30274, (678)777-3322
Nightingale Res. Found. [IO], Ottawa, ON, Canada
Nihon Afurika Gakkai [★IO]
Nihon Arerugi Gakkai [★IO]
Nihon Bengoshi Rengokai [★IO]
Nihon Boseki Kyokai [★IO]
Nihon Boueki Shinkou Kai, Ajia Keizai Kenkyusho [★IO]
Nihon Bunseki Kagaku-Kai [★IO]
Nihon Do Senta [★IO]
Nihon Doro Kensetsugyo Kyokai [★IO]
Nihon Electronics Show Kyokai [★IO]
Nihon Gakujutsu Shinko-kai [★IO]
Nihon Gazo Jyohou Manejimento Kyokai [★IO]
Nihon Genshiryoku Gakkai [★IO]
Nihon Gomu Kyokai [★IO]
Nihon Hinyokika Gakkai [★IO]
Nihon Ishi-Kai [★IO]
Nihon Jidosha Yunyu Kumiai [★IO]
Nihon Jui Gakkai [★IO]
Nihon Kagakushi Gakkai [★IO]
Nihon Kairui Gakkai [★IO]
Nihon Kensetsu Kikai-ka Kyokai [★IO]
Nihon Kikai Gakkai [★IO]
Nihon Kikai Kougyou Rengokai [★IO]
Nihon Kikaku Kyokai Gaikoku Kikaku Raiburari [★IO]
Nihon Koku Eisei Gakkai [★IO]
Nihon Kokusai Koryu Center [★IO]
Nihon Kokusai Mondai Kenkyusho [★IO]
Nihon Kokusai Volunteer Center [★IO]
Nihon Maku Gakkai [★IO]
Nihon Masuka Gakkai [★IO]
Nihon Naika Gakkai [★IO]
Nihon Nettai Igakukai [★IO]
Nihon Noritsu Kyokai [★IO]
Nihon Oyo Toshitsu Kagaku Kai [★IO]
Nihon Recreation Kyokai [★IO]
Nihon Reito Kucho Gakkai [★IO]
Nihon Ryukoshoku Kyokai [★IO]
Nihon Sakumotsu Gakkai [★IO]
Nihon Sangyo Kikai Kogyo-kai [★IO]
Nihon Seikatsu Kyodo Kumiai Rengokai [★IO]
Nihon Seishin Shinkei Gakkai [★IO]
Nihon Seitai Gakkai [★IO]
Nihon Shakai Shinri Gakkai [★IO]
Nihon Shichokaku Kyoiku Kyokai [★IO]
Nihon Shinbun Kyokai [★IO]
Nihon Shinju Yushutsu Kumiai [★IO]
Nihon Shokaki Naishikyo Gakkai [★IO]
Nihon Shonika Gakkai [★IO]
Nihon Shutei Kogyo-kai [★IO]
Nihon Takkyu Kyokai [★IO]
Nihon Tanners Kyokai [★IO]
Nihon Tenmon Gakkai [★IO]
Nihon Tokei Gakkai [★IO]
Nihon Toshokan Kyokai [★IO]
Nihon Tsushin Hanbai Kyokai [★IO]
Nihon UNESCO Kyokai Renmei [★IO]
Nihon YMCA Domei [★IO]
Nikon Historical Soc. [10441], RJR Publishing Inc., PO Box 3213, Munster, IN 46321
Nile Children and Family Support Org. [IO], Addis Ababa, Ethiopia
NIMA Intl. [★2401]
NIMA Intl. [★2401]
Nims Family Assn. [20565], Nancy Garreaud, Treas., 921 E 100 S, Salt Lake City, UT 84102
Nine Lives Associates [3224], Executive Protection Inst., 16 Penn Pl., Ste. 1570, New York, NY 10001, (212)268-4555
Nine Lives Associates [3224], Executive Protection Inst., 16 Penn Pl., Ste. 1570, New York, NY 10001, (212)268-4555
Ninety-Nines, Intl. Org. of Women Pilots [151], 4300 Amelia Earhart Rd., Oklahoma City, OK 73159, (405)685-7969
Ninety-Nines, Intl. Org. of Women Pilots [151], 4300 Amelia Earhart Rd., Oklahoma City, OK 73159, (405)685-7969

Ninety-Nines Intl. Women Pilots [★151]
Ninety-Nines Intl. Women Pilots [★151]
Ninos del Lago [11370], PO Box 1005, Silverton, OR 97381
Ninos del Lago [11370], PO Box 1005, Silverton, OR 97381
Nippon Badminton Assn. [IO], Tokyo, Japan
Nippon Bitamin Gakkai [★IO]
Nippon Butsuri Gakkai [★IO]
Nippon Byori Gakkai [★IO]
Nippon Chiri Gakkai [★IO]
Nippon Chishitsu Gakkai [★IO]
Nippon Cho Gakkai [★IO]
Nippon Club [19084], 145 W 57th St., New York, NY 10019, (212)581-2223
Nippon Dai-Yonki Gakkai [★IO]
Nippon Dam Kyokai [★IO]
Nippon Dobutsu Gakkai [★IO]
Nippon Dojo-Hiryo Gakkai [★IO]
Nippon Ganka Gakkai [★IO]
Nippon Ganseki Kobutsu Kosho Gakkai [★IO]
Nippon Geka Gakkai [★IO]
Nippon Hifuka Gakkai [★IO]
Nippon Hoshasen Eikyo Gakkai [★IO]
Nippon Hotetsu Gakkai [★IO]
Nippon Iden Gakkai [★IO]
Nippon Igaku Hoshasen Gakkai [★IO]
Nippon Interior Fabrics Assn. [IO], Tokyo, Japan
Nippon Junkatsu Gakkai [★IO]
Nippon Kaiji Kyokai [IO], Tokyo, Japan
Nippon Kaiyo Gakkai [★IO]
Nippon Kazan Gakkai [★IO]
Nippon Keidanren [★IO]
Nippon Keiho Gakkai [★IO]
Nippon Keizai Seisaku Gakkai [★IO]
Nippon Ketsueki Gakkai [★IO]
Nippon Kin Gakkai [★IO]
Nippon Kinzoku Gakkai [★IO]
Nippon Kodo Bunseki Gakkai [★IO]
Nippon Kokai Gakkai [★IO]
Nippon Koseibutsu Gakkai [★IO]
Nippon Koshu-Eisei Kyokai [★IO]
Nippon Mokuzai Gakkai [★IO]
Nippon No-Shinkei Gek Gakkai [★IO]
Nippon Nogei Kagaku Kai [★IO]
Nippon Nogyo-Kisho Gakkai [★IO]
Nippon Ongaku Gakkai [★IO]
Nippon Rikusui Gakkai [★IO]
Nippon Ringyo Gijutsu Kyokai [★IO]
Nippon Sei Ko Kai [★IO]
Nippon Seikei Geka Gakkai [★IO]
Nippon Seiri Gakkai [★IO]
Nippon Seramikkusu Kyokai [★IO]
Nippon Shakai Gakkai [★IO]
Nippon Shashin Gakkai [★IO]
Nippon Shashin Sokuryo Gakkai [★IO]
Nippon Shinkeikagaku Gakkai [★IO]
Nippon Shokubutsu Gakkai [★IO]
Nippon Sokuchi Gakkai [★IO]
Nippon Suisan Gakkai [★IO]
Nippon Toshi Keikaku Gakkai [★IO]
Nippon Yakugakkai [★IO]
Nirnaya [IO], Secunderabad, India
Nisaa Inst. for Women's Development [IO], Lenasia, Republic of South Africa
NISH [11820], 8401 Old Courthouse Rd., Ste. 200, Vienna, VA 22182, (571)226-4660
Nissan Infiniti Car Owners Club [21135], 237 Fernwood Blvd., Ste. 111, Fern Park, FL 32730-2116, (407)828-8908
Nitrogen Fixing Tree Assn. - Defunct.
NiUG Intl. [6989], 208 Eagle Valley Mall, No. 124, East Stroudsburg, PA 18301, (570)595-0110
Niwano Heiwa Zaidan [★IO]
Niwano Peace Found. [IO], Tokyo, Japan
Nixon Center [17706], 1615 L St. NW, Ste. 1250, Washington, DC 20036, (202)887-1000
Nixon Center for Peace and Freedom [★17706]
Nkwen Cultural and Development Assn. USA - Address unknown since 2010.
NLDA Associates [★2204]
NMC [17035], 421 S Nine Mound Rd., Verona, WI 53593, (608)848-4615
No-Code Intl. [20939], 4991 Shimerville Rd., Emmaus, PA 18049

No Compromise Majority - Defunct.
No Greater Love - Address unknown since 2010.
No-Load Mutual Fund Assn. [★3201]
No Peace Without Justice [18269], 866 Union Plz., No. 408, New York, NY 10017, (212)980-2558
No Peace Without Justice [18269], 866 Union Plz., No. 408, New York, NY 10017, (212)980-2558
NOAH Friends of the Earth - Denmark [IO], Copenhagen, Denmark
NOAH Nature Alliance [5090], PO Box 6768, San Antonio, TX 78209, (210)826-0599
Noah Webster Found. [★9719]
Noah Webster House [9719], 227 S Main St., West Hartford, CT 06107, (860)521-5362
Noah's Ark Spay and Neuter Gp. - Address unknown since 2011.
Noah's Never Ending Rainbow [14618], 7737 6th Ave., Kenosha, WI 53143, (262)605-3690
Noble Aims Welfare Assn. [IO], Rawalpindi, Pakistan
Noctis [IO], Stockport, United Kingdom
Nocturnal Adoration Soc. [19481], St. Jean Baptiste Catholic Church, 184 E 76th St., New York, NY 10021, (212)288-5082
Noetic Soc. [★9641]
NOF Energy [IO], Durham, United Kingdom
Noise Control
  Inst. of Noise Control Engg. [7162]
  Noise Free Am. [4739]
Noise Control Assn. - Defunct.
Noise Free Am. [4739], 1971 Western Ave., No. 1111, Albany, NY 12203, (877)664-7366
Nomads Outdoor Gp. [IO], Melbourne, Australia
Nomads of the Time Streams - Intl. Michael Moorcock Appreciation Soc. - Defunct.
Non Commissioned Officers Assn. of the U.S.A. [5827], 9330 Corporate Dr., Ste. 701, Selma, TX 78154, (800)662-2620
Non-Executive Directors Assn. [IO], Berkshire, United Kingdom
Non-Ferrous Founders' Soc. [1854], 1480 Renaissance Dr., Ste. 310, Park Ridge, IL 60068, (847)299-0950
Non-Ferrous Metals Producers Comm. [2487], 2030 M St. NW, Ste. 800, Washington, DC 20036, (202)466-7720
Non Governmental Org. BIOS [IO], Chisinau, Moldova
Non-Governmental Org. Comm. on Disarmament [★17555]
Non-Governmental Org. Comm. on Disarmament [★17555]
Non-Powder Gun Products Assn. - Defunct.
Non-Profit Chiropractic Org. [14142], 601 Brady St., Ste. 201, Davenport, IA 52803, (708)459-8080
Non-profit Mgt. Assn. and Support Centers of Am. [★260]
Non-Resident Nepali Assn. [IO], Kathmandu, Nepal
Non-Traditional Casting Proj. [★10559]
Nonferrous Metals Soc. of China [IO], Beijing, People's Republic of China
Nongovernmental Organizations Comm. on Youth [13547], Conf. of NGOs, 777 United Nations Plz., 6th Fl., New York, NY 10017, (212)986-8557
Nonprescription Drug Mfrs. Assn. [★2692]
Nonprescription Drug Mfrs. Assn. of Canada [★20908]
Nonprofit Academic Centers Coun. [8684], 10900 Euclid Ave., Cleveland, OH 44106, (216)368-0969
Nonprofit Australia [IO], Sydney, Australia
Nonprofit Leadership Alliance [8493], 1100 Walnut St., Ste. 1900, Kansas City, MO 64106, (816)561-6415
Nonprofit Mailers Fed. [★264]
NonProfit Necessity - Address unknown since 2011.
Nonprofit Organizations
  Asia Catalyst [12580]
  Economic Justice Inst. [5933]
  HandsNet [12581]
  Natl. Center on Nonprofit Enterprise [12582]
  Nonprofit Academic Centers Coun. [8684]
  Nonprofit VOTE [18162]
  Southeastern Fisheries Assn. [3190]
  Work for Progress [12583]
Nonprofit VOTE [18162], 89 South St., Ste. 203, Boston, MA 02111, (617)357-8683

A star before a book entry number signifies that the name is not listed separately, but is mentioned within the entry.

Nonprofit Voter Engagement Network [★18162]
Nonverbal Learning Disorders Assn. [15239], 507 Hopmeadow St., Simsbury, CT 06070, (860)658-5522
Nonverbal Learning Disorders Assn. [15239], 507 Hopmeadow St., Simsbury, CT 06070, (860)658-5522
Nonviolence
  A. J. Muste Memorial Inst. [18228]
  Africa Peace and Conflict Network [12625]
  Albert Einstein Institution [18163]
  Amer. Patriots Assn. [20742]
  Assn. for Peace and Understanding in the Middle East [18117]
  Benedictines for Peace [19392]
  Canadian Intl. Inst. of Applied Negotiation [13507]
  Catholic Worker Movement [18164]
  Center for Nonviolent Commun. [18165]
  Citizens to Stop Nuclear Terrorism [18711]
  Coalition for Peace with Justice [18236]
  Conflict Solutions Intl. [17405]
  Daisy Alliance [18239]
  Earth Coun. Alliance [12584]
  Earth Coun. Alliance [12584]
  Empower Peace [18241]
  Environmentalists Against War [18777]
  The ETHIC - The Essence of True Humanity is Compassion [18166]
  European Bur. for Conscientious Objection [10879]
  FootPrints for Peace [18243]
  Fourth Freedom Forum [18167]
  Fourth Freedom Forum [18167]
  Friends of Tent of Nations North Am. [12629]
  Global Action to Prevent War [18168]
  Global Action to Prevent War [18168]
  Global Inheritance [18826]
  Global Peace Initiative of Women [18250]
  Global Peace Services [18251]
  Guitars Not Guns [18169]
  Intl. Coalition for the Responsibility to Protect [18498]
  Intl. Coun. for Middle East Stud. [18125]
  Invisible Children [17237]
  Ishmael and Isaac [18126]
  Just Vision [17409]
  Martin Luther King, Jr. Center for Nonviolent Social Change [18170]
  Men Stopping Violence [18171]
  Monks Without Borders [19826]
  Musical Missions of Peace [10352]
  Musicians for Harmony [10353]
  Natl. Assn. of Students Against Violence Everywhere [18172]
  Natl. Assn. of Students Against Violence Everywhere [18172]
  Natl. Endowment for the Animals [11010]
  Natl. Org. of Iraqi Christians [12630]
  Native Amer. Leadership Alliance [20147]
  Nonviolence Intl. [18173]
  Nonviolence Intl. [18173]
  Nonviolent Peaceforce [18174]
  Nonviolent Peaceforce [18174]
  One Voice of Peace [8694]
  Partnership for Global Security [18600]
  Pax Christi U.S.A. [18175]
  Peace of Art [10354]
  Peace Boat US [8695]
  Peace in Focus [18275]
  Prevent Nuclear Terrorism Org. [18718]
  Rsrc. Center for Nonviolence [18176]
  Rsrc. Center for Nonviolence [18176]
  Student Peace Alliance [18290]
  Sudan Sunrise [12636]
  Trans Youth Family Allies [12585]
  U.S. Assn. for the Univ. for Peace [18294]
  U.S. Fed. for Middle East Peace [18295]
  Voters for Peace [18300]
  War Resisters League [18177]
  Where Peace Lives [10355]
  Win Without War [18178]
  Women in Black [18302]
  You Have the Power [18179]
Nonviolence Intl. [18173], 4000 Albemarle St., Ste. 401, Washington, DC 20016, (202)244-0951

Nonviolence Intl. [18173], 4000 Albemarle St., Ste. 401, Washington, DC 20016, (202)244-0951
Nonviolence.Org - Address unknown since 2011.
Nonviolent Peaceforce [18174], 425 Oak Grove St., Minneapolis, MN 55403, (612)871-0005
Nonviolent Peaceforce [18174], 425 Oak Grove St., Minneapolis, MN 55403, (612)871-0005
Noor Educational and Capacity Development Org. [IO], Kabul, Afghanistan
Noortevahetuse Arengu Uhing [★IO]
NOPA Norwegian Soc. of Composers and Lyricists [IO], Oslo, Norway
Norcross Wildlife Found. [5091], 250 W 88th St., Ste. 806, New York, NY 10024-1767, (212)362-4831
Nordens Fackliga Samorganisation [★IO]
Nordens Institut pa Aland [★IO]
Nordic Africa Inst. [IO], Uppsala, Sweden
Nordic Alcohol and Drug Policy Network [IO], Helsinki, Finland
Nordic Assn. of Agricultural Scientists [IO], Stockholm, Sweden
Nordic Assn. for Amer. Stud. [IO], Oslo, Norway
Nordic Assn. for Andrology [IO], Huddinge, Sweden
Nordic Assn. for Canadian Stud. [IO], Turku, Finland
Nordic Assn. for China Stud. [IO], Stockholm, Sweden
Nordic Assn. for Computational Mechanics [IO], Trondheim, Norway
Nordic Assn. for Hydrology [IO], Norrkoping, Sweden
Nordic Assn. of Lexicography [IO], Oslo, Norway
Nordic Assn. for Palliative Care [IO], Copenhagen, Denmark
Nordic Assn. for Psychiatric Epidemiology [IO], Bronshoj, Denmark
Nordic Assn. for Semiotic Stud. [IO], Lund, Sweden
Nordic Assn. for South Asian Stud. [IO], Bergen, Norway
Nordic Assn. of Univ. Administrators [IO], Stockholm, Sweden
Nordic Audiological Soc. [IO], Copenhagen, Denmark
Nordic Centre for Alcohol and Drug Res. [IO], Helsinki, Finland
Nordic Church Coun. for Seamen [IO], Copenhagen, Denmark
Nordic Coll. of Caring Sciences [IO], Radal, Norway
Nordic Comm. on Food Anal. [IO], Oslo, Norway
Nordic Comm. of Schools of Social Work [IO], Frederiksberg, Denmark
Nordic Cooperation on Disability [IO], Vallingby, Sweden
Nordic Coun. [IO], Copenhagen, Denmark
Nordic Coun. of Ministers [IO], Copenhagen, Denmark
Nordic Coun. for Reindeer Husbandry Res. [IO], Tromso, Norway
Nordic Educational Res. Assn. [IO], Orebro, Sweden
Nordic Fed. of Societies of Obstetrics and Gynecology [IO], Reykjavik, Iceland
Nordic Folkecenter for Renewable Energy [IO], Hurup Thy, Denmark
Nordic Forest Res. Cooperation Comm. [IO], Copenhagen, Denmark
Nordic Gerontological Fed. [IO], Norrkoping, Sweden
Nordic IN [IO], Stockholm, Sweden
Nordic Info. Center for Media and Commun. Res. [IO], Goteborg, Sweden
Nordic Info. Center for Media and Commun. Res. - Denmark [IO], Goteborg, Sweden
Nordic Inst. for Advanced Training in Occupational Hea. [IO], Helsinki, Finland
Nordic Inst. on Aland [IO], Mariehamn, Finland
Nordic Inst. of Asian Stud. [IO], Copenhagen, Denmark
Nordic Inst. of Dental Materials [IO], Haslum, Norway
Nordic Inst. for Theoretical Physics [IO], Stockholm, Sweden
Nordic Inst. for Women's Stud. and Gender Res. [IO], Oslo, Norway
Nordic Intl. Stud. Assn. [IO], Helsinki, Finland
Nordic Joint Comm. for Agricultural Res. [IO], Jokioinen, Finland
Nordic Lichen Soc. [IO], Lund, Sweden

Nordic Microscopy Soc. [IO], Jyvaskyla, Finland
Nordic Nuclear Safety Res. [IO], Roskilde, Denmark
Nordic Proj. Fund [IO], Helsinki, Finland
Nordic Rheuma Coun. [IO], Gentofte, Denmark
Nordic Soc. for Aerosol Res. [IO], Copenhagen, Denmark
Nordic Soc. for Middle Eastern Stud. [IO], Bergen, Norway
Nordic Soc. for Radiation Protection [IO], Reykjavik, Iceland
Nordic Swimming Federations Assn. [IO], Helsinki, Finland
Nordic Tax Res. Coun. [IO], Arhus, Denmark
Nordic Teachers' Coun. [IO], Copenhagen, Denmark
Nordic Telemedicine Assn. [IO], Odense, Denmark
Nordic Women's Peace Network [IO], Sandefjord, Norway
Nordic Wood Preservation Coun. [IO], Stockholm, Sweden
Nordisk Arbetsmiljoutbildning [★IO]
Nordisk Audiologisk Selskab [★IO]
Nordisk Copyright Bur. [IO], Copenhagen, Denmark
Nordisk Forening For Fysiologi [★IO]
Nordisk Forening for Leksikografi [★IO]
Nordisk Forening for Obstetrik och Gynekologi [★IO]
Nordisk Forening for Pedagogisk Forskning [★IO]
Nordisk Gerontologisk Forening [★IO]
Nordisk Herpetologisk Forening [★IO]
Nordisk Hydrologisk Forening [★IO]
Nordisk Institut for Asienstudier [★IO]
Nordisk Institut for Teoretisk Fysik [★IO]
Nordisk Institutt for Kvinne- og Kjonnsforskning [★IO]
Nordisk Institutt for Odontologiske Materialer [★IO]
Nordisk Institutt for Sjorett [★IO]
Nordisk Kernesikkerhedsforskning [★IO]
Nordisk Kontaktorgan for Jordbrugsforskning [★IO]
Nordisk Lichenologisk Forening [★IO]
Nordisk Metodikkommitte for Livsmedel [★IO]
Nordisk Ministerrad [★IO]
Nordisk Neurokirurgisk Forening [★IO]
Nordisk Organ for Reindriftsforskning [★IO]
Nordisk Selskap for Midtaustenstudiar [★IO]
Nordisk Selskap for Stralevern [★IO]
Nordisk Skattevitenskapelig Forskningsrad [★IO]
Nordisk Skibsrederforening [★IO]
Nordisk Thoraxkirurgisk Forening [★IO]
Nordiska Afrikainstitutet [★IO]
Nordiska Biskopskonferensen [★IO]
Nordiska Finansanstalldas Union [★IO]
Nordiska Glastekniska Foreningen [★IO]
Nordiska Jordbruksforskares Foerening [★IO]
Nordiska foreningen for Kinastudier [★IO]
Nordiska Lararorganisationers Samrad [★IO]
Nordiska Nykterhetsradet [★IO]
Nordiska Projektexportfonden [★IO]
Nordiska Radet [★IO]
Nordiska Samarbetsorganet for Handikappfragor [★IO]
Nordiska Samarbetsradet for Kriminologi [★IO]
Nordiska Traskyddsradet [★IO]
Nordiska Universitets Administrators-Samarbetet [★IO]
Nordiske Kvinners Fredsnettverk [★IO]
Nordiskt Center for Alkohol- och Drogforskning [★IO]
Nordiskt Informationscenter for Medie- och Kommunikationsforskning [★IO]
Nordiskt Reumarad [★IO]
Nordmanns-Forbundet [★IO]
Norfolk Chamber of Commerce and Indus. [IO], Norwich, United Kingdom
Norfolk Island Judo Assn. [IO], Queensland, Norfolk Island
Norfolk Island Triathlon Fed. [IO], Norfolk Island, Norfolk Island
Norge-Amerika Foreningen [★IO]
Norges Aikidoforbund [★IO]
Norges Ake-, Bob- og skeletonforbund [★IO]
Norges Astma- og Allergiforbund [★IO]
Norges Bandyforbund/Innebandyseksjonen [★IO]
Norges Biljardforbund [★IO]
Norges Bondelag [★IO]
Norges Danseforbund [IO], Oslo, Norway
Norges Diabetesforbund [★IO]

Reference to "IO" in place of a book number signifies that the association may be found in the 50th edition of International Organizations.

Norges Fibromyalgi Forbund [★IO]
Norges Fotballforbund [★IO]
Norges Fredslag [★IO]
Norges Fredsrad [★IO]
Norges Fri-Idrettsforbund [★IO]
Norges Geotekniske Institutt [★IO]
Norges Idrettsforbund og Olympiske og paralympiske Komite [★IO]
Norges Ingenior og Teknologorganisasjon [★IO]
Norges Kunst - og Antikvitetshandleres Forening [IO], Oslo, Norway
Norges Kvinne og Familieforbund [★IO]
Norges Luftsportsforbund [★IO]
Norges Miljovernforbund [★IO]
Norges Naturvernforbund [★IO]
Norges Padleforbund [★IO]
Norges Parkinsonforbund [★IO]
Norges Pelsdyralslag [★IO]
Norges Rafisklags [★IO]
Norges Rederiforbund [★IO]
Norges Sildesalgslag [★IO]
Norges Squashforbund [★IO]
Norges Taekwondo Forbund [★IO]
Norges Tekniske Vitenskapsakademi [★IO]
Norges Tennisforbund [★IO]
Norks Virologisk Forening [★IO]
Norma Terris Humane Educ. Center [★10986]
Norman Found. [13142], 147 E 48th St., New York, NY 10017, (212)230-9830
Norman Mailer Soc. [10728], David Light, Treas., 75 Jennings Ln., Windham, CT 06280
Normes Canadiennes de la Publicite [★IO]
Norrie Disease Assn. [14415], PO Box 3244, Munster, IN 46321
NORSAR [IO], Kjeller, Norway
Norse
    Asatru Alliance [19301]
Norse Fed. [IO], Oslo, Norway
Norsk forening for internasjonal rett [★IO]
Norsk fagbibliotekforening [★IO]
Norsk lokalhistorisk institutt [★IO]
Norsk akupunkturforening [★IO]
Norsk Astronautisk Forening [★IO]
Norsk Bibliotekforening [★IO]
Norsk Biokjemisk Selskap [★IO]
Norsk Botanisk Forening [★IO]
Norsk institutt for by- og regionforskning [★IO]
Norsk Cardiologisk Selskap [★IO]
Norsk Dermatologisk Selskap [★IO]
Norsk Dykkenhistorisk Forening [★IO]
Norsk Elektroteknisk Komite [★IO]
Norsk Epilepsiforbund [★IO]
Norsk Ergoterapeutforbund [★IO]
Norsk Faglitterae Forfatter- og Oversetterforening [★IO]
Norsk Forening for Cystisk Fibrose [★IO]
Norsk Forening for Komponister og Tekstforfattere [★IO]
Norsk Forening for Kvalitet i Helsetjenesten [★IO]
Norsk Forening for Osteogenesis Imperfecta [★IO]
Norsk Forening for Prosjektledelse [★IO]
Norsk Forening for Stomi-og Reservoaropererte [★IO]
Norsk Forskerforbund [★IO]
Norsk Fysioterapeutforbund [★IO]
Norsk Fysisk Selskap [★IO]
Norsk Geoteknisk Forening [★IO]
Norsk Heraldisk Forening [★IO]
Norsk Immunsviktforening [★IO]
Norsk gren av Intl. Fellowship Reconciliation [★IO]
Norsk Jockey Club [IO], Jar, Norway
Norsk Journalistag [★IO]
Norsk Kabel-TV Forbund [★IO]
Norsk Kommunalteknisk Forening [★IO]
Norsk Komponistforening [★IO]
Norsk Kulturrad [★IO]
Norsk Landbruksjournalistlag [★IO]
Norsk Oppfinnerforening [★IO]
Norsk Oversetterforening [★IO]
Norsk PEN [★IO]
Norsk Presseforbund [★IO]
Norsk Psoriasisforbund [★IO]
Norsk Psykologforening [★IO]
Norsk Revmatikerforbund [★IO]
Norsk Roseforening [★IO]

Norsk Selskap for Farmakologi og Toksikologi [★IO]
Norsk Selskap for Immunologi [★IO]
Norsk Skuespillerforbund [★IO]
Norsk Slektshistorisk Forening [★IO]
Norsk Sykepleierforbund [★IO]
Norsk Utenrikspolitisk Institutt [★IO]
Norsk Venturkapitalforeningen [★IO]
Norsk Yngling Klubb [IO], Kolsas, Norway
Norske interiorarkitekters og mobeldesigneres landsforening [★IO]
Norske Arbeiderparti [★IO]
Norske Arkitekters Landsforbund [★IO]
Norske Barne-og Ungdomsbokforfattere [★IO]
Norske Billedkunstnere [★IO]
Norske Dramatikeres Forbund [★IO]
Norske Finansanalytikeres Forening [★IO]
Norske Landskapsarkitekters Forening [★IO]
Norske Sjomatbedrifters Landsforening [★IO]
Norske Symfoni-Orkestres Landsforbund [IO], Oslo, Norway
Norske Vandrerhjem [★IO]
North America
    Before Columbus Found. [10036]
    Hemispheric Cong. of Latin Chambers of Commerce [23367]
    Ugandan North Amer. Assn. [18841]
North Am. Chinese Clean-tech and Semiconductor Assn. [1112], PO Box 61086, Sunnyvale, CA 94088-1086
North Am. Chinese Overseas Trans. Assn. [★3507]
North Am. Chinese Semiconductor Assn. [1112], PO Box 61086, Sunnyvale, CA 94088-1086
North Am. Christian Creative Assn. [19595], PO Box 93027, Hacienda Heights, CA 91745-3027
North America Coordinating Center for Responsible Tourism - Defunct.
North Am. Indian Ministries [★20076]
North Am. Indian Mission [★20076]
North Am. Indigenous Ministries [20076], PO Box 499, Sumas, WA 98295, (604)850-3052
North America-Mongolia Bus. Coun. [2104], 1015 Duke St., Alexandria, VA 22314, (703)549-8444
North America-Mongolia Bus. Coun. [2104], 1015 Duke St., Alexandria, VA 22314, (703)549-8444
North Am. Native Amer. Info. and Trade Center [10334], PO Box 27626, Tucson, AZ 85726-7626, (520)622-4900
North Am. Taiwanese Engineers' Assn. [6817], PO Box 360776, Milpitas, CA 95036
North Am. Taiwanese Engineers' Assn. [6817], PO Box 360776, Milpitas, CA 95036
North Am. Taiwanese Professors' Assn. [19253], PO Box 873704, Vancouver, WA 98687
North Am. Taiwanese Professors' Assn. [19253], PO Box 873704, Vancouver, WA 98687
North Am. Wu(Hao) Taiji Fed.
North Am. Wu(Hao) Taiji Fed. - Address unknown since 2011.
North Amer. Acad. of Ecumenists [19664], Oblates of St. Francis de Sales, 1621 Otis St. NE, Washington, DC 20018, (703)501-6586
North Amer. Agricultural Marketing Officials [4720], Amy Pettit, Sec.-Treas., Alabama Dept. of Agriculture, 1800 Glenn Hwy., Ste. 12, Palmer, AK 99645, (907)761-3864
North Amer. Alliance for the Advancement of Native Peoples [12569], 29780 Hwy. UU, Keytesville, MO 65261
North Amer. Alliance for the Advancement of Native Peoples [12569], 29780 Hwy. UU, Keytesville, MO 65261
North Amer. Alliance for Fair Employment [1158], 33 Harrison Ave., 5th Fl., Boston, MA 02111, (617)482-6300
North Amer. Alliances for Social Relief [12352], PO Box 468, Tucker, GA 30085, (770)330-3897
North Amer. Amateur Paintball Sports Assn. - Defunct.
North Amer. Apio-Therapy Soc. [★13651]
North Amer. Araucanian Royalist Soc. [9720], PO Box 211, Bryn Athyn, PA 19009
North Amer. Assn. for Belarusian Stud. [9434], Harvard Univ., Dept. of Slavic Languages and Literatures, Barker Ctr. 327, 12 Quincy St., Cambridge, MA 02138-3804

North Amer. Assn. for Belarusian Stud. [9434], Harvard Univ., Dept. of Slavic Languages and Literatures, Barker Ctr. 327, 12 Quincy St., Cambridge, MA 02138-3804
North Amer. Assn. for the Catechumenate [19482], 2915 NE Flanders, Portland, OR 97232, (503)502-6251
North Amer. Assn. for the Catechumenate [19482], 2915 NE Flanders, Portland, OR 97232, (503)502-6251
North Amer. Assn. for Celtic Language Teachers [8479], Robert S. Burke, Treas., 1306 NW 32nd Ave., Camas, WA 98607-9336, (360)954-5529
North Amer. Assn. of Central Cancer Registries [13960], 2121 W White Oaks Dr., Ste. B, Springfield, IL 62704-7412, (217)698-0800
North Amer. Assn. of Central Cancer Registries [13960], 2121 W White Oaks Dr., Ste. B, Springfield, IL 62704-7412, (217)698-0800
North Amer. Assn. of Christians in Social Work [13225], PO Box 121, Botsford, CT 06404-0121, (888)426-4712
North Amer. Assn. of Commencement Officers [8242], 191 Clarksville Rd., Princeton Junction, NJ 08550, (512)475-6060
North Amer. Assn. for the Diaconate [★19692]
North Amer. Assn. of Educational Negotiators [23182], OSBA, PO Box 1068, Salem, OR 97308, (503)588-2800
North Amer. Assn. for Environmental Educ. [8148], 2000 P St. NW, Ste. 540, Washington, DC 20036, (202)419-0412
North Amer. Assn. of Fisheries Economists [1362], Ann L. Shriver, Oregon State Univ., 213 Ballard Hall, Corvallis, OR 97331, (541)737-1416
North Amer. Assn. of Floor Covering Distributors [602], 401 N Michigan Ave., Ste. 2200, Chicago, IL 60611, (312)321-6836
North Amer. Assn. of Food Equip. Mfrs. [1441], 161 N Clark St., Ste. 2020, Chicago, IL 60601, (312)821-0201
North Amer. Assn. of Hunter Safety Coordinators [★22698]
North Amer. Assn. of Hunter Safety Coordinators [★22698]
North Amer. Assn. of the Intl. Cooperative Insurance Fed. [★1985]
North Amer. Assn. of Inventory Services [696], PO Box 120145, St. Paul, MN 55112, (888)529-3282
North Amer. Assn. of Jewish Homes and Housing for the Aging [★10834]
North Amer. Assn. for Laser Therapy [15238], Columbia Univ., Coll. of Physicians and Surgeons, 66 E 80th St., New York, NY 10075, (212)535-6040
North Amer. Assn. of Medical Educ. and Commun. Companies - Address unknown since 2011.
North Amer. Assn. of Mirror Mfrs. [★1575]
North Amer. Assn. of Neuro-Linguistic Programming [★16464]
North Amer. Assn. of Neuro-Linguistic Programming [★16464]
North Amer. Assn. of Professors of Christian Educ. [★7858]
North Amer. Assn. of State and Provincial Lotteries [5776], 1 S Broadway, Geneva, OH 44041, (440)466-5630
North Amer. Assn. of State and Provincial Lotteries [5776], 1 S Broadway, Geneva, OH 44041, (440)466-5630
North Amer. Assn. for the Stud. of Jean-Jacques Rousseau [★9411]
North Amer. Assn. for the Stud. of Jean-Jacques Rousseau [★9411]
North Amer. Assn. for the Stud. of Welsh Culture and History [10637], Univ. of Michigan, Dept. of History, Flint, MI 48502, (810)762-3366
North Amer. Assn. for the Stud. of Welsh Culture and History [10637], Univ. of Michigan, Dept. of History, Flint, MI 48502, (810)762-3366
North Amer. Assn. of Subway Franchisees [1530], PO Box 320955, Fairfield, CT 06825, (203)579-7779
North Amer. Assn. of Summer Sessions [8935], Bradley Univ., 1501 W Bradley Ave., Peoria, IL 61625, (309)677-2374

A star before a book entry number signifies that the name is not listed separately, but is mentioned within the entry.

North Amer. Assn. of Summer Sessions **[8935]**, Bradley Univ., 1501 W Bradley Ave., Peoria, IL 61625, (309)677-2374

North Amer. Assn. of Synagogue Executives **[20206]**, Rapaport House, 820 Second Ave., New York, NY 10017, (212)533-7800

North Amer. Assn. of Teachers of Czech **[★9529]**

North Amer. Assn. of Teachers of Czech **[★9529]**

North Amer. Assn. of Telecommunications Dealers **[7548]**, 131 NW 1st Ave., Delray Beach, FL 33444, (561)266-9440

North Amer. Assn. of Urgent Care Medicine **[★13727]**

North Amer. Assn. of Wardens and Superintendents **[11727]**, PO Box 11037, Albany, NY 12211-0037, (518)786-6801

North Amer. Assn. of Wardens and Superintendents **[11727]**, PO Box 11037, Albany, NY 12211-0037, (518)786-6801

North Amer. Babydoll Southdown Sheep Assn. and Registry **[4917]**, PO Box 146, Wellsville, KS 66092, (785)883-4811

North Amer. Babydoll Southdown Sheep Assn. and Registry **[4917]**, PO Box 146, Wellsville, KS 66092, (785)883-4811

North Amer. Band Directors Coordinating Comm. - Defunct.

North Amer. Banding Coun. **[7202]**, Mark Shield-castle, Chm., USFS Redwood Sci. Lab., 1700 Bay-view Dr., Arcata, CA 95521

North Amer. Banding Coun. **[7202]**, Mark Shield-castle, Chm., USFS Redwood Sci. Lab., 1700 Bay-view Dr., Arcata, CA 95521

North Amer. Bangladeshi Assn. for Bangladesh - Ad-dress unknown since 2010.

North Amer. Bar-Related Title Insurers **[2026]**, 1430 Lee St., Des Plaines, IL 60018, (847)298-8300

North Amer. Bear Center **[5092]**, 1926 Hwy. 169, Ely, MN 55731, (218)365-7879

North Amer. Benefit Assn. **[★19064]**

North Amer. Benthological Soc. **[★4220]**

North Amer. Benthological Soc. **[4220]**, SFS Membership Services, 5400 Bosque Blvd., Ste. 680, Waco, TX 76710, (254)399-9636

North Amer. Blueberry Coun. **[4463]**, PO Box 1036, Folsom, CA 95763, (916)983-2279

North Amer. Bluebird Soc. **[5093]**, PO Box 7844, Bloomington, IN 47407, (812)988-1876

North Amer. Bluebird Soc. **[5093]**, PO Box 7844, Bloomington, IN 47407, (812)988-1876

North Amer. Bd. of Certified Energy Practitioners **[6744]**, 56 Clifton Country Rd., Ste. 202, Clifton Park, NY 12065, (800)654-0021

North Amer. Booster Club Assn. **[3337]**, 100 N Mo-rain St., Ste. 215, Kennewick, WA 99336, (509)735-2878

North Amer. Border Terrier Welfare **[11877]**, 532 Mill Creek Crossing, Millboro, VA 24460, (540)997-5570

North Amer. Bowhunting Coalition **[21866]**, PO Box 493, Chatfield, MN 55923

North Amer. Boxing Fed. **[22438]**, 911 Kimbark St., Longmont, CO 80501, (303)442-0258

North Amer. Boxing Fed. **[IO]**, Edmonton, AB, Canada

North Amer. Brain Tumor Coalition **[13961]**, Turner and Goss LLP, 2446 39th St. NW, Washington, DC 20007

North Amer. Br. (1940) Dunkirk Veterans Assn. - Defunct.

North Amer. Br. of Intl. Life Sciences Inst. **[★15836]**

North Amer. Br. of Intl. Life Sciences Inst. **[★15836]**

North Amer. Brass Band Assn. **[10269]**, PO Box 11336, Charleston, WV 25339

North Amer. Brewers' Assn. **[188]**, 2845 Holly Pl., Idaho Falls, ID 83402, (208)589-7231

North Amer. Brewers' Assn. **[188]**, 2845 Holly Pl., Idaho Falls, ID 83402, (208)589-7231

North Amer. British Music Stud. Assn. **[10270]**, St. Michael's Coll., One Winooski Park, Box 377, Colchester, VT 05439, (802)654-2284

North Amer. British Music Stud. Assn. **[10270]**, St. Michael's Coll., One Winooski Park, Box 377, Colchester, VT 05439, (802)654-2284

North Amer. Broadcasters Assn. **[IO]**, Toronto, ON, Canada

North Amer. Building Material Distribution Assn. **[603]**, 401 N Michigan Ave., Chicago, IL 60611, (312)321-6845

North American-Bulgarian Chamber of Commerce **[23375]**, 851 Irwin St., Ste. 200, San Rafael, CA 94901, (415)251-2322

North American-Bulgarian Chamber of Commerce **[23375]**, 851 Irwin St., Ste. 200, San Rafael, CA 94901, (415)251-2322

North Amer. Bullriding Assn. - Address unknown since 2011.

North Amer. Bungee Assn. **[22999]**, PO Box 121, Fairview, OR 97024, (503)520-0303

North Amer. Bungee Assn. **[22999]**, PO Box 121, Fairview, OR 97024, (503)520-0303

North Amer. Butterfly Assn. **[7030]**, 4 Delaware Rd., Morristown, NJ 07960, (973)285-0907

North Amer. Canon Law Soc. **[★19470]**

North Amer. Carbon Capture and Storage Assn. **[6818]**, Michael Moore, Exec. Dir., Blue Source LLC, 12012 Wickchester Ln., Ste. 660, Houston, TX 77079, (281)668-8475

North Amer. Cartographic Info. Soc. **[6381]**, AGS Lib., PO Box 399, Milwaukee, WI 53201-0399, (414)229-6282

North Amer. Case Res. Assn. **[3708]**, Robert C. Crowner, Sec.-Treas., 3719 Meadow Ln., Saline, MI 48176, (734)429-5032

North Amer. Catalysis Soc. **[7383]**, Univ. of California-Berkeley, 103 Gilman Hall, Berkeley, CA 94720, (925)323-5559

North Amer. Celtic Buyers Assn. **[729]**, 27 Addison Ave., Rutherford, NJ 07070, (201)842-9922

North Amer. Celtic Buyers Assn. **[729]**, 27 Addison Ave., Rutherford, NJ 07070, (201)842-9922

North Amer. Center for Emergency Communications - Defunct.

North American-Chilean Chamber of Commerce **[23376]**, 866 United Nations Plz., Ste. 4019, New York, NY 10017, (212)317-1959

North Amer. Chinese Clinical Chemists Assn. **[6416]**, Shu-Ling Fan, PhD, Beth Israel Deaconess Medi-cal Center, Dept. of Pathology, Division of Lab. Medicine, 330 Brookline Ave., Boston, MA 02215, (617)667-3648

North Amer. Chinese Clinical Chemists Assn. **[6416]**, Shu-Ling Fan, PhD, Beth Israel Deaconess Medi-cal Center, Dept. of Pathology, Division of Lab. Medicine, 330 Brookline Ave., Boston, MA 02215, (617)667-3648

North Amer. Chinese Soccer League **[22940]**, 1 Crossan Ct., Landenberg, PA 19350, (302)831-0625

North Amer. Chinese Soccer League **[22940]**, 1 Crossan Ct., Landenberg, PA 19350, (302)831-0625

North Amer. Christian Foreign Language Assn. **[8480]**, Baylor Univ., Dept. of Modern Foreign Languages, 1 Bear Pl., No. 97390, Waco, TX 76798-7390

North Amer. Clinical Dermatologic Soc. **[14337]**, Dermatologist Medical Gp. of North County, 9850 Genesee Ave., Ste. 530, La Jolla, CA 92037, (858)558-0677

North Amer. Clinical Dermatologic Soc. **[14337]**, Dermatologist Medical Gp. of North County, 9850 Genesee Ave., Ste. 530, La Jolla, CA 92037, (858)558-0677

North Amer. Clivia Soc. **[4674]**, 4661 Jeanean Ln., Yorba Linda, CA 92886

North Amer. Clun Forest Assn. **[4918]**, Bramble Hill, 21727 Randall Dr., Houston, MN 55943, (507)864-7585

North Amer. Coalition for Christian Admissions Professionals **[7686]**, PO Box 5211, Huntington, IN 46750-5211, (260)356-5211

North Amer. Cockatiel Soc. **[21226]**, PO Box 143, Bethel, CT 06801-0143

North Amer. Cockatiel Soc. **[21226]**, PO Box 143, Bethel, CT 06801-0143

North Amer. Collectors **[21984]**, 16000 Ventura Blvd., Ste. 1100, Encino, CA 91436, (800)370-4720

North Amer. Colleges and Teachers of Agriculture **[7716]**, 151 W 100 S, Rupert, ID 83350, (208)436-0692

North Amer. Comm. - Defunct.

North Amer. Computational Social and Org. Sci-ences **[6466]**, Carnegie Mellon Univ., ISRI, Wean Hall 1325, 5000 Forbes Ave., Pittsburgh, PA 15213, (412)268-3163

North Amer. Conf. on British Stud. **[9456]**, Univ. of Texas at Austin, Harry Ransom Center, PO Box 7219, Austin, TX 78712-7219, (512)232-1236

North Amer. Conf. on Ethiopian Jewry **[18021]**, 255 W 36th St., Ste. 701, New York, NY 10018, (212)233-5200

North Amer. Conf. on Ethiopian Jewry **[18021]**, 255 W 36th St., Ste. 701, New York, NY 10018, (212)233-5200

North Amer. Conf. of Separated and Divorced Catholics **[11868]**, PO Box 10, Hancock, MI 49930-0010, (906)482-0494

North Amer. Cong. on Latin Am. **[17180]**, 38 Greene St., 4th Fl., New York, NY 10013, (646)613-1440

North Amer. Connection **[IO]**, Solihull, United Kingdom

North Amer. Coordinating Coun. on Japanese Lib. Resources **[10000]**, 149 Upland Rd., Cambridge, MA 02140, (617)945-7294

North Amer. Coordinating Coun. on Japanese Lib. Resources **[10000]**, 149 Upland Rd., Cambridge, MA 02140, (617)945-7294

North Amer. Corriente Assn. **[3928]**, PO Box 12359, North Kansas City, MO 64116, (816)421-1992

North Amer. Coun. on Adoptable Children **[10798]**, 970 Raymond Ave., Ste. 106, St. Paul, MN 55114, (651)644-3036

North Amer. Coun. of Automotive Teachers **[7763]**, PO Box 80010, Charleston, SC 29416, (843)556-7068

North Amer. Coun. for Muslim Women - Defunct.

North Amer. Coun. for Online Learning **[★7719]**

North Amer. Coun. for Online Learning **[★7719]**

North Amer. Crane Working Group **[5094]**, 14223 Greenview Dr., Laurel, MD 20708

North Amer. Dairy Sheep Assn. - Defunct.

North Amer. Danish Warmblood Assn. **[4627]**, 32781 Chadlyn Ct., Wildomar, CA 92595-9310, (951)609-3787

North Amer. Danish Warmblood Assn. **[4627]**, 32781 Chadlyn Ct., Wildomar, CA 92595-9310, (951)609-3787

North Amer. Deer Farmers Assn. **[4362]**, 104 S Lakeshore Dr., Lake City, MN 55041, (651)345-5600

North Amer. Dept. of the Royal Warmblood Studbook of the Netherlands **[4628]**, PO Box 0, Sutherlin, OR 97479, (541)459-3232

North Amer. Deutsch Kurzhaar Club **[21617]**, 1017 S Fourth Ave., Libertyville, IL 60048

North Amer. Dhrupad Assn. **[10271]**, PO Box 361, Agoura Hills, CA 91376, (818)991-0825

North Amer. Dhrupad Assn. **[10271]**, PO Box 361, Agoura Hills, CA 91376, (818)991-0825

North Amer. Die Casting Assn. **[1855]**, 241 Holbrook Dr., Wheeling, IL 60090-5809, (847)279-0001

North Amer. Diecast Toy Collectors Assn. **[★22171]**

North Amer. Diecast Toy Collectors Assn. **[★22171]**

North Amer. Dog Agility Coun. **[22548]**, PO Box 1206, Colbert, OK 74733

North Amer. Dostoevsky Soc. - Defunct.

North Amer. Draft Cross Assn. - Defunct.

North Amer. Economic Stud. Assn. **[★6624]**

North Amer. Economics and Finance Assn. **[★6624]**

North Amer. Elec. Reliability Corp. **[1083]**, 116-390 Village Blvd., Princeton, NJ 08540-5721, (609)452-8060

North Amer. Elec. Reliability Coun. **[★1083]**

North Amer. Elk Breeders Assn. **[5095]**, 4985 W Blue Hill Rd., Ayr, NE 68925-2632, (402)756-3ELK

North Amer. English and European Ford Registry **[21136]**, PO Box 11415, Olympia, WA 98508, (360)754-9585

North Amer. Equine Ranching Info. Coun. **[1734]**, PO Box 43968, Louisville, KY 40253-0968, (502)245-0425

North Amer. Equip. Dealers Assn. **[172]**, 1195 Smizer Mill Rd., Fenton, MO 63026-3480, (636)349-5000

North Amer. Export Grain Assn. **[1595]**, 1250 I St. NW, Ste. 1003, Washington, DC 20005-3939, (202)682-4030

North Amer. Export Grain Assn. [1595], 1250 I St. NW, Ste. 1003, Washington, DC 20005-3939, (202)682-4030

North Amer. Falconers Assn. [22561], Donna Vorce, Corresponding Sec., 601 E 6th St., Davenport, NE 68335

North Amer. Family Campers Assn. [22446], PO Box 318, Lunenburg, MA 01462, (401)828-0579

North Amer. Farm Show Coun. [3763], 590 Woody Hayes Dr., Columbus, OH 43210, (614)292-4278

North Amer. Farmers' Direct Marketing Assn. [4721], 62 White Loaf Rd., Southampton, MA 01073, (413)529-0386

North Amer. Fastpitch Assn. [22955], PO Box 566, Dayton, OR 97114, (503)864-4487

North Amer. Fastpitch Assn. [22955], PO Box 566, Dayton, OR 97114, (503)864-4487

North Amer. Fed. of German Folk Dance Groups [9535], 308 Magnolia Dr., Plainfield, IN 46168

North Amer. Fed. of German Folk Dance Groups [★9535]

North Amer. Fed. of Temple Brotherhoods [★19882]

North Amer. Fed. of Temple Youth [19093], Union for Reform Judaism - Youth Div., 633 3rd Ave., 7th Fl., New York, NY 10017, (212)650-4070

North Amer. Fichte Soc. [10402], Univ. of Kentucky, Dept. of Philosophy, Lexington, KY 40506, (859)257-4376

North Amer. Fishing Club [22583], 12301 Whitewater Dr., Minnetonka, MN 55343, (800)843-6232

North Amer. Flowerbulb Wholesalers Assn. [4675], Marlboro Bulb Company, 2424 Hwy. 72/221 E, Greenwood, SC 29649, (864)229-1618

North Amer. Folk Music and Dance Alliance [★9619]

North Amer. Folk Music and Dance Alliance [★9619]

North Amer. Foodservice Companies [★1433]

North Amer. Football League [22593], 5775 Glenridge Dr. NE, Ste. 100B, Atlanta, GA 30328, (404)475-1803

North Amer. Football League [22593], 5775 Glenridge Dr. NE, Ste. 100B, Atlanta, GA 30328, (404)475-1803

North Amer. Forensic Entomology Assn. [6847], Dr. Christine Picard, PhD, Treas., 6104 Rucker Rd., Indianapolis, IN 46220

North Amer. Forensic Entomology Assn. [6847], Dr. Christine Picard, PhD, Treas., 6104 Rucker Rd., Indianapolis, IN 46220

North Amer. Formula 18 Assn. [22380], 1925 144th St. SE, Mill Creek, WA 98012

North Amer. Forum on the Catechumenate [19483], 125 Michigan Ave. NE, Washington, DC 20017, (202)884-9758

North Amer. Fruit Explorers [21812], 1716 Apples Rd., Chapin, IL 62628-4048, (800)588-3854

North Amer. Game Breeders and Shooting Preserve Assn. [★3797]

North Amer. Gamebird Assn. [3797], PO Box 338, Cambridge, MD 21613, (800)624-2967

North Amer. Gaming Regulators Assn. [5494], 1000 Westgate Dr., Ste. 252, St. Paul, MN 55114, (651)203-7244

North Amer. Geosynthetics Soc. [6429], PO Box 12063, Albany, NY 12212-2063, (518)869-2917

North Amer. Geosynthetics Soc. [6429], PO Box 12063, Albany, NY 12212-2063, (518)869-2917

North Amer. Gladiolus Coun. [21813], 230 Shiloh Dr., Colville, WA 99114, (509)684-5407

North Amer. Graphic Arts Suppliers Assn. - Defunct.

North Amer. Grappling Assn. [23133], 36 Saner Rd., Marlborough, CT 06447, (860)295-0403

North Amer. Grouse Partnership [5096], C. Sealing, 1670 N 1/2 Rd., Fruita, CO 81521, (970)858-9659

North Amer. Guild of Change Ringers [10272], 229 Howard Ave., Woodstown, NJ 08098-1249, (856)769-7264

North Amer. Gun Dog Assn. [21618], 17850 County Rd. 54, Burlington, CO 80807, (719)342-0776

North Amer. Hair Res. Soc. [14677], Wake Forest Univ. School of Medicine, Dept. of Dermatology, Medical Center Blvd., Winston-Salem, NC 27157, (336)716-2768

North Amer. Hardwood Preservation Soc. - Defunct.

North Amer. Hazardous Materials Mgt. Assn. [4520], 3030 W 81st Ave., Westminster, CO 80031-4111, (303)433-4446

North Amer. Heather Soc. [21814], John Calhoun, Treas., 31100 Country Rd., Fort Bragg, CA 95437, (541)929-6272

North Amer. Heather Soc. [21814], John Calhoun, Treas., 31100 Country Rd., Fort Bragg, CA 95437, (541)929-6272

North Amer. Horsemen's Assn. [4629], PO Box 223, Paynesville, MN 56362, (320)243-7250

North Amer. Horticultural Supply Assn. [4676], 100 N 20th St., 4th Fl., Philadelphia, PA 19103-1443, (215)564-3484

North Amer. Hunting Club [22700], 12301 Whitewater Dr., PO Box 3401, Minnetonka, MN 55343, (952)988-9333

North Amer. Hyperthermia Soc. [★16876]

North Amer. Importers Assn. [2105], 1250 Connecticut Ave. NW, Ste. 200, Washington, DC 20036, (888)483-5777

North Amer. Importers Assn. [2105], 1250 Connecticut Ave. NW, Ste. 200, Washington, DC 20036, (888)483-5777

North Amer. Indian Chamber of Commerce of North Am. [★23429]

North Amer. Indian Museums Assn. - Defunct.

North Amer. Indus. Hemp Coun. [6861], PO Box 259329, Madison, WI 53725-9329, (608)835-0428

North Amer. Insulation Mfrs. Assn. [604], 44 Canal Center Plz., Ste. 310, Alexandria, VA 22314, (703)684-0084

North Amer. Interfraternal Found. [23541], 1750 Royalton Dr., Carmel, IN 46032-9620, (317)595-9613

North-American Interfraternity Conf. [23542], 3901 W 86th St., Ste. 390, Indianapolis, IN 46268-1791, (317)872-1112

North Amer. Irish Dance Fed. [9563], Sharon Stidham, Chair, 2317 Peppermill Pointe Ct., Springfield, IL 62712

North Amer. Islamic Trust [9894], 721 Enterprise Dr., Oak Brook, IL 60523, (630)789-9191

North Amer. Judges Assn. [★5612]

North Amer. Jules Verne Soc. [10729], Henry G. Franke, III, Treas., 318 Patriot Way, Yorktown, VA 23693

North Amer. Jules Verne Soc. [10729], Henry G. Franke, III, Treas., 318 Patriot Way, Yorktown, VA 23693

North Amer. Kai Assn. [21619], 3410 Galbraith Line Rd., Yale, MI 48097, (810)956-4863

North Amer. Kant Soc. [10403], Univ. of Southern Maine, 96 Falmouth St., Portland, ME 04104-9300, (207)780-4248

North Amer. Lake Mgt. Soc. [7024], PO Box 5443, Madison, WI 53705-0443, (608)233-2836

North Amer. Laminate Flooring Assn. [605], 1747 Pennsylvania Ave. NW, Ste. 1000, Washington, DC 20006, (202)785-9500

North Amer. Laminate Flooring Assn. [605], 1747 Pennsylvania Ave. NW, Ste. 1000, Washington, DC 20006, (202)785-9500

North Amer. Levinas Soc. [10404], Sol Neely, Co-Sec., Purdue Univ., Dept. of English, 500 Oval Dr., West Lafayette, IN 47907-2038

North Amer. Lily Soc. [21815], Stephanie Sims, Exec. Sec., PO Box W, Bonners Ferry, ID 83805

North Amer. Limousin Found. [3929], 7383 S Alton Way, Ste. 100, Centennial, CO 80112-2339, (303)220-1693

North Amer. Limousin Junior Assn. [3930], North Amer. Limousin Found., 7383 S Alton Way, Ste. 100, Centennial, CO 80112, (303)220-1693

North Amer. Lionhead Rabbit Club [4852], Jennifer Hack, Sec., 4098 N Hwy. 67, Sedalia, CO 80135, (765)346-7604

North Amer. Lionhead Rabbit Club [4852], Jennifer Hack, Sec., 4098 N Hwy. 67, Sedalia, CO 80135, (765)346-7604

North Amer. Llewellin Breeders Assn. [21620], 3413 Forrester Ln., Waco, TX 76708, (254)752-1526

North Amer. Llewellin Breeders Assn. [21620], 3413 Forrester Ln., Waco, TX 76708, (254)752-1526

North Amer. Lumbar Spine Assn. [★15672]

North Amer. Lumbar Spine Assn. [★15672]

North Amer. Man/Boy Love Assn. [13110], PO Box 174, New York, NY 10018, (212)631-1194

North Amer. Manx Assn. [19120], 10251 S Bell Ave., Chicago, IL 60643

North Amer. Manx Assn. [19120], 10251 S Bell Ave., Chicago, IL 60643

North Amer. Maritime Ministry Assn. [13029], PO Box 2434, Niagara Falls, NY 14302, (905)892-7525

North Amer. Maritime Ministry Assn. [13029], PO Box 2434, Niagara Falls, NY 14302, (905)892-7525

North Amer. Masonic Historical Assn. - Defunct.

North Amer. Meat Processors Assn. [2434], 1910 Assn. Dr., Reston, VA 20191, (703)758-1900

North Amer. Meat Processors Assn. [2434], 1910 Assn. Dr., Reston, VA 20191, (703)758-1900

North Amer. Medical/Dental Assn. - Defunct.

North Amer. Membrane Soc. [7086], Univ. of Toledo, Chem. and Env. Engg. (MS 305), 2801 W Bancroft St., Toledo, OH 43606-3390, (419)530-3649

North Amer. Menopause Soc. [15890], 5900 Landerbrook Dr., Ste. 390, Mayfield Heights, OH 44124-4085, (440)442-7550

North Amer. Meteor Network [7107], Mark Davis, Coor., 101 Margate Cir., Goose Creek, SC 29445

North Amer. Meteor Network [7107], Mark Davis, Coor., 101 Margate Cir., Goose Creek, SC 29445

North Amer. Millers' Assn. [2502], 600 Maryland Ave. SW, Ste. 825 W, Washington, DC 20024, (202)484-2200

North Amer. Mini Moke Registry [21137], Sherry Chandler, Ed., 1779 Kickapoo St., South Lake Tahoe, CA 96150, (530)577-7895

North Amer. Model Boat Assn. [21908], 1815 Halley St., San Diego, CA 92154, (619)424-6380

North Amer. Model Boat Assn. [21908], 1815 Halley St., San Diego, CA 92154, (619)424-6380

North Amer. Model Horse Shows Assn. [21857], PO Box 1271, Decatur, TX 76234

North Amer. Morab Horse Association/Registry [★4641]

North Amer. Morab Horse Association/Registry [★4641]

North Amer. Mycological Assn. [7131], PO Box 64, Christiansburg, VA 24068, (540)230-7603

North Amer. Native Fishes Assn. [6955], PO Box 1596, Milton, WA 98354-1596, (256)824-6992

North Amer. Native Fishes Assn. [6955], PO Box 1596, Milton, WA 98354-1596, (256)824-6992

North Amer. Native Plant Soc. [IO], Etobicoke, ON, Canada

North Amer. Natural Bodybuilding Fed. [22420], 180 Peachtree Dr., Waukee, IA 50263, (515)238-6020

North Amer. Natural Casing Assn. [1423], Leon Van Leeuwen Corp., 494 8th Ave., Ste. 805, New York, NY 10001, (212)695-4980

North Amer. Natural Casing Assn. [1423], Leon Van Leeuwen Corp., 494 8th Ave., Ste. 805, New York, NY 10001, (212)695-4980

North Amer. Nature Photography Assn. [2727], 10200 W 44th Ave., Ste. 304, Wheat Ridge, CO 80033-2840, (303)422-8527

North Amer. Neuro-Ophthalmology Soc. [15970], 5841 Cedar Lake Rd., Ste. 204, Minneapolis, MN 55416, (952)646-2037

North Amer. Neuro-Ophthalmology Soc. [15970], 5841 Cedar Lake Rd., Ste. 204, Minneapolis, MN 55416, (952)646-2037

North Amer. NeuroEndocrine Tumor Soc. [14494], 800 NE Tenney Rd., Ste. 110-412, Vancouver, WA 98685, (360)314-4112

North Amer. Neuromodulation Soc. [16106], 4700 W Lake Ave., Glenview, IL 60025, (847)375-4398

North Amer. Nietzsche Soc. [10405], Univ. of Illinois, Dept. of Philosophy, 105 Gregory Hall, 810 S Wright St., Urbana, IL 61801, (217)333-1939

North Amer. Nietzsche Soc. [10405], Univ. of Illinois, Dept. of Philosophy, 105 Gregory Hall, 810 S Wright St., Urbana, IL 61801, (217)333-1939

North Amer. Normande Assn. [3931], 748 Enloe Rd., Rewey, WI 53580, (608)943-6091

North Amer. Nursing Diagnosis Assn. [★15761]

North Amer. Nursing Diagnosis Assn. [★15761]

North Amer. Ohara Teachers Assn. [9617], 750 Braewick Rd., Tryon, NC 28782, (864)654-0657

North Amer. Olive Oil Assn. [2591], 3301 Rte. 66, Bldg. C, Ste. 205, Neptune, NJ 07753-2705, (732)922-3008

A star before a book entry number signifies that the name is not listed separately, but is mentioned within the entry.

North Amer. Olive Oil Assn. [2591], 3301 Rte. 66, Bldg. C, Ste. 205, Neptune, NJ 07753-2705, (732)922-3008

North Amer. One-Armed Golfer Assn. [22521], 8406 Cloverport Dr., Louisville, KY 40228, (502)614-8595

North Amer. Packaging Assn. - Address unknown since 2010.

North Amer. Packgoat Assn. [4506], PO Box 170166, Boise, ID 83717, (435)764-1111

North Amer. Parrot Soc. [21227], 15341 Kingston St., Brighton, CO 80602-7439, (303)659-9544

North Amer. Patristics Soc. [20150], Johns Hopkins Univ., Press Journals Div., 2715 N Charles St., Baltimore, MD 21218, (800)548-1784

North Amer. Peregrine Found. [★22561]

North Amer. Performing Arts Managers and Agents [164], 459 Columbus Ave., No. 133, New York, NY 10024, (718)797-4577

North Amer. Peruvian Horse Assn. [4630], PO Box 2187, Santa Rosa, CA 95405, (707)544-5807

North Amer. Peruvian Horse Assn. [4630], PO Box 2187, Santa Rosa, CA 95405, (707)544-5807

North Amer. Pet Hea. Insurance Assn. [14863], Loran Hickton, Exec. Dir., 434 Salvini Dr., Pittsburgh, PA 15243, (412)319-7730

North Amer. Piedmontese Assn. [3932], 1740 County Rd. 185, Ramah, CO 80832, (306)329-8600

North Amer. Piedmontese Assn. [3932], 1740 County Rd. 185, Ramah, CO 80832, (306)329-8600

North Amer. Plant Protection Org. [IO], Ottawa, ON, Canada

North Amer. Police Work Dog Assn. [5736], 4222 Manchester Ave., Perry, OH 44081-9611, (440)259-3169

North Amer. Potbellied Pig Assn. [3798], 15525 E Via Del Palo, Gilbert, AZ 85298, (480)899-8941

North Amer. Power Sweeping Assn. [2256], 136 S Keowee St., Dayton, OH 45402, (888)757-0130

North Amer. Powerlifting Fed. [22815], Robert Keller, Gen. Sec.-Treas., PO Box 291571, Davie, FL 33329-1571, (907)334-9977

North Amer. Primary Care Res. Gp. [13728], 11400 Tomahawk Creek Pkwy., Ste. 540, Leawood, KS 66211-2681, (913)906-6000

North Amer. Professional Driver Education Assn. - Defunct.

North Amer. Professors of Christian Educ. [7858], Biola Univ., 13800 Biola Ave., La Mirada, CA 90639

North Amer. Pt-to-Pt Assn. - Address unknown since 2011.

North Amer. Punch Mfrs. Assn. [1856], 21 Turquoise Ave., Naples, FL 34114, (239)775-7245

North Amer. Quilling Guild [20969], 2422 Torrington Dr., Toms River, NJ 08755

North Amer. Radio Archives [22120], PO Box 1392, Lake Elsinore, CA 92531, (888)33-AVPRO

North Amer. Rail Shippers Assn. [3529], 2115 Portsmouth Dr., Richardson, TX 75082-4839, (972)690-4740

North Amer. Railcar Operators Assn. [3530], Mark Hudson, Sec., PO Box 321, Dry Ridge, KY 41035-0321

North Amer. Reggio Emilia Alliance [11371], Inspired Practices in Early Educ., Inc., 2040 Wilson Ridge Ct., Roswell, GA 30075, (770)552-0179

North Amer. Registry of Midwives [14108], 5257 Rosestone Dr., Lilburn, GA 30047, (770)381-9051

North Amer. Retail Dealers Assn. [1113], 222 S Riverside Plz., Ste. 2100, Chicago, IL 60606, (312)648-0649

North Amer. Retail Hardware Assn. [1656], 6325 Digital Way, No. 300, Indianapolis, IN 46278-1787, (317)290-0338

North Amer. Riding for the Handicapped Assn. [22522], PO Box 33150, Denver, CO 80233, (303)452-1212

North Amer. Ring Assn. [21621], PO Box 146, Gig Harbor, WA 98335, (206)219-9072

North Amer. Ring Assn. [21621], PO Box 146, Gig Harbor, WA 98335, (206)219-9072

North Amer. Rock Garden Soc. [21816], PO Box 18604, Raleigh, NC 27619

North Amer. Rock Garden Soc. [21816], PO Box 18604, Raleigh, NC 27619

North Amer. Romagnola and RomAngus Assn. [3933], 14305 W 379th St., LaCygne, KS 66040-4077, (913)594-1080

North Amer. Saddle Mule Assn. [20953], 56695 Ginny Belle Ln., New London, MO 63459

North Amer. Sankethi Assn. [9492], 34 Longwood Dr., Clifton Park, NY 12065

North Amer. Sartre Soc. [10406], 150 Broadway, Ste. 812, New York, NY 10038

North Amer. Saxophone Alliance [10273], Drake Univ., Harmon Fine Arts Center, Dept. of Music, Des Moines, IA 50311, (515)271-3104

North Amer. Sea Plant Soc. - Defunct.

North Amer. Securities Administrators Assn. [3205], 750 1st St. NE, Ste. 1140, Washington, DC 20002-8034, (202)737-0900

North Amer. Security Products Org. [3225], 1425 K St. NW, Ste. 350, Washington, DC 20005, (202)587-5743

North Amer. Selle Francais Assn. - Defunct.

North Amer. Serials Interest Gp. [10001], PMB 305, 1902 Ridge Rd., West Seneca, NY 14224

North Amer. Shagya-Arabian Soc. [4631], Gwyn Davis, Info. Off., 9797 S Rangeline Rd., Clinton, IN 47842, (765)665-3851

North Amer. Shetland Sheepbreeders Assn. [4919], NASSA Registry, 15603 173rd Ave., Milo, IA 50166, (641)942-6402

North Amer. Shippers Assn. [3265], 1600 St. Georges Ave., PO Box 249, Rahway, NJ 07065, (732)680-4540

North Amer. Shortwave Assn. [20940], 45 Wildflower Rd., Levittown, PA 19057

North Amer. Sikh Medical and Dental Assn. [15429], 4104 Old Vestal Rd., Ste. 108, Vestal, NY 13850, (607)729-0726

North Amer. Sikh Medical and Dental Assn. [15429], 4104 Old Vestal Rd., Ste. 108, Vestal, NY 13850, (607)729-0726

North Amer. Simulation and Gaming Assn. [8209], PO Box 78636, Indianapolis, IN 46278, (317)387-1424

North Amer. Ski Joring Assn. [23000], 990 Monegan Rd., Whitefish, MT 59937, (406)261-7464

North Amer. Skull Base Soc. [15671], 11300 W Olympic Blvd., Ste. 600, Los Angeles, CA 90064, (310)424-3326

North Amer. Small Bus. Intl. Trade Educators [★7798]

North Amer. Small Bus. Intl. Trade Educators [★7798]

North Amer. Snowsports Journalists Assn. [IO], Kelowna, BC, Canada

North Amer. Soc. of Adlerian Psychology [16415], 614 Old W Chocolate Ave., Hershey, PA 17033, (717)579-8795

North Amer. Soc. of Ancient and Medieval Wargamers [21754], David Schlanger, Sec., 6374 Arbor Way, Elkridge, MD 21075, (410)379-5041

North Amer. Soc. for Cardiovascular Imaging [14036], 1891 Preston White Dr., Reston, VA 20191, (703)476-1350

North Amer. Soc. for Cardiovascular Imaging [14036], 1891 Preston White Dr., Reston, VA 20191, (703)476-1350

North Amer. Soc. for Childhood Onset Schizophrenia [15479], 88 Briarwood Dr. E, Berkeley Heights, NJ 07922

North Amer. Soc. for Dialysis and Transplantation [15555], Phyllis Helderman, 1113 Chickering Park Dr., Nashville, TN 37215, (615)665-0566

North Amer. Soc. of Head and Neck Pathology [16129], Manju Prasad, MD, VP, Yale Univ. School of Medicine, Dept. of Pathology, PO Box 208070, New Haven, CT 06520-8070, (203)737-4862

North Amer. Soc. of Homeopaths [15022], PO Box 450039, Sunrise, FL 33345-0039, (206)720-7000

North Amer. Soc. of Obstetric Medicine [15891], Sandra Medina, Women and Infants' Hosp., 101 Dudley St., 1st Fl., Ste. 1440, Providence, RI 02905, (401)274-1122

North Amer. Soc. of Obstetric Medicine [15891], Sandra Medina, Women and Infants' Hosp., 101 Dudley St., 1st Fl., Ste. 1440, Providence, RI 02905, (401)274-1122

North Amer. Soc. for Oceanic History [10062], Dept. of History, Texas Christian Univ., Box 297260, Fort Worth, TX 76129

North Amer. Soc. for Oceanic History [10062], Dept. of History, Texas Christian Univ., Box 297260, Fort Worth, TX 76129

North Amer. Soc. of Pacing and Electrophysiology [★14016]

North Amer. Soc. of Pacing and Electrophysiology [★14016]

North Amer. Soc. for Pediatric Gastroenterology [★14570]

North Amer. Soc. for Pediatric Gastroenterology, Hepatology and Nutrition [14570], PO Box 6, Flourtown, PA 19031, (215)233-0808

North Amer. Soc. for Pediatric Medicine - Address unknown since 2010.

North Amer. Soc. of Phlebology [★16956]

North Amer. Soc. of Pipe Collectors [21387], PO Box 9642, Columbus, OH 43209-0642

North Amer. Soc. for the Psychology of Sport and Physical Activity [22819], 1607 N Market St., Champaign, IL 61820

North Amer. Soc. for Social Philosophy [10407], Philosophy Documentation Center, PO Box 7147, Charlottesville, VA 22906-7147, (434)220-3300

North Amer. Soc. for the Sociology of Sport [7430], PO Box 291, Bowling Green, OH 43403, (419)352-1928

North Amer. Soc. for Sport History [9789], Ronald A. Smith, Sec.-Treas., PO Box 1026, Lemont, PA 16851-1026

North Amer. Soc. for Sport Mgt. [8722], 135 Winterwood Dr., Butler, PA 16001, (724)482-6277

North Amer. Soc. for Sport Mgt. [8722], 135 Winterwood Dr., Butler, PA 16001, (724)482-6277

North Amer. Soc. for the Stud. of Hypertension in Pregnancy [16591], Keisha Staley, 409 12th St. SW, Washington, DC 20024, (202)863-2570

North Amer. Soc. for the Stud. of Romanticism [IO], London, ON, Canada

North Amer. Soc. for Trenchless Tech. [7588], Losi & Ranger, PLLC, 7445 Morgan Rd., Liverpool, NY 13090, (703)351-5252

North Amer. South Asian Bar Assn. [5678], Inderpreet Sawhney, Pres., 4800 Great Am. Pkwy., Ste. 310, Santa Clara, CA 95054-1227, (408)970-0100

North Amer. South Asian Law Student Assn. [8511], Nina Patel, Co-Pres., PO Box 951476, Los Angeles, CA 90095

North Amer. South Asian Law Student Assn. [8511], Nina Patel, Co-Pres., PO Box 951476, Los Angeles, CA 90095

North Amer. South Devon Assn. [3934], 19590 E Main St., Ste. 202, Parker, CO 80138, (303)770-3130

North Amer. Specialized Coagulation Lab. Assn. [15235], Massachusetts Gen. Hosp., Coagulation Lab., 55 Fruit St., Gray 218, Boston, MA 02114, (617)726-2969

North Amer. Specialized Coagulation Lab. Assn. [15235], Massachusetts Gen. Hosp., Coagulation Lab., 55 Fruit St., Gray 218, Boston, MA 02114, (617)726-2969

North Amer. Spine Soc. [15672], 7075 Veterans Blvd., Burr Ridge, IL 60527, (630)230-3600

North Amer. Spine Soc. [15672], 7075 Veterans Blvd., Burr Ridge, IL 60527, (630)230-3600

North Amer. Sports Fed. [22236], Suzanne Robison, Sec., 1081 Pebble Ct., Mechanicsburg, PA 17050, (717)737-5800

North Amer. Sports Fed. [22236], Suzanne Robison, Sec., 1081 Pebble Ct., Mechanicsburg, PA 17050, (717)737-5800

North Amer. Spotted Draft Horse Assn. [4632], Sherry Shank, Sec.-Treas./Registrar, 17594 U.S. Hwy. 20, Goshen, IN 46528, (574)821-4226

North Amer. Spotted Draft Horse Assn. [4632], Sherry Shank, Sec.-Treas./Registrar, 17594 U.S. Hwy. 20, Goshen, IN 46528, (574)821-4226

North Amer. Squirrel Assn. [22001], PO Box 186, Holmen, WI 54636, (608)234-5988

North Amer. Steam Boat Assn. [22381], 1165 Jacks Hill Rd., Oxford, CT 06478, (203)463-8288

North Amer. Steam Boat Assn. [22381], 1165 Jacks Hill Rd., Oxford, CT 06478, (203)463-8288

Reference to "IO" in place of a book number signifies that the association may be found in the 50th edition of International Organizations.

North Amer. Steel Alliance **[2488]**, 23151 Plaza Pointe Dr., Ste. 120, Laguna Hills, CA 92653, (949)855-3321

North Amer. Stone Skipping Assn. **[22131]**, PO Box 2986, Wimberley, TX 78676-7886

North Amer. Stone Skipping Assn. **[22131]**, PO Box 2986, Wimberley, TX 78676-7886

North Amer. Strawberry Growers Assn. **[4464]**, Bardenhagen Berries, 1888 N Eagle Hwy., Lake Leelanau, MI 49653, (231)271-0072

North Amer. Strawberry Growers Assn. **[4464]**, Bardenhagen Berries, 1888 N Eagle Hwy., Lake Leelanau, MI 49653, (231)271-0072

North Amer. St. Newspaper Assn. **[2954]**, 2201 P St. NW, Washington, DC 20037, (202)462-0011

North Amer. Strongman **[22421]**, 11676 Mark Twain Ln., Bridgeton, MO 63044, (314)770-9279

North Amer. Student Cooperative Org. **[★8927]**

North Amer. Students of Cooperation **[8927]**, PO Box 180048, Chicago, IL 60618, (773)404-2667

North Amer. Studio Alliance **[13698]**, 2313 Hastings Dr., Belmont, CA 94002-3317, (877)626-2782

North Amer. Sundial Soc. **[9014]**, 8 Sachem Dr., Glastonbury, CT 06033

North Amer. Sundial Soc. **[9014]**, 8 Sachem Dr., Glastonbury, CT 06033

North Amer. Swing Club Assn. **[★13108]**

North Amer. Swing Club Assn. **[★13108]**

North Amer. Sys. Builders Assn. **[★3373]**

North Amer. Taiwan Stud. Assn. **[8938]**, Huey-Tyng Gau, Treas., PO Box 50096, Seattle, WA 98145-5096

North Amer. Taiwan Stud. Assn. **[8938]**, Huey-Tyng Gau, Treas., PO Box 50096, Seattle, WA 98145-5096

North Amer. Taiwanese Medical Assn. **[14886]**, 11650 Country Club Rd., West Frankfort, IL 62896

North Amer. Tang Shou Tao Assn. **[13699]**, PO Box 36235, Tucson, AZ 85740, (520)498-0678

North Amer. Tasar Assn. **[IO]**, Vancouver, BC, Canada

North Amer. Technician Excellence **[1717]**, 2111 Wilson Blvd., No. 510, Arlington, VA 22201, (703)276-7247

North Amer. Teckel Club **[21622]**, 9621 Bachelor Rd., Kutztown, PA 19530

North Amer. Thermal Anal. Soc. **[7564]**, Lois Hall, Staff Mgt: Dir., Western Kentucky Univ., Center for Res. and Development, Thermal Anal. Lab., 2413 Nashville Rd., Bowling Green, KY 42101-4101, (270)901-3490

North Amer. Thoroughbred Soc. **[22694]**, 79 Brittin St., Madison, NJ 07940-2138

North Amer. Tiddlywinks Assn. **[21755]**, Rick Tucker, PO Box 1701, Falls Church, VA 22041-0701

North Amer. Tornado Assn. - Address unknown since 2011.

North Amer. Torquay Soc. **[21388]**, R.L. Lookabill, 13607 Maxson Ct., Spotsylvania, VA 22553

North Amer. Trail Ride Conf. **[23091]**, PO Box 224, Sedalia, CO 80135, (303)688-1677

North Amer. Trailer Dealers Assn. **[3531]**, 5901 Sun Blvd., Ste. 100A, St. Petersburg, FL 33715, (727)360-0304

North Amer. Trakehner Assn. **[★4558]**

North Amer. Trakehner Assn. **[★4558]**

North Amer. Transplant Coordinators Org. **[16916]**, PO Box 15384, Lenexa, KS 66285-5384, (913)895-4612

North Amer. Trans. Mgt. Inst. **[7981]**, 2460 W 26th Ave., Ste. 245-C, Denver, CO 80211, (303)952-4013

North Amer. Trap Collector Assn. **[21389]**, PO Box 94, Galloway, OH 43119

North Amer. Travel Journalist Assn. **[3709]**, 3579 E Foothill Blvd., No. 744, Pasadena, CA 91107, (626)376-9754

North Amer. Truck Camper Owners Assn. **[22198]**, PO Box 30408, Bellingham, WA 98228

North Amer. Truck Stop Network **[3122]**, PO Box 337, Sullivan, MO 63080, (573)468-6288

North Amer. Truffling Soc. **[7132]**, PO Box 296, Corvallis, OR 97339

North Amer. Tug of War Fed. **[★23101]**

North Amer. Tuli Assn. - Address unknown since 2010.

North Amer. Union Life Assurance Soc. **[★18960]**

North Amer. Union Life Assurance Soc. - Defunct.

North Amer. Vascular Biology Org. **[16965]**, 18501 Kingshill Rd., Germantown, MD 20874-2211, (301)760-7745

North Amer. Vegetarian Soc. **[10625]**, PO Box 72, Dolgeville, NY 13329, (518)568-7970

North Amer. Vexillological Assn. **[10631]**, 1977 N Olden Ave. Extension, PMB 225, Trenton, NJ 08618-2193

North Amer. Victorian Stud. Assn. **[10633]**, Prof. Dino Franco Felluga, Chm., Purdue Univ., Dept. of English, 500 Oval Dr., West Lafayette, IN 47907

North Amer. Vodder Assn. of Lymphatic Therapy **[15256]**, 317 Cherokee St., Ste. 101, Kingsport, TN 37660-4335, (423)367-8064

North Amer. Vodder Assn. of Lymphatic Therapy **[15256]**, 317 Cherokee St., Ste. 101, Kingsport, TN 37660-4335, (423)367-8064

North Amer. Voyageur Coun. **[9721]**, 4449 Xerxes Ave. S, Minneapolis, MN 55410

North Amer. Warmblood Assn. **[★4561]**

North Amer. Waterfowlers **[★4159]**

North Amer. Weed Mgt. Assn. **[3746]**, PO Box 687, Meade, KS 67864, (620)873-8730

North Amer. Weed Mgt. Assn. **[3746]**, PO Box 687, Meade, KS 67864, (620)873-8730

North Amer. Wensleydale Sheep Assn. **[4920]**, 4589 Fruitland Rd., Loma Rica, CA 95901, (530)745-5262

North Amer. Wensleydale Sheep Assn. **[4920]**, 4589 Fruitland Rd., Loma Rica, CA 95901, (530)745-5262

North Amer. Wholesale Lumber Assn. **[1471]**, 3601 Algonquin Rd., Ste. 400, Rolling Meadows, IL 60008, (847)870-7470

North Amer. Wildlife Enforcement Officers Assn. **[5097]**, Steve Kleiner, Sec.-Treas., PO Box 22, Hollidaysburg, PA 16648, (801)942-9432

North Amer. Wildlife Found. **[★5044]**

North Amer. Wildlife Park Found. **[5098]**, Wolf Park, 4004 E 800 N, Battle Ground, IN 47920, (765)567-2265

North Amer. Wolf Assn. **[5099]**, Indigo Mountain Nature Center, PO Box 208, Lake George, CO 80827, (719)748-5550

North Amer. Working Bouvier Assn. **[21623]**, 1677 Dexter St., Broomfield, CO 80020, (303)520-0924

North Amer. World Music Coalition - Address unknown since 2011.

North Amer. Yacht Racing Union **[★22406]**

North Amer. YMCA Development Org. **[13501]**, 21 Chateau Trianon Dr., Kenner, LA 70065, (504)464-7845

North Amer. YMCA Development Org. **[13501]**, 21 Chateau Trianon Dr., Kenner, LA 70065, (504)464-7845

North Amer. Yngling Assn. **[★22412]**

North Amer. Young Generation in Nuclear **[7168]**, PO Box 32642, Charlotte, NC 28232-2642

North America's Corridor Coalition **[3532]**, 901 Main St., Ste. 4400, Dallas, TX 75202, (214)744-1042

North Atlantic Coun. **[IO]**, Brussels, Belgium

North Atlantic Salmon Conservation Org. **[IO]**, Edinburgh, United Kingdom

North Atlantic Treaty Org. **[IO]**, Brussels, Belgium

North Central Assn. Commn. on Accreditation and School Improvement **[8831]**, Arizona State Univ., PO Box 871008, Tempe, AZ 85287-1008, (800)525-9517

North Central Conf. on Summer Schools **[8936]**, Natalie Kokorudz, Sec.-Treas., Univ. of Illinois Chicago, 1333 S Halsted St., Ste. 225, MC 165, Chicago, IL 60607-5019, (312)413-9075

North Central Wholesalers Assn. **[2782]**, 3271 Springcrest Dr., Hamilton, OH 45011, (513)895-0695

North Country Trail Assn. **[23092]**, 229 E Main St., Lowell, MI 49331-1711, (616)897-5987

North Dakota Historical Soc. of Germans from Russia **[★19005]**

North Dakota Historical Soc. of Germans from Russia **[★19005]**

North Dakota State Univ. Alumni Assn. **[18889]**, 1241 N Univ. Dr., Fargo, ND 58102-2524, (701)231-6800

North-East Atlantic Fisheries Commn. **[IO]**, London, United Kingdom

North East Chamber of Commerce **[IO]**, Durham, United Kingdom

North Eastern Counties Welsh Pony and Cob Assn. **[IO]**, Durham, United Kingdom

North of England Inst. of Mining and Mech. Engineers **[IO]**, Newcastle upon Tyne, United Kingdom

North of England Zoological Soc. **[IO]**, Chester, United Kingdom

North Hampshire Chamber of Commerce and Indus. **[IO]**, Basingstoke, United Kingdom

North of Ireland Family History Soc. **[IO]**, Belfast, United Kingdom

North Korea Freedom Coalition **[18035]**, 9689 Main St., Ste. C, Fairfax, VA 22031, (703)503-0791

North Pacific Anadromous Fish Commn. **[IO]**, Vancouver, BC, Canada

North-South Inst. **[IO]**, Ottawa, ON, Canada

North South Roundtable - Defunct.

North-South Skirmish Assn. **[22885]**, PO Box 218, Crozet, VA 22932-0218

North Staffordshire Chamber of Commerce and Indus. **[IO]**, Stoke-on-Trent, United Kingdom

North Star Fund **[12598]**, 520 8th Ave., Rm. 2203, 36th and 37th St., New York, NY 10018, (212)620-9110

North West England and North Wales Narcotics Anonymous **[IO]**, Manchester, United Kingdom

North Yorkshire AIDS Action **[IO]**, York, United Kingdom

Northamerican Assn. of Masters in Psychology **[8763]**, PO Box 721270, Norman, OK 73070, (405)329-3030

Northamerican Assn. of Masters in Psychology **[8763]**, PO Box 721270, Norman, OK 73070, (405)329-3030

Northamerican Heating, Refrigeration and Airconditioning Wholesalers Association **[★1702]**

Northamerican Heating, Refrigeration, and Airconditioning Wholesalers Assn. **[★1702]**

Northamerican Heating, Refrigeration, and Airconditioning Wholesalers Assn. - Defunct.

Northamerican Ingredient Marketing Specialists **[★1422]**

Northamptonshire Chamber of Commerce **[IO]**, Northampton, United Kingdom

Northeast Conf. on the Teaching of Foreign Languages **[8481]**, Dickinson Coll., PO Box 1773, Carlisle, PA 17013-2896, (717)245-1977

Northeast-Midwest Inst. **[18481]**, 50 F St. NW, Ste. 950, Washington, DC 20001, (202)464-4014

Northeast-Midwest Senate Coalition **[18482]**, Northeast Midwest Inst., 50 F St. NW, Ste. 950, Washington, DC 20001, (202)464-4014

Northeast Organic Farming Assn. - Defunct.

Northeast Sustainable Energy Assn. **[6745]**, 50 Miles St., Greenfield, MA 01301, (413)774-6051

Northeast Waterfowl Comm. **[★5030]**

Northeastern Bird-Banding Assn. **[★7193]**

Northeastern Gay and Lesbian Alumni/ae Assn. **[★18888]**

Northeastern Loggers Assn. **[1472]**, PO Box 69, Old Forge, NY 13420, (315)369-3078

Northeastern Lumber Mfrs. Assn. **[1514]**, PO Box 87A, Cumberland, ME 04021, (207)829-6901

Northeastern Retail Lumber Assn. **[1515]**, 585 N Greenbush Rd., Rensselaer, NY 12144, (518)286-1010

Northeastern Retail Lumberman's Assn. **[★1515]**

Northeastern Spoon Collectors Guild **[21390]**, PO Box 12072, Albany, NY 12212

Northeastern Weed Sci. Soc. **[4682]**, PO Box 307, Fredericksburg, PA 17026, (717)787-7204

Northeastern Wood Utilization Coun. **[★1472]**

Northern Alberta Brain Injury Soc. **[IO]**, Edmonton, AB, Canada

Northern Frontier Visitors Assn. **[IO]**, Yellowknife, NT, Canada

Northern Ireland

    Doors of Hope **[18006]**

Northern Ireland Archery Soc. **[IO]**, Craigavon, United Kingdom

Northern Ireland Assn. for Mental Hea. **[IO]**, Belfast, United Kingdom

---

A star before a book entry number signifies that the name is not listed separately, but is mentioned within the entry.

Northern Ireland Bat Gp. [IO], Newtownabbey, United Kingdom

Northern Ireland Chamber of Commerce and Indus. [IO], Belfast, United Kingdom

Northern Ireland Chest Heart and Stroke Assn. [IO], Belfast, United Kingdom

Northern Ireland Fed. of Housing Associations [IO], Belfast, United Kingdom

Northern Ireland Food and Drink Assn. [IO], Belfast, United Kingdom

Northern Ireland Grain Trade Assn. [IO], Moira, United Kingdom

Northern Ireland Hotels Fed. [IO], Belfast, United Kingdom

Northern Ireland Human Rights Commn. [IO], Belfast, United Kingdom

Northern Ireland Local Govt. Assn. [IO], Belfast, United Kingdom

Northern Ireland Meat Exporters Assn. [IO], Lisburn, United Kingdom

Northern Ireland Mixed Marriage Assn. [IO], Belfast, United Kingdom

Northern Ireland Orienteering Assn. [IO], Lisburn, United Kingdom

Northern Ireland Public Ser. Alliance [IO], Belfast, United Kingdom

Northern Libraries Colloquy [★10004]

Northern Libraries Colloquy [★10004]

Northern Mariana Islands Coun. for the Humanities [IO], Saipan, Northern Mariana Islands

Northern Mariana Islands Tennis Assn. [IO], Saipan, Northern Mariana Islands

Northern Marianas Amateur Sports Assn. [IO], Saipan, Northern Mariana Islands

Northern Marianas Athletics [IO], Saipan, Northern Mariana Islands

Northern Marianas Islands Volleyball Assn. [IO], Saipan, Northern Mariana Islands

Northern Marianas Judo Assn. [IO], Saipan, Northern Mariana Islands

Northern Marianas Protection and Advocacy Systems, Inc. [IO], Saipan, Northern Mariana Islands

Northern Marianas Weightlifting Assn. [IO], Saipan, Northern Mariana Islands

Northern Michigan Univ. Alumni Assn. [18890], 1401 Presque Isle Ave., Marquette, MI 49855, (906)227-2610

Northern Nut Growers Assn. [4754], William Sachs, Treas., PO Box 6216, Hamden, CT 06517-0216

Northern Nut Growers Assn. [IO], Niagara-on-the-Lake, ON, Canada

Northern Rockies Alaska Highway Tourism Assn. [IO], Fort St. John, BC, Canada

Northern Sash and Door Jobbers Assn. [★531]

Northern Shipowners' Defence Club [IO], Oslo, Norway

Northern Textile Assn. [★3451]

Northern Trail Horse Riders Club [IO], Watervale, Australia

Northhamptonshire Chamber of Commerce, Training and Enterprise [★20639]

Northland Miniature Horse Club [IO], Dargaville, New Zealand

Northwest Accreditation Commn. [8055], 1510 Robert St., Ste. 103, Boise, ID 83705, (208)493-5077

Northwest Alaska Native Assn. [★12562]

Northwest Assn. of Accredited Schools [★8055]

Northwest Assn. of Accredited Schools [8055], 1510 Robert St., Ste. 103, Boise, ID 83705, (208)493-5077

Northwest Assn. of Schools and Colleges [★8055]

Northwest Assn. of Schools and Colleges [★8055]

Northwest Assn. of Schools and Colleges Commn. on Schools [★8055]

Northwest Assn. of Schools and Colleges Commn. on Schools [★8055]

Northwest Assn. of Secondary and Higher Schools [★8055]

Northwest Assn. of Secondary and Higher Schools [★8055]

Northwest Atlantic Fisheries Org. [IO], Dartmouth, NS, Canada

Northwest Cartoonists Assn. [★9285]

Northwest Cherry Growers [4465], 105 S 18th St., Ste. 205, Yakima, WA 98901-2149, (509)453-4837

Northwest Coalition for Alternatives to Pesticides [13325], PO Box 1393, Eugene, OR 97440-1393, (541)344-5044

Northwest Ecosystem Alliance [★4247]

Northwest Energy Efficiency Alliance [4229], 421 SW 6th Ave., Ste. 600, Portland, OR 97204, (503)688-5400

Northwest Farm Managers Assn. - Address unknown since 2011.

Northwest Fisheries Assn. [3186], 2208 NW Market St., Ste. 318, Seattle, WA 98107, (206)789-6197

Northwest Forestry Assn. [1473], 1500 SW 1st Ave., Ste. 700, Portland, OR 97201, (503)222-9505

Northwest Hardwood Assn. [★1490]

Northwest Horticultural Coun. [4466], 105 S 18th St., Ste. 105, Yakima, WA 98901, (509)453-3193

Northwest Marine Indus. [★2367]

Northwest Marine Trade Assn. [2367], 1900 N Northlake Way, No. 233, Seattle, WA 98103-9087, (206)634-0911

Northwest Medical Teams Intl. [★12866]

Northwest Medical Teams Intl. [★12866]

Northwest Mining Assn. [2515], 10 N Post St., Ste. 305, Spokane, WA 99201, (509)624-1158

Northwest Nazarene Univ. Alumni Assn. [18891], 623 Holly St., Nampa, ID 83686, (208)467-8011

Northwest Pine Assn. [★1473]

Northwest Regional Spinners' Assn. [21460], 22440 SE, 419th St., Enumclaw, WA 98022, (360)825-1634

Northwest Schooner Soc. [22382], PO Box 75421, Seattle, WA 98175, (206)577-7233

Northwest Steam Soc. [22156], PO Box 73, Hansville, WA 98340-0073, (206)310-4565

Northwest Territory Alliance [9118], 8417 Adbeth Ave., Woodridge, IL 60517

Northwest Territory, Canadian and French Heritage Center [★20628]

Northwest Territory, Canadian and French Heritage Center [★20628]

Northwestern Lumber Assn. [1474], 5905 Golden Valley Rd., No. 110, Minneapolis, MN 55422, (763)544-6822

Northwestern Lumbermen's Assn. [★1474]

Norway

   Norwegian Lundehund Assn. of Am. [21625]

Norway-America Assn. [IO], Oslo, Norway

Norwegian

   Innovation Norway - U.S. [23368]

   Norwegian-American Historical Assn. [10339]

   Norwegian-American Historical Assn. [10339]

   Norwegian Forest Cat Breed Coun. [21255]

   Norwegian Lundehund Assn. of Am. [21625]

   Sons of Norway [19180]

   Sons of Norway [19180]

Norwegian Acad. of Sci. and Letters [IO], Oslo, Norway

Norwegian Acad. of Technological Sciences [IO], Trondheim, Norway

Norwegian Actors' Equity Assn. [IO], Oslo, Norway

Norwegian Acupuncture Assn. [IO], Oslo, Norway

Norwegian Aero Club [IO], Oslo, Norway

Norwegian Aikido Fed. [IO], Broettum, Norway

Norwegian-American Chamber of Commerce [23377], 655 3rd Ave., Ste. 1810, New York, NY 10017, (212)885-9737

Norwegian-American Chamber of Commerce [23377], 655 3rd Ave., Ste. 1810, New York, NY 10017, (212)885-9737

Norwegian Amer. Genealogical Center [20651], 415 W Main St., Madison, WI 53703, (608)255-2224

Norwegian-American Historical Assn. [10339], 1510 St. Olaf Ave., Northfield, MN 55057-1097, (507)786-3221

Norwegian-American Historical Assn. [10339], 1510 St. Olaf Ave., Northfield, MN 55057-1097, (507)786-3221

Norwegian Assn. of Advertisers [IO], Oslo, Norway

Norwegian Assn. of Agricultural Journalists [IO], Oslo, Norway

Norwegian Assn. for Energy Economics [IO], Stavanger, Norway

Norwegian Assn. of Geomorphologists [IO], Blindern, Norway

Norwegian Assn. of Landscape Architects [IO], Oslo, Norway

Norwegian Assn. of Literary Translators [IO], Oslo, Norway

Norwegian Assn. of Municipal Engineers [IO], Oslo, Norway

Norwegian Assn. of Occupational Therapists [IO], Oslo, Norway

Norwegian Assn. of Res. Workers [IO], Oslo, Norway

Norwegian Assn. of Special Libraries [IO], Oslo, Norway

Norwegian Asthma and Allergy Assn. [IO], Oslo, Norway

Norwegian Astronautical Soc. [IO], Oslo, Norway

Norwegian Athletics Fed. [IO], Oslo, Norway

Norwegian Authors' Union [IO], Oslo, Norway

Norwegian Bandy Federation/Floorball Sect. [IO], Oslo, Norway

Norwegian Bible Soc. [IO], Oslo, Norway

Norwegian Billiard Fed. [IO], Oslo, Norway

Norwegian Biochemical Soc. [IO], Oslo, Norway

Norwegian Bioindustry Assn. [IO], Oslo, Norway

Norwegian Botanical Soc. [IO], Oslo, Norway

Norwegian Br. of the Intl. Law Assn. [IO], Oslo, Norway

Norwegian Brewers and Soft Drink Producers [IO], Oslo, Norway

Norwegian Bus. Gp. [IO], Dubai, United Arab Emirates

Norwegian Cable-TV Assn. [IO], Fetsund, Norway

Norwegian Canoe Assn. [IO], Oslo, Norway

Norwegian Church Aid [IO], Oslo, Norway

Norwegian Coun. for Cultural Affairs [IO], Oslo, Norway

Norwegian Coun. On Cardiovascular Diseases [IO], Oslo, Norway

Norwegian Cystic Fibrosis Assn. [IO], Oslo, Norway

Norwegian Defence and Security Indus. Assn. [IO], Oslo, Norway

Norwegian Dental Assn. [IO], Oslo, Norway

Norwegian Dermatological Soc. [IO], Oslo, Norway

Norwegian Diabetes Assn. [IO], Oslo, Norway

Norwegian Electrotechnical Comm. [IO], Lysaker, Norway

Norwegian Elkhound Assn. of Am. [21624], Margaret Williamson, Corresponding Sec., PO Box 932, Imperial Beach, CA 91933

Norwegian Epilepsy Assn. [IO], Oslo, Norway

Norwegian Farmers' Union [IO], Oslo, Norway

Norwegian Fed. of Organisations of Disabled People [IO], Oslo, Norway

Norwegian Fibromyalgia Patients' Assn. [IO], Drammen, Norway

Norwegian Fishermen's Sales Org. for Pelagic Fish [IO], Bergen, Norway

Norwegian Fjord Horse Registry [4633], 1801 W County Rd. 4, Berthoud, CO 80513, (303)684-6466

Norwegian Football Assn. [IO], Oslo, Norway

Norwegian Forest Cat Breed Coun. [21255], 260 E Main St., Alliance, OH 44601, (330)680-4070

Norwegian Formation Evaluation Soc. [IO], Stavanger, Norway

Norwegian Fur Breeders' Assn. [IO], Oslo, Norway

Norwegian Genealogical Soc. [IO], Oslo, Norway

Norwegian Geotechnical Inst. [IO], Oslo, Norway

Norwegian Geotechnical Soc. [IO], Oslo, Norway

Norwegian Gerontological Soc. [IO], Oslo, Norway

Norwegian Heraldic Assn. [IO], Oslo, Norway

Norwegian Hospitality Assn. [IO], Oslo, Norway

Norwegian Immunodeficiency Org. [IO], Alesund, Norway

Norwegian Independent Meat Assn. [IO], Oslo, Norway

Norwegian Inst. of Intl. Affairs [IO], Oslo, Norway

Norwegian Inst. of Local History [IO], Oslo, Norway

Norwegian Inst. of Public Accountants [IO], Oslo, Norway

Norwegian Inst. for Urban and Regional Res. [IO], Oslo, Norway

Norwegian Inventors' Assn. [IO], Stavanger, Norway

Norwegian Labour Party [IO], Oslo, Norway

Norwegian Lib. Assn. [IO], Oslo, Norway

Norwegian Literature Abroad [IO], Oslo, Norway

Norwegian Luge, Bobsleigh and Skeleton Fed. [IO], Oslo, Norway

Reference to "IO" in place of a book number signifies that the association may be found in the 50th edition of International Organizations.

Reference to "IO" in place of a book number signifies that the association may be found in the 50th edition of International Organizations.

Norwegian Lundehund Assn. of Am. [21625], Sue St. Cyr, 9932 Spring Beauty, San Antonio, TX 78254

Norwegian Martial Arts Fed. [IO], Oslo, Norway

Norwegian Media Businesses' Assn. [IO], Oslo, Norway

Norwegian Medical Assn. [IO], Oslo, Norway

Norwegian Multiple Sclerosis Soc. [IO], Oslo, Norway

Norwegian Neuroscience Soc. [IO], Oslo, Norway

Norwegian Non-Fiction Writers and Translators Assn. [IO], Oslo, Norway

Norwegian Nurses Org. [IO], Oslo, Norway

Norwegian Oil Indus. Assn. [IO], Stavanger, Norway

Norwegian Oil Spill Control Assn. [IO], Horten, Norway

Norwegian Olympic and Paralympic Comm. and Confed. of Sports [IO], Oslo, Norway

Norwegian Operations Res. [IO], Oslo, Norway

Norwegian Org. for Children and Youth with Rheumatism [IO], Oslo, Norway

Norwegian Org. of Interior Architects and Furniture Designers [IO], Oslo, Norway

Norwegian Osteogenesis Imperfecta Found. [IO], Oslo, Norway

Norwegian Ostomy Assn. [IO], Oslo, Norway

Norwegian Parkinson Assn. [IO], Oslo, Norway

Norwegian Peace Assn. [IO], Oslo, Norway

Norwegian Peace Coun. [IO], Oslo, Norway

Norwegian PEN [IO], Oslo, Norway

Norwegian Physical Soc. [IO], Bergen, Norway

Norwegian Physiotherapist Assn. [IO], Oslo, Norway

Norwegian Playwrights' Assn. [IO], Oslo, Norway

Norwegian Press Assn. [IO], Oslo, Norway

Norwegian Proj. Mgt. Assn. [IO], Oslo, Norway

Norwegian Proj. Office/Rural Rehabilitation Assn. for Afghanistan [IO], Kabul, Afghanistan

Norwegian Psoriasis Assn. [IO], Oslo, Norway

Norwegian Psychological Assn. [IO], Oslo, Norway

Norwegian Publishers' Assn. [IO], Oslo, Norway

Norwegian Raw Fish Org. [IO], Tromso, Norway

Norwegian Rheumatism Assn. [IO], Oslo, Norway

Norwegian Rose Soc. [IO], Holmsbu, Norway

Norwegian Route 66 Assn. [IO], Radal, Norway

Norwegian Seafood Assn. [IO], Trondheim, Norway

Norwegian Seafood Fed. [IO], Oslo, Norway

Norwegian Sect. of the Intl. Confed. for Electroacoustic Music [IO], Oslo, Norway

Norwegian Shipowners' Assn. [IO], Oslo, Norway

Norwegian Soc. for Biomedical Engg. [IO], Harstad, Norway

Norwegian Soc. of Cardiology [IO], Oslo, Norway

Norwegian Soc. of Chartered Tech. and Sci. Professionals [IO], Oslo, Norway

Norwegian Soc. of Composers [IO], Oslo, Norway

Norwegian Soc. for the Conservation of Nature/ Friends of the Earth Norway [IO], Oslo, Norway

Norwegian Soc. of Dermatology [IO], Oslo, Norway

Norwegian Soc. of Engineers and Technologists [IO], Oslo, Norway

Norwegian Soc. of Financial Analysts [IO], Oslo, Norway

Norwegian Soc. for Immunology [IO], Oslo, Norway

Norwegian Soc. for Medical Informatics [IO], Oslo, Norway

Norwegian Soc. of Pharmacology and Toxicology [IO], Oslo, Norway

Norwegian Soc. for Quality in Healthcare [IO], Horten, Norway

Norwegian Soc. for Virology [IO], Bergen, Norway

Norwegian Squash Assn. [IO], Stavanger, Norway

Norwegian Tennis Assn. [IO], Oslo, Norway

Norwegian Trade Coun. [★23368]

Norwegian Trade Coun. [★23368]

Norwegian Trade Coun. - U.S. [★23368]

Norwegian Trade Coun. - United States [★23368]

Norwegian Trekking Assn. [IO], Oslo, Norway

Norwegian Union of Journalists [IO], Oslo, Norway

Norwegian Venture Capital and Private Equity Assn. [IO], Oslo, Norway

Norwegian Veterinary Assn. [IO], Oslo, Norway

Norwegian Women and Family Assn. [IO], Oslo, Norway

Norwegian Wood - Den norske Beatlesklubben [★IO]

Norwegian Wood - The Beatles Fan Club of Norway [IO], Oslo, Norway

Norwegian Writers for Children [IO], Oslo, Norway

Norwich Campaign for Nuclear Disarmament [IO], Norwich, United Kingdom

Norwich and Norfolk Terrier Club - Address unknown since 2010.

Noshaq [12958], PO Box 296, Collegedale, TN 37315, (423)615-9227

Noshaq [12958], PO Box 296, Collegedale, TN 37315, (423)615-9227

Nosk Gruppe for Geomorfologes [★IO]

Not-For-Profit Services Assn. [50], 624 Grassmere Park Dr., Ste. 15, Nashville, TN 37211, (615)377-3392

Not Forgotten Assn. [IO], London, United Kingdom

Not on Our Watch [17857], 162 5th Ave., 8th Fl., New York, NY 10010

Notaries Public

Amer. Soc. of Notaries [5867]

Natl. Notary Assn. [5868]

Notion Round Table - Defunct.

notMYkid [13548], 5230 E Shea Blvd., Ste. 100, Scottsdale, AZ 85254, (602)652-0163

Nourish Am. [15842], PO Box 567, Ojai, CA 93024, (805)715-2693

Nourish Intl. [11075], 133 1/2 E Franklin St., Ste. 105, Chapel Hill, NC 27514, (919)338-2599

Nouveau Parti Democratique du Canada [★IO]

NOVA Hope for Haiti [12474], 176 Palisade Ave., Emerson, NJ 07630, (201)675-9413

Nova Scotia Arm Wrestling Assn. [IO], Lower Sackville, NS, Canada

Nova Scotia Assn. of Naturopathic Doctors [IO], Halifax, NS, Canada

Nova Scotia Curling Assn. [IO], Halifax, NS, Canada

Nova Scotia Equestrian Fed. [IO], Halifax, NS, Canada

Nova Scotia Hospice Palliative Care Assn. [IO], Truro, NS, Canada

Nova Scotia Lib. Assn. [IO], Halifax, NS, Canada

Nova Scotia Salmon Assn. [IO], Chester, NS, Canada

Nova Scotia Snowboard Assn. [IO], Halifax, NS, Canada

Nova Scotia Trails Fed. [IO], Halifax, NS, Canada

Novelists, Inc. [3710], PO Box 2037, Manhattan, KS 66505

Novell Users Intl. [3393], 404 Wyman St., Waltham, MA 02451, (801)861-4272

Novelty Salt and Pepper Shakers Club [21391], 16468 W Juniper Ct., Surprise, AZ 85387, (623)975-6870

November Coalition [18681], 282 W Astor Ave., Colville, WA 99114, (509)684-1550

Now Christian Freedom Intl. [★20210]

Now Christian Freedom Intl. [★20210]

NOW Legal Comm. [★17653]

NOW Legal Defense and Educ. Fund [★17653]

NOWZUWAN [IO], Chittagong, Bangladesh

NPES: Assn. for Suppliers of Printing, Publishing and Converting Technologies [1624], 1899 Preston White Dr., Reston, VA 20191, (703)264-7200

NPTA Alliance [2620], 401 N Michigan Ave., Ste. 2200, Chicago, IL 60611, (312)321-4092

NRN Natl. Coordination Coun. of U.S. [19173], 2036 S Church St., Murfreesboro, TN 37130

NROTC Colleges and Universities; Assn. of [8624]

NSAC, The Natl. Soc. for Children and Adults with Autism [★13786]

NSF Intl. [16493], 789 N Dixboro Rd., PO Box 130140, Ann Arbor, MI 48113-0140, (734)769-8010

NSF Intl. [16493], 789 N Dixboro Rd., PO Box 130140, Ann Arbor, MI 48113-0140, (734)769-8010

NSGA Team Dealer Div. - Address unknown since 2010.

NSO of COSA [★13082]

NSO of COSA [★13082]

NSU Enthusiasts U.S.A. - Address unknown since 2010.

NSW Bus. Chamber [IO], North Sydney, Australia

NSW Fed. of Housing Associations [IO], Surry Hills, Australia

NSW Ferret Welfare Soc. [IO], Dee Why, Australia

NSW Right to Life Assn. [IO], Sydney, Australia

NSX Club of Am. [21138], 333 Mamaroneck Ave., PMB No. 399, White Plains, NY 10605, (877)679-2582

NTID's Center on Employment [11954], Rochester Inst. of Tech., Lyndon Baines Johnson Bldg., 52 Lomb Memorial Dr., Rochester, NY 14623-5604, (585)475-6219

NTL Inst. [★8178]

NTL Inst. [★8178]

NTL Inst. for Applied Behavioral Sciences [8178], 1901 S Bell St., Ste. 300, Arlington, VA 22202, (703)548-8840

NTL Inst. for Applied Behavioral Sciences [8178], 1901 S Bell St., Ste. 300, Arlington, VA 22202, (703)548-8840

Nubian United Benevolent Intl. Assn. [12787], 2 Tufts St., Charlestown, MA 02129, (617)669-2642

Nuclear

Amer. Coun. on Global Nuclear Competitiveness [7174]

Amer. Glovebox Soc. [7163]

Amer. Nuclear Soc. [7164]

Beyond Nuclear [18192]

Citizens to Stop Nuclear Terrorism [18711]

Clean and Safe Energy Coalition [6707]

Focus Fusion Soc. [6725]

IEEE | Nuclear and Plasma Sciences Soc. [7165]

Inst. of Nuclear Materials Mgt. [7166]

Intl. Panel on Fissile Materials [18203]

Middle Powers Initiative [17554]

Natl. Org. of Test, Res., and Training Reactors [7167]

North Amer. Young Generation in Nuclear [7168]

Nuclear Info. and Records Mgt. Assn. [7169]

Nuclear Info. Tech. Strategic Leadership [7170]

Nuclear Suppliers Assn. [7171]

Partnership for Global Security [18600]

Professional Reactor Operator Soc. [7172]

Radiochemistry Soc. [6418]

Soc. of Nuclear Medicine Technologist Sect. [15697]

United Against Nuclear Iran [18218]

U.S. Women in Nuclear [7173]

Nuclear Age Peace Found. [18270], 1187 Coast Village Rd., Ste. 1, PMB 121, Santa Barbara, CA 93108-2794, (805)965-3443

Nuclear Age Peace Found. [18270], 1187 Coast Village Rd., Ste. 1, PMB 121, Santa Barbara, CA 93108-2794, (805)965-3443

Nuclear Age Rsrc. Center [★18198]

Nuclear Club [★18210]

Nuclear Control Inst. [18210], 1000 Connecticut Ave. NW, Ste. 400, Washington, DC 20036, (202)822-8444

Nuclear Energy

Alliance for Nuclear Accountability [18180]

Amer. Coun. on Global Nuclear Competitiveness [7174]

Beyond Nuclear [18192]

Clean and Safe Energy Coalition [6707]

Comm. for Nuclear Responsibility [18181]

Comm. for Nuclear Responsibility [18181]

Inst. of Nuclear Power Operations [7175]

Natl. Org. of Test, Res., and Training Reactors [7167]

Nuclear Energy Info. Ser. [18182]

Nuclear Info. and Rsrc. Ser. [18183]

Nuclear Info. Tech. Strategic Leadership [7170]

Nukewatch [18184]

Public Citizen's Critical Mass Energy and Env. Prog. [18185]

Three Mile Island Alert [18186]

Union of Concerned Scientists [18187]

U.S. Women in Nuclear [7173]

We the People [18188]

Western Interstate Energy Bd. [18189]

Nuclear Energy Info. Ser. [18182], 3411 W Diversey Ave., No. 16, Chicago, IL 60647, (773)342-7650

Nuclear Energy Inst. [6746], 1776 I St. NW, Ste. 400, Washington, DC 20006-3708, (202)739-8000

Nuclear Free Philippines Coalition [IO], Quezon City, Philippines

Nuclear Info. and Records Mgt. Assn. [7169], 10 Almas Rd., Windham, NH 03087-1105, (603)432-6476

A star before a book entry number signifies that the name is not listed separately, but is mentioned within the entry.

Nuclear Info. and Rsrc. Ser. [18183], 6930 Carroll Ave., Ste. 340, Takoma Park, MD 20912, (301)270-6477

Nuclear Info. Tech. Strategic Leadership [7170], PO Box 262, Mohnton, PA 19540, (610)880-0055

Nuclear Inst. [IO], London, United Kingdom

Nuclear Mgt. and Resources Coun. [★6746]

Nuclear Medicine
Amer. Bd. of Nuclear Medicine [15691]
Amer. Bd. of Sci. in Nuclear Medicine [15692]
Amer. Coll. of Nuclear Medicine [15693]
Chinese-American Soc. of Nuclear Medicine [15694]
Chinese-American Soc. of Nuclear Medicine [15694]
Nuclear Medicine Tech. Certification Bd. [15695]
Soc. of Nuclear Medicine [15696]
Soc. of Nuclear Medicine Technologist Sect. [15697]

Nuclear Medicine Soc. of Thailand [IO], Bangkok, Thailand

Nuclear Medicine Tech. Certification Bd. [15695], 3558 Habersham at Northlake, Bldg. I, Tucker, GA 30084, (404)315-1739

Nuclear Network [★18601]
Nuclear Network [★18601]
Nuclear Records Mgt. Assn. [★7169]
Nuclear Safety Standards Commn. [IO], Salzgitter, Germany
Nuclear Steam Sys. Supply [★7169]
Nuclear Suppliers Assn. [7171], PO Box 1354, Westerly, RI 02891, (401)637-4224

Nuclear Threat Initiative [18211], 1747 Pennsylvania Ave. NW, 7th Fl., Washington, DC 20006, (202)296-4810

Nuclear Threat Reduction Campaign [18212], Veterans for Am., 1025 Vermont Ave. NW, 7th Fl., Washington, DC 20005, (202)483-9222

Nuclear War and Weapons
ALEPH: Alliance for Jewish Renewal [18190]
ALEPH: Alliance for Jewish Renewal [18190]
Architects/Designers/Planners for Social Responsibility [18191]
Beyond Nuclear [18192]
Citizens to Stop Nuclear Terrorism [18711]
Comm. to Bridge the Gap [18193]
Cmpt. Professionals for Social Responsibility [18194]
Concerned Citizens for Nuclear Safety [18195]
Concerned Educators Allied for a Safe Env. [18196]
Corporate Accountability Intl. [18197]
Corporate Accountability Intl. [18197]
Daisy Alliance [18239]NuclearDownwinders
Global Issues Rsrc. Center [18198]
Global Network Against Weapons and Nuclear Power in Space [18199]
Global Security Inst. [18200]
Global Security Inst. [18200]
Grandmothers for Peace Intl. [18201]
Grandmothers for Peace Intl. [18201]
High Frontier Org. [18678]
Inst. for Space and Security Stud. [18202]
Intl. Panel on Fissile Materials [18203]
Intl. Panel on Fissile Materials [18203]
Intl. Philosophers for the Prevention of Nuclear Omnicide [18204]
Intl. Philosophers for the Prevention of Nuclear Omnicide [18204]
Intl. Physicians for the Prevention of Nuclear War [18205]
Intl. Physicians for the Prevention of Nuclear War [18205]
Lawyers Alliance for World Security [18206]
Lawyers Alliance for World Security [18206]
Lawyers' Comm. on Nuclear Policy [18207]
Middle Powers Initiative [17554]
Natl. No-Nukes Prison Support Collective [18208]
Natl. No-Nukes Prison Support Collective [18208]
Nevada Desert Experience [18209]NuclearNever Again Campaign
Nuclear Control Inst. [18210]
Nuclear Threat Initiative [18211]
Nuclear Threat Reduction Campaign [18212]
Nukewatch [18184]

Partnership for Global Security [18600]
Peace Action [18213]
Peace Action Educ. Fund [18214]
Peace Pac [18215]
Physicians for Social Responsibility [18216]
Physicians for Social Responsibility [18216]
Prevent Nuclear Terrorism Org. [18718]
Psychologists for Social Responsibility [18217]
United Against Nuclear Iran [18218]
UrgentCall.org [18219]
WAND Educ. Fund [18220]
Western States Legal Found. [5869]
Women's Action for New Directions [18221]
Nuclear Weapons Freeze Campaign [★18213]

Nudism
Amer. Assn. for Nude Recreation [10340]
Beach Educ. Advocates for Culture, Hea., Env. and Safety [10341]
BeachFront USA [10342]
The Naturist Soc. [10343]

Nuestros Pequenos Hermanos [IO], Milan, Italy
Nuestros Pequenos Hermanos Intl. [20077], PO Box 3134, Alexandria, VA 22302, (703)836-1233
Nuffield Coun. on Bioethics [IO], London, United Kingdom
Nujeen For Family Democratizing Org. [IO], Duhok, Iraq
Nukewatch [18184], 740-A Round Lake Rd., Luck, WI 54853, (715)472-4185
NumbersUSA [18483], 1601 N Kent St., Ste. 1100, Arlington, VA 22209, (703)816-8820
Numerical Control Soc./AIM Tech - Defunct.

Numismatic
American-Israel Numismatic Assn. [21962]
Amer. Numismatic Assn. [21963]
Amer. Numismatic Soc. [21964]
Amer. Soc. of Check Collectors [21965]
Amer. Tax Token Soc. [21966]
Ancient Coin Collectors Guild [21967]
Ancient Coins for Educ. [8685]
Armenian Numismatic Soc. [21968]
Canadian Assn. of Wooden Money Collectors [16549]
Challenge Coin Assn. [21969]
Civil War Token Soc. [21970]
Colonial Coin Collectors Club [21971]
Combined Organizations of Numismatic Error Collectors of Am. [21972]
Cuban Numismatic Assn. [21973]
Early Amer. Coppers [21974]
The Elongated Collectors [21975]
Intl. Bank Note Soc. [21976]
John Reich Collectors Soc. [21977]
Latin Amer. Paper Money Soc. [21978]
Liberty Seated Collectors Club [21979]
Love Token Soc. [21980]
Medal Collectors of Am. [21981]
Natl. Collectors Assn. of Die Doubling [21982]
Natl. Token Collectors Assn. [21983]
North Amer. Collectors [21984]
Numismatic Bibliomania Soc. [21985]
Numismatic Literary Guild [21986]
Numismatics Intl. [21987]
Numismatics Intl. [21987]
One Cent Intl. [21988]
One Cent Intl. [21988]
Original Hobo Nickel Soc. [21989]
Professional Currency Dealers Assn. [21990]
Professional Numismatists Guild [21991]
Russian Numismatic Soc. [21992]
Soc. of Paper Money Collectors [21993]
Soc. of U.S. Pattern Collectors [21994]
Token and Medal Soc. [21995]
U.S. Mexican Numismatic Assn. [21996]
Unrecognised States Numismatic Soc. [21997]
World Internet Numismatic Soc. [21998]
World Internet Numismatic Soc. [21998]
World Proof Numismatic Assn. [21999]
World Proof Numismatic Assn. [21999]
Numismatic Bibliomania Soc. [21985], PO Box 82, Littleton, NH 03561
Numismatic Error Collectors of Am. [★21972]
Numismatic Literary Guild [21986], 1517 Stewart Dr., Nanticoke, PA 18634
Numismatics Intl. [21987], PO Box 570842, Dallas, TX 75357-0842

Numismatics Intl. [21987], PO Box 570842, Dallas, TX 75357-0842
Nunatsinni Katersugaasiviit Kattuffiat [★IO]
Nunavut Tourism [IO], Nunavut, NT, Canada
Nuorten Naisten Kristillinen Yhdistys [★IO]
Nuova Lamborghini Club [★21090]
Nurse Anesthesia Overseas [★16044]
Nurse Anesthesia Overseas [★16044]
Nurse Healers Professional Associates [★15003]
Nurse Healers Professional Associates Intl. [★15003]
Nurse Practitioner Associates for Continuing Educ. [15787], 209 W Central St., Ste. 228, Natick, MA 01760, (508)907-6424

Nurseries
Amer. Nursery and Landscape Assn. [4740]
Amer. Penstemon Soc. [21779]
Garden Centers of Am. [4741]
The Gardeners of Am. [21794]
Horticultural Res. Inst. [4742]
Indoor Gardening Soc. of Am. [21801]
Natl. Day Nurseries Assn. [19544]
North Amer. Lily Soc. [21815]
Nursery and Landscape Assn. Executives of North Am. [4743]
Plumeria Soc. of Am. [21817]
Nursery Assn. Executives [★4743]
Nursery Assn. Executives of North Am. [★4743]
Nursery Assn. Secretaries [★4743]
Nursery and Garden Indus. Australia [IO], Epping, Australia
Nursery and Landscape Assn. Executives of North Am. [4743], 2130 Stella Ct., Columbus, OH 43215, (614)487-1117
Nurses Anonymous; Intl.
Nurses Assoc. Alumnae of U.S. and Canada [★15722]
Nurses Assn. of the Amer. Coll. of Obstetricians and Gynecologists [★15741]
Nurses Assn. of the Amer. Coll. of Obstetricians and Gynecologists [★15741]
Nurses Educational Funds [15788], 304 Park Ave. S, 11th Fl., New York, NY 10010, (212)590-2443
Nurses in Genetics; Intl. Soc. of [14650]
Nurses for a Healthier Tomorrow [15789], Honor Soc. of Nursing, Sigma Theta Tau Intl., 550 W North St., Indianapolis, IN 46202, (888)634-7575
Nurses' House [15790], 2113 Western Ave., Ste. 2, Guilderland, NY 12084-9559, (518)456-7858
Nurses' Hypertension Assn. [IO], London, United Kingdom
Nurses Org. of the Veterans Admin. [★15791]
Nurses Org. of Veterans Affairs [15791], 47595 Watkins Island Sq., Sterling, VA 20165, (703)444-5587
Nurses for the Rights of the Child [11523], 369 Montezuma Ave., No. 354, Santa Fe, NM 87501, (505)989-7377

Nursing
Acad. of Medical Surgical Nurses [15698]
Acad. of Spinal Cord Injury Professionals, Nurses Sect. [15699]
Air and Surface Transport Nurses Assn. [15700]
Alpha Tau Delta [23608]
Amer. Acad. of Ambulatory Care Nursing [15701]
Amer. Acad. of Medical Esthetic Professionals [15702]
Amer. Acad. of Nurse Practitioners [15703]
Amer. Acad. of Nursing [15704]
Amer. Assembly for Men in Nursing [15705]
Amer. Assisted Living Nurses Assn. [15706]
Amer. Assn. of Critical-Care Nurses [15707]
Amer. Assn. of Heart Failure Nurses [15708]
Amer. Assn. of Managed Care Nurses [15709]
Amer. Assn. of Neuroscience Nurses [15710]
Amer. Assn. of Neuroscience Nurses [15710]
Amer. Assn. of Nurse Anesthetists [15711]
Amer. Assn. of Nurse Life Care Planners [15712]
Amer. Assn. of Occupational Hea. Nurses [15713]
Amer. Bd. of Managed Care Nursing [15714]
Amer. Bd. of Neuroscience Nursing [15715]
Amer. Bd. of Nursing Specialties [15716]
Amer. Bd. for Occupational Hea. Nurses [15717]
Amer. Bd. of Perianesthesia Nursing Certification [15718]
Amer. Coll. of Nurse-Midwives [15719]

Reference to "IO" in place of a book number signifies that the association may be found in the 50th edition of International Organizations.

Encyclopedia of Associations, 51st Edition

3067

Amer. Coll. of Nurse Practitioners [15720]
Amer. Forensic Nurses [15721]
Amer. Nurses Assn. [15722]
Amer. Nurses Credentialing Center [15723]
Amer. Nurses Found. [15724]
Amer. Nursing Informatics Assn. [15725]
Amer. Org. of Nurse Executives [15726]
Amer. Pediatric Surgical Nurses Assn. [15727]
Amer. Psychiatric Nurses Assn. [15728]
Amer. Soc. of Ophthalmic Registered Nurses [15729]
Amer. Soc. for Pain Mgt. Nursing [15730]
Amer. Soc. of PeriAnesthesia Nurses [15731]
Amer. Soc. of PeriAnesthesia Nurses [15731]
Amer. Soc. of Plastic Surgical Nurses [15732]
Asian American/Pacific Islander Nurses Assn. [15733]
Asian American/Pacific Islander Nurses Assn. [15733]
Assn. of Camp Nurses [15734]
Assn. of Camp Nurses [15734]
Assn. of Child Neurology Nurses [15735]
Assn. of Child Neurology Nurses [15735]
Assn. of Community Hea. Nursing Educators [15736]
Assn. of Pediatric Hematology/Oncology Nurses [15737]
Assn. of PeriOperative Registered Nurses [15738]
Assn. of PeriOperative Registered Nurses [15738]
Assn. for Radiological and Imaging Nursing [15739]
Assn. of Rehabilitation Nurses [15740]
Assn. of Women's Hea., Obstetric and Neonatal Nurses [15741]
Assn. of Women's Hea., Obstetric and Neonatal Nurses [15741]
Baromedical Nurses Assn. [15742]
Canadian Fed. of Nurses Unions [12557]
Canadian Nurses Protective Soc. [13540]
Certification Bd. for Urologic Nurses and Associates [16944]
Certifying Bd. of Gastroenterology Nurses and Associates [15743]
Chi Eta Phi Sorority [23609]
Commn. on Graduates of Foreign Nursing Schools [15744]
Coun. of Intl. Neonatal Nurses [15745]
Democratic Nursing Org. of South Africa [5694]
Dermatology Nurses' Assn. [15746]
Developmental Disabilities Nurses Assn. [15747]
Fed. for Accessible Nursing Educ. and Licensure [15748]
Frontier Nursing Ser. [15749]
HealthShare Intl. [15750]
Helene Fuld Hea. Trust [15751]
Home Healthcare Nurses Assn. [15752]
Hospice and Palliative Nurses Assn. [15753]
Intl. Assn. of Forensic Nurses [15754]
Intl. Assn. of Forensic Nurses [15754]
Intl. Bilingual Nurses Alliance [15755]
Intl. Nurses Soc. on Addictions [15756]
Intl. Nurses Soc. on Addictions [15756]
Intl. Nursing Assn. for Clinical Simulation and Learning [15757]
Intl. Nursing Assn. for Clinical Simulation and Learning [15757]
Intl. Org. of Multiple Sclerosis Nurses [15758]
Intl. Org. of Multiple Sclerosis Nurses [15758]
Intl. Soc. of Psychiatric-Mental Hea. Nurses [15759]
Intl. Soc. of Psychiatric-Mental Hea. Nurses [15759]
Intl. Transplant Nurses Soc. [15760]
Intl. Transplant Nurses Soc. [15760]
NANDA Intl. [15761]
NANDA Intl. [15761]
Natl. Amer. Arab Nurses Assn. [15762]
Natl. Assn. of Catholic Nurses - U.S.A. [15763]
Natl. Assn. of Clinical Nurse Specialists [15764]
Natl. Assn. of Directors of Nursing Admin. in Long Term Care [15765]
Natl. Assn. of Hispanic Nurses [15766]
Natl. Assn. of Neonatal Nurses [15767]
Natl. Assn. of Nurse Massage Therapists [15768]
Natl. Assn. of Nurse Practitioners in Women's Hea. [15769]

Natl. Assn. of Orthopaedic Nurses [15770]
Natl. Assn. of Pediatric Nurse Practitioners [15771]
Natl. Assn. of School Nurses [15772]
Natl. Assn. of State School Nurse Consultants [15773]
Natl. Black Nurses Assn. [15774]
Natl. Bd. on Certification and Recertification of Nurse Anesthetists [15775]
Natl. Certification Corp. for the Obstetric, Gynecologic and Neonatal Nursing Specialties [15776]
Natl. Coalition of Ethnic Minority Nurse Associations [15777]
Natl. Coalition of Oncology Nurse Navigators [15778]
Natl. Coun. of State Boards of Nursing [15779]
Natl. Fed. of Licensed Practical Nurses [15780]
Natl. League for Nursing [15781]
Natl. Nursing Staff Development Org. [15782]
Natl. Org. for Associate Degree Nursing [15783]
Natl. Org. of Nurse Practitioners Faculties [15784]
Natl. Org. of Nurses with Disabilities [15785]
Navy Nurse Corps Assn. [15786]
Nurse Practitioner Associates for Continuing Educ. [15787]
Nurses Educational Funds [15788]
Nurses for a Healthier Tomorrow [15789]
Nurses' House [15790]
Nurses Org. of Veterans Affairs [15791]
Nurses for the Rights of the Child [11523]Nursing-Nursing Emergency Preparedness Educ. Coalition
Oncology Nursing Certification Corp. [15792]
Oncology Nursing Soc. [15793]
One Nurse At A Time [15794]
Pediatric Nursing Certification Bd. [15795]
Philippine Nurses Assn. of Am. [15796]
Preventive Cardiovascular Nurses Assn. [15797]
Respiratory Nursing Soc. [15798]
Sigma Theta Tau Intl. [23610]
Sigma Theta Tau Intl. [23610]
Soc. of Otorhinolaryngology and Head/Neck Nurses [15799]
Soc. of Pediatric Nurses [15800]
Soc. of Trauma Nurses [15801]
Soc. of Urologic Nurses and Associates [15802]
Soc. for Vascular Nursing [15803]
Transcultural Nursing Soc. [15804]
Transcultural Nursing Soc. [15804]
Univ. of Colorado Hea. Sciences Center Alumni Assn. [23547]
Vietnamese-American Nurses Assn. [15805]
Visiting Nurse Associations of Am. [15806]
Wound, Ostomy and Continence Nurses Soc.: An Assn. of E.T. Nurses [15807]
Wound, Ostomy and Continence Nurses Soc.: An Assn. of E.T. Nurses [15807]
Wound, Ostomy and Continence Nursing Certification Bd. [15808]
Nursing; Amer. Assn. for the History of [9742]
Nursing Emergency Preparedness Educ. Coalition
Nursing Emergency Preparedness Educ. Coalition - Defunct.
Nursing Home Information Service - National Council of Senior Citizens - Defunct.
Nursing Home Reform Coalition [★17465]
Nursing Home Reform; Natl. Citizens Coalition for [★17465]

Nursing Homes
Amer. Assn. of Caregiving Youth [13505]
Amer. Coll. of Hea. Care Administrators [15809]
Amer. Medical Directors Assn. [15810]
Center for the Stud. of Aging of Albany [10838]
Found. Aiding the Elderly [17458]
Natl. Assn. of Boards of Examiners of Long Term Care Administrators [15811]
Natl. Assn. of Professional Geriatric Care Managers [15812]
Nursing; Interagency Coun. on Info. Resources in [9988]
Nursing Mothers Counsel [11490], PO Box 5024, San Mateo, CA 94402-0024, (650)327-6455
Nursing Overseas [★16044]
Nursing Overseas [★16044]

NURTUREart Non-Profit [9247], 910 Grand St., Brooklyn, NY 11211, (718)782-7755
NURTUREart Non-Profit [9247], 910 Grand St., Brooklyn, NY 11211, (718)782-7755
The Nurturing Network [13472], PO Box 1489, White Salmon, WA 98672, (509)493-4026
Nuru Intl. [11076], 71 Manzanita Rd., Atherton, CA 94027, (949)366-6878
Nutraceutical Assn; Amer. [14754]
Nutrition
Advocates for Better Children's Diets [15813]
Amer. Assn. of Nutritional Consultants [15814]
Amer. Bd. of Nutrition [15815]
Amer. Bd. of Physician Nutrition Specialists [15816]
Amer. Celiac Society | Dietary Support Coalition [15817]
Amer. Coll. of Nutrition [15818]
Amer. Coll. of Nutrition [15818]
Amer. Dietetic Assn. [15819]
Amer. Nutrition Assn. [15820]
Amer. Soc. for Clinical Nutrition [15821]
Amer. Soc. for Nutrition [15822]
Amer. Soc. for Parenteral and Enteral Nutrition [15823]
Assn. of Nutrition Departments and Programs [8686]
Assn. for the Stud. of Food and Soc. [6871]
Beyond Hunger [14431]
Calorie Restriction Soc. [15824]
Coalition for a Healthy and Active Am. [15852]
Commn. on Dietetic Registration [15825]
Commn. on Dietetic Registration [15825]
Community Systems Found. [15826]
Comparative Nutrition Soc. [15827]
Coun. for Responsible Nutrition [8687]
Dietary Managers Assn. [15828]
Dietetics in Hea. Care Communities [15829]
Egg Nutrition Center [15830]
End Childhood Hunger [12271]
Feingold Assn. of the U.S. [15831]
Food and Nutrition Bd. [15832]
Friends of Nutre Hogar [14112]
Gardens for Hea. Intl. [13604]
Genetic Metabolic Dietitians Intl. [15497]
Global FoodBanking Network [12281]
Global Initiative for the Advancement of Nutritional Therapy [16851]
Global Nutrition Alliance [15833]
Global Nutrition Alliance [15833]
Gluten Intolerance Gp. [15834]
Indian Soc. for Parenteral and Enteral Nutrition [9901]
Intl. and Amer. Associations of Clinical Nutritionists [15835]
Intl. and Amer. Associations of Clinical Nutritionists [15835]
Intl. Life Sciences Inst. - North Am. [15836]
Intl. Life Sciences Inst. - North Am. [15836]
Intl. Sci. Assn. for Probiotics and Prebiotics [7176]
Intl. Soc. of Sports Nutrition [15837]
Intl. Soc. of Sports Nutrition [15837]
Latino Nutrition Coalition [15838]
Natl. Assn. of Bionutritionists [15839]
Natl. Assn. of Nutrition and Aging Services Programs [15840]
Natl. Assn. of Sports Nutrition [15841]
Natl. Dairy Coun. [4183]
Nourish Am. [15842]
Nutrition and Educ. Intl. [12586]
OrganicAthlete [22232]
Price-Pottenger Nutrition Found. [15843]
Soc. for Animal Homeopathy [15023]
Soc. for Nutrition Educ. [15844]
Spoons Across Am. [15845]
Vitamin Angel Alliance [15846]
Vitamin Angel Alliance [15846]
Vitamin D Coun. [15847]
Weston A. Price Found. [15848]
Whole Grains Coun. [15849]
Nutrition Assn; School [8909]
Nutrition Australia [IO], Melbourne, Australia
Nutrition Education Assn. - Defunct.
Nutrition and Educ. Intl. [12586], 2500 E Foothill Blvd., Ste. 200C, Pasadena, CA 91107, (626)744-0270

A star before a book entry number signifies that the name is not listed separately, but is mentioned within the entry.

Nutrition Found. [★15836]
Nutrition Found. [★15836]
Nutrition; Found. for Digestive Hea. and [14562]
Nutrition Found. of the Philippines [IO], Quezon City, Philippines
Nutrition; Oley Found. for Home Parenteral and Enteral [15014]
Nutrition for Optimal Hea. Assn. [★15820]
Nutrition Soc. [IO], London, United Kingdom
Nutrition Soc. of Australia [IO], Kent Town, Australia
Nutrition Soc. of Southern Africa [IO], Brits, Republic of South Africa
Nuts
  Almond Bd. of California [4744]
  Amer. Peanut Coun. [4745]
  Amer. Peanut Coun. - European Off. [19568]
  Amer. Peanut Res. and Educ. Soc. [4746]
  Amer. Peanut Shellers Assn. [4747]
  California Walnut Bd. [4748]
  Georgia Peanut Commn. [4749]
  Hazelnut Coun. [4750]
  Natl. Peanut Buying Points Assn. [4751]
  Natl. Peanut Festival Assn. [4752]
  Natl. Pecan Shellers Assn. [4753]
  Northern Nut Growers Assn. [4754]
  Peanut Inst. [4755]
  Southern Peanut Growers [4756]
  Virginia-Carolina Peanut Promotions [4757]
  Virginia-Carolina Peanuts [4758]
  Walnut Coun. [4759]
Nuttall Ornithological Club [7203], PO Box 686, Hanson, MA 02341
Nyaya Hea. [15201], 666 Dorchester Ave., South Boston, MA 02127
Nyaya Hea. [15201], 666 Dorchester Ave., South Boston, MA 02127
Nystagmus Network; Amer. [17061]
NYZS/The Wildlife Conservation Soc. [★4162]
NZX [IO], Wellington, New Zealand

O

O-Sport Assn. of Iran [IO], Hamedan, Iran
Oak Flooring Mfrs. of U.S. [★600]
Oak Ridge Assoc. Universities [7384], PO Box 117, Oak Ridge, TN 37831-0117, (865)576-3146
Oak Ridge Boys Intl. Fan Club [23879], 88 New Shackle Island Rd., Hendersonville, TN 37075, (615)824-4924
Oak Ridge Inst. of Nuclear Stud. [★7384]
Oaktree Found. [IO], Melbourne, Australia
OAS Staff Assn. [23260], 1889 F St. NW, Ste. 691, Washington, DC 20006, (202)458-6230
Oasis [IO], London, United Kingdom
Obec Architektu [★IO]
Oberhasli Breeders of Am. [3799], Elise Shope Anderson, Sec.-Treas., 1035 Bardin Rd., Palatka, FL 32177
Obesity
  Amer. Bd. of Bariatric Medicine [15850]
  Amer. Soc. of Bariatric Physicians [15851]
  Coalition for a Healthy and Active Am. [15852]
  Coalition to Promote Minority Hea. [15853]
  Coun. on Size and Weight Discrimination [12587]
  Intl. Size Acceptance Assn. [12588]
  Intl. Size Acceptance Assn. [12588]
  Largely Positive [15854]
  Natl. Assn. to Advance Fat Acceptance [12589]
  Natl. Assn. of Bariatric Nurses [15855]
  Natl. Coalition for a Healthy Am. [15856]
  Obesity Action Coalition [15857]
  The Obesity Soc. [15858]
  The Obesity Soc. [15858]
  Overeaters Anonymous World Ser. Off. [12590]
  Overeaters Anonymous World Ser. Off. [12590]
  Take Off Pounds Sensibly [12591]
  Weight-Control Info. Network [15859]
Obesity Action Coalition [15857], 4511 N Himes Ave., Ste. 250, Tampa, FL 33614, (813)872-7835
The Obesity Found. - Defunct.
The Obesity Soc. [15858], 8757 Georgia Ave., Ste. 1320, Silver Spring, MD 20910, (301)563-6526
The Obesity Soc. [15858], 8757 Georgia Ave., Ste. 1320, Silver Spring, MD 20910, (301)563-6526
The Objectivist Center [10408], The Atlas Soc., 1001 Connecticut Ave. NW, Ste. 425, Washington, DC 20036, (202)296-7263

Oblate Conf. of the U.S. - Defunct.
Obscure Org. [7522], 300 S Jackson St., Arlington, VA 22204, (703)979-4380
Observatoire des Fonctions Publiques Africaines [★IO]
Obsessive-Compulsive Anonymous [12491], PO Box 215, New Hyde Park, NY 11040, (516)739-0662
Obsessive Compulsive Disorder Found. [★15457]
Obsessive-Compulsive Found. [★15457]
Obstetric Anaesthetists' Assn. [IO], London, United Kingdom
Obstetric Anesthesia and Perinatology; Soc. for [16160]
Obstetric, Gynecologic and Neonatal Nursing Specialties; Natl. Certification Corp. for the [15776]
Obstetrical and Gynaecological Soc. of Hong Kong [IO], Hong Kong, People's Republic of China
Obstetrical and Gynaecological Soc. of Singapore [IO], Singapore, Singapore
Obstetrics and Gynecology
  Amer. Acad. of Husband-Coached Childbirth [15860]
  Amer. Assn. of Birth Centers [15861]
  Amer. Assn. of Gynecologic Laparoscopists [15862]
  Amer. Assn. of Naturopathic Midwives [15530]
  Amer. Bd. of Obstetrics and Gynecology [15863]
  Amer. Coll. of Community Midwives [15864]
  Amer. Coll. of Obstetricians and Gynecologists [15865]
  Amer. Coll. of Obstetricians and Gynecologists I Coun. on Resident Educ. in Obstetrics and Gynecology [15866]
  Amer. Coll. of Osteopathic Obstetricians and Gynecologists [15867]
  Amer. Gynecological and Obstetrical Soc. [15868]
  Amer. Pregnancy Assn. [15869]
  Amer. Soc. for Colposcopy and Cervical Pathology [15870]
  Assn. of Physician Assistants in Obstetrics and Gynecology [15871]
  Assn. of Professors of Gynecology and Obstetrics [15872]
  Australasian Menopause Soc. [18733]
  Better BedRest [15873]
  Center for Humane Options in Childbirth Experiences [15874]
  Childbirth Connection [15875]
  Coalition for Improving Maternity Services [15876]
  Coun. of Intl. Neonatal Nurses [15745]
  DONA Intl. [15877]
  Endometriosis Assn. [15878]
  Endometriosis Assn. [15878]
  Endometriosis UK [3565]
  Gynecologic Surgery Soc. [15879]
  Hysterectomy Educational Resources and Services Found. [15880]
  Hysterectomy Educational Resources and Services Found. [15880]
  Intl. Cesarean Awareness Network [15881]
  Intl. Cesarean Awareness Network [15881]
  Intl. Childbirth Educ. Assn. [15882]
  Intl. Childbirth Educ. Assn. [15882]
  Intl. Midwife Assistance [15883]
  Intl. Partnership for Reproductive Hea. [16587]
  Intl. Premature Ovarian Failure Assn. [15884]
  Intl. Premature Ovarian Failure Assn. [15884]
  Lamaze Intl. [15885]
  Lamaze Intl. [15885]
  Midwives Alliance of North Am. [15886]
  Natl. Assn. of Certified Professional Midwives [15887]
  Natl. Healthy Mothers, Healthy Babies Coalition [15888]
  Natl. Healthy Start Assn. [15889]
  North Amer. Menopause Soc. [15890]
  North Amer. Soc. of Obstetric Medicine [15891]
  North Amer. Soc. of Obstetric Medicine [15891]
  Polycystic Ovarian Syndrome Assn. [15892]
  Polycystic Ovarian Syndrome Assn. [15892]
  Preimplantation Genetic Diagnosis Intl. Soc. [14656]
  Sidelines Natl. High-Risk Pregnancy Support Network [15893]
  Soc. for Gynecologic Investigation [15894]

  Soc. for Menstrual Cycle Res. [15895]
  Vulvar Pain Found. [15896]
  Vulvar Pain Found. [15896]
O.C. Intl. [20078], PO Box 36900, Colorado Springs, CO 80936, (719)592-9292
O.C. Intl. [20078], PO Box 36900, Colorado Springs, CO 80936, (719)592-9292
O.C. Ministries [★20078]
O.C. Ministries [★20078]
OCADES - Caritas Burkina Faso [IO], Ouagadougou, Burkina Faso
Occult
  USCCCN Natl. CH on Satanic Crime in Am. [11695]
Occupational and Environmental Medical Assn. of Canada [IO], Oakville, ON, Canada
Occupational Hea. Inst. Trust; Sheet Metal [13007]
Occupational Hea. Nurses; Amer. Assn. of [15713]
Occupational Hea. Nurses; Amer. Bd. for [15717]
Occupational Knowledge Intl. [4798], 4444 Geary Blvd., Ste. 300, San Francisco, CA 94118, (415)221-8900
Occupational Knowledge Intl. [4798], 4444 Geary Blvd., Ste. 300, San Francisco, CA 94118, (415)221-8900
Occupational Medicine
  Acad. of Organizational and Occupational Psychiatry [15897]
  Acad. of Organizational and Occupational Psychiatry [15897]
  Amer. Acad. of Physician Assistants in Occupational Medicine [15898]
  Amer. Bd. of Indus. Hygiene [15899]
  Amer. Coll. of Occupational and Environmental Medicine [15900]
  Amer. Conf. of Governmental Indus. Hygienists [15901]
  Amer. Indus. Hygiene Assn. [15902]
  Amer. Occupational Therapy Found. [15903]
  Assn. of Occupational and Environmental Clinics [15904]
  Assn. of Occupational Hea. Professionals in Healthcare [15905]
  Assn. for Repetitive Motion Syndromes [15906]
  Coalition for Tactical Medicine [15907]
  Coun. for Accreditation in Occupational Hearing Conservation [15908]
  Soc. for Occupational and Environmental Hea. [15909]
Occupational Safety and Health
  Amer. Assn. of Safety Councils [12974]
  European Safety Fed. [10254]
  Voluntary Protection Prog. Assn. for Constr. [15910]
  Voluntary Protection Programs Participants' Assn. [15911]
Occupational Therapists Assn. Mauritius [IO], Port Louis, Mauritius
Occupational Therapists Assn., Tanzania [IO], Moshi, United Republic of Tanzania
Occupational Therapists Assn. of Thailand [IO], Chiang Mai, Thailand
Occupational Therapy Assn. of the Philippines [IO], Quezon City, Philippines
Occupational Therapy Assn. of South Africa [IO], Hatfield, Republic of South Africa
Occupational Therapy Found; Amer. [15903]
Occupational Therapy; Natl. Bd. for Certification in [16863]
Ocean Champions [17417], PO Box 381596, Cambridge, MA 02238, (617)661-6647
Ocean Conservancy [4115], 1300 19th St. NW, 8th Fl., Washington, DC 20036, (202)429-5609
Ocean Conservancy [4115], 1300 19th St. NW, 8th Fl., Washington, DC 20036, (202)429-5609
Ocean Conservation Res. [4116], PO Box 559, Lagunitas, CA 94938, (415)488-0553
Ocean Futures [★5002]
Ocean Futures [★5002]
Ocean Futures [5002], 325 Chapala St., Santa Barbara, CA 93101, (805)899-8899
Ocean Futures Soc. [5002], 325 Chapala St., Santa Barbara, CA 93101, (805)899-8899
Ocean Renewable Energy Coalition [6747], 12909 Scarlet Oak Dr., Darnestown, MD 20878, (301)869-3790

Reference to "IO" in place of a book number signifies that the association may be found in the 50th edition of International Organizations.

Encyclopedia of Associations, 51st Edition   3069

Ocean Res. and Conservation Assn. **[4117]**, Duerr Lab. for Marine Conservation, 1420 Seaway Dr., 2nd Fl., Fort Pierce, FL 34949, (772)467-1600

Ocean Soc. **[7183]**, 30 Sir Frances Drake Blvd., Ross, CA 94957, (415)441-1106

Ocean Spirits **[IO]**, St. George's, Grenada

Ocean Youth Club Scotland **[★9687]**

Ocean Youth Trust Scotland **[IO]**, Greenock, United Kingdom

Oceana **[4118]**, 1350 Connecticut Ave. NW, 5th Fl., Washington, DC 20036, (202)833-3900

Oceana **[4118]**, 1350 Connecticut Ave. NW, 5th Fl., Washington, DC 20036, (202)833-3900

Oceania Natl. Olympic Committees **[IO]**, Suva, Fiji

Oceania Tennis Fed. **[IO]**, Auckland, New Zealand

Oceania Weightlifting Fed. **[IO]**, Noumea, New Caledonia

Oceanic Educational Found. - Defunct.

Oceanic Preservation Soc. **[4119]**, 3063 Sterling Cir. E, No. 7, Boulder, CO 80301

Oceanic Preservation Soc. **[4119]**, 3063 Sterling Cir. E, No. 7, Boulder, CO 80301

Oceanic Soc. **[★4061]**

Oceanic Soc. **[7184]**, PO Box 437, Ross, CA 94957, (415)441-1106

Oceanic Soc. Expeditions **[22191]**, Ft. Mason, Quarters 35 N, San Francisco, CA 94123-1394, (415)441-1106

Oceanographic Soc. of Japan **[IO]**, Tokyo, Japan

Oceanographic Soc. of the Pacific **[★7177]**

Oceanographic Soc. of the Pacific **[★7177]**

Oceanography
  Amer. Soc. of Limnology and Oceanography **[7177]**
  Assn. for the Sciences of Limnology and Oceanography **[7177]**
  Center for Oceans Law and Policy **[7178]**
  The Coastal Soc. **[7179]**
  Coastal States Org. **[7180]**
  IEEE | Oceanic Engg. Soc. **[7181]**
  MarineBio Conservation Soc. **[4714]**
  Natl. Ocean Indus. Assn. **[7182]**
  Natl. Oceanic Soc. **[4102]**
  Ocean Conservation Res. **[4116]**
  Ocean Soc. **[7183]**
  Oceanic Preservation Soc. **[4119]**
  Oceanic Soc. **[7184]**
  The Oceanography Soc. **[7185]**
  The Oceanography Soc. **[7185]**
  World Ocean Coun. **[5009]**

Oceanography; Amer. Soc. of Limnology and **[★7177]**

Oceanography; Amer. Soc. of Limnology and **[7177]**

The Oceanography Soc. **[7185]**, PO Box 1931, Rockville, MD 20849-1931, (301)251-7708

The Oceanography Soc. **[7185]**, PO Box 1931, Rockville, MD 20849-1931, (301)251-7708

Ockenden Intl. - England **[IO]**, Woking, United Kingdom

Odborovy svaz Unios **[IO]**, Prague, Czech Republic

Odd Fellows
  Independent Order of Odd Fellows **[19181]**
  Intl. Assn. of Rebekah Assemblies, IOOF **[19182]**
  Intl. Assn. of Rebekah Assemblies, IOOF **[19182]**
  Junior Lodge, Independent Order of Odd Fellows **[19183]**

ODF Alliance **[6990]**, 1090 Vermont Ave. NW, 6th Fl., Washington, DC 20005, (202)789-4450

ODF Alliance **[6990]**, 1090 Vermont Ave. NW, 6th Fl., Washington, DC 20005, (202)789-4450

Odinism
  Asatru Alliance **[19301]**

O'Dochartaigh Clann Assn. **[IO]**, Buncrana, Ireland

Odontology; Amer. Bd. of Forensic **[14544]**

ODPHP Hea. Info. Center **[★14730]**

ODPHP Natl. Hea. Info. Center **[★14730]**

OECD Nuclear Energy Agency **[IO]**, Issy-les-Moulineaux, France

Oekologischer Aerztebund **[★IO]**

Oesterreichische Forschungsstiftung fuer Entwicklungshilfe **[★IO]**

Oesterreichische Gesellschaft fur Musik **[★IO]**

Oesterreichische HochschuelerInnenschaft **[★IO]**

Oesterreichische Theatertechnische Gesellschaft **[★IO]**

Oesterreichischer Astronomischer Verein **[★IO]**

Oesterreichischer Kaffee- und Tee-Verband **[★IO]**

Oesterreichischer Tennisverband **[★IO]**

Oesterreichischer Zeitschriften-und Fachmedien-Verband **[★IO]**

Oesterreichisches Nord-Sud Institut fur Entwicklung-szusammenarbeit **[★IO]**

Of a Like Mind **[★20290]**

Offender Aid and Restoration - Defunct.

Office for the Advancement of Public Black Colleges **[★7873]**

Off. of the Americas **[17233]**, 8124 W 3rd St., Ste. 202, Los Angeles, CA 90048, (323)852-9808

Off. of the Americas **[17233]**, 8124 W 3rd St., Ste. 202, Los Angeles, CA 90048, (323)852-9808

Office Automation Soc. Intl. - Defunct.

Off. Bus. Center Assn. Intl. **[73]**, 2030 Main St., Ste. 1300, Irvine, CA 92614, (949)260-9023

Off. des normes generales du Canada **[★IO]**

Office for Church in Soc. - Defunct.

Off. Du Haut Commissaire Aux Droits de l'Homme **[★IO]**

Off. Educ. Assn. **[★9042]**

Off. on Educational Credit **[★8171]**

Off. on Educational Credit and Credentials **[★8171]**

Off. Employees Intl. Union **[★23141]**

Office Equipment
  Bus. Solutions Assn. **[3346]**
  Bus. Tech. Assn. **[2577]**
  Copier Dealers Assn. **[2578]**
  ISDA - Assn. of Storage and Retrieval Professionals **[2579]**
  Modular Building Inst. **[2580]**
  MultiFunction Products Assn. **[2581]**
  School and Off. Products Network **[2582]**

Off. Equip. Mfrs. Inst. **[★6539]**

Off. Furniture Dealers Alliance **[★1552]**

Off. Furniture Distribution Assn. **[3665]**, 282 N Ridge Rd., Brooklyn, MI 49230, (517)467-9355

Off. of Hea. Economics **[IO]**, London, United Kingdom

Off. of the High Commissioner for Human Rights **[IO]**, Geneva, Switzerland

Off. for Intellectual Freedom **[10002]**, 50 E Huron St., Chicago, IL 60611, (312)280-4223

Off. Intl. de l'Eau **[★IO]**

Off. Intl. de l'Enseignement Catholique **[★IO]**

Off. of Minorities in Higher Educ. **[★8627]**

Off. Natl. Du Film Du Canada **[★IO]**

Off. Natl. Interprofessionnel des Fruits, des Legumes et de l'Horticulture **[★IO]**

Off. Natl. Interprofessionnel des Vins **[★IO]**

Off. of Paranormal Investigation and Res. Intl. - Defunct.

Off. of Population Affairs CH **[12700]**, PO Box 30686, Bethesda, MD 20824, (866)640-7827

Off. Products of the Bus. Products Indus. Assn. Dealers Alliance **[★3353]**

Office Products Mfrs. Alliance - Defunct.

Office Products Representatives Alliance - Defunct.

Off. and Professional Employees Intl. Union **[23141]**, Mary Mahoney, Sec.-Treas., 80 Eighth Ave., Ste. 610, New York, NY 10011, (212)367-0902

Off. Systems Res. Assn. **[★8969]**

Officers
  Amer. Heraldry Soc. **[20618]**
  Amer. Soc. of Medication Safety Officers **[14869]**
  Assn. of Certified Green Tech. Auditors **[6692]**
  Assn. of Climate Change Officers **[4237]**
  CEO Netweavers **[962]**
  Corporate Responsibility Officers Assn. **[963]**
  Govt. Investment Officers Assn. **[5611]**
  Intl. Assn. of Independent Private Sector Inspectors Gen. **[5546]**
  Military Officers Assn. of Am. **[20740]**
  SATS/EAF Assn. **[20686]**
  Sea Ser. Leadership Assn. **[20741]**

Officers' Christian Fellowship of the U.S.A. **[19596]**, 3784 S Inca St., Englewood, CO 80110-3405, (800)424-1984

Official Betty Boop Fan Club - Address unknown since 2011.

Official Elvis Presley Fan Club of Great Britain **[IO]**, Leicester, United Kingdom

Official Fan Club of the Grand Ole Opry **[23880]**, 2804 Opryland Dr., Nashville, TN 37214, (615)871-OPRY

Official Gilligan's Island Fan Club **[23926]**, 12429 Dormouse Rd., San Diego, CA 92129

Official Gumby Fan Club **[23793]**, Toon's Sta., Inc., 5 Hanley Ct., Tabernacle, NJ 08088, (609)268-6680

Official Intl. Michael York Fan Club **[23779]**, Peter Strain, 5455 Wilshire Blvd., Ste. 1812, Los Angeles, CA 90036, (323)525-3391

Official International Toy Center Dir. - Defunct.

Official Leonard Nimoy Fan Club **[IO]**, Coventry, United Kingdom

Official Red Dwarf Fan Club **[23927]**, Jupiter Mining Company, PO Box 3152, Waquoit, MA 02536

Official Robert Newman Fan Club **[23780]**, PO Box 102, Hope Mills, NC 28348, (877)809-1659

Offshore Contractors Assn. **[IO]**, Aberdeen, United Kingdom

Offshore Marine Ser. Assn. **[2368]**, 990 N Corporate Dr., Ste. 210, Harahan, LA 70123, (504)734-7622

Offshore Pollution Liability Assn. **[IO]**, Ewell, United Kingdom

Ogbaru Natl. Assn. **[12579]**, 2019 Knoll Crest, Arlington, TX 76014, (817)724-7804

Ogden House Seniors 50 Club **[IO]**, Calgary, AB, Canada

Ogolnopolskie Porozumienie Zwiazkow Zawodowych **[★IO]**

OGR **[★2537]**

OGR **[★2537]**

Ogwashi-Uku Assn., USA **[19177]**, 10575 Westpark Dr., No. 424, Houston, TX 77042

Ogwashi-Uku Assn., USA **[19177]**, 10575 Westpark Dr., No. 424, Houston, TX 77042

Ohashi Inst. **[16017]**, PO Box 505, Kinderhook, NY 12106, (518)758-6879

Ohashi Inst. **[16017]**, PO Box 505, Kinderhook, NY 12106, (518)758-6879

Ohio Assn. of Christian Schools **[★7851]**

Ohio Assn. of Christian Schools **[★7851]**

Ohio Ceramics Assn. **[★731]**

Ohio Genealogical Soc. **[20652]**, 611 State Rte. 97 W, Bellville, OH 44813-8813, (419)886-1903

Ohio Herpetological Soc. **[★6941]**

Ohio Org. Development Network **[★2596]**

Ohio Org. Development Network **[★2596]**

Ohio Standard Breeding Assn. Youth Found. **[22652]**

Ohio Wage and Salary Assn. **[★1162]**

Ohio Wage and Salary Assn. **[★1162]**

Ohr Torah Institutions of Israel **[8421]**, 49 W 45th St., Ste. 701, New York, NY 10036-4603, (212)935-8672

An Oige **[★IO]**

Oikonos **[4213]**, PO Box 1918, Kailua, HI 96734, (415)868-1399

Oikonos **[4213]**, PO Box 1918, Kailua, HI 96734, (415)868-1399

Oil
  Citizens for Energy Freedom **[6703]**
  Completion Engg. Assn. **[6961]**
  Crude Oil Quality Assn. **[2647]**
  Domestic Energy Producers Alliance **[1166]**
  Intl. Coun. for Machinery Lubrication **[7034]**
  Oil Change Intl. **[4230]**
  Securing America's Future Energy **[6755]**

Oil Change Intl. **[4230]**, 236 Massachusetts Ave. NE, No. 203, Washington, DC 20002, (202)518-9029

Oil and Colour Chemists' Assn. **[IO]**, Leighton Buzzard, United Kingdom

Oil Companies' European Org. for Environmental and Hea. Protection **[IO]**, Brussels, Belgium

Oil Companies Intl. Marine Forum **[IO]**, London, United Kingdom

Oil Firing Tech. Assn. for the Petroleum Indus. **[IO]**, Ipswich, United Kingdom

Oil Painters of Am. **[9248]**, PO Box 2488, Crystal Lake, IL 60039-2488, (815)356-5987

Oil Pastel Assn. Intl. - Defunct.

Oil Spill Control Assn. of Amer. **[★2788]**

Oilfields Workers' Trade Union **[IO]**, San Fernando, Trinidad and Tobago

Oils and Fats
  Argentine Oil Indus. Chamber **[12919]**
  Fats and Proteins Res. Found. **[2583]**
  Fats and Proteins Res. Found. **[2583]**

A star before a book entry number signifies that the name is not listed separately, but is mentioned within the entry.

Greek Assn. of Indus. and Processors of Olive Oil [20603]
Inst. of Shortening and Edible Oils [2584]
Intl. Castor Oil Assn. [2585]
Intl. Castor Oil Assn. [2585]
Intl. Soc. for Fat Res. [7186]
Intl. Soc. for Fat Res. [7186]
Natl. Assn. of the Edible Oils and Fats Indus. [13303]
Natl. Assn. of Margarine Mfrs. [2586]
Natl. Cottonseed Products Assn. [2587]
Natl. Inst. of Oilseed Products [2588]
Natl. Inst. of Oilseed Products [2588]
Natl. Oilseed Processors Assn. [2589]
Natl. Renderers Assn. [2590]
North Amer. Olive Oil Assn. [2591]
North Amer. Olive Oil Assn. [2591]
Taiwan Margarine Indus. Assn. [13639]
Oilwatch Network [IO], Port Harcourt, Nigeria
OISTAT Centre of Great Britain [IO], London, United Kingdom
OISTAT Japan Centre [IO], Tokyo, Japan
Oita Sports Assn. for the Disabled [IO], Oita, Japan
O.J. Noer Res. Found. [4511], PO Box 94, Juneau, WI 53039-0094
OK Kosher Certification [19892], 391 Troy Ave., Brooklyn, NY 11213, (718)756-7500
OK Labs - Kosher Certification [★19892]
Oklahoma Baptist Univ. Alumni Assn. [18892], Oklahoma Baptist Univ., 500 W Univ., Shawnee, OK 74804, (405)275-2850
Oklahoma City Univ. Alumni Off. [18893], 2501 N Blackwelder, Oklahoma City, OK 73106-1493, (405)208-5117
Oklahoma Univ. Alumni Assn. [18894], 900 Asp Ave., Ste. 427, Norman, OK 73019-4051, (405)325-1710
Okologischer Arztebund eV Ecological Physicians Assn. [★IO]
Okologisk Landslag [★IO]
Olajmagfeldolgozok Magyarorszagi Egyesulete [IO], Budapest, Hungary
The Old Appliance Club [20964], PO Box 65, Ventura, CA 93002, (805)643-3532
Old English Sheepdog Club of Am. [21626], 21802 Roosevelt Rd., Merrill, MI 48637, (989)643-5671
Old Guard Soc. [★1393]
Old Lesbians Organizing [★10867]
Old Lesbians Organizing for Change [10867], PO Box 5853, Athens, OH 45701, (888)706-7506
Old Old Timers Club [20941], 230 Fremont St., Redlands, CA 92373-5078
Old Reel Collectors Assn. [21392], 160 Shoreline Walk, Alpharetta, GA 30022
Old Reel Collectors Assn. [21392], 160 Shoreline Walk, Alpharetta, GA 30022
Old Sleepy Eye Collectors' Club of Am. [21268], 2009 N Park Ave., Oskaloosa, IA 52577-2490, (641)676-1637
Old Time Dance Soc. [IO], Bath, United Kingdom
Oldenburg Registry N.A. [4634], 517 DeKalb Ave., Sycamore, IL 60178, (815)899-7803
Older Women's League [★13473]
Older Women's Network NSW [IO], Millers Point, Australia
Oldsmobile Club of Am. [21139], PO Box 80318, Lansing, MI 48908, (517)663-1811
Oldsmobile Club; Natl. Antique [21122]
Oley Found. for Home Parenteral and Enteral Nutrition [15014], Albany Medical Ctr., 214 Hun Memorial, MC-28, Albany, NY 12208-3478, (518)262-5079
Olfactory Res. Fund [★1524]
Olfactory Res. Fund [★1524]
Oligonucleotide Therapeutics Soc. [16866], 4377 Newport Ave., San Diego, CA 92107, (619)795-9458
Olimpiadas Especiales de Hondras [★IO]
Olimpiadas Especiales de Paraguay [★IO]
Olimpiadas Especiales de Uruguay [★IO]
Olimpiady Specjalne Polska [★IO]
Olimpijski komite slovenije [★IO]
Olimpijski Komitet Srbije [★IO]
Olive Assn. Midnorth South Australia [IO], Adelaide, Australia

Olive Growers Mudgee [IO], Mudgee, Australia
Olive Oil Assn. [★2591]
Olive Oil Assn. [★2591]
Olive Oil Assn. of Am. [★1378]
Olive Oil Gp. [★2591]
Olive Oil Gp. [★2591]
Olive Producers North East Victoria [IO], Benalla, Australia
Olives South Australia [IO], Adelaide, Australia
Oljeindustriens Landsforening [★IO]
Olson 30 Natl. Class Assn. [22383], Aaron Feves, Sec.-Treas., 12 La Linda Dr., Long Beach, CA 90807
Oluklu Mukavva Sanayicileri Dernegi [★IO]
Olympic Comm. of the Former Yugoslav Republic of Macedonia [IO], Skopje, Macedonia
Olympic Comm. of Israel [IO], Tel Aviv, Israel
Olympic Comm. of Portugal [IO], Lisbon, Portugal
Olympic Comm. of Serbia and Montenegro [IO], Belgrade, Serbia
Olympic Comm. of Slovenia [IO], Ljubljana, Slovenia
Olympic Coun. of Asia [IO], Hawalli, Kuwait
Olympic Coun. of Ireland [IO], Dublin, Ireland
Olympic Coun. of Malaysia [IO], Kuala Lumpur, Malaysia
Olympic Educ. Center [★22791]
Olympic Games
  Greek Olympic Soc. [22789]
  Greek Olympic Soc. [22789]
  Guam Natl. Olympic Comm. [22790]
  U.S. Bobsled and Skeleton Fed. [22926]
  U.S. Modern Pentathlon Assn. [23071]
  U.S. Olympic Comm. [22791]
  Virgin Islands Olympic Comm. [22792]
  Virgin Islands Olympic Comm. [22792]
  World Olympians Assn. [22793]
  World Olympians Assn. [22793]
Olympiques Speciaux Canada [★IO]
Oman Assn. for Consumer Protection [IO], Ruwi, Oman
Oman Athletic Assn. [IO], Muscat, Oman
Oman Chamber of Commerce and Indus. [IO], Muscat, Oman
Oman Dental Soc. [IO], Muscat, Oman
Oman Dermatology Soc. [IO], Ruwi, Oman
Oman Opthalmic Soc. [IO], Ruwi, Oman
Oman Orthopaedic Soc. [IO], Ruwi, Oman
Oman Pharmaceutical Soc. [IO], Muscat, Oman
Oman Soc. of Engineers [IO], Muscat, Oman
Oman Tennis Assn. [IO], Muscat, Oman
Omani Charitable Org. [IO], Ruwi, Oman
Omani Economic Assn. [IO], Muscat, Oman
Omani Soc. for Fine Arts [IO], Muttrah, Oman
Omani Spanish Friendship Assn. [IO], Jibroo, Oman
Omas Taekwondo [IO], Nassau, Bahamas
OMB Watch [17752], 1742 Connecticut Ave. NW, Washington, DC 20009, (202)234-8494
Omega Arts Network [★9310]
Omega Chi Epsilon [23519], Univ. Minnesota-Duluth, Chem. Engg. Dept., 176 Engg. Bldg., 1303 Ordean Ct., Duluth, MN 55812-3025, (218)726-6162
Omega Delta [23612], Southern Coll. of Optometry, 1245 Madison Ave., Memphis, TN 38104-2211, (901)722-3200
Omega First Amendment Legal Fund [17314], 1790 30th St., Ste. 418, Boulder, CO 80301, (303)449-3060
Omega Psi Phi Fraternity [23677], 3951 Snapfinger Pkwy., Decatur, GA 30035, (404)284-5533
Omega Theatre and the Omega Arts Network [9310], 41 Greenough Ave., Jamaica Plain, MA 02130, (617)522-8300
OMF Intl. - Singapore [IO], Singapore, Singapore
OMF Intl. U.S.A. [20079], 10 W Dry Creek Cir., Littleton, CO 80120-4413, (303)730-4160
OMF Intl. U.S.A. [20079], 10 W Dry Creek Cir., Littleton, CO 80120-4413, (303)730-4160
Omicron Chi Epsilon [★23506]
Omicron Delta Epsilon [23506], PO Box 1486, Hattiesburg, MS 39402, (601)264-3115
Omicron Delta Gamma [★23506]
Omicron Delta Kappa Foundation [★23566]
Omicron Delta Kappa Soc. [23566], 224 McLaughlin St., Lexington, VA 24450-2002, (540)458-5336
Omicron Kappa Upsilon [23499], Univ. of Nebraska, Coll. of Dentistry, 40th and Holdrege St., Rm. 105, Lincoln, NE 68583-0740, (402)472-1345

Omicron Nu [★23549]
Omnibus Soc. [IO], Walsall, United Kingdom
Omnilogy, Inc. [12353], 22 Camp Fire Ln., Coram, NY 11727
Omohundro Inst. of Early Amer. History and Culture [9790], PO Box 8781, Williamsburg, VA 23187-8781, (757)221-1114
Omospondia Ergodoton ke Biomichanon Kyprou [★IO]
OMS Intl. [20080], PO Box A, Greenwood, IN 46142, (317)888-3333
OMS Intl. [20080], PO Box A, Greenwood, IN 46142, (317)888-3333
Omslag Werkplaats voor Duurzame Ontwikkeling [★IO]
Omslag Workshop for Sustainable Development [IO], Eindhoven, Netherlands
On the Lighter Side, Intl. Lighter Collectors [21393], PO Box 1733, Quitman, TX 75783-2733, (903)763-2795
On the Lighter Side, Intl. Lighter Collectors [21393], PO Box 1733, Quitman, TX 75783-2733, (903)763-2795
On-line Audiovisual Catalogers [★10003]
Oncology
  4K for Cancer [13874]
  Amer. Assn. for Cancer Res. [15912]
  Amer. Assn. for Cancer Res. [15912]
  Amer. Coll. of Mohs Surgery [15913]
  Amer. Joint Comm. on Cancer [15914]
  Amer. Psychosocial Oncology Soc. [15915]
  Amer. Radium Soc. [15916]
  Amer. Soc. of Clinical Oncology [15917]
  Amer. Soc. of Clinical Radiation Oncology [15918]
  Amer. Soc. for Mohs Surgery [15919]
  Amer. Soc. for Mohs Surgery [15919]
  Amer. Soc. of Preventive Oncology [15920]
  Assn. of Residents in Radiation Oncology [15921]
  Cancer Support Community [13903]
  Chemotherapy Found. [15922]
  Children's Cancer and Blood Found. [14964]
  Community Oncology Alliance [15923]
  Connective Tissue Oncology Soc. [15924]
  Connective Tissue Oncology Soc. [15924]
  Friends-4-Cures [13923]
  Golf Fights Cancer [13926]
  Gynecologic Oncology Gp. [15925]
  Hematology/Oncology Pharmacy Assn. [16194]
  Indian Assn. of Surgical Oncology [16712]
  Intl. Assn. for Comparative Res. on Leukemia and Related Diseases [15926]
  Intl. Assn. for Comparative Res. on Leukemia and Related Diseases [15926]
  Intl. Skeletal Soc. [16533]
  Intl. Soc. of Gastrointestinal Oncology [14568]
  Leukemia and Lymphoma Soc. [13936]
  Melanoma Awareness [13940]
  Natl. Assn. for Proton Therapy [15927]
  Natl. Cancer Center [15928]
  Natl. Cancer Registrars Assn. [15929]
  Natl. Coalition of Oncology Nurse Navigators [15778]
  Natl. Found. for Cancer Res. [15930]
  Natl. Found. for Cancer Res. [15930]
  Natl. Melanoma Alliance [13956]
  Oncology Assn. of Naturopathic Physicians [15539]
  Patients Against Lymphoma [15257]
  Radiation Therapy Oncology Gp. [15931]
  Sino-American Network for Therapeutic Radiology and Oncology [16871]
  Soc. of Gynecologic Oncologists [15932]
  Soc. for Integrative Oncology [15933]
  Soc. of Surgical Oncology [15934]
  Soc. for Translational Oncology [15935]
Oncology Administrators; Amer. Coll. of [15284]
Oncology Administrators; Soc. for Radiation [16547]
Oncology; Amer. Soc. of Pediatric Hematology/ [14961]
Oncology; Amer. Soc. for Therapeutic Radiology and [16529]
Oncology Assn. of Naturopathic Physicians [15539], 216 NE Fremont St., Portland, OR 97212, (800)490-8509
Oncology Centers; Assn. of Freestanding Radiation [16513]

Reference to "IO" in place of a book number signifies that the association may be found in the 50th edition of International Organizations.

Encyclopedia of Associations, 51st Edition   **3071**

Oncology Nursing Certification Corp. [15792], 125 Enterprise Dr., Pittsburgh, PA 15275-1214, (412)859-6104

Oncology Nursing Soc. [15793], 125 Enterprise Dr., Pittsburgh, PA 15275, (412)859-6100

Oncology Social Work; Assn. of [13214]

Oncology Social Workers; Assn. of Pediatric [16143]

One-Arm Dove Hunt Assn. [22523], PO Box 582, Olney, TX 76374, (940)564-8867

One Cent Intl. [21988], 2838 County Rd. 12, Fayette, AL 35555

One Cent Intl. [21988], 2838 County Rd. 12, Fayette, AL 35555

One Child at a Time [11372], AIAA/Corporate Office, 2151 Livernois, Ste. 200, Troy, MI 48083, (248)362-1207

One Common Unity [11618], 1525 Newton St. NW, Washington, DC 20010, (202)529-2125

One-Design Class Coun. - Address unknown since 2010.

One Earth Designs [4293], PO Box 382559, Cambridge, MA 02238, (617)671-0727

One Economy [7523], 1220 19th St. NW, Ste. 610, Washington, DC 20036, (202)393-0051

One Family [IO], Dublin, Ireland

One in Four [13095], 10 Shirlawn Dr., Short Hills, NJ 07078

ONE Freedom [20708], PO Box 7418, Boulder, CO 80306, (303)444-1221

One Heart Bulgaria [11373], 165 N Main St., Providence, UT 84332, (435)764-3093

One Heart Bulgaria [11373], 165 N Main St., Providence, UT 84332, (435)764-3093

One Hen [7821], PO Box 990781, Boston, MA 02199

One Hundred Days [14732], PO Box 29715, Atlanta, GA 30359

One-in-a-Million Soc. [★9641]

ONE, Inc. - Address unknown since 2010.

One Laptop Per Child [11665], PO Box 425087, Cambridge, MA 02142, (617)452-5663

One Love Worldwide [12874], 1223 El Caminito Dr., Hobbs, NM 88240

One Missing Link [12545], PO Box 10581, Springfield, MO 65808, (417)886-5836

One More Soul [18561], 1846 N Main St., Dayton, OH 45405-3832, (937)279-5433

One Nurse At A Time [15794], Sue Averill, RN, Pres./Treas., 7747 38th Ave. NE, Seattle, WA 98115

One Parent Families Scotland [IO], Edinburgh, United Kingdom

One Village [IO], Chipping Norton, United Kingdom

One Vision Intl. [11619], PO Box 20608, Knoxville, TN 37940, (865)579-3353

One Voice, Natl. Alliance for Abuse Awareness - Defunct.

One Voice of Peace [8694], 522 S Sunrise Way, Ste. 32, Palm Springs, CA 92264, (760)202-2330

One Warm Coat [12744], PO Box 642850, San Francisco, CA 94164, (877)663-9276

One to World [8372], 285 W Broadway, Ste. 450, New York, NY 10013, (212)431-1195

One World Action [IO], London, United Kingdom

One World Beat [IO], Lausanne, Switzerland

One World Educ. [8928], 1678 Oak St. NW, Washington, DC 20010, (202)558-8899

One World Healthcare USA [14823], 7737 Southwest Fwy., Ste. 819, Houston, TX 77074, (713)504-1173

One World Medical Relief [15202], 933 S Utah Ave., Idaho Falls, ID 83402, (208)552-1759

One World Medical Relief [15202], 933 S Utah Ave., Idaho Falls, ID 83402, (208)552-1759

OneAmerica [17528], 1225 S Weller St., Ste. 200, Seattle, WA 98144, (206)723-2203

OneChildhood - Address unknown since 2011.

O'Neill Critics Inst. [10596], Eugene O'Neill Theater Ctr., 305 Great Neck Rd., Waterford, CT 06385, (860)443-5378

O'Neill Natl. Theater Inst. [9003], Eugene O'Neill Theater Center, 305 Great Neck Rd., Waterford, CT 06385, (860)443-7139

O'Neill Theater Center [★10577]

OneWorld Now! [8929], 600 First Ave., Ste. 600, Seattle, WA 98104, (206)223-7703

OneWorld U.S. [17858], 1721 20th St. NW, Washington, DC 20009

OneWorld United States [17858], 1721 20th St. NW, Washington, DC 20009

Oneworld Works [12354], 2138 Penmar Ave., Ste. 3, Venice, CA 90291, (310)572-1090

Online Audiovisual Catalogers [10003], Florida State Univ., 711 W Madison St., Tallahassee, FL 32306, (850)644-6321

Online Imperial Club [21140], 40 Signal Hill Ct., Rock Spring, GA 30739

Online News Assn. [2863], PO Box 65741, Washington, DC 20035, (646)290-7900

Online Policy Gp. [17397], 1800 Market St., No. 123, San Francisco, CA 94102

Online Privacy Alliance [17315], Hogan and Hartson, 555 13th St. NW, Washington, DC 20004, (202)637-5600

Online Publishers Assn. [2955], 249 W 17th St., New York, NY 10011, (212)204-1495

Online Publishers Assn. Europe [IO], Paris, France

Online Trust Alliance [6550], PO Box 803, Bellevue, WA 98009-0803, (425)455-7400

Only a Child [11374], PO Box 990885, Boston, MA 02199, (617)848-8940

Only a Child [11374], PO Box 990885, Boston, MA 02199, (617)848-8940

Onomatology

Amer. Name Soc. [10344]

Amer. Name Soc. [10344]

Ontario Arts Council/Ontario Arts Coun. Found. [IO], Toronto, ON, Canada

Ontario Assn. for the Application of Personality Type [IO], Concord, ON, Canada

Ontario Assn. of Naturopathic Doctors [IO], Toronto, ON, Canada

Ontario Assn. of Social Workers [IO], Toronto, ON, Canada

Ontario Assn. of Social Workers - Hamilton Area and District Br. [IO], Hamilton, ON, Canada

Ontario Assn. of Youth Employment Centres [IO], Toronto, ON, Canada

Ontario Brain Injury Assn. [IO], St. Catharines, ON, Canada

Ontario Conf. of Catholic Bishops [IO], Toronto, ON, Canada

Ontario Fabricare Assn. [IO], North York, ON, Canada

Ontario Lawn Bowls Assn. [IO], Maberly, ON, Canada

Ontario Native Educ. Counselling Assn. [IO], Naughton, ON, Canada

Ontario Nature [IO], Toronto, ON, Canada

Ontario Psychological Assn. [IO], Toronto, ON, Canada

Ontario Recreational Canoeing and Kayaking Assn. [IO], Toronto, ON, Canada

Ontario School Counsellor's Assn. [IO], Bridgenorth, ON, Canada

Ontario Soc. of Psychotherapists [IO], Toronto, ON, Canada

Ontario and Western Railroad Historical Soc. [★10494]

Ontario and Western Railway Historical Soc. [10494], PO Box 713, Middletown, NY 10940

Ontario Wheelchair Sports Assn. [IO], Toronto, ON, Canada

OPEC Fund for Intl. Development [IO], Vienna, Austria

OPEC News Agency [IO], Vienna, Austria

Opel Assn. of North Am. [21141], 630 Watch Hill Rd., Midlothian, VA 23113, (804)379-9737

Opel Motorsports Club [21142], 3824 Franklin St., La Crescenta, CA 91214

Opel Motorsports Club AG [★21142]

Open Air Campaigners U.S.A. [19767], PO Box D, Nazareth, PA 18064, (610)746-0508

Open Applications Gp. [6491], PO Box 4897, Marietta, GA 30061, (404)402-1962

Open Caribbean Internet eXchange [IO], Philipsburg, Netherlands Antilles

Open Debates [17611], 636 S Columbus St., Alexandria, VA 22314, (703)299-6045

Open DeviceNet Vendor Assn. [6492], 4220 Varsity Dr., Ste. A, Ann Arbor, MI 48108-5006, (734)975-8840

Open DeviceNet Vendor Assn. [6492], 4220 Varsity Dr., Ste. A, Ann Arbor, MI 48108-5006, (734)975-8840

Open and Distance Learning Quality Coun. [IO], London, United Kingdom

Open Door Educ. Found. [8977], 1420 King St., Ste. 610, Alexandria, VA 22314, (703)838-2050

Open Door Student Exchange [★8370]

Open Geospatial Consortium [6551], Jeff Burnet, VP Operations and Finance, 35 Main St., Ste. 5, Wayland, MA 01778-5037, (508)655-5858

Open GIS Consortium [★6551]

The Open Gp. [1906], 44 Montgomery St., Ste. 960, San Francisco, CA 94104-4704, (415)374-8280

Open Mobile Alliance [7549], 4330 La Jolla Village Dr., Ste. 110, San Diego, CA 92122, (858)623-0742

Open Mobile Architecture Initiative [★7549]

OPEN Mortgage [★17894]

Open Pit Mining Assn. [★2513]

The Open Planning Proj. [6493], 148 Lafayette St., New York, NY 10013, (212)796-4220

Open Soc. Assn. [IO], Male, Maldives

Open Soc. Found. for Albania [IO], Tirana, Albania

Open Soc. Found. - Sofia Bulgaria [IO], Sofia, Bulgaria

Open Soc. Inst. [17948], 400 W 59th St., New York, NY 10019, (212)548-0600

Open Soc. Inst. [17948], 400 W 59th St., New York, NY 10019, (212)548-0600

Open Space Action Comm. [★4294]

Open Space Inst. [4294], 1350 Broadway, Ste. 201, New York, NY 10018-7799, (212)290-8200

Open Spaces Soc. [IO], Henley-on-Thames, United Kingdom

Open Voting Consortium [17612], 4941 Forest Creek Way, Granite Bay, CA 95746, (916)209-6620

Open Voting Consortium [17612], 4941 Forest Creek Way, Granite Bay, CA 95746, (916)209-6620

Opening Door [3570], 8049 Ormesby Ln., Woodford, VA 22580-3211

OpenView Forum Intl. [★6523]

Opera

Gerda Lissner Found. [10345]

OPERA Am. [10274], 330 7th Ave., 16th Fl., New York, NY 10001, (212)796-8620

Opera Assn; Metropolitan [10241]

Opera; Center for Contemporary [10172]

Opera Found. [10275], Mannheim LLC, 712 5th Ave., 32nd Fl., New York, NY 10019, (212)664-8843

Opera Guild; Metropolitan [10242]

Opera for Youth [★10261]

Opera for Youth - Defunct.

Opera.ca [IO], Toronto, ON, Canada

Operacao Sorriso - Brasil [★IO]

Operacion Sonrisa Honduras [★IO]

Operacion Sonrisa Nicaragua [★IO]

Operacion Sonrisa - Paraguay [★IO]

Operacion Sonrisa Peru [★IO]

Operacion Sonrisa Venezuela [★IO]

Operasionele Navorsingsvereniging van Suid-Afrika [★IO]

Operating Room Nurses Assn. of the Philippines [IO], Manila, Philippines

Oper. AC - Address unknown since 2011.

Oper. Appreciation [20415], Non-Commissioned Officers Assn. of the U.S.A., 9330 Corporate Dr., Ste. 701, Selma, TX 78154, (703)549-0311

Oper. Big Vote - Address unknown since 2010.

Oper. Blessing Intl. [19597], 977 Centerville Tpke., Virginia Beach, VA 23463, (757)226-3401

Oper. Blessing Intl. [19597], 977 Centerville Tpke., Virginia Beach, VA 23463, (757)226-3401

Oper. Blessing Intl. Relief and Development Corp. [★19597]

Oper. Blessing Intl. Relief and Development Corp. [★19597]

Oper. Brother's Keeper [★12812]

Oper. Brother's Keeper [★12812]

Oper. California [★12476]

Oper. Crossroads Africa [17152], PO Box 5570, New York, NY 10027, (212)289-1949

Oper. Crossroads Africa [17152], PO Box 5570, New York, NY 10027, (212)289-1949

A star before a book entry number signifies that the name is not listed separately, but is mentioned within the entry.

Oper. Eyesight Universal [IO], Calgary, AB, Canada
Oper. First Response [11096], 20037 Dove Hill Rd., Culpeper, VA 22701, (888)289-0280
Oper. Gratitude [11097], 16444 Refugio Rd., Encino, CA 91436, (818)909-0039
Oper. Gratitude [11097], 16444 Refugio Rd., Encino, CA 91436, (818)909-0039
Oper. Happy Note [12556], PO Box 509, Osakis, MN 56360, (320)859-7600
Oper. Help The Children [11375], 2200 Ben Franklin Pkwy. E, 905 A, Philadelphia, PA 19130, (215)557-1999
Oper. Help The Children [11375], 2200 Ben Franklin Pkwy. E, 905 A, Philadelphia, PA 19130, (215)557-1999
Oper. Homefront [12532], 8930 Fourwinds Dr., Ste. 340, San Antonio, TX 78239, (210)659-7756
Oper. Homelink [11098], 25 E Washington St., Ste. 1206, Chicago, IL 60602, (312)863-6337
Oper. HOPE, Inc. [11620], 707 Wilshire Blvd., 30th Fl., Los Angeles, CA 90017, (213)891-2900
Oper. Hug-A-Hero [12533], 1335-E Western Blvd., Jacksonville, NC 28546
Oper. Identity [10799], 1818 Somervell St. NE, Albuquerque, NM 87112-2836, (505)293-3144
Oper. Interdependence [12530], 2830 North Ave., Ste. C5B, PMB 147, Grand Junction, CO 81501-5367
Oper. Joshua [★12392]
Oper. Kid-To-Kid [11376], 100 Biblica Way, Elizabethton, TN 37643-6061
Oper. Lifesaver [13001], 1420 King St., Ste. 401, Alexandria, VA 22314, (703)739-0308
Oper. Lifesaver [13001], 1420 King St., Ste. 401, Alexandria, VA 22314, (703)739-0308
Operation Liftoff - Defunct.
Oper. Never Forgotten [11099], PO Box 132, Saline, MI 48176, (406)581-8358
Oper. Paperback [11100], PO Box 347, Dunstable, MA 01827, (214)602-1726
Oper. PUSH [★13199]
Oper. Quiet Comfort [11101], PO Box 263, La Salle, MI 48145
Oper. Rainbow [15311], PMB 157, 4200 Park Blvd., Oakland, CA 94602, (510)273-2485
Oper. Rescue [★18562]
Oper. Respect [8168], 2 Penn Plz., 5th Fl., New York, NY 10121, (212)904-5243
Oper. Save Am. [18562], PO Box 740066, Dallas, TX 75374, (704)933-3414
Oper. SER [★11959]
Oper. ShoeBox [11102], PO Box 1465, Belleview, FL 34421-1465, (352)307-6723
Oper. Smile [12475], 6435 Tidewater Dr., Norfolk, VA 23509, (757)321-7645
Oper. Smile [12475], 6435 Tidewater Dr., Norfolk, VA 23509, (757)321-7645
Oper. Smile - Australia [IO], Brisbane, Australia
Oper. Smile - Bolivia [IO], Santa Cruz, Bolivia
Oper. Smile - Brazil [IO], Sao Paulo, Brazil
Oper. Smile - Cambodia [IO], Phnom Penh, Cambodia
Oper. Smile - Colombia [IO], Bogota, Colombia
Oper. Smile - Ecuador [IO], Quito, Ecuador
Oper. Smile - Egypt [IO], Heliopolis, Egypt
Oper. Smile - Ethiopia [IO], Addis Ababa, Ethiopia
Oper. Smile - Hangzhou [IO], Hangzhou, People's Republic of China
Oper. Smile - Honduras [IO], Tegucigalpa, Honduras
Oper. Smile - Hong Kong [IO], Hong Kong, People's Republic of China
Oper. Smile - India [IO], Mumbai, India
Oper. Smile Intl. [★12475]
Oper. Smile Intl. [★12475]
Oper. Smile Intl. - Vietnam [IO], Hanoi, Vietnam
Oper. Smile - Ireland [IO], Dublin, Ireland
Oper. Smile - Italy [IO], Rome, Italy
Oper. Smile - Jordan [IO], Amman, Jordan
Oper. Smile - Kenya [IO], Nairobi, Kenya
Oper. Smile - Mexico [IO], Zapopan, Mexico
Oper. Smile - Morocco [IO], Casablanca, Morocco
Oper. Smile - Nicaragua [IO], Managua, Nicaragua
Oper. Smile - Panama [IO], Panama City, Panama
Oper. Smile - Paraguay [IO], Asuncion, Paraguay
Oper. Smile - Peru [IO], Lima, Peru

Oper. Smile - Philippines [IO], Makati City, Philippines
Oper. Smile - Russia [IO], Moscow, Russia
Oper. Smile - Singapore [IO], Singapore, Singapore
Oper. Smile - Thailand [IO], Bangkok, Thailand
Oper. Smile - United Kingdom [IO], London, United Kingdom
Oper. Smile - Venezuela [IO], Caracas, Venezuela
Oper. Sourire Morocco [★IO]
Oper. Stars and Stripes [11103], 483 Old Canton Rd., Ste. 100, Marietta, GA 30068, (770)509-1156
Oper. Support Our Troops [11104], PO Box 3113, Issaquah, WA 98027, (425)369-2215
Oper.: Take a Soldier to the Movies [11105], 17047 W Greenfield Ave., New Berlin, WI 53151-4434, (262)754-4300
Oper. Troop Aid [11106], 7191 Kingsland Dr., Memphis, TN 38125, (901)355-8844
Oper. Truth [★20791]
Oper. U.S.A. [12476], 7421 Beverly Blvd., Los Angeles, CA 90036, (323)413-2353
Operational Res. Soc. of Hong Kong [IO], Hong Kong, People's Republic of China
Operational Res. Soc. of India [IO], Calcutta, India
Operational Res. Soc. of New Zealand [IO], Auckland, New Zealand
Operational Res. Soc. of Singapore [IO], Singapore, Singapore
Operational Res. Soc. of Turkey [IO], Ankara, Turkey
Operational Res. Soc. of the United Kingdom [IO], Birmingham, United Kingdom

Operations Research
Military Operations Res. Soc. [7187]
Operations Res. Soc. of China [IO], Beijing, People's Republic of China
Operations Res. Soc. of Israel [IO], Haifa, Israel
Operations Res. Soc. of the Philippines [IO], Quezon City, Philippines
Operations Res. Soc. of South Africa [IO], Matieland, Republic of South Africa
Operative Dentistry; Acad. of [14226]
Operative Plasterers and Cement Masons Intl. Assn. of U.S. and Canada [23168], 11720 Beltsville Dr., Ste. 700, Beltsville, MD 20705, (301)623-1000
Operative Plasterers and Cement Masons Intl. Assn. of U.S. and Canada [23168], 11720 Beltsville Dr., Ste. 700, Beltsville, MD 20705, (301)623-1000
Operative Registered Nurses; Assn. of Peri [15738]
Opetusalan Ammattijarjesto [★IO]
Ophelia Proj. [13549], 718 Nevada Dr., Erie, PA 16505, (814)456-5437
Ophelia Proj. [13549], 718 Nevada Dr., Erie, PA 16505, (814)456-5437
Ophthalmic Administrators; Amer. Soc. of [15287]
Ophthalmic Care for Underserved Sectors; Interprofessional Fostering of [17090]
Ophthalmic Photographers' Soc. [15971], 1887 W Ranch Rd., Nixa, MO 65714-8262, (417)725-0181
Ophthalmic Plastic and Reconstructive Surgery; Amer. Soc. of [14176]
Ophthalmic Registered Nurses; Amer. Soc. of [15729]
Ophthalmological Found. [★17112]
Ophthalmological Soc. of Taiwan [IO], Taipei, Taiwan
Ophthalmologists; Amer. Coll. of Veterinary [17001]

Ophthalmology
Achromatopsia Network [17055]
Amer. Acad. of Ophthalmology [15936]
Amer. Assn. of Certified Orthoptists [15937]
Amer. Assn. for Ophthalmic Standardized Echography [15938]
Amer. Assn. for Pediatric Ophthalmology and Strabismus [15939]
Amer. Bd. of Ophthalmology [15940]
Amer. Ophthalmological Soc. [15941]
Amer. Orthoptic Coun. [15942]
Amer. Soc. of Cataract and Refractive Surgery [15943]
Amer. Uveitis Soc. [15944]
Assn. for Macular Diseases [15945]
Assn. of Nurses Endorsing Transplantation [15946]
Assn. for Ocular Pharmacology and Therapeutics [15947]

Assn. for Ocular Pharmacology and Therapeutics [15947]
Assn. for Res. in Vision and Ophthalmology [15948]
Assn. for Res. in Vision and Ophthalmology [15948]
Assn. for Retinopathy of Prematurity and Related Diseases [15949]
Assn. of Tech. Personnel in Ophthalmology [15950]
Assn. of Univ. Professors of Ophthalmology [15951]
Assn. of Veterans Affairs Ophthalmologists [15952]
Assn. of Veterans Affairs Ophthalmologists [15952]
Assn. of Vision Educators [15953]
Assn. of Vision Educators [15953]
Better Vision Inst. [15954]
Children's Eye Found. [15955]
Contact Lens Assn. of Ophthalmologists [15956]
Contact Lens Coun. [15957]
Eye Surgery Educ. Coun. [15958]
The Glaucoma Found. [15959]
Glaucoma Res. Found. [15960]
Global Vision 2020 [17077]
Intercontinental Fed. of Behavioral Optometry [15994]
Intl. Coun. of Ophthalmology [15961]
Intl. Eye Found. [15962]
Intl. Eye Found. [15962]
Intl. Fed. of Ophthalmological Societies [15961]
Intl. Iridology Practitioners Assn. [15963]
Intl. Iridology Practitioners Assn. [15963]
Intl. Soc. for Genetic Eye Diseases and Retinoblastoma [15964]
Intl. Soc. of Geographical and Epidemiological Ophthalmology [20801]
Intl. Soc. for Low Vision Res. and Rehabilitation [15965]
Intl. Soc. on Metabolic Eye Disease [15966]
Intl. Soc. on Metabolic Eye Disease [15966]
Joint Commn. on Allied Hea. Personnel in Ophthalmology [15967]
Natl. Assn. of Vision Professionals [15968]
Natl. Examining Bd. of Ocularists [15969]
Neuro-Optometric Rehabilitation Assn. Intl. [15559]
North Amer. Neuro-Ophthalmology Soc. [15970]
North Amer. Neuro-Ophthalmology Soc. [15970]
Ophthalmic Photographers' Soc. [15971]
Optometric Glaucoma Soc. [15972]
ORBIS Intl. [15973]
ORBIS Intl. [15973]
Outpatient Ophthalmic Surgery Soc. [15974]
Pan-American Assn. of Ophthalmology [15975]
Pan-American Assn. of Ophthalmology [15975]
Pediatric Keratoplasty Assn. [15976]
Scandinavian Soc. of Cataract and Refractive Surgery [2479]
Scleral Lens Educ. Soc. [14168]
Soc. for Excellence in Eyecare [15977]
Soc. of Eye Surgeons [15978]
Vision Sciences Soc. [7394]
VOSH Intl. [12482]
World Glaucoma Patient Assn. [15979]
Ophthalmology; Amer. Acad. of [15936]
Ophthalmology; Amer. Bd. of [15940]
Ophthalmology; Assn. for Res. in Vision and [15948]
Ophthalmology; Assn. for Res. in Vision and [15948]
Ophthalmology and Strabismus; Amer. Assn. for Pediatric [15939]
Opimian, the Wine Soc. of Canada [IO], Montreal, QC, Canada
Opintotoiminnan Keskusliitto [★IO]
Opioid Dependence; Amer. Assn. for the Treatment of [16734]
OPP Concerned Sheep Breeders Soc. [17036], 228 Main St., Jordanville, NY 13361, (315)858-6042
Opportunities Industrialization Centers of Am. [11955], 1415 N Broad St., Ste. 227, Philadelphia, PA 19122-3323, (215)236-4500
Opportunities Industrialization Centers Intl. [13198], 1500 Walnut St., Ste. 1304, Philadelphia, PA 19102, (215)842-0220

Reference to "IO" in place of a book number signifies that the association may be found in the 50th edition of International Organizations.

Opportunities Industrialization Centers Intl. [13198], 1500 Walnut St., Ste. 1304, Philadelphia, PA 19102, (215)842-0220

Opportunity Finance Network [17390], Public Ledger Bldg., 620 Chestnut St., Ste. 572, Philadelphia, PA 19106, (215)923-4754

Opportunity International-U.S.A. [12261], 2122 York Rd., Ste. 150, Oak Brook, IL 60523, (630)242-4100

OPSEC Professionals Soc. [18599], PO Box 150515, Alexandria, VA 22315-0515

Optical Equipment
  Global Vision 2020 [17077]
  Optical Storage Tech. Assn. [2592]
  Optical Storage Tech. Assn. [2592]
  Optoelectronics Indus. Development Assn. [2593]
  Optoelectronics Indus. Development Assn. [2593]
  VOSH Intl. [12482]
  Zeiss Historical Soc. of Am. [21415]

Optical Imaging Assn. [4727], PO Box 428, Fairfax, VA 22038, (703)836-1360

Optical Industry Assn. - Defunct.

Optical Internetworking Forum [3394], 48377 Fremont Blvd., Ste. 117, Fremont, CA 94538, (510)492-4040

Optical Labs. Assn. [1687], 11096 Lee Hwy., Ste. A-101, Fairfax, VA 22030-5039, (703)359-2830

Optical Labs. Assn. [1687], 11096 Lee Hwy., Ste. A-101, Fairfax, VA 22030-5039, (703)359-2830

Optical Prdt. Code Coun. - Address unknown since 2011.

Optical Soc. of Am. [7188], 2010 Massachusetts Ave. NW, Washington, DC 20036-1023, (202)223-8130

Optical Soc. of India [IO], Calcutta, India

Optical Storage Tech. Assn. [2592], 19925 Stevens Creek Blvd., Cupertino, CA 95014, (408)253-3695

Optical Storage Tech. Assn. [2592], 19925 Stevens Creek Blvd., Cupertino, CA 95014, (408)253-3695

Optical Video Disc Assn. - Defunct.

Optical Wholesalers Assn. [★1687]

Optical Wholesalers Assn. [★1687]

Optical Wholesalers Natl. Assn. [★1687]

Optical Wholesalers Natl. Assn. [★1687]

Optical Women's Assn. [7189], Dave Beebe, Exec. Dir., 14070 Proton Rd., Ste. 100, LB9, Dallas, TX 75244, (972)233-9107

Optician Assn. [IO], Dusseldorf, Germany

Opticianry
  Amer. Bd. of Opticianry [15980]
  Amer. Bd. of Opticianry [15980]
  BiOptic Driving Network U.S.A. [15981]
  Commn. on Opticianry Accreditation [15982]
  Intercontinental Fed. of Behavioral Optometry [15994]
  Intl. Soc. on Metabolic Eye Disease [15966]
  Natl. Acad. of Opticianry [15983]
  Natl. Fed. of Opticianry Schools [15984]
  Opticians Assn. of Am. [15985]
  Scleral Lens Educ. Soc. [14168]

Opticians Assn. of Am. [15985], 4064 E Fir Hill Dr., Lakeland, TN 38002, (901)388-2423

Opticians Assn. of Canada [IO], Winnipeg, MB, Canada

Optics
  Intercontinental Fed. of Behavioral Optometry [15994]
  Optical Soc. of Am. [7188]
  Optical Women's Assn. [7189]
  Optometric Glaucoma Soc. [15972]
  Plastic Optical Fiber Trade Org. [2594]
  SPIE [7190]
  SPIE [7190]
  VOSH Intl. [12482]
  World Glaucoma Patient Assn. [15979]

Optimist Intl. [13071], 4494 Lindell Blvd., St. Louis, MO 63108, (314)371-6000

Optimist Intl. [13071], 4494 Lindell Blvd., St. Louis, MO 63108, (314)371-6000

The Optimists [11377], 2578 31st St., Astoria, NY 11102, (718)278-4953

Optimum Population Trust [IO], Manchester, United Kingdom

Option Inst. and Fellowship [★16867]

Option Inst. and Fellowship [★16867]

Option Inst. Intl. Learning and Training Center [16867], 2080 S Undermountain Rd., Sheffield, MA 01257-9643, (413)229-2100

Option Inst. Intl. Learning and Training Center [16867], 2080 S Undermountain Rd., Sheffield, MA 01257-9643, (413)229-2100

Options for Animals [★17037]

Options for Animals Found. [★17037]

Options for Animals Intl. [17037], Robbie Hroza, PO Box 3682, Cartersville, GA 30120, (309)658-2920

Options for Children in Zambia [11378], 8 Stonegate Ln., Bedford, MA 01730

OPTIONS Service of Project Concern - Defunct.

Optoelectronics Indus. Development Assn. [2593], 2010 Massachusetts Ave. NW, Washington, DC 20036, (202)416-1449

Optoelectronics Indus. Development Assn. [2593], 2010 Massachusetts Ave. NW, Washington, DC 20036, (202)416-1449

Optometric Editors Assn. - Defunct.

Optometric Extension Prog. Found. [15998], 1921 E Carnegie Ave., Ste. 3L, Santa Ana, CA 92705-5510, (949)250-8070

Optometric Glaucoma Soc. [15972], Michael A. Chaglasian, Sec., Illinois Eye Inst., 3241 S Michigan Ave., Chicago, IL 60616-4201, (312)949-7303

Optometric Historical Soc. [15999], 243 N Lindbergh Blvd., St. Louis, MO 63141

Optometrists Assn. Australia [IO], Carlton South, Australia

Optometry
  Accreditation Coun. on Optometric Educ. [15986]
  Amer. Acad. of Optometry [15987]
  Amer. Acad. of Optometry [15987]
  Amer. Optometric Assn. [15988]
  Amer. Optometric Found. [15989]
  Amer. Optometric Student Assn. [15990]
  Assn. of Regulatory Boards of Optometry [15991]
  Assn. of Regulatory Boards of Optometry [15991]
  Assn. of Schools and Colleges of Optometry [15992]
  Beta Sigma Kappa [23611]
  Coll. of Optometrists in Vision Development [15993]
  Giving Vision [17076]
  Global Vision 2020 [17077]
  Intercontinental Fed. of Behavioral Optometry [15994]
  Intercontinental Fed. of Behavioral Optometry [15994]
  Intl. Soc. for Low Vision Res. and Rehabilitation [15965]
  Intl. Soc. on Metabolic Eye Disease [15966]
  Natl. Bd. of Examiners in Optometry [15995]
  Natl. Contact Lens Examiners [15996]
  Natl. Optometric Assn. [15997]
  Neuro-Optometric Rehabilitation Assn. Intl. [15559]
  Omega Delta [23612]
  Optometric Extension Prog. Found. [15998]
  Optometric Historical Soc. [15999]
  Scleral Lens Educ. Soc. [14168]
  Swiss Soc. of Optometry [9675]
  Tear Film and Ocular Surface Soc. [16000]
  Tear Film and Ocular Surface Soc. [16000]
  Vision USA [16001]
  VOSH Intl. [12482]

Oracle Applications Users Gp. [6494], 3525 Piedmont Rd. NE, Bldg. 5, Ste. 300, Atlanta, GA 30305, (404)240-0897

Oracle Development Tools User Gp. [6495], 2520 Independence Blvd., Ste. 201, Wilmington, NC 28412, (910)452-7444

ORACLE Religious Assn. [20193], Sr. Dr. Oralisa Martin, Founder, PO Box 697, Beltsville, MD 20705, (202)635-2672

Orah Gp. NA'AMAT [IO], Melbourne, Australia

Oral Hea. Am. [7966], 410 N Michigan Ave., Ste. 352, Chicago, IL 60611-4211, (312)836-9900

Oral Hearing-Impaired Sect. - Address unknown since 2010.

Oral History Assn. [9791], Madelyn Campbell, Exec. Sec., Dickinson Coll., PO Box 1773, Carlisle, PA 17013-2896, (717)245-1036

Oral History Soc. [IO], Hertfordshire, United Kingdom

Oral and Maxillofacial Pathology; Amer. Acad. of [16109]

Oral and Maxillofacial Pathology; Amer. Bd. of [16112]

Oral and Maxillofacial Surgery
  Amer. Acad. of Restorative Dentistry [14244]
  Amer. Assn. of Endodontists I Amer. Bd. of Endodontics [14250]
  Amer. Assn. of Oral and Maxillofacial Surgeons [16002]
  Amer. Bd. of Oral and Maxillofacial Surgery [16003]
  Amer. Coll. of Oral and Maxillofacial Surgeons [16004]
  Amer. Coll. of Oral and Maxillofacial Surgeons [16004]
  Amer. Soc. of Maxillofacial Surgeons [16005]
  Face Forward [11885]
  Intl. Assn. of Oral and Maxillofacial Surgeons [16006]
  Intl. Assn. of Oral and Maxillofacial Surgeons [16006]
  Uplift Internationale [16007]
  Uplift Internationale [16007]

Oral and Maxillofacial Surgery Overseas [★16044]

Oral and Maxillofacial Surgery Overseas [★16044]

Oral Medicine; Amer. Acad. of [14240]

Oral Roberts Univ. Educational Fellowship [7859], Oral Roberts Univ., 2448 E 81st St., Ste. 600, Tulsa, OK 74137, (918)493-8880

Orangeburg German Swiss Genealogical Soc. [20653], PO Box 974, Orangeburg, SC 29116-0974

Orangutan Conservancy [5100], PO Box 513, Los Angeles, CA 90036

ORBEL [★IO]

ORBIS Intl. [15973], 520 8th Ave., 11th Fl., New York, NY 10018, (646)674-5500

ORBIS Intl. [15973], 520 8th Ave., 11th Fl., New York, NY 10018, (646)674-5500

ORBIS Macau [IO], Macau, Macao

Orchard House [★9393]

Orchestra Librarians' Assn; Major [9994]

Orchestras
  Intl. Conf. of Symphony and Opera Musicians [10218]
  World Fed. of Amateur Orchestras [10346]
  World Fed. of Amateur Orchestras [10346]

Orchestras Canada [IO], Toronto, ON, Canada

Orchestre national des jeunes du Canada [★IO]

Orchestre des Jeunes de l'Union Europeenne [★IO]

Orchestras Canada [★IO]

Orchid Conservation Alliance [4120], 564 Arden Dr., Encinitas, CA 92024-4501, (760)753-3173

Orchids
  Intl. Phalaenopsis Alliance [4671]
  Orchid Conservation Alliance [4120]

Orchids Dominican, S.A. [IO], Santo Domingo, Dominican Republic

Ordem dos Medicos [IO], Lisbon, Portugal

Order of AHEPA [★19010]

Order of the Alhambra [★18953]

Order of Alhambra [★18953]

Order of the Alhambra [★18953]

Order of Alhambra [★18953]

Order of Americans of Armorial Ancestry [20404], Mr. David Carline Smith, Registrar Gen., PO Box 339, Pembroke, KY 42266, (270)475-4572

Order of Architects and Consulting Engineers [IO], Luxembourg, Luxembourg

Order of the Arrow [13027], 1325 W Walnut Hill Ln., PO Box 152079, Irving, TX 75015-2079, (972)580-2438

Order of the Canons Regular of Premontre [IO], Rome, Italy

Order of the Coif [23567], Univ. of North Carolina, School of Law, CB No. 3380, Chapel Hill, NC 27599-3380, (919)962-1322

Order of the Daughters of the King [19714], 101 Weatherstone Dr., Ste. 870, Woodstock, GA 30188, (770)517-8552

Order of DeMolay [★19240]

Order of DeMolay [★19240]

A star before a book entry number signifies that the name is not listed separately, but is mentioned within the entry.

Order of Discalced Carmelites [IO], Rome, Italy
Order of the Founders and Patriots of Am. [20405],
Natl. Soc., Daughters of Founders and Patriots of
Am., The Woodward Bldg., 733 15th St. NW, No.
915, Washington, DC 20005-2112
Order of Friars Minor [IO], Rome, Italy
Order Fulfillment Coun. | Material Handling Indus. of
Am. [3623], 8720 Red Oak Blvd., Ste. 201,
Charlotte, NC 28217-3992, (704)676-1190
Order of the Indian Wars [10095], PO Box 1650,
Johnstown, CO 80534, (970)589-9530
Order of Indian Wars of the U.S. [★10098]
Order of Kush - Address unknown since 2010.
Order of Lafayette [20875], 243 W 70th St., Apt. 6f,
New York, NY 10023-4321, (212)873-9162
Order of the Noble Companions of the Swan [9630],
PO Box 404, Milltown, NJ 08850
Order of the Noble Companions of the Swan [9630],
PO Box 404, Milltown, NJ 08850
Order of Railway Conductors and Brakemen
[★23292]
Order of Saint Andrew the Apostle [19806], 8 E 79th
St., New York, NY 10075-0106, (212)570-3550
Order of Saint Augustine [IO], Rome, Italy
Order of St. Lazarus [IO], Ottawa, ON, Canada
Order of St. Vincent Soc. [★19711]
Order of St. Vincent Soc. [★19711]
Order Selection, Staging and Storage Coun. of the
Material Handling Indus. of Am. [★3623]
Order Sons of Italy in Am. [19080], 219 E St. NE,
Washington, DC 20002, (202)547-2900
Order of Sons of Zion [★19087]
Order of the Stars and Bars [★20387]
Order of United Commercial Travelers of Am.
[19054], 1801 Watermark Dr., Ste. 100, Columbus,
OH 43215, (614)487-9680
Order of United Commercial Travelers of Am. -
Canadian Off. [IO], Calgary, AB, Canada
Orders and Medals Res. Soc. [IO], High Wycombe,
United Kingdom
Orders and Medals Soc. of Am. [21887], PO Box
198, San Ramon, CA 94583
Orders and Medals Soc. of Am. [21887], PO Box
198, San Ramon, CA 94583
Ordinary Assembly of Catholics of the Holy Land
[IO], Jerusalem, Israel
Ordine dei Carmelitani Scalzi [★IO]
Ordine di Sant'Agostino [★IO]
Ordo Fratrum Excalceatorum Beatissimae Mariae
Virginis de Monte Carmelo [★IO]
Ordo Fratrum Minorum [★IO]
Ordre des Architectes et des Ingenieurs-Conseils
[★IO]
L'Ordre de Bienfaisance et de Protection de l'Ordre
des Elans [★IO]
Ordre des Experts Comptables Agrees au Liban
[★IO]
Ordre de Premontre [★IO]
Ordre des Psychologues du Quebec [IO], Montreal,
QC, Canada
Ordre de Saint-Lazare au Canada [★IO]
L'Ordre Souverain Militaire Hospitalier de Malte
Assn. Canadienne [★IO]
Oregon-California Trails Assn. [9722], PO Box 1019,
Independence, MO 64051-0519, (816)252-2276
Oregon Horsemen's Benevolent Protective Assn.
[22664], 10350 N Vancouver Way, No. 351,
Portland, OR 97217-7530, (503)285-4941
Oregon Ryegrass Growers Seed Commn. [4512],
PO Box 3366, Salem, OR 97302-0366, (503)364-
2944
Orgalime - the European engineering industries as-
sociation [IO], Brussels, Belgium
Organ
    Reed Organ Soc. [10284]
Organ Center [★16920]
Organ CH LLC [10276], PO Box 290786, Charles-
town, MA 02129-0214, (617)241-8550
Organ Historical Soc. [10277], PO Box 26811,
Richmond, VA 23261, (804)353-9226
Organ Historical Trust of Australia [IO], Camberwell,
Australia
Organ Literature Found. - Defunct.
Organ Recovery [★14424]
Organ Recovery and Educ; Center for [16905]

Organ Sharing; United Network for [16920]
Organ Transplant Assn; Amer. [16897]
Organ Transplant Fund [★16913]
Organic Acidemia Assn. [14619], PO Box 1008, Pi-
nole, CA 94564, (510)672-2476
Organic Agriculture Assn. [IO], Bairnsdale, Australia
Organic Certifiers Caucus [★4722]
Organic Consumers Assn. [4762], 6771 S Silver Hill
Dr., Finland, MN 55603, (218)226-4164
Organic Crop Improvement Assn. [4363], 1340 N
Cotner Blvd., Lincoln, NE 68505, (402)477-2323
Organic Crop Improvement Assn. [4363], 1340 N
Cotner Blvd., Lincoln, NE 68505, (402)477-2323
Organic Farming
    Accredited Certifiers Assn. [4760]
    Demeter Biodynamic Trade Assn. [4350]
    Food Trade Sustainability Leadership Assn.
        [1387]
    Independent Organic Inspectors Assn. [4761]
    Organic Consumers Assn. [4762]
    Organic Growers Assn. Western Australia [14898]
    Organic Seed Growers and Trade Assn. [4883]
    Textile Exchange [4763]
    Universal Proutist Farmers Fed. [4365]
    World Wide Opportunities on Organic Farms -
        USA [17173]
Organic Food Alliance [★4722]
Organic Food Fed. [IO], Swaffham, United Kingdom
Organic Growers Assn. Western Australia [IO],
Booragoon, Australia
Organic Growers of Australia [IO], Chermside,
Australia
Organic Reactions Catalysis Soc. [6417], Lilly
Corporate Ctr., DC 1940, Indianapolis, IN 46285,
(317)433-0372
Organic Seed Alliance [4882], PO Box 772, Port
Townsend, WA 98368, (360)385-7192
Organic Seed Growers and Trade Assn. [4883], PO
Box 512, Montrose, CO 81402, (970)275-3409
Organic Textile [★4763]
Organic Trade Assn. [4722], 28 Vernon St., Ste.
413, Brattleboro, VT 05301, (802)275-3800
OrganicAthlete [22232], PO Box 33, Graton, CA
95444, (707)861-0004
Organisatie Van Advies en Ingenieursbureaus [★IO]
Org. mondiale des douanes [★IO]
Org. mondiale des personnes handicapees [★IO]
L'Organisation pour les carrieres en environnement
[★IO]
Org. Africaine de la Propriete Intellectuelle [★IO]
Org. Afro-Asiatique pour la Developpement Rural
[★IO]
Org. of Asia Pacific News Agencies [IO], Jakarta,
Indonesia
L'Organisation des Assurances Africaines [★IO]
Org. Canadienne pour l'Education au Ser. du Devel-
oppement [★IO]
Org. des Capitales et des Villes Islamiques [★IO]
Org. of Caribbean Utility Regulators [IO], George-
town, Guyana
Org. Catholique pour la Promotion Humaine - Cari-
tas Rep. de Guinee [IO], Conakry, Guinea
Org. de la Charite pour un Developpement Integral -
Caritas Togo [IO], Lome, Togo
Org. Cooperation et de Developpement
Economiques [★IO]
Org. for the Cooperation of Railways [IO], Warsaw,
Poland
Org. mondiale d'endoscopie digestive [★IO]
Org. mondiale d'Etudes Specialisees pour les
Maladies de l'Oesophage [★IO]
Org. of Eastern Caribbean States [IO], Castries, St.
Lucia
Org. for Economic Co-Operation and Development
[IO], Paris, France
Org. of European Aluminium Refiners and Remelters
[IO], Dusseldorf, Germany
Org. for European Economic Co-operation [★17585]
Org. of European Indus. Transforming Fruit and
Vegetables [IO], Brussels, Belgium
Org. Europeenne des Indus. Transformatics de Fruits
et de Legumes [★IO]
Org. Europeenne pour l'Equipement de l'Aviation
Civile [★IO]
Org. Europeenne pour l'Exploitation de Satellites
Meteorologiques [★IO]

Org. Europeenne et Mediterraneenne pour la Protec-
tion des Plantes [★IO]
Org. Europeenne pour la Qualite [★IO]
Org. Europeenne pour la Recherche Nucleaire
[★IO]
Org. Europeenne pour la Recherche et le Traitement
du Cancer [★IO]
Org. Europeenne pour des Recherches As-
tronomiques dans l'Hemisphere Austral [★IO]
Org. Europeenne pour les Recherches Chimiosenso-
rielles [★IO]
Org. Europeenne de Telecommunications par Satel-
lite [★IO]
Org. de Femmes pour les Prisonnieres Politiques
[★IO]
Org. Gestosis - Soc. for the Stud. of Pathophysiol-
ogy of Pregnancy [IO], Basel, Switzerland
Org. of Huntington in Greece [IO], Athens, Greece
Org. Interafricaine du Cafe [★IO]
Org. Intergouvernementale pour les Transports Inter-
nationaux Ferroviaires [★IO]
Org. Internationale de Biophysique Pure et Appli-
quee [★IO]
L'Organisation Internationale du Cafe [★IO]
Org. Internationale des Commissions de Valeurs
[★IO]
Org. Internationale des Constructeurs d'Automobiles
[★IO]
Org. Internationale des Femmes Sionistes [★IO]
Org. Internationale des Institutions Superieures de
Control des Finances Publiques [★IO]
Org. Internationale pour l'Elimination de Toutes les
Formes de Discrimination Raciale [★IO]
Org. Internationale de Lutte Biologique Contre les
Animaux et les Plantes Nuisibles [★IO]
Org. Internationale de Metrologie Legale [★IO]
Org. Internationale de Normalisation [★IO]
Org. Internationale de Police Criminelle [★IO]
Org. Internationale pour le Progres [★IO]
Org. Internationale de Recherche sur la Cellule
[★IO]
Org. Internationale de Recherche sur le Cerveau
[★IO]
Org. Internationale des Scenographes, Techniciens
et Architectes de Theatre [★IO]
Org. Internationale des Telecommunications Spa-
tiales [★IO]
Org. Internationale de la Vigne et du Vin [★IO]
Org. Islamique pour l'Education, les Sciences et la
Culture [★IO]
Org. de l'Aviation Civile Internationale [★IO]
Org. pour l'Etude Phyto-Taxonomique de la Region
Mediterraneenne [★IO]
Org. pour l'histoire du Canada [★IO]
Org. Maritime Internationale [★IO]
Org. Meteorologique Mondiale [★IO]
Org. Mondiale Contre la Torture/SOS-Torture [★IO]
Org. Mondiale de Gastroenterologie [★IO]
Org. Mondiale de Labourage [★IO]
Org. Mondiale pour l'Education Prescolaire [★IO]
Org. Mondiale de la Propriete Intellectuelle [★IO]
Org. Mondiale de la Sante [★IO]
Org. Mondiale de la Sante Animale [★IO]
Org. Mondiale pour la Systemique et la Cybernet-
ique [★IO]
Org. Nationale de la sante autochtone [★IO]
Org. Nationale des Femmes Immigrantes et des
Femmes Appartement a une Minorite Visible du
Canada [★IO]
Org. des Nations Unies pour le Developpement In-
dustriel [★IO]
Org. des Nations Unies pour l'Education, la Sci. et la
Culture [★IO]
Org. Neederlandaise de Developpement - Mali
[★IO]
Org. Neerlandaise de Developpement - Cameroon
[★IO]
Org. Nord Americaine Pour La Protection des Plan-
tes [★IO]
Org. for Nordic Elecl. Cooperation [IO], Oslo,
Norway
Org. des Pays Exportateurs de Petrole [★IO]
Org. des Peches de l'Atlantique Nord-Ouest [★IO]
Org. of Pharmaceutical Producers of India [IO],
Mumbai, India

Reference to "IO" in place of a book number signifies that the association may be found in the 50th edition of International Organizations.

L'Organisation Pour La Conservation Du Saumon De l'Atlantique Nord [★IO]

Org. de Producteurs dans le Secteur de la Peche Belge [★IO]

Org. for Professionals in Regulatory Affairs [IO], London, United Kingdom

Org. des Radiodiffusions des Etats Islamiques [★IO]

Org. Regionale Africaine De Communications Par Satellite [★IO]

Org. Regionale Africaine de Normalisation [★IO]

Org. of Rwandese Potters' [IO], Kigali, Rwanda

Org. pour la Sauvegarde des Droits des Enfants [★IO]

Org. Suisse pour l'Information Geographique [★IO]

Org. of Swedish-Speaking Teachers in Finland [IO], Helsinki, Finland

Org. du Traite de l'Atlantique Nord [★IO]

Org. Universitaire Interamericaine [★IO]

Org. des Villes Arabes [★IO]

Org. Werbungtreibende im Markenverband [IO], Berlin, Germany

Org. fur die Zusammenarbeit der Eisenbahnen [★IO]

Organisme Europeen de Recherche sur la Carie [★IO]

Organismo Internacional Regional de Sanidad Agropecuaria [★IO]

Organismo para la Proscripcion de las Armas Nucleares en la Am. Latin y el Caribe [★IO]

Organizacion Arabe de Derchos Humanos [★IO]

Organizacion de las Ciudades del Patrimonio Mundial [★IO]

Organizacion Empresarial Espanola de la Peleteria [IO], Madrid, Spain

Organizacion de las Entidades Fiscalizadoras Superiores de Europa [★IO]

Organizacion de Entidades Fiscalizadoras Superiors de Africa [★IO]

Organizacion de Estados Iberoamericanos para la Educacion, la Ciencia y la Cultura [★IO]

Organizacion para Estudios Tropicales [★7586]

Organizacion para Estudios Tropicales [★IO]

Organizacion para Estudios Tropicales [★7586]

Organizacion Internacional del Azucar [★IO]

Organizacion Internacional para las Migraciones [★IO]

Organizacion Internacional para las Migraciones - Guatemala [★IO]

Organizacion Intl. para las Migraciones - Costa Rica [★IO]

Organizacion Internationale del Cacao [★IO]

Organizacion Latinoamericana de Energia [★IO]

Organizacion Mundial del Comercio [★IO]

Organizacion Mundial de Peronas con Discapacidad [★IO]

Organizacion Mundial del Turismo [★IO]

Organizacion de la Naciones Unidas para La Agricultura y la Alimentacion [★IO]

Organizacion PROFAUNA [IO], Buenos Aires, Argentina

Organizacion Regional del Oriente para la Administracion Publica [★IO]

Organizatia neguvernamentala BIOS [★IO]

Org. for the Advancement of Knowledge [3958], 1212 SW 5th St., Grants Pass, OR 97526-6104, (541)476-5588

Org. for the Advancement of Structured Info. Standards [7524], 25 Corporate Dr., Ste. 103, Burlington, MA 01803-4238

Org. of Agreement States [5955], Off. of Radiation Control, State Dept. of Public Hea., PO Box 303017, Montgomery, AL 36130-3017, (334)206-5391

Org. of Amer. Historians [9792], 112 N Bryan Ave., Bloomington, IN 47408-4141, (812)855-7311

Org. of Amer. Kodaly Educators [8668], 1612 29th Ave. S, Moorhead, MN 56560, (218)227-6253

Org. of Amer. States [17181], 17th St. and Constitution Ave. NW, Washington, DC 20006, (202)458-3000

Org. of Amer. States [17181], 17th St. and Constitution Ave. NW, Washington, DC 20006, (202)458-3000

Org. of Arab Petroleum Exporting Countries [IO], Safat, Kuwait

Org. for Autism Res. [13800], 2000 N 14th St., Ste. 710, Arlington, VA 22201, (703)243-9710

Org. for Bat Conservation [5101], PO Box 801, Bloomfield Hills, MI 48303, (248)645-3232

Org. of Biological Field Stations [6312], Jasper Ridge Biological Preserve, Stanford Univ., 4001 Sandhill Rd., Woodside, CA 94062, (650)861-6814

Org. of Black Airline Pilots [152], 1 Westbrook Corporate Center, Westchester, IL 60154, (703)753-2047

Org. of Black Designers [9574], 300 M St. SW, Ste. N110, Washington, DC 20024, (202)659-3918

Org. of Black Screenwriters [1215], 3010 Wilshire Blvd., No. 269, Los Angeles, CA 90010, (323)735-2050

Org. of Black Screenwriters [1215], 3010 Wilshire Blvd., No. 269, Los Angeles, CA 90010, (323)735-2050

Org. of the Black Sea Economic Cooperation [IO], Istanbul, Turkey

Org. of Bricklin Owners [21143], PO Box 24775, Rochester, NY 14624-0775, (585)247-1575

Org. of CANDU Indus. [IO], Pickering, ON, Canada

Org. of Chinese Amer. Women [17670], 4641 Montgomery Ave., Ste. 208, Bethesda, MD 20814, (301)907-3898

Org. of Chinese Americans [17243], 1322 18th St. NW, Washington, DC 20036-1803, (202)223-5500

Org. of Chinese Americans [17243], 1322 18th St. NW, Washington, DC 20036-1803, (202)223-5500

Org. for Competitive Markets [3723], PO Box 6486, Lincoln, NE 68506, (402)817-4443

Org. of Country Radio Broadcasters [★488]

Org. for Defending Victims of Violence [IO], Tehran, Iran

Org. Design Forum [2300], 5713 Carriage House Ct., Apex, NC 27539, (919)662-8548

Org. Design Forum [2300], 5713 Carriage House Ct., Apex, NC 27539, (919)662-8548

Organization Development

Bus. Architects Assn. [2595]

Bus. Retention and Expansion Intl. [1055]

Intl. Soc. for Organization Development [2596]

Org. Development Inst. [2596]

Org. Development Network [2597]

RandomKid [13554]

Ruckus Soc. [18222]

Soc. for Organizational Learning [2598]

Soc. for Organizational Learning [2598]

Org. Development Inst. [2596], 11234 Walnut Ridge Rd., Chesterland, OH 44026, (440)729-7419

Org. Development Inst. [★2596]

Org. Development Network [2597], 401 N Michigan Ave., Ste. 2200, Chicago, IL 60611, (312)321-5136

Org. des Directeurs des Musees d'art du Canada [★IO]

Org. for Economic Cooperation and Development [17585], 2001 L St. NW, Ste. 650, Washington, DC 20036-4922, (202)785-6323

Org. for the Enforcement of Child Support - Defunct.

Org. for Entrepreneurial Development [7806], 25 Pine St., Ste. 204, Rockaway, NJ 07866, (800)767-0999

Org. of European Cancer Institutes [IO], Brussels, Belgium

Org. for Fair Treatment of Intl. Investment [★18484]

Org. for Fair Treatment of Intl. Investment [★18484]

Org. for Flora Neotropica [6363], New York Botanical Garden, Bronx, NY 10458-5126, (718)817-8625

Org. for Flora Neotropica [6363], New York Botanical Garden, Bronx, NY 10458-5126, (718)817-8625

Org. of Greenlandic Employers [IO], Nuuk, Greenland

Org. for the History of Canada [IO], Ottawa, ON, Canada

Org. for Human Brain Mapping [7159], 5841 Cedar Lake Rd., Ste. 204, Minneapolis, MN 55416, (952)646-2029

Org. of Ibero-American States for Educ., Sci. and Culture - Spain [IO], Madrid, Spain

Org. for Indus., Spiritual and Cultural Advancement - Intl. [IO], Tokyo, Japan

Org. of Inland Biological Field Stations [★6312]

Org. for Intl. Cooperation [17980], Bldg. C, Ste. 196, 100 Conestoga Dr., Marlton, NJ 08053, (856)596-6679

Org. for Intl. Investment [18484], 1225 Nineteenth St. NW, Ste. 501, Washington, DC 20036-2453, (202)659-1903

Org. for Intl. Investment [18484], 1225 Nineteenth St. NW, Ste. 501, Washington, DC 20036-2453, (202)659-1903

Org. Intl. de Protection Civile [★IO]

Org. Internationale du Travail Bur. de l'OIT pour l'Union Europeenne et le Benelux [★IO]

Org. of Islamic Capitals and Cities [IO], Jeddah, Saudi Arabia

Org. for Medical and Psychological Assistance for Children Overseas [14094], 14 Curve St., Lexington, MA 02420

Org. for Medical and Psychological Assistance for Children Overseas [14094], 14 Curve St., Lexington, MA 02420

Org. of News Ombudsmen [2864], Debbie Kornmiller, Treas., The Arizona Daily Star, 4850 S Park Ave., Tucson, AZ 85714

Org. of News Ombudsmen [2864], Debbie Kornmiller, Treas., The Arizona Daily Star, 4850 S Park Ave., Tucson, AZ 85714

Org. of Newspaper Ombudsmen [★2864]

Org. of Newspaper Ombudsmen [★2864]

Org. de Paises Arabes Exportadores de Petroleo [★IO]

Org. of Pakistani Entrepreneurs of North Am. - Address unknown since 2011.

Org. of Parents Through Surrogacy [13305], PO Box 611, Gurnee, IL 60031, (847)782-0224

Org. of the Petroleum Exporting Countries [IO], Vienna, Austria

Org. for the Phyto-Taxonomic Investigation of the Mediterranean Area [IO], Palermo, Italy

Org. for Professional Astrology - Address unknown since 2011.

Org. for the Promotion and Advancement of Small Telecommunications Companies [3602], 2020 K St. NW, 7th Fl., Washington, DC 20006, (202)659-5990

Org. for the Protection and Advancement of Small Telephone Companies [★3602]

Org. for the Protection of Children's Rights [IO], St.-Leonard, QC, Canada

Org. of Regulatory and Clinical Associates [458], PO Box 3490, Redmond, WA 98073, (206)464-0825

Org. for the Relief of Underprivileged Women and Children in Africa [12875], PO Box 278, Waldorf, MD 20604, (202)239-0134

Org. for the Relief of Underprivileged Women and Children in Africa [12875], PO Box 278, Waldorf, MD 20604, (202)239-0134

Org. for Res. on Women and Commun. [10645], Dr. Valerie Renegar, San Diego State Univ., School of Commun., 5500 Campanile Dr., San Diego, CA 92182

Org. for Safety and Asepsis Procedures [14308], PO Box 6297, Annapolis, MD 21401, (410)571-0003

Org. for Security and Co-operation in Europe [IO], Vienna, Austria

Org. for Social Development of Unemployed Youth [IO], Dhaka, Bangladesh

Org. for Social Sci. Res. in Eastern and Southern Africa [IO], Addis Ababa, Ethiopia

Org. of Spirit Indus. Providers [22452], PO Box 752790, Memphis, TN 38175-2790, (800)238-0286

Org. for the Stud. of Sex Differences [7406], 1025 Connecticut Ave. NW, Ste. 701, Washington, DC 20036, (202)496-5002

Org. of Teratology Info. Services [13846], Univ. of Arizona, Drachman Hall, PO Box 210202, Tucson, AZ 85721-0202, (520)626-3547

Org. for Tropical Stud. - Costa Rica [IO], San Jose, Costa Rica

Org. for Tropical Stud., North Amer. Office [7586], Duke Univ., PO Box 90630, Durham, NC 27708-0630, (919)684-5774

Org. for Tropical Stud., North Amer. Off. [7586], Duke Univ., PO Box 90630, Durham, NC 27708-0630, (919)684-5774

Org. for Understanding Cluster Headaches [14690], 3225 Winding Way, Round Rock, TX 78664

Org. of Wildlife Planners [5102], Nebraska Game and Parks Commn., 2200 N 33rd St., Lincoln, NE 68503, (402)471-5448

A star before a book entry number signifies that the name is not listed separately, but is mentioned within the entry.

Org. of Women in Intl. Trade Alberta [IO], Calgary, AB, Canada

Org. of Women Writers of Africa - Address unknown since 2010.

Org. of World Heritage Cities [IO], Quebec, QC, Canada

Organizational Behavior Teaching Soc. [6262], Dr. Cynthia Krom, Treas., Marist Coll., School of Mgt., 3399 North Rd., Poughkeepsie, NY 12601

Organizational Systems Res. Assn. [8969], Morehead State Univ., 150 Univ. Blvd., Box 2478, Morehead, KY 40351-1689, (606)783-2718

Organizations
BoardSource [12592]
Corporate Social Responsibility Assn. [964]
Coun. on Foundations [12593]
Found. Center [12594]
Intl. Soc. for Third-Sector Res. [12595]
Intl. Soc. for Third-Sector Res. [12595]
Mgt. Assistance Gp. [12596]
Natl. Black United Fund [12597]
North Star Fund [12598]
Social Contract Press [12599]
United Way of Am. [12056]

Organizations Staff
Intl. Civil Ser. Commn. [23259]
Intl. Civil Ser. Commn. [23259]
OAS Staff Assn. [23260]
United Nations Staff Union [23261]
United Nations Staff Union [23261]

Organize, Inc. [★11657]

Organize Training Center [11657], 442 Vicksburg St., San Francisco, CA 94114, (415)648-6894

Organized Flying Adjusters [2027], 1439 Skyhawk Pl., Wright City, MO 63390

Organizers' Collaborative [17398], 14 Beacon St., Ste. 720, Boston, MA 02108, (617)720-6190

Organizing Bur. of European School Student Unions [IO], Brussels, Belgium

Organizing Comm. for a Natl. Writers Union [★23320]

Organizzazione Internazionale del Lavoro Ufficio per Italia e San Marino [★IO]

Orgonomy
Amer. Coll. of Orgonomy [16008]

Orient Crusades-Gospel Outreach [★20078]
Orient Crusades-Gospel Outreach [★20078]
Orientacijska Zveza Slovenije [★IO]
Oriental Boat Mission [★20023]
Oriental Boat Mission [★20023]
Oriental Ceramic Soc. [IO], Cambridge, United Kingdom

Oriental Healing
Accreditation Commn. for Acupuncture and Oriental Medicine [16009]
Amer. Acad. of Medical Acupuncture [16010]
Amer. Assn. of Acupuncture and Oriental Medicine [16011]
Amer. Assn. of Acupuncture and Oriental Medicine [16011]
Community Acupuncture Network [13579]
Coun. of Colleges of Acupuncture and Oriental Medicine [16012]
East West Acad. of Healing Arts [16013]
G-Jo Inst. [16014]
Jin Shin Do Found. for Bodymind Acupressure [16015]
Jin Shin Do Found. for Bodymind Acupressure [16015]
Natl. Certification Commn. for Acupuncture and Oriental Medicine [16016]
Ohashi Inst. [16017]
Ohashi Inst. [16017]
ZY Qigong [13722]

Oriental Missionary Soc. [★20080]
Oriental Missionary Soc. [★20080]
Oriental Numismatic Soc. [IO], Lekkerkerk, Netherlands

Oriental Rug Importers Assn. [2071], 100 Park Plaza Dr., Secaucus, NJ 07094, (201)866-5054

Oriental Rug Retailers of Am. [2072], Elizabeth Arnold, Exec. Dir., PO Box 71831, Richmond, VA 23255, (804)270-3195

Orientation Directors Conf. [★7674]

Orienteering
Natl. Assn. of Competitive Mounted Orienteering [22794]

Natl. Assn. of Competitive Mounted Orienteering [22794]
U.S. Orienteering Fed. [22795]

Orienteering Assn. of Hong Kong [IO], Hong Kong, People's Republic of China

Orienteering Australia [IO], Mitchell, Australia

Origami
Origami U.S.A. [22000]

Origami U.S.A. [22000], 15 W 77th St., New York, NY 10024-5192, (212)769-5635

Original Doll Artists Coun. of Am. [21697], Myra Sherrod, 2nd VP, 1251 Garden Circle Dr., St. Louis, MO 63125, (314)894-1489

Original Equip. Suppliers Assn. [697], 1301 W Long Lake Rd., Ste. 225, Troy, MI 48098, (248)952-6401

Original Hobo Nickel Soc. [21989], Verne Walrafen, Sec./Webmaster, 12000 Sunset Ridge Dr., Ozawkie, KS 66070-6045

Original Paper Doll Artists Guild [21698], PO Box 14, Kingfield, ME 04947, (207)265-2500

Orillia Against Drunk Driving [IO], Orillia, ON, Canada

Orioles
Fraternal Order Orioles [19184]

Orion [★19800]
Orion [★19800]

Ornamental Aquatic Trade Assn. [IO], Westbury, United Kingdom

Ornamental Concrete Producers Assn. [835], 759 Phelps Johnson Rd., Leitchfield, KY 42754, (270)879-6319

Ornamental Fish Intl. - Defunct.

Ornithological Coun. [7204], 8722 Preston Pl., Chevy Chase, MD 20815, (301)986-8568

Ornithological Societies of North Am. [7205], 5400 Bosque Blvd., Ste. 680, Waco, TX 76710, (254)399-9636

Ornithological Soc. of Japan [IO], Nara, Japan

Ornithological Soc. of the Middle East [IO], Sandy, United Kingdom

Ornithological Soc. of New Zealand [IO], Nelson, New Zealand

Ornithological Soc. of Polynesia [IO], Tahiti, French Polynesia

Ornithology
Amer. Birding Assn. [7191]
Amer. Birding Assn. [7191]
Amer. Ornithologists' Union [7192]
Assn. of Field Ornithologists [7193]
Avicultural Soc. of Am. [7194]
Avicultural Soc. of Am. [7194]
Cooper Ornithological Soc. [7195]
Cooper Ornithological Soc. [7195]
Cornell Lab of Ornithology [7196]
Eastern Bird Banding Assn. [7197]
Hartz Club of Am. [7198]
Hawk Migration Assn. of North Am. [7199]
Hawkwatch Intl. [7200]
Hawkwatch Intl. [7200]
Inland Bird Banding Assn. [7201]
The Intl. Osprey Found. [5068]
North Amer. Banding Coun. [7202]
North Amer. Banding Coun. [7202]
Nuttall Ornithological Club [7203]
Ornithological Coun. [7204]
Ornithological Societies of North Am. [7205]
Wilson Ornithological Soc. [7206]

Orofacial Pain; Amer. Acad. of [14241]

Oromo-American Citizens Coun. - Address unknown since 2011.

Orphan Found. [★11491]

Orphan Found. of Am. [11491], 21351 Gentry Dr., Ste. 130, Sterling, VA 20166, (571)203-0270

Orphan Resources Intl. [11379], 550 W Trout Run Rd., Ephrata, PA 17522, (717)733-7444

Orphan Resources Intl. [11379], 550 W Trout Run Rd., Ephrata, PA 17522, (717)733-7444

Orphan Support Africa [11380], 2424 York St., Ste. 248, Philadelphia, PA 19125, (215)454-2832

Orphan Train Heritage Soc. of Am. [★20647]

Orphan Voyage - Address unknown since 2010.

Orphan World Relief [11381], 417 W Kanawha Ave., Columbus, OH 43214, (614)596-5306

OrphanAid Africa [11382], 268 Bush St., No. 3100, San Francisco, CA 94104, (415)830-3823

OrphanAid Africa [11382], 268 Bush St., No. 3100, San Francisco, CA 94104, (415)830-3823

Orphans Africa [11621], 2610 N 8th St., Tacoma, WA 98406-7207, (253)549-0089

Orphans Against AIDS [11383], 1110 Knollwood Dr., Buffalo Grove, IL 60089

Orphans to Ambassadors [11384], 126 SW 148th St., Ste. C100-26, Seattle, WA 98166, (206)245-4522

Orphans Intl. Worldwide [11492], 540 Main St., Ste. 418, New York, NY 10044, (212)755-7302

Orphan's Lifeline of Hope Intl. [11385], PO Box 1100, Kalispell, MT 59901, (406)257-0868

Orphan's Lifeline of Hope Intl. [11385], PO Box 1100, Kalispell, MT 59901, (406)257-0868

Orphans of Rwanda, Inc. [★13525]

Orquideas Del Valle [IO], Cali, Colombia

Orr Shalom Children's Homes [IO], Beit Shemesh, Israel

Orsagos Magyar Banyaszati Es Kohaszati Egyesulet [★IO]

ORT Am. [12413], 75 Maiden Ln., 10th Fl., New York, NY 10038, (212)505-7700

ORT Am. [12413], 75 Maiden Ln., 10th Fl., New York, NY 10038, (212)505-7700

ORT Canada [IO], Toronto, ON, Canada

Ortho-Bionomy Intl; Soc. of [13709]
Ortho-Bionomy Intl; Soc. of [13709]

Orthodontic Soc; Amer. [14268]

Orthodontic Soc. of Ireland [IO], Dublin, Ireland

Orthodontics; Amer. Bd. of [14255]

Orthodontists; Amer. Assn. of [14251]

Orthodox and Anglican Fellowship - Defunct.

Orthodox Christian Assn. of Medicine, Psychology and Religion [16416], 50 Goddard Ave., Brookline, MA 02445, (303)278-0815

Orthodox Christians for Life [20223], PO Box 805, Melville, NY 11747, (516)271-4408

Orthodox Theological Soc. in Am. [19647], Penn State Univ., Dept. of History, 312 Weaver Bldg., University Park, PA 16802-5500

Orthodox Union [19893], 11 Broadway, New York, NY 10004, (212)563-4000

Orthopaedic Physician's Assistants; Amer. Soc. of [16027]

Orthopaedic Res. and Educ. Found. [16041], 6300 N River Rd., Ste. 700, Rosemont, IL 60018, (847)698-9980

Orthopaedic Res. Soc. [16042], 6300 N River Rd., Ste. 602, Rosemont, IL 60018-4237, (847)823-5770

Orthopaedic Technologists; Natl. Assn. of [15380]

Orthopaedic Trauma Assn. [16043], 6300 N River Rd., Ste. 727, Rosemont, IL 60018-4226, (847)698-1631

Orthopaedics Overseas [16044], 1900 L St. NW, Ste. 310, Washington, DC 20036, (202)296-0928

Orthopaedics Overseas [16044], 1900 L St. NW, Ste. 310, Washington, DC 20036, (202)296-0928

Orthopedic Appliance and Limb Mfrs. Assn. [★1679]

Orthopedic Found. for Animals [17038], 2300 E Nifong Blvd., Columbia, MO 65201-3806, (573)442-0418

Orthopedic Soc; Veterinary [17051]

Orthopedic Surgical Mfrs. Assn. [1688], PO Box 38805, Germantown, TN 38183-0805, (901)758-0806

Orthopedics
Amer. Acad. of Craniofacial Pain [16018]
Amer. Acad. of Orthopaedic Surgeons [16019]
Amer. Acad. of Orthopaedic Surgeons [16019]
Amer. Assn. of Orthopaedic Executives [16020]
Amer. Assn. of Orthopedic Medicine [16021]
Amer. Back Soc. [16022]
Amer. Bd. of Orthopaedic Surgery [16023]
Amer. Orthopaedic Assn. [16024]
Amer. Orthopaedic Foot and Ankle Soc. [16025]
Amer. Osteopathic Acad. of Orthopedics [16026]
Amer. Soc. of Orthopaedic Physician's Assistants [16027]
Amer. Soc. of Orthopedic Professionals [16028]
Arthroscopy Assn. of North Am. [16029]
Assn. of Bone and Joint Surgeons [16030]
Chiropractic Orthopedists of North Am. [14126]
Clinical Orthopaedic Soc. [16031]

Reference to "IO" in place of a book number signifies that the association may be found in the 50th edition of International Organizations.

Compassion Care for Disabled Children [16032]
Compassion Care for Disabled Children [16032]
Coun. on Chiropractic Orthopedics [16033]
Egyptian Orthopaedic Assn. [15747]
Hip Soc. [16034]
Intl. Coll. of Cranio-Mandibular Orthopedics [16035]
Intl. Coll. of Cranio-Mandibular Orthopedics [16035]
Intl. Soc. of Arthroscopy, Knee Surgery and Ortho-paedic Sports Medicine [16036]
Intl. Soc. of Arthroscopy, Knee Surgery and Ortho-paedic Sports Medicine [16036]
J. Robert Gladden Orthopaedic Soc. [16037]
Jaw Joints and Allied Musculo-Skeletal Disorders Found. [16038]
Natl. Bd. for Certification of Orthopaedic Technolo-gists [16039]
Natl. Osteoporosis Found. [16040]
Orthopaedic Res. and Educ. Found. [16041]
Orthopaedic Res. Soc. [16042]
Orthopaedic Trauma Assn. [16043]
Orthopaedics Overseas [16044]
Orthopaedics Overseas [16044]
Osteogenesis Imperfecta Found. [16045]
Pediatric Orthopedic Soc. of North Am. [16046]
Ruth Jackson Orthopaedic Soc. [16047]
Spine Arthroplasty Soc. [15688]
Orthopedics and Medicine; Amer. Coll. of Foot and Ankle [16291]
Orthopedics and Primary Podiatric Medicine; Amer. Bd. of Podiatric [16289]
Orthopedists; Amer. Coll. of Chiropractic [14120]
Orthopedists; Amer. Coll. of Chiropractic [14120]
Orthopsychiatric Assn; Amer. [16329]
Orthopterists' Soc. [6848], Univ. of Wisconsin - Stout, Biology Dept., 331D Sci. Wing, Menomonie, WI 54751, (715)232-2562
Orthopterists' Soc. [6848], Univ. of Wisconsin - Stout, Biology Dept., 331D Sci. Wing, Menomonie, WI 54751, (715)232-2562
Orthoptic Coun; Amer. [15942]
Orthoptists; Amer. Assn. of Certified [15937]
Orthotics and Prosthetics
Amer. Acad. of Orthotists and Prosthetists [16048]
Amer. Bd. for Certification in Orthotics, Prosthetics and Pedorthics [16049]
Assn. of Children's Prosthetic-Orthotic Clinics [16050]
Bd. for Orthotist/Prosthetist Certification [16051]
Intl. Campaign to Ban Landmines [17553]
A Leg To Stand On [12600]
Natl. Assn. for the Advancement of Orthotics and Prosthetics [16052]
Orton Dyslexia Soc. [★14428]
Orton Dyslexia Soc. [★14428]
Orton Soc. [★14428]
Orton Soc. [★14428]
Osaka Chamber of Commerce and Indus. [IO], Osaka, Japan
Osborne Assn. [11728], 809 Westchester Ave., Bronx, NY 10455, (718)707-2600
Osho Chidvilas - Defunct.
Oslo Chamber of Commerce [IO], Oslo, Norway
OSPAR Commn. [IO], London, United Kingdom
Osseointegration; Acad. of [14227]
Osseous Heteroplasia Assn; Progressive [14624]
OsteoArthritis Res. Soc. Intl. [16623], 15000 Com-merce Pkwy., Ste. C, Mount Laurel, NJ 08054, (856)439-1385
OsteoArthritis Res. Soc. Intl. [16623], 15000 Com-merce Pkwy., Ste. C, Mount Laurel, NJ 08054, (856)439-1385
Osteogenesis Imperfecta Found. [16045], 804 W Diamond Ave., Ste. 210, Gaithersburg, MD 20878, (301)947-0083
Osteology
Amer. Soc. for Bone and Mineral Res. [16053]
Intl. Soc. for Clinical Densitometry [16054]
Intl. Soc. for Clinical Densitometry [16054]
Osteopathic Acad. of Addiction Medicine; Amer. [16735]
Osteopathic Acad. of Orthopedics; Amer. [16026]
Osteopathic Cranial Assn. [★16076]
Osteopathic Found. [★16073]

Osteopathic Intl. Alliance [16078], Amer. Osteopathic Assn., 142 E Ontario St., Chicago, IL 60611
Osteopathic Intl. Alliance [16078], Amer. Osteopathic Assn., 142 E Ontario St., Chicago, IL 60611
Osteopathic Manipulative Therapeutic and Clinical Res. Assn. [★16056]
Osteopathic Medicine
Advocates for the Amer. Osteopathic Assn. [16055]
Amer. Acad. of Osteopathy [16056]
Amer. Assn. of Colleges of Osteopathic Medicine [16057]
Amer. Assn. of Physician Specialists [16058]
Amer. Coll. of Osteopathic Family Physicians [16059]
Amer. Coll. of Osteopathic Internists [16060]
Amer. Coll. of Osteopathic Pediatricians [16061]
Amer. Coll. of Osteopathic Sclerotherapeutic Pain Mgt. [16062]
Amer. Coll. of Osteopathic Surgeons [16063]
Amer. Osteopathic Assn. [16042]
Amer. Osteopathic Assn. of Medical Informatics [16065]
Amer. Osteopathic Bd. of Family Physicians [16066]
Amer. Osteopathic Bd. of Pediatrics [16067]
Amer. Osteopathic Bd. of Preventive Medicine [16068]
Amer. Osteopathic Coll. of Occupational and Preventive Medicine [16069]
Amer. Osteopathic Coll. of Pathologists [16070]
Amer. Osteopathic Coll. of Physical Medicine and Rehabilitation [16071]
Amer. Osteopathic Colleges of Opthalmology and Otolaryngology - Head and Neck Surgery [16072]
Amer. Osteopathic Found. [16073]
Assn. of Military Osteopathic Physicians and Surgeons [16074]
Assn. of Osteopathic Directors and Medical Educators [16075]
Cranial Acad. [16076]
Natl. Bd. of Osteopathic Medical Examiners [16077]
Natl. Osteopathic Women Physician's Assn. [23613]
Osteopathic Intl. Alliance [16078]
Osteopathic Intl. Alliance [16078]
Sigma Sigma Phi [23614]
Student Osteopathic Medical Assn. [16079]
Osteopathic Medicine; Center for Sports and [16309]
Osteopathy
Amer. Osteopathic Assn. of Medical Informatics [16065]
Osteoporose Canada [★IO]
Osteoporosis Australia [IO], Sydney, Australia
Osteoporosis Australian Capital Territory [IO], Weston, Australia
Osteoporosis Canada [IO], Toronto, ON, Canada
Osteoporosis Canada - Ottawa Chap. [IO], Ottawa, ON, Canada
Osteoporosis Comm. of China Gerontological Soc. [IO], Beijing, People's Republic of China
The Osteoporosis Found. [★16040]
Osteoporosis Found; Natl. [16040]
Osteoporosis New South Wales [IO], North Ryde, Australia
Osteoporosis New Zealand [IO], Wellington, New Zealand
Osteoporosis Northern Territory [IO], Nightcliff, Australia
Osteoporosis Soc. of Canada - Hamilton Chap. [IO], Hamilton, ON, Canada
Osteoporosis Soc. of Canada - Kelowna Chap. [IO], Westbank, BC, Canada
Osteoporosis Soc. of Canada - London and Thames Valley Chap. [IO], London, ON, Canada
Osteoporosis Soc. of Canada - Manitoba Chap. [IO], Winnipeg, MB, Canada
Osteoporosis Soc. of Canada - New Brunswick Chap. [IO], Fredericton, NB, Canada
Osteoporosis Soc. of Canada - Niagara Chap. [IO], St. Catharines, ON, Canada
Osteoporosis Soc. of Canada - North Shore Chap. [IO], North Vancouver, BC, Canada

Osteoporosis Soc. of Canada - Nova Scotia Chap. [IO], Dartmouth, NS, Canada
Osteoporosis Soc. of Canada - Peterborough Chap. [IO], Peterborough, ON, Canada
Osteoporosis Soc. of Canada - Quebec City Chap. [IO], Ste.-Foy, QC, Canada
Osteoporosis Soc. of Canada - Regina Chap. [IO], Regina, SK, Canada
Osteoporosis Soc. of Canada - Saskatoon Chap. [IO], Saskatoon, SK, Canada
Osteoporosis Soc. of Canada - Sudbury Chap. [IO], Garson, ON, Canada
Osteoporosis Soc. of Canada - Toronto Chap. [IO], Toronto, ON, Canada
Osteoporosis Soc. of Hong Kong [IO], Hong Kong, People's Republic of China
Osteoporosis Soc. of India [IO], New Delhi, India
Osteoporosis Soc. of Pakistan [IO], Karachi, Pakistan
Osteoporosis Soc. of Singapore [IO], Singapore, Singapore
Osteoporosis Soc. of Sri Lanka [IO], Colombo, Sri Lanka
Osteoporosis South Australia [IO], Marleston, Australia
Osteoporosis Tasmania [IO], Hobart, Australia
Osteoporosis Victoria [IO], Caulfield South, Australia
Osteoporosis Western Australia [IO], Wembley, Australia
Osterreichische Akademie der Wissenschaften [★IO]
Osterreichische Arbeitsgemeinschaft fur Mus-tererkennung [★IO]
Osterreichische Bundes Sportorganisation [★IO]
Osterreichische Cmpt. Gesellschaft [★IO]
Osterreichische Finn Vereinigung [★IO]
Osterreichische Gesellschaft fur Akupunktur [★IO]
Osterreichische Gesellschaft fur Amerikastudien [★IO]
Osterreichische Gesellschaft fur Angewandte Fors-chung in der Tourismusund Freizeitwirtschaft [★IO]
Osterreichische Gesellschaft fur Antimikrobielle Che-motherapie [★IO]
Osterreichische Gesellschaft fur Dermatologie und Venerologie [★IO]
Osterreichische Gesellschaft fur Elektronenmikrosko-pie [★IO]
Osterreichische Gesellschaft zur Erforschung des Knochens und Mineralstoffwechsels [★IO]
Osterreichische Gesellschaft fur Familienplanung [IO], Vienna, Austria
Osterreichische Gesellschaft fur Geriatrie and Ger-ontologie [★IO]
Osterreichische Gesellschaft fur Landschaftsplanung und Landschaftsarchitektur [IO], Vienna, Austria
Osterreichische Gesellschaft fuer Neurowissen-schaften [★IO]
Osterreichische Gesellschaft fur Operations Res. [★IO]
Osterreichische Gesellschaft fur Rheumatologie [IO], Vienna, Austria
Osterreichische Huntington Hilfe [★IO]
Osterreichische Kommission Iustitia Et Pax [IO], Vi-enna, Austria
Osterreichische Landjugend [IO], Vienna, Austria
Osterreichische Pharmakologische Gessellschaft [★IO]
Osterreichische Physiologische Gesellschaft [★IO]
Osterreichische Psysikalische Gesellschaft [★IO]
Osterreichische Rheumaliga [IO], Vienna, Austria
Osterreichische Rosenfreunde in der Osterreichis-chen Gartenbau-Gessellschaft [IO], Vienna, Austria
Osterreichische Statistische Gesellschaft [★IO]
Osterreichische Werbewissenschaftliche Gesell-schaft [★IO]
Osterreichischen Rollsport und Inline-Skate Verband [★IO]
Osterreichischen TanzSport Verbandes [★IO]
Osterreichischer Aero Club [IO], Vienna, Austria
Osterreichischer Arztekammer [★IO]
Osterreichischer Automobil-, Motorrad-, und Touring Club [★IO]
Osterreichischer Badminton Verband [★IO]
Osterreichischer Baseball- und Softballverband [★IO]
Osterreichischer Dachverband fur Geographische Info. [★IO]

A star before a book entry number signifies that the name is not listed separately, but is mentioned within the entry.

Osterreichischer Eishockey-Verband [★IO]
Osterreichischer Floorball Verband [★IO]
Osterreichischer Frisbee-Sport Verband [★IO]
Osterreichischer Golf-Verband [★IO]
Osterreichischer Judo Verband [IO], Vienna, Austria
Osterreichischer Jugendherbergsverband [★IO]
Osterreichischer Komponistenbund [★IO]
Osterreichischer P.E.N-Club [★IO]
Osterreichischer Squash Rackets Verband [IO], Vienna, Austria
Osterreichischer Taekwondo Verband [★IO]
Osterreichischer Tennisverband [IO], Vosendorf, Austria
Osterreichischer Verein fur Kraftfahrzeugtechnik [★IO]
Osterreichischer Wasserskiverband [★IO]
Osterreichisches Institut fur Wirtschaftsforschung [★IO]
Osterreichisches Komitee fur UNICEF [★IO]
Osterreichisches Kuratorium fur Landtechnik und Landentwicklung [★IO]
Osterreichisches Olympisches Comite [★IO]
Osterreichisches Paralympisches Comm. [★IO]
OstomyOstomyIntl. Ostomy Assn.
Ostomy Assn. of China [IO], Shanghai, People's Republic of China
Ostomy and Continence Nursing Certification Bd; Wound, [15808]
OSU Tour [11973], PO Box 701731, Dallas, TX 75370
OT Australia: Australian Assn. of Occupational Therapists [IO], Fitzroy, Australia
Ota Benga Alliance [10825], PO Box 2847, Berkeley, CA 94702
Otesha Proj. [IO], Ottawa, ON, Canada
Othello Assn. Singapore [IO], Singapore, Singapore
The Other Economic Summit of North Am. [★6631]
The Other Economic Summit of the U.S. [6631], 777 UN Plz., Ste. 3C, New York, NY 10017
Other Minds [10278], 333 Valencia St., Ste. 303, San Francisco, CA 94103-3552, (415)934-8134
Otolaryngic Allergy and Found; Amer. Acad. of [13633]
Otolaryngologists - Head and Neck Surgeons; Soc. of Military [15514]
Otolaryngologists - Head and Neck Surgeons; Soc. of Univ. [16090]
Otolaryngology Administrators; Assn. of [15292]
Otolaryngology; Assn. for Res. in [16088]
Otolaryngology - Head and Neck Surgery; Amer. Acad. of [16081]
Otological Soc; Amer. [16086]
Otomotiv Sanayii Dernegi [★IO]
Otorhinolaryngology
    Acoustic Neuroma Assn. [16080]
    Amer. Acad. of Otolaryngology - Head and Neck Surgery [16081]
    Amer. Bd. of Otolaryngology [16082]
    Amer. Head and Neck Soc. [16083]
    Amer. Laryngological Assn. [16084]
    Amer. Laryngological, Rhinological and Otological Soc. [16085]
    Amer. Otological Soc. [16086]
    Amer. Rhinologic Soc. [16087]
    Assn. for Res. in Otolaryngology [16088]
    Soc. for Ear, Nose, and Throat Advances in Children [16089]
    Soc. of Univ. Otolaryngologists - Head and Neck Surgeons [16090]
    Vestibular Disorders Assn. [16091]
    Vestibular Disorders Assn. [16091]
Otosclerosis Study Group - Defunct.
Ottawa Field-Naturalists' Club [IO], Ottawa, ON, Canada
Otterhound Club of Am. [21627], 805 Blackhawk Ln., Riverwoods, IL 60015, (847)945-3234
Ouachita Baptist Univ. Alumni Assn. [18895], 410 Ouachita St., Arkadelphia, AR 71998, (870)245-5506
Ouderkerk Family Genealogical Assn. [20566], 700 Atlanta Country Club Dr., Marietta, GA 30067
Ouellette Family Assn. of Am. [IO], La Pocatiere, QC, Canada
Oughtred Soc. [21394], 9 Stephens Ct., Roseville, CA 95678

Our Bodies, Ourselves [17135], 5 Upland Rd., No. 3, Cambridge, MA 02140, (617)245-0200
Our Developing World [17981], 13004 Paseo Presada, Saratoga, CA 95070-4125, (408)379-4431
Our Developing World [17981], 13004 Paseo Presada, Saratoga, CA 95070-4125, (408)379-4431
Our Family Orphan Communities [11493], PO Box 906, Alamosa, CO 81101-0906, (719)379-3755
Our Giving Community - Address unknown since 2011.
Our Global Heritage [IO], Ho, Ghana
Our Military Kids [12534], 6861 Elm St., Ste. 2-A, McLean, VA 22101, (703)734-6654
Our Task [4295], PO Box 17076, Arlington, VA 22216, (703)981-0010
Our Voices Together [★17514]
Our World-Underwater Scholarship Soc. - Defunct.
Our Youths Found. [IO], San Antonio de Pichincha, Ecuador
OurEarth.org [4121], PO Box 212, Painted Post, NY 14870, (410)878-6485
OURMedia Network [18100], 610 Elm Ave., Norman, OK 73019, (405)325-1570
Out and Equal Workplace Advocates [12105], 155 Sansome St., Ste. 450, San Francisco, CA 94104, (415)694-6500
Out of Love Sugar Glider Rescue [11017], PO Box 183, Medina, OH 44258-0183, (330)722-1627
Out-of-Home Measurement Bur. [★56]
Out of Poverty thru Educ. [7731], 2128 William St., No. 107, Cape Girardeau, MO 63703, (573)334-0930
Out on the Screen [★9607]
Out to Swim London [IO], London, United Kingdom
Outboard Motor Mfrs. Assn. [★2365]
Outdoor Advt. Assn. of Am. [101], 1850 M St. NW, Ste. 1040, Washington, DC 20036, (202)833-5566
Outdoor Advt. Assn. of Great Britain [IO], London, United Kingdom
Outdoor Amusement Bus. Assn. [1216], 1035 S Semoran Blvd., Ste. 1045A, Winter Park, FL 32792, (407)681-9444
Outdoor Education
    Assn. of Outdoor Recreation and Educ. [8688]
    Boy Scouts of Am. [13018]
    Global Explorers [9017]
    Hungarian Scouts Assn. [13020]
    Intl. BioExploration Soc. [8180]
    WAVES for Development [18683]
    Wilderness Classroom Org. [8689]
    Wilderness Educ. Assn. [8690]
Outdoor Education Assn. - Defunct.
Outdoor Ethics Guild - Defunct.
Outdoor Indus. Assn. [IO], Edinburgh, United Kingdom
Outdoor Indus. Women's Coalition [2600], PO Box 36261, Cincinnati, OH 45236, (208)860-6370
Outdoor Indus. Assn. [2601], 4909 Pearl East Cir., Ste. 200, Boulder, CO 80301, (303)444-3353
Outdoor Power Equip. Aftermarket Assn. [1182], 341 S Patrick St., Alexandria, VA 22314, (703)549-7608
Outdoor Power Equip. Aftermarket Assn. [1182], 341 S Patrick St., Alexandria, VA 22314, (703)549-7608
Outdoor Power Equip. Distributors Assn. [★1183]
Outdoor Power Equipment Distributors Assn. - Defunct.
Outdoor Power Equip. and Engine Ser. Assn. [1183], 37 Pratt St., Essex, CT 06426-1159, (860)767-1770
Outdoor Power Equip. Inst. [1184], 341 S Patrick St., Alexandria, VA 22314, (703)549-7600
Outdoor Recreation
    Am. Outdoors Assn. [22835]
    Amer. Canoe Assn. [23120]
    Amer. Carp Soc. [21730]
    Amer. Ski-Bike Assn. [22963]
    Antique Motorcycle Club of Am. [21919]
    Assn. for Challenge Course Tech. [2599]
    Bass Anglers Sportsman Soc. [22572]
    Boy Scouts of Am. [13018]
    Camping Women [22441]
    Carp Anglers Gp. [21732]
    Christian Camp and Conf. Assn. [22442]
    Christian Hunters and Anglers Assn. [21279]
    Family Campers and RVers [22443]

    Fed. of Fly Fishers [22574]
    Hungarian Scouts Assn. [13020]
    Intl. Scale Soaring Assn. [21904]
    Natl. Alliance for the Development of Archery [22222]
    Natl. Archery Assn. of the U.S. [22223]
    Natl. Bass Anglers Assn. [22581]
    Natl. Versatility Ranch Horse Assn. [22686]
    New England Trails Conf. [23090]
    North Amer. Bowhunting Coalition [21866]
    North Amer. Family Campers Assn. [22446]
    North Amer. Hunting Club [22700]
    North Amer. Squirrel Assn. [22001]
    Outdoor Indus. Women's Coalition [2600]
    Outdoor Indus. Assn. [2601]
    Scale Warbird Racing Assn. [21910]
    Self-Guided Hunting Assn. [21867]
    Tree Climbing USA [21286]
    U.S. Lawn Bowls Assn. [22430]
    U.S. Mountain Guides Assn. [22456]
    U.S. Powered Paragliding Assn. [22796]
    U.S. Ski Mountaineering Assn. [22917]
    Up2Us [13563]
    U.S.A. Cricket Assn. [23016]
    USA Professional Platform Tennis Assn. [23066]
    USGA Green Sect. [22628]
    WAVES for Development [18683]
    Wilderness Volunteers [22002]
    Women Outdoors [22797]
Outdoor Recreation Coalition of Am. [★2601]
Outdoor Writers Assn. of Am. [2865], 615 Oak St., Ste. 201, Missoula, MT 59801, (406)728-7434
Outdoor Writers of Canada [IO], Cochrane, AB, Canada
Outdoor Writers and Photographers Guild [IO], Preston, United Kingdom
Outer Critics Circle [10597], 101 W 57th St., New York, NY 10019, (212)765-8557
Outfest [9607], 3470 Wilshire Blvd., Ste. 935, Los Angeles, CA 90010, (213)480-7088
Outpatient Ophthalmic Surgery Soc. [15974], Ms. Claudia A. McDougal, Exec. Dir., 6564 Umbers Cir., Arvada, CO 80007, (866)892-1001
Outpost for Hope [12546], 3438 E Lake Rd., Ste. 14, PO Box 629, Palm Harbor, FL 34685
OutProud - Address unknown since 2011.
Outreach Africa [11386], PO Box 361, Union, IA 50258, (641)486-2550
Outreach Asia [11116], 5608 Benton Ave., Edina, MN 55436, (952)922-8536
Outside Sales Support Network [3571], 22410 68th Ave. E, Bradenton, FL 34211, (941)322-9700
Outsiders Club [IO], London, United Kingdom
Outsourcing
    Global Sourcing Coun. [2602]
    Intl. Assn. of Outsourcing Professionals [2603]
    Intl. Assn. of Outsourcing Professionals [2603]
Outsourcing Inst. [698], Jericho Atrium, 500 N Broadway, Ste. 141, Jericho, NY 11753, (516)681-0066
Outstretched Hands [IO], Milan, Italy
Outward Bound [8937], 100 Mystery Point Rd., Garrison, NY 10524, (845)424-4000
OV-10 Bronco Assn. [9107], PO Box 161966, Fort Worth, TX 76161, (800)575-0535
Ovarian Cancer Coalition; Natl. [13957]
Ovarian Cancer Natl. Alliance [13962], 910 17th St. NW, Ste. 1190, Washington, DC 20006-2605, (202)331-1332
Ovarian Cancer Registry; Gilda Radner Familial [13924]
Ovarian Cancer Registry; Gilda Radner Familial [13924]
Ovations for the Cure [13963], 251 W Central St., Ste. 32, Natick, MA 01760, (508)655-5412
Over the Front [★20905]
Over the Front [★20905]
Over the Hill Gang, Intl. [23001], 2121 N Weber St., Colorado Springs, CO 80907, (719)389-0022
Over the Hill Gang, Intl. [23001], 2121 N Weber St., Colorado Springs, CO 80907, (719)389-0022
Overeaters Anonymous World Ser. Off. [12590], PO Box 44020, Rio Rancho, NM 87174-4020, (505)891-2664
Overeaters Anonymous World Ser. Off. [12590], PO Box 44020, Rio Rancho, NM 87174-4020, (505)891-2664

Reference to "IO" in place of a book number signifies that the association may be found in the 50th edition of International Organizations.

Overhead Components Mfrs. Prdt. Sect. of the Material Handling Inst. [★1847]
Overhead Components Mfrs. Production Sect. of the Material Handling Inst. of Am. [★1847]
Overseas Assn. for Coll. Admission Counseling [7687], 36 Reservoir Rd., Marlboro, NY 12542-5029, (845)236-3074
Overseas Automotive Club [★306]
Overseas Automotive Coun. [306], PO Box 13966, Research Triangle Park, NC 27709-3966, (919)406-8846
Overseas Brats [19245], PO Box 47112, Wichita, KS 67201, (316)269-9610
Overseas Chinese-American Entrepreneurs Assn. [775], 219 Quincy Ave., Quincy, MA 02169
Overseas Chinese Entomologists Assn. [6849], 4287 Farm Meadows Ct., Okemos, MI 48864
Overseas Chinese Entomologists Assn. [6849], 4287 Farm Meadows Ct., Okemos, MI 48864
Overseas Chinese Landscape Architects Assn. [2182], Texas A&M Univ., Dept. of Landscape Architecture, College Station, TX 77843-3137
Overseas Chinese Physics Assn. [★7267]
Overseas Constr. Assn. of Japan, Inc. [IO], Tokyo, Japan
Overseas Crusades [★20078]
Overseas Crusades [★20078]
Overseas Development Inst. [IO], London, United Kingdom
Overseas EDU Assn. [★23179]
Overseas Investors Chamber of Commerce and Indus. [IO], Karachi, Pakistan
Overseas Missionary Fellowship Canada [IO], Mississauga, ON, Canada
Overseas Missionary Fellowship, U.S.A. [★20079]
Overseas Missionary Fellowship, U.S.A. [★20079]
Overseas Press Club of Am. [2866], 40 W 45 St., New York, NY 10036, (212)626-9220
Overseas Press Club of Am. [2866], 40 W 45 St., New York, NY 10036, (212)626-9220
Overseas Press and Media Assn. [IO], Cambridge, United Kingdom
Overseas Teachers Assn. [★23179]
Overseas Writers - Defunct.
Overseas Young Chinese Forum [7845], 11423 Potomac Oaks Dr., Rockville, MD 20850, (301)838-0829
Ovulation Method Res. and Reference Centre of Australia [IO], North Fitzroy, Australia
Owen Family Assn. [20567], George N. Shirley, Jr., Treas., 4190 Hurricane Shores Dr., Benton, AR 72019
OWL - The Voice of Midlife and Older Women [13473], 1025 Connecticut Ave. NW Ste. 701, Washington, DC 20036, (877)653-7966
Owner-Operator Independent Drivers Assn. [3533], 1 NW OOIDA Dr., Grain Valley, MO 64029-7903, (816)229-5791
Owsley Family Historical Soc. [20568], Floyd L. Owsley, Membership Dir., 6185 Oilskin Dr., Ooltewah, TN 37363, (423)910-0058
Oxalosis and Hyperoxaluria Found. [15556], 201 E 19th St., Ste. 12E, New York, NY 10003, (212)777-0470
OXFAM Am. [12355], 226 Causeway St., 5th Fl., Boston, MA 02114, (617)482-1211
OXFAM Am. [12355], 226 Causeway St., 5th Fl., Boston, MA 02114, (617)482-1211
Oxfam - Australia [IO], Carlton, Australia
Oxfam - Canada [IO], Ottawa, ON, Canada
Oxfam France - Agir ici [IO], Paris, France
Oxfam - GB in Vietnam [IO], Hanoi, Vietnam
Oxfam - Germany [IO], Berlin, Germany
Oxfam - Hong Kong [IO], Hong Kong, People's Republic of China
Oxfam Intl. Advocacy Off. [12876], 1100 15th St. NW, Ste. 600, Washington, DC 20005, (202)496-1170
Oxfam Intl. Advocacy Off. [12876], 1100 15th St. NW, Ste. 600, Washington, DC 20005, (202)496-1170
Oxfam - Ireland [IO], Dublin, Ireland
Oxfam-Magasins du monde [★IO]
Oxfam - New Zealand [IO], Auckland, New Zealand
Oxfam - Quebec [IO], Montreal, QC, Canada

Oxfam - Solidarity [IO], Brussels, Belgium
Oxfam - U.K. [IO], Oxford, United Kingdom
Oxfam World Shops [IO], Bierges, Belgium
Oxford Comm. for Famine Relief [★12355]
Oxford Gp. - Moral Re-Armament [★17801]
Oxford Gp. - Moral Re-Armament [★17801]
Oxygen Soc. [★6332]
Oxygen Soc. [★6332]
Oyate [19167], 330 E Thomson Ave., Sonoma, CA 95476, (707)996-6700
Oyo-buturi Gakkai [★IO]
Oz GREEN - Global Rivers Environmental Educ. Network - Australia [IO], Brookvale, Australia
Oz Veshalom-Netivot Shalom [IO], Jerusalem, Israel
Ozark Soc. [4122], PO Box 2914, Little Rock, AR 72203, (479)587-8757
O'zbekiston Bibliya Jamiyati [★IO]

P

P6 Rover Owners Club [IO], Huddersfield, United Kingdom
Pace Intl. Union - Defunct.
PACER Center - Parent Advocacy Coalition for Educational Rights [14368], 8161 Normandale Blvd., Minneapolis, MN 55437, (952)838-0190
Pachamama Alliance [4858], PO Box 29191, San Francisco, CA 94129-0191, (415)561-4522
Pachamama Alliance [4858], PO Box 29191, San Francisco, CA 94129-0191, (415)561-4522
Pacific
    Asian Pacific Americans for Progress [17205]
    Asian and Pacific Islander Inst. on Domestic Violence [11880]
    Indo-Pacific Conservation Alliance [4079]
    Kollaboration [13534]
    Pacific Islanders' Cultural Assn. [10347]
    Pacifica Found. [18223]
    Polynesian Voyaging Soc. [22003]
Pacific 10 Conf. [23002], 1350 Treat Blvd., Ste. 500, Walnut Creek, CA 94597-8853, (925)932-4411
Pacific Amer. Steamship Assn. [★5789]
Pacific Antique Label Soc. [★21324]
Pacific Area Newspaper Publishers' Assn. [IO], Pyrmont, Australia
Pacific Area Travel Assn. [★3572]
Pacific Area Travel Assn. [★3572]
Pacific Arts Assn. [9195], Christina Hellmich, Admin., de Young Museum, 50 Hagiwara Tea Garden Dr., San Francisco, CA 94118
Pacific Arts Assn. [9195], Christina Hellmich, Admin., de Young Museum, 50 Hagiwara Tea Garden Dr., San Francisco, CA 94118
Pacific Asia Travel Assn. [3572], 164 Loop Pl., Trinidad, CA 95570, (707)232-2102
Pacific Asia Travel Assn. [3572], 164 Loop Pl., Trinidad, CA 95570, (707)232-2102
Pacific Asia Travel Assn. - Singapore [IO], Singapore, Singapore
Pacific Asia Travel Assn. - Thailand [IO], Bangkok, Thailand
Pacific Assn. of Quantity Surveyors [IO], Selangor, Malaysia
Pacific Bantam Austin Club [★21002]
Pacific Basin Economic Coun. - Canadian Comm. [IO], Vancouver, BC, Canada
Pacific Basin (Honolulu) [★17249]
Pacific Basin Medical Assn. [IO], Kolonia, Federated States of Micronesia
Pacific Christian Coll. Alumni Assn. [★18874]
Pacific Class Catamaran Assn. - Defunct.
Pacific Coast Cichlid Assn. [21728], PO Box 28145, San Jose, CA 95159-8145
Pacific Coast Economics Assn. [★6637]
Pacific Coast Economics Assn. [★6637]
Pacific Coast Fed. of Fishermen's Associations [4382], PO Box 29370, San Francisco, CA 94129-0370, (415)561-5080
Pacific Coast Garment Mfrs. Assn. [★199]
Pacific Coast Marine Firemen, Oilers, Watertenders and Wipers Assn. [23249], 240 2nd St., San Francisco, CA 94105, (415)362-4592
Pacific Coast Marine Firemen's Union [★23249]
Pacific Coast Oyster Growers Assn. [★3187]
Pacific Coast Paper Box Mfrs'. Assn. - Address unknown since 2010.

Pacific Coast Rugby Union [★22861]
Pacific Coast Shellfish Growers Assn. [3187], 120 State Ave. NE, PMB No. 142, Olympia, WA 98501, (360)754-2744
Pacific Coun. on Intl. Policy [17707], 801 S Figueroa St., Ste. 1130, Los Angeles, CA 90017, (213)221-2000
Pacific Cruise Conf. [★3557]
Pacific Dermatologic Assn. [14338], 575 Market St., Ste. 2125, San Francisco, CA 94105, (415)927-5729
Pacific Dermatologic Assn. [14338], 575 Market St., Ste. 2125, San Francisco, CA 94105, (415)927-5729
Pacific Dragon Boat Assn. [22384], Diane McCab, Treas., 607 30th St., Hermosa Beach, CA 90254
Pacific e-Commerce Development Corp. [IO], Pago Pago, American Samoa
Pacific Economic Cooperation Coun. [IO], Singapore, Singapore
Pacific Endowment for Art Culture and Env. [IO], Koror, Palau
Pacific Fishery Mgt. Coun. [5456], 7700 NE Ambassador Pl., Ste. 101, Portland, OR 97220-1384, (503)820-2280
Pacific Gamefish Res. Found. [★6956]
Pacific Inst. [★11976]
Pacific Inst. [★18485]
Pacific Inst. for Stud. in Development, Env., and Security [11976], 654 13th St., Preservation Park, Oakland, CA 94612, (510)251-1600
Pacific Intl. Trapshooting Assn. [22886], PO Box 770, Lebanon, OR 97355, (541)258-8766
Pacific Intl. Trapshooting Assn. [22886], PO Box 770, Lebanon, OR 97355, (541)258-8766
Pacific Islanders in Communications [10073], 1221 Kapiolani Blvd., Ste. 6A-4, Honolulu, HI 96814, (808)591-0059
Pacific Islanders' Cultural Assn. [10347], 1016 Lincoln Blvd., No. 5, San Francisco, CA 94129, (415)281-0221
Pacific Islands Conservation Res. Assn. [4123], PO Box 302, South Beach, OR 97366
Pacific Islands Museums Assn. [IO], Port Vila, Vanuatu
Pacific Islands News Assn. [IO], Suva, Fiji
Pacific Legal Found. [5937], 3900 Lennane Dr., Ste. 200, Sacramento, CA 95834-2918, (916)419-7111
Pacific Logging Cong. [1475], PO Box 1281, Maple Valley, WA 98038, (425)413-2808
Pacific Logging Cong. [1475], PO Box 1281, Maple Valley, WA 98038, (425)413-2808
Pacific Lumber Exporters Assn. [1476], 2633 NW Raleigh St., No. 39, Portland, OR 97210, (503)598-3325
Pacific Lumber Exporters Assn. [1476], 2633 NW Raleigh St., No. 39, Portland, OR 97210, (503)598-3325
Pacific Lumber Inspection Bur. [1477], 1010 S 36th St., Ste. 300, Federal Way, WA 98003, (253)835-3344
Pacific Lumber Inspection Bur. [1477], 1010 S 36th St., Ste. 300, Federal Way, WA 98003, (253)835-3344
Pacific Marine Fisheries Commn. [★5457]
Pacific Marine Mammal Center [5103], 20612 Laguna Canyon Rd., Laguna Beach, CA 92651, (949)494-3050
Pacific Maritime Assn. [3266], 555 Market St., San Francisco, CA 94105-2800, (415)576-3200
Pacific Northwest Bird and Mammal Soc. [★7144]
Pacific Northwest Christmas Tree Assn. [4975], PO Box 3366, Salem, OR 97302, (503)364-2942
Pacific Northwest Grain Dealers [★3959]
Pacific Northwest Grain and Feed Assn. [3959], 200 SW Market St., Ste. 190, Portland, OR 97201, (503)227-0234
Pacific Northwest Heather Soc. [★21814]
Pacific Northwest Heather Soc. [★21814]
Pacific Northwest Pea Growers and Dealers [★3959]
Pacific Northwest Region of the Lincoln and Continental Owners Club [21144], 21920 SE Mark Rd., Damascus, OR 97089-8756, (866)427-7583
Pacific Northwest Ski Assn. [22913], 2671 Flowery Trail Rd., Usk, WA 99180, (509)445-4454

A star before a book entry number signifies that the name is not listed separately, but is mentioned within the entry.

Pacific Northwest Ski Educ. Found. [★22913]

Pacific Northwest Trail Assn. [23093], North Cascades Gateway Center, 24854 Charles Jones Memorial Cir., Unit 4, Sedro Woolley, WA 98284, (877)854-9415

Pacific Ocean Res. Found. [6956], PO Box 4800, 74-381 Kealakehe Pkwy., Ste. C, Kailua-Kona, HI 96740, (808)329-6105

Pacific Orchid Soc. of Hawaii - Address unknown since 2010.

Pacific Peoples' Partnership [IO], Victoria, BC, Canada

Pacific Post Partum Support Soc. [IO], Burnaby, BC, Canada

Pacific Printing and Imaging Assn. [1625], PO Box 23575, Portland, OR 97281-3575, (503)221-3944

Pacific Railroad Soc. [10495], PO Box 80726, San Marino, CA 91118-8726, (714)637-4676

Pacific Regional Br. of the Intl. Coun. on Archives [IO], Wellington, New Zealand

Pacific Res. Inst. [18485], 1 Embarcadero Ctr., Ste. 350, San Francisco, CA 94111, (415)989-0833

Pacific Res. Inst. for Public Policy [★18485]

Pacific Riding for Developing Abilities [IO], Langley, BC, Canada

Pacific Rocket Soc. [6093], PO Box 662, Mojave, CA 93502-0662, (661)824-1662

Pacific Salmon Commn. [IO], Vancouver, BC, Canada

Pacific Sci. Assn. [7385], Bishop Museum, 1525 Bernice St., Honolulu, HI 96817, (808)848-4124

Pacific Sci. Assn. [7385], Bishop Museum, 1525 Bernice St., Honolulu, HI 96817, (808)848-4124

Pacific Seabird Gp. [5104], Ron LeValley, Treas., PO Box 324, Little River, CA 95456, (707)442-4302

Pacific Seafood Processors Assn. [3188], 1900 W Emerson Pl., No. 205, Seattle, WA 98119, (206)281-1667

Pacific Shellfish Inst. [3829], 120 State Ave. NE, No. 1056, Olympia, WA 98501, (360)754-2741

Pacific Soc. for Women in Philosophy [10409], Emily Lee, Exec. Sec., PO Box 6868, Fullerton, CA 92834-6868

Pacific Southwest Railway Museum [10496], 4695 Nebo Dr., La Mesa, CA 91941-5259, (619)465-7776

Pacific States Marine Fisheries Commn. [5457], 205 SE Spokane St., Ste. 100, Portland, OR 97202, (503)595-3100

Pacific Telecommunications Coun. [7550], 914 Coolidge St., Honolulu, HI 96826-3085, (808)941-3789

Pacific Telecommunications Coun. [7550], 914 Coolidge St., Honolulu, HI 96826-3085, (808)941-3789

Pacific Whale Found. [5105], 300 Maalaea Rd., Ste. 211, Wailuku, HI 96793, (808)249-8811

Pacific Women's Resources [★12097]

Pacifica Found. [18223], 1925 Martin Luther King Jr. Way, Berkeley, CA 94704, (510)849-2590

Packaged Ice Assn. [★1712]

Packaging

Amer. Chemistry Coun. I Plastics Foodservice Packaging Gp. [2604]

Center for Electronic Packaging Res. [7207]

Contract Packaging Assn. [2605]

Coopers' Company [16068]

Corrugated Packaging Alliance [2606]

European Org. for Packaging and the Env. [18895]

Flexible Packaging Assn. [2607]

Inst. of Packaging Professionals [7208]

Inst. of Packaging - South Africa [11536]

Italian Inst. of Packaging [4604]

Natl. Inst. of Packaging, Handling and Logistics Engineers [7209]

Packaging Coun. of Australia [20549]

Packaging Coun. of South Africa [173]

Packaging Machinery Mfrs. Inst. [2608]

Paper Packaging Canada [13752]

Paperboard Packaging Coun. [2609]

Petroleum Packaging Coun. [2610]

Retail Packaging Assn. [2611]

Reusable Packaging Assn. [3072]

Sustainable Packaging Coalition [4764]

Women in Packaging [2612]

Packaging Assn. of Canada [IO], Toronto, ON, Canada

Packaging Coun. of Australia [IO], South Melbourne, Australia

Packaging Coun. of Malaysia [IO], Kuala Lumpur, Malaysia

Packaging Coun. of New Zealand [IO], Manukau City, New Zealand

Packaging Coun. of South Africa [IO], Johannesburg, Republic of South Africa

Packaging Fed. [IO], London, United Kingdom

Packaging and Indus. Films Assn. [IO], Nottingham, United Kingdom

Packaging and Label Gravure Assn. Global [1626], 18481 Royal Hammock Blvd., Naples, FL 34114, (920)217-6059

Packaging and Label Gravure Assn. Global [1626], 18481 Royal Hammock Blvd., Naples, FL 34114, (920)217-6059

Packaging Machinery Mfrs. Inst. [2608], 4350 N Fairfax Dr., Ste. 600, Arlington, VA 22203-1632, (703)243-8555

Packard Auto. Classics [21145], PO Box 360806, Columbus, OH 43236-0806, (614)478-4946

Packard Club [21146], PO Box 360806, Columbus, OH 43236-0806, (614)478-4946

Packard Club [21146], PO Box 360806, Columbus, OH 43236-0806, (614)478-4946

Packards Intl. Motor Car Club [21147], 302 French St., Santa Ana, CA 92701, (714)541-8431

Packards Intl. Motor Car Club [21147], 302 French St., Santa Ana, CA 92701, (714)541-8431

PACON Intl. [4706], 2525 Correa Rd., HIG 407A, Honolulu, HI 96822, (808)956-6163

PACON Intl. [4706], 2525 Correa Rd., HIG 407A, Honolulu, HI 96822, (808)956-6163

PACT [12356], 1828 L St. NW, Ste. 300, Washington, DC 20036, (202)466-5666

Pact, An Adoption Alliance [10800], 4179 Piedmont Ave., Ste. 101, Oakland, CA 94611, (510)243-9460

Pact Training [11680], PO Box 106, New Kingston, NY 12459-0106, (845)586-3992

Paddle Alberta [IO], Edmonton, AB, Canada

Paddle Canada [IO], Kingston, ON, Canada

Paddle Manitoba [IO], Winnipeg, MB, Canada

Paddle Steamer Preservation Soc. [IO], High Wycombe, United Kingdom

Paddlesports Indus. Assn. [3316], PO Box 5204, Frankfort, KY 40602, (502)395-1513

PADI Travel Network [★23105]

PADI Travel Network [★23105]

PAF Users Unlimited - Defunct.

Pagaie Canada [★IO]

Pagan Fed. [IO], London, United Kingdom

Paganism

Alternative Religions Educational Network [20148]

Covenant of Unitarian Universalist Pagans [20149]

Pageant for Peace [★17987]

Pageant for Peace [★17987]

Paget Found. for Paget's Disease of Bone and Related Disorders [15504], 120 Wall St., Ste. 1602, New York, NY 10005-4001, (212)509-5335

Paget's Disease of Bone and Related Disorders; Paget Found. for [15504]

Paget's Disease Found. [★15504]

Pago Pago Game Fishing Assn. [IO], Pago Pago, American Samoa

PAHAL [IO], Jalandhar, India

Pain

Amer. Acad. of Pain Mgt. [16092]

Amer. Acad. of Pain Medicine [16093]

Amer. Bd. of Pain Medicine [16094]

Amer. Chronic Pain Assn. [16095]

Amer. Pain Found. [16096]

Amer. Pain Soc. [16097]

Amer. Soc. of Interventional Pain Physicians [16098]

Amer. Soc. of Pain Educators [16099]

Intl. Adhesions Soc. [16100]

Intl. Adhesions Soc. [16100]

Intl. Assn. for Pain and Chem. Dependency [16101]

Intl. Assn. for the Stud. of Pain [16102]

Intl. Assn. for the Stud. of Pain [16102]

Intl. MYOPAIN Soc. [16103]

Intl. Pelvic Pain Soc. [16104]

Intl. Pelvic Pain Soc. [16104]

Let's Talk Pain [16105]

Natl. Fibromyalgia and Chronic Pain Assn. [14540]

North Amer. Neuromodulation Soc. [16106]

Soc. of Chest Pain Centers and Providers [16107]

TMJ Assn. [16108]

Pain Assn. of Singapore [IO], Singapore, Singapore

Pain Found; Vulvar [15896]

Pain Soc. of the Philippines [IO], Quezon City, Philippines

Paine Natl. Historical Assn; Thomas [10694]

Paint, Body and Equipment Assn. - Defunct.

Paint and Decorating Retailers Assn. [2073], 1401 Triad Center Dr., St. Peters, MO 63376-7353, (636)326-2636

Paint and Decorating Retailers Assn. [2073], 1401 Triad Center Dr., St. Peters, MO 63376-7353, (636)326-2636

Paint and Wallpaper Assn. of Am. [★2073]

Paint and Wallpaper Assn. of Am. [★2073]

PaintAmerica [9311], PO Box 4031, Topeka, KS 66604, (816)806-3340

Paintball

Amer. Paintball Players Assn. [22798]

Natl. Collegiate Paintball Assn. [22799]

Painted Desert Sheep Soc. [4921], 11819 Puska Rd., Needville, TX 77461, (979)793-4207

Painter-Stainers' Company [IO], London, United Kingdom

Painting and Decorating Assn. of Great Britain [IO], Nuneaton, United Kingdom

Painting and Decorating Contractors of Am. [944], 1801 Park 270 Dr., Ste. 220, St. Louis, MO 63146, (314)514-7322

Paints and Finishes

Amer. Coatings Assn. [2613]

Intl. Union of Painters and Allied Trades [23262]

Natl. Acrylic Painters' Assn. [18405]

Natl. Coun. on Paint Disposition [4765]

Natl. Guild of Decoupeurs [21457]

Natl. Paint and Ink Mfrs'. Assn. [4762]

Professional Decorative Painters Assn. [2614]

SSPC: The Soc. for Protective Coatings [2615]

SSPC: The Soc. for Protective Coatings [2615]

Pairti Soisialta Daonlathach an Lucht Oibre [★IO]

Paisley Family Soc. [20569], Martha Pasley Milam Brown, Commissioner, 2205 Pine Knoll Cir., Conyers, GA 30013, (770)483-6949

Paivittaistavarakauppa ry [★IO]

Pakistan

Asian-American Network Against Abuse of Human Rights [17814]

Assn. for the Development of Pakistan [12601]

Eco Energy Finance [6712]

Pakistan Chamber of Commerce USA [23435]

Pakistan Chamber of Commerce USA [23435]

Pakistan Acad. of Sciences [IO], Islamabad, Pakistan

Pakistan Advertisers Soc. [IO], Karachi, Pakistan

Pakistan Advt. Assn. [IO], Karachi, Pakistan

Pakistan Assn. of Automotive Parts and Accessories Mfrs. [IO], Karachi, Pakistan

Pakistan Assn. of Dermatologists [IO], Karachi, Pakistan

Pakistan Assn. of Free Flying [IO], Rawalpindi, Pakistan

Pakistan Assn. of Medical Editors [IO], Karachi, Pakistan

Pakistan Assn. of Orthodontists [IO], Lahore, Pakistan

Pakistan Assn. of Petroleum Geoscientists [IO], Islamabad, Pakistan

Pakistan Assn. of Plastic Surgeons [IO], Karachi, Pakistan

Pakistan Assn. for Res. in Educ. [IO], Karachi, Pakistan

Pakistan Assn. of Urological Surgeons [IO], Karachi, Pakistan

Pakistan Banks' Assn. [IO], Karachi, Pakistan

Pakistan-Belgium Bus. Forum [IO], Karachi, Pakistan

Reference to "IO" in place of a book number signifies that the association may be found in the 50th edition of International Organizations.

Encyclopedia of Associations, 51st Edition   3081

Pakistan Broadcasters Assn. [IO], Karachi, Pakistan
Pakistan Canvas and Tents Mfrs. and Exporters
  Assn. [IO], Lahore, Pakistan
Pakistan Cardiac Soc. [IO], Karachi, Pakistan
Pakistan Cave Res. Assn. [IO], Quetta, Pakistan
Pakistan Chamber of Commerce USA [23435],
  11110 Bellaire Blvd., Ste. 202, Houston, TX 77072-
  2600, (832)877-1234
Pakistan Chamber of Commerce USA [23435],
  11110 Bellaire Blvd., Ste. 202, Houston, TX 77072-
  2600, (832)877-1234
Pakistan Cleft Lip and Palate Assn. [IO], Gujrat,
  Pakistan
Pakistan Coalition for Educ. [IO], Islamabad,
  Pakistan
Pakistan Cmpt. Assn. [IO], Islamabad, Pakistan
Pakistan Cotton Ginners' Assn. [IO], Multan,
  Pakistan
Pakistan Coun. of Renewable Energy Technologies
  [IO], Karachi, Pakistan
Pakistan Coun. for Social Welfare and Human
  Rights [IO], Sialkot, Pakistan
Pakistan Cricket Bd. [IO], Lahore, Pakistan
Pakistan DanceSport Fed. [IO], Lahore, Pakistan
Pakistan Dental Assn. [IO], Lahore, Pakistan
Pakistan Dental Hygienist Assn. [IO], Lahore,
  Pakistan
Pakistan Ex-Servicemen Assn. [IO], Rawalpindi,
  Pakistan
Pakistan Fed. of Floorball [IO], Faisalabad, Pakistan
Pakistan Fed. of Univ. Women [IO], Karachi,
  Pakistan
Pakistan Food Assn. [IO], Karachi, Pakistan
Pakistan Footwear Mfrs. Assn. [IO], Lahore,
  Pakistan
Pakistan Foundry Assn. [IO], Lahore, Pakistan
Pakistan Geotechnical Engg. Soc. [IO], Lahore,
  Pakistan
Pakistan Hosiery Mfrs. Assn. [IO], Karachi, Pakistan
Pakistan Huntington Disease Soc. [IO], Peshawar,
  Pakistan
Pakistan HVACR Soc. [IO], Islamabad, Pakistan
Pakistan Hypertension League [IO], Karachi,
  Pakistan
Pakistan Inst. of Intl. Affairs [IO], Karachi, Pakistan
Pakistan Intl. Freight Forwarders Assn. [IO], Karachi,
  Pakistan
Pakistan Intl. Human Rights Org. [IO], Islamabad,
  Pakistan
Pakistan Ju Jitsu Fed. [IO], Lahore, Pakistan
Pakistan Jute Mills Assn. [IO], Lahore, Pakistan
Pakistan Malaysia Friendship Assn. [IO], Karachi,
  Pakistan
Pakistan Mathematical Soc. [IO], Islamabad,
  Pakistan
Pakistan Natl. Rose Soc. [IO], Islamabad, Pakistan
Pakistan Netball Fed. [IO], Karachi, Pakistan
Pakistan Nuclear Soc. [IO], Islamabad, Pakistan
Pakistan Nutrition and Dietetic Soc. [IO], Karachi,
  Pakistan
Pakistan Occupational Therapy Assn. [IO], Karachi,
  Pakistan
Pakistan Parkinson's Soc. [IO], Karachi, Pakistan
Pakistan Peace Coalition [IO], Karachi, Pakistan
Pakistan Pharmacists Assn. [IO], Lahore, Pakistan
Pakistan Physical Therapy Assn. [IO], Islamabad,
  Pakistan
Pakistan Physiological Soc. [IO], Abbottabad,
  Pakistan
Pakistan Powerlifting Fed. [IO], Lahore, Pakistan
Pakistan Press Found. [IO], Karachi, Pakistan
Pakistan Readymade Garments Mfrs'. and Export-
  ers' Assn. [IO], Karachi, Pakistan
Pakistan Red Crescent Soc. [IO], Islamabad,
  Pakistan
Pakistan Relief [IO], Islamabad, Pakistan
Pakistan Sailing Fed. [IO], Karachi, Pakistan
Pakistan School Sports Assn. [IO], Karachi, Pakistan
Pakistan Ship's Agents Assn. [IO], Karachi, Pakistan
Pakistan Soc. of Actuaries [IO], Karachi, Pakistan
Pakistan Soc. of Cardiovascular and Thoracic
  Surgeons [IO], Lahore, Pakistan
Pakistan Soc. of Criminology [IO], Peshawar,
  Pakistan
Pakistan Soc. of Gastroenterology and G.I. Endos-
  copy [IO], Karachi, Pakistan

Pakistan Soc. of Geographic Info. Systems [IO],
  Lahore, Pakistan
Pakistan Soc. of Hematology [IO], Rawalpindi,
  Pakistan
Pakistan Soc. of Horticultural Sciences [IO], Faisala-
  bad, Pakistan
Pakistan Soc. for Quality Mgt. [IO], Karachi,
  Pakistan
Pakistan Soc. for Rheumatology [IO], Lahore,
  Pakistan
Pakistan Software Export Bd. [IO], Islamabad,
  Pakistan
Pakistan Software Houses Assn. [IO], Islamabad,
  Pakistan
Pakistan Sports Medicine Assn. [IO], Karachi,
  Pakistan
Pakistan Squash Fed. [IO], Islamabad, Pakistan
Pakistan Sugar Mills Assn. [IO], Islamabad, Pakistan
Pakistan Taekwondo Fed. [IO], Rawalpindi, Pakistan
Pakistan Tax Bar Assn. [IO], Karachi, Pakistan
Pakistan Tehreek-e-Insaf [IO], Islamabad, Pakistan
Pakistan Tennis Fed. [IO], Islamabad, Pakistan
Pakistan Tourism Development Corp. [IO], Rawal-
  pindi, Pakistan
Pakistan Trade Union Defence Campaign [IO],
  Lahore, Pakistan
Pakistan Voluntary Hea. and Nutrition Assn. [IO],
  Karachi, Pakistan
Pakistan Waste Products Assn. [IO], Karachi,
  Pakistan
Pakistan Welfare Soc. [IO], Chowk Azam, Pakistan
Pakistani
  Pakistan Chamber of Commerce USA [23435]
Pakistani Amer. Bus. Executives Assn. [699], 23105
  Kashiwa Ct., Torrance, CA 90505, (310)534-1505
Pakistani Amer. Bus. Executives Assn. [699], 23105
  Kashiwa Ct., Torrance, CA 90505, (310)534-1505
Pakistani Youth Org. [IO], Karachi, Pakistan
Pakolaisneuvonta [★IO]
Palaeontographical Soc. - United Kingdom [IO],
  Maidenhead, United Kingdom
Palaeontological Assn. [IO], Aberystwyth, United
  Kingdom
Palaeontological Soc. of Japan [IO], Tokyo, Japan
Palang Merah Indonesia [★IO]
Palatines to Am.: Researching German-Speaking
  Ancestry [20654], PO Box 141260, Columbus, OH
  43214, (614)267-4700
Palatines to Am.: Researching German-Speaking
  Ancestry [20654], PO Box 141260, Columbus, OH
  43214, (614)267-4700
Palau Amateur Volleyball Assn. [IO], Koror, Palau
Palau Conservation Soc. [IO], Koror, Palau
Palau Judo Fed. [IO], Koror, Palau
Palau Red Cross Soc. [IO], Koror, Palau
Palau Tennis Fed. [IO], Koror, Palau
Palau Track and Field Assn. [IO], Koror, Palau
Palau Triathlon Fed. [IO], Koror, Palau
Palau Weightlifting Assn. [IO], Koror, Palau
Paleoanthropology Soc. [7211], 810 E St. SE,
  Washington, DC 20003, (703)292-8759
Paleontological Res. Institution [7212], Museum of
  the Earth, 1259 Trumansburg Rd., Ithaca, NY
  14850, (607)273-6623
Paleontological Soc. [7213], The Coll. of Wooster,
  Dept. of Geology, Wooster, OH 44691, (330)263-
  2247
Paleontological Soc. [7213], The Coll. of Wooster,
  Dept. of Geology, Wooster, OH 44691, (330)263-
  2247
Paleontological Soc. - Germany [IO], Munich,
  Germany
Paleontology
  Cushman Found. for Foraminiferal Res. [7210]
  Intl. Biogeography Soc. [6904]
  Paleoanthropology Soc. [7211]
  Paleontological Res. Institution [7212]
  Paleontological Soc. [7213]
  Paleontological Soc. [7213]
  Soc. for Sedimentary Geology [7214]
  Soc. of Vertebrate Paleontology [7215]
  Soc. of Vertebrate Paleontology [7215]
Palestine
  House of Palestine [10348]
  Intl. Palestinian Cardiac Relief Org. [14021]

  Middle East Investment Initiative [1313]
Palestine Arab Delegation - Defunct.
Palestine Badminton Fed. [IO], Palestine, Israel
Palestine Center [8373], The Jerusalem Fund, 2425
  Virginia Ave. NW, Washington, DC 20037,
  (202)338-1290
Palestine Liberation Org. - Address unknown since
  2010.
Palestinian
  Just Vision [17409]
Palestinian Academic Soc. for the Stud. of Intl. Af-
  fairs [IO], Jerusalem, Israel
Palestinian Agricultural Relief Comm. [IO], Jerusa-
  lem, Israel
Palestinian Family Planning and Protection Assn.
  [IO], Jerusalem, Israel
Palestinian Hydrology Gp. for Water and
  Environmental Resources Development [IO], Ra-
  mallah, Israel
Palestinian Info. Tech. Assn. of Companies [IO], Ra-
  mallah, Israel
Palestinian Tennis Assn. [IO], Palestine, Israel
Pali Text Soc. [IO], Melksham, United Kingdom
Palladium Alliance Intl. [2489], PO Box 81511, Bill-
  ings, MT 59108, (877)473-7873
Palliative Care Assn. of NSW [IO], Camperdown,
  Australia
Palliative Care; Center to Advance [15048]
Palliative Care Org; Natl. Hospice and [15028]
Palliative Care Policy Center [11746], RAND Hea.,
  1200 S Hayes St., Ste. 6402, Arlington, VA 22202-
  5050, (703)413-1100
Palliative Care Victoria [IO], Melbourne, Australia
Pallotti Center [★20088]
Palm Soc. [★6359]
Palm Soc. [★6359]
Palmtherapy Assn; Intl. [16859]
Palomino Horse Assn. [4635], 10171 Nectar Ave.,
  Nelson, MO 65347, (660)859-2064
Palomino Horse Breeders of Am. [4636], 15253 E
  Skelly Dr., Tulsa, OK 74116-2637, (918)438-1234
PALTEX - Expanded Textbook and Instructional
  Materials Prog. [8997], 525 23rd St. NW,
  Washington, DC 20037, (202)974-3451
Palynology
  AASP - The Palynological Soc. [7216]
  Amer. Assn. of Stratigraphic Palynologists [7216]
Pam Tillis Fan Club [23881], PO Box 128575,
  Nashville, TN 37212
Pambansang Komisyon para sa Kultura at mga Sin-
  ing [★IO]
Pambansang Sangguunian sa Pananaliksik ng Pilipi-
  nas [★IO]
Pan African Fed. of the Disabled [IO], Zanzibar,
  United Republic of Tanzania
Pan African Inst. for Development - Burkina Faso
  [IO], Ouagadougou, Burkina Faso
Pan African Postal Union [IO], Arusha, United
  Republic of Tanzania
Pan African Sanctuary Alliance [5106], PO Box
  83741, Portland, OR 97283, (503)238-8077
Pan African Sanctuary Alliance [5106], PO Box
  83741, Portland, OR 97283, (503)238-8077
Pan-African Soc. of Cardiology [IO], Cape Town,
  Republic of South Africa
Pan-American Acridological Soc. [★6848]
Pan-American Acridological Soc. [★6848]
Pan-American Aerobiology Assn. [6313], Michael L.
  Muilenberg, Membership Sec.-Treas., Univ. Of
  Mass-Amherst, 639 N Pleasant St., N239B Morril-l,
  Amherst, MA 01003, (413)545-3052
Pan-American Aerobiology Assn. [6313], Michael L.
  Muilenberg, Membership Sec.-Treas., Univ. Of
  Mass-Amherst, 639 N Pleasant St., N239B Morril-l,
  Amherst, MA 01003, (413)545-3052
Pan-American Allergy Soc. [13643], 1317 Wooded
  Knoll, San Antonio, TX 78258, (210)495-9853
Pan-American Assn. for Biochemistry and Molecular
  Biology - Address unknown since 2010.
Pan-American Assn. of Educational Credit Institu-
  tions [IO], Bogota, Colombia
Pan-American Assn. of Ophthalmology [15975],
  1301 S Bowen Rd., No. 450, Arlington, TX 76013,
  (817)275-7553
Pan-American Assn. of Ophthalmology [15975],
  1301 S Bowen Rd., No. 450, Arlington, TX 76013,
  (817)275-7553

A star before a book entry number signifies that the name is not listed separately, but is mentioned within the entry.

Pan Amer. Center for Sanitary Engg. and Environmental Sciences [IO], Lima, Peru

Pan Amer. Development Found. [17182], 1889 F St. NW, Washington, DC 20006, (202)458-3969

Pan Amer. Development Found. [17182], 1889 F St. NW, Washington, DC 20006, (202)458-3969

Pan-American Fed. of Consultants [IO], Rio de Janeiro, Brazil

Pan-American Fed. for Info. Tech. in Agriculture [6106], Univ. of Florida, Turlington Hall, 1012, Gainesville, FL 32611

Pan-American Fed. for Info. Tech. in Agriculture [6106], Univ. of Florida, Turlington Hall, 1012, Gainesville, FL 32611

Pan Amer. Hea. and Educ. Found. [12477], PO Box 27733, Washington, DC 20038-7733, (202)974-3416

Pan Amer. Hea. and Educ. Found. [12477], PO Box 27733, Washington, DC 20038-7733, (202)974-3416

Pan Amer. Hea. Org. [14733], 525 23rd St. NW, Washington, DC 20037, (202)974-3000

Pan Amer. Hea. Org. [14733], 525 23rd St. NW, Washington, DC 20037, (202)974-3000

Pan Amer. Hea. Org. | Pan Amer. Sanitary Bur. [14734], 525 23rd St. NW, Washington, DC 20037, (202)974-3000

Pan Amer. Hea. Org. | Pan Amer. Sanitary Bur. [14734], 525 23rd St. NW, Washington, DC 20037, (202)974-3000

Pan Amer. Highway Congresses - Defunct.

Pan Amer. Indian Assn. [10335], Loving Hands Inst., 739 12th St., Fortuna, CA 95540, (707)725-9627

Pan Amer. Inst. of Geography and History [IO], Mexico City, Mexico

Pan-American Inst. of Naval Engg. [IO], Rio de Janeiro, Brazil

Pan Amer. Standards Commn. [IO], Caracas, Venezuela

Pan Amer. Taekwondo Union [22749], One Olympic Plz., Ste. 104C, Colorado Springs, CO 80909, (719)866-4632

Pan Amer. Taekwondo Union [22749], One Olympic Plz., Ste. 104C, Colorado Springs, CO 80909, (719)866-4632

Pan Amer. Union [★17181]

Pan Amer. Union [★17181]

Pan Arcadian Fed. of Am. [19016], 880 N York Rd., Elmhurst, IL 60126, (630)833-1900

Pan-Pacific and South-East Asia Women's Assn. [IO], Turramurra, Australia

Pan-Pacific and Southeast Asia Women's Assn. of the U.S.A. - Address unknown since 2010.

Panafstrag - Suriname [IO], Paramaribo, Suriname

Panama League Against Epilepsy [IO], Panama City, Panama

Panama Maritime Law Assn. [IO], Panama City, Panama

Panamanian Assn. for Planned Parenthood [IO], Panama City, Panama

Panamanian Food Retailers and Distributors Assn. [IO], Panama City, Panama

Panamerican Cultural Circle [9949], PO Box 469, Cedar Grove, NJ 07009-0469

Panamerican Cultural Circle [9949], PO Box 469, Cedar Grove, NJ 07009-0469

Panamerican Dairy Fed. [IO], Montevideo, Uruguay

Panamerican/Panafrican Assn. [17497], 3986 Melting Snow Pl., Dumfries, VA 22025, (202)487-4143

PanAmerican Soc. for Pigment Cell Res. [15349], Dr. Andrzej T. Slominski, Sec.-Treas., Univ. of Tennessee Hea. Sci. Center, Dept. of Pathology and Lab. Medicine, 930 Madison Ave., Ste. 599, Memphis, TN 38163, (901)448-3741

Pancreatic Cancer Action Network [13964], 1500 Rosecrans Ave., Ste. 200, Manhattan Beach, CA 90266, (310)725-0025

Pancreatic Diseases
European Pancreatic Club [17828]

Pancyprian Fed. of Labor [IO], Nicosia, Cyprus

Pancyprian Veterinary Assn. [IO], Nicosia, Cyprus

Pandas Intl. [5107], PO Box 620335, Littleton, CO 80162, (303)933-2365

Pandora's Proj. [13096], 3109 W 50th St., Ste. 320, Minneapolis, MN 55410, (612)234-4204

Panel on World Data Centers [6991], 325 Broadway St., Boulder, CO 80305

Panel on World Data Centers [6991], 325 Broadway St., Boulder, CO 80305

Panetics; Intl. Soc. for [18622]

PANGEA - Comunicacio per a la Cooperacio [IO], Barcelona, Spain

Panhellenic Assn. of Landscape Architects [IO], Athens, Greece

Panhellenic Physiotherapists Assn. [IO], Athens, Greece

Panic Anxiety Disorder Assn. [IO], Everald Park, Australia

Panic Anxiety Disorder Assn. Queensland [IO], Stafford, Australia

Panimo-ja Virvoitusjuomateollisuusliitto [★IO]

Pankypria Ergatiki Omospondia [★IO]

Pannellinios Syllogos Epikiaston [IO], Athens, Greece

Panos Inst. [12357], Webster House, 1718 P St. NW, Ste. T-6, Washington, DC 20036, (202)429-0730

Panos Inst. [12357], Webster House, 1718 P St. NW, Ste. T-6, Washington, DC 20036, (202)429-0730

Panos Inst. - London [IO], London, United Kingdom

Panos Inst. - Western Africa [IO], Dakar, Senegal

Pantera Intl. [21148], PO Box 920, Ventura, CA 93002, (805)648-6464

Pantera Intl. [21148], PO Box 920, Ventura, CA 93002, (805)648-6464

Pantheist Soc; Universal [20258]

Pantheon de l'Aviation de Canada [★IO]

Panthera [5108], 8 W 40th St., 18th Fl., New York, NY 10018, (646)786-0400

Panthessalonikan Athletic Org. of Konstantinople [IO], Melbourne, Australia

Papanicolaou Soc. of Cytopathology [14218], Eric Suba, MD, Treas., 2295 Vallejo St., No. 508, San Francisco, CA 94123, (415)833-3871

Paper
100
Recycled Paperboard Alliance [2616]
ASSOCARTA - Italian Assn. of Paper, Cardboard and Pulp Mfrs. [4663]
Assn. of the Austrian Paper Indus. [17452]
Fibre Box Assn. [2617]
French Confed. of the Paper, Cardboard and Cellulose Indus. [7518]
Inst. of Paper Sci. and Tech. [7217]
Inst. of Paper Sci. and Tech. [7217]
Intl. Molded Fibre Assn. [2618]
Intl. Molded Fibre Assn. [2618]
Intl. Paperweight Soc. [22004]
Natl. Assn. of Paperstock Women [2619]
Natl. Coun. for Air and Stream Improvement [4406]
Natl. Guild of Decoupeurs [21457]
NPTA Alliance [2620]
Paper Indus. Mgt. Assn. [2621]
Pulp and Paper Safety Assn. [7218]
TAPPI - Tech. Assn. of the Pulp and Paper Indus. [2622]
Venezuelan Assn. of Paper, Pulp and Carton Producers [15648]

Paper Agents' Assn. [IO], Fleet, United Kingdom

Paper for All [IO], Ouagadougou, Burkina Faso

Paper Bag Inst. - Defunct.

Paper Cup and Container Inst. [★1041]

Paper Distribution Coun. - Address unknown since 2010.

Paper Indus. Mgt. Assn. [2621], 15 Tech. Pkwy. S, Norcross, GA 30092, (770)209-7230

Paper Indus. Tech. Assn. [IO], Bury, United Kingdom

Paper Packaging Canada [IO], Brampton, ON, Canada

Paper and Plastic Representatives Mgt. Coun. [2420], PO Box 150229, Arlington, TX 76015, (682)518-6008

Paper Plate Assn. [★1041]

Paper and Pulp Processing Indus. Assn. [IO], Vienna, Austria

Paper Shipping Sack Mfrs'. Assn. [885], 520 E Oxford St., Coopersburg, PA 18036, (610)282-6845

Paper Stock Indus. Chap. of ISRI [3641], PO Box 64999, Fayetteville, NC 28306, (910)426-7400

Paper Stock Inst. of Am; PSI Chap. [★3641]

Paperboard Packaging Coun. [2609], 1350 Main St., Ste. 1508, Springfield, MA 01103-1628, (413)686-9191

The Papers of Jefferson Davis [★10673]

Paperweight Collectors' Assn. [21395], PO Box 334, Fairless Hills, PA 19030-0334

Paperweights
Intl. Paperweight Soc. [22004]

Papillon Club of Am. [21628], 2633 Pickett Downs Dr., Chuluota, FL 32766

Papillon Incorporated - Address unknown since 2011.

Papua New Guinea Amateur Volleyball Fed. [IO], Boroko, Papua New Guinea

Papua New Guinea Athletic Union [IO], Lae, Papua New Guinea

Papua New Guinea Chamber of Commerce and Indus. [IO], Port Moresby, Papua New Guinea

Papua New Guinea Chamber of Mines and Petroleum [IO], Port Moresby, Papua New Guinea

Papua New Guinea Forest Indus. Assn. [IO], Waigani, Papua New Guinea

Papua New Guinea Lawn Tennis Assn. [IO], Boroko, Papua New Guinea

Papua New Guinea Red Cross Soc. [★IO], Boroko, Papua New Guinea

Papua New Guinea Sports Fed. and Olympic Comm. [IO], Boroko, Papua New Guinea

Papua New Guinea Squash Rackets Fed. [IO], Port Moresby, Papua New Guinea

Papua New Guinea Tourism Indus. Assn. [IO], Port Moresby, Papua New Guinea

Papua New Guinea Tourism Promotion Authority [IO], Port Moresby, Papua New Guinea

Papua New Guinea Yachting Assn. [IO], Port Moresby, Papua New Guinea

Papyrology
Amer. Soc. of Papyrologists [10349]

Para-Amps - Defunct.

Para Sa Bata [11387], 11331 Cedar Springs Dr., Frisco, TX 75035, (469)579-4544

Parachute Club of Am. [★22800]

Parachute Indus. Assn. [2623], 3833 W Oakton St., Skokie, IL 60076, (847)674-9742

Parachute Medical Rescue Ser. [★12480]

Parachute Medical Rescue Ser. [★12480]

Parachuting
Parachute Indus. Assn. [2623]
U.S. Parachute Assn. [22800]

Paraclete [20081], PO Box 1970, Gilbert, AZ 85299, (480)854-4444

Paraffin Safety Assn. of Southern Africa [IO], Cape Town, Republic of South Africa

Paraguay Squash Assn. [IO], Asuncion, Paraguay

Paraguayan-American Chamber of Commerce [IO], Asuncion, Paraguay

Paraguayan Bible Soc. [IO], Asuncion, Paraguay

Paraguayan Chamber of Cereals and Oilseed Exporters [IO], Asuncion, Paraguay

Paraguayan Indus. Union [IO], Asuncion, Paraguay

Paraguayan League Against Epilepsy [IO], Asuncion, Paraguay

Paraguayan Soc. of Dermatology [IO], Asuncion, Paraguay

Paraguayan Soc. of Hypertension [IO], Asuncion, Paraguay

Paralegal Educ; Amer. Assn. for [8497]

Paralegals
Alliance of Legal Document Asst. Professionals [5751]
Amer. Alliance of Paralegals, Inc. [5870]
Natl. Assn. of Legal Assistants [5871]
Natl. Fed. of Paralegal Associations [5872]
Natl. Paralegal Assn. [5873]
Total Practice Mgt. Assn. [5287]

Parallax Soc.

Parallax Soc. - Address unknown since 2011.

Paralympic Comm. of Azerbaijan Republic [IO], Baku, Azerbaijan

Paralympic Comm. of Moldova [IO], Chisinau, Moldova

Paralympic Comm. of Moscow [IO], Moscow, Russia

Reference to "IO" in place of a book number signifies that the association may be found in the 50th edition of International Organizations.

Encyclopedia of Associations, 51st Edition

3083

Paralympic Comm. of the Republic of Belarus [IO], Minsk, Belarus

Paralympic Comm. of Russia [IO], Moscow, Russia

Paralympic Comm. of Serbia [IO], Belgrade, Serbia

Paralympic Coun. of Ireland [IO], Dublin, Ireland

Paralympic Sports Assn. [IO], Edmonton, AB, Canada

Paralympics New Zealand [IO], Auckland, New Zealand

Paralysis Assn; Periodic [15360]

Paralysis Cure Res. Found. [★16700]

Paralyzed Veterans of Am. [20416], 801 18th St. NW, Washington, DC 20006-3517, (800)555-9140

Paramount Orchids [IO], Calgary, AB, Canada

Paranormal

Amer. Assn. of Paranormal Investigators [2624]

Amer. Ghost Soc. [7219]

Intl. Soc. for a Complete Earth [12217]

Intl. Soc. for Paranormal Res. [2625]

Intl. Soc. for Paranormal Res. [2625]

Paraolimpijski komitet Srbije [★IO]

Paraprofessional Healthcare Inst. [★1677]

Parapsychological Assn. [7227], PO Box 24173, Columbus, OH 43224, (202)318-2364

Parapsychology

Acad. of Psychic Arts and Sciences [7220]

Acad. of Spirituality and Paranormal Stud., Inc. [7221]

Acad. of Spirituality and Paranormal Stud., Inc. [7221]

Amer. Soc. for Psychical Res. [7222]

Assn. for Res. and Enlightenment [7223]

Assn. for Res. and Enlightenment [7223]

Comm. for Skeptical Inquiry [7224]

Intl. Soc. for the Stud. of Ghosts and Apparitions [7225]

Intl. Soc. for the Stud. of Ghosts and Apparitions [7225]

Mind Sci. Found. [7226]

Parapsychological Assn. [7227]

Parapsychology Found. [7228]

Rhine Res. Center [7229]

U.S. Psychotronics Assn. [7230]

Parapsychology Found. [7228], PO Box 1562, New York, NY 10021-0043, (212)628-1550

Parapsychology Lab. of Duke Univ. [★7229]

Parasitological Soc. of Southern Africa [IO], Pretoria, Republic of South Africa

Parasitologiese Vereniging van Suidelike Afrika [★IO]

Parasitologists; Amer. Assn. of Veterinary [16987]

Paratuberculosis Awareness and Res. Assn. [14571], PO Box 16219, Temple Terrace, FL 33687-6219

Paratuberculosis Awareness and Res. Assn. [14571], PO Box 16219, Temple Terrace, FL 33687-6219

Parbatya Bouddha Mission [IO], Khagrachari, Bangladesh

Parcel Post Assn. [★2237]

Parcel Shippers Assn. [2237], 1420 King St., Ste. 620, Alexandria, VA 22314, (571)257-7617

Parent Cooperative Preschools Intl. [7834], Natl. Cooperative Bus. Center, 1401 New York Ave. NW, Ste. 1100, Washington, DC 20005

Parent Cooperative Preschools Intl. [7834], Natl. Cooperative Bus. Center, 1401 New York Ave. NW, Ste. 1100, Washington, DC 20005

Parent Finders of Canada [IO], Ottawa, ON, Canada

Parent Network [8693], The Montessori Acad., 530 E Day Rd., Mishawaka, IN 46545, (574)256-5313

Parent Resources and Info. on Drug Educ. [★13284]

Parent Support Assn. of Calgary [IO], Calgary, AB, Canada

Parenteral Drug Assn. [★2699]

Parenteral Drug Assn. [★2699]

Parenteral and Enteral Nutrition Soc. of Asia [IO], Bangkok, Thailand

Parenteral Soc. [★5655]

Parenthood Fed. of Am; Planned [12040]

Parenting Publications of Am. [2956], 1970 E Grand Ave., Ste. 330, El Segundo, CA 90245, (310)364-0193

Parentless Children's Comm. [IO], Yerevan, Armenia

Parentline Plus [IO], London, United Kingdom

Parents

Adoptee-Birthparent Support Network [10774]

ALMA Soc. [10777]

Amer. Coalition for Fathers and Children [12602]

Attachment Parenting Intl. [12603]

Attachment Parenting Intl. [12603]

Center for Loss in Multiple Birth [12604]

Christian Family Life [12001]

Citizenship Through Sports Alliance [22972]

The Compassionate Friends [12605]

Dads Rights [11865]

EcoMom Alliance [13459]

Families for Private Adoption [10788]

Family Equality Coun. [12079]

Family and Home Network [12606]

Father Matters [18224]

FosterClub [13522]

Friends in Adoption [10789]

Generation Green [14077]

Great Dads [12607]

GreatSchools [7831]

Green Parent Assn. [4075]

Holistic Moms Network [12608]

Kids Need Both Parents [17623]

MISS Found. | Alliance of Grandparents, A Support in Tragedy Intl. [12123]

Mocha Moms [13466]

Natl. Assn. of Mothers' Centers [12609]

Natl. Assn. of Non-Custodial Moms [12610]

Natl. Center for Fathering [18225]

Natl. Center for Fathering [18225]

Natl. Fed. of Services for Unmarried Parents and Their Children [6792]

Natl. Foster Parent Assn. [12611]

Natl. Infertility Network Exchange [12612]

Natl. Org. of Single Mothers [13119]

Natl. Practitioners Network for Fathers and Families [12018]

Natl. PTA [8691]

Native Amer. Fatherhood and Families Assn. [12613]

New Parents Network [8692]

Parent Network [8693]

Parents' Action For Children [12614]

Parents' Choice Found. [12615]

Parents Helping Parents [12616]

Parents of Murdered Children [12617]

Parents of Premature Babies [12618]

Parents Without Partners [12619]

Partners in Foster Care [12046]

Postpartum Support Intl. [12620]

Postpartum Support Intl. [12620]

Professional Football Players Mothers' Assn. [22595]

SHARE: Pregnancy and Infant Loss Support [12621]

Single Mothers By Choice [12622]

Single Parent Rsrc. Center [12623]

Surviving Parents Coalition [11511]

Twins Found. [12551]

UNITE [12624]

Welfare Warriors [18226]

Parents' Action For Children [12614], PO Box 2096, Culver City, CA 90231, (888)447-3400

Parents Active for Vision Educ. [17110], 4135 54th Pl., San Diego, CA 92105-2303, (619)287-0081

Parents Against Childhood Epilepsy [14522], 7 E 85th St., Ste. A3, New York, NY 10028, (212)665-7223

Parents Against Tired Truckers [★13011]

Parents' Alliance to Protect Our Children - Defunct.

Parents Anonymous [11388], 675 W Foothill Blvd., Ste. 220, Claremont, CA 91711-3475, (909)621-6184

Parents Assn. for Children with Retarded Mental Development [★12505]

Parents Assn. for Jewish Residential Care [★12503]

Parents Campaign for Handicapped Children and Youth [★11816]

Parents Centres New Zealand [IO], Mana, New Zealand

Parents' Choice Found. [12615], 201 W Padonia Rd., Ste. 303, Timonium, MD 21093, (410)308-3858

Parents-Coaches Assn. [22427], PO Box 224, Odenton, MD 21113, (410)207-1570

Parents in Control [8093], 2511 Jasu Dr., Lawrence, KS 66046, (785)749-0083

Parents, Families, and Friends of Lesbians and Gays [12106], 1828 L St. NW, Ste. 660, Washington, DC 20036, (202)467-8180

Parents and Friends of Ex-Gays and Gays [12107], PO Box 510, Reedville, VA 22539, (804)453-4737

Parents and Friends of Lesbians and Gays [★12106]

Parents of Galactosemic Children [15505], Michelle Fowler, Pres., PO Box 2401, Mandeville, LA 70470, (866)900-7421

Parents Helping Parents [12616], Sobrato Center for Nonprofits-San Jose, 1400 Parkmoor Ave., Ste. 100, San Jose, CA 95126-3429, (408)727-5775

Parents of Infants and Children with Kernicterus [15628], One W Superior St., Ste. 2410, Chicago, IL 60610, (312)274-9695

Parents of Kids with Infectious Diseases [15123], PO Box 5666, Vancouver, WA 98668, (360)695-0293

Parents for MPS [★15501]

Parents of Murdered Children [12617], 100 E 8th St., Ste. 202, Cincinnati, OH 45202, (513)721-5683

Parents of Near Drownings - Defunct.

Parents Network for the Post Institutionalized Child - Address unknown since 2011.

Parents Of Autistic Children [13801], 1999 Rte. 88, Brick, NJ 08724, (732)785-1099

Parents of Premature Babies [12618], 21 Lansing Ln., East Northport, NY 11731

Parents and Professionals and Autism Northern Ireland [IO], Belfast, United Kingdom

Parents for Public Schools [11908], 200 N Cong. St., Ste. 500, Jackson, MS 39201, (601)969-6936

Parents Rights, Inc. [★7725]

Parents' Rights Org. [7725], Citizen's For Educational Freedom - Missouri Fed., 498 Woods Mill Rd., Manchester, MO 63011, (636)686-7101

Parents' Sect. of the Alexander Graham Bell Assn. for the Deaf [★14955]

Parents' Sect. of the Alexander Graham Bell Assn. for the Deaf and Hard of Hearing [14955], 3417 Volta Pl. NW, Washington, DC 20007, (202)337-5220

Parents Sharing Custody - Defunct.

Parents of Surrogate-Borne Infants and Toddlers in Verbal Exchange - Defunct.

Parents and Teachers Against Violence in Educ. [7977], PO Box 1033, Alamo, CA 94507-7033, (925)831-1661

Parents and Teachers in Lutheran Schools - Defunct.

Parents United - Address unknown since 2010.

Parents Volunteer Assn. [★12511]

Parents With a Purpose [★12500]

Parents Without Partners [12619], 1100-H Brandywine Blvd., Zanesville, OH 43701-7303, (800)637-7974

Parents Without Partners - Australia [IO], Lower Templestowe, Australia

Paris Chamber of Commerce and Indus. [IO], Paris, France

Park Law Enforcement Assn. [5881], 1401 Ned Moore Rd., Timberlake, NC 27583-8849, (336)364-4744

Park Ridge Center - Defunct.

Parke Soc. [20570], Paul Jordan-Smith, Ed., 13038 6th Ave. NW, Seattle, WA 98177-4211, (206)366-1532

Parker Gun Collectors Assn. [21717], PO Box 115, Mayodan, NC 27027

Parking

Intl. Parking Inst. [2626]

Intl. Parking Inst. [2626]

Natl. Parking Assn. [2627]

Parking Assn. of Australia [IO], Crows Nest, Australia

Parkinson Alliance [15629], PO Box 308, Kingston, NJ 08528-0308, (609)688-0870

Parkinson Disease Assn; Amer. [15567]

Parkinson Found; Natl. [15621]

Parkinson Soc. of Canada [IO], Toronto, ON, Canada

A star before a book entry number signifies that the name is not listed separately, but is mentioned within the entry.

Parkinson Soc. Canada - Maritime Region **[IO]**, Halifax, NS, Canada

Parkinson Soc. Canada - Southwestern Ontario Region **[IO]**, London, ON, Canada

Parkinson Soc. Manitoba **[IO]**, Winnipeg, MB, Canada

Parkinson Soc. Newfoundland and Labrador **[IO]**, St. John's, NL, Canada

Parkinson Soc. Ottawa **[IO]**, Ottawa, ON, Canada

Parkinson Soc. Quebec **[IO]**, Montreal, QC, Canada

Parkinson's Action Network **[14416]**, 1025 Vermont Ave. NW, Ste. 1120, Washington, DC 20005, (202)638-4101

Parkinson's Assn. of Ireland **[IO]**, Dublin, Ireland

Parkinson's Australia **[IO]**, Calwell, Australia

Parkinson's Disease Found. **[15630]**, 1359 Broadway, Ste. 1509, New York, NY 10018, (212)923-4700

Parkinson's Disease Nurse Specialist Assn. **[IO]**, Wellingborough, United Kingdom

Parkinson's Disease Soc. of the United Kingdom **[IO]**, London, United Kingdom

Parkinson's New South Wales **[IO]**, North Ryde, Australia

Parkinsons New Zealand **[IO]**, Wellington, New Zealand

Parkinson's Soc. of Alberta **[IO]**, Edmonton, AB, Canada

Parkinson's Soc. of Southern Alberta **[IO]**, Calgary, AB, Canada

Parkinson's Victoria **[IO]**, Cheltenham, Australia

Parkinson's Western Australia **[IO]**, Nedlands, Australia

Parks and Recreation

Assn. of Natl. Park Rangers **[5874]**

City Parks Alliance **[18227]**

Coalition of Natl. Park Ser. Retirees **[4766]**

Friends of Virgin Islands Natl. Park **[4767]**

Global Parks **[4070]**

Greensward Found. **[4077]**

Natl. Amusement Park Historical Assn. **[20946]**

Natl. Assn. of County Park and Recreation Officials **[5875]**

Natl. Assn. of Recreation Rsrc. Planners **[5876]**

Natl. Assn. of State Park Directors **[5877]**

Natl. Park Found. **[5878]**

Natl. Park Trust **[4768]**

Natl. Parks Conservation Assn. **[5879]**

Natl. Recreation and Park Assn. **[5880]**

North Amer. Wildlife Park Found. **[5098]**

Park Law Enforcement Assn. **[5881]**

Proj. for Public Spaces **[17394]**

Public Art Fund **[17395]**

Sculpture in the Env. **[17396]**

Soc. of Park and Recreation Educators **[5882]**

Parliamentarians For Global Action **[17556]**, 211 E 43rd St., Ste. 1604, New York, NY 10017, (212)687-7755

Parliamentarians For Global Action **[17556]**, 211 E 43rd St., Ste. 1604, New York, NY 10017, (212)687-7755

Parliamentarians Global Action for Disarmament, Development, and World Reform **[★17556]**

Parliamentarians Global Action for Disarmament, Development, and World Reform **[★17556]**

Parliamentarians for World Order **[★17556]**

Parliamentarians for World Order **[★17556]**

Parliamentary Centre **[IO]**, Ottawa, ON, Canada

Parliaments

Amer. Inst. of Parliamentarians **[10350]**ParliamentsConf. of Speakers and Presiding Officers of the Commonwealth

Natl. Assn. of Parliamentarians **[10351]**

Natl. Assn. of Parliamentarians **[10351]**

Parole

ACLU I Natl. Prison Proj. **[11699]**

Amer. Probation and Parole Assn. **[5883]**

Assn. of Paroling Authorities Intl. **[5884]**

Assn. of Paroling Authorities Intl. **[5884]**

Assn. of State Correctional Administrators **[11706]**

Center for Stud. in Criminal Justice **[11707]**

Intl. Assn. for Correctional and Forensic Psychology **[11715]**

Parrot Intl. **[3851]**, 15332 Antioch Ave., No. 417, Pacific Palisades, CA 90272

Parrot Soc. of Australia **[IO]**, Brisbane, Australia

Parrot Soc. - U.K. **[IO]**, Berkhamsted, United Kingdom

Parrotlet Alliance **[3852]**, 3405 Camden Rd., Marshville, NC 28103

Parrots and People **[3853]**, 521 Essex Pl., Euless, TX 76039, (817)498-9636

PARSA **[IO]**, Kabul, Afghanistan

Parson Russell Terrier Assn. of Am. **[21629]**, Joe Pavlic, Sec., 1450 Priory Rd., Eau Claire, WI 54701, (414)581-9091

partei des Demokratischen Sozialismus **[★IO]**

Parthenais Cattle Breeders Assn. **[3935]**, 982 Hutchins Ln., Chipley, FL 32428, (850)638-8873

Parti Abolitionniste du Canada **[★IO]**

Parti liberal du Canada **[★IO]**

Parti Chretien Social **[★IO]**

Parti Europeen des Liberaux Democrates et Reformateurs **[★IO]**

Parti Gerakan Rakyat Malaysia **[IO]**, Kuala Lumpur, Malaysia

Parti de L'Heritage Chretien **[★IO]**

Parti Ouvrier Socialiste Luxembourgeois **[★IO]**

Parti Populaire Europeen **[★IO]**

Parti Socialiste **[★IO]**

Partial Hospitalization Study Group **[★16335]**

Partially Sighted Soc. **[IO]**, Doncaster, United Kingdom

Participa **[IO]**, Santiago, Chile

Partij van de Arbeid **[★IO]**

Partit Laburista **[★IO]**

Partner for Surgery **[16818]**, PO Box 388, McLean, VA 22101, (703)893-4335

Partner for Surgery **[16818]**, PO Box 388, McLean, VA 22101, (703)893-4335

Partners **[★17918]**

Partners of the Americas **[17183]**, 1424 K St. NW, Ste. 700, Washington, DC 20005, (202)628-3300

Partners of the Americas **[17183]**, 1424 K St. NW, Ste. 700, Washington, DC 20005, (202)628-3300

Partners for Christian Development **[★19598]**

Partners in Community Development Fiji **[IO]**, Suva, Fiji

Partners for Democratic Change **[17918]**, 1779 Massachusetts Ave. NW, Ste. 515, Washington, DC 20036, (202)942-2166

Partners for Development/Cambodia **[IO]**, Phnom Penh, Cambodia

Partners for Effective Parenting - Defunct.

Partners in Foster Care **[12046]**, PO Box 2534, Madison, WI 53701, (608)274-9111

Partners in Hea. **[12132]**, 888 Commonwealth Ave., 3rd Fl., Boston, MA 02215, (617)998-8922

Partners in Hea. **[12132]**, 888 Commonwealth Ave., 3rd Fl., Boston, MA 02215, (617)998-8922

Partners for Livable Communities **[5332]**, 1429 21st St. NW, Washington, DC 20036, (202)887-5990

Partners for Livable Places **[★5332]**

Partners in Parks **[4124]**, PO Box 13601, Wauwatosa, WI 53213-0601, (262)251-2542

Partners for Peace **[18271]**, 1250 4th St. SW, Ste. WG-1, Washington, DC 20024, (202)863-2951

Partners in Peace **[★12627]**

Partners for Peace **[18271]**, 1250 4th St. SW, Ste. WG-1, Washington, DC 20024, (202)863-2951

Partners in Peace **[★12627]**

Partners for Rural Am. **[18574]**, Britta Fuller, Admin. Asst., PO Box 21177, Cheyenne, WY 82003, (307)777-5271

Partners for Rural Improvement and Development in Ethiopia **[12959]**, Zewge Gebre-Mariam, Chm., 2828 Kenyon Cir., Boulder, CO 80305, (303)543-0515

Partners for Rural Improvement and Development in Ethiopia **[12959]**, Zewge Gebre-Mariam, Chm., 2828 Kenyon Cir., Boulder, CO 80305, (303)543-0515

Partners for Sacred Places **[20194]**, 1700 Sansom St., 10th Fl., Philadelphia, PA 19103, (215)567-3234

Partners in Sustainable Development Intl. **[12745]**, 9005 Greenridge Dr., St. Louis, MO 63117, (314)993-5599

Partners Task Force for Gay and Lesbian Couples **[12108]**, Box 9685, Seattle, WA 98109-0685, (206)935-1206

Partners for World Hea. **[15203]**, 7 Glasgow Rd., Scarborough, ME 04074, (207)885-1011

Partners Worldwide **[19598]**, 6139 Tahoe Dr. SE, Grand Rapids, MI 49546, (616)818-4900

Partnership for Advancing the Transition to Hydrogen **[6748]**, 1211 Connecticut Ave. NW, Ste. 600, Washington, DC 20036, (202)457-0076

Partnership for Civil Justice Legal Defense and Educ. Fund **[17316]**, Partnership for Civil Justice, 617 Florida Ave. NW, Washington, DC 20001-1852, (202)232-1180

Partnership to Cut Hunger and Poverty in Africa **[12746]**, 499 S Capitol St. SW, Ste. 500B, Washington, DC 20003, (202)479-4501

Partnership to Cut Hunger and Poverty in Africa **[12746]**, 499 S Capitol St. SW, Ste. 500B, Washington, DC 20003, (202)479-4501

Partnership for a Drug-Free Am. **[★13281]**

Partnership at Drugfree.org **[13281]**, 352 Park Ave. S 9th Fl., New York, NY 10010, (212)922-1560

Partnership for Educ. of Children in Afghanistan **[11494]**, PO Box 201542, Bloomington, MN 55420, (612)821-8759

Partnership for Employment and Training Careers **[★11947]**

Partnership for Food Safety Educ. **[14542]**, 2345 Crystal Dr., Ste. 800, Arlington, VA 22202, (202)220-0651

Partnership for Global Security **[18600]**, 1911 Pine St., Philadelphia, PA 19103, (215)523-9041

Partnership for Global Security **[18600]**, 1911 Pine St., Philadelphia, PA 19103, (215)523-9041

Partnership for Human Res. Protection - Defunct.

Partnership Mission **[★20015]**

Partnership Mission **[★20015]**

Partnership for Patient Safety **[14824]**, 405 N Wabash Ave., Ste. P2W, Chicago, IL 60611, (312)464-0600

Partnership for Philanthropic Planning **[1542]**, 233 McCrea St., Ste. 400, Indianapolis, IN 46225, (317)269-6274

Partnership for Prevention **[14735]**, 1015 18th St. NW, Ste. 300, Washington, DC 20036, (202)833-0009

Partnership for Public Ser. **[17331]**, 1100 New York Ave. NW, Ste. 1090 E, Washington, DC 20005, (202)775-9111

Partnership for Quality Medical Donations **[12478]**, 12600 Deerfield Pkwy., Ste. 100, Alpharetta, GA 30004, (678)566-3628

Partnership for Quality Medical Donations **[12478]**, 12600 Deerfield Pkwy., Ste. 100, Alpharetta, GA 30004, (678)566-3628

Partnership for Res. Integrity in Sci. and Medicine **[18500]**, Professional & Scholarly Publishing, Assn. of Amer. Publishers, 71 5th Ave., 2nd Fl., New York, NY 10003, (212)255-0200

Partnership for Safe Driving **[13002]**, 1312 18th St. NW, Rm. 501, Washington, DC 20036

Partnership for Sustainable Development - Nepal **[IO]**, Kathmandu, Nepal

Party of Democratic Socialism **[IO]**, Berlin, Germany

Party of European Socialists **[IO]**, Brussels, Belgium

Paso Fino Horse Assn. **[4637]**, 4047 Iron Works Pkwy., Ste. 1, Lexington, KY 40511, (859)825-6000

Paso Fino Horse Assn. **[4637]**, 4047 Iron Works Pkwy., Ste. 1, Lexington, KY 40511, (859)825-6000

Paso Fino Owners and Breeders Assn. **[★4637]**

Paso Fino Owners and Breeders Assn. **[★4637]**

Paso Pacifico **[4125]**, PO Box 1244, Ventura, CA 93002-1244, (805)643-7044

Passaic River Coalition **[7609]**, 330 Speedwell Ave., Morristown, NJ 07960, (973)532-9830

Passenger Shipping Assn. **[IO]**, London, United Kingdom

Passenger Vessel Assn. **[2369]**, 103 Oronoco St., Ste. 200, Alexandria, VA 22314, (703)518-5005

Passiflora Soc. Intl. **[4677]**, Butterfly World, 3600 Sample Rd., Coconut Creek, FL 33073

PASSION: Pursuing A Successful Seed In-spite of Negativity **[13550]**, PO Box 112069, Stamford, CT 06911-2069, (888)831-4079

Passionists Intl. **[IO]**, Rome, Italy

Pastel Artists Canada **[IO]**, Flesherton, ON, Canada

Pastel Soc. **[IO]**, London, United Kingdom

Reference to "IO" in place of a book number signifies that the association may be found in the 50th edition of International Organizations.

Pastel Soc. of Am. **[9196]**, 15 Gramercy Park S, New York, NY 10003, (212)533-6931

Pastel Soc. of Am. **[9196]**, 15 Gramercy Park S, New York, NY 10003, (212)533-6931

Pastel Soc. of Australia **[IO]**, Moorooka, Australia

Pastel Soc. of Eastern Canada **[IO]**, Chambly, QC, Canada

Patee House Museum **[★9795]**

Patent and Enamelled Leather Mfrs. Assn. **[★2202]**

Patent Law
Assn. of Patent Law Firms **[5885]**
Coalition Against Counterfeiting and Piracy **[5564]**
Coalition for Intellectual Property Rights **[5565]**
Embroidery Software Protection Coalition **[2049]**
Inventors Workshop Intl. **[5574]**
Natl. Assn. of Patent Practitioners **[5886]**
Public Interest Intellectual Property Advisors **[5580]**

Patent Law Assn. of Washington **[★5559]**

Patent Off. Professional Assn. **[5578]**, PO Box 25287, Alexandria, VA 22313, (571)272-0897

Patent Off. Soc. **[★5579]**

Patent Protection Assn. of China **[IO]**, Beijing, People's Republic of China

Patent and Trademark Off. Soc. **[5579]**, PO Box 2089, Arlington, VA 22202, (571)272-8575

Path-Finder Guide Dogs **[★17094]**

Path-Finder Guide Dogs **[★17094]**

Path of Success **[9079]**, 139 Lake Ave., West Haven, CT 06516, (203)937-7519

Pathfinder do Brasil **[★IO]**

Pathfinder Intl. **[12039]**, 9 Galen St., Ste. 217, Watertown, MA 02472, (617)924-7200

Pathfinder Intl. **[12039]**, 9 Galen St., Ste. 217, Watertown, MA 02472, (617)924-7200

Pathfinder Intl. - Brazil **[IO]**, Salvador, Brazil

Pathological Soc. of Great Britain and Ireland **[IO]**, London, United Kingdom

Pathologists; Amer. Coll. of Veterinary **[17002]**

Pathologists; Amer. Osteopathic Coll. of **[16070]**

Pathology
Amer. Acad. of Oral and Maxillofacial Pathology **[16109]**
Amer. Assn. of Neuropathologists **[16110]**
Amer. Assn. of Pathologists' Assistants **[16111]**
Amer. Bd. of Oral and Maxillofacial Pathology **[16112]**
Amer. Bd. of Pathology **[16113]**
Amer. Pathology Found. **[16114]**
Amer. Soc. for Clinical Pathology **[16115]**
Amer. Soc. for Investigative Pathology **[16116]**
Armed Forces Inst. of Pathology | Dept. of Environmental and Toxicologic Pathology **[16117]**
Armed Forces Inst. of Pathology | Dept. of Environmental and Toxicologic Pathology **[16117]**
Assn. of Indian Pathologists in North America **[16118]**
Assn. for Molecular Pathology **[16119]**
Assn. of Pathology Chairs **[16120]**
Assn. for Pathology Informatics **[16121]**
Clinical Cytometry Soc. **[16122]**
Coll. of Amer. Pathologists **[16123]**
Corporate Speech Pathology Network **[3303]**
Digital Pathology Assn. **[16124]**
European Found. for Plant Pathology **[2675]**
Intl. Acad. of Pathology **[16125]**
Intl. Acad. of Pathology **[16125]**
Intl. Assn. of Orofacial Myology **[16126]**
Intl. Assn. of Orofacial Myology **[16126]**
Intl. Soc. for Plastination **[16127]**
Intl. Soc. for Plastination **[16127]**
Intersociety Coun. for Pathology Info. **[16128]**
North Amer. Soc. of Head and Neck Pathology **[16129]**
Renal Pathology Soc. **[16130]**
Renal Pathology Soc. **[16130]**
Soc. for Applied Immunohistochemistry **[16131]**
Soc. for Hematopathology **[16132]**
Soc. for Pediatric Pathology **[16133]**
Soc. of Toxicologic Pathology **[16134]**
Soc. for Ultrastructural Pathology **[16135]**
U.S. and Canadian Acad. of Pathology **[16136]**
U.S. and Canadian Acad. of Pathology **[16136]**

Pathology; Soc. for Cardiovascular **[14043]**

Pathology; Soc. for Cardiovascular **[14043]**

Pathways to Coll. Network **[8243]**, Inst. for Higher Educ. Policy, 1320 19th St. NW, Ste. 400, Washington, DC 20036, (202)861-8223

Pathways to Peace **[12631]**, PO Box 1057, Larkspur, CA 94977, (415)461-0500

Pathways to Peace **[12631]**, PO Box 1057, Larkspur, CA 94977, (415)461-0500

Pathwork Helpers Assn. of North Am. **[20252]**, 301 E 4th St., Apt. 328, Austin, TX 78701, (512)215-2544

Patidar Cultural Assn. of USA - Address unknown since 2010.

Patience T'ai Chi Assn. **[22750]**, PO Box 350-532, Brooklyn, NY 11235, (718)332-3477

Patient Advocate Found. **[14825]**, 421 Butler Farm Rd., Hampton, VA 23666, (800)532-5274

Patient Advocates for Advanced Cancer Treatments **[13965]**, PO Box 141695, Grand Rapids, MI 49514-1695, (616)453-1477

Patient Privacy Rights **[18104]**, PO Box 248, Austin, TX 78767

Patient Safety Inst. - Defunct.

Patients Against Lymphoma **[15257]**, 3774 Buckwampum Rd., Riegelsville, PA 18077, (610)346-8419

Patinage Canada **[★IO]**

Patinage de Vitesse Canada **[★IO]**

Patriot Network - The Natl. Assn. of Independent Patriot Clubs - Defunct.

Patriotic Educ. Inc. **[7862]**, 107 Heritage Ln., Madison, AL 35758-7974, (256)461-0612

Patriotic Order Sons of Am. **[20744]**, 240 S Centre Ave., Leesport, PA 19533, (610)926-3324

Patriotic Pets - Address unknown since 2011.

Patriotism
Amer. Patriots Assn. **[20742]**
Centennial Legion of Historic Military Commands **[20743]**
Natl. Graves Assn. **[5220]**
Natl. Traditionalist Caucus **[17429]**
Patriotic Order Sons of Am. **[20744]**
A Soldier's Wish List **[11108]**
Twelve Lights League **[18073]**

Patristics
North Amer. Patristics Soc. **[20150]**

Patrol Craft Sailors Assn. **[20724]**, Jim Heywood, 7005 Bridge Rd., Cincinnati, OH 45230, (513)233-2775

Patrouille canadienne de ski **[★IO]**

Patt Family Assn. - Defunct.

Patterdale Terrier Club of Am. **[21630]**, 108 Olde Towne Rd., Paradise, TX 76073

Pattern Makers' League of North Am. **[★23153]**

Pattern, Model, and Mould Mfrs. Assn. **[IO]**, West Bromwich, United Kingdom

Pattern Recognition
Classification Soc. **[7231]**
Pattern Recognition Soc. **[7232]**

Pattern Recognition Assn. of South Africa **[IO]**, Matieland, Republic of South Africa

Pattern Recognition and Machine Intelligence Assn. **[IO]**, Singapore, Singapore

Pattern Recognition Soc. **[7232]**, Natl. Biomedical Res. Found., 3900 Reservoir Rd. NW, Washington, DC 20007, (202)687-2121

Pattern Recognition Soc. of Finland **[IO]**, Oulu, Finland

Patti Page Appreciation Soc. **[23882]**, Rene Paquette, Pres., 4565 S Atlantic Ave., Ste. 5103, Ponce Inlet, FL 32127, (386)756-6682

Patti Page Appreciation Soc. **[23882]**, Rene Paquette, Pres., 4565 S Atlantic Ave., Ste. 5103, Ponce Inlet, FL 32127, (386)756-6682

Patton Soc. **[10682]**, 17010 S Potter Rd., Oregon City, OR 97045

Pauktuutit Inuit Women of Canada **[IO]**, Ottawa, ON, Canada

Paul-Ehrlich-Gesellschaft fur Chemotherapie **[★IO]**

Paul-Ehrlich-Society for Chemotherapy **[IO]**, Rheinbach, Germany

Paul and Lisa Found. **[★13097]**

Paul and Lisa Prog. **[13097]**, PO Box 348, Westbrook, CT 06498, (860)767-7660

Paulist Evangelization Ministries **[19484]**, 3031 4th St. NE, Washington, DC 20017-1102, (202)832-5022

Paulist Father **[★19454]**

Paulist Natl. Catholic Evangelization Assn. **[★19484]**

Paved Arts New Media **[IO]**, Saskatoon, SK, Canada

Paviors' Company **[IO]**, Enfield, United Kingdom

Paw Paw Found. **[4467]**, Kentucky State Univ., 129 Atwood Res. Fac., Frankfort, KY 40601-2355, (502)597-6375

PAWS For A Cause **[11018]**, 2708 Freeman Mill Rd., Suffolk, VA 23438, (757)986-2287

Paws for Friendship **[13402]**, PO Box 341378, Tampa, FL 33694, (813)961-2822

Paws With a Cause **[11821]**, 4646 South Div., Wayland, MI 49348, (616)877-7297

Pax Christi - Aotearoa New Zealand **[IO]**, Auckland, New Zealand

Pax Christi - Australia **[IO]**, Carlton, Australia

Pax Christi - Australia New South Wales Br. **[IO]**, Sydney, Australia

Pax Christi - Austria **[IO]**, Linz, Austria

Pax Christi - Denmark **[IO]**, Copenhagen, Denmark

Pax Christi - Flanders **[IO]**, Antwerp, Belgium

Pax Christi - France **[IO]**, Paris, France

Pax Christi - Germany **[IO]**, Berlin, Germany

Pax Christi - Goma **[IO]**, Goma, Republic of the Congo

Pax Christi - Great Britain **[IO]**, London, United Kingdom

Pax Christi - Hungary **[IO]**, Szeged, Hungary

Pax Christi - Intl. **[IO]**, Brussels, Belgium

Pax Christi - Ireland **[IO]**, Dublin, Ireland

Pax Christi - Italy **[IO]**, Florence, Italy

Pax Christi - Kikwit **[IO]**, Kikwit, Republic of the Congo

Pax Christi - Luxembourg **[IO]**, Luxembourg, Luxembourg

Pax Christi - Netherlands **[IO]**, Utrecht, Netherlands

Pax Christi Osterreich **[★IO]**

Pax Christi - Philippines **[IO]**, Bacolod City, Philippines

Pax Christi - Port-au-Prince **[IO]**, Croix-des-Bouquets, Haiti

Pax Christi - Portugal **[IO]**, Lisbon, Portugal

Pax Christi - Queensland Br. **[IO]**, Cleveland, Australia

Pax Christi - Sect. Francaise **[★IO]**

Pax Christi - Switzerland **[IO]**, Villars-sur-Glane, Switzerland

Pax Christi U.S.A. **[18175]**, 532 W 8th St., Erie, PA 16502, (814)453-4955

Pax Christi Vlaanderen **[★IO]**

Pax Christi - Wallonie-Bruxelles **[IO]**, Brussels, Belgium

Pax Christi - Warsaw **[IO]**, Warsaw, Poland

PAX: Real Solutions to Gun Violence **[★17685]**

Pax Romana, Intl. Catholic Movement for Intellectual and Cultural Affairs **[IO]**, Geneva, Switzerland

Pax Romana, Movimento Internacional de Intelectuales Catolicos **[★IO]**

Pax World Found. **[★17919]**

Pax World Found. **[★17919]**

Pax World Ser. **[17919]**, Mercy Corps., Dept. W, PO Box 2669, Portland, OR 97208-2669, (800)292-3355

Pax World Ser. **[17919]**, Mercy Corps., Dept. W, PO Box 2669, Portland, OR 97208-2669, (800)292-3355

Pay for Schools by Regulating Cannabis **[18337]**, PO Box 86741, Portland, OR 97286, (503)229-0428

Payasos Sin Fronteras **[★IO]**

Payment Card Indus. Security Alliance **[1053]**, 48377 Fremont Blvd., No. 117, Fremont, CA 94538, (510)492-4027

Payments Assn. of South Africa **[IO]**, Marshalltown, Republic of South Africa

Payroll Assn.; Amer. **[1140]**

Paz y Cooperacion **[★IO]**

Pazarlama ve Kamuoyu Arastirmacilari Dernegi **[★IO]**

PBCers Org. - Address unknown since 2011.

PBR Forces Veterans Assn. **[20833]**, 693 Evangeline Rd., Cincinnati, OH 45240-3011

PC/104 Consortium **[3395]**, 16795 Lark Ave., Ste. 104, Los Gatos, CA 95032, (408)337-0904

PC Gaming Alliance **[6552]**, 2400 Camino Ramon, Ste. 375, San Ramon, CA 94583, (925)275-6647

A star before a book entry number signifies that the name is not listed separately, but is mentioned within the entry.

PC Hackers - Defunct.

PCI Indus. Cmpt. Mfrs. Gp. [6553], Virtual, Inc., 401 Edgewater Pl., Ste. 600, Wakefield, MA 01880, (781)246-9318

PCI-Media Impact [12701], 777 United Nations Plz., 5th Fl., 44th St. at 1st Ave., New York, NY 10017, (212)687-3366

PCI-Media Impact [12701], 777 United Nations Plz., 5th Fl., 44th St. at 1st Ave., New York, NY 10017, (212)687-3366

PCIA - The Wireless Infrastructure Assn. [3416], 901 N Washington St., Ste. 600, Alexandria, VA 22314-1535, (703)836-1608

PCIA - The Wireless Infrastructure Assn. [3416], 901 N Washington St., Ste. 600, Alexandria, VA 22314-1535, (703)836-1608

PCOStrategies - Address unknown since 2010.

PCPCI-The Transformer Assn. [★1662]

PCPCI-The Transformer Assn. [★1662]

PDA [2699], Bethesda Towers, 4350 E West Hwy., Ste. 150, Bethesda, MD 20814, (301)656-5900

PDA [2699], Bethesda Towers, 4350 E West Hwy., Ste. 150, Bethesda, MD 20814, (301)656-5900

PDCI [★17918]

PE4life [8723], 127 W 10th St., Ste. 101, Kansas City, MO 64105, (816)472-7345

Peace

A. J. Muste Memorial Inst. [18228]

A. J. Muste Memorial Inst. [18228]

Abrahamic Alliance Intl. [19824]

Acad. for Peace Res. [18229]

Afghanistan Peace Assn. [18230]

Afghanistan Peace Assn. [18230]

Africa Peace and Conflict Network [12625]

Africa Peace and Conflict Network [12625]

African Great Lakes Initiative [13165]PeaceAmer. Comm. for Peace in Chechnya

Americans for Peace Now [18010]

Assn. for Communal Harmony in Asia [12626]

Assn. for Peace and Understanding in the Middle East [18117]

Athletes United for Peace [18231]

Baptist Peace Fellowship of North Am. [18232]

Baptist Peace Fellowship of North Am. [18232]

Buddhist Peace Fellowship [18233]

Buddhist Peace Fellowship [18233]

Catholic Peace Fellowship [18234]

Catholic Worker Movement [18164]

Center on Conscience and War [17560]

Central Comm. for Conscientious Objectors [17561]

Children of the Earth [12627]

Children of the Earth [12627]

The Children of War [18235]

The Children of War [18235]

Citizens to Stop Nuclear Terrorism [18711]

Coalition for Peace with Justice [18236]

Code Pink Women's Pre-Emptive Strike for Peace [18237]

Code Pink Women's Pre-Emptive Strike for Peace [18237]

Coexistence Intl. [12628]

Coexistence Intl. [12628]

Conflict Solutions Intl. [17405]

Consistent Life [18238]

Daisy Alliance [18239]

Darfur Peace and Development Org. [12324]

Disciples Peace Fellowship [18240]

Empower Peace [18241]

Empower Peace [18241]

Environmentalists Against War [18777]PeaceEuropean Univ. Center for Peace Stud.

Family Fed. for World Peace and Unification [20151]

Fellowship of Reconciliation - USA [18242]

Fellowship of Reconciliation - USA [18242]

FootPrints for Peace [18243]

FootPrints for Peace [18243]

Found. for Global Community [18244]

Found. for P.E.A.C.E. [18245]

Found. for P.E.A.C.E. [18245]

Friends of Mali [18246]

Friends of Mali [18246]

Friends of Sabeel - North Am. [18247]

Friends of Sabeel - North Am. [18247]

Friends of Tent of Nations North Am. [12629]

Friends of Tent of Nations North Am. [12629]

Friends World Comm. for Consultation [18248]

Friends World Comm. for Consultation [18248]

Generation for Change and Growth [12328]

Global Ambassadors for Children [18249]

Global Inheritance [18826]

Global Peace Initiative of Women [18250]

Global Peace Services [18251]

Global Vision for Peace [18252]

Global Youth Connect [18828]

Global Youth Partnership for Africa [9875]

GlobalSecurity.org [18253]

Inst. for Peace and Justice [18254]

Intl. A.N.S.W.E.R. - Act Now to Stop War and End Racism [18255]

Intl. A.N.S.W.E.R. - Act Now to Stop War and End Racism [18255]

Intl. Assn. of Educators for World Peace USA [18256]

Intl. Assn. of Educators for World Peace USA [18256]

Intl. Coun. for Middle East Stud. [18125]

Intl. Peace Operations Assn. [18257]

Intl. Soc. for a Complete Earth [12217]

Intl. Stability Operations Assn. [18257]

Irish Amer. Unity Conf. [18009]

Ishmael and Isaac [18126]

Israeli Comm. Against House Demolitions - USA [18258]

Jane Addams Peace Assn. [18259]

Jane Addams Peace Assn. [18259]

Jewish Peace Fellowship [18260]

Joan B. Kroc Inst. for Intl. Peace Stud. [18261]

Joan B. Kroc Inst. for Intl. Peace Stud. [18261]

Just Vision [17409]

Kids for Peace [18262]

Lutheran Peace Fellowship [18263]

Mennonite Central Comm. Overseas Peace Off. [18264]

Mennonite Central Comm. Overseas Peace Off. [18264]

Men's Intl. Peace Exchange [18265]

Men's Intl. Peace Exchange [18265]

Meretz U.S.A. [18266]

Middle East Peace Dialogue Network [12515]

Monks Without Borders [19826]

Mt. Diablo Peace Center [18267]

Musical Missions of Peace [10352]

Musicians for Harmony [10353]

Natl. Org. of Iraqi Christians [12630]

Natl. Peace Found. [18268]

Native Amer. Leadership Alliance [20147]

No Peace Without Justice [18269]

No Peace Without Justice [18269]

Nuclear Age Peace Found. [18270]

Nuclear Age Peace Found. [18270]

One Voice of Peace [8694]

Partners for Peace [18271]

Partners for Peace [18271]

Partnership for Global Security [18600]

Pathways to Peace [12631]

Pathways to Peace [12631]

Peace Alliance [18272]

Peace of Art [10354]

Peace of Art [10354]

Peace Boat US [8695]

Peace Brigades Intl. U.S.A. [18273]

Peace Brigades Intl. U.S.A. [18273]

Peace Development Fund [18274]

Peace First [12632]

Peace in Focus [18275]

Peace and Justice Stud. Assn. [18276]

Peace Sci. Soc. Intl. [18277]

Peace Sci. Soc. Intl. [18277]

Peace X Peace [18278]

PeaceJam [8696]

Peacework Volunteer Org. [18279]

Peacework Volunteer Org. [18279]

Peaceworkers Nonviolent Peaceforce [18280]

Peaceworkers Nonviolent Peaceforce [18280]

Play for Peace [12633]

Play for Peace [12633]

Plowshares Inst. [18281]

Presbyterian Peace Fellowship [18282]

Prevent Nuclear Terrorism Org. [18718]

Prog. for the Advancement of Res. on Conflict and Collaboration [18283]

Promoting Enduring Peace [18284]

Pups for Peace [12634]

Pups for Peace [12634]

Race for Peace [18285]

Roots of Peace [18286]

Rumi Forum [18287]

Save Darfur Coalition [17744]

Seeds of Peace [18288]

September Eleventh Families for Peaceful Tomorrows [12635]

Ser. for Peace [18289]

Student Peace Alliance [18290]

Sudan Sunrise [12636]

Traprock Center for Peace and Justice [18291]

Troops Out Now Coalition [18292]

UNANIMA Intl. [18645]

United Nations | Women's Fed. for World Peace Intl. [12637]

United for Peace and Justice [18293]

United for Peace and Justice [18293]

U.S. Assn. for the Univ. for Peace [18294]

U.S. Canada Peace Anniversary Assn. [19185]

U.S. Canada Peace Anniversary Assn. [19185]

U.S. Fed. for Middle East Peace [18295]

U.S. Inst. of Peace [18296]

U.S. Inst. of Peace [18296]

U.S. Peace Govt. [18297]

Universal Peace Fed. [18298]

Universal Peace Fed. [18298]

Veterans for Peace [18299]

Veterans for Peace [18299]

Voices of African Mothers [12638]

Voices of African Mothers [12638]PeaceVoices in the Wilderness

Voters for Peace [18300]

War and Peace Found. [18301]

War and Peace Found. [18301]

Where Peace Lives [10355]

Win Without War [18178]

Women in Black [18302]

Women's Alliance for Peace and Human Rights in Afghanistan [12253]

Women's Intl. League for Peace and Freedom U.S. Sect. [18303]

Women's Intl. League for Peace and Freedom U.S. Sect. [18303]

World Conf. of Religions for Peace [18304]

World Conf. of Religions for Peace [18304]

World Peace Prayer Soc. [18305]

World Peace Prayer Soc. [18305]

World Peace Through Tech. Org. [12639]

World Peace Through Tech. Org. [12639]

World Sound Healing Org. [12640]

Worldwide Forgiveness Alliance [12641]

Worldwide Forgiveness Alliance [12641]

Youth Action for Peace - Deutschland [21562]

Peace Action [18213], 8630 Fenton St., Ste. 524, Silver Spring, MD 20910, (301)565-4050

Peace Action Educ. Fund [18214], Montgomery Center, 8630 Fenton St., Ste. 524, Silver Spring, MD 20910, (301)565-4050

Peace Action Soc. Org. for Somalia [IO], Nairobi, Kenya

Peace Alliance [18272], PO Box 27601, Washington, DC 20038, (202)684-2553

Peace of Art [10354], PO Box 52416, Boston, MA 02205, (617)435-7608

Peace of Art [10354], PO Box 52416, Boston, MA 02205, (617)435-7608

Peace Boat US [8695], 777 United Nations Plz., Rm. 3E, New York, NY 10017, (212)687-7214

Peace Brigades Intl. - Australia [IO], Fitzroy, Australia

Peace Brigades Intl. - Belgium [IO], Brussels, Belgium

Peace Brigades Intl. - Canada [IO], Ottawa, ON, Canada

Peace Brigades Intl. - Luxembourg [IO], Syren, Luxembourg

Peace Brigades Intl. - Netherlands [IO], Utrecht, Netherlands

Peace Brigades Intl. - Switzerland [IO], Bern, Switzerland

Reference to "IO" in place of a book number signifies that the association may be found in the 50th edition of International Organizations.

Peace Brigades Intl. - United Kingdom [IO], London, United Kingdom

Peace Brigades Intl. U.S.A. [18273], 1326 9th St. NW, Washington, DC 20001, (202)232-0142

Peace Brigades Intl. U.S.A. [18273], 1326 9th St. NW, Washington, DC 20001, (202)232-0142

Peace Builders [★17986]

Peace Builders [★17986]

Peace Child Intl. [IO], Buntingford, United Kingdom

Peace Child Sierra Leone [IO], Freetown, Sierra Leone

Peace and Cooperation [IO], Madrid, Spain

Peace Corps [18309], 1111 20th St. NW, Washington, DC 20526, (202)692-1040

Peace Corps

    Friends of Mali [18246]

    Friends of Tent of Nations North Am. [12629]

    Lesbian, Gay, Bisexual and Transgender U.S. Peace Corps Alumni [18306]

    Minority Peace Corps Assn. [18307]

    Natl. Peace Corps Assn. [18308]

    Peace Corps [18309]

    Peace Corps Partnership Prog. [18310]

Peace Corps Inst. - Defunct.

Peace Corps Partnership Prog. [18310], 1111 20th St. NW, Washington, DC 20526, (202)692-2170

Peace Corps School Partnership Prog. [★18310]

Peace Corps School to School Prog. [★18310]

Peace Corps of the U.S. [★18309]

Peace Development Fund [18274], 44 N Prospect St., PO Box 1280, Amherst, MA 01004, (413)256-8306

Peace Educ. Found. [★17407]

Peace First [12632], 280 Summer St., Boston, MA 02210, (617)261-3833

Peace in Focus [18275], PO Box 170820, Boston, MA 02117

Peace and Freedom Party [18361], PO Box 24764, Oakland, CA 94623, (510)465-9414

Peace Games [★12632]

PEACE for Guatemala [★12789]

Peace, Hea. and Human Development Found. [IO], Kobe, Japan

Peace History Soc. [9793], PO Box 506, Shepherdstown, WV 25443, (651)793-1468

Peace Hostage Exchange Found. [★17496]

Peace Hostage Exchange Found. [★17496]

Peace House Africa [11389], 6581 City W Pkwy., Eden Prairie, MN 55344, (952)465-0050

Peace and Justice Ser. in Argentina [IO], Buenos Aires, Argentina

Peace and Justice Stud. Assn. [18276], Prescott Coll., 220 Grove Ave., Prescott, AZ 86301, (928)350-2008

Peace Movement of Esbjerg [IO], Esbjerg, Denmark

Peace Museum - Address unknown since 2010.

Peace and Neutrality Alliance [IO], Dalkey, Ireland

Peace Now [★18010]

Peace Now [IO], Jerusalem, Israel

Peace Now [★18010]

Peace Officers for Christ Intl. [19599], 3000 W MacArthur Blvd., Ste. 426, Santa Ana, CA 92704-6962, (714)426-7632

Peace Officers for Christ Intl. [19599], 3000 W MacArthur Blvd., Ste. 426, Santa Ana, CA 92704-6962, (714)426-7632

Peace Pac [18215], Coun. for a Livable World, 322 4th St. NE, Washington, DC 20002, (202)543-4100

Peace Partnership Intl. - Defunct.

Peace Pledge Union [IO], London, United Kingdom

Peace Res. Center [IO], Madrid, Spain

Peace Res. Inst. [★18469]

Peace Res. Inst. [★18469]

Peace Res. Network [★18276]

Peace Res. Soc. - Intl. [★18277]

Peace Res. Soc. - Intl. [★18277]

Peace Rsrc. Proj. [18625], PO Box 1122, Arcata, CA 95518-1122, (707)268-1106

Peace Sci. Soc. Intl. [18277], Pennsylvania State Univ., Dept. of Political Sci., 202 Pond Bldg., University Park, PA 16802

Peace Sci. Soc. Intl. [18277], Pennsylvania State Univ., Dept. of Political Sci., 202 Pond Bldg., University Park, PA 16802

Peace Taxpayers - Defunct.

Peace Tour [★12639]

Peace Tour [★12639]

Peace Villages Found. Venezuela [IO], Santa Elena de Uairen, Venezuela

Peace Winds Am. [11859], 2517 Eastlake Ave. E, Ste. 103, Seattle, WA 98102, (206)432-3712

Peace X Peace [18278], 1776 I St. NW, 9th Fl., Washington, DC 20006, (877)684-3770

PeaceArt Intl. [9312], PO Box 40028, Rochester, NY 14604-0028, (585)482-0778

Peacebuild [IO], Ottawa, ON, Canada

Peacefund Canada [IO], Ottawa, ON, Canada

PeaceJam [8696], 11200 Ralston Rd., Arvada, CO 80004, (303)455-2099

PeaceQuest - Sweden [IO], Stockholm, Sweden

PeaceTrees Vietnam [11842], 1301 5th Ave., Ste. 2500, Seattle, WA 98101, (206)441-6136

Peacework Volunteer Org. [18279], 209 Otey St., Blacksburg, VA 24060-7426, (800)272-5519

Peacework Volunteer Org. [18279], 209 Otey St., Blacksburg, VA 24060-7426, (800)272-5519

Peaceworkers [★18280]

Peaceworkers [★18280]

Peaceworkers Nonviolent Peaceforce [18280], 425 Oak Grove St., Minneapolis, MN 55403, (612)871-0005

Peaceworkers Nonviolent Peaceforce [18280], 425 Oak Grove St., Minneapolis, MN 55403, (612)871-0005

Peanut

    Peanut Pals [21396]

Peanut Advisory Bd. [★4756]

Peanut Butter Mfrs. Assn. [★1424]

Peanut Butter Mfrs. and Nut Salters Assn. [★1424]

Peanut Butter and Nut Processors Assn. [★1424]

Peanut Butter Sandwich and Cookie Mfrs. Assn. [★1424]

Peanut Improvement Working Group [★4746]

Peanut Inst. [4755], PO Box 70157, Albany, GA 31708-0157, (229)888-0216

Peanut and Nut Salters Assn. [★1424]

Peanut Pals [21396], 6052 Canter Glen Ave., Las Vegas, NV 89122

Peanut and Tree Nut Processors Assn. [1424], PO Box 2660, Alexandria, VA 22301, (301)365-2521

Pear Bur. Northwest [4468], 4382 SE Intl. Way, Ste. A, Milwaukie, OR 97222-4635, (503)652-9720

Pearl Harbor History Associates [9794], PO Box 1007, Stratford, CT 06615

Pearl Harbor Survivors Assn. [20865], PO Box 1816, Carlsbad, CA 92018-1816, (760)727-9027

Pearl S. Buck Birthplace Found. [9406], Pearl S. Buck Museum, PO Box 126, Hillsboro, WV 24946, (304)653-4430

Pearl S. Buck Found. [★11390]

Pearl S. Buck Found. [★11390]

Pearl S. Buck Intl. [11390], 520 Dublin Rd., Perkasie, PA 18944, (215)249-0100

Pearl S. Buck Intl. [11390], 520 Dublin Rd., Perkasie, PA 18944, (215)249-0100

Peat Soc. of Czech Republic [IO], Prague, Czech Republic

Peat Soc. of Lithuania [IO], Taurage, Lithuania

Peat Soc. of Netherlands [IO], Eelde, Netherlands

Peat Soc. of Poland [IO], Olsztyn, Poland

Peat Soc. of Russia [IO], Moscow, Russia

Peat Soc. of Ukraine [IO], Kiev, Ukraine

Peck Pioneers - Defunct.

Peckglo Org. [IO], Uyo, Nigeria

Pedal Power ACT [IO], Canberra, Australia

Pedal Steel Guitar Assn. [10279], PO Box 20248, Floral Park, NY 11002-0248, (516)616-9214

Pedestrians

    Am. Walks [18775]

Pediatric/Adolescent Gastroesophageal Reflux Assn. [14572], PO Box 7728, Silver Spring, MD 20907, (301)601-9541

Pediatric/Adolescent Gastroesophageal Reflux Assn. [14572], PO Box 7728, Silver Spring, MD 20907, (301)601-9541

Pediatric AIDS Found. [13622], 11150 Santa Monica Blvd., Ste. 1050, Los Angeles, CA 90025, (310)314-1459

Pediatric Assn. of Naturopathic Physicians [8681], 216 NE Fremont St., Portland, OR 97212

Pediatric Brain Tumor Found. of the U.S. [13966], 302 Ridgefield Ct., Asheville, NC 28806, (828)665-6891

Pediatric Cardiac Intensive Care Soc. [16150], Anthony C. Chang, MD, VP of Intl. Affairs, CHOC Heart Inst., 455 S Main St., LLW-108, Orange, CA 92868

Pediatric Cardiac Intensive Care Soc. [16150], Anthony C. Chang, MD, VP of Intl. Affairs, CHOC Heart Inst., 455 S Main St., LLW-108, Orange, CA 92868

Pediatric Chaplains Network [19529], Chaplain Del Farris, Bus. Mgr., Arkansas Children's Hosp., 1 Children's Way, Little Rock, AR 72202

Pediatric Dermatology; Soc. for [14340]

Pediatric Digestion and Motility Disorders Soc. [16151], PO Box 1360, Buffalo, NY 14205

Pediatric Endocrinology Nursing Soc. [16152], PO Box 14516, Lenexa, KS 66285, (913)895-4628

Pediatric Hematology/Oncology; Amer. Soc. of [14961]

Pediatric Infectious Diseases Soc. [15124], 1300 Wilson Blvd., Ste. 300, Arlington, VA 22209, (703)299-6764

Pediatric Infectious Diseases Soc. [15124], 1300 Wilson Blvd., Ste. 300, Arlington, VA 22209, (703)299-6764

Pediatric Keratoplasty Assn. [15976], Westchester Medical Ctr., Dept. of Ophthalmology, Valhalla, NY 10595, (914)493-1599

Pediatric Nephrology; Amer. Soc. of [15546]

Pediatric Neuroradiology; Amer. Soc. of [16527]

Pediatric Neurotransmitter Disease Assn. [15631], PO Box 180622, Delafield, WI 53018, (603)733-8409

Pediatric Nurse Practitioners; Natl. Assn. of [15771]

Pediatric Nursing Certification Bd. [15795], 800 S Frederick Ave., Ste. 204, Gaithersburg, MD 20877-4152, (301)330-2921

Pediatric Orthopedic Soc. of North Am. [16046], 6300 N River Rd., Ste. 727, Rosemont, IL 60018-4226, (847)698-1692

Pediatric Pathology; Soc. for [16133]

Pediatric Pharmacy Advocacy Gp. [16153], 7953 Stage Hills Blvd., Ste. 101, Memphis, TN 38133, (901)380-3617

Pediatric Projects - Defunct.

Pediatric Psychology; Soc. for [16425]

Pediatric Psychology; Soc. for [16425]

Pediatric Radiology; Soc. for [16546]

Pediatric Therapists; Assn. of [16842]

Pediatricians; Amer. Coll. of Osteopathic [16061]

Pediatrics

    Academic Pediatric Assn. [16137]

    Amer. Acad. of Pediatrics [16138]

    Amer. Bd. of Pediatrics [16139]

    Amer. Pediatric Soc. [16140]

    Amer. Pediatric Surgical Assn. [16141]

    Assn. of Medical School Pediatric Dept. Chairs [16142]

    Assn. of Pediatric Oncology Social Workers [16143]

    Coun. of Pediatric Subspecialties [16144]

    Creative Children Therapy [16846]

    Fed. of Pediatric Organizations [16145]

    Global Neuro Rescue [15593]

    Global Pediatric Alliance [16146]

    Global Pediatric Alliance [16146]

    Holistic Pediatric Assn. [13682]

    Humanity for Children [16147]

    Hypospadias and Epispadias Assn. [13842]

    Intl. Pediatric Endosurgery Gp. [16148]

    Intl. Pediatric Endosurgery Gp. [16148]

    It's My Heart [14028]

    Natl. Pediatrics AIDS Network [16149]

    Pediatric Assn. of Naturopathic Physicians [8681]

    Pediatric Cardiac Intensive Care Soc. [16150]

    Pediatric Cardiac Intensive Care Soc. [16150]

    Pediatric Digestion and Motility Disorders Soc. [16151]

    Pediatric Endocrinology Nursing Soc. [16152]

    Pediatric Pharmacy Advocacy Gp. [16153]

    Puerto Rico Assn. of Pediatric Surgeons [16154]

    Soc. for Developmental and Behavioral Pediatrics [16155]

A star before a book entry number signifies that the name is not listed separately, but is mentioned within the entry.

Soc. for Pediatric Res. [16156]
Together for Kids [15070]
Pediatrics; Amer. Osteopathic Bd. of [16067]
Pediatrics Overseas [★16044]
Pediatrics Overseas [★16044]
Pediatrics; Soc. for Physician Assistants in [16243]
Pediculosis Assn; Natl. [16491]
Pedorthic Footwear Assn. [1460], 2025 M St. NW, Ste. 800, Washington, DC 20036, (202)367-1145
Pedro Rescue Helicopter Assn. [20316], 16610 14th Ave. SW, Burien, WA 98166, (503)653-7727
Peer Hea. Exchange [9080], 545 Sansome St., Ste. 900, San Francisco, CA 94111, (415)684-1234
PEF Israel Endowment Funds [12395], 317 Madison Ave., Ste. 607, New York, NY 10017, (212)599-1260
PEF Israel Endowment Funds [12395], 317 Madison Ave., Ste. 607, New York, NY 10017, (212)599-1260
Peggy Browning Fund [6075], 1528 Walnut St., Ste. 1904, Philadelphia, PA 19103-3648, (267)273-7990
Pekingese Club of Am. [21631], Col. Ret. Clifford Jones, Jr., Treas., 22 Middlebury Rd., Orchard Park, NY 14127-3962, (716)662-1510
Pelastakaa Lapset [★IO]
Pele Defense Fund - Address unknown since 2011.
Pellet Fuels Inst. [4493], 1901 N Moore St., Ste. 600, Arlington, VA 22209-1708, (703)522-6778
Pelsinform [IO], Oslo, Norway
Peltier Defense Comm; Leonard [17507]
Pembina Inst. for Appropriate Development [IO], Drayton Valley, AB, Canada
Pembroke Welsh Corgi Club of Am. [21632], Patty Gailey, Corresponding Sec., 94 S 250 E, Blackfoot, ID 83221, (208)782-2510
Pemphigus and Pemphigoid Found; Intl. [14394]
PEN Amer. Center [10730], 588 Broadway, Ste. 303, New York, NY 10012, (212)334-1660
Pen and Brush [9249], 16 E 10th St., New York, NY 10003, (212)475-3669
PEN Canada [IO], Toronto, ON, Canada
PEN Center USA [10731], PO Box 6037, Beverly Hills, CA 90212, (323)424-4939
PEN Club Italiano [★IO]
P.E.N. Club - Poland [IO], Warsaw, Poland
Pen Collectors of Am. [21397], Lisa Anderson, PO Box 992, Appleton, WI 54912, (575)491-3025
P.E.N. The Austrian Center [IO], Vienna, Austria
Penal Reform Intl. [IO], London, United Kingdom
Penang Turf Club [IO], Penang, Malaysia
Pencil Makers Assn. [★3356]
Peninsula Hang Glider Club [★22214]
Peninsula Woodturners Guild [IO], Frankston, Australia
Penn House; William [17710]
Penn State Alumni Assn. - Austria [IO], Vienna, Austria
Penn State Alumni Assn. - Brazil [IO], Ribeirao Preto, Brazil
Penn State Alumni Assn. - Canada [IO], Edmonton, AB, Canada
Penn State Alumni Assn. - China [IO], Beijing, People's Republic of China
Penn State Alumni Assn. - Hong Kong [IO], Hong Kong, People's Republic of China
Penn State Alumni Assn. - India [IO], Mumbai, India
Penn State Alumni Assn. - Indonesia [IO], Jakarta, Indonesia
Penn State Alumni Assn. - Iran [IO], Mashhad, Iran
Penn State Alumni Assn. - Japan [IO], Tokyo, Japan
Penn State Alumni Assn. - Karachi [IO], Karachi, Pakistan
Penn State Alumni Assn. - Lesotho [IO], Maseru, Lesotho
Penn State Alumni Assn. - New Zealand [IO], Palmerston North, New Zealand
Penn State Alumni Assn. - Pakistan [IO], Islamabad, Pakistan
Penn State Alumni Assn. - Philippines [IO], Caloocan City, Philippines
Penn State Alumni Assn. - Saudi Arabia [IO], Riyadh, Saudi Arabia
Penn State Alumni Assn. - Spain [IO], Madrid, Spain
Penn State Alumni Assn. - Taiwan [IO], Taipei, Taiwan

Penn State Alumni Assn. - Thailand [IO], Bangkok, Thailand
Penn State Alumni Assn. - Trinidad [IO], Port of Spain, Trinidad and Tobago
Pennsylvania Dutch
Pennsylvania German Soc. [10356]
Pennsylvania German Soc. [10356]
Soc. of the Descendants of the Schwenkfeldian Exiles [10357]
Pennsylvania German Folklore Soc. [★10356]
Pennsylvania German Folklore Soc. [★10356]
Pennsylvania German Soc. [10356], PO Box 244, Kutztown, PA 19530, (717)597-7940
Pennsylvania German Soc. [10356], PO Box 244, Kutztown, PA 19530, (717)597-7940
Pennsylvania Grade Crude Oil Assn. - Defunct.
Pennsylvania Mfg. Confectioner's Assn. [★1426]
Pennsylvania Mfg. Confectioner's Assn. [★1426]
Pennsylvania Scotch-Irish Soc. [★20662]
Penny Resistance - Defunct.
Penobscot Marine Museum [10063], PO Box 498, Searsport, ME 04974-0498, (207)548-2529
Pension Real Estate Assn. [3036], 100 Pearl St., 13th Fl., Hartford, CT 06103, (860)692-6341
Pension Res. Coun. [12642], The Wharton School of the Univ. of Pennsylvania, 3620 Locust Walk, 3000 Steinberg Hall - Dietrich Hall, Philadelphia, PA 19104-6302, (215)898-7620
Pension Res. Coun. [12642], The Wharton School of the Univ. of Pennsylvania, 3620 Locust Walk, 3000 Steinberg Hall - Dietrich Hall, Philadelphia, PA 19104-6302, (215)898-7620
Pension Rights Center [12643], 1350 Connecticut Ave. NW, Ste. 206, Washington, DC 20036-1739, (202)296-3776
Pensions
Amer. Benefits Coun. [5887]
Assn. of Public Pension Fund Auditors [23263]
Church Benefits Assn. [20152]
Pension Res. Coun. [12642]
Pension Res. Coun. [12642]
Pension Rights Center [12643]
Retirement Indus. Trust Assn. [435]
Pensions Mgt. Inst. [IO], London, United Kingdom
Pentathlon
U.S. Modern Pentathlon Assn. [23071]
Pentathlon Canada [IO], Quebec, QC, Canada
Pentecostal
Pentecostal Assemblies of the World [20153]
Pentecostal Assemblies of the World [20153]
Pentecostal Charismatic Churches of North Am. [20154]
Pentecostal Charismatic Churches of North Am. [20154]
Soc. for Pentecostal Stud. [20155]
Pentecostal Assemblies of the World [20153], 3939 N Meadows Dr., Indianapolis, IN 46205, (317)547-9541
Pentecostal Assemblies of the World [20153], 3939 N Meadows Dr., Indianapolis, IN 46205, (317)547-9541
Pentecostal Charismatic Churches of North Am. [20154], Open Bible Churches, 2020 Bell Ave., Des Moines, IA 50315, (515)288-6761
Pentecostal Charismatic Churches of North Am. [20154], Open Bible Churches, 2020 Bell Ave., Des Moines, IA 50315, (515)288-6761
Pentecostal Faith Missions [★20042]
Pentecostal Faith Missions [★20042]
Pentecostal Fellowship of North Am. [★20154]
Pentecostal Fellowship of North Am. [★20154]
PEO Intl. [9063], 3700 Grand Ave., Des Moines, IA 50312, (515)255-3153
PEO Intl. [9063], 3700 Grand Ave., Des Moines, IA 50312, (515)255-3153
PEO Sisterhood [★9063]
PEO Sisterhood [★9063]
People 4 Earth [4296], 1612 K St. NW, Ste. 600, Washington, DC 20006, (484)919-1488
People Against Cancer [13967], PO Box 10, Otho, IA 50569, (515)972-4444
People Against Impaired Driving [IO], Edmonton, AB, Canada
People Against Racist Terror [★17270]
People Against Racist Terror [★17270]

People Against Rape [13098], 2154 N Centre St., Ste. 302, North Charleston, SC 29406, (843)745-0144
People for the Amer. Way [17317], 1101 15th St. NW, Ste. 600, Washington, DC 20005, (202)467-4999
People-Animals-Love [16868], 4900 Massachusetts Ave. NW, Ste. 330, Washington, DC 20016, (202)966-2171
People, Animals, Nature - Address unknown since 2011.
People Before Lawyers [5280], Marc Perkel, 309 N Jefferson, No. 220, Springfield, MO 65802, (417)866-1222
People for Children [11495], Ricky Martin Found., PO Box 13534, San Juan, PR 00908-3534
People for Children [11495], Ricky Martin Found., PO Box 13534, San Juan, PR 00908-3534
People with Disabilities - Ireland [IO], Dublin, Ireland
People with Disabilities - Uganda [IO], Kampala, Uganda
People and Dogs Soc. [IO], Normanton, United Kingdom
People of the Earth [★4126]
People of the Earth [★4126]
People for the Ethical Treatment of Animals [11019], 501 Front St., Norfolk, VA 23510, (757)622-7382
People for the Ethical Treatment of Animals Europe [IO], London, United Kingdom
People of Faith Against the Death Penalty [17221], 110 W Main St., Ste. 2-G, Carrboro, NC 27510, (919)933-7567
People for Haiti [12877], 2132 Flameflower Ct., Trinity, FL 34655, (727)457-7272
People Improvement Org. [IO], Phnom Penh, Cambodia
People In Aid [IO], London, United Kingdom
People for Internet Responsibility - Address unknown since 2010.
People for Life [12942], PO Box 1126, Erie, PA 16512, (814)459-1333
People Living with HIV/AIDS SA [IO], Adelaide, Australia
People Opposing Women Abuse [IO], Yeoville, Republic of South Africa
People Organized to Stop Rape of Imprisoned Persons [★11720]
People to People Ambassador Prog. [17982], Dwight D. Eisenhower Bldg., 1956 Ambassador Way, Spokane, WA 99224-4002, (509)568-7000
People to People Ambassador Prog. [17982], Dwight D. Eisenhower Bldg., 1956 Ambassador Way, Spokane, WA 99224-4002, (509)568-7000
People to People Citizen Ambassador Prog. [★17982]
People to People Citizen Ambassador Prog. [★17982]
People to People Comm. on Fungi [★7131]
People to People Intl. [17983], 911 Main St., Ste. 2110, Kansas City, MO 64105-5305, (816)531-4701
People to People Intl. [17983], 911 Main St., Ste. 2110, Kansas City, MO 64105-5305, (816)531-4701
People and Planet [IO], Oxford, United Kingdom
People Protecting Animals and Their Habitats [11020], 151 First Ave., Ste. 161, New York, NY 10003, (617)354-2826
People Protecting Animals and Their Habitats [11020], 151 First Ave., Ste. 161, New York, NY 10003, (617)354-2826
People-to-People Hea. Found. - Address unknown since 2010.
People With AIDS Coalition - Defunct.
People's Commm. on Env. and Development India [IO], New Delhi, India
People's Decade of Human Rights Educ. [17859], 526 W 111th St., Ste. 4E, New York, NY 10025, (212)749-3156
People's Decade of Human Rights Educ. [★17859]
People's Democratic Party of Bhutan [IO], Thimphu, Bhutan
Peoples Dispensary for Sick Animals [IO], Telford, United Kingdom
People's Inst. for Survival and Beyond [18626], 601 N Carrollton Ave., New Orleans, LA 70119, (504)301-9292

Reference to "IO" in place of a book number signifies that the association may be found in the 50th edition of International Organizations.

People's Lobby [18389], 359 Jean St., Mill Valley, CA 94941, (415)383-7880

People's Medical Soc. [17768], PO Box 868, Allentown, PA 18105-0868, (610)770-1670

People's Movement for Human Rights Learning [17859], 526 W 111th St., Ste. 4E, New York, NY 10025, (212)749-3156

People's Org. for Peace and Educ. [IO], Islamabad, Pakistan

People's Progressive Party of Guyana [IO], George-town, Guyana

People's Relief Comm. [★12401]

People's Relief Comm. [★12401]

People's Rights Fund [17318], 55 W 17th St., Ste. 500, New York, NY 10011, (212)633-6646

Peoples Rights Org. [17319], 4292 Indianola Ave., Columbus, OH 43214-2226, (614)268-0122

People's Trust for Endangered Species [IO], London, United Kingdom

Pepsi-Cola Collectors Club [21398], Diane Gabriel, 335 Mathews Way, New Castle, PA 16101-8625

Per Scholas [8056], 804 E 138th St., Bronx, NY 10454, (718)991-8400

PERA [IO], Melton Mowbray, United Kingdom

Perbutuhan Kebangsaan St. Vincent de Paul [★IO]

Percussion Marketing Coun. [2569], PO Box 33252, Cleveland, OH 44133, (440)582-7006

Percussion Marketing Coun. [2569], PO Box 33252, Cleveland, OH 44133, (440)582-7006

Percussive Arts Soc. [10280], 110 W Washington St., Ste. A, Indianapolis, IN 46204, (317)974-4488

Percy Grainger Lib. Soc. [★9500]

Percy Grainger Lib. Soc. [★9500]

Percy Grainger Soc. [IO], Aylesbury, United Kingdom

The Peregrine Fund [5109], 5668 W Flying Hawk Ln., Boise, ID 83709, (208)362-3716

The Peregrine Fund [5109], 5668 W Flying Hawk Ln., Boise, ID 83709, (208)362-3716

Perennial Plant Assn. [4678], 3383 Schirtzinger Rd., Hilliard, OH 43026, (614)771-8431

Perfins Club [22062], Ken Rehfeld, Sec., PO Box 125, Spokane Valley, WA 99016-0125

Performance Mgt. Assn. [★2276]

Performance Mgt. Assn. [★2276]

Performance Warehouse Assn. [3624], 41701 Corporate Way, Ste. 1, Palm Desert, CA 92260, (760)346-5647

Performing Animal Welfare Soc. [11021], PO Box 849, Galt, CA 95632, (209)745-2606

Performing Arts

Actors' Equity Assn. [23264]

Amer. Dance Guild [9534]

Amer. Fed. of Musicians of the U.S. and Canada [23265]

Amer. Fed. of Musicians of the U.S. and Canada [23265]

Amer. Guild of Musical Artists [23266]

Amer. Theatre Arts for Youth [10566]

Assoc. Actors and Artistes of Am. [23267]

Assoc. Actors and Artistes of Am. [23267]

Assn. for Korean Music Res. [10165]

Assn. of Theatrical Press Agents and Managers [23268]

Chris Young Fan Club [23825]

Dance/Drill Team Directors of Am. [9544]

Dart Music Intl. [10187]

Diverse Emerging Music Org. [10188]

Drama Desk [10573]

Global Alliance of Performers [10358]

Global Alliance of Performers [10358]

The Grascals Fan Club [23851]

Guild of Italian Amer. Actors [23269]

Independent Arts and Media [9179]

Insight Arts [9293]

Intl. Alliance of Composers [10213]

Intl. Alliance of Theatrical Stage Employees, Moving Picture Technicians, Artists and Allied Crafts of the U.S., Its Territories and Canada [23270]

Intl. Alliance of Theatrical Stage Employees, Moving Picture Technicians, Artists and Allied Crafts of the U.S., Its Territories and Canada [23270]

Intl. Guild of Musicians in Dance [23271]

Intl. Guild of Musicians in Dance [23271]

Intl. Guild of Symphony, Opera and Ballet Musicians [23272]

Intl. Performing Arts for Youth [10359]

Intl. Soc. for Improvised Music [10226]

Jeannie Seely's Circle of Friends [23860]

Johnnie Ray Intl. Fan Club [23865]

Media, Entertainment and Arts Alliance [21699]

Michael Jackson Fan Club [23878]

Musical Missions of Peace [10352]

Musicians for Harmony [10353]

Natl. New Deal Preservation Assn. [10360]

Natl. Puro Conjunto Music Assn. [10263]

North Amer. Irish Dance Fed. [9563]

O'Neill Critics Inst. [10596]

PeaceArt Intl. [9312]

Richard Burgi Fan Club [23781]

Screen Actors Guild [23273]

Soc. for Eighteenth-Century Music [10291]

Stage Directors and Choreographers Soc. [23274]

Subud Intl. Cultural Assn. U.S.A. [9320]

Sword Swallowers Assn. Intl. [10361]

Union Internationale de la Marionette l Amer. CTR [22112]

United Scenic Artists [23275]

Voices Breaking Boundaries [10362]

WordTheatre [10550]

World Artists Experiences [9325]

Performing Arts Alliance [9313], 1211 Connecticut Ave. NW, Ste. 200, Washington, DC 20036, (202)207-3850

Performing Arts for Crisis Training [★11680]

Performing Arts Found. [9314], 401 N 4th St., Wausau, WI 54403, (715)842-0988

Performing Arts Medicine Assn. [16417], PO Box 440301, Aurora, CO 80044-0301, (303)632-9255

Performing Right Soc. [IO], London, United Kingdom

Performing and Visual Arts Soc. - Defunct.

Perfume and Scent Bottle Collectors [★21359]

Perfume and Scent Bottle Collectors [★21359]

Perfusion Prog. Directors' Coun. [14037], Medical Univ. of South Carolina, Division of Cardiovascular Perfusion, 151B Rutledge Ave., Charleston, SC 29425, (843)792-9262

Perhaps Kids Meeting Kids Can Make a Difference [17984], 380 Riverside Dr., Box 8H, New York, NY 10025

Perhaps Kids Meeting Kids Can Make a Difference [17984], 380 Riverside Dr., Box 8H, New York, NY 10025

Perhimpunan Dokter Spesialis Kulit dan Kelamin Indonesia [★IO]

Perhimpunan Pembina Kesehatan Olahraga Indonesia [★IO]

Perianesthesia Nursing Certification; Amer. Bd. of [15718]

Perinatology

Amer. Coll. of Community Midwives [15864]

Natl. Perinatal Assn. [16157]

Natl. Perinatal Info. Center [16158]

Purine Res. Soc. [15506]

Soc. for Maternal-Fetal Medicine [16159]

Soc. for Obstetric Anesthesia and Perinatology [16160]

Periodic Paralysis Assn. [15360], 155 W 68th St., Ste. 1732, New York, NY 10023, (407)339-9499

Periodical and Book Assn. of Am. [2957], 481 8th Ave., Ste. 526, New York, NY 10001, (212)563-6502

Periodical Publishers Assn. [IO], London, United Kingdom

Periodical Wholesalers of North Am. - Defunct.

Periodontology; Amer. Bd. of [14257]

Periodontology; Western Soc. of [14311]

Periodontology; Western Soc. of [14311]

Peripheral Arterial Disease Coalition [14038], Vascular Disease Found., 1075 S Yukon St., Ste. 320, Lakewood, CO 80226, (303)989-0500

Perkumpulan Keluarga Berencana Indonesia [★IO]

Perlite Inst. [2516], 4305 N 6th St., Ste. A, Harrisburg, PA 17110, (717)238-9723

Permacultura Am. Latina [4684], PO Box 2372, Santa Fe, NM 87504, (505)989-1695

Permaculture Assn. [IO], London, United Kingdom

Permaculture Trust of Botswana [IO], Serowe, Botswana

Permanent Blind Relief War Fund [★17085]

Permanent Blind Relief War Fund [★17085]

Permanent Charities Comm. of the Entertainment Indus. [★11970]

Permanent Commn. for the South Pacific [IO], Guayaquil, Ecuador

Permanent Court of Arbitration [IO], The Hague, Netherlands

Permanent European Conf. on Probation and Aftercare [IO], Utrecht, Netherlands

Permanent Intl. Commn. for the Proof of Small-Arms [IO], Liege, Belgium

Permanent Magnet Producers Assn. [★1652]

Permanent Magnet Producers Assn. [★1652]

Permanent Secretariat of the Hemispheric Cong. of Latin C.O.C. and Indiana [★23367]

Permanent Secretariat of the Hemispheric Cong. of Latin C.O.C. and Indiana [★23367]

Permanent Ser. for Mean Sea Level [IO], Liverpool, United Kingdom

Permanent Way Institution [IO], Stoke-on-Trent, United Kingdom

Permanent Working Group of European Junior Doctors [IO], Lisbon, Portugal

Persatuan Ahli-Ahli Sains Malaysia [★IO]

Persatuan Alergi and Imunologi Malaysia [★IO]

Persatuan Automobil Malaysia [★IO]

Persatuan Bagi Orang Buta Malaysia [★IO]

Persatuan Bantuan Perubatan Malaysia [★IO]

Persatuan Bulan Sabit Merah Malaysia [★IO]

Persatuan Dermatologi Malaysia [★IO]

Persatuan Ekonomi Malaysia [★IO]

Persatuan Elektrik Dan Elektronik Malaysia [★IO]

Persatuan Farmakologi dan Fisiologi Malaysia [★IO]

Persatuan Farmaseutikal Malaysia [★IO]

Persatuan Floorball Malaysia [★IO]

Persatuan Geologi Malaysia [★IO]

Persatuan Gerontologi Malaysia [★IO]

Persatuan Hosp. Swasta Malaysia [★IO]

Persatuan Hotel Budget Malaysia [★IO]

Persatuan Industri Komputer Dan Multimedia Malaysia [★IO]

Persatuan Juru X-Ray Malaysia [★IO]

Persatuan Jurupulih Carakerja Malaysia [★IO]

Persatuan Jurutera Perunding Malaysia [★IO]

Persatuan Kebangsaan Autism Malaysia [★IO]

Persatuan Kebangsaan Pembeli Rumah [★IO]

Persatuan Komputer Brunei Darussalam [★IO]

Persatuan Minyak Sawit Malaysia [★IO]

Persatuan Nuklear Malaysia [★IO]

Persatuan Panahan Indonesia [★IO]

Persatuan Pandu Puteri Malaysia [★IO]

Persatuan Pejenamaan Malaysia [★IO]

Persatuan Pemborong Binaan Malaysia [★IO]

Persatuan Pengilang-Pengilang Tekstil Malaysia [★IO]

Persatuan Perancang Keluarga Sabah [★IO]

Persatuan Perubatan Malaysia [★IO]

Persatuan Perusahaan Periklanan Indonesia [★IO]

Persatuan Pustakawan Malaysia [★IO]

Persatuan Squash Indonesia [IO], Jakarta, Indonesia

Persatuan Tenis Seluruh Indonesia [★IO]

Persatuan Transplan Malaysia [★IO]

Persatuan Wanita Kristian Malaysia [★IO]

Persatuan Warga Emas Malaysia [★IO]

Persian Orthopedic Trauma Assn. [IO], Tehran, Iran

Personal Care Prdt. Coun. [1670], 1101 17th St. NW, Ste. 300, Washington, DC 20036-4702, (202)331-1770

Personal Communications Indus. Assn. [★3416]

Personal Communications Indus. Assn. [★3416]

Personal Computer Mgt. Assn. - Defunct.

Personal Cmpt. Memory Card Intl. Assn.

Personal Cmpt. Memory Card Intl. Assn. - Address unknown since 2011.

Personal Computers

E-quip Africa [12644]

E-quip Africa [12644]

Personal Development

4 Real Women Intl. [13447]

Alliance for Full Participation [11754]

Beauty 4 Ashes Intl. [13452]

Career Gear [12645]

Destination ImagiNation [8697]

Enrichment Educ. [8276]

Grooming Future World Leaders [13528]

A star before a book entry number signifies that the name is not listed separately, but is mentioned within the entry.

Intl. Assn. for Human Values [12216]
Intl. Enneagram Assn. [16161]
Intl. Enneagram Assn. [16161]
Soc. for Res. on Identity Formation [8698]
Soc. for Res. on Identity Formation [8698]
Personal Freedom Outreach [19641], PO Box
26062, St. Louis, MO 63136-0062, (314)921-9800
Personal Injury Lawyers Marketing and Mgt. Assn.
[268], 607 Briarwood Dr., Ste. 4, Myrtle Beach, SC
29572, (800)497-1890
Personal Managers' Assn. [IO], London, United
Kingdom
Personal Ponies Ltd. [11822], 17401 Conoy Rd.,
Barnesville, MD 20838, (301)349-2161
Personal Power Development Corp. - Defunct.
Personal Retirement Alliance Ltd. - Defunct.
Personal Submersibles Org. [7148], PO Box 53,
Weare, NH 03281
Personal Watercraft Indus. Assn. [3066], 444 N
Capitol St., Ste. 645, Washington, DC 20001,
(202)737-9768
Personalized Medicine Coalition [15430], 1225 New
York Ave. NW, Ste. 450, Washington, DC 20005,
(202)589-1770

Personnel
Amer. Coll. Personnel Assn. [8699]
America's Edge [17599]
Coll. and Univ. Professional Assn. for Human
Resources [8700]
Human Rsrc. Certification Inst. [2628]
Human Resources Benchmarking Assn. [666]Per-
sonnelMedia Human Resources Assn.
Natl. Assn. for Govt. Training and Development
[2629]
Natl. Human Resources Assn. [2630]
SHRM Global Forum [2631]
SHRM Global Forum [2631]
Soc. for Human Rsrc. Mgt. [2632]
Personnel Accreditation Inst. [★2628]
Persons United Limiting Substandards and Errors in
Hea. Care [14826], PO Box 353, Wantagh, NY
11793-0353, (516)579-4711
Perth Australia ACM SIGGRAPH [IO], Nedlands,
Australia
Pertubuhan Akitek Malaysia [★IO]
Pertubuhan Pertolongan Wanita [★IO]

Peru
Amazon Promise [16162]
Community Promotion Development Liberation
[12646]
Peruvian Heart Assn. [14039]

Peruvian
Peruvian Heart Assn. [14039]
Peruvian Assn. of Advt. Agencies [IO], Lima, Peru
Peruvian Assn. for Conservation of Nature [IO],
Lima, Peru
Peruvian Bible Soc. [IO], Lima, Peru
Peruvian Constr. Indus. Chamber [IO], Lima, Peru
Peruvian Heart Assn. [14039], PO Box 797, Fabens,
TX 79838-0797, (915)764-4321
Peruvian Heart Assn. [14039], PO Box 797, Fabens,
TX 79838-0797, (915)764-4321
Peruvian Horse Assn. of Canada [IO], Acheson, AB,
Canada
Peruvian Inca Orchid Dog Club of Am. [21633],
17502 S 750 W, Wanatah, IN 46390, (219)733-
9480
Peruvian Inst. for Educ. in Human Rights and Peace
[IO], Lima, Peru
Peruvian League Against Epilepsy [IO], Lima, Peru
Peruvian Paso Horse Registry of North Am. [★4630]
Peruvian Paso Horse Registry of North Am. [★4630]
Peruvian Paso Part-Blood Registry [★4630]
Peruvian Paso Part-Blood Registry [★4630]
Peruvian Soc. of Arterial Hypertension [IO], Lima,
Peru
Peruvian Soc. of Cardiology [IO], Lima, Peru
Peruvian Soc. of Clinical Neurophysiology [IO],
Lima, Peru
Peruvian Soc. of Dermatology [IO], Lima, Peru

Pest Control
Amer. Mosquito Control Assn. [4769]
Amer. Mosquito Control Assn. [4769]
Assn. of Amer. Pesticide Control Officials [5888]
Assn. of Applied IPM Ecologists [4770]

Assn. of Natural Biocontrol Producers [4771]
Assn. of Structural Pest Control Regulatory Of-
ficials [4772]
Bio-Integral Rsrc. Center [4773]
Biopesticide Indus. Alliance [7233]
Natl. Assn. of Exotic Pest Plant Councils [4774]
Natl. Entomology Scent Detection Canine Assn.
[2633]
Natl. Gypsy Moth Mgt. Bd. [4775]
Natl. Pest Mgt. Assn. Intl. [2634]
Natl. Pest Mgt. Assn. Intl. [2634]
Pesticide Applicators Professional Assn. [2635]
Responsible Indus. for a Sound Env. [2636]
Soc. for Vector Ecology [4776]
Pesticide Action Network North Am. Regional Center
[13326], 49 Powell St., Ste. 500, San Francisco,
CA 94102, (415)981-1771
Pesticide Action Network UK [IO], London, United
Kingdom
Pesticide Applicators Professional Assn. [2635], PO
Box 80095, Salinas, CA 93912-0095, (831)442-
3536
Pesticide Educ. and Action Proj. [★13326]
Pesticide Info. Center; Natl. [13324]
Pesticide Safety Educators; Amer. Assn. of [4326]
The Pesticide Stewardship Alliance [6850], 11327
Gravois Rd., No. 201, St. Louis, MO 63126,
(314)849-9137
Pet Assistance and Welfare Services [IO], Saipan,
Northern Mariana Islands
Pet Care Services Assn. [2683], 2670 Acad. Blvd.,
Colorado Springs, CO 80917, (719)667-1600
Pet Care Trust [11022], 2105 Laurel Bush Blvd.,
Ste. 200, Bel Air, MD 21015, (443)640-1060
Pet Care Trust [IO], Bedford, United Kingdom
Pet Food Assn. of Canada [IO], Toronto, ON,
Canada
Pet Food Inst. [2684], 2025 M St. NW, Ste. 800,
Washington, DC 20036-2422, (202)367-1120
Pet Food Mfrs'. Assn. [IO], London, United Kingdom
Pet Indus. Distributors Assn. [2685], 2105 Laurel
Bush Rd., Ste. 200, Bel Air, MD 21015-5200,
(443)640-1060
Pet Indus. Joint Advisory Coun. [2686], 1140 19th
St. NW, Ste. 300, Washington, DC 20036,
(202)452-1525
Pet Pride [11023], PO Box 1055, Pacific Palisades,
CA 90272, (310)836-5427
PET Resin Assn. [2772], 355 Lexington Ave., Ste.
1500, New York, NY 10017-6603, (212)297-2125
PET Resin Assn. [2772], 355 Lexington Ave., Ste.
1500, New York, NY 10017-6603, (212)297-2125
Pet Savers Found. [11024], 750 Port Washington
Blvd., Port Washington, NY 11050, (516)883-1461
Pet Sitters Intl. [2687], 201 E King St., King, NC
27021, (336)983-9222
Pet Sitters Intl. [2687], 201 E King St., King, NC
27021, (336)983-9222
Pet Therapy Soc. of Northern Alberta [IO], Edmon-
ton, AB, Canada
PETA India [IO], Mumbai, India

Petanque
Fed. of Petanque U.S.A. [22801]
Peter Burwash Intl. Special Tennis Programs
[23059], 4200 Res. Forest Dr., Ste. 250, The
Woodlands, TX 77381, (281)363-4707
Peter Burwash Intl. Special Tennis Programs
[23059], 4200 Res. Forest Dr., Ste. 250, The
Woodlands, TX 77381, (281)363-4707
Peter Warlock Soc. [IO], London, United Kingdom
Petfood and Accessories Mfrs. Assn. [IO], Dussel-
dorf, Germany
Petite World - Defunct.
Petites Soeurs de Jesus [★IO]
Petites Soeurs de l'Assomption [★IO]
Petrochemical Indus. Assn. of Taiwan [IO], Taipei,
Taiwan

Petroleum
Amer. Assn. of Drilling Engineers [7234]
Amer. Assn. of Professional Landmen [2637]
Amer. Exploration and Production Coun. [2638]
Amer. Oil and Gas Historical Soc. [2639]
Amer. Petroleum Inst. [2640]
America's Natural Gas Alliance [2641]
Assn. of Desk and Derrick Clubs [2642]

Assn. of Energy Ser. Companies
[2643]PetroleumAssn. of the German
Petroleum Indus.
Assn. of Nigerian Petroleum Professionals Abroad
[7235]
Assn. of Nigerian Petroleum Professionals Abroad
[7235]
Assn. of Oil Pipe Lines [2644]
Assn. for the Stud. of Peak Oil and Gas U.S.A.
[7236]
BP Amoco Marketers Assn. [2645]
Citizens for Affordable Energy [6701]
Citizens for Energy Freedom [6703]
Citizens Energy Plan [6704]
Completion Engg. Assn. [6961]
Coordinating Res. Coun. [2646]
Crude Oil Quality Assn. [2647]
Deep Draft Lubricant Assn. [2225]
Distribution Contractors Assn. [23276]
Domestic Energy Producers Alliance [1166]
Drilling Engg. Assn. [2648]
EndOil [6716]
Energy Policy Res. Found., Inc. [7237]
Energy Traffic Assn. [2649]
Energy Vision [6724]
Gas Processors Assn. [2650]
Gas Processors Suppliers Assn. [2651]
Growth Energy [6728]
HALTER, Inc. [16852]
Independent Lubricant Mfrs. Assn. [2652]
Independent Lubricant Mfrs. Assn. [2652]
Independent Petroleum Assn. of Am. [2653]
Intl. Assn. of Directional Drilling [7238]
Intl. Assn. of Drilling Contractors [2654]
Intl. Assn. of Drilling Contractors [2654]
Intl. Assn. of Geophysical Contractors [2655]
Intl. Assn. of Geophysical Contractors [2655]
Intl. Coun. for Machinery Lubrication [7034]
Intl. Oil Scouts Assn. [2656]
Intl. Oil Scouts Assn. [2656]
Leadership for Energy Automated Processing
[1171]
Natl. Assn. of Div. Order Analysts [2657]
Natl. Assn. of Royalty Owners [2658]
Natl. Assn. of Shell Marketers [2659]
Natl. Lubricating Grease Inst. [2660]
Natl. Oil Recyclers Assn. [2661]
Natl. Petrochemical and Refiners Assn. [2662]
Natl. Petroleum Mgt. Assn. [2663]
New Fuels Alliance [6885]
Oil Firing Tech. Assn. for the Petroleum Indus.
[13925]
Org. of the Petroleum Exporting Countries [6201]
Petroleum Convenience Alliance for Tech.
Standards [2664]
Petroleum Equip. Inst. [2665]
Petroleum Equip. Inst. [2665]
Petroleum Equip. Suppliers Assn. [2666]
Petroleum Tech. Transfer Coun. [2667]
Pipe Line Contractors Assn. [2668]
Pipeline Assn. for Public Awareness [2755]
Res. Partnership to Secure Energy for Am. [6752]
Securing America's Future Energy [6755]
Ser. Sta. Dealers of America/National Coalition of
Petroleum Retailers and Allied Trades [2669]
Set Am. Free [17619]
Soc. of Independent Gasoline Marketers of Am.
[2670]
The Soc. for Organic Petrology [7239]
The Soc. for Organic Petrology [7239]
Soc. of Petroleum Engineers [7240]
Soc. of Petroleum Engineers [7240]
Soc. of Petroleum Evaluation Engineers [7241]
Soc. of Petrophysicists and Well Log Analysts
[7242]
Soc. of Professional Women in Petroleum [2671]
Soc. of Professional Women in Petroleum [2671]
Texas Independent Producers and Royalty Own-
ers Assn. [2672]
U.S. Oil and Gas Assn. [2673]
Veggie Van Org. [4872]
Western States Petroleum Assn. [2674]
World Energy Cities Partnership [1179]
Petroleum Assn. of Japan [IO], Tokyo, Japan
Petroleum Br. of AIME [★7240]

Reference to "IO" in place of a book number signifies that the association may be found in the 50th edition of International Organizations.

Petroleum Br. of AIME [★7240]
Petroleum Convenience Alliance for Tech. Standards [2664], 2773 Jefferson Davis Hwy., Ste. 115, Stafford, VA 22554, (703)836-0919
Petroleum Equip. Inst. [2665], PO Box 2380, Tulsa, OK 74101-2380, (918)494-9696
Petroleum Equip. Inst. [2665], PO Box 2380, Tulsa, OK 74101-2380, (918)494-9696
Petroleum Equip. Suppliers Assn. [2666], 1240 Blalock Rd., Ste. 110, Houston, TX 77055, (713)932-0168
Petroleum Exploration Soc. of Australia [IO], Perth, Australia
Petroleum Exploration Soc. of Great Britain [IO], London, United Kingdom
Petroleum Indus. Elecl. Assn. [★1074]
Petroleum Indus. Res. Found. [★7237]
Petroleum Indus. Security Coun. [★1889]
Petroleum Joint Venture Assn. [IO], Calgary, AB, Canada
Petroleum Packaging Coun. [2610], 1519 via Tulipan, San Clemente, CA 92673, (949)369-7102
Petroleum Services Assn. of Canada [IO], Calgary, AB, Canada
Petroleum Tech. Alliance Canada [IO], Calgary, AB, Canada
Petroleum Tech. Transfer Coun. [2667], PO Box 246, Sand Springs, OK 74063, (918)241-5801

Pets
Alaskan Malamute Club of Am. [21478]
Alliance for Contraception in Cats and Dogs [12647]
Amer. Assn. of Cat Enthusiasts [21243]
Amer. Canine Educ. Found. [21488]
Amer. Fox Terrier Club [21495]
Amer. Kuvasz Assn. [11870]
Amer. Mobile Groomers Assn. [2675]
Amer. Pet Products Assn. [2676]
Amer. Rottweiler Club [21504]
Amer. Shetland Sheepdog Assn. [21506]
Amer. Veterinary Distributors Assn. [2677]
Animal House Rescue [10913]
Animal Welfare Advocacy [10922]
Animal Welfare Coun. [3807]
Assn. for Pet Loss and Bereavement [12648]
Assn. for Veterinary Family Practice [17016]
Australian Shepherd Club of Am. [21517]
Berger Picard Club of Am. [21523]
Bluetick Breeders of Am. [21527]
Canine Defense Fund [10936]
Canine Freestyle Fed. [22545]
CATalyst Coun. [10938]
Caucasian Ovcharka Club of Am. [21536]
Chinese Shar-Pei Club of Am. [21539]
Club de l'Epagneul Breton of the U.S. [21541]
Cockapoo Club of Am. [21543]
Companion Animal Protection Soc. [12649]
Compassion Without Borders [10948]
Continental Mi-Ki Assn. [21546]
The Designer Cat Assn. [21248]
Doberman Assistance Network [11871]
Dogue de Bordeaux Soc. of Am. [21555]
Feral Cat Caretakers' Coalition [3810]
Field Spaniel Soc. of Am. [21562]
Friends of Roman Cats [3859]
Galgo Rescue Intl. Network [10969]
German Shepherd Dog Club of Am. | Working Dog Assn. [21569]
Global Animal Relief [3812]
Global Fed. of Animal Sanctuaries [10970]
Grey Muzzle Org. [10971]
Hartz Club of Am. [7198]
Havana Silk Dog Assn. of Am. [21578]
Icelandic Sheepdog Assn. of Am. [21582]
Independent Pet and Animal Trans. Assn. Intl. [2678]
Intl. Aid for Korean Animals [10988]
Intl. Assn. of Pet Cemeteries and Crematories [2679]
Intl. Assn. of Pet Cemeteries and Crematories [2679]
Intl. Defenders of Animals [10989]
Intl. German Coolie Soc. and Registry [21585]
Intl. Professional Groomers [2680]
Jews for Animal Rights [10996]

Missing Pet Partnership [12650]
Natl. Assn. of Professional Pet Sitters [2681]
Natl. Birman Fanciers [21254]
Natl. Dog Groomers Assn. of Am. [2682]
Natl. Dog Registry [11009]
North Amer. Deutsch Kurzhaar Club [21617]
North Amer. Dog Agility Coun. [22548]
North Amer. Llewellin Breeders Assn. [21620]
North Amer. Pet Hea. Insurance Assn. [14863]
North Amer. Teckel Club [21622]
Norwegian Forest Cat Breed Coun. [21255]
Norwegian Lundehund Assn. of Am. [21625]
Out of Love Sugar Glider Rescue [11017]
Personal Ponies Ltd. [11822]
Peruvian Inca Orchid Dog Club of Am. [21633]
Pet Care Services Assn. [2683]
Pet Food Inst. [2684]
Pet Indus. Distributors Assn. [2685]
Pet Indus. Joint Advisory Coun. [2686]
Pet Sitters Intl. [2687]
Pet Sitters Intl. [2687]
Pets Am. [12651]
The Pig Preserve Assn. [11025]
Precious Paws Rescue and Adoption [12652]
Rescue Alliance of Hairless and Other Breeds [11031]
Ridgeback Rescue of the U.S. [11034]
Samoyed Club of Am. [21646]
Savannah Cat Club [3864]
Share a Pet [12653]
Soul Friends [16873]
Spanish Water Dog Assn. of Am. [21654]
SPCA Intl. [11041]
United Beagle Gundog Fed. [21661]
United Natl. Weight Pull Assn. [22550]
U.S.A. Coton de Tulear Club [21666]
U.S. Complete Shooting Dog Assn. [21668]
U.S. Mondioring Assn. [22552]
United Yorkie Rescue [11052]
VeterinaryVentures [11055]
West Highland White Terrier Club of Am. [21677]
World Pet Assn. [2688]
World Pet Assn. [2688]

Pets Am. [12651], 1286 Univ. Ave., Ste. 507, San Diego, CA 92103, (512)497-7535
Pew Charitable Trusts [13143], 2005 Market St., Ste. 1700, Philadelphia, PA 19103-7077, (215)575-9050
Pewter Soc. [IO], Macclesfield, United Kingdom
The Peyote Way Church [★20141]
Peyote Way Church of God [20141], 30800 W Bonita Klondyke Rd., Willcox, AZ 85643, (928)828-3444
PF [★12039]
PF [★12039]
PGAA - Defunct.
PGI [337], The Terminus Bldg., 3280 Peachtree Rd. NW, Atlanta, GA 30305, (866)548-3203
Pharma Indus. Finland [IO], Helsinki, Finland
Pharmaceutical Assn. of Malaysia [IO], Petaling Jaya, Malaysia
Pharmaceutical Bus. Intelligence and Res. Gp. [2705], 114 Madison Way, Lansdale, PA 19446, (215)855-5255
Pharmaceutical Care Mgt. Assn. [16211], 601 Pennsylvania Ave. NW, Ste. 740 S, Washington, DC 20004, (202)207-3610
Pharmaceutical Gp. of the European Union [IO], Brussels, Belgium
Pharmaceutical and Healthcare Assn. of the Philippines [IO], Makati City, Philippines
Pharmaceutical and Healthcare Sciences Soc. [IO], Swindon, United Kingdom
Pharmaceutical Indus. Labor-Management Assn. [2700], 101 N Union St., Ste. 305, Alexandria, VA 22314, (703)548-4721
Pharmaceutical Info. and Pharmacovigilance Assn. [IO], Haslemere, United Kingdom
Pharmaceutical Printed Literature Assn. [2706], PO Box 722, Batavia, IL 60510, (630)777-5709
Pharmaceutical Res. and Mfrs. of Am. [2701], 950 F St. NW, Ste. 300, Washington, DC 20004, (202)835-3400
Pharmaceutical Soc. of Australia [IO], Deakin West, Australia

Pharmaceutical Soc. of Denmark [IO], Copenhagen, Denmark
Pharmaceutical Soc. of Ireland [IO], Dublin, Ireland
Pharmaceutical Soc. of Japan [IO], Tokyo, Japan
Pharmaceutical Soc. of New Zealand [IO], Wellington, New Zealand
Pharmaceutical Soc. of Northern Ireland [IO], Belfast, United Kingdom
Pharmaceutical Soc. of Singapore [IO], Singapore, Singapore
Pharmaceutical Soc. of South Africa [IO], Arcadia, Republic of South Africa

Pharmaceuticals
Amer. Assn. of Pharmaceutical Scientists [7243]
Amer. Assn. of Pharmaceutical Scientists [7243]
Amer. Pharmacists Assn. | Acad. of Pharmacy Practice and Mgt. [16176]
Amer. Soc. for Automation in Pharmacy [2689]
Analytical and Life Sci. Systems Assn. [7358]
Animal Hea. Inst. [2690]
Chain Drug Marketing Assn. [2691]
Chain Drug Marketing Assn. [2691]PharmaceuticalsConsumer Hea. Products Canada
Consumer Healthcare Products Assn. [2692]
Danish Assn. of the Pharmaceutical Indus. [10384]
Drug, Chem. and Assoc. Technologies Assn. [2693]
European Behavioral Pharmacology Soc. [5980]
French Pharmaceutical Distribution Assn. [3038]
Generic Pharmaceutical Assn. [2694]PharmaceuticalsHea. Products Assn. of Southern Africa
Intl. Fed. of Pharmaceutical Wholesalers [2695]
Intl. Fed. of Pharmaceutical Wholesalers [2695]
Intl. Pharmaceutical Excipients Coun. of the Americas [2696]
Intl. Pharmaceutical Excipients Coun. of the Americas [2696]
Intl. Soc. for Pharmaceutical Engg. [7244]
Intl. Soc. for Pharmaceutical Engg. [7244]
Medicines Australia [13892]
Natl. Assn. of Pharmaceutical Representatives [2697]
Natl. Chamber of the Pharmaceutical Indus. [8859]
Natl. Pharmaceutical Coun. [2698]
PDA [2699]
PDA [2699]
Pharmaceutical and Healthcare Sciences Soc. [5655]
Pharmaceutical Indus. Labor-Management Assn. [2700]
Pharmaceutical Res. and Mfrs. of Am. [2701]
Pharmaceutical Soc. of South Africa [3644]
Soc. For Clinical Data Mgt. [2702]
Pharmachemical Ireland [IO], Dublin, Ireland
Pharmacists; Assn. of Natural Medicine [15533]
Pharmacists for Life [★18563]
Pharmacists for Life [★18563]
Pharmacists for Life Intl. [18563], PO Box 1281, Powell, OH 43065-1281, (740)881-5520
Pharmacists for Life Intl. [18563], PO Box 1281, Powell, OH 43065-1281, (740)881-5520
Pharmacology; Intl. Soc. for Anaesthetic [13749]
Pharmacology; Intl. Soc. for Anaesthetic [13749]

Pharmacy
Acad. of Managed Care Pharmacy [16163]
Acad. of Pharmaceutical Res. and Sci. [16164]
Accreditation Coun. for Pharmacy Educ. [16165]
Alliance for the Prudent Use of Antibiotics [16166]
Alpha Zeta Omega [23615]
Amer. Assn. of Colleges of Pharmacy [16167]
Amer. Assn. of Pharmacy Technicians [16168]
Amer. Chinese Pharmaceutical Assn. [16169]
Amer. Coll. of Apothecaries [16170]
Amer. Coll. of Clinical Pharmacology [16171]
Amer. Coll. of Clinical Pharmacy [16172]
Amer. Coll. of Neuropsychopharmacology [16173]
Amer. Found. for Pharmaceutical Educ. [16174]
Amer. Inst. of the History of Pharmacy [16175]
Amer. Pharmacists Assn. | Acad. of Pharmacy Practice and Mgt. [16176]
Amer. Pharmacists Assn. | Acad. of Student Pharmacists [16177]

A star before a book entry number signifies that the name is not listed separately, but is mentioned within the entry.

Amer. Soc. for Clinical Pharmacology and Therapeutics [16178]
Amer. Soc. of Clinical Psychopharmacology [16179]
Amer. Soc. of Consultant Pharmacists [16180]
Amer. Soc. of Hea. Sys. Pharmacists [16181]
Amer. Soc. of Pharmacognosy [16182]
Amer. Soc. of Pharmacognosy [16182]
Amer. Soc. for Pharmacology and Experimental Therapeutics [16183]
ASHP Found. [16184]
Assn. of Clinical Res. Professionals [16185]
Assn. of Clinical Res. Professionals [16185]
Bangladeshi-American Pharmacists' Assn. [16186]
Canadian Assn. of Pharmacy in Oncology [16548]
Canadian Assn. of Pharmacy Technicians [16950]
Chinese Biopharmaceutical Assn., U.S.A. [16187]
Christian Pharmacists Fellowship Intl. [16188]
Christian Pharmacists Fellowship Intl. [16188]
Commn. for Certification in Geriatric Pharmacy [16189]
Drug Info. Assn. [16190]
Drug Info. Assn. [16190]PharmacyEthiopian Pharmacists Assn. in North Am.
Foreign Pharmacy Graduate Examination Comm. [16191]
HealthCare Compliance Packaging Coun. [16192]
Healthcare Distribution Mgt. Assn. [16193]
Hematology/Oncology Pharmacy Assn. [16194]PharmacyIndian Pharmacological Soc.
Intl. Acad. of Compounding Pharmacists [16195]
Intl. Biopharmaceutical Assn. [16196]
Intl. Biopharmaceutical Assn. [16196]
Intl. Soc. of Oncology Pharmacy Practitioners [16197]
Intl. Soc. of Oncology Pharmacy Practitioners [16197]
Intl. Soc. for Pharmacoeconomics and Outcomes Res. [16198]
Intl. Soc. for Pharmacoeconomics and Outcomes Res. [16198]
Intl. Soc. for Pharmacoepidemiology [16199]
Intl. Soc. for Pharmacoepidemiology [16199]
Intl. Soc. of Pharmacogenomics [16200]
Kappa Psi [23616]
Lambda Kappa Sigma [23617]
Medical Letter [16201]
Multidisciplinary Assn. for Psychedelic Stud. [16202]
Natl. Alliance of State Pharmacy Associations [16203]
Natl. Assn. of Boards of Pharmacy [16204]
Natl. Assn. of Chain Drug Stores [16205]
Natl. Assn. of Pharmaceutical Representatives [2697]
Natl. Coalition of Pharmaceutical Distributors [2703]
Natl. Community Pharmacists Assn. [16206]
Natl. Coun. on Patient Info. and Educ. [16207]
Natl. Coun. for Prescription Drug Programs [16208]
Natl. Pharmaceutical Assn. [16209]
Natl. Pharmacy Technician Assn. [16210]
Nigerian Assn. of Pharmacists and Pharmaceutical Scientists in the Americas [2704]
Pharmaceutical Bus. Intelligence and Res. Gp. [2705]
Pharmaceutical Care Mgt. Assn. [16211]
Pharmaceutical Indus. Labor-Management Assn. [2700]
Pharmaceutical Printed Literature Assn. [2706]
Pharmacy Technician Educators Coun. [16212]
Pharmacy Technician Educators Coun. [16212]
Phi Delta Chi [23618]
Rho Chi - Alpha Beta Chap. [23619]
SAFE-BioPharma Assn. [2707]
Safety Net Hospitals for Pharmaceutical Access [16213]
Safety Pharmacology Soc. [16214]
Sino-American Pharmaceutical Professionals Assn. [16215]
Sino-American Pharmaceutical Professionals Assn. [16215]
Soc. of Infectious Diseases Pharmacists [16216]

U.S. Pharmacopeia [16217]
U.S. Pharmacopeia [16217]
Pharmacy Advocacy Gp; Pediatric [16153]
Pharmacy Coun. of St. Lucia [IO], Castries, St. Lucia
Pharmacy Defence Assn. [IO], Wellington, New Zealand
Pharmacy Guild of Australia [IO], Canberra, Australia
Pharmacy Guild of New Zealand [IO], Wellington, New Zealand
Pharmacy Technician Educators Coun. [16212], Mary Mohr, Pres., Clarian Hea. Partners Inc., 6144 Knyghton Rd., Indianapolis, IN 46220, (317)962-0919
Pharmacy Technician Educators Coun. [16212], Mary Mohr, Pres., Clarian Hea. Partners Inc., 6144 Knyghton Rd., Indianapolis, IN 46220, (317)962-0919
Pheasants Forever [5110], 1783 Buerkle Cir., St. Paul, MN 55110, (651)773-2000
Phelps-Stokes Fund [8057], 1400 Eye St. NW, Ste. 750, Washington, DC 20005, (202)371-9544
Phelps-Stokes Fund [8057], 1400 Eye St. NW, Ste. 750, Washington, DC 20005, (202)371-9544
Phenix Soc. - Defunct.

Phenomena
  Amer. Soc. of Dowsers [7245]
  Assn. TransCommunication [7246]
  Assn. TransCommunication [7246]
  Borderland Sciences Res. Found. [7247]
  Center for Bigfoot Stud. [7248]
  Fund for UFO Res. [7249]
  Ghost Res. Soc. [7250]
  Intl. Assn. for Near-Death Stud. [7251]
  Intl. Assn. for Near-Death Stud. [7251]
  Intl. Fortean Org. [7252]
  Intl. Fortean Org. [7252]
  Intl. UFO Museum and Res. Center at Roswell, New Mexico [7253]
  Intl. UFO Museum and Res. Center at Roswell, New Mexico [7253]
  J. Allen Rynek Center for UFO Stud. [7254]
  Mutual UFO Network [7255]
  Natl. Investigations Comm. on Unidentified Flying Objects [7256]
  Natl. Investigations Comm. on Unidentified Flying Objects [7256]
  Soc. for Sci. Exploration [7257]
  UFO Info. Retrieval Center [7258]
  UFO Info. Retrieval Center [7258]
PHI [1677], 349 E 149th St., 10th Fl., Bronx, NY 10451, (718)402-7766
Phi Alpha Delta [23579], 345 N Charles St., 3rd Fl., Baltimore, MD 21201, (410)347-3118
Phi Alpha Epsilon [23520], Univ. of Kansas, Civil, Environmental, and Architectural Engg. Dept., 2150 Learned Hall, 1530 W 15th St., Lawrence, KS 66045-7609, (785)864-3603
Phi Alpha Sigma [23593], 313 S 10th St., Philadelphia, PA 19107
Phi Alpha Theta [23548], Univ. of South Florida, 4202 E Fowler Ave., SOC107, Tampa, FL 33620-8100, (813)974-8212
Phi Beta [23468], 377 Pearl St., Jackson, OH 45640
Phi Beta Chi [23728], PO Box 65426, West Des Moines, IA 50265, (515)334-0933
Phi Beta Delta [23568], 1630 Connecticut Ave. NW, 3rd Fl., Washington, DC 20009, (202)518-2052
Phi Beta Kappa [23469], 1606 New Hampshire Ave. NW, Washington, DC 20009, (202)265-3808
Phi Beta Kappa Foundation [★23469]
Phi Beta Mu [23603], 7 Surry Run Pl., The Woodlands, TX 77384-4786
Phi Beta Mu [23603], 7 Surry Run Pl., The Woodlands, TX 77384-4786
Phi Beta Sigma Fraternity [23637], 145 Kennedy St. NW, Washington, DC 20011-5294, (202)726-5434
Phi Chi [★23594]
Phi Chi Medical Fraternity [23594], 2039 Ridgeview Dr., Floyds Knobs, IN 47119, (812)923-7270
Phi Chi Theta [23483], 1508 E Beltline Rd., Ste. 104, Carrollton, TX 75006, (972)245-7202
Phi Chi Welfare Association [★23594]
Phi Delta Chi [23618], 116 N Lafayette, Ste. B, South Lyon, MI 48178, (800)PDC-1883

Phi Delta Delta [★23579]
Phi Delta Epsilon Medical Fraternity [23590], 1005 N Northlake Dr., Hollywood, FL 33019, (786)302-1120
Phi Delta Epsilon Medical Fraternity [23590], 1005 N Northlake Dr., Hollywood, FL 33019, (786)302-1120
Phi Delta Gamma [23623], 1201 Red Mile Rd., PO Box 4599, Lexington, KY 40544-4599, (859)255-1848
Phi Delta Kappa [23624], 408 N Union St., PO Box 7888, Bloomington, IN 47402-0789, (812)339-1156
Phi Delta Phi Intl. Legal Fraternity [23581], 1426 21st St. NW, Washington, DC 20036, (202)223-6801
Phi Delta Phi Intl. Legal Fraternity [23581], 1426 21st St. NW, Washington, DC 20036, (202)223-6801
Phi Delta Phi Legal Inst. [★23581]
Phi Delta Phi Legal Inst. [★23581]
Phi Delta Theta Intl. Fraternity [23678], 2 S Campus Ave., Oxford, OH 45056-1801, (513)523-6345
Phi Epsilon Kappa [23620], 901 W New York St., Indianapolis, IN 46202, (317)627-8745
Phi Gamma Delta [23679], PO Box 4599, Lexington, KY 40544-4599, (859)255-1848
Phi Gamma Nu [23484], 6745 Cheryl Ann Dr., Seven Hills, OH 44131-3720, (216)524-0019
Phi Kappa [★23682]
Phi Kappa Epsilon [★23483]
Phi Kappa Phi [23569], 7576 Goodwood Blvd., Baton Rouge, LA 70806, (225)388-4917
Phi Kappa Sigma [23680], 2 Timber Dr., Chester Springs, PA 19425, (610)469-3282
Phi Kappa Sigma [23680], 2 Timber Dr., Chester Springs, PA 19425, (610)469-3282
Phi Kappa Tau [23681], 5221 Morning Sun Rd., Oxford, OH 45056-8928, (513)523-4193
Phi Kappa Theta Natl. Fraternity [23682], 9640 N Augusta Dr., Ste. 420, Carmel, IN 46032-9602, (317)872-9934
Phi Kappa Upsilon Fraternity [23521], 21000 W 9 Mile Rd., Southfield, MI 48075, (734)775-3164
Phi Lambda Kappa Medical Fraternity - Defunct.
Phi Mu Alpha Sinfonia Fraternity and Found. Natl. HQ [23604], 10600 Old State Rd., Evansville, IN 47711, (812)867-2433
Phi Mu Delta [23683], 316 Cherry Hill Blvd., Cherry Hill, NJ 08002, (888)401-2213
Phi Mu Fraternity [23729], 400 Westpark Dr., Peachtree City, GA 30269, (770)632-2090
Phi Omega Pi [★23723]
Phi Pi Epsilon [★13112]
Phi Pi Phi [★23657]
Phi Rho Sigma Medical Soc. [23595], PO Box 90264, Indianapolis, IN 46290-0264
Phi Sigma [23471], Quinnipiac Univ., Dept. of Biological Sciences, 275 Mt. Carmel Ave., Hamden, CT 06518-1905
Phi Sigma Delta [★23707]
Phi Sigma Epsilon [★23684]
Phi Sigma Iota [23577], Roz Macken, Admin. Dir., Allegheny Coll., 520 N Main St., Box 30, Meadville, PA 16335-3902, (814)332-4886
Phi Sigma Kappa [23684], 2925 E 96th St., Indianapolis, IN 46240, (317)573-5420
Phi Sigma Nu Native Amer. Fraternity [23685], PO Box 2040, Pembroke, NC 28372
Phi Sigma Pi Natl. Honor Fraternity [23582], 2119 Ambassador Cir., Lancaster, PA 17603-2391, (717)299-4710
Phi Sigma Sigma [23730], 8178 Lark Brown Rd., Ste. 202, Elkridge, MD 21075-6424, (410)799-1224
Phi Theta Kappa [★23483]
Phi Theta Kappa [★23514]
Phi Theta Kappa [★23514]
Phi Theta Kappa Intl. [★23514]
Phi Theta Kappa Intl. [★23514]
Phi Theta Kappa, Intl. Honor Soc. [23514], PO Box 13729, Jackson, MS 39236-3729, (601)984-3504
Phi Theta Kappa, Intl. Honor Soc. [23514], PO Box 13729, Jackson, MS 39236-3729, (601)984-3504
Phi Theta Pi [23485], 6552 Bradford Dr., West Des Moines, IA 50266-2308, (515)440-2045
Phi Upsilon Omicron [23550], PO Box 329, Fairmont, WV 26555-0329, (304)368-0612

Reference to "IO" in place of a book number signifies that the association may be found in the 50th edition of International Organizations.

Phi Zeta [23757], Dr. James E. Smallwood, Sec.-Treas., North Carolina State Univ., Coll. of Veterinary Medicine, MBS Dept., Raleigh, NC 27606, (919)513-6223
Philadelphia Flyers Fan Club [23909], PO Box 610, Plymouth Meeting, PA 19462
Philadelphia Soc. [18486], 11620 Rutan Cir., Jerome, MI 49249, (517)688-5111
Philalethes Soc. [19139], John C. Householder, Jr., Bus. Mgr., 800 S 15th St., No. 1803, Sebring, OH 44672, (330)938-7582
Philanthropic Roundtable [★12682]
Philanthropy
  AlKoura League [12428]
  Amer. Grant Writers' Assn. [12654]
  Amer. Inst. of Philanthropy [12655]
  Andrew W. Mellon Found. [10363]
  Arcus Found. [18311]
  Asian Americans/Pacific Islanders in Philanthropy [12656]
  Assn. of Donor Relations Professionals [12657]
  Assn. of Small Foundations [18312]
  BAPS Charities [18313]
  BAPS Charities [18313]
  Bread for the Journey Intl. [12658]
  Bread for the Journey Intl. [12658]
  Building Tomorrow [12659]
  Building Tomorrow [12659]
  Caring Voice Coalition [12660]
  Catholic Campaign for Human Development [12661]
  ChildFund Intl. [11231]
  Comm. Encouraging Corporate Philanthropy [12662]
  Coun. of Religious Volunteer Agencies [13390]
  Drishtipat Worldwide [11124]
  Dyson Found. [12663]
  East West Educ. Development Found. [12664]
  East West Educ. Development Found. [12664]
  Emerging Practitioners in Philanthropy [12665]
  First Foundations [13188]
  Forum of Regional Associations of Grantmakers [12666]
  Funders' Collaborative on Youth Organizing [12667]
  Funders' Network for Smart Growth and Livable Communities [11587]
  G. Unger Vetlesen Found. [12668]
  G. Unger Vetlesen Found. [12668]
  Giving U.S.A. Found. [12669]
  Global Civic Preservation [12329]
  Good360 [12670]
  Grant Professionals Assn. [12671]
  Grantmakers in the Arts [12672]
  Grantmakers for Children, Youth, and Families [12673]
  Grantmakers in Hea. [16218]
  Grantmakers Without Borders [12674]
  Grantmakers Without Borders [12674]
  Humanitarian Intl. Ser. Gp. [12260]
  Humanitarian Travels Intl. [13338]
  Independent Sector [12675]
  Intl. Corrugated Packaging Found. [12676]
  Intl. Corrugated Packaging Found. [12676]
  Israel Humanitarian Found. [12393]
  Jessie Ball duPont Fund [12677]
  Ladies of Charity of the U.S.A. [13191]
  Local Independent Charities of Am. [12678]PhilanthropyMakassed Found. of Am.
  Natl. Comm. for Responsive Philanthropy [12679]
  Native Americans in Philanthropy [12680]
  Neighborhood Funders Gp. [12681]
  Omnilogy, Inc. [12353]
  Philanthropy Roundtable [12682]
  Rebuilding Together [12200]
  Recycling for Charities [4871]
  Rockefeller Bros. Fund [12683]
  Rockefeller Bros. Fund [12683]
  Rockefeller Family Fund [12684]
  Senior Gleaners [12291]
  Soc. of Young Philanthropists [12685]
  Surdna Found. [12686]
  Trull Found. [12687]
  Twenty-First Century Found. [12688]
  United Way of Am. [12056]

  The Urban Inst. I Natl. Center for Charitable Statistics [12689]
  U.S.A. Harvest [12298]
  Women's Philanthropy Inst. [12690]
Philanthropy Roundtable [12682], 1730 M St. NW, Ste. 601, Washington, DC 20036, (202)822-8333
Philatelic
  Alaska Collectors' Club [22005]
  Amer. Air Mail Soc. [22006]
  Amer. First Day Cover Soc. [22007]
  Amer. Helvetia Philatelic Soc. [22008]
  Amer. Helvetia Philatelic Soc. [22008]
  Amer. Philatelic Cong. [22009]
  Amer. Philatelic Res. Lib. [22010]
  Amer. Philatelic Soc. [22011]
  Amer. Philatelic Soc. Writers Unit [22012]
  Amer. Plate Number Single Soc. [22013]
  Amer. Revenue Assn. [22014]
  Amer. Revenue Assn. [22014]
  Amer. Soc. of Polar Philatelists [22015]
  Amer. Topical Assn. [22016]
  Amer. Topical Assn., Americana Unit [22017]
  Amer. Topical Assn., Biology Unit [22018]
  Amer. Topical Assn. I Casey Jones Railroad Unit [22019]
  Assoc. Collectors of El Salvador [22020]
  Bicycle Stamps Club [22021]
  Brazil Philatelic Assn. [22022]
  Bullseye Cancel Collectors' Club [22023]
  CartoPhilatelic Soc. [22024]
  Chemistry and Physics on Stamps Stud. Unit [22025]
  China Stamp Soc. [22026]
  Christmas Philatelic Club [22027]
  Christopher Columbus Philatelic Soc. [22028]
  Citizens' Stamp Advisory Comm. [22029]
  Civil Censorship Study Group [22030]
  Civil Censorship Study Group [22030]
  Collectors Club [22031]
  Collectors of Religion on Stamps [22032]
  Confederate Stamp Alliance [22033]
  Cover Collectors Circuit Club [22034]
  Earth's Physical Features Stud. Unit [22035]
  Eire Philatelic Assn. [22036]
  Errors, Freaks and Oddities Collectors' Club [22037]
  First Issues Collectors Club [22038]
  France and Colonies Philatelic Soc. [22039]
  German Colonies Collectors Gp. [22040]
  German Colonies Collectors Gp. [22040]
  Germany Philatelic Soc. [22041]
  Germany Philatelic Soc. [22041]
  Graphics Philately Assn. [22042]
  Haiti Philatelic Soc. [22043]
  India Stud. Circle for Philately [22044]
  Inter-Governmental Philatelic Corp. [22045]
  Intl. Soc. of Worldwide Stamp Collectors [22046]
  Intl. Soc. of Worldwide Stamp Collectors [22046]
  Jack Knight Air Mail Soc. [22047]
  Jack Knight Air Mail Soc. [22047]
  Korea Stamp Soc. [22048]
  Machine Cancel Soc. [22049]
  Mailer's Postmark Permit Club [22050]
  Maritime Postmark Soc. [22051]
  Maritime Postmark Soc. [22051]
  Mathematical Stud. Unit [22052]
  Meter Stamp Soc. [22053]
  Metropolitan Air Post Soc. [22054]
  Metropolitan Air Post Soc. [22054]
  Mexico Elmhurst Philatelic Soc. Intl. [22055]
  Mexico Elmhurst Philatelic Soc. Intl. [22055]
  Military Postal History Soc. [22056]
  Mobile Post Off. Soc. [22057]
  Napoleonic Age Philatelists [22058]
  Natl. Duck Stamp Collectors Soc. [22059]
  Natl. Stamp Dealers Assn. [22060]
  Nepal and Tibet Philatelic Stud. Circle [22061]
  Perfins Club [22062]
  Philatelic Found. [22063]
  Polonus Philatelic Soc. [22064]
  Post Mark Collectors Club [22065]
  Postal History Soc. [22066]
  Precancel Stamp Soc. [22067]
  Rossica Soc. of Russian Philately [22068]
  Rossica Soc. of Russian Philately [22068]

  Rotary on Stamps Fellowship [22069]
  Rotary on Stamps Fellowship [22069]
  Ryukyu Philatelic Specialist Soc. [22070]
  Ryukyu Philatelic Specialist Soc. [22070]
  St. Helena, Ascension, and Tristan da Cunha Philatelic Soc. [22071]
  Scandinavian Collectors Club [22072]
  Scandinavian Collectors Club [22072]
  Scouts on Stamps Soc. Intl. [22073]
  Ships on Stamps Unit [22074]
  Soc. of Australasian Specialists/Oceania [22075]
  Soc. for Costa Rica Collectors [22076]
  Soc. for Hungarian Philately [22077]
  Soc. for Hungarian Philately [22077]
  Soc. of Israel Philatelists [22078]
  Soc. for Thai Philately [22079]
  Space Topic Stud. Unit [22080]
  Space Topic Stud. Unit [22080]
  Sports Philatelists Intl. [22081]
  Sports Philatelists Intl. [22081]
  Stamps on Stamps Collectors Club [22082]
  Stamps on Stamps Collectors Club [22082]
  State Revenue Soc. [22083]
  Tannu Tuva Collectors' Soc. [22084]
  Tannu Tuva Collectors' Soc. [22084]
  Ukrainian Philatelic and Numismatic Soc. [22085]
  Ukrainian Philatelic and Numismatic Soc. [22085]
  United Nations Philatelists, Inc. [22086]
  United Postal Stationery Soc. [22087]
  U.S. Cancellation Club [22088]
  U.S. Philatelic Classics Soc. [22089]
  U.S. Stamp Soc. [22090]
  Universal Ship Cancellation Soc. [22091]
  Western Cover Soc. [22092]
  Wreck and Crash Mail Soc. [22093]
  Young Stamp Collectors of Am. [22094]
Philatelic Found. [22063], 70 W 40th St., 15th Fl., New York, NY 10018, (212)221-6555
Philatelic Lib. Assn. [★22010]
Philatelic Literature Assn. [★22010]
Philatelic Traders' Soc. [IO], Fleet, United Kingdom
Philately
  Amer. Philatelic Res. Lib. [22010]
  Amer. Philatelic Soc. Writers Unit [22012]
  Amer. Topical Assn. [22016]
  Assoc. Collectors of El Salvador [22020]
  Brazil Philatelic Assn. [22022]
  Citizens' Stamp Advisory Comm. [22029]
  Collectors of Religion on Stamps [22032]
  Confederate Stamp Alliance [22033]
  Cover Collectors Circuit Club [22034]
  Errors, Freaks and Oddities Collectors' Club [22037]
  First Issues Collectors Club [22038]
  France and Colonies Philatelic Soc. [22039]
  Intl. Fed. of Amer. Homing Pigeon Fanciers [22097]
  Intl. Soc. of Worldwide Stamp Collectors [22046]
  Jack Knight Air Mail Soc. [22047]
  Korea Stamp Soc. [22048]
  Mailer's Postmark Permit Club [22050]
  Meter Stamp Soc. [22053]
  Mexico Elmhurst Philatelic Soc. Intl. [22055]
  Napoleonic Age Philatelists [22058]
  Rossica Soc. of Russian Philately [22068]
  Ships on Stamps Unit [22074]
  Soc. of Australasian Specialists/Oceania [22075]
  Soc. for Thai Philately [22079]
  Space Topic Stud. Unit [22080]
  Wreck and Crash Mail Soc. [22093]
Philip Boileau Collectors' Soc. [20970], 1025 Redwood Blvd., Redding, CA 96003-1905
Philip Larkin Soc. [IO], Hornsea, United Kingdom
Philip Roth Soc. [10732], Central Connecticut State Univ., Dept. of English, New Britain, CT 06050, (860)832-2773
Philippine Airlines Mountaineering Club [IO], Makati City, Philippines
Philippine Amateur Track and Field Assn. [IO], Manila, Philippines
Philippine Amer. Chamber of Commerce [23436], Chris Baltazar, 5400 Shawnee Rd., Ste. 102, Alexandria, VA 22312, (202)486-8600
Philippine Amer. Writers and Artists [10733], PO Box 31928, San Francisco, CA 94131-0928

A star before a book entry number signifies that the name is not listed separately, but is mentioned within the entry.

Philippine Assn. of Entomologists [IO], Los Banos, Philippines
Philippine Assn. of Gerontology [IO], Valenzuela City, Philippines
Philippine Assn. of the Record Indus. [IO], Manila, Philippines
Philippine Assn. of Secretaries and Administrative Professionals [IO], Makati City, Philippines
Philippine Assn. of Ser. Exporters, Inc. [IO], Mandaluyong City, Philippines
Philippine Assn. of Univ. Women [IO], Manila, Philippines
Philippine Badminton Assn. [IO], Manila, Philippines
Philippine Bible Soc. [IO], Manila, Philippines
Philippine Chamber of Commerce and Indus. [IO], Makati City, Philippines
Philippine Coconut Oil Producers Assn. [IO], Pasig City, Philippines
Philippine Convention and Visitors Corp. [IO], Manila, Philippines
Philippine Dermatological Soc. [IO], Quezon City, Philippines
Philippine Diabetes Assn. [IO], Mandaluyong City, Philippines
Philippine Exporters Confed. [IO], Pasay City, Philippines
Philippine Franchise Assn. [IO], Pasig City, Philippines
Philippine League Against Epilepsy [IO], Manila, Philippines
Philippine Medical Assn. [IO], Quezon City, Philippines
Philippine Medical Informatics Soc. [IO], Manila, Philippines
Philippine Natl. AIDS Coun. [IO], Manila, Philippines
Philippine Natl. Red Cross [IO], Manila, Philippines
Philippine Nurses Assn. of Am. [15796], 73 Hawkins Cir., Wheaton, IL 60187, (630)653-0630
Philippine Olympic Comm. [IO], Pasig City, Philippines
Philippine Partnership for the Development of Human Resources in Rural Areas [IO], Quezon City, Philippines
Philippine Physical Therapy Assn. [IO], Quezon City, Philippines
Philippine Retailers Assn. [IO], Pasig City, Philippines
Philippine Sailing Assn. [IO], Makati City, Philippines
Philippine Skating Union [IO], Pasay City, Philippines
Philippine Social Sci. Coun. [IO], Quezon City, Philippines
Philippine Soc. of Anesthesiologists [IO], Quezon City, Philippines
Philippine Soc. of Gastrointestinal Endoscopy [IO], Quezon City, Philippines
Philippine Soc. of Hypertension [IO], Pasig City, Philippines
Philippine Soc. for Microbiology and Infectious Diseases [IO], Quezon City, Philippines
Philippine Soc. of Photogrammetry and Remote Sensing [IO], Quezon City, Philippines
Philippine Software Indus. Assn. [IO], Makati City, Philippines
Philippine Sports Assn. of the Differently Abled [IO], Pasig City, Philippines
Philippine Sugar Millers Assn. [IO], Makati City, Philippines
Philippine Taekwondo Assn. [IO], Manila, Philippines
Philippine Tennis Assn. [IO], Manila, Philippines
Philippine Travel Agencies Assn. [IO], Pasay City, Philippines
Philippine Tropical Fish Exporters Assn. [IO], Paranaque, Philippines
Philippine Urological Assn. [IO], Quezon City, Philippines

Philippines
Filipina Women's Network [18792]
Filipino Amer. Natl. Historical Soc. [10364]
Filipino Amer. Natl. Historical Soc. [10364]
Filipinos for Affirmative Action [18314]
Intl. Soc. of Filipinos in Finance and Accounting [36]
Mamburao-U.S.A. Assn. [10365]
Military Order of the Carabao [20745]

Natl. Alliance for Filipino Concerns [17200]
Natl. Fed. of Filipino Amer. Associations [10366]
Philippine Amer. Chamber of Commerce [23436]
Philolexian Soc. [10046], Columbia Univ., 515 Lerner Hall, 2920 Broadway, New York, NY 10027
Philological Soc. [IO], London, United Kingdom
Philomathean Soc. of the Univ. of Pennsylvania [10047], Coll. Hall, Box H, Philadelphia, PA 19104
Philosophical Res. Soc. [10410], 3910 Los Feliz Blvd., Los Angeles, CA 90027, (323)663-2167

Philosophy
Aesthetic Realism Found. [10367]
Amer. Assn. of Philosophy Teachers [8701]
Amer. Catholic Philosophical Assn. [8702]
Amer. Maritain Assn. [10368]
Amer. Philosophical Assn. [10369]
Amer. Philosophical Practitioners Assn. [8703]
Assn. for the Advancement of Philosophy and Psychiatry [8704]
Assn. for the Advancement of Philosophy and Psychiatry [8704]
Assn. for Feminist Ethics and Social Theory [10370]
Assn. for Informal Logic and Critical Thinking [10371]
Assn. for Practical and Professional Ethics [8705]
Ayn Rand Inst. [10372]
Ayn Rand Soc. [10373]
Camus Stud. Assn. [10374]
Center for Process Stud. [10375]
Concerned Philosophers for Peace [10376]
Coun. for Res. in Values and Philosophy [10377]
Coun. for Res. in Values and Philosophy [10377]
FreeThoughtAction [10378]
Gabriel Marcel Soc. [10379]
HOPOS - The Intl. Soc. for the History of Philosophy of Sci. [8839]
Inst. for the Advancement of Philosophy for Children [10380]
Inst. for the Advancement of Philosophy for Children [10380]
Intl. Adam Smith Soc. [10381]
Intl. Assn. for Environmental Philosophy [10382]
Intl. Assn. for Philosophy and Literature [10383]
Intl. Assn. for Philosophy and Literature [10383]
Intl. Berkeley Soc. [10384]
Intl. Boethius Soc. [10385]
Intl. Fed. of Philosophical Societies [10386]
Intl. Fed. of Philosophical Societies [10386]
Intl. Husserl and Phenomenological Res. Soc. [10387]
Intl. Husserl and Phenomenological Res. Soc. [10387]
Intl. Inst. for Field-Being [8706]
Intl. New Thought Alliance [10388]
Intl. Plutarch Soc. [10389]
Intl. Soc. for Comparative Stud. of Chinese and Western Philosophy [8707]
Intl. Soc. for Neoplatonic Stud. [10390]
Intl. Soc. for Neoplatonic Stud. [10390]
Intl. Soc. for Phenomenological Stud. [10391]
Intl. Soc. for Phenomenological Stud. [10391]
Intl. Soc. for Phenomenology and Literature [10392]
Intl. Soc. for Phenomenology and Literature [10392]
Intl. Soc. for Phenomenology and the Sciences of Life [10393]
Intl. Soc. for Phenomenology and the Sciences of Life [10393]
Internet Infidels [10394]
Jagannath Org. for Global Awareness [20213]
Josiah Royce Soc. [10395]
Karl Jaspers Soc. of North Am. [10396]
Libertarian SIG [10397]
Lonergan Philosophical Soc. [10398]
Lonergan Philosophical Soc. [10398]
Merleau-Ponty Circle [10399]
Metaphysical Soc. of Am. [10400]
Michael Oakeshott Assn. [10401]
North Amer. Fichte Soc. [10402]
North Amer. Kant Soc. [10403]
North Amer. Levinas Soc. [10404]
North Amer. Nietzsche Soc. [10405]
North Amer. Nietzsche Soc. [10405]

North Amer. Sartre Soc. [10406]
North Amer. Soc. for Social Philosophy [10407]
The Objectivist Center [10408]
Pacific Soc. for Women in Philosophy [10409]
Philosophical Res. Soc. [10410]
Philosophy Documentation Center [10411]
Philosophy of Educ. Soc. [8708]
Philosophy of Sci. Assn. [10412]
Philosophy of Time Soc. [10413]
Radical Philosophy Assn. [10414]
Resources for Independent Thinking [10415]
Soc. for the Advancement of Amer. Philosophy [10416]
Soc. for Analytical Feminism [10417]
Soc. for Ancient Greek Philosophy [10418]
Soc. for Asian and Comparative Philosophy [10419]
Soc. of Christian Philosophers [10420]
Soc. of Christian Philosophers [10420]
Soc. for Exact Philosophy [10421]
Soc. for Exact Philosophy [10421]
Soc. for Phenomenology and Existential Philosophy [10422]
Soc. for the Philosophical Stud. of Genocide and the Holocaust [10423]
Soc. for the Philosophical Stud. of Genocide and the Holocaust [10423]
Soc. for Philosophy in the Contemporary World [10424]
Soc. for Philosophy in the Contemporary World [10424]
Soc. for Philosophy and Psychology [10425]
Soc. for Philosophy and Tech. [10426]
Soc. for Philosophy and Tech. [10426]
Soc. for Skeptical Stud. [10427]
Soc. for Social and Political Philosophy [10428]
Soc. for the Stud. of Process Philosophies [10429]
Soc. for Utopian Stud. [10430]
Soc. for Utopian Stud. [10430]
Southern Soc. for Philosophy and Psychology [10431]
Theosophical Book Assn. for the Blind [20264]
Undergraduate Philosophy Assn. [8709]
World Inst. for Advanced Phenomenological Res. and Learning [10432]
World Inst. for Advanced Phenomenological Res. and Learning [10432]
Philosophy Documentation Center [10411], PO Box 7147, Charlottesville, VA 22906-7147, (434)220-3300
Philosophy of Educ. Soc. [8708], Univ. of Illinois, 1310 S 6th St., Champaign, IL 61820, (217)333-3673
Philosophy of Educ. Soc. of Australasia [IO], Perth, Australia
Philosophy of Sci. Assn. [10412], Bloomsburg Univ., Dept. of Philosophy, Bloomsburg, PA 17815, (570)389-4174
Philosophy; Soc. for Natural [7078]
Philosophy of Time Soc. [10413], Messiah Colorado, Dept. of Philosophy, 1 Coll. Ave., Grantham, PA 17027
Phlebology; Amer. Coll. of [16956]
Phlebotomy Assn; Natl. [14973]
Phobia Clinic [★12693]
Phobia Soc. of Am. [★12692]

Phobias
Agoraphobics in Motion [12691]
Anxiety Disorders Assn. of Am. [12692]
Anxiety and Phobia Treatment Center [12693]
Phoenix Center [★13873]
Phoenix House [13282], 164 W 74th St., New York, NY 10023, (646)505-2080
Phoenix House Found. [★13282]
Phoenix Proj. [★16561]
Phoenix Soc. for Burn Survivors [13873], 1835 R W Berends Dr. SW, Grand Rapids, MI 49519-4955, (616)458-2773
Phonemic Spelling Coun. [★8523]
Phones For Life - Address unknown since 2011.

Phonetics
Amer. Assn. of Phonetic Sciences [10433]
Phonograph Soc; Vintage Radio and [22123]
Phonographic Performances New Zealand [IO], Auckland, New Zealand

Reference to "IO" in place of a book number signifies that the association may be found in the 50th edition of International Organizations.

Phosphate Chemicals Export Assn. [761], PO Box 3320, Northbrook, IL 60062, (847)849-4305

Phosphoric Acid and Phosphates Producers Assn. [IO], Brussels, Belgium

Photo Art Assn. of Singapore [IO], Singapore, Singapore

Photo-Chemical Machining Inst. [2490], 11 Robert Toner Blvd., Ste. 234, North Attleboro, MA 02763, (508)385-0085

Photo-Chemical Machining Inst. [2490], 11 Robert Toner Blvd., Ste. 234, North Attleboro, MA 02763, (508)385-0085

Photo Imaging Coun. [IO], Croydon, United Kingdom

Photo Imaging Educ. Assn. [8711], 3000 Picture Pl., Jackson, MI 49201, (517)788-8100

Photo Marketing Assn. - Australia [IO], Frenchs Forest, Australia

Photo Marketing Assn. - Canada [IO], Ancaster, ON, Canada

Photo Marketing Assn. Intl. [★2730]

Photo Marketing Assn. Intl. [IO], Welwyn Garden City, United Kingdom

Photo Marketing Assn. Intl. [★2730]

Photo Marketing Assn. - New Zealand [IO], Auckland, New Zealand

Photobiology; Amer. Soc. for [6289]

Photobiology; Amer. Soc. for [6289]

Photogrammetry
ASPRS - The Imaging and Geospatial Info. Soc. [7259]
Mgt. Assn. for Private Photogrammetric Surveyors [7260]

Photographers' Assn. of Am. [★2732]

Photographes Professionnels du Canada [★IO]

Photographic Art and Sci. Found. [8712], Intl. Photography Hall of Fame and Museum, 2100 NE 52nd St., Kirkpatrick Ctr., Oklahoma City, OK 73111, (405)424-4055

Photographic Art and Sci. Found. [8712], Intl. Photography Hall of Fame and Museum, 2100 NE 52nd St., Kirkpatrick Ctr., Oklahoma City, OK 73111, (405)424-4055

The Photographic Historical Soc. [10442], 350 Whiting Rd., Webster, NY 14580

Photographic Historical Soc. of Canada [IO], Toronto, ON, Canada

Photographic and Imaging Mfrs. Assn. [★2722]

Photographic and Imaging Mfrs. Assn. [★2722]

Photographic Mfrs. and Distributors Assn. [★2728]

Photographic Merchandising and Distributing Assn. [★2728]

Photographic Soc. of Am. [22095], 3000 United Founders Blvd., Ste. 103, Oklahoma City, OK 73112-3940, (405)843-1437

Photographic Soc. of Southern Africa [IO], Gauteng, Republic of South Africa

Photographic Stud. Workshop [★9613]

Photography
Amer. Photographic Artists [2708]
Amer. Photographic Artists Guild [2709]
Amer. Professional Wedding Photographers Assn. [2710]
Amer. Soc. of Media Photographers [2711]
Amer. Soc. of Photographers [10434]
Amer. Soc. of Picture Professionals [2712]
Antique and Amusement Photographers Intl. [2713]
Architectural League of New York [17392]
Assoc. Press Photo Managers [2714]
Assn. of Intl. Photography Art Dealers [10435]
Assn. of Intl. Photography Art Dealers [10435]
Blue Earth Alliance [10436]
British Press Photographers Assn. [2197]
Commercial Photographers Intl. [2715]
Commercial Photographers Intl. [2715]
Daguerreian Soc. [10437]
Editorial Photographers [2716]
En Foco [10438]
Flashes of Hope [11135]
Glamour Photographers Intl. [2717]
Glamour Photographers Intl. [2717]
Independent Photo Imagers [2718]
Intl. Assn. of Architectural Photographers [2719]
Intl. Assn. of Architectural Photographers [2719]
Intl. Assn. of Panoramic Photographers [2720]

Intl. Assn. of Panoramic Photographers [2720]
Intl. Center of Photography [8710]
Intl. Center of Photography [8710]
Intl. Fire Photographers Assn. [2721]
Intl. Fire Photographers Assn. [2721]
Intl. Imaging Indus. Assn. [2722]
Intl. Imaging Indus. Assn. [2722]
Intl. Inst. of Photographic Arts [2723]
Intl. Inst. of Photographic Arts [2723]
Intl. League of Conservation Photographers [4777]
Intl. League of Conservation Photographers [4777]
Intl. Photographic Historical Org. [10439]
Intl. Photographic Historical Org. [10439]
Intl. Soc. for Aviation Photography [2724]
Intl. Visual Sociology Assn. [7428]
Kids with Cameras [12694]
Natl. Assn. of Photographic Equip. Technicians [2725]
Natl. Press Photographers Assn. [2726]
Natl. Stereoscopic Assn. [10440]
Nikon Historical Soc. [10441]
North Amer. Nature Photography Assn. [2727]
Peace in Focus [18275]
Photo Imaging Educ. Assn. [8711]
Photographic Art and Sci. Found. [8712]
Photographic Art and Sci. Found. [8712]
The Photographic Historical Soc. [10442]
Photographic Soc. of Am. [22095]
Photographic Soc. of Southern Africa [4611]
Photoimaging Mfrs. and Distributors Assn. [2728]
Pictorial Photographers of Am. [10443]
Picture Archv. Coun. of Am. [2729]
PMA - The Worldwide Community of Imaging Associations [2730]
PMA - The Worldwide Community of Imaging Associations [2730]
Professional Aerial Photographers Assn. [2731]
Professional Aerial Photographers Assn. [2731]
Professional Photographers of Am. [2732]
Professional School Photographers Assn. Intl. [2733]
Professional School Photographers Assn. Intl. [2733]
Professional Women Photographers [2734]
Silent Images [13148]
Soc. for Imaging Sci. and Tech. [7261]
Soc. of Photo-Technologists [2735]
Soc. of Photo-Technologists [2735]
Soc. for Photographic Educ. [8713]
Soc. of Sport and Event Photographers [2736]
Soc. of Sport and Event Photographers [2736]
Stock Artists Alliance [2737]
Student Photographic Soc. [10444]
U.S. Senate Press Photographers Gallery [2738]
Univ. Photographers Assn. of Am. [8714]
Visual Artists and Galleries Assn. [5583]
Wedding and Portrait Photographers Intl. [2739]
Wedding and Portrait Photographers Intl. [2739]
White House News Photographers Assn. [2740]
Women in Photography Intl. [2741]

Photoimaging Mfrs. and Distributors Assn. [2728], 7600 Jericho Tpke., Ste. 301, Woodbury, NY 11797, (516)802-0895

Photoluminescent Safety Products Assn. [IO], Surrey, United Kingdom

Phrenocon [★23681]

Phycological Soc. of Am. [6364], John Wiley & Sons Inc., 350 Main St., Malden, MA 02148, (781)388-8599

Phycological Soc. of Am. [6364], John Wiley & Sons Inc., 350 Main St., Malden, MA 02148, (781)388-8599

Phylloxera and Grape Indus. Bd. of South Australia [IO], Stepney, Australia

Physiatrists; Assn. of Academic [16560]

Physical Disability Australia [IO], Willawarrin, Australia

Physical Education
Amer. Alliance for Hea., Physical Educ., Recreation and Dance [8715]
Intl. Coun. for Hea., Physical Educ., Recreation, Sport, and Dance [8716]
Intl. Coun. for Hea., Physical Educ., Recreation, Sport, and Dance [8716]

Natl. Acad. of Kinesiology [8717]
Natl. Assn. of Collegiate Women Athletics Administrators [8718]
Natl. Assn. for Girls and Women in Sport [8719]
Natl. Assn. for Sport and Physical Educ. [8720]
Natl. Interscholastic Athletic Administrators Assn. [8721]
NFHS Coaches Assn. [22465]
North Amer. Soc. for Sport Mgt. [8722]
North Amer. Soc. for Sport Mgt. [8722]
PE4life [8723]
Phi Epsilon Kappa [23620]
Soc. of State Directors of Hea., Physical Educ. and Recreation [8724]
Sport and Recreation Law Assn. [23022]

Physical Educ. Assn. of Ireland [IO], Limerick, Ireland

Physical Fitness
Aerobics and Fitness Assn. of Am. [16219]
Aerobics and Fitness Assn. of Am. [16219]
Alliance for Wellness ROI [16303]
Am. Outdoors Assn. [22835]
Amer. Barefoot Waterski Club [23114]
Amer. Coun. on Exercise [16220]
Amer. Junior Rodeo Assn. [22839]
Amer. Medical Athletic Assn. [22802]
Amer. Nordic Walking Assn. [16221]
Amer. Running Assn. [22803]
Amer. Senior Fitness Assn. [16222]
Aquatic Exercise Assn. [22804]
Aquatic and Fitness Professional Assn. Intl. [22805]
Assn. of Ayurvedic Professionals of North Am. [13664]
Breathecure [13669]
Center for the Stud. of Aging of Albany [10838]
Cinderella Softball Leagues [22951]
Coalition for a Healthy and Active Am. [15852]
Cooper Inst. [16223]
Cooper Inst. [16223]
Dance It Forward USA [9546]
Energy Kinesiology Assn. [13674]
Exercise Safety Assn. [16224]
Fed. of Intl. Lacrosse [22713]
Fitness Forward [16225]
Fitness Indus. Suppliers Assn. - North Am. [2742]
Fitness Indus. Suppliers Assn. - North Am. [2742]
Girls on the Run Intl. [22863]
Hampton One-Design Class Racing Assn. [22340]
Harness Horse Youth Found. [22652]
IDEA Hea. and Fitness Assn. [16226]
Intl. Assn. of Gay and Lesbian Martial Artists [22734]
Intl. Female Boxers Assn. [22437]
Intl. Fitness Assn. [16227]
Intl. Fitness Professionals Assn. [16228]
Intl. Hea., Racquet and Sportsclub Assn. [2743]
Intl. Hea., Racquet and Sportsclub Assn. [2743]
Intl. Natural Bodybuilding and Fitness Fed. [22418]
Intl. Sungja-Do Assn. [22738]
Intl. Youth Conditioning Assn. [23139]
Journey to Solidarity [14139]
Kids Enjoy Exercise Now [21474]
Maccabi USA/Sports for Israel [22985]
Martial Arts Teachers' Assn. [22743]
Medical Fitness Assn. [16229]
Natl. Assn. for Hea. and Fitness [16230]
Natl. Assn. of Underwater Instructors [23104]
Natl. Coalition for Promoting Physical Activity [22806]
Natl. Gym Assn. [22807]
Natl. Junior Baseball League [22285]
Natl. Scholastic Surfing Assn. [23035]
Natl. Senior Games Assn. [22808]
Natl. Softball Assn. [22954]
Natl. Starwind/Spindrift Class Assn. [22377]
Natl. Team Cheng Martial Arts Assn. [22747]
Native Amer. Fitness Coun. [16231]
Natural Fitness Trainers Assn. [22809]
New England Trails Conf. [23090]
OrganicAthlete [22232]
Pilates Method Alliance [16232]
Professional Baseball Athletic Trainers Soc. [22289]

A star before a book entry number signifies that the name is not listed separately, but is mentioned within the entry.

Professional Football Players Mothers' Assn. [22595]
Shape Up Am. [16233]
Spirit Indus. Trade Assn. [733]
Spoons Across Am. [15845]
Sportscar Vintage Racing Assn. [22249]
U.S. Bobsled and Skeleton Fed. [22926]
U.S. Competitive Aerobics Fed. [22209]
U.S. Dental Tennis Assn. [23062]
U.S. Disc Sports [22536]
U.S. Kuo Shu Fed. [22759]
U.S. Ski Team Found. [22919]
U.S. Water Fitness Assn. [22810]
USA Diving [22544]
U.S.A. Karate Fed. [22766]
USA Professional Platform Tennis Assn. [23066]
USA Pulling [23074]
USA Volleyball [23111]
USGA Green Sect. [22628]
Women Outdoors [22797]
Women's All-Star Assn. [22432]
World Fast-Draw Assn. [22891]
World Fed. of Athletic Training and Therapy [16722]
The World Kuoshu Fed. [22770]
World Masters Cross-Country Ski Assn. [22921]
World Mudo Fed. [22773]
ZY Qigong [13722]
Physical and Hea. Educ. Canada [IO], Ottawa, ON, Canada
Physical Security Interoperability Alliance [6819], 65 Washington St., Ste. 170, Santa Clara, CA 95050, (650)938-6945
Physical Soc. of Japan [IO], Tokyo, Japan
Physical Soc. of Republic of China [IO], Taipei, Taiwan
Physical Therapy
Amer. Hosp. Assn., Sect. for Long Term Care and Rehabilitation [15039]
Univ. of Colorado Hea. Sciences Center Alumni Assn. [23547]
Physical Therapy Assn; Amer. [16838]
Physical Therapy Assn. of Thailand [IO], Nakhon Nayok, Thailand
Physical Therapy Overseas [★16044]
Physical Therapy Overseas [★16044]
Physically Impaired
Amer. Amputee Soccer Assn. [22932]
Amer. Assn. of People with Disabilities [11757]
Amer. Bd. of Disability Analysts [16553]
Amputees in Motion Intl. [11759]
BlazeSports Am. [22508]
Christian Overcomers [11771]
Disability Resources [11776]
Extensions for Independence [11786]
Gospel Assn. for the Blind [17078]
Kids Together [11802]
Natl. Assn. of the Physically Handicapped [11811]
Natl. Inst. for Rehabilitation Engg. [11817]
North Amer. One-Armed Golfer Assn. [22521]
Special Recreation for disABLED Intl. [11831]
Support Dogs, Inc. [11832]
Watering Seeds Org. [22532]
World T.E.A.M. Sports [22534]
Physician Asst. Educ. Assn. [16239], 300 N Washington St., Ste. 710, Alexandria, VA 22314-2544, (703)548-5538
Physician Assistants
Accreditation Rev. Commn. on Educ. for the Physician Asst. [16234]
Amer. Acad. of Physician Assistants [16235]
Assn. of Neurosurgical Physician Assistants [16236]
Assn. of Physician Assistants in Cardiology [14006]
Natl. Assn. of Physician Assistants [16237]
Natl. Commn. on Certification of Physician Assistants [16238]
Physician Asst. Educ. Assn. [16239]
Soc. of Army Physician Assistants [16240]
Soc. of Dermatology Physician Assistants [16241]
Soc. of Emergency Medicine Physician Assistants [16242]
Soc. for Physician Assistants in Pediatrics [16243]
Soc. of Physician Assistants in Rheumatology [16626]

Physician Assistants in Dermatology [★16241]
Physician Assistants; Soc. of Air Force [20330]
Physician Hospitals of Am. [15431], 2025 M St. NW, Ste. 800, Washington, DC 20036, (202)367-1113
Physician Insurers Assn. of Am. [15131], 2275 Res. Blvd., Ste. 250, Rockville, MD 20850, (301)947-9000
Physician Specialists; Amer. Assn. of [16058]
Physicians
Acad. of Clinical Lab. Physicians and Scientists [16244]
Acad. of Clinical Lab. Physicians and Scientists [16244]
Adopt a Dr. [16245]
Air Medical Physician Assn. [16246]
Amer. Acad. on Commun. in Healthcare [16247]
Amer. Acad. of Hospice and Palliative Medicine [16248]
Amer. Assn. of Clinical Directors [16249]
Amer. Assn. of Nutritional Consultants [15814]
Amer. Assn. of Orthopaedic Executives [16020]
Amer. Assn. of Physicians of Indian Origin [16250]
Amer. Bd. of Integrative Holistic Medicine [14991]
Amer. Bd. of Nutrition [15815]
Amer. Celiac Society | Dietary Support Coalition [15817]
Amer. Coll. of Community Midwives [15864]
Amer. Coll. of Physicians [15133]
Amer. Hosp. Assn., Sect. for Long Term Care and Rehabilitation [15039]
Amer. Medical Assn. | Fed. of State Physician Hea. Programs [16251]
Amer. Muslim Women Physicians Assn. [16252]
Amer. Muslim Women Physicians Assn. [16252]
Amer. Osteopathic Coll. of Anesthesiologists [13735]
Amer. Physician Art Assn. [9156]
Amer. Physician Scientists Assn. [8588]
Amer. Registry of Medical Assistants [15316]
Amer. Soc. for Clinical Nutrition [15821]
Assn. of Amer. Indian Physicians [16253]
Assn. of Amer. Physicians and Surgeons [16254]
Assn. of Chinese Amer. Physicians [16255]
Assn. of French-Speaking Physicians of Canada [19603]
Assn. of Nigerian Physicians in the Americas [16256]
Assn. of Nigerian Physicians in the Americas [16256]
Assn. of Physicians of Pakistani Descent of North Am. [16257]
Assn. of Prog. Directors in Internal Medicine [15134]
Assn. of Ringside Physicians [16258]
Assn. of Staff Physician Recruiters [16259]
Assn. of Staff Physician Recruiters [16259]
Avenues, Natl. Support Gp. for Arthrogryposis Multiplex Congenita [15573]
Benign Essential Blepharospasm Res. Found. [15575]
Catholic Medical Assn. [16260]
Certification Bd. for Urologic Nurses and Associates [16944]
Children's Tumor Found. [15579]
Chinese Amer. Doctors Assn. [16261]
Chinese Amer. Doctors Assn. [16261]
Chinese Amer. Soc. Of Anesthesiology [13745]
Educational Commn. for Foreign Medical Graduates [16262]
Educational Commn. for Foreign Medical Graduates [16262]
Fed. Physicians Assn. [16263]
Fed. of Pediatric Organizations [16145]
Forbes Norris MDA/ALS Res. Center [15590]
Global Physicians Corps [15174]
Heart Rhythm Soc. [14016]
Interamerican Coll. of Physicians and Surgeons [16264]
Interamerican Coll. of Physicians and Surgeons [16264]
Intercontinental Fed. of Behavioral Optometry [15994]
Intl. Anesthesia Res. Soc. [13748]
Intl. Assn. of Healthcare Central Ser. Material Mgt. [15058]

Intl. Assn. of Physicians in AIDS Care [16265]
Intl. Assn. of Physicians in AIDS Care [16265]
Intl. Fed. of Psoriasis Associations [14328]
Intl. Skeletal Soc. [16533]
The IPA Assn. of Am. [16266]
Iraqi Medical Sciences Assn. [15193]
Islamic Medical Assn. of North Am. [16267]
Natl. Assn. of Locum Tenens Org. [16268]
Natl. Assn. of Managed Care Physicians [16269]
Natl. Assn. of Medics and Corpsmen [5219]
Natl. Assn. of Physician Recruiters [16270]
Natl. Assn. of Residents and Interns [15425]
Natl. Assn. of Veterans Affairs Physicians and Dentists [16271]
Natl. Coalition of Healthcare Recruiters [15298]
Natl. Org. of Rheumatology Managers [16621]
Natl. Physicians Alliance [16272]
Naturopathic Physicians Bd. of Aesthetic Medicine [15537]
North Amer. Clinical Dermatologic Soc. [14337]
North Amer. Sikh Medical and Dental Assn. [15429]
Oncology Assn. of Naturopathic Physicians [15539]
Pediatric Assn. of Naturopathic Physicians [8681]
Physicians Against World Hunger [12287]
Qualified Private Medical Practitioners' and Hospitals' Assn. [14104]
Royal Coll. of Physicians of Ireland [16247]
Semmelweis Soc. Intl. [16510]
Soc. of Correctional Physicians [16273]
Soc. of Nuclear Medicine Technologist Sect. [15697]
Soc. for Worldwide Medical Exchange [15212]
Thai Physicians Assn. of Am. [16274]
Tourette Syndrome Assn. [15636]
US Doctors for Africa [15221]
Physicians Against World Hunger [12287], 2 Stowe Rd., Peekskill, NY 10566
Physicians Against World Hunger [12287], 2 Stowe Rd., Peekskill, NY 10566
Physicians; Amer. Assn. of Naturopathic [15531]
Physicians; Amer. Osteopathic Bd. of Family [16066]
Physicians; Amer. Soc. of Psychoanalytic [16354]
Physicians Assoc. for AIDS Care [★16265]
Physicians Assoc. for AIDS Care [★16265]
Physicians' Assn. for Anthroposophic Medicine [13700], 1923 Geddes Ave., Ann Arbor, MI 48104-1797, (734)930-9462
Physicians Assn. of Uzbekistan [IO], Tashkent, Uzbekistan
Physicians for Choice - Defunct.
Physicians Coalition for Injectable Safety [14181], Amer. Soc. for Aesthetic Plastic Surgery, 11262 Monarch St., Garden Grove, CA 92841, (888)272-7711
Physicians Comm. for Responsible Medicine [14736], 5100 Wisconsin Ave. NW, Ste. 400, Washington, DC 20016, (202)686-2210
Physicians and Dentists; Union of Amer. [23216]
Physicians for Global Survival [IO], Ottawa, ON, Canada
Physicians for Human Rights [17860], 2 Arrow St., Ste. 301, Cambridge, MA 02138, (617)301-4200
Physicians for Human Rights [17860], 2 Arrow St., Ste. 301, Cambridge, MA 02138, (617)301-4200
Physicians for Human Rights - Israel [IO], Tel Aviv, Israel
Physicians for a Natl. Hea. Prog. [18347], 29 E Madison St., Ste. 602, Chicago, IL 60602, (312)782-6006
Physicians for Peace [15312], 229 W Bute St., Ste. 200, Norfolk, VA 23510, (757)625-7569
Physicians for Peace [15312], 229 W Bute St., Ste. 200, Norfolk, VA 23510, (757)625-7569
Physicians for Reproductive Choice and Hea. [16592], 55 W 39th St., Ste. 1001, New York, NY 10018-3889, (646)366-1890
Physicians for Social Responsibility [18216], 1875 Connecticut Ave. NW, Ste. 1012, Washington, DC 20009, (202)667-4260
Physicians for Social Responsibility [18216], 1875 Connecticut Ave. NW, Ste. 1012, Washington, DC 20009, (202)667-4260
Physicians for Social Responsibility - Finland [IO], Helsinki, Finland

Reference to "IO" in place of a book number signifies that the association may be found in the 50th edition of International Organizations.

Physicians; Soc. of Air Force [15511]
Physicians and Surgeons of the U.S.A; Royal Coll. of [16933]
Physicians; Uniformed Services Acad. of Family [15515]
Physicians Who Care - Defunct.

Physics

Amer. Assn. of Physicists in Medicine [16275]
Amer. Assn. of Physicists in Medicine [16275]
Amer. Assn. of Physics Teachers [8725]
Amer. Bd. of Hea. Physics [16276]
Amer. Center for Physics [7262]
Amer. Inst. of Physics [7263]
Amer. Physical Soc. [7264]
Amer. Physical Soc. [7264]
Australasian Coll. of Physical Scientists and Engineers in Medicine [1210]
Combustion Inst. [7265]
Ethiopian Geophysical Union Intl. [6920]
Hea. Physics Soc. [16277]
Inst. of Physics [7266]PhysicsIntl. Assn. of Physics Students
Intl. Org. of Chinese Physicist and Astronomers [7267]
JILA [7268]
Natl. Soc. of Black Physicists [7269]
Natl. Soc. of Hispanic Physicists [7270]
Neutron Scattering Soc. of Am. [7271]
Sci. Comm. on Solar Terrestrial Physics [7272]
Sci. Comm. on Solar Terrestrial Physics [7272]
Sigma Pi Sigma [23621]
Soc. of Physics Students [7273]
Physics Teacher Educ. Coalition [8960], Amer. Physical Soc., 1 Physics Ellipse, College Park, MD 20740, (301)209-3251
Physiological and Pharmacological Soc. - Belgium [IO], Gent, Belgium
Physiological Soc. - Ghana [IO], Accra, Ghana
Physiological Soc. - Hungary [IO], Debrecen, Hungary
Physiological Soc. - Italy [IO], Genoa, Italy
Physiological Soc. - Japan [IO], Tokyo, Japan
Physiological Soc. - Latvia [IO], Riga, Latvia
Physiological Soc. - Lithuania [IO], Kaunas, Lithuania
Physiological Soc. - Netherlands [IO], Maastricht, Netherlands
Physiological Soc. - New Zealand [IO], Otago, New Zealand
Physiological Soc. - Poland [IO], Krakow, Poland
Physiological Soc. - Romania [IO], Cluj-Napoca, Romania
Physiological Soc. - Spain [IO], Caceres, Spain
Physiological Soc. - Thailand [IO], Bangkok, Thailand
Physiological Soc. - Turkey [IO], Konya, Turkey
Physiological Soc. - UK [IO], London, United Kingdom
Physiological Soc. - Ukraine [IO], Kiev, Ukraine

Physiology

Amer. Physiological Soc. [7274]
Amer. Soc. of Exercise Physiologists [16278]PhysiologyCanadian Alliance of Physiotherapy Regulators
Scandinavian Physiological Soc. [2006]
Soc. of Gen. Physiologists [7275]
Physiology Soc. - the Philippines [IO], Quezon City, Philippines
Physiology Soc. - Southern Africa [IO], Stellenbosch, Republic of South Africa
Physiology Soc. - Sri Lanka [IO], Nugegoda, Sri Lanka
Physiotherapeuten Verband Furstentum Liechtenstein [IO], Schaan, Liechtenstein
Physiotherapy Assn. of Malawi [IO], Lilongwe, Malawi
Physiotherapy Assn. of Trinidad and Tobago [IO], San Fernando, Trinidad and Tobago
Physiotherapy and Rehabilitation Support for Afghanistan [IO], Kabul, Afghanistan
Phytochemical Soc. of Europe [IO], London, United Kingdom
Phytochemical Soc. of Europe - United Kingdom [IO], London, United Kingdom
Phytopathological Soc. of Japan [IO], Tokyo, Japan

Pi Alpha Alpha [23627], NASPAA, 1029 Vermont Ave. NW, Ste. 1100, Washington, DC 20005, (202)628-8965
Pi Beta Phi [23686], 1154 Town and Country Commons Dr., Town and Country, MO 63017-8200, (636)256-0680
Pi Delta Phi [23544], Idaho State Univ., Dept. of Foreign Languages, Box 8350, Pocatello, ID 83209, (208)282-3740
Pi Delta Psi Fraternity [23687], PO Box 520269, Flushing, NY 11352-0269
Pi Gamma Mu [23709], 1001 Millington St., Ste. B, Winfield, KS 67156, (620)221-3128
Pi Gamma Mu [23709], 1001 Millington St., Ste. B, Winfield, KS 67156, (620)221-3128
Pi Kappa Alpha [23688], 8347 W Range Cove, Memphis, TN 38125, (901)748-1868
Pi Kappa Phi [23689], PO Box 240526, Charlotte, NC 28224, (704)504-0888
Pi Kappa Sigma [★23732]
Pi Lambda Phi Fraternity [23690], 60 Newtown Rd., No. 118, Danbury, CT 06810, (203)740-1044
Pi Lambda Theta [23515], 408 N Union St., PO Box 7888, Bloomington, IN 47407-7888, (812)339-1156
Pi Mu Epsilon [23589], Hendrix Coll., Dept. of Mathematics and Cmpt. Sci., Conway, AR 72032, (501)450-1253
Pi Omega Pi [23488], Box 9730, Mississippi State, MS 39762, (662)325-7528
Pi Sigma Alpha [23622], 1527 New Hampshire Ave. NW, Washington, DC 20036-1203, (202)483-2512
Pi Sigma Alpha, the Natl. Political Sci. Honor Soc. [★23622]
Pi Sigma Epsilon [23586], 3747 S Howell Ave., Milwaukee, WI 53207-3870, (414)328-1952
Pi Tau Sigma [23522], Univ. of Connecticut, Dean of the School of Engg., 338 Caslte Hall, 261 Glenbrook Rd., Unit 2237, Storrs, CT 06269, (860)486-6218
Pi Tau Sigma [23522], Univ. of Connecticut, Dean of the School of Engg., 338 Caslte Hall, 261 Glenbrook Rd., Unit 2237, Storrs, CT 06269, (860)486-6218
PIA Natl. [★2012]
Piaget Soc.: Soc. for the Stud. of Knowledge and Development; Jean [16407]
Piano Mfrs. Assn. Intl. [2570], 14070 Proton Rd., Ste. 100, LB9, Dallas, TX 75244, (972)233-9107
Piano Mfrs. Assn. Intl. [2570], 14070 Proton Rd., Ste. 100, LB9, Dallas, TX 75244, (972)233-9107
Piano Technicians Guild [2571], 4444 Forest Ave., Kansas City, KS 66106, (913)432-9975
Pianoforte Tuners' Assn. [IO], Lightwater, United Kingdom
Pickard Collectors Club [21399], PO Box 317, Glencoe, IL 60022
Pickle Packers Intl. [1425], 1620 I St. NW, Ste. 925, Washington, DC 20006, (202)331-2456
Pickle Packers Intl. [1425], 1620 I St. NW, Ste. 925, Washington, DC 20006, (202)331-2456
Picon [IO], Hitchin, United Kingdom
Pictorial Photographers of Am. [10443], Jack Levy, Treas., 300 E 74th St., Apt. 35G, New York, NY 10021-3746, (212)243-0273
Picture Agency Coun. of Am. [★2729]
Picture Archv. Coun. of Am. [2729], 23046 Avenida de la Carlota, Ste. 600, Laguna Hills, CA 92653-1537, (714)815-8427
Picture the Homeless [17792], 2427 Morris Ave., 2nd Fl., Bronx, NY 10468, (646)314-6423
Piedmontese Assn. of the U.S. [3936], 343 Barrett Rd. 1, Elsberry, MO 63343-4137, (573)384-5685
Pierce-Arrow Soc. [21149], Chris Diekman, Membership Chm., PO Box 2636, Cedar Rapids, IA 52406-2636
Pierce Butler, Jr. Found. for Educ. in World Law [★18812]
Pierre Chastain Family Assn. [20571], Mary Chastain Kitchings, Membership Chair, 1649 Rocky Top Dr. SW, Lilburn, GA 30047-2593
Pierre Fauchard Acad. [14309], PO Box 3718, Mesquite, NV 89024-3718, (702)345-2950
Pierre Robin Network [14620], 3604 Biscayne St., Quincy, IL 62305
The Pig Preserve Assn. [11025], Richard Hoyle, Sec., PO Box 555, Jamestown, TN 38556, (504)272-3958

Pigeons

Amer. Racing Pigeon Union [22096]
Intl. Fed. of Amer. Homing Pigeon Fanciers [22097]
Intl. Fed. of Amer. Homing Pigeon Fanciers [22097]
Intl. Modena Club [22098]
Pigging Products and Services Assn. [IO], Kesgrave, United Kingdom
PIJAC Canada [IO], Ottawa, ON, Canada
Pilates Method Alliance [16232], PO Box 370906, Miami, FL 33137, (305)573-4946
Pilatus Owners and Pilots Assn. [153], 6890 E Sunrise Dr., Ste. 120-114, Tucson, AZ 85702, (520)299-7485
Pile Driving Contractors Assn. [945], PO Box 66208, Orange Park, FL 32065, (904)215-4771
Pilgrim Africa [12878], 4000 Aurora Ave. N, Ste. 111, Seattle, WA 98103-7853, (206)706-0350
Pilgrim Africa [12878], 4000 Aurora Ave. N, Ste. 111, Seattle, WA 98103-7853, (206)706-0350
Pilgrim Edward Doty Soc. [20406], Mary Lee Merrill, Membership Chair, PO Box 45, Warren, ME 04864
Pilgrim Soc. [20747], Pilgrim Hall Museum, 75 Court St., Plymouth, MA 02360, (508)746-1620

Pilgrims

Gen. Soc. of Mayflower Descendants [20746]
Gen. Soc. of Mayflower Descendants [20746]
Pilgrim Soc. [20747]
Pilipinas Aikido Propagation Assn. [IO], Quezon City, Philippines
Pillar Nonprofit Network [IO], London, ON, Canada
Pills Anonymous [13283], 2740 Grant St., Concord, CA 94520
Pilot Class 43-D Assn. - Defunct.
Pilot Dogs [17111], 625 W Town St., Columbus, OH 43215, (614)221-6367
Pilot Intl. and Pilot Intl. Found. [13072], 102 Preston Ct., Macon, GA 31210, (478)477-1208
Pilot Intl. and Pilot Intl. Found. [13072], 102 Preston Ct., Macon, GA 31210, (478)477-1208
Pilot Parents of Southern Arizona [12512], 2600 N Wyatt Dr., Tucson, AZ 85712, (520)324-3150
Pilots' Assn; Cherokee [20887]
Pilots for Christ Intl. [19768], 890 22 Mile Rd., Sand Lake, MI 49343-9503, (616)884-6241
Pilots for Christ Intl. [19768], 890 22 Mile Rd., Sand Lake, MI 49343-9503, (616)884-6241
Pinball Owner's Assn. [IO], Kent, United Kingdom
Pine Chemicals Assn. [762], 3350 Riverwood Pkwy. SE, Ste. 1900, Atlanta, GA 30339, (770)984-5340
Pine Creek Railroad [22127], New Jersey Museum of Trans., PO Box 622, Farmingdale, NJ 07727-0622, (732)938-5524
Pink Door Nonprofit Org. [13968], PO Box 6990, Houston, TX 77265-6990, (713)899-1245
Pink Isn't Always Pretty [13969], 9642 Anderson Way, Converse, TX 78109, (877)495-PIAP
Pintaurakoitsijat ry [★IO]
Pinto Horse Assn. of Am. [4638], 7330 NW 23rd St., Bethany, OK 73008, (405)491-0111
Pioneer Clubs [20307], PO Box 788, Wheaton, IL 60189-0788, (630)293-1600
Pioneer Girls [★20307]
Pioneer Girls, Pioneer Boys [★20307]
Pioneer Total Abstinence Assn. [IO], Dublin, Ireland
Pioneer Women/Na'amat, the Women's Labor Zionist Org. of Am. [★19884]
Pioneer Women, The Women's Labor Zionist Org. of Am. [★19884]
Pioneers [12054], 930 15th St., 12th Fl., Denver, CO 80202, (303)571-1200

Pioneers

Intl. Soc. Daughters of Utah Pioneers [20748]
Intl. Soc. Daughters of Utah Pioneers [20748]
Natl. Soc. of the Sons of Utah Pioneers [20749]
Soc. of California Pioneers [20750]
Soc. of Indiana Pioneers [20751]
Sons and Daughters of Oregon Pioneers [20752]
Sons and Daughters of Pioneer Rivermen [20753]
Pionus Breeders Assn. [21228], PO Box 150, Pilot Hill, CA 95664, (530)885-7868
Pionus Breeders Assn. [21228], PO Box 150, Pilot Hill, CA 95664, (530)885-7868
Pipe Fabrication Inst. [2754], 511 Avenue of the Americas, No. 601, New York, NY 10011, (514)634-3434

A star before a book entry number signifies that the name is not listed separately, but is mentioned within the entry.

Pipe Jacking Assn. [IO], London, United Kingdom

Pipe Line Contractors Assn. [2668], 1700 Pacific Ave., Ste. 4100, Dallas, TX 75201-4675, (214)969-2700

Pipe Smoking

Intl. Assn. of Pipe Smokers Clubs [22099]

Intl. Assn. of Pipe Smokers Clubs [22099]

Pipeline Assn. for Public Awareness [2755], 16361 Table Mountain Pkwy., Golden, CO 80403

Pipeline Indus. Guild [IO], London, United Kingdom

Piper Owner Soc. [20912], N7450 Aanstad Rd., Iola, WI 54945, (715)445-5000

Pipes

Amer. Concrete Pipe Assn. [2744]

Amer. Concrete Pressure Pipe Assn. [2745]

Canadian Concrete Pipe Assn. [14484]

Cast Iron Soil Pipe Inst. [2746]

Concrete Pipeline Systems Assn. [5775]

Ductile Iron Pipe Res. Assn. [2747]

Expansion Joint Mfrs. Assn. [2748]

Intervention and Coiled Tubing Assn. [7276]

Natl. Assn. of Pipe Fabricators [2749]

Natl. Assn. of Steel Pipe Distributors [2750]

Natl. Certified Pipe Welding Bur. [2751]

Natl. Clay Pipe Inst. [2752]

Natl. Corrugated Steel Pipe Assn. [2753]

Pipe Fabrication Inst. [2754]

Pipeline Assn. for Public Awareness [2755]

Plastic Pipe and Fittings Assn. [2756]

Plastics Pipe Inst. [2757]

Pressure Vessel Res. Coun. [2758]

Tube and Pipe Assn., Intl. [2759]

Tube and Pipe Assn., Intl. [2759]

Uni-Bell PVC Pipe Assn. [2760]

Uni-Bell PVC Pipe Assn. [2760]

United Assn. of Journeymen and Apprentices of the Plumbing, Pipe Fitting, Sprinkler Fitting Indus. of the U.S. and Canada [23277]

PIRA Intl. [IO], Leatherhead, United Kingdom

Pirandello Soc. of Am. [9407], CNL Anne and Henry Paolucci Intl. Conf. Center, 68-02 Metropolitan Ave., Middle Village, NY 11379, (718)821-3916

Pitch-In Canada [IO], White Rock, BC, Canada

Pitch and Putt Union of Ireland [IO], Dublin, Ireland

Pitless Adapter Division of Water Systems Coun. [★3653]

Pittsburgh Hornets Booster Club [★23910]

Pittsburgh Penguins Booster Club [23910], PO Box 903, Pittsburgh, PA 15230

Pittsburgh Transplant Found. [★16905]

Pituitary

Human Growth Found. [16279]

Natl. Hormone and Pituitary Prog. [16280]

Pituitary Network Assn. [16281]

Pituitary Found. [IO], Bristol, United Kingdom

Pituitary Network Assn. [16281], PO Box 1958, Thousand Oaks, CA 91358, (805)499-9973

Pituitary Tumor Network Assn. [★16281]

Pius X Secular Inst. [19485], 27 Cove St., Manchester, NH 03104, (603)622-4849

Pius X Secular Inst. [19485], 27 Cove St., Manchester, NH 03104, (603)622-4849

Pizza, Pasta and Italian Food Assn. [IO], Chepstow, United Kingdom

PKF North Amer. Network [51], 1745 N Brown Rd., Ste. 350, Lawrenceville, GA 30043, (770)279-4560

PKF North Amer. Network [51], 1745 N Brown Rd., Ste. 350, Lawrenceville, GA 30043, (770)279-4560

PKS Kids [14621], PO Box 94, Florissant, MO 63032-0094

Placement

Amer. Assn. for Employment in Educ. [8726]

Natl. Assn. of Colleges and Employers [8727]

Natl. Student Employment Assn. [8728]

Plaid Cymru - The Party of Wales [IO], Cardiff, United Kingdom

Plain Talk - Defunct.

Plains Cotton Growers [3960], 4517 W Loop 289, Lubbock, TX 79414, (806)792-4904

Plaintiff Employment Lawyers Assn. [★5273]

Plan of Action for Challenging Times [8085], 635 Divisadero St., San Francisco, CA 94117, (415)922-2550

Plan Cambodia [IO], Phnom Penh, Cambodia

Plan Canada [IO], Toronto, ON, Canada

Plan Intl. [IO], Woking, United Kingdom

Plan Intl. Deutschland e.V. [★IO]

PLAN Intl. - U.S.A. [★11496]

PLAN Intl. - U.S.A. [★11496]

Plan Japan [IO], Tokyo, Japan

Plan Netherlands [IO], Amsterdam, Netherlands

Plan Pakistan [IO], Islamabad, Pakistan

Plan - United Kingdom [IO], London, United Kingdom

Plan U.S.A. [11496], 155 Plan Way, Warwick, RI 02886, (401)738-5600

Plan U.S.A. [11496], 155 Plan Way, Warwick, RI 02886, (401)738-5600

Planet 21 [IO], Bern, Switzerland

Planet Aid [13163], 1 Cross St., Holliston, MA 01746, (508)893-0644

Planet Aid [13163], 1 Cross St., Holliston, MA 01746, (508)893-0644

Planet Ark [IO], Sydney, Australia

Planet Club [IO], Budapest, Hungary

Planet Drum Found. [17196], PO Box 31251, San Francisco, CA 94131, (415)285-6556

Planet Drum Found. [17196], PO Box 31251, San Francisco, CA 94131, (415)285-6556

PlaNet Finance US [17920], 195 Broadway, 12th Fl., New York, NY 10007, (646)587-5018

Planeta Sustenable [IO], Mexico City, Mexico

Planetarium Soc; Middle Atlantic [8841]

Planetary Assn. for Clean Energy [IO], Ottawa, ON, Canada

Planetary Citizens [18816], PO Box 1056, Mount Shasta, CA 96067, (530)926-6424

Planetary Citizens [18816], PO Box 1056, Mount Shasta, CA 96067, (530)926-6424

Planetary Gemologists Assn. [IO], Bangkok, Thailand

Planetary Soc. [6094], 85 S Grand Ave., Pasadena, CA 91106-2301, (626)793-5100

Planetary Soc. [6094], 85 S Grand Ave., Pasadena, CA 91106-2301, (626)793-5100

PlanetMUG - Address unknown since 2010.

PlanetQuest [6235], PO Box 211, Sausalito, CA 94966

PlanetRead [8537], 26 Manor Dr., Piedmont, CA 94611, (510)435-3175

PlanetRead [8537], 26 Manor Dr., Piedmont, CA 94611, (510)435-3175

Planetree [14737], 130 Div. St., Derby, CT 06418, (203)732-1365

Planetwork [4214], 1230 Market St., No. 517, San Francisco, CA 94102, (415)721-1591

Planned Parenthood [★12040]

Planned Parenthood Assn. of Sierra Leone [IO], Freetown, Sierra Leone

Planned Parenthood Assn. of Thailand [IO], Bangkok, Thailand

Planned Parenthood Edmonton [IO], Edmonton, AB, Canada

Planned Parenthood Fed. of Am. [12040], 434 W 33rd St., New York, NY 10001, (212)541-7800

Planned Parenthood Fed. of Nigeria [IO], Abuja, Nigeria

Planned Parenthood/World Population [★12040]

Planners Network [18487], Cornell Univ., 106 W Sibley Hall, Ithaca, NY 14853, (607)254-8890

Planning

Assn. of Divorce Financial Planners [1335]

Assn. for Institutional Res. [8729]

Assn. for Strategic Planning [2761]

Building Commissioning Assn. [538]

Bus. Retention and Expansion Intl. [1055]PlanningEuropean Coun. of Spatial Planners

Fusion Architecture [6197]

Green Home Coun. [567]

Intl. Assn. for China Planning [18315]

Intl. Soc. for Educational Planning [8730]

Intl. Soc. for Educational Planning [8730]

Ministry Architecture [6200]

Natl. Assn. of County Planners [5329]

Natl. Assn. of Financial and Estate Planning [1316]

Natl. Assn. of Planning Councils [18316]

Public Architecture [243]

Soc. for Coll. and Univ. Planning [8731]

Soc. of Iranian Architects and Planners [6206]

State Higher Educ. Executive Officers [8732]

Urbanists Intl. [6207]

Wedding Indus. Professionals Assn. [475]

Planning Assistance - Address unknown since 2010.

Planning and Development Collaborative Intl.

Planning and Development Collaborative Intl. - Address unknown since 2011.

Planning Inst. Australia [IO], Kingston, Australia

Planning and Mgt. Assistance Proj. of the Center for Community Change [★12596]

Planning and Visual Educ. Partnership [3123], 4651 Sheridan St., Ste. 470, Hollywood, FL 33021, (954)893-7225

Plant Conservation Action Gp. [IO], Victoria, Seychelles

Plant Engg. and Maintenance Assn. of Canada [IO], Mississauga, ON, Canada

Plant Growth Regulation Soc. of Am. [6365], 1018 Duke St., Alexandria, VA 22314, (703)836-4606

Plant Growth Regulator Soc. of Am. [★6365]

Plant Growth Regulator Working Group [★6365]

Plant Molecular Biology Assn. [★6384]

Plant Sci. Seminar [★16182]

Plant Sci. Seminar [★16182]

Plant Yng Nghymru [★IO]

Planters' Labor and Supply Company [★4936]

Planting Empowerment [4410], 1348 Euclid St. NW, No. 305, Washington, DC 20009, (202)470-2432

Planting Empowerment [4410], 1348 Euclid St. NW, No. 305, Washington, DC 20009, (202)470-2432

Planting Hope [11622], PO Box 56, Montpelier, VT 05601, (802)229-4145

Plantio La Orquidea [IO], Caracas, Venezuela

Plasma Protein Therapeutics Assn. [13852], 147 Old Solomons Island Rd., Ste. 100, Annapolis, MD 21401, (202)789-3100

Plaster

Natl. Plasterers Coun. [2762]

Plastic Bag Assn. [★878]

Plastic Coatings and Film Assn. [★2766]

Plastic Coatings and Film Assn. [★2766]

Plastic Container Mfrs. Inst. - Defunct.

Plastic Loose Fill Coun. [4778], 1298 Cronson Blvd., Ste. 201, Crofton, MD 21114, (510)654-0756

Plastic Lumber Trade Assn. [2773], PO Box 211, Worthington, MN 56187, (507)372-5558

Plastic Optical Fiber Trade Org. [2594], 1340 Soldiers Field Rd., Ste. 2, Brighton, MA 02135, (617)782-5033

Plastic Pipe and Fittings Assn. [2756], Bldg. C, Ste. 312, 800 Roosevelt Rd., Glen Ellyn, IL 60137, (630)858-6540

Plastic Pollution Coalition [4799], 2150 Allston Way, Ste. 460, Berkeley, CA 94704, (510)394-5772

Plastic Shipping Container Inst. [886], 1701 Pennsylvania Ave. NW, Ste. 300, Washington, DC 20006, (202)253-4347

Plastic Surgery Administrative Assn. [14182], 6324 Fairview Ave. N, Crystal, MN 55428, (800)373-0302

Plastic Surgery Educational Found. [★14183]

Plastic Surgery Found. [14183], Michael D. Costello, Exec. VP, 444 E Algonquin Rd., Arlington Heights, IL 60005, (847)228-9900

Plastic Surgery Res. Coun. [14184], 45 Lyme Rd., Ste. 304, Hanover, NH 03755, (603)643-2325

Plastic Surgery Res. Coun. [14184], 45 Lyme Rd., Ste. 304, Hanover, NH 03755, (603)643-2325

Plastica Infantil con Excelencia en el Logro [IO], Buenos Aires, Argentina

Plastics

Assn. of Postconsumer Plastic Recyclers [2763]

Assn. of Rotational Molders Intl. [2764]

Assn. of Rotational Molders Intl. [2764]

Center for the Polyurethanes Indus. [2765]

Chem. Fabrics and Film Assn. [2766]

Chem. Fabrics and Film Assn. [2766]

Dual Laminate Fabrication Assn. [2767]

EPS Molders Assn. [2768]

European Comm. of Machinery Mfrs. for the Plastics and Rubber Indus. [23885]

European Coun. for Plasticisers and Intermediates [21034]

Intl. Assn. of Plastics Distribution [2769]

Intl. Assn. of Plastics Distribution [2769]

Reference to "IO" in place of a book number signifies that the association may be found in the 50th edition of International Organizations.

Encyclopedia of Associations, 51st Edition

3099

Intl. Assn. of Used Equip. Dealers [2770]
Intl. Assn. of Used Equip. Dealers [2770]
Intl. Card Mfrs. Assn. [2771]
Intl. Card Mfrs. Assn. [2771]
PET Resin Assn. [2772]
PET Resin Assn. [2772]
Plastic Loose Fill Coun. [4778]
Plastic Lumber Trade Assn. [2773]
Plastic Pollution Coalition [4799]
Plastics Division of the Amer. Plastics Coun.
  [2774]
Plastics Fed. of South Africa [16628]
Plastics Inst. of Am. [7277]PlasticsPlasticsEurope
Plasticville Collectors Assn. [22100]
Polyurethane Foam Assn. [2775]
Polyurethane Mfrs. Assn. [2776]
Soc. of Plastics Engineers [7278]
Soc. of Plastics Engineers [7278]
Soc. of the Plastics Indus. [2777]
Plastics and Chemicals Indus. Assn. [IO], Abbots-
ford, Australia
Plastics Division of the Amer. Plastics Coun. [2774],
700 2nd St. NE, Washington, DC 20002, (202)249-
6623
Plastics Education Found. - Defunct.
Plastics Export Promotion Coun. [IO], Mumbai, India
Plastics Fed. [IO], Paris, France
Plastics Fed. of South Africa [IO], Halfway House,
Republic of South Africa
Plastics Historical Soc. [IO], Burghclere, United
Kingdom
Plastics Injection Moulders Assn. [IO], Sydney,
Australia
Plastics Inst. of Am. [7277], 1 Univ. Ave., Lowell, MA
01854, (978)934-2575
Plastics Pipe Inst. [2757], 105 Decker Ct., Ste. 825,
Irving, TX 75062, (469)499-1044
Plastics Window Fed. [IO], Luton, United Kingdom
PlasticsEurope [IO], Brussels, Belgium
Plasticville Collectors Assn. [22100], 601 SE Second
St., Ankeny, IA 50021-3207
Plastindustrien i Danmark [★IO]
Plate, Cup, Container and Doily Inst. [★1041]
Plate, Cup and Container Inst. [★1041]
Platelet Disorder Support Assn. [13810], 133 Rollins
Ave., Potomac, MD 20859, (301)770-6636
Platemakers Educational and Res. Inst. [★6934]
Platemakers Educational and Res. Inst. [★6934]
Platslageriernas Riksforbund [★IO]
Platt Family Assn. [20572], 4081 Greystone Dr., Har-
risburg, PA 17112
Plattelands Jongeren Nederland [IO], Utrecht,
Netherlands
Play
  The Assn. for the Stud. of Play [10445]
  Collegiate Assn. of Table Top Gamers [21745]
  Intl. Play Equip. Mfrs. Assn. [2778]
  Intl. Play Equip. Mfrs. Assn. [2778]
  KaBOOM! [12695]
  Playworks [12696]
Play for Peace [12633], 500 N Michigan Ave., Ste.
300, Chicago, IL 60611, (312)675-8568
Play for Peace [12633], 500 N Michigan Ave., Ste.
300, Chicago, IL 60611, (312)675-8568
Play Soccer [10826], PO Box 106, Princeton, NJ
08542-0106, (609)683-4941
Play Therapy Intl. [IO], Uckfield, United Kingdom
Player Piano Gp. [IO], Essex, United Kingdom
The Players [10598], 16 Gramercy Park S, New
York, NY 10003, (212)475-6116
Playground Safety; Natl. Prog. for [18578]
Playing for Keeps [11166], Assn. of Children's
Museums, 2711 Jefferson Davis Hwy., Ste. 600,
Arlington, VA 22202, (703)224-3100
PLAYLINK [IO], London, United Kingdom
Playworks [12696], 380 Washington St., Oakland,
CA 94607, (510)893-4180
Playwrights Guild of Canada [IO], Toronto, ON,
Canada
Pleiades Found. for Peace and Space Education -
Defunct.
Plenty [★12879]
Plenty [★12879]
Plenty Canada [IO], Lanark, ON, Canada
Plenty Intl. [12879], PO Box 394, Summertown, TN
38483, (931)964-4323

Plenty Intl. [12879], PO Box 394, Summertown, TN
38483, (931)964-4323
Plenty - U.S.A. [★12879]
Plenty - U.S.A. [★12879]
Plesna Zveza Slovenije [★IO]
Plesni Sporstki Savez Bosne I Hercegovine [★IO]
Plowshares Inst. [18281], PO Box 243, Simsbury,
CT 06070-0243, (860)651-4304
Plug In Am. [6118], 2370 Market St., No. 419, San
Francisco, CA 94114, (415)323-3329
Plumbers' Company [IO], London, United Kingdom
Plumbing
  Amer. Supply Assn. [2779]
  Bath Enclosure Mfrs. Assn. [2780]
  Bathroom Mfrs. Assn. [8558]
  Decorative Plumbing and Hardware Assn. [2781]
  North Central Wholesalers Assn. [2782]
  Plumbing and Drainage Inst. [2783]
  Plumbing Mfrs. Inst. [2784]
  Plumbing Mfrs. Inst. [2784]
  United Assn. of Journeymen and Apprentices of
    the Plumbing, Pipe Fitting, Sprinkler Fitting
    Indus. of the U.S. and Canada [23277]
  Wholesale Distributors Assn. [2785]
Plumbing Brass Inst. [★2784]
Plumbing Brass Inst. [★2784]
Plumbing Distributors Assn. of New Zealand [IO],
Auckland, New Zealand
Plumbing and Drainage Inst. [2783], 800 Turnpike
St., Ste. 300, North Andover, MA 01845, (978)557-
0720
Plumbing and Drainage Mfrs. Assn. [★2783]
Plumbing, Heating-Cooling Contractors Assn. [946],
PO Box 6808, Falls Church, VA 22046, (703)237-
8100
Plumbing, Heating and Cooling Information Bur. -
Defunct.
Plumbing Mfrs. Inst. [2784], 1921 Rohlwing Rd., Unit
G, Rolling Meadows, IL 60008, (847)481-5500
Plumbing Mfrs. Inst. [2784], 1921 Rohlwing Rd., Unit
G, Rolling Meadows, IL 60008, (847)481-5500
Plumeria Soc. of Am. [21817], PO Box 22791,
Houston, TX 77227-2791, (713)946-9175
Plunkett Found. [IO], Oxford, United Kingdom
Plymouth Barracuda/Cuda Owners Club [21150],
Ann M. Curman, Sec., 36 Woodland Rd., East
Greenwich, RI 02818-3430, (401)884-4449
Plymouth Four Cylinder Owners Club [★21151]
Plymouth Four and Six Cylinder Owners Club
[★21151]
Plymouth Owners Club [21151], PO Box 416,
Cavalier, ND 58220-0416, (701)549-3746
Plymouth Rock Fanciers Club [4812], Robert Blosl,
Sec.-Treas., 14390 S Blvd., Silverhill, AL 36576
Plymouth Rock Found. [8058], 1120 Long Pond Rd.,
Plymouth, MA 02360, (800)210-1620
Plywood Res. Found. [★1506]
PM - Greece [IO], Athens, Greece
PMA - Independent Book Publishers Assn. [★2937]
PMA - The Worldwide Community of Imaging As-
sociations [2730], 3000 Picture Pl., Jackson, MI
49201-8853, (517)788-8100
PMA - The Worldwide Community of Imaging As-
sociations [2730], 3000 Picture Pl., Jackson, MI
49201-8853, (517)788-8100
PMC Sect. of the Sci. Apparatus Makers Assn.
[★3177]
PMCA: An Intl. Assn. of Confectioners [1426], 2980
Linden St., Ste. E3, Bethlehem, PA 18017,
(610)625-4655
PMCA: An Intl. Assn. of Confectioners [1426], 2980
Linden St., Ste. E3, Bethlehem, PA 18017,
(610)625-4655
P.N. Elrod Fan Club [9408], PO Box 60391, Fort
Worth, TX 76115
P.N. Elrod Fan Club [9408], PO Box 60391, Fort
Worth, TX 76115
PNG-Australia Alumni Assn. [IO], Port Moresby,
Papua New Guinea
Poale Zion - United Labor Zionist Org. of Am.
[★19086]
Pocket Testament League [19352], PO Box 800,
Lititz, PA 17543-7026, (800)636-8785
Pocket Testament League [19352], PO Box 800,
Lititz, PA 17543-7026, (800)636-8785

Pocketful of Joy [11391], 24 Goose Ln., Tolland, CT
06084
POD Network [★8244]
POD Network [★8244]
Podiatric Sports Medicine; Amer. Acad. of [16710]
Podiatry
  Acad. of Ambulatory Foot and Ankle Surgery
    [16282]
  Acad. of Ambulatory Foot and Ankle Surgery
    [16282]
  Amer. Acad. of Podiatric Practice Mgt. [16283]
  Amer. Assn. of Colleges of Podiatric Medicine
    [16284]
  Amer. Assn. of Hosp. and Healthcare Podiatrists
    [16285]
  Amer. Assn. for Women Podiatrists [16286]
  Amer. Bd. of Lower Extremity Surgery [16287]
  Amer. Bd. of Multiple Specialties in Podiatry
    [16288]
  Amer. Bd. of Podiatric Orthopedics and Primary
    Podiatric Medicine [16289]
  Amer. Bd. of Podiatric Surgery [16290]
  Amer. Coll. of Foot and Ankle Orthopedics and
    Medicine [16291]
  Amer. Coll. of Foot and Ankle Surgeons [16292]
  Amer. Podiatric Medical Assn. [16293]
  Amer. Podiatric Medical Students' Assn. [16294]
  Amer. Soc. of Forensic Podiatry [14545]
  Amer. Soc. of Podiatric Medical Assistants
    [16295]
  Coun. on Podiatric Medical Educ. [16296]
  Fed. of Podiatric Medical Boards [16297]
  Intl. Fed. of Foot and Ankle Societies [16298]
  Intl. Fed. of Foot and Ankle Societies [16298]
  Natl. Bd. of Podiatric Medical Examiners [16299]
  Natl. Podiatric Medical Assn. [16300]
PODS Assn. [3343], PO Box 1726, Sand Springs,
OK 74063, (918)246-9343
Poe Found. [9409], Poe Museum, 1914-16 E Main
St., Richmond, VA 23223, (804)648-5523
The Poe Shrine [★9409]
Poe Soc. of Baltimore; Edgar Allan [9361]
Poe Stud. Assn. [9410], Ohio Univ., Dept. of English,
360 Ellis Hall, Athens, OH 45701
Poetic Unity [11623], 491 8th St., Bohemia, NY
11716
Poetics and Linguistics Assn. [IO], Middelburg,
Netherlands
Poetry
  Acad. of Amer. Poets [10446]
  Friends of Robert Frost [10447]
  Haiku Soc. of Am. [10448]
  Intl. Marie de France Soc. [8733]
  Intl. Poetry Forum [10449]
  Intl. Poetry Forum [10449]
  Natl. Fed. of State Poetry Societies [10450]
  Natl. Poetry Found. [10451]
  PEN Center USA [10731]
  Poetry Found. [10452]
  Poetry Found. [10452]
  Poetry Proj. [10453]
  Poetry Soc. of Am. [10454]
  Poets and Writers [10455]
  Tanka Soc. of Am. [10456]
  World Cong. of Poets [10457]
  World Cong. of Poets [10457]
  Yuki Teikei Haiku Soc. [10458]
Poetry Assn; Sci. Fiction [10522]
Poetry Found. [10452], 61 W Superior St., Chicago,
IL 60611-4034, (312)787-7070
Poetry Found. [10452], 61 W Superior St., Chicago,
IL 60611-4034, (312)787-7070
Poetry Ireland [IO], Dublin, Ireland
Poetry Proj. [10453], St. Mark's Church, 131 E 10th
St., New York, NY 10003, (212)674-0910
The Poetry Proj. at St. Mark's Church [★10453]
Poetry Soc. [IO], London, United Kingdom
Poetry Soc. of Am. [10454], 15 Gramercy Park, New
York, NY 10003, (212)254-9628
Poets
  Natl. Fed. of State Poetry Societies [10450]
  PEN Center USA [10731]
  Poetic Unity [11623]
Poets Against the War [10734], Box 1614, Port
Townsend, WA 98368

A star before a book entry number signifies that the name is not listed separately, but is mentioned within the entry.

Poets and Writers [10455], 90 Broad St., Ste. 2100, New York, NY 10004, (212)226-3586

Pogo Fan Club and Walt Kelly Soc. [23794], Spring Hollow Books, 6908 Wentworth Ave., Richfield, MN 55423

Pogranicze Found. [IO], Sejny, Poland

POINT [★20658]

POINT [★20658]

Point Found. [4215], 5757 Wilshire Blvd., Ste. 370, Los Angeles, CA 90036, (323)933-1234

Point-of-Purchase Advt. Inst. [★102]

Point-of-Purchase Advt. Intl. [102], 1600 Duke St., Ste. 610, Alexandria, VA 22314, (703)373-8800

Pointer Club Francais [IO], St. Maurice Sur Fessard, France

POINTers [★20658]

POINTers [★20658]

Poison Control Centers; Amer. Assn. of [16891]

Pokdi Neurofisiologi [★IO]

Poker
 Poker Players Alliance [22101]

Poker Players Alliance [22101], 1325 G St. NW, Ste. 500, Washington, DC 20005, (888)448-4PPA

Poland
 Polish Amer. Golf Assn. [22620]

Poland ACM Chap. [IO], Wroclaw, Poland

Poland China Record Assn. [4956], PO Box 9758, Peoria, IL 61612-9758, (309)691-6301

Poland Sports Medicine Assn. [IO], Warsaw, Poland

Polar Bears Intl. [5111], PO Box 3008, Bozeman, MT 59772

Polar Bears Intl. [5111], PO Box 3008, Bozeman, MT 59772

Polar Libraries Colloquy [10004], Byrd Polar Res. Center Archival Prog., 134 Univ. Archives, 2700 Kenny Rd., Columbus, OH 43210, (614)688-8173

Polar Libraries Colloquy [10004], Byrd Polar Res. Center Archival Prog., 134 Univ. Archives, 2700 Kenny Rd., Columbus, OH 43210, (614)688-8173

Polar Studies
 Amer. Polar Soc. [7279]
 Amer. Polar Soc. [7279]
 Antarctic and Southern Ocean Coalition [7280]
 Antarctic and Southern Ocean Coalition [7280]
 Assn. of Polar Early Career Scientists [7281]
 Intl. Arctic Sci. Comm. [13782]
 Intl. Soc. for a Complete Earth [12217]
 U.S. Antarctic Prog. [7282]

Polaris Intl. North Amer. Network [★51]

Polaris Intl. North Amer. Network [★51]

Polaris Proj. [17861], PO Box 53315, Washington, DC 20009, (202)745-1001

Polarity Therapy Assn; Amer. [13657]

Police
 Intl. Police and Fire Chaplain's Assn. [19522]

Police Assn. for Coll. Educ. [5737], 63 Lake Forest Dr., Mineral, VA 23117, (540)894-8781

Police Associations; Intl. Union of [23242]

Police Car Owners of Am. [21152], 172 County Rd. 136, Eureka Springs, AR 72631-9138, (479)253-2364

Police Executive Res. Forum [5738], 1120 Connecticut Ave. NW, Ste. 930, Washington, DC 20036, (202)466-7820

Police Fed. of England and Wales [IO], Leatherhead, United Kingdom

Police and Fire Professionals of Am; Intl. Union, Security, [23295]

Police and Fire Professionals of Am; Intl. Union, Security, [23295]

Police and Firemen's Insurance Assn. [19055], 101 E 116th St., Carmel, IN 46032, (317)581-1913

Police Found. [5739], 1201 Connecticut Ave. NW, Washington, DC 20036-2636, (202)833-1460

Police History Soc. [IO], Bletchley, United Kingdom

Police Marksman Assn. [5740], 200 Green St., 2nd Fl., San Francisco, CA 94111, (888)765-4231

Police Martial Arts Assn. [IO], Riverview, NB, Canada

Police Officers; Intl. Brotherhood of [23241]

Police Superintendents' Assn. of England and Wales [IO], Pangbourne, United Kingdom

Policy
 Citizens Energy Plan [6704]
 Coalition for a Realistic Foreign Policy [17698]

 Friends of Africa Intl. [17830]
 Global Migration Gp. [5790]
 Iran Policy Comm. [17998]
 MOMSTELL [13265]
 PolicyLink [18317]
 U.S. Off. on Colombia [17956]
 Water Resources Coalition [7615]

Policy Stud. Gp. of the Amer. Political Sci. Assn. [★18488]

Policy Stud. Org. [18488], 1527 New Hampshire Ave. NW, Washington, DC 20036, (202)483-2512

Policy and Taxation Gp. [18687], PO Box 53454, Washington, DC 20009, (714)641-6913

PolicyLink [18317], 1438 Webster St., Ste. 303, Oakland, CA 94612, (510)663-2333

Polio
 Intl. Post Polio Support Org. [16301]
 Intl. Post Polio Support Org. [16301]
 Polio Fellowship of Ireland [14860]

Polio Fellowship of Ireland [IO], Dublin, Ireland

Polio Soc. - Address unknown since 2011.

Polish
 Amer. Coun. for Polish Culture [19186]
 Amer. Inst. of Polish Culture [10459]
 Amer. Inst. of Polish Culture [10459]
 Assn. of the Sons of Poland [19187]
 Jozef Pilsudski Inst. of Am. for Res. in the Modern History of Poland [10460]
 Jozef Pilsudski Inst. of Am. for Res. in the Modern History of Poland [10460]
 Kosciuszko Found. [10461]
 Kosciuszko Found. [10461]
 Legion of Young Polish Women [19188]
 Natl. Medical and Dental Assn. [19189]
 Polish Amer. Cong. [19190]
 Polish Amer. Golf Assn. [22620]
 Polish Amer. Historical Assn. [10462]
 Polish Amer. Historical Assn. [10462]
 Polish-American-Jewish Alliance for Youth Action [13551]
 Polish Arts and Culture Found. [19191]
 Polish Assistance, Inc. [19192]
 Polish Beneficial Assn. [19193]
 Polish Falcons of Am. [19194]
 Polish Inst. of Arts and Sciences of Am. [10463]
 Polish Museum of Am. [10464]
 Polish Natl. Alliance of the U.S. of North Am. [19195]
 Polish Natl. Union of Am. [19196]
 Polish Nobility Assn. Found. [19197]
 Polish Roman Catholic Union of Am. [19198]
 Polish Union of Am. [19199]
 Polish Union of the U.S. of North Am. [19200]
 Polish Women's Alliance of Am. [19201]
 Union of Poles in Am. [19202]

Polish Acad. of Sciences [IO], Warsaw, Poland

Polish Actors Assn. [IO], Warsaw, Poland

Polish Alma Mater of Am. [★19195]

Polish Amer. Chamber of Commerce [23378], 4800 N Milwaukee Ave., Ste. 206, Chicago, IL 60630, (773)205-1998

Polish Amer. Chamber of Commerce [23378], 4800 N Milwaukee Ave., Ste. 206, Chicago, IL 60630, (773)205-1998

Polish Amer. Cong. [19190], 5711 N Milwaukee Ave., Chicago, IL 60646-6215, (773)763-9944

Polish-American Cultural Inst. of Miami [★10459]

Polish-American Cultural Inst. of Miami [★10459]

Polish Amer. Golf Assn. [22620], 616 Manhattan Ave., Brooklyn, NY 11222, (718)389-8536

Polish-Amer. Guardian Soc. - Defunct.

Polish Amer. Historical Assn. [10462], Central Connecticut State Univ., 1615 Stanley St., New Britain, CT 06050, (860)832-3010

Polish Amer. Historical Assn. [10462], Central Connecticut State Univ., 1615 Stanley St., New Britain, CT 06050, (860)832-3010

Polish Amer. Historical Commn. of the Polish Inst. of Arts and Sciences in Am. [★10462]

Polish Amer. Historical Commn. of the Polish Inst. of Arts and Sciences in Am. [★10462]

Polish Amer. Immigration and Relief Comm. - Defunct.

Polish-American-Jewish Alliance for Youth Action [13551], Jay Pollack, Treas., 13B Pipe Hill Ct., Baltimore, MD 21209, (410)486-0698

 Polish-American-Jewish Alliance for Youth Action [13551], Jay Pollack, Treas., 13B Pipe Hill Ct., Baltimore, MD 21209, (410)486-0698

Polish Arts and Culture Found. [19191], 4077 Waterhouse Rd., Oakland, CA 94602, (510)599-2244

Polish Assistance, Inc. [19192], 15 E 65th St., New York, NY 10065-6501, (212)570-5560

Polish Assn. for Amer. Stud. [IO], Lublin, Poland

Polish Assn. of Dermatology [IO], Warsaw, Poland

Polish Assn. for Landscape Ecology [IO], Warsaw, Poland

Polish Assn. for Spina Bifida and Hydrocephalus [IO], Lublin, Poland

Polish Assn. of Tenants [IO], Krakow, Poland

Polish Auto. and Motorcycle Fed. [IO], Warsaw, Poland

Polish Baseball and Softball Fed. [IO], Warsaw, Poland

Polish Beneficial Assn. [19193], 2595 Orthodox St., Philadelphia, PA 19137, (215)535-2626

Polish Canoe Fed. [IO], Warsaw, Poland

Polish Cardiac Soc. [IO], Warsaw, Poland

Polish Chamber of Books [IO], Warsaw, Poland

Polish Chamber of the Chem. Indus. [IO], Warsaw, Poland

Polish Chamber of Commerce [IO], Warsaw, Poland

Polish Chamber of Commerce of Importers, Exporters and Cooperation [IO], Poznan, Poland

Polish Chamber of Exhibition Indus. [IO], Poznan, Poland

Polish Chamber of Pharmaceutical Indus. and Medical Devices [IO], Warsaw, Poland

Polish Chem. Soc. [IO], Warsaw, Poland

Polish Commn. for Electron Microscopy [IO], Krakow, Poland

Polish Composers Union [IO], Warsaw, Poland

Polish Draughts Fed. [IO], Minsk Mazowiecki, Poland

Polish Economic Soc. [IO], Warsaw, Poland

Polish Entomological Soc. [IO], Poznan, Poland

Polish Falcons of Am. [19194], 381 Mansfield Ave., Pittsburgh, PA 15220-2751, (412)922-2244

Polish Figure Skating Assn. [IO], Warsaw, Poland

Polish Filmmakers Assn. [IO], Warsaw, Poland

Polish Floorball Fed. [IO], Gdynia, Poland

Polish Football Assn. [IO], Warsaw, Poland

Polish Genealogical Soc. [★20655]

Polish Genealogical Soc. [★20655]

Polish Genealogical Soc. of Am. [20655], 984 N Milwaukee Ave., Chicago, IL 60622-4101

Polish Genealogical Soc. of Am. [20655], 984 N Milwaukee Ave., Chicago, IL 60622-4101

Polish Geographical Soc. [IO], Warsaw, Poland

Polish Geological Soc. [IO], Krakow, Poland

Polish Geotechnical Soc. [IO], Gdansk, Poland

Polish Info. Processing Soc. [IO], Warsaw, Poland

Polish Inst. of Arts and Sci. of Am. [★10463]

Polish Inst. of Arts and Sciences of Am. [10463], 208 E 30th St., New York, NY 10016, (212)686-4164

Polish Jet Sports Boating Assn. [IO], Gdansk, Poland

Polish Journalists' Assn. [IO], Warsaw, Poland

Polish Librarians Assn. [IO], Warsaw, Poland

Polish Meat Assn. [IO], Warsaw, Poland

Polish Medical Assn. [IO], Warsaw, Poland

Polish Medical Assn., Sect. of Chemotherapy [IO], Warsaw, Poland

Polish Museum of Am. [10464], 984 N Milwaukee Ave., Chicago, IL 60622-4101, (773)384-3352

Polish Mutual Assistance [★19192]

Polish Natl. Alliance of the U.S. of North Am. [19195], 6100 N Cicero Ave., Chicago, IL 60646, (773)286-0500

Polish Natl. Union of Am. [19196], 1002 Pittston Ave., Scranton, PA 18505, (800)724-6352

Polish Nobility Assn. [★19197]

Polish Nobility Assn. Found. [19197], Villa Anneslie, 529 Dunkirk Rd., Baltimore, MD 21212-2014

Polish Olympic Comm. [IO], Warsaw, Poland

Polish Orienteering Assn. [IO], Warsaw, Poland

Polish Orthodontic Assn. [IO], Lublin, Poland

Polish Osteoarthrology Soc. [IO], Krakow, Poland

Polish Paralympic Comm. [IO], Warsaw, Poland

Polish Phonetic Assn. [IO], Poznan, Poland

Reference to "IO" in place of a book number signifies that the association may be found in the 50th edition of International Organizations.

Encyclopedia of Associations, 51st Edition

3101

Polish Physical Soc. **[IO]**, Warsaw, Poland
Polish Physiological Soc. **[IO]**, Krakow, Poland
Polish Private Equity Assn. **[IO]**, Warsaw, Poland
Polish Psychological Assn. **[IO]**, Warsaw, Poland
Polish Red Cross **[IO]**, Warsaw, Poland
Polish Roman Catholic Union of Am. **[19198]**, 984 N Milwaukee Ave., Chicago, IL 60642-4101, (773)782-2600
Polish Seed Trade Assn. **[IO]**, Poznan, Poland
Polish Singers Alliance of Am. **[10281]**, Mrs. Teresa Krenglicki, Pres., 208 Caesar Blvd., Williamsville, NY 14221
Polish Singers Alliance of Am. **[10281]**, Mrs. Teresa Krenglicki, Pres., 208 Caesar Blvd., Williamsville, NY 14221
Polish Social and Cultural Assn. **[IO]**, London, United Kingdom
Polish Soc. of Agricultural Engg. **[IO]**, Krakow, Poland
Polish Soc. for Contemporary Music **[IO]**, Warsaw, Poland
Polish Soc. of Gerontology **[IO]**, Warsaw, Poland
Polish Soc. of Hypertension **[IO]**, Poznan, Poland
Polish Soc. of Multiple Sclerosis **[IO]**, Warsaw, Poland
Polish Soc. of the Phonographic Indus. **[IO]**, Warsaw, Poland
Polish Soc. for Photogrammetry and Remote Sensing **[IO]**, Warsaw, Poland
Polish Soc. of Physiotherapy **[IO]**, Pabianice, Poland
Polish Soc. of Rose Fanciers **[IO]**, Warsaw, Poland
Polish Soc. for the Stud. of Pain **[IO]**, Krakow, Poland
Polish Soc. of Veterinary Sci. **[IO]**, Warsaw, Poland
Polish Sociological Assn. **[IO]**, Warsaw, Poland
Polish Speed Skating Assn. **[IO]**, Warsaw, Poland
Polish Surname Network - Defunct.
Polish Taekwondo Fed. **[IO]**, Warsaw, Poland
Polish Tatra Sheepdog Club of Am. **[21634]**, Anita Liebl, Sec., 7119 W Lakefield Dr., Milwaukee, WI 53219, (414)329-1373
Polish Tourist Country-Lovers' Soc. **[IO]**, Warsaw, Poland
Polish Underground Movement (1939-1945) Stud. Trust **[IO]**, London, United Kingdom
Polish Union of Am. **[19199]**, 745 Center Rd., West Seneca, NY 14224-2108, (716)677-0220
Polish Union of the U.S. of North Am. **[19200]**, PO Box 660, Wilkes-Barre, PA 18703-0660, (570)823-1611
Polish-U.S. Bus. Coun. - Address unknown since 2011.
Polish Western Assn. of America - Defunct.
Polish Women's Alliance of Am. **[19201]**, 6643 N Northwest Hwy., 2nd Fl., Chicago, IL 60631, (847)384-1200
Polish Youth Hostels Assn. **[IO]**, Warsaw, Poland

Political Action
AIDS United **[18318]**
Alcohol Beverage Legislative Coun. **[5196]**
Amer. Medical Political Action Comm. **[18319]**
Amer. Renewal Found. **[18320]**
Asian Pacific Americans for Progress **[17205]**
BANKPAC **[18321]**
Better Govt. Assn. **[18322]**
Bus. Alliance for Commerce in Hemp **[18323]**
Business-Industry Political Action Comm. **[18324]**
Campaign for Working Families **[18325]**
Common Cause **[18326]**
The Conservation Campaign **[17416]**
Consumers United for Rail Equity **[18327]**
The Creative Coalition **[18328]**
Debt AIDS Trade Africa **[17149]**
Democracy for Am. **[18329]**
Democracy Intl. **[18330]**
Democracy Intl. **[18330]**
Democrats for Educ. Reform **[17600]**
Dredging Indus. Size Standard Comm. **[18331]**
EMILY's List **[18332]**
Free Cong. Found. **[18333]**
FreedomWorks **[18334]**
League of Revolutionaries for a New Am. **[18335]**
Natl. Assn. of Bus. Political Action Committees **[18336]**
Natl. Jewish Democratic Coun. **[18387]**

Natl. Law Center on Homelessness and Poverty **[12163]**
Pay for Schools by Regulating Cannabis **[18337]**
Resist **[18338]**
Social Democrats, U.S.A. **[18339]**
Turkish Coalition U.S.A. Political Action Comm. **[18340]**
UAW | Community Action Prog. **[18341]**
U.S.-English **[18342]**
Political Action Comm. of Young Americans for Freedom **[★17418]**
Political Assn. for Animal Rights in Europe **[IO]**, Dusseldorf, Germany
Political Campaign Inst. - Defunct.
Political Economy and Economic History Soc. **[IO]**, Tokyo, Japan
Political Economy Res. Center - The Center for Free Market Environmentalism **[★4297]**

Political Education
Celebration U.S.A. **[8734]**
Democracy for Am. **[18329]**
Natl. Jewish Democratic Coun. **[18387]**
Political Educ. Comm. **[★18744]**

Political Federations
Ashburn Inst. **[18343]**
Ashburn Inst. **[18343]**
Coun. of Volunteer Americans **[18344]**
Independent Women's Forum **[18345]**
League of Conservation Voters **[18346]**
Physicians for a Natl. Hea. Prog. **[18347]**
Semisocialist Coalition of Earth **[18348]**
Semisocialist Coalition of Earth **[18348]**
United Fascist Union **[18349]**
U.S. Term Limits Found. **[18350]**
World Ser. Authority **[18351]**
World Ser. Authority **[18351]**

Political Items
Amer. Political Items Collectors **[22102]**

Political Parties
Amer. Muslim Alliance **[18142]**
Amer. Nationalist Union **[18352]**
Campus Greens **[18353]**
Comm. for a Unified Independent Party **[18354]**
Communist Party of the U.S.A. **[18355]**
Conservative Party **[18356]**
Expansionist Party of the U.S. **[18357]**
Expansionist Party of the U.S. **[18357]**
Green Party of the U.S. **[18358]**
La Raza Unida Party **[18359]**
Libertarian Natl. Comm. **[18360]**
Natl. Jewish Democratic Coun. **[18387]**
Peace and Freedom Party **[18361]**
Progressive Democrats of Am. **[17542]**
Progressive Labor Party **[18362]**
Prohibition Natl. Comm. **[18363]**
Republicans Abroad Intl. **[18364]**
Republicans Abroad Intl. **[18364]**
Socialist Labor Party of Am. **[18365]**
Socialist Party U.S.A. **[18366]**
U.S. Pacifist Party **[18367]**
Working Families Party **[18368]**
World Socialist Party of the U.S. **[18369]**
Political Party Democrats 66 **[IO]**, The Hague, Netherlands

Political Reform
Brennan Center for Justice | NYU School of Law **[5889]**
CIVICUS: World Alliance for Citizen Participation **[18370]**
CIVICUS: World Alliance for Citizen Participation **[18370]**
Comm. to Support the Revolution in Peru **[18371]**
Debt AIDS Trade Africa **[17149]**
Political Res. Associates **[5890]**, 1310 Broadway, Ste. 201, Somerville, MA 02144, (617)666-5300

Political Science
Acad. of Political Sci. **[7283]**
Albanian Political Sci. Assn. **[5703]**
Amer. Acad. of Political and Social Sci. **[7284]**
Amer. Muslim Alliance **[18142]**
Amer. Political Sci. Assn. **[7285]**
Assn. for Political Theory **[7286]**
Caucus for a New Political Sci. **[7287]**
Inter-University Consortium for Political and Social Res. **[7288]**

Intl. Conf. for the Stud. of Political Thought **[7289]**
Jefferson Legacy Found. **[8735]**
Joint Center for Political and Economic Stud. **[7290]**
Pi Sigma Alpha **[23622]**
Political Stud. Assn. of Ireland **[10447]**
Public Choice Soc. **[7291]**
Robert H. Smith Intl. Center for Jefferson Stud. **[8736]**
Soc. for Terrorism Res. **[7554]**
Political Stud. Assn. **[IO]**, Newcastle upon Tyne, United Kingdom
Political Stud. Assn. of Ireland **[IO]**, Dublin, Ireland

Politics
Aaron Burr Assn. **[10650]**
Amer. Assn. of Political Consultants **[18372]**
Amer. Conservative Union **[17418]**
Amer. League of Lobbyists **[18373]**
Amer. Muslim Alliance **[18142]**
Arab Amer. Inst. **[18374]**
Arab Amer. Inst. **[18374]**
Asian Pacific Americans for Progress **[17205]**
Asian and Pacific Islander Amer. Vote **[18375]**
Ataturk Soc. of Am. **[18376]**
Black Women's Roundtable on Voter Participation **[18377]**
Center for Responsive Politics **[18378]**
Center for the Stud. of the Presidency **[17246]**
Center for Voting and Democracy **[18379]**
Change Bangladesh **[17275]**
Commn. on Presidential Debates **[18380]**
Election Defense Alliance **[17607]**
Hereditary Order of the Families of the Presidents and First Ladies of Am. **[20754]**
Indian Amer. Forum for Political Educ. **[18381]**
Indus. Areas Found. **[17379]**
Inst. for America's Future **[18382]**
Intl. Conf. for the Stud. of Political Thought **[7289]**
Korean Amer. Voters' Coun. **[18034]**
League of Women Voters of the U.S. **[18383]**
League of Young Voters **[18384]**
Mobile Voter **[18096]**
Natl. Coalition on Black Civic Participation **[18385]**
Natl. Fed. of Pachyderm Clubs **[18386]**
Natl. Jewish Democratic Coun. **[18387]**
Natl. Women's Political Caucus **[17669]**
Natl. Write Your Congressman **[18388]**
Nonprofit VOTE **[18162]**
People's Lobby **[18389]**
Political Res. Associates **[5890]**
Progressive Democrats of Am. **[17542]**
Proj. Vote! **[18390]**
Reagan Alumni Assn. **[18391]**
Scientists and Engineers for Am. **[5314]**
South Asian Amer. Voting Youth **[18392]**
Southwest Voter Registration Educ. Proj. **[18393]**
Turkish Coalition U.S.A. Political Action Comm. **[18340]**
Ulysses S. Grant Assn. **[10695]**
Voter Action **[18394]**
Politieke Partij Democraten 66 **[★IO]**
Politischer Arbeitskreis fur Tierrechte in Europa **[★IO]**
Politzer Soc. - Intl. Soc. for Otological Surgery **[IO]**, Ankara, Turkey
Polk Memorial Assn; James K. **[10671]**
Pollock-Krasner Found. **[9250]**, 863 Park Ave., New York, NY 10075, (212)517-5400
Pollock-Krasner Found. **[9250]**, 863 Park Ave., New York, NY 10075, (212)517-5400

Polls
Amer. Assn. for Public Opinion Res. **[18395]**
Coun. of Amer. Survey Res. Organizations **[18396]**
Election Defense Alliance **[17607]**
Natl. Coun. on Public Polls **[18397]**
Voters for Peace **[18300]**
World Assn. for Public Opinion Res. **[18398]**
World Assn. for Public Opinion Res. **[18398]**

Pollution Control
Air and Waste Mgt. Assn. **[4779]**
Air and Waste Mgt. Assn. **[4779]**
Amer. Coun. for Accredited Certification **[4780]**
Canadian Centre for Pollution Prevention **[4229]**
CarFree City, USA **[4961]**

A star before a book entry number signifies that the name is not listed separately, but is mentioned within the entry.

Center for Clean Air Policy [4781]
Citizens for Alternatives to Chem. Contamination [4782]
Clean Air Task Force [4783]
Clean Air Watch [4784]
Clean Fuels Development Coalition [4785]
Clean Water Am. Alliance [4988]
Climate Registry [4786]
Climate Trust [4787]
Energy Action Coalition [6717]
Environmental Cleanup Coalition [4788]
Environmental Cleanup Coalition [4788]
ETAD: Ecological and Toxicological Assn. of Dyes and Organic Pigments Mfrs. [4789]
Fed. of Environmental Technologists [4790]
Freshwater Soc. [4791]
Get Oil Out! [4792]
Global Warming Initiatives [4793]
Global Warming Initiatives [4793]
Indoor Air Quality Assn. [4794]
Inst. of Clean Air Companies [2786]
Mfrs. of Emission Controls Assn. [2787]
Natl. Biosolids Partnership [4795]
Natl. Environmental, Safety and Hea. Training Assn. [4796]
Natl. Environmental, Safety and Hea. Training Assn. [4796]
Natl. Pollution Prevention Roundtable [4797]
Noise Free Am. [4739]
Occupational Knowledge Intl. [4798]
Occupational Knowledge Intl. [4798]
Oil Change Intl. [4230]
Plastic Pollution Coalition [4799]
Practice Greenhealth [14506]
Responsible Purchasing Network [1222]
Solar Cookers Intl. [4800]
Solar Cookers Intl. [4800]
Spill Control Assn. of Am. [2788]
Water Env. Fed. [4801]
Water Env. Fed. [4801]
Worldwide Pollution Control Assn. [2789]
Worldwide Pollution Control Assn. [2789]
Pollution Probe [IO], Toronto, ON, Canada
Polly Klaas Found. [12540], PO Box 800, Petaluma, CA 94953, (800)587-4357
Polo
Amer. Bicycle Polo Assn. [22811]
Amer. Polo Horse Assn. [22812]
U.S. Bicycle Polo Assn. [22813]
U.S. Polo Assn. [22814]
Polonus Philatelic Soc. [22064], PO Box 489, Maryville, IL 62062
Polska Akademia Nauk [★IO]
Polska Asocjacja Ekologii Krajobrazu [★IO]
Polska Federacja Aikido [IO], Warsaw, Poland
Polska Federacja Squasha [IO], Warsaw, Poland
Polska Federacja Unihokeja - Floorball [★IO]
Polska Izba Ksiazki [★IO]
Polska Izba Nasienna [★IO]
Polska Izba Przemyslu Chemicznego [★IO]
Polska Izba Przemyslu Farmaceutycznego i Wyrobow Medycznych [★IO]
Polska Izba Przemyslu Targowego [★IO]
Polska Unia W Ameryce [★19199]
Polski Komitet Olimpijski [★IO]
Polski Komitet Paraolimpijski [★IO]
Polski Komitet Swiatowej Rady Energetycznej [★IO]
Polski Osrodek Spoleczno Kulturalny [★IO]
Polski Towarzystwo Milosnikow Roz [★IO]
Polski Zwiazek Badmintona [IO], Warsaw, Poland
Polski Zwiazek Kajakowy [★IO]
Polski Zwiazek Lekkiej Atletyki [IO], Warsaw, Poland
Polski Zwiazek Lyzwiarstwa Szybkiego [★IO]
Polski Zwiazek Lyzwiarswa Figurowego [★IO]
Polski Zwiazek Motorowy [★IO]
Polski Zwiazek Orientacji Sportowej [★IO]
Polski Zwiazek Pilki Noznej [★IO]
Polski Zwiazek Taekwondo [★IO]
Polskie Stowarzyszenie Inwestorow Kapitalowych [★IO]
Polskie Towarzystwo Badania Bolu [★IO]
Polskie Towarzystwo Chemiczne [★IO]
Polskie Towarzystwo Ekonomiczne [★IO]
Polskie Towarzystwo Entomologiczne [★IO]
Polskie Towarzystwo Fizjoterapii [★IO]

Polskie Towarzystwo Fizyczne [★IO]
Polskie Towarzystwo Fonetyczne [★IO]
Polskie Towarzystwo Geograficzne [★IO]
Polskie Towarzystwo Geologiczne [★IO]
Polskie Towarzystwo Informatyczne [★IO]
Polskie Towarzystwo Inzynierii Rolniczej [★IO]
Polskie Towarzystwo Kardiologiczne [★IO]
Polskie Towarzystwo Lekarskie [★IO]
Polskie Towarzystwo Mineralogiczne [★IO]
Polskie Towarzystwo Muzyki Wspolczesnej [★IO]
Polskie Towarzystwo Nadcisnienia Tetniczego [★IO]
Polskie Towarzystwo Nauk Weterynaryjnych [★IO]
Polskie Towarzystwo Ortodontyczne [★IO]
Polskie Towarzystwo Psychologiczne [★IO]
Polskie Towarzystwo Schronisk Mlodziezowych [★IO]
Polskie Towarzystwo Socjologiczne [★IO]
Polskie Towarzystwo Stwardnienia Rozsianego [★IO]
Polskie Towarzystwo Taneczne [IO], Krakow, Poland
Polskie Towarzystwo Turystyczno-Krajoznawcze [★IO]
Polskie Zrzeszenie Lokatorow [★IO]
Polyacrylate Absorbents; Inst. for [756]
Polyacrylate Absorbents; Inst. for [756]
Polycystic Ovarian Syndrome Assn. [15892], PO Box 3403, Englewood, CO 80155-3403
Polycystic Ovarian Syndrome Assn. [15892], PO Box 3403, Englewood, CO 80155-3403
Polycystic Ovarian Syndrome Assn. of Australia [IO], Baulkham Hills, Australia
Polyisocyanurate Insulation Mfrs. Assn. [606], 7315 Wisconsin Ave., Ste. 400E, Bethesda, MD 20814, (301)654-0000
Polymer Machinery, Mfrs. and Distributors Assn. [IO], Rugby, United Kingdom
Polynesian
Polynesian Cultural Center [10465]
Polynesian Cultural Center [10465]
Polynesian Cultural Center [10465], 55-370 Kamehameha Hwy., Laie, HI 96762, (808)293-3333
Polynesian Cultural Center [10465], 55-370 Kamehameha Hwy., Laie, HI 96762, (808)293-3333
Polynesian Soc. [IO], Auckland, New Zealand
Polynesian Voyaging Soc. [22003], 10 Sand Island Pkwy., Honolulu, HI 96819, (808)842-1101
Polysomnographic Technologists; Bd. of Registered [15371]
Polystyrene Packaging Coun. [★2604]
Polyurethane Div., Soc. of the Plastics Indus. [★2765]
Polyurethane Foam Assn. [2775], 334 Lakeside Plz., Loudon, TN 37774, (865)657-9840
Polyurethane Mfrs. Assn. [2776], 6737 W Washington Ave., Ste. 1300, Milwaukee, WI 53214, (414)431-3094
Pomegranate Guild of Judaic Needlework [21461], Ethel Marcus, Treas., 1942 E Main St., 3rd Fl., Waterbury, CT 06705
Pompeiiana, Inc. - Defunct.
Ponderosa Pine Woodwork Assn. [★635]
Ponies Assn. - UK [IO], Huntingdon, United Kingdom
Pontiac-Oakland Club Intl. [21153], PO Box 68, Maple Plain, MN 55359, (877)368-3454
Pontifica Academia delle Scienze [★IO]
Pontifical Acad. of Sciences [IO], Vatican City, Vatican City
Pontifical Assn. of the Holy Childhood [★19428]
Pontifical Coun. for Culture [IO], Rome, Italy
Pontifical Coun. for the Pastoral Care of Migrants and Itinerant People [IO], Vatican City, Vatican City
Pontifical Mission for Palestine [12775], 1011 1st Ave., New York, NY 10022-4195, (212)826-1480
Pontifical Mission Societies - Canada [IO], Toronto, ON, Canada
Pontifical Mission Societies in the U.S. [19486], 70 W 36th St., 8th Fl., New York, NY 10018, (212)563-8700
Pontifical Mission Soc. [IO], Aachen, Germany
Pontifical Missionary Union [★19486]
Pontifical Missionary Union of Priests and Religious [★19486]
Pontificium Consilium de Cultura [★IO]
Pontius Family Assn. [20573], B.J. Bongo, Treas., 21810 Fairmont Blvd., Shaker Heights, OH 44118-4816, (937)339-5211

Pony of the Americas Club [4639], 3828 S Emerson Ave., Indianapolis, IN 46203, (317)788-0107
Pony Baseball and Softball [22288], PO Box 225, Washington, PA 15301, (724)225-1060
Pony Club [IO], Kenilworth, United Kingdom
Pony Club Australia [IO], Goodwood, Australia
Pony and Colt Boys Baseball [★22288]
Pony Express Historical Assn. [9795], PO Box 1022, St. Joseph, MO 64502, (816)232-8206
Pony League [★22288]
Poodle Club of Am. [21635], Kay Tripp, Corresponding Sec., 5604 Merion Sta. Dr., Apex, NC 27539, (919)387-8780
Poolplayer Assn; Natl. Wheelchair [22519]
Pop Music
Chicago Fan Club [23822]
Cliff Richard Fan Club of Am. [23826]
Donny Osmond Intl. Network [23835]
Pop Warner Junior League Football [★22594]
Pop Warner Little Scholars [22594], 586 Middletown Blvd., Ste. C-100, Langhorne, PA 19047, (215)752-2691
Popcorn Bd. [1427], 401 N Michigan Ave., Chicago, IL 60611-4267, (312)644-6610
Popcorn and Concessions Assn. [★1451]
Popcorn Inst. [★1427]
Popcorn Processors Assn. [★1427]
Pope and Young Club [22227], PO Box 548, Chatfield, MN 55923-0548, (507)867-4144
Poplar Coun. of Canada [IO], Edmonton, AB, Canada
Poplar and Fast Growing Forest Trees Res. Inst. [IO], Izmit, Turkey
Popotnisko zdruzenje Slovenije [★IO]
Popular Culture
Amer. Culture Assn. [10466]
Hip-Hop Assn. [10467]
Hip-Hop Summit Youth Coun. [10468]
Popular Culture Assn. [10469]
Popular Culture Assn. [10469], 276 Bessey Hall, East Lansing, MI 48824, (517)355-6660
Popular Price Shoe Retailer Assn. [★1458]
Popular Rotorcraft Assn. [20913], PO Box 68, Mentone, IN 46539-0068, (574)353-7227
Population
Alliance for Contraception in Cats and Dogs [12647]
Anita Borg Inst. for Women and Tech. [12697]
Anita Borg Inst. for Women and Tech. [12697]
Assn. of Population Centers [6594]
Center for Commun. Programs [12698]
Center for Commun. Programs [12698]
Global Migration Gp. [5790]
Negative Population Growth [12699]
Off. of Population Affairs CH [12700]
PCI-Media Impact [12701]
PCI-Media Impact [12701]
Population Action Intl. [12702]
Population Action Intl. [12702]
Population Commun. [12703]
Population Commun. [12703]
Population Connection [12704]
Population Coun. [12705]
Population Coun. [12705]
Population-Environment Balance [12706]
Population Inst. [12707]
Population Inst. [12707]
Population Rsrc. Center [12708]
Population Rsrc. Center [12708]
Rotarian Action Gp. for Population Growth and Sustainable Development [12709]
Rotarian Action Gp. for Population Growth and Sustainable Development [12709]
Soc. of Family Planning [14528]
Sustainable Population Australia [22141]
Population Action Intl. [12702], 1300 19th St. NW, Ste. 200, Washington, DC 20036, (202)557-3400
Population Action Intl. [12702], 1300 19th St. NW, Ste. 200, Washington, DC 20036, (202)557-3400
Population Assn. of Am. [6596], 8630 Fenton St., Ste. 722, Silver Spring, MD 20910-3812, (301)565-6710
Population Assn. of New Zealand [IO], Wellington, New Zealand
Population Assn. of Pakistan [IO], Islamabad, Pakistan

Reference to "IO" in place of a book number signifies that the association may be found in the 50th edition of International Organizations.

Population Commun. **[12703]**, 1250 E Walnut St., Ste. 220, Pasadena, CA 91106, (626)793-4750
Population Commun. **[12703]**, 1250 E Walnut St., Ste. 220, Pasadena, CA 91106, (626)793-4750
Population Communications Intl. **[★12701]**
Population Communications Intl. **[★12701]**
Population and Community Development Assn. **[IO]**, Bangkok, Thailand
Population Connection **[12704]**, 2120 L St. NW, Ste. 500, Washington, DC 20037, (202)332-2200
Population Coun. **[12705]**, 1 Dag Hammarskjold Plz., New York, NY 10017, (212)339-0500
Population Coun. **[12705]**, 1 Dag Hammarskjold Plz., New York, NY 10017, (212)339-0500
Population Crisis Comm. **[★12702]**
Population Crisis Comm. **[★12702]**
Population and Development Intl. - Vietnam **[IO]**, Hanoi, Vietnam
Population-Environment Balance **[12706]**, PO Box 1059, Anaheim, CA 92815, (714)204-3466
Population Inst. **[12707]**, 107 2nd St. NE, Washington, DC 20002, (202)544-3300
Population Inst. **[12707]**, 107 2nd St. NE, Washington, DC 20002, (202)544-3300
Population Inst. Advocates, Inc. **[★12707]**
Population Inst. Advocates, Inc. **[★12707]**
Population Reference Bur. **[6597]**, 1875 Connecticut Ave. NW, Ste. 520, Washington, DC 20009-5728, (202)483-1100
Population Reference Bur. **[6597]**, 1875 Connecticut Ave. NW, Ste. 520, Washington, DC 20009-5728, (202)483-1100
Population Rsrc. Center **[12708]**, One Highland Rd., Princeton, NJ 08540, (609)924-7004
Population Rsrc. Center **[12708]**, One Highland Rd., Princeton, NJ 08540, (609)924-7004
Populist Party of Am. **[★18352]**
Porcelain
　Intl. Doll Makers Assn. **[21692]**
Porcelain Enamel Inst. **[607]**, PO Box 920220, Norcross, GA 30010, (770)676-9366
Pornography
　Anti-Child Pornography Org. **[12710]**
　Anti-Child Pornography Org. **[12710]**
　Morality in Media **[18399]**
　pureHOPE **[18400]**
Porphyria Found; Amer. **[15491]**
Porsche Club of Am. **[21154]**, PO Box 6400, Columbia, MD 21045, (410)381-0911
Port Douglas Daintree Tourism Assn. **[IO]**, Port Douglas, Australia
Port and Douro Wines Inst. **[IO]**, Porto, Portugal
Portable Rechargeable Battery Assn. **[★1114]**
Portable Sanitation Assn. **[★3642]**
Portable Sanitation Assn. **[★3642]**
Portable Sanitation Assn. Intl. **[3642]**, 7800 Metro Pkwy., Ste. 104, Bloomington, MN 55425, (952)854-8300
Portable Sanitation Assn. Intl. **[3642]**, 7800 Metro Pkwy., Ste. 104, Bloomington, MN 55425, (952)854-8300
Portland Cement Assn. **[836]**, 5420 Old Orchard Rd., Skokie, IL 60077-1053, (847)966-6200
Portland Cement Mfrs'. Assn. **[IO]**, Buenos Aires, Argentina
Portland Grain Exchange - Defunct.
Portmarnock Sub-Aqua Club **[IO]**, Portmarnock, Ireland
Portobello Antique Dealers Assn. **[IO]**, London, United Kingdom
Portrait Soc. of Am. **[9197]**, PO Box 11272, Tallahassee, FL 32302, (850)878-9996
Ports Australia **[IO]**, Sydney, Australia
Portsmouth and South East Hampshire Chamber of Commerce and Indus. **[IO]**, Havant, United Kingdom
Portugal
　Luso-American Educ. Found. **[10470]**
Portugese Soc. of Osteoporosis and other Metabolic Bone Disease **[IO]**, Lisbon, Portugal
Portuguesa Multiple Sclerosis Soc. **[IO]**, Lisbon, Portugal
Portuguese
　Amer. Portuguese Stud. Assn. **[8737]**
　Luso-American Educ. Found. **[10470]**

Portuguese Amer. Leadership Coun. of the U.S. **[19203]**
Portuguese Historical and Cultural Soc. **[19204]**
Portuguese Acad. of History **[IO]**, Lisbon, Portugal
Portuguese Amer. Leadership Coun. of the U.S. **[19203]**, 9255 Center St., Ste. 404, Manassas, VA 20110, (202)466-4664
Portuguese Antique Dealers' Assn. **[IO]**, Lisbon, Portugal
Portuguese Assn. of Automotive Suppliers **[IO]**, Porto, Portugal
Portuguese Assn. of Booksellers and Publishers **[IO]**, Lisbon, Portugal
Portuguese Assn. of Music Educ. **[IO]**, Lisbon, Portugal
Portuguese Assn. of the Pharmaceutical Indus. **[IO]**, Lisbon, Portugal
Portuguese Assn. of Retail Companies **[IO]**, Lisbon, Portugal
Portuguese Assn. for Technicians of the Pulp and Paper Indus. **[IO]**, Thomar, Portugal
Portuguese Assn. for Telework **[IO]**, Cascais, Portugal
Portuguese Broadcasting Assn. **[IO]**, Lisbon, Portugal
Portuguese Cancer Soc. **[IO]**, Porto, Portugal
Portuguese Chamber **[IO]**, London, United Kingdom
Portuguese Chamber of Commerce in Britain **[IO]**, London, United Kingdom
Portuguese Confed. of Bus. and Services **[IO]**, Lisbon, Portugal
Portuguese Continental Union of the U.S.A. **[★19053]**
Portuguese Coun. of Shopping Centers **[IO]**, Lisbon, Portugal
Portuguese Fiscal Assn. **[IO]**, Lisbon, Portugal
Portuguese Football Fed. **[IO]**, Lisbon, Portugal
Portuguese Footwear, Components, Leather Goods Manufacturer's Assn. **[IO]**, Porto, Portugal
Portuguese Gp. of the Intl. Assn. of Hydrogeologists **[IO]**, Aveiro, Portugal
Portuguese Historical and Cultural Soc. **[19204]**, PO Box 161990, Sacramento, CA 95816, (916)391-7356
Portuguese Hotel Assn. **[IO]**, Lisbon, Portugal
Portuguese League Against Epilepsy **[IO]**, Porto, Portugal
Portuguese Leather Assn. **[IO]**, Alcanena, Portugal
Portuguese Mineral Water Producers' Assn. **[IO]**, Lisbon, Portugal
Portuguese Operations Res. Soc. **[IO]**, Lisbon, Portugal
Portuguese Orienteering Fed. **[IO]**, Mafra, Portugal
Portuguese Osteoporosis Assn. **[IO]**, Porto, Portugal
Portuguese Paper Indus. Assn. **[IO]**, Lisbon, Portugal
Portuguese Petroleum Enterprises' Assn. **[IO]**, Lisbon, Portugal
Portuguese Pharmacological Soc. **[IO]**, Lisbon, Portugal
Portuguese Physiological Soc. **[IO]**, Carcavelos, Portugal
Portuguese Plastics Mfrs'. Assn. **[IO]**, Lisbon, Portugal
Portuguese Podengo Club of Am. **[21636]**, Becky Berkley, Membership Chair, 11655 Vaca Pl., San Diego, CA 92124
Portuguese Soc. of Cardiology **[IO]**, Lisbon, Portugal
Portuguese Soc. of Dermatology and Venereology **[IO]**, Lisbon, Portugal
Portuguese Soc. of Digestive Endoscopy **[IO]**, Lisbon, Portugal
Portuguese Soc. of Infectious Diseases **[IO]**, Lisbon, Portugal
Portuguese Soc. of Rheumatology **[IO]**, Lisbon, Portugal
Portuguese Soc. of Stomatology and Dental Medicine **[IO]**, Lisbon, Portugal
Portuguese Squash Assn. **[IO]**, Braga, Portugal
Portuguese Trade Commn. - Address unknown since 2011.
Portuguese Water Dog Club of Am. **[21637]**, Pat Qvigstad, Membership Chair, 111 Foxtail Cir., Black Hawk, CO 80422-8861, (303)582-5009
Portugueses Travel and Tourism Agencies' Assn. **[IO]**, Lisbon, Portugal

Positional Plagiocephaly Support; Craniosynostosis and **[14196]**
Positive Coaching Alliance **[22467]**, 1001 N Rengstorff Ave., Ste. 100, Mountain View, CA 94043, (650)210-0803
Positive Discipline Assn. **[7308]**, 9417 Remuda Path, San Antonio, TX 78254, (866)767-3472
Positive Futures Network - Address unknown since 2011.
Positive Music Assn. **[10282]**, Scott Johnson, 4593 Maple Ct., Boulder, CO 80301-5829, (303)581-9083
Positive Youth Found. - Address unknown since 2011.
Positively Addictive Dog Sports **[IO]**, Brisbane, Australia
Positively UK **[IO]**, London, United Kingdom
Post and Antenatal Depression Assn. **[IO]**, Fitzroy North, Australia
Post Card Distributors Assn. of North Am. **[★2791]**
Post Card and Souvenir Distributors Assn. **[★2791]**
Post Mark Collectors Club **[22065]**, 7014 Woodland Oaks Dr., Magnolia, TX 77354-4898
Post Natal Depression Support Assn. **[IO]**, Subiaco, Australia
Post Natal Depression Support Assn. South Africa **[IO]**, Cape Town, Republic of South Africa
Post-Polio Hea. Intl. **[11823]**, 4207 Lindell Blvd., No. 110, St. Louis, MO 63108-2930, (314)534-0475
Post-Polio Hea. Intl. **[11823]**, 4207 Lindell Blvd., No. 110, St. Louis, MO 63108-2930, (314)534-0475
Post Primary Teachers Assn. **[IO]**, Wellington, New Zealand
Post-Tensioning Inst. **[608]**, 38800 Country Club Dr., Farmington Hills, MI 48331, (248)848-3180
Post-Traumatic Stress
　Amer. Combat Veterans of War **[20771]**
　EMDR - Humanitarian Assistance Programs **[12711]**
　EMDR - Humanitarian Assistance Programs **[12711]**
　Forgotten Victims **[13363]**
　Gift From Within **[12712]**
Postal Cancellation Soc. **[★22065]**
Postal Card Soc. of Am. **[★22087]**
Postal History Soc. **[22066]**, 869 Bridgewater Dr., New Oxford, PA 17350
Postal History Soc. of Canada **[IO]**, Ottawa, ON, Canada
Postal Service
　Air Mail Pioneers **[20879]**
　Amer. Philatelic Res. Lib. **[22010]**
　Amer. Philatelic Soc. Writers Unit **[22012]**
　Amer. Postal Workers Union **[23278]**
　Amer. Topical Assn. **[22016]**
　Assoc. Collectors of El Salvador **[22020]**
　Brazil Philatelic Assn. **[22022]**
　Carriers and Locals Soc. **[22103]**
　Citizens' Stamp Advisory Comm. **[22029]**
　Collectors of Religion on Stamps **[22032]**
　Confederate Stamp Alliance **[22033]**
　Cover Collectors Circuit Club **[22034]**
　Errors, Freaks and Oddities Collectors' Club **[22037]**
　France and Colonies Philatelic Soc. **[22039]**
　Intl. Fed. of Amer. Homing Pigeon Fanciers **[22097]**
　Jack Knight Air Mail Soc. **[22047]**
　Korea Stamp Soc. **[22048]**
　Mailer's Postmark Permit Club **[22050]**
　Meter Stamp Soc. **[22053]**
　Mexico Elmhurst Philatelic Soc. Intl. **[22055]**
　Natl. Alliance of Postal and Fed. Employees **[23279]**
　Natl. Assn. of Coll. and Univ. Mail Services **[2790]**
　Natl. Assn. of Letter Carriers of the U.S.A. **[23280]**
　Natl. Assn. of Postal Supervisors **[23281]**
　Natl. Assn. of Postmasters of the U.S. **[5891]**
　Natl. League of Postmasters of the U.S. **[23282]**
　Natl. Postal Forum **[5892]**
　Natl. Postal Mail Handlers Union **[23283]**
　Natl. Rural Letter Carriers' Assn. **[23284]**
　Retired League Postmasters of the Natl. League of Postmasters **[5893]**

A star before a book entry number signifies that the name is not listed separately, but is mentioned within the entry.

Rossica Soc. of Russian Philately [22068]
Ships on Stamps Unit [22074]
Soc. of Australasian Specialists/Oceania [22075]
Soc. for Thai Philately [22079]
Space Topic Stud. Unit [22080]
Wreck and Crash Mail Soc. [22093]
Postal Union of the Americas, Spain, and Portugal [IO], Montevideo, Uruguay
Postal Workers
Air Mail Pioneers [20879]
Amer. Philatelic Res. Lib. [22010]
Amer. Philatelic Soc. Writers Unit [22012]
Amer. Topical Assn. [22016]
Assoc. Collectors of El Salvador [22020]
Brazil Philatelic Assn. [22022]
Citizens' Stamp Advisory Comm. [22029]
Collectors of Religion on Stamps [22032]
Confederate Stamp Alliance [22033]
Cover Collectors Circuit Club [22034]
Errors, Freaks and Oddities Collectors' Club [22037]
France and Colonies Philatelic Soc. [22039]
Intl. Fed. of Amer. Homing Pigeon Fanciers [22097]
Jack Knight Air Mail Soc. [22047]
Korea Stamp Soc. [22048]
Mailer's Postmark Permit Club [22050]
Meter Stamp Soc. [22053]
Mexico Elmhurst Philatelic Soc. Intl. [22055]
Rossica Soc. of Russian Philately [22068]
Ships on Stamps Unit [22074]
Soc. of Australasian Specialists/Oceania [22075]
Soc. for Thai Philately [22079]
Space Topic Stud. Unit [22080]
Wreck and Crash Mail Soc. [22093]
Postcards
Intl. Fed. of Postcard Dealers [22104]
Intl. Fed. of Postcard Dealers [22104]
Souvenir Wholesale Distributors Assn. [2791]
PostEurop [IO], Brussels, Belgium
Postgraduate Center for Mental Hea. - Address unknown since 2010.
Postpartum Support Intl. [12620], 6706 SW 54th Ave., Portland, OR 97219, (503)894-9453
Postpartum Support Intl. [12620], 6706 SW 54th Ave., Portland, OR 97219, (503)894-9453
Postsecondary Electronic Standards Coun. [8902], 1250 Connecticut Ave. NW, Ste. 200, Washington, DC 20036, (202)261-6516
Posttraumatic Stress Disorder; Natl. Center for [16727]
Pot Belly Pig Rescue - Address unknown since 2010.
Potato Assn. of Am. [4469], Univ. of Maine, 5719 Crossland Hall, Rm. 220, Orono, ME 04469-5719, (207)581-3042
The Potato Bd. [★4480]
Potato Chip Inst., Intl. [★1430]
Potato Chip/Snack Food Assn. [★1430]
Potency Restored - Defunct.
Potomac Antique Tools and Indus. Assn. [21871], 9121 Bramble Pl., Annandale, VA 22003
Potters Coun. [9472], Ceramic Publications Co., 600 N Cleveland Ave., Ste. 210, Westerville, OH 43082, (800)424-8698
Potters Coun. [9472], Ceramic Publications Co., 600 N Cleveland Ave., Ste. 210, Westerville, OH 43082, (800)424-8698
Potters for Peace [21462], Peter Chartrand, Dir., PO Box 1043, Bisbee, AZ 85603, (520)249-8093
Potters for Peace [21462], Peter Chartrand, Dir., PO Box 1043, Bisbee, AZ 85603, (520)249-8093
Poultry
Amer. Bantam Assn. [4802]
Amer. Egg Bd. [4803]
Amer. Pastured Poultry Producers Assn. [4804]
Amer. Poultry Assn. [4805]
Amer. Poultry Intl. [4806]
Amer. Poultry Intl. [4806]
Amer. Silkie Bantam Club [4807]
Egg CH, Inc. [4808]
Further Poultry Processors Assn. of Canada [17861]
Intl. HACCP Alliance [4809]
Natl. Chicken Coun. [4810]

Natl. Turkey Fed. [4811]
Plymouth Rock Fanciers Club [4812]
Poultry Breeders of Am. [4813]
Poultry and Egg Farmers and Processors Assn. [10402]PoultryPoultry Indus. Assn. of New Zealand
Poultry Sci. Assn. [4814]
Soc. for the Preservation of Poultry Antiquities [4815]
United Egg Processors [4816]
United Egg Producers [4817]
U.S. Poultry and Egg Assn. [4818]
U.S.A. Poultry and Egg Export Coun. [4819]
Virginia Poultry Breeders Assn. [4820]
World's Poultry Sci. Assn., U.S.A. Br. [4821]
Poultry Breeders of Am. [4813], 1530 Cooledge Rd., Tucker, GA 30084-7303, (770)493-9401
Poultry and Egg Farmers and Processors Assn. [IO], Buenos Aires, Argentina
Poultry and Egg Natl. Bd. [★4803]
Poultry Indus. Assn. of New Zealand [IO], Auckland, New Zealand
Poultry Sci. Assn. [4814], 2441 Village Green Pl., Champaign, IL 61822, (217)356-5285
Pound Civil Justice Inst. [6048], 777 6th St. NW, Ste. 200, Washington, DC 20001, (202)944-2841
Poured Concrete Contractors Assn. [★908]
Poverty
1000 Jobs [12713]
1000 Jobs [12713]
African Sky [11542]
Aid Africa [12714]
Aid Africa [12714]
Aid for the World [12715]
Amer. Bar Assn. Commn. on Homelessness and Poverty [12153]
Amer. Outreach to Ethiopia [12265]
Ardent Lion Soc. [11659]
Artists for Peace and Justice [13152]
Artists Striving to End Poverty [12716]
Bahia St. [12717]
Bahia St. [12717]
Because Intl. [12718]
Blessings on Africa [12719]
Blessings on Africa [12719]
Bridges to Prosperity [12952]
Bright Hope Intl. [12720]
Bright Hope Intl. [12720]
Catholic Worker Movement [18164]
Center for Community Change [12721]
Center on Urban Poverty and Community Development [12722]
Challah for Hunger [12266]
Child Empowerment Intl. [11214]
Chris Cares Intl. [11560]
Christ for the Poor [8789]
Community Action Partnership [12723]
Community Solutions for Africa's Development [11570]
Conservation through Poverty Alleviation Intl. [4030]
Debt AIDS Trade Africa [17149]
EarthSpark Intl. [6711]
Economic Success CH [12724]
Egyptians Relief Assn. [11577]
Eliminate Poverty Now [11066]
Empowering the Poor [12326]
Empowerment Works [11579]
Equator Initiative [11581]
Eurostep: European Solidarity Towards Equal Participation of People [10467]
Everyone Needs a Hero [11582]
Exit Poverty Empowerment [11067]
Fashion Fights Poverty [12725]
Feed My Hungry Children [11274]
Flying Doctors of Am. [12454]
Food-Aid [12275]
Food for the Poor [12726]
Food for the Poor [12726]
Food Res. and Action Center [12278]
For Victims of War and Poverty [12455]
Free Store/Food Bank [12727]
Friends of the Third World [12728]
Friends of the Third World [12728]
From Hunger to Harvest [12280]

From Us With Love [12235]
A Future Without Poverty [12729]
Global Fac. for Disaster Reduction and Recovery [11851]
Global Family Rescue [13158]
Global FoodBanking Network [12281]
Global Goods Partners [12330]
Global Partnership for Afghanistan [3716]
Governors' Wind Energy Coalition [6070]
Green for All [17189]
HANDS for Cambodia [11593]
Hearts for Kenya [11070]
Helping Hand for Nepal [12847]
Helping Hearts Helping Hands [12730]
Humanitarian Services for Children of Vietnam [11318]
Indus. Areas Found. [17379]
Initiative for Global Development [12731]
Innovations for Poverty Action [17190]
Inst. for Children, Poverty and Homelessness [11320]
Inter-Faith Community Services [12732]
Intl. Agro Alliance [4940]
Intl. Crisis Aid [12854]
Intl. Partners [12345]
Jewish Fund for Justice [12733]
KickStart Intl. [12734]
Krochet Kids Intl. [12735]
Ladies of Charity of the U.S.A. [13191]
Liberian Anti Poverty Assn. [11071]
LIFT [11072]
Lighthouse Sta. [12736]
Long Way Home [11073]
Matanya's Hope [12737]
Matanya's Hope [12737]
Mercy Beyond Borders [12738]
Mercy Corps [12739]
Mercy Corps [12739]
Millennium Campus Network [17191]
Miracles in Action [12740]
Mission of Mercy [12741]
Mission of Mercy [12741]
Moms Against Poverty [12742]
Natl. Center for Children in Poverty [11488]
Natl. Student Campaign Against Hunger and Homelessness [12286]
Natl. Title I Assn. [7677]
Nepal SEEDS: Social Educational Environmental Development Services in Nepal [11615]
New Reality Intl. [12743]
Not on Our Watch [17857]
Nuru Intl. [11076]
Nyaya Hea. [15201]
One Warm Coat [12744]
Organize Training Center [11657]
Partners in Sustainable Development Intl. [12745]
Partnership to Cut Hunger and Poverty in Africa [12746]
Partnership to Cut Hunger and Poverty in Africa [12746]
Physicians Against World Hunger [12287]
Poverty Alliance [15802]
Poverty Awareness Coalition for Equality [12747]
Poverty Awareness Coalition for Equality [12747]
Poverty and Race Res. Action Coun. [12748]
Prana Intl. [12749]
Prana Intl. [12749]
Reach Global [13146]
Reach Out to Romania [12750]
Rebuilding Together [12200]
Red Feather Development Gp. [12201]
Relief for Africa [12882]
Restoring Institutions Services and Empowering Liberia [11625]
Rights and Resources Initiative [4412]
RISE-UP From Poverty [12751]
Rising Intl. [11078]
rock CAN roll [12289]
Rotarian Action Gp. for the Alleviation of Hunger and Malnutrition [12290]
Rural Initiative Development Assn. [12961]
Scattering Resources [12888]
Seeds For Hope [11861]
SHIP Aid: Shipping Humanitarian Aid to Impoverished People [12889]

Reference to "IO" in place of a book number signifies that the association may be found in the 50th edition of International Organizations.

Sierra Leone Relief and Development Outreach [12890]
Simple Hope [12891]
SingleStop USA [12752]
Skills for Humanity [12753]
Sky of Love [11406]
Synergos Inst. [12754]
Synergos Inst. [12754]
Tech. for the Poor [4945]
Teens Fighting Hunger [12295]
ThinkImpact [12373]
Touching Hearts [10817]
Tusubira - We Have Hope [12755]
Ugandan Amer. Partnership Org. [12307]
Union Settlement Assn. [12756]
U.S.A. Harvest [12298]
Vietnam Relief Effort [12896]
Village Missions Intl. [11651]
Well Done Org. [11653]
Why Hunger [17876]
World Bicycle Relief [12898]
World Concern [12757]
World Concern [12757]
Poverty Alleviation Cambodia [IO], Phnom Penh, Cambodia
Poverty Alliance [IO], Glasgow, United Kingdom
Poverty, Anti-
Inter-Faith Community Services [12732]
Jewish Fund for Justice [12733]
PlaNet Finance US [17920]
Umoja Intl. [12969]
Why Hunger [17876]
Poverty Awareness Coalition for Equality [12747], Virginia Tech, 418 Durham Hall, Blacksburg, VA 24061, (703)501-7844
Poverty Awareness Coalition for Equality [12747], Virginia Tech, 418 Durham Hall, Blacksburg, VA 24061, (703)501-7844
Poverty; Natl. Law Center on Homelessness and [12163]
Poverty and Race Res. Action Coun. [12748], 1200 18th St. NW, No. 200, Washington, DC 20036, (202)906-8023
P.O.W. Network [20757], PO Box 68, Skidmore, MO 64487-0068, (660)928-3304
Powder Actuated Tool Mfrs'. Inst. [1857], 136 S Main St., Ste. 2E, St. Charles, MO 63301, (314)889-7117
Powder Coating Inst. [791], 2170 Buckthorne Pl., Ste. 250, The Woodlands, TX 77380, (832)585-0770
Power
Amer. Coun. on Global Nuclear Competitiveness [7174]
America's Natural Gas Alliance [2641]
Biomass Power Assn. [7292]
Citizens' Alliance for Responsible Energy [6702]
Citizens for Energy Freedom [6703]
Clean and Safe Energy Coalition [6707]
Demand Response and Smart Grid Coalition [6649]
Distributed Wind Energy Assn. [3666]
Eco Energy Finance [6712]
Energy Efficiency Bus. Coalition [1167]
Energy Info. Standards Alliance [1168]
FutureGen Alliance [6112]
GridWise Alliance [6727]
GridWise Architecture Coun. [7293]
Growth Energy [6728]
Indus. Energy Consumers of Am. [1169]
Intl. Assn. for the Advancement of Steam Power [7480]
Intl. Photovoltaic Equip. Assn. [1170]
Natl. Alliance for Advanced Tech. Batteries [441]
Natl. Assn. of Power Engineers [7294]
Natl. Renewables Cooperative Org. [6741]
Natl. Wind Watch [18788]
New Energy Indus. Assn. for Asia and the Pacific [6742]
New Generation Energy [6743]
Nuclear Info. Tech. Strategic Leadership [7170]
Power to the People [7440]
Power Sources Mfrs. Assn. [2792]
Pro Energy Alliance [1175]
Renewable Energy Markets Assn. [1176]

Res. Partnership to Secure Energy for Am. [6752]
Securing America's Future Energy [6755]
Show Me Solar [7443]
STG Intl. [7449]
U.S. Water and Power [6121]
Vote Solar Initiative [7451]
Wind Energy Works! [7625]
Power and Commun. Contractors Assn. [947], 1908 Mt. Vernon Ave., Alexandria, VA 22314, (703)212-7734
Power Conversion Products Coun. Intl. [★1662]
Power Conversion Products Coun. Intl. [★1662]
Power Crane and Shovel Assn. [1858], Assn. of Equip. Mfrs., 6737 W Washington St., Ste. 2400, Milwaukee, WI 53214-5647, (414)272-0943
Power Fan Mfrs. Assn. [★1697]
Power Fan Mfrs. Assn. [★1697]
Power Fastenings Assn. [IO], Birmingham, United Kingdom
Power-Motion Tech. Representatives Assn. [1859], 16A Journey, Ste. 200, Aliso Viejo, CA 92656, (949)859-2885
Power to the People [7440], 1113 Parker St., Berkeley, CA 94702
POWER: People Organized to Win Employment Rights [11956], 335 S Van Nes Ave., 2nd Fl., San Francisco, CA 94103, (415)864-8372
Power Sources Mfrs. Assn. [2792], PO Box 418, Mendham, NJ 07945-0418, (973)543-9660
Power Tool Inst. [1657], 1300 Sumner Ave., Cleveland, OH 44115-2851, (216)241-7333
Power Transmission Distributors Assn. [1860], 230 W Monroe St., Ste. 1410, Chicago, IL 60606-4703, (312)516-2100
Power Transmission Distributors Assn. [1860], 230 W Monroe St., Ste. 1410, Chicago, IL 60606-4703, (312)516-2100
Power Transmission Representatives Assn. [★1859]
Power Up Gambia [7441], 4724 Kingsessing Ave., Philadelphia, PA 19143
POWER UP: Professional Org. of Women in Entertainment Reaching UP! [17737], 419 N Larchmont Blvd., No. 283, Los Angeles, CA 90004, (323)463-3154
Power Washers of North Am. [2257], 1410 Energy Park Dr., Ste. 6, St. Paul, MN 55108, (800)393-7962
Power Washers of North Am. [2257], 1410 Energy Park Dr., Ste. 6, St. Paul, MN 55108, (800)393-7962
Power for Women [13474], 28 E Jackson Blvd., Ste. 1900, Chicago, IL 60604, (312)957-0195
Powerlifting
North Amer. Powerlifting Fed. [22815]
U.S. Powerlifting Fed. [22816]
U.S.A. Powerlifting [22817]
Powerlifting Comm. of the Amateur Athletic Union [★22816]
Powys Soc. [IO], London, United Kingdom
Powys Soc. of North Am. - Address unknown since 2011.
PPFA Guild [★9199]
PRA Coatings Tech. Centre [IO], Hampton, United Kingdom
Practical Action [IO], Rugby, United Kingdom
Practical Action - Bangladesh [IO], Dhaka, Bangladesh
Practical Allergy Res. Found. [★13638]
Practice Greenhealth [14506], 12355 Sunrise Valley Dr., Ste. 680, Reston, VA 20191, (888)688-3332
Practice Greenhealth [14506], 12355 Sunrise Valley Dr., Ste. 680, Reston, VA 20191, (888)688-3332
Practising Law Inst. [8512], 810 7th Ave., 21st Fl., New York, NY 10019-5818, (212)824-5700
Prader-Willi Connection - Defunct.
Prader-Willi Syndrome Assn. [★14622]
Prader-Willi Syndrome Assn. - South Africa [IO], Pretoria, Republic of South Africa
Prader-Willi Syndrome Assn. U.S.A [★14622]
Prader-Willi Syndrome Assn. USA [14622], 8588 Potter Park Dr., Ste. 500, Sarasota, FL 34238, (941)312-0400
Prader-Willi Syndrome Parents and Friends [★14622]
Prairie Club [12767], 12 E Willow St., Unit A, Lombard, IL 60148, (630)620-9334

Prairie Dog Coalition [11026], 2525 Arapahoe Rd., No. E4-527, Boulder, CO 80302, (720)938-0788
Prairie Implement Mfrs'. Assn. [★20811]
Prall Family Assn. - Address unknown since 2010.
Prana Intl. [12749], PO Box 362, Flourtown, PA 19031-0362, (267)460-5551
Prana Intl. [12749], PO Box 362, Flourtown, PA 19031-0362, (267)460-5551
Pratham U.S.A. [12305], 9703 Richmond Ave., Ste. 102, Houston, TX 77042, (713)774-9599
Pravah [IO], New Delhi, India
Praxis Proj. [11535], 1750 Columbia Rd. NW, 2nd Fl., Washington, DC 20009, (202)234-5921
Prayers for Life [19665], Salve Regina Univ., Ochre Ct., Newport, RI 02840, (401)849-5421
PRBA- The Rechargeable Battery Assn. [1114], 1776 K St., 4th Fl., Washington, DC 20006, (202)719-4978
Pre-Eclampsia Soc. [IO], Caernarfon, United Kingdom
Pre-Raphaelite Soc. [IO], Coventry, United Kingdom
Pre-school Learning Alliance [IO], London, United Kingdom
Precancel Stamp Soc. [22067], James Hirstein, Sec., PO Box 4072, Missoula, MT 59806-4072
Precast Flooring Fed. [IO], Leicester, United Kingdom
Precast/Prestressed Concrete Inst. [837], 200 W Adams St., No. 2100, Chicago, IL 60606, (312)786-0300
Precious Metal Clay Guild
Precious Metal Clay Guild - Address unknown since 2011.
Precious Paws Rescue and Adoption [12652], 15 Main St., Van Buren, ME 04785, (207)868-2828
Precision Aerobatics Model Pilots Assn. [20914], 180 Lake Hill Rd., Burnt Hills, NY 12027-9403, (518)399-5939
Precision Chiropractic Res. Soc. - Defunct.
Precision Machined Products Assn. [1658], 6700 W Snowville Rd., Brecksville, OH 44141, (440)526-0300
Precision Measurements Assn. - Defunct.
Precision Metalforming Assn. [2491], 6363 Oak Tree Blvd., Independence, OH 44131-2556, (216)901-8800
Precision Potentiometer Mfrs. Assn. [★1118]
Predator Conservation Alliance [★5076]
Predator Proj. [★5076]
Predmore - Pridmore - Pridemore - Prigmore Assn. - Defunct.
Preemptive Love Coalition [14040], 2012 Monterrey Dr., Hewitt, TX 76643
Prefab. Home Mfrs. Inst. [★2311]
Preferred Funeral Directors Intl. [2543], PO Box 335, Indian Rocks Beach, FL 33785, (888)655-1566
Preferred Funeral Directors Intl. [2543], PO Box 335, Indian Rocks Beach, FL 33785, (888)655-1566
Preferred Hotels Assn. - Defunct.
Pregnancy and Infant Loss Support; SHARE: [12621]
Prehistoric Soc. [IO], London, United Kingdom
Preimplantation Genetic Diagnosis Intl. Soc. [14656], 2825 N Halsted St., Chicago, IL 60657, (773)472-4900
Prejudice Institute/Center for the Applied Stud. of Ethnoviolence [17320], 2743 Maryland Ave., Baltimore, MD 21218, (410)243-6987
Premature Birth
Global Alliance to Prevent Prematurity and Stillbirth [14105]
Parents of Premature Babies [12618]
Premedical Summer Institute [★8196]
Premenstrual Soc. [IO], Addlestone, United Kingdom
Premier Assistants Intl. - Address unknown since 2010.
Premium Advt. Assn. of Am. [★2422]
Preoperative Assn. [IO], London, United Kingdom
Preparatory Commn. for the Comprehensive Nuclear-Test-Ban Treaty Org. [IO], Vienna, Austria
Prepare Tomorrow's Parents [13552], 454 NE 3rd St., Boca Raton, FL 33432, (561)620-0256
Presbyterian
Assn. of Presbyterian Colleges and Universities [8738]

A star before a book entry number signifies that the name is not listed separately, but is mentioned within the entry.

Independent Bd. for Presbyterian Foreign Missions [20156]
Mission to the World [20157]
Mission to the World [20157]
Natl. Ghost Ranch Found. [20158]
Presbyterian Church Bus. Administrators' Assn. [20159]
Presbyterian Evangelistic Fellowship [20160]
Presbyterian Historical Soc. [10471]
Presbyterian Lay Comm. [20161]
Presbyterian Men [20162]
Presbyterian-Reformed Ministries Intl. [20163]
Presbyterian-Reformed Ministries Intl. [20163]
Presbyterian Women [20164]
Presbyterians for Renewal [20165]
Presbyterian Assn. of Musicians [20129], 100 Witherspoon St., Louisville, KY 40202-1396, (502)569-5288
Presbyterian Church of Aotearoa New Zealand [IO], Wellington, New Zealand
Presbyterian Church Bus. Administrators' Assn. [20159], Mindi Stivers, Presbyterian Distribution Ser., 3904 Produce Rd., Ste. 2201, Louisville, KY 40218, (800)524-2612
Presbyterian Coll. Union [★8738]
Presbyterian Evangelistic Fellowship [20160], 425 State St., Ste. 312, Bristol, VA 24201, (276)591-5335
Presbyterian Frontier Fellowship [20082], 7132 Portland Ave., Ste. 136, Richfield, MN 55423-3264, (612)869-0062
Presbyterian Hea. Educ. and Welfare Assn. - Address unknown since 2010.
Presbyterian Historical Assn. [★10471]
Presbyterian Historical Soc. [10471], 425 Lombard St., Philadelphia, PA 19147-1516, (215)627-1852
Presbyterian Hunger Prog. [12288], Presbyterian Church (U.S.A.), 100 Witherspoon St., Louisville, KY 40202-1396, (800)728-7228
Presbyterian Lay Comm. [20161], PO Box 2210, Lenoir, NC 28645-2210, (828)758-8716
Presbyterian Men [20162], 100 Witherspoon St., Louisville, KY 40202, (800)728-7228
Presbyterian Missionary Comm. [★14276]
Presbyterian Parents of Gays and Lesbians [12109], 6100 Colwell Blvd., Ste. 250, Irving, TX 75039, (972)219-6063
Presbyterian Peace Fellowship [18282], 17 Cricket-town Rd., Stony Point, NY 10980, (845)786-6743
Presbyterian-Reformed Ministries Intl. [20163], PO Box 429, Black Mountain, NC 28711-0429, (828)669-7373
Presbyterian-Reformed Ministries Intl. [20163], PO Box 429, Black Mountain, NC 28711-0429, (828)669-7373
Presbyterian and Reformed Renewal Ministries Intl. [★20163]
Presbyterian and Reformed Renewal Ministries Intl. [★20163]
Presbyterian Women [20164], 100 Witherspoon St., Louisville, KY 40202, (888)728-7228
Presbyterians for Biblical Concerns [★20165]
Presbyterians for Lesbian and Gay Concerns [★19798]
Presbyterians Pro-Life [12943], 3942 Middle Rd., Allison Park, PA 15101, (412)487-1990
Presbyterians for Renewal [20165], 8134 New LaGrange Rd., Louisville, KY 40222-4673, (502)425-4630

Preschool Education
Brick by Brick for Tanzania! [8739]
Give Children a Choice [8740]
Natl. Head Start Assn. [8741]
Natl. Kindergarten Alliance [8742]
Waldorf Early Childhood Assn. of North Am. [8743]
Prescott Coll. Alumni Assn. [18896], 220 Grove Ave., Prescott, AZ 86301, (877)350-4502
Prescription Footwear Assn. [★1460]
Presentation Bros. of Mary [IO], Cork, Ireland
Preservation Action [9723], 401 F St. NW, Ste. 331, Washington, DC 20001, (202)637-7873
Preservation du bois Canada [★IO]
Preservation Inst. [13144], 2140 Shattuck Ave., Ste. 2122, Berkeley, CA 94704

Preservation Trades Network [609], PO Box 151, Burbank, OH 44214-0151, (330)465-1504
Preservation Volunteers [9724], 1995 Broadway, Ste. 605, New York, NY 10023, (212)769-2900
Pres. Benjamin Harrison Found. [10683], 1230 N Delaware St., Indianapolis, IN 46202, (317)631-1888
Presidential Classroom [8494], 119 Oronoco St., Alexandria, VA 22314-2015
Presidential Classroom for Young Americans [★8494]
Presidential and Democratic Party Victory Fund - Defunct.
Presidential Families of Am. [20656], 633 S Columbus St., Alexandria, VA 22314-4101
Presidential Prayer Team [19919], PO Box 15040, Scottsdale, AZ 85267-5040, (866)433-PRAY
Presidents Assn. - Defunct.
President's Award for Educational Excellence [★8749]
President's Commn. on the Holocaust [★17791]
Presidents Forum [★661]
Press
Alternative Press Center [10472]
Amer. Agricultural Editors' Assn. [2793]
Amer. Amateur Press Assn. [22105]
Amer. Assn. of Dental Editors [2794]
Amer. Assn. of Independent News Distributors [2795]
Amer. Copy Editors Soc. [2796]
Amer. Jewish Press Assn. [2797]
Amer. Medical Writers Assn. [2798]
Amer. News Women's Club [2799]
Amer. Soc. of Bus. Publication Editors [2800]
Amer. Soc. of Magazine Editors [2801]
Amer. Soc. of News Editors [2802]
Asian Amer. Journalists Assn. [2803]
Assoc. Press [2804]
Assoc. Press Managing Editors [2805]
Assn. of Alternative Newsweeklies [2806]
Assn. of Amer. Editorial Cartoonists [2807]
Assn. of Capitol Reporters and Editors [5894]
Assn. of Earth Sci. Editors [2808]
Assn. of Earth Sci. Editors [2808]
Assn. of Educational Publishers [8744]
Assn. of Food Journalists [2809]
Assn. of Food Journalists [2809]
Assn. of Hea. Care Journalists [2810]
Assn. of Hea. Care Journalists [2810]
Assn. for Independent Creative Editors [2811]
Assn. for Women Journalists [2812]
Assn. for Women in Sports Media [2813]
Austrian Magazines Assn. [16152]
Austrian Newspaper Assn. [18596]
Baseball Writers Assn. of Am. [2814]
Boating Writers Intl. [2815]
Boating Writers Intl. [2815]
Bowling Writers Assn. of Am. [2816]
Catholic News Ser. [2817]
Chess Journalists of Am. [2818]
Columbia Scholastic Press Advisers Assn. [8745]
Columbia Scholastic Press Assn. [8746]
Comm. of Concerned Journalists [2819]
Community Newspapers of Australia [16163]
Constr. Writers Assn. [2820]
Constr. Writers Assn. [2820]
Coun. for the Advancement of Sci. Writing [2821]
Coun. of Literary Magazines and Presses [10473]
Coun. of Sci. Editors [2822]
Deadline Club [2823]
Dog Writers' Assn. of Am. [2824]
Editorial Freelancers Assn. [2825]
Educ. Writers Assn. [2826]
Fine Press Book Assn. [2827]
Foreign Press Assn. [2828]
Graphic Arts Employers of Am. [23211]
Hollywood Foreign Press Assn. [2829]
Intl. Center for Journalists [2830]
Intl. Center for Journalists [2830]
Intl. Food, Wine and Travel Writers Assn. [2831]
Intl. Food, Wine and Travel Writers Assn. [2831]
Intl. Foodservice Editorial Coun. [2832]
Intl. Foodservice Editorial Coun. [2832]
Intl. Motor Press Assn. [2833]
Intl. Motor Press Assn. [2833]

Intl. Newspaper Gp. [2834]
Intl. Sci. Writers Assn. [2835]
Intl. Sci. Writers Assn. [2835]
Intl. Soc. of Weekly Newspaper Editors [2836]
Intl. Soc. of Weekly Newspaper Editors [2836]
Investigative Reporters and Editors [2837]
Investigative Reporters and Editors [2837]
Jazz Journalists Assn. [2838]
Jazz Journalists Assn. [2838]
Military Reporters and Editors [5895]
Millwright Gp. [23221]
Natl. Acad. of TV Journalists [2839]
Natl. Amateur Press Assn. [22106]
Natl. Arab Amer. Journalists Assn. [2840]
Natl. Assn. of Black Journalists [2841]
Natl. Assn. of Hispanic Journalists [2842]
Natl. Assn. of Home and Workshop Writers [2843]
Natl. Assn. of Independent Writers and Editors [2844]
Natl. Assn. of Real Estate Editors [2845]
Natl. Assn. of Sci. Writers [2846]
Natl. Assn. of Sci. Writers [2846]
Natl. Collegiate Baseball Writers Assn. [2847]
Natl. Conf. of Editorial Writers [2848]
Natl. Elementary Schools Press Assn. [8747]
Natl. Fed. of Press Women [2849]
Natl. Lesbian and Gay Journalists Assn. [2850]
Natl. News Bur. [2851]
Natl. Newspaper Assn. [2852]
Natl. Press Club [2853]
Natl. Press Found. [2854]
Natl. Scholastic Press Assn. [8748]
Natl. Soc. of Newspaper Columnists [2855]
Natl. Sportscasters and Sportswriters Assn. [2856]
Natl. Turf Writers Assn. [2857]
Natl. Writers Assn. [2858]
Native Amer. Journalists Assn. [2859]
New York Financial Writers' Assn. [2860]
Newspaper Assn. Managers [2861]
Newspaper Target Marketing Coalition [2576]
Newswomen's Club of New York [2862]
Online News Assn. [2863]
Org. of News Ombudsmen [2864]
Org. of News Ombudsmen [2864]
Outdoor Writers Assn. of Am. [2865]
Overseas Press Club of Am. [2866]
Overseas Press Club of Am. [2866]
Red Tag News Publications Assn. [2238]
Regional Reporters Assn. [2867]
Religion News Ser. [2868]
Religion News Ser. [2868]
Religion Newswriters Assn. [2869]
Soc. of Amer. Bus. Editors and Writers [2870]
Soc. of Amer. Travel Writers [2871]
Soc. for Features Journalism [2872]
Soc. for News Design [2873]
Soc. for News Design [2873]
Soc. of Professional Journalists [2874]
Soc. of the Silurians [2875]
South Asian Journalists Assn. [2876]
South Asian Journalists Assn. [2876]
Student Press Law Center [17358]
Travel Journalists Guild [2877]
United Amateur Press Assn. of Am. [22107]
United Nations Correspondents Assn. [2878]
United Nations Correspondents Assn. [2878]
United Press Intl. [2879]
United Press Intl. [2879]
U.S. Harness Writers' Assn. [2880]
U.S. Marine Corps Combat Correspondents Assn. [2881]
UNITY: Journalists of Color [2882]
White House Correspondents' Assn. [2883]
Women's Natl. Book Assn. [2884]
World Bowling Writers [2885]
World Bowling Writers [2885]
Press Complaints Commn. [IO], London, United Kingdom
Pressed Metal Inst. [★2491]
Pressure Gauge and Dial Thermometer Assn. [IO], Birmingham, United Kingdom
Pressure Sensitive Tape Coun. [58], 1833 Center Point Cir., Ste. 123, Naperville, IL 60563, (630)544-5048

Reference to "IO" in place of a book number signifies that the association may be found in the 50th edition of International Organizations.

Pressure Vessel Mfrs. Assn. [1861], 800 Roosevelt Rd., Bldg. C, Ste. 312, Glen Ellyn, IL 60137, (630)942-6590

Pressure Vessel Res. Coun. [2758], PO Box 1942, New York, NY 10156, (216)658-3847

Pressure Washer Mfrs. Assn. [1862], 1300 Sumner Ave., Cleveland, OH 44115-2851, (216)241-7333

Prestressed Concrete Assn. [IO], Leicester, United Kingdom

Pretrial Justice Inst. [5765], 730 11th St. NW, Ste. 302, Washington, DC 20001, (202)638-3080

Pretrial Services Rsrc. Center [★5765]

Prevent Blindness Am. [17112], 211 W Wacker Dr., Ste. 1700, Chicago, IL 60606, (800)331-2020

Prevent Cancer Found. [13970], 1600 Duke St., Ste. 500, Alexandria, VA 22314, (703)836-4412

Prevent Child Abuse [11392], 228 S Wabash Ave., 10th Fl., Chicago, IL 60611-3703, (312)663-3520

Prevent Child Abuse [11392], 228 S Wabash Ave., 10th Fl., Chicago, IL 60611-3703, (312)663-3520

Prevent a Litter Coalition [11027], PO Box 688, Great Falls, VA 22066, (703)818-8009

Prevent Nuclear Terrorism Org. [18718], PO Box 60489, Palo Alto, CA 94306, (650)857-0898

Preventive Cardiovascular Nurses Assn. [15797], 613 Williamson St., Ste. 200, Madison, WI 53703, (608)250-2440

Preventive Medicine
 Alliance for Natural Hea. USA [16302]
 Alliance for Wellness ROI [16303]
 Amer. Assn. of Nutritional Consultants [15814]
 Amer. Bd. of Nutrition [15815]
 Amer. Bd. of Preventive Medicine [16304]
 Amer. Coll. for Advancement in Medicine [16305]
 Amer. Coll. for Advancement in Medicine [16305]
 Amer. Coll. of Preventive Medicine [16306]
 Amer. Inst. for Preventive Medicine [16307]
 Amer. Inst. for Preventive Medicine [16307]
 Amer. Soc. for Clinical Nutrition [15821]
 Assn. for Prevention Teaching and Res. [16308]
 Center for Sports and Osteopathic Medicine [16309]
 Hearing Educ. and Awareness for Rockers [16310]
 Natl. Insulin Resistance Coun. [16311]
 Natl. Wellness Inst. [16312]
 Natl. Wellness Inst. [16312]
 San Francisco AIDS Found. [13624]
 Soft Power Hea. [15213]

Priatelia Zeme Slovensko [★IO]

Price-Pottenger Found. [★15843]

Price-Pottenger Nutrition Found. [15843], 7890 Broadway, Lemon Grove, CA 91945, (619)462-7600

PRICE Users Assn. [★6460]

PRICE Users Assn. [★6460]

PRIDE Found. - Promote Real Independence for the Disabled and Elderly [11824], 391 Long Hill Rd., Groton, CT 06340-1293, (860)455-7320

PRIDE Youth Programs [13284], 4 W Oak St., Fremont, MI 49412, (231)924-1662

Priests for Equality - Address unknown since 2010.

Priests Eucharistic League [★19416]

Priests for Life [18564], PO Box 141172, Staten Island, NY 10314, (718)980-4400

Primarily Primates, Inc. [11028], 26099 Dull Knife Trail, San Antonio, TX 78255, (830)755-4616

Primary Biliary Cirrhosis Org. [14417], 1430 Garden Rd., Pearland, TX 77581, (281)997-1516

Primary Glass Mfrs. Coun. - Defunct.

Primary Immunodeficiency Assn. [IO], London, United Kingdom

Primate Rescue Center [11029], 2515 Bethel Rd., Nicholasville, KY 40356, (859)858-4866

Primate Soc. of Great Britain [IO], St. Andrews, United Kingdom

Primates
 Ape Action Africa [5027]
 Ape Conservation Effort [5028]
 Pan African Sanctuary Alliance [5106]

Primatological Soc; Intl. [6143]

Primatological Soc; Intl. [6143]

Primatologists; Amer. Soc. of [6131]

Primer [★18586]

Primero Agua [13428], 2675 Stonecrest Dr., Washington, MO 63090, (636)239-1573

Prince of Asturias Found. [IO], Oviedo, Spain

Prince Edward Island 4-H [IO], Charlottetown, PE, Canada

Prince Edward Island Assn. of Social Workers [IO], Charlottetown, PE, Canada

Prince Edward Island Coun. of the Arts [IO], Charlottetown, PE, Canada

Prince George Brain Injured Gp. Soc. [IO], Prince George, BC, Canada

Prince of Wales Intl. Bus. Leaders Forum [IO], London, United Kingdom

Princess Kitty Fan Club [23788], PO Box 430784, Miami, FL 33243-0784, (305)661-0528

Principals
 Natl. Assn. of Elementary School Principals [8749]
 Natl. Assn. of Principals of Schools for Girls [8750]
 Natl. Assn. of Secondary School Principals [8751]

Principals Australia [IO], Hindmarsh, Australia

Prindle Class Assn. - Address unknown since 2010.

Print Alliance Credit Exchange [1324], ABC - Amega, Inc., 1100 Main St., Buffalo, NY 14209, (716)878-9504

Print Associates Credit Exchange [★1324]

The Print Center [9251], 1614 Latimer St., Philadelphia, PA 19103, (215)735-6090

The Print Center [9251], 1614 Latimer St., Philadelphia, PA 19103, (215)735-6090

The Print Club [★9251]

The Print Club [★9251]

Print Coun. of Am. [9198], The Art Inst. of Chicago, Dept. of Drawings and Prints, 111 S Michigan Ave., Chicago, IL 60603, (312)857-7162

Print and Media Assn. Singapore [IO], Singapore, Singapore

Print Media South Africa [IO], Parklands, Republic of South Africa

Print Services and Distribution Assn. [3354], 401 N Michigan Ave., Ste. 2200, Chicago, IL 60611, (800)230-0175

Printing Brokerage Assn. [★1627]

Printing Brokerage Assn. [★1627]

Printing Brokerage/Buyers Assn. [1627], PO Box 744, Palm Beach, FL 33480, (215)821-6581

Printing Brokerage/Buyers Assn. [1627], PO Box 744, Palm Beach, FL 33480, (215)821-6581

Printing Brokerage/Buyers Assn. Intl. [★1627]

Printing Brokerage/Buyers Assn. Intl. [★1627]

Printing Equip. and Supply Dealers' Assn. [IO], Bolton, ON, Canada

Printing and Graphics Indus. Assn. of Alberta [IO], Calgary, AB, Canada

Printing Historical Soc. [IO], London, United Kingdom

Printing Indus. of Am. [1628], 200 Deer Run Rd., Sewickley, PA 15143, (412)741-6860

Printing Indus. Fed. of South Africa [IO], Honeydew, Republic of South Africa

Printing Indus. of Am. [★1628]

Printing Indus. Assn. of the Slovak Republic [IO], Bratislava, Slovakia

Printing Indus. Credit Executives [993], 1100 Main St., Buffalo, NY 14209, (800)226-0722

Prism Comics [803], 12111 Marlowe Dr., Garden Grove, CA 92841, (714)258-6457

PRISM Intl. [1907], 1418 Aversboro Rd., Ste. 201, Garner, NC 27529, (919)771-0657

PRISM Intl. [1907], 1418 Aversboro Rd., Ste. 201, Garner, NC 27529, (919)771-0657

PRISMS: Parents and Researchers Interested In Smith-Magenis Syndrome [14623], 21800 Town Center Plz., Ste. No. 266A-633, Sterling, VA 20164, (972)231-0035

PRISMS: Parents and Researchers Interested In Smith-Magenis Syndrome [14623], 21800 Town Center Plz., Ste. No. 266A-633, Sterling, VA 20164, (972)231-0035

Prison-Ashram Proj. [11729], Human Kindness Found., PO Box 61619, Durham, NC 27715, (919)383-5160

Prison Atheist League of America - Defunct.

Prison Fellowship [★11731]

Prison Fellowship Intl. [11730], PO Box 17434, Washington, DC 20041, (703)481-0000

Prison Fellowship Intl. [11730], PO Box 17434, Washington, DC 20041, (703)481-0000

Prison Fellowship Ministries [11731], PO Box 1550, Merrifield, VA 22116-1550, (877)478-0100

Prison Fellowship Scotland [IO], Glasgow, United Kingdom

Prison Hospice Assn; Natl. [15030]

Prison Mission Assn. [20083], PO Box 2300, Port Orchard, WA 98366-0690, (360)876-0918

Prison Pen Pals - Address unknown since 2010.

Prison Res. Educ. Action Proj. [★11733]

Prisoners
 Acad. of Criminal Justice Sciences [11698]
 ACLU | Natl. Prison Proj. [11699]
 All of Us or None [17256]
 Assn. of State Correctional Administrators [11706]
 Bible Believers Fellowship [20166]
 Center for Stud. in Criminal Justice [11707]
 Christ Truth Ministries [19346]
 Critical Resistance [18401]
 Hea. through Walls [15182]
 Intl. Assn. for Correctional and Forensic Psychology [11715]
 Intl. Network of Prison Ministries [19992]
 Jewish Prisoner Services Intl. [19874]
 November Coalition [18681]

Prisoners Abroad [IO], London, United Kingdom

Prisoners Bible Broadcast [★19346]

Prisoners' Friends' Assn. [IO], Hong Kong, People's Republic of China

Prisoners' Rights Union [11732], PO Box 161321, Sacramento, CA 95816-1321, (916)422-2240

Prisoner's Union [★11732]

Prisoners of War
 Amer. Ex-Prisoners of War [20755]
 Natl. Alliance of Families for the Return of America's Missing Servicemen [20756]
 P.O.W. Network [20757]
 Rolling Thunder [20758]

Privacy Intl. [IO], London, United Kingdom

Privacy Rights CH [2886], 3100 5th Ave., Ste. B, San Diego, CA 92103, (619)298-3396

Private Agencies Collaborating Together [★12356]

Private Agencies Collaborating Together [6062], 1828 L St. NW, Ste. 300, Washington, DC 20036, (202)466-5666

Private Agencies Collaborating Together [6062], 1828 L St. NW, Ste. 300, Washington, DC 20036, (202)466-5666

Private Art Dealers Assn. [258], PO Box 872, Lenox Hill Sta., New York, NY 10021, (212)572-0772

Private Citizen, Inc. [17321], PO Box 233, Naperville, IL 60566, (630)393-2370

Private Communications Assn. [★8894]

Private Duty Homecare Assn. [15015], 228 7th St. SE, Washington, DC 20003, (202)547-7424

Private Enterprise Res. Center [17722], Texas A&M Univ., 4231 TAMU, College Station, TX 77843-4231, (979)845-7722

Private Equity CFO Assn. [1325], 28 State St., 14th Fl., Boston, MA 02109

Private Label Assn. [IO], Lisbon, Portugal

Private Label Mfrs. Assn. [2421], 630 3rd Ave., New York, NY 10017, (212)972-3131

Private Libraries Assn. [IO], Middlesex, United Kingdom

Private Motor Truck Coun. of Canada [IO], Oakville, ON, Canada

Private Practitioners of Pathology Found. [★16114]

Private Radio
 Assn. of Clandestine Radio Enthusiasts [20934]

Private Schools
 The Assn. of Boarding Schools [8752]
 Assn. of Private Enterprise Educ. [8753]
 Assn. of Private Enterprise Educ. [8753]
 Coun. for Amer. Private Educ. [8754]
 Natl. Assn. of State Administrators and Supervisor of Private Schools [8755]

Private Sector Coun. [17476], Partnership for Public Ser., 1100 New York Ave. NW, Ste. 1090 E, Washington, DC 20005, (202)775-9111

Private Sector Org. of Jamaica [IO], Kingston, Jamaica

Private Security Liaison Coun. - Defunct.

Private Truck Coun. of Am. [★3525]

A star before a book entry number signifies that the name is not listed separately, but is mentioned within the entry.

Privatization
Privacy Rights CH **[2886]**
Privatization Center **[★5855]**
Privatization Coun., Inc. **[★17720]**
Prize4Life **[15632]**, PO Box 425783, Cambridge, MA 02142-0015, (617)500-7527
Pro Athletes Outreach **[19769]**, PO Box 801, Palo Alto, CA 94302, (650)206-2962
Pro Bike **[★22484]**
Pro-Choice Am; NARAL **[18525]**
Pro-Choice Public Educ. Proj. **[10770]**, PO Box 3952, New York, NY 10163, (212)977-4266
Pro Energy Alliance **[1175]**, PO Box 3983, Salt Lake City, UT 84110, (888)316-8285
Pro Familia: Deutsche Gesellschaft fur Familienplanung, Sexualpadagogik und Sexualberatung **[IO]**, Frankfurt, Germany
Pro Familia Hungarian Sci. Soc. **[IO]**, Budapest, Hungary
Pro Helvetia Arts Coun. of Switzerland **[IO]**, Zurich, Switzerland
Pro Legends **[★22592]**
Pro-Life Action League **[18565]**, 6160 N Cicero Ave., Ste. 600, Chicago, IL 60646, (773)777-2900
Pro-Life Action League **[18565]**, 6160 N Cicero Ave., Ste. 600, Chicago, IL 60646, (773)777-2900
Pro-Life Alliance of Gays and Lesbians **[12944]**, PO Box 3005, York, PA 17402, (202)223-6697
Pro-Life Movement of the Czech Republic **[IO]**, Prague, Czech Republic
Pro Mujer **[13475]**, 253 W 35th St., 11th Fl., New York, NY 10001, (646)626-7000
Pro Natura **[★IO]**
Pro Players Assn. **[13403]**, PO Box 1233, Castle Rock, CO 80104, (720)327-9207
Pro Sanctity Movement **[19487]**, 11002 N 204th St., Elkhorn, NE 68022-3800, (402)289-2670
Pro Stock Owners Assn. - Defunct.
Pro Vita Advisors **[20224]**, PO Box 292813, Dayton, OH 45429, (937)306-1504
Pro vs. GI Joe **[21762]**, 4 Montage, Irvine, CA 92614-8112, (818)371-1283
Probate Law
Amer. Coll. of Trust and Estate Counsel **[5896]**
Probation Boards' Assn. **[IO]**, London, United Kingdom
Probe Intl. **[IO]**, Toronto, ON, Canada
Probe Ministries Intl. **[7860]**, 2001 W Plano Pkwy., Ste. 2000, Plano, TX 75075, (972)941-4565
Probe Ministries Intl. **[7860]**, 2001 W Plano Pkwy., Ste. 2000, Plano, TX 75075, (972)941-4565
Process Equip. Mfrs. Assn. **[1863]**, 201 Park Washington Ct., Falls Church, VA 22046-4527, (703)538-1796
Process Gas Consumers Gp. **[17468]**, 601 13th St. NW, Washington, DC 20004-2415, (202)661-2225
Process Serving
Natl. Assn. of Professional Process Servers **[5897]**
Processed Apples Inst. **[★449]**
Processed Apples Inst. **[★4426]**
Processed Vegetable Growers Assn. **[IO]**, Louth, United Kingdom
Processors' and Growers' Res. Org. **[IO]**, Peterborough, United Kingdom
ProChiropractic Europe **[IO]**, Copenhagen, Denmark
ProChoice Rsrc. Center - Defunct.
Procicaribe - Caribbean Agricultural Sci. and Tech. Network Sys. **[IO]**, St. Augustine, Trinidad and Tobago
Proctology
Amer. Bd. of Colon and Rectal Surgery **[16313]**
Amer. Soc. of Colon and Rectal Surgeons **[16314]**
Intl. Assn. of Colon Therapy **[16315]**
Intl. Assn. of Colon Therapy **[16315]**
Procurement and Supply Chain Benchmarking Assn. **[700]**, 4606 FM 1960 W, Ste. 250, Houston, TX 77069-9949, (281)440-5044
Produce
Natl. Barley Growers Assn. **[4373]**
Produce Marketing Assn. **[4723]**, PO Box 6036, Newark, DE 19714-6026, (302)738-7100
Produce Marketing Assn. **[4723]**, PO Box 6036, Newark, DE 19714-6026, (302)738-7100
Produce Packaging Assn. **[★4723]**

Produce Packaging Assn. **[★4723]**
Produce Packaging and Marketing Assn. **[★4723]**
Produce Packaging and Marketing Assn. **[★4723]**
Produce Prepackaging Assn. **[★4723]**
Produce Prepackaging Assn. **[★4723]**
Producers Alliance for Cinema and TV **[IO]**, London, United Kingdom
Producers Commn. Assn. **[★4724]**
Producers and Composers of Applied Music **[IO]**, Malvern, United Kingdom
Producers Guild of Am. **[1266]**, 8530 Wilshire Blvd., Ste. 450, Beverly Hills, CA 90211-3115, (310)358-9020
Producers Livestock Marketing Assn. **[4724]**, PO Box 540477, North Salt Lake, UT 84054-0477, (801)936-2424
Producers and Mfrs. Assn. **[★4933]**
Prdt. Development and Mgt. Assn. **[2301]**, 401 N Michigan Ave., Chicago, IL 60611, (856)439-9052
The Prdt. Liability Alliance - Address unknown since 2010.
Product Testing
CR Found. **[14277]**
Intl. Air Filtration Certifiers Assn. **[1705]**
Intl. Assn. for Prdt. Development **[2887]**
Intl. Assn. for Prdt. Development **[2887]**
Intl. Consumer Prdt. Hea. and Safety Org. **[2888]**
Intl. Consumer Prdt. Hea. and Safety Org. **[2888]**
Intl. Coun. for Quality Function Deployment **[2889]**
Producteurs d'oeufs d'incubation du Canada **[★IO]**
Production Engine Rebuilders Assn. **[★1185]**
Production Engine Remanufacturers Assn. **[1185]**, 28203 Woodhaven Rd., Edwards, MO 65326, (417)998-5057
Production Engg. Assn. **[IO]**, Guildford, United Kingdom
Production Equip. Rental Assn. - Address unknown since 2011.
Production Guild of Great Britain **[IO]**, Aylesbury, United Kingdom
Production Managers Assn. **[IO]**, London, United Kingdom
Production Music Library Assn. - Defunct.
Production and Operations Mgt. Soc. **[2302]**, Prof. Chelliah Sriskandarajah, PhD, Assoc. Exec. Dir., The Univ. of Texas at Dallas, School of Mgt., 2601 N Floyd Rd., Richardson, TX 75080, (972)883-4047
Production and Operations Mgt. Soc. **[2302]**, Prof. Chelliah Sriskandarajah, PhD, Assoc. Exec. Dir., The Univ. of Texas at Dallas, School of Mgt., 2601 N Floyd Rd., Richardson, TX 75080, (972)883-4047
Production Services Assn. **[IO]**, Bath, United Kingdom
Productivity Assn. of Pakistan **[IO]**, Islamabad, Pakistan
Productschap Vis **[★IO]**
Produits alimentaires et de consommation du Canada **[★IO]**
ProEnglish **[9579]**, 1601 N Kent St., Ste. 1100, Arlington, VA 22209, (703)816-8821
Proetica **[IO]**, Lima, Peru
Prof. Dr. G.A. Lindeboom Inst. **[IO]**, Ede, Netherlands
Prof. Dr. G.A. Lindeboom Instituut **[★IO]**
Professional Accounting Soc. of Am. **[52]**, 986 Colina Vista, Ventura, CA 93003
Professional Administrative Co-Employers **[1159]**, Ray O'Leary, Admin., 3535 S Woodland Cir., Quinton, VA 23141, (804)932-9159
Professional Aerial Photographers Assn. **[2731]**, 10351 Stella Link Rd., Houston, TX 77025, (713)721-6593
Professional Aerial Photographers Assn. **[2731]**, 10351 Stella Link Rd., Houston, TX 77025, (713)721-6593
Professional Aeromedical Transport Assn. - Defunct.
Professional Airways Systems Specialists **[23155]**, 1150 17th St. NW, Ste. 702, Washington, DC 20036-4603, (202)293-7277
Professional Anglers Assn. **[IO]**, Stoneleigh, United Kingdom
Professional Animal Auditor Certification Org. **[53]**, PO Box 31, Redfield, IA 50233-0031, (402)403-0104

Professional Archers Assn. - Defunct.
Professional Armed Forces Rodeo Assn. **[22848]**, Val Baker, Sec., 1985 1st St. W, No. 2523, Randolph, TX 78150-4312
Professional Armed Forces Rodeo Assn. **[22848]**, Val Baker, Sec., 1985 1st St. W, No. 2523, Randolph, TX 78150-4312
Professional Assn. of Alexander Teachers **[IO]**, Birmingham, United Kingdom
Professional Assn. of Canadian Theatres **[IO]**, Toronto, ON, Canada
Professional Assn. for Contract Employment - Address unknown since 2011.
Professional Assn. of Custom Clothiers **[★202]**
Professional Assn. of Diving Instructors **[23105]**, 30151 Tomas St., Rancho Santa Margarita, CA 92688-2125, (949)858-7234
Professional Assn. of Diving Instructors **[23105]**, 30151 Tomas St., Rancho Santa Margarita, CA 92688-2125, (949)858-7234
Professional Assn. of Foreign Ser. Officers **[IO]**, Ottawa, ON, Canada
Professional Assn. of German Yoga Instructors **[IO]**, Gottingen, Germany
Professional Assn. of Hea. Care Off. Mgt. **[15300]**, 1576 Bella Cruz Dr., Ste. 360, Lady Lake, FL 32159, (800)451-9311
Professional Assn. of Hea. Care Off. Managers **[★15300]**
Professional Assn. of Innkeepers Intl. **[1771]**, 207 White Horse Pike, Haddon Heights, NJ 08035, (856)310-1102
Professional Assn. of Innkeepers Intl. **[1771]**, 207 White Horse Pike, Haddon Heights, NJ 08035, (856)310-1102
Professional Assn. for Investment Communications Resources **[2150]**, 12100 Sunset Hills Rd., Ste. 130, Reston, VA 20190, (866)993-0999
Professional Assn. of Parasail Operators **[23123]**, 844 W Mission Bay Dr., Ste. A, San Diego, CA 92109, (858)488-9100
Professional Assn. of Resume Writers and Career Coaches **[11957]**, 1388 Brightwaters Blvd. NE, St. Petersburg, FL 33704-1336, (727)821-2274
Professional Assn. of Small Bus. Accountants **[54]**, 6405 Metcalf Ave., Ste. 503, Shawnee Mission, KS 66202, (866)296-0001
Professional Assn. for SQL Server **[6554]**, 203 N LaSalle St., Ste. 2100, Chicago, IL 60601, (425)967-8000
Professional Assn. of Volleyball Officials **[23027]**, PO Box 780, Oxford, KS 67119, (888)791-2074
Professional Audio Mfrs. Alliance **[1115]**, 11242 Waples Mill Rd., Ste. 200, Fairfax, VA 22030, (703)279-9938
Professional Audiovideo Retailers Assn. **[★1094]**
Professional Audiovideo Retailers Assn. - Defunct.
Professional Autograph Dealers Assn. **[797]**, PO Box 1729W, Murray Hill Sta., New York, NY 10016
Professional Aviation Maintenance Assn. **[154]**, 400 N Washington St., Ste. 300, Alexandria, VA 22314, (703)778-4647
Professional Bail Agents of the U.S. **[5297]**, 1301 Pennsylvania Ave. NW, Ste. 925, Washington, DC 20004, (202)783-4120
Professional Baseball Athletic Trainers Soc. **[22289]**, PO Box 386, Atlanta, GA 30361
Professional Basketball Writers' Assn. - Defunct.
Professional Beauty Assn. | Nail Mfrs. Coun. **[974]**, 15825 N 71st St., Ste. 100, Scottsdale, AZ 85254, (480)281-0424
Professional Beauty Assn. | Natl. Cosmetology Assn. **[975]**, 15825 N 71st St., Ste. 100, Scottsdale, AZ 85254, (480)281-0424
Professional Boatman's Assn. **[IO]**, Yapton, United Kingdom
Professional Bodyguard Assn. **[IO]**, Durham, United Kingdom
Professional Bowhunter's Soc. **[22228]**, PO Box 246, Terrell, NC 28682, (704)664-2534
Professional Bowlers Assn. of Am. **[22428]**, 719 2nd Ave., Ste. 701, Seattle, WA 98104-1747, (206)332-9688
Professional Bowls Assn. **[IO]**, Blackpool, United Kingdom

Reference to "IO" in place of a book number signifies that the association may be found in the 50th edition of International Organizations.

Professional Car Soc. [21155], Jeff Hookway, Sec./ Membership Dir., 201 Glenside Trail, Sparta, NJ 07871-1249

Professional Climbing Instructors Assn. [22455], PO Box 784, Bishop, CA 93515, (310)455-1830

Professional Coaches, Mentors and Advisors [22468], PO Box 265, Palos Verdes Estates, CA 90274-0265, (800)768-6017

Professional Coaches and Mentors Assn. [★22468]

Professional Cmpt. Assn. of Lebanon [IO], Beirut, Lebanon

Professional Computing Assn. [IO], Royston, United Kingdom

Professional Constr. Estimators Assn. of Am. [948], PO Box 680336, Charlotte, NC 28216, (704)489-1494

Professional Contractors Gp. [IO], West Drayton, United Kingdom

Professional Convention Mgt. Assn. [2457], 35 E Wacker Dr., Ste. 500, Chicago, IL 60601-2105, (312)423-7262

Professional Currency Dealers Assn. [21990], James A. Simek, Sec., PO Box 7157, Westchester, IL 60154

Professional Dance Teachers Assn. - Address unknown since 2011.

Professional Dancers Fed. [22495], 6830 N Broadway, Ste. D, Denver, CO 80221, (303)412-7712

Professional Decorative Painters Assn. [2614], PO Box 13427, Denver, CO 80201, (303)433-7372

Professional Development League [★5437]

Professional Disc Golf Assn. [IO], Toronto, ON, Canada

Professional Drag Racing Assn. [★22244]

Professional Drivers Coun. [★23302]

Professional Elecl. Apparatus Recyclers League [1084], 4255 S Buckley Rd., No. 118, Aurora, CO 80013, (877)AT-PEARL

Professional Engineers Ontario [IO], Toronto, ON, Canada

Professional Farmers of Am. [4364], PO Box 36, Cedar Falls, IA 50613, (319)277-1278

Professional Figure Skaters Cooperative [22897], PO Box 893, Park Forest, IL 60466, (312)296-7864

Professional Film and Video Equipment Assn. - Defunct.

Professional Football Chiropractic [14143], PO Box 842, Sumner, WA 98390, (253)948-6039

Professional Football Players Mothers' Assn. [22595], Gloria McDuffie, PO Box 451175, Sunrise, FL 33345

Professional Football Researchers Assn. [22596], 740 Deerfield Rd., Warminster, PA 18974

Professional Football Writers of Am. [22597], 12030 Cedar Lake Ct., Maryland Heights, MO 63043

Professional Footballers' Assn. [IO], Docklands, Australia

Professional Footballers' Assn. United Kingdom [IO], Manchester, United Kingdom

Professional Fraternity Assn. [23543], 1011 San Jacinto, Ste. 205, Austin, TX 78701, (512)789-9530

Professional Gardeners Guild [IO], Cambridge, United Kingdom

Professional Golf Club Repairmen's Assn. - Defunct.

Professional Golf Teachers Assn. of Am. [22621], PO Box 912, La Quinta, CA 92247, (760)777-1925

Professional Golfers' Assn. of Am. [22622], 100 Ave. of the Champions, Palm Beach Gardens, FL 33418, (561)624-8400

Professional Golfers' Assn. - England [IO], Sutton Coldfield, United Kingdom

Professional Golfers' Associations of Europe [IO], Sutton Coldfield, United Kingdom

Professional Grounds Mgt. Soc. [4517], 720 Light St., Baltimore, MD 21230-3816, (410)223-2861

Professional Handlers' Assn. [21638], 17017 Norbrook Dr., Olney, MD 20832-2623, (301)924-0089

Professional Housing Mgt. Assn. [5524], 154 Ft. Evans Rd. NE, Leesburg, VA 20176, (703)771-1888

Professional Hunters' Assn. of South Africa [IO], Centurion, Republic of South Africa

Professional Independent Mass Marketing Administrators [★2028]

Professional Inst. of the Public Ser. of Canada [IO], Ottawa, ON, Canada

Professional Insurance Communicators of Am. [815], PO Box 68700, Indianapolis, IN 46268-0700, (317)875-5250

Professional Insurance Marketing Assn. [2028], 230 E Ohio St., Ste. 400, Chicago, IL 60611, (817)569-7462

Professional Insurance Mass-Marketing Assn. [★2028]

Professional Intl. Network Soc. - Defunct.

Professional Knifemakers Assn. [21463], 2905 N Montana Ave., Ste. 30027, Helena, MT 59601, (903)489-1026

Professional Knitwear Designers Guild [★201]

Professional Knitwear Designers Guild [★201]

Professional Lacrosse Players Assn. [23299], 52 Haynes Rd., Sudbury, MA 01776

Professional Landcare Network [2183], 950 Herndon Pkwy., Ste. 450, Herndon, VA 20170, (703)736-9666

Professional Lawn Tennis Assn. of U.S. [★23064]

Professional Lawn Tennis Assn. of U.S. [★23064]

Professional Liability Underwriting Soc. [2029], 5353 Wayzata Blvd., Ste. 600, Minneapolis, MN 55416, (952)746-2580

Professional Liability Underwriting Soc. [2029], 5353 Wayzata Blvd., Ste. 600, Minneapolis, MN 55416, (952)746-2580

Professional Lighting and Sign Mgt. Companies of Am. [2223], 1100-H Brandywine Blvd., Zanesville, OH 43701-7303, (740)452-4541

Professional Lighting and Sound Assn. [IO], Eastbourne, United Kingdom

Professional Loadmaster Assn. [5828], PO Box 4351, Tacoma, WA 98438, (253)215-0118

Professional Managers Assn. [5435], PO Box 77235, Washington, DC 20013, (202)874-0126

Professional Mediation Assn. [5211], 1645 Martha Leeville Rd., Lebanon, TN 37090, (800)305-5978

Professional Numismatic Guild [★21991]

Professional Numismatists Guild [21991], 28441 Rancho California Rd., Ste. 106, Temecula, CA 92590, (951)587-8300

Professional Org. of Women in the Arts [9315], 365 Bridge St., Ste. 7F, Brooklyn, NY 11201

Professional and Organizational Development Network in Higher Educ. [8244], PO Box 3318, Nederland, CO 80466, (303)258-9521

Professional and Organizational Development Network in Higher Educ. [8244], PO Box 3318, Nederland, CO 80466, (303)258-9521

Professional Outdoor Media Assn. [2439], PO Box 1569, Johnstown, PA 15907, (814)254-4719

Professional Paddlesports Assn. [★3316]

Professional Photographers of Am. [2732], 229 Peachtree St. NE, Ste. 2200, Atlanta, GA 30303-1608, (404)522-8600

Professional Photographers of Canada [IO], Woodstock, ON, Canada

Professional Photographic Labs. Assn. [IO], Welwyn Garden City, United Kingdom

Professional Picture Framers Assn. [9199], 3000 Picture Pl., Jackson, MI 49201, (517)788-8100

Professional Pilots Fed. - Address unknown since 2011.

Professional Plant Users Gp. [IO], London, United Kingdom

Professional Putters Assn. [22623], 28 Sioux Trail, Ransom Canyon, TX 79366, (434)237-7888

Professional Rabbit Meat Assn. [4853], Denise Konzek, Sec.-Treas., 627 S Union St., Kennewick, WA 99336

Professional Racing Org. of Am. [★22489]

Professional Reactor Operator Soc. [7172], PO Box 484, Byron, IL 61010-0484, (815)234-8140

Professional Risk Managers' Intl. Assn. [2030], 400 Washington St., Northfield, MN 55057

Professional Rodeo Cowboys Assn. [22849], 101 Pro Rodeo Dr., Colorado Springs, CO 80919-2301, (719)593-8840

Professional School Photographers of Am. [★2733]

Professional School Photographers of Am. [★2733]

Professional School Photographers Assn. Intl. [2733], 11000 Viking Dr., 5th Fl., Eden Prairie, MN 55344, (952)826-4278

Professional School Photographers Assn. Intl. [2733], 11000 Viking Dr., 5th Fl., Eden Prairie, MN 55344, (952)826-4278

Professional Scripophily Trade Assn. [701], PO Box 223795, Chantilly, VA 20153, (703)579-4209

Professional Ser. Assn. [3238], 71 Columbia St., Cohoes, NY 12047, (518)237-7777

Professional Services Bus. Mgt. Assn. [★2266]

Professional Services Coun. [17723], 4401 Wilson Blvd., Ste. 1110, Arlington, VA 22203, (703)875-8059

Professional Services Mgt. Assn. [★2266]

Professional Skaters Assn. [22898], 3006 Allegro Park SW, Rochester, MN 55902, (507)281-5122

Professional Skaters Guild of Am. [★22898]

Professional Ski Instructors of Am. [22914], 133 S Van Gordon St., Ste. 200, Lakewood, CO 80228, (303)987-9390

Professional Ski Instructors of Am. Educational Foundation [★22914]

Professional Soc. of Forensic Mapping [5490], 4891 Independence St., Ste. 140, Wheat Ridge, CO 80033

Professional Soc. for Sales and Marketing Training [3166], 113 McHenry Rd., No. 141, Buffalo Grove, IL 60089, (973)882-3931

Professional Speakers Assn. of the Middle East [IO], Dubai, United Arab Emirates

Professional Sports Car Racing [★22246]

Professional Squash Assn. [IO], Cardiff, United Kingdom

Professional Teacher Associations Network [IO], Karachi, Pakistan

Professional and Tech. Consultants Assn. [867], PO Box 2261, Santa Clara, CA 95055, (408)971-5902

Professional Tennis Registry [23060], PO Box 4739, Hilton Head Island, SC 29938, (843)785-7244

Professional Tennis Registry - U.S.A. [★23060]

Professional Tour Guide Assn. of Australia [IO], Melbourne, Australia

Professional Truck Driver Inst. [3534], 555 E Braddock Rd., Alexandria, VA 22314-2182, (703)647-7015

Professional Truck Driver Inst. of Am. [★3534]

Professional Turf and Landscape Conf. [★2181]

Professional Union of the Building Sector [IO], Brussels, Belgium

Professional Union of Insurance Companies [IO], Brussels, Belgium

Professional Windsurfers Assn. [22385], PO Box 791656, Paia, HI 96779

Professional Women of Color Network [3688], PO Box 22367, Seattle, WA 98122, (206)568-3044

Professional Women in Constr. [949], 315 E 56th St., New York, NY 10022-3730, (212)486-4712

Professional Women Controllers [1326], PO Box 950085, Oklahoma City, OK 73195-0085

Professional Women in Healthcare [3689], 2200 Wilson Blvd., No. 102-364, Arlington, VA 22201, (703)243-1620

Professional Women Photographers [2734], 119 W 72nd St., No. 223, New York, NY 10023

Professional Women Singers Assn. [10283], PO Box 884, New York, NY 10159

Professional Women's Bowling Assn. - Defunct.

Professional Women's Rodeo Assn. [★22851]

Professional Yachtsmen's Assn. [IO], Antibes, France

Professionals

100 Women in Hedge Funds Assn. [1275]

146th Alumni Assn. [7727]

Accountability in Intl. Development [12308]

African Amer. Fed. Executive Assn. [5504]

Agricultural Commodities Certification Assn. [3749]

Algerian Amer. Scientists Assn. [7353]

Alliance of Legal Document Asst. Professionals [5751]

Alliance of Supplier Diversity Professionals [2969]

Alliance for Work-Life Progress [2890]

Amer. Accounts Payable Assn. [6]

Amer. Assn. of Anthropological Genetics [6895]

Amer. Assn. of Electronic Reporters and Transcribers [2891]

Amer. Assn. of Inside Sales Professionals [3156]

A star before a book entry number signifies that the name is not listed separately, but is mentioned within the entry.

Amer. Assn. of Snowboard Instructors [22923]
Amer. Assn. for Teaching and Curriculum [8941]
Amer. Bus. Assn. of Russian-speaking Professionals [2892]
Amer. Guild of Town Criers [10475]
Amer. Professional Wedding Photographers Assn. [2710]
Amer. Soc. of Cost Segregation Professionals [3381]
Amer. Soc. for Training and Development [2893]
Amer. Soc. for Training and Development [2893]
Arab Amer. Women's Coun. [18922]
ArchVoices [6190]
Asian Hea. Care Leaders Assn. [15288]
Assn. of African Amer. Financial Advisors [1334]
Assn. of Appraiser Regulatory Officials [227]
Assn. of Biblical Counselors [19631]
Assn. of Divorce Financial Planners [1335]
Assn. of Haitian Professionals [19021]
Assn. of Liberian Engineers USA [6786]
Assn. for Medical Ethics [14872]
Assn. of Nigerian Petroleum Professionals Abroad [7235]
Assn. of Professional Reserve Analysts [2894]
Assn. for Refugee Ser. Professionals [12301]
Assn. of Residential Cleaning Services Intl. [2240]
Assn. of Thai Professionals in Am. and Canada [19255]
Australian Soc. of Assn. Executives [6390]
Automotive Women's Alliance Found. [294]
Bionomics Intl. [7363]
Bridge Engg. Assn. [6789]
Bus. Architects Assn. [2595]
CARTHA [18402]
Chartered Alternative Investment Analyst Assn. [2134]
Coalition of Organic Landscapers [2179]
Coalition on the Public Understanding of Sci. [7365]
Continental Basketball League [22294]
Corporate Responsibility Officers Assn. [963]
Corporate Speech Pathology Network [3303]
Coun. of Supplier Diversity Professionals [715]
Creativity Coaching Assn. [22458]
Delta Sigma Delta [23498]
Energy Training Coun. [6723]
Ethiopian Geophysical Union Intl. [6920]
Football Writers Assn. of Am. [22588]
Fusion Architecture [6197]
Global Alliance of Artists [9234]
Global Sourcing Coun. [2602]
Govt. Investment Officers Assn. [5611]
Gp. Underwriters Assn. of Am. [1962]
Haitian Amer. Professionals Coalition [11592]
Humane Soc. Veterinary Medical Assn. [10985]
Interior Redesign Indus. Specialists [2060]
Intl. Amusement and Leisure Defense Assn. [3057]
Intl. Assn. of Certified Surveillance Professionals [3213]
Intl. Assn. for Cmpt. and Info. Sci. [6456]
Intl. Assn. of Facilitators [2895]
Intl. Assn. of Facilitators [2895]
Intl. Assn. of Torch Clubs [10474]
Intl. Intelligence Ethics Assn. [7001]
Intl. Janitorial Cleaning Services Assn. [2248]
Intl. League of Professional Baseball Clubs [22272]
Intl. Soc. for Aeolian Res. [6926]
Intl. Soc. for Aviation Photography [2724]
Intl. Soc. of Filipinos in Finance and Accounting [36]
Intl. Soc. for Hyaluronan Sciences [6274]
Intl. Soc. for Intelligence Res. [7002]
Intl. Soc. of Six Sigma Professionals [7295]
Intl. Soc. of Six Sigma Professionals [7295]
Intl. Soc. of Sustainability Professionals [4340]
Intl. Tamil Tech. Professionals' Org. [12346]
Kidney Community Emergency Response Coalition [15552]
Latino Engineers, Architects and Developers Soc. [7029]
Moroccan-American Soc. for Life Sciences [7141]
MSPAlliance [6547]
Natl. Amer. Semi-Professional Baseball Assn. [22279]

Natl. Assn. of Certified Public Bookkeepers [43]
Natl. Assn. of Diversity Officers in Higher Educ. [8238]
Natl. Assn. of Farm Bus. Anal. Specialists [165]
Natl. Assn. of Foreclosure Prevention Professionals [2899]
Natl. Assn. of Independent Real Estate Brokers [3021]
Natl. Assn. of Left-Handed Golfers [22617]
Natl. Assn. of Minority Govt. Contractors [928]
Natl. Assn. of Mortgage Processors [428]
Natl. Assn. of Pond Professionals [237]
Natl. Assn. of Professional Baseball Leagues [22280]
Natl. Assn. of Real Estate Consultants [3027]
Natl. Assn. of Reunion Managers [2896]
Natl. Assn. of Subrogation Professionals [2897]
Natl. Block and Bridle Club [23464]
Natl. Football League [22591]
Natl. Governmental Collectors Assn. [5500]
Natl. Latina Bus. Women Assn. [2188]
Natl. Org. of Professional Hispanic Natural Resources Conservation Ser. Employees [4521]
Natl. Soc. for Hispanic Professionals [695]
Natl. Title I Assn. [7677]
North Am. Chinese Clean-tech and Semiconductor Assn. [1112]
North Amer. Football League [22593]
North Amer. Young Generation in Nuclear [7168]
Overseas Chinese Entomologists Assn. [6849]
Philippine Nurses Assn. of Am. [15796]
PlanetQuest [6235]
Professional Climbing Instructors Assn. [22455]
Professional Golf Teachers Assn. of Am. [22621]
Professional Lighting and Sign Mgt. Companies of Am. [2223]
Professionals in Workers' Compensation [3704]
Public Architecture [243]
Scientists and Engineers for Am. [5314]
Security Anal. and Risk Mgt. Assn. [3227]
Slate Roofing Contractors Assn. of North Am. [617]
Soc. for Design and Process Sci. [6601]
Soc. for the History of Psychology [7312]
Soc. of Iranian Architects and Planners [6206]
Soc. of Sensory Professionals [7391]
Soc. for Terrorism Res. [7554]
Stock Artists Alliance [2737]
TechAssure Assn. [2045]
Total Practice Mgt. Assn. [5287]
Transported Asset Protection Assn. [7396]
U.S. Mountain Guides Assn. [22456]
U.S. Women in Nuclear [7173]
Upwardly Global [2898]
Urban Teacher Residency United [8962]
Water Innovations Alliance [7614]
Wedding Indus. Professionals Assn. [475]
Women's High Tech Coalition [7535]
Young Professionals in Energy [6763]
Professionals - Nicaragua - Defunct.
Professionals in Workers' Compensation [3704], PO Box 4435, Federal Way, WA 98063, (206)824-2899
Professionels Canadiens du ski et du surf des neiges [★IO]
Professionels en Produits Promotionnels du Canada [★IO]

Professions
Amer. Accounts Payable Assn. [6]
Amer. Guild of Town Criers [10475]
Amer. Professional Wedding Photographers Assn. [2710]
ArchVoices [6190]
Black Career Women [19205]
Bus. Architects Assn. [2595]
Catholic Social Workers Natl. Assn. [13216]
Community Managers Intl. Assn. [2277]
Delta Sigma Delta [23498]
Global Alliance of Artists [9234]
Interior Redesign Indus. Specialists [2060]
Intl. Assn. of Torch Clubs [10474]
Natl. Assn. of Workforce Development Professionals [11947]
Natl. Org. for Career Credentialing [727]
Overseas Chinese Entomologists Assn. [6849]

Phi Delta Gamma [23623]
Phi Delta Kappa [23624]
Total Practice Mgt. Assn. [5287]
Urban Teacher Residency United [8962]
Young Professionals in Energy [6763]
Professor Chen Wen-Chen Memorial Found. [18685], PO Box 136, Kingston, NJ 08528, (609)936-1352
Professors
Amer. Assn. of Univ. Professors [8756]
Assn. of Chinese Professors of Social Sciences in the U.S. [7409]
Assn. of Environmental Engg. and Sci. Professors [8757]
Assn. of Professors and Scholars of Iranian Heritage [8411]
Chinese-American Professors in Environmental Engg. and Sci. [6425]
Intercollegiate Stud. Inst. [17425]
Soc. of Chinese Amer. Professors and Scientists [8758]
Univ. Faculty for Life [8759]
Univ. Faculty for Life [8759]
Professors and Res. Sect. of the Division of Christian Educ. of the Natl. Coun. of Churches [★19686]
Profit Sharing/401k Coun. of Am. [1160], 20 N Wacker Dr., Ste. 3700, Chicago, IL 60606, (312)419-1863
Profit Sharing/401k Educ. Found. [1161], 20 N Wacker Dr., Ste. 3700, Chicago, IL 60606, (312)419-1863
Profit Sharing Coun. of Am. [★1160]
Profit Sharing Res. Found. [★1161]
Progeria Res. Found. [16779], PO Box 3453, Peabody, MA 01961-3453, (978)535-2594
Progeria Res. Found. [16779], PO Box 3453, Peabody, MA 01961-3453, (978)535-2594
Prog. of Academic Exchange [8374], 14 Willett Ave., Port Chester, NY 10573, (914)690-1340
Prog. of Academic Exchange [8374], 14 Willett Ave., Port Chester, NY 10573, (914)690-1340
Prog. for the Advancement of Res. on Conflict and Collaboration [18283], Syracuse Univ., 400 Eggers Hall, Syracuse, NY 13244-1020, (315)443-2367
Prog. on the Anal. and Resolution of Conflicts [★18283]
Prog. for Appropriate Tech. in Hea. [17197], 2201 Westlake Ave., Ste. 200, Seattle, WA 98121, (206)285-3500
Prog. for Appropriate Tech. in Hea. [17197], 2201 Westlake Ave., Ste. 200, Seattle, WA 98121, (206)285-3500
Prog. in Ethnographic Film [★6158]
Prog. for the Introduction and Adaptation of Contraceptive Tech. [★17197]
Prog. for the Introduction and Adaptation of Contraceptive Tech. [★17197]
Program for New Americans [★17249]
Prog. for Res. and Documentation for a Sustainable Soc. [IO], Oslo, Norway
Programa de las Naciones Unidas para el Desarrollo [★IO]
Programa de las Naciones Unidas para el Medio Ambiente [IO], Panama City, Panama
Programas Interculturales de Honduras [★IO]
Programme Alimentaire Mondiale [★IO]
Programme for Belize [IO], Belize City, Belize
Programme Intl. sur la Securite des Substances Chimiques [★IO]
Programme sur l'Homme et la Biosphere [★IO]
Programme des Nations Unies pour le developpement [★IO]
Programme des Nations Unies pour le developpment Cote d'Ivoire [★IO]
Programme des Nations Unies pour le developpement - Mali [★IO]
Programme des Nations Unies pour le developpement en Mauritanie [★IO]
Programme des Nations Unies pour le developpement - Togo [★IO]
Programme Parents-Secours du Canada [★IO]
Programme for the Stud. and Promotion of Representative Institutions [IO], Geneva, Switzerland

---

Reference to "IO" in place of a book number signifies that the association may be found in the 50th edition of International Organizations.

Programmers Guild [7525], PO Box 1250, Summit, NJ 07902-1250

Programming Languages

Assn. for Computing Machinery | Special Interest Gp. on Algorithms and Computation Theory [7296]

Assn. for Computing Machinery | Special Interest Gp. on the APL and J Languages [7297]

FORTH Interest Gp. [7298]

League for Programming Freedom [7299]

Rexx Language Assn. [7300]

Rexx Language Assn. [7300]

Special Interest Gp. on Ada [7301]

Special Interest Gp. on Programming Languages [7302]

Progress Educational Trust [IO], London, United Kingdom

Progress and Freedom Found. [17352], 1444 Eye St. NW, Ste. 500, Washington, DC 20005, (202)289-8928

Progressio [IO], London, United Kingdom

Progressive Democrats of Am. [17542], PO Box 150064, Grand Rapids, MI 49515, (877)239-2093

Progressive Found. - Address unknown since 2010.

Progressive Gardening Trade Assn. [4496], 10210 Leatherleaf Ct., Manassas, VA 20111-4245, (703)392-5890

Progressive Hea. Partnership [15204], PO Box 98025, Durham, NC 27708, (708)365-9564

Progressive Jewish Network/New Jewish Agenda - Defunct.

Progressive Labor Party [18362], PO Box 808, Brooklyn, NY 11202, (212)629-0002

Progressive Librarians Guild [10005], Rider Univ. Lib., 2083 Lawrenceville Rd., Lawrenceville, NJ 08648

Progressive Osseous Heteroplasia Assn. [14624], 5327 Westpointe Plaza Dr., No. 113, Columbus, OH 43228, (614)887-7642

Progressive Policy Inst. [18489], 1101 14th St. NW, Ste. 1250, Washington, DC 20005, (202)525-3926

Progressive Supranuclear Palsy Assn. - Europe [IO], Towcester, United Kingdom

Progressive Tech. Proj. [7526], 2801 21st Ave. S, Ste. 132E, Minneapolis, MN 55407, (612)724-2600

Prohibition Natl. Comm. [18363], PO Box 2635, Denver, CO 80201, (303)237-4947

Project Africa [★23646]

Proj. Americana [★18634]

Proj. Appleseed: The Natl. Campaign for Public School Improvement [8086], 520 Melville Ave., St. Louis, MO 63130-4506, (314)292-9760

Proj. Baobab [13553], 340 Churchill Ave., Palo Alto, CA 94301-1704, (650)328-9332

Proj. Censored [17227], PO Box 571, Cotati, CA 94931-0571, (707)874-2695

Proj. Children [11497], PO Box 933, Greenwood Lake, NY 10925, (845)477-3472

Proj. Children [11497], PO Box 933, Greenwood Lake, NY 10925, (845)477-3472

Proj. Concern, Inc. [★15205]

Proj. Concern, Inc. [★15205]

Proj. Concern Intl. [15205], 5151 Murphy Canyon Rd., Ste. 320, San Diego, CA 92123-4339, (858)279-9690

Proj. Concern Intl. [15205], 5151 Murphy Canyon Rd., Ste. 320, San Diego, CA 92123-4339, (858)279-9690

Project Connect - Defunct.

Proj. Cuddle [11393], 2973 Harbor Blvd., No. 326, Costa Mesa, CA 92626, (714)432-9681

Proj. on Defense Alternatives [17511], The Commonwealth Inst., PO Box 398105, Inman Sq. Post Off., Cambridge, MA 02139, (617)547-4474

Project Equus - Defunct.

Proj. on Ethnic Relations [17862], 15 Chambers St., Princeton, NJ 08542-3707, (609)683-5666

Proj. EverGreen [4683], PO Box 156, New Prague, MN 56071, (952)758-9135

Proj. Exports Promotion Coun. of India [IO], New Delhi, India

Proj. Food, Land and People [3764], 65 Poinsettia Rd. SE, Scio, OH 43988, (330)627-5712

Proj. Genesis [8432], 122 Slade Ave., Ste. 250, Baltimore, MD 21208, (410)602-1350

Proj. on Govt. Oversight [18138], 1100 G St. NW, Ste. 900, Washington, DC 20005-3806, (202)347-1122

Proj. Harmony [8375], 5197 Main St., Unit 6, Waitsfield, VT 05673, (802)496-4545

Proj.: Hearts and Minds [12479], PO Box 252, Thornwood, NY 10594

Proj. HOPE [14738], 255 Carter Hall Ln., Millwood, VA 22646, (540)837-2100

Proj. HOPE [14738], 255 Carter Hall Ln., Millwood, VA 22646, (540)837-2100

Proj. Hope to Abolish the Death Penalty [17222], PO Box 1362, Lanett, AL 36863, (334)499-0003

Proj. Human Aid [IO], Konstanz, Germany

Proj. Inform [13623], 1375 Mission St., San Francisco, CA 94103-2621, (415)558-8669

Proj. Kids Worldwide [14095], 530 1st Ave., Ste. 9Z, New York, NY 10016, (212)263-8141

Proj. Lighthawk [★4092]

Proj. Magic [16869], Stormont-Vail West, 3707 SW 6th Ave., Topeka, KS 66606, (785)270-4610

Proj. Mgt. Assn. of Denmark [IO], Hillerod, Denmark

Proj. Mgt. Assn. of Finland [IO], Helsinki, Finland

Proj. Mgt. Assn. of Iceland [IO], Reykjavik, Iceland

Proj. Mgt. Assn. of Slovakia [IO], Trnava, Slovakia

Proj. Mgt. Inst. [2303], 14 Campus Blvd., Newtown Square, PA 19073-3299, (610)356-4600

Proj. Mgt. Inst. [2303], 14 Campus Blvd., Newtown Square, PA 19073-3299, (610)356-4600

Proj. Mgt. South Africa [IO], Johannesburg, Republic of South Africa

Proj. on Military Procurement [★18138]

Proj. Mind Found. [IO], Jerusalem, Israel

Proj. Orbis [★15973]

Proj. Orbis [★15973]

Project Overcome - Defunct.

Proj. Ploughshares [IO], Waterloo, ON, Canada

Proj. for Public Spaces [17394], 700 Broadway, 4th Fl., New York, NY 10003-9536, (212)620-5660

Proj. RACE [18986], PO Box 2366, Los Banos, CA 93635-2366

Proj. READ Literacy Network [IO], Kitchener, ON, Canada

Project Reassurance [★23646]

Proj. Renewal [13285], 200 Varick St., New York, NY 10014, (212)620-0340

Project to Res. Objects Theories, Extraterrestrials and Unusual Sightings - Defunct.

Proj. ROSE (Recycled Oil Saves Energy) - Defunct.

Project SHARE - Defunct.

Proj. South: Inst. for the Elimination of Poverty and Genocide [17949], 9 Gammon Ave., Atlanta, GA 30315, (404)622-0602

Proj. South: Inst. for the Elimination of Poverty and Genocide [17949], 9 Gammon Ave., Atlanta, GA 30315, (404)622-0602

Proj. S.T. [★15623]

Proj. Sunshine [11394], 108 W 39th St., Ste. 725, New York, NY 10018, (212)354-8035

Proj. on Tech., Work and Character [6950], The Maccoby Gp., 4825 Linnean Ave. NW, Washington, DC 20008, (202)895-8922

Proj. Tibet [18724], 403 Canyon Rd., Santa Fe, NM 87501, (505)982-3002

Proj. Tibet [18724], 403 Canyon Rd., Santa Fe, NM 87501, (505)982-3002

Proj. Tomorrow [8076], 15707 Rockfield Blvd., Ste. 250, Irvine, CA 92618, (949)609-4660

Proj. Trust [IO], Isle of Coll, United Kingdom

Proj. Underground [18140], 8 Radford St., Ste. 201, Christiansburg, VA 24073, (540)394-2553

Proj. Vote! [18390], 737 1/2 8th St. SE, Washington, DC 20003, (202)546-4173

Project Yedid - Defunct.

Proj. YES [9081], 5275 Sunset Dr., Miami, FL 33143, (305)663-7195

Projekt Mgt. Austria [IO], Vienna, Austria

Projektiyhdistys ry [★IO]

ProJet Assn. - Defunct.

Projet Otesha [★IO]

Projets pour une Agriculture Ecologique [★IO]

Pro-Life

Republican Majority for Choice [18539]

ProLiteracy Worldwide [8538], 1320 Jamesville Ave., Syracuse, NY 13210, (315)422-9121

ProLiteracy Worldwide [8538], 1320 Jamesville Ave., Syracuse, NY 13210, (315)422-9121

ProLitteris [IO], Zurich, Switzerland

Prolotherapy Assn. [★16021]

PROMAX Intl. [★508]

PROMAX Intl. [★508]

PROMAXBDA [508], 1522e Cloverfield Blvd., Santa Monica, CA 90404, (310)788-7600

PROMAXBDA [508], 1522e Cloverfield Blvd., Santa Monica, CA 90404, (310)788-7600

Prometheus Radio Proj. [18101], PO Box 42158, Philadelphia, PA 19101, (215)727-9620

Prometheus Soc. - Address unknown since 2010.

PROMETRA - France [IO], Lanuejols, France

PROMETRA - Spain [IO], Las Palmas de Gran Canaria, Spain

Promicrofinance Intl. [IO], Kinshasa, Democratic Republic of the Congo

A Promise of Hea. [14827], 419 E Fraser Dr., Pueblo West, CO 81007, (719)547-1995

Promise Keepers [19600], PO Box 11798, Denver, CO 80211-0798, (866)PRO-MISE

Promise World Wide [12358], 173 Ivy Hill Way, Los Gatos, CA 95032, (408)358-0160

Promised Land Intl. [19376], PO Box 149, Haymarket, VA 20168, (703)723-0089

ProMoM: Promotion of Mother's Milk - Address unknown since 2011.

Promoting Enduring Peace [18284], 39 Goodrich St., New Haven, CT 06517-3202, (202)573-7322

Promotion Industry Coun. - Defunct.

Promotion Marketing Assn. [2422], 650 First Ave., Ste. 2-5W, New York, NY 10016, (212)420-1100

Promotion Marketing Assn. of Am. [★2422]

Promotional Glass Collectors Assn. [21400], 4595 Limestone Ln., Memphis, TN 38141, (901)794-8723

Promotional Products Assn. Intl. [103], 3125 Skyway Cir. N, Irving, TX 75038-3526, (972)252-0404

Promotional Products Assn. Intl. [103], 3125 Skyway Cir. N, Irving, TX 75038-3526, (972)252-0404

Promotional Products Professionals of Canada [IO], St.-Laurent, QC, Canada

Promotora de las Comunidades Municipales [IO], Bogota, Colombia

Promusicae [IO], Madrid, Spain

Proofreaders Club of New York - Defunct.

Propane Gas Assn. of Canada [IO], Calgary, AB, Canada

Propeller Club of the U.S. [3267], 3927 Old Lee Hwy., Ste. 101A, Fairfax, VA 22030, (703)691-2777

Property

Amer. Soc. of Cost Segregation Professionals [3381]

Assn. of Appraiser Regulatory Officials [227]

Assn. of Green Property Owners and Managers [2900]

Castle Coalition [18403]

Indus. Asset Mgt. Coun. [3014]

Natl. Assn. of Foreclosure Prevention Professionals [2899]

Natl. Assn. of Independent Real Estate Brokers [3021]

Natl. Assn. of Real Estate Consultants [3027]

Natl. Assn. State Agencies for Surplus Property [5898]

Natl. Assn. of Unclaimed Property Administrators [5899]

Unclaimed Property Professionals Org. [5900]

Property Admin. Assn. [★2903]

Property Casualty Insurers Assn. of Am. [2031], 2600 S River Rd., Des Plaines, IL 60018-3286, (847)297-7800

Property Consultants Soc. [IO], Arundel, United Kingdom

Property Coun. of Australia [IO], Sydney, Australia

Property and Env. Res. Center [4297], 2048 Anal. Dr., Ste. A, Bozeman, MT 59718, (406)587-9591

Property Loss Res. Bur. [2032], 3025 Highland Pkwy., Ste. 800, Downers Grove, IL 60515-1291, (630)724-2200

Property Management

Assn. of Green Property Owners and Managers [2900]

Coalition of Landlords, Homeowners and Merchants [18404]

A star before a book entry number signifies that the name is not listed separately, but is mentioned within the entry.

Reference to "IO" in place of a book number signifies that the association may be found in the 50th edition of International Organizations.

Psychic Arts and Sciences; Acad. of [7220]
Psychoanalysis
Amer. Acad. of Psychoanalysis and Dynamic Psychiatry [16351]
Amer. Psychoanalytic Assn. [16352]
Amer. Psychoanalytic Found. [16353]
Amer. Psychological Assn. | Soc. of Psychological Hypnosis [16380]
Amer. Soc. of Psychoanalytic Physicians [16354]
Assn. for Child Psychoanalysis [16355]
Assn. for Psychoanalytic Medicine [16356]
European Fed. for Psychoanalytic Psychotherapy [20477]
Intl. Assn. for Relational Psychoanalysis and Psychotherapy [16357]
Intl. Assn. for Relational Psychoanalysis and Psychotherapy [16357]
Intl. Fed. for Psychoanalytic Educ. [8760]
Intl. Forum for Psychoanalytic Educ. [8760]
Intl. Positive Psychology Assn. [16401]
Karen Horney Clinic [16358]
Natl. Assn. for the Advancement of Psychoanalysis [16359]
Natl. Assn. for the Advancement of Psychoanalysis [16359]
Natl. Psychological Assn. for Psychoanalysis [16360]
Radical Psychology Network [16421]
Sandtray Network [16361]
Sandtray Network [16361]
Sigmund Freud Archives [16362]
World Org. and Public Educ. Corp. of the Natl. Assn. for the Advancement of Psychoanalysis [16363]
World Org. and Public Educ. Corp. of the Natl. Assn. for the Advancement of Psychoanalysis [16363]
Psychoanalytic Assistance Fund [★16353]
Psychoanalytic Res. Soc. - Address unknown since 2010.
Psychological Soc. of Ireland [IO], Dublin, Ireland
Psychological Soc. of Northern Greece [IO], Thessaloniki, Greece
Psychological Soc. of South Africa [IO], Houghton, Republic of South Africa
Psychologists' Assn. of Alberta [IO], Edmonton, AB, Canada
Psychologists For Legislative Action Now [★16385]
Psychologists Interested in the Advancement of Psychotherapy [★16368]
Psychologists Interested in Religious Issues [★16382]
Psychologists for Social Responsibility [18217], 258 Harvard St., PMB 282, Brookline, MA 02446, (202)543-5347
Psychology
Alfred Adler Inst. [16364]
Amer. Balint Soc. [16365]
Amer. Bd. of Professional Neuropsychology [16366]
Amer. Bd. of Professional Psychology [16367]
Amer. Psychological Assn. [16368]
Amer. Psychological Assn. | Amer. Soc. for the Advancement of Pharmacotherapy [16369]
Amer. Psychological Assn. | Division of Family Psychology [16370]
Amer. Psychological Assn. | Division of Independent Practice [16371]
Amer. Psychological Assn. | Division of Intl. Psychology [16372]
Amer. Psychological Assn. - Division of Intl. Psychology [16372]
Amer. Psychological Assn. | Division of of Psychotherapy [16373]
Amer. Psychological Assn. | Div. of State, Provincial, and Territorial Psychological Assn. Affairs [16374]
Amer. Psychological Assn. | Division of Trauma Psychology [16375]
Amer. Psychological Assn. of Graduate Students [16376]
Amer. Psychological Assn. - Hea. Psychology Div. [16377]
Amer. Psychological Assn. - Media Psychology Div. [16378]

Amer. Psychological Assn. | Soc. of Addictions Psychology [16379]
Amer. Psychological Assn. | Soc. of Psychological Hypnosis [16380]
Amer. Psychological Assn. | Soc. for the Study of Peace, Conflict and Violence [16381]
Amer. Psychological Assn. | Soc. for the Study of Religion and Spirituality [16382]
Amer. Psychology-Law Soc. [16383]
Assn. for Advanced Training in the Behavioral Sciences [8761]
Assn. for the Advancement of Gestalt Therapy [16384]
Assn. for the Advancement of Psychology [16385]
Assn. for Birth Psychology [16386]
Assn. of Black Psychologists [16387]
Assn. for Humanistic Psychology [16388]
Assn. for Integrative Psychology [16389]
Assn. for Psychological Sci. [16390]
Assn. for Psychological Type Intl. [16391]
Assn. for Res. in Personality [7303]
Assn. of State and Provincial Psychology Boards [16392]
Assn. of State and Provincial Psychology Boards [16392]
Assn. for Women in Psychology [16393]
Athletic Success Inst. [22818]PsychologyBelgian Fed. of Psychologists
Binge Eating Disorder Assn. [14432]
Center for Applications of Psychological Type [16394]
C.G. Jung Found. for Analytical Psychology [16395]
China Amer. Psychoanalytic Alliance [16396]
Christian Assn. for Psychological Stud. [16397]
Cognitive Development Soc. [13825]
Consciousness-Based Educ. Assn. [8762]
Coun. for the Natl. Register of Hea. Ser. Providers in Psychology [16398]
Coun. of Professional Geropsychology Training Programs [14663]
Czech-Moravian Psychological Soc. [14315]
European Assn. of Psychological Assessment [16440]
False Memory Syndrome Found. [16399]
German Assn. of Sport Psychology [19506]
Intl. Assn. for Correctional and Forensic Psychology [11715]
Intl. Assn. for Psychoanalytic Self Psychology [16400]
Intl. Positive Psychology Assn. [16401]
Intl. Remote Viewing Assn. [7304]
Intl. Soc. for Comparative Psychology [16402]
Intl. Soc. for Comparative Psychology [16402]
Intl. Soc. for Developmental Psychobiology [16403]
Intl. Soc. for Developmental Psychobiology [16403]
Intl. Soc. for Dialogical Sci. [7305]
Intl. Soc. for Dialogical Sci. [7305]
Intl. Soc. for Ecological Psychology [7306]
Intl. Soc. for Ecological Psychology [7306]
Intl. Soc. for Intelligence Res. [7002]
Intl. Soc. of Political Psychology [16404]
Intl. Soc. of Political Psychology [16404]
Intl. Soc. for Self and Identity [7307]
Intl. Soc. for Self and Identity [7307]
Intl. Soc. of Sports Psychology [16405]
Intl. Soc. of Sports Psychology [16405]
Iranian Amer. Psychological Assn. [16406]
Japanese Soc. of Adlerian Psychology [17563]
Jean Piaget Soc.: Soc. for the Stud. of Knowledge and Development [16407]
Julian Jaynes Soc. [16408]
Midwestern Psychological Assn. [16409]
Natl. Acad. of Neuropsychology [16410]
Natl. Alliance of Professional Psychology Providers [16411]
Natl. Assn. of Psychometrists [16412]
Natl. Assn. of School Psychologists [16413]
Natl. Register of Hea. Ser. Providers in Psychology [16414]
North Amer. Soc. of Adlerian Psychology [16415]
North Amer. Soc. for the Psychology of Sport and Physical Activity [22819]

Northamerican Assn. of Masters in Psychology [8763]
Northamerican Assn. of Masters in Psychology [8763]PsychologyNorwegian Psychological Assn.
Orthodox Christian Assn. of Medicine, Psychology and Religion [16416]
Performing Arts Medicine Assn. [16417]
Positive Discipline Assn. [7308]
Psi Beta [23625]
Psi Chi, the Natl. Honor Soc. in Psychology [23626]
Psychological Soc. of Ireland [12947]
Psychology Beyond Borders [11860]
Psychometric Soc. [16418]
Psychonomic Soc. [16419]
Psychosynthesis Intl. [16420]
Psychosynthesis Intl. [16420]
Radical Psychology Network [16421]
Radical Psychology Network [16421]
Sandtray Network [16361]
Sculpture in the Env. [17396]
Sigmund Freud Archives [16362]
Singapore Psychological Soc. [16914]
Six Seconds [7309]
Soc. for Applied Res. in Memory and Cognition [7310]
Soc. for Chaos Theory in Psychology and Life Sciences [7311]
Soc. of Clinical Child and Adolescent Psychology [16422]
Soc. of Consulting Psychology [16423]
Soc. for the History of Psychology [7312]
Soc. for the History of Psychology [7312]
Soc. for Indus. and Organizational Psychology [16424]
Soc. for Indus. and Organizational Psychology [16424]
Soc. for Pediatric Psychology [16425]
Soc. for Pediatric Psychology [16425]
Soc. for Personality Assessment [16426]
Soc. for Personality Assessment [16426]
Soc. for Personality and Social Psychology [7313]
Soc. for Police and Criminal Psychology [16427]
Soc. for Psychological Anthropology [7314]
Soc. of Psychological Hypnosis [16380]
Soc. for the Psychological Stud. of Ethnic Minority Issues [16428]
Soc. for the Psychological Stud. of Lesbian, Gay, Bisexual and Transgender Issues [16429]
Soc. for the Psychological Stud. of Men and Masculinity [16430]
Soc. for the Psychological Stud. of Social Issues [16431]
Soc. for Psychophysiological Res. [16432]
Soc. for Psychophysiological Res. [16432]
Soc. for a Sci. of Clinical Psychology [16433]
Soc. for the Stud. of Human Development [6946]
Soc. for Theoretical and Philosophical Psychology [16434]
Soc. for Theoretical and Philosophical Psychology [16434]
Soc. for Vocational Psychology [7315]
Sri Aurobindo Assn. [20301]
Sufi Psychology Assn. [16435]
Turkish Psychological Assn. [15136]
U.S. Assn. for Body Psychotherapy [16436]
Vision Sciences Soc. [7394]
Workplace Bullying Inst. [16437]
Psychology; Assn. for Transpersonal [9821]
Psychology Beyond Borders [11860], 1000 Rio Grande St., Austin, TX 78701, (512)579-3825
Psychology Beyond Borders [11860], 1000 Rio Grande St., Austin, TX 78701, (512)579-3825
Psychology; Intl. Assn. for Correctional and Forensic [11715]
Psychology; Intl. Center for the Stud. of Psychiatry and
Psychology; Southern Soc. for Philosophy and [10431]
Psychometric Soc. [16418], PO Box 26170, Greensboro, NC 27402-6170
Psychoneuroendocrinology; Intl. Soc. of [15346]
Psychoneuroendocrinology; Intl. Soc. of [15346]
Psychoneuroimmunology Res. Soc. [13820], Susan Keran Solomon, Exec. Dir., 10724 Wilshire Blvd., No. 602, Los Angeles, CA 90024

A star before a book entry number signifies that the name is not listed separately, but is mentioned within the entry.

Psychonomic Soc. [16419], 2424 Amer. Ln., Madison, WI 53704-3102, (608)441-1070

Psychopathology
Amer. Psychopathological Assn. [16438]
Assn. for Comprehensive Energy Psychology [16439]
Assn. for Comprehensive Energy Psychology [16439]
Natl. Assn. of Cognitive-Behavioral Therapists [16440]
Soc. for Psychotherapy Res. [16441]
Psychopharmacology; Amer. Soc. of Clinical [16179]
Psychosocial Development and Advisory Center [IO], Lima, Peru

Psychosomatic Medicine
Acad. of Psychosomatic Medicine [16442]
Amer. Psychosomatic Soc. [16443]
Psychosynthesis Intl. [16420], PO Box 3551, Westlake Village, CA 91359
Psychosynthesis Intl. [16420], PO Box 3551, Westlake Village, CA 91359
Psychotherapists and Counsellors Assn. of Western Australia [IO], Subiaco, Australia

Psychotherapy
Albert Ellis Inst. [16444]
Amer. Acad. of Psychotherapists [16445]
Amer. Art Therapy Assn. [16446]
Amer. Assn. for Marriage and Family Therapy [16447]
Amer. Bd. of Examiners of Psychodrama, Sociometry, and Gp. Psychotherapy [16448]
Amer. Dance Therapy Assn. [16449]
Amer. Gp. Psychotherapy Assn. [16450]
Amer. Music Therapy Assn. [16451]
Amer. Psychological Assn. I Division of of Psychotherapy [16373]
Amer. Psychological Assn. I Soc. of Psychological Hypnosis [16380]
Amer. Psychotherapy Assn. [16452]
Amer. Soc. of Gp. Psychotherapy and Psychodrama [16453]
Angel Harps [16454]
Art Therapy Connection [13772]
Assn. for the Advancement of Psychotherapy [16455]
Assn. for Applied Poetry [16456]
Assn. of Mormon Counselors and Psychotherapists [16457]
Certification Bd. for Music Therapists [16458]
EMDR Intl. Assn. [16459]
EMDR Intl. Assn. [16459]
Equine Assisted Growth and Learning Assn. [16460]
Equine Assisted Growth and Learning Assn. [16460]
Inst. for Expressive Anal. [16461]
Intl. Alliance of Professional Hypnotists [15089]
Intl. Assn. for Cognitive Psychotherapy [16462]
Intl. Assn. for Cognitive Psychotherapy [16462]
Intl. Assn. for Women's Mental Hea. [15456]
Intl. Integrative Psychotherapy Assn. [16463]
Intl. Neuro-Linguistic Programming Assn. [16464]
Intl. Neuro-Linguistic Programming Assn. [16464]
Intl. Neuro-Linguistic Programming Trainers Assn. [16465]
Kate's Voice [8764]
Milton H. Erickson Found. [16466]
Music Therapy for Healing [16467]
Natl. Anger Mgt. Assn. [15465]
Natl. Assn. of Certified Professionals of Equine Therapy [13694]
Natl. Assn. for Drama Therapy [16468]
Natl. Assn. for Poetry Therapy [16469]
Natl. Coalition of Creative Arts Therapies Associations [16470]
Natl. Fed. for Biblio/Poetry Therapy [16471]
Psychotherapy Network [16472]
Rabbinic Center for Res. and Counseling [16473]
Sandtray Network [16361]
Soc. for the Exploration of Psychotherapy Integration [16474]
Soc. for the Exploration of Psychotherapy Integration [16474]
William Glasser Inst. [16475]
Psychotherapy and Counselling Fed. of Australia [IO], Fitzroy, Australia

Psychotherapy Network [16472], 5135 MacArthur Blvd. NW, Washington, DC 20016, (202)537-8950
Psynetics Found. [★9828]
PT Boats All Hands [★20866]
PT Boats All Hands [★20866]
PT Boats, Bases and Tenders [★20866]
PT Boats, Bases and Tenders [★20866]
PT Boats, Inc. [20866], PO Box 38070, Germantown, TN 38183-0070, (901)755-8440
PT Boats, Inc. [20866], PO Box 38070, Germantown, TN 38183-0070, (901)755-8440
PTNA [★16281]

Public Administration
80-20 Initiative [17204]
Amer. Assn. of State Ser. Commissions [5903]
Amer. Soc. for Public Admin. [5904]
Amer. Soc. for Public Admin. [5904]
Conf. of Minority Public Administrators [5905]
Inst. of Public Admin. Australia [6523]
Inst. of Public Admin. USA [5906]
Inst. of Public Admin. USA [5906]
Natl. Acad. of Public Admin. [5907]
Natl. Acad. of Public Admin. [5907]
Natl. Assn. of Schools of Public Affairs and Admin. [5908]
Natl. Assn. of State Facilities Administrators [5909]
Natl. Forum for Black Public Administrators [5910]
Partnership for Public Ser. [17331]
Public Tech. Inst. [5911]
Sect. for Women in Public Admin. [5912]
Southern Public Admin. Educ. Found. [5913]
Public Advocate of the U.S. [16677], 5613 Leesburg Pike, Ste. 17, Falls Church, VA 22041, (703)845-1808

Public Affairs
9/11 Families for a Secure Am. Found. [18710]
80-20 Initiative [17204]
Ad Coun. [18410]
Advancing Human Rights [17807]
Air Force Public Affairs Alumni Assn. [5914]
Alfred P. Sloan Found. [18411]
Alliance for Democracy [18412]
Amer. Energy Alliance [17614]
Amer. Libyan Freedom Alliance [17513]
Amer. Muslim Alliance [18142]
The Asia Found. [18413]
Assn. for a More Just Soc. [17272]
Bosniak Amer. Advisory Coun. for Bosnia and Herzegovina [17895]
Breakthrough [17815]
Bus. Leaders for Sensible Priorities [18414]
Buying Influence [17446]
Campaign for America's Future [18415]
Carter Center [18416]
Center for Strategic and Intl. Stud. [18417]
Center for Strategic and Intl. Stud. [18417]
Change Bangladesh [17275]
Coalition for a Realistic Foreign Policy [17698]
Coalition for Tax Fairness [18694]
Commercial Alert [18418]
Concerned Citizens for Nuclear Safety [18195]
Conflict Solutions Intl. [17405]
Corporate Voices for Working Families [17479]
Dalit Freedom Network [17823]
Dalit Solidarity [17824]
Darfur Human Rights Org. [17825]
Democrats for Educ. Reform [17600]
EarthRights Intl. [17827]
Eisenhower Inst. [18419]
Election Defense Alliance [17607]
European-American Unity and Rights Org. [17288]
First Amendment Proj. [18420]
Focus the Nation [17616]
Ford Found. [18421]
Ford Found. [18421]
Friends of Africa Intl. [17830]
Fuel for Truth [18608]
Genocide Intervention Network [17739]
Girls for a Change [11290]
Global Network Against Weapons and Nuclear Power in Space [18199]
Global Peace Services [18251]
Global Youth Action Network [18827]

Hands Across the Mideast Support Alliance [18124]
Heart of Am. Northwest [18422]
Inst. of Public Affairs [16106]
Intl. Inst. for Strategic Stud. US [18423]
Intl. Inst. for Strategic Stud. US [18423]
Intl. Professional Partnerships for Sierra Leone [17917]
Intl. Refugee Rights Initiative [17843]·
Iran Policy Comm. [17998]
Joseph and Edna Josephson Inst. of Ethics [11982]
Korean Amer. Voters' Coun. [18034]
League of Young Voters [18384]
Light Millennium [17299]
Mainstream Media Proj. [18503]
Media and Democracy Coalition [18094]
Mobile Voter [18096]
Natl. Alliance of Community Economic Development Associations [17582]PublicNatl. Civic Coun.
Natl. Coalition of Pro-Democracy Advocates [17526]
Natl. Priorities Proj. [17625]
Native Public Media [18098]
New Am. Media [18099]
Nonprofit VOTE [18162]
OURMedia Network [18100]
Partnership for Public Ser. [17331]
Peace Alliance [18272]
Pi Alpha Alpha [23627]
Progressive Democrats of Am. [17542]
Prometheus Radio Proj. [18101]
Public Campaign [18424]
Public Educ. Center [18425]
Pushback Network [18491]
School of the Americas Watch [18426]
South Asian Amer. Voting Youth [18392]
Turkish Coalition U.S.A. Political Action Comm. [18340]
Twelve Lights League [18073]
United Nations I Emergenccy Coalition for U.S. Financial Support of the United Nations [18750]
Universal Human Rights Network [17865]
US-Azerbaijan Coun. [17958]
USAction [18633]
Voices for Global Change [17254]
Vote Hemp [18609]
W.K. Kellogg Found. [18427]
Women's Voices. Women Vote [18802]
Young Americans for Liberty [18836]
Public Affairs Coun. [17482], 2033 K St. NW, Ste. 700, Washington, DC 20006, (202)872-1790
Public Affairs of Iranian Americans [18002], 1614 20th St. NW, Washington, DC 20009, (202)828-8370
Public Agency Risk Managers Assn. [5557], PO Box 6810, San Jose, CA 95150, (530)823-4957
Public Agenda [18490], 6 E 39th St., 9th Fl., New York, NY 10016, (212)686-6610
Public Agenda Found. [★18490]
Public Architecture [243], 1211 Folsom St., 4th Fl., San Francisco, CA 94103, (415)861-8200
Public Archives Commn. of the Amer. Historical Assn. [★9145]
Public Art Fund [17395], 1 E 53rd St., New York, NY 10022, (212)223-7800
Public Arts Coun. [★17395]
Public Broadcasting Mgt. Assn. [509], 939 S Stadium Rd., Columbia, SC 29201-4724, (803)799-5517
Public Broadcasting Ser. [9464], 2100 Crystal Dr., Arlington, VA 22202
Public Campaign [18424], 1133 19th St. NW, Ste. 900, Washington, DC 20036, (202)640-5600
Public Choice Soc. [7291], Univ. of Florida, Warrington Colorado of Bus. Admin., Dept. of Economics, PO Box 117140, Gainesville, FL 32611-7140, (352)392-0117
Public Citizen [17469], 1600 20th St. NW, Washington, DC 20009, (202)588-1000
Public Citizen Hea. Res. Gp. [16494], 1600 20th St. NW, Washington, DC 20009, (202)588-1000
Public Citizen Litigation Gp. [17470], 1600 20th St. NW, Washington, DC 20009, (202)588-1000

Reference to "IO" in place of a book number signifies that the association may be found in the 50th edition of International Organizations.

Encyclopedia of Associations, 51st Edition
3115

Public Citizen's Cong. Watch [17471], 1600 20th St. NW, Washington, DC 20009, (202)588-1000

Public Citizen's Critical Mass Energy and Env. Prog. [18185], 215 Pennsylvania Ave. SE, Washington, DC 20003, (202)546-4996

Public Citizen's Critical Mass Energy and Env. Proj. [★18185]

Public and Commercial Services Union [IO], London, United Kingdom

Public Conversations Proj. [17353], 46 Kondazian St., Watertown, MA 02472-2832, (617)923-1216

Public Dreams Soc. [IO], Vancouver, BC, Canada

Public Educ. Center [18425], 1830 Connecticut Ave. NW, Washington, DC 20009, (202)466-4310

Public Educ. Corp. of the Natl. Assn. for the Advancement of Psychoanalysis [★16363]

Public Educ. Corp. of the Natl. Assn. for the Advancement of Psychoanalysis [★16363]

Public Educ. Network [8776], 601 13th St. NW, Ste. 710 S, Washington, DC 20005-3812, (202)628-7460

Public Employee Dept. (of AFL-CIO) - Defunct.

Public Employees Roundtable [5313], PO Box 75248, Washington, DC 20013-5248, (202)927-4926

Public Finance
Amer. Assn. for Budget and Prog. Anal. [5915]
Assn. for Governmental Leasing and Finance [5916]
Assn. of Public Treasurers of the U.S. and Canada [5917]
Bus. Coun. [18428]
Bus. Roundtable [18429]
Center on Budget and Policy Priorities [18430]
Comm. for a Responsible Fed. Budget [18431]
Found. for Economic Educ. [18432]
Govt. Finance Officers Assn. of U.S. and Canada [5918]
Govt. Finance Officers Assn. of U.S. and Canada [5918]
Manhattan Inst. for Policy Res. [18433]
Natl. Assn. of County Collectors, Treasurers and Finance Officers [5919]
Natl. Assn. of State Auditors, Comptrollers, and Treasurers [5920]
Natl. Assn. of State Budget Officers [5921]
Natl. Assn. of State Treasurers [5922]
PlaNet Finance US [17920]
Pro Mujer [13475]
Soc. of Financial Examiners [5923]
Public-General Hosp. Sect. [★15040]

Public Health
Alliance for Rabies Control [14370]
Amer. Assn. for Hea. Educ. [16476]
Amer. Assn. of Public Hea. Physicians [16477]
Amer. Public Hea. Assn. [16478]
Assn. for Community Hea. Improvement [16479]
Assn. for Community Hea. Improvement [16479]
Assn. of Hea. Fac. Survey Agencies [5924]
Assn. of Public Hea. Labs. [16480]
Assn. of Public Hea. Labs. [16480]
Assn. of Schools of Public Hea. [16481]
Assn. of State Drinking Water Administrators [5925]
Assn. of State and Territorial Hea. Officials [5926]
Assn. of State and Territorial Local Hea. Liaison Officials [5927]
CarFree City, USA [4961]
Caribbean Public Hea. Coalition [16482]
Clinic at a Time [15152]
Coalition for Anabolic Steroid Precursor and Ephedra Regulation [16718]
Coalition to Protect America's Hea. Care [15049]
Coalition for Safe Community Needle Disposal [14842]
Coalition for SafeMinds [15580]
CodeBlueNow! [16483]
Collaborative on Hea. and the Env. [14500]
Commonwealth Fund [16484]
Community Oncology Alliance [15923]
Coun. on Educ. for Public Hea. [16485]
A Cup of Water Intl. [20282]
Delta Omega [23628]
Directors of Hea. Promotion and Educ. [5928]
Env. and Human Hea., Inc. [14501]

Environmental Outreach and Stewardship Alliance [4259]
Fluoride Action Network [14281]
Food and Drug Admin. Alumni Assn. [17697]
Global Network for Neglected Tropical Diseases [14388]
Global Partnership for Family Hea. [13608]
Global Solutions for Infectious Diseases [15116]
GlobeMed [15175]
Hea. Care for Am. Now [17771]
Hea. Justice Collaborative [15181]
Hea. Wrights [16486]
HIS Nets [13588]
Intl. HACCP Alliance [4809]
Intl. Soc. for Disease Surveillance [14395]
Intl. Union Against Sexually Transmitted Infections, Regional Off. for North Am. [16656]
Medicine for Peace [18434]
Medicine for Peace [18434]
mHealth Alliance [15198]
Moms Against Mercury [13322]
Natl. Assn. of County and City Hea. Officials [5929]
Natl. Assn. of Local Boards of Hea. [16487]
Natl. Assn. for Public Hea. Statistics and Info. Systems [5930]
Natl. Assn. of Rural Hea. Clinics [16488]
Natl. Conf. of Local Environmental Hea. Administrators [16489]
Natl. Hea. Freedom Coalition [14816]
Natl. Org. of State Offices of Rural Hea. [16490]
Natl. Pediculosis Assn. [16491]
Natl. Rural Hea. Assn. [16492]
Natl. Transitions of Care Coalition [14821]
Nature Healing Nature [11614]
Network for the Improvement of World Hea. [15200]
Norrie Disease Assn. [14415]
NSF Intl. [16493]
NSF Intl. [16493]
Public Citizen Hea. Res. Gp. [16494]
Public Hea. Assn. of Australia [18708]
Public Hea. Found. [16495]
Public Hea. Leadership Soc. [16496]
Safety Net Hospitals for Pharmaceutical Access [16213]
Soc. for the Anal. of African-American Public Hea. Issues [16497]
Soc. for Public Hea. Educ. [16498]
Soc. for Public Hea. Educ. [16498]
South Asian Public Hea. Assn. [16499]
Trust for America's Hea. [16500]
U.S.-Mexico Border Hea. Assn. [16501]
U.S.-Mexico Border Hea. Assn. [16501]
U.S. Public Hea. Ser. I Commissioned Officers Assn. [5931]
Universities Allied for Essential Medicines [8384]
Venous Disease Coalition [16970]
Water is Life Intl. [13435]
Water for People I PlayPumps Intl. [10827]
WaterAid Am. [13441]
World Fed. of Public Hea. Associations [16502]
World Fed. of Public Hea. Associations [16502]
Public Hea. Assn. of Australia [IO], Curtin, Australia
Public Hea. Assn. of Australia - Australian Capital Territory [IO], Frankston, Australia
Public Hea. Assn. of Australia - New South Wales [IO], Frankston, Australia
Public Hea. Assn. of Australia - Victoria [IO], Hampton, Australia
Public Hea. Assn. of Australia - Western Australia [IO], Perth, Australia
Public Hea. Assn. of New Zealand [IO], Wellington, New Zealand
Public Hea. Found. [16495], 1300 L St. NW, Ste. 800, Washington, DC 20005, (202)218-4400
Public Hea. Leadership Soc. [16496], An Nguyen, Prog. Coor., 1515 Poydras St., Ste. 1200, New Orleans, LA 70112, (504)301-9821
Public Hosp. Pharmacy Coalition [★16213]
Public Housing Authorities Directors Assn. [5525], 511 Capitol Ct. NE, Washington, DC 20002-4937, (202)546-5445

Public Information
Amer. Guild of Town Criers [10475]

Amer. Lib. Assn. - Public Info. Off. [10476]
Buying Influence [17446]
DataCenter [18435]
Natl. Anxiety Center [18436]
Natl. Freedom of Info. Coalition [18437]
ODF Alliance [6990]
OURMedia Network [18100]
Public Interest Advocacy Centre [IO], Ottawa, ON, Canada
Public Interest Communications [★17354]
Public Interest Intellectual Property Advisors [5580], PO Box 65245, Washington, DC 20035, (401)374-0607

Public Interest Law
Alliance for Justice [5932]
Amer. Non-Governmental Organizations Coalition for the Intl. Criminal Court [17488]
Economic Justice Inst. [5933]
Equal Rights Advocates [5934]
Natl. Chamber Litigation Center [5935]
Natl. Legal Found. [5936]
Pacific Legal Found. [5937]
Public Interest Intellectual Property Advisors [5580]
Public Justice [5938]
U.S. Justice Found. [5939]
Washington Legal Found. [5940]
Public Investors Arbitration Bar Assn. - Address unknown since 2011.
Public Justice [5938], 1825 K St. NW, Ste. 200, Washington, DC 20006-1220, (202)797-8600

Public Lands
The Conservation Campaign [17416]
Defense of Place [4039]
Forest Ser. Employees for Environmental Ethics [4822]
LandChoices [4089]
Natl. Brownfield Assn. [2905]
Natural Trails and Waters Coalition [4823]
Proj. for Public Spaces [17394]
Public Art Fund [17395]
Public Lands Coun. [4824]
Public Lands Found. [4825]
Sculpture in the Env. [17396]
Sustainable Obtainable Solutions [4826]
Public Lands Coun. [4824], 1301 Pennsylvania Ave. NW, Ste. 300, Washington, DC 20004-1701, (202)347-0228
Public Lands Found. [4825], 3032 N Homestead Pl., Tucson, AZ 85749
Public Leadership Educ. Network [9064], 1001 Connecticut Ave. NW, Ste. 900, Washington, DC 20036, (202)872-1585
Public Libraries Div. [★10006]
Public Lib. Assn. [10006], Amer. Lib. Assn., 50 E Huron St., Chicago, IL 60611, (312)280-5028
Public Lib. of Sci. [10007], Koshland Bldg., 1160 Battery St., Ste. 100, San Francisco, CA 94111, (415)624-1200
Public Media Center [17354], 466 Green St., Ste. 300, San Francisco, CA 94133-4067, (415)434-1403
Public Media Found. [18102], Northeastern Univ., PO Box 167, Boston, MA 01944, (978)768-7469
Public Monuments and Sculpture Assn. [IO], London, United Kingdom
Public Personnel Assn. [★1153]
Public Personnel Assn. [★1153]

Public Policy
Amer. Assembly [18438]
Amer. Assn. of Women [18439]
Amer. Energy Alliance [17614]
Amer. Enterprise Inst. for Public Policy Res. [18440]
Amer. Legislative Exchange Coun. [18441]
Assn. for Public Policy Anal. and Mgt. [18442]
Assn. for Public Policy Anal. and Mgt. [18442]
Brookings Institution [18443]
Cato Inst. [18444]
Center for Advancement of Public Policy [18445]
Center for Governmental Res. [18446]
Center for Liberal Strategies [17285]
Center for Natl. Policy [18447]
Center for Public Justice [18448]
Center for the Stud. of Social Policy [18449]

A star before a book entry number signifies that the name is not listed separately, but is mentioned within the entry.

The Century Found. [18450]
Common Sense for Drug Policy [18451]
Communitarian Network [18452]
Coro [18453]
Corporate Voices for Working Families [17479]
Coun. for Social and Economic Stud. [18454]
Economic Policy Inst. [18455]
Economic Success CH [12724]
Eisenhower Inst. [18419]
Eisenhower World Affairs Inst. [18456]
Eisenhower World Affairs Inst. [18456]
Emergency Comm. to Defend Constitutional
   Welfare Rights USA [18457]
Equine Land Conservation Rsrc. [4827]
Ethics and Public Policy Center [18458]
Fed. of Amer. Scientists [18459]
Found. for Natl. Progress [18460]
Found. for Public Affairs [18461]
Freedom Found. [5941]
Global Options [18462]
Global Options [18462]
Governmental Res. Assn. [18463]
Harry Singer Found. [18464]
HIV/AIDS Prevention Grants Prog. [10884]
Hudson Inst. [18465]
The Independent Inst. [18466]
Inst. for Contemporary Stud. [18467]
Inst. for Philosophy and Public Policy [18468]
Inst. for Policy Stud. [18469]
Inst. for Policy Stud. [18469]
Inst. for Public Accuracy [18470]
Inst. for Rsrc. and Security Stud. [18471]
Inst. for SocioEconomic Stud. [18472]
Intl. Professional Partnerships for Sierra Leone
   [17917]
Leadership Coun. of Aging Organizations [10850]
League of Women Voters Educ. Fund [18473]
League of Young Voters [18384]
Marijuana Policy Proj. [18086]
Nation Inst. [18474]
Natl. Center for Policy Anal. [18475]
Natl. Center for Public Policy Res. [18476]
Natl. Chamber Found. [18477]
Natl. Inst. for Public Policy [18478]
Natl. Issues Forums Inst. [18479]
New Am. Found. [18480]
Northeast-Midwest Inst. [18481]
Northeast-Midwest Senate Coalition [18482]
NumbersUSA [18483]
Online Privacy Alliance [17315]
Org. for Intl. Investment [18484]
Org. for Intl. Investment [18484]
Pacific Res. Inst. [18485]
Philadelphia Soc. [18486]
Planners Network [18487]
Policy Stud. Org. [18488]
Progressive Policy Inst. [18489]
Public Agenda [18490]
Public Policy Assessment Soc. [13575]
Pushback Network [18491]
R2P Coalition [13376]
RESOLVE [18492]
Sarah Scaife Found. [18493]
Sarah Scaife Found. [18493]
South Asian Amer. Voting Youth [18392]
Unitarian Universalist Assn. of Congregations
   [12903]
Vision New Am. [18494]
Women's Economic Round Table [18495]Public-
   World Priorities
Youth Policy Inst. [18496]
Public Policy Assessment Soc. [IO], Woden,
   Australia
Public Radio Capital [10483], 834 Marshall Rd.,
   Boulder, CO 80305, (720)304-7274
Public Radio News Directors Incorporated [510],
   Christine Paige Diers, Bus. Mgr., PO Box 838, St-
   urgis, SD 57785-0838, (605)490-3033
Public Radio Prog. Directors Assn. [2980], 38 Milford
   St., Hamilton, NY 13346, (315)824-8226
Public Radio Programmer's Assn. [★2980]
Public Relations
   80-20 Initiative [17204]
   Agricultural Relations Coun. [2906]
   Assn. of Entertainment Marketing Agencies [1189]

Coun. of Alumni Marketing and Membership
   Professionals [2397]
Coun. of Public Relations Firms [18497]
Inst. for Public Relations [8765]
Natl. Black Public Relations Soc. [2907]
Natl. Coun. for Marketing and Public Relations
   [8766]
Natl. Info. Officers Assn. [5942]
Natl. School Public Relations Assn. [8767]
Public Relations Soc. of Am. [2908]
Public Relations Student Soc. of Am. [8768]
Publicity Club of London [5837]
Religion Communicators Coun. [20168]
Soc. of Consumer Affairs Professionals [2909]
Public Relations Consultants Assn. [IO], London,
   United Kingdom
Public Relations Inst. of Australia [IO], Darlinghurst,
   Australia
Public Relations Inst. of Southern Africa [IO], Pine-
   gowrie, Republic of South Africa
Public Relations Soc. of Am. [2908], 33 Maiden Ln.,
   11th Fl., New York, NY 10038-5150, (212)460-
   1400
Public Relations Student Soc. of Am. [8768], 33
   Maiden Ln., 11th Fl., New York, NY 10038-5150,
   (212)460-1474
Public Responsibility in Medicine and Res. [18586],
   126 Brookline Ave., Ste. 202, Boston, MA 02215-
   3920, (617)423-4112
Public Risk Mgt. Assn. [5558], 700 S Washington
   St., Ste. 218, Alexandria, VA 22314, (703)528-7701
Public Safety Writers Assn. [3711], 2024 Falcon Ct.,
   Bellingham, WA 98229
Public Schools
   Amer. Assn. of Classified School Employees
      [23177]
   Assn. of Latino Administrators and
      Superintendents [7661]
   Citizens for Effective Schools [8769]
   Culturatti Kids Resource Network [9074]
   Democrats for Educ. Reform [17600]
   Designs for Change [8770]
   Educ. Voters of Am. [8771]
   Horace Mann League of the U.S.A. [8772]
   Natl. Alliance for Public Charter Schools [8773]
   Natl. Assn. for Single Sex Public Educ. [8774]
   Natl. Coalition for Public School Options [8775]
   Public Educ. Network [8776]
   Resources for Indispensable Schools and Educa-
      tors [8961]
Public Service
   Consumer Web Watch [17455]
Public Ser. Alliance of Canada [IO], Ottawa, ON,
   Canada
Public Ser. Res. Coun. [18046], 320-D Maple Ave.
   E, Vienna, VA 22180-4742, (703)242-3575
Public Services Intl. [IO], Ferney-Voltaire, France
Public Speaking
   Canadian Assn. of Professional Speakers [20528]
   Gavel Clubs [10477]
   Genealogical Speakers Guild [10478]
   Intl. Assn. of Speakers Bureaus [10479]
   Intl. Assn. of Speakers Bureaus [10479]
   Intl. Public Debate Assn. [8777]
   Intl. Public Debate Assn. [8777]
   Natl. Coalition for Dialogue and Deliberation
      [8778]
   Natl. Forensic Assn. [8895]
   Natl. Speakers Assn. [10480]
   Toastmasters Intl. [10481]
   Toastmasters Intl. [10481]
Public Speaking and Humor Club - Defunct.
Public Tech., Inc. [★5911]
Public Tech. Inst. [5911], 1426 Prince St.,
   Alexandria, VA 22314, (202)626-2400
Public Telecommunications Financial Mgt. Assn.
   [★509]
**Public TransitPublicScottish Assn. for Public
Transport**
Public Utilities Advt. Assn. [★818]
Public Utilities Advt. Assn. [★818]
Public Utilities Communicators Assn. [★818]
Public Utilities Communicators Assn. [★818]
Public Voice for Food and Health Policy - Defunct.
Public Welfare
   Amer. Public Human Services Assn. | Natl. Coun.
      of State Human Ser. Administrators [13171]

Assn. for a More Just Soc. [17272]
Burmese Amer. Democratic Alliance [17213]
Corporate Voices for Working Families [17479]
Crime Survivors [17487]
Daisy Alliance [18239]
EarthRights Intl. [17827]
Environmentalists Against War [18777]
Intl. Coalition for the Responsibility to Protect
   [18498]
Invisible Children [17237]
Light Millennium [17299]
The Love Alliance [17365]
Moms Against Mercury [13322]
Natl. Alliance of Community Economic Develop-
   ment Associations [17582]
Natl. Alliance for Filipino Concerns [17200]
Natl. Center for Law and Economic Justice [5943]
Natl. Traffic Incident Mgt. Coalition [13330]
Safer Racer Tour [13006]
Spirit of Am. [18499]
USAction [18633]
Water for People | PlayPumps Intl. [10827]
Public Welfare Found. [13145], 1200 U St. NW,
   Washington, DC 20009-4443, (202)965-1800
Public Works
   80-20 Initiative [17204]
   Amer. Public Works Assn. [5944]
   Clean Water Constr. Coalition [4989]
   Coun. of Infrastructure Financing Authorities
      [5945]
   Coun. of Infrastructure Financing Authorities
      [5945]
   Global Village Inst. [5946]
   Global Village Inst. [5946]
   Intl. Assn. for Public Participation Practitioners
      [5947]
   Intl. Assn. for Public Participation Practitioners
      [5947]
   Natl. Alliance of Highway Beautification Agencies
      [5948]
   Natl. Assn. of Clean Water Agencies [5949]
   Proj. for Public Spaces [17394]
Public Works Historical Soc. [9796], Amer. Public
   Works Assn., 2345 Grand Blvd., Ste. 700, Kansas
   City, MO 64108, (816)472-6100
Publicity Club of London [IO], London, United
   Kingdom
Publishers Assn. [IO], London, United Kingdom
Publishers Assn. for Cultural Exchange, Japan [IO],
   Tokyo, Japan
Publishers Assn. of New Zealand [IO], Auckland,
   New Zealand
Publishers Assn. of South Africa [IO], Cape Town,
   Republic of South Africa
Publishers Info. Bur. [115], 810 7th Ave., 24th Fl.,
   New York, NY 10019, (212)872-3700
Publishers Licensing Soc. [IO], London, United
   Kingdom
Publishers Marketing Assn. [★2937]
Publishers Publicity Circle [IO], London, United
   Kingdom
Publishing
   About Books, Inc. [2910]
   AFL-CIO | Intl. Labor Communications Assn.
      [2911]
   Alliance of Area Bus. Publications [2912]
   Amer. Book Producers Assn. [2913]
   Amer. Bus. Media [2914]
   Amer. Court and Commercial Newspapers [2915]
   Amer. Horse Publications [2916]
   Assoc. Church Press [2917]
   Assn. of Amer. Publishers [2918]
   Assn. of Art Editors [2919]
   Assn. of Catholic Publishers [2920]
   Assn. of Dir. Publishers [2921]
   Assn. of Free Community Papers [2922]
   Assn. of Free Community Papers [2922]
   Assn. of Test Publishers [2923]
   Bay Area Independent Publishers Assn. [2924]
   Book Indus. Study Group [2925]
   Book Indus. Study Group [2925]
   Catholic Press Assn. [2926]
   The Christian Sci. Publishing Soc. [2927]
   Christian Small Publishers Assn. [2928]
   Christian Small Publishers Assn. [2928]

Reference to "IO" in place of a book number signifies that the association may be found in the 50th edition of International Organizations.

City and Regional Magazine Assn. **[2929]**
CrossRef **[2930]**
CrossRef **[2930]**
Custom Content Coun. **[2931]**
Educational Book and Media Assn. **[2932]**
English Westerners Soc. **[3693]**
EPIC - Electronically Published Internet Connection **[22110]**
European Publishers Coun. **[13878]**
European Rotogravure Assn. **[9572]**
Evangelical Christian Publishers Assn. **[2933]**
Evangelical Christian Publishers Assn. **[2933]**
Fed. of German Newspaper Publishers **[23891]**
Financial Publishers Assn. **[2934]**
Fulfillment Mgt. Assn. **[2935]**
German Publishers and Booksellers Assn. **[19985]**
Great Lakes Independent Booksellers Assn. **[2936]**
Independent Assn. of Publishers' Employees **[23285]**
Independent Book Publishers Assn. **[2937]**
Independent Free Papers of Am. **[2938]**
Inland Press Assn. **[2939]**
Intl. Assn. of Cross-Reference Dir. Publishers **[2940]**
Intl. Newsmedia Marketing Assn. **[2941]**
Intl. Newsmedia Marketing Assn. **[2941]**
Intl. Newspaper Gp. **[2834]**
The Intl. Publication Planning Assn. **[2942]**
The Intl. Publication Planning Assn. **[2942]**
Intl. Regional Magazine Assn. **[2943]**
Intl. Soc. of Managing and Tech. Editors **[2944]**
Intl. Soc. for Medical Publication Professionals **[16503]**
Intl. Soc. for Medical Publication Professionals **[16503]**
Jewish Student Press Ser. **[8428]**
Livestock Publications Coun. **[2945]**
Macrocosm USA **[2946]**
Magazine Publishers of Am. **[2947]**
Midwest Free Community Papers **[2948]**
Natl. Assn. of Hispanic Publications **[2949]**
Natl. Assn. of Independent Publishers Representatives **[2950]**
Natl. Assn. of Publishers' Representatives **[2951]**
Natl. Assn. of Trade Press Publishers **[4614]**
Natl. Trade Circulation Found., Inc. **[2952]**
Newspaper Assn. of Am. **[2953]**
Newspaper Target Marketing Coalition **[2576]**
North Amer. St. Newspaper Assn. **[2954]**
Online Publishers Assn. **[2955]**
Parenting Publications of Am. **[2956]**
Partnership for Res. Integrity in Sci. and Medicine **[18500]**
Periodical and Book Assn. of Am. **[2957]**
Protestant Church-Owned Publishers Assn. **[2958]**
Publishers Assn. **[13887]**
Red Tag News Publications Assn. **[2238]**
Scholarly Publishing and Academic Resources Coalition **[2959]**
Singles Press Assn. **[2960]**
Small Publishers, Artists and Writers Network **[2961]**
Small Publishers, Artists and Writers Network **[2961]**
Small Publishers Assn. of North Am. **[2962]**
Soc. for the Promotion of Sci. and Scholarship **[2963]**
Soc. for Scholarly Publishing **[2964]**
Southern Newspaper Publishers Assn. **[2965]**
Specialized Info. Publishers Assn. **[2966]**
Specialized Info. Publishers Assn. **[2966]**
Suburban Newspapers of Am. **[2967]**
Theosophical Book Assn. for the Blind **[20264]**
United Amateur Press Assn. of Am. **[22107]**
Yellow Pages Assn. **[2968]**
Publishing Ireland **[IO]**, Dublin, Ireland
Publishing Scotland **[IO]**, Edinburgh, United Kingdom
Puebla Inst. **[★17818]**
Puebla Inst. **[★17818]**
Pueblo a Pueblo **[12124]**, PO Box 11486, Washington, DC 20008, (202)302-0622
Puerto Rican Family Inst. **[12148]**, 145 W 15th St., New York, NY 10011, (212)924-6320

Puerto Rican Hispanic Genealogical Soc. **[20657]**, PO Box 260118, Bellerose, NY 11426-0118
Puerto Rican Legal Defense and Educ. Fund **[17322]**, 99 Hudson St., 14th Fl., New York, NY 10013-2815, (212)219-3360
Puerto Rican Stud. Assn. **[19206]**, Cornell Univ., Latino Studies Program, 434 Rockefeller Hall, Ithaca, NY 14853-2502, (607)255-3197
Puerto Rican Traveling Theatre Company **[10599]**, 304 W 47th St., New York, NY 10036, (212)354-1293
Puerto Rico
   Natl. Assn. State Agencies for Surplus Property **[5898]**
   Natl. Puerto Rican Coalition **[18501]**
   Natl. Puerto Rican Coalition **[18501]**
   Puerto Rican Stud. Assn. **[19206]**
   Puerto Rico U.S.A. Citizenship Found. **[18502]**
   Puerto Rico Water and Env. Assn. **[5006]**
Puerto Rico Alpha 1 Support Gp. **[★16609]**
Puerto Rico Alpha 1 Support Gp. **[★16609]**
Puerto Rico Assn. of Pediatric Surgeons **[16154]**, PO Box 10426, Caparra Heights Sta., San Juan, PR 00922-0426, (787)777-3535
Puerto Rico Soc. of Microbiologists **[7112]**, PO Box 360175, San Juan, PR 00936-0175, (787)751-3057
Puerto Rico U.S.A. Citizenship Found. **[18502]**, 600 13th St. NW, Washington, DC 20005, (202)756-8213
Puerto Rico, U.S.A. Found. **[★18502]**
Puerto Rico Water and Env. Assn. **[5006]**, PO Box 13702, San Juan, PR 00908-3702, (787)478-3716
Pug Dog Club of Am. **[21639]**, Donna Manha, Sec., 449 Maar Ave., Fremont, CA 94536
Pugwash Conferences on Sci. and World Affairs **[17403]**, Washington Off., 1111 19th St. NW, No. 1200, Washington, DC 20036, (202)478-3440
Pugwash Conferences on Sci. and World Affairs **[17403]**, Washington Off., 1111 19th St. NW, No. 1200, Washington, DC 20036, (202)478-3440
Puli Club of Am. **[21640]**, S. Eniko Szeremy, Corresponding Sec., 10305 N Chatfield Pl., Littleton, CO 80125, (303)791-6306
Pull-thru Network **[14573]**, 2312 Savoy St., Hoover, AL 35226-1528, (205)978-2930
Pulling Foundation **[★23073]**
Pulmonary and Allergy Patients' Assn. of Slovenia **[IO]**, Ljubljana, Slovenia
Pulmonary Fibrosis; Coalition for **[16606]**
Pulmonary Hypertension Assn. **[15079]**, 801 Roeder Rd., Ste. 1000, Silver Spring, MD 20910, (301)565-3004
Pulmonary Hypertension Assn. - United Kingdom **[IO]**, Rotherham, United Kingdom
Pulp Chemicals Assn. **[★762]**
Pulp and Paper Engineers and Technicians Assn. of Slovenia **[IO]**, Ljubljana, Slovenia
Pulp and Paper Indus. Fed. of the Slovak Republic **[IO]**, Banska Bystrica, Slovakia
Pulp and Paper Machinery Assn. **[★1809]**
Pulp and Paper Machinery Mfrs. Assn. **[★1809]**
Pulp and Paper Res. and Tech. Center **[IO]**, Grenoble, France
Pulp and Paper Safety Assn. **[7218]**, PO Box 531, Perry, FL 32348, (850)584-3639
Pulverized Limestone Assn. **[★3366]**
Pump Distributors Assn. **[IO]**, Woodbridge, United Kingdom
Pump Indus. Australia **[IO]**, Stuarts Point, Australia
Punjabi-American Cultural Assn. **[9860]**, 5055 Bus. Center Dr., Ste. 108, No. 165, Fairfield, CA 94534
Puppet Centre Trust **[IO]**, London, United Kingdom
Puppeteers of Am. **[22111]**, Fred Thompson, 26 Howard Ave., New Haven, CT 06519-2809
Puppetry
   Union Internationale de la Marionnette I Amer. CTR **[22112]**
Puppets
   Puppeteers of Am. **[22111]**
   Union Internationale de la Marionnette I Amer. CTR **[22112]**
Pups for Peace **[12634]**, 8424A Santa Monica Blvd., Ste. 112, West Hollywood, CA 90069-4267, (800)669-8930

Pups for Peace **[12634]**, 8424A Santa Monica Blvd., Ste. 112, West Hollywood, CA 90069-4267, (800)669-8930
Pura Vida for Children **[11395]**, PO Box 1692, New Canaan, CT 06840, (203)644-4404
Purcell Family of Am. **[20574]**, 2138 Harris Ave., Richland, WA 99354
Purchasing
   Alliance of Supplier Diversity Professionals **[2969]**
   Amer. Purchasing Soc. **[2970]**
   Buying Influence **[17446]**
   European Inst. of Purchasing Mgt. **[8233]**
   Inst. for Supply Mgt. **[2971]**
   Natl. Assn. of Purchasing Card Professionals **[2972]**
   Natl. Assn. of Purchasing and Payables **[2973]**
   Natl. Assn. of State Procurement Officials **[5950]**
   Natl. Inst. of Governmental Purchasing **[5951]**
   Natl. Inst. of Governmental Purchasing **[5951]**
   Natl. Purchasing Inst. **[2974]**
   Procurement and Supply Chain Benchmarking Assn. **[700]**
   Responsible Purchasing Network **[1222]**
Purchasing Mgt. Assn. of Canada **[IO]**, Toronto, ON, Canada
Pure Puerto Rican Paso Fino Fed. of Am. **[4640]**, PO Box 280444, Columbia, SC 29228-0444, (503)799-9792
Purebred Dexter Cattle Assn. of North Am. **[3937]**, 25979 Hwy. EE, Prairie Home, MO 65068, (660)841-9502
Purebred Morab Horse Association/Registry **[4641]**, W2802 Emons Rd., Appleton, WI 54915, (920)687-0188
Purebred Morab Horse Association/Registry **[4641]**, W2802 Emons Rd., Appleton, WI 54915, (920)687-0188
pureHOPE **[18400]**, 800 Compton Rd., Ste. 9224, Cincinnati, OH 45231, (513)521-6227
Purine 24, Inc. **[★15506]**
Purine Res. Soc. **[15506]**, 5424 Beech Ave., Bethesda, MD 20814-1730, (301)530-0354
Purple Flower Gang **[23883]**, 1803 Lucas St., Muscatine, IA 52761
Purple Martin Conservation Assn. **[5112]**, 301 Peninsula Dr., Ste. 6, Erie, PA 16505, (814)833-7656
Pursuing Our Italian Names Together **[20658]**, Box 82309, Las Vegas, NV 89180-3209
Pursuing Our Italian Names Together **[20658]**, Box 82309, Las Vegas, NV 89180-3209
PUSH Coalition; Rainbow/ **[13199]**
Pushback Network **[18491]**, 330 7th Ave., 19th Fl., New York, NY 10001
Put and Call Brokers and Dealers Assn. - Defunct.
Puthi Komar Org. **[IO]**, Battambang City, Cambodia
Puu- ja Erityisalojen Liitto **[★IO]**
Puusepaenteollisuuden Liitto Ry **[★IO]**
Puzzle Buffs Intl. **[21756]**, 41 Park Dr., Port Clinton, OH 43452, (419)734-2600
PWSA USA **[★14622]**
PXE Intl. **[14626]**, 4301 Connecticut Ave. NW, Ste. 404, Washington, DC 20008-2369, (202)362-9599
PXI Systems Alliance **[6555]**, PO Box 1016, Niwot, CO 80544-1016, (303)652-2585
Pyrenean Mastiff Club of Am. **[21641]**, 4083 W Ave. L, No. 107, Quartz Hill, CA 93536, (661)724-0268
Pyrotechnics
   Alliance of Special Effects and Pyrotechnic Operators **[2975]**
   Amer. Pyrotechnics Assn. **[2976]**
   Pyrotechnics Guild Intl. **[2977]**
   Pyrotechnics Guild Intl. **[2977]**
Pyrotechnics Guild Intl. **[2977]**, PO Box 52, Manchester, MI 48158, (734)428-0900
Pyrotechnics Guild Intl. **[2977]**, PO Box 52, Manchester, MI 48158, (734)428-0900

Q

Qajaq U.S.A. **[23124]**, PO Box 333, Andover, NJ 07821
Qatar Amateur Radio Soc. **[IO]**, Doha, Qatar
Qatar Animal Welfare Soc. **[IO]**, Doha, Qatar
Qatar Assn. of Athletics Fed. **[IO]**, Doha, Qatar

A star before a book entry number signifies that the name is not listed separately, but is mentioned within the entry.

Qatar British Bus. Forum [IO], Doha, Qatar
Qatar Chamber of Commerce and Indus. [IO], Doha, Qatar
Qatar Charity [IO], Doha, Qatar
Qatar Diabetes Assn. [IO], Doha, Qatar
Qatar Fencing Fed. [IO], Doha, Qatar
Qatar Gen. Org. for Standards and Metrology [IO], Doha, Qatar
Qatar Geological Soc. [IO], Doha, Qatar
Qatar Golf Assn. [IO], Doha, Qatar
Qatar Gymnastics Fed. [IO], Doha, Qatar
Qatar Judo Fed. [IO], Doha, Qatar
Qatar League Against Epilepsy [IO], Doha, Qatar
Qatar Marine Sport Fed. [IO], Doha, Qatar
Qatar Natl. Cancer Soc. [IO], Doha, Qatar
Qatar Olympic Comm. [IO], Doha, Qatar
Qatar Red Crescent Soc. [IO], Doha, Qatar
Qatar Sailing and Rowing Fed. [IO], Doha, Qatar
Qatar Squash Fed. [IO], Doha, Qatar
Qatar Swimming Assn. [IO], Doha, Qatar
Qatar Taekwondo and Karate Fed. [IO], Doha, Qatar
Qatar Tamizhar Sangam [IO], Doha, Qatar
Qatar Tennis Fed. [IO], Doha, Qatar
Qatar Weightlifting Fed. [IO], Doha, Qatar
QatarDebate [IO], Doha, Qatar
Qatari Businessmen Assn. [IO], Doha, Qatar
Qigong Alliance Intl. [13701], PO Box 750, Ely, MN 55731, (800)341-8895
QiGong Res. Soc. [13702], 3201 Rte. 38, Ste. 201, Mount Laurel, NJ 08054, (856)234-3056
Quackwatch [★17765]
Quadex Users' Org. - Defunct.
Quail Forever [5113], 1783 Buerkle Cir., St. Paul, MN 55110, (651)209-4980
Quail Unlimited [5114], PO Box 70518, Albany, GA 31708, (803)637-5731
Quaker Coun. for European Affairs [IO], Brussels, Belgium
Quaker Parakeet Soc. [3854], PO Box 7241, Springfield, OR 97475
Quaker Parakeet Soc. [3854], PO Box 7241, Springfield, OR 97475
Quaker Peace and Social Witness [IO], London, United Kingdom
Quaker Ser. Australia [IO], Surry Hills, Australia
Quaker United Nations Off. - Switzerland [IO], Geneva, Switzerland
Quakers Fostering Justice [IO], Mission, BC, Canada
Qualifications and Curriculum Authority [IO], London, United Kingdom
Qualified Private Medical Practitioners' and Hospitals' Assn. [IO], Kochi, India
Qualitative Res. Consultants Assn. [7334], 1000 Westgate Dr., Ste. 252, St. Paul, MN 55114, (651)290-7491
Quality Assurance
  Amer. Bd. of Quality Assurance and Utilization Rev. Physicians [16504]
  Amer. Coll. of Medical Quality [16505]
  Amer. Hea. Quality Assn. [16506]
  Amer. Soc. for Quality [7316]
  British Assn. of Res. Quality Assurance [630]
  Inst. for Medical Quality [16507]
  Intl. Acad. for Quality [7317]
  Intl. Acad. for Quality [7317]
  Intl. Air Filtration Certifiers Assn. [1705]
  Intl. Assn. of Ser. Evaluators [2978]
  Intl. Assn. of Ser. Evaluators [2978]
  Natl. Assn. for Healthcare Quality [16508]
  Natl. Comm. for Quality Assurance [16509]
  Semmelweis Soc. Intl. [16510]
  Soc. of Quality Assurance [2979]
  Soc. of Quality Assurance [2979]
  Statistical Process Controls [7318]
  Statistical Process Controls [7318]
  Team and Workplace Excellence Forum [7319]
Quality Bakers of Am. Cooperative [393], 1055 Parsippany Blvd., Ste. 201, Parsippany, NJ 07054, (973)263-6970
Quality Chekd Dairies [1026], 1733 Park St., Naperville, IL 60563, (800)222-6455
Quality Chekd Ice Cream Assn. [★1026]
Quality Educ. for Minorities Network [8059], 1818 N St. NW, Ste. 350, Washington, DC 20036, (202)659-1818

Quality Educ. for Minorities Proj. [★8059]
Quality Meat Scotland [IO], Edinburgh, United Kingdom
Quality and Productivity Mgt. Assn. - Defunct.
Quality and Productivity Soc. of Pakistan [IO], Lahore, Pakistan
Quality Scheme for Ready Mixed Concrete [IO], Hampton, United Kingdom
Quality Systems Assessment Registrar [IO], Milton, ON, Canada
Quality Tourism Services Assn. [IO], Hong Kong, People's Republic of China
Quantal Energy [8121], 97 Mt. Warner Rd., Hadley, MA 01035
Quarter Century Wireless Assn. [20942], PO Box 3247, Framingham, MA 01705-3247, (508)405-1930
Quarter Sport Horse Registry [★4561]
Quartermaster Assn. [★5794]
Quartus Found. for Spiritual Res. [12223], PO Box 1768, Boerne, TX 78006-6768, (830)249-3985
Quartzite Rock Assn. [850], PO Box 661, Sioux Falls, SD 57101, (605)339-1520
Quaternary Assn; Amer. [7137]
Quaternary and Geomorphological Assn. of Vietnam [IO], Hanoi, Vietnam
Quaternary Res. Assn. [IO], Menai Bridge, United Kingdom
Quebec Assn. of Independent Schools [IO], Montreal, QC, Canada
Quebec Assn. of Marriage and Family Therapy [IO], Westmount, QC, Canada
Quebec Fed. of Historical Societies [IO], Montreal, QC, Canada
Quebec-Labrador Foundation I Atlantic Center for the Env. [4299], 55 S Main St., Ipswich, MA 01938, (978)356-0038
Quebec-Labrador Found. I Atlantic Center for the Env. [4299], 55 S Main St., Ipswich, MA 01938, (978)356-0038
Quebec dans le Monde [IO], Ste.-Foy, QC, Canada
Quebec Wheelchair Assn. [IO], Montreal, QC, Canada
Quebec Writers' Fed. [IO], Westmount, QC, Canada
Queen Fan Club [IO], West Horsley, United Kingdom
Queen Isabella Foundation [★18952]
Queen Isabella Foundation [★18952]
Queen Sofia Spanish Inst. [10539], 684 Park Ave., New York, NY 10065, (212)628-0420
Queen Sofia Spanish Inst. [10539], 684 Park Ave., New York, NY 10065, (212)628-0420
Queen's English Soc. [IO], Reading, United Kingdom
Queensland Chamber of Commerce and Indus. [IO], Brisbane, Australia
Queensland Counsellors Assn. [IO], Brisbane, Australia
Queensland History Teachers Assn. [IO], New Farm, Australia
Queensland Master Builders Assn. [IO], Brisbane, Australia
Queensland Secondary Principals Assn. [IO], Runcorn, Australia
Queensland Weightlifting Assn. [IO], Capalaba, Australia
Queer West Arts and Culture Centre [IO], Toronto, ON, Canada
Quekett Microscopical Club [IO], South Ruislip, United Kingdom
Quest Books [★20265]
Quest, Inc. [★7968]
Quest Intl. [★7968]
Quest Intl. Users Gp. [6593], 2365 Harrodsburg Rd., Ste. A325, Lexington, KY 40504, (859)226-4307
Quest Natl. Center [★7968]
Quest for Peace [18160], PO Box 5206, Hyattsville, MD 20782, (301)699-0042
Quest for Peace [18160], PO Box 5206, Hyattsville, MD 20782, (301)699-0042
The Questers [20962], 210 S Quince St., Philadelphia, PA 19107-5534, (215)923-5183
Questscope for Social Development in the Middle East - Jordan [IO], Amman, Jordan
Questscope for Social Development in the Middle East - United Kingdom [IO], London, United Kingdom

Quetzaltrekkers - Guatemala [IO], Quetzaltenango, Guatemala
Quetzaltrekkers - Nicaragua [IO], Leon, Nicaragua
Quickdraw Animation Soc. [IO], Calgary, AB, Canada
Quiet Valley Living Historical Farm [9797], 1000 Turkey Hill Rd., Stroudsburg, PA 18360, (570)992-6161
Quill and Scroll Soc. [23574], Univ. of Iowa, School of Journalism and Mass Commun., 100 Adler Journalism Bldg., Rm. E346, Iowa City, IA 52242, (319)335-3457
Quilt Art Assn; Contemporary [21434]
Quilt Assn; Intl. [21447]
Quilters' Guild of the British Isles [IO], York, United Kingdom
The Quilters Hall of Fame [21464], 926 S Washington St., Marion, IN 46953, (765)664-9333
Quilter's Soc; Amer. [21430]
Quilting Assn; Natl. [21458]
Quilts; Alliance for Amer. [21423]
Quimper Club Intl. [20971], Janet Fox, Treas., 2315 Spruce St., Philadelphia, PA 19103
Quit [IO], London, United Kingdom
Quixote Center [18628], PO Box 5206, Hyattsville, MD 20782-0206, (301)699-0042
Quixote Center [18628], PO Box 5206, Hyattsville, MD 20782-0206, (301)699-0042
Quixote Center [19488], PO Box 5206, Hyattsville, MD 20782, (301)699-0042
Quota Club Intl. [★13073]
Quota Club Intl. [★13073]
Quota Intl. [13073], 1420 21st St. NW, Washington, DC 20036, (202)331-9694
Quota Intl. [13073], 1420 21st St. NW, Washington, DC 20036, (202)331-9694

R

R.A. Bloch Cancer Found. [13972], One H&R Block Way, Kansas City, MO 64105, (816)854-5050
Raad voor Cultuur [★IO]
Rabbinic Center for Res. and Counseling [16473], Rabbinic Center Synagogue, 128 E Dudley ave., Westfield, NJ 07090, (908)233-0419
Rabbinical Assembly [19894], 3080 Broadway, New York, NY 10027, (212)280-6000
Rabbinical Assembly [19894], 3080 Broadway, New York, NY 10027, (212)280-6000
Rabbinical Assembly of Am. [★19894]
Rabbinical Assembly of Am. [★19894]
Rabbinical Coun. of Am. [19895], 305 7th Ave., 12th Fl., New York, NY 10001, (212)807-9000
Rabbis; Central Conf. of Amer. [19853]
Rabbits
  Amer. Belgian Hare Club [4828]
  Amer. Checkered Giant Rabbit Club [4829]
  Amer. Dutch Rabbit Club [4830]
  Amer. Fed. of New Zealand Rabbit Breeders [4831]
  Amer. Fuzzy Lop Rabbit Club [22113]
  Amer. Harlequin Rabbit Club [4832]
  Amer. Himalayan Rabbit Assn. [4833]
  Amer. Himalayan Rabbit Assn. [4833]
  Amer. Netherland Dwarf Rabbit Club [4834]
  Amer. Rabbit Breeders Assn. [4835]
  Amer. Satin Rabbit Breeders' Assn. [4836]
  Amer. Standard Chinchilla Rabbit Breeders Assn. [4837]
  Californian Rabbit Specialty Club [4838]
  Cinnamon Rabbit Breeders Assn. [4839]
  Havana Rabbit Breeders Assn. [4840]
  Holland Lop Rabbit Specialty Club [4841]
  Hotot Rabbit Breeders Intl. [4842]
  Hotot Rabbit Breeders Intl. [4842]
  Lop Rabbit Club of Am. [4843]
  Mini Lop Rabbit Club of Am. [4844]
  Natl. Angora Rabbit Breeders Club [4845]
  Natl..Fed. of Flemish Giant Rabbit Breeders [4846]
  Natl. Jersey Wooly Rabbit Club [4847]
  Natl. Jersey Wooly Rabbit Club [4847]
  Natl. Lilac Rabbit Club of Am. [4848]
  Natl. Mini Rex Rabbit Club [4849]
  Natl. Mini Rex Rabbit Club [4849]

Reference to "IO" in place of a book number signifies that the association may be found in the 50th edition of International Organizations.

Natl. Rex Rabbit Club [4850]
Natl. Silver Rabbit Club [4851]
North Amer. Lionhead Rabbit Club [4852]
North Amer. Lionhead Rabbit Club [4852]
Professional Rabbit Meat Assn. [4853]
Rhinelander Rabbit Club of Am. [4854]
Silver Marten Rabbit Club [4855]
Race Horse Club [★4619]
Race for Peace [18285], PO Box 195, Armonk, NY 10504, (914)299-6193
Race Track Chaplaincy of Am. [19530], 2365 Harrodsburg Rd., Ste. A120, Lexington, KY 40504, (859)410-7822
Racecourse Assn. [IO], Ascot, United Kingdom
Racegoers Club [IO], Ascot, United Kingdom
Racehorse Owners Assn. of Great Britain [IO], London, United Kingdom
Rachel Carson Coun. [13327], PO Box 10779, Silver Spring, MD 20914-0779, (301)593-7507
Rachel Carson Homestead Assn. [10684], PO Box 46, Springdale, PA 15144-0046, (724)274-5459
Rachel Carson Trust for the Living Env. [★13327]
Racial Justice 911 [17323], CAAAV: Organizing Asian Communities, 2473 Valentine Ave., Bronx, NY 10458, (718)220-7391

Racing
Amer. Bicycle Racing [22820]
Amer. Mule Racing Assn. [22821]
Amer. Power Boat Assn. [22316]
Amer. Swan Boat Assn. [22822]
Assn. of Racing Commissioners Intl. [5952]
Assn. of Racing Commissioners Intl. [5952]
Auto. Racing Club of Am. [22243]
Buick St. Rod Assn. [22114]
Diesel Hot Rod Assn. [22823]
East Coast Timing Assn. [22115]
Electrathon Am. [22824]
Force 5 Class Assn. [22336]
Gay and Lesbian Rowing Fed. [22855]
Geary 18 Intl. Yacht Racing Assn. [22338]
Godolphin Soc. [10482]
Hampton One-Design Class Racing Assn. [22340]
Harness Horse Youth Found. [22652]
Highlander Class Intl. Assn. [22341]
Intl. Hobie Class Assn. [22353]
Intl. Laser Class Assn. - North Amer. Region [22356]
Intl. Trotting and Pacing Assn. [22656]
Johnny Benson Fan Club [23791]
Kustoms of Am. [22116]
MG Vintage Racers [22117]
Monster Truck Racing Assn. [22825]
Monster Truck Racing Assn. [22825]
Natl. Butterfly Assn. [22371]
Natl. Championship Racing Assn. [22826]
Natl. Christian Barrel Racers Assn. [22660]
Natl. Starwind/Spindrift Class Assn. [22377]
Professional Windsurfers Assn. [22385]
Safer Racer Tour [13006]
Scale Warbird Racing Assn. [21910]
Sportscar Vintage Racing Assn. [22249]
Thoroughbred Club of Am. [22666]
United Barrel Racing Assn. [22670]
U.S. A-Class Catamaran Assn. [22400]
U.S. Adventure Racing Assn. [22827]
U.S. Albacore Assn. [22401]
U.S. Auto Club [22250]
U.S. Lawn Mower Racing Assn. [22828]
U.S. Power Squadrons [22405]
U.S. Ski Team Found. [22919]
U.S. Wayfarer Assn. [22410]
World Championship Cutter and Chariot Racing Assn. [22448]
Young Racers of Am. [22829]

Racism
Black Holocaust Soc. [17154]
Facing History and Ourselves Natl. Found. [9764]
Natl. Alliance Against Racist and Political Repression [17304]
Turkish Amer. Alliance for Fairness [19260]
Racism No Way [IO], Darlinghurst, Australia
Rack Mfrs. Inst. [1864], 8720 Red Oak Blvd., Ste. 201, Charlotte, NC 28217-3992, (704)676-1190
Rack Mfrs. Inst. [1864], 8720 Red Oak Blvd., Ste. 201, Charlotte, NC 28217-3992, (704)676-1190

Racking Horse Breeders' Assn..of Am. [4642], 67 Horse Center Rd., Ste. B, Decatur, AL 35603, (256)353-7225
Racquet Sports
U.S. Dental Tennis Assn. [23062]
USA Professional Platform Tennis Assn. [23066]
Racquetball
Guam Racquetball Fed. [22830]
Guam Racquetball Fed. [22830]
Intl. Racquetball Fed. [22831]
Intl. Racquetball Fed. [22831]
U.S. Racquetball Assn. [22832]
Racquetball Assn. of Ireland [IO], Cork, Ireland
Racquetball Canada [IO], Ottawa, ON, Canada
Rader Assn. [20575], 2633 Gilbert Way, Rancho Cordova, CA 95670-3513, (916)366-6833
Radgivende Ingeniorers Forening [★IO]
Radiance Technique Assn. Intl. [★13703]
Radiance Technique Assn. Intl. [★13703]
The Radiance Technique Intl. Assn. [13703], PO Box 40570, St. Petersburg, FL 33743-0570, (727)347-2106
The Radiance Technique Intl. Assn. [13703], PO Box 40570, St. Petersburg, FL 33743-0570, (727)347-2106
Radiance Technique and Radiant Peace Assn. Intl. [★13703]
Radiance Technique and Radiant Peace Assn. Intl. [★13703]
Radiant Panel Assn. [★1718]
Radiant Professionals Alliance [1718], 8512 Oswego Rd., Ste. 180, Baldwinsville, NY 13027, (315)303-4735
Radiation
Amer. Coll. of Radiation Oncology [16511]
Assn. for Directors of Radiation Oncology Programs [16512]
Assn. of Freestanding Radiation Oncology Centers [16513]
Assn. for Radiological and Imaging Nursing [15739]
Conf. of Radiation Control Prog. Directors [5953]
Coun. on Ionizing Radiation Measurements and Standards [7320]
Intl. Commn. on Radiation Units and Measurements [7321]
Intl. Commn. on Radiation Units and Measurements [7321]
Intl. Isotope Soc. [6271]
Intl. RadioSurgery Assn. [16514]
Intl. RadioSurgery Assn. [16514]
Intl. Skeletal Soc. [16533]
Natl. Coun. on Radiation Protection and Measurements [5954]
Org. of Agreement States [5955]
Radiation and Public Hea. Proj. [16515]
Radiation Res. Soc. [7322]
RadTech Intl. North Am. [7323]
RadTech Intl. North Am. [7323]
Radiation Effects Res. Found. [IO], Hiroshima, Japan
Radiation Oncology Administrators [★16547]
Radiation Oncology; Assn. of Residents in [15921]
Radiation and Public Hea. Proj. [16515], PO Box 1260, Ocean City, NJ 08226
Radiation Res. Soc. [7322], PO Box 7050, Lawrence, KS 66044, (800)627-0326
Radiation Safety Inst. of Canada [IO], Toronto, ON, Canada
Radiation Therapy Oncology Gp. [15931], 1818 Market St., Ste. 1600, Philadelphia, PA 19103, (215)574-3189
Radical
Catholic Worker Movement [18164]
Radical Art Caucus [9200], Depaul Univ., Art History Dept., 1150 W Fullerton, Chicago, IL 60614, (773)325-4890
Radical Caucus [★10414]
Radical Philosophy Assn. [10414], 215 W 88th St., Apt. 3B, New York, NY 10024-2324
Radical Psychology Network [16421], PO Box 35384, Brighton, MA 02135
Radical Psychology Network [16421], PO Box 35384, Brighton, MA 02135
Radical Res. Center [★10472]

Radical Women [17671], New Valencia Hall, 625 Larkin St., Ste. 202, San Francisco, CA 94109, (415)864-1278
Radikale Venstre [★IO]
Radio
Africa News Ser. [17144]
Amer. Lib. Assn. - Public Info. Off. [10476]
Amer. Radio Relay League [20931]
Amer. Shortwave Listeners Club [20932]
Antique Wireless Assn. [22118]
Antique Wireless Assn. [22118]
ARRL Found. [20933]
Catholic Radio Assn. [19406]
The Christian Sci. Publishing Soc. [2927]
Intl. Radio Club of Am. [20937]
Mainstream Media Proj. [18503]
Mainstream Media Proj. [18503]
Natl. Assn. Broadcast Employees and Technicians l Communications Workers of Am. [23162]
Natl. Lum and Abner Soc. [22119]
No-Code Intl. [20939]
North Amer. Radio Archives [22120]
Old Old Timers Club [20941]
Prometheus Radio Proj. [18101]
Public Radio Capital [10483]
Public Radio Prog. Directors Assn. [2980]
Radio Club of Am. [22121]
Soc. to Preserve and Encourage Radio Drama, Variety and Comedy [22122]
Vintage Radio and Phonograph Soc. [22123]
Western Public Radio [2981]
Radio Advt. Bur. [104], 1320 Greenway Dr., Ste. 500, Irving, TX 75038-2587, (212)681-7214
Radio Advisory Bd. of Canada [IO], Ottawa, ON, Canada
Radio Amateur Assn. of Greece [IO], Athens, Greece
Radio Amateur Satellite Corp. [7551], 850 Sligo Ave., Ste. 600, Silver Spring, MD 20910-4787, (301)589-6062
Radio Amateurs du Canada [★IO]
Radio Amateurs of Canada [IO], Ottawa, ON, Canada
Radio Amateurs of Lebanon [IO], Beirut, Lebanon
Radio Club of Am. [22121], PO Box 621074, Littleton, CO 80162, (303)948-4921
Radio Club Venezolano [IO], Caracas, Venezuela
Radio, Elecl. and TV Retailers' Assn. [IO], Bedford, United Kingdom
Radio Executives Club [★494]
Radio Free Europe/Radio Liberty [17355], 1201 Connecticut Ave. NW, Washington, DC 20036-2605, (202)457-6948
Radio Info. Center for the Blind [★17063]
Radio Internacional Feminista [★IO]
Radio Liberty Comm. [★17355]
Radio Marketing Bur. [IO], Toronto, ON, Canada
Radio Pioneers Club [★486]
Radio Soc. of Bermuda [IO], Hamilton, Bermuda
Radio Soc. of Great Britain [IO], Bedford, United Kingdom
Radio Soc. of Sri Lanka [IO], Colombo, Sri Lanka
Radio Tech. Commn. for Aeronautics [★6024]
Radio Tech. Commn. for Marine Ser. [★3417]
Radio Tech. Commn. for Marine Ser. [★3417]
Radio Tech. Commn. for Maritime Services [3417], 1800 N Kent St., Ste. 1060, Arlington, VA 22209-2109, (703)527-2000
Radio Tech. Commn. for Maritime Services [3417], 1800 N Kent St., Ste. 1060, Arlington, VA 22209-2109, (703)527-2000
Radio-Television Digital News Assn. [511], 529 14th St. NW, Ste. 425, Washington, DC 20045, (202)659-6510
Radio and TV Directors Guild [★23187]
Radio and TV Executive Soc. [★494]
Radio and TV Fed. [IO], Rome, Italy
Radio-Television News Directors' Assn. [IO], Toronto, ON, Canada
Radio-Television News Directors Assn. [★511]
Radioactive Waste
Beyond Nuclear [18192]
Concerned Citizens for Nuclear Safety [18195]
Radioactive Waste Mgt. Advisory Comm. [IO], London, United Kingdom

A star before a book entry number signifies that the name is not listed separately, but is mentioned within the entry.

Radiochemistry Soc. **[6418]**, PO Box 3091, Richland, WA 99354, (800)371-0542

Radiocommunication Bur. **[IO]**, Geneva, Switzerland

Radiographers; Assn. of Vascular and Interventional **[16959]**

Radiologic Technologists; Amer. Registry of **[15365]**

Radiologic Technologists; Amer. Soc. of **[15368]**

Radiological Soc. of North Am. **[16537]**, 820 Jorie Blvd., Oak Brook, IL 60523, (630)571-2670

Radiological Soc. of Pakistan **[IO]**, Lahore, Pakistan

Radiological Soc. of the Republic of China **[IO]**, Taipei, Taiwan

Radiologists Bus. Managers Assn. **[★15301]**

Radiologists in Ultrasound; Soc. of **[16548]**

Radiology

AHRA: The Assn. for Medical Imaging Mgt. **[16516]**

Amer. Assn. for Women Radiologists **[16517]**

Amer. Bd. of Radiology **[16518]**

Amer. Chiropractic Registry of Radiologic Technologists **[16519]**

Amer. Coll. of Radiology **[16520]**

Amer. Osteopathic Coll. of Radiology **[16521]**

Amer. Roentgen Ray Soc. **[16522]**

Amer. Roentgen Ray Soc. **[16522]**

Amer. Soc. of Clinical Radiation Oncology **[15918]**

Amer. Soc. of Emergency Radiology **[16523]**

Amer. Soc. of Head and Neck Radiology **[16524]**

Amer. Soc. of Neuroimaging **[16525]**

Amer. Soc. of Neuroradiology **[16526]**

Amer. Soc. of Pediatric Neuroradiology **[16527]**

Amer. Soc. of Spine Radiology **[16528]**

Amer. Soc. for Therapeutic Radiology and Oncology **[16529]**

Assn. of Prog. Coordinators in Radiology **[16530]**

Assn. for Radiological and Imaging Nursing **[15739]**

Assn. of Univ. Radiologists **[16531]**

Coun. on Diagnostic Imaging **[16532]**

Intl. Skeletal Soc. **[16533]**

Intl. Skeletal Soc. **[16533]**

Intl. Soc. for Magnetic Resonance in Medicine **[16534]**

Intl. Soc. for Magnetic Resonance in Medicine **[16534]**

Intl. Soc. of Radiology **[16535]**

Intl. Soc. of Radiology **[16535]**

Magnetic Resonance Managers Soc. **[16536]**

Radiological Soc. of North Am. **[16537]**

Sino-American Network for Therapeutic Radiology and Oncology **[16871]**

Soc. for the Advancement of Women's Imaging **[16538]**

Soc. of Breast Imaging **[16539]**

Soc. of Chairs of Academic Radiology Departments **[16540]**

Soc. of Computed Body Tomography and Magnetic Resonance **[16541]**

Soc. of Gastrointestinal Radiologists **[16542]**

Soc. for Imaging Informatics in Medicine **[16543]**

Soc. of Interventional Radiology **[16544]**

Soc. of NeuroInterventional Surgery **[16545]**

Soc. for Pediatric Radiology **[16546]**

Soc. for Radiation Oncology Administrators **[16547]**

Soc. of Radiologists in Ultrasound **[16548]**

Soc. of Skeletal Radiology **[16549]**

Soc. of Thoracic Radiology **[16550]**

World Fed. of Neuroradiological Societies **[16551]**

World Fed. of Neuroradiological Societies **[16551]**

Radiology; Amer. Acad. of Oral and Maxillofacial **[14239]**

Radiology; Amer. Chiropractic Coll. of **[14118]**

Radiology; Amer. Coll. of Veterinary **[17003]**

Radiology Bus. Mgt. Assn. **[15301]**, 10300 Eaton Pl., Ste. 460, Fairfax, VA 22030, (703)621-3355

Radiology Info. Sys. Consortium **[★16543]**

Radiology Mammography Intl. **[13861]**, 1037 Robinwood Hills Dr., Akron, OH 44333, (330)666-1967

Radiology Mammography Intl. **[13861]**, 1037 Robinwood Hills Dr., Akron, OH 44333, (330)666-1967

Radionic Assn. **[IO]**, Banbury, United Kingdom

Radios Rurales Internationales **[★IO]**

Radium Soc; Amer. **[15916]**

Radix Inst. **[13704]**, 3212 Monte Vista NE, Albuquerque, NM 87106-2120, (310)570-2439

Radner Familial Ovarian Cancer Registry; Gilda **[13924]**

RadTech Intl. North Am. **[7323]**, 7720 Wisconsin Ave., Ste. 208, Bethesda, MD 20814, (240)497-1242

RadTech Intl. North Am. **[7323]**, 7720 Wisconsin Ave., Ste. 208, Bethesda, MD 20814, (240)497-1242

RAFAD Found. **[IO]**, Geneva, Switzerland

RAFI-USA **[★3747]**

RAFI-USA **[★3747]**

RAID Advisory Board - Defunct.

The Rail Archive - Defunct.

Rail Freight Gp. **[IO]**, London, United Kingdom

Rail and Maritime Transport Union **[IO]**, Wellington, New Zealand

Rail, Tram and Bus Union **[IO]**, Redfern, Australia

Railfuture **[IO]**, Leeds, United Kingdom

Railroad Advancement Through Information and Law Found. - Defunct.

Railroad Constr. and Maintenance Assn. **[★2991]**

Railroad Historical Soc; Illinois Central **[9775]**

Railroad Public Relations Assn. - Defunct.

Railroad Sta. Historical Soc. **[10497]**, 26 Thackeray Rd., Oakland, NJ 07436-3312, (212)818-8085

Railroad Yardmasters of Am. **[★23292]**

Railroader Club; Lionel **[21890]**

Railroadiana Collectors Assn. Incorporated **[22128]**, 17675 W 113th St., Olathe, KS 66061

Railroads

Air Brake Assn. **[2982]**

Alliance for Rail Competition **[2983]**

Amer. Assn. of Private Railroad Car Owners **[2984]**

Amer. Assn. of Railroad Superintendents **[2985]**

Amer. Railway Engg. and Maintenance of Way Assn. **[2986]**

Amer. Railway Engg. and Maintenance of Way Assn. **[2986]**

Amer. Short Line and Regional Railroad Assn. **[2987]**

Amer. Train Dispatchers Assn. **[23286]**

Anthracite Railroads Historical Soc. **[10484]**

Assn. of Amer. Railroads **[2988]**

Assn. of Railway Museums **[10485]**

Baltimore and Ohio Railroad Historical Soc. **[10486]**

Bluebell Railway Preservation Soc. **[1005]**

Bridge Line Historical Soc. **[22124]**

Brotherhood of Locomotive Engineers and Trainmen **[23287]**

Brotherhood of Locomotive Engineers and Trainmen **[23287]**

Brotherhood of Maintenance of Way Employees **[23288]**

Brotherhood of Railroad Signalmen **[23289]**

Central Elec. Railfans' Assn. **[22125]**

Chesapeake and Ohio Historical Soc. **[10487]**

Elec. Railroaders' Assn. **[10488]**

European Fed. of Museum and Tourist Railways **[9557]**

Friends of the Valley Railroad **[10489]**

Highland Railway Soc. **[10208]**

Lexington Gp. in Trans. History **[10490]**

Marklin Digital Special Interest Gp. **[21891]**

Massachusetts Bay Railroad Enthusiasts **[10491]**

Mid-Continent Railway Historical Soc. **[22126]**

Mystic Valley Railway Soc. **[10492]**

Natl. Assn. of Railroad Passengers **[2989]**

Natl. Assn. of Railway Bus. Women **[2990]**

Natl. Railroad Constr. and Maintenance Assn. **[2991]**

Natl. Railway Historical Soc. **[10493]**

Ontario and Western Railway Historical Soc. **[10494]**

Pacific Railroad Soc. **[10495]**

Pacific Southwest Railway Museum **[10496]**

Pine Creek Railroad **[22127]**

Railroad Sta. Historical Soc. **[10497]**

Railroadiana Collectors Assn. Incorporated **[22128]**

Railway Engineering-Maintenance Suppliers Assn. **[2992]**

Railway Engineering-Maintenance Suppliers Assn. **[2992]**

Railway Enthusiasts Soc. **[11922]**

Railway and Locomotive Historical Soc. **[10498]**

Railway Supply Inst. **[2993]**

Railway Systems Suppliers, Inc. **[2994]**

Railway Tie Assn. **[2995]**

Soo Line Historical and Tech. Soc. **[10499]**

Spokane, Portland and Seattle Railway Historical Soc. **[10500]**

Terminal Railroad Assn. Historical and Tech. Soc. **[10501]**

Tourist Railway Assn. **[2996]**

Tourist Railway Assn. **[2996]**

Toy Train Collectors Soc. **[21894]**

Transport Museum Assn. **[10502]**

Trans. Communications Intl. Union **[23290]**

Trans. Communications Union I Brotherhood Railway Carmen Div. **[23291]**

United Trans. Union **[23292]**

Wabash, Frisco and Pacific Assn. **[10503]**RailroadsWorld War Two Railway Study Group

Youth in Model Railroading **[21897]**

Rails-to-Trails Conservancy **[23094]**, 2121 Ward Ct. NW, 5th Fl., Washington, DC 20037, (202)331-9696

Railton Owners Club **[IO]**, Faversham, United Kingdom

Railtrails Australia **[IO]**, Oak Park, Australia

Railway Assn. of Canada **[IO]**, Ottawa, ON, Canada

Railway Bus. Assn. **[★2993]**

Railway Bus. Women's Assn. **[★2990]**

Railway and Canal Historical Soc. **[IO]**, Oxford, United Kingdom

Railway Children **[IO]**, Cheshire, United Kingdom

Railway Communications Suppliers Assn. **[★2994]**

Railway Correspondence and Travel Soc. **[IO]**, Slough, United Kingdom

Railway Engineering-Maintenance Suppliers Assn. **[2992]**, 500 New Jersey Ave. NW, Ste. 400, Washington, DC 20001, (202)715-2921

Railway Engineering-Maintenance Suppliers Assn. **[2992]**, 500 New Jersey Ave. NW, Ste. 400, Washington, DC 20001, (202)715-2921

Railway Enthusiasts Soc. **[IO]**, Auckland, New Zealand

Railway Historical Soc. of Milwaukee **[★22126]**

Railway Indus. Clearance Assn. **[3535]**, 10330 Lake Rd., Bldg. K, Houston, TX 77070, (281)826-0009

Railway Indus. Assn. **[IO]**, London, United Kingdom

Railway Indus. Clearance Assn. **[★3535]**

Railway Labor Executives' Assn. - Defunct.

Railway and Locomotive Historical Soc. **[10498]**, PO Box 62698, Colorado Springs, CO 80962-2698

Railway Patrolmen's Intl. Union **[★23290]**

Railway Preservation Soc. of Ireland **[IO]**, Newtownabbey, United Kingdom

Railway Progress Inst. **[★2993]**

Railway Signal and Communications Suppliers Assn. **[★2994]**

Railway Supply Assn. **[★2993]**

Railway Supply Inst. **[2993]**, 425 3rd St. SW, Ste. 920, Washington, DC 20024-3229, (202)347-4664

Railway Systems Suppliers, Inc. **[2994]**, 9306 New LaGrange Rd., Ste. 100, Louisville, KY 40242-3671, (502)327-7774

Railway Tech. Soc. of Australasia **[IO]**, Kingston, Australia

Railway Tie Assn. **[2995]**, 115 Commerce Dr., Ste. C, Fayetteville, GA 30214-7335, (770)460-5553

Rain Forests

Coalition for Rainforest Nations **[4856]**

Intl. Soc. for Preservation of the Tropical Rainforest **[4857]**

Intl. Soc. for Preservation of the Tropical Rainforest **[4857]**

Pachamama Alliance **[4858]**

Pachamama Alliance **[4858]**

Rainforest Partnership **[4859]**

Rainforest Relief **[4860]**

Tropical Forest and Climate Coalition **[4861]**

Tropical Forest and Climate Coalition **[4861]**

Rain for the Sahel and Sahara **[12359]**, PO Box 545, Newmarket, NH 03857, (603)371-0676

Rain for the Sahel and Sahara **[12359]**, PO Box 545, Newmarket, NH 03857, (603)371-0676

Rainbow Alliance of the Deaf **[12110]**, Henry Carter, Sec., 731 Lake Dr., Snellville, GA 30039

Reference to "IO" in place of a book number signifies that the association may be found in the 50th edition of International Organizations.

Rainbow Div. Veterans Memorial Found. [20876], 750 Vanderbilt Rd., Ellensburg, WA 98926

Rainbow/PUSH Coalition [13199], 930 E 50th St., Chicago, IL 60615-2702, (773)373-3366

Rainbow Rsrc. Centre: Serving Manitoba's Gay, Lesbian, Bisexual, Transgendered, and Two-Spirited Communities [IO], Winnipeg, MB, Canada

Rainbowfish Study Group of North Am.

Rainbowfish Study Group of North Am. - Address unknown since 2011.

RAINBOWS [11498], 1360 Hamilton Pkwy., Itasca, IL 60143, (847)952-1770

RAINBOWS [11498], 1360 Hamilton Pkwy., Itasca, IL 60143, (847)952-1770

Rainbows for All God's Children [★11498]

Rainbows for All God's Children [★11498]

Rainforest Action Network [4126], 221 Pine St., 5th Fl., San Francisco, CA 94104, (415)398-4404

Rainforest Action Network [4126], 221 Pine St., 5th Fl., San Francisco, CA 94104, (415)398-4404

Rainforest Alliance [4127], 665 Broadway, Ste. 500, New York, NY 10012, (212)677-1900

Rainforest Alliance [4127], 665 Broadway, Ste. 500, New York, NY 10012, (212)677-1900

Rainforest Info. Centre [IO], Lismore, Australia

Rainforest Partnership [4859], PO Box 49268, Austin, TX 78765, (512)420-0101

Rainforest Relief [4860], PO Box 298, New York, NY 10008-0298, (917)543-4064

Rainwater Assn. of Somalia [IO], Baidoa, Somalia

Raisin Bargaining Assn. [4470], 1300 E Shaw Ave., Ste. 175, Fresno, CA 93710-7911, (559)221-1925

Raising a Reader [8783], 2440 W El Camino Real, Ste. 300, Mountain View, CA 94040, (650)450-5566

Raittiuden Ystavat [★IO]

Rajagiri Outreach Ser. Soc. [IO], Kochi, India

Rakennusliitto [★IO]

Ralph Waldo Emerson Study Group - Defunct.

Ramakrishna - Vivekananda Center [20278], 17 E 94th St., New York, NY 10128, (212)534-9445

Ramblers' Assn. [IO], London, United Kingdom

Ranch HQ Assn. [★9798]

Ranchers for Peace - Defunct.

Ranching Heritage Assn. [9798], PO Box 43201, Lubbock, TX 79409-3201, (806)742-0497

Rand Soc; Ayn [10373]

Randolph-Sheppard Vendors of Am. [3614], 940 Parc Helene Dr., Marrero, LA 70072-2421, (504)328-6373

RandomKid [13554], PO Box 102, Waukee, IA 50263-9581, (612)210-9952

Randonneurs USA [22485], 226 West Ave., Santa Cruz, CA 95060, (831)227-6266

Rangeland

   Amer. Forage and Grassland Coun. [4862]

   Soc. for Range Mgt. [4863]

   Working Ranch Cowboys Assn. [2997]

Rangers Fan Club [★23908]

Rangers and Rangerettes [★19285]

Rangpur Dinajpur Rural Ser. Bangladesh [IO], Dhaka, Bangladesh

Rank and File [IO], Montreal, QC, Canada

Rannsoknarrad Islands [★IO]

Raoul Wallenberg Comm. [IO], Stockholm, Sweden

Raoul Wallenberg Comm. of the U.S. [17569], 15 W 16th St., 6th Fl., New York, NY 10011, (917)606-8260

Raoul Wallenberg Comm. of the U.S. [17569], 15 W 16th St., 6th Fl., New York, NY 10011, (917)606-8260

Raoul Wallenberg Kommitten [★IO]

Raoul Wallenberg Working Group [★17569]

Raoul Wallenberg Working Group [★17569]

Rape

   MaleSurvivor: The Natl. Org. Against Male Sexual Victimization [13089]

   Pandora's Proj. [13096]

   Rape, Abuse and Incest Natl. Network [12758]

   Rwanda Gift for Life [13099]

   Sex Abuse Treatment Alliance [13100]

   Speaking Out About Rape [12759]

   Students Active for Ending Rape [12760]

   Women for Women [12761]

Rape, Abuse and Incest Natl. Network [12758], 2000 L St. NW, Ste. 406, Washington, DC 20036, (202)544-3064

Rape; People Against [13098]

Rapid Technologies and Additive Mfg. Community [7047], SME, 1 SME Dr., Dearborn, MI 48121, (313)425-3000

RapidIO Trade Assn. [6467], 12343 Hymeadow Dr., Ste. 2R, Austin, TX 78750, (512)401-2900

RAPRA Tech. [IO], Shrewsbury, United Kingdom

Raptor Educ. Found. [5115], PO Box 200400, Denver, CO 80220, (303)680-8500

Raptor Rehabilitation and Propagation Proj. [★5158]

Raptor Rehabilitation and Propagation Proj. [★5158]

Raptor Res. Found. [5116], 101 12th Ave., Rm. 110, Box 19, Fairbanks, AK 99701, (907)456-0041

RARE [5117], 1840 Wilson Blvd., Ste. 204, Arlington, VA 22201, (703)522-5070

Rare Animal Relief Effort [★5117]

Rare Breeds Canada [IO], Notre-Dame-de-l'Ile-Perrot, QC, Canada

RARE Center [★5117]

Rare Center for Tropical Bird Conservation [★5117]

RARE Center for Tropical Conservation [★5117]

Rare-Earth Information Center - Defunct.

Rare Fruit Coun. [★4471]

Rare Fruit Coun. [★4471]

Rare Fruit Coun. Intl. [4471], 14735 SW 48 Terr., Miami, FL 33185-4066, (305)554-1333

Rare Fruit Coun. Intl. [4471], 14735 SW 48 Terr., Miami, FL 33185-4066, (305)554-1333

Raskob Found. for Catholic Activities [19489], PO Box 4019, Wilmington, DE 19807-0019, (302)655-4440

Raskob Found. for Catholic Activities [19489], PO Box 4019, Wilmington, DE 19807-0019, (302)655-4440

Raspberry Indus. Development Coun. [IO], Abbotsford, BC, Canada

Rassemblement des Amateurs de Levriers d'Irlande et d'Ecosse [IO], St.-Souplet-sur-Py, France

Rat Assistance and Teaching Soc. [21950], 857 Lindo Ln., Chico, CA 95973, (530)899-0605

Rat Fan Club [21951], 857 Lindo Ln., Chico, CA 95973, (530)899-0605

Rat fur Formgebung [★IO]

Rat and Mouse Club of Am. [21952], 6082 Modoc Rd., Westminster, CA 92683

Rat, Mouse, and Hamster Fanciers - Address unknown since 2011.

Rat Terrier Club of Am. [21642], 47044 5th St. W, Lancaster, CA 93534-7501, (661)945-5663

Rathkamp Matchcover Soc. [21882], 1509 S Dugan Rd., Urbana, OH 43078-9209

Rating Surveyors' Assn. [IO], Leeds, United Kingdom

Rational Recovery Systems [16752], PO Box 800, Lotus, CA 95651, (530)621-2667

Ratkaisiya Kansainvalistymiseen [★IO]

Rattan Assn. of Cambodia [IO], Phnom Penh, Cambodia

Raueddi kross Islands [★IO]

Rauma Chamber of Commerce [IO], Rauma, Finland

Rauman Kauppakamari [★IO]

Rawlin(g)s-Rollin(g)s Family History Assn. - Defunct.

Ray Helfer Soc. [14100], Tammy Hurley, 12865 Parkside Dr., Palos Park, IL 60464

Ray of Hope [13297], 2778 Snapfinger Rd., Decatur, GA 30034, (770)696-5100

Ray Price Intl. Fan Club [23884], Sandra Orwig, Pres., 4205 Catalina Ln., Harrisburg, PA 17109

Ray Soc. [IO], London, United Kingdom

Raynaud's and Scleroderma Assn. [IO], Alsager, United Kingdom

RAZZIE Awards [★21706]

RC-Unionen [IO], Lystrup, Denmark

Rdeci Kriz Slovenije [★IO]

RDMA Consortium - Address unknown since 2011.

Re-Formed Congregation of the Goddess - Intl. [20290], PO Box 6677, Madison, WI 53716-0677, (608)226-9998

Re-Solv, the Soc. for the Prevention of Solvent and Volatile Substance Abuse [IO], Stone, United Kingdom

Reach Across [20084], PO Box 2047, Lexington, SC 29071-2047, (803)358-2330

Reach Across [20084], PO Box 2047, Lexington, SC 29071-2047, (803)358-2330

REACH Charity: Assn. for Children with Upper Limb Deficiency [IO], Cornwall, United Kingdom

Reach the Children [11396], 14 Chesham Way, Fairport, NY 14450, (585)223-3344

Reach the Children [11396], 14 Chesham Way, Fairport, NY 14450, (585)223-3344

Reach Global [13146], 2150 Allston Way, Ste. 400, Berkeley, CA 94704, (415)742-8048

Reach Global [13146], 2150 Allston Way, Ste. 400, Berkeley, CA 94704, (415)742-8048

Reach Intl. Healthcare and Training [15206], PO Box 152, Caulfield, MO 65626

Reach Out to Romania [12750], PO Box 18016, Anaheim, CA 92817-8016

Reach Out To Asia [IO], Doha, Qatar

Reach Out To Help [★20709]

Reach Out for Youth with Ileitis and Colitis [16780], 84 Northgate Cir., Melville, NY 11747, (631)293-3102

Reach to Recovery [13973], Amer. Cancer Soc., PO Box 22718, Oklahoma City, OK 73123-1718, (800)ACS-2345

Reach to Recovery Found. [★13882]

Reach the World [8179], 329 E 82nd St., 2nd Fl., New York, NY 10028, (212)288-6987

Reaching Critical Will [17558], Women's Intl. League for Peace and Freedom, 777 UN Plz., 6th Fl., New York, NY 10017, (212)682-1265

REACT [★5967]

REACT [★5967]

REACT Intl. [5967], 12114 Boydton Plank Rd., Dinwiddie, VA 23841, (301)316-2900

REACT Intl. [5967], 12114 Boydton Plank Rd., Dinwiddie, VA 23841, (301)316-2900

Read Horn of Africa USA [12360], 310 E 38th St., Ste. CR-A, Minneapolis, MN 55409, (612)821-2364

Read Horn of Africa USA [12360], 310 E 38th St., Ste. CR-A, Minneapolis, MN 55409, (612)821-2364

Reading

   Coll. Reading and Learning Assn. [8779]

   Intl. Reading Assn. [8780]

   Intl. Reading Assn. [8780]

   Literacy Res. Assn. [8781]

   Movable Book Soc. [21233]

   Natl. Right to Read Found. [8782]

   Raising a Reader [8783]

   Reading Is Fundamental [8784]

   Reading Recovery Coun. of North Am. [8785]

   Reading Recovery Coun. of North Am. [8785]

   Soc. for the Sci. Stud. of Reading [8786]

Reading Is Fundamental [8784], 1255 23rd St. NW, Ste. 300, Washington, DC 20037, (202)536-3400

Reading Recovery Coun. of North Am. [8785], 500 W Wilson Bridge Rd., Ste. 250, Worthington, OH 43085-5218, (614)310-7323

Reading Recovery Coun. of North Am. [8785], 500 W Wilson Bridge Rd., Ste. 250, Worthington, OH 43085-5218, (614)310-7323

Reagan Alumni Assn. [18391], 904 Vicar Ln., Alexandria, VA 22302-3421, (703)461-7250

Reagan Appointees Alumni Assn. [★18391]

Real Academia Nacional Farmacia [★IO]

Real Diaper Assn. [11750], 3401 Adams Ave., Ste. A, PMB No. 155, San Diego, CA 92116-2490

Real Estate

   AIR Commercial Real Estate Assn. [2998]

   Amer. Land Title Assn. [2999]

   Amer. Real Estate Soc. [8787]

   Amer. Real Estate and Urban Economics Assn. [8788]

   Amer. Resort Development Assn. [3000]

   Amer. Soc. of Cost Segregation Professionals [3381]

   Asian Amer. Real Estate Assn. [3001]

   Assn. of Appraiser Regulatory Officials [227]

   Assn. of Energy and Environmental Real Estate Professionals [8150]

   Assn. of Green Property Owners and Managers [2900]

   Assn. of Real Estate License Law Officials [5956]

   Assn. of Real Estate License Law Officials [5956]

   Assn. of Real Estate Women [3002]

   Bahamas Real Estate Assn. [13724]

   BOMI Intl. - The Independent Inst. for Property and Fac. Mgt. Educ. [3003]

A star before a book entry number signifies that the name is not listed separately, but is mentioned within the entry.

Building Owners and Managers Assn. Intl. [3004]
Building Owners and Managers Assn. Intl. [3004]
Building Professionals' Consortium [6501]
Castle Coalition [18403]
CCIM Inst. [3005]
CCIM Inst. [3005]
CoreNet Global [3006]
CoreNet Global [3006]
Coun. of Real Estate Brokerage Managers [3007]
Coun. of Real Estate Brokerage Managers [3007]
Coun. of Residential Specialists [3008]
Counselors of Real Estate [3009]
Counselors of Real Estate [3009]
CRE Finance Coun. [3010]
CREW Network [3011]
FIABCI-U.S.A. [3012]
Hotel Brokers Intl. [3013]
Hotel Brokers Intl. [3013]
Indus. Asset Mgt. Coun. [3014]
Inst. of Real Estate Mgt. [3015]
Intl. Assn. of Attorneys and Executives in Corporate Real Estate [3016]
Intl. Assn. of Attorneys and Executives in Corporate Real Estate [3016]
Intl. Bus. Brokers Assn. [3017]
Intl. Bus. Brokers Assn. [3017]
Intl. Real Estate Inst. [3018]
Intl. Real Estate Inst. [3018]
Natl. Apartment Assn. [3019]
Natl. Assn. of Exclusive Buyer Agents [18504]
Natl. Assn. of Hispanic Real Estate Professionals [3020]
Natl. Assn. of Independent Real Estate Brokers [3021]
Natl. Assn. of Indus. and Off. Properties [3022]
Natl. Assn. of Land Title Examiners and Abstractors [3023]
Natl. Assn. of Media Brokers [3024]
Natl. Assn. of Real Estate Brokers [3025]
Natl. Assn. of Real Estate Companies [3026]
Natl. Assn. of Real Estate Consultants [3027]
Natl. Assn. of Real Estate Investment Managers [3028]
Natl. Assn. of Real Estate Investment Trusts [3029]
Natl. Assn. of Realtors [3030]
Natl. Assn. of Rev. Appraisers and Mortgage Underwriters [3031]
Natl. Coun. of Exchangors [3032]
Natl. Multi Housing Coun. [3033]
Natl. Multifamily Resident Info. Coun. [3034]
Natl. Residential Appraisers Inst. [3035]
Pension Real Estate Assn. [3036]
Property Mgt. Assn. [3037]
Real Estate Buyer's Agent Coun. [3038]
Real Estate Educators Assn. [3039]
Real Estate Info. Professionals Assn. [3040]
Real Estate Roundtable [3041]
Real Estate Services Providers Coun. [3042]
Realtors Land Inst. [3043]
Soc. of Indus. and Off. Realtors [3044]
Vacation Rental Managers Assn. [3045]
Women's Coun. of Realtors [3046]
Real Estate Aviation Chap. - Defunct.
Real Estate Brokerage Coun. [★3007]
Real Estate Brokerage Coun. [★3007]
Real Estate Brokerage Managers Coun. [★3007]
Real Estate Brokerage Managers Coun. [★3007]
Real Estate Buyer's Agent Coun. [3038], 430 N Michigan Ave., Chicago, IL 60611, (312)329-8656
Real Estate Developers' Assn. of Singapore [IO], Singapore, Singapore
Real Estate Educators Assn. [3039], 2000 Interstate Park Dr., Ste. 306, Montgomery, AL 36109-5420, (334)625-4686
Real Estate Indus. Assn. [IO], Port Moresby, Papua New Guinea
Real Estate Info. Professionals Assn. [3040], 2501 Aerial Center Pkwy., Ste. 103, Morrisville, NC 27560, (919)459-2070
Real Estate Info. Providers Assn. [★3040]
Real Estate Inst. of Canada [IO], Toronto, ON, Canada
Real Estate Investment Securities Assn. [1785], Two Meridian Plz., 10401 N Meridian St., Ste. 202, Indianapolis, IN 46290, (317)663-4180

Real Estate Law Inst. - Defunct.
Real Estate Roundtable [3041], 801 Pennsylvania Ave. NW, Ste. 720, Washington, DC 20004, (202)639-8400
Real Estate Services Providers Coun. [3042], 2000 L St. NW, Ste. 522, Washington, DC 20036, (202)862-2051
Real Estate's Roundtable [★3041]
Real Federacion Espanola de Squash [IO], Madrid, Spain
Real Federacion Espanola de Tenis [IO], Barcelona, Spain
Real Found. [13476], 550 Hinesburg Rd., South Burlington, VT 05403, (802)846-7871
Real Property Assn. of Canada [IO], Toronto, ON, Canada
Real Sociedad Economica de Amigos del Pais de Tenerife [★IO]
Real Sociedad Espanola de Fisica [★IO]
Real Sociedad Espanola de Historia Natural [IO], Madrid, Spain
Real Sociedad Espanola de Quimica [★IO]
Real Sociedad Matematica Espanola [IO], Madrid, Spain
REAL Women of Canada [IO], Ottawa, ON, Canada
Reality Relief [12880], 834 Ave. F, Billings, MT 59102, (706)201-8520
Realizing Rights: The Ethical Globalization Initiative - Defunct.
Realtors Land Inst. [3043], 430 N Michigan Ave., Chicago, IL 60611, (312)329-8446
Realtors Natl. Marketing Inst. - Defunct.
Reason Found. [5855], 3415 S Sepulveda Blvd., Ste. 400, Los Angeles, CA 90034, (310)391-2245
Reason Public Policy Inst. [★5855]
Reasoning Mind [8569], 3050 Post Oak Blvd., Ste. 1200, Houston, TX 77056, (281)579-1110
Reasons to Believe [20235], 731 E Arrow Hwy., Glendora, CA 91740, (626)335-1480
Rebecca Clarke Soc. [9504], Brandeis Univ., Women's Stud. Res. Center, Mailstop 079, Waltham, MA 02454-9110, (617)776-1809
Reblooming Iris Soc. [21818], 341 Schwatz Rd., Gettysburg, PA 17325, (717)338-1657
Rebuild A Nation [11077], 129 Fabyan Pl., 3rd Fl., Newark, NJ 07112-1106, (718)207-7142
Rebuild A Nation [11077], 129 Fabyan Pl., 3rd Fl., Newark, NJ 07112-1106, (718)207-7142
Rebuilding Alliance [12199], 178 South Blvd., San Mateo, CA 94402, (650)325-4663
Rebuilding Alliance [12199], 178 South Blvd., San Mateo, CA 94402, (650)325-4663
Rebuilding Haiti Now [12881], 2314 Alamance Dr., West Chicago, IL 60185
Rebuilding Together [12200], 1899 L St. NW, Ste. 1000, Washington, DC 20036-3810, (800)473-4229
Rebuilding Together with Christmas in April - U.S.A. [★12200]
RECAP [★11522]
Recent Past Preservation Network [6943], PO Box 3072, Burlington, VT 05408
Reciclanet Hezgarri Elkartea [IO], Bilbao, Spain
Reciprocal Meat Conf. [★6869]
ReclaimDemocracy.org [17529], 222 S Black Ave., Bozeman, MT 59715, (406)582-1224
Recognition Professionals Intl. [17613], 1000 Westgate Dr., Ste. 252, St. Paul, MN 55114, (651)290-7490
Recognition Technologies Users Assn., OCR/Scanner/Fax Assn. [★6512]
Reconciling Congregation Prog. [★19799]
Reconciling Ministries Network [19799], 3801 N Keeler Ave., Chicago, IL 60641-3007, (773)736-5526
Reconnecting Am. [13336], 436 14th St., Ste. 1005, Oakland, CA 94612, (510)268-8602
Reconnexion [IO], Glen Iris, Australia
Reconstruction Efforts Aiding Children without Homes [11624], PO Box 4141, Winchester, VA 22604
Reconstructionist Fed. of Congregations and Fellowships [★19875]
Reconstructionist Fellowship of Congregations [★19875]
Reconstructionist Rabbinical Assn. [19896], 1299 Church Rd., Wyncote, PA 19095, (215)576-5210

Reconstructive Microsurgery; Amer. Soc. for [16802]
Reconstructive Microsurgery; Amer. Soc. for [16802]
Reconstructive Surgery; Amer. Bd. of Facial Plastic and [16794]
Record Indus. Assn. of Am. [★3052]
The Recording Acad. [★10505]
Recording Artists, Actors and Athletes Against Drunk Driving [13003], 4370 Tujunga Ave., Ste. 212, Studio City, CA 91604, (818)752-7799
Recording Artists, Actors and Athletes Against Drunk Driving [13003], 4370 Tujunga Ave., Ste. 212, Studio City, CA 91604, (818)752-7799
Recording Artists, Actors and Athletes Against Drunk Driving - Australia [IO], Crows Nest, Australia
Recording for the Blind [★17095]
Recording for the Blind and Dyslexic [★17095]
Recording Indus. Music Performance Trust Funds [★10246]
Recording Industry
Natl. Acad. of Recording Arts and Sciences [10505]
Tamizdat [9518]
Recording Indus. Assn. of Am. [3052], 1025 F St. NW, 10th Fl., Washington, DC 20004, (202)775-0101
Recording Indus. Assn. of Jamaica [IO], Kingston, Jamaica
Recording Indus. Assn. of Japan [IO], Tokyo, Japan
Recording Indus. Assn. of Malaysia [IO], Kuala Lumpur, Malaysia
Recording Indus. Assn. of New Zealand [IO], Auckland, New Zealand
Recording Indus. Assn. of Singapore [IO], Singapore, Singapore
Recording Indus. of South Africa [IO], Randburg, Republic of South Africa
Recordings
Alliance of Artists and Recording Companies [3047]
Alliance of Artists and Recording Companies [3047]
Amer. Assn. of Independent Music [3048]
Audio Publishers Assn. [3049]
British Assn. of Record Dealers [14368]
Music Video Production Assn. [3050]
Musical Heritage Soc. [10504]
Natl. Acad. of Recording Arts and Sciences [10505]
Natl. Assn. of Recording Merchandisers [3051]
Recording Indus. Assn. of Am. [3052]
Soc. of Professional Audio Recording Services [3053]
Records Mgt. Assn. of Australasia [IO], St. Helens, Australia
Records Mgt. Soc. [IO], Newcastle upon Tyne, United Kingdom
Recovered Alcoholic Clergy Assn. [13286], 127 Inverness Rd., Athens, GA 30606, (706)546-5281
Recovered Medical Equip. for the Developing World [15313], PO Box 208051, New Haven, CT 06520-8051, (203)737-5356
Recovered Medical Equip. for the Developing World [15313], PO Box 208051, New Haven, CT 06520-8051, (203)737-5356
Recovery Ministries [13287], 218 Oakview Dr., Mooresville, IN 46158, (317)797-3813
Recovery from Mormonism [12902], Richard Packham, 2145 Melton Rd., Roseburg, OR 97470, (541)672-2360
Recreation
92nd St. Y [12400]
Am. Outdoors Assn. [22835]
Amer. Assn. for Physical Activity and Recreation [12762]
Amer. Blind Bowling Assn. [22502]
Amer. Boating Assn. [22315]
Amer. Canoe Assn. [23120]
Amer. Carp Soc. [21730]
Amer. Lands Access Assn. [22129]
Amer. Recreation Coalition [12763]
Amer. Ski-Bike Assn. [22963]
Angels With Special Needs [11760]
Antique Motorcycle Club of Am. [21919]
Assn. of Pool and Spa Professionals [3054]
Assn. of Pool and Spa Professionals [3054]

Reference to "IO" in place of a book number signifies that the association may be found in the 50th edition of International Organizations.

Bass Anglers Sportsman Soc. [22572]
Best Holiday Trav-L-Park Assn. [3055]
Break Away: The Alternative Break Connection [12764]
Camping Women [22441]
Carp Anglers Gp. [21732]
Christian Camp and Conf. Assn. [22442]
Christian Hunters and Anglers Assn. [21279]
Collegiate Assn. of Table Top Gamers [21745]
Employee Services Mgt. Found. [12765]
Family Campers and RVers [22443]
Fed. of Fly Fishers [22574]
Fed. of Metal Detector and Archaeological Clubs [21851]
Green Spa Network [3056]
Harley Hummer Club [21929]
Hostelling Intl. USA [12766]
Intl. Amusement and Leisure Defense Assn. [3057]
Intl. Assn. of Skateboard Companies [22833]
Intl. Assn. of Skateboard Companies [22833]
Intl. Dodge Ball Fed. [22981]
Intl. Fitness Assn. [16227]
Intl. Miniature Aircraft Assn. [22130]
Intl. Scale Soaring Assn. [21904]
Intl. Spa Assn. [3058]
Intl. Spa Assn. [3058]
KampGround Owners Assn. [3059]
Kids Enjoy Exercise Now [21474]
Natl. 42 Players Assn. [21750]
Natl. Amateur Dodgeball Assn. [22253]
Natl. Amusement Park Historical Assn. [20946]
Natl. Assn. of RV Parks and Campgrounds [3060]
Natl. Bass Anglers Assn. [22581]
Natl. Forest Recreation Assn. [3061]
Natl. Swimming Pool Found. [3062]
Natl. Versatility Ranch Horse Assn. [22686]
North Amer. Bowhunting Coalition [21866]
North Amer. Family Campers Assn. [22446]
North Amer. Stone Skipping Assn. [22131]
North Amer. Stone Skipping Assn. [22131]
Prairie Club [12767]
Pro vs. GI Joe [21762]
Resort and Commercial Recreation Assn. [3063]
Ride to Work [21936]
Riva Club USA [21232]
Scale Warbird Racing Assn. [21910]
Senior Roller Skaters of Am. [22899]
Special Recreation for disABLED Intl. [11831]
Sport and Recreation Law Assn. [23022]
Stars for Stripes [20417]
Suntanning Assn. for Educ. [3064]
Tread Lightly! [4864]
Tree Climbing USA [21286]
U.S. Boomerang Assn. [22422]
U.S. Bridge Fed. [21240]
U.S. Lawn Bowls Assn. [22430]
U.S. Mountain Guides Assn. [22456]
U.S. Naval Sailing Assn. [20727]
U.S. Parachute Assn. [22800]
U.S. Powered Paragliding Assn. [22796]
U.S. Ski Team Found. [22919]
Up2Us [13563]
U.S.A. Cricket Assn. [23016]
Veterans Educ. Proj. [13357]
WAVES for Development [18683]
Recreation Division of the Amer. Alliance for Hea., Physical Educ. and Recreation [★12762]
Recreation Vehicle Dealers Assn. of Am. [3067], 3930 Univ. Dr., Fairfax, VA 22030-2515, (703)591-7130
Recreation Vehicle Dealers Assn. of Canada [IO], Richmond, BC, Canada
Recreation Vehicle Indus. Assn. [3068], 1896 Preston White Dr., Reston, VA 20191, (703)620-6003
Recreation Vehicle Rental Assn. [3069], 3930 Univ. Dr., Fairfax, VA 22030-2515, (703)591-7130
Recreational Canoeing Assn. of British Columbia [IO], Vancouver, BC, Canada
Recreational Fishing Alliance [4383], PO Box 3080, New Gretna, NJ 08224, (609)404-1060
Recreational Park Trailer Indus. Assn. [3070], 30 Greenville St., 2nd Fl., Newnan, GA 30263-2602, (770)251-2672
Recreational Scuba Training Coun. [23106], PO Box 11083, Jacksonville, FL 32239-1083

Recreational Vehicle Aftermarket Assn. [3625], 1833 Centre Point Cir., Ste. 123, Naperville, IL 60563-4848, (630)596-9004
Recreational Vehicle Club Directors Assn. [★22146]
Recreational Vehicle Division of the Trailer Coach Assn. [★3068]
Recreational Vehicle Inst. [★3068]
Recreational Vehicles
  Alpine Coach Assn. [22132]
  Antique Snowmobile Club of Am. [22133]
  Arctic Cat Club of Am. [22134]
  Beaver Ambassador Club [22135]
  BlueRibbon Coalition [22834]
  Carriage Travel Club [22186]
  Discovery Owners Assn., Inc. [22136]
  Escapees [22137]
  Family Campers and RVers [22443]
  Family Motor Coach Assn. [22138]
  Good Sam Recreational Vehicle Club [22139]
  Handicapped Travel Club [22140]
  HitchHikers of Am. Intl. [22141]
  Holiday Rambler Recreational Vehicle Club [22142]
  Intl. Snowmobile Mfrs. Assn. [3065]
  Intl. Snowmobile Mfrs. Assn. [3065]
  Jayco Travel Club [22143]
  Loners on Wheels [22144]
  Natl. African-American RV'ers Assn. [22145]
  North Amer. Family Campers Assn. [22446]
  Personal Watercraft Indus. Assn. [3066]
  Recreation Vehicle Dealers Assn. of Am. [3067]
  Recreation Vehicle Indus. Assn. [3068]
  Recreation Vehicle Rental Assn. [3069]
  Recreational Park Trailer Indus. Assn. [3070]
  RV Mfrs'. Clubs Assn. [22146]
  RVing Women [22147]
  SunnyTravelers [22148]
  Supreme Travel Club [22149]
  Toyota Territory Off-Roaders Assn. [22150]
  Vagabundos Del Mar RV, Boat and Travel Club [22151]
  Vagabundos Del Mar RV, Boat and Travel Club [22151]
  Wally Byam Caravan Club Intl. [22152]
Recruitment and Consulting Services Assn. [IO], Melbourne, Australia
Recruitment and Employment Confed. [IO], London, United Kingdom
Recruitment Process Outsourcing Assn. [1791], Scott Foos, Exec. Dir., 6619 S Dixie Hwy., No. 355, Miami, FL 33143, (305)799-3237
ReCycle BiCycle of Sydney Australia [IO], Camperdown, Australia
Recycled Paperboard Tech. Assn. [887], PO Box 5774, Elgin, IL 60121-5774, (847)622-2544
Recycling
  Action for Clean Energy [4224]
  Ag Container Recycling Coun. [4865]
  Aircraft Fleet Recycling Assn. [12768]
  Aircraft Fleet Recycling Assn. [12768]
  Assn. of Lighting and Mercury Recyclers [4866]
  Battery Recycling Assn. of North Am. [3071]
  Biofuel Recycling [4867]
  Cement Kiln Recycling Coalition [4868]
  CHWMEG [3633]
  Clean the World [4869]
  East West Educ. Development Found. [12664]
  Free Geek [12769]
  Freecycle Network [4870]
  GAIA Movement USA [4066]
  The Green Standard [4208]
  Natl. Coun. on Paint Disposition [4765]
  Recycling for Charities [4871]
  Reusable Packaging Assn. [3072]
  Sustainable Biomaterials Collaborative [6119]
  Sustainable Packaging Coalition [4764]
  Veggie Van Org. [4872]
  Vishwam [12770]
  Vishwam [12770]
  Waste-to-Energy Res. and Tech. Coun. [7593]
  World Reuse, Repair and Recycling Assn. [4873]
Recycling Assn. [IO], Daventry, United Kingdom
Recycling for Charities [4871], 5763 Arapahoe Ave., Unit G, Boulder, CO 80303, (866)630-7557
Recycling Coun. of Alberta [IO], Bluffton, AB, Canada

Recycling Coun. of Ontario [IO], Toronto, ON, Canada
Red Angus Assn. of Am. [3938], 4201 N, Interstate 35, Denton, TX 76207-3415, (940)387-3502
Red de Automatica de Cuba [IO], Havana, Cuba
Red Badge of Courage - Defunct.
Red Bancos [IO], Montevideo, Uruguay
Red Barnet Danmark [★IO]
Red Cedar Shingle Bur. [★1500]
Red Cedar Shingle Bur. [★1500]
Red Cedar Shingle and Handsplit Shake Bur. [★1500]
Red Cedar Shingle and Handsplit Shake Bur. [★1500]
Red Crescent Soc. of Djibouti [IO], Djibouti, Djibouti
Red Crescent Soc. of the United Arab Emirates [IO], Abu Dhabi, United Arab Emirates
Red Cross
  Amer. Friends of Magen David Adom [12801]
Red Cross of Benin [IO], Porto-Novo, Benin
Red Cross of Cape Verde [IO], Praia, Cape Verde
Red Cross of Chad [IO], N'Djamena, Chad
Red Cross of Constantine I United Grand Imperial Coun. [19140], PO Box 1606, El Cajon, CA 92022-1606, (619)456-4652
Red Cross of the Democratic Republic of the Congo [IO], Kinshasa, Democratic Republic of the Congo
Red Cross of Equatorial Guinea [IO], Malabo, Equatorial Guinea
Red Cross Natl. HQ; Amer. [12803]
Red Cross Overseas Assn; Amer. [12804]
Red Cross Soc. of Bosnia and Herzegovina [IO], Sarajevo, Bosnia-Hercegovina
Red Cross Soc. of China [IO], Beijing, People's Republic of China
Red Cross Soc. of Cote d'Ivoire [IO], Abidjan, Cote d'Ivoire
Red Cross Soc. of Eritrea [IO], Asmara, Eritrea
Red Cross Soc. of Guinea [IO], Conakry, Guinea
Red Cross Soc. of Guinea-Bissau [IO], Bissau, Guinea-Bissau
Red Cross of The Former Yugoslav Republic of Macedonia [IO], Skopje, Macedonia
Red Cross - Ukraine [IO], Kiev, Ukraine
Red Earth [19168], 6 Santa Fe Plz., Oklahoma City, OK 73102, (405)427-5228
Red Espanola de Albergues Juveniles [★IO]
Red Feather Development Gp. [12201], PO Box 907, Bozeman, MT 59771-0907, (406)585-7188
Red Hat Soc. [10646], 431 S Acacia Ave., Fullerton, CA 92831, (714)738-0001
Red Hills Conservation Prog. [★4148]
Red Men
  Degree of Pocahontas, Improved Order of Red Men [19207]
  Great Coun. of U.S. Improved Order of Red Men [19208]
Red Mogen David [★12801]
Red Mogen David [★12801]
Red Poll Beef Breeders Intl. [★3895]
Red Poll Cattle Club of Am. [★3895]
Red Poll Cattle Soc. [IO], Chelmsford, United Kingdom
Red River Valley Fighter Pilots Assn. [20802], PO Box 1553, Front Royal, VA 22630-0033, (540)636-9798
Red River Valley Sugarbeet Growers Assn. [4937], 1401 32nd St. SW, Fargo, ND 58103-3428, (701)239-4151
Red Sea Mission Team [★20084]
Red Sea Mission Team [★20084]
Red Sea Team Intl. [★20084]
Red Sea Team Intl. [★20084]
Red Tag News Publications [★2238]
Red Tag News Publications Assn. [2238], 1415 N Dayton St., Chicago, IL 60622, (312)274-2215
Red and White Dairy Cattle Assn. - Defunct.
Red Wing Collectors Soc. [21401], PO Box 50, Red Wing, MN 55066, (651)388-4004
Red Wing For'em Club [23911], PO Box 007, Allen Park, MI 48101, (313)300-7082
Redbirds Vision [19169], PO Box 702, Simi Valley, CA 93062, (805)217-0364
Redd Barna [★IO]
Rede Brasileira Agroflorestal [★IO]

A star before a book entry number signifies that the name is not listed separately, but is mentioned within the entry.

Redeem Our Country - Defunct.
Redefining Progress [17586], 1904 Franklin St., Ste.
600, Oakland, CA 94612, (510)444-3041
Rederscentrale [IO], Ostend, Belgium
RedLight Children [11144], 75 Rockefeller Plz., 17th
Fl., New York, NY 10019
RedR Australia [IO], North Melbourne, Australia
RedR Canada [IO], Ottawa, ON, Canada
RedR India [IO], Pune, India
RedR Intl. [IO], Tiverton, United Kingdom
RedR London - Intl. Hea. Exchange [IO], London,
United Kingdom
RedR New Zealand [IO], Auckland, New Zealand
REDRESS [IO], London, United Kingdom
RedRover [11030], PO Box 188890, Sacramento,
CA 95818, (916)429-2457
Redwood Alliance [17618], PO Box 293, Arcata, CA
95518, (707)822-7884
Redwood Inspection Ser. [1478], 818 Grayson Rd.,
Ste. 201, Pleasant Hill, CA 94523, (925)935-1499
Redwood Region Logging Conf. [4411], 5601 S
Broadway St., Eureka, CA 95502-7127, (707)443-
4091
Reed Organ Soc. [10284], Charlie Robison,
Membership Sec., PO Box 47, Independence, MO
64051-0047
Reed Organ Soc. of Am. [★10284]
Reef Check [4707], PO Box 1057, Pacific Palisades,
CA 90272-1057, (310)230-2371
Reef Check [4707], PO Box 1057, Pacific Palisades,
CA 90272-1057, (310)230-2371
Reef Check Europe [IO], Bremen, Germany
Reef Relief [4708], PO Box 430, Key West, FL
33041, (305)294-3100
Reef Relief [4708], PO Box 430, Key West, FL
33041, (305)294-3100
ReefGuardian Intl. [4709], PO Box 1316, Middle-
town, MD 21769-4668
ReefGuardian Intl. [4709], PO Box 1316, Middle-
town, MD 21769-4668
Reel Recovery [11138], 160 Brookside Rd.,
Needham, MA 02492, (800)699-4490
Reeve Found; Christopher and Dana [16700]
Referees' Assn. [IO], Coventry, United Kingdom
Reference and Adult Services Division of ALA
[★10008]
Reference Point Found. - Defunct.
Reference Services Division of ALA [★10008]
Reference and User Services Assn. of Amer. Lib.
Assn. [10008], Barb Macikas, 50 E Huron St.,
Chicago, IL 60611, (312)280-4395
Refined Bitumen Assn. [IO], Harrogate, United
Kingdom
Refined Sugar Assn. [IO], London, United Kingdom
Reflex Sympathetic Dystrophy Assn. [★15633]
Reflex Sympathetic Dystrophy Syndrome Assn. of
Am. [15633], PO Box 502, Milford, CT 06460,
(203)877-3790
Reflexology Assn. of Am. [13705], PO Box 714,
Chepachet, RI 02814, (980)234-0159
Reflexology Assn. of Am. [13705], PO Box 714,
Chepachet, RI 02814, (980)234-0159
Reflexology Assn. of Australia [IO], Wynnum,
Australia
Reflexology Assn. of Canada [IO], Winnipeg, MB,
Canada
Reflexology Certification Bd; Amer. [13658]
Reflexology; Intl. Inst. of [16858]
Reflexology; Intl. Inst. of [16858]
Reform
Anglicans United [19689]
Natl. Alliance for Family Court Justice [5624]
Reform Jewish Appeal [19897], Union for Reform
Judaism, 633 3rd Ave., New York, NY 10017-6778,
(212)650-4000
Reform Judaism [19898], 2027 Massachusetts Ave.
NW, Washington, DC 20036, (202)387-2800
REFORMA: Natl. Assn. of Lib. Services to the
Spanish-Speaking [★10009]
REFORMA: Natl. Assn. to Promote Lib. Services to
the Spanish-Speaking [10009], Sandra Rios
Balderrama, PO Box 4386, Fresno, CA 93744,
(480)734-4460
REFORMA: Natl. Assn. of Spanish-Speaking Librar-
ians [★10009]

ReformAMT [18688], PO Box 915, Cupertino, CA
95015, (408)482-2400
Reformation
Soc. for Reformation Res. [10506]
Reformed Ecumenical Coun. - Defunct.
REFORMERS, Pakistan [IO], Faisalabad, Pakistan
Refounded Natl. Party of South Africa [IO], Pretoria,
Republic of South Africa
The Refractories Inst. [6384], PO Box 8439,
Pittsburgh, PA 15218, (412)244-1880
Refractory Ceramic Fibers Coalition [732], 2300 N
St. NW, Rm. 6178, Washington, DC 20037,
(202)663-9188
Refreshments Canada [IO], Toronto, ON, Canada
Refrigerated Foods Assn. [1428], 2971 Flowers Rd.
S, Ste. 266, Atlanta, GA 30341, (770)452-0660
Refrigerating Engineers and Technicians Assn.
[6820], PO Box 1819, Salinas, CA 93902,
(831)455-8783
Refrigeration Compressor Rebuilders Assn. [★1708]
Refrigeration Compressor Rebuilders Assn. [★1708]
Refrigeration Equip. Mfrs. Assn. [★1695]
Refrigeration; Inst. of [IO]
Refrigeration Res. and Educ. Found. [★3628]
Refrigeration Res. and Educ. Found. [★3628]
The Refrigeration Res. Found. [★3628]
The Refrigeration Res. Found. [★3628]
Refrigeration Ser. Engineers Soc. [1719], 1666 Rand
Rd., Des Plaines, IL 60016-3552, (847)297-6464
Refrigeration Ser. Engineers Soc. [1719], 1666 Rand
Rd., Des Plaines, IL 60016-3552, (847)297-6464
Refugee Advice Centre [IO], Helsinki, Finland
Refugee Coun. of Australia [IO], Surry Hills,
Australia
Refugee Coun. of New Zealand [IO], Auckland, New
Zealand
Refugee Coun. U.S.A. [18508], 1628 16th St. NW,
Washington, DC 20009, (202)319-2102
Refugee Coun. U.S.A. [18508], 1628 16th St. NW,
Washington, DC 20009, (202)319-2102
Refugee Legal Support Ser. [★18053]
Refugee Legal Support Ser. [★18053]
Refugee Relief Intl. [12480], 2995 Woodside Rd.,
No. 400-244, Woodside, CA 94062
Refugee Relief Intl. [12480], 2995 Woodside Rd.,
No. 400-244, Woodside, CA 94062
Refugee Women's Network [13477], 1431A McLen-
don Dr., Decatur, GA 30033, (404)299-0180
Refugees
Amer. Fund for Czech and Slovak Relief [12771]
Amer. Fund for Czech and Slovak Relief [12771]
Amer. Near East Refugee Aid [12772]
Amer. Near East Refugee Aid [12772]
Amer. Refugee Comm. [12773]
Amer. Refugee Comm. [12773]
Art for Refugees in Transition [12774]
Assn. for Refugee Ser. Professionals [12301]
Bridging Refugee Youth and Children's Services
[11452]
Catholic Near East Welfare Assn. | Pontifical Mis-
sion for Palestine [12775]
Catholic Relief Services [12776]
Catholic Relief Services [12776]
Central Amer. Rsrc. Center [18505]
Central Amer. Rsrc. Center [18505]
Church World Ser., Immigration and Refugee
Prog. [18506]
Church World Ser., Immigration and Refugee
Prog. [18506]
Comm. for Humanitarian Assistance to Iranian
Refugees [12777]
Comm. for Humanitarian Assistance to Iranian
Refugees [12777]
El Rescate [12778]
Ethiopian Community Development Coun. [12779]
Ethiopian Community Development Coun. [12779]
FilmAid Intl. [12780]
FilmAid Intl. [12780]
FORGE [12781]
Heshima Kenya [11310]
Humanitarian Law Proj. [18507]
Humanitarian Law Proj. [18507]
Intl. Refugee Rights Initiative [17843]
Intl. Rescue Comm. | Spanish Refugee Aid
[12782]

Intl. Rescue Comm. USA [12783]
Intl. Rescue Comm. USA [12783]
Iranian Refugees' Alliance [12784]
Iranian Refugees' Alliance [12784]
Jesuit Refugee Service/U.S.A. [12785]
Jesuit Refugee Service/U.S.A. [12785]
Lutheran Immigration and Refugee Ser. [12786]
Lutheran Immigration and Refugee Ser. [12786]
Nubian United Benevolent Intl. Assn. [12787]
Orphans to Ambassadors [11384]
Pontifical Mission for Palestine [12775]
Refugee Coun. U.S.A. [18508]
Refugee Coun. U.S.A. [18508]
Refugees Intl. [12788]
Refugees Intl. [12788]
Rights Action/Guatemala Partners [12789]
Shelter for Life Intl. [19209]
South-East Asia Center [18509]
South-East Asia Center [18509]
Southeast Asia Rsrc. Action Center [12790]
Tibetan Aid Proj. [12791]
Tibetan Aid Proj. [12791]
U.S. Comm. for Refugees and Immigrants
[18510]
U.S. Comm. for Refugees and Immigrants
[18510]
U.S. Conf. of Catholic Bishops/Migration and
Refugee Services [12792]
USA for the United Nations High Commissioner
for Refugees [12793]
USA for the United Nations High Commissioner
for Refugees [12793]
WITNESS [17868]
Refugees Intl. [12788], 2001 S St. NW, Ste. 700,
Washington, DC 20009, (202)828-0110
Refugees Intl. [12788], 2001 S St. NW, Ste. 700,
Washington, DC 20009, (202)828-0110
Refuseniks
NCSJ: Advocates on Behalf of Jews in Russia,
Ukraine, the Baltic States and Eurasia [17568]
RÉG - The Intl. Roger Waters Fan Club [23885],
128 Onyx Dr., Watsonville, CA 95076
REGAP [★11054]
Regency Found. Networx [IO], London, United
Kingdom
Regeneration [19637], PO Box 9830, Baltimore, MD
21284-9830, (410)661-0284
Regent St. Assn. [IO], London, United Kingdom
Regional African Satellite Communications Org. [IO],
Abidjan, Cote d'Ivoire
Regional Airline Assn. [155], 2025 M St. NW, Ste.
800, Washington, DC 20036-3309, (202)367-1170
Regional Assn. of Oil and Natural Gas Companies in
Latin Am. and the Caribbean [IO], Montevideo,
Uruguay
Regional Aviation Assn. of Australia [IO], Mitchell,
Australia
Regional Centre for Mapping of Resources for
Development [IO], Nairobi, Kenya
Regional Centre for Seismology for South Am. [IO],
Lima, Peru
Regional and Distribution Carriers Conf. [★3246]
Regional Environmental Center for Central and
Eastern Europe - Albania [IO], Tirana, Albania
Regional Environmental Center for Central and
Eastern Europe - Hungary [IO], Szentendre,
Hungary
Regional Environmental Center for Central and
Eastern Europe - Latvia [IO], Riga, Latvia
Regional Integration Energy Commn. [IO], Montev-
ideo, Uruguay
Regional Org. for the Protection of the Marine Env.
[IO], Safat, Kuwait
Regional Reporters Assn. [2867], Cincinnati En-
quirer, 1100 New York Ave. NW, Ste. 2005,
Washington, DC 20005
Regional Sci. Assn. [★5333]
Regional Sci. Assn. [★5333]
Regional Sci. Assn. Intl. [5333], 2149 Grey Ave.,
Evanston, IL 60201, (847)570-9501
Regional Sci. Assn. Intl. [5333], 2149 Grey Ave.,
Evanston, IL 60201, (847)570-9501
Regional Stud. Assn. [IO], Seaford, United Kingdom
Regionalais Vides Centrs Centralai un Austrumeiro-
pai [★IO]

Reference to "IO" in place of a book number signifies that the association may be found in the 50th edition of International Organizations.

Regis Sys. Users' Gp. - Address unknown since 2011.
The Register [★21134]
Register of Elecl. Contractors of Ireland [IO], Dublin, Ireland
Register of Professional Archaeologists [6175], 5024-R Campbell Blvd., Baltimore, MD 21236, (410)933-3486
Registered Financial Planners Inst. [1346], 2001 Cooper Foster Park Rd., Amherst, OH 44001, (440)282-7176
Registered Master Builders Fed. [IO], Wellington, New Zealand
Registered Nursing Home Assn. [IO], Birmingham, United Kingdom
Registro Aprilia [IO], Vicenza, Italy
Registro Aurelia Italiano [IO], Milan, Italy
Registry of Comparative Pathology - Defunct.
Registry of Emergency Medical Technicians - Ambulance [★14477]
Registry of Interpreters for the Deaf [14956], 333 Commerce St., Alexandria, VA 22314, (703)838-0030
Registry of Tissue Reactions to Drugs [★16117]
Registry of Tissue Reactions to Drugs [★16117]
Regroupement des consultants canadiens en developpement internationale [★IO]
Regroupement pour la surveillance du nucleaire [★IO]
Regular Common Carrier Conf. [★3246]
Regulation Found. [★18440]
Regulatory Affairs Professionals Soc. [14739], 5635 Fishers Ln., Ste. 550, Rockville, MD 20852, (301)770-2920
Regulatory Affairs Professionals Soc. [14739], 5635 Fishers Ln., Ste. 550, Rockville, MD 20852, (301)770-2920
Regulatory Assistance Proj. [6055], PO Box 507, Hallowell, ME 04347, (207)319-6000

Rehabilitation
Amer. Acad. of Physical Medicine and Rehabilitation [16552]
Amer. Blind Bowling Assn. [22502]
Amer. Bd. of Disability Analysts [16553]
Amer. Bd. of Physical Medicine and Rehabilitation [16554]
Amer. Cong. of Rehabilitation Medicine [16555]
Amer. Friends of ALYN Hosp. [12794]
Amer. Friends of ALYN Hosp. [12794]
Amer. Kinesiotherapy Assn. [16556]
Amer. Medical Rehabilitation Providers Assn. [16557]
Amer. RehabACTion Network [18511]
Amer. Rehabilitation Counseling Assn. [16558]
Amer. Therapeutic Recreation Assn. [16559]
Amputees in Motion Intl. [11759]
Anahata Intl. [13662]
Assn. of Academic Physiatrists [16560]
Assn. of Recovering Motorcyclists [13236]
Brain Injury Rsrc. Center [16561]
Continuing Care Accreditation Commn. [16562]
Coun. on Rehabilitation Educ. [16563]
Coun. of State Administrators of Vocational Rehabilitation [16564]
Hospitalized Veterans Writing Proj. [16565]
Inter-National Assn. of Bus., Indus. and Rehabilitation [11794]
Intl. Assn. of Addictions and Offender Counselors [11674]
Intl. Assn. of Rehabilitation Professionals [16566]
Intl. Soc. for Low Vision Res. and Rehabilitation [15965]
Irob Relief and Rehabilitation Operations Brotherhood [11986]
MOMSTELL [13265]
Narcotic Educational Found. of Am. [13267]
Natl. Assn. of Peoplecultural Rehabilitation Concerns [16567]
Natl. Assn. for Rehabilitation Leadership [16568]
Natl. Assn. of Rehabilitation Providers and Agencies [16569]
Natl. Assn. of Ser. Providers in Private Rehabilitation [16570]
Natl. Coun. on Rehabilitation Educ. [16571]
Natl. Rehabilitation Assn. [16572]

Natl. Rehabilitation Counseling Assn. [16573]
Natl. Rehabilitation Info. Center [16574]
Neuro-Optometric Rehabilitation Assn. Intl. [15559]
Permacultura Am. Latina [4684]
Rehabilitation Intl. [16575]
Rehabilitation Intl. [16575]
Rwanda Gift for Life [13099]
Salute Military Golf Assn. [22624]
Sex Abuse Treatment Alliance [13100]
Sister Kenny Rehabilitation Inst. [16576]
U.S. Psychiatric Rehabilitation Assn. [16577]
U.S. Psychiatric Rehabilitation Assn. [16577]
Veterans Educ. Proj. [13357]
Vocational Evaluation and Career Assessment Professionals [16578]
Vocational Evaluation and Career Assessment Professionals [16578]
Watering Seeds Org. [22532]
World Assn. for Psychosocial Rehabilitation - U.S. Br. [16579]
Rehabilitation Engg. and Assistive Tech. Soc. of North Am. [11825], 1700 N Moore St., Ste. 1540, Arlington, VA 22209-1903, (703)524-6686
Rehabilitation Engg. Center [★13140]
Rehabilitation Gazette [★11823]
Rehabilitation Gazette [★11823]
Rehabilitation Intl. [16575], 25 E 21st St., 4th Fl., New York, NY 10010, (212)420-1500
Rehabilitation Intl. [16575], 25 E 21st St., 4th Fl., New York, NY 10010, (212)420-1500
Rehabilitation Nurses; Assn. of [15740]
Rehabilitation Nursing Found. [★15740]

Reiki
Intl. Center for Reiki Training [22153]
Intl. Center for Reiki Training [22153]
Reiki Educ. [16580]
Shelter Animal Reiki Assn. [16581]
Shibumi Intl. Reiki Assn. [16582]
Reiki Alliance [13706], PO Box 451, Belchertown, MA 01007, (413)323-4381
Reiki Alliance [13706], PO Box 451, Belchertown, MA 01007, (413)323-4381
The Reiki Assn. [IO], Haverfordwest, United Kingdom
Reiki Educ. [16580], PO Box 298, Pineville, NC 28134, (704)644-3644
Reiki Rays of Hope for Caregivers [13707], 9592 Dublin Ln., Mentor, OH 44060, (440)357-6517
Reinsurance Assn. of Am. [2033], 1445 New York Ave., 7th Fl., Washington, DC 20005, (202)638-3690
Reinsurance Brokers' Assn. Singapore [IO], Singapore, Singapore
Reiselivsbedriftenes Landsforening [★IO]
Reklamcilar Dernegi [★IO]
Relate [IO], Rugby, United Kingdom
Relate Scotland [IO], Edinburgh, United Kingdom
Relationships Australia [IO], Curtin, Australia
Relationships Scotland [IO], Edinburgh, United Kingdom
Relatives and Residents Assn. [IO], London, United Kingdom
Relax and Rebound Centre [★9831]
Relax Tension Centre [★9831]
Relay and Switch Indus. Assn. [1085], 2500 Wilson Blvd., Ste. 310, Arlington, VA 22201, (703)907-8021
Reliability Engg. and Mgt. Institute/Reliability Testing Inst. - Address unknown since 2010.

Relief
ACCORD [20169]
Adopt-a-Village Intl. [11540]
Adventist Development and Relief Agency - Canada [10139]
Adventist Development and Relief Agency Intl. [12795]
Adventist Development and Relief Agency Intl. [12795]
Afghanistan Relief Org. [12796]
Africa Am. Crisis Assistance Network [12797]
Aid Still Required [11845]
Aid for the World [12715]
Aiding Romania's Children [11181]
AIDS Relief Intl. [10873]

Air Serv Intl. [12798]
Air Serv Intl. [12798]
All Hands Volunteers [11846]
Alliance For Relief Mission in Haiti [12799]
Am. Continental 2000 [11847]
Amer. Belarussian Relief Org. [12800]
Amer. Friends of Magen David Adom [12801]
Amer. Friends of Magen David Adom [12801]
Amer. Fund for Czech and Slovak Relief [12771]
Amer. Jewish World Ser. [12802]
Amer. Jewish World Ser. [12802]
Amer. Outreach to Ethiopia [12265]
Amer. Red Cross Natl. HQ [12803]
Amer. Red Cross Overseas Assn. [12804]
Americans Care and Share [12805]
AmeriCares Found. [12806]
AmeriGhana [12312]
Ardent Lion Soc. [11659]
Aviation for Humanity [12807]
Baitulmaal [12808]
Baptist Global Response [12809]
Batey Relief Alliance [12810]
Batey Relief Alliance [12810]
Blessings on Africa [12719]
Box Proj. [12811]
Box Proj. [12811]
Bridges Cambodia Intl. [11203]
Brother's Brother Found. [12812]
Brother's Brother Found. [12812]
Burma Relief Network [12813]
Burma Relief Network [12813]
Burundi Friends Intl. [11555]
Care 2 Share [13373]
CARE Deutschland-Luxemburg [6057]
Care Highway Intl. [12814]
Care Highway Intl. [12814]
CARE Intl. USA [12815]
CARE Intl. USA [12815]
CARE Netherlands [10373]
CARE Norge Norway [20280]
Caritas Puerto Rico [12816]
CHAP Intl. [12817]
charity: water [13414]
Chefs for Humanity [12267]
Chernobyl Children Proj., U.S.A. [12818]
Child Empowerment Intl. [11214]
Child Hope Intl. [11218]
Children's Cup [12819]
Children's Relief Mission [11250]
Christ for the Poor [8789]
Christian Action and Relief for Haiti [12820]
Christian Alliance For Humanitarian Aid [12821]
Christian Relief Services [12822]
Christian Relief Services [12822]
Church World Ser. [12823]
Church World Ser. [12823]
CitiHope Intl. [12824]
CitiHope Intl. [12824]
CityTeam Ministries [12825]
Community Aid Relief and Development [12826]
Compassion into Action Network - Direct Outcome Org. [11849]
Compassion First [12827]
Compassion First [12827]
Concern Am. [12828]
Concern Am. [12828]
Concern Worldwide [12829]
Concern Worldwide [12829]
Connecting Congo [11573]
Convoy of Hope [12830]
Convoy of Hope [12830]
Covenant World Relief [12831]
Covenant World Relief [12831]
Darfur Peace and Development Org. [12324]
Direct Aid Intl. [12832]
Direct Aid Intl. [12832]
Doctors in Christ [15303]
Doctors Without Borders USA [12833]
Edurelief [12834]
Edurelief [12834]
Episcopal Relief and Development [12835]
Episcopal Relief and Development [12835]
Estonian Relief Comm. [12836]
Estonian Relief Comm. [12836]
Ethiopian Orphan Relief [11271]

A star before a book entry number signifies that the name is not listed separately, but is mentioned within the entry.

Feed the Children [12837]
Feed the Children [12837]
Feed My Hungry Children [11274]
Fight Against Hunger Org. [12274]
Flying Doctors of Am. [12454]
Food-Aid [12275]
Food for Life Global [12838]
Food for Life Global [12838]
For Victims of War and Poverty [12455]
From Hunger to Harvest [12280]
Ghana Relief Org. [11289]
Gleaning for the World [12839]
Global Action Intl. [12840]
Global Action Intl. [12840]
Global Emergency Relief [11923]
Global Hope Network Intl. [12841]
Global MissionAir [20170]
Global MissionAir [20170]
Global Partners Running Waters [11590]
GlobeMed [15175]
Globus Relief [12458]
Great Commn. Alliance [11852]
Hand in Hand USA [12842]
Hand in Hand USA [12842]
Hands Across the Water [11297]
Hannah's Promise Intl. Aid [12843]
Hea. For All Missions [12459]
HEART 9/11: Healing Emergency Aid Response
    Team 9/11 [11853]
Heart for Africa [11299]
Heart to Heart Intl. [12844]
Heart to Heart Intl. [12844]
Help Aid Africa [11594]
Help Brings Hope for Haiti [12845]
Help the Children [12846]
Helping Hand for Nepal [12847]
Hope Force Intl. [11854]
Hope and Future for Children in Bolivia [11314]
Hope for Haiti's Children [11315]
HumaniNet [12848]
HumaniNet [12848]
Humanitarian African Relief Org. [12849]
Humanitarian Intl. Ser. Gp. [12260]
Humanitarian Resources Intl. [12850]
Humanitarian Resources Intl. [12850]
Humanitarian Services for Children of Vietnam
    [11318]
Humanity First USA [11855]
Humans in Crisis Intl. Corp. [12851]
Indian Muslim Relief and Charities [12852]
Indian Muslim Relief and Charities [12852]
Indonesia Relief - USA [11856]
Intl. Aid [12853]
Intl. Aid [12853]
Intl. Coalition for Haiti [11599]
Intl. Crisis Aid [12854]
Intl. Crisis Aid [12854]
Intl. Development Missions [12342]
Intl. Medical Corps [12855]
Intl. Medical Corps [12855]
Intl. Relief Teams [12856]
Intl. Relief Teams [12856]
InterServe U.S.A. [20054]
Iraqi Christian Relief Coun. [12857]
Irob Relief and Rehabilitation Operations Brother-
    hood [11986]
Islamic Relief U.S.A. [12858]
Islamic Relief U.S.A. [12858]
Island Aid [11858]
Ivory Coast Medical Relief Team [16583]
Ivory Coast Medical Relief Team [16583]
Jamaica Unite [11602]
Jewish World Watch [17743]
JOY for Our Youth [11330]
Kenya Medical Outreach [12462]
Khadarlis for Sierra Leone [11607]
Kids Against Hunger [12283]
Kindness in a Box [11339]
Knightsbridge Intl. [12859]
Korean Amer. Sharing Movement [12860]
Lalmba Assn. [12861]
Lalmba Assn. [12861]
Life for Relief and Development [12862]
Life for Relief and Development [12862]
Mapendo Intl. [12863]

Mapendo Intl. [12863]
Medical Aid to Haiti [12467]
Medical Relief Alliance [12864]
Medical Relief Alliance [12864]
Medical Relief Intl. [12865]
Medical Teams Intl. [12866]
Medical Teams Intl. [12866]
Mennonite Disaster Ser. [12867]
Mennonite Disaster Ser. [12867]
Mercy - U.S.A. for Aid and Development [12868]
Mercy - U.S.A. for Aid and Development [12868]
Mir Pace Intl. [12869]
Mir Pace Intl. [12869]
Mobile Medical Disaster Relief [12472]
Move For Hunger [12285]
Natl. Relief Network [12870]
Natl. Voluntary Organizations Active in Disaster
    [12871]
Near East Found. [18134]
Nepal SEEDS: Social Educational Environmental
    Development Services in Nepal [11615]
NetHope [12872]
New Frontiers Hea. Force [12873]
North Amer. Alliances for Social Relief [12352]
Nuestros Pequenos Hermanos Intl. [20077]
One Love Worldwide [12874]
One World Medical Relief [15202]
Org. for the Relief of Underprivileged Women and
    Children in Africa [12875]
Org. for the Relief of Underprivileged Women and
    Children in Africa [12875]
Orphan World Relief [11381]
Oxfam Intl. Advocacy Off. [12876]
Oxfam Intl. Advocacy Off. [12876]
Para Sa Bata [11387]
Partnership for Quality Medical Donations [12478]
Peace Winds Am. [11859]
People for Haiti [12877]
Pilgrim Africa [12878]
Pilgrim Africa [12878]
Plenty Intl. [12879]
Plenty Intl. [12879]
Reach Out to Romania [12750]
Reality Relief [12880]
Rebuilding Haiti Now [12881]
Relief for Africa [12882]
Relief for Africa [12882]
Relief Intl. [12883]
Relief Liberia Intl. [12884]
Religious Freedom Coalition [12885]
Restoring Institutions Services and Empowering
    Liberia [11625]
RHEMA Intl. [12886]
RHEMA Intl. [12886]
River Intl. [12887]
rock CAN roll [12289]
Romania Reborn [11397]
Rotarian Action Gp. for the Alleviation of Hunger
    and Malnutrition [12290]
Samaritan's Feet [11402]
Scattering Resources [12888]
Scattering Resources [12888]
Serving Our World [11405]
Share Our Strength [12292]
SHIP Aid: Shipping Humanitarian Aid to
    Impoverished People [12889]
SHIP Aid: Shipping Humanitarian Aid to
    Impoverished People [12889]
Sierra Leone Relief and Development Outreach
    [12890]
Simple Hope [12891]
Soc. for Orphaned Armenian Relief [12892]
Soc. for Orphaned Armenian Relief [12892]
Somali Medical and Supplies Relief Org. [12893]
Somali Medical and Supplies Relief Org. [12893]
Sri Lanka Medical Assn. of North Am. [14830]
Start Thinking About Romanian Children Relief
    [11410]
Stop Hunger Now [12294]
Teens Fighting Hunger [12295]
Thirst Relief Intl. [13432]
To Love a Child [11417]
Ukrainian Children's Aid and Relief Effort [11422]
UNICEF | Change for Good [12894]
U.S.A. for Africa [12895]

U.S.A. for Africa [12895]
Vietnam Relief Effort [12896]
Vishwam [12770]
Well Done Org. [11653]
Wings of Hope [12897]
Wings of Hope [12897]
World Assn. of Natural Disaster Awareness and
    Assistance [12572]
World Bicycle Relief [12898]
World Bicycle Relief [12898]
World Community Chaplains [12899]
World Community Chaplains [12899]
World Emergency Relief [12900]
World Emergency Relief [12900]
World Mercy Fund [12901]
World Mercy Fund [12901]
World Relief Org. for Children [11434]
World Vision Intl. [20171]
World Vision Intl. [20171]
World Water Relief [13445]
Relief for Africa [12882], 1100 N Main St., Ann
    Arbor, MI 48104, (734)846-9119
Relief for Africa [12882], 1100 N Main St., Ann
    Arbor, MI 48104, (734)846-9119
Relief Found. [IO], Chennai, India
Relief Intl. [12883], 5455 Wilshire Blvd., Ste. 1280,
    Los Angeles, CA 90036, (323)932-7888
Relief Liberia Intl. [12884], 10186 Lancaster Ln. N,
    Maple Grove, MN 55369, (763)607-4233

Religion

Abrahamic Alliance Intl. [19824]
Acad. of Homiletics [19814]
Acton Inst. for the Stud. of Religion and Liberty
    [20172]
Administrative Personnel Assn. of the
    Presbyterian Church [19609]
Adopt-A-Church Intl. [19610]
Advent Christian Gen. Conf. [19287]
Adventist Hea. Intl. [15138]
Afghan Hindu Assn. of Am. [19810]
African Amer. Lutheran Assn. [19920]
Alliance of Faith and Feminism [17628]
Amer. Buddhist Stud. Center [19358]
Amer. Clergy Leadership Conf. [20173]
Amer. Hindu Assn. [19811]
Amer. Jewish Comm. [19840]
Amer. Vinland Assn. [19300]
Anglicans United [19689]
ASGM [19339]
Asociacion para la Educacion Teologica Hispana
    [9006]
Assn. of Biblical Counselors [19631]
Assn. of Islamic Charitable Projects [19830]
Assn. of Presbyterian Church Educators [19612]
Assn. of Reformed Baptist Churches of Am.
    [19309]
Assn. for Religion and Intellectual Life [19669]
Assn. for the Restoration of Church and Home
    [19613]
Athletes in Action [19731]
Baptist Mid-Missions [19314]
BCM Intl. [19341]
Beatitudes Soc. [19540]
Biblical Inst. for Social Change [20174]
Black Holocaust Soc. [17154]
Brotherhood of Saint Andrew [19693]
Bros. and Sisters in Christ [19541]
Buddhist Churches of Am. Fed. of Buddhist
    Women's Associations [19359]
Cambridge Buddhist Assn. [19363]
Catholic Acad. of Sciences in the U.S.A. [19670]
Catholic Assn. of Latino Leaders [19398]
Catholic Campus Ministry Assn. [19399]
Catholic Central Union of Am. I Central Bur.
    [19400]
Catholic War Veterans Auxiliary of the U.S.A.
    [20704]
Catholic War Veterans of the U.S.A. [20781]
Center for Christian/Jewish Understanding
    [19650]
Center for Confucian Sci. [20175]
Center on Conscience and War [17560]
Center for the Evangelical United Brethren
    Heritage [19719]
Center for the Ministry of Teaching [19671]

Reference to "IO" in place of a book number signifies that the association may be found in the 50th edition of International Organizations.

Center for Reduction of Religious-Based Conflict [18512]
Center for Reduction of Religious-Based Conflict [18512]
Central Rabbinical Cong. of the U.S.A. and Canada [19854]
China Aid Assn. [20209]
Christ Truth Ministries [19346]
Christian Camp and Conf. Assn. [22442]
Christian Media Assn. [19947]ReligionChristian Res. Assn.
Christian Universalist Assn. [19560]
Christian Wrestling Fed. [23131]
ChristianTrade Assn. Intl. [19561]
Church Universal and Triumphant [20176]
Claretian Volunteers and Lay Missionaries [19413]
Coalition of Spirit-filled Churches [19616]
Collectors of Religion on Stamps [22032]
Commn. of the Churches on Intl. Affairs [19828]
Confessing Synod Ministries [20242]
Coun. for a Parliament of the World's Religions [20177]
Coun. for a Parliament of the World's Religions [20177]ReligionDay One Christian Ministries
Dharma Drum Mountain Buddhist Assn. [19364]
Dharma Realm Buddhist Assn. [19365]
Disciples Ecumenical Consultative Coun. [19618]
Disciples Justice Action Network [19566]
Divine Sci. Ministers Assn. [19645]
Do Right Found. [20178]
ECKANKAR [20179]
Episcopal Women's Caucus [19702]
Episcopalians for Global Reconciliation [19703]
Equestrian Ministries Intl. [19816]
European Soc. for the Stud. of Sci. and Theology [18226]
Evangelical Educ. Soc. [19704]
Family Fed. for World Peace and Unification [20151]
Fed. of Jain Associations in North America [20180]
Fiqh Coun. of North Am. [19831]
Forum for Scriptural Christianity [19972]
Found. for the Preservation of the Mahayana Tradition [19367]
Found. for Traditional Values [18513]
Full Gospel Bus. Men's Fellowship Intl. [19574]
Global Teams [19709]
The Gospel Coalition [19576]
Great Commission Res. Network [19619]
Greek Orthodox Ladies Philoptochos Soc. [19804]
Hagiography Soc. [20212]
Hea. Ministries Assn. [20181]
High School Evangelism Fellowship [19751]
Historical Soc. of the United Methodist Church [9768]
Holy Childhood Assn. [19428]
Holy Shroud Guild [19431]
Interdisciplinary Biblical Res. Inst. [19677]
Interfaith Alliance [20182]
Intl. Alumni Assn. of Shri Mahavir Jain Vidyalaya [19219]
Intl. Assn. of Christian Chaplains [19520]
Intl. Assn. of Missionary Aviation [20052]
Intl. Catholic Deaf Assn. U.S. Sect. [19435]
Intl. Centers for Spiritual Living [20183]
Intl. Centers for Spiritual Living [20183]
Intl. Coalition of Apostles [19991]
Intl. Fellowship of Christians and Jews [20184]
Intl. Fellowship of Christians and Jews [20184]
Intl. Order of Saint Luke the Physician [20185]
Intl. Order of Saint Luke the Physician [20185]
Intl. Org. for Septuagint and Cognate Stud. [19349]
Intl. Police and Fire Chaplain's Assn. [19522]
Intl. Soc. for the Stud. of Religion, Nature and Culture [8329]
InterServe U.S.A. [20054]
Jagannath Org. for Global Awareness [20213]
Jewish Orthodox Feminist Alliance [19873]
Jewish Prisoner Services Intl. [19874]
Jews for Judaism [20186]
Jews for Judaism [20186]
John Templeton Found. [20187]

Legatus [19445]
Liberal Religious Educators Assn. [20268]
Life Action Revival Ministries [19757]
Lollard Soc. [20188]
Lollard Soc. [20188]
Maclellan Found. [20189]
Maclellan Found. [20189]
Makatab Tarighat OveyssiShahmaghsoudi [20249]
Mariannhill Mission Soc. [19447]
Master's Men of the Natl. Assn. of Free Will Baptists [19323]
Mentalphysics [20190]
Mission Soc. of the Mother of God of Boronyavo [20191]
Missionary Soc. of Saint Paul the Apostle [19454]
Monks Without Borders [19826]
Mooncircles [20250]
Morris Pratt Inst. Assn. [20142]
Muslim Alliance in North America [19147]
Muslim Amer. Soc. [20135]
Muslim Women's Coalition [20136]
Natl. Alliance Against Christian Discrimination [19589]
Natl. Assn. of Asian-Pacific Amer. Deacons [20202]
Natl. Assn. of Catholic Family Life Ministers [19997]
Natl. Assn. of Catholic Youth Ministry Leaders [19455]
Natl. Assn. of Evangelicals [19766]
Natl. Assn. of Family Ministries [19998]
Natl. Assn. of Hispanic Priests of the USA [19457]
Natl. Assn. of Jewish Chaplains [19526]
Natl. Assn. of Melkite Youth [19591]
Natl. Assn. of Priest Pilots [19459]
Natl. Assn. of Veterans Affairs Chaplains [19527]
Natl. Conf. of Catholic Airport Chaplains [19528]
Natl. Spiritual Assembly of the Baha'is of the U.S. [20192]
Natl. Spiritualist Assn. of Churches I Healers League [20145]
New Hope Intl. [20073]
New Life Intl. Alliance [19999]
New Wineskins Missionary Network [20075]
North Am. Christian Creative Assn. [19595]
Nuestros Pequenos Hermanos Intl. [20077]
ORACLE Religious Assn. [20193]
Partners for Sacred Places [20194]
Pocket Testament League [19352]
Polish-American-Jewish Alliance for Youth Action [13551]
Quixote Center [19488]
Reach Across [20084]
Recovery from Mormonism [12902]
Response-Ability [20085]
Saq' Be': Org. for Mayan and Indigenous Spiritual Bodies [9867]
Seventh Day Adventist Kinship Intl. [19800]
Seventh Day Baptist Missionary Soc. [19330]
Seventh Day Baptist World Fed. [19331]
Sikh Coun. on Religion and Educ. [20241]
Soc. of the Companions of the Holy Cross [19716]
Soc. for Hindu-Christian Stud. [20215]
Soc. for Old Testament Stud. [13915]
Soc. for the Sci. Stud. of Religion [20195]
Soc. for the Sci. Stud. of Religion [20195]
Soc. for the Stud. of Christian Spirituality [19601]
Spiritual Directors Intl. [20196]
Spiritual Directors Intl. [20196]
Spirituality and Practice [7929]
Teen Missions Intl. [20099]
Theosophical Book Assn. for the Blind [20264]
Triratna Buddhist Community [19374]
UNANIMA Intl. [18645]
Unitarian Universalist Assn. of Congregations [12903]
United Indian Missions Intl. [20102]
U.S. Assn. of Consecrated Virgins [19507]
U.S. Christian Chamber of Commerce [23393]
U.S. Conf. of Catholic Bishops I Bishops' Comm. on Priestly Formation [19688]
United States Conference of Catholic Bishops I Comm. on Divine Worship [19510]
United Synagogue Youth [19907]

Universal Muslim Assn. of Am. [20137]
Universal Torah Registry [19908]
URANTIA Assn. of the U.S. [20197]
Westar Inst. [20198]
WordAlone Ministries [19943]
Zarathushtrian Assembly [20199]
Religion in an Age of Sci; Inst. on [20234]
Religion; Amer. Acad. of [7993]
Religion in Amer. Life - Defunct.
Religion Communicators Coun. [20168], 475 Riverside Dr., Rm. 1355, New York, NY 10115, (212)870-2985
Religion; Coun. of Societies for the Stud. of [9011]
Religion and Ethics Network - Defunct.
Religion and Family Life Sect. [★12017]
Religion and Family Life Sect. [★12017]
Religion News Ser. [2868], 1930 18th St. NW, Ste. B2, Washington, DC 20009, (202)463-8777
Religion News Ser. [2868], 1930 18th St. NW, Ste. B2, Washington, DC 20009, (202)463-8777
Religion Newswriters Assn. [2869], Univ. of Missouri, School of Journalism, 30 Neff Annex, Columbia, MO 65211, (573)882-9257
Religion and Socialism Commn. of the Democratic Socialists of Am. [18658], 536 W 111th St., No. 37, New York, NY 10025
Religion and Socialism Comm. of DSA [★18658]
Religiosos Terciarios Capuchinos de Nuestra Senora de los Dolores [★IO]
Religious Action Center of Reform Judaism [18022], Arthur and Sara Jo Kobacker Bldg., 2027 Massachusetts Ave. NW, Washington, DC 20036, (202)387-2800
Religious Action Center of Reform Judaism [18022], Arthur and Sara Jo Kobacker Bldg., 2027 Massachusetts Ave. NW, Washington, DC 20036, (202)387-2800
Religious Action Center of the Union of Amer. Hebrew Congregations [★18022]
Religious Action Center of the Union of Amer. Hebrew Congregations [★18022]
Religious Activities Task Force, Natl. Safety Coun. - Defunct.

Religious Administration
Administrative Personnel Assn. of the Presbyterian Church [19609]
Assn. of Presbyterian Church Educators [19612]
Christian Leadership Alliance [20200]
Coalition of Spirit-filled Churches [19616]
Episcopal Women's Caucus [19702]
HealthCare Chaplaincy [20201]
Intl. Assn. of Christian Chaplains [19520]
Intl. Catholic Deaf Assn. U.S. Sect. [19435]
Natl. Assn. of Asian-Pacific Amer. Deacons [20202]
Natl. Assn. of Church Bus. Admin. [20203]
Natl. Assn. of Church Facilities Managers [20204]
Natl. Assn. of Church Personnel Administrators [20205]
Natl. Assn. of Hispanic Priests of the USA [19457]
Natl. Assn. of Jewish Chaplains [19526]
Natl. Assn. of Veterans Affairs Chaplains [19527]
North Amer. Assn. of Synagogue Executives [20206]
Seventh Day Baptist Missionary Soc. [19330]
Seventh Day Baptist World Fed. [19331]
United Religions Initiative [20207]
United States Conference of Catholic Bishops I Comm. on Divine Worship [19510]
World Coun. of Religious Leaders [20208]
World Coun. of Religious Leaders [20208]
Religious Affairs; Assn. of Coll. and Univ. [8905]
Religious Bros. Conf. [19490], 5401 S Cornell Ave., Chicago, IL 60615, (773)595-4023
Religious Coalition for Abortion Rights [★18526]
Religious Coalition for Reproductive Choice [18526], 1413 K St. NW, 14th Fl., Washington, DC 20005, (202)628-7700
Religious Commun. Assn. [7888], Univ. of Texas at Tyler, Dept. of Commun., 3900 Univ. Blvd., Tyler, TX 75799, (903)566-7093
Religious Conf. Mgt. Assn. [2458], 7702 Woodland Dr., Ste. 120, Indianapolis, IN 46278, (317)632-1888
Religious Conf. Mgt. Assn. [2458], 7702 Woodland Dr., Ste. 120, Indianapolis, IN 46278, (317)632-1888

A star before a book entry number signifies that the name is not listed separately, but is mentioned within the entry.

Religious Convention Managers Assn. [★2458]
Religious Convention Managers Assn. [★2458]
Religious Educ. Assn.: An Assn. of Professors, Practitioners, and Researchers in Religious Educ. [19686], PO Box 200392, Evans, CO 80620-0392, (765)225-8836
Religious Experience Res. Centre [IO], Lampeter, United Kingdom
Religious Formation Conf. [19491], 8820 Cameron St., Silver Spring, MD 20910-4152, (301)588-4938
Religious Freedom
Albanian Catholic Inst. [18514]
Albanian Catholic Inst. [18514]
Amer. Freedom Alliance [18515]
Appeal of Conscience Found. [18516]
Atheists For Human Rights [17207]
Becket Fund for Religious Liberty [18517]
Center for Christian/Jewish Understanding [19650]
Center for Law and Religious Freedom [18518]
China Aid Assn. [20209]
Christian Freedom Intl. [20210]
Christian Freedom Intl. [20210]
Christian Solidarity Intl. [20211]
Christian Solidarity Intl. [20211]
Christian Universalist Assn. [19560]
Intl. Coalition for Religious Freedom [18519]
Intl. Coalition for Religious Freedom [18519]
Intl. Religious Liberty Assn. [18520]
Intl. Religious Liberty Assn. [18520]
Natl. Alliance Against Christian Discrimination [19589]
Rutherford Inst. [18521]
Sikh Coun. on Religion and Educ. [20241]
Religious Freedom Coalition [12885], PO Box 77511, Washington, DC 20013, (202)543-0300
Religious News Ser. [★2868]
Religious News Ser. [★2868]
Religious Newswriters Assn. [★2869]
Religious Public Relations Coun. [★20168]
Religious Reform
Anglicans United [19689]
Religious Res. Assn. [20222], 618 SW 2nd Ave., Galva, IL 61434-1912, (309)932-2727
Religious Res. Fellowship [★20222]
Religious Sci. Intl. [★20183]
Religious Sci. Intl. [★20183]
Religious Speech Commun. Assn. [★7888]
Religious Speech Division of Speech Commun. Assn. [★7888]
Religious Studies
Acad. of Homiletics [19814]
Amer. Buddhist Stud. Center [19358]
ASGM [19339]
Assn. for Religion and Intellectual Life [19669]
Beatitudes Soc. [19540]
Buddhist Churches of Am. Fed. of Buddhist Women's Associations [19359]
China Aid Assn. [20209]
Christ Truth Ministries [19346]
Christian Universalist Assn. [19560]
Deaf-Intl. [12139]
Dharma Drum Mountain Buddhist Assn. [19364]
Hagiography Soc. [20212]
Historical Soc. of the United Methodist Church [9768]
Holy Shroud Guild [19431]
Intl. Org. for Septuagint and Cognate Stud. [19349]
Intl. Soc. for the Stud. of Religion, Nature and Culture [8329]
Jagannath Org. for Global Awareness [20213]
Jews for Judaism [20186]
Natl. Coun. on Bible Curriculum in Public Schools [20214]
Reach Across [20084]
Soc. for Hindu-Christian Stud. [20215]
Soc. for the Stud. of Christian Spirituality [19601]
Soc. for the Stud. of Japanese Religions [20216]
Soc. for the Stud. of Japanese Religions [20216]
Tyndale Soc. [20217]
Tyndale Soc. [20217]
Westar Inst. [20198]
World Union of Deists [20218]
World Union of Deists [20218]

Religious Supplies
Natl. Church Goods Assn. [3073]
Religious Understanding
Afghan Hindu Assn. of Am. [19810]
Amer. Buddhist Stud. Center [19358]
Amer. Hindu Assn. [19811]
Assn. for the Restoration of Church and Home [19613]
Beatitudes Soc. [19540]
Buddhist Churches of Am. Fed. of Buddhist Women's Associations [19359]
Center for Christian/Jewish Understanding [19650]
China Aid Assn. [20209]
Dharma Drum Mountain Buddhist Assn. [19364]
Disciples Ecumenical Consultative Coun. [19618]
Evangelical Educ. Soc. [19704]
Jews for Judaism [20186]
Makatab Tarighat OveyssiShahmaghsoudi [20249]
Muslim Amer. Soc. [20135]
New Wineskins Missionary Network [20075]
Polish-American-Jewish Alliance for Youth Action [13551]
Reach Across [20084]
Scottish Bible Soc. [4060]
Sikh Coun. on Religion and Educ. [20241]
Soc. for the Stud. of Christian Spirituality [19601]
Universal Muslim Assn. of Am. [20137]
Religious Witness for the Earth [4341], PO Box 642, Littleton, MA 01460-2642
Religious Zionists of America - Defunct.
The Remain Intact "ORGAN"ization - Defunct.
Remanufacturing Industries Coun. Intl. - Defunct.
The Remanufacturing Inst. [2343], Ron Giuntini, Advisor, PO Box 48, Lewisburg, PA 17837, (570)523-0992
The Remanufacturing Inst. [2343], Ron Giuntini, Advisor, PO Box 48, Lewisburg, PA 17837, (570)523-0992
Remedios AIDS Found. [IO], Manila, Philippines
Remembering ADAM [13288], PO Box 665, Hastings, PA 16646, (814)344-8026
Remineralize the Earth [4927], 152 South St., Northampton, MA 01060, (413)586-4429
Remnant Of Israel [19770], PO Box 142633, Irving, TX 75014-2633
Remote Sensing and Photogrammetry Soc. [IO], Nottingham, United Kingdom
Remove Intoxicated Drivers - U.S.A. [★13004]
Renaissance
Massachusetts Center for Renaissance Stud. [10507]
Massachusetts Center for Renaissance Stud. [10507]
Renaissance Lawyer Soc. [5281]
Renaissance Soc. of Am. [10508]
Renaissance Soc. of Am. [10508]
Renaissance Artists and Writers Assn. [9847], RAWA New York Sector, 97-38 42nd Ave., 1st Fl., Corona, NY 11368, (718)898-1603
Renaissance Development Org. [IO], Gujranwala, Pakistan
Renaissance Educ. Assn. [★13111]
Renaissance English Texts Soc. [★10507]
Renaissance English Texts Soc. [★10507]
Renaissance Lawyer Soc. [5281], 211 Vale Rd., Jamestown, KS 66948
Renaissance Soc. of Am. [10508], CUNY, 365 5th Ave., Rm. 5400, New York, NY 10016-4309, (212)817-2130
Renaissance Soc. of Am. [10508], CUNY, 365 5th Ave., Rm. 5400, New York, NY 10016-4309, (212)817-2130
Renaissance Transgender Assn. [13111], 987 Old Eagle School Rd., Ste. 719, Wayne, PA 19087, (610)975-9119
Renaissance Universal [18817], 3001 58th Ave. S, Apt. 511, St. Petersburg, FL 33712, (727)867-1813
Renaissance Universal [IO], London, United Kingdom
Renal Administrators Assn; Natl. [15299]
Renal Assn. [IO], Petersfield, United Kingdom
Renal Pathology Soc. [16130], UNC Division of Nephropathology, 409 Brinkhous-Bullitt Bldg., CB No. 7525, Chapel Hill, NC 27599, (919)966-2421

Renal Pathology Soc. [16130], UNC Division of Nephropathology, 409 Brinkhous-Bullitt Bldg., CB No. 7525, Chapel Hill, NC 27599, (919)966-2421
Renal Physicians Assn. [15557], 1700 Rockville Pike, Ste. 220, Rockville, MD 20852-1631, (301)468-3515
Renal Support Network [15558], 1311 N Maryland Ave., Glendale, CA 91207, (818)543-0896
Renault Owners Club of North Am. [21156], 7467 Mission Gorge Rd., No. 81, Santee, CA 92071, (619)334-1711
Rene Dubos Center for Human Environments [4300], The Rene Dubos Ctr., 279 Bronxville Rd., Bronxville, NY 10708, (914)337-1636
Rene Dubos Forum [★4300]
Renew Am. [★7442]
Renew Am. [3973], PO Box 50502, Provo, UT 84605-0502
Renew Am. [★7442]
Renew the Earth [7442], 1850 Centennial Park Dr., Ste. 105, Reston, VA 20191, (703)689-4670
Renew the Earth [7442], 1850 Centennial Park Dr., Ste. 105, Reston, VA 20191, (703)689-4670
Renewable and Alternative Energy Assn. of Pakistan [IO], Islamabad, Pakistan
Renewable Energy Assn. [IO], London, United Kingdom
Renewable Energy Assn. of Swaziland [IO], Mbabane, Swaziland
Renewable Energy Markets Assn. [1176], 1211 Connecticut Ave. NW, Ste. 600, Washington, DC 20036, (202)640-6597
Renewable Energy for Medicine and Educ. [6749], PO Box 732, Cardiff, CA 92007
Renewable Energy Resources [6750], 769 Harrison Ave., Salt Lake City, UT 84105, (801)699-5705
Renewable Fuels Assn. [6751], 425 3rd St. SW, Ste. 1150, Washington, DC 20024, (202)289-3835
Renewable Natural Resources Found. [4128], 5430 Grosvenor Ln., Bethesda, MD 20814-2142, (301)493-9101
RenewableUK [IO], London, United Kingdom
Renting and Leasing
Amer. Automotive Leasing Assn. [3074]
Amer. Car Rental Assn. [3075]
Amer. Rental Assn. [3076]
Assn. of Progressive Rental Organizations [3077]
Equip. Leasing and Finance Assn. [3078]
Equip. Leasing and Finance Assn. [3078]
Natl. Assn. of Equip. Leasing Brokers [3079]
Natl. Retail Tenants Assn. [3080]
Natl. Truck Leasing Sys. [3081]
Natl. Vehicle Leasing Assn. [3082]
Tenants and Residents Org. of England [11761]
Textile Rental Services Assn. of Am. [3083]
Truck Renting and Leasing Assn. [3084]
REO Club of Am. [21157], 1323 W Maple Ave., Enid, OK 73703-4512, (651)457-6968
REO Club of Am. [21157], 1323 W Maple Ave., Enid, OK 73703-4512, (651)457-6968
Repair
House of Heroes [13350]
Repatriation Found; Amer. Indian Ritual Object [18149]
Repertoire Canadien des Psychologues Offrant des Services de Sante [★IO]
Rephael Soc. - Defunct.
Reporters Comm. for Freedom of the Press [17356], 1101 Wilson Blvd., Ste. 1100, Arlington, VA 22209, (703)807-2100
Reporters sans Frontieres [★IO]
Reporters Network - Address unknown since 2011.
Reporters Without Borders - France [IO], Paris, France
Repossessions Division of Amer. Collectors Assn. [★1031]
Representative of German Indus. and Trade [702], 1776 I St. NW, Ste. 1000, Washington, DC 20006, (202)659-4777
Representative of German Indus. and Trade [702], 1776 I St. NW, Ste. 1000, Washington, DC 20006, (202)659-4777
Representatives of Electronic Products Mfrs. [★1099]
Representatives of Radio Parts Mfrs. [★1099]

Reference to "IO" in place of a book number signifies that the association may be found in the 50th edition of International Organizations.

REPROBEL **[IO]**, Brussels, Belgium
Reproduction Rights Soc. of Nigeria **[IO]**, Ibadan, Nigeria
Reproductive and Family Hea. Assn. of Fiji **[IO]**, Suva, Fiji
Reproductive Freedom
  Exhale **[10766]**
  One More Soul **[18561]**
Reproductive Health
  Amer. Bd. of Oriental Reproductive Medicine **[16595]**
  Amer. Coll. of Community Midwives **[15864]**
  Exhale **[10766]**
  Family of the Americas Found. **[12032]**
  Family Hea. Alliance **[16584]**
  Fertile Dreams **[14531]**
  Ibis Reproductive Hea. **[16585]**
  Intl. Midwife Assistance **[15883]**
  Intl. Org. for Women and Development **[16586]**
  Intl. Partnership for Reproductive Hea. **[16587]**
  Intl. Union Against Sexually Transmitted Infections, Regional Off. for North Am. **[16656]**
  Ipas **[16588]**
  Maternal Life Intl. **[16589]**
  Maternal Life Intl. **[16589]**
  Medical Students for Choice **[16590]**
  North Amer. Soc. for the Stud. of Hypertension in Pregnancy **[16591]**
  Physicians for Reproductive Choice and Hea. **[16592]**
  Soc. of Family Planning **[14528]**
  Soc. for Male Reproduction and Urology **[16593]**
  Soc. for the Stud. of Male Reproduction **[16594]**
  Support for Intl. Change **[15214]**
  WINGS **[12904]**
  WINGS **[12904]**
  World Hea. Partners **[15225]**
Reproductive Hea. Assn. of Cambodia **[IO]**, Phnom Penh, Cambodia
Reproductive Hea. Assn; Natl. Family Planning and **[12038]**
Reproductive Hea. Professionals; Assn. of **[12027]**
Reproductive Medicine
  Amer. Bd. of Oriental Reproductive Medicine **[16595]**
  Amer. Coll. of Community Midwives **[15864]**
  Exhale **[10766]**
  Ibis Reproductive Hea. **[16585]**
  Inst. for Female Alternative Medicine **[16596]**
  Intl. Midwife Assistance **[15883]**
  Intl. Union Against Sexually Transmitted Infections, Regional Off. for North Am. **[16656]**
  Natl. Campaign to Prevent Teen Pregnancy **[13540]**
  Preimplantation Genetic Diagnosis Intl. Soc. **[14656]**
  Soc. for Assisted Reproductive Tech. **[16597]**
  Soc. for Prevention of Human Infertility **[16598]**
  Soc. for Prevention of Human Infertility **[16598]**
  Soc. for Reproductive Endocrinology and Infertility **[16599]**
  Soc. of Reproductive Surgeons **[16600]**
  Soc. for the Stud. of Reproduction **[16601]**
Reproductive Rights
  Catholics for Choice **[18522]**
  Center for Reproductive Rights **[18523]**
  Center for Reproductive Rights **[18523]**
  Exhale **[10766]**
  Family Hea. Alliance **[16584]**
  Fertile Dreams **[14531]**
  Ibis Reproductive Hea. **[16585]**
  Law Students for Reproductive Justice **[18524]**
  NARAL Pro-Choice Am. **[18525]**
  Natl. Advocates for Pregnant Women **[17854]**
  Natl. Pro-Life Alliance **[18558]**
  One More Soul **[18561]**
  Religious Coalition for Reproductive Choice **[18526]**
  Republicans for Choice **[18527]**
Reproductive Toxicology Center **[14534]**, 2737 Devonshire Pl. NW, No. 120, Washington, DC 20008-3459, (301)514-3081
Reproductive Toxicology Center **[14534]**, 2737 Devonshire Pl. NW, No. 120, Washington, DC 20008-3459, (301)514-3081

Reptile and Amphibian Ecology Intl. **[5118]**, 3901 W Calle Don Miguel, Tucson, AZ 85746, (520)647-1434
Reptile and Amphibian Ecology Intl. **[5118]**, 3901 W Calle Don Miguel, Tucson, AZ 85746, (520)647-1434
Reptiles
  Global Gecko Assn. **[4874]**
  Save the Turtles **[5123]**
Reptilian and Amphibian Veterinarians; Assn. of **[17014]**
Reptilian and Amphibian Veterinarians; Assn. of **[17014]**
Republic of China Aikido Assn. **[IO]**, Taipei, Taiwan
Republic of the Marshall Islands Volleyball Fed. **[IO]**, Majuro, Marshall Islands
Republic of Trinidad and Tobago Taekwondo Assn. **[IO]**, Port of Spain, Trinidad and Tobago
Republican Coalition for Choice **[★18539]**
Republican Governors Assn. **[6001]**, 1747 Pennsylvania Ave. NW, Ste. 250, Washington, DC 20006, (202)662-4140
Republican Jewish Coalition **[18537]**, 50 F St. NW, Ste. 100, Washington, DC 20001, (202)638-6688
Republican Liberty Caucus **[18538]**, PO Box 410045, Melbourne, FL 32941, (202)239-6207
Republican Majority for Choice **[18539]**, 1900 L St. NW, Ste. 320, Washington, DC 20036-5676, (202)629-1300
Republican Natl. Coalition for Life **[18566]**, PO Box 618, Alton, IL 62002, (618)462-5415
Republican Natl. Comm. **[18540]**, 310 1st St. SE, Washington, DC 20003, (202)863-8500
Republican Natl. Hispanic Assembly of the U.S. **[18541]**, PO Box 5991, Lakeland, FL 33807, (206)337-1464
Republican Party
  Coll. Republican Natl. Comm. **[18528]**
  Congressional Automotive Caucus **[17410]**
  Log Cabin Republicans **[18529]**
  Madison Proj. **[5957]**
  Mainstream Republicans of Washington **[18530]**
  Natl. Black Republican Assn. **[18531]**
  Natl. Comm. for an Effective Cong. **[17413]**
  Natl. Fed. of Republican Women **[18532]**
  Natl. Republican Club of Capitol Hill **[18533]**
  Natl. Republican Congressional Comm. **[18534]**
  Natl. Republican Senatorial Comm. **[18535]**
  Natl. Teen Age Republicans **[18536]**
  Republican Jewish Coalition **[18537]**
  Republican Liberty Caucus **[18538]**
  Republican Majority for Choice **[18539]**
  Republican Natl. Coalition for Life **[18566]**
  Republican Natl. Comm. **[18540]**
  Republican Natl. Hispanic Assembly of the U.S. **[18541]**
  Republican Presidential Task Force **[18542]**
  Ripon Soc. **[18543]**
  United Black Republican Coalition **[18544]**
  U.S. Assn. of Former Members of Cong. **[17414]**
  Women's Natl. Republican Club **[18545]**
  Young Republican Natl. Fed. **[18546]**
Republican Presidential Task Force **[18542]**, Natl. Republican Senatorial, Ronald Reagan Republican Center Comm., 425 2nd St. NE, Washington, DC 20002, (202)675-6000
Republican Pro-Choice Coalition **[★18539]**
Republicans Abroad Intl. **[18364]**, 1275 K St. NW, Ste. 102, Washington, DC 20005, (202)608-1423
Republicans Abroad Intl. **[18364]**, 1275 K St. NW, Ste. 102, Washington, DC 20005, (202)608-1423
Republicans for Choice **[18527]**, 3213 Duke St., Ste. 808, Alexandria, VA 22314, (703)508-5897
Republicans for Environmental Protection **[4129]**, 971 S Centerville Rd., No. 139, Sturgis, MI 49091-2502, (269)651-1808
Republicko Udruzenje Srbije za Pomoc Osobama sa Autizmom **[★IO]**
ReRun **[17796]**, PO Box 113, Helmetta, NJ 08828, (732)521-1370
RESCARE **[IO]**, Stockport, United Kingdom
Rescue
  129th Alumni and Heritage Assn. **[19270]**
  Amer. Rescue Dog Assn. **[12905]**
  Amer. Rescue Dog Assn. **[12905]**

  Animal House Rescue **[10913]**
  Coast to Coast Dachshund Rescue **[10944]**
  Compassion Without Borders **[10948]**
  Echo Dogs White Shepherd Rescue **[10954]**
  HOPE Animal-Assisted Crisis Response **[12906]**
  Intl. Comm. for the Rescue of KAL 007 Survivors **[18547]**
  Marine Animal Rescue Soc. **[4093]**
  Mountain Rescue Assn. **[12907]**
  Natl. Assn. for Search and Rescue **[12908]**
  Natl. Disaster Search Dog Found. **[12909]**
  Natl. Search Dog Alliance **[12910]**
  Natl. Wolfdog Alliance **[21615]**
  Out of Love Sugar Glider Rescue **[11017]**
  The Pig Preserve Assn. **[11025]**
  Rescue Alliance of Hairless and Other Breeds **[11031]**
  Ridgeback Rescue of the U.S. **[11034]**
  Saving Horses, Inc. **[12167]**
  U.S. Homeland Emergency Response Org. **[12911]**
  U.S. Lifesaving Assn. **[12912]**
  United Yorkie Rescue **[11052]**
Rescue Alliance of Hairless and Other Breeds **[11031]**, 5116 Brookside Ln., New Port Richey, FL 34653
Research
  1st Special Response Gp. **[11843]**
  Addgene **[7110]**
  Alliance in Support of Independent Res. **[3085]**
  Amer. Assn. of Wine Economists **[3670]**
  Amer. Educational Res. Assn. **[8790]**
  Amer. Institutes for Res. **[7324]**
  Amer. Lib. Assn. I Off. for Res. and Statistics **[10509]**
  Amer. Philatelic Res. Lib. **[22010]**
  Amer. Psychological Assn. I Soc. of Psychological Hypnosis **[16380]**
  Analytical and Life Sci. Systems Assn. **[7358]**
  Assn. of Independent Res. Institutes **[7325]**
  Assn. for Korean Music Res. **[10165]**
  Assn. of Population Centers **[6594]**
  Assn. of Res. Directors **[7326]**
  Assn. for the Stud. of the Middle East and Africa **[8619]**
  Assn. of Univ. Res. Parks **[8791]**
  Carnegie Institution for Sci. **[7327]**
  Chalcedon Found. **[20219]**
  Church Growth Inc. **[20220]**
  Cmpt. Ethics Inst. **[8792]**
  Consortium on Financing Higher Educ. **[8793]**
  Coun. of Amer. Overseas Res. Centers **[7328]**
  Coun. on Governmental Relations **[8794]**
  Coun. on Undergraduate Res. **[8795]**
  Drilling, Observation and Sampling of the Earth's Continental Crust **[6602]**
  Dysphagia Res. Soc. **[14383]**
  Elliot Inst. **[10765]**
  Environmental Res. Found. **[13638]**
  European Assn. for Institutional Res. **[14044]**ResearchExecutive Search Roundtable
  Fed. of Earth Sci. Info. Partners **[6603]**
  Global Hea. Technologies Coalition **[15172]**
  Hagiography Soc. **[20212]**
  Hawaii Agriculture Res. Center **[4936]**
  HopeLab **[15342]**
  Indus. Res. Inst. **[7329]**
  Inner Light Found. **[7330]**
  Inst. for Creation Res. **[20221]**
  Inst. of Environmental Sciences and Tech. **[7331]**
  Inst. of Environmental Sciences and Tech. **[7331]**
  Inst. of Public Admin. USA **[5906]**
  Intl. Assn. for Relationship Res. **[7332]**
  Intl. Assn. of Word and Image Stud. **[8796]**
  Intl. Assn. of Word and Image Stud. **[8796]**
  Intl. Atherosclerosis Soc. **[14020]**
  Intl. Intelligence Ethics Assn. **[7001]**
  Intl. Mammalian Genome Soc. **[6900]**
  Intl. Pedigree Assignment and Bloodline Res. Assn. **[4602]**
  Intl. Soc. for Aeolian Res. **[6926]**
  Intl. Soc. for Autism Res. **[13797]**
  Intl. Soc. for Hyaluronan Sciences **[6274]**
  Intl. Soc. for IGF Res. **[6851]**
  Intl. Soc. for Intelligence Res. **[7002]**

A star before a book entry number signifies that the name is not listed separately, but is mentioned within the entry.

Intl. Soc. for Nanoscale Sci., Computation and Engg. [7376]
Intl. Soc. for Neuroimmunomodulation [15664]
Intl. Soc. for Plasmid Biology and other Mobile Genetic Elements [7111]
Intl. Soc. for Presence Res. [7333]
Knowledge Alliance [8797]
NAMM Found. [10248]
Natl. Assn. of Sci. Materials Managers [3179]
Natl. Assn. of Univ. Fisheries and Wildlife Programs [8146]
Natl. Conferences on Undergraduate Res. [8798]
Natl. Coun. of Univ. Res. Administrators [8799]
Natl. Dairy Coun. [4183]
Natl. Found. for Brain Res. [15666]
Natl. Postdoctoral Assn. [8800]
Natural History Network [7143]
North Amer. Meteor Network [7107]
North Amer. Taiwan Stud. Assn. [8938]
PlanetQuest [6235]
Qualitative Res. Consultants Assn. [7334]
Quantal Energy [8121]
Religious Res. Assn. [20222]
Res. for Hea. [15207]
Res. Prog. at Earthwatch Inst. [7335]
Res. Prog. at Earthwatch Inst. [7335]
ResearchChannel [7336]
Soc. for the Anal. of African-American Public Hea. Issues [16497]
Soc. of Herbarium Curators [6368]
Soc. for Hindu-Christian Stud. [20215]
Soc. for the History of Psychology [7312]
Soc. of Res. Administrators [7337]
Soc. of Sensory Professionals [7391]
Soc. for Terrorism Res. [7554]
U.S. Coun. for Automotive Res. [6245]
Universities Res. Assn. [7338]
Universities Res. Assn. [7338]
University-Community Partnership for Social Action Res. [7895]
Women Educators [9067]
World Assn. for Case Method Res. and Application [7339]
World Assn. for Case Method Res. and Application [7339]
Res.! Am. [15350], 1101 King St., Ste. 520, Alexandria, VA 22314-2960, (703)739-2577
Res. Associates of Am. - Address unknown since 2010.
Res. Assn. of the German Glass Indus. [IO], Offenbach, Germany
Res. Center Against Meningitis and Schistosomiasis [IO], Niamey, Niger
Res. Center for Economic Growth and Bus. Development [IO], Paris, France
Res. Center for Religion and Human Rights in Closed Societies - Defunct.
Res. Center; Sultan Qaboos bin Said [★18129]
Res. Centre for Islamic History, Art and Culture [IO], Istanbul, Turkey
Res. Chefs Assn. [1011], 1100 Johnson Ferry Rd., Ste. 300, Atlanta, GA 30342, (404)252-3663
Res. Commn. of Natl. Sunday School [★7858]
Research and Community Development Institute [★18817]
Res. Coun. of the Great Cities Prog. for School Improvement [★9028]
Res. Coun. on Riveted and Bolted Structural Joints [★7481]
Res. Coun. on Structural Connections [7481], 1 E Wacker Dr., Ste. 700, Chicago, IL 60601, (312)670-5414
Res. and Development Associates [★6879]
Res. and Development Associates for Military Food and Packaging Systems [6879], 16607 Blanco Rd., Ste. 501, San Antonio, TX 78232, (210)493-8024
Res. and Development Division of Planned Parenthood Fed. of Am. [★12034]
Res. and Development Soc. [IO], London, United Kingdom
Res. for Hea. [15207], 4321 Northampton Rd., Cuyahoga Falls, OH 44223
Res. for Hea. [15207], 4321 Northampton Rd., Cuyahoga Falls, OH 44223
Res. Inst. of the Assn. of the Austrian Cement Indus. [IO], Vienna, Austria

Res. Inst. of Chem. Processing and Utilization of Forest Products [IO], Nanjing, People's Republic of China
Res. Inst. of Forestry, Policy and Info. [IO], Beijing, People's Republic of China
Res. Inst. for Fragrance Materials [1523], 50 Tice Blvd., Woodcliff Lake, NJ 07677, (201)689-8089
Res. Inst. of Investment Analysts Malaysia [IO], Kuala Lumpur, Malaysia
Res. Inst. - Subtropical Forestry [IO], Fuyang, People's Republic of China
Res. Inst. of the Wood Indus. [IO], Beijing, People's Republic of China
Res. Interest Groups [★7431]
Res. Partnership to Secure Energy for Am. [6752], 1650 Hwy. 6, Ste. 325, Sugar Land, TX 77478, (281)313-9555
Res. to Prevent Blindness [17113], 645 Madison Ave., 21st Fl., New York, NY 10022-1010, (212)752-4333
Res. Prog. at Earthwatch Inst. [7335], PO Box 75, Maynard, MA 01754, (978)461-0081
Res. Prog. at Earthwatch Inst. [7335], PO Box 75, Maynard, MA 01754, (978)461-0081
Res. Security Administrators [5971], Robert B. Iannone, Exec. Dir., 11137 McGee River Cir., Fountain Valley, CA 92708-4824, (714)839-7804
Res. Soc. on Alcoholism [16753], 7801 N Lamar Blvd., Ste. D-89, Austin, TX 78752-1038, (512)454-0022
Res. Soc. for Victorian Periodicals [10634], 939 Ridge Court, No. 2, Evanston, IL 60202
Res. Soc. for Victorian Periodicals [10634], 939 Ridge Court, No. 2, Evanston, IL 60202
Res. and Technological Exchange Gp. - France [IO], Nogent-sur-Marne, France
Res. and Tech. Exchange Gp. - Vietnam [IO], Hanoi, Vietnam
Res. and Training Center on Independent Living [11826], Univ. of Kansas, Dole Center, Ste. 4089, 1000 Sunnyside Ave., Lawrence, KS 66045-7561, (785)864-4095
ResearchChannel [7336], 93 S Jackson St., No. 31285, Seattle, WA 98104-2818, (877)616-7265
Researched Medicines Indus. Assn. of New Zealand [IO], Wellington, New Zealand
Reseau canadien de maladies genetiques [★IO]
Reseau Africain d'Institutions Scientifiques et Technologiques [★IO]
Reseau Canadien du Cancer de la Prostate [★IO]
Reseau Canadien d'info-traitements sida [★IO]
Reseau d'acces a la Justice [★IO]
Reseau d'action des femmes handicapees du Canada [★IO]
Reseau des aliments et des materiaux davant-garde [★IO]
Reseau d'information sur le patrimoine Canadien [★IO]
Reseau euro-mediterraneen des droits de l'homme [★IO]
Reseau Europeen des Centres de Formation d' Administrateurs Culturels [★IO]
Reseau Europeen Droit et Societe [★IO]
Reseau Europeen des Instituts de Sciences du Sport et pour l' Emploi [★IO]
Reseau des Femmes Chefs d'Enterprises du Gabon [★IO]
Reseau Foi and Justice Afrique - Europe [★IO]
Reseau Intl. des Institutions de Financement Alternatif [★IO]
Reseau Intl. pour l'Analyse des Reseaux Sociaux [★7415]
Reseau Intl. pour l'Analyse des Reseaux Sociaux [★7415]
Reseau canadien des cardiopathies congenitales de l'adulte [★IO]
Reseau canadien pour le traitement de l'asthma [★IO]
Reseau canadien de l'environment [★IO]
Reseau canadien pour l'innovation en education [★IO]
Reseau Mondial des femmes pour les droits sur la Reproduction [★IO]
Reseau de Sante de Femmes d'Amerique Latine et des Caraibes [★IO]

Reseau juridique canadien VIH/SIDA [★IO]
Reserve Officers Assn. of the U.S. [5829], 1 Constitution Ave. NE, Washington, DC 20002-5618, (202)479-2200
Reserve Officers of the Naval Services [★5829]
Reserve Police Officers Assn. [5741], 89 Rockland Ave., Yonkers, NY 10705, (800)326-9416

Resettlement
Amer. Fund for Czech and Slovak Relief [12771]
Residency Rev. Comm. for Emergency Medicine [14478], Accreditation Coun. for Graduate Medical Educ., 515 N State St., Ste. 2000, Chicago, IL 60610, (312)755-5000
Residential Boat Owners' Assn. [IO], Ely, United Kingdom
Residential Constr. Workers' Assn. [851], 3660D Wheeler Ave., Alexandria, VA 22304, (703)212-8294
Residential Energy Services Network [610], PO Box 4561, Oceanside, CA 92052-4561, (760)806-3448
Residential Sales Coun. [★3008]
Resilient Floor Covering Inst. [611], 115 Broad St., Ste. 201, LaGrange, GA 30240, (706)882-3833
Resilient Tile Inst. [★611]
Resin Flooring Assn. [IO], Farnham, United Kingdom
Resist [18338], 259 Elm St., Somerville, MA 02144, (617)623-5110
Resistance Task Force - Defunct.
Resistance Welder Mfrs. Assn. [★1865]
Resistance Welding Mfg. Alliance [1865], 550 NW Lejeune Rd., Miami, FL 33126, (305)443-9353
Resisting Defamation [17324], 2341 Darnell Ct., San Jose, CA 95133, (408)923-0908
RESNA: Assn. for the Advancement of Rehabilitation Tech. [★11825]
Resolution - First for Family Law [IO], Orpington, United Kingdom
RESOLVE [★14535]
RESOLVE [18492], 1255 23rd St. NW, Ste. 275, Washington, DC 20037, (202)944-2300
Resolve, The Natl. Infertility Assn. [14535], 1760 Old Meadow Rd., Ste. 500, McLean, VA 22102, (703)556-7172
Resolve Through Sharing [★11127]
Resort and Commercial Recreation Assn. [3063], PO Box 1564, Dubuque, IA 52004
Resort Development Org. [IO], Brussels, Belgium
Resort Hotel Assn. [1772], 2100 E Cary St., Ste. 3, Richmond, VA 23223, (804)525-2020
Rsrc. Center for Nonviolence [18176], 515 Broadway, Santa Cruz, CA 95060, (831)423-1626
Rsrc. Center for Nonviolence [18176], 515 Broadway, Santa Cruz, CA 95060, (831)423-1626
Rsrc. Centre on Nonviolence [IO], Montreal, QC, Canada
Rsrc. Development Intl. Cambodia [12361], PO Box 9144, Louisville, KY 40209
Rsrc. Development Intl. - Cambodia [IO], Phnom Penh, Cambodia
Rsrc. Development Intl. Cambodia [12361], PO Box 9144, Louisville, KY 40209
Rsrc. Efficient Agricultural Production - Canada [IO], Ste.-Anne-de-Bellevue, QC, Canada
Rsrc. Generation [13154], 220 E 23rd St., Ste. 509, New York, NY 10010, (646)461-3043
Resources for Independent Thinking [10415], 484 Lake Park Ave., No. 24, Oakland, CA 94610-2730, (925)228-0565
Resources for Indispensable Schools and Educators [8961], PO Box 70065, Oakland, CA 94612, (877)631-7473
Resources and Tech. Services Div. - of ALA [★9968]

Respiratory Diseases
Allergy and Asthma Network Mothers of Asthmatics [16602]
Alpha-1 Assn. [16603]
Amer. Lung Assn. [16604]
Assn. of Asthma Educators [16605]
Asthma Soc. of Ireland [18457]
Coalition for Pulmonary Fibrosis [16606]
Cystic Fibrosis Found. [16607]
Cystic Fibrosis Worldwide [16608]
Fundacion Alfa-1 de Puerto Rico [16609]
Fundacion Alfa-1 de Puerto Rico [16609]
Intl. Bronchoesophagological Soc. [13869]

Reference to "IO" in place of a book number signifies that the association may be found in the 50th edition of International Organizations.

LAM Treatment Alliance **[16610]**
Second Wind Lung Transplant Assn. **[16611]**
United Mitochondrial Disease Found. **[16612]**
U.S. Adult Cystic Fibrosis Assn. **[16613]**
Respiratory Nursing Soc. **[15798]**, PO Box 980567, Richmond, VA 23298-0567
Response-Ability **[20085]**, 1341 Montgomery Ave., Rosemont, PA 19010, (610)626-1400
Responsible Endowments Coalition **[9082]**, 33 Flatbush Ave., 5th Fl., Brooklyn, NY 11217, (718)989-3949
Responsible Hospitality Inst. **[11827]**, 740 Front St., Ste. 318, Santa Cruz, CA 95060, (831)469-3396
Responsible Hospitality Inst. **[11827]**, 740 Front St., Ste. 318, Santa Cruz, CA 95060, (831)469-3396
Responsible Indus. for a Sound Env. **[2636]**, 1156 15th St. NW, Ste. 400, Washington, DC 20005, (202)872-3860
Responsible Investment Assn. Australasia **[IO]**, Sydney, Australia
Responsible Policies for Animals **[11032]**, PO Box 891, Glenside, PA 19038, (215)886-RPA1
Responsible Purchasing Network **[1222]**, 1201 Martin Luther King Jr. Way, Oakland, CA 94612, (866)776-1330
Responsible Wealth **[★17594]**
Restaurant
Asian Chefs Assn. **[736]**
Confrerie de la Chaine des Rotisseurs, Bailliage des U.S.A. **[21845]**
Coun. of Intl. Restaurant Real Estate Brokers **[3086]**
Coun. of Intl. Restaurant Real Estate Brokers **[3086]**
Coun. of State Restaurant Associations **[3087]**
Distinguished Restaurants of North Am. **[3088]**
Fed. of Dining Room Professionals **[3089]**
Fed. of Dining Room Professionals **[3089]**
Green Restaurant Assn. **[4875]**
Intl. Soc. of Restaurant Assn. Executives **[3087]**
McDonald's Hispanic Operators Assn. **[3090]**
Restaurant Fac. Mgt. Assn. **[3091]**
Restaurant Assn. **[IO]**, London, United Kingdom
Restaurant Assn. of New Zealand **[IO]**, Auckland, New Zealand
Restaurant Assn. of Singapore **[IO]**, Singapore, Singapore
Restaurant Assn. of South Africa **[IO]**, Douglasdale, Republic of South Africa
Restaurant and Catering New South Wales **[IO]**, Surry Hills, Australia
Restaurant Fac. Mgt. Assn. **[3091]**, 5068 W Plano Pkwy., Ste. 300, Plano, TX 75093, (972)805-0905
Restaurant Marketing and Delivery Assn. **[1454]**, 4921 Boone Ave. N, New Hope, MN 55428
Restaurants' Assn. **[IO]**, Vienna, Austria
Restaurants Assn. of Ireland **[IO]**, Dublin, Ireland
Restless Development **[IO]**, London, United Kingdom
Restless Legs Syndrome Found. **[16781]**, 1610 14th St. NW, Ste. 300, Rochester, MN 55901, (507)287-6465
Restoration Indus. Assn. **[2258]**, 9810 Patuxent Woods Dr., Ste. K, Columbia, MD 21046-1595, (443)878-1000
Restore America's Estuaries **[4999]**, 2020 N 14th St., Ste. 210, Arlington, VA 22201-2524, (703)524-0248
Restore Humanity **[12362]**, 1655 Woolsey Ave., Fayetteville, AR 72703, (479)841-2841
Restoring Hope through Educational and Medical Aid **[★12886]**
Restoring Hope through Educational and Medical Aid **[★12886]**
Restoring Institutions Services and Empowering Liberia **[11625]**, 1250 4th St. SW, Washington, DC 20024
Restricted Growth Assn. **[IO]**, Solihull, United Kingdom
Restroom Assn. of Singapore **[IO]**, Singapore, Singapore
Resultats **[★IO]**
RESULTS **[17875]**, 750 First St. NE, Ste. 1040, Washington, DC 20002, (202)783-7100
RESULTS **[17875]**, 750 First St. NE, Ste. 1040, Washington, DC 20002, (202)783-7100

Results - Australia **[IO]**, Belgrave, Australia
Results - Canada **[IO]**, Ottawa, ON, Canada
Results - United Kingdom **[IO]**, London, United Kingdom
ReSurge Intl. **[14185]**, 857 Maude Ave., Mountain View, CA 94043, (650)962-0123
Retail Advt. Conf. **[★105]**
Retail Advt. and Marketing Assn. **[105]**, 325 7th St. NW, Ste. 1100, Washington, DC 20004-2818, (202)661-3052
Retail Advt. and Marketing Assn., Intl. **[★105]**
Retail Bakers of Am. **[394]**, 202 Village Cir., Ste. 1, Slidell, LA 70458, (985)643-6504
Retail Clerks Intl. Union **[★23191]**
Retail Confectioners Intl. **[1429]**, 2053 S Waverly, Ste. C, Springfield, MO 65804, (417)883-2775
Retail Confectioners Intl. **[1429]**, 2053 S Waverly, Ste. C, Springfield, MO 65804, (417)883-2775
Retail Coun. of Canada **[IO]**, Toronto, ON, Canada
Retail Credit Inst. of Am. **[★2212]**
Retail Design Inst. **[3124]**, 25 N Broadway, Tarrytown, NY 10591-3221, (800)379-9912
Retail Design Inst. **[3124]**, 25 N Broadway, Tarrytown, NY 10591-3221, (800)379-9912
Retail Energy Supply Assn. **[1177]**, PO Box 6089, Harrisburg, PA 17112, (717)566-5405
Retail Grocery, Dairy and Allied Trades Assn. **[IO]**, Dublin, Ireland
Retail Indus. Leaders Assn. **[3125]**, 1700 N Moore St., Ste. 2250, Arlington, VA 22209, (703)841-2300
Retail Jewelers of Am. **[★2163]**
Retail Merchant Bakers of Am. **[★394]**
Retail Motor Indus. Fed. **[IO]**, London, United Kingdom
Retail Motor Indus. Org. **[IO]**, Randburg, Republic of South Africa
Retail Packaging Assn. **[2611]**, PO Box 43517, Cincinnati, OH 45243, (513)527-4333
Retail Packaging Mfrs. Assn. **[★2611]**
Retail Paint and Wallpaper Distributors of Am. **[★2073]**
Retail Paint and Wallpaper Distributors of Am. **[★2073]**
Retail Print Music Dealers Assn. **[2572]**, 14070 Proton Rd., Ste. 100, Dallas, TX 75244, (972)233-9107
Retail Solutions Providers Assn. **[6556]**, 10130 Perimeter Pkwy., Ste. 420, Charlotte, NC 28216, (704)357-3124
Retail Tobacco Dealers of Am. **[★3109]**
Retail, Wholesale and Dept. Store Union **[23293]**, 30 E 29th St., New York, NY 10016, (212)684-5300
Retailers of Art Glass and Supplies **[1581]**, Bonnie Wentz, 48 York St., Gettysburg, PA 17325, (717)334-0906
Retailers of Art Glass and Supplies **[1581]**, Bonnie Wentz, 48 York St., Gettysburg, PA 17325, (717)334-0906
Retailing
Agricultural Retailers Assn. **[3092]**
Amer. Booksellers Assn. **[3093]**
Antiquarian Booksellers' Assn. of Canada **[21261]**
Asian Amer. Convenience Stores Assn. **[3094]**
Assn. of Coupon Professionals **[3095]**
Assn. for Retail Tech. Standards **[3096]**
Black Retail Action Gp. **[3097]**
Bd. Retailers Assn. **[3098]**
Brazilian Assn. of Shopping Centers **[17591]**
CBA **[3099]**
CBA **[3099]**
Consumer Electronics Retailers Coalition **[3100]**
Consumer Goods Forum **[3101]**
Consumer Goods Forum **[3101]**
Contemporary Design Gp. **[1547]**
Craft Retailers Assn. for Tomorrow **[987]**
Direct Gardening Assn. **[3102]**
Food Indus. Assn. Executives **[3103]**
Food Marketing Inst. **[3104]**
Gift and Home Trade Assn. **[3161]**
Gift Sales Manager Assn. **[3162]**
Intl. Assn. of Airport Duty Free Stores **[3105]**
Intl. Assn. of Airport Duty Free Stores **[3105]**
Intl. Coun. of Shopping Centers **[3106]**
Intl. Coun. of Shopping Centers **[3106]**
Intl. League of Antiquarian Booksellers **[3107]**

Intl. League of Antiquarian Booksellers **[3107]**
Intl. Mystery Shopping Alliance **[3108]**
Intl. Premium Cigar and Pipe Retailers **[3109]**
Joint Labor Mgt. Comm. of the Retail Food Indus. **[23190]**
Merchants Payment Coalition **[12913]**
Mobile Enhancement Retailers Assn. **[3110]**
Museum Store Assn. **[3111]**
NARTS - The Assn. of Resale Professionals **[3112]**
Natl. Assn. of Coll. Stores **[3113]**
Natl. Assn. of Convenience Stores **[3114]**
Natl. Assn. of Convenience Stores **[3114]**
Natl. Assn. for Retail Marketing Services **[3115]**
Natl. Confectionery Sales Assn. **[3116]**
Natl. Grocers Assn. **[3117]**
Natl. Retail Fed. **[3118]**
NATSO **[3119]**
NATSO Found. **[3120]**
Natural Products Assn. **[3121]**
North Amer. Truck Stop Network **[3122]**
Planning and Visual Educ. Partnership **[3123]**
Retail Design Inst. **[3124]**
Retail Design Inst. **[3124]**
Retail Energy Supply Assn. **[1177]**
Retail Indus. Leaders Assn. **[3125]**
Retail, Wholesale and Dept. Store Union **[23293]**
Retailers of Art Glass and Supplies **[1581]**
Shop Am. Alliance **[3126]**
Singapore Retailers Assn. **[18923]**
Spa Assn. **[3127]**
Women Grocers of Am. **[3128]**
World Floor Covering Assn. **[3129]**
World Floor Covering Assn. **[3129]**
Retardation, Mental
Aicardi Syndrome Newsl. **[14581]**
Arc of the U.S. **[12495]**
Assn. for Children with Down Syndrome **[12496]**
Retarded Infants Ser. **[★12500]**
Rethink **[IO]**, London, United Kingdom
Reticuloendothelial Soc. **[★16614]**
Reticuloendothelial System
Soc. for Leukocyte Biology **[16614]**
Retina Hong Kong **[IO]**, Hong Kong, People's Republic of China
Retinitis Pigmentosa
Retinitis Pigmentosa Intl. **[17114]**
Retinitis Pigmentosa Intl. **[17114]**, PO Box 900, Woodland Hills, CA 91365, (818)992-0500
Retinitis Pigmentosa Intl. **[17114]**, PO Box 900, Woodland Hills, CA 91365, (818)992-0500
Retinoblastoma Intl. **[13974]**, 18030 Brookhurst St., Box 408, Fountain Valley, CA 92708, (323)669-2299
Retinoblastoma Intl. **[13974]**, 18030 Brookhurst St., Box 408, Fountain Valley, CA 92708, (323)669-2299
Retinopathy of Prematurity and Related Diseases; Assn. for **[15949]**
Retired Activities Br. **[5830]**, Navy Personnel Command, 5720 Integrity Dr., Millington, TN 38055-6220, (866)827-5672
Retired Affairs Officers **[★5830]**
Retired Affairs Sect. **[★5830]**
Retired Army Nurse Corps Assn. **[★15509]**
The Retired Enlisted Assn. **[20803]**, 1111 S Abilene Ct., Aurora, CO 80012, (303)752-0660
Retired Foreign Ser. Officers Assn. **[★5467]**
Retired Greyhound Trust **[IO]**, Worcester Park, United Kingdom
Retired Greyhounds As Pets **[★11054]**
Retired League Postmasters of the Natl. League of Postmasters **[5893]**, Natl. League of Postmasters, 1 Beltway Ctr., 5904 Richmond Hwy., Ste. 500, Alexandria, VA 22303-1864, (703)329-4550
Retired Military Police Assn. **[20716]**, PO Box 25343, Fayetteville, NC 28314, (910)867-4292
The Retired Officers Assn. **[★20740]**
Retired and Pioneer Rural Carriers of U.S. - Defunct.
Retired and Senior Volunteer Prog. **[13404]**, Senior Corps, 1201 New York Ave. NW, Washington, DC 20525, (202)606-5000
Retired Ser. Personnel Assn. of Bhutan **[IO]**, Thimphu, Bhutan
Retired Teamsters Fellowship Club - Defunct.

A star before a book entry number signifies that the name is not listed separately, but is mentioned within the entry.

Retired Western Union Employees Assn. [434], PO
Box 413, Montgomery, NY 12549
Retirees
Assn. of Retirement Housing Managers [17799]
Food and Drug Admin. Alumni Assn. [17697]
Gay and Lesbian Assn. of Retiring Persons
[10843]
Gray is Green: The Natl. Senior Conservation
Corps [4072]
Leadership Coun. of Aging Organizations [10850]
Retirement
AARP [12914]
Alliance for Retired Americans [18548]
Amer. Assn. of Retirement Communities [12915]
Assn. of Retired Americans [12916]
Coalition of Natl. Park Ser. Retirees [4766]
Gay and Lesbian Assn. of Retiring Persons
[10843]
Inst. for Retired Professionals [12917]
Leadership Coun. of Aging Organizations [10850]
Mennonite Assn. of Retired Persons [12918]
Natl. Retired Teachers Assn. [8801]
Retirement Income Indus. Assn. [3130]
Setting Priorities for Retirement Years [12919]
TIAA-CREF [8802]
Retirement Income Indus. Assn. [3130], 101 Fed.
St., Ste. 1900, Boston, MA 02110, (617)342-7390
Retirement Indus. Trust Assn. [435], 820 Jorie Blvd.,
Ste. 420, Oak Brook, IL 60523-2284, (941)724-
0900
Retirement Planning Assn. of Canada [IO], Stratford,
ON, Canada
Retirement Res. Found. [10868], 8765 W Higgins
Rd., Ste. 430, Chicago, IL 60631-4170, (773)714-
8080
Retread Mfrs. Assn. [IO], Crewe, United Kingdom
Retreat Assn. [IO], Amersham, United Kingdom
Return to Freedom [11033], PO Box 926, Lompoc,
CA 93438, (805)737-9246
Reumapatientenbond [IO], Amersfoort, Netherlands
Reunion des Amateurs de Fox-Terriers [IO], Bros-
ville, France
Reunion Internationale des Laboratoires et Experts
des Materiaux, Systemes de Constructions et Ou-
vrages [★IO]
Reunion pour la Promotion et l'Enseignement de la
Musique Electroacoustique [IO], Paris, France
Reunite - Intl. Child Abduction Centre [IO], Leicester,
United Kingdom
Reusable Indus. Packaging Assn. [888], 8401
Corporate Dr., Ste. 450, Landover, MD 20785,
(301)577-3786
Reusable Packaging Assn. [3072], 1100 N Glebe
Rd., Ste. 1010, Arlington, VA 22201, (703)224-
8284
Reuse Development Org. [4984], The Loading Dock,
2 N Kresson St., Baltimore, MD 21224, (410)558-
3625
Reverb [4130], 386 Fore St., No. 202, Portland, ME
04101, (207)221-6553
Revma Liga V Ceske Republice [★IO]
Revolutionary Assn. of the Women of Afghanistan
[IO], Quetta, Pakistan
Revolutionary Mexican Historical Soc. - Defunct.
Rex Breeders United [21256], 446 Itasca Ct. NW,
Rochester, MN 55901
Rexx Language Assn. [7300], 7028 W Waters Ave.,
Tampa, FL 33634-2292
Rexx Language Assn. [7300], 7028 W Waters Ave.,
Tampa, FL 33634-2292
Reye's Syndrome
Natl. Reye's Syndrome Found. [16615]
Reye's Syndrome Soc. [★16615]
Reynolds Family Assn. [20576], 2240 130th St.,
Winterset, IA 50273-8479
RGK Found. [15351], 1301 W 25th St., Ste. 300,
Austin, TX 78705-4236, (512)474-9298
RHEMA Intl. [12886], PO Box 82085, Rochester, MI
48308-2085, (248)652-2450
RHEMA Intl. [12886], PO Box 82085, Rochester, MI
48308-2085, (248)652-2450
Rheology
Soc. of Rheology [7340]
Rhetoric
Assn. for the Rhetoric of Sci. and Tech. [10510]

Intl. Soc. for the History of Rhetoric [10511]
Intl. Soc. for the History of Rhetoric [10511]
Rhetoric Soc. of Am. [10512]
Rhetoric Soc. of Am. [10512], Cara A. Finnegan,
Comm. Chair, Univ. of Illinois, 103 Commun. Bldg.
MC-456, 1207 W Oregon Ave., Urbana, IL 61801
Rheuma Assn. of Slovenia [IO], Ljubljana, Slovenia
Rheumatic Diseases
Amer. Coll. of Rheumatology [16616]
Amer. Coll. of Rheumatology [16616]
Arthritis Found. [16617]
Arthritis Ireland [2780]
The Arthritis Soc. [5869]
Childhood Arthritis and Rheumatology Res. Alli-
ance [16618]
Childhood Arthritis and Rheumatology Res. Alli-
ance [16618]
Coalition of State Rheumatology Organizations
[16619]
Natl. Inst. of Arthritis and Musculoskeletal and
Skin Diseases Info. CH [16620]
Natl. Org. of Rheumatology Managers [16621]
Natl. Sjogren's Syndrome Assn. [16622]
OsteoArthritis Res. Soc. Intl. [16623]
OsteoArthritis Res. Soc. Intl. [16623]
Roger Wyburn-Mason and Jack M. Blount Found.
for the Eradication of Rheumatoid Disease
[16624]
Sjogren's Syndrome Found. [16625]
Sjogren's Syndrome Found. [16625]
Soc. of Physician Assistants in Rheumatology
[16626]
Spondylitis Assn. of Am. [16627]
Rheumatism Soc. [IO], Istanbul, Turkey
Rheumatoid Disease Found. [★16624]
Rheumatology Assn. of Bosnia and Herzegovina
[IO], Sarajevo, Bosnia-Hercegovina
Rheumatology Assn. of Georgia [IO], Tbilisi, Georgia
Rhine Res. Center [7229], Inst. for Parapsychology,
2741 Campus Walk Ave., Bldg. 500, Durham, NC
27705, (919)309-4600
Rhinelander Rabbit Club of Am. [4854], 11237 Sum-
mit School Rd., Huntingdon, PA 16652, (814)667-
2406
Rhinologic Soc; Amer. [16087]
Rhinology Res. Soc. [IO], Tehran, Iran
Rho Chi [★23619]
Rho Chi - Alpha Beta Chap. [23619], Univ. of North
Carolina, 3210 Kerr Hall, CB 7569, Chapel Hill, NC
27599, (919)843-9001
Rhodes (9 Class Assn. [22386], Tom Carville,
Treas., 1402 Main St., La Place, LA 70068,
(312)642-1006
Rhodesian Ridgeback Club of the U.S. [21643],
Ross Jones, Corresponding Sec., 2008 Dorothy St.
NE, Albuquerque, NM 87112, (505)296-3611
Rhodesian Ridgeback Klubben [IO], Svendborg,
Denmark
Rhododendron Res. Found. [★21782]
Rhododendron Species Botanical Garden [★6366]
Rhododendron Species Found. [6366], PO Box
3798, Federal Way, WA 98063, (253)838-4646
Rice Assn. [IO], London, United Kingdom
Rice Coun. of Am. [★3965]
Rice Coun. for Market Development [★3965]
Rice Design Alliance [6203], MS 51, PO Box 1892,
Houston, TX 77251-1892, (713)348-4876
The Rice Indus. [★3965].
Rice Millers' Assn. [2503], U.S.A. Rice Fed., 4301 N
Fairfax Dr., Ste. 425, Arlington, VA 22203,
(703)236-2300
Ricegrowers' Assn. of Australia [IO], Leeton,
Australia
Rich Family Assn. [20577], PO Box 142, Wellfleet,
MA 02667
Richard Burgi Fan Club [23781], 11155 Aqua Vista
St., No. 302, Studio City, CA 91602-3700
Richard the III Found. [10685], 34 Hillside Dr., Sab-
attus, ME 04280
Richard III Soc., Amer. Br. [10686], Pamela J. Butler,
11000 Anaheim Ave. NE, Albuquerque, NM 87122
Richard III Soc. of Canada [IO], Burlington, ON,
Canada
Richard Jefferies Soc. [IO], Longcot, United
Kingdom

Richard "Rock" Taylor Descendants - Defunct.
Richard Wagner Verband Intl. e.V. [★IO]
Richardson Boat Owners Assn. [22387], 15 Webster
St., North Tonawanda, NY 14120, (845)595-6127
Rick's Loyal Supporters [23886], Vivian Acinelli, Ed.,
4530 E Four Ridge Rd., Imperial, MO 63052
Ricky Skaggs Intl. Fan Club [23887], Skaggs Family
Records, PO Box 2478, Hendersonville, TN 37077,
(615)264-8877
Ricsel Orchids [IO], Porto Alegre, Brazil
Ricsel Orquideas [★IO]
RID - Capital Area [★13004]
RID U.S.A. [13004], PO Box 520, Schenectady, NY
12301, (518)372-0034
Ridden Standardbred Assn. - Defunct.
Ride and Tie Assn. [23004], 8215 E White Oak
Ridge, No. 41, Orange, CA 92869, (714)321-3695
Ride to Work [21936], PO Box 1072, Proctor, MN
55810, (218)722-9806
Ride for World Hea. [14213], PO Box 8234,
Columbus, OH 43201
Rider Haggard Soc. [IO], Whitley Bay, United
Kingdom
Riders for Hea. [15519], Lisa Bakker, Development
Dir., 440 W Ontario St., Chicago, IL 60610,
(312)373-1447
Riders for Justice [21937], PO Box 1192, Clifton, CO
81520-1192
Ridgeback Rescue of the U.S. [11034], Mariann
Stone, Sec., 13200 Matador Dr., Creve Coeur, MO
63141, (605)348-3202
Riding for the Disabled Assn. - Ireland [IO], Delgany,
Ireland
Riding for the Disabled Assn. of Singapore [IO], Sin-
gapore, Singapore
Rifles
Browning Collectors Assn. [21712]
Natl. Firearms Act Trade and Collectors Assn.
[1354]
Natl. Mossberg Collectors Assn. [21716]
North-South Skirmish Assn. [22885]
Right for Children, Youth and Social Development
[IO], Lagos, Nigeria
Right to Know Comm. of Correspondence - Defunct.
Right to Life
Amer. Assn. of Pro Life Obstetricians and
Gynecologists [18549]
Amer. Center for Law and Justice [12920]
Amer. Life League [12921]
Americans United for Life [12922]
Anglicans for Life [12923]
Assn. for Interdisciplinary Res. in Values and
Social Change [12924]
Baptists for Life [12925]
Birthright U.S.A. [12926]
Black Americans for Life [12927]
Catholics United for Life [12928]
Center for Bio-Ethical Reform [18550]
Children of the Rosary [18551]
Collegians Activated to Liberate Life [12929]
Democrats for Life of Am. [18552]
Dentists for Life [18553]
Feminists for Life of Am. [18554]
Healing the Culture [12930]
Heartbeat Intl. [12931]
Heartbeat Intl. [12931]
Helpers of God's Precious Infants [18555]
Human Development Rsrc. Coun. [12932]
Human Life Found. [12933]
Human Life Intl. [12934]
Human Life Intl. [12934]
Last Harvest Ministries [12935]
Liberty Godparent Home [12936]RightLife Coali-
tion Intl.
Life Decisions Intl. [12937]
Life Decisions Intl. [12937]
Lutherans for Life [12938]
March for Life Educ. and Defense Fund [18556]
Natl. Assn. of Pro-Life Nurses [16628]
Natl. Comm. for a Human Life Amendment
[18557]
Natl. Life Center [12939]
Natl. Pro-Life Alliance [18558]
Natl. Pro-Life Religious Coun. [18559]
Natl. Right to Life Comm. [12940]

Reference to "IO" in place of a book number signifies that the association may be found in the 50th edition of International Organizations.

Natl. Right to Life Educational Trust Fund [18560]
Natl. Teens for Life [12941]
One More Soul [18561]
Oper. Save Am. [18562]
Orthodox Christians for Life [20223]
People for Life [12942]
Pharmacists for Life Intl. [18563]
Pharmacists for Life Intl. [18563]
Presbyterians Pro-Life [12943]
Priests for Life [18564]
Pro-Life Action League [18565]
Pro-Life Action League [18565]
Pro-Life Alliance of Gays and Lesbians [12944]
Pro Vita Advisors [20224]
Republican Natl. Coalition for Life [18566]
Rock For Life [18567]
Sisters of Life [20225]
STOPP Intl. [18568]
Students for Life of Am. [12945]
Teachers Saving Children Natl. [18569]
Right Turn, Intl. [13200], 1901 N Tamarind Ave.,
    West Palm Beach, FL 33407-6283, (561)767-2257
Rights Action/Guatemala Partners [12789], PO Box
    50887, Washington, DC 20091, (202)783-1123
Rights and Resources Initiative [4412], 1238
    Wisconsin Ave. NW, Ste. 204, Washington, DC
    20007, (202)470-3900
Rights and Resources Initiative [4412], 1238
    Wisconsin Ave. NW, Ste. 204, Washington, DC
    20007, (202)470-3900
Rights of Way
    Intl. Right of Way Assn. [5958]
    Intl. Right of Way Assn. [5958]
Rights of Women [IO], London, United Kingdom
Rigoberta Menchu Tum Found. [17325], 11
    Broadway, 2nd Fl., New York, NY 10004,
    (212)982-5358
Rigoberta Menchu Tum Found. [17325], 11
    Broadway, 2nd Fl., New York, NY 10004,
    (212)982-5358
Riksfoereningen Autism [★IO]
Riksforbundet for Sexuell Upplysning [★IO]
Riksorganisationen for Kvinnojourer Och Tjejjourer i
    Sverige [★IO]
Riksorganisationen Unga Reumatiker [★IO]
Riksutstallningar [★IO]
Rin Tin Tin Fan Club [23928], PO Box 27, Crockett,
    TX 75835, (936)545-0471
Ring of Troth [★19300]
Riot Relief Fund [19150], 87 Water St., Stonington,
    CT 06378
Ripon Soc. [18543], 1300 L St. NW, Ste. 900,
    Washington, DC 20005, (202)216-1008
RISE [★2636]
RISE-UP From Poverty [12751], 15613 5th Ave. NE,
    Shoreline, WA 98155
Rising Intl. [11078], 300 Potrero St., Santa Cruz, CA
    95060, (831)429-7473
Rising Leaders [18067], 5011 Spruce Dr., Moon
    Township, PA 15108-9058, (412)262-6145
Rising Tide Capital [1060], 348 Martin Luther King
    Dr., Jersey City, NJ 07305, (201)432-4316
Rising Tide North Am. [4131], PO Box 3928,
    Oakland, CA 94609, (503)438-4697
Risk and Insurance Mgt. Assn. of Singapore [IO],
    Singapore, Singapore
Risk and Insurance Mgt. Soc. [2034], 1065 Ave. of
    the Americas, 13th Fl., New York, NY 10018,
    (212)286-9292
Risk Mgt. Assn. [436], 1801 Market St., Ste. 300,
    Philadelphia, PA 19103-1628, (215)446-4000
Risk Mgt. Institution of Australasia [IO], Melbourne,
    Australia
Risk Mgt. Soc. of Taiwan, R.O.C. [IO], Taoyuan City,
    Taiwan
Risk Managers and Consultants Assn. of Japan [IO],
    Tokyo, Japan
Risley Family Assn. [20578], PO Box 552, Clarkson,
    NY 14430
Risley Family Assn. [20578], PO Box 552, Clarkson,
    NY 14430
Rita Hayworth Fan Club [23782], 3943 York Ave. S,
    Minneapolis, MN 55410
Rites and Reason Theatre [10600], Brown Univ.,
    155 Angell St., Providence, RI 02912, (401)863-
    3558

Rithofundasamband Islands [★IO]
Riva Club USA [21232], PO Box 724, Carnelian
    Bay, CA 96140
Rivendell Resources [★13301]
River Conservation Fund [★3996]
River Fund [10891], 11155 Roseland Rd., No. 16,
    Sebastian, FL 32958, (772)589-5076
River Intl. [12887], 2380 W Monte Vista Ave., Tur-
    lock, CA 95382
River Mgt. Soc. [4132], PO Box 5750, Takoma Park,
    MD 20913-5750, (301)585-4677
River Network [4133], 520 SW 6th Ave., Ste. 1130,
    Portland, OR 97204, (503)241-3506
River Rats [★20802]
River Sports
    Am. Outdoors Assn. [22835]
    Amer. Canoe Assn. [23120]
    Amer. Whitewater [22836]
    Intl. Rafting Fed. [22837]
    Natl. Org. for Rivers [22838]
    Qajaq U.S.A. [23124]
River of Words [3835], PO Box 4000-J, Berkeley,
    CA 94704, (510)548-7636
Rivera Policy Inst; Tomas [19105]
Riverland and Mallee Trail Horse Riders' Club [IO],
    Barmera, Australia
Rivers Without Borders [4134], PO Box 154, Clinton,
    WA 98236, (360)341-1976
Riviera Owners Assn. [21158], PO Box 261218,
    Denver, CO 80226-9218, (303)233-2987
RNA Soc. [6276], 9650 Rockville Pike, Bethesda,
    MD 20814-3998, (301)634-7120
Road to 100G Alliance - Address unknown since
    2010.
Road Emulsion Assn. Limited [IO], West Sussex,
    United Kingdom
Road Engg. Assn. of Malaysia [IO], Shah Alam,
    Malaysia
Road Freight Assn. [IO], Isando, Republic of South
    Africa
Road Haulage Assn. [IO], Weybridge, United
    Kingdom
The Road Info. Prog. [3536], 1726 M St. NW, Ste.
    401, Washington, DC 20036-4521, (202)466-6706
Road Map Collectors of Am. [★21402]
Road Map Collectors Assn. [21402], PO Box 158,
    Channelview, TX 77530-0158
Road Operators' Safety Coun. [IO], Olney, United
    Kingdom
Road Race Lincoln Register [21159], 640
    Homestead Ave., Metairie, LA 70005
Road Race Lincoln Register [21159], 640
    Homestead Ave., Metairie, LA 70005
Road Recovery Found. [16754], PO Box 1680,
    Radio City Sta., New York, NY 10101-1680,
    (212)489-2425
Road Runners Club of Am. [22866], 1501 Lee Hwy.,
    Ste. 140, Arlington, VA 22209, (703)525-3890
Road Surface Dressing Assn. [IO], Colchester,
    United Kingdom
Roadway Safety Found. [13005], 1101 14th St. NW,
    Ste. 750, Washington, DC 20005, (202)857-1200
Robert Brookings Graduate School of Economics
    and Govt. [★18443]
Robert Burns World Fed. [IO], Kilmarnock, United
    Kingdom
Robert E. Lee Memorial Assn. [10687], Stratford Hall
    Plantation, 483 Great House Rd., Stratford, VA
    22558-0001, (804)493-8038
Robert E. Lee Memorial Found. [★10687]
Robert F. Kennedy Center for Justice and Human
    Rights [13555], 1367 Connecticut Ave. NW, Ste.
    200, Washington, DC 20036, (202)463-7575
Robert F. Kennedy Memorial [★13555]
Robert Flaherty Found. [★9604]
Robert Flaherty Found. [★9604]
Robert H. Smith Intl. Center for Jefferson Stud.
    [8736], PO Box 316, Charlottesville, VA 22902,
    (434)984-9864
Robert L. Gale Fund for the Stud. of Trusteeship
    [★7659]
Robert Morris Associates-Association of Bank Loan
    and Credit Officers [★436]
Robert Morris Associates/Association of Lending and
    Credit Risk [★436]

Robert Redford Fan Club [23783], Trudy J. Hoffman,
    517 William St., Dunmore, PA 18510
Robert Roesler de Villiers Found. [★13936]
Robert Sterling Clark Found. [11743], 135 E 64th
    St., New York, NY 10021, (212)288-8900
Robinson Jeffers Assn. [10735], Mr. Robert Kafka,
    Treas., UCLA Extension, Rm. 214, 10995 Le
    Conte Ave., Los Angeles, CA 90024
Robinson Jeffers Comm. - Defunct.
Robot Inst. of Am. [★7344]
Robotic Indus. Assn. [7344], PO Box 3724, Ann
    Arbor, MI 48106, (734)994-6088
Robotics
    Assn. for Unmanned Vehicle Systems Intl. [7341]
    Assn. for Unmanned Vehicle Systems Intl. [7341]
    Automated Imaging Assn. [7342]
    IEEE I Robotics and Automation Soc. [7343]
    Robotic Indus. Assn. [7344]
A Rocha Canada [IO], Surrey, BC, Canada
A Rocha France [IO], Arles, France
A Rocha Ghana [IO], Accra, Ghana
A Rocha India [IO], Bangalore, India
A Rocha Intl. [IO], Cambridge, United Kingdom
A Rocha Kenya [IO], Watamu, Kenya
A Rocha Lebanon [IO], Jal el Dib, Lebanon
Rochester Bur. of Municipal Res. [★18446]
Rock Against Cancer [13975], 4711 Hope Valley
    Rd., Durham, NC 27707, (877)246-0976
rock CAN roll [12289], PO Box 700, Jericho, NY
    11753, (516)822-3457
Rock Detective Geoscience Educ. [7983], 14655
    Betz Ln., Red Bluff, CA 96080, (530)529-4890
Rock the Earth [4301], 1536 Wynkoop St., Ste.
    B200, Denver, CO 80202, (303)454-3304
Rock For Life [18567], PO Box 333, Locust Grove,
    VA 22508, (540)322-3761
Rock Music
    KISS Rocks Fan Club [23869]
    Lou Christie Intl. Fan Club [23874]
The Rock Poster Soc. [9201], PO Box 20309,
    Oakland, CA 94620-0309
Rock the Vote [17228], 1001 Connecticut Ave. NW,
    Ste. 640, Washington, DC 20036-5563, (202)719-
    9910
Rockefeller Bros. Fund [12683], 475 Riverside Dr.,
    Ste. 900, New York, NY 10115, (212)812-4200
Rockefeller Bros. Fund [12683], 475 Riverside Dr.,
    Ste. 900, New York, NY 10115, (212)812-4200
Rockefeller Family Fund [12684], 475 Riverside Dr.,
    Ste. 900, New York, NY 10115, (212)812-4252
Rocket City Astronomical Assn. [★6237]
Rocky Mountain Cichlid Assn. [21729], Sam Chin,
    Treas., 2309 Oswego St., Aurora, CO 80010,
    (303)364-7983
Rocky Mountain Elk Found. [5119], 5705 Grant
    Creek Rd., Missoula, MT 59808, (406)523-4500
Rocky Mountain Horse Assn. [4643], 4037 Iron
    Works Pkwy., Ste. 160, Lexington, KY 40511,
    (859)243-0260
Rocky Mountain Inst. [4737], 2317 Snowmass Creek
    Rd., Snowmass, CO 81654-9199, (970)927-3851
Rocky Mountain Llama and Alpaca Assn. [3800],
    Bob Hance, Treas., 11818 W 52nd Ave., Wheat
    Ridge, CO 80033, (303)422-4681
Rocky Mountain Mineral Law Found. [5864], 9191
    Sheridan Blvd., Ste. 203, Westminster, CO 80031,
    (303)321-8100
Rocky Mountain Mineral Law Found. [5864], 9191
    Sheridan Blvd., Ste. 203, Westminster, CO 80031,
    (303)321-8100
Rocky Mountain Social Sci. Assn. [★7420]
Rodeo
    Amer. Junior Rodeo Assn. [22839]
    Intl. Gay Rodeo Assn. [22840]
    Intl. Gay Rodeo Assn. [22840]
    Intl. Professional Rodeo Assn. [22841]
    Natl. Bucking Bull Assn. [22842]
    Natl. Day of the Cowboy [9124]
    Natl. Fed. of Professional Bullriders [22843]
    Natl. Finals Rodeo Comm. [22844]
    Natl. High School Rodeo Assn. [22845]
    Natl. InterCollegiate Rodeo Assn. [22846]
    Natl. Little Britches Rodeo Assn. [22847]
    Professional Armed Forces Rodeo Assn. [22848]
    Professional Armed Forces Rodeo Assn. [22848]

A star before a book entry number signifies that the name is not listed separately, but is mentioned within the entry.

Professional Rodeo Cowboys Assn. [22849]
Rodeo Historical Soc. [9125]
United Barrel Racing Assn. [22670]
U.S. Calf Ropers Assn. [22850]
Women's Professional Rodeo Assn. [22851]
Rodeo Historical Soc. [9125], Natl. Cowboy and Western Heritage Museum, 1700 NE 63rd St., Oklahoma City, OK 73111, (405)478-2250
Roentgen Ray Soc; Amer. [16522]
Roentgen Soc. of the U.S. [★16522]
Roentgen Soc. of the U.S. [★16522]
Roger Baldwin Found. of ACLU [★17261]
Roger Sessions Soc. [9505], Univ. of North Carolina Wilmington, Dept. of Music, 601 S Coll. Rd., Wilmington, NC 28403-5975, (910)962-3890
Roger Wyburn-Mason and Jack M. Blount Found. for the Eradication of Rheumatoid Disease [16624], 7376 Walker Rd., Fairview, TN 37062-8141, (615)799-1002
Rolf Inst. [★13708]
Rolf Inst. of Structural Integration [13708], 5055 Chaparral Ct., Ste. 103, Boulder, CO 80301, (303)449-5903
Roller Bearing Engineers Comm. [★1796]
Roller Skating Assn. Intl. [3279], 6905 Corporate Dr., Indianapolis, IN 46278, (317)347-2626
Roller Skating Assn. Intl. [3279], 6905 Corporate Dr., Indianapolis, IN 46278, (317)347-2626
Roller Skating Operators Assn. of Am. [★3279]
Roller Skating Operators Assn. of Am. [★3279]
Roller Skating Rink Operators Assn. [★3279]
Roller Skating Rink Operators Assn. [★3279]
RollerSoccer Intl. Fed. [23005], PO Box 423318, San Francisco, CA 94142-3318, (415)864-6879
RollerSoccer Intl. Fed. [23005], PO Box 423318, San Francisco, CA 94142-3318, (415)864-6879
Rolling Readers [12432], 2515 Camino del Rio S, Ste. 330, San Diego, CA 92108, (619)516-4095
Rolling Stones Fan Club Off. [IO], Copenhagen, Denmark
Rolling Thunder [20758], PO Box 216, Neshanic Station, NJ 08853, (908)369-5439
Rolls-Royce Enthusiasts' Club [IO], Towcester, United Kingdom
Rolls-Royce Owners' Club [21160], 191 Hempt Rd., Mechanicsburg, PA 17050, (717)697-4671
Roma Women Assn. in Romania [IO], Bucharest, Romania
Roman
Friends of Roman Cats [3859]
Roman-Germanic Commn. of German Archaeological Inst. [IO], Frankfurt, Germany
Romance Writers of Am. [10736], 14615 Benfer Rd., Houston, TX 77069, (832)717-5200
Romania
Oper. Help The Children [11375]
Reach Out to Romania [12750]
Romania ACM SIGCHI [IO], Bucharest, Romania
Romania Reborn [11397], PO Box 2027, Purcellville, VA 20134, (540)751-9490
Romania Soc. Against Epilepsy [IO], Bucharest, Romania
Romanian
Christian Aid Ministries [18570]
Christian Aid Ministries [18570]
Cong. of Romanian Americans [19210]
Oper. Help The Children [11375]
Romanian-American Chamber of Commerce [23437]
Romanian Stud. Assn. of Am. [10513]
Romanian-U.S. Bus. Coun. [23438]
Soc. for Romanian Stud. [10514]
Soc. for Romanian Stud. [10514]
Start Thinking About Romanian Children Relief [11410]
Union and League of Romanian Societies [19211]
Romanian Acad. [IO], Bucharest, Romania
Romanian Alzheimer Soc. [IO], Bucharest, Romania
Romanian-American Chamber of Commerce [23437], 2 Wisconsin Cir., Ste. 700, Chevy Chase, MD 20815, (240)235-6060
Romanian Assn. for Telework and Teleactivities [IO], Drobeta-Turnu Severin, Romania
Romanian Assn. for Transpersonal Psychology [IO], Bucharest, Romania

Romanian Badminton Fed. [IO], Bucharest, Romania
Romanian Banking Assn. [IO], Bucharest, Romania
Romanian Baseball and Softball Fed. [IO], Bucharest, Romania
Romanian Dental Assn. of Private Practitioners [IO], Bucharest, Romania
Romanian Dermatological Soc. [IO], Bucharest, Romania
Romanian EMC Assn. [IO], Craiova, Romania
Romanian Fed. for Physiotherapy [IO], Oradea, Romania
Romanian League Against Rheumatism [IO], Bucharest, Romania
Romanian Local Press Editors Assn. [IO], Brasov, Romania
Romanian Medical Assn. [IO], Bucharest, Romania
Romanian Missionary Soc. [20086], PO Box 527, Wheaton, IL 60187, (630)665-6503
Romanian Natl. Coun. - Defunct.
Romanian Natl. Tourist Off. [3573], 355 Lexington Ave., 8th Fl., New York, NY 10017, (212)545-8484
Romanian Natl. Tourist Off. [3573], 355 Lexington Ave., 8th Fl., New York, NY 10017, (212)545-8484
Romanian Olympic and Sports Comm. [IO], Bucharest, Romania
Romanian Orthodox
Amer. Romanian Orthodox Youth [20226]
Amer. Romanian Orthodox Youth [20226]
Romanian Press Club [IO], Bucharest, Romania
Romanian Skating Fed. [IO], Bucharest, Romania
Romanian Soc. of Cardiology [IO], Bucharest, Romania
Romanian Soc. for Electron Microscopy [IO], Bucharest, Romania
Romanian Soc. of Gastrointestinal Endoscopy [IO], Bucharest, Romania
Romanian Soc. of Medical Informatics [IO], Timisoara, Romania
Romanian Soc. for Meteors and Astronomy [IO], Targoviste, Romania
Romanian Soc. of Osteoporosis and Musculoskeletal Diseases [IO], Bucharest, Romania
Romanian Soc. of Photogrammetry and Remote Sensing [IO], Bucharest, Romania
Romanian Soc. of Physiological Sciences [IO], Targu Mures, Romania
Romanian Soc. of Rheumatology [IO], Cluj-Napoca, Romania
Romanian Soc. for the Stud. of Chemotherapics [IO], Iasi, Romania
Romanian Stud. Assn. of Am. [10513], Univ. of Mississippi, 208 E Bondurant Hall, University, MS 38677, (662)915-7716
Romanian Stud. Gp. [★10514]
Romanian Stud. Gp. [★10514]
Romanian Taekwondo Fed. [IO], Bucharest, Romania
Romanian Tourist Bd. [★3573]
Romanian Tourist Bd. [★3573]
Romanian Union of Public Transport [IO], Bucharest, Romania
Romanian-U.S. Bus. Coun. [23438], 1615 H St. NW, Washington, DC 20062-2000, (202)463-5570
Romanian-U.S. Economic Coun. [★23438]
Romanian-U.S. Working Group [★23438]
Romanian Visual Arts Copyright Collecting Soc. [IO], Bucharest, Romania
Romantic Novelists' Assn. [IO], Swindon, United Kingdom
Romany
Gypsy Lore Soc. [10515]
Gypsy Lore Soc. [10515]
Romany Soc. [IO], Macclesfield, United Kingdom
Romisch-Germanische Kommission des Deutschen Archaeologischen Instituts [★IO]
Ronald Reagan Home Preservation Found. [10688], 816 S Hennepin Ave., Dixon, IL 61021, (815)288-5176
Ronald Reagan Restoration and Preservation Assn. [★10688]
Ronald Stevenson Soc. [IO], Edinburgh, United Kingdom
Ronny and the Daytonas Fan Club [23888], Robert J. McKenzie, Pres., 114 Prince George Dr., Hampton, VA 23669-3604, (757)838-2059

Roof Coatings Mfrs. Assn. [792], 750 Natl. Press Bldg., 529 14th St. NW, Washington, DC 20045, (202)207-0919
Roof Consultants Inst. [950], 1500 Sunday Dr., Ste. 204, Raleigh, NC 27607, (919)859-0742
Roof Tile Inst. [★629]
Roofing Indus. Comm. on Weather Issues [612], 6314 Kungle Rd., Clinton, OH 44216, (330)671-4569
Rooftops Canada [IO], Toronto, ON, Canada
Room to Read [11909], 111 Sutter St., 16th Fl., San Francisco, CA 94104, (415)561-3331
Room to Read [11909], 111 Sutter St., 16th Fl., San Francisco, CA 94104, (415)561-3331
ROOMatRTPI [IO], London, United Kingdom
Roosevelt Assn; Theodore [10693]
Roosevelt Centennial Youth Proj. [★13080]
Roosevelt Inst. [10689], 570 Lexington Ave., 18th Fl., New York, NY 10022, (212)444-9130
Roosevelt Memorial Assn. [★10693]
Root Cause [18629], 1 Canal Park, 3rd Fl., Cambridge, MA 02141, (617)492-2300
Roots of Development [12960], 1325 18th St. NW, Ste. 303, Washington, DC 20036, (202)466-0805
Roots of Peace [18286], 990 A St., Ste. 402, San Rafael, CA 94901, (415)455-8008
Roots and Wings Intl. [12363], 5018 N Allen Pl., Spokane, WA 99205, (503)564-8831
Rope Jumping
Amer. Double Dutch League [22852]
U.S. Amateur Jump Rope Fed. [22853]
Rope Paper Sack Mfrs. Assn. [★885]
Rorschach Res. Exchange [★16426]
Rorschach Res. Exchange [★16426]
Rosa Klub CR [★IO]
Rosacea Soc; Natl. [14335]
Rosary for Life Org. - Defunct.
Roscoe Pound-American Trial Lawyers Found. [★6048]
Roscoe Pound Found. [★6048]
Roscoe Pound Inst. [★6048]
Roscoe Pound-NACCA Found. [★6048]
Rose Family Assn. [20579], 1474 Montelegre Dr., San Jose, CA 95120-4831, (408)268-2137
Rose Hybridizers Assn. [21819], 21 S Wheaton Rd., Horseheads, NY 14845-1077
Rose Kushner Breast Cancer Advisory Center [13976], PO Box 757, Palos Verdes Estates, CA 90274
Rose Soc. of Argentina [IO], Buenos Aires, Argentina
Rosedale Mennonite Missions [19962], 9920 Rosedale-Milford Center Rd., Irwin, OH 43029, (740)857-1366
Rosedale Mennonite Missions [19962], 9920 Rosedale-Milford Center Rd., Irwin, OH 43029, (740)857-1366
Rosenberg Fund for Children [11499], 116 Pleasant St., Ste. 348, Easthampton, MA 01027-2759, (413)529-0063
Roses Incorporated [★4744]
Rosicrucian
Rosicrucian Fellowship [20227]
Rosicrucian Fellowship [20227]
Rosicrucian Fraternity [19212]
Rosicrucian Order, AMORC English Grand Lodge [19213]
Rosicrucian Fellowship [20227], 2222 Mission Ave., Oceanside, CA 92058-2329, (760)757-6600
Rosicrucian Fellowship [20227], 2222 Mission Ave., Oceanside, CA 92058-2329, (760)757-6600
Rosicrucian Fraternity [19212], PO Box 220, Quakertown, PA 18951
Rosicrucian Order [★19213]
Rosicrucian Order, AMORC English Grand Lodge [19213], 1342 Naglee Ave., San Jose, CA 95126-2007, (408)947-3600
Rossica [★22068]
Rossica [★22068]
Rossica Soc. of Russian Philately [22068], Dr. Ed Laveroni, Sec., PO Box 320997, Los Gatos, CA 95032-0116
Rossica Soc. of Russian Philately [22068], Dr. Ed Laveroni, Sec., PO Box 320997, Los Gatos, CA 95032-0116

Reference to "IO" in place of a book number signifies that the association may be found in the 50th edition of International Organizations.

Rossiiskoe Mineralogicheskoe Obshchestvo [★IO]
Rossika [★22068]
Rossika [★22068]
Roster of Certified Engineers of the ASEIB [★6766]
Rotaplast Intl. [14202], 3317 26th St., San Francisco, CA 94110, (415)252-1111
Rotarian Action Gp. for the Alleviation of Hunger and Malnutrition [12290], Charles Cotten, Treas., 4015 Boulder Ave., Odessa, TX 79762, (432)550-5193
Rotarian Action Gp. for the Alleviation of Hunger and Malnutrition [12290], Charles Cotten, Treas., 4015 Boulder Ave., Odessa, TX 79762, (432)550-5193
Rotarian Action Gp. for Population Growth and Sustainable Development [12709], 344 W Pike St., Lawrenceville, GA 30046, (770)407-5633
Rotarian Action Gp. for Population Growth and Sustainable Development [12709], 344 W Pike St., Lawrenceville, GA 30046, (770)407-5633
Rotary Intl. [13074], One Rotary Center, 1560 Sherman Ave., Evanston, IL 60201, (847)866-3000
Rotary Intl. [13074], One Rotary Center, 1560 Sherman Ave., Evanston, IL 60201, (847)866-3000
Rotary on Stamps Fellowship [22069], 1327 Prince Albert Dr., St. Louis, MO 63146
Rotary on Stamps Fellowship [22069], 1327 Prince Albert Dr., St. Louis, MO 63146
Rotary on Stamps Unit [★22069]
Rotary on Stamps Unit [★22069]
Rotating Elecl. Machines Assn. [IO], London, United Kingdom
ROTH [★20709]
Rotorcraft
    Popular Rotorcraft Assn. [20913]
    Whirly-Girls - Intl. Women Helicopter Pilots [20923]
Rottweiler Club of Am. [★21504]
Rottweilerklubben Danmark [★IO]
Rough Fell Sheep Breeders Assn. [IO], Ripon, United Kingdom
Rough and Smooth Collie Training Assn. [IO], Uttoxeter, United Kingdom
Rough and Tumble Engineers' Historical Assn. [22157], PO Box 9, Kinzers, PA 17535-0009, (717)442-4249
ROUNDALAB [★9552]
Rounders England [IO], Sheffield, United Kingdom
Rousseau Assn. [9411], Univ. of La Verne, Dept. of History and Political Sci., 1950 3rd St., La Verne, CA 91750
Rousseau Assn. [9411], Univ. of La Verne, Dept. of History and Political Sci., 1950 3rd St., La Verne, CA 91750
Routes to Learning Canada [IO], Kingston, ON, Canada
Rover P4 Drivers Guild [IO], Milton Keynes, United Kingdom
Roving Volunteers in Christ's Ser. [22192], 1800 SE 4th St., Smithville, TX 78957, (800)727-8914
Rowing
    Eastern Assn. of Rowing Colleges [22854]
    Gay and Lesbian Rowing Fed. [22855]
    Intercollegiate Rowing Assn. [22856]
    Intl. Rafting Fed. [22837]
    Natl. Rowing Found. [22857]
    Scholastic Rowing Assn. of Am. [22858]
    U.S. Rowing Assn. [22859]
Rowing Canada Aviron [IO], Victoria, BC, Canada
Roy Rogers - Dale Evans Collectors Assn. [23889], PO Box 1166, Portsmouth, OH 45662, (740)353-0900
Royal Academies for Sci. and the Arts of Belgium [IO], Brussels, Belgium
Royal Acad. of Arts [IO], London, United Kingdom
Royal Acad. of Dance [IO], London, United Kingdom
Royal Acad. of Dance [9564], 1712 19th St., No. 215 B, Bakersfield, CA 93301-4313, (661)336-0160
Royal Acad. of Dancing, U.S. Br. [★9564]
Royal Acad. of Dramatic Art [IO], London, United Kingdom
Royal Acad. of Dutch Language and Literature [IO], Gent, Belgium
Royal Acad. of Engg. [IO], London, United Kingdom
Royal Acad. of Letters, History and Antiquities [IO], Stockholm, Sweden
Royal Acad. of Medicine of Belgium [IO], Brussels, Belgium

Royal Acad. of Medicine in Ireland [IO], Dublin, Ireland
Royal Acad. of Music [IO], London, United Kingdom
Royal Acad. of Overseas Sciences [IO], Brussels, Belgium
Royal Acad. of Sci., Humanities, and Fine Arts of Belgium [IO], Brussels, Belgium
Royal Aeronautical Soc. - Australia [IO], Mascot, Australia
Royal Aeronautical Soc., New Zealand Div. [IO], Wellington, New Zealand
Royal Aeronautical Soc. - United Kingdom [IO], London, United Kingdom
Royal African Soc. [IO], London, United Kingdom
Royal Agricultural and Horticultural Soc. of South Australia [IO], Goodwood, Australia
Royal Agricultural Soc. of the Commonwealth [IO], Edinburgh, United Kingdom
Royal Agricultural Soc. of England [IO], Coventry, United Kingdom
Royal Agricultural Soc. of New Zealand [IO], Woodend, New Zealand
Royal Agricultural Soc. of NSW [IO], Sydney, Australia
Royal Air Force Benevolent Fund [IO], London, United Kingdom
Royal Air Force Historical Soc. [IO], Wotton-under-Edge, United Kingdom
Royal Air Forces Assn. [IO], Leicester, United Kingdom
Royal and Ancient Golf Club [IO], Fife, United Kingdom
Royal and Ancient Golf Club of St. Andrews [IO], Fife, United Kingdom
Royal Anthropological Inst. of Great Britain and Ireland [IO], London, United Kingdom
Royal Archaeological Inst. [IO], London, United Kingdom
Royal Architectural Inst. of Canada [IO], Ottawa, ON, Canada
Royal Asiatic Soc. of Great Britain and Ireland [IO], London, United Kingdom
Royal Asiatic Soc. - Hong Kong Br. [IO], Hong Kong, People's Republic of China
Royal Assn. of British Dairy Farmers [IO], Kenilworth, United Kingdom
Royal Assn. for Deaf People [IO], Colchester, United Kingdom
Royal Assn. for Disability and Rehabilitation [IO], London, United Kingdom
Royal Assn. of Dutch Wine Traders [IO], Amsterdam, Netherlands
Royal Assn. of Netherlands' Shipowners [IO], Rotterdam, Netherlands
Royal Astronomical Soc. [IO], London, United Kingdom
Royal Astronomical Soc. of Canada [IO], Toronto, ON, Canada
Royal Astronomical Soc. of New Zealand [IO], Wellington, New Zealand
Royal Australasian Coll. of Dental Surgeons [IO], Sydney, Australia
Royal Australasian Coll. of Physicians [IO], Sydney, Australia
Royal Australasian Coll. of Surgeons [IO], Melbourne, Australia
Royal Australian Chem. Inst. [IO], North Melbourne, Australia
Royal Australian Chem. Inst. - ACT Br. [IO], Canberra, Australia
Royal Australian Chem. Inst. - NSW Br. [IO], Sydney, Australia
Royal Australian Chem. Inst. - NT Br. [IO], Casuarina, Australia
Royal Australian Chem. Inst. - SA Br. [IO], Bedford Park, Australia
Royal Australian Chem. Inst. - Tasmanian Br. [IO], Hobart, Australia
Royal Australian Chem. Inst. - Victorian Br. [IO], Melbourne, Australia
Royal Australian Chem. Inst. - WA Br. [IO], West Leederville, Australia
Royal Australian Coll. of Gen. Practitioners [IO], South Melbourne, Australia
Royal Australian Historical Soc. [IO], Sydney, Australia

Royal Australian and New Zealand Coll. of Obstetricians and Gynaecologists [IO], East Melbourne, Australia
Royal Australian and New Zealand Coll. of Ophthalmologists [IO], Surry Hills, Australia
Royal Australian and New Zealand Coll. of Psychiatrists [IO], Melbourne, Australia
Royal Australian and New Zealand Coll. of Radiologists [IO], Sydney, Australia
Royal Bath and West of England Soc. [IO], Shepton Mallet, United Kingdom
Royal Belgian Aero Club [IO], Brussels, Belgium
Royal Belgian Assn. of Biscuit, Chocolate, Pralines and Confectionery [IO], Brussels, Belgium
Royal Belgian Football Assn. [IO], Brussels, Belgium
Royal Belgian Shipowners' Assn. [IO], Antwerp, Belgium
Royal Belgian Tennis Fed. [IO], Brussels, Belgium
Royal Booksellers Assn. [IO], Bilthoven, Netherlands
Royal British Legion Women's Sect. [IO], London, United Kingdom
Royal British Soc. of Sculptors [IO], London, United Kingdom
Royal British Virgin Islands Yacht Club [IO], Tortola, British Virgin Islands
Royal Canadian Coll. of Organists [IO], Toronto, ON, Canada
Royal Canadian Geographical Soc. [IO], Ottawa, ON, Canada
Royal Canadian Golf Assn. [IO], Oakville, ON, Canada
Royal Canadian Legion [IO], Ottawa, ON, Canada
Royal Canadian Numismatic Assn. [IO], Markham, ON, Canada
Royal Canadian Regiment Assn. [IO], London, ON, Canada
Royal Celtic Soc. [IO], Edinburgh, United Kingdom
Royal Chamber of the Belgian Antique Dealers [IO], Brussels, Belgium
Royal Choral Soc. [IO], London, United Kingdom
Royal Cliff Wine Club [IO], Pattaya, Thailand
Royal Coll. of Anaesthetists [IO], London, United Kingdom
Royal Coll. of Dentists of Canada [IO], Toronto, ON, Canada
Royal Coll. of Gen. Practitioners [IO], London, United Kingdom
Royal Coll. of Midwives [IO], London, United Kingdom
Royal Coll. of Nursing [IO], London, United Kingdom
Royal Coll. of Nursing - Australia [IO], Deakin West, Australia
Royal Coll. of Obstetricians and Gynaecologists - United Kingdom [IO], London, United Kingdom
Royal Coll. of Ophthalmologists [IO], London, United Kingdom
Royal Coll. of Organists [IO], London, United Kingdom
Royal Coll. of Paediatrics and Child Hea. [IO], London, United Kingdom
Royal Coll. of Pathologists of Australasia [IO], Surry Hills, Australia
Royal Coll. of Pathologists - United Kingdom [IO], London, United Kingdom
Royal Coll. of Physicians [IO], London, United Kingdom
Royal Coll. of Physicians of Edinburgh [IO], Edinburgh, United Kingdom
Royal Coll. of Physicians of Ireland [IO], Dublin, Ireland
Royal Coll. of Physicians and Surgeons of Canada [IO], Ottawa, ON, Canada
Royal Coll. of Physicians and Surgeons of Glasgow [IO], Glasgow, United Kingdom
Royal Coll. of Physicians and Surgeons of the U.S.A. [16933], PO Box 24224, Detroit, MI 48224-0224, (313)882-0641
Royal Coll. of Physicians and Surgeons of the U.S.A. [16933], PO Box 24224, Detroit, MI 48224-0224, (313)882-0641
Royal Coll. of Psychiatrists [IO], London, United Kingdom
Royal Coll. of Radiologists - United Kingdom [IO], London, United Kingdom
Royal Coll. of Speech and Language Therapists [IO], London, United Kingdom

---

A star before a book entry number signifies that the name is not listed separately, but is mentioned within the entry.

Royal Coll. of Surgeons of Edinburgh [IO], Edinburgh, United Kingdom

Royal Coll. of Surgeons of England [IO], London, United Kingdom

Royal Coll. of Surgeons in Ireland [IO], Dublin, Ireland

Royal Coll. of Veterinary Surgeons [IO], London, United Kingdom

Royal Commonwealth Ex-Services League [IO], London, United Kingdom

Royal Commonwealth Soc. [IO], London, United Kingdom

Royal Conservatory of Music [IO], Toronto, ON, Canada

Royal Danish Acad. of Fine Arts [IO], Copenhagen, Denmark

Royal Danish Acad. of Sciences and Letters [IO], Copenhagen, Denmark

Royal Danish Aeroclub [IO], Roskilde, Denmark

Royal Danish Agricultural Soc. [IO], Copenhagen, Denmark

Royal Danish Geographical Soc. [IO], Copenhagen, Denmark

Royal Dublin Soc. [IO], Dublin, Ireland

Royal Dutch Cricket Assn. [IO], Nieuwegein, Netherlands

Royal Dutch Geographical Soc. [IO], Utrecht, Netherlands

Royal Dutch Korfball Assn. [IO], Zeist, Netherlands

Royal Dutch Medical Assn. [IO], Utrecht, Netherlands

Royal Economic Soc. [IO], Fife, United Kingdom

Royal Economic Soc. of Friends of Tenerife [IO], San Cristobal de La Laguna, Spain

Royal Enfield Owners Club of North Am. [IO], Oshawa, ON, Canada

Royal Entomological Soc. [IO], St. Albans, United Kingdom

Royal Entomological Soc. of Antwerp, Belgium [IO], Hoboken, Belgium

Royal Environmental Hea. Inst. of Scotland [IO], Edinburgh, United Kingdom

Royal Fed. of Aero Clubs of Australia [IO], Canberra, Australia

Royal Fed. of Water and Soft Drinks Indus. [IO], Brussels, Belgium

Royal Flying Dr. Ser. of Australia [IO], Sydney, Australia

Royal Forest and Bird Protection Soc. of New Zealand [IO], Wellington, New Zealand

Royal Forestry Soc. [IO], Tring, United Kingdom

Royal Geographical Soc. with the Inst. of British Geographers [IO], London, United Kingdom

Royal Geographical Soc. of Queensland [IO], Milton, Australia

Royal Heraldry Soc. of Canada [IO], Ottawa, ON, Canada

Royal Highland and Agricultural Soc. of Scotland [IO], Edinburgh, United Kingdom

Royal Highland Educ. Trust [IO], Edinburgh, United Kingdom

Royal Historical Soc. of Queensland [IO], Brisbane, Australia

Royal Historical Soc. - United Kingdom [IO], London, United Kingdom

Royal Historical Soc. of Victoria [IO], Melbourne, Australia

Royal Horticultural Soc. [IO], London, United Kingdom

Royal Horticultural Soc. of Ireland [IO], Dublin, Ireland

Royal Humane Soc. [IO], London, United Kingdom

Royal Incorporation of Architects in Scotland [IO], Edinburgh, United Kingdom

Royal Inst. of the Architects of Ireland [IO], Dublin, Ireland

Royal Inst. of British Architects [IO], London, United Kingdom

Royal Inst. for Deaf and Blind Children [IO], Sydney, Australia

Royal Inst. of Dutch Architects [IO], Amsterdam, Netherlands

Royal Inst. of Intl. Relations [IO], Brussels, Belgium

Royal Inst. of Navigation [IO], London, United Kingdom

Royal Inst. of Oil Painters [IO], London, United Kingdom

Royal Inst. of Painters in Water Colours [IO], London, United Kingdom

Royal Inst. of Philosophy [IO], London, United Kingdom

Royal Inst. of Public Hea. [IO], London, United Kingdom

Royal Institution of Chartered Surveyors [IO], London, United Kingdom

Royal Institution of Engineers in the Netherlands [IO], The Hague, Netherlands

Royal Institution of Great Britain [IO], London, United Kingdom

Royal Institution of Naval Architects [IO], London, United Kingdom

Royal Irish Acad. [IO], Dublin, Ireland

Royal Irish Acad. of Music [IO], Dublin, Ireland

Royal Irish Auto. Club [IO], Dublin, Ireland

Royal Isle of Wight Agricultural Soc. [IO], Newport, United Kingdom

Royal Life Saving Soc. [IO], Alcester, United Kingdom

Royal Life Saving Soc. Australia [IO], Broadway, Australia

Royal Medical Soc. [IO], Edinburgh, United Kingdom

Royal Mencap Soc. [IO], London, United Kingdom

Royal Meteorological Soc. [IO], Reading, United Kingdom

Royal Microscopical Soc. [IO], Oxford, United Kingdom

Royal Musical Assn. [IO], Manchester, United Kingdom

Royal Natl. Acad. of Pharmacy [IO], Madrid, Spain

Royal Natl. Inst. of Blind People - UK [IO], London, United Kingdom

Royal Natl. Inst. for Deaf People [IO], London, United Kingdom

Royal Natl. Lifeboat Institution - Ireland [IO], Dun Laoghaire, Ireland

Royal Natl. Mission to Deep Sea Fishermen [IO], Whiteley, United Kingdom

Royal Natl. Rose Soc. [IO], St. Albans, United Kingdom

Royal Neighbors of Am. [19056], 230 16th St., Rock Island, IL 61201-8645, (309)788-4561

Royal Netherlands Acad. of Arts and Sciences [IO], Amsterdam, Netherlands

Royal Netherlands Aeronautical Assn. [IO], Woerden, Netherlands

Royal Netherlands Assn. of Musicians [IO], Amsterdam, Netherlands

Royal Netherlands Chem. Soc. [IO], Leidschendam, Netherlands

Royal Netherlands Soc. for Agricultural Sciences [IO], Wageningen, Netherlands

Royal New South Wales Bowling Assn. [IO], Sydney, Australia

Royal New Zealand Aero Club [IO], Blenheim, New Zealand

Royal New Zealand Naval Women's Assn. [IO], Auckland, New Zealand

Royal Norwegian Soc. of Sciences and Letters [IO], Trondheim, Norway

Royal Numismatic Soc. [IO], London, United Kingdom

Royal Oak Found. [9725], 35 W 35th St., Ste. 1200, New York, NY 10001-2205, (212)480-2889

Royal Oman Polo Club [IO], Muscat, Oman

Royal Order of Scotland [19141], PO Box 11, Charleroi, PA 15022-0011, (724)489-0670

Royal Over-Seas League [IO], London, United Kingdom

Royal Pharmaceutical Soc. of Great Britain [IO], London, United Kingdom

Royal Philatelic Soc. [IO], London, United Kingdom

Royal Philatelic Soc. of Canada [IO], Toronto, ON, Canada

Royal Philharmonic Soc. [IO], London, United Kingdom

Royal Philosophical Soc. of Glasgow [IO], Glasgow, United Kingdom

Royal Photographic Soc. of Great Britain [IO], Bath, United Kingdom

Royal Physiographical Soc. of Lund [IO], Lund, Sweden

Royal Sailors' Rests [IO], Portsmouth, United Kingdom

Royal Scottish Acad. [IO], Edinburgh, United Kingdom

Royal Scottish Acad. of Music and Drama [IO], Glasgow, United Kingdom

Royal Scottish Country Dance Soc. [IO], Edinburgh, United Kingdom

Royal Scottish Forestry Soc. [IO], Newton Stewart, United Kingdom

Royal Scottish Geographical Soc. [IO], Perth, United Kingdom

Royal Soc. [IO], London, United Kingdom

Royal Soc. of Antiquaries of Ireland [IO], Dublin, Ireland

Royal Soc. for Asian Affairs [IO], London, United Kingdom

Royal Soc. of British Artists [IO], London, United Kingdom

Royal Soc. of Canada [IO], Ottawa, ON, Canada

Royal Soc. of Chemistry [IO], London, United Kingdom

Royal Soc. of Edinburgh [IO], Edinburgh, United Kingdom

Royal Soc. for the Encouragement of Arts, Manufactures, and Commerce [IO], London, United Kingdom

Royal Soc. of Literature [IO], London, United Kingdom

Royal Soc. of Marine Artists [IO], London, United Kingdom

Royal Soc. of Medicine [IO], London, United Kingdom

Royal Soc. of Miniature Painters, Sculptors and Gravers [IO], London, United Kingdom

Royal Soc. for Music History of the Netherlands [IO], Utrecht, Netherlands

Royal Soc. of Musicians of Great Britain [IO], London, United Kingdom

Royal Soc. of New South Wales [IO], Sydney, Australia

Royal Soc. of New Zealand [IO], Wellington, New Zealand

Royal Soc. of New Zealand, Canterbury Br. [IO], Christchurch, New Zealand

Royal Soc. of New Zealand, Manawatu Br. [IO], Palmerston North, New Zealand

Royal Soc. of New Zealand, North Shore Br. [IO], Auckland, New Zealand

Royal Soc. of New Zealand, Rotorua Br. [IO], Rotorua, New Zealand

Royal Soc. of Painter-Printmakers [IO], London, United Kingdom

Royal Soc. of Portrait Painters [IO], London, United Kingdom

Royal Soc. for the Prevention of Accidents [IO], Birmingham, United Kingdom

Royal Soc. for the Prevention of Cruelty to Animals Natl. HQ [IO], Horsham, United Kingdom

Royal Soc. for the Protection of Birds [IO], Sandy, United Kingdom

Royal Soc. for Protection and Care of Animals [IO], Thimphu, Bhutan

Royal Soc. for Protection of Nature [IO], Thimphu, Bhutan

Royal Soc. of South Africa [IO], Cape Town, Republic of South Africa

Royal Soc. of South Australia [IO], Adelaide, Australia

Royal Soc. of Tropical Medicine and Hygiene [IO], London, United Kingdom

Royal Soc. of Ulster Architects [IO], Belfast, United Kingdom

Royal Soc. of Victoria [IO], Melbourne, Australia

Royal Soc. of Western Australia [IO], Welshpool, Australia

Royal Soc. of Wildlife Trusts [IO], Newark, United Kingdom

Royal Statistical Soc. [IO], London, United Kingdom

Royal Surgical Aid Soc. [IO], London, United Kingdom

Royal Swedish Acad. of Engg. Sciences [IO], Stockholm, Sweden

Royal Swedish Acad. of Sciences [IO], Stockholm, Sweden

Reference to "IO" in place of a book number signifies that the association may be found in the 50th edition of International Organizations.

Royal TV Soc. **[IO]**, London, United Kingdom
Royal Town Planning Inst. **[IO]**, London, United Kingdom
Royal Tropical Inst. **[IO]**, Amsterdam, Netherlands
Royal Ulster Agricultural Soc. **[IO]**, Belfast, United Kingdom
Royal United Services Inst. for Defence and Security Stud. **[IO]**, London, United Kingdom
Royal Victorian Bowls Assn. **[IO]**, Hawthorn, Australia
Royal Watercolour Soc. **[IO]**, London, United Kingdom
Royal Welsh Agricultural Soc. **[IO]**, Builth Wells, United Kingdom
Royal Western Australian Historical Soc. **[IO]**, Nedlands, Australia
Royal Western India Turf Club **[IO]**, Mumbai, India
Royal Winnipeg Ballet Alumni Assn. **[IO]**, Winnipeg, MB, Canada
Royal Yachting Assn. **[IO]**, Southampton, United Kingdom
Royal Zoological Soc. of New South Wales **[IO]**, Mosman, Australia
Royal Zoological Soc. of Scotland **[IO]**, Edinburgh, United Kingdom
Royal Zoological Soc. of South Australia **[IO]**, Adelaide, Australia
Roycrofters-at-Large Assn. **[21465]**, 21 S Grove St., Ste. 110, East Aurora, NY 14052, (716)655-7252
Roycrofters-At-Large Association/Elbert Hubbard Found. **[★21465]**
RPO Am. **[★5959]**
RSNZ Wellington Br. **[IO]**, Wellington, New Zealand
RTCA **[6024]**, 1828 L St. NW, Ste. 805, Washington, DC 20036, (202)833-9339
RTCM **[★3417]**
RTCM **[★3417]**
RTS Bereavement Services **[★11127]**
RTS Parent Gp. U.S.A. **[★13847]**
Rubber
  Amer. Chem. Soc., Rubber Div. **[3131]**
  European Tyre and Rubber Mfrs'. Assn. **[197]**
  French Rubber Mfrs. Assn. **[20843]**
  Intl. Inst. of Synthetic Rubber Producers **[3132]**
  Intl. Inst. of Synthetic Rubber Producers **[3132]**
  Natl. Assn. of Hose and Accessories Distribution **[1850]**
  Natl. Plastics Indus. Assn. **[13393]**
  Rubber Assn. of Canada **[4761]**
  Rubber Mfrs. Assn. **[3133]**
Rubber Assn. of Am. **[★3133]**
Rubber Assn. of Canada **[IO]**, Mississauga, ON, Canada
Rubber Assn. of Indonesia **[IO]**, Jakarta, Indonesia
Rubber Club of Am. **[★3133]**
Rubber Mfrs. Assn. **[3133]**, 1400 K St. NW, Ste. 900, Washington, DC 20005, (202)682-4800
Rubber Mfrs'. Assn. of Finland **[IO]**, Helsinki, Finland
Rubber Pavements Assn. **[613]**, 1801 S Jentilly Ln., Ste. A-2, Tempe, AZ 85281-5738, (480)517-9944
Rubber Pavements Assn. **[613]**, 1801 S Jentilly Ln., Ste. A-2, Tempe, AZ 85281-5738, (480)517-9944
Rubber and Plastic Adhesive and Sealant Mfrs. Coun. **[★57]**
Rubber Stamp Manufacturer's Guild **[IO]**, London, United Kingdom
Rubicon - Defunct.
Rubin Found; Samuel **[13202]**
Rubinstein-Taybi Parent Gp. U.S.A. **[13847]**, Ms. Lorrie Baxter, Coor., PO Box 146, Smith Center, KS 66967, (785)697-2984
Ruckus Soc. **[18222]**, PO Box 28741, Oakland, CA 94604, (510)931-6339
Rudd Family Res. Assn. - Defunct.
Rudjer Boskovic Inst. **[IO]**, Zagreb, Croatia
Ruffed Grouse Soc. **[5120]**, 451 McCormick Rd., Coraopolis, PA 15108, (412)262-4044
Ruffed Grouse Soc. of Am. **[★5120]**
Ruffed Grouse Soc. of North Am. **[★5120]**
Rug Soc. of Washington, District of Columbia **[★9185]**
Rug Soc. of Washington, District of Columbia **[★9185]**
Rugby
  U.S. Quad Rugby Assn. **[22860]**

U.S. Quad Rugby Assn. **[22860]**
U.S. Rugby Football Union **[22861]**
Welsh Rugby Union **[5451]**
Rugby Fives Assn. **[IO]**, London, United Kingdom
Rugby Football League **[IO]**, Leeds, United Kingdom
Rugby Football Union **[IO]**, Twickenham, United Kingdom
Rugby Players' Assn. **[IO]**, Twickenham, United Kingdom
Rugby Union Players' Assn. **[IO]**, Sydney, Australia
RUGMARK Found. **[11398]**, 2001 S St. NW, Ste. 510, Washington, DC 20009, (202)234-9050
RUGMARK Found. **[11398]**, 2001 S St. NW, Ste. 510, Washington, DC 20009, (202)234-9050
Rule of Law Consortium - Defunct.
Rumi Forum **[18287]**, 1150 17th St., Ste. 408, Washington, DC 20036, (202)429-1690
Runaways
  Amer. Youth Work Center **[13508]**
  Children of the Night **[12946]**
  Girls and Boys Town **[12947]**
  Natl. Network for Youth **[12948]**
  Natl. Runaway Switchboard **[12949]**
  One Missing Link **[12545]**
Runkle Family Assn. **[20580]**, PO Box 14, Ringoes, NJ 08551
Running
  Amer. Ultrarunning Assn. **[22862]**
  Girls on the Run Intl. **[22863]**
  Natl. Intercollegiate Running Club Assn. **[22864]**
  New York Road Runners Club **[22865]**
  Race for Peace **[18285]**
  Road Runners Club of Am. **[22866]**
  Running USA **[22867]**
  U.S. Cross Country Coaches Assn. **[22868]**
  U.S. Running Streak Assn. **[22869]**
Running Strong for Amer. Indian Youth **[★12558]**
Running USA **[22867]**, 1631 Mesa Ave., Ste. A, Colorado Springs, CO 80906, (719)434-2575
Runnymede Trust **[IO]**, London, United Kingdom
Rural Advancement Found. Intl. USA **[3747]**, PO Box 640, Pittsboro, NC 27312, (919)542-1396
Rural Advancement Found. Intl. USA **[3747]**, PO Box 640, Pittsboro, NC 27312, (919)542-1396
Rural Advancement Fund Intl. **[★3747]**
Rural Advancement Fund Intl. **[★3747]**
Rural Am., Inc. **[★11571]**
Rural Amer. Women - Defunct.
Rural and Assoc. Contractors Fed. of New Zealand **[IO]**, Lower Hutt, New Zealand
Rural Centre For Human Interests **[IO]**, Solan, India
Rural Coalition **[18575]**, 1012 14th St. NW, Ste. 1100, Washington, DC 20005, (202)628-7160
Rural Community Assistance Partnership **[7610]**, 1701 K St. NW, Ste. 700, Washington, DC 20006, (202)408-1273
Rural Community Assistance Prog. **[★7610]**
Rural Crafts Assn. **[IO]**, Godalming, United Kingdom
Rural Development
  Abriendo Mentes **[12950]**
  Act for Africa Intl. **[12951]**
  Agricultural Development Initiatives **[3727]**
  Bridges to Prosperity **[12952]**
  Building Community Bridges **[11554]**
  Chris Cares Intl. **[11560]**
  Community Development Intl. **[11567]**
  Community Empowerment Network **[12953]**
  Computers for Africa **[7910]**
  Connecting Congo **[11573]**
  Drinking Water for India **[13419]**
  Elephant Energy **[6715]**
  Empower Tanzania, Inc. **[12954]**
  Empower Tanzania, Inc. **[12954]**
  Farmer-Veteran Coalition **[20610]**
  Fed. of Southern Cooperatives Land Assistance Fund **[12955]**
  Fields of Growth Intl. **[12416]**
  From Hunger to Harvest **[12280]**
  Global Partners Running Waters **[11590]**
  Greener Pastures Inst. **[12178]**
  Haiti Convention Assn. **[12966]**
  HELPSudan **[11442]**
  Humans in Crisis Intl. Corp. **[12851]**
  India Development Ser. **[18571]**
  India Development Ser. **[18571]**

Inter-American Found. **[18572]**
Inter-American Found. **[18572]**
Intl. Agro Alliance **[4940]**
Intl. Development Collaborative **[12341]**
Intl. Inst. of Rural Reconstruction U.S. Chap. **[12956]**
Intl. Inst. of Rural Reconstruction U.S. Chap. **[12956]**
Into Your Hands **[12967]**
Jewish Heart for Africa **[10822]**
Long Way Home **[11073]**
Miracles in Action **[12740]**
Namlo Intl. **[12349]**
Natl. Coalition for Food and Agricultural Res. **[3744]**
Natl. Org. of State Offices of Rural Hea. **[16490]**
Natl. Rural Economic Developers Assn. **[18573]**
Natl. Rural Water Assn. **[12957]**
Natl. Women in Agriculture Assn. **[3762]**
North Amer. Alliances for Social Relief **[12352]**
Noshaq **[12958]**
Noshaq **[12958]**
Partners for Rural Am. **[18574]**
Partners for Rural Improvement and Development in Ethiopia **[12959]**
Partners for Rural Improvement and Development in Ethiopia **[12959]**
Partners in Sustainable Development Intl. **[12745]**
Partnership to Cut Hunger and Poverty in Africa **[12746]**
Reconstruction Efforts Aiding Children without Homes **[11624]**
Roots of Development **[12960]**
Rural Coalition **[18575]**
Rural Initiative Development Assn. **[12961]**
Rural Initiative Development Assn. **[12961]**
Rural Planning Organizations of Am. **[5959]**
Rural School and Community Trust (Rural Trust) **[8803]**
Sabu Help **[12962]**
SeaAid **[11628]**
Solar Light for Africa **[11640]**
Sunstove Org. **[11643]**
Sustainable Biomaterials Collaborative **[6119]**
Sustainable Smiles **[4876]**
TERRA - Rsrc. Development Intl. **[12963]**
TERRA - Rsrc. Development Intl. **[12963]**
Under The Baobab Tree **[7901]**
Union MicroFinanza **[12964]**
Village Volunteers **[12379]**
Well Done Org. **[11653]**
World Sustainable Agriculture Assn. **[12965]**
World Sustainable Agriculture Assn. **[12965]**
Rural Doctors Assn. of Australia **[IO]**, Manuka, Australia
Rural Doctors Assn. of Southern Africa **[IO]**, Tygerberg, Republic of South Africa
Rural Education
  Agami **[7824]**
  Haiti Convention Assn. **[12966]**
  HELPSudan **[11442]**
  Into Your Hands **[12967]**
  Magis Americas **[12968]**
  Natl. Rural Educ. Advocacy Coalition **[8804]**
  Natl. Rural Educ. Assn. **[8805]**
  Two Cents of Hope **[8292]**
  Under The Baobab Tree **[7901]**
Rural Educ. Assn. **[★8805]**
Rural Electricity Rsrc. Coun. **[6753]**, PO Box 309, Wilmington, OH 45177-0309, (937)383-0001
Rural Hea. Intl. Non-Profit Org. **[15208]**, 4447 Clarke Dr., Troy, MI 48085, (248)238-0636
Rural Housing Alliance **[★11571]**
Rural and Indus. Design and Building Assn. **[IO]**, Stowmarket, United Kingdom
Rural Initiative Development Assn. **[12961]**, 511 S Magnolia Dr., Glenshaw, PA 15116, (412)969-7626
Rural Initiative Development Assn. **[12961]**, 511 S Magnolia Dr., Glenshaw, PA 15116, (412)969-7626
The Rural Inst.: Center for Excellence in Disability Educ., Res. and Ser. **[11828]**, Univ. of Montana Rural Inst., 52 Corbin Hall, Missoula, MT 59812, (406)243-5467
Rural Planning Organizations of Am. **[5959]**, Natl. Assn. of Development Organizations, 400 N Capitol St. NW, Ste. 390, Washington, DC 20001, (202)624-7806

A star before a book entry number signifies that the name is not listed separately, but is mentioned within the entry.

Rural Reconstruction Nepal **[IO]**, Kathmandu, Nepal
Rural/Regional Educational Assn. **[★8805]**
Rural Renewable Energy Alliance **[6754]**, 2330 Dancing Wind Rd. SW, Pine River, MN 56474, (218)587-4753
Rural Restoration Adopt Ministry - Address unknown since 2011.
Rural School and Community Trust (Rural Trust) **[8803]**, 4455 Connecticut Ave. NW, Ste. 310, Washington, DC 20008, (202)822-3919
Rural Sect. of the Amer. Sociological Soc. **[★7431]**
Rural Self-Help Development Assn. **[IO]**, Maseru, Lesotho
Rural Sociological Soc. **[7431]**, Brigham Young Univ., 2019 JFSB, Provo, UT 84602, (801)422-7386
Rural Support Programmes Network **[IO]**, Islamabad, Pakistan
Rural Theology Assn. **[IO]**, East Yorkshire, United Kingdom
Rural Women New Zealand **[IO]**, Wellington, New Zealand
Rural Youth
 African Kids In Need **[11179]**
 Long Way Home **[11073]**
 Umoja Intl. **[12969]**
Rural Youth Europe **[IO]**, Helsinki, Finland
Ruralite - Environnement - Developpement **[★IO]**
Rurality - Env. - Development **[IO]**, Attert, Belgium
Ruritan Natl. **[13075]**, PO Box 487, Dublin, VA 24084, (540)674-5431
Ruritan Natl. Foundation **[★13075]**
Rushlight Club **[10020]**, 4508 Elsrode Ave., Baltimore, MD 21214-3107, (443)433-6071
Rushmore Natl. Memorial Soc; Mount **[9709]**
Russell Sage Found. **[7417]**, 112 E 64th St., New York, NY 10065, (212)750-6000
Russian
 Amer. Assn. for Russian Language, Culture and Educ. **[10516]**
 Carpatho-Rusyn Soc. **[10517]**
 Cong. of Russian Americans **[19214]**
 Early Slavic Stud. Assn. **[8863]**
 High School Evangelism Fellowship **[19751]**
 Intl. Found. for Terror Act Victims **[12970]**
 Intl. Found. for Terror Act Victims **[12970]**
 Rossica Soc. of Russian Philately **[22068]**
 Russian-American Chamber of Commerce **[23439]**
 Russian-American Chamber of Commerce **[23439]**
 Russian Brotherhood Org. of the U.S.A. **[19215]**
 Tolstoy Found. **[19216]**
Russian Acad. of Entrepreneurship **[IO]**, Moscow, Russia
Russian Acad. of Sciences **[IO]**, Moscow, Russia
Russian-American Chamber of Commerce **[23439]**, 970 Sidney Marcus Blvd., Ste. 1504, Atlanta, GA 30324, (404)667-9319
Russian-American Chamber of Commerce **[23439]**, 970 Sidney Marcus Blvd., Ste. 1504, Atlanta, GA 30324, (404)667-9319
Russian Amer. Medical Assn. **[15432]**, 36100 Euclid Ave., Ste. 330-B, Willoughby, OH 44094, (440)953-8055
Russian Amer. Medical Assn. **[15432]**, 36100 Euclid Ave., Ste. 330-B, Willoughby, OH 44094, (440)953-8055
Russian Assn. of Bidders and Cost Engg. **[IO]**, Moscow, Russia
Russian Assn. of Bus. Educ. **[IO]**, Moscow, Russia
Russian Assn. of Engineers for Heating, Ventilation, Air-Conditioning, Heat Supply and Building Thermal Physics **[IO]**, Moscow, Russia
Russian Assn. of Marine and River Bunker Suppliers **[IO]**, St. Petersburg, Russia
Russian Assn. of Networks and Services **[IO]**, Moscow, Russia
Russian Assn. of Occupational Therapists **[IO]**, St. Petersburg, Russia
Russian Assn. of Orthodontists **[IO]**, Moscow, Russia
Russian Assn. on Osteoporosis **[IO]**, Moscow, Russia
Russian Assn. of Wind Indus. **[IO]**, St. Petersburg, Russia

Russian Authors' Soc. **[IO]**, Moscow, Russia
Russian Bird Conservation Union **[IO]**, Moscow, Russia
Russian Brotherhood Org. of the U.S.A. **[19215]**, 1733 Spring Garden St., Philadelphia, PA 19130, (215)563-2537
Russian Children's Welfare Soc. **[11399]**, 200 Park Ave. S, Ste. 1508, New York, NY 10003, (212)473-6263
Russian Children's Welfare Soc. **[11399]**, 200 Park Ave. S, Ste. 1508, New York, NY 10003, (212)473-6263
Russian Coun. of Shopping Centers **[IO]**, Moscow, Russia
Russian Cycle Touring Club **[IO]**, Moscow, Russia
Russian Fed. Assn. for Pattern Recognition and Image Anal. **[IO]**, Moscow, Russia
Russian Gestosis Assn. **[IO]**, Moscow, Russia
Russian Historical and Genealogical Soc. in Am. **[★20659]**
Russian Independent Mutual Aid Soc. - Defunct.
Russian League Against Epilepsy **[IO]**, Moscow, Russia
Russian Lib. Assn. **[IO]**, St. Petersburg, Russia
Russian Marketing Assn. **[IO]**, Moscow, Russia
Russian Medical Soc. **[IO]**, Moscow, Russia
Russian Mineralogical Soc. **[IO]**, St. Petersburg, Russia
Russian Natl. Billiard Fed. **[IO]**, St. Petersburg, Russia
Russian Nobility Assn. in Am. **[20659]**, 971 1st Ave., New York, NY 10022
Russian Numismatic Soc. **[21992]**, PO Box 3684, Santa Rosa, CA 95402-3684, (707)527-1007
Russian Orthodox
 Fellowship of Orthodox Christians in Am. **[20228]**
Russian Orthodox Catholic Women's Mutual Aid Soc. - Defunct.
Russian Orthodox Fraternity Lubov - Defunct.
Russian Rightholders' Soc. for Collective Mgt. of Reprographic Reproduction Rights **[IO]**, Moscow, Russia
Russian Skating Union **[IO]**, Moscow, Russia
Russian Soc. of Aesthetic Medicine **[IO]**, Moscow, Russia
Russian Soc. for Digestive Endoscopy **[IO]**, Moscow, Russia
Russian Soc. for Electron Microscopy **[IO]**, Moscow, Russia
Russian Soc. of Hypertension **[IO]**, Moscow, Russia
Russian Soc. of Nematologists **[IO]**, Petrozavodsk, Russia
Russian Soc. of Scanning Probe Microscopy and Nanotechnology **[IO]**, Moscow, Russia
Russian Soc. of Sociologists **[IO]**, Moscow, Russia
Russian Software Developers Assn. **[IO]**, St. Petersburg, Russia
Russian Squash Fed. **[IO]**, Moscow, Russia
Russian Taekwondo Union **[IO]**, Moscow, Russia
Russian Union of Exhibitions and Fairs **[IO]**, Nizhny Novgorod, Russia
Russian Union of Travel Indus. **[IO]**, Moscow, Russia
Russian Venture Capital Assn. **[IO]**, St. Petersburg, Russia
Russian Wolfhound Club of Am. **[★21529]**
Russo-British Chamber of Commerce **[IO]**, London, United Kingdom
Rutenberg and Everett Yiddish Film Lib. **[★9606]**
Ruth Jackson Orthopaedic Soc. **[16047]**, 6300 N River Rd., Ste. 727, Rosemont, IL 60018-4226, (847)698-1626
Rutherford B. Hayes Lib. and Museum **[★10690]**
Rutherford B. Hayes Presidential Center **[10690]**, Spiegel Grove, Fremont, OH 43420-2796, (419)332-2081
Rutherford Inst. **[18521]**, PO Box 7482, Charlottesville, VA 22906-7482, (434)978-3888
RV Mfrs'. Clubs Assn. **[22146]**, 413 Walnut St., Green Cove Springs, FL 32043-3443, (904)529-6575
RVing Women **[22147]**, PO Box 1940, Apache Junction, AZ 85217-1940, (480)671-6226
Rwanda Assn. of Univ. Women **[IO]**, Kigali, Rwanda
Rwanda Gift for Life **[13099]**, PO Box 840, Montclair, NJ 07042, (973)783-4057

Rwanda Knits **[11626]**, 5 Emmons St., No. 2, Montpelier, VT 05602, (518)791-0212
Rwanda Natl. Examinations Coun. **[IO]**, Kigali, Rwanda
Rwanda Network of Christian Organizations **[IO]**, Kigali, Rwanda
Rwanda Partners **[12364]**, 159 Western Ave. W, Ste. No. A455, Seattle, WA 98119, (206)838-8698
Rwanda Pharmaceutical Students' Assn. **[IO]**, Butare, Rwanda
Rwanda Rural Development Assn. **[IO]**, Kigali, Rwanda
Rwanda Rural Rehabilitation Initiative **[IO]**, Kigali, Rwanda
Rwanda Tours and Travel Assn. **[IO]**, Kigali, Rwanda
Rwanda Women's Network **[IO]**, Kigali, Rwanda
Rwanda Works **[IO]**, Kigali, Rwanda
Rwandan Natl. Assn. of the Deaf **[IO]**, Kigali, Rwanda
Rwandan Red Cross **[IO]**, Kigali, Rwanda
Rwandese Assn. of Local Govt. Authorities **[IO]**, Kigali, Rwanda
Ryan's Reach **[16782]**, 22 Panorama, Coto de Caza, CA 92679, (949)733-0046
Rybarske Sdruzeni Ceske Republiky **[★IO]**
Ryukyu Philatelic Specialist Soc. **[22070]**, PO Box 240177, Charlotte, NC 28224-0177
Ryukyu Philatelic Specialist Soc. **[22070]**, PO Box 240177, Charlotte, NC 28224-0177

S

Saab Club of North Am. **[21161]**, 30 Puritan Dr., Port Chester, NY 10573
Saathi **[IO]**, Mumbai, India
Sabah Family Planning Assn. **[IO]**, Kota Kinabalu, Malaysia
Sabbath
 Bible Sabbath Assn. **[20229]**
 Lord's Day Alliance of the U.S. **[20230]**
 Seventh Day Baptist World Fed. **[19331]**
Sabre Found. **[17921]**, 872 Massachusetts Ave., Ste. 2-1, Cambridge, MA 02139, (617)868-3510
Sabre Found. **[17921]**, 872 Massachusetts Ave., Ste. 2-1, Cambridge, MA 02139, (617)868-3510
Sabu Help **[12962]**, PO Box 912, La Grande, OR 97850, (801)834-4992
Sabun ve Deterjan Sanayicileri Dernegi **[★IO]**
Sackville Rivers Assn. **[IO]**, Lower Sackville, NS, Canada
Sacred Cat of Burma Fanciers **[21257]**, 5395 Ridge Ave. SW, East Sparta, OH 44626-2332, (330)484-4739
Sacred Dance Guild **[9565]**, Pat Troy, Admin., 550M Ritchie Hwy., No. 271, Severna Park, MD 21146, (877)422-8678
Sacred Dance Guild **[9565]**, Pat Troy, Admin., 550M Ritchie Hwy., No. 271, Severna Park, MD 21146, (877)422-8678
Sacred Dying Found. **[11747]**, PO Box 210328, San Francisco, CA 94121, (415)585-9455
Sacred Earth Network **[4302]**, 93A Glasheen Rd., Petersham, MA 01366, (978)724-0120
Sacred Earth Network **[4302]**, 93A Glasheen Rd., Petersham, MA 01366, (978)724-0120
Sacred Heart League **[19492]**, PO Box 300, Walls, MS 38680-0300, (800)232-9079
Sacred Journey **[★19654]**
Sacred Journey **[★19654]**
Sacred Passage, NatureQuest **[★12224]**
Sacred Passage, NatureQuest **[★12224]**
Sacred Passage and the Way of Nature Fellowship **[12224]**, PO Box 3388, Tucson, AZ 85722-3388, (520)623-3588
Sacred Passage and the Way of Nature Fellowship **[12224]**, PO Box 3388, Tucson, AZ 85722-3388, (520)623-3588
Sacro Occipital Res. Soc. **[★14144]**
Sacro Occipital Res. Soc. **[★14144]**
Sacro Occipital Res. Soc. Intl. **[14144]**, PO Box 24361, Overland Park, KS 66283, (239)513-9800
Sacro Occipital Res. Soc. Intl. **[14144]**, PO Box 24361, Overland Park, KS 66283, (239)513-9800
Sacro Occipital Technique Org. U.S.A. **[14145]**, PO Box 1357, Sparta, NC 28675, (336)793-6524

Reference to "IO" in place of a book number signifies that the association may be found in the 50th edition of International Organizations.

SADC Plant Genetic Resources Centre [IO], Lusaka, Zambia
Saddle, Harness and Allied Trades Assn. [2205], Proleptic, Inc., PO Box 497, Belgrade, ME 04917, (207)495-3600
SADSA [★10587]
SAE Intl. [6243], 400 Commonwealth Dr., Warrendale, PA 15096-0001, (724)776-4841
SAE Intl. [6243], 400 Commonwealth Dr., Warrendale, PA 15096-0001, (724)776-4841
SAE Ser. Tech. Prog. Off. - Address unknown since 2011.
SAF - The Center for Commercial Floriculture [★1369]
Safari Club Intl. [5121], 4800 W Gates Pass Rd., Tucson, AZ 85745-9490, (520)620-1220
Safari Club Intl. [5121], 4800 W Gates Pass Rd., Tucson, AZ 85745-9490, (520)620-1220
Safaris
  North Amer. Hunting Club [22700]
SAFE Assn. [6095], PO Box 130, Creswell, OR 97426-0130, (541)895-3012
SAFE-BioPharma Assn. [2707], 1 Bridge Plz., Ste. 275, Fort Lee, NJ 07024, (201)849-4545
Safe Energy Communication Coun. - Defunct.
Safe Haven Proj. - Address unknown since 2011.
Safe Kids Canada [IO], Toronto, ON, Canada
Safe Kids Worldwide [11400], 1301 Pennsylvania Ave. NW, Ste. 1000, Washington, DC 20004-1707, (202)662-0600
Safe Passage [11401], The Sparhawk Mill, 81 Bridge St., Ste. 104, Yarmouth, ME 04096, (207)846-1188
Safe Passage [11401], The Sparhawk Mill, 81 Bridge St., Ste. 104, Yarmouth, ME 04096, (207)846-1188
Safe Sitter [11159], 8604 Allisonville Rd., Ste. 248, Indianapolis, IN 46250-1597, (317)596-5001
Safe States Alliance [18581], 2200 Century Pkwy., Ste. 700, Atlanta, GA 30345, (770)690-9000
Safe and Vault Technicians Assn. [3226], 3500 Easy St., Dallas, TX 75247, (214)819-9771
Safe Water Coalition - Defunct.
Safe Water Network [13429], 10 Saugatuck Ave., Westport, CT 06880, (203)341-8865
Safely in Mothers Arms [★13033]
Safer Racer Tour [13006], 4537 Orphanage Rd., Concord, NC 28027, (704)795-7474
Safer Soc. Found. [11733], PO Box 340, Brandon, VT 05733-0340, (802)247-3132
Safer Soc. Prog. and Press [★11733]
SaferAfrica [IO], Pretoria, Republic of South Africa
Safety
  AAA Found. for Traffic Safety [12971]
  Advocates for Highway and Auto Safety [12972]
  Amer. Assn. for Horsemanship Safety [12973]
  Amer. Assn. of Safety Councils [12974]
  Amer. Assn. of Safety Councils [12974]
  Amer. Avalanche Assn. [12975]
  Amer. Biological Safety Assn. [3134]
  Amer. Boating Assn. [22315]
  Amer. Fire Sprinkler Assn. [3135]
  Amer. Highway Users Alliance [12976]
  Amer. Soc. of Medication Safety Officers [14869]
  Amer. Soc. of Safety Engineers [7345]
  Amer. Traffic Safety Services Assn. [3136]
  Arts, Crafts and Theatre Safety [12977]
  Assn. for the Advancement of Automotive Medicine [12978]
  Assn. of Needle-Free Injection Mfrs. [2330]
  Assn. of Public-Safety Communications Officials Intl. [5960]
  Assn. of Public-Safety Communications Officials Intl. [5960]
  Assn. of State Dam Safety Officials [5961]
  Automatic Fire Alarm Assn. [3137]
  Bicycle Helmet Safety Inst. [12979]
  Bd. of Certified Hazard Control Mgt. [3138]
  Bd. of Certified Prdt. Safety Mgt. [3139]
  Bd. of Certified Safety Professionals [7346]
  Building Security Coun. [3210]
  Canadian Assn. of Road Safety Professionals [15848]
  Center for Auto Safety [12980]
  Central Sta. Alarm Assn. [3140]

Cherokee Pilots' Assn. [20887]
Citizens for Reliable and Safe Highways [18576]
Coalition for Safe Community Needle Disposal [14842]
Common Ground Alliance [12981]
Coun. for Amusement and Recreational Equip. Safety [5962]
Dam Safety Coalition [13418]
Document Security Alliance [5539]
driveAWARE [12982]
Energy Training Coun. [6723]
Farm Safety 4 Just Kids [12983]
Fire Dept. Safety Officers Assn. [5963]
Fire Equip. Mfrs'. Assn. [3141]
Fire Suppression Systems Assn. [3142]
Found. for Aquatic Injury Prevention [12984]
Harley Hummer Club [21929]
InfraGard Natl. Members Alliance [5968]
Insurance Inst. for Highway Safety [12985]
Intl. Assn. for Bridge Maintenance and Safety [6369]
Intl. Assn. of Certified Surveillance Professionals [3213]
Intl. Campaign to Ban Landmines [17553]
Intl. Coalition for the Responsibility to Protect [18498]
Intl. Fed. of Competitive Eating [22982]
Intl. HACCP Alliance [4809]
Intl. Municipal Signal Assn. [5964]
Intl. Municipal Signal Assn. [5964]
Intl. Safety Equip. Assn. [3143]
Intl. Safety Equip. Assn. [3143]
Intl. Sharps Injury Prevention Soc. [16629]
Intl. Sharps Injury Prevention Soc. [16629]
Intl. Soc. for Agricultural Safety and Hea. [12986]
Intl. Soc. of Air Safety Investigators [12987]
Intl. Soc. of Air Safety Investigators [12987]
Intl. Sys. Safety Soc. [3144]
Internet Keep Safe Coalition [17996]
Kidpower Teenpower Fullpower Intl. [12988]
Kidpower Teenpower Fullpower Intl. [12988]
Kids and Cars [18577]
Knights of Life Motorcycle Club [12989]
Lightning Protection Inst. [3145]
Mothers Against Drunk Driving [12990]
Motorcycle Safety Found. [3146]
Natl. Alliance for the Primary Prevention of Sharps Injuries [16630]
Natl. Assn. Citizens on Patrol [12991]
Natl. Assn. of Fire Equip. Distributors [3147]
Natl. Assn. of Professional Accident Reconstruction Specialists [5965]
Natl. Assn. of State Motorcycle Safety Administrators [5966]
Natl. Assn. of Triads [12992]
Natl. Assn. of Women Highway Safety Leaders [12993]
Natl. Drowning Prevention Alliance [12994]
Natl. Fire Protection Assn. [12995]
Natl. Fire Sprinkler Assn. [3148]
Natl. Floor Safety Inst. [3149]
Natl. Inst. for Farm Safety [12986]
Natl. Motorists Assn. [13335]
Natl. Operating Comm. on Standards for Athletic Equip. [3150]
Natl. Org. of Alternative Programs [16631]
Natl. Prog. for Playground Safety [18578]
Natl. Safe Boating Coun. [12996]
Natl. Safety Coun. [12997]
Natl. Safety Mgt. Soc. [12998]
Natl. Student Safety Prog. [18579]
Natl. Traffic Incident Mgt. Coalition [13330]
Natl. Water Safety Cong. [12999]
Natl. Water Safety Cong. [12999]
Natl. Whistleblower Center [13000]
NEHRP Coalition [7402]
Network of Employers for Traffic Safety [18580]
Oper. Lifesaver [13001]
Oper. Lifesaver [13001]
Org. of Spirit Indus. Providers [22452]
Partnership for Safe Driving [13002]
Photoluminescent Safety Products Assn. [19537]
Physical Security Interoperability Alliance [6819]
Physicians Coalition for Injectable Safety [14181]
Pipeline Assn. for Public Awareness [2755]

Professional Airways Systems Specialists [23155]
Professional Climbing Instructors Assn. [22455]
REACT Intl. [5967]
REACT Intl. [5967]
Recording Artists, Actors and Athletes Against Drunk Driving [13003]
Recording Artists, Actors and Athletes Against Drunk Driving [13003]
RID U.S.A. [13004]
Roadway Safety Found. [13005]
Safe States Alliance [18581]
Safer Racer Tour [13006]
Safety Equip. Distributors Assn. [3151]
Safety Equip. Inst. [3152]
SafetyBeltSafe U.S.A. [18582]
Security Anal. and Risk Mgt. Assn. [3227]
Sheet Metal Occupational Hea. Inst. Trust [13007]
Specialty Vehicle Inst. of Am. I ATV Safety Inst. [13008]
Students Against Destructive Decisions [13009]
Terra Segura Intl. [17559]
Traffic Records Comm. [13010]
Trans. Safety Equip. Inst. [3153]
Truck Safety Coalition [13011]
Underwriters Labs. [3154]
Underwriters' Labs. of Canada [9222]
United Lightning Protection Assn. [3155]
Univ. of Iowa Injury Prevention Res. Center [7347]
Veterans of Safety [13012]
Voluntary Protection Prog. Assn. for Constr. [15910]
World Safety Org. [18583]
World Safety Org. [18583]
Safety Assessment Fed. [IO], London, United Kingdom
Safety Center; Natl. School [8821]
Safety Education
  Amer. Assn. of Safety Councils [12974]
  driveAWARE [12982]
  Partnership for Safe Driving [13002]
Safety Equip. Distributors Assn. [3151], 2105 Laurel Bush Rd., Ste. 200, Bel Air, MD 21015, (443)640-1065
Safety Equip. Inst. [3152], 1307 Dolley Madison Blvd., Ste. 3A, McLean, VA 22101, (703)442-5732
Safety Glazing Certification Coun. [614], PO Box 730, Sackets Harbor, NY 13685-0730, (315)646-2234
Safety and Hea. Assn; Semiconductor Environmental, [6672]
Safety, Health, and Environmental Resource Center Intl. - Defunct.
Safety Net Hospitals for Pharmaceutical Access [16213], 1101 15th St. NW, Ste. 910, Washington, DC 20005, (202)552-5850
Safety Pharmacology Soc. [16214], 1821 Michael Faraday Dr., Ste. 300, Reston, VA 20190, (703)547-0874
SafetyBeltSafe U.S.A. [18582], PO Box 553, Altadena, CA 91003, (310)222-6860
S'Affirmer Ensemble [★IO]
Sahabat Alam Malaysia [★IO]
Sahaya Intl. [12365], Koen Van Rompay, Sec.-Treas., 2949 Portage Bay Ave., Apt. No. 195, Davis, CA 95616, (530)756-9074
Sahil [IO], Islamabad, Pakistan
Sahko-ja teleurakoitsijaliitto [★IO]
Sahkoinsinooriliitto [★IO]
Saigon Mission Assn. [18764], 1135 Devonshire Dr., San Diego, CA 92107, (619)225-1180
Saigon Mission Assn. [18764], 1135 Devonshire Dr., San Diego, CA 92107, (619)225-1180
Sail Am. [463], 850 Aquidneck Ave., Unit B-4, Middletown, RI 02842-7244, (401)841-0900
Sail and Life Training Soc. [IO], Victoria, BC, Canada
Sail Training Assn; Amer. [22317]
Sailing Assn; Amer. [22318]
Sailing Assn; Annapolis Naval [22321]
Sailing Assn; Catalina 22 Natl. [22326]
Sailing Assn; Flying Scot [22335]
Sailing Assn. of the Principality of Liechtenstein [IO], Schaan, Liechtenstein
Sailing Assn. of Zimbabwe [IO], Harare, Zimbabwe

A star before a book entry number signifies that the name is not listed separately, but is mentioned within the entry.

Sailing Barge Assn. [IO], Bournemouth, United Kingdom
Sailing Class Assn; Interlake [22344]
Sailing and Cruising Assn. [IO], London, United Kingdom
Sailing Fed. of Azerbaijan [IO], Baku, Azerbaijan
Sailing Fed. of Peru [IO], Callao, Peru
SailMail Assn. [6679], 39270 Paseo Padre Pkwy., No. 850, Fremont, CA 94538, (619)980-6215
Sailors for the Sea [4135], 18 Market Sq., Newport, RI 02840, (401)846-8900
Sailors' Union of the Pacific [23250], 450 Harrison St., San Francisco, CA 94105, (415)777-3400
Saint Andrew's Soc. of the State of New York [19225], 150 E 55th St., Ste. 3, New York, NY 10022, (212)223-4248
Saint Andrew's Ukrainian Orthodox Soc. [18739], Vitali Vizir, 1023 Yorkshire Dr., Los Altos, CA 94024, (440)582-1051
Saint Andrew's Ukrainian Orthodox Soc. [18739], Vitali Vizir, 1023 Yorkshire Dr., Los Altos, CA 94024, (440)582-1051
St. Anthony's Guild [20087], 4 Jersey St., East Rutherford, NJ 07073-1012, (973)778-1915
Saint Bernard Club of Am. [21644], Cheryl Zappala, Corresponding Sec., 1043 S 140th St., Seattle, WA 98168, (206)242-7480
St. Clare's Home for Children [★13596]
St. Clare's Home Properties [★13596]
Saint Croix Hotel and Tourism Assn. [1773], PO Box 24238, Gallows Bay, St. Croix, VI 00824, (340)773-7117
Saint Croix Hotel and Tourism Assn. [1773], PO Box 24238, Gallows Bay, St. Croix, VI 00824, (340)773-7117
Saint Francis Burial and Counseling Soc. [★13317]
St. Francis Center [★13317]
St. Gabriel Possenti Soc. [17689], PO Box 2844, Arlington, VA 22202-0844, (202)239-8005
St. George Assn. of the U.S.A. - Defunct.
St. Helena, Ascension, and Tristan da Cunha Philatelic Soc. [22071], Mr. Tom Bowman, Sec., 901 Aspen Dr., Mountain Top, PA 18707-9104
St. Helens Chamber of Commerce [IO], St. Helens, United Kingdom
Saint Hubert Soc. of America - Defunct.
Saint John of Damascus Assn. of Orthodox Iconographers, Iconologists, and Architects - Defunct.
Saint John River Salmon Anglers Assn. [IO], Fredericton, NB, Canada
St. John's Guild - The Floating Hosp. [★15055]
Saint Joseph Congregation [IO], Rome, Italy
St. Joseph Grain Exchange - Defunct.
Saint Jude Children's Res. Hosp. [14096], 262 Danny Thomas Pl., Memphis, TN 38105, (901)595-3300
St. Jude League [19493], 205 W Monroe St., Chicago, IL 60606-5013, (312)544-8230
Saint Karl Borromaus Assn. for the Dissemination of Good Literature [IO], Bonn, Germany
St. Kitt-Nevis Chamber of Indus. and Commerce [IO], Basseterre, St. Kitts and Nevis
St. Kitts Lawn Tennis Assn. [IO], Basseterre, St. Kitts and Nevis
Saint Kitts and Nevis Amateur Athletic Assn. [IO], Basseterre, St. Kitts and Nevis
St. Kitts/Nevis Assn. of Disabled Persons [IO], Basseterre, St. Kitts and Nevis
St. Kitts - Nevis Football Assn. [IO], Basseterre, St. Kitts and Nevis
St. Kitts and Nevis Hotel and Tourism Assn. [IO], Basseterre, St. Kitts and Nevis
St. Kitts/Nevis Netball Assn. [IO], Basseterre, St. Kitts and Nevis
St. Kitts and Nevis Olympic Comm. [IO], Basseterre, St. Kitts and Nevis
St. Kitts and Nevis Red Cross Soc. [IO], Basseterre, St. Kitts and Nevis
St. Kitts and Nevis Taekwondo Fed. [IO], Basseterre, St. Kitts and Nevis
Saint Kitts-Nevis Tourist Off. [★23344]
Saint Kitts Tourism Authority [23344], 414 E 75th St., Ste. 5, New York, NY 10021, (212)535-1234
St. Lawrence Shipoperators [IO], Quebec, QC, Canada

Saint Louis Blueliners [★23899]
St. Louis Railway Historical Soc. [★10502]
Saint Lucia Amateur Swimming Assn. [IO], Castries, St. Lucia
St. Lucia Animal Protection Soc. [IO], Castries, St. Lucia
St. Lucia Arthritis and Lupus Assn. [IO], Castries, St. Lucia
Saint Lucia Athletics Assn. [IO], Castries, St. Lucia
St. Lucia Chamber of Commerce, Indus. and Agriculture [IO], Castries, St. Lucia
St. Lucia Hotel and Tourism Assn. [IO], Castries, St. Lucia
St. Lucia Indus. and Small Bus. Assn. [IO], Castries, St. Lucia
St. Lucia Lawn Tennis Assn. [IO], Castries, St. Lucia
St. Lucia Mfrs'. Assn. [IO], Castries, St. Lucia
St. Lucia Netball Assn. [IO], Castries, St. Lucia
St. Lucia Planned Parenthood Assn. [IO], Castries, St. Lucia
St. Lucia Red Cross [IO], Castries, St. Lucia
St. Lucia Sailing Assn. [IO], Castries, St. Lucia
Saint Lucia Shooting Assn. [IO], Castries, St. Lucia
St. Lucia Tourist Bd. [IO], Castries, St. Lucia
Saint Lucia Tourist Bd. [23345], 800 2nd Ave., 9th Fl., New York, NY 10017, (212)867-2950
St. Maarten Hospitality and Trade Assn. [IO], Philipsburg, Netherlands Antilles
St. Mary's Coll. of California Alumni Assn. [18897], PO Box 3400, Moraga, CA 94575-3400, (925)631-4200
Saint Nicholas Soc. of the City of New York [20660], Jill Spiller, Exec. Dir., 20 W 44th St., Rm. 508, New York, NY 10036-6603, (212)991-9944
Saint Patrick's Missionary Soc. [IO], Kiltegan, Ireland
St. Paul Soc. [IO], Islamabad, Pakistan
Saint Photios Found. [19807], PO Box 1960, St. Augustine, FL 32085, (904)829-8205
St. Photios Greek Orthodox Natl. Shrine [★19807]
St. Vincent and the Grenadines Natl. Olympic Comm. [IO], Kingstown, St. Vincent and the Grenadines
St. Vincent and the Grenadines Netball Assn. [IO], Kingstown, St. Vincent and the Grenadines
St. Vincent and the Grenadines Red Cross [IO], Kingstown, St. Vincent and the Grenadines
St. Vincent Pallotti Center for Apostolic Development [20088], 415 Michigan Ave. NE, Washington, DC 20017, (202)529-3330
Saint Vincent de Paul Soc. - Australia [IO], Deakin West, Australia
Saint Vincent de Paul Soc. - Lesotho [IO], Maseru, Lesotho
St. Vincent and The Grenadines Lawn Tennis Assn. [IO], Kingstown, St. Vincent and the Grenadines
Saints Alive in Jesus [19771], PO Box 1347, Issaquah, WA 98027, (800)861-9888
Saints' Stories [19494], 520 Oliphant Ln., Middletown, RI 02842-4600, (401)849-5421
Sakhartvelos Mtsvaneta Modzraoba [★IO]
Salad Mfrs. Assn. [★1428]
Saleeby-Saliba Assn. of Families [20581], PO Box 87094, Fayetteville, NC 28304
Saleen Club of Am. [21162], 6181 Linden Dr. E, West Bend, WI 53095, (414)234-7472
Salem Hebrew Lutheran Mission [★19756]
Salers Assn. of Canada [IO], Carstairs, AB, Canada
Salers Cattle Soc. of the UK and Ireland [IO], Shrewsbury, United Kingdom
Sales
 Accountants Motivational Marketing Org. [2]
 Amer. Assn. of Inside Sales Professionals [3156]
 Direct Selling Assn. [3157]
 Direct Selling Assn. of New Zealand [21933]
 Direct Selling Assn. - South Africa [9514]
 Direct Selling Educ. Found. [3158]
 Direct Selling Educ. Found. [3158]
 Direct Selling Women's Alliance [3159]
 Foodservice Gp. [3160]
 Foodservice Gp. [3160]
 Gift and Home Trade Assn. [3161]
 Gift Sales Manager Assn. [3162]
 Marketing Agencies Assn. Worldwide [3163]
 Marketing Agencies Assn. Worldwide [3163]
 Natl. Assn. of Sales Professionals [3164]

 Natl. Field Selling Assn. [3165]
 Professional Soc. for Sales and Marketing Training [3166]
 Promotion Marketing Assn. [2422]
 Sales and Marketing Executives Intl. [3167]
 Sales and Marketing Executives Intl. [3167]
 Soc. of Pharmaceutical and Biotech Trainers [3168]
 World Fed. of Direct Selling Associations [3169]
 World Fed. of Direct Selling Associations [3169]
Sales Assn. of the Graphic Arts - Defunct.
Sales Exchange for Refugee Rehabilitation and Vocation [3488], PO Box 365, New Windsor, MD 21776-0365, (608)255-0440
Sales Exchange for Refugee Rehabilitation and Vocation [3488], PO Box 365, New Windsor, MD 21776-0365, (608)255-0440
Sales and Marketing Executives Intl. [3167], PO Box 1390, Sumas, WA 98295-1390, (312)893-0751
Sales and Marketing Executives Intl. [3167], PO Box 1390, Sumas, WA 98295-1390, (312)893-0751
Salesian Lay Missioners [★20089]
Salesian Lay Missioners [★20089]
Salesian Missioners [20089], 2 Lefevre Ln., New Rochelle, NY 10801-5710, (914)633-8344
Salesian Missioners [20089], 2 Lefevre Ln., New Rochelle, NY 10801-5710, (914)633-8344
Salesian Volunteers [★20089]
Salesian Volunteers [★20089]
Salisbury Hunt Club [IO], Salisbury, Australia
Salisbury Sound Assn. [20725], Capt. Marian Bruce, Sec., 813 Branding Iron St. SE, Albuquerque, NM 87123, (505)293-3841
Salisbury Univ. I Ward Museum of Wildfowl Art [9252], 909 S Schumaker Dr., Salisbury, MD 21804, (410)742-4988
Sallie Mae Fund [8194], 11100 USA Pkwy., Fishers, IN 46037
Salmagundi Club [9317], 47 5th Ave., New York, NY 10003, (212)255-7740
Salmon Preservation Assn. for the Waters of Newfoundland [IO], Corner Brook, NL, Canada
Salmon and Trout Assn. [IO], London, United Kingdom
Salmonid Assn. of Eastern Newfoundland [IO], St. John's, NL, Canada
Salt Inst. [2507], 700 N Fairfax St., Ste. 600, Alexandria, VA 22314-2085, (703)549-4648
Salt Producers Assn. [★2507]
Salt Shaker Collectors Club [★21304]
Salt Water Fly Rodders of Am. [★22578]
Salters' Company [IO], London, United Kingdom
Salters' Inst. [IO], London, United Kingdom
Saltire Soc. [IO], Edinburgh, United Kingdom
Saluki Club of Am. [21645], Terry Smith, Futurity Sec., PO Box 1367, Placitas, NM 87043, (505)771-8459
Saluki Tree of Life Alliance [11878], 3701 Sacramento St., No. 345, San Francisco, CA 94118-1705
Salute Military Golf Assn. [22624], PO Box 83893, Gaithersburg, MD 20883, (301)500-7449
Salute Our Services [11107], 2100 Reston Pkwy., Ste. 300, Reston, VA 20191, (703)234-1773
Salvador Sailing Fed. [IO], San Salvador, El Salvador
Salvadoran Amer. Leadership and Educational Fund [17603], 1625 W Olympic Blvd., Ste. 718, Los Angeles, CA 90015, (213)480-1052
Salvadoran Amer. Leadership and Educational Fund [17603], 1625 W Olympic Blvd., Ste. 718, Los Angeles, CA 90015, (213)480-1052
Salvadoran Amer. Medical Soc. [15326], 1631 N Loop W, No. 570, Houston, TX 77008, (713)864-1150
Salvadoran Amer. Medical Soc. [15326], 1631 N Loop W, No. 570, Houston, TX 77008, (713)864-1150
Salvadoran Amer. Natl. Network [18979], 2845 W 7th St., Los Angeles, CA 90005
Salvadoran Assn. of Industrials [IO], San Salvador, El Salvador
Salvadoran Chamber of the Constr. Indus. [IO], San Salvador, El Salvador
Salvadoran Chamber of Tourism [IO], San Salvador, El Salvador

Reference to "IO" in place of a book number signifies that the association may be found in the 50th edition of International Organizations.

Encyclopedia of Associations, 51st Edition

3141

Salvadoran Demographic Assn. **[IO]**, San Salvador, El Salvador

Salvadoran Exporters' Assn. **[IO]**, San Salvador, El Salvador

Salvadoran Soc. of Gynecological Endoscopy and Medicine **[IO]**, San Salvador, El Salvador

Salvadoran Soc. of Dermatology **[IO]**, San Salvador, El Salvador

Salvati Copiii Romania **[★IO]**

Salvation Army **[13201]**, PO Box 269, Alexandria, VA 22313, (703)684-5500

Salvation Army **[13201]**, PO Box 269, Alexandria, VA 22313, (703)684-5500

Salvation Army **[★13172]**

Salvation Army - Caribbean Territory **[IO]**, Kingston, Jamaica

Salvation Army Home League - Intl. **[IO]**, London, United Kingdom

Salvation Army Intl. HQ **[IO]**, London, United Kingdom

Salvation Army UK and Ireland **[IO]**, London, United Kingdom

Salvation Army Women's, Adult and Family Ministries - New Zealand **[IO]**, Wellington, New Zealand

Salvation Army Women's Ministries **[IO]**, Wellington, New Zealand

Salzburg Global Seminar **[9870]**, 1730 Pennsylvania Ave. NW, Ste. 250, Washington, DC 20006, (202)637-7683

Sam Adams Alliance **[17753]**, 400 W Erie, Ste. 407, Chicago, IL 60654, (312)920-0080

Sam Davis Memorial Assn. **[10691]**, 1399 Sam Davis Rd., Smyrna, TN 37167, (615)459-2341

SAMA Gp. of Associations **[3180]**, PO Box 428, Fairfax, VA 22038, (703)836-1360

Samahang Malakolohiya ng Pilipinas **[★IO]**

Samanbaya no Kai **[★IO]**

Samantha Smith Found. - Defunct.

Samarbetsnamnden for Folklig Dans **[★IO]**

Samarbetsorganisationen for Emballagefragor i Skandinavien **[★IO]**

Samaritan Lay Missioners - Defunct.

Samaritans **[★20090]**

Samaritans **[★20090]**

Samaritans - England **[IO]**, Ewell, United Kingdom

Samaritan's Feet **[11402]**, 1900 Associates Ln., Charlotte, NC 28217, (704)341-1630

Samaritans Intl. **[20090]**, 370 E Cedar St., Moores-ville, NC 28115-2806, (704)663-7951

Samaritans Intl. **[20090]**, 370 E Cedar St., Moores-ville, NC 28115-2806, (704)663-7951

Samaritan's Purse **[20000]**, PO Box 3000, Boone, NC 28607, (828)262-1980

Samaritans - Western Australia **[IO]**, Subiaco, Australia

Samband Islenskra Auglysingastofa **[★IO]**

Sambhav **[IO]**, Gwalior, India

Samfundet til Udgivelse of Dansk Musik **[★IO]**

Samfunnsokonomenes Forening **[★IO]**

Sammy Kershaw Fan Club **[23890]**, 833 Todd Preis Dr., Nashville, TN 37221

SamNordisk Skogforskning **[★IO]**

Samoa Assn. of Women Graduates **[IO]**, Apia, Western Samoa

Samoa Badminton Assn. **[IO]**, Apia, Western Samoa

Samoa Chamber of Commerce and Indus. **[IO]**, Apia, Western Samoa

Samoa Family Hea. Assn. **[IO]**, Apia, Western Samoa

Samoa Nurses Assn. **[IO]**, Apia, Western Samoa

Samoa Red Cross Soc. **[IO]**, Apia, Western Samoa

Samoa Sailing Assn. **[IO]**, Apia, Western Samoa

Samoa Squash Rackets Assn. **[IO]**, Apia, Western Samoa

Samoa Taekwondo Fed. **[IO]**, Apia, Western Samoa

Samoa Tourism Authority **[IO]**, Apia, Western Samoa

Samojedhunde Klubben I Danmark **[★IO]**

Samoyed

Samoyed Club of Am. **[21646]**

Samoyed Club of Am. **[21646]**, Tasha Libby, Membership Chair, 44 Jenny Ln., Oxford, ME 04270-3348, (207)743-6273

Samtok Atvinnulifsins **[★IO]**

Samtok Idnadarins **[★IO]**

Samuel H. Kress Found. **[13147]**, 174 E 80th St., New York, NY 10075, (212)861-4993

Samuel Roberts Noble Found. **[3724]**, 2510 Sam Noble Pkwy., Ardmore, OK 73401, (580)223-5810

Samuel Rubin Found. **[13202]**, 777 United Nations Plz., New York, NY 10017-3521, (212)697-8945

San Diego County Railway Museum **[★10496]**

San Diego Railroad Museum **[★10496]**

San Francisco African Amer. Historical and Cultural Soc. **[9104]**, 762 Fulton St., 2nd Fl., San Francisco, CA 94102, (415)292-6172

San Francisco AIDS Found. **[13624]**, 1035 Market St., Ste. 400, San Francisco, CA 94103, (415)487-3000

San Francisco Camerawork **[9608]**, 657 Mission St., 2nd Fl., San Francisco, CA 94105-4104, (415)512-2020

San Francisco Maritime Natl. Park Assn. **[10128]**, PO Box 470310, San Francisco, CA 94147-0310, (415)561-6662

San Francisco Social Psychiatry Seminar **[★16341]**

San Francisco Social Psychiatry Seminar **[★16341]**

San Jose Rescue Mission **[★12825]**

San Juan 21 Class Assn. **[22388]**, 211 Gloria St., Greenville, NC 27858-8627, (252)355-6974

San Marino Soc. of Cardiology **[IO]**, Dogana, San Marino

San Marino Tennis Fed. **[IO]**, San Marino, San Marino

Sanayee Development Org. **[IO]**, Kabul, Afghanistan

Sanctuary Workers and Volunteers Assn. **[11035]**, PO Box 637, Boyd, TX 76023, (940)433-5091

Sandicast Collectors Guild **[20974]**, 3300 W Castor St., Santa Ana, CA 92704-3908, (714)424-0111

Sandplay Therapists of Am. **[16870]**, PO Box 4847, Walnut Creek, CA 94596, (925)825-9277

Sandtray Network **[16361]**, 1946 Clemens Rd., Oakland, CA 94602, (510)530-1383

Sandtray Network **[16361]**, 1946 Clemens Rd., Oakland, CA 94602, (510)530-1383

SANE Australia **[IO]**, South Melbourne, Australia

SANE/FREEZE: Campaign for Global Security **[★18213]**

SANE/FREEZE Educ. Fund **[★18214]**

Sanex WTA Tour **[★23061]**

Sanex WTA Tour **[★23061]**

Sangeet Natak Akademi **[★IO]**

Sanitarians

Amer. Acad. of Sanitarians **[16632]**

Sanitary Brass Inst. **[★2784]**

Sanitary Brass Inst. **[★2784]**

Sanitary Inst. of Am. **[★1866]**

Sanitary Inst. of Am. **[★1866]**

Sanitary Supply Wholesaling Assn. **[2259]**, PO Box 98, Swanton, OH 43558, (419)825-3055

Sanitation

Agua Muisne **[13411]**

Aguayuda **[13412]**

AIDIS-USA **[7348]**

AIDIS-USA Sect. **[7348]**

Amer. Restroom Assn. **[13013]**

Amer. Soc. of Sanitary Engg. **[7349]**

charity: water **[13414]**

A Child's Right **[13415]**

Clean Water for Haiti **[4991]**

Clean the World **[4869]**

Community Water Solutions **[13417]**

Give Clean Water **[13421]**

Global Water Challenge **[4993]**

H2O for Life **[13422]**

In Our Own Quiet Way **[13424]**

Millennium Water Alliance **[13427]**

Pan Amer. Center for Sanitary Engg. and Environmental Sciences **[14474]**

Primero Agua **[13428]**

Safe Water Network **[13429]**

SURGE **[13431]**

Thirst Relief Intl. **[13432]**

Water 1st Intl. **[13433]**

Water for Life Intl. **[13436]**

Water to Thrive **[13439]**

Water for Waslala **[13440]**

WaterAid Am. **[13441]**

WaterPartners Intl. **[13442]**

Sanomalehtien Liitto Tidningarnas Forbund **[★IO]**

Santa Am. **[11500]**, 308 Belrose Ave., Ste. 200 E, Daphne, AL 36526, (251)626-6609

Santa Barbara Medical Res. Found. **[★15843]**

Santa Cruz Mountain Vintners **[★5172]**

Santa Cruz Mountains Winegrowers Assn. **[5172]**, 7605-A Old Dominion Ct., Aptos, CA 95003, (831)685-8463

Santa Fe Indian School **[★10329]**

Santa Gertrudis Breeders Intl. **[3939]**, PO Box 1257, Kingsville, TX 78364, (361)592-9357

Santa Gertrudis Breeders Intl. **[3939]**, PO Box 1257, Kingsville, TX 78364, (361)592-9357

Santana 20 Class Assn. **[22389]**, 1266 Napa Creek Dr., Eugene, OR 97404, (541)517-8690

Santiago Chamber of Commerce **[IO]**, Santiago, Chile

Santini's Porpoise School **[★7041]**

Santo Domingo Chamber of Commerce and Produc-tion **[IO]**, Santo Domingo, Dominican Republic

Sao Tome and Principe Red Cross **[IO]**, Sao Tome, Sao Tome and Principe

Saq' Be': Org. for Mayan and Indigenous Spiritual Bodies **[9867]**, PO Box 31111, Santa Fe, NM 87594, (505)466-4044

Saq' Be': Org. for Mayan and Indigenous Spiritual Bodies **[9867]**, PO Box 31111, Santa Fe, NM 87594, (505)466-4044

Sarah Scaife Found. **[18493]**, One Oxford Ctre., 301 Grant St., Ste. 3900, Pittsburgh, PA 15219-6401, (412)392-2900

Sarah Scaife Found. **[18493]**, One Oxford Ctre., 301 Grant St., Ste. 3900, Pittsburgh, PA 15219-6401, (412)392-2900

Sarawak Campaign Comm. **[IO]**, Tokyo, Japan

Sarawak Teachers' Union **[IO]**, Kuching, Malaysia

Sarawak United People's Party **[IO]**, Kuching, Malaysia

Sarcoid Networking Assn. **[14418]**, 5302 S Sheridan Ave., Tacoma, WA 98408-3535, (253)826-7737

Sarcoma Alliance **[13977]**, 775 E Blithedale, No. 334, Mill Valley, CA 94941, (415)381-7236

SAREKA Cambodian Children's Arts **[IO]**, Siha-noukville, Cambodia

Sartre Soc. **[★10406]**

Sarvodaya U.S.A. **[11627]**, 122 State St., Ste. 510, Madison, WI 53703, (608)442-5945

SAS Global Forum **[6516]**, SAS Inst. Inc., 100 SAS Campus Dr., Cary, NC 27513-2414, (919)677-8000

SAS Global Forum **[6516]**, SAS Inst. Inc., 100 SAS Campus Dr., Cary, NC 27513-2414, (919)677-8000

SAS Users Gp. Intl. **[★6516]**

SAS Users Gp. Intl. **[★6516]**

Sasakawa Peace Found. **[IO]**, Tokyo, Japan

Saskatchewan 4-H Coun. **[IO]**, Saskatoon, SK, Canada

Saskatchewan Angus Assn. **[IO]**, Regina, SK, Canada

Saskatchewan Dental Therapists Assn. **[IO]**, Gull Lake, SK, Canada

Saskatchewan Environmental Soc. **[IO]**, Saskatoon, SK, Canada

Saskatchewan Horse Fed. **[IO]**, Regina, SK, Canada

Saskatchewan Hospice Palliative Care Assn. **[IO]**, Regina, SK, Canada

Saskatchewan Lib. Assn. **[IO]**, Regina, SK, Canada

Saskatchewan Music Festival Assn. **[IO]**, Regina, SK, Canada

Saskatchewan Snowboard Assn. **[IO]**, Lebret, SK, Canada

Saskatchewan Wheelchair Sports Assn. **[IO]**, Saska-toon, SK, Canada

SATELLIFE Global Hea. Info. Network **[14828]**, 30 California St., Watertown, MA 02472, (617)926-9400

SATELLIFE Global Hea. Info. Network **[14828]**, 30 California St., Watertown, MA 02472, (617)926-9400

Satellite Broadcasting and Communications Assn. **[3418]**, 1100 17th St. NW, Ste. 1150, Washington, DC 20036, (202)349-3620

Satellite Broadcasting and Communications Assn. **[3418]**, 1100 17th St. NW, Ste. 1150, Washington, DC 20036, (202)349-3620

Satellite Dealers Assn. Inc. **[★1100]**

Satellite Dealers Assn. Inc. **[★1100]**

A star before a book entry number signifies that the name is not listed separately, but is mentioned within the entry.

Satellite Dishes

Mobile Satellite Users Assn. **[7350]**

Satellite Indus. Assn. **[816]**, 1200 18th St. NW, Ste. 1001, Washington, DC 20036, (202)503-1560

Satellite TV Indus. Assn. **[★3418]**

Satellite TV Indus. Assn. **[★3418]**

Satellite Video Exchange Soc. **[IO]**, Vancouver, BC, Canada

SATS/EAF Assn. **[20686]**, Alvin Wilder, Treas., 2514 Hickory St., New Bern, NC 28562

Saudi Arabian Athletics Fed. **[IO]**, Riyadh, Saudi Arabia

Saudi Arabian Judo and Taekwondo Fed. **[IO]**, Riyadh, Saudi Arabia

Saudi Arabian Olympic Comm. **[IO]**, Riyadh, Saudi Arabia

Saudi Arabian Sports Medicine Assn. **[IO]**, Riyadh, Saudi Arabia

Saudi Arabian Tennis Fed. **[IO]**, Riyadh, Saudi Arabia

Saudi Arabian Weightlifting and Body Building Fed. **[IO]**, Riyadh, Saudi Arabia

Saudi Arabian Youth Hostels Assn. **[IO]**, Riyadh, Saudi Arabia

Saudi British Soc. **[IO]**, London, United Kingdom

Saudi Chap. of Epilepsy **[IO]**, Riyadh, Saudi Arabia

Saudi Osteoporosis Soc. **[IO]**, Riyadh, Saudi Arabia

Saudi Pediatric Assn. **[IO]**, Riyadh, Saudi Arabia

Saudi Physical Therapy Assn. **[IO]**, Riyadh, Saudi Arabia

Saudi Public Assistance for Pakistan Earthquake Victims **[IO]**, Islamabad, Pakistan

Saudi Soc. of Dermatology and Venereology **[IO]**, Riyadh, Saudi Arabia

Saudi Sports Fed. for Special Needs **[IO]**, Riyadh, Saudi Arabia

Saudi Squash Fed. **[IO]**, Riyadh, Saudi Arabia

Savannah Cat Club **[3864]**, 571 Millcross Rd., Lancaster, PA 17601

Savannah Cat Club **[3864]**, 571 Millcross Rd., Lancaster, PA 17601

Save-A-Baby **[★12936]**

Save-A-Vet **[11036]**, 387 Northgate Rd., Lindenhurst, IL 60046, (815)349-9647

Save Africa's Children **[11501]**, PO Box 8386, Los Angeles, CA 90008, (323)733-1048

Save America's Forests **[4136]**, 4 Lib. Ct. SE, Washington, DC 20003-1049, (202)544-9219

Save the Apollo Launch Tower **[★9086]**

Save a Baby - Defunct.

Save the Children **[11502]**, 54 Wilton Rd., Westport, CT 06880, (203)221-4030

Save the Children Australia **[IO]**, Fitzroy, Australia

Save the Children Australia - New South Wales Div. **[IO]**, Sydney, Australia

Save the Children Australia - South Australia Div. **[IO]**, Glenside, Australia

Save the Children Australia - Tasmania Div. **[IO]**, Hobart, Australia

Save the Children Australia - Victoria Div. **[IO]**, Fitzroy, Australia

Save the Children Australia - Western Australia Div. **[IO]**, West Perth, Australia

Save the Children Canada **[IO]**, Toronto, ON, Canada

Save the Children Denmark **[IO]**, Copenhagen, Denmark

Save the Children Dominican Republic **[IO]**, Santo Domingo, Dominican Republic

Save the Children Egypt **[IO]**, Cairo, Egypt

Save the Children Fiji **[IO]**, Suva, Fiji

Save the Children Finland **[IO]**, Helsinki, Finland

Save the Children Fund - Swaziland **[IO]**, Mbabane, Swaziland

Save the Children Germany **[IO]**, Berlin, Germany

Save the Children Hong Kong **[IO]**, Hong Kong, People's Republic of China

Save the Children Italia **[IO]**, Rome, Italy

Save the Children Korea **[IO]**, Seoul, Republic of Korea

Save the Children Netherlands **[IO]**, The Hague, Netherlands

Save the Children New Zealand **[IO]**, Wellington, New Zealand

Save the Children Norway **[IO]**, Oslo, Norway

Save the Children Romania **[IO]**, Bucharest, Romania

Save the Children Spain **[IO]**, Madrid, Spain

Save the Children Sweden **[IO]**, Stockholm, Sweden

Save the Children UK **[IO]**, London, United Kingdom

Save the Chimps **[11037]**, PO Box 12220, Fort Pierce, FL 34979, (772)429-0403

Save Darfur Coalition **[17744]**, 1025 Connecticut Ave. NW, Ste. 310, Washington, DC 20036, (800)917-2034

Save the Elephants **[IO]**, Nairobi, Kenya

Save a Family Plan **[12019]**, PO Box 610157, Port Huron, MI 48061-0157, (519)672-1115

Save a Family Plan **[12019]**, PO Box 610157, Port Huron, MI 48061-0157, (519)672-1115

Save the Frogs! **[4137]**, 303 Potrero St., No. 51, Santa Cruz, CA 95060, (831)621-6215

SAVE Intl. **[6964]**, 136 S Keowee St., Dayton, OH 45402, (937)224-7283

SAVE Intl. **[6964]**, 136 S Keowee St., Dayton, OH 45402, (937)224-7283

Save Life On Earth - Defunct.

Save the Manatee Club **[5122]**, 500 N Maitland Ave., Maitland, FL 32751, (407)539-0990

Save Our Barns Comm. - Defunct.

Save Our Constitution - Defunct.

Save Our Schools **[18704]**, Maureen P. Madden, Founder/CEO, PO Box 175, Annapolis, MD 21404, (410)552-5331

Save Our Seas **[4138]**, PO Box 813, Hanalei, HI 96714, (808)651-3452

Save Our Seas **[4138]**, PO Box 813, Hanalei, HI 96714, (808)651-3452

Save the Patient **[14740]**, 260 E Chestnut St., No. 1712, Chicago, IL 60611-2455, (312)440-0630

Save the Rain **[13430]**, PO Box 1510, Mount Shasta, CA 96067, (530)926-9999

Save the Redwoods League **[4139]**, 114 Sansome St., Ste. 1200, San Francisco, CA 94104-3823, (415)362-2352

Save the Refugees Fund **[★12739]**

Save the Refugees Fund **[★12739]**

Save Somali Women and Children **[IO]**, Mogadishu, Somalia

Save the Turtles **[5123]**, PO Box 738, Occidental, CA 95465, (707)538-8084

Save the Turtles **[5123]**, PO Box 738, Occidental, CA 95465, (707)538-8084

Save the Waves Coalition **[5007]**, PO Box 183, Davenport, CA 95017, (831)426-6169

Save the Whales **[5124]**, 1192 Waring St., Seaside, CA 93955, (831)899-9957

Save Yemen's Flora and Fauna **[4140]**, 1523 River Terrace Dr., East Lansing, MI 48823

Savers and Investors League - Address unknown since 2011.

SavetheInternet.com Coalition **[17997]**, Free Press Action Fund, 40 Main St., Ste. 301, Florence, MA 01062, (413)585-1533

Savez Klizackih Sportava Bosne I Hercegovine **[★IO]**

Saving Animals Via Educ. **[11038]**, PO Box 2961, Ponte Vedra Beach, FL 32004, (904)476-7532

Saving Antiquities for Everyone **[9131]**, PO Box 231172, New York, NY 10023-0020

Saving the Arts - Address unknown since 2011.

Saving Horses, Inc. **[12167]**, 8840 Hunter Pass, Alpine, CA 91901-2622, (619)445-2917

Saving Little Hearts **[14041]**, 5629 Barineau Ln., Knoxville, TN 37920-7907, (866)748-4605

Saving and Preserving Arts and Cultural Environments **[9202]**, 9053 Soquel Dr., Ste. 205, Aptos, CA 95003, (831)662-2907

Saving Wildlife Intl. **[5125]**, PO Box 2626, Malibu, CA 90265, (800)945-3794

Saving Wildlife Intl. **[5125]**, PO Box 2626, Malibu, CA 90265, (800)945-3794

Savings and Credit Co-operative League of South Africa **[IO]**, Roggebaai, Republic of South Africa

Sawin Soc. - Defunct.

SAY Soccer U.S.A. **[★22941]**

Say Yes to Better Sports for Kids **[★22461]**

SB Latex Coun. **[763]**, 1250 Connecticut Ave. NW, Ste. 700, Washington, DC 20036, (202)419-1500

SBGI **[IO]**, Kenilworth, United Kingdom

Scaffold Contractors Assn. **[★615]**

Scaffold Indus. Assn. **[615]**, 400 Admiral Blvd., Kansas City, MO 64106, (816)595-4860

Scaffolding, Shoring and Forming Inst. **[616]**, 1300 Sumner Ave., Cleveland, OH 44115, (216)241-7333

Scale Mfrs. Assn. **[3657]**, PO Box 26972, Columbus, OH 43226, (866)372-4627

Scale Ship Modelers Assn. of North Am. **[21909]**, 412 W Gard Dr., Crown Point, IN 46307-2342

Scale Warbird Racing Assn. **[21910]**, PO Box 328, Muncie, IN 47302

Scalp

Natl. Alopecia Areata Found. **[16633]**

Scandinavian

American-Scandinavian Found. **[10518]**

American-Scandinavian Found. **[10518]**

Independent Order of Svithiod **[19217]**

Scandinavian Tourist Boards **[23440]**

Soc. for the Advancement of Scandinavian Stud. **[8806]**

Scandinavian-Amer. Genealogical Soc. - Defunct.

Scandinavian Assn. for Gastrointestinal Motility **[IO]**, Goteborg, Sweden

Scandinavian Assn. for the Stud. of Pain **[IO]**, Oslo, Norway

Scandinavian Assn. for Thoracic Surgery **[IO]**, Turku, Finland

Scandinavian-Baltic Soc. for Parasitology **[IO]**, Daugavpils, Latvia

Scandinavian Bishops Conf. **[IO]**, Woodstock, United Kingdom

Scandinavian Collectors Club **[22072]**, Donald Brent, Exec. Sec., PO Box 13196, El Cajon, CA 92020

Scandinavian Collectors Club **[22072]**, Donald Brent, Exec. Sec., PO Box 13196, El Cajon, CA 92020

Scandinavian Copper Development Assn. **[IO]**, Espoo, Finland

Scandinavian Fraternity of America - Defunct.

Scandinavian Herpetological Soc. **[IO]**, Roskilde, Denmark

Scandinavian Inst. of Maritime Law **[IO]**, Oslo, Norway

Scandinavian Natl. Tourist Offices **[★23440]**

Scandinavian Neurosurgical Soc. **[IO]**, Stockholm, Sweden

Scandinavian Packaging Assn. **[IO]**, Taastrup, Denmark

Scandinavian Physiological Soc. **[IO]**, Uppsala, Sweden

Scandinavian Plant Physiology Soc. **[IO]**, Helsinki, Finland

Scandinavian Res. Coun. for Criminology **[IO]**, Reykjavik, Iceland

Scandinavian Seminar **[8376]**, 24 Dickinson St., Amherst, MA 01002-2310, (413)253-9736

Scandinavian Seminar **[8376]**, 24 Dickinson St., Amherst, MA 01002-2310, (413)253-9736

Scandinavian Soc. of Antimicrobial Chemotherapy **[IO]**, Skien, Norway

Scandinavian Soc. of Cataract and Refractive Surgery **[IO]**, Karlstad, Sweden

Scandinavian Soc. for Cell Toxicology **[IO]**, Kiel, Germany

Scandinavian Soc. of Clinical Physiology and Nuclear Medicine **[IO]**, Copenhagen, Denmark

Scandinavian Soc. of Glass Tech. **[IO]**, Vaxjo, Sweden

Scandinavian Soc. for Head and Neck Oncology **[IO]**, Bergen, Norway

Scandinavian Soc. for Lab. Animal Sci. **[IO]**, Tyreso, Sweden

Scandinavian Soc. for Prehistoric Art **[IO]**, Tanumshede, Sweden

Scandinavian Soc. for Prosthetic Dentistry **[IO]**, Arhus, Denmark

Scandinavian Soc. for Res. in CardioThoracic Surgery **[IO]**, Arhus, Denmark

Scandinavian Soc. for the Stud. of Diabetes **[IO]**, Trondheim, Norway

Scandinavian Tire and Rim Org. **[IO]**, Uppsala, Sweden

Scandinavian Tourist Boards **[23440]**, 655 3rd Ave., Ste. 1810, New York, NY 10017-5617, (212)885-9700

Reference to "IO" in place of a book number signifies that the association may be found in the 50th edition of International Organizations.

Scattering Resources **[12888]**, PO Box 725215, Atlanta, GA 31139

Scattering Resources **[12888]**, PO Box 725215, Atlanta, GA 31139

Scenarios U.S.A. **[18832]**, 80 Hanson Pl., Ste. 305, Brooklyn, NY 11217, (718)230-5125

Scenic Am. **[4303]**, 1250 Eye St. NW, Ste. 750, Washington, DC 20005, (202)638-0550

Schechter Day School Network **[8433]**, 820 2nd Ave., New York, NY 10017, (212)533-7800

Schedules Direct **[6557]**, 8613 42nd Ave. S, Seattle, WA 98118, (206)701-7800

Scherman Found. **[13203]**, 16 E 52nd St., Ste. 601, New York, NY 10022-5306, (212)832-3086

Schiffli Embroidery Inst. **[★3453]**

Schiffli Embroidery Mfrs. Promotion Found. **[★3453]**

Schiffli Embroidery Mfrs. Promotion Fund **[3453]**, 7 Commercial Ave., Fairview, NJ 07022

Schiffli Embroidery Promotion Coun. **[★3453]**

Schiffli Lace and Embroidery Mfrs. Assn. **[3454]**, 7 Commercial Ave., Fairview, NJ 07022, (201)654-3575

Schiffli Mfrs. Promotion Fund **[★3453]**

Schipperke Club of Am. **[21647]**, Beverly Henry, Membership Chair, 1129 Lake Bluff Dr., Little Elm, TX 75068-5301, (972)294-4371

Schizophrenia Intl. Res. Soc. **[15481]**, 5034-A Thoroughbred Ln., Brentwood, TN 37027

Schizophrenia Intl. Res. Soc. **[15481]**, 5034-A Thoroughbred Ln., Brentwood, TN 37027

Schizophrenia Ireland **[IO]**, Dublin, Ireland

Schizophrenia; North Amer. Soc. for Childhood Onset **[15479]**

Schizophrenia Soc. of Canada **[IO]**, Winnipeg, MB, Canada

Scholarly Publishing and Academic Resources Coalition **[2959]**, 21 Dupont Cir. NW, Ste. 800, Washington, DC 20036, (202)296-2296

Scholars for Peace in the Middle East **[18135]**, PO Box 48, Grantham, PA 17027-0048, (800)732-0999

Scholars for Peace in the Middle East **[18135]**, PO Box 48, Grantham, PA 17027-0048, (800)732-0999

Scholarship
Amer. Sociological Assn. | Honors Prog. **[23738]**
Assn. of African Women Scholars **[8807]**
Assn. of African Women Scholars **[8807]**
Assn. for Africanist Anthropology **[6133]**
Assn. for Borderlands Stud. **[8400]**
Assn. of Concerned African Scholars **[17147]**
Assn. of Marshall Scholars **[8808]**
Assn. of Marshall Scholars **[8808]**
Astronaut Scholars Honor Soc. **[23629]**
Beta Beta Beta **[23470]**
Beta Gamma Sigma **[23476]**
Beta Phi Mu **[23583]**
Beta Sigma Kappa **[23611]**
Delta Phi Epsilon Professional Foreign Ser. Sorority **[23529]**
Delta Sigma Delta **[23498]**
Gamma Sigma Delta **[23463]**
Intl. Alumni Assn. of Shri Mahavir Jain Vidyalaya **[19219]**
Intl. Soc. for the Scholarship of Teaching and Learning **[8809]**
Intl. Soc. for the Scholarship of Teaching and Learning **[8809]**
Mu Beta Psi **[23601]**
Natl. Assn. of Fellowships Advisors **[8810]**
Natl. Block and Bridle Club **[23464]**
Natl. Scholarship Providers Assn. **[8811]**
Natl. Scholarship Providers Assn. **[8811]**
Natl. Soc. of Collegiate Scholars **[8812]**
Natl. Soc. of High School Scholars **[8813]**
Phi Chi Medical Fraternity **[23594]**
Scholarship Am. **[8814]**
Sigma Alpha Iota Intl. Music Fraternity **[23605]**
Soc. for the Stud. of Early China **[7846]**
Scholarship Alumni
Assn. of Amer. Rhodes Scholars **[19218]**
Astronaut Scholars Honor Soc. **[23629]**
Intl. Alumni Assn. of Shri Mahavir Jain Vidyalaya **[19219]**
Intl. Alumni Assn. of Shri Mahavir Jain Vidyalaya **[19219]**
Scholarship Am. **[8814]**, 1550 Amer. Blvd. E, Ste. 155, Minneapolis, MN 55425, (952)830-7300

Scholarship Societies of the South **[★23551]**
Scholarship Societies of Texas **[★23551]**
Scholarships
Amer. Sociological Assn. | Honors Prog. **[23738]**
Astronaut Scholars Honor Soc. **[23629]**
Beta Beta Beta **[23470]**
Beta Gamma Sigma **[23476]**
Beta Phi Mu **[23583]**
Beta Sigma Kappa **[23611]**
Delta Phi Epsilon Professional Foreign Ser. Sorority **[23529]**
Delta Sigma Delta **[23498]**
Gamma Sigma Delta **[23463]**
Intl. Alumni Assn. of Shri Mahavir Jain Vidyalaya **[19219]**
Mu Beta Psi **[23601]**
Natl. Block and Bridle Club **[23464]**
Natl. Forensic Assn. **[8895]**
Sigma Alpha Iota Intl. Music Fraternity **[23605]**
Scholastic Rowing Assn. of Am. **[22858]**, PO Box 528, Berlin, NJ 08009
Schomburg Center for Res. in Black Culture **[9105]**, 515 Malcolm X Blvd., New York, NY 10037-1801, (212)491-2200
Schomburg Center for Res. in Black Culture **[9105]**, 515 Malcolm X Blvd., New York, NY 10037-1801, (212)491-2200
School Administrators and Supervisors Organizing Comm. **[★7656]**
School of the Americas Watch **[18426]**, PO Box 4566, Washington, DC 20017, (202)234-3440
School Boards
Inst. for the Transfer of Tech. to Educ. **[8314]**
Natl. Assn. of Diversity Officers in Higher Educ. **[8238]**
Natl. Assn. of State Boards of Educ. **[8815]**
Natl. School Boards Assn. **[8816]**
School and Community Safety Soc. of Am. of the Amer. Assn. for Active Lifestyles and Fitness - Address unknown since 2010.
School Facilities Coun. of Architecture, Educ. and Indus. **[★7662]**
School Facilities Coun. of Architecture, Educ. and Indus. **[★7662]**
School Hea. Division of Amer. Assn. for Hea., Physical Educ. and Recreation **[★16476]**
School and Home Off. Products Assn. **[★2582]**
School of Islamic Sufism **[★20249]**
School Journey Assn. **[IO]**, London, United Kingdom
School Leaders Scotland **[IO]**, Glasgow, United Kingdom
School Libraries Division of the Amer. Lib. Assn. **[★9952]**
School Lib. Assn. **[IO]**, Swindon, United Kingdom
School of Living **[9830]**, 215 Julian Woods Ln., Julian, PA 16844, (814)353-0130
School Nutrition Assn. **[8909]**, 120 Waterfront St., Ste. 300, Oxon Hill, MD 20745, (301)686-3100
School and Off. Products Network **[2582]**, 3131 Elbee Rd., Dayton, OH 45439, (937)610-3333
School Sci. and Mathematics Assn. **[8851]**, Oklahoma State Univ., Coll. of Educ., 245 Willard, Stillwater, OK 74078, (405)744-8018
School Sci. and Mathematics Assn. **[8851]**, Oklahoma State Univ., Coll. of Educ., 245 Willard, Stillwater, OK 74078, (405)744-8018
School Security
Intl. Assn. of Campus Law Enforcement Administrators **[8817]**
Intl. Assn. of Campus Law Enforcement Administrators **[8817]**
Natl. Alliance for Safe Schools **[8818]**
Natl. Assn. of School Rsrc. Officers **[8819]**
Natl. Assn. of School Safety and Law Enforcement Officers **[8820]**
Natl. School Safety Center **[8821]**
School Services
Educ. Conservancy **[7683]**
Natl. Assn. of Coll. Auxiliary Services **[3170]**
Natl. School Supply and Equip. Assn. **[3171]**
School and Off. Products Network **[2582]**
School Sisters of Notre Dame **[IO]**, Rome, Italy
School Social Work Assn. of Am. **[8872]**, PO Box 1086, Sumner, WA 98390
School Sport Fed. of Ukraine **[IO]**, Kiev, Ukraine

School Supplies
Natl. Assn. for Health Science Educ. Partnerships **[8318]**
Schoolboy Rowing Assn. of Am. **[★22858]**
Schools
Alliance for School Choice **[8822]**
Amer. Assn. of Classified School Employees **[23177]**
Amer. Collegiate Hockey Assn. **[22639]**
Assn. for the Advancement of Intl. Educ. **[8388]**
Assn. of Amer. Intl. Colleges and Universities **[8389]**
Assn. of Classical and Christian Schools **[8823]**
Assn. of Classical and Christian Schools **[8823]**
Assn. of Episcopal Colleges **[8162]**
Assn. of Latino Administrators and Superintendents **[7661]**
Better School Food **[8824]**
Brick by Brick for Tanzania! **[8739]**
Campaign for High School Equity **[13014]**
Chinese School Assn. in the U.S. **[8825]**
Circle of Women: Reach and Teach Across Borders **[13015]**
Coalition for Community Schools **[8826]**
Coalition on the Public Understanding of Sci. **[7365]**
Coll. Summit **[8234]**
Consciousness-Based Educ. Assn. **[8762]**
CORE: Coalition for Residential Educ. **[8827]**
Coun. for the Advancement of Standards in Higher Educ. **[8914]**
Dance/Drill Team Directors of Am. **[9544]**
Democrats for Educ. Reform **[17600]**
Destination ImagiNation **[8697]**
Educ. Conservancy **[7683]**
Educational Help for Afghanistan Assn. **[8916]**
Giraffe Club **[18680]**
Go Green Initiative Assn. **[8156]**
GreatSchools **[7831]**
Green Schools Alliance **[8158]**
H2O for Life **[13422]**
Haiti Convention Assn. **[12966]**
Home and School Inst. **[8026]**
LearnServe Intl. **[8828]**
Natl. Assn. of Diversity Officers in Higher Educ. **[8238]**
Natl. Assn. for Episcopal Christian Educ. Directors **[7856]**
Natl. Assn. of Hea. Sci. Educ. Partnership **[8843]**
Natl. Assn. for Professional Development Schools **[8829]**
Natl. Assn. of University-Model Schools **[7885]**
Natl. Assn. for Year-Round Educ. **[8044]**
Natl. Coalition for Public School Options **[8775]**
Natl. History Club **[8261]**
Natl. Middle Level Sci. Teachers' Assn. **[8848]**
Natl. Service-Learning CH **[8830]**
Network of Intl. Christian Schools **[7857]**
NFHS Coaches Assn. **[22465]**
North Central Assn. Commn. on Accreditation and School Improvement **[8831]**
One World Educ. **[8928]**
OneWorld Now! **[8929]**
Out of Poverty thru Educ. **[7731]**
Playworks **[12696]**
Resources for Indispensable Schools and Educators **[8961]**
Solace Intl. **[13479]**
StandardsWork **[8832]**
Urban Teacher Residency United **[8962]**
Schools for Hea. in Europe **[IO]**, Woerden, Netherlands
Schools Interoperability Framework Assn. **[6468]**, 1090 Vermont Ave. NW, 6th Fl., Washington, DC 20005, (202)789-4460
Schools Music Assn. **[IO]**, London, United Kingdom
Schools and Universities Polo Assn. **[IO]**, Sunninghill, United Kingdom
Schubert Soc. of the U.S.A. - Defunct.
Schuss Ski Club **[IO]**, Torrens Park, Australia
Schweiz Basketball-Verband **[IO]**, Fribourg, Switzerland
Schweiz Blinden- und Sehbehindertenverband **[★IO]**
Schweiz Chorvereinigung **[★IO]**
Schweizer Allianz Mission **[★IO]**

A star before a book entry number signifies that the name is not listed separately, but is mentioned within the entry.

Schweizer Brauerei-Verband [★IO]
Schweizer Buchhaendler - und Verleger - Verband [★IO]
Schweizer Finnsegler - Vereinigung [★IO]
Schweizer Forum fur Kommunikationsrecht [★IO]
Schweizer Franchise Verband [★IO]
Schweizer Heimatwerk [★IO]
Schweizer Hochschulsport-Verband [★IO]
Schweizer Jugendherbergen [★IO]
Schweizer Milchproduzenten [★IO]
Schweizer Physiotherapie Verband [★IO]
Schweizer Tanzsportverbande [★IO]
Schweizer Wanderwege [★IO]
Schweizer Werbe-Auftraggeberverband [IO], Zurich, Switzerland
Schweizerische Akademie der Geistes- und Sozial- wissenschaften [★IO]
Schweizerische Akademie der Medizinischen Wis- senschaften [★IO]
Schweizerische Akademie der Technischen Wissen- schaften [★IO]
Schweizerische Arbeitsgemeinschaft fur Logopadie [★IO]
Schweizerische Bankiervereinigung [★IO]
Schweizerische Bibelgesellschaft [★IO]
Schweizerische Chemische Gesellschaft [★IO]
Schweizerische Direktoren-Konferenz Gewerblich Industrieller Berufsund Fachschulen [★IO]
Schweizerische Fachvereinigung fur Ener- giewirtschaft [★IO]
Schweizerische Geomorphologische Gesellschaft [★IO]
Schweizerische Gesellschaft fur Astrophysik und As- tronomie [★IO]
Schweizerische Gesellschaft fur Ernahrung [★IO]
Schweizerische Gesellschaft fur Gerontologie [★IO]
Schweizerische Gesellschaft fur Infektiologie [★IO]
Schweizerische Gesellschaft fur Kardiologie [★IO]
Schweizerische Gesellschaft fur Kartografie [★IO]
Schweizerische Gesellschaft fur Kieferorthopadie [★IO]
Schweizerische Gesellschaft fur Medizinische Infor- matik [★IO]
Schweizerische Gesellschaft fur Photogrammetrie Bildanalyse und Fernerkundung [★IO]
Schweizerische Gesellschaft fur Rheumatologie [IO], Zurich, Switzerland
Schweizerische Gesellschaft fur Soziologie/Societe suisse de sociologie [★IO]
Schweizerische Gesellschaft fur Strahlenbiologie und Medizinische Physik [★IO]
Schweizerische Gesellschaft zum Studium des Schmerzes [★IO]
Schweizerische Gesellschaft fur Theaterkultur [★IO]
Schweizerische Gesellschaft fur Versuchstierkunde [★IO]
Schweizerische Huntington Vereinigung [IO], Feld- meilen, Switzerland
Schweizerische Hypertonie Gesellschaft [★IO]
Schweizerische Lebenstrettungs-Gesellschaft [★IO]
Schweizerische Liga gegen Epilepsie [★IO]
Schweizerische Mgt. Gesellschaft [★IO]
Schweizerische Nationalkommission Justitia et Pax [IO], Bern, Switzerland
Schweizerische Normen-Vereinigung [★IO]
Schweizerische Physikalische Gesellschaft [★IO]
Schweizerische Vereinigung gegen die Osteoprorose [★IO]
Schweizerische Vereinigung fur Schiedsgerichts- barkeit [★IO]
Schweizerische Vereinigung fur Sonnenenergie [★IO]
Schweizerische Zentralstelle fur Heilpadagogik [★IO]
Schweizerischen Textil- und Bekleidungsindustrie [★IO]
Schweizerischer Anwaltsverband [★IO]
Schweizerischer Arbeitgeberverband [★IO]
Schweizerischer Drogistenverband [★IO]
Schweizerischer Elektrotechnischer Verein [★IO]
Schweizerischer Forstverein [★IO]
Schweizerischer Friedensrat [★IO]
Schweizerischer Ingenieur- und Architektenverein [★IO]
Schweizerischer Kanu-Verband [★IO]

Schweizerischer Konditor-Confiseurmeister-Verband [★IO]
Schweizerischer Kosmetik- und Waschmittelverband [★IO]
Schweizerischer Landfrauenverband [★IO]
Schweizerischer Leichtathletikverband [★IO]
Schweizerischer Spirituosenverband [★IO]
Schweizerischer Squash-Verband [★IO]
Schweizerischer Tennisverband [★IO]
Schweizerischer Unihockey Verband [★IO]
Schweizerischer Verband der Akademikerinnen [★IO]
Schweizerischer Verband der Akademikerinnen [IO], Fribourg, Switzerland
Schweizerischer Verband Akademischen Volks- und Betriebswirtschafter [IO], Embrach, Switzerland
Schweizerischer Verband Diplomierter Ernahrungs- beraterInnen [★IO]
Schweizerischer Verband fuer Geomatik und Land- management [★IO]
Schweizerischer Verband der Ingenieur- Agronominnen und der Lebensmittel- Ingenieurinnen [★IO]
Schweizerischer Verband fur interne Kommunikation [★IO]
Schweizerischer Verband fur Landtechnik [IO], Rini- ken, Switzerland
Schweizerischer Verband der Lebensmittel- Detaillisten [★IO]
Schweizerischer Verband alleinerziehender Muetter und Vater [★IO]
Schweizerischer Verband des Personals Oeffentli- cher Dienste [IO], Zurich, Switzerland
Schweizerischer Verband fur Weiterbildung [★IO]
Schweizerischer Volleyball-Verband [★IO]
Schweizerisches Arbeiterhilfswerk [★IO]
Schweizerrisher Ruderverband [★IO]
Schwenkfeldian Exile Soc. [★10357]
Schwestern von der Gottlichen Vorsehung [★IO]
SCI - Intl. Voluntary Ser. [13405], 232 Hartman's Mill Rd., Charlottesville, VA 22902, (303)440-7244
SCI - Intl. Voluntary Ser. [13405], 232 Hartman's Mill Rd., Charlottesville, VA 22902, (303)440-7244

Science
AAAS Sci. and Human Rights Coalition [17806]
AASP - The Palynological Soc. [7216]
Acad. of Applied Sci. [7351]
Access Res. Network [8833]
Addgene [7110]
African Sci. Inst. [7352]
Algal Biomass Org. [6680]
Algerian Amer. Scientists Assn. [7353]
Alliance for Sci. and Tech. Res. in Am. [7354]
Allied Social Sci. Associations [7408]
Amer. Anthropological Assn. I Soc. for the Anthropology of Europe [6128]
Amer. Assn. for the Advancement of Sci. [7355]
Amer. Assn. of Anthropological Genetics [6895]
Amer. Comm. for the Weizmann Inst. of Sci. [7356]
Amer. Philosophical Soc. [7357]
Amer. Physician Scientists Assn. [8588]
Amer. Psychological Assn. I Soc. of Psychological Hypnosis [16380]
Amer. Sci. Affiliation [20231]
Analytical and Life Sci. Systems Assn. [7358]
Armenian Engineers and Scientists of Am. [7359]
Armenian Engineers and Scientists of Am. [7359]
Assn. of African Biomedical Scientists [7360]
Assn. for Africanist Anthropology [6133]
Assn. of Chinese Professors of Social Sciences in the U.S. [7409]
Assn. of Educators in Imaging and Radiologic Sci- ences [8834]
Assn. for Humanist Sociology [7424]
Assn. of Orthodox Jewish Scientists [7361]
Assn. for the Sci. Stud. of Consciousness [7914]
Assn. for the Stud. of Food and Soc. [6871]
Assn. of Thai Professionals in Am. and Canada [19255]
Assn. for Women in Sci. [7362]
Astronaut Scholars Honor Soc. [23629]
Beta Beta Beta [23470]
Beta Kappa Chi [23630]
Bill and Melinda Gates Found. [12134]

BIO IT Coalition [6333]
Bionomics Intl. [7363]
Black Entomologists [6840]
Bulgarian Acad. of Sciences [2098]
Bulletin of the Atomic Scientists [7364]
Chinese-American Professors in Environmental Engg. and Sci. [6425]
Chinese Amer. Soc. Of Anesthesiology [13745]
Coalition for Educ. in the Life Sciences [8835]
Coalition on the Public Understanding of Sci. [7365]
Coalition for Sci. After School [8836]
Commn. on Professionals in Sci. and Tech. [7366]
Comm. on the Status of Women in Microbiology [6297]
Coun. for Elementary Sci. Intl. [8837]
Coun. for Elementary Sci. Intl. [8837]
Coun. of Sci. Soc. Presidents [7367]
Coun. of State Sci. Supervisors [8838]
Creation Res. Soc. [20232]
Drilling, Observation and Sampling of the Earth's Continental Crust [6602]
Ethiopian Geophysical Union Intl. [6920]
Fed. of Earth Sci. Info. Partners [6603]
Focus Fusion Soc. [6725]
Fuel Cell and Hydrogen Energy Assn. [7368]
Genesis Inst. [20233]
Global Wildlife Conservation [5060]
Hellenic Bioscientific Assn. in the USA [7369]
History of Sci. Soc. [9774]
HOPOS - The Intl. Soc. for the History of Philosophy of Sci. [8839]
Human Behavior and Evolution Soc. [6255]
Inst. for Chem. Educ. [7820]
Inst. on Religion in an Age of Sci. [20234]
Inst. for Sci. and Intl. Security [18584]
Inst. for Sci. and Intl. Security [18584]
Inst. for Women in Trades, Tech. and Sci. [3684]
Intl. Aeronauts League [21203]
Intl. Assn. for Ecology and Hea. [6604]
Intl. Biogeography Soc. [6904]
Intl. Coun. of Academies of Engg. and Technologi- cal Sciences [8840]
Intl. Coun. of Academies of Engg. and Technologi- cal Sciences [8840]
Intl. Coun. for the Life Sciences [7370]
Intl. Fed. of Nonlinear Analysts [7371]
Intl. Fed. of Nonlinear Analysts [7371]
Intl. Graphic Arts Educ. Assn. [8220]
Intl. Humic Substances Soc. [7372]
Intl. Humic Substances Soc. [7372]
The Intl. Lepidoptera Survey [6845]
Intl. Lunar Observatory Assn. [6231]
Intl. Mammalian Genome Soc. [6900]
Intl. Org. of Plant Biosystematists [6358]
Intl. Soc. for Aeolian Res. [6926]
Intl. Soc. of African Scientists [7373]
Intl. Soc. of African Scientists [7373]
Intl. Soc. for Bioluminescence and Chemilumines- cence [7374]
Intl. Soc. for Bioluminescence and Chemilumines- cence [7374]
Intl. Soc. for Hyaluronan Sciences [6274]
Intl. Soc. for IGF Res. [6851]
Intl. Soc. for Intelligence Res. [7002]
Intl. Soc. of Iraqi Scientists [7375]
Intl. Soc. of Iraqi Scientists [7375]
Intl. Soc. for Nanoscale Sci., Computation and Engg. [7376]
Intl. Soc. for Nanoscale Sci., Computation and Engg. [7376]
Intl. Soc. for Neuroimmunomodulation [15664]
Intl. Soc. for Plasmid Biology and other Mobile Genetic Elements [7111]
Middle Atlantic Planetarium Soc. [8841]
Moroccan-American Soc. for Life Sciences [7141]
Natl. Acad. of Sciences [7377]
Natl. Alliance of State Sci. and Mathematics Coali- tions [8842]
Natl. Assn. of Academies of Sci. [7378]
Natl. Assn. of Hea. Sci. Educ. Partnership [8843]
Natl. Assn. for Res. in Sci. Teaching [8844]
Natl. Center for Improving Sci. Educ. [8845]
Natl. Center for Sci. Educ. [8846]
Natl. Earth Sci. Teachers Assn. [8847]

Reference to "IO" in place of a book number signifies that the association may be found in the 50th edition of International Organizations.

A star before a book entry number signifies that the name is not listed separately, but is mentioned within the entry.

Scottish Agricultural Org. Soc. **[IO]**, Newbridge, United Kingdom

Scottish Aikido Fed. **[IO]**, Innerleithen, United Kingdom

Scottish Amateur Football Assn. **[IO]**, Glasgow, United Kingdom

Scottish Amateur Music Assn. **[IO]**, Alva, United Kingdom

Scottish Anglers Natl. Assn. **[IO]**, Kinross, United Kingdom

Scottish Arts Coun. **[IO]**, Edinburgh, United Kingdom

Scottish Assn. of Family History Societies **[IO]**, Edinburgh, United Kingdom

Scottish Assn. of Geography Teachers **[IO]**, Tranent, United Kingdom

Scottish Assn. of Hea. Councils **[IO]**, Edinburgh, United Kingdom

Scottish Assn. for Marine Sci. **[IO]**, Oban, United Kingdom

Scottish Assn. of Master Bakers **[IO]**, Edinburgh, United Kingdom

Scottish Assn. of Meat Wholesalers **[IO]**, Edinburgh, United Kingdom

Scottish Assn. for Mental Hea. **[IO]**, Glasgow, United Kingdom

Scottish Assn. for Public Transport **[IO]**, Glasgow, United Kingdom

Scottish Assn. of Sign Language Interpreters **[IO]**, Glasgow, United Kingdom

Scottish Assn. of Young Farmers' Clubs **[IO]**, Edinburgh, United Kingdom

Scottish Athletics **[IO]**, Edinburgh, United Kingdom

Scottish Beekeepers' Assn. **[IO]**, Inverness, United Kingdom

Scottish Bible Soc. **[IO]**, Edinburgh, United Kingdom

Scottish Bowling Assn. **[IO]**, Ayr, United Kingdom

Scottish Building Contractors Assn. **[IO]**, Glasgow, United Kingdom

Scottish Building Fed. **[IO]**, Edinburgh, United Kingdom

Scottish Campaign for Nuclear Disarmament **[IO]**, Glasgow, United Kingdom

Scottish Canoe Assn. **[IO]**, Edinburgh, United Kingdom

Scottish Catholic Intl. Aid Fund **[IO]**, Glasgow, United Kingdom

Scottish Childminding Assn. **[IO]**, Stirling, United Kingdom

Scottish Church History Soc. **[IO]**, Edinburgh, United Kingdom

Scottish Churches Housing Action **[IO]**, Edinburgh, United Kingdom

Scottish Churches Housing Agency **[★20385]**

Scottish Comm. of Optometrists **[IO]**, Edinburgh, United Kingdom

Scottish Community Care Forum **[IO]**, Dumbarton, United Kingdom

Scottish Correspondence Chess Assn. **[IO]**, Dundee, United Kingdom

Scottish Coun. on Alcohol **[★5216]**

Scottish Coun. on Deafness **[IO]**, Glasgow, United Kingdom

Scottish Coun. for Development and Indus. **[IO]**, Glasgow, United Kingdom

Scottish Coun. on Human Bioethics **[IO]**, Edinburgh, United Kingdom

Scottish Coun. of Independent Schools **[IO]**, Edinburgh, United Kingdom

Scottish Coun. for Intl. Arbitration **[IO]**, Edinburgh, United Kingdom

Scottish Coun. for Postgraduate Medical and Dental Educ. **[IO]**, Edinburgh, United Kingdom

Scottish Coun. for Res. in Educ. **[IO]**, Glasgow, United Kingdom

Scottish Coun. for Single Homeless **[IO]**, Edinburgh, United Kingdom

Scottish Coun. for Voluntary Organisations **[IO]**, Edinburgh, United Kingdom

Scottish Crop Res. Inst. **[IO]**, Dundee, United Kingdom

Scottish Croquet Assn. **[IO]**, Edinburgh, United Kingdom

Scottish Croquet Assn. - Defunct.

Scottish Cyclists' Union **[IO]**, Edinburgh, United Kingdom

Scottish Daily Newspaper Soc. **[IO]**, Edinburgh, United Kingdom

Scottish Dance Teacher's Alliance **[IO]**, Glasgow, United Kingdom

Scottish Decorators Fed. **[IO]**, Stirling, United Kingdom

Scottish Deerhound Club of Am. **[21648]**, Ruth Piwonka, Membership Sec., PO Box 472, Kinderhook, NY 12106

Scottish Disability Sport **[IO]**, Edinburgh, United Kingdom

Scottish Ecological Design Assn. **[IO]**, Edinburgh, United Kingdom

Scottish Educ. and Action for Development **[IO]**, Edinburgh, United Kingdom

Scottish Engg. **[IO]**, Glasgow, United Kingdom

Scottish Enterprise Energy Team **[IO]**, Aberdeen, United Kingdom

Scottish Equestrian Assn. **[IO]**, Kilmaurs, United Kingdom

Scottish Esperanto Assn. **[IO]**, Motherwell, United Kingdom

Scottish Farm and Countryside Educational Trust **[★17419]**

Scottish Fed. of Housing Associations **[IO]**, Glasgow, United Kingdom

Scottish Fed. of Meat Traders Assn. **[IO]**, Perth, United Kingdom

Scottish Fed. of Model Boat Clubs **[IO]**, Edinburgh, United Kingdom

Scottish Fed. of Sea Anglers **[IO]**, Fife, United Kingdom

Scottish Fishermen's Fed. **[IO]**, Aberdeen, United Kingdom

Scottish Food and Drink Fed. **[IO]**, Edinburgh, United Kingdom

Scottish Football Assn. **[IO]**, Glasgow, United Kingdom

Scottish Further and Higher Educ. Funding Coun. **[IO]**, Edinburgh, United Kingdom

Scottish Games Assn. **[IO]**, St. Andrews, United Kingdom

Scottish Genealogy Soc. **[IO]**, Edinburgh, United Kingdom

Scottish Golf Union **[IO]**, St. Andrews, United Kingdom

Scottish Grocers' Fed. **[IO]**, Edinburgh, United Kingdom

Scottish Gymnastics Assn. **[IO]**, Stirling, United Kingdom

Scottish Harp Soc. of Am. **[10287]**, Kathleen Bingaman, Membership Comm. Chair, PO Box 57, Snellville, GA 30078

Scottish Heritage U.S.A. **[19226]**, PO Box 457, Pinehurst, NC 28370, (910)295-4448

Scottish History Soc. **[IO]**, St. Andrews, United Kingdom

Scottish Hockey Union **[IO]**, Edinburgh, United Kingdom

Scottish Huntington's Assn. **[IO]**, Paisley, United Kingdom

Scottish Ice Skating Assn. **[IO]**, Edinburgh, United Kingdom

Scottish Inland Waterways Assn. **[IO]**, Fife, United Kingdom

Scottish Joint Indus. Bd. for the Elecl. Contracting Indus. **[IO]**, Midlothian, United Kingdom

Scottish Ladies Golfing Assn. **[IO]**, Perth, United Kingdom

Scottish Language Dictionaries **[IO]**, Edinburgh, United Kingdom

Scottish Law Agents Soc. **[IO]**, Glasgow, United Kingdom

Scottish Licensed Trade Assn. **[IO]**, Edinburgh, United Kingdom

Scottish Local Authority Network of Physical Educ. **[IO]**, Fife, United Kingdom

Scottish Master Wrights and Builders Assn. **[IO]**, Glasgow, United Kingdom

Scottish Microbiology Assn. **[IO]**, Dumfries, United Kingdom

Scottish Microbiology Soc. **[IO]**, Glasgow, United Kingdom

Scottish Motor Neurone Disease Assn. **[IO]**, Glasgow, United Kingdom

Scottish Motor Trade Assn. **[IO]**, Edinburgh, United Kingdom

Scottish Museums Coun. **[IO]**, Edinburgh, United Kingdom

Scottish Natl. Coun. of YMCA's **[IO]**, Edinburgh, United Kingdom

Scottish Natl. Party **[IO]**, Edinburgh, United Kingdom

Scottish Natural Heritage **[IO]**, Inverness, United Kingdom

Scottish Newspaper Publishers Assn. **[IO]**, Edinburgh, United Kingdom

Scottish and Northern Ireland Plumbing Employers' Fed. **[IO]**, Edinburgh, United Kingdom

Scottish and Northern Welsh Pony and Cob Assn. **[IO]**, Northumberland, United Kingdom

Scottish Official Bd. of Highland Dancing **[IO]**, Edinburgh, United Kingdom

Scottish Ornithologists' Club **[IO]**, East Lothian, United Kingdom

Scottish Out of School Care Network **[IO]**, Glasgow, United Kingdom

Scottish Parent Teacher Coun. **[IO]**, Edinburgh, United Kingdom

Scottish Photographic Fed. **[IO]**, Carluke, United Kingdom

Scottish Plant Owners Assn. **[IO]**, Glasgow, United Kingdom

Scottish Police Fed. **[IO]**, Glasgow, United Kingdom

Scottish Pre-School Play Assn. **[IO]**, Glasgow, United Kingdom

Scottish Qualifications Authority **[IO]**, Glasgow, United Kingdom

Scottish Railway Preservation Soc. **[IO]**, West Lothian, United Kingdom

Scottish Refugee Coun. **[IO]**, Glasgow, United Kingdom

Scottish Retail Consortium **[IO]**, Gullane, United Kingdom

Scottish Right of Way Soc. **[★1274]**

Scottish Rights of Way and Access Soc. **[IO]**, Edinburgh, United Kingdom

Scottish Rock Garden Club **[IO]**, Leicester, United Kingdom

Scottish Rural Property and Bus. Assn. **[IO]**, Musselburgh, United Kingdom

Scottish Screen **[IO]**, Glasgow, United Kingdom

Scottish Secondary Teachers' Assn. **[IO]**, Edinburgh, United Kingdom

Scottish Ski Club **[IO]**, Fort William, United Kingdom

Scottish Soc. for Autism **[IO]**, Alloa, United Kingdom

Scottish Soc. for Conservation and Restoration **[IO]**, Edinburgh, United Kingdom

Scottish Soc. for Contamination Control **[IO]**, Glasgow, United Kingdom

Scottish Soc. of the History of Medicine **[IO]**, Edinburgh, United Kingdom

Scottish Soc. for the Prevention of Cruelty to Animals **[IO]**, Dunfermline, United Kingdom

Scottish Soc. for Psychical Res. **[IO]**, Fife, United Kingdom

Scottish SPCA **[IO]**, Dunfermline, United Kingdom

Scottish Spina Bifida Assn. **[IO]**, Cumbernauld, United Kingdom

Scottish Sports Assn. **[IO]**, Edinburgh, United Kingdom

Scottish Squash Assn. **[IO]**, Edinburgh, United Kingdom

Scottish Storytelling Forum **[IO]**, Edinburgh, United Kingdom

Scottish Stud. Program/Scottish Stud. Found. **[IO]**, Toronto, ON, Canada

Scottish Sub Aqua Club **[IO]**, Edinburgh, United Kingdom

Scottish Swimming **[IO]**, Stirling, United Kingdom

Scottish Terrier Club of Am. **[21649]**, Liz Heywood, Membership Chair, 30 Starbarrack Rd., Red Hook, NY 12571-2249, (845)758-8088

Scottish Text Soc. **[IO]**, Nottingham, United Kingdom

Scottish Timber Trade Assn. **[IO]**, Stirling, United Kingdom

Scottish Urban Archaeological Trust **[IO]**, Perth, United Kingdom

Scottish Volleyball Assn. **[IO]**, Edinburgh, United Kingdom

Scottish Welsh Pony and Cob Assn. **[IO]**, Lanark, United Kingdom

Reference to "IO" in place of a book number signifies that the association may be found in the 50th edition of International Organizations.

Scottish Wild Land Gp. [IO], Glasgow, United Kingdom

Scottish Wildlife Trust [IO], Edinburgh, United Kingdom

Scottish Women's Aid [IO], Edinburgh, United Kingdom

Scottish Women's Football [IO], Glasgow, United Kingdom

Scottish Women's Indoor Bowling Assn. [IO], Letham, United Kingdom

Scottish Women's Rural Institutes [IO], Edinburgh, United Kingdom

Scottish Youth Hostels Assn. [IO], Stirling, United Kingdom

Scottsdale Inst. [14887], 1660 Hwy. 100 S, Ste. 306, Minneapolis, MN 55416, (952)545-5880

Scout Assn. [IO], London, United Kingdom

Scout Assn. of Argentina [IO], Buenos Aires, Argentina

Scout Assn. of Belize [IO], Belize City, Belize

Scout Assn. of Jamaica [IO], Kingston, Jamaica

Scouting
    Assn. of Baptists for Scouting [13016]
    Assn. of Girl Scout Executive Staff [13017]
    Boy Scouts of Am. [13018]
    Girl Guiding Scotland [5054]
    Girl Scouts of the U.S.A. [13019]
    Hungarian Scouts Assn. [13020]
    Natl. Assn. of Presbyterian Scouters [13021]
    Natl. Catholic Comm. on Scouting [13022]
    Natl. Eagle Scout Assn. [13023]
    Natl. Episcopal Scouters Assn. [13024]
    Natl. Jewish Comm. on Girl Scouting [13025]
    Natl. Jewish Comm. on Scouting [13026]
    Order of the Arrow [13027]
    Scouting For All [13028]
    Singapore Scout Assn. [10600]

Scouting Assn. of Canada [IO], Montreal, QC, Canada

Scouting For All [13028], PO Box 600841, San Diego, CA 92160-0841, (619)229-1612

Scouting Ireland CSI [IO], Dublin, Ireland

Scouts de Argentina Asociacion Civil [★IO]

Scouts Canada [IO], Ottawa, ON, Canada

Scouts on Stamps Soc. [★22073]

Scouts on Stamps Soc. Intl. [22073], PO Box 6228, Kennewick, WA 99336, (509)735-3731

Scrabble Crossword Game Players [★21753]

Scrabble Players [★21753]

Scrambl-Gram [★21756]

Scrap Tire Management Council - Defunct.

Screen Actors Guild [23273], 5757 Wilshire Blvd., 7th Fl., Los Angeles, CA 90036-3600, (323)954-1600

Screen Advt. World Assn. [IO], London, United Kingdom

Screen Directors Guild of Am. [★23187]

Screen Directors Intl. Guild [★23187]

Screen Mfrs. Assn. [1659], Jeff Sawyers, VP, 311 W Coleman St., Rice Lake, WI 54868, (715)236-4575

Screen Mfrs. Assn. [1659], Jeff Sawyers, VP, 311 W Coleman St., Rice Lake, WI 54868, (715)236-4575

Screen Printing Assn. of Canada [★1631]

Screen Printing Assn. of Canada [★1631]

Screen Printing Assn. Intl. [★1631]

Screen Printing Assn. Intl. [★1631]

Screen Printing Tech. Found. [1629], Specialty Graphic Imaging Assn., 10015 Main St., Fairfax, VA 22031, (703)385-1335

Screen Printing Tech. Found. [1629], Specialty Graphic Imaging Assn., 10015 Main St., Fairfax, VA 22031, (703)385-1335

Screen Process Printing Assn. [★1631]

Screen Process Printing Assn. [★1631]

Screen Producers Assn. of Australia [IO], Surry Hills, Australia

Screen Producers Guild [★1266]

Screen Producers Ireland [IO], Dublin, Ireland

Screen Production and Development Assn. of New Zealand [IO], Wellington, New Zealand

Screenprinting and Graphic Imaging Assn. Intl. [★1631]

Screenprinting and Graphic Imaging Assn. Intl. [★1631]

Screenrights [IO], Neutral Bay, Australia

Screenwriters Assn. Singapore [IO], Singapore, Singapore

Scriabin Soc. of Am. [10288], 353 Lindsey Dr., Berwyn, PA 19312

Scribes Administrative Off. [★5325]

Scribes - The Amer. Soc. of Legal Writers [5325], PO Box 13038, Lansing, MI 48901, (517)371-5140

Scripps Assn. of Families [7886], Scripps Coll., 1030 Columbia Ave., Claremont, CA 91711, (909)607-1542

Scripps Howard Found. [8447], PO Box 5380, Cincinnati, OH 45201, (513)977-3035

Scripture Gift Mission/U.S.A. [★19339]

Scripture Union - Australia [IO], Chapel Hill, Australia

Scripture Union - Benin [IO], Cotonou, Benin

Scripture Union - Botswana [IO], Gaborone, Botswana

Scripture Union - Burundi [IO], Bujumbura, Burundi

Scripture Union - Cambodia [IO], Phnom Penh, Cambodia

Scripture Union - Cameroon [IO], Yaounde, Cameroon

Scripture Union - Canada [IO], Pickering, ON, Canada

Scripture Union - Democratic Republic of Congo [IO], Kinshasa, Republic of the Congo

Scripture Union - Egypt [IO], Cairo, Egypt

Scripture Union - England and Wales [IO], Milton Keynes, United Kingdom

Scripture Union - Equatorial Guinea [IO], Malabo, Equatorial Guinea

Scripture Union - Fiji [IO], Suva, Fiji

Scripture Union - India [IO], Chennai, India

Scripture Union - Indonesia [IO], Jakarta, Indonesia

Scripture Union - Israel [IO], Netanya, Israel

Scripture Union - Japan [IO], Kawasaki, Japan

Scripture Union - Kenya [IO], Nairobi, Kenya

Scripture Union - Kyrgyzstan [IO], Bishkek, Kirgizstan

Scripture Union - Lesotho [IO], Maseru, Lesotho

Scripture Union - Liberia [IO], Monrovia, Liberia

Scripture Union - Lithuania [IO], Vilnius, Lithuania

Scripture Union - Malawi [IO], Lilongwe, Malawi

Scripture Union - Mongolia [IO], Ulan Bator, Mongolia

Scripture Union - Namibia [IO], Windhoek, Namibia

Scripture Union - Nepal [IO], Kathmandu, Nepal

Scripture Union - New Caledonia [IO], Noumea, New Caledonia

Scripture Union - New South Wales [IO], West Ryde, Australia

Scripture Union - New Zealand [IO], Wellington, New Zealand

Scripture Union - Niger [IO], Niamey, Niger

Scripture Union - Northern Ireland [IO], Belfast, United Kingdom

Scripture Union - Pakistan [IO], Lahore, Pakistan

Scripture Union - Philippines [IO], Manila, Philippines

Scripture Union - Romania [IO], Timisoara, Romania

Scripture Union - Russia [IO], Moscow, Russia

Scripture Union - Rwanda [IO], Kigali, Rwanda

Scripture Union - Samoa [IO], Apia, Western Samoa

Scripture Union - Scotland [IO], Glasgow, United Kingdom

Scripture Union - Sierra Leone [IO], Freetown, Sierra Leone

Scripture Union - Singapore [IO], Singapore, Singapore

Scripture Union - Sri Lanka [IO], Colombo, Sri Lanka

Scripture Union - Sudan [IO], Juba, Sudan

Scripture Union - Swaziland [IO], Mbabane, Swaziland

Scripture Union - Taiwan [IO], Taipei, Taiwan

Scripture Union - Tanzania [IO], Dar es Salaam, United Republic of Tanzania

Scripture Union - Togo [IO], Lome, Togo

Scripture Union - Tonga [IO], Nuku'alofa, Tonga

Scripture Union - Uganda [IO], Kampala, Uganda

Scripture Union - Vanuatu [IO], Port Vila, Vanuatu

Scripture Union - Victoria [IO], Northcote, Australia

Scripture Union - Zambia [IO], Kitwe, Zambia

Scrollsaw Assn. of the World [22204], PO Box 340, Botkins, OH 45306, (937)693-3309

Scrollsaw Assn. of the World [22204], PO Box 340, Botkins, OH 45306, (937)693-3309

Scruggs Family Assn. [20582], Mary Beth Scruggs Rephlo, Sec.-Treas., 6130 Sherborn Ln., Springfield, VA 22152, (703)451-9473

Scrum Alliance [6558], PO Box 40097, Indianapolis, IN 46240-0097

SCSI Trade Assn. [1908], Presidio of San Francisco, Bldg. 572B, Ruger St., PO Box 29920, San Francisco, CA 94129, (415)561-6273

Scuba Assn; Handicapped [22511]

Scuba Assn; Handicapped [22511]

Scuba Diving
    Natl. Assn. of Underwater Instructors [23104]
    Scuba Training Coun; Recreational [23106]

Sculptors Guild [10530], 55 Washington St., Ste. 256, Brooklyn, NY 11201, (718)422-0555

Sculptors Soc. of Canada [IO], Toronto, ON, Canada

Sculpture
    Assn. of Lifecasters Intl. [10527]
    Assn. of Lifecasters Intl. [10527]
    Fed. of Modern Painters and Sculptors [9230]
    Intl. Sculpture Center [10528]
    Natl. Sculpture Soc. [10529]
    Sculptors Guild [10530]
    Sculpture in the Env. [17396]

Sculpture in the Env. [17396], 25 Maiden Ln., New York, NY 10038-4008, (212)285-0120

SD Assn. [6469], 2400 Camino Ramon, Ste. 375, San Ramon, CA 94583, (925)275-6615

SDA Kindred [★19800]

SDA Kinship [★19800]

SDA Kinship Intl. [★19800]

SDA Kinship Intl. [★19800]

Sdruzeni Automobiloveho Prumyslu [★IO]

Sdruzeni zastancu detskych prav - ceska sekce DCI [★IO]

Sdruzeni Najemniku [★IO]

S.E. Asia Vets [★20786]

Sea Educ. Assn. [8551], PO Box 6, Woods Hole, MA 02543, (508)540-3954

Sea Grant Assn. [7057], Univ. of New Hampshire, 24 Colovos Rd., Durham, NH 03824, (603)862-2921

Sea Kayak Operators Assn. of New Zealand [IO], Auckland, New Zealand

Sea Ser. Leadership Assn. [20741], PO Box 40371, Arlington, VA 22204

Sea Shepherd Conservation Soc. [5126], PO Box 2616, Friday Harbor, WA 98250, (360)370-5650

Sea Shepherd Conservation Soc. [5126], PO Box 2616, Friday Harbor, WA 98250, (360)370-5650

Sea to Sky Freenet Assn. [IO], Squamish, BC, Canada

Sea Stud. Found. [IO], Rio de Janeiro, Brazil

Sea Turtle Conservancy [5127], 4424 NW 13th St., Ste. B-11, Gainesville, FL 32609, (352)373-6441

Sea Turtle Conservancy [5127], 4424 NW 13th St., Ste. B-11, Gainesville, FL 32609, (352)373-6441

Sea Turtle Rescue Fund [★4115]

Sea Turtle Rescue Fund [★4115]

Sea Turtle Survival League [★5127]

Sea Turtle Survival League [★5127]

SeaAid [11628], PO Box 6688, Portland, OR 97228, (877)850-2525

Seabee Veterans of Am. [★20723]

Seabird Gp. [IO], Cambridge, United Kingdom

Seacoast Anti-Pollution League - Address unknown since 2010.

Seacology [4141], 1623 Solano Ave., Berkeley, CA 94707, (510)559-3505

Seafarers/Harry Lundberg School of Seamanship [★23251]

Seafarers and Intl. House [19940], 123 E 15th St., New York, NY 10003, (212)677-4800

Seafarers' Intl. Union of North Am. [23251], 5201 Auth Way, Camp Springs, MD 20746, (301)899-0675

Seafood
    FishWise [1359]
    Intl. Seafood Sustainability Assn. [1361]
    Maine Lobstermen's Assn. [3183]
    Marine Stewardship Coun. [4877]
    Natl. Fisheries Inst. [3184]
    Natl. Seafood Educators [3185]
    Northwest Fisheries Assn. [3186]
    Pacific Coast Shellfish Growers Assn. [3187]

A star before a book entry number signifies that the name is not listed separately, but is mentioned within the entry.

Pacific Seafood Processors Assn. [3188]
Seafood Choices Alliance [3189]
Seafood Choices Alliance [3189]
Shrimp Coun. [4878]
Southeastern Fisheries Assn. [3190]
Sustainable Fisheries Partnership [3830]
U.S. Freshwater Prawn and Shrimp Growers Assn. [3191]
Seafood Choices Alliance [3189], 8401 Colesville Rd., Ste. 500, Silver Spring, MD 20910, (301)495-9570
Seafood Choices Alliance [3189], 8401 Colesville Rd., Ste. 500, Silver Spring, MD 20910, (301)495-9570
Sealant and Waterproofers Inst. [★59]
Sealant and Waterproofers Inst. [★59]
Sealant Waterproofing and Restoration Inst. [59], 400 Admiral Blvd., Kansas City, MO 64106, (816)472-7974
Sealant Waterproofing and Restoration Inst. [59], 400 Admiral Blvd., Kansas City, MO 64106, (816)472-7974
Seaman's Church Inst. of New York [★19715]
Seamen
North Amer. Maritime Ministry Assn. [13029]
North Amer. Maritime Ministry Assn. [13029]
United Seamen's Ser. [13030]
United Seamen's Ser. [13030]
Seamen and Intl. House [★19940]
Seamen's Center [★19940]
Seamen's Church Inst. of New York and New Jersey [19715], 241 Water St., New York, NY 10038, (212)349-9090
SEAMEO Regional Centre for Educ. in Sci. and Mathematics [IO], Penang, Malaysia
SEAMEO Regional Centre for Educational Innovation and Tech. [IO], Quezon City, Philippines
SEAMEO Regional Centre for Public Hea. [IO], Manila, Philippines
SEAMEO Regional Centre for Tropical Biology [IO], Bogor, Indonesia
SEAMEO Regional Language Centre [IO], Singapore, Singapore
Seamless Garment Network [★18238]
SEAMS [★2344]
SEAMS Assn. [2344], 4921-C Broad River Rd., Columbia, SC 29212, (803)772-5861
Seaplane Pilots Assn. [156], 3859 Laird Blvd., Lakeland, FL 33811, (863)701-7979
Search for Common Ground [18601], 1601 Connecticut Ave. NW, Ste. 200, Washington, DC 20009-1035, (202)265-4300
Search for Common Ground [18601], 1601 Connecticut Ave. NW, Ste. 200, Washington, DC 20009-1035, (202)265-4300
Search Engine Marketing Professional Org. [2423], 401 Edgewater Pl., Ste. 600, Wakefield, MA 01880, (781)876-8866
Search for Extra-Terrestrial Intelligence League [★6236]
Search for the Great Bear - Defunct.
Search Inst. [★13557]
Search for Justice and Equality in Palestine/Israel - Address unknown since 2010.
Search and Rescue Dogs of the U.S. [11879], PO Box 85, Otis, CO 80743
SEARCH - The Natl. Consortium for Justice Info. and Statistics [11734], 7311 Greenhaven Dr., Ste. 145, Sacramento, CA 95831, (916)392-2550
Sears Family Assn. [20583], 2208 Amber Rd., Oklahoma City, OK 73170, (405)703-0779
Seaside Support League - POW/MIA - Defunct.
SEASONS: Suicide Bereavement - Defunct.
Seatbelt Law Opposition Forum - Address unknown since 2011.
SeaWeb [4710], 8401 Colesville Rd., Ste. 500, Silver Spring, MD 20910, (301)495-9570
Secadev - Caritas Chad [IO], N'Djamena, Chad
SECO: Tech. Control Bur. for Constr. [IO], Brussels, Belgium
Second Amendment Comm. [5452], PO Box 1776, Hanford, CA 93232, (559)584-5209
Second Amendment Found. [17326], James Madison Bldg., 12500 NE 10th Pl., Bellevue, WA 98005, (425)454-7012

Second Amendment Sisters [17690], 900 RR 620 S, Ste. C-101, PMB 228, Lakeway, TX 78734, (877)271-6216
Second Bombardment Assn. [20329], Matt R. Bryner, Treas., 8386 Fenton Way, Arvada, CO 80003, (303)412-0030
Second Harvest [★12272]
Second Harvest, The Natl. Food Bank Network [★12272]
Second Husbands Alliance for Fair Treatment - Defunct.
Second Marine Div. Assn. [20687], PO Box 8180, Camp Lejeune, NC 28547-8180, (910)451-3167
Second Nature [8245], 18 Tremont St., Ste. 308, Boston, MA 02108, (617)722-0036
Second Sight [★17079]
Second Wind Lung Transplant Assn. [16611], 52 Mountainside Rd., Mendham, NJ 07945, (973)543-3035
Second Wind Org. [★16611]
Second World War Aircraft Preservation Soc. [IO], Alton, United Kingdom
Secondary Education
Alliance for Excellent Educ. [8854]
Amer. Legion Auxiliary Girls Nation [17245]
Amer. Mgt. Assn. I Oper. Enterprise [8547]
Natl. Alliance for Secondary Educ. and Transition [8855]
Natl. High School Alliance [8856]
Natl. History Club [8261]
Natl. Traditionalist Caucus [17429]
One World Educ. [8928]
OneWorld Now! [8929]
Student Press Law Center [17358]
Women and Youth Supporting Each Other [9069]
Secondary Educ. Union [IO], Paris, France
Secondary Materials and Recycled Textiles [1866], 2105 Laurel Bush Rd., Ste. 200, Bel Air, MD 21015, (443)640-1050
Secondary Materials and Recycled Textiles [1866], 2105 Laurel Bush Rd., Ste. 200, Bel Air, MD 21015, (443)640-1050
Secondary Principals Assn. of New Zealand [IO], Auckland, New Zealand
Secondary School Admission Test Bd. [8993], CN 5339, Princeton, NJ 08543, (609)683-4440
Secours Quaker Canadien [★IO]
Secret Soc. of Happy People [9854], 240 N Denton Tap Rd., PMB No. 112, Coppell, TX 75019, (972)459-7031
Secretariat for Family, Laity, Women, and Youth [12020], 3211 4th St. NE, Washington, DC 20017-1194, (202)541-3040
Secretariat for Hispanic Affairs/National Conf. of Catholic Bishops [★12149]
Secretariat on Laity and Family Life [★12020]
Secretariat of the Pacific Community [IO], Noumea, New Caledonia
Secretariat of the Pacific Regional Env. Programme [IO], Apia, Western Samoa
Secretariat du Programme Regional Oceanien de l'Environnement [★IO]
Secretariat for the Spanish Speaking [★12149]
Secretive Societies, Mind Control and Ritual Abuse [13303], PO Box 1295, Easthampton, MA 01027
Sect. 23 Leased Housing Assn. [★12192]
Sect. of Criminal Law [★5642]
Sect. of the Division of Libraries for Children and Young People of the Amer. Lib. Assn. [★9952]
Sect. on Gay and Lesbian Legal Issues, Assn. of Amer. Law Schools [★8500]
Sect. for Magnetic Resonance Technologists [15384], 2030 Addison St., 7th Fl., Berkeley, CA 94704, (510)841-1899
Sect. Nationale de la CIME [IO], Moscow, Russia
Sect. on Women in Legal Education of the AALS - Defunct.
Sect. for Women in Public Admin. [5912], 1301 Pennsylvania Ave. NW, Ste. 840, Washington, DC 20004-1735, (202)393-7878
Sectoral Assn. of Trans. Equip. and Machines Mfg. [IO], Montreal, QC, Canada
Sectoral Roundtable Assn. for the Hea. and Safety of Metal and Elecl. Workers [IO], Longueuil, QC, Canada

Secular Coalition for Am. [20236], PO Box 66096, Washington, DC 20009, (202)299-1091
Secular Inst. Little Apostoles of Charity [IO], Ponte Lambro, Italy
Secular Inst. of Saint Francis de Sales [19495], 104 W Main St., Middletown, PA 17057
Secular Inst. of Saint Francis de Sales [19495], 104 W Main St., Middletown, PA 17057
Secular Organizations for Sobriety [13289], 4773 Hollywood Blvd., Hollywood, CA 90027, (323)666-4295
Secular Student Alliance [17869], PO Box 2371, Columbus, OH 43216, (614)441-9588
SecuriJeunes Canada [★IO]
Securing America's Future Energy [6755], 1111 19th St. NW, Ste. 406, Washington, DC 20036, (202)461-2360
Securities
Amer. Assn. of Professional Tech. Analysts [3387]
Assn. of Securities and Exchange Commn. Alumni [3192]
Chicago Bd. Options Exchange [3193]
Chicago Stock Exchange [3194]
Consolidated Tape Assn. [3195]
Coun. of Institutional Investors [3196]
EMTA [3197]
EMTA [3197]
Financial Indus. Regulatory Authority [3198]
Investment Adviser Assn. [3199]
Investment Company Inst. [3200]
Mutual Fund Educ. Alliance [3201]
Natl. Assn. of Securities Professionals [3202]
New York Soc. of Security Analysts [3203]
New York Stock Exchange [3204]
North Amer. Securities Administrators Assn. [3205]
Securities Indus. and Financial Markets Assn. [3206]
Securities Transfer Assn. [3207]
Security Traders Assn. [3208]
Securities Analysts Assn., Chinese Taipei [IO], Taipei, Taiwan
Securities Analysts Assn., Thailand [IO], Bangkok, Thailand
Securities Indus. Assn. and The Bond Market Assn. [★3206]
Securities Indus. and Financial Markets Assn. [3206], 120 Broadway, 35th Fl., New York, NY 10271-0080, (212)313-1200
Securities and Insurance Licensing Assn. [2035], PO Box 498, Zionsville, IN 46077, (317)709-7452
Securities Investors Assn. - Singapore [IO], Singapore, Singapore
Securities Transfer Assn. [3207], PO Box 5220, Hazlet, NJ 07730, (732)888-6040
Security
9/11 Families for a Secure Am. Found. [18710]
Aircraft Carrier Indus. Base Coalition [1034]
Amer. Security Coun. [18587]
Amer. Security Coun. Found. [18588]
Assn. of Governmental Risk Pools [5549]
Assn. of Threat Assessment Professionals [3209]
Atlantic Coun. of the U.S. [18589]
British Amer. Security Info. Coun. [17501]
Building Security Coun. [3210]
Bus. Executives for Natl. Security [18590]
Center for Natl. Security Stud. [18591]
Center for Security Policy [18592]
Citizens to Stop Nuclear Terrorism [18711]
Coalition to Insure Against Terrorism [1949]
Coalition for a Realistic Foreign Policy [17698]
Coalition for a Secure Driver's License [18593]
Coun. for Emerging Natl. Security Affairs [18594]
Cyber Security Indus. Alliance [6974]
Daisy Alliance [18239]
Defense Orientation Conf. Assn. [18595]
Document Security Alliance [5539]
Electronic Security Assn. [3211]
Fuel for Truth [18608]
GlobalSecurity.org [18253]
InfraGard Natl. Members Alliance [5968]
The Infrastructure Security Partnership [3212]
Inst. for Defense Analyses [5969]
Intl. Assn. of Certified Surveillance Professionals [3213]

Reference to "IO" in place of a book number signifies that the association may be found in the 50th edition of International Organizations.

Intl. Assn. of Independent Private Sector Inspectors Gen. [5546]
Intl. Assn. of Investigative Locksmiths [3214]
Intl. Assn. of Investigative Locksmiths [3214]
Intl. Assn. of Professional Security Consultants [3215]
Intl. Assn. of Professional Security Consultants [3215]
Intl. Cargo Security Coun. [3216]
Intl. Coalition for the Responsibility to Protect [18498]
Intl. Found. for Protection Officers [3217]
Intl. Found. for Protection Officers [3217]
Intl. Guards Union of Am. [23294]
Intl. Intelligence Ethics Assn. [7001]
Intl. Intelligence Network [3218]
Intl. Intelligence Network [3218]
Intl. Org. of Black Security Executives [3219]
Intl. Security Mgt. Assn. [3220]
Intl. Security Mgt. Assn. [3220]SecurityIntl. Security, Trust and Privacy Alliance
Intl. Union, Security, Police and Fire Professionals of Am. [23295]
Intl. Union, Security, Police and Fire Professionals of Am. [23295]
Mine Warfare Assn. [18596]
Natl. Alarm Assn. of Am. [3221]
Natl. Assn. of Security Companies [3222]
Natl. Coun. of Investigation and Security Services [3223]
Natl. Cyber Security Alliance [7395]
Natl. Security and Law Soc. [5970]
Natl. Security Whistleblowers Coalition [18597]
Nautilus Inst. [18598]
Nautilus Inst. [18598]
Nine Lives Associates [3224]
Nine Lives Associates [3224]
North Amer. Security Products Org. [3225]
OPSEC Professionals Soc. [18599]
Partnership for Global Security [18600]
Partnership for Global Security [18600]
Physical Security Interoperability Alliance [6819]
Prevent Nuclear Terrorism Org. [18718]
Res. Security Administrators [5971]
Safe and Vault Technicians Assn. [3226]
Search for Common Ground [18601]
Search for Common Ground [18601]
Security Anal. and Risk Mgt. Assn. [3227]
Security Indus. Assn. [3228]
Set Am. Free [17619]
Transported Asset Protection Assn. [7396]
U.S. Indus. Coalition [7397]
U.S. Indus. Coalition [7397]
Women in Intl. Security [18602]
Women in Intl. Security [18602]
Security Anal. and Risk Mgt. Assn. [3227], PO Box 100284, Arlington, VA 22210, (703)635-7906
Security Assn. of South Africa [IO], Kloof, Republic of South Africa
Security on Campus [11693], 133 Ivy Ln., Ste. 200, King of Prussia, PA 19406-2101, (610)768-9330
Security Equip. Indus. Assn. [★3228]
Security Equip. Mfrs. Assn. [★3228]
Security Hardware Distributors Assn. [1660], 105 Eastern Ave., Ste. 104, Annapolis, MD 21403, (410)940-6346
Security Indus. Assn. [3228], 635 Slaters Ln., Ste. 110, Alexandria, VA 22314, (703)683-2075
Security Systems and Alarms Inspection Bd. [IO], North Shields, United Kingdom
Security Traders Assn. [3208], 80 Broad St., 5th Fl., New York, NY 10004, (203)202-7680

Security Training
Intl. Assn. of Certified Surveillance Professionals [3213]
Sedgwick Soc. [10738], 619 Wayne Ave., Haddonfield, NJ 08033

Seed
Abundant Life Seeds [3976]
Amer. Seed Res. Found. [4879]
Amer. Seed Trade Assn. [4880]
Assn. of Amer. Seed Control Officials [5187]
Natl. Coun. of Commercial Plant Breeders [4881]
Natl. Garden Bur. [4673]
Organic Seed Alliance [4882]

Organic Seed Growers and Trade Assn. [4883]
Soc. of Commercial Seed Technologists [4884]
Seed Assn. of Kyrgyzstan [IO], Bishkek, Kirgizstan
Seed Crushers' and Oil Processors' Assn. [IO], Beckenham, United Kingdom
Seed Savers Exchange [21820], 3094 N Winn Rd., Decorah, IA 52101, (563)382-5990
Seed Saver's Network [IO], Byron Bay, Australia
Seedlings Braille Books for Children [9036], PO Box 51924, Livonia, MI 48151-5924, (734)427-8552
Seeds of Diversity Canada [IO], Toronto, ON, Canada
Seeds For Hope [11861], PO Box 145, Plainview, NY 11803
Seeds For Hope [11861], PO Box 145, Plainview, NY 11803
Seeds of HOPE Intl. [11403], PO Box 49458, Colorado Springs, CO 80949, (719)473-8494
Seeds of Peace [18288], 370 Lexington Ave., Ste. 2103, New York, NY 10017, (212)573-8040
Seeing Eye [17115], PO Box 375, Morristown, NJ 07963-0375, (973)539-4425
Seeking Common Ground [13556], PO Box 101958, Denver, CO 80250, (303)691-2393
Seeking Ecology Educ. and Design Solutions [4216], 1015 Red Dr., Traverse City, MI 49684, (231)947-0312
Seeley Genealogical Soc. [20584], Terry Tietjens, Dir., PO Box 337, Abilene, KS 67410-0337, (785)263-1084
Seimos Planavimo Ir Seksualines Sveikatos Asociacija [★IO]
Seingalt Soc. - Defunct.
Seismological Soc. of Am. [7403], 201 Plaza Professional Bldg., El Cerrito, CA 94530, (510)525-5474
Seismological Soc. of Japan [IO], Tokyo, Japan

Seismology
Australian Earthquake Engg. Soc. [3669]
Earthquake Engg. Res. Inst. [7398]
European-Mediterranean Seismological Centre [16605]
Intl. Assn. of Seismology and Physics of the Earth's Interior [7399]
Intl. Assn. of Seismology and Physics of the Earth's Interior [7399]
Intl. Tsunami Info. Center [7400]
Intl. Tsunami Info. Center [7400]
Natl. Info. Ser. for Earthquake Engg. [7401]
NEHRP Coalition [7402]
Seismological Soc. of Am. [7403]
Vibration Isolation and Seismic Control Mfrs. Assn. [7404]
Sejours [★21853]
Sekai Boeki Center Tokyo [★IO]
Sekcija za arterijsko hipertenzijo [★IO]
Sekiyu Remmei Kohobu Shiryoka [★IO]
Selden Soc. [IO], London, United Kingdom
SELECT [IO], Midlothian, United Kingdom
Selected Independent Funeral Homes [2544], 500 Lake Cook Rd., Ste. 205, Deerfield, IL 60015, (847)236-9401
Selective Mutism Found. [15482], PO Box 13133, Sissonville, WV 25360-0133

Selenology
Amer. Lunar Soc. [6223]
Self-Employed Women's Assn. [IO], Ahmedabad, India
Self-Government Advocates [★18076]
Self-Guided Hunting Assn. [21867], PO Box 2771, Pinetop, AZ 85935, (800)518-4868
Self Help Africa [IO], Shrewsbury, United Kingdom
Self Help Found. [★12366]
Self Help Found. [★12366]
Self Help for Hard of Hearing People [★14940]
Self-Help Initiative for Sustainable Development [IO], Accra, Ghana
Self Help Intl. [12366], 703 2nd Ave. NW, Waverly, IA 50677-2308, (319)352-4040
Self Help Intl. [12366], 703 2nd Ave. NW, Waverly, IA 50677-2308, (319)352-4040
Self-Help Soc. - Defunct.
Self-Insurance Inst. of Am. [2036], PO Box 1237, Simpsonville, SC 29681, (800)851-7789
Self-Realization Fellowship [20300], 3880 San Rafael Ave., Dept. 9W, Los Angeles, CA 90065-3298, (818)549-5151

Self Reliance Assn. of Amer. Ukrainians [19263], 2332 W Chicago Ave., Chicago, IL 60622, (773)328-7500
Self-Rising Flour and Corn Meal Prog. [★1395]
Self-Rising Flour Inst. [★1395]
Self-Service and Kiosk Assn. and Digital Signage Assn. [★3233]
Self-Service Storage Assn. [★3626]
Self Storage Assn. [3626], 1901 N Beauregard St., Ste. 450, Alexandria, VA 22311, (703)575-8000
Self Storage Assn. of Australasia [IO], Bundoora, Australia
Self Storage Assn. of the United Kingdom [IO], Nantwich, United Kingdom

Self Defense
Aikido Assn. of Am. [22216]
All Japan Ju-Jitsu Intl. Fed. [22720]
Alliance of Guardian Angels [11681]
Amer. Self-Protection Assn. [22870]
Assn. of Defensive Spray Mfrs. [3229]
Assn. for Women's Self Defense Advancement [13031]
Assn. for Women's Self Defense Advancement [13031]
Chen Qingzhou Martial Arts Assn., USA [22728]
Gin Soon Tai Chi Chuan Fed. [22733]
Intl. Chinese Boxing Assn. [22436]
Intl. Disabled Self-Defense Assn. [13032]
Intl. Modern Hapkido Fed. [22735]
Intl. Seven-Star Mantis Style Lee Kam Wing Martial Art Assn. USA [22736]
Intl. Sungja-Do Assn. [22738]
Intl. Yang Style Tai Chi Chuan Assn. [22740]
Martial Arts Intl. Fed. [22742]
Martial Arts Teachers' Assn. [22743]
Mothers Arms [13033]
Natl. Coun. for Taekwondo Masters Certification [22746]
Natl. Team Cheng Martial Arts Assn. [22747]
U.S. Kuo Shu Fed. [22759]
U.S. Muay Thai Assn. [22761]
U.S. Taekwondo Union [22763]
USA Natl. Karate-do Fed. [22710]
World Hapkido Assn. [22767]
The World Kuoshu Fed. [22770]
World Martial Arts Assn. [22771]
World Mudo Fed. [22773]

Selfhelp
4 Real Women Intl. [13447]
Adult Children of Alcoholics World Ser. Org. [13034]
Adult Children of Alcoholics World Ser. Org. [13034]
Amer. Self-Help Gp. CH [13035]
A.R.T.S. Anonymous [13036]
Clutterers Anonymous [13037]
Co-Dependents Anonymous [13038]
Coalition for Emotional Literacy [13039]
Debtors Anonymous [13040]
Delancey St. Found. [13041]
Deliver the Dream [13042]
ManKind Proj. [13043]
Marijuana Anonymous World Services [13044]
Messies Anonymous [13045]
Natl. Assn. for Native Amer. Children of Alcoholics [11356]
Natl. Assn. for Shoplifting Prevention [13046]
Nicotine Anonymous World Services [13047]
Nicotine Anonymous World Services [13047]
Workaholics Anonymous [13048]
Selkirk Rex Breed Club - Address unknown since 2011.
Sellin Center for Studies in Criminology and Criminal Law - Defunct.
SEMA Found. [★6244]

Semantics
Inst. of Gen. Semantics [10531]
Inst. of Gen. Semantics [10531]
Intl. Soc. of Neuro-Semantics [16642]
Intl. Soc. of Neuro-Semantics [16642]
Semences du Patrimoine Canada [★IO]
SEMI Intl. [1116], 3081 Zanker Rd., San Jose, CA 95134, (408)943-6900
SEMI Intl. [1116], 3081 Zanker Rd., San Jose, CA 95134, (408)943-6900

A star before a book entry number signifies that the name is not listed separately, but is mentioned within the entry.

Semiconductor Environmental, Safety and Hea. Assn. **[6672]**, 1313 Dolley Madison Blvd., Ste. 402, McLean, VA 22101-3926, (703)790-1745
Semiconductor Equip. and Materials Inst. **[★1116]**
Semiconductor Equip. and Materials Inst. **[★1116]**
Semiconductor Equip. and Materials Intl. **[★1116]**
Semiconductor Equip. and Materials Intl. **[★1116]**
Semiconductor Indus. Assn. **[1117]**, 1101 K St. NW, Ste. 450, Washington, DC 20005, (202)446-1700
Semiconductor Safety Assn. **[★6672]**
Semillas - Sociedad Mexicana Pro Derechos de la Mujer, AC **[IO]**, Mexico City, Mexico
Seminar on the Acquisition of Latin Amer. Lib. Materials **[10010]**, Tulane Univ., The Latin Amer. Lib., 422 Howard-Tilton Memorial Lib., 7001 Freret St., New Orleans, LA 70118, (504)247-1366
Seminar on the Acquisition of Latin Amer. Lib. Materials **[10010]**, Tulane Univ., The Latin Amer. Lib., 422 Howard-Tilton Memorial Lib., 7001 Freret St., New Orleans, LA 70118, (504)247-1366
Semiotic Soc. of Am. **[7405]**, Univ. of West Florida, Box 32009, Pensacola, FL 32514, (850)474-2186
Semiotics
  Semiotic Soc. of Am. **[7405]**
Semisocialist Coalition of Earth **[18348]**, PO Box 4051, Bluefield, WV 24701
Semisocialist Coalition of Earth **[18348]**, PO Box 4051, Bluefield, WV 24701
Semmelweis Soc. Intl. **[16510]**, 6984 Knighthood Ln., Columbia, MD 21045, (714)995-7242
Senate Copper Caucus - Defunct.
Senegal League Against Epilepsy **[IO]**, Dakar, Senegal
Senegalese Red Cross Soc. **[IO]**, Dakar, Senegal
Senepol Cattle Breeders Assn. **[3940]**, PO Box 429, O'Fallon, IL 62269, (910)617-6355
SENEVOLU **[IO]**, Dakar, Senegal
Senior Action in a Gay Env. **[12111]**, 305 7th Ave., 6th Fl., New York, NY 10001, (212)741-2247
Senior Beta Club **[★23636]**
Senior Community Ser. Employment Prog. **[11958]**, U.S. Dept. of Labor, Frances Perkins Bldg., 200 Constitution Ave. NW, Washington, DC 20210, (877)872-5627
Senior Conformation Judges Assn. **[21650]**, 7200 Tanager St., Springfield, VA 22150, (703)451-5656
Senior Conformation Judges Assn. Educ. Fund **[★21488]**
Senior Corps **[13406]**, 1201 New York Ave. NW, Washington, DC 20525, (202)606-5000
Senior Executives Assn. **[5436]**, 77 K St. NE, Ste. 2600, Washington, DC 20002, (202)927-7000
Senior Executives Assn. Professional Development League **[5437]**, SEA, 77 K St. NE, Ste. 2600, Washington, DC 20002, (202)927-7000
Senior Experten Ser. **[IO]**, Bonn, Germany
Senior Gleaners **[12291]**, 1951 Bell Ave., Sacramento, CA 95838, (916)925-3240
Senior Masters - Defunct.
Senior Men's Boxing Comm. of the Amateur Athletic Union **[★22439]**
Senior Roller Skaters of Am. **[22899]**, 119 Yorkshire Ct., Elyria, OH 44035, (440)365-6843
SeniorNet **[13308]**, 12801 Worldgate Dr., Ste. 500, Herndon, VA 20170, (571)203-7100
SeniorNet **[13308]**, 12801 Worldgate Dr., Ste. 500, Herndon, VA 20170, (571)203-7100
The Seniors Coalition **[10869]**, 1250 Connecticut Ave. NW, Ste. 200, Washington, DC 20036, (202)261-3594
Seniors Cooperative Alert Network - Defunct.
Senmon Toshokan Kyogikai **[★IO]**
Sennacieca Asocio Tutmonda **[★IO]**
SENSE **[IO]**, London, United Kingdom
Sense of Smell Inst. **[1524]**, 545 5th Ave., Ste. 900, New York, NY 10017, (212)725-2755
Sense of Smell Inst. **[1524]**, 545 5th Ave., Ste. 900, New York, NY 10017, (212)725-2755
Sensus Educational Assn. **[IO]**, Alvsjo, Sweden
Sensus Studieforbund **[★IO]**
Sentencing Proj. **[11735]**, 1705 DeSales St. NW, 8th Fl., Washington, DC 20036, (202)628-0871
Sepak Takraw Assn. of Canada **[IO]**, Regina, SK, Canada
Sephardic House **[★19843]**

September 11 Digital Archv. **[18719]**, George Mason Univ., Center for History and New Media, Dept. of History and Art History, MSN 1E7, 4400 Univ. Dr., Fairfax, VA 22030, (703)993-9277
September 11th Families' Assn. **[11862]**, 22 Cortlandt St., Ste. 801, New York, NY 10007, (212)422-3520
September 11th Fund - Defunct.
September Eleventh Families for Peaceful Tomorrows **[12635]**, PO Box 1818, Peter Stuyvesant Sta., New York, NY 10009, (212)598-0970
September's Mission **[13312]**, 548 Broadway, 3rd Fl., New York, NY 10012, (888)424-4685
Sequoia Helping Hands **[11404]**, PO Box 13015, Durham, NC 27709, (919)469-3095
SER **[★11959]**
SER - Jobs for Progress **[★11959]**
SER - Jobs for Progress Natl. **[11959]**, 100 E Royal Ln., Ste. 130, Irving, TX 75039, (469)549-3600
Serama Coun. of North Am. - Address unknown since 2010.
Serb Natl. Fed. **[19227]**, 938 Penn Ave., 4th Fl., Pittsburgh, PA 15222, (412)642-7372
Serbia and Montenegro Tennis Fed. **[IO]**, Belgrade, Serbia
Serbian
  Serb Natl. Fed. **[19227]**
  Serbian-American Chamber of Commerce **[23441]**
  Serbian-American Chamber of Commerce **[23441]**
Serbian Acad. of Sciences and Arts **[IO]**, Belgrade, Serbia
Serbian-American Chamber of Commerce **[23441]**, 448 W Barry Ave., Chicago, IL 60657, (773)388-3404
Serbian-American Chamber of Commerce **[23441]**, 448 W Barry Ave., Chicago, IL 60657, (773)388-3404
Serbian Amer. Medical and Dental Soc.
Serbian Amer. Medical and Dental Soc. - Address unknown since 2011.
Serbian Bar Assn. of Am. **[5282]**, 20 S Clark, Ste. 700, Chicago, IL 60603, (312)782-8500
Serbian Physiological Soc. **[IO]**, Belgrade, Serbia
Serendib **[11629]**, PO Box 11081, Columbia, SC 29211, (877)573-5399
Serial ATA Intl. Org. **[6559]**, 3855 SW 153rd Dr., Beaverton, OR 97006, (503)619-0572
Serials Round Table - of ALA **[★9968]**
Serra Intl. **[19496]**, 70 E Lake St., Ste. 1210, Chicago, IL 60601-5938, (312)419-7411
Serra Intl. **[19496]**, 70 E Lake St., Ste. 1210, Chicago, IL 60601-5938, (312)419-7411
Sertoma Intl. **[13076]**, 1912 E Meyer Blvd., Kansas City, MO 64132-1174, (816)333-8300
Sertoma Intl. **[13076]**, 1912 E Meyer Blvd., Kansas City, MO 64132-1174, (816)333-8300
Servants in Faith and Tech. **[17198]**, 2944 County Rd. 113, Lineville, AL 36266, (256)396-2015
Servants in Faith and Tech. **[17198]**, 2944 County Rd. 113, Lineville, AL 36266, (256)396-2015
Servas Intl. **[★17986]**
Servas Intl. **[★17986]**
ServeHAITI **[11630]**, 999 Peachtree St. NE, Ste. 2300, Atlanta, GA 30309
ServeHAITI **[11630]**, 999 Peachtree St. NE, Ste. 2300, Atlanta, GA 30309
Service
  Assn. of Residential Cleaning Services Intl. **[2240]**
  Assn. of Support Professionals **[3230]**
  Assn. of Support Professionals **[3230]**
  Coalition of Ser. Indus. **[3231]**
  Custom Electronic Design Installation Assn. **[3232]**
  Customer Relationship Mgt. Assn. **[869]**
  Digital Screenmedia Assn. **[3233]**
  Equip. Ser. Assn. **[3234]**
  Fed. Consumer Info. Center Prog. **[5540]**
  Gyro Intl. **[13058]**
  Help Desk Inst. **[3235]**
  Intl. Customer Ser. Assn. **[3236]**
  Intl. Janitorial Cleaning Services Assn. **[2248]**
  Junior Optimist Octagon Intl. **[13060]**
  Key Club Intl. **[13061]**
  Kiwanis Intl. **[13062]**
  Natl. Assn. of Ser. Managers **[3237]**

Natl. Service-Learning Partnership **[8857]**
Optimist Intl. **[13071]**
Professional Ser. Assn. **[3238]**
Ser. Contract Indus. Coun. **[3239]**
Ser. Employees Intl. Union **[23296]**
Ser. Employees Intl. Union **[23296]**
Ser. Indus. Assn. **[3240]**ServeSer. and Support Professionals Assn.
United States Women of Today **[13079]**
Utility Indus. Gp. **[3607]**
Veteran's Coalition **[20810]**
Veterans and Military Families for Progress **[20815]**
Ser. Civil Intl., Austrian Br. **[IO]**, Vienna, Austria
Ser. Civil Intl. - Germany **[IO]**, Bonn, Germany
Ser. Civil Intl., Osterreichische Zweig **[★IO]**
Ser. Civil Intl. - U.S.A. **[★13405]**
Ser. Civil Intl. - U.S.A. **[★13405]**
Service Clubs
Active 20-30 Assn. of U.S./Canada **[13049]**
Altrusa Intl. **[13050]**
Altrusa Intl. **[13050]**
AMBUCS **[13051]**
Assistance League **[13052]**
Carnegie Hero Fund Commn. **[13053]**
Circle K Intl. **[13054]**
Circle K Intl. **[13054]**
Civitan Intl. **[13055]**
Civitan Intl. **[13055]**
Cosmopolitan Intl. **[13056]**
Cosmopolitan Intl. **[13056]**
Good Bears of the World **[13057]**
Good Bears of the World **[13057]**
Gyro Intl. **[13058]**
Gyro Intl. **[13058]**
Junior Chamber Intl. **[13059]**
Junior Chamber Intl. **[13059]**
Junior Optimist Octagon Intl. **[13060]**
Junior Optimist Octagon Intl. **[13060]**
Key Club Intl. **[13061]**
Key Club Intl. **[13061]**
Kiwanis Intl. **[13062]**
Kiwanis Intl. **[13062]**
La Sertoma Intl. **[13063]**
La Sertoma Intl. **[13063]**
Links Found. **[13064]**
Lions Clubs Intl. **[13065]**
Lions Clubs Intl. **[13065]**
Natl. Assn. of Colored Women's Clubs **[13066]**
Natl. Assn. of Junior Auxiliaries **[13067]**
Natl. Assn. of Negro Bus. and Professional Women's Clubs **[13068]**
Natl. Exchange Club **[13069]**
NGA **[13070]**
Optimist Intl. **[13071]**
Optimist Intl. **[13071]**
Pilot Intl. and Pilot Intl. Found. **[13072]**
Pilot Intl. and Pilot Intl. Found. **[13072]**
Quota Intl. **[13073]**
Quota Intl. **[13073]**
Rotary Intl. **[13074]**
Rotary Intl. **[13074]**
Ruritan Natl. **[13075]**
Sertoma Intl. **[13076]**
Sertoma Intl. **[13076]**
Soroptimist Intl. of the Americas **[13077]**
Soroptimist Intl. of the Americas **[13077]**
Theta Rho Girls' Club **[13561]**
United Nations Women's Guild **[13078]**
United Nations Women's Guild **[13078]**
United States Women of Today **[13079]**
Youth Ser. Am. **[13080]**
Zonta Intl. **[13081]**
Zonta Intl. **[13081]**
Ser. Contract Indus. Coun. **[3239]**, 204 S Monroe St., Tallahassee, FL 32301, (850)681-1058
Ser. Corps of Retired Executives **[★3296]**
Ser. d'assistance canadienne aux organismes **[★IO]**
Ser. d'Entretien et de Reparation Automobiles du Canada **[★IO]**
Ser. Employees Intl. Union **[23296]**, 1800 Massachusetts Ave. NW, Washington, DC 20036, (202)730-7000
Ser. Employees Intl. Union **[23296]**, 1800 Massachusetts Ave. NW, Washington, DC 20036, (202)730-7000

Reference to "IO" in place of a book number signifies that the association may be found in the 50th edition of International Organizations.

Ser. and Food Workers' Union [IO], Auckland, New Zealand

Ser. For Peace - Sierra Leone [IO], Freetown, Sierra Leone

Service Fraternities
   Alpha Phi Alpha Fraternity [23634]
   Alpha Phi Omega Natl. Ser. Fraternity [23635]
   Natl. Beta Club [23636]
   Phi Beta Sigma Fraternity [23637]
   Psi Sigma Phi Multicultural Fraternity [23638]

Ser. Indus. Assn. [3240], 2164 Historic Decatur Rd., Villa 19, San Diego, CA 92106, (619)221-9200

Ser. de liaison non gouvernemental de l'ONU [★IO]

Ser. for the Love of God [11631], 291 Dutch Ln., Pittsburgh, PA 15236, (412)650-6292

Ser. Managers of Am. [★3237]

Ser. for Peace [18289], 360 Fairfield Ave., Ste. 200, Bridgeport, CT 06604, (203)339-0064

Ser. of Peace and Justice, Chile [IO], Valparaiso, Chile

Ser. Permanent du Niveau Moyen des Mers [★IO]

Ser. Social Intl. [★IO]

Service Sororities
   Alpha Kappa Alpha [23639]
   Beta Sigma Phi [23640]
   Delta Gamma Pi Multicultural Sorority [23739]
   Delta Sigma Chi Sorority [23741]
   Delta Sigma Theta [23641]
   Delta Tau Lambda Sorority [23742]
   Epsilon Sigma Alpha [23642]
   Gamma Alpha Omega Sorority [23643]
   Gamma Sigma Sigma [23644]
   Kappa Phi Gamma Sorority [23746]
   Lambda Psi Delta Sorority [23747]
   Sigma Alpha Sorority [23645]
   Sigma Gamma Rho Sorority [23646]
   Zeta Chi Phi Multicultural Sorority [23752]
   Zeta Phi Beta Sorority [23647]

Ser. Specialists Assn. [368], 160 Symphony Way, Ste. 2, Elgin, IL 60120, (847)760-0067

Ser. Sta. Dealers of Am. [★2669]

Ser. Sta. Dealers of Am. and Allied Trades [★2669]

Ser. Sta. Dealers of America/National Coalition of Petroleum Retailers and Allied Trades [2669], 1532 Pointer Ridge Pl., Ste. E, Bowie, MD 20716, (301)390-4405

Ser. and Support Professionals Assn.

Ser. and Support Professionals Assn. - Address unknown since 2011.

Ser. Technicians Soc. [★3460]

Ser. Tools Inst. [★1650]

Ser. Workers United [23230], 330 W 42nd St., Rm. 900, New York, NY 10036, (888)798-6466

Servicemembers Legal Defense Network [5837], PO Box 65301, Washington, DC 20035-5301, (202)328-3244

Services pour femmes immigrantes d'Ottawa [★IO]

Services for the Hea. in Asian and African Regions [IO], Tokyo, Japan

Services, Indus. Professional and Tech. Union [IO], Dublin, Ireland

Servicio Colombiano de Comunicacion [IO], Bogota, Colombia

Servicio Paz y Justicia en Argentina [★IO]

Servicio Paz y Justicia, Chile [★IO]

Serving Our World [11405], 30025 Alicia Pkwy., No. 179, Laguna Niguel, CA 92677, (949)363-7343

Serving Our World [11405], 30025 Alicia Pkwy., No. 179, Laguna Niguel, CA 92677, (949)363-7343

Servizio dei Gesuiti per i Rifugiati in Italia [★IO]

Servizio Volontariato Giovanile [★IO]

Sesame Workshop [9474], PO Box 5136, Toms River, NJ 08754-5136

SESKO Electrotechnical Standardization in Finland [IO], Helsinki, Finland

Set Am. Free [17619], 7811 Montrose Rd., Ste. 505, Potomac, MD 20854-3368

Set Decorators Soc. of Am. [2074], 7100 Tujunga Ave., Ste. No. A, North Hollywood, CA 91605, (818)255-2425

Seth and Della Cummings Family Assn. - Defunct.

SETI League [6236], PO Box 555, Little Ferry, NJ 07643, (201)641-1770

Seton Hill University's E-magnify - Address unknown since 2010.

Seton Shrine Center [★19480]

Setting Priorities for Retirement Years [12919], 3916 Rosemary St., Chevy Chase, MD 20815, (301)656-3405

Seva Found. [12367], 1786 5th St., Berkeley, CA 94710, (510)845-7382

Seva Found. [12367], 1786 5th St., Berkeley, CA 94710, (510)845-7382

Seven Generations Ahead [11632], PO Box 3125, Oak Park, IL 60303, (708)660-9909

Seven Seas Cruising Assn. [22390], 2501 E Commercial Blvd., Ste. 203, Fort Lauderdale, FL 33308, (954)771-5660

Seventh Day Adventist
   Adventist Community Services [20237]
   Assn. of Adventist Forums [20238]
   Assn. of Adventist Forums [20238]
   Christians in Crisis [20239]
   Seventh Day Adventist Kinship Intl. [19800]

Seventh Day Adventist Kinship Intl. [19800], PO Box 69, Tillamook, OR 97141-0069

Seventh Day Adventist Kinship Intl. [19800], PO Box 69, Tillamook, OR 97141-0069

Seventh-Day Adventist Welfare Services [★12795]

Seventh-Day Adventist Welfare Services [★12795]

Seventh-Day Adventist World Ser. [★12795]

Seventh-Day Adventist World Ser. [★12795]

Seventh Day Baptist Gen. Conf. [19327], PO Box 1678, Janesville, WI 53547-1678, (608)752-5055

Seventh Day Baptist Gen. Conf. of the U.S. and Canada [19328], PO Box 1678, Janesville, WI 53547-1678, (608)752-5055

Seventh Day Baptist Historical Soc. [19329], PO Box 1678, Janesville, WI 53547-1678, (608)752-5055

Seventh Day Baptist Missionary Soc. [19330], 19 Hillside Ave., Ashaway, RI 02804, (401)596-4326

Seventh Day Baptist World Fed. [19331], 88 Terrace Ave., Salem, WV 26426, (304)782-1727

Seventh Day Baptist World Fed. [19331], 88 Terrace Ave., Salem, WV 26426, (304)782-1727

Seventh Generation Advisors [4304], 2601 Ocean Park Blvd., Ste. 311, Santa Monica, CA 90405, (310)664-0300

Seventh Generation Fund for Indian Development [18156], PO Box 4569, Arcata, CA 95518, (707)825-7640

Seventh Step Soc. of Canada [IO], Calgary, AB, Canada

Severn Valley Welsh Pony and Cob Assn. [IO], Welshpool, United Kingdom

Sew Much Comfort [11079], 13805 Frontier Ln., Burnsville, MN 55337

Sewa Intl. U.S.A. [12368], 3908 Westhollow Pkwy., Houston, TX 77082, (708)USA-SEWA

Sewa Org. [IO], Lahore, Pakistan

Sewalanka Found. [IO], Boralesgamuwa, Sri Lanka

Sewing
   Canadian Quilters' Assn. [20989]
   Sewing Educator Alliance [8858]
   Spinning and Weaving Assn. [3456]
   Spirit Quilts [11408]

Sewing Educator Alliance [8858], Sewing Dealers Trade Association/Vacuum Dealers Trade Assn., 2724 2nd Ave., Des Moines, IA 50313, (515)282-9101

Sewn Products Equip. and Suppliers of the Americas [1867], 9650 Strickland Rd., Ste. 103-324, Raleigh, NC 27615, (919)872-8909

Sewn Products Equip. Suppliers Assn. of the Americas [★1867]

Sex Abuse Treatment Alliance [13100], PO Box 761, Milwaukee, WI 53201-0761, (517)482-2085

Sex Addiction
   COSA [13082]
   COSA [13082]
   Sex Addicts Anonymous [13083]
   Sex and Love Addicts Anonymous [13084]
   Sexaholics Anonymous [13085]
   Sexaholics Anonymous [13085]

Sex Addicts Anonymous [13083], PO Box 70949, Houston, TX 77270, (713)869-4902

Sex Info. and Educ. Coun. of Canada [IO], Toronto, ON, Canada

Sex Info. and Educ. Coun. of the U.S. [★16651]

Sex and Love Addicts Anonymous [13084], 1550 NE Loop 410, Ste. 118, San Antonio, TX 78209, (210)828-7900

Sex Worker Found. for Art, Culture and Educ. [★13106]

Sex Workers Anonymous - Address unknown since 2011.

Sexaholics Anonymous [13085], PO Box 3565, Brentwood, TN 37024, (615)370-6062

Sexaholics Anonymous [13085], PO Box 3565, Brentwood, TN 37024, (615)370-6062

Sexual Abuse
   Anti-Child Pornography Org. [12710]
   DeafHope [12141]
   DOVE: Advocacy Services for Abused Deaf Women and Children [12142]
   Generation Five [13086]
   Girls Educational and Mentoring Services [18603]
   Global Centurion [11292]
   Hope of Survivors [13087]
   Incest Survivors Anonymous [13088]
   Incest Survivors Anonymous [13088]
   MaleSurvivor: The Natl. Org. Against Male Sexual Victimization [13089]
   Minga [11351]
   Mothers Against Sexual Abuse [13090]
   Mothers Against Sexual Predators At Large [13091]
   Natl. Assn. to Prevent Sexual Abuse of Children [13092]
   Natl. Org. of Sisters of Color Ending Sexual Assault [13093]
   Natl. Sexual Violence Rsrc. Center [13094]
   One in Four [13095]
   Pandora's Proj. [13096]
   Paul and Lisa Prog. [13097]
   People Against Rape [13098]
   RedLight Children [11144]
   Rwanda Gift for Life [13099]
   Sex Abuse Treatment Alliance [13100]
   Survivor Connections [13101]
   Survivors of Incest Anonymous [13102]
   Transitions Global [12248]
   WINGS Found. [13103]

Sexual Abuse Anonymous [★13102]

Sexual Abusers; Assn. for the Treatment of [6253]

Sexual Advice Assn. [IO], London, United Kingdom

Sexual Assault Res. Assn. [★6253]

Sexual Freedom
   Atticus Circle [17735]
   Center for Sex and Culture [8859]SexualCross-dressers Intl.
   Gender Educ. and Advocacy [13104]
   Intl. Found. for Gender Educ. [13105]
   Intl. Sex Worker Found. for Art, Culture and Educ. [13106]SexualIntersex Soc. of North Am.
   Loving More [13107]
   NASCA Intl. [13108]
   NASCA Intl. [13108]
   Natl. Coalition for Sexual Freedom [18604]
   Natl. Coming Out Day [12102]
   Natl. Leather Assn. - Intl. [13109]
   North Amer. Man/Boy Love Assn. [13110]
   Renaissance Transgender Assn. [13111]
   Seventh Day Adventist Kinship Intl. [19800]
   Soc. for the Second Self [13112]
   Sylvia Rivera Law Proj. [18730]
   World Professional Assn. for Transgender Hea. [13113]
   World Professional Assn. for Transgender Hea. [13113]

Sexual Harassment
   Minga [11351]
   Transitions Global [12248]

Sexual Health
   Abstinence CH [16643]
   Accord Alliance [13114]
   Aim For Success [8860]
   Amer. Assn. of Sexuality Educators, Counselors and Therapists [16644]
   Amer. Bd. of Sexology [16645]
   Cervical Barrier Advancement Soc. [16646]
   Family Care Intl. [16647]
   Family Care Intl. [16647]
   Fertile Dreams [14531]

A star before a book entry number signifies that the name is not listed separately, but is mentioned within the entry.

Friends-4-Cures [13923]
Intl. Professional Surrogates Assn. [16648]
Intl. Professional Surrogates Assn. [16648]
Intl. Soc. for the Stud. of Women's Sexual Hea.
[16649]
Intl. Soc. for the Stud. of Women's Sexual Hea.
[16649]
Intl. Union Against Sexually Transmitted Infec-
tions, Regional Off. for North Am. [16656]
Internet Sexuality Info. Services [8861]
Natl. Abstinence Educ. Assn. [8862]
Natl. Black Gay Men's Advocacy Coalition [12099]
Sexual Medicine Soc. of North Am. [16650]
Sexuality Info. and Educ. Coun. of the U.S.
[16651]
Soc. for the Sci. Stud. of Sexuality [16652]
Soc. for Sex Therapy and Res. [16653]
World Against AIDS [12386]
Sexual Hea. and Family Planning Australia - Intl.
Prog. [IO], Canberra, Australia
Sexual Medicine Soc. of North Am. [16650], 1100 E
Woodfield Rd., Ste. 520, Schaumburg, IL 60173,
(847)517-7225
Sexual Orientation and Gender Expression; Coun.
on [8869]
Sexuality
Natl. Coming Out Day [12102]
Org. for the Stud. of Sex Differences [7406]
Seventh Day Adventist Kinship Intl. [19800]
Soc. for the Psychological Stud. of Lesbian, Gay,
Bisexual and Transgender Issues [16429]
Sylvia Rivera Law Proj. [18730]
Youth Pride Alliance [12117]
Sexuality Info. and Educ. Coun. of the U.S. [16651],
90 John St., Ste. 402, New York, NY 10038,
(212)819-9770
Sexually Transmitted Diseases
AIDS-Free World [13594]
Amer. Social Hea. Assn. [16654]
Amer. Social Hea. Assn. I Herpes Rsrc. Center
[16655]
Blood: Water Mission [10809]
Gardens for Hea. Intl. [13604]
Global AIDS Interfaith Alliance [13607]
Global Youth Coalition on HIV/AIDS [10881]
HomeAID for Africa [10812]
Intl. Alliance for the Prevention of AIDS [13614]
Intl. Union Against Sexually Transmitted Infec-
tions, Regional Off. for North Am. [16656]
Intl. Union Against Sexually Transmitted Infec-
tions, Regional Off. for North Am. [16656]
Internet Sexuality Info. Services [8861]
Lily of the Valley Endeavor [10886]
Natl. Black Gay Men's Advocacy Coalition [12099]
Natl. Coalition of Anti-Violence Programs [18770]
Natl. Coalition of STD Directors [16657]
San Francisco AIDS Found. [13624]
Soc. for Prevention of Human Infertility [16598]
SOTENI Intl. [10893]
World Against AIDS [12386]
World Hea. Clinicians [13630]
Seyaj Org. for Childhood Protection [IO], Sana'a,
Yemen
Seychelles Amateur Athletics Fed. [IO], Victoria,
Seychelles
Seychelles Assn. Of Offshore Practitioners and
Registered Agents [IO], Victoria, Seychelles
Seychelles Bird Records Comm. [IO], Victoria, Sey-
chelles
Seychelles Canoe Assn. [IO], Victoria, Seychelles
Seychelles Cricket Assn. [IO], Mahe, Seychelles
Seychelles Disabled People's Org. [IO], Victoria,
Seychelles
Seychelles Hospitality and Tourism Assn. [IO], Victo-
ria, Seychelles
Seychelles Karting Assn. [IO], Victoria, Seychelles
Seychelles Natl. Coun. for Children [IO], Victoria,
Seychelles
Seychelles Natl. Youth Coun. [IO], Victoria, Sey-
chelles
Seychelles Olympians Assn. [IO], Victoria, Sey-
chelles
Seychelles Soc. for the Prevention of Cruelty to
Animals [IO], Victoria, Seychelles
Seychelles Squash Rackets Assn. [IO], Victoria,
Seychelles

Seychelles Tennis Assn. [IO], Roche Caiman, Sey-
chelles
Seychelles Yachting Assn. [IO], Victoria, Seychelles
SFI Found. [6244], 15708 Pomerado Rd., Ste.
N208, Poway, CA 92064-2066, (858)451-8868
SFPE Educational and Sci. Foundation [★6863]
SGCI Chemie Pharma Schweiz [IO], Zurich,
Switzerland
SGM International/U.S.A. [★19339]
SGML Open [★7524]
Shadan Hojin Nihon Ryokogyo Kyokai [★IO]
Shadanhojin Nipon Yakurigakkai [★IO]
ShadowBlossom [11633], PO Box 1887, Decatur,
GA 30031, (678)999-6020
SHAEF and ETOUSA Veterans Assn. - Defunct.
Shakers
Antique Glass Salt and Sugar Shaker Club
[21304]
Friends of the Shakers [10532]
Shakespeare Assn. of America - Defunct.
Shakespeare Birthplace Trust [IO], Warwickshire,
United Kingdom
Shakespeare Oxford Soc. [9412], PO Box 808,
Yorktown Heights, NY 10598, (914)962-1717
Shakespeare Oxford Soc. [9412], PO Box 808,
Yorktown Heights, NY 10598, (914)962-1717
Shakespeare Soc. [9413], 45 E 78th St., New York,
NY 10075, (212)967-6802
Shakespeare Soc. of Southern Africa [IO], Graham-
stown, Republic of South Africa
Shakespeare Theatre Assn. of Am. [10601], Mr.
Philip Sneed, Member-at-Large, 277 UCB, Boulder,
CO 80309, (303)492-2782
Shakey's Franchised Dealers Assn. - Defunct.
Shalom Achshav [★18010]
Shalom Achshav [★IO]
Shalom Achshav [★18010]
Shape Up Am. [16233], PO Box 149, Clyde Park,
MT 59018, (406)686-4844
SHARE [★12621]
Share and Care Cockayne Syndrome Network
[14627], PO Box 282, Waterford, VA 20197,
(703)727-0404
Share Found. [★17604]
Share Found. [★17604]
SHARE Found.: Building a New El Salvador Today
[17604], 2425 Coll. Ave., Berkeley, CA 94704,
(510)848-8487
SHARE Found.: Building a New El Salvador Today
[17604], 2425 Coll. Ave., Berkeley, CA 94704,
(510)848-8487
Share Our Strength [12292], 1730 M St. NW, Ste.
700, Washington, DC 20036, (202)393-2925
Share a Pet [12653], 3699 N Dixie Hwy., Oakland
Park, FL 33334, (954)630-8763
SHARE: Pregnancy and Infant Loss Support
[12621], 402 Jackson St., St. Charles, MO 63301,
(636)947-6164
Shared Hope Intl. [13498], PO Box 65337, Vancou-
ver, WA 98665, (360)693-8100
Shared Hope Intl. [13498], PO Box 65337, Vancou-
ver, WA 98665, (360)693-8100
Shared Housing Rsrc. Center [★12196]
SHARED, Inc. [15209], 1018 Beacon St., Ste. 201,
Brookline, MA 02446, (617)277-7800
Shared Living Rsrc. Center - Defunct.
Sharing Info. and Experience for Safer Operations
[IO], Pulborough, United Kingdom
Sharing of Ministries Abroad U.S.A. [20091], 2501
Ridgmar Plz., No. 99, Fort Worth, TX 76116,
(817)737-7662
Sharing Resources Worldwide [15210], 4417 Rob-
ertson Rd., Madison, WI 53714
Shark Alliance [5128], 901 E St. NW, 10th Fl.,
Washington, DC 20004, (202)552-2000
Shark Found. Switzerland [IO], Zurich, Switzerland
Shark Res. Inst. [7061], PO Box 40, Princeton, NJ
08540, (609)921-3522
Shark Res. Inst. [7061], PO Box 40, Princeton, NJ
08540, (609)921-3522
Shark Savers [5129], 419 Lafayette St., 2nd Fl.,
New York, NY 10003
Shark Savers [5129], 419 Lafayette St., 2nd Fl.,
New York, NY 10003
Sharkhunters Intl. [10096], PO Box 1539, Hernando,
FL 34442, (352)637-2917

Sharkhunters Intl. [10096], PO Box 1539, Hernando,
FL 34442, (352)637-2917
Sharps Collector Assn. [21718], PO Box 81566, Bill-
ings, MT 59108
Sharsheret [13978], 1086 Teaneck Rd., Ste. 3A,
Teaneck, NJ 07666, (201)833-2341
Shatner and Friends Intl. [23784], PO Box 1345,
Studio City, CA 91614
Shaw Soc; Bernard [9351]
Shea Yeleen Intl. [1671], 280 Madison Ave., Ste.
912, New York, NY 10016, (212)386-5576
Sheep
Amer. Border Leicester Assn. [4885]
Amer. Cheviot Sheep Soc. [4886]
Amer. Cormo Sheep Assn. [4887]
Amer. Corriedale Assn. [4888]
Amer. Cotswold Record Assn. [4889]
Amer. Delaine and Merino Record Assn. [4890]
Amer. Dorper Sheep Breeders' Soc. [4891]
Amer. Dorper Sheep Breeders' Soc. [4891]
Amer. Hampshire Sheep Assn. [4892]
Amer. Karakul Sheep Registry [4893]
Amer. Miniature Cheviot Sheep Breeders Assn.
[4894]
Amer. North Country Cheviot Sheep Assn. [4895]
Amer. Oxford Sheep Assn. [4896]
Amer. Polypay Sheep Assn. [4897]
Amer. Rambouillet Sheep Breeders' Assn. [4898]
Amer. Romney Breeders' Assn. [4899]
Amer. Sheep Indus. Assn. [4900]
Amer. Shetland Sheepdog Assn. [21506]
Amer. Shropshire Registry Assn. [4901]
Amer. Southdown Breeders' Assn. [4902]
ARCA: Amer. Romeldale/CVM Assn. [4903]
Australian Corriedale Assn. [14783]
Australian Texel Stud Breeders Assn. [5749]
Barbados Blackbelly Sheep Assn. Intl. [4904]
Barbados Blackbelly Sheep Assn. Intl. [4904]
Bluefaced Leicester Union of North Am. [4905]
Bluefaced Leicester Union of North Am. [4905]
Columbia Sheep Breeders Assn. of Am. [4906]
Continental Dorset Club [4907]
Finnsheep Breeders Assn. [4908]
Icelandic Sheepdog Assn. of Am. [21582]
Jacob Sheep Breeders Assn. [4909]
Jacob Sheep Soc. [3508]
Miniature and Novelty Sheep Breeders Assn. and
Registry [4910]
Montadale Sheep Breeders Assn. [4911]
Natl. Lamb Feeders Assn. [4912]
Natl. Lincoln Sheep Breeders' Assn. [4913]
Natl. Tunis Sheep Registry, Inc. [4914]
Natural Colored Wool Growers Assn. [4915]
Natural Colored Wool Growers Assn. [4915]
Navajo-Churro Sheep Assn. [4916]
North Amer. Babydoll Southdown Sheep Assn.
and Registry [4917]
North Amer. Babydoll Southdown Sheep Assn.
and Registry [4917]
North Amer. Clun Forest Assn. [4918]
North Amer. Shetland Sheepbreeders Assn.
[4919]
North Amer. Wensleydale Sheep Assn. [4920]
North Amer. Wensleydale Sheep Assn. [4920]
Painted Desert Sheep Soc. [4921]
Public Lands Coun. [4824]
Rough Fell Sheep Breeders Assn. [2346]
Soays of Am. [4922]
Soays of Am. [4922]
Soc. for the Conservation of Bighorn Sheep
[5131]
United Suffolk Sheep Assn. [4923]
Wild Sheep Found. [5148]
Sheepdog
Amer. Shetland Sheepdog Assn. [21506]
Icelandic Sheepdog Assn. of Am. [21582]
Sheet Metal and Air Conditioning Contractors' Natl.
Assn. [1720], 4201 Lafayette Center Dr., Chantilly,
VA 20151-1209, (703)803-2980
Sheet Metal Contractors Assn. of Alberta [IO], Cal-
gary, AB, Canada
Sheet Metal Contractors Natl. Assn. [★1720]
Sheet Metal Occupational Hea. Inst. [★13007]
Sheet Metal Occupational Hea. Inst. Trust [13007],
601 N Fairfax St., Ste. 250, Alexandria, VA 22314,
(703)739-7130

Reference to "IO" in place of a book number signifies that the association may be found in the 50th edition of International Organizations.

Sheet Metal Workers' Intl. Assn. **[23255]**, 1750 New York Ave. NW, 6th Fl., Washington, DC 20006, (202)783-5880

Sheffield Chamber of Commerce and Indus. **[IO]**, Sheffield, United Kingdom

Sheffield Conservation Volunteers **[IO]**, Sheffield, United Kingdom

Shelby Amer. Auto. Club **[21163]**, PO Box 788, Sharon, CT 06069

Shellac Export Promotion Coun. **[IO]**, Calcutta, India

Shellfish Assn. of Great Britain **[IO]**, London, United Kingdom

Shelter
Natl. Domestic Violence Hotline **[11894]**
Out of Love Sugar Glider Rescue **[11017]**
The Shelter Alliance **[11634]**
Shelter Animal Reiki Assn. **[16581]**

Shelter Advt. Assn. **[★101]**

The Shelter Alliance **[11634]**, 1719 State Rte. 10, Ste. 235, Parsippany, NJ 07054

Shelter Animal Reiki Assn. **[16581]**, 369B 3rd St., No. 156, San Rafael, CA 94901

Shelter for Life Intl. **[19209]**, 10201 Wayzata Blvd., Ste. 230, Hopkins, MN 55305, (763)253-4082

Shelter Now Intl. **[★19209]**

Shelterforce Collective **[★12190]**

Shelving Mfrs. Assn. **[★1871]**

Shema Yisrael **[★19859]**

Shenandoah Natl. Park Assn. **[9726]**, 3655 U.S. Hwy. 211 E, Luray, VA 22835, (540)999-3582

Shenandoah Natural History Assn. **[★9726]**

Shepaug Valley Archaeological Soc. **[★6169]**

Shepway Chamber of Commerce and Indus. **[★12983]**

Sherwood Anderson Soc. - Defunct.

Shetland Aquaculture **[IO]**, Lerwick, United Kingdom

Shevchenko Sci. Soc. **[19264]**, 63 4th Ave., New York, NY 10003-5200, (212)254-5130

Shevchenko Sci. Soc. **[19264]**, 63 4th Ave., New York, NY 10003-5200, (212)254-5130

SHHH **[★14940]**

Shiatsu Educ. Center of Am. **[★16017]**

Shiatsu Educ. Center of Am. **[★16017]**

Shiatsu Therapy Assn. of Australia **[IO]**, Surrey Hills, Australia

Shibumi Intl. Reiki Assn. **[16582]**, PO Box 1776, Berthoud, CO 80513

Shidhulai Swanirvar Sangstha **[IO]**, Dhaka, Bangladesh

Shields Class Assn. **[★22391]**

Shields Class Sailing Assn. **[★22391]**

Shields Natl. Class Assn. **[22391]**, 3225 W St. Joseph, Lansing, MI 48917, (517)372-9207

Shih Tzu Club of Am. **[★21507]**

Shindokay Org. **[IO]**, Quetta, Pakistan

Shine Therapy **[15274]**, PO Box 12325, Fort Worth, TX 76110, (817)372-8998

Shingles Support Soc. **[IO]**, London, United Kingdom

Shining Hope for Communities **[11635]**, 14 Red Glen Rd., Middletown, CT 06457, (860)218-9854

SHIP Aid: Shipping Humanitarian Aid to Impoverished People **[12889]**, 1216 Monica Ln., San Jose, CA 95128-4121

SHIP Aid: Shipping Humanitarian Aid to Impoverished People **[12889]**, 1216 Monica Ln., San Jose, CA 95128-4121

Ship Info. Center **[★10057]**

Shipbuilders' Assn. of Japan **[IO]**, Tokyo, Japan

Shipbuilders Coun. of Am. **[2370]**, 1455 F St. NW, Ste. 225, Washington, DC 20005, (202)347-5462

Shipbuilders and Shiprepairers Assn. **[IO]**, Egham, United Kingdom

Shipbuilding Assn. of Canada **[IO]**, Ottawa, ON, Canada

Shipmasters' Assn. of Montenegro **[IO]**, Kotor, Montenegro

Shipowners Claims Bur. **[2037]**, 1 Battery Park Plz., 31st Fl., New York, NY 10004, (212)847-4500

Shippers for Competitive Ocean Transportation - Defunct.

Shippers Natl. Freight Claim Coun., Inc. **[★3275]**

Shippers Oil Field Traffic Assn. **[★2649]**

Shippers of Recycled Textiles **[3268]**, 2105 Laurel Bush Rd., Ste. 200, Bel Air, MD 21015, (443)640-1050

Shipping
Amer. Import Shippers Assn. **[3241]**
Amer. Inst. for Shippers' Associations **[3242]**
Amer. Moving and Storage Assn. **[3243]**
Amer. Moving and Storage Assn. **[3243]**ShippingAustralian Ship Repairers Gp.
Coun. on Safe Trans. of Hazardous Articles **[3244]**
Dangerous Goods Advisory Coun. **[3245]**
Distribution and LTL Carriers Assn. **[3246]**
Doc to Dock **[15302]**
Express Delivery and Logistics Assn. **[3247]**
Hong Kong Assn. of Freight Forwarding and Logistics **[9495]**
Independent Armored Car Operators Assn. **[3248]**
Intl. Assn. of Movers **[3249]**
Intl. Assn. of Movers **[3249]**
Intl. Assn. of Structural Movers **[3250]**
Intl. Assn. of Structural Movers **[3250]**
Intl. Furniture and Trans. Logistics Coun. **[3251]**
Intl. Furniture Trans. and Logistics Coun. **[3251]**
Intl. Safe Transit Assn. **[3252]**
Intl. Safe Transit Assn. **[3252]**
LTD Shippers Assn. **[3486]**
Maritime Assn. of the Port of New York and New Jersey **[3253]**
Messenger Courier Assn. of Am. **[3254]**
NASSTRAC **[3255]**
Natl. Armored Car Assn. **[3256]**
Natl. Cargo Bur. **[3257]**
Natl. Motor Freight Traffic Assn. **[3258]**
Natl. Shippers Strategic Trans. Coun. **[3259]**
Natl. Solid Wastes Mgt. Assn. **[3260]**
Natl. Tank Truck Carriers **[3261]**
Natl. Waterways Conf. **[3262]**
New York/New Jersey Foreign Freight Forwarders and Brokers Assn. **[3263]**
New York Shipping Assn. **[3264]**
North Amer. Shippers Assn. **[3265]**
Pacific Maritime Assn. **[3266]**
Propeller Club of the U.S. **[3267]**
Shippers of Recycled Textiles **[3268]**
Shipping Assn. of Trinidad and Tobago **[2648]**
Soc. of Marine Port Engineers **[3269]**
Specialized Carriers and Rigging Assn. **[3270]**
Specialized Carriers and Rigging Assn. **[3270]**
Sporting Goods Shippers Assn. **[3271]**
Trans-Atlantic Amer. Flag Liner Operators/Trans-Pacific Amer. Flag Berth Operators **[3272]**
Trans. Inst. **[3273]**
Trans. Intermediaries Assn. **[3274]**
Trans. and Logistics Coun. **[3275]**
Women's Intl. Shipping and Trading Assn. **[3276]**
Women's Intl. Shipping and Trading Assn. **[3276]**

Shipping Assn. of Trinidad and Tobago **[IO]**, Port of Spain, Trinidad and Tobago

Shipping Fed. of Canada **[IO]**, Montreal, QC, Canada

Ships-in-Bottles Assn. of Am. **[21911]**, PO Box 180550, Coronado, CA 92178

Ships on Stamps Unit **[22074]**, Myron P. Molnau, Sec., 2117 E 6th St., Moscow, ID 83843-9709

Shirika la Utafiti na Maendeleo va Viwanda, Tanzania **[★IO]**

Shirkat Gah **[★IO]**

Shirley Family Assn. **[20585]**, 10256 Glencoe Dr., Cupertino, CA 95014

Shoe Ser. Inst. of Am. **[1461]**, 305 Huntsman Ct., Bel Air, MD 21015, (410)569-3425

Shomrim Societies; Natl. Conf. of **[12412]**

Shomrim Soc. **[12414]**, Murry Ellman, Financial Sec., PO Box 598, Knickerbocker, NY 10002, (718)543-4825

Shon Branham Fan Club **[23891]**, 206 Doel Bean, Kirbyville, TX 75956, (409)423-3319

Shooting
Amateur Trapshooting Assn. **[22871]**
Amer. Single Shot Rifle Assn. **[22872]**
Amer. Single Shot Rifle Assn. **[22872]**
Browning Collectors Assn. **[21712]**
Cast Bullet Assn. **[22873]**
Cowboy Mounted Shooting Assn. **[22874]**
Fifty Caliber Shooters Assn. **[22154]**
Fifty Caliber Shooters Assn. **[22154]**
Intl. Benchrest Shooters **[22875]**
Intl. Defensive Pistol Assn. **[22876]**
Intl. Defensive Pistol Assn. **[22876]**
Intl. Handgun Metallic Silhouette Assn. **[22877]**
Intl. Handgun Metallic Silhouette Assn. **[22877]**
Natl. Alliance for the Development of Archery **[22222]**
Natl. Archery Assn. of the U.S. **[22223]**
Natl. Assn. of Arms Shows **[21715]**
Natl. Assn. of Shooting Sports Athletes **[22878]**
Natl. Bench Rest Shooters Assn. **[22879]**
Natl. Firearms Act Trade and Collectors Assn. **[1354]**
Natl. Mossberg Collectors Assn. **[21716]**
Natl. Muzzle Loading Rifle Assn. **[22880]**
Natl. Rifle Assn. of Am. **[22881]**
Natl. Shooting Sports Found. **[22882]**
Natl. Skeet Shooting Assn. **[22883]**
Natl. Sporting Clays Assn. **[22884]**
North Amer. Bowhunting Coalition **[21866]**
North Amer. Hunting Club **[22700]**
North-South Skirmish Assn. **[22885]**
Pacific Intl. Trapshooting Assn. **[22886]**
Pacific Intl. Trapshooting Assn. **[22886]**
U.S. Complete Shooting Dog Assn. **[21668]**
U.S. Helice Assn. **[22887]**
U.S. Practical Shooting Assn. **[22888]**
U.S. Revolver Assn. **[22889]**
USA Shooting **[22890]**
World Fast-Draw Assn. **[22891]**

Shooting Fed. of Canada **[IO]**, Ottawa, ON, Canada

Shop Am. Alliance **[3126]**, 1308 Westhampton Woods Ct., Chesterfield, MO 63005, (707)224-3795

Shop and Display Equip. Assn. **[IO]**, Caterham, United Kingdom

Shop, Distributive, and Allied Employees' Assn. **[IO]**, Melbourne, Australia

Shoplifters Alternative **[★13046]**

Shoplifters Anonymous **[★13046]**

Shoplifters Anonymous Intl. **[★13046]**

Shoqata Shqiptare E Dhimbjes **[★IO]**

Shoqata Shqiptare e Shkencave Politike **[★IO]**

Shoraye Ketabe Koodak **[★IO]**

Short Span Steel Bridge Alliance **[6371]**, 1140 Connecticut Ave., Ste. 705 NW, Washington, DC 20036, (301)367-6179

Short Stature Found. **[★13116]**

Short Wing Piper Club **[20915]**, 15841 Pear Cir., Fayetteville, AR 72704, (479)521-2609

Shorthand Reporters Assn. of Australia **[IO]**, Sydney, Australia

Shorthanded Sailing Assn. of Australia **[IO]**, McMahons Point, Australia

Shortness
Billy Barty Found. **[13115]**
Little People of Am. **[13116]**
Natl. Org. of Short Statured Adults **[13117]**

Shortwave Listeners Club; Amer. **[20932]**

Shosin Soc. - Defunct.

Shout Global Hea. **[15211]**, 103 Azalea Ct., No. 18-2, Largo, MD 20774, (240)293-3652

Show Horse Alliance **[4644]**, 10368 Bluegrass Pkwy., Louisville, KY 40299, (502)266-5100

Show Me A Cure **[13979]**, PO Box 2283, Florissant, MO 63032, (314)799-9700

Show Me Solar **[7443]**, 5402 Mirasol Manor Way, Eureka, MO 63025, (314)324-5250

Show Mercy Intl. **[11503]**, PO Box 607, Albany, OR 97321, (541)791-3566

Showboat **[★20870]**

Showmen's Guild of Great Britain **[IO]**, Drighlington, United Kingdom

Showmen's League of Am. **[8138]**, PO Box 64980, Chicago, IL 60664, (312)332-6236

Shrimp Coun. **[4878]**, 7918 Jones Br. Dr., Ste. 700, McLean, VA 22102, (703)752-8880

Shriners **[★19132]**

Shriner's Burns Inst. for Children **[★23648]**

Shriners Hospitals for Children **[14097]**, Shriners Intl. HQ, 2900 Rocky Point Dr., Tampa, FL 33607-1460, (813)281-0300

Shriners Hospitals for Children Endowment Fund **[★14097]**

SHRM Global Forum **[2631]**, 1800 Duke St., Alexandria, VA 22314-3494, (703)548-3440

A star before a book entry number signifies that the name is not listed separately, but is mentioned within the entry.

SHRM Global Forum **[2631]**, 1800 Duke St., Alexandria, VA 22314-3494, (703)548-3440

Shropshire Chamber of Commerce and Enterprise **[IO]**, Telford, United Kingdom

Shropshire Soc. - Defunct.

Shudokan Martial Arts Assn. **[22751]**, PO Box 6022, Ann Arbor, MI 48106, (734)645-6441

Shuffleboard
  Intl. Shuffleboard Assn. **[22892]**
  Intl. Shuffleboard Assn. **[22892]**
  Table Shuffleboard Assn. **[22893]**

Shutdown Proj. **[★5946]**

Shutdown Proj. **[★5946]**

Shuttleworth Leadership Soc. Intl. **[8495]**, PO Box 27306, Los Angeles, CA 90027, (323)663-5797

Shwachman Diamond Am. **[14628]**, 931-B S Main St., No. 332, Kernersville, NC 27284, (336)423-8158

Shwachman-Diamond Syndrome Canada **[IO]**, Mississauga, ON, Canada

Shwachman-Diamond Syndrome Found. **[16783]**, 127 Western Ave., Sherborn, MA 01770, (888)825-7373

Shwachman-Diamond Syndrome Found. **[16783]**, 127 Western Ave., Sherborn, MA 01770, (888)825-7373

Shwachman-Diamond Syndrome Intl. **[★16783]**

Shwachman-Diamond Syndrome Intl. **[★16783]**

Shy Drager Syndrome/Multiple Sys. Atrophy Support Gp. **[15634]**, 8311 Brier Creek Pkwy., Ste. 105-434, Raleigh, NC 27617, (866)737-5999

Sialkot Chamber of Commerce and Indus. **[IO]**, Sialkot, Pakistan

SIAMA World Mission Travel **[IO]**, Leiden, Netherlands

Siberian Husky Club of Am. **[21651]**, Barbara Horsey, Corresponding Sec., 10194 Old Kent Ln., Clarkston, MI 48348

Sibling Information Network - Defunct.

Sicilian
  Arba Sicula **[19228]**
  Arba Sicula **[19228]**

Sicilian Bioethical Inst. **[IO]**, Acireale, Italy

Sickle Cell Anemia
  Amer. Sickle Cell Anemia Assn. **[16658]**

Sickle Cell Disease Assn. of Am. **[14974]**, 231 E Baltimore St., Ste. 800, Baltimore, MD 21202, (410)528-1555

Side Saddle Assn. **[IO]**, Lincolnshire, United Kingdom

Sidelines Natl. High-Risk Pregnancy Support Network **[15893]**, PO Box 1808, Laguna Beach, CA 92652, (949)497-2265

Sidelines Natl. Support Network **[★15893]**

Sidran Found. and Press **[★12492]**

Sidran Inst. for Traumatic Stress Educ. and Advocacy **[12492]**, 200 E Joppa Rd., Ste. 207, Baltimore, MD 21286-3107, (410)825-8888

Sidran Traumatic Stress Found. **[★12492]**

Sierra Club **[4217]**, 85 2nd St., 2nd Fl., San Francisco, CA 94105, (415)977-5500

Sierra Club of Canada **[IO]**, Ottawa, ON, Canada

Sierra Club Legal Defense Fund **[★5414]**

Sierra Club Legal Defense Fund **[★5414]**

Sierra Leone Amateur Athletic Assn. **[IO]**, Freetown, Sierra Leone

Sierra Leone Bar Assn. **[IO]**, Freetown, Sierra Leone

Sierra Leone Lawn Tennis Assn. **[IO]**, Freetown, Sierra Leone

Sierra Leone Olympian Assn. **[IO]**, Freetown, Sierra Leone

Sierra Leone Powerlifting Assn. **[IO]**, Freetown, Sierra Leone

Sierra Leone Red Cross Soc. **[IO]**, Freetown, Sierra Leone

Sierra Leone Relief and Development Outreach **[12890]**, 4231 B Duke St., Alexandria, VA 22304, (703)823-3600

Sierra Leone Weightlifting Assn. **[IO]**, Freetown, Sierra Leone

Sierra Leone Youth Empowerment Org. **[IO]**, Freetown, Sierra Leone

Sierra Student Coalition **[4218]**, 408 C St. NE, Washington, DC 20002, (202)548-4592

Sierra Visions **[12369]**, PO Box 3435, Laurel, MD 20709-3271, (240)554-1555

Sierra Visions **[12369]**, PO Box 3435, Laurel, MD 20709-3271, (240)554-1555

SIGAPP - Special Interest Gp. on Applied Computing **[6560]**, ACM, 2 Penn Plz., Ste. 701, New York, NY 10121-0701

SIGCAPH **[★6517]**

SIGForth - Defunct.

Sight Savers Intl. - England **[IO]**, Haywards Heath, United Kingdom

Siglingasamband Islands **[★IO]**

Sigma Alpha Epsilon **[23692]**, 1856 Sheridan Rd., Evanston, IL 60201-3837, (847)475-1856

Sigma Alpha Epsilon **[23692]**, 1856 Sheridan Rd., Evanston, IL 60201-3837, (847)475-1856

Sigma Alpha Eta **[★16690]**

Sigma Alpha Iota Intl. Music Fraternity **[23605]**, 1 Tunnel Rd., Asheville, NC 28805-1229, (828)251-0606

Sigma Alpha Lambda **[23570]**, 501 Village Green Pkwy., Ste. 1, Bradenton, FL 34209, (941)866-5614

Sigma Alpha Mu **[23693]**, 9245 N Meridian St., Ste. 105, Indianapolis, IN 46260-1812, (317)846-0600

Sigma Alpha Phi **[★8926]**

Sigma Alpha Sorority **[23645]**, 2713 Ubly Rd., Bad Axe, MI 48413, (989)658-2780

Sigma Beta Rho Fraternity **[23694]**, PO Box 4668, New York, NY 10163, (888)333-1449

Sigma Chi Intl. Corp. **[★23695]**

Sigma Chi Intl. Fraternity **[23695]**, 1714 Hinman Ave., Evanston, IL 60201-4517, (847)869-3655

Sigma Delta Chi **[★2874]**

Sigma Delta Chi Found. **[23575]**, 3909 N Meridian St., Indianapolis, IN 46208-4011, (317)927-8000

Sigma Delta Epsilon **[★23631]**

Sigma Delta Epsilon, Graduate Women in Sci. **[23631]**, PO Box 240607, St. Paul, MN 55124, (952)236-9112

Sigma Delta Pi **[23753]**, Coll. of Charleston, Hispanic Stud., 66 George St., Charleston, SC 29424-0001, (843)953-6748

Sigma Delta Tau **[23731]**, 714 Adams St., Carmel, IN 46032, (317)846-7747

Sigma Gamma Epsilon **[23545]**, Univ. of Norther Iowa, Dept. of Earth Sci., Cedar Falls, IA 50614-0335, (319)273-2707

Sigma Gamma Phi **[★23655]**

Sigma Gamma Rho Sorority **[23646]**, 1000 Southill Dr., Ste. 200, Cary, NC 27513, (919)678-9720

Sigma Gamma Tau **[23523]**, Wichita State Univ., Aerospace Engg. Dept., 1845 Fairmount St., Wichita, KS 67260-0044, (316)978-5935

Sigma Iota Epsilon **[23584]**, Colorado State Univ., 312 Rockwell Hall, Fort Collins, CO 80521, (970)491-6265

Sigma Kappa **[23732]**, 8733 Founders Rd., Indianapolis, IN 46268, (317)872-3275

Sigma Kappa Found. **[23733]**, 8733 Founders Rd., Indianapolis, IN 46268, (317)872-3275

Sigma Lambda Alpha Sorority **[23748]**, PO Box 424296, Denton, TX 76204-4296, (888)475-2462

Sigma Lambda Gamma Natl. Sorority **[23749]**, 125 E Zeller St., Suites D & E, North Liberty, IA 52317, (319)626-7679

Sigma Nu Fraternity **[23696]**, 9 N Lewis St., PO Box 1869, Lexington, VA 24450, (540)463-1869

Sigma Phi Alpha **[23501]**, Northern Arizona Univ., PO Box 15065, Flagstaff, AZ 86011-5065, (928)523-0520

Sigma Phi Beta Fraternity **[23697]**, PO Box 937, Tempe, AZ 85280-0937, (888)744-2382

Sigma Phi Delta - Defunct.

Sigma Phi Educational Foundation **[★23699]**

Sigma Phi Epsilon **[23698]**, 310 S Blvd., PO Box 1901, Richmond, VA 23218, (804)353-1901

Sigma Phi Epsilon Educational Found. **[★23698]**

Sigma Phi Soc. **[23699]**, PO Box 4633, Chapel Hill, NC 27515

Sigma Pi **[★23700]**

Sigma Pi Fraternity, Intl. **[23700]**, PO Box 1897, Brentwood, TN 37024, (615)373-5728

Sigma Pi Sigma **[23621]**, 1 Physics Ellipse, College Park, MD 20740, (301)209-3007

Sigma Sigma Phi **[23614]**, 4810 Snowdrop Dr., Garland, TX 75043, (972)303-2050

Sigma Sigma Sigma **[23734]**, 225 N Muhlenberg St., Woodstock, VA 22664-1424, (540)459-4212

Sigma Sigma Sigma Foundation **[★23734]**

Sigma Tau **[★23525]**

Sigma Tau Delta **[★23527]**

Sigma Tau Delta **[★23527]**

Sigma Tau Delta, the Intl. English Honor Soc. **[23527]**, Northern Illinois Univ., Dept. of English, DeKalb, IL 60115-2863, (815)981-9974

Sigma Tau Delta, Intl. English Honor Soc. **[23527]**, Northern Illinois Univ., Dept. of English, DeKalb, IL 60115-2863, (815)981-9974

Sigma Tau Gamma **[23701]**, PO Box 54, Warrensburg, MO 64093-0054, (660)747-2222

Sigma Theta Tau **[★23610]**

Sigma Theta Tau **[★23610]**

Sigma Theta Tau Intl. **[23610]**, 550 W North St., Indianapolis, IN 46202, (317)634-8171

Sigma Theta Tau Intl. **[23610]**, 550 W North St., Indianapolis, IN 46202, (317)634-8171

Sigma Xi **[★23632]**

Sigma Xi, The Sci. Res. Soc. **[23632]**, PO Box 13975, Research Triangle Park, NC 27709, (919)549-4691

Sigma Zeta **[23633]**, Our Lady of the Lake Univ., Dept. of Biology, 411 SW 24th St., San Antonio, TX 78207-4689, (210)434-6711

Sigma Zeta Development Fund **[★23633]**

Sigmund Freud Archives **[16362]**, 23 The Hemlocks, Roslyn, NY 11576

Sign Assn. of Canada **[IO]**, Woodbridge, ON, Canada

Sign Language Interpreters Assn. of New Zealand **[IO]**, Auckland, New Zealand

Signal Appliance Assn. **[★2994]**

Signal Company Aircraft Warning Hawaii - Signal Aircraft Warning Regiment Hawaii Assn. - Defunct.

Signal Corps Regimental Assn. **[20367]**, 4570 Dewey Dr., Martinez, GA 30907, (706)364-1755

Signal Processing Soc. **[★6079]**

Signature-Durham **[IO]**, Durham, United Kingdom

Significant Living **[10870]**, 2880 Vision Ct., Aurora, IL 60506, (630)801-3838

Signing Exact English Center for the Advancement of Deaf Children **[14957]**, PO Box 1181, Los Alamitos, CA 90720, (562)430-1467

SIGNIS, World Catholic Assn. for Communication **[IO]**, Brussels, Belgium

Sikh
  Bus. Assn. of Sikh Entrepreneurs **[3277]**
  Coun. of Khalistan **[20240]**
  Coun. of Khalistan **[20240]**
  North Amer. Sikh Medical and Dental Assn. **[15429]**
  Sikh Amer. Legal Defense and Educ. Fund **[18605]**
  Sikh Coalition **[18606]**
  Sikh Coun. on Religion and Educ. **[20241]**
  Sikh Sports Assn. of the U.S.A. **[22894]**
  UNITED SIKHS **[12228]**

Sikh Amer. Legal Defense and Educ. Fund **[18605]**, 1413 K St. NW, 5th Fl., Washington, DC 20005-3405, (202)393-2700

Sikh Coalition **[18606]**, 40 Exchange Pl., Ste. 728, New York, NY 10005, (212)655-3095

Sikh Coun. on Religion and Educ. **[20241]**, 2621 Univ. Blvd. W, Silver Spring, MD 20902, (301)946-2800

Sikh Sports Assn. of the U.S.A. **[22894]**, 4430 Deer Field Way, Danville, CA 94506, (925)383-5605

Silent Images **[13148]**, PO Box 667, Matthews, NC 28106, (704)999-5010

Silent Running Soc. - Defunct.

Silica and Moulding Sands Assn. **[IO]**, London, United Kingdom

Silicon Valley Chinese Engineers Assn. **[6822]**, PO Box 642, Mountain View, CA 94042

Silicon Valley Chinese Engineers Assn. **[6822]**, PO Box 642, Mountain View, CA 94042

Silicones Environmental, Hea. and Safety Coun. **[764]**, 2325 Dulles Corner Blvd., Ste. 500, Herndon, VA 20171, (703)788-6570

Silicones Hea. Coun. **[★764]**

Silk Assn. of Great Britain **[IO]**, London, United Kingdom

Reference to "IO" in place of a book number signifies that the association may be found in the 50th edition of International Organizations.

Silk Assn. of India [IO], Calcutta, India
Silk Painters Intl. [9253], PO Box 1074, East Point, FL 32328, (850)670-8323
Silky Terrier Club of Am. [21652], Carol Zaretski, Membership Chair, 160 Hillside Dr., North Haledon, NJ 07508
Silva Forest Found. [IO], Slocan Park, BC, Canada
Silver Age Yoga [17138], 7968 Arjons Dr., Ste. 213, San Diego, CA 92126, (858)693-3110
Silver Ghost Assn. [21164], Jim Bannon, Membership Dir., 1115 Western Blvd., Arlington, TX 76013-3838, (817)861-6605
Silver Info. Center - Defunct.
Silver Inst. [2492], 888 16th St., Ste. 303, Washington, DC 20006, (202)835-0185
Silver Marten Rabbit Club [4855], 8538 Hwy. E, Pittsville, WI 54466, (715)207-8485
Silver Star Families of Am. [12535], 525 Cave Hollow Rd., Clever, MO 65631-6313, (417)743-2508
Silver Users Assn. [2493], 11240 Waples Mill Rd., No. 200, Fairfax, VA 22030, (703)930-7790
Silver Wings Fraternity [20916], PO Box 1694, Oldsmar, FL 34677-1694
Silvermine Guild of Artists [★9203]
Silvermine Guild Arts Center [9203], 1037 Silvermine Rd., New Canaan, CT 06840-4398, (203)966-9700
Silvermine Guild Center for the Arts [★9203]
Simcoe County Brain Injury Assn. [IO], Barrie, ON, Canada
Simian Soc. of Am. [11040], Mel Orr, Sec., 6 Stephens St., Dillsburg, PA 17019, (717)432-9205
Simon DeMontfort Soc. - Defunct.
Simon Found. [★16948]
Simon Found. for Continence [16948], PO Box 815, Wilmette, IL 60091, (847)864-3913
Simon Wiesenthal Center [17790], 1399 S Roxbury Dr., Los Angeles, CA 90035, (310)553-9036
Simon Wiesenthal Center [17790], 1399 S Roxbury Dr., Los Angeles, CA 90035, (310)553-9036
Simple Hope [12891], PO Box 4, Menomonee Falls, WI 53052, (262)569-9919
Simulation Councils, Inc. [★6471]
Simulation Councils, Inc. [★6471]
Simulation Indus. Assn. of Australia [IO], Lindfield, Australia
Simulation Interoperability Standards Org. [7527], PO Box 781238, Orlando, FL 32878-1238, (407)882-1348
Simulation and Learning; Intl. Nursing Assn. for Clinical [15757]
Sindacato Nazionale Scuola CGIL [★IO]
Sindacato Unitario Nazionale Inquilini ed Assegnatari [IO], Rome, Italy
Sindh Journalists' Network for Children [IO], Karachi, Pakistan
Sindicato da Industria da Construcao Civil no Estado do Rio de Janeiro [★IO]
Sindicato de Industriales de Panama [★IO]
Sindicato Nacional da Industria de Componentes para Veiculos Automotores [★IO]
Sindikat vzgoje izobrazevanja, znanosti in kulture Slovenije [★IO]
The Sinfonia Fraternity [★23604]
Singapore ACM SIGGRAPH [IO], Singapore, Singapore
Singapore Aircargo Agents Assn. [IO], Singapore, Singapore
Singapore Am. Bus. Assn. [703], 3 Twin Dolphin Dr., Ste. 150, Redwood City, CA 94065, (650)260-3388
Singapore Am. Bus. Assn. [703], 3 Twin Dolphin Dr., Ste. 150, Redwood City, CA 94065, (650)260-3388
Singapore Assn. of Administrative Professionals [IO], Singapore, Singapore
Singapore Assn. of Convention and Exhibition Organisers and Suppliers [IO], Singapore, Singapore
Singapore Assn. for the Deaf [IO], Singapore, Singapore
Singapore Assn. of the Inst. of Chartered Secretaries and Administrators [IO], Singapore, Singapore
Singapore Assn. of Myanmar [IO], Yangon, Myanmar
Singapore Assn. of Occupational Therapists [IO], Singapore, Singapore
Singapore Assn. of Pharmaceutical Indus. [IO], Singapore, Singapore

Singapore Assn. of Social Workers [IO], Singapore, Singapore
Singapore Assn. of the Visually Handicapped [IO], Singapore, Singapore
Singapore Badminton Assn. [IO], Singapore, Singapore
Singapore Baseball and Softball Assn. [IO], Singapore, Singapore
Singapore Bus. and Professional Women's Assn. [IO], Singapore, Singapore
Singapore Chamber of Commerce - Hong Kong [IO], Hong Kong, People's Republic of China
Singapore Chefs Assn. [IO], Raffles City, Singapore
Singapore Chinese Chamber of Commerce and Indus. [IO], Singapore, Singapore
Singapore Clock and Watch Trade Assn. [IO], Singapore, Singapore
Singapore Cmpt. Soc. [IO], Singapore, Singapore
Singapore Contractors Assn. Ltd. [IO], Singapore, Singapore
Singapore Corporate Counsel Assn. [IO], Singapore, Singapore
Singapore Cycle and Motor Traders' Assn. [IO], Singapore, Singapore
Singapore DanceSport Fed. [IO], Singapore, Singapore
Singapore Dental Assn. [IO], Singapore, Singapore
Singapore Disability Sports Coun. [IO], Singapore, Singapore
Singapore Drama Educators Assn. [IO], Singapore, Singapore
Singapore Economic Development Bd. [IO], Singapore, Singapore
Singapore Env. Coun. [IO], Singapore, Singapore
Singapore Fruits and Vegetables Importers and Exporters Assn. [IO], Singapore, Singapore
Singapore Furniture Assn. [IO], Singapore, Singapore
Singapore Furniture Indus. Coun. [IO], Singapore, Singapore
Singapore Hotel Assn. [IO], Singapore, Singapore
Singapore Indian Chamber of Commerce and Indus. [IO], Singapore, Singapore
Singapore Indian Fine Arts Soc. [IO], Singapore, Singapore
Singapore Indus. Automation Assn. [IO], Singapore, Singapore
Singapore Infocomm Tech. Fed. [IO], Singapore, Singapore
Singapore Inst. of Architects [IO], Singapore, Singapore
Singapore Inst. of Food Sci. and Tech. [IO], Singapore, Singapore
Singapore Inst. of Intl. Affairs [IO], Singapore, Singapore
Singapore Inst. of Landscape Architects [IO], Singapore, Singapore
Singapore Intl. Arbitration Centre [IO], Singapore, Singapore
Singapore Intl. Chamber of Commerce [IO], Singapore, Singapore
Singapore Inventors' Development Assn. [IO], Singapore, Singapore
Singapore Investment Banking Assn. [IO], Singapore, Singapore
Singapore Jewellers Assn. [IO], Singapore, Singapore
Singapore Logistics Assn. [IO], Singapore, Singapore
Singapore Malay Teachers' Union [IO], Singapore, Singapore
Singapore Mfrs. Fed. [IO], Singapore, Singapore
Singapore Mathematical Soc. [IO], Singapore, Singapore
Singapore Medical Assn. [IO], Singapore, Singapore
Singapore Metal and Machinery Assn. [IO], Singapore, Singapore
Singapore Natl. Comm. of the Intl. Water Assn. [IO], Singapore, Singapore
Singapore Natl. Employers Fed. [IO], Singapore, Singapore
Singapore Natl. Olympic Coun. [IO], Singapore, Singapore
Singapore Natl. Shippers' Coun. [IO], Singapore, Singapore

Singapore Natl. Stroke Assn. [IO], Singapore, Singapore
Singapore Netherlands Assn. [IO], Brussels, Belgium
Singapore Penjing and Stone Appreciation Soc. [IO], Singapore, Singapore
Singapore Planned Parenthood Assn. [IO], Singapore, Singapore
Singapore Plastic Indus. Assn. [IO], Singapore, Singapore
Singapore Productivity Assn. [IO], Singapore, Singapore
Singapore Psychological Soc. [IO], Singapore, Singapore
Singapore Radiological Soc. [IO], Singapore, Singapore
Singapore Red Cross [IO], Singapore, Singapore
Singapore Reinsurers' Assn. [IO], Singapore, Singapore
Singapore Retailers Assn. [IO], Singapore, Singapore
Singapore Sailing Fed. [IO], Singapore, Singapore
Singapore Scout Assn. [IO], Singapore, Singapore
Singapore Squash Rackets Assn. [IO], Singapore, Singapore
Singapore Taekwondo Fed. [IO], Singapore, Singapore
Singapore Timber Assn. [IO], Singapore, Singapore
Singapore Tourism Bd. [IO], Singapore, Singapore
Singapore Turf Club [IO], Singapore, Singapore
Singapore Venture Capital and Private Equity Assn. [IO], Singapore, Singapore
Singapore Veterinary Assn. [IO], Singapore, Singapore
Singapore Water Assn. [IO], Singapore, Singapore
Singapore Water Ski and Wakeboard Fed. [IO], Singapore, Singapore
Singaporean Soc. for Mass Spectrometry [IO], Singapore, Singapore
Singer Owners' Club [IO], Stamford, United Kingdom
Single Booklovers [21420], PO Box 214, Media, PA 19063, (610)212-7332
A Single Drop - Defunct.
Single Global Currency Assn. [437], PO Box 390, Newcastle, ME 04553, (207)586-6078
Single Global Currency Assn. [437], PO Box 390, Newcastle, ME 04553, (207)586-6078
Single Mothers By Choice [12622], PO Box 1642, New York, NY 10028, (212)988-0993
Single Parent Rsrc. Center [12623], 228 E 45th St., New York, NY 10017, (212)951-7030
Single Ply Roofing Assn. [IO], London, United Kingdom
Single Ser. Inst. [★1041]
Singles
    Natl. Assn. of Single People [13118]
    Natl. Org. of Single Mothers [13119]
Singles in Agriculture [21421], 118 E Front Ave., Stockton, IL 61085, (815)947-3559
Singles Press Assn. [2960], PO Box 2139, Sioux Falls, SD 57101, (605)335-4125
SingleStop USA [12752], 1825 Park Ave., Ste. 503, New York, NY 10035, (212)480-2870
Sinkies Intl. [★21862]
Sino-American Bridge for Educ. and Hea. [9876], Anne S. Watt, EdD, Vice Chair, 15R Sargent St., Cambridge, MA 02140
Sino-American Buddhist Assn. [★19365]
Sino-American Cooperative Org. [20867], Willie Baker, 2810 Highlands Blvd., Spring Valley, CA 91977
Sino-American Network for Therapeutic Radiology and Oncology [16871], Yue Cao, PhD, Treas., 1261 Creal Crescent, Ann Arbor, MI 48103
Sino-American Pharmaceutical Professionals Assn. [16215], PO Box 282, Nanuet, NY 10954
Sino-American Pharmaceutical Professionals Assn. [16215], PO Box 282, Nanuet, NY 10954
Sir Arthur Sullivan Soc. [IO], Looe, United Kingdom
Sir Henry Royce Memorial Found. [IO], Sydney, Australia
Sirenian Intl. [4711], 200 Stonewall Dr., Fredericksburg, VA 22401
Sirenian Intl. [4711], 200 Stonewall Dr., Fredericksburg, VA 22401
Sirius Astronomy Assn. [IO], Constantine, Algeria

A star before a book entry number signifies that the name is not listed separately, but is mentioned within the entry.

SISTAS [13478], PO Box 2845, Vacaville, CA 95696, (707)317-9478
Sistema de la Integracion CentroAmericana [IO], Antiguo Cuscatlan, El Salvador
Sistema Internacional de Informacion y Documentacion de Derechos Humanos [★IO]
Sister Cities Intl. [17985], 915 15th St. NW, 4th Fl., Washington, DC 20005, (202)347-8630
Sister Cities Intl. [17985], 915 15th St. NW, 4th Fl., Washington, DC 20005, (202)347-8630
Sister Formation Conf. [★19491]
Sister Island Proj. [11636], PO Box 1413, Langley, WA 98260, (360)321-4012
Sister Kenny Found. [★16576]
Sister Kenny Inst. [★16576]
Sister Kenny Rehabilitation Inst. [16576], 800 E 28th St., Minneapolis, MN 55407, (612)863-4200
Sister to Sister Network - Defunct.
Sisterhood Agenda [10647], Sisterhood Agenda Global Training Acad., 16213 Spring Garden, St. John, VI 00830, (973)893-7608
Sisterhood of Shoers - Address unknown since 2011.
Sisters of Charity - Halifax [IO], Halifax, NS, Canada
Sisters of Charity of Saint Jeanne Antide Thouret [IO], Rome, Italy
Sisters Concerned for the Rural Poor [★12523]
Sisters of the Congregation of Saint Agnes [★19417]
Sisters in Crime [3712], PO Box 442124, Lawrence, KS 66044, (785)842-1325
Sisters of the Cross of Chavanod [IO], Geneva, Switzerland
Sisters of Divine Providence [IO], Munster, Germany
Sisters of Life [20225], St. Frances de Chantal Convent, 198 Hollywood Ave., Bronx, NY 10465-3350, (718)863-2264
Sisters Network [13980], 2922 Rosedale St., Houston, TX 77004, (713)781-0255
Sisters of Our Lady of Charity of the Good Shepherd [IO], Rome, Italy
Sisters of Saint Joseph of the Sacred Heart [IO], North Sydney, Australia
Sisters of Saint Louis [IO], Killiney, Ireland
SisterSong Women of Color Reproductive Hea. Collective [★18806]
SisterSong Women of Color Reproductive Justice Collective [18806], 1237 Ralph David Abernathy Blvd. SW, Atlanta, GA 30310, (404)756-2680
Site Safe New Zealand [IO], Wellington, New Zealand
Situational Mgt. and Inter-Learning Est. Soc. [IO], Calcutta, India
Six of One Club: The Prisoner Appreciation Soc. [23929], 871 Clover Dr., North Wales, PA 19454-2749, (215)699-2527
Six Seconds [7309], PO Box 1985, Freedom, CA 95019, (831)684-1800
Sixth Marine Div. Assn. [20868], 1108 W Wellington Ave., Chicago, IL 60657-4338, (773)472-0225
Sjoessuradoerernas Foerening [★IO]
Sjogren's Syndrome Assn; Natl. [16622]
Sjogren's Syndrome Found. [16625], 6707 Democracy Blvd., Ste. 325, Bethesda, MD 20817, (301)530-4420
Sjogren's Syndrome Found. [16625], 6707 Democracy Blvd., Ste. 325, Bethesda, MD 20817, (301)530-4420
Sjoraddningssallskapet [★IO]
Skat Found. [IO], St. Gallen, Switzerland
Skate Canada [IO], Ottawa, ON, Canada
Skate Park Assn. of the U.S.A. [22900], 2118 Wilshire Blvd., No. 622, Santa Monica, CA 90403, (310)495-7112

Skating
Grind for Life [11136]
Ice Skating Inst. [3278]
Ice Skating Inst. [3278]
Intl. Gay Figure Skating Union [22895]
Marathon Skating Intl. [22896]
Professional Figure Skaters Cooperative [22897]
Professional Skaters Assn. [22898]
Roller Skating Assn. Intl. [3279]
Roller Skating Assn. Intl. [3279]
Senior Roller Skaters of Am. [22899]

Skate Park Assn. of the U.S.A. [22900]
Skating Assn. for the Blind and Handicapped [22901]
U.S. Figure Skating Assn. [22902]
U.S. Speedskating [22903]
U.S.A. Roller Sports [22904]
Women's Flat Track Derby Assn. [22905]
Skating Assn. for the Blind and Handicapped [22901], 2607 Niagara St., Buffalo, NY 14207, (716)362-9600
Skating Assn. of The Democratic People's Republic of Korea [IO], Pyongyang, Democratic People's Republic of Korea
Skating Fed. of Azerbaijan Republic [IO], Baku, Azerbaijan
Skating Fed. of Bosnia and Herzegovina [IO], Sarajevo, Bosnia-Hercegovina
Skating Fed. of The Republic of Kazakhstan [IO], Almaty, Kazakhstan
Skating Union of Belarus [IO], Minsk, Belarus
Skating Union of Mongolia [IO], Ulan Bator, Mongolia
Skeleton Fed; U.S. Bobsled and [22926]
Skeptics Soc. [7386], PO Box 338, Altadena, CA 91001, (626)794-3119
Ski Area Management - Defunct.
Ski nautique et planche Canada [★IO]
Ski Indus. Assn. [★3338]
Ski for Light [22524], 1455 W Lake St., Minneapolis, MN 55408, (612)827-3232
Ski for Light [22524], 1455 W Lake St., Minneapolis, MN 55408, (612)827-3232
Ski and Snowboard Assn; U.S. Deaf [22529]

Skiing
Amateur Ski Instructors Assn. [22906]
Amer. Barefoot Waterski Club [23114]
Amer. Birkebeiner Ski Found. [22907]
Amer. Cross Country Skiers [22908]
Amer. Ski-Bike Assn. [22963]
Camping Women [22441]
Icelandic Ski Assn. [16899]
Intl. Ski Dancing Assn. [22909]
Intl. Skiing History Assn. [10533]
Intl. Skiing History Assn. [10533]
Natl. Brotherhood of Skiers [22910]
Natl. Ski Coun. Fed. [22911]
Natl. Ski Patrol Sys. [22912]
Pacific Northwest Ski Assn. [22913]
Professional Ski Instructors of Am. [22914]
U.S. Biathlon Assn. [22915]
U.S. Collegiate Ski and Snowboard Assn. [22916]
U.S. Mountain Guides Assn. [22456]
U.S. Ski Mountaineering Assn. [22917]
U.S. Ski and Snowboard Assn. [22918]
U.S. Ski Team Found. [22919]
U.S. Telemark Ski Assn. [22920]
World Masters Cross-Country Ski Assn. [22921]
World Masters Cross-Country Ski Assn. [22921]
Worldloppet/American Birkebeiner [22922]
Worldloppet/American Birkebeiner [22922]
Skills for Humanity [12753], 412 N Coast Hwy., No. 114, Laguna Beach, CA 92651
Skillshare Botswana [IO], Gaborone, Botswana
Skillshare Intl. [IO], Leicester, United Kingdom
SkillsUSA [8298], 14001 SkillsUSA Way, Leesburg, VA 20176, (703)777-8810
Skin Cancer Found. [13981], 149 Madison Ave., Ste. 901, New York, NY 10016, (212)725-5176
Skinner Family Assn. [20586], PO Box 2594, Rancho Cucamonga, CA 91729
Skinner Leadership Inst. [19772], PO Box 190, Tracys Landing, MD 20779, (301)261-9800
Skinner Surname Org. [★20586]
Skinners' Company [IO], London, United Kingdom
Skioasamband Islands [★IO]
Skogsindustrierna [★IO]
Skolenes Landsforbund [IO], Oslo, Norway
Skripja Yunyon Vanuatu [★IO]
Sky Help [16930], 218 Evergreen Dr., Moorestown, NJ 08057
Sky of Love [11406], PO Box 170241, Brooklyn, NY 11217
Skye Terrier Club of Am. [21653], 2213 Flagler Pl. NW, Washington, DC 20001, (202)210-5142
Skyline Hikers of the Canadian Rockies [IO], Vegreville, AB, Canada

SkyTruth [4342], PO Box 3283, Shepherdstown, WV 25443-3283, (304)885-4581
Slag Cement Assn. [838], 2516 Waukegan Rd., Ste. 349, Glenview, IL 60025, (847)977-6920
Slate Roofing Contractors Assn. of North Am. [617], 143 Forest Ln., Grove City, PA 16127, (814)786-7015
Slavery and Trafficking; Coalition to Abolish [12233]
Slavic
Amer. Assn. of Teachers of Slavic and East European Languages [8462]
Assn. for Slavic, East European and Eurasian Stud. [10534]
Early Slavic Stud. Assn. [8863]
Natl. Coun. for Eurasian and East European Res. [10535]
Slavic Heritage Coalition [10536]
Slavic and East European Folklore Assn. [9625], Univ. of Kentucky, Russian and Eastern Stud. and Linguistics, 1055 Patterson Off. Tower, Lexington, KY 40506-0027, (859)257-1756
Slavic and East European Folklore Assn. [9625], Univ. of Kentucky, Russian and Eastern Stud. and Linguistics, 1055 Patterson Off. Tower, Lexington, KY 40506-0027, (859)257-1756
Slavic Gospel Assn. [20092], 6151 Commonwealth Dr., Loves Park, IL 61111, (815)282-8900
Slavic Gospel Assn. [20092], 6151 Commonwealth Dr., Loves Park, IL 61111, (815)282-8900
Slavic Heritage Coalition [10536], 51 W 14th St., Ste. 4R, New York, NY 10011, (212)366-5406
Slavonic Benevolent Order of the State of Texas [★19058]
Sleep
Amer. Acad. of Dental Sleep Medicine [16659]
Amer. Acad. of Sleep Medicine [16660]
Amer. Assn. of Sleep Technologists [16661]
Amer. Bd. of Sleep Medicine [16662]
Amer. Sleep Apnea Assn. [16663]
Assoc. Professional Sleep Societies [16664]
Awake in Am. [18607]
Better Sleep Coun. [16665]
Intl. Assn. for the Stud. of Dreams [16666]
Narcolepsy Network [16667]
Natl. Sleep Found. [16668]
Sleep Res. Soc. [16669]
World Assn. of Sleep Medicine [16670]
World Assn. of Sleep Medicine [16670]
Sleep Res. Soc. [16669], 2510 N Frontage Rd., Darien, IL 60561, (630)737-9701
Sliding Glass Door and Window Inst. [★518]
Sligo Chamber of Commerce and Indus. [IO], Sligo, Ireland
Slo-Pitch Natl. Softball [IO], Toronto, ON, Canada
Sloan Consortium [8060], PO Box 1238, Newburyport, MA 01950, (781)583-7561
Slocum Soc. [★22366]
Sloga Fraternal Life Insurance Soc. [★18967]
Slovak
First Catholic Slovak Ladies Assn. [19229]
First Catholic Slovak Union of the U.S.A. and Canada [19230]
Natl. Slovak Soc. of the U.S.A. [19231]
Slovak-American Cultural Center [10537]
Slovak Catholic Fed. [19232]
Slovak Catholic Sokol [19233]
Slovak Stud. Assn. [10538]
SOKOL U.S.A. [19234]
Slovak Acad. of Sciences [IO], Bratislava, Slovakia
Slovak Aikido Assn. - Aikikai Slovakia [IO], Trnava, Slovakia
Slovak-American Cultural Center [10537], PO Box 5395, New York, NY 10185
Slovak Assn. for Branded Products [IO], Bratislava, Slovakia
Slovak Athletic Fed. [IO], Bratislava, Slovakia
Slovak Badminton Fed. [IO], Presov, Slovakia
Slovak Baseball Fed. [IO], Bratislava, Slovakia
Slovak Catholic Fed. [19232], 173 Berner Ave., Hazleton, PA 18201
Slovak Catholic Fed. of Am. [★19232]
Slovak Catholic Sokol [19233], 205 Madison St., PO Box 899, Passaic, NJ 07055, (800)886-7656
Slovak Chamber of Commerce and Indus. [IO], Bratislava, Slovakia

Reference to "IO" in place of a book number signifies that the association may be found in the 50th edition of International Organizations.

Encyclopedia of Associations, 51st Edition

3157

Slovak Chamber of Dentists [IO], Bratislava, Slovakia

Slovak Dance Sport Fed. [IO], Bratislava, Slovakia

Slovak Dermatovenereological Soc. [IO], Bratislava, Slovakia

Slovak Family Planning Assn. [IO], Bratislava, Slovakia

Slovak Figure Skating Assn. [IO], Bratislava, Slovakia

Slovak Floorball Assn. [IO], Bratislava, Slovakia

Slovak Gymnastic Union Sokol of the U.S.A. [★19234]

Slovak Intl. Fed. of Automatic Control - Natl. Member Org. [IO], Bratislava, Slovakia

Slovak League Against Epilepsy [IO], Bratislava, Slovakia

Slovak League Against Hypertension [IO], Martin, Slovakia

Slovak Marfan Assn. [IO], Bratislava, Slovakia

Slovak Medical Assn. [IO], Bratislava, Slovakia

Slovak Medical Soc. of Infectiology [IO], Bratislava, Slovakia

Slovak Multiple Sclerosis Soc. [IO], Trnava, Slovakia

Slovak Olympic Comm. [IO], Bratislava, Slovakia

Slovak Orienteering Assn. [IO], Bratislava, Slovakia

Slovak Orthodontic Soc. [IO], Bratislava, Slovakia

Slovak Paralympic Comm. [IO], Bratislava, Slovakia

Slovak Pharmacological Soc. [IO], Martin, Slovakia

Slovak Physical Soc. [IO], Bratislava, Slovakia

Slovak Republic Public Relations Assn. [IO], Bratislava, Slovakia

Slovak Rheumatological Soc. [IO], Piestany, Slovakia

Slovak Schoolsport Assn. [IO], Bratislava, Slovakia

Slovak Soc. of Biomedical Engg. and Medical Informatics [IO], Bratislava, Slovakia

Slovak Soc. of Cardiology [IO], Bratislava, Slovakia

Slovak Soc. of Chemotherapy [IO], Bratislava, Slovakia

Slovak Soc. of Gerontology and Geriatrics [IO], Bratislava, Slovakia

Slovak Soc. for Operations Res. [IO], Bratislava, Slovakia

Slovak Soc. of Sports Medicine [IO], Bratislava, Slovakia

Slovak Speed Skating Union [IO], Spisska Nova Ves, Slovakia

Slovak Squash Assn. [IO], Bratislava, Slovakia

Slovak Stud. Assn. [10538], Wayne Sta. Univ., Dept. of Political Sci., 2040 F/AB, Detroit, MI 48220, (313)577-2630

Slovak Tennis Assn. [IO], Bratislava, Slovakia

Slovak Union of Newspaper Publishers [IO], Bratislava, Slovakia

Slovak Union against Osteoporosis [IO], Piestany, Slovakia

Slovak Venture Capital Assn. [IO], Bratislava, Slovakia

Slovakian Physiological Soc. [IO], Bratislava, Slovakia

Slovene Bone Soc. [IO], Ljubljana, Slovenia

Slovene Dance Sport Fed. [IO], Ljubljana, Slovenia

Slovene Franciscan Fathers - Address unknown since 2010.

Slovene Natl. Benefit Soc. [19236], 247 W Allegheny Rd., Imperial, PA 15126-9774, (724)695-1100

Slovene Osteoporosis Patient Soc. [IO], Ljubljana, Slovenia

Slovene Physiological Soc. [IO], Maribor, Slovenia

Slovene Skating Union [IO], Ljubljana, Slovenia

Slovene Soc. for Microscopy [IO], Ljubljana, Slovenia

Slovene Tennis Assn. [IO], Ljubljana, Slovenia

Slovene Writers' Assn. [IO], Ljubljana, Slovenia

Slovenia Sports Medicine Soc. [IO], Celje, Slovenia

Slovenian
  Amer. Mutual Life Assn. [19235]
  Slovene Natl. Benefit Soc. [19236]
  Slovenian Women Union of Am. [19237]
  Soc. for Slovene Stud. [19238]
  Soc. for Slovene Stud. [19238]

Slovenian Acad. of Sciences and Arts [IO], Ljubljana, Slovenia

Slovenian ACM Chap. [IO], Ljubljana, Slovenia

Slovenian Advt. Chamber [IO], Ljubljana, Slovenia

Slovenian Assn. of Occupational Therapists [IO], Ljubljana, Slovenia

Slovenian Assn. for Pain Mgt. [IO], Maribor, Slovenia

Slovenian Assn. of Physiotherapists [IO], Ljubljana, Slovenia

Slovenian Biochemical Soc. [IO], Ljubljana, Slovenia

Slovenian Geotechnical Soc. [IO], Ljubljana, Slovenia

Slovenian Hypertension Soc. [IO], Ljubljana, Slovenia

Slovenian League Against Epilepsy [IO], Ljubljana, Slovenia

Slovenian Medical Assn. [IO], Ljubljana, Slovenia

Slovenian Medical Informatics Assn. [IO], Ljubljana, Slovenia

Slovenian Medical Soc. [IO], Ljubljana, Slovenia

Slovenian Mutual Benefit Assn. [★19235]

Slovenian Orienteering Fed. [IO], Ljubljana, Slovenia

Slovenian Orthodontic Soc. [IO], Ljubljana, Slovenia

Slovenian Pharmaceutical Soc. [IO], Ljubljana, Slovenia

Slovenian Pharmacological Soc. [IO], Ljubljana, Slovenia

Slovenian Proj. Mgt. Assn. [IO], Ljubljana, Slovenia

Slovenian Publishers Assn. [IO], Ljubljana, Slovenia

Slovenian Red Cross [IO], Ljubljana, Slovenia

Slovenian Soc. of Cardiology [IO], Ljubljana, Slovenia

Slovenian Soc. of Chemotherapy [IO], Ljubljana, Slovenia

Slovenian Soc. for Pattern Recognition [IO], Ljubljana, Slovenia

Slovenian Squash Assn. [IO], Ljubljana, Slovenia

Slovenian Taekwondo Assn. [IO], Celje, Slovenia

Slovenian Turf Club [IO], Maribor, Slovenia

Slovenian Women Union of Am. [19237], 431 N Chicago St., Joliet, IL 60432, (815)727-1926

Slovenian Women's Union [★19237]

Slovenian Writers' Assn. [IO], Ljubljana, Slovenia

Slovenska Aikido Asociacia - Aikikai Slovakia [★IO]

Slovenska Akademia Vied [★IO]

Slovenska Akademija Znanosti in Umetnosti [★IO]

Slovenska Asociacia Skolskeho Sportu [★IO]

Slovenska Asociacia Spravcovskych Spolocnosti [★IO]

Slovenska Bankova Asociacia [★IO]

Slovenska Baseballova Federacia [★IO]

Slovenska Dermatovenerologicka Spolocnost [★IO]

Slovenska Fyzikalna Spolocnost [★IO]

Slovenska Kardiologicka Spolocnost [★IO]

Slovenska Komora Zubnych Lekarov [★IO]

Slovenska Liga Proti Hypertenzii [★IO]

Slovenska Oglasevalska Zbornica [★IO]

Slovenska Spolocnost pre Operacny Vyskum [★IO]

Slovenska Squashova Asociacia [★IO]

Slovenske hnutie specialnych olympiad [★IO]

Slovenske zdruzenie pre znackove vyrobky [★IO]

Slovenski nacionalni komite Svetovnega energetskega sveta [IO], Ljubljana, Slovenia

Slovensko-Americke Kulturne Stredisko [★10537]

Slovensko Biokemijsko Drustvo [★IO]

Slovensko Drustvo Farmakologov [★IO]

Slovensko Drustvo za Medicinsko Informatiko [★IO]

Slovensko Drustvo Za Mikroskopijo [★IO]

Slovensko Farmacevtsko Drustvo [★IO]

Slovensko Galopsko Drustvo [★IO]

Slovensko Zdruzenje za Projektni Mgt. [★IO]

Slovensko Zdruzenje Za Zdravljenje Bolecin [★IO]

Slovensky krasokorculiarsky zvaz [★IO]

Slovensky paralympijsky vybor [★IO]

Slovensky Atleticky Zvaz [★IO]

Slovensky Cerveny Kriz [IO], Bratislava, Slovakia

Slovensky Olympijsky Vybor [★IO]

Slovensky Tenisovy Zvaz [★IO]

Slovensky Zvaz Florbalu [★IO]

Slovensky Zvaz Orientacnych Sportov [★IO]

Slovensky Zvaz Sclerosis Mulitplex [★IO]

Slovensky Zvaz Tanecneho Sportu [★IO]

Slow Food USA [9632], 20 Jay St., Ste. M04, Brooklyn, NY 11201, (718)260-8000

Slow Food USA [9632], 20 Jay St., Ste. M04, Brooklyn, NY 11201, (718)260-8000

Slurry Tech. Assn. [★782]

Slurry Transport Assn. [★782]

SMA Fathers [★19497]

SMA Fathers [★19497]

SMA Lay Missionaries [20093], 256 Manor Cir., Takoma Park, MD 20912, (301)891-2037

Small Acts - Address unknown since 2011.

Small Brewers Assn. [★179]

Small Brewers Comm. [★179]

Small Business
  Amer. Independent Bus. Alliance [3280]
  Amer. Senior Benefits Assn. [3281]
  Amer. Small Bus. Coalition [3282]
  Amer. Small Bus. League [3283]
  Amer. Small Mfrs. Coalition [2328]
  Assn. for Enterprise Opportunity [3284]
  Assn. of Small Bus. Development Centers [3285]
  BEST Employers Assn. [3286]
  Employers of Am. [3287]
  Family Firm Inst. [3288]
  Family Firm Inst. [3288]
  Intl. Assn. of Women in Family Enterprises [3289]
  Intl. Coun. for Small Bus. [3290]
  Intl. Coun. for Small Bus. [3290]
  Natl. Assn. for Bus. Organizations [3291]
  Natl. Assn. for the Self-Employed [3292]
  Natl. Assn. of Small Bus. Contractors [931]
  Natl. Assn. of Small Bus. Investment Companies [3293]
  Natl. Bus. Assn. [3294]
  Natl. Coalition for Capital [1058]
  Natl. Small Bus. Assn. [3295]
  Noshaq [12958]
  SCORE [3296]
  Small Bus. and Entrepreneurship Coun. [3297]
  Small Bus. Legislative Coun. [3298]
  Small Bus. Ser. Bur. [3299]
  Support Services Alliance [3300]
  U.S. Assn. for Small Bus. and Entrepreneurship [3301]

Small Bus. Assistance Center [★3299]

Small Bus. Coun. of Am. [17477], PO Box 1229, Wilmington, DE 19899, (302)691-7222

Small Bus. and Entrepreneurship Coun. [3297], 2944 Hunter Mill Rd., Ste. 204, Oakton, VA 22124, (703)242-5840

Small Bus. Exporters Assn. [★2106]

Small Bus. Exporters Assn. of the U.S. [2106], 1156 15th St. NW, Ste. 1100, Washington, DC 20005, (202)659-9320

Small Bus. Legislative Coun. [3298], 1100 H St. NW, Ste. 540, Washington, DC 20005, (202)639-8500

Small Bus. Ser. Bur. [3299], 554 Main St., PO Box 15014, Worcester, MA 01615-0014, (800)343-0939

Small Bus. Survival Comm. [★3297]

Small Bus. in Telecommunications - Address unknown since 2011.

Small Domestic Elecl. Appliance Mfrs'. Assn. [IO], Barcelona, Spain

Small Elecl. Appliance Marketing Assn. [IO], Croydon, United Kingdom

Small Explorers and Producers Assn. of Canada [IO], Calgary, AB, Canada

Small Firms Assn. [IO], Dublin, Ireland

Small Independent Record Mfrs. Assn. - Defunct.

Small Investor Protection Assn. [IO], Markham, ON, Canada

Small Luxury Hotels [★1774]

Small Luxury Hotels Assn. [★1774]

Small Luxury Hotels of the World [1774], 370 Lexington Ave., Ste. 1506, New York, NY 10017, (212)953-2064

Small Motor Mfr. Assn. [★1086]

Small Motor Mfr. Assn. [★1086]

Small Motors and Motion Assn. [★1086]

Small Motors and Motion Assn. [★1086]

Small Museum Assn. [10129], Dayna Aldridge, Membership Coor., Historic Ships in Baltimore, Pier 1, 301 E Pratt St., Baltimore, MD 21202-3110

Small Publishers, Artists and Writers Network [2961], PMB 123, 323 E Matilija St., Ste. 110, Ojai, CA 93023, (805)646-3045

Small Publishers, Artists and Writers Network [2961], PMB 123, 323 E Matilija St., Ste. 110, Ojai, CA 93023, (805)646-3045

Small Publishers Assn. of North Am. [2962], PO Box 9725, Colorado Springs, CO 80932-0725, (719)924-5534

A star before a book entry number signifies that the name is not listed separately, but is mentioned within the entry.

Small Towns Inst. - Defunct.
A Small Victory - Defunct.
Small World Found. [16820], PO Box 25004, Asheville, NC 28813
SmallCommunity.org [★17368]
Smaller Mfrs. Medical Device Assn. [★3178]
Smart Card Alliance [7528], 191 Clarksville Rd., Princeton Junction, NJ 08550, (609)587-4208
Smart Card Indus. Assn. [★7528]
Smart Growth Am. [11637], 1707 L St. NW, Ste. 1050, Washington, DC 20036, (202)207-3355
SMART Recovery [16755], 7304 Mentor Ave., Ste. F, Mentor, OH 44060, (440)951-5357
Smart Women's Inst. of Entrepreneurial Learning [10739], 24165 IH-10 W, Ste. 217-637, San Antonio, TX 78257, (866)821-5829
SMARTER Brunei [IO], Bandar Seri Begawan, Brunei Darussalam
SmartPower [4231], 1120 Connecticut Ave. NW, Washington, DC 20036, (202)775-2040
SMARTRISK [IO], Toronto, ON, Canada
Smartshoppers Intl. - Defunct.
SME Found. [★8129]
SME Union - Small and Medium Enterprises Union of the EPP [IO], Brussels, Belgium
Smile Alliance Intl. [11504], PO Box 240, Cle Elum, WA 98922, (509)674-2274
Smile Alliance Intl. [11504], PO Box 240, Cle Elum, WA 98922, (509)674-2274
Smile Network Intl. [14203], 211 N First St., Ste. 150, Minneapolis, MN 55401, (612)377-1800
SMMA - The Assn. for Elec. Motors, Their Control and Application [★1086]
SMMA - The Assn. for Elec. Motors, Their Control and Application [★1086]
SMMA - The Motor and Motion Assn. [1086], PO Box P182, South Dartmouth, MA 02748, (508)979-5935
SMMA - The Motor and Motion Assn. [1086], PO Box P182, South Dartmouth, MA 02748, (508)979-5935
Smocking Arts Guild of Am. [21466], PO Box 2846, Grapevine, TX 76099, (800)520-3101
Smoke Free Soc. Corp. - Address unknown since 2010.
Smoke Prevention Assn. of Amer. [★4779]
Smoke Prevention Assn. of Amer. [★4779]
SmokeFree Educational Services - Address unknown since 2011.
Smokenders [16674], PO Box 316, Kensington, MD 20895, (800)828-4357
Smoking
   Action on Smoking and Hea. [16671]
   Americans for Nonsmokers' Rights [16672]
   European Network for Smoking Prevention [16222]
   Natl. Center for Tobacco-Free Kids [16673]
   Smokenders [16674]
   Tobacco Control Rsrc. Center [13328]
SMOLOSKYP Publishes - Defunct.
SMOLOSKYP, Ukrainian Info. Ser.
SMOLOSKYP, Ukrainian Info. Ser. - Address unknown since 2011.
Snack Food Assn. [1430], 1600 Wilson Blvd., Ste. 650, Arlington, VA 22209, (703)836-4500
Snipe Class Intl. Racing Assn. [22392], 2812 Canon St., San Diego, CA 92106-2742, (619)224-6998
Snipe Class Intl. Racing Assn. [22392], 2812 Canon St., San Diego, CA 92106-2742, (619)224-6998
Snodgrass Clan Soc. [20587], 8221 Stonewall Dr., Vienna, VA 22180-6947
Snow and Ice Mgt. Assn. [6039], 7670 N Port Washington Rd., Ste. 105, Milwaukee, WI 53217, (414)375-1940
Snow Leopard Network [5130], 4649 Sunnyside Ave. N, Seattle, WA 98103, (206)632-2421
Snow Leopard Network [5130], 4649 Sunnyside Ave. N, Seattle, WA 98103, (206)632-2421
Snow Sports
   Amer. Assn. of Snowboard Instructors [22923]
   Amer. Coun. of Snowmobile Associations [22924]
   Amer. Ski-Bike Assn. [22963]
   Professional Figure Skaters Cooperative [22897]
   SOS Outreach [22925]
   U.S. Bobsled and Skeleton Fed. [22926]

U.S. Cross Country Snowmobile Racing Assn, [22927]
U.S. Ski Team Found. [22919]
U.S. Snowshoe Assn. [22928]
World Masters Cross-Country Ski Assn. [22921]
Snow Sports New Zealand [IO], Wanaka, New Zealand
Snowboard Assn; U.S. Ski and [22918]
Snowmobile Associations; Amer. Coun. of [22924]
Snowmobile Club of Am; Antique [22133]
Snowsport England [IO], Halesowen, United Kingdom
Snowsport GB [IO], Edinburgh, United Kingdom
Snowsport Scotland [IO], Edinburgh, United Kingdom
Snowsport Wales [IO], Cardiff, United Kingdom
SnowSports Indus. Am. [3338], 8377-B Greensboro Dr., McLean, VA 22102, (703)556-9020
SNV/Organisation Neerlandaise de Developpement au Burkina Faso [★IO]
Soap Box Derby
   All-Amer. Soap Box Derby [22929]
   Natl. Derby Rallies [22930]
Soap and Detergent Assn. [★744]
Soaps and Detergents Indus. Assn. [IO], Istanbul, Turkey
Soaring Assn. of Canada [IO], Ottawa, ON, Canada
Soaring Soc. of Am. [22213], PO Box 2100, Hobbs, NM 88241-2100, (575)392-1177
Soays of Am. [4922], PO Box 551, Gig Harbor, WA 98335
Soays of Am. [4922], PO Box 551, Gig Harbor, WA 98335
Soccer
   Am. Scores [22931]
   Amer. Amputee Soccer Assn. [22932]
   Amer. Youth Soccer Org. [22933]
   Cosmopolitan Soccer League [22934]
   Coun. of Ivy Gp. Presidents [22975]
   Eastern Coll. Soccer Assn. [22935]
   Intl. Gay and Lesbian Football Assn. [22936]
   Natl. Goalie War Assn. [22937]
   Natl. Intercollegiate Soccer Officials Assn. [22938]
   Natl. Soccer Coaches Assn. of Am. [22939]
   North Amer. Chinese Soccer League [22940]
   North Amer. Chinese Soccer League [22940]
   Soccer Assn. for Youth [22941]
   Soccer Without Borders [22942]
   Southeastern Conf. [23006]
   U.S. Adult Soccer Assn. [22943]
   U.S. Club Soccer [22944]
   U.S. Indoor Sports Assn. [22945]
   U.S. Power Soccer Assn. [22946]
   U.S. Soccer Fed. [22947]
   U.S. Youth Soccer Assn. [22948]
   U.S.A. Sanatan Sports and Cultural Assn. [22949]
Soccer Assn. for Youth [22941], 1 N Commerce Park Dr., Ste. 306-320, Cincinnati, OH 45215, (513)769-3800
Soccer Indus. Coun. of Am. [3317], Sporting Goods Mfrs. Assn., 8505 Fenton St., Ste. 211, Silver Spring, MD 20910, (301)495-6321
Soccer in the Streets [11638], 2323 Perimeter Park Dr. NE, Atlanta, GA 30341, (770)452-0505
Soccer Without Borders [22942], PO Box 3443, Oakland, CA 94609, (510)859-4874
Social Accountability Intl. [18809], 15 W 44th St., 6th Fl., New York, NY 10036, (212)684-1414
Social Accountability Intl. [18809], 15 W 44th St., 6th Fl., New York, NY 10036, (212)684-1414
Social Action
   Alliance of Jamaican and Amer. Humanitarians [11543]
   Anti-Child Pornography Org. [12710]
   Artists United for Social Justice [18640]
   Breakthrough [17815]
   Catholic Central Union of Am. I Central Bur. [19400]
   Debt AIDS Trade Africa [17149]
   Democracy for Am. [18329]
   Disciples Justice Action Network [19566]
   Election Defense Alliance [17607]
   FootPrints for Peace [18243]
   Fuel for Truth [18608]
   Generation Green [14077]

   Genocide Intervention Network [17739]
   Global Youth Connect [18828]
   Goree Inst. [5361]
   Kids for Peace [18262]
   Natl. Assn. of Evangelicals [19766]
   Natl. Black Environmental Justice Network [4284]
   Organize Training Center [11657]
   Reality Relief [12880]
   RedLight Children [11144]
   Rotarian Action Gp. for the Alleviation of Hunger and Malnutrition [12290]
   Seventh Generation Advisors [4304]
   TransWorld Development Initiatives [12262]
   UNANIMA Intl. [18645]
   Vote Hemp [18609]
   World Action for Humanity [13120]
Social Care Assn. [IO], Surrey, United Kingdom
Social Change
   A. Philip Randolph Inst. [18610]
   African Fed., Inc. [17900]
   African Great Lakes Initiative [13165]
   Artists United for Social Justice [18640]
   Asian Pacific Americans for Progress [17205]
   Behaviorists for Social Responsibility [18611]
   Black Leadership Forum [18844]
   Breakthrough [17815]
   Brotherhood Org. of a New Destiny [18612]
   Brotherhood Org. of a New Destiny [18612]
   Catholic Central Union of Am. I Central Bur. [19400]SocialCoalition for Justice in the Maquiladoras
   Context Inst. [18613]
   Creative Resources Guild [18614]
   Eco-Justice Working Group [18615]
   Edurelief [12834]
   Episcopal Peace Fellowship [18616]
   ESA [18617]
   FootPrints for Peace [18243]
   Found. on Economic Trends [18618]
   Friends of Liberia [13121]
   Girls for a Change [11290]
   Global Inheritance [18826]
   Graduation Pledge Alliance [18619]
   Graduation Pledge Alliance [18619]
   HandsOn Network [13394]
   Independent Progressive Politics Network [18620]
   Insight Arts [9293]
   Interhelp [18621]
   Interhelp [18621]
   Intl. Soc. for Panetics [18622]
   Intl. Soc. for Panetics [18622]
   Intl. Sustainability Coun. [4212]
   Intl. Symbiosis Soc. [18623]
   Intl. Symbiosis Soc. [18623]
   Justice Stud. Assn. [13122]
   Krochet Kids Intl. [12735]
   LIFT [11072]
   The Love Alliance [17365]
   Natl. Assn. of Evangelicals [19766]
   Natl. Org. for African-American Women [10829]
   NETWORK, A Natl. Catholic Social Justice Lobby [18624]
   North Amer. Alliances for Social Relief [12352]
   Oil Change Intl. [4230]
   One Voice of Peace [8694]
   Peace Rsrc. Proj. [18625]
   People's Inst. for Survival and Beyond [18626]
   Poverty Awareness Coalition for Equality [12747]
   Prana Intl. [12749]
   Proutist Universal [18627]
   Quixote Center [18628]
   Quixote Center [18628]
   Root Cause [18629]
   Social Enterprise Alliance [3302]
   Southeast Inst. for Gp. and Family therapy [18630]
   TeamPact [18631]
   Technocracy Inc. [18632]
   ThinkImpact [12373]
   TransWorld Development Initiatives [12262]
   Ugandan Amer. Partnership Org. [12307]
   UNANIMA Intl. [18645]
   USAction [18633]
   Venus Proj. [18634]
   Village Focus Intl. [11650]

Reference to "IO" in place of a book number signifies that the association may be found in the 50th edition of International Organizations.

Voices for Global Change [17254]
We, The World [13123]
Women Proutists [18635]
Women's Proj. [18636]
Social Clubs
Chemists' Club [19239]
DeMolay Intl. [19240]
DeMolay Intl. [19240]
Everyday Democracy [19241]
Jim Smith Soc. [19242]
Jim Smith Soc. [19242]
Lois Link Intl. - USA [19243]
Lois Link Intl. - USA [19243]
The Moles [19244]
Overseas Brats [19245]
Soc. for the Second Self [13112]
Stunts Unlimited [19246]
Tall Persons Club - Great Britain and Ireland
[15480]
Social Contract Press [12599], 445 E Mitchell St.,
Petoskey, MI 49770, (231)347-1171
Social Cooperative Grado 16 [IO], Milan, Italy
Social Democratic and Labour Party [IO], Belfast,
United Kingdom
Social Democratic Party of Austria [IO], Vienna,
Austria
Social Democratic Party of Denmark [IO], Frederiks-
berg, Denmark
Social Democratic Party of Germany [IO], Berlin,
Germany
Social Democratic Youth of Denmark [IO], Frederiks-
berg, Denmark
Social Democrats, U.S.A. [18339], PO Box 5307,
Johnstown, PA 15904-5288, (814)262-8941
Social and Educational Development Assn., Pakistan
[IO], Mardan, Pakistan
Social, Emotional and Behavioural Difficulties Assn.
[IO], Manchester, United Kingdom
Social Enterprise Alliance [3302], 11525 Springridge
Rd., Potomac, MD 20854, (202)758-0194
Social Fraternities
Acacia Fraternity [23648]
Alpha Chi Rho [23649]
Alpha Delta Gamma [23650]
Alpha Delta Phi [23651]
Alpha Delta Pi [23652]
Alpha Epsilon Pi [23653]
Alpha Kappa Lambda [23654]
Alpha Phi Delta [23655]
Alpha Psi Lambda Natl. [23656]
Alpha Sigma Phi [23657]
Alpha Tau Omega [23658]
Beta Chi Theta Natl. Fraternity [23659]
Beta Sigma Psi Natl. Lutheran Fraternity [23660]
Beta Theta Pi [23661]
Chi Phi [23662]
Chi Psi [23663]
Delta Kappa Epsilon [23664]
Delta Lambda Phi Natl. Social Fraternity [23665]
Delta Psi [23666]
Delta Sigma Pi [23667]
Delta Upsilon [23668]
Delta Upsilon [23668]
Farmhouse [23669]
Groove Phi Groove, Social Fellowship [23670]
Kappa Alpha Order [23671]
Kappa Alpha Psi Fraternity [23672]
Kappa Alpha Psi Fraternity [23672]
Kappa Alpha Soc. [23673]
Kappa Delta Rho [23674]
Kappa Sigma [23675]
Lambda Chi Alpha [23676]
Omega Psi Phi Fraternity [23677]
Phi Delta Theta Intl. Fraternity [23678]
Phi Gamma Delta [23679]
Phi Kappa Sigma [23680]
Phi Kappa Sigma [23680]
Phi Kappa Tau [23681]
Phi Kappa Theta Natl. Fraternity [23682]
Phi Mu Delta [23683]
Phi Sigma Kappa [23684]
Phi Sigma Nu Native Amer. Fraternity [23685]
Pi Beta Phi [23686]
Pi Delta Psi Fraternity [23687]
Pi Kappa Alpha [23688]

Pi Kappa Phi [23689]
Pi Lambda Phi Fraternity [23690]
Psi Sigma Phi Multicultural Fraternity [23638]
Psi Upsilon [23691]
Psi Upsilon [23691]
Sigma Alpha Epsilon [23692]
Sigma Alpha Epsilon [23692]
Sigma Alpha Mu [23693]
Sigma Beta Rho Fraternity [23694]
Sigma Chi Intl. Fraternity [23695]
Sigma Nu Fraternity [23696]
Sigma Phi Beta Fraternity [23697]
Sigma Phi Epsilon [23698]
Sigma Phi Soc. [23699]
Sigma Pi Fraternity, Intl. [23700]
Sigma Tau Gamma [23701]
Tau Epsilon Phi [23702]
Tau Kappa Epsilon [23703]
Theta Chi Fraternity [23704]
Theta Delta Chi [23705]
Theta Delta Chi [23705]
Theta Xi [23706]
Zeta Beta Tau [23707]
Zeta Psi Fraternity of North Am. [23708]
Social History Soc. [IO], Lancaster, United Kingdom
Social Housing Neighbourhood Fed. of Catalonia
[IO], Barcelona, Spain
Social Integration and Community Development
Assn. [11639], 3 Church Cir., Ste. 294, Annapolis,
MD 21401, (443)569-3578
Social Investment Forum [★18649]
Social Investment Org. [IO], Toronto, ON, Canada
Social Issues
African Great Lakes Initiative [13165]
Ambrose Monell Found. [13124]
Ambrose Monell Found. [13124]
Applied Res. Center [18637]
Artists for Peace and Justice [13152]
Assn. for a More Just Soc. [17272]
Because Intl. [12718]
Brecht Forum [13125]
Brecht Forum [13125]
Center for Assessment and Policy Development
[18638]
Center for Human Services [13126]
Center for Human Services [13126]
Charles Stewart Mott Found. [13127]
Compton Found. [13128]
Compton Found. [13128]
Disciples Justice Action Network [19566]
Discover Worlds [13129]
Doris Duke Charitable Found. [13130]
Earth Coun. Alliance [12584]
Edward E. Ford Found. [13131]
Edward E. Ford Found. [13131]
Election Defense Alliance [17607]
Faceless Intl. [13362]
Faith Alliance Against Slavery and Trafficking
[17289]
FootPrints for Peace [18243]
Friends of Africa Intl. [17830]
Fuller Found. [13132]
Geraldine R. Dodge Found. [13133]
Global Centurion [11292]
Global Community Initiatives [11589]
Global Visionaries [13134]
Hands Across the Mideast Support Alliance
[18124]
HandsOn Network [13394]
Hearst Found. [13135]
Heartland Inst. [13136]
Human Development and Capability Assn.
[12210]
Innocents at Risk [12241]
Ittleson Found. [13137]
Jewish World Watch [17743]
Kresge Found. [13138]
Kresge Found. [13138]
Leadership Coun. of Aging Organizations [10850]
LIFT [11072]
The Love Alliance [17365]
Media Action Grassroots Network [18092]
Millennium Campus Network [17191]
Nathan Cummings Found. [13139]
Natl. Coalition of Pastors' Spouses [13195]

Natl. Sci. and Tech. Educ. Partnership [13140]
Needmor Fund [13141]
Norman Found. [13142]
Oil Change Intl. [4230]
Pew Charitable Trusts [13143]
Poverty Awareness Coalition for Equality [12747]
Preservation Inst. [13144]
Public Welfare Found. [13145]
Reach Global [13146]
Reach Global [13146]
Responsible Policies for Animals [11032]
Samuel H. Kress Found. [13147]
Silent Images [13148]
Soc. for the Stud. of Social Problems [13149]
South Asian Americans Leading Together [18644]
TeamPact [18631]
Training for Change [13150]
Trans Youth Family Allies [12585]
USAction [18633]
We, The World [13123]
Wheel Wishers [7407]
Women in Fatherhood, Inc. [13151]
Women's Intl. Coalition for Economic Justice
[17596]
Social Justice
A. J. Muste Memorial Inst. [18228]
And Justice for All [18639]
Artists for Peace and Justice [13152]
Artists United for Social Justice [18640]
Assn. for a More Just Soc. [17272]
Catholic Central Union of Am. I Central Bur.
[19400]
Center for Economic and Social Justice [11900]
Children Beyond Our Borders [17235]
Coalition Against Genocide [17738]
Crime Survivors [17487]
Dalit Freedom Network [17823]
Dalit Solidarity [17824]
Disciples Justice Action Network [19566]
Earth Coun. Alliance [12584]
Educating for Justice [8864]
Educating for Justice [8864]
Ensaaf [18641]
Equal Justice Soc. [5972]
Friends of Africa Intl. [17830]
Hagar USA [12237]
Healing the Divide [12238]
Intl. Possibilities Unlimited [18642]
Intl. Possibilities Unlimited [18642]
The Love Alliance [17365]
Media Action Grassroots Network [18092]
MediaGlobal [12348]
Natl. Alliance for Family Court Justice [5624]
Natl. Black Environmental Justice Network [4284]
Natl. Black Justice Coalition [18643]
Natl. Organizers Alliance [13153]
Poverty Awareness Coalition for Equality [12747]
Rsrc. Generation [13154]
Ruckus Soc. [18222]
South Asian Americans Leading Together [18644]
UNANIMA Intl. [18645]
Universal Human Rights Network [17865]
USAction [18633]
Women's Intl. Coalition for Economic Justice
[17596]
Social Legislation Information Service - Defunct.
Social Policy Assn. [IO], Suffolk, United Kingdom
Social Problems
ABLE: Assn. for Better Living and Educ. Intl.
[11537]
Catholic Central Union of Am. I Central Bur.
[19400]
Disciples Justice Action Network [19566]
Eliminate Poverty Now [11066]
Genocide Intervention Network [17739]
Innocents at Risk [12241]
Unitarian Universalist Assn. of Congregations
[12903]
Social Progress Trust Fund [★17579]
Social Progress Trust Fund [★17579]
Social Psychiatry Res. Inst. [16344], 423 E 138th
St., Ste. 201, Bronx, NY 10454, (212)249-6829
Social Relief Intl. [12370], PO Box 540765, Omaha,
NE 68154, (402)403-0130
Social Relief Intl. [12370], PO Box 540765, Omaha,
NE 68154, (402)403-0130

A star before a book entry number signifies that the name is not listed separately, but is mentioned within the entry.

Social Res. Assn. [IO], London, United Kingdom
Social Responsibilities Round Table of the Amer. Lib.
   Assn. [10011], 50 E Huron St., Chicago, IL 60611,
   (312)280-4294
Social Responsibility
   Accountability in Intl. Development [12308]
   BuildingBlocks Intl. [11666]
   Campaign for Fresh Air and Clean Politics
      [18646]
   CARTHA [18402]
   Corporate Social Responsibility Assn. [964]
   Friends of Liberia [13121]
   Global Brigades [11588]
   Gyro Intl. [13058]
   HandsOn Network [13394]
   INFORM [18647]
   Intl. Development Stewardship [12343]
   Junior Optimist Octagon Intl. [13060]
   Key Club Intl. [13061]
   Kiwanis Intl. [13062]
   Ladies of Charity of the U.S.A. [13191]
   Message! Products [18648]
   Optimist Intl. [13071]
   R2P Coalition [13376]
   Rwanda Knits [11626]
   US SIF: The Forum for Sustainable and
      Responsible Investment [18649]
   World Partners for Development [13210]
Social Sci. History Assn. [7418], Journals Dept.,
   Duke Univ. Press, PO Box 90660, Durham, NC
   27708
Social Sci. Res. Coun. [7419], 1 Pierrepont Plz.,
   15th Fl., Brooklyn, NY 11201, (212)377-2700
Social Sciences
   Allied Social Sci. Associations [7408]
   Amer. Psychological Assn. l Soc. of Psychological
      Hypnosis [16380]
   Assn. for Africanist Anthropology [6133]
   Assn. of Chinese Professors of Social Sciences in
      the U.S. [7409]
   Assn. for Humanist Sociology [7424]
   Assn. of Muslim Social Scientists of North Am.
      [7410]
   Assn. of Population Centers [6594]SocialAssn. of
      Social Sci. Researchers
   Center for Pacific Northwest Stud. [7411]
   Center for the Stud. of Gp. Processes [7412]
   Coalition of Handwriting Analysts Intl. [6937]
   Consortium of Social Sci. Associations [7413]
   European and Mediterranean Network of the
      Social Sciences [586]
   German-Japanese Soc. for Social Sciences
      [16384]
   HOPOS - The Intl. Soc. for the History of
      Philosophy of Sci. [8839]
   Indian Assn. of Social Sci. Institutions [1935]
   Inst. for Social Res. [7414]
   Intl. Adam Smith Soc. [10381]
   Intl. Assn. for Comparative Mythology [7133]
   Intl. Intelligence Ethics Assn. [7001]
   Intl. Network for Social Network Anal. [7415]
   Intl. Network for Social Network Anal. [7415]
   Intl. Soc. for the Comparative Stud. of Civilizations
      [7416]
   Intl. Soc. for the Comparative Stud. of Civilizations
      [7416]
   Intl. Soc. for the Social Stud. [8865]
   Intl. Visual Sociology Assn. [7428]
   Legacies of War [8259]
   Paleoanthropology Soc. [7211]
   Pi Gamma Mu [23709]
   Pi Gamma Mu [23709]
   Russell Sage Found. [7417]
   Social Sci. History Assn. [7418]
   Social Sci. Res. Coun. [7419]
   Soc. for the History of Psychology [7312]
   Soc. for the Stud. of Human Development [6946]
   Soc. for the Stud. of Symbolic Interaction [7432]
   Soc. for Terrorism Res. [7554]
   Western Social Sci. Assn. [7420]
Social Sciences and Humanities Res. Coun. of
   Canada [IO], Ottawa, ON, Canada
**Social SecuritySocialEuropean Inst. of Social
Security**
   Natl. Acad. of Social Insurance [18650]

Natl. Assn. of Disability Representatives [18651]
Natl. Comm. to Preserve Social Security and
   Medicare [18652]
Natl. Conf. of State Social Security Administrators
   [5973]
Natl. Coun. of Social Security Mgt. Associations
   [5974]
Natl. Org. of Social Security Claimants'
   Representatives [18653]
Social Security and Medicare; Natl. Comm. to
   Preserve [18652]
Social Service
   1-2-3 Intl. [12573]
   1st Special Response Gp. [11843]
   200 Orphanages Worldwide [11172]
   1000 Jobs [12713]
   Accountability in Intl. Development [12308]
   Act for Africa Intl. [12951]
   Active: Water [13410]
   Adopt-a-Village Intl. [11540]
   Adventrek [12256]
   Africa Am. Crisis Assistance Network [12797]
   Africa Bridge [11177]
   Africa Hope [11178]
   African Cultural Alliance of North Am. [10818]
   African Sky [11542]
   AfriHope Intl., Inc. [10806]
   AHOPE for Children [11180]
   Aid Africa [12714]
   Aid Still Required [11845]
   AlKoura League [12428]
   All for Africa [10807]
   All the Children are Children [11182]
   All Hands Volunteers [11846]
   All Kids Can Learn Intl. [11446]
   All One People [10808]
   All Our Children Intl. Outreach [11183]
   Alliance For Relief Mission in Haiti [12799]
   Alliance for Full Participation [11754]
   Alliance of Jamaican and Amer. Humanitarians
      [11543]
   Am. Continental 2000 [11847]
   Amer. Bar Assn. Commn. on Homelessness and
      Poverty [12153]
   Amer. Soc. for the Support of Injured Survivors of
      Terrorism [13359]
   Amer. Sunrise [12170]
   Amman Imman: Water is Life [13413]
   Angel Covers [11190]
   Anti-Poverty Initiative [17188]
   Ark Mission [11191]
   Art Aids Art [10819]
   Artfully AWARE [9275]
   Aviation for Humanity [12807]
   Bahia St. [12717]
   Baitulmaal [12808]
   Baptist Global Response [12809]
   Be The Change Intl. [13344]
   Because Intl. [12718]
   Benefit4Kids [11196]
   Bethany Christian Services Intl. [11197]
   Birambye Intl. [11550]
   Blessings on Africa [12719]
   blueEnergy [11966]
   Brave Intl. [19808]
   Breaking Ground [11552]
   Bridge Kids Intl. [13515]
   Bridges Cambodia Intl. [11203]
   Building Community Bridges [11554]
   BuildingBlocks Intl. [11666]
   Burundi Friends Intl. [11555]
   Camp To Belong [11205]
   Care 2 Share [13373]
   Care Highway Intl. [12814]
   Care Through Educ. Intl. [11453]
   Catholic Social Workers Natl. Assn. [13216]
   Challah for Hunger [12266]
   ChangeALife Uganda [11209]
   CHAP Intl. [12817]
   Charities Aid Found. Am. [13155]
   charity: water [13414]
   CHEER for Viet Nam [13374]
   Chefs for Humanity [12267]
   Chemists Without Borders [12449]
   Child Vikaas Intl. [11161]

   Child Welfare and Policy and Practice Gp.
      [11229]
   Children of the Americas [11234]
   Children of Grace [11236]
   Children's Vision Intl., Inc. [11458]
   Choices [12258]
   Chosen Children Intl. [11255]
   Christian Alliance For Humanitarian Aid [12821]
   Christian Ladies All together Standing against
      Social Injustice Corp. [13456]
   Clinic at a Time [15152]
   Common Hope for Hea. [14768]
   Community Aid Relief and Development [12826]
   Community Members Interested [11569]
   Community Solutions for Africa's Development
      [11570]
   Community Water Solutions [13417]
   Compassion into Action Network - Direct Outcome
      Org. [11849]
   Compassion First [12827]
   Complementary and Alternative Medicine Initiative
      [13671]
   Confessing Synod Ministries [20242]
   Connecting Congo [11573]
   Coun. on Accreditation [13182]
   Coun. of Religious Volunteer Agencies [13390]
   Coun. for Zimbabwe [12322]
   Cover Me With Love [11261]
   Damien Ministries [19633]
   Developing Hands [11264]
   Distressed Children and Infants Intl. [11265]
   Drinking Water for India [13419]
   Drishtipat Worldwide [11124]
   DROKPA [11575]
   EarthSpark Intl. [6711]
   Ecuador Children's Hope Org. [11266]
   Educational Help for Afghanistan Assn. [8916]
   Embracing Orphans [11267]
   Emerging Humanity [12325]
   Emerging Practitioners in Philanthropy [12665]
   Empower Tanzania, Inc. [12954]
   Enable Intl. [13156]
   Encephalitis Global [14384]
   Esther's Aid for Needy and Abandoned Children
      [11270]
   Ethiopia's Tomorrow [11272]
   Everyone Needs a Hero [11582]
   Executives Without Borders [60]
   Exodus Guild [10821]
   Farm Rescue [12041]
   Fields of Growth Intl. [12416]
   Fight Against Hunger Org. [12274]
   Flashes of Hope [11135]
   Food-Aid [12275]
   Forgotten Victims [13363]
   FosterClub [13522]
   Freedom Fields USA [11529]
   Friends of the Children of Angola [11284]
   Funders' Network for Smart Growth and Livable
      Communities [11587]
   A Future Without Poverty [12729]
   Gay and Lesbian Assn. of Retiring Persons
      [10843]
   Gift of Water [13420]
   Give Clean Water [13421]
   Global AIDS Interfaith Alliance [13607]
   Global Alliance for Community Empowerment
      [10811]
   Global Children's Org. [11467]
   Global Civic Preservation [12329]
   Global Family [13157]
   Global Family [13157]
   Global Family Rescue [13158]
   Global FoodBanking Network [12281]
   Global Goods Partners [12330]
   Global Partners Running Waters [11590]
   Global Peace Services [18251]
   Global Water Challenge [4993]
   Glocal Ventures [12331]
   Great Commn. Alliance [11852]
   Gyro Intl. [13058]
   H2O for Life [13422]
   Haiti Works! [12333]
   Hand in Hand USA [12842]
   HandReach [11517]

Reference to "IO" in place of a book number signifies that the association may be found in the 50th edition of International Organizations.

A star before a book entry number signifies that the name is not listed separately, but is mentioned within the entry.

Social Sororities
Alpha Chi Omega [23710]
Alpha Epsilon Phi [23711]
Alpha Gamma Delta [23712]
Alpha Omicron Pi [23713]
Alpha Phi Intl. Fraternity [23714]
Alpha Phi Intl. Fraternity [23714]
Alpha Sigma Alpha [23715]
Alpha Sigma Tau [23716]
Alpha Xi Delta Women's Fraternity [23717]
Chi Omega [23718]
Delta Delta Delta [23719]
Delta Gamma [23720]
Delta Gamma [23720]
Delta Gamma Pi Multicultural Sorority [23739]
Delta Phi Epsilon [23721]
Delta Sigma Chi Sorority [23741]
Delta Xi Phi Multicultural Sorority [23722]
Delta Zeta [23723]
Gamma Phi Beta [23724]
Gamma Phi Beta [23724]
Kappa Alpha Theta [23725]
Kappa Delta [23726]
Kappa Kappa Gamma [23727]
Kappa Phi Gamma Sorority [23746]
Lambda Psi Delta Sorority [23747]
Phi Beta Chi [23728]
Phi Mu Fraternity [23729]
Phi Sigma Sigma [23730]
Sigma Delta Tau [23731]
Sigma Kappa [23732]
Sigma Kappa Found. [23733]
Sigma Sigma Sigma [23734]
Theta Phi Alpha [23735]
Zeta Chi Phi Multicultural Sorority [23752]
Zeta Tau Alpha [23736]

Social Studies
Intl. Soc. for the Social Stud. [8865]
Legacies of War [8259]
Natl. Coun. for the Social Stud. [8866]
Social Venture Network [704], PO Box 29221, San Francisco, CA 94129-0221, (415)561-6501

Social Welfare
1-2-3 Intl. [12573]
4 Real Women Intl. [13447]
9/11 Families for a Secure Am. Found. [18710]
200 Orphanages Worldwide [11172]
1000 Jobs [12713]
Abriendo Mentes [12950]
Achieve in Africa [11173]
Active: Water [13410]
Adventrek [12256]
African Cultural Alliance of North Am. [10818]
African Great Lakes Initiative [13165]
African Sky [11542]
AfriHope Intl., Inc. [10806]
Aid Africa [12714]
Aid Still Required [11845]
Aid for the World [12715]
Airline Ambassadors Intl. [13166]
Airline Ambassadors Intl. [13166]
AlKoura League [12428]
All for Africa [10807]
All Hands Volunteers [11846]
All Kids Can Learn Intl. [11446]
All One People [10808]
Alliance for Full Participation [11754]
Alliance of Jamaican and Amer. Humanitarians [11543]
Am. Continental 2000 [11847]
Amer. Assn. of SNAP Directors [5975]
Amer. Bar Assn. Commn. on Homelessness and Poverty [12153]
Amer. Friends Ser. Comm. [13167]
Amer. Friends Ser. Comm. [13167]
Amer. Humane Assn. [13168]
Amer. Public Human Services Assn. [13169]
Amer. Public Human Services Assn. l IT Solutions Mgt. for Human Services [13170]
Amer. Public Human Services Assn. l Natl. Coun. of State Human Ser. Administrators [13171]
Amer. Rescue Workers [13172]
Amer. Soc. for Kurds [13173]
Amer. Soc. for Kurds [13173]
Amer. Soc. for the Support of Injured Survivors of Terrorism [13359]

Amer. Sunrise [12170]
AmeriGhana [12312]
Amman Imman: Water is Life [13413]
Angel Wing Flights [12445]
Animals Deserve Absolute Protection Today and Tomorrow [10924]
Art Aids Art [10819]
Artists for Peace and Justice [13152]
Assn. of Gospel Rescue Missions [13174]
Assn. of Gospel Rescue Missions [13174]
Aviation for Humanity [12807]
Bahia St. [12717]
Baitulmaal [12808]
Be The Change Intl. [13344]
Because Intl. [12718]
BERWA [12315]
Birambye Intl. [11550]
Blessings on Africa [12719]
Blood: Water Mission [10809]
BLOOM Africa [11199]
blueEnergy [11966]
Brave Intl. [19808]
A Bridge for Children [11201]
Bridge Kids Intl. [13515]
Bridge of Love [11202]
Bridges Cambodia Intl. [11203]
Building Bridges Worldwide [11553]
Building Tomorrow [12659]
Cambodian Amer. Mobile Clinic [14110]
Camp To Belong [11205]
Care 2 Share [13373]
Care Highway Intl. [12814]
Care Through Educ. Intl. [11453]
Carrie Estelle Doheny Found. [13175]
CATalyst Coun. [10938]
Catholic Central Union of Am. l Central Bur. [19400]
Catholic Charities USA [13176]
Challah for Hunger [12266]
CHAP Intl. [12817]
CHEER for Viet Nam [13374]
Chemists Without Borders [12449]
The Child is Innocent [11219]
Child Literacy [11221]
Child Vikaas Intl. [11161]
Child Welfare and Policy and Practice Gp. [11229]
Children of the Americas [11234]
Children of the Dump [11235]
Children's Cup [12819]
Children's Vision Intl., Inc. [11458]
ChildVoice Intl. [11254]
Choices [12258]
Christian Found. for Children and Aging [13177]
Christian Found. for Children and Aging [13177]
Christian Ladies All together Standing against Social Injustice Corp. [13456]
Clean the World [4869]
Coalition for Economic Survival [13178]
Coalition on Human Needs [13179]
Coleman Found. [13180]
Community Members Interested [11569]
Community Water Solutions [13417]
Compassion First [12827]
Connecting Congo [11573]
Conrad N. Hilton Found. [13181]
Coun. on Accreditation [13182]
Coun. for Hea. and Human Ser. Ministries of the United Church of Christ [13183]
Coun. of Religious Volunteer Agencies [13390]
Coun. for Standards in Human Ser. Educ. [8867]
Coun. for Zimbabwe [12322]
Cover Me With Love [11261]
CRISTA Ministries [13184]
Crutches 4 Kids [11262]
Cuban Amer. Natl. Coun. [13185]
Debt AIDS Trade Africa [17149]
Developing Hands [11264]
Distressed Children and Infants Intl. [11265]
Drishtipat Worldwide [11124]
Educate the Children [11461]
Educate These Children [11462]
Educ. for Prosperity [11576]
Edurelief [12834]
Embracing Orphans [11267]

Emergency Relief Response Fund [13186]
Emergency Relief Response Fund [13186]
Emerging Humanity [12325]
Emerging Practitioners in Philanthropy [12665]
Empower Orphans [11269]
Empower Tanzania, Inc. [12954]
Empowerment Works [11579]
Enable Intl. [13156]
Esther's Aid for Needy and Abandoned Children [11270]
Evangelical Lutheran Good Samaritan Soc. [13187]
Everyone Needs a Hero [11582]
Exodus Guild [10821]
Faceless Intl. [13362]
Farm Rescue [12041]
Feral Cat Caretakers' Coalition [3810]
Fight Against Hunger Org. [12274]
First Foundations [13188]
First Star [11278]
Flying Kites [11279]
Forgotten Victims [13363]
Friends of Liberia [13121]
Friends Women's Assn. [13461]
FUNDaFIELD [11288]
A Future Without Poverty [12729]
Generation Five [13086]
Generations United [13189]
Global Alliance for Community Empowerment [10811]
Global Children [11293]
Global Children's Org. [11467]
Global Civic Preservation [12329]
Global FoodBanking Network [12281]
Global Goods Partners [12330]
Goods for Good [11296]
Guitars For Vets [11840]
Gyro Intl. [13058]
H2O for Life [13422]
Haiti Works! [12333]
Hand in Hand USA [12842]
HandReach [11517]
Hands Across the Water [11297]
Hands to Hearts Intl. [11298]
HandsOn Network [13394]
HavServe Volunteer Ser. Network [11069]
Hea. Justice Collaborative [15181]
Hearts for the Hungry [12282]
Hedge Funds Care [11143]
Helping Children Worldwide [11304]
Helping Hearts Helping Hands [12730]
Helping and Loving Orphans [11307]
Helping Orphans Worldwide [11308]
HelpMercy Intl. [14791]
Hero Initiative [9490]
Hollywood Unites For Haiti [12128]
HomeAID for Africa [10812]
Hope for the Child [11313]
Hope Force Intl. [11854]
Hope for Haiti [11595]
Hope Through Hea. [12385]
HumaniNet [12848]
Humanitarian African Relief Org. [12849]
Humanitarian Intl. Ser. Gp. [12260]
Humans in Crisis Intl. Corp. [12851]
Igbere Progressive Assn. Intl. [12576]
In Our Own Quiet Way [13424]
Indigo Threads [11596]
Innocents at Risk [12241]
InterConnection [11664]
Intl. Assn. for Human Values [12216]
Intl. Partners [12345]
Intl. Relief Friendship Found. [13190]
Intl. Relief Friendship Found. [13190]
Inyana - League of Rwandan Children and Youth [11474]
Junior Optimist Octagon Intl. [13060]
Key Club Intl. [13061]
Kids Against Hunger [12283]
Kids Together [11802]
Kiwanis Intl. [13062]
Kollaboration [13534]
Korean Amer. Sharing Movement [12860]
Ladies of Charity of the U.S.A. [13191]
Life in Abundance Intl. [10814]

Reference to "IO" in place of a book number signifies that the association may be found in the 50th edition of International Organizations.

Lighthouse Sta. [12736]
Lily of the Valley Endeavor [10886]
Living Waters Org. [11608]
Louis and Harold Price Found. [13192]
Magic Johnson Found. [13193]
Malawi Children's Mission [11347]
Mali Assistance Proj. [10816]
Matanya's Hope [12737]
Medicine for Mali [12468]
Meds and Food for Kids [11348]
Mike's Angels [11349]
Mil Milagros [11350]
Minga [11351]
Miracles of Hope Network [11352]
Moringa Community [11610]
Move For Hunger [12285]
Muslim Alliance in North America [19147]
Namlo Intl. [12349]
Natl. Alliance for Hispanic Hea. [13194]
Natl. Assn. of Ser. Dogs [11876]
Natl. Assn. of The Bahamas [11141]
Natl. Assn. of Victim Ser. Professionals in Corrections [13366]
Natl. Coalition of Pastors' Spouses [13195]
Natl. Foster Care Coalition [11366]
Natl. Furniture Bank Assn. [12059]
Natl. Local Tech. Assistance Prog. Assn. [13196]
Natl. Minorities with Disabilities Coalition [17545]
Natl. Org. for Human Services [8868]
Natl. Org. of Iraqi Christians [12630]
Natl. Staff Development and Training Assn. [13197]
Natl. WIC Assn. [5976]
Nature Healing Nature [11614]
Neighbors Without Borders [12350]
New Ecology, Inc. [11616]
New Hope Constr. [12198]
New Reality Intl. [12743]
NextAid [11369]
Ninos del Lago [11370]
Nubian United Benevolent Intl. Assn. [12787]
Nuru Intl. [11076]
Nutrition and Educ. Intl. [12586]
One Love Worldwide [12874]
One Missing Link [12545]
One Vision Intl. [11619]
Oneworld Works [12354]
Oper. Help The Children [11375]
Oper. Interdependence [12530]
Opportunities Industrialization Centers Intl. [13198]
Opportunities Industrialization Centers Intl. [13198]
Optimist Intl. [13071]
The Optimists [11377]
Options for Children in Zambia [11378]
Organize Training Center [11657]
OrphanAid Africa [11382]
Orphans to Ambassadors [11384]
Para Sa Bata [11387]
Partnership for Quality Medical Donations [12478]
Peace Winds Am. [11859]
People for Haiti [12877]
Picture the Homeless [17792]
Pilgrim Africa [12878]
Planting Hope [11622]
Prana Intl. [12749]
Proj. Baobab [13553]
Promise World Wide [12358]
Pueblo a Pueblo [12124]
Pura Vida for Children [11395]
Rainbow/PUSH Coalition [13199]
Read Horn of Africa USA [12360]
Reality Relief [12880]
Rebuild A Nation [11077]
Reconstruction Efforts Aiding Children without Homes [11624]
Relief for Africa [12882]
Relief Liberia Intl. [12884]
Rsrc. Development Intl. Cambodia [12361]
Restore Humanity [12362]
Right Turn, Intl. [13200]
Rising Intl. [11078]
River Intl. [12887]
Roots and Wings Intl. [12363]

Rotarian Action Gp. for the Alleviation of Hunger and Malnutrition [12290]
Rotarian Action Gp. for Population Growth and Sustainable Development [12709]
Rural Hea. Intl. Non-Profit Org. [15208]
Rwanda Gift for Life [13099]
Rwanda Partners [12364]
Sabu Help [12962]
Safe Passage [11401]
Safe Water Network [13429]
Salvation Army [13201]
Salvation Army [13201]
Samaritan's Feet [11402]
Samuel Rubin Found. [13202]
Save Darfur Coalition [17744]
Scattering Resources [12888]
Scherman Found. [13203]
Seeds For Hope [11861]
ServeHAITI [11630]
Ser. for the Love of God [11631]
Seven Generations Ahead [11632]
Sex Abuse Treatment Alliance [13100]
SHIP Aid: Shipping Humanitarian Aid to Impoverished People [12889]
Simple Hope [12891]
SingleStop USA [12752]
Skills for Humanity [12753]
Soc. of St. Vincent de Paul Coun. of the U.S. [13204]
Soc. of Young Philanthropists [12685]
Somali Medical and Supplies Relief Org. [12893]
SOTENI Intl. [10893]
SpanAfrica [11642]
Spark Ventures [11407]
Spirit Quilts [11408]
StandUp for Kids [11409]
Stop Hunger Now [12294]
Strategies for Intl. Development [12372]
SunPower Afrique [13227]
Sunstove Org. [11643]
Surviving Parents Coalition [11511]
Sustainable Organic Integrated Livelihoods [11645]
SustainUS [13559]
Team Success [13560]
TERRA - Rsrc. Development Intl. [12963]
Threads Weaving Dreams [12374]
To Love a Child [11417]
Together for Tanzania [11646]
Tomorrow's Youth Org. [13562]
Touching Hearts [10817]
TransWorld Development Initiatives [12262]
Travelers Aid Intl. [13205]
Travelers Aid Intl. [13205]
Tusubira - We Have Hope [12755]
Twinkle Little Stars [11419]
Ubuntu Africa [11421]
Ugandan Amer. Partnership Org. [12307]
Umoja Intl. [12969]
UNANIMA Intl. [18645]
Uncharterd Intl. [12377]
United Nations I Vietnam Relief Effort [13372]
United People in Christ [19980]
UNITED SIKHS [12228]
U.S. Conf. of City Human Services Officials [5977]
United We Serve [20712]
Venture Strategies Innovations [14833]
Village Focus Intl. [11650]
Village Volunteers [12379]
Vishwam [12770]
Volunteers of Am. [13206]
VOSH Intl. [12482]
Water 1st Intl. [13433]
Water is Life Intl. [13435]
Water for People I PlayPumps Intl. [10827]
WaterAid Am. [13441]
We, The World [13123]
Welfare Res., Inc. [13207]
Wheel Wishers [7407]
William and Flora Hewlett Found. [13208]
Windward Found. [13209]
Wine to Water [13443]
WINGS [12904]
Woman Within Intl. Ltd. [13486]

Women of Hope Proj. [13487]
Women of Yemen Assn. [11080]
Women's Global Connection [13493]
World Action for Humanity [13120]
World of Good Development Org. [12382]
World Orphans [11433]
World Partners for Development [13210]
World Partners for Development [13210]
World Spark [11435]
World Wins Intl. [11654]
Worldhealer [12384]
WorldHope Corps [11655]
Wounded Warrior Proj. [20822]
Zambia Hope Intl. [11437]
Zarrow Families Found. [13211]

Social Work

1-2-3 Intl. [12573]
Accountability in Intl. Development [12308]
Achieve in Africa [11173]
Active: Water [13410]
Adventrek [12256]
Africa Am. Crisis Assistance Network [12797]
African Cultural Alliance of North Am. [10818]
AfriHope Intl., Inc. [10806]
Aid Africa [12714]
Aid Still Required [11845]
AlKoura League [12428]
All for Africa [10807]
All Hands Volunteers [11846]
All Kids Can Learn Intl. [11446]
All One People [10808]
ALMA Soc. [10777]
Amer. Assn. for Psychoanalysis in Clinical Social Work [13212]
Amer. Bar Assn. Commn. on Homelessness and Poverty [12153]
Amer. Sunrise [12170]
AmeriGhana [12312]
Art Aids Art [10819]
Artfully AWARE [9275]
Artists Striving to End Poverty [12716]
Assn. for Advanced Training in the Behavioral Sciences [8761]
Assn. for Community Org. and Social Admin. [13213]
Assn. of Oncology Social Work [13214]
Assn. for Schools of Social Work in Africa [383]
Assn. of Social Work Boards [13215]
Aviation for Humanity [12807]
Bahia St. [12717]
Be The Change Intl. [13344]
Because Intl. [12718]
BERWA [12315]
Blood: Water Mission [10809]
blueEnergy [11966]
Brave Intl. [19808]
Bridge Kids Intl. [13515]
Bridge of Love [11202]
Bridges to Prosperity [12952]
Building Bridges Worldwide [11553]
Building Tomorrow [12659]
Care Highway Intl. [12814]
Care Through Educ. Intl. [11453]
Catholic Social Workers Natl. Assn. [13216]
Challah for Hunger [12266]
CHAP Intl. [12817]
Chefs for Humanity [12267]
Chemists Without Borders [12449]
Child Vikaas Intl. [11161]
Children of the Dump [11235]
Children's Cup [12819]
Children's Hope Intl. Literacy and Development [11245]
Children's Vision Intl., Inc. [11458]
ChildVoice Intl. [11254]
Clinical Social Work Assn. [13217]
Common Hope for Hea. [14768]
Community Aid Relief and Development [12826]
Community Members Interested [11569]
Compassion First [12827]
Coun. of Intl. Programs USA [13218]
Coun. of Intl. Programs USA [13218]
Coun. on Sexual Orientation and Gender Expression [8869]
Coun. on Social Work Educ. [8870]

A star before a book entry number signifies that the name is not listed separately, but is mentioned within the entry.

3164   Encyclopedia of Associations, 51st Edition

Coun. for Zimbabwe [12322]
Developing Hands [11264]
Distressed Children and Infants Intl. [11265]
Drishtipat Worldwide [11124]
Emerging Humanity [12325]
Emerging Practitioners in Philanthropy [12665]
Employee Assistance Professionals Assn. [13219]
Empower Tanzania, Inc. [12954]
Enable Intl. [13156]
Esther's Aid for Needy and Abandoned Children [11270]
Faceless Intl. [13362]
Families for Private Adoption [10788]
Farm Rescue [12041]
Fight Against Hunger Org. [12274]
First Star [11278]
Flying Kites [11279]
Food-Aid [12275]
Freedom Fields USA [11529]
Friends of Liberia [13121]
A Future Without Poverty [12729]
Global Children [11293]
Global Civic Preservation [12329]
Global Goods Partners [12330]
Global Rsrc. Alliance [3974]
Great Commn. Alliance [11852]
Hand in Hand USA [12842]
HandReach [11517]
HandsOn Network [13394]
Hannah's Promise Intl. Aid [12843]
Healing the Divide [12238]
Hea. Justice Collaborative [15181]
Hearts for the Hungry [12282]
Hearts for Kenya [11070]
Helping Children Worldwide [11304]
Helping and Loving Orphans [11307]
Hero Initiative [9490]
Hollywood Unites For Haiti [12128]
HomeAID for Africa [10812]
Hope for the Child [11313]
Hope Force Intl. [11854]
HumaniNet [12848]
Humanitarian African Relief Org. [12849]
Humanitarian Intl. Ser. Gp. [12260]
Humanitarian Resources Intl. [12850]
Humans in Crisis Intl. Corp. [12851]
Igbere Progressive Assn. Intl. [12576]
Infancy Intl. [14113]
Integrative Clinics Intl. [14899]
InterConnection [11664]
Intl. Crisis Aid [12854]
Intl. Development Stewardship [12343]
Intl. Partners [12345]
Irish Assn. of Social Workers [8228]
Irob Relief and Rehabilitation Operations Brotherhood [11986]
Ivory Coast Medical Relief Team [16583]
Kids Against Hunger [12283]
Kindness in a Box [11339]
Libraries Without Borders [8519]
Life in Abundance Intl. [10814]
Lighthouse Sta. [12736]
Little By Little [14802]
Living Waters Org. [11608]
Mali Assistance Proj. [10816]
Matanya's Hope [12737]
MediaGlobal [12348]
Medical Bridges [15307]
Medicine for Mali [12468]
Meds and Food for Kids [11348]
Miracles of Hope Network [11352]
Missing Children in Am. [11353]
Moms Against Poverty [12742]
Move For Hunger [12285]
Namlo Intl. [12349]
Natl. Assn. of Black Social Workers [13220]
Natl. Assn. of Deans and Directors of Schools of Social Work [8871]
Natl. Assn. of Puerto Rican Hispanic Social Workers [13221]
Natl. Assn. of Ser. Dogs [11876]
Natl. Assn. of Social Workers [13222]
Natl. Assn. of The Bahamas [11141]
Natl. Furniture Bank Assn. [12059]
Natl. Local Tech. Assistance Prog. Assn. [13196]

Natl. Network for Social Work Managers [13223]
Nature Healing Nature [11614]
Neighbors Without Borders [12350]
Netting Nations [14413]
New Hope Constr. [12198]
New Reality Intl. [12743]
Nigerian Social Workers Assn. [13224]
Ninos del Lago [11370]
North Amer. Assn. of Christians in Social Work [13225]
Nuru Intl. [11076]
Nutrition and Educ. Intl. [12586]
Omnilogy, Inc. [12353]
One Love Worldwide [12874]
One Nurse At A Time [15794]
Oneworld Works [12354]
Oper. Help The Children [11375]
Outreach Asia [11116]
People for Haiti [12877]
Picture the Homeless [17792]
Pilgrim Africa [12878]
Planting Hope [11622]
Prana Intl. [12749]
Proj. Baobab [13553]
Pueblo a Pueblo [12124]
Pura Vida for Children [11395]
Rain for the Sahel and Sahara [12359]
Read Horn of Africa USA [12360]
Reality Relief [12880]
Relief for Africa [12882]
Rsrc. Development Intl. Cambodia [12361]
Restore Humanity [12362]
RISE-UP From Poverty [12751]
Roots and Wings Intl. [12363]
Rural Hea. Intl. Non-Profit Org. [15208]
Safe Passage [11401]
Scattering Resources [12888]
School Social Work Assn. of Am. [8872]
ServeHAITI [11630]
Ser. for the Love of God [11631]
Serving Our World [11405]
SHIP Aid: Shipping Humanitarian Aid to Impoverished People [12889]
Singapore Assn. of Social Workers [5652]
SingleStop USA [12752]
Skills for Humanity [12753]
Soccer Without Borders [22942]
Soc. for Social Work Leadership in Hea. Care [13226]
Soc. for Social Work and Res. [8873]
Soc. for Social Work and Res. [8873]
Somali Medical and Supplies Relief Org. [12893]
SOTENI Intl. [10893]
SpanAfrica [11642]
Spark Ventures [11407]
Stop Hunger Now [12294]
Sudan Sunrise [12636]
SURGE [13431]
Sustainable Organic Integrated Livelihoods [11645]
Teens Fighting Hunger [12295]
TERRA - Rsrc. Development Intl. [12963]
To Love a Child [11417]
Tomorrow's Youth Org. [13562]
Twinkle Little Stars [11419]
Ugandan Amer. Partnership Org. [12307]
United People in Christ [19980]
United We Serve [20712]
Venture Strategies Innovations [14833]
Village Volunteers [12379]
Vishwam [12770]
Water is Life Intl. [13435]
Water for Sudan [13438]
Water for Waslala [13440]
WaterAid Am. [13441]
Wheel Wishers [7407]
Wine to Water [13443]
Women of Hope Proj. [13487]
Women of Yemen Assn. [11080]
Women's Global Connection [13493]
World of Good Development Org. [12382]
World Wins Intl. [11654]
Worldhealer [12384]
Wounded Warrior Proj. [20822]
Zambia Hope Intl. [11437]

Social Work Res. Gp. [★13222]
Social Workers
   Accountability in Intl. Development [12308]
   ALMA Soc. [10777]
   Amer. Bar Assn. Commn. on Homelessness and Poverty [12153]
   Assn. for Community Org. and Social Admin. [13213]
   Assn. for Humanist Sociology [7424]
   Building Tomorrow [12659]
   Emerging Practitioners in Philanthropy [12665]
   Families for Private Adoption [10788]
   Fight Against Hunger Org. [12274]
   A Future Without Poverty [12729]
   Global Goods Partners [12330]
   Humanitarian Resources Intl. [12850]
   Intl. Development Stewardship [12343]
   Move For Hunger [12285]
   Neighbors Without Borders [12350]
   Soc. for Social Work Leadership in Hea. Care [13226]
   SpanAfrica [11642]
   Spark Ventures [11407]
   Village Volunteers [12379]
Social Workers in the Field of Learning Disability [IO], Dublin, Ireland
Socialdemokraterne [★IO]
Socialism
   Caucus for a New Political Sci. [7287]
   Committees of Correspondence for Democracy and Socialism [5978]
   Democratic Socialists of Am. [18654]
   Freedom Road Socialist Org. [5979]
   Freedom Socialist Party [18655]
   League for the Revolutionary Party [18656]
   News and Letters Comm. [18657]
   Religion and Socialism Commn. of the Democratic Socialists of Am. [18658]
   Socialist Action [18659]
   Socialist Alternative [5980]
   Workers World Party [18660]
   Workers World Party [18660]
   Young Communist League USA [18661]
   Young Democratic Socialists [18662]
   Youth for Intl. Socialism [18663]
   Youth for Intl. Socialism [18663]
Socialist Action [18659], PO Box 10328, Oakland, CA 94610, (415)255-1080
Socialist Alliance [IO], Canberra, Australia
Socialist Alternative [5980], PO Box 45343, Seattle, WA 98145, (206)526-7185
Socialist Educational Soc. [★18369]
Socialist Gp. in the European Parliament [IO], Brussels, Belgium
Socialist Intl. [IO], London, United Kingdom
Socialist Intl. Women [IO], London, United Kingdom
Socialist Labor Party of Am. [18365], PO Box 218, Mountain View, CA 94042-0218, (408)280-7266
Socialist Party [IO], London, United Kingdom
Socialist Party of Canada [IO], Victoria, BC, Canada
Socialist Party-Democratic Socialist Fed. [★18339]
Socialist Party - France [IO], Paris, France
Socialist Party U.S.A. [18366], 339 Lafayette St., Ste. 303, New York, NY 10012, (212)982-4586
Socialist Party, U.S.A. [★18339]
Socialistic Labor Party [★18365]
Sociedad Anatomica Espanola [★IO]
Sociedad de Anestesiologia de Chile [IO], Santiago, Chile
Sociedad Anglo-Chilena [★IO]
Sociedad Argentina de Biofisica [★IO]
Sociedad Argentina de Bioingeniera [★IO]
Sociedad Argentina de Biologia [★IO]
Sociedad Argentina de Botanica [★IO]
Sociedad Argentina de Cardiologia [★IO]
Sociedad Argentina De Informatica E Investigacion Operativa [IO], Buenos Aires, Argentina
Sociedad Argentina de Dermatologia [★IO]
Sociedad Argentina de Endocrinologia y Metabolismo [★IO]
Sociedad Argentina de Estudios Geograficos [★IO]
Sociedad Argentina de Fisiologica [IO], Buenos Aires, Argentina
Sociedad Argentina de Gastroenterologia [★IO]
Sociedad Argentina de Genetica [★IO]

Reference to "IO" in place of a book number signifies that the association may be found in the 50th edition of International Organizations.

Sociedad Argentina de Hematologia [★IO]
Sociedad Argentina de Oftalmologia [★IO]
Sociedad Argentina de Osteoporosis [★IO]
Sociedad Argentina de Patologia [IO], Buenos Aires, Argentina
Sociedad Argentina de Pediatria [★IO]
Sociedad Argentina de Psicotrauma [★IO]
Sociedad Biblica Chilena [★IO]
Sociedad Biblica Colombiana [★IO]
Sociedad Biblica de Costa Rica [★IO]
Sociedad Biblica de Honduras [★IO]
Sociedad Biblica de Mexico [★IO]
Sociedad Biblica de Nicaragua [★IO]
Sociedad Biblica Peruana [★IO]
Sociedad Biblica de el Salvador [★IO]
Sociedad de Biologia de Chile [IO], Santiago, Chile
Sociedad Boliviana de Gastroenterologia y Endoscopia [★IO]
Sociedad Boliviana de Osteologia y Metabolismo Mineral [★IO]
Sociedad Boliviana de Terapia Fisica [IO], Santa Cruz, Bolivia
Sociedad Chilena de Cardiologia y Cirugia Cardiovascular [★IO]
Sociedad Chilena de Ciencia de la Computacion [★IO]
Sociedad Chilena De Fertilidad [IO], Santiago, Chile
Sociedad Chilena del Derecho de Autor [IO], Santiago, Chile
Sociedad Chilena de Dermatologia y Venereologia [★IO]
Sociedad Chilena de Endocrinologia y Diabetes [IO], Santiago, Chile
Sociedad Chilena de Fotogrametria y Percepcion Remota [IO], Santiago, Chile
Sociedad Chilena de Gastroenterologia [IO], Santiago, Chile
Sociedad Chilena de Geotecnica [IO], Santiago, Chile
Sociedad Chilena de Infectologia [★IO]
Sociedad Chilena de Medicina del Deporte [IO], Santiago, Chile
Sociedad Chilena de Obstetricia y Ginecologia [★IO]
Sociedad Chilena de Urologia [IO], Santiago, Chile
Sociedad de Ciencias Aranzadi [IO], Donostia-San Sebastian, Spain
Sociedad Colombiana de Cardiologia [★IO]
Sociedad Colombiana de Fisica [★IO]
Sociedad Colombiana de Ingenieros [★IO]
Sociedad Colombiana de Matematicas [IO], Bogota, Colombia
Sociedad Colombiana de Ortodoncia [IO], Medellin, Colombia
Sociedad Colombiana de Percepcion Remota y Sistemas de Informacion Geografica [IO], Bogota, Colombia
Sociedad Cubana de Endoscopia Digestiva [IO], Havana, Cuba
Sociedad de Derechos Literarios [IO], Santiago, Chile
Sociedad Dominicana de Cardiologia [★IO]
Sociedad Dominicana de Menopausia y Osteoporosis [★IO]
Sociedad Dominicane de Medicina del Deporte [IO], Santo Domingo, Dominican Republic
Sociedad Ecuatoriana De Medicina Reproductiva [★IO]
Sociedad Ecuatoriana de Dermatologia [★IO]
Sociedad Espanola de Agroingenieria [IO], Valencia, Spain
Sociedad Espanola de Bioquimica y Biologia Molecular [★IO]
Sociedad Espanola de Cardiologia [★IO]
Sociedad Espanola de Ceramica y Vidrio [★IO]
Sociedad Espanola de Ciencias Fisologicas [★IO]
Sociedad Espanola de Cirugia Plastica, Reparadora y Estetica [★IO]
Sociedad Espanola para el Estudio de la Obesidad [IO], Madrid, Spain
Sociedad Espanola de Etologia [★IO]
Sociedad Espanola de Farmacologia [★IO]
Sociedad Espanola de Geomorfologia [IO], Saragossa, Spain
Sociedad Espanola de Geriatria y Gerontologia [IO], Madrid, Spain

Sociedad Espanola de Ginecologia y Obstetricia [★IO]
Sociedad Espanola de Gravitacion y Relatividad [★IO]
Sociedad Espanola de Informatica de la Salud [★IO]
Sociedad Espanola de Ingenieria Biomedica [★IO]
Sociedad Espanola de Investigaciones Oseas y Metabolismo Mineral [IO], Madrid, Spain
Sociedad Espanola de Ortodoncia [IO], Madrid, Spain
Sociedad Espanola de Proteomica [★IO]
Sociedad Espanola de Quimicos Cosmeticos [★IO]
Sociedad Espanola de Reumatologia [★IO]
Sociedad de Estadistica e Investigacion Operativa [★IO]
Sociedad de Fomento Fabril [★IO]
Sociedad de Gastroenterologia del Peru [IO], Lima, Peru
Sociedad de Genetica de Chile [IO], Santiago, Chile
Sociedad Geografica de Lima [★IO]
Sociedad Geologica de Espana [★IO]
Sociedad Geologica Mexicana [IO], Mexico City, Mexico
Sociedad Honoraria Hispanica [8250], PO Box 5318, Buffalo Grove, IL 60089-5318, (847)550-0455
Sociedad Interamericana de Cardiologia [★IO]
Sociedad Internacional de Bioetica [★IO]
Sociedad Internacional Brecht [★9374]
Sociedad Internacional Brecht [★9374]
Sociedad Latinoamericana de Cardiologia Intervencionista [★IO]
Sociedad Latinoamericana de Nefrologia e Hipertension [★IO]
Sociedad de Linguistica del Caribe [★IO]
Sociedad de Matematica de Chile [IO], Santiago, Chile
Sociedad Matematica Mexicana [IO], Mexico City, Mexico
Sociedad Mexicana de Ciencias Fisiologicas, A.C. [IO], Mexico City, Mexico
Sociedad Mexicana de Dermatologia [★IO]
Sociedad Mexicana de Entomologia [IO], Tlalnepantla, Mexico
Sociedad Mexicana de Historia de la Ciencia y de la Tecnologia [★IO]
Sociedad Mexicana de Historia Natural [IO], Mexico City, Mexico
Sociedad Mexicana de Ingenieria Biomedica [IO], Mexico City, Mexico
Sociedad Mexicana de Ingenieria Economica, Financiera y de Costos [★IO]
Sociedad Mexicana de Pediatria [IO], Mexico City, Mexico
Sociedad Mexicana de Psicologia [★IO]
Sociedad de Microscopia de Espana [★IO]
Sociedad Nacional de Mineria, Petroleo y Energia [★IO]
Sociedad de Obstetricia y Ginecologia de Venezuela [IO], Caracas, Venezuela
Sociedad Paraguaya De Fertilidad [IO], Asuncion, Paraguay
Sociedad Paraguaya de Dermatologia [★IO]
Sociedad Paraguaya de Medicina del Deporte [IO], Asuncion, Paraguay
Sociedad Paraguayana de Gastroenterologia [IO], Asuncion, Paraguay
Sociedad Peruana de Cardiologia [★IO]
Sociedad Peruana De Fertilidad [IO], Lima, Peru
Sociedad Peruana de Dermatologia [★IO]
Sociedad Peruana de Geotecnia [IO], Lima, Peru
Sociedad Peruana de Hipertension Arterial [★IO]
Sociedad Peruana de Medicina y Ciencias Aplicadas al Deporte [IO], Lima, Peru
Sociedad Perunana de Reumatologia [IO], Lima, Peru
Sociedad de Psiquiatria del Uruguay [IO], Montevideo, Uruguay
Sociedad Quimica de Mexico [★IO]
Sociedad Salvadorena De Endoscopia Ginecologica Y Medicina [★IO]
Sociedad de San Vicente de Paul - Colombia [IO], Medellin, Colombia
Sociedad de San Vicente de Paul - Costa Rica [IO], Heredia, Costa Rica
Sociedad de San Vicente de Paul - Ecuador [IO], Quito, Ecuador

Sociedad de San Vicente de Paul - Guatemala [IO], Quetzaltenango, Guatemala
Sociedad de San Vicente de Paul - Nicaragua [IO], Leon, Nicaragua
Sociedad de San Vicente de Paul - Republica Dominicana [IO], Santo Domingo, Dominican Republic
Sociedad Uruguaya de Cardiologia [★IO]
Sociedad Uruguaya de Endoscopia Digestiva [IO], Montevideo, Uruguay
Sociedad Uruguaya de Informatica en la Salud [★IO]
Sociedad Venezolana de Cirugia [IO], Caracas, Venezuela
Sociedad Venezolana de Dermatologia [IO], Caracas, Venezuela
Sociedad Venezolana de Medicina Deportiva [IO], Caracas, Venezuela
Sociedad Venezolana de Menopausia y Osteoporosis [★IO]
Sociedad Venezolana de Oftalmologia [IO], Caracas, Venezuela
Sociedad Venezolana de Puericultura y Pediatria [IO], Caracas, Venezuela
Sociedade Biblica do Brasil [★IO]
Sociedade Biblica de Portugal [★IO]
Sociedade Brasileira de Automatica [★IO]
Sociedade Brasileira de Automatica [IO], Porto Alegre, Brazil
Sociedade Brasileira de Bioquimica e Biologia Molecular [★IO]
Sociedade Brasileira de Dermatologia [★IO]
Sociedade Brasileira de Engenharia Biomedica [★IO]
Sociedade Brasileira de Entomologia [★IO]
Sociedade Brasileira de Farmacologia e Terapeutica Experimental [★IO]
Sociedade Brasileira de Fisiologica [★IO]
Sociedade Brasileira de Genetica [★IO]
Sociedade Brasileira de Geofisica [★IO]
Sociedade Brasileira de Geologia Nucleo de Minas Gerais [IO], Belo Horizonte, Brazil
Sociedade Brasileira de Hipertensao [★IO]
Sociedade Brasileira de Informatica em Saude [★IO]
Sociedade Brasileira de Medicina do Esporte [IO], Sao Paulo, Brazil
Sociedade Brasileira de Medicina Estetica [★IO]
Sociedade Brasileira de Metrologia [★IO]
Sociedade Brasileira de Microscopia e Microanalise [★IO]
Sociedade Brasileira de Odontologia Estetica [★IO]
Sociedade Brasileira de Osteoporose [★IO]
Sociedade Brasileira de Pesquisa Operacional [★IO]
Sociedade Civil Bem-Estar Familiar no Brazil [IO], Rio de Janeiro, Brazil
Sociedade de Geografia de Lisboa [★IO]
Sociedade Internacional de Trilogia Analitica [★IO]
Sociedade Portuguesa de Autores [IO], Lisbon, Portugal
Sociedade Portuguesa de Cardiologia [★IO]
Sociedade Portuguesa de Doencas Infecciosas [★IO]
Sociedade Portuguesa de Endoscopia Digestiva [★IO]
Sociedade Portuguesa de Esclerose Multipla [★IO]
Sociedade Portuguesa de Estomatologia E Medicina Dentaria [★IO]
Sociedade Portuguesa de Farmacologia [★IO]
Sociedade Portuguesa de Medicina Desportiva [IO], Lisbon, Portugal
Sociedade Portuguesa de Ortopedia Dento Facial [IO], Porto, Portugal
Sociedade Potuguesa de Dermatologia e Venereologia [★IO]
Sociedade Rural Brasileira [★IO]
Sociedades Biblicas Unidas [★IO]
Socieded de Epileptologia de Chile [★IO]
Societa di Bioinformatica Italiana [★IO]
Societa Chimica Italiana [★IO]
Societa Europea di Cultura [★IO]
Societa Geologica Italiana [★IO]
Societa Italiana di Anatomia [★IO]
Societa Italiana di Biofisica [★IO]
Societa Italiana di Chirurgia Endoscopica e Nuove Tecnologie [★IO]

A star before a book entry number signifies that the name is not listed separately, but is mentioned within the entry.

Societa Italiana di Dermatologia Chirurgica ed Oncologica [★IO]
Societa Italiana di Dermatologia Medica, Chirurgica, Estetica e delle Malattie Sessualmente Tramesse [★IO]
Societa Italiana Di Chemioterapia [★IO]
Societa Italiana Di Endoscopia Digestiva [★IO]
Societa Italiana di Ecologia [★IO]
Societa Italiana di Endocrinologia [IO], Rome, Italy
Societa Italiana di Endocrinologia e Diabetologia Pediatrica [★IO]
Societa Italiana di Farmacia Ospedaliera [★IO]
Societa Italiana di Farmacologia [★IO]
Societa Italiana di Fertilita e Sterilita e Medicina della Riproduzione [★IO]
Societa Italiana di Fisica [★IO]
Societa Italiana di Fisiologia [★IO]
Societa Italiana di Fotogrammetria e Topografia [IO], Turin, Italy
Societa Italiana di Genetica Agraria [★IO]
Societa Italiana di Geologia Ambientale [★IO]
Societa Italiana di Gerontologia e Geriatria [★IO]
Societa Italiana di Ginecologia e Ostetricia [IO], Rome, Italy
Societa Italiana per l'Organizzazione Internazionale [★IO]
Societa Italiana di Medicina Generale [IO], Florence, Italy
Societa Italiana di Medicina Interna [★IO]
Societa Italiana di Mineralogia e Petrologia [IO], Pisa, Italy
Societa Italiana di Neurofisiologia Clinica [IO], Naples, Italy
Societa Italiana di Neuroscienze [★IO]
Societa Italiana di Patologia Vegetale [★IO]
Societa Italiana di Pediatria [IO], Milan, Italy
Societa Italiana di Psicologia [IO], Rome, Italy
Societa' Italiana di Psicosintesi Terapeutica [★IO]
Societa Italiana per la Psicosomatica in Ginecologia e Ostetroicia [★IO]
Societa Italiana di Radiologia Medica [★IO]
Societa Italiana di Scienze Microscopiche [★IO]
Societa Italiana di Tossicologia [★IO]
Societa Medica Italiana di Paraplegia [IO], Florence, Italy
Societa Meteorologica Italiana [★IO]
Societa Sammarinese di Cardiologia [★IO]
Societa per lo Studio dei Problemi Fiscali [★IO]
Societadi di Scienze Farmacologiche Applicate [★IO]
Societas Biochemica, Biophysica et Microbiologica Fenniae [★IO]
Societas Biochemica, Biophysica et Microbiological Fenniae [★IO]
Societas Biologica Fennica Vanamo [★IO]
Societas Europaea Anatomorum Veterinariorum [★IO]
Societas Europaea Herpetologica [★IO]
Societas Heraldica Scandinavica [IO], Landskrona, Sweden
Societas Internationalis Aerosolibus in Medicina [★IO]
Societas Internationalis pro Diagnostica Ultrasonica in Ophthalmologia [★IO]
Societas Internationalis Studiis NeoLatinis Provehendis [★IO]
Societas Linguistica Europaea [★IO]
Societas Liturgica [19666], Alan Barthel, Sec., 100 Witherspoon St., Louisville, KY 40202, (502)569-5759
Societas Liturgica [19666], Alan Barthel, Sec., 100 Witherspoon St., Louisville, KY 40202, (502)569-5759
Societas Neurologica Japonica [★IO]
Societas Physiologia Plantarum Scandinavica [★IO]
Societas Scientiarum Fennica [★IO]
Societate de Gestiune Colectiva a Dreptunior de Autor [IO], Bucharest, Romania
Societatea Astronomica Romana de Meteori [★IO]
Societatea de Educatie Contraceptiva si Sexuala [IO], Bucharest, Romania
Societatea de Gestiune Colectiva a Drepturilor de Autor in Domeniul Artelor Vizuale [★IO]
Societatea de Mgt., Consulting si Tehnologie in Constructii [★IO]

Societatea Romana Alzheimer [★IO]
Societatea Romana de Cardiologie [★IO]
Societatea Romana De Stiinte Fiziologice [★IO]
Societatea Romana de Endoscopie Digestiva [★IO]
Societatea Romana de Informatica Medicala [★IO]
Societatea Romana de Medicina Sportiva [IO], Bucharest, Romania
Societe canadienne de biomecanique [★IO]
Societe canadienne de recherches cliniques [★IO]
Societe canadienne de medecine nucleaire [★IO]
Societe canadienne de medecine interne [★IO]
Societe canadienne de technologie chimique [★IO]
Societe canadienne de chimie [★IO]
Societe quebecoise de gestion collective des droits de reproduction [IO], Montreal, QC, Canada
Societe Africaine de Reassurance [★IO]
Societe des Africanistes [★IO]
Societe Alzheimer du Canada [★IO]
Societe des Amís d'Alexandre Dumas [IO], Le Port-Marly, France
Societe Anatomique de Paris [★IO]
Societe Astronomique de France [IO], Paris, France
Societe Astronomique de France [★IO]
Societe Astronomique de Suisse [★IO]
Societe du droit de reproduction des auteurs, compositeurs et editeurs au Canada [★IO]
Societe des Auteurs et Compositeurs Dramatiques [★IO]
Societe des Auteurs, Compositeurs et Editeurs de Musique [IO], Neuilly-sur-Seine, France
Societe Belge des Auteurs, Compositeurs et Editeurs [IO], Brussels, Belgium
Societe Belge de Cardiologie/Belgische Vereniging Voor Cardiologie [IO]
Societe Belge de Microscopie [★IO]
Societe Belge de Photogrammetrie, de Teledetection et de Cartographie [IO], Brussels, Belgium
Societe Belge de Physiologie et de Pharmacologie Fondamentales et Cliniques [★IO]
Societe Bernoulli pour la Statistique Mathematique et la Probabilite [★IO]
Societe Bibliographique du Canada [★IO]
Societe Biblique Canadienne [★IO]
Societe de Biologie Experimentale [★IO]
Societe Botanique Suisse [★IO]
Societe statistique du Canada [★IO]
Societe historique du Canada [★IO]
Societe de la medecine rurale du Canada [★IO]
Societe pour la nature et les parcs du Canada [★IO]
Societe des designers graphiques du Canada [★IO]
Societe Canadienne des Anesthesiologistes [★IO]
Societe Canadienne des Auteurs, Illustrateurs, et Artistes pour Enfants [★IO]
Societe Canadienne des Biologistes l'Environnement [★IO]
Societe Canadienne du Cancer [★IO]
Societe Canadienne de Cardiologie [★IO]
Societe Canadienne des Chavaux Belges [★IO]
Societe Canadienne des Chirurgiens Plasticiens [★IO]
Societe Canadienne des Clinico-Chimistes [★IO]
Societe Canadienne d'Agronomie [★IO]
Societe Canadienne d'Allergie et d'Immunologie Clinique [★IO]
Societe Canadienne d'Astronomie [★IO]
Societe Canadienne d'Atherosclerose, de Thrombose et de Biologie Vasculaire [★IO]
Societe Canadienne d'Education par l'Art [★IO]
Societe Canadienne D'endocrinologie et metabolisme [★IO]
Societe Canadienne d'Esthetique [★IO]
Societe Canadienne d'Evaluation [★IO]
Societe Canadienne d'Hematologie [★IO]
Societe Canadienne d'Histoire de l'Eglise Catholique - Sect. Francaise [★IO]
Societe Canadienne d'Histoire Orale [★IO]
Societe Canadienne d'Histoire et Philosophie des Sciences [★IO]
Societe Canadienne d'historie de l'Eglise [★IO]
Societe Canadienne des pharmaciens d'Hopitaux [★IO]
Societe Canadienne d'Hypertension Arterielle [★IO]
Societe Canadienne du Dialogue Humaine Machine [★IO]
Societe Canadienne d'Immunologie [★IO]

Societe Canadienne D'indexation [★IO]
Societe Canadienne d'Ingenierie des Services de Sante [★IO]
Societe Canadienne des Directeurs de Clubs [★IO]
Societe Canadienne des Directeurs d'Association [★IO]
Societe Canadienne d'Ophthalmologie [★IO]
Societe Canadienne de Droit Canonique [★IO]
Societe Canadienne des Etudes Bibliques [★IO]
Societe Canadienne pour les Etudes Italiennes [★IO]
Societe Canadienne de Fertilite et d'Andrologie [★IO]
Societe Canadienne pour la Formation et le Perfectionnement [★IO]
Societe Canadienne de Genie Biomedical [★IO]
Societe Canadienne de Genie Chimique [★IO]
Societe Canadienne de Genie Civil [★IO]
Societe Canadienne de Genie Mecanique [★IO]
Societe Canadienne de Geotechnique [★IO]
Societe Canadienne de Geriatrie [★IO]
Societe Canadienne des Infirmieres et Infirmiers en Gastoenterologie et Travailleurs Associes [★IO]
Societe Canadienne de l'Autisme [★IO]
Societe Canadienne de l'Energie du sol [★IO]
Societe Canadienne pour l'Etude de la Religion [★IO]
Societe Canadienne de l'Hemophilie [★IO]
Societe Canadienne de Mfrs. de Chaudieres [★IO]
Societe Canadienne de Meteorologie et d'Oceanographique [★IO]
Societe Canadienne des Microbiologistes [★IO]
Societe Canadienne de Navigation [★IO]
Societe Canadienne de Neurochirurgie [★IO]
Societe Canadienne de Pediatrie [★IO]
Societe Canadienne de Peintres en Aquarelle [★IO]
Societe Canadienne de Pharmacologie Clinique [★IO]
Societe Canadienne de Physiologie Vegetale [★IO]
Societe Canadienne de Phytopathologie [★IO]
Societe Canadienne pour la Prevention de la Cruaute les Enfants [★IO]
Societe Canadienne des Professeurs de la Technique Alexander [★IO]
Societe Canadienne de Psychanalyse [★IO]
Societe Canadienne de Psychologie [★IO]
Societe Canadienne de Recherche Operationnelle [★IO]
Societe Canadienne des Relations Publiques [★IO]
Societe Canadienne de Rhumatologie [★IO]
Societe Canadienne de la Sante et de la Securite au Travail [★IO]
Societe Canadienne de la Schizophrenie [★IO]
Societe Canadienne de Sci. animale [★IO]
Societe Canadienne de Sci. de Laboratoire Medical [★IO]
Societe Canadienne de la Sci. du Sol [★IO]
Societe Canadienne des Sciences du Cerveau, du Comportement et de la Cognition [★IO]
Societe Canadienne des Sciences Judiciaires [★IO]
Societe Canadienne de la Sclerose Laterale Amyotrophique [★IO]
Societe Canadienne de la Sclerose en Plaques [★IO]
Societe Canadienne du Sida [★IO]
Societe Canadienne de Soins Intensifs [★IO]
Societe Canadienne du Sommeil [★IO]
Societe Canadienne de la Surete Industrielle [★IO]
Societe Canadienne des Technologistes en Cardiologie [★IO]
Societe Canadienne des Technologistes en Orthopedie [★IO]
Societe Canadienne de Teledetection [★IO]
Societe Canadienne des Therapeutes Respiratoires [★IO]
Societe Canadienne de Thoracologie [★IO]
Societe Canadienne pour les Traditions Musicales [★IO]
Societe Canadienne de Zoologie [★IO]
Societe des Canadiennes dans la Sci. et la Technologies [★IO]
Societe de Chimie Industrielle, Amer. Sect. [6419], Danielle Fraser, Admin., 80 Hathaway Dr., Stratford, CT 06615, (212)725-9539
Societe de Chimie Industrielle, Amer. Sect. [6419], Danielle Fraser, Admin., 80 Hathaway Dr., Stratford, CT 06615, (212)725-9539

Reference to "IO" in place of a book number signifies that the association may be found in the 50th edition of International Organizations.

Societe de Chimie Industrielle - French Sect. [IO], Paris, France
Societe de Chimie Therapeutique [IO], Chatenay-Malabry, France
Societe Civile des Auteurs Multimedia [★IO]
Societe Collective de Retransmission du Canada [★IO]
Societe Congolaise d'Osteoporose [★IO]
Societe Culinaire Philanthropique [19057], 305 E 47th St., Ste. 11B, New York, NY 10017, (212)308-0628
Societe Culturelle Canadienne des Sourds [★IO]
Societe canadienne d'agroeconomie [★IO]
Societe de genealogie et d'archives de Rimouski [IO], Rimouski, QC, Canada
Societe d'arthrite [★IO]
Societe educative de visites et d'echanges au Canada [★IO]
Societe d'Entomologie du Canada [★IO]
Societe Des Psychologues Du Manitoba [★IO]
Societe canadienne d'etude du dix-huiteme siecle [★IO]
Societe d'etudes socialistes [★IO]
Societe Ecossaise d'Heraldique [★IO]
Societe des Editeurs et Auteurs de Musique [IO], Paris, France
Societe des Editeurs de la Presse Privee [IO], Ouagadougou, Burkina Faso
Societe des Etudes Cauvsiennes [★10374]
Societe Europeene de Culture de Tissus [★IO]
Societe Europeene d'Ichthyologie [★IO]
Societe Europeene de Psychiatrie de l'Enfant et de l'Adolescent [★IO]
Societe Europeenne de Chirurgie Cardiovasculaire [★IO]
Societe Europeenne pour la Chirurgie de L'Epaule et du Coude [★IO]
Societe Europeenne pour la Formation des Ingenieurs [★IO]
Societe Europeenne de Gynecologie [★IO]
Societe Europeenne des Ophtalmologistes Contactologues [★IO]
Societe des Exportateurs de Vins Suisses [★IO]
Societe Finno-Ougrienne [★IO]
Societe Francaise de Cardiologie [★IO]
Societe Francaise de Ceramique [★IO]
Societe Francaise de Chimie [★IO]
Societe Francaise d'Acoustique [IO], Paris, France
Societe Francaise d'Anesthesie et de Reanimation [★IO]
Societe Francaise d'Economie Rurale [★IO]
Societe Francaise d'Endoscopie Digestive [★IO]
Societe Francaise de Dermatologie [★IO]
Societe Francaise d'Histoire Outre-Mer [★IO]
Societe Francaise d'Orchidophilie [★IO]
Societe Francaise d'Osteodensitometrie Clinic [★IO]
Societe Francaise de Genetique [★IO]
Societe Francaise de Geriatrie et Gerontologie [★IO]
Societe Francaise de Gynecologie et Obstetique Psychosomatique [★IO]
Societe Francaise de Medecine Manuelle Orthopedique et Osteopathique [★IO]
Societe Francaise de Medecine du Sport [IO], Montpellier, France
Societe Francaise de Metallurgie et de Materiaux [★IO]
Societe Francaise des Microscopies [IO], Paris, France
Societe Francaise de Musicologie [★IO]
Societe Francaise de Pharmacologie et de Therapeutique [★IO]
Societe Francaise de Physique [★IO]
Societe Francaise de Rhumatologie [IO], Paris, France
Societe Francaise des Roses 'Les Amis des Roses' [IO], Lyon, France
Societe Francaise du Vide [★IO]
Societe Francophone Vitamines et Biofacteurs [★IO]
Societe Genealogique Canadienne-Francaise [★IO]
Societe des Gens de Lettres [IO], Paris, France
Societe de Geologie Appliquee aux Gites Mineraux [★IO]
Societe Geologique de France [★IO]
Societe des Gynecologues Oncologues du Canada [★IO]

Societe H.G. Wells [★IO]
Societe Huntington du Canada [★IO]
Societe des Indexateurs [★IO]
Societe des Ingenieurs de l'Automobile [★IO]
Societe Intl. d'Ethologie Applie [★IO]
Societe Intl. d'Etudes Gemellaires [★IO]
Societe Internationale de Brecht [★9374]
Societe Internationale de Brecht [★9374]
Societe Internationale de Chimiotherapie [★IO]
Societe Internationale de Chirurgie [★IO]
Societe Internationale de Chirurgie Orthopedique et de Traumatologie [★IO]
Societe Internationale de Criminologie [★IO]
Societe Internationale de Defense Sociale [★IO]
Societe Internationale d'Etude du XVIIIe Siecle [★IO]
Societe Internationale pour le Developpement [★IO]
Societe Internationale d'Hydrologie et de Climatologie Medicale [★IO]
Societe Internationale d'Oncologie Pediatrique [★IO]
Societe Internationale de Droit Militaire et de Droit de la Guerre [★IO]
Societe Internationale de Droit du Travail et de la Securite Sociale [★IO]
Societe Internationale d'Urologie [IO], Montreal, QC, Canada
Societe Internationale Kodaly [★IO]
Societe Internationale pour l'Etude de la Philosophie Medievale [★IO]
Societe Internationale de Mecanique des Roches [★IO]
Societe Internationale de Mecanique des Sols et de la Geotechnique [★IO]
Societe Internationale de Medecine Interne [★IO]
Societe Internationale des Morphologistes de la Vie Vegetale [★IO]
Societe Internationale de Mycologie Humaine et Animales [★IO]
Societe Internationale de Neurochimie [★IO]
Societe Internationale de Neuropathologie [★IO]
Societe Internationale de Psychopathologie de l'Expression d'Art Therapie [★IO]
Societe Internationale des Radiographes et Techniciens de Radiologie [★IO]
Societe Internationale de Recherche sur le Folklore Oral [★IO]
Societe Internationale du Rorschach et des Methodes Projectives [★IO]
Societe Internationale de la Sci. Horticole [★IO]
Societe Internationale Scientifique des Champignons Comestibles [★IO]
Societe Internationale de Sociologie des Religions [★IO]
Societe Internationale pour la Stereologie [★IO]
Societe Internationale de Transfusion Sanguine [★IO]
Societe Jean-Jacques Rousseau [IO], Geneva, Switzerland
Societe Jersiaise [IO], Jersey, United Kingdom
Societe Kipling [★IO]
Societe de Legislation Comparee [★IO]
Societe pour l'Etude de la Coherence [★IO]
Societe canadienne pour l'etude de l'education [★IO]
Societe pour l'Etude de l'Egypte Ancienne [★IO]
Societe canadienne pour l'etude de l'enseignement superieur [★IO]
Societe Libanaise de Gastroenterologie [★IO]
Societe Libanaise de Rhumatologie [★IO]
Societe Luxembourgeoise d'Orthodontie [IO], Luxembourg, Luxembourg
Societe Marcoaine De Fertilite Et De Contraception [★IO]
Societe Marocaine de Rhumatologie [★IO]
Societe Mathematique du Canada [★IO]
Societe de Microscopie du Canada [★IO]
Societe Mondiale pour la Protection des Animaux [★IO]
Societe de Musique des Universites Canadiennes [★IO]
Societe Mycologique de Nouvelle-Caledonie [★IO]
Societe Nationale Canadienne des Sourds-Aveugles [★IO]
Societe des Naturalistes Luxembourgeois [★IO]
Societe de Neuroendocrinologie [IO], Paris, France

Societe Nucleaire Canadienne [★IO]
Societe de Numismatique Orientale [★IO]
Societe des Obstetriciens et Gynecologues du Canada [★IO]
Societe des Ornithologistes du Canada [★IO]
Societe Pan-Africaine de Cardiologie [★IO]
Societe Parkinson Canada [★IO]
Societe Parkinson d'Ottawa [★IO]
Societe Parkinson du Quebec [★IO]
Societe de Pastel de L'est du Canada [★IO]
Societe de Pathologie Exotique [IO], Paris, France
Societe de Pathologie Exotique [★IO]
Societe de Physiologie [IO], Montaigu, France
Societe Planetaire pour l'Assainissement de l'Energie [★IO]
Societe pour la Protection de la Nature en Israel [★IO]
Societe de Recherche sur le Cancer [★IO]
Societe Royale Belge des Electriciens [IO], Brussels, Belgium
Societe Royale Belge de Rhumatologie [★IO]
Societe Royale de Chimie [IO], Brussels, Belgium
Societe Royale D'Economie Politique De Belgique [IO], Charleroi, Belgium
Societe Royale Du Canada [★IO]
Societe Royale Heraldique du Canada [★IO]
Societe Royale de Numismatique de Belgique [IO], Brussels, Belgium
Societe Royale des Sciences de Liege [IO], Liege, Belgium
Societe Saint-Jean-Baptiste de Montreal [IO], Montreal, QC, Canada
Societe de Saint Vincent de Paul [★IO]
Societe de Saint-Vincent de Paul - Algeria [IO], Algiers, Algeria
Societe de Saint Vincent de Paul du Burundi [IO], Bujumbura, Burundi
Societe de Saint-Vincent de Paul - Canada [★IO]
Societe de Saint-Vincent de Paul - Cote d' Ivoire [IO], Abidjan, Cote d'Ivoire
Societe Suisse de Biochimie [★IO]
Societe Suisse de Biochimie [★IO]
Societe Suisse d'Ethique Biomedicale [★IO]
Societe Suisse d'Heraldique [★IO]
Societe Suisse d'Hydrogeologie [★IO]
Societe Suisse pour l'Optique et l'Optometrie [★IO]
Societe Suisse de Pharmacologie et de Toxicologie [★IO]
Societe Swisse de Medecine du Sport [IO], Bern, Switzerland
Societe des Textes Anglais Anciens [★IO]
Societe Tunisien de Medecine du Sport [IO], Tunis, Tunisia
Societe Tunisienne de Cardiologie et de Chirurgie Cardiovasculaire [★IO]
Societe Tunisienne de Codification [★IO]
Societe Universitaire Europeenne de Recherches Financieres [★IO]
Societes des Auters dans les Arts Graphiques et Plastiques [IO], Paris, France
Societes Internationales Limnologiae Theoreticae et Applicatae [★7023]
Societes Internationales Limnologiae Theoreticae et Applicatae [★7023]
Soc. of the 3rd Infantry Div. [20696], 1515 Ramblewood Dr., Hanover Park, IL 60133-2230
Soc. for Academic Continuing Medical Educ. [8617], 3416 Primm Ln., Birmingham, AL 35216, (205)978-7990
Soc. for Academic Continuing Medical Educ. [8617], 3416 Primm Ln., Birmingham, AL 35216, (205)978-7990
Soc. for Academic Emergency Medicine [14479], 2340 S River Rd., Ste. 200, Des Plaines, IL 60018, (847)813-9823
Soc. of Academic and Res. Surgery [IO], London, United Kingdom
Soc. for Accessible Travel for the Handicapped [★11829]
Soc. for Accessible Travel and Hospitality [11829], 347 5th Ave., Ste. 605, New York, NY 10016, (212)447-7284
Soc. of Accredited Marine Surveyors [7489], 7855 Argyle Forest Blvd., Ste. 203, Jacksonville, FL 32244, (904)384-1494

A star before a book entry number signifies that the name is not listed separately, but is mentioned within the entry.

Soc. of Accredited Marine Surveyors **[7489]**, 7855 Argyle Forest Blvd., Ste. 203, Jacksonville, FL 32244, (904)384-1494

Soc. of Actuaries **[2038]**, 475 N Martingale Rd., Ste. 600, Schaumburg, IL 60173, (847)706-3500

Soc. for Acupuncture Res. **[13581]**, 130 Cloverhurst Ct., Winston-Salem, NC 27103

Soc. for Acupuncture Res. **[13581]**, 130 Cloverhurst Ct., Winston-Salem, NC 27103

Soc. for Adolescent Hea. and Medicine **[14098]**, 111 Deer lake Rd., Ste. 100, Deerfield, IL 60015, (847)753-5226

Soc. for Adolescent Medicine **[★14098]**

Soc. for Advanced Legal Stud. **[IO]**, London, United Kingdom

Soc. for the Advancement of Amer. Philosophy **[10416]**, Birmingham Southern Coll., BSC Box 549013, Birmingham, AL 35254, (205)226-4868

Soc. for the Advancement of Anaesthesia in Dentistry **[IO]**, London, United Kingdom

Soc. for the Advancement of Behavior Anal. **[6263]**, 550 W Centre Ave., Ste. 1, Portage, MI 49024, (269)492-9310

Soc. for the Advancement of Blood Mgt. **[14975]**, 350 Engle St., Englewood, NJ 07631, (602)343-7458

Soc. for the Advancement of Blood Mgt. **[14975]**, 350 Engle St., Englewood, NJ 07631, (602)343-7458

Soc. for Advancement of Chicanos and Native Americans in Sci. **[7387]**, PO Box 8526, Santa Cruz, CA 95061-8526, (831)459-0170

Soc. for the Advancement of Community, Hea., Educ. and Training **[IO]**, Islamabad, Pakistan

Soc. for the Advancement of Criminology **[★11740]**

Soc. for the Advancement of Economic Theory **[6632]**, Univ. of Illinois at Urbana-Champaign, Dept. of Economics, 410 David Kinley Hall, 1407 W Gregory Dr., Urbana, IL 61801, (217)333-0120

Soc. for the Advancement of Educ. - Address unknown since 2010.

Soc. for the Advancement of Excellence in Educ. **[IO]**, Kelowna, BC, Canada

Soc. for the Advancement of Gastroenterology **[★14550]**

Soc. for the Advancement of Judaism **[19899]**, 15 W 86th St., New York, NY 10024, (212)724-7000

Soc. for Advancement of Mgt. **[2304]**, 6300 Ocean Dr., OCNR 330, Unit 5807, Corpus Christi, TX 78412, (361)825-6045

Soc. for the Advancement of Material and Process Engg. **[7067]**, 1161 Park View Dr., Ste. 200, Covina, CA 91724-3751, (626)331-0616

Soc. for the Advancement of Scandinavian Stud. **[8806]**, Brigham Young Univ., 3168 JFSB, Provo, UT 84602-6702, (801)422-5598

Soc. for the Advancement of Socio-Economics **[17593]**, PO Box 39008, Baltimore, MD 21212, (410)435-6617

Soc. for the Advancement of Women's Hea. Res. **[★17136]**

Soc. for the Advancement of Women's Imaging **[16538]**, PO Box 885, Schererville, IN 46375, (219)864-2119

Soc. of Aeronautical Weight Engineers, Inc. **[★7468]**

Soc. of Aerospace Material and Process Engineers **[★7067]**

Soc. of African Missions **[19497]**, 23 Bliss Ave., Tenafly, NJ 07670-3001, (201)567-0450

Soc. of African Missions **[★20093]**

Soc. of African Missions **[19497]**, 23 Bliss Ave., Tenafly, NJ 07670-3001, (201)567-0450

Soc. of Africanists **[IO]**, Paris, France

Soc. of Agricultural Meteorology of Japan **[IO]**, Tokyo, Japan

Soc. of Air Force Anesthesiologists **[★13747]**

Soc. of Air Force Clinical Surgeons **[16821]**, 1511 Paddington Way, Plumas Lake, CA 95961-9129, (530)741-0682

Soc. of Air Force Physician Assistants **[20330]**, PO Box 340597, San Antonio, TX 78234-0838

Soc. of Air Force Physicians **[15511]**, PO Box 64, Devine, TX 78016-0064, (830)665-4048

Soc. of Air Safety Investigators **[★12987]**

Soc. of Air Safety Investigators **[★12987]**

Soc. of Aircraft Material and Process Engineers **[★7067]**

Soc. for All Artists **[IO]**, Newark, United Kingdom

Soc. of Allied Weight Engineers **[7468]**, PO Box 60024, Los Angeles, CA 90060, (562)596-2873

Soc. for Alternative Media and Res. **[IO]**, Islamabad, Pakistan

Soc. for Amateur Radio in The Netherlands **[IO]**, Arnhem, Netherlands

Soc. for Amateur Scientists **[7388]**, 1356 Saxon Ln., Naperville, IL 60564, (630)487-9566

Soc. for Ambulatory Anesthesia **[13752]**, 520 N Northwest Hwy., Park Ridge, IL 60068-2573, (847)825-5586

Soc. for Amer. Archaeology **[6176]**, 1111 14th St. NW, Ste. 800, Washington, DC 20005, (202)789-8200

Soc. of Amer. Archivists **[9145]**, 17 N State St., Ste. 1425, Chicago, IL 60602-4061, (312)606-0722

Society of Amer. Artists **[★9226]**

Soc. of Amer. Bacteriologists **[★6288]**

Soc. for Amer. Baseball Res. **[22290]**, 4455 E Camelback Rd., Ste. D-140, Phoenix, AZ 85018, (602)343-6455

Soc. of Amer. Bus. and Economic Writers **[★2870]**

Soc. of Amer. Bus. Editors and Writers **[2870]**, Walter Cronkite Scholarship of Journalism and Mass Commun., 555 N Central Ave., Ste. 416, Phoenix, AZ 85004-1248, (602)496-7862

Soc. of Amer. Bus. Writers **[★2870]**

Soc. of Amer. Etchers **[★9645]**

Soc. of Amer. Etchers, Gravers, Lithographers and Woodcutters **[★9645]**

Soc. of Amer. Fight Directors **[9004]**, 1350 E Flamingo Rd., No. 25, Las Vegas, NV 89119

Soc. of Amer. Florists **[1369]**, 1601 Duke St., Alexandria, VA 22314-3406, (703)836-8700

Soc. of Amer. Florists and Ornamental Horticulturists **[★1369]**

Soc. of Amer. Foresters **[4413]**, 5400 Grosvenor Ln., Bethesda, MD 20814-2198, (301)897-8720

Soc. of Amer. Gastrointestinal and Endoscopic Surgeons **[14574]**, 11300 W Olympic Blvd., Ste. 600, Los Angeles, CA 90064, (310)437-0544

Soc. of Amer. Gastrointestinal and Endoscopic Surgeons **[14574]**, 11300 W Olympic Blvd., Ste. 600, Los Angeles, CA 90064, (310)437-0544

Soc. of Amer. Graphic Artists **[9645]**, 32 Union Sq., Rm. 1214, New York, NY 10003

Soc. of Amer. Historians - Defunct.

Soc. of Amer. Historical Artists - Defunct.

Soc. of Amer. Indian Govt. Employees **[23209]**, PO Box 7715, Washington, DC 20044, (202)564-0375

Soc. of Amer. Law Teachers - Defunct.

Soc. of Amer. Magicians **[21881]**, PO Box 505, Parker, CO 80134, (303)362-0575

Soc. of Amer. Military Engineers **[6823]**, 607 Prince St., Alexandria, VA 22314-3117, (703)549-3800

Soc. of Amer. Mosaic Artists **[9254]**, PO Box 624, Ligonier, PA 15658, (724)238-3087

Soc. for Amer. Music **[10289]**, Univ. of Pittsburgh, Stephen Foster Memorial, Pittsburgh, PA 15260, (412)624-3031

Soc. of Amer. Period Furniture Makers **[9631]**, 423-A S Galena Rd., Sunbury, OH 43074

Soc. of Amer. Registered Architects **[6204]**, PO Box 280, Newport, TN 37822, (423)721-0129

Soc. of Amer. Silversmiths **[3377]**, PO Box 786, West Warwick, RI 02893, (401)461-6840

Soc. for Amer. Travel Writers **[2871]**, 11950 W Lake Park Dr., Ste. 320, Milwaukee, WI 53224, (414)359-1625

Soc. of Amer. Value Engineers **[★6964]**

Soc. for Amer. Value Engineers **[★6964]**

Soc. for Anaerobic Microbiology **[IO]**, London, United Kingdom

Soc. for the Anal. of African-American Public Hea. Issues **[16497]**, Dr. Cheryl B. Prince, Treas., PO Box 360350, Decatur, GA 30036

Soc. for Analytical Cytology **[★6305]**

Soc. for Analytical Cytology **[★6305]**

Soc. for Analytical Feminism **[10417]**, Carol Hay, Sec.-Treas., Univ. of Massachusetts Lowell, Dept. of Philosophy, One Univ. Ave., Lowell, MA 01854

Soc. for Ancient Greek Philosophy **[10418]**, Binghamton Univ., Dept. of Philosophy, Binghamton, NY 13902-6000, (607)777-2886

Soc. of Ancient Military Historians **[10097]**, Western Illinois Univ., Dept. of History, Morgan Hall 445, Macomb, IL 61455-1390, (309)298-1053

Soc. of Anglican Missionaries and Senders **[20094]**, PO Box 399, Ambridge, PA 15003, (724)266-0669

Soc. for Anglo-Chinese Understanding **[IO]**, Barrow-in-Furness, United Kingdom

Soc. for Animal Artists **[9255]**, 5451 Sedona Hills Dr., Berthoud, CO 80513, (970)532-3127

Soc. for Animal Homeopathy **[15023]**, 272 Lucille Dr., Walker Lake, NV 89415, (775)313-5884

Soc. for Animal Protective Legislation - Address unknown since 2010.

Soc. for Animal Rights **[★10994]**

Soc. for Animal Rights **[★10994]**

Soc. for Anthropology in Community Colleges **[7729]**, San Diego Miramar Coll., Dept. of Anthropology, 10440 Black Mountain Rd., San Diego, CA 92126, (619)388-7534

Soc. for the Anthropology of Consciousness **[7730]**, Amer. Anthropological Assn., 2200 Wilson Blvd., Ste. 600, Arlington, VA 22201, (703)528-1902

Soc. for the Anthropology of Europe **[6128]**, 2200 Wilson Blvd., Ste. 600, Arlington, VA 22201, (703)528-1902

Soc. for the Anthropology of Food and Nutrition **[6147]**, Univ. of Pennsylvania, Anthropology Dept., 323 Museum, Spruce St. and S 33rd St., Philadelphia, PA 19104, (215)898-7461

Soc. for the Anthropology of North Am. **[6148]**, Amer. Anthropological Assn., 2200 Wilson Blvd., Ste. 600, Arlington, VA 22201, (703)528-1902

Soc. for the Anthropology of Religion **[6149]**, Andrew Buckser, Purdue Univ., Dept. of Sociology and Anthropology, 700 W State St., West Lafayette, IN 47907-1365

Soc. for the Anthropology of Visual Commun. **[★6158]**

Soc. of Antiquaries of London **[IO]**, London, United Kingdom

Soc. of Antiquaries of Newcastle-upon-Tyne **[IO]**, Newcastle upon Tyne, United Kingdom

Soc. of Antiquaries of Scotland **[IO]**, Edinburgh, United Kingdom

Soc. of Antique Modelers **[20917]**, 3379 Crystal Ct., Napa, CA 94558, (707)255-3547

Soc. for Applied Anthropology **[6150]**, PO Box 2436, Oklahoma City, OK 73101-2436, (405)843-5113

Soc. for Applied Anthropology **[6150]**, PO Box 2436, Oklahoma City, OK 73101-2436, (405)843-5113

Soc. of Applied Botany **[IO]**, Braunschweig, Germany

Soc. for Applied Immunohistochemistry **[16131]**, Richard W. Cartun, PhD, Sec.-Treas., Hartford Hosp., Dept. of Pathology, 80 Seymour St., Hartford, CT 06102, (860)545-1596

Soc. for Applied Learning Tech. **[8320]**, 50 Culpeper St., Warrenton, VA 20186, (540)347-0055

Soc. for Applied Microbiology **[IO]**, Bedford, United Kingdom

Soc. for Applied Pharmacological Sciences **[IO]**, Milan, Italy

Soc. for Applied Philosophy **[IO]**, Aberdeen, United Kingdom

Soc. for Applied Res. in Memory and Cognition **[7310]**, Robert Belli, Ed., Univ. of Nebraska-Lincoln, Dept. of Psychology, 223 Burnett Hall, Lincoln, NE 68588-0308

Soc. for Applied Spectroscopy **[7459]**, 5320 Spectrum Dr., Ste. C, Frederick, MD 21703, (301)694-8122

Soc. of Archer-Antiquaries **[IO]**, South Gloucestershire, United Kingdom

Soc. of Architectural Historians **[9799]**, 1365 N Astor St., Chicago, IL 60610-2144, (312)573-1365

Soc. of Architectural Historians of Great Britain **[IO]**, London, United Kingdom

Soc. of Archivists - Ireland **[IO]**, Dublin, Ireland

Soc. of Archivists - United Kingdom **[IO]**, Taunton, United Kingdom

Soc. of the Ark and the Dove **[20407]**, PO Box 401, Riderwood, MD 21139-0401

Soc. for Armenian Stud. **[9150]**, Armenian Stud. Prog., California State Univ., 5245 N Backer Ave., PB4, Fresno, CA 93740-8001, (559)278-2669

Reference to "IO" in place of a book number signifies that the association may be found in the 50th edition of International Organizations.

Soc. for Armenian Stud. **[9150]**, Armenian Stud. Prog., California State Univ., 5245 N Backer Ave., PB4, Fresno, CA 93740-8001, (559)278-2669

Soc. of Army Historical Res. **[IO]**, London, United Kingdom

Soc. of Army Physician Assistants **[16240]**, PO Box 07490, Fort Myers, FL 33919, (239)482-2162

Soc. for the Arts in Healthcare **[13771]**, 2647 Connecticut Ave. NW, Ste. 200, Washington, DC 20008, (202)299-9770

Soc. for the Arts in Healthcare **[13771]**, 2647 Connecticut Ave. NW, Ste. 200, Washington, DC 20008, (202)299-9770

Soc. for the Arts, Religion and Contemporary Culture **[9318]**, PO Box 15, Maxatawny, PA 19538, (610)683-7581

Soc. for Asian Art **[9204]**, Asian Art Museum, 200 Larkin St., San Francisco, CA 94102, (415)581-3701

Soc. for Asian and Comparative Philosophy **[10419]**, Prof. Michael Barnhart, Treas., Kingsborough/CUNY, Dept. of History, 2001 Oriental Blvd., Brooklyn, NY 11235

Soc. of Asian Fed. Officers **[5742]**, PO Box 2978, New York, NY 10008, (212)436-1655

Soc. for Asian Music **[10290]**, PO Box 7819, Austin, TX 78713-7819, (512)232-7621

Soc. for Asian Music **[10290]**, PO Box 7819, Austin, TX 78713-7819, (512)232-7621

Soc. of Assistants Teaching in Preparatory Schools **[IO]**, Great Dunmow, United Kingdom

Soc. for Assisted Reproductive Tech. **[16597]**, 1209 Montgomery Hwy., Birmingham, AL 35216-2809, (205)978-5000

Soc. of Atherosclerosis Imaging and Prevention **[16966]**, 8601 Aqueduct Rd., Potomac, MD 20854, (301)251-8864

Soc. of Australasian Specialists/Oceania **[22075]**, PO Box 24764, San Jose, CA 95154-4764, (408)978-0193

Soc. of Australian Genealogists **[IO]**, Sydney, Australia

Soc. of Authors - England **[IO]**, London, United Kingdom

Soc. of Authors' Representatives **[★161]**

Soc. for Automation in Bus. Educ. **[★7907]**

Soc. for Automation in Bus. Educ. **[★7907]**

Soc. for Automation in English and the Humanities **[★7907]**

Soc. for Automation in English and the Humanities **[★7907]**

Soc. for Automation in Fine Arts **[★7907]**

Soc. for Automation in Fine Arts **[★7907]**

Soc. for Automation in Professional Educ. **[★7907]**

Soc. for Automation in Professional Educ. **[★7907]**

Soc. for Automation in the Social Sciences **[★7907]**

Soc. for Automation in the Social Sciences **[★7907]**

Soc. of Auto. Engineers **[★6243]**

Soc. of Automotive Analysts **[307]**, PO Box 94, Rockwood, MI 48173, (248)804-6433

Soc. of Automotive Engineers **[7389]**, 400 Commonwealth Dr., Warrendale, PA 15096-0001, (724)776-4970

Soc. of Automotive Engineers **[7389]**, 400 Commonwealth Dr., Warrendale, PA 15096-0001, (724)776-4970

Soc. of Automotive Engineers - Australasia **[IO]**, Southbank, Australia

Soc. of Automotive Engineers - Japan **[IO]**, Tokyo, Japan

Soc. of Automotive Engineers - Thailand **[IO]**, Bangkok, Thailand

Soc. of Automotive Historians **[21165]**, Patrick D. Bisson, Treas., 8537 Tim Tam Trail, Flushing, MI 48433

Soc. for Basic Urologic Res. **[16949]**, 1100 E Woodfield Rd., Ste. 520, Schaumburg, IL 60173, (847)517-7225

Soc. of Basque Stud. in Am. **[9433]**, 19 Colonial Gardens, Brooklyn, NY 11209

Soc. of Basque Stud. in Am. **[9433]**, 19 Colonial Gardens, Brooklyn, NY 11209

Soc. of Bead Researchers **[6177]**, Alice Scherer, Sec.-Treas., PO Box 13719, Portland, OR 97213

Soc. of Bead Researchers **[6177]**, Alice Scherer, Sec.-Treas., PO Box 13719, Portland, OR 97213

Soc. of Bead Researchers - Canada **[IO]**, Ottawa, ON, Canada

Soc. of Beaux-Arts Architects **[★7737]**

Soc. of Behavioral Medicine **[13821]**, 555 E Wells St., Ste. 1100, Milwaukee, WI 53202-3800, (414)918-3156

Soc. for Behavioral Neuroendocrinology **[13822]**, 1100 E Woodfield Rd., Ste. 520, Schaumburg, IL 60173, (847)517-7225

Soc. for Behavioral Pediatrics **[★16155]**

Soc. of Biblical Literature **[19353]**, Luce Center, 825 Houston Mill Rd., Atlanta, GA 30329, (404)727-3100

Soc. of Biblical Literature and Exegesis **[★19353]**

Soc. for Bioethics Consultation **[★8589]**

Soc. of Biological Chemists, India **[IO]**, Bangalore, India

Soc. of Biological Inorganic Chemistry **[6420]**, 9650 Rockville Pike, Rm. L-3503A, Bethesda, MD 20814-3998, (301)634-7194

Soc. of Biological Psychiatry **[16345]**, Mayo Clinic of Jacksonville, Research-Birdsall 310, 4500 San Pablo Rd., Jacksonville, FL 32224, (904)953-2842

Soc. of Biological Psychiatry **[16345]**, Mayo Clinic of Jacksonville, Research-Birdsall 310, 4500 San Pablo Rd., Jacksonville, FL 32224, (904)953-2842

Soc. for Biological Therapy **[★13982]**

Soc. for Biological Therapy **[★13982]**

Soc. of Biology **[IO]**, London, United Kingdom

Soc. for Biomedical Engg. **[IO]**, Wetzlar, Germany

Soc. for Biomedical Equipment Technicians - Defunct.

Soc. for Biomolecular Sciences **[6423]**, 100 Illinois St., Ste. 242, St. Charles, IL 60174, (630)256-7527

Soc. for Biomolecular Sciences and Assn. for Lab. Automation **[★6423]**

Soc. for Biomolecular Screening **[★6423]**

Soc. for Biomolecular Screening **[★6423]**

Soc. for Biotechnology, Japan **[IO]**, Osaka, Japan

Soc. of Blessed Gianna Beretta Molla **[19776]**, PO Box 2946, Warminster, PA 18974, (215)657-3101

Soc. of Blessed Gianna Beretta Molla **[19776]**, PO Box 2946, Warminster, PA 18974, (215)657-3101

Soc. of Boat and Yacht Designers **[1039]**, 117 E Louisa St., No. 268, Seattle, WA 98102-3203, (801)225-6060

Soc. of Bookbinders **[IO]**, Shepperton, United Kingdom

Soc. of Border Leicester Sheep Breeders **[IO]**, Alnwick, United Kingdom

Soc. of Breast Imaging **[16539]**, 1891 Preston White Dr., Reston, VA 20191-4397, (703)715-4390

Soc. of British Aerospace Companies **[IO]**, London, United Kingdom

Soc. of British Neurological Surgeons **[IO]**, London, United Kingdom

Soc. of British Water and Wastewater Indus. **[IO]**, Leamington Spa, United Kingdom

Soc. of Brooklyn Etchers **[★9645]**

Soc. of Building Sci. Educators **[8117]**, Leonard Bachman, Pres., 122 Coll. of Architecture, Univ. of Houston, Houston, TX 77204-4000

Soc. of Bus. Economists **[IO]**, Andover, United Kingdom

Soc. for Bus. Ethics **[11984]**, 28 Westhampton Way, Richmond, VA 23173, (804)287-6083

Soc. for Bus. Ethics **[11984]**, 28 Westhampton Way, Richmond, VA 23173, (804)287-6083

Soc. of Bus. Magazine Editors **[★2800]**

Soc. of Cable Telecommunication Engineers **[IO]**, Watford, United Kingdom

Soc. of Cable Telecommunications Engineers **[6824]**, 140 Philips Rd., Exton, PA 19341-1318, (610)363-6888

Soc. of Cable TV Engineers **[★6824]**

Soc. of California Pioneers **[20750]**, 300 4th St., San Francisco, CA 94107-1272, (415)957-1849

Soc. for Calligraphy **[10757]**, PO Box 64174, Los Angeles, CA 90064-0174

Soc. of Canadian Ornithologists **[IO]**, Regina, SK, Canada

Soc. for Canadian Women in Sci. and Tech. **[IO]**, Vancouver, BC, Canada

Soc. for Carbide Engineers **[★7101]**

Soc. of Carbide and Tool Engineers **[7101]**, Pittsburgh Chap. No. 10, PO Box 77, McKeesport, PA 15135, (724)539-6118

Soc. for Cardiological Sci. and Tech. **[IO]**, Lichfield, United Kingdom

Soc. for Cardiothoracic Surgery in Great Britain and Ireland **[IO]**, London, United Kingdom

Soc. of Cardiovascular Anesthesiologists **[13753]**, 2209 Dickens Rd., Richmond, VA 23230-2005, (804)282-0084

Soc. of Cardiovascular Anesthesiologists **[13753]**, 2209 Dickens Rd., Richmond, VA 23230-2005, (804)282-0084

Soc. for Cardiovascular Angiography and Interventions **[14042]**, 2400 North St. NW, Ste. 500, Washington, DC 20037-1153, (202)741-9854

Soc. of Cardiovascular and Interventional Radiology **[★16544]**

Soc. for Cardiovascular Magnetic Resonance **[15385]**, 19 Mantua Rd., Mount Royal, NJ 08061, (856)423-8955

Soc. for Cardiovascular Magnetic Resonance **[15385]**, 19 Mantua Rd., Mount Royal, NJ 08061, (856)423-8955

Soc. for Cardiovascular Mgt. **[★13997]**

Soc. for Cardiovascular Pathology **[14043]**, Silvio H. Litovsky, MD, Treas., Univ. of Alabama Birmingham, 619 19th St. S, PDA6A 175L, Birmingham, AL 35249

Soc. for Cardiovascular Pathology **[14043]**, Silvio H. Litovsky, MD, Treas., Univ. of Alabama Birmingham, 619 19th St. S, PDA6A 175L, Birmingham, AL 35249

Soc. for Caribbean Linguistics **[IO]**, St. Augustine, Trinidad and Tobago

Soc. of Cartographers **[IO]**, Glasgow, United Kingdom

Soc. of Catholic Coll. Teachers of Sacred Doctrine **[★9010]**

Soc. of Certified Credit Executives - Address unknown since 2011.

Soc. of Certified Data Pros **[★7906]**

Soc. of Certified Insurance Counselors **[8324]**, Natl. Alliance for Insurance Educ. and Res., PO Box 27027, Austin, TX 78755-2027, (800)633-2165

Soc. of Chairs of Academic Radiology Departments **[16540]**, 820 Jorie Blvd., Oak Brook, IL 60523, (630)368-3731

Soc. for Chaos Theory in Psychology and Life Sciences **[7311]**, PO Box 484, Pewaukee, WI 53072

Soc. of Chartered Property and Casualty Underwriters **[★1954]**

Soc. of Chartered Surveyors in the Republic of Ireland **[IO]**, Dublin, Ireland

Soc. for Chem. Engg. and Biotechnology **[IO]**, Frankfurt, Germany

Soc. for Chem. Hazard Commun. **[765]**, PO Box 1392, Annandale, VA 22003-9392, (703)658-9246

Soc. of Chem. Indus. **[IO]**, London, United Kingdom

Soc. of Chem. Mfrs. and Affiliates **[766]**, 1850 M St. NW, Ste. 700, Washington, DC 20036-5810, (202)721-4100

Soc. of Chest Pain Centers and Providers **[16107]**, 6161 Riverside Dr., Dublin, OH 43017, (614)442-5950

Soc. of Children's Book Writers **[★10740]**

Soc. of Children's Book Writers and Illustrators **[10740]**, 8271 Beverly Blvd., Los Angeles, CA 90048, (323)782-1010

Soc. Chilena de Osteologia y Metabolismo Mineral **[★IO]**

Soc. of Chinese Amer. Professors and Scientists **[8758]**, PO Box 5735, Woodridge, IL 60517

Soc. of Chinese Scholars on Exercise Physiology and Fitness **[IO]**, Hong Kong, People's Republic of China

Soc. of Chiropodists and Podiatrists **[IO]**, London, United Kingdom

Soc. of Chiropractic Orthospinology **[14146]**, 2500 Flowers Chapel Rd., Dothan, AL 36305, (334)793-7992

Soc. of Christian Ethics **[11985]**, PO Box 5126, St. Cloud, MN 56302-5126, (320)253-5407

Soc. of Christian Philosophers **[10420]**, Calvin Coll., Dept. of Philosophy, 1845 Knollcrest Cir. SE, Grand Rapids, MI 49546-4402

Soc. of Christian Philosophers **[10420]**, Calvin Coll., Dept. of Philosophy, 1845 Knollcrest Cir. SE, Grand Rapids, MI 49546-4402

A star before a book entry number signifies that the name is not listed separately, but is mentioned within the entry.

Soc. for Church Archaeology **[IO]**, York, United Kingdom

Soc. of the Cincinnati **[20341]**, 2118 Massachusetts Ave. NW, Washington, DC 20008-2810, (202)785-2040

Soc. of the Cincinnati **[20341]**, 2118 Massachusetts Ave. NW, Washington, DC 20008-2810, (202)785-2040

Soc. for Cinema and Media Stud. **[9609]**, Wallace Old Sci. Hall, Rm. 300, 640 Parrington Oval, Norman, OK 73019, (405)325-8075

Soc. for Cinema Stud. **[★9609]**

Soc. of Cinematologists **[★9609]**

Soc. for Cinephiles/Cinecon **[9610]**, 3727 W Magnolia Blvd., No. 760, Burbank, CA 91505, (800)411-0455

Soc. of Civil War Historians **[9800]**, Penn State Univ., Civil War Era Ctr., 108 Weaver Bldg., University Park, PA 16802-5500, (814)863-0151

Soc. of Cleaning and Restoration Technicians **[2260]**, 234 Cedric St., Leesburg, GA 31763, (229)883-1202

Soc. of Cleaning Technicians **[★2260]**

Soc. of Clinical Child and Adolescent Psychology **[16422]**, Karen Roberts, Exec. Sec., PO Box 3968, Lawrence, KS 66046

Soc. for Clinical Ecology **[★14496]**

Soc. for Clinical Ecology **[★14496]**

Soc. for Clinical and Experimental Hypnosis **[15094]**, PO Box 252, Southborough, MA 01772, (508)598-5553

Soc. for Clinical and Medical Electrologists **[★14446]**

Soc. for Clinical and Medical Hair Removal **[14446]**, 2424 Amer. Ln., Madison, WI 53704-3102, (608)443-2470

Soc. of Clinical Res. Associates **[14157]**, 530 W Butler Ave., Ste. 109, Chalfont, PA 18914, (215)822-8644

Soc. of Clinical Res. Associates **[14157]**, 530 W Butler Ave., Ste. 109, Chalfont, PA 18914, (215)822-8644

Soc. for Clinical and Translational Sci. **[14158]**, 2025 M St. NW, Ste. 800, Washington, DC 20036, (202)367-1119

Soc. for Clinical Trials **[14159]**, 100 N 20th St., 4th Fl., Philadelphia, PA 19103, (215)564-3484

Soc. for Clinical Vascular Surgery **[14044]**, 500 Cummings Ctr., Ste. 4550, Beverly, MA 01915, (978)927-8330

Soc. for Co-operation in Russian and Soviet Stud. **[IO]**, London, United Kingdom

Soc. of Coll., Natl. and Univ. Libraries **[IO]**, London, United Kingdom

Soc. for Coll. and Univ. Planning **[8731]**, 1330 Eisenhower Pl., Ann Arbor, MI 48108, (734)764-2000

Soc. of Collision Repair Specialists **[369]**, PO Box 909, Prosser, WA 99350, (302)423-3537

Soc. for Colposcopy and Cervical Pathology of Singapore **[IO]**, Singapore, Singapore

Soc. for Commercial Archeology **[9215]**, PO Box 45828, Madison, WI 53744-5828

Soc. of Commercial Seed Technologists **[4884]**, 101 E State St., No. 214, Ithaca, NY 14850, (607)256-3313

Soc. for Companion Animal Stud. **[IO]**, Burford, United Kingdom

Soc. of the Companions of the Holy Cross **[19716]**, Adelynrood Retreat and Community Center, 46 Elm St., Byfield, MA 01922-2812, (978)462-6721

Soc. of Comparative Legislation **[IO]**, Paris, France

Soc. for the Comparative Stud. of Soc. and History **[9801]**, Univ. of Michigan, 1007 E Huron, Ann Arbor, MI 48109-1690, (734)764-6362

Soc. of the Compassionate Friends **[★12605]**

Soc. of Competitive Intelligence Professionals **[★6993]**

Soc. of Competitive Intelligence Professionals **[6993]**, 1700 Diagonal Rd., Ste. 600, Alexandria, VA 22314, (703)739-0696

Soc. of Competitor Intelligence Professionals **[★6993]**

Soc. of Competitor Intelligence Professionals **[★6993]**

Soc. of Composers, Authors and Music Publishers of Canada **[IO]**, Toronto, ON, Canada

Soc. of Composers, Inc. **[9506]**, PO Box 687, Mineral Wells, TX 76068-0687

Soc. of Computed Body Tomography **[★16541]**

Soc. of Computed Body Tomography and Magnetic Resonance **[16541]**, 1891 Preston White Dr., Reston, VA 20191, (703)476-1117

Soc. for Cmpt. Applications in Radiology **[★16543]**

Soc. for Cmpt. Simulation **[★6471]**

Soc. for Cmpt. Simulation **[★6471]**

Soc. for Computerized Tomography and Neuroimaging **[★16525]**

Soc. for Computers and Law **[IO]**, Bristol, United Kingdom

Soc. for Computing and Tech. in Anaesthesia **[IO]**, London, United Kingdom

Soc. for the Conservation of Bighorn Sheep **[5131]**, PO Box 94182, Pasadena, CA 91109-4182, (310)339-4677

Soc. for Conservation GIS **[6569]**, PO Box 7183, Redlands, CA 92375

Soc. of Constr. Law **[IO]**, Wantage, United Kingdom

Soc. of Constr. and Quantity Surveyors **[IO]**, Huddersfield, United Kingdom

Soc. of Consulting Marine Engineers and Ship Surveyors **[IO]**, London, United Kingdom

Soc. of Consulting Psychology **[16423]**, 336 Bon Air Center, No. 444, Greenbrae, CA 94904, (415)710-8097

Soc. of Consumer Affairs Professionals **[2909]**, 675 N Washington St., Ste. 200, Alexandria, VA 22314, (703)519-3700

Soc. for Consumer Psychology **[17472]**, PO Box 5795, Potsdam, NY 13699, (315)268-6605

Soc. of Corporate Meeting Professionals - Defunct.

Soc. of Corporate Secretaries and Governance Professionals **[74]**, 521 5th Ave., New York, NY 10175, (212)681-2000

Soc. of Correctional Physicians **[16273]**, PO Box 11760, Chicago, IL 60611-0760, (800)229-7380

Soc. of Cosmetic Chemists **[6421]**, 120 Wall St., Ste. 2400, New York, NY 10005-4088, (212)668-1500

Soc. of Cosmetic Chemists of South Africa **[IO]**, Johannesburg, Republic of South Africa

Soc. of Cosmetic Scientists **[IO]**, Luton, United Kingdom

Soc. of Cosmetic Scientists Singapore **[IO]**, Singapore, Singapore

Soc. of Cost Estimating and Anal. **[1327]**, 527 Maple Ave. E, Ste. 301, Vienna, VA 22180, (703)938-5090

Soc. for Costa Rica Collectors **[22076]**, 4204 Haring Rd., Metairie, LA 70006

Soc. for Cotton Products Analysts **[★6395]**

Soc. for Cotton Products Analysts **[★6395]**

Soc. of Counselling and Psychotherapy Educators **[IO]**, Weipa, Australia

Soc. of County Treasurers **[IO]**, Taunton, United Kingdom

Soc. for Court Stud. **[IO]**, London, United Kingdom

Soc. for Craniofacial Morphometry **[14204]**, Shriver Center, Harvard Medical School, 200 Trapelo Rd., Waltham, MA 02452-6332, (781)642-0163

Soc. for Creative Anachronism **[10079]**, PO Box 360789, Milpitas, CA 95036-0789, (408)263-9305

Soc. for Creative Anachronism, New Zealand **[IO]**, Wellington, New Zealand

Soc. of Critical Care Medicine **[14209]**, 500 Midway Dr., Mount Prospect, IL 60056, (847)827-6869

Soc. of Critical Care Medicine **[14209]**, 500 Midway Dr., Mount Prospect, IL 60056, (847)827-6869

Soc. for Cross-Cultural Res. **[9871]**, San Jose Sta. Univ., Dept. of Counselor Educ., Sweeney Hall 420, San Jose, CA 95192, (408)924-3767

Soc. for Cryobiology **[6585]**, Wendell Q. Sun, Treas., 1 Millennium Way, Branchburg, NJ 08876, (908)947-1176

Soc. of Crystallographers in Australia and New Zealand **[IO]**, Clayton, Australia

Soc. for Cultural Anthropology **[6151]**, Univ. of California, Santa Cruz, Dept. of Anthropology, 1156 High St., Santa Cruz, CA 95064, (831)459-5717

Soc. for Curriculum Development **[★7950]**

Soc. of Czech Architects **[IO]**, Prague, Czech Republic

Soc. of Dairy Tech. **[IO]**, Appleby-in-Westmorland, United Kingdom

Soc. of Dance History Scholars **[9802]**, Robert Ranieri, 3416 Primm Ln., Birmingham, AL 35216, (205)978-1404

Soc. for Data Educators **[★7907]**

Soc. for Data Educators **[★7907]**

Soc. of Daughters of Holland Dames **[20408]**, 308 Tunbridge Rd., Baltimore, MD 21212-3803

Soc. of Decorative Painters **[21467]**, 393 N McLean Blvd., Wichita, KS 67203-5968, (316)269-9300

Soc. of Depreciation Professionals **[55]**, 347 5th Ave., Ste. 703, New York, NY 10016, (646)417-6378

Soc. of Dermatologists, Venereologists and Leprologists of Nepal **[IO]**, Kathmandu, Nepal

Soc. of Dermatology Physician Assistants **[16241]**, 4111 W Alameda Ave., Ste. 412, Burbank, CA 91505, (800)380-3992

Soc. of the Descendants of the Colonial Clergy **[20409]**, 17 Lowell Mason Rd., Medfield, MA 02052-1709

Soc. of the Descendants of the Schwenkfeldian Exiles **[10357]**, 105 Seminary St., Pennsburg, PA 18073-1898, (215)679-3103

Soc. of the Descendants of Washington's Army at Valley Forge **[20342]**, PO Box 1779, Doylestown, PA 18902, (215)348-1047

Soc. for Design Admin. **[6205]**, 2400 Ardmore Blvd., Ste. 302, Pittsburgh, PA 15221, (800)711-8199

Soc. for Design and Process Sci. **[6601]**, 3824 Cedar Springs Rd., Ste. 368, Dallas, TX 75219-4136, (214)253-9025

Soc. of Designer Craftsmen **[IO]**, London, United Kingdom

Soc. for the Development of Austrian Economics **[6633]**, Peter Lewin, Treas., 7708 Queens Garden Dr., Dallas, TX 75248

Soc. for the Development of Women and Children **[IO]**, Sana'a, Yemen

Soc. for Developmental and Behavioral Pediatrics **[16155]**, 6728 Old McLean Village Dr., McLean, VA 22101, (703)556-9222

Soc. for Developmental Biology **[6314]**, 9650 Rockville Pike, Bethesda, MD 20814-3998, (301)634-7815

Soc. for Developmental Biology **[6314]**, 9650 Rockville Pike, Bethesda, MD 20814-3998, (301)634-7815

Soc. of the Devotees of Jerusalem **[★19878]**

Soc. of Diagnostic Medical Sonography **[16678]**, 2745 N Dallas Pkwy., Ste. 350, Plano, TX 75093-8730, (214)473-8057

Soc. of Die Casting Engineers **[★1855]**

Soc. for Disability Stud. **[11830]**, Soc. for Disability Stud., 107 Commerce Center Dr., Ste. 204, Huntersville, NC 28078, (704)274-9240

Soc. for Disabled Women Pakistan **[IO]**, Faisalabad, Pakistan

Soc. of Dramatic Authors and Composers **[IO]**, Paris, France

Soc. of Dyers and Colourists - England **[IO]**, Bradford, United Kingdom

Soc. for Ear, Nose, and Throat Advances in Children **[16089]**, Children's Hosp. of San Diego, 3030 Children's Way, Ste. 402, San Diego, CA 92123, (858)576-4085

Soc. of Early Amer. Decoration **[★9212]**

Soc. of Early Americanists **[9113]**, 1104 7th Ave. S, Moorhead, MN 56563, (800)593-7246

Soc. for Earthquake and Civil Engg. Dynamics **[IO]**, London, United Kingdom

Soc. for East Asian Anthropology **[6152]**, Prof. Jennifer Robertson, Pres., Univ. of Michigan, Dept. of Anthropology, 1085 S Univ. Ave., Ann Arbor, MI 48109

Soc. for Ecological Restoration **[★4219]**

Soc. for Ecological Restoration Intl. **[4219]**, 1017 O St. NW, Washington, DC 20001, (202)299-9518

Soc. for Ecological Restoration and Mgt. **[★4219]**

Soc. for Economic Anthropology **[6153]**, Dr. Mark Moritz, Mgr., Ohio State Univ., Dept. of Anthropology, 4058 Smith Lab., 174 W 18th Ave., Columbus, OH 43210-1106, (614)247-7426

Soc. for Economic Botany **[6367]**, PO Box 299, St. Louis, MO 63166-0299

Reference to "IO" in place of a book number signifies that the association may be found in the 50th edition of International Organizations.

Soc. of Economic Geologists [6914], 7811 Shaffer Pkwy., Littleton, CO 80127-3732, (720)981-7882

Soc. of Economic Paleontologists and Mineralogists [★7214]

Soc. of Editors [IO], Cambridge, United Kingdom

Soc. for Editors and Proofreaders [IO], London, United Kingdom

Soc. for Educ. in Anesthesia [13754], 520 N Northwest Hwy., Park Ridge, IL 60068-2573, (847)825-5586

Soc. for Educ., Music and Psychology Res. [IO], London, United Kingdom

Soc. for Educational Data Systems [★7907]

Soc. for Educational Data Systems [★7907]

Soc. of Educational Programmers and Systems Analysts [★7907]

Soc. of Educational Programmers and Systems Analysts [★7907]

Soc. for Educational Visits and Exchanges in Canada [IO], Ottawa, ON, Canada

Soc. of Educators and Scholars [9872], Inter Amer. Univ. of Puerto Rico, Metropolitan Campus, PO Box 191293, San Juan, PR 00919-1293

Soc. of Educators and Scholars [9872], Inter Amer. Univ. of Puerto Rico, Metropolitan Campus, PO Box 191293, San Juan, PR 00919-1293

Soc. for Eighteenth-Century Music [10291], 298 Blue Sage Dr., Allentown, PA 18104

Soc. for Electro-Acoustic Music in the U.S. [10292], PO Box 272, Milltown, NJ 08850

Soc. of Emergency Medicine Physician Assistants [16242], 1125 Executive Cir., Irving, TX 75038, (877)297-7594

Soc. for Emotional Well-Being Worldwide [15483], PO Box 41, New York, NY 10024

Soc. for Endangered Languages [IO], Cologne, Germany

Soc. for Endocrinology [IO], Bristol, United Kingdom

Soc. for Endocrinology, Metabolism and Diabetes of South Africa [IO], Sandton, Republic of South Africa

Soc. of Endocrinology and Metabolism of Turkey [IO], Ankara, Turkey

Soc. of Endovascular Veterinary Surgery - Address unknown since 2010.

Soc. for Energy Educ. [6756], 2526 Van Hise Ave., Madison, WI 53705, (608)246-6487

Soc. of Energy Professionals Intl. - Defunct.

Soc. for Engg. in Agriculture [IO], Barton, Australia

The Soc. for Engg. in Agriculture, Food and Biological Systems [★6774]

The Soc. for Engg. in Agriculture, Food and Biological Systems [★6774]

Soc. of Engineering Illustrators - Address unknown since 2010.

Soc. of Engg. Sci. [6825], S. White, Univ. of Illinois at Urbana-Champaign, Beckman Inst. for Advanced Sci. and Tech., 405 N Mathews Ave., Rm. 3361, Urbana, IL 61801

Soc. for Env. and Human Development [IO], Dhaka, Bangladesh

Soc. for Environmental Engineers [★7331]

Soc. for Environmental Engineers [IO], Buntingford, United Kingdom

Soc. for Environmental Exploration [IO], London, United Kingdom

Soc. for Environmental Graphic Design [1639], 1000 Vermont Ave. NW, Ste. 400, Washington, DC 20005, (202)638-5555

Soc. for Environmental Graphic Designers [★1639]

Soc. of Environmental Journalists [8448], PO Box 2492, Jenkintown, PA 19046, (215)884-8174

Soc. of Environmental Toxicology and Chemistry [14508], 229 S Baylen St., 2nd Fl., Pensacola, FL 32502, (850)469-1500

Soc. for Environmental Truth - Defunct.

Soc. of Environmental Understanding and Sustainability [5000], 716 Kent Rd., Kenilworth, IL 60043, (847)251-2079

Soc. for Epidemiologic Res. [14515], PO Box 990, Clearfield, UT 84089, (801)525-0231

Soc. of Epileptologists of Lithuania [IO], Kaunas, Lithuania

Soc. of Equestrian Artists [IO], Kent, United Kingdom

Soc. for the Eradication of TV [17357], Box 10491, Oakland, CA 94610-0491

Soc. of Ethical Attorneys at Law [5283], PO Box 5993, San Antonio, TX 78201, (210)785-0935

Soc. of Ethnobiology [6315], Steve Wolverton, Treas., Univ. of North Texas, Dept. of Geography, 1155 Union Cir., No. 305279, Denton, TX 76203-5017, (940)565-4987

Soc. of Ethnobiology [6315], Steve Wolverton, Treas., Univ. of North Texas, Dept. of Geography, 1155 Union Cir., No. 305279, Denton, TX 76203-5017, (940)565-4987

Soc. for Ethnomusicology [10293], The Musical Instrument Museum, 8550 S Priest Dr., Tempe, AZ 85284, (480)309-4077

Society of European Stage Authors and Composers [★9506]

Soc. for Evolutionary Anal. in Law [6264], Vanderbilt Univ. Law School, 131 21st Ave. S, Nashville, TN 37203-1181, (615)343-2034

Soc. for Evolutionary Anal. in Law [6264], Vanderbilt Univ. Law School, 131 21st Ave. S, Nashville, TN 37203-1181, (615)343-2034

Soc. for Exact Philosophy [10421], Univ. of Florida, Dept. of Philosophy, 330 Griffin-Floyd Hall, Gainesville, FL 32611-8545, (352)392-2084

Soc. for Exact Philosophy [10421], Univ. of Florida, Dept. of Philosophy, 330 Griffin-Floyd Hall, Gainesville, FL 32611-8545, (352)392-2084

Soc. for Excellence in Eyecare [15977], PO Box 2153, Goodlettsville, TN 37070-2153, (615)892-0863

Soc. for Executive Leadership in Academic Medicine Intl. [15433], 100 N 20th St., 4th Fl., Philadelphia, PA 19103-1443, (215)564-3484

Soc. for Executive Leadership in Academic Medicine Intl. [15433], 100 N 20th St., 4th Fl., Philadelphia, PA 19103-1443, (215)564-3484

Soc. for Existential Anal. [IO], London, United Kingdom

Soc. for Existential and Phenomenological Theory and Culture [IO], Edmonton, AB, Canada

Soc. for Experimental Biology [IO], London, United Kingdom

Soc. for Experimental Biology and Medicine [6316], 130 W Pleasant Ave., No. 334, Maywood, NJ 07607, (201)962-3519

Soc. for Experimental Mechanics [7482], 7 School St., Bethel, CT 06801, (203)790-6373

Soc. of Experimental Psychologists - Defunct.

Soc. for Experimental Stress Anal. [★7482]

Soc. of Experimental Test Pilots [6096], PO Box 986, Lancaster, CA 93584-0986, (661)942-9574

Soc. of Exploration Geophysicists [6929], PO Box 702740, Tulsa, OK 74170-2740, (918)497-5500

Soc. of Exploration Geophysicists of Japan [IO], Tokyo, Japan

Soc. for the Exploration of Psychotherapy Integration [16474], 3100 N Leisure World Blvd., Apt. 1021, Silver Spring, MD 20906

Soc. for the Exploration of Psychotherapy Integration [16474], 3100 N Leisure World Blvd., Apt. 1021, Silver Spring, MD 20906

Soc. of Explosives Engineers [★6803]

Soc. of Explosives Engineers [★6803]

Soc. of Eye Surgeons [15978], Intl. Eye Found., 10801 Connecticut Ave., Kensington, MD 20895, (240)290-0263

Soc. of Family Planning [14528], 255 S 17th St., Ste. 1102, Philadelphia, PA 19103, (866)584-6758

Soc. Farsarotul [9525], PO Box 753, Trumbull, CT 06611

Soc. for Features Journalism [2872], 200 E Las Olas Blvd., 9th Fl., Fort Lauderdale, FL 33301, (954)356-4718

Soc. of Fed. Labor and Employee Relations Professionals [5637], PO Box 25112, Arlington, VA 22202, (703)403-3039

Soc. of Fed. Labor Relations Professionals [★5637]

Soc. of Federal Linguists - Defunct.

Soc. of Feed Technologists [IO], Reading, United Kingdom

Soc. for Fetal Urology [16950], Dept. of Surgery/Pediatrics, Division of Urology/Section Pediatric Urology, 1600 7th Ave. S, ACC No. 318, Birmingham, AL 35233, (205)939-9840

Soc. for Field Experience Educ. [★8177]

Soc. of the Fifth Div. [20697], 8653 Miroballi Dr., Hickory Hills, IL 60457-1062

Soc. for Financial Educ. and Professional Development [7811], 2120 Washington Blvd., Ste. 400, Arlington, VA 22204, (202)842-3807

Soc. of Financial Examiners [5923], 12100 Sunset Hills Rd., Ste. 130, Reston, VA 20190, (703)234-4140

Soc. of Financial Ser. Professionals [2039], 19 Campus Blvd., Ste. 100, Newtown Square, PA 19073-3239, (610)526-2500

Soc. of Financial Ser. Professionals [2039], 19 Campus Blvd., Ste. 100, Newtown Square, PA 19073-3239, (610)526-2500

Soc. of Fine Art Auctioneers and Valuers [IO], East Molesey, United Kingdom

Soc. of Finnish Composers [IO], Helsinki, Finland

Soc. of Fire Protection Engineers [6863], 7315 Wisconsin Ave., Ste. 620E, Bethesda, MD 20814, (301)718-2910

Soc. of the First Infantry Div. [20368], 1933 Morris Rd., Blue Bell, PA 19422-1422, (888)324-4733

Soc. of Flavor Chemists [6422], 3301 Rte. 66, Bldg. C, Ste. 205, Neptune, NJ 07753, (732)922-3393

Soc. of Flight Test Engineers [6097], 44814 N Elm Ave., Lancaster, CA 93534, (661)949-2095

Soc. of Floristry [IO], Shropshire, United Kingdom

Soc. for Folk Arts Preservation [9626], 75 Timberhill Ln., South Fallsburg, NY 12779, (845)436-7314

Soc. for Folk Life Stud. [IO], Durham, United Kingdom

Soc. for Food Hygiene and Tech. [IO], Middleton, United Kingdom

Soc. for Foodservice Mgt. [1455], 15000 Commerce Pkwy., Ste. C, Mount Laurel, NJ 08054, (856)380-6829

Soc. For Biomaterials [6329], 15000 Commerce Pkwy., Ste. C, Mount Laurel, NJ 08054, (856)439-0826

Soc. For Clinical Data Mgt. [2702], 555 E Wells St., Ste. 1100, Milwaukee, WI 53202-3823, (414)226-0362

Soc. of Forensic Toxicologists [5488], One MacDonald Center, 1 N MacDonald St., Ste. 15, Mesa, AZ 85201, (480)839-9106

Soc. of Former Special Agents of the Fed. Bur. of Investigation [19111], 3717 Fettler Park Dr., Dumfries, VA 22025, (703)445-0026

Soc. of the Founders and Friends of Norwich, Connecticut [9727], PO Box 62, Norwich, CT 06360, (860)889-9440

Soc. of the Founders of Norwich, Connecticut [★9727]

Soc. for Free Radical Biology and Medicine [6332], 8365 Keystone Crossing, Ste. 107, Indianapolis, IN 46240, (317)205-9482

Soc. for Free Radical Biology and Medicine [6332], 8365 Keystone Crossing, Ste. 107, Indianapolis, IN 46240, (317)205-9482

Soc. of Freelance Editors and Proofreaders [★18730]

Soc. for French Amer. Cultural Services and Educational Aid [★8312]

Soc. for French Historical Stud. [9803], 551-101 Milton Ct., Long Beach, CA 90803, (562)494-6764

Soc. for French Stud. [IO], Bristol, United Kingdom

Soc. for Freshwater Sci. [4220], SFS Membership Services, 5400 Bosque Blvd., Ste. 680, Waco, TX 76710, (254)399-9636

Soc. of the Friendly Sons of St. Patrick in the City of New York [19072], 80 Wall St., New York, NY 10005, (212)269-1770

Soc. of Friends of Touro Synagogue [★9733]

Soc. of Garden Designers [IO], Ross-on-Wye, United Kingdom

Soc. of Gastroenterology Nurses and Associates [14575], 401 N Michigan Ave., Chicago, IL 60611, (312)321-5165

Soc. of Gastrointestinal Assistants [★14575]

Soc. of Gastrointestinal Radiologists [16542], Intl. Meeting Managers, Inc., 4550 Post Oak Pl., Ste. 342, Houston, TX 77027, (713)965-0566

Soc. of Genealogists [IO], London, United Kingdom

Soc. of Gen. Internal Medicine [15137], 1500 King St., Ste. 303, Alexandria, VA 22314, (202)887-5150

A star before a book entry number signifies that the name is not listed separately, but is mentioned within the entry.

Soc. for Gen. Microbiology **[IO]**, Reading, United Kingdom

Soc. for Gen. Music - Address unknown since 2010.

Soc. of Gen. Physiologists **[7275]**, PO Box 257, Woods Hole, MA 02543-0257, (508)540-6719

Soc. of Geography of Lisbon **[IO]**, Lisbon, Portugal

Soc. of Geology Applied to Mineral Deposits **[IO]**, Prague, Czech Republic

Soc. of Geomagnetism and Earth, Planetary and Space Sciences **[IO]**, Kobe, Japan

Soc. of Geriatric Cardiology - Defunct.

Soc. of Geriatric Ophthalmology - Defunct.

Soc. for German-American Stud. **[9636]**, Wabash Coll., Crawfordsville, IN 47933, (765)361-6129

Soc. of German Cooks **[IO]**, Frankfurt, Germany

Soc. for German Idealism **[9637]**, Lewis & Clark Coll., Dept. of Philosophy, 615 SW Palatine Hill Rd., Portland, OR 97219-7879, (503)768-7477

Soc. of Glass and Ceramic Decorated Products **[1582]**, PO Box 2489, Zanesville, OH 43702, (740)588-9882

Soc. of Glass Decorators **[★1582]**

Soc. of Glass Tech. **[IO]**, Sheffield, United Kingdom

Soc. of the Golden Sect. - Defunct.

Soc. of Govt. Economists **[5393]**, PO Box 77082, Washington, DC 20013, (202)643-1743

Soc. of Govt. Meeting Professionals **[2459]**, 908 King St., Lower Level, Alexandria, VA 22314, (703)549-0892

Soc. of Govt. Ser. Urologists **[16951]**, 1100 E Woodfield Rd., Ste. 520, Schaumburg, IL 60173, (847)517-7225

Soc. of Govt. Travel Professionals **[3574]**, PO Box 158, Glyndon, MD 21071-0158, (202)363-7487

Soc. of Grain Elevator Superintendents **[★1593]**

Soc. of Graphic Designers of Canada **[IO]**, Ottawa, ON, Canada

Soc. of Grasslands Naturalists **[IO]**, Medicine Hat, AB, Canada

Soc. of Gynecologic Investigation **[15894]**, 888 Bestgate Rd., Ste. 420, Annapolis, MD 21401, (404)727-8600

Soc. of Gynecologic Oncologists **[15932]**, 230 W Monroe St., Ste. 710, Chicago, IL 60606, (312)235-4060

Soc. of Gynecologic Oncologists of Canada **[IO]**, Ottawa, ON, Canada

Soc. of the Hawley Family **[20588]**, 450 E Waterside Dr., Unit 209, Chicago, IL 60601

Soc. of Head and Neck Surgeons **[★16083]**

Soc. of Headmasters and Headmistresses of Independent Schools **[IO]**, Market Harborough, United Kingdom

Soc. for Hea. Educ. **[IO]**, Male, Maldives

Soc. for Hea. and Human Values **[★8589]**

Soc. of Healthcare Epidemiologists of Am. **[★14516]**

Soc. for Healthcare Epidemiology of Am. **[14516]**, 1300 Wilson Blvd., Ste. 300, Arlington, VA 22209, (703)684-1006

Soc. of Healthcare Executive Assistants - Defunct.

Soc. for Healthcare Planning and Marketing of the Amer. Hosp. Assn. **[★15041]**

Soc. of Hearing Aid Audiologists **[★14944]**

Soc. of Hearing Aid Audiologists **[★14944]**

Soc. for Heart Attack Prevention and Eradication **[14045]**, 710 N Post Oak Rd., Ste. 204, Houston, TX 77024, (713)529-4484

Soc. for Heart Brain Medicine **[14046]**, 9500 Euclid Ave., Mail Code JJ40, Cleveland, OH 44195, (216)636-2424

Soc. for Heart Valve Disease **[14959]**, 900 Cummings Ctr., Ste. 221-U, Beverly, MA 01915, (978)927-8330

Soc. of Heating, Airconditioning and Sanitary Engineers of Japan **[IO]**, Tokyo, Japan

Soc. for Helping People with Autism **[IO]**, Bratislava, Slovakia

Soc. for Hematology and Stem Cells **[14976]**, 401 N Michigan Ave., Ste. 2200, Chicago, IL 60611, (312)321-5114

Soc. for Hematology and Stem Cells **[14976]**, 401 N Michigan Ave., Ste. 2200, Chicago, IL 60611, (312)321-5114

Soc. for Hematopathology **[16132]**, 3643 Walton Way Extension, Augusta, GA 30909, (706)733-7550

Soc. of Heraldic Arts **[IO]**, Devon, United Kingdom

Soc. of Herbarium Curators **[6368]**, Dr. Lucile McCook, Treas., PO Box 1848, University, MS 38677, (662)915-5488

Soc. for Heritage, Architectural Preservation and Enhancement **[IO]**, Roseau, Dominica

Soc. for Hindu-Christian Stud. **[20215]**, Bradley J. Malkovsky, Treas./Ed., Univ. of Notre Dame, 232 Malloy Hall, Notre Dame, IN 46556, (574)631-7128

Soc. of Hispanic Professional Engineers **[6826]**, 13181 Crossroads Pkwy. N, Ste. 450, City of Industry, CA 91746-3496, (323)725-3970

Soc. for Historians of Amer. Foreign Relations **[9804]**, Dept. of History, Ohio State Univ., 106 Dulles Hall, 230 W 17th Ave., Columbus, OH 43210, (614)292-1951

Soc. for Historians of the Early Amer. Republic **[9805]**, 3355 Woodland Walk, Philadelphia, PA 19104-4531, (215)746-5393

Soc. for Historical Archaeology **[6178]**, 9707 Key West Ave., Ste. 100, Rockville, MD 20850, (301)990-2454

Soc. for Historical Archaeology **[6178]**, 9707 Key West Ave., Ste. 100, Rockville, MD 20850, (301)990-2454

Soc. for the History of Alchemy and Chemistry **[IO]**, Oxford, United Kingdom

Soc. for the History of Authorship, Reading and Publishing **[9450]**, The John Hopkins Univ. Press, Journals Publishing Div., PO Box 19966, Baltimore, MD 21211-0966, (410)516-6987

Soc. for the History of Authorship, Reading and Publishing **[9450]**, The John Hopkins Univ. Press, Journals Publishing Div., PO Box 19966, Baltimore, MD 21211-0966, (410)516-6987

Soc. for the History of Discoveries **[9806]**, Donald Perkins, Treas., 5904 Mt. Eagle Dr., Apt. 118, Alexandria, VA 22303-2535

Soc. for the History of Discoveries **[9806]**, Donald Perkins, Treas., 5904 Mt. Eagle Dr., Apt. 118, Alexandria, VA 22303-2535

Soc. for History Educ. **[8263]**, California State Univ., Long Beach, 1250 Bellflower Blvd., Long Beach, CA 90840, (562)985-2573

Soc. for History in the Fed. Govt. **[9807]**, Box 14139, Benjamin Franklin Sta., Washington, DC 20044, (301)279-9697

Soc. for the History of Natural History **[IO]**, London, United Kingdom

Soc. for the History of Navy Medicine **[9808]**, 131 El Camino Real, Vallejo, CA 94590-3464, (707)373-3989

Soc. for the History of Psychology **[7312]**, Trey Buchanan, Sec.-Treas., 501 Coll. Ave., Wheaton, IL 60187

Soc. for the History of Psychology **[7312]**, Trey Buchanan, Sec.-Treas., 501 Coll. Ave., Wheaton, IL 60187

Soc. for the History of Tech. **[9809]**, PO Box 400744, Charlottesville, VA 22904-4744, (434)975-2190

Soc. of Homeopaths **[IO]**, Northampton, United Kingdom

Soc. of Hosp. Attorneys **[★5510]**

Soc. of Hosp. Epidemiologists of Am. **[★14516]**

Soc. of Hosp. Linen Ser. and Laundry Managers **[IO]**, Bolton, United Kingdom

Soc. of Hosp. Medicine **[15067]**, 1500 Spring Garden St., Ste. 501, Philadelphia, PA 19130, (267)702-2601

Soc. for Human Ecology **[14509]**, Ms. Barbara Carter, Sec., Coll. of the Atlantic, 105 Eden St., Bar Harbor, ME 04609, (207)288-5015

Soc. for Human Ecology **[14509]**, Ms. Barbara Carter, Sec., Coll. of the Atlantic, 105 Eden St., Bar Harbor, ME 04609, (207)288-5015

Soc. for Human Performance in Extreme Environments **[6265]**, 2652 Corbyton Ct., Orlando, FL 32828, (407)381-7762

Soc. for Human Rsrc. Mgt. **[2632]**, 1800 Duke St., Alexandria, VA 22314-3499, (703)548-3440

Soc. for Human Rights and Prisoners Aid **[IO]**, Islamabad, Pakistan

Soc. for Humanistic Judaism **[19900]**, 28611 W 12 Mile Rd., Farmington Hills, MI 48334, (248)478-7610

Soc. for Humanistic Judaism **[19900]**, 28611 W 12 Mile Rd., Farmington Hills, MI 48334, (248)478-7610

Soc. for the Humanities **[9848]**, Cornell Univ., Andrew D. White House, 27 East Ave., Ithaca, NY 14853-1101, (607)255-9274

Soc. for Hungarian Philately **[22077]**, Jim Gaul, Auction Chm., 1920 Fawn Ln., Hellertown, PA 18055-2117, (610)838-8162

Soc. for Hungarian Philately **[22077]**, Jim Gaul, Auction Chm., 1920 Fawn Ln., Hellertown, PA 18055-2117, (610)838-8162

Soc. of Icelandic Advt. Agencies **[IO]**, Reykjavik, Iceland

Soc. of Illustrators **[9256]**, 128 E 63rd St., New York, NY 10021-7303, (212)838-2560

Soc. of Illustrators **[9256]**, 128 E 63rd St., New York, NY 10021-7303, (212)838-2560

Soc. for Imaging Informatics in Medicine **[16543]**, 19440 Golf Vista Plz., Ste. 330, Leesburg, VA 20176, (703)723-0432

Soc. for Imaging Sci. and Tech. **[7261]**, 7003 Kilworth Ln., Springfield, VA 22151, (703)642-9090

Soc. for Immunotherapy and Cancer **[13982]**, 555 E Wells St., Ste. 1100, Milwaukee, WI 53202-3823, (414)271-2456

Soc. for In Vitro Biology **[6317]**, 514 Daniels St., Ste. 411, Raleigh, NC 27605-1317, (919)562-0600

Soc. of Incentive and Travel Executives **[3575]**, 401 N Michigan Ave., Chicago, IL 60611, (312)321-5148

Soc. of Incentive Travel Executives **[★3575]**

Soc. of Incentive and Travel Executives **[3575]**, 401 N Michigan Ave., Chicago, IL 60611, (312)321-5148

Soc. of Incentive Travel Executives **[★3575]**

Soc. for the Increase of the Ministry **[20001]**, 924 Farmington Ave., No. 100, West Hartford, CT 06107, (860)233-1732

Soc. of Independent Brewers **[IO]**, Thirsk, United Kingdom

Soc. of Independent Financial Advisors - Defunct.

Soc. of Independent Gasoline Marketers of Am. **[2670]**, 3930 Pender Dr., Ste. 340, Fairfax, VA 22030, (703)709-7000

Soc. of Independent and Private School Data Educ. **[★7907]**

Soc. of Independent and Private School Data Educ. **[★7907]**

Soc. of Independent Professional Earth Scientists **[6915]**, 4925 Greenville Ave., Ste. 1106, Dallas, TX 75206, (214)363-1780

Soc. of Independent Roundabout Proprietors **[IO]**, Retford, United Kingdom

Soc. of Independent Show Organizers **[1237]**, 2601 Ocean Park Blvd., Ste. 200, Santa Monica, CA 90405, (310)450-8831

Soc. of Indexers **[IO]**, Sheffield, United Kingdom

Soc. of Indian Auto. Mfrs. **[IO]**, New Delhi, India

Soc. for Indian Philosophy and Religion **[9861]**, PO Box 79, Elon, NC 27244

Soc. of Indiana Pioneers **[20751]**, 140 N Senate Ave., Indianapolis, IN 46204-2207, (317)233-6588

Soc. for Individual Liberty **[★18078]**

Soc. for Individual Liberty **[★18078]**

Soc. for Indonesian-Americans

Soc. for Indonesian-Americans - Address unknown since 2010.

Soc. for Indus. and Applied Mathematics **[7077]**, 3600 Market St., 6th Fl., Philadelphia, PA 19104-2688, (215)382-9800

Soc. for Indus. Archeology **[6179]**, Michigan Technological Univ., Social Sciences Dept., 1400 Townsend Dr., Houghton, MI 49931-1295, (906)487-1889

Soc. of Indus. Engineers **[★2304]**

Soc. for Indus. Microbiology **[6318]**, 3929 Old Lee Hwy., Ste. 92A, Fairfax, VA 22030-2421, (703)691-3357

Soc. of Indus. and Off. Realtors **[3044]**, 1201 New York Ave. NW, Ste. 350, Washington, DC 20005-6126, (202)449-8200

Soc. of Indus. and Organizational Psychology **[16424]**, 440 E Poe Rd., Ste. 101, Bowling Green, OH 43402-1355, (419)353-0032

Reference to "IO" in place of a book number signifies that the association may be found in the 50th edition of International Organizations.

Soc. for Indus. and Organizational Psychology **[16424]**, 440 E Poe Rd., Ste. 101, Bowling Green, OH 43402-1355, (419)353-0032

Soc. of Indus. Realtors **[★3044]**

Soc. of Infectious Diseases Pharmacists **[16216]**, 823 Cong. Ave., Ste. 230, Austin, TX 78701, (512)479-0425

Soc. of Infectious Diseases Singapore **[IO]**, Singapore, Singapore

Soc. for Info. Display **[6470]**, 1475 S Bascom Ave., Ste. 114, Campbell, CA 95008-0628, (408)879-3901

Soc. for Info. Display **[6470]**, 1475 S Bascom Ave., Ste. 114, Campbell, CA 95008-0628, (408)879-3901

Soc. for Info. Mgt. **[2305]**, 401 N Michigan Ave., Chicago, IL 60611-4267, (312)527-6734

Soc. of Info. Tech. Mgt. **[IO]**, Northampton, United Kingdom

Soc. of Info. Tech. and Teacher Educ. **[8978]**, PO Box 1545, Chesapeake, VA 23327-1545, (757)366-5606

Soc. of Inkwell Collectors **[21403]**, 2203 39th St. SE, Puyallup, WA 98372, (301)919-6322

Soc. of Inkwell Collectors **[21403]**, 2203 39th St. SE, Puyallup, WA 98372, (301)919-6322

Soc. of Instrument and Control Engineers **[IO]**, Tokyo, Japan

Soc. of Insurance Accountants **[★1328]**

Soc. of Insurance Financial Mgt. **[1328]**, PO Box 9001, Mount Vernon, NY 10552, (914)966-3180

Soc. of Insurance Res. **[2040]**, 631 Eastpointe Dr., Shelbyville, IN 46176, (317)398-3684

Soc. of Insurance Trainers and Educators **[8325]**, 1821 Univ. Ave. W, Ste. S256, St. Paul, MN 55104, (651)999-5354

Soc. for Integrative and Comparative Biology **[7638]**, 1313 Dolley Madison Blvd., Ste. 402, McLean, VA 22101-3926, (703)790-1745

Soc. for Integrative Oncology **[15933]**, Lorenzo Cohen, PhD, Pres., UTMD Anderson Cancer Center, 1515 Holcombe Blvd., Box 243, Houston, TX 77030, (713)745-4260

Soc. for Intercultural Educ., Training and Res. **[★8410]**

Soc. for Intercultural Educ., Training and Res. **[★8410]**

Soc. for Intercultural Educ., Training and Res. U.S.A. **[8410]**, 603 Stewart St., Ste. 610, Seattle, WA 98101, (206)859-4351

Soc. for Intercultural Educ., Training and Res. U.S.A. **[8410]**, 603 Stewart St., Ste. 610, Seattle, WA 98101, (206)859-4351

Soc. of Intl. Bus. Fellows **[2088]**, 191 Peachtree St. NE, Ste. 3950, Atlanta, GA 30303-1740, (404)525-7423

Soc. of Intl. Bus. Fellows **[2088]**, 191 Peachtree St. NE, Ste. 3950, Atlanta, GA 30303-1740, (404)525-7423

Soc. of Intl. Chinese in Educational Tech. **[8970]**, Dr. Hong Zhan, Treas., 7200 E Pioneer Ln., Prescott Valley, AZ 86314, (928)523-0408

Soc. of Intl. Chinese in Educational Tech. **[8970]**, Dr. Hong Zhan, Treas., 7200 E Pioneer Ln., Prescott Valley, AZ 86314, (928)523-0408

Soc. for Intl. Development - Italy **[IO]**, Rome, Italy

Soc. for Intl. Development - USA **[17922]**, 1875 Connecticut Ave. NW, Ste. 720, Washington, DC 20009-5728, (202)884-8590

Soc. for Intl. Development - USA **[17922]**, 1875 Connecticut Ave. NW, Ste. 720, Washington, DC 20009-5728, (202)884-8590

Soc. of Intl. Gas Tanker and Terminal Operators **[IO]**, London, United Kingdom

Soc. for Intl. Hockey Res. **[IO]**, Toronto, ON, Canada

Soc. of Internet Professionals **[IO]**, Toronto, ON, Canada

Soc. of Interventional Pain Mgt. Surgery Centers **[16822]**, Amer. Soc. of Interventional Pain Physicians, 81 Lakeview Dr., Paducah, KY 42001, (270)554-9412

Soc. of Interventional Radiology **[16544]**, 3975 Fair Ridge Dr., Ste. 400 N, Fairfax, VA 22033, (703)691-1805

Soc. of Invasive Cardiovascular Professionals **[14047]**, 1500 Sunday Dr., Ste. 102, Raleigh, NC 27607-5151, (919)861-4546

Soc. for Invertebrate Pathology - Defunct.

Soc. for Investigative Dermatology **[14339]**, 526 Superior Ave. E, Ste. 540, Cleveland, OH 44114-1999, (216)579-9300

Soc. of Iranian Architects and Planners **[6206]**, PO Box 643066, Los Angeles, CA 90064

Soc. of Iranian Architects and Planners **[6206]**, PO Box 643066, Los Angeles, CA 90064

Soc. of Iranian Doctors **[IO]**, Tehran, Iran

Soc. of Iranian Petroleum Indus. Equip. Mfrs. **[IO]**, Tehran, Iran

Soc. of the Irish Motor Indus. **[IO]**, Dublin, Ireland

Soc. of Israel Philatelists **[22078]**, PO Box 507, Northfield, OH 44067, (330)467-7446

Soc. for Italian Historical Stud. **[9904]**, 1500 SW 5th Ave., No. 1106, Portland, OR 97201-5425

Soc. for Italic Handwriting **[IO]**, Birmingham, United Kingdom

Soc. for Italic Stud. **[★9903]**

Soc. of Japanese Aerospace Companies **[IO]**, Tokyo, Japan

Soc. of Japanese Arts **[IO]**, Aerdenhout, Netherlands

Soc. for Japanese Irises **[21821]**, PO Box 390, Millington, MD 21651

Soc. of Japanese Women Scientists **[IO]**, Hiratsuka, Japan

Soc. of Jewish Ethics **[19901]**, 1531 Dickey Dr., Atlanta, GA 30322, (404)712-8550

Soc. of Jewish Sci. **[19902]**, 109 E 39th St., New York, NY 10016, (212)682-2626

Soc. for Judgment and Decision Making **[7807]**, Florida State Univ., Coll. of Bus., PO Box 3061110, Tallahassee, FL 32306-1110, (850)644-8231

Soc. for Judgment and Decision Making **[7807]**, Florida State Univ., Coll. of Bus., PO Box 3061110, Tallahassee, FL 32306-1110, (850)644-8231

Soc. of Kabalarians of Canada **[IO]**, Vancouver, BC, Canada

Soc. of Kastorians Omonoia **[19017]**, 150-28 14th Ave., Whitestone, NY 11357, (718)746-4505

Soc. of King Charles the Martyr **[19296]**, 291 Bacon St., Piety Corner, Waltham, MA 02451

Soc. for Korean-American Scholars **[8451]**, PO Box 90305, Durham, NC 27708

Soc. for Lab. Animal Sci. **[IO]**, Berlin, Germany

Soc. for Lab. Automation and Screening **[6423]**, 100 Illinois St., Ste. 242, St. Charles, IL 60174, (630)256-7527

Soc. of Laparoendoscopic Surgeons **[16823]**, 7330 SW 62nd Pl., Ste. 410, Miami, FL 33143-4825, (305)665-9959

Soc. for Latin Amer. Anthropology **[6154]**, AAA Membership Services, 4350 N Fairfax Dr., Ste. 640, Arlington, VA 22203-1620, (703)528-1902

Soc. for Latin Amer. Anthropology **[6154]**, AAA Membership Services, 4350 N Fairfax Dr., Ste. 640, Arlington, VA 22203-1620, (703)528-1902

Soc. for Latin Amer. Stud. **[IO]**, Oxford, United Kingdom

Soc. of Laundry Engineers and Allied Trades **[IO]**, Chessington, United Kingdom

Soc. of Leather Technologists and Chemists **[IO]**, Northampton, United Kingdom

Soc. of Leather Technologists and Chemists South African Sect. **[IO]**, Pietermaritzburg, Republic of South Africa

Soc. of Legal Scholars in the United Kingdom and Ireland **[IO]**, Southampton, United Kingdom

Soc. of Lesbian and Gay Anthropologists **[★6135]**

Soc. for Leukocyte Biology **[16614]**, 9650 Rockville Pike, Bethesda, MD 20814, (301)634-7451

Soc. for Libyan Stud. **[IO]**, London, United Kingdom

Soc. for Life with Osteoporosis **[IO]**, Ankara, Turkey

Soc. for Light Treatment and Biological Rhythms **[16872]**, Namni Goel, PhD, Pres., Univ. of Pennsylvania, School of Medicine, 1013 Blockley Hall, Philadelphia, PA 19104-6021, (215)898-1742

Soc. for Light Treatment and Biological Rhythms **[16872]**, Namni Goel, PhD, Pres., Univ. of Pennsylvania, School of Medicine, 1013 Blockley Hall, Philadelphia, PA 19104-6021, (215)898-1742

Soc. of Limerents - Defunct.

Soc. for Lincolnshire History and Archaeology **[IO]**, Lincoln, United Kingdom

Soc. for Linguistic Anthropology **[6155]**, UCSD, Dept. of Anthropology, 0532, 9500 Gilman Dr., La Jolla, CA 92093-5004, (858)534-4639

Soc. of the Little Flower **[19498]**, 1313 N Frontage Rd., Darien, IL 60561-5340, (630)968-9400

Soc. of Local Authority Chief Executives and Senior Managers **[IO]**, London, United Kingdom

Soc. of Local Coun. Clerks **[IO]**, Taunton, United Kingdom

Soc. of Logistics Engineers **[★6965]**

Soc. of Logistics Engineers **[★6965]**

Soc. of London Art Dealers **[IO]**, London, United Kingdom

Soc. of London Theatre **[IO]**, London, United Kingdom

Soc. for Louisiana Irises **[21822]**, Ron Killingsworth, Treas., 10329 Caddo Lake Rd., Mooringsport, LA 71060

Soc. for Low Temperature Biology **[IO]**, London, United Kingdom

Soc. for Luminescence Microscopy and Spectroscopy - Defunct.

Soc. of Magazine Photographers **[★2711]**

Soc. of Magazine Writers **[★10700]**

Soc. for Magnetic Resonance **[★16534]**

Soc. for Magnetic Resonance **[★16534]**

Soc. for Maintenance and Reliability Professionals **[2261]**, 8400 Westpark Dr., 2nd Fl., McLean, VA 22102, (703)245-8011

Soc. for Male Reproduction and Urology **[16593]**, 1209 Montgomery Hwy., Birmingham, AL 35216-2809, (205)978-5000

Soc. of Mgt. Accountants of Canada **[IO]**, Mississauga, ON, Canada

Soc. for the Mgt. of Autism Related Issues in Training, Educ. and Resources **[IO]**, Negara, Brunei Darussalam

Soc. for Mgt. Info. Systems **[★2305]**

Soc. of Mfg. Emgineers I Composites Mfg. Tech Gp. **[2345]**, One SME Dr., Dearborn, MI 48128, (313)425-3000

Soc. of Mfg. Engineers **[7048]**, One SME Dr., Dearborn, MI 48121, (313)425-3000

Soc. for Mfg. Engineers I Assn. for Finishing Processes **[6432]**, 1 SME Dr., Dearborn, MI 48121, (313)425-3000

Soc. for Mfg. Engineers I Assn. for Finishing Processes **[6432]**, 1 SME Dr., Dearborn, MI 48121, (313)425-3000

Soc. of Mfg. Engineers I Composites Mfg. Tech Gp. **[2345]**, One SME Dr., Dearborn, MI 48128, (313)425-3000

Soc. of Mfg. Engineers Educ. Found. **[8129]**, PO Box 930, Dearborn, MI 48121, (313)425-3300

Soc. of Mfg. Engineers I Electronics Mfg. Tech Gp. **[6673]**, 1 SME Dr., Dearborn, MI 48121-0930, (313)425-3000

Soc. of Mfg. Engineers I Electronics Mfg. Tech Gp. **[6673]**, 1 SME Dr., Dearborn, MI 48121-0930, (313)425-3000

Soc. of Mfg. Engineers I Machining and Material Removal Community **[7529]**, 1 SME Dr., Dearborn, MI 48128-2408, (313)425-3000

Soc. of Mfg. Engineers I North Amer. Mfg. Res. Institution **[7049]**, 1 SME Dr., Dearborn, MI 48121, (313)425-3000

Soc. of Mareen Duvall Descendants **[20589]**, 3580 S River Terr., Edgewater, MD 21037, (410)798-4531

Soc. of Marine Consultants - Defunct.

Soc. for Marine Mammalogy **[4712]**, Univ. of North Carolina at Wilmington, 601 S Coll. Rd., Wilmington, NC 28403, (910)962-7199

Soc. for Marine Mammalogy **[IO]**, Edmonton, AB, Canada

Soc. of Marine Port Engineers **[3269]**, PO Box 369, Eatontown, NJ 07724, (732)389-2009

Soc. of Maritime Arbitrators **[5212]**, 30 Broad St., 7th Fl., New York, NY 10004-2304, (212)344-2400

Soc. of Maritime Indus. **[IO]**, London, United Kingdom

Soc. for Marketing Professional Services **[2424]**, 44 Canal Center Plz., Ste. 444, Alexandria, VA 22314, (703)549-6117

Soc. for Maternal-Fetal Medicine **[16159]**, 409 12th St. SW, Washington, DC 20024-2125, (202)863-2476

A star before a book entry number signifies that the name is not listed separately, but is mentioned within the entry.

Soc. for Mathematical Biology [6319], PO Box 11283, Boulder, CO 80301, (303)661-9942

Soc. of Mathematicians, Physicists and Astronomers of Slovenia [IO], Ljubljana, Slovenia

Soc. for Medical Anthropology [6156], Carolyn Sargent, Washington Univ. in St. Louis, 1 Brookings Dr., St. Louis, MO 63130-4862, (314)935-3860

Soc. of Medical Banking Excellence - Address unknown since 2010.

Soc. of Medical Consultants to the Armed Forces [15512], 5 Southern Way, Fredericksburg, VA 22406, (540)361-2587

Soc. for Medical Decision Making [15434], 390 Amwell Rd., Ste. 402, Hillsborough, NJ 08844, (908)359-1184

Soc. of Medical Friends of Wine [22200], Susan Guerguy, Exec. Sec., 511 Jones Pl., Walnut Creek, CA 94597-3141, (925)933-9691

Soc. of Medical Informatics of Bosnia and Herzegovina [IO], Sarajevo, Bosnia-Hercegovina

Soc. of Medical Lab. Technologists of South Africa [IO], Roggebaai, Republic of South Africa

Soc. for Medicinal Plant Res. [IO], Neunkirchen am Brand, Germany

Soc. for Medicines Res. [IO], Leicester, United Kingdom

Soc. for Medieval Archaeology [IO], Leeds, United Kingdom

Soc. for Medieval and Renaissance Philosophy [10080], Univ. of Missouri, St. Louis, Dept. of Philosophy, 599 Lucas Hall, MC 73, 1 Univ. Blvd., St. Louis, MO 63121-4400, (314)516-5439

Soc. for Melanoma Res. [13983], Site Solutions Worldwide, PO Box 215, Burnt Hills, NY 12027, (866)374-6338

Soc. for Melanoma Res. [13983], Site Solutions Worldwide, PO Box 215, Burnt Hills, NY 12027, (866)374-6338

Soc. for Menstrual Cycle Res. [15895], Eastern Washington Univ., 229 Communications Bldg., Cheney, WA 99004

Soc. of Metaphysicians [IO], Hastings, United Kingdom

Soc. of Mexican Amer. Engineers and Scientists [6827], 2437 Bay Area Blvd., No. 100, Houston, TX 77058, (281)557-3677

Soc. of Midland Authors [3713], PO Box 10419, Chicago, IL 60610

Soc. for Military History [10098], Virginia Military Inst., George C. Marshall Lib., Lexington, VA 24450, (540)464-7468

Soc. of Military Orthopaedic Surgeons [15513], 110 W Rd., Ste. 227, Towson, MD 21204, (866)494-1778

Soc. of Military Otolaryngologists [★15514]

Soc. of Military Otolaryngologists - Head and Neck Surgeons [15514], PO Box 923, Converse, TX 78109, (210)945-9006

Soc. of Military Widows [20709], Cathy Mcgraw, Treas., 4374 Via San Jose, Riverside, CA 92504-2449, (800)842-3451

Soc. of Mineral Analysts [7124], PO Box 404, Lewiston, ID 83501, (208)799-3286

Soc. of Mining Engineers [★7128]

Soc. for Mining, Metallurgy, and Exploration [7128], 12999 E Adam Aircraft Cir., Englewood, CO 80112, (303)948-4200

Soc. for Mining, Metallurgy, Rsrc. and Environmental Tech. [IO], Clausthal-Zellerfeld, Germany

Soc. of Missionaries of Africa [19499], 1624 21st St. NW, Washington, DC 20009-1003, (202)232-5154

Soc. for Modeling and Simulation Intl. [6471], 2598 Fortune Way, Ste. I, Vista, CA 92081, (858)277-3888

Soc. for Modeling and Simulation Intl. [6471], 2598 Fortune Way, Ste. I, Vista, CA 92081, (858)277-3888

Soc. of Modern Grammar [IO], Taegu City, Republic of Korea

Soc. for Molecular Biology and Evolution [6320], Prof. Manyuan Long, PhD, Sec., Univ. of Chicago, Dept. of Ecology and Evolution, 1101 E 57th St., Chicago, IL 60637, (773)702-0557

Soc. for Molecular Imaging [15435], PO Box 293878, Kerrville, TX 78029-3878, (830)257-0112

Soc. for Molecular Imaging [15435], PO Box 293878, Kerrville, TX 78029-3878, (830)257-0112

Soc. of Mortgage Consultants [★427]

Soc. of Motion Picture Art Directors [★9595]

Soc. of Motion Picture and TV Art Directors [★9595]

Soc. of Motion Picture and TV Engineers [6828], 3 Barker Ave., 5th Fl., White Plains, NY 10601, (914)761-1100

Soc. of Motor Mfrs. and Traders [IO], London, United Kingdom

Soc. for Mucopolysaccharide Diseases [IO], Amersham, United Kingdom

Soc. for Mucosal Immunology [15112], 11950 W Lake Park Dr., Ste. 320, Milwaukee, WI 53224-3049, (414)359-1650

Soc. for Mucosal Immunology [15112], 11950 W Lake Park Dr., Ste. 320, Milwaukee, WI 53224-3049, (414)359-1650

Soc. of Municipal Arborists [4414], PO Box 641, Watkinsville, GA 30677, (706)769-7412

Soc. for Muscular Dystrophy Info. Intl. [IO], Bridgewater, NS, Canada

Soc. of Museum Archaeologists [IO], Oxford, United Kingdom

Soc. for Music Anal. [IO], Lancaster, United Kingdom

Soc. for Music Perception and Cognition [10294], Scott Lipscomb, Treas., Univ. of Minnesota School of Music, 148 Ferguson Hall, 2106 4th St. S, Minneapolis, MN 55455, (612)624-2843

Soc. for Music Teacher Educ. [8669], MENC: Natl. Assn. for Music Educ., 1806 Robert Fulton Dr., Reston, VA 20191, (703)860-4000

Soc. for Music Theory [10295], Univ. of Chicago, Dept. of Music, 1010 E 59th St., Chicago, IL 60637, (773)834-3821

Soc. for Music Theory [10295], Univ. of Chicago, Dept. of Music, 1010 E 59th St., Chicago, IL 60637, (773)834-3821

Soc. for Name Stud. in Britain and Ireland [IO], Stow-on-the-Wold, United Kingdom

Soc. for Natal Effects on Hea. in Adult Life [IO], Mumbai, India

Soc. of Natl. Assn. Publications [★263]

Soc. for Natural Philosophy [7078], Thomas J. Pence, Treas., Michigan Sta. Univ., Dept. of Mech. Engg., 2452 Engg. Bldg., East Lansing, MI 48824-1226

Soc. for the Nature Protection of Croatia [IO], Zagreb, Croatia

Soc. for Nautical Res. [IO], Hailsham, United Kingdom

Soc. of Naval Architects and Marine Engineers [7149], 601 Pavonia Ave., Jersey City, NJ 07306, (201)798-4800

Soc. of Nematologists [7152], PO Box 311, Marceline, MO 64658, (660)256-3331

Soc. for Neonatology and Paediatric Intensive Care [IO], Lubeck, Germany

Soc. of Netherlands Literature [IO], Leiden, Netherlands

Soc. for Neuroeconomics [6634], Samanta Shaw, 4 Washington Pl., Rm. 809, New York, NY 10003

Soc. of NeuroInterventional Surgery [16545], 3975 Fair Ridge Dr., Ste. 200 N, Fairfax, VA 22033, (703)691-2272

Soc. of Neurological Surgeons [15686], Kim J. Burchiel, MD, Sec., 3303 SW Bond Ave., Portland, OR 97239, (503)494-9635

Soc. for Neuronal Regulation [★15663]

Soc. for Neuronal Regulation [★15663]

Soc. for Neuroscience [7160], 1121 14th St. NW, Ste. 1010, Washington, DC 20005, (202)962-4000

Soc. for Neuroscience in Anesthesiology and Critical Care [15687], 520 N Northwest Hwy., Park Ridge, IL 60068-2573, (847)825-5586

Soc. of Neurosurgical Anesthesia and Critical Care [★15687]

Soc. for New Communications Res. [6439], 266 Hillsdale Ave., San Jose, CA 95136, (408)266-9658

Soc. for New Language Stud. - Address unknown since 2010.

Soc. for New Testament Stud. [IO], Amsterdam, Netherlands

Soc. for News Design [2873], 424 E Central Blvd., Ste. 406, Orlando, FL 32801, (407)420-7748

Soc. for News Design [2873], 424 E Central Blvd., Ste. 406, Orlando, FL 32801, (407)420-7748

Soc. of Newspaper Design [★2873]

Soc. of Newspaper Design [★2873]

Soc. of Non-Invasive Vascular Tech. [★16969]

Soc. for Nondestructive Testing [★7555]

Soc. for Nonprofit Organizations [267], 5820 Canton Center Rd., Ste. 165, Canton, MI 48187-2683, (734)451-3582

Soc. of North Amer. Goldsmiths [21468], 540 Oak St., Ste. A, Eugene, OR 97401, (541)345-5689

Soc. for Northwestern Vertebrate Biology [7144], Tiffany Sacra Garcia, Treas., Oregon State Univ., Dept. of Fisheries and Wildlife, 104 Nash Hall, Corvallis, OR 97333

Soc. of Nuclear Medicine [15696], 1850 Samuel Morse Dr., Reston, VA 20190-5316, (703)708-9000

Soc. of Nuclear Medicine Technologist Sect. [15697], 1850 Samuel Morse Dr., Reston, VA 20190, (703)708-9000

Soc. for Nutrition Educ. [15844], 9100 Purdue Rd., Ste. 200, Indianapolis, IN 46268, (317)328-4627

Soc. for Obstetric Anesthesia and Perinatology [16160], 520 N Northwest Hwy., Park Ridge, IL 60068-2573, (847)825-6472

Soc. of Obstetricians and Gynaecologists of Canada [IO], Ottawa, ON, Canada

Soc. for Occupational and Environmental Hea. [15909], 6728 Old McLean Village Dr., McLean, VA 22101, (703)556-9222

Soc. of Occupational Medicine [IO], London, United Kingdom

Soc. for Office-Based Surgery [★16789]

Soc. for Old Testament Stud. [IO], Oxford, United Kingdom

Soc. of Operations Engineers [IO], London, United Kingdom

The Soc. for Organic Petrology [7239], Paul Hackley, Membership Chm., U.S. Geological Survey, 956 Natl. Ctr., Reston, VA 20192, (703)648-6458

The Soc. for Organic Petrology [7239], Paul Hackley, Membership Chm., U.S. Geological Survey, 956 Natl. Ctr., Reston, VA 20192, (703)648-6458

Soc. for Organizational Learning [2598], PO Box 425005, Cambridge, MA 02142, (617)300-9500

Soc. for Organizational Learning [2598], PO Box 425005, Cambridge, MA 02142, (617)300-9500

Soc. of Ornamental Turners [IO], London, United Kingdom

Soc. for Orphaned Armenian Relief [12892], 1060 1st Ave., Ste. 400, King of Prussia, PA 19406, (610)213-3452

Soc. for Orphaned Armenian Relief [12892], 1060 1st Ave., Ste. 400, King of Prussia, PA 19406, (610)213-3452

Soc. of Ortho-Bionomy Intl. [13709], 5335 N Tacoma St., Ste. 21G, Indianapolis, IN 46220, (317)536-0064

Soc. of Ortho-Bionomy Intl. [13709], 5335 N Tacoma St., Ste. 21G, Indianapolis, IN 46220, (317)536-0064

Soc. of Orthodox Youth Organizations [★19646]

Soc. for Orthomolecular Hea. Medicine [13710], 2698 Pacific Ave., San Francisco, CA 94115, (415)922-6462

Soc. of Otorhinolaryngology and Head/Neck Nurses [15799], 207 Downing St., New Smyrna Beach, FL 32168, (386)428-1695

Soc. of Our Lady of the Most Holy Trinity [19500], PO Box 152, 3816 County Rd. 61, Robstown, TX 78380, (361)387-2754

Soc. for Pacific Coast Native Iris [21823], 7417 92nd Pl. SE, Mercer Island, WA 98040, (206)232-7745

Soc. for Pacific Coast Native Iris [21823], 7417 92nd Pl. SE, Mercer Island, WA 98040, (206)232-7745

Soc. of Paper Money Collectors [21993], PO Box 117060, Carrollton, TX 75011

Soc. of Park and Recreation Educators [5882], Natl. Recreational and Park Assn., 22377 Belmont Ridge Rd., Ashburn, VA 20148-4501, (800)626-4501

Soc. of Parrot Breeders and Exhibitors [21229], PO Box 546, Hollis, NH 03049, (603)878-3435

Soc. for Participatory Medicine [14829], PO Box 1183, Newburyport, MA 01950

Reference to "IO" in place of a book number signifies that the association may be found in the 50th edition of International Organizations.

Soc. for Participatory Res. in Asia [IO], New Delhi, India

Soc. of Patient Representatives [★15243]

Soc. for Pediatric Anesthesia [13755], 2209 Dickens Rd., Richmond, VA 23230-2005, (804)282-9780

Soc. for Pediatric Dermatology [14340], 8365 Keystone Crossing, Ste. 107, Indianapolis, IN 46240, (317)202-0224

Soc. of Pediatric Nurses [15800], 7044 S 13th St., Oak Creek, WI 53154, (414)908-4950

Soc. for Pediatric Pathology [16133], U.S. and Canada Acad. of Pathology, 3643 Walton Way Extension, Augusta, GA 30909, (706)364-3375

Soc. for Pediatric Psychology [16425], Karen Roberts, Admin. Off./Database Mgr., PO Box 3968, Lawrence, KS 66046

Soc. for Pediatric Psychology [16425], Karen Roberts, Admin. Off./Database Mgr., PO Box 3968, Lawrence, KS 66046

Soc. for Pediatric Radiology [16546], 1891 Preston White Dr., Reston, VA 20191, (703)648-0680

Soc. for Pediatric Res. [16156], 3400 Res. Forest Dr., Ste. B-7, The Woodlands, TX 77381, (281)419-0052

Soc. for Pediatric Urology [16952], 900 Cummings Ctr., Ste. 4550, Beverly, MA 01915, (978)927-8330

Soc. for Pelvic Surgeons - Defunct.

Soc. of Pension Consultants [IO], London, United Kingdom

Soc. for Pentecostal Stud. [20155], 1435 N Glenstone Ave., Springfield, MO 65802, (417)268-1084

Soc. of Perinatal Obstetricians [★16159]

Soc. for Peripheral Vascular Nursing [★15803]

Soc. of Permanent Cosmetic Professionals [976], 69 N Broadway, Des Plaines, IL 60016, (847)635-1330

Soc. for Personal Growth [IO], Edmonton, AB, Canada

Soc. for Personality Assessment [16426], 6109H Arlington Blvd., Falls Church, VA 22044, (703)534-4772

Soc. for Personality Assessment [16426], 6109H Arlington Blvd., Falls Church, VA 22044, (703)534-4772

Soc. for Personality and Social Psychology [7313], Christie Marvin, Exec. Asst., Cornell Univ., Dept. of Psychology, 239 Uris Hall, Ithaca, NY 14853, (607)254-5416

Soc. for Personnel Admin. [★1153]

Soc. for Personnel Admin. [★1153]

Soc. of Petroleum Engineers [7240], 222 Palisades Creek Dr., PO Box 833836, Richardson, TX 75083-3836, (972)952-9393

Soc. of Petroleum Engineers [7240], 222 Palisades Creek Dr., PO Box 833836, Richardson, TX 75083-3836, (972)952-9393

Soc. of Petroleum Engineers - Iran Sect. [IO], Tehran, Iran

Soc. of Petroleum Engineers - London Off. [IO], London, United Kingdom

Soc. of Petroleum Evaluation Engineers [7241], 5535 Memorial Dr., No. F654, Houston, TX 77007, (713)651-1639

Soc. of Petroleum Geophysicists [★6929]

Soc. of Petrophysicists and Well Log Analysts [7242], 8866 Gulf Fwy., Ste. 320, Houston, TX 77017, (713)947-8727

Soc. of Phantom Friends [9451], 40 S Vine St., Mount Carmel, PA 17851

Soc. of Phantom Friends [9451], 40 S Vine St., Mount Carmel, PA 17851

Soc. of Pharmaceutical and Biotech Trainers [3168], 4423 Pheasant Ridge Rd., Ste. 100, Roanoke, VA 24014-5274, (540)725-3859

Soc. of Pharmaceutical Medicine [IO], London, United Kingdom

Soc. for Phenomenology and Existential Philosophy [10422], Emory Univ., Dept. of Philosophy, 214 Bowden Hall, Atlanta, GA 30322

Soc. for the Philosophical Stud. of Genocide and the Holocaust [10423], Prof. James R. Watson, Pres., Loyola Univ. - New Orleans, Dept. of Philosophy, New Orleans, LA 70118

Soc. for the Philosophical Stud. of Genocide and the Holocaust [10423], Prof. James R. Watson, Pres., Loyola Univ. - New Orleans, Dept. of Philosophy, New Orleans, LA 70118

Soc. for the Philosophical Stud. of Marxism [★10070]

Soc. for Philosophy in the Contemporary World [10424], PO Box 7147, Charlottesville, VA 22906-7147, (434)220-3300

Soc. for Philosophy in the Contemporary World [10424], PO Box 7147, Charlottesville, VA 22906-7147, (434)220-3300

Soc. for Philosophy and Psychology [10425], Thomas W. Polger, Sec.-Treas., Univ. of Cincinnati, Dept. of Philosophy, 206 McMicken Hall, Cincinnati, OH 45221, (513)556-6328

Soc. for Philosophy and Tech. [10426], Philosophy Documentation Center, PO Box 7147, Charlottesville, VA 22906-7147, (434)220-3300

Soc. for Philosophy and Tech. [10426], Philosophy Documentation Center, PO Box 7147, Charlottesville, VA 22906-7147, (434)220-3300

Soc. of Photo-Optical Instrumentation Engineers [★7190]

Soc. of Photo-Optical Instrumentation Engineers [★7190]

Soc. of Photo-Technologists [2735], 11112 S Spotted Rd., Cheney, WA 99004-9038, (509)624-9621

Soc. of Photo-Technologists [2735], 11112 S Spotted Rd., Cheney, WA 99004-9038, (509)624-9621

Soc. for Photographic Educ. [8713], 2530 Superior Ave., No. 403, Cleveland, OH 44114, (216)622-2733

Soc. of Photographic Engg. [★7261]

Soc. of Photographic Instrumentation Engineers [★7190]

Soc. of Photographic Instrumentation Engineers [★7190]

Soc. of Photographic Sci. and Tech. of Japan [IO], Tokyo, Japan

Soc. of Photographic Scientists and Engg. [★7261]

Soc. for Physical Regulation in Biology and Medicine [6277], Columbia Univ., 1210 Amsterdam Ave., New York, NY 10027

Soc. for Physical Regulation in Biology and Medicine [6277], Columbia Univ., 1210 Amsterdam Ave., New York, NY 10027

Soc. for Physician Assistants in Pediatrics [16243], 1212 Turncreek Ln., Schertz, TX 78154, (210)722-7622

Soc. of Physician Assistants in Rheumatology [16626], PO Box 82501, Tampa, FL 33682, (813)988-7795

Soc. of Physicists of Macedonia [IO], Skopje, Macedonia

Soc. of Physics Students [7273], Amer. Inst. of Physics, 1 Physics Ellipse, College Park, MD 20740-3843, (301)209-3007

Soc. of Pi Kappa Lambda [23606], Capital Univ., Conservatory of Music, 1 Coll. and Main, Columbus, OH 43209, (614)236-7211

Soc. of Piping Engineers and Designers [6829], 9211 West Rd., Ste. 143-219, Houston, TX 77064, (832)286-3404

Soc. for Plant Morphology and Physiology [★6351]

Soc. for Plastic Surgical Skin Care Specialists [14186], 11262 Monarch St., Garden Grove, CA 92841, (562)799-0466

Soc. of Plastics Engineers [7278], 13 Church Hill Rd., PO Box 403, Newtown, CT 06470, (203)775-0471

Soc. of Plastics Engineers [7278], 13 Church Hill Rd., PO Box 403, Newtown, CT 06470, (203)775-0471

Soc. of the Plastics Indus. [2777], 1667 K St. NW, Ste. 1000, Washington, DC 20006, (202)974-5200

Soc. of Ploughmen [IO], Doncaster, United Kingdom

Soc. for Police and Criminal Psychology [16427], 750 Veterans Memorial Hwy., Hauppauge, NY 11788, (631)724-5522

Soc. of Polish-American Travel Agents [3576], Mrs. Honorata Pierwola, Pres., 36 Main St., South River, NJ 08882, (732)390-1750

Soc. for Polish Philately [IO], London, United Kingdom

Soc. of Polish Town Planners [IO], Warsaw, Poland

Soc. for Popular Astronomy [IO], Nottingham, United Kingdom

Soc. of Population Ecology [IO], Kyoto, Japan

Soc. for Post-Medieval Archaeology [IO], London, United Kingdom

Soc. of the Postal History of Eretz Israel [IO], Jerusalem, Israel

Soc. of Practising Veterinary Surgeons [IO], Warwick, United Kingdom

Soc. of Prayer for World Peace [★18305]

Soc. of Prayer for World Peace [★18305]

Soc. for the Preservation and Advancement of the Harmonica [10296], PO Box 865, Troy, MI 48099-0865, (586)771-4866

Soc. for the Preservation and Advancement of the Harmonica [10296], PO Box 865, Troy, MI 48099-0865, (586)771-4866

Soc. for the Preservation of Afghanistan's Cultural Heritage [IO], Kabul, Afghanistan

Soc. for the Preservation of Amer. Business History - Defunct.

Soc. for the Preservation and Appreciation of Antique Motor Fire Apparatus in Am. [21710], Barbara Connors, Membership Sec., 5420 S Kedvale Ave., Chicago, IL 60632-4232

Soc. for the Preservation and Appreciation of Old Time Music and Dancing [★8782]

Soc. for the Preservation and Encouragement of Barber Shop Quartet Singing in Am. [10297], 110 Seventh Ave. N, Nashville, TN 37203-3704, (615)823-3993

Soc. for the Preservation of English Language and Literature [8136], PO Box 321, Braselton, GA 30517, (770)586-0184

Soc. for the Preservation of Film Music [★10196]

Soc. for the Preservation of the Greek Heritage [9650], 5125 MacArthur Blvd. NW, Ste. 11B, Washington, DC 20016, (202)363-4337

Soc. for the Preservation of Natural History Collections [9728], PO Box 526, New York, NY 10044-0526, (212)769-5864

Soc. for the Preservation of New England Antiquities [★9695]

Soc. for the Preservation of Old Mills [9729], Robert Lundegard, PO Box 422, Great Falls, VA 22066, (703)759-2626

Soc. for the Preservation of Poultry Antiquities [4815], 1057 Nick Watts Rd., Lugoff, SC 29078

Soc. for the Preservation and Propagation of Barber Shop Quartet Singing in the U.S. [★10297]

Soc. for the Preservation of Variety Arts - Defunct.

Soc. to Preserve and Encourage Radio Drama, Variety and Comedy [22122], PO Box 669, Manhattan Beach, CA 90266, (310)219-0053

Soc. for Prevention of Human Infertility [16598], 877 Park Ave., New York, NY 10021, (212)744-5500

Soc. for Prevention of Human Infertility [16598], 877 Park Ave., New York, NY 10021, (212)744-5500

Soc. for Prevention Res. [16756], 11240 Waples Mill Rd., Ste. 200, Fairfax, VA 22030, (703)934-4850

Soc. for Prevention Res. [16756], 11240 Waples Mill Rd., Ste. 200, Fairfax, VA 22030, (703)934-4850

Soc. of Procurement Officers in Local Govt. [IO], Leicester, United Kingdom

Soc. of Professional Accountants [IO], Great Missenden, United Kingdom

Soc. of Professional Accountants of Canada [IO], Toronto, ON, Canada

Soc. of Professional Archaeologists [★6175]

Soc. of Professional Audio Recording Services [3053], 441 W 53rd St., New York, NY 10019, (212)765-7500

Soc. of Professional Audio Recording Studios [★3053]

Soc. of Professional Benefit Administrators [1133], Two Wisconsin Cir., Ste. 670, Chevy Chase, MD 20815-7003, (301)718-7722

Soc. of Professional Business Consultants - Defunct.

Soc. of Professional Drivers - Address unknown since 2011.

Soc. of Professional Engineers [IO], Northampton, United Kingdom

Soc. of Professional Investigators [5610], 233 Broadway, Ste. 2201, New York, NY 10279, (646)584-9081

Soc. of Professional Journalists [2874], Eugene S. Pulliam Natl. Journalism Center, 3909 N Meridian St., Indianapolis, IN 46208, (317)927-8000

A star before a book entry number signifies that the name is not listed separately, but is mentioned within the entry.

Soc. of Professional Journalists, Sigma Delta Chi [★2874]

Soc. of Professional Mgt. Consultants [★2288]

Soc. of Professional Rope Access Technicians [1868], 994 Old Eagle School Rd., Ste. 1019, Wayne, PA 19087-1866, (610)971-4850

Soc. of Professional Well Log Analysts [★7242]

Soc. of Professional Wireless Pioneers [★3421]

Soc. of Professional Women in Petroleum [2671], PO Box 420957, Houston, TX 77242

Soc. of Professional Women in Petroleum [2671], PO Box 420957, Houston, TX 77242

Soc. of Professors of Child and Adolescent Psychiatry [16346], 3615 Wisconsin Ave. NW, Washington, DC 20010, (202)476-3922

Soc. of Professors of Child Psychiatry [★16346]

Soc. of Professors of Educ. [8061], Univ. of West Georgia, Coll. of Educ., Dept. of Educational Leadership and Professional Stud., 1600 Maple St., Carrollton, GA 30118-5160, (770)836-4426

Soc. for Progressive Supranuclear Palsy [★14387]

Soc. for Projective Techniques and Personality Assessment [★16426]

Soc. for Projective Techniques and Personality Assessment [★16426]

Soc. for Projective Techniques and Rorschach Inst. [★16426]

Soc. for Projective Techniques and Rorschach Inst. [★16426]

Soc. for Promoting Christian Knowledge [IO], London, United Kingdom

Soc. for Promoting and Encouraging Arts and Knowledge of the Church [19717], 805 County Rd. 102, Eureka Springs, AR 72632-9705, (479)253-9701

Soc. Promoting Environmental Conservation [IO], Vancouver, BC, Canada

Soc. for the Promotion of African, Asian, and Latin Amer. Literature [IO], Frankfurt, Germany

Soc. for the Promotion of Byzantine Stud. [IO], Birmingham, United Kingdom

Soc. for the Promotion of Educ. and Res. [IO], Belize City, Belize

Soc. for the Promotion of Hellenic Stud. [IO], London, United Kingdom

Soc. for the Promotion of Japanese Animation [9205], 1733 S Douglass Rd., Ste. F, Anaheim, CA 92806, (714)937-2994

Soc. for the Promotion of Roman Stud. [IO], London, United Kingdom

Soc. for the Promotion of Sci. and Scholarship [2963], 4139 El Camino Way, Palo Alto, CA 94306, (650)906-0714

Soc. for Promotion of Youth and Masses [IO], New Delhi, India

Soc. for the Propagation of the Faith [IO], Toronto, ON, Canada

Soc. for the Propagation of the Faith [19501], 70 W 36th St., 8th Fl., New York, NY 10018, (212)563-8700

Soc. of Prospective Medicine - Defunct.

Soc. for Protecting the Rights of the Child [IO], Tehran, Iran

Soc. for the Protection of Ancient Buildings [IO], London, United Kingdom

Soc. for the Protection of Animals Abroad [IO], London, United Kingdom

Soc. for the Protection of Nature in Israel [IO], Tel Aviv, Israel

Soc. for Protection of Nature in Lebanon [IO], Beirut, Lebanon

Soc. for the Protection for the Rights of the Child [IO], Islamabad, Pakistan

Soc. for the Protection of the Socially Disadvantaged Individuals [IO], Tehran, Iran

Soc. for the Protection of Unborn Children [IO], London, United Kingdom

Soc. for the Protection of Unborn Children - Scotland [IO], Glasgow, United Kingdom

Soc. of Protozoologists [★7637]

Soc. for the Provision of Educ. in Rural Australia [IO], Perth, Australia

Soc. for Psychical Res. [IO], London, United Kingdom

Soc. for Psychological Anthropology [7314], PO Box 951553, Los Angeles, CA 90095-1553, (310)825-3366

Soc. for Psychological Assistance - Croatia [IO], Zagreb, Croatia

Soc. for Psychological Hypnosis [16380], Division Services Office, 750 First St NE, Washington, DC 20002-4242

Soc. for the Psychological Stud. of Ethnic Minority Issues [16428], Adelphi Univ., 1 South Ave., Garden City, NY 11530, (516)877-4185

Soc. for the Psychological Stud. of Lesbian, Gay, Bisexual and Transgender Issues [16429], Amer. Psychological Assn., 750 1st St. NE, Washington, DC 20002

Soc. for the Psychological Stud. of Lesbian and Gay Issues [★16429]

Soc. for the Psychological Stud. of Men and Masculinity [16430], Am. Psychological Associates, 750 1st St. NE, Washington, DC 20002-4242

Soc. for the Psychological Stud. of Social Issues [16431], 208 I St. NE, Washington, DC 20002-4340, (202)675-6956

Soc. for Psychophysiological Res. [16432], 2424 Amer. Ln., Madison, WI 53704, (608)443-2472

Soc. for Psychophysiological Res. [16432], 2424 Amer. Ln., Madison, WI 53704, (608)443-2472

Soc. of Psychosomatic Obstetrics and Gynaecology, Brazil [IO], Sao Paulo, Brazil

Soc. for Psychotherapy Res. [16441], Univ. of Louisville, 401 E Chestnut St., Ste. 610, Louisville, KY 40202, (502)852-1937

Soc. for Public Hea. Educ. [16498], 10 G St. NE, Ste. 605, Washington, DC 20002-4242, (202)408-9804

Soc. for Public Hea. Educ. [16498], 10 G St. NE, Ste. 605, Washington, DC 20002-4242, (202)408-9804

Soc. of Public Hea. Educators [★16498]

Soc. of Public Hea. Educators [★16498]

Soc. for the Publication of Danish Music [IO], Copenhagen, Denmark

Soc. of Publication Designers [1640], 27 Union Sq. W, Ste. 207, New York, NY 10003, (212)223-3332

Soc. of Publishers in Asia [IO], Hong Kong, People's Republic of China

Soc. of Quality Assurance [2979], 154 Hansen Rd., Ste. 201, Charlottesville, VA 22911, (434)297-4772

Soc. of Quality Assurance [2979], 154 Hansen Rd., Ste. 201, Charlottesville, VA 22911, (434)297-4772

Soc. for Quantitative Analyses of Behavior [6266], 234 Huron Ave., Cambridge, MA 02138, (617)497-5270

Soc. of Quantitative Analysts [1329], PO Box 6, Rutledge, MO 63563, (800)918-7930

Soc. for Radiation Oncology Administrators [16547], 5272 River Rd., Ste. 630, Bethesda, MD 20816, (301)718-6510

Soc. of Radiographers of South Africa [IO], Cape Town, Republic of South Africa

Soc. for Radiological Protection [IO], London, United Kingdom

Soc. of Radiologists in Ultrasound [16548], 1891 Preston White Dr., Reston, VA 20191-4326, (703)858-9210

Soc. for Range Mgt. [4863], 10030 W 27th Ave., Wheat Ridge, CO 80215-6601, (303)986-3309

Soc. of Real Estate Appraisers [★225]

Soc. of Recorder Players [IO], Guildford, United Kingdom

Soc. of Recreation Executives - Address unknown since 2010.

Soc. for Reformation Res. [10506], Luther Coll., Dept. of History, 700 Coll. Dr., Decorah, IA 52101-1045

Soc. of Registered Professional Adjusters [2041], PO Box 876, Downers Grove, IL 60515, (630)515-9340

Soc. of Registered Professional Adjusters [2041], PO Box 876, Downers Grove, IL 60515, (630)515-9340

Soc. of Rehabilitation and Crime Prevention [IO], Hong Kong, People's Republic of China

Soc. for the Rehabilitation of the Facially Disfigured [★14201]

Soc. of Reliability Engineers [6830], Dr. J.A. Nachlas, Virginia Tech, 250 Durham Hall, Blacksburg, VA 24061-0118, (540)231-5357

Soc. for Religion in Higher Educ. [★19687]

Soc. for Renaissance Stud. [IO], Nottingham, United Kingdom

Soc. for the Renewal of the Sacred Liturgy [★19378]

Soc. for the Renewal of the Sacred Liturgy [★19378]

Soc. for Reproduction Rights of Authors, Composers and Publishers in Canada [IO], Montreal, QC, Canada

Soc. for Reproductive Biology [IO], Balnarring, Australia

Soc. for Reproductive Endocrinology and Infertility [16599], Amer. Soc. for Reproductive Medicine, 1209 Montgomery Hwy., Birmingham, AL 35216-2809, (205)978-5000

Soc. of Reproductive Surgeons [16600], 1209 Montgomery Hwy., Birmingham, AL 35216-2809, (205)978-5000

Soc. of Res. Administrators [7337], 1901 N Moore St., Ste. 1004, Arlington, VA 22209, (703)741-0140

Soc. for Res. on Adolescence [13557], 2950 S State St., Ste. 401, Ann Arbor, MI 48104, (734)926-0700

Soc. for Res. in Child Development [11168], 2950 S State St., Ste. 401, Ann Arbor, MI 48104, (734)926-0600

Soc. for Res. in Child Development [11168], 2950 S State St., Ste. 401, Ann Arbor, MI 48104, (734)926-0600

Soc. for Res. and Educ. in Primary Care Internal Medicine [★15137]

Soc. for Res. into Higher Educ. [IO], London, United Kingdom

Soc. for Res. into Hydrocephalus and Spina Bifida [IO], Middlesborough, United Kingdom

Soc. for Res. on Identity Formation [8698], Florida Intl. Univ., Dept. of Psychology, 11200 SW 8th St., Univ. Park, DM 269-F, Miami, FL 33199, (305)348-3941

Soc. for Res. on Identity Formation [8698], Florida Intl. Univ., Dept. of Psychology, 11200 SW 8th St., Univ. Park, DM 269-F, Miami, FL 33199, (305)348-3941

Soc. for Res. and Initiatives for Sustainable Technologies and Institution [IO], Ahmedabad, India

Soc. for Res. on Meteorites [★6928]

Soc. for Res. on Nicotine and Tobacco [4959], 2424 Amer. Ln., Madison, WI 53704, (608)443-2462

Soc. for the Responsible Use of Resources in Agriculture and on the Land [IO], Fordingbridge, United Kingdom

Soc. of Rheology [7340], Univ. of Wisconsin, Rheology Res. Ctr., Madison, WI 53706, (608)262-7473

Soc. for Risk Anal. [2042], 1313 Dolley Madison Blvd., Ste. 402, McLean, VA 22101, (703)790-1745

Soc. of Risk Mgt. Consultants [2043], 330 S Executive Dr., Ste. 301, Brookfield, WI 53005-4275, (800)765-SRMC

Soc. of Roller Skating Teachers of Am. - Address unknown since 2011.

Soc. for Romanian Stud. [10514], Paul E. Michelson, Sec., Huntington Coll., Dept. of History, Huntington, IN 46750, (260)359-4242

Soc. for Romanian Stud. [10514], Paul E. Michelson, Sec., Huntington Coll., Dept. of History, Huntington, IN 46750, (260)359-4242

Soc. for Rousseau Stud. [★9411]

Soc. for Rousseau Stud. [★9411]

Soc. of Rubber Indus., Japan [IO], Tokyo, Japan

Soc. of Rural Physicians of Canada [IO], Shawville, QC, Canada

Soc. of St. Andrew [12293], 3383 Sweet Hollow Rd., Big Island, VA 24526, (434)299-5956

Soc. of Saint Mary Magdalene [19502], PO Box 28423, St. Petersburg, FL 33709

Soc. of St. Monica - Defunct.

Soc. of Saint Peter Apostle [19503], 70 W 36th St., 8th Fl., New York, NY 10018, (212)563-8700

Soc. of St. Peter the Apostle for Native Clergy [★19503]

Soc. of Saint Pius X [IO], Menzingen, Switzerland

Soc. of Saint Stephen - Address unknown since 2011.

Soc. of Saint Vincent de Paul - Bangladesh [IO], Dhaka, Bangladesh

---

Reference to "IO" in place of a book number signifies that the association may be found in the 50th edition of International Organizations.

Soc. of Saint Vincent de Paul - Botswana [IO], Serowe, Botswana

Soc. of Saint Vincent de Paul - Cameroon [IO], Limbe, Cameroon

Soc. of Saint Vincent de Paul - Canada [IO], Ottawa, ON, Canada

Soc. of Saint Vincent de Paul - Central African Republic [IO], Bangui, Central African Republic

Soc. of Saint Vincent de Paul Central Coun. - Hong Kong [IO], Hong Kong, People's Republic of China

Soc. of St. Vincent de Paul Coun. of the U.S. [13204], 58 Progress Pkwy., Maryland Heights, MO 63043-3706, (314)576-3993

Soc. of Saint Vincent de Paul - Egypt [IO], Cairo, Egypt

Soc. of Saint Vincent de Paul - El Salvador [IO], San Salvador, El Salvador

Soc. of Saint Vincent de Paul - Ethiopia [IO], Addis Ababa, Ethiopia

Soc. of Saint Vincent de Paul - India [IO], Mumbai, India

Soc. of Saint Vincent de Paul - Intl. [IO], Paris, France

Soc. of Saint Vincent de Paul - Ireland [IO], Dublin, Ireland

Soc. of Saint Vincent de Paul - Jamaica [IO], Kingston, Jamaica

Soc. of Saint Vincent de Paul - Korea [IO], Seoul, Republic of Korea

Soc. of Saint Vincent de Paul - Liberia [IO], Monrovia, Liberia

Soc. of Saint Vincent de Paul - Lithuania [IO], Vilnius, Lithuania

Soc. of Saint Vincent de Paul - Mozambique [IO], Maputo, Mozambique

Soc. of Saint Vincent de Paul - Namibia [IO], Windhoek, Namibia

Soc. of Saint Vincent de Paul - New Zealand [IO], Wellington, New Zealand

Soc. of Saint Vincent de Paul - Nigeria [IO], Ibadan, Nigeria

Soc. of Saint Vincent de Paul - Pakistan [IO], Karachi, Pakistan

Soc. of Saint Vincent de Paul - Peru [IO], Lima, Peru

Soc. of Saint Vincent de Paul - Philippines [IO], Manila, Philippines

Soc. of Saint Vincent de Paul - Rwanda [IO], Kigali, Rwanda

Soc. of Saint Vincent de Paul - Scotland [IO], Glasgow, United Kingdom

Soc. of Saint Vincent de Paul - Slovenia [IO], Miren, Slovenia

Soc. of Saint Vincent de Paul - South Africa [IO], Overport, Republic of South Africa

Soc. of Saint Vincent de Paul - Sri Lanka [IO], Negombo, Sri Lanka

Soc. of Saint Vincent de Paul - Sudan [IO], Khartoum, Sudan

Soc. of Saint Vincent de Paul - Trinidad and Tobago [IO], Port of Spain, Trinidad and Tobago

Soc. of Sales and Marketing [IO], London, United Kingdom

Soc. of Satellite Professionals [★3419]

Soc. of Satellite Professionals [★3419]

Soc. of Satellite Professionals Intl. [3419], The New York Info. Tech. Center, 55 Broad St., 14th Fl., New York, NY 10004, (212)809-5199

Soc. of Satellite Professionals Intl. [3419], The New York Info. Tech. Center, 55 Broad St., 14th Fl., New York, NY 10004, (212)809-5199

Soc. of Savings and Loan Controllers [★2282]

Soc. for Scholarly Publishing [2964], 10200 W 44th Ave., Ste. 304, Wheat Ridge, CO 80033, (303)422-3914

Soc. of School Librarians Intl. [10012], 19 Savage St., Charleston, SC 29401, (843)577-5351

Soc. of School Librarians Intl. [10012], 19 Savage St., Charleston, SC 29401, (843)577-5351

Soc. of School Masters and School Mistresses [IO], Kent, United Kingdom

Soc. for a Sci. of Clinical Psychology [16433], Lynn Peterson, PO Box 1082, Niwot, CO 80544

Soc. for Sci. and the Public [7390], 1719 N St. NW, Washington, DC 20036, (202)785-2255

Soc. for Sci. and the Public [7390], 1719 N St. NW, Washington, DC 20036, (202)785-2255

Soc. for Sci. Exploration [7257], Mark Urban-Lurain, Sec., Michigan State Univ., 111 N Kedzie Lab., East Lansing, MI 48824, (517)432-2152

Soc. for the Sci. Investigation of Para-Sciences [IO], Rossdorf, Germany

Soc. for the Sci. Stud. of Reading [8786], Darlene Beeman, PO Box 290, Cameron, MO 64429, (816)235-2245

Soc. for the Sci. Stud. of Religion [20195], Indiana Univ. - Purdue Univ. Indianapolis, Cavanaugh Hall 417, 425 Univ. Blvd., Indianapolis, IN 46202, (317)278-6491

Soc. for the Sci. Stud. of Religion [20195], Indiana Univ. - Purdue Univ. Indianapolis, Cavanaugh Hall 417, 425 Univ. Blvd., Indianapolis, IN 46202, (317)278-6491

Soc. for the Sci. Stud. of Sex [★16652]

Soc. for the Sci. Stud. of Sexuality [16652], PO Box 416, Allentown, PA 18105-0416, (610)443-3100

Soc. of Scottish Artists [IO], Glasgow, United Kingdom

Soc. of Scribes [10758], PO Box 933, New York, NY 10150, (212)452-0139

Soc. of Scribes and Illuminators [IO], London, United Kingdom

Soc. for the Second Self [13112], PO Box 980638, Houston, TX 77098-0638, (713)349-8969

Soc. for Sedimentary Geology [7214], 4111 S Darlington Ave., Ste. 100, Tulsa, OK 74135-6373, (918)610-3361

Soc. for Self-Playing Musical Instruments [IO], Essen, Germany

Soc. of Sensory Professionals [7391], 10860 Kenwood Rd., Cincinnati, OH 45242, (513)891-9100

Soc. for Seventeenth-Century Music [10298], Prof. Kimberly Montford, VP, Trinity Univ., Dept. of Music, San Antonio, TX 78212-7200, (210)999-8214

Soc. for Sex Therapy and Res. [16653], 6311 W Gross Point Rd., Niles, IL 60714, (847)647-8832

Soc. of Shoe Fitters [IO], Hingham, United Kingdom

Soc. for Siberian Irises [21824], Box 315, Biglerville, PA 17307, (717)677-7818

Soc. of the Silurians [2875], PO Box 1195, Madison Square Sta., New York, NY 10159, (212)532-0887

Soc. for Simulation in Healthcare [15386], Don Giroux, 5353 Wayzata Blvd., Ste. 207, Minneapolis, MN 55416, (952)358-2440

Soc. for Simulation in Healthcare [15386], Don Giroux, 5353 Wayzata Blvd., Ste. 207, Minneapolis, MN 55416, (952)358-2440

Soc. of Singers [12557], 26500 W Agoura Rd., No. 102-554, Calabasas, CA 91302, (818)995-7100

Soc. of Skeletal Radiology [16549], 1100 E Woodfield Rd., Ste. 520, Schaumburg, IL 60173, (847)517-3302

Soc. for Skeptical Stud. [10427], Weber State Univ., Dept. of Political Sci. and Philosophy, 1203 Univ. Cir., Ogden, UT 84408-1203

Soc. for Slovene Stud. [19238], Dr. Carole Rogel, Treas., 45 Neil Ave., Apt. 805, Columbus, OH 43215-1650

Soc. for Slovene Stud. [19238], Dr. Carole Rogel, Treas., 45 Neil Ave., Apt. 805, Columbus, OH 43215-1650

Soc. for the Social History of Medicine [IO], Stockton-on-Tees, United Kingdom

Soc. for Social Medicine [IO], London, United Kingdom

Soc. for Social and Political Philosophy [10428], PO Box 7147, Charlottesville, VA 22906-7147, (800)444-2419

Soc. for Social Stud. of Sci. [7392], Louisiana State Univ., Dept. of Sociology, 126 Stubbs Hall, Baton Rouge, LA 70803, (225)578-5311

Soc. for Social Work Admin. in Hea. Care [★13226]

Soc. for Social Work Leadership in Hea. Care [13226], 100 N 20th St., 4th Fl., Philadelphia, PA 19103, (215)564-3484

Soc. for Social Work and Res. [8873], 11240 Waples Mill Rd., Ste. 200, Fairfax, VA 22030, (703)352-7797

Soc. for Social Work and Res. [8873], 11240 Waples Mill Rd., Ste. 200, Fairfax, VA 22030, (703)352-7797

Soc. for Socialist Stud. [IO], Thompson, MB, Canada

Soc. of Soft Drink Technologists [★448]

Soc. of Soft Drink Technologists [★448]

Soc. for Software Quality [6496], PO Box 27634, San Diego, CA 92198

Soc. of South African Geographers [IO], Bloemfontein, Republic of South Africa

Soc. of Spanish Engineers, Planners and Architects - Defunct.

Soc. of Spanish and Spanish-American Stud.

Soc. of Spanish and Spanish-American Stud. - Address unknown since 2011.

Soc. of Sport and Event Photographers [2736], 229 Peachtree St. NE, Ste. 2200, Atlanta, GA 30303-1608, (877)427-3778

Soc. of Sport and Event Photographers [2736], 229 Peachtree St. NE, Ste. 2200, Atlanta, GA 30303-1608, (877)427-3778

Soc. of Sports Therapists [IO], Glasgow, United Kingdom

Soc. of Stage Directors and Choreographers [★23274]

Soc. of State Directors of Hea., Physical Educ. and Recreation [8724], PO Box 40186, Arlington, VA 22204

Soc. of State Directors of Physical and Hea. Educ. [★8724]

Soc. for Storytelling [IO], Reading, United Kingdom

Soc. for Strings - Address unknown since 2010.

Soc. for the Stud. of Addiction to Alcohol and Other Drugs [IO], Leeds, United Kingdom

Soc. for the Stud. of Amer. Women Writers [10741], Karen A. Weyler, VP, Membership and Finances, Univ. of North Carolina at Greensboro, Dept. of English, 3143 Moore Humanities Bldg., Greensboro, NC 27402-6170

Soc. for the Stud. of Amer. Women Writers [10741], Karen A. Weyler, VP, Membership and Finances, Univ. of North Carolina at Greensboro, Dept. of English, 3143 Moore Humanities Bldg., Greensboro, NC 27402-6170

Soc. for the Stud. of Amphibians and Reptiles [6941], Zoo Atlanta, 800 Cherokee Ave. SE, Atlanta, GA 30315, (404)624-5655

Soc. for the Stud. of Architecture in Canada [IO], Ottawa, ON, Canada

Soc. for the Stud. of Biological Rhythms [★6309]

Soc. for the Stud. of Biological Rhythms [★6309]

Soc. for the Stud. of Breast Disease [★13859]

Soc. for the Stud. of Christian Spirituality [19601], The Johns Hopkins Univ. Press, PO Box 19966, Baltimore, MD 21211-0966, (800)548-1784

Soc. for the Stud. of Coherence [IO], Paris, France

Soc. for the Stud. of Development and Growth [★6314]

Soc. for the Stud. of Development and Growth [★6314]

Soc. for the Stud. of Dictionaries and Lexicography [★9443]

Soc. for the Stud. of Early China [7846], Inst. of East Asian Stud., Univ. of California, Publications Off., 2223 Fulton St., 6th Fl., Berkeley, CA 94720-2318, (510)643-6325

Soc. for the Stud. of Early China [7846], Inst. of East Asian Stud., Univ. of California, Publications Off., 2223 Fulton St., 6th Fl., Berkeley, CA 94720-2318, (510)643-6325

Soc. for the Stud. of Early Modern Women [9065], Nancy A. Guttierez, Treas., Univ. of North Carolina at Charlotte, Coll. of Arts and Sciences, 9201 Univ. City Blvd., Charlotte, NC 28223, (704)687-3388

Soc. for the Stud. of Egyptian Antiquities [IO], Toronto, ON, Canada

Soc. for the Stud. of Evolution [6855], Judy Stone, Sec., Colby Coll., 5720 Mayflower Hill Dr., Waterville, ME 04901, (207)859-5736

Soc. for the Stud. of German Art [IO], Berlin, Germany

Soc. for the Stud. of the Holy Roman Empire [9810], Amy R. Caldwell, Co-VP/Treas., California State Univ., Channel Islands, History Dept., One Univ. Dr., Camarillo, CA 93012

Soc. for the Stud. of Human Biology [IO], Loughborough, United Kingdom

A star before a book entry number signifies that the name is not listed separately, but is mentioned within the entry.

Soc. for the Stud. of Human Development **[6946]**, William Kurtines, PhD, Exec. Sec., Florida Intl. Univ., Dept. of Psychology, Univ. Park, 11200 SW 8th St., Miami, FL 33199, (305)348-3941

Soc. for the Stud. of Inborn Errors of Metabolism **[IO]**, Zurich, Switzerland

Soc. for the Stud. of Indigenous Languages of the Americas **[9944]**, PO Box 1295, Denton, TX 76202

Soc. for the Stud. of Indigenous Languages of the Americas **[9944]**, PO Box 1295, Denton, TX 76202

Soc. for the Stud. of Ingestive Behavior **[13823]**, 5250 Old Orchard Rd., Ste. 300, Skokie, IL 60077, (312)283-0900

Soc. for the Stud. of Internationalism **[★9793]**

Soc. for the Stud. of Japanese Religions **[20216]**, Univ. of North Carolina, Dept. of Religious Stud., 125 Saunders Hall, CB No. 3225, Chapel Hill, NC 27599-3225

Soc. for the Stud. of Japanese Religions **[20216]**, Univ. of North Carolina, Dept. of Religious Stud., 125 Saunders Hall, CB No. 3225, Chapel Hill, NC 27599-3225

Soc. for the Stud. of Labour History **[IO]**, Leeds, United Kingdom

Soc. for the Study of Male Psychology and Physiology - Defunct.

Soc. for the Stud. of Male Reproduction **[16594]**, 1100 E Woodfield Rd., Ste. 520, Schaumburg, IL 60173, (847)517-7225

Soc. for the Stud. of Medieval Languages and Literature **[IO]**, Oxford, United Kingdom

Soc. for the Stud. of Midwestern Literature **[10048]**, Mr. Roger J. Bresnahan, PhD, Sec.-Treas., Michigan State Univ., 235 Bessey Hall, East Lansing, MI 48824-1033

Soc. for the Stud. of Myth and Tradition - Address unknown since 2010.

Soc. for the Stud. of Neuronal Regulation **[★15663]**

Soc. for the Stud. of Neuronal Regulation **[★15663]**

Soc. for the Stud. of Normal Psychology **[IO]**, London, United Kingdom

Soc. for the Stud. of Occupation: U.S.A. **[7767]**, Univ. of Oklahoma Hea. Sciences Center, 1200 N Stonewall Ave., Oklahoma City, OK 73117, (405)271-2131

Soc. for the Stud. of Pain, Nigeria **[IO]**, Ibadan, Nigeria

Soc. for the Stud. of Pre-Han China **[★7846]**

Soc. for the Stud. of Pre-Han China **[★7846]**

Soc. for the Stud. of Process Philosophies **[10429]**, Fordham Univ., Dept. of Philosophy, Collins Hall, 441 E Fordham Rd., Bronx, NY 10458, (718)817-4721

Soc. for the Stud. of Psychiatry and Culture **[16347]**, Oregon Hea. and Sci. Univ., Dept. of Psychiatry (UHN80T), 3181 SW Sam Jackson Park Rd., Portland, OR 97239, (503)494-6653

Soc. for the Stud. of Reproduction **[16601]**, 1619 Monroe St., Madison, WI 53711-2063, (608)256-2777

Soc. for the Stud. of Social Biology **[6598]**, Syracuse Univ., Ctr. for Policy Res., 426 Eggers Hall, Syracuse, NY 13244-1020

Soc. for the Stud. of Social Problems **[13149]**, 901 McClung Tower, Univ. of Tennessee, Knoxville, TN 37996-0490, (865)689-1531

Soc. for the Stud. of Southern Literature **[10049]**, Univ. of Mississippi, PO Box 1848, Barnard Observatory, University, MS 38677-9700

Soc. for the Stud. of Symbolic Interaction **[7432]**, Linda Morrison, PhD, Treas., Duquesne Univ., Dept. of Sociology, 600 Forbes Ave., Pittsburgh, PA 15282, (412)396-6489

Soc. for the Study of Women in Legal History - Defunct.

Soc. of Stukely Westcott Descendants of Am. **[20590]**, 8121 Beverly Dr., Prairie Village, KS 66208

Soc. of Sudanese Colleges of Agricultural Sector **[IO]**, Khartoum, Sudan

Soc. for Surgery of the Alimentary Tract **[16824]**, 900 Cummings Ctr., No. 221-U, Beverly, MA 01915, (978)927-8330

Soc. of Surgical Oncology **[15934]**, 85 W Algonquin Rd., Ste. 550, Arlington Heights, IL 60005, (847)427-1400

Soc. of Swedish Authors in Finland **[IO]**, Helsinki, Finland

Soc. of Systematic Biologists **[7639]**, California Acad. of Sciences, Golden Gate Park, San Francisco, CA 94118

Soc. of Systematic Zoology **[★7639]**

Soc. of Teachers of the Alexander Technique **[IO]**, London, United Kingdom

Soc. of Teachers of Emergency Medicine **[★14479]**

Soc. of Teachers of Family Medicine **[14527]**, 11400 Tomahawk Creek Pkwy., Ste. 540, Leawood, KS 66211, (913)906-6000

Soc. of Teachers of Speech and Drama **[IO]**, Mansfield, United Kingdom

Soc. of Tech. Analysts **[IO]**, Vernham Dean, United Kingdom

Soc. for Tech. Commun. **[817]**, 9401 Lee Hwy., Ste. 300, Fairfax, VA 22031, (703)522-4114

Soc. for Tech. Commun. **[817]**, 9401 Lee Hwy., Ste. 300, Fairfax, VA 22031, (703)522-4114

Soc. for Tech. Commun., Eastern Ontario Chap. **[IO]**, Nepean, ON, Canada

Soc. of Tech. Writers and Editors **[★817]**

Soc. of Tech. Writers and Publishers **[★817]**

Soc. for the Technological Advancement of Reporting **[5360]**, 222 S Westmonte Dr., Ste. 101, Altamonte Springs, FL 32714, (407)774-7880

Soc. for Tech. in Anesthesia **[13756]**, 6736 W Washington St., Ste. 1300, Milwaukee, WI 53214, (414)389-8600

Soc. for Tech. in Anesthesia **[13756]**, 6736 W Washington St., Ste. 1300, Milwaukee, WI 53214, (414)389-8600

Soc. of Telecommunications Consultants **[3420]**, PO Box 70, Old Station, CA 96071-0070, (530)335-7313

Soc. of TV Lighting Directors **[IO]**, West Sussex, United Kingdom

Soc. of Tempera Painters **[9257]**, Michael Bergt, Pres., PO Box 30766, Santa Fe, NM 87592-0766, (505)473-9654

Soc. for Terrorism Res. **[7554]**, PO Box 590094, Newton, MA 02459

Soc. for Textual Scholarship **[10050]**, Indiana Univ. Press, 601 N Morton St., Bloomington, IN 47404

Soc. for Thai Philately **[22079]**, 9379 W Escuda Dr., Peoria, AZ 85382

Soc. for Theatre Res. **[IO]**, London, United Kingdom

Soc. for Theoretical and Philosophical Psychology **[16434]**, Montana Sta. Univ., Hea. and Human Development, Herrick Hall, Bozeman, MT 59717, (406)581-6215

Soc. for Theoretical and Philosophical Psychology **[16434]**, Montana Sta. Univ., Hea. and Human Development, Herrick Hall, Bozeman, MT 59717, (406)581-6215

Soc. for Theriogenology **[17039]**, PO Box 3007, Montgomery, AL 36109-3007, (334)395-4666

Soc. for Thermal Medicine **[16876]**, PO Box 1897, Lawrence, KS 66044, (800)627-0326

Soc. of the Third Infantry Div. **[20369]**, 1515 Ramblewood Dr., Hanover Park, IL 60133-2230

Soc. of Thoracic Radiology **[16550]**, PO Box 7169, Rochester, MN 55903-7169, (507)288-5620

Soc. of Thoracic Surgeons **[16881]**, 633 N St. Clair St., Ste. 2320, Chicago, IL 60611, (312)202-5800

Soc. for Threatened Peoples **[IO]**, Gottingen, Germany

Soc. of Tobacco Jar Collectors - Address unknown since 2011.

Soc. of Token, Medal and Obsolete Paper Money Collectors **[★21995]**

Soc. of Toxicologic Pathologists **[★16134]**

Soc. of Toxicologic Pathology **[16134]**, 1821 Michael Faraday Dr., Ste. 300, Reston, VA 20190, (703)438-7508

Soc. of Toxicology **[7574]**, 1821 Michael Faraday Dr., Ste. 300, Reston, VA 20190-5348, (703)438-3115

Soc. of Tractor Engineers **[★6243]**

Soc. for Traditional Music in Switzerland **[IO]**, Pfaffikon, Switzerland

Soc. of Traditional Roman Catholics **[19504]**, PO Box 130, Mead, WA 99021-0130

Soc. for Translational Oncology **[15935]**, 318 Blackwell St., Ste. 270, Durham, NC 27701, (919)433-0489

Soc. of Trauma Nurses **[15801]**, 3493 Lansdowne Dr., Ste. 2, Lexington, KY 40517, (859)977-7456

Soc. for Traumatic Stress Stud. **[★16726]**

Soc. for Traumatic Stress Stud. **[★16726]**

Soc. of Travel Agents in Govt. **[★3574]**

Soc. of Travel and Tourism Educators **[★3564]**

Soc. of Travel and Tourism Educators **[★3564]**

Soc. for Treatment of Autism **[IO]**, Calgary, AB, Canada

Soc. for Treatment and Stud. of Pain **[IO]**, Rawalpindi, Pakistan

Soc. of Tribologists and Lubrication Engineers **[6831]**, 840 Busse Hwy., Park Ridge, IL 60068, (847)825-5536

Soc. of Tribologists and Lubrication Engineers **[6831]**, 840 Busse Hwy., Park Ridge, IL 60068, (847)825-5536

Soc. for Tropical Veterinary Medicine **[17040]**, Oklahoma State Univ., Dept. of Veterinary Pathobiology, Center for Veterinary Hea. Sciences, 250 McElroy Hall, Stillwater, OK 74078, (405)744-6726

Soc. for Tropical Veterinary Medicine **[17040]**, Oklahoma State Univ., Dept. of Veterinary Pathobiology, Center for Veterinary Hea. Sciences, 250 McElroy Hall, Stillwater, OK 74078, (405)744-6726

Soc. of Trust and Estate Practitioners **[IO]**, London, United Kingdom

Soc. of Trust and Estate Practitioners Ireland **[IO]**, Dublin, Ireland

Soc. of Trust and Estate Practitioners USA **[1226]**, 40 E 84th St., Ste. 5D, New York, NY 10028, (212)737-3690

Soc. of Turkish Amer. Architects, Engineers and Scientists **[6832]**, 821 United Nations Plz., Turkish Ctr., 2nd Fl., New York, NY 10017, (646)312-3366

Soc. of Turkish Amer. Architects, Engineers and Scientists **[6832]**, 821 United Nations Plz., Turkish Ctr., 2nd Fl., New York, NY 10017, (646)312-3366

Soc. of Turkish Architects, Engineers and Scientists in Am. **[★6832]**

Soc. of Turkish Architects, Engineers and Scientists in Am. **[★6832]**

Soc. of Typographic Aficionados **[1630]**, 3415 Richmond Blvd., Apt. C, Oakland, CA 94611-5849, (510)414-6406

Soc. of Ukrainian Engineers in Am. **[★6834]**

Soc. of Ukrainian Philatelists **[★22085]**

Soc. of Ukrainian Philatelists **[★22085]**

Soc. for Ultrastructural Pathology **[16135]**, Duke Univ. Medical Ctr., Dept. of Pathology, PO Box 3712, Durham, NC 27710, (919)286-0411

Soc. for Underwater Tech. **[IO]**, London, United Kingdom

Soc. of U.S. Air Force Flight Surgeons **[13586]**, PO Box 35387, Brooks City Base, TX 78235

Soc. for U.S. Commemorative Coins - Address unknown since 2011.

Soc. of U.S. Medical Consultants in World War II **[★15512]**

Soc. of U.S. Naval Flight Surgeons **[13587]**, PO Box 33008, Pensacola, FL 32508-3008, (850)452-2257

Soc. of U.S. Pattern Collectors **[21994]**, PO Box 806, Nyack, NY 10960, (845)321-0249

Soc. of Univ. Olodaryngologists **[★16090]**

Soc. of Univ. Otolaryngologists - Head and Neck Surgeons **[16090]**, 2709 San Marcos Dr., Pasadena, CA 91107, (626)683-7313

Soc. of Univ. Patent Administrators **[★5561]**

Soc. of Univ. Surgeons **[16825]**, 341 N Maitland Ave., Ste. 130, Maitland, FL 32751, (407)647-7714

Soc. of Univ. Urologists **[16953]**, 1100 E Woodfield Rd., Ste. 520, Schaumburg, IL 60173, (847)517-7225

Soc. for Upgrading the Built Env. **[IO]**, Giza, Egypt

Soc. for Urban, Natl. and Transnational/Global Anthropology **[6157]**, Univ. of North Carolina, Dept. of Anthropology, 301 Alumni Bldg., CB No. 3115, Chapel Hill, NC 27599-3115

Soc. of Urologic Nurses and Associates **[15802]**, PO Box 56, E Holly Ave., Pitman, NJ 08071-0056, (856)256-2335

Soc. of Uroradiology **[16954]**, Intl. Meeting Managers, 4550 Post Oak Pl., Ste. 342, Houston, TX 77027, (713)965-0566

Soc. for Utopian Stud. **[10430]**, Univ. of Florida, PO Box 117310, Gainesville, FL 32611-7310, (352)392-6650

Reference to "IO" in place of a book number signifies that the association may be found in the 50th edition of International Organizations.

Soc. for Utopian Stud. [10430], Univ. of Florida, PO Box 117310, Gainesville, FL 32611-7310, (352)392-6650

Soc. for Vacuum Coaters [793], 71 Pinon Hill Pl. NE, Albuquerque, NM 87122-1914, (505)856-7188

Soc. for Values in Higher Educ. [19687], Portland State Univ., PO Box 751, Portland, OR 97207-0751, (503)725-2575

Soc. for Vascular Medicine [16967], 111 Deer Lake Rd., Ste. 100, Deerfield, IL 60015, (847)480-2961

Soc. for Vascular Medicine and Biology [★16967]

Soc. for Vascular Nursing [15803], 100 Cummings Ctr., Ste. 124 A, Beverly, MA 01915, (978)927-7800

Soc. for Vascular Surgery [16968], 633 N St. Clair, 22nd Fl., Chicago, IL 60611, (312)334-2300

Soc. of Vascular Tech. [★16969]

Soc. for Vascular Ultrasound [16969], 4601 Presidents Dr., Ste. 260, Lanham, MD 20706-4831, (301)459-7550

Soc. of Vector Ecologists [★4776]

Soc. for Vector Ecology [4776], 1966 Compton Ave., Corona, CA 92881-3318, (951)340-9792

Soc. of Vertebrate Paleontology [7215], 111 Deer Lake Rd., Ste. 100, Deerfield, IL 60015, (847)480-9095

Soc. of Vertebrate Paleontology [7215], 111 Deer Lake Rd., Ste. 100, Deerfield, IL 60015, (847)480-9095

Soc. of Veterinary Behavior Technicians [17041], Danielle Woodgate, Treas., 4840 Oakview Ln. N, Plymouth, MN 55442

Soc. for Veterinary Medical Ethics [17042], John S. Wright, DVM, Treas., Coll. of Veterinary Medicine, Univ. of Minnesota, Veterinary Clinical Sciences Dept., C339 Veterinary Medical Center, 1352 Boyd Ave., St. Paul, MN 55108

Soc. for Visual Anthropology [6158], Reading Area Community Coll., Soc. Sciences Div., 10 S 2nd St., Reading, PA 19603

Soc. for Vocational Psychology [7315], Patrick J. Rottinghaus, PhD, Communications Off., Southern Illinois Univ. at Carbondale, Dept. of Psychology, Life Sci. II, Rm. 222C, Carbondale, IL 62901, (618)453-3573

Soc. for Voluntary Control of Trade Fair and Exhibition Statistics [IO], Berlin, Germany

Soc. of the War of 1812 in Connecticut [★20840]

Soc. of the War of 1812 in Pennsylvania [★20840]

Soc. for Welfare Awakening Training and Hea. Implementation [IO], Warangal, India

Soc. of Wetland Scientists [4142], 1313 Dolley Madison Blvd., Ste. 402, McLean, VA 22101, (703)790-1745

Soc. for Whole Body Autoradiography [15387], Stefan Linehan, Pres.-Elect, XenoBiotic Labs., Inc., 107 Morgan Ln., Plainsboro, NJ 08536, (609)799-2295

Soc. of Wildlife Artists [IO], London, United Kingdom

Soc. of Wildlife Specialists [★5156]

Soc. of Wine Educators [22201], 1319 F St. NW, Ste. 303, Washington, DC 20004, (202)408-8777

Soc. of Wireless Pioneers [3421], 12 Chapala Dr., Santa Rosa, CA 95403

Soc. of Woman Geographers [6906], 415 E Capitol St. SE, Washington, DC 20003, (202)546-9228

Soc. of Woman Geographers [6906], 415 E Capitol St. SE, Washington, DC 20003, (202)546-9228

Soc. for Women and AIDS in Africa [IO], Dakar, Senegal

Soc. of Women Artists [IO], Gillingham, United Kingdom

Soc. of Women Engineers [6833], 203 N La Salle St., Ste. 1675, Chicago, IL 60601, (312)596-5223

Soc. for Women in Philosophy, Eastern Div. - Defunct.

Soc. of Women in Urology [16955], 1110 E Woodfield Rd., Ste. 520, Schaumburg, IL 60173, (847)517-7225

Soc. of Women Writers and Journalists [IO], West Sussex, United Kingdom

Soc. of Women Writers - Victoria [IO], Carrum, Australia

Soc. for Women's Hea. Res. [17136], 1025 Connecticut Ave. NW, Ste. 701, Washington, DC 20036, (202)223-8224

Soc. of Wood Engravers [IO], Peterborough, United Kingdom

Soc. of Wood Sci. and Tech. [4415], PO Box 6155, Monona, WI 53716, (608)577-1342

Soc. for Worldwide Medical Exchange [15212], 1666 Kennedy Causeway, Ste. 702, North Bay Village, FL 33141, (305)407-9222

Soc. for Worldwide Medical Exchange [15212], 1666 Kennedy Causeway, Ste. 702, North Bay Village, FL 33141, (305)407-9222

Soc. of Writers to Her Majesty's Signet [IO], Edinburgh, United Kingdom

Soc. of Young Philanthropists [12685], 9107 Wilshire Blvd., Ste. 725, Beverly Hills, CA 90210, (310)275-0483

Soc. of Young Publishers [IO], London, United Kingdom

Socio-Ecological Union [IO], Moscow, Russia

Socio-Legal Stud. Assn. [IO], Belfast, United Kingdom

Sociological Assn. of Ireland [IO], Cork, Ireland

Sociological Practice Assn. and Soc. for Applied Sociology [★7422]

Sociologists' AIDS Network [13625], Carrie E. Foote, Treas., Indiana University-Purdue Univ., Dept. of Sociology, 425 Univ. Blvd., CA 306b, Indianapolis, IN 46228

Sociologists Without Borders [18664], David Brunsma, Treas., Univ. of Missouri, 312 Middlebush Hall, Columbia, MO 65211, (537)882-1067

Sociologists Without Borders [18664], David Brunsma, Treas., Univ. of Missouri, 312 Middlebush Hall, Columbia, MO 65211, (537)882-1067

Sociologists for Women in Soc. [9590], 10 Chaffee Rd., Kingston, RI 02881, (401)874-9510

Sociologists for Women in Soc. [9590], 10 Chaffee Rd., Kingston, RI 02881, (401)874-9510

Sociology

Alpha Kappa Delta [23737]

Alpha Kappa Delta [23737]

Amer. Sociological Assn. [7421]

Amer. Sociological Assn. l Comm. on the Status of Women in Sociology [9589]

Amer. Sociological Assn. l Honors Prog. [23738]

Assn. for Africanist Anthropology [6133]

Assn. for Applied and Clinical Sociology [7422]

Assn. of Black Sociologists [7423]

Assn. for Humanist Sociology [7424]

Assn. of Population Centers [6594]

Assn. for the Sociology of Religion [7425]

Christian Sociological Soc. [7426]

Intl. Rural Sociology Assn. [7427]

Intl. Rural Sociology Assn. [7427]

Intl. Visual Sociology Assn. [7428]

Natl. Coun. of State Sociological Associations [7429]

North Amer. Soc. for the Sociology of Sport [7430]

Rural Sociological Soc. [7431]

Soc. for the Stud. of Symbolic Interaction [7432]

Sociologists Without Borders [18664]

Sociologists Without Borders [18664]

Sodality Movement and Queens Work [★19471]

Soeurs du Bon Pasteur [★IO]

Soeurs de la Charite de Sainte Jeanne Antide Thouret [★IO]

Soeurs de la Croix de Chavanod [★IO]

Soeurs de Saint Louis [★IO]

Soft Drink and Fruit Juice Producers' Assn. [IO], Lisbon, Portugal

Soft Furnishing Indus. Assn. of Australia [IO], Reservoir, Australia

Soft Furnishing Indus. Assn. of Australia - New South Wales [IO], Mortdale, Australia

Soft Furnishing Indus. Assn. of Australia - Queensland [IO], Brisbane, Australia

Soft Furnishing Indus. Assn. of Australia - South Australia [IO], Adelaide, Australia

Soft Furnishing Indus. Assn. of Australia - Tasmania [IO], Reservoir, Australia

Soft Furnishing Indus. Assn. of Australia - Victoria [IO], Reservoir, Australia

Soft Furnishing Indus. Assn. of Australia - Western Australia [IO], Joondalup, Australia

Soft Power Hea. [15213], 2887 Purchase St., Purchase, NY 10577, (914)694-2442

Softball

Amateur Softball Assn. of Am. [22950]

Babe Ruth Baseball/Softball [22268]

Cinderella Softball Leagues [22951]

Intl. Senior Softball Assn. [22952]

Intl. Senior Softball Assn. [22952]

Intl. Softball Fed. [22953]

Intl. Softball Fed. [22953]

Natl. Softball Assn. [22954]

North Amer. Fastpitch Assn. [22955]

North Amer. Fastpitch Assn. [22955]

Softball Players Assn. [22956]

U.S. Fastpitch Assn. [22957]

U.S. Specialty Sports Assn. [22958]

Softball Assn; Natl. Wheelchair [22520]

Softball Canada [IO], Ottawa, ON, Canada

Softball Players Assn. [22956], PO Box 1307, Mustang, OK 73064, (405)376-7034

Software Contractors' Guild [1029], 7151 S US Hwy. 60, No. 704, Gold Canyon, AZ 85118

Software Defined Radio Forum [★6501]

Software Distributors' Assn. [IO], Santiago, Chile

Software Indus. Division of ADAPSO [★6499]

Software and Info. Indus. Assn. [5581], 1090 Vermont Ave. NW, 6th Fl., Washington, DC 20005-4095, (202)289-7442

Software Management Assn. - Defunct.

Software New Zealand [IO], North Shore City, New Zealand

Software Productivity Consortium [★6498]

Software in the Public Interest [6497], PO Box 501248, Indianapolis, IN 46250-6248

Software Publishers Assn. and Info. Indus. Assn. [★5581]

Software and Tech. Vendors' Assn. [819], 555 8th Ave., Ste. 1902, New York, NY 10018, (646)233-0167

Software Testing Inst. - Address unknown since 2011.

Softwood Export Coun. [1479], PO Box 80517, Portland, OR 97280, (503)620-5946

Softwood Export Coun. [1479], PO Box 80517, Portland, OR 97280, (503)620-5946

Soil

Assn. for Environmental Hea. and Sciences [4924]

Assn. of Women Soil Scientists [7433]

Erosion Control Tech. Coun. [4925]

Erosion Control Tech. Coun. [4925]

Intl. Biochar Initiative [6115]

Natl. Soc. of Consulting Soil Scientists [4926]

Remineralize the Earth [4927]

Soil Carbon Coalition [4928]

Soil and Plant Anal. Coun. [7434]

Soil Sci. Soc. of Am. [7435]

U.S. Consortium of Soil Sci. Associations [4929]

U.S. Permafrost Assn. [7436]

Soil Assn. [IO], Bristol, United Kingdom

Soil Carbon Coalition [4928], PO Box 393, Enterprise, OR 97828, (541)263-1888

Soil Conservation

Intl. Biochar Initiative [6115]

Soil Carbon Coalition [4928]

Soil Conservation Soc. of Am. [★4143]

Soil and Hea. Assn. of New Zealand [IO], Auckland, New Zealand

Soil and Plant Anal. Coun. [7434], 347 N Shores Cir., Windsor, CO 80550, (970)686-5702

Soil Sci. Soc. of Am. [7435], 677 S Segoe Rd., Madison, WI 53711, (608)273-8080

Soil Sci. Soc. of South Africa [IO], Erasmusrand, Republic of South Africa

Soil and Water Conservation Soc. [4143], 945 SW Ankeny Rd., Ankeny, IA 50023-9723, (515)289-2331

Sojourners [19602], 3333 14th St. NW, Ste. 200, Washington, DC 20010, (202)328-8842

Sojourners Club [★19138]

Sojuzpushnina [IO], Moscow, Russia

Sojuzupak [★IO]

Soka Gakkai International-United States of Am. [19372], 606 Wilshire Blvd., Santa Monica, CA 90401, (310)260-8900

Soka Gakkai International-United States of Am. [19372], 606 Wilshire Blvd., Santa Monica, CA 90401, (310)260-8900

A star before a book entry number signifies that the name is not listed separately, but is mentioned within the entry.

Sokol [★18971]
SOKOL U.S.A. [19234], PO Box 189, East Orange, NJ 07019-0189, (973)676-0280
Solace Intl. [13479], 282 E Croydon Park Rd., Tucson, AZ 85704, (520)208-7940
Solace Intl. [13479], 282 E Croydon Park Rd., Tucson, AZ 85704, (520)208-7940
Solar
  Sunstove Org. [11643]
Solar Box Cookers Intl. [★4800]
Solar Box Cookers Intl. [★4800]
Solar Cookers Intl. [4800], 1919 21st St., Ste. 101, Sacramento, CA 95811, (916)455-4499
Solar Cookers Intl. [4800], 1919 21st St., Ste. 101, Sacramento, CA 95811, (916)455-4499
Solar Elec. Power Assn. [7444], 1220 19th St. NW, Ste. 800, Washington, DC 20036-2400, (202)857-0898
Solar Energy
  Amer. Solar Action Plan [7437]
  Amer. Solar Energy Soc. [7438]
  Australian and New Zealand Solar Energy Soc. [6491]
  blueEnergy [11966]
  Eco Energy Finance [6712]
  Fifty Lanterns Intl. [7439]
  Global Possibilities [4930]
  Innovation: Africa [6114]
  Intergovernmental Renewable Energy Org. [6731]
  Intl. Photovoltaic Equip. Assn. [1170]
  Power to the People [7440]
  Power Up Gambia [7441]
  Renew the Earth [7442]
  Renew the Earth [7442]
  Renewable Energy for Medicine and Educ. [6749]
  Rural Renewable Energy Alliance [6754]
  Show Me Solar [7443]
  Solar Elec. Power Assn. [7444]
  Solar Energy Indus. Assn. [7445]
  Solar Energy Intl. [7446]
  Solar Energy Intl. [7446]
  Solar Energy Soc. [2611]
  Solar Household Energy [4931]
  Solar Household Energy [4931]
  Solar Light for Africa [11640]
  Solar for Peace [7447]
  Solar Rating and Certification Corp. [7448]
  STG Intl. [7449]
  SunPower Afrique [13227]
  SunPower Afrique [13227]
  Sunstove Org. [11643]
  Sustainable Buildings Indus. Coun. [7450]
  Vote Solar Initiative [7451]
Solar Energy Indus. Assn. [7445], 575 7th St. NW, Ste. 400, Washington, DC 20004, (202)682-0556
Solar Energy Intl. [7446], PO Box 715, Carbondale, CO 81623, (970)963-8855
Solar Energy Intl. [7446], PO Box 715, Carbondale, CO 81623, (970)963-8855
Solar Energy Res. and Educ. Foundation [★7445]
Solar Energy Soc. [IO], Abingdon, United Kingdom
Solar Energy Soc. of Canada [IO], Ottawa, ON, Canada
Solar Household Energy [4931], PO Box 15063, Chevy Chase, MD 20825
Solar Household Energy [4931], PO Box 15063, Chevy Chase, MD 20825
Solar Light for Africa [11640], 2475 Northwinds Pkwy., Ste. 200, Alpharetta, GA 30009, (770)753-6000
Solar Light for Africa [11640], 2475 Northwinds Pkwy., Ste. 200, Alpharetta, GA 30009, (770)753-6000
Solar Lobby [★7442]
Solar Lobby [★7442]
Solar for Peace [7447], PO Box 764, Danville, CA 94526-0764, (925)208-4989
Solar Rating and Certification Corp. [7448], 400 High Point Dr., Ste. 400, Cocoa, FL 32926, (321)213-6037
Solar Trade Assn. [IO], Milton Keynes, United Kingdom
Solbrekken Evangelistic Assn. of Canada [IO], Edmonton, AB, Canada
Soldier of Fortune
  Omega First Amendment Legal Fund [17314]

Soldiers' Angels [18930], 1792 E Washington Blvd., Pasadena, CA 91104, (626)529-5114
Soldiers for Peace - Defunct.
Soldiers, Sailors, Airmen and Families Assn. Forces Help [IO], London, United Kingdom
A Soldier's Wish List [11108], Mrs. Julieann Najar, Founder, 11143 Larimore Rd., St. Louis, MO 63138, (314)868-2264
SOLE - The Intl. Soc. of Logistics [6965], 8100 Professional Pl., Ste. 111, Hyattsville, MD 20785-2229, (301)459-8446
SOLE - The Intl. Soc. of Logistics [6965], 8100 Professional Pl., Ste. 111, Hyattsville, MD 20785-2229, (301)459-8446
Solent Skiers Assn. [IO], Fareham, United Kingdom
Soles for Kidz [19531], 5821 Imes Ln., Fort Worth, TX 76179, (866)905-5439
Solid Axle Corvette Club [21166], PO Box 1134, El Dorado, CA 95623, (916)991-7040
Solid Axle Corvette Club [21166], PO Box 1134, El Dorado, CA 95623, (916)991-7040
Solid Fuel Assn. [IO], Alfreton, United Kingdom
Solid Waste Assn. of North Am. [6067], 1100 Wayne Ave., Ste. 700, Silver Spring, MD 20910, (240)494-2242
Solid Waste Composting Coun. [★6068]
Solidaridad Internacional [IO], Madrid, Spain
Solidaritat mit Frauen in Not [★IO]
Solidarity and Action Against the HIV Infection in India [10892], 20 Plaza St. E, Apt. C11, Brooklyn, NY 11238
Solidarity and Action Against the HIV Infection in India [10892], 20 Plaza St. E, Apt. C11, Brooklyn, NY 11238
Solidarity for Afghan Families [IO], Kabul, Afghanistan
Solidarity for Children in Africa and the World [IO], Cotonou, Benin
Solidarity Philippines Australia Network [IO], Brisbane, Australia
Solidarity with Women in Distress [IO], Boppard, Germany
Solids Handling and Processing Assn. [IO], Leicester, United Kingdom
Soliya [18833], 6 E 39th St., Ste. 301, New York, NY 10016, (718)701-5855
Solomon Island Graduate Women's Assn. [IO], Honiara, Solomon Islands
Solomon Islands Judo Assn. [IO], Honiara, Solomon Islands
Solomon Islands Red Cross [IO], Honiara, Solomon Islands
Solomon Islands Taekwondo Union [IO], Honiara, Solomon Islands
Solomon Islands Tennis Assn. [IO], Honiara, Solomon Islands
Solomon Islands Volleyball Fed. [IO], Honiara, Solomon Islands
Solomon Islands Weightlifting Fed. [IO], Honiara, Solomon Islands
Solomon Islands Yachting Assn. [IO], Honiara, Solomon Islands
Solomon Schechter Day School Assn. [★8433]
Solvent Extractors' Assn. of India [IO], Mumbai, India
Solvents Indus. Assn. [IO], Harwich, United Kingdom
SOMA U.S.A. [★20091]
Somali Athletics Fed. [IO], Sharjah, United Arab Emirates
Somali Badminton Fed. [IO], Mogadishu, Somalia
Somali Cat Club of Am. - Address unknown since 2011.
Somali Child Soldier Relief Org. [IO], Toronto, Canada
Somali Coalition for Freedom of Expression [IO], Mogadishu, Somalia
Somali Community Concern [IO], Mogadishu, Somalia
Somali Disabled People Coun. [IO], Mogadishu, Somalia
Somali Family Care Network [19247], 2724 Dorr Ave., Ste. 102, Fairfax, VA 22031, (703)560-0005
Somali Foreign Correspondents Assn. [IO], Mogadishu, Somalia
Somali Info. Tech. Professionals Assn. [IO], Mogadishu, Somalia

Somali Intl. Cat Club [21258], George Hilton, Treas., 2210 21st St., Lake Charles, LA 70601
Somali Journalists Soc. [IO], Mogadishu, Somalia
Somali Judo Fed. [IO], Mogadishu, Somalia
Somali Medical and Supplies Relief Org. [12893], PO Box 86212, Portland, OR 97286, (503)317-7011
Somali Medical and Supplies Relief Org. [12893], PO Box 86212, Portland, OR 97286, (503)317-7011
Somali Natl. Assn. of the Deaf [IO], Mogadishu, Somalia
Somali Powerlifting Fed. [IO], Mogadishu, Somalia
Somali Refugees Development Assn. [IO], Sana'a, Yemen
Somali Weightlifting Fed. [IO], Mogadishu, Somalia
Somalia
  Read Horn of Africa USA [12360]
  Somali Family Care Network [19247]
  Somali Medical and Supplies Relief Org. [12893]
Somalia Squash Fed. [IO], Mogadishu, Somalia
Somatics Soc. [12225], 1516 Grant Ave., Ste. 212, Novato, CA 94945, (415)892-0617
Somerset Chamber of Commerce and Indus. [IO], Taunton, United Kingdom
Sommelier Soc. of Am. [189], PO Box 20080, West Village Sta., New York, NY 10014, (212)679-4190
Sonar Class Assn. [22393], Bruce McArthur, Class Admin., 44 Brookside Rd., Darien, CT 06820, (203)655-6665
Songsmith Soc. - Defunct.
Songwriters Assn. of Canada [IO], Toronto, ON, Canada
Songwriters, Composers And Lyricists Assn. [IO], Blackwood, Australia
Songwriters Guild [★5582]
Songwriters Guild of Am. [5582], 209 Tenth Ave. S, Ste. 321, Nashville, TN 37203, (615)742-9945
Songwriters and Lyricists Club - Defunct.
Songwriters Protective Assn. [★5582]
Songwriters of Wisconsin Intl. [9507], PO Box 1027, Neenah, WI 54957-1027, (920)725-5129
Sonneck Soc. [★10289]
Sonography
  Amer. Inst. of Ultrasound in Medicine [16675]
  Amer. Registry of Diagnostic Medical Sonography [16676]
  Hope Imaging [16677]
  Intl. Soc. of Cardiovascular Ultrasound [14440]
  Soc. of Diagnostic Medical Sonography [16678]
Sonography; Joint Rev. Comm. on Educ. in Diagnostic Medical [8581]
Sonoma County Vintners [5173], 420 Aviation Blvd., Ste. 106, Santa Rosa, CA 95403-1039, (707)522-5840
Sonoma County Wine Growers Assn. [★5173]
Sonoma County Winegrape Commission [5174], PO Box 1959, Sebastopol, CA 95473, (707)829-3963
Sonoma County Wineries Assn. [★5173]
Sons of the Amer. Legion [20710], PO Box 1055, Indianapolis, IN 46206, (317)630-1200
Sons of Charity [IO], Paris, France
Sons of Colonial New England Natl. Soc. [20410], 3504 Wilson St., Fairfax, VA 22030-2936
Sons of Confederate Veterans [20388], PO Box 59, Columbia, TN 38402-0059, (931)380-1844
Sons and Daughters In Touch [20711], PO Box 100366, Arlington, VA 22210, (800)984-9994
Sons and Daughters of Oregon Pioneers [20752], PO Box 6685, Portland, OR 97228
Sons and Daughters of Pioneer Rivermen [20753], 102 Front St., Marietta, OH 45750, (740)373-4068
Sons of the Desert [23807], PO Box 2102, Natick, MA 01760
Sons of Norway [19180], 1455 W Lake St., Minneapolis, MN 55408-2666, (612)827-3611
Sons of Norway [19180], 1455 W Lake St., Minneapolis, MN 55408-2666, (612)827-3611
Sons of Pericles [19018], 1909 Q St. NW, Ste. 500, Washington, DC 20009, (202)232-6300
Sons of Scotland Benevolent Assn. [IO], Toronto, ON, Canada
Sons of Spanish Amer. War Veterans [20760], 185 Jordan Rd., Plymouth, MA 02360
Sons of Union Veterans of the Civil War [20389], PO Box 1865, Harrisburg, PA 17105-1865, (717)232-7000

Reference to "IO" in place of a book number signifies that the association may be found in the 50th edition of International Organizations.

Sons of Utah Pioneers [★20749]
Sons of Veterans, USA [★20389]
Sony Ericsson WTA Tour [23061], 1 Progress Plz., Ste. 1500, St. Petersburg, FL 33701, (727)895-5000
Sony Ericsson WTA Tour [23061], 1 Progress Plz., Ste. 1500, St. Petersburg, FL 33701, (727)895-5000
Soo Line Historical and Tech. Soc. [10499], 39105 Fishermans Ln., Chassell, MI 49916
Soong Ching Ling Found. [IO], Beijing, People's Republic of China
SOPAR [IO], Gatineau, QC, Canada
Sophus Frederick Hansen Family Org. - Defunct.
Soroptimist Fed. of the Americas [★13077]
Soroptimist Fed. of the Americas [★13077]
Soroptimist Found. of Canada [IO], Richmond Hill, ON, Canada
Soroptimist Intl. [IO], Cambridge, United Kingdom
Soroptimist Intl. of the Americas [13077], 1709 Spruce St., Philadelphia, PA 19103-6103, (215)893-9000
Soroptimist Intl. of the Americas [13077], 1709 Spruce St., Philadelphia, PA 19103-6103, (215)893-9000
Soroptimist Intl. of Anguilla [IO], The Valley, Anguilla
Soroptimist Intl. d'Europe [★IO]
Soroptimist Intl. of Europe [IO], Geneva, Switzerland
Soroptimist Intl. of Great Britain and Ireland [IO], Stockport, United Kingdom
Soroptimist Intl. of the South West Pacific [IO], Waterloo, Australia
Sororities
Delta Gamma Pi Multicultural Sorority [23739]
Delta Phi Omega Sorority [23740]
Delta Sigma Chi Sorority [23741]
Delta Tau Lambda Sorority [23742]
Delta Xi Nu Multicultural Sorority [23743]
Gamma Delta Pi [23744]
Gamma Gamma Chi Sorority [23745]
Kappa Phi Gamma Sorority [23746]
Lambda Psi Delta Sorority [23747]
Sigma Lambda Alpha Sorority [23748]
Sigma Lambda Gamma Natl. Sorority [23749]
Theta Chi Omega Multicultural Sorority [23750]
Theta Nu Xi Multicultural Sorority [23751]
Zeta Chi Phi Multicultural Sorority [23752]
Sororities, Service
Delta Gamma Pi Multicultural Sorority [23739]
Delta Sigma Chi Sorority [23741]
Delta Sigma Theta [23641]
Delta Tau Lambda Sorority [23742]
Kappa Phi Gamma Sorority [23746]
Lambda Psi Delta Sorority [23747]
Zeta Chi Phi Multicultural Sorority [23752]
Sororities, Social
Delta Gamma Pi Multicultural Sorority [23739]
Delta Sigma Chi Sorority [23741]
Kappa Phi Gamma Sorority [23746]
Lambda Psi Delta Sorority [23747]
Sigma Delta Tau [23731]
Zeta Chi Phi Multicultural Sorority [23752]
Sorority Editors Conf. [★23508]
Soros Found. Romania [IO], Bucharest, Romania
Sorptive Minerals Inst. [2508], 1155 15th St. NW, Ste. 500, Washington, DC 20005, (202)289-2760
Sortir du Nucleaire [★IO]
SOS Children's Villages - India [IO], New Delhi, India
SOS Children's Villages - Jamaica [IO], Montego Bay, Jamaica
SOS Children's Villages - Kenya [IO], Nairobi, Kenya
SOS Children's Villages of Pakistan [IO], Lahore, Pakistan
SOS Femmes [IO], St. Dizier, France
SOS Outreach [22925], PO Box 2020, Avon, CO 81620, (970)926-9292
SOS Sahel Intl. - UK [IO], Oxford, United Kingdom
SOS Sexisme [IO], Meudon, France
SOSA Gliding Club [IO], Rockton, ON, Canada
Sosiaa-ja terveydenhuollon tietojenkasittely-yhdistys ry [★IO]
SOTENI Intl. [10893], 2366 Kemper Ln., Cincinnati, OH 45206, (513)961-2100

Sotos Syndrome Support Assn. [14629], PO Box 4626, Wheaton, IL 60189, (630)682-8815
Sotos Syndrome Support Assn. [14629], PO Box 4626, Wheaton, IL 60189, (630)682-8815
Sotsialno-Ekologicheskiy Soyuz [★IO]
SOUL [IO], Sana'a, Yemen
Soul Friends [16873], 300 Church St., Ste. 105, Wallingford, CT 06492, (203)679-0849
Soulforce [12112], PO Box 2499, Abilene, TX 79604, (434)384-7696
Soumen kielitieteellinen yhdistys [★IO]
Soumen Sulkapalloliitto [★IO]
Sound Healers Assn. [13711], PO Box 2240, Boulder, CO 80306, (303)443-8181
Sound and Music [IO], London, United Kingdom
SoundAid [★14924]
SoundAid [★14924]
SoundExchange [2573], 1121 Fourteenth St. NW, Ste. 700, Washington, DC 20005, (202)640-5858
South Africa
Art Aids Art [10819]
From Us With Love [12235]
South Africa Partners [18665]
South Africa Partners [18665]
South African Tourism [23442]
South African USA Chamber of Commerce [23379]
South Africa ACM SIGCHI [IO], Port Elizabeth, Republic of South Africa
South Africa Assn. of Tourism Professionals [IO], Johannesburg, Republic of South Africa
South Africa Inst. of Race Relations [IO], Johannesburg, Republic of South Africa
South Africa Partners [18665], 89 South St., Ste. 701, Boston, MA 02111, (617)443-1072
South Africa Partners [18665], 89 South St., Ste. 701, Boston, MA 02111, (617)443-1072
South Africa Stainless Steel Development Assn. [IO], Rivonia, Republic of South Africa
South African Acad. for Sci. and Arts [IO], Arcadia, Republic of South Africa
South African Aerospace Maritime and Defence Indus. Assn. [IO], Centurion, Republic of South Africa
South African Antique Dealers Assn. [IO], Parkhurst, Republic of South Africa
South African Archaeological Soc. [IO], Vlaeberg, Republic of South Africa
South African Article Numbering Assn. [★22943]
South African Assn. of Botanists [IO], Matieland, Republic of South Africa
South African Assn. of Competitive Intelligence Professionals [IO], Pretoria, Republic of South Africa
South African Assn. for Food Sci. and Tech. [IO], Durban, Republic of South Africa
South African Assn. of Freight Forwarders [IO], Bedfordview, Republic of South Africa
South African Assn. for Learning and Educational Difficulties [IO], Johannesburg, Republic of South Africa
South African Assn. for Marine Biological Res. [IO], Durban, Republic of South Africa
South African Assn. of Physicists in Medicine and Biology [IO], Bloemfontein, Republic of South Africa
South African Assn. of Women Graduates [IO], Benmore, Republic of South Africa
South African Avocado Growers' Assn. [IO], Tzaneen, Republic of South Africa
South African Boerboel Breeders Assn. - U.S.A. and Canada [22549], PO Box 532, Live Oak, FL 32064, (386)397-1172
South African Br. of the Intl. Law Assn. [IO], Sandton, Republic of South Africa
South African Broadcasting Corp. [IO], Auckland Park, Republic of South Africa
South African Chefs Assn. [IO], Melville, Republic of South Africa
South African Chem. Inst. [IO], Wits, Republic of South Africa
South African Coal Processing Soc. [IO], Johannesburg, Republic of South Africa
South African Cong. for Early Childhood Development [IO], Pretoria, Republic of South Africa

South African Coun. of Churches [IO], Marshalltown, Republic of South Africa
South African Coun. for the Proj. and Constr. Mgt. Professions [IO], Halfway House, Republic of South Africa
South African Coun. for the Quantity Surveying Profession [IO], Halfway House, Republic of South Africa
South African Coun. of Shopping Centres [IO], Sandton, Republic of South Africa
South African Coun. of World Affiliated YWCA [IO], Johannesburg, Republic of South Africa
South African Dental Assn. [IO], Gauteng, Republic of South Africa
South African Depression and Anxiety Gp. [IO], Benmore, Republic of South Africa
South African Educ. and Env. Proj. U.S.A. [12371], Charles Elkins, 4505 Lowell St. NW, Washington, DC 20016, (202)686-3518
South African Electrotechnical Export Coun. [IO], Halfway House, Republic of South Africa
South African Fed. of Civil Engg. Contractors [IO], Bedfordview, Republic of South Africa
South African Figure Skating Assn. [IO], Cape Town, Republic of South Africa
South African Fiscal Assn. [IO], Cape Town, Republic of South Africa
South African Freelancer's Assn. [IO], Phalaborwa, Republic of South Africa
South African Geophysical Assn. [IO], Gardenview, Republic of South Africa
South African Hea. Informatics Assn. [IO], Cape Town, Republic of South Africa
South African Holstein Breeders' Assn. [IO], Bloemfontein, Republic of South Africa
South African Inst. of Architects [IO], Randburg, Republic of South Africa
South African Inst. of Chartered Accountants [IO], Johannesburg, Republic of South Africa
South African Inst. of Forestry [IO], Pietermaritzburg, Republic of South Africa
South African Inst. of Intl. Affairs [IO], Braamfontein, Republic of South Africa
South African Inst. of Mining and Metallurgy [IO], Marshalltown, Republic of South Africa
South African Insurance Assn. [IO], Braamfontein, Republic of South Africa
South African Marfan Syndrome Org. [IO], Queenswood, Republic of South Africa
South African Masters Sports Assn. [IO], Johannesburg, Republic of South Africa
South African Mathematical Soc. [IO], Pietermaritzburg, Republic of South Africa
South African Medical Assn. [IO], Pretoria, Republic of South Africa
South African Medical Physics Soc. [IO], Cape Town, Republic of South Africa
South African Medical Res. Coun. [IO], Cape Town, Republic of South Africa
South African Museums Assn. [IO], Port Elizabeth, Republic of South Africa
South African Music Rights Org. [IO], Braamfontein, Republic of South Africa
South African Nasionale Verbruikerunie [★IO]
South African Natl. Biodiversity Inst. [IO], Pretoria, Republic of South Africa
South African Natl. Consumer Union [IO], Pretoria, Republic of South Africa
South African Natl. Coun. for the Blind [IO], Pretoria, Republic of South Africa
South African Natl. Coun. of YMCA's [IO], Braamfontein, Republic of South Africa
South African Natl. Seed Org. [IO], Lynnwood Ridge, Republic of South Africa
South African Natl. Tuberculosis Assn. [IO], Edenvale, Republic of South Africa
South African Nursing Assn. [★5694]
South African Optometric Assn. [IO], Halfway House, Republic of South Africa
South African Orchid Coun. [IO], Edenvale, Republic of South Africa
South African Orthopaedic Assn. [IO], Brandhof, Republic of South Africa
South African Paint Mfrs. Assn. [IO], Johannesburg, Republic of South Africa

A star before a book entry number signifies that the name is not listed separately, but is mentioned within the entry.

South African Petroleum Indus. Assn. [IO], Sandton, Republic of South Africa
South African Protea Producers and Exporters Assn. [IO], Paarl, Republic of South Africa
South African Red Cross Soc. [IO], Pretoria, Republic of South Africa
South African Reinforced Concrete Engineers' Assn. [IO], Bedfordview, Republic of South Africa
South African Scout Assn. [IO], Clareinch, Republic of South Africa
South African Soc. for Basic and Clinical Pharmacology [IO], Potchefstroom, Republic of South Africa
South African Soc. of Biochemistry and Molecular Biology [IO], Durban, Republic of South Africa
South African Soc. for Enology and Viticulture [IO], Dennesig, Republic of South Africa
South African Soc. of Music Teachers [IO], Menlo Park, Republic of South Africa
South African Soc. of Occupational Hea. Nursing Practitioners [IO], Boksburg, Republic of South Africa
South African Soc. of Physiotherapy [IO], Gardenview, Republic of South Africa
South African Soc. for Professional Engineers [IO], Sandton, Republic of South Africa
South African Soc. of Psychiatrists [IO], Wonderboom Poort, Republic of South Africa
South African Soc. of Teachers of the Alexander Technique [IO], Cape Town, Republic of South Africa
South African Soc. of Travel Medicine [IO], Johannesburg, Republic of South Africa
South African Speed Skating Assn. [IO], Gauteng, Republic of South Africa
South African Sports Confed. and Olympic Comm. [IO], Melrose, Republic of South Africa
South African Sports Medicine Assn. [IO], Bloemfontein, Republic of South Africa
South African Statistical Assn. [IO], Matieland, Republic of South Africa
South African Sugar Technologists' Assn. [IO], Mount Edgecombe, Republic of South Africa
South African Sugarcane Indus. Agronomists Assn. [IO], Durban, Republic of South Africa
South African Sugarcane Res. Inst. [IO], Mount Edgecombe, Republic of South Africa
South African Taekwondo Fed. [IO], Pretoria, Republic of South Africa
South African Tennis Assn. [IO], Saxonwold, Republic of South Africa
South African Textile Indus. Export Coun. [IO], Westlake, Republic of South Africa
South African Tourism [23442], 500 5th Ave., 20th Fl., Ste. 2040, New York, NY 10110, (212)730-2929
South African Tourism Bd. [★23442]
South African Tourist Corp. [★23442]
South African Translators' Inst. [IO], Johannesburg, Republic of South Africa
South African USA Chamber of Commerce [23379], 515 E Las Olas Blvd., Ste. 950, Fort Lauderdale, FL 33301-2278, (954)776-8158
South African USA Chamber of Commerce [23379], 515 E Las Olas Blvd., Ste. 950, Fort Lauderdale, FL 33301-2278, (954)776-8158
South African Venture Capital Assn. [IO], Houghton, Republic of South Africa
South African Veterinary Assn. [IO], Pretoria, Republic of South Africa
South African Water Ski Fed. [IO], Centurion, Republic of South Africa
South African Wind Energy Assn. [IO], Cape Town, Republic of South Africa
South African Women's Agricultural Union [IO], Centurion, Republic of South Africa
South African Youth Hostels Assn. [IO], Muizenberg, Republic of South Africa
South Am. Mission [20095], 1021 Maxwell Mill Rd., Ste. B, Fort Mill, SC 29708, (803)802-8580
South Amer. Athletic Confed. [IO], Manaus, Brazil
South Amer. Commn. for the Control of Foot-and-Mouth Disease [IO], Sao Bento, Brazil
South Amer. Explorers [3577], 126 Indian Creek Rd., Ithaca, NY 14850, (607)277-0488
South Amer. Explorers [3577], 126 Indian Creek Rd., Ithaca, NY 14850, (607)277-0488

South Amer. Explorers Club [★3577]
South Amer. Explorers Club [★3577]
South Amer. Indian Mission [★20095]
South Amer. Mission Prayer League [★19944]
South Amer. Mission Prayer League [★19944]
South Amer. Missionary Soc. - USA [★20094]
South Asia Alliance for Poverty Eradication [IO], Kathmandu, Nepal
South Asian Amer. Leaders of Tomorrow [18666], 6930 Carroll Ave., Ste. 506, Takoma Park, MD 20912, (301)270-1855
South Asian Amer. Voting Youth [18392], 1718 M St. NW, No. 290, Washington, DC 20036
South Asian Americans Leading Together [18644], 6930 Carroll Ave., Ste. 506, Takoma Park, MD 20912, (301)270-1855
South Asian Assn. for Regional Cooperation [IO], Kathmandu, Nepal
South Asian Journalists Assn. [2876], Columbia Graduate School of Journalism, 2950 Broadway, New York, NY 10027-7060, (212)854-5979
South Asian Journalists Assn. [2876], Columbia Graduate School of Journalism, 2950 Broadway, New York, NY 10027-7060, (212)854-5979
South Asian Language Teachers Assn. - Address unknown since 2010.
South Asian Public Hea. Assn. [16499], Mayur A. Patel, MS, Treas., 1105 Grant St., Evanston, IL 60201
South Asian Women's Centre [IO], Toronto, ON, Canada
South Australia Arts and Indus. Development [IO], Adelaide, Australia
South Australian Croquet Assn. [IO], Adelaide, Australia
South Australian Employers Chamber of Commerce and Indus. [IO], Unley, Australia
South Australian English Teachers Assn. [IO], Medindie, Australia
South Australian Photographic Fed. [IO], Park Holme, Australia
South Carolina Therapeutic Assn. [★11701]
South Centre [IO], Geneva, Switzerland
South Chesire Chamber [IO], Crewe, United Kingdom
South Dublin Chamber of Commerce [IO], Dublin, Ireland
South-East Asia Center [18509], 5120 N Broadway St., Chicago, IL 60640, (773)989-7433
South-East Asia Center [18509], 5120 N Broadway St., Chicago, IL 60640, (773)989-7433
South East Asia Investigations into Social and Humanitarian Activities [IO], Phnom Penh, Cambodia
South East Asia Iron and Steel Inst. [IO], Shah Alam, Malaysia
South East Folk Arts Network [IO], Brighton, United Kingdom
South Eastern Welsh Pony and Cob Assn. [IO], Heathfield, United Kingdom
South India ACM SIGCHI [IO], Chennai, India
South Okanagan Similkameen Brain Injury Soc. [IO], Penticton, BC, Canada
South Pacific Applied Geoscience Commn. [IO], Suva, Fiji
South Pacific Underwater Medicine Soc. [IO], Melbourne, Australia
South Rugby Union [★22861]
South Slavonic Catholic Union [★19043]
South St. Seaport Museum [10064], 12 Fulton St., New York, NY 10038, (212)748-8725
South Wales Chamber of Commerce [IO], Swansea, United Kingdom
South West Fed. of Croquet Clubs [IO], Budleigh Salterton, United Kingdom
South West Olive Assn. [IO], Balingup, Australia
South West Region Campaign for Nuclear Disarmament [IO], Exeter, United Kingdom
South-West Univ. for Nationalities [IO], Chengdu, People's Republic of China
South Western Assn. of WPCS [IO], Sherborne, United Kingdom
Southampton and Fareham Chamber of Commerce and Indus. [IO], Southampton, United Kingdom
Southeast Asia
Champa Cultural Preservation Assn. of USA [10636]

Southeast Asia Rsrc. Action Center [12790], 1628 16th St. NW, Washington, DC 20009-3099, (202)667-4690
Southeast Asian Geotechnical Soc. [IO], Pathumthani, Thailand
Southeast Asian Ministers of Educ. Org. [IO], Bangkok, Thailand
Southeast Asian Ministers of Educ. Org. Regional Centre for Archaeology and Fine Arts [IO], Bangkok, Thailand
Southeast Asian Regional Center for Graduate Stud. and Res. in Agriculture [IO], Laguna, Philippines
Southeast Desalting Assn. [5008], 2409 SE Dixie Hwy., Stuart, FL 34996, (772)781-7698
Southeast Inst. [★18630]
Southeast Inst. for Gp. and Family therapy [18630], 659 Edwards Ridge Rd., Chapel Hill, NC 27517-9201, (919)929-1171
Southeast Waterfowl Comm. [★5030]
Southeastern Assn. of Fish and Wildlife Agencies [5458], 8005 Freshwater Farms Rd., Tallahassee, FL 32308, (850)893-0084
Southeastern Assn. of Game and Fish Commissioners [★5458]
Southeastern Composers' League [10299], 4810 Cedarline Dr., Greensboro, NC 27409
Southeastern Conf. [23006], 2201 Richard Arrington Blvd. N, Birmingham, AL 35203, (205)458-3000
Southeastern Fisheries Assn. [3190], 1118-B Thomasville Rd., Tallahassee, FL 32303, (850)224-0612
Southeastern Florida Holocaust Memorial Center [★17785]
Southeastern Historical Keyboard Soc. [21959], PO Box 50092, Austin, TX 78763
Southeastern Legal Found. [5679], 2255 Sewell Mill Rd., Ste. 320, Marietta, GA 30062-7218, (770)977-2131
Southeastern Lumber Mfrs. Assn. [1480], 200 Greencastle Rd., Tyrone, GA 30290, (770)631-6701
Southeastern Manufactured Housing Inst. [★2309]
Southeastern Peanut Assn. [★4747]
Southeastern Poultry and Egg Assn. [★4818]
Southeastern Theatre Conf. [10602], 1175 Revolution Mill Dr., Ste. 14, Greensboro, NC 27405, (336)272-3645
Southern Africa Assn. for the Advancement of Sci. [IO], Irene, Republic of South Africa
Southern Africa Cat Coun. [IO], Kensington, Republic of South Africa
Southern Africa Fed. of the Disabled [IO], Bulawayo, Zimbabwe
Southern Africa HIV and AIDS Info. Dissemination Ser. [IO], Harare, Zimbabwe
Southern Africa Inst. for Mgt. Services [IO], Pretoria, Republic of South Africa
Southern Africa Network - Defunct.
Southern Africa Res. and Documentation Centre [IO], Harare, Zimbabwe
Southern African Acoustics Inst. [IO], Pierre van Ryneveld, Republic of South Africa
Southern African Assn. for Learning and Educational Difficulties [IO], Johannesburg, Republic of South Africa
Southern African Biofuels Assn. [IO], Vorna Valley, Republic of South Africa
Southern African Bird Ringing Unit [IO], Rondebosch, Republic of South Africa
Southern African Catholic Bishops' Conf. [IO], Pretoria, Republic of South Africa
Southern African Catholic Bishops' Conf. - Justice and Peace [IO], Pretoria, Republic of South Africa
Southern African Center for Cooperation in Agricultural and Natural Resources Res. and Training [IO], Gaborone, Botswana
Southern African Digital Broadcasting Assn. [IO], Cresta, Republic of South Africa
Southern African Hypertension Soc. [IO], Pretoria, Republic of South Africa
Southern African Inst. of Ecologists and Environmental Scientists [IO], Cape Town, Republic of South Africa
Southern African Inst. of Forestry [IO], Menlo Park, Republic of South Africa

Reference to "IO" in place of a book number signifies that the association may be found in the 50th edition of International Organizations.

Southern African Marketing Res. Assn. **[IO]**, Randburg, Republic of South Africa
Southern African Network of AIDS Ser. Organizations **[IO]**, Harare, Zimbabwe
Southern African Non-Governmental Org. Network **[IO]**, Braamfontein, Republic of South Africa
Southern African Soc. of Human Genetics **[IO]**, Johannesburg, Republic of South Africa
Southern African Soc. for Plant Pathology **[IO]**, Stellenbosch, Republic of South Africa
Southern Alberta Brain Injury Soc. **[IO]**, Calgary, AB, Canada
Southern Alberta Curling Assn. **[IO]**, Calgary, AB, Canada
Southern Alberta Epilepsy Assn. **[IO]**, Lethbridge, AB, Canada
Southern Apparel Contractors Assn. **[★200]**
Southern Apparel Contractors Assn. **[★200]**
Southern Asians
  Kappa Phi Gamma Sorority **[23746]**
  North Amer. South Asian Bar Assn. **[5678]**
  North Amer. South Asian Law Student Assn. **[8511]**
  South Asian Amer. Leaders of Tomorrow **[18666]**
  South Asian Americans Leading Together **[18644]**
Southern Assn. of Baptist Colleges and Schools **[★9012]**
Southern Assn. on Children Under Six **[★11505]**
Southern Assn. of Colleges and Schools **[8062]**, 1866 Southern Ln., Decatur, GA 30033-4033, (404)679-4500
Southern Assn. of Independent Fastener Distributors **[★1655]**
Southern Baptist Found. **[19332]**, 901 Commerce St., Ste. 600, Nashville, TN 37203, (615)254-8823
Southern Baptist Historical Lib. and Archives **[19333]**, 901 Commerce St., Ste. 400, Nashville, TN 37203-3630, (615)244-0344
Southern Bean Assn. - Address unknown since 2011.
Southern California Advt. Agencies Assn. **[★109]**
Southern California Hang Glider Assn. **[★22214]**
Southern California Right of Way Assn. **[★5958]**
Southern California Right of Way Assn. **[★5958]**
Southern California Souvenir Spoon Collectors Soc. **[★21299]**
Southern California Souvenir Spoon Collectors Soc. **[★21299]**
Southern Case Writers **[★3708]**
Southern Casualty and Surety Conf. **[★1990]**
Southern Center for Human Rights **[17223]**, 83 Poplar St. NW, Atlanta, GA 30303-2122, (404)688-1202
Southern Classified Advt. Managers Assn. **[106]**, PO Box 531335, Mountain Brook, AL 35253-1335, (205)592-0389
Southern Conf. **[23007]**, 702 N Pine St., Spartanburg, SC 29303, (864)591-5100
Southern Conf. of Black Mayors **[★5853]**
Southern Connecticut State Univ. Alumni Assn. **[18898]**, 501 Crescent St., New Haven, CT 06515, (203)392-8824
Southern Cotton Assn. **[985]**, 88 Union Ave., Ste. 1204, Memphis, TN 38103, (901)525-2272
Southern Cotton Ginners Assn. **[986]**, 874 Cotton Gin Pl., Memphis, TN 38106, (901)947-3104
Southern Counties Folk Fed. **[IO]**, Southampton, United Kingdom
Southern Counties Welsh Pony and Cob Assn. **[IO]**, Southampton, United Kingdom
Southern Cypress Mfrs. Assn. **[1481]**, 100 First Ave., Ste. 525, Pittsburgh, PA 15222, (412)244-0440
Southern Dental Assn. **[★14262]**
Southern Early Childhood Assn. **[11505]**, PO Box 55930, Little Rock, AR 72215-5930, (501)221-1648
Southern and Eastern African Mineral Centre **[IO]**, Dar es Salaam, United Republic of Tanzania
Southern Economic Assn. **[6635]**, Univ. of Tennessee at Chattanooga, 313 Fletcher Hall, Dept. 6106, 615 McCallie Ave., Chattanooga, TN 37403-2598, (423)425-4118
Southern Educ. Found. **[8063]**, 135 Auburn Ave. NE, 2nd Fl., Atlanta, GA 30303, (404)523-0001
Southern Environmental Assn. - Belize **[IO]**, Dangriga, Belize

Southern Flinders Olive Growers Assn. **[IO]**, Jamestown, Australia
Southern Forest Products Assn. **[1482]**, Southern Pine Coun., 2900 Indiana Ave., Kenner, LA 70065, (504)443-4464
Southern Furniture Mfrs. Assn. **[★1543]**
Southern Furniture Market **[★1550]**
Southern Governors' Assn. **[6002]**, Hall of the States, 444 N Capitol St. NW, Ste. 200, Washington, DC 20001, (202)624-5897
Southern Governors' Conf. **[★6002]**
Southern Hardwood Lumber Mfrs. Assn. **[★1509]**
Southern Hardwood Producers **[★1509]**
Southern Historical Assn. **[9121]**, Univ. of Georgia, Dept. of History, Rm. 111A, LeConte Hall, Athens, GA 30602-1602, (706)542-8848
Southern Humanities Conf. **[★9849]**
Southern Humanities Coun. **[9849]**, Mark Ledbetter, Exec. Dir., 228 Pine Grove Church Rd., Culloden, GA 31016, (478)960-0140
Southern Indus. Insurers' Conf. **[★1990]**
Southern Inst. for Appropriate Tech. **[★17198]**
Southern Inst. for Appropriate Tech. **[★17198]**
Southern Mutual Help Assn. **[11641]**, 3602 Old Jeanerette Rd., New Iberia, LA 70563, (337)367-3277
Southern Newspaper Publishers Assn. **[2965]**, 3680 N Peachtree Rd., Ste. 300, Atlanta, GA 30341, (404)256-0444
Southern Oak Flooring Indus. **[★600]**
Southern Paint and Wallcovering Dealers Assn. **[★2073]**
Southern Paint and Wallcovering Dealers Assn. **[★2073]**
Southern Peanut Growers **[4756]**, 1025 Sugar Pike Way, Canton, GA 30115, (770)751-6615
Southern Peanut Warehousemen's Assn. **[★4751]**
Southern Pine Coun. **[3703]**, SFPA, 2900 Indiana Ave., Kenner, LA 70065-4605, (504)443-4464
Southern Pine Inspection Bur. **[1483]**, PO Box 10915, Pensacola, FL 32524-0915, (850)434-2611
Southern Plywood Mfrs. Assn. **[★1510]**
Southern Poverty Law Center **[17327]**, 400 Washington Ave., Montgomery, AL 36104, (334)956-8200
Southern Poverty Law Center **[17327]**, 400 Washington Ave., Montgomery, AL 36104, (334)956-8200
Southern Presbyterian Peace Fellowship **[★18282]**
Southern Pressure Treaters' Assn. **[1484]**, PO Box 3219, Pineville, LA 71361-3219, (318)619-8589
Southern Public Admin. Educ. Found. **[5913]**, 122 W High St., Elizabethtown, PA 17022, (717)540-6126
Southern Pulp and Paper Safety Assn. **[★7218]**
Southern Purchasing Inst. **[★2974]**
Southern Region Campaign for Nuclear Disarmament **[IO]**, Southampton, United Kingdom
Southern Regional Coun. **[17328]**, 1201 W Peachtree St. NE, Ste. 2000, Atlanta, GA 30309-3453, (404)522-8764
Southern Sash and Door Jobbers Assn. **[★531]**
Southern Soc. for Philosophy and Psychology **[10431]**, Michael J. Beran, Treas., Language Res. Center, 3401 Panthersville Rd., Decatur, GA 30034
Southern Speech Assn. **[★8899]**
Southern Speech Commun. Assn. **[★8899]**
Southern States Commun. Assn. **[8899]**, Valdosta State Univ., 1500 N Patterson St., Valdosta, GA 31698, (229)333-5820
Southern States Indus. Coun. **[★17725]**
Southern Textile Assn. **[3455]**, PO Box 66, Gastonia, NC 28054, (704)215-4543
Southern U.S. Trade Assn. **[3725]**, 701 Poydras St., Ste. 3725, New Orleans, LA 70139, (504)568-5986
SouthernChristian Leadership Conf. **[17329]**, PO Box 89128, Atlanta, GA 30312, (404)522-1420
Southface Energy Inst. **[6757]**, 241 Pine St. NE, Atlanta, GA 30308, (404)872-3549
Southland Head Injury Soc. **[IO]**, Invercargill, New Zealand
Southwark Habitat for Humanity **[IO]**, London, United Kingdom
Southwest Assn. of Petroleum Geologists **[★6907]**
Southwest Bluegrass Assn. **[10300]**, PO Box 720974, Pinon Hills, CA 92372-0974
Southwest Case Res. Assn. **[7808]**, Univ. of South Alabama, Mitchell Coll. of Bus., Dept. of Mgt., Mobile, AL 36688, (251)460-6730

Southwest Celtic Music Assn. **[9471]**, 1920 Abrams Pkwy., No. 382, Dallas, TX 75214-6270
Southwest Coun. of La Raza **[★12146]**
Southwest Coun. of La Raza **[★12146]**
Southwest Developmental Vision Soc. **[★15993]**
Southwest Parks and Monuments Assn. **[★7145]**
Southwest Res. and Info. Center **[17473]**, PO Box 4524, Albuquerque, NM 87106, (505)262-1862
Southwest Spanish Mustang Assn. **[4645]**, PO Box 948, Antlers, OK 74523, (580)326-6005
Southwest Traditional Crop Conservancy Garden and Seed Bank **[★4107]**
Southwest Vintage Radio and Phonograph Soc. **[★22123]**
Southwest Voter Registration Educ. Proj. **[18393]**, Kelly USA, Bldg. 1670, 206 Lombard St., 2nd Fl., San Antonio, TX 78226, (210)922-0225
Southwestern Athletic Conf. **[23008]**, 2101 6th Ave. N, Ste. 700, Birmingham, AL 35203, (205)251-7573
Southwestern Bigfoot Res. Team **[★7248]**
Southwestern Donkey and Mule Soc. **[20954]**, Shirley Knott, Sec., PO Box 869, Collinsville, TX 76233, (254)947-4065
Southwestern Legal Found. **[★5656]**
Southwestern Legal Found. **[★5656]**
Southwestern Monuments Assn. **[★7145]**
Southwestern Peanut Growers Assn. - Address unknown since 2010.
Souvenir Building Collectors Soc. **[21404]**, 987 Safflower Ct., Rockwall, TX 75087-6106, (972)772-5755
Souvenir Napoleonien **[IO]**, Paris, France
Souvenir Spoon Collectors of Am. **[★21299]**
Souvenir Spoon Collectors of Am. **[★21299]**
Souvenir Wholesale Distributors Assn. **[2791]**, Marci L. Hickey, CMP, Exec. VP, 2105 Laurel Bush Rd., Ste. 200, Bel Air, MD 21015, (443)640-1055
Sovereign Hospitaller Order of Saint John - Defunct.
Sovereign Military Order of Malta - Canadian Assn. **[IO]**, Ottawa, ON, Canada
Sovereignty Intl. **[17950]**, PO Box 191, Hollow Rock, TN 38342, (731)986-3999
Sovereignty Intl. **[17950]**, PO Box 191, Hollow Rock, TN 38342, (731)986-3999
Soviet Union
  Ashburn Inst. **[18343]**
  Rossica Soc. of Russian Philately **[22068]**
  Soc. for Co-operation in Russian and Soviet Stud. **[540]**
  U.S. Assn. of Former Members of Cong. **[17414]**
Soycrafters Assn. of North Am. **[★3961]**
Soyfoods Assn. of North Am. **[3961]**, 1050 17th St. NW, Ste. 600, Washington, DC 20036, (202)659-3520
Soyuz Arkhitektorov Rossii **[★IO]**
Sozialdemokratische Partei Deutschlands **[★IO]**
Sozialdemokratische Partei Osterreichs **[★IO]**
Sozialdienst Katholischer Frauen **[IO]**, Dortmund, Germany
Sozialverband Vdk Deutschland **[IO]**, Bonn, Germany
SP 250 Register **[IO]**, Dorking, United Kingdom
Spa Assn. **[3127]**, PO Box 270637, Fort Collins, CO 80527, (970)218-5414
Spa Assn. Singapore **[IO]**, Singapore, Singapore
Spa Bus. Assn. **[IO]**, Rayleigh, United Kingdom
Space
  Fed. of Galaxy Explorers **[8874]**
  Global Network Against Weapons and Nuclear Power in Space **[18199]**
  Intl. Lunar Observatory Assn. **[6231]**
  Intl. Soc. for Aviation Photography **[2724]**
  Lifeboat Found. **[18667]**
  Mars Soc. **[7452]**
  Moon Soc. **[7453]**
  Space Access Soc. **[7454]**
  Space Frontier Found. **[7455]**
  Space Frontier Found. **[7455]**
  Space Stud. Bd. **[7456]**
  Space Stud. Inst. **[6099]**
  Space Topic Stud. Unit **[22080]**
Space Access Soc. **[7454]**, 5515 N 7th St., No. 134-348, Phoenix, AZ 85014
Space Assn. of Australia **[IO]**, Mulgrave, Australia

A star before a book entry number signifies that the name is not listed separately, but is mentioned within the entry.

Space Coast Writers' Guild [10742], PO Box 262, Melbourne, FL 32902-0262

Space Energy Assn. [6098], PO Box 1136, Clearwater, FL 33757-1136, (954)749-6553

Space Enterprise Coun. [157], 1615 H St. NW, Washington, DC 20062-2000, (800)638-6582

Space and Flight Equip. Assn. [★6095]

Space Found. [7696], 4425 Arrowswest Dr., Colorado Springs, CO 80907, (719)576-8000

Space Frontier Found. [7455], 16 1st Ave., Nyack, NY 10960, (800)787-7223

Space Frontier Found. [7455], 16 1st Ave., Nyack, NY 10960, (800)787-7223

Space Stud. Bd. [7456], Natl. Res. Coun., 500 5th St. NW, Washington, DC 20001, (202)334-3477

Space Stud. Inst. [6099], 1434 Flightline St., Mojave, CA 93501, (661)750-2774

Space Topic Educ. Program [★7697]

Space Topic Stud. Unit [22080], Carmine Torrisi, Sec., PO Box 780241, Maspeth, NY 11378

Space Topic Stud. Unit [22080], Carmine Torrisi, Sec., PO Box 780241, Maspeth, NY 11378

Space Topics Study Group [★22080]

Space Topics Study Group [★22080]

Space Trans. Assn. [6100], Richard Coleman, Pres., 4305 Underwood St., University Park, MD 20782, (703)855-3917

Space Unit [★22080]

Space Unit [★22080]

Spain

Spanish Water Dog Assn. of Am. [21654]

Spain-United States Chamber of Commerce [23380], Empire State Bldg., 350 5th Ave., Ste. 2600, New York, NY 10118, (212)967-2170

Spain-United States Chamber of Commerce [23380], Empire State Bldg., 350 5th Ave., Ste. 2600, New York, NY 10118, (212)967-2170

Spalding Univ. Alumni Assn. [18899], 845 S 3rd St., Louisville, KY 40203, (502)585-7111

SpanAfrica [11642], 736 Cole St., San Francisco, CA 94117

SpanAfrica [11642], 736 Cole St., San Francisco, CA 94117

Spaniel Club Francais [IO], Lussac-les-Chateaux, France

Spanish

Amer. Assn. of Teachers of Spanish and Portuguese [8463]

Queen Sofia Spanish Inst. [10539]

Queen Sofia Spanish Inst. [10539]

Sigma Delta Pi [23753]SpanishSoc. of Spanish and Spanish-American Stud.

Spanish Water Dog Assn. of Am. [21654]

Twentieth Century Spanish Assn. of Am. [10540]

Twentieth Century Spanish Assn. of Am. [10540]

Spanish Aerosols Assn. [IO], Barcelona, Spain

Spanish Alpha 1 Assn. [IO], Cadiz, Spain

Spanish ALS Assn. [IO], Madrid, Spain

Spanish American War

Independence Seaport Museum [20759]

Sons of Spanish Amer. War Veterans [20760]

Spanish Article Numbering Assn. [IO], Barcelona, Spain

Spanish Assn. Against Osteoporosis [IO], Madrid, Spain

Spanish Assn. of Beer and Malt Technicians [IO], Madrid, Spain

Spanish Assn. of Bioenterprises [IO], Madrid, Spain

Spanish Assn. of Dance Sport and Competition Dancing [IO], Barcelona, Spain

Spanish Assn. of Digestive Endoscopy [IO], Pamplona, Spain

Spanish Assn. of Egg Producers [IO], Madrid, Spain

Spanish Assn. of Flour and Semolina Mfrs. [IO], Madrid, Spain

Spanish Assn. of Irrigation Mfrs. [IO], Madrid, Spain

Spanish Assn. of the Meat Indus. [IO], Madrid, Spain

Spanish Assn. of Multiple Sclerosis [IO], Madrid, Spain

Spanish Assn. for Parents with Autistic Children [IO], Madrid, Spain

Spanish Assn. for Pattern Recognition and Image Anal. [IO], Granada, Spain

Spanish Assn. of Petroleum Products Operators [IO], Madrid, Spain

Spanish Assn. of Sugar Confectionery and Chewing Gum Mfrs. [IO], Barcelona, Spain

Spanish Assn. of Toy Mfrs. [IO], Ibi, Spain

Spanish-Barb Breeders Assn. [4646], PO Box 1628, Silver City, NM 88062

Spanish Bottled Water Assn. [IO], Madrid, Spain

Spanish Bus. Coun. [IO], Dubai, United Arab Emirates

Spanish Chamber of Commerce in Great Britain [IO], London, United Kingdom

Spanish Colonial Arts Soc. [9658], PO Box 5378, Santa Fe, NM 87502-5378, (505)982-2226

Spanish Confed. of Animal Feed Mfrs. [IO], Madrid, Spain

Spanish Confed. of Bus. Organisations [IO], Madrid, Spain

Spanish Confed. of Family Alzheimer Associations [IO], Pamplona, Spain

Spanish Confed. of Medical and Tech. Advisers Associations [IO], Ourense, Spain

Spanish Confed. of Plastics Indus. [IO], Madrid, Spain

Spanish Confed. of Small and Medium-Sized Companies [IO], Madrid, Spain

Spanish Cotton Spinners and Weavers Assn. [IO], Barcelona, Spain

Spanish Dairy Fed. [IO], Madrid, Spain

Spanish Economic Assn. [IO], Bilbao, Spain

Spanish Entomological Assn. [IO], Alicante, Spain

Spanish Ethological Soc. [IO], Barcelona, Spain

Spanish Exporters and Mfrs. of Table Olives Assn. [IO], Seville, Spain

Spanish Fed. of Clothing Companies [IO], Madrid, Spain

Spanish Fed. of Elecl. Appliances Retailers [IO], Madrid, Spain

Spanish Food and Drink Indus. Fed. [IO], Madrid, Spain

Spanish Gas Assn. [IO], Barcelona, Spain

Spanish Heritage Assn. [★8378]

Spanish Heritage Assn. [★8378]

Spanish Heritage-Herencia Espanola [★8378]

Spanish Heritage-Herencia Espanola [★8378]

Spanish Hotel Fed. [IO], Madrid, Spain

Spanish Inventors Club [IO], Barcelona, Spain

Spanish Jewelry, Silverware and Watches Assn. [IO], Madrid, Spain

Spanish Knitting Assn. [IO], Barcelona, Spain

Spanish League Against Epilepsy [IO], Madrid, Spain

Spanish Microscopy Soc. [IO], Cadiz, Spain

Spanish Motor Vehicle Manufactures' Assn. [IO], Madrid, Spain

Spanish Mustang Registry [4647], 323 County Rd. 419, Chilton, TX 76632, (254)546-2177

Spanish Natl. Honor Soc. [★8250]

Spanish Neuromodulation Soc. [IO], Florence, Italy

Spanish-Norman Horse Registry [4648], Linda Osterman-Hamid, Registrar, PO Box 985, Woodbury, CT 06798, (203)266-4048

Spanish Olive Oil Exporters Assn. [IO], Madrid, Spain

Spanish Paint and Printing Inks Manufactures' Assn. [IO], Madrid, Spain

Spanish Paper Inst. [IO], Madrid, Spain

Spanish Paralympic Comm. [IO], Madrid, Spain

Spanish Reproduction Rights Centre [IO], Madrid, Spain

Spanish Royal Soc. of Physics [IO], Madrid, Spain

Spanish Soc. of Anatomy [IO], Madrid, Spain

Spanish Soc. for Biochemistry and Molecular Biology [IO], Madrid, Spain

Spanish Soc. of Biomedical Engg. [IO], Madrid, Spain

Spanish Soc. of Cardiology [IO], Madrid, Spain

Spanish Soc. for Cartography, Photogrammetry and Remote Sensing [IO], Madrid, Spain

Spanish Soc. of Ceramic and Glass [IO], Madrid, Spain

Spanish Soc. of Cosmetic Chemists [IO], Barcelona, Spain

Spanish Soc. of Gravitation and Relativity [IO], Leioa, Spain

Spanish Soc. of Hea. Informatics [IO], Madrid, Spain

Spanish Soc. and League of Hypertension [IO], Madrid, Spain

Spanish Soc. of Pharmacology [IO], Barcelona, Spain

Spanish Soc. of Plastic, Reconstructive and Aesthetic Surgery [IO], Madrid, Spain

Spanish Soc. of Proteomics [IO], Cordoba, Spain

Spanish Soc. of Psychosomatic Obstetrics and Gynaecology [IO], Madrid, Spain

Spanish Soc. of Real Chemistry [IO], Madrid, Spain

Spanish Soc. of Rheumatology [IO], Madrid, Spain

Spanish Stainless Steel Development Assn. [IO], Madrid, Spain

Spanish Statistical and Operations Res. Soc. [IO], Madrid, Spain

Spanish Textile Machinery Mfrs. Assn. [IO], Barcelona, Spain

Spanish Unihockey and Floorball Assn. [IO], Madrid, Spain

Spanish Water Dog Assn. of Am. [21654], Nancy P. Valley, Treas., 308 Granite Rd., Guilford, CT 06437

Spanish Wine Fed. [IO], Madrid, Spain

Spanish World Gospel Broadcasting [★20096]

Spanish World Gospel Broadcasting [★20096]

Spanish World Gospel Mission [★20096]

Spanish World Gospel Mission [★20096]

Spanish World Ministries [20096], PO Box 542, Winona Lake, IN 46590-0542, (574)267-8821

Spanish World Ministries [20096], PO Box 542, Winona Lake, IN 46590-0542, (574)267-8821

Spanish Youth Hostels [IO], Madrid, Spain

Spark Ventures [11407], PO Box 479329, Chicago, IL 60647, (773)293-6710

Sparks Family Assn. [20591], Nancy Sparks Frank, 6395 Black Water Trail, Atlanta, GA 30328-2756

Sparrow Clubs U.S.A. [11506], 906 NE Greenwood Ave., Ste. 2, Bend, OR 97701, (541)312-8630

Spartacist League - Address unknown since 2010.

Spasmodic Dysphonia Assn; Natl. [15622]

Spasmodic Torticollis Assn; Natl. [15623]

The Spastic Centre of New South Wales [IO], Sydney, Australia

SPCA of Illinois [★10928]

SPCA Intl. [11041], PO Box 8682, New York, NY 10001

Speakability [IO], London, United Kingdom

Speakers on Asian Topics [17708], 18600 Walkers Choice Rd., Ste. 4, Montgomery Village, Gaithersburg, MD 20886, (301)990-8831

Speakers Res. Comm. for the United Nations [★18745]

Speakers Res. Comm. for the United Nations [★18745]

Speaking Out About Rape [12759], 3208 E Colonial Dr., Unit 243, Orlando, FL 32803, (321)278-5246

Special Care Dentistry Assn. [14310], 401 N Michigan Ave., Ste. 2200, Chicago, IL 60611, (312)527-6764

Special Comm. of 24 [★17330]

Special Comm. of 24 [★17330]

Special Comm. on Decolonization [★17330]

Special Comm. on Decolonization [★17330]

Special Comm. on the Situation with Regard to the Implementation of the Declaration on the Granting of Independence to Colonial Countries and Peoples [17330], UN HQ, Rm. IN-637A, 300 East 42nd St., New York, NY 10017, (212)963-3051

Special Comm. on the Situation with Regard to the Implementation of the Declaration on the Granting of Independence to Colonial Countries and Peoples [17330], UN HQ, Rm. IN-637A, 300 East 42nd St., New York, NY 10017, (212)963-3051

Special Constituency Sect. for Mental Hea. and Psychiatric Services [★16327]

Special Constituency Sect. for Psychiatric and Substance Abuse Services [★16327]

Special Days

Arbor Day Found. [18668]

Golden Glow of Christmas Past [22155]

Natl. Father's Day/Mother's Day Coun. [18669]

Thanks-Giving Found. [18670]

Thanks-Giving Found. [18670]

Special Education

Amer. Coun. on Rural Special Educ. [8875]

AVKO Educational Res. Found. [8876]

Coun. of Administrators of Special Educ. [8877]

Coun. for Children with Behavioral Disorders [8878]

Reference to "IO" in place of a book number signifies that the association may be found in the 50th edition of International Organizations.

Coun. for Exceptional Children [8879]
Coun. of Parent Attorneys and Advocates [8880]
Div. on Career Development and Transition [8881]
Div. for Early Childhood of the Coun. for Exceptional Children [8882]
Div. on Visual Impairments [8883]
Found. for Exceptional Children [11788]
Gifted Learning Proj. [12424]
Inter-American Conductive Educ. Assn. [8884]
Inter-American Conductive Educ. Assn. [8884]
Kate's Voice [8764]
Natl. Assn. of Parents with Children in Special Educ. [8885]
Natl. Assn. of Private Special Educ. Centers [8886]
Natl. Assn. of Special Educ. Teachers [8887]
Natl. Assn. of State Directors of Special Educ. [8888]
Natl. Rsrc. Center for Paraprofessionals in Educ. and Related Services [8889]

Special Forces
Special Forces Assn. [20761]
Special Forces Assn. [20761], PO Box 41436, Fayetteville, NC 28309-1436, (910)485-5433
Special Indus. Radio Ser. Assn. [★3407]
Special Interest Comm. for Computers and the Physically Handicapped [★6517]
Special Interest Gp. on Accessible Computing [6517], 2 Penn Plz., Ste. 701, New York, NY 10121-0701, (212)626-0500
Special Interest Gp. on Ada [7301], Ricky E. Sward, Chm., The MITRE Corp., 1155 Acad. Park Loop, Colorado Springs, CO 80910, (719)572-8263
Special Interest Gp. on Algorithms Computability Theory [★7296]
Special Interest Gp. on Artificial Intelligence [6212], Assn. for Computing Machinery, 2 Penn Plz., Ste. 701, New York, NY 10121-0701, (212)626-0605
Special Interest Gp. on Automata and Computability Theory [★7296]
Special Interest Gp. on Biomedical Computing [★6504]
Special Interest Gp. for Biomedical Info. Processing [★6504]
Special Interest Gp. on Cmpt. and Human Interaction [6267], 1515 Broadway, New York, NY 10036, (212)626-0500
Special Interest Gp. for Cmpt. Personnel Res. [★6527]
Special Interest Group for Computer Personnel Res. - Defunct.
Special Interest Group for Computer Uses in Education - Defunct.
Special Interest Gp. for Computers and the Physically Handicapped [★6517]
Special Interest Gp. on Data Commun. [★6473]
Special Interest Gp. on Data Communications of the Assn. for Computing Machinery [6518], 1414 Massachusetts Ave., Boxborough, MA 01719, (978)936-1292
Special Interest Gp. for Design Automation [6472], PO Box 6000, Binghamton, NY 13902, (607)777-2943
Special Interest Gp. on Design of Commun. [6561], Assn. for Computing Machinery, 2 Penn Plz., Ste. 701, New York, NY 10121-0701, (212)626-0605
Special Interest Gp. for Documentation [★6561]
Special Interest Gp. on Info. Retrieval [6992], 140 Governors Dr., Amherst, MA 01003-9264, (413)545-3240
Special Interest Gp. on Mgt. of Data [6473], Univ. of Pittsburgh, Dept. of Cmpt. Sci., Pittsburgh, PA 15260-9161, (412)624-8843
Special Interest Gp. on Mobility of Systems Users, Data, and Computing [6562], Fran Spinola, Prog. Coor., 2 Penn Plz., Ste. 701, New York, NY 10121-0701, (212)626-0603
Special Interest Group on Numerical Mathematics - Defunct.
Special Interest Gp. on Programming Languages [7302], Matthew Flatt, 50 Central Campus Dr., Rm. 3190, Salt Lake City, UT 84112, (801)587-9091
Special Interest Gp. on Simulation [6474], PO Box 3082, Auburn, AL 36831, (334)844-6360
Special Interest Gp. for Social and Behavioral Sci. Computing [★6267]

Special Interest Gp. on Supporting Work Gp. - Defunct.
Special Interest Group for Univ. and Coll. Computing Services - Defunct.
Special Libraries Assn. [10013], 331 S Patrick St., Alexandria, VA 22314-3501, (703)647-4900
Special Libraries Assn. [10013], 331 S Patrick St., Alexandria, VA 22314-3501, (703)647-4900
Special Military Active Retired Travel Club [20690], 600 Univ. Off. Blvd., Ste. 1A, Pensacola, FL 32504, (850)478-1986
Special Military Active Retired Travel Club [20690], 600 Univ. Off. Blvd., Ste. 1A, Pensacola, FL 32504, (850)478-1986
Special Olympics [22525], 1133 19th St. NW, Washington, DC 20036, (202)628-3630
Special Olympics [22525], 1133 19th St. NW, Washington, DC 20036, (202)628-3630
Special Olympics Albania [IO], Tirana, Albania
Special Olympics Algeria [IO], Algiers, Algeria
Special Olympics Andorra [IO], Andorra la Vella, Andorra
Special Olympics Armenia [IO], Yerevan, Armenia
Special Olympics Australia [IO], Concord, Australia
Special Olympics Austria [IO], Schladming, Austria
Special Olympics Bahrain [IO], Manama, Bahrain
Special Olympics Bangladesh [IO], Dhaka, Bangladesh
Special Olympics Belarus [IO], Minsk, Belarus
Special Olympics Benin [IO], Cotonou, Benin
Special Olympics Bolivia [IO], La Paz, Bolivia
Special Olympics Bosnia and Herzegovina [IO], Sarajevo, Bosnia-Hercegovina
Special Olympics Botswana [IO], Gaborone, Botswana
Special Olympics Bulgaria [IO], Sofia, Bulgaria
Special Olympics Burkina Faso [IO], Ouagadougou, Burkina Faso
Special Olympics Cameroon [IO], Yaounde, Cameroon
Special Olympics Canada [IO], Toronto, ON, Canada
Special Olympics Chad [IO], N'Djamena, Chad
Special Olympics Congo [IO], Brazzaville, Republic of the Congo
Special Olympics Costa Rica [IO], San Jose, Costa Rica
Special Olympics Cote d'Ivoire [IO], Abidjan, Cote d'Ivoire
Special Olympics Croatia [IO], Zagreb, Croatia
Special Olympics Cuba [IO], Havana, Cuba
Special Olympics Cyprus [IO], Nicosia, Cyprus
Special Olympics Czech Republic [IO], Prague, Czech Republic
Special Olympics Deutschland [IO], Berlin, Germany
Special Olympics East Asia [IO], Beijing, People's Republic of China
Special Olympics Ecuador [IO], Quito, Ecuador
Special Olympics Egypt [IO], Giza, Egypt
Special Olympics El Salvador [IO], San Salvador, El Salvador
Special Olympics Emirates [IO], Sharjah, United Arab Emirates
Special Olympics Finland [IO], Slu, Finland
Special Olympics Gambia [IO], Bakau, Gambia
Special Olympics Ghana [IO], Accra, Ghana
Special Olympics Greece [IO], Athens, Greece
Special Olympics Honduras [IO], Tegucigalpa, Honduras
Special Olympics Iceland [IO], Reykjavik, Iceland
Special Olympics Iran [IO], Tehran, Iran
Special Olympics Ireland [IO], Dublin, Ireland
Special Olympics Italy [IO], Rome, Italy
Special Olympics Jordan [IO], Amman, Jordan
Special Olympics Kenya [IO], Nairobi, Kenya
Special Olympics Kuwait [IO], Hawalli, Kuwait
Special Olympics Latvia [IO], Riga, Latvia
Special Olympics Lebanon [IO], Beirut, Lebanon
Special Olympics Lesotho [IO], Maseru, Lesotho
Special Olympics Libya [IO], Tripoli, Libyan Arab Jamahiriya
Special Olympics Malawi [IO], Blantyre, Malawi
Special Olympics Malaysia [IO], Selangor, Malaysia
Special Olympics Mali [IO], Bamako, Mali
Special Olympics Mauritania [IO], Nouakchott, Mauritania

Special Olympics Mauritius [IO], Beau Bassin, Mauritius
Special Olympics Moldova [IO], Chisinau, Moldova
Special Olympics Namibia [IO], Windhoek, Namibia
Special Olympics Netherlands [IO], Bunnik, Netherlands
Special Olympics Niger [IO], Niamey, Niger
Special Olympics Nippon Japan [IO], Tokyo, Japan
Special Olympics Norway [IO], Oslo, Norway
Special Olympics Oman [IO], Muscat, Oman
Special Olympics Paraguay [IO], Asuncion, Paraguay
Special Olympics Philippines [IO], Quezon City, Philippines
Special Olympics Poland [IO], Warsaw, Poland
Special Olympics Portugal [IO], Lisbon, Portugal
Special Olympics Qatar [IO], Doha, Qatar
Special Olympics Reunion [IO], La Possession, France
Special Olympics Russia [IO], Moscow, Russia
Special Olympics Rwanda [IO], Kigali, Rwanda
Special Olympics Saudi Arabia [IO], Riyadh, Saudi Arabia
Special Olympics Senegal [IO], Dakar, Senegal
Special Olympics Seychelles [IO], Victoria, Seychelles
Special Olympics Slovakia [IO], Bratislava, Slovakia
Special Olympics Slovenia [IO], Ljubljana, Slovenia
Special Olympics South Africa [IO], Sandton, Republic of South Africa
Special Olympics Spain [IO], Barcelona, Spain
Special Olympics Sudan [IO], Khartoum, Sudan
Special Olympics Swaziland [IO], Mbabane, Swaziland
Special Olympics Sweden [IO], Stockholm, Sweden
Special Olympics Switzerland [IO], Fribourg, Switzerland
Special Olympics Syria [IO], Damascus, Syrian Arab Republic
Special Olympics Tanzania [IO], Dar es Salaam, United Republic of Tanzania
Special Olympics Thailand [IO], Bangkok, Thailand
Special Olympics Togo [IO], Lome, Togo
Special Olympics Uganda [IO], Kampala, Uganda
Special Olympics Uruguay [IO], Montevideo, Uruguay
Special Olympics Yemen [IO], Sana'a, Yemen
Special Olympics Zambia [IO], Lusaka, Zambia
Special Olympics Zimbabwe [IO], Harare, Zimbabwe
Special Recreation for Disabled [★11831]
Special Recreation for Disabled [★11831]
Special Recreation for disABLED Intl. [11831], 701 Oaknoll Dr., Iowa City, IA 52246-5168, (319)466-3192
Special Recreation for disABLED Intl. [11831], 701 Oaknoll Dr., Iowa City, IA 52246-5168, (319)466-3192
A Special Wish Found. [11507], 1250 Memory Ln., Columbus, OH 43209, (614)258-3186
Specialist Access Engg. and Maintenance Assn. [IO], Chesterfield, United Kingdom
Speciality Automotive Mfrs. Assn. [★337]
Specialized Carriers and Rigging Assn. [3270], 2750 Prosperity Ave., Ste. 620, Fairfax, VA 22031-4312, (703)698-0291
Specialized Carriers and Rigging Assn. [3270], 2750 Prosperity Ave., Ste. 620, Fairfax, VA 22031-4312, (703)698-0291
Specialized Info. Publishers Assn. [2966], 8229 Boone Blvd., Ste. 260, Vienna, VA 22182, (703)992-9339
Specialized Info. Publishers Assn. [2966], 8229 Boone Blvd., Ste. 260, Vienna, VA 22182, (703)992-9339
Specialized Info. Publishers Assn. - United Kingdom [IO], Surrey, United Kingdom
Specialty Advt. Assn. [★103]
Specialty Advt. Assn. [★103]
Specialty Advt. Assn. Intl. [★103]
Specialty Advt. Assn. Intl. [★103]
Specialty Advt. Guild Intl. [★103]
Specialty Advt. Guild Intl. [★103]
Specialty Advt. Natl. Assn. [★103]
Specialty Advt. Natl. Assn. [★103]
Specialty Coffee Assn. of Am. [452], 330 Golden Shore, Ste. 50, Long Beach, CA 90802, (562)624-4100

A star before a book entry number signifies that the name is not listed separately, but is mentioned within the entry.

Specialty Coffee Assn. of Europe [IO], Chelmsford, United Kingdom

Specialty Crop Trade Coun. [4472], 710 Striker Ave., Sacramento, CA 95834, (916)561-5900

Specialty Equip. Mfrs. Assn. [★338]

Specialty Equip. Market Assn. [338], 1575 S Valley Vista Dr., Diamond Bar, CA 91765, (909)396-0289

Specialty Graphic Imaging Assn. [1631], 10015 Main St., Fairfax, VA 22031-3489, (703)385-1335

Specialty Graphic Imaging Assn. [1631], 10015 Main St., Fairfax, VA 22031-3489, (703)385-1335

Specialty Sleep Assn. [1556], 46639 Jones Ranch Rd., Friant, CA 93626, (559)868-4187

Specialty Steel Indus. of North Am. [2494], 3050 K St. NW, Washington, DC 20007, (202)342-8630

Specialty Steel Indus. of the U.S. [★2494]

Specialty Tools and Fasteners Distributors Assn. [1869], PO Box 44, Elm Grove, WI 53122, (262)784-4774

Specialty Vehicle Inst. of Am. [339], ATV Safety Inst., 2 Jenner St., Ste. 150, Irvine, CA 92618-3806, (949)727-3727

Specialty Vehicle Inst. of Am. I ATV Safety Inst. [13008], 2 Jenner St., Ste. 150, Irvine, CA 92618-3806, (949)727-3727

Specialty Wine Retailers Assn. [3671], 915 L St., Ste. 1000, Sacramento, CA 95814, (707)266-1449

Specialty Wire Assn. [★1804]

Species Alliance [5132], 5200 San Pablo Ave., Emeryville, CA 94608, (510)594-8355

Species Iris Gp. of North Am. [21825], Rodney Barton, Membership Sec., 3 Wolters St., Hickory Creek, TX 75065

Spectroscopy

Amer. Soc. for Mass Spectrometry [7457]

Coblentz Soc. [7458]

Soc. for Applied Spectroscopy [7459]

Speech

Acad. of Rehabilitative Audiology [14910]

Amer. Forensic Assn. [8890]

Amer. Parliamentary Debate Assn. [8891]

Corporate Speech Pathology Network [3303]

Deaf Bilingual Coalition [12137]

Deaf and Hard of Hearing Alliance [14929]

Deaf Intl. [12139]

Delta Sigma Rho - Tau Kappa Alpha [23754]

Dogs for the Deaf [14933]

Intl. Debate Educ. Assn. [18671]

Model Secondary School for the Deaf [14946]

Natl. Assn. of Urban Debate Leagues [8892]

Natl. Catholic Forensic League [8893]

Natl. Commun. Assn. [8894]

Natl. Forensic Assn. [8895]

Natl. Forensic League [8896]

Natl. Parliamentary Debate Assn. [8897]

NFHS Speech, Debate and Theatre Assn. [8898]

Rhetoric Soc. of Am. [10512]

Southern States Commun. Assn. [8899]

VoiceCare Network [8900]

Speech Arts; Natl. Assn. of Dramatic and [10587]

Speech Assn. of Am. [★8894]

Speech Commun. Assn. [★8894]

Speech Found. of Am. [★16692]

Speech and Hearing

Acad. of Rehabilitative Audiology [14910]

Amer. Acad. of Audiology [16679]

Amer. Inst. for Stuttering Treatment and Professional Training [16680]

Amer. Neurotology Soc. [16681]

Amer. Speech Language Hearing Assn. [16682]

Amer. Tinnitus Assn. [16683]

Canadian Stuttering Assn. [16915]

Childhood Apraxia of Speech Assn. [16684]

Deaf Bilingual Coalition [12137]

Deaf and Hard of Hearing Alliance [14929]

Deaf Intl. [12139]

DeafHope [12141]

DOVE: Advocacy Services for Abused Deaf Women and Children [12142]

Friends: The Natl. Assn. of Young People Who Stutter [16685]

House Ear Inst. [16686]

Intl. Catholic Deaf Assn. U.S. Sect. [19435]

Model Secondary School for the Deaf [14946]

Natl. Black Assn. for Speech-Language and Hearing [16687]

Natl. Center for Voice and Speech [16688]

Natl. Coalition on Auditory Processing Disorders [14949]

Natl. Cued Speech Assn. [16689]

Natl. Student Speech Language Hearing Assn. [16690]

Natl. Stuttering Assn. [16691]

Stuttering Found. of Am. [16692]

Voice Found. [16693]

Speech Language Hearing Assn. Singapore [IO], Singapore, Singapore

Speech Pathology Australia [IO], Melbourne, Australia

Speed Equip. Mfrs. Assn. [★338]

Speed Skating Canada [IO], Ottawa, ON, Canada

Speedskating; U.S. [22903]

SPEEDUP Soc.: Swiss Forum for GRID and High Performance Computing [IO], Zurich, Switzerland

Speleological Fed. of Latin Am. and the Caribbean [IO], Havana, Cuba

Speleology

Assn. for Mexican Cave Stud. [7460]

Assn. for Mexican Cave Stud. [7460]

Cave Res. Found. [7461]

Natl. Speleological Soc. [7462]

Spellbinders [10547], PO Box 1986, Basalt, CO 81621, (970)544-2389

The Spelling Soc. [IO], Wellesbourne, United Kingdom

Spencer Family Assn. [★20663]

Spencer Found. [11910], 625 N Michigan Ave., Ste. 1600, Chicago, IL 60611, (312)337-7000

Spencer Historical and Genealogical Soc. [20663], Debbie Diekema, Registrar, 68281 Birch St., South Haven, MI 49090-9780

Sphere Proj. [IO], Geneva, Switzerland

Sphinx Org. [10301], 400 Renaissance Ctr., Ste. 2550, Detroit, MI 48243, (313)877-9100

SPI Composites Inst. - Defunct.

Spice Indus. Assn. [IO], Bonn, Germany

Spices Bd. of India [IO], Cochin, India

Spidshundeklubben [★IO]

SPIE [7190], PO Box 10, Bellingham, WA 98227-0010, (360)676-3290

SPIE [7190], PO Box 10, Bellingham, WA 98227-0010, (360)676-3290

Spill Control Assn. of Am. [2788], 2105 Laurel Bush Rd., Ste. 200, Bel Air, MD 21015, (443)640-1085

Spina Bifida

Spina Bifida Assn. of Am. [16694]

Spina Bifida Assn. of Am. [16694], 4590 MacArthur Blvd. NW, Washington, DC 20007-4226, (202)944-3285

Spina Bifida Assn. of Japan [IO], Tokyo, Japan

Spina-bifida et Hydrocephalie Canada [★IO]

Spina Bifida and Hydrocephalus Assn. of Canada [IO], Winnipeg, MB, Canada

Spina Bifida und Hydrocephalus Osterreich [IO], Vienna, Austria

Spinal Cord Injuries Australia [IO], Matraville, Australia

Spinal Cord Injury Professionals, Nurses Sect; Amer. Assn. of [★15699]

Spinal Cord Res. Found. [★20416]

Spinal Cord Soc. [16704], 19051 County Hwy. 1, Fergus Falls, MN 56537-7609, (218)739-5252

Spinal Cord Tumor Assn. [16705], PO Box 461, Jay, FL 32565, (850)675-6663

Spinal Hea. Intl. [16706], 2221 NW 3rd Pl., Gainesville, FL 32603

Spinal Injuries Action Assn. [IO], Dublin, Ireland

Spinal Injuries Assn. [IO], Milton Keynes, United Kingdom

Spinal Injury

Amer. Assn. of Spinal Cord Injury Professionals, Psychologists and Social Workers Sect. [16695]

Amer. Paraplegia Soc. [16696]

Amer. Spinal Injury Assn. [16697]

Assn. for Medical Ethics [16698]

Cervical Spine Res. Soc. [16699]

Cervical Spine Res. Soc. [16699]

Christopher and Dana Reeve Found. [16700]SpinalIntl. Intradiscal Therapy Soc.

Intl. Soc. for Minimal Intervention in Spinal Surgery [16701]SpinalIntl. Spinal Development and Res. Found.

Intl. Spine Intervention Soc. [16702]

Natl. Spinal Cord Injury Assn. [16703]

Spinal Cord Soc. [16704]

Spinal Cord Tumor Assn. [16705]

Spinal Hea. Intl. [16706]

Spinal Injuries Action Assn. [11987]

ThinkFirst Natl. Injury Prevention Found. [16707]

World Spine Care [16708]

Spinal Injury Assn; Amer. [16697]

Spine Arthroplasty Soc. [15688], 2323 Cheshire Dr., Ste. 101, Aurora, IL 60502, (630)995-9994

Spine Radiology; Amer. Soc. of [16528]

Spine Soc. of Europe [IO], Uster, Switzerland

Spine Soc; North Amer. [15672]

Spine Soc; North Amer. [15672]

Spinners and Weavers Assn. of Korea [IO], Seoul, Republic of Korea

Spinning and Weaving Assn. [3456], PO Box 7506, Loveland, CO 80537, (970)613-4629

Spirit of Am. [18499], 12021 Wilshire Blvd., Ste. 507, Los Angeles, CA 90025, (310)405-0220

Spirit of Drum Corps Alumni Assn. [IO], Calgary, AB, Canada

Spirit Indus. Trade Assn. [733], 6992 Dublin Rd., Dublin, OH 43017

Spirit Quilts [11408], PO Box 3268, Paradise, CA 95967, (530)873-2765

Spirit of the Sage Coun. [4144], 439 Westwood Ctr., No. 144, Fayetteville, NC 28314, (626)676-4116

Spirit of Women [15068], 2424 N Fed. Hwy., Ste. 100, Boca Raton, FL 33431, (561)544-0755

Spirits Indus. Fed. [IO], Buenos Aires, Argentina

Spiritual Assembly of the Baha'is of Malaysia [IO], Kuala Lumpur, Malaysia

Spiritual Counterfeits Proj. [19642], PO Box 4308, Berkeley, CA 94704-0308, (510)540-0300

Spiritual Directors Intl. [20196], PO Box 3584, Bellevue, WA 98009-3584, (425)455-1565

Spiritual Directors Intl. [20196], PO Box 3584, Bellevue, WA 98009-3584, (425)455-1565

Spiritual Life

Afghan Hindu Assn. of Am. [19810]

Amer. Hindu Assn. [19811]

Arthur Morgan Inst. for Community Solutions [17368]

Assn. for the Restoration of Church and Home [19613]

Catholic Athletes for Christ [22230]

Dharma Drum Mountain Buddhist Assn. [19364]

Found. for the Preservation of the Mahayana Tradition [19367]

Hanuman Found. [12208]

Inst. for Theological Encounter With Sci. and Tech. [12215]

Jagannath Org. for Global Awareness [20213]

Makatab Tarighat OveyssiShahmaghsoudi [20249]

Mooncircles [20250]

Morris Pratt Inst. Assn. [20142]

Natl. Spiritualist Assn. of Churches I Healers League [20145]

Soc. of the Companions of the Holy Cross [19716]

Soc. for the Stud. of Christian Spirituality [19601]

Sri Aurobindo Assn. [20301]

Theosophical Book Assn. for the Blind [20264]

U.S. Assn. of Consecrated Virgins [19507]

Spiritual Life Inst. [20253], NADA Hermitage, PO Box 219, Crestone, CO 81131, (719)256-4778

Spiritual Life Inst. [20253], NADA Hermitage, PO Box 219, Crestone, CO 81131, (719)256-4778

Spiritual Life Inst. of Am. [★20253]

Spiritual Life Inst. of Am. [★20253]

Spiritual Ministry - Defunct.

Spiritual Sci. Fellowship [IO], Montreal, QC, Canada

Spiritual Understanding

Aetherius Soc. [20243]

Aetherius Soc. [20243]

Amer. Hindu Assn. [19811]

Assn. for the Restoration of Church and Home [19613]

Black Holocaust Soc. [17154]

Christian Universalist Assn. [19560]

Circle Sanctuary [20244]

Circle Sanctuary [20244]

Coun. on Spiritual Practices [20245]

Reference to "IO" in place of a book number signifies that the association may be found in the 50th edition of International Organizations.

Dharma Drum Mountain Buddhist Assn. [19364]
Found. for a Course in Miracles [20246]
Found. for the Preservation of the Mahayana Tradition [19367]
Hanuman Found. [12208]
Inst. of Noetic Sciences [10541]
Inst. for Theological Encounter With Sci. and Tech. [12215]
Interfaith Church of Metaphysics [20247]
Intl. Center for Spirit at Work [20248]
Intl. Center for Spirit at Work [20248]
Jagannath Org. for Global Awareness [20213]
Jews for Judaism [20186]
Makatab Tarighat OveyssiShahmaghsoudi [20249]
Monks Without Borders [19826]
Mooncircles [20250]
Morris Pratt Inst. Assn. [20142]
Muhyiddin Ibn Arabi Soc. [20251]
Natl. Spiritualist Assn. of Churches | Healers League [20145]
Pathwork Helpers Assn. of North Am. [20252]
Pediatric Chaplains Network [19529]
Saq' Be': Org. for Mayan and Indigenous Spiritual Bodies [9867]
Soc. of the Companions of the Holy Cross [19716]
Soc. for the Stud. of Christian Spirituality [19601]
Spiritual Life Inst. [20253]
Spiritual Life Inst. [20253]
Spiritual Unity of Nations [20254]
Sri Aurobindo Assn. [20301]
The Swedenborg Proj. [8901]
Tayu Center [20255]
Temple of Understanding [20256]
Thanks-Giving Square [20257]
Thanks-Giving Square [20257]
Theosophical Book Assn. for the Blind [20264]
Universal Pantheist Soc. [20258]
Urantia Found. [20259]
Urantia Found. [20259]
Vedic Friends Assn. [10542]
Wainwright House [20260]
White Mountain Educ. Assn. [20261]
World Sound Healing Org. [12640]
Spiritual Unity of Nations [20254], PO Box 9553, Wyoming, MI 49509, (616)531-1339
Spiritualist
Saq' Be': Org. for Mayan and Indigenous Spiritual Bodies [9867]
Spiritualist Yoga Fellowship [IO], Montreal, QC, Canada
Spirituality and Practice [7929], 15 W 24th St., 10th Fl., New York, NY 10010, (212)691-5240
Spitz Dog Club [IO], Ebeltoft, Denmark
SPJST [19058], PO Box 100, Temple, TX 76503, (800)727-7578
Spohr Soc. of Great Britain [IO], Sheffield, United Kingdom
Spokane, Portland and Seattle Railway Historical Soc. [10500], 2618 NW 113th St., Vancouver, WA 98685
Spolecenstvo organizatoru veletrznich a vystavnich akci [★IO]
Spolecnost pro Elektroakustickou Hudbu [IO], Prague, Czech Republic
Spolecnost pro Projektove Rizeni [★IO]
Spolecnost pro Vedy a Umeni [★9528]
Spolecnost pro Vedy a Umeni [★9528]
Spolecnost na pomoc osobam s autizmom [★IO]
Spolecnost biomedicinskeho inzinierstva a medicinskej informatiky [★IO]
Spolecnost pre Planovane Rodicovstvo [★IO]
Spolecnost pre Projektove Riadenie [★IO]
Spondylitis Assn. of Am. [16627], PO Box 5872, Sherman Oaks, CA 91413, (818)981-1616
Sponge and Chamois Inst. [2206], 10024 Off. Center Ave., Ste. 203, St. Louis, MO 63128, (314)842-2230
Sponsors of Open Housing Investment [★17894]
Spoons Across Am. [15845], 540 Pres. St., 3rd Fl., Brooklyn, NY 11215, (718)522-4921
Sport Aircraft Assn. of Australia - Chap. 2 Camden [IO], Picton, Australia
Sport Aircraft Assn. of Australia - Chap. 4 South Coast [IO], Figtree, Australia

Sport Aircraft Assn. of Australia - Chap. 5 Central Coast [IO], Toronto, Australia
Sport Aircraft Assn. of Australia - Chap. 6 Coffs Harbour [IO], Nambucca Heads, Australia
Sport Aircraft Assn. of Australia - Chap. 8 Mangalore [IO], Newport, Australia
Sport Aircraft Assn. of Australia - Chap. 11 Hills District, New South Wales [IO], Richmond, Australia
Sport Aircraft Assn. of Australia - Chap. 12 Sydney Southern [IO], Oatley, Australia
Sport Aircraft Assn. of Australia - Chap. 13 Albany District, Western Australia [IO], Redmond, Australia
Sport Aircraft Assn. of Australia - Chap. 14 Latrobe Valley [IO], Newborough, Australia
Sport Aircraft Assn. of Australia - Chap. 15 Queensland [IO], Sunnybank Hills, Australia
Sport Aircraft Assn. of Australia - Chap. 17 Pallamana-Murray Bridge [IO], Norwood, Australia
Sport Aircraft Assn. of Australia - Chap. 18 Melbourne [IO], Templestowe, Australia
Sport Aircraft Assn. of Australia - Chap. 19 Gold Coast [IO], Hope Island, Australia
Sport Aircraft Assn. of Australia - Chap. 20 Kyneton District [IO], Newham, Australia
Sport Aircraft Assn. of Australia - Chap. 22 Sunshine Coast, Queensland [IO], Beerwah, Australia
Sport Aircraft Assn. of Australia - Chap. 23 Frogs Hollow, New South Wales [IO], Merimbula, Australia
Sport Aircraft Assn. of Australia - Chap. 24 Jandakot, Western Australia [IO], South Perth, Australia
Sport Aircraft Assn. of Australia - Chap. 25 Port Lincoln [IO], Port Lincoln, Australia
Sport Balloon Soc. of the U.S.A. - Defunct.
Sport Canada [IO], Gatineau, QC, Canada
Sport Climbing Australia [IO], St. Peters, Australia
Sport Fishery Res. Found. [★22570]
Sport Interuniversitaire Canadien [★IO]
Sport Mgt. Assn. of Australia and New Zealand [IO], Lindfield, Australia
Sport Marketing Assn. [3339], Univ. of Memphis, 204B Fieldhouse, Memphis, TN 38152
Sport Northern Ireland [IO], Belfast, United Kingdom
Sport Nova Scotia [IO], Halifax, NS, Canada
Sport Physiotherapy Canada [IO], Ottawa, ON, Canada
Sport and Recreation Law Assn. [23022], Mary Myers, Asst. Exec. Dir., 1608 N Redbarn St., Wichita, KS 67212
Sport Taekwondo Papua New Guinea [IO], Boroko, Papua New Guinea
Sport Wales [IO], Cardiff, United Kingdom
SportAccord [IO], Lausanne, Switzerland
Sporting Arms and Ammunitions Mfrs. Inst. [1355], 11 Mile Hill Rd., Newtown, CT 06470-2359, (203)426-4358
Sporting Goods
Amer. Fly-Fishing Trade Assn. [3304]
Archery Trade Assn. [3305]
Archery Trade Assn. [3305]
Assn. of Golf Merchandisers [3306]
Bicycle Prdt. Suppliers Assn. [3307]
Billiard and Bowling Inst. of Am. [3308]
Diving Equip. and Marketing Assn. [3309]
Diving Equip. and Marketing Assn. [3309]
Fed. of the European Sporting Goods Indus. [18872]
Fletchers' Company [13814]
Intl. Clubmakers' Guild [3310]
Kite Trade Assn. Intl. [3311]
Kite Trade Assn. Intl. [3311]
Natl. Assn. of Sporting Goods Wholesalers [3312]
Natl. Bicycle Dealers Assn. [3313]
Natl. Ski and Snowboard Retailers Assn. [3314]
Natl. Sporting Goods Assn. [3315]
Paddlesports Indus. Assn. [3316]
Soccer Indus. Coun. of Am. [3317]
Sporting Goods Mfrs. Assn. [3318]
Sporting Goods Mfrs. Assn. [3318]
Tennis Indus. Assn. [3319]
Trade Assn. of Paddlesports [3320]
Trade Assn. of Paddlesports [3320]
Water Sports Indus. Assn. [3321]
Sporting Goods Mfrs. Assn. [★3318]

Sporting Goods Mfrs. Assn. [3318], 8505 Fenton St., Ste. 211, Silver Spring, MD 20910, (301)495-6321
Sporting Goods Mfrs. Assn. [3318], 8505 Fenton St., Ste. 211, Silver Spring, MD 20910, (301)495-6321
Sporting Goods Shippers Assn. [3271], 3250 Spanish Springs Ct., Sparks, NV 89434, (775)356-9931
Sporting Wheelies and Disabled Sport and Recreation Assn. of Queensland [IO], Bowen Hills, Australia
Sports
Access Fund [22959]
African Baseball Network [22260]
Aikido Assn. of Am. [22216]
All Japan Ju-Jitsu Intl. Fed. [22720]
Amateur Athletic Union [22960]
Am. Outdoors Assn. [22835]
Amer. Amputee Hockey Assn. [22961]
Amer. Amputee Soccer Assn. [22932]
Amer. Assn. of Snowboard Instructors [22923]
Amer. Barefoot Waterski Club [23114]
Amer. Boating Assn. [22315]
Amer. Canoe Assn. [23120]
Amer. Collegiate Hockey Assn. [22639]
Amer. Coon Hunters Assn. [22696]
Amer. Junior Rodeo Assn. [22839]
Amer. Legion Baseball [22265]
Amer. Lumberjack Assn. [22962]
Amer. Polo Horse Assn. [22812]
Amer. Power Boat Assn. [22316]
Amer. Ski-Bike Assn. [22963]
Amer. Sports Assn. [3322]
Amer. Turners [22964]
Amer. Ultrarunning Assn. [22862]
Amer. Volkssport Assn. [22965]
Archery Range and Retailers Org. [3323]
Assn. of Canadian Mountain Guides [13150]
Assn. of Luxury Suite Directors [3324]
Assn. of Minor League Umpires [22266]
Assn. for Professional Basketball Res. [22293]
Assn. of Professional Towsurfers [23030]
Assn. of Volleyball Professionals [23297]
Athletes in Action [19731]
Athletic Equip. Managers Assn. [22966]
Athletic Inst. [3325]
Atlantic Coast Conf. [22967]
Bass Anglers Sportsman Soc. [22572]
Big East Conf. [22968]
Big Ten Conf. [22969]
Big West Conf. [22970]
Billiard Cong. of Am. [22308]
BlazeSports Am. [22508]
Blind Sailing Intl. [23109]
Blueliners [23899]
Bobby Labonte Fan Club [23900]
Bowling Proprietors' Assn. of Am. [3326]
Canine Freestyle Fed. [22545]
Catholic Athletes for Christ [22230]
Central Intercollegiate Athletic Assn. [22971]
Chen Qingzhou Martial Arts Assn., USA [22728]
Christian Cheerleaders of Am. [22450]
Christian Wrestling Fed. [23131]
Cinderella Softball Leagues [22951]
Citizenship Through Sports Alliance [22972]
Cleveland Hockey Booster Club [23901]
Coalition for Anabolic Steroid Precursor and Ephedra Regulation [16718]
Coll. Athletic Bus. Mgt. Assn. [22973]
Coll. Sports Info. Directors of Am. [22974]
Continental Basketball League [22294]
Coun. of Ivy Gp. Presidents [22975]
Cross Country Ski Areas Assn. [3327]
Dale Jarrett Fan Club [23902]
Devils Fan Club [23903]
Diesel Hot Rod Assn. [22823]
Eastern Coll. Athletic Conf. [22643]
Eastern Winter Sports Representatives Assn. [3328]
Fantasy Sports Trade Assn. [3329]
Fed. of Fly Fishers [22574]
Fed. of Gay Games [22976]
Fed. of Gay Games [22976]
Fed. of Intl. Lacrosse [22713]
Football Writers Assn. of Am. [22588]
Force 5 Class Assn. [22336]
FUNDaFIELD [11288]

A star before a book entry number signifies that the name is not listed separately, but is mentioned within the entry.

Gay and Lesbian Rowing Fed. [22855]
Geary 18 Intl. Yacht Racing Assn. [22338]
Gin Soon Tai Chi Chuan Fed. [22733]
Global Sports Alliance USA [22977]
Golf Coaches Assn. of Am. [22608]
Golf Course Builders Assn. of Am. [3330]
Golf Course Superintendents Assn. of Am. [3331]
Golf Range Assn. of Am. [3332]
Golf Writers Assn. of Am. [22610]
Hampton One-Design Class Racing Assn. [22340]
Harness Horse Youth Found. [22652]
Hartford Whalers Booster Club [23904]
Highlander Class Intl. Assn. [22341]
Home School Sports Network [22978]
Impact Sports Intl. [22979]
Intercollegiate Assn. of Amateur Athletes of Am.
[22980]
InterCollegiate Horse Show Assn. [22682]
Intercollegiate Women's Lacrosse Coaches Assn.
[22714]
Intl. Aeronauts League [21203]
Intl. Assn. of Gay and Lesbian Martial Artists
[22734]
Intl. Athletic Found. [14904]
Intl. Chinese Boxing Assn. [22436]
Intl. Dodge Ball Fed. [22981]
Intl. Fed. of Competitive Eating [22982]
Intl. Female Boxers Assn. [22437]
Intl. Fitness Assn. [16227]
Intl. Gravity Sports Assn. [22983]
Intl. Gravity Sports Assn. [22983]
Intl. Hobie Class Assn. [22353]
Intl. Laser Class Assn. - North Amer. Region
[22356]
Intl. League of Professional Baseball Clubs
[22272]
Intl. Modern Hapkido Fed. [22735]
Intl. Natural Bodybuilding and Fitness Fed.
[22418]
Intl. Physical Fitness Assn. [3333]
Intl. Physical Fitness Assn. [3333]
Intl. Rafting Fed. [22837]
Intl. Seven-Star Mantis Style Lee Kam Wing
Martial Art Assn. USA [22736]
Intl. Shuffleboard Assn. [22892]
Intl. Sports Heritage Assn. [22984]
Intl. Sungja-Do Assn. [22738]
Intl. Trotting and Pacing Assn. [22656]
Intl. Women's Flag Football Assn. [22589]
Intl. Yang Style Tai Chi Chuan Assn. [22740]
Intl. Youth Conditioning Assn. [23139]
Japanese Assn. for Women in Sport [5890]
Johnny Benson Fan Club [23791]
Kids Enjoy Exercise Now [21474]
Los Angeles Kings Booster Club [23905]
Maccabi USA/Sports for Israel [22985]
Martial Arts Intl. Fed. [22742]
Martial Arts Teachers' Assn. [22743]
Men's Collegiate Lacrosse Assn. [22715]
Midwest Winter Sports Representatives Assn.
[3334]
Miniature Golf Assn. of the U.S. [22986]
Mountaineering Ireland [3675]
Mounted Games Across Am. [22987]
Natl. Advt. Golf Assn. [22616]
Natl. Alliance for the Development of Archery
[22222]
Natl. Amer. Semi-Professional Baseball Assn.
[22279]
Natl. Archery Assn. of the U.S. [22223]
Natl. Assn. of Athletic Development Directors
[22988]
Natl. Assn. of Collegiate Directors of Athletics
[22989]
Natl. Assn. of Collegiate Gymnastics Coaches/
Women [22633]
Natl. Assn. of Collegiate Marketing Administrators
[22990]
Natl. Assn. of Intercollegiate Athletics [22991]
Natl. Assn. of Left-Handed Golfers [22617]
Natl. Assn. of Professional Baseball Leagues
[22280]
Natl. Assn. of Underwater Instructors [23104]
Natl. Basketball Players Assn. [23298]
Natl. Bass Anglers Assn. [22581]

Natl. Butterfly Assn. [22371]
Natl. Christian Barrel Racers Assn. [22660]
Natl. Christian Coll. Athletic Assn. [22992]
Natl. Club Baseball Assn. [22283]
Natl. Coalition Against Violent Athletes [22231]
Natl. Collegiate Athletic Assn. [22993]
Natl. Coun. for Taekwondo Masters Certification
[22746]
Natl. Coun. of Youth Sports [22994]
Natl. Fastpitch Coaches Assn. [22995]
Natl. Fed. of State High School Associations
[22996]
Natl. Finals Rodeo Comm. [22844]
Natl. Football League [22591]
Natl. Golf Course Owners Assn. [3335]
Natl. Golf Found. [3336]
Natl. Hockey League Booster Clubs [23906]
Natl. Horseshoe Pitchers Assn. of Am. [22695]
Natl. Intramural-Recreational Sports Assn. [22997]
Natl. Junior Baseball League [22285]
Natl. Junior Coll. Athletic Assn. [22998]
Natl. Scholastic Surfing Assn. [23035]
Natl. Softball Assn. [22954]
Natl. Starwind/Spindrift Class Assn. [22377]
Natl. Surf Schools and Instructors Assn. [23036]
Natl. Team Cheng Martial Arts Assn. [22747]
Natl. Versatility Ranch Horse Assn. [22686]
Natural Fitness Trainers Assn. [22809]
New England Trails Conf. [23090]
New York Islanders Booster Club [23907]
New York Rangers Fan Club [23908]
NFHS Coaches Assn. [22465]
North Amer. Booster Club Assn. [3337]
North Amer. Bowhunting Coalition [21866]
North Amer. Bungee Assn. [22999]
North Amer. Bungee Assn. [22999]
North Amer. Dog Agility Coun. [22548]
North Amer. Football League [22593]
North Amer. Hunting Club [22700]
North Amer. One-Armed Golfer Assn. [22521]
North Amer. Ski Joring Assn. [23000]
North-South Skirmish Assn. [22885]
OrganicAthlete [22232]
Org. of Spirit Indus. Providers [22452]
Over the Hill Gang, Intl. [23001]
Over the Hill Gang, Intl. [23001]
Pacific 10 Conf. [23002]
Philadelphia Flyers Fan Club [23909]
Pittsburgh Penguins Booster Club [23910]
Polish Amer. Golf Assn. [22620]
Professional Baseball Athletic Trainers Soc.
[22289]
Professional Climbing Instructors Assn. [22455]
Professional Figure Skaters Cooperative [22897]
Professional Football Chiropractic [14143]
Professional Football Players Mothers' Assn.
[22595]
Professional Golf Teachers Assn. of Am. [22621]
Professional Lacrosse Players Assn. [23299]
Professional Putters Assn. [22623]
Professional Windsurfers Assn. [22385]
Protect Our Winters [4298]
Protection Sports Assn. [23003]
Qajaq U.S.A. [23124]
Race for Peace [18285]
Red Wing For'em Club [23911]
Ride and Tie Assn. [23004]
RollerSoccer Intl. Fed. [23005]
RollerSoccer Intl. Fed. [23005]
Salute Military Golf Assn. [22624]
Scottish Athletics [15617]
Self-Guided Hunting Assn. [21867]
Senior Roller Skaters of Am. [22899]
Sikh Sports Assn. of the U.S.A. [22894]
SnowSports Indus. Am. [3338]
Soccer Without Borders [22942]
Southeastern Conf. [23006]
Southern Conf. [23007]
Southwestern Athletic Conf. [23008]
Spirit Indus. Trade Assn. [733]
Sport Marketing Assn. [3339]
Sport and Recreation Law Assn. [23022]
Sports Charities U.S.A. [23009]
Sportscar Vintage Racing Assn. [22249]
Sportsplex Operators and Developers Assn.
[23010]

Table Shuffleboard Assn. [22893]
Thoroughbred Club of Am. [22666]
United Barrel Racing Assn. [22670]
United Natl. Weight Pull Assn. [22550]
U.S. A-Class Catamaran Assn. [22400]
U.S. Albacore Assn. [22401]
U.S.A. Deaf Basketball [22300]
U.S. Assn. of Independent Gymnastic Clubs
[3340]
U.S. Auto Club [22250]
U.S. Bobsled and Skeleton Fed. [22926]
U.S. Boomerang Assn. [22422]
U.S. Broomball Assn. [23011]
U.S. Club Soccer [22944]
U.S. Collegiate Athletic Assn. [23012]
U.S. Competitive Aerobics Fed. [22209]
U.S. Dental Tennis Assn. [23062]
U.S. Disc Sports [22536]
U.S. Flag Football League [22599]
U.S. Futsal Fed. [23013]
U.S. Hunter Jumper Assn. [22691]
U.S. Kuo Shu Fed. [22759]
U.S. Lawn Bowls Assn. [22430]
U.S. Modern Pentathlon Assn. [23071]
U.S. Mondioring Assn. [22552]
U.S. Muay Thai Assn. [22761]
U.S. Olympic Comm. [22791]
U.S. Parachute Assn. [22800]
U.S. Power Squadrons [22405]
U.S. Powered Paragliding Assn. [22796]
U.S. ProMiniGolf Assn. [22627]
U.S. Racquet Stringers Assn. [3341]
U.S. Ski Mountaineering Assn. [22917]
U.S. Ski Team Found. [22919]
U.S. Snooker Assn. [22311]
U.S. Sports Acad. [23014]
U.S. Taekwondo Union [22763]
U.S. Twirling Assn. [22306]
U.S. Wayfarer Assn. [22410]
U.S. Women's Curling Assn. [22473]
Univ. Athletic Assn. [23015]
Up2Us [13563]
USA Athletes Intl. [22233]
U.S.A. Cricket Assn. [23016]
USA Diving [22544]
USA Gymnastics [22636]
USA Hockey [22647]
U.S.A. Karate Fed. [22766]
USA Natl. Karate-do Fed. [22710]
USA Professional Platform Tennis Assn. [23066]
USA Pulling [23074]
USA Volleyball [23111]
USGA Green Sect. [22628]
Vintage Base Ball Assn. [22292]
Washington Capitals Fan Club [23912]
Watering Seeds Org. [22532]
Western Athletic Conf. [23017]
Western Winter Sports Representatives Assn.
[3342]
Women Outdoors [22797]
Women's All-Star Assn. [22432]
Women's Sports Found. [23018]
World Confed. of Billiard Sports [22313]
World Fast-Draw Assn. [22891]
World Fed. of Athletic Training and Therapy
[16722]
World Footbag Assn. [23019]
World Footbag Assn. [23019]
World Hapkido Assn. [22767]
The World Kuoshu Fed. [22770]
World Martial Arts Assn. [22771]
World Masters Cross-Country Ski Assn. [22921]
World Mudo Fed. [22773]
World Sport Stacking Assn. [23020]
World Sport Stacking Assn. [23020]
World T.E.A.M. Sports [22534]
Sports Ambassadors [20097], Dwight D. Eisenhower
Bldg., 1956 Ambassador Way, Spokane, WA
99224, (509)568-7000
Sports Car Club of Am. [21167], PO Box 19400,
Topeka, KS 66619-0400, (785)357-7222
Sports Charities U.S.A. [23009], 1100 Larkspur
Landing Cir., Ste. 340, Larkspur, CA 94939,
(800)874-0740
Sports Coach UK [IO], Leeds, United Kingdom

Reference to "IO" in place of a book number signifies that the association may be found in the 50th edition of International Organizations.

Sports Dietitians Australia **[IO]**, South Melbourne, Australia
Sports Facilities
   Am. Outdoors Assn. **[22835]**
   Amer. Barefoot Waterski Club **[23114]**
   Amer. Blind Bowling Assn. **[22502]**
   Amer. Junior Rodeo Assn. **[22839]**
   Cinderella Softball Leagues **[22951]**
   Fed. of Intl. Lacrosse **[22713]**
   Hampton One-Design Class Racing Assn. **[22340]**
   Harness Horse Youth Found. **[22652]**
   Intl. Assn. of Gay and Lesbian Martial Artists **[22734]**
   Maccabi USA/Sports for Israel **[22985]**
   Natl. Assn. of Underwater Instructors **[23104]**
   Natl. Junior Baseball League **[22285]**
   Natl. Scholastic Surfing Assn. **[23035]**
   Natl. Softball Assn. **[22954]**
   Natl. Starwind/Spindrift Class Assn. **[22377]**
   New England Trails Conf. **[23090]**
   Professional Baseball Athletic Trainers Soc. **[22289]**
   Sportscar Vintage Racing Assn. **[22249]**
   Stadium Managers Assn. **[23021]**
   U.S. Bobsled and Skeleton Fed. **[22926]**
   U.S. Competitive Aerobics Fed. **[22209]**
   U.S. Dental Tennis Assn. **[23062]**
   U.S. Disc Sports **[22536]**
   USA Diving **[22544]**
   U.S.A. Karate Fed. **[22766]**
   USA Volleyball **[23111]**
   USGA Green Sect. **[22628]**
   Women Outdoors **[22797]**
   Women's All-Star Assn. **[22432]**
   World Fast-Draw Assn. **[22891]**
   World Masters Cross-Country Ski Assn. **[22921]**
Sports Fed. and Olympic Comm. of Hong Kong, China **[IO]**, Hong Kong, People's Republic of China
Sports Field Contractors Association - Defunct.
Sports Goods Export Promotion Coun. **[IO]**, New Delhi, India
Sports Journalists' Assn. of Great Britain **[IO]**, South Croydon, United Kingdom
Sports Law
   Sport and Recreation Law Assn. **[23022]**
   Sports Lawyers Assn. **[5981]**
Sports Lawyers Assn. **[5981]**, 12100 Sunset Hills Rd., Ste. 130, Reston, VA 20190, (703)437-4377
Sports Leaders UK **[IO]**, Milton Keynes, United Kingdom
Sports Medical Comm. of Ethiopia **[IO]**, Addis Ababa, Ethiopia
Sports Medicine
   Acad. for Sports Dentistry **[16709]**
   Acad. for Sports Dentistry **[16709]**
   Amer. Acad. of Podiatric Sports Medicine **[16710]**
   Amer. Coll. of Sports Medicine **[16711]**
   Amer. Medical Soc. for Sports Medicine **[16712]**
   Amer. Orthopaedic Soc. for Sports Medicine **[16713]**
   Amer. Osteopathic Acad. of Sports Medicine **[16714]**
   Amer. Sports Medicine Inst. **[16715]**
   Assn. for Applied Sport Psychology **[16716]**
   Assn. for Applied Sport Psychology **[16716]**
   Big Picture Alliance **[16717]**
   Coalition for Anabolic Steroid Precursor and Ephedra Regulation **[16718]**
   European Soc. of Sports Traumatology, Knee Surgery and Arthroscopy **[18418]**
   Joint Commn. on Sports Medicine and Sci. **[16719]**
   Natl. Honor Soc. of Sports Medicine **[16720]**
   Natl. Youth Sports Safety Found. **[16721]**
   World Fed. of Athletic Training and Therapy **[16722]**
Sports Medicine Assn. of Belgium **[IO]**, Leuven, Belgium
Sports Medicine Assn. of Greece **[IO]**, Thessaloniki, Greece
Sports Medicine Assn. of the Philippines **[IO]**, Manila, Philippines
Sports Medicine Australia **[IO]**, Hackett, Australia
Sports Medicine Australia - New South Wales Br. **[IO]**, Rhodes, Australia

Sports Medicine Australia - Northern Territory Br. **[IO]**, Darwin, Australia
Sports Medicine Australia - Queensland Br. **[IO]**, Milton, Australia
Sports Medicine Australia - Victoria Br. **[IO]**, South Melbourne, Australia
Sports Medicine Australia - Western Australia Br. **[IO]**, Claremont, Australia
Sports Medicine Fed. of Iran **[IO]**, Tehran, Iran
Sports Officials
   Am. Outdoors Assn. **[22835]**
   Amer. Barefoot Waterski Club **[23114]**
   Amer. Junior Rodeo Assn. **[22839]**
   Assn. of Minor League Umpires **[22266]**
   Assn. for Professional Basketball Res. **[22293]**
   Cinderella Softball Leagues **[22951]**
   Fed. of Intl. Lacrosse **[22713]**
   Hampton One-Design Class Racing Assn. **[22340]**
   Harness Horse Youth Found. **[22652]**
   Intercollegiate Women's Lacrosse Coaches Assn. **[22714]**
   Intl. Assn. of Gay and Lesbian Martial Artists **[22734]**
   Maccabi USA/Sports for Israel **[22985]**
   Natl. Alliance for the Development of Archery **[22222]**
   Natl. Assn. of Sports Commissions **[23023]**
   Natl. Assn. of Sports Officials **[23024]**
   Natl. Assn. of Sports Officials - Organizations Network **[23025]**
   Natl. Assn. of Underwater Instructors **[23104]**
   Natl. Coalition Against Violent Athletes **[22231]**
   Natl. Junior Baseball League **[22285]**
   Natl. Scholastic Surfing Assn. **[23035]**
   Natl. Softball Assn. **[22954]**
   Natl. Starwind/Spindrift Class Assn. **[22377]**
   Natl. Surf Schools and Instructors Assn. **[23036]**
   New England Trails Conf. **[23090]**
   NFHS Officials Assn. **[23026]**
   Professional Assn. of Volleyball Officials **[23027]**
   Professional Baseball Athletic Trainers Soc. **[22289]**
   Sportscar Vintage Racing Assn. **[22249]**
   U.S. Bobsled and Skeleton Fed. **[22926]**
   U.S. Competitive Aerobics Fed. **[22209]**
   U.S. Disc Sports **[22536]**
   USA Athletes Intl. **[22233]**
   USA Diving **[22544]**
   U.S.A. Karate Fed. **[22766]**
   USA Volleyball **[23111]**
   USGA Green Sect. **[22628]**
   Women Outdoors **[22797]**
   Women's All-Star Assn. **[22432]**
   World Fast-Draw Assn. **[22891]**
   World Masters Cross-Country Ski Assn. **[22921]**
Sports Officials' Development Prog. and Media Center **[★22997]**
Sports Officials Youth Alliance - Address unknown since 2011.
Sports Philatelists Intl. **[22081]**, Norman Jacobs, Advt., 2712 N Decatur Rd., Decatur, GA 30033
Sports Philatelists Intl. **[22081]**, Norman Jacobs, Advt., 2712 N Decatur Rd., Decatur, GA 30033
Sports Sect., Amer. Coll. Public Relations Assn. **[★22974]**
Sports Turf Managers Assn. **[2184]**, 805 New Hampshire St., Ste. E, Lawrence, KS 66044, (800)323-3875
Sports Turf Managers Assn. **[2184]**, 805 New Hampshire St., Ste. E, Lawrence, KS 66044, (800)323-3875
Sports Turf Res. Inst. **[IO]**, Bingley, United Kingdom
Sportscar Vintage Racing Assn. **[22249]**, 1 Maple St., Hanover, NH 03755, (603)640-6161
SportScotland **[IO]**, Glasgow, United Kingdom
Sportsmen's Assn. for Firearms Educ. **[17691]**, PO Box 343, Commack, NY 11725, (631)475-8125
Sportsmen's Ser. Bur. **[★22882]**
Sportsplex Operators and Developers of Am. **[★23010]**
Sportsplex Operators and Developers Assn. **[23010]**, PO Box 24263, Westgate Sta., Rochester, NY 14624-0263, (585)426-2215
Sportsplex Owners and Directors of Am. **[★23010]**
Spotted Saddle Horse Breeders' and Exhibitors' Assn. **[4649]**, PO Box 1046, Shelbyville, TN 37162, (931)684-7496

Spotted Swine Record **[★4952]**
Sprayberry/Spraberry/Sprabary Family Assn. - Defunct.
Sprayed Concrete Assn. **[IO]**, Hampshire, United Kingdom
SPRI **[852]**, 411 Waverly Oaks Rd., Ste. 331B, Waltham, MA 02452, (781)647-7026
Spring Mfrs. Assn. **[★1661]**
Spring Mfrs. Inst. **[1661]**, 2001 Midwest Rd., Ste. 106, Oak Brook, IL 60523-1335, (630)495-8588
Spring Res. Inst. **[340]**, 422 Kings Way, Naples, FL 34104, (317)439-4811
Spring Ser. Assn., Suspension Specialists **[★368]**
Springboard Enterprises **[3690]**, 2100 Foxhall Rd. NW, Washington, DC 20007, (202)242-6282
Springtide Resources **[IO]**, Toronto, ON, Canada
Sprinkler Irrigation Assn. **[★170]**
Sprinkler Irrigation Assn. **[★170]**
Sprit and Vinleverantorsforeningen **[★IO]**
Spuria Iris Soc. **[21826]**, Rte. 1, Box 258, Gower, MO 64454-8613, (816)424-6436
Spuria Iris Soc. **[21826]**, Rte. 1, Box 258, Gower, MO 64454-8613, (816)424-6436
Squash
   Natl. Urban Squash and Educ. Assn. **[23028]**
   U.S. Squash Racquets Assn. **[23029]**
Squash Australia **[IO]**, Milton, Australia
Squash Bond Nederland **[IO]**, Zoetermeer, Netherlands
Squash Canada **[IO]**, Ottawa, ON, Canada
Squash Fed. of Chile **[IO]**, Santiago, Chile
Squash Fed. of Oman **[IO]**, Muscat, Oman
Squash Fiji **[IO]**, Suva, Fiji
Squash Malawi **[IO]**, Blantyre, Malawi
Squash New Zealand **[IO]**, Henderson, New Zealand
Squash Rackets Assn. of Chinese Taipei **[IO]**, Taipei, Taiwan
Squash Rackets Assn. of the Philippines **[IO]**, Makati City, Philippines
Squash Rackets Fed. of India **[IO]**, Chennai, India
Squash South Africa **[IO]**, Northlands, Republic of South Africa
Squash Zveza Slovenije **[★IO]**
Squire SS-100 Club **[★21168]**
Squire SS-100 Registry **[21168]**, 11826 S 51st St., Phoenix, AZ 85044-2313, (480)893-9451
Srer Khmer **[IO]**, Phnom Penh, Cambodia
Sri Aurobindo Assn. **[20301]**, 2715 W Ketteleman Ln., Ste. 203-174, Lodi, CA 95242, (209)339-3710
Sri Aurobindo Soc. **[IO]**, Pondicherry, India
Sri Lanka
   Serendib **[11629]**
   Sri Lanka Medical Assn. of North Am. **[14830]**
   Sri Lanka Wildlife Conservation Soc. **[5133]**
Sri Lanka Amateur Baseball and Softball Assn. **[IO]**, Boralesgamuwa, Sri Lanka
Sri Lanka Assn. of Administrative and Professional Secretaries **[IO]**, Colombo, Sri Lanka
Sri Lanka Assn. for the Advancement of Sci. **[IO]**, Colombo, Sri Lanka
Sri Lanka Badminton Assn. **[IO]**, Colombo, Sri Lanka
Sri Lanka Coll. of Dermatologists **[IO]**, Colombo, Sri Lanka
Sri Lanka Heart Assn. **[IO]**, Colombo, Sri Lanka
Sri Lanka Lib. Assn. **[IO]**, Colombo, Sri Lanka
Sri Lanka Medical Assn. of North Am. **[14830]**, 2500 Nesconset Hwy., Bldg. 16A, Stony Brook, NY 11790, (631)246-5454
Sri Lanka Prajathantravadi Samajavadi Janarajaye Eksath Jatheenge Sangamaya **[★IO]**
Sri Lanka Proj. **[IO]**, London, United Kingdom
Sri Lanka Red Cross Soc. **[IO]**, Colombo, Sri Lanka
Sri Lanka Soc. of Occupational Therapists **[IO]**, Kadawatha, Sri Lanka
Sri Lanka Soc. of Physiotherapy **[IO]**, Colombo, Sri Lanka
Sri Lanka Sports Medicine Assn. **[IO]**, Colombo, Sri Lanka
Sri Lanka Squash Fed. **[IO]**, Colombo, Sri Lanka
Sri Lanka Standards Institution **[IO]**, Colombo, Sri Lanka
Sri Lanka Tea Bd. **[IO]**, Colombo, Sri Lanka
Sri Lanka Tennis Assn. **[IO]**, Colombo, Sri Lanka
Sri Lanka Wildlife Conservation Soc. **[5133]**, 127 Kingsland St., Nutley, NJ 07110, (973)667-0576

A star before a book entry number signifies that the name is not listed separately, but is mentioned within the entry.

Sri Lanka Wildlife Conservation Soc. **[5133]**, 127 Kingsland St., Nutley, NJ 07110, (973)667-0576

Sri Lankan
Ceylon (Sri Lanka) Tourist Dept. **[23443]**

Sri Lankan Geotechnical Soc. **[IO]**, Colombo, Sri Lanka

SSPC: The Soc. for Protective Coatings **[2615]**, 40 24th St., 6th Fl., Pittsburgh, PA 15222-4656, (412)281-2331

SSPC: The Soc. for Protective Coatings **[2615]**, 40 24th St., 6th Fl., Pittsburgh, PA 15222-4656, (412)281-2331

Stable Value Assn. **[★2151]**

Stable Value Investment Assn. **[2151]**, 1025 Connecticut Ave. NW, Ste. 1000, Washington, DC 20036, (202)580-7620

Stadium Managers Assn. **[23021]**, 525 SW 5th St., Ste. A, Des Moines, IA 50309-4501, (515)282-8192

Staff Assn. of the Org. of Amer. States **[★23260]**

Staff and Educational Development Assn. **[IO]**, London, United Kingdom

Staff Union of the Intl. Labour Org. **[IO]**, Geneva, Switzerland

Stafford Canary Club of Am. **[21230]**, 851 Neptune St., Port Charlotte, FL 33948, (941)764-7877

Stafford Canary Club of Am. **[21230]**, 851 Neptune St., Port Charlotte, FL 33948, (941)764-7877

Staffordshire Terrier Club of Am. **[21655]**, Monica Davi, Corresponding Sec., 11781 Arguello Dr., Mira Loma, CA 91752, (951)360-6003

STAG **[★3574]**

Stage Directors and Choreographers Found. **[10603]**, 1501 Broadway, Ste. 1701, New York, NY 10036-5600, (212)391-1070

Stage Directors and Choreographers Soc. **[23274]**, 1501 Broadway, Ste. 1701, New York, NY 10036, (212)391-1070

Stage Mgt. Assn. **[IO]**, London, United Kingdom

Stained Glass Assn. of Am. **[1583]**, 9313 E 63rd St., Raytown, MO 64133, (816)737-2090

Stained Glass Professionals Assn. - Defunct.

Stair Soc. **[IO]**, Edinburgh, United Kingdom

Stamp Out AIDS - Defunct.

Stampe Club Intl. - Address unknown since 2011.

Stamps on Stamps - Centenary Unit **[★22082]**

Stamps on Stamps - Centenary Unit **[★22082]**

Stamps on Stamps Collectors Club **[22082]**, Michael Merritt, Sec.-Treas., 73 Mountainside Rd., Mendham, NJ 07945

Stamps on Stamps Collectors Club **[22082]**, Michael Merritt, Sec.-Treas., 73 Mountainside Rd., Mendham, NJ 07945

Stamps on Stamps Unit **[★22082]**

Stamps on Stamps Unit **[★22082]**

Stamps for the Wounded - Address unknown since 2011.

Stan Mikita Hockey School for the Hearing Impaired **[★22504]**

Stand for the Troops **[20350]**, PO Box 11179, Greenwich, CT 06831

Stand Up For Africa **[IO]**, London, United Kingdom

Standard Independent Data Format Assn. - Defunct.

Standard Jack and Jennet Registry of Am. **[★3784]**

Standard Schnauzer Club of Am. **[21656]**, 7907 S 44th West Ave., Tulsa, OK 74132-3466, (918)446-6761

Standard Schnauzer Club of Am. **[21656]**, 7907 S 44th West Ave., Tulsa, OK 74132-3466, (918)446-6761

Standardbred Owners Assn. **[22665]**, 733 Yonkers Ave., Ste. 102, Yonkers, NY 10704-2659, (914)968-3599

Standardbred Retirement Found. **[4650]**, 108 Old York Rd., Hamilton, NJ 08620, (609)324-1500

Standards
Alliance for Building Regulatory Reform in the Digital Age **[6372]**
Amer. Measuring Tool Mfrs. Assn. **[7463]**
Amer. Natl. Metric Coun. **[18672]**
Amer. Natl. Standards Inst. **[5982]**
Americans for Customary Weight and Measure **[18673]**
Anti-Malware Testing Standards Org. **[6478]**
Building Commissioning Assn. **[538]**
Coalition for Healthcare eStandards **[14765]**

Coalition for Intellectual Property Rights **[5565]**
Consumer Products Codification Assn. **[5737]**
Data Interchange Standards Assn. **[18674]**
Dozenal Soc. of Am. **[7464]**
Egyptian Article Numbering Assn. **[14015]**
Embroidery Software Protection Coalition **[2049]**
GS1 Denmark **[21219]**
GS1 Mauritius **[18889]**
GS1 South Africa **[22943]**
GS1 Tunisia **[107]**
GS1 Ukraine **[16763]**
Healthcare Laundry Accreditation Coun. **[2192]**
High Performance Building Coun. **[6376]**
Intl. Air Filtration Certifiers Assn. **[1705]**
Intl. Assn. of Forensic and Security Metrology **[7465]**
Intl. Assn. for the Properties of Water and Steam **[5983]**
Intl. Assn. for the Properties of Water and Steam **[5983]**
Intl. Soc. for Structural Hea. Monitoring of Intelligent Infrastructure **[6428]**
Mfg. Skill Standards Coun. **[7466]**
Natl. Conf. on Weights and Measures **[5984]**
NCSL Intl. **[7467]**
NCSL Intl. **[7467]**
PODS Assn. **[3343]**
Postsecondary Electronic Standards Coun. **[8902]**
Soc. of Allied Weight Engineers **[7468]**
Standards Engg. Soc. **[7469]**
Storage Performance Coun. **[3344]**
Unicode Consortium **[18675]**
U.S. Metric Assn. **[7470]**
Utility Indus. Gp. **[3607]**

Standards Assn. of Zimbabwe **[IO]**, Harare, Zimbabwe

Standards Coun. of Canada **[IO]**, Ottawa, ON, Canada

Standards Engg. Soc. **[7469]**, 1950 Lafayette Rd., Portsmouth, NH 03801, (603)926-0750

Standards Engineers Soc. **[★7469]**

Standards New Zealand **[IO]**, Wellington, New Zealand

StandardsWork **[8832]**, 1001 Connecticut Ave. NW, Ste. 640, Washington, DC 20036, (202)835-2000

Standing Commn. on Ecumenical Relations of the Episcopal Church - Address unknown since 2011.

Standing Comm. of the European Glass Indus. **[IO]**, Brussels, Belgium

Standing Comm. for Nobel Prize Winners' Congresses **[IO]**, Lindau, Germany

Standing Conf. of the Canonical Orthodox Bishops in the Americas **[19648]**, 10 E 79th St., New York, NY 10075, (212)774-0526

Standing Conf. of the Canonical Orthodox Bishops in the Americas **[19648]**, 10 E 79th St., New York, NY 10075, (212)774-0526

Standing Conf. on Lib. Materials on Africa **[IO]**, London, United Kingdom

Standing Liaison Comm. of EU Speech and Language Therapists and Logopedists **[IO]**, Paris, France

Standing Up for SUV, Pickup and Van Owners of Am. - Address unknown since 2011.

StandUp for Kids **[11409]**, 83 Walton St., Ste. 100, Atlanta, GA 30303, (800)365-4KID

StandWithUs **[18015]**, PO Box 341069, Los Angeles, CA 90034-1069, (310)836-6140

Stanford Chicano/Latino Alumni Assn. **[18900]**, PO Box 86204, Los Angeles, CA 90086-0204, (213)473-7528

Stanley Badminton Club **[IO]**, Fleetwood, United Kingdom

Staples Family History Assn. - Defunct.

STAR Kampuchea **[IO]**, Phnom Penh, Cambodia

Star-Spangled Banner Flag House Assn. **[20613]**, 844 E Pratt St., Baltimore, MD 21202, (410)837-1793

Star Trek
STARFLEET **[23913]**
Starfleet Command **[23914]**
United Fed. of Planets Internationale **[23915]**

StarFabric Trade Assn. - Address unknown since 2010.

STARFLEET **[23913]**, PO Box 8213, Bangor, ME 04402, (888)734-8735

Starfleet Command **[23914]**, PO Box 33565, Indianapolis, IN 46203-0565, (317)508-9351

Starlight Children's Found. **[11508]**, 2049 Century Plz. E Ste. 4320, Los Angeles, CA 90067, (310)479-1212

Starlight Starbright Children's Found. **[★11508]**

Starptautiskas Apmainas Centrs **[★IO]**

Stars of David **[★10801]**

Stars of David **[★10801]**

Stars of David Intl. **[10801]**, 3175 Commercial Ave., Ste. 100, Northbrook, IL 60062-1915, (800)STAR-349

Stars of David Intl. **[10801]**, 3175 Commercial Ave., Ste. 100, Northbrook, IL 60062-1915, (800)STAR-349

Stars for Stripes **[20417]**, 109 Rivers Edge Ct., Nashville, TN 37214, (615)872-2122

Starships of the Third Fleet **[10523]**, 10358 Aquilla Dr., Lakeside, CA 92040-2236

START **[IO]**, Dubai, United Arab Emirates

Start Thinking About Romanian Children Relief **[11410]**, 100 Traylee Dr., Wake Forest, NC 27587, (919)521-5851

Starwind/Spindrift 19 Assn. **[★22377]**

Starwind/Spindrift Assn. **[★22377]**

State Beer Assn. of Executives of Am. **[★185]**

State Beer Wholesalers Secretaries **[★185]**

State Capital Global Law Firm Gp. **[5284]**, 1717 Pennsylvania Ave. NW, Ste. 1200, Washington, DC 20006, (202)659-6601

State Capital Global Law Firm Gp. **[5284]**, 1717 Pennsylvania Ave. NW, Ste. 1200, Washington, DC 20006, (202)659-6601

State Capital Law Firm Gp. **[★5284]**

State Capital Law Firm Gp. **[★5284]**

State Chamber of Commerce New South Wales **[IO]**, Sydney, Australia

State Debt Mgt. Network **[6003]**, Natl. Assn. of State Treasurers, 2760 Res. Park Dr., PO Box 11910, Lexington, KY 40578-1910, (859)244-8175

State Defense Force Assn. of the U.S. **[★5831]**

State Dept. Watch **[17709]**, PO Box 65398, Washington, DC 20035

State Educational Tech. Directors Assn. **[8979]**, PO Box 10, Glen Burnie, MD 21060, (202)715-6636

State Government
Coun. on Governmental Ethics Laws **[5985]**
Coun. on Licensure, Enforcement and Regulation **[5986]**
Coun. of State Community Development Agencies **[5987]**
Coun. of State Governments **[5988]**
Democratic Governors Assn. **[5989]**
Fiscal Stud. Prog. **[5990]**
Natl. Assn. of Attorneys Gen. **[5991]**
Natl. Assn. of Secretaries of State **[5992]**
Natl. Assn. of State Chief Administrators **[5993]**
Natl. Assn. for State Community Services Programs **[5994]**
Natl. Assn. of State Personnel Executives **[5995]**
Natl. Black Caucus of State Legislators **[5996]**
Natl. Conf. of Commissioners on Uniform State Laws **[5997]**
Natl. Conf. of State Legislatures **[5998]**
Natl. Coun. of County Assn. Executives **[5353]**
Natl. Governors Assn. **[5999]**
Natl. Lieutenant Governors Assn. **[6000]**
Reason Found. **[5855]**
Republican Governors Assn. **[6001]**
Southern Governors' Assn. **[6002]**
State Debt Mgt. Network **[6003]**

State Govt. Affairs Coun. **[1589]**, 515 King St., Ste. 325, Alexandria, VA 22314, (703)684-0967

State Governmental Affairs Coun. **[★1589]**

State Guard Assn. of the U.S. **[5831]**, PO Box 1416, Fayetteville, GA 30214-1416

State Higher Educ. Executive Officers **[8732]**, 3035 Center Green Dr., Ste. 100, Boulder, CO 80301-2205, (303)541-1600

State Revenue Soc. **[22083]**, Kent Gray, Sec., PO Box 67842, Albuquerque, NM 87193

State and Territorial Air Pollution Prog. Administrators and Assn. of Local Air Pollution Control Officials **[★5419]**

State and Territorial Injury Prevention Directors Assn. **[★18581]**

Reference to "IO" in place of a book number signifies that the association may be found in the 50th edition of International Organizations.

State of the World Forum [18818], 35 Miller Ave., No. 314, Mill Valley, CA 94941, (415)388-2114
State of the World Forum [18818], 35 Miller Ave., No. 314, Mill Valley, CA 94941, (415)388-2114
State of the World's Sea Turtles [5134], 2011 Crystal Dr., Ste. 500, Arlington, VA 22202, (703)341-2433
State of the World's Sea Turtles [5134], 2011 Crystal Dr., Ste. 500, Arlington, VA 22202, (703)341-2433
Statens Kulturrad [★IO]
States Org. for Boating Access [464], 231 S LaSalle St., Ste. 2050, Chicago, IL 60604, (312)946-6283
States Rights
　Coun. of Conservative Citizens [18676]
　Public Advocate of the U.S. [18677]
Statewide Steering Comm. [★9694]
Sta. Helena and Dependencies Philatelic Soc. [★22071]
Station Representatives Assn. - Defunct.
Stationary Engine Soc. [★22331]
Stationers' and Newspaper Makers' Company [IO], London, United Kingdom
Stationery
　Argentine Chamber of Stationers, Bookshops and Related Businesses [7388]
　British Engraved Stationery Assn. [6545]
　Bus. Forms Mgt. Assn. [3345]
　Bus. Solutions Assn. [3346]
　Check Payment Systems Assn. [3347]
　Envelope Mfrs. Assn. [3348]
　Global Envelope Alliance [3349]
　Global Envelope Alliance [3349]
　Greeting Card Assn. [3350]
　Intl. Marking and Identification Assn. [3351]
　Intl. Marking and Identification Assn. [3351]
　Label Printing Indus. of Am. [3352]
　Natl. Off. Products Alliance [3353]
　Print Services and Distribution Assn. [3354]
　Tag and Label Mfrs. Inst. [3355]
　Writing Instrument Mfrs. Assn. [3356]
Statistical, Economic and Social Res. and Training Centre for the Islamic Countries [IO], Ankara, Turkey
Statistical Inst. for Asia and the Pacific [IO], Chiba, Japan
Statistical Off. of the European Communities [IO], Luxembourg, Luxembourg
Statistical Process Control Soc. [★7318]
Statistical Process Control Soc. [★7318]
Statistical Process Controls [7318], 5908 Toole Dr., Ste. C, Knoxville, TN 37919, (865)584-5005
Statistical Process Controls [7318], 5908 Toole Dr., Ste. C, Knoxville, TN 37919, (865)584-5005
Statistical and Social Inquiry Soc. of Ireland [IO], Dublin, Ireland
Statistical Soc. of Australia, Inc. [IO], Belconnen, Australia
Statistical Soc. of Canada [IO], Ottawa, ON, Canada
Statistics
　Amer. Statistical Assn. [7471]
　Assn. of Population Centers [6594]
　Caucus for Women in Statistics [7472]
　Caucus for Women in Statistics [7472]
　Comm. of Presidents of Statistical Societies [7473]
　Econometric Soc. [7474]
　Econometric Soc. [7474]
　Inst. of Mathematical Statistics [7475]
　Intl. Biometric Soc. [7476]
　Intl. Biometric Soc. [7476]
　Intl. Biometric Soc., Eastern North Amer. Region [7477]
　Intl. Biometric Soc., Western North Amer. Region [7478]
　Intl. Biometric Soc., Western North Amer. Region [7478]
　Natl. Inst. of Statistical Sciences [7479]
　Netherlands Soc. for Statistics and Operations Res. [1717]
Statistiek en Economische Informatie - Statistique et Info. Economique [IO], Brussels, Belgium
Statstjanstemannaforbundet [★IO]
Statue of Liberty Club [21405], 7116 Treasure Isle, Lansing, MI 48917
Statue of Liberty - Ellis Island Found. [9730], History Center, 17 Battery Pl., No. 210, New York, NY 10004-3507, (212)561-4588

Steam Auto. Club of Am. [21169], PO Box 8, Berrien Springs, MI 49103, (269)471-7408
Steam Engines
　Intl. Assn. for the Advancement of Steam Power [7480]SteamIntl. Stationary Steam Engine Soc. Northwest Steam Soc. [22156]
　Rough and Tumble Engineers' Historical Assn. [22157]
　Steamship Historical Soc. of Am. [22158]
Steam Plough Club [IO], Hereford, United Kingdom
Steamboat Assn. of Sweden [IO], Akersberga, Sweden
The Steamboaters [4145], PO Box 41266, Eugene, OR 97404
Steamfitting Indus. Promotion Fund [1721], 44 W 28th St., New York, NY 10001-4212, (212)481-1493
Steamship Historical Soc. of Am. [22158], 1029 Waterman Ave., East Providence, RI 02914, (401)274-0805
Steamship Sailors' Union [★23250]
Steamtown Museum Assn. - Defunct.
Stearman Restorers Assn. [20918], Chino Airport, 7000 Merrill Ave., Box 90, Chino, CA 91710-8800
Steel Bar Mills [★2496]
Steel Can Recycling Inst. [★3643]
Steel Constr. Inst. [IO], Ascot, United Kingdom
Steel Deck Inst. [618], PO Box 25, Fox River Grove, IL 60021, (847)458-4647
Steel Door Inst. [619], 30200 Detroit Rd., Westlake, OH 44145, (440)899-0010
Steel Erectors Assn. of Am. [6578], 2216 W Meadowview Dr., Ste. 115, Greensboro, NC 27407, (336)294-8880
Steel Founders' Soc. of Am. [1870], 780 McArdle Dr., Unit G, Crystal Lake, IL 60014-8155, (815)455-8240
Steel Founders' Soc. of Am. [1870], 780 McArdle Dr., Unit G, Crystal Lake, IL 60014-8155, (815)455-8240
Steel Framing Alliance [2495], 1140 Connecticut Ave. NW, Ste. 705, Washington, DC 20036, (202)785-2022
Steel Framing Alliance [2495], 1140 Connecticut Ave. NW, Ste. 705, Washington, DC 20036, (202)785-2022
Steel Joist Inst. [620], 234 W Cheves St., Florence, SC 29501, (843)407-4091
Steel Mfrs. Assn. [2496], 1150 Connecticut Ave. NW, Ste. 715, Washington, DC 20036-4131, (202)296-1515
Steel Recycling Inst. [3643], 680 Andersen Dr., Pittsburgh, PA 15220-2700, (412)922-2772
Steel Scaffolding and Shoring Inst. [★616]
Steel Ser. Center Inst. [★2482]
Steel Shipping Container Inst. [889], PO Box 100907, Arlington, VA 22210, (571)527-0779
Steel Structures Painting Coun. [★2615]
Steel Structures Painting Coun. [★2615]
Steel Tank Inst. and Steel Plate Fabricators Assn. [890], 944 Donata Ct., Lake Zurich, IL 60047, (847)438-8265
Steel Treating Res. Soc. [★7090]
Steel Treating Res. Soc. [★7090]
Steel Truss and Component Assn. [★622]
Steel Tube Inst. of North Am. [891], 2516 Waukegan Rd., Ste. 172, Glenview, IL 60025, (847)461-1701
Steel Tube Inst. of North Am. [891], 2516 Waukegan Rd., Ste. 172, Glenview, IL 60025, (847)461-1701
Steel Window Assn. [IO], Tamworth, United Kingdom
Steel Window Inst. [621], 1300 Sumner Ave., Cleveland, OH 44115-2851, (216)241-7333
Steel Workers Organizing Comm. [★23256]
STEER [20098], PO Box 1236, Bismarck, ND 58502, (701)258-4911
STEER [20098], PO Box 1236, Bismarck, ND 58502, (701)258-4911
Steering Comm. for Sustainable Agriculture [★3740]
Stefan Batory Found. [IO], Warsaw, Poland
Stefanie Powers' Official Fan Club [23785], PO Box 5087, Sherman Oaks, CA 91403
Steiff Club [21406], 24 Albion Rd., Ste. 220, Lincoln, RI 02865, (401)312-0080
Stein Collectors Intl. [21407], PO Box 502, Fairless Hills, PA 19030-0502

Stein Collectors Intl. [21407], PO Box 502, Fairless Hills, PA 19030-0502
Steinbeck Center Found. [★9404]
Steinbeck Center; Natl. [9404]
The Stelle Gp. - Defunct.
Stencilers and Decorative Artists Guild [20972], William Woody, 1751 State Rte. 32, Round Pond, ME 04564, (207)529-2209
Step Up 4 Vets [13354], 9903 Santa Monica Blvd., No. 700, Beverly Hills, CA 90212-1671
Step-Up Found. [★16948]
Step Up Women's Network [13480], 510 S Hewitt St., No. 111, Los Angeles, CA 90013, (213)382-9161
Stepfamily Assn. of Am. - Defunct.
Stepfamily Found. [12021], 310 W 85th St., No. 1B, New York, NY 10024, (212)877-3244
Stephen Leacock Assn. [IO], Orillia, ON, Canada
Stephenson Locomotive Soc. [IO], Cheshire, United Kingdom
STEPS: Assn. for People with Lower Limb Abnormalities [★3694]
Steps Charity Worldwide [IO], Lymm, United Kingdom
Stereo Photographers, Collectors and Enthusiasts Club [★10440]
Stereoscopic Soc. [IO], Greenford, United Kingdom
Stereoscopic Soc. of America - Defunct.
Sterling Silversmiths Guild of America - Defunct.
Steuben Soc. of Am. [19007], 1 S Ocean Ave., Ste. 217, Patchogue, NY 11772, (631)730-5111
Steven Spielberg Film Soc. - Defunct.
Steward/Stewardess Div., Air Line Pilots Assn. [★23150]
Steward/Stewardess Div., Air Line Pilots Assn. [★23150]
Stewards of the Range [18407], PO Box 1190, Taylor, TX 76574, (512)365-8038
STG Intl. [7449], PO Box 426152, Cambridge, MA 02142
Stichting Agromisa [★IO]
Stichting ALS Onderzoekfonds [★IO]
Stichting Dierenbescherming Suriname [★IO]
Stichting Eurodata [★IO]
Stichting voor Fundamenteel Onderzoek der Materie [★IO]
Stichting Gilles de la Tourette [★IO]
Stichting Lobi [IO], Paramaribo, Suriname
Stichting Natuur en Milieu [★IO]
Stichting Nederlandse Industrie voor Defensie en Veiligheid [★IO]
Stichting Platform Bio-Energie [★IO]
Stichting Ruimteonderzoek Nederland [★IO]
Stichting Transnational Inst. [★IO]
Stichting VONK Projecten [★IO]
Stichting tegen Vrouwenhandel [★IO]
Stichting Werkgroep Urgenta [★IO]
Stickler Involved People [14630], 15 Angelina Dr., Augusta, KS 67010, (316)259-5194
Stickler Involved People [14630], 15 Angelina Dr., Augusta, KS 67010, (316)259-5194
Stiftelsen IMTEC [★IO]
Stiftelsen for Industriell og Teknisk Forskning ved Norges Tekniske Hogskole [★IO]
Stiftelsen Skogsbrukets Forskningsinstitut [★IO]
Stiftung DIAKONIA Weltbund von Verbaenden und Gemeinschaften der DIAKONIE [★IO]
Stiftung fur Europaische Sprach- und Bildungszentren [★IO]
Stiftung Europaisches Naturerbe [★IO]
Stiftung Frauen-Literatur-Forschung e.V. [★IO]
Stiftung Global Harmony [★IO]
Stiftung Niedersachsen [★IO]
Still Bank Collectors Club of Am. [21205], 440 Homestead Ave., Metairie, LA 70005, (504)833-2715
Stillbirth and Neonatal Death Soc. [IO], London, United Kingdom
Stilton Cheesemakers' Assn. [IO], Surbiton, United Kingdom
Stock Artists Alliance [2737], 229 Peachtree St., Ste. 2200, Atlanta, GA 30303, (888)722-1334
Stock Transfer Assn. [★3207]
Stockholm Chamber of Commerce [IO], Stockholm, Sweden

A star before a book entry number signifies that the name is not listed separately, but is mentioned within the entry.

Stockholm Env. Inst. - Sweden [IO], Stockholm, Sweden

Stockholm Environmental Inst. - Tallinn [IO], Tallinn, Estonia

Stockholm Herpetological Soc. [IO], Stockholm, Sweden

Stockholmi Keskkonnainstituudi Tallinna Keskus [★IO]

Stockholms Herpetologiska Forening [★IO]

Stolen Horse Intl. [11042], PO Box 1341, Shelby, NC 28151, (704)484-2165

Stolen Horse Intl. [11042], PO Box 1341, Shelby, NC 28151, (704)484-2165

Stoma Care Soc. [IO], Kuala Lumpur, Malaysia

Stomatological Soc. of Greece [IO], Athens, Greece

Stone
  Allied Stone Indus. [3357]
  Amer. Rock Mechanics Assn. [3358]
  Barre Granite Assn. [3359]
  Building Stone Inst. [3360]
  Elberton Granite Assn. [3361]
  Indiana Limestone Inst. of Am. [3362]
  Intl. Colored Gemstone Assn. [3363]
  Intl. Colored Gemstone Assn. [3363]
  Intl. Meteorite Collectors Assn. [22159]
  Marble Inst. of Am. [3364]
  Marble Inst. of Am. [3364]
  Natl. Building Granite Quarries Assn. [3365]
  Natl. Stone, Sand and Gravel Assn. [3366]

Stone Assn. of Iran [IO], Tehran, Iran

Stop Abuse by Counselors - Defunct.

Stop Abuse for Everyone [11897], 16869 SW 65th Ave., PMB 212, Lake Oswego, OR 97035-7865, (503)853-8686

Stop Calling It Autism! [13802], PO Box 155728, Fort Worth, TX 76155, (888)SCIA-123

STOP Forced Busing - Defunct.

Stop Hunger Now [12294], 615 Hillsborough St., Ste. 200, Raleigh, NC 27603, (919)839-0689

Stop Hunger Now [12294], 615 Hillsborough St., Ste. 200, Raleigh, NC 27603, (919)839-0689

Stop it Now! [11411], 351 Pleasant St., Ste. B-319, Northampton, MA 01060, (413)587-3500

Stop Planned Parenthood [★18568]

Stop Predatory Gambling Found. [12065], 100 Maryland Ave. NE, Rm. 311, Washington, DC 20002, (202)567-6996

Stop Prisoner Rape [★11720]

Stop the Silence [11145], PO Box 127, Glenn Dale, MD 20769-0127, (301)464-4791

Stop TB Partnership [IO], Geneva, Switzerland

Stop the War Coalition [IO], London, United Kingdom

Stop War Toys Campaign - Defunct.

STOPP Intl. [18568], Amer. Life League, PO Box 1350, Stafford, VA 22555, (540)659-4171

Storage Coun. [★3623]

Storage Equip. Mfrs. Assn. [1871], Material Handling Indus. of Am., 8720 Red Oak Blvd., Ste. 201, Charlotte, NC 28217, (704)676-1190

Storage and Handling Equip. Distributors' Assn. [IO], Birmingham, United Kingdom

Storage Networking Indus. Assn. [6475], 425 Market St., Ste. 1020, San Francisco, CA 94105, (415)402-0006

Storage Performance Coun. [3344], 643 Bair Island Rd., Ste. 103, Redwood City, CA 94063, (650)556-9384

Stories of Autism [13803], 13110 NE 177th Pl., No. 237, Woodinville, WA 98072, (425)485-9919

Story Circle Network [10548], PO Box 500127, Austin, TX 78750-0127, (512)454-9833

Story Circle Network [10548], PO Box 500127, Austin, TX 78750-0127, (512)454-9833

Story Rhymes for Educ. [10549], PO Box 416, Denver, CO 80201-0416

Storytelling
  Intl. Order of E.A.R.S. [10543]
  Intl. Order of E.A.R.S. [10543]
  Jewish Storytelling Coalition [10544]
  Natl. Assn. of Black Storytellers [10545]
  Natl. Storytelling Network [10546]
  Silent Images [13148]
  Spellbinders [10547]
  Story Circle Network [10548]
  Story Circle Network [10548]
  Story Rhymes for Educ. [10549]
  WordTheatre [10550]

Storytelling Assn. - Singapore [IO], Singapore, Singapore

Stoval, Stoveal, Stoball [★20592]

Stovall Family Assn. [20592], Linda M. Stovall, Pres., 3345 Tibey Ct., Dubuque, IA 52002-2849, (563)557-9227

Stove, Furnace and Allied Appliance Workers Intl. Union of North Am. [★23144]

Stowarzy Szenie Mlodych Chorych [IO], Poznan, Poland

Stowarzysenie Bibliotekarzy Polskich [★IO]

Stowarzyszeine Miedzynarodowe Triennale Grafiki [★IO]

Stowarzyszenie Antywariuszy Polskich [★IO]

Stowarzyszenie Chorych z Przepuklina Oponowo-Rdzeniowa R.P. [★IO]

Stowarzyszenie Dziennikarzy Polskich [★IO]

Stowarzyszenie Filmowcow Polskich [★IO]

Stowarzyszenie Gazet Lokalnych [★IO]

Stowarzyszenie Geomorfologow Polskich [★IO]

Stowarzyszenie Inzynierow i Technikow Lesnictwa i Drzewnictwa [★IO]

Stowarzyszenie Papiernikow Polskich [★IO]

Stowarzyszenie Polskiej Filatelistyki [★IO]

Stowarzyszenie na Rzecz Osob z Choroba Huntingtona w Polsce [IO], Warsaw, Poland

Stowe-Day Found. [★10716]

Straight Spouse Network [12440], PO Box 507, Mahwah, NJ 07430, (201)825-7763

Straight Spouse Support Network [★12440]

Strangers Club [★10521]

Strategic Account Mgt. Assn. [2425], 33 N LaSalle St., Ste. 3700, Chicago, IL 60602, (312)251-3131

Strategic Account Mgt. Assn. [2425], 33 N LaSalle St., Ste. 3700, Chicago, IL 60602, (312)251-3131

Strategic Air Command Judo Assn. [★22705]

Strategic and Competitive Intelligence Professionals [6993], 1700 Diagonal Rd., Ste. 600, Alexandria, VA 22314, (703)739-0696

Strategic Defense Initiative
  High Frontier Org. [18678]

Strategic Energy, Environmental and Trans. Alternatives [8122], 18340 Yorba Linda Blvd., Ste. 107-509, Yorba Linda, CA 92886-4058, (714)777-7729

Strategic Planning Soc. [IO], London, United Kingdom

Strategic Services on Unemployment and Workers' Compensation and the Natl. Found. for UC & WC [★13343]

Strategies for Intl. Development [12372], 2525 Wilson Blvd., Arlington, VA 22201, (703)875-0500

Strategy Gaming Soc. - Address unknown since 2010.

Stratis Hea. [14741], 2901 Metro Dr., Ste. 400, Bloomington, MN 55425-1525, (952)854-3306

Strawberry Shortcake Chat Gp. [21699], 138 E Main Cross St., Greenville, KY 42345, (270)338-4318

Strawberry Shortcake Doll Club [★21699]

St. Child Rescue Ghana [IO], Accra, Ghana

St. Law [5766], 1010 Wayne Ave., Ste. 870, Silver Spring, MD 20910, (301)589-1130

Streeter Family Assn. [20593], 3273 State Rte. 248, Canisteo, NY 14823, (607)225-4246

StreetSchool Network [9083], PO Box 140069, Denver, CO 80214, (303)830-8213

Strengthening Participatory Org. [IO], Islamabad, Pakistan

Stress
  Amer. Inst. of Stress [16723]
  Cell Stress Soc. Intl. [16724]
  Cell Stress Soc. Intl. [16724]
  Intl. Critical Incident Stress Found. [16725]
  Intl. Critical Incident Stress Found. [16725]
  Intl. Soc. for Traumatic Stress Stud. [16726]
  Intl. Soc. for Traumatic Stress Stud. [16726]
  Natl. Center for Posttraumatic Stress Disorder [16727]
  VietNow Natl. [13358]

Stress Analysis
  Res. Coun. on Structural Connections [7481]
  Soc. for Experimental Mechanics [7482]
  Structural Stability Res. Coun. [7483]

Stress and Anxiety Res. Soc. [IO], Meerbusch, Germany

Stress Management
  Natl. Center for Posttraumatic Stress Disorder [16727]

Strict Baptist Historical Soc. [IO], Caterham, United Kingdom

STRIDE, Inc. [7974], PO Box 778, Rensselaer, NY 12144, (518)598-1279

STRIDE: Sports and Therapeutic Recreation Instruction/Developmental Educ. [★7974]

Striped Bass Growers Assn. [4384], PO Box 1647, Pine Bluff, AR 71613, (870)850-7900

Stripers Unlimited - Defunct.

Stroke
  Amer. Stroke Assn. [16728]
  Brain Attack Coalition [16729]
  Children's Hemiplegia and Stroke Assn. [16730]
  Natl. Stroke Assn. [16731]
  Stroke Awareness for Everyone [16732]
  Stroke Awareness for Everyone [16732]
  Stroke Network [16733]
  Stroke Network [16733]

Stroke Assn. [IO], London, United Kingdom

Stroke Awareness for Everyone [16732], PO Box 36186, Los Angeles, CA 90036

Stroke Awareness for Everyone [16732], PO Box 36186, Los Angeles, CA 90036

Stroke Info. and Referral Center [★16731]

Stroke Network [16733], PO Box 492, Abingdon, MD 21009

Stroke Network [16733], PO Box 492, Abingdon, MD 21009

Stroke Soc. of Australasia [IO], Crows Nest, Australia

Strong Family Assn. of Am. [20594], Kathleen A. Strong, Sec., 7239 65th Pl., Glendale, NY 11385-6929

Strong Women, Strong Girls [13481], 1 Milk St., Ste. 300, Boston, MA 02109, (617)338-4833

Structural Building Components Assn. [622], 6300 Enterprise Ln., Madison, WI 53719, (608)274-4849

Structural Clay Products Inst. [★536]

Structural Clay Products Res. Found. [★536]

Structural Clay Tile Assn. [★536]

Structural Insulated Panel Assn. [623], PO Box 1699, Gig Harbor, WA 98335, (253)858-7472

Structural Stability Res. Coun. [7483], 301 Butler Carlton Hall, 1401 N Pine St., Rolla, MO 65409-0030, (573)341-6610

Structured Employment Economic Development Corp. [17587], 915 Broadway, 17th Fl., New York, NY 10010, (212)473-0255

Stuart, Charles
  Soc. of King Charles the Martyr [19296]

Stucco Mfrs. Assn. [624], 2402 Vista Nobleza, Newport Beach, CA 92660, (949)640-9902

Studebaker Driver's Club [21170], PO Box 1715, Maple Grove, MN 55311-6715, (763)420-7829

Studebaker Family Natl. Assn. [20595], 6555 S State Rte. 202, Tipp City, OH 45371-9444, (937)667-7013

Studebaker Owners Club [★21170]

Student Affl. Gp. [8930], Univ. of Akron, Dept. of Psychology, Arts and Sciences Bldg., Akron, OH 44325-4301, (330)972-7280

Student African Amer. Brotherhood [19288], The Univ. of Toledo, PO Box 350842, Toledo, OH 43635, (419)530-3221

Student Amer. Dental Assn. [★7965]

Student Amer. Medical Assn. [★8587]

Student Amer. Pharmaceutical Assn. [★16177]

Student Amer. Veterinary Medical Assn. [17043], AVMA, 1931 N Meacham Rd., Ste. 100, Schaumburg, IL 60173, (847)925-8070

Student Amer. Veterinary Medical Assn. [17043], AVMA, 1931 N Meacham Rd., Ste. 100, Schaumburg, IL 60173, (847)925-8070

Student Animal Rights Alliance - Address unknown since 2011.

Student Assn. for Voter Empowerment - Address unknown since 2011.

Student Christian Movement of Hong Kong [IO], Hong Kong, People's Republic of China

Student Conservation Assn. [4146], PO Box 550, Charlestown, NH 03603-0550, (603)543-1700

Reference to "IO" in place of a book number signifies that the association may be found in the 50th edition of International Organizations.

Student Environmental Action Coalition [4305], 2206 Washington St. E, Charleston, WV 25311, (304)414-0143
Student Foreign Missions Fellowship [★20051]
Student Global AIDS Campaign - Address unknown since 2011:
Student Homophile League [★12075]
Student Jour. Gp. of the Amer. Speech and Hearing Assn. [★16690]
Student Letter Exchange [21422], 1111 Broadhollow Rd., Ste. 329, Farmingdale, NY 11735, (631)393-0216
Student Missions Fellowship [★20051]
Student Natl. Dental Assn. [7967], Obianuju Mbamalu, Treas., 125 Kirkbride Apt. 5, Voorhees, NJ 08043
Student Natl. Educ. Assn. [★23181]
Student Natl. Medical Assn. [8618], 5113 Georgia Ave. NW, Washington, DC 20011, (202)882-2881
Student Nurses' Assn; Natl. [8616]
Student Org. of North Am. [8931], Univ. of Arizona, Univ. Services Annex Bldg. 300A, Rm. 108, 220 W 6th St., Tucson, AZ 85721-0300, (520)626-0120
Student Osteopathic Medical Assn. [16079], 142 E Ontario St., Chicago, IL 60611, (312)202-8193
Student Peace Alliance [18290], PO Box 27601, Washington, DC 20038, (202)684-2553
Student Personnel Assn. for Teacher Educ. [★8278]
Student Photographic Soc. [10444], 229 Peachtree St. NE, Ste. 2200, Atlanta, GA 30303, (866)886-5325
Student Pledge Against Gun Violence [17692], 112 Nevada St., Northfield, MN 55057, (507)645-5378
Student Press Law Center [17358], 1101 Wilson Blvd., Ste. 1100, Arlington, VA 22209, (703)807-1904
Student Pugwash U.S.A. [18819], 1015 18th St. NW, Ste. 704, Washington, DC 20036, (202)429-8900
Student Services
  Assn. of Coll. Unions Intl. [8903]
  Assn. of Coll. Unions Intl. [8903]
  Assn. of Coll. and Univ. Housing Officers Intl. [8904]
  Assn. of Coll. and Univ. Housing Officers Intl. [8904]
  Assn. of Coll. and Univ. Religious Affairs [8905]
  Assn. for Support of Graduate Students [8231]
  Natl. Assn. for Campus Activities [8906]
  Natl. Coun. on Student Development [8907]
  Natl. Student Exchange [8908]
  School Nutrition Assn. [8909]
  Students Serve [8910]
Student Services West [★8353]
Student Services West [★8353]
Student Soc. for Stem Cell Res. [15352], 303 Bannockburn Ave., Tampa, FL 33617, (813)368-8937
Student Soc. for Stem Cell Res. [15352], 303 Bannockburn Ave., Tampa, FL 33617, (813)368-8937
Student Union of Latvia [IO], Riga, Latvia
Student Veterans of Am. [9032], PO Box 77673, Washington, DC 20013-8673, (866)320-3826
Student Veterinary Emergency and Critical Care Soc. [17044], 6335 Camp Bullis Rd., Ste. 23, San Antonio, TX 78257-9722, (210)698-5575
Student Veterinary Emergency and Critical Care Soc. [17044], 6335 Camp Bullis Rd., Ste. 23, San Antonio, TX 78257-9722, (210)698-5575
Student and Youth Travel Assn. [3578], 8400 Westpark Dr., 2nd Fl., McLean, VA 22102, (703)610-1263
Student and Youth Travel Assn. [3578], 8400 Westpark Dr., 2nd Fl., McLean, VA 22102, (703)610-1263
Studentrad Haskola Islands [IO], Reykjavik, Iceland
Students
  Alliance for Preventive Hea. [14864]
  Alliance for Student Activities [8911]
  Amer. Assn. of Human Design Practitioners [1036]
  Amer. Collegiate Hockey Assn. [22639]
  Amer. Mgt. Assn. I Oper. Enterprise [8547]
  Amer. Physician Scientists Assn. [8588]
  Amer. Student Assn. of Community Colleges [8912]

Amer. Student Govt. Assn. [8913]
ASSE Intl. Student Exchange Programs [8346]
Assn. for Borderlands Stud. [8400]
Assn. for Support of Graduate Students [8231]
Assn. of Teachers of Tech. Writing [9072]
Astronaut Scholars Honor Soc. [23629]
Battelle for Kids [7826]
Break Away: The Alternative Break Connection [12764]
Campus Pride [12072]
Close Up Found. [17249]
Coll. Summit [8234]
Collegiate Assn. of Table Top Gamers [21745]
Coun. for the Advancement of Standards in Higher Educ. [8914]
Coun. for Children with Behavioral Disorders [8878]
Crystal Ball Cruise Assn. [13228]
Culturatti Kids Resource Network [9074]
Dance/Drill Team Directors of Am. [9544]
Destination ImagiNation [8697]
Ecology Proj. Intl. [8154]
Educ. Conservancy [7683]
Educ. Pioneers [8915]
Educational Help for Afghanistan Assn. [8916]
Educational Help for Afghanistan Assn. [8916]
Egyptian Student Assn. in North America [8917]
Egyptian Student Assn. in North America [8917]
Europeans Students' Union [18]
Fed. des Etudiant(e)s Francophones [17]
Global Brigades [11588]
Global Explorers [9017]
Go Green Initiative Assn. [8156]
GreatSchools [7831]
Green Schools Alliance [8158]StudentsHallgatoi Onkormanyzatok Orszagos Konferenciaja
Hispanic Educational Tech. Services [8973]
Humanity in Action [8277]
IES Abroad [8170]
Intercollegiate Stud. Inst. [17425]
Intl. Alumni Assn. of Shri Mahavir Jain Vidyalaya [19219]
Intl. Assn. for the Exchange of Students for Tech. Experience [8918]
Intl. Assn. for the Exchange of Students for Tech. Experience [8918]
Intl. Fed. of Engg. Educ. Societies [8124]
Intl. Soc. for the Social Stud. [8865]
InterVarsity Link [8919]
InterVarsity Link [8919]
Jesuit Assn. of Student Personnel Administrators [7665]
Jewish Student Press Ser. [8428]
Journey Toward Sustainability [8159]
Leadership Enterprise for a Diverse Am. [8920]
Millennium Campus Network [17191]
Minority Access, Inc. [8631]
Muslim Students Assn. of the U.S. and Canada [8921]
Muslim Students Assn. of the U.S. and Canada [8921]
Natl. Assn. of Graduate-Professional Students [8922]
Natl. Assn. of Hea. Sci. Educ. Partnership [8843]
Natl. Assn. of Math Circles [8566]
Natl. Assn. of Student Councils [8923]
Natl. Center for Student Leadership [8924]
Natl. CH for Commuter Programs [8925]
Natl. Club Baseball Assn. [22283]
Natl. Coalition for Public School Options [8775]
Natl. Forensic Assn. [8895]
Natl. History Club [8261]
Natl. Latina/Latino Law Student Assn. [18057]
Natl. Middle Level Sci. Teachers' Assn. [8848]
Natl. Senior Classical League [7866]
Natl. Soc. of Leadership and Success [8926]
Natl. Student Union of Macedonia [14274]
Natl. Title I Assn. [7677]
Natl. Traditionalist Caucus [17429]
Natl. Union of Students - United Kingdom [8191]
Naturopathic Medical Student Assn. [15535]
North Amer. South Asian Law Student Assn. [8511]
North Amer. Students of Cooperation [8927]
One World Educ. [8928]

OneWorld Now! [8929]
Overseas Young Chinese Forum [7845]
Responsible Endowments Coalition [9082]
Rock Detective Geoscience Educ. [7983]
Security on Campus [11693]
Soliya [18833]
Student Affl. Gp. [8930]
Student African Amer. Brotherhood [19288]
Student Org. of North Am. [8931]
Student Peace Alliance [18290]StudentsStudentrad Haskola Islands
Students for the Second Amendment [17693]
Swedish Natl. Union of Students [2389]
Union of North Amer. Vietnamese Students Assn. [19275]
U.S. Assn. of Former Members of Cong. [17414]
U.S. Student Assn. [8932]
USSA Found. [8933]
World Savvy [9084]
Students Active for Ending Rape [12760], 32 Broadway, Ste. 1101, Brooklyn, NY 11249, (347)293-0953
Students Against Destructive Decisions [13009], 255 Main St., Marlborough, MA 01752, (508)481-3568
Students Against Drunk Driving [★13009]
Students for Change - Defunct.
Students for the Exploration and Development of Space [7697], MIT Rm. W20-445, 77 Massachusetts Ave., Cambridge, MA 02139
Students in Free Enterprise [17724], The Jack Shewmaker SIFE World HQ, 1959 E Kerr St., Springfield, MO 65803-4775, (417)831-9505
Students Helping St. Kids Intl. [11509], PO Box 2069, Eugene, OR 97402, (877)543-7697
Students Helping St. Kids Intl. [11509], PO Box 2069, Eugene, OR 97402, (877)543-7697
Students for Life of Am. [12945], 4141 N Henderson Rd., Ste. 7, Arlington, VA 22203, (703)351-6280
Students for the Second Amendment [17693], 9624 Braun Run, San Antonio, TX 78254, (210)674-5559
Students Serve [8910], 1733 Cy Ct., Vienna, VA 22182, (703)865-8790
Students for Social Responsibility - Address unknown since 2010.
Studiengesellschaft fur Unterirdische Verkehrsanlagen [★IO]
Studio Art Quilt Associates [9319], PO Box 572, Storrs, CT 06268-0572, (860)487-4199
Studiorum Novi Testamenti Societas [★IO]
Studium Polski Podziemnej [★IO]
Stud. Circles Rsrc. Center [★19241]
Stuntmen's Assn. of Motion Pictures [1267], 5200 Lankershim Blvd., Ste. 190, North Hollywood, CA 91601, (818)766-4334
Stunts Unlimited [19246], 15233 Ventura Blvd., Ste. 425, Sherman Oaks, CA 91403, (818)501-1970
Stuntwomen's Assn. of Motion Pictures [1268], 12457 Ventura Blvd., No. 208, Studio City, CA 91604-2411, (818)762-0907
Sturge-Weber Found. [15635], PO Box 418, Mount Freedom, NJ 07970-0418, (973)895-4445
Stuttering Found. of Am. [16692], 1805 Moriah Woods Blvd., Ste. 3, PO Box 11749, Memphis, TN 38117-0749, (901)761-0343
Stutz Club [21171], PO Box 86, Greenford, OH 44422, (330)730-9498
Styrene Butadiene Latex Mfrs. Coun. [★763]
Styrene and Ethylbenzene Assn. - Defunct.
Styrene Info. and Res. Center [767], 801 N Quincy St., 7th Fl., Arlington, VA 22203, (703)875-0736
Sub Aqua Assn. [IO], Liverpool, United Kingdom
Subaru 360 Drivers' Club [21172], 23251 Hansen Rd., Tracy, CA 95304
Submarine Indus. Base Coun. [1035], 1825 I St. NW, Ste. 600, Washington, DC 20006-5403, (202)207-3633
Submarine League; Naval [17510]
Submersible Wastewater Pump Assn. [625], 1866 Sheridan Rd., Ste. 201, Highland Park, IL 60035-2545, (847)681-1868
Subscription Fulfillment Managers Assn. [★2935]
Substance Abuse
  ABLE: Assn. for Better Living and Educ. Intl. [11537]

A star before a book entry number signifies that the name is not listed separately, but is mentioned within the entry.

Addiction Res. and Treatment Corp. [13229]
Al-Anon Family Gp. HQ World Ser. Off. [13230]
Al-Anon Family Gp. HQ World Ser. Off. [13230]
Alateen [839]
Alateen [13231]SubstanceAlcohol Focus Scotland
Alcohol Res. Info. Ser. [13232]
Alcoholics Anonymous World Services [13233]
Alcoholics Anonymous World Services [13233]
Amer. Assn. for the Treatment of Opioid
  Dependence [16734]
Amer. Coun. for Drug Educ. [13234]
Amer. Osteopathic Acad. of Addiction Medicine
  [16735]
Amer. Soc. of Addiction Medicine [16736]
Assn. of Halfway House Alcoholism Programs of
  North Am. [13235]
Assn. of Recovering Motorcyclists [13236]
Assn. for the Treatment of Tobacco Use and
  Dependence [16737]
Australian Drug Found. [8629]
BACCHUS Network [13237]
BACCHUS Network [13237]
Calix Soc. [13238]
Calix Soc. [13238]
Center on Addiction and the Family [13239]
Center for Substance Abuse Prevention [16738]
Century Coun. [16739]
Choose Responsibility [13240]
Christian Addiction Rehabilitation Assn. [13241]
Co-Anon Family Groups [13242]
Coalition of Higher Educ. Associations for
  Substance Abuse Prevention [13243]
Cocaine Anonymous World Services [13244]
Cocaine Anonymous World Services [13244]
Community Anti-Drug Coalitions of Am. [13245]
DanceSafe [13246]
DanceSafe [13246]
D.A.R.E. Am. [13247]
Do It Now Found. [13248]
Drug and Alcohol Testing Indus. Assn. [13249]
Entertainment Indus. Coun. [13250]
Faces and Voices of Recovery [18679]
Families Anonymous [13251]
Families Anonymous [13251]
Families Worldwide [13252]
Families Worldwide [13252]
Family Coun. on Drug Awareness [13253]
Family Coun. on Drug Awareness [13253]
Giraffe Club [18680]
Harm Reduction Coalition [13254]
Harm Reduction Coalition [13254]
Hazelden Found. [13255]
Informed Families Educ. Center l Natl. Family
  Partnership [13256]
Inst. for a Drug-Free Workplace [13257]
Inst. on Global Drug Policy [13258]
Inst. on Global Drug Policy [13258]
Intl. Assn. of Addictions and Offender Counselors
  [11674]
Intl. Coalition for Addiction Stud. Educ. [8934]
Intl. Coun. on Alcohol, Drugs and Traffic Safety
  [16740]
Intl. Coun. on Alcohol, Drugs and Traffic Safety
  [16740]
Intl. Doctors in Alcoholics Anonymous [13259]
Intl. Doctors in Alcoholics Anonymous [13259]
Intl. Lawyers in Alcoholics Anonymous
  [13260]SubstanceIntl. Nurses Anonymous
Intl. Soc. for Biomedical Res. on Alcoholism
  [16741]
Intl. Soc. for Biomedical Res. on Alcoholism
  [16741]
Jewish Alcoholics, Chemically Dependent Persons
  and Significant Others [13261]
Jewish Alcoholics, Chemically Dependent Persons
  and Significant Others [13261]
Leadership to Keep Children Alcohol Free [13262]
Luz Social Services [13263]
Men Against Destruction - Defending Against
  Drugs and Social Disorder [13264]
Moderation Mgt. [16742]
MOMSTELL [13265]
Mothers Against Misuse and Abuse [16743]
NAADAC: The Assn. for Addiction Professionals
  [16744]

NALGAP: The Assn. of Lesbian, Gay, Bisexual,
  and Transgender Addiction Professionals and
  Their Allies [13266]
Narcotic Educational Found. of Am. [13267]
Narcotics Anonymous [13268]
Narcotics Anonymous [13268]
Natl. Acupuncture Detoxification Assn. [16745]
Natl. Acupuncture Detoxification Assn. [16745]
Natl. African Amer. Drug Policy Coalition [13269]
Natl. Alliance of Advocates for Buprenorphine
  Treatment [16746]
Natl. Alliance for Drug Endangered Children
  [13270]
Natl. Alliance for Medication Assisted Recovery
  [16747]
Natl. Alliance for Medication Assisted Recovery
  [16747]
Natl. Asian Pacific Amer. Families Against
  Substance Abuse [13271]
Natl. Assn. of Addiction Treatment Providers
  [13272]
Natl. Assn. on Alcohol, Drugs and Disability
  [16748]
Natl. Assn. for Children of Alcoholics [13273]
Natl. Assn. on Drug Abuse Problems [13274]
Natl. Assn. of Drug Court Professionals [6004]
Natl. Assn. of Drug Court Professionals [6004]
Natl. Assn. of State Alcohol and Drug Abuse
  Directors [13275]
Natl. Black Alcoholism and Addiction Coun.
  [13276]
Natl. Catholic Coun. on Alcoholism and Related
  Drug Problems [13277]
Natl. Catholic Coun. on Alcoholism and Related
  Drug Problems [13277]
Natl. CH for Alcohol and Drug Info. [16749]
Natl. Coun. on Alcoholism and Drug Dependence
  [13278]
Natl. Families in Action [13279]
Natl. Inhalant Prevention Coalition [16750]
Natl. Inst. on Drug Abuse [6005]
Natl. Org. on Fetal Alcohol Syndrome [16751]
New Hope Found. [13280]
notMYkid [13548]
November Coalition [18681]
Partnership at Drugfree.org [13281]
Phoenix House [13282]
Pills Anonymous [13283]
PRIDE Youth Programs [13284]
Proj. Renewal [13285]
Rational Recovery Systems [16752]
Recovered Alcoholic Clergy Assn. [13286]
Recovery Ministries [13287]
Remembering ADAM [13288]
Res. Soc. on Alcoholism [16753]
Road Recovery Found. [16754]
Secular Organizations for Sobriety [13289]
SMART Recovery [16755]
Soc. for Prevention Res. [16756]
Soc. for Prevention Res. [16756]
Substance Abuse Prog. Administrators Assn.
  [16757]
Substance Abuse Prog. Administrators Assn.
  [16757]
Treatment Communities of Am. [13290]
Triangle Club [13291]
VietNow Natl. [13358]
Way to Work [11962]
Women for Sobriety [13292]
Substance Abuse; Assn. for Medical Educ. and Res.
in [8593]
Substance Abuse Librarians and Info. Specialists
  [10014], PO Box 9513, Berkeley, CA 94709-0513,
  (510)769-1831
Substance Abuse Librarians and Info. Specialists
  [10014], PO Box 9513, Berkeley, CA 94709-0513,
  (510)769-1831
Substance Abuse Prog. Administrators Assn.
  [16757], 1014 Whispering Oak Dr., Bardstown, KY
  40004, (860)690-3392
Substance Abuse Prog. Administrators Assn.
  [16757], 1014 Whispering Oak Dr., Bardstown, KY
  40004, (860)690-3392
Subterranean Construction
  Amer. Underground Constr. Assn. [7484]

Subud
  Subud Intl. Cultural Assn. U.S.A. [9320]
  Subud U.S.A. [20262]
Subud Intl. Cultural Assn. [★9320]
Subud Intl. Cultural Assn. U.S.A. [9320], 9509 Ke-
  tona Cove, Austin, TX 78759-6260
Subud North Am. [★20262]
Subud U.S.A. [20262], 14019 NE 8th St., Ste. A,
  Bellevue, WA 98007, (425)643-1904
Subud Youth Assn. [13558], 14019 NE 8th St., Ste.
  A, Bellevue, WA 98007, (425)643-1904
Suburban Newspapers of Am. [2967], 116 Cass St.,
  Traverse City, MI 49684, (888)486-2466
Suburban Sect. of the Natl. Newspaper Assn.
  [★2967]
S.U.C.C.E.S.S. for Autism [13804], 28700 Euclid
  Ave., Mailbox No. 120, Wickliffe, OH 44092
Succulent Soc. of South Africa [IO], Pretoria,
  Republic of South Africa
Sudan-American Found. for Educ. [7837], 3122
  Ross Rd., Ames, IA 50014
Sudan Athletic Assn. [IO], Khartoum, Sudan
Sudan Development Assn. - Defunct.
Sudan Internet Soc. [IO], Khartoum, Sudan
Sudan Lawn Tennis Assn. [IO], Khartoum, Sudan
Sudan Population Network [IO], Khartoum, Sudan
Sudan Squash Fed. [IO], Khartoum, Sudan
Sudan Stud. Assn. [7703], Rhode Island Coll., Dept.
  of Anthropology, 600 Mt. Pleasant Ave.,
  Providence, RI 02908, (401)467-2857
Sudan Stud. Assn. [7703], Rhode Island Coll., Dept.
  of Anthropology, 600 Mt. Pleasant Ave.,
  Providence, RI 02908, (401)467-2857
Sudan Stud. Soc. of the United Kingdom [IO],
  London, United Kingdom
Sudan Sunrise [12636], 8643 Hauser Ct., Ste. 240,
  Lenexa, KS 66215, (913)599-0800
SUDANAID - Caritas Sudan [IO], Khartoum, Sudan
Sudanese Assn. in Petroleum Geoscientists [IO],
  Khartoum, Sudan
Sudanese Chambers of Indus. Assn. [IO], Khartoum,
  Sudan
Sudanese Development Initiative [IO], Khartoum,
  Sudan
Sudanese Medical Engg. Soc. [IO], Khartoum,
  Sudan
Sudanese Org. for Educ. Development [IO], Khar-
  toum, Sudan
Sudanese Standard and Metrology Org. [IO], Khar-
  toum, Sudan
Sudanese Taekwondo Fed. [IO], Khartoum, Sudan
Sudanese Weightlifting Fed. [IO], Khartoum, Sudan
Sudanese Women Artists Assn. [IO], Khartoum,
  Sudan
Sudanese Women Empowerment for Peace [IO],
  Khartoum, Sudan
Sudden Arrhythmia Death Syndromes Found.
  [14631], 508 E South Temple, Ste. 202, Salt Lake
  City, UT 84102-1013, (801)531-0937
Sudden Cardiac Arrest Assn. [14048], 1133 Con-
  necticut Ave. NW, 11th Fl., Washington, DC 20036,
  (202)719-8909
Sudden Infant Death Syndrome
  Amer. Guild for Infant Survival [16758]
  Amer. Sudden Infant Death Syndrome Inst.
  [16759]
  Assn. of SIDS and Infant Mortality Programs
  [16760]
  First Candle/SIDS Alliance [16761]
  Natl. Sudden and Unexpected Infant/Child Death
  and Pregnancy Loss Rsrc. Center [16762]
Sudden Infant Death Syndrome Alliance [★16761]
Sudden Infant Death Syndrome Awareness for Africa
  [IO], Lagos, Nigeria
Sueriges Skeppsmaklareforening [★IO]
Suffolk Chamber of Commerce [IO], Ipswich, United
  Kingdom
Sufi Psychology Assn. [16435], PO Box 19922,
  Sacramento, CA 95819, (916)368-5530
Sugar
  All Trinidad Sugar and Gen. Workers' Trade Union
  [2219]
  Amer. Soc. of Sugar Cane Technologists [4932]
  Amer. Sugar Cane League of the U.S.A. [4933]
  Amer. Sugarbeet Growers Assn. [4934]

Reference to "IO" in place of a book number signifies that the association may be found in the 50th edition of International Organizations.

Argentine Sugar Center [22206]
Australian Soc. of Sugar Cane Technologists [13751]
Beet Sugar Development Found. [4935]
Chamber of Sugar Producers [652]
Hawaii Agriculture Res. Center [4936]
Intl. Stevia Coun. [1404]
Intl. Sugar Trade Coalition [3367]
Intl. Sugar Trade Coalition [3367]
Red River Valley Sugarbeet Growers Assn. [4937]
South African Sugarcane Indus. Agronomists Assn. [11870]
Sugar Assn. [1431], 1300 L St. NW, Ste. 1001, Washington, DC 20005, (202)785-1122
Sugar Assn. of London [IO], London, United Kingdom
Sugar Bur. [IO], London, United Kingdom
Sugar Indus. Technologists [6880], 201 Cypress Ave., Clewiston, FL 33440, (863)983-3637
Sugar Indus. Technologists [6880], 201 Cypress Ave., Clewiston, FL 33440, (863)983-3637
Sugar Milling Res. Inst. [IO], Durban, Republic of South Africa
Sugarbugs - Address unknown since 2010.
Suicide
Amer. Assn. of Suicidology [13293]
Amer. Found. for Suicide Prevention [13294]
Girls and Boys Town [12947]
Heartbeat [13295]
Natl. Org. for People of Color Against Suicide [13296]
Ray of Hope [13297]
Suicide Prevention Action Network U.S.A. [13298]
Suicide Prevention Intl. [13299]
Trans Youth Family Allies [12585]
Suicide Info. and Educ. Coll. [IO], Calgary, AB, Canada
Suicide and Mental Hea. Assn. Intl.
Suicide and Mental Hea. Assn. Intl. - Address unknown since 2011.
Suicide Prevention Action Network U.S.A. [13298], 1010 Vermont Ave. NW, Ste. 408, Washington, DC 20005, (202)449-3600
Suicide Prevention Intl. [13299], 1045 Park Ave., Ste. 3C, New York, NY 10028
Suid-Afrikaanse Avokadokwekersverening [★IO]
Suid Afrikaanse Beestelergenootskap [★IO]
Suid-Afrikaanse Chemiese Instituut [★IO]
Suid-Afrikaanse Federasie van Druknywerhede [★IO]
Suid-Afrikaanse Marfansindroom Ondersteunings-groep [★IO]
Suid-Afrikaanse Mediese Fisika Vereniging [★IO]
Suid-Afrikaanse Orgideeraad [★IO]
Suid-Afrikaanse Ortopediese Vereniging [★IO]
Suid-Afrikaanse Vertalersinstituut [★IO]
Suid Afrikaanse Wingerd en Wynkundevereniging [★IO]
Suid-Afrikaanse Wiskundevereniging [★IO]
Suider-Afrika Genootskap vir die Bevordering van die Wetenskap [★IO]
Suider Afrikaanse Akoestiekinstituut [★IO]
Suider Afrikaanse Museumvereniging [★IO]
Sulabh Intl. Social Ser. Org. [IO], New Delhi, India
Sulfate of Potash Magnesia Export Assn. - Defunct.
Sullivant Moss Soc. [★6341]
Sullivant Moss Soc. [★6341]
The Sulphur Inst. [768], 1140 Connecticut Ave. NW, Ste. 612, Washington, DC 20036, (202)331-9660
The Sulphur Inst. [768], 1140 Connecticut Ave. NW, Ste. 612, Washington, DC 20036, (202)331-9660
Sultan Qaboos bin Said Res. Center [★18129]
Sultan Qaboos bin Said Res. Center [★18129]
Sumatran Orangutan Soc. USA [5135], 1029 Ray Andra Dr., DeSoto, TX 75115, (301)648-3855
Sumatran Orangutan Soc. USA [5135], 1029 Ray Andra Dr., DeSoto, TX 75115, (301)648-3855
Sumi-e Soc. of Am. [9206], 122 Denton St., Patchogue, NY 11772, (631)475-6779
Summer and Casual Furniture Mfrs. Assn. [1557], 317 W High Ave., High Point, NC 27260, (336)884-5000
Summer School
North Amer. Assn. of Summer Sessions [8935]
North Amer. Assn. of Summer Sessions [8935]

North Central Conf. on Summer Schools [8936]
Summerbridge Natl. [★8005]
Summerland Olives [IO], Casino, Australia
The Summit Lighthouse [★20176]
Sumner Family Assn. [20596], Mr. Charles Hanson Sumner, Dir., 7540 Rolling River Pkwy., Nashville, TN 37221-3322, (615)646-9946
Sumner Family Assn. [20596], Mr. Charles Hanson Sumner, Dir., 7540 Rolling River Pkwy., Nashville, TN 37221-3322, (615)646-9946
Sump Pump Mfrs. Assn. [★626]
Sump Pump Mfrs. Assn. [★626]
Sump and Sewage Pump Mfrs. Assn. [626], PO Box 647, Northbrook, IL 60065-0647, (847)559-9233
Sump and Sewage Pump Mfrs. Assn. [626], PO Box 647, Northbrook, IL 60065-0647, (847)559-9233
Sun Do Mountain Taoist Breathing Meditation Center [★9933]
Sun Do Mountain Taoist Breathing Meditation Center [★9933]
Sun-Maid Growers of California [4473], 13525 S Bethel Ave., Kingsburg, CA 93631, (559)896-8000
Sun Marine Employees Assn. - Defunct.
Sun Safety Alliance [13984], 1856 Old Reston Ave., Ste. 215, Reston, VA 20190, (703)481-1414
SUN Symphony Soc. Inc. [★9321]
SUN Symphony Soc. Inc. [★9321]
Sunbeam Rapier Registry [21173], 3212 Orchard Cir., West Des Moines, IA 50266, (515)226-9475
Sunbeam Rapier Registry of North Am. [★21173]
SunCoast Fundogs Agility Club [IO], Brisbane, Australia
SunDance [IO], Frenkendorf, Switzerland
Sundance Inst. [9611], PO Box 684429, Park City, UT 84068, (435)658-3456
Sunflower Alliance - Defunct.
Sunflower Assn. of Am. [★3956]
SunGard Public Sector Users' Gp. Assn. [6519], PO Box 402456, Atlanta, GA 30384-2456
Sunny Von Bulow Natl. Victim Advocacy Center [★13367]
SunnyTravelers [22148], 58800 Executive Dr., Mishawaka, IN 46544, (574)258-0571
SunPower Afrique [13227], 212 Christian St., 1st Fl., Philadelphia, PA 19147
SunPower Afrique [13227], 212 Christian St., 1st Fl., Philadelphia, PA 19147
Sunshine Found. [11510], 1041 Mill Creek Dr., Feasterville, PA 19053, (215)396-4770
Sunstove Org. [11643], 2165 Underwood Pkwy., Elm Grove, WI 53122
Sunsweet Growers [4474], 901 N Walton Ave., Yuba City, CA 95993, (800)417-2253
Suntanning Assn. for Educ. [3064], PO Box 1181, Gulf Breeze, FL 32562, (800)536-8255
Suomen hahmontunnistustutkimusken seura ry [★IO]
Suomen fysiologiyhdistys [★IO]
Suomen 4H-liitto [★IO]
Suomen Aikidoliitto [★IO]
Suomen Akateemisten Naisten Liitto - Finlands Kvinnliga Akademikers Forbund [★IO]
Suomen Ammattilittojen Solidaarissuskeskus [★IO]
Suomen Ampumahiihtoliito [★IO]
Suomen Ampumaurheiluliitto [★IO]
Suomen Anaetesiologiyhdistys [★IO]
Suomen Apteekkariliitto [★IO]
Suomen Autokoululiitto [★IO]
Suomen Automaatioseura [★IO]
Suomen Autoteknillinen Liitto ry [★IO]
Suomen Bensiinikauppiaitten ja Liikennepalvelua-lojen Liitto SBL ry [★IO]
Suomen Biljardiliitto [★IO]
Suomen Biologian Seura Vanamo [IO], Helsinki, Finland
Suomen Curlingliitto [★IO]
Suomen Egyptologinen Seura [★IO]
Suomen Elintarviketyoelaeisten Liitto [★IO]
Suomen Farmakologiyhdistys [★IO]
Suomen Franchising-Yhdistys [★IO]
Suomen Fyysikkoseura Finlands Fysikerforening r.y. [★IO]
Suomen Gynekologiyhdistys Ry [★IO]
Suomen Historiallinen Seura [★IO]
Suomen Journalistiliitto [★IO]

Suomen Kalankasvattajaliitto [★IO]
Suomen Kansanopistoyhdistys [★IO]
Suomen Kardiologinen Seura [★IO]
Suomen Kehitysvammaisten Liikunta ja Urheilu ry [★IO]
Suomen Kelloseppaliitto ry [★IO]
Suomen Kirjailijaliitto [★IO]
Suomen Kirjastoseura [★IO]
Suomen Krikettiliitto RY [★IO]
Suomen Kulttuurirahasto [★IO]
Suomen Kustannusyhdistys [★IO]
Suomen Laakariliitto [★IO]
Suomen Laulajain ja Soittajain Liitto [★IO]
Suomen Leipuriliitto ry [★IO]
Suomen Liikennelentajaliitto [★IO]
Suomen Liikunta ja Urheilu [★IO]
Suomen Liitokiekkoliitto ry [★IO]
Suomen Maisema-arkkitehtiliitto [★IO]
Suomen Marfan-yhdistyksen [★IO]
Suomen Merimies-Unioni [★IO]
Suomen Mielenterveysseura [★IO]
Suomen MS-liitto [★IO]
Suomen Museoliitto [★IO]
Suomen Musiikkikustantajat ry [★IO]
Suomen Musiikkiopplaitosten Liitto [★IO]
Suomen Muusikkojen Liitto [★IO]
Suomen Naytelmakirjailijaliitto [★IO]
Suomen Nuorisoyhteistyo Allianssi [★IO]
Suomen Nuorkauppakamarit ry [★IO]
Suomen Olympiakomitea [★IO]
Suomen Operaatiotutkimusseura ry [★IO]
Suomen Osteoporoosiliitto ry [★IO]
Suomen Pakolaisapu [★IO]
Suomen Paralympiakomitea [★IO]
Suomen Parkinson- liitto ry Finlands Parkinson for-bund rf [★IO]
Suomen Perhostutkijain Seura ry [★IO]
Suomen Radioamatooriliitto ry [★IO]
Suomen Rakennusinsinoeoerien Liitto RIL [★IO]
Suomen Retkeilymajajarjesto [★IO]
Suomen Ruususeura r.y. - Finska Rosensallskapet r.f. [★IO]
Suomen Sadankomitealiitto [★IO]
Suomen Sahkotukkuliikkeiden Liitto ry [★IO]
Suomen Salibandyliitto [★IO]
Suomen Satamaliitto [★IO]
Suomen Saveltajat [★IO]
Suomen Sinfoniaorkesterit [★IO]
Suomen Sosialidemokraattinen Puolue [★IO]
Suomen Suoramarkkinointiliitto [★IO]
Suomen Sydanliitto ry [★IO]
Suomen Taekwondoliitto [★IO]
Suomen Taideyhdistys [★IO]
Suomen Taiteilijaseura [★IO]
Suomen Tennisliitto [★IO]
Suomen Tiedeakatemiain Valtuuskunta [★IO]
Suomen Turkiselainten Kasvattajain Liitto ry [★IO]
Suomen Tuulivoimayhdistys ry [★IO]
Suomen Uimaliitto [★IO]
Suomen Valkonauhaliitto [★IO]
Suomen Varustamoyhdistys Ry [★IO]
Suomen Vesihiihtourheilu ry [★IO]
Suomen YK-Liitto [★IO]
Suomi-Amerikka Yhdistysten Liitto [★IO]
Suore Missionarie del Preziosissimo Sangue [★IO]
Suore Missionarie di San Pietro Claver [★IO]
Super Coupe Club of Am. [21174], 4322 Hamilton Rd., Medina, OH 44256, (330)242-1122
Superconductor Applications Assn. - Defunct.
Superior Coun. of U.S. Soc. of St. Vincent de Paul [★13204]
Supermarket Inst. [★3104]
Superstition Mountain Historical Soc. [9126], 4087 N Apache Trail, Apache Junction, AZ 85219, (480)983-4888
Superstition Mountain/Lost Dutchman Museum [★9126]
Supervised Visitation Network [11412], 3955 Riverside Ave., Jacksonville, FL 32205, (904)419-7861
Supervised Visitation Network [11412], 3955 Riverside Ave., Jacksonville, FL 32205, (904)419-7861
Supima [3962], 4141 E Broadway Rd., Phoenix, AZ 85040, (602)792-6002

A star before a book entry number signifies that the name is not listed separately, but is mentioned within the entry.

Supima Assn. of Am. [★3962]

Supplier Excellence Alliance [1872], 2062 Bus. Center Dr., Ste. 225, Irvine, CA 92612, (949)476-1144

Suppliers of Advanced Composite Materials Assn. [★519]

Suppliers of Advanced Composite Materials Assn. - Defunct.

Supply-Chain Coun. [1909], 12320 Barker Cypress Rd., Ste. 600, PMB 321, Cypress, TX 77429-8329, (202)962-0440

Supply-Chain Coun. [1909], 12320 Barker Cypress Rd., Ste. 600, PMB 321, Cypress, TX 77429-8329, (202)962-0440

Supply-Chain Coun. - Brazil Chap. [IO], Vinhedo, Brazil

Supply-Chain Coun. - Europe Chap. [IO], Amsterdam, Netherlands

Supply-Chain Coun. - Greater China Chap. [IO], Hong Kong, People's Republic of China

Supply-Chain Coun. - South East Asia Chap. [IO], Singapore, Singapore

Supply-Chain Coun. - Southern African Chap. [IO], Cape Town, Republic of South Africa

Supply Chain and Logistics Assn. Canada [IO], Markham, ON, Canada

Supply Chain and Logistics Gp. [IO], Dubai, United Arab Emirates

Support Assn. for the Women of Afghanistan - Australia [IO], Bedford Park, Australia

Support Coalition Intl. [★17852]

Support Connection [13985], 40 Triangle Ctr., Ste. 100, Yorktown Heights, NY 10598, (914)962-6402

Support Dogs for the Handicapped [★11832]

Support Dogs for the Handicapped [★11832]

Support Dogs, Inc. [11832], 11645 Lilburn Park Rd., St. Louis, MO 63146, (314)997-2325

Support Dogs, Inc. [11832], 11645 Lilburn Park Rd., St. Louis, MO 63146, (314)997-2325

Support Groups

4 Real Women Intl. [13447]

Aicardi Syndrome Newsl. [14581]

Amer. Self-Help Gp. CH [13035]

Angelman Syndrome Found. [16763]

AppleWorks Users Gp. [6479]

Avenues, Natl. Support Gp. for Arthrogryposis Multiplex Congenita [15573]

Because I Love You: The Parent Support Gp. [13300]

Billy Barty Found. [13115]

CDG Family Network Found. [16764]

Children's Tumor Found. [15579]

Co-Anon Family Groups [13242]

COLAGE [12074]

Columbia Queer Alliance [12075]

Debtors Anonymous [13040]

Exhale [10766]

Families of Adults Afflicted with Asperger's Syndrome [16765]

Family Equality Coun. [12079]

Fatty Oxidation Disorders Family Support Gp. [16766]

FG Syndrome Family Alliance [16767]

FG Syndrome Family Alliance [16767]

Five P Minus Soc. [16768]

FRAXA Res. Found. [16769]

Generation Five [13086]

Genetic Alliance [16770]

GriefNet [13301]

Heartbeat [13295]

Hold the Door for Others [11129]

Incontinentia Pigmenti Intl. Found. [14601]

Intl. Center for Fabry Disease [16771]

Intl. Center for Fabry Disease [16771]

Intl. Size Acceptance Assn. [12588]

It's My Heart [14028]

Klinefelter Syndrome and Associates [16772]

Loved Ones and Drivers Support [13342]

ManKind Proj. [13043]

Melanoma Awareness [13940]

Miscarriage Infant Death and Stillbirth Support Gp. [16773]

MISS Found. I Alliance of Grandparents, A Support in Tragedy Intl. [12123]

Mocha Moms [13466]

MUMS Natl. Parent-to-Parent Network [16774]

Myotubular Myopathy Rsrc. Gp. [16775]

Natl. Assn. for Native Amer. Children of Alcoholics [11356]

Natl. Assn. of Non-Custodial Moms [12610]

Natl. Necrotizing Fasciitis Found. [16776]

Natl. Org. for Empowering Caregivers [13302]

Natl. Org. for Empowering Caregivers [13302]

Natl. Potter Syndrome Forum [16777]

Natl. Practitioners Network for Fathers and Families [12018]

Nevus Network [16778]

Nevus Network [16778]

One Missing Link [12545]

Pandora's Proj. [13096]

Pediatric Chaplains Network [19529]

Progeria Res. Found. [16779]

Progeria Res. Found. [16779]

Reach Out for Youth with Ileitis and Colitis [16780]

Restless Legs Syndrome Found. [16781]

Rwanda Gift for Life [13099]

Ryan's Reach [16782]

Secretive Societies, Mind Control and Ritual Abuse [13303]

Shwachman-Diamond Syndrome Found. [16783]

Shwachman-Diamond Syndrome Found. [16783]

A Soldier's Wish List [11108]

Special Recreation for disABLED Intl. [11831]

Survivor Connections [13101]

Syndromes Without a Name USA [14419]

Tourette Syndrome Assn. [15636]

Vasculitis Found. [16784]

Vasculitis Found. [16784]

Well Spouse Assn. [16785]

Wide Smiles [16786]

Woman to Woman Support Network [16787]

World Arnold Chiari Malformation Assn. [16788]

World Arnold Chiari Malformation Assn. [16788]

Support Groups for Monosomy 9P [★14589]

Support Groups for Monosomy 9P [★14589]

The Support-In [★17852]

Support for Intl. Change [15214], PO Box 25803, Los Angeles, CA 90025

Support Org. for Trisomy 13/18 Ireland [IO], Athlone, Ireland

Support Org. for Trisomy 13/18 and Related Disorders - UK [IO], Sutton Coldfield, United Kingdom

Support Org. for Trisomy 18, 13, and Related Disorders [14632], 2982 S Union St., Rochester, NY 14624, (585)594-4621

Support Our Aging Religious [10871], 900 Varnum St. NE, Washington, DC 20017, (202)529-7627

Support Our Shelters [11043], 100 Walsh Rd., Lansdowne, PA 19050, (610)626-6647

Support Our Soldiers Am. [11109], 55 Bergen St., Brooklyn, NY 11201, (718)237-1097

Support Our Troops [11110], PO Box 70, Daytona Beach, FL 32115-0070, (386)767-8887

Support for People with Oral and Head and Neck Cancer [13986], PO Box 53, Locust Valley, NY 11560-0053, (516)759-5333

Support Services Alliance [3300], PO Box 130, Schoharie, NY 12157, (518)295-7966

Supranuclear Palsy; Soc. for Progressive [★14387]

Supreme Camp of the Amer. Woodmen [★19286]

Supreme Camp of the Amer. Woodmen - Defunct.

Supreme Commandery Knights of Saint John [★18957]

Supreme Commandery Knights of Saint John [★18957]

Supreme Coun. 33rd Degree, Ancient and Accepted Scottish Rite of Freemasonry - Southern Masonic Jurisdiction [★19125]

Supreme Coun. Catholic Benevolent Legion [★18955]

Supreme Coun. Catholic Benevolent Legion [★18955]

Supreme Coun. of the Royal Arcanum [19059], 61 Batterymarch St., Boston, MA 02110-3208, (617)426-4135

Supreme Coun. of the Western Catholic Union [★18960]

Supreme Court Historical Soc. [9811], Opperman House, 224 E Capitol St. NE, Washington, DC 20003, (202)543-0400

Supreme Emblem Club of the U.S.A. [18981], 130 Queen Dr., West Wareham, MA 02576, (617)818-6608

Supreme Forest Woodmen Circle [★19286]

Supreme Ladies Auxiliary Knights of Saint John [18959], Mrs. Ann Friday, Supreme Sec., 2330 Kirby Dr., Hillcrest Heights, MD 20748-3265, (301)423-6516

Supreme Lodge of the Danish Sisterhood of Am. [18975], Christine Hix, Natl. Trustee, 6396 Noble Ct., Arvada, CO 80403

Supreme Lodge Knights of Pythias [19096], 25 S Morton Ave., Morton, PA 19070, (610)544-3500

Supreme Lodge of the World, Loyal Order of Moose [★18989]

Supreme Lodge of the World, Loyal Order of Moose [★18989]

Supreme Master Ching Hai Meditation Assn. [19373], PO Box 730247, San Jose, CA 95173-0247, (408)603-5037

Supreme Master Ching Hai Meditation Assn. [19373], PO Box 730247, San Jose, CA 95173-0247, (408)603-5037

Supreme Temple Order Pythian Sisters [19097], 315 Third St., Findlay, OH 45840-5065

Supreme Travel Club [22149], PO Box 191, Osceola, IN 46561, (574)258-0571

Surdna Found. [12686], 330 Madison Ave., 30th Fl., New York, NY 10017, (212)557-0010

Surety Assn. of Am. [★2044]

Surety and Fidelity Assn. of Am. [2044], 1101 Connecticut Ave. NW, Ste. 800, Washington, DC 20036, (202)463-0600

Surf Life Saving Assn. of Great Britain [IO], Exeter, United Kingdom

Surf Life Saving Australia [IO], Bondi Beach, Australia

Surface Coatings Assn. Australia [IO], Toorak, Australia

Surface Coatings Assn. New Zealand [IO], Auckland, New Zealand

Surface Contractors Assn. [IO], Helsinki, Finland

Surface Design Assn. [3457], PO Box 360, Sebastopol, CA 95473-0360, (707)829-3110

Surface Engg. Assn. [IO], Birmingham, United Kingdom

Surface Engg. Coating Assn. [6433], Vantage Ctr., Ste. 8, 6311 Inducon Corporate Dr., Sanborn, NY 14132, (716)791-8100

Surface Mount Tech. Assn. [1873], 5200 Willson Rd., Ste. 215, Edina, MN 55424, (952)920-7682

Surface Trans. Policy Proj. [18734], 1707 L St. NW, Ste. 1050, Washington, DC 20036, (202)466-2636

Surfaces in Biomaterials Found. [6336], 1000 Westgate Dr., Ste. 252, St. Paul, MN 55114, (651)290-6267

SurfAid Intl. [11644], 530 Second St., Encinitas, CA 92024, (760)753-1103

SurfAid Intl. [11644], 530 Second St., Encinitas, CA 92024, (760)753-1103

Surfers Against Sewage [IO], Cornwall, United Kingdom

Surfer's Medical Assn. [15436], PO Box 454, Aptos, CA 95001, (831)601-7873

Surfing

Assn. of Professional Towsurfers [23030]

Assn. of Surfing Lawyers [23031]

Assn. of Surfing Professionals [23032]

Eastern Surfing Assn. [23033]

Intl. Surfing Assn. [23034]

Natl. Scholastic Surfing Assn. [23035]

Natl. Surf Schools and Instructors Assn. [23036]

Professional Windsurfers Assn. [22385]

Surfrider Found. [18682]

Surfrider Found. [18682]

WAVES for Development [18683]

Surfing Medicine Intl. [13712], PO Box 548, Waialua, HI 96791, (518)635-0899

Surfing South Africa [IO], Rondebosch, Republic of South Africa

Surfrider Found. [18682], PO Box 6010, San Clemente, CA 92674-6010, (949)492-8170

Surfrider Found. [18682], PO Box 6010, San Clemente, CA 92674-6010, (949)492-8170

Surfun: The Official Jan and Dean Fan Club [23892], 328 Sumner Ave., Sumner, WA 98390

Reference to "IO" in place of a book number signifies that the association may be found in the 50th edition of International Organizations.

SURGE [13431], 521 S 7th St., Ste. 214, Minneapolis, MN 55415
Surgeons; Amer. Acad. of Neurological and Orthopaedic [15681]
Surgeons; Amer. Acad. of Orthopaedic [16019]
Surgeons; Amer. Acad. of Orthopaedic [16019]
Surgeons; Amer. Assn. of Plastic [14172]
Surgeons; Amer. Coll. of Foot and Ankle [16292]
Surgeons; Amer. Coll. of Oral and Maxillofacial [16004]
Surgeons; Amer. Coll. of Oral and Maxillofacial [16004]
Surgeons; Amer. Coll. of Osteopathic [16063]
Surgeons; Amer. Coll. of Veterinary [17004]
Surgeons; Amer. Soc. of Colon and Rectal [16314]
Surgeons; Amer. Soc. of Maxillofacial [16005]
Surgeons; Assn. of Bone and Joint [16030]
Surgeons; Assn. of Military Osteopathic Physicians and [16074]
Surgeons; Puerto Rico Assn. of Pediatric [16154]
Surgeons; Soc. of Eye [15978]
Surgeons; Soc. of Military Orthopaedic [15513]
Surgeons; Soc. of Military Otolaryngologists - Head and Neck [15514]
Surgeons; Soc. of Reproductive [16600]
Surgeons; Soc. of U.S. Air Force Flight [13586]
Surgeons; Soc. of Univ. Otolaryngologists - Head and Neck [16090]
Surgeons of the U.S.A; Royal Coll. of Physicians and [16933]
Surgeons of the U.S; Assn. of Military [15510]
Surgery
    Alliance for Contraception in Cats and Dogs [12647]
    Alliance for Smiles [14189]
    Ambulatory Surgery Center Assn. [16789]
    Amer. Assn. for Accreditation of Ambulatory Surgery Facilities [16790]
    Amer. Assn. of Hip and Knee Surgeons [16791]
    Amer. Assn. of Orthopaedic Executives [16020]
    Amer. Assn. of Surgical Physician Assistants [16792]
    Amer. Bd. of Abdominal Surgery [16793]
    Amer. Bd. of Facial Plastic and Reconstructive Surgery [16794]
    Amer. Bd. of Surgery [16795]
    Amer. Coll. of Eye Surgeons [16796]
    Amer. Coll. of Surgeons [16797]
    Amer. Coll. of Surgeons [16797]
    Amer. Hernia Soc. [16798]
    Amer. Hernia Soc. [16798]
    Amer. Shoulder and Elbow Surgeons [16799]
    Amer. Soc. of Abdominal Surgeons [16800]
    Amer. Soc. for Aesthetic Plastic Surgery [14175]
    Amer. Soc. of Breast Surgeons [16801]
    Amer. Soc. forReconstructive Microsurgery [16802]
    Amer. Soc. of Gen. Surgeons [16803]
    Amer. Soc. for Metabolic and Bariatric Surgery [16804]
    Amer. Soc. of Plastic Surgeons | Plastic Surgery Educ. Found. [14178]
    Amer. Soc. for Reconstructive Microsurgery [16802]
    Amer. Surgical Assn. [16805]
    Assn. for Academic Surgery [16806]
    Assn. of Prog. Directors in Surgery [16807]
    Assn. of Prog. Directors in Vascular Surgery [16808]
    Assn. of Women Surgeons [16809]
    Assn. of Women Surgeons [16809]
    Changing Children's Lives [15150]
    Children's Corrective Surgery Soc. [16810]
    Coun. for Refractive Surgery Quality Assurance [16811]
    CyberKnife Soc. [16812]
    DAST Intl. [16813]
    Face Forward [11885]
    Global Partners in Anesthesia and Surgery [16814]
    Global Partners in Anesthesia and Surgery [16814]
    Intl. Alliance of Hair Restoration Surgeons [14675]
    Intl. Coll. of Surgeons [16815]
    Intl. Coll. of Surgeons [16815]

Intl. Palestinian Cardiac Relief Org. [14021]
Intl. Soc. for Vascular Surgery [16816]
Intl. Soc. for Vascular Surgery [16816]
Natl..Surgical Asst. Assn. [16817]
Partner for Surgery [16818]
Partner for Surgery [16818]
Physicians Coalition for Injectable Safety [14181]
Plastic Surgery Found. [14183]
Prosthetics Outreach Found. [16819]
Small World Found. [16820]
Smile Network Intl. [14203]
Soc. of Air Force Clinical Surgeons [16821]
Soc. of Interventional Pain Mgt. Surgery Centers [16822]
Soc. of Laparoendoscopic Surgeons [16823]
Soc. for Surgery of the Alimentary Tract [16824]
Soc. of Univ. Surgeons [16825]
Spine Arthroplasty Soc. [15688]
Western Surgical Assn. [16826]
Surgery; Amer. Acad. of Facial Plastic and Reconstructive [14170]
Surgery; Amer. Assn. for Hand [14678]
Surgery; Amer. Bd. of Colon and Rectal [16313]
Surgery; Amer. Bd. of Neurological [15683]
Surgery; Amer. Bd. of Oral and Maxillofacial [16003]
Surgery; Amer. Bd. of Orthopaedic [16023]
Surgery; Amer. Bd. of Plastic [14173]
Surgery; Amer. Bd. of Podiatric [16290]
Surgery; Amer. Soc. of Cataract and Refractive [15943]
Surgery; Amer. Soc. of Ophthalmic Plastic and Reconstructive [14176]
Surgery of the Hand; Amer. Found. for [14679]
Surgery of the Hand; Amer. Soc. for [14681]
Surgery; Intl. Soc. of Hair Restoration [14676]
Surgery Soc; Gynecologic [15879]
Surgery of Trauma; Amer. Assn. for the [16923]
Surgical Assn; Amer. Pediatric [16141]
Surgical Dressing Mfrs. Assn. [IO], Chesterfield, United Kingdom
Surgical Eye Expeditions Intl. [17116], 6950 Hollister Ave., Ste. 250, Santa Barbara, CA 93117-2807, (805)963-3303
Surgical Eye Expeditions Intl. [17116], 6950 Hollister Ave., Ste. 250, Santa Barbara, CA 93117-2807, (805)963-3303
Surgical Instrument Mfrs. Assn. of Pakistan [IO], Sialkot, Pakistan
Surgical Nurses; Acad. of Medical [15698]
Surgical Oncology; Soc. of [15934]
Surgical Oncology Soc. Pakistan [IO], Lahore, Pakistan
Surgical Technologists; Assn. of [15370]
Surgical Trade Found. [★1683]
Surinaams Olympisch Comite [★IO]
Surinaamse Athletiek Bond [IO], Paramaribo, Suriname
Surinaamse Badminton Bond [IO], Paramaribo, Suriname
Surinaamse Vereniging voor Fysiotherapie [IO], Paramaribo, Suriname
Suriname Animal Protection Soc. [IO], Paramaribo, Suriname
Suriname Olympic Comm. [IO], Paramaribo, Suriname
Suriname Red Cross [IO], Paramaribo, Suriname
Surinamese Weightlifting and Bodybuilding Fed. [IO], Paramaribo, Suriname
Surplus
    Assoc. Surplus Dealers [3368]
    Investment Recovery Assn. [3369]
Surratt Soc. [9731], 9118 Brandywine Rd., Box 427, Clinton, MD 20735, (301)868-1121
Surrey Chambers of Commerce [IO], Woking, United Kingdom
Surrogate Parent Found. [★13304]
Surrogate Parenthood
    Center for Surrogate Parenting [13304]
    Org. of Parents Through Surrogacy [13305]
Sursawera [IO], New Delhi, India
Surtees Soc. [IO], Durham, United Kingdom
Surtsey Res. Soc. [IO], Reykjavik, Iceland
Surtseyjarfelagid [★IO]
The Survey Assn. [IO], Newark-on-Trent, United Kingdom

Surveying
    Amer. Assn. for Geodetic Surveying [7485]
    Amer. Cong. on Surveying and Mapping [7486]
    Amer. Coun. of Engg. Companies | Coun. of Professional Surveyors [3370]
    Australian Inst. of Quantity Surveyors [2438]
    The Hydrographic Soc. of Am. [7487]
    Natl. Soc. of Professional Surveyors [7488]
    Soc. of Accredited Marine Surveyors [7489]
    Soc. of Accredited Marine Surveyors [7489]
    U.S. Surveyors Assn. [7490]
Surveyors Historical Soc. [9812], 628 Ridge Ave., Lawrenceburg, IN 47025-1912, (812)537-2000
Surveyors; Mgt. Assn. for Private Photogrammetric [7260]
Survival [IO], London, United Kingdom
Survival
    Amer. Friends of "For Survival" [13306]
        Crime Survivors [17487]
        Outward Bound [8937]
        Pandora's Proj. [13096]
    Survival Deutschland [IO], Berlin, Germany
    Survival and Flight Equip. Assn. [★6095]
    Survival Intl. - Espana [IO], Madrid, Spain
    Survival Intl. - France [IO], Paris, France
    Survival Intl. - Italia [IO], Milan, Italy
Surviving Parents Coalition [11511], 1414 22nd St. NW, Ste. 4, Washington, DC 20037, (888)301-4343
Survivor Connections [13101], 52 Lyndon Rd., Cranston, RI 02905-1121, (401)941-2548
Survivor Corps - Defunct.
Survivors And Victims Empowered [11413], 38 Doe Run Rd., Ste. 250, Manheim, PA 17545, (717)665-0006
Survivors of Incest Anonymous [13102], World Ser. Off., PO Box 190, Benson, MD 21018-0190, (410)893-3322
Survivors Network of Those Abused by Priests [13370], PO Box 6416, Chicago, IL 60680, (312)455-1499
Survivors of Torture Intl. [17863], PO Box 151240, San Diego, CA 92175, (619)278-2400
Survivorship [13377], Family Justice Center, 470 27th St., Oakland, CA 94612
Susan G. Komen Breast Cancer Found. [★13987]
Susan G. Komen for the Cure [13987], 5005 LBJ Fwy., Ste. 250, Dallas, TX 75244, (877)465-6636
Susan G. Komen Found. [★13987]
Susan Glaspell Soc. [10743], 555 Jefferson St., Northumberland, PA 17857
Susila Dharma Intl. [IO], Montreal, QC, Canada
Suspension Specialists Assn. [★368]
Sussex Cattle Assn. of America - Defunct.
Sussex Chamber of Commerce and Enterprise [IO], Burgess Hill, United Kingdom
Sussex Peace Alliance [IO], Hailsham, United Kingdom
Sustain: The Alliance for Better Food and Farming [IO], London, United Kingdom
Sustainable Agriculture
    Agricultural Commodities Certification Assn. [3749]
    Agricultural Development Initiatives [3727]
    Alliance for Sustainability [4345]
    Brighter Green [4014]
    Community Agroecology Network [4938]
    Ecoagriculture Partners [4939]
    Ecova Mali [3754]
    Farm and Ranch Freedom Alliance [4352]
    Global Urban Development [11591]
    Intl. Agro Alliance [4940]
    Multinational Exchange for Sustainable Agriculture [4941]
    Natl. Sustainable Agriculture Coalition [4942]
    Natl. Women in Agriculture Assn. [3762]
    Partnership to Cut Hunger and Poverty in Africa [12746]
    Permacultura Am. Latina [4684]
    Protected Harvest [4943]
    Sustainable Agriculture Educ. [4944]
    Sustainable Agriculture Educ. Assn. [7717]
    Sustainable Biomaterials Collaborative [6119]
    Tech. for the Poor [4945]
    Tech. for the Poor [4945]

A star before a book entry number signifies that the name is not listed separately, but is mentioned within the entry.

Urban Farming [4366]
World Wide Opportunities on Organic Farms - USA [17173]
Sustainable Agriculture Educ. [4944], 2150 Allston Way, Ste. 320, Berkeley, CA 94704, (510)526-1793
Sustainable Agriculture Educ. Assn. [7717], Univ. of Missouri, Dept. of Rural Sociology, 120 Gentry Hall, Columbia, MO 65211, (573)882-0861
Sustainable Biodiesel Alliance [4494], PO Box 6028, Austin, TX 78762, (512)410-7841
Sustainable Biomaterials Collaborative [6119], Heeral Bhalala, Inst. for Local Self-Reliance, 2001 S St. NW, Ste. 570, Washington, DC 20009, (202)898-1610
Sustainable Buildings Indus. Coun. [7450], 1112 16th St. NW, Ste. 240, Washington, DC 20036, (202)628-7400
Sustainable Development Network [IO], Bristol, United Kingdom
Sustainable Development Tech. Canada [IO], Ottawa, ON, Canada
Sustainable Electricity Assn. New Zealand [IO], Paraparaumu, New Zealand
Sustainable Fisheries Partnership [3830], 4348 Waialae Ave., No. 692, Honolulu, HI 96816, (202)580-8187
Sustainable Furnishings Coun. [1558], PO Box 205, Chapel Hill, NC 27514, (919)967-1137
Sustainable Harvest Intl. [3765], 779 N Bend Rd., Surry, ME 04684, (207)669-8254
Sustainable Hospitals Proj. [15069], Kitson 200, 1 Univ. Ave., Lowell, MA 01854, (978)934-3386
Sustainable Obtainable Solutions [4826], PO Box 1424, Helena, MT 59624, (406)495-0738
Sustainable Organic Integrated Livelihoods [11645], 124 Church Rd., Sherburne, NY 13460
Sustainable Org. for Community Peasant Labourer Student Development and Orphans [IO], Siem Reap, Cambodia
Sustainable Packaging Coalition [4764], 600 E Water St., Ste. C, Charlottesville, VA 22902, (434)817-1424
Sustainable Population Australia [IO], Weston Creek, Australia
Sustainable Smiles [4876], PO Box 148, Alberton, MT 59820, (406)370-0226
Sustainable Travel Intl. [4965], PO Box 1313, Boulder, CO 80306, (720)273-2975
Sustainable Travel Intl. [4965], PO Box 1313, Boulder, CO 80306, (720)273-2975
Sustainable World Coalition [4147], Earth Island Inst., 2150 Allston Way. No. 460, Berkeley, CA 94704, (415)737-0235
SustainUS [13559], 1718 21st St. NW, Washington, DC 20009
Suunnittelu- ja konsulttitoimistojen liitto [★IO]
Suzuki Assn. of the Americas [8670], PO Box 17310, Boulder, CO 80308, (303)444-0948
Suzy Bogguss Fan Club [23893], Suzy Bogguss Concerts, Suzy Fan Mail, PMB 186, 8161 Hwy. 100, Nashville, TN 37220
Svaz knihovniku a informacnich pracovniku Ceske republiky [★IO]
Svaz Ceskych A Moravskych Vyrobnich Druzstev [★IO]
Svaz prumyslu a dopravy CR [★IO]
Svaz Obchodu A Cestovniho Ruchu Cr [★IO]
Svensk Armaturindustri [★IO]
Svensk Beteendemedicinsk Forening [★IO]
Svensk Biblioteksforening [★IO]
Svensk-Botswanska Vanskapsforeningen [★IO]
Svensk Flyghistorisk Forening [★IO]
Svensk Forening for Geriatrik and Gerontologi [★IO]
Svensk Form [★IO]
Svensk Gastroenterologisk Forening [★IO]
Svensk Handel [★IO]
Svensk-Irlandska Foreningen [★IO]
Svensk Kirurgisk Forening [★IO]
Svensk Mjolk [★IO]
Svensk Samhallsvetenskaplig Datatjanst [★IO]
Svensk Teaterunion - Svenska ITI [★IO]
Svensk Teknik och Design [★IO]
Svensk Ungdom - Svenska Folkpartiets Ungdomsorganisation [★IO]
Svenska lantbruksproducenternas centralforbund [★IO]

Svenska Akademien [★IO]
Svenska Arkeologiska Samfundet [★IO]
Svenska Arkivsamfundet [★IO]
Svenska Astronomiska Sallskapet [★IO]
Svenska Bankforeningen [★IO]
Svenska Baseboll och Softboll Forbundet [★IO]
Svenska Betongforeningen [★IO]
Svenska Bokhandlareforeningen [IO], Stockholm, Sweden
Svenska Bryggareforeningen [★IO]
Svenska Budoforbundet Aikidosektionen [IO], Stockholm, Sweden
Svenska Cardiologforeningen [★IO]
Svenska Danssportforbundet [★IO]
Svenska Filminstitutet [★IO]
Svenska Folkhogskolans Laraforbund [IO], Stockholm, Sweden
Svenska Folkpartiet [★IO]
Svenska Foreningen OIKOS [★IO]
Svenska Fornminnesforeningen [★IO]
Svenska Forsakringsforeningen [★IO]
Svenska Forskningsgruppen i Geomorfologi [★IO]
Svenska Fotografers Forbund [IO], Stockholm, Sweden
Svenska Franchise Foreningen [★IO]
Svenska Freds och Skiljedomsforeningen [★IO]
Svenska Friidrottsforbundet [★IO]
Svenska Frisbeesport Forbundet [★IO]
Svenska Fysikersamfundet [★IO]
Svenska Gasforeningen [★IO]
Svenska Geotekniska Foreningen [★IO]
Svenska Gjuteriforeningen [★IO]
Svenska Glasbruksforeningen [★IO]
Svenska Hypertonisallskapet [★IO]
Svenska Innebandyforbundet [★IO]
Svenska Kanot Forbundet [★IO]
Svenska Kvinnoforbundet [★IO]
Svenska Lakaresallskapet [★IO]
Svenska Ljussattare Foreningen [★IO]
Svenska Marfanforeningen [★IO]
Svenska Matematikersamfundet [★IO]
Svenska Mineralogiska Sallskapet [★IO]
Svenska Musikerforbundet [★IO]
Svenska Naturskyddsforeningen [★IO]
Svenska OptikSallskapet [★IO]
Svenska Orienteringsforbundet [★IO]
Svenska Ortodontiforeningen [★IO]
Svenska PEN [★IO]
Svenska Petroleum Institutet [★IO]
Svenska Psykoanalytiska Foreningen [★IO]
Svenska Reumatikerforbundet [★IO]
Svenska Sallskapet for Antropologi och Geografi [★IO]
Svenska Sallskapet for Automatiserad Bildanalys [★IO]
Svenska Samfundet for Musikforskning [★IO]
Svenska Skolidrottsforbundet [IO], Stockholm, Sweden
Svenska Squash Forbundet [IO], Malmo, Sweden
Svenska Tennisforbundet [★IO]
Svenska Tidningsutgivarefoereningen [★IO]
Svenska Tidningsutgivareforeningen [★IO]
Svenska Unescoradet [★IO]
Svenska Uppfinnare Foreningen [★IO]
Svenska Vattenskidforbundet [★IO]
Svenska Vegetariska Foreningen [★IO]
Svenska Yngling Forbundet [IO], Helsingborg, Sweden
Svenskt Naringsliv [★IO]
Svenskt ProjektForum [★IO]
Sveriges advokatsamfund [★IO]
Sveriges 4H [★IO]
Sveriges Angbats Forening [★IO]
Sveriges Annonsorer [★IO]
Sveriges Bageriforbund [★IO]
Sveriges Begravningsbyraers Forbund [IO], Stockholm, Sweden
Sveriges Dovas Riksforbund [★IO]
Sveriges Fackoversattarforening [★IO]
Sveriges Faerghandlares Riksfoerbund [★IO]
Sveriges Film- och Videofoerbund [★IO]
Sveriges Forenade Studentkarer [★IO]
Sveriges Forfattarforbund [★IO]
Sveriges Gerontologiska Sallskap [★IO]
Sveriges Hotell-och Restaurangforetagare [★IO]

Sveriges Konst Och Antikhandlarforening [IO], Stockholm, Sweden
Sveriges Korforbund [★IO]
Sveriges Kristna Rad [★IO]
Sveriges Lakarforbund [★IO]
Sveriges Lakarforbund [★IO]
Sveriges Moebelhandlare [★IO]
Sveriges Olympiska Kommitte [★IO]
Sveriges Psykologforbund [★IO]
Sveriges Redare-Forening [★IO]
Sveriges Redovisningskonsulters Forbund [★IO]
Sveriges Reklamfoerbund [★IO]
Sveriges Skolledarforbund [★IO]
Sveriges Skorstensfejaremaestares Riksfoerbund [★IO]
Sveriges Tandlakarforbund [★IO]
Sveriges Tidskrifter [★IO]
Sveriges Universitetslararforbund [★IO]
Sveriges Verkstadsindustrier [★IO]
Sveriges Veterinarforbund [★IO]
Swadhina [IO], Calcutta, India
Swan-Avon Olive Assn. [IO], Midland, Australia
Swan Owners Assn. of Am. [22394], Hank Schmitt, PO Box 347, Jamestown, RI 02835, (631)423-4988
Swat Youth Front [IO], Saidu Sharif, Pakistan
Swaziland Action Gp. Against Abuse [IO], Matsapha, Swaziland
Swaziland Athletics Assn. [IO], Mbabane, Swaziland
Swaziland Breast Cancer Network [IO], Mbabane, Swaziland
Swaziland Coalition of Concerned Civic Organisations [IO], Mbabane, Swaziland
Swaziland Natl. Badminton Assn. [IO], Mbabane, Swaziland
Swaziland Natl. Tennis Union [IO], Manzini, Swaziland
Swaziland Olympic and Commonwealth Games Assn. [IO], Mbabane, Swaziland
Swaziland Scout Assn. [IO], Mbabane, Swaziland
Swaziland Squash Assn. [IO], Mbabane, Swaziland
Swaziland Sugar Assn. [IO], Mbabane, Swaziland
SweatFree Communities [23231], 30 Blackstone St., Bangor, ME 04401, (207)262-7277
Sweatshop Watch - Address unknown since 2011.
Sweden
Swedish Translators in North America [10615]
Swedenborg Found. [9414], 320 N Church St., West Chester, PA 19380, (610)430-3222
The Swedenborg Proj. [8901], PO Box 9111, Lutherville, MD 21093, (410)773-9844
Swedenborg Soc. [IO], London, United Kingdom
Swedish
Amer. Swedish Historical Museum [10551]
Amer. Swedish Inst. [10552]
Amer. Swedish Inst. [10552]
Swedish-American Historical Soc. [10553]
Swedish Amer. Museum Assn. of Chicago [10554]
Swedish Amer. Museum Assn. of Chicago [10554]
Swedish Colonial Soc. [10555]
Swedish Colonial Soc. [10555]
Swedish Coun. of Am. [19248]
Swedish Trade Coun. [3489]
Swedish Translators in North America [10615]
Swedish Women's Educational Assn. Intl. [19249]
Swedish Women's Educational Assn. Intl. [19249]
Swedish 4H Assn. [IO], Katrineholm, Sweden
Swedish Acad. [IO], Stockholm, Sweden
Swedish Acad. of Pharmaceutical Sciences [IO], Stockholm, Sweden
Swedish Advertisers' Assn. [IO], Stockholm, Sweden
Swedish Amateur Theatre Coun. [IO], Vasteras, Sweden
Swedish-American Bar Assn. [5285], Mikael Koltai, Esq., Founder, 5020 Campus Dr., Newport Beach, CA 92660, (949)706-9111
Swedish-American Chamber of Commerce [★23381]
Swedish-American Chamber of Commerce [★23381]
Swedish-American Chambers of Commerce, U.S.A. [23381], 2900 K St. NW, Ste. 403, Washington, DC 20007, (202)536-1520
Swedish-American Chambers of Commerce, U.S.A. [23381], 2900 K St. NW, Ste. 403, Washington, DC 20007, (202)536-1520

Reference to "IO" in place of a book number signifies that the association may be found in the 50th edition of International Organizations.

Swedish-American Historical Soc. **[10553]**, 3225 W Foster Ave., Box 48, Chicago, IL 60625, (773)583-5722

Swedish Amer. Museum Assn. of Chicago **[10554]**, 5211 N Clark St., Chicago, IL 60640, (773)728-8111

Swedish Amer. Museum Assn. of Chicago **[10554]**, 5211 N Clark St., Chicago, IL 60640, (773)728-8111

Swedish Anti-Nuclear Movement **[IO]**, Stockholm, Sweden

Swedish Archaeological Soc. **[IO]**, Molndal, Sweden

Swedish Archival Assn. **[IO]**, Lund, Sweden

Swedish Arts Coun. **[IO]**, Stockholm, Sweden

Swedish Assn. of Accounting Consultants **[IO]**, Falun, Sweden

Swedish Assn. of Agents **[IO]**, Stockholm, Sweden

Swedish Assn. for Amer. Stud. **[IO]**, Harnosand, Sweden

Swedish Assn. of Dietitians **[IO]**, Stockholm, Sweden

Swedish Assn. of Door and Shutter Suppliers **[IO]**, Stockholm, Sweden

Swedish Assn. for the Electro HyperSensitive **[IO]**, Stockholm, Sweden

Swedish Assn. for Energy Economics **[IO]**, Stockholm, Sweden

Swedish Assn. of Graduate Engineers **[IO]**, Stockholm, Sweden

Swedish Assn. of Marine Underwriters **[IO]**, Stockholm, Sweden

Swedish Assn. of Mines, Minerals and Metal Producers **[IO]**, Stockholm, Sweden

Swedish Assn. of Neurologically Disabled **[IO]**, Stockholm, Sweden

Swedish Assn. of Occupational Therapists **[IO]**, Nacka, Sweden

Swedish Assn. of Orthodontists **[IO]**, Linkoping, Sweden

Swedish Assn. of the Pharmaceutical Indus. **[IO]**, Stockholm, Sweden

Swedish Assn. of Professional Translators **[IO]**, Bastad, Sweden

Swedish Assn. for the Protection of Ancient Monuments **[IO]**, Stockholm, Sweden

Swedish Assn. of Registered Physiotherapists **[IO]**, Stockholm, Sweden

Swedish Assn. of School Principals and Directors of Educ. **[IO]**, Stockholm, Sweden

Swedish Assn. for Sexuality Educ. **[IO]**, Stockholm, Sweden

Swedish Assn. of Suppliers of Effluent and Water Treatment Equip. **[IO]**, Stockholm, Sweden

Swedish Assn. of Suppliers of Elecl. Household Appliances **[IO]**, Stockholm, Sweden

Swedish Assn. of Univ. Teachers **[IO]**, Stockholm, Sweden

Swedish Assn. of Univ. Women **[IO]**, Stockholm, Sweden

Swedish Astronomical Soc. **[IO]**, Stockholm, Sweden

Swedish Athletic Assn. **[IO]**, Solna, Sweden

Swedish Aviation Historical Soc. **[IO]**, Stockholm, Sweden

Swedish Bankers' Assn. **[IO]**, Stockholm, Sweden

Swedish Bar Assn. **[IO]**, Stockholm, Sweden

Swedish Baseball and Softball Fed. **[IO]**, Skovde, Sweden

Swedish Brewers' Assn. **[IO]**, Stockholm, Sweden

Swedish Bus. Assn. of Singapore **[IO]**, Singapore, Singapore

Swedish-Canadian Chamber of Commerce **[IO]**, Toronto, ON, Canada

Swedish Canoe Fed. **[IO]**, Nykoping, Sweden

Swedish Cartographic Soc. **[IO]**, Gavle, Sweden

Swedish Chimney Sweep Masters Assn. **[IO]**, Stockholm, Sweden

Swedish Choral Assn. **[IO]**, Stockholm, Sweden

Swedish Colonial Soc. **[10555]**, 916 S Swanson St., Philadelphia, PA 19147-4332

Swedish Colonial Soc. **[10555]**, 916 S Swanson St., Philadelphia, PA 19147-4332

Swedish Concrete Assn. **[IO]**, Stockholm, Sweden

Swedish Confed. of Professional Associations **[IO]**, Stockholm, Sweden

Swedish Confed. of Professional Employees **[IO]**, Stockholm, Sweden

Swedish Cosmetic, Toiletry and Household Products Suppliers' Assn. **[IO]**, Stockholm, Sweden

Swedish Coun. of Am. **[19248]**, 2600 Park Ave., Minneapolis, MN 55407, (612)871-0593

Swedish Crystal Mfrs. Assn. **[IO]**, Stockholm, Sweden

Swedish Dairy Assn. **[IO]**, Stockholm, Sweden

Swedish Dance Sport Fed. **[IO]**, Farsta, Sweden

Swedish Dental Assn. **[IO]**, Stockholm, Sweden

Swedish Dental Trade Assn. **[IO]**, Stockholm, Sweden

Swedish Direct Marketing Assn. **[IO]**, Stockholm, Sweden

Swedish Doctors for the Env. **[IO]**, Stockholm, Sweden

Swedish-English Literary Translators' Assn. **[IO]**, London, United Kingdom

Swedish Farmers Safety and Preventive Hea. Assn. **[IO]**, Stockholm, Sweden

Swedish Fed. of Consulting Engineers and Architects **[IO]**, Stockholm, Sweden

Swedish Fed. of Film and Video Amateurs **[IO]**, Stockholm, Sweden

Swedish Fellowship of Reconciliation **[IO]**, Sundbyberg, Sweden

Swedish Film Inst. **[IO]**, Stockholm, Sweden

Swedish Finn Assn. **[IO]**, Karlstad, Sweden

Swedish-Finnish Benevolent and Aid Assn. of Am. and Swedish-Finnish Temperance Assn. **[★9616]**

Swedish-Finnish Benevolent and Aid Assn. of Am. and Swedish-Finnish Temperance Assn. **[★9616]**

Swedish Floorball Fed. **[IO]**, Solna, Sweden

Swedish Flooring Trade Assn. **[IO]**, Stockholm, Sweden

Swedish Forensic Sci. Assn. **[IO]**, Goteborg, Sweden

Swedish Forest Indus. Fed. **[IO]**, Stockholm, Sweden

Swedish Foundry Assn. **[IO]**, Jonkoping, Sweden

Swedish Franchise Assn. **[IO]**, Goteborg, Sweden

Swedish Frisbeesport Fed. **[IO]**, Goteborg, Sweden

Swedish Furniture Indus. Assn. **[IO]**, Stockholm, Sweden

Swedish Furniture Retailers' Assn. **[IO]**, Stockholm, Sweden

Swedish Gas Assn. **[IO]**, Stockholm, Sweden

Swedish Geotechnical Soc. **[IO]**, Linkoping, Sweden

Swedish Geriatric Assn. **[IO]**, Norrkoping, Sweden

Swedish Gerontological Soc. **[IO]**, Norrkoping, Sweden

Swedish Heating Boilers and Burners Assn. **[IO]**, Stockholm, Sweden

Swedish Hemophilia Soc. **[IO]**, Sundbyberg, Sweden

Swedish Hotel and Restaurant Assn. **[IO]**, Stockholm, Sweden

Swedish Hypertension Soc. **[IO]**, Stockholm, Sweden

Swedish Inst. for Fibre and Polymer Res. **[IO]**, Molndal, Sweden

Swedish Inst. of Intl. Affairs **[IO]**, Stockholm, Sweden

Swedish Insurance Soc. **[IO]**, Stockholm, Sweden

Swedish Inventors' Assn. **[IO]**, Stockholm, Sweden

Swedish-Irish Soc. **[IO]**, Kista, Sweden

Swedish Lib. Assn. **[IO]**, Stockholm, Sweden

Swedish Machine Tool and Cutting Tool Mfrs. Assn. **[IO]**, Stockholm, Sweden

Swedish Magazine Publishers' Assn. **[IO]**, Stockholm, Sweden

Swedish Marfan Assn. **[IO]**, Tungelsta, Sweden

Swedish Mathematical Soc. **[IO]**, Goteborg, Sweden

Swedish Meat Indus. Assn. **[IO]**, Stockholm, Sweden

Swedish Medical Assn. **[IO]**, Stockholm, Sweden

Swedish Mineralogical Soc. **[IO]**, Stockholm, Sweden

Swedish Musicians' Union **[IO]**, Stockholm, Sweden

Swedish Natl. Assn. of the Deaf **[IO]**, Stockholm, Sweden

Swedish Natl. Commn. for UNESCO **[IO]**, Stockholm, Sweden

Swedish Natl. Comm. on Physiology **[IO]**, Stockholm, Sweden

Swedish Natl. Coun. of Adult Educ. **[IO]**, Stockholm, Sweden

Swedish Natl. Coun. for Cultural Affairs **[IO]**, Stockholm, Sweden

Swedish Natl. Union of Students **[IO]**, Stockholm, Sweden

Swedish Newspaper Publishers Assn. **[IO]**, Stockholm, Sweden

Swedish Newspapers' Assn. **[IO]**, Stockholm, Sweden

Swedish Olympic Comm. **[IO]**, Stockholm, Sweden

Swedish Operations Res. Soc. **[IO]**, Vasteras, Sweden

Swedish Optical Soc. **[IO]**, Stockholm, Sweden

Swedish Org. of Youth with Rheumatism **[IO]**, Stockholm, Sweden

Swedish Orienteering Fed. **[IO]**, Solna, Sweden

Swedish Osteoporosis Soc. **[IO]**, Goteborg, Sweden

Swedish Paint Trade Fed. **[IO]**, Stockholm, Sweden

Swedish Peace and Arbitration Soc. **[IO]**, Stockholm, Sweden

Swedish PEN Centre **[IO]**, Stockholm, Sweden

Swedish People's Party of Finland **[IO]**, Helsinki, Finland

Swedish Petroleum Inst. **[IO]**, Stockholm, Sweden

Swedish Physical Soc. **[IO]**, Uppsala, Sweden

Swedish Pioneer Centennial Comm. **[★10553]**

Swedish Pioneer Historical Soc. **[★10553]**

Swedish Plastics and Chem. Fed. **[IO]**, Stockholm, Sweden

Swedish Precast Concrete Fed. **[IO]**, Stockholm, Sweden

Swedish Proj. Mgt. Soc. **[IO]**, Stockholm, Sweden

Swedish Psoriasis Assn. **[IO]**, Johanneshov, Sweden

Swedish Psychoanalytical Soc. **[IO]**, Stockholm, Sweden

Swedish Psychological Assn. **[IO]**, Stockholm, Sweden

Swedish Res. Coun. for Env., Agricultural Sciences and Spatial Planning **[IO]**, Stockholm, Sweden

Swedish Res. Gp. in Geomorphology **[IO]**, Uppsala, Sweden

Swedish Rheumatism Assn. **[IO]**, Stockholm, Sweden

Swedish Sea Rescue Soc. **[IO]**, Vastra Frolunda, Sweden

Swedish Shipbrokers' Assn. **[IO]**, Goteborg, Sweden

Swedish Shipowners' Assn. **[IO]**, Goteborg, Sweden

Swedish Social Sci. Data Archv. **[IO]**, Goteborg, Sweden

Swedish Soc. of Aeronautics and Astronautics **[IO]**, Solna, Sweden

Swedish Soc. Against Painful Experiments on Animals **[IO]**, Alvsjo, Sweden

Swedish Soc. for Anthropology and Geography **[IO]**, Stockholm, Sweden

Swedish Soc. for Automated Image Anal. **[IO]**, Lund, Sweden

Swedish Soc. of Behavioral Medicine **[IO]**, Stockholm, Sweden

Swedish Soc. of Cardiology **[IO]**, Stockholm, Sweden

Swedish Soc. of Crafts and Design **[IO]**, Stockholm, Sweden

Swedish Soc. of Gastroenterology **[IO]**, Linkoping, Sweden

Swedish Soc. of Medicine **[IO]**, Stockholm, Sweden

Swedish Soc. for Musicology **[IO]**, Stockholm, Sweden

Swedish Soc. for Nature Conservation **[IO]**, Stockholm, Sweden

Swedish Soc. OIKOS **[IO]**, Lund, Sweden

Swedish Soc. of Organbuilding **[IO]**, Stockholm, Sweden

Swedish Soc. of Popular Music Composers **[IO]**, Stockholm, Sweden

Swedish Soc. of Psychosomatic Obstetrics and Gynaecology **[IO]**, Stockholm, Sweden

Swedish Soc. for Rheumatology **[IO]**, Stockholm, Sweden

Swedish Spirits and Wine Suppliers **[IO]**, Stockholm, Sweden

Swedish Steel Producers' Assn. **[IO]**, Stockholm, Sweden

Swedish Surgical Soc. **[IO]**, Stockholm, Sweden

Swedish Teachers' Union **[IO]**, Stockholm, Sweden

Swedish Tennis Assn. **[IO]**, Stockholm, Sweden

Swedish Theater Union - Swedish ITI **[IO]**, Stockholm, Sweden

A star before a book entry number signifies that the name is not listed separately, but is mentioned within the entry.

Swedish Trade Commn. [★3489]
Swedish Trade Commn. [★3489]
Swedish Trade Coun. [3489], 150 N Michigan Ave., Ste. 1950, Chicago, IL 60601, (312)781-6222
Swedish Trade Coun. [3489], 150 N Michigan Ave., Ste. 1950, Chicago, IL 60601, (312)781-6222
Swedish Trade Coun.- North Am. [★3489]
Swedish Trade Coun.- North Am. [★3489]
Swedish Trade Coun. - U.S. [★3489]
Swedish Trade Coun. - U.S. [★3489]
Swedish Trade Fed. [IO], Stockholm, Sweden
Swedish Translators in North America [10615], 6008 Corliss Ave. N, Seattle, WA 98103
Swedish Translators in North America [10615], 6008 Corliss Ave. N, Seattle, WA 98103
Swedish Travelling Exhibitions [IO], Visby, Sweden
Swedish Union of Tenants [IO], Stockholm, Sweden
Swedish Vegetarian Fed. [IO], Stockholm, Sweden
Swedish Veterinary Assn. [IO], Stockholm, Sweden
Swedish Warm Blood Assn. of North Am. [★4651]
Swedish Warmblood Assn. of North Am. [4651], PO Box 788, Socorro, NM 87801, (575)835-1318
Swedish Water Ski Fed. [IO], Trollhattan, Sweden
Swedish Women's Educational Assn. Intl. [19249], 552 S El Camino Real, Encinitas, CA 92024, (760)942-1100
Swedish Women's Educational Assn. Intl. [19249], 552 S El Camino Real, Encinitas, CA 92024, (760)942-1100
Swedish Writers' Union [IO], Stockholm, Sweden
Swedish Youth of Finland - Youth Org. of the Swedish People's Party [IO], Helsinki, Finland
Sweet Adelines, Inc. [★10302]
Sweet Adelines, Inc. [★10302]
Sweet Adelines Intl. [10302], PO Box 470168, Tulsa, OK 74147-0168, (918)622-1444
Sweet Adelines Intl. [10302], PO Box 470168, Tulsa, OK 74147-0168, (918)622-1444
Sweet and Fortified Wine Assn. - Address unknown since 2010.
Sweet Mother Intl. [IO], Gawler, Australia
Sweet Sleep [11414], PO Box 40486, Nashville, TN 37204-9998, (615)730-7671
Sweet Sorghum Ethanol Assn. [6120], 8912 Brandon Sta. Rd., Raleigh, NC 27613, (919)870-0782
Sweets Global Network [IO], Munich, Germany
Swift Boat Veterans for Truth - Defunct.
Swift Museum Found. [20919], PO Box 644, Athens, TN 37371-0644, (423)745-9547
Swim America [★23037]
Swim Ireland [IO], Dublin, Ireland
Swimming
   Amer. Swimming Coaches Assn. [23037]
   Coll. Swimming Coaches Assn. of Am. [23038]
   Intl. Acad. of Aquatic Art [23039]
   Intl. Gay and Lesbian Aquatics [23040]
   Intl. Swimming Hall of Fame [23041]
   Intl. Swimming Hall of Fame [23041]
   Natl. InterScholastic Swimming Coaches Assn. of Am. [23042]
   U.S. Aquatic Sports [23043]
   U.S. Masters Swimming [23044]
   U.S. Swim School Assn. [23045]
   U.S. Synchronized Swimming [23046]
   U.S.A. Swimming [23047]
   World Aquatic Babies and Children [23048]
   World Aquatic Babies and Children [23048]
Swimming/Natation Canada [IO], Ottawa, ON, Canada
Swimming Pool and Allied Trades Assn. [IO], Andover, United Kingdom
Swimming Teachers' Assn. [IO], Walsall, United Kingdom
Swine
   Amer. Berkshire Assn. [4946]
   Amer. Guinea Hog Assn. [4947]
   Chester White Swine Record Assn. [4948]
   Natl. Hereford Hog Record Assn. [4949]
   Natl. Junior Swine Assn. [4950]
   Natl. Pork Producers Coun. [4951]
   Natl. Spotted Swine Record [4952]
   Natl. Swine Improvement Fed. [4953]
   Natl. Swine Registry [4954]
   Natl. Swine Registry l United Duroc Swine Registry [4955]

The Pig Preserve Assn. [11025]
Poland China Record Assn. [4956]
Swiss
   American-Swiss Found. [19250]
   American-Swiss Found. [19250]
   Swiss-American Chamber of Commerce [23444]
   Swiss Amer. Historical Soc. [10556]
   Swiss Amer. Historical Soc. [10556]
   Swiss Benevolent Soc. of New York [19251]
   Switzerland Convention and Incentive Bur. [23445]
Swiss Acad. of Engg. Sciences [IO], Zurich, Switzerland
Swiss Acad. of Humanities and Social Sciences [IO], Bern, Switzerland
Swiss Acad. of Medical Sciences [IO], Basel, Switzerland
Swiss Acad. of Sciences [IO], Bern, Switzerland
Swiss ACM SIGCHI [IO], Zurich, Switzerland
Swiss Alliance of Development Organisations [IO], Bern, Switzerland
Swiss Alliance Mission [IO], Winterthur, Switzerland
Swiss Aluminium Assn. [IO], Zurich, Switzerland
Swiss-American Bus. Coun. [2107], PO Box 641724, Chicago, IL 60601, (312)624-7697
Swiss-American Bus. Coun. [2107], PO Box 641724, Chicago, IL 60601, (312)624-7697
Swiss-American Chamber of Commerce [23444], PO Box 26007, San Francisco, CA 94126-6007, (415)433-6679
Swiss - Amer. Chamber of Commerce [IO], Zurich, Switzerland
Swiss-American Coun. of Women [18794], 222 E 44th St., 9th Fl., New York, NY 10017, (212)433-0293
Swiss Amer. Historical Soc. [10556], Marianne Burkhard, 5521 Rosalie Dr., Peoria, IL 61614
Swiss Amer. Historical Soc. [10556], Marianne Burkhard, 5521 Rosalie Dr., Peoria, IL 61614
Swiss Amer. Stamp Soc. [★22008]
Swiss Amer. Stamp Soc. [★22008]
Swiss Arbitration Assn. [IO], Basel, Switzerland
Swiss-Argentine Chamber of Commerce [IO], Buenos Aires, Argentina
Swiss Assn. of Agricultural and Food Stuff Engineers [IO], Zollikofen, Switzerland
Swiss Assn. of Consulting Engineers [IO], Bern, Switzerland
Swiss Assn. of Dealers in Antiques and Arts [IO], Zurich, Switzerland
Swiss Assn. for Energy Economics [IO], Zurich, Switzerland
Swiss Assn. of Geomatics and Landmanagement [IO], Solothurn, Switzerland
Swiss Assn. of High School Principals [IO], Lucerne, Switzerland
Swiss Assn. of Insurance and Risk Managers [IO], Bern, Switzerland
Swiss Assn. for Internal Commun. [IO], Bern, Switzerland
Swiss Assn. for Intl. Cooperation - Helvetas Vietnam [IO], Hanoi, Vietnam
Swiss Assn. of Logopedics [IO], Zurich, Switzerland
Swiss Assn. for Nutrition [IO], Bern, Switzerland
Swiss Assn. against Osteoporosis [IO], Basel, Switzerland
Swiss Assn. for Pattern Recognition [IO], Bern, Switzerland
Swiss Assn. of Physiotherapy [IO], Sursee, Switzerland
Swiss Assn. for Standardization [IO], Winterthur, Switzerland
Swiss Assn. for the Stud. of Pain [IO], Zurich, Switzerland
Swiss Assn. of Tenants [IO], Geneva, Switzerland
Swiss Assn. for Theatre Stud. [IO], Basel, Switzerland
Swiss Athletic Fed. [IO], Bern, Switzerland
Swiss-Australian Chamber of Commerce and Indus. [IO], Sydney, Australia
Swiss Bankers Assn. [IO], Basel, Switzerland
Swiss Bar Assn. [IO], Bern, Switzerland
Swiss Benevolent Soc. of New York [19251], 500 5th Ave., Rm. 1800, New York, NY 10110-1804, (212)246-0655

Swiss Bible Soc. [IO], Bienne, Switzerland
Swiss Biochemical Soc. [IO], Lausanne, Switzerland
Swiss Bone and Mineral Soc. [IO], Zurich, Switzerland
Swiss Booksellers and Publishers Assn. [IO], Zurich, Switzerland
Swiss Botanical Soc. [IO], Bern, Switzerland
Swiss Br. of the Intl. Fiscal Assn. [IO], Basel, Switzerland
Swiss Brewers' Assn. [IO], Zurich, Switzerland
Swiss Bus. Assn. Singapore [IO], Singapore, Singapore
Swiss Bus. Coun. [IO], Dubai, United Arab Emirates
Swiss Bus. Fed. [IO], Zurich, Switzerland
Swiss Canoe Fed. [IO], Zurich, Switzerland
Swiss Chem. Soc. [IO], Bern, Switzerland
Swiss Christian Democratic Party [IO], Bern, Switzerland
Swiss Comm. for the Jews in the Former Soviet Union [IO], Bottmingen, Switzerland
Swiss Confectionery and Pastry Bakers' Assn. [IO], Bern, Switzerland
Swiss Conf. of Directors of Professional and Indus. Schools [IO], Elsau, Switzerland
Swiss Cosmetic and Detergent Assn. [IO], Zurich, Switzerland
Swiss Craft Found. [IO], Zurich, Switzerland
Swiss DanceSport Fed. [IO], Glattbrugg, Switzerland
Swiss Dietetic Assn. [IO], Bern, Switzerland
Swiss Egg Producers' Assn. [IO], Zurich, Switzerland
Swiss Electrotechnical Assn. [IO], Fehraltorf, Switzerland
Swiss Fed. for Adult Learning [IO], Zurich, Switzerland
Swiss Fed. of the Blind and Visually Impaired [IO], Bern, Switzerland
Swiss Fed. of Cricket Umpires and Scorers [IO], Winterthur, Switzerland
Swiss Fed. of Trade Unions [IO], Bern, Switzerland
Swiss Floorball Assn. [IO], Bern, Switzerland
Swiss Food Retailers' Assn. [IO], Bern, Switzerland
Swiss Forestry Soc. [IO], Frenkendorf, Switzerland
Swiss Forum for Communications Law [IO], Zurich, Switzerland
Swiss Found. for Sexual and Reproductive Hea. [IO], Lausanne, Switzerland
Swiss Franchise Assn. [IO], Zurich, Switzerland
Swiss Geomorphological Soc. [IO], Fribourg, Switzerland
Swiss Golf Assn. [IO], Epalinges, Switzerland
Swiss Graphic Designers [IO], Flawil, Switzerland
Swiss Heraldry Soc. [IO], Vetroz, Switzerland
Swiss Hiking Fed. [IO], Bern, Switzerland
Swiss Hosp. Assn. [IO], Bern, Switzerland
Swiss Hydrogeological Soc. [IO], Lausanne, Switzerland
Swiss Inst. of Special Educ. [IO], Bern, Switzerland
Swiss Lab. Animal Sci. Assn. [IO], Reinach, Switzerland
Swiss Labour Assistance [IO], Zurich, Switzerland
Swiss League Against Epilepsy [IO], Zurich, Switzerland
Swiss Lifesaving Assn. [IO], Sursee, Switzerland
Swiss Malaysian Bus. Assn. [IO], Kuala Lumpur, Malaysia
Swiss Mgt. Assn. [IO], Zurich, Switzerland
Swiss Medical Assn. [IO], Bern, Switzerland
Swiss Mineral Water and Soft Drink Producers' Assn. [IO], Zurich, Switzerland
Swiss Museums Assn. [IO], Zurich, Switzerland
Swiss Musicians' Assn. [IO], Lausanne, Switzerland
Swiss Natl. Tourist Off. [★23445]
Swiss Olympic Assn. [IO], Bern, Switzerland
Swiss Operations Res. Soc. [IO], Lausanne, Switzerland
Swiss Org. for Geographic Info. [IO], Lucerne, Switzerland
Swiss Orthodontic Soc. [IO], Gumligen-Bern, Switzerland
Swiss Paralympic Comm. [IO], Bern, Switzerland
Swiss Peace Coun. [IO], Zurich, Switzerland
Swiss Physical Soc. [IO], Basel, Switzerland
Swiss Physiological Soc. [IO], Bern, Switzerland
Swiss Private Bankers Assn. [IO], Geneva, Switzerland

Reference to "IO" in place of a book number signifies that the association may be found in the 50th edition of International Organizations.

Swiss Pulp, Paper and Cardboard Indus. Assn. **[IO]**, Zurich, Switzerland

Swiss Radio and TV Retailers' Assn. **[IO]**, Grenchen, Switzerland

Swiss Retail Chemists' Assn. **[IO]**, Biel, Switzerland

Swiss Retail Fed. **[IO]**, Bern, Switzerland

Swiss Rowing Fed. **[IO]**, Sarnen, Switzerland

Swiss Soc. of Astrophysics and Astronomy **[IO]**, Bern, Switzerland

Swiss Soc. for Biochemistry **[IO]**, Zurich, Switzerland

Swiss Soc. for Biomedical Ethics **[IO]**, Basel, Switzerland

Swiss Soc. of Cardiology **[IO]**, Bern, Switzerland

Swiss Soc. of Cartography **[IO]**, Wabern, Switzerland

Swiss Soc. of Engineers and Architects **[IO]**, Zurich, Switzerland

Swiss Soc. of Gerontology **[IO]**, Bern, Switzerland

Swiss Soc. of Hypertension **[IO]**, Bern, Switzerland

Swiss Soc. for Infectious Diseases **[IO]**, Basel, Switzerland

Swiss Soc. for Medical Informatics **[IO]**, Bern, Switzerland

Swiss Soc. for Microbiology **[IO]**, Schwarzenburg, Switzerland

Swiss Soc. for Optics and Microscopy **[IO]**, Basel, Switzerland

Swiss Soc. of Optometry **[IO]**, Adligenswil, Switzerland

Swiss Soc. of Pharmacology and Toxicology **[IO]**, Zug, Switzerland

Swiss Soc. of Photogrammetry. Image Anal. and Remote Sensing **[IO]**, Wabern, Switzerland

Swiss Soc. of Radiobiology and Medical Physics **[IO]**, Bern, Switzerland

Swiss Sociological Assn. **[IO]**, Geneva, Switzerland

Swiss Solar Energy Soc. **[IO]**, Bern, Switzerland

Swiss Spirits Producers' Assn. **[IO]**, Bern, Switzerland

Swiss Squash **[IO]**, Langnau am Albis, Switzerland

Swiss Tchoukball Fed. **[IO]**, Geneva, Switzerland

Swiss Teachers Fed. **[IO]**, Zurich, Switzerland

Swiss Tech. Distributors' Assn. **[IO]**, Basel, Switzerland

Swiss Tennis **[IO]**, Bienne, Switzerland

Swiss Textile Fed. **[IO]**, Zurich, Switzerland

Swiss Tropical Inst. **[IO]**, Basel, Switzerland

Swiss Univ. Sports Fed. **[IO]**, St. Gallen, Switzerland

Swiss Volleyball Fed. **[IO]**, Bern, Switzerland

Swiss Wine Exporters Assn. **[IO]**, Penthalaz, Switzerland

Swiss Youth Hostels **[IO]**, Zurich, Switzerland

Swissmem L'Industrie Suisse de Machines, des Equipements Electriques et des Metaux **[★IO]**

Swissmem - Swiss Mech. and Elecl. Engg. Indus. **[IO]**, Zurich, Switzerland

Switchmen's Union of North Am. **[★23292]**

Switzerland
    Swiss Amer. Historical Soc. **[10556]**

Switzerland Convention and Incentive Bur. **[23445]**, Switzerland Tourism, 608 5th Ave., New York, NY 10020, (212)757-5944

Switzerland Convention and Incentive Bur. **[IO]**, Zurich, Switzerland

Switzerland Tourism **[★23445]**

Sword Swallowers Assn. Intl. **[10361]**, 3004 W Goodman Ave., Muncie, IN 47304-4418

Sydney ACM SIGGRAPH Chap. **[IO]**, Clovelly, Australia

Sydney Medical School Found. **[IO]**, Sydney, Australia

Sydney SIGMOBILE ACM Chap. **[IO]**, Mosman, Australia

Sydney Ski Club **[IO]**, Sydney, Australia

Sydney Underwater Bushwalking Soc. **[IO]**, Sydney, Australia

Sylvia Rivera Law Proj. **[18730]**, 147 W 24th St., 5th Fl., New York, NY 10011, (212)337-8550

Symbolic Interaction; Soc. for the Stud. of **[7432]**

Symbral Found. for Community Services - Address unknown since 2011.

Symphonic Music
    Classical Music Lovers' Exchange **[10177]**
    Intl. Conf. of Symphony and Opera Musicians **[10218]**

Symphony, Opera and Ballet Musicians; Intl. Guild of **[23272]**

Symphony for United Nations **[9321]**, 20 Glenmore Dr., Durham, NC 27707, (919)381-5219

Symphony for United Nations **[9321]**, 20 Glenmore Dr., Durham, NC 27707, (919)381-5219

Symposium on Cmpt. Applications in Medical Care **[★14219]**

Syna die Gewerkschaft **[IO]**, Zurich, Switzerland

Synagogue Youth; Natl. Conf. of **[19887]**

Synagogue Youth; United **[19907]**

Synagogues: Transformation and Renewal - Address unknown since 2011.

Synchro Canada **[IO]**, Gloucester, ON, Canada

Synchro Swimming U.S.A. **[★23046]**

Synchronized Swimming Division of the Amateur Athletic Union **[★23046]**

Syndesmos **[IO]**, Holargos, Greece

Syndesmos Epistimonon Michanikon Kyprou **[★IO]**

Syndicat Canadien des Communications, de l'Energie et du Papier **[★IO]**

Syndicat Canadien des Telecommunications Transmarines **[★IO]**

Syndicat des Communications d'Amerique **[★IO]**

Syndicat Educ. et Sciences **[★IO]**

Syndicat des Enseignants **[IO]**, Paris, France

Syndicat des Enseignants de Hongrie **[★IO]**

Syndicat Europeen de l'Industrie des Futs Fibre **[★IO]**

Syndicat Gen. de l'Education Nationale **[IO]**, Paris, France

Syndicat de l'Eclairage **[★IO]**

Syndicat de l'emploi et de l'immigration du Canada **[★IO]**

Syndicat des Locataires - Huurdersbond **[IO]**, Brussels, Belgium

Syndicat Natl. du Caoutchouc et des Polymeres **[★IO]**

Syndicat Natl. des Employees et Employes Generaux et du Secteur Public **[★IO]**

Syndicat Natl. des Enseignants **[★IO]**

Syndicat Natl. des Enseignements de Second Degre **[★IO]**

Syndicat Natl. des Fabricants de Boites, Emballages et Bouchages Metalliques **[★IO]**

Syndicat Natl. des Fabricants de Bouillons et Potages **[IO]**, Paris, France

Syndicat Natl. de l'Edition **[★IO]**

Syndicat Natl. de l'Edition Phonographique **[★IO]**

Syndicat Natl. de l'Edition Phonographique **[IO]**, Paris, France

Syndicat Natl. des Residences de Tourisme **[★IO]**

Syndicat de la Presse Quotidienne Nationale **[IO]**, Paris, France

Syndicat de la Presse Quotidienne Regionale **[IO]**, Paris, France

Syndicat Suisse des Antiquares et Commercants d'Art **[★IO]**

Syndicat des Travailleurs et Travailleuses des Postes **[★IO]**

Syndicate of Journalists of the Czech Republic **[IO]**, Prague, Czech Republic

Syndicated Network TV Assn. **[107]**, 1 Penn Plz., Ste. 5310, New York, NY 10119, (212)259-3740

Syndikat novinaru Ceske republiky **[★IO]**

Syndrome X Assn. **[15507]**, PO Box 331, Munroe Falls, OH 44262

Syndromes Without a Name USA **[14419]**, 1745 Lorna Ln., Otsego, MI 49078, (269)692-2090

Synergos Inst. **[12754]**, 51 Madison Ave., 21st Fl., New York, NY 10010, (212)447-8111

Synergos Inst. **[12754]**, 51 Madison Ave., 21st Fl., New York, NY 10010, (212)447-8111

Synthetic Amorphous Silica and Silicates Indus. Assn. **[769]**, 116 Countryside Dr., Chagrin Falls, OH 44022, (440)897-8780

Synthetic and Rayon Textiles Export Promotion Coun. **[IO]**, Mumbai, India

Synthetic Yarn and Fiber Assn. **[3458]**, 737 Park Trail Ln., Clover, SC 29710, (704)589-5895

Synthetics Soc; Intl. Geo **[6427]**

Synthetics Soc; North Amer. Geo **[6429]**

Syrian Amateur Astronomers Assn. **[IO]**, Damascus, Syrian Arab Republic

Syrian-American Relations Coun. **[17951]**, 28 E Jackson Blvd., Ste. 405, Chicago, IL 60604, (312)212-1520

Syrian-American Relations Coun. **[17951]**, 28 E Jackson Blvd., Ste. 405, Chicago, IL 60604, (312)212-1520

Syrian Arab Amateur Athletic Fed. **[IO]**, Damascus, Syrian Arab Republic

Syrian Arab Red Crescent **[IO]**, Damascus, Syrian Arab Republic

Syrian Arab Soc. of Dermatology **[IO]**, Aleppo, Syrian Arab Republic

Syrian Arab Taekwondo Fed. **[IO]**, Damascus, Syrian Arab Republic

Syrian Arab Tennis Fed. **[IO]**, Damascus, Syrian Arab Republic

Syrian Assn. of Laparoscopic Surgery **[IO]**, Damascus, Syrian Arab Republic

Syrian Assn. for Rheumatology **[IO]**, Damascus, Syrian Arab Republic

Syrian Canadian Bus. Assn. **[IO]**, Damascus, Syrian Arab Republic

Syrian Cardiovascular Assn. **[IO]**, Damascus, Syrian Arab Republic

Syrian Chap. of Epilepsy **[IO]**, Damascus, Syrian Arab Republic

Syrian Family Planning Assn. **[IO]**, Damascus, Syrian Arab Republic

Syrian Intl. Freight Forwarders Assn. **[IO]**, Damascus, Syrian Arab Republic

Syrian Mgt. Consultants Assn. **[IO]**, Damascus, Syrian Arab Republic

Syrian Muay Thai Assn. **[IO]**, Damascus, Syrian Arab Republic

Syrian Orthodontic Soc. **[IO]**, Damascus, Syrian Arab Republic

Syrian Orthodox Youth Org. **[★19646]**

Syrian Physical Therapy Assn. **[IO]**, Damascus, Syrian Arab Republic

Syrian Soc. of Nephrology and Transplantation **[IO]**, Damascus, Syrian Arab Republic

Syrian Stud. Assn. **[8620]**, Prof. Fred H. Lawson, Pres., Mills Coll., 5000 MacArthur Bldg., Oakland, CA 94613, (510)430-2342

Syrian Textile and Garment Exporters Assn. **[IO]**, Damascus, Syrian Arab Republic

Syringomyelia and Chiari Alliance Proj; Amer. **[15568]**

Sys. Administrators Guild **[★6522]**

System Independent Data Format Assn. - Defunct.

System Safety Soc. **[★3144]**

Systematic and Applied Acarology Soc. **[IO]**, Canberra, Australia

Systematics Assn. **[IO]**, London, United Kingdom

Systematics Assn. of New Zealand **[IO]**, Auckland, New Zealand

Systeme Economique Latinoamericain et Caribeen **[★IO]**

Systeme informatise sur les stagiaires post-M.D. en formation clinique **[★IO]**

Systems Builders Assn. **[★2310]**

Systems Building Res. Alliance **[1786]**, 1776 Broadway, Ste. 2205, New York, NY 10019, (212)496-0900

Systems Integrators
    Clean Tech. and Sustainable Indus. Org. **[3856]**
    Control and Info. Systems Integrators Assn. **[3371]**
    LonMark Intl. **[3372]**
    NASBA - The Assn. of Sys. Builders and Integrators **[3373]**
    Natl. Assn. of Campus Card Users **[3374]**

Systems and Software Consortium, Inc. **[6498]**, 2214 Rock Hill Rd., Herndon, VA 20170-4227, (703)896-4360

Szkolny Zwiazek Sportowy **[IO]**, Warsaw, Poland

T

T-34 Assn. **[21202]**, 880 N County Rd., 900-E, Tuscola, IL 61953

T. Rextasy Japanese Fan Club **[IO]**, Saitama, Japan

T. Rextasy UK Fan Club **[IO]**, Halstead, United Kingdom

T-Ten Class Assn. **[22395]**, Ted Mahoney, Fleet Capt., 2655 S Belvoir Blvd., University Heights, OH 44118, (216)321-0275

TAALK: Talk About Abuse to Liberate Kids **[11512]**, 30251 Golden Lantern, No. E283, Laguna Niguel, CA 92677, (949)495-4553

A star before a book entry number signifies that the name is not listed separately, but is mentioned within the entry.

Table and Art Glassware Mfrs. - Defunct.
Table Shuffleboard Assn. **[22893]**, 8155 Meadow Lark Dr., Wynnewood, OK 73098-8847, (512)619-6030

Table Tennis
   Natl. Collegiate Table Tennis Assn. **[23049]**
   U.S.A. Table Tennis **[23050]**

Tableware
   Amer. Edged Products Mfrs. Assn. **[3375]**
   Butter Pat Patter Assn. **[21313]**
   Gift Associates Interchange Network **[3376]**
   Soc. of Amer. Silversmiths **[3377]**

Tackett Family Assn. **[20597]**, 260 Bella Vista Way, Rio Vista, CA 94571
Tackle/Shooting Sports Agents Assn. - Defunct.
Tadamun Social Soc. **[IO]**, Dubai, United Arab Emirates
Taekwon-Do Zveza Slovenije **[★IO]**
Taekwondo Assn. of Thailand **[IO]**, Bangkok, Thailand
Taekwondo Australia **[IO]**, Sydney, Australia
Taekwondo Bond Nederland **[IO]**, Arnhem, Netherlands
Taekwondo Fed. of Armenia **[IO]**, Yerevan, Armenia
Taekwondo Fed. of Bosnia and Herzegovina **[IO]**, Sarajevo, Bosnia-Hercegovina
Taekwondo Fed. of India **[IO]**, New Delhi, India
Taekwondo Fed. of Islamic Republic of Iran **[IO]**, Tehran, Iran
Taekwondo Fed. of the Republic of Kazakhstan **[IO]**, Almaty, Kazakhstan
Taekwondo Fed. of the Republic of Tajikistan **[IO]**, Dushanbe, Tajikistan
Taekwondo Fed. of Turkey **[IO]**, Ankara, Turkey
Taekwondo New Zealand **[IO]**, Auckland, New Zealand
Taekwondo Union; U.S. **[22763]**
Taft Family Assn. **[20598]**, Patricia Allen, Sec.-Treas., 77 Greenfield Rd., Montague, MA 01351
TAG Intl. **[★4]**
Tag and Label Mfrs. Inst. **[3355]**, 1 Blackburn Center, Gloucester, MA 01930, (978)282-1400
Tag Mfrs. Inst. **[★3355]**
Tahiti Jet Club **[IO]**, Tahiti, French Polynesia
Tahoe Improvement and Conservation Assn. **[★4091]**
Tahtitieteellinen yhdistys Ursa **[★IO]**

T'ai Chi
   Amer. Tai Chi and Qigong Assn. **[16827]**
   Gin Soon Tai Chi Chuan Fed. **[22733]**
   Intl. Yang Style Tai Chi Chuan Assn. **[22740]**

Tai Chi Assn. of Australia **[IO]**, Jannali, Australia
Tai Chi Chuan/Shaolin Chuan Assn. - Defunct.
Taidemaalariliitto **[★IO]**
Taiga Rescue Network **[IO]**, Helsinki, Finland
Tailhook Assn. **[5832]**, 9696 Businesspark Ave., San Diego, CA 92131, (858)689-9223
Taipei Assn. of Advt. Agencies **[IO]**, Taipei, Taiwan
Taipei Bus. Assn. in Singapore **[IO]**, Singapore, Singapore
Taipei Economic and Cultural Off. in New York **[9480]**, 1 E 42nd St., 11th Fl., Press Div., New York, NY 10017, (212)557-5122
Taipei Soc. of Infectious Diseases **[IO]**, Taipei, Taiwan
Taipei World Trade Center and China External Trade Development Coun. **[IO]**, Taipei, Taiwan
An Taisce **[★IO]**

Taiwan
   Formosan Assn. for Public Affairs **[18684]**
   Formosan Assn. for Public Affairs **[18684]**
   Friends of Taiwan Intl. **[17945]**
   Intercollegiate Taiwanese Amer. Students Assn. **[19252]**
   North Am. Taiwanese Professors' Assn. **[19253]**
   North Am. Taiwanese Professors' Assn. **[19253]**
   North Amer. Taiwan Stud. Assn. **[8938]**
   North Amer. Taiwan Stud. Assn. **[8938]**
   Professor Chen Wen-Chen Memorial Found. **[18685]**
   Taipei Economic and Cultural Off. in New York **[9480]**
   Taiwanese Amer. Citizens League **[19254]**

Taiwan Assn. of Machinery Indus. **[IO]**, Taipei, Taiwan

Taiwan Assn. of Stationery Indus. **[IO]**, Taipei, Taiwan
Taiwan Bags Assn. **[IO]**, Taipei, Taiwan
Taiwan Bicycle Exporters' Assn. **[IO]**, Taipei, Taiwan
Taiwan Chain Store and Franchise Assn. **[IO]**, Taipei, Taiwan
Taiwan Cotton Spinners' Assn. **[IO]**, Taipei, Taiwan
Taiwan Elec. and Electronic Mfrs'. Assn. **[IO]**, Taipei, Taiwan
Taiwan Elec. Wire and Cable Indus'. Assn. **[IO]**, Taipei, Taiwan
Taiwan Epilepsy Soc. **[IO]**, Taipei, Taiwan
Taiwan External Trade Development Coun. **[IO]**, Taipei, Taiwan
Taiwan Footwear Mfrs. Assn. **[IO]**, Taipei, Taiwan
Taiwan Frozen Seafood Indus. Assn. **[IO]**, Kaohsiung, Taiwan
Taiwan Garment Indus. Assn. **[IO]**, Taipei, Taiwan
Taiwan Gas Appliance Mfrs'. Assn. **[IO]**, Taipei, Taiwan
Taiwan Gift and Houseware Exporters Assn. **[IO]**, Taipei, Taiwan
Taiwan Hand Tool Mfrs'. Assn. **[IO]**, Taipei, Taiwan
Taiwan Handicraft Promotion Center **[IO]**, Taipei, Taiwan
Taiwan Jewelry Indus. Assn. **[IO]**, Taipei, Taiwan
Taiwan Junior Chamber **[IO]**, Taipei, Taiwan
Taiwan Knitting Indus. Assn. **[IO]**, Taipei, Taiwan
Taiwan Man-Made Fiber Indus. Assn. **[IO]**, Taipei, Taiwan
Taiwan Margarine Indus. Assn. **[IO]**, Taipei, Taiwan
Taiwan Medical Assn. **[IO]**, Taipei, Taiwan
Taiwan Mold and Die Indus. Assn. **[IO]**, Taipei, Taiwan
Taiwan Non-Woven Fabrics Indus. Assn. **[IO]**, Taipei, Taiwan
Taiwan Occupational Therapy Assn. **[IO]**, Taipei, Taiwan
Taiwan Pediatric Assn. **[IO]**, Taipei, Taiwan
Taiwan Private Equity and Venture Capital Assn. **[IO]**, Taipei, Taiwan
Taiwan Regional Assn. of Adhesive Tape Mfrs. **[IO]**, Taipei, Taiwan
Taiwan Regional Assn. of Filament Fabrics Printing, Dyeing and Finishing Indus. **[IO]**, Taipei, Taiwan
Taiwan Rubber Indus. Assn. **[IO]**, Taipei, Taiwan
Taiwan Soc. of Cardiology **[IO]**, Taipei, Taiwan
Taiwan Soc. of Clinical Neurophysiology **[IO]**, Taipei, Taiwan
Taiwan Sporting Goods Mfrs. Assn. **[IO]**, Taipei, Taiwan
Taiwan Textile Fed. **[IO]**, Taipei, Taiwan
Taiwan Toy Mfrs'. Assn. **[IO]**, Taipei, Taiwan
Taiwan Visitors Assn. - Taipei **[IO]**, Taipei, Taiwan
Taiwan Youth Hostel Assn. **[IO]**, Taipei, Taiwan
Taiwan Zippers Mfrs. Assn. **[IO]**, Taipei, Taiwan

Taiwanese
   North Am. Taiwan Stud. Assn. **[8938]**
   Taipei Economic and Cultural Off. in New York **[9480]**

Taiwanese Amer. Citizens League **[19254]**, 3001 Walnut Grove Ave., No. 7, Rosemead, CA 91770
Taiwanese Amer. Lawyers Assn. **[5286]**, Tony M. Lu, Esq., Pres., 3333 S Brea Canyon Rd., Ste. 213, Diamond Bar, CA 91765, (909)468-4650
Taiwanese Amer. Lawyers Assn. **[5286]**, Tony M. Lu, Esq., Pres., 3333 S Brea Canyon Rd., Ste. 213, Diamond Bar, CA 91765, (909)468-4650
Taiwanese Assn. for Artificial Intelligence **[IO]**, Taipei, Taiwan
Tajik Academician Res. and Educational Network Assn. **[IO]**, Dushanbe, Tajikistan
Tajikistan Alumni Assn. **[IO]**, Dushanbe, Tajikistan
Take Off Pounds Sensibly **[12591]**, PO Box 070360, Milwaukee, WI 53207, (414)482-4620
Take Root **[12541]**, PO Box 930, Kalama, WA 98625, (360)673-3720
Takemusu Aiki Assn. of Australia **[IO]**, Sydney, Australia
Taking Control of Your Diabetes **[14358]**, 1110 Camino Del Mar, Ste. B, Del Mar, CA 92014, (858)755-5683
Talent Managers Assn. **[1217]**, 4821 Lankershim Blvd., Ste. F149, North Hollywood, CA 91601, (818)487-5556

Talk About Curing Autism **[13805]**, 3070 Bristol St., Ste. 340, Costa Mesa, CA 92626, (949)640-4401
Talking Newspaper Assn. of the United Kingdom **[IO]**, Heathfield, United Kingdom
Talking Page Literacy Org. **[8539]**, 1738 Tradewinds Ln., Newport Beach, CA 92660, (949)650-8101
Tall Bearded Iris Soc. **[21827]**, PO Box 6991, Lubbock, TX 79493, (806)792-1878
Tall Cedar Foundation **[★19142]**
Tall Cedars of Lebanon of North Am. **[19142]**, 2609 N Front St., Harrisburg, PA 17110, (717)232-5991
Tall Cedars of Lebanon of the U.S.A. **[★19142]**
Tall Clubs Intl. **[13307]**, 8466 N Lockwood Ridge Rd. 188, Sarasota, FL 34243, (888)468-2552
Tall Clubs Intl. **[13307]**, 8466 N Lockwood Ridge Rd. 188, Sarasota, FL 34243, (888)468-2552
Tall Oil Assn. **[★762]**
Tall Persons Club - Great Britain and Ireland **[IO]**, London, United Kingdom
Tall Timbers **[★4149]**
Tall Timbers Land Conservancy **[4148]**, Tall Timbers Res. Sta., 13093 Henry Beadel Dr., Tallahassee, FL 32312, (850)893-4153
Tall Timbers Res. **[★4149]**
Tall Timbers Res. Sta. **[4149]**, 13093 Henry Beadel Dr., Tallahassee, FL 32312-0918, (850)893-4153
Taller Ecologista **[★IO]**
Tallgrass Prairie Found. **[★4071]**
Tallinn Frisbee Club **[IO]**, Tallinn, Estonia

Tallness
   Tall Clubs Intl. **[13307]**
   Tall Clubs Intl. **[13307]**

Talyllyn Railway Preservation Soc. **[IO]**, Tywyn, United Kingdom
TAMAR Proj. **[★IO]**
Tamarind Inst. **[8221]**, 2500 Central Ave. SE, Albuquerque, NM 87106, (505)277-3901
Tamarind Lithography Workshop **[★8221]**
Tamburitza Assn. of Am. **[10303]**, 3894 Spartan Dr., Fort Gratiot, MI 48059, (810)385-9667
Tamika and Friends **[13988]**, PO Box 2942, Upper Marlboro, MD 20773-2942, (866)595-2448
Tamir Welfare Org. **[IO]**, Faisalabad, Pakistan
Tamizdat **[9518]**, PO Box 20618, New York, NY 10009, (212)260-8444
Tamworth and District Olive Growers Assn. **[IO]**, Tamworth, Australia
Tan Son Nhut Assn. **[20823]**, PO Box 236, Penryn, PA 17564-0236
Tandem Club of Am. **[22486]**, 10708 Cambium Ct., Raleigh, NC 27613-6304
Tang Center for Herbal Medicine Res. **[15215]**, Univ. of Chicago, Pritzker School of Medicine, Dept. of Anesthesia and Critical Care, 5841 S Maryland Ave., MC 4028, Chicago, IL 60637, (773)834-2399
Tang Center for Herbal Medicine Res. **[15215]**, Univ. of Chicago, Pritzker School of Medicine, Dept. of Anesthesia and Critical Care, 5841 S Maryland Ave., MC 4028, Chicago, IL 60637, (773)834-2399
Tangent Gp. **[12113]**, 8721 Santa Monica Blvd., Ste. 37, West Hollywood, CA 90069, (818)527-5442
Tangents **[★12113]**

Tangible Assets
   Indus. Coun. for Tangible Assets **[3378]**

Tank Conf. of the Truck Trailer Mfrs. Assn. **[892]**, 1020 Princess St., Alexandria, VA 22314, (703)549-3010
Tanka Soc. of Am. **[10456]**, PO Box 521084, Tulsa, OK 74152
Tanners' Coun. of Am. **[★2202]**
Tanners' Coun. of Japan **[IO]**, Hyogo, Japan
Tannu Tuva Collectors' Soc. **[22084]**, 513 6th Ave. S, Lake Worth, FL 33460
Tannu Tuva Collectors' Soc. **[22084]**, 513 6th Ave. S, Lake Worth, FL 33460
Tantalum-Niobium Intl. Stud. Center **[IO]**, Lasne, Belgium
Tantur Ecumenical Inst. **[IO]**, Jerusalem, Israel
The Tanygnathus Soc. **[3855]**, 4510 Buckingham Rd., Fort Myers, FL 33905-7208
Tanzania Amateur Athletic Assn. **[IO]**, Dar es Salaam, United Republic of Tanzania
Tanzania Amateur Radio Club **[IO]**, Dar es Salaam, United Republic of Tanzania
Tanzania Assn. of Non Governmental Organizations **[IO]**, Dar es Salaam, United Republic of Tanzania

Reference to "IO" in place of a book number signifies that the association may be found in the 50th edition of International Organizations.

Encyclopedia of Associations, 51st Edition   **3203**

Tanzania Assn. of Tour Operators [IO], Arusha, United Republic of Tanzania
Tanzania Badminton Assn. [IO], Morogoro, United Republic of Tanzania
Tanzania Consumers Protection Assn. [IO], Dar es Salaam, United Republic of Tanzania
Tanzania Debate Assn. [IO], Dar es Salaam, United Republic of Tanzania
Tanzania Fed. of Cooperatives [IO], Dar es Salaam, United Republic of Tanzania
Tanzania Gender Networking Prog. [IO], Dar es Salaam, United Republic of Tanzania
Tanzania Indus. Res. and Development Org. [IO], Dar es Salaam, United Republic of Tanzania
Tanzania Lawn Tennis Assn. [IO], Dar es Salaam, United Republic of Tanzania
Tanzania Lib. Assn. [IO], Dar es Salaam, United Republic of Tanzania
Tanzania Red Cross Natl. Soc. [IO], Dar es Salaam, United Republic of Tanzania
Tanzania Sports Medicine Assn. [IO], Dar es Salaam, United Republic of Tanzania
Tanzania Squash Rackets Assn. [IO], Dar es Salaam, United Republic of Tanzania
Tanzania Teachers' Union [IO], Dar es Salaam, United Republic of Tanzania
Tanzania Trade Development Authority [IO], Dar es Salaam, United Republic of Tanzania
Tanzania eco Volunteerism [IO], Tanga, United Republic of Tanzania
Tanzania Weightlifting Fed. [IO], Dar es Salaam, United Republic of Tanzania
Tanzania Women Graduates Fed. [IO], Dar es Salaam, United Republic of Tanzania
Tanzania Youth in Action for Development [IO], Dar es Salaam, United Republic of Tanzania
Tanzer 16 Class Assn. [22396], 7111 Crescent Dr., Chapel Hill, NC 27516, (919)933-8208
Tanzer 22 Class Assn. [IO], Nepean, ON, Canada
Taoist Tai Chi Soc. of Australia [IO], Bayswater, Australia
Taos Natl. Soc. of Watercolorists [9207], PO Box 2943, Taos, NM 87571
Tapori Intl. ATD Fourth World [IO], Geneva, Switzerland
Tapori Intl. ATD Quart Monde [★IO]
TAPPI - Tech. Assn. of the Pulp and Paper Indus. [2622], 15 Tech. Pkwy. S, Norcross, GA 30092, (770)446-1400
Taralye [★850]
Tarlton Inst. for Marine Education - Defunct.
Tarot
Amer. Tarot Assn. [22160]
Amer. Tarot Assn. [22160]
Tarot Guild of Australia [IO], Melbourne, Australia
TARP Assn. [308], 1801 County Rd. B W, Roseville, MN 55113, (651)222-2508
Tartans of Scotland [IO], Dunkeld, United Kingdom
Tarten Ten
T-Ten Class Assn. [22395]
TASH [11833], 1001 Connecticut Ave. NW, Ste. 235, Washington, DC 20036, (202)540-9020
Task Force on Alternatives in Print [★9956]
Task Force for Child Survival and Development [12481], 325 Swanton Way, Decatur, GA 30030, (404)371-0466
Task Force on Gay Liberation [★9633]
Task Force on Lesbian/Gay Issues [★8869]
Task Force on Using Mass Media [★8316]
Task Force on Using Mass Media [★8316]
Task Force for Women in Public Admin. [★5912]
Task Force on World Hunger/Presbyterian Church in the U.S. [★12288]
Tasmanian Canine Assn. [IO], Glenorchy, Australia
Tasmanian Chamber of Commerce and Indus. [IO], Hobart, Australia
Tasmanian History Teachers' Assn. [IO], Bellerive, Australia
Tasmanian Infection Control Assn. [IO], Hobart, Australia
Tasmanian Olive Coun. [IO], Brighton, Australia
Tasmanian Secondary Principals Assn. [IO], Devonport, Australia
Tasters Guild Intl. [190], 1515 Michigan NE, Grand Rapids, MI 49503, (616)454-7815

Tattoo-a-Pet [11044], 6571 SW 20th Ct., Fort Lauderdale, FL 33317, (954)581-5834
Tattoo Club of Great Britain [IO], Oxford, United Kingdom
Tattooing
Alliance of Professional Tattooists [3379]
Assn. of Professional Piercers [3380]
Natl. Tattoo Assn. [10557]
Natl. Tattoo Assn. [10557]
Tau Alpha Pi [23524], 1818 N St. NW, Ste. 600, Washington, DC 20036, (202)350-5762
Tau Beta Pi Assn. [23525], PO Box 2697, Knoxville, TN 37901-2697, (865)546-4578
Tau Beta Sigma [23607], PO Box 849, Stillwater, OK 74076-0849, (405)372-2333
Tau Epsilon Phi [23702], 1000 White Horse Rd., Ste. 512, Voorhees, NJ 08043, (856)782-9837
Tau Epsilon Phi Found. [★23702]
Tau Epsilon Rho Law Fraternity [★23580]
Tau Epsilon Rho Law Soc. [23580], 133 Paisley Pl., Hainesport, NJ 08036, (609)864-1838
Tau Kappa Alpha [★23754]
Tau Kappa Epsilon [23703], 7439 Woodland Dr., Indianapolis, IN 46268, (317)872-6533
Tau Omega [★23523]
Tau Sigma Delta [23466], Texas A & M Univ., Coll. of Architecture, Langford A411, College Station, TX 77843, (979)847-2787
Tavistock Inst. [IO], London, United Kingdom
Tax Analysts [18705], 400 S Maple Ave., Ste. 400, Falls Church, VA 22046, (703)533-4400
Tax Analysts and Advocates [★18705]
Tax Coun. [6019], 1301 K St. NW, Ste. 800W, Washington, DC 20005-3317, (202)822-8062
Tax Council-Alcoholic Beverage Indus. [★180]
Tax Executives Inst. [6020], 1200 G St. NW, Ste. 300, Washington, DC 20005-3814, (202)638-5601
Tax Found. [6021], 529 14th St. NW, Ste. 420, Washington, DC 20045-1000, (202)464-6200
Tax Free America - Defunct.
Tax Reform
Coalition for Tax Fairness [18694]
Howard Jarvis Taxpayers Assn. [18686]
Policy and Taxation Gp. [18687]
ReformAMT [18688]
Taxpayers for Common Sense [18689]
Tax Reform Action Coalition - Defunct.
Taxation
Amer. Soc. of Cost Segregation Professionals [3381]
Amer. Soc. of Tax Problem Solvers [6006]
Amer. Tax Policy Inst. [18690]
Amer. Taxation Assn. [6007]
Americans for Tax Reform [18691]
Assn. for Computers and Taxation [3382]
Center for the Stud. of Economics [18692]
Citizens for Tax Justice [18693]
Coalition for Tax Fairness [18694]
Common Ground - U.S.A. [18695]
Coun. of Georgist Organizations [18696]
Coun. On State Taxation [18697]
Fed. of Exchange Accommodators [3383]
Fed. of Tax Administrators [6008]
Forest Landowners Tax Coun. [6009]
Henry George Inst. - New York [18698]
Inst. for Professionals in Taxation [6010]
Inst. of Tax Consultants [6011]
Intl. Assn. of Assessing Officers [6012]
Intl. Assn. of Assessing Officers [6012]
MultiState Tax Commn. [6013]
Natl. Assn. of Computerized Tax Processors [6014]
Natl. Assn. of Enrolled Agents [6015]
Natl. Assn. of Tax Consultants [6016]
Natl. Assn. of Tax Professionals [6017]
Natl. Campaign for a Peace Tax Fund [18699]
Natl. Community Tax Coalition [18700]
Natl. Governmental Collectors Assn. [5500]
Natl. Tax Assn. [6018]
Natl. Tax-Limitation Comm. [18701]
Natl. Taxpayers Union [18702]
Natl. War Tax Resistance Coordinating Comm. [18703]
Save Our Schools [18704]
Tax Analysts [18705]

Tax Coun. [6019]
Tax Executives Inst. [6020]
Tax Found. [6021]
Taxpayers Against Fraud [18706]
Urban-Brookings Tax Policy Center [18707]
Taxation Inst. of Australia [IO], Sydney, Australia
Taxation With Representation [★18705]
Taxation With Representation Fund [★18705]
Taxi-Stop [★21853]
Taxicab, Limousine and Paratransit Assn. [3537], 3200 Tower Oaks Blvd., Ste. 220, Rockville, MD 20852, (301)984-5700
Taxicab, Limousine and Paratransit Assn. [3537], 3200 Tower Oaks Blvd., Ste. 220, Rockville, MD 20852, (301)984-5700
Taxidermy
Natl. Taxidermists Assn. [3384]
Taxpayers Against Fraud [18706], 1220 19th St. NW, Ste. 501, Washington, DC 20036, (202)296-4826
Taxpayers Assn. of Europe [IO], Munich, Germany
Taxpayers for Common Sense [18689], 651 Pennsylvania Ave. SE, Washington, DC 20003, (202)546-8500
Taxpayers Educ. Lobby [★18704]
Tay-Sachs and Allied Diseases Assn; Natl. [15624]
Tay-Sachs and Allied Diseases Assn; Natl. [15624]
Taylor Soc. [★2304]
Tayu Center [20255], PO Box 11554, Santa Rosa, CA 95406, (707)829-9579
Tayu Fellowship [★20255]
Tayu Inst. [★20255]
TDI [★14958]
Te Kaunihera O Nga Neehi Maori O Aotearoa [★IO]
Te Kaunihera Wahine O Aotearoa [★IO]
TE Lawrence Soc. [IO], Oxford, United Kingdom
Te Mana o Te Moana [IO], Moorea, French Polynesia
Te Petereihana o Whare Tapere o Aotearoa [★IO]
Te Pouhere Whakaako o Te Reo Pakeha o Aotearoa [★IO]
Te Roopu Turi o Aoearoa [★IO]
Te Roopu Whaka Waihanga Iwi O Aotearoa [★IO]
Te Roopu Whakaritenga o nga Ture [★IO]
Te Ropu Kairangahau Tikanga-a-iwi o Aotearoa [★IO]
Te Ropu Kaiwhakamaori a-waha, a tuhi o Aotearoa [★IO]
Te Tari Puna Ora o Aotearoa [★IO]
Tea
Caffeine Awareness Assn. [13828]
Tea Assn. of Canada [IO], Toronto, ON, Canada
Tea Assn. of the U.S.A. [453], 362 5th Ave., Ste. 801, New York, NY 10001, (212)986-9415
Tea Bd. of Kenya [IO], Nairobi, Kenya
Tea Coun. [IO], London, United Kingdom
Tea Coun. of Canada [★7062]
Tea Coun. of the U.S.A. [454], 362 5th Ave., Ste. 801, New York, NY 10001, (212)986-9415
Tea Coun. of the U.S.A. [454], 362 5th Ave., Ste. 801, New York, NY 10001, (212)986-9415
Tea Family Org. - Defunct.
Tea Leaf Club Intl. [21269], 3120 E Titus Ave., Des Moines, IA 50320
TEACH (Teaching Each Other About Conquering Handicaps) - Defunct.
Teacher Education
Amer. Assn. for Teaching and Curriculum [8941]
Assn. for the Advancement of Intl. Educ. [8388]
Care Through Educ. Intl. [11453]
Resources for Indispensable Schools and Educators [8961]
Teacher Trainers Sect. of the Agricultural Division of the Assn. for Career and Tech. Educ. [★7706]
Teachers
African Language Teachers Assn. [8939]
Amer. Assn. of Classified School Employees [23177]
Amer. Assn. of Colleges for Teacher Educ. [8940]
Amer. Assn. of Snowboard Instructors [22923]
Amer. Assn. of Teachers of French [8459]
Amer. Assn. for Teaching and Curriculum [8941]
Amer. Coun. on Immersion Educ. [8942]
Art Teachers' Assn. [16803]
Assn. for the Advancement of Intl. Educ. [8388]

A star before a book entry number signifies that the name is not listed separately, but is mentioned within the entry.

Assn. of Canadian Univ. and Coll. Teachers of French [5092]
Assn. for Constructivist Teaching [8943]
Assn. for Sci. Teacher Educ. [8944]
Assn. of Teacher Educators [8945]
Assn. of Teachers of Tech. Writing [9072]
Canadian Assn. of Immersion Teachers [4292]
Care Through Educ. Intl. [11453]
Carnegie Found. for the Advancement of Teaching [8946]
Conf. on Coll. Composition and Commun. [8132]
Coun. for the Advancement of Standards in Higher Educ. [8914]
Dance Masters of Am. [7959]
Educ. Indus. Assn. [8947]
Go Green Initiative Assn. [8156]
Inst. for Chem. Educ. [7820]
Intl. Assn. for Jazz Educ. [8653]
Intl. Assn. for Teachers of Chinese to Speakers of Other Languages [7844]
Intl. Coun. on Educ. for Teaching [8948]
Intl. Coun. on Educ. for Teaching [8948]
Intl. Soc. for the Social Stud. [8865]
Joseph Campbell Found. [8949]
Martial Arts Teachers' Assn. [22743]
Medau Movement [3297]
Middle Atlantic Planetarium Soc. [8841]
Natl. Alliance of Black School Educators [8950]
Natl. Assn. for the Advancement of Caring Teachers [8951]
Natl. Assn. for Beginning Teachers [8952]
Natl. Assn. of Blind Teachers [8953]
Natl. Assn. of Community Coll. Teacher Educ. Programs [8954]
Natl. Assn. of Early Childhood Teacher Educators [8955]
Natl. Assn. of Hea. Sci. Educ. Partnership [8843]
Natl. Assn. of Math Circles [8566]
Natl. Assn. of State Directors of Teacher Educ. and Certification [8956]
Natl. Bd. for Professional Teaching Standards [8957]
Natl. Coun. of Japanese Language Teachers [8958]
Natl. Coun. on Teacher Quality [8959]
Natl. History Club [8261]
Natl. Middle Level Sci. Teachers' Assn. [8848]
Natl. Schools Comm. for Economic Educ. [7988]
Natl. Surf Schools and Instructors Assn. [23036]
Network of Intl. Christian Schools [7857]
North Amer. Irish Dance Fed. [9563]
One World Educ. [8928]
Organizational Behavior Teaching Soc. [6262]
Physics Teacher Educ. Coalition [8960]
Professional Golf Teachers Assn. of Am. [22621]
Resources for Indispensable Schools and Educators [8961]
Rock Detective Geoscience Educ. [7983]
Sino-American Bridge for Educ. and Hea. [9876]
Soc. for Music Teacher Educ. [8669]
Spirituality and Practice [7929]
Tech. Inst. for Music Educators [8671]
U.S. Ski Team Found. [22919]
Urban Teacher Residency United [8962]
Women Educators [9067]
Teachers' Division of Natl. Assn. of Cosmetology Schools [★7935]
Teachers' Educational Coun. - Natl. Assn. of Accredited Cosmetology Schools [★7935]
Teachers' Educational Coun. - Natl. Assn. of Cosmetology Schools [★7935]
Teachers of English to Speakers of Other Languages [8137], 1925 Ballenger Ave., Ste. 550, Alexandria, VA 22314-6820, (703)836-0774
Teachers of English to Speakers of Other Languages Aotearoa New Zealand [IO], Wellington, New Zealand
Teachers of English to Speakers of Other Languages - Arabia [IO], Dubai, United Arab Emirates
Teachers of English to Speakers of Other Languages - France [IO], Paris, France
Teachers Insurance and Annuity Assn. [8326], TIAA-CREF, PO Box 1259, Charlotte, NC 28201, (800)842-2252

Teachers Resisting Unhealthy Children's Entertainment [11415], 160 Lakeview Ave., Cambridge, MA 02138
Teachers Saving Children Natl. [18569], PO Box 125, Damascus, OH 44619-0125, (330)821-2747
Teachers' Union of Hungary [IO], Budapest, Hungary
Teachers' Union of Ireland [IO], Dublin, Ireland
Teachers Union Norway [IO], Oslo, Norway
Teachers and Writers Collaborative [9076], 520 8th Ave., Ste. 2020, New York, NY 10018, (212)691-6590
Teaching Aids at Low Cost [IO], St. Albans, United Kingdom
Teaching for Change [8111], PO Box 73038, Washington, DC 20056, (202)588-7204
Teaching-Family Assn. [12022], PO Box 2007, Midlothian, VA 23113, (804)632-0155
Teaching Individual Protective Strategies [★11694]
Teaching Individuals Positive Solutions [★11694]
Teaching and Learning About Aging Proj. [★10854]
Teaching, Learning and Tech. Gp. [7530], PO Box 5643, Takoma Park, MD 20913, (301)270-8312
Teaching, Learning and Tech. Gp. [7530], PO Box 5643, Takoma Park, MD 20913, (301)270-8312
Team Drivers Intl. Union [★23301]
Team HOPE: Help Offering Parents Empowerment - Address unknown since 2011.
Team Ironclad [★22478]
Team Ironclad [★22478]
Team Success [13560], 5050 Laguna Blvd., Ste. 112-415, Elk Grove, CA 95758, (916)629-4229
Team and Workplace Excellence Forum [7319], PO Box 3005, Milwaukee, WI 53201-3005, (414)272-1734
TeamPact [18631], 2897 N Druid Hills Rd., Ste. 166, Atlanta, GA 30329, (404)683-1044
Teamsters for a Democratic Union [23302], PO Box 10128, Detroit, MI 48210, (313)842-2600
Teamsters Natl. Union [★23301]
Tear Australia [IO], Blackburn, Australia
Tear Film and Ocular Surface Soc. [16000], PO Box 130146, Boston, MA 02113
Tear Film and Ocular Surface Soc. [16000], PO Box 130146, Boston, MA 02113
Tearfund [IO], Teddington, United Kingdom
TECH CORPS [13407], 112 Jefferson Ave., Columbus, OH 43215, (614)583-9211
TECH, Tech. Exchange for Christian Healthcare [19954], PO Box 1912, Midland, MI 48641-1912, (989)837-5515
TechAmerica [6499], 601 Pennsylvania Ave. NW, North Bldg., Ste. 600, Arlington, VA 22209, (202)682-9110
TechAssure Assn. [2045], 23655 Currant Dr., Golden, CO 80401, (703)470-8324
TechLaw Gp. [5680], Ackermann Pr., 1111 N Shore Dr., Ste. N-400, Knoxville, TN 37919, (865)588-7456
Tech. Advisors Gp. [IO], London, United Kingdom
Tech. Anal. Soc. of St. Lucia [IO], Castries, St. Lucia
Tech. Analysts Soc. Singapore [IO], Singapore, Singapore
Tech. Assistance Collaborative [13164], 31 St. James Ave., Ste. 710, Boston, MA 02116, (617)266-5657
Tech. Assn. of the Graphic Arts [6935], 200 Deer Run Rd., Sewickley, PA 15143, (412)259-1706
Tech. Assn. of the Graphic Arts [6935], 200 Deer Run Rd., Sewickley, PA 15143, (412)259-1706
Tech. Assn. of the Lithographic Indus. [★6935]
Tech. Assn. of the Lithographic Indus. [★6935]
Tech. Assn. for Solid Wastes Mgt. [IO], Bilbao, Spain
Tech. Center for Clay, Tiles, and Bricks [IO], Clamart, France
Technical Ceramics Mfrs. Assn. - Defunct.
Tech. Commn. for Oceanography and Marine Meteorology [IO], Geneva, Switzerland
Tech. Communicators Assn. of New Zealand [IO], Auckland, New Zealand

Technical Consulting
Am. Continental 2000 [11847]
Mfg. Enterprise Solutions Assn. Intl. [7491]
Mfg. Enterprise Solutions Assn. Intl. [7491]
Natl. Local Tech. Assistance Prog. Assn. [13196]

Technical Education
Amer. Foundry Soc. [8963]

Amer. Tech. Educ. Assn. [8964]
Amer. Tech. Educ. Assn. [8964]
Caribbean Engg. and Tech. Professionals [1456]
Gen. Soc. of Mechanics and Tradesmen of the City of New York [8965]
Intl. Coun. for Machinery Lubrication [7034]
Intl. Fire Ser. Training Assn. [8966]
Intl. Fire Ser. Training Assn. [8966]
Intl. Tech. and Engineering Educ. Assn. [8967]
Intl. Tech. and Engg. Educators Assn. [8967]
Intl. Tech. and Engg. Educators Assn. l Coun. for Supervision and Leadership [8968]
Intl. Tech. and Engg. Educators Assn. - Coun. for Supervision and Leadership [8968]
Natl. Local Tech. Assistance Prog. Assn. [13196]
Organizational Systems Res. Assn. [8969]
WoodLINKS USA [8300]
World Partners for Development [13210]
Tech. Educational and Skill Training Org. [IO], Kabul, Afghanistan
Tech., Engg. and Elecl. Union [IO], Dublin, Ireland
Technical Info. Center [★8963]
Tech. Publishing Soc. [★817]
Tech. Textile and Nonwoven Assn. [IO], Melbourne, Australia
Tech. Valuation Soc. [★2550]
Tech. Writing; Assn. of Teachers of [9072]
Technische Org. der Europaischen Reifen- und Felgenhersteller [★IO]
Technocracy Inc. [18632], 2475 Harksell Rd., Ferndale, WA 98248-9764, (360)366-1012
Technologies du Developpement Durable du Canada [★IO]
Technologist Sect. of the Soc. of Nuclear Medicine [★15697]

Technology
911 Indus. Alliance [804]
1394 High Performance Serial Bus Trade Assn. [3385]
ACT Canada [17769]
Advanced Biofuels Assn. [1533]
Advanced Biofuels USA [6108]
Advanced Media Workflow Assn. [3386]
Aguayuda [13412]
Algal Biomass Org. [6680]
Alliance for Building Regulatory Reform in the Digital Age [6372]
Alliance for Digital Equality [7492]
Alliance for Renewable Energy [6683]
Alternative Tech. Assn. [16079]
Amer. Assn. of Professional Tech. Analysts [3387]
Amer. Farmers for the Advancement and Conservation of Tech. [4347]
Amer. Filtration and Separations Soc. [7493]
Amer. Soc. of Digital Forensics and eDiscovery [6883]
Amer. Supplier Inst. [7494]
Anti-Malware Testing Standards Org. [6478]
Application Ser. Provider Indus. Consortium [3388]
Assn. of Certified Green Tech. Auditors [6692]
Assn. for Competitive Tech. [3389]
Assn. of Liberian Engineers USA [6786]
Assn. of Teachers of Tech. Writing [9072]
Assn. of Tech., Mgt. and Applied Engg. [8296]
Assn. of Thai Professionals in Am. and Canada [19255]
Bill and Melinda Gates Found. [12134]
BIO IT Coalition [6333]
Biomass Power Assn. [7292]
Biomass Thermal Energy Coun. [6697]
Bionomics Intl. [7363]
Bridge Engg. Assn. [6789]
Building Enclosure Coun. Natl. [6374]
Building Enclosure Tech. and Env. Coun. [539]
Building Tech. Educators' Soc. [7732]
CARTHA [18402]
CDMA Development Gp. [7495]
Charles A. and Anne Morrow Lindbergh Found. [4240]
Clean Economy Network [6605]
Clean Tech. and Sustainable Indus. Org. [3856]
Clean Tech. Trade Alliance [6110]
CommerceNet [7496]
Cooperative Assn. for Internet Data Anal. [7007]

Reference to "IO" in place of a book number signifies that the association may be found in the 50th edition of International Organizations.

Cyber Security Indus. Alliance [6974]
Demand Response and Smart Grid Coalition [6649]
Digital Pathology Assn. [16124]
Digital Signage Assn. [90]
Digital Watermarking Alliance [6932]
Drilling, Observation and Sampling of the Earth's Continental Crust [6602]
EarthSpark Intl. [6711]
Edutechnia [6976]
Electrification Coalition [3510]
Electrocoat Assn. [7497]
Electronic Frontier Found. [7498]
Electronic Indus. Citizenship Coalition [1098]
Energy Efficiency Bus. Coalition [1167]
Energy Extraction Technologies [6718]
Energy Farm [6719]
Energy Info. Standards Alliance [1168]
Energy Storage Coun. [6722]
Enterprise for a Sustainable World [1056]
Epsilon Pi Tau [23755]
Epsilon Pi Tau [23755]
Ethernet Alliance [7499]
Financial Services Tech. Consortium [7500]
FlexTech Alliance [3390]
Focus Fusion Soc. [6725]
Foresight Nanotech Inst. [7501]
FutureGen Alliance [6112]
Geekcorps [3391]
Geosynthetics Materials Assn. [6426]
Global Hea. Technologies Coalition [15172]
Global Medical Knowledge [15375]
Global Spatial Data Infrastructure Assn. [7502]
Global Spatial Data Infrastructure Assn. [7502]
Global Tech. Distribution Coun. [3392]
GlobalPlatform [7503]
Green Computing Impact Org. [1221]
GridWise Alliance [6727]
HeatGreen Coun. [6113]
HIMSS Electronic Hea. Record Assn. [15332]
Hispanic Educational Tech. Services [8973]
Hotel Tech. Next Generation [1753]
HumaniNet [12848]
Hydrogen 2000 [6729]
IEEE | Soc. on Social Implications of Tech. [7504]
InCommon [6537]
Info. Tech. Services Marketing Assn. [2405]
InfraGard Natl. Members Alliance [5968]
Innovation: Africa [6114]
Inst. for the Transfer of Tech. to Educ. [8314]
Inst. for Women in Trades, Tech. and Sci. [3684]
Interactive Media Entertainment and Gaming Assn. [7008]
InterConnection [11664]
Intl. Aesthetic and Laser Assn. [15237]
Intl. Assn. for the Advancement of Steam Power [7480]
Intl. Assn. for Cmpt. and Info. Sci. [6456]
Intl. Assn. for Impact Assessment [7505]
Intl. Assn. for Impact Assessment [7505]
Intl. Assn. for the Mgt. of Tech. [7506]
Intl. Assn. of Nanotechnology [7507]
Intl. Assn. of Nanotechnology [7507]
Intl. Assn. of Space Entrepreneurs [139]
Intl. Assn. for Structural Mechanics in Reactor Tech. [7508]
Intl. Assn. for Structural Mechanics in Reactor Tech. [7508]
Intl. Avaya Users Gp. [3410]
Intl. Biometric Identification Assn. [7509]
Intl. Building Performance Simulation Assn. [6377]
Intl. Christian Technologists Assn. [19990]
InterNational Comm. for Info. Tech. Standards [7510]
Intl. Coun. for Machinery Lubrication [7034]
Intl. Coun. on Nanotechnology [6430]
Intl. DB2 Users Gp. [6592]
Intl. Hospitality Info. Tech. Assn. [7511]
Intl. Radio Club of Am. [20937]
Intl. Soc. for Ethics and Info. Tech. [6979]
Intl. Soc. for Nanoscale Sci., Computation and Engg. [7376]
Intl. Soc. for Quality Electronic Design [6600]TechnologyIntl. Tech. Inst.
Internet Merchants Assn. [2117]

Jewish Heart for Africa [10822]
Joint Venture: Silicon Valley Network [7512]
JumpStart Intl. [11605]
The Keystone Center [7513]
Knowledge Ecology Intl. [7514]
Latinos in Info. Sciences and Tech. Assn. [6983]
Metro Ethernet Forum [7515]
Metro Ethernet Forum [7515]
Mobile Voter [18096]
Monte Jade Sci. and Tech. Assn. [7516]
MSPAlliance [6547]
NanoBusiness Alliance [7517]
Natl. Assn. of State 911 Administrators [7547]
Natl. Center For Advanced Technologies [7518]
Natl. Coalition for Telecommunications Educ. and Learning [8981]
Natl. LambdaRail [7519]
Natl. Tech. Assn. [7520]
Natl. Urban Tech. Center [7521]
North Am. Chinese Clean-tech and Semiconductor Assn. [1112]
North Amer. Radio Archives [22120]
North Amer. Security Products Org. [3225]
North Amer. Young Generation in Nuclear [7168]
Novell Users Intl. [3393]
Obscure Org. [7522]
Ocean Renewable Energy Coalition [6747]
ODF Alliance [6990]
One Economy [7523]
Optical Internetworking Forum [3394]
Org. for the Advancement of Structured Info. Standards [7524]
Pan-American Fed. for Info. Tech. in Agriculture [6106]
PC/104 Consortium [3395]
Physical Security Interoperability Alliance [6819]
Plug In Am. [6118]
Programmers Guild [7525]
Progressive Tech. Proj. [7526]
Recycling for Charities [4871]
Rural Renewable Energy Alliance [6754]
SailMail Assn. [6679]
Serial ATA Intl. Org. [6559]
Simulation Interoperability Standards Org. [7527]
Smart Card Alliance [7528]
Soc. for Design and Process Sci. [6601]
Soc. of Intl. Chinese in Educational Tech. [8970]
Soc. of Intl. Chinese in Educational Tech. [8970]
Soc. of Mfg. Engineers | Machining and Material Removal Community [7529]
Software and Tech. Vendors' Assn. [819]
Soliya [18833]
Sweet Sorghum Ethanol Assn. [6120]
Teaching, Learning and Tech. Gp. [7530]
Teaching, Learning and Tech. Gp. [7530]
TECH CORPS [13407]
Tech. Inst. for Music Educators [8671]
Tech. for the Poor [4945]
Tech. Services Indus. Assn. [7531]
Tech. Without Borders [7532]
TechSoup [7533]
Tissue Engg. Intl. and Regenerative Medicine Soc. [13835]
Transported Asset Protection Assn. [7396]
Truth About Trade and Tech. [6337]
U.S. Coun. for Automotive Res. [6245]
U.S. Women in Nuclear [7173]
Utility Tech. Assn. [7591]
Waste-to-Energy Res. and Tech. Coun. [7593]
Water Innovations Alliance [7614]
Welders Without Borders [7619]
The Wind Alliance [7624]
Wireless-Life Sciences Alliance [16829]
Women in Tech. Intl. [7534]
Women in Tech. Intl. [7534]
Women of Wind Energy [7627]
Women's High Tech Coalition [7535]
World Bamboo Org. [4738]
World Sci. and Engg. Acad. and Soc. [6837]
Tech. Applications Prog., Intl. City Mgt. Assn. [★5911]
Tech. Assn. of the Automotive Indus. [IO], Orbassano, Italy
Tech. Councils of North Am. [6994], Paige Rasid, Exec. Mgr., 222 Pitkin St., Ste. 113, East Hartford, CT 06108, (860)289-0878

Tech. Councils of North Am. [6994], Paige Rasid, Exec. Mgr., 222 Pitkin St., Ste. 113, East Hartford, CT 06108, (860)289-0878
Technology Education
Alliance for Digital Equality [7492]
Assn. for the Advancement of Computing in Educ. [8971]
Building Tech. Educators' Soc. [7732]
Fiber Optic Assn. [8972]
Fiber Optic Assn. [8972]
Hispanic Educational Tech. Services [8973]
Intl. Tamil Tech. Professionals' Org. [12346]
Internet Bus. Alliance [3396]
Link Found. [7536]
Natl. Assn. for Tech Prep Leadership [8974]
Natl. Coalition of Advanced Tech. Centers [8975]
Natl. Coalition of Advanced Tech. Centers [8975]
Natl. Coalition for Tech. in Educ. and Training [8976]
Natl. Coalition for Telecommunications Educ. and Learning [8981]
Open Door Educ. Found. [8977]
SeniorNet [13308]
SeniorNet [13308]
Soc. for Info. Tech. and Teacher Educ. [8978]
State Educational Tech. Directors Assn. [8979]
Urban Ed [9031]
Utility Tech. Assn. [7591]
Welders Without Borders [7619]
Youth Media Minds of Am. [8980]
Tech. Indus. of Finland [IO], Helsinki, Finland
Tech. Inst. for Music Educators [8671], 7503 Kingwood Ct., Fairview, TN 37062, (615)285-9750
Tech. New Zealand [IO], Wellington, New Zealand
Tech. for the Poor [4945], 877 Pelham Ct., Westerville, OH 43081, (614)841-9086
Tech. for the Poor [4945], 877 Pelham Ct., Westerville, OH 43081, (614)841-9086
Tech. Services Indus. Assn. [7531], 17065 Camino San Bernadino, Ste. 200, San Diego, CA 92127, (858)674-5491
Tech. Student Assn. [8299], 1914 Assn. Dr., Reston, VA 20191-1540, (703)860-9000
Tech. Transfer Soc. - Address unknown since 2010.
Tech. Without Borders [7532], PO Box 445, The Plains, VA 20198, (703)220-7327
Technonet Asia [IO], Singapore
TechnoServe [17923], 1120 19th St. NW, 8th Fl., South Tower, Washington, DC 20036, (202)785-4515
TechnoServe [17923], 1120 19th St. NW, 8th Fl., South Tower, Washington, DC 20036, (202)785-4515
TechnoServe - Tanzania [IO], Dar es Salaam, United Republic of Tanzania
TechServe Alliance [868], 1420 King St., Ste. 610, Alexandria, VA 22314, (703)838-2050
TechSoup [7533], 435 Brannan St., Ste. 100, San Francisco, CA 94107, (415)633-9300
Tee it up for the Troops [13355], 2422 E 117th St., No. 102, Burnsville, MN 55337, (952)646-2490
Teen-Age Assembly of America - Defunct.
Teen Assn. of Model Railroaders [21893], 3645 Toronto Ct., Indianapolis, IN 46268
Teen Assn. of Model Railroading [★21893]
Teen Challenge Intl. [20308], 5250 N Towne Centre Dr., Ozark, MO 65721, (417)581-2181
Teen Challenge Intl. [20308], 5250 N Towne Centre Dr., Ozark, MO 65721, (417)581-2181
Teen Challenge Intl., USA [★20308]
Teen Challenge Intl., USA [★20308]
Teen Challenge Natl. [★20308]
Teen Challenge Natl. [★20308]
Teen Challenge World Wide Network [★20308]
Teen Challenge World Wide Network [★20308]
Teen Mission [★20099]
Teen Mission [★20099]
Teen Missions Intl. [20099], 885 E Hall Rd., Merritt Island, FL 32953, (321)453-0350
Teen Missions Intl. [20099], 885 E Hall Rd., Merritt Island, FL 32953, (321)453-0350
Teens Fighting Hunger [12295], 3 Monroe Pkwy., Ste. P, Lake Oswego, OR 97035, (971)285-5588
Teens Teaching AIDS Prevention - Defunct.
Teeth In the Neck Gang [★9408]

A star before a book entry number signifies that the name is not listed separately, but is mentioned within the entry.

Reference to "IO" in place of a book number signifies that the association may be found in the 50th edition of International Organizations.

Tenant Farmers Assn. [IO], Reading, United Kingdom

Tenant-in-Common Assn. [★1785]

Tenant Participation Advisory Ser. [IO], Manchester, United Kingdom

Tenants Advice Ser. [IO], East Perth, Australia

Tenants Org. of Denmark [IO], Copenhagen, Denmark

Tenants Org. - Norway [IO], Oslo, Norway

Tenants and Residents Org. of England [IO], Runcorn, United Kingdom

Tenants Union of New South Wales [IO], Surry Hills, Australia

Tenants Union of Queensland [IO], Fortitude Valley, Australia

Tenants Union of Victoria [IO], Fitzroy, Australia

Teniska Zveza Slovenije [★IO]

Tennessee Assn. of Economics Educators - Defunct.

Tennessee Folklore Soc. [9627], 1538 Laurel Ave., Knoxville, TN 37916-2016

Tennessee Regulatory Authority [6056], 460 James Robertson Pkwy., Nashville, TN 37243-0505, (615)741-2904

Tennessee Walking Horse Breeders' Assn. of Am. [★4652]

Tennessee Walking Horse Breeders' Assn. of Am. [★4652]

Tennessee Walking Horse Breeders' and Exhibitors' Assn. [4652], PO Box 286, Lewisburg, TN 37091, (931)359-1574

Tennessee Walking Horse Breeders' and Exhibitors' Assn. [4652], PO Box 286, Lewisburg, TN 37091, (931)359-1574

Tennis

Amer. Medical Tennis Assn. [23051]

Amer. Platform Tennis Assn. [23052]

Amer. Tennis Assn. [23053]

Gay and Lesbian Tennis Alliance [23054]

Gay and Lesbian Tennis Alliance [23054]

InterCollegiate Tennis Assn. [23055]

Intl. Tennis Hall of Fame [23056]

Intl. Tennis Hall of Fame [23056]

Natl. Public Parks Tennis Assn. [23057]

Natl. Senior Women's Tennis Assn. [23058]

Peter Burwash Intl. Special Tennis Programs [23059]

Peter Burwash Intl. Special Tennis Programs [23059]

Professional Tennis Registry [23060]

Sony Ericsson WTA Tour [23061]

Sony Ericsson WTA Tour [23061]

U.S. Dental Tennis Assn. [23062]

U.S. Natl. Tennis Acad. [23063]

U.S. Professional Tennis Assn. [23064]

U.S. Professional Tennis Assn. [23064]

U.S. Tennis Assn. [23065]

USA Professional Platform Tennis Assn. [23066]

U.S.A. Tennis | NJTL [23067]

WTA Tour Players Assn. [23068]

Tennis Assn. of Austria [IO], Vosendorf, Austria

Tennis Assn. of Bosnia and Herzegovina [IO], Sarajevo, Bosnia-Hercegovina

Tennis Assn. of Democratic People's Republic of Korea [IO], Pyongyang, Democratic People's Republic of Korea

Tennis Assn. of the Maldives [IO], Male, Maldives

Tennis Canada [IO], Toronto, ON, Canada

Tennis Cook Islands [IO], Rarotonga, Cook Islands

Tennis Educational Found. [★23056]

Tennis Educational Found. [★23056]

Tennis Fed. of the Cayman Islands [IO], George Town, Cayman Islands

Tennis Fed. of Islamic Republic of Iran [IO], Tehran, Iran

Tennis Fed. of Myanmar [IO], Yangon, Myanmar

Tennis Found. of North Am. [★3319]

Tennis Indus. Assn. [3319], 117 Executive Center, 1 Corpus Christie Pl., Hilton Head Island, SC 29928, (843)686-3036

Tennis Ireland [IO], Dublin, Ireland

Tennis Jamaica [IO], Kingston, Jamaica

Tennis Mfrs. Assn. [★3319]

Tennis Samoa [IO], Apia, Western Samoa

Tennis Scotland [IO], Edinburgh, United Kingdom

Tennis Wales [IO], Cardiff, United Kingdom

Tennis Zimbabwe [IO], Harare, Zimbabwe

Tennissamband Island [★IO]

Tennyson Soc. [IO], Lincoln, United Kingdom

Tenovus Scotland [IO], Glasgow, United Kingdom

Teollisuustaiteen Liitto Ornamo [★IO]

Teratology Info. Services; Org. of [13846]

Teratology Soc. [6321], 1821 Michael Faraday Dr., Ste. 300, Reston, VA 20190, (703)438-3104

Teratology Soc; Neurobehavioral [15626]

Terminal Elevator Grain Assn. [★1596]

Terminal Grain - Defunct.

Terminal Railroad Assn. Historical and Tech. Soc. [10501], PO Box 1688, St. Louis, MO 63188-1688, (314)535-3101

Terminally III

Sacred Dying Found. [11747]

TERRA - Rsrc. Development Intl. [12963], 1617 Hillcrest Dr., Laguna Beach, CA 92651, (949)680-7850

TERRA - Rsrc. Development Intl. [12963], 1617 Hillcrest Dr., Laguna Beach, CA 92651, (949)680-7850

Terra Segura Intl. [17559], 1219 23rd St., San Diego, CA 92102, (619)546-0748

Terrazzo Tile and Marble Assn. of Canada [IO], Concord, ON, Canada

terre des homes Deutschland e.V. [★IO]

Terre des Femmes [★IO]

Terre des Hommes [IO], Basel, Switzerland

Terre des Hommes Germany [IO], Osnabruck, Germany

Terre des Hommes Germany - India [IO], Pune, India

Terre des Hommes Intl. Fed. [IO], Geneva, Switzerland

Terror Free Tomorrow [18720], PO Box 5704, Washington, DC 20016, (202)274-1800

Terror Free Tomorrow [18720], PO Box 5704, Washington, DC 20016, (202)274-1800

Terrorism

9/11 Families for a Secure Am. Found. [18710]

Amer. Soc. for the Support of Injured Survivors of Terrorism [13359]

Citizens to Stop Nuclear Terrorism [18711]

Coalition to Insure Against Terrorism [1949]

Families of September 11 [18712]

Fuel for Truth [18608]

Hearts and Minds Network [18713]

Intl. Assn. for Counterterrorism and Security Professionals [18714]

Intl. Assn. for Counterterrorism and Security Professionals [18714]

Intl. Counter-Terrorism Officers Assn. [18715]

Intl. Counter-Terrorism Officers Assn. [18715]

Move Am. Forward [18716]

My Good Deed [13310]

Natl. Memorial Inst. for the Prevention of Terrorism [18717]

NAVAH [13311]

Prevent Nuclear Terrorism Org. [18718]

Psychology Beyond Borders [11860]

September 11 Digital Archv. [18719]

September's Mission [13312]

Soc. for Terrorism Res. [7554]

Terror Free Tomorrow [18720]

Terror Free Tomorrow [18720]

United Against Nuclear Iran [18218]

Voices of September 11th [18721]

Win Without War [18178]

World Trade Center Survivors' Network [13313]

WTC Families For Proper Burial [13314]

Terry Fox Found. [IO], Chilliwack, BC, Canada

Tertiary Capuchins of Our Lady of Sorrows [IO], Rome, Italy

Tesla Coil Builders Assn. - Defunct.

Tesla Engine Builders Assn. [627], 5464 N Port Washington Rd., No. 293, Milwaukee, WI 53217-4925

Tesla Memorial Soc. [10692], William H. Terbo, Exec. Sec., Southwyck Village, 21 Maddaket, Scotch Plains, NJ 07076-3136, (732)396-8852

Tesla Memorial Soc. [10692], William H. Terbo, Exec. Sec., Southwyck Village, 21 Maddaket, Scotch Plains, NJ 07076-3136, (732)396-8852

Testing

ACT [8982]

Amer. Soc. for Nondestructive Testing [7555]

Amer. Soc. of Test Engineers [7556]

Anti-Malware Testing Standards Org. [6478]

Assn. for Assessment in Counseling and Educ. [8983]

ASTM Intl. [7557]TestingCanadian Testing Assn. The Coll. Bd. [8984]

Controlled Env. Testing Assn. [7558]

Educational Records Bur. [8985]

Educational Records Bur. [8985]

Educational Testing Ser. [8986]

Graduate Record Examinations Bd. [8987]

Intl. Air Filtration Certifiers Assn. [1705]

Intl. Soc. for Performance Improvement [8988]

Intl. Soc. for Performance Improvement [8988]

Intl. Test and Evaluation Assn. [7559]

Intl. Test and Evaluation Assn. [7559]

Natl. Assessment of Educational Progress [8989]

Natl. Assn. for Proficiency Testing [7560]

Natl. Assn. of Test Directors [8990]

Natl. Center for Fair and Open Testing [8991]

Natl. Coun. on Measurement in Educ. [8992]

Natl. Fair Access Coalition on Testing [7561]

Secondary School Admission Test Bd. [8993]

VXIbus Consortium [7562]

Teton Club Intl. [21888], 3700 S Westport Ave., No. 2590, Sioux Falls, SD 57106-6360

Teton Club Intl. [21888], 3700 S Westport Ave., No. 2590, Sioux Falls, SD 57106-6360

Tex Ritter Fan Club

Tex Ritter Fan Club - Address unknown since 2010.

Texans for Educational Excellence [★7769]

Texans for Educational Excellence [★7769]

Texas A&M Univ. - Commerce Alumni Assn. [18901], PO Box 3011, Commerce, TX 75429-3011, (903)886-5765

Texas Date Nail Collectors Assn. - Address unknown since 2010.

Texas Independent Producers and Royalty Owners Assn. [2672], 919 Cong. Ave., Ste. 1000, Austin, TX 78701, (512)477-4452

Texas Intl. Theatrical Arts Soc. [10604], 3625 N Hall St., Ste. 740, Dallas, TX 75219, (214)528-6112

Texas Intl. Theatrical Arts Soc. [10604], 3625 N Hall St., Ste. 740, Dallas, TX 75219, (214)528-6112

Texas Longhorn Breeders Assn. of Am. [3941], 2315 N Main St., Ste. 402, PO Box 4430, Fort Worth, TX 76164, (817)625-6241

Text and Academic Authors Assn. [10744], PO Box 56359, St. Petersburg, FL 33732-6359, (727)563-0020

Textbook Authors Assn. [★10744]

Textbooks

Amer. Textbook Coun. [8994]

Educational Res. Analysts [8995]

Natl. Assn. of State Textbook Administrators [8996]

PALTEX - Expanded Textbook and Instructional Materials Prog. [8997]

Used Textbook Assn. [8998]

Textile Bag Mfrs. Assn. - Defunct.

Textile Bag and Packaging Assn. [893], 3000 Royal Marco Way PH-N, Marco Island, FL 34145, (616)481-4739

Textile Bag Processors Assn. [★893]

Textile Care Allied Trades Assn. [2194], 271 Rte. 46 W, No. D203, Fairfield, NJ 07004, (973)244-1790

Textile Clothing and Footwear Union of Australia [IO], Carlton South, Australia

Textile Coun. of Hong Kong [IO], Hong Kong, People's Republic of China

Textile Exchange [4763], 822 Baldridge St., O'Donnell, TX 79351, (806)428-3411

Textile and Fashion Fed. Singapore [IO], Singapore, Singapore

Textile Fed. [IO], Bruma, Republic of South Africa

Textile Fibers and By-Products Assn. [3459], 1531 Indus. Dr., Griffin, GA 30224, (770)412-2325

Textile Importers' Assn. in Sweden [IO], Stockholm, Sweden

Textile Inst. [IO], Manchester, United Kingdom

Textile Laundry Coun. - Defunct.

Textile Machinery Assn. [IO], Frankfurt, Germany

Textile Machinery Assn. of Sweden [IO], Stockholm, Sweden

A star before a book entry number signifies that the name is not listed separately, but is mentioned within the entry.

Textile Recycling Assn. [IO], Maidstone, United
Kingdom
Textile Rental Services Assn. of Am. [3083], 1800
Diagonal Rd., Ste. 200, Alexandria, VA 22314,
(703)519-0029
Textile Res. Inst. [★3461]
Textile Res. Inst. [★3461]
Textile Services Assn. [IO], London, United Kingdom
Textile Soc. of Am. [3460], PO Box 193, Middletown,
DE 19709, (302)378-9636
Textile Soc. of Am. [3460], PO Box 193, Middletown,
DE 19709, (302)378-9636
Textile Soc. for the Stud. of Art, Design and History
[IO], St. Albans, United Kingdom
Textile Waste Assn. [★3459]
Textile Waste Exchange [★3459]
Textiles
Amer. Assn. of Textile Chemists and Colorists
[7563]
Amer. Assn. of Textile Chemists and Colorists
[7563]
Amer. Fiber Mfrs. Assn. [3432]
Amer. Flock Assn. [3433]
Amer. Reusable Textile Assn. [3434]
Amer. Wool Coun. [3435]
Amer. Yarn Spinners Assn. [3436]
Assn. for Contract Textiles [3437]
Brazilian Assn. of the Nonwoven and Tech.
Textiles Indus. [15944]
Brazilian Dimensional Embroidery Intl. Guild
[22164]
Brazilian Dimensional Embroidery Intl. Guild
[22164]
Brazilian Textile and Apparel Indus. Assn. [18938]
Bus. Alliance for Commerce in Hemp [18323]
Cashmere and Camel Hair Mfrs. Inst. [3438]
Chilean Textile Inst. [1790]
Colonial Coverlet Guild of Am. [21326]
Costa Rican Textile Chamber [14793]
Craft Retailers Assn. for Tomorrow [987]
Embroidery Trade Assn. [3439]
Fabric Shop Network [3440]
Fed. of Argentine Textile Indus. [1064]
Geosynthetics Materials Assn. [6426]
Healthcare Laundry Accreditation Coun. [2192]
Hemp Indus. Assn. [3441]
Hemp Indus. Assn. [3441]
INDA, Assn. of the Nonwoven Fabrics Indus.
[3442]
Independent Textile Rental Assn. [3443]
Independent Textile Rental Assn. [3443]
Indus. Fabrics Assn. Intl. [3444]
Indus. Fabrics Assn. Intl. [3444]
Intl. Textile and Apparel Assn. [3445]
Intl. Textile and Apparel Assn. [3445]
Intl. Textile Market Assn. [3446]
Narrow Fabrics Inst. [3447]
Narrow Fabrics Inst. [3447]
Natl. Assn. of Decorative Fabric Distributors
[3448]
Natl. Coun. of Textile Organizations [3449]
The Natl. Needle Arts Assn. [3450]
Natl. Textile Assn. [3451]
Natl. Textile, l Wool Mfrs. Coun. [3452]
Schiffli Embroidery Mfrs. Promotion Fund [3453]
Schiffli Lace and Embroidery Mfrs. Assn. [3454]
Southern Textile Assn. [3455]
Spinning and Weaving Assn. [3456]
Surface Design Assn. [3457]
Synthetic Yarn and Fiber Assn. [3458]
Textile Fibers and By-Products Assn. [3459]
Textile Soc. of Am. [3460]
Textile Soc. of Am. [3460]
TRI/Princeton [3461]
TRI/Princeton [3461]
U.S. Assn. of Importers of Textiles and Apparel
[3462]
U.S. Indus. Fabrics Inst. [3463]
Textilimportoererna [★IO]
Textilipari Muszaki es Tudomanyos Egyesulet [★IO]
Textured Yarn Assn. of Am. [★3458]
Tezkoatletska Zveza Slovenije [★IO]
T.G. Sheppard Intl. Fan Club [23894], 5123 Secor
Rd., No. 6, Toledo, OH 43623-2326
Thai
Assn. of Thai Professionals in Am. and Canada
[19255]

Karen Natl. League [18722]
Soc. for Thai Philately [22079]
Thai U.S.A. Assn. [19256]
U.S. Muay Thai Assn. [22761]
Thai Assn. of Conf. Interpreters [IO], Bangkok,
Thailand
Thai Assn. of Orthodontists [IO], Bangkok, Thailand
Thai Assn. for the Stud. of Pain [IO], Bangkok,
Thailand
Thai Assn. of Univ. Women [IO], Bangkok, Thailand
Thai Bankers' Assn. [IO], Bangkok, Thailand
Thai Chamber of Commerce [IO], Bangkok, Thailand
Thai Coffee Exporters Assn. [IO], Bangkok, Thailand
Thai Cosmetic Mfrs. Assn. [IO], Bangkok, Thailand
Thai Entertainment Content Trade Assn. [IO],
Bangkok, Thailand
Thai Food Processors' Assn. [IO], Bangkok,
Thailand
Thai Frozen Foods Assn. [IO], Bangkok, Thailand
Thai Furniture Indus. Assn. [IO], Bangkok, Thailand
Thai Garment Mfrs. Assn. [IO], Bangkok, Thailand
Thai Gem and Jewelry Traders' Assn. [IO], Bangkok,
Thailand
Thai Healing Alliance Intl. [15275], PO Box 16247,
Chapel Hill, NC 27516
Thai Hypertension League [IO], Bangkok, Thailand
Thai Indus. Standards Inst. [IO], Bangkok, Thailand
Thai Insurance Brokers' Assn. [IO], Bangkok,
Thailand
Thai Jet Sports Boating Assn. [IO], Bangkok,
Thailand
Thai Life Assurance Assn. [IO], Bangkok, Thailand
Thai Natl. Shippers' Coun. [IO], Bangkok, Thailand
Thai Packaging Assn. [IO], Bangkok, Thailand
Thai Physicians Assn. of Am. [16274], PO Box 208,
Bethalto, IL 62010, (618)463-0317
Thai Population Assn. [IO], Nakhon Pathom,
Thailand
Thai Red Cross Soc. [IO], Bangkok, Thailand
Thai Silk Assn. [IO], Bangkok, Thailand
Thai Soc. of Clinical Neurophysiology [IO], Bangkok,
Thailand
Thai Soc. for the Prevention of Cruelty to Animals
[IO], Bangkok, Thailand
Thai Spa Assn. [IO], Bangkok, Thailand
Thai Spa Operators Assn. [IO], Bangkok, Thailand
Thai Synthetic Fiber Mfrs'. Assn. [IO], Bangkok,
Thailand
Thai Tapioca Trade Assn. [IO], Bangkok, Thailand
Thai Textile Mfg. Assn. [IO], Bangkok, Thailand
Thai U.S.A. Assn. [19256], 628 10th Ave., New York,
NY 10036, (212)245-4660
Thai Vacation Ownership Assn. [IO], Bangkok,
Thailand
Thai Venture Capital Assn. [IO], Bangkok, Thailand
Thai Weaving Indus. Assn. [IO], Bangkok, Thailand
Thai Youth Hostels Assn. [IO], Bangkok, Thailand
Thailand
Assn. of Thai Professionals in Am. and Canada
[19255]
Serendib [11629]
Soc. for Thai Philately [22079]
Thai U.S.A. Assn. [19256]
U.S. Muay Thai Assn. [22761]
Thailand Bus. Coun. for Sustainable Development
[IO], Nonthaburi, Thailand
Thailand Chap. of the ACM [IO], Bang Sao Thong,
Thailand
Thailand Chap. of the Internet Soc. [IO], Samut Pra-
kan, Thailand
Thailand Dance Sport Assn. [IO], Bangkok, Thailand
Thailand Golf Assn. [IO], Bangkok, Thailand
Thailand Incentive and Convention Assn. [IO],
Bangkok, Thailand
Thailand Squash Rackets Assn. [IO], Bangkok,
Thailand
Thailand Textile Inst. [IO], Bangkok, Thailand
Thalassaemia Fed. of Pakistan [IO], Lahore,
Pakistan
Thalassaemia Soc. of Pakistan [IO], Lahore,
Pakistan
Thalidomide Soc. [IO], Hitchin, United Kingdom
Thames Valley Chamber of Commerce [IO], Slough,
United Kingdom
ThanaCAP [★17459]

Thanatology
Americans for Better Care of the Dying [13315]
Living/Dying Proj. [13316]
William Wendt Center for Loss and Healing
[13317]
Thanet and East Kent Chamber [IO], Broadstairs,
United Kingdom
Thanet and East Kent Chamber of Commerce
[★18899]
Thanks-Giving Found. [18670], PO Box 131770,
Dallas, TX 75313-1770, (214)969-1977
Thanks-Giving Found. [18670], PO Box 131770,
Dallas, TX 75313-1770, (214)969-1977
Thanks-Giving Square [20257], PO Box 131770,
Dallas, TX 75313-1770, (214)969-1977
Thanks-Giving Square [20257], PO Box 131770,
Dallas, TX 75313-1770, (214)969-1977
Thanks to Scandinavia [8195], 165 E 56th St., New
York, NY 10022, (212)891-1403
Thanks to Scandinavia [8195], 165 E 56th St., New
York, NY 10022, (212)891-1403
THE NETWORK [★9054]
Theater
Amer. Soc. for Aesthetics [9270]
Amer. Theatre Arts for Youth [10566]
Drama Desk [10573]
O'Neill Critics Inst. [10596]
Outer Critics Circle [10597]
University/Resident Theatre Assn. [9005]
Theater of Dreams [IO], Culemborg, Netherlands
Theater Workshop Boston [★9310]
Theatre
Alliance for Inclusion in the Arts [10559]
Alliance of Resident Theatres/New York [10560]
Amer. Alliance for Theatre and Educ. [10561]
Amer. Assn. of Community Theatre [10562]
Amer. Conservatory Theater Found. [10563]
Amer. Russian Theatrical Alliance [10564]
Amer. Soc. for Theatre Res. [10565]
Amer. Theatre Arts for Youth [10566]
Amer. Theatre Critics Assn. [10567]
Amer. Theatre and Drama Soc. [10568]
Amer. Theatre and Drama Soc. [10568]
Assn. for Theatre in Higher Educ. [8999]
Assn. of Theatre Movement Educators [9000]
Assn. of Theatre Movement Educators [9000]
Audience Development Comm. [10569]
Bilingual Found. of the Arts [10570]
Black Theatre Network [10571]
Broadway League [10572]
Drama Desk [10573]
Drama League [10574]
Dramatists Guild of Am. [10575]
Educational Theatre Assn. [9001]
Episcopal Actors' Guild of Am. [10576]
Eugene O'Neill Memorial Theater Center [10577]
Ford's Theatre Soc. [10578]
Friars Club [10579]
Hosp. Audiences [10580]
Inst. of Outdoor Drama [10581]
Jack Point Preservation Soc. [9501]
The Lambs [10582]
League of Historic Amer. Theatres [10583]
League of Resident Theatres [10584]
Literary Managers and Dramaturgs of the
Americas [10585]
The Masquers [10586]
Natl. Assn. of Dramatic and Speech Arts [10587]
Natl. Assn. of Schools of Theatre [9002]
Natl. Corporate Theatre Fund [10588]
Natl. Music Theater Network [10589]
Natl. New Play Network [10590]
Natl. Performance Network [10591]
Natl. Theatre Conf. [10592]
Natl. Theatre Workshop of the Handicapped
[10593]
New Dramatists [10594]
New England Theatre Conf. [10595]
O'Neill Critics Inst. [10596]
O'Neill Natl. Theater Inst. [9003]
Outer Critics Circle [10597]
The Players [10598]
Puerto Rican Traveling Theatre Company [10599]
Rites and Reason Theatre [10600]
Shakespeare Theatre Assn. of Am. [10601]

Reference to "IO" in place of a book number signifies that the association may be found in the 50th edition of International Organizations.

Soc. of Amer. Fight Directors [9004]
Southeastern Theatre Conf. [10602]
Stage Directors and Choreographers Found.
[10603]
Texas Intl. Theatrical Arts Soc. [10604]
Texas Intl. Theatrical Arts Soc. [10604]
Theatre Communications Gp. [10605]
Theatre Development Fund [10606]
Theatre Historical Soc. of Am. [10607]
Theatre for Young Audiences USA [10608]
U.S. Inst. for Theatre Tech. [10609]
University/Resident Theatre Assn. [9005]
Ziegfeld Club [10610]
Theatre Alliance; Intl. Museum
Theatre Comm. for Eugene O'Neill - Defunct.
Theatre Communications Gp. [10605], 520 8th Ave.,
24th Fl., New York, NY 10018-4156, (212)609-
5900
Theatre Development Fund [10606], 520 8th Ave.,
Ste. 801, New York, NY 10018-6507, (212)912-
9770
Theatre Education Assn. - Defunct.
Theatre in Education - Defunct.
Theatre Equip. Assn. [★1260]
Theatre Equip. Assn. [★1260]
Theatre Historical Soc. of Am. [10607], York Theatre
Bldg., 152 N York, 2nd Fl., Elmhurst, IL 60126-
2806, (630)782-1800
Theatre Inst. [IO], Prague, Czech Republic
Theatre Lib. Assn. [10015], The New York Public
Lib. for the Performing Arts, 40 Lincoln Center Plz.,
New York, NY 10023
Theatre Organ Soc. Intl. [10304], PO Box 251,
O'Fallon, IL 62269, (618)632-8455
Theatre Owners of Am. [★1209]
Theatre Recording Soc. - Defunct.
Theatre for Young Audiences USA [10608], Theatre
School at DePaul Univ., 2135 N Kenmore Ave.,
Chicago, IL 60614, (773)325-7981
Theatrical, Literary and Audiovisual Agency [IO],
Prague, Czech Republic
Themed Entertainment Assn. [1218], 150 E Olive
Ave., Ste. 306, Burbank, CA 91502, (818)843-8497
Themed Entertainment Assn. [1218], 150 E Olive
Ave., Ste. 306, Burbank, CA 91502, (818)843-8497
TheNetwork for Consumer Protection [IO], Islama-
bad, Pakistan
THEO BC [IO], Vancouver, BC, Canada
Theodore Roosevelt Assn. [10693], PO Box 719,
Oyster Bay, NY 11771, (516)921-6319
Theodore Roosevelt Conservation Partnership
[4150], 1660 L St. NW, Ste. 208, Washington, DC
20036, (202)639-8727
Theology
Acad. of Homiletics [19814]
Arthur Vining Davis Foundations [11902]
ASGM [19339]
Asociacion para la Educacion Teologica Hispana
[9006]
Assn. of Theological Schools in the U.S. and
Canada [9007]
Assn. of Theological Schools in the U.S. and
Canada [9007]
Boston Theological Inst. [9008]
Caribbean Assn. of Theological Schools [5527]
Catholic Biblical Assn. of Am. [9009]
Chatlos Found. [20263]
Chatlos Found. [20263]
Christian Universalist Assn. [19560]
Coll. Theology Soc. [9010]
Coun. of Societies for the Stud. of Religion [9011]
The Gospel Coalition [19576]
Interdisciplinary Biblical Res. Inst. [19677]
Intl. Assn. of Baptist Colleges and Universities
[9012]
Intl. Org. for Septuagint and Cognate Stud.
[19349]
Jews for Judaism [20186]
Natl. Assn. of Baptist Professors of Religion
[9013]
Soc. for the Stud. of Christian Spirituality [19601]
Westar Inst. [20198]
Theology; Found. for Christian [19708]
Theology; Found. for Christian [19708]
Theorie et Culture Existentialiste et Phenom-
enologiques [★IO]

Theosophical
Theosophical Book Assn. for the Blind [20264]
Theosophical Soc. in Am. [20265]
United Lodge of Theosophists [20266]
United Lodge of Theosophists [20266]
Theosophical Book Assn. for the Blind [20264], 54
Krotona Hill, Ojai, CA 93023, (805)614-4977
Theosophical Publishing House [★20265]
Theosophical Soc. [IO], Chennai, India
Theosophical Soc. in Am. [20265], PO Box 270,
Wheaton, IL 60187-0270, (630)668-1571
Theosophical Soc. in England [IO], London, United
Kingdom
Therapet Animal Assisted Therapy Found. [16874],
PO Box 130118, Tyler, TX 75713-0118
Therapeutic Communities of Am. [★13290]
Therapeutic Touch Intl. Assn. [15003], PO Box 419,
Craryville, NY 12521, (518)325-1185
Therapy
Adventures in Movement for the Handicapped
[16830]
Alliance for Addiction Solutions [15561]
Alliance for Biotherapies [16831]
Alliance for Massage Therapy Educ. [8560]
Amer. Acad. of Hea. Physics [16832]
Amer. Acad. of Orthopaedic Manual Physical
Therapists [16833]
Amer. Assn. for Respiratory Care [16834]
Amer. Commn. for Accreditation of Reflexology
Educ. and Training [7726]
Amer. Hippotherapy Assn. [16835]
Amer. Hippotherapy Assn. [16835]
Amer. Horticultural Therapy Assn. [16836]
Amer. Occupational Therapy Assn. [16837]
Amer. Physical Therapy Assn. [16838]
Amer. Physical Therapy Assn., Orthopaedic Sect.
[16839]
American Physical Therapy Assn., Private
Practice Sect. [16840]
Aromatherapy Registration Coun. [13663]
Art Therapy Connection [13772]
Assn. for Advanced Training in the Behavioral Sci-
ences [8761]
Assn. for Applied and Therapeutic Humor [16841]
Assn. of Pediatric Therapists [16842]
Assn. for Play Therapy [16843]
Assn. of Therapeutic Communities [15286]
Biomagnetic Therapy Assn. [16844]
Comm. on Accreditation for Respiratory Care
[16845]
Create A Smile Dental Found. [13318]
Creative Children Therapy [16846]
Delta Soc. [16847]
Disabled Drummers Assn. [11780]
Divine Canines [16848]
Emergency Response Massage Intl. [15266]
Family Therapy Sect. of the Natl. Coun. on Family
Relations [16849]
Found. for Physical Therapy [16850]
Global Initiative for the Advancement of Nutritional
Therapy [16851]
Global Initiative for the Advancement of Nutritional
Therapy [16851]
HALTER, Inc. [16852]
Infusion Nurses Soc. [16853]
Intl. Alliance of Professional Hypnotists [15089]
Intl. Assn. of Human-Animal Interaction Organiza-
tions [16854]
Intl. Assn. of Human-Animal Interaction Organiza-
tions [16854]
Intl. Assn. of Medical and Therapeutic Specialists
[13686]
Intl. Assn. for Regression Res. and Therapies
[16855]
Intl. Bd. for Regression Therapy [16856]
Intl. Bd. for Regression Therapy [16856]
Intl. Cellular Medicine Soc. [14649]
Intl. ECP Therapists Assn. [16857]
Intl. EECP Therapists Assn. [16857]
Intl. Inst. of Reflexology [16858]
Intl. Inst. of Reflexology [16858]
Intl. Palmtherapy Assn. [16859]
Intl. Palmtherapy Assn. [16859]
Intl. Soc. for Ayurveda and Hea. [13691]
Island Dolphin Care [11797]

Kate's Voice [8764]
Laughter Therapy [16860]
Love on a Leash - The Found. for Pet Provided
Therapy [16861]
Medical Spa Soc. [14902]
Music Therapy for Healing [16467]
Natl. Anger Mgt. Assn. [15465]
Natl. Assn. of Certified Professionals of Equine
Therapy [13694]
Natl. Assn. of Myofascial Trigger Point Therapists
[16862]
Natl. Bd. for Certification in Occupational Therapy
[16863]
Natl. Bd. for Respiratory Care [16864]
Natl. Coun. for Therapeutic Recreation Certifica-
tion [16865]
North Amer. Assn. for Laser Therapy [15238]
Oligonucleotide Therapeutics Soc. [16866]
Option Inst. Intl. Learning and Training Center
[16867]
Option Inst. Intl. Learning and Training Center
[16867]
People-Animals-Love [16868]
Proj. Magic [16869]
Rock Against Cancer [13975]
Sandplay Therapists of Am. [16870]
Sandtray Network [16361]
Shine Therapy [15274]
Sigmund Freud Archives [16362]
Sino-American Network for Therapeutic Radiology
and Oncology [16871]
Soc. for Light Treatment and Biological Rhythms
[16872]
Soc. for Light Treatment and Biological Rhythms
[16872]
Soc. of Sports Therapists [907]
Soul Friends [16873]
Spa Assn. [3127]
Therapet Animal Assisted Therapy Found. [16874]
Therapy Dogs Intl. [16875]
Therapy Dogs Intl. [16875]
Touch of Relief [15004]
World Fed. of Therapeutic Communities [13719]
Therapy Dogs Intl. [16875], 88 Bartley Rd.,
Flanders, NJ 07836, (973)252-9800
Therapy Dogs Intl. [16875], 88 Bartley Rd.,
Flanders, NJ 07836, (973)252-9800
Theriogenology; Soc. for [17039]
Thermal Analysis
North Amer. Thermal Anal. Soc. [7564]
Soc. for Thermal Medicine [16876]
Thermal Insulation Contractors Assn. [IO], Darling-
ton, United Kingdom
Thermal Insulation Mfrs. Assn. - Defunct.
Thermal Insulation Mfrs. and Suppliers Assn. [IO],
Bordon, United Kingdom
Thermal and Nuclear Power Engg. Soc. [IO], Tokyo,
Japan
Thermal Spraying and Surface Engg. Assn. [IO],
Rugby, United Kingdom
Thermology
Intl. Assn. of Certified Thermographers [7565]
Thermoplastic Exterior Building Division of the Soc.
of the Plastics Indus. [★633]
Thermoplastic Pipe Division of the Soc. of the
Plastics Indus. [★2757]
Thermoset Resin Formulators Assn. [794], 800
Roosevelt Rd., Bldg. C, Ste. 312, Glen Ellyn, IL
60137, (630)942-6596
Theta Chi Fraternity [23704], 3330 Founders Rd.,
Indianapolis, IN 46268-1333, (317)824-1881
Theta Chi Omega Multicultural Sorority [23750], PO
Box 190837, Arlington, TX 76019, (817)272-2293
Theta Delta Chi [23705], 214 Lewis Wharf, Boston,
MA 02110, (800)999-1847
Theta Delta Chi [23705], 214 Lewis Wharf, Boston,
MA 02110, (800)999-1847
Theta Delta Chi Educational Found. [★23705]
Theta Delta Chi Educational Found. [★23705]
Theta Delta Chi Founder's Corporation [★23705]
Theta Delta Chi Founder's Corporation [★23705]
Theta Kappa Nu [★23567]
Theta Kappa Nu [★23676]
Theta Kappa Phi [★23682]
Theta Nu Xi Multicultural Sorority [23751], Rashida
Rawls, Dir. of Communications, PO Box 32987,
Phoenix, AZ 85064

A star before a book entry number signifies that the name is not listed separately, but is mentioned within the entry.

Theta Phi Alpha [23735], 27025 Knickerbocker Rd., Bay Village, OH 44140-2300, (440)899-9282

Theta Rho Girls' Club [13561], 422 Trade St., Winston-Salem, NC 27101-2830, (336)725-5955

Theta Sigma Phi [★806]

Theta Tau [23526], 1011 San Jacinto, Ste. 205, Austin, TX 78701, (512)472-1904

Theta Upsilon [★23723]

Theta Xi [23706], PO Box 411134, St. Louis, MO 63141-3134, (314)993-6294

Thimble Collectors Intl. [21408], 1209 Hill Rd. N, No. 253, Pickerington, OH 43147

Think First Found.: Natl. Injury Prevention Programs [★16707]

Think Pink Qatar [IO], Doha, Qatar

ThinkFirst Natl. Injury Prevention Found. [16707], 1801 N Mill St., Ste. F, Naperville, IL 60563, (630)961-1400

ThinkImpact [12373], 1755 S St. NW, Ste. 6A, Washington, DC 20009, (202)657-6616

thinkLA [109], 4223 Glencoe Ave., Ste. C-100, Marina del Rey, CA 90292, (310)823-7320

ThinkTwice Global Vaccine Inst. [15113], PO Box 9638, Santa Fe, NM 87504, (505)983-1856

Third Class Mail Assn. [★2232]

Third Generation [17430], Heritage Found., 214 Massachusetts Ave. NE, Washington, DC 20002-4999, (202)546-4400

Third Order of Carmel [IO], Rome, Italy

Third Order Carmelites [★19441]

Third World

Flying Doctors of Am. [12454]

Small World Found. [16820]

Strategies for Intl. Development [12372]

Uncharted Intl. [12377]

Third World Conf. Found. [17924], 1507 E 53rd St., Ste. 305, Chicago, IL 60615-4575, (773)241-6688

Third World Conf. Found. [17924], 1507 E 53rd St., Ste. 305, Chicago, IL 60615-4575, (773)241-6688

Third World Network - Malaysia [IO], Penang, Malaysia

Third World Org. for Women in Sci. [IO], Trieste, Italy

Thirst Relief Intl. [13432], PO Box 436, Lewis Center, OH 43035-0436, (614)529-8335

Thirst Relief Intl. [13432], PO Box 436, Lewis Center, OH 43035-0436, (614)529-8335

This Life Cambodia [IO], Siem Reap, Cambodia

Thistle Class Assn. [22397], Patty Lawrence, Sec.-Treas., 6758 Little River Ln., Loveland, OH 45140, (513)583-5080

Thomas A. Dooley Found. [★15190]

Thomas A. Dooley Found. [★15190]

Thomas A. Dooley Foundation/INTERMED U.S.A. [★15190]

Thomas A. Dooley Foundation/INTERMED U.S.A. [★15190]

Thomas B. Fordham Found. [11911], 1016 16th St. NW, 8th Fl., Washington, DC 20036, (202)223-5452

Thomas Blair Family Org. - Defunct.

Thomas Borland Family Org. - Defunct.

Thomas Guthrie Family Org. - Defunct.

The Thomas Hardy Assn. [9415], Rosemarie Morgan, Pres./Ed., 124 Bishop St., New Haven, CT 06511, (203)624-6976

Thomas Hardy Soc. [IO], Dorchester, United Kingdom

Thomas Jefferson's Poplar Forest [9732], PO Box 419, Forest, VA 24551-0419, (434)525-1806

Thomas Legal Defense Fund - Defunct.

Thomas Lovell Beddoes Soc. [IO], Belper, United Kingdom

Thomas Minor Family Soc. [★20600]

Thomas Minor Soc. [20600], Ray Howell, Sec., 38 W 1600 S, Orem, UT 84058

Thomas Nast Soc. [9208], Morristown-Morris Township Lib., 1 Miller Rd., Morristown, NJ 07960, (973)538-3473

Thomas Paine Natl. Historical Assn. [10694], 983 North Ave., New Rochelle, NY 10804-3609

Thomas Rivera Center [★19105]

Thomas Thorn and Mary Ann Downman Family Org. - Defunct.

Thomas Wolfe Soc. [9416], PO Box 1146, Bloomington, IN 47402-1146

Thompson Collectors Assn. [21719], PO Box 1675, Ellicott City, MD 21041-1675

Thompson Collectors Assn. [21719], PO Box 1675, Ellicott City, MD 21041-1675

Thomson Found. [IO], Cardiff, United Kingdom

Thomson Reuters Found. [IO], London, United Kingdom

Thomson Sci. - Europe, Middle East, and Africa [IO], London, United Kingdom

Thoracic Medicine

Amer. Assn. for Thoracic Surgery [16877]

Amer. Bd. of Thoracic Surgery [16878]

Amer. Thoracic Soc. [16879]

Amer. Thoracic Soc. [16879]

CTSNet: Cardiothoracic Surgery Network [16880]

CTSNet: Cardiothoracic Surgery Network [16880]

European Soc. of Thoracic Surgeons [19933]

Soc. of Thoracic Surgeons [16881]

Thoracic Radiology; Soc. of [16550]

Thoracic Surgery

Thoracic Surgery Residents Assn. [16882]

Thoracic Surgery Residents Assn. [16882], PO Box 3496, Durham, NC 27710, (919)684-2890

Thoreau Lyceum - Defunct.

Thoreau Soc. [9417], 341 Virginia Rd., Concord, MA 01742, (978)369-5310

Thorne Ecological Found. [★4221]

Thorne Ecological Inst. [4221], PO Box 19107, Boulder, CO 80308-2107, (303)499-3647

Thornton W. Burgess Soc. [4306], 6 Discovery Hill Rd., East Sandwich, MA 02537, (508)888-6870

Thornton Wilder Soc. [10745], Coll. of New Jersey, PO Box 7718, Ewing, NJ 08628-0718, (609)771-2346

Thornton Wilder Soc. [10745], Coll. of New Jersey, PO Box 7718, Ewing, NJ 08628-0718, (609)771-2346

Thoroughbred Breeders' Assn. [IO], Newmarket, United Kingdom

Thoroughbred Club of Am. [22666], PO Box 8098, Lexington, KY 40533-8098, (859)254-4282

Thoroughbred Owners and Breeders Assn. [22667], PO Box 910668, Lexington, KY 40591, (859)276-2291

Thoroughbred Racing Associations [22668], 420 Fair Hill Dr., Ste. 1, Elkton, MD 21921-2573, (410)392-9200

Thoroughbred Racing Protective Bur. [22669], 420 Fair Hill Dr., Ste. 2, Elkton, MD 21921, (410)398-2261

Thoroughbred Retirement Found. [11045], PO Box 3387, Saratoga Springs, NY 12866, (518)226-0028

Thoroughbred United Retirement Fund - Defunct.

Thousand [★9639]

Thousand [★9639]

A Thousand Books - Address unknown since 2011.

Threads Weaving Dreams [12374], 4050 Lakewood Dr., Bessemer, AL 35020

Threads Weaving Dreams [12374], 4050 Lakewood Dr., Bessemer, AL 35020

The Three Cent 1851-57 Unit [★22089]

Three Dog Night Fan Club [23895], PO Box 1975, Rowlett, TX 75030, (615)383-8787

Three Hundred Third BGA Membership [★20847]

Three Mile Island Alert [18186], 315 Peffer St., Harrisburg, PA 17102

Three Stooges Fan Club [23798], PO Box 747, Gwynedd Valley, PA 19437, (267)468-0810

Threefold Educational Found. and School [8280], 260 Hungry Hollow Rd., Chestnut Ridge, NY 10977, (845)352-5020

Threshold [4307], 976 E Univ. Blvd., Tucson, AZ 85719, (520)623-3588

Threshold Ministries [IO], St. John, NB, Canada

Thrive [IO], Reading, United Kingdom

Thrivent Financial for Lutherans [19941], 4321 N Ballard Rd., Appleton, WI 54919-0001, (920)734-5721

Throw the Hypocritical Rascals Out - Defunct.

Thunderbird Class Assn. [★22363]

Thunderbird and Cougar Club of Am. [21175], 422 Cooper St., Mountain Home, AR 72653

Thunderhead Alliance [★18731]

Thunderhead Alliance [★18731]

Thurgood Marshall Coll. Fund [7705], 80 Maiden Ln., Ste. 2204, New York, NY 10038, (212)573-8888

Thurgood Marshall Scholarship Fund [★7705]

Thyroid

Amer. Thyroid Assn. [16883]

Natl. Graves' Disease Found. [16884]

Thyroid Cancer Survivors' Assn. [16885]

Thyroid Cancer Survivors' Assn. [16885], PO Box 1545, New York, NY 10159-1545, (877)588-7904

TI Personal Programmable Calculator Club - Defunct.

TIAA-CREF [8802], PO Box 1259, Charlotte, NC 28201, (800)842-2252

Tibet

Antahkarana Soc. Intl. [13319]

DROKPA [11575]

Found. for the Preservation of the Mahayana Tradition [19367]

Intl. Campaign for Tibet [18723]

Intl. Campaign for Tibet [18723]

Proj. Tibet [18724]

Proj. Tibet [18724]

Tibet Fund [10611]

Tibet Justice Center [18725]

Tibet Justice Center [18725]

U.S.-Tibet Comm. [18726]

U.S.-Tibet Comm. [18726]

Tibet AID - Japan [IO], Kyoto, Japan

Tibet Fund [10611], 241 E 32nd St., New York, NY 10016, (212)213-5011

Tibet Justice Center [18725], 440 Grand Ave., Ste. 425, Oakland, CA 94610, (510)486-0588

Tibet Justice Center [18725], 440 Grand Ave., Ste. 425, Oakland, CA 94610, (510)486-0588

Tibet Soc. - Defunct.

Tibet Soc. of the United Kingdom [IO], London, United Kingdom

Tibetan

Found. for the Preservation of the Mahayana Tradition [19367]

Tibetan Aid Proj. [12791], 2210 Harold Way, Berkeley, CA 94704, (510)848-4238

Tibetan Aid Proj. [12791], 2210 Harold Way, Berkeley, CA 94704, (510)848-4238

Tibetan Found. [★10611]

Tibetan Nyingma Relief Foundation [★12791]

Tibetan Nyingma Relief Foundation [★12791]

Tibetan Spaniel Club of Am. [21657], Bonnie Bieber, Membership Chair, 7 Lennox Dr., Middletown, DE 19709, (434)525-7710

Tibetan Terrier Club of Am. [21658], 945 Clairemont Ave., Decatur, GA 30030

Tibetan Women's Assn. [IO], Dharamsala, India

Tibetan Youth Cong. [IO], Dharamsala, India

Tidewater Guild for Infant Survival, Inc. [★16758]

Tiers Ordre Carmelitaine [★IO]

Tietotekniikan liitto ry [★IO]

Tiffany Club [★13105]

Tiffin Glass Collectors Club [21843], PO Box 554, Tiffin, OH 44883, (419)448-0200

Tiger Horse Assn. [4653], 1604 Fescue Cir., Huddleston, VA 24104, (540)297-2276

Tigers East/Alpines East [21176], PO Box 1260, Kulpsville, PA 19443-1260, (717)600-2021

Tigers East/Alpines East [21176], PO Box 1260, Kulpsville, PA 19443-1260, (717)600-2021

Tilapia Intl. Found. [IO], Utrecht, Netherlands

The Tile Assn. [IO], Beckenham, United Kingdom

Tile Contractors Assn. of Am. [951], 10434 Indiana Ave., Kansas City, MO 64137, (800)655-8453

Tile Coun. of Am. [★628]

Tile Coun. of North Am. [628], 100 Clemson Res. Blvd., Anderson, SC 29625, (864)646-8453

Tile and Mantel Contractors Assn. of Am. [★951]

Tile, Marble, Terrazzo, Finishers, Shopworkers, and Granite Cutters Intl. Union [★23169]

Tile Partners for Humanity [12202], 505 Sable Ct., Alpharetta, GA 30004, (678)366-1815

Tile Partners for Humanity [12202], 505 Sable Ct., Alpharetta, GA 30004, (678)366-1815

Tile Roofing Inst. [629], 230 E Ohio St., Ste. 400, Chicago, IL 60611, (312)670-4177

Tiles and Architectural Ceramics Soc. [IO], Oldham, United Kingdom

Tillers Intl. [12375], 10515 E OP Ave., Scotts, MI 49088, (269)626-0223

Tilling Soc. [IO], Hastings, United Kingdom

Reference to "IO" in place of a book number signifies that the association may be found in the 50th edition of International Organizations.

Tilt-Up Concrete Assn. [952], PO Box 204, Mount
Vernon, IA 52314, (319)895-6911
Tilt-Up Concrete Assn. [952], PO Box 204, Mount
Vernon, IA 52314, (319)895-6911
Timap for Justice [IO], Freetown, Sierra Leone
Timber Assn. of California [★1466]
Timber Decking Assn. [IO], Castleford, United
Kingdom
Timber Frame Bus. Coun. [630], 46 Chambersburg
St., Gettysburg, PA 17325, (717)334-5234
Timber Framers Guild [1485], PO Box 295, Alstead,
NH 03602-0295, (559)834-8453
Timber Framers Guild [1485], PO Box 295, Alstead,
NH 03602-0295, (559)834-8453
Timber Packaging and Pallet Confed. [IO], Leicester,
United Kingdom
Timber Preservers Assn. of Australia [IO], Brighton,
Australia
Timber Products Mfrs. [1486], 951 E 3rd Ave.,
Spokane, WA 99202-2215, (509)535-4646
Timber Products Mfrs. Assn. [★1486]
Timber Res. and Development Assn. [IO], High Wy-
combe, United Kingdom
Timber Trade Fed. [IO], London, United Kingdom
Time
   Intl. Soc. for the Stud. of Time [10612]
   Intl. Soc. for the Stud. of Time [10612]
Time for Lyme [15125], 30 Myano Ln., Ste. 20,
Stamford, CT 06902, (203)969-1333
Timepieces
   Independent Time and Labor Mgt. Assn. [3464]
   Intl. Watch Collectors Soc. [22165]
   Intl. Watch Fob Assn. [22166]
   Intl. Watch Fob Assn. [22166]
   Natl. Assn. of Watch and Clock Collectors [22167]
   North Amer. Sundial Soc. [9014]
   North Amer. Sundial Soc. [9014]
Timeshare Consumers Assn. [IO], Blyth, United
Kingdom
Timothy Demonbreun Soc. [★20397]
Tin Can Sailors - The Natl. Assn. of Destroyer
Veterans [20726], PO Box 100, Somerset, MA
02726, (508)677-0515
Tinker Found. [9950], 55 E 59th St., New York, NY
10022, (212)421-6858
Tinker Found. [9950], 55 E 59th St., New York, NY
10022, (212)421-6858
Tinnitus Assn; Amer. [16683]
Tinnitus Intl. Service Assn. - Defunct.
Tiny Hands Intl. [11416], PO Box 67195, Lincoln, NE
68506, (402)601-4816
Tippers Anonymous - Defunct.
TIPS Prog. [11694], 1400 Key Blvd., Ste. 700,
Arlington, VA 22209-1547, (800)GET-TIPS
Tire Assn. of North Am. [★3465]
Tire Indus. Assn. [3465], 1532 Pointer Ridge Pl.,
Ste. G, Bowie, MD 20716-1883, (301)430-7280
Tire Retread Info. Bur. [★3466]
Tire Retread Info. Bur. [★3466]
Tire Retread and Repair Info. Bur. [3466], 1013
Birch St., Falls Church, VA 22046, (703)533-7677
Tire Retread and Repair Info. Bur. [3466], 1013
Birch St., Falls Church, VA 22046, (703)533-7677
Tire Retreading Inst. [★3465]
Tire and Rim Assn. [3467], 175 Montrose West Ave.,
Ste. 150, Copley, OH 44321, (330)666-8121
Tire Soc. [7566], PO Box 1502, Akron, OH 44309-
1502, (330)972-7814
Tire Soc. [7566], PO Box 1502, Akron, OH 44309-
1502, (330)972-7814
Tires
   Imported Tyre Mfrs'. Assn. [4226]
   Natl. Assn. of Tire and Renovating Plants Distribu-
   tors [22270]
   Natl. Assn. of Tire Specialists [13886]
   Tire Indus. Assn. [3465]
   Tire Retread and Repair Info. Bur. [3466]
   Tire Retread and Repair Info. Bur. [3466]
   Tire and Rim Assn. [3467]
   Tire Soc. [7566]
   Tire Soc. [7566]
Tirisanyo Catholic Commn. - Caritas Botswana [IO],
Gaborone, Botswana
Tissue
   Ehlers Danlos Natl. Found. [16886]

Natl. Marfan Found. [16887]
USBloodDonors.org [13853]
Tissue Banks Intl. [16917], 815 Park Ave.,
Baltimore, MD 21201, (410)752-3800
Tissue Banks Intl. [16917], 815 Park Ave.,
Baltimore, MD 21201, (410)752-3800
Tissue Culture Assn. [★6317]
Tissue Culture Commn. [★6317]
Tissue Engg. Intl. and Regenerative Medicine Soc.
[13835], Sarah Wilburn, Admin., 223 Park Pl., San
Ramon, CA 94583, (925)362-0998
Tissue Viability Nurses Assn. [IO], Plymouth, United
Kingdom
Titanic Enthusiasts of Am. [★10065]
Titanic Enthusiasts of Am. [★10065]
Titanic Historical Soc. [10065], PO Box 51053,
Indian Orchard, MA 01151-0053, (413)543-4770
Titanic Historical Soc. [10065], PO Box 51053,
Indian Orchard, MA 01151-0053, (413)543-4770
Titanic Intl. [★10066]
Titanic Intl. [★10066]
Titanic Intl. Soc. [10066], Robert Bracken, Treas.,
PO Box 416, Midland Park, NJ 07432-0416
Titanic Intl. Soc. [10066], Robert Bracken, Treas.,
PO Box 416, Midland Park, NJ 07432-0416
Titanium Development Assn. [★2475]
Titanium Development Assn. [★2475]
Titanium Dioxide Mfrs. Sector Gp. [IO], Brussels,
Belgium
Tithing
   NewTithing Gp. [18727]
   Tithing and Stewardship Found. [20267]
Tithing Found. [★20267]
Tithing and Stewardship Found. [20267], Book
Center, 1100 E 55th St., Chicago, IL 60615,
(773)256-0679
Tjanstemannens Centralorganisation [★IO]
The TLT Gp. [★7530]
The TLT Gp. [★7530]
TMJ Assn. [16108], PO Box 26770, Milwaukee, WI
53226-0770, (262)432-0350
TMJ and Orofacial Pain Soc. of Am. [15523], 1020
12th St., Ste. 303, Sacramento, CA 95814,
(916)444-1985
Tmmob Jeoloji Muhendisleri Odasi [★IO]
To Love a Child [11417], PO Box 165, Clifton Park,
NY 12065, (518)859-4424
Toastmasters Intl. [10481], PO Box 9052, Mission
Viejo, CA 92690-9052, (949)858-8255
Toastmasters Intl. [10481], PO Box 9052, Mission
Viejo, CA 92690-9052, (949)858-8255
Toastmasters New Zealand [IO], Canterbury, New
Zealand
Tobacco
   Amer. Legacy Found. [18728]
   Brazilian Tobacco Indus. Assn. [11800]
   Burley Stabilization Corp. [4957]
   Burley Tobacco Growers Cooperative Assn.
   [4958]
   Natl. Assn. of Tobacco Outlets [3468]
   Soc. for Res. on Nicotine and Tobacco [4959]
   Tobacco Associates [3469]
   Tobacco Assn. of Malawi [22673]
   Tobacco Merchants Assn. [3470]
   Tobacconists' Assn. of Am. [3471]
   U.S. Tobacco Cooperative [4960]
Tobacco Associates [3469], 8452 Holly Leaf Dr.,
McLean, VA 22102, (703)821-1255
Tobacco Assn. of Malawi [IO], Lilongwe, Malawi
Tobacco Assn. of the U.S. - Defunct.
Tobacco Control Rsrc. Center [13328], Public Hea.
Advocacy Inst., 102 The Fenway, Cushing Hall,
Ste. 117, Boston, MA 02115, (617)373-2026
Tobacco Experts Assn. [IO], Izmir, Turkey
Tobacco Growers' Assn. of Brazil [IO], Santa Cruz
do Sul, Brazil
Tobacco Inst. - Defunct.
Tobacco Mfrs. Assn. [IO], London, United Kingdom
Tobacco Merchants Assn. [3470], PO Box 8019,
Princeton, NJ 08543-8019, (609)275-4900
Tobacco Workers Intl. Union [★23225]
Tobacconists' Assn. of Am. [3471], 19 S Wabash
Ave., Chicago, IL 60603, (312)351-2444
Tobago Hotel and Tourism Assn. [IO], Scarborough,
Trinidad and Tobago

Toc H [IO], Whitchurch, United Kingdom
TOCA - Defunct.
Tochi Seidoshi Gakkai [★IO]
Together [IO], London, United Kingdom
Together for Kids [15070], 14103 Seabiscuit, Al-
pharetta, GA 30004, (704)438-1834
Together for Tanzania [11646], PO Box 395, Powha-
tan, VA 23139
Togolese Red Cross [IO], Lome, Togo
Toho Gakkai [★IO]
Toilet Goods Assn. [★1670]
Toimihenkilokeskusjarjesto [★IO]
Token and Medal Soc. [21995], Kathy Freeland,
Sec., 6125 Fourth St., Ste. 194, Mayville, MI
48744
Tokushima Intl. Cooperation [IO], Tokushima, Japan
Tokyo ACM SIGGRAPH [IO], Tokyo, Japan
Tokyo Bar Assn. [IO], Tokyo, Japan
Tokyo Bengoshikai Toshokan [★IO]
Tokyo Chigaku Kyokai [★IO]
Tokyo Geographical Soc. [IO], Tokyo, Japan
Tokyo Inst. of Psychiatry [IO], Tokyo, Japan
Tokyo Sangyo Boeki Kyokai [★IO]
Tokyo Trade and Indus. Assn. [IO], Tokyo, Japan
Tolkien Soc. [IO], Oxford, United Kingdom
Tolstoy Found. [19216], PO Box 578, Valley Cot-
tage, NY 10989, (845)268-6722
Tom Jones Tom Terrific Fan Club [23896], 411 Co-
ram Ave., Shelton, CT 06484-3134
Tom Lee Music Found. [IO], Hong Kong, People's
Republic of China
Tom Skinner Associates [★19772]
Tomas Rivera Policy Inst. [19105], Univ. of Southern
California, School of Policy, Planning, and
Development, Ralph and Goldie Lewis Hall, 650
Childs Way, Ste. 102, Los Angeles, CA 90089-
0626, (213)821-5615
Tomato Genetics Cooperative [4475], Univ. of
Florida, Gulf Coast Res. and Educ. Center, 14625
County Rd. 672, Wimauma, FL 33598-6101,
(813)633-4135
Tomato Genetics Cooperative [4475], Univ. of
Florida, Gulf Coast Res. and Educ. Center, 14625
County Rd. 672, Wimauma, FL 33598-6101,
(813)633-4135
Tomiki Aikido of the Americas [22752], 5752 S King-
ston Way, Englewood, CO 80111, (303)740-7424
Tomorrow's Youth Org. [13562], 1356 Beverly Rd.,
Ste. 200, McLean, VA 22101, (703)893-1143
Toned Coin Collectors Soc. - Address unknown
since 2011.
Tonga Amateur Athletic Assn. [IO], Nuku'alofa,
Tonga
Tonga Amateur Sports Assn. and Natl. Olympic
Comm. [IO], Nuku'alofa, Tonga
Tonga Archery Assn. [IO], Nuku'alofa, Tonga
Tonga Chamber of Commerce and Indus. [IO],
Nuku'alofa, Tonga
Tonga Family Hea. Assn. [IO], Nuku'alofa, Tonga
Tonga Judo Assn. [IO], Nuku'alofa, Tonga
Tonga Natl. Volleyball Assn. [IO], Nuku'alofa, Tonga
Tonga Powerlifting Fed. [IO], Nuku'alofa, Tonga
Tonga Red Cross Soc. [IO], Nuku'alofa, Tonga
Tonga Squash Rackets Assn. [IO], Nuku'alofa,
Tonga
Tonga Tennis Assn. [IO], Nuku'alofa, Tonga
Tonga Visitors Bur. [IO], Nuku'alofa, Tonga
Tool Collectors Assn; Mid-West [21869]
Tool and Gauge Mfrs. Assn. of India [IO], Mumbai,
India
Tool and Stainless Steel Indus. Comm. [★2494]
Tooling and Mfg. Assn. [2346], 1177 S Dee Rd.,
Park Ridge, IL 60068, (847)825-1120
Tooling, Mfg. and Technologies Assn. [1874], PO
Box 2204, Farmington Hills, MI 48333-2204,
(248)488-0300
Tools for Self Reliance [IO], Southampton, United
Kingdom
Tools and Trades History Soc. [IO], Devon, United
Kingdom
Toonan Ajia Shigakkai [★IO]
Toothpick Holder Collectors' Soc. [★21385]
Top End Assn. for Mental Hea. [IO], Darwin,
Australia
Top Level Domain Assn. [2118], 620 Sea Island Rd.,
No. 123, St. Simons Island, GA 31522, (912)634-
9168

A star before a book entry number signifies that the name is not listed separately, but is mentioned within the entry.

Topaz Arts [9322], PO Box 770150, Woodside, NY 11377-0150, (718)505-0440

Toplumsal Saydamlik Hareketi Dernegi [★IO]

TopTen USA [1178], 1620 St. NW, Ste. 210, Washington, DC 20006

Torah Fund - a Campaign [★19910]

Tornado and Storm Res. Org. [IO], Warrington, United Kingdom

Toronto Action for Social Change [IO], Toronto, ON, Canada

Toronto Area of Narcotics Anonymous [IO], Toronto, ON, Canada

Toronto Hard of Hearing Br. [IO], Alliston, ON, Canada

Torquay Pottery Collectors' Soc. [IO], Torquay, United Kingdom

Tortilla Indus. Assn. [1432], 1600 Wilson Blvd., Ste. 650, Arlington, VA 22209, (703)245-8034

Tortilla Indus. Assn. [1432], 1600 Wilson Blvd., Ste. 650, Arlington, VA 22209, (703)245-8034

TortoiseAid Intl.

TortoiseAid Intl. - Address unknown since 2011.

Torture Abolition and Survivors Support Coalition Intl. [17864], 4121 Harewood Rd. NE, Ste. B, Washington, DC 20017, (202)529-2991

Torture Abolition and Survivors Support Coalition Intl. [17864], 4121 Harewood Rd. NE, Ste. B, Washington, DC 20017, (202)529-2991

Total Educ. in the Total Env. [★4300]

Total Energy Mgt. Professionals [★6693]

Total Energy Mgt. Professionals [★6693]

Total Family Care Coalition [12023], 1214 I St. SE, Ste. 11, Washington, DC 20003-4103, (202)758-3281

Total Immersion Fluency Training [★16680]

Total Practice Mgt. Assn. [5287], 25 E Washington St., Ste. 510, Chicago, IL 60602, (312)496-6074

Touch Football Australia [IO], Deakin, Australia

Touch-Healing
Coun. for Healing [13672]
Hospital-Based Massage Network [15267]
Shine Therapy [15274]

Touch for Hea. Assn. [★13713]

Touch for Hea. Assn. of Am. [★13713]

Touch for Hea. Found. [★13713]

Touch for Hea. Kinesiology Assn. [13713], 7121 New Light Trail, Chapel Hill, NC 27516, (919)969-0027

Touch the Life of a Child Org. [11418], 31811 Pacific Hwy. S, Ste. B-220, Federal Way, WA 98003, (253)838-2038

Touch the Life of a Child Org. [11418], 31811 Pacific Hwy. S, Ste. B-220, Federal Way, WA 98003, (253)838-2038

Touch of Relief [15004], 1500 Hadden Manor Ct., Silver Spring, MD 20904, (301)680-8867

Touched By Elvis Fan Club - Address unknown since 2011.

Touching Hearts [10817], 5555 Corporate Ave., Cypress, CA 90630, (714)229-8700

Tour Operators Assn. of Papua New Guinea [IO], Port Moresby, Papua New Guinea

Tourette Syndrome Assn. [15636], 42-40 Bell Blvd., Ste. 205, Bayside, NY 11361-2820, (718)224-2999

Tourette Syndrome Assn. of Australia [IO], Maroubra, Australia

Tourettes Action [IO], London, United Kingdom

Touring
Belgian Tourist Off. [23333]
Ceylon (Sri Lanka) Tourist Dept. [23443]
Cyprus Tourism Org. [23396]
European Travel Commn. [3558]
Greek Natl. Tourist Org. [3512]
Grenada Bd. of Tourism [23343]
Jordan Info. Bur. [23421]
Malaysia Tourism Promotion Bd. [23427]
Mexico Tourism Bd. [23428]
Saint Kitts Tourism Authority [23344]

Tourism
Anguilla Tourist Bd. [23446]
Antigua Hotels and Tourist Assn. [1906]
Assn. of Chilean Tourism Agencies [5735]
Assn. for the Promotion of Tourism to Africa [3472]
Assn. for the Promotion of Tourism to Africa [3472]

Belgian Tourist Off. [23333]
Bermuda Dept. of Tourism [23447]
Binational Tourism Alliance [3473]
Cayman Islands Dept. of Tourism [23448]
Ceylon (Sri Lanka) Tourist Dept. [23443]
Convention Indus. Coun. [3474]
Cyprus Tourism Org. [23396]
European Travel Commn. [3558]
Global Explorers [9017]
Greek Natl. Tourist Org. [3512]
Grenada Bd. of Tourism [23343]
Intl. Assn. of Reservation Executives [3475]
Intl. Assn. of Reservation Executives [3475]
Intl. Assn. of Tour Managers - North Amer. Region [3562]
The Intl. Ecotourism Soc. [3476]
The Intl. Ecotourism Soc. [3476]
Jordan Info. Bur. [23421]
Malaysia Tourism Promotion Bd. [23427]
Mexico Tourism Bd. [23428]
Natl. Coun. of State Tourism Directors [23449]
Natl. Fed. of Tourist Guide Associations USA [23450]
Natl. Tourism Org. of Serbia [7992]
Professional Tour Guide Assn. of Australia [4754]
Saint Kitts Tourism Authority [23344]
St. Lucia Hotel and Tourism Assn. [1165]
Soc. for Accessible Travel and Hospitality [11829]
Tourist Assn. of Slovenia [13870]
Trinidad Restaurants, Hotels and Tourism Assn. [3371]
U.S. Travel Data Center [3584]

Tourism Authority of Thailand [IO], Bangkok, Thailand

Tourism Employees Assn. of Maldives [IO], Male, Maldives

Tourism and Hospitality Chamber of Slovenia [IO], Ljubljana, Slovenia

Tourism Indus. Assn. of Canada [IO], Ottawa, ON, Canada

Tourism Indus. Assn. New Zealand [IO], Wellington, New Zealand

Tourism Indus. Assn. of the Yukon [IO], Whitehorse, YT, Canada

Tourism Soc. [IO], Sutton, United Kingdom

Tourist Assn. of Slovenia [IO], Ljubljana, Slovenia

Tourist Railway Assn. [2996], 1016 Rosser St., Co-nyers, GA 30012, (770)278-0088

Tourist Railway Assn. [2996], 1016 Rosser St., Co-nyers, GA 30012, (770)278-0088

Tournament of Roses Assn. [9581], 391 S Orange Grove Blvd., Pasadena, CA 91105, (626)449-4100

Touro Synagogue Found. [9733], 85 Touro St., Newport, RI 02840, (401)847-4794

Toward Freedom [17732], PO Box 468, Burlington, VT 05402, (802)657-3733

Toward Freedom [17732], PO Box 468, Burlington, VT 05402, (802)657-3733

Towards Freedom [17620], 2116 Pico Blvd., Ste. B, Santa Monica, CA 90405, (310)315-0961

Towarzystwo Biblijne w Polsce [★IO]

Towarzystwo imienia Fryderyka Chopina [★IO]

Towarzystwo Przetwarzania Obrazow [★IO]

Towarzystwo Urbanistow Polskich [★IO]

Towing and Recovery Assn. of Am. [370], 2121 Eisenhower Ave., Ste. 200, Alexandria, VA 22314, (703)684-7713

Town Affiliation Assn. of the U.S., Inc. [★17985]

Town Affiliation Assn. of the U.S., Inc. [★17985]

Town and Country Planning Assn. [IO], London, United Kingdom

Town and Country Religious Res. Center [★19426]

Town Creek Found. - Defunct.

Towner Rating Bur. [★2044]

Townswomen's Guilds [IO], Birmingham, United Kingdom

Toxic Exposure
Alliance for Healthy Homes [13320]
Asbestos Disease Awareness Org. [16888]
Asbestos Disease Awareness Org. [16888]
Beyond Pesticides [13321]
Chem. Injury Info. Network [16889]
Chem. Injury Info. Network [16889]
Coalition for SafeMinds [15580]
Fluoride Action Network [14281]

Mercury Policy Proj. [18729]
Moms Against Mercury [13322]
Natl. Inst. for Chem. Stud. [13323]
Natl. Pesticide Info. Center [13324]
Northwest Coalition for Alternatives to Pesticides [13325]
Pesticide Action Network North Am. Regional Center [13326]
Rachel Carson Coun. [13327]
Tobacco Control Rsrc. Center [13328]
White Lung Assn. [13329]
White Lung Assn. [13329]

Toxicologic Pathology; Soc. of [16134]

Toxicology
African Soc. for Toxicological Sciences [7567]
Amer. Acad. of Clinical Toxicology [16890]
Amer. Assn. of Poison Control Centers [16891]
Amer. Bd. of Clinical Metal Toxicology [16892]
Amer. Bd. of Toxicology [7568]
Amer. Bd. of Toxicology [7568]
Amer. Coll. of Medical Toxicology [16893]
Amer. Coll. of Toxicology [7569]
Amer. Coll. of Toxicology [7569]
Fluoride Action Network [14281]
Genetic Toxicology Assn. [7570]
Hamner Institutes for Hea. Sciences [7571]
Intl. Endotoxin and Innate Immunity Soc. [7572]
Intl. Endotoxin and Innate Immunity Soc. [7572]
Intl. Neurotoxicology Assn. [7573]
Natl. Eosinophilia-Myalgia Syndrome Network [16894]
Soc. of Toxicology [7574]
Toxicology Excellence for Risk Assessment [7575]
Toxicology Forum [7576]

Toxicology Center; Reproductive [14534]

Toxicology Center; Reproductive [14534]

Toxicology Excellence for Risk Assessment [7575], 2300 Montana Ave., Ste. 409, Cincinnati, OH 45211, (513)542-7475

Toxicology Forum [7576], 1300 Eye St. NW, Ste. 1010 E, Washington, DC 20005-3328, (202)659-0030

Toy
A.C. Gilbert Heritage Soc. [22168]
Amy's Doll Lover's Club [21687]
Doll Costumer's Guild [21690]
Intl. Doll Makers Assn. [21692]
Strawberry Shortcake Chat Gp. [21699]
Toy Train Collectors Soc. [21894]
Women in Toys [3479]
Youth in Model Railroading [21897]

Toy Australian Shepherd Assn. of Am. [21659], 557 Forest Way Dr., Fort Mill, SC 29715, (803)548-7048

Toy Car Collectors Assn. [22171], PO Box 1824, Bend, OR 97709-1824, (541)419-6491

Toy Car Collectors Assn. [22171], PO Box 1824, Bend, OR 97709-1824, (541)419-6491

Toy Dish Collectors [★22173]

Toy Indus. of Europe [IO], Brussels, Belgium

Toy Indus. Assn. [3478], 1115 Broadway, Ste. 400, New York, NY 10010, (212)675-1141

Toy Mfrs. of Am. [★3478]

Toy Mfrs'. Assn. [IO], Sao Paulo, Brazil

Toy Retailers Assn. [IO], Gainsborough, United Kingdom

Toy Stitchers Intl., Inc. [22172], Lynn Furman, Treas., PO Box 200, Savannah, NY 13146-0200

Toy Traders of Europe [IO], Nuremberg, Germany

Toy Train Collectors Soc. [21894], Louis A. Bohn, Membership Chm., 109 Howedale Dr., Rochester, NY 14616-1534, (585)663-4188

Toy Train Operating Soc. [21895], PO Box 6710, Fullerton, CA 92834, (714)449-9391

Toyota Owner's and Restorer's Club [21177], 2849 Long Beach Blvd., Long Beach, CA 90806, (562)412-3932

Toyota Territory Off-Roaders Assn. [22150], PO Box 2323, Mont Belvieu, TX 77580, (281)414-1645

Toys
A.C. Gilbert Heritage Soc. [22168]
Amy's Doll Lover's Club [21687]
Doll Costumer's Guild [21690]
Fisher-Price Collector's Club [22169]
Fisher-Price Collector's Club [22169]

Reference to "IO" in place of a book number signifies that the association may be found in the 50th edition of International Organizations.

GI Joe Collectors' Club [22170]
Intl. Coun. of Toy Indus. [3477]
Intl. Coun. of Toy Indus. [3477]
Intl. Doll Makers Assn. [21692]
Strawberry Shortcake Chat Gp. [21699]
Toy Car Collectors Assn. [22171]
Toy Car Collectors Assn. [22171]
Toy Indus. Assn. [3478]
Toy Mfrs'. Assn. [14754]
Toy Stitchers Intl., Inc. [22172]
Toy Train Collectors Soc. [21894]
Treasures for Little Children [22173]
Women in Toys [3479]
Youth in Model Railroading [21897]
Toys Mfrs'. Assn. of Hong Kong [IO], Hong Kong,
    People's Republic of China
Toys for Tots Found. [★11483]
TR8 Car Club of Am. [★21179]
Tra- och Mobelindustriforbundet [★IO]
TRACE Intl. [5347], 151 West St., Ste. 300, An-
    napolis, MD 21401, (410)990-0076
Trachoma Initiative; Intl. [17089]
Trachoma Initiative; Intl. [17089]

Track and Field
DECA, The Decathlon Assn. [23069]
Lifelong Fitness Alliance [23070]
U.S. Modern Pentathlon Assn. [23071]
U.S.A. Track and Field [23072]

Tractor Pulling
Natl. Tractor Pullers Assn. [23073]
Professional Putters Assn. [22623]
USA Pulling [23074]

Tractors
Ferguson Enthusiasts of North Am. [22174]
Ford/Fordson Collectors Assn. [22175]
Gravely Tractor Club of Am. [22176]
Intl. Harvester Collectors [22177]
Massey Collectors Assn. [22178]
Natl. Antique Tractor Pullers Assn. [22179]
Natl. Russell Collectors Assn. [21382]
Natl. Vintage Tractor and Engine Club [11911]
Two-Cylinder Club [22180]
USA Pulling [23074]
Vintage Garden Tractor Club of Am. [22181]
Tracy Byrd Online Fan Club - Address unknown
    since 2011.

Trade
1-800 Amer. Free Trade Assn. [3588]
Accountants Motivational Marketing Org. [2]
Alliance for Amer. Mfg. [2325]
Alliance for Responsible Trade [3480]
Alliance for Responsible Trade [3480]
Amer. Assn. of Inside Sales Professionals [3156]
Amer. Assn. of Professional Tech. Analysts [3387]
Amer. Chamber of Commerce Executives [23451]
Amer. Small Mfrs. Coalition [2328]
Assn. of African Amer. Financial Advisors [1334]
Assn. of Manufactured Goods Exporters [21613]
Australian New Zealand - Amer. Chambers of
    Commerce [23339]
Australian Trade Commn. [23452]
Austrian Trade Commn. [23329]
Automotive Undercar Trade Org. [293]
Brazil-U.S. Bus. Coun. [23354]
Brazilian Govt. Trade Bur. of the Consulate Gen.
    of Brazil in New York [23335]
Bridal Show Producers Intl. [471]
British Trade Off. at Consulate-General [23336]
Buying Influence [17446]
Canadian/American Border Trade Alliance [3481]
Canadian/American Border Trade Alliance [3481]
Centre for Importers of Paraguay [1322]
ChristianTrade Assn. Intl. [19561]
Coalition Against Counterfeiting and Piracy [5564]
Coalition for Intellectual Property Rights [5565]
Community Development Bankers Assn. [406]
Coun. on Competitiveness [3482]
Cyprus-US Chamber of Commerce [23360]
Debt AIDS Trade Africa [17149]
Efficiency First [4046]
Embroidery Software Protection Coalition [2049]
Export Inst. of the U.S. [3483]
Export Inst. of the U.S. [3483]
Fair Trade USA [3484]
FishWise [1359]

Gift and Home Trade Assn. [3161]
Global Envelope Alliance [3349]
Global Sourcing Coun. [2602]
Hazelnut Coun. [4750]
Innovation Norway - U.S. [23368]
Intl. Air Filtration Certifiers Assn. [1705]
Intl. Assn. of Directional Drilling [7238]
Intl. Bridal Mfrs. Assn. [472]
Intl. Economic Alliance [1065]
Intl. Reciprocal Trade Assn. [3485]
Intl. Reciprocal Trade Assn. [3485]
Intl. Sugar Trade Coalition [3367]
Iraqi Amer. Chamber of Commerce and Indus.
    [23370]
Jordan Info. Bur. [23421]
Korean Amer. Soc. of Entrepreneurs [718]
Latin Am. Trade Coalition [2187]
Leadership for Energy Automated Processing
    [1171]
LTD Shippers Assn. [3486]
LTD Shippers Assn. [3486]
Military Heraldry Soc. [2896]
Natl. Assn. of Trade Exchanges [3487]TradeNatl.
    Guild of Master Craftsmen
Natl. Roof Certification and Inspection Assn. [596]
Natl. United States-Arab Chamber of Commerce
    [23374]
North Amer. Trailer Dealers Assn. [3531]
Organic Seed Growers and Trade Assn. [4883]
Professional Decorative Painters Assn. [2614]
Reusable Packaging Assn. [3072]
Romanian-U.S. Bus. Coun. [23438]
Sales Exchange for Refugee Rehabilitation and
    Vocation [3488]
Sales Exchange for Refugee Rehabilitation and
    Vocation [3488]
Slate Roofing Contractors Assn. of North Am.
    [617]
Software and Tech. Vendors' Assn. [819]
South African USA Chamber of Commerce
    [23379]
Spirit Indus. Trade Assn. [733]
Swedish Trade Coun. [3489]
Swedish Trade Coun. [3489]
Truth About Trade and Tech. [6337]
Turkish-American Chamber of Commerce and
    Indus. [23455]
Uganda Export Promotion Bd. [21208]
Union of Exporters of Uruguay [5748]
U.S. ASEAN Bus. Coun. [3490]
U.S. ASEAN Bus. Coun. [3490]
U.S. Indian Amer. Chamber of Commerce [23407]
U.S.-U.A.E. Bus. Coun. [2115]
U.S.-Ukraine Bus. Coun. [721]
U.S.-Vietnam WTO Coalition [18762]
Western and English Sales Assn. [3491]
Women's Intl. Shipping and Trading Assn. [3276]
World Economic Processing Zones Assn. [3492]
World Economic Processing Zones Assn. [3492]
World Energy Cities Partnership [1179]
World Trade Centers Assn. [3493]
World Trade Centers Assn. [3493]
Trade Assn. of Paddlesports [3320], 11781 A. Water-
    tank Rd., Burlington, WA 98233, (559)340-8277
Trade Assn. of Paddlesports [3320], 11781 A. Water-
    tank Rd., Burlington, WA 98233, (559)340-8277
Trade Assn. of Proprietary Plants - Defunct.
Trade Card Collectors Assn. - Address unknown
    since 2011.
Trade Commn. of Norway [★23368]
Trade Commn. of Norway [★23368]
Trade Press Assn. [IO], Barcelona, Spain
Trade Promotion Mgt. Associates [110], 51 Crag-
    wood Rd., Ste. 200, South Plainfield, NJ 07080,
    (646)442-3746
Trade Show Bur. [★1228]
Trade Show Exhibitors Assn. [1238], 2301 S Lake
    Shore Dr., Ste. 1005, Chicago, IL 60616, (312)842-
    8732
Trade Union Advisory Comm. to the OECD [IO],
    Paris, France
Trade Union Cong. of the Philippines [IO], Quezon
    City, Philippines
Trade Union of Educ. in Finland [IO], Helsinki,
    Finland

Trade Union Solidarity Centre of Finland [IO], Hels-
    inki, Finland
Trades Union Cong. - England [IO], London, United
    Kingdom
Trades Union Cong. - Women's Comm. [IO],
    London, United Kingdom
Tradeswomen [11960], 1433 Webster St., Oakland,
    CA 94612, (510)891-8773
Trading Standards Inst. [IO], Basildon, United
    Kingdom
Traditional Boat Squadron of Australia - Australian
    Capital Territory [IO], Erindale Centre, Australia
Traditional Cat Assn. [21259], PO Box 178, Heisson,
    WA 98622-0178
Traditional Chinese Medicine Assn. and Alumni
    [13714], 108-A E 38th St., New York, NY 10016,
    (212)889-4802
Traditional Country Music Assn. [★10265]
Traditional Cowboy Arts Assn. [9127], Don Bellamy,
    PO Box 2002, Salmon, ID 83467, (208)865-2006
Traditional Fine Arts Org. [9323], 90 Via Regalo,
    San Clemente, CA 92673, (714)997-8500
Traditional Irish Music, Singing and Dancing Soc.
    [IO], Monkstown, Ireland
Traditional Siamese Breeders and Fanciers Assn.
    [★21259]
Traditional Small Craft Assn. [22398], PO Box 350,
    Mystic, CT 06355, (425)361-7758
Traditional Tae Kwon Do Chung Do Assn. [22753],
    1209 Gilmore Ln., Louisville, KY 40213, (502)964-
    3800
Traditions pour Demain [★IO]
Traditions for Tomorrow [IO], Rolle, Switzerland
Traffic
driveAWARE [12982]
Motorcycle Safety Found. [3146]
Natl. Comm. on Uniform Traffic Laws and
    Ordinances [6025]
Natl. Motorists Assn. [13335]
Natl. Traffic Incident Mgt. Coalition [13330]
Trans. Safety Equip. Inst. [3153]
Traffic Accident Data Comm. [★13010]
Traffic Accident Data Proj. Comm. [★13010]
Traffic Audit Bur. [★56]
Traffic Audit Bur. for Media Measurement [56], 271
    Madison Ave., Ste. 1504, New York, NY 10016,
    (212)972-8075
Traffic Clubs Intl. [★3538]
Traffic Clubs Intl. [★3538]
Traffic Directors Guild of Am. [512], 26000 Avenida
    Aeropuerto, No. 114, San Juan Capistrano, CA
    92675, (949)429-7063
Traffic Injury Res. Found. [IO], Ottawa, ON, Canada
TRAFFIC North Am. [5136], WWF-US, 1250 24th St.
    NW, Washington, DC 20037, (202)293-4800
Traffic Records Comm. [13010], Natl. Safety Coun.,
    1121 Spring Lake Dr., Itasca, IL 60143-3201,
    (630)285-1121
TRAFFIC - U.S.A. [★5136]
Tragedy Assistance Prog. for Survivors [11111],
    1777 F St. NW, Ste. 600, Washington, DC 20006,
    (202)588-8277
Traidcraft [IO], Gateshead, United Kingdom
Trail Riders of the Canadian Rockies [IO], Calgary,
    AB, Canada
Trail Riders of Today [22687], Margaret Scarff,
    Membership Comm., 4406 Carico Ln., White Hall,
    MD 21161, (301)622-4157
Trail of Tears Assn. [10613], 1100 N Univ., Ste. 143,
    Little Rock, AR 72207, (501)666-9032
Trailer Coach Assn. [★2309]
Trailer Coach Mfrs. Assn. [★2309]
Trailer Hitch Mfrs. Assn. - Defunct.
Trails
Adirondack Forty-Sixers [23075]
Adirondack Mountain Club [23076]
Adirondack Trail Improvement Soc. [23077]
Am. Outdoors Assn. [22835]
Amer. Endurance Ride Conf. [23078]
Amer. Hiking Soc. [23079]
Amer. Trails [23080]
Appalachian Mountain Club [23081]
Appalachian Trail Conservancy [23082]
Continental Divide Trail Soc. [23083]
Florida Trail Assn. [23084]

A star before a book entry number signifies that the name is not listed separately, but is mentioned within the entry.

InterCollegiate Outing Club Assn. [23085]
Intl. Soc. of Professional Trackers [3494]
IOCALUM [23086]
Montana Outfitters and Guides Assn. [23087]
Mountaineers [23088]
New England Trail Rider Assn. [23089]
New England Trails Conf. [23090]
North Amer. Trail Ride Conf. [23091]
North Country Trail Assn. [23092]
Pacific Northwest Trail Assn. [23093]
Rails-to-Trails Conservancy [23094]
Scottish Rights of Way and Access Soc. [1274]
Trail of Tears Assn. [10613]
Tree Climbing USA [21286]
U.S. Mountain Guides Assn. [22456]
U.S. Ski Mountaineering Assn. [22917]
Train Collectors Assn. [21896], PO Box 248, Strasburg, PA 17579-0248, (717)687-8623
Train Collectors Assn. [21896], PO Box 248, Strasburg, PA 17579-0248, (717)687-8623
Trainers
Innovation Network [1912]
Intl. Modern Hapkido Fed. [22735]
Natl. Athletic Trainers' Assn. [23095]
Natl. Coun. on Strength and Fitness [23096]
Natl. Fed. of Professional Trainers [23097]
Natl. Strength and Conditioning Assn. [23098]
New Zealand Assn. for Training and Development [5638]
Professional Baseball Athletic Trainers Soc. [22289]
Professional Climbing Instructors Assn. [22455]
Professional Golf Teachers Assn. of Am. [22621]
Thoroughbred Club of Am. [22666]
Walking Horse Trainers Assn. [4660]
Training for Change [13150], PO Box 30914, Philadelphia, PA 19104, (215)776-8444
Training Directors' Forum - Defunct.
Training Media Assn. - Defunct.
Training and Productivity Authority of Fiji [IO], Nasinu, Fiji
Training Res. Assessment Consultants [★6251]
Training Res. Assessment Consultants [★6251]
Tramway and Light Railway Soc. [IO], Brightlingsea, United Kingdom
Trans-Atlantic Amer. Flag Liner Operators/Trans-Pacific Amer. Flag Berth Operators [3272], 80 Wall St., Ste. 1117, New York, NY 10005-3688, (212)269-2415
Trans European Policy Stud. Assn. [IO], Brussels, Belgium
Trans Lunar Res. [6101], Randa Milliron, Co-Founder, PO Box 661, Mojave, CA 93502-0661, (661)824-1662
Trans-Species Unlimited [★10920]
Trans World Radio [20100], PO Box 8700, Cary, NC 27512-8700, (919)460-3700
Trans World Radio [20100], PO Box 8700, Cary, NC 27512-8700, (919)460-3700
Trans Youth Family Allies [12585], PO Box 1471, Holland, MI 49422-1471, (888)462-8932
TransAct - Dutch Center for Gender Issues in Healthcare and Prevention of Sexual Violence [IO], Utrecht, Netherlands
Transaction Processing Performance Coun. [6476], PO Box 29920, San Francisco, CA 94129-0920, (415)561-6272
TransAfrica [★17153]
TransAfrica [★17153]
TransAfrica Forum [17153], 1629 K St. NW, Ste. 1100, Washington, DC 20006, (202)223-1960
TransAfrica Forum [17153], 1629 K St. NW, Ste. 1100, Washington, DC 20006, (202)223-1960
Transamerican Advt. Agency Network [★111]
Transamerican Advt. Agency Network [★111]
Transcultural Nursing Soc. [15804], Madonna Univ., Coll. of Nursing and Hea., 36600 Schoolcraft Rd., Livonia, MI 48150, (888)432-5470
Transcultural Nursing Soc. [15804], Madonna Univ., Coll. of Nursing and Hea., 36600 Schoolcraft Rd., Livonia, MI 48150, (888)432-5470
TransFair Canada [IO], Ottawa, ON, Canada
TransFair USA [★3484]
Transferware Collectors Club [21270], 734 Torreya Ct., Palo Alto, CA 94303

Transfiguration Prison Ministry - Defunct.
The Transformer Assn. [1662], 1300 Sumner Ave., Cleveland, OH 44115-2851, (216)241-7333
The Transformer Assn. [1662], 1300 Sumner Ave., Cleveland, OH 44115-2851, (216)241-7333
Transfrigoroute Intl. [IO], Brussels, Belgium
Transgender
Atticus Circle [17735]
Campus Pride [12072]
CenterLink [11661]
Equality Fed. [17736]
Gay and Lesbian Assn. of Retiring Persons [10843]
LEAGUE [12096]
Natl. Coalition of Anti-Violence Programs [18770]
Sylvia Rivera Law Proj. [18730]
Youth Pride Alliance [12117]
Transgender Amer. Veterans Assn. [20804], PO Box 4513, Akron, OH 44310, (718)849-5665
The Transition Network [13482], PO Box 231240, New York, NY 10023-0021, (212)714-8040
Transition U.S. [4343], PO Box 917, Sebastopol, CA 95473, (707)763-1100
Transitions Global [12248], 7723 Tylers Place Blvd., No. 330, West Chester, OH 45069, (513)898-9372
Translation
The Amer. Assn. of Language Specialists [3495]
The Amer. Assn. of Language Specialists [3495]
Amer. Literary Translators Assn. [10614]
Amer. Translation and Interpreting Stud. Assn. [9015]
Amer. Translators Assn. [3496]
Assn. for Machine Translation in the Americas [7577]
Assn. for Machine Translation in the Americas [7577]
Intl. Org. for Septuagint and Cognate Stud. [19349]
Natl. Alliance of Black Interpreters [3497]
Swedish Translators in North America [10615]
Swedish Translators in North America [10615]
Translators Assn. [IO], London, United Kingdom
Transmission Rebuilders Network Intl. [341], 6501 E Greenway Pkwy., Ste. 103/298, Scottsdale, AZ 85254, (888)582-8764
Transnational Found. for Peace and Future Res. [IO], Lund, Sweden
Transnational Inst. [IO], Amsterdam, Netherlands
Transocean Marine Paint Assn. [IO], Rotterdam, Netherlands
Transparence-International (France) [★IO]
Transparencia, Consciencia and Cidadania [★IO]
Transparencia Internacional Costa Rica [★IO]
Transparencia Paraguay [IO], Asuncion, Paraguay
Transparencia Venezuela [IO], Caracas, Venezuela
Transparency, Consciousness and Citizenship [IO], Brasilia, Brazil
Transparency Intl. - Argentina [IO], Buenos Aires, Argentina
Transparency Intl. - Australia [IO], Melbourne, Australia
Transparency Intl. - Azerbaijan [IO], Baku, Azerbaijan
Transparency Intl. - Bangladesh [IO], Dhaka, Bangladesh
Transparency Intl. - Bosnia and Herzegovina [IO], Banja Luka, Bosnia-Hercegovina
Transparency Intl. - Brazil [IO], Sao Paulo, Brazil
Transparency Intl. - Brussels [IO], Brussels, Belgium
Transparency Intl. - Bulgaria [IO], Sofia, Bulgaria
Transparency Intl. - Burundi [IO], Bujumbura, Burundi
Transparency Intl. - Cameroon [IO], Yaounde, Cameroon
Transparency Intl. - Canada [IO], Toronto, ON, Canada
Transparency Intl. - Chile [IO], Santiago, Chile
Transparency Intl. - Colombia [IO], Bogota, Colombia
Transparency Intl. - Costa Rica [IO], San Jose, Costa Rica
Transparency Intl. - Croatia [IO], Zagreb, Croatia
Transparency Intl. - Czech Republic [IO], Prague, Czech Republic
Transparency Intl. - Denmark [IO], Copenhagen, Denmark

Transparency Intl. Deutschland e.V. [★IO]
Transparency Intl. - Dominican Republic [IO], Santo Domingo, Dominican Republic
Transparency Intl. - Estonia [IO], Tallinn, Estonia
Transparency Intl. - Ethiopia [IO], Addis Ababa, Ethiopia
Transparency Intl. - Fiji [IO], Suva, Fiji
Transparency Intl. - France [IO], Levallois Perret, France
Transparency Intl. - Georgia [IO], Tbilisi, Georgia
Transparency Intl. - Germany [IO], Berlin, Germany
Transparency Intl. - Greece [IO], Athens, Greece
Transparency Intl. - Haiti [IO], Petionville, Haiti
Transparency Intl. Hrvatska [★IO]
Transparency Intl. - Hungary [IO], Budapest, Hungary
Transparency Intl. - India [IO], New Delhi, India
Transparency Intl. - Indonesia [IO], Jakarta, Indonesia
Transparency Intl. - Initiative Madagascar [IO], Antananarivo, Madagascar
Transparency Intl. - Ireland [IO], Dublin, Ireland
Transparency Intl. - Israel [IO], Tel Aviv, Israel
Transparency Intl. - Italy [IO], Milan, Italy
Transparency Intl. - Kazakhstan [IO], Almaty, Kazakhstan
Transparency Intl. - Kenya [IO], Nairobi, Kenya
Transparency Intl. - Korea [IO], Seoul, Republic of Korea
Transparency Intl. - Lithuania [IO], Vilnius, Lithuania
Transparency Intl. - Malaysia [IO], Kuala Lumpur, Malaysia
Transparency Intl. - Moldova [IO], Chisinau, Moldova
Transparency Intl. - Mongolia [IO], Ulan Bator, Mongolia
Transparency Intl. - Nepal [IO], Kathmandu, Nepal
Transparency Intl. - New Zealand [IO], Wellington, New Zealand
Transparency Intl. - Nigeria [IO], Abuja, Nigeria
Transparency Intl. - Pakistan [IO], Karachi, Pakistan
Transparency Intl. - Papua New Guinea [IO], Port Moresby, Papua New Guinea
Transparency Intl. - Philippine Chap. [IO], Manila, Philippines
Transparency Intl. - Poland [IO], Warsaw, Poland
Transparency Intl. - Romania [IO], Bucharest, Romania
Transparency Intl. - Russia [IO], Moscow, Russia
Transparency Intl. - Slovakia [IO], Bratislava, Slovakia
Transparency Intl. - Solomon Islands [IO], Honiara, Solomon Islands
Transparency Intl. - South Africa [IO], Braamfontein, Republic of South Africa
Transparency Intl. - Sri Lanka [IO], Colombo, Sri Lanka
Transparency Intl. - Sweden [IO], Stockholm, Sweden
Transparency Intl. - Switzerland [IO], Bern, Switzerland
Transparency Intl. - Taiwan [IO], Taipei, Taiwan
Transparency Intl. - Thailand [IO], Bangkok, Thailand
Transparency Intl. - Turkey [IO], Istanbul, Turkey
Transparency Intl. - Uganda [IO], Kampala, Uganda
Transparency Intl. - UK [IO], London, United Kingdom
Transparency Intl. - Ukraine [IO], Kiev, Ukraine
Transparency Intl. - Vanuatu [IO], Port Vila, Vanuatu
Transparency Intl. - Zambia [IO], Lusaka, Zambia
Transparency Intl. - Zimbabwe [IO], Harare, Zimbabwe
Transparency Maldives [IO], Male, Maldives
Transparency Mauritius [IO], Port Louis, Mauritius
Transpersonal Institute [★9821]
Transplant Australia [IO], North Sydney, Australia
Transplant Organ Procurement Org. [★16905]
Transplant Recipients Intl. Org. [16918], 2100 M St. NW, No. 170-353, Washington, DC 20037-1233, (202)293-0980
Transplant Recipients Intl. Org. [16918], 2100 M St. NW, No. 170-353, Washington, DC 20037-1233, (202)293-0980
Transplant Speakers Intl. [16919], PO Box 6395, Freehold, NJ 07728-6395, (877)609-4615

Reference to "IO" in place of a book number signifies that the association may be found in the 50th edition of International Organizations.

Transplant Speakers Intl. [16919], PO Box 6395, Freehold, NJ 07728-6395, (877)609-4615
Transplantation
AlloSource [16895]
Amer. Assn. of Tissue Banks [16896]
Amer. Organ Transplant Assn. [16897]
Amer. Soc. for Blood and Marrow Transplantation [16898]
Amer. Soc. of Multicultural Hea. and Transplant Professionals [16899]
Amer. Soc. of Transplant Surgeons [16900]
Amer. Soc. of Transplantation [16901]
Amer. Transplant Assn. [16902]
Asians for Miracle Marrow Matches [16903]
Blood and Marrow Transplant Info. Network [16904]
Center for Organ Recovery and Educ. [16905]
Intl. Assn. for Organ Donation [16906]
Intl. Assn. for Organ Donation [16906]
Intl. Liver Transplantation Soc. [16907]
Intl. Liver Transplantation Soc. [16907]
Intl. Pediatric Transplant Assn. [16908]
Intl. Pediatric Transplant Assn. [16908]
Intl. Soc. for Heart and Lung Transplantation [16909]
Intl. Soc. for Heart and Lung Transplantation [16909]
Kidney Community Emergency Response Coalition [15552]
Kidney Transplant/Dialysis Assn. [16910]
LifeSharers [16911]
Natl. Bone Marrow Transplant Link [16912]
Natl. Found. for Transplants [16913]
Natl. Inst. of Transplantation [16914]
Natl. Transplant Soc. [16915]
North Amer. Transplant Coordinators Org. [16916]
Tissue Banks Intl. [16917]
Tissue Banks Intl. [16917]
Transplant Recipients Intl. Org. [16918]
Transplant Recipients Intl. Org. [16918]
Transplant Speakers Intl. [16919]
Transplant Speakers Intl. [16919]
United Network for Organ Sharing [16920]
Transplantation; Assn. of Nurses Endorsing [15946]
The Transplantation Soc. [IO], Montreal, QC, Canada
Transport 2000 - Canada [IO], Ottawa, ON, Canada
Transport Assn. [IO], Leatherhead, United Kingdom
Transport for Christ [★20101]
Transport for Christ [★20101]
Transport for Christ, Intl. [20101], PO Box 117, Marietta, PA 17547-0117, (717)426-9977
Transport for Christ, Intl. [20101], PO Box 117, Marietta, PA 17547-0117, (717)426-9977
Transport and Gen. Workers' Union [IO], London, United Kingdom
Transport and Indus. Workers Union [IO], Port of Spain, Trinidad and Tobago
Transport Museum Assn. [10502], 2967 Barrett Sta. Rd., St. Louis, MO 63122, (314)965-6885
Transport Planning Soc. [IO], London, United Kingdom
Transport Salaried Staffs' Assn. - Ireland [IO], Dublin, Ireland
Transport Salaried Staffs Assn. - United Kingdom [IO], London, United Kingdom
Transport Ticket Soc. [IO], Mansfield, United Kingdom
Transport Workers Union of Am. [23303], 501 3rd St. NW, 9th Fl., Washington, DC 20001, (202)719-3900
Transport Workers' Union of Australia [IO], Parramatta, Australia
Transportation
Advanced Transit Assn. [7578]
Agricultural and Food Transporters Conf. [3498]
Airport Ground Trans. Assn. [3499]
Alliance for Biking and Walking [18731]
Alliance for Biking and Walking [18731]
Alliance for a New Trans. Charter [6026]
Amalgamated Transit Union [23300]
Amer. Assn. of State Highway and Trans. Officials [6027]
Amer. Bus Assn. [3500]
Amer. Dream Coalition [17264]

Amer. Public Trans. Assn. [3501]
Amer. Public Trans. Assn. [3501]
Amer. Road and Trans. Builders Assn. [6028]
Amer. Soc. of Trans. and Logistics [3502]
Amer. Truck Dealers [3503]
Amer. Trucking Associations [3504]
Amer. Trucking Associations | Tech. and Maintenance Coun. [3505]
Amer. Vecturist Assn. [22182]
Americans for Trans. Mobility [6029]
Angel Wing Flights [12445]
Assn. for Commuter Trans. [13331]
Assn. for Commuter Trans. [13331]
Assn. of Pedestrian and Bicycle Professionals [18732]
Assn. for Safe Intl. Road Travel [13332]
Assn. for Safe Intl. Road Travel [13332]
Assn. of Trans. Law Professionals [6030]
Bigfoot Owners Clubs Intl. [21008]
CarFree City, USA [4961]
Certified Claims Professional Accreditation Coun. [3506]
Chinese Overseas Trans. Assn. [3507]
Coach Operators Fed. [8706]
Coalition Against Bigger Trucks [13333]
Conf. of Minority Trans. Officials [3508]
Delta Nu Alpha Trans. Fraternity [23756]
driveAWARE [12982]
Driver Employment Coun. of Am. [3509]
Electrification Coalition [3510]
Elevator U [555]
Eno Trans. Found. [7579]
Equip. Managers Coun. of Am. [845]Transportation European Fed. for Transport and Env.
European Intermodal Assn. [3385]
Governors Highway Safety Assn. [6031]
Gray Line Sightseeing Assn. [3511]
Greek Natl. Tourist Org. [3512]
Greek Natl. Tourist Org. [3512]
High Speed Ground Trans. Assn. [7580]
Inst. of Trans. Engineers [7581]
Inst. of Trans. Engineers [7581]
Intelligent Trans. Soc. of Am. [3513]
Intermodal Assn. of North Am. [3514]
The Intl. Air Cargo Assn. [3515]
The Intl. Air Cargo Assn. [3515]
Intl. Assn. for the Advancement of Steam Power [7480]
Intl. Bicycle Fund [13334]
Intl. Bicycle Fund [13334]
Intl. Bridge, Tunnel and Turnpike Assn. [6032]
Intl. Bridge, Tunnel and Turnpike Assn. [6032]
Intl. Brotherhood of Teamsters [23301]
Intl. Coun. on Clean Trans. [3516]Transportation Intl. Fed. of Bike Messenger Associations
Intl. Human Powered Vehicle Assn. [7582]
Intl. Human Powered Vehicle Assn. [7582]
Intl. Road Fed. [3517]
Intl. Road Fed. [3517]
Intl. Trans. Mgt. Assn. [6033]
Intl. Trans. Mgt. Assn. [6033]
Japan Road Contractors Assn. [15]
Light Elec. Vehicle Assn. [3518]
Loved Ones and Drivers Support [13342]
Massachusetts Bay Railroad Enthusiasts [10491]
Mid-West Truckers Assn. [3519]
The Monorail Soc. [22183]
Natl. Alliance of Highway Beautification Agencies [5948]
Natl. Assn. of Publicly Funded Truck Driving Schools [3520]
Natl. Assn. for Pupil Trans. [6034]
Natl. Assn. of Railroad Trial Counsel [6035]
Natl. Assn. of Show Trucks [3521]
Natl. Assn. of Timetable Collectors [22184]
Natl. Bus Traffic Assn. [3522]
Natl. Conf. of State Fleet Administrators [6036]
Natl. Conf. of State Trans. Specialists [6037]
Natl. Indus. Trans. League [3523]
Natl. Limousine Assn. [3524]
Natl. Motorists Assn. [13335]
Natl. Private Truck Coun. [3525]
Natl. Safe Skies Alliance [18733]
Natl. School Trans. Assn. [3526]

Natl. Traffic Incident Mgt. Coalition [13330]
Natl. Trailer Dealers Assn. [3527]
Natl. Transit Benefit Assn. [6038]
Natl. Truckers Assn. [3528]
North Amer. Rail Shippers Assn. [3529]
North Amer. Railcar Operators Assn. [3530]
North Amer. Trailer Dealers Assn. [3531]
North America's Corridor Coalition [3532]
Owner-Operator Independent Drivers Assn. [3533]
Partnership for Safe Driving [13002]
Personal Submersibles Org. [7148]
Plug In Am. [6118]
Professional Truck Driver Inst. [3534]
Railway Indus. Clearance Assn. [3535]
Railway and Locomotive Historical Soc. [10498]
Reconnecting Am. [13336]
Ride to Work [21936]
The Road Info. Prog. [3536]
Snow and Ice Mgt. Assn. [6039]
Surface Trans. Policy Proj. [18734]
Taxicab, Limousine and Paratransit Assn. [3537]
Taxicab, Limousine and Paratransit Assn. [3537]
Teamsters for a Democratic Union [23302]
Transport Salaried Staffs Assn. - United Kingdom [18774]
Transport Workers Union of Am. [23303]
Trans. Alternatives [7583]
Trans. Clubs Intl. [3538]
Trans. Clubs Intl. [3538]
Trans. Communications Intl. Union [23290]
Trans. Communications Union | Brotherhood Railway Carmen Div. [23291]
Trans. Lawyers Assn. [6040]
Trans. Res. Bd. [7584]
Trans. Res. Forum [7585]
Trans. Safety Equip. Inst. [3153]
Trucking Indus. Defense Assn. [3539]
Trucking Mgt., Inc. [3540]
Truckload Carriers Assn. [3541]
United Motorcoach Assn. [3542]
Vespa Club of Am. [21942]
Wabash, Frisco and Pacific Assn. [10503]
Women in Trucking [3543]
Women's Intl. Shipping and Trading Assn. [3276]
Women's Trans. Seminar [3544]
Women's Trans. Seminar [3544]
World Bicycle Relief [12898]
Trans. Alternatives [7583], 127 W 26th St., Ste. 1002, New York, NY 10001, (212)629-8080
Trans. Assn. of Am; Community [11571]
Trans. Assn. of Canada [IO], Ottawa, ON, Canada
Trans. Brokers Conf. of Am. [★3274]
Trans. Claims and Prevention Coun. [★3275]
Trans. Clubs Intl. [3538], PO Box 2223, Ocean Shores, WA 98569, (877)858-8627
Trans. Clubs Intl. [3538], PO Box 2223, Ocean Shores, WA 98569, (877)858-8627
Transportation-Communication Employees Union [★23290]
Trans. Communications Intl. Union [23290], 3 Res. Pl., Rockville, MD 20850, (301)948-4910
Trans. Communications Union | Brotherhood Railway Carmen Div. [23291], 3 Res. Pl., Rockville, MD 20850, (301)948-4910
Trans. Consumer Protection Coun. [★3275]
Trans., Elevator and Grain Merchants Assn. [1596], PO Box 26426, Kansas City, MO 64196, (816)569-4020
Trans. Inst. [3273], 5201 Auth Way, Camp Springs, MD 20746-4211, (301)423-3335
Trans. Insurance Rating Bur. [★1926]
Trans. Intermediaries Assn. [3274], 1625 Prince St., Ste. 200, Alexandria, VA 22314, (703)299-5700
Trans. Lawyers Assn. [6040], PO Box 15122, Lenexa, KS 66285-5122, (913)895-4615
Trans. and Logistics Coun. [3275], 120 Main St., Huntington, NY 11743, (631)549-8988
Trans. Res. Bd. [7584], The Natl. Academies, 500 5th St. NW, Washington, DC 20001, (202)334-2167
Trans. Res. Forum [7585], NDSU Dept. 2880, PO Box 6050, Fargo, ND 58108-6050, (701)231-7766
Trans. Safety Equip. Inst. [3153], PO Box 13966, Research Triangle Park, NC 27709, (919)406-8823
Transported Asset Protection Assn. [7396], Purdue Pharma Technologies, Inc., 498 Washington St., Coventry, RI 02816, (401)823-2059

A star before a book entry number signifies that the name is not listed separately, but is mentioned within the entry.

TransportGroup [IO], Stockholm, Sweden
TransportGruppen [★IO]
Transportokonomisk institutt [★IO]
Transsexual
   Gender Educ. and Advocacy [13104]
   Natl. Coalition of Anti-Violence Programs [18770]
   Sylvia Rivera Law Proj. [18730]
Transverse Myelitis Assn. [15637], Sanford J. Sie-
   gel, Pres./Newsletter Ed., 1787 Sutter Pkwy., Pow-
   ell, OH 43065-8806, (614)766-1806
Transverse Myelitis Assn. [15637], Sanford J. Sie-
   gel, Pres./Newsletter Ed., 1787 Sutter Pkwy., Pow-
   ell, OH 43065-8806, (614)766-1806
Transvestite
   Soc. for the Second Self [13112]
Transworld Advt. Agency Network [111], 814 Water-
   town St., Newton, MA 02465, (617)795-1706
Transworld Advt. Agency Network [111], 814 Water-
   town St., Newton, MA 02465, (617)795-1706
TransWorld Development Initiatives [12262], PO Box
   105, Brentwood, MD 20722, (301)793-7551
TransWorld Development Initiatives [12262], PO Box
   105, Brentwood, MD 20722, (301)793-7551
Transylvania Soc. of Dracula [IO], St. John's, NL,
   Canada
Transylvania Soc. of Dracula - Italy [IO], Turin, Italy
Trappers
   Natl. Trappers Assn. [4963]
Trapping
   Fur Takers of Am. [4962]
   Natl. Trappers Assn. [4963]
Traprock Center for Peace and Justice [18291], PO
   Box 1201, Greenfield, MA 01302-1201, (413)773-
   7427
Traprock Peace Center [★18291]
Trauma
   Amer. Acad. of Experts in Traumatic Stress
    [16921]
   Amer. Acad. of Wound Mgt. [16922]
   Amer. Assn. for the Surgery of Trauma [16923]
   Amer. Professional Wound Care Assn. [16924]
   Amer. Trauma Soc. [16925]
   Anahata Intl. [13662]
   Coalition for Amer. Trauma Care [16926]
   Forgotten Victims [13363]
   Give an Hour [11088]
   Harvard Injury Control Res. Center [16927]
   Hold the Door for Others [11129]
   Medically Induced Trauma Support Services
    [16928]
   Natl. Child Traumatic Stress Network [16929]
   NAVAH [13311]
   Sky Help [16930]
   Transitions Global [12248]
   Trauma Found. at San Francisco Gen. Hosp.
    [18735]
   Traumatic Incident Reduction Assn. [16931]
Trauma Care Intl. [★13750]
Trauma Care Intl. [★13750]
Trauma Found. at San Francisco Gen. Hosp.
   [18735], 233 Captain Nurse Cir., Novato, CA
   94949, (415)380-9230
Traumatic Incident Reduction Assn. [16931], 5145
   Pontiac Trail, Ann Arbor, MI 48105, (734)761-6268
Travel
   Adventrek [12256]
   Adventure Travel Trade Assn. [3545]
   Africa Travel Assn. [3546]
   Africa Travel Assn. [3546]
   Amer. Auto. Touring Alliance [3547]
   Amer. Small Bus. Travelers Alliance [3548]
   Amer. Soc. of Travel Agents [3549]
   Assist Card Intl. [3550]
   Assist Card Intl. [3550]
   Assn. of Corporate Travel Executives [3551]
   Assn. of Destination Mgt. Executives [3552]
   Assn. of Destination Mgt. Executives [3552]
   Assn. of Retail Travel Agents [3553]
   Assn. of Travel Marketing Executives [3554]
   Belgian Tourist Off. [23333]
   Bermuda Dept. of Tourism [23447]
   Binational Tourism Alliance [3473]
   Bounders United [22185]
   Bus. Travel Coalition [23453]
   Caribbean Hotel and Tourism Assn. [3555]

Caribbean Hotel and Tourism Assn. [3555]
Carriage Travel Club [22186]
Ceylon (Sri Lanka) Tourist Dept. [23443]
Coun. for Educational Travel U.S.A. [9016]
Country Coach Intl. [22187]
Cruise Club of Am. [3556]
Cruise Lines Intl. Assn. [3557]
Cruise Lines Intl. Assn. [3557]
Cyprus Tourism Org. [23396]
Escapees [22137]
Estonian Assn. of Travel Agencies [22494]
European Travel Commn. [3558]
European Travel Commn. [3558]
European Union Fed. of Youth Hostel Associa-
   tions [5721]
Extra Miler Club [22188]
Faceless Intl. [13362]
Fed. of Amer. Consumers and Travelers [13337]
German Natl. Tourist Bd. [3559]
German Natl. Tourist Off. [3559]
Global Explorers [9017]
Global Explorers [9017]
Greek Natl. Tourist Org. [3512]
Grenada Bd. of Tourism [23343]
Hellenic Assn. of Travel and Tourist Agencies
   [12083]
Highpointers Club [22189]
Hostelling Intl. USA [12766]
Humanitarian Travels Intl. [13338]
Humanitarian Travels Intl. [13338]
Interactive Travel Services Assn. [3560]
Intl. Airline Passengers Assn. [22190]
Intl. Airline Passengers Assn. [22190]
Intl. Assn. of Antarctica Tour Operators [3561]
Intl. Assn. of Antarctica Tour Operators [3561]
Intl. Assn. for Medical Assistance to Travellers
   [13339]
Intl. Assn. for Medical Assistance to Travellers
   [13339]
Intl. Assn. of Tour Managers - North Amer. Region
   [3562]
Intl. BioExploration Soc. [8180]
Intl. Galapagos Tour Operators Assn. [23454]
Intl. Galapagos Tour Operators Assn. [23454]
Intl. Gay and Lesbian Travel Assn. [3563]
Intl. Soc. of Travel and Tourism Educators [3564]
Intl. Soc. of Travel and Tourism Educators [3564]
Interval Intl. [21854]
Irish Travel Agents Assn. [11362]
Italian Fed. of Tour Operators and Travel Agen-
   cies [6479]
Japan Natl. Tourist Org. [23417]
Jordan Info. Bur. [23421]
Kenya Assn. of Tour Operators [5531]
Malaysia Tourism Promotion Bd. [23427]
Mesoamerican Ecotourism Alliance [4964]
Mexico Tourism Bd. [23428]
Motorist Info. and Services Assn. [13340]
My Travel Bug [9018]
My Travel Bug [9018]
Natl. Assn. of Commissioned Travel Agents [3565]
Natl. Assn. of Cruise-Oriented Agencies [3566]
Natl. Assn. of Passport and Visa Services [3567]
Natl. Assn. of Travel Agents Singapore [9136]
Natl. Bus. Travel Assn. [3568]
Natl. Tour Assn. [3569]
Oceanic Soc. Expeditions [22191]
Opening Door [3570]
Order of United Commercial Travelers of Am. -
   Canadian Off. [1985]
Outside Sales Support Network [3571]
Pacific Asia Travel Assn. [3572]
Pacific Asia Travel Assn. [3572]
Romanian Natl. Tourist Off. [3573]
Romanian Natl. Tourist Off. [3573]
Roving Volunteers in Christ's Ser. [22192]
RV Mfrs'. Clubs Assn. [22146]
Saint Kitts Tourism Authority [23344]
Soc. for Accessible Travel and Hospitality [11829]
Soc. of Govt. Travel Professionals [3574]
Soc. of Incentive and Travel Executives [3575]
Soc. of Incentive and Travel Executives [3575]
Soc. of Polish-American Travel Agents [3576]
South Amer. Explorers [3577]
South Amer. Explorers [3577]

Student and Youth Travel Assn. [3578]
Student and Youth Travel Assn. [3578]
Sustainable Travel Intl. [4965]
Sustainable Travel Intl. [4965]
The Travel Inst. [3579]
Travel and Tourism Res. Assn. [3580]
Travel and Tourism Res. Assn. [3580]
Travelers' Century Club [22193]
U.S. Air Consolidator Assn. [3581]
U.S. Tour Operators Assn. [3582]
U.S. Tour Operators Assn. [3582]
U.S. Travel Assn. [3583]
U.S. Travel Data Center [3584]
U.S. Travel Insurance Assn. [3585]
Venezuelan Tourism Assn. [3586]
Venezuelan Tourism Assn. [3586]
Visitor Stud. Assn. [9019]
Visitor Stud. Assn. [9019]
VisitSweden [3587]
VisitSweden [3587]
WAVES for Development [18683]
Women Outdoors [22797]
World Ocean and Cruise Liner Soc. [22194]
World Ocean and Cruise Liner Soc. [22194]
Travel Agencies Assn. [IO], Madrid, Spain
Travel Agents Assn. of India [IO], Mumbai, India
Travel Agents Assn. of New Zealand [IO], Welling-
   ton, New Zealand
Travel Agents Assn. of Sri Lanka [IO], Colombo, Sri
   Lanka
Travel China Roads [7847], 1719 E Feemster Ct.,
   Visalia, CA 93292, (559)636-6026
Travel Goods Assn. [2226], 301 N Harrison St., No.
   412, Princeton, NJ 08540-3512, (877)TGA-1938
Travel Indus. Coun. of Hong Kong [IO], Hong Kong,
   People's Republic of China
Travel Industry and Disabled Exchange - Defunct.
The Travel Inst. [3579], 148 Linden St., Ste. 305,
   Wellesley, MA 02482, (781)237-0280
Travel Journalists Guild [2877], PO Box 10643,
   Chicago, IL 60610-4952, (312)664-9279
Travel Professionals Assn. - Defunct.
Travel Professionals Intl. [IO], Winnipeg, MB,
   Canada
Travel Services
   Belgian Tourist Off. [23333]
   Cyprus Tourism Org. [23396]
   Greek Natl. Tourist Org. [3512]
   Humanitarian Travels Intl. [13338]
   Interval Intl. [21854]
   Jordan Info. Bur. [23421]
   Mexico Tourism Bd. [23428]
Travel and Tourism Government Affairs Coun. -
   Defunct.
Travel and Tourism Res. Assn. [3580], 3048 W
   Clarkston Rd., Lake Orion, MI 48362, (248)708-
   8872
Travel and Tourism Res. Assn. [3580], 3048 W
   Clarkston Rd., Lake Orion, MI 48362, (248)708-
   8872
Travel Trust Assn. [IO], Woking, United Kingdom
Travelers Aid Intl. [13205], 1612 K St. NW, Ste. 206,
   Washington, DC 20006, (202)546-1127
Travelers Aid Intl. [13205], 1612 K St. NW, Ste. 206,
   Washington, DC 20006, (202)546-1127
Travelers' Century Club [22193], PO Box 7050,
   Santa Monica, CA 90406-7050, (310)458-3454
Travelers Protective Assn. of Am. [19060], 3755 Lin-
   dell Blvd., St. Louis, MO 63108-3476, (314)371-
   0533
Tread Lightly! [4864], 298 24th St., Ste. 325, Ogden,
   UT 84401, (801)627-0077
Treasure State Outfitters [★23087]
Treasures for Little Children [22173], PO Box 118,
   Chardon, OH 44024
Treasury Historical Assn. [9813], PO Box 28118,
   Washington, DC 20038-8118, (202)298-0550
Treasury Mgt. Assn. [★1283]
Treatment Action Gp. [13626], 261 5th Ave., Ste.
   2110, New York, NY 10016-7701, (212)253-7922
Treatment Communities of Am. [13290], 1601 Con-
   necticut Ave., Ste. 803, Washington, DC 20009,
   (202)296-3503
Treatment and Res. Advancements Assn. for
   Personality Disorder [15484], 23 Greene St., New
   York, NY 10013, (212)966-6514

Reference to "IO" in place of a book number signifies that the association may be found in the 50th edition of International Organizations.

Tree Care Indus. Assn. **[4976]**, 136 Harvey Rd., Ste. 101, Londonderry, NH 03053, (603)314-5380

Tree Care Indus. Assn. **[4976]**, 136 Harvey Rd., Ste. 101, Londonderry, NH 03053, (603)314-5380

Tree Climber's Coalition **[21284]**, 6625 Hwy. 53 E, Ste. 410, PMB 43, Dawsonville, GA 30534, (706)216-1679

Tree Climbers Intl. **[21285]**, PO Box 5588, Atlanta, GA 31107, (404)377-3150

Tree Climbing USA **[21286]**, PO Box 142062, Fayetteville, GA 30214, (770)487-6929

Tree Coun. **[IO]**, London, United Kingdom

Tree House Animal Found. **[★11046]**

Tree House Humane Soc. **[11046]**, 1212 W Carmen Ave., Chicago, IL 60640-2999, (773)784-5488

Tree Musketeers **[4151]**, 305 Richmond St., El Segundo, CA 90245, (310)322-0263

Tree of Peace Soc. **[9582]**, 326 Cook Rd., Hogansburg, NY 13655, (518)358-2641

Tree-Ring Soc. **[4416]**, Univ. of Arizona, Lab. of Tree-Ring Res., Bldg. 58, Tucson, AZ 85721, (520)621-1608

Treeing Walker Breeders and Fanciers Assn. **[21660]**, Grant Noeske, Sec., 9680 W Northern Ave., No. 3306, Peoria, AZ 85345, (815)275-6233

TreePeople **[4152]**, 12601 Mulholland Dr., Beverly Hills, CA 90210, (818)753-4600

Trees
Elm Res. Inst. **[4393]**
Intl. Wood Collectors Soc. **[22203]**
Tree Climbing USA **[21286]**

Trees for the Future **[4977]**, PO Box 7027, Silver Spring, MD 20907, (301)565-0630

Trees for Life **[12296]**, 3006 W St. Louis St., Wichita, KS 67203-5129, (316)945-6929

Trees for Life **[12296]**, 3006 W St. Louis St., Wichita, KS 67203-5129, (316)945-6929

Trees and Shrubs
Amer. Conifer Soc. **[4966]**
Amer. Soc. of Consulting Arborists **[4967]**
Amer. Willow Growers Network **[4968]**
European Palm Soc. **[21282]**
Growing Planet **[4400]**
Holly Soc. of Am. **[4969]**
Intl. Fruit Tree Assn. **[4970]**
Intl. Fruit Tree Assn. **[4970]**
Intl. Oak Soc. **[4971]**
Intl. Oak Soc. **[4971]**
Intl. Soc. of Arboriculture **[4972]**
Intl. Soc. of Arboriculture **[4972]**
Intl. Wood Collectors Soc. **[22203]**
Metropolitan Tree Improvement Alliance **[4973]**
Natl. Christmas Tree Assn. **[4974]**
Pacific Northwest Christmas Tree Assn. **[4975]**
Tree Care Indus. Assn. **[4976]**
Tree Care Indus. Assn. **[4976]**
Trees for the Future **[4977]**

Trees for Tomorrow **[4417]**, 519 Sheridan St., PO Box 609, Eagle River, WI 54521, (715)479-6456

Trees, Water and People **[4308]**, 633 Remington St., Fort Collins, CO 80524, (970)484-3678

Trees, Water and People **[4308]**, 633 Remington St., Fort Collins, CO 80524, (970)484-3678

Trekking Agencies' Assn. of Nepal **[IO]**, Kathmandu, Nepal

Trekking for Kids **[22638]**, PO Box 25493, Washington, DC 20027, (202)651-1387

Trekking Union of Kyrgyzstan **[IO]**, Bishkek, Kirgizstan

Tremor Action Network **[15638]**, PO Box 5013, Pleasanton, CA 94566, (510)681-6565

Tremor Action Network **[15638]**, PO Box 5013, Pleasanton, CA 94566, (510)681-6565

Tremor Found; Intl. Essential **[15600]**

Tremor Found; Intl. Essential **[15600]**

Trenaunay Support Gp; Klippel- **[13843]**

Tri-College Coun. **[★15358]**

Tri-County Citrus Label Collectors **[★21324]**

Tri-Ess Sorority **[★13112]**

TRI-M Music Honor Soc. **[10305]**, 1806 Robert Fulton Dr., Reston, VA 20191, (703)860-4000

Tri-Pacer Owners Club **[★20915]**

TRI/Princeton **[3461]**, 601 Prospect Ave., Princeton, NJ 08540, (609)430-4820

TRI/Princeton **[3461]**, 601 Prospect Ave., Princeton, NJ 08540, (609)430-4820

Tri-State Dental Assn. **[★14301]**

Trial Advocacy
Amer. Assn. for Justice **[6041]**
Amer. Bd. of Trial Advocates **[6042]**
Amer. Coll. of Trial Lawyers **[6043]**
Amer. Mock Trial Assn. **[9020]**
Intl. Soc. of Barristers **[6044]**
Intl. Soc. of Barristers **[6044]**
ITC Trial Lawyers Assn. **[6045]**
Natl. Bd. of Trial Advocacy **[6046]**
Natl. Inst. for Trial Advocacy **[6047]**
Pound Civil Justice Inst. **[6048]**

Trial Lawyers for Public Justice **[★5938]**

Triangle Club **[13291]**, PO Box 65458, Washington, DC 20035, (202)659-8641

Triangle Coalition for Sci. and Tech. Educ. **[8852]**, 1840 Wilson Blvd., Ste. 201, Arlington, VA 22201, (703)516-5960

Triangle Martial Arts Assn. **[22754]**, PO Box 111, San Francisco, CA 94102, (415)992-5551

Triangles **[IO]**, London, United Kingdom

Triathlon
New York Triathlon Club **[23099]**
U.S.A. Triathlon **[23100]**

Triathlon Assn. of Singapore **[IO]**, Singapore, Singapore

Triathlon; U.S.A. **[23100]**

Tribal Court CH **[5681]**, 8235 Santa Monica Blvd., Ste. 211, West Hollywood, CA 90046, (323)650-5467

Tribal Preservation Prog. **[10336]**, Heritage Preservation Services, Natl. Park Ser., 1201 Eye St. NW, 2255, Washington, DC 20005, (202)354-1837

Tribal Sovereignty Prog. **[★18156]**

TriBeta **[★23470]**

Tribunal Arbitral du Sport **[★IO]**

Tributyl Phosphate Task Force **[770]**, SOCMA VISIONS, 1850 M St. NW, Ste. 700, Washington, DC 20036-5810, (202)721-4154

Trichotillomania Learning Center **[15485]**, 207 McPherson St., Ste. H, Santa Cruz, CA 95060-5863, (831)457-1004

Trickle Up Prog. **[12376]**, 104 W 27th St., 12th Fl., New York, NY 10001-6210, (212)255-9980

Tricycle Assn. **[IO]**, Newark, United Kingdom

The Tried and True Warriors **[★23862]**

Trigeminal Neuralgia Assn. **[★15587]**

Trikon **[★12114]**

Trikone **[12114]**, PO Box 14475, San Francisco, CA 94114

Trilateral Commn. **[17952]**, 1156 15th St. NW, Washington, DC 20005, (202)467-5410

Trilateral Commn. **[17952]**, 1156 15th St. NW, Washington, DC 20005, (202)467-5410

Trinidad Restaurants, Hotels and Tourism Assn. **[IO]**, Chaguaramas, Trinidad and Tobago

Trinidad and Tobago Amateur Radio Soc. **[IO]**, Port of Spain, Trinidad and Tobago

Trinidad and Tobago Badminton Assn. **[IO]**, Port of Spain, Trinidad and Tobago

Trinidad and Tobago Chamber of Indus. and Commerce **[IO]**, Port of Spain, Trinidad and Tobago

Trinidad and Tobago Coalition Against Domestic Violence **[IO]**, Port of Spain, Trinidad and Tobago

Trinidad and Tobago Draughts Assn. **[IO]**, Carapichaima, Trinidad and Tobago

Trinidad and Tobago Football Fed. **[IO]**, Port of Spain, Trinidad and Tobago

Trinidad and Tobago Inst. of Architects **[IO]**, Port of Spain, Trinidad and Tobago

Trinidad and Tobago Mfrs. Assn. **[IO]**, Barataria, Trinidad and Tobago

Trinidad and Tobago Olympic Comm. **[IO]**, Port of Spain, Trinidad and Tobago

Trinidad and Tobago Red Cross Soc. **[IO]**, Port of Spain, Trinidad and Tobago

Trinidad and Tobago Reprographic Rights Org. **[IO]**, El Socorro, Trinidad and Tobago

Trinidad and Tobago Tourism Development Authority - Defunct.

Trinity Hea. Intl. **[14907]**, 34605 12 Mile Rd., Farmington Hills, MI 48331, (248)489-6100

Triological Soc. **[★16085]**

Triple Nine Soc. **[9642]**, Dr. Ina Bendis, Membership Off., 3129 Barkley Ave., Santa Clara, CA 95051

The Triplet Connection **[12549]**, PO Box 429, Spring City, UT 84662, (435)851-1105

Tripoli Rocketry Assn. **[8853]**, PO Box 87, Bellevue, NE 68005, (402)884-9530

Tripoli Sci. Assn. **[★8853]**

Trips for Kids **[8161]**, 138 Sunnyside Ave., Mill Valley, CA 94941, (415)458-2986

Triratna Buddhist Community **[19374]**, Aryaloka Buddhist Centre, 14 Heartwood Cir., Newmarket, NH 03857, (603)659-5456

Trisha Yearwood Fan Club **[23897]**, PO Box 120895, Nashville, TN 37212

Trisomy 18, 13, and Related Disorders; Support Org. for **[14632]**

Triumph Intl. Owners Assn. **[★21938]**

Triumph Intl. Owners Assn. **[★21938]**

Triumph Intl. Owners Club **[21938]**, PO Box 158, Plympton, MA 02367-0158, (508)946-1939

Triumph Intl. Owners Club **[21938]**, PO Box 158, Plympton, MA 02367-0158, (508)946-1939

Triumph Over Phobia **[IO]**, Bath, United Kingdom

Triumph Register of Am. **[21178]**, 934 Coachway, Annapolis, MD 21401, (410)974-6707

Triumph Sports Owners Assn. **[★21191]**

Triumph Wedge Owners Assn. **[21179]**, 1591 Peoples Creek Rd., Advance, NC 27006-7451, (336)998-6501

Trollope Soc. **[9418]**, 1235 Park Ave., Ste. 15-D, New York, NY 10128, (212)683-4023

Troops Out Now Coalition **[18292]**, 55 W 17th St., No. 5C, New York, NY 10011, (212)633-6646

Tropenbos Intl. **[IO]**, Wageningen, Netherlands

Trophy Dealers of Am. **[★382]**

Trophy Dealers and Mfrs. Assn. **[★382]**

Tropic Lightning Assn. **[★20352]**

Tropical Agricultural Res. and Higher Educ. Centre **[IO]**, Turrialba, Costa Rica

Tropical Biology Assn. **[IO]**, Cambridge, United Kingdom

Tropical Clinics **[15216]**, Margaret Kilibwa, PhD, Founder/Dir., PO Box 622, Kingston, NJ 08528-0622, (732)331-6859

Tropical Flowering Tree Soc. **[4679]**, Fairchild Tropical Botanical Garden, 10901 Old Cutler Rd., Coral Gables, FL 33156

Tropical Flowering Tree Soc. **[4679]**, Fairchild Tropical Botanical Garden, 10901 Old Cutler Rd., Coral Gables, FL 33156

Tropical Forest and Climate Coalition **[4861]**, 1616 P St. NW, Ste. 403, Washington, DC 20036, (202)552-1828

Tropical Forest and Climate Coalition **[4861]**, 1616 P St. NW, Ste. 403, Washington, DC 20036, (202)552-1828

Tropical Forest Found. **[4418]**, 2121 Eisenhower Ave., Ste. 200, Alexandria, VA 22314, (703)518-8834

Tropical Forest Gp. **[4153]**, 1125 Ft. Stockton Dr., San Diego, CA 92103

Tropical Forest Rsrc. Gp. **[IO]**, Craven Arms, United Kingdom

Tropical Forestry Initiative **[4154]**, PO Box 15, Binghamton, NY 13903, (607)772-2160

Tropical Forestry Initiative **[4154]**, PO Box 15, Binghamton, NY 13903, (607)772-2160

Tropical Grassland Soc. of Australia **[IO]**, St. Lucia, Australia

Tropical Growers' Assn. **[IO]**, London, United Kingdom

Tropical Hea. and Educ. Trust **[IO]**, London, United Kingdom

Tropical Medicine
Amer. Soc. of Tropical Medicine and Hygiene **[16932]**
Royal Coll. of Physicians and Surgeons of the U.S.A. **[16933]**
Royal Coll. of Physicians and Surgeons of the U.S.A. **[16933]**

Tropical Sci. Center **[IO]**, San Jose, Costa Rica

Tropical Studies
Assn. for Fire Ecology of the Tropics **[4195]**
Org. for Tropical Stud., North Amer. Office **[7586]**
Org. for Tropical Stud., North Amer. Off. **[7586]**
Plumeria Soc. of Am. **[21817]**

Trotskyist League of Canada **[IO]**, Toronto, ON, Canada

A star before a book entry number signifies that the name is not listed separately, but is mentioned within the entry.

Trotting Horse Museum [★22653]
Troubles d'Apprentissage - Assn. Canadienne [★IO]
Troubles d'apprentissage - Assn. Nouveau-Brunswick [★IO]
Trout Unlimited [5137], 1300 N 17th St., Ste. 500, Arlington, VA 22209-2404, (703)522-0200
Trout Unlimited Canada [IO], Calgary, AB, Canada
TRRA Historical Soc. [★10501]
Truck Cap and Accessory Alliance - a SEMA Coun. [★333]
Truck Cap and Accessory Assn. [★333]
Truck Cap Indus. Assn. [★333]
Truck Cover and Tarp Assn. [★308]
Truck-Frame and Axle Repair Assn. [371], Ken Dias, 364 W 12th St., Erie, PA 16501, (877)735-1687
Truck and Heavy Equip. Claims Coun. [★2024]
Truck Mfrs. Assn. [342], 333 W Wacker Dr., Ste. 810, Chicago, IL 60606, (312)929-1979
Truck Mfrs. Assn. [342], 333 W Wacker Dr., Ste. 810, Chicago, IL 60606, (312)929-1979
Truck Mixer Mfrs. Bur. [343], 900 Spring St., Silver Spring, MD 20910, (301)587-1400
Truck Renting and Leasing Assn. [3084], 675 N Washington St., Ste. 410, Alexandria, VA 22314, (703)299-9120
Truck Safety Coalition [13011], 2020 14th St. N, Ste. 710, Arlington, VA 22201, (703)294-6404
Truck Safety Equip. Inst. [★3153]
Truck Trailer Mfrs. Assn. [344], 1020 Princess St., Alexandria, VA 22314-2247, (703)549-3010
Truck Trailer Mfrs. Assn. [344], 1020 Princess St., Alexandria, VA 22314-2247, (703)549-3010
Trucker Buddy Intl. [7838], 3200 Rice Mine Rd., Tuscaloosa, AL 35406, (205)248-1261
Truckers for Christ [19603], 8455 S Kirby Ct., Haysville, KS 67060, (316)554-0644
Trucking
  Amer. Alliance of Ethical Movers [13341]
  Loved Ones and Drivers Support [13342]
  Natl. Truck Leasing Sys. [3081]
Trucking Employers [★3540]
Trucking Indus. Defense Assn. [3539], 6311 W Gross Point Rd., Niles, IL 60714, (847)647-7226
Trucking Mgt., Inc. [3540], PO Box 860725, Shawnee, KS 66286, (913)568-5873
Truckload Carriers Assn. [3541], 555 E Braddock Rd., Alexandria, VA 22314-2182, (703)838-1950
Trucks
  Amer. Truck Historical Soc. [22195]
  Antique Truck Club of Am. [22196]
  Bigfoot Owners Clubs Intl. [21008]
  Citizens for Reliable and Safe Highways [18576]
  Dodge Pilothouse Era Truck Club of Am. [22197]
  Ferguson Enthusiasts of North Am. [22174]
  Ford/Fordson Collectors Assn. [22175]
  Kustom Kemps of Am. [21089]
  Massey Collectors Assn. [22178]
  North Amer. Truck Camper Owners Assn. [22198]
  United St. Machine Assn. [21185]
  USA Pulling [23074]
  Vintage Garden Tractor Club of Am. [22181]
True Food Network [6881], 660 Pennsylvania Ave. SE, No. 302, Washington, DC 20003, (202)547-9359
The True Nature Network [11047], PO Box 20672, Columbus Circle Sta., New York, NY 10023-1487
True Seed Exchange [★21820]
Trull Found. [12687], 404 4th St., Palacios, TX 77465, (361)972-5241
Truman Scholarship Found; Harry S. [8192]
The Trumpeter Swan Soc. [5138], 12615 County Rd. 9, Plymouth, MN 55441-1248, (763)694-7851
Truss Plate Inst. [631], 218 N Lee St., Ste. 312, Alexandria, VA 22314, (703)683-1010
Trussed Rafter Assn. [IO], Chesterfield, United Kingdom
The Trust [★17161]
Trust for America's Hea. [16500], 1730 M St. NW, Ste. 900, Washington, DC 20006, (202)223-9870
Trust Companies' Assn. of Japan [IO], Tokyo, Japan
Trust in Educ. [11647], PO Box 936, Lafayette, CA 94549, (925)299-2010
Trust for Mutual Understanding [9874], 6 W 48th St., 12th Fl., New York, NY 10036, (212)843-0404
Trust for Mutual Understanding [9874], 6 W 48th St., 12th Fl., New York, NY 10036, (212)843-0404

Trust for Public Land [4155], 101 Montgomery St., Ste. 900, San Francisco, CA 94104, (415)495-4014
Trustee Div. [★9970]
Truth About Trade and Tech. [6337], 309 Court Ave., Ste. 214, Des Moines, IA 50309, (515)274-0800
Truth Wins Out [12115], PO Box 96, Burlington, VT 05402
Try Us Resources [★2519]
TTS Inst. [IO], Rajamaki, Finland
Tube Collectors Assn. [21409], PO Box 636, Ashland, OR 97520, (407)401-4407
Tube and Pipe Assn., Intl. [2759], 833 Featherstone Rd., Rockford, IL 61107-6301, (815)399-8775
Tube and Pipe Assn., Intl. [2759], 833 Featherstone Rd., Rockford, IL 61107-6301, (815)399-8775
Tuberculosis Controllers Assn; Natl. [14412]
Tuberous Sclerosis Alliance [15639], 801 Roeder Rd., Ste. 750, Silver Spring, MD 20910, (301)562-9890
Tuberous Sclerosis Assn. [IO], Birmingham, United Kingdom
Tubists Universal Brotherhood Assn. [★10229]
Tubists Universal Brotherhood Assn. [★10229]
Tubular Brass Inst. [★2784]
Tubular Brass Inst. [★2784]
Tubular Exchanger Mfrs. Assn. [1722], 25 N Broadway, Tarrytown, NY 10591, (914)332-0040
Tucker Auto. Club of Am. [21180], 9509 Hinton Dr., Santee, CA 92071-2760
Tucker's Orchid Nursery [IO], Auckland, New Zealand
Tuerkiye Isci Sendikalari Konfederasyonu [★IO]
Tuerkiye Kimya Sanayicileri Dernegi [★IO]
Tuesday's Children [11863], 390 Plandome Rd., Ste. 217, Manhasset, NY 11030, (516)562-9000
Tuetuen Eksperleri Dernegi [★IO]
Tufts Center for Animals and Public Policy [11048], Tufts Univ., Cummings School of Veterinary Medicine, 200 Westboro Rd., North Grafton, MA 01536, (508)839-7991
Tufts Univ. Alumni Assn. [18902], Off. Of Alumni Relations, 80 George St., Ste. 100-3, Medford, MA 02155, (617)627-3532
Tug of War
  U.S. Amateur Tug of War Assn. [23101]
Tugboat Enthusiasts Soc. of the Americas [22399], PO Box 710, Winterport, ME 04496
Tum Gida Ithalatcilari Dernegi [★IO]
Tumblehome Recreational Canoe Club [IO], St. John's, NL, Canada
Tumor Soc; Musculoskeletal [15522]
Tumor Soc; Natl. Brain [14404]
Tun Abdul Razak Res. Centre [IO], Hertford, United Kingdom
Tunas Harapan Found. [IO], Pati, Indonesia
Tune-Up Mfrs. Coun. [345], Motor and Equip. Mfrs. Assn., PO Box 13966, Research Triangle Park, NC 27709-3966, (919)406-8821
Tune-up Mfrs. Inst. [★345]
Tunisian Assn. Against Epilepsy [IO], Sfax, Tunisia
Tunisian Chap. of IASP [IO], Tunis, Tunisia
Tunisian Economic Assn. [IO], Tunis, Tunisia
Tunisian Red Crescent [IO], Tunis, Tunisia
Tunisian Soc. of Cardiology and Cardiovascular Surgery [IO], Tunis, Tunisia
Tunisian Soc. of Dermatology and Venereology [IO], Tunis, Tunisia
Turbine Inlet Cooling Assn. [6838], 427 Prairie Knoll Dr., Ste. 102, Naperville, IL 60565, (630)357-3960
Turf and Ornamental Communicators Assn. [2185], PO Box 156, New Prague, MN 56071, (952)758-6340
Turfgrass Producers Intl. [4513], 2 E Main St., East Dundee, IL 60118, (847)649-5555
Turfgrass Producers Intl. [4513], 2 E Main St., East Dundee, IL 60118, (847)649-5555
Turfgrass Visiting Ser. [★22625]
Turisticka Organizacija Srbije [★IO]
Turk Dishekimleri Birligi [★IO]
Turk Elektron Mikroskopi Dernegi [★IO]
Turk Elektronik Sanayicileri Dernegi [★IO]
Turk Farmakoloji Dernegi [★IO]
Turk Kardiyoloji Dernegi [★IO]
Turk Musavir Muhendisler ve Mimarlar Birligi [★IO]

Turk Ortodonti Dernegi [★IO]
Turk Ortopedi ve Travmatoloji Dernegi [★IO]
Turk Tabipleri Birligi [★IO]
Turk Universiteli Kadinlar Dernegi [★IO]
Turkey Farmers of Canada [IO], Mississauga, ON, Canada
Turkey Vulture Soc. [5139], 2327 Polksville Rd., Oakland, KY 42159
Turkhana Desert Fund [★12897]
Turkhana Desert Fund [★12897]
Turkish
  Amer. Assn. of Teachers of Turkic Languages [9021]
  Amer. Friends of Turkey [18736]
  Amer. Friends of Turkey [18736]
  Amer. Res. Inst. in Turkey [10616]
  Amer. Res. Inst. in Turkey [10616]
  American-Turkish Coun. [18737]
  American-Turkish Coun. [18737]
  Amer. Turkish Friendship Coun. [17937]
  Amer. Turkish Soc. [19257]
  Amer. Turkish Soc. [19257]
  Assembly of Turkish Amer. Associations [19258]
  Fed. of Turkish Amer. Associations [19259]
  Inst. of Turkish Stud. [10617]
  Soc. of Turkish Amer. Architects, Engineers and Scientists [6832]
  Turkish Amer. Alliance for Fairness [19260]
  Turkish-American Chamber of Commerce and Indus. [23455]
  Turkish-American Chamber of Commerce and Indus. [23455]
  Turkish Coalition of Am. [18738]
  Turkish Coalition of Am. [18738]
  Turkish Coalition U.S.A. Political Action Comm. [18340]
  Turkish Stud. Assn. [10618]
  Turkish Stud. Assn. [10618]
Turkish Acad. of Sciences [IO], Ankara, Turkey
Turkish Amer. Alliance for Fairness [19260], PO Box 6151, San Rafael, CA 94903, (641)715-3900
Turkish Amer. Bus. Connection [705], 2784 Homestead Rd., No. 118, Santa Clara, CA 95051, (408)404-5208
Turkish-American Chamber of Commerce and Indus. [23455], 2 W 45th St., Ste. 1709, New York, NY 10036, (212)354-5470
Turkish-American Chamber of Commerce and Indus. [23455], 2 W 45th St., Ste. 1709, New York, NY 10036, (212)354-5470
Turkish Amer. Scientists and Scholars Assn. [7393], 1526 18th St. NW, Washington, DC 20036, (800)620-4120
Turkish Amer. Scientists and Scholars Assn. [7393], 1526 18th St. NW, Washington, DC 20036, (800)620-4120
Turkish Assn. for Energy Economics [IO], Istanbul, Turkey
Turkish Assn. for Hypertension Control [IO], Izmir, Turkey
Turkish Assn. of Marketing and Public Opinion Researchers [IO], Istanbul, Turkey
Turkish Assn. of Sports Medicine [IO], Izmir, Turkey
Turkish Assn. of Trauma and Emergency Surgery [IO], Istanbul, Turkey
Turkish Assn. of Univ. Women [IO], Istanbul, Turkey
Turkish Athletic Fed. [IO], Ankara, Turkey
Turkish Badminton Fed. [IO], Ankara, Turkey
Turkish British Chamber of Commerce and Indus. [IO], London, United Kingdom
Turkish Businessmen Assn. Qatar [IO], Doha, Qatar
Turkish Chem. Mfrs'. Assn. [IO], Istanbul, Turkey
Turkish Clothing Mfrs. Assn. [IO], Istanbul, Turkey
Turkish Coalition of Am. [18738], 1510 H St. NW, Ste. 900, Washington, DC 20005, (202)370-1399
Turkish Coalition of Am. [18738], 1510 H St. NW, Ste. 900, Washington, DC 20005, (202)370-1399
Turkish Coalition U.S.A. Political Action Comm. [18340], 1025 Connecticut Ave. NW, Ste. 1000, Washington, DC 20036, (866)314-7977
Turkish Confed. of Employer Associations [IO], Ankara, Turkey
Turkish Contractors Assn. [IO], Ankara, Turkey
Turkish DanceSport Fed. [IO], Ankara, Turkey
Turkish Dental Assn. [IO], Ankara, Turkey

Reference to "IO" in place of a book number signifies that the association may be found in the 50th edition of International Organizations.

Turkish Electronics and Info. Indus. Assn. **[IO]**, Istanbul, Turkey

Turkish Foundrymen's Assn. **[IO]**, Istanbul, Turkey

Turkish Ice Skating Fed. **[IO]**, Ankara, Turkey

Turkish Iron and Steel Producers Assn. **[IO]**, Ankara, Turkey

Turkish League Against Epilepsy **[IO]**, Istanbul, Turkey

Turkish League Against Rheumatism **[IO]**, Ankara, Turkey

Turkish Medical Informatics Assn. **[IO]**, Ankara, Turkey

Turkish Natl. Paralympic Comm. **[IO]**, Istanbul, Turkey

Turkish Orthodontic Soc. **[IO]**, Ankara, Turkey

Turkish Osteoporosis Soc. **[IO]**, Istanbul, Turkey

Turkish Pharmacological Soc. **[IO]**, Ankara, Turkey

Turkish Physiotherapy Assn. **[IO]**, Ankara, Turkey

Turkish Psychological Assn. **[IO]**, Ankara, Turkey

Turkish Red Crescent Soc. **[IO]**, Ankara, Turkey

Turkish Retired Officers Assn. **[IO]**, Ankara, Turkey

Turkish Soc. of Antimicrobial Chemotherapy **[IO]**, Istanbul, Turkey

Turkish Sóc. of Cardiology **[IO]**, Istanbul, Turkey

Turkish Soc. of Chemotherapy **[IO]**, Istanbul, Turkey

Turkish Soc. of Dermatology **[IO]**, Ankara, Turkey

Turkish Soc. of Dermatopathology **[IO]**, Ankara, Turkey

Turkish Soc. for Electron Microscopy **[IO]**, Istanbul, Turkey

Turkish Soc. for Image Anal. and Pattern Recognition **[IO]**, Istanbul, Turkey

Turkish Soc. of Orthopaedic Surgery and Traumatology **[IO]**, Ankara, Turkey

Turkish Soc. of Physiological Sciences **[IO]**, Konya, Turkey

Turkish Squash Fed. **[IO]**, Ankara, Turkey

Turkish Stud. Assn. **[10618]**, Princeton Univ., 110 Jones Hall, Princeton, NJ 08544, (609)258-4280

Turkish Stud. Assn. **[10618]**, Princeton Univ., 110 Jones Hall, Princeton, NJ 08544, (609)258-4280

Turkish Tourism Investors Assn. **[IO]**, Istanbul, Turkey

Turkish Underwater Sports, Life-Saving, Water Ski and Fin Swimming Fed. **[IO]**, Ankara, Turkey

Turkiskaupan Liitto ry **[★IO]**

Turkiye Atletizm Federasyonu **[★IO]**

Turkiye Badminton Federasyonu **[★IO]**

Turkiye Bankalar Birligi **[★IO]**

Turkiye Bilimler Akademisi **[★IO]**

Turkiye Bilimsel ve Teknolojik Arastirma Kurumu **[★IO]**

Turkiye Buz Pateni Federasyonu **[★IO]**

Turkiye Damizlik Sigir Yetistiricileri Merkez Birligi **[★IO]**

Turkiye Dokum Sanayicileri Dernegi **[★IO]**

Turkiye Emekli Subaylar Dernegi **[★IO]**

Turkiye Endokrinoloji Ve Metabolizma Dernegi **[★IO]**

Turkiye Fizyoterapistler Dernegi **[★IO]**

Turkiye Giyim Sanayicileri Dernigi **[★IO]**

Turkiye Isveren Sendikalari Konfederasyonu **[★IO]**

Turkiye Jokey Kulubu **[★IO]**

Turkiye Kizilay Dernegi **[★IO]**

Turkiye Milli Olimpiyat Komitesi **[★IO]**

Turkiye Milli Paralimpik Komitesi **[★IO]**

Turkiye Muteahhitler Birligi **[★IO]**

Turkiye Osteoporoz Dernegi **[★IO]**

Turkiye Romatizma Arastirma ve Savas Dernegi **[★IO]**

Turkiye Sigorta ve Reasurans Sirketleri Birligi **[★IO]**

Turkiye Spor Hekimleri Dernegi **[★IO]**

Turkiye Sualti Sporlari Federasyonu **[★IO]**

Turkiye Turizm Dernegi **[★IO]**

Turkmen Women Actives Rights Assn., Afghanistan **[IO]**, Kabul, Afghanistan

Turkmenistan Badminton Fed. **[IO]**, Ashgabat, Turkmenistan

Turkmenistan Tennis Assn. **[IO]**, Ashgabat, Turkmenistan

Turks and Caicos Assn. of Off. Professionals **[IO]**, Providenciales, Turks and Caicos Islands

Turks and Caicos Islands Amateur Athletic Assn. **[IO]**, Grand Turk Island, Turks and Caicos Islands

Turks and Caicos Tennis Fed. **[IO]**, Orton, Turks and Caicos Islands

Turnaround Mgt. Assn. **[2306]**, 150 S Wacker Dr., Ste. 900, Chicago, IL 60606, (312)578-6900

Turnbull Clan Assn. **[20601]**, 8216 S 101st St., La Vista, NE 68128, (402)715-5733

Turnbull Clan Assn. of North Am. **[★20601]**

Turner Found. **[4309]**, 133 Luckie St. NW, 2nd Fl., Atlanta, GA 30303, (404)681-9900

Turner Soc. **[IO]**, London, United Kingdom

Turner Syndrome Assn. of Australia **[IO]**, Warner, Australia

Turner Syndrome Soc. of the U.S. **[14633]**, 11250 West Rd., Ste. G, Houston, TX 77065, (800)365-9944

Turner's Syndrome Soc. **[IO]**, Ottawa, ON, Canada

Turners Syndrome Support Soc. **[IO]**, Clydebank, United Kingdom

Turtle Island Restoration Network **[4156]**, PO Box 370, Forest Knolls, CA 94933, (415)663-8590

Turtle Survival Alliance **[5140]**, Heather Lowe, Prog. Coor., 1989 Colonial Pkwy., Fort Worth, TX 76110, (817)759-7262

Tuskegee Airmen, Inc. **[20317]**, PO Box 830060, Tuskegee, AL 36083, (334)421-0198

Tusubira - We Have Hope **[12755]**, PO Box 482, Mercer Island, WA 98040

Tutmonda Esperantista Junulara Organizo **[★IO]**

Tutoring

Natl. Tutoring Assn. **[9022]**

Tuvalu Athletics Assn. **[IO]**, Funafuti, Tuvalu

Tuvalu Rugby Union **[IO]**, Funafuti, Tuvalu

Tuvalu Tennis Assn. **[IO]**, Funafuti, Tuvalu

Tuvalu Weightlifting Fed. **[IO]**, Funafuti, Tuvalu

TV-Free Am. **[★11998]**

TVR Car Club **[★21181]**

TVR Car Club of England, U.S. Area **[★21181]**

TVR Car Club North Am. **[21181]**, Marshall Moore, Pres., 3559 Overbrook Dr., Roanoke, VA 24018, (540)772-0952

Twain Boyhood Home Associates; Mark **[9395]**

Twain Circle of New York; Mark **[9396]**

Tweed Shire Coun. **[IO]**, Murwillumbah, Australia

Twelve Lights League **[18073]**, PO Box 1415, Bremerton, WA 98337, (360)373-9999

Twentieth Century Fund **[★18450]**

Twentieth Century Soc. **[IO]**, London, United Kingdom

Twentieth Century Spanish Assn. of Am. **[10540]**, Temple Univ., Dept. of Spanish and Portuguese, 1114 W Berks St., Philadelphia, PA 19122

Twentieth Century Spanish Assn. of Am. **[10540]**, Temple Univ., Dept. of Spanish and Portuguese, 1114 W Berks St., Philadelphia, PA 19122

Twenty-First Century Found. **[12688]**, 132 W 112th St., Lower Level, No. 1, New York, NY 10026, (212)662-3700

Twenty Year Club **[★486]**

TWIN **[IO]**, London, United Kingdom

Twin Bonanza Assn. - Address unknown since 2011.

Twin Towers Fund - Defunct.

Twinkle Little Stars **[11419]**, PO Box 182, Euless, TX 76039, (817)891-3579

Twinless Twins Support Gp. **[★12550]**

Twinless Twins Support Gp. **[★12550]**

Twinless Twins Support Gp. Intl. **[12550]**, PO Box 980481, Ypsilanti, MI 48198-0481, (888)205-8962

Twinless Twins Support Gp. Intl. **[12550]**, PO Box 980481, Ypsilanti, MI 48198-0481, (888)205-8962

Twins

Twins Found. **[12551]**

Twins Found. **[12551]**, PO Box 6043, Providence, RI 02940-6043, (401)751-8946

Twins and Multiple Births Assn. **[IO]**, Guildford, United Kingdom

Twins Support Gp. Intl; Twinless **[12550]**

Twins Support Gp. Intl; Twinless **[12550]**

Twins, Triplets, and More Assn. of Calgary **[IO]**, Calgary, AB, Canada

Twirly Birds **[20920]**, 21588 Sarahills Dr., Saratoga, CA 95070

Two Cents of Hope **[8292]**, 423 Westfalen Dr., Cary, NC 27519, (919)389-3430

Two-Cylinder Club **[22180]**, PO Box 430, Grundy Center, IA 50638-0430, (319)824-6060

Two-Cylinder Worldwide **[★22180]**

Two Hearts for Hope **[11420]**, PO Box 1928, Lebanon, MO 65536

Two Moon Dive Club **[IO]**, Sana'a, Yemen

Two Spirited People of the First Nations **[IO]**, Toronto, ON, Canada

Two/Ten Associates **[★1462]**

Two/Ten Footwear Found. **[1462]**, 1466 Main St., Waltham, MA 02451-1623, (781)736-1522

Two/Ten Found. **[★1462]**

Two/Ten Natl. Found. **[★1462]**

Tylers' and Bricklayers' Company **[IO]**, Seer Green, United Kingdom

Tyndale Soc. **[20217]**, PO Box 643, Unionville, PA 19375, (610)869-9087

Tyndale Soc. **[20217]**, PO Box 643, Unionville, PA 19375, (610)869-9087

Tyne and Wear Campaign for Nuclear Disarmament **[IO]**, Newcastle upon Tyne, United Kingdom

Type Directors Club **[6936]**, 347 W 36th St., Ste. 603, New York, NY 10018, (212)633-8943

Typophiles **[9646]**, 15 Gramercy Park S, No. 6C, New York, NY 10003

Tyrone Guthrie Centre **[IO]**, Newbliss, Ireland

Tzeirai Etr Tzion **[★19864]**

Tzivos Hashem **[9930]**, 792 Eastern Pkwy., Brooklyn, NY 11213, (718)467-6630

U

UAE Genetic Diseases Assn. **[IO]**, Dubai, United Arab Emirates

UAE Powerlifting Assn. **[IO]**, Dubai, United Arab Emirates

UAW I Community Action Prog. **[18341]**, Solidarity House, 8000 E Jefferson Ave., Detroit, MI 48214, (313)926-5000

Ubuntu Africa **[11421]**, PO Box 7906, Greenwich, CT 06836-7906

Ubuntu Africa **[11421]**, PO Box 7906, Greenwich, CT 06836-7906

UCA Intl. Users Gp. **[7589]**, 10604 Candler Falls Ct., Raleigh, NC 27614, (919)847-2241

Udruzenje kardiologa Bosne i Hercegovine **[★IO]**

Udruzenje pomorskih kapetana trgovacke mornarice Crne Gore **[★IO]**

Udruzenje Hotela Crne Gore **[★IO]**

Udruzenje Poslovnih Zena **[★IO]**

Udruzenje Stanara Hrvatske **[★IO]**

Udruzenje-Udruga Stanjara BIHUSS-Saravejo **[★IO]**

Udruzenje Za Gas Srbije **[★IO]**

Udruzenjeza Numeraciju Artikala Bosne I Hercegovine **[★IO]**

UERMMMC Nursing Alumni Assn. U.S.A. **[18903]**, 9 Mimosa Ln., Piscataway, NJ 08854, (732)463-0504

UFM Intl. **[★20034]**

UFM Intl. **[★20034]**

UFO Info. Retrieval Center **[7258]**, 3131 W Cochise Dr., No. 158, Phoenix, AZ 85051-9511, (602)284-5427

UFO Info. Retrieval Center **[7258]**, 3131 W Cochise Dr., No. 158, Phoenix, AZ 85051-9511, (602)284-5427

Uganda Amateur Athletics Fed. **[IO]**, Kampala, Uganda

Uganda Amateur Draughts Assn. **[IO]**, Kampala, Uganda

Uganda Assn. of Consulting Engineers **[IO]**, Kampala, Uganda

Uganda Assn. of Physiotherapy **[IO]**, Kampala, Uganda

Uganda Assn. of Univ. Women **[IO]**, Kampala, Uganda

Uganda Diabetis Assn. **[IO]**, Kampala, Uganda

Uganda Export Promotion Bd. **[IO]**, Kampala, Uganda

Uganda Games and Sports Medicine Assn. **[IO]**, Kampala, Uganda

Uganda Girl Guides Assn. **[IO]**, Kampala, Uganda

Uganda Junior Chamber **[IO]**, Kampala, Uganda

Uganda Medical Assn. **[IO]**, Kampala, Uganda

Uganda Newspaper Editors and Proprietors Assn. **[IO]**, Kampala, Uganda

Uganda Red Cross Soc. **[IO]**, Kampala, Uganda

Uganda Soc. **[IO]**, Kampala, Uganda

Uganda Squash Rackets Assn. **[IO]**, Kampala, Uganda

Uganda Tennis Assn. **[IO]**, Kampala, Uganda

A star before a book entry number signifies that the name is not listed separately, but is mentioned within the entry.

Uganda Weightlifting Fed. **[IO]**, Kampala, Uganda

Uganda Women's Effort to Save Orphans **[IO]**, Kampala, Uganda

Ugandan Amer. Partnership Org. **[12307]**, PO Box 250328, Atlanta, GA 30325, (404)856-3709

Ugandan Amer. Partnership Org. **[12307]**, PO Box 250328, Atlanta, GA 30325, (404)856-3709

Ugandan North Amer. Assn. **[18841]**, PO Box 20167, Bloomington, MN 55420, (651)983-5288

Ugbajo Itsekiri U.S.A. **[19145]**, PO Box 11465, Washington, DC 20008

Ughdarras a Chlo Hearaich **[★IO]**

Uglies Unlimited - Address unknown since 2010.

UHAI for Hea. **[15217]**, 37 Sophia Dr., Worcester, MA 01607

UHL Collectors Soc. **[21410]**, 398 S Star Dr., Santa Claus, IN 47579, (812)544-2987

UIL-Scuola **[IO]**, Rome, Italy

UIM Intl. **[★20102]**

UIM Intl. **[★20102]**

UJA Fed. - Jewish Info. Ser. of Greater Toronto **[IO]**, Toronto, ON, Canada

UK Apitherapy Soc. **[IO]**, Cheshunt, United Kingdom

UK Assn. of Online Publishers **[IO]**, London, United Kingdom

UK Athletics **[IO]**, Solihull, United Kingdom

UK Cleaning Products Indus. Assn. **[IO]**, Tattenhall, United Kingdom

UK Coalition of People Living with HIV and AIDS **[IO]**, London, United Kingdom

UK Comm. for UNICEF **[IO]**, London, United Kingdom

UK Coun. on Deafness **[IO]**, Colchester, United Kingdom

UK Fashion Exports **[IO]**, London, United Kingdom

UK Forest Products Assn. **[IO]**, Stirling, United Kingdom

UK Inbound **[IO]**, London, United Kingdom

UK Indus. Vision Assn. **[IO]**, Royston, United Kingdom

U.K. Irrigation Assn. **[IO]**, Rushden, United Kingdom

UK Metric Assn. **[IO]**, London, United Kingdom

UK Paruresis Trust **[IO]**, Kendal, United Kingdom

UK Public Hea. Assn. **[IO]**, London, United Kingdom

UK Pyrotechnics Soc. **[IO]**, London, United Kingdom

U.K. Sailing Acad. **[IO]**, Isle of Wight, United Kingdom

UK Soc. for Modelling and Simulation **[IO]**, Nottingham, United Kingdom

UK Sports Assn. for People with Learning Disability **[IO]**, London, United Kingdom

UK Steel Assn. **[IO]**, London, United Kingdom

UK Timber Frame Assn. **[IO]**, Alloa, United Kingdom

UK Web Design Assn. **[IO]**, Gosport, United Kingdom

UK Windsurfing Assn. **[IO]**, Haywards Heath, United Kingdom

UKCMG **[IO]**, Watford, United Kingdom

Ukraine Assn. of Cartoonists **[IO]**, Kiev, Ukraine

Ukraine Floorball Fed. **[IO]**, Kiev, Ukraine

Ukraine/Kiev Chap. of the Assn. of Energy Engineers **[IO]**, Kiev, Ukraine

Ukraine Physiological Soc. **[IO]**, Kiev, Ukraine

Ukraine Squash Fed. **[IO]**, Kiev, Ukraine

Ukrainian

League of Ukrainian Catholics of Am. **[19261]**

Providence Assn. of Ukrainian Catholics in Am. **[19262]**

Saint Andrew's Ukrainian Orthodox Soc. **[18739]**

Saint Andrew's Ukrainian Orthodox Soc. **[18739]**

Self Reliance Assn. of Amer. Ukrainians **[19263]**

Shevchenko Sci. Soc. **[19264]**

Shevchenko Sci. Soc. **[19264]**

Ukrainian Acad. of Arts and Sciences in the U.S. **[10619]**

Ukrainian Acad. of Arts and Sciences in the U.S. **[10619]**

Ukrainian Cong. Comm. of Am. **[18740]**

Ukrainian Cong. Comm. of Am. **[18740]**

Ukrainian Educational Coun. **[10620]**

Ukrainian Educational Coun. **[10620]**

Ukrainian Fraternal Assn. **[19265]**

Ukrainian Fraternal Assn. **[19265]**

Ukrainian Inst. of Am. **[10621]**

Ukrainian Inst. of Am. **[10621]**

Ukrainian Natl. Assn. **[19266]**

Ukrainian Natl. Women's League of Am. **[19267]**

Ukranian Cong. Comm. of Am. **[18741]**

Ukranian Congress Committee of Am. **[18741]**

U.S.-Ukraine Bus. Coun. **[721]**

U.S. Ukraine Found. **[18742]**

U.S. Ukraine Found. **[18742]**

United Ukrainian Amer. Relief Comm. **[19268]**

The Washington Gp. **[19269]**

Ukrainian Acad. of Arts and Sciences in the U.S. **[10619]**, 206 W 100 St., New York, NY 10021-1018, (212)222-1866

Ukrainian Acad. of Arts and Sciences in the U.S. **[10619]**, 206 W 100 St., New York, NY 10021-1018, (212)222-1866

Ukrainian-American Environmental Assn. - Address unknown since 2011.

Ukrainian Amer. Veterans **[20805]**, PO Box 172, Holmdel, NJ 07733-0172, (732)888-0494

Ukrainian Amer. War Veterans **[★20805]**

Ukrainian Assn. of Automatic Control **[IO]**, Kiev, Ukraine

Ukrainian Assn. of Dermatologists, Venereologists and Cosmetologists **[IO]**, Kiev, Ukraine

Ukrainian Assn. of Orthodontists **[IO]**, Lviv, Ukraine

Ukrainian Assn. on Osteoporosis **[IO]**, Kiev, Ukraine

Ukrainian Assn. of Rheumatologists **[IO]**, Kiev, Ukraine

Ukrainian Athletic Fed. **[IO]**, Kiev, Ukraine

Ukrainian Badminton Fed. **[IO]**, Kiev, Ukraine

Ukrainian Catholic Youth League **[★19261]**

Ukrainian Center for Independent Political Res. **[IO]**, Kiev, Ukraine

Ukrainian Center for Intl. Security Stud. **[IO]**, Kiev, Ukraine

Ukrainian Center for Social Res. **[★10620]**

Ukrainian Center for Social Res. **[★10620]**

Ukrainian Children's Aid and Relief Effort **[11422]**, PO Box 123, Glencoe, MO 63038

Ukrainian Cong. Comm. of Am. **[18740]**, 203 2nd Ave., New York, NY 10003, (212)228-6840

Ukrainian Cong. Comm. of Am. **[18740]**, 203 2nd Ave., New York, NY 10003, (212)228-6840

Ukrainian Dance Sport Assn. **[IO]**, Kiev, Ukraine

Ukrainian Draughts Fed. **[IO]**, Kiev, Ukraine

Ukrainian Educational Coun. **[10620]**, PO Box 391, Cooper Sta., New York, NY 10276-0391, (212)477-1200

Ukrainian Educational Coun. **[10620]**, PO Box 391, Cooper Sta., New York, NY 10276-0391, (212)477-1200

Ukrainian Energy Brigades **[IO]**, Rivne, Ukraine

Ukrainian Engineers' Soc. of Am. **[6834]**, 2 E 79th St., New York, NY 10021

Ukrainian Figure Skating Fed. **[IO]**, Kiev, Ukraine

Ukrainian Fraternal Assn. **[19265]**, 371 N 9th Ave., Scranton, PA 18504-2005, (570)342-0937

Ukrainian Fraternal Assn. **[19265]**, 371 N 9th Ave., Scranton, PA 18504-2005, (570)342-0937

Ukrainian Gerontology and Geriatrics Soc. **[IO]**, Kiev, Ukraine

Ukrainian Inst. of Am. **[10621]**, 2 E 79th St., New York, NY 10021, (212)288-8660

Ukrainian Inst. of Am. **[10621]**, 2 E 79th St., New York, NY 10021, (212)288-8660

Ukrainian Internet Assn. **[IO]**, Kiev, Ukraine

Ukrainian League Against Epilepsy **[IO]**, Kiev, Ukraine

Ukrainian Marketing Assn. **[IO]**, Kiev, Ukraine

Ukrainian Medical Assn. of North Am. **[15437]**, 2247 W Chicago Ave., Chicago, IL 60622, (888)RXU-MANA

Ukrainian Mineralogical Soc. **[IO]**, Kiev, Ukraine

Ukrainian Natl. Assn. **[19266]**, 2200 Rte. 10 W, Parsippany, NJ 07054, (973)292-9800

Ukrainian Natl. Info. Ser. **[★18741]**

Ukrainian Natl. Info. Ser. **[★18741]**

Ukrainian Natl. Sportive Billiard Fed. **[IO]**, Kiev, Ukraine

Ukrainian Natl. Women's League of Am. **[19267]**, 203 2nd Ave., New York, NY 10003, (212)533-4646

Ukrainian Philatelic and Numismatic Soc. **[22085]**, 1235 Fairview Dr., Kent, OH 44240-2807

Ukrainian Philatelic and Numismatic Soc. **[22085]**, 1235 Fairview Dr., Kent, OH 44240-2807

Ukrainian Physical Soc. **[IO]**, Kiev, Ukraine

Ukrainian Res. and Documentation Center **[★10621]**

Ukrainian Res. and Documentation Center **[★10621]**

Ukrainian Res. Found. - Defunct.

Ukrainian Soc. of Cardiology **[IO]**, Kiev, Ukraine

Ukrainian Soc. of Gastrointestinal Endoscopy **[IO]**, Kiev, Ukraine

Ukrainian Soc. of Photogrammetry and Remote Sensing **[IO]**, Lviv, Ukraine

Ukrainian Taekwondo Fed. **[IO]**, Kharkov, Ukraine

Ukrainian Tennis Fed. **[IO]**, Kiev, Ukraine

Ukrainian Weightlifting Fed. **[IO]**, Kiev, Ukraine

Ukrainian Workingmen's Assn. **[19265]**

Ukrainian Workingmen's Assn. **[★19265]**

Ukrainian Youth Hostels Assn. **[IO]**, Kiev, Ukraine

Ukrains'ke Mineralogichne Tovarystvo **[★IO]**

Ukranian Congress Committee of Am. **[18741]**, 203 2nd Ave., New York, NY 10003, (212)228-6840

Ukranian Cong. Comm. of Am. **[18741]**, 203 2nd Ave., New York, NY 10003, (212)228-6840

Ulcer Advisory Panel; Natl. Pressure **[14819]**

ULI Found. **[18757]**, 1025 Thomas Jefferson St. NW, Ste. 500 W, Washington, DC 20007-5201, (202)624-7000

Ulster Archaeological Soc. **[IO]**, Belfast, United Kingdom

Ulster Architectural Heritage Soc. **[IO]**, Belfast, United Kingdom

Ulster Cancer Found. **[IO]**, Belfast, United Kingdom

Ulster Farmers' Union **[IO]**, Belfast, United Kingdom

Ulster Folk Life Soc. **[★18581]**

Ulster Folk and Transport Museum **[IO]**, Holywood, United Kingdom

Ulster Historical Found. **[IO]**, Belfast, United Kingdom

Ulster-Scots Language Soc. **[IO]**, Belfast, United Kingdom

Ulster-Scots Soc. of Am. **[20664]**, PO Box 3969, Amarillo, TX 79116

Ulster Soc. of Organists and Choirmasters **[IO]**, Belfast, United Kingdom

Ulster Teachers' Union **[IO]**, Belfast, United Kingdom

Ultimate Players Assn. **[★22537]**

Ultra Marathon Cycling Assn. **[22487]**, PO Box 18028, Boulder, CO 80308-1028, (303)545-9566

Ultra Marathon Cycling Assn. **[22487]**, PO Box 18028, Boulder, CO 80308-1028, (303)545-9566

Ultrasonic Indus. Assn. **[3182]**, PO Box 2307, Dayton, OH 45401-2307, (937)586-3725

Ultrasonic Indus. Coun. **[★3182]**

Ultrasonic Mfrs. Assn. **[★3182]**

Ultrasound

Intl. Soc. of Cardiovascular Ultrasound **[14440]**

Musculoskeletal Ultrasound Soc. **[16934]**

Musculoskeletal Ultrasound Soc. **[16934]**

Ultrasound in Medicine; Amer. Inst. of **[16675]**

Ultrasound; Soc. for Vascular **[16969]**

Ultrastructural Pathology; Soc. for **[16135]**

Ulusal Travma ve Acil Cerrahi Dernegi **[★IO]**

Uluslararasi Mavi Hilal **[★IO]**

Ulysses S. Grant Assn. **[10695]**, Mississippi State Univ. Libraries, 395 Hardy Rd., PO Box 5408, Mississippi State, MS 39762-5408, (662)325-7668

Umanotera, Slovenian Found. for Sustainable Development **[IO]**, Ljubljana, Slovenia

Umanotera, Slovenska fundacija za trajnostni razvoj, ustanova **[★IO]**

Umbrella Assn. of German Pig Production **[IO]**, Bonn, Germany

Umoja Intl. **[12969]**, PO Box 1256, Silver Spring, MD 20910

Umpires' Assn; Amateur Baseball **[22261]**

Umuryango w'Abasoma Bibiliya **[★IO]**

U.N. Reform Electoral Campaign Comm. **[★18744]**

UN Sys. Network on Rural Development and Food Security **[IO]**, Rome, Italy

UNA Intl. Ser. **[IO]**, York, United Kingdom

UNAIDS - Joint United Nations Programme on HIV/AIDS **[IO]**, Geneva, Switzerland

UNANIMA Intl. **[18645]**, 211 E 43rd St., Rm. 1207, New York, NY 10017, (212)370-0075

Unarius Acad. of Sci. **[12227]**, 145 S Magnolia Ave., El Cajon, CA 92020-4522, (619)444-7062

Unarius Acad. of Sci. **[12227]**, 145 S Magnolia Ave., El Cajon, CA 92020-4522, (619)444-7062

Reference to "IO" in place of a book number signifies that the association may be found in the 50th edition of International Organizations.

Unarius Educational Found. [★12227]
Unarius Educational Found. [★12227]
Unchartered Intl. [12377], 1130 Washington Sq., Evansville, IN 47715, (812)473-7701
Unclaimed Property Professionals Org. [5900], 110 Wall St., 11th Fl., No. 0080, New York, NY 10005-3111, (508)883-9065
U.N.C.L.E. HQ Inc. [★23924]
U.N.C.L.E. HQ [23930], 1903 60th Pl. E, Ste. M4391, Bradenton, FL 34203, (941)256-0704
Uncle Remus Museum [9419], Highway 441, Eaton-ton, GA 31024, (706)485-6856
The Unconservatory [10306], 8035 SW 26th St., Miami, FL 33155, (305)266-9673
UNDA U.S.A. Natl. Catholic Assn. for Communica-tors [★9457]
Undeb Badminton Cymru [★IO]
Undeb Rygbi Cymru [★IO]
Under The Baobab Tree [7901], 1725 E Bayshore Rd., Ste. 103, Redwood City, CA 94063
Underfashion Club [112], 326 Field Rd., Clinton Corners, NY 12514, (845)758-6405
Undergraduate Philosophy Assn. [8709], Univ. of Texas, Dept. of Philosophy, 313 Waggener Hall, Austin, TX 78712, (512)475-9185
Underground Engg. Contractors' Assn. [★911]
Underground Injection Practices Coun. [★3636]
Underground Trans. Res. Assn. [IO], Cologne, Germany
Underground Utility and Leak Locators Assn. [3603], US Sewer and Drain, 210 Field End St., Sarasota, FL 34240, (800)977-5325
Undersea and Hyperbaric Medical Soc. [16935], 21 W Colony Pl., Ste. 280, Durham, NC 27705, (919)490-5140
Undersea Medical Soc. [★16935]
Undersea Medicine
  Undersea and Hyperbaric Medical Soc. [16935]
Underwater Soc. of Am. [23107], PO Box 628, Daly City, CA 94017, (650)583-8492
Underwater Sports
  Assn. of Commercial Diving Educators [23102]
  Natl. Assn. for Cave Diving [23103]
  Natl. Assn. of Underwater Instructors [23104]
  Professional Assn. of Diving Instructors [23105]
  Professional Assn. of Diving Instructors [23105]
  Recreational Scuba Training Coun. [23106]
  Underwater Soc. of Am. [23107]
Underwriters
  Amer. Legal Finance Assn. [1279]
  Environmental Risk Resources Assn. [4260]
  Gp. Underwriters Assn. of Am. [1962]
  TechAssure Assn. [2045]
Underwriters Labs. [3154], 2600 NW Lake Rd., Ca-mas, WA 98607-8542, (877)854-3577
Underwriters' Labs. of Canada [IO], Toronto, ON, Canada
Unemployment
  UWC: Strategic Services on Unemployment and Workers' Compensation [13343]
UNESCO-ASCHBERG Bursaries for Artists Pro-gramme [IO], Paris, France
UNESCO Club - Malta [IO], Hamrun, Malta
UNESCO Co-Action Programme [IO], Paris, France
UNESCO Dhaka Off. [IO], Dhaka, Bangladesh
UNESCO-IHE Inst. for Water Educ. [IO], Delft, Netherlands
UNESCO Inst. for Lifelong Learning [IO], Hamburg, Germany
UNESCO Regional Bur. for Sci. and Culture in Europe [IO], Venice, Italy
Unevangelized Fields Missions [★20034]
Unevangelized Fields Missions [★20034]
Unexpected Wildlife Refuge [11049], PO Box 765, Newfield, NJ 08344-0765, (856)697-3541
Unfinished Furniture Assn. [1559], PO Box 520, Spofford, NH 03462, (518)832-7939
Unger Vetlesen Found; G. [12668]
Uni-Bell Plastic Pipe Assn. [★2760]
Uni-Bell Plastic Pipe Assn. [★2760]
Uni-Bell PVC Pipe Assn. [2760], 2711 LBJ Fwy., Ste. 1000, Dallas, TX 75234, (972)243-3902
Uni-Bell PVC Pipe Assn. [2760], 2711 LBJ Fwy., Ste. 1000, Dallas, TX 75234, (972)243-3902
Unia Wolnosci [★IO]

Uniao Biblica Mocambique [IO], Maputo, Mozam-bique
Uniao Brasileira de Compositores [★IO]
Uniao Cultural Brasil Estados Unidos [★IO]
Uniao da Geomorfologia Brasileira [★IO]
Uniao Portuguesa Continental do Estado da California [★19053]
UNICEF - Afghanistan [IO], Kabul, Afghanistan
UNICEF - Albania [IO], Tirana, Albania
UNICEF - Algeria [IO], Algiers, Algeria
UNICEF - Angola [IO], Luanda, Angola
UNICEF - Antigua and Barbuda [IO], Bridgetown, Barbados
UNICEF - Argentina [IO], Buenos Aires, Argentina
UNICEF - Austria [IO], Vienna, Austria
UNICEF - Azerbaijan [IO], Baku, Azerbaijan
UNICEF - Bahrain [IO], Manama, Bahrain
UNICEF - Bangladesh [IO], Dhaka, Bangladesh
UNICEF - Barbados [IO], Bridgetown, Barbados
UNICEF - Belarus [IO], Minsk, Belarus
UNICEF - Belgium [IO], Brussels, Belgium
UNICEF - Belize [IO], Belize City, Belize
UNICEF - Benin [IO], Cotonou, Benin
UNICEF - Bhutan [IO], Thimphu, Bhutan
UNICEF - Bolivia [IO], Cochabamba, Bolivia
UNICEF - Bolivia [IO], La Paz, Bolivia
UNICEF - Bosnia and Herzegovina [IO], Sarajevo, Bosnia-Hercegovina
UNICEF, Brazil-Brasilia [IO], Brasilia, Brazil
UNICEF, Brazil-Fortaleza [IO], Fortaleza, Brazil
UNICEF, Brazil-Recife [IO], Recife, Brazil
UNICEF, Brazil-Rio de Janeiro [IO], Rio de Janeiro, Brazil
UNICEF, Brazil-Salvador [IO], Salvador, Brazil
UNICEF, Brazil-Sao Luis [IO], Sao Luis, Brazil
UNICEF - Bulgaria [IO], Sofia, Bulgaria
UNICEF - Burkina Faso [IO], Ouagadougou, Burkina Faso
UNICEF - Burundi [IO], Bujumbura, Burundi
UNICEF - Cambodia [IO], Phnom Penh, Cambodia
UNICEF - Cameroon [IO], Yaounde, Cameroon
UNICEF - Canada [IO], Toronto, ON, Canada
UNICEF - Cape Verde [IO], Praia, Cape Verde
UNICEF - Central African Republic [IO], Bangui, Central African Republic
UNICEF - Chad [IO], N'Djamena, Chad
UNICEF | Change for Good [12894], 3 United Na-tions Plz., New York, NY 10017, (212)326-7000
UNICEF - Chile [IO], Santiago, Chile
UNICEF - China [IO], Beijing, People's Republic of China
UNICEF - Colombia [IO], Bogota, Colombia
UNICEF - Comoros [IO], Moroni, Comoros
UNICEF - Costa Rica [IO], San Jose, Costa Rica
UNICEF - Cote d'Ivoire [IO], Abidjan, Cote d'Ivoire
UNICEF - Croatia [IO], Zagreb, Croatia
UNICEF - Cuba [IO], Havana, Cuba
UNICEF - Czech Republic [IO], Prague, Czech Republic
UNICEF - Denmark [IO], Copenhagen, Denmark
UNICEF - Djibouti [IO], Djibouti, Djibouti
UNICEF - Dominican Republic [IO], Santo Domingo, Dominican Republic
UNICEF - Ecuador [IO], Quito, Ecuador
UNICEF - Egypt [IO], Cairo, Egypt
UNICEF - El Salvador [IO], San Salvador, El Salvador
UNICEF - Equatorial Guinea [IO], Malabo, Equato-rial Guinea
UNICEF - Estonia [IO], Tallinn, Estonia
UNICEF - Ethiopia [IO], Addis Ababa, Ethiopia
UNICEF - Fiji [IO], Suva, Fiji
UNICEF - Finland [IO], Helsinki, Finland
UNICEF - France [IO], Paris, France
UNICEF - Gabon [IO], Libreville, Gabon
UNICEF - Gambia [IO], Banjul, Gambia
UNICEF - Georgia [IO], Tbilisi, Georgia
UNICEF - Germany [IO], Cologne, Germany
UNICEF - Ghana [IO], Accra, Ghana
UNICEF - Greece [IO], Athens, Greece
UNICEF - Grenada [IO], Bridgetown, Barbados
UNICEF - Guatemala [IO], Guatemala City, Guatemala
UNICEF - Guinea [IO], Conakry, Guinea
UNICEF - Guinea-Bissau [IO], Bissau, Guinea-Bissau

UNICEF - Guyana [IO], Georgetown, Guyana
UNICEF - Hungary [IO], Budapest, Hungary
UNICEF - Iceland [IO], Reykjavik, Iceland
UNICEF - Ireland [IO], Dublin, Ireland
UNICEF - Israel [IO], Tel Aviv, Israel
UNICEF - Japan [IO], Tokyo, Japan
UNICEF - Jordan [IO], Amman, Jordan
UNICEF - Lithuania [IO], Vilnius, Lithuania
UNICEF - Luxembourg [IO], Luxembourg, Luxembourg
UNICEF - Madagascar [IO], Antananarivo, Madagas-car
UNICEF - Malawi [IO], Lilongwe, Malawi
UNICEF - Malaysia [IO], Kuala Lumpur, Malaysia
UNICEF - Mali [IO], Bamako, Mali
UNICEF - Mauritania [IO], Nouakchott, Mauritania
UNICEF - Mexico [IO], Mexico City, Mexico
UNICEF - Mongolia [IO], Ulan Bator, Mongolia
UNICEF - Mozambique [IO], Maputo, Mozambique
UNICEF - Myanmar [IO], Yangon, Myanmar
UNICEF - Nepal [IO], Kathmandu, Nepal
UNICEF - Netherlands [IO], The Hague, Netherlands
UNICEF - New Zealand [IO], Wellington, New Zealand
UNICEF - Nicaragua [IO], Managua, Nicaragua
UNICEF - Niger [IO], Niamey, Niger
UNICEF - Nigeria [IO], Abuja, Nigeria
UNICEF - Norway [IO], Oslo, Norway
UNICEF - Oman [IO], Muscat, Oman
UNICEF - Pakistan [IO], Islamabad, Pakistan
UNICEF - Panama [IO], Panama City, Panama
UNICEF - Papua New Guinea [IO], Port Moresby, Papua New Guinea
UNICEF - Paraguay [IO], Asuncion, Paraguay
UNICEF - Peru [IO], Lima, Peru
UNICEF - Philippines [IO], Makati City, Philippines
UNICEF - Poland [IO], Warsaw, Poland
UNICEF - Portugal [IO], Lisbon, Portugal
UNICEF - Republic of the Congo [IO], Brazzaville, Republic of the Congo
UNICEF - Republic of Korea [IO], Seoul, Republic of Korea
UNICEF - Republic of Moldova [IO], Chisinau, Moldova
UNICEF - Romania [IO], Bucharest, Romania
UNICEF - Russian Fed. [IO], Moscow, Russia
UNICEF - Rwanda [IO], Kigali, Rwanda
UNICEF - San Marino [IO], San Marino, San Marino
UNICEF - Saudi Arabia [IO], Riyadh, Saudi Arabia
UNICEF - Senegal [IO], Dakar, Senegal
UNICEF - Slovakia [IO], Bratislava, Slovakia
UNICEF - Somalia [IO], Nairobi, Kenya
UNICEF - South Africa [IO], Pretoria, Republic of South Africa
UNICEF - Spain [IO], Madrid, Spain
UNICEF - Sri Lanka [IO], Colombo, Sri Lanka
UNICEF - Sudan [IO], Khartoum, Sudan
UNICEF - Swaziland [IO], Mbabane, Swaziland
UNICEF - Sweden [IO], Stockholm, Sweden
UNICEF - Switzerland [IO], Zurich, Switzerland
UNICEF - Syrian Arab Republic [IO], Damascus, Syrian Arab Republic
UNICEF - Tajikistan [IO], Dushanbe, Tajikistan
UNICEF - Thailand [IO], Bangkok, Thailand
UNICEF - Togo [IO], Lome, Togo
UNICEF - Tunisia [IO], Tunis, Tunisia
UNICEF - Turkey [IO], Ankara, Turkey
UNICEF - Uganda [IO], Kampala, Uganda
UNICEF - Ukraine [IO], Kiev, Ukraine
UNICEF - United Kingdom [IO], London, United Kingdom
UNICEF - United Republic of Tanzania [IO], Dar es Salaam, United Republic of Tanzania
UNICEF - Uruguay [IO], Montevideo, Uruguay
UNICEF - Uzbekistan [IO], Tashkent, Uzbekistan
UNICEF - Vanuatu [IO], Port Vila, Vanuatu
UNICEF - Venezuela [IO], Caracas, Venezuela
UNICEF - Vietnam [IO], Hanoi, Vietnam
UNICEF - Yemen [IO], Sana'a, Yemen
UNICEF - Zambia [IO], Lusaka, Zambia
UNICEF - Zimbabwe [IO], Harare, Zimbabwe
Unico Natl. [19081], 271 U.S. Hwy. 46 W, Ste. A-108, Fairfield, NJ 07004, (973)808-0035
Unicode Consortium [18675], Microsoft Bldg. 5, 1065 L'Avenida St., Mountain View, CA 94043, (650)693-3921

A star before a book entry number signifies that the name is not listed separately, but is mentioned within the entry.

Unicorn Users Gp. Intl. [★6973]

Unicycling Soc. of Am. [22488], PO Box 21487, Minneapolis, MN 55421-0487

Unicyclist's Assn. of Am. [★22488]

UNIDO Center for Regional Cooperation in Turkey [IO], Ankara, Turkey

Unie der Belgische Adverteerders [★IO]

Unie der Designers in Belgie [★IO]

Unie van Soroptimist Clubs in Nederland, Suriname en de Nederlandse Antillen [IO], Amsterdam, Netherlands

Unie van de Uitgevers van de Periodieke Pers [★IO]

Unie Vydavatelu [★IO]

UNIFEM Natl. Comm. Japan [IO], Yokohama, Japan

UNIFEM New Zealand [IO], Wellington, New Zealand

Unified Abrasives Mfrs'. Assn. [2347], 30200 Detroit Rd., Cleveland, OH 44145-1967, (440)899-0010

Unified Abrasives Mfrs'. Assn. - Grain Comm. [1875], 30200 Detroit Rd., Cleveland, OH 44145-1967, (440)899-0010

Unified Abrasives Mfrs'. Assn. - Superabrasives Div. [1876], 30200 Detroit Rd., Cleveland, OH 44145-1967, (440)899-0010

Unified for Global Healing [15218], 487 Myrtle Ave., Unit B-7, Brooklyn, NY 11205

Uniform Code Coun. [★281]

Uniform Grocery Prdt. Code Coun. [★281]

Uniform Law Commissioners [★5997]

Uniform Mfrs. Exchange [★211]

Uniform Prdt. Code Coun. [★281]

Uniform and Textile Service Assn. - Address unknown since 2010.

Uniformed Services Acad. of Family Physicians [15515], 1503 Santa Rosa Rd., Ste. 207, Richmond, VA 23229, (804)968-4436

UniForum Assn. [6520], PO Box 3177, Annapolis, MD 21403, (410)715-9500

UniForum Assn. [6520], PO Box 3177, Annapolis, MD 21403, (410)715-9500

UniForum New Zealand [IO], Wellington, New Zealand

uNight [11423], 139 Mulberry St., Ste. 19, New York, NY 10013, (646)649-4961

Unija poslodavaca Crne Gore [★IO]

UNIMA [IO], Charleville-Mezieres, France

Unio de Radioaficionats Andorrans [★IO]

Union europeenne des veterinaires praticiens [★IO]

Union mondiale des societes catholiques de philosophie [★IO]

Union europeenne de et des petites et moyennes enterprises [★IO]

Union Africaine des Aveugles [★IO]

Union for African Population Stud. [IO], Accra, Ghana

Union de Agencias de Viajes [★IO]

Union Aid Abroad - Australian People for Hea., Educ. and Development Abroad [IO], Sydney, Australia

Union of Amer. Physicians and Dentists [23216], 180 Grand Ave., Ste. 1380, Oakland, CA 94612, (510)839-0193

Union of Amer. Physicians and Dentists [★23216]

Union des Annonceurs [IO], Paris, France

L'Union Arabe de Ciment et des Materiaux de Constr. [★IO]

Union of Architects in Bulgaria [IO], Sofia, Bulgaria

Union of Architects of Romania [IO], Bucharest, Romania

Union of Architects of Russia [IO], Moscow, Russia

Union des Artistes de la Reunion [IO], St.-Denis, France

Union de Asociaciones de Estanqueros de Espana [★IO]

Union des Assn. des Personnes Handicapees du Tchad [IO], N'Djamena, Chad

Union des Associations de Boissons des Pays Membres de l' UE [★IO]

Union des Associations Europeennes de Football [★IO]

Union of Associations of Slovene Librarians [IO], Ljubljana, Slovenia

Union des Assurances du Burkina [★IO]

Union Astronomique Internationale [★IO]

Union of Australian Women [IO], Melbourne, Australia

Union des Avocats Europeens [★IO]

Union Belge des Annonceurs [IO], Brussels, Belgium

Union of Belgian Brewers [IO], Brussels, Belgium

Union Biblica Argentina [IO], Buenos Aires, Argentina

Union Biblica Chile [IO], Santiago, Chile

Union Biblica Chilena [★IO]

Union Biblica de Colombia [IO], Barranquilla, Colombia

Union Biblica Ecuatorina [IO], Quito, Ecuador

Union Bouddhique d'Europe [★IO]

Union of Brazilian Composers [IO], Rio de Janeiro, Brazil

Union of Bulgarian Artists [IO], Sofia, Bulgaria

Union of Bulgarian Composers [IO], Sofia, Bulgaria

Union of Bulgarian Motorists [IO], Sofia, Bulgaria

Union of Canadian Trans. Employees [IO], Ottawa, ON, Canada

Union of Catholic Asian News [IO], Hong Kong, People's Republic of China

Union of Chemists in Bulgaria [IO], Sofia, Bulgaria

Union Chretienne Feminine [★IO]

Union Chretienne de Jeunes Gens du Cameroun [★IO]

Union Chretienne de Jeunes Gens du Senegal [★IO]

Union Chretienne des Pensionnes [IO], Brussels, Belgium

Union of Civil Servants [IO], Stockholm, Sweden

Union of Concerned Scientists [18187], 2 Brattle Sq., Cambridge, MA 02138-3780, (617)547-5552

Union of Constr., Allied Trades and Technicians - United Kingdom [IO], London, United Kingdom

Union des Cooperatives des Planteurs de Tabac de France [★IO]

Union Costarricense de Camaras y Asociaciones de la Empresa Privada [★IO]

Union of Councils [★17570]

Union of Councils [★17570]

Union of Councils for Jews in the Former Soviet Union [17570], PO Box 11676, Cleveland Park, Washington, DC 20008, (202)237-8262

Union of Councils for Jews in the Former Soviet Union [17570], PO Box 11676, Cleveland Park, Washington, DC 20008, (202)237-8262

Union of Councils for Soviet Jews [★17570]

Union of Councils for Soviet Jews [★17570]

Union Cycliste Internationale [★IO]

Union of Czech Mathematicians and Physicists [IO], Prague, Czech Republic

Union of Czech and Moravian Production Co-Operatives [IO], Prague, Czech Republic

Union of the Deaf in Bulgaria [IO], Sofia, Bulgaria

Union for Democratic Communications [17360], Florida State Univ., Dept. of Commun., Univ. Ctr., Bldg. C, Ste. 3100, Tallahassee, FL 32306-2664, (850)644-8748

Union for Democratic Communications [17360], Florida State Univ., Dept. of Commun., Univ. Ctr., Bldg. C, Ste. 3100, Tallahassee, FL 32306-2664, (850)644-8748

Union Democratique Bretonne [★IO]

Union of Denturists in Finland [IO], Helsinki, Finland

Union of Designers in Belgium [IO], Brussels, Belgium

Union of Economists of Slovenia [IO], Ljubljana, Slovenia

Union des Ecrivaines et des Ecrivains Quebecois [IO], Montreal, QC, Canada

Union des Editeurs de la Presse Periodique [IO], Brussels, Belgium

Union of the Elec. Indus. - EURELECTRIC [IO], Brussels, Belgium

Union of Estonian Emergency Medical Services [IO], Tartu, Estonia

Union of Estonian Psychologists [IO], Tartu, Estonia

Union for Ethical BioTrade [IO], Geneva, Switzerland

Union of European Beverages Associations [IO], Brussels, Belgium

Union of European Football Associations [IO], Nyon, Switzerland

Union of European Historic Houses Associations [IO], Brussels, Belgium

Union of European Petroleum Independents [IO], Brussels, Belgium

Union of European Railway Indus. [IO], Brussels, Belgium

Union Europeene de Judo [★IO]

Union Europeenne des Associations Nationales de Services d'Eau [★IO]

Union Europeenne des Aveugles [★IO]

Union Europeenne de la Carrosserie [★IO]

Union Europeenne du Commerce du Betail et de la Viande [★IO]

Union Europeenne du Commerce des Produits Laitiers et Derives [★IO]

Union Europeenne Des Medecins Specialistes [★IO]

Union Europeenne des Entrepeneurs du Paysage [★IO]

Union Europeenne pour l'Agrement technique dans la construction [★IO]

Union Europeenne de l'Ameublement [★IO]

Union Europeenne de l'Hopitalisation Privee [★IO]

Union Europeenne des Miroitiers Vitriers [★IO]

Union Europeenne de la Navigation Fluviale [★IO]

Union Europeenne de la Presse Sportive [★IO]

Union Europeenne des Producteurs de Granulats [★IO]

Union Europeenne des Promoteurs Constructeurs [★IO]

Union Europeenne de Radio-Television [★IO]

Union Evangelica Bautista Espanola [IO], Valencia, Spain

Union de Exportadores del Uruguay [★IO]

Union of Exporters of Uruguay [IO], Montevideo, Uruguay

Union of Finance Personnel in Europe [IO], Berlin, Germany

Union des Finanzpersonals in Europa [★IO]

Union of Finnish Writers [IO], Helsinki, Finland

Union des Foires Internationales [★IO]

Union Francaise des Indus. Petrolieres [★IO]

Union of French Aerospace and Space Indus. [IO], Paris, France

Union of French Tobacco Growers' Co-operatives [IO], Paris, France

Union Gen. de Trabajadores [★IO]

Union Geographique Internationale [★IO]

Union Geophysique Canadienne [★IO]

Union of German Catholic Women [IO], Cologne, Germany

Union des Groupements de Detaillants independants de l'Europe a.i.s.b.l. [★IO]

Union of Groups of Independent Retailers of Europe a.i.s.b.l. [IO], Brussels, Belgium

Union Haddiema Maghqudin [★IO]

Union Indus. Argentina [★IO]

Union Indus. Paraguaya [★IO]

Union des Indus. et de la Distribution des Plastiques et du Caoutchouc [★IO]

Union des Indus. Ferroviaires Europeenes [★IO]

Union of Info. Tech. Enterprises [IO], Yerevan, Armenia

Union of Insurance Employees in Finland [IO], Helsinki, Finland

Union Internacional de Tecnicos de la Industria del Calzado [★IO]

Union of Intl. Fairs [IO], Paris, France

Union for the Intl. Language Ido [IO], Arzon, France

Union Internationale pour les livres de jeunesse [★IO]

Union Internationale des Architectes [★IO]

Union Internationale des Associations et Organismes Techniques [★IO]

Union Internationale des Assureurs Aviation [★IO]

Union Internationale des Avocats [★IO]

Union Internationale des Centres du Batiment [★IO]

Union Internationale des Chauffeurs Routiers [★IO]

Union Internationale des Chemins de Fer [★IO]

Union Internationale Chretienne des Dirigeants d'Entreprise [★IO]

Union Internationale Contre le Cancer [★IO]

Union Internationale Contre la Tuberculose et les Maladies Respiratoires [★IO]

Union Internationale de Cristallographie [★IO]

Union Internationale d'Angiologie [★IO]

Union Internationale des Editeurs [★IO]

Union Internationale des Etudiants [★IO]

Union Internationale des Guides et Scouts d'Europe [★IO]

Reference to "IO" in place of a book number signifies that the association may be found in the 50th edition of International Organizations.

Union Internationale Humaniste et Laique [★IO]
Union Internationale des Instituts de Recherches Forestieres [★IO]
Union Internationale pour les applications d l'electricite [★IO]
Union Internationale pour l'Etude du Quarternaire [★IO]
Union Internationale pour l'Etude Scientifique de la Population [★IO]
Union Internationale de l'Industrie du Gaz [★IO]
Union Internationale des Magistrats [★IO]
Union Internationale de la Marionnette I Amer. CTR [22112], Vincent Anthony, Gen. Sec., 1404 Spring St. NW, Atlanta, GA 30309-2820, (404)881-5110
Union Internationale Motonautique [IO], Monaco, Monaco
Union Internationale de la Presse Electronique [IO], Tettnang, Germany
Union Internationale de Promotion de la Sante et d'Education pour la Sante [★IO]
Union Internationale pour la Protection des Obtentions Vegetales [★IO]
Union Internationale de Radioecologie [★IO]
Union Internationale pour la Sci., la Technique et les Applications du Vide [★IO]
Union Internationale de Sci. et de Technologie Alimentaires [★IO]
Union Internationale des Sciences Anthropologiques et Ethnologiques [★IO]
Union Internationale des Sciences Biologiques [★IO]
Union Internationale des Sciences Geologiques [★IO]
Union Internationale des Societes de Microbiologie [★IO]
Union Internationale de Speleologie [★IO]
L'Union Internationale pour la Taxatione sur la Valeur de la Terre et la Libre-Echange [★IO]
Union Internationale des Telecommunications [★IO]
Union Internationale des Transports Publics [★IO]
Union Internationale des Transports Routiers [★IO]
Union Internationale Vegetarienne [★IO]
Union Internationale des Wagons Prives [★IO]
Union Interparlementaire [★IO]
Union of Inventors of Bulgaria [IO], Sofia, Bulgaria
Union of Japanese Scientists and Engineers [IO], Tokyo, Japan
Union of Journalists in Finland [IO], Helsinki, Finland
Union of Latin Amer. Universities [IO], Mexico City, Mexico
Union Latinoamericana de Ciegos [★IO]
Union and League of Romanian Societies [19211], PO Box 1037, Andover, OH 44003-1037, (440)293-5335
Union and League of Romanian Societies of Am. [★19211]
Union pour l'Etude de la Population Africaine [★IO]
Union de l'Europe Occidentale [★IO]
Union Luxembourgeoise de Ski Nautique [★IO]
Union of Macedonian Political Organizations [★19119]
Union of Macedonian Political Organizations [★19119]
Union du Mahgreb Arabe [★IO]
Union des Maisons de Bordeaux [★IO]
Union des Maisons de Bordeaux [IO], Bordeaux, France
Union des Maisons de Champagne [★IO]
Union of the Mfrs. and Consumers of Packages and Packaging Products [IO], Moscow, Russia
Union Matematica Argentina [★IO]
Union Medica Nacional [IO], San Jose, Costa Rica
Union MicroFinanza [12964], 1485 Getty St., Muskegon, MI 49442
Union Mondiale des Organisations Feminines Catholiques [★IO]
Union Mundial pro Interlingua [IO], Helsinki, Finland
Union Mundial para la Naturaleza Oficina Regional para Mesoamerica [IO], San Jose, Costa Rica
Union of Myanmar Travel Assn. [IO], Yangon, Myanmar
Union Nationale des Associations de Tourisme et de Plein Air [★IO]
Union Nationale Des Handicapes Du Congo [IO], Brazzaville, Democratic Republic of the Congo
Union Nationale des Entrepreneurs du Paysage [★IO]

Union Nationale de la Femme Tunisienne [★IO]
Union Nationale des Pharmacies de France [★IO]
Union Nationale du Sport Scolaire [IO], Paris, France
Union Network Intl. - Asian and Pacific Regional Off. [IO], Singapore, Singapore
Union of North Amer. Vietnamese Students Assn. [19275], PO Box 433, Westminster, CA 92684
Union of North Amer. Vietnamese Students Assn. [19275], PO Box 433, Westminster, CA 92684
Union Panafricaine des Postes [★IO]
Union Petroliere Europeenne Independante [★IO]
Union of the Physicists in Bulgaria [IO], Sofia, Bulgaria
Union of the Plastics and Rubber Indus. [IO], Paris, France
Union of Poles in Am. [19202], 9999 Granger Rd., Garfield Heights, OH 44125, (216)478-0120
Union Postal De Las Americas, Espana, y Portugal [★IO]
Union Postale Universelle [★IO]
Union de la Presse Francophone [★IO]
Union des Producteurs Agricoles [★IO]
Union of Professional Airmen [★23146]
Union of Professional Airmen [★23146]
Union Professionnelle des Entreprises d'Assurances [★IO]
Union Professionnelle du Secteur Immobilier [★IO]
Union for Protection of Tenants MakeDom [IO], Skopje, Macedonia
Union of Public Transport [IO], Paris, France
Union for Radical Political Economics [6636], Univ. of Massachusetts, URPE Gordon Hall, 418 N Pleasant St., Amherst, MA 01002-1735, (413)577-0806
Union Radio Scientifique Internationale [★IO]
Union for Reform Judaism [19903], 633 3rd Ave., New York, NY 10017-6778, (212)650-4000
Union for Reform Judaism I Commn. on Outreach and Synagogue Community [19904], Dept. of Outreach and Membership m, 633 3rd Ave., New York, NY 10017-6778, (212)650-4230
Union Routiere de France [★IO]
Union Royale des Armateurs Belges [★IO]
Union Royale Belge des Societes de Football-Association [★IO]
Union Saint-Jean-Baptiste [18993], Saint-Jean-Baptiste Educ. Found., PO Box F, Woonsocket, RI 02895-0989, (800)225-USJB
Union of Sci. and Educ. [IO], Luxembourg, Luxembourg
Union of Scientists in Bulgaria [IO], Sofia, Bulgaria
Union Settlement Assn. [12756], 237 E 104th St., New York, NY 10029, (212)828-6000
Union of Shop, Distributive and Allied Workers [IO], Manchester, United Kingdom
Union Sindical Obrera [★IO]
Union of Students in Ireland [IO], Dublin, Ireland
Union Suisse des Chorales [IO], Aarau, Switzerland
Union Suisse des Societes d'Ingenieurs-Conseils [★IO]
Union of Swiss Chocolate Mfrs. [IO], Bern, Switzerland
Union of the Swiss Country-Women [IO], Brugg, Switzerland
Union Syndicale Suisse [★IO]
Union Syndicat Veterinaire Belge [★IO]
Union des Syndicats de Monaco [★IO]
Union Textile Merchants' Assn. [IO], Bangkok, Thailand
Union for Traditional Judaism [19905], 668 Amer. Legion Dr., Ste. B, Teaneck, NJ 07666, (201)801-0707
Union des Transports Publics [★IO]
Union des Travailleurs Esperantistes des Pays de Langue Francaise/Esperanto-Informations [IO], Paris, France
Union de Universidades de Am. Latina y El Caribe [★IO]
Union of YMCA's in Bulgaria YMCA-YWCA [IO], Sofia, Bulgaria
Union Youth Football Assn. [22598], 10026-A S Mingo Rd., No. 124, Tulsa, OK 74133, (918)289-8916
Unione Costruttori Italiani Stampi E Attrezzature di Precisione [★IO]

Unione Cristiana Delle Giovani [★IO]
Unione Industriali Pastai Italiani [★IO]
Unione Italiana dei Ciechi [★IO]
Unione Matematica Italiana [★IO]
Unione Nazionale dell'Avicoltura [★IO]
Unione Nazionale Industria Conciaria [★IO]
Unione Nazionale Industrie Dentarie Italiane [★IO]
Unione Nazionale Rappresentanti Autoveicoli Esteri [★IO]
Unione Petrolifera [IO], Rome, Italy
Unione Produttori Italiani Viteria e Bulloneria [★IO]
Uniono por la Linguo Internaciona Ido [★IO]
Unions
    AFL-CIO I Union Label and Ser. Trades Dept. [23304]
    Amer. Assn. of Classified School Employees [23177]
    Assn. of Minor League Umpires [22266]
    Australian Workers' Union [3358]
    Change to Win [23305]
    Change to Win [23305]
    Coalition of Black Trade Unionists [23306]
    Coalition of Labor Union Women [23307]
    Coalition of Labor Union Women I Center for Educ. and Res. [23308]
    Coun. of Engineers and Scientists Organizations [23309]
    Coun. on Union-Free Env. [23310]
    Directors Guild of Am. [23187]
    Graphic Arts Employers of Am. [23211]
    Indus. Workers of the World Starbucks Workers Union [23311]
    Intl. Brotherhood of DuPont Workers [23171]
    Intl. Brotherhood of Teamsers I Brewery and Soft Drink Workers Conf. [23158]
    Intl. Union of Electronic, Elecl., Salaried, Machine, and Furniture Workers [23184]
    Intl. Union of Indus. and Independent Workers [23312]
    Intl. Union of Indus. and Independent Workers [23312]
    Joint Labor Mgt. Comm. of the Retail Food Indus. [23190]
    Labor Res. Assn. [23239]
    Machinists Non-Partisan Political League [23220]
    Millwright Gp. [23221]
    Natl. Conservation District Employees Assn. [23313]
    Natl. Fed. of Independent Unions [23314]
    Professional Airways Systems Specialists [23155]
    Trans. Communications Intl. Union [23290]
    Trans. Communications Union I Brotherhood Railway Carmen Div. [23291]
    United Assn. of Journeymen and Apprentices of the Plumbing, Pipe Fitting, Sprinkler Fitting Indus. of the U.S. and Canada [23277]
    United Brotherhood of Carpenters and Joiners of Am. [23169]
    United Nations Staff Union [23261]
Unions Chretiennes Feminines du Cameroun [★IO]
UniPro Foodservice [1433], 2500 Cumberland Pkwy., Ste. 600, Atlanta, GA 30339, (770)952-0871
UNISON [IO], London, United Kingdom
Unit Production Managers Guild of Hollywood [★23187]
Unitarian Christian Advance [★20269]
Unitarian Christian Comm. [★20269]
Unitarian Christian Fellowship [★20269]
Unitarian Educational Directors Assn. [★20268]
Unitarian Historical Soc. [IO], Manchester, United Kingdom
Unitarian Ser. Comm. [★20272]
Unitarian Ser. Comm. [★20272]
Unitarian Universalist
    Liberal Religious Educators Assn. [20268]
    Unitarian Universalist Christian Fellowship [20269]
    Unitarian Universalist Historical Soc. [20270]
    Unitarian Universalist Ministers Assn. [20271]
    Unitarian Universalist Ministers Assn. [20271]
    Unitarian Universalist Ser. Comm. [20272]
    Unitarian Universalist Ser. Comm. [20272]
    Unitarian Universalist Women's Fed. [20273]
Unitarian Universalist Assn. of Congregations [12903], 25 Beacon St., Boston, MA 02108, (617)742-2100

A star before a book entry number signifies that the name is not listed separately, but is mentioned within the entry.

Unitarian Universalist Assn. of Congregations - Washington Off. for Faith in Action [★12903]

Unitarian Universalist Assn. of Congregations-Washington Off. for Social Justice [★12903]

Unitarian Universalist Assn. Jubilee Working Group for Anti-Racism - Defunct.

Unitarian Universalist Assn. - Washington Off. for Social Concern [★12903]

Unitarian Universalist Christian Fellowship [20269], PO Box 6702, Tulsa, OK 74156, (918)794-4637

Unitarian Universalist Historical Soc. [20270], 27 Grove St., Scituate, MA 02066

Unitarian Universalist Ministers Assn. [20271], 25 Beacon St., Boston, MA 02108, (617)848-0498

Unitarian Universalist Ministers Assn. [20271], 25 Beacon St., Boston, MA 02108, (617)848-0498

Unitarian Universalist Musicians' Network [20130], 2208 Henery Tuckers Ct., Charlotte, NC 28270, (800)969-8866

Unitarian Universalist Ser. Comm. [20272], 689 Massachusetts Ave., Cambridge, MA 02139-3302, (617)868-6600

Unitarian Universalist Ser. Comm. [20272], 689 Massachusetts Ave., Cambridge, MA 02139-3302, (617)868-6600

Unitarian Universalist Women's Fed. [20273], 25 Beacon St., Boston, MA 02108, (617)948-4692

Unitarian Universalists for Lesbian and Gay Concerns [★19794]

UNITE [12624], PO Box 65, Drexel Hill, PA 19026, (888)488-6483

Unite for HER [13989], PO Box 351, Pocopson, PA 19366, (610)322-9552

Unite Here [23240], 275 7th Ave., New York, NY 10001-6708, (212)265-7000

Unite for Sight [13380], 234 Church St., 7th Fl., New Haven, CT 06510

Unite for Sight [13380], 234 Church St., 7th Fl., New Haven, CT 06510

United Abrasives Mfrs'. Assn. - Superabrasives Div. [★1876]

United Action for Animals [11050], PO Box 635, New York, NY 10021, (212)249-9178

United Against Nuclear Iran [18218], PO Box 1028, New York, NY 10008-1021, (212)554-3296

United Agribusiness League [3726], 54 Corporate Park, Irvine, CA 92606-5105, (949)975-1424

United Amateur Press [★22107]

United Amateur Press Assn. [★22107]

United Amateur Press Assn. of Am. [22107], Deborah Beachboard, Sec.-Treas., 343 SW Pacific Ave., Chehalis, WA 98532-2925

United Amputee Services Assn. [15314], PO Box 4277, Winter Park, FL 32793-4277, (407)359-5500

United Animal Nations [★11030]

United Animal Nations U.S.A. [★11030]

United Arab Emirates Athletics Assn. [IO], Dubai, United Arab Emirates

United Arab Emirates Interschool Sports Assn. [IO], Dubai, United Arab Emirates

United Arab Emirates Sports Medicine Comm. [IO], Dubai, United Arab Emirates

United Arab Emirates Squash Rackets Assn. [IO], Dubai, United Arab Emirates

United Arab Emirates Tennis Assn. [IO], Dubai, United Arab Emirates

United Assn. of Equip. Leasing - Address unknown since 2011.

United Assn. of Journeymen and Apprentices of the Plumbing and Pipe Fitting Indus. of the U.S. and Canada [★23277]

United Assn. of Journeymen and Apprentices of the Plumbing, Pipe Fitting, Sprinkler Fitting Indus. of the U.S. and Canada [23277], 3 Park Pl., Annapolis, MD 21401, (410)269-2000

United Assn. for Labor Educ. [8453], 14951 SW 157 Terr., Miami, FL 33187, (305)348-3271

United Assn. Mfrs'. Representatives [2324], PO Box 784, Branson, MO 65615, (417)779-1575

United Assn. of Mobile Contract Cleaners [2262], 314 Marlow Ct., Chesapeake, VA 23322, (800)816-3240

United Assn. of Oil Services - Defunct.

United Auto Workers [★23145]

United Auto Workers Community Action Prog. [★18341]

United Baltic Appeal [18942], 115 W 183 St., Bronx, NY 10453-1103, (718)367-8802

United Baltic Appeal [18942], 115 W 183 St., Bronx, NY 10453-1103, (718)367-8802

United Barrel Racing Assn. [22670], 960 Bunyan Ave., Balsam Lake, WI 54810, (715)857-6343

United Beagle Gundog Fed. [21661], 529 Coppage Rd., Russell Springs, KY 42642, (270)384-1095

United Beauty Assn. [★975]

United Better Dress Mfrs. Assn. - Defunct.

United Bible Societies [IO], Reading, United Kingdom

United Bible Societies in Venezuela [IO], Caracas, Venezuela

United Black Drag Racers Assn. [22560], 17 Santa Fe Dr., Rock Hill, St. Louis, MO 63119, (314)968-1720

United Black Fund [12055], 2500 Martin Luther King Jr. Ave. SE, Washington, DC 20020, (202)783-9300

United Black Fund of Am. [★12055]

United Black Republican Coalition [18544], PO Box 4585, Wichita, KS 67204, (316)265-5209

United Bd. for Christian Colleges in China [★8396]

United Bd. for Christian Colleges in China [★8396]

United Bd. for Christian Higher Educ. in Asia [8396], 475 Riverside Dr., Ste. 1221, New York, NY 10115, (212)870-2600

United Bd. for Christian Higher Educ. in Asia [8396], 475 Riverside Dr., Ste. 1221, New York, NY 10115, (212)870-2600

United Brachial Plexus Network [15673], 1610 Kent St., Kent, OH 44240, (866)877-7004

United Brachial Plexus Network [15673], 1610 Kent St., Kent, OH 44240, (866)877-7004

United Braford Breeders [3942], 422 E Main, No. 218, Nacogdoches, TX 75961, (936)569-8200

United Brotherhood of Carpenters and Joiners of Am. [23169], UBC Order Dept., 14110 Sullyfield Cir., Chantilly, VA 20151, (703)378-9000

United Burundian-American Community Assn. [17953], 14339 Rosetree Ct., Silver Spring, MD 20906, (240)669-6305

United Bus Owners of Am. [★3542]

United Bus. Educ. Assn. [★7804]

United Calvinist Youth [★19606]

United Campuses to Prevent Nuclear War - Defunct.

United Catholic Music and Video Assn. [19506], PO Box 230, Donnellson, IA 52625, (319)835-9314

United Cerebral Palsy Associations [15640], 1660 L St. NW, Ste. 700, Washington, DC 20036, (202)776-0406

United Cerebral Palsy Res. and Educational Found. [★15640]

United Chainsaw Carvers Guild [21469], PO Box 255, Ridgway, PA 15853-0255

United Church Bd. for World Ministries - Defunct.

United Church of Christ

Biblical Witness Fellowship [20274]

Evangelical and Reformed Historical Soc. [20275]

United Church of Christ Justice and Witness Ministries [20276]

United Church of Christ Coalition for Lesbian, Gay, Bisexual and Transgender Concerns [19801], 2592 W 14th St., Cleveland, OH 44113, (216)861-0799

United Church of Christ Commn. for Racial Justice [★20276]

United Church of Christ Coordinating Center for Women in Church and Soc. - Defunct.

United Church of Christ Gay Caucus [★19801]

United Church of Christ Justice and Witness Ministries [20276], United Church of Christ, 700 Prospect Ave., Cleveland, OH 44115-1110, (216)736-2100

United Church of Christ Ministers for Racial and Social Justice [★20276]

United Church Coalition for Lesbian/Gay Concerns [★19801]

United Church People for Biblical Witness [★20274]

United Church Women [IO], Etobicoke, ON, Canada

United Civil Party [IO], Minsk, Belarus

United Community Funds and Councils of Am. [★12056]

United Confederate Veterans [★20388]

United Confed. of Taino People [18945], Off. of Intl. Relations and Regional Coordination, PO Box 4515, New York, NY 10163, (212)604-4186

United Cooperatives [★4176]

United Coun. of Church Women [★20286]

United Coun. of Corvette Clubs [21182], PO Box 532605, Indianapolis, IN 46253, (866)457-2582

United Coun. for Neurological Subspecialties [15674], 1080 Montreal Ave., St. Paul, MN 55116, (651)695-2762

United Dairy [★1014]

United Dance Merchants of Am. [1028], PO Box 218, Granville, MA 01034, (800)304-8362

United Daughters of the Confederacy [20390], UDC Bus. Off., 328 North Blvd., Richmond, VA 23220-4009, (804)355-1636

United Designers Assn. [★6184]

United Doberman Club [21662], PO Box 58455, Renton, WA 98058-1455, (636)629-4553

United Drive-In Theatre Owners Assn. [1269], PO Box 24771, Middle River, MD 21220, (443)490-1250

United Egg Assn. [★4817]

United Egg Processors [4816], 1720 Windwind Concourse, Ste. 230, Alpharetta, GA 30005, (770)360-9220

United Egg Producers [4817], 1720 Windward Concourse, Ste. 230, Alpharetta, GA 30005, (770)360-9220

United Elecl., Radio and Machine Workers of Am. [23185], 1 Gateway Ctr., Ste. 1400, Pittsburgh, PA 15222-1416, (412)471-8919

United Engg. Found. [6835], PO Box 70, Mount Vernon, VA 22121-0070, (973)244-2328

United Engg. Soc. [★6835]

United Engg. Trustees [★6835]

United European Gastroenterology Fed. [IO], Vienna, Austria

United for a Fair Economy [17594], 29 Winter St., Boston, MA 02108, (617)423-2148

United Farm Workers of Am. [23143], PO Box 62, Keene, CA 93531, (661)823-6151

United Farm Workers Organizing Comm. [★23143]

United Fascist Union [18349], PO Box 384, Wilmington, DE 19899

United Fathers of Am. [11869], 1651 E 4th St., Ste. 122, Santa Ana, CA 92701, (714)558-7949

United Fed. of CFS/CFIDS/CEBV Orgs. - Defunct.

United Fed. of Doll Clubs [21700], 10900 N Pomona Ave., Kansas City, MO 64153, (816)891-7040

United Fed. of Planets Internationale [23915], Helene Donohue, 217 W Nebraska Ave., No. 218, St. Paul, MN 55117

United Fed. of Postal Clerks [★23278]

United Fed. of Travel Agents' Associations [IO], Monaco, Monaco

United Fellowship for Christian Ser. [★20054]

United Fellowship for Christian Ser. [★20054]

United Firefighters' Union of Australia, Queensland Br. [IO], West End, Australia

United Fly Tyers [22584], 7 Beaver Pond Dr., Brookline, NH 03033

United Fly Tyers [22584], 7 Beaver Pond Dr., Brookline, NH 03033

United Flying Octogenarians [20921], 19 Bay State Rd., Natick, MA 01760-2942

United Food and Commercial Workers Intl. Union [23191], 1775 K St. NW, Washington, DC 20006-1598, (202)223-3111

United Ford Owners [21183], PO Box 32419, Columbus, OH 43232, (740)607-1451

United Four-Wheel Drive Associations [21184], PO Box 316, Swartz Creek, MI 48473, (800)448-3932

United Fresh Fruit and Vegetable Assn. and Intl. Fresh-Cut Produce Assn. [★4476]

United Fresh Produce Assn. [4476], 1901 Pennsylvania Ave. NW, Ste. 1100, Washington, DC 20006, (202)303-3400

United Furniture Workers of Am. [★23193]

United Furniture Workers Insurance Fund [23193], 1910 Air Lane Dr., Nashville, TN 37210, (615)889-8860

United Future New Zealand [IO], Wellington, New Zealand

United Garment Workers of Am. [★23191]

United Global Org. of Development [IO], Islamabad, Pakistan

United Gloster Breeders [21231], 715 Avocado Ct., Del Mar, CA 92014-3911

Reference to "IO" in place of a book number signifies that the association may be found in the 50th edition of International Organizations.

United Grief Support [★12624]

United in Gp. Harmony Assn. [10307], 1135 Main Ave., Clifton, NJ 07011, (973)365-0049

United Hellenic Voters of Am. [19019], 525 W Lake St., Addison, IL 60101, (630)628-0820

United Hellenic Voters of Illinois [★19019]

United HIAS Ser. [★12406]

United HIAS Ser. [★12406]

United Horological Assn. of Amer. [★2155]

United Hunts Racing Assn. [★22662]

United Indian Development Assn. [★12563]

United Indian Missions Intl. [20102], PO Box 336010, Greeley, CO 80633-0601, (970)785-1176

United Indian Missions, Intl. [20102], PO Box 336010, Greeley, CO 80633-0601, (970)785-1176

United Indians of All Tribes Found. [18157], Discovery Park, PO Box 99100, Seattle, WA 98199, (206)285-4425

United Infants' and Children's Wear Assn. - Defunct.

United Inventors Assn. of the U.S.A. [7015], 1025 Connecticut Ave. NW, Ste. 1000, Washington, DC 20036, (800)701-8595

United Israel World Union [20118], PO Box 561476, Charlotte, NC 28256

United Israel World Union [20118], PO Box 561476, Charlotte, NC 28256

United Jewish Appeal [★12410]

United Jewish Appeal - Fed. of Jewish Philanthropies of New York - Address unknown since 2010.

United Jewish Appeal - Fed. of Jewish Philanthropies of New York Task Force on Compulsive Gambling - Defunct.

United Jewish Communities [★12410]

United Kennel Club [21663], 100 E Kilgore Rd., Portage, MI 49002-0506, (269)343-9020

United Kingdom
  British Trade Off. at Consulate-General [23336] Cambridge in Am. [9023]

United Kingdom Assn. for European Law [IO], London, United Kingdom

United Kingdom Assn. for Milk Banking [IO], London, United Kingdom

United Kingdom Assn. of Professional Engineers [IO], Bromley, United Kingdom

United Kingdom Automatic Control Coun. [IO], Stevenage, United Kingdom

United Kingdom Bartenders Guild [IO], Linlithgow, United Kingdom

United Kingdom Cast Stone Assn. [IO], Northampton, United Kingdom

United Kingdom Comm. of Intl. Water Assn. [IO], London, United Kingdom

United Kingdom Coun. for Psychotherapy [IO], London, United Kingdom

United Kingdom Dodge Ball Assn. [IO], Kettering, United Kingdom

United Kingdom eInformation Gp. [IO], Leyburn, United Kingdom

United Kingdom Environmental Law Assn. [IO], Dorking, United Kingdom

United Kingdom Environmental Mutagen Soc. [IO], Edinburgh, United Kingdom

United Kingdom Forum for Organisational Hea. [IO], East Molesey, United Kingdom

United Kingdom Home Care Assn. [IO], Sutton, United Kingdom

United Kingdom Housekeepers Assn. [IO], London, United Kingdom

United Kingdom Hydrogen Assn. [IO], Newcastle upon Tyne, United Kingdom

United Kingdom Indus. Vision Assn. [IO], Royston, United Kingdom

United Kingdom Inst. for Conservation of Historic and Artistic Works [IO], London, United Kingdom

United Kingdom-Ireland Controlled Release Soc. [IO], Hoddesdon, United Kingdom

United Kingdom Jujitsu Assn. Intl. [IO], Rochdale, United Kingdom

United Kingdom Literacy Assn. [IO], Leicester, United Kingdom

United Kingdom Major Ports Gp. [IO], London, United Kingdom

United Kingdom Maritime Pilots' Assn. [IO], London, United Kingdom

United Kingdom Multiple Sclerosis Specialist Nurse Assn. [IO], Ledbury, United Kingdom

United Kingdom Offshore Operators' Assn. [IO], London, United Kingdom

United Kingdom Onshore Operators Gp. [IO], Bournemouth, United Kingdom

United Kingdom Paintball Sports Fed. [IO], Rochdale, United Kingdom

United Kingdom Petroleum Indus. Assn. [IO], London, United Kingdom

United Kingdom Polocrosse Assn. [IO], Sheffield, United Kingdom

United Kingdom Practical Shooting Assn. [IO], Weymouth, United Kingdom

United Kingdom Rocketry Assn. [IO], Canterbury, United Kingdom

United Kingdom Sci. Park Assn. [IO], Cambridge, United Kingdom

United Kingdom Skateboarding Assn. [IO], Waltham Abbey, United Kingdom

United Kingdom Soc. for Trenchless Tech. [IO], Leamington Spa, United Kingdom

United Kingdom Spring Mfrs. Assn. [IO], Sheffield, United Kingdom

United Kingdom Tang Soo Soo Bahk Do Fed. [IO], Watford, United Kingdom

United Kingdom Transplant Coordinators Assn. [IO], Kingsbridge, United Kingdom

United Kingdom Warehousing Assn. [IO], London, United Kingdom

United Kingdom Wayfarer Assn. [IO], Colchester, United Kingdom

United Kingdom Weighing Fed. [IO], Birmingham, United Kingdom

United Kingdom's Disabled People's Coun. [IO], Derby, United Kingdom

United Knitwear Mfrs. League - Defunct.

United Leukodystrophy Found. [15641], 2304 Highland Dr., Sycamore, IL 60178, (815)895-3211

United Leukodystrophy Found. [15641], 2304 Highland Dr., Sycamore, IL 60178, (815)895-3211

United Lightning Protection Assn. [3155], 426 North Ave., Libertyville, IL 60048, (800)668-8572

United Lodge of Theosophists [20266], 245 W 33rd St., Los Angeles, CA 90007, (213)748-7244

United Lodge of Theosophists [20266], 245 W 33rd St., Los Angeles, CA 90007, (213)748-7244

United Lodge of Theosophists - Belgium [IO], Antwerp, Belgium

United Lodge of Theosophists - India [IO], Mumbai, India

United Lodge of Theosophists - Ottawa [IO], Ottawa, ON, Canada

United Lodge of Theosophists - United Kingdom [IO], London, United Kingdom

United Methodist Assn. of Hea. and Welfare Ministries [14742], 407-B Corporate Center Dr., Ste. B, Vandalia, OH 45377, (937)415-3624

United Methodist Church I Gen. Bd. of Church and Soc. [19975], 100 Maryland Ave. NE, Washington, DC 20002, (202)488-5600

United Methodist Comm. on Overseas Relief [★19976]

United Methodist Comm. on Overseas Relief [★19976]

United Methodist Comm. on Relief [19976], 475 Riverside Dr., Rm. 1522, New York, NY 10115, (212)870-3951

United Methodist Comm. on Relief [19976], 475 Riverside Dr., Rm. 1522, New York, NY 10115, (212)870-3951

United Methodist Coun. on Youth Ministry [★19977]

United Methodist Youth Org. [19977], PO Box 340003, Nashville, TN 37203-0003, (615)340-7079

United Mine Workers of Am. [23257], 18354 Quantico Gateway Dr., Ste. 200, Triangle, VA 22172-1179, (703)291-2400

United Missionary Church [★20065]

United Missionary Church [★20065]

United Missionary Fellowship [★19732]

United Missionary Fellowship [★19732]

United Mitochondrial Disease Found. [16612], 8085 Saltsburg Rd., Ste. 201, Pittsburgh, PA 15239, (412)793-8077

United Motorcoach Assn. [3542], 113 S West St., 4th Fl., Alexandria, VA 22314-2824, (703)838-2929

United Natl. Indian Tribal Youth [10337], PO Box 800, Oklahoma City, OK 73101, (405)236-2800

United Natl. Life Insurance Soc. [★19053]

United Natl. Weight Pull Assn. [22550], Karyn Dawes, Treas., PO Box 1719, San Marcos, CA 92079

United Nations [18747], First Ave., 46th St., New York, NY 10017, (212)963-4475

United Nations [18747], First Ave., 46th St., New York, NY 10017, (212)963-4475

United Nations
  Be The Change Intl. [13344]
  Center for U.N. Reform Educ. [18743]
  Citizens for Global Solutions [18744]
  Communications Coordination Comm. for the United Nations [18745]
  Communications Coordination Comm. for the United Nations [18745]
  Friends of the United Nations [18746]
  Global Vision for Peace [18252]
  MediaGlobal [12348]
  United Nations [18747]
  United Nations [18747]
  United Nations Assn. of the U.S.A. [18748]
  United Nations I Commn. on the Status of Women [18749]
  United Nations Commn. on the Status of Women [18749]
  United Nations I Emergenccy Coalition for U.S. Financial Support of the United Nations [18750]
  United Nations Staff Union [23261]
  U.S. Assn. for the Univ. for Peace [18294]
  U.S. Fund for UNICEF [18751]
  U.S.A. Coun. of Organizations I United Nations Assn. [18752]
  World Federalist Movement [18753]
  World Federalist Movement [18753]

United Nations Asia and Far East Inst. for the Prevention of Crime and the Treatment of Offenders [IO], Tokyo, Japan

United Nations Assn. of Australia [IO], Canberra, Australia

United Nations Assn. of Australia - Australian Capital Territory [IO], Canberra, Australia

United Nations Assn. of Australia - New South Wales [IO], Sydney, Australia

United Nations Assn. of Australia - South Australia [IO], Adelaide, Australia

United Nations Assn. of Australia - Victoria [IO], Melbourne, Australia

United Nations Assn. of Australia - Western Australia [IO], East Perth, Australia

United Nations Assn. in Canada [IO], Ottawa, ON, Canada

United Nations Assn. in Canada Calgary Br. [IO], Calgary, AB, Canada

United Nations Assn. in Canada Edmonton Br. [IO], Edmonton, AB, Canada

United Nations Assn. in Canada Hamilton Br. [IO], Dundas, ON, Canada

United Nations Assn. in Canada Kootenay Region Br. [IO], Grand Forks, BC, Canada

United Nations Assn. in Canada Montreal [IO], Montreal, QC, Canada

United Nations Assn. in Canada Natl. Capital Region Br. [IO], Ottawa, ON, Canada

United Nations Assn. in Canada Quebec Br. [IO], Quebec, QC, Canada

United Nations Assn. in Canada Quinte and District Br. [IO], Belleville, ON, Canada

United Nations Assn. in Canada Saguenay Lac-Saint-Jean Br. [IO], Chicoutimi, QC, Canada

United Nations Assn. in Canada St. John's Br. [IO], Paradise, NL, Canada

United Nations Assn. in Canada Toronto Region Br. [IO], Toronto, ON, Canada

United Nations Assn. in Canada Vancouver Br. [IO], Vancouver, BC, Canada

United Nations Assn. in Canada Victoria Br. [IO], Victoria, BC, Canada

United Nations Assn. in Canada Winnipeg Br. [IO], Winnipeg, MB, Canada

United Nations Assn. in the Democratic Socialist Republic of Sri Lanka [IO], Panadura, Sri Lanka

United Nations Assn. of Great Britain and Northern Ireland [IO], London, United Kingdom

United Nations Assn. of Hungary **[IO]**, Budapest, Hungary

United Nations Assn. of Iran **[IO]**, Tehran, Iran

United Nations Assn. of the U.S.A. **[18748]**, 801 2nd Ave., 2nd Fl., New York, NY 10017, (212)907-1300

United Nations Children's Fund - Armenia **[IO]**, Yerevan, Armenia

United Nations Children's Fund - Botswana **[IO]**, Gaborone, Botswana

United Nations Children's Fund - Namibia **[IO]**, Windhoek, Namibia

United Nations Commn. on the Status of Women **[18749]**, Div. for the Advancement of Women, 2 United Nations Plz., 12th Fl., Rm. DC2, New York, NY 10017

United Nations I Commn. on the Status of Women **[18749]**, Div. for the Advancement of Women, 2 United Nations Plz., 12th Fl., Rm. DC2, New York, NY 10017

United Nations Comm. on the Peaceful Uses of Outer Space **[IO]**, Vienna, Austria

United Nations Conf. on Trade and Development **[IO]**, Geneva, Switzerland

United Nations Correspondents Assn. **[2878]**, United Nations, 405 E 42nd St., Rm. L-213, New York, NY 10017, (212)963-7137

United Nations Correspondents Assn. **[2878]**, United Nations, 405 E 42nd St., Rm. L-213, New York, NY 10017, (212)963-7137

United Nations Delegations; Hospitality Comm. for **[17972]**

United Nations Development Fund for Women **[17672]**, 304 E 45th St., 15th Fl., New York, NY 10017, (212)906-6400

United Nations Development Fund for Women **[17672]**, 304 E 45th St., 15th Fl., New York, NY 10017, (212)906-6400

United Nations Development Programme **[17925]**, 1 United Nations Plz., New York, NY 10017, (212)906-5000

United Nations Development Programme **[17925]**, 1 United Nations Plz., New York, NY 10017, (212)906-5000

United Nations Development Programme - Afghanistan **[IO]**, Kabul, Afghanistan

United Nations Development Programme - Angola **[IO]**, Luanda, Angola

United Nations Development Programme - Armenia **[IO]**, Yerevan, Armenia

United Nations Development Programme - Burkina Faso **[IO]**, Ouagadougou, Burkina Faso

United Nations Development Programme - Burundi **[IO]**, Bujumbura, Burundi

United Nations Development Programme - Cambodia **[IO]**, Phnom Penh, Cambodia

United Nations Development Programme - Cameroon **[IO]**, Yaounde, Cameroon

United Nations Development Programme - Central African Republic **[IO]**, Bangui, Central African Republic

United Nations Development Programme - China **[IO]**, Beijing, People's Republic of China

United Nations Development Programme - Cote d'Ivoire **[IO]**, Abidjan, Cote d'Ivoire

United Nations Development Programme - Cuba **[IO]**, Havana, Cuba

United Nations Development Programme - Djibouti **[IO]**, Djibouti, Djibouti

United Nations Development Programme - Eritrea **[IO]**, Asmara, Eritrea

United Nations Development Programme - Ethiopia **[IO]**, Addis Ababa, Ethiopia

United Nations Development Programme - Gabon **[IO]**, Libreville, Gabon

United Nations Development Programme - Gambia **[IO]**, Cape Point, Gambia

United Nations Development Programme - Ghana **[IO]**, Accra, Ghana

United Nations Development Programme - Guinea **[IO]**, Conakry, Guinea

United Nations Development Programme - Haiti **[IO]**, Port-au-Prince, Haiti

United Nations Development Programme - Iran **[IO]**, Tehran, Iran

United Nations Development Programme - Kyrgyzstan **[IO]**, Bishkek, Kirgizstan

United Nations Development Programme - Lesotho **[IO]**, Maseru, Lesotho

United Nations Development Programme - Liberia **[IO]**, Monrovia, Liberia

United Nations Development Programme - Madagascar **[IO]**, Antananarivo, Madagascar

United Nations Development Programme - Malawi **[IO]**, Lilongwe, Malawi

United Nations Development Programme - Mali **[IO]**, Bamako, Mali

United Nations Development Programme - Mauritania **[IO]**, Nouakchott, Mauritania

United Nations Development Programme - Mauritius and Seychelles **[IO]**, Port Louis, Mauritius

United Nations Development Programme - Montenegro **[IO]**, Podgorica, Montenegro

United Nations Development Programme - Mozambique **[IO]**, Maputo, Mozambique

United Nations Development Programme - Niger **[IO]**, Niamey, Niger

United Nations Development Programme - Nigeria **[IO]**, Abuja, Nigeria

United Nations Development Programme - Pakistan **[IO]**, Islamabad, Pakistan

United Nations Development Programme - Papua New Guinea **[IO]**, Port Moresby, Papua New Guinea

United Nations Development Programme - Regional Bur. for Asia and the Pacific **[17926]**, United Nations Development Programme, 1 United Nations Plz., New York, NY 10017, (212)906-5000

United Nations Development Programme - Regional Bur. for Asia and the Pacific **[17926]**, United Nations Development Programme, 1 United Nations Plz., New York, NY 10017, (212)906-5000

United Nations Development Programme - Rwanda **[IO]**, Kigali, Rwanda

United Nations Development Programme - Sudan **[IO]**, Khartoum, Sudan

United Nations Development Programme - Swaziland **[IO]**, Mbabane, Swaziland

United Nations Development Programme - Tajikistan **[IO]**, Dushanbe, Tajikistan

United Nations Development Programme - Tanzania **[IO]**, Dar es Salaam, United Republic of Tanzania

United Nations Development Programme - Togo **[IO]**, Lome, Togo

United Nations Development Programme - Turkmenistan **[IO]**, Ashgabat, Turkmenistan

United Nations Development Programme - Uganda **[IO]**, Kampala, Uganda

United Nations Development Programme - Uzbekistan **[IO]**, Tashkent, Uzbekistan

United Nations Div. for the Advancement of Women **[13483]**, 2 United Nations Plz., DC2-1270, New York, NY 10017, (212)963-3171

United Nations Div. for the Advancement of Women **[13483]**, 2 United Nations Plz., DC2-1270, New York, NY 10017, (212)963-3171

United Nations Economic Commn. for Africa **[IO]**, Addis Ababa, Ethiopia

United Nations Economic Commn. for Europe **[IO]**, Geneva, Switzerland

United Nations Economic and Social Commn. for Asia and the Pacific **[IO]**, Bangkok, Thailand

United Nations Educational, Sci. and Cultural Org. **[IO]**, Paris, France

United Nations I Emergenccy Coalition for U.S. Financial Support of the United Nations **[18750]**, 110 Maryland Ave. NE, Ste. 409, Washington, DC 20002, (202)546-1572

United Nations Env. Program/Global Rsrc. Info. Database **[4310]**, USGS Natl. Center of EROS, 47914 252nd St., Sioux Falls, SD 57198-0001, (605)594-6117

United Nations Env. Programme - Regional Off. for Africa **[IO]**, Nairobi, Kenya

United Nations Env. Programme - Regional Off. for Asia and the Pacific **[IO]**, Bangkok, Thailand

United Nations Env. Programme - Regional Off. for Europe **[IO]**, Geneva, Switzerland

United Nations Framework Convention on Climate Change **[IO]**, Bonn, Germany

United Nations HQ Nongovernmental Organizations Comm. on Youth **[★13547]**

United Nations High Commissioner for Refugees - Regional Off. Mexico **[IO]**, Polanco, Mexico

United Nations High Commissioner for Refugees - Switzerland **[IO]**, Geneva, Switzerland

United Nations Indus. Development Org. **[IO]**, Vienna, Austria

United Nations Indus. Development Org. - Algeria **[IO]**, Algiers, Algeria

United Nations Indus. Development Org. - Bolivia **[IO]**, La Paz, Bolivia

United Nations Indus. Development Org. - Cameroon **[IO]**, Yaounde, Cameroon

United Nations Indus. Development Org. - China **[IO]**, Beijing, People's Republic of China

United Nations Indus. Development Org. - Colombia **[IO]**, Bogota, Colombia

United Nations Indus. Development Org. - Cote d'Ivoire **[IO]**, Abidjan, Cote d'Ivoire

United Nations Indus. Development Org. - Egypt **[IO]**, Cairo, Egypt

United Nations Indus. Development Org. - Eritrea **[IO]**, Asmara, Eritrea

United Nations Indus. Development Org. - Ethiopia **[IO]**, Addis Ababa, Ethiopia

United Nations Indus. Development Org. - Ghana **[IO]**, Accra, Ghana

United Nations Indus. Development Org. - Guinea **[IO]**, Conakry, Guinea

United Nations Indus. Development Org. - India **[IO]**, New Delhi, India

United Nations Indus. Development Org. - Indonesia **[IO]**, Jakarta, Indonesia

United Nations Indus. Development Org. - Iran **[IO]**, Tehran, Iran

United Nations Indus. Development Org. - Kenya **[IO]**, Nairobi, Kenya

United Nations Indus. Development Org. - Lebanon **[IO]**, Beirut, Lebanon

United Nations Indus. Development Org. - Madagascar **[IO]**, Antananarivo, Madagascar

United Nations Indus. Development Org. - Mexico **[IO]**, Mexico City, Mexico

United Nations Indus. Development Org. - Morocco **[IO]**, Rabat, Morocco

United Nations Indus. Development Org. - Mozambique **[IO]**, Maputo, Mozambique

United Nations Indus. Development Org. - Nigeria **[IO]**, Abuja, Nigeria

United Nations Indus. Development Org. - Pakistan **[IO]**, Islamabad, Pakistan

United Nations Indus. Development Org. - Philippines **[IO]**, Makati City, Philippines

United Nations Indus. Development Org. - Senegal **[IO]**, Dakar, Senegal

United Nations Indus. Development Org. - Sudan **[IO]**, Khartoum, Sudan

United Nations Indus. Development Org. - Thailand **[IO]**, Bangkok, Thailand

United Nations Indus. Development Org. - Tunisia **[IO]**, Tunis, Tunisia

United Nations Indus. Development Org. - Uruguay **[IO]**, Montevideo, Uruguay

United Nations Indus. Development Org. - Vietnam **[IO]**, Hanoi, Vietnam

United Nations Indus. Development Org. - Zimbabwe **[IO]**, Harare, Zimbabwe

United Nations Info. Centre - Lagos **[IO]**, Lagos, Nigeria

United Nations Inst. for Training and Res. **[IO]**, Geneva, Switzerland

United Nations Non-Governmental Liaison Ser. **[IO]**, Geneva, Switzerland

United Nations Off. of the High Commissioner for Human Rights **[IO]**, Geneva, Switzerland

United Nations Philatelists, Inc. **[22086]**, Blanton Clement, Jr., Sec., PO Box 146, Morrisville, PA 19067-0146

United Nations Population Fund - Afghanistan **[IO]**, Kabul, Afghanistan

United Nations Population Fund - Armenia **[IO]**, Yerevan, Armenia

United Nations Population Fund - Azerbaijan **[IO]**, Baku, Azerbaijan

United Nations Population Fund - Bangladesh **[IO]**, Dhaka, Bangladesh

Reference to "IO" in place of a book number signifies that the association may be found in the 50th edition of International Organizations.

United Nations Population Fund - Belgium **[IO]**, Brussels, Belgium

United Nations Population Fund - Benin **[IO]**, Cotonou, Benin

United Nations Population Fund - Bolivia **[IO]**, La Paz, Bolivia

United Nations Population Fund - Brazil **[IO]**, Brasilia, Brazil

United Nations Population Fund - Cambodia **[IO]**, Phnom Penh, Cambodia

United Nations Population Fund - Cameroon **[IO]**, Yaounde, Cameroon

United Nations Population Fund - Colombia **[IO]**, Bogota, Colombia

United Nations Population Fund - Costa Rica **[IO]**, San Jose, Costa Rica

United Nations Population Fund - Cote d'Ivoire **[IO]**, Abidjan, Cote d'Ivoire

United Nations Population Fund - Democratic Republic of Congo **[IO]**, Kinshasa, Republic of the Congo

United Nations Population Fund - Dominican Republic **[IO]**, Santo Domingo, Dominican Republic

United Nations Population Fund - Ecuador **[IO]**, Quito, Ecuador

United Nations Population Fund - Egypt **[IO]**, Cairo, Egypt

United Nations Population Fund - Estonia **[IO]**, Tallinn, Estonia

United Nations Population Fund - Fiji **[IO]**, Suva, Fiji

United Nations Population Fund - Georgia **[IO]**, Tbilisi, Georgia

United Nations Population Fund - Guatemala **[IO]**, Guatemala City, Guatemala

United Nations Population Fund - Guinea **[IO]**, Conakry, Guinea

United Nations Population Fund - Haiti **[IO]**, Port-au-Prince, Haiti

United Nations Population Fund - Honduras **[IO]**, Tegucigalpa, Honduras

United Nations Population Fund - India **[IO]**, New Delhi, India

United Nations Population Fund - Iran **[IO]**, Tehran, Iran

United Nations Population Fund - Jamaica **[IO]**, Kingston, Jamaica

United Nations Population Fund - Japan **[IO]**, Tokyo, Japan

United Nations Population Fund - Kazakhstan **[IO]**, Almaty, Kazakhstan

United Nations Population Fund - Kenya **[IO]**, Nairobi, Kenya

United Nations Population Fund - Kyrgyzstan **[IO]**, Bishkek, Kirgizstan

United Nations Population Fund - Lebanon **[IO]**, Beirut, Lebanon

United Nations Population Fund - Madagascar **[IO]**, Antananarivo, Madagascar

United Nations Population Fund - Malawi **[IO]**, Lilongwe, Malawi

United Nations Population Fund - Malaysia **[IO]**, Kuala Lumpur, Malaysia

United Nations Population Fund - Maldives **[IO]**, Male, Maldives

United Nations Population Fund - Mali **[IO]**, Bamako, Mali

United Nations Population Fund - Mauritania **[IO]**, Nouakchott, Mauritania

United Nations Population Fund - Mauritius **[IO]**, Port Louis, Mauritius

United Nations Population Fund - Mexico **[IO]**, Mexico City, Mexico

United Nations Population Fund - Mongolia **[IO]**, Ulan Bator, Mongolia

United Nations Population Fund - Morocco **[IO]**, Rabat, Morocco

United Nations Population Fund - Mozambique **[IO]**, Maputo, Mozambique

United Nations Population Fund - Myanmar **[IO]**, Yangon, Myanmar

United Nations Population Fund - Nepal **[IO]**, Kathmandu, Nepal

United Nations Population Fund - Nicaragua **[IO]**, Managua, Nicaragua

United Nations Population Fund - Nigeria **[IO]**, Abuja, Nigeria

United Nations Population Fund - Pakistan **[IO]**, Islamabad, Pakistan

United Nations Population Fund - Paraguay **[IO]**, Asuncion, Paraguay

United Nations Population Fund - Peru **[IO]**, Lima, Peru

United Nations Population Fund - Philippines **[IO]**, Makati City, Philippines

United Nations Population Fund - Republic of Moldova **[IO]**, Chisinau, Moldova

United Nations Population Fund - Romania **[IO]**, Bucharest, Romania

United Nations Population Fund - Rwanda **[IO]**, Kigali, Rwanda

United Nations Population Fund - Senegal **[IO]**, Dakar, Senegal

United Nations Population Fund - Sri Lanka **[IO]**, Colombo, Sri Lanka

United Nations Population Fund - Syrian Arab Republic **[IO]**, Damascus, Syrian Arab Republic

United Nations Population Fund - Tajikistan **[IO]**, Dushanbe, Tajikistan

United Nations Population Fund - Tanzania **[IO]**, Dar es Salaam, United Republic of Tanzania

United Nations Population Fund - Thailand **[IO]**, Bangkok, Thailand

United Nations Population Fund - Turkey **[IO]**, Ankara, Turkey

United Nations Population Fund - Turkmenistan **[IO]**, Ashgabat, Turkmenistan

United Nations Population Fund - Ukraine **[IO]**, Kiev, Ukraine

United Nations Population Fund - United Arab Emirates **[IO]**, Abu Dhabi, United Arab Emirates

United Nations Population Fund - Uzbekistan **[IO]**, Tashkent, Uzbekistan

United Nations Population Fund - Venezuela **[IO]**, Caracas, Venezuela

United Nations Population Fund - Yemen **[IO]**, Sana'a, Yemen

United Nations Res. Inst. for Social Development **[IO]**, Geneva, Switzerland

United Nations Special Comm. Against Apartheid - Defunct.

United Nations Staff Assn. **[★23261]**

United Nations Staff Assn. **[★23261]**

United Nations Staff Union **[23261]**, 866 United Nations Plz., Rm. A-0248, 2nd Fl., New York, NY 10017, (212)963-7075

United Nations Staff Union **[23261]**, 866 United Nations Plz., Rm. A-0248, 2nd Fl., New York, NY 10017, (212)963-7075

United Nations Sys. Standing Comm. on Nutrition **[IO]**, Geneva, Switzerland

United Nations I Vietnam Relief Effort **[13372]**, 845 United Nations Plaza, 90A, New York, NY 10017, (917)668-2600

United Nations Volunteers **[IO]**, Bonn, Germany

United Nations I Women's Fed. for World Peace Intl. **[12637]**, 4 W 43rd St., New York, NY 10036, (914)946-3017

United Nations Women's Guild **[13078]**, One United Nations Plaza, DC-1, Rm. 0775, New York, NY 10017, (212)963-8279

United Nations Women's Guild **[13078]**, One United Nations Plaza, DC-1, Rm. 0775, New York, NY 10017, (212)963-8279

United Natural Products Alliance **[14845]**, Lindsay Wright, Dir. of Programs and Seminars, 1075 Hollywood Ave., Salt Lake City, UT 84105, (801)474-2572

United Negro Coll. Fund **[8196]**, 8260 Willow Oaks Corporate Dr., PO Box 10444, Fairfax, VA 22031-8044, (703)205-3400

United Negro Coll. Fund I Natl. Alumni Coun. **[18904]**, 8260 Willow Oaks Corporate Dr., Fairfax, VA 22031, (703)205-3400

United Neighborhood Centers of Am. **[11648]**, 11700 W Lake Park Dr., Milwaukee, WI 53224, (414)359-6576

United Network Command **[23931]**, PO Box 275, Buffalo, NY 14201

United Network for Organ Sharing **[16920]**, PO Box 2484, Richmond, VA 23218-2484, (804)782-4800

United New Conservationists - Defunct.

United Order of the Golden Cross **[★19286]**

United Order True Sisters **[19283]**, Linton Intl. Plaza, 660 Linton Blvd., Ste. 6, Delray Beach, FL 33444, (561)265-1557

United Orthodox Rabbinate - Defunct.

United Ostomy Assn. of Canada **[IO]**, Toronto, ON, Canada

United Ostomy Assn. - Defunct.

United Parents and Teachers Assn. of Jewish Schools - Defunct.

United Parkinson Found. **[★15630]**

United Patients Assn. for Pulmonary Hypertension **[★15079]**

United for Peace **[★18293]**

United for Peace **[★18293]**

United for Peace and Justice **[18293]**, PO Box 607, New York, NY 10108, (212)868-5545

United for Peace and Justice **[18293]**, PO Box 607, New York, NY 10108, (212)868-5545

United Pegasus Found. **[17797]**, PO Box 173, Tehachapi, CA 93581, (661)823-9672

United People in Christ **[19980]**, PO Box 162601, Altamonte Springs, FL 32716-2601, (407)862-0107

United Plant Savers **[13715]**, PO Box 400, East Barre, VT 05649, (802)476-6467

United Plant Savers **[13715]**, PO Box 400, East Barre, VT 05649, (802)476-6467

United Plastics Distributors Assn. **[★2769]**

United Plastics Distributors Assn. **[★2769]**

United Polish Women of Am. **[★19195]**

United Poodle Breeds Assn. **[21664]**, 5 Helena Cir., Columbia, SC 29209

United Postal Stationery Soc. **[22087]**, PO Box 3982, Chester, VA 23831

United Poultry Concerns **[11051]**, PO Box 150, Machipongo, VA 23405-0150, (757)678-7875

United Presbyterian Peace Fellowship **[★18282]**

United Presbyterian Women **[★20164]**

United Press Associations **[★2879]**

United Press Associations **[★2879]**

United Press Intl. **[2879]**, 1133 19th St. NW, Washington, DC 20036, (202)898-8000

United Press Intl. **[2879]**, 1133 19th St. NW, Washington, DC 20036, (202)898-8000

United Press Intl. - Chile **[IO]**, Santiago, Chile

United Press Intl. - Hong Kong **[IO]**, Hong Kong, People's Republic of China

United Press Intl. - Japan **[IO]**, Tokyo, Japan

United Press Intl. - Korea **[IO]**, Seoul, Republic of Korea

United Press Intl. - Middle East **[IO]**, Beirut, Lebanon

United Producers Assn. **[IO]**, Karachi, Pakistan

United Producers, Inc. **[4725]**, 8351 N High St., Ste. 250, Columbus, OH 43235, (614)433-2150

United Professional Horsemen's Assn. **[4654]**, 4059 Iron Works Pkwy., Ste. 2, Lexington, KY 40511, (859)231-5070

United Religions Initiative **[20207]**, PO Box 29242, 1009 Gen. Kennedy Ave., San Francisco, CA 94129, (415)561-2300

United Republicans for Equality and Privacy **[★18529]**

United Retail Workers **[★23191]**

United Road Transport Union **[IO]**, Cheadle Hulme, United Kingdom

United Scenic Artists **[23275]**, 29 W 38th St., 15th Fl., New York, NY 10018, (212)581-0300

United Schutzhund Clubs of Am. **[21665]**, 3810 Paule Ave., St. Louis, MO 63125-1718, (314)638-9686

United Scleroderma Found. - Defunct.

United Seamen's Ser. **[13030]**, 635 4th Ave., Ground Fl., Brooklyn, NY 11232, (718)369-3818

United Seamen's Ser. **[13030]**, 635 4th Ave., Ground Fl., Brooklyn, NY 11232, (718)369-3818

United Ser. Organizations **[★18931]**

United Ser. Organizations **[★18931]**

United Services for New Americans **[★12406]**

United Services for New Americans **[★12406]**

United Shoe Retailers Assn. **[1463]**, PO Box 4931, West Hills, CA 91308, (818)703-6062

United Sidecar Assn. **[21939]**, 5201 Cook Rd., St. Joseph, MO 64505, (816)232-2726

UNITED SIKHS **[12228]**, PO Box 7203, New York, NY 10116, (646)688-3525

A star before a book entry number signifies that the name is not listed separately, but is mentioned within the entry.

United Silver Fanciers [★21260]

United Silver and Golden Fanciers [21260], Sally Daniels, Treas., 5242 Vista Grande Dr., Santa Rosa, CA 95403

United Slate, Tile and Composition Roofers, Damp and Waterproof Workers Assn. [★23170]

United Soccer League - Defunct.

United Soc. for the Propagation of the Gospel [IO], London, United Kingdom

United South and Eastern Tribes [12570], 711 Stewarts Ferry Pike, Ste. 100, Nashville, TN 37214, (615)872-7900

United Southeastern Tribes [★12570]

United Soybean Bd. [4477], 16305 Swingley Ridge Rd., Ste. 150, Chesterfield, MO 63017, (636)530-1777

United Sportsmans Assn. of North Am. - Address unknown since 2010.

United Square Dancers of Am. [9566], 7547 Westlake Rd., Sterlington, LA 71280, (318)665-9085

U.S. [★12599]

United States

Africa News Ser. [17144]

Amer. Civil Liberties Union [17260]

Amer. Coun. on Consumer Interests [17442]

Assn. of Concerned African Scholars [17147]

Assn. of Thai Professionals in Am. and Canada [19255]

Building Bridges: Middle East-US [8385]

Center for Constitutional Rights [17273]

Close Up Found. [17249]

Congressional Automotive Caucus [17410]

Constitutional Rights Found. [17437]

Natl. Center for Constitutional Stud. [17440]

Natl. Comm. for an Effective Cong. [17413]

Partners for Rural Am. [18574]

People for the Amer. Way [17317]

Sino-American Bridge for Educ. and Hea. [9876]

Thai U.S.A. Assn. [19256]

United Nations | Emergenccy Coalition for U.S. Financial Support of the United Nations [18750]

U.S. Women and Cuba Collaboration [17957]

U.S. 6 Metre Assn. - Defunct.

U.S. 1869 Pictoral Res. Associates [★22089]

U.S. A-Class Catamaran Assn. [22400], Hall Spars, 33 Broadcommon Rd., Bristol, RI 02809

U.S. Adult Cystic Fibrosis Assn. [16613], PO Box 1618, Gresham, OR 97030-0519, (503)669-3561

U.S. Adult Soccer Assn. [22943], 7000 S Harlem Ave., Bridgeview, IL 60455-1160, (708)496-6870

U.S. Adventure Racing Assn. [22827], PO Box 514, Wellborn, TX 77881, (979)703-5018

U.S.-Afghanistan Reconstruction Coun. [10805], 8201 Greensboro Dr., Ste. 105, McLean, VA 22102, (703)462-8252

U.S. African Development Found. [17927], 1400 I St. NW, Ste. 1000, Washington, DC 20005, (202)673-3916

U.S. African Development Found. [17927], 1400 I St. NW, Ste. 1000, Washington, DC 20005, (202)673-3916

U.S. Aikido Fed. [22219], New York Aikikai, 142 W 18th St., New York, NY 10011, (212)242-6246

U.S. Air Consolidator Assn. [3581], 16 W 46th St., 2nd Flr., New York, NY 10036, (212)764-6161

U.S. Air Force Judo Assn. [★22705]

U.S. Air Racing Assn. [★22212]

U.S. Albacore Assn. [22401], 1031 Graham St., Bethlehem, PA 18015-2520

U.S.-Algeria Bus. Coun. [2108], 2001 Jefferson Davis Hwy., Ste. 208, Arlington, VA 22202, (703)418-4150

U.S. Amateur Ballroom Dancers Assn. [★9567]

U.S. Amateur Confed. of Roller Skating [★22904]

U.S. Amateur Confed. of Roller Skating - Address unknown since 2010.

U.S. Amateur Jai Alai Players Assn. - Defunct.

U.S. Amateur Jump Rope Fed. [22853], PO Box 569, Huntsville, TX 77342-0569, (936)295-3332

U.S. Amateur Racquetball Assn. [★22832]

U.S. Amateur Tug of War Assn. [23101], Amy Breuscher, Sec., PO Box 68, Hollandale, WI 53544, (800)TUGOWAR

U.S. Amateur Wrestling Found. - Defunct.

U.S.A. Amateur Boxing Fed. [★22439]

U.S.A. Chap. of AIDA [★5553]

U.S.A. Chap. of AIDA [★5553]

U.S. of America-China Chamber of Commerce [23391], 55 W Monroe St., Ste. 630, Chicago, IL 60603, (312)368-9911

U.S. of America-China Chamber of Commerce [23391], 55 W Monroe St., Ste. 630, Chicago, IL 60603, (312)368-9911

U.S.A. Coton de Tulear Club [21666], J.J. Walker, Sec., PO Box 3792, Pikeville, KY 41502, (606)639-0364

U.S.A. Deaf Basketball [22300], Brian Fruits, Treas., 5313 Windwood Cir., McFarland, WI 53558

U.S.A. Field Hockey [★22568]

U.S.A. Netball Assn. [22788], PO Box 1105, New York, NY 10274-1105, (561)738-3174

U.S.A. Slo-Pitch Softball Assn. [★22958]

U.S.A. Sports Fed. [★22791]

U.S.A. Standards Inst. [★5982]

U.S.A. Transactional Anal. Assn. [13824], 7891 Westwood Dr., Ste. 103, Gilroy, CA 95020, (408)848-2293

U.S.A. Underwater Fed. - Defunct.

U.S.A. Wushu-Kungfu Fed. [22755], 6313 Harford Rd., Baltimore, MD 21214, (410)444-6666

U.S. of Amer. Amateur Boxing Fed. [★22439]

U.S. Amputee Athletic Assn. [★22510]

U.S.-Angola Chamber of Commerce [23382], 1100 17th St. NW, Ste. 1000, Washington, DC 20036, (202)857-0789

U.S.-Angola Chamber of Commerce [23382], 1100 17th St. NW, Ste. 1000, Washington, DC 20036, (202)857-0789

U.S. Animal Hea. Assn. [17045], 4221 Mitchell Ave., St. Joseph, MO 64507, (816)671-1144

U.S. Antarctic Prog. [7282], Off. of Polar Programs, Natl. Sci. Found., 4201 Wilson Blvd., Ste. 755, Arlington, VA 22203, (703)292-8030

U.S. Antiaircraft Assn. [★5801]

U.S. Apnea Assn. [22542], 3642 Seahorn Dr., Malibu, CA 90265, (310)560-6104

U.S. Apnea Assn. [22542], 3642 Seahorn Dr., Malibu, CA 90265, (310)560-6104

U.S. Apple Assn. [4478], 8233 Old Courthouse Rd., Ste. 200, Vienna, VA 22182, (703)442-8850

U.S. Apple Assn. [4478], 8233 Old Courthouse Rd., Ste. 200, Vienna, VA 22182, (703)442-8850

U.S. Aquaculture Soc. [3831], Virginia Seafood AREC, 102 S King St., Hampton, VA 23669, (757)727-4861

U.S. Aquatic Sports [23043], Debra Turner, Coor., 325 Rolling Trails Rd., Greenwood, IN 46142, (317)223-0702

U.S. Armor Assn. [5833], PO Box 607, Fort Knox, KY 40121-0607, (502)942-8624

U.S. Armored Cavalry Assn. [★5833]

U.S. Army Ranger Assn. [20370], PO Box 52126, Fort Benning, GA 31995-2126, (706)457-6379

U.S. Army Special Forces Decade Assn. [★20761]

U.S. Army Special Forces Decade Club [★20761]

U.S. Army Warrant Officers Assn. [5834], 462 Herndon Pkwy., Ste. 207, Herndon, VA 20170-5235, (703)742-7727

U.S. Artists [9258], 5757 Wilshire Blvd., Ste. 580, Los Angeles, CA 90036, (323)857-5857

U.S. ASEAN Bus. Coun. [3490], 1101 17th St. NW, Ste. 411, Washington, DC 20036, (202)289-1911

U.S. ASEAN Bus. Coun. [3490], 1101 17th St. NW, Ste. 411, Washington, DC 20036, (202)289-1911

U.S. - ASEAN Coun. for Bus. and Tech. [★3490]

U.S. - ASEAN Coun. for Bus. and Tech. [★3490]

U.S.-Asia Inst. [17201], 232 E Capitol St. NE, Washington, DC 20003, (202)544-3181

U.S.-Asia Inst. [17201], 232 E Capitol St. NE, Washington, DC 20003, (202)544-3181

U.S. Asian Bus. Coun. - Address unknown since 2011.

U.S. Associates of the Intl. Chamber of Commerce [★707]

U.S. Associates of the Intl. Chamber of Commerce [★707]

U.S. Assn. for Blind Athletes [22526], 33 N Indus. St., Colorado Springs, CO 80903, (719)630-0422

U.S. Assn. for Body Psychotherapy [16436], 8639 B 16th St., Ste. 119, Silver Spring, MD 20910, (202)466-1619

U.S. Assn. for Computational Mechanics [7080], PO Box 8137, Austin, TX 78713, (512)529-7333

U.S. Assn. of Consecrated Virgins [19507], 300 W Ottawa St., Lansing, MI 48933-1577

U.S. Assn. for Energy Economics [6758], Mr. David L. Williams, Exec. Dir., 28790 Chagrin Blvd., Ste. 350, Cleveland, OH 44122, (216)464-2785

U.S. Assn. of Former Members of Cong. [17414], 1401 K St. NW, Ste. 503, Washington, DC 20005, (202)222-0972

U.S. Assn. of Importers of Textiles and Apparel [3462], 1140 Connecticut Ave., Ste. 950, Washington, DC 20036, (202)419-0444

U.S. Assn. of Independent Gymnastic Clubs [3340], 450 N End Ave., Ste. 20F, New York, NY 10282, (212)227-9792

U.S. Assn. of Museum Volunteers [★10106]

U.S. Assn. for Small Bus. and Entrepreneurship [3301], Belmont Univ., 1900 Belmont Blvd., Nashville, TN 37212, (615)460-2615

U.S. Assn. for the Univ. for Peace [18294], 218 D St. SE, 3rd Fl., Washington, DC 20003-1900, (202)683-4081

U.S. Athletes Assn. - Defunct.

U.S. Austrian Chamber of Commerce [23330], 165 W 46th St., New York, NY 10036, (212)819-0117

U.S. Autism and Asperger Assn. [13806], PO Box 532, Draper, UT 84020-0532, (801)816-1234

U.S. Auto Club [22250], 4910 W 16th St., Speedway, IN 46224, (317)247-5151

United States-Azerbaijan Chamber of Commerce [23383], 1212 Potomac St. NW, Washington, DC 20007, (202)333-8702

United States-Azerbaijan Chamber of Commerce [23383], 1212 Potomac St. NW, Washington, DC 20007, (202)333-8702

U.S. Badminton Assn. [★22252]

U.S.-Bahrain Bus. Coun. [2109], 1615 H St. NW, Washington, DC 20062, (202)463-5628

U.S.-Bahrain Bus. Coun. [2109], 1615 H St. NW, Washington, DC 20062, (202)463-5628

U.S. Baseball Fed. [★22291]

U.S. Basketball Writers Assn. [22301], 1818 Chouteau Ave., St. Louis, MO 63103, (314)444-4300

U.S. Beet Sugar Assn. [1434], 1156 15th St. NW, Ste. 1019, Washington, DC 20005, (202)296-4820

U.S. Beet Sugar Indus. [★1434]

U.S. Biathlon Assn. [22915], 49 Pineland Dr., Ste. 301A, New Gloucester, ME 04260, (207)688-6500

U.S. Bicycle Assn. [★22475]

U.S. Bicycle Polo Assn. [22813], PO Box 19424, Sacramento, CA 95819-0424, (916)487-1670

U.S. Billiard Assn. [22309], Jim Shovak, Sec.-Treas., 58 Hawthorne Ave., East Islip, NY 11730, (516)238-6193

U.S. Blind Golf Assn. [22527], 125 Gilberts Hill Rd., Lehighton, PA 18235, (615)385-0784

U.S. Bd. on Books for Young People [9452], 5503 N El Adobe Dr., Fresno, CA 93711-2373, (559)351-6119

U.S. Bd. Sailing Assn. [★22411]

U.S. Bobsled and Skeleton Fed. [22926], 196 Old Military Rd., Lake Placid, NY 12946, (518)523-1842

U.S. Bocce Fed. [22416], 14107 W Dublin Dr., Homer Glen, IL 60491, (630)257-2854

U.S. Boer Goat Assn. [4507], PO Box 663, Spicewood, TX 78669, (866)668-7242

U.S. Book Exchange [10016], 2969 W 25th St., Cleveland, OH 44113, (216)241-6960

U.S. Boomerang Assn. [22422], 3351 236th St. SW, Brier, WA 98036-8421, (425)485-1672

U.S. Border Collie Club [21667], Laura Carson, Treas., 1712 Hertford St., Greensboro, NC 27403

U.S. Border Control [17886], PO Box 97115, Washington, DC 20090-7115, (703)740-8668

U.S. Bowling Cong. [22429], 621 Six Flags Dr., Arlington, TX 76011, (800)514-2695

U.S. Bowling Cong. [22429], 621 Six Flags Dr., Arlington, TX 76011, (800)514-2695

U.S. Boxer Assn. - Address unknown since 2010.

U.S. Braille Chess Assn. [21277], Jay Leventhal, Sec., 5 Moore Ave., Freeport, NY 11520, (516)223-8685

U.S. Breastfeeding Comm. [13866], 2025 M St. NW, Ste. 800, Washington, DC 20036, (202)367-1132

Reference to "IO" in place of a book number signifies that the association may be found in the 50th edition of International Organizations.

U.S. Bridge Assn. [★21239]

U.S. Bridge Assn. [★21239]

U.S. Bridge Fed. [21240], 2990 Airways Blvd., Memphis, TN 38116-3828

U.S. Broomball Assn. [23011], 26676 Berg Dr., Monroe, OR 97456

U.S. Bus. Coun. for Sustainable Development [1061], Bldg. II, Ste. 202, 4425 S Mopac Expy., Austin, TX 78735, (512)892-6411

U.S. Bus. and Indus. Coun. [★17725]

U.S. Bus. and Indus. Coun. [17725], 512 C St. NE, Washington, DC 20002, (202)266-3980

U.S. Calf Ropers Assn. [22850], PO Box 690, Giddings, TX 78942, (979)542-1239

U.S. Camaro Club [★21197]

U.S. Canada Peace Anniversary Assn. [19185], PO Box 4564, Blaine, WA 98231-4564, (360)332-7165

U.S. Canada Peace Anniversary Assn. [19185], PO Box 4564, Blaine, WA 98231-4564, (360)332-7165

U.S. and Canadian Acad. of Pathology [16136], 3643 Walton Way Extension, Augusta, GA 30909, (706)733-7550

U.S. and Canadian Acad. of Pathology [16136], 3643 Walton Way Extension, Augusta, GA 30909, (706)733-7550

U.S. Cancellation Club [22088], Roger Rhoads, Sec.-Treas., 6160 Brownstone Ct., Mentor, OH 44060

U.S. Cane Sugar Refiners' Assn. - Defunct.

U.S. Canoe Assn. [23125], Paula Thiel, Membership Chair, 487 Wylie School Rd., Voluntown, CT 06384, (860)564-2443

U.S. Canoe and Kayak Team [★23127]

U.S. Canola Assn. [1435], 600 Pennsylvania Ave. SE, Ste. 320, Washington, DC 20003, (202)969-8113

U.S. Capitol Historical Soc. [9814], 200 Maryland Ave., Ste. 400 NE, Washington, DC 20002, (202)543-8919

U.S. Catholic Bishops' Natl. Advisory Coun. - Defunct.

U.S. Catholic Conf. [★12149]

U.S. Catholic Conf. Migration and Refugee Services [★12792]

U.S. Catholic Conference/Migration and Refugee Services [★12792]

U.S. Catholic Mission Assn. [19508], 3025 4th St. NE, Ste. 100, Washington, DC 20017-1102, (202)832-3112

U.S. Catholic Mission Coun. [★19508]

U.S. Cavalry Assn. [★5833]

U.S. Cavalry Assn. and Memorial Res. Lib. [10099], PO Box 2325, Fort Riley, KS 66442-0325, (785)784-5797

U.S. Chamber of Commerce [23384], 1615 H St. NW, Washington, DC 20062-2000, (202)659-6000

U.S. Chamber of Shipping [★5789]

U.S. Chap., Intl. Real Estate Fed. [★3012]

U.S. Cheng Ming Martial Arts Assn. [22756], 3916 McDermott Dr., No. 160, Plano, TX 75025, (972)740-8458

U.S. Chess Fed. [21278], PO Box 3967, Crossville, TN 38557, (931)787-1234

U.S.-China Bus. Coun. [2110], 1818 N St. NW, Ste. 200, Washington, DC 20036-2470, (202)429-0340

U.S.-China Educ. Found. [8377], 4140 Oceanside Blvd., Ste. 159, No. 112, Oceanside, CA 92056-6005

U.S.-China Educ. Found. [8377], 4140 Oceanside Blvd., Ste. 159, No. 112, Oceanside, CA 92056-6005

United States-China Educational Inst. [★9481]

United States-China Educational Inst. [★9481]

U.S.-China Exchange Assn. [17954], 52 Bridge St., Metuchen, NJ 08840, (732)494-2724

U.S.-China Peoples Friendship Assn. [17244], 402 E 43rd St., Indianapolis, IN 46205, (317)283-7735

U.S.-China Peoples Friendship Assn. [17244], 402 E 43rd St., Indianapolis, IN 46205, (317)283-7735

U.S. Christian Chamber of Commerce [23393], PO Box 33581, Northglenn, CO 80233-0581, (303)246-0007

U.S. Churchill Found. [★8197]

U.S. Civil Defense Coun. [★5307]

U.S. Civil Defense Coun. [★5307]

U.S. Classic Racing Assn. [21940], 441 Athol Rd., Richmond, NH 03470, (603)239-6778

U.S. Clean Heat and Power Assn. [7590], 105 N Virginia Ave., Ste. 204, Falls Church, VA 22046, (703)647-6244

U.S. Climate Emergency Coun. [4157], PO Box 11138, Takoma Park, MD 20912, (240)396-2155

U.S. Club Soccer [22944], 716 8th Ave. N, Myrtle Beach, SC 29577, (843)429-0006

U.S. Coast Guard Chief Petty Officers Assn. [20392], 5520-G Hempstead Way, Springfield, VA 22151-4009, (703)941-0395

U.S. Coast Guards
  Burton Island Assn. [20717]

U.S. Collegiate Athletic Assn. [23012], 4101 Washington Ave., Bldg. 601, Newport News, VA 23607, (757)706-3756

U.S. Collegiate Ski and Snowboard Assn. [22916], PO Box 180, Cummington, MA 01026, (413)634-0110

U.S. Combined Heat and Power Assn. [★7590]

U.S. Combined Training Assn. [★22690]

U.S. Comm. of the Blue Shield [9526], 5136 15th Ave. S, Minneapolis, MN 55417, (612)839-7654

U.S. Comm. for a Free Lebanon [18070], 445 Park Ave., 9th Fl., New York, NY 10022

U.S. Comm. on Irrigation and Drainage [7611], 1616 17th St., No. 483, Denver, CO 80202, (303)628-5430

U.S. Comm. on Irrigation, Drainage and Flood Control [★7611]

U.S. Comm. on Large Dams [★7612]

U.S. Comm. for Refugees [★18510]

U.S. Comm. for Refugees [★18510]

U.S. Comm. for Refugees and Immigrants [18510], 2231 Crystal Dr., Ste. 350, Arlington, VA 22202-3711, (703)310-1130

U.S. Comm. for Refugees and Immigrants [18510], 2231 Crystal Dr., Ste. 350, Arlington, VA 22202-3711, (703)310-1130

U.S. Comm. in Solidarity With the People of El Salvador [★17602]

U.S. Comm. in Solidarity With the People of El Salvador [★17602]

U.S. Comm. Sports for Israel [★22985]

U.S. Comm. for Sports in Israel [★22985]

U.S. Comm. for the United Nations [★18748]

U.S. Competitive Aerobics Fed. [22209], 8033 Sunset Blvd., No. 920, Los Angeles, CA 90046, (323)850-3777

U.S. Complete Shooting Dog Assn. [21668], 3329 Redlawn Rd., Boydton, VA 23917, (434)738-9757

U.S. Composting Coun. [6068], One Comac Loop 14B1, Ronkonkoma, NY 11779, (631)737-4931

U.S. Conf. of Catholic Bishops [19509], 3211 4th St. NE, Washington, DC 20017-1104, (202)541-3000

U.S. Conf. of Catholic Bishops | Bishops' Comm. on Priestly Formation [19688], 3211 4th St. NE, Washington, DC 20017-1194, (202)541-3033

United States Conference of Catholic Bishops | Comm. on Divine Worship [19510], 3211 4th St. NE, Washington, DC 20017-1194, (202)541-3060

U.S. Conf. of Catholic Bishops | Ecumenical and Interreligious Affairs [19511], 3211 4th St. NE, Washington, DC 20017-1194, (202)541-3000

U.S. Conf. of Catholic Bishops/Migration and Refugee Services [12792], 3211 4th St. NE, Washington, DC 20017-1194, (202)541-3352

U.S. Conf. of Catholic Bishops | Secretariat for Hispanic Affairs [12149], 3211 4th St. NE, Washington, DC 20017, (202)541-3150

U.S. Conf. of City Human Services Officials [5977], U.S. Conf. of Mayors, 1620 Eye St. NW, 4th Fl., Washington, DC 20006, (202)293-7330

U.S. Conf. of Local Health Officers - Defunct.

U.S. Conf. of Mayors [5856], 1620 Eye St. NW, Washington, DC 20006, (202)293-7330

U.S. Conf. for the World Coun. of Churches - Defunct.

U.S. Connected Communities Assn. [6440], 1901 Pennsylvania Ave. NW, 5th Fl., Washington, DC 20006

U.S. Consortium of Soil Sci. Associations [4929], 611 Jeffrey Dr., Lincoln, NE 68505, (402)483-0604

U.S. Constitution
  Center for Constitutional Rights [17273]

Congressional Automotive Caucus [17410]

Constitutional Rights Found. [17437]

Natl. Center for Constitutional Stud. [17440]

Natl. Comm. for an Effective Cong. [17413]

People for the Amer. Way [17317]

U.S. Assn. of Former Members of Cong. [17414]

U.S. Copper Assn. [★7088]

U.S. Copts Assn. [12249], 5116 Arlington Blvd., Ste. 155, Falls Church, VA 22042

U.S. Copts Assn. [12249], 5116 Arlington Blvd., Ste. 155, Falls Church, VA 22042

U.S. Coun. for Automotive Res. [6245], 1000 Town Center Dr., Ste. 300, Southfield, MI 48075, (248)223-9000

U.S. Coun. of Better Bus. Bureaus [706], 4200 Wilson Blvd., Ste. 800, Arlington, VA 22203-1838, (703)276-0100

U.S. Coun. for Energy Awareness [★6746]

U.S. Coun. on Intl. Banking [★420]

U.S. Coun. for Intl. Bus. [707], 1212 Avenue of the Americas, New York, NY 10036, (212)354-4480

U.S. Coun. for Intl. Bus. [707], 1212 Avenue of the Americas, New York, NY 10036, (212)354-4480

U.S. Coun. of the Intl. Chamber of Commerce [★707]

U.S. Coun. of the Intl. Chamber of Commerce [★707]

U.S. Coun. for Intl. Friendship - Defunct.

U.S. Court Reporters Assn. [5361], 8430 Gross Point Rd., Ste. 115, Skokie, IL 60077, (847)470-9500

U.S. Croquet Assn. [22471], 700 Florida Mango Rd., West Palm Beach, FL 33406-4461, (561)478-0760

U.S. Cross Country Coaches Assn. [22868], Walt Drenth, Pres., Michigan State Univ., Jenison Fieldhouse, East Lansing, MI 48824, (517)355-1640

U.S. Cross Country Snowmobile Racing Assn. [22927], PO Box 273, Minto, ND 58261, (701)248-2029

U.S.-Cuba Trade Assn. [2111], 2300 M St. NW, Ste. 800, Washington, DC 20037, (202)530-5236

U.S.-Cuba Trade Assn. [2111], 2300 M St. NW, Ste. 800, Washington, DC 20037, (202)530-5236

U.S. Curling Assn. [22472], 5525 Clem's Way, Stevens Point, WI 54482, (715)344-1199

U.S. Cutting Tool Inst. [1877], 1300 Sumner Ave., Cleveland, OH 44115-2851, (216)241-7333

U.S. Cycling Fed. [22489], U.S.A. Cycling, 210 U.S.A. Cycling Point, Ste. 100, Colorado Springs, CO 80919, (719)434-4200

U.S. Dairy Export Coun. [4186], 2101 Wilson Blvd., Ste. 400, Arlington, VA 22201-3061, (703)528-3049

U.S. Deaf Cycling Assn. [22528], Bobby Skedsmo, Sec.-Treas., 247 Jack London Ct., Pittsburg, CA 94565-3661

U.S. Deaf Ski and Snowboard Assn. [22529], PO Box 4, Cambridge, VT 05444

U.S. Dental Tennis Assn. [23062], 1414 Rhorer Rd., Bloomington, IN 47401, (800)445-2524

U.S. Dept. of Agriculture | Forest Ser. Volunteers Prog. [4419], 1400 Independence Ave. SW, Washington, DC 20250-0003, (202)205-1661

U.S. Dept. of Agriculture | Org. of Professional Employees [5194], PO Box 23762, Washington, DC 20026, (202)720-4898

U.S. Deputy Sheriffs' Assn. [5743], 1304 Langham Creek Dr., Ste. 324, Houston, TX 77084, (866)933-7889

U.S. Disc Sports [22536], World Flying Disc Fed., 8550 Tujunga Valley St., Sunland, CA 91040, (818)353-6339

U.S. Display Consortium [★3390]

U.S. Distance Learning Assn. [8274], 76 Canal St., Ste. 400, Boston, MA 02114, (617)399-1770

U.S. Dog Agility Assn. [22551], PO Box 850955, Richardson, TX 75085, (972)487-2200

U.S. Dressage Fed. [22688], 4051 Iron Works Pkwy., Lexington, KY 40511, (859)971-2277

U.S. Dry Bean Coun. [4479], PO Box 1026, Pierre, SD 57501, (605)494-0280

U.S. Durum Growers Assn. [3963], 2409 Jackson Ave., Bismarck, ND 58501, (701)214-3203

U.S. Dye Mfrs. Operating Comm. of ETAD [★4789]

U.S. Elite Coaches' Assn. for Women's Gymnastics [22469], 10 Quail Point Pl., Carmichael, CA 95608, (916)487-3559

A star before a book entry number signifies that the name is not listed separately, but is mentioned within the entry.

U.S. Energy Assn. **[6759]**, 1300 Pennsylvania Ave. NW, Ste. 550, Mailbox 142, Washington, DC 20004-3022, (202)312-1230

U.S. Energy Assn. **[6759]**, 1300 Pennsylvania Ave. NW, Ste. 550, Mailbox 142, Washington, DC 20004-3022, (202)312-1230

U.S.-English **[18342]**, 1747 Pennsylvania Ave. NW, Ste. 1050, Washington, DC 20006, (202)833-0100

U.S. Entertainment Force **[11112]**, 6504 N 7th St., Fresno, CA 93710, (559)981-5132

U.S. Equal Employment Opportunity Commn. **[5403]**, 131 M St. NE, Washington, DC 20507, (202)663-4900

U.S. Equestrian Fed. **[22689]**, 4047 Iron Works Pkwy., Lexington, KY 40511-8483, (859)258-2472

U.S. Equestrian Team **[★22689]**

U.S. Equestrian Team - Defunct.

U.S. Equine Rescue League **[12168]**, 9660 Falls of Neuse Rd., Ste. 138, Raleigh, NC 27615, (800)650-8549

U.S. Eventing Assn. **[22690]**, 525 Old Waterford Rd. NW, Leesburg, VA 20176, (703)779-0440

U.S. Faceters Guild **[6590]**, 2410 N 2nd St., Kalamazoo, MI 49009

U.S. Fastpitch Assn. **[22957]**, 22912 Ann Miller Rd., Panama City, FL 32413, (850)234-2839

U.S. Fed. for Culture Collections **[6322]**, Mary Meeker, Treas., 1519 Little Farms Rd., Oxnard, CA 93030-4738, (805)984-6947

U.S. Fed. for Middle East Peace **[18295]**, 777 United Nations Plz., 44th St. and 1st Ave., Ste. C, New York, NY 10017, (212)922-0300

U.S. Fed. of Police **[★5686]**

U.S. Fed. of Scholars and Scientists - Address unknown since 2010.

U.S. Fed. of Worker Cooperatives **[23318]**, PO Box 170701, San Francisco, CA 94117-0701, (415)379-9201

U.S. Feed Grains Coun. **[★4376]**

U.S. Feed Grains Coun. **[★4376]**

U.S. Fencing Assn. **[22565]**, 1 Olympic Plz., Colorado Springs, CO 80909-5780, (719)866-4511

U.S. Fencing Coaches Assn. **[22566]**, Carolyn Gresham-Fiegel, Treas., 514 NW 164th St., Edmond, OK 73013-2001

U.S. Field Artillery Assn. **[★5801]**

U.S. Field Hockey Assn. **[22568]**, 1 Olympic Plz., Colorado Springs, CO 80909, (719)866-4339

U.S. Figure Skating Assn. **[22902]**, 20 1st St., Colorado Springs, CO 80906, (719)635-5200

U.S. Flag Assn. **[★20612]**

U.S. Flag Football Assn. **[★22599]**

U.S. Flag Football for the Deaf **[22530]**, PO Box 150221, Austin, TX 78715

U.S. Flag Football League **[22599]**, 763 Ridge Rd., Angier, NC 27501, (919)894-7976

U.S. Flag Found. **[10632]**, Flag Plz., 1275 Bedford Ave., Pittsburgh, PA 15219, (412)261-1776

U.S. Flag and Touch Football League **[22600]**, 7709 Ohio St., Mentor, OH 44060, (440)974-8735

U.S. Floorball Assn. **[22255]**, 10037 Scenic Blvd., Cupertino, CA 95014

U.S. Football Alliance **[22601]**, PO Box 607, New Castle, PA 16103, (724)866-1714

U.S. Found. for Intl. Scouting - Defunct.

U.S. Freshwater Prawn and Shrimp Growers Assn. **[3191]**, 655 Napanee Rd., Leland, MS 38756, (662)686-2894

U.S. Fund for UNICEF **[18751]**, 125 Maiden Ln., 11th Fl., New York, NY 10038, (212)922-2651

U.S. Futsal Fed. **[23013]**, PO Box 40077, Berkeley, CA 94704-4077, (510)836-8733

U.S. Geodynamics Comm. - Defunct.

U.S. Girls' Wrestling Assn. **[23134]**, 3105 Hickory Ridge Ln., Ortonville, MI 48462, (248)627-8066

U.S. Global Strategy Coun. - Defunct.

U.S. Golf Assn. **[22625]**, PO Box 708, Far Hills, NJ 07931, (908)234-2300

U.S. Golf Teachers Fed. **[22626]**, 1295 SE Port St. Lucie Blvd., Port St. Lucie, FL 34952, (772)335-3216

U.S. Grains Coun. **[4376]**, 1400 K St. NW, Ste. 1200, Washington, DC 20005, (202)789-0789

U.S. Grains Coun. **[4376]**, 1400 K St. NW, Ste. 1200, Washington, DC 20005, (202)789-0789

U.S. Green Building Coun. **[632]**, 2101 L St. NW, Ste. 500, Washington, DC 20037, (202)742-3792

U.S. Green Network **[★18358]**

U.S. Group of the Inter-Parliamentary Union - Defunct.

U.S./Guatemala Labor Educ. Proj. **[★18047]**

U.S./Guatemala Labor Educ. Proj. **[★18047]**

U.S. Gymnastics Fed. **[★22636]**

U.S. Handball Assn. **[22637]**, 2333 N Tucson Blvd., Tucson, AZ 85716, (520)795-0434

U.S. Handcycling Fed. **[22490]**, PO Box 3538, Evergreen, CO 80437, (303)459-4159

U.S. Hang Gliding Assn. **[★22214]**

U.S. Hang Gliding and Paragliding Assn. **[22214]**, PO Box 1330, Colorado Springs, CO 80901-1330, (719)632-8300

U.S. Hapki Hae **[22757]**, 4826 Old Natl. Hwy., College Park, GA 30337, (404)768-0507

U.S. Harness Writers' Assn. **[2880]**, Jerry Connors, Sec., PO Box 1314, Mechanicsburg, PA 17055, (717)651-5889

U.S. Helice Assn. **[22887]**, 10701 CR 1200, Malakoff, TX 75148, (817)233-1025

U.S. Helsinki Watch **[★17836]**

U.S. Helsinki Watch **[★17836]**

U.S. Hereditary Angioedema Assn. **[14634]**, 7 Waterfront Plz., 500 Ala Moana Blvd., Ste. 400, Honolulu, HI 96813, (866)798-5598

U.S. Hide, Skin and Leather Assn. **[2207]**, 1150 Connecticut Ave. NW, 12th Fl., Washington, DC 20036, (202)587-4250

U.S. Hispanic Advocacy Assn. **[17781]**, 601 Pennsylvania Ave. NW, Ste. 900, Washington, DC 20004, (215)520-8850

U.S. Hispanic Chamber of Commerce **[23405]**, 1424 K St. NW, Ste. 401, Washington, DC 20005, (202)842-1212

U.S. Historical Soc. - Address unknown since 2011.

U.S. Holocaust Memorial Coun. **[17791]**, 100 Raoul Wallenberg Pl. SW, Washington, DC 20024-2126, (202)488-0400

U.S. Homeland Emergency Response Org. **[12911]**, PO Box 90453, Austin, TX 78709-0453, (512)585-0256

U.S. Horse Cavalry Assn. **[★10099]**

U.S. Human Proteome Org. **[6323]**, 2019 Galisteo St., Bldg. I-1, Santa Fe, NM 87505, (505)989-4876

U.S. Human Proteome Org. **[6323]**, 2019 Galisteo St., Bldg. I-1, Santa Fe, NM 87505, (505)989-4876

U.S. Hunter Jumper Assn. **[22691]**, 3870 Cigar Ln., Lexington, KY 40511, (859)225-6706

U.S. Hydrofoil Assn. **[23118]**, 320 Starlight Pl., Lutherville, MD 21093, (800)533-2972

U.S. ICE Hispanic Agents Assn. **[5514]**, PO Box 212, Lemon Grove, CA 91946, (602)721-3077

U.S. Icelandic Horse Cong. **[4655]**, 4525 Hewitts Point Rd., Oconomowoc, WI 53066, (907)357-4233

U.S. Independent Telephone Assn. **[★3604]**

U.S. Indian Amer. Chamber of Commerce **[23407]**, 6030 Daybreak Cir., Ste. A150/164, Clarksville, MD 21029, (240)393-2945

U.S. Indian Amer. Chamber of Commerce **[23407]**, 6030 Daybreak Cir., Ste. A150/164, Clarksville, MD 21029, (240)393-2945

United States-Indonesia Soc. **[720]**, 1625 Massachusetts Ave. NW, Ste. 550, Washington, DC 20036-2260, (202)232-1400

United States-Indonesia Soc. **[720]**, 1625 Massachusetts Ave. NW, Ste. 550, Washington, DC 20036-2260, (202)232-1400

U.S. Indoor Soccer Assn. **[★22945]**

U.S. Indoor Sports Assn. **[22945]**, 1340 N Great Neck Rd., Ste. 1272-142, Virginia Beach, VA 23454-2268, (703)820-2810

U.S. Indus. Coun. **[★17725]**

U.S. Indus. Fabrics Inst. **[3463]**, 1801 County Rd. B.W., Roseville, MN 55113-4061, (651)222-2508

U.S. Indus. Coalition **[7397]**, 1600 Wilson Blvd., Ste. 1010, Arlington, VA 22209, (703)526-9447

U.S. Indus. Coalition **[7397]**, 1600 Wilson Blvd., Ste. 1010, Arlington, VA 22209, (703)526-9447

U.S. Infantry Assn. **[★5801]**

U.S. Inst. of Peace **[18296]**, 2301 Constitution Ave. NW, Washington, DC 20037, (202)457-1700

U.S. Inst. of Peace **[18296]**, 2301 Constitution Ave. NW, Washington, DC 20037, (202)457-1700

U.S. Inst. for Textile Res. **[★3461]**

U.S. Inst. for Textile Res. **[★3461]**

U.S. Inst. for Theatre Tech. **[10609]**, 315 S Crouse Ave., Ste. 200, Syracuse, NY 13210, (315)463-6463

U.S. Intercollegiate Lacrosse Assn. **[22716]**, 3738 W Lake Rd., Perry, NY 14530, (585)237-5886

U.S. Intl. Coun. on Disabilities **[11834]**, 1012 14th St. NW, Ste. 105, Washington, DC 20005, (202)347-0102

U.S. Intl. Coun. on Disabilities **[11834]**, 1012 14th St. NW, Ste. 105, Washington, DC 20005, (202)347-0102

U.S. Intl. Sailing Assn. **[★22408]**

U.S. Intl. Skating Assn. **[★22903]**

U.S. Intl. Speedskating Assn. **[★22903]**

U.S. Internet Indus. Assn. **[6521]**, 1800 Diagonal Rd., Ste. 600, Alexandria, VA 22314, (703)647-7440

U.S. Internet Ser. Provider Assn. **[6563]**, 700 12th St. NW, Ste. 700E, Washington, DC 20005, (202)904-2351

U.S. Interreligious Comm. on Peace **[★18304]**

U.S. Interreligious Comm. on Peace **[★18304]**

U.S.-Israel Binational Sci. Found. **[IO]**, Jerusalem, Israel

U.S. Isshinryu Karate Assn. **[22758]**, 2202 Surfside Dr., Anderson, SC 29625, (864)225-8610

U.S. ITU Assn. **[7552]**, Leslie Joseph Martinkovics, Dir., Verizon Communications Inc., 1300 I St. NW, Ste. 400 W, Washington, DC 20005, (202)515-2433

U.S. J/24 Class Assn. **[22402]**, 900 Old Koenig Ln., Ste. 114, Austin, TX 78756, (512)266-0033

U.S. J/24 Class Assn. **[22402]**, 900 Old Koenig Ln., Ste. 114, Austin, TX 78756, (512)266-0033

U.S.-Japan Bus. Coun. **[23418]**, 2101 L St. NW, Ste. 1000, Washington, DC 20037, (202)728-0068

U.S.-Japan Coun. **[17955]**, 1225 Nineteenth St. NW, Ste. 700, Washington, DC 20036, (202)223-6840

U.S./Japan Cultural Trade Network **[9519]**, 1471 Guerrero St., Ste. 3, San Francisco, CA 94110, (415)867-7080

United States-Japan Found. **[18969]**, 145 E 32nd St., New York, NY 10016, (212)481-8753

United States-Japan Found. **[18969]**, 145 E 32nd St., New York, NY 10016, (212)481-8753

U.S. Jaycees **[★23458]**

U.S. Judo **[22704]**, 1 Olympic Plz., Ste. 505, Colorado Springs, CO 80909, (719)866-4730

U.S. Judo Assn. **[22705]**, PO Box 1880, Tarpon Springs, FL 34688-1880, (877)411-3409

U.S. Judo Fed. **[22706]**, PO Box 338, Ontario, OR 97914, (541)889-8753

U.S. Junior Chamber of Commerce **[23458]**, 7447 S Lewis Ave., Tulsa, OK 74136-6808, (918)584-2481

U.S. Junior Chamber of Commerce **[★23458]**

U.S. Justice Found. **[5939]**, 932 D St., Ste. 2, Ramona, CA 92065-2355, (760)788-6624

U.S.-Kazakhstan Bus. Assn. **[2112]**, 1200 G St. NW, Ste. 827, Washington, DC 20005, (202)434-8791

U.S. Kerry Blue Terrier Club **[21669]**, Brian Tormey, Membership Chm., 4916 Standing Stone Rd., Huntingdon, PA 16652, (814)667-3828

U.S.-Korea Economic Coun. **[★23422]**

U.S.-Korea Soc. **[★23422]**

U.S. Kuo Shu Fed. **[22759]**, PO Box 20269, Baltimore, MD 21284-0269, (443)394-9200

U.S. Labor Educ. in the Americas Proj. **[18047]**, PO Box 268-290, Chicago, IL 60626, (773)262-6502

U.S. Labor Educ. in the Americas Proj. **[18047]**, PO Box 268-290, Chicago, IL 60626, (773)262-6502

U.S. Lacrosse **[22717]**, 113 W Univ. Pkwy., Baltimore, MD 21210, (410)235-6882

U.S. Lacrosse Assn., Women's Div. **[22718]**, 113 W Univ. Pkwy., Baltimore, MD 21210, (410)235-6882

U.S. Lactation Consultant Assn. **[13867]**, 2501 Aerial Center Pkwy., Ste. 103, Morrisville, NC 27560, (919)861-4543

U.S. Lakeland Terrier Club **[21670]**, 10301 Brangus Dr., Crowley, TX 76036, (817)297-2398

U.S. Late Model Assn. **[22251]**, 701 W 4th St., Pueblo, CO 81003, (719)543-0218

U.S. Law Firm Gp. **[5288]**, Quarles and Brady LLP, 411 E Wisconsin Ave., Milwaukee, WI 53202-4497, (414)277-5879

Reference to "IO" in place of a book number signifies that the association may be found in the 50th edition of International Organizations.

U.S. Law Firm Gp. **[5288]**, Quarles and Brady LLP, 411 E Wisconsin Ave., Milwaukee, WI 53202-4497, (414)277-5879

U.S. Lawn Bowls Assn. **[22430]**, 10639 Lindamere Dr., Los Angeles, CA 90077, (310)440-9400

U.S. Lawn Mower Racing Assn. **[22828]**, 1544 Shermer Rd., Ste. F, Northbrook, IL 60062, (847)272-2120

U.S. Lawn Tennis Assn. **[★23065]**

U.S. Les Autres Sports Assn. - Defunct.

U.S. Letter Carriers Mutual Benefit Assn. **[19061]**, 100 Indiana Ave. NW, Ste. 510, Washington, DC 20001-2144, (202)638-4318

U.S. Life-Saving Ser. Heritage Assn. **[9734]**, PO Box 213, Hull, MA 02045-0213, (781)724-7131

U.S. Lifesaving Assn. **[12912]**, PO Box 366, Huntington Beach, CA 92648, (866)367-8752

U.S. Lighthouse Soc. **[9735]**, 9005 Point No Point Rd. NE, Hansville, WA 98340, (415)362-7255

U.S. Lipizzan Registry **[4656]**, 8480 O'Hare Rd., Las Vegas, NV 89143-1235, (503)589-3172

U.S. Livestock Sanitary Assn. **[★17045]**

U.S. Log Rolling Assn. **[★23126]**

U.S. Log Rolling Assn. **[23126]**, 2217 W Lawn Ave., Madison, WI 53711

U.S. Luge Assn. **[22719]**, 57 Church St., Lake Placid, NY 12946, (518)523-2071

U.S. Marine Corps Combat Correspondents Assn. **[2881]**, 110 Fox Ct., Wildwood, FL 34785-9081, (352)748-4698

U.S. Marine Corps Drill Instructors Assn. - Address unknown since 2011.

U.S. Marine Corps Motor Transport Assn. **[2500]**, PO Box 1372, Jacksonville, NC 28541-1372, (910)450-1841

U.S. Marine Corps Scout/Sniper Assn. **[20688]**, PO Box 762, Quantico, VA 22134

U.S. Marine Raider Assn. **[5835]**, Hon. Florence R. Dornan, Sec., 704 Cooper Ct., Arlington, TX 76011-5550, (817)275-1552

U.S. Marine Safety Assn. **[5778]**, 5050 Indus. Rd., Ste. 2, Wall Township, NJ 07727, (732)751-0102

U.S. Mariner Class Assn. **[22403]**, PO Box 273, Ship Bottom, NJ 08008

U.S. Maritime Alliance **[2371]**, 485C U.S. Hwy. 1 S, Ste. 100, Iselin, NJ 08830, (732)404-2960

U.S. Martial Arts Assn. **[22760]**, 8011 Mariposa Ave., Citrus Heights, CA 95610-1514, (916)727-1486

U.S. Martial Arts Assn. **[22760]**, 8011 Mariposa Ave., Citrus Heights, CA 95610-1514, (916)727-1486

U.S. Masters Swimming **[23044]**, 655 N Tamiami Trail, Sarasota, FL 34236, (941)256-8767

U.S. Meat Export Fed. **[2435]**, 1855 Blake St., Ste. 200, Denver, CO 80202, (303)623-6328

U.S. Meat Export Fed. **[2435]**, 1855 Blake St., Ste. 200, Denver, CO 80202, (303)623-6328

U.S. Men's Curling Assn. **[★22472]**

U.S. Merchant Marine Veterans of World War II **[20869]**, PO Box 629, San Pedro, CA 90733-0629, (310)519-9545

U.S. Metric Assn. **[7470]**, 10245 Andasol Ave., Northridge, CA 91325-1504, (818)363-5606

U.S. Mexican Numismatic Assn. **[21996]**, PO Box 5270, Carefree, AZ 85377, (480)921-2562

U.S.-Mexico Border Hea. Assn. **[16501]**, 211 Florence St., Ste. 101, El Paso, TX 79901, (915)532-1006

United States-Mexico Border Hea. Assn. **[★16501]**

United States-Mexico Border Hea. Assn. **[★16501]**

U.S.-Mexico Border Hea. Assn. **[16501]**, 211 Florence St., Ste. 101, El Paso, TX 79901, (915)532-1006

United States Mexico Chamber of Commerce **[23385]**, PO Box 14414, Washington, DC 20004, (703)752-4886

U.S. Mexico Chamber of Commerce **[23385]**, PO Box 14414, Washington, DC 20004, (703)752-4886

U.S. Mine Rescue Assn. **[12536]**, PO Box 1010, Uniontown, PA 15401, (724)366-5272

U.S. Mine Rescue Assn. **[12536]**, PO Box 1010, Uniontown, PA 15401, (724)366-5272

U.S. Modern Pentathlon Assn. **[23071]**, 1 Olympic Plz., Colorado Springs, CO 80909-5780, (719)866-3035

U.S. Modern Pentathlon and Biathlon Assn. **[★23071]**

U.S. Mondioring Assn. **[22552]**, Kyle Sprague, Treas., 401 Park Way W, Las Vegas, NV 89106, (702)301-9843

U.S. Mountain Guides Assn. **[22456]**, PO Box 267, Intervale, NH 03845

U.S. Muay Thai Assn. **[22761]**, 6535 Broadway, Ste. 1K, Bronx, NY 10471

U.S. Natl. Amateur Athletic Union Taekwondo Comm. **[★22763]**

U.S. Natl. Comm. for Byzantine Stud. **[9815]**, 214 St. Mark's Sq., Philadelphia, PA 19104

U.S. Natl. Comm. on the History of Geology - Defunct.

U.S. Natl. Comm., Intl. Commn. on Irrigation and Drainage **[★7611]**

U.S. Natl. Comm. for the Intl. Union of Pure and Applied Chemistry **[6424]**, The Natl. Academies, Keck Center, 500 5th St. NW, Washington, DC 20001, (202)334-2807

U.S. Natl. Comm. for the Intl. Union of Pure and Applied Chemistry **[6424]**, The Natl. Academies, Keck Center, 500 5th St. NW, Washington, DC 20001, (202)334-2807

U.S. Natl. Comm. for Pacific Economic Cooperation

U.S. Natl. Comm. for Pacific Economic Cooperation - Address unknown since 2011.

U.S. Natl. Comm. on Theoretical and Applied Mechanics **[7081]**, Bd. on Intl. Sci. Organizations, The Natl. Academies, 500 5th St., Washington, DC 20001-2736, (202)334-2807

U.S. Natl. Comm. for World Food Day **[12297]**, 2175 K St. NW, Washington, DC 20037, (202)653-2404

U.S. Natl. Comm. for World Food Day **[12297]**, 2175 K St. NW, Washington, DC 20037, (202)653-2404

U.S. Natl. Fed. of Christian Life Communities **[★19471]**

U.S. Natl. and Olympic Teams **[★22950]**

U.S. Natl. Sect. of IBBY **[★9452]**

U.S. Natl. Senior Sports Org. **[★22808]**

U.S. Natl. Soc. for the Intl. Soc. of Soil Mechanics and Found. Engg. **[★6927]**

U.S. Natl. Soc. for the Intl. Soc. of Soil Mechanics and Found. Engg. **[★6927]**

U.S. Natl. Soc. for the Intl. Soc. of Soil Mechanics and Geotechnical Engg. **[★6927]**

U.S. Natl. Soc. for the Intl. Soc. of Soil Mechanics and Geotechnical Engg. **[★6927]**

U.S. Natl. Student Assn. **[★8932]**

U.S. Natl. Tennis Acad. **[23043]**, 3523 McKinney Ave., No. 208, Dallas, TX 75204, (800)452-8519

U.S. Naval Cryptologic Veterans Assn. **[20806]**, PO Box 16009, Pensacola, FL 32507-6009, (850)455-6026

U.S. Naval Inst. **[5836]**, 291 Wood Rd., Annapolis, MD 21402, (410)268-6110

U.S. Naval Sailing Assn. **[20727]**, PO Box 4702, Annapolis, MD 21403, (443)510-1421

U.S. Navy Beach Jumpers Assn. **[20728]**, 450-106 State Rd. 13N, Ste. 407, St. Johns, FL 32259-3860, (727)487-6252

U.S. Navy Memorial Found. **[20729]**, 701 Pennsylvania Ave. NW, Ste. 123, Washington, DC 20004, (202)737-2300

U.S. Neapolitan Mastiff Club **[21671]**, PO Box 66, Vienna, NJ 07880, (908)637-8957

U.S. New Zealand Coun. **[2113]**, DACOR Bacon House, 1801 F St. NW, Washington, DC 20006, (202)842-0772

U.S. Norton Owners' Assn. **[★21932]**

U.S. Norton Owners' Assn. **[★21932]**

U.S. Off. on Colombia **[17956]**, 1100 G St. NW, Ste. 800, Washington, DC 20005, (202)232-8090

U.S. Off. on Colombia **[17956]**, 1100 G St. NW, Ste. 800, Washington, DC 20005, (202)232-8090

U.S. Offshore Wind Collaborative **[7623]**, 1 Broadway, 14th Fl., Cambridge, MA 02142, (617)401-3145

U.S. Oil and Gas Assn. **[2673]**, 513 N State St., Ste. 202, Jackson, MS 39201, (601)948-8903

U.S. Olympic Assn. **[★22791]**

U.S. Olympic Comm. **[22791]**, 27 S Tejon, Colorado Springs, CO 80903, (719)866-4529

U.S. Operating Comm. of ETAD **[★4789]**

U.S. Optimist Dinghy Assn. **[22404]**, PO Box 311, North Kingstown, RI 02852, (609)510-0798

U.S. Orienteering Fed. **[22795]**, PO Box 505, Riderwood, MD 21139, (410)802-1125

U.S. Othello Assn. - Address unknown since 2011.

U.S. Pacifist Party **[18367]**, 5729 S Dorchester Ave., Chicago, IL 60637, (773)324-0654

U.S.-Pakistan Bus. Coun. **[708]**, 1615 H St. NW, Washington, DC 20062, (202)463-5732

U.S. Pan Asian Amer. Chamber of Commerce **[23386]**, 1329 18th St. NW, Washington, DC 20036, (202)296-5221

U.S. Pan Asian Amer. Chamber of Commerce **[23386]**, 1329 18th St. NW, Washington, DC 20036, (202)296-5221

U.S. Parachute Assn. **[22800]**, 5401 Southpoint Centre Blvd., Fredericksburg, VA 22407, (540)604-9740

U.S. Peace Corps **[★18309]**

U.S. Peace Corps - Zambia **[IO]**, Lusaka, Zambia

U.S. Peace Govt. **[18297]**, 2000 Capital Blvd., Fairfield, IA 52556, (877)424-3546

U.S. Permafrost Assn. **[7436]**, PO Box 750141, Fairbanks, AK 99775-0141, (302)831-0852

U.S. Personal Chef Assn. **[738]**, 5728 Major Blvd., Ste. 750, Orlando, FL 32819, (505)994-6372

U.S. Peruvian Horse Assn. **[4657]**, PO Box 249, Morrison, CO 80465, (303)697-9567

U.S. Pharmacopeia **[16217]**, 12601 Twinbrook Pkwy., Rockville, MD 20852-1790, (301)881-0666

U.S. Pharmacopeia **[16217]**, 12601 Twinbrook Pkwy., Rockville, MD 20852-1790, (301)881-0666

U.S. Pharmacopeial Convention **[★16217]**

U.S. Pharmacopeial Convention **[★16217]**

U.S. Philatelic Classics Soc. **[22089]**, 102 Old Pawling Rd., Pawling, NY 12564-2121

U.S. Pilots Assn. **[158]**, 1652 Indian Point Rd., Branson, MO 65616, (417)338-2225

U.S. Police Canine Assn. **[5744]**, PO Box 80, Springboro, OH 45066-0080, (937)751-6469

U.S. Polo Assn. **[22814]**, 4037 Iron Works Pkwy., Ste. 110, Lexington, KY 40511, (859)219-1000

U.S. Pony Clubs **[22692]**, 4041 Iron Works Pkwy., Lexington, KY 40511-8483, (859)254-7669

U.S. PostgreSQL Assn. **[6500]**, 1767 12th St., No. 149, Hood River, OR 97031, (503)778-5428

U.S. Potato Bd. **[4480]**, 7555 E Hampden Ave., Ste. 412, Denver, CO 80231-4835, (303)369-7783

U.S. Poultry and Egg Assn. **[4818]**, 1530 Cooledge Rd., Tucker, GA 30084-7303, (770)493-9401

U.S. Power Soccer Assn. **[22946]**, Nancy Mitchell, Treas., PO Box 15668, Fremont, CA 94539

U.S. Power Squadrons **[22405]**, 1504 Blue Ridge Rd., Raleigh, NC 27607, (888)367-8777

U.S. Powered Paragliding Assn. **[22796]**, 931 W 75th St., Ste. 137-150, Naperville, IL 60565, (866)378-7772

U.S. Powerlifting Fed. **[22816]**, PO Box 231, Parkersburg, WV 26102, (304)489-2428

U.S. Powerlifting Fed. of the AAU **[★22816]**

U.S. Practical Shooting Assn. **[22888]**, PO Box 811, Sedro Woolley, WA 98284, (360)855-2245

U.S. Professional Diving Coaches Assn. **[22543]**, PO Box 268, Milford, OH 45150

U.S. Professional Lawn Tennis Assn. **[★23064]**

U.S. Professional Lawn Tennis Assn. **[★23064]**

U.S. Professional Poolplayers Assn. **[22310]**, 4340 E Indian School Rd., Ste. 21-115, Phoenix, AZ 85018-5375, (877)788-7227

U.S. Professional Tennis Assn. **[23064]**, 3535 Briarpark Dr., Ste. 1, Houston, TX 77042, (713)978-7782

U.S. Professional Tennis Assn. **[23064]**, 3535 Briarpark Dr., Ste. 1, Houston, TX 77042, (713)978-7782

U.S. Professional Tennis Registry **[★23060]**

U.S. ProMiniGolf Assn. **[22627]**, 3210 Hwy. 17 S, North Myrtle Beach, SC 29582, (843)458-2585

U.S. Province of Congregation of Mariannhill Missionaries **[★19447]**

U.S. Psychiatric Rehabilitation Assn. **[16577]**, 601 Global Way, Ste. 106, Linthicum, MD 21090, (410)789-7054

U.S. Psychiatric Rehabilitation Assn. **[16577]**, 601 Global Way, Ste. 106, Linthicum, MD 21090, (410)789-7054

A star before a book entry number signifies that the name is not listed separately, but is mentioned within the entry.

U.S. Psychotronics Assn. [7230], 409 Marquette Dr., Louisville, KY 40222, (502)429-6600

U.S. Public Hea. Ser. Clinical Soc. [★5931]

U.S. Public Hea. Ser. I Commissioned Officers Assn. [5931], 8201 Corporate Dr., Ste. 200, Landover, MD 20785, (301)731-9080

U.S. Qatar Bus. Coun. [23387], 1341 Connecticut Ave. NW, Ste. 4A, Washington, DC 20036, (202)457-8555

United States Qatar Bus. Coun. [23387], 1341 Connecticut Ave. NW, Ste. 4A, Washington, DC 20036, (202)457-8555

U.S. Quad Rugby Assn. [22860], 11104 Spicewood Club Dr., Austin, TX 78750, (512)791-2644

U.S. Quad Rugby Assn. [22860], 11104 Spicewood Club Dr., Austin, TX 78750, (512)791-2644

U.S. Racquet Stringers Assn. [3341], 330 Main St., Vista, CA 92084, (760)536-1177

U.S. Racquetball Assn. [22832], 1685 W Uintah St., Colorado Springs, CO 80904-2969, (719)635-5396

U.S. Radionics Assn. [★7230]

U.S. Region of Congregation of Mariannhill Missionaries [★19447]

U.S. Revolver Assn. [22889], RR 1 Box 548, Scotrun, PA 18355

U.S. Rice Export Development, Assn. [★3965]

U.S. Rice Producers Assn. [4508], 2825 Wilcrest Dr., Ste. 505, Houston, TX 77042-6041, (713)974-7423

U.S. Ride Directors Assn. [★22477]

U.S.-ROC Taiwan Bus. Coun. [★2090]

U.S.-ROC (Taiwan) Bus. Coun. [★2090]

U.S. Rottweiler Club [21672], Leslie Fried, Membership Off., 107 Colony Pl., Woolwich Township, NJ 08085

U.S. Rowing Assn. [22859], 2 Wall St., Princeton, NJ 08540, (609)751-0700

U.S. Rugby Football Union [22861], 2500 Arapahoe Ave., Ste. 200, Boulder, CO 80302, (303)539-0300

U.S. Running Streak Assn. [22869], 294 Chalet Dr., Millersville, MD 21108-1118, (410)987-5215

U.S. Russia Bus. Coun. [2089], 1110 Vermont Ave. NW, Ste. 350, Washington, DC 20005-3544, (202)739-9180

U.S. Russia Bus. Coun. [2089], 1110 Vermont Ave. NW, Ste. 350, Washington, DC 20005-3544, (202)739-9180

U.S. Sailing Assn. [22406], PO Box 1260, Portsmouth, RI 02871-0907, (401)683-0800

U.S. Sailing Assn. [★22406]

U.S. Sailing Assn. I Coun. of Sailing Associations [22407], 15 Maritime Dr., PO Box 1260, Portsmouth, RI 02871-0907, (401)683-0800

U.S. Sailing Assn. I U.S. Sailing Found. [22408], 15 Maritime Dr., PO Box 1260, Portsmouth, RI 02871-0907, (401)683-0800

U.S.-Saudi Arabian Bus. Coun. [2114], 8081 Wolftrap Rd., Ste. 300, Vienna, VA 22182, (703)962-9300

U.S. Scale Masters Assn. [21912], 415 Charman St., Oregon City, OR 97045, (859)881-8347

U.S. Seaplane Pilots Assn. [★156]

U.S. Senate Press Photographers Gallery [2738], U.S. Capitol, S-317, Washington, DC 20510, (202)224-6548

U.S. Seniors Bowling Assn. [★22429]

U.S. Seniors Bowling Assn. [★22429]

U.S. Servas [17986], 1125 16th St., Ste. 201, Arcata, CA 95521-5585, (707)825-1714

U.S. Servas [17986], 1125 16th St., Ste. 201, Arcata, CA 95521-5585, (707)825-1714

U.S. Shellac Importers Assn. - Defunct.

U.S. Ski Assn. [★22918]

U.S. Ski Mountaineering Assn. [22917], PO Box 495, Wilson, WY 83014

U.S. Ski and Snowboard Assn. [22918], PO Box 100, Park City, UT 84060, (435)649-9090

U.S. Ski Team Found. [22919], 1500 Kearns Blvd., Park City, UT 84060, (435)649-9090

U.S. Skiing [★22918]

U.S. Snooker Assn. [22311], 1000 Kiely Blvd., No. 86, Santa Clara, CA 95051, (408)615-7479

U.S. Snowshoe Assn. [22928], 678 County Rte. 25, Corinth, NY 12822, (518)654-7648

U.S. Soccer Fed. [22947], 1801 S Prairie Ave., Chicago, IL 60616, (312)808-1300

U.S. Soccer Football Assn. [★22947]

U.S. Soc. for Augmentative and Alternative Commun. [17361], 100 E Pennsylvania Ave., Towson, MD 21286

U.S. Soc. on Dams [7612], 1616 17th St., No. 483, Denver, CO 80202-1277, (303)628-5430

U.S. Soc. for Ecological Economics [4222], 617 Main St., Burlington, VT 05405, (802)656-2906

U.S. Soc. for Ecological Economics [4222], 617 Main St., Burlington, VT 05405, (802)656-2906

U.S. Soc. for Educ. Through Art [7754], East Carolina Univ., Jenkins Fine Arts Ctr., E 5th St., Greenville, NC 27858-4353, (252)328-1298

U.S. Soc. of Esperanto Instructors [★8458]

U.S. Soda Ash Export Assn. [★1573]

U.S. Soling Assn. [22409], Ashley Henderson, 605 Farmhurst Dr., No. 20, Charlotte, NC 28217, (704)264-0996

U.S. Sommelier Assn. [191], 1111 Lincoln Rd., Ste. 400-9, Miami Beach, FL 33139, (954)437-0449

U.S. Space Education Assn. - Defunct.

U.S. Space Found. [★7696]

U.S. Specialty Sports Assn. [22958], 611 Line Dr., Kissimmee, FL 34744, (321)697-3637

U.S. Speedskating [22903], PO Box 18370, Kearns, UT 84118, (801)417-5360

U.S. Sport Jujitsu Assn. [22762], PO Box 566, Nitro, WV 25143, (304)755-1394

U.S. Sports Acad. [23014], One Acad. Dr., Daphne, AL 36526-7055, (251)626-3303

U.S. Sports Acrobatics - Address unknown since 2011.

United States Sports Chiropractic Fed. - Address unknown since 2011.

U.S. Sportsmen's Alliance [22701], 801 Kingsmill Pkwy., Columbus, OH 43229, (614)888-4868

U.S. Squash Racquets Assn. [23029], 555 8th Ave., Ste. 1102, New York, NY 10018-4311, (212)268-4090

U.S. Stamp Soc. [22090], PO Box 6634, Katy, TX 77491-6634

U.S. Student Assn. [8932], 1211 Connecticut Ave. NW, Ste. 406, Washington, DC 20036, (202)640-6570

U.S. Student Travel Ser. [★8363]

U.S. Student Travel Ser. [★8363]

U.S. Sugar Mfrs. Assn. [★1434]

U.S. Superyacht Assn. [465], 757 SE 17th St., No. 662, Fort Lauderdale, FL 33316, (954)792-8666

U.S. Surveyors Assn. [7490], 13430 McGregor Blvd., Fort Myers, FL 33919, (800)245-4425

U.S. Sweet Potato Coun. [4481], 12 Nicklaus Ln., Ste. 101, Columbia, SC 29229-3363, (803)788-7101

U.S. Sweetener Producers Gp. [★1374]

U.S. Swim School Assn. [23045], PO Box 17208, Fountain Hills, AZ 85269, (480)837-5525

U.S. Swimming Found. [★23048]

U.S. Swimming Found. [★23048]

U.S. Synchronized Swimming [23046], 132 E Washington St., Ste. 820, Indianapolis, IN 46204, (317)237-5700

U.S. Table Soccer Fed. [21757], PO Box 14455, Washington, DC 20044

U.S. Table Tennis Assn. [★23050]

U.S. Taekwondo Union [22763], 1 Olympic Plz., Colorado Springs, CO 80909, (719)866-4632

U.S.-Taiwan Bus. Coun. [2090], 1700 N Moore St., Ste. 1703, Arlington, VA 22209, (703)465-2930

U.S.-Taiwan Bus. Coun. [2090], 1700 N Moore St., Ste. 1703, Arlington, VA 22209, (703)465-2930

U.S. Tanzer 16 Class Assn. [★22396]

U.S. Tchoukball Assn. [22256], 4250 W Cramer St., Seattle, WA 98199, (240)505-5951

U.S. Team Handball Fed. [★22258]

U.S. Team Penning Assn. [22671], 3609 Acton Hwy., Ste. 21, Granbury, TX 76049, (817)326-4444

U.S. Team Penning Assn. [22671], 3609 Acton Hwy., Ste. 21, Granbury, TX 76049, (817)326-4444

U.S. Telecom Assn. [3604], 607 14th St. NW, Ste. 400, Washington, DC 20005, (202)326-7300

U.S. Telecommunications Suppliers Assn. [★3422]

U.S. Telemark Ski Assn. [22920], PO Box 775570, Steamboat Springs, CO 80477, (406)862-3303

U.S. Telephone Assn. [★3604]

U.S. Tennis Assn. [23065], 70 W Red Oak Ln., White Plains, NY 10604, (914)696-7000

U.S. Term Limits Found. [18350], 9900 Main St., Ste. 303, Fairfax, VA 22031, (703)383-0907

U.S.-Tibet Comm. [18726], 241 E 32nd St., New York, NY 10016, (212)481-3569

U.S.-Tibet Comm. [18726], 241 E 32nd St., New York, NY 10016, (212)481-3569

U.S. Tobacco Cooperative [4960], 1304 Annapolis Dr., Raleigh, NC 27608-2130, (919)821-4560

U.S. Tour Operators Assn. [3582], 275 Madison Ave., Ste. 2014, New York, NY 10016-1101, (212)599-6599

U.S. Tour Operators Assn. [3582], 275 Madison Ave., Ste. 2014, New York, NY 10016-1101, (212)599-6599

U.S. Trademark Assn. [★5573]

U.S. Trademark Assn. [★5573]

U.S. Trager Assn. [13716], Anna Marie Bowers, Admin. Dir., PO Box 1009, Burton, OH 44021, (440)834-0308

U.S. Travel Assn. [3583], 1100 New York Ave. NW, Ste. 450, Washington, DC 20005-3934, (202)408-8422

U.S. Travel Data Center [3584], Travel Indus. Assn. of Am., 1100 New York Ave. NW, Ste. 450, Washington, DC 20005-3934, (202)408-8422

U.S. Travel Insurance Assn. [3585], 1333 H St. NW, Ste. 820, Washington, DC 20005, (800)224-6164

U.S. Treasury Agents Assn. [★5383]

U.S. Triathlon Assn. [★23100]

U.S. Trotting Assn. [22672], 750 Michigan Ave., Columbus, OH 43215, (614)224-2291

U.S. Trout Farmers Assn. [3832], PO Box 1647, Pine Bluff, AR 71613, (870)850-7900

U.S. Truck Historical Soc. [★22195]

U.S. Tuna Found. - Address unknown since 2010.

U.S. Twirling Assn. [22306], 1608 Wortell Dr., Lincoln, CA 95648, (916)343-0062

U.S.-U.A.E. Bus. Coun. [2115], 505 Ninth St. NW, Ste. 5010, Washington, DC 20004, (202)863-7285

U.S.-Ukraine Bus. Coun. [721], 1300 I St. NW, Ste. 720 W, Washington, DC 20005, (202)429-0551

U.S. Ukraine Found. [18742], 1 Thomas Cir. NW, Ste. 900-B, Washington, DC 20005, (202)223-2228

U.S. Ukraine Found. [18742], 1 Thomas Cir. NW, Ste. 900-B, Washington, DC 20005, (202)223-2228

U.S. Ultralight Assn. [20922], PO Box 3501, Gettysburg, PA 17325, (717)339-0200

U.S. Venetian Blind Assn. [★2076]

U.S. Veterinary Medical Assn. [★17010]

U.S.-Vietnam Trade Coun. [17202], 1025 Vermont Ave. NW, Ste. 300, Washington, DC 20005, (202)580-6950

U.S.-Vietnam Trade Coun. [17202], 1025 Vermont Ave. NW, Ste. 300, Washington, DC 20005, (202)580-6950

U.S.-Vietnam WTO Coalition [18762], 1101 17th St. NW, Ste. 411, Washington, DC 20036, (202)289-1912

U.S. War Dogs Assn. [20691], 1313 Mt. Holly Rd., Burlington, NJ 08016, (609)234-4539

U.S. Water Fitness Assn. [22810], PO Box 243279, Boynton Beach, FL 33424-3279, (561)732-9908

U.S. Water Polo [23113], 2124 Maine St., Ste. 240, Huntington Beach, CA 92648, (714)500-5445

U.S. Water and Power [6121], 1179 Nelrose Ave., Venice, CA 90291

U.S. Wayfarer Assn. [22410], 6907 Valley Haven Dr., Charlotte, NC 28211, (704)366-6250

U.S. Wheat Associates [3964], 3103 10th St. N, Ste. 300, Arlington, VA 22201, (202)463-0999

U.S. Wheat Associates [3964], 3103 10th St. N, Ste. 300, Arlington, VA 22201, (202)463-0999

U.S. Windsurfing Assn. [22411], 817 79th Ave., St. Pete Beach, FL 33706, (877)386-8708

U.S. Women and Cuba Collaboration [17957], 6508 27th Ave. NW, Seattle, WA 98115

U.S. Women in Nuclear [7173], Carol Berrigan, Nuclear Energy Inst., 1776 I St. NW, Ste. 400, Washington, DC 20006

United States Women of Today [13079], 728 Prospect St., York, PA 17403-2426

U.S. Women's Chamber of Commerce [23457], 700 12th St. NW, Ste. 700, Washington, DC 20005, (888)418-7922

Reference to "IO" in place of a book number signifies that the association may be found in the 50th edition of International Organizations.

U.S. Women's Curling Assn. **[22473]**, Cleveland Skating Club, Shaker Heights, OH 44120

U.S. Women's Track Coaches Assn. - Defunct.

U.S. Wrestling Fed. **[★23135]**

U.S. Yacht Racing Union **[★22406]**

U.S. Yngling Assn. **[22412]**, 7171 U.S. 23 S, Ossineke, MI 49766, (989)471-3545

U.S. Youth Soccer Assn. **[22948]**, 9220 World Cup Way, Frisco, TX 75033, (800)476-2237

U.S. Yudo Assn. **[22764]**, Intl. Yudo Fed., PO Box 620395, Orlando, FL 32862-0395

United Steelworkers of Am. **[23256]**, 5 Gateway Ctr., Pittsburgh, PA 15222, (412)562-2400

United Steelworkers of Am. - Canadian Br. **[IO]**, Toronto, ON, Canada

United Stockgrowers of Am. I Ranchers-Cattlemen Action Legal Fund **[3943]**, PO Box 30715, Billings, MT 59107, (406)252-2516

United Stone and Allied Products Workers of Am. **[★23256]**

United St. Machine Assn. **[21185]**, 430 N Batchewana St., Clawson, MI 48017, (248)435-3091

United Student Aid Funds **[★8194]**

United Suffolk Sheep Assn. **[4923]**, PO Box 995, Ottumwa, IA 52501-0995, (641)684-5291

United Support of Artists for Africa **[★12895]**

United Support of Artists for Africa **[★12895]**

United Synagogue of Am. **[★19906]**

United Synagogue of Am. **[★19906]**

United Synagogue of Conservative Judaism **[19906]**, 820 2nd Ave., New York, NY 10017-4504, (212)533-7800

United Synagogue of Conservative Judaism **[19906]**, 820 2nd Ave., New York, NY 10017-4504, (212)533-7800

United Synagogue Youth **[19907]**, Rapaport House, 820 2nd Ave., 10th Fl., New York, NY 10010, (212)533-7800

United Transport Ser. Employees **[★23290]**

United Trans. Union **[23292]**, 24950 Country Club Blvd., Ste. 340, North Olmsted, OH 44070-5333, (216)228-9400

United Trotting Assn. **[★22672]**

United Typothetae of Am. **[★1628]**

United Ukrainian Amer. Relief Comm. **[19268]**, 1206 Cottman Ave., Philadelphia, PA 19111, (215)728-1630

United Union of Roofers, Waterproofers and Allied Workers **[23170]**, 1660 L St. NW, Ste. 800, Washington, DC 20036-5646, (202)463-7663

United Way of Am. **[12056]**, 701 N Fairfax St., Alexandria, VA 22314, (703)683-7800

United Way of Canada - Centraide Canada **[IO]**, Ottawa, ON, Canada

United Way Intl. **[12057]**, 701 N Fairfax St., Alexandria, VA 22314-2045, (703)836-7112

United Way Intl. **[12057]**, 701 N Fairfax St., Alexandria, VA 22314-2045, (703)836-7112

United We Serve **[20712]**, 5645 US Hwy., 59 S, Jefferson, TX 75657, (903)665-2647

United White Shepherd Club **[21673]**, 663 E 150 S, Valparaiso, IN 46383, (219)733-2810

United World Atheists/Amer. Atheists - Defunct.

United World Mission **[20103]**, PO Box 602002, Charlotte, NC 28260-2002, (704)357-3355

United World Mission **[20103]**, PO Box 602002, Charlotte, NC 28260-2002, (704)357-3355

United Yorkie Rescue **[11052]**, Carl Sullenberger, Treas., 7170 Deer Run Dr., Amherst, OH 44001

Unitus **[12378]**, 2030 1st Ave., 3rd Fl., Seattle, WA 98121, (206)926-3700

Unity **[IO]**, Stoke-on-Trent, United Kingdom

Unity-and-Diversity World Coun. **[17987]**, Leland P. Stewart, BSE, Founder/Coor., PO Box 661401, Los Angeles, CA 90066-9201, (310)391-5735

Unity-and-Diversity World Coun. **[17987]**, Leland P. Stewart, BSE, Founder/Coor., PO Box 661401, Los Angeles, CA 90066-9201, (310)391-5735

Unity Coalition for Israel **[8422]**, 3965 W 83rd St., No. 292, Shawnee Mission, KS 66208, (913)648-0022

Unity Coalition for Israel **[8422]**, 3965 W 83rd St., No. 292, Shawnee Mission, KS 66208, (913)648-0022

Unity Corps **[11536]**, PO Box 29219, Los Angeles, CA 90029-0219, (323)850-8700

Unity of Czech Ladies and Men **[★18972]**

Unity in Diversity Coun. **[★17987]**

Unity in Diversity Coun. **[★17987]**

Unity and Diversity World Org. **[★17987]**

Unity and Diversity World Org. **[★17987]**

Unity Fellowship Church Movement **[19802]**, 5149 W Jefferson Blvd., Los Angeles, CA 90016, (323)938-8322

UNITY: Journalists of Color **[2882]**, 7950 Jones Br. Dr., McLean, VA 22107, (703)854-3585

Unity Network **[★10337]**

Uniunea Arhitectilor din Romania **[★IO]**

Uniunea Generala a Industriasilor din Romania **[★IO]**

Uniunea Romana De Transport Public **[★IO]**

Universal Articulate Interdimensional Understanding of Sci. **[★12227]**

Universal Articulate Interdimensional Understanding of Sci. **[★12227]**

Universal Autograph Collectors Club **[21411]**, PO Box 1392, Mount Dora, FL 32756

Universal Cooperatives **[4176]**, 1300 Corporate Center Curve, Eagan, MN 55121, (651)239-1000

Universal Design Alliance **[1040]**, 3651-E Peachtree Pkwy., Ste. 311, Suwanee, GA 30024, (813)368-7420

Universal Esperanto Assn. **[IO]**, Rotterdam, Netherlands

Universal Fellowship of Metropolitan Community Churches **[★19797]**

Universal Gym Affiliates **[★3333]**

Universal Gym Affiliates **[★3333]**

Universal Hea. Care Action Network **[14831]**, 2800 Euclid Ave., No. 520, Cleveland, OH 44115-2418, (216)241-8422

Universal Human Rights Network **[17865]**, 1050 17th St. NW, Ste. 1000, Washington, DC 20036, (202)955-1010

Universal Martial Arts Brotherhood **[22765]**, 2427 Buckingham Rd., Ann Arbor, MI 48104, (734)971-7040

Universal Martial Arts Brotherhood **[22765]**, 2427 Buckingham Rd., Ann Arbor, MI 48104, (734)971-7040

Universal Masonic Brotherhood **[19143]**, PO Box 6410, Seffner, FL 33583, (813)662-3597

Universal Muslim Assn. of Am. **[20137]**, PO Box 313, Burtonsville, MD 20866, (646)932-8622

Universal Pantheist Soc. **[20258]**, PO Box 3499, Visalia, CA 93278

Universal Peace Fed. **[18298]**, 200 White Plains Rd., Tarrytown, NY 10591, (914)631-1331

Universal Peace Fed. **[18298]**, 200 White Plains Rd., Tarrytown, NY 10591, (914)631-1331

Universal Postal Union **[IO]**, Bern, Switzerland

Universal Proutist Farmers Fed. **[4365]**, 6810 Tilden Ln., Rockville, MD 20852, (301)231-0110

Universal Proutist Intellectual Fed. **[★18627]**

Universal Proutist Youth Fed. - Address unknown since 2010.

Universal Proutists Women **[★18635]**

Universal Serials and Book Exchange **[★10016]**

Universal Ship Cancellation Soc. **[22091]**, 747 Shard Ct., Fremont, CA 94539-7419

Universal Ship Cancellation Soc., Savannah Chap. **[★22051]**

Universal Ship Cancellation Soc., Savannah Chap. **[★22051]**

Universal Torah Registry **[19908]**, 225 W 34th St., Ste. 1607, New York, NY 10122-1693, (212)983-4800

Universal White Brotherhood **[IO]**, Sevres, France

Universala Esperanto-Asocio **[★IO]**

Universalist Ser. Comm. **[★20272]**

Universalist Ser. Comm. **[★20272]**

Universities Allied for Essential Medicines **[8384]**, 2625 Alcatraz Ave., No. 180, Berkeley, CA 94705, (510)868-1159

Universities Associated for Res. and Education in Pathology - Defunct.

Universities Assn. for Lifelong Learning **[IO]**, Leicester, United Kingdom

Universities Australia **[IO]**, Canberra, Australia

Universities Coun. for the Educ. of Teachers **[IO]**, London, United Kingdom

Universities Coun. on Hydrology **[★7613]**

Universities Coun. on Water Resources **[7613]**, Southern Illinois Univ. Carbondale, 1000 Faner Dr., Rm. 4543, Carbondale, IL 62901-4526, (618)536-7571

Universities Fed. for Animal Welfare **[IO]**, Wheathampstead, United Kingdom

Universities Field Staff Intl. -Inst. of World Affairs **[★8407]**

Universities Field Staff Intl. -Inst. of World Affairs **[★8407]**

Universities Res. Assn. **[7338]**, 1111 19th St. NW, Ste. 400, Washington, DC 20036, (202)293-1382

Universities Res. Assn. **[7338]**, 1111 19th St. NW, Ste. 400, Washington, DC 20036, (202)293-1382

Universities Space Res. Assn. **[6102]**, 10211 Wincopin Cir., Ste. 500, Columbia, MD 21044-3432, (410)730-2656

Universities UK **[IO]**, London, United Kingdom

Univ. of Advancing Cmpt. Tech. Alumni Assn. - Address unknown since 2010.

Univ. of Alaska Fairbanks Alumni Assn. **[18905]**, PO Box 750126, Fairbanks, AK 99775, (907)474-7081

Univ. Assn. for Contemporary European Stud. **[IO]**, London, United Kingdom

Univ. Assn. for Emergency Medicine **[★14479]**

Univ. Athletic Assn. **[23015]**, 151 Sully's Trail, Ste. 14, Pittsford, NY 14534-4562, (585)419-0575

Univ. Aviation Assn. **[7698]**, 3410 Skyway Dr., Auburn, AL 36830-6444, (334)844-2434

Univ. of Bremen, Res. Gp. on African Development Perspectives **[IO]**, Bremen, Germany

Univ. of Calgary Ballroom Dance Club **[IO]**, Calgary, AB, Canada

Univ. and Coll. Designers Assn. **[8321]**, 199 W Enon Spring Rd., Ste. 300, Smyrna, TN 37167, (615)459-4559

Univ. and Coll. Designers Assn. **[8321]**, 199 W Enon Spring Rd., Ste. 300, Smyrna, TN 37167, (615)459-4559

Univ. and Coll. Labor Educ. Assn. **[★8453]**

Univ. and Coll. Theater Assn. **[★8999]**

Univ. and Coll. Union **[IO]**, London, United Kingdom

Univ. and Coll. Union Scotland **[★IO]**

Univ. of Colorado Hea. Sciences Center Alumni Assn. **[23547]**, 13100 E 17th Pl., Rm. CG009, Aurora, CO 80045, (303)724-2518

University-Community Partnership for Social Action Res. **[7895]**, PO Box 871104, Tempe, AZ 85287-1104, (480)965-6253

Univ. Consortium for Instructional Development and Technology - Defunct.

Univ. Continuing Educ. Assn. **[★7930]**

Univ. Continuing Educ. Assn. **[7930]**, 1 Dupont Cir., Ste. 615, Washington, DC 20036, (202)659-3130

Univ. Corp. for Atmospheric Res. **[7108]**, PO Box 3000, Boulder, CO 80307-3000, (303)497-1000

Univ. Coun. for Educational Admin. **[7678]**, Univ. of Virginia, Curry School of Educ., 405 Emmett St., Charlottesville, VA 22904-0265, (434)243-1041

Univ. Economic Development Assn. **[9047]**, 7801 York Rd., Ste. 260, Towson, MD 21204, (877)583-UEDA

Univ. Faculty for Life **[8759]**, Georgetown Univ., Wolffington Hall, Washington, DC 20057, (718)817-3291

Univ. Faculty for Life **[8759]**, Georgetown Univ., Wolffington Hall, Washington, DC 20057, (718)817-3291

Univ. Film Assn. **[★8183]**

Univ. Film Producers Assn. **[★8183]**

Univ. Film and Video Assn. **[8183]**, 3800 Barham Blvd., Ste. 103, Los Angeles, CA 90068, (866)647-8382

Univ. Found. **[IO]**, Brussels, Belgium

Univ. Insurance Managers Assn. **[★8327]**

Univ. of Iowa Alumni Assn. **[18906]**, 100 Levitt Center, Iowa City, IA 52242-1797, (319)335-3294

Univ. of Iowa Injury Prevention Res. Center **[7347]**, 202 IREH Oakdale Res. Campus, Iowa City, IA 52242-5000, (319)335-4458

Univ. Labor Educ. Assn. **[★8453]**

Univ. Lab. Managers Assn. **[★7021]**

A star before a book entry number signifies that the name is not listed separately, but is mentioned within the entry.

Univ. of Louisville Alumni Assn. [18907], Univ. of Louisville, Malcolm B. Chancey Center, Alumni Off. , Louisville, KY 40292, (502)852-6186

Univ. of Mary Alumni Assn. [18908], 7500 Univ. Dr., Bismarck, ND 58504, (701)355-8030

Univ. of Minnesota - Crookston Alumni Assn. [18909], 2900 Univ. Ave., Crookston, MN 56716-5001, (218)281-8434

Univ. of Minnesota Human Rights Center [★17833]

Univ. of Oklahoma Assn. [★18894]

Univ. Peace Studies Network - Defunct.

Univ. Philosophical Soc. [IO], Dublin, Ireland

Univ. Photographers Assn. of Am. [8714], Community Coll., 9000 W Coll. Pkwy., Palos Hills, IL 60465

Univ. Professional & Continuing Educ. Assn. [7930], 1 Dupont Cir., Ste. 615, Washington, DC 20036, (202)659-3130

University Res. Comm. [★7620]

University/Resident Theatre Assn. [9005], 1560 Broadway, Ste. 1103, New York, NY 10036, (212)221-1130

Univ. Risk and Insurance Managers Assn. [★8327]

Univ. Risk Mgt. and Insurance Assn. [8327], PO Box 1027, Bloomington, IN 47402-1027, (812)855-6683

Univ. of South Dakota Alumni Assn. [18910], 414 E Clark St., Vermillion, SD 57069-2390, (605)677-6734

Univ. of Texas at Brownsville and Texas Southmost Coll. Alumni Assn. [18911], 80 Ft. Brown, Brownsville, TX 78520-4956, (956)882-4327

Univ. of Texas I Pan-American Alumni Assn. [18912], 1201 W Univ. Dr., UC108, Edinburg, TX 78541, (956)381-2500

Univ. of Virginia I Bibliographical Soc. [9453], Alderman Lib., PO Box 400152, Charlottesville, VA 22904, (434)924-7013

Univ. of Wisconsin I Eau Claire Alumni Assn. [18913], PO Box 4004, Eau Claire, WI 54702-4004, (715)836-3266

Univ. of Wisconsin - Platteville Alumni Assn. - Address unknown since 2010.

Univ. Women of Europe [IO], Paris, France

Univ. Women's Assn. - Singapore [IO], Singapore, Singapore

Unlimited Scale Racing Assn. [21913], PO Box 819, Brea, CA 92822

Unlocking Autism [13807], PO Box 208, Tyrone, GA 30290, (866)366-3361

UNOS [★16920]

Unplug [★8009]

Unrecognised States Numismatic Soc. [21997], PO Box 0534, Castaic, CA 91310-0534

Unreserved Amer. Indian Fashion and Art Alliance [9134], 55 Bethune St., 13th Fl., New York, NY 10014, (212)206-6580

Unwanted Horse Coalition [11053], 1616 H St. NW, 7th Fl., Washington, DC 20006, (202)296-4031

Unwed Parents Anonymous - Defunct.

UOTS, Inc. [★19283]

UP Micro-Loans: Unlimiting People [IO], Berlin, Germany

Up With People [8065], 6830 Broadway, Unit A, Denver, CO 80221-2851, (303)460-7100

Up2Us [13563], 520 Eight Ave., 2nd Fl., New York, NY 10018, (212)563-3031

Upenyu [15219], 1 Mary Ct., Cranbury, NJ 08512, (317)460-6792

Upholstered Furniture Action Coun. [1560], Box 2436, High Point, NC 27261, (336)885-5065

Upholsterers' Intl. Union of North Am. [★23256]

UPL-AOPA Luxembourg [★IO]

Upledger Inst. [13717], 11211 Prosperity Farms Rd., Ste. D-325, Palm Beach Gardens, FL 33410, (561)622-4334

Upledger's Intl. Assn. of Healthcare Practitioners [★14796]

Upledger's Intl. Assn. of Healthcare Practitioners [★14796]

Uplift a Child Intl. [11513], 8705 Kodiak Dr., Silver Spring, MD 20903-3500, (301)445-4665

Uplift Intl. [15220], PO Box 27696, Seattle, WA 98165, (206)455-0916

Uplift Internationale [16007], PO Box 181658, Denver, CO 80218, (303)707-1361

Uplift Internationale [16007], PO Box 181658, Denver, CO 80218, (303)707-1361

Upper Mississippi River Conservation Comm. [4158], 555 Lester Ave., Onalaska, WI 54650, (608)783-8432

Upsilon Pi Epsilon Assn. [23495], 158 Wetlands Edge Rd., American Canyon, CA 94503, (530)518-8488

Upsilon Pi Epsilon Assn. [23495], 158 Wetlands Edge Rd., American Canyon, CA 94503, (530)518-8488

Upwardly Global [2898], San Francisco Off., 582 Market St., Ste. 1207, San Francisco, CA 94104, (415)834-9901

Urania Trust [IO], Old Windsor, United Kingdom

URANTIA Assn. of the U.S. [20197], URANTIA Found., 533 Diversey Pkwy., Chicago, IL 60614, (773)525-3319

Urantia Found. [20259], 533 Diversey Pkwy., Chicago, IL 60614, (773)525-3319

Urantia Found. [20259], 533 Diversey Pkwy., Chicago, IL 60614, (773)525-3319

Urasenke Tea Ceremony Soc. [9913], Urasenke Chanoyu Center, 153 E 69th St., New York, NY 10021, (212)988-6161

Urbain Baudreau Graveline Genealogical Assn. [20602], PO Box 905, Palmer, MA 01069, (413)283-8378

Urban Affairs

Assn. of Collegiate Schools of Planning [9024]UrbanAssn. of Town Centre Mgt.

Center for Urban and Regional Stud. [10622]

Center for Urban and Regional Stud. [10622]

CEOs for Cities [18754]

Coalition on Urban Renewal and Educ. [18755]

Cong. for the New Urbanism [6049]

European Forum for Urban Safety [14982]

Greener Pastures Inst. [12178]

Higher Educ. Consortium for Urban Affairs [9025]

Higher Educ. Consortium for Urban Affairs [9025]

Intl. Assn. for China Planning [18315]

Intl. Healthy Cities Found. [13345]

Intl. Healthy Cities Found. [13345]

Natl. Neighborhood Coalition [17389]

Natl. Urban Fellows [18756]UrbanPlanning and Development Collaborative Intl.

ULI Found. [18757]

Urban Affairs Assn. [9026]

Urban Inst. [18758]

Urban Superintendent's Assn. of Am. [9027]

Urban Affairs Assn. [9026], Univ. of Delaware, 298 Graham Hall, Newark, DE 19716, (302)831-1681

Urban Alliance on Race Relations [IO], Toronto, ON, Canada

Urban Art Intl. - Address unknown since 2010.

Urban Awareness USA [19604], 601 Dinwiddie St., Portsmouth, VA 23704, (866)975-8722

Urban-Brookings Tax Policy Center [18707], 2100 M St. NW, Washington, DC 20037, (202)833-7200

Urban Coalition Action Coun. [★18326]

Urban Ecology Australia [IO], Adelaide, Australia

Urban Ed [9031], 2041 Martin Luther King, Jr. Ave. SE, Ste. M2, Washington, DC 20020, (202)610-2344

Urban Education

Coun. of the Great City Schools [9028]

Natl. Educ. Assn. I Natl. Coun. of Urban Educ. Associations [9029]

Natl. Urban Alliance for Effective Educ. [9030]

Urban Ed [9031]

Urban Teacher Residency United [8962]

Urban Environment Conf. - Defunct.

Urban Farming [4366], 19785 W 12 Mile Rd., Southfield, MI 48076, (313)664-0615

Urban Financial Services Coalition [438], 1200 G St. NW, Ste. 800, Washington, DC 20005, (202)289-8335

Urban Homesteading Assistance Bd. [12203], 120 Wall St., 20th Fl., New York, NY 10005, (212)479-3300

Urban Inst. [18758], 2100 M St. NW, Washington, DC 20037, (202)833-7200

The Urban Inst. I Natl. Center for Charitable Statistics [12689], 2100 M St. NW, 5th Fl., Washington, DC 20037, (866)518-3874

Urban Land Found. [★18757]

Urban Land Inst. [5334], 1025 Thomas Jefferson St. NW, Ste. 500, Washington, DC 20007-5230, (202)624-7000

Urban Land Inst. Found. [★18757]

Urban Land Res. Found. [★18757]

Urban League; Natl. [17312]

Urban Libraries Coun. [10017], 125 S Wacker Dr., Ste. 1050, Chicago, IL 60606, (312)676-0999

Urban Lib. Trustees Coun. [★10017]

Urban and Regional Info. Systems Assn. [6995], 701 Lee St., Ste. 680, Des Plaines, IL 60016, (847)824-6300

Urban Superintendent's Assn. of Am. [9027], PO Box 1248, Chesapeake, VA 23327-1248, (757)436-1032

Urban Teacher Residency United [8962], 1332 N Halsted St., Ste. 204, Chicago, IL 60642, (312)397-8878

Urbanists Intl. [6207], 134 The Uplands, Berkeley, CA 94705, (510)547-5500

Urethane Inst., Soc. of the Plastics Indus. Polyurethane Div. [★2765]

Urgent Care Assn. of Am. [13729], 4320 Winfield Rd., Ste. 200, Warrenville, IL 60555, (630)836-8514

Urgenta Found. [IO], Utrecht, Netherlands

UrgentCall.org [18219], Inst. for Defense and Disarmament Stud., 675 Massachusetts Ave., Cambridge, MA 02139, (617)354-4337

Urhobo Natl. Assn. of North Am. [19178], 133-18 Guy Brewer Blvd., 2nd Fl., Jamaica, NY 11434

Urine Disease Family Support Gp; Maple Syrup [15499]

Urogynecologic Soc; Amer. [16941]

Urologic Nurses and Associates; Soc. of [15802]

Urological Soc. of Australia and New Zealand [IO], Edgecliff, Australia

Urological Soc. of India [IO], Ludhiana, India

Urology

Amer. Assn. of Clinical Urologists [16936]

Amer. Assn. of Genito-Urinary Surgeons [16937]

Amer. Bd. of Urology [16938]

Amer. Prostate Soc. [16939]

Amer. Soc. of Andrology [16940]

Amer. Urogynecologic Soc. [16941]

Amer. Urological Assn. [16942]

Amer. Urological Assn. Found. [16943]

Certification Bd. for Urologic Nurses and Associates [16944]

Interstitial Cystitis Assn. [16945]

Kidney Community Emergency Response Coalition [15552]

Natl. Assn. for Continence [16946]

Natl. Assn. for Continence [16946]

Natl. Kidney and Urologic Diseases Info. CH [16947]

Simon Found. for Continence [16948]

Soc. for Basic Urologic Res. [16949]

Soc. for Fetal Urology [16950]

Soc. of Govt. Ser. Urologists [16951]

Soc. for Pediatric Urology [16952]

Soc. of Univ. Urologists [16953]

Soc. of Uroradiology [16954]

Soc. of Women in Urology [16955]

Urostomy Assn. [IO], Uttoxeter, United Kingdom

Ursa Astronomical Assn. [IO], Helsinki, Finland

Uruguay Transparente [IO], Montevideo, Uruguay

Uruguayan Assn. of the Analytical Psychotherapy [IO], Montevideo, Uruguay

Uruguayan Assn. for the Stud. of Pain [IO], Montevideo, Uruguay

Uruguayan Circle of Advt. Agencies [IO], Montevideo, Uruguay

Uruguayan Dermatological Soc. [IO], Montevideo, Uruguay

Uruguayan Family Planning Assn. [IO], Montevideo, Uruguay

Uruguayan Found. of Joint Cooperation and Development [IO], Montevideo, Uruguay

Uruguayan Hypertension Comm. [IO], Montevideo, Uruguay

Uruguayan League Against Epilepsy [IO], Montevideo, Uruguay

Uruguayan Rose Assn. [IO], Montevideo, Uruguay

Reference to "IO" in place of a book number signifies that the association may be found in the 50th edition of International Organizations.

Uruguayan Soc. of Cardiology **[IO]**, Montevideo, Uruguay

Uruguayan Soc. of Clinical Neurophysiology **[IO]**, Montevideo, Uruguay

Uruguayan Soc. of Hea. Informatics **[IO]**, Montevideo, Uruguay

Ururka Dhagoolayaasha Qaranka Soomaaliyeed **[★IO]**

Ururka Dhaqdhaqaaqa Nabaddda Bulshada Soomaaliyeed **[★IO]**

US-Azerbaijan Coun. **[17958]**, 1212 Potomac St. NW, Washington, DC 20007, (202)333-8702

US-Azerbaijan Coun. **[17958]**, 1212 Potomac St. NW, Washington, DC 20007, (202)333-8702

US-China Green Energy Coun. **[6760]**, 1964 Deodara Dr., Los Altos, CA 94024-7054

US-China Higher Educ. Alliance **[7848]**, 133-28 41 Ave., Ste. 2B, Flushing, NY 11355, (718)661-1068

US-China Peoples Friendship Assn. **[★8305]**

US Coalition for Child Survival **[11514]**, 1616 Ft. Myer Dr., 11th Fl., Arlington, VA 20598, (703)312-6800

US-Cuba Reconciliation Initiative **[17754]**, 355 W 39th St., New York, NY 10118, (212)760-9903

US-Cuba Reconciliation Initiative **[17754]**, 355 W 39th St., New York, NY 10118, (212)760-9903

US Doctors for Africa **[15221]**, 14945 Ventura Blvd., Ste. 224, Sherman Oaks, CA 91403, (818)728-6629

US Doctors for Africa **[15221]**, 14945 Ventura Blvd., Ste. 224, Sherman Oaks, CA 91403, (818)728-6629

US Flag Football League **[★22600]**

US Foreclosure Network **[★5289]**

US Human Rights Network **[17866]**, 250 Georgia Ave. SW, Ste. 330, Atlanta, GA 30312, (404)588-9761

US Human Rights Network **[17866]**, 250 Georgia Ave. SW, Ste. 330, Atlanta, GA 30312, (404)588-9761

U.S., Inc. **[★12599]**

US-Ireland Alliance **[722]**, 2800 Clarendon Blvd., Ste. 502 W, Arlington, VA 22201, (202)643-8742

US-Ireland Alliance **[722]**, 2800 Clarendon Blvd., Ste. 502 W, Arlington, VA 22201, (202)643-8742

US SIF: The Forum for Sustainable and Responsible Investment **[18649]**, 910 17th St. NW, Ste. 1000, Washington, DC 20006, (202)872-5361

Us TOO Intl. **[13990]**, 5003 Fairview Ave., Downers Grove, IL 60515, (630)795-1002

Us TOO Intl. **[13990]**, 5003 Fairview Ave., Downers Grove, IL 60515, (630)795-1002

U.S.A. for Africa **[12895]**, 5670 Wilshire Blvd., Ste. 1450, Los Angeles, CA 90036, (323)954-3124

U.S.A. for Africa **[12895]**, 5670 Wilshire Blvd., Ste. 1450, Los Angeles, CA 90036, (323)954-3124

USA Athletes Intl. **[22233]**, 13095 S Mur-Len Rd., Ste. 140, Olathe, KS 66062, (913)397-9024

U.S.A. Badminton **[22252]**, 1 Olympic Plz., Colorado Springs, CO 80909, (719)866-4808

U.S.A. Baseball **[22291]**, 403 Blackwell St., Durham, NC 27701, (919)474-8721

U.S.A. Basketball **[22302]**, 5465 Mark Dabling Blvd., Colorado Springs, CO 80918-3842, (719)590-4800

USA-BIAC **[★707]**

USA-BIAC **[★707]**

U.S.A. Boxing **[22439]**, 30 Cimino Dr., Colorado Springs, CO 80903, (719)866-2300

U.S.A. Broomball **[22257]**, PO Box 20201, Bloomington, MN 55420, (763)241-1789

U.S.A. - Bus. and Indus. Advisory Comm. to the OECD **[17588]**, U.S. Coun. for Intl. Bus., 1212 Avenue of the Americas, New York, NY 10036, (212)354-4480

U.S.A. Canoe/Kayak **[23127]**, 330 S Tryon St., Lower Level, Charlotte, NC 28202, (704)348-4330

U.S.A. Climbing **[21287]**, 2031 Broadway, Ste. 8, Boulder, CO 80302, (888)944-4244

U.S.A. Coun. of Organizations | United Nations Assn. **[18752]**, 801 2nd Ave., 2nd Fl., New York, NY 10017, (212)907-1300

U.S.A. Cricket Assn. **[23016]**, 429 Lenox Ave., Ste. P405, Miami Beach, FL 33139, (305)537-3764

U.S.A. Dance **[9567]**, PO Box 152988, Cape Coral, FL 33915-2988, (239)242-0805

U.S.A. Deaf Sports Fed. **[22531]**, PO Box 910338, Lexington, KY 40591-0338, (605)367-5760

U.S.A. Defenders of Greyhounds **[11054]**, PO Box 1256, Carmel, IN 46082, (317)244-0113

USA Diving **[22544]**, 132 E Washington St., Ste. 850, Indianapolis, IN 46204, (317)237-5252

USA Dry Pea and Lentil Coun. **[3766]**, 2780 W Pullman Rd., Moscow, ID 83843-4024, (208)882-3023

USA Engage **[17589]**, 1625 K St. NW, Ste. 200, Washington, DC 20006, (202)887-0278

U.S.A. Equestrian Assn. **[★22689]**

U.S.A. Fed. of Bocce **[★22416]**

U.S.A. Fed. of Pankration Ethlima **[22237]**, 1935 S Plum Grove Rd., No. 321, Palatine, IL 60067, (847)971-2343

U.S.A. Field Hockey Assn. **[★22568]**

U.S.A. Film Festival **[9612]**, 6116 N Central Expy., Ste. 105, Dallas, TX 75206, (214)821-6300

U.S.A. Finn Assn. - Address unknown since 2011.

U.S.A. Football **[22602]**, 45 N Pennsylvania St., Ste. 700, Indianapolis, IN 46204, (317)614-7750

USA Gp. **[★8194]**

USA Gymnastics **[22636]**, 132 E Washington St., Ste. 700, Indianapolis, IN 46204, (317)237-5050

U.S.A. Harvest **[12298]**, PO Box 1628, Louisville, KY 40201-1628, (502)895-3924

USA Hockey **[22647]**, 1775 Bob Johnson Dr., Colorado Springs, CO 80906-4090, (719)576-8724

U.S.A. Karate Fed. **[22766]**, 1550 Ritchie Rd., Stow, OH 44224

U.S.A.-Korean Karate Assn. - Defunct.

USA Natl. Host - Defunct.

USA Natl. Karate-do Fed. **[22710]**, 1631 Mesa Ave., Ste. A-1, Colorado Springs, CO 80906, (719)477-6925

USA Pentathlon **[★23071]**

U.S.A. Ploughing Org. **[4367]**, Roger Neate, Sec.-Treas., 14837 Greenville Rd., Van Wert, OH 45891, (419)965-2284

U.S.A. Poultry and Egg Export Coun. **[4819]**, 2300 W Park Place Blvd., Ste. 100, Stone Mountain, GA 30087, (770)413-0006

U.S.A. Powerlifting **[22817]**, PO Box 668, Columbia City, IN 46725, (260)248-4889

USA Professional Platform Tennis Assn. **[23066]**, PO Box 666, Summit, NJ 07902, (847)274-8998

USA Pulling **[23074]**, 15501 WCR 13, Platteville, CO 80651, (800)750-7048

USA Racquetball **[★22832]**

U.S.A.-Republic of China Economic Coun. **[★2090]**

U.S.A.-Republic of China Economic Coun. **[★2090]**

U.S.A. Rice Coun. **[3965]**, 4301 N Fairfax Dr., Ste. 425, Arlington, VA 22203, (703)236-2300

U.S.A. Rice Fed. **[1597]**, 4301 N Fairfax Dr., Ste. 425, Arlington, VA 22203, (703)236-2300

U.S.A-ROC Economic Coun. **[★2090]**

U.S.A-ROC Economic Coun. **[★2090]**

U.S.A. Roller Skating **[★22904]**

U.S.A. Roller Sports **[22904]**, PO Box 6579, Lincoln, NE 68506-0579, (402)483-7551

U.S.A. Sanatan Sports and Cultural Assn. **[22949]**, 8637 Wilhert Ct., Sacramento, CA 95828

USA Shooting **[22890]**, 1 Olympic Plz., Colorado Springs, CO 80909, (719)866-4670

USA Softball **[★22950]**

U.S.A. Swimming **[23047]**, 1 Olympic Plz., Colorado Springs, CO 80909, (719)866-4578

U.S.A. Table Tennis **[23050]**, 1 Olympic Plz., Colorado Springs, CO 80909-5769, (719)866-4583

U.S.A Team-Handball **[22258]**, 2330 W California Ave., Salt Lake City, UT 84104, (801)463-2000

U.S.A. Tennis | NJTL **[23067]**, U.S. Tennis Assn., 70 W Red Oak Ln., White Plains, NY 10604-3602, (914)696-7000

U.S.A. Toy Lib. Assn. **[11169]**, 2719 Broadway Ave., Evanston, IL 60201, (847)612-6966

U.S.A. Track and Field **[23072]**, 132 E Washington St., Ste. 800, Indianapolis, IN 46204, (317)261-0500

U.S.A. Triathlon **[23100]**, 5825 Delmonico Dr., Colorado Springs, CO 80919, (719)597-9090

U.S.A. Ultimate **[22537]**, 4730 Table Mesa Dr., Ste. I-200C, Boulder, CO 80305, (303)447-3472

USA for the United Nations High Commissioner for Refugees **[12793]**, 1775 K St. NW, Ste. 290, Washington, DC 20006, (202)296-1115

USA for the United Nations High Commissioner for Refugees **[12793]**, 1775 K St. NW, Ste. 290, Washington, DC 20006, (202)296-1115

USA Volleyball **[23111]**, 715 S Circle Dr., Colorado Springs, CO 80910-2368, (719)228-6800

U.S.A. Water Ski **[23119]**, 1251 Holy Cow Rd., Polk City, FL 33868, (863)324-4341

USA Weightlifting **[23129]**, 1 Olympic Plz., Colorado Springs, CO 80909, (719)866-4508

U.S.A. Wrestling **[23135]**, 6155 Lehman Dr., Colorado Springs, CO 80918, (719)598-8181

Usability Professionals' Assn. **[1910]**, 140 N Bloomingdale Rd., Bloomingdale, IL 60108-1017, (630)980-4997

Usability Professionals' Assn. **[1910]**, 140 N Bloomingdale Rd., Bloomingdale, IL 60108-1017, (630)980-4997

USAction **[18633]**, 1825 K St. NW, Ste. 210, Washington, DC 20006, (202)263-4520

USAF Medical Ser. Corps Assn. **[15516]**, 860 Oak Hills Dr., Monument, CO 80132-8829, (866)818-2110

USASPCA - U.S. Animal Soc. for the Prevention of Cruelty to Animals **[★11067]**

USB Implementers Forum **[6564]**, 3855 SW 153rd Dr., Beaverton, OR 97006, (503)619-0426

USBE **[★10016]**

USBloodDonors.org **[13853]**, 9220 Sunset Blvd., Ste. 310, Los Angeles, CA 90069

USC Canada **[IO]**, Ottawa, ON, Canada

USCCCN Natl. CH on Satanic Crime in Am. **[11695]**, USCCCN Intl., PO Box 663, South Plainfield, NJ 07080-0663, (908)226-8715

Used Building Materials Assn. **[★541]**

Used Textbook Assn. **[8998]**, 7375 Day Creek Blvd., Ste. 103-211, Rancho Cucamonga, CA 91739, (888)724-3338

Used Truck Assn. **[372]**, 325 Country Club Dr., Ste. A, Stockbridge, GA 30281, (877)438-7882

Used Truck Sales Network **[★372]**

USENIX Assn. **[6522]**, 2560 9th St., Ste. 215, Berkeley, CA 94710, (510)528-8649

USF Constellation Found. **[★10059]**

USFN-America's Mortgage Banking Attorneys **[5289]**, 625 The City Dr., Ste. 310, Orange, CA 92868-4949, (714)838-7167

USGA Green Sect. **[22628]**, PO Box 708, Far Hills, NJ 07931-0708, (908)234-2300

Usher Syndrome Self-Help Network - Defunct.

Ushers
  Natl. United Church Ushers Assn. of Am. **[20277]**

USMC Vietnam Tankers Assn. **[20824]**, 5537 Lower Mountain Rd., New Hope, PA 18938

USO-All Ser. Postal Chess Club **[★21273]**

USO World HQ **[18931]**, PO Box 96322, Washington, DC 20090, (703)908-6400

USO World HQ **[18931]**, PO Box 96322, Washington, DC 20090, (703)908-6400

Usratuna Sudanese Assn. for Disabled Children **[IO]**, Omdurman, Sudan

USRowing **[★22859]**

USS BB-42 Idaho Assn. **[20730]**, 113 Hillcrest Dr., Greenville, AL 36037, (334)371-1849

USS Constellation Museum **[★10059]**

USS Intrepid Assn. of Former Crew Members **[20731]**, PO Box 140471, Staten Island, NY 10314, (800)343-CVII

U.S.S. LCI Natl. Assn. **[20807]**, 101 Rice Bent Way, No. 6, Columbia, SC 29229, (803)865-5665

USS Leyte CV32 Assn. **[20732]**, PO Box 275, Mountain Ranch, CA 95246, (209)754-1022

USS Liberty Veterans Assn. **[20733]**, PO Box 789, Woodinville, WA 98072

USS LSM-LSMR Assn. **[20734]**, 21850 Vista Dr., Saegertown, PA 16433, (814)763-3090

USS Nimitz CVN-68 Assn. **[20735]**, John Wilder, Treas., 54 Jackson Rd., Medford, MA 02155

USS Nitro AE-2/AE-23 Assn. **[5220]**, Robert F. Eberlein, VP/Founder, 12215 Ashland St., Granger, IN 46530-9654, (574)277-3128

USS North Carolina Battleship Assn. **[20870]**, PO Box 480, Wilmington, NC 28402, (910)251-5797

USS Oklahoma Assn. - Defunct.

USS Pyro AE-1 and AE-24 Assn. **[20736]**, 3808 Brighton Ct., Alexandria, VA 22305-1571, (703)837-1977

A star before a book entry number signifies that the name is not listed separately, but is mentioned within the entry.

USS St. Louis CL-49 Assn. [10067], 1112 N 18th St., Cambridge, OH 43725, (740)432-5305

USS Wainwright Veterans Assn. [20808], 168 Locust Dr., Rocky Point, NY 11778

USS Wisconsin Assn. [20737], PO Box 227, Marion, MS 39342

USSA Found. [8933], U.S. Student Assn., 1211 Connecticut Ave. NW, Ste. 406, Washington, DC 20036, (202)640-6570

USTA/National Junior Tennis League [★23067]

Ustav Mezinarodnich Vztahu Praha [★IO]

Utdanningsforbundet [★IO]

Utenti Pubblicita Associati [IO], Milan, Italy

Utilimetrics - The Utility Tech. Assn. [3605], 1400 E Touhy Ave., Ste. 258, Des Plaines, IL 60018-3345, (847)480-9628

Utilities
1-800 Amer. Free Trade Assn. [3588]
AFL-CIO | Utility Workers Union of Am. [23315]
Amer. Backflow Prevention Assn. [7587]
Amer. Backflow Prevention Assn. [7587]
Amer. Public Gas Assn. [3589]
Amer. Public Power Assn. [6050]
Assn. of Boards of Certification [6051]
Assn. of Edison Illuminating Companies [3590]
Clean Water Constr. Coalition [4989]
Communications Supply Ser. Assn. [3591]
COMPTEL [3592]
Edison Elec. Inst. [3593]
Edison Elec. Inst. [3593]
Elec. Utility Indus. Sustainable Supply Chain Alliance [3594]
Electricity Storage Assn. [3595]
Electricity Storage Assn. [3595]
Energy Storage Coun. [6722]
Equip. Managers Coun. of Am. [845]
European Fed. of Local Public Energy Distribution Companies [14430]
European Small Hydropower Assn. [18897]
Fifty Lanterns Intl. [7439]
GridWise Alliance [6727]
GridWise Architecture Coun. [7293]
Inst. of Public Utilities [3596]
Intl. Utilities Revenue Protection Assn. [6052]
Intl. Utilities Revenue Protection Assn. [6052]
Large Public Power Coun. [5406]
LEAGUE [12096]
NASSCO [3597]
Natl. Assn. of Regulatory Utility Commissioners [6053]
Natl. Assn. of State Utility Consumer Advocates [6054]
Natl. Exchange Carrier Assn. [3598]
Natl. Governmental Collectors Assn. [5500]
Natl. Renewables Cooperative Org. [6741]
Natl. Telecommunications Cooperative Assn. [3599]
Natl. Utilities Diversity Coun. [3600]
Natl. Utility Training and Safety Educ. Assn. [3601]
North Amer. Soc. for Trenchless Tech. [7588]
Ocean Renewable Energy Coalition [6747]
Org. for the Promotion and Advancement of Small Telecommunications Companies [3602]
Pro Energy Alliance [1175]
Regulatory Assistance Proj. [6055]
Ride to Work [21936]
Tennessee Regulatory Authority [6056]
Tropical Forestry Initiative [4154]
UCA Intl. Users Gp. [7589]
Underground Utility and Leak Locators Assn. [3603]
United Kingdom Soc. for Trenchless Tech. [12932]
U.S. Clean Heat and Power Assn. [7590]
U.S. Telecom Assn. [3604]
Utilimetrics - The Utility Tech. Assn. [3605]
Utilities Ser. Alliance [3606]
Utility Indus. Gp. [3607]
Utility Mgt. and Conservation Assn. [3608]
Utility Supply Mgt. Alliance [3609]
Utility Tech. Assn. [7591]
Water and Sewer Distributors of Am. [3610]

Utilities Ser. Alliance [3606], 9200 Indian Creek Pkwy., Ste. 201, Overland Park, KS 66210, (913)451-5641

Utilities Telecom Coun. [3425], 1129 20th St. NW, Ste. 350, Washington, DC 20036, (202)872-0030

Utilities Telecommunications Coun. [★3425]

Utility Communicators Intl. [818], 735 Delaware Rd., No. 380, Buffalo, NY 14223-1231, (716)957-4505

Utility Communicators Intl. [818], 735 Delaware Rd., No. 380, Buffalo, NY 14223-1231, (716)957-4505

Utility Indus. Gp. [3607], Robert Dempsey, Chm., Southern California Edison Co., Bldg. 3-2 MD3, 4910 Rivergrade Rd., Irwindale, CA 91706, (626)543-6291

Utility Mgt. and Conservation Assn. [3608], PO Box 318, Eden Prairie, MN 55343

Utility Supply Mgt. Alliance [3609], PO Box 2932, Olathe, KS 66063, (817)215-5516

Utility Tech. Assn. [7591], PO Box 695, Clermont, GA 30527, (770)519-1676

Utrikespolitiska Institutet [★IO]

Uttaranchal Assn. of North Am. [9862], 10560 Main St., Ste. LL-1, Fairfax, VA 22030, (703)273-7982

UWC: Strategic Services on Unemployment and Workers' Compensation [13343], 910 17th St. NW, Ste. 315, Washington, DC 20006, (202)223-8902

Uyghur Amer. Assn. [17867], 1420 K St. NW, Ste. 350, Washington, DC 20005, (202)478-1920

Uyghur Amer. Assn. [17867], 1420 K St. NW, Ste. 350, Washington, DC 20005, (202)478-1920

Uzbek Intl. Forwarders Assn. [IO], Tashkent, Uzbekistan

Uzbekistan Assn. of Enterprises, Radio-Electronic, Electrotechnical and Instrument Enterprises [IO], Tashkent, Uzbekistan

Uzbekistan Badminton Fed. [IO], Tashkent, Uzbekistan

Uzbekistan Lessors Assn. [IO], Tashkent, Uzbekistan

Uzbekistan Lib. Assn. [IO], Tashkent, Uzbekistan

Uzbekistan-Malaysia Friendship Soc. [IO], Tashkent, Uzbekistan

Uzbekistan Soc. for the Protection of Birds [IO], Tashkent, Uzbekistan

Uzbekistan Taekwondo Assn. [IO], Tashkent, Uzbekistan

Uzbekistan Teachers of English Assn. [IO], Tashkent, Uzbekistan

Uzbekistan Tennis Fed. [IO], Tashkent, Uzbekistan

V

Vacation Exchange Club [★21853]

Vacation Rental Housekeeping Professionals [1045], 5380 Gulf of Mexico Dr., Ste. 105, Longboat Key, FL 34228, (850)303-1358

Vacation Rental Managers Assn. [3045], 9100 Purdue Rd., Ste. 200, Indianapolis, IN 46268, (317)454-8315

Vacation Samaritans [★20090]

Vacation Samaritans [★20090]

Vacations for Veterans [13356], 9435 Lorton Market St., No. 105, Lorton, VA 22079, (800)831-8803

Vaccine Awareness League; Global [14709]

Vaccine and Infectious Disease Org. [IO], Saskatoon, SK, Canada

Vaccine Inst; ThinkTwice Global [15113]

Vachel Lindsay Assn. [9420], PO Box 9356, Springfield, IL 62791-9356

Vacuum Cleaner Mfrs. Assn. [★218]

Vacuum Cleaner Mfrs. Assn. - Defunct.

Vacuum Dealers Trade Assn. [221], 2724 2nd Ave., Des Moines, IA 50313-4933, (515)282-9101

Vacuum Metallizers Assn. [★788]

Vacuum Soc. of Australia [IO], Callaghan, Australia

Vacuum Technology
AVS Sci. and Tech. Soc. [7592]
Israel Vacuum Soc. [2315]

Vaestoliitto [★IO]

Vagabundos Del Mar RV, Boat and Travel Club [22151], 190 Main St., Rio Vista, CA 94571, (707)374-5511

Vagabundos Del Mar RV, Boat and Travel Club [22151], 190 Main St., Rio Vista, CA 94571, (707)374-5511

Vahey Family Assn. - Defunct.

Vakgroep Voor KinderVerpleegkunde [★IO]

Vakuutusvaeen Liitto VvL ry [★IO]

Valley Fig Growers [4482], 2028 S 3rd St., Fresno, CA 93702, (559)237-3893

Valley Intl. Foosball Assn. [21758], PO Box 656, Bay City, MI 48707, (800)544-1346

Valley Intl. Foosball Assn. [21758], PO Box 656, Bay City, MI 48707, (800)544-1346

Valley of the Kings Found. [IO], Kent, United Kingdom

Valorisation de Innovation dans l'Ameublement [★IO]

Value Found. [★6963]

Values and Visions [★7929]

Valve Mfrs. Assn. [★1663]

Valve Mfrs. Assn. of Am. [1663], 1050 17th St. NW, Ste. 280, Washington, DC 20036, (202)331-8105

Valve Remanufacturers Coun. [★1664]

Valve Repair Coun. [1664], 1050 17th St. NW, Ste. 280, Washington, DC 20036, (202)331-8105

Valves and Fittings Sweden [IO], Stockholm, Sweden

The Vampire Empire - Address unknown since 2010.

Vampire Res. Center - Defunct.

Vampire's Vault - Defunct.

Van Alen Inst.: Projects in Public Architecture [7737], 30 W 22nd St., 6th Fl., New York, NY 10010-5801, (212)924-7000

Van Andel Educ. Inst. [8066], 333 Bostwick Ave. NE, Grand Rapids, MI 49503, (616)234-5528

Van Voorhees Assn. [20603], Mr. Albert T. Van Voorhies, 9 Purdy Ave., East Northport, NY 11731-4501

Vanadium Producers and Reclaimers Assn. [2497], 900 2nd St. NE, Ste. 201, Washington, DC 20002, (202)842-0219

Vancouver ACM SIGGRAPH [IO], Vancouver, BC, Canada

Vancouver Chinese Choir Assn. [IO], Vancouver, BC, Canada

Vancouver Univ. Worldwide [★7973]

The Vanguard Found. [★814]

Vanished Children's Alliance - Defunct.

Vanuatu Amateur Volleyball [IO], Port Vila, Vanuatu

Vanuatu Archery Assn. [IO], Port Vila, Vanuatu

Vanuatu Assn. of Sports and Natl. Olympic Comm. [IO], Port Vila, Vanuatu

Vanuatu Athletics Assn. [IO], Port Vila, Vanuatu

Vanuatu Chefs and Food Handlers Assn. [IO], Port Vila, Vanuatu

Vanuatu Family Hea. Assn. [IO], Port Vila, Vanuatu

Vanuatu IT Users Soc. [IO], Port Vila, Vanuatu

Vanuatu Judo Fed. [IO], Port Vila, Vanuatu

Vanuatu Laebri Asosiesen [★IO]

Vanuatu Lib. Assn. [IO], Port Vila, Vanuatu

Vanuatu Netball Assn. [IO], Port Vila, Vanuatu

Vanuatu Red Cross Soc. [IO], Port Vila, Vanuatu

Vanuatu Renewable Energy and Power Assn. [IO], Port Vila, Vanuatu

Vanuatu Sport Fed. Blind Disabled [IO], Port Vila, Vanuatu

Vanuatu Squash Rackets Assn. [IO], Port Vila, Vanuatu

Vanuatu Tennis Fed. [IO], Port Vila, Vanuatu

Vanuatu Tourism Off. [IO], Port Vila, Vanuatu

Vanuatu Triathlon Assn. [IO], Port Vila, Vanuatu

Vanuatu Weightlifting Fed. [IO], Port Vila, Vanuatu

Variable Electronic Components Inst. [1118], PO Box 1070, Vista, CA 92085-1070, (760)631-0178

Variable Resistive Components Inst. [★1118]

Variable Resistive Components Inst. - Defunct.

Variety Clubs Intl. [★11424]

Variety Clubs Intl. [★11424]

Variety Intl. - The Children's Charity [11424], 4601 Wilshire Blvd., Ste. 260, Los Angeles, CA 90010, (323)934-4688

Variety Intl. - The Children's Charity [11424], 4601 Wilshire Blvd., Ste. 260, Los Angeles, CA 90010, (323)934-4688

Vasa Order of Am. [19062], 5971 W Walbrook Dr., San Jose, CA 95129

Vasa Order of Am. [19062], 5971 W Walbrook Dr., San Jose, CA 95129

Vascular Nursing; Soc. for [15803]

Vascular Surgery; Soc. for Clinical [14044]

Vascular System
Amer. Coll. of Phlebology [16956]
Amer. Venous Forum [16957]
Assn. for Vascular Access [16958]

Reference to "IO" in place of a book number signifies that the association may be found in the 50th edition of International Organizations.

Assn. of Vascular and Interventional Radiographers [16959]
Canadian Soc. of Atherosclerosis, Thrombosis and Vascular Biology [15265]
Intl. Coll. of Angiology [16960]
Intl. Coll. of Angiology [16960]
Intl. Soc. of Endovascular Specialists [16961]
Intl. Soc. of Endovascular Specialists [16961]
Intersocietal Commn. for the Accreditation of Vascular Labs. [16962]
Microcirculatory Soc. [16963]
Natl. Org. of Vascular Anomalies [16964]
North Amer. Vascular Biology Org. [16965]
Soc. of Atherosclerosis Imaging and Prevention [16966]
Soc. for Vascular Medicine [16967]
Soc. for Vascular Surgery [16968]
Soc. for Vascular Ultrasound [16969]
Venous Disease Coalition [16970]
Vasculitis Found. [16784], PO Box 28660, Kansas City, MO 64188-8660, (816)436-8211
Vasculitis Found. [16784], PO Box 28660, Kansas City, MO 64188-8660, (816)436-8211
Vaseline Glass Collectors, Inc. [21412], 14560 Schleisman Rd., Corona, CA 92880
Vatican Lib; Amer. Friends of the [9953]
Vaulting
Amer. Vaulting Assn. [23108]VaultingIntl. Vaulting Club
Vawter - Vauter - Vaughter Family Assn. [20604], 14586 W Merrell St., Goodyear, AZ 85338, (309)928-2956
Vedanta
Ramakrishna - Vivekananda Center [20278]
Vedic Friends Assn. [10542], PO Box 15082, Detroit, MI 48215
Vegaaniliitto [★IO]
Vegan Action [10626], PO Box 4288, Richmond, VA 23220, (804)502-8736
Vegan Awareness Found. [★10626]
Vegan Soc; Amer. [10623]
Vegan Soc. of Australia [IO], Seaford, Australia
Vegan Soc. of England [IO], Birmingham, United Kingdom
Vegan Soc. of Finland [IO], Helsinki, Finland
Vegetarian Gourmet Society [★16014]
Vegetarian Info. Ser. [★10961]
Vegetarian Rsrc. Gp. [10627], PO Box 1463, Baltimore, MD 21203, (410)366-8343
Vegetarian Soc. of Ireland [IO], Dublin, Ireland
Vegetarian Soc. of Singapore [IO], Singapore, Singapore
Vegetarian Soc. of the United Kingdom [IO], Altrincham, United Kingdom
Vegetarian Youth Network - Defunct.
Vegetarianism
Amer. Vegan Soc. [10623]
Australian Vegetarian Soc. [5309]
Christian Vegetarian Assn. [20279]
Christian Vegetarian Assn. [20279]
Compassionate Cooks [13346]
Feminists for Animal Rights [10964]
Jewish Vegetarians of North Am. [10624]
North Amer. Vegetarian Soc. [10625]
Vegan Action [10626]
Vegetarian Rsrc. Gp. [10627]
Vegetarians Intl. Voice for Animals [★11056]
Vegetarians Intl. Voice for Animals [★11056]
Veggie Van Org. [4872], 8033 W Sunset Blvd., Ste. 154, West Hollywood, CA 90046
Vehicle Builders and Repairers Assn. [IO], Leeds, United Kingdom
Veitch Historical Soc. [20605], Patricia A. McConnell, VP for Membership, 134 Rhonda Dr., Universal City, TX 78148-3420, (210)659-6813
Velasquez Inst; William C. [19106]
Velo-Cardio-Facial Syndrome [14635], PO Box 12591, Dallas, TX 75225, (732)238-5494
Velo-Cardio-Facial Syndrome [14635], PO Box 12591, Dallas, TX 75225, (732)238-5494
Velocette Owners Club of North Am. [21941], 13029 SW Bachelor Rd., Vashon, WA 98070
Venceremos Brigade [17988], PO Box 5202, Englewood, NJ 07631-5202, (212)560-4360
Vending
Intl. Assn. of Ice Cream Distributors and Vendors [3611]

Intl. Assn. of Ice Cream Vendors [3611]
Natl. Automatic Merchandising Assn. [3612]
Natl. Bulk Vendors Assn. [3613]
Randolph-Sheppard Vendors of Am. [3614]
Venezuela
Venezuelan Amer. Assn. of the U.S. [23456]
Venezuelan Amer. Assn. of the U.S. [23456], 30 Vesey St., Ste. 506, New York, NY 10007, (212)233-7776
Venezuelan-American Chamber of Commerce [23388], 1600 Ponce de Leon, Ste. 1004, Coral Gables, FL 33134, (786)350-1190
Venezuelan-American Chamber of Commerce [★23388]
Venezuelan-American Chamber of Commerce and Indus. [IO], Caracas, Venezuela
Venezuelan Assn. of the Chem. and Petrochemical Indus. [IO], Caracas, Venezuela
Venezuelan Assn. of Mining and Metallurgical Indus. [IO], Caracas, Venezuela
Venezuelan Assn. of Paper, Pulp and Carton Producers [IO], Caracas, Venezuela
Venezuelan Assn. of the Plastics Indus. [IO], Caracas, Venezuela
Venezuelan Chamber of the Automotive Indus. [IO], Caracas, Venezuela
Venezuelan Chamber of Commerce of the U.S. [★23456]
Venezuelan Chamber of Info. Tech. Businesses [IO], Caracas, Venezuela
Venezuelan Chamber of Insurance Companies [IO], Caracas, Venezuela
Venezuelan Confed. of Indus. [IO], Caracas, Venezuela
Venezuelan Exporters' Assn. [IO], Caracas, Venezuela
Venezuelan Physiological Soc. [IO], Caracas, Venezuela
Venezuelan Soc. of Menopause and Osteoporosis [IO], Caracas, Venezuela
Venezuelan Tourism Assn. [3586], PO Box 3010, Sausalito, CA 94966-3010, (415)331-0100
Venezuelan Tourism Assn. [3586], PO Box 3010, Sausalito, CA 94966-3010, (415)331-0100
Venezuelan Trust Fund [★17579]
Venezuelan Trust Fund [★17579]
Venezuelean League Against Epilepsy [IO], Caracas, Venezuela
Venous Disease Coalition [16970], 1075 S Yukon St., Ste. 320, Lakewood, CO 80226, (303)989-0500
Venstre [★IO]
Venture Capital Alliance; Community Development [11568]
Venture Scotland [IO], Edinburgh, United Kingdom
Venture Strategies for Hea. and Development [14832], 2140 Shattuck Ave., Ste. 1110, Berkeley, CA 94704-1234, (510)665-1880
Venture Strategies for Hea. and Development [14832], 2140 Shattuck Ave., Ste. 1110, Berkeley, CA 94704-1234, (510)665-1880
Venture Strategies Innovations [14833], 2401 E Katella Ave., Ste. 400, Anaheim, CA 92806, (714)221-2040
Venture Touring Soc. [★22781]
Venue Mgt. Assn. - Asia Pacific [IO], Toowong, Australia
Venus Proj. [18634], 21 Valley Ln., Venus, FL 33960, (863)465-0321
Vera Found. [★11736]
Vera Found. [★23174]
Vera Inst. of Justice [11736], 233 Broadway, 12th Fl., New York, NY 10279-1299, (212)334-1300
Verband der Akademikerinnen Osterreichs [★IO]
Verband deutscher Archivarinnen und Archivare [★IO]
Verband der Automobilindustrie [★IO]
Verband Beratender Ingenieure [★IO]
Verband Bildung und Erziehung [★IO]
Verband der Brauereien Oesterreichs [★IO]
Verband der Chemischen Industrie [★IO]
Verband der Deutschen Dental-Industrie [★IO]
Verband der Deutschen Heimtextilien-Industrie [★IO]
Verband der Deutschen Lederindustrie [★IO]
Verband der Deutschen Margarineindustrie [★IO]

Verband der Deutschen Milchwirtschaft [★IO]
Verband Deutscher Antiquare [IO], Elbingen, Germany
Verband Deutscher Grossbackereien [★IO]
Verband Deutscher Konzert Choere [★IO]
Verband Deutscher Maschinen- und Anlagenbau [IO], Frankfurt, Germany
Verband Deutscher Metallhaendler e.v. [★IO]
Verband Deutscher Oelmuhlen e.v. [IO], Berlin, Germany
Verband Deutscher Papierfabriken [★IO]
Verband Deutscher Pfandbriefbanken [★IO]
Verband Deutscher Reeder [★IO]
Verband Deutscher Schiffsausruester e.V. [★IO]
Verband Deutscher Schulmusiker [★IO]
Verband Deutscher Verkehrsunternehmen [★IO]
Verband Deutscher Vermessungsingenieure e.V. [★IO]
Verband Deutscher Wirtschaftsingenieure [★IO]
Verband Deutscher Zeitschriftenverleger [IO], Berlin, Germany
Verband der Diatassistenten - Deutscher Bundesverband [★IO]
Verband der Elektrotechnik Elektronik und Informationstechnik [★IO]
Verband der Europaischen Angelgeratehersteller [★IO]
Verband der Europaischen Bettfedern- und Bettwarenindustrie [★IO]
Verband der Europaischen Elektrowerkzeug-Hersteller [★IO]
Verband der Fleischwirtschaft e.V. [★IO]
Verband der Fluglinien Europaischer Regionen [★IO]
Verband der deutschen Fruchtsaft-Industrie e.V. [★IO]
Verband Hannoverscher Warmblutzuechter [IO], Verden, Germany
Verband der Internationalen Kraftfahrzeughersteller [★IO]
Verband der Internationalen Lyceum-Clubs in Deutschland [IO], Hamburg, Germany
Verband der Koche Deutschlands [★IO]
Verband der Landesarchaologen in der Bundesrepublik Deutschland [★IO]
Verband der Museen der Schweiz [★IO]
Verband Oesterreichischer Verkehrspiloten [★IO]
Verband der Osterreichischen Musikwirtschaft [IO], Vienna, Austria
Verband Osterreichischer Banken und Bankiers [★IO]
Verband Osterreichischer Ingenieure [IO], Vienna, Austria
Verband Osterreichischer Zeitungen [★IO]
Verband der Polyurethan-Weichschaum Industrie [IO], Frankfurt, Germany
Verband der deutschen Rauchtabakindustrie [★IO]
Verband der Reformwaren-Hersteller [★IO]
Verband fur Schiffbau und Meerestechnik [★IO]
Verband Schweizer Galerien [★IO]
Verband der Schweizer Unternehmen [★IO]
Verband der Schweizerischen Uhrenindustrie [★IO]
Verband der Schweizerischen Zellstoff-, Papier- und Kartonindustrie [★IO]
Verband Schweizerischer Mineralquellen und Soft Drink-Produzenten [★IO]
Verband Schweizerischer Radio- und Televisions-fachgeschaefte [★IO]
Verband Schweizerischer Technischer Handler [★IO]
Verband Selbstandiger Ingenieure und Architekten [IO], Ettlingen, Germany
Verbindung der Schweizer Arztinnen und Arzte [★IO]
Verbond der Vlaamse Tandartsen [IO], Brussels, Belgium
Vereeniging van Handelaren in Oude Kunst in Nederland [★IO]
Verein Demokratischer Pharmazeutinnen und Pharmazeuten [★IO]
Verein Deutscher Bibliothekare [★IO]
Verein Deutscher Ingenieure [★IO]
Verein Deutscher Textilveredlungsfachleute e.V [IO], Leimen, Germany
Verein Deutscher Werkzeugmaschinenfabriken [★IO]

A star before a book entry number signifies that the name is not listed separately, but is mentioned within the entry.

Verein Deutscher Zementwerke [★IO]

Verein zur Forderung des Offentlichen Bewegten und Unbewegten Datenverkehrs [IO], Bielefeld, Germany

Verein Fur Socialpolitik [IO], Frankfurt, Germany

Verein vom Heiligen Karl Borromaeus zur Verbreitung Guter Literatur [★IO]

Verein ICC - Schweiz [IO], Nyon, Switzerland

Verein fur Internationale Jugendarbeit - Arbeitsgemeinschaft Christlicher Frauen Bundesverein [★IO]

Verein der Kohlenimporteure e.V. [★IO]

Verein Ungarischer Chemiker [★IO]

Verein unabhangiger Vermogensverwalter in Liechtenstein [★IO]

Verein der Zellstoff-und Papier-Chemiker und-Ingenieure [★IO]

Vereinigung fur Angewandte Botanik e.V. [★IO]

Vereinigung zur Erforschung der Neueren Geschichte [★IO]

Vereinigung der Ernahrungsindustriens der EWG [★IO]

Vereinigung der Freunde Antiker Kunst [★IO]

Vereinigung der Osterreichischen Zementindustrie [★IO]

Vereinigung Osterreichischer Bibliothekarinnen und Bibliothekare [★IO]

Vereinigung der Schmelzkaseindustrie in der EU [★IO]

Vereinigung des Schweizerischen Import- und Grosshandels [★IO]

Vereniging voor de Bakkerij en Zoetwarenindustrie [★IO]

Vereniging voor de Bakkerij- en Zoetwarenindustrie [★IO]

Vereniging van Communicatie-adviesbureaus [★IO]

Vereniging voor Experimenteel Radio Onderzoek In Nederland [★IO]

Vereniging van Geneeskundige Laboratorium Tegnoloe van Suid-Afrika [★IO]

Vereniging van Huntington [★IO]

Vereniging van Huntington [IO], The Hague, Netherlands

Vereniging voor Infectieziekten [★IO]

Vereniging voor Japanse Kunst [★IO]

Vereniging Leveranciers Huishoudelijke Apparaten Nederland [★IO]

Vereniging voor Mededingingsrecht [IO], Amsterdam, Netherlands

Vereniging Milieudefensie [★IO]

Vereniging Mitex [★IO]

Vereniging van Nederlandse Agenten, Commissionairs, Makelaars en Taxateurs in Wijn en Gedistilleerd [★IO]

Vereniging van de Nederlandse Chemische Industrie [★IO]

Vereniging van Nederlandse Fabrikanten van Eetbare Olien en Vetten [IO], The Hague, Netherlands

Vereniging Nederlandse Lijmindustrie [★IO]

Vereniging van de Nederlandse Pluimveeverwerkende Industrie [★IO]

Vereniging Nederlandse Scheepsbouw Industrie [★IO]

Vereniging van Openbare Bibliotheken [★IO]

Vereniging van Radiograwe van Suid-Afrika [★IO]

Vereniging Spierziekten Nederland [★IO]

Vereniging Spierziekten Nederland [IO], Baarn, Netherlands

Vereniging voor Statistiek en Operationele Res. [★IO]

Vereniging van Verfgroothandelaren in Nederland [★IO]

Vereniging van Vrouwen met Hogere Opleiding [IO], Gorinchem, Netherlands

Vereniging voor Zorgadministratie en Informatie [★IO]

Vergilian Soc. [9421], Wayland Acad., 101 N Univ. Ave., Beaver Dam, WI 53916, (920)356-2120

Veriniging van Bloemenveilingen [★IO]

Veris Res. Info. Ser. - Defunct.

Verite [11924], 44 Belchertown Rd., Amherst, MA 01002, (413)253-9227

Verite [11924], 44 Belchertown Rd., Amherst, MA 01002, (413)253-9227

Verkefnastjornunarfelag Islands [★IO]

Vermazen/Vermason Family Org. - Defunct.

The Vermiculite Assn. [IO], Lincoln, United Kingdom

Vernacular Architecture Forum [6208], PO Box 1511, Harrisonburg, VA 22803-1511

Versatility in Poodles [4190], Susan Dearholt, Treas., 1929 Van Buren Ave. SE, Bemidji, MN 56601, (218)755-9727

Vertebrate Paleontology; Soc. of [7215]

Vertebrate Paleontology; Soc. of [7215]

Very Special Arts [★11835]

Very Special Arts [★11835]

Very Special Arts Bahamas [IO], Nassau, Bahamas

Very Special Arts do Brasil [★IO]

Vesalius Trust [8222], Lisa Warren, Exec. Dir., 20751 W Chartwell Dr., Kildeer, IL 60047, (847)540-8671

Vespa Club of Am. [21942], PO Box 54825, Oklahoma City, OK 73154-1825, (719)473-4692

Vesterheim Genealogical Center [★20651]

Vesterheim Genealogical Center and Naeseth Lib. [★20651]

Vestibular Disorders Assn. [16091], PO Box 13305, Portland, OR 97213, (503)229-7705

Vestibular Disorders Assn. [16091], PO Box 13305, Portland, OR 97213, (503)229-7705

Veteran-Cycle Club [IO], Dursley, United Kingdom

Veteran Feminists of Am. [17673], PO Box 44551, Phoenix, AZ 85064

Veteran Motor Car Club of Am. [21186], Mike Welsh, Sec., 7501 Manchester Ave., Kansas City, MO 64138, (816)298-6412

Veteran Wireless Operators Assn. [3426], PO Box 1003, Peck Slip, New York, NY 10272-1003

Veterans

11th Armored Cavalry's Veterans of Vietnam and Cambodia [20828]

78th Div. Veterans Assn. [20762]

82nd Airborne Div. Assn. [20763]

90th Div. Assn. [20764]

129th Alumni and Heritage Assn. [19270]

369th Veterans' Assn. [20765]

494th Bombardment Gp. (H) Assn. 7th Air Force [20324]

Acupuncture for Veterans [13576]

African Amer. Post Traumatic Stress Disorder Assn. [20766]

Air Commando Assn. [20767]

Air Compassion for Veterans [20768]

Air Weather Assn. [20769]

Air Weather Reconnaissance Assn. [20770]

Amer. Combat Veterans of War [20771]

Amer. GI Forum of U.S. [20772]

Amer. Gulf War Veterans Assn. [20773]

Amer. Military Retirees Assn. [20774]

Amer. Patriots Assn. [20742]

Amer. Veterans Alliance [20775]

Amer. Veterans for Equal Rights [12067]

AMVETS [20776]

Army, Navy, and Air Force Veterans in Canada [1350]

Army and Navy Union U.S.A. [20777]

Assn. for Counselors and Educators in Govt. [11669]

Beirut Veterans of Am. [20778]

Black Veterans for Social Justice [20779]

Bullwhip Squadron Assn. [20780]

Burton Island Assn. [20717]

Canadian Peacekeeping Veterans Assn. [14284]

Catholic War Veterans Auxiliary of the U.S.A. [20704]

Catholic War Veterans of the U.S.A. [20781]

Centennial Legion of Historic Military Commands [20743]

Center for Veterans Issues [20782]

Center for Women Veterans [20783]

Chosin Few [20674]

Circle of Friends for Amer. Veterans [20784]

Coalition to Salute America's Heroes [20785]

Coast Guard Combat Veterans Assn. [20786]

Cold War Veterans Assn. [20787]

Combat Helicopter Pilots Assn. [20313]

Desert Storm Veterans Assn. [20788]

Disabled Amer. Veterans [20412]

Disabled Amer. Veterans Auxiliary [20413]

Distinguished Flying Cross Soc. [20374]

Farmer-Veteran Coalition [20610]

Forgotten Heroes [13347]

Grosse Pointe War Memorial Assn. [20789]

Guitars For Vets [11840]

Help Hospitalized Veterans [13348]

Hof Reunion Assn. [20349]

Homefront Hugs U.S.A. [13349]

Homes for Our Troops [20790]

Homosexual Info. Center [12088]

House of Heroes [13350]

Intl. Submariners Association-USA [20678]

Iraq and Afghanistan Veterans of Am. [20791]

Japanese Amer. Veterans Assn. [20792]

Jewish War Veterans of the U.S.A. [20793]

Korean War Proj. [6057]

Military Order of the Loyal Legion of the U.S. [20386]

Military Order of the Purple Heart of the U.S.A. [20378]

Military Order of the Stars and Bars [20387]

Montford Point Marine Assn. [5810]

Mothers of Military Support [12529]

Natl. Assn. of Atomic Veterans [13351]

Natl. Assn. for Black Veterans [20794]

Natl. Assn. of County Veterans Ser. Officers [20795]

Natl. Assn. of State Approving Agencies [6058]

Natl. Assn. of State Directors of Veterans Affairs [6059]

Natl. Assn. of State Veterans Homes [13352]

Natl. Assn. of Veterans Affairs Chaplains [19527]

Natl. Assn. of Veterans Prog. Administrators [20796]

Natl. Assn. of Veterans' Res. and Educ. Foundations [6060]

Natl. Coalition for Homeless Veterans [20797]

Natl. Gulf War Rsrc. Center [20798]

Natl. Gulf War Rsrc. Center [20798]

Natl. Museum of Amer. Jewish Military History [20799]

Natl. Native Amer. Veterans Assn. [20800]

Natl. Order of Trench Rats [20414]

Natl. Org. of Veterans' Advocates [6061]

Natl. Soc. of Women Descendants of the Ancient and Honorable Artillery Company [20403]

Natl. Veteran-Owned Bus. Assn. [3615]

Natl. Veterans Legal Services Prog. [20801]

Natl. Veterans Services Fund [13353]

Not Forgotten Assn. [11006]

Pedro Rescue Helicopter Assn. [20316]

Private Agencies Collaborating Together [6062]

Private Agencies Collaborating Together [6062]

Red River Valley Fighter Pilots Assn. [20802]

The Retired Enlisted Assn. [20803]

Salute Military Golf Assn. [22624]

SATS/EAF Assn. [20686]

Soc. of the Ark and the Dove [20407]

Stars for Stripes [20417]

Step Up 4 Vets [13354]

Student Veterans of Am. [9032]

Tan Son Nhut Assn. [20823]

Tee it up for the Troops [13355]

Transgender Amer. Veterans Assn. [20804]

Ukrainian Amer. Veterans [20805]

U.S. Marine Corps Scout/Sniper Assn. [20688]

U.S. Naval Cryptologic Veterans Assn. [20806]

U.S. Navy Beach Jumpers Assn. [20728]

United We Serve [20712]

USMC Vietnam Tankers Assn. [20824]

U.S.S. LCI Natl. Assn. [20807]

USS LSM-LSMR Assn. [20734]

USS North Carolina Battleship Assn. [20870]

USS Wainwright Veterans Assn. [20808]

Vacations for Veterans [13356]

Veterans Assn. of Am. [20809]

Veteran's Coalition [20810]

Veterans for Common Sense [20811]

Veterans Educ. Proj. [13357]

Veterans and Families [20812]

Veterans of Foreign Wars of the U.S. [20813]

Veterans of Foreign Wars of the U.S. | Ladies Auxiliary [20814]

Veterans and Military Families for Progress [20815]

Veterans of Modern Warfare [20816]

Reference to "IO" in place of a book number signifies that the association may be found in the 50th edition of International Organizations.

Veterans' Widows Intl. Network [20817]
Veterans' Widows Intl. Network [20817]
Veterans2Work [20818]
Vets4Vets [20819]
Vietnam Dustoff Assn. [20836]
Vietnam Era Seabees [20826]
Vietnam Veteran Wives [20820]
VietNow Natl. [13358]
Women's Overseas Ser. League [20821]
Wounded Warrior Proj. [20822]
Veterans of the Abraham Lincoln Brigade - Defunct.
Veterans Affairs; Nurses Org. of [15791]
Veterans Against the War Anti-Imperialist; Vietnam
  [18766]
Veterans Against the War; Vietnam [18765]
Veterans for Am. [17989], 1025 Vermont Ave. NW,
  7th Fl., Washington, DC 20005, (202)483-9222
Veterans of Am; Vietnam [18767]
Veterans Assn. of Am. [20809], PO Box 309, New
  York, NY 10032, (800)590-2173
Veterans Assn; Blinded [17068]
Veteran's Assn. of the USS Iowa [20738], 8314 W
  Promenade Dr., Homosassa, FL 34448, (352)621-
  0675
Veterans Auxiliary of the U.S.A; Catholic War
  [20704]
Veterans of the Battle of the Bulge [20871], PO Box
  27430, Philadelphia, PA 19118, (703)528-4058
Veterans Bedside Network [11972], 10 Fiske Pl.,
  Rm. 328, Mount Vernon, NY 10550, (914)699-6069
Veterans of the Civil War; Auxiliary to Sons of Union
  [20381]
Veteran's Coalition [20810], 2800 S Shirlington Rd.,
  Ste. 325, Arlington, VA 22206
Veterans Coalition; Natl. Vietnam and Gulf War
  [18763]
Veterans for Common Sense [20811], 900 2nd St.
  NE, Ste. 216, Washington, DC 20002-3559,
  (202)558-4553
Veterans; Descendants of Mexican War [20692]
Veterans Educ. Proj. [13357], PO Box 416, Amherst,
  MA 01004-0416, (413)253-4947
Veterans English Table Tennis Soc. [IO], Letchworth,
  United Kingdom
Veterans and Families [20812], 657 Brickyard Dr.,
  Sacramento, CA 95831, (916)320-4395
Veterans of Foreign Wars
  Salute Military Golf Assn. [22624]
  Tan Son Nhut Assn. [20823]
  Vietnam Dustoff Assn. [20836]
Veterans of Foreign Wars of the U.S. [20813], 406
  W 34th St., Kansas City, MO 64111, (816)756-
  3390
Veterans of Foreign Wars of the U.S. I Ladies
  Auxiliary [20814], 406 W 34th St., 10th Fl., Kansas
  City, MO 64111, (816)561-8655
Veterans; Friends of Israel Disabled [20672]
Veterans Hosp. Radio and TV Guild [★11972]
Veterans Intl. [★17989]
Veterans and Military Families for Progress [20815],
  PO Box 66353, Washington, DC 20035-6353,
  (202)841-1687
Veterans of Modern Warfare [20816], PO Box
  96503, No. 33107, Washington, DC 20090,
  (888)445-9891
Veterans for Peace [18299], 216 S Meramec Ave.,
  St. Louis, MO 63105, (314)725-6005
Veterans for Peace [18299], 216 S Meramec Ave.,
  St. Louis, MO 63105, (314)725-6005
Veterans of Safety [13012], Univ. of Central Mis-
  souri, Humphreys 304, Warrensburg, MO 64093,
  (660)543-4971
Veterans of the Vietnam War [20834], 805 S Town-
  ship Blvd., Pittston, PA 18640-3327, (570)603-9740
Veterans' Widows Intl. Network [20817], 3657E S
  Laredo St., Aurora, CO 80013, (303)693-4745
Veterans' Widows Intl. Network [20817], 3657E S
  Laredo St., Aurora, CO 80013, (303)693-4745
Veterans of World War I of U.S.A. [20844], PO Box
  8027, Alexandria, VA 22306-8027, (703)780-5660
Veterans Writing Proj; Hospitalized [16565]
Veterans2Work [20818], 345 E Blithedale Ave., Mill
  Valley, CA 94941, (415)925-1515
Veterinary Assn. for Arbitration and Jurisprudence
  [IO], Carlisle, United Kingdom

Veterinary Assn. of Malaysia [IO], Petaling Jaya,
  Malaysia
Veterinary Botanical Medicine Assn. [17046], 6410
  Hwy. 92, Acworth, GA 30102
Veterinary Cancer Soc. [17047], PO Box 30855,
  Columbia, MO 65205, (573)823-8497
Veterinary Coun. of Ireland [IO], Dublin, Ireland
Veterinary Education
  Intl. Veterinarians Dedicated to Animal Hea.
    [17029]
Veterinary Emergency and Critical Care Soc.
  [17048], 6335 Camp Bullis Rd., Ste. 12, San
  Antonio, TX 78257, (210)698-5575
Veterinary History Soc. [IO], Cirencester, United
  Kingdom
Veterinary Hosp. Managers Assn. [17049], PO Box
  2280, Alachua, FL 32616-2280, (518)433-8911
Veterinary Inst. of Integrative Medicine [17050], PO
  Box 740053, Arvada, CO 80006, (303)277-8227
Veterinary Medicine
  Acad. of Veterinary Homeopathy [16971]
  Amer. Acad. of Veterinary Nutrition [16972]
  Amer. Acad. of Veterinary Pharmacology and
    Therapeutics [16973]
  Amer. Animal Hosp. Assn. [16974]
  Amer. Assn. of Avian Pathologists [16975]
  Amer. Assn. of Bovine Practitioners [16976]
  Amer. Assn. of Equine Practitioners [16977]
  Amer. Assn. of Equine Veterinary Technicians
    [16978]
  Amer. Assn. of Equine Veterinary Technicians
    [16978]
  Amer. Assn. of Feline Practitioners [16979]
  Amer. Assn. of Housecall and Mobile Veterinar-
    ians [16980]
  Amer. Assn. of Public Hea. Veterinarians [16981]
  Amer. Assn. of Small Ruminant Practitioners
    [16982]
  Amer. Assn. of Swine Veterinarians [16983]
  Amer. Assn. of Swine Veterinarians [16983]
  Amer. Assn. of Traditional Chinese Veterinary
    Medicine [13653]
  Amer. Assn. of Veterinary Clinicians [16984]
  Amer. Assn. of Veterinary Immunologists [16985]
  Amer. Assn. of Veterinary Lab. Diagnosticians
    [16986]
  Amer. Assn. of Veterinary Parasitologists [16987]
  Amer. Assn. of Veterinary State Boards [16988]
  Amer. Assn. of Wildlife Veterinarians [16989]
  Amer. Assn. of Zoo Veterinarians [16990]
  Amer. Bd. of Veterinary Practitioners [16991]
  Amer. Bd. of Veterinary Specialties [16992]
  Amer. Bd. of Veterinary Toxicology [16993]
  Amer. Canine Sports Medicine Assn. [16994]
  Amer. Coll. of Lab. Animal Medicine [16995]
  Amer. Coll. of Theriogenologists [16996]
  Amer. Coll. of Veterinary Anesthesiologists
    [16997]
  Amer. Coll. of Veterinary Dermatology [16998]
  Amer. Coll. of Veterinary Emergency and Critical
    Care [16999]
  Amer. Coll. of Veterinary Internal Medicine
    [17000]
  Amer. Coll. of Veterinary Ophthalmologists
    [17001]
  Amer. Coll. of Veterinary Pathologists [17002]
  Amer. Coll. of Veterinary Radiology [17003]
  Amer. Coll. of Veterinary Surgeons [17004]
  Amer. Heartworm Soc. [17005]
  Amer. Holistic Veterinary Medical Assn. [17006]
  Amer. Pre-Veterinary Medical Assn. [17007]
  Amer. Veterinary Chiropractic Assn. [17008]
  Amer. Veterinary Dental Soc. [17009]
  Amer. Veterinary Medical Assn. [17010]
  Amer. Veterinary Soc. of Animal Behavior [17011]
  Animal Hea. Found. [17012]
  Assn. of Amer. Veterinary Medical Colleges [9033]
  Assn. of Avian Veterinarians USA [17013]
  Assn. of Avian Veterinarians USA [17013]
  Assn. of Reptilian and Amphibian Veterinarians
    [17014]
  Assn. of Reptilian and Amphibian Veterinarians
    [17014]
  Assn. of Shelter Veterinarians [17015]
  Assn. of Shelter Veterinarians [17015]

  Assn. for Veterinary Family Practice [17016]
  Assn. of Veterinary Hematology and Transfusion
    Medicine [17017]
  Assn. of Veterinary Technician Educators [9034]
  Assn. for Women Veterinarians Found. [17018]
  Assn. of Zoo Veterinary Technicians [17019]
  Canine Cancer Awareness [17020]
  Cats in Crisis [10939]
  Companion Animal Parasite Coun. [17021]
  Conf. of Res. Workers in Animal Diseases
    [17022]
  Conf. of Res. Workers in Animal Diseases
    [17022]
  Controlled Release Soc. [6404]
  Cornell Feline Hea. Center [17023]
  Darwin Animal Doctors [3809]VeterinaryEuropean
    Assn. of Veterinary Diagnostic Imaging
  European Soc. of Veterinary Neurology [18015]
  European Soc. of Veterinary Orthopaedics and
    Traumatology [1114]
  Evidenced-Based Veterinary Medicine Assn.
    [17024]
  Fed. of European Companion Animal Veterinary
    Associations [10478]
  Humane Soc. Veterinary Medical Assn. [10985]
  Intl. Assn. for Aquatic Animal Medicine [17025]
  Intl. Assn. for Aquatic Animal Medicine [17025]
  Intl. Assn. for Paratuberculosis [17026]
  Intl. Assn. for Paratuberculosis [17026]
  Intl. Embryo Transfer Soc. [17027]
  Intl. Embryo Transfer Soc. [17027]
  Intl. Soc. of Veterinary Dermatopathology [17028]
  Intl. Soc. of Veterinary Dermatopathology [17028]
  Intl. Veterinarians Dedicated to Animal Hea.
    [17029]
  Intl. Veterinary Acupuncture Soc. [17030]
  Intl. Veterinary Acupuncture Soc. [17030]
  Intl. Veterinary Ultrasound Soc. [17031]
  Intl. Veterinary Ultrasound Soc. [17031]
  Mid-Atlantic States Assn. of Avian Veterinarians
    [17032]
  Natl. Assn. of Fed. Veterinarians [17033]
  Natl. Assn. of Veterinary Technicians in Am.
    [17034]
  NMC [17035]
  North Amer. Pet Hea. Insurance Assn. [14863]
  OPP Concerned Sheep Breeders Soc. [17036]
  Options for Animals Intl. [17037]
  Orthopedic Found. for Animals [17038]
  Phi Zeta [23757]VeterinarySingapore Veterinary
    Assn.
  Soc. for Animal Homeopathy [15023]
  Soc. for Theriogenology [17039]
  Soc. for Tropical Veterinary Medicine [17040]
  Soc. for Tropical Veterinary Medicine [17040]
  Soc. of Veterinary Behavior Technicians [17041]
  Soc. for Veterinary Medical Ethics [17042]
  Student Amer. Veterinary Medical Assn. [17043]
  Student Amer. Veterinary Medical Assn. [17043]
  Student Veterinary Emergency and Critical Care
    Soc. [17044]
  Student Veterinary Emergency and Critical Care
    Soc. [17044]
  U.S. Animal Hea. Assn. [17045]
  Veterinary Botanical Medicine Assn. [17046]
  Veterinary Cancer Soc. [17047]
  Veterinary Emergency and Critical Care Soc.
    [17048]
  Veterinary Hosp. Managers Assn. [17049]
  Veterinary Inst. of Integrative Medicine [17050]
  Veterinary Orthopedic Soc. [17051]
  VeterinaryVentures [11055]
  Western Veterinary Conf. [17052]
  World Assn. for the Advancement of Veterinary
    Parasitology [17053]
  World Assn. for the Advancement of Veterinary
    Parasitology [17053]
  World Assn. of Veterinary Lab. Diagnosticians
    [17054]
  World Assn. of Veterinary Lab. Diagnosticians
    [17054]
  World Vets [11064]
Veterinary Orthopedic Soc. [17051], PO Box 705,
  Okemos, MI 48805-0705, (517)381-2468
VeterinaryVentures [11055], Amber Holland, Treas.,
  2613 NW Raleigh St., No. 25, Portland, OR 97210

A star before a book entry number signifies that the name is not listed separately, but is mentioned within the entry.

Vetlesen Found; G. Unger [12668]

Vetplantvereniging van Suid-Afrika [★IO]

Vets Care Org., Pakistan [IO], Lahore, Pakistan

Vets With a Mission [17203], PO Box 202, Newberry, SC 29108, (803)405-9926

Vets With a Mission [17203], PO Box 202, Newberry, SC 29108, (803)405-9926

Vets4Vets [20819], 4192 E Boulder Springs Way, Tucson, AZ 85712, (520)319-5500

Vexillology

    Flag Res. Center [10628]

    Intl. Fed. of Vexillological Associations [10629]

    Intl. Fed. of Vexillological Associations [10629]

    Natl. Flag Found. [10630]

    North Amer. Vexillological Assn. [10631]

    U.S. Flag Found. [10632]

VHA [15071], PO Box 140909, Irving, TX 75014-0909, (972)830-0626

VHL Family Alliance [14636], 2001 Beacon St., Ste. 208, Boston, MA 02135-7787, (617)277-5667

Vi Hjaelper Hinanden [★IO]

Vibha [11425], 1030 E El Camino Real, No. 424, Sunnyvale, CA 94087, (408)997-9992

Vibration Found. [★7082]

Vibration Inst. [7082], 6262 S Kingery Hwy., Ste. 212, Willowbrook, IL 60527-2284, (630)654-2254

Vibration Isolation and Seismic Control Mfrs. Assn. [7404], 994 Old Eagle School Rd., Ste. 1019, Wayne, PA 19087-1866, (610)971-4850

Victim Offender Mediation Assn. [18761], Doreene Langason, Admin., Center for Policy, Planning and Performance, 2233 Univ. Ave. W, Ste. 300, St. Paul, MN 55114, (612)874-0570

Victim Offender Mediation Assn. [18761], Doreene Langason, Admin., Center for Policy, Planning and Performance, 2233 Univ. Ave. W, Ste. 300, St. Paul, MN 55114, (612)874-0570

Victim Support [IO], London, United Kingdom

Victim Support Europe [IO], Utrecht, Netherlands

Victims

    9/11 Families for a Secure Am. Found. [18710]

    Amer. Soc. for the Support of Injured Survivors of Terrorism [13359]

    Amer. Soc. of Victimology [13360]

    Center for Victims of Torture [13361]

    Dreamcatchers for Abused Children [11142]

    Faceless Intl. [13362]

    For Victims of War and Poverty [12455]

    Forgotten Victims [13363]

    Intl. Cruise Victims [18759]

    Intl. Org. for Victim Assistance [13364]

    MaleSurvivor: The Natl. Org. Against Male Sexual Victimization [13089]

    Natl. Assn. of Crime Victim Compensation Boards [13365]

    Natl. Assn. of Victim Ser. Professionals in Corrections [13366]

    Natl. Center for Victims of Crime [13367]

    Natl. Child Abuse Defense and Rsrc. Center [13368]

    Natl. Coalition of Anti-Violence Programs [18770]

    Natl. Crime Victim Bar Assn. [6063]

    Natl. Org. for Victim Assistance [13369]

    Natl. Victims' Constitutional Amendment Partnership [18760]

    NAVAH [13311]

    Pandora's Proj. [13096]

    Sex Abuse Treatment Alliance [13100]

    Survivors Network of Those Abused by Priests [13370]

    Transitions Global [12248]

    Victim Offender Mediation Assn. [18761]

    Victim Offender Mediation Assn. [18761]

    Victim Support Europe [12156]

    Victims of Crime and Leniency [13371]

    Vietnamese Alliance to Combat Trafficking [12251]

    Wounded Warrior Proj. [20822]

Victims' Assistance Legal Org. [11696], 8180 Greensboro Dr., Ste. 1070, McLean, VA 22102-3860, (703)748-0011

Victims of Chiropractic Abuse [14147], PO Box 3278, New Haven, CT 06515

Victims of Choice - Defunct.

Victims of Crime and Leniency [13371], PO Box 4449, Montgomery, AL 36103, (334)262-7197

Victims of Violence [IO], Ottawa, ON, Canada

Victoria Habitat for Humanity [IO], Victoria, BC, Canada

Victoria League for Commonwealth Friendship [IO], London, United Kingdom

Victorian

    Antique Glass Salt and Sugar Shaker Club [21304]

    Fairy Lamp Club [21337]

    North Amer. Victorian Stud. Assn. [10633]

    Res. Soc. for Victorian Periodicals [10634]

    Res. Soc. for Victorian Periodicals [10634]

    Victorian Soc. in Am. [10635]

Victorian Area of Narcotics Anonymous [IO], Melbourne, Australia

Victorian Artists Soc. [IO], East Melbourne, Australia

Victorian Assn. for the Teaching of English [IO], Melbourne, Australia

Victorian Dental and Oral Therapists' Assn. [IO], Parkville, Australia

Victorian Employers' Chamber of Commerce and Indus. [IO], Melbourne, Australia

Victorian Farmers Fed. [IO], Melbourne, Australia

Victorian Hairwork Soc. [21470], 1333 S Noland Rd., Independence, MO 64055, (816)833-2955

Victorian Infection Control Professionals Assn. [IO], Carlton, Australia

Victorian Ladies' Bowling Assn. [IO], Hawthorn, Australia

Victorian Military Soc. [IO], Newbury, United Kingdom

Victorian Model Aeronautical Assn. [IO], Cranbourne, Australia

Victorian Olive Coun. [IO], Alpine Shire, Australia

Victorian Soc. [IO], London, United Kingdom

Victorian Soc. in Am. [10635], 1634 Sansom St., Philadelphia, PA 19103, (215)636-9872

Vida Humana Internacional [★IO]

Video

    Christian Media Assn. [19947]

    United Catholic Music and Video Assn. [19506]

Video Electronics Standards Assn. [6674], 39899 Balentine Dr., Ste. 125, Newark, CA 94560, (510)651-5122

Video Software Dealers Assn. [★275]

Videotex Indus. Assn. [★678]

Videotex Indus. Assn. [★678]

Vidskiptarad Islands [★IO]

Vie autonome Canada [★IO]

Vienna Inst. for Intl. Dialogue and Cooperation [IO], Vienna, Austria

Viers/Veirs Family Org. - Defunct.

VietHope [13375], 423 Brookline Ave., No. 199, Boston, MA 02215

Vietnam

    Care 2 Share [13373]

    Champa Cultural Preservation Assn. of USA [10636]

    CHEER for Viet Nam [13374]

    Children of Vietnam [11242]

    Glocal Ventures [12331]

    Hannah's Promise Intl. Aid [12843]

    Tan Son Nhut Assn. [20823]

    United Nations | Vietnam Relief Effort [13372]

    United Nations | Vietnam Relief Effort [13372]

    U.S.-Vietnam WTO Coalition [18762]

    USMC Vietnam Tankers Assn. [20824]

    Vietnam Dustoff Assn. [20836]

    Vietnam Era Seabees [20826]

Vietnam Assistance for the Handicapped - Ho Chi Minh City [IO], Ho Chi Minh City, Vietnam

Vietnam Assn. of Certified Public Accountants [IO], Hanoi, Vietnam

Vietnam Assn. of Seafood Exporters and Producers [IO], Hanoi, Vietnam

Vietnam Athletic Fed. [IO], Hanoi, Vietnam

Vietnam Badminton Fed. [IO], Hanoi, Vietnam

Vietnam Charities - Defunct.

Vietnam Combat Veterans [20835], PO Box 715, White Pine, MI 49971, (906)885-5599

Vietnam Dog Handler Assn. [20825], 1712 Crescent Dr., Pekin, IL 61554-1637, (309)202-5542

Vietnam Dustoff Assn. [20836], Richard Dean, 2929 Cedar Mill Crossing, Acworth, GA 30101

Vietnam Engg. Consultant Assn. [IO], Hanoi, Vietnam

Vietnam Era Seabees [20826], PO Box 5177, Midlothian, VA 23112-0020

Vietnam Found. - Defunct.

Vietnam Gastroenterology Assn. [IO], Hanoi, Vietnam

Vietnam Gen. Assn. of Medicine and Pharmacy [IO], Hanoi, Vietnam

Vietnam Helicopter Pilots Assn. [20837], 407 W Coll. St., Grapevine, TX 76051-5218, (800)505-8472

Vietnam Human Rights Network [12250], 14550 Magnolia St., Ste. 203, Westminster, CA 92683, (714)657-9488

Vietnam Human Rights Network [12250], 14550 Magnolia St., Ste. 203, Westminster, CA 92683, (714)657-9488

Vietnam Medical Assn. [IO], Hanoi, Vietnam

Vietnam Natl. Heart Assn. [IO], Hanoi, Vietnam

Vietnam Olympic Comm. [IO], Hanoi, Vietnam

Vietnam Proj. [★17989]

Vietnam Red Cross Soc. [IO], Hanoi, Vietnam

Vietnam Relief Effort [12896], 845 United Nations Plz., 90A, New York, NY 10017, (917)668-2600

Vietnam Rheumatology Assn. [IO], Hanoi, Vietnam

Vietnam Security Police Assn. [20827], Bill Marshall, Membership Chm., 24450 Alta Vista Dr., Dana Point, CA 92629

Vietnam Software Assn. [IO], Hanoi, Vietnam

Vietnam Taekwondo Fed. [IO], Ho Chi Minh City, Vietnam

Vietnam Tennis Fed. [IO], Hanoi, Vietnam

Vietnam Veteran Wives [20820], PO Box 396, Republic, WA 99166, (509)775-2096

Vietnam Veterans

    Natl. Vietnam and Gulf War Veterans Coalition [18763]

    Saigon Mission Assn. [18764]

    Saigon Mission Assn. [18764]

    Tan Son Nhut Assn. [20823]

    USMC Vietnam Tankers Assn. [20824]

    Vietnam Dog Handler Assn. [20825]

    Vietnam Era Seabees [20826]

    Vietnam Security Police Assn. [20827]

    Vietnam Veterans Against the War [18765]

    Vietnam Veterans Against the War Anti-Imperialist [18766]

    Vietnam Veterans of Am. [18767]

Vietnam Veterans Against the War [18765], PO Box 2065, Sta. A, Chicago, IL 60690-2065, (773)276-4189

Vietnam Veterans Against the War Anti-Imperialist [18766], PO Box 21604, Seattle, WA 98111-3604, (206)374-2215

Vietnam Veterans Against the War/Winter Soldier Org. [★18765]

Vietnam Veterans of Am. [18767], 8719 Colesville Rd., Ste. 100, Silver Spring, MD 20910, (301)585-4000

Vietnam Veterans of Amer. Found. [★17989]

Vietnam Veterans Assn. of Australia - Natl. Coun. [IO], Melbourne, Australia

Vietnam Veterans Memorial Fund [20838], 2600 Virginia Ave. NW, Ste. 104, Washington, DC 20037, (202)393-0090

Vietnam War

    11th Armored Cavalry's Veterans of Vietnam and Cambodia [20828]

    77th Artillery Assn. [20829]

    Associates of Vietnam Veterans of Am. [20830]

    Gamewardens of Vietnam Assn. [20831]

    Legacies of War [8259]

    Mobile Riverine Force Assn. [20832]

    PBR Forces Veterans Assn. [20833]

    Tan Son Nhut Assn. [20823]

    USMC Vietnam Tankers Assn. [20824]

    Veterans of the Vietnam War [20834]

    Vietnam Combat Veterans [20835]

    Vietnam Dustoff Assn. [20836]

    Vietnam Era Seabees [20826]

    Vietnam Helicopter Pilots Assn. [20837]

    Vietnam Veterans Memorial Fund [20838]

    Vietnam Women's Memorial Found. [20839]

Vietnam Women's Memorial Found. [20839], 1735 Connecticut Ave. NW, 3rd Fl., Washington, DC 20009, (866)822-8963

Vietnam Women's Memorial Proj. [★20839]

Reference to "IO" in place of a book number signifies that the association may be found in the 50th edition of International Organizations.

Vietnamese
Cambodian Mutual Assistance Assn. [19271]
Care 2 Share [13373]
Champa Cultural Preservation Assn. of USA [10636]
Champa Cultural Preservation Assn. of USA [10636]
CHEER for Viet Nam [13374]
Gp. of Universities for the Advancement of Vietnamese Abroad [9035]
Humanitarian Services for Children of Vietnam [11318]
Natl. Alliance of Vietnamese Amer. Ser. Agencies [19272]
Natl. Assn. for the Educ. and Advancement of Cambodian, Laotian, and Vietnamese Americans [19273]
Natl. Center for Victims of Crime [13367]
Natl. Cong. of Vietnamese Americans [19274]
Union of North Amer. Vietnamese Students Assn. [19275]
Union of North Amer. Vietnamese Students Assn. [19275]
VietHope [13375]
Vietnamese Alliance to Combat Trafficking [12251]
Vietnamese Amer. Coun. [19276]
Vietnamese Professionals Soc. [19277]
Vietnamese Professionals Soc. [19277]
Vietnamese Alliance to Combat Trafficking [12251], PO Box 218, Westminster, CA 92684-0218
Vietnamese Amer. Coun. [19276], 780 S 1st St., San Jose, CA 95113, (408)518-0759
Vietnamese Amer. Medical Assn. [★15438]
Vietnamese Amer. Medical Assn. [★15438]
Vietnamese-American Nurses Assn. [15805], PO Box 691994, Houston, TX 77269-1994
Vietnamese Amer. Soc. - Defunct.
Vietnamese Canadian Fed. [IO], Ottawa, ON, Canada
Vietnamese Catholic Fed. in the U.S.A. - Defunct.
Vietnamese Geotechnical Soc. [IO], Hanoi, Vietnam
Vietnamese Medical Assn. of the U.S.A. [15438], 4108 Surfside Ct., Arlington, TX 76016, (682)667-1016
Vietnamese Medical Assn. of the U.S.A. [15438], 4108 Surfside Ct., Arlington, TX 76016, (682)667-1016
Vietnamese Nom Preservation Found. [10051], 229 Beachers Brook Ln., Cary, NC 27511
Vietnamese Nom Preservation Found. [10051], 229 Beachers Brook Ln., Cary, NC 27511
Vietnamese Professionals Soc. [19277], 5150 Fair Oaks Blvd., Ste. 101-128, Carmichael, CA 95608-5758, (916)484-3519
Vietnamese Professionals Soc. [19277], 5150 Fair Oaks Blvd., Ste. 101-128, Carmichael, CA 95608-5758, (916)484-3519
VietNow [★13358]
VietNow Natl. [13358], 1835 Broadway, Rockford, IL 61104, (815)227-5100
VIEW Clubs of Australia [IO], Sydney, Australia
Viewers for Quality TV - Defunct.
Viking Brotherhood [★19301]
Viking Soc. for Northern Res. [IO], London, United Kingdom
Villa-Lobos Music Soc. - Defunct.
Village Earth: CSVBD [11649], PO Box 797, Fort Collins, CO 80522, (970)237-3002
Village Earth: CSVBD [11649], PO Box 797, Fort Collins, CO 80522, (970)237-3002
Village Educ. Rsrc. Center [IO], Dhaka, Bangladesh
Village Focus Intl. [11650], 14 Wall St., 20th Fl., New York, NY 10005, (917)621-7167
Village Missions Intl. [11651], 10945 Reed Hartman Hwy., Ste. 201, Cincinnati, OH 45242, (513)791-2066
Village Volunteers [12379], 5100 S Dawson St., Ste. 202, Seattle, WA 98118, (206)577-0515
Villers Found. [★10842]
Vilnius Chamber of Commerce, Indus., and Crafts [IO], Vilnius, Lithuania
VIM, Inc. - Defunct.
Vin og Spiritus Organisationen i Danmark [★IO]
Vindmolleindustrien [★IO]

The Vine Gp. USA - Address unknown since 2011.
Vinegar Connoisseurs Intl. [21849], PO Box 41, Roslyn, SD 57261, (800)342-4519
Vinegar Connoisseurs Intl. [21849], PO Box 41, Roslyn, SD 57261, (800)342-4519
Vinegar Inst. [1436], 1100 Johnson Ferry Rd., Ste. 300, Atlanta, GA 30342, (404)252-3663
Vinifera Wine Growers Assn. [★5165]
Vinland Alliance [★19300]
Vintage Austin Register [IO], Alfreton, United Kingdom
Vintage Base Ball Assn. [22292], Rich Arpi, Treas., 2445 Londin Ln. E, Unit 410, Maplewood, MN 55119, (651)739-6986
Vintage BMW [★21943]
The Vintage BMW Club [★21943]
Vintage BMW Motorcycle Owners [21943], Roland Slabon, PO Box 599, Troy, OH 45373-0599, (770)235-5281
Vintage Chevrolet Club of Am. [21187], Mike McGowan, Membership Sec., PO Box 609, Lemont, IL 60439-0609, (708)455-8222
Vintage Drivers Club of Am. [21188], 13505 Running Water Rd., Palm Beach Gardens, FL 33418-7933, (561)622-7554
Vintage Fashion and Costume Jewelry Club
Vintage Fashion and Costume Jewelry Club - Address unknown since 2011.
Vintage Garden Tractor Club of Am. [22181], 412 W Chestnut, Pardeeville, WI 53954, (608)429-4520
Vintage Locomotive Soc. [IO], Winnipeg, MB, Canada
Vintage Motor Bike Club [21944], 537 W Huntington St., Montpelier, IN 47359, (417)881-7411
Vintage Radio and Phonograph Soc. [22123], PO Box 165345, Irving, TX 75016, (972)742-8085
Vintage Sailplane Assn. [22215], 31757 Honey Locust Rd., Jonesburg, MO 63351-3195
Vintage Sports Car Club of Am. [21189], PO Box 60425, Florence, MA 01062, (413)584-4210
Vintage Thunderbird Club of Am. [★21190]
Vintage Thunderbird Club of Am. [★21190]
Vintage Thunderbird Club Intl. [21190], Bob McNeill, Exec. Sec., PO Box 58872, Tukwila, WA 98138-2872
Vintage Thunderbird Club Intl. [21190], Bob McNeill, Exec. Sec., PO Box 58872, Tukwila, WA 98138-2872
Vintage Triumph Register [21191], PO Box 655, Howell, MI 48844
Vintage Volkswagen Club of Am. [21192], 629 S Mississippi Ave., Mason City, IA 50401, (641)421-0965
Vintage Wooden Boat Assn. [IO], Potton, United Kingdom
Vintners' Fed. of Ireland [IO], Dublin, Ireland
Vinyl Coun. of Australia [IO], Laverton, Australia
Vinyl Fabrics Inst. [★2766]
Vinyl Fabrics Inst. [★2766]
Vinyl Siding Inst. [633], 1201 15th St. NW, Ste. 220, Washington, DC 20005, (202)587-5100
Viola d'Amore Soc. of Am. [10308], 10917 Pickford Way, Culver City, CA 90230, (310)838-5509
Viola da Gamba Soc. of Am. [10309], Mr. Ken Perlow, Treas., 131 S Humphrey Ave., Oak Park, IL 60302, (708)383-4608
Viola Res. Soc. [★10158]
Violence
Amer. Family Assn. [17334]
Assassination Archives and Res. Center [18768]
Bahia St. [12717]
Coalition to Stop Gun Violence [17686]
Face Forward [11885]
INCITE! Women of Color Against Violence [18769]
Intl. Refugee Rights Initiative [17843]
Natl. Coalition Against Violent Athletes [22231]
Natl. Coalition of Anti-Violence Programs [18770]
Natl. Org. of Sisters of Color Ending Sexual Assault [13093]
North Korea Freedom Coalition [18035]
R2P Coalition [13376]
Survivorship [13377]
Violence Policy Center [18771]
Witness Justice [18772]

Women Against Gun Violence [18773]
Women in Black [18302]
Violence Everywhere; Natl. Assn. of Students Against [18172]
Violence Everywhere; Natl. Assn. of Students Against [18172]
Violence Policy Center [18771], 1730 Rhode Island Ave. NW, Ste. 1014, Washington, DC 20036, (202)822-8200
Violent Death Bereavement Soc. [11130], PO Box 1930, Seattle, WA 98199, (206)223-6398
Violin Soc. of Am. [10310], 341 N Maitland Ave., Ste. 130, Maitland, FL 32751, (407)647-8839
VIP Div. [★11737]
Virago Owners Club [21945], 1386 Reynolds Cir., Binghamton, NY 13903
Virgin Islands
Natl. Assn. State Agencies for Surplus Property [5898]
Virgin Islands Dept. of Economic Development and Agriculture - Defunct.
Virgin Islands Olympic Comm. [22792], PO Box 366, Frederiksted, VI 00841, (340)719-8462
Virgin Islands Olympic Comm. [22792], PO Box 366, Frederiksted, VI 00841, (340)719-8462
Virginia-Carolina Peanut Promotions [4757], 103 Triangle Ct., Nashville, NC 27856-0008, (252)459-9977
Virginia-Carolina Peanuts [4758], 103 Triangle Ct., Nashville, NC 27856-0008, (252)459-9977
Virginia Poultry Breeders Assn. [4820], 6453 Silky Way, Gloucester, VA 23061
Virginia Poultry Breeders Club [★4820]
Virginia Woolf Soc. [★9379]
Virginia Woolf Soc. [★9379]
Virology; Amer. Soc. for [6269]
Virtual Private Network Consortium [2119], 127 Segre Pl., Santa Cruz, CA 95060, (831)426-9827
Virtual Private Network Consortium [2119], 127 Segre Pl., Santa Cruz, CA 95060, (831)426-9827
Visao Mundial - Brazil [★IO]
Vishwam [12770], 3 Eastmans Rd., Parsippany, NJ 07054-3702, (973)886-8170
Vishwam [12770], 3 Eastmans Rd., Parsippany, NJ 07054-3702, (973)886-8170
Vision-Aid [17117], 8 Vine Brook Rd., Lexington, MA 02421, (781)333-5252
Vision Australia [IO], Enfield, Australia
Vision Australia Found. [IO], Kooyong, Australia
Vision Coun. [1689], 225 Reinekers Ln., Ste. 700, Alexandria, VA 22314, (703)548-4560
Vision Earth Soc. [4223], 1825 NE 149 St., Miami, FL 33181, (305)945-2727
Vision Educational Found. - Defunct.
Vision Gp. of the Robotic Indus. Assn. [★7342]
Vision Indus. Coun. of Am. [★1689]
Vision Intl; Coun. of Citizens With Low [11774]
Vision Mondiale Canada [★IO]
Vision Mundial Colombia [★IO]
Vision New Am. [18494], 4340 Stevens Creek Blvd., Ste. 166, San Jose, CA 95129, (408)260-0116
Vision and Ophthalmology; Assn. for Res. in [15948]
Vision Sciences Soc. [7394], 19 Richardson Rd., Novato, CA 94949, (415)883-3301
Vision USA [16001], 243 N Lindbergh Blvd., St. Louis, MO 63141-7881, (800)766-4466
Vision U.S.A. [★15988]
Vision World Wide
Vision World Wide - Address unknown since 2011.
Visionaries In Action - Across Africa [IO], Johannesburg, Republic of South Africa
Visionary Alternatives [13718], 7725 Kenway Pl. E, Boca Raton, FL 33433, (561)750-4551
Visions in Action [12380], 2710 Ontario Rd. NW, Washington, DC 20009, (202)625-7402
Visions in Action [12380], 2710 Ontario Rd. NW, Washington, DC 20009, (202)625-7402
Visit Denmark [IO], Copenhagen, Denmark
Visiting Nurse Associations of Am. [15806], 900 19th St. NW, Ste. 200, Washington, DC 20006, (202)384-1420
Visitor Prog. Ser. of Meridian House Intl. [★17978]
Visitor Stud. Assn. [9019], PO Box 10668, Rockville, MD 20849-0668, (301)762-1450
Visitor Stud. Assn. [9019], PO Box 10668, Rockville, MD 20849-0668, (301)762-1450

A star before a book entry number signifies that the name is not listed separately, but is mentioned within the entry.

VisitScotland [IO], Edinburgh, United Kingdom
VisitSweden [3587], PO Box 4649, Grand Central Sta., New York, NY 10163-4649, (212)885-9700
VisitSweden [3587], PO Box 4649, Grand Central Sta., New York, NY 10163-4649, (212)885-9700
Visual Artists and Galleries Assn. [5583], 350 5th Ave., Ste. 2820, New York, NY 10118, (212)736-6666
Visual Artists Ireland [IO], Dublin, Ireland
Visual Arts Ontario [IO], Toronto, ON, Canada
Visual Effects Soc. [1270], 5535 Balboa Blvd., Ste. 205, Encino, CA 91316, (818)981-7861
Visual Indicators Coun. [6836], 188 Rte. 10, Ste. 307, East Hanover, NJ 07936, (973)884-1668
Visual Resources Assn. [278], 2174 W Rocking-horse Rd., Rancho Palos Verdes, CA 90275-1604, (310)489-3792
Visual Resources Assn. [278], 2174 W Rocking-horse Rd., Rancho Palos Verdes, CA 90275-1604, (310)489-3792
Visual Stud. Workshop [9613], 31 Prince St., Rochester, NY 14607, (585)442-8676

Visually Impaired
Achromatopsia Network [17055]
Aicardi Syndrome Newsl. [14581]
Amer. Action Fund for Blind Children and Adults [17056]
Amer. Blind Bowling Assn. [22502]
Amer. Coun. of the Blind [17057]
Amer. Coun. of the Blind | Amer. Coun. of Blind Students [17058]
Amer. Coun. of the Blind Lions [17059]
Amer. Found. for the Blind [17060]
Amer. Nystagmus Network [17061]
Amer. Printing House for the Blind [17062]
Assoc. Services for the Blind [17063]
Assn. for the Advancement of Blind and Retarded [17064]
Assn. for Educ. and Rehabilitation of the Blind and Visually Impaired [17065]
Blind Children's Fund [17066]
Blind Sailing Intl. [23109]
Blind Ser. Assn. [17067]
Blinded Veterans Assn. [17068]
Braille Authority of North Am. [17069]
Braille Authority of North Am. [17069]
Canadian Guide Dogs for the Blind [19113]
Care Ministries [20280]
Carroll Center for the Blind [17070]
Christian Blind Mission Intl. [17071]
Christian Blind Mission Intl. [17071]
Christian Record Services [17072]
Clearer Vision Ministries [13378]
Clearer Vision Ministries [13378]
Coun. of Families with Visual Impairment [17073]
Div. on Visual Impairments [8883]
European Eye Bank Assn. [1325]
Fidelco Guide Dog Found. [17074]
Found. Fighting Blindness [17075]
Giving Vision [17076]
Global Vision 2020 [17077]
Gospel Assn. for the Blind [17078]
Guide Dog Found. for the Blind [17079]
Guide Dog Users, Inc. [17080]
Guide Dogs of Am. [17081]
Guide Dogs for the Blind [17082]
Guide Dogs for the Blind [17082]
Guiding Eyes for the Blind [17083]
Guiding Eyes for the Blind [17083]
Guild for Human Services [17084]
Helen Keller Intl. [17085]
Helen Keller Intl. [17085]
Independent Visually Impaired Enterprisers [17086]
Intercontinental Fed. of Behavioral Optometry [15994]
Intl. Assn. of Audio Info. Services [17087]
Intl. Assn. of Audio Info. Services [17087]
Intl. Children's Anophthalmia Network [17088]
Intl. Children's Anophthalmia Network [17088]
Intl. Soc. for Low Vision Res. and Rehabilitation [15965]
Intl. Trachoma Initiative [17089]
Intl. Trachoma Initiative [17089]
Interprofessional Fostering of Ophthalmic Care for Underserved Sectors [17090]

JBI Intl. - Jewish Braille Inst. of Am. [17091]
JBI Intl. - Jewish Braille Inst. of Am. [17091]
Jewish Guild for the Blind [17092]
Keren Or [17093]
Keren Or [17093]
Leader Dogs for the Blind [17094]
Leader Dogs for the Blind [17094]
Learning Ally [17095]
Lighthouse Intl. [17096]
Lighthouse Intl. [17096]
Lutheran Braille Evangelism Assn. [17097]
Lutheran Braille Evangelism Assn. [17097]
Lutheran Braille Workers [17098]
Lutheran Braille Workers [17098]
Macular Degeneration Found. [17099]
Mission Cataract USA [17100]
Natl. Accreditation Coun. for Agencies Serving the Blind and Visually Impaired [17101]
Natl. Alliance for Eye and Vision Res. [17102]
Natl. Assn. of Blind Merchants [3616]
Natl. Assn. for Parents of Children With Visual Impairments [17103]
Natl. Braille Assn. [17104]
Natl. Braille Press [17105]
Natl. Church Conf. of the Blind [13379]
Natl. Consortium of Deaf-Blindness [17106]VisuallyNatl. Coun. for the Blind of Ireland
Natl. Fed. of the Blind [17107]
Natl. Indus. for the Blind [17108]
Natl. Org. of Parents of Blind Children [17109]
Optometric Glaucoma Soc. [15972]
Parents Active for Vision Educ. [17110]
Pilot Dogs [17111]
Prevent Blindness Am. [17112]
Res. to Prevent Blindness [17113]
Retinitis Pigmentosa Intl. [17114]
Retinitis Pigmentosa Intl. [17114]
Seedlings Braille Books for Children [9036]
Seeing Eye [17115]
Surgical Eye Expeditions Intl. [17116]
Surgical Eye Expeditions Intl. [17116]
Unite for Sight [13380]
Unite for Sight [13380]
Veterans Educ. Proj. [13357]
Vision-Aid [17117]VisuallyVision World Wide
VOSH Intl. [12482]
World Access for the Blind [17118]
World Access for the Blind [17118]
World Glaucoma Patient Assn. [15979]
Xavier Soc. for the Blind [17119]
Visually Impaired Data Processors Intl. - Address unknown since 2010.
Visually Impaired Veterans of Am. - Address unknown since 2010.
VITA [6565], PO Box 19658, Fountain Hills, AZ 85269, (480)837-7486
Vital Voices Global Partnership [13484], 1625 Massachusetts Ave. NW, Ste. 850, Washington, DC 20036, (202)861-2625
Vitalise [IO], London, United Kingdom
Vitamin Angel Alliance [15846], PO Box 42029, Santa Barbara, CA 93140, (805)564-8400
Vitamin Angel Alliance [15846], PO Box 42029, Santa Barbara, CA 93140, (805)564-8400
Vitamin D Coun. [15847], 1241 Johnson Ave., No. 134, San Luis Obispo, CA 93401
Vitamin Soc. of Japan [IO], Kyoto, Japan
Vitiligo Found; Natl. [14336]
Vitiligo Support Intl. [14341], 808 Wiggington Rd., Ste. D, Lynchburg, VA 24502, (818)752-9002
Vitreous Enamel Services [IO], St. Helens, United Kingdom
Viva! USA [11056], 1123 Broadway, Ste. 912, New York, NY 10010
Viva! USA [11056], 1123 Broadway, Ste. 912, New York, NY 10010
ViviendasLeon [12575], 1585 Folsom St., San Francisco, CA 94103, (415)255-2920
Vivit [6523], PO Box 18510, Boulder, CO 80308
Vizsla Club of Am. [21674], Shella A. Fuhrman, PO Box 90, Friendsville, TN 37737-0090, (865)603-9335
Vizsla Club of France [IO], Walincourt, France
Vlaamse Reumaliga Belgium [IO], Mechelen, Belgium

Vlaamse Squash Federatie [★IO]
Vlaamse Taekwondo Bond [★IO]
Vlaamse Vereniging voor Entomologie [★IO]
Vlaamse Vereniging voor Spina Bifida en Hydro-cephalus vzw [IO], Oosterzele, Belgium
Vlaamse Vereniging voor Watersport [★IO]
Vlaamse Vereniging voor Ontwikkelings Samen-werking [★IO]
Vladimir Nabokov Soc. [★9380]
Vladimir Nabokov Soc. [★9380]
VNO-NCW Confed. of Netherlands Indus. and Employers [IO], The Hague, Netherlands
Vocational Assn. of the Middle West [★9039]
Vocational Education
Amer. Assn. for Vocational Instructional Materials [9037]
Amer. Bd. of Vocational Experts [9038]
Assn. for Career and Tech. Educ. [9039]
Assn. for Career and Tech. Educ. Res. [9040]
Assn. of Private Sector Colleges and Universities [9041]
Bus. Professionals of Am. [9042]
Center on Educ. and Training for Employment [9043]
Intl. Assn. of Jewish Vocational Services [9044]
Intl. Assn. of Jewish Vocational Services [9044]
Intl. Vocational Educ. and Training Assn. [9045]
Intl. Vocational Educ. and Training Assn. [9045]
Iota Lambda Sigma [23758]
Israel Humanitarian Found. [12393]
Natl. Assn. of State Directors of Career Tech. Educ. Consortium [9046]
Natl. Tech. Honor Soc. [23759]
Univ. Economic Development Assn. [9047]
WoodLINKS USA [8300]
Vocational Evaluation and Career Assessment Professionals [16578], 5500 Univ. Pkwy., Rm. CE-120, San Bernardino, CA 92407, (909)537-3696
Vocational Evaluation and Career Assessment Professionals [16578], 5500 Univ. Pkwy., Rm. CE-120, San Bernardino, CA 92407, (909)537-3696
Vocational Evaluation and Work Adjustment Assn. [★16578]
Vocational Evaluation and Work Adjustment Assn. [★16578]
Vocational Found. Bur. of the Assn. for the Preven-tion of Crime [★11962]
Vocational Found., Inc. [★11962]
Vocational Guidance and Workshop Center [★23646]
Vocational Indus. Clubs of Am. [★8298]
Vocational Instructional Materials Sect. - Address unknown since 2010.
Vocational Rehabilitation Assn. of Canada [IO], Tor-onto, ON, Canada
VOICE [IO], Mumbai, India
Voice for Animals [11057], PO Box 120095, San Antonio, TX 78212, (210)737-3138
Voice of China and Asia Missionary Soc. [20104], PO Box 702015, Tulsa, OK 74170-2015, (918)392-0560
Voice of China and Asia Missionary Soc. [20104], PO Box 702015, Tulsa, OK 74170-2015, (918)392-0560
Voice Found. [16693], 1721 Pine St., Philadelphia, PA 19103, (215)735-7999
Voice of Healing [★20022]
Voice of Healing [★20022]
Voice of Liberty Assn. - Defunct.
Voice for Life [IO], Wellington, New Zealand
Voice of the Listener and Viewer [IO], Gravesend, United Kingdom
Voice of the Martyrs [20105], PO Box 443, Bartles-ville, OK 74005-0443, (918)337-8015
Voice of Reason [★17267]
Voice Rehabilitation Inst. [★11795]
Voice Rehabilitation Inst. [★11795]
Voice of the Retarded [★12513]
Voice of Tangier [★20100]
Voice of Tangier [★20100]
Voice: The Union for Educ. Professionals [IO], Derby, United Kingdom
Voice of Women Org. [IO], Herat, Afghanistan
VoiceCare Network [8900], Dept. of Music, St. John's Univ., Collegeville, MN 56321, (320)363-3374

Reference to "IO" in place of a book number signifies that the association may be found in the 50th edition of International Organizations.

VOICES in Action - Address unknown since 2010.
Voices of African Mothers **[12638]**, 13 Glenbrook Ave., Yonkers, NY 10705-1650, (914)963-8725
Voices of African Mothers **[12638]**, 13 Glenbrook Ave., Yonkers, NY 10705-1650, (914)963-8725
Voices for America's Children **[11426]**, 1000 Vermont Ave. NW, Ste. 700, Washington, DC 20005, (202)289-0777
Voices Breaking Boundaries **[10362]**, PO Box 541247, Houston, TX 77254-1247, (713)524-7821
Voices for Global Change **[17254]**, 505 Wythe St., Alexandria, VA 22314, (703)549-7077
Voices of September 11th **[18721]**, 161 Cherry St., New Canaan, CT 06840, (203)966-3911
Voices in the Wilderness
Voices in the Wilderness - Address unknown since 2011.
Voix des Femmes Canadiennes pour la Paix **[★IO]**
Volcanological Soc. of Japan **[IO]**, Tokyo, Japan
Volks-wagen Amer. Dealers Assn. **[★347]**
Volks-wagen Amer. Dealers Assn. **[★347]**
Volkspartij voor Vrijheid en Democratie **[IO]**, The Hague, Netherlands
Volkswagen Club of Am. **[21193]**, PO Box 154, North Aurora, IL 60542
Volleyball
 Amer. Volleyball Coaches Assn. **[23110]**
 USA Volleyball **[23111]**
Volleyball Assn. of Ireland **[IO]**, Dublin, Ireland
Volleyball Professionals; Assn. of **[23297]**
Volontaire-Globalisation **[IO]**, Lome, Togo
Volontariato Internazionale per lo Sviluppo **[★IO]**
Volta Speech Assn. for the Deaf **[★14912]**
Volta Speech Assn. for the Deaf **[★14912]**
Volume Footwear Retailers of Am. **[★1458]**
Volume Footwear Retailers Assn. **[★1458]**
Voluntarios de las Naciones Unidas **[★IO]**
Voluntarism
 Alliance for Preventive Hea. **[14864]**
 AmeriCorps VISTA **[13381]**
 Amigos de las Americas **[13382]**
 Amigos de las Americas **[13382]**
 Amizade Global Service-Learning and Volunteer Programs **[13383]**
 Amizade Global Service-Learning and Volunteer Programs **[13383]**
 Assn. for Healthcare Volunteer Rsrc. Professionals **[13384]**
 Assn. of Junior Leagues Intl. **[13385]**
 Assn. of Junior Leagues Intl. **[13385]**
 Assn. for Res. on Nonprofit Organizations and Voluntary Action **[13386]**
 Assn. for Res. on Nonprofit Organizations and Voluntary Action **[13386]**
 Brethren Volunteer Ser. **[13387]**
 Brethren Volunteer Ser. **[13387]**
 Bridges to Community **[13388]**
 Bridges to Community **[13388]**
 Bus. Volunteers Unlimited **[13389]**
 ChildFund Intl. **[11231]**
 Coun. of Religious Volunteer Agencies **[13390]**
 Drishtipat Worldwide **[11124]**
 Emerging Practitioners in Philanthropy **[12665]**
 Flying Doctors of Am. **[12454]**
 Give an Hour **[11088]**
 Global Rsrc. Alliance **[3974]**
 Global Ser. Corps **[13391]**
 Global Ser. Corps **[13391]**
 Globe Aware **[13392]**
 Globe Aware **[13392]**
 Good Shepherd Volunteers **[13393]**
 HandsOn Network **[13394]**
 HavServe Volunteer Ser. Network **[11069]**
 HealthCare Volunteer **[14790]**
 Holiday Express **[13395]**
 Holiday Proj. **[13396]**
 Intl. Assn. for Volunteer Effort **[13397]**
 Intl. Assn. for Volunteer Effort **[13397]**
 Intl. Volunteer Prog. **[13398]**
 Intl. Volunteer Prog. **[13398]**
 Intl. Volunteer Programs Assn. **[13399]**
 Intl. Volunteer Programs Assn. **[13399]**
 Kids Korps USA **[13400]**
 Natl. Assn. of Volunteer Programs in Local Govt. **[6064]**

 Natl. Human Services Assembly **[13401]**
 One Nurse At A Time **[15794]**
 Outreach Asia **[11116]**
 Paws for Friendship **[13402]**
 Pro Players Assn. **[13403]**
 Retired and Senior Volunteer Prog. **[13404]**
 SCI - Intl. Voluntary Ser. **[13405]**
 SCI - Intl. Voluntary Ser. **[13405]**
 Senior Corps **[13406]**
 SpanAfrica **[11642]**
 TECH CORPS **[13407]**
 Village Volunteers **[12379]**VoluntarismVolunteer Development - Scotland
 VolunteerMatch **[18774]**
 Volunteers in Asia **[13408]**
 Volunteers in Asia **[13408]**
 Winant and Clayton Volunteers **[13409]**
 Winant and Clayton Volunteers **[13409]**
Voluntary Action Network India **[IO]**, New Delhi, India
Voluntary Cooperation Movement
Voluntary Cooperation Movement - Address unknown since 2011.
Voluntary Euthanasia Soc. of New Zealand **[IO]**, Auckland, New Zealand
Voluntary Euthanasia Soc. of Scotland **[★18513]**
Voluntary Fund for the United Nations Decade for Women **[★17672]**
Voluntary Fund for the United Nations Decade for Women **[★17672]**
Voluntary Hospitals of Am. **[★15071]**
Voluntary Organisations in Cooperation in Emergencies **[IO]**, Brussels, Belgium
Voluntary Protection Prog. Assn. for Constr. **[15910]**, PO Box 751222, Dayton, OH 45475-1222, (937)321-7233
Voluntary Protection Programs Participants' Assn. **[15911]**, 7600-E Leesburg Pike, Ste. 100, Falls Church, VA 22043, (703)761-1146
Voluntary Ser. Intl. **[IO]**, Dublin, Ireland
Voluntary Ser. Overseas - England **[IO]**, London, United Kingdom
Voluntary Workcamps Assn. of Uganda **[IO]**, Kampala, Uganda
The Voluntaryists - Address unknown since 2010.
Volunteer Canada **[IO]**, Ottawa, ON, Canada
Volunteer Committees of Art Museums of Canada and the U.S. **[10130]**, 5139 Thorncroft Ct., Royal Oak, MI 48073
Volunteer Development - Scotland **[IO]**, Stirling, United Kingdom
Volunteer Gp. Khoop Khun Maak **[IO]**, Chiba, Japan
Volunteer Lawyers for the Arts **[5767]**, 1 E 53rd St., 6th Fl., New York, NY 10022, (212)319-2787
Volunteer Missionary Movement - Europe **[IO]**, Dublin, Ireland
Volunteer Missionary Movement - U.S. Off. **[19512]**, 5980 W Loomis Rd., Greendale, WI 53129-1824, (414)423-8660
Volunteer Optometric Services to Humanity/International **[★12482]**
Volunteer Optometric Services to Humanity/International **[★12482]**
Volunteer Ser. Abroad - New Zealand **[IO]**, Wellington, New Zealand
Volunteer Ser. Overseas - United Kingdom **[IO]**, London, United Kingdom
Volunteer Services for the Blind **[★17063]**
Volunteer Soc. Nepal **[IO]**, Kathmandu, Nepal
Volunteering Ecuador Org. **[IO]**, Quito, Ecuador
Volunteering Ireland **[IO]**, Dublin, Ireland
Volunteering New Zealand **[IO]**, Wellington, New Zealand
VolunteerMatch **[18774]**, 717 California St., 2nd Fl., San Francisco, CA 94108, (415)241-6868
Volunteers in Action - Defunct.
Volunteers of Am. **[13206]**, 1660 Duke St., Alexandria, VA 22314, (703)341-5000
Volunteers in Asia **[13408]**, 1663 Mission St., Ste. 504, San Francisco, CA 94103, (415)904-8033
Volunteers in Asia **[13408]**, 1663 Mission St., Ste. 504, San Francisco, CA 94103, (415)904-8033
Volunteers' Circle of the Natl. Gallery of Canada **[IO]**, Ottawa, ON, Canada
Volunteers in Hea. Care **[14834]**, 111 Brewster St., Pawtucket, RI 02860, (401)729-3284

Volunteers for Intl. Development **[★18280]**
Volunteers for Intl. Development **[★18280]**
Volunteers and Interns for Balinese Educ. Found. **[IO]**, Bali, Indonesia
Volunteers for Israel **[18016]**, 330 W 42nd St., Ste. 1618, New York, NY 10036, (212)643-4848
Volunteers for Israel **[18016]**, 330 W 42nd St., Ste. 1618, New York, NY 10036, (212)643-4848
Volunteers in Overseas Assistance **[★4174]**
Volunteers in Overseas Assistance **[★4174]**
Volunteers for Peace **[17990]**, 7 Kilburn St., Ste. 316, Burlington, VT 05401, (802)540-3060
Volunteers for Peace **[17990]**, 7 Kilburn St., Ste. 316, Burlington, VT 05401, (802)540-3060
Volunteers in Prevention, Probation, Prisons **[11737]**, Grand Park Ctre., 28 W Adams, Ste. 1310, Detroit, MI 48226, (313)964-1110
Volunteers in Probation **[★11737]**
Volunteers for Rural India **[IO]**, South Harrow, United Kingdom
Volunteers in Ser. to Am. **[★13381]**
Volunteers for TAU - Defunct.
Volvo Club of Am. **[21194]**, PO Box 16, Afton, NY 13730
Von Braun Astronomical Soc. **[6237]**, PO Box 1142, Huntsville, AL 35807
VON Coalition **[2120]**, 2300 N St. NW, Washington, DC 20037, (202)663-8215
Von Hippel-Lindau Family Alliance **[★14636]**
Vonumu Intl. **[★11513]**
Voorlichtingsbureau Vlees **[★IO]**
VOR **[12513]**, 836 S Arlington Heights Rd., No. 351, Elk Grove Village, IL 60007-3667, (877)399-4867
VOSH Intl. **[12482]**, PO Box 209, Ipswich, MA 01938, (407)328-5825
VOSH Intl. **[12482]**, PO Box 209, Ipswich, MA 01938, (407)328-5825
Vote Hemp **[18609]**, PO Box 1571, Brattleboro, VT 05302, (202)318-8999
Vote Solar Initiative **[7451]**, 300 Brannan St., Ste. 609, San Francisco, CA 94107, (415)817-5062
Voter Action **[18394]**, 2366 Eastlake Ave. E, Ste. 311, Seattle, WA 98102, (206)723-1941
Voter Participation; Black Women's Roundtable on **[18377]**
Voter Registration
 Korean Amer. Voters' Coun. **[18034]**
 Mobile Voter **[18096]**
Voter Rights March - Address unknown since 2011.
Voters for Peace **[18300]**, 2842 N Calvert St., Baltimore, MD 21218, (443)708-8360
Voters Telecomm Watch - Defunct.
The VP Found. **[★15896]**
The VP Found. **[★15896]**
VPP; Assn. of Intellectual Property Rights **[IO]**, Duisburg, Germany
Vrouwen Overleg Komitee **[IO]**, Brussels, Belgium
VSA arts **[11835]**, 818 Connecticut Ave. NW, Ste. 600, Washington, DC 20006, (202)628-2800
VSA Arts **[★11835]**
VSA Arts of Albania **[IO]**, Tirana, Albania
VSA Arts of Argentina **[IO]**, Buenos Aires, Argentina
VSA Arts of Brazil **[IO]**, Rio de Janeiro, Brazil
VSA Arts of Cyprus **[IO]**, Nicosia, Cyprus
VSA - The Intl. Org. on Arts and Disability **[11835]**, 818 Connecticut Ave. NW, Ste. 600, Washington, DC 20006, (202)628-2800
Vserossiiskoe Obschestvo Slepykn **[★IO]**
VUFO-NGO Rsrc. Centre **[IO]**, Hanoi, Vietnam
Vulval Pain Soc. **[IO]**, Nottingham, United Kingdom
Vulvar Pain Found. **[15896]**, PO Box 177, Graham, NC 27253, (336)226-0704
Vulvar Pain Found. **[15896]**, PO Box 177, Graham, NC 27253, (336)226-0704
Vulvodynia Assn; Natl. **[17131]**
Vuokralaisten Keskusliito **[★IO]**
VXIbus Consortium **[7562]**, PO Box 1016, Niwot, CO 80544-1016, (303)652-2585

W

W. E. Upjohn Inst. for Community Res. **[★11961]**
W. E. Upjohn Inst. for Employment Res. **[11961]**, 300 S Westnedge Ave., Kalamazoo, MI 49007-4686, (269)343-5541

A star before a book entry number signifies that the name is not listed separately, but is mentioned within the entry.

W. Maurice Young Centre for Applied Ethics [IO], Vancouver, BC, Canada

W. T. Bandy Center for Baudelaire Stud. [★9429]

WA Horse Trekkers Club [IO], Burekup, Australia

WAAG Agility Dog Club [IO], Ashmore, Australia

Waan Aelon in Majel [★IO]

Wabash, Frisco and Pacific Assn. [10503], Mr. Jim Greathouse, Treas., 11 Manas Dr., Belleville, IL 62226

Wagner And Griswold Soc. [21859], 3514 66th Ave. W, University Place, WA 98466, (253)566-0854

Wagner Soc. of New York [10311], PO Box 230949, Ansonia Sta., New York, NY 10023-0949, (212)749-4561

Wahana Lingkungan Hidup Indonesia [★IO]

Waikato Head Injury Soc. [IO], Hamilton, New Zealand

Wainwright House [20260], 260 Stuyvesant Ave., Rye, NY 10580-3115, (914)967-6080

Wainwright House Center for Development of Human Potential [★20260]

Waiters Assn. - Address unknown since 2011.

Wakeboarding New Zealand [IO], Auckland, New Zealand

Waksman Found. for Microbiology [6324], Swarthmore Coll., Dept. of Biology, 500 Coll. Ave., Swarthmore, PA 19081-1390, (610)328-8044

Wal-Mart Workers for Change [23232], 1775 K St. NW, Washington, DC 20006, (866)587-2299

Walden Woods Proj. [9736], 44 Baker Farm Rd., Lincoln, MA 01773-3004, (781)259-4700

Waldensian

Amer. Waldensian Soc. [20281]

Waldorf Early Childhood Assn. of North Am. [8743], 285 Hungry Hollow Rd., Chestnut Ridge, NY 10977, (845)352-1690

Waldorf Kindergarten Assn. of North Am. [★8743]

Wales Craft Coun. [IO], Welshpool, United Kingdom

Wales North Am. Bus. Chamber [23389], 69 Closter Rd., Palisades, NY 10964, (845)398-0619

Wales North Am. Bus. Chamber [23389], 69 Closter Rd., Palisades, NY 10964, (845)398-0619

Wales Young Farmers' Clubs [IO], Builth Wells, United Kingdom

Wales Young Farmers' Clubs - Carmarthenshire Fed. [IO], Carmarthen, United Kingdom

Wales Young Farmers' Clubs - Clwyd Fed. [IO], Ruthin, United Kingdom

Wales Young Farmers' Clubs - Eryri Fed. [IO], Caernarfon, United Kingdom

Wales Young Farmers' Clubs - Glamorgan Fed. [IO], Pencoed, United Kingdom

Wales Young Farmers' Clubs - Gwent Fed. [IO], Usk, United Kingdom

Wales Young Farmers' Clubs - Meirionnydd Fed. [IO], Dolgellau, United Kingdom

Wales Young Farmers' Clubs - Montgomery Fed. [IO], Newtown, United Kingdom

Wales Young Farmers' Clubs - Pembrokeshire Fed. [IO], Haverfordwest, United Kingdom

Wales Young Farmers' Clubs - Radnor Fed. [IO], Llandrindod Wells, United Kingdom

Wales Young Farmers' Clubs - Ynys Mon Fed. [IO], Holyhead, United Kingdom

WALHI [IO], Jakarta, Indonesia

Walk Across Am. and Europe [★17890]

Walkaloosa Horse Assn. [4658], 4055 Villa Creek Rd., Cayucos, CA 93430, (805)995-1894

Walkaloosa Horse Assn. [4658], 4055 Villa Creek Rd., Cayucos, CA 93430, (805)995-1894

Walking

Am. Walks [18775]

Walking Assn. - Defunct.

Walking Horse Owners' Assn. [4659], PO Box 4007, Murfreesboro, TN 37129, (615)494-8822

Walking Horse Trainers Assn. [4660], 1101 N Main St., PO Box 61, Shelbyville, TN 37162, (931)684-5866

Walking on Water [19605], 5928 Balfour Ct., Ste. C, Carlsbad, CA 92008, (760)438-1111

Wallace Found. [11912], 5 Penn Plz., 7th Fl., New York, NY 10001, (212)251-9700

Wallace Genetic Found. [3767], 4910 Massachusetts Ave. NW, Ste. 221, Washington, DC 20016, (202)966-2932

Wallcovering Distributors Assn. [★2075]

Wallcovering Mfrs. Assn. [★2075]

Wallcoverings Assn. [2075], 401 N Michigan Ave., Ste. 2200, Chicago, IL 60611, (312)321-5166

Wallenberg Comm. of the U.S; Raoul [17569]

Wallpaper Wholesalers Assn. [★2075]

Wally Byam Caravan Club Intl. [22152], PO Box 612, Jackson Center, OH 45334, (937)596-5211

Walmsley Soc. [IO], Eastbourne, United Kingdom

Walnut Coun. [4759], Wright Forestry Center, 1007 N 725 W, West Lafayette, IN 47906-9431, (765)583-3501

Walnut Marketing Bd. [★4748]

Walpole Soc. [IO], London, United Kingdom

Walt Disney Collectors Soc. - Address unknown since 2011.

Walt Whitman Birthplace Assn. [9422], 246 Old Walt Whitman Rd., Huntington Station, NY 11746-4148, (631)427-5240

Walter Burley Griffin Soc. of Am. [9142], 1152 Center Dr., St. Louis, MO 63117, (314)644-4546

Walters Intl. Speakers Bur. - Address unknown since 2011.

WAM Intl.: Women Advancing Microfinance [1330], 402 Constitution Ave. NE, Washington, DC 20002, (202)547-4546

WAND Educ. Fund [18220], 691 Massachusetts Ave., Arlington, MA 02476, (781)643-6740

Wanderer Forum Found. [19513], PO Box 542, Hudson, WI 54016-0542, (651)276-1429

WAP Forum [★7549]

War Agencies Employee Protection Agency [★5502]

War Agencies Employee Protection Agency [★5502]

War on Drugs - Defunct.

War of 1812

Gen. Soc. of the War of 1812 [20840]

Natl. Soc., U.S. Daughters of 1812 [20841]

War and Peace Found. [18301], 20 E 9th St., No. 23E, New York, NY 10003, (212)228-5836

War and Peace Found. [18301], 20 E 9th St., No. 23E, New York, NY 10003, (212)228-5836

War; Poets Against the [10734]

War Relief Services - Natl. Catholic Welfare Conf. [★12776]

War Relief Services - Natl. Catholic Welfare Conf. [★12776]

War Resistance

Americans Against World Empire [18776]

Center on Conscience and War [17560]

Central Comm. for Conscientious Objectors [17561]

Environmentalists Against War [18777]

Historians Against the War [18778]

Invisible Children [17237]

Iraq Veterans Against the War [20842]

Military Families Speak Out [18779]

Voters for Peace [18300]

War Resisters' Intl. [IO], London, United Kingdom

War Resisters League [18177], 339 Lafayette St., New York, NY 10012, (212)228-0450

War on Want [IO], London, United Kingdom

War Widows' Assn. of Great Britain [IO], London, United Kingdom

Ward Found. [★9252]

Wardens Assn. of Am. [★11727]

Wardens Assn. of Am. [★11727]

Warehouse Distributors Assn. [★3625]

Warehouse Distributors Assn. for Leisure and Mobile Products - Defunct.

Warehousing

Affiliated Warehouse Companies [3617]

Amer. Chain of Warehouses [3618]

Intl. Assn. of Refrigerated Warehouses [3619]

Intl. Assn. of Refrigerated Warehouses [3619]

Intl. Liquid Terminals Assn. [3620]

Intl. Warehouse Logistics Assn. [3621]

Intl. Warehouse Logistics Assn. [3621]

Mobile Self-Storage Assn. [3622]

Order Fulfillment Coun. | Material Handling Indus. of Am. [3623]

Performance Warehouse Assn. [3624]

Recreational Vehicle Aftermarket Assn. [3625]

Self Storage Assn. [3626]

Warehousing Educ. and Res. Coun. [3627]

World Food Logistics Org. [3628]

World Food Logistics Org. [3628]

Warehousing Educ. and Res. Coun. [3627], 1100 Jorie Blvd., Ste. 170, Oak Brook, IL 60523-4423, (630)990-0001

Warm Blankets Orphan Care Intl. [11515], 5105 Tollview Dr., Ste. 155, Rolling Meadows, IL 60008, (847)577-1070

Warringah Coun. [IO], Dee Why, Australia

Warrington Anglers Assn. [IO], Warrington, United Kingdom

Warrington Chamber of Commerce and Indus. [IO], Warrington, United Kingdom

Washburn Alumni Assn. [18914], 1700 SW Coll. Ave., Topeka, KS 66621, (785)670-1171

Washington Calligraphers Guild [10759], PO Box 3688, Merrifield, VA 22116-3688

Washington Capitals Fan Club [23912], PO Box 2802, Springfield, VA 22152-0802

Washington Ethical Soc. [19821], 7750 16th St. NW, Washington, DC 20012-1462, (202)882-6650

Washington Feed Assn. [★3959]

Washington Forest Protection Assn. [1487], 724 Columbia St. NW, Ste. 250, Olympia, WA 98501, (360)352-1500

Washington Friends Seminar Prog. [★17710]

The Washington Gp. [19269], PO Box 11248, Washington, DC 20008, (202)586-7227

Washington HQ Assn. [★10679]

Washington Home Center for Palliative Care Stud. [★11746]

Washington Inst. of Foreign Affairs

Washington Inst. of Foreign Affairs - Address unknown since 2011.

Washington Journalism Center [8449], Boston Univ., 2807 Connecticut Ave. NW, Washington, DC 20008, (202)756-7804

Washington Legal Found. [5940], 2009 Massachusetts Ave. NW, Washington, DC 20036-1011, (202)588-0302

Washington Natl. Monument Assn. - Defunct.

Washington Off. on Latin Am. [18058], 1666 Connecticut Ave. NW, Ste. 400, Washington, DC 20009, (202)797-2171

Washington Off. on Latin Am. [18058], 1666 Connecticut Ave. NW, Ste. 400, Washington, DC 20009, (202)797-2171

Washington Press Club [★2853]

Washington State Apple Commn. [4483], PO Box 18, Wenatchee, WA 98807-0018, (509)663-9600

Washington Workshops Found. [7863], 1250 24th St. NW, Ste. 300, Washington, DC 20037, (202)965-3434

Washington's Army at Valley Forge [★20342]

Waste

Alliance of Foam Packaging Recyclers [4978]

Amer. Coal Ash Assn. [3629]

Asphalt Recycling and Reclaiming Assn. [3630]

Assn. of Professional Animal Waste Specialists [3631]

Assn. of State and Territorial Solid Waste Mgt. Officials [6065]

Automotive Recyclers Assn. [3632]

Basel Action Network [18780]

Basel Action Network [18780]

Battery Recycling Assn. of North Am. [3071]

Biomass Power Assn. [7292]

Center For Hea., Env. and Justice [4979]

CHWMEG [3633]

Clean Water Constr. Coalition [4989]

Clean the World [4869]

Coalition for Responsible Waste Incineration [3634]

Community Environmental Coun. [4980]

EcoLogical Mail Coalition [4698]

Energy Recovery Coun. [4981]

Environmental Cleanup Coalition [4788]

Environmental Indus. Associations [3635]

Equip. Managers Coun. of Am. [845]

Freecycle Network [4870]

Global Alliance for Incinerator Alternatives [4982]

Global Alliance for Incinerator Alternatives [4982]

Ground Water Protection Coun. [3636]

Inst. of Scrap Recycling Indus. [3637]

Inst. of Scrap Recycling Indus. [3637]

Municipal Waste Mgt. Assn. [6066]

Reference to "IO" in place of a book number signifies that the association may be found in the 50th edition of International Organizations.

Natl. Assn. for PET Container Resources [3638]
Natl. Assn. of Wastewater Transporters [3639]
Natl. Coun. on Paint Disposition [4765]
Natl. Onsite Wastewater Recycling Assn. [4983]
Natl. Recycling Coalition [3640]
Paper Stock Indus. Chap. of ISRI [3641]
Portable Sanitation Assn. Intl. [3642]
Portable Sanitation Assn. Intl. [3642]
Reuse Development Org. [4984]
Solid Waste Assn. of North Am. [6067]
Steel Recycling Inst. [3643]
Sustainable Packaging Coalition [4764]
U.S. Composting Coun. [6068]
Waste Equip. Tech. Assn. [3644]
Waste-to-Energy Res. and Tech. Coun. [7593]
Zero Waste Alliance [4985]
Zero Waste Alliance [4985]
Waste Care [IO], Leeds, United Kingdom
Waste Equip. Mfrs. Inst. [★3644]
Waste Equip. Tech. Assn. [3644], 4301 Connecticut
Ave. NW, Ste. 300, Washington, DC 20008-2304,
(202)244-4700
Waste Mgt. Assn. of Australia [IO], Burwood,
Australia
Waste Mgt. and Recycling Assn. of Singapore [IO],
Singapore, Singapore
Waste-to-Energy Res. and Tech. Coun. [7593],
Columbia Univ., Earth Engg. Ctr., Mudd Bldg., Rm.
926, 500 W 120th St., New York, NY 10027,
(212)854-9136
Waste Watch [IO], London, United Kingdom
Watchable Wildlife [5141], PO Box 319, Marine on
St. Croix, MN 55047, (651)433-4100
Watchlist on Children and Armed Conflict [11427],
Women's Refugee Commn., 122 E 42nd St., 12th
Fl., New York, NY 10168-1289, (212)551-2941
Watchlist on Children and Armed Conflict [11427],
Women's Refugee Commn., 122 E 42nd St., 12th
Fl., New York, NY 10168-1289, (212)551-2941
Watchman Fellowship [19643], PO Box 13340,
Arlington, TX 76094, (817)277-0023
Water
 Active: Water [13410]
 Agua Muisne [13411]
 Agua Muisne [13411]
 Aguayuda [13412]
 Aguayuda [13412]
 Alliance for Water Educ. [8149]
 Alliance for Water Efficiency [4986]
 Amer. Decentralized Wastewater Assn. [3645]
 Amer. Ground Water Trust [3646]
 Amer. Rivers [3996]
 Amer. Shore and Beach Preservation Assn.
  [3997]
 Amer. Water Works Assn. [3647]
 Amer. Water Works Assn. [3647]
 Amman Imman: Water is Life [13413]
 Assn. of Water Technologies [3648]
 Australasian Bottled Water Inst. [3272]
 charity: water [13414]
 charity: water [13414]
 A Child's Right [13415]
 Clean Water Action [4987]
 Clean Water Am. Alliance [4988]
 Clean Water Constr. Coalition [4989]
 Clean Water Fund [4990]
 Clean Water for Haiti [4991]
 Clean Water for Haiti [4991]
 Clean Water for the World [13416]
 Community Water Solutions [13417]
 A Cup of Water Intl. [20282]
 Dam Safety Coalition [13418]
 Deep Springs Intl. [4992]
 Drinking Water for India [13419]
 Environmental Cleanup Coalition [4788]
 Gift of Water [13420]
 Give Clean Water [13421]
 Global Water Challenge [4993]
 Global Water Challenge [4993]
 Groundwater Found. [4994]
 Groundwater Mgt. Caucus [7599]
 Groundwater Mgt. Districts Assn. [4995]
 H2O for Life [13422]
 H2O for Life [13422]
 Healing Waters Intl. [13423]

 Healing Waters Intl. [13423]
 In Our Own Quiet Way [13424]
 Intl. Action [13425]
 Intl. Water Level Coalition [5004]
 Irrigation Water Mgt. Soc. [5005]
 Keepers of the Waters [4996]
 Keepers of the Waters [4996]
 League to Save Lake Tahoe [4091]
 Liquid Water [13426]
 Millennium Water Alliance [13427]
 Natl. Assn. of Pond Professionals [237]
 Natl. Assn. of Water Companies [3649]
 Natl. Flood Determination Assn. [4732]
 Natl. Ground Water Assn. [3650]
 Natl. Ground Water Assn. [3650]
 Natl. Utility Contractors Assn. I Clean Water Coun.
  [4997]
 Native Amer. Water Assn. [3651]
 Nature Healing Nature [11614]
 Nature's Voice Our Choice [4998]
 Personal Submersibles Org. [7148]
 Primero Agua [13428]
 Restore America's Estuaries [4999]
 Rivers Without Borders [4134]
 Safe Water Network [13429]
 Save the Rain [13430]
 Seeking Ecology Educ. and Design Solutions
  [4216]
 Soc. of Environmental Understanding and Sus-
  tainability [5000]
 Solar for Peace [7447]
 SURGE [13431]
 Thirst Relief Intl. [13432]
 Thirst Relief Intl. [13432]
 U.S. Water and Power [6121]
 Water 1st Intl. [13433]
 Water 1st Intl. [13433]
 Water Alliance for Africa [13434]
 Water Design-Build Coun. [634]
 Water Innovations Alliance [7614]
 Water for Life Intl. [13436]
 Water is Life Intl. [13435]
 Water Missions Intl. [13437]
 Water Missions Intl. [13437]
 Water Quality Assn. [3652]
 Water Resources Coalition [7615]
 Water for Sudan [13438]
 Water Systems Coun. [3653]
 Water to Thrive [13439]
 Water to Thrive [13439]
 Water for Waslala [13440]
 Water for Waslala [13440]
 WaterAid Am. [13441]
 WateReuse Assn. [5001]
 WaterPartners Intl. [13442]
 WaterPartners Intl. [13442]
 Wine to Water [13443]WaterWorld Water Coun.
 World Water Org. [13444]
 World Water Org. [13444]
 World Water Relief [13445]
Water 1st Intl. [13433], 1904 3rd Ave., Ste. 1012,
Seattle, WA 98101, (206)297-3024
Water 1st Intl. [13433], 1904 3rd Ave., Ste. 1012,
Seattle, WA 98101, (206)297-3024
Water Advocates [9049], 1506 21st St. NW, Ste.
200, Washington, DC 20036, (202)293-4002
Water Advocates [9049], 1506 21st St. NW, Ste.
200, Washington, DC 20036, (202)293-4002
Water Alliance for Africa [13434], 3267 E 3300 S,
No. 535, Salt Lake City, UT 84109
Water Conditioning Intl. [★3652]
Water Conditioning Found. [★3652]
Water Conservation
 Alliance for Water Educ. [8149]
 Clean Water for Haiti [4991]
 Environmental Commons [4049]
 Global Water Challenge [4993]
 Irrigation Water Mgt. Soc. [5005]
 Save the Rain [13430]
 Water Resources Coalition [7615]
 World Water Org. [13444]
Water Design-Build Coun. [634], Sarah Chittenden,
Exec. Dir., 1025 Connecticut Ave. NW, Ste. 1204,
Washington, DC 20036, (202)833-1950
Water Env. Fed. [4801], 601 Wythe St., Alexandria,
VA 22314-1994, (703)684-2400

Water Env. Fed. [4801], 601 Wythe St., Alexandria,
VA 22314-1994, (703)684-2400
Water Innovations Alliance [7614], 4 Res. Dr., Ste.
402, Shelton, CT 06484, (203)733-1949
Water Inst. of Southern Africa [IO], Halfway House,
Republic of South Africa
Water Jetting Assn. [IO], Erith, United Kingdom
Water for Life Intl. [13436], 514 Via de la Valle, Ste.
207, Solana Beach, CA 92075, (858)509-9445
Water is Life Intl. [13435], 399 Carolina Ave., Ste.
200, Winter Park, FL 32789, (407)435-2112
Water Lily Soc. [★21806]
Water Lily Soc. [★21806]
Water Missions Intl. [13437], PO Box 31258,
Charleston, SC 29417, (843)769-7395
Water Missions Intl. [13437], PO Box 31258,
Charleston, SC 29417, (843)769-7395
Water New Zealand [IO], Wellington, New Zealand
Water for People [17928], 6666 W Quincy Ave.,
Denver, CO 80235-3098, (720)488-4590
Water for People I PlayPumps Intl. [10827], 1717
Rhode Island Ave. NW, Ste. 700, Washington, DC
20036, (720)488-4590
Water Planet USA [4713], 203 Greenwood Dr.,
Panama City Beach, FL 32407, (850)230-6030
Water Planet USA [4713], 203 Greenwood Dr.,
Panama City Beach, FL 32407, (850)230-6030
Water Pollution
 Clean Water Am. Alliance [4988]
 Ocean Futures Soc. [5002]
 Ocean Futures Soc. [5002]
 Water for Life Intl. [13436]
Water Pollution Control Fed. [★4801]
Water Pollution Control Fed. [★4801]
Water Polo
 Collegiate Water Polo Assn. [23112]
 U.S. Water Polo [23113]
Water Polo Canada [IO], Gloucester, ON, Canada
Water Polo Comm. of the Amateur Athletic Union
 [★23113]
Water Quality Assn. [3652], 4151 Naperville Rd.,
Lisle, IL 60532-1088, (630)505-0160
Water Quality Insurance Syndicate [2046], 60 Broad
St., 33rd Fl., New York, NY 10004, (212)292-8700
Water Resources
 Active: Water [13410]
 Agricultural Drainage Mgt. Coalition [5003]
 Agua Muisne [13411]
 Aguayuda [13412]
 Alliance for Water Educ. [8149]
 Alliance for Water Efficiency [4986]
 Amer. Inst. of Hydrology [7594]
 Amer. Membrane Tech. Assn. [7595]
 Amer. Membrane Tech. Assn. [7595]
 Amer. Rainwater Catchment Systems Assn.
  [7596]
 Amer. Soc. of Irrigation Consultants [7597]
 Amer. Water Resources Assn. [7598]
 Amer. Water Resources Assn. [7598]
 Amman Imman: Water is Life [13413]
 Aquatic Resources Educ. Assn. [9048]
 charity: water [13414]
 A Child's Right [13415]
 Clean Water Am. Alliance [4988]
 Clean Water Constr. Coalition [4989]
 Clean Water for Haiti [4991]
 Clean Water for the World [13416]
 Community Water Solutions [13417]
 A Cup of Water Intl. [20282]
 Dam Safety Coalition [13418]
 Drinking Water for India [13419]
 Environmental Cleanup Coalition [4788]
 Give Clean Water [13421]
 Global Water Challenge [4993]
 Groundwater Mgt. Caucus [7599]
 H2O for Life [13422]
 In Our Own Quiet Way [13424]
 Intl. Action [13425]
 Intl. Desalination Assn. [7600]
 Intl. Desalination Assn. [7600]
 Intl. Network on Participatory Irrigation Mgt.
  [7016]
 Intl. Rainwater Catchment Systems Assn. [7601]
 Intl. Rainwater Catchment Systems Assn. [7601]
 Intl. Rivers [7602]

A star before a book entry number signifies that the name is not listed separately, but is mentioned within the entry.

Intl. Rivers [7602]
Intl. Water Level Coalition [5004]
Irrigation Water Mgt. Soc. [5005]
Liquid Water [13426]
Millennium Water Alliance [13427]
Natl. Groundwater Assn. I Assn. of Ground Water Scientists and Engineers [7603]
Natl. Hydrologic Warning Coun. [7604]
Natl. Institutes for Water Resources [7605]
Natl. Water Center [7606]
Natl. Water Resources Assn. [7607]
Nature's Voice Our Choice [4998]
New Water Supply Coalition [7608]
Ocean Renewable Energy Coalition [6747]
Passaic River Coalition [7609]
Primero Agua [13428]
Puerto Rico Water and Env. Assn. [5006]
Rivers Without Borders [4134]
Rural Community Assistance Partnership [7610]
Safe Water Network [13429]
Save the Waves Coalition [5007]
Southeast Desalting Assn. [5008]
SURGE [13431]
Thirst Relief Intl. [13432]
U.S. Comm. on Irrigation and Drainage [7611]
U.S. Soc. on Dams [7612]
Universities Coun. on Water Resources [7613]
Water 1st Intl. [13433]
Water Advocates [9049]
Water Advocates [9049]
Water Alliance for Africa [13434]
Water Innovations Alliance [7614]
Water for Life Intl. [13436]
Water is Life Intl. [13435]
Water Resources Coalition [7615]
Water for Sudan [13438]
Water to Thrive [13439]
Water for Waslala [13440]
WaterPartners Intl. [13442]
Wine to Water [13443]
World Ocean Coun. [5009]
World Ocean Coun. [5009]
World Water Org. [13444]
World Water Relief [13445]
Water Resources Coalition [7615], Amer. Soc. of Civil Engineers, 101 Constitution Ave. NW, Washington, DC 20001, (202)789-7850
Water Safety Cong; Natl. [12999]
Water Safety Cong; Natl. [12999]
Water Safety New Zealand [IO], Wellington, New Zealand
Water Sci. and Tech. Assn. [IO], Manama, Bahrain
Water Services Assn. of Australia [IO], Melbourne, Australia
Water and Sewage Works Mfrs. Assn. [★1878]
Water and Sewer Distributors of Am. [3610], 100 N 20th St., 4th Fl., Philadelphia, PA 19103-1443, (215)564-3484
Water Ski Indus. Assn. [★3321]
Water Ski and Wakeboard Canada [IO], Ottawa, ON, Canada
Water Skiing
   Amer. Barefoot Waterski Club [23114]
   Amer. Water Ski Educational Found. [23115]
   Intl. Jet Sports Boating Assn. and Amer. Watercraft Assn. [23116]
   Intl. Jet Sports Boating Assn. and Amer. Watercraft Assn. [23116]
   Natl. Collegiate Water Ski Assn. [23117]
   U.S. Hydrofoil Assn. [23118]
   U.S.A. Water Ski [23119]
Water Sports
   Amer. Barefoot Waterski Club [23114]
   Amer. Boating Assn. [22315]
   Amer. Canoe Assn. [23120]
   Amer. Power Boat Assn. [22316]
   Amer. Watercraft Assn. [23121]
   Blind Sailing Intl. [23109]
   Force 5 Class Assn. [22336]
   Geary 18 Intl. Yacht Racing Assn. [22338]
   Hampton One-Design Class Racing Assn. [22340]
   Highlander Class Intl. Assn. [22341]
   Intl. Hobie Class Assn. [22353]
   Intl. Laser Class Assn. - North Amer. Region [22356]

Intl. Rafting Fed. [22837]
Natl. Assn. of Black Scuba Divers [23122]
Natl. Assn. of Underwater Instructors [23104]
Natl. Butterfly Assn. [22371]
Natl. Starwind/Spindrift Class Assn. [22377]
Professional Assn. of Parasail Operators [23123]
Professional Windsurfers Assn. [22385]
Qajaq U.S.A. [23124]
Ships on Stamps Unit [22074]
U.S. A-Class Catamaran Assn. [22400]
U.S. Albacore Assn. [22401]
U.S. Canoe Assn. [23125]
U.S. Log Rolling Assn. [23126]
U.S. Power Squadrons [22405]
U.S. Wayfarer Assn. [22410]
U.S.A. Canoe/Kayak [23127]
USA Diving [22544]
World Freestyle Watercraft Alliance [23128]
World Freestyle Watercraft Alliance [23128]
World Masters Cross-Country Ski Assn. [22921]
Water Sports Indus. Assn. [3321], PO Box 568512, Orlando, FL 32856-8512, (407)251-9039
Water for Sudan [13438], PO Box 25551, Rochester, NY 14625, (585)383-0410
Water Supply Improvement Assn. [★7600]
Water Supply Improvement Assn. [★7600]
Water Systems Coun. [3653], 1101 30th St. NW, Ste. 500, Washington, DC 20007, (202)625-4387
Water to Thrive [13439], PO Box 26747, Austin, TX 78755, (512)206-4495
Water to Thrive [13439], PO Box 26747, Austin, TX 78755, (512)206-4495
Water Transport Assn. - Defunct.
Water UK [IO], London, United Kingdom
Water for Waslala [13440], Justin Knabb, Treas., 2000 Friedensburg Rd., Reading, PA 19606, (646)463-3391
Water for Waslala [13440], Justin Knabb, Treas., 2000 Friedensburg Rd., Reading, PA 19606, (646)463-3391
Water and Wastewater Equip. Mfrs. Assn. [1878], PO Box 17402, Washington, DC 20041, (703)444-1777
Water and Wastewater Instrumentation Testing Assn. of North Am. [★1920]
Water and Wastewater Instrumentation Testing Assn. of North Am. [★1920]
Water Works Mfrs. Assn. [★1878]
WaterAid Am. [13441], 315 Madison Ave., Ste. 2301, New York, NY 10017, (212)683-0430
WaterAid Burkina Faso [IO], Ouagadougou, Burkina Faso
Waterbed Coun. [★1556]
Waterbed Mfrs. Assn. [★1556]
Waterbirth Intl. [14109], PO Box 5578, Lighthouse Point, FL 33074, (954)821-9125
Waterbirth Intl. [14109], PO Box 5578, Lighthouse Point, FL 33074, (954)821-9125
WateReuse Assn. [5001], 1199 N Fairfax St., Ste. 410, Alexandria, VA 22314, (703)548-0880
Waterford Chamber [IO], Waterford, Ireland
Waterfowl U.S.A. [4159], Waterfowl Bldg., Box 50, Edgefield, SC 29824, (803)637-5767
Waterfront and Allied Workers' Union [IO], Roseau, Dominica
The Waterfront Center [11652], PO Box 53351, Washington, DC 20009, (202)337-0356
Watering Seeds Org. [22532], 6303 Owensmouth Ave., 10th Fl., Woodland Hills, CA 91367-2262, (818)936-3476
WaterJet Tech. Assn. [★6867]
WaterJet Tech. Association-Industrial and Municipal Cleaning Assn. [6867], 906 Olive St., Ste. 1200, St. Louis, MO 63101-1448, (314)241-1445
Waterless Printing Assn. [1632], PO Box 1252, Woodstock, IL 60098, (815)337-7681
Watermark Assn. of Artisans - Address unknown since 2011.
WaterPartners Intl. [13442], 920 Main St., Ste. 1800, Kansas City, MO 64105-2008, (913)312-8600
WaterPartners Intl. [13442], 920 Main St., Ste. 1800, Kansas City, MO 64105-2008, (913)312-8600
Waterski Assn. Zimbabwe [IO], Bulawayo, Zimbabwe
Wathnakpheap [IO], Phnom Penh, Cambodia

Watusi Intl. Assn. [★3944]
Watusi Intl. Assn. [★3944]
WAVES for Development [18683], 345 W 48th St., Ste. 1A, New York, NY 10036
Waves of Hea. [15222], 206 Bergen Ave., Ste. 203, Kearny, NJ 07032, (201)436-8888
WAVES Natl. [20739], Monica O'Hara, Natl. Treas., 6383 Kimmy Ct., San Diego, CA 92114-5631
Waves Natl. Corp. [★20739]
Waxed Paper Inst. [★2607]
The Way [★20106]
The Way [★20106]
The Way Intl. [20106], PO Box 328, New Knoxville, OH 45871-0328, (419)753-2523
The Way Intl. [20106], PO Box 328, New Knoxville, OH 45871-0328, (419)753-2523
Way to Work [11962], 52 Broadway, 6th Fl., New York, NY 10004, (212)823-1035
W.C. Fields Fan Club [23799], PO Box 506, Stratford, NJ 08084-0506
WDA: The RV Aftermarket Assn. [★3625]
We Are AWARE [13485], PO Box 242, Bedford, MA 01730-0242, (781)893-0500
We Are Family [12116], PO Box 21806, Charleston, SC 29413, (843)637-9379
We Care Prog. [11738], 3493 Hwy. 21, Atmore, AL 36502, (251)368-8818
We Interrupt This Message [18103], 1215 York St., San Francisco, CA 94110
We Love Lucy/International Lucille Ball Fan Club [23786], PO Box 56234, Sherman Oaks, CA 91413-1234
We the People [18188], 200 Harrison St., Oakland, CA 94607-4114, (510)836-DARE
We, The World [13123], 211 E 43rd St., Ste. 710, New York, NY 10017, (212)867-0846
WEA Intl. [★6637]
WEA Intl. [★6637]
WEA Scottish Assn. [IO], Edinburgh, United Kingdom
Weather
   Alliance for Climate Educ. [4315]
   Assn. of Climate Change Officers [4237]
   Catholic Coalition on Climate Change [4016]
   Climate Gp. [4023]
   Inst. of Global Env. and Soc. [4271]
   Natl. Assn. of Storm Chasers and Spotters [7616]
   Natl. Storm Shelter Assn. [3654]
   Natl. Weather Ser. Employees Org. [6069]
   Rising Tide North Am. [4131]
   Tropical Forest and Climate Coalition [4861]
   Weather Risk Mgt. Assn. [3655]
   Weather Risk Mgt. Assn. [3655]
Weather Control Res. Assn. [★7109]
Weather Modification Assn. [7109], PO Box 26926, Fresno, CA 93729-6926, (559)434-3486
Weather Risk Mgt. Assn. [3655], 529 14th St. NW, Ste. 750, Washington, DC 20045, (202)289-3800
Weather Risk Mgt. Assn. [3655], 529 14th St. NW, Ste. 750, Washington, DC 20045, (202)289-3800
Weatherby Collectors Assn. [21720], PO Box 1217, Washington, MO 63090, (636)239-0348
Weatherford Family Assn. - Defunct.
Weatherhead Center for Intl. Affairs [17959], Harvard Univ., 1737 Cambridge St., Cambridge, MA 02138-3016, (617)495-4420
Weatherhead Center for Intl. Affairs [17959], Harvard Univ., 1737 Cambridge St., Cambridge, MA 02138-3016, (617)495-4420
Weave a Real Peace [11115], 3102 N Classen Blvd., Oklahoma City, OK 73118-3899
WEB [★1134]
WEB [★1134]
Web Analytics Assn. [7009], 401 Edgewater Pl., Ste. 600, Wakefield, MA 01880, (781)876-8933
Web Host Guild - Defunct.
Web Network of Employee Benefits [★1134]
Web Network of Employee Benefits [★1134]
Web Network of Professional Benefits [★1134]
Web Network of Professional Benefits [★1134]
Web Offset Assn. [1633], Printing Indus. of Am., 200 Deer Run Rd., Sewickley, PA 15143, (412)259-1802
Web Sling Assn. [★1879]
Web Sling and Tie Down Assn. [1879], 2105 Laurel Bush Rd., Ste. 200, Bel Air, MD 21015, (443)640-1070

Reference to "IO" in place of a book number signifies that the association may be found in the 50th edition of International Organizations.

Web Wise Kids **[11428]**, PO Box 27203, Santa Ana, CA 92799, (714)435-2885

WEB - Worldwide Employee Benefits Network **[1134]**, 1701 Pennsylvania Ave. NW, Ste. 300, Washington, DC 20006, (888)795-6862

WEB - Worldwide Employee Benefits Network **[1134]**, 1701 Pennsylvania Ave. NW, Ste. 300, Washington, DC 20006, (888)795-6862

Web3D Consortium **[6566]**, 650 Castro St., Ste. 120-490, Mountain View, CA 94041, (248)342-7662

Webb Deep-Sky Soc. **[6238]**, 10575 Darrel Dr., Hanover, MI 49241

Webb Deep-Sky Soc. **[6238]**, 10575 Darrel Dr., Hanover, MI 49241

Webb Soc. **[★6238]**

Webb Soc. **[★6238]**

Webgrrls Intl. **[3691]**, PO Box 2425, New York, NY 10021, (888)932-4775

WEC Intl. **[19773]**, PO Box 1707, Fort Washington, PA 19034, (215)646-2322

WEC Intl. **[19773]**, PO Box 1707, Fort Washington, PA 19034, (215)646-2322

WECAI Network **[1054]**, PO Box 550856, Fort Lauderdale, FL 33355-0856, (954)625-6606

Wedding and Event Videographers Assn. Intl. **[1271]**, 8499 S Tamiami Trail, PMB 208, Sarasota, FL 34238, (941)923-5334

Wedding and Event Videographers Assn. Intl. **[1271]**, 8499 S Tamiami Trail, PMB 208, Sarasota, FL 34238, (941)923-5334

Wedding Indus. Professionals Assn. **[475]**, 8912 E Pinnacle Peak Rd., Ste. F9-111, Scottsdale, AZ 85255, (480)626-1657

Wedding Photographers of Am. **[★2739]**

Wedding Photographers of Am. **[★2739]**

Wedding Photographers Intl. **[★2739]**

Wedding Photographers Intl. **[★2739]**

Wedding and Portrait Photographers Intl. **[2739]**, 6059 Bristol Pkwy., Ste. 100, Culver City, CA 90230, (310)846-4770

Wedding and Portrait Photographers Intl. **[2739]**, 6059 Bristol Pkwy., Ste. 100, Culver City, CA 90230, (310)846-4770

Weddings Beautiful Worldwide **[476]**, 1004 N Thompson St., Ste. 101, Richmond, VA 23230, (804)342-6061

Weddings Beautiful Worldwide **[476]**, 1004 N Thompson St., Ste. 101, Richmond, VA 23230, (804)342-6061

Wedgwood Intl. Seminar **[21271]**, PO Box 674, Ontario, CA 91762-8674

Wedgwood Intl. Seminar **[21271]**, PO Box 674, Ontario, CA 91762-8674

Wedgwood Soc. of Great Britain **[IO]**, London, United Kingdom

Weed Sci. Soc. of Am. **[3748]**, 810 E 10th St., Lawrence, KS 66044-3018, (785)843-1235

Weed Sci. Soc. of Pakistan **[IO]**, Peshawar, Pakistan

Weed Soc. of Am. **[★3748]**

Weed Soc. of Victoria **[IO]**, Frankston, Australia

Weedman Family Genealogy - Defunct.

WEF Ministries **[★19732]**

WEF Ministries **[★19732]**

Wegener's Granulomatosis Assn. **[★16784]**

Wegener's Granulomatosis Assn. **[★16784]**

Wegener's Granulomatosis Support Gp. **[★16784]**

Wegener's Granulomatosis Support Gp. **[★16784]**

Wegener's Granulomatosis Support Gp. Intl. **[★16784]**

Wegener's Granulomatosis Support Gp. Intl. **[★16784]**

Weighing
  Intl. Soc. of Weighing and Measurement **[3656]**
  Intl. Soc. of Weighing and Measurement **[3656]**
  Scale Mfrs. Assn. **[3657]**

Weight-Control Info. Network **[15859]**, 1 WIN Way, Bethesda, MD 20892-3665, (202)828-1025

Weightlifting
  Intl. Natural Bodybuilding and Fitness Fed. **[22418]**
  Natural Fitness Trainers Assn. **[22809]**
  USA Weightlifting **[23129]**
  World Assn. of Benchers and Dead Lifters **[23130]**

World Assn. of Benchers and Dead Lifters **[23130]**

Weightlifting Assn. of Amer. Samoa **[IO]**, Pago Pago, American Samoa

Weightlifting and Body Building Assn. of Swaziland **[IO]**, Mbabane, Swaziland

Weightlifting Fed. of Azerbaijan **[IO]**, Baku, Azerbaijan

Weightlifting Fed. of Kyrgyzstan **[IO]**, Bishkek, Kirgizstan

Weightlifting Fed. of the Republic of Kazakhstan **[IO]**, Almaty, Kazakhstan

Weightlifting Fed. of Slovenia **[IO]**, Velenje, Slovenia

Weightlifting Fed. of Tonga **[IO]**, Nuku'alofa, Tonga

Weightlifting Fed. of Turkmenistan **[IO]**, Ashgabat, Turkmenistan

Weightlifting Fed. of Vietnam **[IO]**, Hanoi, Vietnam

Weimaraner Club of Am. **[21675]**, PO Box 489, Wakefield, RI 02880-0489, (401)782-3725

Welded Steel Tube Inst. **[★891]**

Welded Steel Tube Inst. **[★891]**

Welders Without Borders **[7619]**, Prof. Samuel Colton, Sr., Founder, 1931 W Allen St., Yuma, AZ 85364, (928)344-7570

Welders Without Borders **[7619]**, Prof. Samuel Colton, Sr., Founder, 1931 W Allen St., Yuma, AZ 85364, (928)344-7570

Welding
  Amer. Welding Soc. **[7617]**
  Amer. Welding Soc. **[7617]**
  Edison Welding Inst. **[7618]**
  European Fed. for Welding, Joining and Cutting **[23815]**
  Welders Without Borders **[7619]**
  Welders Without Borders **[7619]**
  Welding Res. Coun. **[7620]**

The Welding Inst. **[IO]**, Cambridge, United Kingdom

Welding Mfrs. Assn. **[IO]**, London, United Kingdom

Welding Res. Coun. **[7620]**, PO Box 1942, New York, NY 10156, (216)658-3847

Welding Tech. Inst. of Australia **[IO]**, Newington, Australia

Welfare Assn. for the Development of Afghanistan **[IO]**, Kabul, Afghanistan

Welfare of the Blind - Defunct.

Welfare Info. Network **[★12724]**

Welfare Law Center **[★5943]**

Welfare League Assn. of New York **[★11728]**

Welfare Org. for Women **[IO]**, Lahore, Pakistan

Welfare Res., Inc. **[13207]**, 112 State St., Ste. 1340, Albany, NY 12207, (518)432-2563

Welfare Warriors **[18226]**, 2711 W Michigan Ave., Milwaukee, WI 53208, (414)342-6662

Well Done Org. **[11653]**, 10813 27th St. SE, Lake Stevens, WA 98258, (206)349-1574

Well Drillers Assn. **[IO]**, Nuneaton, United Kingdom

Well Proj. **[13627]**, PO Box 768, Nellysford, VA 22958, (888)616-9355

Well Services Contractors Assn. **[IO]**, Aberdeen, United Kingdom

Well Spouse Assn. **[16785]**, 63 W Main St., Ste. H, Freehold, NJ 07728, (732)577-8899

Well Spouse Found. **[★16785]**

Well-Springs Found. **[9831]**, Pat Kinnamon, Exec. Dir., 550 W Butternut Rd., Summerville, SC 29483, (843)873-1960

Wellesley Centers for Women **[9066]**, Wellesley Coll., 106 Central St., Wellesley, MA 02481, (781)283-2500

Wellesley Coll. Alumnae Assn. **[18915]**, Green Hall, Rm. 246, 106 Central St., Wellesley, MA 02481-8203, (781)283-2331

Wellness Center - Defunct.

Wellness Councils of Am. **[14908]**, 17002 Marcy St., Ste. 140, Omaha, NE 68118, (402)827-3590

Wells Family Res. Assn. **[20606]**, PO Box 5427, Kent, WA 98064-5427

Wells Family Res. Assn. **[20606]**, PO Box 5427, Kent, WA 98064-5427

Wellstart Intl. **[14835]**, PO Box 602, Blue Jay, CA 92317-0602, (714)724-1675

Welsh
  Natl. Welsh-American Found. **[19278]**
  North Amer. Assn. for the Stud. of Welsh Culture and History **[10637]**

North Amer. Assn. for the Stud. of Welsh Culture and History **[10637]**

Welsh Natl. Gymanfa Ganu Assn. **[19279]**

Welsh Natl. Gymanfa Ganu Assn. **[19279]**

Welsh Amateur Dance Sport Assn. **[IO]**, Merthyr Tydfil, United Kingdom

Welsh Amateur Music Fed. **[IO]**, Cardiff, United Kingdom

Welsh-American Genealogical Soc. **[20665]**, 60 Norton Ave., Poultney, VT 05764-1029

Welsh Badminton Union **[IO]**, Cardiff, United Kingdom

Welsh Black Cattle Assn. - Defunct.

Welsh Black Cattle Soc. **[IO]**, Caernarfon, United Kingdom

Welsh Books Coun. **[IO]**, Aberystwyth, United Kingdom

Welsh Centre for Intl. Affairs **[IO]**, Cardiff, United Kingdom

Welsh Croquet Assn. **[IO]**, Caldicot, United Kingdom

Welsh Judo Assn. **[IO]**, Cardiff, United Kingdom

Welsh Liberal Democrats **[IO]**, Cardiff, United Kingdom

Welsh Music Guild **[IO]**, Barry, United Kingdom

Welsh Natl. Gymanfa Ganu Assn. **[19279]**, PO Box 410, Granville, OH 43023, (740)587-3936

Welsh Natl. Gymanfa Ganu Assn. **[19279]**, PO Box 410, Granville, OH 43023, (740)587-3936

Welsh Pony and Cob Soc. **[IO]**, Aberystwyth, United Kingdom

Welsh Pony and Cob Soc. of Am. **[4661]**, 720 Green St., Stephens City, VA 22655, (540)868-7669

Welsh Pony Soc. of Am. **[★4661]**

Welsh Propriety Soc. - Defunct.

Welsh Rugby Union **[IO]**, Cardiff, United Kingdom

Welsh Springer Spaniel Club of am. **[21676]**, Carla Vooris, Corresponding Sec., 783 Ellington Farm Rd., Manson, NC 27553, (252)456-3645

Welsh Terrier Club of Am. Rescue Ser. **[★21685]**

Welsh Women's Aid - Cardiff Natl. Off. **[IO]**, Cardiff, United Kingdom

Welt-Gesellschaft fur Buiatrik **[★IO]**

Welt-Tierarztgesellschaft **[★IO]**

Welthaus Bielefeld **[★IO]**

Weltorganisation fur Schiffsmodellbau und Schiffsmodellsport **[★IO]**

Weltrat fur Erneuerbare Energien **[★IO]**

Welttierschutzgesellschaft e.V. **[★IO]**

Weltverband der Sportartikel-Industrie **[★IO]**

Wemos **[IO]**, Amsterdam, Netherlands

Wensleydale Longwool Sheep Breeders' Assn. **[IO]**, Heighington, United Kingdom

WERA Motorcycle Roadracing **[22782]**, 2555 Marietta Hwy., Ste. 104, Canton, GA 30114, (770)720-5010

We're Welcome on Organic Farms - Austria **[IO]**, Stainz, Austria

Wereldsolidariteit **[★IO]**

Werkstatt 3 **[★IO]**

Wert Family History Assn. **[20607]**, PO Box 240, Port Royal, PA 17082-0240, (717)527-4399

Wesleyan/Holiness Women Clergy **[20002]**, 8611 Mayhew Rd., Fort Wayne, IN 46835, (260)241-2993

Wesleyan/Holiness Women Clergy **[20002]**, 8611 Mayhew Rd., Fort Wayne, IN 46835, (260)241-2993

West Africa
  Bodomase Development Assn. USA **[11551]**
  Medicine for Mali **[12468]**

West Africa Network for Peacebuilding **[IO]**, Accra, Ghana

West Africa Telecommunication Regulators Assn. **[IO]**, Abuja, Nigeria

West African Coll. of Surgeons **[IO]**, Lagos, Nigeria

West Australian Croquet Assn. **[IO]**, Mount Lawley, Australia

West Australian Olive Coun. **[IO]**, Warnbro, Australia

West Coast Book Prize Soc. **[IO]**, Vancouver, BC, Canada

West Coast Electronics Mfrs. Assn. **[★1122]**

West Coast Environmental Law **[IO]**, Vancouver, BC, Canada

West Coast Lumber Inspection Bur. **[1488]**, PO Box 23145, Tigard, OR 97281, (503)639-0651

A star before a book entry number signifies that the name is not listed separately, but is mentioned within the entry.

West Coast Lumbermen's Assn. [★1491]
West Coast Velocette Owners Club [★21941]
West-Europaisches Institut fur Holzimpragnierung [★IO]
West Gulf Maritime Assn. [2372], 1717 E Loop, Portway Plz., Ste. 200, Houston, TX 77029, (713)678-7655
West Highland White Terrier Club of Am. [21677], Cheryl Stinson, Membership Chair, 10613 Elder Ln., Prospect, KY 40059, (502)423-1668
West Indian
   Grenada Bd. of Tourism [23343]
   Montserrat Progressive Soc. of New York [19280]
West-Indian Amer. Military Members Assn. [5221], Joel Robertson, Webmaster, 7026 Commander Howe Terr., Brandywine, MD 20613, (301)782-4854
West Indies Mission [★20111]
West Indies Mission [★20111]
West Kent Chamber of Commerce and Indus. [IO], Tonbridge, United Kingdom
West Kootenay Brain Injury Assn. [IO], Castlegar, BC, Canada
West Midlands Campaign for Nuclear Disarmament [IO], Birmingham, United Kingdom
West Wales Chamber of Commerce [★18878]
West World Holiday Exchange [★21853]
Westar Inst. [20198], PO Box 7268, Santa Rosa, CA 95407, (707)523-1323
Western Apparel and Equip. Mfrs. Assn. [★3491]
Western Assoc. Modelers - Address unknown since 2010.
Western Assn. of Architects [★6183]
Western Assn. for Art Conservation [259], Natl. Park Ser., Intermountain Region Museum Services Prog., 255 N Commerce Park Loop, Tucson, AZ 85745, (520)791-6430
Western Assn. of Art Conservators [★259]
Western Assn. of Christian Schools [★7851]
Western Assn. of Christian Schools [★7851]
Western Assn. of Fish and Wildlife Agencies [5459], 522 Notre Dame Ct., Cheyenne, WY 82009, (307)638-1470
Western Assn. of Map Libraries [10018], Univ. of California, Sci. Lib., 1156 High St., Santa Cruz, CA 95064, (831)459-3187
Western Assn. of Schools and Colleges [8067], 985 Atlantic Ave., Ste. 100, Alameda, CA 94501, (510)748-9001
Western Assn. of State Game and Fish Commissioners [★5459]
Western Athletic Conf. [23017], 9250 E Costilla Ave., Ste. 300, Englewood, CO 80112, (303)799-9221
Western Australia Scripture Union [IO], Mount Hawthorn, Australia
Western Australian Assn. for Mental Hea. [IO], Perth, Australia
Western Australian Farmers Fed. [IO], East Perth, Australia
Western Australian Secondary School Executives Assn. [IO], West Leederville, Australia
Western Bohemian Fraternal Assn. [★18974]
Western Building Material Assn. [1489], PO Box 1699, Olympia, WA 98507, (360)943-3054
Western Canada Psychoanalytic Psychotherapy Assn. [IO], Vancouver, BC, Canada
Western Canada Wilderness Comm. [IO], Vancouver, BC, Canada
Western Canadian Watercross Assn. [IO], Fort McMurray, AB, Canada
Western Catholic Union [18960], 510 Maine St., Quincy, IL 62301, (217)223-9721
Western Center on Law and Poverty [5768], 3701 Wilshire Blvd., Ste. 208, Los Angeles, CA 90010-2809, (213)487-7211
Western Central Atlantic Fishery Commn. [IO], Bridgetown, Barbados
Western Coal Coun. Mission [★778]
Western Coal Trans. Assn. [★784]
Western Coll. Assn. - Defunct.
Western Coll. Reading Assn. [★8779]
Western Coll. Reading and Learning Assn. [★8779]
Western Collegiate Hockey Assn. [22648], 2211 S Josephine St., Denver, CO 80208, (303)871-4223
Western Coun. of Constr. Consumers [853], 1731 Howe Ave., Ste. 613, Sacramento, CA 95825-2209, (916)599-8020

Western Coun. on Intl. Banking [★420]
Western Coun. of Model Boating [★21908]
Western Coun. of Model Boating [★21908]
Western Cover Soc. [22092], 15370 Skyview Terr., San Jose, CA 95132-3042
Western Dredging Assn. [2373], PO Box 5797, Vancouver, WA 98668-5797, (360)750-0209
Western Eastern Roadracers Assn. [★22782]
Western Eastern Roadracer's Assn., Inc. [★22782]
Western Economic Assn. Intl. [6637], 18837 Brookhurst St., Ste. 304, Fountain Valley, CA 92708-7302, (714)965-8800
Western Economic Assn. Intl. [6637], 18837 Brookhurst St., Ste. 304, Fountain Valley, CA 92708-7302, (714)965-8800
Western Electronics Mfrs. Assn. [★1122]
Western Engine Rebuilders Assn. [★1185]
Western and English Mfrs. Assn. [★3491]
Western and English Sales Assn. [3491], 451 E 58th Ave., Ste. 4128, Denver, CO 80216, (800)295-1041
Western European Inst. for Wood Preservation [IO], Brussels, Belgium
Western European Union [IO], Brussels, Belgium
Western Fairs Assn. [1219], 1776 Tribute Rd., Ste. 210, Sacramento, CA 95815-4495, (916)927-3100
Western Fast-Draw Assn. [★22891]
Western Floor Covering Assn. [★3129]
Western Floor Covering Assn. [★3129]
Western Forestry Center [★4422]
Western Forestry Center [★4422]
Western Forestry and Conservation Assn. [4420], 4033 SW Canyon Rd., Portland, OR 97221, (503)226-4562
Western Forestry and Conservation Assn. [4420], 4033 SW Canyon Rd., Portland, OR 97221, (503)226-4562
Western Found. for Raptor Conservation [★7200]
Western Found. for Raptor Conservation [★7200]
Western Fraternal Life Assn. [18974], 1900 1st Ave. NE, Cedar Rapids, IA 52402-5321, (319)363-2653
Western Front Assn. - U.S. Br. [10100], Jeffrey Lamonica, Sec., 3116 S 17th St., Philadelphia, PA 19145, (845)486-6189
Western Fruit Jobbers Assn. [★4476]
Western Gerontological Soc. [★10833]
Western Golf Assn. [22629], 1 Briar Rd., Golf, IL 60029, (847)724-4600
Western Growers Assn. [4484], PO Box 2130, Newport Beach, CA 92658, (949)863-1000
Western Growers Protective Assn. [★4484]
Western Hardwood Assn. [1490], PO Box 1095, Camas, WA 98607, (360)835-1600
Western History Assn. [9128], Univ. of Missouri - St. Louis, 152C Univ. Center, 1 Univ. Blvd., St. Louis, MO 63121, (314)516-7282
Western Home Furnishings Assn. [1561], 500 Giuseppe Ct., Ste. 6, Roseville, CA 95678, (916)784-7677
Western Humor and Irony Membership [★9853]
Western Humor and Irony Membership [★9853]
Western Independent Bankers [439], 601 Montgomery St., Ste. 1200, San Francisco, CA 94111, (415)352-2323
Western Intl. Walking Horse Assn. [4662], PO Box 872288, Vancouver, WA 98687-2228, (503)349-5265
Western Intl. Walking Horse Assn. [4662], PO Box 872288, Vancouver, WA 98687-2228, (503)349-5265
Western Interpreters Assn. [★7142]
Western Interstate Energy Bd. [18189], 1600 Broadway, Ste. 1700, Denver, CO 80202, (303)573-8910
Western Interstate Nuclear Compact [★18189]
Western Literature Assn. [10052], Utah State Univ., English Dept., 3200 Old Main Hill, Logan, UT 84322-3200, (435)797-1603
Western Manufactured Housing Communities Assn. [2315], 455 Capitol Mall, Ste. 800, Sacramento, CA 95814, (916)448-7002
Western Mobilehome Parkowners Assn. [★2315]
Western Music Assn. [10312], 972 Mesquite Dr., Sierra Vista, AZ 85635, (520)456-7229
Western Natl. Parks Assn. [7145], 12880 N Vistoso Village Dr., Tucson, AZ 85755, (520)622-1999

Western New Mexico Univ. Alumni Assn. [18916], PO Box 680, Silver City, NM 88062, (575)538-6675
Western Oil and Gas Assn. [★2674]
Western Olive Assn. [IO], Warren, Australia
Western Pacific Assn. of Transactional Analysts [IO], Mosman, Australia
Western Payments Alliance [1331], 685 Market St., Ste. 540, San Francisco, CA 94105, (415)433-1230
Western Petroleum Refiners Assn. [★2662]
Western Pine Assn. [★1491]
Western Plumbing Officials Assn. [★5301]
Western Plumbing Officials Assn. [★5301]
Western Public Radio [2981], Ft. Mason Ctr., Bldg. D, San Francisco, CA 94123, (415)771-1160
Western Railway Supervisors Assn. [★23290]
Western Red Cedar Lumber Assn. [IO], Vancouver, BC, Canada
Western Retail Lumbermen's Assn. [★1489]
Western River Guides Assn. [★22835]
Western Roentgen Soc. [★16537]
Western Rugby Union of the United States [★22861]
Western Saddle Clubs Assn. [4663], Teri Spence, Sec., 47009 Company Rd. 13, St. Peter, MN 56082, (507)345-5856
Western Sahara Campaign for Human Rights and Humanitarian Relief - Defunct.
Western Shoe Retailers Assn. [★1463]
Western Slavonic Assn. [★19067]
Western Snow Conf. - Address unknown since 2011.
Western Social Sci. Assn. [7420], Yuma Br. Campus - NAU, PO Box 6236, Yuma, AZ 85366-6236, (928)317-6475
Western Soc. of Malacologists [7037], 16391 Del Oro Cir., Huntington Beach, CA 92649, (714)593-7460
Western Soc. of Naturalists [7146], San Diego State Univ., Dept. of Biology, 5500 Campanile Dr., San Diego, CA 92182
Western Soc. of Periodontology [14311], PO Box 458, Artesia, CA 90702-0458, (562)493-4080
Western Soc. of Periodontology [14311], PO Box 458, Artesia, CA 90702-0458, (562)493-4080
Western States Advt. Agencies Assn. [★109]
Western States Legal Found. [5869], 655 13th St., Ste. 201, Preservation Park, Oakland, CA 94612, (510)839-5877
Western States Petroleum Assn. [2674], 1415 L St., Ste. 600, Sacramento, CA 95814, (916)498-7750
Western Surgical Assn. [16826], Nonie Lowry, PO Box 411654, Kansas City, MO 64141, (913)402-7102
Western Timber Assn. [★1466]
Western Traders Assn. [★21361]
Western U.S. Agricultural Trade Assn. [3768], 4601 NE 77th Ave., Ste. 240, Vancouver, WA 98662-4730, (360)693-3373
Western Vehicle Leasing Assn. [★3082]
Western Veterinary Conf. [17052], 2425 E Oquendo Rd., Las Vegas, NV 89120, (702)739-6698
Western Wheat Assn. [★3964]
Western Wholesale Druggists [★16193]
Western Wholesale Pet Supply Assn. [★2688]
Western Wholesale Pet Supply Assn. [★2688]
Western Winter Sports Representatives Assn. [3342], 726 Tenacity Dr., Unit B, Longmont, CO 80504, (303)532-4002
Western Women Bowlers [★22431]
Western Women Premier Bowlers [22431], Mrs. Laura Hardeman, Sec., 938 Redbud Rd., Chula Vista, CA 91910
Western Women Professional Bowlers [★22431]
Western Wood Moulding Producers [★583]
Western Wood Moulding Producers [★583]
Western Wood Products Assn. [1491], 522 SW 5th Ave., Ste. 500, Portland, OR 97204-2122, (503)224-3930
Western World Pet Supply Assn. [★2688]
Western World Pet Supply Assn. [★2688]
Western Writers of Am. [10746], Rod Miller, 1665 E Julio St., Sandy, UT 84093, (505)277-5234
Westerners Found. [★9129]
Westerners Found. [★9129]

Reference to "IO" in place of a book number signifies that the association may be found in the 50th edition of International Organizations.

Westerners Intl. **[9129]**, 1700 NE 63rd St., Oklahoma City, OK 73111, (800)541-4650
Westerners Intl. **[9129]**, 1700 NE 63rd St., Oklahoma City, OK 73111, (800)541-4650
Westland Training - Defunct.
Westminster Kennel Club **[21678]**, 149 Madison Ave., Ste. 402, New York, NY 10016-6722, (212)213-3165
Weston A. Price Found. **[15848]**, PMB 106-380, 4200 Wisconsin Ave. NW, Washington, DC 20016, (202)363-4394
Weston A. Price Memorial Found. **[★15843]**
WeTip **[11697]**, PO Box 1296, Rancho Cucamonga, CA 91729-1296, (909)987-2477
Wetlands Intl. **[IO]**, Wageningen, Netherlands
Wetlands Intl. Asia Pacific-Indonesia Programme **[IO]**, Jawa Barat, Indonesia
Wett Ones **[IO]**, Newtown, Australia
Wexford Chamber of Indus. and Commerce **[IO]**, Wexford, Ireland
Whale and Dolphin Conservation Soc. **[IO]**, Chippenham, United Kingdom
Whale and Dolphin Watch Australia **[IO]**, Urangan, Australia
Whale Protection Fund **[★4115]**
Whale Protection Fund **[★4115]**
Whale Res; Center for **[7040]**
Whales
　Ocean Soc. **[7183]**
　World Whale Police **[5018]**
Whaling Museum Soc. **[10068]**, PO Box 25, Cold Spring Harbor, NY 11724, (631)367-3418
What Kids Can Do **[18834]**, PO Box 603252, Providence, RI 02906, (401)247-7665
Wheat Flour Inst. **[★2502]**
Wheat Foods Coun. **[1598]**, 51 D Red Fox Ln., Ridgway, CO 81432, (970)626-9828
Wheat Gluten Industry Coun. - Defunct.
Wheat Quality Coun. **[3966]**, PO Box 966, Pierre, SD 57501-0966, (605)224-5187
Wheat Ridge Found. **[★19942]**
Wheat Ridge Ministries **[19942]**, 1 Pierce Pl., Ste. 250E, Itasca, IL 60143-2634, (630)766-9066
Wheel Wishers **[7407]**, 26 Ave. Port Imperial, West New York, NJ 07093
Wheelchair and Ambulatory Sports, USA **[22533]**, Ralph Armento, Operations Mgr., PO Box 5266, Kendall Park, NJ 08824-5266, (732)266-2634
Wheelchair Basketball Canada **[IO]**, Ottawa, ON, Canada
Wheelchair Poolplayer Assn; Natl. **[22519]**
Wheelchair Poolplayer Assn; Natl. **[22519]**
Wheelchair Sports Alberta **[IO]**, Edmonton, AB, Canada
Wheelchair Sports Assn. of Newfoundland and Labrador **[IO]**, Paradise, NL, Canada
Wheelchair Sports Assn. of South Australia **[IO]**, Marleston, Australia
Wheelchair Sports New South Wales **[IO]**, Putney, Australia
Wheelchair Sports U.S.A. **[★22533]**
Wheelchair Sports Victoria **[IO]**, Abbotsford, Australia
The Wheelmen **[22491]**, 1552 Autumn Ridge Cir., Reston, VA 20194-1563
WheelPower - British Wheelchair Sport **[IO]**, Stoke Mandeville, United Kingdom
Wheels for the World **[11836]**, Joni and Friends Intl. Disability Center, PO Box 3333, Agoura Hills, CA 91376-3333, (818)707-5664
Wheels for the World **[11836]**, Joni and Friends Intl. Disability Center, PO Box 3333, Agoura Hills, CA 91376-3333, (818)707-5664
Where Peace Lives **[10355]**, PO Box 2007, Red Bank, NJ 07701
Whey Products Inst. **[★1017]**
Whirly-Girls - Intl. Women Helicopter Pilots **[20923]**, 4617 Gilronan Ct., Palm Harbor, FL 34685
Whisky Pitcher Collectors Assn. of Am. **[21413]**, 22862 Bluejay Ave., Mattawan, MI 49071, (269)668-4169
Whisky Pitcher Collectors Assn. of Am. **[21413]**, 22862 Bluejay Ave., Mattawan, MI 49071, (269)668-4169
Whisper - Defunct.
White Bison **[10338]**, 701 N 20th St., Colorado Springs, CO 80904, (719)548-1000

White German Shepherd Dog Club of Am. **[21679]**, 8837 N Mountain Dr., Mercersburg, PA 17236, (717)328-3339
White Goods Suppliers' Assn. **[IO]**, Istanbul, Turkey
White House Correspondents' Assn. **[2883]**, 600 New Hampshire Ave., Ste. 800, Washington, DC 20037, (202)266-7453
White House Historical Assn. **[9816]**, PO Box 27624, Washington, DC 20038-7624, (202)737-8292
White House News Photographers Assn. **[2740]**, 7119 Ben Franklin Sta., Washington, DC 20044-7119, (202)785-5230
White House Proj. **[18795]**, 12 MetroTech Ctr., 26th Fl., Brooklyn, NY 11201, (212)709-4450
White Ironstone China Assn. **[21272]**, Suzanne Nielsen, PO Box 6052, Chesterfield, MO 63006-6052, (212)744-0872
White Lung Assn. **[13329]**, PO Box 1483, Baltimore, MD 21203-1483, (410)243-5864
White Lung Assn. **[13329]**, PO Box 1483, Baltimore, MD 21203-1483, (410)243-5864
White Mountain Educ. Assn. **[20261]**, PO Box 11975, Prescott, AZ 86304, (928)778-0638
White Park Cattle Assn. of Am. **[★3872]**
White Plate Flat Trackers Assn. **[22783]**, PO Box 897, Sturgis, SD 57785
White Ribbon Alliance for Safe Motherhood **[11439]**, 1 Thomas Cir. NW, Ste. 200, Washington, DC 20005, (202)777-9758
White Supremacy
　The Creativity Movement **[18781]**
　The Creativity Movement **[18781]**
　Knights of the Ku Klux Klan **[18782]**
　Natl. Alliance **[18783]**
　Natl. Socialist Movement **[18784]**
　Natl. Socialist Movement **[18784]**
　The Nationalist Movement **[18785]**
　New Order **[18786]**
　New Order **[18786]**
Whitebred Shorthorn Assn. **[IO]**, Brampton, United Kingdom
Whitehall Found. **[7161]**, PO Box 3423, Palm Beach, FL 33480, (561)655-4474
Whiteruthenian Amer. Relief - Defunct.
Whitetails Unlimited **[5142]**, PO Box 720, Sturgeon Bay, WI 54235, (920)743-6777
Whitewater NZ **[IO]**, Wellington, New Zealand
Whitman Birthplace Assn; Walt **[9422]**
Whole Child Intl. **[11429]**, 11726 San Vicente Blvd., Ste. 222, Los Angeles, CA 90049, (310)820-0018
Whole Grains Coun. **[15849]**, 266 Beacon St., Boston, MA 02116, (617)421-5500
Wholesale Beer Assn. Executives of Am. **[★185]**
Wholesale Commn. Florists of Am. **[★1370]**
Wholesale Distribution
　Coun. of Supply Chain Mgt. Professionals **[3658]**
　Distribution Bus. Mgt. Assn. **[3659]**
　Global Market Development Center **[3660]**
　Intl. Sealing Distributors Assn. **[3661]**
　Natl. Assn. of Sign Supply Distributors **[3662]**
　Natl. Assn. of Wholesaler-Distributors **[3663]**
　NAW Inst. for Distribution Excellence **[3664]**
　Off. Furniture Distribution Assn. **[3665]**
　Wholesale Markets Brokers' Assn. **[1358]**
Wholesale Distributors Assn. **[2785]**, 2121 Butler St., Dallas, TX 75235
Wholesale Distributors Assn. Educational Foundation **[★2785]**
Wholesale Florist and Florist Supplier Assn. **[1370]**, 147 Old Solomons Island Rd., Ste. 302, Annapolis, MD 21401, (410)573-0400
Wholesale Florists and Florist Suppliers of Am. **[★1370]**
Wholesale Markets Brokers' Assn. **[IO]**, London, United Kingdom
Whoo Who Sprue **[★15817]**
Whooping Crane Conservation Assn. **[5143]**, 5840 Forrests Edge Ln., Gloucester, VA 23061
Whooping Crane Conservation Gp. **[★5143]**
Who's Positive **[10894]**, PO Box 8314, Charlottesville, VA 22906, (434)260-1330
WHTour **[IO]**, Brussels, Belgium
Why Hunger **[17876]**, 505 8th Ave., Ste. 2100, New York, NY 10018, (800)548-6479
Why Hunger **[17876]**, 505 8th Ave., Ste. 2100, New York, NY 10018, (800)548-6479

Wi-Fi Alliance **[6567]**, 10900B Stonelake Blvd., Ste. 126, Austin, TX 78759, (512)498-9434
WiccanWiccanChurch and School of Wicca
　The Witches' Voice **[20283]**
WICUDA-USA **[9095]**, PO Box 3108, Bellaire, TX 77402
WIDE network **[IO]**, Brussels, Belgium
Wide Smiles **[16786]**, PO Box 5153, Stockton, CA 95205-0153, (209)942-2812
Wider Opportunities for Women **[11963]**, 1001 Connecticut Ave. NW, Ste. 930, Washington, DC 20036, (202)464-1596
Wider Quaker Fellowship **[19782]**, 1506 Race St., Philadelphia, PA 19102-1406, (215)241-7250
Widowed Persons Ser. **[★13446]**
Widowhood
　AARP | Grief and Loss Prog. **[13446]**
　Global Action on Widowhood **[18787]**
　Single Mothers By Choice **[12622]**
Widows of World War I - Defunct.
Wiener Institut fur Entwicklungsfragen und Zusammenarbeit **[★IO]**
Wilbur Found. - Address unknown since 2011.
Wilbur Hot Springs Hea. Sanctuary **[9832]**, 3375 Wilbur Springs Rd., Williams, CA 95987-9709, (530)473-2306
Wild Animal Orphanage **[11058]**, PO Box 690422, San Antonio, TX 78269, (210)688-2511
Wild Animals Worldwide **[5144]**, 1100 Larkspur Landing Cir., Ste. 340, Larkspur, CA 94939, (866)439-0989
Wild Bird Feeding Indus. **[4377]**, PO Box 502, West End, NC 27376, (888)839-1237
Wild Bird Soc. of Japan **[IO]**, Tokyo, Japan
Wild Blueberry Assn. of North Am. **[4485]**, PO Box 100, Old Town, ME 04468, (207)570-3535
Wild Blueberry Assn. of North Am. **[4485]**, PO Box 100, Old Town, ME 04468, (207)570-3535
Wild Burro Rescue and Preservation Proj. **[11059]**, PO Box 10, Olancha, CA 93549-0010, (760)384-8523
Wild Canid Survival and Res. Center **[★5052]**
Wild Earth
Wild Earth - Address unknown since 2011.
Wild Farm Alliance **[4368]**, PO Box 2570, Watsonville, CA 95077, (831)761-8408
Wild Felid Res. and Mgt. Assn. **[5145]**, PO Box 3335, Montrose, CO 81402, (970)252-1928
Wild Gift **[5146]**, PO Box 3064, Sun Valley, ID 83353, (208)726-7475
Wild Goose Assn. **[★7151]**
Wild Goose Assn. **[★7151]**
Wild Horse Sanctuary **[11060]**, PO Box 30, Shingletown, CA 96088-0030, (530)474-5770
Wild Horse Spirit **[11061]**, 25 Lewers Creek Rd., Carson City, NV 89704, (775)883-5488
Wild Horses of Am. Registry **[5147]**, PO Box 55, Lantry, SD 57636-0055, (605)964-6866
Wild Horses of Am. Registry **[★5070]**
Wild Horses of Am. Registry **[★5070]**
Wild Sheep Found. **[5148]**, 720 Allen Ave., Cody, WY 82414-3402, (307)527-6261
Wild Steelhead Coalition **[5149]**, Box 264, Kirkland, WA 98033
Wild Water Kayak Club **[IO]**, Chapelizod, Ireland
WildAid **[5150]**, 744 Montgomery St., Ste. 300, San Francisco, CA 94111, (415)834-3174
WildAid **[5150]**, 744 Montgomery St., Ste. 300, San Francisco, CA 94111, (415)834-3174
WildCat Conservation Legal Aid Soc. **[5016]**, PO Box 65495, Washington, DC 20035
Wildcat Ser. Corp. **[11964]**, 2 Washington St., 3rd Fl., New York, NY 10004, (212)209-6000
Wilderness Classroom Org. **[8689]**, 4605 Grand Ave., Western Springs, IL 60558, (312)505-9973
Wilderness Educ. Assn. **[8690]**, 1900 E 10th St., Bloomington, IN 47406, (812)855-4095
Wilderness Inquiry **[22447]**, 808 14th Ave. SE, Minneapolis, MN 55414-1516, (612)676-9400
Wilderness Intl. **[4160]**, PO Box 491, Canby, OR 97013, (503)593-0199
Wilderness Medical Soc. **[15439]**, 2150 S 1300 E, Ste. 500, Salt Lake City, UT 84106, (801)990-2988
The Wilderness Soc. **[4161]**, 1615 M St. NW, Washington, DC 20036, (202)833-2300

A star before a book entry number signifies that the name is not listed separately, but is mentioned within the entry.

The Wilderness Soc. [4161], 1615 M St. NW, Washington, DC 20036, (202)833-2300
The Wilderness Soc. - Australia [IO], Hobart, Australia
Wilderness Volunteers [22002], PO Box 22292, Flagstaff, AZ 86002-2292, (928)556-0038
Wilderness Watch - Defunct.
Wildflowers Inst. [9481], 1144 Pacific Ave., San Francisco, CA 94133, (415)775-1151
Wildflowers Inst. [9481], 1144 Pacific Ave., San Francisco, CA 94133, (415)775-1151
The Wildfowl Trust [★5276]
Wildfowl Trust of North Am. [5151], PO Box 519, Grasonville, MD 21638, (410)827-6694
Wildfowl and Wetlands Trust [IO], Gloucester, United Kingdom
Wildlands Network [4311], PO Box 5284, Titusville, FL 32783, (520)558-0165
Wildlands Proj. [★4311]

Wildlife
Advanced Conservation Strategies [3979]
Alliance for Global Conservation [3983]
Amara Conservation [5022]
Amer. Wilderness Coalition [5010]
Animal Venom Res. Intl. [13759]
Animal World USA [3808]
Ape Conservation Effort [5028]
Assn. of Professional Wildlife Educators [9050]
Atlantic Flyway Coun. [5030]
Audubon Intl. [4008]
Audubon Naturalist Soc. of the Central Atlantic States [4009]
Big Wildlife [5034]
BlueVoice.org [4013]
Bonobo Conservation Initiative [5038]
Born Free USA [10934]
Cetos Res. Org. [4199]
Coun. for Endangered Species Act Reliability [5413]
Darwin Animal Doctors [3809]
Elephants Without Borders [5011]
Forest Bird Soc. [4056]
Forest Partners Intl. [4395]
Friends of the Osa [4063]
Fur Free Alliance [10968]
Global Animal Relief [3812]
Global Fed. of Animal Sanctuaries [10970]
Global Res. and Rescue [5012]
Global Res. and Rescue [5012]
Global Wildlife Conservation [5060]
Global Wildlife Resources [5013]
Global Wildlife Resources [5013]
Hawk Mountain Sanctuary [5063]
Human-Wildlife Conflict Collaboration [5014]
Hummingbird Monitoring Network [3848]
Iemanya Oceanica [5064]
Intl. Defenders of Animals [10989]
Kasese Wildlife Conservation Awareness Org. [5074]
Marine Animal Rescue Soc. [4093]
Marine Mammal Conservancy [5079]
Millennium Wildlife Sciences [5015]
Natl. Wildlife Fed. [4103]
NOAH Nature Alliance [5090]
North Amer. Wildlife Park Found. [5098]
North Amer. Wolf Assn. [5099]
Pan African Sanctuary Alliance [5106]
Reptile and Amphibian Ecology Intl. [5118]
Save the Frogs! [4137]
Save the Turtles [5123]
Saving Wildlife Intl. [5125]
Shark Alliance [5128]
Snow Leopard Network [5130]
Soc. for the Conservation of Bighorn Sheep [5131]
Sri Lanka Wildlife Conservation Soc. [5133]
State of the World's Sea Turtles [5134]
Turtle Survival Alliance [5140]
Unexpected Wildlife Refuge [11049]
Wild Animals Worldwide [5144]
Wild Felid Res. and Mgt. Assn. [5145]
Wild Gift [5146]
Wild Sheep Found. [5148]
WildCat Conservation Legal Aid Soc. [5016]
Wilderness Intl. [4160]

Wildlife Conservation Network [5152]
Wildlife Media [5155]
Wildlife in Need [5017]
Wonderful World of Wildlife [5157]
World Nature Coalition [5159]
World Whale Police [5018]
World Whale Police [5018]
Wildlife Aid [IO], Leatherhead, United Kingdom
Wildlife Clubs of Kenya [IO], Nairobi, Kenya
Wildlife Conservation
Abundant Wildlife Soc. of North Am. [5019]
African Wild Dog Conservancy [5020]
African Wild Dog Conservancy [5020]
African Wildlife Found. [5021]
African Wildlife Found. [5021]
Alliance for Global Conservation [3983]
Alliance for Tompotika Conservation [3985]
Amara Conservation [5022]
Amer. Bird Conservancy [5023]
Amer. Deer and Wildlife Alliance [5024]
Amer. Pheasant and Waterfowl Soc. [5025]
Amer. Tortoise Rescue [5026]
Amer. Wilderness Coalition [5010]
Animal World USA [3808]
Ape Action Africa [5027]
Ape Conservation Effort [5028]
Assn. for Professional Observers [4379]
Assn. of Professional Wildlife Educators [9050]
Assn. Promoting Educ. and Conservation in Amazonia [5029]
Assn. Promoting Educ. and Conservation in Amazonia [5029]
Atlantic Flyway Coun. [5030]
Audubon Naturalist Soc. of the Central Atlantic States [4009]
Bat Conservation Intl. [5031]
Bat Conservation Intl. [5031]
Bear Trust Intl. [5032]
Bear Trust Intl. [5032]
Big Wild Advocates [5033]
Big Wildlife [5034]
The Billfish Found. [5035]
Bird Strike Comm. U.S.A. [5036]
Birds of Prey Found. [5037]
BlueVoice.org [4013]
Bonobo Conservation Initiative [5038]
Bonobo Conservation Initiative [5038]
Boone and Crockett Club [5039]
Boreal Songbird Initiative [5040]
Boreal Songbird Initiative [5040]
Born Free USA [10934]
Brooks Bird Club [5041]
Cetacean Soc. Intl. [5042]
Cetacean Soc. Intl. [5042]
Cetos Res. Org. [4199]
Conservation Alliance for Tigers [5159]
Conservation Leaders Network [4734]
Coun. for Endangered Species Act Reliability [5413]
Darwin Animal Doctors [3809]
Defenders of Wildlife [5043]
Delta Waterfowl Found. [5044]
Desert Tortoise Coun. [5045]
Dian Fossey Gorilla Fund Intl. [5046]
Dian Fossey Gorilla Fund Intl. [5046]
Ducks Unlimited [5047]
Earthtrust [5048]
Earthtrust [5048]
EcoHealth Alliance [5049]
Elephant Care Intl. [5050]
Elephant Care Intl. [5050]
Elephants Without Borders [5011]
Endangered Species Coalition [5051]
Endangered Wolf Center [5052]
Env. for the Americas [3845]
Environmental Commons [4049]
Equine Protection Network [5053]
Exotic Wildlife Assn. [5054]
Florida Keys Wild Bird Rehabilitation Center [5055]
Fly By Night: The Bat Specialists [5056]
Forest Bird Soc. [4056]
Forest Partners Intl. [4395]
Freshwater Mollusk Conservation Soc. [5057]
Friends of the Australian Koala Found. [5058]

Friends of the Sea Otter [5059]
Fur Free Alliance [10968]
Global Animal Relief [3812]
Global Res. and Rescue [5012]
Global Wildlife Conservation [5060]
Global Wildlife Resources [5013]
Great Bear Found. [5061]
Great Lakes Indian Fish and Wildlife Commn. [5062]
Hawk Mountain Sanctuary [5063]
Human-Wildlife Conflict Collaboration [5014]
Hummingbird Monitoring Network [3848]
Iemanya Oceanica [5064]
Intl. Assn. for Bear Res. and Mgt. [5065]
Intl. Assn. for Bear Res. and Mgt. [5065]
Intl. Bird Rescue Res. Center [5066]
Intl. Bird Rescue Res. Center [5066]
Intl. Crane Found. [5067]
Intl. Crane Found. [5067]
Intl. Defenders of Animals [10989]
The Intl. Osprey Found. [5068]
The Intl. Osprey Found. [5068]
Intl. Snow Leopard Trust [5069]
Intl. Snow Leopard Trust [5069]
Intl. Soc. for the Protection of Mustangs and Burros [5070]
Intl. Soc. for the Protection of Mustangs and Burros [5070]
Intl. Wild Waterfowl Assn. [5071]
Intl. Wild Waterfowl Assn. [5071]
Intl. Wildlife Rehabilitation Coun. [5072]
Intl. Wildlife Rehabilitation Coun. [5072]
Jane Goodall Inst. for Wildlife Res., Educ., and Conservation [5073]
Kasese Wildlife Conservation Awareness Org. [5074]
Kasese Wildlife Conservation Awareness Org. [5074]
Keeping Track [5075]
Keystone Conservation [5076]
Kids Ecology Corps [4322]
Last Chance Forever [5077]
Lewa Wildlife Conservancy (U.S.A.) [5078]
Marine Animal Rescue Soc. [4093]
Marine Mammal Conservancy [5079]
Marine Mammal Stranding Center [5080]
Millennium Wildlife Sciences [5015]
Mission: Wolf [5081]
Mountain Lion Found. [5082]
Natl. Endowment for the Animals [11010]
Natl. Military Fish and Wildlife Assn. [5083]
Natl. Wild Turkey Fed. [5084]
Natl. Wildlife Control Operators Assn. [5085]
Natl. Wildlife Fed. [4103]
Natl. Wildlife Refuge Assn. [5086]
Natl. Wildlife Rehabilitators Assn. [5087]
Natl. Wolfdog Alliance [21615]
Native Fish Soc. [5088]
New York Turtle and Tortoise Soc. [5089]
NOAH Nature Alliance [5090]
Norcross Wildlife Found. [5091]
North Amer. Bear Center [5092]
North Amer. Bluebird Soc. [5093]
North Amer. Bluebird Soc. [5093]
North Amer. Crane Working Group [5094]
North Amer. Elk Breeders Assn. [5095]
North Amer. Grouse Partnership [5096]
North Amer. Wildlife Enforcement Officers Assn. [5097]
North Amer. Wildlife Park Found. [5098]
North Amer. Wolf Assn. [5099]
Ocean Soc. [7183]
Orangutan Conservancy [5100]
Org. for Bat Conservation [5101]
Org. of Wildlife Planners [5102]
OurEarth.org [4121]
Pacific Marine Mammal Center [5103]
Pacific Seabird Gp. [5104]
Pacific Whale Found. [5105]
Pan African Sanctuary Alliance [5106]
Pan African Sanctuary Alliance [5106]
Pandas Intl. [5107]
Panthera [5108]
Paso Pacifico [4125]
The Peregrine Fund [5109]

Reference to "IO" in place of a book number signifies that the association may be found in the 50th edition of International Organizations.

The Peregrine Fund [5109]
Pheasants Forever [5110]
Polar Bears Intl. [5111]
Polar Bears Intl. [5111]
Purple Martin Conservation Assn. [5112]
Quail Forever [5113]
Quail Unlimited [5114]
Raptor Educ. Found. [5115]
Raptor Res. Found. [5116]
RARE [5117]
Reptile and Amphibian Ecology Intl. [5118]
Reptile and Amphibian Ecology Intl. [5118]
Rocky Mountain Elk Found. [5119]
Ruffed Grouse Soc. [5120]
Safari Club Intl. [5121]
Safari Club Intl. [5121]
Save the Frogs! [4137]
Save the Manatee Club [5122]
Save the Turtles [5123]
Save the Turtles [5123]
Save the Whales [5124]
Save Yemen's Flora and Fauna [4140]
Saving Wildlife Intl. [5125]
Saving Wildlife Intl. [5125]
Sea Shepherd Conservation Soc. [5126]
Sea Shepherd Conservation Soc. [5126]
Sea Turtle Conservancy [5127]
Sea Turtle Conservancy [5127]
Shark Alliance [5128]
Shark Savers [5129]
Shark Savers [5129]
Snow Leopard Network [5130]
Snow Leopard Network [5130]
Soc. for the Conservation of Bighorn Sheep
    [5131]
Species Alliance [5132]
Sri Lanka Wildlife Conservation Soc. [5133]
Sri Lanka Wildlife Conservation Soc. [5133]
State of the World's Sea Turtles [5134]
State of the World's Sea Turtles [5134]
Sumatran Orangutan Soc. USA [5135]
Sumatran Orangutan Soc. USA [5135]WildlifeTor-
    toiseAid Intl.
TRAFFIC North Am. [5136]
Trout Unlimited [5137]
The Trumpeter Swan Soc. [5138]
Turkey Vulture Soc. [5139]
Turtle Survival Alliance [5140]
Unexpected Wildlife Refuge [11049]
Watchable Wildlife [5141]
Whitetails Unlimited [5142]
Whooping Crane Conservation Assn. [5143]
Wild Animals Worldwide [5144]
Wild Felid Res. and Mgt. Assn. [5145]
Wild Gift [5146]
Wild Horses of Am. Registry [5147]
Wild Sheep Found. [5148]
Wild Steelhead Coalition [5149]
WildAid [5150]
WildAid [5150]
WildCat Conservation Legal Aid Soc. [5016]
Wilderness Intl. [4160]
Wildfowl Trust of North Am. [5151]
Wildlife Conservation Network [5152]
Wildlife Disease Assn. [5153]
Wildlife Disease Assn. [5153]
Wildlife Forever [5154]
Wildlife Media [5155]
Wildlife in Need [5017]
The Wildlife Soc. [5156]
Wonderful World of Wildlife [5157]
World Bird Sanctuary [5158]
World Bird Sanctuary [5158]
World Nature Coalition [5159]
World Whale Police [5018]
Xerces Soc. [5160]
Xerces Soc. [5160]
Wildlife Conservation Intl. [★4162]
Wildlife Conservation Network [5152], 25745 Bassett
    Ln., Los Altos Hills, CA 94022, (650)949-3533
Wildlife Conservation Soc. [4162], 2300 Southern
    Blvd., Bronx, NY 10460, (718)220-5100
Wildlife Conservation Soc. of Tanzania [IO], Arusha,
    United Republic of Tanzania
Wildlife Coordinating Committee - Defunct.

Wildlife Disease Assn. [5153], PO Box 7065,
    Lawrence, KS 66044-7065, (800)627-0326
Wildlife Disease Assn. [5153], PO Box 7065,
    Lawrence, KS 66044-7065, (800)627-0326
Wildlife and Env. Soc. of Malawi [IO], Limbe, Malawi
Wildlife and Env. Soc. of South Africa [IO], Howick,
    Republic of South Africa
Wildlife and Environmental Conservation Soc. of
    Zambia [IO], Lusaka, Zambia
Wildlife Forever [5154], 2700 Freeway Blvd., No.
    1000, Brooklyn Center, MN 55430, (763)253-0222
Wildlife Habitat Canada [IO], Ottawa, ON, Canada
Wildlife Habitat Coun. [4163], 8737 Colesville Rd.,
    Ste. 800, Silver Spring, MD 20910, (301)588-8994
Wildlife Habitat Enhancement Coun. [★4163]
Wildlife Legislative Fund of Am. [★22701]
Wildlife Mgt. Inst. [4164], Richard E. McCabe, VP,
    1424 NW Carlson Rd., Topeka, KS 66614,
    (410)562-5341
Wildlife Media [5155], 1208 Bay St., Ste. 202, Bell-
    ingham, WA 98225-4304, (360)734-6060
Wildlife in Need [5017], 7651 Santos Rd., Lompoc,
    CA 93436-9428, (805)737-3700
Wildlife Preservation Soc. of Australia [IO], Brighton-
    Le-Sands, Australia
Wildlife Preservation Trust Intl. [★5049]
Wildlife Protection Soc. of India [IO], New Delhi,
    India
Wildlife Refuge Reform Coalition - Defunct.
Wildlife Rehabilitation Coun. [★5072]
Wildlife Rehabilitation Coun. [★5072]
The Wildlife Soc. [5156], 5410 Grosvenor Ln., Ste.
    200, Bethesda, MD 20814-2144, (301)897-9770
Wildlife Trust [★5049]
Wildlife Trusts [IO], Newark, United Kingdom
Wilhelm Furtwangler Soc. of Am. - Address unknown
    since 2011.
Wilkie Collins Soc. [IO], London, United Kingdom
Willa Cather Found. [★9423]
Willa Cather Pioneer Memorial and Educational
    Found. [9423], 413 N Webster St., Red Cloud, NE
    68970, (402)746-2653
Willa Cather Soc. [★9423]
Willem Mengelberg Soc. - Defunct.
William Allen White Found. [9424], Univ. Kansas,
    William Allen White School of Journalism and
    Mass Commun., Stauffer-Flint Hall, 1435 Jayhawk
    Blvd., Lawrence, KS 66045-7575, (785)864-4755
William Armstrong and Mary Kirk Family Org. -
    Defunct.
William Barnes Soc. [IO], Dorchester, United
    Kingdom
William C. Velasquez Inst. [19106], Kelly U.S.A.
    Bldg. 1670, 206 Lombard St., 1st Fl., San Antonio,
    TX 78226, (210)922-3118
William Cobbett Soc. [IO], Tillington, United Kingdom
William Dean Howells Soc. [9425], Prof. Mischa
    Renfroe, Sec.-Treas., Box 70, Murfreesboro, TN
    37132-0001
William E. Simon Found. [17595], 140 E 45th St.,
    Ste. 14D, New York, NY 10017, (212)661-8366
William Faulkner Soc. [10747], Univ. of Mississippi,
    Dept. of English, PO Box 1848, University, MS
    38677-1848
William and Flora Hewlett Found. [13208], 2121
    Sand Hill Rd., Menlo Park, CA 94025, (650)234-
    4500
William Gilmore Simms Soc. [10748], South Caro-
    liniana Lib., Univ. of South Carolina, 910 Sumter
    St., Columbia, SC 29208
William Glasser Inst. [16475], PO Box 2666, Country
    Club Hills, IL 60478, (708)957-6047
William H. Donner Found. [13991], 60 E 42nd St.,
    Ste. 1560, New York, NY 10165, (212)949-0404
William H. Whitsitt Baptist Heritage Soc. [19334],
    1028 S Haven Dr., Hewitt, TX 76643
William Herschel Soc. [IO], Bath, United Kingdom
William Hutchinson and Jane Penman Family Org. -
    Defunct.
William J. Clinton Found. [17929], 1200 Pres. Clin-
    ton Ave., Little Rock, AR 72201, (501)748-0471
William J. Murray Evangelistic Assn. [★12885]
William J. Murray Faith Found. [★12885]
William James Soc. [10696], Todd Lekan, Sec.-
    Treas., Muskingum Univ., 163 Stormont St., New
    Concord, OH 43762

William Morris Soc. [IO], London, United Kingdom
William Morris Soc., Amer. Br. [★9426]
William Morris Soc., North Amer. Br. [★9426]
William Morris Soc. in the U.S. [9426], PO Box
    53263, Washington, DC 20009
William Penn Assn. [19063], 709 Brighton Rd.,
    Pittsburgh, PA 15233, (412)231-2979
William Penn Coll. Alumni Assn. [★18917]
William Penn Fraternal Assn. [★19063]
William Penn House [17710], 515 E Capitol St. SE,
    Washington, DC 20003, (202)543-5560
William Penn Univ. Alumni Assn. [18917], 201 True-
    blood Ave., Oskaloosa, IA 52577-1799, (641)673-
    1046
William Shatner Connection [★23784]
William T. Grant Found. [11170], 570 Lexington Ave.,
    18th Fl., New York, NY 10022-6837, (212)752-
    0071
William T. Grant Found. [11170], 570 Lexington Ave.,
    18th Fl., New York, NY 10022-6837, (212)752-
    0071
William Wendt Center for Loss and Healing [13317],
    4201 Connecticut Ave. NW, Ste. 300, Washington,
    DC 20008, (202)624-0010
Williams Family Assn. - Defunct.
Williams Grove Old Timers [★21046]
Williams Syndrome Assn. [14637], 570 Kirts Blvd.,
    Ste. 223, Troy, MI 48084-4156, (248)244-2229
Willing Workers on Organic Farms [★16088]
Willing Workers on Organic Farms - Australia [IO],
    Buchan, Australia
Willing Workers on Organic Farms - Denmark [IO],
    Tars, Denmark
Willing Workers on Organic Farms - Ghana [IO], Ac-
    cra, Ghana
Willing Workers on Organic Farms - Japan [IO],
    Sapporo, Japan
Willing Workers on Organic Farms - New Zealand
    [IO], Nelson, New Zealand
Willing Workers on Organic Farms - Norway [IO],
    Oslo, Norway
Willkommen im Curling Club Hamburg e.V. [★IO]
Willow Creek Assn. [19623], PO Box 3188, Bar-
    rington, IL 60011-3188, (800)570-9812
Willow Mixed Media - Address unknown since 2010.
Willys-Overland-Knight Registry [21195], 1749 Chain
    Bridge Rd., McLean, VA 22102-2934
Willys-Overland-Knight Registry [21195], 1749 Chain
    Bridge Rd., McLean, VA 22102-2934
Wilson Knight Interdiscipline Soc. and Found. -
    Defunct.
Wilson Natl. Fellowship Found; Woodrow [8198]
Wilson Ornithological Soc. [7206], OSNA Bus. Off.,
    5400 Bosque Blvd., Ste. 680, Waco, TX 76710,
    (254)399-9636
Wilson Orthological Club [★7206]
Wilson Presidential Lib. Found; Woodrow [10697]
Wilson's Disease Assn. Intl. [15508], 5572 N Diver-
    sey Blvd., Milwaukee, WI 53217, (414)961-0533
WiMedia Alliance [6568], 2400 Camino Ramon, Ste.
    375, San Ramon, CA 94583, (925)275-6604
Win Without War [18178], 1717 Massachusetts Ave.
    NW, Ste. 801, Washington, DC 20036-2000,
    (202)232-3317
Winant and Clayton Volunteers [13409], 1393 York
    Ave., New York, NY 10021, (212)737-2720
Winant and Clayton Volunteers [13409], 1393 York
    Ave., New York, NY 10021, (212)737-2720
Winchester Arms Collectors Assn. [20968], PO Box
    30047, Lumberton, TX 77657-0047, (409)755-4488
The Wind Alliance [7624], 1100 Louisiana St., Ste.
    5005, Houston, TX 77002, (713)600-9994

Wind Energy
    Amer. Solar Action Plan [7437]
    Amer. Wind Energy Assn. [7621]
    blueEnergy [11966]
    Distributed Wind Energy Assn. [3666]
    Governors' Wind Energy Coalition [6070]
    Intergovernmental Renewable Energy Org. [6731]
    Latin Am. Wind Energy Assn. - U.S. [7622]
    Natl. Wind Watch [18788]
    Renewable Energy for Medicine and Educ. [6749]
    U.S. Offshore Wind Collaborative [7623]
    The Wind Alliance [7624]
    Wind Energy Mfrs. Assn. [3667]

A star before a book entry number signifies that the name is not listed separately, but is mentioned within the entry.

Wind Energy Works! **[7625]**
Windustry **[7626]**
Women of Wind Energy **[7627]**
Wind Energy Mfrs.' Assn. **[3667]**, 345 S High St., Muncie, IN 47305, (317)733-9797
Wind Energy Works! **[7625]**, Amer. Wind Energy Assn., 1501 M St. NW, Ste. 1000, Washington, DC 20005, (202)383-2538
Windmill Class Assn. **[22413]**, 1571 Quarrier St., Charleston, WV 25311
Windmill Stud. Unit **[IO]**, Sittingbourne, United Kingdom

Window
Efficient Windows Collaborative **[3668]**
Window Covering Safety Coun. **[3669]**
A Window Between Worlds **[11898]**, 710 4th Ave., Ste. 5, Venice, CA 90291, (310)396-0317
Window Covering Mfrs. Assn. **[2076]**, 355 Lexington Ave., 15th Fl., New York, NY 10017, (212)297-2122
Window Covering Safety Coun. **[3669]**, 355 Lexington Ave., Ste. 1500, New York, NY 10017, (212)297-2100
Window Coverings Assn. of Am. **[2077]**, 11230 Gold Express Dr., Ste. 310-149, Gold River, CA 95670, (916)943-0979
Window and Door Mfrs. Assn. **[635]**, 401 N Michigan Ave., Ste. 2200, Chicago, IL 60611, (312)321-6802
Windsor Family Historical Assn. - Defunct.
Windstar Found. **[4312]**, 2317 Snowmass Creek Rd., Snowmass, CO 81654, (970)927-5430
Windsurfing Assn. of Maldives **[IO]**, Male, Maldives
Windustry **[7626]**, 2105 1st Ave. S, Minneapolis, MN 55404, (612)870-3461
Windward Found. **[13209]**, 55 Windward Ln., Klickitat, WA 98628, (509)369-2000

Wine
Amer. Assn. of Wine Economists **[3670]**
Amer. Soc. for Enology and Viticulture **[5161]**
Amer. Vineyard Found. **[5162]**
Amer. Wine Alliance for Res. and Educ. **[5163]**
Amer. Wine Soc. **[5164]**
Atlantic Seaboard Wine Assn. **[5165]**
Australian Soc. of Viticulture and Oenology **[16832]**
Australian Wine Consumers' Co-operative Soc. **[15563]**
Brotherhood of the Knights of the Vine **[5166]**
California Assn. of Winegrape Growers **[5167]**
Confrerie de la Chaine des Rotisseurs, Bailliage des U.S.A. **[21845]**
Monterey County Vintners and Growers Assn. **[5168]**
Napa Valley Grapegrowers **[5169]**
Napa Valley Vintners Assn. **[5170]**
Napa Valley Wine Lib. Assn. **[22199]**WineNatl. Viticulture Inst.
New York Wine/Grape Found. **[5171]**
Santa Cruz Mountains Winegrowers Assn. **[5172]**
Soc. of Medical Friends of Wine **[22200]**
Soc. of Wine Educators **[22201]**
Sonoma County Vintners **[5173]**
Sonoma County Winegrape Commission **[5174]**
Specialty Wine Retailers Assn. **[3671]**
Wine Appreciation Guild **[5175]**
Wine Inst. **[5176]**
Wine to Water **[13443]**
WineAmerica Natl. Assn. of Amer. Wineries **[3672]**
Women for Winesense **[22202]**
Wine Advisory Bd. **[★5175]**
Wine Appreciation Guild **[5175]**, 360 Swift Ave., Unit 30-40, South San Francisco, CA 94080-6228, (650)866-3020
Wine Development Bd. of Ireland **[IO]**, Dublin, Ireland
Wine Futures Exchange - Defunct.
Wine Indus. Suppliers Australia **[IO]**, Adelaide, Australia
Wine Inst. **[5176]**, 425 Market St., Ste. 1000, San Francisco, CA 94105, (415)512-0151
Wine Inst. of New Zealand **[IO]**, Auckland, New Zealand
Wine Soc. **[IO]**, Stevenage, United Kingdom
Wine Soc. of Macau **[IO]**, Macau, Macao
Wine and Spirit Trade Assn. **[IO]**, London, United Kingdom

Wine and Spirits Shippers Assn. **[192]**, 11800 Sunrise Valley Dr., Ste. 425, Reston, VA 20191, (703)860-2300
Wine and Spirits Wholesalers of Am. **[193]**, 805 15th St. NW, Ste. 430, Washington, DC 20005, (202)371-9792
Wine and Vineyards Inst. **[IO]**, Lisbon, Portugal
Wine to Water **[13443]**, PO Box 2567, Boone, NC 28607, (828)355-9655
WineAmerica Natl. Assn. of Amer. Wineries **[3672]**, 1015 18th St. NW, Ste. 500, Washington, DC 20036, (202)783-2756
Winemakers' Fed. of Australia **[IO]**, Manuka, Australia
Wines of South Africa **[IO]**, Stellenbosch, Republic of South Africa
Wingate Inst. for Physical Educ. in Israel **[★22985]**
Winged Warriors/National B-Body Owners Assn. **[21196]**, 216 12th St., Boone, IA 50036-2019, (515)432-3001
Wingfield Family Soc. **[20608]**, John D. Wingfield, Treas., 1004 Cherokee Rd., Perry, GA 31069-2243
Wingfield Family Soc. **[20608]**, John D. Wingfield, Treas., 1004 Cherokee Rd., Perry, GA 31069-2243
WINGS **[12904]**, 793 Ashbury St., San Francisco, CA 94117, (415)230-0441
WINGS **[12904]**, 793 Ashbury St., San Francisco, CA 94117, (415)230-0441
Wings Club - Defunct.
Wings and Dreams for Kids **[14099]**, 3210 E Fur Hollow Dr., Sandy, UT 84092-4268
WINGS Found. **[13103]**, 7550 W Yale Ave., Ste. B-201, Denver, CO 80227, (303)238-4739
Wings of Hope **[12897]**, 18370 Wings of Hope Blvd., Chesterfield, MO 63005, (800)448-9487
Wings of Hope **[12897]**, 18370 Wings of Hope Blvd., Chesterfield, MO 63005, (800)448-9487
Winrock Intl. **[17171]**, 2101 Riverfront Dr., Little Rock, AR 72202-1748, (501)280-3000
Winrock Intl. **[17171]**, 2101 Riverfront Dr., Little Rock, AR 72202-1748, (501)280-3000
Winrock Intl. Inst. for Agricultural Development **[★17171]**
Winrock Intl. Inst. for Agricultural Development **[★17171]**
Winrock Intl. Livestock Res. and Training Center **[★17171]**
Winrock Intl. Livestock Res. and Training Center **[★17171]**
Winston Churchill Found. of the U.S. **[8197]**, 600 Madison Ave., Ste. 1601, New York, NY 10022-1737, (212)752-3200
Winston S. Churchill Stud. Unit **[★10657]**
Winta - Eritrean Resources Assn. e.V. **[IO]**, Bonn, Germany
Wire Assn. **[★7102]**
Wire Assn. **[★7102]**
Wire Assn. Intl. **[7102]**, PO Box 578, Guilford, CT 06437, (203)453-2777
Wire Assn. Intl. **[7102]**, PO Box 578, Guilford, CT 06437, (203)453-2777
Wire and Cable Indus. Suppliers Assn. **[1119]**, 1867 W Market St., Akron, OH 44313, (330)864-2122
Wire Fabricators Assn. **[1665]**, PO Box 304, Montgomery, IL 60538, (630)896-1469
Wire Fabricators Assn. **[1665]**, PO Box 304, Montgomery, IL 60538, (630)896-1469
Wire Reinforcement Inst. **[636]**, 942 Main St., Ste. 300, Hartford, CT 06103, (860)808-3000
Wirebound Box Mfrs. Assn. - Defunct.
Wired Intl. **[15223]**, Drawer 371132, Montara, CA 94037-1132, (650)728-2828
Wired Woman **[IO]**, Vancouver, BC, Canada
Wirehaired Vizsla Club of Am. **[21680]**, 9992 S Old Hwy. 81, Assaria, KS 67416
Wireless Communications Assn. Intl. **[3427]**, 1333 H St. NW, Ste. 700 W, Washington, DC 20005-4754, (202)452-7823
Wireless Communications Assn. Intl. **[3427]**, 1333 H St. NW, Ste. 700 W, Washington, DC 20005-4754, (202)452-7823
Wireless Indus. Assn. **[3428]**, 9746 Tappenbeck Dr., Houston, TX 77055-4102, (713)467-0077
Wireless Innovation Forum **[6501]**, 18631 N 19th Ave., Ste. 158-436, Phoenix, AZ 85027-5800, (604)828-9846

Wireless Inst. of Australia **[IO]**, Bayswater, Australia
Wireless-Life Sciences Alliance **[16829]**, PO Box 910543, San Diego, CA 92121
Wiring Harness Manufacturer's Assn. **[1087]**, 7500 Flying Cloud Dr., Ste. 900, Eden Prairie, MN 55344, (952)253-6225
Wirral Chamber of Commerce and Indus. **[IO]**, Wirral, United Kingdom
Wirtschafts Junioren Deutschland **[★IO]**
Wirtschaftskammern Osterreichs **[★IO]**
Wirtschaftsverband Erdol- und Erdgasgewinnung **[★IO]**
Wirtschaftsverband Grosshandel Metallhalbzeug **[IO]**, Berlin, Germany
Wirtschaftsverband der deutschen Kautschukindustrie **[★IO]**
Wirtschaftsverband Stahl - und Metallverarbeitung **[★IO]**
Wirtschaftsvereinigung Alkoholfreie Getranke e.V. **[★IO]**
Wirtschaftsvereinigung Bergbau E.v. **[★IO]**
Wisconsin Cheese Makers' Assn. **[1027]**, 8030 Excelsior Dr., Ste. 305, Madison, WI 53717-1950, (608)828-4550
Wisconsin Cheese Seminar **[★1398]**
Wisconsin Cheese Seminar **[★1398]**
Wisconsin Cheese and Specialty Food Merchants Assn. - Defunct.
Wisconsin Coordinating Coun. on Nicaragua **[★17991]**
Wisconsin Coordinating Coun. on Nicaragua **[★17991]**
Wisconsin Creameries Assn. **[★4187]**
Wisconsin Dairy Foods Assn. **[★4187]**
Wisconsin Dairy Products Assn. **[4187]**, 8383 Greenway Blvd., No. 130, Middleton, WI 53562, (608)836-3336
Wisdom of the Heart Found. **[IO]**, Tijuana, Mexico
WISH **[★5492]**
WISH List **[5492]**, 333 N Fairfax St., Ste. 302, Alexandria, VA 22314, (703)778-5550
A Wish With Wings **[11516]**, 917 W Sanford St., Arlington, TX 76012, (817)469-9474

Witches
Assoc. Daughters of Early Amer. Witches **[20843]**
Witches Anti-Discrimination Lobby - Defunct.
The Witches' Voice **[20283]**, PO Box 341018, Tampa, FL 33694-1018
WITH/Curam, Parent and Carer NGO in Ireland **[IO]**, Dun Laoghaire, Ireland
WITNESS **[17868]**, 80 Hanson Pl., 5th Fl., Brooklyn, NY 11217, (718)783-2000
Witness Anonymous Program **[★11697]**
Witness Justice **[18772]**, PO Box 475, Frederick, MD 21705-0475, (301)846-9110
Witness for Peace **[18161]**, 3628 12th St. NE, 1st Fl., Washington, DC 20017, (202)547-6112
Witness for Peace **[18161]**, 3628 12th St. NE, 1st Fl., Washington, DC 20017, (202)547-6112
Wives of Older Men - Defunct.
W.K. Kellogg Found. **[18427]**, 1 Michigan Ave. E, Battle Creek, MI 49017-4012, (269)968-1611
W.M. Keck Found. **[15353]**, 550 S Hope St., Ste. 2500, Los Angeles, CA 90071, (213)680-3833
Wobblies **[★23218]**
Wobblies **[★23218]**
Wobbly Parrot Rescue **[IO]**, Reading, United Kingdom
The Wodehouse Soc. **[9427]**, 1388 Wellesley Ave., St. Paul, MN 55105-2417
Wofford Coll. Natl. Alumni Assn. **[18918]**, 429 N Church St., Spartanburg, SC 29303-3663, (864)597-4000
Wolf Haven Intl. **[4165]**, 3111 Offut Lake Rd., Tenino, WA 98589, (360)264-4695
Wolf Haven Intl. **[4165]**, 3111 Offut Lake Rd., Tenino, WA 98589, (360)264-4695
Wolf Trap Found. for the Performing Arts **[9324]**, 1645 Trap Rd., Vienna, VA 22182, (703)255-1900
Wolfe Pack **[9428]**, PO Box 230822, New York, NY 10023, (212)949-0867
Wolfensberger Family Assn. **[20609]**, David E. Wolfenbarger, Treas., 768 Chain Ridge Rd., St. Louis, MO 63122, (314)961-5032
Wolfpack Fan Club **[23898]**, PO Box 17311, Nashville, TN 37217, (615)780-3579

Reference to "IO" in place of a book number signifies that the association may be found in the 50th edition of International Organizations.

Wolseley Register [IO], Roade, United Kingdom
Woman and Family [IO], Minsk, Belarus
Woman Within Intl. Ltd. [13486], 10051 E Highland Rd., Ste. 29-280, Howell, MI 48843-6317, (519)962-8512
Woman to Woman Support Network [16787], 164 Broadway, Newport, RI 02840, (401)841-9211
Womankind Worldwide [IO], London, United Kingdom
Woman's Amer. Baptist Foreign Mission Soc. [★19317]
Woman's Amer. Baptist Foreign Mission Soc. [★19317]
Woman's Benefit Assn. [★19064]
Woman's Foreign Missionary Soc. [★20072]
Woman's Foreign Missionary Soc. [★20072]
Woman's Life Insurance Soc. [19064], PO Box 5020, Port Huron, MI 48061-5020, (810)985-5191
Woman's Missionary Soc. [★20072]
Woman's Missionary Soc. [★20072]
Woman's Missionary Union [19335], PO Box 830010, Birmingham, AL 35283-0010, (205)991-8100
Woman's Natl. Auxiliary Convention of Free Will Baptists [★19336]
Woman's Natl. Democratic Club [17543], 1526 New Hampshire Ave. NW, Washington, DC 20036, (202)232-7363

Women
4 Real Women Intl. [13447]
About-Face [13448]
Advancing Women Professionals and the Jewish Community [13449]WomenAfghan Women's Assn. Intl.
African-American Female Entrepreneurs Alliance [3673]
African Amer. Women in Cinema Org. [9592]
African Women Global Network [18789]
Aglow Intl. [20284]
Aglow Intl. [20284]
Alliance of Faith and Feminism [17628]
Alliance for Intl. Women's Rights [18804]
Alliance for Natl. Defense [6071]
Amer. Assn. of Breast Care Professionals [13858]
Amer. Assn. for Cancer Res. I Women in Cancer Res. [17120]
Amer. Assn. of Univ. Women [9051]
Amer. Assn. of Univ. I Women Educational Found. [9052]
Amer. Assn. of Univ. Women I Legal Advocacy Fund [6072]
Amer. Assn. for Women in Community Colleges [9053]
Amer. Coun. on Educ. I Off. of Women in Higher Educ. [9054]
Amer. Legion Auxiliary Girls Nation [17245]
Amer. Menopause Found. [17121]
Amer. Muslim Women Physicians Assn. [16252]
Amer. Sociological Assn. I Comm. on the Status of Women in Sociology [9589]
Arab Amer. Bus. Women's Coun. [3674]
Arab Amer. Women's Coun. [18922]
Arab Women's Solidarity Assn. [13450]
Arab Women's Solidarity Assn. UNITED [13450]
Armed Females of Am. [17682]
Armenian Intl. Women's Assn. [13451]
Asociatia Nationala A Femeilor Cu Diploma Universitara Din Romania [16169]
Assn. of Black Women in Higher Educ. [9055]WomenAssn. Burkinabe des Femmes Diplomees des Universites
Assn. for Pelvic Organ Prolapse Support [14760]
Assn. for Women in Aviation Maintenance [3675]
Assn. of Women in the Metal Indus. [3676]
Assn. of Women's Bus. Centers [3677]
Austrian Fed. of Univ. Women [16435]
Automotive Women's Alliance Found. [294]
Basic Hea. Intl. [17122]
Beauty 4 Ashes Intl. [13452]
Black Women in Church and Soc. [20285]
Black Women in Sisterhood for Action [13453]
Black Women United for Action [13454]
Black Women United for Action [13454]
Black Women's Hea. Imperative [17123]
Bright Pink [17124]

Buddhist Churches of Am. Fed. of Buddhist Women's Associations [19359]
Bus. Coun. for Peace [13455]
Bus. and Professional Women's Found. [10638]
Camping Women [22441]
Catalyst [10639]
Center for African Studies [18789]
Center for the Educ. of Women [9056]
Center for Women Veterans [20783]
Center for Women's Bus. Res. [3678]
Christian Ladies All together Standing against Social Injustice Corp. [13456]
Church Women United [20286]
Cinderella Softball Leagues [22951]
Command Trust Network [17125]
Comm. on the Status of Women in Microbiology [6297]
Congressional Club [19281]
Danish Assn. of Univ. Women [18314]
DeafHope [12141]
Defense Advisory Comm. on Women in the Services [5805]
Delta Gamma Pi Multicultural Sorority [23739]
Delta Sigma Chi Sorority [23741]
Delta Tau Lambda Sorority [23742]
Deutscher Akademikerinnenbund [14115]
Dining for Women [13457]
Dress for Success Worldwide [13458]
Dress for Success Worldwide [13458]
Dwa Fanm [17826]
EcoMom Alliance [13459]
Educational Found. for Women in Accounting [9057]
Egyptian Assn. of Univ. Women [18102]
Emerge Am. [18790]
Episcopal Women's Caucus [19702]
Estonian Assn. of Univ. Women [250]
Ethiopian North Amer. Hea. Professionals Assn. [14776]
Every Mother is a Working Mother Network [18791]
Executive Women Intl. [66]
Executive Women's Coun. [3679]
Exhale [10766]
Face Forward [11885]
Female Leadership Interest Coun. [3680]
Feminists for Animal Rights [10964]
Fianna Fail [13970]
Filipina Women's Network [18792]
Finnish and Amer. Women's Network [13460]
Found. for Women's Resources [9058]
Friends Women's Assn. [13461]
Gen. Fed. of Women's Clubs [19282]
Gen. Fed. of Women's Clubs [19282]
German Professional Women's Assn. [3681]
German Professional Women's Assn. [3681]
Girls Educ. Intl. [9059]
Girls Educational and Mentoring Services [18603]
Girls Helping Girls [12118]
Global Action on Widowhood [18787]
Global Alliance for Women's Hea. [17126]
Global Alliance for Women's Hea. [17126]
Global Grassroots [13497]
Greek Orthodox Ladies Philoptochos Soc. [19804]
Hagar USA [12237]
Hands to Hearts Intl. [11298]
Hard Hatted Women [3682]
Hispanas Organized for Political Equality [17776]
Hispanic Professional Women's Assn. [3683]
Hong Kong Assn. of Univ. Women [19024]
Hope Intl. [13462]
HOPE Intl. [13462]
Ibis Reproductive Hea. [16585]
Innocents at Risk [12241]
Inst. for Women in Trades, Tech. and Sci. [3684]
Intercollegiate Women's Lacrosse Coaches Assn. [22714]
Intl. Assn. of Women in Family Enterprises [3289]
Intl. Assn. of Women Ministers [20287]
Intl. Assn. of Women Ministers [20287]
Intl. Assn. for Women's Mental Hea. [15456]
Intl. Disciples Women's Ministries [20288]
Intl. Disciples Women's Ministries [20288]
Intl. Female Boxers Assn. [22437]
Intl. Healthcare Volunteers [14798]

Intl. Partnership for Reproductive Hea. [16587]
Intl. Women's Flag Football Assn. [22589]
Intl. Women's Forum [13463]
Intl. Women's Forum [13463]
Intl. Women's Hea. Coalition [17127]
Intl. Women's Hea. Coalition [17127]
Intl. Women's Media Found. [3685]
Intl. Women's Media Found. [3685]
Iris Films/Iris Feminist Collective [10640]
Irish Fed. of Univ. Women [14118]
Jamaica Unite [11602]
Jewish Orthodox Feminist Alliance [19873]
Kappa Phi Gamma Sorority [23746]
KEZA [210]
Korean Assn. of Univ. Women [13649]
Ladyslipper [10641]
Lambda Psi Delta Sorority [23747]
Latin Amer. Women's Assn. [13464]
Lesbian Herstory Educational Found. [10642]
Lesbian Herstory Educational Found. [10642]
Maitri [13465]
Matrix Found. [18793]
Melpomene Inst. [17128]
Mercado Global [3686]
Mercy Beyond Borders [12738]
Mocha Moms [13466]
Moms in Touch Intl. [20289]
Moms in Touch Intl. [20289]
Mooncircles [20250]
Mothers Acting Up [13467]
Mothers' Home Bus. Network [1731]
Muslim Women's Coalition [20136]
Narika [13468]
Natl. Action Org. [13469]
Natl. Advocates for Pregnant Women [17854]
Natl. Asian Women's Hea. Org. [17129]
Natl. Asian Women's Hea. Org. [17129]
Natl. Assn. of Baby Boomer Women [13470]
Natl. Assn. of Black Women in Constr. [848]
Natl. Assn. of Female Paramedics [14472]
Natl. Assn. of Univ. Women [9060]
Natl. Black Herstory Task Force [10643]
Natl. Coalition for Women and Girls in Educ. [9061]
Natl. Coun. on Women's Hea. [17130]
Natl. Found. for Women Legislators [6073]
Natl. Latina Bus. Women Assn. [2188]
Natl. Network to End Violence Against Immigrant Women [13471]
Natl. Org. for African-American Women [10829]
Natl. Org. of Sisters of Color Ending Sexual Assault [13093]
Natl. Soc. of Women Descendants of the Ancient and Honorable Artillery Company [20403]
Natl. Vulvodynia Assn. [17131]
Natl. Women in Agriculture Assn. [3762]
Natl. Women's Bus. Coun. [3687]
Natl. Women's Hea. Alliance [14822]
Natl. Women's Hea. Network [17132]
Natl. Women's Hea. Rsrc. Center [17133]
Natl. Women's History Proj. [10644]
Natl. Women's Political Caucus [17669]
Natl. Women's Stud. Assn. [9062]
Native Amer. Women's Hea. Educ. Rsrc. Center [17134]
Native Amer. Women's Hea. Educ. Rsrc. Center [17134]
Nepal Assn. of Univ. Women [252]
News Brunswick Advisory Coun. on the Status of Women [2251]
Nigeria Assn. of Univ. Women [256]
The Nurturing Network [13472]
Older Women's Network NSW [1389]
Org. for Res. on Women and Commun. [10645]
Orphans Africa [11621]
Our Bodies, Ourselves [17135]
OWL - The Voice of Midlife and Older Women [13473]
Pakistan Fed. of Univ. Women [11115]
PEO Intl. [9063]
PEO Intl. [9063]
Physicians Against World Hunger [12287]
Pink Isn't Always Pretty [13969]
POWER UP: Professional Org. of Women in Entertainment Reaching UP! [17737]

A star before a book entry number signifies that the name is not listed separately, but is mentioned within the entry.

Power for Women [13474]
Pro Mujer [13475]
Professional Football Players Mothers' Assn. [22595]
Professional Org. of Women in the Arts [9315]
Professional Women of Color Network [3688]
Professional Women in Healthcare [3689]
Promise World Wide [12358]
Public Leadership Educ. Network [9064]
Re-Formed Congregation of the Goddess - Intl. [20290]
Reach Global [13146]
Real Found. [13476]
Red Hat Soc. [10646]
Refugee Women's Network [13477]
Rising Intl. [11078]
Rwanda Gift for Life [13099]
Rwanda Knits [11626]
Secretariat for Family, Laity, Women, and Youth [12020]
Single Mothers By Choice [12622]
SISTAS [13478]
Sisterhood Agenda [10647]
Soc. of the Companions of the Holy Cross [19716]
Soc. for the Stud. of Early Modern Women [9065]
Soc. of Women Artists [4727]
Soc. for Women's Hea. Res. [17136]
Solace Intl. [13479]
Solace Intl. [13479]
Springboard Enterprises [3690]
Step Up Women's Network [13480]
Strong Women, Strong Girls [13481]
Stuntwomen's Assn. of Motion Pictures [1268]
Swiss-American Coun. of Women [18794]
Threads Weaving Dreams [12374]
The Transition Network [13482]
Transitions Global [12248]
Uganda Assn. of Univ. Women [21728]
United Nations Div. for the Advancement of Women [13483]
United Nations Div. for the Advancement of Women [13483]
United Order True Sisters [19283]
U.S. Assn. of Consecrated Virgins [19507]
U.S. Women and Cuba Collaboration [17957]
U.S. Women in Nuclear [7173]
United States Women of Today [13079]
U.S. Women's Chamber of Commerce [23457]
U.S. Women's Curling Assn. [22473]
Venture Strategies for Hea. and Development [14832]
Venture Strategies Innovations [14833]
Veteran Feminists of Am. [17673]
Vital Voices Global Partnership [13484]
Voices of African Mothers [12638]
WAM Intl.: Women Advancing Microfinance [1330]
We Are AWARE [13485]
Webgrrls Intl. [3691]
Wellesley Centers for Women [9066]
Whirly-Girls - Intl. Women Helicopter Pilots [20923]
White House Proj. [18795]
Woman Within Intl. Ltd. [13486]
Women Against Prostate Cancer [13992]
Women as Allies [18796]
Women in Aviation Intl. [3692]
Women in Aviation Intl. [3692]
Women in Balance [17137]
Women Church Convergence [20291]
Women Contractors Assn. [3693]
Women Educators [9067]
Women in Engg. ProActive Network [3694]
Women Entrepreneurs in Sci. and Tech. [3695]
Women and the Env. Org. [4323]
Women in Fatherhood, Inc. [13151]
Women in Flavor and Fragrance Commerce [3696]
Women, Food and Agriculture Network [5177]
Women of Hope Proj. [13487]
Women in Informal Employment: Globalizing and Organizing [13488]WomenWomen, Ink
Women Make Movies [10648]
Women in Mgt. [2307]
Women in Military Ser. for Am. Memorial Found. [6074]

Women Organizing for Change in Agriculture and NRM [3769]
Women Outdoors [22797]
Women in Photography Intl. [2741]
Women in Progress [13489]
Women in Progress [13489]
Women in Real Estate [9068]
Women in Toys [3479]
Women in Transition [13490]
Women Watch Afrika [18797]
Women of Wind Energy [7627]
Women With Disabilities Australia [1988]
Women for Women Intl. [13491]
Women of Yemen Assn. [11080]
Women and Youth Supporting Each Other [9069]
Women's All-Star Assn. [22432]
Women's Alliance for Theology, Ethics and Ritual [20292]
Women's Alliance for Theology, Ethics and Ritual [20292]
Women's Bus. Enterprise Natl. Coun. [3697]
Women's Coll. Coalition [9070]
Women's Earth Alliance [5178]
Women's Employment Opportunity Proj. [18798]
Women's Foreign Policy Gp. [18799]
Women's Foreign Policy Gp. [18799]
Women's Funding Network [13492]
Women's Global Connection [13493]
Women's High Tech Coalition [7535]
Women's History Network [10649]
Women's Intl. Center [13494]
Women's Intl. Center [13494]
Women's Intl. Coalition for Economic Justice [17596]
Women's Intl. Shipping and Trading Assn. [3276]
Women's Learning Partnership for Rights, Development, and Peace [13495]
Women's Learning Partnership for Rights, Development, and Peace [13495]
Women's Missionary Soc., AME Church [20293]
Women's Missionary Soc., AME Church [20293]
Women's Org. of Rebirth Through Healing [18800]
Women's Policy, Inc. [18801]
Women's Regional Publications of Am. [3698]
Women's Voices Now [18807]
Women's Voices. Women Vote [18802]
Women's World Banking - USA [13496]
Women's World Banking - USA [13496]
Women's World Org. for Rights, Literature and Development [18803]
Women's World Org. for Rights, Literature and Development [18803]
World Day of Prayer Intl. Comm. [20294]
World Day of Prayer Intl. Comm. [20294]
World of Good Development Org. [12382]
Zeta Chi Phi Multicultural Sorority [23752]
Women in Adult and Vocational Educ. [IO], Carlton North, Australia
Women in Advt. and Marketing [★806]
Women in Aerospace [6103], 204 E St. NE, Washington, DC 20002, (202)547-0229
Women Affirming Life - Address unknown since 2011.
Women for Afghan Women [12252], 158-24 73rd Ave., Fresh Meadows, NY 11366, (718)591-2434
Women for Afghan Women [12252], 158-24 73rd Ave., Fresh Meadows, NY 11366, (718)591-2434
Women Against Gun Control [17694], PO Box 95357, South Jordan, UT 84095, (801)328-9660
Women Against Gun Control [17694], PO Box 95357, South Jordan, UT 84095, (801)328-9660
Women Against Gun Violence [18773], 8800 Venice Blvd., Ste. 304, Los Angeles, CA 90034, (310)204-2348
Women Against Lung Cancer [★13955]
Women Against Military Madness [18139], 310 E 38th St., Ste. 222, Minneapolis, MN 55409-1337, (612)827-5364
Women Against Prostate Cancer [13992], 236 Massachusetts Ave. NE, Ste. 301, Washington, DC 20002, (202)580-5730
Women Airforce Ser. Pilots WWII - Defunct.
Women Alive Coalition [13628], 1566 Burnside Ave., Los Angeles, CA 90019, (323)965-1564

Women as Allies [18796], PO Box 2193, Los Banos, CA 93635, (831)246-3954
Women in Animation [1272], PO Box 17706, Encino, CA 91416, (818)759-9596
Women in Aviation Intl. [3692], Morningstar Airport, 3647 State Rte. 503 S, West Alexandria, OH 45381, (937)839-4647
Women in Aviation Intl. [3692], Morningstar Airport, 3647 State Rte. 503 S, West Alexandria, OH 45381, (937)839-4647
Women in Balance [17137], PO Box 12004, Overland Park, KS 66282, (888)820-5295
Women Band Directors Intl. [8672], 1603 10th Ave. W, Bradenton, FL 34205, (423)718-2622
Women Band Directors Intl. [8672], 1603 10th Ave. W, Bradenton, FL 34205, (423)718-2622
Women Band Directors Natl. Assn. [★8672]
Women Band Directors Natl. Assn. [★8672]
Women in Banking and Finance [IO], West Wickham, United Kingdom
Women in Bio [6338], PO Box 34043, Bethesda, MD 20827, (703)819-7647
Women in Black [18302], PO Box 20554, New York, NY 10021, (212)560-0905
Women in Bus. Development, Inc. [IO], Apia, Western Samoa
Women Bus. Owners - Address unknown since 2010.
Women in Cable [★513]
Women in Cable Telecommunications [513], 14555 Avion Pkwy., Ste. 250, Chantilly, VA 20151, (703)234-9810
Women in Cancer Res. [★17120]
Women Chefs and Restaurateurs [739], PO Box 1875, Madison, AL 35758, (256)975-1346
Women Chiefs of Enterprises Intl. [IO], Kingston, Australia
Women, Children and Family Ser. Charities of Am. [12058], 1100 Larkspur Landing Cir., Ste. 340, Larkspur, CA 94939, (800)626-6481
Women of the Church [★20164]
Women in the Church Coalition [★20291]
Women Church Convergence [20291], PO Box 806, Mill Valley, CA 94942, (908)753-4636
Women of the Church of God [★19615]
Women Climbing [IO], Wellington, New Zealand
Women of Color Partnership Program - Defunct.
Women of Color Rsrc. Center - Address unknown since 2011.
Women in Communications [★806]
Women in Communications Found. [★814]
Women Constr. Owners and Executives U.S.A. [953], 1004 Duke St., Alexandria, VA 22314, (800)788-3548
Women Contractors Assn. [3693], 10807 Jones Rd., PMB 164, Houston, TX 77065, (713)807-9977
Women in Defense [★17512]
Women in Defense, a Natl. Security Org. [17512], 2111 Wilson Blvd., Ste. 400, Arlington, VA 22201-3001, (703)247-2552
Women in Direct Marketing Intl. - Address unknown since 2010.
Women Educators [9067], Retired - UCSB, Graduate School of Educ., 536 E Lake St., Pentwater, MI 49449, (231)869-5939
Women Employed [11965], 65 E Wacker Pl., Ste. 1500, Chicago, IL 60601, (312)782-3902
Women and Employment [★11934]
Women in Endocrinology [14495], Mary Ruppe, MD, Sec.-Treas., Univ. of Texas, 6431 Fannin St., Ste. 5106, Houston, TX 77030, (858)534-1312
Women in Energy - Defunct.
Women in Engg. ProActive Network [3694], 1901 E Asbury Ave., Ste. 220, Denver, CO 80208, (303)871-4643
Women Entrepreneurs of Canada [IO], Toronto, ON, Canada
Women Entrepreneurs in Sci. and Tech. [3695], 485 Mass Ave., Ste. 300, Cambridge, MA 02139, (857)998-4040
Women and the Env. Org. [4323], 1629 K St. NW, Ste. 300, Washington, DC 20006, (202)355-6397
Women for Faith and Family [19514], PO Box 300411, St. Louis, MO 63130-0261, (314)863-8385
Women in Fatherhood, Inc. [13151], 236 Massachusetts Ave. NE, Ste. 610, Washington, DC 20002, (202)544-1936

Reference to "IO" in place of a book number signifies that the association may be found in the 50th edition of International Organizations.

Women in Fed. Law Enforcement [5745], 2200 Wilson Blvd., Ste. 102, PMB 204, Arlington, VA 22201-3324, (703)548-9211

Women in Film [1273], 6100 Wilshire Blvd., Ste. 710, Los Angeles, CA 90048, (323)935-2211

Women in Film and TV - United Kingdom [IO], London, United Kingdom

Women in Film and Video [1274], 3628 12th St. NE, Washington, DC 20017, (202)429-9438

Women in Fire Suppression [★5443]

Women in Flavor and Fragrance Commerce [3696], 3301 Rte. 66, Ste. 205, Bldg. C, Neptune, NJ 07753, (732)922-0500

Women, Food and Agriculture Network [5177], PO Box 611, Ames, IA 50010, (515)460-2477

Women in Food Indus. Mgt. [IO], Mississauga, ON, Canada

Women in Franchising [1531], 53 W Jackson Blvd., Ste. 1157, Chicago, IL 60604, (312)431-1467

Women in Govt. [5857], 1319 F St. NW, Ste. 710, Washington, DC 20004, (202)333-0825

Women in Govt. [5857], 1319 F St. NW, Ste. 710, Washington, DC 20004, (202)333-0825

Women in Govt. Relations [17755], 801 N Fairfax St., Ste. 211, Alexandria, VA 22314-1757, (703)299-8546

Women in Govt. Relations LEADER Found. [17756], Women in Govt. Relations, 801 N Fairfax St., Ste. 211, Alexandria, VA 22314-1757, (703)299-8546

Women Grocers of Am. [3128], 1005 N Glebe Rd., Ste. 250, Arlington, VA 22201-5758, (703)516-0700

Women in Hea. Care Mgt. [14836], PO Box 66, Stow, MA 01775

Women Helping Women - Defunct.

Women of Hope Proj. [13487], 4876-118 Princess Anne Rd., No. 203, Virginia Beach, VA 23462

Women in Housing and Finance [1332], 400 N Washington St., Ste. 300, Alexandria, VA 22314, (703)683-4742

Women in Informal Employment: Globalizing and Organizing [13488], Harvard Univ., 79 John F. Kennedy St., Cambridge, MA 02138, (617)496-7037

Women, Ink

Women, Ink - Address unknown since 2011.

Women Inst. [IO], Santiago, Chile

Women in Insurance and Financial Services [2047], 136 Everett Rd., Albany, NY 12205, (518)694-5506

Women in Insurance and Financial Services [2047], 136 Everett Rd., Albany, NY 12205, (518)694-5506

Women and Intl. Affairs CH [★17676]

Women in Intl. Security [18602], 3600 North St. NW, Lower Level, Washington, DC 20007, (202)687-3366

Women in Intl. Security [18602], 3600 North St. NW, Lower Level, Washington, DC 20007, (202)687-3366

Women Involved in Farm Economics [17172], 8463 20th St. SW, Richardton, ND 58652, (702)938-4246

Women Journalists Without Chains [IO], Sana'a, Yemen

Women Judges' Fund for Justice [★5627]

Women in Law and Development in Africa [IO], Accra, Ghana

Women Lawyers' Club [★5266]

Women Life Underwriters Confed. [★2047]

Women Life Underwriters Confed. [★2047]

Women Life Underwriters Conf. of the Natl. Assn. of Life Underwriters [★2047]

Women Life Underwriters Conf. of the Natl. Assn. of Life Underwriters [★2047]

Women in Livestock Development [3913], 1 World Ave., Little Rock, AR 72202, (800)422-0474

Women Living Under Muslim Laws [IO], London, United Kingdom

Women Make Movies [10648], 462 Broadway, Ste. 500WS, New York, NY 10013, (212)925-0606

Women in Managed Care

Women in Managed Care - Address unknown since 2011.

Women in Mgt. [2307], PO Box 1032, Dundee, IL 60118-7032, (708)386-0496

Women and Manual Trades [IO], London, United Kingdom

Women Marines Assn. [20689], PO Box 377, Oaks, PA 19456-0377, (888)525-1943

Women and Mathematics Educ. [8570], Mathematics Dept., Dept. 3036, 1000 E Univ., Laramie, WY 82071

Women Members Network of the Royal Soc. of Chemistry [IO], Cambridge, United Kingdom

Women and Men Against Sexual Harassment and Other Abuses - Address unknown since 2011.

Women in Military Ser. for Am. Memorial Found. [6074], Dept. 560, Washington, DC 20042-0560, (703)533-1155

Women in Mining [2517], PO Box 260246, Lakewood, CO 80226-0246, (303)298-1535

Women in Municipal Govt. [5858], Natl. League of Cities, 1301 Pennsylvania Ave. NW, Ste. 550, Washington, DC 20004, (202)626-3000

Women in Music Natl. Network - Address unknown since 2011.

Women of the Natl. Agricultural Aviation Assn. [3838], 1005 E St. SE, Washington, DC 20003-2847, (202)546-5722

Women Nationally Active for Christ [19336], PO Box 5002, Antioch, TN 37011-5002, (615)731-6812

Women in Neurosurgery [15689], AANS, 5550 Meadowbrook Dr., Rolling Meadows, IL 60008, (847)378-0500

Women in Neurotrauma Res. - Address unknown since 2011.

Women in Nuclear Global [IO], London, United Kingdom

Women in Nuclear Korea [IO], Daejeon, Republic of Korea

Women Officers Professional Assn. [★20741]

Women On Wheels Motorcycle Assn. [22784], PO Box 83076, Lincoln, NE 68501, (402)477-1280

Women Org. for Development and Capacity Building Labena [IO], Khartoum, Sudan

Women Organized to Respond to Life-Threatening Diseases [13629], 449 15th St., Ste. 303, Oakland, CA 94612-2821, (510)986-0340

Women Organized to Respond to Life-Threatening Diseases [13629], 449 15th St., Ste. 303, Oakland, CA 94612-2821, (510)986-0340

Women Organizing for Change in Agriculture and NRM [3769], 1775 K St. NW, Ste. 410, Washington, DC 20006, (202)331-9099

Women Outdoors [22797], PO Box 158, Northampton, MA 01061

Women in Packaging [2612], 4290 Bells Ferry Rd., Ste. 106-17, Kennesaw, GA 30144-1300, (678)594-6872

Women for Peace - Switzerland [IO], Volketswil, Switzerland

Women in Philanthropy - Address unknown since 2010.

Women in Photography Intl. [2741], 569 N Rossmore Ave., No. 604, Los Angeles, CA 90004, (303)462-1444

Women in Physics Gp. [IO], London, United Kingdom

Women in Progress [13489], PO Box 18323, Minneapolis, MN 55418, (800)338-3032

Women in Progress [13489], PO Box 18323, Minneapolis, MN 55418, (800)338-3032

Women Proutists [18635], 2005 Wheaton Haven Ct., Silver Spring, MD 20902, (202)239-1171

Women in Publishing [IO], London, United Kingdom

Women in Publishing Soc. Hong Kong [IO], Hong Kong, People's Republic of China

Women in Real Estate [9068], Architectural Resources Gp., Pier 9, San Francisco, CA 94111, (415)421-1680

Women of Reform Judaism [19909], 633 3rd Ave., New York, NY 10017, (212)650-4050

Women Refugees Community in Zambia [IO], Lusaka, Zambia

Women Riding For Res. [★21947]

Women into Sci. and Engg. [IO], London, United Kingdom

Women in Sci. Enquiry Network [IO], Malvern, Australia

Women in Security Electronics - Address unknown since 2010.

Women for Sobriety [13292], PO Box 618, Quakertown, PA 18951-0618, (215)536-8026

Women in Spanish [★9653]

Women Strike for Peace - Defunct.

Women in Tech. Intl. [7534], 11500 Olympic Blvd., Ste. 400, Los Angeles, CA 90064, (818)788-9484

Women in Tech. Intl. [7534], 11500 Olympic Blvd., Ste. 400, Los Angeles, CA 90064, (818)788-9484

Women in Tech. and Sci. [IO], Dublin, Ireland

Women in Tech. Yemen [IO], Sana'a, Yemen

Women in Tourism [IO], Athens, Greece

Women in Toys [3479], Joan Packard Luks, 300 Winston Dr., Cliffside Park, NJ 07010

Women in Transition [13490], 21 S 12th St., 6th Fl., Philadelphia, PA 19107, (215)564-5301

Women in Trucking [3543], PO Box 400, Plover, WI 54467-0400, (888)464-9482

Women Watch Afrika [18797], 4151 Memorial Dr., Ste. 205-A, Decatur, GA 30032, (404)759-6419

Women Welcome Women World Wide [IO], High Wycombe, United Kingdom

Women on Wheels [★22784]

Women in the Wind [21946], PO Box 8392, Toledo, OH 43615

Women of Wind Energy [7627], 155 Water St., Brooklyn, NY 11201, (718)210-3666

Women for Winesense [22202], PO Box 10549, Napa, CA 94581, (707)253-7100

Women With Disabilities Australia [IO], Rosny Park, Australia

Women Without Osteoporosis [IO], Sofia, Bulgaria

Women for Women [12761], 4455 Connecticut Ave. NW, Ste. 200, Washington, DC 20008, (202)737-7705

Women for Women in Bosnia [★12761]

Women for Women Intl. [13491], 4455 Connecticut Ave. NW, Ste. 200, Washington, DC 20008, (202)737-7705

Women for Women's Human Rights - New Ways [IO], Istanbul, Turkey

Women Working Worldwide [IO], Manchester, United Kingdom

Women for World Hea. [14837], 16291 Fantasia Ln., Huntington Beach, CA 92649, (714)846-4524

Women Writing the West [3714], 8547 E Arapahoe Rd., No. J-541, Greenwood Village, CO 80112-1436

Women of Yemen Assn. [11080], PO Box 16215, San Francisco, CA 94116

Women and Youth Supporting Each Other [9069], PO Box 712189, Los Angeles, CA 90071, (714)390-8363

WomenHeart: Natl. Coalition for Women with Heart Disease [14049], 818 18th St. NW, Ste. 1000, Washington, DC 20006, (202)728-7199

Women's Action Alliance [IO], Camberwell, Australia

Women's Action Gp. [IO], Harare, Zimbabwe

Women's Action for New Directions [18221], 691 Massachusetts Ave., Arlington, MA 02476, (781)643-6740

Women's Action for Nuclear Disarmament [★18221]

Women's Advocacy Office - Defunct.

Women's Africa Comm. of the African-American Inst. - Defunct.

Women's Aglow Fellowship Intl. [★20284]

Women's Aglow Fellowship Intl. [★20284]

Women's Aid - Ireland [IO], Dublin, Ireland

Women's Aid Org. [IO], Petaling Jaya, Malaysia

Women's All-Star Assn. [22432], Linda Rose-Keefe, Exec. Dir., 21 Eckhardt Terr., North Arlington, NJ 07031, (201)997-3125

Women's Alliance for a Democratic Iraq - Address unknown since 2011.

Women's Alliance for Peace and Human Rights in Afghanistan [12253], PO Box 77057, Washington, DC 20013-7057

Women's Alliance for Peace and Human Rights in Afghanistan [12253], PO Box 77057, Washington, DC 20013-7057

Women's Alliance for Theology, Ethics and Ritual [20292], 8121 Georgia Ave., Ste. 310, Silver Spring, MD 20910, (301)589-2509

Women's Alliance for Theology, Ethics and Ritual [20292], 8121 Georgia Ave., Ste. 310, Silver Spring, MD 20910, (301)589-2509

Women's Aquatic Network [7058], PO Box 57158, Washington, DC 20037

A star before a book entry number signifies that the name is not listed separately, but is mentioned within the entry.

Women's Army Corps Veterans' Assn. [20371], PO Box 5577, Fort McClellan, AL 36205-0577, (256)820-6824

Women's Art Club of the City of New York [★9242]

Women's Assn. for Educ. and Social Action [IO], Montreal, QC, Canada

Women's Assn. of the Mining Indus. of Canada Found. [IO], Toronto, ON, Canada

Women's Assn. of Romania [IO], Bucharest, Romania

Women's Assn. of Small and Medium Businesses [IO], Phnom Penh, Cambodia

Women's Automotive Assn. Intl. [309], PO Box 2535, Birmingham, MI 48012, (248)646-5250

Women's Automotive Assn. Intl. [309], PO Box 2535, Birmingham, MI 48012, (248)646-5250

Women's Auxiliary to the Amer. Dental Assn. [★14228]

Women's Auxiliary to the Amer. Medical Assn. [★15396]

Women's Auxiliary of the ICA - Address unknown since 2011.

Women's Auxiliary to the Natl. Medical Assn. [★15404]

Women's Basketball Coaches Assn. [22303], 4646 Lawrenceville Hwy., Lilburn, GA 30047, (770)279-8027

Women's Breast Cancer Advisory Center [★13976]

Women's Bus. Enterprise Natl. Coun. [3697], 1120 Connecticut Ave. NW, Ste. 1000, Washington, DC 20036, (202)872-5515

Women's Campaign Fund [17674], 1900 L St. NW, Ste. 500, Washington, DC 20036, (202)393-8164

Women's Cancer Network [13993], Found. for Women's Cancer, 230 W Monroe St., Ste. 2528, Chicago, IL 60606, (312)578-1439

Women's Catholic Order of Foresters [★18958]

Women's Caucus for Art [9259], Canal St. Sta., PO Box 1498, New York, NY 10013, (212)634-0007

Women's Caucus of the Coll. Art Assn. [★9259]

Women's Caucus for Political Sci. - Address unknown since 2010.

Women's Classical Caucus [9488], Baylor Univ., Dept. of Classics, One Bear Pl., No. 97352, Waco, TX 76798

Women's Coll. Coalition [9070], PO Box 1952, Hartford, CT 06144, (860)306-0291

Women's Correctional Assn. [★11705]

Women's Coun. on Energy and the Env. [6761], PO Box 33211, Washington, DC 20033, (202)997-4512

Women's Coun. of Realtors [3046], 430 N Michigan Ave., Chicago, IL 60611, (312)329-8481

Women's Coun. of Realtors of the Natl. Assn. of Realtors [★3046]

Women's Dermatologic Soc. [14342], 700 N Fairfax St., Ste. 510, Alexandria, VA 22314, (571)527-3115

Women's Dermatologic Soc. [14342], 700 N Fairfax St., Ste. 510, Alexandria, VA 22314, (571)527-3115

Women's Distance Comm. - Defunct.

Women's Documentation Center [IO], Lima, Peru

Women's Earth Alliance [5178], 2150 Allston Way, Ste. 460, Berkeley, CA 94704, (510)859-9110

Women's Economic Rights Project - Defunct.

Women's Economic Round Table [18495], Columbia Univ., Graduate School of Journalism, Knight-Bagehot Fellowship Prog., 2950 Broadway, Mail Code 3850, New York, NY 10027, (914)922-1747

Women's Electoral Lobby - Australia [IO], Canberra, Australia

Women's Employment Opportunity Proj. [18798], 250 Georgia Ave., No. 213, Atlanta, GA 30312, (404)681-2497

Women's Engg. Soc. [IO], Stevenage, United Kingdom

Women's Env. and Development Org. [17675], 355 Lexington Ave., 3rd Fl., New York, NY 10017, (212)973-0325

Women's Env. and Development Org. [17675], 355 Lexington Ave., 3rd Fl., New York, NY 10017, (212)973-0325

Women's Environmental Network [IO], London, United Kingdom

Women's Fisheries Network [4385], 2442 NW Market St., No. 243, Seattle, WA 98107

Women's Flat Track Derby Assn. [22905], PO Box 14100, Austin, TX 78761, (512)587-1859

Women's Food and Farming Union [IO], Lincoln, United Kingdom

Women's Foodservice Forum [1456], 6750 LBJ Fwy., Dallas, TX 75240, (972)770-9100

Women's Foreign Policy Gp. [18799], 1875 Connecticut Ave. NW, Ste. 720, Washington, DC 20009-5728, (202)884-8597

Women's Foreign Policy Gp. [18799], 1875 Connecticut Ave. NW, Ste. 720, Washington, DC 20009-5728, (202)884-8597

Women's Forum For Res. and Training [IO], Taiz, Yemen

Women's Funding Network [13492], 505 Sansome St., 2nd Fl., San Francisco, CA 94111, (415)441-0706

Women's Global Connection [13493], PO Box 34833, San Antonio, TX 78265, (210)832-3208

Women's Global Network for Reproductive Rights - Netherlands [IO], Amsterdam, Netherlands

Women's Gp. for the Abolition of Sexual Mutilation [IO], Paris, France

Women's Hall of Fame [★20379]

Women's Health Action and Mobilization - Defunct.

Women's Hea. and Economic Development Assn. [IO], Uyo, Nigeria

Women's Healthy Environments Network [IO], Toronto, ON, Canada

Women's High Tech Coalition [7535], MaryClare Fitzgerald, Pres./CEO, The Dutko Gp., 410 1st St. SE, Washington, DC 20003-1819, (202)479-7141

Women's History Network [10649], Natl. Women's History Proj., 3440 Airway Dr., Ste. F, Santa Rosa, CA 95403-2060, (707)636-2888

Women's Home and Foreign Missionary Soc. [★20293]

Women's Horticultural Assn. [4680], PO Box 7217, Appleton, WI 54912, (920)993-5134

Women's Humane Soc. Animal Shelter [11062], PO Box 1470, Bensalem, PA 19020, (215)750-3100

Women's Information Exchange - Defunct.

Women's Infoteka [IO], Zagreb, Croatia

Women's Initiatives for Gender Justice [IO], The Hague, Netherlands

Women's Innovation Projects East-West [IO], Moscow, Russia

Women's Inst. for Freedom of the Press [17362], 1940 Calvert St. NW, Washington, DC 20009-1502, (202)656-0893

The Women's Inst. Press - Defunct.

Women's Inter-Church Coun. of Canada [IO], Toronto, ON, Canada

Women's Intl. Center [13494], PO Box 669, Rancho Santa Fe, CA 92067-0669, (858)759-3567

Women's Intl. Center [13494], PO Box 669, Rancho Santa Fe, CA 92067-0669, (858)759-3567

Women's Intl. Coalition for Economic Justice [17596], 12 Dongan Pl., No. 206, New York, NY 10040, (212)304-9106

Women's Intl. Coalition for Economic Justice [17596], 12 Dongan Pl., No. 206, New York, NY 10040, (212)304-9106

Women's Intl. League for Peace and Freedom - Albania [IO], Tirana, Albania

Women's Intl. League for Peace and Freedom - Australia [IO], Adelaide, Australia

Women's Intl. League for Peace and Freedom - Belarus [IO], Minsk, Belarus

Women's Intl. League for Peace and Freedom - Bolivia [IO], Santa Cruz, Bolivia

Women's Intl. League for Peace and Freedom - Burundi [IO], Bujumbura, Burundi

Women's Intl. League for Peace and Freedom - Canada [IO], Vancouver, BC, Canada

Women's Intl. League for Peace and Freedom - Chile [IO], Las Condes, Chile

Women's Intl. League for Peace and Freedom - Colombia [IO], Bogota, Colombia

Women's Intl. League for Peace and Freedom - Costa Rica [IO], San Jose, Costa Rica

Women's Intl. League for Peace and Freedom - Denmark [IO], Copenhagen, Denmark

Women's Intl. League for Peace and Freedom - Finland [IO], Helsinki, Finland

Women's Intl. League for Peace and Freedom - France [IO], Paris, France

Women's Intl. League for Peace and Freedom - Germany [IO], Nuremberg, Germany

Women's Intl. League for Peace and Freedom - India [IO], Ahmedabad, India

Women's Intl. League for Peace and Freedom - Ireland [IO], Carrick-on-Suir, Ireland

Women's Intl. League for Peace and Freedom - Israel [IO], Bat Yam, Israel

Women's Intl. League for Peace and Freedom - Italy [IO], Rome, Italy

Women's Intl. League for Peace and Freedom - Japan [IO], Tokyo, Japan

Women's Intl. League for Peace and Freedom - Lebanon [IO], Beirut, Lebanon

Women's Intl. League for Peace and Freedom - Nepal [IO], Kathmandu, Nepal

Women's Intl. League for Peace and Freedom - Netherlands [IO], Utrecht, Netherlands

Women's Intl. League for Peace and Freedom - New Zealand [IO], Wellington, New Zealand

Women's Intl. League for Peace and Freedom - Norway [IO], Oslo, Norway

Women's Intl. League for Peace and Freedom - Peru [IO], Lima, Peru

Women's Intl. League for Peace and Freedom - Philippines [IO], Quezon City, Philippines

Women's Intl. League for Peace and Freedom - Russia [IO], Moscow, Russia

Women's Intl. League for Peace and Freedom - Sierra Lone [IO], Freetown, Sierra Leone

Women's Intl. League for Peace and Freedom - Sri Lanka [IO], Colombo, Sri Lanka

Women's Intl. League for Peace and Freedom - Sweden [IO], Stockholm, Sweden

Women's Intl. League for Peace and Freedom - Switzerland [IO], Geneva, Switzerland

Women's Intl. League for Peace and Freedom - United Kingdom Sect. [IO], London, United Kingdom

Women's Intl. League for Peace and Freedom U.S. Sect. [18303], 11 Arlington St., Boston, MA 02116, (617)266-0999

Women's Intl. League for Peace and Freedom U.S. Sect. [18303], 11 Arlington St., Boston, MA 02116, (617)266-0999

Women's Intl. League for Peace and Freedom - Venezuela [IO], Caracas, Venezuela

Women's Intl. Motorcycle Assn. [IO], Wirral, United Kingdom

Women's Intl. Motorcycle Assn. - Australia [IO], Carnegie, Australia

Women's Intl. Motorcycle Assn. - New South Wales [IO], St. Peters, Australia

Women's Intl. Motorcycle Assn. - New Zealand [IO], Auckland, New Zealand

Women's Intl. Motorcycle Assn. - Queensland [IO], Fortitude Valley, Australia

Women's Intl. Motorcycle Assn. - South Australia [IO], Hamley Bridge, Australia

Women's Intl. Motorcycle Assn. - Tasmania [IO], Carnegie, Australia

Women's Intl. Motorcycle Assn. - Victoria [IO], Ingle Farm, Australia

Women's Intl. Network [17676], WIN News, 187 Grant St., Lexington, MA 02420-2126, (781)862-9431

Women's Intl. Network [17676], WIN News, 187 Grant St., Lexington, MA 02420-2126, (781)862-9431

Women's Intl. Network of Utility Professionals [1088], PO Box 817, Fergus Falls, MN 56538-0817, (218)731-1659

Women's Intl. News Gathering Ser. [IO], Vancouver, BC, Canada

Women's Intl. Professional Tennis Coun. [★23061]

Women's Intl. Professional Tennis Coun. [★23061]

Women's Intl. Shipping and Trading Assn. [3276], Blank Rome, LLP, 600 New Hampshire Ave. NW, Washington, DC 20037

Women's Intl. Shipping and Trading Assn. [3276], Blank Rome, LLP, 600 New Hampshire Ave. NW, Washington, DC 20037

Women's Intl. Shipping and Trading Assn. Hellas [IO], Piraeus, Greece

Women's Intl. Shipping and Trading Assn. Italy [IO], Genoa, Italy

Reference to "IO" in place of a book number signifies that the association may be found in the 50th edition of International Organizations.

Women's Intl. Shipping and Trading Assn.
Netherlands [IO], Hellevoetsluis, Netherlands
Women's Intl. Shipping and Trading Assn. Singapore
[IO], Singapore, Singapore
Women's Intl. Stud. Europe [IO], Nicosia, Cyprus
Women's Intl. Tennis Assn. [★23068]
Women's Intl. Zionist Org. - Israel [IO], Tel Aviv,
Israel
Women's Intl. Zionist Org. - Netherlands [IO], Am-
sterdam, Netherlands
Women's Issues, Status, and Education - Defunct.
Women's Jewelry Assn. [2173], 52 Vanderbilt Ave.,
19th Fl., New York, NY 10017-3827, (212)687-
2722
Women's Law Proj. [17677], 125 S 9th St., No. 300,
Philadelphia, PA 19107, (215)928-9801
Women's Leadership Forum - Address unknown
since 2010.
Women's Leadership Network, Natl. Student Educ.
Fund [★8932]
Women's League for Conservative Judaism [19910],
475 Riverside Dr., Ste. 820, New York, NY 10115,
(212)870-1260
Women's League of the United Synagogue of Am.
[★19910]
Women's Learning Partnership for Rights, Develop-
ment, and Peace [13495], 4343 Montgomery Ave.,
Ste. 201, Bethesda, MD 20814, (301)654-2774
Women's Learning Partnership for Rights, Develop-
ment, and Peace [13495], 4343 Montgomery Ave.,
Ste. 201, Bethesda, MD 20814, (301)654-2774
Women's Legal Defense Fund [★17666]
Women's Legal Educ. and Action Fund [IO], Toronto,
ON, Canada
Women's Missionary and Ser. Commn. of the Men-
nonite Church [★19961]
Women's Missionary Soc., AME Church [20293],
1134 11th St. NW, Washington, DC 20001,
(202)371-8886
Women's Missionary Soc., AME Church [20293],
1134 11th St. NW, Washington, DC 20001,
(202)371-8886
Women's Motorcyclist Found. [21947], 7 Lent Ave.,
Le Roy, NY 14482-1009, (585)768-6054
Women's Mountain Bike and Tea Soc. [22492], PO
Box 757, Fairfax, CA 94978, (415)459-0980
Women's Natl. Basketball Players Assn. [22304],
310 Lenox Ave., New York, NY 10027, (212)655-
0880
Women's Natl. Book Assn. [2884], PO Box 237,
New York, NY 10150-0231, (212)208-4629
Women's Natl. Commn. [IO], London, United
Kingdom
Women's Natl. Republican Club [18545], 3 W 51st
St., New York, NY 10019, (212)582-5454
Women's Network in Aquatic and Marine Affairs
[★7058]
Women's Network Australia [IO], Sunnybank Hills,
Australia
Women's Network of the Methodist Church [IO],
London, United Kingdom
Women's Ordination Conf. [19515], PO Box 15057,
Washington, DC 20003, (202)675-1006
Women's Org. of Hapoel Hamizrachi [★19860]
Women's Org. of Hapoel Hamizrachi [★19860]
Women's Org. for Political Prisoners [IO], Tel Aviv,
Israel
Women's Org. of Rebirth Through Healing [18800],
PO Box 575, Atlanta, GA 30301, (404)496-4073
Women's Org. of the Social Democratic Party of
Austria [IO], Vienna, Austria
Women's Org. of the Swedish People's Party in
Finland [IO], Helsinki, Finland
Women's Overseas Ser. League [20821], PO Box
7124, Washington, DC 20044-7124
Women's Parent Mite Missionary Soc. [★20293]
Women's Party for Survival [★18221]
Women's Peace Party [★18303]
Women's Peace Party [★18303]
Women's Philanthropy Inst. [12690], 550 W North
St., Ste. 301, Indianapolis, IN 46202-3272,
(317)274-4200
Women's Policy, Inc. [18801], 409 12th St. SW, Ste.
310, Washington, DC 20024, (202)554-2323
Women's Prison Assn. [11739], 110 2nd Ave., New
York, NY 10003, (646)336-6100

Women's Professional Billiard Assn. [22312], 416
County Rd. 501, Bayfield, CO 81122, (615)859-
9722
Women's Professional Golf Assn. [★22614]
Women's Professional Rodeo Assn. [22851], 431 S
Cascade, Colorado Springs, CO 80903, (719)447-
4627
Women's Proj. [18636], 55 W End Ave., New York,
NY 10023, (212)765-1706
Women's Regional Publications of Am. [3698], Jill
Duval, VP/Membership Chair, PO Box 12955,
Albuquerque, NM 87195, (505)247-9195
Women's Res. and Educ. Inst. [17678], 714 G St.
SE, Ste. 200, Washington, DC 20003, (202)280-
2720
Women's Rsrc. Centre [IO], Karachi, Pakistan
Women's Rights
  Alliance for Intl. Women's Rights [18804]
  Armenian Intl. Women's Assn. [13451]
  Beauty 4 Ashes Intl. [13452]
  Dwa Fanm [17826]
  Family Hea. Alliance [16584]
  Gender Action [18805]
  Girls Educational and Mentoring Services [18603]
  Global Action on Widowhood [18787]
  Global Grassroots [13497]
  Innocents at Risk [12241]
  Jewish Orthodox Feminist Alliance [19873]
  Natl. Advocates for Pregnant Women [17854]
  Natl. Org. for African-American Women [10829]
  Shared Hope Intl. [13498]
  Shared Hope Intl. [13498]
  Shining Hope for Communities [11635]
  SisterSong Women of Color Reproductive Justice
    Collective [18806]
  U.S. Women and Cuba Collaboration [17957]
  US Human Rights Network [17866]
  Veteran Feminists of Am. [17673]
  Voices of African Mothers [12638]
  Woman Within Intl. Ltd. [13486]
  Women Watch Afrika [18797]
  Women's Alliance for Peace and Human Rights in
    Afghanistan [12253]
  Women's Intl. Coalition for Economic Justice
    [17596]
  Women's Voices Now [18807]
  Women's Voices. Women Vote [18802]
Women's Rights Comm. [17679], Amer. Fed. of
Teachers, Human Rights Dept., 555 New Jersey
Ave. NW, Washington, DC 20001, (202)879-4400
Women's Rights Proj. of the Center for Law and
Social Policy [★17668]
Women's Royal Voluntary Ser. [IO], Abingdon,
United Kingdom
Women's Sailing Found. [★22378]
Women's Soc. of Christian Ser. Gen. Conf. [IO], Sin-
gapore, Singapore
Women's Sport and Fitness Found. [IO], London,
United Kingdom
Women's Sports Found. [23018], 1899 Hempstead
Tpke., Ste. 400, East Meadow, NY 11554,
(516)542-4700
Women's Studies
  Global Grassroots [13497]
Women's Stud. Assn. [IO], Wellington, New Zealand
Women's Support Proj. [IO], Glasgow, United
Kingdom
Women's Supreme Coun. [★19876]
Women's Supreme Coun. [★19876]
Women's Tennis Assn. [★23068]
Women's Tennis Coun. [★23061]
Women's Tennis Coun. [★23061]
Women's Theodore Roosevelt Memorial Assn.
[★10693]
Women's Trans. Seminar [3544], 1701 K St. NW,
Ste. 800, Washington, DC 20006, (202)955-5085
Women's Trans. Seminar [3544], 1701 K St. NW,
Ste. 800, Washington, DC 20006, (202)955-5085
Women's Union of Russia [IO], Moscow, Russia
Women's Veterinary Medical Assn. [★17018]
Women's Voices for the Earth [4313], PO Box 8743,
Missoula, MT 59807, (406)543-3747
Women's Voices Now [18807], 119 W 72nd St., No.
167, New York, NY 10023, (919)475-8407
Women's Voices. Women Vote [18802], 1640 Rhode
Island Ave. NW, Ste. 825, Washington, DC 20036,
(202)659-9570

Women's Work Force Network [★11963]
Women's WORLD [★18803]
Women's WORLD [★18803]
Women's World Banking - USA [13496], 8 W 40th
St., 9th Fl., New York, NY 10018, (212)768-8513
Women's World Banking - USA [13496], 8 W 40th
St., 9th Fl., New York, NY 10018, (212)768-8513
Women's World Org. for Rights, Literature and
Development [18803], PO Box 250 891, Columbia
Univ. Sta., New York, NY 10025, (212)947-2915
Women's World Org. for Rights, Literature and
Development [18803], PO Box 250 891, Columbia
Univ. Sta., New York, NY 10025, (212)947-2915
Women's World Summit Found. [IO], Geneva,
Switzerland
WomensLaw.org - Address unknown since 2011.
Wonderful World of Wildlife [5157], 88 E Main St.,
No. 134, Mendham, NJ 07945, (908)380-8810
Wood
  Amer. Wood Coun. [3699]
  Assn. of Woodworking and Furnishings Suppliers
    [3700]
  Hardwood Coun. [3701]
  Hardwood Coun. [3701]
  Hardwood Fed. [1508]
  Hardwood Mfrs. Assn. I Amer. Hardwood Info.
    Center [3702]
  Intl. Wood Collectors Soc. [22203]
  Natl. Coun. for Air and Stream Improvement
    [4406]
  Natl. Guild of Decoupeurs [21457]
  Scrollsaw Assn. of the World [22204]
  Scrollsaw Assn. of the World [22204]
  Southern Pine Coun. [3703]
  Wood I-Joist Mfrs. Assn. [1517]
  Wooden Canoe Heritage Assn. [22414]
  WoodLINKS USA [8300]
Wood Collectors Soc. [★22203]
Wood Coll. Alumni Assn. - Defunct.
Wood Component Mfrs. Assn. [1516], 741 Butlers
Gate, Ste. 100, Marietta, GA 30068, (770)565-
6660
Wood Energy Inst. [★1699]
Wood Engravers Network [21471], 1455 Jefferson
Ave., St. Paul, MN 55105
Wood Engravers Network [21471], 1455 Jefferson
Ave., St. Paul, MN 55105
Wood and Forestry Products Exporters Union [IO],
Istanbul, Turkey
Wood Heating Alliance [★1699]
Wood Heating Educ. and Res. Found. [★1700]
Wood I-Joist Mfrs. Assn. [1517], PO Box 1088,
Roseburg, OR 97470, (541)784-2817
Wood Machinery Mfrs. of Am. [1880], 500 Citadel
Dr., Ste. 200, Commerce, CA 90040, (323)215-
0330
Wood Moulding and Millwork Producers [★583]
Wood Moulding and Millwork Producers [★583]
Wood Moulding and Millwork Producers Assn. [583],
507 1st St., Woodland, CA 95695, (530)661-9591
Wood Moulding and Millwork Producers Assn.
[★583]
Wood Preservation Canada [IO], Ottawa, ON,
Canada
Wood Products Mfrs. Assn. [1518], PO Box 761,
Westminster, MA 01473-0761, (978)874-5445
Wood and Synthetic Flooring Inst. [★578]
Wood and Synthetic Flooring Inst. [★578]
Wood Trades
  Intl. Wood Collectors Soc. [22203]
  Wood I-Joist Mfrs. Assn. [1517]
  Wooden Canoe Heritage Assn. [22414]
Wood Truss Coun. of Am. [★622]
Wood-Turners Ser. Bur. [★1518]
Wood Turners and Shapers Assn. [★1518]
Wood, Wire and Metal Lathers' Intl. Union [★23169]
Woodcarvings
  Intl. Wood Collectors Soc. [22203]
  Wooden Canoe Heritage Assn. [22414]
Wooden Boat Assn. of New South Wales [IO],
Gladesville, Australia
Wooden Boat Assn. - Queensland [IO], Brisbane,
Australia
Wooden Boat Assn. - Victoria [IO], Glen Huntly,
Australia

A star before a book entry number signifies that the name is not listed separately, but is mentioned within the entry.

Wooden Boat Guild of Tasmania [IO], Battery Point, Australia
Wooden Canoe Heritage Assn. [22414], PO Box 117, Tamworth, NH 03886, (603)323-8992
Woodlands Inst. [★9623]
Woodlands Mountain Inst. [★9623]
WoodLINKS USA [8300], PO Box 445, Tuscola, IL 61953, (217)253-3239
WoodLINKS USA [8300], PO Box 445, Tuscola, IL 61953, (217)253-3239
Woodmen
Intl. Wood Collectors Soc. [22203]
Modern Woodmen of Am. [19284]
Woodmen Rangers [19285]
Woodmen of the World/Omaha Woodmen Life Insurance Soc. [19286]
Woodmen Rangers [19285], Woodmen of the World/ Omaha Woodmen Life Insurance Soc., Woodmen Tower, 1700 Farnam St., Omaha, NE 68102, (800)225-3108
Woodmen of the World/Omaha Woodmen Life Insurance Soc. [19286], Woodmen Tower, 1700 Farnam St., Omaha, NE 68102-2002, (800)225-3108
Woodrow Wilson Birthplace Found. [★10697]
Woodrow Wilson Intl. Center for Scholars [9850], 1 Woodrow Wilson Plz., 1300 Pennsylvania Ave. NW, Washington, DC 20004-3027, (202)691-4000
Woodrow Wilson Intl. Center for Scholars [9850], 1 Woodrow Wilson Plz., 1300 Pennsylvania Ave. NW, Washington, DC 20004-3027, (202)691-4000
Woodrow Wilson Natl. Fellowship Found. [8198], PO Box 5281, Princeton, NJ 08543-5281, (609)452-7007
Woodrow Wilson Presidential Lib. Found. [10697], 18-24 N Coalter St., PO Box 24, Staunton, VA 24402-0024, (540)885-0897
Woodworking Machinery Distributors Assn. - Defunct.
Woodworking Machinery Importers Assn. of Am. [★1881]
Woodworking Machinery Indus. Assn. [1881], 3313 Paper Mill Rd., Ste. 202, Phoenix, MD 21131, (410)628-1970
Woodworking Machinery Mfrs. of Am. [★1880]
Woodworking Machinery Mfrs. Assn. [★1880]
Woodworking Machinery Suppliers Assn. [IO], Matlock, United Kingdom
Wool
Amer. Wool Coun. [3435]
Natl. Textile Assn. I Wool Mfrs. Coun. [3452]
Woolmens' Company [IO], Great Brickhill, United Kingdom
WOOMB Philippines [IO], Manila, Philippines
WOOMB Tanzania [IO], Mtwara, United Republic of Tanzania
Worcester Polytechnic Inst. Alumni [★18919]
Worcester Polytechnic Inst. Alumni Assn. [18919], 100 Inst. Rd., Worcester, MA 01609-2280, (508)831-5600
Word of Life Fellowship [19774], PO Box 600, Schroon Lake, NY 12870, (518)494-6000
Word of Mouth Marketing Assn. [2426], 65 E Wacker Pl., Ste. 500, Chicago, IL 60601, (312)853-4400
WordAlone Ministries [19943], PO Box 521, Maple Lake, MN 55358, (612)216-2055
WordAlone Network [★19943]
Wordcraft Circle of Native Writers and Storytellers [9527], Univ. of Oklahoma, Native Amer. Stud. Prog., 633 Elm Ave., Rm. 208, Norman, OK 73019
Wordcraft Circle of Native Writers and Storytellers [9527], Univ. of Oklahoma, Native Amer. Stud. Prog., 633 Elm Ave., Rm. 208, Norman, OK 73019
WordTheatre [10550], PO Box 5554, Santa Monica, CA 90409, (310)915-5150
Work in America Inst. - Defunct.
Work Found. [IO], London, United Kingdom
Work Glove Inst. [★1833]
Work Glove Inst. [★1833]
Work Glove Mfrs. Assn. [★1833]
Work Glove Mfrs. Assn. [★1833]
Work at Home Moms [★665]
Work for Progress [12583], 1536 Wynkoop St., Ste. 300, Denver, CO 80202, (303)623-4900
Workaholics Anonymous [13048], PO Box 289, Menlo Park, CA 94026-0289, (510)273-9253

Workers
Alliance for Worker Freedom [23316]
Amer. Assn. of Working People [11928]
Annapolis Coalition on the Behavioral Hea. Workforce [15446]
Coalition of Immokalee Workers [13499]
Faith Alliance Against Slavery and Trafficking [17289]
Fed. of Employers and Workers of Am. [1147]
Freelancers Union [23317]
Green Collar Assn. [1148]
Intl. Assn. of Heat and Frost Insulators and Allied Workers [1707]
Intl. Union of Indus. and Independent Workers [23312]
Jobs With Justice [18808]
Natl. Org. of Injured Workers [23319]
Peggy Browning Fund [6075]
Professionals in Workers' Compensation [3704]
Social Accountability Intl. [18809]
Social Accountability Intl. [18809]
U.S. Fed. of Worker Cooperatives [23318]
Waterfront and Allied Workers' Union [9516]
Youth for Intl. Socialism [18663]
Workers Compensation Insurance Organizations [2048], Pennsylvania Compensation Rating Bur., United Plaza Bldg., Ste. 1500, 30 S 17th St., Philadelphia, PA 19103, (215)568-2371
Workers' Educational Assn. [IO], Stockholm, Sweden
Workers' Educational Assn. - East Midlands Region [IO], Nottingham, United Kingdom
Workers' Educational Assn. - Eastern Region [IO], Cambridge, United Kingdom
Workers' Educational Assn. - London Region [IO], London, United Kingdom
Workers' Educational Assn. - North East Region [IO], Jesmond, United Kingdom
Workers' Educational Assn. - North West Region [IO], Liverpool, United Kingdom
Workers' Educational Assn. - Northern Ireland [IO], Belfast, United Kingdom
Workers' Educational Assn. - South Wales [IO], Cardiff, United Kingdom
Workers' Educational Assn. - South Western Region [IO], Exeter, United Kingdom
Workers' Educational Assn. - Southern Region [IO], Rochester, United Kingdom
Workers' Educational Assn. - United Kingdom [IO], London, United Kingdom
Workers' Educational Assn. - West Midlands Region [IO], Birmingham, United Kingdom
Workers' Educational Assn. - Yorkshire and Humber [IO], Leeds, United Kingdom
Workers' Music Assn. [IO], London, United Kingdom
Worker's Socialist Party [★18369]
Workers Solidarity Alliance [17184], 339 Lafayette St., Rm. 202, New York, NY 10012
Workers' Trade Union [IO], Madrid, Spain
Workers World Party [18660], 55 W 17th St., New York, NY 10011, (212)627-2994
Workers World Party [18660], 55 W 17th St., New York, NY 10011, (212)627-2994
Workflow Mgt. Coalition [2308], 759 CJC Hwy., Ste. No. 363, Cohasset, MA 02025-2115, (781)719-9209
The Workforce Alliance [★11952]
Workgroup for Electronic Data Interchange [1678], 12020 Sunrise Valley Dr., Ste. 100, Reston, VA 20191, (703)391-2716
Working Capital for Community Needs [17991], PO Box 1534, Madison, WI 53701, (608)257-7230
Working Capital for Community Needs [17991], PO Box 1534, Madison, WI 53701, (608)257-7230
Working Class Stud. Assn. [8455], Cherie Rankin, Treas., PO Box 264, Emden, IL 62635
Working in Employee Benefits [★1134]
Working in Employee Benefits [★1134]
Working Families [IO], London, United Kingdom
Working Families Party [18368], 2 Nevins St., 3rd Fl., Brooklyn, NY 11217, (718)222-3796
Working Films [12043], 602 S 5th Ave., Wilmington, NC 28401, (910)342-9000
Working Group of Alpine Regions [IO], Innsbruck, Austria

Working Group on Applied Physical Geography [IO], Amsterdam, Netherlands
Working Group on Untouchables - Defunct.
Working Kelpie Coun. of Australia [IO], Castle Hill, Australia
Working Pit Bull Terrier Club of Am. [21681], Aja Harris, Treas., 2608 Kentucky Ave., Baltimore, MD 21213
Working Ranch Cowboys Assn. [2997], PO Box 7765, Amarillo, TX 79114-7765, (806)374-9722
Working Riesenschnauzer Fed. [21682], Martha Galuszka, Membership Dir., 324 Oakwood Ave., West Hartford, CT 06110, (860)233-2286
Working Riesenschnauzer Fed. [21682], Martha Galuszka, Membership Dir., 324 Oakwood Ave., West Hartford, CT 06110, (860)233-2286
Working Today [1532], 45 Main St., Ste. 710, Brooklyn, NY 11201, (718)222-1099
Working Women Educ. Fund [★17627]
Working Women, Natl. Assn. of Off. Workers [★17626]
Working Women Organizing Proj. [★17626]
Working Women's Forum India [IO], Chennai, India
WorkingAbroad Projects [IO], Lewes, United Kingdom
Workingmen's Party [★18365]
Workmen's Benefit Fund of the U.S.A. [19065], 399 Conklin St., Ste. 310, Farmingdale, NY 11735-2614, (516)938-6060
Workmen's Circle [19066], 247 W 37th St., 5th Fl., New York, NY 10018, (212)889-6800
Workmen's Compensation
Canadian Injured Workers Alliance [20179]
Fed. of Employers and Workers of Am. [1147]
Natl. Org. of Injured Workers [23319]
Professionals in Workers' Compensation [3704]
Workplace Benefits Assn. [1135], 9221 Ravenna Rd., Ste. No. D8, Twinsburg, OH 44087, (330)425-8399
Workplace Bullying Inst. [16437], PO Box 29915, Bellingham, WA 98228, (360)656-6630
Workplace Bullying and Trauma Inst. [★16437]
Workplace Fairness [11925], 920 U St. NW, Washington, DC 20001, (202)243-7660
Workroom Assn. of Am. [2078], 802 N Robinson Dr., Waco, TX 76706, (254)662-4021
Workshop 3 [IO], Hamburg, Germany
WORLD [★13629]
WORLD [★13629]
World Ability Fed. [11837], 120 S Riverside Plz., Ste. 1050, Chicago, IL 60606, (312)207-0000
World Ability Fed. [11837], 120 S Riverside Plz., Ste. 1050, Chicago, IL 60606, (312)207-0000
World Acad. of Art and Sci. [9331], 657 Coventry Rd., Kensington, CA 94707
World Acad. of Art and Sci. [9331], 657 Coventry Rd., Kensington, CA 94707
World Access for the Blind [17118], 17328 Ventura Blvd., No. 195, Encino, CA 91316, (866)396-7035
World Access for the Blind [17118], 17328 Ventura Blvd., No. 195, Encino, CA 91316, (866)396-7035
World Action for Humanity [13120], PO Box 193584, San Francisco, CA 94119-3584, (415)321-0701
World Affairs
Assn. of World Citizens [18810]
Assn. of World Citizens [18810]
Bosniak Amer. Advisory Coun. for Bosnia and Herzegovina [17895]
Coun. on Intl. and Public Affairs [18811]
Coun. on Intl. and Public Affairs [18811]
Fund for Peace [18812]
Global Interdependence Center [18813]
Hoover Institution on War, Revolution and Peace [18814]
Inst. of Current World Affairs [18815]
Inst. of Current World Affairs [18815]
Planetary Citizens [18816]
Planetary Citizens [18816]
Renaissance Universal [18817]
State of the World Forum [18818]
State of the World Forum [18818]
Student Pugwash U.S.A. [18819]
U.S. Assn. for the Univ. for Peace [18294]
World Affairs Councils of Am. [18820]
World Affairs Councils of Am. [18820]

Reference to "IO" in place of a book number signifies that the association may be found in the 50th edition of International Organizations.

Worldwatch Inst. [18821]
Worldwatch Inst. [18821]
World Affairs Center for the U.S. [★17700]
World Affairs Center for the U.S. [★17700]
World Affairs Councils of Am. [18820], 1200 18th St. NW, Ste. 902, Washington, DC 20036, (202)833-4557
World Affairs Councils of Am. [18820], 1200 18th St. NW, Ste. 902, Washington, DC 20036, (202)833-4557
World Against AIDS [12386], 707 E 215 St., Bronx, NY 10467, (917)500-5289
World Against AIDS [12386], 707 E 215 St., Bronx, NY 10467, (917)500-5289
World Agroforestry Centre [IO], Nairobi, Kenya
World Airline Entertainment Assn. [373], 355 Lexington Ave., 15th Fl., New York, NY 10017, (212)297-2177
World Airline Entertainment Assn. [★373]
World Airline Historical Soc. [20924], PO Box 489, Ocoee, FL 34761
World Airline Historical Soc. [20924], PO Box 489, Ocoee, FL 34761
World Airline Hobby Club [★20924]
World Airline Hobby Club [★20924]
World Airlines Clubs Assn. [IO], Montreal, QC, Canada
World Allergy Org. [13644], 555 E Wells St., Ste. 1100, Milwaukee, WI 53202-3823, (414)276-1791
World Allergy Org. [13644], 555 E Wells St., Ste. 1100, Milwaukee, WI 53202-3823, (414)276-1791
World Alliance for Breastfeeding Action [IO], Penang, Malaysia
World Alliance for Decentralized Energy [6762], 1513 16th St. NW, Washington, DC 20036, (202)667-5600
World Alliance of Gourmet Robustas [1584], 360 E 72nd St., Ste. C 3000, New York, NY 10021, (212)737-2548
World Alliance of Gourmet Robustas [1584], 360 E 72nd St., Ste. C 3000, New York, NY 10021, (212)737-2548
World Alliance of Reformed Churches [IO], Geneva, Switzerland
World Amateur Golf Coun. [★22613]
World Amateur Golf Coun. [★22613]
World Apheresis Assn. [IO], Paris, France
World Apostolate of Fatima [★19394]
World Apple and Pear Assn. [IO], Brussels, Belgium
World Aquaculture Soc. [3833], Louisiana State Univ., 143 J.M. Parker Coliseum, Baton Rouge, LA 70803, (225)578-3137
World Aquaculture Soc. [3833], Louisiana State Univ., 143 J.M. Parker Coliseum, Baton Rouge, LA 70803, (225)578-3137
World Aquatic Babies and Children [23048], 838 20th Ave. N, St. Petersburg, FL 33704, (727)804-3399
World Aquatic Babies and Children [23048], 838 20th Ave. N, St. Petersburg, FL 33704, (727)804-3399
World Aquatic Babies Cong. [★23048]
World Aquatic Babies Cong. [★23048]
World Aquatic Coalition, Inc. [★22804]
World Arabian Horse Org. [IO], Gloucester, United Kingdom
World Archaeological Soc. [6180], Ron Miller, Founder, 120 Lakewood Dr., Hollister, MO 65672, (417)334-2377
World Archaeological Soc. [6180], Ron Miller, Founder, 120 Lakewood Dr., Hollister, MO 65672, (417)334-2377
World Arnold Chiari Malformation Assn. [16788], 31 Newtown Woods Rd., Newtown Square, PA 19073, (610)353-4737
World Arnold Chiari Malformation Assn. [16788], 31 Newtown Woods Rd., Newtown Square, PA 19073, (610)353-4737
World Artists Experiences [9325], PO Box 9753, Arnold, MD 21012
World Assistance [★17993]
World Assistance [★17993]
World Assn. for the Advancement of Veterinary Parasitology [17053], Tom Kennedy, Pres., Central Life Sciences, 301 W Osborn Rd., Phoenix, AZ 85013, (602)664-1258

World Assn. for the Advancement of Veterinary Parasitology [17053], Tom Kennedy, Pres., Central Life Sciences, 301 W Osborn Rd., Phoenix, AZ 85013, (602)664-1258
World Assn. of the Alcohol Beverage Indus. [194], 4211 Oakhill Rd., Fredericksburg, VA 22408, (513)948-4706
World Assn. of the Alcohol Beverage Indus. [194], 4211 Oakhill Rd., Fredericksburg, VA 22408, (513)948-4706
World Assn. for Allied Disciplines and Infant Psychiatry [★16349]
World Assn. for Allied Disciplines and Infant Psychiatry [★16349]
World Assn. of Animal Production [IO], Rome, Italy
World Assn. of Beet and Cane Growers [IO], Paris, France
World Assn. of Benchers and Dead Lifters [23130], PO Box 27499, Golden Valley, MN 55427, (763)545-8654
World Assn. of Benchers and Dead Lifters [23130], PO Box 27499, Golden Valley, MN 55427, (763)545-8654
World Assn. for Buiatrics [IO], Budapest, Hungary
World Assn. for Case Method Res. and Application [7339], 23 Mackintosh Ave., Needham, MA 02492-1218, (781)444-8982
World Assn. for Case Method Res. and Application [7339], 23 Mackintosh Ave., Needham, MA 02492-1218, (781)444-8982
World Assn. of Center Associates [★5592]
World Assn. of Center Associates [★5592]
World Assn. for Children and Parents [11430], 315 S Second St., Renton, WA 98057, (206)575-4550
World Assn. for Children and Parents [11430], 315 S Second St., Renton, WA 98057, (206)575-4550
World Assn. for Chinese Biomedical Engineers [6330], 210 Lothrop St., E1641 BST, Pittsburgh, PA 15219, (412)648-1494
World Assn. for Chinese Biomedical Engineers [6330], 210 Lothrop St., E1641 BST, Pittsburgh, PA 15219, (412)648-1494
World Assn. for Christian Commun. [IO], London, United Kingdom
World Assn. of Christian Radio Amateurs and Listeners [IO], Brixham, United Kingdom
World Assn. of Community Radio Broadcasters [IO], Montreal, QC, Canada
World Assn. of Cultural Psychiatry [16348], Wen-Shing Tseng, MD, Pres., Univ. of Hawaii School, Dept. of Psychiatry, 1356 Lusitana St., Honolulu, HI 96813-2421
World Assn. of Cultural Psychiatry [16348], Wen-Shing Tseng, MD, Pres., Univ. of Hawaii School, Dept. of Psychiatry, 1356 Lusitana St., Honolulu, HI 96813-2421
World Assn. of Detectives [IO], Karachi, Pakistan
World Assn. of Girl Guides and Girl Scouts [IO], London, United Kingdom
World Assn. for the History of Veterinary Medicine [IO], Vienna, Austria
World Assn. of Indus. and Technological Res. Organizations [IO], Shah Alam, Malaysia
World Assn. for Infant Mental Hea. [16349], Neil Boris, MD, Tulane Public Hea., Ste. 2301, New Orleans, LA 70112
World Assn. for Infant Mental Hea. [16349], Neil Boris, MD, Tulane Public Hea., Ste. 2301, New Orleans, LA 70112
World Assn. of Judges - Address unknown since 2010.
World Assn. of Law Professors - Address unknown since 2010.
World Assn. of Lawyers [5591], 7910 Woodmont Ave., Ste. 20814, Bethesda, MD 20814, (202)466-5428
World Assn. of Lawyers [5591], 7910 Woodmont Ave., Ste. 20814, Bethesda, MD 20814, (202)466-5428
World Assn. of Marching Show Bands [IO], Calgary, AB, Canada
World Assn. of Natural Disaster Awareness and Assistance [12572], 1865 SW 4th Ave., Ste. D5-A, Delray Beach, FL 33444, (561)450-5690
World Assn. of Newspapers [IO], Paris, France

World Assn. of Non-Governmental Organizations [11117], 200 White Plains Rd., 1st Fl., Tarrytown, NY 10591, (914)631-8990
World Assn. of Persons with disAbilities [14369], 112 Herweck Dr., San Antonio, TX 78213
World Assn. of Persons with disAbilities [14369], 112 Herweck Dr., San Antonio, TX 78213
World Assn. for Positive Psychotherapy, Transcultural Family Therapy Psychosomatic Medicine [IO], Wiesbaden, Germany
World Assn. for Professional Investigators [IO], London, United Kingdom
World Assn. for Psychosocial Rehabilitation - U.S. Br. [16579], 174 Avenue B, Ste. 1, New York, NY 10009, (646)872-8006
World Assn. for Public Opinion Res. [18398], Univ. of Nebraska-Lincoln, UNL Gallup Res. Ctr., 201 N 13th St., Lincoln, NE 68588-0242, (402)472-7720
World Assn. for Public Opinion Res. [18398], Univ. of Nebraska-Lincoln, UNL Gallup Res. Ctr., 201 N 13th St., Lincoln, NE 68588-0242, (402)472-7720
World Assn. of Res. Professionals [IO], Amsterdam, Netherlands
World Assn. of Sarcoidosis and Other Granulomatous Disorders [IO], Stockholm, Sweden
World Assn. for the School as an Instrument of Peace [IO], Geneva, Switzerland
World Assn. of Sleep Medicine [16670], 2358 68th St. NW, Rochester, MN 55901, (507)206-1235
World Assn. of Sleep Medicine [16670], 2358 68th St. NW, Rochester, MN 55901, (507)206-1235
World Assn. for Small and Medium Enterprises [IO], Noida, India
World Assn. of Societies of Pathology and Lab. Medicine [IO], Tokyo, Japan
World Assn. of Soil and Water Conservation [4166], John M. Laflen, Treas., 5784 Hwy. 9, Buffalo Center, IA 50424
World Assn. of Soil and Water Conservation [4166], John M. Laflen, Treas., 5784 Hwy. 9, Buffalo Center, IA 50424
World Assn. of Theoretically Oriented Chemists [IO], Marburg, Germany
World Assn. of Travel Agencies [IO], Nyon, Switzerland
World Assn. of Valuation Organizations [IO], Singapore, Singapore
World Assn. for Vedic Stud. [9520], Prof. BhuDev Sharma, Pres., Clark Atlanta Univ., 223 James P. Brawley Dr. SW, Box 764, Atlanta, GA 30314, (404)880-6912
World Assn. for Vedic Stud. [9520], Prof. BhuDev Sharma, Pres., Clark Atlanta Univ., 223 James P. Brawley Dr. SW, Box 764, Atlanta, GA 30314, (404)880-6912
World Assn. of Veterinary Anatomists [IO], Budapest, Hungary
World Assn. of Veterinary Lab. Diagnosticians [17054], PO Box 14125, Lexington, KY 40512-4125, (859)253-0571
World Assn. of Veterinary Lab. Diagnosticians [17054], PO Box 14125, Lexington, KY 40512-4125, (859)253-0571
World Atlatl Assn. [21872], Richard Lyons, Treas., 5024 King Rd., Jeffersonville, IN 47130, (812)246-9987
World Atlatl Assn. [21872], Richard Lyons, Treas., 5024 King Rd., Jeffersonville, IN 47130, (812)246-9987
World Bamboo Org. [4738], Ms. Susanne Lucas, CEO, 9 Bloody Pond Rd., Plymouth, MA 02360
World Bamboo Org. [4738], Ms. Susanne Lucas, CEO, 9 Bloody Pond Rd., Plymouth, MA 02360
The World Bank [★17915]
The World Bank [★17915]
World Bank Gp. [17930], 1818 H St. NW, Washington, DC 20433, (202)473-1000
World Bank Gp. [17930], 1818 H St. NW, Washington, DC 20433, (202)473-1000
World Bicycle Polo Fed. - Defunct.
World Bicycle Relief [12898], 1333 N Kingsbury St., 4th Fl., Chicago, IL 60642, (312)664-3836
World Bicycle Relief [12898], 1333 N Kingsbury St., 4th Fl., Chicago, IL 60642, (312)664-3836
World Bird Sanctuary [5158], 125 Bald Eagle Ridge Rd., Valley Park, MO 63088, (636)861-3225

A star before a book entry number signifies that the name is not listed separately, but is mentioned within the entry.

World Bird Sanctuary **[5158]**, 125 Bald Eagle Ridge Rd., Valley Park, MO 63088, (636)861-3225

World Blind Union **[IO]**, Madrid, Spain

World Blue Chain: For the Protection of Animals and Nature **[IO]**, Brussels, Belgium

World Bocce Assn. **[★22417]**

World Bocce Assn. **[★22417]**

World Bocce League **[22417]**, PO Box 286, Bensenville, IL 60106, (847)669-9444

World Bocce League **[22417]**, PO Box 286, Bensenville, IL 60106, (847)669-9444

World Bowling Writers **[2885]**, 122 S Michigan Ave., Ste. 1506, Chicago, IL 60603, (312)341-1110

World Bowling Writers **[2885]**, 122 S Michigan Ave., Ste. 1506, Chicago, IL 60603, (312)341-1110

World Boxing Coun. **[IO]**, Mexico City, Mexico

World Boxing - Defunct.

World Bulldog Alliance **[21683]**, 1700 Ridgewood Ave., Ste. D, Holly Hill, FL 32117, (386)437-4762

World Bur. of Metal Statistics **[IO]**, Ware, United Kingdom

World Bus. Associates **[5592]**, World Jurist Assn., 7910 Woodmont Ave., Ste. 1440, Bethesda, MD 20814, (202)466-5428

World Bus. Associates **[5592]**, World Jurist Assn., 7910 Woodmont Ave., Ste. 1440, Bethesda, MD 20814, (202)466-5428

World Bus. Coun. **[★709]**

World Bus. Coun. **[★709]**

World Camp for Kids **[11431]**, 157 S Lexington Ave., Ste. B-1, Asheville, NC 28801, (828)254-2339

World Cancer Res. Fund **[IO]**, London, United Kingdom

World Canine Freestyle Org. **[22553]**, PO Box 350122, Brooklyn, NY 11235-0122, (718)332-8336

World Care **[11913]**, 3538 E Ellington Pl., Tucson, AZ 85713, (520)514-1588

World Care **[11913]**, 3538 E Ellington Pl., Tucson, AZ 85713, (520)514-1588

World Chamberlain Genealogical Soc. **[20666]**, Patricia Sugg, Corresponding Sec., 13305 Cloverdale Pl., Germantown, MD 20874

World Championship Cutter and Chariot Racing Assn. **[22448]**, 2632 S 4300 W, Ogden, UT 84401, (801)731-8021

World Chap. of Disneyana Enthusiasts **[21414]**, PO Box 470116, Celebration, FL 34747-0116, (407)275-2756

World Chap. of Disneyana Enthusiasts **[21414]**, PO Box 470116, Celebration, FL 34747-0116, (407)275-2756

World Chess Fed. **[IO]**, Athens, Greece

World Chiropractic Alliance **[14148]**, 2683 Via de La Valle, Ste. G, Del Mar, CA 92014-1961, (480)786-9235

World Chiropractic Alliance **[14148]**, 2683 Via de La Valle, Ste. G, Del Mar, CA 92014-1961, (480)786-9235

World for Christ Crusade **[20107]**, 1005 Union Valley Rd., West Milford, NJ 07480, (973)728-3267

World for Christ Crusade **[20107]**, 1005 Union Valley Rd., West Milford, NJ 07480, (973)728-3267

World Church of the Creator **[★18781]**

World Church of the Creator **[★18781]**

World Citizens **[★18810]**

World Citizens **[★18810]**

World Citizens Assembly **[★18810]**

World Citizens Assembly **[★18810]**

World Clown Assn. **[21290]**, PO Box 12215, Merrillville, IN 46410, (219)487-5317

World Coal Inst. **[IO]**, London, United Kingdom

World Cocoa Found. **[4369]**, 1411 K St. NW, Ste. 1300, Washington, DC 20005, (202)737-7870

World Commn. on Protected Areas **[IO]**, Gland, Switzerland

World Commun. Assn. **[7775]**, 527 Lodge Ln., Kalamazoo, MI 49009, (269)387-3132

World Commun. Assn. **[7775]**, 527 Lodge Ln., Kalamazoo, MI 49009, (269)387-3132

World Community **[★12899]**

World Community **[★12246]**

World Community **[★12899]**

World Community **[★12246]**

World Community Chaplains **[12899]**, 24303 Woolsey Canyon Rd., No. 142, West Hills, CA 91304-1130, (818)884-6568

World Community Chaplains **[12899]**, 24303 Woolsey Canyon Rd., No. 142, West Hills, CA 91304-1130, (818)884-6568

World Community Projects **[★12899]**

World Community Projects **[★12899]**

World Cmpt. Exchange **[7913]**, 936 Nantasket Ave., Hull, MA 02045

World Computer Graphics Assn. - Defunct.

World Concern **[12757]**, 19303 Fremont Ave. N, Seattle, WA 98133, (206)546-7201

World Concern **[12757]**, 19303 Fremont Ave. N, Seattle, WA 98133, (206)546-7201

World Confed. of Billiard Sports **[22313]**, 4345 Beverly St., Ste. D, Colorado Springs, CO 80918, (719)264-8300

World Confed. of Jewish Community Centers **[IO]**, Jerusalem, Israel

World Confed. for Physical Therapy **[IO]**, London, United Kingdom

World Confed. of Productivity Sci. **[IO]**, Montreal, QC, Canada

World Conf. of Religions for Peace **[18304]**, 777 United Nations Plz., New York, NY 10017, (212)687-2163

World Conf. of Religions for Peace **[18304]**, 777 United Nations Plz., New York, NY 10017, (212)687-2163

World Cong. of Faiths **[IO]**, London, United Kingdom

World Cong. of Gay, Lesbian, Bisexual, and Transgender Jews **[19803]**, PO Box 23379, Washington, DC 20026-3379

World Cong. of Gay, Lesbian, Bisexual, and Transgender Jews **[19803]**, PO Box 23379, Washington, DC 20026-3379

World Cong. of Poets **[10457]**, 4423 Pitch Pine Ct., San Jose, CA 95136

World Cong. of Poets **[IO]**, Paris, France

World Conservation Union **[IO]**, Gland, Switzerland

World Convention of Churches of Christ **[19626]**, PO Box 50998, Nashville, TN 37205-0998, (615)298-1824

World Convention of Churches of Christ **[19626]**, PO Box 50998, Nashville, TN 37205-0998, (615)298-1824

World Corrosion Org. **[4178]**, PO Box 2544, New York, NY 10016-2544

World Coun. of Blind Lions **[★17059]**

World Coun. for Cardiovascular and Pulmonary Rehabilitation - Address unknown since 2010.

World Coun. of Churches **[IO]**, Geneva, Switzerland

World Coun. of Comparative Educ. Societies **[IO]**, Rondebosch, Republic of South Africa

World Coun. of Conservative/Masorti Synagogues **[19911]**, 3080 Broadway, New York, NY 10027, (212)280-6039

World Coun. of Conservative/Masorti Synagogues **[19911]**, 3080 Broadway, New York, NY 10027, (212)280-6039

World Coun. of Credit Unions **[1008]**, 5710 Mineral Point Rd., Madison, WI 53705-4454, (608)395-2000

World Coun. of Credit Unions **[1008]**, 5710 Mineral Point Rd., Madison, WI 53705-4454, (608)395-2000

World Coun. for Curriculum and Instruction **[7954]**, Alliant Intl. Univ., Shirley M. Hufstedler School of Educ., 10455 Pomerado Rd., San Diego, CA 92131-1799, (858)635-4718

World Coun. for Curriculum and Instruction **[7954]**, Alliant Intl. Univ., Shirley M. Hufstedler School of Educ., 10455 Pomerado Rd., San Diego, CA 92131-1799, (858)635-4718

World Coun. of Elders **[9521]**, PO Box 7915, Boulder, CO 80306, (303)444-9263

World Coun. of Elders **[9521]**, PO Box 7915, Boulder, CO 80306, (303)444-9263

World Coun. of Enterostomal Therapists **[IO]**, Mississauga, ON, Canada

World Coun. of Hellenes Abroad **[19020]**, 801 W Adams St., Ste. 235, Chicago, IL 60607, (312)627-1821

World Coun. of Hellenes Abroad **[19020]**, 801 W Adams St., Ste. 235, Chicago, IL 60607, (312)627-1821

World Coun. of Jewish Archives - Defunct.

World Coun. of Religious Leaders **[20208]**, Empire State Bldg., 350 5th Ave., 59th Fl., New York, NY 10118, (212)967-2891

World Coun. of Religious Leaders **[20208]**, Empire State Bldg., 350 5th Ave., 59th Fl., New York, NY 10118, (212)967-2891

World Coun. for Renewable Energy **[IO]**, Bonn, Germany

World Coun. of Synagogues **[★19911]**

World Coun. of Synagogues **[★19911]**

World Craniofacial Found. **[14205]**, PO Box 515838, Dallas, TX 75251-5838, (972)566-6669

World Cultural Coun. **[IO]**, Mexico City, Mexico

World Curling Fed. **[IO]**, Perth, United Kingdom

World Customs Org. **[IO]**, Brussels, Belgium

World Dance Alliance Americas **[9568]**, UW-Madison Dance Prog., Lathrop Hall, 1050 Univ. Ave., Madison, WI 53706, (608)262-6655

World Dance Alliance Americas **[9568]**, UW-Madison Dance Prog., Lathrop Hall, 1050 Univ. Ave., Madison, WI 53706, (608)262-6655

World Dance Coun. **[IO]**, Mitcham, United Kingdom

World Dance Coun. - Germany **[IO]**, Hamburg, Germany

The World of Dark Shadows **[23932]**, PO Box 17666, Temple City, CA 91780

World Darts Fed. **[IO]**, London, United Kingdom

World Day for Peace - Defunct.

World Day of Prayer Intl. Comm. **[20294]**, 475 Riverside Dr., Rm. 729, New York, NY 10115, (212)870-3049

World Day of Prayer Intl. Comm. **[20294]**, 475 Riverside Dr., Rm. 729, New York, NY 10115, (212)870-3049

World Development Fed. **[12381]**, 6625 The Corners Pkwy., Ste. 200, Norcross, GA 30092-2901, (770)446-6996

World Development Fed. **[12381]**, 6625 The Corners Pkwy., Ste. 200, Norcross, GA 30092-2901, (770)446-6996

World Development Movement **[IO]**, London, United Kingdom

A World of Difference Inst. **[11525]**, 605 3rd Ave., New York, NY 10158, (212)885-7811

A World of Difference Inst. **[11525]**, 605 3rd Ave., New York, NY 10158, (212)885-7811

World Div. CUNA Intl. **[★1008]**

World Div. CUNA Intl. **[★1008]**

World Draughts Fed. **[IO]**, Amsterdam, Netherlands

World of Dreams Found. Canada **[IO]**, Montreal, QC, Canada

World Dredging Assn. **[★2374]**

World Dredging Assn. **[★2374]**

World Economic Forum **[IO]**, Geneva, Switzerland

World Economic Processing Zones Assn. **[3492]**, 3 Bullet Hill Rd., Danbury, CT 06811-2906, (203)798-9394

World Economic Processing Zones Assn. **[3492]**, 3 Bullet Hill Rd., Danbury, CT 06811-2906, (203)798-9394

World Educ. **[7692]**, 44 Farnsworth St., Boston, MA 02210, (617)482-9485

World Educ. **[7692]**, 44 Farnsworth St., Boston, MA 02210, (617)482-9485

World Emergency Relief **[12900]**, PO Box 1760, Temecula, CA 92593, (951)225-6700

World Emergency Relief **[12900]**, PO Box 1760, Temecula, CA 92593, (951)225-6700

World Energy Cities Partnership **[1179]**, 1200 Smith St., Ste. 700, Houston, TX 77002, (713)844-3636

World Energy Coun. Argentina Comm. **[IO]**, Cordoba, Argentina

World Energy Coun. - England **[IO]**, London, United Kingdom

World Energy Coun. Indian Member Comm. **[IO]**, New Delhi, India

World Energy Coun. Italian Natl. Comm. **[IO]**, Rome, Italy

World Energy Coun. Polish Member Comm. **[IO]**, Warsaw, Poland

World Energy Coun. Turkish Natl. Comm. **[IO]**, Ankara, Turkey

World Env. Center **[4167]**, 734 15th St. NW, Ste. 720, Washington, DC 20005, (202)312-1370

World Env. Center **[4167]**, 734 15th St. NW, Ste. 720, Washington, DC 20005, (202)312-1370

Reference to "IO" in place of a book number signifies that the association may be found in the 50th edition of International Organizations.

World Environmental Org. [4168], 2020 Pennsylvania Ave. NW, No. 2001, Washington, DC 20006, (800)800-2099

World Evangelical Alliance [19726], 644 Strander Blvd., No. 154, Seattle, WA 98188

World Evangelical Alliance [19726], 644 Strander Blvd., No. 154, Seattle, WA 98188

World Evangelical Fellowship [★19726]

World Evangelical Fellowship [★19726]

World Evangelism [★19764]

World Evangelism [★19764]

World Expeditionary Assn. Intl. [IO], London, United Kingdom

World Export Processing Zones Assn. [★3492]

World Export Processing Zones Assn. [★3492]

World Family Ethiopian Orphans and Medical Care [11432], 15 Ross Ave., San Anselmo, CA 94960, (415)302-3037

World Farriers Assn. [1243], PO Box 1102, Albuquerque, NM 87103, (505)345-7550

World Farriers Assn. [1243], PO Box 1102, Albuquerque, NM 87103, (505)345-7550

World Fast-Draw Assn. [22891], 6000 Wilkins Ave., Oakdale, CA 95361-9797, (209)847-0483

World Federalist Assn. [★18744]

World Federalist Movement [18753], 708 3rd Ave., 24th Fl., New York, NY 10017, (212)599-1320

World Federalist Movement [18753], 708 3rd Ave., 24th Fl., New York, NY 10017, (212)599-1320

World Fed. of Advertisers [IO], Brussels, Belgium

World Fed. of Agriculture, Food, Hotel and Allied Workers [IO], Brussels, Belgium

World Fed. of Amateur Orchestras [10346], Paul Todd, Honorary Vice-Chm., 15676 Fountain Hills Dr., Omaha, NE 68118, (402)333-3497

World Fed. of Amateur Orchestras [10346], Paul Todd, Honorary Vice-Chm., 15676 Fountain Hills Dr., Omaha, NE 68118, (402)333-3497

World Fed. of Athletic Training and Therapy [16722], UT Hea. Sci. Center at San Antonio, School of Allied Hea. Sciences, 7703 Floyd Curl Dr., San Antonio, TX 78229-3901, (210)567-8755

World Fed. of Catholic Medical Associations [IO], Vatican City, Vatican City

World Fed. of Chinese Medicine Societies [IO], Beijing, People's Republic of China

World Fed. of Chiropractic [IO], Toronto, ON, Canada

World Fed. of Clerical Workers [IO], Brussels, Belgium

World Fed. for Coral Reef Conservation [4169], PO Box 942, Safety Harbor, FL 34695

World Fed. for Coral Reef Conservation [4169], PO Box 942, Safety Harbor, FL 34695

World Fed. of the Cossack Natl. Liberation Movement of Cossackia - Defunct.

World Fed. for Culture Collections [IO], Surrey, United Kingdom

World Fed. of Dark Shadows Clubs [★23918]

World Fed. of the Deaf [IO], Helsinki, Finland

World Fed. of Direct Selling Associations [3169], 1667 K St. NW, Ste. 1100, Washington, DC 20006, (202)452-8866

World Fed. of Direct Selling Associations [3169], 1667 K St. NW, Ste. 1100, Washington, DC 20006, (202)452-8866

World Fed. of Doctors Who Respect Human Life [IO], Ostend, Belgium

World Fed. of Engg. Organisations [IO], Paris, France

World Fed. of Free Latvians - Address unknown since 2010.

World Fed. of Great Towers [IO], Tuross Head, Australia

World Fed. of Hemophilia [IO], Montreal, QC, Canada

World Fed. of Intl. Music Competitions [IO], Geneva, Switzerland

World Fed. of Investors Corp. [IO], Stockholm, Sweden

World Fed. of Islamic Missions [IO], Karachi, Pakistan

World Fed. for Medical Educ. [IO], Copenhagen, Denmark

World Fed. for Mental Hea. [15486], 12940 Harbor Dr., Ste. 101, Woodbridge, VA 22192, (703)494-6515

World Fed. for Mental Hea. [15486], 12940 Harbor Dr., Ste. 101, Woodbridge, VA 22192, (703)494-6515

World Fed. of Methodist and Uniting Church Women - USA

World Fed. of Methodist and Uniting Church Women - USA - Address unknown since 2011.

World Fed. of Methodist Women [★20062]

World Fed. of Neurology [IO], Richmond, United Kingdom

World Fed. of Neurology Res. Gp. on Motor Neuron Diseases [15642], Robert G. Miller, MD, Chm., Dept. of Neurology, 2324 Sacramento St., No. 150, San Francisco, CA 94115, (415)600-3604

World Fed. of Neurology Res. Gp. on Motor Neuron Diseases/Amyotropic Lateral Sclerosis [15642], Robert G. Miller, MD, Chm., Dept. of Neurology, 2324 Sacramento St., No. 150, San Francisco, CA 94115, (415)600-3604

World Fed. of Neuroradiological Societies [16551], 2210 Midwest Rd., Ste. 207, Oak Brook, IL 60523-8205, (630)574-0220

World Fed. of Neuroradiological Societies [16551], 2210 Midwest Rd., Ste. 207, Oak Brook, IL 60523-8205, (630)574-0220

World Fed. of Neurosurgical Societies [IO], Nyon, Switzerland

World Fed. of Occupational Therapists [IO], Forrestfield, Australia

World Fed. of Orthodontists [14312], 401 N Lindbergh Blvd., St. Louis, MO 63141-7816, (314)993-1700

World Fed. of Orthodontists [14312], 401 N Lindbergh Blvd., St. Louis, MO 63141-7816, (314)993-1700

World Fed. of Pipe Line Contractors Associations - Address unknown since 2010.

World Fed. of Public Hea. Associations [16502], Amer. Public Hea. Assn., 800 I St. NW, Washington, DC 20001-3710, (202)777-2506

World Fed. of Public Hea. Associations [16502], Amer. Public Hea. Assn., 800 I St. NW, Washington, DC 20001-3710, (202)777-2506

World Fed. of Sci. Workers [IO], Montreuil, France

World Fed. of Societies of Anaesthesiologists [IO], London, United Kingdom

World Fed. of the Sporting Goods Indus. [IO], Lausanne, Switzerland

World Fed. of Surgical Oncology Societies [IO], London, United Kingdom

World Fed. of Tech. Organizations [IO], Surrey, BC, Canada

World Fed. of Therapeutic Communities [13719], 54 W 40th St., New York, NY 10018

World Fed. of Trade Unions [IO], Athens, Greece

World Fed. of Ukrainian Women's Organizations [IO], Toronto, ON, Canada

World Fed. for Ultrasound in Medicine and Biology [IO], Sao Paulo, Brazil

World Fellowship of Buddhists [IO], Bangkok, Thailand

World Floor Covering Assn. [3129], 2211 E Howell Ave., Anaheim, CA 92806, (714)978-6440

World Floor Covering Assn. [3129], 2211 E Howell Ave., Anaheim, CA 92806, (714)978-6440

World Folk Music Assn. [10313], PO Box 83583, Gaithersburg, MD 20883, (202)362-2225

World Folk Music Assn. [10313], PO Box 83583, Gaithersburg, MD 20883, (202)362-2225

World Food Logistics Org. [3628], 1500 King St., Ste. 201, Alexandria, VA 22314, (703)373-4300

World Food Logistics Org. [3628], 1500 King St., Ste. 201, Alexandria, VA 22314, (703)373-4300

World Food Prog. USA [12299], 1819 L St. NW, Ste. 900, Washington, DC 20036, (202)530-1694

World Food Programme - Afghanistan [IO], Kabul, Afghanistan

World Food Programme - Algeria [IO], Algiers, Algeria

World Food Programme - Angola [IO], Luanda, Angola

World Food Programme - Armenia [IO], Yerevan, Armenia

World Food Programme - Azerbaijan [IO], Baku, Azerbaijan

World Food Programme - Bangladesh [IO], Dhaka, Bangladesh

World Food Programme - Benin [IO], Cotonou, Benin

World Food Programme - Bhutan [IO], Thimphu, Bhutan

World Food Programme - Bolivia [IO], La Paz, Bolivia

World Food Programme - Burkina Faso [IO], Ouagadougou, Burkina Faso

World Food Programme - Burundi [IO], Bujumbura, Burundi

World Food Programme - Cambodia [IO], Phnom Penh, Cambodia

World Food Programme - Cameroon [IO], Yaounde, Cameroon

World Food Programme - Cape Verde [IO], Praia, Cape Verde

World Food Programme - Central African Republic [IO], Bangui, Central African Republic

World Food Programme - Chad [IO], N'Djamena, Chad

World Food Programme - Congo [IO], Brazzaville, Republic of the Congo

World Food Programme - Cote d'Ivoire [IO], Abidjan, Cote d'Ivoire

World Food Programme - Cuba [IO], Havana, Cuba

World Food Programme - Djibouti [IO], Djibouti, Djibouti

World Food Programme - Ecuador [IO], Quito, Ecuador

World Food Programme - Egypt [IO], Cairo, Egypt

World Food Programme - El Salvador [IO], San Salvador, El Salvador

World Food Programme - Eritrea [IO], Asmara, Eritrea

World Food Programme - Ethiopia [IO], Addis Ababa, Ethiopia

World Food Programme - Gambia [IO], Banjul, Gambia

World Food Programme - Georgia [IO], Tbilisi, Georgia

World Food Programme - Ghana [IO], Accra, Ghana

World Food Programme - Guatemala [IO], Guatemala City, Guatemala

World Food Programme - Guinea [IO], Conakry, Guinea

World Food Programme - Guinea Bissau [IO], Bissau, Guinea-Bissau

World Food Programme - Haiti [IO], Port-au-Prince, Haiti

World Food Programme - Honduras [IO], Tegucigalpa, Honduras

World Food Programme - India [IO], New Delhi, India

World Food Programme - Indonesia [IO], Jakarta, Indonesia

World Food Programme - Iran [IO], Tehran, Iran

World Food Programme - Italy [IO], Rome, Italy

World Food Programme - Jordan [IO], Amman, Jordan

World Food Programme - Kenya [IO], Nairobi, Kenya

World Food Programme - Korea DPR [IO], Pyongyang, Democratic People's Republic of Korea

World Food Programme - Laos [IO], Vientiane, Lao People's Democratic Republic

World Food Programme - Lesotho [IO], Maseru, Lesotho

World Food Programme - Liberia [IO], Monrovia, Liberia

World Food Programme - Madagascar [IO], Antananarivo, Madagascar

World Food Programme - Malawi [IO], Lilongwe, Malawi

World Food Programme - Mali [IO], Bamako, Mali

World Food Programme - Mauritania [IO], Nouakchott, Mauritania

World Food Programme - Mozambique [IO], Maputo, Mozambique

World Food Programme - Myanmar [IO], Yangon, Myanmar

World Food Programme - Nepal [IO], Kathmandu, Nepal

World Food Programme - Nicaragua [IO], Managua, Nicaragua

A star before a book entry number signifies that the name is not listed separately, but is mentioned within the entry.

World Food Programme - Niger **[IO]**, Niamey, Niger

World Food Programme - Occupied Palestinian Territories **[IO]**, Jerusalem, Israel

World Food Programme - Pakistan **[IO]**, Islamabad, Pakistan

World Food Programme - Peru **[IO]**, Lima, Peru

World Food Programme - Russian Fed. Caucasus **[IO]**, Moscow, Russia

World Food Programme - Rwanda **[IO]**, Kigali, Rwanda

World Food Programme - Sao Tome and Principe **[IO]**, Sao Tome, Sao Tome and Principe

World Food Programme - Senegal **[IO]**, Dakar, Senegal

World Food Programme - Sierra Leone **[IO]**, Freetown, Sierra Leone

World Food Programme - Sri Lanka **[IO]**, Colombo, Sri Lanka

World Food Programme - Sudan **[IO]**, Khartoum, Sudan

World Food Programme - Swaziland **[IO]**, Mbabane, Swaziland

World Food Programme - Syria **[IO]**, Damascus, Syrian Arab Republic

World Food Programme - Tajikistan **[IO]**, Dushanbe, Tajikistan

World Food Programme - Tanzania **[IO]**, Dar es Salaam, United Republic of Tanzania

World Food Programme - Uganda **[IO]**, Kampala, Uganda

World Food Programme - Yemen **[IO]**, Sana'a, Yemen

World Food Programme - Zambia **[IO]**, Lusaka, Zambia

World Food Programme - Zimbabwe **[IO]**, Harare, Zimbabwe

World Footbag Assn. **[23019]**, PO Box 775208, Steamboat Springs, CO 80477, (970)870-9898

World Footbag Assn. **[23019]**, PO Box 775208, Steamboat Springs, CO 80477, (970)870-9898

World Forest Inst. **[4421]**, World Forestry Center, 4033 SW Canyon Rd., Portland, OR 97221, (503)228-1367

World Forest Inst. **[4421]**, World Forestry Center, 4033 SW Canyon Rd., Portland, OR 97221, (503)228-1367

World Forestry Center **[4422]**, 4033 SW Canyon Rd., Portland, OR 97221, (503)228-1367

World Forestry Center **[4422]**, 4033 SW Canyon Rd., Portland, OR 97221, (503)228-1367

World Foundrymen Org. **[IO]**, West Bromwich, United Kingdom

World Foundrymen Org. - United Kingdom **[IO]**, Kington, United Kingdom

World Freestyle Watercraft Alliance **[23128]**, 1060 Old Rte. 220 S, Duncansville, PA 16635, (734)652-1481

World Freestyle Watercraft Alliance **[23128]**, 1060 Old Rte. 220 S, Duncansville, PA 16635, (734)652-1481

World Future Soc. **[6891]**, 7910 Woodmont Ave., Ste. 450, Bethesda, MD 20814, (301)656-8274

World Future Soc. **[6891]**, 7910 Woodmont Ave., Ste. 450, Bethesda, MD 20814, (301)656-8274

World Gastroenterology Org. **[IO]**, Munich, Germany

World Glacier Monitoring Ser. **[IO]**, Zurich, Switzerland

World Glaucoma Patient Assn. **[15979]**, Scott Christensen, Pres., The Glaucoma Found., 80 Maiden Ln., Ste. 1206, New York, NY 10038, (212)651-1900

World Gold Coun. **[2509]**, 424 Madison Ave., 3rd Fl., New York, NY 10017, (212)317-3800

World Gold Coun. **[2509]**, 424 Madison Ave., 3rd Fl., New York, NY 10017, (212)317-3800

World of Good Development Org. **[12382]**, 1500 Broadway, Ste. 400, Oakland, CA 94612, (510)844-1418

World Goodwill - Commonwealth **[IO]**, London, United Kingdom

World Goodwill U.S.A. **[17805]**, 120 Wall St., 24th Fl., New York, NY 10005, (212)292-0707

World Goodwill U.S.A. **[17805]**, 120 Wall St., 24th Fl., New York, NY 10005, (212)292-0707

World Gospel Mission **[20108]**, PO Box 948, Marion, IN 46952-0948, (765)664-7331

World Gospel Mission **[20108]**, PO Box 948, Marion, IN 46952-0948, (765)664-7331

World Govt. of World Citizens **[★18351]**

World Growth **[2079]**, PO Box 3693, Arlington, VA 22203-3693, (866)467-7200

World Growth **[2079]**, PO Box 3693, Arlington, VA 22203-3693, (866)467-7200

World Hapkido Assn. **[22767]**, 1789 Thousand Oaks Blvd., Thousand Oaks, CA 91362, (805)495-9622

World Head of Family Sokeship Coun. **[22768]**, 6035 Ft. Caroline Rd., Ste. 22, Jacksonville, FL 32277, (904)745-6019

World Hea. Ambassador **[14838]**, 7611 Little River Tpke., Ste. 108W, Annandale, VA 22003, (703)658-7060

World Hea. Clinicians **[13630]**, 153 East Ave., Ste. 32, Norwalk, CT 06851, (203)852-9525

World Hea. Imaging, Telemedicine and Informatics Alliance **[15224]**, 47 W Polk St., Ste. 100-289, Chicago, IL 60605, (312)994-9940

World Hea. Org. **[IO]**, Geneva, Switzerland

World Hea. Org. - Regional Off. for the Eastern Mediterranean **[IO]**, Cairo, Egypt

World Hea. Org. - Regional Off. for Europe **[IO]**, Copenhagen, Denmark

World Hea. Org. - Regional Off. for South-East Asia **[IO]**, New Delhi, India

World Hea. Org. - Regional Off. for the Western Pacific **[IO]**, Manila, Philippines

World Hea. Org. - Zimbabwe **[IO]**, Harare, Zimbabwe

World Hea. Partners **[15225]**, 2140 Shattuck Ave., Ste. 1110, Berkeley, CA 94704

World Hea. Services **[15226]**, 21122 Cabin Point Rd., Disputanta, VA 23842, (817)933-2088

World Heart Fed. **[IO]**, Geneva, Switzerland

World Heritage **[8378]**, 277 Lower Cliff Dr., Laguna Beach, CA 92651, (949)342-1777

World Heritage **[8378]**, 277 Lower Cliff Dr., Laguna Beach, CA 92651, (949)342-1777

World Heritage Alliance - Defunct.

World Heritage Centre **[IO]**, Paris, France

World History Assn. **[9817]**, Univ. of Hawaii at Manoa, Sakamaki Hall A-203, 2530 Dole St., Honolulu, HI 96822-2283, (808)956-7688

World History Assn. **[9817]**, Univ. of Hawaii at Manoa, Sakamaki Hall A-203, 2530 Dole St., Honolulu, HI 96822-2283, (808)956-7688

World Holstein-Friesian Fed. **[IO]**, Leuven, Belgium

World Home Bible League **[★19343]**

World Home Bible League **[★19343]**

World Homecare and Hospice Org. **[15016]**, 228 Seventh St. SE, Washington, DC 20003, (202)547-7424

World Homecare and Hospice Org. **[15016]**, 228 Seventh St. SE, Washington, DC 20003, (202)547-7424

World Homeopathy Awareness Org., Pakistan **[IO]**, Rawalpindi, Pakistan

World Hope Intl. **[20003]**, PO Box 17151, Baltimore, MD 21297-1151, (703)923-9414

World of Hope Intl. **[12383]**, 884 2nd Ave., UN Plz., No. 20149, New York, NY 10017, (212)580-2501

World Hope Intl. **[20003]**, PO Box 17151, Baltimore, MD 21297-1151, (703)923-9414

World Horse Welfare **[IO]**, Snetterton, United Kingdom

World House **[IO]**, Bielefeld, Germany

World Humor and Irony Membership **[★9853]**

World Humor and Irony Membership **[★9853]**

World Humor and Irony Movement **[★9853]**

World Humor and Irony Movement **[★9853]**

World Hunger Educ. Ser. **[17877]**, PO Box 29056, Washington, DC 20017, (202)269-6322

World Hunger Educ. Ser. **[17877]**, PO Box 29056, Washington, DC 20017, (202)269-6322

World Hunger Year **[★17876]**

World Impact **[20109]**, 2001 S Vermont Ave., Los Angeles, CA 90007-1279, (323)735-1137

World Impact **[20109]**, 2001 S Vermont Ave., Los Angeles, CA 90007-1279, (323)735-1137

World Info. Ser. on Energy **[IO]**, Amsterdam, Netherlands

World Inst. for Advanced Phenomenological Res. and Learning **[10432]**, 1 Ivy Pointe Way, Hanover, NH 03755, (802)295-3487

World Inst. for Advanced Phenomenological Res. and Learning **[10432]**, 1 Ivy Pointe Way, Hanover, NH 03755, (802)295-3487

World Inst. Coun. - Defunct.

World Inst. for Development Economics Res. of the United Nations Univ. **[IO]**, Helsinki, Finland

World Inst. on Disability **[11838]**, 3075 Adeline St., Ste. 280, Berkeley, CA 94703, (510)225-6400

World Inst. on Disability **[11838]**, 3075 Adeline St., Ste. 280, Berkeley, CA 94703, (510)225-6400

World Inst. of Holistic Therapies **[★15001]**

World Intellectual Property Org. **[IO]**, Geneva, Switzerland

World Internet Numismatic Soc. **[21998]**, PO Box 220904, St. Louis, MO 63122

World Internet Numismatic Soc. **[21998]**, PO Box 220904, St. Louis, MO 63122

World Investigators Network **[2126]**, 7501 Sparrows Point Blvd., Baltimore, MD 21219, (410)477-8879

World Investigators Network **[2126]**, 7501 Sparrows Point Blvd., Baltimore, MD 21219, (410)477-8879

World Jeet Kune Do Fed. **[22769]**, PO Box 52820, Tulsa, OK 74152-0820

World Jersey Cattle Bur. **[IO]**, Jersey, United Kingdom

World Jewish Cong., Amer. Sect. **[18023]**, 501 Madison Ave., 17th Fl., New York, NY 10022, (212)755-5770

World Jewish Cong., Amer. Sect. **[18023]**, 501 Madison Ave., 17th Fl., New York, NY 10022, (212)755-5770

World Jewish Relief **[IO]**, London, United Kingdom

World Juggling Fed. **[22708]**, 8560 Greenwood Ave. N, No. 315, Seattle, WA 98103

World Jurist Assn. **[5593]**, 7910 Woodmont Ave., Ste. 1440, Bethesda, MD 20814, (202)466-5428

World Jurist Assn. **[5593]**, 7910 Woodmont Ave., Ste. 1440, Bethesda, MD 20814, (202)466-5428

World Karate Fed. **[IO]**, Athens, Greece

World Kouk Sun Do Soc. **[9933]**, 45 S Main St., Ste. 90, West Hartford, CT 06107-2402, (860)523-5260

World Kouk Sun Do Soc. **[9933]**, 45 S Main St., Ste. 90, West Hartford, CT 06107-2402, (860)523-5260

The World Kuoshu Fed. **[22770]**, PO Box 20269, Baltimore, MD 21284-0269, (443)394-9222

World Land Trust U.S.A. **[4314]**, 2806 P St. NW, Washington, DC 20007, (800)456-4930

World Land Trust U.S.A. **[4314]**, 2806 P St. NW, Washington, DC 20007, (800)456-4930

World Learning **[8379]**, PO Box 676, Brattleboro, VT 05302-0676, (802)257-7751

World Learning **[8379]**, PO Box 676, Brattleboro, VT 05302-0676, (802)257-7751

World Learning Visitor Exchange Prog. **[17992]**, 1015 15th St. NW, 7th Fl., Washington, DC 20005, (202)408-5420

World Learning Visitor Exchange Prog. **[17992]**, 1015 15th St. NW, 7th Fl., Washington, DC 20005, (202)408-5420

World Libertarian Order **[18081]**, PO Box 1911, Las Vegas, NV 89125

World Literacy of Canada **[IO]**, Toronto, ON, Canada

World Literacy, Inc. **[★7692]**

World Literacy, Inc. **[★7692]**

World Lottery Assn. - Canada **[IO]**, Montreal, QC, Canada

World LP Gas Assn. **[IO]**, Paris, France

World Malayalee Coun. **[19039]**, PO Box 823, Sugar Land, TX 77487-0823, (281)723-8520

World Manx Association **[★19120]**

World Manx Association **[★19120]**

World Mariculture Soc. **[★3833]**

World Mariculture Soc. **[★3833]**

World Marrow Donor Assn. **[IO]**, Leiden, Netherlands

World Martial Arts Assn. **[22771]**, Redeemer St. John's Church, 939 - 83rd St., Brooklyn, NY 11228, (718)833-9039

World Masters Athletics **[IO]**, Hemel Hempstead, United Kingdom

World Masters Cross-Country Ski Assn. **[22921]**, PO Box 604, Bend, OR 97709, (541)317-0217

World Masters Cross-Country Ski Assn. **[22921]**, PO Box 604, Bend, OR 97709, (541)317-0217

World Media Assn.

World Media Assn. - Address unknown since 2011.

World Medical Assn. [IO], Ferney-Voltaire, France
World Medical Corps [★12855]
World Medical Corps [★12855]
World Medical Mission [19955], Samaritan's Purse, PO Box 3000, Boone, NC 28607, (828)262-1980
World Medical Mission [19955], Samaritan's Purse, PO Box 3000, Boone, NC 28607, (828)262-1980
World Medical Relief [12483], 11745 Rosa Parks Blvd., Detroit, MI 48206-1270, (313)866-5333
World Medical Relief [12483], 11745 Rosa Parks Blvd., Detroit, MI 48206-1270, (313)866-5333
World Memon Org. - Pakistan Chap. [IO], Karachi, Pakistan
World Mercy Fund [12901], PO Box 227, Waterford, VA 20197-0227, (540)882-3226
World Mercy Fund [12901], PO Box 227, Waterford, VA 20197-0227, (540)882-3226
World Meteorological Org. [IO], Geneva, Switzerland
World Methodist Coun. [19978], PO Box 518, Lake Junaluska, NC 28745, (828)456-9432
World Methodist Coun. [19978], PO Box 518, Lake Junaluska, NC 28745, (828)456-9432
World Methodist Historical Soc. [19979], PO Box 127, Madison, NJ 07940, (973)408-3189
World Methodist Historical Soc. [19979], PO Box 127, Madison, NJ 07940, (973)408-3189
World Miniature Warbird Assn. [21914], Ed Irons, Sec./Ed., 7100 Cottonwood Dr., Grant, FL 32949, (321)724-0584
World Mission Prayer League [19944], 232 Clifton Ave., Minneapolis, MN 55403-3497, (612)871-6843
World Mission Prayer League [19944], 232 Clifton Ave., Minneapolis, MN 55403-3497, (612)871-6843
World Modern Arnis Alliance [22772], PO Box 5, West Seneca, NY 14224, (716)771-1291
World Movement of Christian Workers [IO], Brussels, Belgium
World Movement of Mothers [IO], Paris, France
World Mudo Fed. [22773], 5050A Nicholson Ln., Rockville, MD 20852, (301)929-8880
World Muscle Soc. [IO], Ankara, Turkey
World Music Contest Found., Kerkrade [IO], Kerkrade, Netherlands
World Nature Assn. - Defunct.
World Nature Coalition [5159], 601 Pennsylvania Ave. NW, South Bldg., Ste. 900, Washington, DC 20004, (202)379-2974
World Neighbors [17993], 4127 NW 122nd St., Oklahoma City, OK 73120-9933, (405)752-9700
World Neighbors [17993], 4127 NW 122nd St., Oklahoma City, OK 73120-9933, (405)752-9700
World Ninepin Bowling Assn. [IO], Pegnitz, Germany
World Non-national Assn. [IO], Paris, France
World Notables
  Aaron Burr Assn. [10650]
  Abraham Lincoln Assn. [10651]
  Albert Schweitzer Fellowship [10652]
  Amer. Friends of Lafayette [10653]
  Buckminster Fuller Inst. [10654]
  Buffalo Bill Historical Center [10655]
  Calvin Coolidge Memorial Found. [10656]
  Churchill Centre [10657]
  Edison Birthplace Assn. [10658]
  Frederick A. Cook Soc. [10659]
  Friends of the Abraham Lincoln Museum [10660]
  Friends of Franklin [10661]
  Friends of Patrick Henry [10662]
  Friends of Peace Pilgrim [10663]
  Friends of Peace Pilgrim [10663]
  George C. Marshall Found. [10664]
  Hall of Fame for Great Americans [10665]
  Harry S. Truman Lib. Inst. for Natl. and Intl. Affairs [10666]
  Harry S. Truman Lib. Inst. for Natl. and Intl. Affairs [10666]
  Henry Clay Memorial Found. [10667]
  Herbert Hoover Presidential Lib. Assn. [10668]
  Intl. Soc. for Hildegard Von Bingen Stud. [10669]
  Intl. Soc. for Hildegard Von Bingen Stud. [10669]
  James Beard Found. [10670]
  James K. Polk Memorial Assn. [10671]
  James Monroe Memorial Found. [10672]
  Jefferson Davis Assn. [10673]
  John Ericsson Soc. [10674]
  John Pelham Historical Assn. [10675]

  Ladies' Hermitage Assn. [10676]
  Leif Ericson Viking Ship [10677]
  Little Bighorn History Alliance [10678]
  Morris-Jumel Mansion [10679]
  Mount Vernon Ladies' Assn. [10680]
  Napoleonic Historical Soc. [10681]
  Patton Soc. [10682]
  Pres. Benjamin Harrison Found. [10683]
  Rachel Carson Homestead Assn. [10684]
  Richard the III Found. [10685]
  Richard III Soc., Amer. Br. [10686]
  Robert E. Lee Memorial Assn. [10687]
  Ronald Reagan Home Preservation Found. [10688]
  Roosevelt Inst. [10689]
  Rutherford B. Hayes Presidential Center [10690]
  Sam Davis Memorial Assn. [10691]
  Tesla Memorial Soc. [10692]
  Tesla Memorial Soc. [10692]
  Theodore Roosevelt Assn. [10693]
  Thomas Paine Natl. Historical Assn. [10694]
  Ulysses S. Grant Assn. [10695]
  William James Soc. [10696]
  Woodrow Wilson Presidential Lib. Found. [10697]
World Nuclear Assn. [IO], London, United Kingdom
World Ocean Coun. [5009], 3035 Hibiscus Dr., Ste. 1, Honolulu, HI 96815, (808)277-9008
World Ocean Coun. [5009], 3035 Hibiscus Dr., Ste. 1, Honolulu, HI 96815, (808)277-9008
World Ocean and Cruise Liner Soc. [22194], PO Box 329, Northport, NY 11768, (631)261-5556
World Ocean and Cruise Liner Soc. [22194], PO Box 329, Northport, NY 11768, (631)261-5556
World Olympians Assn. [22793], PO Box 1791, Ketchum, ID 83340, (208)578-4801
World Olympians Assn. [22793], PO Box 1791, Ketchum, ID 83340, (208)578-4801
World Org. Against Torture [IO], Geneva, Switzerland
World Org. for Animal Hea. [IO], Paris, France
World Org. Ovulation Method Billings [IO], Burwood, Australia
World Org. Ovulation Method Billings, Argentina [IO], Buenos Aires, Argentina
World Org. Ovulation Method Billings, Canada [IO], Coquitlam, BC, Canada
World Org. Ovulation Method Billings, Italy [IO], Rome, Italy
World Org. of Systems and Cybernetics [IO], Reading, United Kingdom
World Org. Against Torture USA [★12254]
World Org. Against Torture USA [★12254]
World Org. of China Painters [21472], 2641 NW 10th St., Oklahoma City, OK 73107-5407, (405)521-1234
World Org. of China Painters [21472], 2641 NW 10th St., Oklahoma City, OK 73107-5407, (405)521-1234
World Org. for Digestive Endoscopy [IO], Munich, Germany
World Org. of Dredging Associations [2374], PO Box 5797, Vancouver, WA 98668-5797, (360)750-0209
World Org. of Dredging Associations [2374], PO Box 5797, Vancouver, WA 98668-5797, (360)750-0209
World Org. for Early Childhood Educ. [IO], Montreal-Nord, QC, Canada
World Org. for Early Childhood Educ., U.S. Natl. Comm. [7835], Judith Wagner, Whittier Coll., Whittier, CA 90608, (562)907-4250
World Org. of Family Doctors [IO], Singapore, Singapore
World Org. for Human Rights USA [12254], 2029 P St. NW, Ste. 202, Washington, DC 20036, (202)296-5702
World Org. for Human Rights USA [12254], 2029 P St. NW, Ste. 202, Washington, DC 20036, (202)296-5702
World Org. for Jews From Arab Countries [18024], 1125 Park Ave., New York, NY 10128, (212)427-1246
World Org. for Modelship Building and Modelship Sport [IO], Duchcov, Czech Republic
World Org. of the Ovulation Method-Billings, U.S.A. [★12032]
World Org. and Public Educ. Corp. of the Natl. Assn. for the Advancement of Psychoanalysis [16363], 80 8th Ave., Ste. 1501, New York, NY 10011, (212)741-0515

World Org. and Public Educ. Corp. of the Natl. Assn. for the Advancement of Psychoanalysis [16363], 80 8th Ave., Ste. 1501, New York, NY 10011, (212)741-0515
World Org. of the Scout Movement [IO], Geneva, Switzerland
World Org. for Specialized Stud. on Diseases of the Esophagus [IO], Paris, France
World Org. of Webmasters [1911], PO Box 1743, Folsom, CA 95630, (916)989-2933
World Org. of Webmasters [1911], PO Box 1743, Folsom, CA 95630, (916)989-2933
World Org. of Young Esperantists [IO], Rotterdam, Netherlands
World Orphans [11433], PO Box 1840, Castle Rock, CO 80104, (720)362-4881
World Orphans [11433], PO Box 1840, Castle Rock, CO 80104, (720)362-4881
World ORT [IO], London, United Kingdom
World Parkinson Disease Assn. [IO], Milan, Italy
World Partners Adoption - Defunct.
World Partners for Development [13210], PO Box 165, Haymarket, VA 20168, (571)435-2657
World Partners for Development [13210], PO Box 165, Haymarket, VA 20168, (571)435-2657
World Peace Found. [17994], 169 Holland St., Somerville, MA 02144, (617)627-2255
World Peace Found. [17994], 169 Holland St., Somerville, MA 02144, (617)627-2255
World Peace Inst. - Defunct.
World Peace One [12229], 5135 Dearborn St., Pittsburgh, PA 15224, (412)363-9792
World Peace One [12229], 5135 Dearborn St., Pittsburgh, PA 15224, (412)363-9792
World Peace Prayer Soc. [18305], 26 Benton Rd., Wassaic, NY 12592, (845)877-6093
World Peace Prayer Soc. [18305], 26 Benton Rd., Wassaic, NY 12592, (845)877-6093
World Peace Tax Fund Steering Comm. [★18699]
World Peace Through Law Center [★5593]
World Peace Through Law Center [★5593]
World Peace Through Tech. Org. [12639], 150 Folsom St., San Francisco, CA 94105, (415)371-8706
World Peace Through Tech. Org. [12639], 150 Folsom St., San Francisco, CA 94105, (415)371-8706
World Pen Pals [8380], PO Box 337, Saugerties, NY 12477, (845)246-7828
World Pen Pals [8380], PO Box 337, Saugerties, NY 12477, (845)246-7828
World Pet Assn. [2688], 135 W Lemon Ave., Monrovia, CA 91016-2809, (626)447-2222
World Pet Assn. [2688], 135 W Lemon Ave., Monrovia, CA 91016-2809, (626)447-2222
World Petroleum Coun. - The Global Forum for Oil and Gas Sci., Tech., Economics and Mgt. [IO], London, United Kingdom
World Pheasant Assn. [IO], Newcastle upon Tyne, United Kingdom
World Phenomenology Inst. [★10432]
World Phenomenology Inst. [★10432]
World Phosphate Inst. [IO], Casablanca, Morocco
World Piano Competition [10314], 441 Vine St., Ste. 1030, Cincinnati, OH 45202, (513)421-5342
World Ploughing Org. [IO], Hall, Netherlands
World Plumbing Coun. [IO], Marmion, Australia
World Poetry Therapy Assn. [★16469]
World Poker Assn. - Address unknown since 2011.
World Policy Inst. [17711], 220 5th Ave., 9th Fl., New York, NY 10001, (212)481-5005
World Policy Inst. [17711], 220 5th Ave., 9th Fl., New York, NY 10001, (212)481-5005
World Population Emergency Campaign [★12040]
World Prayer Center [★19369]
World Presbyterian Missions [★20157]
World Presbyterian Missions [★20157]
World Preserve - Defunct.
World Presidents Org. [709], 600 E Las Colinas Blvd., Ste. 1000, Irving, TX 75039, (972)587-1500
World Presidents Org. [709], 600 E Las Colinas Blvd., Ste. 1000, Irving, TX 75039, (972)587-1500
World Press Freedom Comm. [17363], 11690-C Sunrise Valley Dr., Reston, VA 20191, (703)715-9811
World Press Freedom Comm. [17363], 11690-C Sunrise Valley Dr., Reston, VA 20191, (703)715-9811

A star before a book entry number signifies that the name is not listed separately, but is mentioned within the entry.

World Press Inst. [**17364**], 3415 Univ. Ave., St. Paul, MN 55114, (612)205-7582

World Press Inst. [**17364**], 3415 Univ. Ave., St. Paul, MN 55114, (612)205-7582

World Print Coun. - Defunct.

World Priorities

World Priorities - Address unknown since 2011.

World Processing Tomato Coun. [**IO**], Sorgues, France

World Professional Assn. for Transgender Hea. [**13113**], 1300 S Second St., Ste. 180, Minneapolis, MN 55454, (612)624-9397

World Professional Assn. for Transgender Hea. [**13113**], 1300 S Second St., Ste. 180, Minneapolis, MN 55454, (612)624-9397

World Proof Numismatic Assn. [**21999**], PO Box 4094, Pittsburgh, PA 15201-0094

World Proof Numismatic Assn. [**21999**], PO Box 4094, Pittsburgh, PA 15201-0094

World Psychiatric Assn. [**16350**], Pedro Ruiz, Pres.-Elect, Univ. of Texas, 1120 NW 14th St., Ste. 1458, Miami, FL 33136, (305)243-2676

World Psychiatric Assn. [**16350**], Pedro Ruiz, Pres.-Elect, Univ. of Texas, 1120 NW 14th St., Ste. 1458, Miami, FL 33136, (305)243-2676

World Rabbit Sci. Assn. [**IO**], Castanet-Tolosan, France

World Refugee Fund [★**18351**]

World Rehabilitation Fund [**11839**], 16 E 40th St., Ste. 704, New York, NY 10016, (212)532-6000

World Rehabilitation Fund [**11839**], 16 E 40th St., Ste. 704, New York, NY 10016, (212)532-6000

World Relief [**19727**], 7 E Baltimore St., Baltimore, MD 21202, (443)451-1900

World Relief [**19727**], 7 E Baltimore St., Baltimore, MD 21202, (443)451-1900

World Relief Commn. [★**19727**]

World Relief Commn. [★**19727**]

World Relief Commn. of the Natl. Assn. of Evangelicals [★**19727**]

World Relief Commn. of the Natl. Assn. of Evangelicals [★**19727**]

World Relief Friendship Found. [★**13190**]

World Relief Friendship Found. [★**13190**]

World Relief Org. for Children [**11434**], 3157 N Rainbow Blvd., No. 234, Las Vegas, NV 89108, (702)481-5178

World Res. Found. [**14743**], 41 Bell Rock Plz., Sedona, AZ 86351, (928)284-3300

World Res. Found. [**14743**], 41 Bell Rock Plz., Sedona, AZ 86351, (928)284-3300

World Resources Inst. [**4170**], 10 G St. NE, Ste. 800, Washington, DC 20002, (202)729-7600

World Resources Inst. [**4170**], 10 G St. NE, Ste. 800, Washington, DC 20002, (202)729-7600

World Reuse, Repair and Recycling Assn. [**4873**], PO Box 1010, Middlebury, VT 05753, (802)377-9166

World Road Assn. - France [**IO**], Paris, France

World Rock 'n' Roll Confed. [**IO**], Ljubljana, Slovenia

World Rock Paper Scissors Soc. [**IO**], Toronto, ON, Canada

World Safety Org. [**18583**], 106 W Young Ave., Ste. F, PO Box 518, Warrensburg, MO 64093, (660)747-3132

World Safety Org. [**18583**], 106 W Young Ave., Ste. F, PO Box 518, Warrensburg, MO 64093, (660)747-3132

World Salsa Fed. [**9569**], 8080 SW 81 Dr., Miami, FL 33143, (786)566-2604

World Salt Found. [**20110**], 6810 Lee St., Hollywood, FL 33024, (954)964-2799

World Salt Found. [**20110**], 6810 Lee St., Hollywood, FL 33024, (954)964-2799

World Savvy [**9084**], 999 Sutter St., 4th Fl., San Francisco, CA 94109, (415)292-7421

World Sci. Fiction Soc. [**10524**], PO Box 426159, Cambridge, MA 02142

World Sci. Fiction Soc. [**10524**], PO Box 426159, Cambridge, MA 02142

World Sci. and Engg. Acad. and Soc. [**6837**], Prof. Charles A. Long, Pres., Univ. of Wisconsin, 2100 Main St., Stevens Point, WI 54481-3897

World Sci. and Engg. Acad. and Soc. [**6837**], Prof. Charles A. Long, Pres., Univ. of Wisconsin, 2100 Main St., Stevens Point, WI 54481-3897

World Scout Bur. [**IO**], Geneva, Switzerland

World Scout Found. [**IO**], Geneva, Switzerland

World Scout Organization [★**9583**]

World Self-Medication Indus. [**IO**], Ferney-Voltaire, France

World Senior Golf Fed. [**22630**], PO Box 350667, Westminster, CO 80035-0667, (303)920-4206

World Senior Golf Fed. [**22630**], PO Box 350667, Westminster, CO 80035-0667, (303)920-4206

World Ser. Authority [**18351**], World Off., 1012 14th St. NW, Ste. 205, Washington, DC 20005, (202)638-2662

World Ser. Authority [**18351**], World Off., 1012 14th St. NW, Ste. 205, Washington, DC 20005, (202)638-2662

World Ser. Authority of the World Govt. of World Citizens [★**18351**]

World Ser. Authority of the World Govt. of World Citizens [★**18351**]

World Ship Soc. [**IO**], Gravesend, United Kingdom

World Ship Trust - United Kingdom [**IO**], London, United Kingdom

World Shoe Assn. [**214**], 15821 Ventura Blvd., Ste. 415, Encino, CA 91436-2974, (818)379-9400

World Shoe Assn. [**214**], 15821 Ventura Blvd., Ste. 415, Encino, CA 91436-2974, (818)379-9400

World Sikh Org. [**IO**], Ottawa, ON, Canada

World Small Animal Veterinary Assn. [**IO**], Dundas, ON, Canada

World Snooker [**IO**], Bristol, United Kingdom

World Socialist Party - New Zealand [**IO**], Auckland, New Zealand

World Socialist Party of the U.S. [**18369**], Box 440247, Boston, MA 02144

World Soc. of the Abdominal Compartment Syndrome [**IO**], Antwerp, Belgium

World Soc. for Ekistics [**IO**], Athens, Greece

World Soc. of Mixed Jurisdiction Jurists [**5682**], Tulane Law School, 6329 Freret St., New Orleans, LA 70118, (504)865-5978

World Soc. of Mixed Jurisdiction Jurists [**5682**], Tulane Law School, 6329 Freret St., New Orleans, LA 70118, (504)865-5978

World Soc. for the Protection of Animals [**11063**], Lincoln Plaza, 89 South St., Ste. 201, Boston, MA 02111, (617)896-9214

World Soc. for the Protection of Animals [**11063**], Lincoln Plaza, 89 South St., Ste. 201, Boston, MA 02111, (617)896-9214

World Soc. for the Protection of Animals - Australia [**IO**], St. Leonards, Australia

World Soc. for the Protection of Animals - Brazil [**IO**], Rio de Janeiro, Brazil

World Soc. for the Protection of Animals - Canada [**IO**], Toronto, ON, Canada

World Soc. for the Protection of Animals - Colombia [**IO**], Bogota, Colombia

World Soc. for the Protection of Animals - Costa Rica [**IO**], Heredia, Costa Rica

World Soc. for the Protection of Animals - Denmark [**IO**], Copenhagen, Denmark

World Soc. for the Protection of Animals - England [**IO**], London, United Kingdom

World Soc. for the Protection of Animals - Germany [**IO**], Berlin, Germany

World Soc. for the Protection of Animals - Netherlands [**IO**], The Hague, Netherlands

World Soc. for the Protection of Animals - New Zealand [**IO**], Auckland, New Zealand

World Soc. for Stereotactic and Functional Neurosurgery [**15690**], Michael Schulder, MD, Sec.-Treas., North Shore Univ. Hosp., Dept. of Neurosurgery, North Shore LIJ Hea. Sys., 9 Tower, 300 Community Dr., Manhasset, NY 11030, (516)562-3065

World Soc. for Stereotactic and Functional Neurosurgery [**15690**], Michael Schulder, MD, Sec.-Treas., North Shore Univ. Hosp., Dept. of Neurosurgery, North Shore LIJ Hea. Sys., 9 Tower, 300 Community Dr., Manhasset, NY 11030, (516)562-3065

World Soc. for Stereotactic and Functional Neurosurgery - Canada [**IO**], Tokyo, Japan

World Soc. of Victimology [**IO**], Tilburg, Netherlands

World Solidarity [**IO**], Brussels, Belgium

World Sound Healing Org. [**12640**], PO Box 389, Ascutney, VT 05030, (802)674-9585

World Spark [**11435**], 1635 SE Malden St., Portland, OR 97202, (503)245-7899

World Spine Care [**16708**], 801 N Tustin Ave., Ste. 202, Santa Ana, CA 92705, (714)547-9822

World Sport Stacking Assn. [**23020**], 11 Inverness Way S, Englewood, CO 80112, (303)962-5672

World Sport Stacking Assn. [**23020**], 11 Inverness Way S, Englewood, CO 80112, (303)962-5672

World Squash Fed. [**IO**], Hastings, United Kingdom

World Steel Assn. [**IO**], Brussels, Belgium

World Stereotactic Soc. [★**15690**]

World Stereotactic Soc. [★**15690**]

World Sturgeon Conservation Soc. U.S.A. [**4171**], Wisconsin Dept. of Natural Resources, 625 City Ctr., Ste. 700, Oshkosh, WI 54901, (920)424-3059

World Sugar Res. Org. [**IO**], London, United Kingdom

World Sustainable Agriculture Assn. [**12965**], 8554 Melrose Ave., West Hollywood, CA 90069, (310)657-7202

World Sustainable Agriculture Assn. [**12965**], 8554 Melrose Ave., West Hollywood, CA 90069, (310)657-7202

World Swing Dance Coun. [**9570**], 4401 E Janice Way, Phoenix, AZ 85032, (602)482-2828

World Swing Dance Coun. [**9570**], 4401 E Janice Way, Phoenix, AZ 85032, (602)482-2828

World Taekwondo Fed. [**IO**], Seoul, Republic of Korea

World Team [**20111**], 1431 Stuckert Rd., Warrington, PA 18976, (215)491-4900

World Team [**20111**], 1431 Stuckert Rd., Warrington, PA 18976, (215)491-4900

World T.E.A.M. Sports [**22534**], 1300 17th St. N, Ste. 750, Arlington, VA 22209-3872, (855)987-8326

World Tech. Volunteers [★**13210**]

World Tech. Volunteers [★**13210**]

World Teleport Assn. [**3429**], 55 Broad St., 14th Fl., New York, NY 10004, (212)825-0218

World Teleport Assn. [**3429**], 55 Broad St., 14th Fl., New York, NY 10004, (212)825-0218

World Timecapsule Fund - Defunct.

World Toilet Org. [**IO**], Singapore, Singapore

World Tourism Org. [**IO**], Madrid, Spain

World Trade Center Assn. of Brussels [**IO**], Kraainem, Belgium

World Trade Center Barcelona [**IO**], Barcelona, Spain

World Trade Center Basel [**IO**], Basel, Switzerland

World Trade Center Bogota [**IO**], Bogota, Colombia

World Trade Center Budapest [**IO**], Budapest, Hungary

World Trade Center Cairo [**IO**], Cairo, Egypt

World Trade Center Curacao [**IO**], Curacao, Netherlands Antilles

World Trade Center Eindhoven [**IO**], Eindhoven, Netherlands

World Trade Center Geneva [**IO**], Geneva, Switzerland

World Trade Center Genoa [**IO**], Genoa, Italy

World Trade Center Grenoble [**IO**], Grenoble, France

World Trade Center Hamburg [**IO**], Hamburg, Germany

World Trade Center Israel [**IO**], Tel Aviv, Israel

World Trade Center Leipzig [**IO**], Leipzig, Germany

World Trade Center Lille [**IO**], Lille, France

World Trade Center Madrid [**IO**], Madrid, Spain

World Trade Center Metro Manila [**IO**], Pasay City, Philippines

World Trade Center Metz-Sarrebruck [**IO**], Metz, France

World Trade Center Mexico City [**IO**], Mexico City, Mexico

World Trade Center Moscow [**IO**], Moscow, Russia

World Trade Center of New Orleans [**2091**], 2 Canal St., Ste. 2900, New Orleans, LA 70130, (504)529-1601

World Trade Center of New Orleans [**2091**], 2 Canal St., Ste. 2900, New Orleans, LA 70130, (504)529-1601

World Trade Center Nigeria [**IO**], Lagos, Nigeria

World Trade Center Panama [**IO**], Panama City, Panama

World Trade Center Paris [**IO**], Paris, France

World Trade Center Rotterdam [**IO**], Rotterdam, Netherlands

---

Reference to "IO" in place of a book number signifies that the association may be found in the 50th edition of International Organizations.

World Trade Center Ruhr Valley [IO], Gelsenkirchen, Germany

World Trade Center Sao Paulo [IO], Sao Paulo, Brazil

World Trade Center Seville [IO], Seville, Spain

World Trade Center Stockholm [IO], Stockholm, Sweden

World Trade Center Survivors' Network [13313], 295 Greenwich St., Ste. 302, New York, NY 10007

World Trade Center Taichung [IO], Taichung, Taiwan

World Trade Center Tokyo [IO], Tokyo, Japan

World Trade Center Vienna Airport [IO], Vienna, Austria

World Trade Center Zurich [IO], Zurich, Switzerland

World Trade Centers Assn. [3493], 420 Lexington Ave., Ste. 518, New York, NY 10170, (212)432-2626

World Trade Centers Assn. [3493], 420 Lexington Ave., Ste. 518, New York, NY 10170, (212)432-2626

World Trade Centers Assn. of Antwerp [IO], Antwerp, Belgium

World Trade Centre Beijing [IO], Beijing, People's Republic of China

World Trade Centre Johannesburg [IO], Sandton, Republic of South Africa

World Trade Centre Montreal [IO], Montreal, QC, Canada

World Trade Centre Shanghai [IO], Shanghai, People's Republic of China

World Trade Centre Vancouver [IO], Vancouver, BC, Canada

World Trade and Convention Centre Halifax [IO], Halifax, NS, Canada

World Trade Org. [IO], Geneva, Switzerland

World Traditional Karate Org. [22774], 138 Bradley Ave., Staten Island, NY 10314

World Traditional Karate Org. [22774], 138 Bradley Ave., Staten Island, NY 10314

World Transhumanist Assn. [★6945]

World Transhumanist Assn. [★6945]

World Travel and Tourism Coun. [IO], London, United Kingdom

World Umpires Assn. [23157], PO Box 394, Neenah, WI 54957, (920)969-1580

World Umpires Assn. [23157], PO Box 394, Neenah, WI 54957, (920)969-1580

World Underwater Fed. [IO], Rome, Italy

World Union of Catholic Philosophical Societies [IO], Antigonish, NS, Canada

World Union of Catholic Women's Organisations [IO], Paris, France

World Union of Deists [20218], PO Box 4052, Clearwater, FL 33758

World Union of Deists [20218], PO Box 4052, Clearwater, FL 33758

World Union of Jewish Students [IO], Tel Aviv, Israel

World Union of Wholesale Markets [IO], The Hague, Netherlands

World Univ. Colleges [★7973]

World Univ. Colleges Consortium [★7973]

World Veterans Fed. [IO], Paris, France

World Veterinary Assn. [IO], Brussels, Belgium

World Veterinary Poultry Assn. [IO], Giessen, Germany

World Vets [11064], 802 1st Ave. N, Fargo, ND 58102, (877)688-8387

World Vision [20112], PO Box 9716, Federal Way, WA 98063-9716, (253)815-1000

World Vision Armenia [IO], Yerevan, Armenia

World Vision Asia Pacific Region [IO], Bangkok, Thailand

World Vision Australia [IO], Melbourne, Australia

World Vision Canada [IO], Mississauga, ON, Canada

World Vision Colombia [IO], Bogota, Colombia

World Vision Hong Kong [IO], Hong Kong, People's Republic of China

World Vision India [IO], Chennai, India

World Vision Intl. [20171], 800 W Chestnut Ave., Monrovia, CA 91016-3198, (626)303-8811

World Vision Intl. [20171], 800 W Chestnut Ave., Monrovia, CA 91016-3198, (626)303-8811

World Vision Intl. Azerbaijan [IO], Baku, Azerbaijan

World Vision Intl. Brazil [IO], Sao Paulo, Brazil

World Vision Intl. Romania [IO], Bucharest, Romania

World Vision Intl. Vietnam [IO], Hanoi, Vietnam

World Vision Ireland [IO], Dublin, Ireland

World Vision Japan [IO], Tokyo, Japan

World Vision Malaysia [IO], Petaling Jaya, Malaysia

World Vision Middle East/Eastern Europe [IO], Nicosia, Cyprus

World Vision New Zealand [IO], Auckland, New Zealand

World Vision Singapore [IO], Singapore, Singapore

World Vision Taiwan [IO], Taipei, Taiwan

World Vision United Kingdom [IO], Milton Keynes, United Kingdom

World Volunteers [IO], Milan, Italy

World War I Aeroplanes [20925], PO Box 730, Red Hook, NY 12571, (845)835-8121

World War II War Brides Assn. [20713], 1125 Pinon Oak Dr., Prescott, AZ 86305, (928)237-1581

World War II War Brides Assn. [20713], 1125 Pinon Oak Dr., Prescott, AZ 86305, (928)237-1581

World War I
Veterans of World War I of U.S.A. [20844]

World War II
70th Infantry Div. Assn. [20845]
86th Chem. Mortar Battalion Assn. [20846]
303rd Bomb Gp. (H) Assn. [20847]
494th Bombardment Gp. (H) Assn. 7th Air Force [20324]
504th Parachute Infantry Regiment Assn. [20848]
508th Parachute Infantry Regiment Assn. [20849]
509th Parachute Infantry Assn. [20850]
517th Parachute Regimental Combat Team Assn. [20851]
526th Armored Infantry Battalion Assn. [20852]
Americal Div. Veterans Assn. [20853]
Amer. Defenders of Bataan and Corregidor [20854]
Amer. Merchant Marine Veterans [20855]
Amer. Rosie the Riveter Assn. [20856]
Amer. Rosie the Riveter Assn. [20856]
B-26 Marauder Historical Soc. [20857]
B-26 Marauder Historical Soc. [20857]
Eighth Air Force Historical Soc. [20858]
Fourth Marine Div. Assn. [20859]
Global Alliance for Preserving the History of WWII in Asia [20860]
Global Alliance for Preserving the History of WWII in Asia [20860]
Intl. B-24 Liberator Club [20861]
Intl. B-24 Liberator Club [20861]
Merrill's Marauders Assn. [20862]
Natl. World War II Glider Pilots Assn. [20315]
Navajo Code Talkers Assn. [20863]
P-47 Thunderbolt Pilots Assn. [20864]
Pearl Harbor History Associates [9794]
Pearl Harbor Survivors Assn. [20865]
PT Boats, Inc. [20866]
PT Boats, Inc. [20866]WorldSecond World War Aircraft Preservation Soc.
Sino-American Cooperative Org. [20867]
Sixth Marine Div. Assn. [20868]
U.S. Merchant Marine Veterans of World War II [20869]
USS North Carolina Battleship Assn. [20870]
Veterans of the Battle of the Bulge [20871]

World War Two Railway Study Group [IO], Leamington Spa, United Kingdom

World War Two Stud. Assn. [9818], Prof. Mark Parillo, Kansas State Univ., Dept. of History, Eisenhower Hall, Manhattan, KS 66506-1002, (913)532-0374

World War Two Stud. Assn. [9818], Prof. Mark Parillo, Kansas State Univ., Dept. of History, Eisenhower Hall, Manhattan, KS 66506-1002, (913)532-0374

World Wars
1st Fighter Assn. [20872]
Fed. of French War Veterans [20873]
Military Order of the World Wars [20874]
Military Order of the World Wars [20874]
Order of Lafayette [20875]
Rainbow Div. Veterans Memorial Found. [20876]
Wounded Warrior Proj. [20822]

World Water Coun. [IO], Marseille, France

World Water Org. [13444], 866 United Nations Plz., New York, NY 10017, (212)759-1639

World Water Org. [13444], 866 United Nations Plz., New York, NY 10017, (212)759-1639

World Water Relief [13445], 8343 Roswell Rd., Ste. 455, Atlanta, GA 30350, (404)242-1601

World Waterpark Assn. [1220], 8826 Santa Fe Dr., Ste. 310, Overland Park, KS 66212, (913)599-0300

World Waterpark Assn. [1220], 8826 Santa Fe Dr., Ste. 310, Overland Park, KS 66212, (913)599-0300

World Watusi Assn. [3944], PO Box 2610, Glen Rose, TX 76043, (254)898-0157

World Watusi Assn. [3944], PO Box 2610, Glen Rose, TX 76043, (254)898-0157

World Whale Police [5018], PO Box 814, Olympia, WA 98506, (360)561-7492

World Whale Police [5018], PO Box 814, Olympia, WA 98506, (360)561-7492

World Wide AIDS Coalition [13631], Lucy Thairu, PhD, Prog. Coor., PO Box 20044, Stanford, CA 94309, (650)568-9771

World Wide Assn. of Treasure Seekers [22109], 1495 FM 49, Gilmer, TX 75644, (903)734-7773

World Wide Essence Soc. [15005], PO Box 285, Concord, MA 01742, (978)369-8454

World Wide Essence Soc. [15005], PO Box 285, Concord, MA 01742, (978)369-8454

World Wide Fund for Nature - India [IO], New Delhi, India

World Wide Fund for Nature - Japan [IO], Tokyo, Japan

World Wide Fund for Nature - Malaysia [IO], Selangor, Malaysia

World Wide Fund for Nature - Sweden [IO], Stockholm, Sweden

World Wide Fund for Nature - WWF Intl. [IO], Gland, Switzerland

World-Wide Missions [20113], PO Box 2300, Redlands, CA 92373-0761, (909)793-2009

World-Wide Missions [20113], PO Box 2300, Redlands, CA 92373-0761, (909)793-2009

World Wide Opportunities on Organic Farms - Canada [IO], Procter, BC, Canada

World Wide Opportunities on Organic Farms - Czech Republic [IO], Valec, Czech Republic

World Wide Opportunities on Organic Farms - Germany [IO], Dresden, Germany

World Wide Opportunities on Organic Farms - Italia [IO], Castagneto Carducci, Italy

World Wide Opportunities on Organic Farms - Korea [IO], Seoul, Republic of Korea

World Wide Opportunities on Organic Farms - Nepal [IO], Kathmandu, Nepal

World Wide Opportunities on Organic Farms - Slovenia [IO], Sencur, Slovenia

World Wide Opportunities on Organic Farms - Sweden [IO], Sunne, Sweden

World Wide Opportunities on Organic Farms - Switzerland [IO], Maur, Switzerland

World Wide Opportunities on Organic Farms - Uganda [IO], Kampala, Uganda

World Wide Opportunities on Organic Farms - UK [IO], Winslow, United Kingdom

World Wide Opportunities on Organic Farms - USA [17173], 430 Forest Ave., Laguna Beach, CA 92651, (949)715-9500

World Wide Opportunities for Women [IO], Kitchener, ON, Canada

World Wide Pet Indus. Assn. [★2688]

World Wide Pet Indus. Assn. [★2688]

World Wide Pet Supply Assn. [★2688]

World Wide Pet Supply Assn. [★2688]

World Wide Web
Anti-Child Pornography Org. [12710]
InterConnection [11664]
Internet Keep Safe Coalition [17996]
Internet Merchants Assn. [2117]
Mobile Voter [18096]
Top Level Domain Assn. [2118]

World Wide Web Consortium [6477], Massachusetts Inst. of Tech., 32 Vassar St., Rm. 32-G515, Cambridge, MA 02139, (617)253-2613

World Wide Web Consortium [6477], Massachusetts Inst. of Tech., 32 Vassar St., Rm. 32-G515, Cambridge, MA 02139, (617)253-2613

A star before a book entry number signifies that the name is not listed separately, but is mentioned within the entry.

World Wildlife Fund [4172], PO Box 97180, Washington, DC 20090-7180, (202)293-4800

World Wildlife Fund [4172], PO Box 97180, Washington, DC 20090-7180, (202)293-4800

World Wildlife Fund - Canada [IO], Toronto, ON, Canada

World Wildlife Fund - Denmark [IO], Copenhagen, Denmark

World Wildlife Fund - U.S. [★4172]

World Wildlife Fund - U.S. [★4172]

World Wind Energy Assn. [IO], Bonn, Germany

World Wins Intl. [11654], PO Box 191091, Boise, ID 83719-1091, (208)585-7370

World Without War Coun. - Address unknown since 2010.

World Witness, Foreign Mission Bd. of the Associate Reformed Presbyterian Church [20114], 1 Cleveland St., Ste. 220, Greenville, SC 29601, (864)233-5226

World Witness, Foreign Mission Bd. of the Associate Reformed Presbyterian Church [20114], 1 Cleveland St., Ste. 220, Greenville, SC 29601, (864)233-5226

World Young Women's Christian Association [IO], Geneva, Switzerland

World Youth Alliance [18835], 228 E 71st St., New York, NY 10021, (212)585-0757

World Youth Alliance [18835], 228 E 71st St., New York, NY 10021, (212)585-0757

World Youth Coun. [★19625]

World Youth Found. [IO], Melaka, Malaysia

World Youth Student and Educational Travel Confed. [IO], Amsterdam, Netherlands

WorldatWork [1162], 14040 N Northsight Blvd., Scottsdale, AZ 85260, (480)951-9191

WorldatWork [1162], 14040 N Northsight Blvd., Scottsdale, AZ 85260, (480)951-9191

Worldcraft Circle of Native Writers' and Storytellers [19170], Minnesota State Univ., Mankato, English Dept., 230 Armstrong Hall, Mankato, MN 56001, (507)389-5508

Worlddidac [IO], Bern, Switzerland

WorldFish Center [IO], Penang, Malaysia

Worldhealer [12384], PO Box 62121, Santa Barbara, CA 93160, (805)253-2324

WorldHope Corps [11655], 11 Ardsleigh Dr., Madison, NJ 07940, (973)714-0023

Worldloppet [★22922]

Worldloppet [★22922]

Worldloppet/American Birkebeiner [22922], PO Box 911, Hayward, WI 54843, (715)634-5025

Worldloppet/American Birkebeiner [22922], PO Box 911, Hayward, WI 54843, (715)634-5025

World's Fairs
1904 World's Fair Soc. [22205]

World's Poultry Sci. Assn. [IO], Ballynahinch, United Kingdom

World's Poultry Sci. Assn. - The Netherlands [IO], Beekbergen, Netherlands

World's Poultry Sci. Assn. - UK [IO], Ballymena, United Kingdom

World's Poultry Sci. Assn., U.S.A. Br. [4821], 1775 E Palm Canyon Dr., Ste. 110, Palm Springs, CA 92264, (760)699-5078

WorldTeach [8068], Center for Intl. Development, Harvard Univ., 79 John F. Kennedy St., Cambridge, MA 02138, (617)495-5527

WorldVenture [19337], 1501 W Mineral Ave., Littleton, CO 80120-5612, (720)283-2000

WorldVenture [19337], 1501 W Mineral Ave., Littleton, CO 80120-5612, (720)283-2000

WorldViews - Defunct.

Worldwatch Inst. [18821], 1776 Massachusetts Ave. NW, Washington, DC 20036-1904, (202)452-1999

Worldwatch Inst. [18821], 1776 Massachusetts Ave. NW, Washington, DC 20036-1904, (202)452-1999

Worldwide Aquatic Bodywork Assn. [13720], PO Box 1817, Middletown, CA 95461, (707)928-5860

Worldwide Assn. of Self-Adhesive Labels and Related Products [IO], The Hague, Netherlands

Worldwide Assurance for Employees of Public Agencies [5502], 433 Park Ave., Falls Church, VA 22046, (703)790-8010

Worldwide Assurance for Employees of Public Agencies [5502], 433 Park Ave., Falls Church, VA 22046, (703)790-8010

Worldwide Camaro Assn. [★21197]

Worldwide Camaro Club [21197], 5200 S Washington Ave., Titusville, FL 32780-7318, (800)283-0691

Worldwide Collectors Club [★22046]

Worldwide Collectors Club [★22046]

Worldwide Dental Hea. Ser. [★12457]

Worldwide Dental Hea. Ser. [★12457]

Worldwide Dragonfly Assn. [IO], Frankfurt, Germany

Worldwide ERC [1163], 4401 Wilson Blvd., Ste. 510, Arlington, VA 22203, (703)842-3400

Worldwide Forgiveness Alliance [12641], 20 Sunnyside Ave., Ste. A268, Mill Valley, CA 94941, (415)381-3372

Worldwide Forgiveness Alliance [12641], 20 Sunnyside Ave., Ste. A268, Mill Valley, CA 94941, (415)381-3372

Worldwide Friendship Intl. - Address unknown since 2011.

Worldwide Kennel Club [21684], PO Box 62, Mount Vernon, NY 10552, (914)771-5219

Worldwide Kennel Club [21684], PO Box 62, Mount Vernon, NY 10552, (914)771-5219

Worldwide Marriage Encounter [12441], 2210 E Highland Ave., Ste. 110, San Bernardino, CA 92404-4666, (909)863-9963

Worldwide Marriage Encounter [12441], 2210 E Highland Ave., Ste. 110, San Bernardino, CA 92404-4666, (909)863-9963

Worldwide Monitors Radio Club [★20943]

Worldwide Monitors Radio Club [★20943]

Worldwide Pollution Control Assn. [2789], 12190 Hubbard St., Livonia, MI 48150, (734)525-0300

Worldwide Pollution Control Assn. [2789], 12190 Hubbard St., Livonia, MI 48150, (734)525-0300

Worldwide Printing Thermographers Assn. - Defunct.

Worldwide Responsible Accredited Production [215], 2200 Wilson Blvd., Ste. 601, Arlington, VA 22201, (703)243-0970

Worldwide Responsible Accredited Production [215], 2200 Wilson Blvd., Ste. 601, Arlington, VA 22201, (703)243-0970

Worldwide Responsible Apparel Production [★215]

Worldwide Responsible Apparel Production [★215]

Worldwide Sys. for Conformity Testing and Certification of Electrotechnical Equip. and Components [IO], Geneva, Switzerland

Worldwide Television-FM DX Assn. [20943], PO Box 501, Somersville, CT 06072

Worldwide Television-FM DX Assn. [20943], PO Box 501, Somersville, CT 06072

Worldwide Univ. Colleges Consortium [★7973]

Worldwide Univ. Consortium

Worldwide Univ. Consortium - Address unknown since 2011.

Worldwide Women Professional Bowlers [★22431]

Worship Resources Office - Defunct.

Worshipful Company of Bakers [IO], London, United Kingdom

Worshipful Company of Farriers [IO], Kings Langley, United Kingdom

Worshipful Company of Framework Knitters [IO], Upminster, United Kingdom

Worshipful Company of Glaziers' and Painters of Glass [IO], London, United Kingdom

Worshipful Company of Grocers [IO], London, United Kingdom

Worshipful Company of Info. Technologists [IO], London, United Kingdom

Worshipful Company of Musicians [IO], London, United Kingdom

Worshipful Company of Pattenmakers [IO], Sutton Valence, United Kingdom

Worshipful Company of Pewterers [IO], London, United Kingdom

Worshipful Company of Sci. Instrument Makers [IO], London, United Kingdom

Worshipful Company of Scriveners of the City of London [IO], London, United Kingdom

Worshipful Company of Shipwrights [IO], London, United Kingdom

Worshipful Company of Tin Plate Workers [IO], Norfolk, United Kingdom

Worshipful Company of Vintners [IO], London, United Kingdom

Worshipful Company of Wheelwrights [IO], Bexleyheath, United Kingdom

Worshipful Soc. of Apothecaries of London [IO], London, United Kingdom

Wound Care Assn; Amer. Professional [16924]

Wound Healing Soc. [14839], 341 N Maitland Ave., Ste. 130, Maitland, FL 32751, (407)647-8839

Wound, Ostomy and Continence Nurses Soc.: An Assn. of E.T. Nurses [15807], 15000 Commerce Pkwy., Ste. C, Mount Laurel, NJ 08054, (888)224-9626

Wound, Ostomy and Continence Nurses Soc., An Assn. of E.T. Nurses [★15807]

Wound, Ostomy and Continence Nurses Soc.: An Assn. of E.T. Nurses [15807], 15000 Commerce Pkwy., Ste. C, Mount Laurel, NJ 08054, (888)224-9626

Wound, Ostomy and Continence Nurses Soc., An Assn. of E.T. Nurses [★15807]

Wound, Ostomy and Continence Nursing Certification Bd. [15808], 555 E Wells St., Ste. 1100, Milwaukee, WI 53202-3823, (888)496-2622

Wounded Warrior Proj. [20822], 4899 Belfort Rd., Ste. 300, Jacksonville, FL 32256, (904)296-7350

Woven Fabric Belting Mfrs. Assn. [★3447]

Woven Fabric Belting Mfrs. Assn. [★3447]

Woven Wire Products Assn. [1882], PO Box 610280, Birmingham, AL 35261-0280, (800)529-6691

WPC Club [21198], PO Box 3504, Kalamazoo, MI 49003-3504

Wreck and Crash Mail Soc. [22093], 12407 Dover Rd., Reisterstown, MD 21136

Wren Family Assn. - Defunct.

Wrestlers WithOut Borders [23136], 63 Whitney St., San Francisco, CA 94131

Wrestling
Christian Wrestling Fed. [23131]
Natl. Wrestling Coaches Assn. [23132]
North Amer. Grappling Assn. [23133]
U.S. Girls' Wrestling Assn. [23134]
U.S.A. Wrestling [23135]
Wrestlers WithOut Borders [23136]

Writers
Alexandra Writers' Centre Soc. [305]
Amer. Christian Fiction Writers [10698]
Amer. Friends of the Shakespeare Birthplace Trust [10699]
Amer. Friends of the Shakespeare Birthplace Trust [10699]
Amer. Philatelic Soc. Writers Unit [22012]
Amer. Soc. of Journalists and Authors [10700]
Aphra Behn Soc. [10701]
Arthur Miller Soc. [10702]
Asian Amer. Writers' Workshop [3705]
Assn. of Writers and Writing Programs [10703]
Authors Guild [10704]
Authors League of Am. [10705]
Baseball Writers Assn. of Am. [2814]
Bread Loaf Writers Conf. [10706]
Broad Universe [22206]
Carson McCullers Soc. [10707]
Charles Johnson Soc. [10708]
Charles W. Chesnutt Assn. [10709]
Charlotte Perkins Gilman Soc. [10710]
Comm. on Scholarly Editions [10711]
Cormac McCarthy Soc. [10712]
Culturatti Kids Resource Network [9074]
Don DeLillo Soc. [10713]
Elizabeth Madox Roberts Soc. [10714]
Football Writers Assn. of Am. [22588]
Gene Stratton Porter Memorial Soc. [9365]
Georgia Writers Assn. [10715]
Golf Writers Assn. of Am. [22610]
Harriet Beecher Stowe Center [10716]
Harriet Beecher Stowe Soc. [10717]
Harry Stephen Keeler Soc. [9368]
Horror Writers Assn. [10718]
Intercultural Alliance of Artists and Scholars [9237]
Intl. Adam Smith Soc. [10381]
Intl. Assn. of Crime Writers, North Amer. Br. [10719]
Intl. Assn. of Crime Writers, North Amer. Br. [10719]

Reference to "IO" in place of a book number signifies that the association may be found in the 50th edition of International Organizations.

Intl. Assn. of Media Tie-in Writers [10720]
Intl. Assn. of Media Tie-in Writers [10720]
Intl. Black Writers [10721]
Intl. Black Writers and Authors [10721]
Intl. Rebecca West Soc. [10722]
Intl. Thriller Writers [10723]
Intl. Thriller Writers [10723]
Intl. Women's Writing Guild [10724]
Intl. Women's Writing Guild [10724]
Irish Playwrights and Screenwriters Guild [2396]
James Jones Literary Soc. [10725]
Jerry B. Jenkins Christian Writers Guild [20295]
Kay Boyle Soc. [10726]
Military Writers Soc. of Am. [22207]
Mystery Writers of Am. [10727]
Natl. Assn. of Independent Writers and Editors
   [2844]
Natl. Resume Writers' Assn. [3706]
Natl. Resume Writers' Assn. [3706]
Natl. Verbatim Reporters Assn. [3707]
Natl. Writers Union [23320]
Norman Mailer Soc. [10728]
North Amer. Case Res. Assn. [3708]
North Amer. Jules Verne Soc. [10729]
North Amer. Jules Verne Soc. [10729]
North Amer. Travel Journalist Assn. [3709]
Novelists, Inc. [3710]
Outer Critics Circle [10597]
PEN Amer. Center [10730]
PEN Center USA [10731]
Philip Roth Soc. [10732]
Philippine Amer. Writers and Artists [10733]
P.N. Elrod Fan Club [9408]
Poets Against the War [10734]
Public Safety Writers Assn. [3711]
Robinson Jeffers Assn. [10735]
Romance Writers of Am. [10736]
Sci. Fiction and Fantasy Writers of Am. [10737]
Sculpture in the Env. [17396]
Sedgwick Soc. [10738]
Silent Images [13148]
Sisters in Crime [3712]
Smart Women's Inst. of Entrepreneurial Learning
   [10739]
Soc. of Children's Book Writers and Illustrators
   [10740]
Soc. of Midland Authors [3713]
Soc. for the Stud. of Amer. Women Writers
   [10741]
Soc. for the Stud. of Amer. Women Writers
   [10741]
Space Coast Writers' Guild [10742]
Susan Glaspell Soc. [10743]
Text and Academic Authors Assn. [10744]
Thornton Wilder Soc. [10745]
Thornton Wilder Soc. [10745]
United Amateur Press Assn. of Am. [22107]
Western Writers of Am. [10746]
William Faulkner Soc. [10747]
William Gilmore Simms Soc. [10748]
Women Writing the West [3714]
Worldcraft Circle of Native Writers' and Storytell-
   ers [19170]
Writers Guild of Am. East [23321]
Writers Guild of Am. West [23322]
Writers Workshop [10749]
Writing Acad. [10750]
Writers Alliance - Defunct.
Writers' Fed. of Nova Scotia [IO], Halifax, NS,
   Canada
Writers Guild of Alberta [IO], Edmonton, AB, Canada
Writers Guild of Am. East [23321], 250 Hudson St.,
   New York, NY 10013, (212)767-7800
Writers Guild of Am. West [23322], 7000 W Third
   St., Los Angeles, CA 90048, (323)951-4000
Writers Guild of Canada [IO], Toronto, ON, Canada
Writers Guild Found. [★23322]
Writers' Guild of Great Britain [IO], London, United
   Kingdom
Writers in Prison Comm. of Intl. P.E.N. [IO], London,
   United Kingdom
Writers and Scholars Educational Trust [IO], London,
   United Kingdom
Writers' Trust of Canada [IO], Toronto, ON, Canada
Writers' Union of Canada [IO], Toronto, ON, Canada

Writers' Union of Iceland [IO], Reykjavik, Iceland
Writers Workshop [10749], Univ. of Illinois at
   Urbana-Champaign, 608 S Wright St., 288 English
   Bldg., Urbana, IL 61801, (217)333-8796
Writing
   826 Natl. [9071]
   Amer. Assn. of Handwriting Analysts [10751]
   Amer. Handwriting Anal. Found. [10752]
   Amer. Pencil Collectors Soc. [21297]
   Amer. Soc. of Greek and Latin Epigraphy [10753]
   Assn. of Legal Writing Directors [6076]
   Assn. of Teachers of Tech. Writing [9072]
   Coalition of Handwriting Analysts Intl. [6937]
   Conf. on Coll. Composition and Commun. [8132]
   Coun. of Graphological Societies [10754]
   Coun. of Writing Prog. Administrators [9073]
   Culturatti Kids Resource Network [9074]
   Gene Stratton Porter Memorial Soc. [9365]
   Hagiography Soc. [20212]
   Harry Stephen Keeler Soc. [9368]
   Intercultural Alliance of Artists and Scholars
      [9237]
   Intl. Adam Smith Soc. [10381]
   Intl. Black Writers and Authors [10721]
   Intl. Graphoanalysis Soc. [10755]
   Intl. Graphoanalysis Soc. [10755]
   James Jones Literary Soc. [10725]
   Military Writers Soc. of Am. [22207]
   Natl. Assn. of Independent Writers and Editors
      [2844]
   Natl. Soc. for Graphology [10756]
   Natl. Writing Proj. [9075]
   PEN Center USA [10731]
   Sedgwick Soc. [10738]
   Silent Images [13148]
   Soc. for Calligraphy [10757]
   Soc. of Scribes [10758]
   Teachers and Writers Collaborative [9076]
   Washington Calligraphers Guild [10759]
Writing Acad. [10750], 4010 Singleton Rd.,
   Rockford, IL 61114, (815)877-9675
Writing Equip. Soc. [IO], Bury St. Edmunds, United
   Kingdom
Writing Instrument Mfrs. Assn. [3356], 1701
   Pennsylvania Ave. NW, Ste. 300, Washington, DC
   20006, (202)253-4347
WSA Fraternal Life [19067], 11265 Decatur St., Ste.
   100, Westminster, CO 80234, (303)451-1494
WSSFN [★15690]
WSSFN [★15690]
W.T. Bandy Center for Baudelaire and Modern
   French Stud. [9429], 419 21st Ave. S, Nashville,
   TN 37240-0007, (615)343-0372
WTA Tour Players Assn. [23068], 1 Progress Plz.,
   Ste. 1500, St. Petersburg, FL 33701, (727)895-
   5000
WTA Tout [★23061]
WTA Tout [★23061]
WTC Families For Proper Burial [13314], PO Box
   236, Fanwood, NJ 07023
WTCARES [21685], 164 N Forrest Ave., Camden,
   TN 38320-1217, (731)584-6530
WTF Taekwondo Assn. of Canada [IO], Ottawa, ON,
   Canada
Wuqu' Kawoq [15227], PO Box 91, Bethel, VT
   05032
WWF - Australia [IO], Sydney, Australia
WWF Intl. [IO], Gland, Switzerland
WWF-UK [IO], Godalming, United Kingdom
WWF Verdensnaturfonden [★IO]
WWII PT Boats, Tenders and Bases [★20866]
WWII PT Boats, Tenders and Bases [★20866]
WWW Wimachtendienk, Wingolauchsik, Witahemui
   [★13027]
Wyburn-Mason and Jack M. Blount Found. for the
   Eradication of Rheumatoid Disease; Roger [16624]
Wyckoff House and Assn. [10131], 5816 Clarendon
   Rd., Brooklyn, NY 11203, (718)629-5400
Wycliffe Bible Translators [19354], PO Box 628200,
   Orlando, FL 32862-8200, (407)852-3600
Wyman Worldwide Hea. Partners [15228], 227
   Mechanic St., Ste. 3, Lebanon, NH 03766

X

Xaverian Missionaries [★20115]

Xaverian Missionaries of the U.S. [20115], 12
   Helene Ct., Wayne, NJ 07470, (973)942-2975
Xaverian Missionary Fathers [★20115]
Xaverian Missioners of the U.S. [★20115]
Xavier Inst. of Development Action and Stud. [IO],
   Jabalpur, India
Xavier Soc. for the Blind [17119], 154 E 23rd St.,
   New York, NY 10010, (212)473-7800
Xerces Soc. [5160], 628 NE Broadway, Ste. 200,
   Portland, OR 97232-1324, (503)232-6639
Xeroderma Pigmentosum Soc. [14638], 437 Snyder-
   town Rd., Craryville, NY 12521, (518)851-9490
Xi Psi Phi [23502], Dr. Keith W. Dickey, Supreme
   Sec.-Treas., 160 S Bellwood Dr., Ste. Z, East Al-
   ton, IL 62024-2086, (618)307-5433
X.Org [★6647]
X.Org Found.
X.Org Found. - Address unknown since 2011.
Xplor Intl. [1634], 4022 Land O'Lakes Blvd., Ste.
   102, Land O'Lakes, FL 34639, (813)929-8100
Xplor Intl. [1634], 4022 Land O'Lakes Blvd., Ste.
   102, Land O'Lakes, FL 34639, (813)929-8100
Xtal Set Soc. [6675], PO Box 3636, Lawrence, KS
   66046, (405)517-7347
XyUser Gp. [6524], 12310 129th St. N, Largo, FL
   33774
XyVision Users Gp. [★6524]

Y

Yacht Architects and Brokers Assn. [★2375]
Yacht Brokers Assn. of Am. [2375], 105 Eastern
   Ave., Ste. 104, Annapolis, MD 21403, (410)940-
   6345
Yacht Brokers, Designers and Surveyors Assn. [IO],
   Petersfield, United Kingdom
Yacht Club Uruguayo [IO], Montevideo, Uruguay
Yacht Harbour Assn. [IO], Egham, United Kingdom
Yacht Racing Assn. of Thailand Under Royal Patron-
   age [IO], Bangkok, Thailand
Yacht Racing Associations Coun. [★22407]
Yachting Assn. of India [IO], New Delhi, India
Yachting Assn. of Sri Lanka [IO], Colombo, Sri
   Lanka
Yachting Club of Am. [22415], Box 1040, Marco
   Island, FL 34146, (239)642-4448
Yachting Journalists' Assn. [IO], Lymington, United
   Kingdom
Yachting New Zealand [IO], Auckland, New Zealand
Yachting Union of Latvia [IO], Riga, Latvia
Yad Sarah [IO], Jerusalem, Israel
Yad Vashem, The Holocaust Martyrs' and Heroes'
   Remembrance Authority [IO], Jerusalem, Israel
YAI Network [12514], 460 W 34th St., New York, NY
   10001-2382, (212)273-6100
Yale-China Assn. [8381], 442 Temple St., Box
   208223, New Haven, CT 06520-8223, (203)432-
   0880
Yale-in-China Assn. [★8381]
Yamaha 650 Soc. [21948], 27 Green Acres Dr.,
   Rolla, MO 65401-3910, (573)368-5852
Yamaha 650 Soc. [21948], 27 Green Acres Dr.,
   Rolla, MO 65401-3910, (573)368-5852
Yang Style Tai Chi Chuan Assn; Intl. [22740]
Yarn Dyers Assn. [★3436]
Yarns of Yesteryear Project - Defunct.
Yas Meyve-Sebze Ihracatcilari Birligi [★IO]
Yasodhara Ashram Soc. [IO], Kootenay Bay, BC,
   Canada
Yayasan Indonesia Aikikai [IO], Jakarta, Indonesia
Yeats Soc. Sligo [IO], Dublin, Ireland
Yeladim - Fair Chance for Children [IO], Tel Aviv,
   Israel
Yellow Pages Assn. [2968], 400 Connell Dr., Ste.
   1100, Berkeley Heights, NJ 07922-2747, (908)286-
   2380
Yellow Pages Integrated Media Assn. [★2968]
Yellow Pages Publishers Assn. [★2968]
Yemen Amateur Athletic Fed. [IO], Sana'a, Yemen
Yemen Assn. Against Epilepsy [IO], Sana'a, Yemen
Yemen Banks Assn. [IO], Sana'a, Yemen
Yemen Red Crescent Soc. [IO], Sana'a, Yemen
Yemen Taekwondo Fed. [IO], Sana'a, Yemen
Yemen Tennis Fed. [IO], Sana'a, Yemen
Yemen Weightlifting Fed. [IO], Sana'a, Yemen

A star before a book entry number signifies that the name is not listed separately, but is mentioned within the entry.

Yemeni Businessmen Club [IO], Sana'a, Yemen
Yemeni Otolaryngology Soc. [IO], Sana'a, Yemen
Yemeni Seafood Exporters Assn. [IO], Sana'a, Yemen
YES Inst. [★9081]
YES Rwanda [IO], Kigali, Rwanda
Yevreiskaya obshtshina Estonii [★IO]
YIVO Inst. for Jewish Res. [9931], 15 W 16th St., New York, NY 10011-6301, (212)246-6080
YIVO Inst. for Jewish Res. [9931], 15 W 16th St., New York, NY 10011-6301, (212)246-6080
YLEM: Artists Using Sci. and Tech. [9260], PO Box 31923, San Francisco, CA 94131-0923, (415)445-0196
YMA Fashion Scholarship Fund [216], 36 W 20th St., 3rd Fl., New York, NY 10011, (212)594-6422

YMCA

Assn. of YMCA Professionals [13500]
North Amer. YMCA Development Org. [13501]
North Amer. YMCA Development Org. [13501]
YMCA Intl. Br. [13502]
YMCA Intl. Br. [13502]
YMCA of the U.S.A. [13503]
Young Men's Christian Association - Canada [8069]
Young Women's Christian Association - Puerto Rico [13567]
Young Women's Christian Association - Rwanda [3393]
Y's Men Intl., U.S. Area [13504]

YMCA Intl. [★13503]
YMCA Intl. Br. [13502], 5 W 63rd St., 2nd Fl., New York, NY 10023, (212)727-8800
YMCA Intl. Br. [13502], 5 W 63rd St., 2nd Fl., New York, NY 10023, (212)727-8800
YMCA Intl. Camp Counselor Prog. [8382], 5 W 63rd St., 2nd Fl., New York, NY 10023, (212)727-8800
YMCA Intl. Camp Counselor Prog. [8382], 5 W 63rd St., 2nd Fl., New York, NY 10023, (212)727-8800
YMCA Intl. - Defunct.
YMCA Intl. Prog. Services [★13502]
YMCA Intl. Prog. Services [★13502]
YMCA Intl. Student Services [★13502]
YMCA Intl. Student Services [★13502]
YMCA na Slovensku [★IO]
YMCA of the U.S.A. [13503], 101 N Wacker Dr., Chicago, IL 60606, (312)977-0031
Ymgyrch Diogelu Cymru Wledig [★IO]
Yngling Assn. of Canada [IO], Kingston, ON, Canada
Yngling Club Holland [IO], Haarlem, Netherlands
Yngling Club Osterreich [IO], Salzburg, Austria

Yoga

3HO Found. [20296]
Agni Yoga Soc. [20297]
Amer. Yoga Assn. [10760]
Anahata Intl. [13662]
Ananda Marga [20298]
Ananda Yoga Teachers Assn. [10761]YogaAssn. of Himalayan Yoga Meditation Societies
B.K.S. Iyengar Yoga Natl. Assn. of the U.S. [23137]
Breathecure [13669]
Eureka Soc. [20299]
Green Yoga Assn. [5179]
Mentalphysics [20190]
Self-Realization Fellowship [20300]
Silver Age Yoga [17138]
Sri Aurobindo Assn. [20301]
Triratna Buddhist Community [19374]
Yoga Alliance [10762]
Yoga Bear [13721]
Yoga Res. Found. [20302]

Yoga Alliance [10762], 1701 Clarendon Blvd., Ste. 110, Arlington, VA 22209, (888)921-YOGA
Yoga Bear [13721], 735 Emerson St., Palo Alto, CA 94301
Yoga Res. Found. [20302], 6111 SW 74th Ave., Miami, FL 33143, (305)666-2006
Yoneylem Arastirmasi Dernegi [★IO]
York and Districts Olive Assn. [IO], York, Australia
Yorkshire Campaign for Nuclear Disarmament [IO], Bradford, United Kingdom
Yorkshire Terrier Club of Am. [21686], Robert Owen, Sec., PO Box 6204, Elizabethtown, KY 42702

Yosemite Conservancy [7147], 101 Montgomery St., Ste. 1700, San Francisco, CA 94104, (415)434-1782
Yosemite Museum Assn. [★7147]
Yosemite Natural History Assn. [★7147]
You Have the Power [18179], 2814 12th Ave. S, Nashville, TN 37204, (615)292-7027
Young Adult Adjustment Center [★12514]
Young Adult Institute/National Inst. for People with Disabilities [★12514]
Young Adult Inst. and Workshop [★12514]
Young Adult Lib. Services Assn. [10019], Amer. Lib. Assn., 50 E Huron St., Chicago, IL 60611, (312)280-4390
Young Americans for Freedom [17431], 2300 M St. NW, Ste. 800, Washington, DC 20037, (202)470-0196
Young Americans for Liberty [18836], PO Box 2751, Arlington, VA 22202
Young America's Found. [17432], F.M. Kirby Freedom Ctr., 110 Elden St., Herndon, VA 20170, (703)318-9608
Young Astronaut Coun. - Address unknown since 2011.
Young Audiences Arts for Learning [9326], 115 E 92nd St., New York, NY 10128-1688, (212)831-8110
Young Australians Best Book Award Coun. [IO], Kew, Australia
Young Black Women's Soc. - Address unknown since 2011.
Young Calvinist Fed. [★19606]
Young Children: Priority One [★13062]
Young Children: Priority One [★13062]
Young Circle League of Am. [★19066]
Young Communist League USA [18661], 235 W 23rd St., Ste. 254, New York, NY 10011-2302, (212)741-2016
Young Concert Artists [10315], 250 W 57th St., Ste. 1222, New York, NY 10107, (212)307-6655
Young Conservatives [IO], Frederiksberg, Denmark
Young Democratic Club of Am. [★17544]
Young Democratic Socialists [18662], 75 Maiden Ln., Ste. 505, New York, NY 10038, (212)727-8610
Young Democrats of Am. [17544], PO Box 77496, Washington, DC 20013-8496, (202)639-8585
Young Entrepreneurs Assn. Brunei [IO], Bandar Seri Begawan, Brunei Darussalam
Young Entrepreneurs' Org. [★660]
Young Guard Soc. [★1393]
Young Judaea [19912], 50 W 58th St., New York, NY 10019, (212)303-8014
Young Judaea/Hashachar [★19912]
Young Koreans United - Defunct.
Young Life [20309], PO Box 520, Colorado Springs, CO 80901, (719)381-1844
Young Life [20309], PO Box 520, Colorado Springs, CO 80901, (719)381-1844
Young Men's Assn. of the Men's Apparel Indus. [★216]
Young Men's Auxiliary Educ. and Missionary Soc. [★19715]
Young Men's Christian Association - Albania [IO], Tirana, Albania
Young Men's Christian Association - Angola [IO], Luanda, Angola
Young Men's Christian Association - Antwerp, Belgium [IO], Antwerp, Belgium
Young Men's Christian Association - Armenia [IO], Yerevan, Armenia
Young Men's Christian Association - Aruba [IO], San Nicolas, Aruba
Young Men's Christian Association - Barbados [IO], Bridgetown, Barbados
Young Men's Christian Association - Belize [IO], Belize City, Belize
Young Men's Christian Association - Benin [IO], Cotonou, Benin
Young Men's Christian Association - Burundi [IO], Bujumbura, Burundi
Young Men's Christian Association - Canada [IO], Toronto, ON, Canada
Young Men's Christian Association - Costa Rica [IO], San Jose, Costa Rica
Young Men's Christian Association - Democratic Republic of Congo [IO], Kinshasa, Republic of the Congo

Young Men's Christian Association - England [IO], London, United Kingdom
Young Men's Christian Association - Ethiopia [IO], Addis Ababa, Ethiopia
Young Men's Christian Association - Fiji [IO], Suva, Fiji
Young Men's Christian Association - Finland [IO], Helsinki, Finland
Young Men's Christian Association - Gambia [IO], Banjul, Gambia
Young Men's Christian Association - Georgia [IO], Tbilisi, Georgia
Young Men's Christian Association - Guyana [IO], Linden, Guyana
Young Men's Christian Association - Haiti [IO], Port-au-Prince, Haiti
Young Men's Christian Association - Hong Kong [IO], Hong Kong, People's Republic of China
Young Men's Christian Association - Hungary [IO], Balatongyorok, Hungary
Young Men's Christian Association - Indonesia [IO], Jakarta, Indonesia
Young Men's Christian Association - Ireland [IO], Belfast, United Kingdom
Young Men's Christian Association - Jordan [IO], Amman, Jordan
Young Men's Christian Association - Korea [IO], Seoul, Republic of Korea
Young Men's Christian Association - Lebanon [IO], Beirut, Lebanon
Young Men's Christian Association - Mauritius [IO], Quatre Bornes, Mauritius
Young Men's Christian Association - Nazareth [IO], Nazareth, Israel
Young Men's Christian Association - Nepal [IO], Kathmandu, Nepal
Young Men's Christian Association - Papua New Guinea [IO], Lae, Papua New Guinea
Young Men's Christian Association - Peru [IO], Lima, Peru
Young Men's Christian Association - Philippines [IO], Manila, Philippines
Young Men's Christian Association - Rwanda [IO], Kigali, Rwanda
Young Men's Christian Association - Samoa [IO], Apia, Western Samoa
Young Men's Christian Association - Senegal [IO], Dakar, Senegal
Young Men's Christian Association - Sierra Leone [IO], Freetown, Sierra Leone
Young Men's Christian Association - Slovakia [IO], Bratislava, Slovakia
Young Men's Christian Association - Spain [IO], Madrid, Spain
Young Men's Christian Association - Suriname [IO], Paramaribo, Suriname
Young Men's Christian Association - Taiwan [IO], Taipei, Taiwan
Young Men's Christian Association - Trinidad and Tobago [IO], Port of Spain, Trinidad and Tobago
Young Men's Christian Association - Ukraine [IO], Kiev, Ukraine
Young Men's Christian Association and Young Women's Christian Association - Denmark [IO], Valby, Denmark
Young Men's Christian Associations of the U.S.A. [★13503]
Young Menswear Assn. [★216]
Young Menswear Assn. of Men's Apparel Indus. [★216]
Young Musicians of Muscat [IO], Seeb, Oman
Young Naturalists' Circle [IO], Montreal, QC, Canada
Young Onset Parkinson's Assn. - Address unknown since 2011.
Young Peoples Socialist League [★18339]
Young Presidents' Org. [710], 600 E Las Colinas Blvd., Ste. 1000, Irving, TX 75039, (972)587-1500
Young Professionals in Energy [6763], 600 Travis St., Ste. 2310, Houston, TX 77002, (832)429-6344
Young Racers of Am. [22829], 1609 Pleasant Run, Keller, TX 76248, (817)431-8309
Young Religious Unitarian Universalists - Defunct.
Young Republican Natl. Fed. [18546], PO Box 15293, Washington, DC 20003, (202)608-1417
Young and the Restless Fan Club [23933], 7800 Beverly Blvd., Ste. 3305, Los Angeles, CA 90036

Reference to "IO" in place of a book number signifies that the association may be found in the 50th edition of International Organizations.

Young Social Democrats [★18339]
Young Stamp Collectors of Am. [22094], 100 Match Factory Pl., Bellefonte, PA 16823, (814)933-3820
Young Surname Org. [★20493]
Young Survival Coalition [13994], 61 Broadway, Ste. 2235, New York, NY 10006, (646)257-3000
Young Survival Coalition [13994], 61 Broadway, Ste. 2235, New York, NY 10006, (646)257-3000
Young Volunteers for the Env. [IO], Lome, Togo
Young Women Social Entrepreneurs [711], 6006 Colton Blvd., Oakland, CA 94611, (415)378-4417
Young Women's Christian Association - Albania [IO], Tirana, Albania
Young Women's Christian Association - Amer. Samoa [IO], Pago Pago, American Samoa
Young Women's Christian Association - Angola [IO], Luanda, Angola
Young Women's Christian Association - Antigua [IO], St. Johns, Antigua-Barbuda
Young Women's Christian Association - Aotearoa/ New Zealand [IO], Wellington, New Zealand
Young Women's Christian Association - Argentina [IO], Buenos Aires, Argentina
Young Women's Christian Association - Australia [IO], Dickson, Australia
Young Women's Christian Association - Bahamas [IO], Nassau, Bahamas
Young Women's Christian Association - Bangladesh [IO], Dhaka, Bangladesh
Young Women's Christian Association - Barbados [IO], St. Michael, Barbados
Young Women's Christian Association - Belarus [IO], Minsk, Belarus
Young Women's Christian Association - Belgium [IO], Antwerp, Belgium
Young Women's Christian Association - Belize [IO], Belize City, Belize
Young Women's Christian Association - Benin [IO], Cotonou, Benin
Young Women's Christian Association - Botswana [IO], Gaborone, Botswana
Young Women's Christian Association - Brazil [IO], Sao Paulo, Brazil
Young Women's Christian Association - Bulgaria [IO], Sofia, Bulgaria
Young Women's Christian Association - Cameroon [IO], Yaounde, Cameroon
Young Women's Christian Association - Canada [IO], Toronto, ON, Canada
Young Women's Christian Association - Chile [IO], Valparaiso, Chile
Young Women's Christian Association - Colombia [IO], Bogota, Colombia
Young Women's Christian Association - Czech Republic [IO], Prague, Czech Republic
Young Women's Christian Association - El Salvador [IO], San Salvador, El Salvador
Young Women's Christian Association - Estonia [IO], Tallinn, Estonia
Young Women's Christian Association - Ethiopia [IO], Addis Ababa, Ethiopia
Young Women's Christian Association - Fiji [IO], Suva, Fiji
Young Women's Christian Association - Finland [IO], Helsinki, Finland
Young Women's Christian Association - Gambia [IO], Banjul, Gambia
Young Women's Christian Association - Germany [IO], Hannover, Germany
Young Women's Christian Association - Ghana [IO], Accra, Ghana
Young Women's Christian Association - Great Britain [IO], Oxford, United Kingdom
Young Women's Christian Association - Greece [IO], Athens, Greece
Young Women's Christian Association - Grenada [IO], St. George's, Grenada
Young Women's Christian Association - Guyana [IO], Georgetown, Guyana
Young Women's Christian Association - Hong Kong [IO], Hong Kong, People's Republic of China
Young Women's Christian Association - Iceland [IO], Reykjavik, Iceland
Young Women's Christian Association - India [IO], New Delhi, India

Young Women's Christian Association - Ireland [IO], Dublin, Ireland
Young Women's Christian Association - Italy [IO], Torre Pellice, Italy
Young Women's Christian Association - Jamaica [IO], Kingston, Jamaica
Young Women's Christian Association - Japan [IO], Tokyo, Japan
Young Women's Christian Association - Kenya [IO], Nairobi, Kenya
Young Women's Christian Association - Korea [IO], Seoul, Republic of Korea
Young Women's Christian Association - Latvia [IO], Riga, Latvia
Young Women's Christian Association - Lebanon [IO], Beirut, Lebanon
Young Women's Christian Association - Lesotho [IO], Maseru, Lesotho
Young Women's Christian Association - Lithuania [IO], Vilnius, Lithuania
Young Women's Christian Association - Madagascar [IO], Antananarivo, Madagascar
Young Women's Christian Association - Malaysia [IO], Petaling Jaya, Malaysia
Young Women's Christian Association - Mauritius [IO], Pointe aux Sables, Mauritius
Young Women's Christian Association - Mexico [IO], Guadalajara, Mexico
Young Women's Christian Association - Myanmar [IO], Yangon, Myanmar
Young Women's Christian Association - Namibia [IO], Windhoek, Namibia
Young Women's Christian Association - Nepal [IO], Kathmandu, Nepal
Young Women's Christian Association - Netherlands [IO], Utrecht, Netherlands
Young Women's Christian Association - Nigeria [IO], Lagos, Nigeria
Young Women's Christian Association - Norway [IO], Oslo, Norway
Young Women's Christian Association - Pakistan [IO], Lahore, Pakistan
Young Women's Christian Association - Palestine [IO], Jerusalem, Israel
Young Women's Christian Association - Papua New Guinea [IO], Boroko, Papua New Guinea
Young Women's Christian Association - Peru [IO], Lima, Peru
Young Women's Christian Association - Philippines [IO], Manila, Philippines
Young Women's Christian Association - Puerto Rico [13567], PO Box 10111, San Juan, PR 00908, (787)724-1037
Young Women's Christian Association - Puerto Rico [13567], PO Box 10111, San Juan, PR 00908, (787)724-1037
Young Women's Christian Association - Romania [IO], Bucharest, Romania
Young Women's Christian Association - Rwanda [IO], Gitarama, Rwanda
Young Women's Christian Association - Samoa [IO], Apia, Western Samoa
Young Women's Christian Association - Sierra Leone [IO], Freetown, Sierra Leone
Young Women's Christian Association - Singapore [IO], Singapore, Singapore
Young Women's Christian Association - Solomon Islands [IO], Honiara, Solomon Islands
Young Women's Christian Association - Sri Lanka [IO], Colombo, Sri Lanka
Young Women's Christian Association - Suriname [IO], Paramaribo, Suriname
Young Women's Christian Association - Taiwan [IO], Taipei, Taiwan
Young Women's Christian Association - Thailand [IO], Bangkok, Thailand
Young Women's Christian Association - Togo [IO], Lome, Togo
Young Women's Christian Association - Trinidad and Tobago [IO], Port of Spain, Trinidad and Tobago
Young Women's Christian Association - Uganda [IO], Kampala, Uganda
Young Women's Christian Association - Ukraine [IO], Kiev, Ukraine
Young Women's Christian Association - Uruguay [IO], Montevideo, Uruguay

Young Women's Christian Association - Young Men's Christian Association of Sweden [IO], Stockholm, Sweden
Young Women's Christian Association - Zambia [IO], Lusaka, Zambia
Young Women's Financial Assn. of New York [★1299]
Young Women's Investment Assn. of New York [★1299]
Young Workers Liberation League [★18661]
Young World Development Regional Center [★12728]
Young World Development Regional Center [★12728]
Youth
All One People [10808]
Amer. Assn. of Caregiving Youth [13505]
Amer. Assn. of Children's Residential Centers [13506]
Amer. Hindu Assn. [19811]
Amer. Legion Baseball [22265]
Amer. Quarter Horse Youth Assn. [4549]
Amer. Youth Found. [20303]
Amer. Youth Policy Forum [13507]
Amer. Youth Work Center [13508]
America's Promise - The Alliance for Youth [13509]
Artists United for Social Justice [18640]
Assn. of Thai Professionals in Am. and Canada [19255]
Athgo Intl. [13510]
Athgo Intl. [13510]
Awana Clubs Intl. [20304]
Awana Clubs Intl. [20304]
Babe Ruth Baseball/Softball [22268]
Boy Scouts of Am. [13018]
Boys and Girls Clubs of Am. [13511]
Boys' and Girls' Clubs of Northern Ireland [5371]
Boys Hope Girls Hope [13512]
Boys Town Jerusalem Found. of Am. [13513]
Boys' Towns of Italy [13514]
Break Away: The Alternative Break Connection [12764]
Bridge Kids Intl. [13515]
Bridging Refugee Youth and Children's Services [11452]
Building Tomorrow [12659]
Camp Fire USA [13516]
Campaign For Our Children [13517]
Center for Youth Development and Policy Res. [18822]
Children Beyond Our Borders [17235]
Children of the Nations Intl. [11237]
CityKids Found. [13518]
Coalition for Juvenile Justice [6077]
Coll. Summit [8234]
Constitutional Rights Found. [17437]
Corps Network [13519]
Covenant House [13520]
CSB Ministries [20305]
EcoVentures Intl. [4319]
Educate Tomorrow [9077]
Enrichment Educ. [8276]
Ewing Marion Kaufman Found. [18823]
Families, 4-H, and Nutrition [13521]
Fed. of Pediatric Organizations [16145]
FosterClub [13522]
Fresh Lifelines for Youth [13523]
Friends for Youth [13524]
FUNDaFIELD [11288]
Future Corvette Owners Assn. [21060]
Future Voters of Am. [18824]
Generation for Change and Growth [12328]
Generation Rwanda [13525]
GesherCity [19091]
Girls for a Change [11290]
Girls Helping Girls [12118]
Girls Inc. [13526]
Girls on the Run Intl. [22863]
Global Action Proj. [18825]
Global Action Proj. [18825]
Global Ambassadors for Children [18249]
Global Family Rescue [13158]
Global Inheritance [18826]
Global Nomads Gp. [9078]

A star before a book entry number signifies that the name is not listed separately, but is mentioned within the entry.

Global Youth Action Network [18827]
Global Youth Action Network [18827]
Global Youth Coalition on HIV/AIDS [10881]
Global Youth Connect [18828]
Global Youth Connect [18828]
Global Youth Partnership for Africa [9875]
Glories Happy HATS [13527]
Grooming Future World Leaders [13528]
Hollywood Unites For Haiti [12128]
Holy Childhood Assn. [19428]
Humanitarian Travels Intl. [13338]
Hungarian Scouts Assn. [13020]
I Have a Dream Found. [13529]
Indify [13530]
Inst. in Basic Life Principles [13531]
Intl. Alliance for Youth Sports [23138]
Intl. Pediatric Hypertension Assn. [15076]
Intl. Performing Arts for Youth [10359]
Intl. Progressive Educ. [8074]
Intl. Youth Conditioning Assn. [23139]
Intl. Youth Found. [13532]
Intl. Youth Found. [13532]
Invisible Children [17237]
Inyana - League of Rwandan Children and Youth [11474]
Iranian Alliances Across Borders [19069]
Jackie Robinson Found. [13533]
Jamaica Unite [11602]
Junior Optimist Octagon Intl. [13060]
Just Think [18829]
Kids Making a Difference [3813]
Kids for Peace [18262]
Kids Without Borders [11337]
Kollaboration [13534]
Korean Amer. Voters' Coun. [18034]
Latin Amer. Women's Assn. [13464]
League of Young Voters [18384]
Masada/Maccabi Israel Summer Programs [19881]
Miracle Corners of the World [13535]
Mobile Voter [18096]
Natl. 4-H Coun. [13536]
Natl. AfterSchool Assn. [11152]
Natl. Assn. of Catholic Youth Ministry Leaders [19455]
Natl. Assn. of Extension 4-H Agents [13537]
Natl. Assn. of Melkite Youth [19591]
Natl. Assn. of Police Athletic Leagues [13538]
Natl. Assn. of Youth Clubs [13539]
Natl. Assn. of Youth Courts [18830]
Natl. Campaign to Prevent Teen Pregnancy [13540]
Natl. Child Labor Comm. [13541]
Natl. Collaboration for Youth [11363]
Natl. Episcopal Scouters Assn. [13024]
Natl. Fellowship of Child Care Executives [13542]
Natl. Foster Care Coalition [11366]
Natl. Junior Horticultural Assn. [21811]
Natl. Network of Youth Ministries [20306]
Natl. Organizations for Youth Safety [13543]
Natl. Tots and Teens [13544]
Natl. Youth Employment Coalition [13545]
Natl. Youth Rights Assn. [18831]
Network of Iranian Amer. Soc. [13546]
Nongovernmental Organizations Comm. on Youth [13547]
North Amer. Young Generation in Nuclear [7168]
notMYkid [13548]
Ocean Youth Trust Scotland [9687]
OneWorld Now! [8929]
Ophelia Proj. [13549]
Ophelia Proj. [13549]
Optimist Intl. [13071]
Overseas Young Chinese Forum [7845]
PASSION: Pursuing A Successful Seed In-spite of Negativity [13550]
Path of Success [9079]
Peace in Focus [18275]
Peer Hea. Exchange [9080]
Pioneer Clubs [20307]
Polish-American-Jewish Alliance for Youth Action [13551]
Polish-American-Jewish Alliance for Youth Action [13551]
Prepare Tomorrow's Parents [13552]

Proj. Baobab [13553]
Proj. YES [9081]
RandomKid [13554]
Responsible Endowments Coalition [9082]
Robert F. Kennedy Center for Justice and Human Rights [13555]
Scenarios U.S.A. [18832]
Secretariat for Family, Laity, Women, and Youth [12020]
Seeking Common Ground [13556]
Soccer Without Borders [22942]
Soc. for Res. on Adolescence [13557]
Soc. of Young Philanthropists [12685]
Soliya [13833]
South Asian Amer. Voting Youth [18392]
StandUp for Kids [11409]
StreetSchool Network [9083]
Student Peace Alliance [18290]
Subud Youth Assn. [13558]
SustainUS [13559]
Syndesmos [14271]
Team Success [13560]
Teen Challenge Intl. [20308]
Teen Challenge Intl. [20308]
Teen Missions Intl. [20099]
Teens Fighting Hunger [12295]
Theta Rho Girls' Club [13561]
Tomorrow's Youth Org. [13562]
Trans Youth Family Allies [12585]
Umoja Intl. [12969]
Union of North Amer. Vietnamese Students Assn. [19275]
U.S. Junior Chamber of Commerce [23458]
United Synagogue Youth [19907]
Up2Us [13563]
Urban Ed [9031]
Way to Work [11962]
What Kids Can Do [18834]
Where Peace Lives [10355]
Whole Child Intl. [11429]
WICUDA-USA [9095]
World Savvy [9084]
World Youth Alliance [18835]
World Youth Alliance [18835]
Young Americans for Liberty [18836]
Young America's Found. [17432]
Young Life [20309]
Young Life [20309]
Young Professionals in Energy [6763]
Youth Action Intl. [11436]
Youth for Christ/U.S.A. [20310]
Youth for Human Rights Intl. [12255]
Youth for Intl. Socialism [18663]
Youth Law Center [13564]
Youth Pride Alliance [12117]
Youth Venture [3715]
Youth to Youth Intl. [13565]
Youth to Youth Intl. [13565]
YouthBuild USA [13566]
Youth in Action Assn. [IO], Kabul, Afghanistan
Youth Action Intl. [11436], 125 Park St., Ste. 450, Traverse City, MI 49684, (231)946-6283
Youth Action Network [IO], Toronto, ON, Canada
Youth Action for Peace [IO], Brussels, Belgium
Youth Action for Peace - Deutschland [IO], Frankfurt, Germany
Youth Action for Peace - Italy [IO], Rome, Italy
Youth Adult Prog. [★8547]
Youth Advocate Prog. Intl.
Youth Advocate Prog. Intl. - Address unknown since 2011.
Youth Against War and Fascism - Defunct.
Youth Assisting Youth [IO], Toronto, ON, Canada
Youth Assn. for Human Rights Promotion and Development [IO], Kigali, Rwanda
Youth Challenge International-Canada [IO], Toronto, ON, Canada
Youth for Christ/U.S.A. [20310], PO Box 4478, Englewood, CO 80155, (303)843-9000
Youth Club of Pakistan [IO], Dubai, United Arab Emirates
Youth Crime Watch of Am. - Address unknown since 2011.
Youth Development Coalition - Defunct.
Youth Editors Assn. of America - Defunct.

Youth Educ. in the Arts [9327], 601 W Hamilton St., Allentown, PA 18101, (610)821-0345
Youth Educ. in the Arts [9327], 601 W Hamilton St., Allentown, PA 18101, (610)821-0345
Youth Empowerment Initiative [IO], New Delhi, India
Youth for Environmental Sanity [4324], 240 Harkleroad Ave., Santa Cruz, CA 95062, (831)465-1091
Youth of the European People's Party [IO], Brussels, Belgium
Youth Evangelism Assn. [19775], 13000 U.S. 41 N, Evansville, IN 47725, (812)867-2418
Youth For Understanding Intl. Exchange [★8383]
Youth For Understanding Intl. Exchange [★8383]
Youth For Understanding USA [8383], 6400 Goldsboro Rd., Ste. 100, Bethesda, MD 20817, (240)235-2100
Youth For Understanding USA [8383], 6400 Goldsboro Rd., Ste. 100, Bethesda, MD 20817, (240)235-2100
Youth Hostel Associations of China [IO], Guangzhou, People's Republic of China
Youth Hostel Romania [IO], Cluj-Napoca, Romania
Youth Hostels Assn. of England and Wales [IO], Matlock, United Kingdom
Youth Hostels Assn. of India [IO], New Delhi, India
Youth Hostels Assn. of New Zealand [IO], Christchurch, New Zealand
Youth Hostels Assn. of Russia [IO], St. Petersburg, Russia
Youth for Human Rights Intl. [12255], 1954 Hillhurst Ave., No. 416, Los Angeles, CA 90027, (323)663-5799
Youth for Human Rights Intl. [12255], 1954 Hillhurst Ave., No. 416, Los Angeles, CA 90027, (323)663-5799
Youth for Intl. Socialism [18663], Wellred Books, PO Box 4244, St. Paul, MN 55104
Youth for Intl. Socialism [18663], Wellred Books, PO Box 4244, St. Paul, MN 55104
Youth Law Center [13564], 200 Pine St., Ste. 300, San Francisco, CA 94104, (415)543-3379
Youth League of the Coalition Party [IO], Helsinki, Finland
Youth Media Minds of Am. [8980], 206 N Clarendon Ave., Avondale Estates, GA 30002, (404)292-1265
Youth Ministry [19945], Lutheran Church-Missouri Synod, 1333 S Kirkwood Rd., St. Louis, MO 63122-7295, (314)996-1732
Youth Ministry, U.S. Catholic Conf. [★12020]
Youth in Model Railroading [21897], 12990 Prince Ct., Broomfield, CO 80020-5419, (303)466-2857
Youth and Music of Germany [IO], Weikersheim, Germany
Youth Org. on Stamps [★22073]
Youth Partnership for Peace and Development - Sierra Leone [IO], Freetown, Sierra Leone
Youth for Peace [IO], Phnom Penh, Cambodia
Youth Policy Inst. [18496], 634 S Spring St., 10th Fl., Los Angeles, CA 90014, (213)688-2802
Youth Pride Alliance [12117], PO Box 33161, Washington, DC 20009, (202)387-4141
Youth in Reconstruction of a World in Destruction [IO], Bujumbura, Burundi
Youth Ser. Am. [13080], 1101 15th St., Ste. 200, Washington, DC 20005, (202)296-2992
Youth for Sierra Leone Improvement [IO], Freetown, Sierra Leone
Youth Soc. for Peace and Development of the Balkans [IO], Plovdiv, Bulgaria
Youth and Student Hostel Found. of the Philippines [IO], Paranaque, Philippines
Youth Taking Charge [12493], PO Box 96, Wimberley, TX 78676, (512)212-0373
Youth for Unity and Voluntary Action [IO], Mumbai, India
Youth Venture [3715], 1700 N Moore Ave., Ste. 2000, Arlington, VA 22209, (703)527-4126
Youth Voluntary Ser. of Italy [IO], Caserta, Italy
Youth With a Mission [20116], PO Box 26479, Colorado Springs, CO 80936-6479, (719)380-0505
Youth to Youth Intl. [13565], 547 E 11th Ave., Columbus, OH 43221, (614)224-4506
Youth to Youth Intl. [13565], 547 E 11th Ave., Columbus, OH 43221, (614)224-4506
YouthBuild USA [13566], 58 Day St., Somerville, MA 02144, (617)623-9900

Reference to "IO" in place of a book number signifies that the association may be found in the 50th edition of International Organizations.

YouthLink Scotland **[IO]**, Edinburgh, United Kingdom
Youths for Transparency Intl. **[IO]**, Lagos, Nigeria
Yrittajanaisten Keskusliitto **[★IO]**
Y's Men Intl. **[IO]**, Geneva, Switzerland
Y's Men Intl., U.S. Area **[13504]**, Dean Currie, Area
  Ser. Dir., 629 Lantana Ln., Imperial, CA 92251
Yugntruf - Youth for Yiddish **[9932]**, 419 Lafayette
  St., 2nd Fl., New York, NY 10003, (212)889-0381
Yugntruf - Youth for Yiddish **[9932]**, 419 Lafayette
  St., 2nd Fl., New York, NY 10003, (212)889-0381
Yugoslav MND Assn. **[IO]**, Belgrade, Serbia
Yugoslav Soc. of Plastic, Reconstructive and
  Aesthetic Surgery **[IO]**, Belgrade, Serbia
Yuki Teikei Haiku Soc. **[10458]**, Anne M. Homan,
  Membership Sec., 10695 Morgan Territory Rd.,
  Livermore, CA 94550
Yukon Conservation Soc. **[IO]**, Whitehorse, YT,
  Canada
Yukon Historical and Museums Assn. **[IO]**, White-
  horse, YT, Canada
Yukon Sci. Inst. **[IO]**, Whitehorse, YT, Canada
Yukon Wheelchair Recreation Soc. **[IO]**, Whitehorse,
  YT, Canada
Yukuhara Haiku Soc., English Language Div.
  [★10458]
Yum-O Org. **[12135]**, 132 E 43rd St., No. 223, New
  York, NY 10017
Yves R. Simon Inst. - Address unknown since 2011.
YWCA
  Young Women's Christian Association - Puerto
    Rico **[13567]**
  YWCA of the U.S.A. **[13568]**
YWCA v Ceske republice **[★IO]**
YWCA of the U.S.A. **[13568]**, 2025 M St. NW, Ste.
  550, Washington, DC 20036, (202)467-0801

Z

Z Car Club Assn. **[21199]**, 6 Jason Dr., Londonderry,
  NH 03053, (603)425-2270
Z Series Car Club of Am. **[21200]**, Chuck Krblich,
  Treas., 1119 SE Third Ave., Fort Lauderdale, FL
  33316
Zalman Shazar Center for Jewish History **[IO]**,
  Jerusalem, Israel
Zambia Amateur Athletic Assn. **[IO]**, Lusaka, Zambia
Zambia Assn. of Chambers of Commerce and Indus.
  [IO], Lusaka, Zambia
Zambia Badminton Assn. **[IO]**, Lusaka, Zambia
Zambia Civic Educ. Assn. **[IO]**, Lusaka, Zambia
Zambia Export Growers' Assn. **[IO]**, Lusaka, Zambia
Zambia Hope Intl. **[11437]**, Hope Mountain Found.,
  5235 Westview Dr., Ste. 100, Frederick, MD
  21703, (301)624-0061
Zambia Lawn Tennis Assn. **[IO]**, Mufulira, Zambia
Zambia Natl. Farmers' Union **[IO]**, Lusaka, Zambia
Zambia Red Cross Soc. **[IO]**, Lusaka, Zambia
Zambia Soc. of Physiotherapy **[IO]**, Lusaka, Zambia
Zambia Squash Assn. **[IO]**, Lusaka, Zambia
Zambia Union of Financial Institutions and Allied
  Workers **[IO]**, Lusaka, Zambia
Zambia Weightlifting Assn. **[IO]**, Kitwe, Zambia
Zane Grey's West Soc. **[9430]**, Sheryle Hodapp,
  Sec.-Treas., 15 Deer Oaks Dr., Pleasanton, CA
  94588-8236, (925)485-1325
Zangle Natl. Users' Gp. **[6996]**, John Getchell,
  Treas., 4653 Majestic Dr., Bellingham, WA 98226
Zarathushtrian Assembly **[20199]**, PO Box 2160,
  Cypress, CA 90630-1660, (714)349-0304
Zarrow Families Found. **[13211]**, 401 S Boston Ave.,
  Ste. 900, Tulsa, OK 74103-4012, (918)295-8008
Zawaya **[9141]**, 3150 18th St., Ste. 523, San
  Francisco, CA 94110, (415)255-9330
Zdruzenie Automobiloveho Priemyslu Slovenskej
  Republiky **[★IO]**
Zdruzenie Podnikatel'ov Slovenska **[★IO]**
Zdruzenie na Stanari na Makedonija **[★IO]**
Zdruzenje Kardiologov Slovenije **[★IO]**
Zdruzenje Multiple Sklerose Slovenije **[IO]**, Ljubljana,
  Slovenia
Zdruzenje Najemnikov Slovenije **[★IO]**
Zeiss Historical Soc. of Am. **[21415]**, PO Box 556,
  Mount Kisco, NY 10549
Zeiss Historical Soc. of Am. **[21415]**, PO Box 556,
  Mount Kisco, NY 10549
Zeleni Crne Gore **[★IO]**
Zellweger Baby Support Network **[14639]**, Pam
  Freeth, Pres., 9310 Groundhog Dr., Richmond, VA
  23235, (919)741-9778

Zen-do Kai Martial Arts **[22775]**, PO Box 186,
  Johnstown, NY 12095, (518)762-1589
Zen-do Kai Martial Arts Assn. **[★22775]**
Zen Stud. Soc. **[19375]**, New York Zendo Shobo-Ji,
  223 E 67th St., New York, NY 10065, (212)861-
  3333
Zenkoku Nogyo Kyodo Kumiai Rengo-kai **[★IO]**
Zenska Infoteka **[★IO]**
Zentralverband der Augenoptiker **[★IO]**
Zentralverband der Deutschen Schweineproduktion
  [★IO]
Zentralverband der Deutschen Schweineproduktion
  e.V. **[★IO]**
Zentralverband Deutscher Ingenieure **[IO]**, Munich,
  Germany
Zentralverband Deutsches Kraftfahrzeuggewerbe
  [★IO]
Zentralverband Elektrotechnik- und Elektronikindus-
  trie **[★IO]**
Zentrum zur Sozialmedizinischen, Rechtlichen und
  Kulturellen Betreuung von Auslandern und Auslan-
  derinnen in Osterreich **[★IO]**
Zero Balancing Assn. **[★15000]**
Zero Balancing Hea. Assn. **[15006]**, Kings Contriv-
  ance Village Ctr., 8640 Guilford Rd., Ste. 241,
  Columbia, MD 21046, (410)381-8956
Zero Corruption Transparency **[IO]**, Skopje, Mace-
  donia
Zero Population Growth - Seattle Chap. **[★12704]**
ZERO - The Proj. to End Prostate Cancer **[13995]**,
  10 G St. NE, Washington, DC 20002, (202)463-
  9455
Zero to Three: Natl. Center for Infants, Toddlers and
  Families **[14053]**, 1255 23rd St. NW, Ste. 350,
  Washington, DC 20037, (202)638-1144
Zero Waste Alliance **[4985]**, One World Trade
  Center, 121 SW Salmon St., Ste. 210, Portland,
  OR 97204, (503)279-9383
Zero Waste Alliance **[4985]**, One World Trade
  Center, 121 SW Salmon St., Ste. 210, Portland,
  OR 97204, (503)279-9383
ZESPRI Intl. **[IO]**, Mount Maunganui, New Zealand
Zeta Beta Tau **[23707]**, 3905 Vincennes Rd., Ste.
  100, Indianapolis, IN 46268, (317)334-1898
Zeta Chi Phi Multicultural Sorority **[23752]**, PO Box
  461583, San Antonio, TX 78246-1583, (210)641-
  7841
Zeta Phi Beta Sorority **[23647]**, 1734 New
  Hampshire Ave. NW, Washington, DC 20009,
  (202)387-3103
Zeta Phi Eta **[23494]**, 95 Park Ave., Washington, NJ
  07882
Zeta Psi **[★23708]**
Zeta Psi Educational Found. **[★23708]**
Zeta Psi Found. of Canada **[★23708]**
Zeta Psi Fraternity of North Am. **[23708]**, 15 S Henry
  St., Pearl River, NY 10965, (845)735-1847
Zeta Tau Alpha **[23736]**, 3450 Founders Rd.,
  Indianapolis, IN 46268, (317)872-0540
ZHABA Facilitators Collective **[IO]**, Budapest,
  Hungary
Ziegfeld Club **[10610]**, 593 Park Ave., New York, NY
  10065, (212)751-6688
ZigBee Alliance **[3430]**, 2400 Camino Ramon, Ste.
  375, San Ramon, CA 94583, (925)275-6607
Zimbabwe Assn. of Consulting Engineers **[IO]**,
  Harare, Zimbabwe
Zimbabwe Assn. of Occupational Therapists **[IO]**,
  Harare, Zimbabwe
Zimbabwe Badminton Assn. **[IO]**, Belvedere,
  Zimbabwe
Zimbabwe Girl Guides Assn. **[IO]**, Harare, Zimbabwe
Zimbabwe Hypertension Soc. **[IO]**, Gaborone,
  Botswana
Zimbabwe Inst. of Engineers **[IO]**, Harare, Zimbabwe
Zimbabwe Medical Assn. **[IO]**, Harare, Zimbabwe
Zimbabwe Music Rights Assn. **[IO]**, Harare,
  Zimbabwe
Zimbabwe Physiotherapy Assn. **[IO]**, Harare,
  Zimbabwe
Zimbabwe Red Cross Soc. **[IO]**, Harare, Zimbabwe
Zimbabwe Sci. Assn. **[IO]**, Harare, Zimbabwe
Zimbabwe Sports Medicine Assn. **[IO]**, Harare,
  Zimbabwe
Zimbabwe Squash Rackets Assn. **[IO]**, Harare,
  Zimbabwe
Zimbabwe Stock Exchange **[IO]**, Harare, Zimbabwe

Zimbabwe Taekwondo Assn. **[IO]**, Harare, Zimbabwe
Zimbabwe Veterinary Assn. **[IO]**, Harare, Zimbabwe
Zimbabwe Weightlifting Assn. **[IO]**, Harare,
  Zimbabwe
Zimbabwe Women's Rsrc. Centre and Network **[IO]**,
  Harare, Zimbabwe
ZimCopy **[IO]**, Harare, Zimbabwe
Zionism
  Central Rabbinical Cong. of the U.S.A. and
    Canada **[19854]**
Zionist Archives and Library of World Zionist Org. -
  Amer. Sect. - Defunct.
Zionist Fed. of Great Britain and Northern Ireland
  [IO], London, United Kingdom
Zionist Movement; Amer. **[19844]**
Zionist Org. of Am. **[19913]**, 4 E 34th St., New York,
  NY 10016, (212)481-1500
Zionist Youth Movement; Hashomer Hatzair **[19864]**
Zisin Gakkai **[★IO]**
ZOA Refugee Care - Netherlands **[IO]**, Apeldoorn,
  Netherlands
ZOA Vluchtelingenzorg **[★IO]**
ZonMw **[★IO]**
Zonta Intl. **[13081]**, 1211 W 22nd St., Ste. 900, Oak
  Brook, IL 60523-3384, (630)928-1400
Zonta Intl. **[13081]**, 1211 W 22nd St., Ste. 900, Oak
  Brook, IL 60523-3384, (630)928-1400
Zoo and Aquarium Assn. **[IO]**, Mosman, Australia
Zoo Veterinary Technicians; Assn. of **[17019]**
Zoological Soc. of Ireland **[IO]**, Dublin, Ireland
Zoological Soc. of Japan **[IO]**, Tokyo, Japan
Zoological Soc. of London **[IO]**, London, United
  Kingdom
Zoological Soc. of Montreal **[IO]**, Montreal, QC,
  Canada
Zoological Soc. of Southern Africa **[IO]**, Scottsville,
  Republic of South Africa
Zoology
  Amer. Assn. of Zoo Keepers **[7628]**
  Animal Behavior Mgt. Alliance **[7629]**
  Animal Behavior Soc. **[7630]**
  Aquarium and Zoo Facilities Assn. **[7631]**
  Assn. of Companion Animal Behavior Counselors
    [7632]
  Assn. of Zoos and Aquariums **[7633]**
  The Crustacean Soc. **[7634]**
  European Assn. for Aquatic Mammals **[3918]**
  European Assn. for Zoological Nomenclature
    [17211]
  Friends of the Natl. Zoo **[7635]**
  Intl. Assn. of Animal Behavior Consultants **[7636]**
  Intl. Assn. of Animal Behavior Consultants **[7636]**
  Intl. Soc. for Anthrozoology **[23310]**
  Intl. Soc. of Protistologists **[7637]**
  Overseas Chinese Entomologists Assn. **[6849]**
  Royal Zoological Soc. of South Australia **[13884]**
  Soc. for Integrative and Comparative Biology
    [7638]
  Soc. of Systematic Biologists **[7639]**
Zumunta Assn. USA **[19179]**, 133 Augur St., Ham-
  den, CT 06517, (203)946-0173
Zurcher Handelskammer **[★IO]**
Zurich Chamber of Commerce **[IO]**, Zurich,
  Switzerland
Zuzu News **[23787]**, Zuzu Appearances, PO Box
  145, Carnation, WA 98014
Zuzu Soc. **[★23787]**
Zvaz celulozo-papierenskeho priemyslu Slovenskej
  republiky **[★IO]**
Zvaz Elektrotechnickeho Priemyslu Slovenskej Re-
  publiky **[★IO]**
Zvaz polygrafie na Slovensku **[★IO]**
Zvaz Strojarskeho Priemyslu Slovenskej Republiky
  [★IO]
Zveza Bibliotekarskih Drustev Slovenije **[★IO]**
Zveza Radioammaterjev Slovenije **[★IO]**
Zwiazek Artystow Scen Polskich **[★IO]**
Zwiazek Kompozytorow Polskich **[★IO]**
Zwiazek Polskie Mieso **[★IO]**
Zwiazek Pracodawcow Innowacyjnych Firm Farma-
  ceutycznych **[★IO]**
Zwiazek Producentow Audio Video **[★IO]**
ZY Qigong **[13722]**, 4033 Stone Way N, Seattle, WA
  98103, (206)726-0088
ZZ Top Intl. Fan Club, Inc. - Defunct.

A star before a book entry number signifies that the name is not listed separately, but is mentioned within the entry.